Stanley Gibbons
STAMP CATALOGUE

PART 1

British Commonwealth 1986

Eighty-eighth edition

Including post-independence issues of
Ireland, Pakistan and South Africa

Stanley Gibbons Publications Ltd
London and Ringwood

By Appointment to Her Majesty The Queen
Stanley Gibbons, London
Philatelists

Published by **Stanley Gibbons Publications Ltd**
Editorial, Sales Offices and Distribution Centre:
5 Parkside, Christchurch Road, Ringwood,
Hants BH24 3SH.

ISSN: 0142–9752 ISBN: 0 85259 109 8

Item No. 0281

Phototypeset by Input Typesetting Ltd, London.
Printed in Great Britain by The Garden City Press, Ltd,
Letchworth, Hertfordshire.

Preface to the 1986 Edition

A HOUSE DIVIDED?

Ever since the genesis of the hobby stamp collecting has attracted adherents by the myriad choices open to the participants in its many facets.

Specialist, average and beginner collectors have happily co-existed, each making their own contribution. Circumstances change, however, and the old patterns are showing signs of strain. The different groups appear to be drifting apart with hints of indifference, or even hostility, replacing the unity of purpose which has previously prevailed.

Before any gaping chasms open the point must be made that if the specialists and leading collectors of tomorrow are not amongst the present members of the Stamp Bug Club, the school groups or the purchasers of packaged collections then it is difficult to see from what other source they can appear. These "new" collectors are equally as enthusiastic as their "traditional" fellows and we must all share the responsibility of making certain that such enthusiasm is not lost, but is introduced to the wider fascination of the hobby.

It is our hope that this particular volume will be used, and appreciated, by every class of collector. It contains, within its pages, research from leading specialists, and corrections from young collectors whose sharp eyes have detected errors, overlooked by both the printer and ourselves. All contributions are welcome – it is, after all, the same hobby from whatever angle you view it.

PRICES

It is encouraging to report that the consolidation of prices, mentioned last year, has, in general, been sustained. The increased demand for stamps from the later part of the reign of Queen Victoria to the end of that of King George V has continued, spreading to the more common stamps of the period. Such movements are particularly pronounced amongst the **West Indies** islands, **Barbados, Bermuda** and others, together with smaller colonies as far-flung as **Fiji, Gibraltar** and the **Seychelles**. Stocks of these stamps no longer exist in quantity and this shortage is reflected in the new prices. Some issues from the reign of King George VI have also risen in value, but here gains are more selective, mostly being restricted to pre-1945 stamps.

India to 1949, together with the **Convention** and **Feudatory States**, continues to be popular, but is now being joined, as a major collecting area, by the territories which now make up **Malaysia**. Prices have improved throughout this group, from early issues to the modern, not forgetting the Japanese Occupation period where many items are now recognised as scarce.

Only the **Australia** group remains depressed and it has been necessary to amend prices for early **New South Wales** and **South Australia** to bring them into line with current market levels.

Most noticeable has been the revival of interest in used stamps, coupled with the increasing demand for errors and varieties. A special effort has been made this year to provide prices for such items previously unpriced.

During the last few months prices for new issues have been oscillating due to currency fluctuations, but with the revival of sterling it is hoped that this period is now at an end.

REVISIONS IN THIS EDITION

1985 marks the 50th anniversary of an important milestone in stamp collecting – the appearance of the first Commonwealth Omnibus issue. The **1935 Silver Jubilee** series, always immensely popular with collectors, initiated the succession of Royal commemorations which have introduced many to the hobby.

To mark the anniversary the coverage of vignette plate varieties on the Windsor Castle design has been expanded to include three additional types of the Bradbury, Wilkinson printings and two on those produced by De La Rue. Less attention has been paid in the past to the stamps printed by Waterlow and the pattern of flaws on these stamps is not yet fully established. We are grateful to Mr. L. Sackstein for his assistance in this project and to Mr. S. Drewett and Mr. S. Ellis for the loan of examples used to prepare the enlarged illustrations which now appear in the Omnibus section following Zululand.

Postage Labels. A number of Commonwealth countries have, in recent months, installed the machines which print and issue these labels in the face value requested by the customer. Such items, often called "Frama" labels, are outside the scope of the listings, but illustrations and descriptions are provided to assist collectors in their identification. Such notes have currently been added for **Great Britain** and **Australia**, together with a similar treatment of the **Canada** "Stick'n Tick" experiments.

Appendix. Following the policy statement in the Preface to the 1985 edition it has been necessary to introduce Appendix listings for **Cayes of Belize**, issues from the **Grenadines of St. Vincent** inscribed "Bequia" or "Union Island" and for those stamps inscribed with the names of the component islands of **Tuvalu.**

Batum. Mr. R. Gibbs, FRPSL, has allowed us access to his research into the comparative scarcities of these neglected issues and the prices have been considerably amended.

Burma. Mr. G. Davis, FRPSL, has assisted in a comprehensive reappraisal of the Japanese Occupation period prices.

Egypt and the **Sudan**. Dr. P. A. S. Smith, FRPSL, of the Egypt Study Circle has provided amendments to Egypt, a number of which appear in this edition. Additional postal history notes are also included for Sudan.

Grenada. A number of additional dates, and corrections to existing ones, have been added from 1895 onwards.

India and States. Interest in the pre-Independence issues for both India and the States continues unabated. With the help of Mr. P. Kinns and Mr. C. T. Sturton, FRPSL, much new date information and a number of new varieties have been added. In response to requests from collectors we have provided further notes as to which Feudatory States stamps exist with gum, and which do not.

We have fallen in line with the general consensus of research into the circular stamps of **Jammu and Kashmir** so that the design previously identified as a 1 a. is now shown as a 4 a. and vice versa. Full details of the resulting number changes can be found in the table on page *vii*.

Dr. E. D. Pereira, FRPSL, has drawn our attention to the three types of the **Soruth** "SARKARI" overprints and the listings have been enlarged to illustrate and list all three.

Long Island. Our coverage of these World War I provisionals has been completely rewritten to provide a clear explanation of the different colours of ribbon and carbon used for the typewritten stamps. We are grateful to Mr. R. Gibbs, FRPSL, for allowing us access to his, as yet unpublished, research on this issue.

Orange Free State. After many years of neglect the issues of Orange Free State are now much in demand and we have hastened, with the help of Mr. A. R. Allison to overhaul this part of the catalogue. Information has been amplified and a number of new varieties added.

Tristan de Cunha. The recent sale, by Stanley Gibbons Auctions Ltd, of the George Crabb collection has enabled us to reassess the value of covers, showing the various cachets, with some startling results.

We do appreciate the continued help given to us by individual collectors, dealers, philatelic societies and postal administrations. Without their assistance the task of revising the annual *Part I* would be impossible. Corrections and suggestions are always welcome, but please do remember to address them to rural Ringwood and not to the bustle of the Strand.

David J. Aggersberg

Prices

The prices quoted in this catalogue are the estimated selling prices of Stanley Gibbons Ltd at the time of publication. They are, *unless it is specifically stated otherwise*, for examples in fine condition for the issue concerned. Superb examples are worth more; those of a lower quality considerably less.

All prices are subject to change without prior notice and Stanley Gibbons Ltd may from time to time offer stamps below catalogue price in consequence of special purchases or particular promotions.

No guarantee is given to supply all stamps priced, since it is not possible to keep every catalogued item in stock.

Quotation of prices. The prices in the left-hand column are for unused stamps and those in the right-hand column are for used.

A dagger (†) denotes that the item listed does not exist in that condition and a blank, or dash, that it exists, or may exist, but no market price is known.

Prices are expressed in pounds and pence sterling. One pound comprises 100 pence (£1 = 100p).

The method of notation is as follows: pence in numerals (e.g. 5 denotes five pence); pound and pence, up to £100, in numerals (e.g. 4·25 denotes four pounds and twenty-five pence); prices above £100 expressed in whole pounds with the "£" sign shown.

Unused stamps. Great Britain and Commonwealth: the prices for unused stamps of Queen Victoria to King Edward VIII are for lightly hinged examples. Unused prices for King George VI and Queen Elizabeth II issues are for unmounted mint.

Some stamps from the King George VI period are often difficult to find in unmounted mint condition. In such instances we would expect that collectors would need to pay a high proportion of the price quoted to obtain mounted mint examples. Generally speaking lightly mounted mint stamps from this reign, issued before 1945, are in considerable demand.

Mounted mint stamps from the reign of Queen Elizabeth II are frequently available at lower prices than those quoted for the stamps unmounted.

Used stamps. The used prices are normally for stamps postally used but may be for stamps cancelled-to-order where this practice exists.

A pen-cancellation on early issues can sometimes correctly denote postal use. Instances are individually noted in the Catalogue in explanation of the used price given.

Prices quoted for bisects on cover or on large piece are for those dated during the period officially authorised.

Stamps not sold unused to the public (e.g. some official stamps) are priced used only.

The use of "unified" designs, that is stamps inscribed for both postal and fiscal purposes, results in a number of stamps of very high face value. In some instances these may not have been primarily intended for postal purposes, but if they are so inscribed we include them. We only price such items used, however, where there is evidence of normal postal usage.

Cover prices. To assist collectors, cover prices are quoted for issues up to 1945 at the beginning of each country.

The system gives a general guide in the form of a factor by which the corresponding used price of the loose stamp should be multiplied when found in fine average condition on cover.

Care is needed in applying the factors and they relate to a cover which bears a single of the denomination listed; strips and blocks would need individual valuation outside the scope. If more than one denomination is present the most highly priced attracts the multiplier and the remainder are priced at the simple figure for used singles in arriving at a total.

The cover should be of non-philatelic origin, bearing the correct postal rate for the period and distance involved and cancelled with the markings normal to the offices concerned. Purely philatelic items have a cover value only slightly greater than the catalogue value for the corresponding used stamps. This applies generally to those high-value stamps used philatelically rather than in the normal course of commerce. Low-value stamps, e.g. ¼d. and ½d., are desirable when used as a single rate on cover and merit an increase in "multiplier" value.

First-day covers in the period up to 1945 are not within the scope of the system and the multiplier should not be used. As a special category of philatelic usage, with wide variations in valuation according to scarcity, they require separate treatment.

Oversized covers, difficult to accommodate on an album page, should be reckoned as worth little more than the corresponding value of the used stamps. The condition of a cover affects its value. Except for "wreck covers", serious damage or soiling reduce the value where the postal markings and stamps are ordinary ones. Conversely, visual appeal adds to the value and this can include freshness of appearance, important addresses, old-fashioned but legible hand-writing, historic town-names, etc.

The multipliers are a base on which further value would be added to take account of the cover's postal historical importance in demonstrating such things as unusual, scarce or emergency cancels, interesting routes, significant postal markings, combination usage, the development of postal rates, and so on.

For *Great Britain*, rather than multiplication factors, the cover price is shown as a third column, following the prices for unused and used stamps. It will be extended beyond King Edward VII in subsequent editions.

Minimum price. The minimum price quoted is five pence. This represents a handling charge rather than a basis for valuing common stamps, for which the 5p price should not be reckoned automatically, since it covers a variation in real scarcity.

Set prices. Set prices are generally for one of each value, excluding shades and varieties, but including major colour changes. Where there are alternative shades, etc., the cheapest is usually included. The number of stamps in the set is always stated for clarity. The mint prices for sets containing *se-tenant* pieces are based on the prices quoted for such combinations, and not on those for the individual stamps.

Specimen stamps. The pricing of these items is explained under that heading.

Repricing. Collectors will be aware that the market factors of supply and demand directly influence the prices quoted in this Catalogue. Whatever the scarcity of a particular stamp, if there is no one in the market who wishes to buy it it cannot be expected to achieve a high price. Conversely, the same item actively sought by numerous potential buyers may cause the price to rise.

All the prices in this Catalogue are examined during the preparation of each new edition by expert staff of Stanley Gibbons and repriced as necessary. They take many factors into account, including supply and demand, and are in close touch with the international stamp market and the auction world.

Commonwealth cover prices and advice on postal history material originally provided by Edward B. Proud.

Stanley Gibbons Addresses

HEAD OFFICE, 399 STRAND, LONDON WC2R 0LX

Auction Room and Specialist Stamp Departments. Open Monday–Friday 9.30 a.m. to 5 p.m.

Shop. Open Monday–Friday 9.30 a.m. to 5.30 p.m. and Saturday 10 a.m. to 12.30 p.m.

Telephone 01 836 8444 and Telex 28883 for all departments.

OTHER UNITED KINGDOM BRANCHES

Stanley Gibbons Publications Ltd. 5, Parkside, Christchurch Road, Ringwood, Hants BH24 3SH. Telephone 04254 2363. Telex 41271.

Urch Harris & Co. Ltd. Clifton Heights, Triangle West; Bristol BS8 1BQ. Telephone 0272 277483 and Telex 44 9522.

OVERSEAS BRANCHES

Stanley Gibbons Australia Pty. Ltd. P.O. Box 863J, Melbourne 3001, Australia. Telephone (01 061) 67 3332 and Telex AA 37223.

Stanley Gibbons (Pty.) Ltd. P.O. Box 62074, Marshalltown 2107, R.S.A. Telephone (01 027) 11 8347616 and Telex 8-8120.

Stanley Gibbons Inc. 124 Charlotte Ave, C.S. 1809, Hicksville, New York 11801, U.S.A. Telephone (01 01516) 935–9490 and Telex 96–7733.

Guarantee

All stamps are guaranteed genuine originals in the following terms:

If not as described, and returned by the purchaser, we undertake to refund the price paid to us in the original transaction. If any stamp is certified as genuine by the Expert Committee of the Royal Philatelic Society, London, or by B.P.A. Expertising Ltd, the purchaser shall not be entitled to make any claim against us for any error, omission or mistake in such certificate.

Consumers' statutory rights are not affected by the above guarantee.

The recognised Expert Committees in this country are those of the Royal Philatelic Society, 41 Devonshire Place, London W1N 1PE, and B.P.A. Expertising Ltd, P.O. Box 33, Bognor Regis, West Sussex PO22 7SR. They do not undertake valuations under any circumstances and fees are payable for their services.

Index

	page
Preface	iii
Prices	iv
Addresses	iv
Stamps Added and Numbers Altered	vii
General Philatelic Information	viii
Abbreviations	xiv

Country	*page*
Abu Dhabi	1
Aden	1
Aitutaki (*see* Cook Islands)	179
Alderney (*see* Guernsey)	GB50
Alwar (*see* Indian States)	332
Andaman and Nicobar Islands (Japanese Occupation)	326
Anguilla	4
Antigua	11
Ascension	27
Australia	32
Australian Antarctic Territory	52
Baghdad (*see* Iraq)	360
Bahamas	53
Bahawalpur (*see* Pakistan)	574
Bahrain	61
Bamra (*see* Indian States)	332
Bangkok (*see* British P.O. in Siam)	109
Bangladesh	62
Barbados	66
Barbuda (*see* Antigua)	21
Barwani (*see* Indian States)	332
Basutoland	74
Batum (British Occupation)	76
Bechuanaland	78
Bechuanaland Protectorate	77
Belize	79
Bermuda	84
Bhopal (*see* Indian States)	333
Bhor (*see* Indian States)	336
Biafra (*see* Nigeria)	538
Bijawar (*see* Indian States)	336
Botswana	90
B.M.A. Malaya (*see* Malaysia)	415
British Antarctic Territory	94
British Bechuanaland	76
British Central Africa (*see* Nyasaland Protectorate)	556
British Columbia	96
British Columbia and Vancouver Island	96
British Commonwealth Occupation Force (Japan)	52
British Commonwealth Omnibus Issues	802
British Consular Mail (*see* Madagascar)	405
British East Africa	96
British Forces in Egypt (*see* Egypt)	211
British Guiana	97
British Honduras	101
British Indian Ocean Territory	104
British Kaffraria (*see* Cape of Good Hope)	150
British Levant	106
British Military Administration, Malaya	415
British New Guinea (*see* Papua)	576
British North Borneo (*see* North Borneo)	548
British Occupation of Iraq (*see* Iraq)	360
British Occupation of Italian Colonies	108
British P.O.s Abroad	GB61
British P.O.s in China	297
British P.O.s in Crete	109
British P.O.s in Morocco	475
British P.O. in Siam	109
British Postal Agencies in Eastern Arabia	109
British Solomon Islands Protectorate (*see* Solomon Islands)	669
British Somaliland (*see* Somaliland Prot)	675
British South Africa Co (*see* Rhodesia)	592
British Virgin Islands	110
Brunei	117
Brunei (Japanese Occupation)	122
Bundi (*see* Indian States)	336, 352
Burma	112
Burma (Japanese Occupation)	123
Bushire (British Occupation)	125
Bussahir (*see* Indian States)	338
Caicos Islands (*see* Turks and Caicos Islands)	769
Cameroons (British Occupation)	125
Canada	125
Cape of Good Hope	149
Cayes of Belize (*see* Belize)	83
Cayman Islands	151
C. E. F. (Cameroons)	125
C. E. F. (*on* India)	325
Ceylon	158
Chamba (*see* Indian States)	326
Channel Islands	GB45
Charkhari (*see* Indian States)	338
China (British P.O.s)	297
China Expeditionary Force (*see* India)	325
Christmas Island	165
Cochin (*see* Indian States)	339
Cocos (Keeling) Islands	167
Cook Islands	169
Crete (British Administration)	109
Crowned-circle handstamps	GB61
Cyprus	187
Cyrenaica	199
Datia (Duttia) (*see* Indian States)	342
Dhar (*see* Indian States)	342
Dominica	199
Duttia (*see* Indian States)	342
East Africa Forces (E.A.F.)	109
East Africa & Uganda (*see* Kenya, Uganda and Tanganyika)	386
East India (India Nos. 35 etc.)	299
E. E. F. (*see* Palestine)	575
Egypt	208
Eire (*see* Ireland Republic)	361
Eritrea (M.E.F. *and* B.M.A.)	108
Falkland Islands	211
Falkland Islands Dependencies	217
Faridkot (*see* Indian States)	327, 342
Federated Malay States (*see* Malaysia)	414
Fiji	219
Gambia	227
G. E. A. (*see* Tanzania)	717
Ghana	234
Gibraltar	246
Gilbert and Ellice Islands	253
Gilbert Islands	255
Gold Coast	256
Graham Land (*see* Falkland Is Deps)	217
Great Britain	GB1
Great Britain (Channel Islands)	GB45
Great Britain (Island Issues)	GB45
Great Britain (Official Stamps)	GB43
Great Britain (Postage Due Stamps)	GB42
Great Britain (Postal Fiscals)	GB44
Great Britain (Regional Stamps)	GB41
Great Britain (Used Abroad)	GB61
Grenada	258
Grenadines (*see* Grenada *and* St. Vincent)	272, 632
Griqualand West	278
Guernsey	GB45
Guyana	279
Gwalior (*see* Indian States)	327
Hadhramaut (*see* Aden)	3
Heligoland	291
Holkar (Indore) (*see* Indian States)	344
Hong Kong	291
Hong Kong (Japanese Occupation)	297
Hyderabad (*see* Indian States)	342
Idar (*see* Indian States)	344
I. E. F. (*see* India)	325
I.E.F. 'D' (*see* Mosul)	360
India	297
Indian Convention States	326
Indian Custodian Forces in Korea	325
Indian Expeditionary Forces, 1914–22	325
Indian Feudatory States	332
Indian National Army	326
Indian U.N. Force in Congo	326
Indian U.N. Force in Gaza (Palestine)	326
Indore (*see* Indian States)	344
International Commission in Indo-China	326
Ionian Islands	360
Iraq	360
Ireland (Republic)	361
Isle of Man	GB50
Jaipur (*see* Indian States)	345
Jamaica	372
Jammu and Kashmir (*see* Indian States)	346
Japanese Occupation of Andaman and Nicobar Islands	326
Japanese Occupation of Brunei	122
Japanese Occupation of Burma	122
Japanese Occupation of Hong Kong	297
Japanese Occupation of Kelantan	438
Japanese Occupation of Malaya	436
Japanese Occupation of North Borneo	553
Japanese Occupation of Sarawak	646
Jasdan (*see* Indian States)	348
Jersey	GB55
Jhalawar (*see* Indian States)	348
Jind (*see* Indian States)	329, 348
Johore (*see* Malaysia)	422
Junagadh (Soruth) (*see* Indian States)	353
Kashmir and Jammu (*see* Indian States)	346
Kathiri State of Seiyun (*see* Aden)	2
Kedah (*see* Malaysia)	424
Kelantan (*see* Malaysia)	426
Kelantan (Japanese Occupation)	438
Kelantan (Thai Occupation)	438
Kenya	382
Kenya, Uganda and Tanganyika	386
King Edward VII Land (*see* New Zealand)	526
Kiribati	391
Kishangarh (*see* Indian States)	349
Korea (Indian Custodian Forces)	325
Kuwait	393
Labuan	395
Lagos	396
Las Bela (*see* Indian States)	350
Leeward Islands	397
Lesotho	398
Levant (British)	106
Long Island	404
Lydenburg (*see* Transvaal)	745
Madagascar (British Consular Mail)	405
Mafeking Siege Stamps (*see* Cape of Good Hope)	150
Mafia (*see* Tanzania)	717
Mahra Sultanate of Qishn and Socotra (*see* Aden)	4
Malacca (*see* Malaysia)	427
Malawi	405
Malaya (B.M.A.)	415
Malaya (Japanese Occupation)	436
Malaya (Thai Occupation)	438
Malayan Federation	416
Malayan Postal Union	415
Malaysia	412, 416
Malaysian States	422
Maldive Islands	439
Malta	449
Mauritius	460

INDEX

Country	*page*
Middle East Forces (M.E.F.)	108
Montserrat	468
Morocco Agencies (British Post Offices)	475
Morvi (*see* Indian States)	350
Mosul (*see* Iraq)	360
Muscat	477
Nabha (*see* Indian States)	330
Nandgaon (*see* Indian States)	350
Natal	478
Nauru	479
Nawanagar (*see* Indian States)	350
Negri Sembilan (*see* Malaysia)	427
Nevis (*see* St. Kitts-Nevis)	604, 611
New Brunswick	484
New Carlisle, Gaspé	125
Newfoundland	484
New Guinea (*late* German)	489
New Hebrides	491
New Republic	497
New South Wales	498
New Zealand	503
Niger Coast Protectorate	529
Niger Company Territories	529
Nigeria	530
Niuafo'ou (*see* Tonga)	738
Niue	538
Norfolk Island	544
North Borneo	548
North Borneo (Japanese Occupation)	553
North West Pacific Islands (*see* New Guinea)	489
Northern Ireland	GB41
Northern Nigeria	554
Northern Rhodesia	554
Nova Scotia	555
Nowanuggur (Nawanagar) (*see* Indian States)	350
Nyasaland Force (N. F.) (*see* Tanzania)	717
Nyasaland Protectorate	555
Oil Rivers (*see* Niger Coast)	528
Omnibus Issues	802
Orange Free State	557
Orange River Colony	559
Orchha (*see* Indian States)	351
Pahang (*see* Malaysia)	429
Pakistan	559
Palestine (British Mandate)	575
Papua	576
Papua New Guinea	578
Patiala (*see* Indian States)	331
Penang (*see* Malaysia)	430
Penrhyn Island (*see* Cook Islands)	183
Perak (*see* Malaysia)	431
Perlis (*see* Malaysia)	433
Pietersburg (*see* Transvaal)	744
Pitcairn Islands	584

Country	*page*
Poonch (*see* Indian States)	351
Prince Edward Island	588
Puttiala (Patiala) (*see* Indian States)	331
Qatar	588
Qu'aiti State in Hadhramaut (*see* Aden)	3
Queensland	589
Rajasthan (*see* Indian States)	352
Rajpipla (*see* Indian States)	352
Rarotonga (Cook Islands, No. 50, etc.)	169
Redonda (*see* Antigua)	27
Rhodesia	592
Rhodesia and Nyasaland	597
Ross Dependency (*see* New Zealand)	526
Rustenburg (*see* Transvaal)	745
Sabah	597
St. Christopher	604
St. Christopher, Nevis and Anguilla	605
St. Helena	598
St. Kitts	609
St. Kitts-Nevis	605
St. Lucia	614
St. Vincent	623
Salonica (*see* British Levant)	108
Samoa	636
Sarawak	644
Sarawak (Japanese Occupation)	646
Saurashtra (Soruth) (*see* Indian States)	353
Schweizer Renecke (*see* Transvaal)	745
Scinde (*see* India)	298
Scotland	GB42
Seiyun (*see* Aden)	2
Selangor (*see* Malaysia)	433
Seychelles	647
Shihr and Mukalla (*see* Aden)	3
Sierra Leone	655
Singapore	663
Sirmoor (*see* Indian States)	352
Solomon Islands	669
Somalia (British Occupation)	109
Somaliland Protectorate	675
Soruth (*see* Indian States)	353
South Africa	677
South African Republic (*see* Transvaal)	741
South Arabian Federation	689
South Australia	689
South Georgia (*see* Falkland Is Deps)	217
South Orkneys (*see* Falkland Is Deps)	217
South Shetlands (*see* Falkland Is Deps)	217
South West Africa	94
Southern Cameroons	700
Southern Nigeria	700
Southern Rhodesia	700
Sri Lanka	702
Stellaland	708
Straits Settlements (*see* Malaysia)	412
Sudan	708

Country	*page*
Sungei Ujong (*see* Malaysia)	42
Swaziland	71
Tanganyika (Tanzania)	71
Tangier (*see* Morocco)	47
Tanzania	717, 71
Tasmania	72
Thai Occupation of Kelantan	43
Thai Occupation of Malaya	43
Thai Occupation of Trengganu	43
Tobago (*see* Trinidad and Tobago)	74
Togo (Anglo-French Occupation)	724
Tokelau (*see* New Zealand)	527
Tonga	72
Transjordan	738
Transvaal	741
Travancore (*see* Indian States)	355
Travancore-Cochin (*see* Indian States)	358
Trengganu (*see* Malaysia)	435
Trengganu (Thai Occupation)	439
Trinidad	746
Trinidad and Tobago	746, 747
Tripolitania (M.E.F. *and* B.M.A.)	108
Tristan da Cunha	754
Trucial States	760
Turkish Cypriot Posts (*see* Cyprus)	196
Turkish Empire (British P.O.) (*see* British Levant)	106
Turks Islands	760
Turks and Caicos Islands	760, 761
Tuvalu	770
Uganda	774
Vancouver Island (*see* British Columbia)	96
Van Diemen's Land (*see* Tasmania)	722
Vanuatu	779
Victoria	780
Victoria Land (*see* New Zealand)	526
Virgin Islands (*see* British Virgin Islands)	110
Volksrust (*see* Transvaal)	745
Vryburg (*see* Cape of Good Hope)	151
Wadhwan (*see* Indian States)	359
Wales	GB42
Western Australia	790
Western Samoa (*see* Samoa)	637
Wolmaransstad (*see* Transvaal)	745
Zambia	792
Zanzibar	797
Zil Elwannyen (Elwagne, Eloigne) Sesel (*see* Seychelles)	653
Zimbabwe	800
Zululand	801
Addenda and Corrigenda	806
Omnibus issues	802

Stamps Added

Excluding new issues which have appeared in Gibbons *Stamp Monthly* Supplements, the following are the Catalogue numbers of stamps listed in this edition for the first time.

Great Britain. 815b, X857a, 1246a.
  Used Abroad. Colombia. Z23*a*, Z123*a*. Peru. Z40*a*.
Anguilla. 384B/7B, 507a, 509a, 510a, 511a, 609a, 610a.
Antigua. 91e, 541a.
  Barbuda. MS328c, 614a, 677c, 678c, 679c, 680c, 681c, 682c.
Ascension. 45a.
Bahamas. CC2, 141f, 142e.
Basutoland. 14f.
Bechuanaland. 111b, 112b/c, 113b/c, 114b/c.
Belize. 577/82, 643a, 728, 735, 743/6.
British Guiana. 301e, 302e, 303e.
British Honduras. 143b/c, 144c/d, 146b/d.
Cayman Is. 96e.
Ceylon. 381e, 497b.
Cook Is. 909b/c.
  Aitutaki. 462a/b, 464a/b.
  Penrhyn Is. 314a, 315a, 316a.
Dominica. 92e, 93e.
Egypt. 41b, 77a, O64a.
Falkland Is. 139b, 139d, 140b, 140d, 140g, 141b, 141d, 142b/d.
  Falkland Is Dependencies. 93a.
Fiji. 243e.
Gambia. 8a, 143b/d, 144b/c, 145c, 146b/c.
Ghana. 1031ab, 1066a.
Gibraltar. 114b/c, 115b, 116b/c, 117b/c, 374a, 379b, 383a, 384a, 386a, 387a.
Gilbert & Ellice Is. 36d, 37d, 38d, 39d.
Gold Coast. 113b/c, 114c, 115b/c, 116b/c.
Grenada. 117a.
Guyana. 775a, 787a, 791a, 841d, 983cc, 1200a, 1245a, OP3.
Hong Kong. 117b, 133c, 134b/c, 136b.
India.
  Indian Convention States – Gwalior. 76b.
  Indian Feudatory States – Charkhari. 28b.
    Cochin. 12a, O20ba/c.
    Jaipur. 20a, 21ab, 34a, 36a.
    Kishangarh. 64a.
    Orchha. 3ba.
    Soruth. O9a, O12a, O15a, O19a.
    Travancore. 42c, 61b, 74c, O52J.
    Travancore – Cochin. 1h, 2f, 3g.
    Wadhwan. 6a.
Jamaica. 115b/c, 116c, 117b/c.
Kenya, Uganda and Tanganyika. 125e, 126e, 127e, 127g.
Kiribati. O16/24.
Malaysia.
  Johore. 13b.
  Selangor. 150a.
Malta. 210b/c, 211b/c, 212b/c, 213b/c.
Mauritius. 639a.
Montserrat. 577c, 578d, 579a, 579c, 580b/e, 581b.
Newfoundland. 280b.
Niger Coast Protectorate. Z17*a*.
Nigeria.
  Biafra. 16dc.
Niue. 518a/b, 520a/b.
Northern Rhodesia. 19e.
Orange Free State. 10c, 12b/c, 26/b, 57c, 59a, 75a, 102o, 103e, 106c/d, 111e, 112j, 114e/f, 120d, 121g, 128b/ba.
Pakistan. 208a, 479a, 480a, O86a, O115b.
Rhodesia. 359a.
St. Helena. 124e, 125e, 423a.
St. Kitts-Nevis – St. Kitts. 45b
  Nevis. 109a.
St Lucia. 109e, 111e.
St. Vincent.
  Grenadines of St. Vincent. 303ab.
Seychelles. 128b, 129b, 130b, 131b, 378a, 573b/e, 574b/e, 577b/c, 578b/c.
  Zil Elwannyen Sesel. 73b/c, 74b/c, 75b/c, 76b/c.
Sierra Leone. 181b/c, 182c, 183c, 184c, 286a.
Singapore. 291a, 361a, 373a.
Solomon Islands. 53e, 56e.
South Africa. 75a, O38a.
Southern Rhodesia. 30a.
Swaziland. 21b/c, 22c, 23b, 24b/c.
Tonga. 36c, 773ba, O13c/cb
  Niuafo'ou. 22a.
Transvaal.
  Pietersburg. 25n, 25o, 26g
Trinidad and Tobago. 239b/c, 240c, 241b/c, 242c.
Zambia. 133a, 234a, 279a, 280a, 281a, 282b, 388a.
Zanzibar. 45j.

Catalogue Numbers Altered

The table below is a cross-reference for those stamps, the Catalogue numbers of which have altered in this edition.

Old	*New*
Great Britain	
X862/93	X864/95
X894/6	X898/900
X897	X902
X898	X904
X902/25	X914/37
X926/9	X934/42
X930	X944
X931/5	X946/50
X936/44	X952/60
Northern Ireland	
NI36/8a	N137/9a
N139/42	N141/4
N143/4	N146/7
Scotland	
S38/40	S39/41
S41/4	S43/46
S45/6	S48/9
Wales	
W37/39a	W38/40a
W40/3	W42/5
W44/5	W47/8
Anguilla	
MS388a	**MS**388b
Bahrain	
94II/III	94a/b
95II	95a
96II/IIa	96a/ab
Bangladesh	
213/15	216/18
Belize	
577/721	583/727
722/7	729/34
728/34	736/42
735/69	747/81
Canada	
944/55	**MS**944
Ghana	
1038/49	1048/59
Gibraltar	
384*a*	384*b*
Grenada	
118	119
119	118
120	120*a*
120*a*	120
212/18	214/20
219/20	212/13
Grenadines of Grenada	
551/81	552/82
Guyana	
775*a*	775*b*
791a	791b
948a	*Deleted*
OP3/4	OP4/5
India	
1089	1092
1090/2	1089/91
1098	1099
1099	1098
Indian Feudatory States–Jammu and Kashmir	
2	3
3	2
5	6
6	5
9	10
10	9
12	13
13	12
15	16
16	15
18	19
19	18
21	22
22	21
24	25
25	24
27	28
28	27
36	37
37	36
45	46
46	45
Kishangarh	
64*b*	64*c*
Kiribati	
O16/20	O25/9
Labuan	
116*c*/d	116*d*/da
Long Island	
4/32	*Rewritten*
Malawi	
D20/5	D21/6
Montserrat	
579a	579b
590/603	595/9
Nigeria	
Biafra	
16b/cb	16c/db
Orange Free State	
8a	9a
12c	10d
36c	*Deleted*
54b	*Deleted*
112h	*Deleted*
121d/e	*Deleted*
Pakistan	
208a	208b
Papua	
37b	*Deleted*
Queensland	
F35/37	*Deleted*
St Kitts-Nevis	
Nevis	
109/13	122/6
114/26	109/21
114a/ab	109b/ba
127/42	132/47
143/7	127/31
Seychelles	
378a	378b
Sierra Leone	
764/83	763/82
Southern Rhodesia	
30a	30b
Tuvalu	
O20	O30

General Philatelic Information

and Guidelines to the Scope of the Part 1 (British Commonwealth) Catalogue

The notes which follow seek to reflect current practice in compiling the Part 1 (British Commonwealth) Catalogue.

It scarcely needs emphasising that the *Stanley Gibbons Stamp Catalogue* has a very long history and that the vast quantity of information it contains has been carefully built up by successive generations through the work of countless individuals. Philately itself is never static and the Catalogue has evolved and developed during this long time-span. Thus, while these notes are important for today's criteria, they may be less precise the farther back in the listings one travels. They are not intended to inaugurate some unwanted series of piecemeal alterations in a widely respected work, but it does seem to us useful that Catalogue users know as exactly as possible the policies currently in operation.

THE CATALOGUE IN GENERAL

Contents. The Catalogue is confined to adhesive postage stamps, including miniature sheets. For particular categories the rules are:

(*a*) Revenue (fiscal) stamps or telegraph stamps are listed only where they have been expressly authorised for postal duty.

(*b*) Stamps issued only precancelled are included, but normally issued stamps available additionally with precancel have no separate precancel listing unless the face value is changed.

(*c*) Stamps prepared for use but not issued, hitherto accorded full listing, are nowadays footnoted with a price (where possible).

(*d*) Bisects (trisects, etc.) are only listed where such usage was officially authorised.

(*e*) Stamps issued only on first day covers and not available separately are not listed but priced (on the cover) in a footnote.

(*f*) New printings are only included in this catalogue where they show a major philatelic variety, such as a change in shade, watermark or paper. Full details of modern new printings, which include changes in imprint dates, are given in the *Elizabethan Catalogue*. (Details for the relevant areas are also given in the *Channel Islands Specialised Catalogue* and *Collect Channel Island and Isle of Man Stamps*.)

(*g*) Official and unofficial reprints are dealt with by footnote.

(*h*) Stamps from imperforate printings of modern issues which also occur perforated are covered by footnotes, but are listed where widely available for postal use.

Exclusions. The following are excluded: (*a*) non-postal revenue or fiscal stamps; (*b*) postage stamps used fiscally; (*c*) local carriage labels and private local issues; (*d*) telegraph stamps; (*e*) bogus or phantom stamps; (*f*) railway or airline letter fee stamps, bus or road transport company labels; (*g*) cut-outs; (*h*) all types of non-postal labels and souvenirs; (*i*) documentary labels for the postal service, e.g. registration, recorded delivery, airmail etiquettes, etc.; (*j*) privately applied embellishments to official issues and privately commissioned items generally; (*k*) stamps for training postal officers.

Legitimate issues. In judging status for inclusion in the catalogue broad considerations are applied to stamps. They must be issued by a legitimate postal authority, recognised by the government concerned, and must be adhesives valid for proper postal use in the class of service for which they are inscribed. We may also, from time to time, indicate where we feel that any particular issue has been restricted in its general availability to the public.

The publishers of this catalogue have observed, with concern, the proliferation of "artificial" stamp-issuing territories. On several occasions this has resulted in separately inscribed issues for various component parts of otherwise united states or territories.

Stanley Gibbons Publications Ltd have decided that where such circumstances occur, they will not, in the future, list these items in the SG catalogue without first satisfying themselves that the stamps represent a genuine political, historical or postal division within the country concerned. Any such issues which do not fulfil this stipulation will be recorded in the Catalogue Appendix only.

For errors and varieties the criterion is legitimate (albeit inadvertent) sale through a postal administration in the normal course of business. Details of provenance are always important; printers' waste and fraudulently manufactured material is excluded.

Certificates. In assessing unlisted items due weight is given to Certificates from recognised Expert Committees and, where appropriate, we will usually ask to see them.

New issues. New issues are listed regularly in the Catalogue Supplement published in Gibbons *Stamp Monthly*, whence they are consolidated into the next available edition of the Catalogue.

Full listing. "Full listing" confers our recognition and implies allotting a catalogue number and (wherever possible) a price quotation. Stamps of each country are catalogued chronologically by date of issue. Subsidiary classes are placed at the end of the country, as separate lists, with a distinguishing letter prefix to the catalogue number, e.g. D for postage due, O for official and E for express delivery stamps.

Date of issue. Where local issue dates differ from dates of release by agencies, "date of issue" is the local date. Fortuitous stray usage before the officially intended date is disregarded in listing. For ease of reference, the Catalogue displays in the top corner the date of issue of the first set listed on each page.

Catalogue numbers. The catalogue number appears in the extreme left column. The boldface Type numbers in the next column are merely cross-references to illustrations. Catalogue numbers in the Gibbons *Stamp Monthly* Supplement are provisional only and may need to be altered when the lists are consolidated. For the numbering of miniature sheets and sheetlets *see* section below.

Once published in the Catalogue, numbers are changed as little as possible; really serious renumbering is reserved for the occasions when a complete country or an entire issue is being rewritten. The edition first affected includes cross-reference tables of old and new numbers.

Our catalogue numbers are universally recognised in specifying stamps and as a hallmark of status.

Illustrations. Stamps are illustrated at three-quarters linear size. Stamps not illustrated are the same size and format as the value shown, unless otherwise indicated. Stamps issued only as miniature sheets have the stamp alone illustrated but sheet size is also quoted. Overprints, surcharges and watermarks are normally actual size. Illustrations of varieties are often enlarged to show the detail.

Designers. Designers' names are quoted where known, though space precludes naming every individual concerned in the production of a set. In particular, photographers supplying material are usually named only when they also make an active contribution in the design stage; posed photographs of reigning monarchs are, however, an exception to this rule.

CONTACTING THE CATALOGUE EDITOR

The editor is always interested in hearing from people who have new information which will improve or correct the Catalogue. As a general rule he must see and examine the actual stamps before they can be considered for listing; photographs or photocopies are insufficient evidence.

Submissions should be made in writing to the Catalogue Editor, Stanley Gibbons Publications Ltd. The cost of return postage for items submitted is appreciated, and this should include the registration fee if required.

Where information is solicited purely for the benefit of the enquirer, the editor cannot undertake to reply if the answer is already contained in these published notes or if return postage is omitted. Written communications are greatly preferred to enquiries by telephone and the editor regrets that he or his staff cannot see personal callers without a prior appointment being made. Correspondence may be subject to delay during the production period of each new edition.

The editor welcomes close contact with study circles and is interested, too, in finding reliable local correspondents who will verify and supplement offical information in countries where this is deficient.

We regret we do not give opinions as to the genuineness of stamps, nor do we identify stamps or number them by our Catalogue.

TECHNICAL MATTERS

The meanings of the technical terms used in the Catalogue will be found in *Philatelic Terms Illustrated* by Russell Bennett and James Watson, published by Stanley Gibbons.

References below to "more specialised" listings are to be taken to indicate, as appropriate, the Stanley Gibbons *Great Britain Specialised Catalogue* in 4 volumes; the *Channel Islands Specialised Catalogue* and (for Commonwealth stamps of the present reign) the *Elizabethan Stamp Catalogue*.

1. Printing

Printing errors. Errors in printing are of major interest to the Catalogue. Authenticated items meriting consideration would include: background, centre or frame inverted or omitted; centre or subject transposed; error of colour; error or omission of value; double prints and impressions; printed both sides; and so on. Designs *tête-bêche*, whether intentionally or by accident, are listable. *Se-tenant* arrangements of stamps are recognised in the listings or footnotes. Gutter pairs (a pair of stamps separated by blank margin) are not included in this volume, but can be found, for certain issues, in the *Elizabethan Catalogue*. Colours only partially omitted are not listed. Stamps with embossing omitted and (for Commonwealth countries) stamps printed on the gummed side are reserved for our more specialised listings.

Printing varieties. Listing is accorded to major changes in the printing base which lead to completely new types. In recess-printing this could be a design re-engraved; in photogravure or photolithography a screen altered in whole or in part. It can also encompass flat-bed and rotary printing if the results are readily distinguishable.

To be considered at all, varieties must be constant.

Early stamps, produced by primitive methods, were prone to numerous imperfections: the lists reflect this, recognising re-entries, retouches, broken frames, misshapen letters, and so on. Printing technology has, however, radically improved over the years, during which time photogravure and lithography have become predominant. Varieties nowadays are more in the nature of flaws and these, being too specialised for this general catalogue, are almost always outside the scope. The development of our range of specialised catalogues allows us now to list those items which have philatelic significance in their appropriate volume.

In no catalogue, however, do we list such items as: dry prints, kiss prints, doctor-blade flaws, colour shifts or registration flaws (unless they lead to the complete omission of a colour from an individual stamp), lithographic ring flaws, and so on. Neither do we recognise fortuitous happenings like paper creases or confetti flaws.

Overprints (and surcharges). Overprints of different types qualify for separate listing. These include overprints in different colours; overprints from different printing processes such as litho and typo; overprints in totally different typefaces, etc.

Overprint errors and varieties. Major errors in machine-printed overprints are important and listable. They include: overprint inverted or omitted; overprint double (treble, etc.); overprint diagonal; overprint double, one inverted; pairs with one overprint omitted, e.g. from a radical shift to an adjoining stamp; error of colour; error of type fount; letters inverted or omitted, etc. If the overprint is handstamped, few of these would qualify and a distinction is drawn. We continue, however, to list pairs of stamps where one has a handstamped overprint and the other has not.

Varieties occurring in overprints will often take the form of broken letters, slight differences in spacing, rising spaces, etc. Only the most important would be considered for footnote mention.

Sheet positions. If space permits we quote sheet positions of listed varieties and authenticated data is solicited for this purpose.

De La Rue plates. The Catalogue classifies the general plates used by De La Rue for printing British Colonial stamps as follows:

VICTORIAN KEY TYPE

Die I

1. The ball of decoration on the second point of the crown appears as a dark mass of lines.
2. Dark vertical shading separates the front hair from the bun.
3. The vertical line of colour outlining the front of the throat stops at the sixth line of shading on the neck.
4. The white space in the coil of the hair above the curl is roughly the shape of a pin's head.

Die II

1. There are very few lines of colour in the ball and it appears almost white.
2. A white vertical strand of hair appears in place of the dark shading.
3. The line stops at the eighth line of shading.
4. The white space is oblong, with a line of colour partially dividing it at the left end.

Plates numbered 1 and 2 are both Die I. Plates 3 and 4 are Die II.

GEORGIAN KEY TYPE

Die I

A. The second (thick) line below the name of the country is cut slanting, conforming roughly to the shape of the crown on each side.
B. The labels of solid colour bearing the words "POSTAGE" and "& REVENUE" are square at the inner top corners.
C. There is a projecting "bud" on the outer spiral of the ornament in each of the lower corners.

Die II

A. The second line is cut vertically on each side of the crown.
B. The labels curve inwards at the top.
C. There is no "bud" in this position.

Unless otherwise stated in the lists, all stamps with watermark Multiple Crown CA (w **8**) are Die I while those with watermark Multiple Crown Script CA (w **9**) are Die II.

2. Paper

All stamps listed are deemed to be on "ordinary" paper of the wove type and white in colour; only departures from this are normally mentioned.

Types. Where classification so requires we distinguish such other types of paper as, for example, vertically and horizontally laid; wove and laid bâtonné; card(board); carton; cartridge; glazed; granite; native; pelure; porous; quadrillé; ribbed; rice; and silk thread.

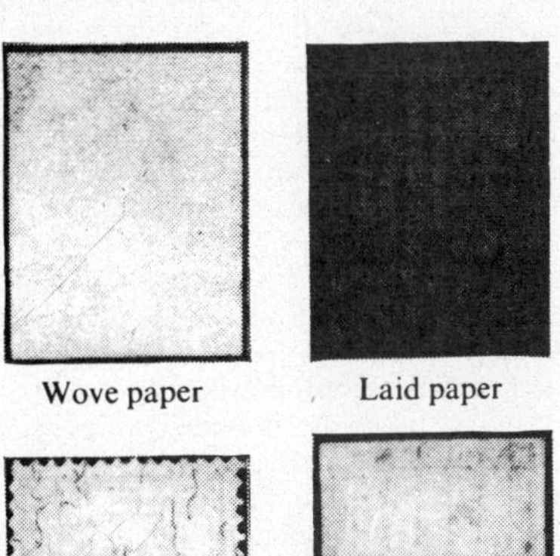

Wove paper

Laid paper

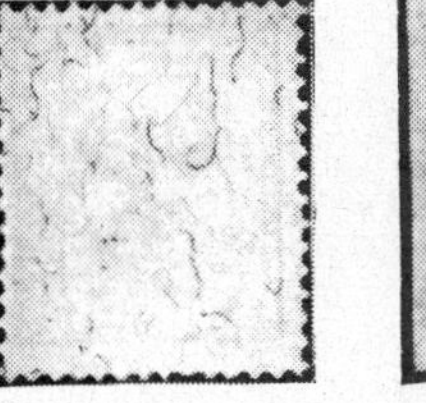

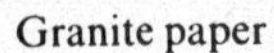

Granite paper

Quadrillé paper

Burelé band

The various makeshifts for normal paper are listed as appropriate. The varieties of double paper and joined paper are recognised. The security device of a printed burelé band on the back of a stamp, as in early Queensland, qualifies for listing.

Descriptive terms. The fact that a paper is handmade (and thus probably of uneven thickness) is mentioned where necessary. Such descriptive terms as "hard" and "soft"; "smooth" and "rough"; "thick", "medium" and "thin" are applied where there is philatelic merit in classifying papers. We do not, for example, even in more specialised listings, classify paper thicknesses in the Wilding and Machin definitives of Great Britain. Weight standards for the paper apply to complete reels only, so that differences on individual stamps are acceptable to the printer provided the reel conforms overall.

Coloured, very white and toned papers. A coloured paper is one that is coloured right through (front and back of the stamp). In the Catalogue the colour of the paper is given in *italics*, thus:

black/*rose* = black design on rose paper.

Papers have been made specially white in recent years by, for example, a very heavy coating of chalk. We do not classify shades of whiteness of paper as distinct varieties. There does exist, however, a type of paper from early days called toned. This is off-white, often brownish or buffish, but it cannot be assigned any definite colour. A toning effect brought on by climate, incorrect storage or gum staining is disregarded here, as this was not the state of the paper when issued.

Modern developments. Two modern developments also affect the listings: printing on self-adhesive paper and the use of metallic foils. For self-adhesive stamps *see* under "Gum", below. Care should be taken not to damage the embossing on stamps impressed on metallic foils, such as Sierra Leone 1965–67, by subjecting the album pages to undue pressure. The possibility of faked "missing gold heads" is noted at the appropriate places in the listing of modern Great Britain.

"Ordinary" and "Chalk-surfaced" papers. The availability of many postage stamps for revenue purposes made necessary some safeguard against the illegitimate re-use of stamps with removable cancellations. This was at first secured by using fugitive inks and later by printing on chalky (chalk-surfaced) paper, both of which made it difficult to remove any form of obliteration without also damaging the stamp design.

With some exceptions we do not list the varieties on chalky paper separately, but we have indicated the existence of the papers by the letters **"O"** (ordinary) and **"C"** (chalky) after the description of all stamps where the chalky paper may be found. Both letters shown together signify that the stamp exists on both papers; if a date is given it is that of the first-mentioned paper and the price quoted is that of the cheaper variety. Where no indication is given, the paper is "ordinary".

Our chalky paper is specifically one which shows a black mark when touched with a silver wire. The paper used during the Second World War for high values, as in Bermuda, the Leeward Islands, etc., was thinly coated with some kind of surfacing which does not react to silver and is therefore regarded (and listed) as "ordinary". Stamps on chalk-surfaced paper can easily lose this coating through immersion in water.

Another paper introduced during the War as a substitute for chalky is rather thick, very white and glossy, and shows little or no watermark, nor does it show a black line when touched with silver. In the Bahamas high values this paper might be mistaken for the chalky (which is thinner and poorer-looking) but for the silver test.

Glazed paper. In 1969 the Crown Agents introduced a new general-purpose paper for use in conjunction with all current printing processes. It generally has a marked glossy surface but the degree varies according to the process used, being more marked in recess-printing stamps. As it does not respond to the silver test this presents a further test where previous printings were on chalky paper. A change of paper to the glazed variety merits separate listing.

Green and yellow papers. Issues of the First World War and immediate postwar period occur on green and yellow papers and these are given separate Catalogue listing. The original coloured papers (coloured throughout) gave way to surface-coloured papers, the stamps having "white backs"; other stamps show one colour on the front and a different one at the back. Because of the numerous variations a grouping of colours is adopted as follows:

YELLOW PAPERS

(1) The original *yellow* paper (throughout), usually bright in colour. The gum is often sparse, of harsh consistency and dull-looking.

(2) The *white backs*.

(3) A bright *lemon* paper. The colour must have a pronounced greenish tinge, different from the "yellow" in (1). As a rule, the gum on stamps using this lemon paper is plentiful- smooth and shiny, and the watermark shows distinctly. Care is needed with stamps printed in green on yellow paper (1) as it may appear that the paper is this lemon.

(4) An *orange-buff* paper. The colour must have a distinct brownish tinge. It is not to be confused with a muddy yellow (1) nor the misleading appearance (on the surface) of stamps printed in red on yellow paper where an engraved plate has been insufficiently wiped.

(5) A *pale yellow* paper that has a creamy tone to the yellow.

GREEN PAPERS

(6) The original "green" paper, varying considerably through shades of *blue-green* and *yellow-green*, the front and back sometimes differing.

(7) The *white backs*.

(8) A paper blue-green on the surface with *pale olive* back. The back must be markedly paler than the front and this and the pronounced olive tinge to the back distinguish it from (6).

(9) Paper with a vivid green surface, commonly called *emerald-green*; it has the olive back of (8).

(10) Paper with *emerald-green* both back and front.

3. Perforation and Rouletting

Perforation gauge. The gauge of a perforation is the number of holes in a length of 2 cm. For correct classification the size of the holes (large or small) may need to be distinguished; in a few cases the actual number of holes on each edge of the stamp needs to be quoted.

Measurement. The Gibbons *Instanta* gauge is the standard for measuring perforations. The stamp is viewed against a dark background with the transparent gauge put on top of it. Though the gauge measures to decimal accuracy, perforations read from it are generally quoted in the Catalogue to the nearest half. For example:

Just over perf 12¾ to just under 13¼ = perf 13
Perf 13¼ exactly, rounded up = perf 13½
Just over perf 13¼ to just under 13¾ = perf 13½
Perf 13¾ exactly, rounded up = perf 14

However, where classification depends on it, actual quarter-perforations are quoted.

Notation. Where no perforation is quoted for an issue it is imperforate. Perforations are usually abbreviated (and spoken) as follows, though sometimes they may be spelled out for clarity. This notation for rectangular stamps (the majority) applies to diamond shapes if "top" is read as the edge to the top right.

P 14: perforated alike on all sides (read: "perf 14").

P 14 × 15: the first figure refers to top and bottom, the second to left and right sides (read: "perf 14 by 15"). This is a compound perforation. For an upright triangular stamp the first figure refers to the two sloping sides and the second to the base. In inverted triangulars the base is first and the second figure refers to the sloping sides.

P 14–15: perforation measuring anything between 14 and 15: the holes are irregularly spaced, thus the gauge may vary along a single line or even along a single edge of the stamp (read: "perf 14 to 15").

P 14 *irregular*: perforated 14 from a worn perforator, giving badly aligned holes irregularly spaced (read: "irregular perf 14").

P comp(ound) 14 × 15: two gauges in use but not necessarily on opposite sides of the stamp. It could be one side in one gauge and three in the other; or two adjacent sides with the same gauge. (Read: "perf compound of 14 and 15".) For three gauges or more, abbreviated as "*P* 14, 14½, 15 *or compound*" for example.

P 14, 14½: perforated approximately 14¼ (read: "perf 14 or 14½"). It does *not* mean two stamps, one perf 14 and the other perf 14½. This obsolescent notation is gradually being replaced in the Catalogue.

Imperf: imperforate (not perforated).

Imperf × *P* 14: imperforate at top and bottom and perf 14 at sides.

Perf × imperf

P 14 × *imperf*: perf 14 at top and bottom and imperforate at sides.

Such headings as "*P* 13 × 14 (*vert*) and *P* 14 × 13 (*horiz*)" indicate which perforations apply to which stamp format—vertical or horizontal.

Some stamps are additionally perforated so that a label or tab is detachable; others have been perforated suitably for use as two halves. Listings are normally for whole stamps, unless stated otherwise.

Other terms. Perforation almost always gives circular holes; where other shapes have been used they are specified, e.g. square holes; lozenge perf. Interrupted perfs are brought about by the omission of pins at regular intervals. Perforations merely simulated by being printed as part of the design are of course ignored. With few exceptions, privately applied perforations are not listed.

Perforation errors and varieties. Authenticated errors, where a stamp normally perforated is accidentally issued imperforate, are listed provided no traces of perforation (blind holes or indentations) remain. They must be provided as pairs, both stamps wholly imperforate, and are only priced in that form.

In Great Britain, numerous of these part-perforated stamps have arisen from the introduction of the Jumelle Press. This has a rotary perforator with rows of pins on one drum engaging with holes on another. Engagement is only gradual when the perforating unit is started up or stopped, giving rise to perforations "fading out", a variety mentioned above as not listed.

Stamps from the Jumelle printings sometimes occur imperforate between stamp and sheet margin. Such errors are not listed in this catalogue, but are covered by the fourth volume of the *Great Britain Specialised Catalogue*.

Pairs described as "imperforate between" have the line of perforations between the two stamps omitted.

Imperf between (*horiz pair*): a horizontal pair of stamps with perfs all around the edges but none between the stamps.

Imperf between (*vert pair*): a vertical pair of stamps with perfs all around the edges but none between the stamps.

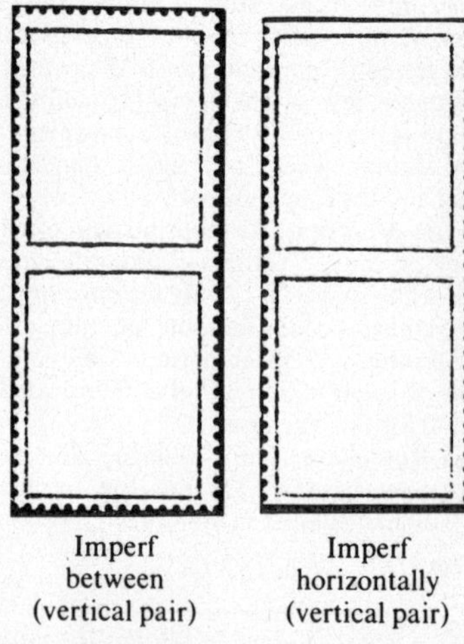

Imperf between (vertical pair) | Imperf horizontally (vertical pair)

Where several of the rows have escaped perforation the resulting varieties are listable. Thus:

Imperf vert (*horiz pair*): a horizontal pair of stamps perforated top and bottom; all three vertical directions are imperf—the two outer edges and between the stamps.

Imperf horiz (*vert pair*): a vertical pair perforated at left and right edges; all three horizontal directions are imperf—the top, bottom and between the stamps.

Straight edges. Large sheets cut up before issue to post offices can cause stamps with straight edges, i.e. imperf on one side or on two sides at right angles. They are not usually listable in this condition and are worth less than corresponding stamps properly perforated all round. This does not, however, apply to certain stamps, mainly from coils and booklets, where straight edges on various sides are the manufacturing norm affecting every stamp. The listings and notes make clear which sides are correctly imperf.

Malfunction. Varieties of double, misplaced or partial perforation caused by error or machine malfunction are not listable, neither are freaks, such as perforations placed diagonally from paper folds, nor missing holes caused by broken pins.

Centering. Well-centred stamps have designs surrounded by equal opposite margins. Where this condition affects the price the fact is stated.

Types of perforating. Where necessary for classification, perforation types are distinguished. These include:

Line perforation from one line of pins punching single rows of holes at a time.

Comb perforation from pins disposed across the sheet in comb formation, punching out holes at three sides of the stamp a row at a time.

Harrow perforation applied to a whole pane or sheet at one stroke.

Rotary perforation from toothed wheels operating across a sheet, then crosswise.

Sewing-machine perforation. The resultant condition, clean-cut or rough, is distinguished where required.

Pin-perforation is the commonly applied term for pin-roulette in which, instead of being punched out, round holes are pricked by sharp-pointed pins and no paper is removed.

Punctured stamps. Perforation holes can be punched into the face of the stamp. Patterns of small holes, often in the shape of initial letters, are privately applied devices against pilferage. These "perfins" are outside the scope. Identification devices, when officially inspired, are listed or noted; they can be shapes, or letters or words formed from holes, sometimes converting one class of stamp into another.

Rouletting. In rouletting the paper is cut, for ease of separation, but none is removed. The gauge is measured, when needed, as for perforations. Traditional French terms descriptive of the type of cut are often used and types include:

Arc roulette (*percé en arc*). Cuts are minute, spaced arcs, each roughly a semicircle.

Cross roulette (*percé en croix*). Cuts are tiny diagonal crosses.

Line roulette (*percé en ligne* or *en ligne droite*). Short straight cuts parallel to the frame of the stamp. The commonest basic roulette. Where not further described, "roulette" means this type.

Rouletted in colour or *coloured roulette* (*percé en lignes colorées* or *en lignes de couleur*). Cuts with coloured edges, arising from notched rule inked simultaneously with the printing plate.

Saw-tooth roulette (*percé en scie*). Cuts applied zigzag fashion to resemble the teeth of a saw.

Serpentine roulette (*percé en serpentin*). Cuts as sharply wavy lines.

Zigzag roulette (*percé en zigzags*). Short straight cuts at angles in alternate directions, producing sharp points on separation. U.S. usage favours "serrate(d) roulette" for this type.

Pin-roulette (originally *percé en points* and now *perforés trous d'epingle*) is commonly called pin-perforation in English.

4. Gum

All stamps listed are assumed to have gum of some kind; if they were issued without gum this is stated. Original gum (o.g.) means that which was present on the stamp as issued to the public. Deleterious climates and the presence of certain chemicals can cause gum to crack and, with early stamps, even make the paper deteriorate. Unscrupulous fakers are adept in removing it and regumming the stamp to meet the unreasoning demand often made for "full o.g." in cases where such a thing is virtually impossible.

The gum normally used on stamps has been gum arabic until the late 1960s when synthetic adhesives were introduced. Harrison and Sons Ltd for instance use *polyvinyl alcohol*, known to philatelists as PVA. This is almost invisible except for a slight yellowish tinge which was incorporated to make it possible to see that the stamps have been gummed. It has advantages in hot countries, as stamps do not curl and sheets are less likely to stick together. Gum arabic and PVA are not distinguished in the lists except that where a stamp exists with both forms this is indicated in footnotes. Our more specialised catalogues provide separate listing of gums for Great Britain.

Self-adhesive stamps are issued on backing paper, from which they are peeled before affixing to mail. Unused examples are priced as for backing paper intact, in which condition they are recommended to be kept. Used examples are best collected on cover or on piece.

5. Watermarks

Stamps are on unwatermarked paper except where the heading to the set says otherwise.

Detection. Watermarks are detected for Catalogue description by one of four methods: (1) holding stamps to the light; (2) laying stamps face down on a dark background; (3) adding a few drops of petroleum ether 40/60 to the stamp laid face down in a watermark tray; or (4) by use of the Morley-Bright Detector, which works by revealing the thinning of the paper at the watermark. (Note that petroleum ether is highly inflammable in use and can damage photogravure stamps.)

Listable types. Stamps occurring on both watermarked and unwatermarked papers are different types and both receive full listing.

Single watermarks (devices occurring once on every stamp) can be modified in size and shape as between different issues; the types are noted but not usually separately listed. Fortuitous absence of watermark from a single stamp or its gross displacement would not be listable.

To overcome registration difficulties the device may be repeated at close intervals (a *multiple watermark*), single stamps thus showing parts of several devices. Similarly, a large *sheet watermark* (or *all-over watermark*) covering numerous stamps can be used. We give informative notes and illustrations for them. The designs may be such that numbers of stamps in the sheet automatically lack watermark: this is not a listable variety. Multiple and all-over watermarks sometimes undergo modifications, but if the various types are difficult to distinguish from single stamps notes are given but not separate listings.

Papermakers' watermarks are noted where known but not listed separately, since most stamps in the sheet will lack them. Sheet watermarks which are nothing more than officially adopted papermakers' watermarks are, however, given normal listing.

Marginal watermarks, falling outside the pane of stamps, are ignored except where misplacement causes the adjoining row to be affected, in which case they are footnoted.

Watermark errors and varieties. Watermark errors are recognised as of major importance. They comprise stamps intended to be on unwatermarked paper but issued watermarked by mistake, or stamps printed on paper with the wrong watermark. Watermark varieties, on the other hand, such as broken or deformed bits on the dandy roll, are not listable.

Watermark positions. The diagram shows how watermark position is described in the Catalogue. Paper has a side intended for printing and watermarks are usually impressed so that they read normally when looked through from that printed side. However, since philatelists customarily detect watermarks by looking at the back of the stamp the watermark diagram also makes clear what is actually seen.

Illustrations in the Catalogue are of watermarks in normal positions (from the front of the stamps) and are actual size where possible.

Differences in watermark position are collectable as distinct varieties. In this Catalogue, however, only normal and sideways watermarks are listed (and "sideways inverted" is treated as "sideways"). Inverted and reversed watermarks have always been outside its scope: in the early days of flat-bed printing sheets of watermarked paper were fed indiscriminately through the press and the resulting watermark positions had no particular philatelic significance. Similarly, the special make-up of sheets for booklets can in some cases give equal quantities of normal and inverted watermarks.

Collectors are reminded that inverted and reversed watermarks are listed (for G.B. and Commonwealth stamps of the present reign) in the *Elizabethan Catalogue* and (for G.B. all reigns) in the *Great Britain Specialised Catalogue* and *Collect British Stamps*.

Where a watermark comes indiscriminately in various positions our policy is to cover this by a general note: we do not give separate listings because the watermark position in these circumstances has no particular philatelic importance. There is a general note of this sort in modern Cyprus, for example. Issues printed since 1962 by Aspioti-Elka occur with the vertical stamps having the watermark normal or inverted, while horizontal stamps are likewise found with the watermark reading upwards or downwards.

Standard types of watermark. Some watermarks have been used generally for various British possessions rather than exclusively for a single colony. To avoid repetition the Catalogue classifies 15 general types, as under, with references in the headings throughout the listings being given either in words or in the form "*W* w **14**" (meaning "watermark type w **14**"). In those cases where watermark illustrations appear in the listings themselves, the respective reference reads, for example, *W* **153**, thus indicating that the watermark will be found in the normal sequence of illustrations as (type) **153**.

The general types are as follows, with an example of each quoted.

AS DESCRIBED (Read through front of stamp)		AS SEEN DURING WATERMARK DETECTION (Stamp face down and back examined)
GvR	Normal	GvR (mirrored)
GvR (inverted)	Inverted	GvR (inverted, mirrored)
GvR (mirrored)	Reversed	GvR
GvR (inverted, mirrored)	Reversed and inverted	GvR (inverted)
GvR (sideways)	Sideways	GvR (sideways, mirrored)
GvR (sideways inverted)	Sideways inverted	GvR (sideways inverted, mirrored)

W	*Description*	*Example*
w **1**	Large Star	St. Helena No. 1
w **2**	Small Star	Turks Is. No. 4
w **3**	Broad (pointed) Star	Grenada No. 24
w **4**	Crown (over) CC, small stamp	Antigua No. 13
w **5**	Crown (over) CC, large stamp	Antigua No. 31
w **6**	Crown (over) CA, small stamp	Antigua No. 21
w **7**	Crown CA (CA over Crown), large stamp	Sierra Leone No. 54
w **8**	Multiple Crown CA	Antigua No. 41
w **9**	Multiple Crown Script CA	Seychelles No. 158
w **9*a***	do. Error	Seychelles No. 158a
w **9*b***	do. Error	Seychelles No. 158b
w **10**	V over Crown	N.S.W. No. 327
w **11**	Crown over A	N.S.W. No. 347
w **12**	Multiple St. Edward's Crown Block CA	Antigua No. 149
w **13**	Multiple PTM	Johore No. 166
w **14**	Multiple Crown CA Diagonal	Antigua No. 426
w **15**	Multiple POST OFFICE	Kiribati No. 141

CC in these watermarks is an abbreviation for "Crown Colonies" and CA for "Crown Agents".

Watermarks w **1**, w **2** and w **3** are on stamps printed by Perkins, Bacon; w **4** onwards on stamps from De La Rue and other printers.

w **1**
Large Star

w **2**
Small Star

w **3**
Broad (pointed) Star

Watermark w **1**, *Large Star*, measures 15 to 16 mm across the star from point to point and about 27 mm from centre to centre vertically between stars in the sheet. It was made for long stamps like Ceylon 1857 and St. Helena 1856.

Watermark w **2**, *Small Star*, is of similar design but measures 12 to 13½ mm from point to point and 24 mm from centre to centre vertically. It was for use with ordinary-size stamps such as Grenada 1863–71.

When the Large Star watermark was used with the smaller stamps it only occasionally comes in the centre of the paper. It is frequently so misplaced as to show portions of two stars above and below and this eccentricity will very often help in determining the watermark.

Watermark w **3**, *Broad* (*pointed*) *Star*, resembles w **1** but the points are broader.

w **4**
Crown (over) CC

w **5**
Crown (over) CC

Two *Crown* (*over*) *CC* watermarks were used: w **4** was for stamps of ordinary size and w **5** for those of larger size.

w **6**
Crown (over) CA

w **7**
CA over Crown

Two watermarks of *Crown CA* type were used, w **6** being for stamps of ordinary size. The other, w **7**, is properly described as *CA over Crown*. It was specially made for paper on which it was intended to print long fiscal stamps: that some were used postally accounts for the appearance of w **7** in the Catalogue. The watermark occupies twice the space of the ordinary Crown CA watermark, w **6**. Stamps of normal size printed on paper with w **7** watermark show it *sideways*; it takes a horizontal pair of stamps to show the entire watermark.

w **8**
Multiple Crown CA

w **9**
Multiple Crown Script CA

Multiple watermarks began in 1904 with w **8**, *Multiple Crown CA*, changed from 1921 to w **9**, *Multiple Crown Script CA*. On stamps of ordinary size portions of two or three watermarks appear and on the large-sized stamps a greater number can be observed. The change to letters in script character with w **9** was accompanied by a Crown of distinctly different shape.

w **9***a*: Error,
Crown missing

w **9***b*: Error,
St. Edward's Crown

The *Multiple Crown Script CA* watermark, w **9**, is known with two errors recurring among the 1950–52 printings of several territories. In the first a crown has fallen away from the dandy-roll that impresses the watermark into the paper pulp. It gives w **9***a*, *Crown missing*, but this omission has been found in both "Crown only" (*illustrated*) and "Crown CA" rows. The resulting faulty paper was used for Seychelles, Johore and the postage due stamps of nine colonies.

When the omission was noticed a second mishap occurred, which was to insert a wrong crown in the space, giving w **9***b*, *St. Edward's Crown*. This produced varieties in Bahamas, St. Kitts-Nevis and Singapore and the incorrect crown likewise occurs in "Crown only" and "Crown CA" rows.

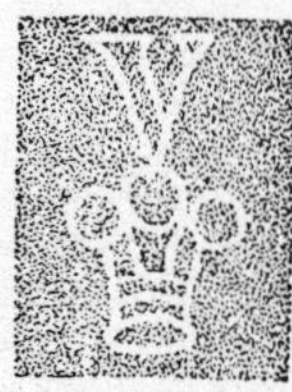

w **10**
V over Crown

w **11**
Crown over A

Resuming the general types, two watermarks found in issues of several Australian States are: w **10**, *V over Crown*, and w **11**, *Crown over A*.

w **12**
Multiple St. Edward's Crown Block CA

The *Multiple St. Edward's Crown Block CA* watermark, w **12**, was introduced in 1957 and besides the change in the Crown (from that used in *Multiple Crown Script CA*, w **9**) the letters reverted to block capitals. The new watermark began to appear sideways in 1966 and these stamps are generally listed as separate sets.

w **13**
Multiple PTM

The watermark w **13**, *Multiple PTM*, was introduced for new Malayan issues in November 1961.

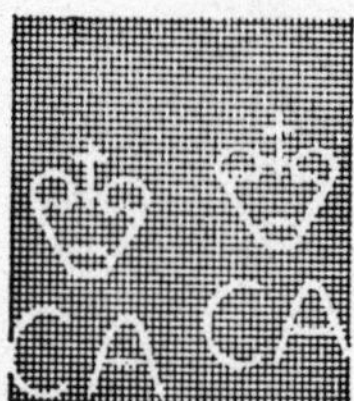

w **14**
Multiple Crown CA Diagonal

By 1974 the two dandy-rolls (the "upright" and the "sideways") for w **12** were wearing out; the Crown Agents therefore discontinued using the sideways-watermark one and retained the other only as a stand-by. A new dandy-roll with the pattern of w **14**, *Multiple Crown CA Diagonal*, was introduced and first saw use with some Churchill Centenary issues.

The new watermark has the design arranged in gradually spiralling rows. It is improved in design to allow smooth passage over the paper (the gaps between letters and rows had caused jolts in previous dandy-rolls) and the sharp corners and angles, where fibres used to accumulate, have been eliminated by rounding.

This watermark has no "normal" sideways position amongst the different printers using it. To avoid confusion our more specialised listings do not rely on such terms as "sideways inverted" but describe the direction in which the watermark points.

w **15**
Multiple POST OFFICE

During 1981 w **15**, *Multiple POST OFFICE*, was introduced for certain issues prepared by Philatelists Ltd, acting for various countries in the Indian Ocean, Pacific and West Indies.

In recent years the use of watermarks has, to a small extent, been superseded by fluorescent security markings. These are often more visible from the reverse of the stamp (Cook Islands from 1970 onwards), but have occurred printed over the design (Hong Kong Nos. 415/30). In 1982 the Crown Agents introduced a new stock paper, without watermark, known as "C-Kurity" on which a fluorescent pattern of blue rosettes is visible on the reverse, beneath the gum. This paper has, so far, been used for issues from Gambia and Norfolk Island.

6. Colours

Stamps in two or three colours have these named in order of appearance, from the centre moving outwards. Four colours or more are usually listed as multicoloured.

In compound colour names the second is the predominant one, thus:

orange-red = a red tending towards orange;

red-orange = an orange containing more red than usual.

Standard colours used. The 100 colours most used for stamp identification are given in the Stanley Gibbons Colour Guide; these, plus a further 100 variations for more specialised use, are included in the Stanley Gibbons Stamp Colour Key. The Catalogue has used the Guide and Key as standards for describing new issues for some years. The names are also introduced as lists are rewritten, though exceptions are made for those early issues where traditional names have become universally established.

Determining colours. When comparing actual stamps with colour samples in the Guide or Key, view in a good north daylight (or its best substitute: fluorescent "colour-matching" light). Sunshine is not recommended. Choose a solid portion of the stamp design; if available, marginal markings such as solid bars of colour or colour check dots are helpful. Shading lines in the design can be misleading as they appear lighter than solid colour. Postmarked portions of a stamp appear darker than normal. If more than one colour is present, mask off the extraneous ones as the eye tends to mix them.

Errors of colour. Major colour errors in stamps or overprints which qualify for listing are: wrong colours; one colour inverted in relation to the rest; albinos (colourless impressions), where these have Expert Committee certificates; prominent colours completely omitted, but only on unused stamps (if found on used stamps the information is footnoted) and with good credentials, missing colours being frequently faked. In this Catalogue "prominent" means the country name or face value or colours that affect a considerable area of the stamp. Missing colours of less magnitude are reserved for the more specialised listings.

Colours only partially omitted are not recognised. Colour shifts, however spectacular, are not listed.

Shades. Shades in philately refer to variations in the intensity of a colour or the presence of differing amounts of other colours. They are particularly significant when they can be linked to specific printings. In general, shades need to be quite marked to fall within the scope of this Catalogue; it does not favour nowadays listing the often numerous shades of a stamp, but chooses a single applicable colour name which will indicate particular groups of outstanding shades. Furthermore, the listings refer to colours as issued: they may deteriorate into something different through the passage of time.

Modern colour printing by lithography is prone to marked differences of shade, even within a single run, and variations can occur within the same sheet. Such shades are not listed.

Aniline colours. An aniline colour meant originally one derived from coal-tar; it now refers more widely to colour of a particular brightness suffused on the surface of a stamp and showing through clearly on the back.

Colours of overprints and surcharges. All overprints and surcharges are in black unless stated otherwise in the heading or after the description of the stamp.

7. Specimen Stamps

Originally, stamps overprinted SPECIMEN were circulated to postmasters or kept in official records, but after the establishment of the Universal Postal Union supplies were sent to Berne for distribution to the postal administrations of member countries.

During the period 1884 to 1928 most of the stamps of British Crown Colonies required for this purpose were overprinted SPECIMEN in various shapes and sizes by their printers from typeset formes. Some locally produced provisionals were handstamped locally, as were sets prepared for presentation. From 1928 stamps were punched with holes forming the word SPECIMEN, each firm of printers using a different machine or machines. From 1948 the stamps supplied for U.P.U. distribution were no longer punctured.

Stamps of some other Commonwealth territories were overprinted or handstamped locally, while stamps of Great Britain and those overprinted for use in overseas postal agencies (mostly of the higher denominations) bore SPECIMEN overprints and handstamps applied by the Inland Revenue or the Post Office.

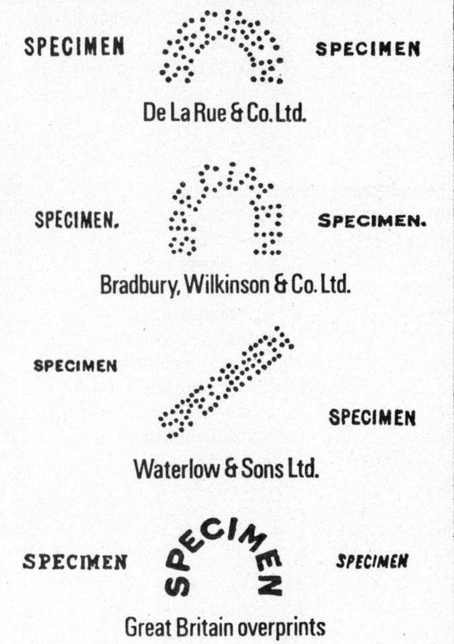

Some of the commoner types of overprints or punctures are illustrated here. Collectors are warned that dangerous forgeries of the punctured type exist.

The *Part 1 (British Commonwealth) Catalogue* records those Specimen overprints or perforations intended for distribution by the U.P.U. to member countries. In addition the Specimen overprints of Australia and its dependent territories, which were sold to collectors by the Post Office, are also included.

All other Specimens are outside the scope of this volume. The *Elizabethan Catalogue* contains details of modern Specimen overprints issued for publicity purposes.

Specimens are not quoted in Great Britain as they are fully listed in the Stanley Gibbons *Great Britain Specialised Catalogue*.

In specifying type of specimen for individual high-value stamps, "H/S" means handstamped, "Optd" is overprinted and "Perf" is punctured. Some sets occur mixed, e.g. "Optd/Perf". If unspecified, the type is apparent from the date or it is the same as for the lower values quoted as a set.

Prices. Prices for stamps up to £1 are quoted in sets; higher values are priced singly after the colours, thus "(S. £20)". Where specimens exist in more than one type the price quoted is for the cheapest. Specimen stamps have rarely survived even as pairs; these and strips of three, four or five are worth considerably more than singles.

8. Luminescence

Machines which sort mail electronically have been introduced in recent years. In consequence some countries have issued stamps on fluorescent or phosphorescent papers, while others have marked their stamps with phosphor bands.

The various papers can only be distinguished by ultraviolet lamps emitting particular wavelengths. They are separately listed only when the stamps have some other means of distinguishing them, visible without the use of these lamps. Where this is not so, the papers are recorded in footnotes or headings.

For this Catalogue we do not consider it appropriate that collectors be compelled to have use of an ultraviolet lamp before being able to identify stamps by our listings. Some experience will also be found necessary in interpreting the results given by ultraviolet. Collectors using the lamps, nevertheless, should exercise great care in their use as exposure to their light is extremely dangerous to the eyes.

Phosphor bands are listable, since they are visible to the naked eye (by holding stamps at an angle to the light and looking along them, the bands appear dark). Stamps existing with and without phosphor bands or with differing numbers of bands are given separate listings. Varieties such as double bands, bands omitted, misplaced or printed on the back are not listed.

Detailed descriptions appear at appropriate places in the listings in explanation of luminescent papers; *see*, for example, Australia above No. 308, Canada above Nos. 472 and 611, Cook Is. above No. 249, etc.

For Great Britain, where since 1959 phosphors have played a prominent and intricate part in stamp issues, the main notes above Nos. 599, 723 and below X960 should be studied, as well as the footnotes to individual listings where appropriate. In general the classification is as follows and is particularly important in understanding the decimal "Machin" definitives (No. X841 onwards).

Stamps with *phosphor bands* are those where a separate cylinder applies the phosphor after the stamps are printed. Issues with "all-over" phosphor have the "band" covering the entire stamp. Parts of the stamp covered by phosphor bands, or the entire surface for "all-over" phosphor versions, appear matt. Stamps on *phosphorised paper* have the phosphor added to the paper coating before the stamps are printed. Issues on this paper have a completely shiny surface.

Further particularisation of phosphor—their methods of printing and the colours they exhibit under ultraviolet—is outside the scope. The more specialised listings should be consulted for this information.

9. Coil Stamps

Stamps issued only in coil form are given full listing. If stamps are issued in both sheets and coils the coil stamps are listed separately only where there is some feature (e.g. perforation or watermark sideways) by which singles can be distinguished. Coil strips containing different stamps *se-tenant* are also listed.

Coil join pairs are too random and too easily faked to permit of listing; similarly ignored are coil stamps which have accidentally suffered an extra row of perforations from the claw mechanism in a malfunctioning vending machine.

10. Booklet Stamps

Stamp booklets are outside the scope of this Catalogue.

Single stamps from booklets are listed if they are distinguishable in some way (such as watermark or perforation) from similar sheet stamps.

Booklet panes are listed where they contain stamps of different denominations *se-tenant*, where stamp-size labels are included, or where such panes are otherwise identifiable. Booklet panes are placed in the listing under the lowest denomination present.

Particular perforations (straight edges) are covered by appropriate notes.

11. Miniature Sheets and Sheetlets

We distinguish between "miniature sheets" and "sheetlets" and this affects the catalogue numbering. An item in sheet form that is postally valid, containing a single stamp, pair, block or set of stamps, with wide, inscribed and/or decorative margins, is a *miniature sheet* if it is sold at post offices as an indivisible entity. As such the Catalogue allots a single **MS** number and describes what stamps make it up. (*See* Great Britain 1978 Historic Buildings, No. **MS**1058, as an example.) The *sheetlet* or *small sheet* differs in that the individual stamps are intended to be purchased separately for postal purposes. For sheetlets, all the component postage stamps are numbered individually and the composition explained in a footnote. (The 1978 Christmas Island Christmas sheetlet, Nos. 99/107, is an example.) Note that the definitions refer to post office sale—not how items may be subsequently offered by stamp dealers.

Production as sheetlets is a modern marketing development chosen by postal administrations to interest collectors in purchasing the item complete; if he has done so he should, as with all *se-tenant* arrangements, keep the sheetlet intact in his collection.

12. Forgeries and Fakes

Forgeries. Where space permits, notes are considered if they can give a concise description that will permit unequivocal detection of a forgery. Generalised warnings, lacking detail, are not nowadays inserted, since their value to the collector is problematic.

Fakes. Unwitting fakes are numerous, particularly "new shades" which are colour changelings brought about by exposure to sunlight, soaking in water contaminated with dyes from adherent paper, contact with oil and dirt from a pocketbook, and so on. Fraudulent operators, in addition, can offer to arrange: removal of hinge marks; repairs of thins on white or coloured papers; replacement of missing margins or perforations; reperforating in true or false gauges; removal of fiscal cancellations; rejoining of severed pairs, strips and blocks; and (a major hazard) regumming. Collectors can only be urged to purchase from reputable sources and to insist upon Expert Committee certification where there is any kind of doubt.

The Catalogue can consider footnotes about fakes where these are specific enough to assist in detection.

Abbreviations

Printers

A.B.N. Co	American Bank Note Co, New York.
A. & M.	Alden & Mowbray Ltd, Oxford.
Ashton-Potter	Ashton-Potter Ltd, Toronto.
Aspioti-Elka (Aspiotis)	Aspioti-Elka, Greece.
B.A.B.N.	British American Bank Note Co, Ottawa.
B.D.T.	B.D.T. International Security Printing Ltd, Dublin, Ireland.
B.W.	Bradbury Wilkinson & Co, Ltd.
C.B.N.	Canadian Bank Note Co, Ottawa.
Continental B.N. Co	Continental Bank Note Co.
Courvoisier	Imprimerie Courvoisier S.A., La-Chaux-de-Fonds, Switzerland.
D.L.R.	De La Rue & Co, Ltd, London, and (from 1961) Bogota, Colombia.
Edila	Editions de l'Aubetin, S.A.
Enschedé	Joh. Enschedé en Zonen, Haarlem, Netherlands.
Format	Format International Security Printers, Ltd, London.
Harrison	Harrison & Sons, Ltd, London.
Heraclio Fournier	Heraclio Fournier S.A., Vitoria, Spain.
J.W.	John Waddington of Kirkstall, Ltd.
P.B.	Perkins Bacon Ltd, London.
Questa	Questa Colour Security Printers, Ltd.
Ueberreuter	(incorporating Brader Rosenbaum), Korneuburg, Austria.
Walsall	Walsall Security Printers, Ltd.
Waterlow	Waterlow & Sons, Ltd, London.

General Abbreviations

Alph	Alphabet
Anniv	Anniversary
C, c	Chalky paper
Comp	Compound (perforation)
Des	Designer; designed
Diag	Diagonal; diagonally
Eng	Engraver; engraved
F.C.	Fiscal Cancellation
H/S	Handstamped
Horiz	Horizontal; horizontally
Imp, Imperf	Imperforate
Inscr	Inscribed
L	Left
Litho	Lithographed
mm	Millimetres
MS	Miniature sheet
N.Y.	New York
O, o	Ordinary paper
Opt(d)	Overprint(ed)
P or P-c	Pen-cancelled
P, Pf or Perf	Perforated
Photo	Photogravure
Pl	Plate
Pr	Pair
Ptd	Printed
Ptg	Printing
R	Right
R.	Row
Recess	Recess-printed
Roto	Rotogravure
Roul	Rouletted
S	Specimen (overprint)
Surch	Surcharge(d)
T.C.	Telegraph Cancellation
T	Type
Typo	Typographed
Un	Unused
Us	Used
Vert	Vertical; vertically
W or wmk	Watermark
Wmk s	Watermark sideways

(†) = Does not exist.

(—) (or blank price column) = Exists, or may exist, but no market price is known.

/ between colours means "on" and the colour following is that of the paper on which the stamp is printed.

Colours of Stamps

Bl (blue); blk (black); brn (brown); car, carm (carmine); choc (chocolate); clar (claret); emer (emerald); grn (green); ind (indigo); mag (magenta); mar (maroon); mult (multicoloured); mve (mauve); ol (olive); orge (orange); pk (pink); pur (purple); scar (scarlet); sep (sepia); turq (turquoise); ultram (ultramarine); verm (vermilion); vio (violet); yell (yellow).

Colours of Overprints and Surcharges

(B.) = blue, (Blk.) = black, (Br.) = brown, (C.) = carmine, (G.) = green, (Mag.) = magenta, (Mve.) = mauve, (Ol.) = olive, (O.) = orange, (P.) = purple, (Pk.) = pink, (R.) = red, (Sil.) = silver, (V.) = violet, (Vm.) or (Verm.) = vermilion, (W.) = white, (Y.) = yellow.

Arabic Numerals

As in the case of European figures, the details of the Arabic numerals vary in different stamp designs, but they should be readily recognised with the aid of this illustration.

٠	١	٢	٣	٤	٥	٦	٧	٨	٩
0	1	2	3	4	5	6	7	8	9

STANLEY GIBBONS STAMP CATALOGUE

Part 1: BRITISH COMMONWEALTH

with Ireland, Pakistan and South Africa

88th EDITION—1986

Great Britain

Great Britain Postage Stamps, GB 1
Regional Issues—
I. Northern Ireland, GB 41
II. Scotland, GB 42
III. Wales, GB 42
Postage Due Stamps, GB 42
Official Stamps, GB 43
Postal Fiscal Stamps, GB 44
Channel Islands General Issue, GB 45
Guernsey, GB 45
Isle of Man, GB 50
Jersey, GB 55
British Post Offices Abroad, GB 61

STAMPS ON COVER. Prices are quoted, as a third price column, for those Victorian and Edwardian issues usually found used on cover. In general these prices refer to the cheapest version of each basic stamp with other shades, plates or varieties, together with unusual frankings and postmarks, being worth more.

QUEEN VICTORIA
20 June 1837—22 January 1901

MULREADY ENVELOPES AND LETTER SHEETS, so called from the name of the designer, William Mulready, were issued concurrently with the first British adhesive stamps.

1d. black

Envelopes: £100 *unused*; £130 *used*.
Letter Sheets: £90 *unused*; £110 *used*.

2d. blue

Envelopes: £150 *unused*; £500 *used*.
Letter Sheets: £130 *unused*; £450 *used*.

LINE-ENGRAVED ISSUES

GENERAL NOTES

Brief notes on some aspects of the line-engraved stamps follow, but for further information and a full specialist treatment of these issues collectors are recommended to consult Volume 1 of the Stanley Gibbons *Great Britain Specialised Catalogue*.

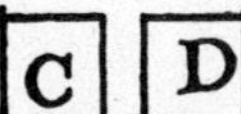

Alphabet I

Alphabet II

Alphabet III

Alphabet IV

Typical Corner Letters of the four Alphabets

Alphabets. Four different letterings were used for the corner letters on stamps prior to the issue with letters in all four corners, these being known to collectors as:

Alphabet I. Used for all plates made from 1840 to the end of 1851. Letters small.

Alphabet II. Plates from 1852 to mid-1855. Letters larger, heavier and broader.

Alphabet III. Plates from mid-1855 to end of period. Letters tall and more slender.

Alphabet IV. 1861. 1d. Die II, Plates 50 and 51 only. Letters were hand-engraved instead of being punched on the plate. They are therefore inconsistent in shape and size but generally larger and outstanding.

While the general descriptions and the illustrations of typical letters given above may be of some assistance, only long experience and published aids can enable every stamp to be allocated to its particular Alphabet without hesitation, as certain letters in each are similar to those in one of the others.

Blued Paper. The blueing of the paper of the earlier issues is believed to be due to the presence of prussiate of potash in the printing ink, or in the paper, which, under certain conditions, tended to colour the paper when the sheets were damped for printing. An alternative term is bleuté paper.

Corner Letters. The corner letters on the early British stamps were intended as a safeguard against forgery, each stamp in the sheet having a different combination of letters. Taking the first 1d. stamp, printed in 20 horizontal rows of 12, as an example, the lettering is as follows:

Row 1. A A, A B, A C, etc. to A L.

Row 2. B A, B B, B C, etc. to B L.

and so on to

Row 20. T A, T B, T C, etc. to T L.

On the stamps with four corner letters, those in the upper corners are in the reverse positions to those in the lower corners. Thus in a sheet of 240 (12 × 20) the sequence is:

Row 1. AA/AA BA/AB CA/AC etc. to LA/AL

Row 2. AB/BA BB/BB CB/BC etc. to LB/BL

and so on to

Row 20. AT/TA BT/TB CT/TC etc. to LT/TL

Placing letters in all four corners was not only an added precaution against forgery but was meant to deter unmarked parts of used stamps being pieced together and passed off as an unused whole.

Dies. The first die of the 1d. was used for making the original die of the 2d., both the No Lines and White Lines issues. In 1855 the 1d. Die I was amended by retouching the head and deepening the lines on a transferred impression of the original. This later version, known to collectors as Die II, was used for making the dies for the 1d. and 2d. with letters in all four corners and also for the 1½d.

The two dies are illustrated above No. 17 in the catalogue.

Double letter

Guide line in corner

Guide line through value

Double Corner Letters. These are due to the workman placing his letter-punch in the wrong position at the first attempt, when lettering the plate, and then correcting the mistake; or to a slight shifting of the punch when struck. If a wrong letter was struck in the first instance, traces of a wrong letter may appear in a corner in addition to the correct one. A typical example is illustrated.

Guide Lines and Dots. When laying down the impressions of the design on the early plates, fine vertical and horizontal guide lines were marked on the plates to assist the operative. These were usually removed from the gutter margins, but could not be removed from the stamp impressions without damage to the plate, so that in such cases they appear on the printed stamps, sometimes in the corners, sometimes through "POSTAGE" or the value. Typical examples are illustrated.

Guide dots or cuts were similarly made to indicate the spacing of the guide lines. These too sometimes appear on the stamps.

Ivory Head

"Ivory Head." The so-called "ivory head" variety is one in which the Queen's Head shows white on the back of the stamp. It arises from the comparative absence of ink in the head portion of the design, with consequent absence of blueing. (*See* "Blued Paper" note above.)

Line-engraving. In this context "line-engraved" is synonymous with recess-printing, in which the engraver cuts recesses in a plate and printing (the coloured areas) is from these recesses. "Line-engraved" is the traditional philatelic description for these stamps; other equivalent terms found are "engraving in *taille-douce*" (French) or "in *intaglio*" (Italian).

Plates. Until the introduction of the stamps with letters in all four corners, the number of the plate was not indicated in the design of the stamp, but was printed on the sheet margin. By long study of identifiable blocks and the minor variations in the design, coupled with the position of the corner letters, philatelists are now able to allot many of these stamps to their respective plates. Specialist collectors often endeavour to obtain examples of a given stamp printed from its different plates and our catalogue accordingly reflects this depth of detail.

Maltese Cross — Type of Town postmark

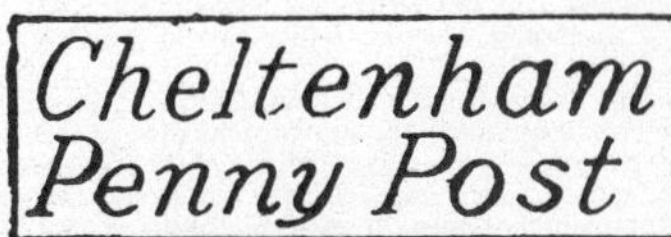

Type of Penny Post cancellation

Example of 1844 type postmark

Postmarks. The so-called "Maltese Cross" design was the first employed for obliterating British postage stamps and was in use from 1840 to 1844. Being hand-cut, the obliterating stamps varied greatly in detail and some distinctive types can be allotted to particular towns or offices. Local types, such as those used at Manchester, Norwich, Leeds, etc., are keenly sought. A red ink was first employed, but was superseded by black, after some earlier experiments, in February 1841. Maltese Cross obliterations in other colours are rare.

Obliterations of this type, numbered 1 to 12 in the centre, were used at the London Chief Office in 1843 and 1844.

Some straight-line cancellations were in use in 1840 at the Penny Post receiving offices, normally applied on the envelope, the adhesives then being obliterated at the Head Office. They are nevertheless known, with or without Maltese Cross, on the early postage stamps.

In 1842 some offices in S.W. England used dated postmarks in place of the Maltese Cross, usually on the back of the letter since they were not originally intended as obliterators. These town postmarks have likewise been found on adhesives.

In 1844 the Maltese Cross design was superseded by numbered obliterators of varied type, one of which is illustrated. They are naturally comparatively scarce on the first 1d. and 2d. stamps. Like the Maltese Cross they are found in various colours, some of which are rare.

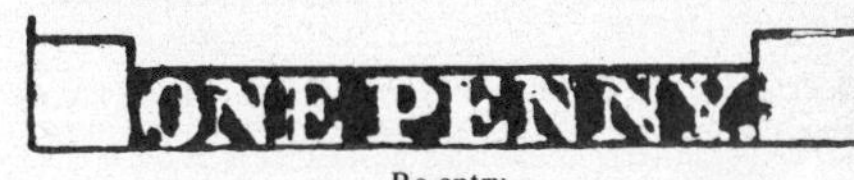

Re-entry

"Union Jack" re-entry

Re-entries. Re-entries on the plate show as a doubling of part of the design of the stamp generally at top or bottom. Many re-entries are very slight while others are most marked. A typical one is illustrated.

The *"Union Jack" re-entry*, so called owing to the effect of the re-entry on the appearance of the corner stars (*see illustration*) occurs on stamp L K of Plate 75 of the 1d. red, Die I.

T A (T L) M A (M L)
Varieties of Large Crown Watermark

I Two states of Large Crown Watermark II

Watermarks. Two watermark varieties, as illustrated, consisting of crowns of entirely different shape, are found in sheets of the Large Crown paper and fall on stamps lettered M A and T A (or M L and T L when the paper is printed on the wrong side). Both varieties are found on the 1d. rose-red of 1857, while the M A (M L) variety comes also on some plates of the 1d. of 1864 (Nos. 43, 44) up to about Plate 96. On the 2d. the T A (T L) variety is known on plates 8 and 9, and the M A (M L) on later prints of plate 9. These varieties may exist inverted, or inverted reversed on stamps lettered A A and A L and H A and H L, and some are known.

In 1861 a minor alteration was made in the Large Crown watermark by the removal of the two vertical strokes, representing *fleurs-de-lis*, which projected upwards from the uppermost of the three horizontal curves at the base of the Crown. Hence two states are distinguishable, as illustrated.

CONDITION—IMPERFORATE LINE-ENGRAVED ISSUES

The prices quoted for the 1840 and 1841 imperforate Line-engraved issues are for "fine" examples. As condition is most important in assessing the value of a stamp, the following definitions will assist collectors in the evaluation of individual examples.

Four main factors are relevant when considering quality.

(a) **Impression.** This should be clean and the surface free of any rubbing or unnatural blurring which would detract from the appearance.

(b) **Margins.** This is perhaps the most difficult factor to evaluate. Stamps described as "fine", the standard adopted in this catalogue for pricing purposes, should have margins of the recognised width, defined as approximately one half of the distance between two adjoining unsevered stamps. Stamps described as "very fine" or "superb" should have margins which are proportionately larger than those of a "fine" stamp. Examples with close margins should not, generally, be classified as "fine".

(c) **Cancellation.** On a "fine" stamp this should be reasonably clear and not noticeably smudged. A stamp described as "superb" should have a neat cancellation, preferably centrally placed or to the right.

(d) **Appearance.** Stamps, at the prices quoted, should always be without any tears, creases, bends or thins and should not be toned on either the front or back. Stamps with such defects are worth only a proportion of the catalogue price.

Good

Fine

Very Fine

Superb

The above actual size illustrations of 1840 1d. blacks show the various grades of quality. When comparing these illustrations it should be assumed that they are all from the same plate and that they are free of any hidden defects.

PRINTERS. Nos. 1/53*a* were recess-printed by Perkins, Bacon & Petch, known from 1852 as Perkins, Bacon & Co.

1

1*a*

2 Small Crown

(Eng Charles and Frederick Heath)

1840 (6–8 May). *Letters in lower corners. Wmk Small Crown. W* **2.** *Imperf.*

No.	Type			Un	Used	Used on cover
1	1	1d. intense black	.. ..	£3250	£190	
2		1d. black	.. ..	£2750	£140	£225
3		1d. grey-black (worn plate)	..	£3000	£180	
4	1*a*	2d. deep full blue (8.5.40)	..	£7000	£375	
5		2d. blue	.. ..	£5500	£275	£550
6		2d. pale blue	.. ..	£7000	£350	

The 1d. stamp in black was printed from Plates 1 to 11. Plate 1 exists in two states (known to collectors as 1*a* and 1*b*), the latter being the result of extensive repairs.

Repairs were also made to plates 2, 5, 6, 8, 9, 10 and 11, and certain impressions exist in two or more states.

The so-called "Royal reprint" of the 1d. black was made in 1864, from Plate 66, Die II, on paper with Large Crown watermark, inverted. A printing was also made in carmine, on paper with the same watermark, normal.

For 1d. black with "VR" in upper corners *see* No. V1 under Official Stamps.

The 2d. stamps were printed from Plates 1 and 2.

Plates of 1d. black

Plate	Un	Used
1*a*	£4500	£175
1*b*	£2750	£140
2	£2750	£140
3	£3500	£190
4	£3000	£160
5	£2750	£150
6	£2750	£140
7	£3250	£180
8	£3500	£190
9	£4000	£225
10	£4500	£300
11	£4500	£1600

Varieties of 1d. black

			Un	Used
a.	On *bleuté* paper (Plates 1 to 8) ..	*from*	—	£160
b.	Double letter in corner ..	*from*	£3000	£160
bb.	Re-entry ..	*from*	£3250	£180
bc.	"PB" re-entry (Plate 5, 3rd state)		—	£3500
cc.	Large letters in each corner (E J, I L, J C and P A) (Plate 1*b*) ..	*from*	£3500	£300
c.	Guide line in corner ..		£3000	£160
d.	„ „ through value ..		£3000	£160
e.	Watermark inverted ..		£3750	£325
g.	Obliterated red Maltese Cross ..		—	£140
h.	„ black „ „ ..		—	£140
i.	„ blue „ „ ..		—	£1000
k.	„ magenta „ „ ..		—	£500
m.	„ yellow „ „ ..		—	£3000
n.	Number (1 to 12) in Maltese Cross	*from*	—	£1000
o.	Town obliteration (without Maltese Cross) in black on stamp ..	*from*	—	£900
p.	Town obliteration (without Maltese Cross) in yellow on stamp ..	*from*	—	£3750
q.	Town obliteration (without Maltese Cross) in red on stamp ..	*from*	—	£950
r.	"Penny Post" obliteration in black on stamp ..	*from*	—	£950
s.	Obliteration of 1844 in black on stamp	*from*	—	£350

Plates of 2d. blue

Plate		Un	Used
1	*Shades from*	£5500	£275
2	*Shades from*	£6500	£350

Varieties of 2d. blue

		Un	Used
a.	Double letter in corner ..	—	£400
aa.	Re-entry ..	—	£450
b.	Guide line in corner ..	—	£350
c.	„ „ through value ..	—	£350
d.	Watermark inverted ..	£7000	£600
e.	Obliterated red Maltese Cross (Plate 1)	—	£275
f.	„ black „ „ ..	—	£275
g.	„ blue „ „ ..	—	£1700
h.	„ magenta „ „ ..	—	£1400
i.	Number (1 to 12) in Maltese Cross .. .. .. *from*	—	£2250
k.	Town obliteration (without Maltese Cross) in black on stamp ..	—	£950
l.	Obliteration of 1844 in black on stamp	—	£500
m.	„ „ „ „ blue „ ..	—	£1100
n.	"Penny Post" obliteration in black on stamp	—	£1100

1841 (10 Feb). *Printed from "black" plates. Wmk W* **2.** *Paper more or less blued. Imperf.*

No.	Type		Un	Used	Used on cover
7	1	1d. red-brown (*shades*) ..	£450	24·00	50·00
		a. "PB" re-entry (Plate 5, 3rd state) ..	—	£1000	

The first printings of the 1d. in red were made from Plates 1*b*, 2, 5 and 8 to 11 used for the 1d. black.

1d. red-brown from "black" plates

Plate	Un	Used
1*b*	£2750	£140
2	£1600	85·00
5	£600	35·00
8	£475	27·00
9	£450	24·00
10	£475	27·00
11	£500	24·00

1841 (late Feb). *Plate 12 onwards. Wmk W* **2.** *Paper more or less blued. Imperf.*

			Un	Used	Used on cover
8	1	1d. red-brown ..	£110	1·75	5·00
8*a*		1d. red-brown on very blue paper	£130	2·00	
9		1d. pale red-brown (worn plates)	£170	6·00	
10		1d. deep red-brown ..	£130	4·00	
11		1d. lake-red ..	£400	£150	
12		1d. orange-brown ..	£250	35·00	

Error. No letter "A" in right lower corner (*Stamp* B (A), *Plate* 77)

			Un	Used
12*a*	1	1d. red-brown ..	—	£3500

The error "No letter A in right corner" was due to the omission to insert this letter on stamp B A of Plate 77. The error was discovered some months after the plate was registered and was then corrected.

There are innumerable variations in the colour and shade of the 1d. "red" and those given in the above list represent colour groups each covering a wide range.

Varieties of 1d. red-brown, etc.

			Un	Used
a.	Re-entry ..	*from*	—	17·00
b.	Double letter in corner ..	*from*	—	8·00
ba.	Double Star (Plate 75) "Union Jack" re-entry		—	350
c.	Guide line in corner ..		—	3·00
d.	„ „ through value ..		—	8·50
e.	Thick outer frame to stamp ..		—	7·00
f.	Ivory head ..		£160	4·00
g.	Watermark inverted ..		£325	35·00
ga.	Left corner letter "S" inverted (Plates 78, 105, 107) ..	*from*	—	30·00
gb.	P converted to R (Plates 30, 33, 83, 86)	*from*	—	20·00
h.	Obliterated red Maltese Cross ..		—	£600
i.	„ black „ „ ..		—	6·00
k.	„ blue „ „ ..		—	80·00
m.	Obliteration No. 1 in Maltese Cross ..		—	22·00
	„ „ 2 „ ..		—	22·00
	„ „ 3 „ ..		—	35·00
	„ „ 4 „ ..		—	70·00
	„ „ 5 „ ..		—	22·00
	„ „ 6 „ ..		—	18·00
	„ „ 7 „ ..		—	16·00
	„ „ 8 „ ..		—	16·00
	„ „ 9 „ ..		—	24·00
	„ „ 10 „ ..		—	30·00
	„ „ 11 „ ..		—	38·00
	„ „ 12 „ ..		—	55·00
n.	Obliteration "Penny Post" in black on stamp		—	£130
o.	Town obliteration (without Maltese Cross) in black on stamp ..	*from*	—	75·00
p.	Town obliteration (without Maltese Cross) in blue on stamp ..	*from*	—	£175
q.	Town obliteration (without Maltese Cross) in green on stamp ..	*from*	—	£300
r.	Town obliteration (without Maltese Cross) in yellow on stamp ..	*from*	—	£3250
ra.	Town obliteration (without Maltese Cross) in red on stamp ..	*from*	—	£1300
s.	Obliteration of 1844 in blue on stamp ..	*from*	—	30·00
t.	„ „ „ red „ ..	*from*	—	£600
u.	„ „ „ green „ ..	*from*	—	50·00
v.	„ „ „ violet „ ..	*from*	—	£300
w.	„ „ „ black „ ..	*from*	—	1·75

Stamps with thick outer frame to the design are from plates on which the frame-lines have been strengthened or recut, particularly Plates 76 and 90.

For "Union Jack" re-entry *see* General Notes to Line-engraved Issues.

In "P converted to R" the corner letter "R" is formed from the "P", the distinctive long tail having been hand-cut.

KEY TO LINE-ENGRAVED ISSUES

S.G. Nos.	Description	Date	Wmk	Perf	Die	Alphabet
THE IMPERFORATE ISSUES						
1/3	1d. black	6.5.40	SC	Imp	I	I
4/6	2d. no lines	8.5.40	SC	Imp	I	I
PAPER MORE OR LESS BLUED						
7	1d. red-brown	10.2.41	SC	Imp	I	I
8/12	1d. red-brown	10.2.41	SC	Imp	I	I
8/12	1d. red-brown	6.2.52	SC	Imp	I	II
13/15	2d. white lines	13.3.41	SC	Imp	I	I
THE PERFORATED ISSUES						
ONE PENNY VALUE						
16*a*	1d. red-brown	1848	SC	Roul	I	I
16*b*	1d. red-brown	1850	SC	16	I	I
16*c*	1d. red-brown	1853	SC	16	I	II
16*d*	1d. red-brown	1854	SC	14	I	I
17/18	1d. red-brown	Feb 1854	SC	16	I	II
22	1d. red-brown	Jan 1855	SC	14	I	II
24/5	1d. red-brown	28.2.55	SC	14	II	II
21	1d. red-brown	1.3.55	SC	16	II	II
26	1d. red-brown	15.5.55	LC	16	II	II
29/33	1d. red-brown	Aug 1855	LC	14	II	III
NEW COLOURS ON WHITE PAPER						
37/41	1d. rose-red	Nov 1856	LC	14	II	III
36	1d. rose-red	26.12.57	LC	16	II	III
42	1d. rose-red	1861	LC	14	II	IV
40b	1d. rose-red	1862	LC	14	II	II
TWO PENCE VALUE						
19, 20	2d. blue	1.3.54	SC	16	I	I
23	2d. blue	22.2.55	SC	14	I	I
23*a*	2d. blue	5.7.55	SC	14	I	II
20*a*	2d. blue	18.8.55	SC	16	I	II
27	2d. blue	20.7.55	LC	16	I	II
34	2d. blue	20.7.55	LC	14	I	II
35	2d. blue	2.7.57	LC	14	I	III
36*a*	2d. blue	1.2.58	LC	16	I	III
LETTERS IN ALL FOUR CORNERS						
48/9	½d. rose-red	1.10.70	W 9	14	—	
43/4	1d. rose-red	1.4.64	LC	14	II	
53*a*	1½d. rosy mauve	1860	LC	14	II	
51/3	1½d. rose-red	1.10.70	LC	14	II	
45	2d. blue	July 1858	LC	14	II	
46/7	2d. thinner lines	7.7.69	LC	14	II	

Watermarks: SC = Small Crown, T **2.**
LC = Large Crown, T **4.**
Dies: *See* notes above No. 17 in the catalogue.
Alphabets: *See* General Notes to this section.

3 White lines added

1841 (13 Mar). *White lines added. Wmk W* **2**. *Paper more or less blued. Imperf.*

			Un	Used	Used on cover
13	3	2d. pale blue	£1300	40·00	
14		2d. blue	£1000	25·00	£100
15		2d. deep full blue	£1300	38·00	
15*aa*		2d. violet-blue	£6000	£350	

The 2d. stamp with white lines was printed from Plates 3 and 4.

Plates of 2d. blue

Plate		Un	Used
3	*Shades from*	£1000	28·00
4	*Shades from*	£1200	25·00

Varieties of 2d. blue

		Un	Used
a.	Guide line in corner	—	27·00
b.	,, ,, through value	£1500	27·00
bb.	Double letter in corner	—	40·00
be.	Re-entry	£1800	50·00
c.	Ivory head	£1600	27·00
d.	Watermark inverted	£2250	£180
e.	Obliterated red Maltese Cross	—	£3000
f.	,, black ,, ,,	—	50·00
g.	,, blue ,, ,,	—	£500
i.	Obliteration No. 1 in Maltese Cross	—	£160
	,, ,, 2 ,,	—	£160
	,, ,, 3 ,,	—	£160
	,, ,, 4 ,,	—	£150
	,, ,, 5 ,,	—	£200
	,, ,, 6 ,,	—	£150
	,, ,, 7 ,,	—	£300
	,, ,, 8 ,,	—	£200
	,, ,, 9 ,,	—	£300
	,, ,, 10 ,,	—	£350
	,, ,, 11 ,,	—	£200
	,, ,, 12 ,,	—	£110
k.	Obliteration of 1844 in black on stamp	—	25·00
l.	,, ,, ,, blue ,,	—	£275
m.	,, ,, ,, red ,,	—	£3250
n.	,, ,, ,, green ,,	—	£350
p.	Town obliteration in black ,,	—	£275
q.	,, ,, blue ,,	—	£500

1841 (April). *Trial printing (unissued) on Dickinson silk-thread paper. Imperf.*

16	1	1d. red-brown (Plate 11)	£1750

Eight sheets were printed on this paper, six being gummed, two ungummed, but we have only seen examples without gum.

1848. *Rouletted approx 11½ by Henry Archer.*

16*a*	1	1d. red-brown (Plates 70, 71)	£3000

1850. *P 16, by Henry Archer.*

16*b*	1	1d. red-brown (Alph I) (from Plates 71, 79, 90–101 and 105. Also Plate 8, unused only) *from*	£500	£130

Stamp on cover, dated prior to February 1854 (*price* £300); dated February and after 1854 (*price* £200).

1853. *Government Trial Perforations.*

16*c*	1	1d. red-brown (*p* 16) (Alph II) (*on cover*)	†	£4250
16*d*		1d. red-brown (*p* 14) (Alph I)	£3250	

SEPARATION TRIALS. Although the various trials of machines for rouletting and perforating were unofficial, Archer had the consent of the authorities in making his experiments, and sheets so experimented upon were afterwards used by the Post Office.

As Archer ended his experiments in 1850 and plates with corner letters Alphabet II did not come into issue until 1852, perforated stamps with corner letters of Alphabet I may safely be assumed to be Archer productions, if genuine.

The Government trial perforations were done on Napier machines in 1853. As Alphabet II was by that time in use, the trials can only be distinguished from the perforated stamps listed below by being dated prior to 28 January 1854, the date when the perforated stamps were officially issued.

Die I

Die II

4 Large Crown

Die I: The features of the portrait are lightly shaded and consequently lack emphasis.

Die II (Die I retouched): The lines of the features have been deepened and appear stronger.

The eye is deeply shaded and made more lifelike. The nostril and lips are more clearly defined, the latter appearing much thicker. A strong downward stroke of colour marks the corner of the mouth. There is a deep indentation of colour between lower lip and chin. The band running from the back of the ear to the chignon has a bolder horizontal line below it than in Die I.

1854–57. *Paper more or less blued.* (*a*) *Wmk Small Crown, W* **2**. *P* 16.

			Un	Used	★ Used on cover
17	1	1d. red-brown (Die I) (2.54)	£100	1·75	7·00
18		1d. yellow-brown (Die I)	£120	4·00	
19	3	2d. deep blue (Plate 4) (1.3.54)	£1100	25·00	50·00
		a. Imperf three sides (horiz pair)	†	—	
20		2d. pale blue (Plate 4)	£1300	40·00	
20*a*		2d. blue (Plate 5) (18.8.55)	£1600	85·00	£175
21	1	1d. red-brown (Die II) (1.3.55)	£120	7·00	17·00
		a. Imperf			
		(*b*) *Wmk Small Crown, W* **2**. *P* 14			
22	1	1d. red-brown (Die I) (1.55)	£225	14·00	25·00
23	3	2d. blue (Plate 4) (22.2.55)	£1600	75·00	£120
23*a*		2d. blue (Plate 5) (5.7.55)	£1600	70·00	£110
		b. Imperf (Plate 5)			
24	1	1d. red-brown (Die II) (28.2.55)	£225	13·00	22·00
24*a*		1d. deep red-brown (very blue paper) (Die II)	£200	15·00	
25		1d. orange-brown (Die II)	£500	30·00	
		(*c*) *Wmk Large Crown, W* **4**. *P* 16			
26	1	1d. red-brown (Die II) (15.5.55)	£400	24·00	35·00
		a. Imperf (Plate 7)			
27	3	2d. blue (Plate 5) (20.7.55)	£2000	£100	£175
		a. Imperf	—	£2000	
		(*d*) *Wmk Large Crown, W* **4**. *P* 14			
29	1	1d. red-brown (Die II) (18.8.55)	£100	65	5·50
		a. Imperf (*shades*) (Plates 22, 25, 43)	£750	£600	
30		1d. brick-red (Die II)	£130	8·00	
31		1d. plum (Die II) (2.56)	£700	£150	
32		1d. brown-rose (Die II)	£150	9·00	
33		1d. orange-brown (Die II) (3.57)	£225	11·00	
34	3	2d. blue (Plate 5) (20.7.55)	£1000	16·00	45·00
35		2d. blue (Plate 6) (2.7.57)	£1100	19·00	60·00
		a. Imperf	—	£2000	
★17/35a		**For well-centred, lightly used**		+125%	

1856–62. *Paper no longer blued.* (*a*) *Wmk Large Crown, W* **4**. *P* 16.

			Un	Used	Used on cover
36	1	1d. rose-red (Die II) (26.12.57)	£500	18·00	32·00
36*a*	3	2d. blue (Plate 6) (1.2.58)	£2750	£100	£200
		(*b*) (Die II) *Wmk Large Crown, W* **4**. *P* 14			
37	1	1d. red-brown (11.56)	£225	25·00	
38		1d. pale red (9.4.57)	40·00	1·50	
		a. Imperf	£425	£350	
39		1d. pale rose (3.57)	40·00	3·00	
40		1d. rose-red (9.57)	25·00	50	1·00
		a. Imperf	£475	£350	
		b. Reserve plates 15 or 16 (Alph II) (1862) *from*	70·00	3·00	
41		1d. deep-rose-red (7.57)	40·00	1·25	

1861. *Letters engraved on plate instead of punched (Alphabet IV).*

			Un	Used	Used on cover
42	1	1d. rose-red (Die II) (Plates 50 and 51)	95·00	5·00	18·00
		a. Imperf	—	£1500	
★36/42a		**For well-centred, lightly used**		+125%	

The original die (Die I) was used to provide roller dies for the laying down of all the line-engraved stamps from 1840 to 1855. In that year a new master die was laid down (by means of a Die I roller die) and the impression was retouched by hand engraving by William Humphrys. This retouched die, always known to philatelists as Die II, was from that time used for preparing all new roller dies.

One Penny. The numbering of the 1d. plates recommenced at 1 on the introduction of Die II. Plates 1 to 21 were Alphabet II from which a scarce plum shade exists. Corner letters of Alphabet III appear on Plate 22 and onwards.

As an experiment, the corner letters were engraved by hand on Plates 50 and 51 in 1856, instead of being punched (Alphabet IV), but punching was again resorted to from Plate 52 onwards. Plates 50 and 51 were not put into use until 1861.

Two Pence. Unlike the 1d. the old sequence of plate numbers continued. Plates 3 and 4 of the 2d. had corner letters of Alphabet I, Plate 5 Alphabet II and Plate 6 Alphabet III. In Plate 6 the white lines are thinner than before.

In both values, varieties may be found as described in the preceding issues—ivory heads, inverted watermarks, re-entries, and double letters in corners.

The change of perforation from 16 to 14 was decided upon late in 1854 since the closer holes of the former gauge tended to cause the sheets of stamps to break up when handled, but for a time both gauges were in concurrent use. Owing to faulty alignment of the impressions on the plates and to shrinkage of the paper when damped, badly perforated stamps are plentiful in the line-engraved issues.

5

6

Showing position of the plate number on the 1d. and 2d. values. (Plate 170 shown)

1858–79. *Letters in all four corners. Wmk Large Crown, W* **4**. *Die* II (1*d. and* 2*d.*). *P* 14.

			Un	Used	★ Used on cover
43	5	1d. rose-red (1.4.64)	9·00	60	1·25
44		1d. lake-red	9·00	60	
		a. Imperf. *from*	£600	£500	
★43/4a		**For well-centred, lightly used**		+125%	

NEW INFORMATION

The editor is always interested to correspond with people who have new information that will improve or correct the Catalogue.

Plate	Un	Used	*Plate*	Un	Used
71	22·00	3·00	150	9·00	60
72	35·00	3·50	151	25·00	9·00
73	25·00	3·00	152	18·00	4·50
74	20·00	75	153	70·00	4·00
76	40·00	75	154	15·00	60
77	£35000	£18000	155	16·00	1·00
78	£100	75	156	15·00	75
79	30·00	60	157	15·00	75
80	20·00	1·25	158	9·00	75
81	60·00	1·50	159	9·00	75
82	£120	2·00	160	9·00	60
83	£140	5·00	161	29·00	2·50
84	60·00	1·50	162	16·00	6·00
85	25·00	1·50	163	15·00	2·00
86	30·00	3·50	164	15·00	3·00
87	9·00	1·00	165	20·00	75
88	£160	6·00	166	15·00	5·00
89	40·00	75	167	10·00	70
90	28·00	75	168	12·00	7·00
91	40·00	5·00	169	30·00	3·50
92	15·00	75	170	11·00	60
93	40·00	75	171	9·00	60
94	40·00	4·00	172	9·00	1·25
95	25·00	75	173	50·00	9·00
96	28·00	60	174	9·00	60
97	15·00	2·50	175	35·00	2·50
98	15·00	5·00	176	25·00	1·25
99	25·00	4·00	177	10·00	75
100	35·00	1·50	178	15·00	2·50
101	50·00	8·00	179	16·00	1·25
102	20·00	80	180	16·00	2·50
103	19·00	2·00	181	15·00	75
104	28·00	2·25	182	£100	3·00
105	65·00	5·50	183	25·00	2·00
106	30·00	80	184	9·00	1·00
107	40·00	5·50	185	15·00	2·00
108	30·00	1·10	186	30·00	1·50
109	75·00	2·00	187	11·00	75
110	19·00	8·00	188	20·00	10·00
111	35·00	1·50	189	35·00	5·00
112	60·00	1·50	190	10·00	5·00
113	15·00	11·00	191	9·00	6·00
114	£350	12·00	192	25·00	75
115	£100	1·50	193	9·00	75
116	75·00	9·00	194	15·00	7·00
117	16·00	60	195	15·00	7·00
118	25·00	75	196	10·00	4·00
119	10·00	1·00	197	16·00	12·00
120	9·00	60	198	9·00	5·00
121	40·00	9·00	199	20·00	5·00
122	9·00	60	200	20·00	75
123	12·00	1·00	201	9·00	6·00
124	12·00	60	202	15·00	7·00
125	15·00	2·00	203	9·00	15·00
127	35·00	2·00	204	12·00	1·00
129	11·00	7·00	205	11·00	3·00
130	18·00	1·50	206	11·00	11·00
131	75·00	16·00	207	12·00	12·00
132	£100	24·00	208	11·00	15·00
133	90·00	9·00	209	15·00	12·00
134	9·00	60	210	20·00	18·00
135	£100	30·00	211	42·00	20·00
136	£100	20·00	212	15·00	15·00
137	15·00	1·25	213	12·00	15·00
138	9·00	60	214	25·00	25·00
139	20·00	16·00	215	25·00	25·00
140	9·00	60	216	20·00	25·00
141	£150	7·50	217	15·00	3·00
142	50·00	25·00	218	11·00	5·50
143	30·00	15·00	219	45·00	75·00
144	£100	20·00	220	9·00	4·50
145	9·00	1·50	221	29·00	20·00
146	10·00	5·00	222	32·00	40·00
147	18·00	3·00	223	38·00	70·00
148	20·00	2·50	224	65·00	65·00
149	15·00	5·00	225	£2000	£500

Error. Imperf. Issued at Cardiff (Plate 116)

			Un	Used
44*b*	5	1d. rose-red (18.1.70)	£900	£650

The following plate numbers are also known imperf and used (No. 44a): 72, 79, 80, 81, 82, 83, 86, 87, 88, 90, 91, 92, 93, 96, 97, 100, 102, 103, 104, 105, 107, 108, 109, 112, 114, 117, 120, 121, 122, 136, 137, 142, 146, 148, 158, 162, 164, 166, 171, 174, 191 and 202.

The numbering of this series of 1d. red plates follows after that of the previous 1d. stamp, last printed from Plate 68.

Plates 69, 70, 75, 126 and 128 were prepared for this issue but rejected owing to defects, and stamps from these plates do not exist, so that specimens which appear to be from these plates (like many of those which optimistic collectors believe to be from Plate 77) bear other plate numbers. Owing to faulty engraving or printing it is not always easy to identify the plate number. Plate 77 was also rejected but some stamps printed from it were used. One specimen is in the Tapling Collection and six or seven others are known. Plates 226 to 228 were made but not used.

Specimens from most of the plates are known with inverted watermark. The variety of watermark described in the General Notes to this section occurs on stamp M A (or M L) on plates up to about 96 (*Prices from £85 used*).

Re-entries in this issue are few, the best being on stamps M K and T K of Plate 71 and on S L and T L, Plate 83.

			Un	Used	★ Used on cover
45	6	2d. blue (thick lines) (7.58)	£150	2·25	14·00
		a. Imperf (Plate 9)	—	£2500	
		Plate			
		7	£400	14·00	
		8	£450	11·00	
		9	£150	2·25	
		12	£700	23·00	
46		2d. blue (thin lines) (1.7.69)	£130	5·50	14·00
47		2d. deep blue (thin lines)	£130	5·50	
		a. Imperf (Plate 13)	£1100		
		Plate			
		13	£175	5·50	
		14	£200	7·50	
		15	£130	7·50	
★45/7		**For well-centred, lightly used**		+125%	

Plates 10 and 11 of the 2d. were prepared but rejected. Plates 13 to 15 were laid down from a new roller impression on which the white lines were thinner.

There are some marked re-entries and repairs, particularly on Plates 7, 8, 9 and 12.

Stamps with inverted watermark may be found and also the T A (T L) and M A (M L) watermark varieties (*see* General Notes to this section).

Though the paper is normally white, some printings showed blueing and stamps showing the "ivory head" may therefore be found.

7

Showing the plate number (9)

9

1870 (1 Oct). *Wmk W* **9**, *extending over three stamps. P* 14.

			Un	★ Used	Used on cover
48	**7**	½d. rose-red	40·00	3·50	22·00
49		½d. rose	40·00	3·50	
		a. Imperf (Plates 1, 4, 5, 6, 8, 14) .. .. .. *from*	£800	£500	
		Plate			
		1	90·00	25·00	
		3	55·00	8·00	
		4	70·00	5·00	
		5	50·00	3·50	
		6	40·00	3·50	
		8	80·00	22·00	
		9	£1700	£250	
		10	70·00	3·50	
		11	40·00	3·50	
		12	40·00	3·50	
		13	40·00	3·50	
		14	40·00	3·50	
		15	55·00	5·00	
		19	85·00	12·00	
		20	90·00	15·00	
★48/9a		**For well-centred, lightly used** ..		+200%	

The ½d. was printed in sheets of 480 (24 × 20) so that the check letters run from A A / A A to X T / T X.

Plates 2, 7, 16, 17 and 18 were not completed while Plates 21 and 22, though made, were not used.

Owing to the method of perforating, the outer side of stamps in either the A or X row (ie the left or right side of the sheet) is imperf.

Stamps may be found with watermark inverted or reversed, or without watermark, the latter due to misplacement of the paper when printing.

8

Position of plate Number

1870 (1 Oct). *Wmk W* **4**. *P* 14.

			Un	★ Used	Used on cover
51	**8**	1½d. rose-red	£150	16·00	£120
52		1½d. lake-red	£150	16·00	
		a. Imperf (Plates 1 and 3) *from*	£1200	†	
		Plate			
		(1)	£400	20·00	
		3	£150	16·00	
		Error of lettering. OP-PC for CP-PC (Plate 1)			
53	**8**	1½d. rose-red	£3250	£500	
★51/3		**For well-centred, lightly used** ..		+125%	

1860. *Prepared for use but not issued; blued paper. Wmk W* **4**. *P* 14.

			Un	Used
53*a*	**8**	1½d. rosy mauve (Plate 1)	£1750	
		b. Error of lettering, OP-PC for CP-PC		

Owing to a proposed change in the postal rates, 1½d. stamps were first printed in 1860, in rosy mauve, No. 53*a*, but the change was not approved and the greater part of the stock was destroyed.

In 1870 a 1½d. stamp was required and was issued in rose-red.

Plate 1 did not have the plate number in the design of the stamps, but on stamps from Plate 3 the number will be found in the frame as shown above.

Plate 2 was defective and was not used.

The error of lettering OP-PC on Plate 1 was apparently not noticed by the printers, and therefore not corrected.

EMBOSSED ISSUES

Volume 1 of the Stanley Gibbons *Great Britain Specialised Catalogue* gives further detailed information on the embossed issues.

PRICES. The prices quoted are for cut-square stamps with average to fine embossing. Stamps with exceptionally clear embossing are worth more.

10

11

12 13

Position of die number

(Primary die engraved at the Royal Mint by William Wyon. Stamps printed at Somerset House)

1847–54. *Imperf*. (For paper and wmk see footnote.)

			Un	Used	Used on cover
54	**10**	1s. pale green (11.9.47) ..	£2750	£325	£450
55		1s. green	£2750	£375	
56		1s. deep green	£3250	£425	
		Die 1 (1847)	£2750	£325	
		Die 2 (1854)	£3250	£375	
57	**11**	10d. brown (6.11.48)	£2250	£475	£900
		Die 1 (1848)	£2500	£525	
		Die 2 (1850)	£2250	£475	
		Die 3 (1853)	£2250	£475	
		Die 4 (1854)	£2500	£525	
		Die 5	£16000		
58	**12**	6d. mauve (1.3.54)	£2500	£325	
59		6d. dull lilac	£2500	£275	£375
60		6d. purple	£2500	£275	
61		6d. violet	£3250	£400	

The 1s. and 10d. are on "Dickinson" paper with silk threads. The 6d. is on paper watermarked V R in single-lined letters, W **13**, which may be found in four ways—upright, inverted, upright reversed, and inverted reversed; none is scarce.

The die numbers are indicated on the base of the bust. Only Die 1 (1 WW) of the 6d. was used for the adhesive stamps. The 10d. is from Die 1 (W.W.1 on stamps), and Dies 2 to 5 (2 W.W., 3 W.W., 4 W.W. and 5 W.W.) but the number and letters on stamps from Die 1 are seldom clear and many specimens are known without any trace of them. Because of this the stamp we previously listed as "No die number" has been deleted. That they are from Die 1 is proved by the existence of blocks showing stamps with and without the die number. The 1s. is from Dies 1 and 2 (W.W.1, W.W.2).

The normal arrangement of the silk threads in the paper was in pairs running down each vertical row of the sheet, the space between the threads of each pair being approximately 5 mm and between pairs of threads 20 mm. Varieties due to misplacement of the paper in printing show a single thread on the first stamp from the sheet margin and two threads 20 mm apart on the other stamps of the row. Faulty manufacture is the cause of stamps with a single thread in the middle.

Through bad spacing of the impressions, which were handstruck, all values may be found with two impressions more or less overlapping. Owing to the small margin allowed for variation of spacing, specimens with good margins on all sides are not common.

Double impressions are known of all values.

Later printings of the 6d. had the gum tinted green to enable the printer to distinguish the gummed side of the paper.

SURFACE-PRINTED ISSUES

GENERAL NOTES

Volume 1 of the Stanley Gibbons *Great Britain Specialised Catalogue* gives further detailed information on the surface-printed issues.

"Abnormals". The majority of the great rarities in the surface-printed group of issues are the so-called "abnormals", whose existence is due to the practice of printing six sheets from every plate as soon as made, one of which was kept for record purposes at Somerset House, while the others were perforated and usually issued. If such plates were not used for general production or if, before they came into full use, a change of watermark or colour took place, the six sheets originally printed would differ from the main issue in plate, colour or watermark and, if issued, would be extremely rare.

The abnormal stamps of this class listed in this Catalogue and distinguished, where not priced, by an asterisk (*) are:

No.		
78	3d.	Plate 3 (with white dots)
152	4d.	vermilion, Plate 16
153	4d.	sage-green, Plate 17
109	6d.	mauve, Plate 10
122/4	6d.	pale chestnut and 6d. chestnut, Plate 12
145	6d.	pale buff, Plate 13
88	9d.	Plate 3 (hair lines)
98	9d.	Plate 5 (*see* footnote to No. 98)
113	10d.	Plate 2
91	1s.	Plate 3 ("Plate 2")
148/50	1s.	green, Plate 14
120	2s.	blue, Plate 3

Those which may have been issued, but of which no specimens are known, are 2½d. wmk. Anchor, Plates 4 and 5; 3d. wmk Emblems, Plate 5; 3d. wmk Spray, Plate 21; 6d. grey, wmk Spray, Plate 18; 8d. orange, Plate 2; 1s. wmk Emblems, Plate 5. 5s. wmk Maltese Cross, Plate 4.

The 10d. Plate 1, wmk Emblems (No. 99), is sometimes reckoned among the abnormals, but was an error, due to the use of the wrong paper.

Corner Letters. With the exception of the 4d., 6d. and 1s. of 1855–57, the ½d., 1½d., 2d. and 5d. of 1880, the 1d. lilac of 1881 and the £5 (which had letters in lower corners only, and in the reverse order to the normal), all the surface-printed stamps issued prior to 1887 had letters in all four corners, as in the later line-engraved stamps. The arrangement is the same, the letters running in sequence right across and down the sheets, whether these were divided into panes or not. The corner letters existing naturally depend on the number of stamps in the sheet and their arrangement.

Imprimaturs and Imperforate Stamps. The Post Office retained in their records (now in the National Postal Museum) one imperforate sheet from each plate, known as the Imprimatur (or officially approved) sheet. Some stamps were removed from time to time for presentation purposes and have come on to the market, but these imperforates are not listed as they were not issued. Full details can be found in Volume I of the *Great Britain Specialised Catalogue*.

However, other imperforate stamps are known to have been issued and these are listed where it has been possible to prove that they do not come from the Imprimatur sheets. It is therefore advisable to purchase these only when accompanied by an Expert Committee certificate of genuineness.

Plate Numbers. All stamps from No. 75 to No. 163 bear in their designs either the plate number or, in one or two earlier instances, some other indication by which one plate can be distinguished from another. With the aid of these and of the corner letters it is thus possible to "reconstruct" a sheet of stamps from any plate of any issue or denomination.

Surface-printing. In this context the traditional designation "surface-printing" is synonymous with typo(graphy)—a philatelic term—or letterpress—the printers' term—as meaning printing from (the surface of) raised type. It is also called relief-printing, as the image is in relief (in French, *en épargne*), unwanted parts of the design having been cut away. Duplicate impressions can be electrotyped or stereotyped from an original die, the resulting *clichés* being locked together to form the printing plate.

Wing Margins. As the vertical gutters (spaces) between the panes, into which sheets of stamps of most values were divided until the introduction of the Imperial Crown watermark, were perforated through the centre with a single row of holes, instead of each vertical row of stamps on the inner side of the panes having its own line of perforation as is now usual, a proportion of the stamps in each sheet have what is called a "wing margin" about 5 mm wide on one or other side.

The stamps with "wing margins" are the watermark Emblems and Spray of Rose series (3d. 6d. 9d. 10d. 1s. and 2s.) with letters D, E, H or I in S.E. corner, and the watermark Garter series (4d. and 8d.) with letters F or G in S.E. corner. Knowledge of this lettering will enable collectors to guard against stamps with wing margin cut down and re-perforated, but note that wing margin stamps of Nos. 62 to 73 are also to be found re-perforated.

PRINTERS. The issues of Queen Victoria, Nos. 62/214, were typo by Thomas De La Rue & Co.

PERFORATIONS. All the surface-printed issues of Queen Victoria are Perf 14, with the exception of Nos. 126/9.

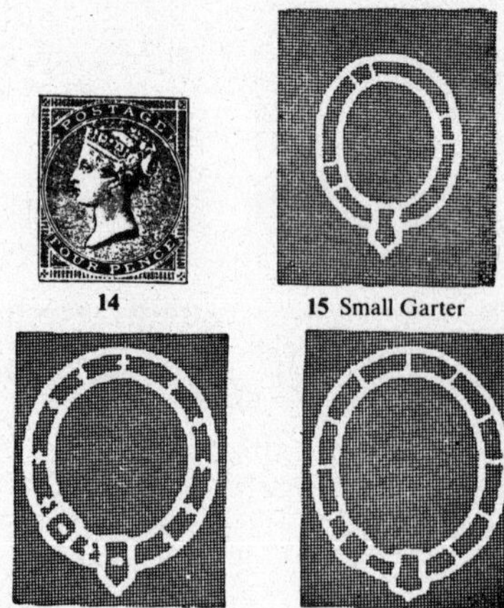

14 · **15** Small Garter · **16** Medium Garter · **17** Large Garter

1855–57. *No corner letters.*

(*a*) *Wmk Small Garter, W* **15**. *Highly glazed, deeply blued paper* (31 July 1855)

			Un	★ Used	Used on cover
62	**14**	4d. carmine (*shades*)	£2250	£130	£200
		a. Paper slightly blued ..	£2500	£120	
		b. White paper	£3000	£325	
		(*b*) *Wmk Medium Garter, W* **16**			
		(i) *Thick, blued highly glazed paper* (25 February 1856)			
63	**14**	4d. carmine (*shades*)	£3250	£130	£225
		a. White paper	£2750		
		(ii) *Ordinary thin white paper* (September 1856)			
64	**14**	4d. pale carmine	£1750	£110	£200
		(iii) *Ordinary white paper, specially prepared ink* (1 November 1856)			
65	**14**	4d. rose *or* deep rose	£1800	£120	£225
		(*c*) *Wmk Large Garter, W* **17**. *Ordinary white paper* (January 1857)			
66	**14**	4d. rose-carmine	£700	25·00	50·00
		a. Rose	£600	25·00	
		b. Thick glazed paper	£1700	65·00	
★62/6b		**For well-centred, lightly used** ..		+125%	

18

19

20 Emblems wmk (normal)

20*a* Wmk error, three roses and shamrock

20*b* Wmk error, three roses and thistle

(*d*) *Wmk Emblems, W* **20**

			Un	Used	★ Used on cover
69	**18**	6d. deep lilac (21.10.56)	£550	50·00	
70		6d. pale lilac	£500	30·00	65·00
		a. Azure paper	£2500	£300	
		b. Thick paper	£750	70·00	
		c. Error. Wmk W **20*a***			
71	**19**	1s. deep green (1.11.56)	£1200	£110	
72		1s. green	£600	90·00	£130
73		1s. pale green	£600	90·00	
		a. Azure paper	—	£450	
		b. Thick paper	—	£125	
★69/73b		**For well-centred, lightly used**		**+125%**	

KEY TO SURFACE-PRINTED ISSUES 1855–83

S.G. Nos.	*Description*	*Watermark*	*Date of Issue*
	NO CORNER LETTERS		
62	4d. carmine	Small Garter	31.7.55
63/5	4d. carmine	Medium Garter	25.2.56
66/*a*	4d. carmine	Large Garter	Jan 1857
69/70	6d. lilac	Emblems	21.10.56
71/3	1s. green	Emblems	1.11.56
	SMALL WHITE CORNER LETTERS		
75/7	3d. carmine	Emblems	1.5.62
78	3d. carmine (dots)	Emblems	Aug 1862
79/82	4d. red	Large Garter	15.1.62
83/5	6d. lilac	Emblems	1.12.62
86/8	9d. bistre	Emblems	15.1.62
89/91	1s. green	Emblems	1.12.62
	LARGE WHITE CORNER LETTERS		
92	3d. rose	Emblems	1.3.65
102/3	3d. rose	Spray	July 1867
93/5	4d. vermilion	Large Garter	4.7.65
96/7	6d. lilac	Emblems	1.4.65
104/7	6d. lilac	Spray	21.6.67
108/9	6d. lilac	Spray	8.3.69
122/4	6d. chestnut	Spray	12.4.72
125	6d. grey	Spray	24.4.73
98	9d. straw	Emblems	1.12.65
110/11	9d. straw	Spray	3.10.67
99	10d. brown	Emblems	11.11.67
112/14	10d. brown	Spray	1.7.67
101	1s. green	Emblems	Feb 1865
115/17	1s. green	Spray	13.7.67
118/20*b*	2s. blue	Spray	1.7.67
121	2s. brown	Spray	27.2.80
126/7	5s. rose	Cross	1.7.67
128	10s. grey	Cross	26.9.78
129	£1 brown-lilac	Cross	26.9.78
130, 134	5s. rose	Anchor	25.11.82
131, 135	10s. grey-green	Anchor	Feb 1883
132, 136	£1 brown-lilac	Anchor	Dec 1882
133, 137	£5 orange	Anchor	21.3.82
	LARGE COLOURED CORNER LETTERS		
138/9	2½d. rosy mauve	Anchor	1.7.75
141	2½d. rosy mauve	Orb	13.5.76
142	2½d. blue	Orb	5.2.80
157	2½d. blue	Crown	23.3.81
143/4	3d. rose	Spray	5.7.73
158	3d. rose	Crown	Feb 1881
159	3d. on 3d. purple	Crown	1.1.83
152	4d. vermilion	Large Garter	1.3.76
153	4d. sage-green	Large Garter	12.3.77
154	4d. brown	Large Garter	15.8.80
160	4d. brown	Crown	9.12.80
145	6d. buff	Spray	15.3.73
146/7	6d. grey	Spray	31.3.74
161	6d. grey	Crown	1.1.81
162	6d. on 6d. purple	Crown	1.1.83
156*a*	8d. purple-brown	Large Garter	July 1876
156	8d. orange	Large Garter	11.9.76
148/50	1s. green	Spray	1.9.73
151	1s. brown	Spray	14.10.80
163	1s. brown	Crown	29.5.81

Watermarks:		
	Anchor	W **40, 47**
	Cross	W **39**
	Crown	W **49**
	Emblems	W **20**
	Large Garter	W **17**
	Medium Garter	W **16**
	Orb	W **48**
	Small Garter	W **15**
	Spray	W **33**

21 **22**

23 **24** **25** Plate 2

A. White dots added

B. Hair lines

1862–64. *A small uncoloured letter in each corner, the* 4*d. wmk Large Garter. W* **17**, *the others Emblems, W* **20**.

			Un	Used	★ Used on cover
75	**21**	3d. deep carmine-rose (Plate 2) (1.5.62)	£1100	£120	
76		3d. bright carmine-rose	£650	90·00	£225
77		3d. pale carmine-rose	£650	90·00	
		b. Thick paper	—	£120	
78		3d. rose (with white dots, Type A, Plate 3) (8.62)	*	£2250	
		a. Imperf (Plate 3)	£1750		
79	**22**	4d. bright red (Plate 3) (15.1.62)	£750	45·00	
80		4d. pale red	£500	28·00	75·00
81		4d. bright red (Hair lines, Type B, Plate 4) (16.10.63)	£650	35·00	
82		4d. pale red (Hair lines, Type B, Plate 4)	£550	24·00	70·00
		a. Imperf (Plate 4)	£1200		
83	**23**	6d. deep lilac (Plate 3) (1.12.62)	£750	50·00	
84		6d. lilac	£650	24·00	65·00
		a. Azure paper	—	£275	
		b. Thick paper	—	40·00	
		c. Error. Wmk W **20*b*** (stamp TF)			
85		6d. lilac (Hair lines, Plate 4) (20.4.64)	£800	50·00	£120
		a. Imperf	£1100		
		c. Thick paper	£1200	65·00	
86	**24**	9d. bistre (Plate 2) (15.1.62)	£1100	£130	£250
87		9d. straw	£1100	£130	
		a. On azure paper			
		b. Thick paper	£1700	£150	
88		9d. bistre (Hair lines, Plate 3) (5.62)	£6000	£1700	
89	**25**	1s. deep green (Plate No. 1 = Plate 2) (1.12.62)	£800	80·00	
90		1s. green (Plate No. 1 = Plate 2)	£700	55·00	£100
		a. "K" in lower left corner in white circle (stamp KD)	£4250	£500	
		aa. "K" normal (stamp KD)	—	£600	
		b. On azure paper			
		c. Thick paper	—	£110	
		ca. Thick paper, "K" in circle as No. 99a	—	£900	
91		1s. deep green (Plate No. 2 = Plate 3)	£11000	*	
		a. Imperf	£1100		
★75/91		**For well-centred, lightly used**		**+125%**	

The 3d. as Type **21**, but with network background in the spandrels which is found overprinted SPECIMEN, was never issued.

The plates of this issue may be distinguished as follows:

3d. Plate 2. No white dots.
Plate 3. White dots as Illustration A.
4d. Plate 3. No hair lines. Roman I next to lower corner letters.
Plate 4. Hair lines in corners. (Illustration B.). Roman II.
6d. Plate 3. No hair lines.
Plate 4. Hair lines in corners.
9d. Plate 2. No hair lines.
Plate 3. Hair lines in corners. Beware of faked lines.
1s. Plate 2. Numbered 1 on stamps.
Plate 3. Numbered 2 on stamps and with hair lines.

The 9d. on azure paper (No. 87a) is very rare, only one specimen being known.

The variety "K" in circle, No. 90a, is believed to be due to a damaged letter having been cut out and replaced. It is probable that the punch was driven in too deeply, causing the flange to penetrate the surface, producing an indentation showing as an uncoloured circle.

The watermark variety "three roses and a shamrock" illustrated in W **20*a*** was evidently due to the substitution of an extra rose for the thistle in a faulty watermark bit. It is found on stamp T A of Plates 2 and 4 of the 3d., Plates 1 (No. 70c), 3, 5 and 6 of the 6d., Plate 4 of the 9d. and Plate 4 of the 1s.

26 **27**

28 (with hyphen) **28*a*** (without hyphen)

29 **30** **31**

1865–67. *Large uncoloured corner letters. Wmk Large Garter* (**4*d.***); *others Emblems.*

			Un	Used	★ Used on cover
92	**26**	3d. rose (Plate 4) (1.3.65)	£375	26·00	90·00
		a. Error. Wmk W **20*a***	£900	£275	
		b. Thick paper	£500	30·00	
93	**27**	4d. dull vermilion (4.7.65)	£200	15·00	35·00
94		4d. vermilion	£175	15·00	
		a. Imperf (Plates 11, 12)	£500		
95		4d. deep vermilion	£200	20·00	
		Plate			
		7 (1865)	£275	19·00	
		8 (1866)	£225	19·00	
		9 (1867)	£225	15·00	
		10 (1868)	£300	26·00	
		11 (1869)	£225	15·00	
		12 (1870)	£200	15·00	
		13 (1872)	£225	17·00	
		14 (1873)	£275	26·00	
96	**28**	6d. deep lilac (with hyphen) (7.3.65)	£400	35·00	
97		6d. lilac (with hyphen)	£350	25·00	60·00
		a. Thick paper	£450	32·00	
		b. Stamp doubly printed (Plate 6)	—	£3750	
		c. Error. Wmk W **20*a*** (Pl 5, 6) *from*	—	£300	
		Plate			
		5 (1865)	£350	25·00	
		6 (1867)	£1000	55·00	
98	**29**	9d. straw (Plate 4) (1.12.65)	£700	£170	£275
		a. Thick paper	£950	£275	
		b. Error. Wmk W **20*a***	—	£350	
99	**30**	10d. red-brn (Plate 1) (11.11.67)	*	£10000	
101	**31**	1s. green (Plate 4) (1.2.65)	£600	45·00	75·00
		a. Error. Wmk W **20*a***	—	£350	
		b. Thick paper	£700	85·00	
		c. Imperf between (vert pair)	—	£3750	
★92/101c		**For well-centred, lightly used**		**+ 100%**	

From mid-1866 to about the end of 1871 4d. stamps of this issue appeared generally with watermark inverted.

Unused copies of No. 98 from Plate 5 exist, but this was never put to press and all evidence points to the existing copies being from a portion of the Imprimatur sheet which was perforated by De La Rue in 1887 for insertion in albums to be presented to members of the Stamp Committee (*Price* £10000 *un*).

The 10d. stamps, No. 99, were printed in *error* on paper watermarked "Emblems" instead of on "Spray of Rose".

32 **33** Spray of Rose **34**

1867–80. *Wmk Spray of Rose, W* **33**.

			Un	Used	★ Used on cover
102	**26**	3d. deep rose (12.7.67)	£225	18·00	
103		3d. rose	£200	12·00	38·00
		a. Imperf (Plates 5, 6, 8) *from*	£500		
		Plate			
		4 (1867)	£300	50·00	
		5 (1868)	£200	14·00	
		6 (1870)	£225	12·00	
		7 (1871)	£275	15·00	
		8 (1872)	£250	14·00	
		9 (1872)	£250	18·00	
		10 (1873)	£275	25·00	
104	**28**	6d. lilac (with hyphen) (Plate 6) (21.6.67)	£550	26·00	90·00
105		6d. deep lilac (with hyphen) (Plate 6)	£550	26·00	
106		6d. purple (with hyphen) (Pl 6)	£550	35·00	
107		6d. bright violet (with hyphen) (Plate 6) (22.7.68)	£550	28·00	
108	**28*a***	6d. dull violet (without hyphen) (Plate 8) (18.3.69)	£325	22·00	
109		6d. mauve (without hyphen)	£275	20·00	55·00
		a. Imperf (Plate Nos. 8 and 9)	£700	£600	
		Plate			
		8 (1869, mauve)	£275	22·00	
		9 (1870, mauve)	£275	20·00	
		10 (1869, mauve)	*	£11000	
110	**29**	9d. straw (Plate No. 4) (3.10.67)	£600	90·00	£200
111		9d. pale straw (Plate No. 4)	£600	90·00	
		a. Imperf (Plate 4)	£1700		
112	**30**	10d. red-brown (1.7.67)	£1000	£120	£325
113		10d. pale red-brown	£1000	£150	
114		10d. deep red-brown	£1200	£130	
		a. Imperf (Plate 1)	£1400		
		Plate			
		1 (1867)	£1000	£120	
		2 (1867)	£12000	£2500	
115	**31**	1s. deep green (13.7.67)	£425	8·50	
117		1s. green	£350	8·50	20·00
		a. Imperf between (pair) (Pl 7)			
		b. Imperf (Plate 4)	£800	£550	
		Plate			
		4 (1867)	£350	12·00	
		5 (1871)	£400	9·00	
		6 (1872)	£525	8·50	
		7 (1873)	£525	20·00	
118	**32**	2s. dull blue (1.7.67)	£950	45·00	£325
119		2s. deep blue	£950	45·00	
		a. Imperf (Plate 1)	£1600		
120		2s. pale blue	£1500	75·00	
		aa. Imperf (Plate 1)	£1700		
120*a*		2s. cobalt	£4750	£700	
120*b*		2s. milky blue	£3000	£300	
		Plate			
		1 (1867)	£950	45·00	
		3 (1868)	*	£2500	
121		2s. brown (Plate No. 1) (27.2.80)	£5500	£800	
		a. Imperf	£3750		
★102/21		**For well-centred, lightly used**		**+75%**	

1872–73. *Uncoloured letters in corners. Wmk Spray, W* **33**.

No.	Type		Un	Used	★ Used on cover
122	**34**	6d. deep chestnut (12.4.72) ..	£425	16·00	50·00
123		6d. chestnut (23.5.72)	£350	16·00	
124		6d. pale buff (26.10.72) ..	£375	26·00	£130
		Plate			
		11 (1872, deep chestnut) ..	£425	16·00	
		11 (1872, chestnut) ..	£350	16·00	
		11 (1872, pale buff) ..	£375	26·00	
		12 (1872, pale chestnut†) ..	*	£1200	
		12 (1872, chestnut†) ..	*	£1200	
		12 (1872, pale buff) ..	£750	45·00	
125		6d. grey (Plate No. 12) (24.4.73)	£550	35·00	85·00
		a. Imperf	£1100		
★122/5		**For well-centred, lightly used** ..		**+50%**	

(†) The prices quoted are for the true pale chestnut and chestnut shades which are very rare (in this plate).

35 36

37

38

39 Maltese Cross   40 Large Anchor

1867–83. *Uncoloured letters in corners.*

(*a*) *Wmk Maltese Cross, W* **39**. *P* 15½ × 15

No.	Type		Un	★ Used
126	**35**	5s. rose (1.7.67)	£2250	£140
127		5s. pale rose	£2500	£140
		a. Imperf (Plate 1)	£3250	
		Plate		
		1 (1867)	£2250	£140
		2 (1874)	£3250	£200
128	**36**	10s. greenish grey (Plate 1) (26.9.78) ..	£16000	£800
129	**37**	£1 brown-lilac (Plate 1) (26.9.78) ..	£20000	£1100
		(*b*) *Wmk Anchor, W* **40**. *P* 14. (i) *Blued paper*		
130	**35**	5s. rose (Plate 4) (25.11.82) ..	£4750	£700
131	**36**	10s. grey-green (Plate 1) (2.83) ..	£18000	£1000
132	**37**	£1 brown-lilac (Plate 1) (12.82) ..	£25000	£1800
133	**38**	£5 orange (Plate 1) (21.3.82) ..	£13000	£2250
		(ii) *White paper*		
134	**35**	5s. rose (Plate 4)	£4500	£700
135	**36**	10s. greenish grey (Plate 1)	£20000	£1000
136	**37**	£1 brown-lilac (Plate 1)	£30000	£1800
137	**38**	£5 orange (Plate 1)	£3250	£1100
★126/37		**For well-centred, lightly used**		**+75%**

41 42 43

44 45 46

47 Small Anchor   48 Orb

1873–80. *Large coloured letters in the corners.*

(*a*) *Wmk Anchor, W* **47**

No.	Type		Un	Used	★ Used on cover
138	**41**	2½d. rosy mauve (*blued paper*) (1.7.75)	£375	28·00	
		a. Imperf			
139		2½d. rosy mauve (*white paper*) ..	£225	16·00	38·00
		Plate			
		1 (*blued paper*) (1875) ..	£375	28·00	
		1 (*white paper*) (1875) ..	£225	16·00	
		2 (*blued paper*) (1875) ..	£3000	£350	
		2 (*white paper*) (1875) ..	£225	16·00	
		3 (*white paper*) (1875) ..	£400	28·00	
		3 (*blued paper*) (1875) ..	—	£1200	
		Error of Lettering L H—F L *for* L H—H L (*Plate* 2)			
140	**41**	2½d. rosy mauve	£7000	£600	
		(*b*) *Wmk Orb, W* **48**			
141	**41**	2½d. rosy mauve (1.5.76) ..	£200	12·00	35·00
		Plate			
		3 (1876)	£500	30·00	
		4 (1876)	£200	12·00	
		5 (1876)	£200	16·00	
		6 (1876)	£200	12·00	
		7 (1877)	£200	12·00	
		8 (1877)	£200	16·00	
		9 (1877)	£200	12·00	
		10 (1878)	£225	17·00	
		11 (1878)	£200	12·00	
		12 (1878)	£200	16·00	
		13 (1878)	£200	16·00	
		14 (1879)	£200	12·00	
		15 (1879)	£200	12·00	
		16 (1879)	£200	12·00	
		17 (1880)	£500	60·00	
142		2½d. blue (5.2.80)	£140	6·00	15·00
		Plate			
		17 (1880)	£140	15·00	
		18 (1880)	£160	10·00	
		19 (1880)	£140	6·00	
		20 (1880)	£140	6·00	
		(*c*) *Wmk Spray, W* **33**			
143	**42**	3d. rose (5.7.73)	£200	11·00	35·00
144		3d. pale rose	£200	11·00	
		Plate			
		11 (1873)	£200	11·00	
		12 (1873)	£225	13·00	
		14 (1874)	£250	14·00	
		15 (1874)	£200	13·00	
		16 (1875)	£200	13·00	
		17 (1875)	£225	13·00	
		18 (1875)	£225	13·00	
		19 (1876)	£200	13·00	
		20 (1879)	£200	25·00	
145	**43**	6d. pale buff (Plate 13) (15.3.73)	*	£4500	
146		6d. deep grey (20.3.74) ..	£225	16·00	38·00
147		6d. grey	£225	16·00	
		Plate			
		13 (1874)	£225	18·00	
		14 (1875)	£225	18·00	
		15 (1876)	£225	16·00	
		16 (1878)	£225	16·00	
		17 (1880)	£300	35·00	
148	**44**	1s. deep green (1.9.73) ..	£325	20·00	
150		1s. pale green	£250	20·00	40·00
		Plate			
		8 (1873)	£325	25·00	
		9 (1874)	£325	25·00	
		10 (1874)	£300	25·00	
		11 (1875)	£300	25·00	
		12 (1875)	£250	20·00	
		13 (1876)	£250	20·00	
		14 (—)	*	£8000	
151		1s. orange-brown (Plate 13) (14.10.80)	£1100	£120	£250
		(*d*) *Wmk Large Garter, W* **17**			
152	**45**	4d. vermilion (1.3.76)	£600	£120	£275
		Plate			
		15 (1876)	£600	£120	
		16 (1877)	*	£8000	
153		4d. sage-green (12.3.77) ..	£400	75·00	£175
		Plate			
		15 (1877)	£450	80·00	
		16 (1877)	£400	75·00	
		17 (1877)	*	£5500	
154		4d. grey-brown (Plate 17) (15.8.80)	£600	80·00	£170
		a. Imperf			
156	**46**	8d. orange (Plate 1) (11.9.76) ..	£500	80·00	£200
★138/56		**For well-centred, lightly used** ..		**+100%**	

1876 (July). *Prepared for use but not issued.*

No.	Type		Un
156*a*	**46**	8d. purple-brown (Plate 1) ..	£2750

49 Imperial Crown   3d (50)

1880–83. *Wmk Imperial Crown, W* **49**.

No.	Type		Un	Used	★ Used on cover
157	**41**	2½d. blue (23.3.81)	£140	5·00	15·00
		Plate			
		21 (1881)	£200	6·00	
		22 (1881)	£140	5·00	
		23 (1881)	£140	5·00	
158	**42**	3d. rose (1.81)	£180	14·00	28·00
		Plate			
		20 (1881)	£225	30·00	
		21 (1881)	£180	14·00	
159		3d. on 3d. lilac (T **50**) (C.) (Plate 21) (1.1.83)	£200	45·00	£200
160	**45**	4d. grey-brown (8.12.80) ..	£150	19·00	60·00
		Plate			
		17 (1880)	£150	19·00	
		18 (1882)	£150	19·00	
161	**43**	6d. grey (1.1.81)	£150	16·00	35·00
		Plate			
		17 (1881)	£180	16·00	
		18 (1882)	£150	16·00	
162		6d. on 6d. lilac (as T **50**) (C.) (Plate 18) (1.1.83)	£200	45·00	£130
		a. Slanting dots (various) *from*	£250	60·00	
		b. Opt double	—	£3500	
163	**44**	1s. orange-brown (29.5.81) ..	£225	35·00	85·00
		Plate			
		13 (1881)	£275	35·00	
		14 (1881)	£225	35·00	2·00
★157/63		**For well-centred, lightly used** ..		**+75%**	

The 1s. Plates 13 and 14 are known in purple, but were not issued thus. They come from the Souvenir Album prepared for members of the "Stamp Committee of 1884".

52 53

54 55 56

1880–81. *Wmk Imperial Crown, W* **49**.

No.	Type		Un	Used	★ Used on cover
164	**52**	½d. deep green (14.10.80) ..	15·00	2·00	4·00
		a. Imperf	£250		
165		½d. pale green	17·00	2·50	
166	**53**	1d. Venetian red (1.1.80) ..	4·00	75	1·25
		a. Imperf	£250		
167	**54**	1½d. Venetian red (14.10.80) ..	60·00	14·00	60·00
168	**55**	2d. pale rose (8.12.80) ..	70·00	20·00	50·00
168*a*		2d. deep rose	70·00	20·00	
169	**56**	5d. indigo (15.3.81)	£400	30·00	£120
		a. Imperf	£600		
★164/9		**For well-centred, lightly used** ..		**+75%**	

Die I   57   Die II

1881. *Wmk Imperial Crown, W* **49**. (*a*) *14 dots in each corner, Die* I (12 July).

No.	Type		Un	Used	★ Used on cover
170	**57**	1d. lilac	75·00	10·00	15·00
171		1d. pale lilac	75·00	10·00	
		(*b*) *16 dots in each corner, Die* II (12 December)			
172	**57**	1d. lilac	80	40	1·10
172*a*		1d. bluish lilac	£180	35·00	
		a. Blued paper	£1400		
173		1d. deep purple	80	30	
		a. Printed both sides	£400	†	
		b. Frame broken at bottom ..	£475	£175	
		c. Printed on gummed side ..	£375	†	
		d. Imperf three sides (pair) ..	£1500	†	
		e. Printed both sides but impression on back inverted	£400	†	
		f. No watermark	£225	†	
174		1d. mauve	80	30	
		a. Imperf (pair)	£700		
★170/4		**For well-centred, lightly used** ..		**+50%**	

1d. stamps with the words "PEARS SOAP" printed on back in *orange, blue* or *mauve* price *from* £300, *unused*.

The variety "frame broken at bottom" (No. 173b) shows a white space just inside the bottom frame-line from between the "N" and "E" of "ONE" to below the first "N" of "PENNY", breaking the pearls and cutting into the lower part of the oval below "PEN".

KEY TO SURFACE-PRINTED ISSUES 1880–1900

S.G. Nos.	Description	Date of Issue
164/5	½d. green	14.10.80
187	½d. slate-blue	1.4.84
197/d	½d. vermilion	1.1.87
213	½d. blue-green	17.4.1900
166	1d. Venetian red	1.1.80
170/1	1d. lilac, Die I	12.7.81
172/4	1d. lilac, Die II	12.12.81
167	1½d. Venetian red	14.10.80
188	1½d. lilac	1.4.84
198	1½d. purple and green	1.1.87
168/a	2d. rose	8.12.80
189	2d. lilac	1.4.84
199/200	2d. green and red	1.1.87
190	2½d. lilac	1.4.84
201	2½d. purple on blue paper	1.1.87
191	3d. lilac	1.4.84
202/4	3d. purple on yellow paper	1.1.87
192	4d. dull green	1.4.84
205/a	4d. green and brown	1.1.87
206	4½d. green and carmine	15.9.92
169	5d. indigo	15.3.81
193	5d. dull green	1.4.84
207	5d. purple and blue, Die I	1.1.87
207a	5d. purple and blue, Die II	—
194	6d. dull green	1.4.84
208/a	6d. purple on rose-red paper	1.1.87
195	9d. dull green	1.8.83
209	9d. purple and blue	1.1.87
210	10d. purple and carmine	24.2.90
196	1s. dull green	1.4.84
211	1s. green	1.1.87
214	1s. green and carmine	11.7.1900
175	2s. 6d. lilac on blued paper	2.7.83
178/9	2s. 6d. lilac	1884
176	5s. rose on blued paper	1.4.84
180/1	5s. rose	1884
177/a	10s. ultramarine on blued paper	1.4.84
182/3a	10s. ultramarine	1884
185	£1 brown-lilac, wmk Crowns	1.4.84
186	£1 brown-lilac, wmk Orbs	1.2.88
212	£1 green	27.1.91

Note that the £5 value used with the above series is listed as Nos. 133 and 137.

58

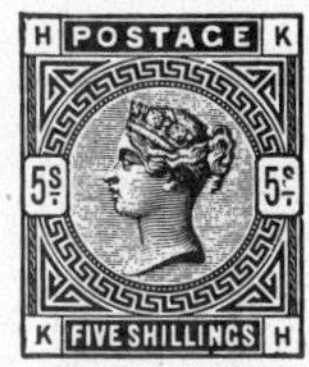

59

60

1883–84. *Coloured letters in the corners. Wmk Anchor, W* **40**.

(a) Blued paper

			Un	★ Used
175	**58**	2s. 6d. lilac (2.7.83)	£1700	£200
176	**59**	5s. rose (1.4.84)	£3250	£550
177	**60**	10s. ultramarine (1.4.84)	£11000	£1300
177a		10s. cobalt (5.84)	£12000	£3000

(b) White paper

			Un	Used
178	**58**	2s. 6d. lilac	£200	50·00
179		2s. 6d. deep lilac	£200	50·00
		a. Deep lilac, blued paper	£1600	£475
180	**59**	5s. rose	£400	60·00
181		5s. crimson	£400	60·00
182	**60**	10s. cobalt	£13000	£3000
183		10s. ultramarine	£700	£175
183a		10s. pale ultramarine	£700	£175
★175/83a		**For well-centred, lightly used**		**+50%**

For No. 180 perf 12 *see* second note below No. 196.

61

Broken frames, Plate 2

1884 (1 April). *Wmk Three Imperial Crowns, W* **49**.

			Un	★ Used
185	**61**	£1 brown-lilac	£8000	£800
		a. Frame broken	£15000	£1300

1888 (1 Feb). *Wmk Three Orbs, W* **48**.

			Un	Used
186	**61**	£1 brown-lilac	£16000	£1000
		a. Frame broken	—	£1900
★185/6a		**For well-centred, lightly used**		+50%

The broken-frame varieties, Nos. 185a and 186a, are on Plate 2 stamps JC and TA, as illustrated. *See also* No. 212a.

62

63

64

65

66

1883 (1 Aug) (*9d.*) *or* **1884** (1 April) (*others*). *Wmk Imperial Crown, W* **49** (*sideways on horiz designs*).

			Un	★ Used	Used on cover
187	**52**	½d. slate-blue	8·00	1·00	2·00
		a. Imperf	£200		
188	**62**	1½d. lilac	55·00	15·00	55·00
		a. Imperf	£225		
189	**63**	2d. lilac	70·00	20·00	50·00
		a. Imperf	£250		
190	**64**	2½d. lilac	40·00	5·00	12·00
		a. Imperf	£300		
191	**65**	3d. lilac	90·00	32·00	55·00
		a. Imperf	£300		
192	**66**	4d. dull green	£150	60·00	£120
		a. Imperf	£350		
193	**62**	5d. dull green	£150	60·00	£110
		a. Imperf	£350		
194	**63**	6d. dull green	£200	70·00	£130
		a. Imperf	£350		
195	**64**	9d. dull green (1.8.83)	£450	£200	£500
196	**65**	1s. dull green	£300	£100	£250
		a. Imperf	£700		
★187/96		**For well-centred, lightly used**		+100%	

The above prices are for stamps in the true dull green colour. Stamps which have been soaked, causing the colour to run, are virtually worthless.

Stamps of the above set and No. 180 are also found perf 12; these are official perforations, but were never issued. A second variety of the 5d. is known with a line instead of a stop under the "d" in the value; this was never issued and is therefore only known *unused* (*Price* £4000).

71

72

73

74

75

76

77

78

79

80

81

82

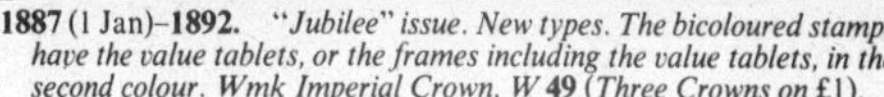

1887 (1 Jan)–**1892.** *"Jubilee" issue. New types. The bicoloured stamps have the value tablets, or the frames including the value tablets, in the second colour. Wmk Imperial Crown, W* **49** (*Three Crowns on* £1).

			Un	★ Used	Used on cover
197	**71**	½d. vermilion	65	20	50
		a. Printed on gummed side	£650	†	
		b. Printed both sides			
		c. Doubly printed	£1100		
		d. Imperf	£200		
197e		½d. orange-vermilion	65	20	
198	**72**	1½d. dull purple and green	8·00	80	15·00
		a. Purple part of design double	—	£2250	
199	**73**	2d. green and vermilion	£300	75·00	
200		2d. green and carmine	13·00	2·50	10·00
201	**74**	2½d. purple/*blue*	8·00	30	4·00
		a. Printed on gummed side	—	†	
		b. Imperf three sides	£600		
202	**75**	3d. purple/*yellow*	13·00	90	20·00
		a. Imperf			
203		3d. deep purple/*yellow*	13·00	90	
204		3d. purple/*orange* (1891)	£400	80·00	
205	**76**	4d. green and purple-brown	16·00	4·00	15·00
		aa. Imperf			
205a		4d. green and deep brown	16·00	3·25	
206	**77**	4½d. green and carmine (15.9.92)	3·25	30·00	55·00
206a		4½d. green & deep brt carmine	£180	75·00	
207	**78**	5d. dull purple and blue (Die I)	£300	25·00	60·00
207a		5d. dull purple and blue (Die II)	18·00	3·00	20·00
208	**79**	6d. purple/*rose-red*	17·00	4·00	15·00
208a		6d. deep purple/*rose-red*	17·00	4·00	
209	**80**	9d. dull purple and blue	50·00	22·00	50·00
210	**81**	10d. dull purple and carmine (24.2.90)	40·00	20·00	60·00
		aa. Imperf	£650		
210a		10d. dull purple and deep bright carmine	£350	50·00	
211	**82**	1s. green	£100	25·00	75·00
212	**61**	£1 green (27.1.91)	£2000	£300	
		a. Frame broken	£5750	£800	
★197/212a		**For well-centred, lightly used**		+50%	

The broken-frame varieties, No. 212a, are on Plate 2 stamps JC or TA, as illustrated above No. 185.

½d. stamps with "PEARS SOAP" printed on the back in *orange, blue* or *mauve*, price *from* £300 each.

1900. *Colours changed. Wmk Imperial Crown, W* **49**.

			Un	★ Used	Used on cover
213	**71**	½d. blue-green (17.4)	55	30	50
		a. Printed on gummed side	—	†	
		b. Imperf	£750		
214	**82**	1s. green and carmine (11.7)	45·00	50·00	£120
197/214		*Set of* 14	£300	£140	
★213/14		**For well-centred, lightly used**		+50%	

The ½d. No. 213, in bright blue, is a colour changeling.

KING EDWARD VII

22 January 1901–6 May 1910

PRINTINGS. Distinguishing De La Rue printings from the provisional printings of the same values made by Harrison & Sons Ltd. or at Somerset House may prove difficult in some cases. For very full guidance Volume 2 of the Stanley Gibbons *Great Britain Specialised Catalogue* should prove helpful.

Note that stamps perforated 15 × 14 must be Harrison; the 2½d., 3d. and 4d. in this perforation are useful reference material, their shades and appearance in most cases matching the Harrison perf 14 printings.

Except for the 6d. value, all stamps on chalk-surfaced paper were printed by De La Rue.

Of the stamps on ordinary paper, the De La Rue impressions are usually clearer and of a higher finish than those of the other printers. The shades are markedly different except in some printings of the 4d., 6d. and 7d. and in the 5s., 10s. and £1.

Used stamps in good, clean, unrubbed condition and with dated postmarks can form the basis of a useful reference collection, the dates often assisting in the assignment to the printers.

USED STAMPS. For well-centred, lightly used examples of King Edward VII stamps, add the following percentages to the used prices quoted below:

De La Rue printings (Nos. 215/66)—3d. values +35%, 4d. orange +100%, 6d. +75%, 7d. and 1s. +25%, all other values +50%.

Harrison printings (Nos. 267/86)—all values and perforations +75%.

Somerset House printings (Nos. 287/320)—1s. values +25%, all other values +50%.

83

84

85

86

87

88

92 93

94

95

96

97

(Des E. Fuchs)

1902 (1 Jan)–**10.** *Printed by De La Rue & Co. Wmk Imperial Crown* (½*d. to* 1*s.*); *Anchor* (2*s.* 6*d. to* 10*s.*); *Three Crowns* (£1). *P* 14.

O = "Ordinary" paper. **C** = Chalk-surfaced paper

No.	Type	Value	Description	*Un*	*Used*	*Used on cover*
215	**83**	½d.	dull blue-green, **O** (1.1.02)	50	30	60
216		½d.	blue-green, **O**	50	30	
217		½d.	pale yellowish green, **O** (26.11.04)	40	20	30
218		½d.	yellowish green, **O** ..	40	20	
		a.	Stamp from booklet with cross label attached ..	£110	£110	
		b.	Doubly printed (bottom row on one pane) (Control H9)	£3250		
219		1d.	scarlet, **O** (1.1.02) ..	35	15	1·50
220		1d.	bright scarlet, **O**	35	15	
		a.	Imperf (pair)	£2750		
221	**84**	1½d.	dull pur & grn, **O** (21.3.02)	22·00	4·75	
222		1½d.	slate-purple and green, **O**	18·00	4·75	12·00
223		1½d.	pale dull purple and green, **C** (8.05)	32·00	5·50	
224		1½d.	slate-pur & bluish green, **C**	23·00	4·25	
225	**85**	2d.	yellowish green & carmine-red, **O** (25.3.02)	24·00	3·25	12·00
226		2d.	grey-green and carmine-red, **O** (1904)	24·00	3·25	
227		2d.	pale grey-green & carmine-red, **C** (4.06)	26·00	3·75	
228		2d.	pale grey-green and scarlet, **C** (1909)	35·00	6·00	
229		2d.	dull blue-green and carmine, **C** (1907)	60·00	32·00	
230	**86**	2½d.	ultramarine, **O** (1.1.02) ..	5·50	2·50	10·00
231		2½d.	pale ultramarine, **O** ..	4·50	1·25	
232	**87**	3d.	dull purple/*orange-yellow*, **O** (20.3.02)	18·00	2·50	20·00
232*a*		3d.	dp purple/*orange-yellow*, **O**	20·00	2·50	
232*b*		3d.	pale reddish purple/*orange-yellow*, **C** (3.06)	70·00	15·00	
233		3d.	dull purple/*orange-yellow*, **C**	80·00	18·00	
233*a*		3d.	dull reddish purple/*yellow* (*lemon* back), **C**	60·00	22·00	
233*b*		3d.	pale purple/*lemon*, **C** ..	18·00	6·00	
234		3d.	purple/*lemon*, **C**	16·00	4·25	
235	**88**	4d.	grn & grey-brn, **O** (27.3.02)	35·00	11·00	
236		4d.	green & chocolate-brn, **O**	40·00	11·00	
237		4d.	green and chocolate-brown, **C** (1.06)	28·00	7·00	25·00
238		4d.	dp grn & chocolate-brn, **C**	32·00	8·50	
239		4d.	brown-orange, **O** (1.11.09)	£140	80·00	
240		4d.	pale orange, **O** (12.09) ..	8·50	6·50	20·00
241		4d.	orange-red, **O** (12.09) ..	8·50	6·00	
242	**89**	5d.	dull purple and ultramarine, **O** (14.5.02)	30·00	6·00	30·00
243		5d.	dull pur & ultram, **C** (5.06)	45·00	10·00	
244		5d.	slate-purple & ultram, **C** ..	35·00	10·00	
245	**83**	6d.	pale dull purple, **O** (1.1.02)	16·00	4·25	30·00
246		6d.	slate-purple, **O**	16·00	4·25	
247		6d.	pale dull purple, **C** (1.06)	32·00	6·00	
248		6d.	dull purple, **C**	22·00	6·00	
249	**90**	7d.	grey-black, **O** (4.5.10) ..	4·00	6·00	£120
249*a*		7d.	deep grey-black, **O** ..	£110	70·00	
250	**91**	9d.	dull purple and ultramarine, **O** (7.4.02)	50·00	24·00	£120
251		9d.	slate-purple & ultram, **O** ..	50·00	24·00	
252		9d.	dull pur & ultram, **C** (6.05)	55·00	30·00	
253		9d.	slate-purple & ultram, **C** ..	55·00	30·00	
254	**92**	10d.	dull purple and carmine, **O** (3.7.02)	50·00	18·00	£120
		a.	No cross on crown ..	£180	80·00	
255		10d.	slate-pur & carm, **C** (9.06)	50·00	28·00	
		a.	No cross on crown ..	£170	75·00	
256	**92**	10d.	dull pur & scar, **C** (9.10) ..	50·00	35·00	
		a.	No cross on crown ..	£170	75·00	
257	**93**	1s.	dull green and carmine, **O** (24.3.02)	45·00	8·50	80·00
258		1s.	dull green & carm, **C** (9.05)	55·00	12·00	
259		1s.	dull green & scar, **C** (9.10)	55·00	20·00	
260	**94**	2s.	6d. lilac, **O** (5.4.02) ..	£250	35·00	£500
261		2s.	6d. pale dull purple, **C** (7.10.05)	£225	80·00	
262		2s.	6d. dull purple, **C**	£275	50·00	
263	**95**	5s.	bright carmine, **O** (5.4.02)	£300	40·00	£500
264		5s.	deep bright carmine, **O** ..	£300	40·00	
265	**96**	10s.	ultramarine, **O** (5.4.02) ..	£650	£200	
266	**97**	£1	dull blue-green, **O** (16.6.02)	£1400	£250	

97*a*

1910 (May). *Prepared for use, but not issued.*

266*a* **97*a*** 2d. Tyrian plum £6000

One example of this stamp is known used, but it was never issued to the public.

1911. *Printed by Harrison & Sons. "Ordinary" paper. Wmk Imperial Crown.* (*a*) *P* 14.

No.	Type	Value	Description	*Un*	*Used*	*Used on cover*
267	**83**	½d.	dull yellow-green (3.5.11)	1·25	40	3·00
268		½d.	dull green	2·00	40	
269		½d.	deep dull green	9·00	2·00	
270		½d.	pale bluish green	22·00	22·00	
		a.	Stamp from booklet with cross label attached ..	£150	£150	
		b.	Wmk sideways	—	£4750	
		c.	Imperf (pair)	£2250		
271		½d.	bright green (fine impression) (6.11)	£250	£110	
272		1d.	rose-red (3.5.11)	1·90	4·00	6·00
		a.	No wmk	75·00	70·00	
273		1d.	deep rose-red	2·75	4·00	
274		1d.	rose-carmine	32·00	9·00	
275		1d.	aniline pink (5.11) ..	£325	£110	
275*a*		1d.	aniline rose	£110	75·00	
276	**86**	2½d.	bright blue (10.7.11) ..	22·00	10·00	18·00
277	**87**	3d.	purple/*lemon* (12.9.11) ..	40·00	90·00	£140
277*a*		3d.	grey/*lemon*	£3500		
278	**88**	4d.	bright orange (13.7.11) ..	45·00	40·00	£100
			(*b*) *P* 15 × 14			
279	**83**	½d.	dull green (30.10.11) ..	20·00	20·00	16·00
279*a*		½d.	deep dull green	24·00	18·00	
280		1d.	rose-red (5.10.11)	20·00	10·00	
281		1d.	rose-carmine	4·00	3·00	15·00
282		1d.	pale rose-carmine ..	4·00	3·50	
283	**86**	2½d.	bright blue (14.10.11) ..	14·00	4·00	12·00
284		2½d.	dull blue	12·00	4·00	
285	**87**	3d.	purple/*lemon* (22.9.11) ..	18·00	3·00	15·00
285*a*		3d.	grey/*lemon*	£3000		
286	**88**	4d.	bright orange (22.11.11) ..	14·00	6·00	40·00

1911–13. *Printed at Somerset House. Ordinary paper, unless marked* **C** (*= chalk-surfaced paper*). *Wmk as* 1902–10. *P* 14.

No.	Type	Value	Description	*Un*	*Used*	*Used on cover*
287	**84**	1½d.	reddish purple and bright green (13.7.11)	28·00	9·50	
288		1½d.	dull purple and green ..	13·00	6·00	30·00
289		1½d.	slate-purple & green (9.12)	17·00	10·00	
290	**85**	2d.	dp dull green & red (8.8.11)	10·00	4·50	30·00
291		2d.	deep dull green and carmine	11·00	4·50	
292		2d.	grey-green and bright carmine (carmine shows clearly on back) (11.3.12)	11·00	6·00	
293	**89**	5d.	dull reddish purple and bright blue (7.8.11) ..	12·00	4·25	50·00
294		5d.	dp dull reddish pur & brt bl	12·00	4·25	
295	**83**	6d.	royal purple, **O** (31.10.11)	38·00	40·00	
296		6d.	brt magenta, **C** (31.10.11)	£2000		
297		6d.	dull purple, **O**	20·00	12·00	60·00
298		6d.	reddish purple, **O** (11.11)	20·00	14·00	
		a.	No cross on crown (*various shades*)	£130		
299		6d.	very deep reddish purple, **O** (11.11)	38·00	18·00	
300		6d.	dark purple, **O** (3.12) ..	20·00	15·00	
301		6d.	dull purple "Dickinson" coated paper* (3.13) ..	£130	80·00	
303		6d.	deep plum, **C** (7.13) ..	16·00	30·00	
		a.	No cross on crown ..	£130		
305	**90**	7d.	slate-grey (1.8.12) ..	5·50	8·50	85·00
306	**91**	9d.	reddish purple and light blue (24.7.11)	60·00	30·00	
306*a*		9d.	deep dull reddish purple and deep bright blue (9.11) ..	50·00	32·00	
307		9d.	dull reddish pur & bl (10.11)	48·00	22·00	85·00
307*a*		9d.	deep plum and blue (7.13)	48·00	30·00	
308		9d.	slate-pur & cobalt-bl (3.12)	60·00	35·00	
309	**92**	10d.	dull purple & scar (9.10.11)	45·00	32·00	
310		10d.	dull reddish purple and aniline pink	£160	£110	
311		10d.	dull reddish pur & car (5.12)	48·00	20·00	85·00
		a.	No cross on crown ..	£160		
312	**93**	1s.	dark green & scar (17.7.11)	70·00	25·00	
313		1s.	dp green & scarlet (9.10.11)	45·00	8·00	85·00
314		1s.	green and carmine (15.4.12)	32·00	8·00	
315	**94**	2s.	6d. dull greyish purple (27.9.11)	£400	£110	
316		2s.	6d. dull reddish pur (10.11)	£200	45·00	
317		2s.	6d. dark purple	£200	50·00	
318	**95**	5s.	carmine (29.2.12)	£300	50·00	
319	**96**	10s.	blue (14.1.12)	£650	£200	
320	**97**	£1	deep green (3.9.11) ..	£1300	£250	
215/320			.. .. *Set of* 15 (*to 1s*)	£220	80·00	

*No. 301 was on an experimental coated paper which does not respond to the silver test.

KING GEORGE V

6 May 1910–20 January 1936

Further detailed information on the issues of King George V will be found in Volume 2 of the Stanley Gibbons *Great Britain Specialised Catalogue*.

PRINTERS. Types **98** to **102** were typographed by Harrison & Sons Ltd, with the exception of certain preliminary printings made at Somerset House and distinguishable by the controls "A.11", B.11" or "B.12" (the Harrison printings do not have a full stop after the letter). The booklet stamps, Nos. 334/7, and 344/5 were printed by Harrisons only.

WATERMARK VARIETIES. Many British stamps to 1967 exist without watermark owing to misplacement of the paper, and with either inverted, reversed, or inverted and reversed watermarks. A proportion of the low-value stamps issued in booklets have the watermark inverted in the normal course of printing.

We do not list such watermark varieties here, but they are listed in the *Great Britain Specialised Catalogue.*

The 1½d. and 5d. 1912–22, and 2d. and 2½d., 1924–26, listed here, are frcm *whole* sheets without watermark.

Low values with *watermark sideways* are normally from stamp rolls used in machines with sideways delivery or, from June 1940, certain booklets.

98

99

For type differences with T **101/2** *see* notes below the latter.

Die A

Die B

Dies of Halfpenny

Die A. The three upper scales on the body of the right hand dolphin form a triangle; the centre jewel of the cross inside the crown is suggested by a comma.

Die B. The three upper scales are incomplete; the centre jewel is suggested by a crescent.

Die A

Die B

Dies of One Penny

Die A. The second line of shading on the ribbon to the right of the crown extends right across the wreath; the line nearest to the crown on the right hand ribbon shows as a short line at the bottom of the ribbon.

Die B. The second line of shading is broken in the middle; the first line is little more than a dot.

(Des Bertram Mackennal and G. W. Eve. Head from photograph by W. & D. Downey. Die eng J. A. C. Harrison)

1911–12. *Wmk Imperial Crown, W* **49.** *P* 15 × 14.

No.	Type	Value	Description	*Un*	*Used*
321	**98**	½d.	pale green (Die A) (22.6.11) ..	3·25	85
322		½d.	green (Die A) (22.6.11)	1·60	55
		a.	Error. Perf 14	£3250	£200
323		½d.	bluish green (Die A)	£375	£100
324		½d.	yellow-green (Die B)	3·50	40
325		½d.	bright green (Die B)	2·75	40
		a.	Wmk sideways	—	£1700
326		½d.	bluish green (Die B)	£160	60·00
327	**99**	1d.	carmine-red (Die A) (22.6.11) ..	1·75	60
		a.	Error. Perf 14	£4000	
		b.	Experimental ptg on chalk-surfaced paper (Control A.11)	£225	
		c.	Wmk sideways	†	
328		1d.	pale carmine (Die A) (22.6.11) ..	3·00	60
		a.	No cross on crown	£275	75·00
329		1d.	carmine (Die B)	1·75	75
330		1d.	pale carmine (Die B)	2·00	75
		a.	No cross on crown	£275	75·00
331		1d.	rose-pink (Die B)	60·00	15·00
332		1d.	scarlet (Die B) (6.12)	11·00	7·00
333		1d.	aniline scarlet (Die B)	£100	50·00

For note on the aniline scarlet No. 333 *see* below No. 343.

ALTERED CATALOGUE NUMBERS

Any Catalogue numbers altered from the last edition are shown as a list in the introductory pages.

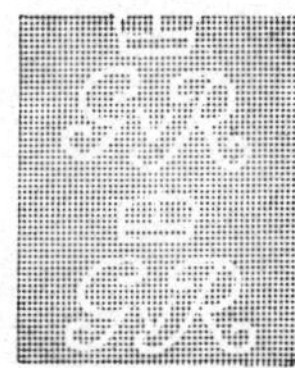

100 Simple Cypher

1912 (Aug). *Booklet stamps. Wmk Royal Cypher* ("*Simple*"), *W* **100.** *P* 15 × 14.

No.	Type	Description	Unused	Used
334	**98**	½d. pale green (Die B)	20·00	16·00
335		½d. green (Die B)	20·00	16·00
336	**99**	1d. scarlet (Die B)	10·00	8·00
337		1d. bright scarlet (Die B)	10·00	8·00

101

102

103 Multiple Cypher

Type differences

½d. In T **98** the ornament above "P" of "HALFPENNY" has two thin lines of colour and the beard is undefined. In T **101** the ornament has one thick line and the beard is well defined.

1d. In T **99** the body of the lion is unshaded and in T **102** it is shaded.

1912 (1 Jan). *Wmk Imperial Crown, W* **49.** *P* 15 × 14.

No.	Type	Description	Unused	Used
338	**101**	½d. deep green	6·00	2·75
339		½d. green	1·25	30
340		½d. yellow-green	1·25	30
		a. No cross on crown	60·00	12·00
341	**102**	1d. bright scarlet	90	30
		a. No cross on crown	45·00	12·00
		b. Printed double, one albino	£100	
342		1d. scarlet	90	30
343		1d. aniline scarlet*	£120	55·00
		a. No cross on crown	£575	

* Our prices for the aniline scarlet 1d. stamps, Nos. 333 and 343, are for specimens in which the colour is suffused on the surface of the stamp and shows through clearly on the back. Specimens without these characteristics but which show "aniline" reactions under the quartz lamp are relatively common.

1912 (Aug). *Wmk Royal Cypher* ("*Simple*"), *W* **100.** *P* 15 × 14.

No.	Type	Description	Unused	Used
344	**101**	½d. green	1·25	45
		a. No cross on crown	65·00	15·00
345	**102**	1d. scarlet	90	30
		a. No cross on crown	55·00	13·00

1912 (Oct). *Wmk Royal Cypher* ("*Multiple*"), *W* **103.** *P* 15 × 14.

No.	Type	Description	Unused	Used
346	**101**	½d. green	3·00	1·50
		a. No cross on crown	65·00	20·00
		b. Imperf	£110	
		c. Wmk sideways	†	£800
347		½d. yellow-green	3·00	2·50
348		½d. pale green	1·90	2·75
349	**102**	1d. bright scarlet	3·75	1·75
350		1d. scarlet	5·00	2·50
		a. No cross on crown	70·00	16·00
		b. Imperf	85·00	
		c. Wmk sideways	£110	55·00
		d. Wmk sideways. No cross on crown	£375	

104

105

106

No. 357a

No. 357ab

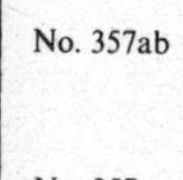

No. 357ac

107

108

Die I

Die II

Dies of 2d.

Die I.— Inner frame-line at top and sides close to solid of background. *Four* complete lines of shading between top of head and oval frame-line. These four lines do *not* extend to the oval itself. White line round "TWOPENCE" thin.

Die II.— Inner frame-line farther from solid of background. *Three* lines between top of head and extending to the oval. White line round "TWOPENCE" thicker.

STAMPS WITHOUT WATERMARK. The listed varieties, Nos. 363a, 421a and 422a, come from sheets completely without watermark. Examples on other issues exist, due to faulty registration of the paper, and these are listed in Stanley Gibbons *Great Britain Specialised Catalogue, Vol.* 2.

(Des Bertram Mackennal (heads) and G. W. Eve (frames). Coinage head (½, 1½, 2, 3 and 4d.); large medal head (1d., 2½d.); intermediate medal head (5d. to 1s.); small medal head used for fiscal stamps. Dies eng J. A. C. Harrison)

(Typo by Harrison & Sons Ltd., except the 6d. printed by the Stamping Department of the Board of Inland Revenue, Somerset House. The latter also made printings of the following which can only be distinguished by the controls: ½d. B.13; 1½d. A.12; 2d. C.13; 2½d. A.12; 3d. A.12, B.13, C.13; 4d. B.13; 5d. B.13; 7d. C.13; 8d. C.13; 9d. agate B.13; 10d. C.13; 1s. C.13)

1912–24. *Wmk Royal Cypher, W* **100.** *P* 15 × 14.

No.	Type	Description	Unused	Used
351	**105**	½d. green (1.13)	30	10
		a. Doubly printed	£3250	
352		½d. bright green	30	15
353		½d. deep green	2·25	90
354		½d. yellow-green	5·00	1·25
355		½d. very yellow (Cyprus) green (1914)	£2250	
356		½d. blue-green	32·00	12·00
357	**104**	1d. bright scarlet (10.12)	15	10
		a. "Q" for "O" (R.1/4) (Control E14)	£200	
		ab. "Q" for "O" (R.4/11) (Control T22)	£350	
		ac. Reversed "Q" for "O" (R.15/9) (Control T22)	£350	
		ad. Inverted "Q" for "O" (R.20/3)	£400	
		b. *Tête-bêche* (pair)	£5500	
358		1d. vermilion	1·50	60
359		1d. pale rose-red	4·75	30
360		1d. carmine-red	7·00	2·25
361		1d. scarlet-vermilion	70·00	20·00
		a. Printed on back†	£100	†
362	**105**	1½d. red-brown (10.12)	40	10
		a. "PENCF" (R.15/12)	£225	90·00
		b. Booklet pane. Four stamps plus two printed labels (2.24)	£180	
363		1½d. chocolate-brown	60	30
		a. Without wmk	£120	
364		1½d. chestnut	85	20
		a. "PENCF" (R.15/12)	£110	50·00
365		1½d. yellow-brown	14·00	9·00
366	**106**	2d. orange-yellow (Die I) (8.12)	3·00	1·50
367		2d. reddish orange (Die I) (11.13)	80	30
368		2d. orange (Die I)	60	30
369		2d. bright orange (Die I)	85	45
370		2d. orange (Die II) (9.21)	2·00	1·50
371	**104**	2½d. cobalt-blue (10.12)	3·25	85
371*a*		2½d. bright blue (1914)	2·75	85
372		2½d. blue	2·75	85
373		2½d. indigo-blue* (toned paper) (1920)	£1600	
373*a*		2½d. dull Prussian blue* (1921)	£550	
374	**106**	3d. dull reddish violet (10.12)	7·00	1·00
375		3d. violet	1·75	45
376		3d. bluish violet (11.13)	2·25	70
377		3d. pale violet	3·50	70
378		4d. deep grey-green (1.13)	18·00	3·50
379		4d. grey-green	4·00	50
380		4d. pale grey-green	3·75	1·75
381	**107**	5d. brown (6.13)	4·00	2·25
382		5d. yellow-brown	4·00	2·25
		a. Without wmk	£450	
383		5d. bistre-brown	55·00	25·00
384		6d. dull purple, **C** (8.13)	14·00	3·00
385		6d. reddish purple, **C**	6·00	90
		a. Perf 14 (10.20)	60·00	75·00
386		6d. deep reddish purple, **C**	8·00	1·25
387		7d. olive (8.13)	12·00	3·25
388		7d. bronze-green (1915)	40·00	8·50
389		7d. sage-green (1917)	22·00	5·00
390		8d. black/*yellow* (8.13)	25·00	6·50
391		8d. blk/*yell-buff* (*granite*) (5.17)	25·00	8·00
392	**108**	9d. agate (6.13)	8·00	1·90
393		9d. deep agate	11·00	2·75
393*a*		9d. olive-green (9.22)	80·00	18·00
393*b*		9d. pale olive-green	80·00	18·00
394		10d. turquoise-blue (8.13)	15·00	11·00
394*a*		10d. deep turquoise-blue	30·00	15·00
395		1s. bistre-brown (8.13)	9·00	75
396		1s. olive-bistre	30·00	3·00
351/95		*Set of* 15	£150	42·00

Imperf stamps of this issue exist but may be war-time colour trials.

† The impression of No. 361a is set sideways and is very pale.

* No. 373 comes from Control O 20 and also exists on white paper.

No. 373*a* comes from Control R 21 and also exists on toned paper, but both are unlike the rare Prussian blue shade of the 1935 2½d. Jubilee issue.

See also Nos. 418/29.

For the 2d., T **106** bisected, see note under Guernsey, War Occupation Issues.

1913 (Aug). *Wmk Royal Cypher* ("*Multiple*"), *W* **103.** *P* 15 × 14.

No.	Type	Description	Unused	Used
397	**105**	½d. bright green	75·00	90·00
398	**104**	1d. dull scarlet	£150	£130

Both these stamps were originally issued in rolls only. Subsequently sheets were found, so that horizontal pairs and blocks are known but are of considerable rariety.

109

A

110 Single Cypher

Major Re-entries on 2s. 6d.

Nos. 400a and 408a

No. 415b

(Des Bertram Mackennal. Dies eng J. A. C. Harrison. Recess)

High values, so-called "Sea Horses" design: T **109**. *Background around portrait consists of horizontal lines, Type* A. *Wmk Single Cypher, W* **110.** *P* 11 × 12.

1913 (30 June–Aug). *Printed by Waterlow Bros & Layton.*

No.	Description	Unused	Used
399	2s. 6d. deep sepia-brown	£200	45·00
400	2s. 6d. sepia-brown	£200	40·00
	a. Re-entry (R.2/1)	£900	£400
401	5s. rose-carmine (4 July)	£450	£120
402	10s. indigo-blue (1 Aug)	£650	£200
403	£1 green (1 Aug)	£1750	£575
404	£1 dull blue-green (1 Aug)	£1750	£575
★399/404	**For well-centred, lightly used**		**+25%**

1915 (Dec)–**18.** *Printed by De La Rue & Co.*

No.	Description	Unused	Used
405	2s. 6d. deep yellow-brown	£225	50·00
406	2s. 6d. yellow-brown	£225	45·00
407	2s. 6d. pale brown (worn plate)	£200	45·00
408	2s. 6d. seal-brown	£225	50·00
	a. Re-entry (R.2/1)	£900	£400
409	5s. bright carmine	£450	£130
410	5s. pale carmine (worn plate)	£450	£130
411	10s. deep blue	£1700	£300
412	10s. blue	£1500	£275
413	10s. pale blue	£1500	£275
★405/13	**For well-centred, lightly used**		**+25%**

1918 (Dec)–**19.** *Printed by Bradbury, Wilkinson & Co, Ltd.*

No.	Description	Unused	Used
413*a*	2s. 6d. olive-brown	90·00	24·00
414	2s. 6d. chocolate-brown	£120	26·00
415	2s. 6d. reddish brown	£120	26·00
415*a*	2s. 6d. pale brown	£110	24·00
	b. Major re-entry (R.1/2)	£800	£250
416	5s. rose-red (1.19)	£200	30·00
417	10s. dull grey-blue (1.19)	£375	75·00
★413*a*/17	**For well-centred, lightly used**		**+25%**

DISTINGUISHING PRINTINGS. Note that the £1 value was only printed by Waterlow.

Waterlow and De La Rue stamps measure exactly 22 mm vertically. In the De La Rue printings the gum is usually patchy and yellowish, and the colour of the stamp, particularly in the 5s., tends to show through the back. The holes of the perforation are smaller than those of the other two printers.

In the Bradbury Wilkinson printings the height of the stamp is 22¾ or 23 mm. On most of the 22¾ mm high stamps a minute coloured guide dot appears in the margin just above the middle of the upper frame-line.

For (1934) re-engraved Waterlow printings *see* Nos. 450/2.

111

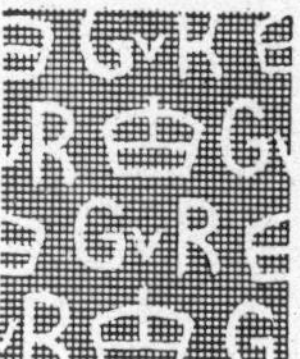

111*a*

Block Cypher

The watermark Type **111*a***, as compared with Type **111**, differs as follows: Closer spacing of horizontal rows (12½ mm instead of 14½ mm). Letters shorter and rounder. Watermark thicker.

(Typo by Waterlow & Sons, Ltd (all values except 6d.) and later, 1934–35, by Harrison & Sons, Ltd (all values). Until 1934 the 6d. was printed at Somerset House where a printing of the 1½d. was also made in 1926 (identifiable only by control E.26). Printings by Harrisons in 1934–35 can be identified, when in mint condition, by the fact that the gum shows a streaky appearance vertically, the Waterlow gum being uniformly applied, but Harrisons also used up the balance of the Waterlow "smooth gum" paper)

1924 (Feb)–**26.** *Wmk Block Cypher, W* **111.** *P* 15 × 14.

418	**105**	½d.	green	12	10
		a.	Wmk sideways (5.24)	7·00	3·50
		b.	Doubly printed	£1500	
419	**104**	1d.	scarlet	25	20
		a.	Wmk sideways	16·00	8·00
		b.	Expermental paper, W **111***a* (10.24)	30·00	
		c.	Inverted "Q" for "O" (R.20/3)	£325	
420	**105**	1½d.	red-brown	20	15
		a.	*Tête-bêche* (pair)	£375	£300
		b.	Wmk sideways (8.24)	4·25	2·25
		c.	Printed on the gummed side	£425	†
		d.	Booklet pane. Four stamps plus two printed labels (6.24)	40·00	
		e.	Ditto. Wmk sideways	£900	
		f.	Experimental paper, W **111***a* (10.24)	40·00	
		g.	Double impression		
421	**106**	2d.	orange (Die II) (9.24)	60	45
		a.	No wmk	£350	
		b.	Wmk sideways (7.26)	70·00	50·00
		c.	Doubly printed	£3250	
422	**104**	2½d.	blue (10.24)	3·25	90
		a.	No wmk	£475	
423	**106**	3d.	violet (10.24)	4·00	60
424		4d.	grey-green (11.24)	8·00	90
		a.	Printed on the gummed side	£800	†
425	**107**	5d.	brown (11.24)	15·00	1·75
426		6d.	reddish purple, **C** (9.24)	3·00	1·50
426*a*		6d.	purple, **O** (6.26)	2·00	35
427	**108**	9d.	olive-green (12.24)	8·00	1·75
428		10d.	turquoise-blue (11.24)	23·00	15·00
429		1s.	bistre-brown (10.24)	18·00	90
418/29			*Set of* 12	70·00	19·00

There are numerous shades in this issue.

The 6d. on both chalky and ordinary papers was printed by both Somerset House and Harrisons. The Harrison printings have streaky gum, differ slightly in shade, and that on chalky paper is printed in a highly fugitive ink. The prices quoted are for the commonest (Harrison) printing in each case.

112

(Des H. Nelson. Eng J. A. C. Harrison. Recess Waterlow)

1924–25. *British Empire Exhibition. W* **111.** *P* 14.

			(*a*) *Dated* "1924" (23.4.24)		
430	**112**	1d.	scarlet	3·00	6·00
431		1½d.	brown	5·00	9·00
			(*b*) *Dated* "1925" (9.5.25)		
432	**112**	1d.	scarlet	10·00	20·00
433		1½d.	brown	30·00	40·00

113

114

115

116 St. George and the Dragon

117

(Des J. Farleigh (T **113** and **115**), E. Linzell (T **114**) and H. Nelson (T **116**). Eng C. G. Lewis (T **113**), T. E. Storey (T **115**), both at the Royal Mint; J. A. C. Harrison, of Waterlow (T **114** and **116**). Typo by Waterlow from plates made at the Royal Mint, except T **116,** recess by Bradbury, Wilkinson from die and plate of their own manufacture)

1929 (10 May). *Ninth U.P.U. Congress, London.*

			(*a*) *W* **111.** *P* 15 × 14		
434	**113**	½d.	green	1·25	12
		a.	Wmk sideways	30·00	28·00
435	**114**	1d.	scarlet	90	80
		a.	Wmk sideways	50·00	38·00
436		1½d.	purple-brown	90	12
		a.	Wmk sideways	28·00	22·00
		b.	Booklet pane. Four stamps plus two printed labels	£130	
437	**115**	2½d.	blue	8·00	5·00
			(*b*) *W* **117.** *P* 12		
438	**116**	£1	black	£800	£550

PRINTERS. All subsequent issues were printed in photogravure by Harrison and Sons, Ltd, *except where otherwise stated.*

118

119

120

121

122

1934–36. *W* **111.** *P* 15 × 14.

439	**118**	½d.	green (19.11.34)	10	15
		a.	Wmk sideways	8·00	1·50
		b.	Imperf three sides	£500	
440	**119**	1d.	scarlet (24.9.34)	10	15
		a.	Imperf (pair)	£500	
		b.	Printed on the gummed side	£325	
		c.	Wmk sideways	10·00	2·75
		d.	Double impression	£950	
441	**118**	1½d.	red-brown (20.8.34)	10	15
		a.	Imperf (pair)	£225	
		b.	Imperf (three sides) (pair)	£275	
		c.	Wmk sideways	6·00	2·00
		d.	Booklet pane. Four stamps plus two printed labels (1.35)	30·00	
442	**120**	2d.	orange (21.1.35)	30	30
		a.	Imperf (pair)	£600	
		b.	Wmk sideways	80·00	45·00
443	**119**	2½d	ultramarine (18.3.35)	75	60
444	**120**	3d.	violet (18.3.35)	1·00	60
445		4d.	deep grey-green (2.12.35)	1·75	65
446	**121**	5d.	yellow-brown (17.2.36)	6·00	2·00
447	**122**	9d.	deep olive-green (2.12.35)	11·00	2·50
448		10d.	turquoise-blue (24.2.36)	12·00	8·00
449		1s.	bistre-brown (24.2.36)	18·00	55
439/49			*Set of* 11	40·00	13·00

Owing to the need for wider space for the perforations the size of the designs of the ½d. and 2d. were once, and the 1d. and 1½d. twice reduced from that of the first printings.

There are also numerous minor variations, due to the photographic element in the process.

The ½d. imperf three sides, No. 439b, is known in a block of four, from a sheet, in which the bottom pair is imperf at top and sides.

For No. 442 bisected, see Guernsey, War Occupation Issues.

B 123

(Eng J. A. C. Harrison. Recess Waterlow)

1934 (Oct). *T* **109** (*re-engraved*). *Background around portrait consists of horizontal and diagonal lines, Type* B. *W* **110.** *P* 11 × 12.

450	**109**	2s.	6d. chocolate-brown	85·00	12·00
451		5s.	bright rose-red	£150	28·00
452		10s.	indigo	£275	35·00

There are numerous other minor differences in the design of this issue.

(Des B. Freedman)

1935 (7 May). *Silver Jubilee. W* **111.** *P* 15 × 14.

453	**123**	½d.	green	25	20
454		1d.	scarlet	45	35
455		1½d.	red-brown	25	20
456		2½d.	blue	5·00	5·00
456*a*		2½d.	Prussian blue	£3500	£2750

The 1d., 1½d. and 2½d. values differ from T **123** in the emblem in the panel at right.

No. 456*a*, from three sheets printed with the wrong ink, was issued at a P.O. in Edmonton, North London.

KING EDWARD VIII
20 January–10 December 1936

Further detailed information on the stamps of King Edward VIII will be found in Volume 2 of the Stanley Gibbons *Great Britain Specialised Catalogue.*

124

125

(Des from photo by Hugh Cecil)

1936. *W* **125.** *P* 15 × 14.

457	**124**	½d.	green (1.9.36)	25	10
		a.	Double impression	—	£500
458		1d.	scarlet (14.9.36)	25	20
459		1½d.	red-brown (1.9.36)	30	10
		a.	Booklet pane. Four stamps plus two printed labels	22·00	
460		2½d.	bright blue (1.9.36)	25	50

KING GEORGE VI
11 December 1936–6 February 1952

Further detailed information on the stamps of King George VI will be found in Volume 2 of the Stanley Gibbons *Great Britain Specialised Catalogue.*

126 King George VI and Queen Elizabeth

(Des E. Dulac)

1937 (13 May). *Coronation. W* **127.** *P* 15 × 14.

461	**126**	1½d.	maroon	20	5

127 128

129 130

King George VI and National Emblems

(Des T **128/9,** E. Dulac (head) and E. Gill (frames). T **130,** E. Dulac (whole stamp))

1937–47. *W* **127.** *P* 15 × 14.

462	**128**	½d.	green (10.5.37)	10	5
		a.	Wmk sideways (1.38)	25	30
		ab.	Booklet pane of 4	6·00	
463		1d.	scarlet (10.5.37)	10	5
		a.	Wmk sideways (2.38)	8·00	5·00
		ab.	Booklet pane of 4	30·00	
464		1½d.	red-brown (30.7.37)	15	5
		a.	Wmk sideways (2.38)	90	75
		b.	Booklet pane. Four stamps plus two printed labels	28·00	
		c.	Imperf three sides (pair)		
465		2d.	orange (31.1.38)	1·10	40
		a.	Wmk sideways (2.38)	48·00	25·00
		b.	Bisected (on cover)	†	15·00
466		2½d.	ultramarine (10.5.37)	25	5
		a.	Wmk sideways (6.40)	65·00	17·00
		b.	*Tête-bêche* (horiz pair)		
467		3d.	violet (31.1.38)	4·00	75
468	**129**	4d.	grey-green (21.11.38)	25	25
		a.	Imperf (pair)	£400	
		b.	Imperf three sides (pair)		
469		5d.	brown (21.11.38)	2·50	40
		a.	Imperf (pair)	£450	
		b.	Imperf three sides (pair)	£350	
470		6d.	purple (30.1.39)	1·10	20
471	**130**	7d.	emerald-green (27.2.39)	4·25	50
		a.	Imperf three sides (pair)	£350	
472		8d.	bright carmine (27.2.39)	7·00	65
473		9d.	deep olive-green (1.5.39)	5·00	60
474		10d.	turquoise-blue (1.5.39)	5·00	60
		aa.	Imperf (pair)		
474*a*		11d.	plum (29.12.47)	3·50	1·00
475		1s.	bistre-brown (1.5.39)	5·00	15
462/75			*Set of* 15	32·00	4·50

For later printings of the lower values in apparently lighter shades and different colours, see Nos. 485/90 and 503/8.

No. 465b was authorised for use in Guernsey. See notes on War Occupation Issues.

131 King George VI

132 King George VI

133

(Des E. Dulac (T **131**) and Hon. G. R. Bellew (T **132**). Eng J. A. C. Harrison. Recess Waterlow)

1939–48. *W* **133.** *P* 14.

476	**131**	2s. 6d. brown (4.9.39)	50·00	9·00
476*a*		2s. 6d. yellow-green (9.3.42)	12·00	60
477		5s. red (21.8.39)	25·00	1·25
478	**132**	10s. dark blue (30.10.39)	£160	21·00
478*a*		10s. ultramarine (30.11.42)	25·00	4·00
478*b*		£1 brown (1.10.48)	25·00	22·00

134 Queen Victoria and King George VI.

(Des H. L. Palmer)

1940 (6 May). *Centenary of First Adhesive Postage Stamps. W* **127.** *P* 14½ × 14.

479	**134**	½d. green	15	10
480		1d. scarlet	30	8
481		1½d. red-brown	30	75
482		2d. orange	50	50
		a. Bisected (on cover)	†	10·00
483		2½d. ultramarine	1·00	15
484		3d. violet	4·00	3·00
479/84		*Set of* 6	5·50	5·00

No. 482a was authorised for use in Guernsey. See notes on War Occupation Issues.

1941–42. *Head as Nos.* 462/7, *but lighter background. W* **127.** *P* 15 × 14.

485	**128**	½d. pale green (1.9.41)	12	5
		a. *Tête-bêche* (horiz pair)	£700	
		b. Imperf (pair)	£600	
486		1d. pale scarlet (11.8.41)	12	5
		a. Wmk sideways (10.42)	5·00	6·00
		b. Imperf (pair)	£500	
		c. Imperf three sides (pair)	£350	
		d. Imperf between (vert pair)		
487		1½d. pale red-brown (28.9.42)	70	45
488		2d. pale orange (6.10.41)	50	25
		a. Wmk sideways (6.42)	6·00	12·00
		b. *Tête-bêche* (horiz pair)	£750	
		c. Imperf (pair)	£900	
		d. Imperf pane*		
489		2½d. light ultramarine (21.7.41)	10	5
		a. Wmk sideways (8.42)	12·00	10·00
		b. *Tête-bêche* (horiz pair)	£700	
		c. Imperf (pair)	£450	
		d. Imperf pane*	£1000	
490		3d. pale violet (3.11.41)	2·00	25
485/90		*Set of* 6	3·00	1·00

The *tête-bêche* varieties are from defectively made-up stamp booklets.

*BOOKLET ERRORS. Those listed as "imperf panes" show one row of perforations either at the top or at the bottom of the pane of 6.

WATERMARK VARIETIES. Please note that *inverted watermarks* are outside the scope of this Catalogue but are fully listed in the *Great Britain Specialised Catalogue.* See also the notes about watermarks at the beginning of the King George V section.

135

136 Symbols of Peace and Reconstruction

(Des H. L. Palmer (T **135**) and R. Stone (T **136**))

1946 (11 June). *Victory. W* **127.** *P* 15 × 14.

491	**135**	2½d. ultramarine	10	5
492	**136**	3d. violet	10	12

137

138 King George VI and Queen Elizabeth

(Des G. Knipe and Joan Hassall from photographs by Dorothy Wilding)

1948 (26 Apr). *Royal Silver Wedding. W* **127.** *P* 15 × 14 (2½*d.*) *or* 14 × 15 (£1).

493	**137**	2½d. ultramarine	10	5
494	**138**	£1 blue	48·00	42·00

1948 (10 May). Stamps of 1d. and 2½d. showing seaweed-gathering were on sale at eight Head Post Offices in Great Britain, but were primarily for use in the Channel Islands and are listed there (see after Great Britain Postal Fiscals).

139 Globe and Laurel Wreath

140 "Speed"

141 Olympic Symbol

142 Winged Victory

(Des P. Metcalfe, A. Games, S. D. Scott and E. Dulac)

1948 (29 July). *Olympic Games. W* **127.** *P* 15 × 14.

495	**139**	2½d. ultramarine	5	5
496	**140**	3d. violet	25	25
497	**141**	6d. bright purple	45	60
498	**142**	1s. brown	95	1·00

143 Two Hemispheres

144 U.P.U. Monument, Berne

145 Goddess Concordia, Globe and Points of Compass

146 Posthorn and Globe

(Des Mary Adshead (T **143**), P. Metcalfe (T **144**), H. Fleury (T **145**) and Hon. G. R. Bellew (T **146**))

1949 (10 Oct). *75th Anniv of Universal Postal Union. W* **127.** *P* 15 × 14.

499	**143**	2½d. ultramarine	5	5
500	**144**	3d. violet	40	30
501	**145**	6d. bright purple	40	40
502	**146**	1s. brown	1·00	1·40

1950–52. *4d. as Nos.* 468 *and others as Nos.* 485/9, *but colours changed.*

503	**128**	½d. pale orange (3.5.51)	10	10
		a. Imperf (pair)		
		b. *Tête-bêche* (horiz pair)	£1300	
		c. Imperf pane*		
504		1d. light ultramarine (3.5.51)	10	10
		a. Wmk sideways (5.51)	20	50
		b. Imperf (pair)	£450	
		c. Imperf three sides (pair)	£225	
		d. Booklet pane. Three stamps plus three printed labels (3.52)	15·00	
		e. Ditto. Partial *tête-bêche* pane	£1300	
505		1½d. pale green (3.5.51)	30	10
		a. Wmk sideways (9.51)	2·25	2·50
506		2d. pale red-brown (3.5.51)	45	12
		a. Wmk sideways (5.51)	45	1·10
		b. *Tête-bêche* (horiz pair)	£1300	
		c. Imperf three sides (pair)	£250	
507		2½d. pale scarlet (3.5.51)	15	10
		a. Wmk sideways (5.51)	80	90
		b. *Tête-bêche* (horiz pair)		
508	**129**	4d. light ultramarine (2.10.50)	1·60	90
503/8		*Set of* 6	2·40	1·10

*BOOKLET ERRORS. Those listed as "imperf panes" show one row of perforations either at the top or at the bottom of the pane of 6.

147 H.M.S. *Victory*

148 White Cliffs of Dover

149 St. George and the Dragon

150 Royal Coat of Arms

(Des Mary Adshead (T **147/8**), P. Metcalfe (T **149/50**). Recess Waterlow)

1951 (3 May). *W* **133.** *P* 11 × 12.

509	**147**	2s. 6d. yellow-green	11·00	60
510	**148**	5s. red	28·00	1·75
511	**149**	10s. ultramarine	18·00	6·00
512	**150**	£1 brown	40·00	15·00

151 "Commerce and Prosperity"

152 Festival Symbol

(Des E. Dulac (T **151**), A. Games (T **152**))

1951 (3 May). *Festival of Britain. W* **127.** *P* 15 × 14.

513	**151**	2½d. scarlet	20	5
514	**152**	4d. ultramarine	20	50

QUEEN ELIZABETH II
6 February 1952

Further detailed information on the stamps of Queen Elizabeth II will be found in volumes 3 and 4 of the Stanley Gibbons *Great Britain Specialised Catalogue*.

153 Tudor Crown

154

155

156

157

158

159

160

Queen Elizabeth II and National Emblems

I II

Types of 2½d. Type I:—In the frontal cross of the diadem, the top line is only half the width of the cross.

Type II:—The top line extends to the full width of the cross and there are signs of strengthening in other parts of the diadem.

(Des Enid Marx (T **154**), M. Farrar-Bell (T **155/6**), G. Knipe (T **157**), Mary Adshead (T **158**), E. Dulac (T **159/60**). Portrait by Dorothy Wilding)

1952–54. *W* **153.** *P* 15 × 14.

No.	Type	Value	Description	Unused	Used
515	**154**	½d.	orange-red (31.8.53)	5	5
516		1d.	ultramarine (31.8.53)	20	5
		a.	Booklet pane. Three stamps plus three printed labels	25·00	
517		1½d.	green (5.12.52)	5	5
		a.	Wmk sideways (15.10.54)	20	75
		b.	Imperf pane*	£600	
518		2d.	red-brown (31.8.53)	20	15
		a.	Wmk sideways (8.10.54)	85	1·25
519	**155**	2½d.	carmine-red (Type I) (5.12.52)	5	5
		a.	Wmk sideways (15.11.54)	6·00	7·00
		b.	Type II (Booklets) (5.53)	50	35
520		3d.	deep lilac (18.1.54)	1·40	30
521	**156**	4d.	ultramarine (2.11.53)	3·50	75
522	**157**	5d.	brown (6.7.53)	1·25	1·50
523		6d.	reddish purple (18.1.54)	2·75	70
		a.	Imperf three sides (pair)		
524		7d.	bright green (18.1.54)	6·00	2·25
525	**158**	8d.	magenta (6.7.53)	1·25	80
526		9d.	bronze-green (8.2.54)	16·00	3·00
527		10d.	Prussian blue (8.2.54)	14·00	3·00
528		11d.	brown-purple (8.2.54)	26·00	12·00
529	**159**	1s.	bistre-brown (6.7.53)	90	50
530	**160**	1s.	3d. green (2.11.53)	7·00	2·00
531	**159**	1s.	6d. grey-blue (2.11.53)	18·00	1·75
515/31			*Set of* 17	90·00	25·00

See also Nos. 540/56, 561/6, 570/94 and 599/618*a*.

*BOOKLET ERRORS.—This pane of 6 stamps is *completely* imperf (see No. 540*a*, etc.).

161

162

163

164

(Des E. Fuller (2½d.), M. Goaman (4d.), E. Dulac (1s. 3d.), M. Farrar-Bell (1s. 6d.), Portrait (except 1s. 3d.) by Dorothy Wilding)

1953 (3 June). *Coronation. W* **153.** *P* 15 × 14.

No.	Type	Value	Description	Unused	Used
532	**161**	2½d.	carmine-red	10	10
533	**162**	4d.	ultramarine	75	1·25
534	**163**	1s.	3d. deep yellow-green	5·00	4·00
535	**164**	1s.	6d. deep grey-blue	8·00	5·00

165 St. Edward's Crown

166 Carrickfergus Castle

167 Caernarvon Castle

168 Edinburgh Castle

169 Windsor Castle

(Des L. Lamb. Portrait by Dorothy Wilding. Recess Waterlow (until 31.12.57) and De La Rue (subsequently))

1955–58. *W* **165.** *P* 11 × 12.

No.	Type	Value	Description	Unused	Used
536	**166**	2s.	6d. black-brown (23.9.55)	9·00	1·50
		a.	De La Rue printing (17.7.58)	20·00	2·75
537	**167**	5s.	rose-carmine (23.9.55)	45·00	5·00
		a.	De La Rue printing (30.4.58)	45·00	9·00
538	**168**	10s.	ultramarine (1.9.55)	80·00	20·00
		a.	De La Rue printing. *Dull ultramarine* (25.4.58)	£150	20·00
539	**169**	£1	black (1.9.55)	£110	30·00
		a.	De La Rue printing (28.4.58)	£300	40·00

See also Nos. 595/8a and 759/62.

On 1 January 1958, the contract for printing the high values, T **166** to **169** was transferred to De La Rue & Co, Ltd.

The work of the two printers is very similar, but the following notes will be helpful to those attempting to identify Waterlow and De La Rue stamps of the W **165** issue.

The De La Rue sheets are printed in pairs and have a ⊣ or ⊢ shaped guide-mark at the centre of one side-margin, opposite the middle row of perforations, indicating left- and right-hand sheets respectively.

The Waterlow sheets have a small circle (sometimes crossed) instead of a "⊢" and this is present in both side-margins opposite the 6th row of stamps, though one is sometimes trimmed off. Short dashes are also present in the perforation gutter between the marginal stamps marking the middle of the four sides and a cross is at the centre of the sheet. The four corners of the sheet have two lines forming a right-angle as trimming marks, but some are usually trimmed off. All these gutter marks and sheet-trimming marks are absent in the De La Rue printings.

De La Rue used the Waterlow die and no alterations were made to it, so that no difference exists in the design or its size, but the making of new plates at first resulted in slight but measurable variations in the width of the gutters between stamps, particularly the horizontal, as follows:

	W.	D.L.R.
Horiz gutters, mm	3.8 to 4.0	3.4 to 3.8

Later D.L.R. plates were however less distinguishable in this respect.

For a short time in 1959 the D.L.R. 2s. 6d. appeared with one dot in the bottom margin below the first stamp.

It is possible to sort singles with reasonable certainty by general characteristics. The individual lines of the D.L.R. impression are cleaner and devoid of the whiskers of colour of Waterlow's, and the whole impression lighter and softer.

Owing to the closer setting of the horizontal rows the strokes of the perforating comb are closer; this results in the topmost tooth on each side of De La Rue stamps being narrower than the corresponding teeth in Waterlow's which were more than normally broad.

Shades also help. The 2s. 6d. D.L.R. is a warmer, more chocolate shade than the blackish brown of W.; the 5s. a lighter red with less carmine than W's; the 10s. more blue and less ultramarine; the £1 less intense black.

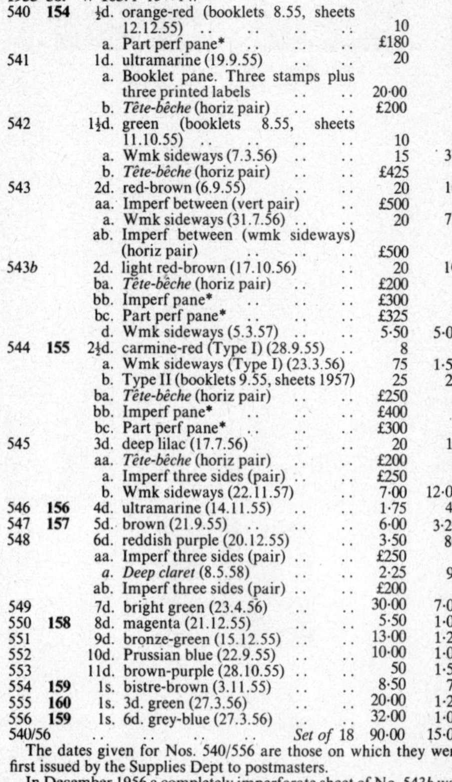

The paper of D.L.R. printings is uniformly white, identical with that of W. printings from February 1957 onwards, but earlier W. printings are on paper which is creamy by comparison.

In this and later issues of T **166/9** the dates of issue given for changes of watermark or paper are those on which supplies were first sent by the Supplies Department to Postmasters.

1955–58. *W* **165.** *P* 15 × 14.

No.	Type	Value	Description	Unused	Used
540	**154**	½d.	orange-red (booklets 8.55, sheets 12.12.55)	10	5
		a.	Part perf pane*	£180	
541		1d.	ultramarine (19.9.55)	20	5
		a.	Booklet pane. Three stamps plus three printed labels	20·00	
		b.	*Tête-bêche* (horiz pair)	£200	
542		1½d.	green (booklets 8.55, sheets 11.10.55)	10	5
		a.	Wmk sideways (7.3.56)	15	35
		b.	*Tête-bêche* (horiz pair)	£425	
543		2d.	red-brown (6.9.55)	20	10
		aa.	Imperf between (vert pair)	£500	
		a.	Wmk sideways (31.7.56)	20	75
		ab.	Imperf between (wmk sideways) (horiz pair)	£500	
543*b*		2d.	light red-brown (17.10.56)	20	10
		ba.	*Tête-bêche* (horiz pair)	£200	
		bb.	Imperf pane*	£300	
		bc.	Part perf pane*	£325	
		d.	Wmk sideways (5.3.57)	5·50	5·00
544	**155**	2½d.	carmine-red (Type I) (28.9.55)	8	5
		a.	Wmk sideways (Type I) (23.3.56)	75	1·50
		b.	Type II (booklets 9.55, sheets 1957)	25	25
		ba.	*Tête-bêche* (horiz pair)	£250	
		bb.	Imperf pane*	£400	
		bc.	Part perf pane*	£300	
545		3d.	deep lilac (17.7.56)	20	15
		aa.	*Tête-bêche* (horiz pair)	£200	
		a.	Imperf three sides (pair)	£250	
		b.	Wmk sideways (22.11.57)	7·00	12·00
546	**156**	4d.	ultramarine (14.11.55)	1·75	40
547	**157**	5d.	brown (21.9.55)	6·00	3·25
548		6d.	reddish purple (20.12.55)	3·50	80
		aa.	Imperf three sides (pair)	£250	
		a.	*Deep claret* (8.5.58)	2·25	95
		ab.	Imperf three sides (pair)	£200	
549		7d.	bright green (23.4.56)	30·00	7·00
550	**158**	8d.	magenta (21.12.55)	5·50	1·00
551		9d.	bronze-green (15.12.55)	13·00	1·25
552		10d.	Prussian blue (22.9.55)	10·00	1·00
553		11d.	brown-purple (28.10.55)	50	1·50
554	**159**	1s.	bistre-brown (3.11.55)	8·50	70
555	**160**	1s.	3d. green (27.3.56)	20·00	1·25
556	**159**	1s.	6d. grey-blue (27.3.56)	32·00	1·00
540/56			*Set of* 18	90·00	15·00

The dates given for Nos. 540/556 are those on which they were first issued by the Supplies Dept to postmasters.

In December 1956 a completely imperforate sheet of No. 543*b* was noticed by clerks in a Kent post office, one of whom purchased it against P.O. regulations. In view of this irregularity we do not consider it properly issued.

Types of 2½d. In this issue, in 1957, Type II formerly only found in stamps from booklets, began to replace Type I on sheet stamps.

*BOOKLET ERRORS. Those listed as "imperf panes" show one row of perforations either at top or bottom of the booklet pane; those as "part perf panes" have one row of 3 stamps imperf on three sides.

170 Scout Badge and "Rolling Hitch"

171 "Scouts coming to Britain"

172 Globe within a Compass

(Des Mary Adshead (2½d.), P. Keely (4d.), W. H. Brown (1s. 3d.))

1957 (1 Aug). *World Scout Jubilee Jamboree. W* **165.** *P* 15 × 14.

No.	Type	Value	Description	Unused	Used
557	**170**	2½d.	carmine-red	15	5
558	**171**	4d.	ultramarine	1·00	1·25
559	**172**	1s.	3d. green	5·50	7·00

173

½d. to 1½d., 2½d., 3d. 2d.

Graphite-line arrangements
(Stamps viewed from back)

1957 (12 Sept). *46th Inter-Parliamentary Union Conference. W* **165.** *P* 15 × 14.

No.	Type	Value	Description	Unused	Used
560	**173**	4d.	ultramarine	95	1·40

GRAPHITE-LINED ISSUES. These were used in connection with automatic sorting machinery, first introduced experimentally at Southampton.

The graphite lines were printed in black on the back, beneath the gum; two lines per stamp, except for the 2d.

In November 1959 phosphor bands were introduced (see notes after No. 598).

1957 (19 Nov). *Graphite-lined issue. Two graphite lines on the back, except 2d. value, which has one line.* *W* **165.** *P* 15 × 14.

No.	Type	Description	Unused	Used
561	**154**	½d. orange-red	15	30
562		1d. ultramarine	15	20
563		1½d. green	50	70
		a. Both lines at left	£300	£170
564		2d. light red-brown	4·00	1·50
		a. Line at left	£200	£120
565	**155**	2½d. carmine-red (Type II)	6·50	7·00
566		3d. deep lilac	80	60
561/6		*Set of* 6	10·00	9·50

No. 564a results from a misplacement of the line and horizontal pairs exist showing one stamp without line. No. 563a results from a similar misplacement.

See also Nos. 587/94.

176 Welsh Dragon

177 Flag and Games Emblem

178 Welsh Dragon

(Des R. Stone (3d.), W. H. Brown (6d.), P. Keely (1s. 3d.))

1958 (18 July). *Sixth British Empire and Commonwealth Games, Cardiff.* *W* **165.** *P* 15 × 14.

No.	Type	Description	Unused	Used
567	**176**	3d. deep lilac	15	5
568	**177**	6d. reddish purple	40	30
569	**178**	1s. 3d. green	3·25	3·75

179 Multiple Crowns

1958–65. *W* **179.** *P* 15 × 14.

No.	Type	Description	Unused	Used
570	**154**	½d. orange-red (25.11.58)	5	5
		a. Wmk sideways (26.5.61)	8	10
		c. Part perf pane*	£200	
		k. Chalky paper (15.7.63)	1·25	2·75
		l. Booklet pane. No. 570k × 3 *se-tenant* with 574k	6·00	
		m. Booklet pane. No. 570a × 2 *se-tenant* with 574l × 2	1·50	
571		1d. ultramarine (booklets 11.58, sheets 24.3.59)	5	5
		aa. Imperf (vert pair from coil)	£300	
		a. Wmk sideways (26.5.61)	75	40
		b. Part perf pane*	£180	
		c. Imperf pane	£600	
		l. Booklet pane. No. 571a × 2 *se-tenant* with 575a × 2†	4·00	
572		1½d. green (booklets 12.58, sheets 30.8.60)	5	5
		a. Imperf three sides (horiz strip of 3)	£425	
		b. Wmk sideways (26.5.61)	7·00	3·00
573		2d. light red-brown (4.12.58)	5	5
		a. Wmk sideways (3.4.59)	50	75
574	**155**	2½d. carmine-red (Type II) (booklets 11.58, sheets 15.9.59)	5	5
		aa. Imperf strip of 3	£125	
		ab. *Tête-bêche* (horiz pr)	£200	
		ac. Imperf pane	£600	
		a. Wmk sideways (Type I) (10.11.60)	20	15
		b. Type I (wmk upright) (4.10.61)	25	35
		ba. Imperf strip of 6		
		k. Type II. Chalky paper (15.7.63)	20	60
		l. Wmk sideways (Type II) Ord paper (1.7.64)	45	75
575		3d. deep lilac (booklets 11.58, sheets 8.12.58)	10	5
		a. Wmk sideways (24.10.58)	10	10
		b. Imperf pane*	£350	
		c. Part perf pane*	£250	
		d. Phantom "R" (Cyl 41 no dot)	£190	
		e. Phantom "R" (Cyl 37 no dot)	28·00	
576	**156**	4d. ultramarine (29.10.58)	40	25
		a. Deep ultramarine†† (28.4.65)	12	10
		ab. Wmk sideways (31.5.65)	12	12
		ac. Imperf pane*	£350	
		ad. Part perf pane*		
577		4½d. chestnut (9.2.59)	10	8
578	**157**	5d. brown (10.11.58)	25	10
579		6d. deep claret (23.12.58)	25	10
		a. Imperf three sides (pair)	£200	
		b. Imperf (pair)	£300	
580		7d. bright green (26.11.58)	45	20
581	**158**	8d. magenta (24.2.60)	45	20
582		9d. bronze-green (24.3.59)	45	20
583		10d. Prussian blue (18.11.58)	80	20
584	**159**	1s. bistre-brown (30.10.58)	35	8
585	**160**	1s. 3d. green (17.6.59)	35	20
586	**159**	1s. 6d. grey-blue (16.12.58)	4·50	30
570/86		*Set of* 17	7·00	1·50

*BOOKLET ERRORS. See note after No. 556.

†Booklet pane No. 571l comes in two forms, with the 1d. stamps on the left or on the right.

††This "shade" was brought about by making more deeply etched cylinders, resulting in apparent depth of colour in parts of the design. There is no difference in the colour of the ink.

Sideways watermark. The 2d., 2½d., 3d. and 4d. come from coils and the ½d., 1d., 1½d., 2½d., 3d. and 4d. come from booklets. In *coil* stamps the sideways watermark shows the top of the watermark to the left. In the *booklet* stamps it comes equally to the left or right.

Nos. 570k and 574k only come from 2s. "Holiday Resort" Experimental undated booklets issued in 1963, in which one page contained 1 × 2½d. *se-tenant* with 3 × ½d. (*See* No. 570l).

No. 574l comes from coils, and the "Holiday Resort" Experimental booklets dated "1964" comprising four panes each containing two of these 2½d. stamps *se-tenant* vertically with two ½d. No. 570a. (*See* No. 570m.)

2½d. imperf. No. 574aa comes from a booklet with watermark upright. No. 574ba is from a coil with sideways watermark.

No. 574b comes from *sheets* bearing cylinder number 42 and is also known on vertical delivery coils.

Nos. 575d and 615a occurred below the last stamp of the sheet from Cyl 41 (no dot), where an incomplete marginal rule revealed an "R". The cylinder was later twice retouched. The stamps listed show the original, unretouched "R". The rare variety, No. 575d, is best collected in a block of 4 or 6 with full margins in order to be sure that it is not No. 615a with phosphor lines removed.

No. 575e is a similar variety but from Cyl. 37 (no dot). The marginal rule is much narrower and only a very small part of the "R" is revealed. The cylinder was later retouched. The listed variety is for the original, unretouched state.

WHITER PAPER. On 18 May 1962 the Post Office announced that a whiter paper was being used for the current issue (including Nos. 595/8). This is beyond the scope of this catalogue, but the whiter papers are listed in Vol. 3 of the Stanley Gibbons *Great Britain Specialised Catalogue.*

1958 (24 Nov)–**61.** *Graphite-lined issue. Two graphite lines on the back, except 2d. value, which has one line.* *W* **179.** *P* 15 × 14.

No.	Type	Description	Unused	Used
587	**154**	½d. orange-red (15.6.59)	2·00	3·00
588		1d. ultramarine (18.12.58)	80	1·25
		a. Misplaced graphite lines (7.61)*	60	80
589		1½d. green (4.8.59)†	22·00	28·00
590		2d. light red-brown (24.11.58)	7·00	1·75
591	**155**	2½d. carmine-red (Type II) (9.6.59)	7·00	7·00
592		3d. deep lilac (24.11.58)	30	30
		a. Misplaced graphite lines (5.61)*	£175	£100
593	**156**	4d. ultramarine (29.4.59)	3·75	4·50
		a. Misplaced graphite lines (1961)*	£600	
594		4½d. chestnut (3.6.59)	5·00	4·50
587/94		*Set of* 8	43·00	45·00

Nos. 587/9 were only issued in booklets or coils (587/8).

*No. 588a (in coils), and Nos. 592a and 593a (both in sheets) result from the use of a residual stock of graphite-lined paper. As the use of graphite lines had ceased, the register of the lines in relation to the stamps was of no importance and numerous misplacements occurred—two lines close together, one line only, etc. No. 588a refers to two lines at left or at right; No. 592a refers to stamps with two lines only at left and both clear of the perforations and No. 593a to stamps with two lines at left (with left line down perforations) and traces of a third line down the opposite perforations.

†The prices quoted are for stamps with the watermark inverted. (*Prices for upright watermark £65 un, £50 us.*)

(Recess D.L.R. (until 31.12.62), then B.W.)

1959–68. *W* **179.** *P* 11 × 12.

No.	Type	Description	Unused	Used
595	**166**	2s. 6d. black-brown (22.7.59)	14·00	65
		a. B.W. printing (1.7.63)	30	20
		k. Chalk-surfaced paper (30.5.68)	25	60
596	**167**	5s. scarlet-vermilion (15.6.59)	50·00	1·25
		a. B.W. ptg. *Red* (*shades*) (3.9.63)	90	60
		ab. Printed on the gummed side	£500	
597	**168**	10s. blue (21.7.59)	45·00	2·00
		a. B.W. ptg. *Bright ultram* (16.10.63)	5·00	3·00
598	**169**	£1 black (23.6.59)	£120	18·00
		a. B.W. printing (14.11.63)	11·00	4·50

The B.W. printings have a marginal Plate Number. They are generally more deeply engraved than the D.L.R., showing more of the Diadem detail and heavier lines on Her Majesty's face. The vertical perf is 11.9 to 12 as against D.L.R. 11.8.

See also Nos. 759/62.

PHOSPHOR BAND ISSUES. These are printed on the front and are wider than graphite lines. They are not easy to see but show as broad vertical bands at certain angles to the light.

Values representing the rate for printed papers (and when this was abolished in 1968 for second class mail) have one band and others two, three or four bands as stated, according to the size and format.

In the small size stamps the bands are on each side with the single band at left (*except where otherwise stated*). In the large-size commemorative stamps the single band may be at left, centre or right, varying in different designs. The bands are vertical on both horizontal and vertical designs *except where otherwise stated.*

The phosphor was originally applied typographically but later usually by photogravure and sometimes using flexography, a typographical process using rubber cylinders.

Three different types of phosphor have been used, distinguishable by the colour emitted under an ultra-violet lamp, the first being green, then blue and now violet. Different sized bands are also known. All these are fully listed in Vol. 3 of the Stanley Gibbons *Great Britain Specialised Catalogue.*

Varieties. Misplaced and missing phosphor bands are known but such varieties are beyond the scope of this Catalogue.

1959 (18 Nov). *Phosphor-Graphite issue. Two phosphor bands on front and two graphite lines on back, except 2d. value, which has one band on front and one line on back.* *P* 15 × 14. (*a*) *W* **165.**

No.	Type	Description	Unused	Used
599	**154**	½d. orange-red	3·00	3·50
600		1d. ultramarine	3·00	4·00
601		1½d. green	3·00	4·50

(*b*) *W* **179**

No.	Type	Description	Unused	Used
605	**154**	2d. light red-brown (1 band)	5·00	4·50
		a. Error. W **165**	£200	£200
606	**155**	2½d. carmine-red (Type II)	9·00	10·00
607		3d. deep lilac	15·00	9·00
608	**156**	4d. ultramarine	8·50	25·00
609		4½d. chestnut	45·00	20·00
599/609		*Set of* 8	75·00	70·00

1960 (22 June)–**67.** *Phosphor issue. Two phosphor bands on front, except where otherwise stated.* *W* **179.** *P* 15 × 14.

No.	Type	Description	Unused	Used
610	**154**	½d. orange-red	5	5
		a. Wmk sideways (26.5.61)	7·50	11·00
611		1d. ultramarine	5	5
		a. Wmk sideways (14.7.61)	25	40
		l. Booklet pane. No. 611a × 2 *se-tenant* with 615d × 2†	12·00	
		m. Booklet pane. No. 611a × 2 *se-tenant* with 615b × 2†† (10.67)	3·00	
612		1½d. green	8	8
		a. Wmk sideways (14.7.61)	7·50	10·00
613		2d. light red-brown (1 band)	24·00	21·00
613*a*		2d. lt red-brown (two bands) (4.10.61)	8	5
		aa. Imperf three sides***		
		ab. Wmk sideways (6.4.67)	8	40
614	**155**	2½d. carmine-red (Type II) (2 bands)*	10	25
614*a*		2½d. carmine-red (Type II) (1 band) (4.10.61)	60	50
614*b*		2½d. carmine-red (Type I) (1 band) (7.11.61)	35·00	26·00
615		3d. deep lilac (2 bands)	50	35
		a. Phantom "R" (Cyl 41 no dot)	20·00	
		b. Wmk sideways (14.7.61)	1·00	1·00
615*c*		3d. deep lilac (1 side band) (29.4.65)	35	30
		d. Wmk sideways (16.8.65)	2·50	3·00
		e. One centre band (8.12.66)	25	30
		ea. Wmk sideways (19.6.67)	15	50
616	**156**	4d. ultramarine	3·75	4·50
		a. Deep ultramarine (28.4.65)	15	10
		aa. Part perf pane**	£250	
		ab. Wmk sideways (16.8.65)	10	15
616*b*		4½d. chestnut (13.9.61)	10	20
616*c*	**157**	5d. brown (9.6.67)	20	20
617		6d. deep claret (27.6.60)	20	20
617*a*		7d. bright green (15.2.67)	20	20
617*b*	**158**	8d. magenta (28.6.67)	20	20
617*c*		9d. bronze-green (29.12.66)	75	25
617*d*		10d. Prussian blue (30.12.66)	1·10	30
617*e*	**159**	1s. bistre-brown (28.6.67)	30	20
618	**160**	1s. 3d. green	3·00	2·00
618*a*	**159**	1s. 6d. grey-blue (12.12.66)	2·25	1·00
610/618*a*		*Set of* 17	7·50	4·50

The automatic facing equipment was brought into use on 6 July 1960 but the phosphor stamps may have been released a few days earlier.

The stamps with watermark sideways are from booklets except Nos. 613ab and 615ea which are from coils. No. 616ab comes from both booklets and coils.

No. 615a. See footnote after No. 586.

*No. 614 with two bands on the creamy paper was originally from cylinder 50 dot and no dot. When the change in postal rates took place in 1965 it was reissued from cylinder 57 dot and no dot on the whiter paper. Some of these latter were also released in error in districts of S.E. London in September 1964. The shade of the reissue is slightly more carmine.

**Booklet error. Two stamps at bottom left imperf on three sides and the third imperf on two sides.

***This comes from the bottom row of a sheet which is imperf at bottom and both sides.

†Booklet pane No. 611l comes in two forms, with the 1d. stamps on the left or on the right. This was printed in this manner to provide for 3d. stamps with only one band.

††Booklet pane No. 611m comes from 2s. booklets of January and March 1968. The two bands on the 3d. stamp thus created are intentional because of the technical difficulty of producing a single band on one stamp *se-tenant* with a two-banded stamp, as this requires perfect registration of the bands.

Unlike previous one-banded phosphor stamps, No. 615c has a broad band extending over two stamps so that alternate stamps have the band at left or right (same prices either way).

180 Postboy of 1660

181 Posthorn of 1660

(Des R. Stone (3d.), Faith Jaques (1s. 3d.))

1960 (7 July). *Tercentenary of Establishment of General Letter Office.* *W* **179** (*sideways on* 1*s.* 3*d.*). *P* 15 × 14 (3*d.*) *or* 14 × 15 (1*s.* 3*d.*).

No.	Type	Description	Unused	Used
619	**180**	3d. deep lilac	5	5
620	**181**	1s. 3d. green	4·00	4·25

182 Conference Emblem

(Des R. Stone (emblem, P. Rahikainen))

1960 (19 Sept). *First Anniv of European Postal and Telecommunications Conference. Chalk-surfaced paper.* *W* **179.** *P* 15 × 14.

No.	Type	Description	Unused	Used
621	**182**	6d. bronze-green and purple	50	60
622		1s. 6d. brown and blue	6·50	6·00

183 Thrift Plant

184 "Growth of Savings"

185 Thrift Plant

(Des P. Gauld (2½d.), M. Goaman (others))

1961 (28 Aug). *Centenary of Post Office Saving Bank. Chalk-surfaced paper. W* **179** *(sideways on 2½d.) P* 14 × 15 *(2½d.) or* 15 × 14 *(others).*

I. "TIMSON" Machine
II. "THRISSELL" Machine

				I		II	
623	**183**	2½d.	black and red ..	15	15	2·00	1·40
		a.	Black omitted ..	—	—	†	
624	**184**	3d.	orange-brown & vio	10	10	40	5
		a.	Orange-brn omitted	65·00	—	£120	—
		x.	Perf through side sheet margin ..	20·00	—	†	
		xa.	Orange-brn omitted	—	—	†	
625	**185**	1s.	6d. red and blue ..	2·75	2·25	†	

2½d. TIMSON. Cyls 1E–1F. Deeply shaded portrait (brownish black).

2½d. THRISSELL. Cyls 1D–1B or 1D (dot)–1B (dot). Lighter portrait (grey-black).

3d. TIMSON. Cyls 3D–3E. Clear, well-defined portrait with deep shadows and bright highlights.

3d. THRISSELL. Cyls 3C–3B or 3C (dot)–3B (dot). Dull portrait, lacking in contrast.

Sheet marginal examples *without* single extension perf hole on the short side of the stamp are always "Timson", as are those with large punch-hole *not* coincident with printed three-sided box guide mark.

The 3d. "Timson" perforated completely through the right-hand side margin comes from a relatively small part of the printing perforated on a sheet-fed machine.

Normally the "Timsons" were perforated in the reel, with three large punch-holes in both long margins and the perforations completely through both short margins. Only one punch-hole coincides with the guide-mark.

The "Thrissells" have one large punch-hole in one long margin, coinciding with guide-mark and one short margin imperf (except sometimes for encroachments).

186 C.E.P.T. Emblem

187 Doves and Emblem

188 Doves and Emblem

(Des M. Goaman (doves T. Kurpershoek))

1961 (18 Sept). *European Postal and Telecommunications (C.E.P.T.) Conference, Torquay. Chalk-surfaced paper. W* **179.** *P* 15 × 14.

626	**186**	2d.	orange, pink and brown	5	5
627	**187**	4d.	buff, mauve and ultramarine ..	20	30
628	**188**	10d.	turquoise, pale green & Prussian bl	30	45
		a.	Pale green omitted	£700	
		b.	Turquoise omitted	£700	

189 Hammer Beam Roof, Westminster Hall

190 Palace of Westminster

(Des Faith Jaques)

1961 (25 Sept). *Seventh Commonwealth Parliamentary Conference. Chalk-surfaced paper. W* **179** *(sideways on* 1*s.* 3*d.). P* 15 × 14 *(6d.) or* 14 × 15 *(1s. 3d.).*

629	**189**	6d.	purple and gold	25	25
		a.	Gold omitted	£300	
630	**190**	1s.	3d. green and blue	2·50	3·00
		a.	Blue (Queen's head) omitted ..	£1000	

191 "Units of Productivity"

192 "National Productivity"

193 "Unified Productivity"

(Des D. Gentleman)

1962 (14 Nov). *National Productivity Year. Chalk-surfaced paper. W* **179** *(inverted on 2½d. and 3d.). P* 15 × 14.

631	**191**	2½d.	myrtle-green & carm-red *(shades)*	8	5
		p.	One phosphor band	60	30
632	**192**	3d.	light blue and violet *(shades)* ..	8	5
		a.	Light blue (Queen's head) omitted	£800	
		p.	Three phosphor bands	1·00	60
633	**193**	1s.	3d. carmine, light blue & dp green	1·75	1·75
		a.	Light blue (Queen's head) omitted	£1100	
		p.	Three phosphor bands	35·00	28·00

194 Campaign Emblem and Family

195 Children of Three Races

(Des M. Goaman)

1963 (21 Mar). *Freedom from Hunger. Chalk-surfaced paper. W* **179** *(inverted). P* 15 × 14.

634	**194**	2½d.	crimson and pink	8	5
		p.	One phosphor band	1·00	2·75
635	**195**	1s.	3d. bistre-brown and yellow ..	2·25	2·25
		p.	Three phosphor bands	28·00	24·00

196 "Paris Conference"

(Des R. Stone)

1963 (7 May). *Paris Postal Conference Centenary. Chalk-surfaced paper. W* **179** *(inverted). P* 15 × 14.

636	**196**	6d.	green and mauve	60	60
		a.	Green omitted	£700	
		p.	Three phosphor bands	8·00	10·00

197 Posy of Flowers

198 Woodland Life

(Des S. Scott (3d.), M. Goaman (4½d.))

1963 (16 May). *National Nature Week. Chalk-surfaced paper. W* **179.** *P* 15 × 14.

637	**197**	3d.	yellow, green, brown and black ..	5	5
		p.	Three phosphor bands	50	60
638	**198**	4½d.	black, blue, yellow, mag & brn-red	25	45
		p.	Three phosphor bands	6·50	7·00

199 Rescue at Sea

200 19th-century Lifeboat

201 Lifeboatmen

(Des D. Gentleman)

1963 (31 May). *Ninth International Lifeboat Conference, Edinburgh. Chalk-surfaced paper. W* **179.** *P* 15 × 14.

639	**199**	2½d.	blue, black and red	10	5
		p.	One phosphor band	50	45
640	**200**	4d.	red, yellow, brown, black and blue	45	50
		p.	Three phosphor bands	40	75
641	**201**	1s.	6d. sepia, yellow and grey-blue ..	3·00	2·75
		p.	Three phosphor bands	45·00	32·00

202 Red Cross

203

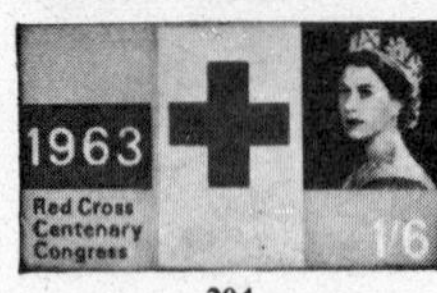

204

(Des H. Bartram)

1963 (15 Aug). *Red Cross Centenary Congress. Chalk-surfaced paper. W* **179.** *P* 15 × 14.

642	**202**	3d.	red and deep lilac	5	5
		a.	Red omitted	£850	
		p.	Three phosphor bands	60	40
		pa.	Red omitted	£1500	
643	**203**	1s.	3d. red, blue and grey	3·75	4·25
		p.	Three phosphor bands	38·00	30·00
644	**204**	1s.	6d. red, blue and bistre	3·75	4·25
		p.	Three phosphor bands	32·00	30·00

205 Commonwealth Cable

(Des P. Gauld)

1963 (3 Dec). *Opening of COMPAC (Trans-Pacific Telephone Cable). Chalk-surfaced paper. W* **179.** *P* 15 × 14.

645	**205**	1s.	6d. blue and black	2·75	2·25
		a.	Black omitted	£850	
		p.	Three phosphor bands	20·00	20·00

206 Puck and Bottom
(*A Midsummer Night's Dream*)

207 Feste (*Twelfth Night*)

208 Balcony Scene (*Romeo and Juliet*)

209 "Eve of Agincourt" (*Henry V*)

210 Hamlet contemplating Yorick's Skull (*Hamlet*) and Queen Elizabeth II

(Des D. Gentleman. Photo Harrison & Sons (3d., 6d., 1s. 3d., 1s. 6d.). Des C. and R. Ironside. Recess B.W. (2s. 6d.))

1964 (23 April). *Shakespeare Festival. Chalk-surfaced paper. W* **179.** *P* 11 × 12 (*2s. 6d.*) *or* 15 × 14 (*others*).

646	**206**	3d. yell-bistre, blk & dp vio-bl (*shades*)	10	5
		p. Three phosphor bands	10	10
647	**207**	6d. yellow, orge, blk & yell-ol (*shades*)	20	15
		p. Three phosphor bands	60	70
648	**208**	1s. 3d. cerise, bl-grn, blk & sep (*shades*)	1·00	1·50
		p. Three phosphor bands	5·00	4·50
649	**209**	1s. 6d. violet, turq, blk & blue (*shades*)	1·60	1·25
		p. Three phosphor bands	19·00	12·00
650	**210**	2s. 6d. deep slate-purple (*shades*) ..	2·00	2·75

211 Flats near Richmond Park ("Urban Development")

212 Shipbuilding Yards, Belfast ("Industrial Activity")

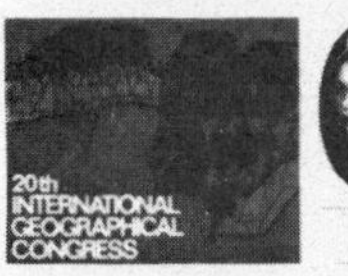

213 Beddgelert Forest Park, Snowdonia ("Forestry")

214 Nuclear Reactor, Dounreay ("Technological Development")

(Des D. Bailey)

1964 (1 July). *20th International Geographical Congress, London. Chalk-surfaced paper. W* **179.** *P* 15 × 14.

651	**211**	2½d. blk, olive-yellow, ol-grey & turq-bl	8	5
		p. One phosphor band	25	50
652	**212**	4d. orge-brn, red-brn, rose, blk & vio	50	60
		a. Violet omitted	£140	
		b. Red-brown omitted	£250	
		c. Violet and red-brown omitted ..	£120	
		p. Three phosphor bands	1·75	2·50
653	**213**	8d. yellow-brown, emerald, grn & blk	75	90
		a. Green (lawn) omitted	£300	
		p. Three phosphor bands	3·75	4·00
654	**214**	1s. 6d. yell-brn, pale pink, blk & brn	3·75	2·75
		p. Three phosphor bands	25·00	20·00

215 Spring Gentian

216 Dog Rose

217 Honeysuckle

218 Fringed Water Lily

(Des M. and Sylvia Goaman)

1964 (5 Aug). *Tenth International Botanical Congress, Edinburgh. Chalk-surfaced paper. W* **179.** *P* 15 × 14.

655	**215**	3d. violet, blue and sage-green ..	5	5
		a. Blue omitted	£750	
		p. Three phosphor bands	25	25
656	**216**	6d. apple-green, rose, scarlet and green	25	35
		p. Three phosphor bands	2·50	5·00
657	**217**	9d. lemon, green, lake and rose-red ..	2·25	2·50
		a. Green (leaves) omitted	£550	
		p. Three phosphor bands	3·00	6·00
658	**218**	1s. 3d. yellow, emerald, reddish violet and grey-green	2·50	2·00
		p. Three phosphor bands	24·00	19·00

219 Forth Road Bridge

220 Forth Road and Railway Bridges

(Des A. Restall)

1964 (4 Sept). *Opening of Forth Road Bridge. Chalk-surfaced paper. W* **179.** *P* 15 × 14.

659	**219**	3d. black, blue and reddish violet ..	5	5
		p. Three phosphor bands	75	75
660	**220**	6d. black, light blue and carmine-red	45	55
		a. Light blue omitted	£700	£500
		p. Three phosphor bands	5·50	4·75

221 Sir Winston Churchill

(Des D. Gentleman and Rosalind Dease, from photograph by Karsh)

1965 (8 July). *Churchill Commemoration. Chalk-surfaced paper. W* **179.** *P* 15 × 14.

I. "REMBRANDT" Machine

661	**221**	4d. black and olive-brown	5	5
		p. Three phosphor bands	50	50

II. "TIMSON" Machine

661*a*	**221**	4d. black and olive-brown	10	15

III. "L. & M. 4" Machine

662	–	1s. 3d. black and grey	40	60
		p. Three phosphor bands	3·25	3·75

The 1s. 3d. shows a closer view of Churchill's head.

4d. REMBRANDT. Cyls 1A–1B dot and no dot. Lack of shading detail on Churchill's portrait. Queen's portrait appears dull and coarse. This is a rotary machine which is sheet-fed.

4d. TIMSON. Cyls 5A–6B no dot. More detail on Churchill's portrait—furrow on forehead, his left eyebrow fully drawn and more shading on cheek. Queen's portrait lighter and sharper. This is a reel-fed, two-colour 12-in. wide rotary machine and the differences in impression are due to the greater pressure applied by this machine.

1s. 3d. Cyls 1A–1B no dot. The "Linotype and Machinery No. 4" machine is an ordinary sheet-fed rotary press machine. Besides being used for printing the 1s. 3d. stamps it was also employed for overprinting the phosphor bands on both values.

Two examples of the 4d. value exist with the Queen's head omitted, one due to something adhering to the cylinder and the other due to a paper fold. The stamp also exists with Churchill's head omitted, also due to a paper fold.

222 Simon de Montfort's Seal

223 Parliament Buildings (after engraving by Hollar, 1647)

(Des S. Black (6d.), R. Guyatt (2s. 6d.))

1965 (19 July). *700th Anniv of Simon de Montfort's Parliament. Chalk-surfaced paper. W* **179.** *P* 15 × 14.

663	**222**	6d. olive-green	15	15
		p. Three phosphor bands	65	1·00
664	**223**	2s. 6d. black, grey and pale drab ..	1·25	1·50

224 Bandsmen and Banner

225 Three Salvationists

(Des M. Farrar-Bell (3d.), G. Trenaman (1s. 6d.))

1965 (9 Aug). *Salvation Army Centenary. Chalk-surfaced paper. W* **179.** *P* 15 × 14.

665	**224**	3d. indigo, grey-blue, cerise, yell & brn	5	5
		p. One phosphor band	50	50
666	**225**	1s. 6d. red, blue, yellow and brown ..	1·10	1·60
		p. Three phosphor bands	5·00	6·50

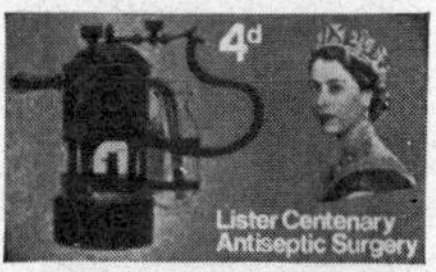

226 Lister's Carbolic Spray

227 Lister and Chemical Symbols

(Des P. Gauld (4d.), F. Ariss (1s.))

1965 (1 Sept). *Centenary of Joseph Lister's Discovery of Antiseptic Surgery. Chalk-surfaced paper. W* **179.** *P* 15 × 14.

667	**226**	4d. indigo, brown-red and grey-black	5	5
		a. Brown-red (tube) omitted	£100	45·00
		b. Indigo omitted	£300	
		p. Three phosphor bands	20	30
		pa. Brown-red (tube) omitted	£200	
668	**227**	1s. black, purple and new blue ..	1·25	1·50
		p. Three phosphor bands	1·75	2·25

228 Trinidad Carnival Dancers

229 Canadian Folk-dancers

(Des D. Gentleman and Rosalind Dease)

1965 (1 Sept). *Commonwealth Arts Festival. Chalk-surfaced paper.* *W* **179.** *P* 15 × 14.

669	**228**	6d. black and orange	30	30
		p. Three phosphor bands	60	75
670	**229**	1s. 6d. black and light reddish violet	1·00	1·50
		p. Three phosphor bands	1·25	2·75

SE-TENANT COMBINATIONS. Where these occur they are listed, and priced in mint condition. Such items can occasionally be supplied in used condition at a premium over the used prices for the single stamps concerned.

230 Flight of Spitfires

231 Pilot in Hurricane

232 Wing-tips of Spitfire and Messerschmitt "ME-109"

233 Spitfires attacking Heinkel "HE-111" Bomber

234 Spitfire attacking Stuka Dive-bomber

235 Hurricanes over Wreck of Dornier "DO-17z2" Bomber

236 Anti-aircraft Artillery in Action

237 Air-battle over St. Paul's Cathedral

(Des D. Gentleman and Rosalind Dease (4d. × 6 and 1s. 3d.), A. Restall (9d.))

1965 (13 Sept). *25th Anniv of Battle of Britain. Chalk-surfaced paper.* *W* **179.** *P* 15 × 14.

671	**230**	4d. yellow-olive and black	25	20
		a. Block of 6. Nos. 671/6	7·00	
		p. Three phosphor bands	35	60
		pa. Block of 6. Nos. 671p/6p	8·00	
672	**231**	4d. yellow-olive, olive-grey and black	25	20
		p. Three phosphor bands	35	60
673	**232**	4d. red, new blue, yell-ol, ol-grey & blk	25	20
		p. Three phosphor bands	35	60
674	**233**	4d. olive-grey, yellow-olive and black	25	20
		p. Three phosphor bands	35	60
675	**234**	4d. olive-grey, yellow-olive and black	25	20
		p. Three phosphor bands	35	60
676	**235**	4d. olive-grey, yell-olive, new blue & blk	25	20
		a. New blue omitted	—	£200
		p. Three phosphor bands	35	60
677	**236**	9d. bluish violet, orange and slate-purple	1·25	1·75
		p. Three phosphor bands	2·50	2·00
678	**237**	1s. 3d. light grey, deep grey, black, light blue and bright blue	1·25	1·75
		p. Three phosphor bands	2·00	2·00
671/8		*Set of* 8	8·50	4·25
671p/8p		*Set of* 8	11·00	7·00

Nos. 671/6 were issued together *se-tenant* in blocks of 6 (3 × 2) within the sheet.

238 Tower and Georgian Buildings

239 Tower and "Nash" Terrace, Regent's Park

(Des C. Abbott)

1965 (8 Oct). *Opening of Post Office Tower. Chalk-surfaced paper.* *W* **179** (*sideways on 3d.*). *P* 14 × 15 (*3d.*) *or* 15 × 14 (*1s. 3d.*).

679	**238**	3d. olive-yell, new blue & bronze-green	5	5
		a. Olive-yellow (Tower) omitted	£600	
		p. One phosphor band	15	15
680	**239**	1s. 3d. bronze-green, yellow-green & bl	65	85
		p. Three phosphor bands	65	75

The one phosphor band on No. 679p was produced by printing broad phosphor bands across alternate vertical perforations. Individual stamps show the band at right or left (same prices either way).

240 U.N. Emblem

241 I.C.Y. Emblem

(Des J. Matthews)

1965 (25 Oct). *20th Anniv of U.N.O. and International Co-operation Year. Chalk-surfaced paper.* *W* **179.** *P* 15 × 14.

681	**240**	3d. black, yellow-orange and light blue	8	5
		p. One phosphor band	15	20
682	**241**	1s. 6d. black, bright purple and lt blue	1·25	1·40
		p. Three phosphor bands	1·25	1·60

242 Telecommunications Network

243 Radio Waves and Switchboard

(Des A. Restall)

1965 (15 Nov). *I.T.U. Centenary. Chalk-surfaced paper.* *W* **179.** *P* 15 × 14.

683	**242**	9d. red, ultram, dp slate, vio, blk & pk	40	80
		p. Three phosphor bands	60	60
684	**243**	1s. 6d. red, greenish bl, ind, blk & lt pk	1·00	1·00
		a. Light pink omitted	£300	
		p. Three phosphor bands	7·00	8·00

Originally scheduled for issue on 17 May 1965, supplies from the Philatelic Bureau were sent in error to reach a dealer on that date and another dealer received his supply on 27 May.

244 Robert Burns (after Skirving chalk drawing)

245 Robert Burns (after Nasmyth portrait)

(Des G. Huntly)

1966 (25 Jan). *Burns Commemoration. Chalk-surfaced paper.* *W* **179.** *P* 15 × 14.

685	**244**	4d. black, deep violet-blue and new blue	5	5
		p. Three phosphor bands	15	15
686	**245**	1s. 3d. black, slate-blue & yellow-orge	60	85
		p. Three phosphor bands	1·25	1·25

246 Westminster Abbey

247 Fan Vaulting, Henry VII Chapel

(Des Sheila Robinson. Photo Harrison (3d.). Des and eng Bradbury, Wilkinson. Recess (2s. 6d.))

1966 (28 Feb). *900th Anniv of Westminster Abbey. Chalk-surfaced paper (3d.).* *W* **179.** *P* 15 × 14 (*3d.*) *or* 11 × 12 (*2s. 6d.*).

687	**246**	3d. black, red-brown and new blue	10	8
		p. One phosphor band	25	25
688	**247**	2s. 6d. black	70	1·10

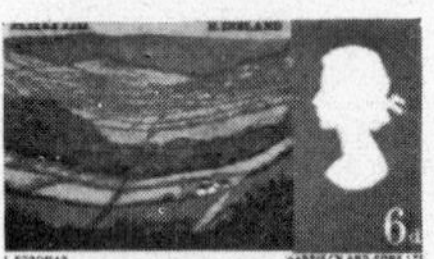

248 View near Hassocks, Sussex

249 Antrim, Northern Ireland

250 Harlech Castle, Wales

251 Cairngorm Mountains, Scotland

(Des L. Rosoman. Queen's portrait, adapted by D. Gentleman from coinage)

1966 (2 May). *Landscapes. Chalk-surfaced paper.* *W* **179.** *P* 15 × 14.

689	**248**	4d. black, yellow-green and new blue	5	5
		p. Three phosphor bands	8	8
690	**249**	6d. black, emerald and new blue	8	15
		p. Three phosphor bands	20	15
691	**250**	1s. 3d. blk, greenish yell & greenish bl	50	50
		p. Three phosphor bands	50	75
692	**251**	1s. 6d. black, orange and Prussian blue	50	70
		p. Three phosphor bands	50	75

252 Players with Ball

253 Goalmouth Mêlée

254 Goalkeeper saving Goal

(Des D. Gentleman (4d.), W. Kempster (6d.), D. Caplan (1s. 3d.). Queen's portrait adapted by D. Gentleman from coinage)

1966 (1 June). *World Cup Football Competition Chalk-surfaced paper.* *W* **179** (*sideways on 4d.*). *P* 14 × 15 (*4d.*) *or* 15 × 14 (*others*).

693	**252**	4d. red, reddish pur, brt bl, flesh & blk	5	5
		p. Two phosphor bands	10	8

694 **253** 6d. black, sepia, red, apple-green & blue 20 20
a. Black omitted .. .. .. 50·00
b. Apple-green omitted £350
c. Red omitted £375
p. Three phosphor bands 20 15
pa. Black omitted £120
695 **254** 1s. 3d. black, blue, yell, red & lt yell-ol 30 45
a. Blue omitted £180
p. Three phosphor bands 15 45

255 Black-headed Gull

256 Blue Tit

257 Robin

258 Blackbird

(Des J. Norris Wood)

1966 (8 Aug). *British Birds. Chalk-surfaced paper.* W **179**. *P* 15 × 14.
696 **255** 4d. grey, black, red, emerald-green, brt blue, greenish yellow and bistre .. 15 5
a. Block of 4. Nos. 696/9 80
ab. Black (value), etc. omitted* (*block of four*) £1400
ac. Black only omitted* .. ..
p. Three phosphor bands 12 30
pa. Block of 4. Nos. 696p/9p 80
697 **256** 4d. black, greenish yellow, grey, reddish brown, emerald-green, bright blue and bistre 15 5
p. Three phosphor bands 12 30
698 **257** 4d. red, greenish yellow, black, grey, bistre, reddish brown & emer-green 15 5
p. Three phosphor bands 12 30
699 **258** 4d. black, reddish brown, greenish yellow and grey 15 5
p. Three phosphor bands 12 30

Nos. 696/9 were issued together *se-tenant* in blocks of four within the sheet.

* In No. 696ab the blue, bistre and reddish brown are also omitted but in No. 696ac only the black is omitted.

Other missing colours known are greenish yellow, red, emerald-green, bright blue, bistre and reddish brown on ordinary paper and emerald-green, bright blue, bistre and reddish brown on phosphor.

MISSING COLOURS IN MULTICOLOURED ISSUES. We only actually list the most outstanding errors, but make footnote mention of others known to us which have full listing in the *Elizabethan Catalogue*.

259 Cup Winners

1966 (18 Aug). *England's World Cup Football Victory. Chalk-surfaced paper.* W **179** (*sideways*). *P* 14 × 15.
700 **259** 4d. red, reddish pur, brt bl, flesh & blk 5 15

These stamps were only put on sale at post offices in England, the Channel Islands and the Isle of Man, and at the Philatelic Bureau in London and also, on 22 August, in Edinburgh on the occasion of the opening of the Edinburgh Festival as well as at Army post offices at home and abroad.

260 Jodrell Bank Radio Telescope

261 British Motor-cars

262 "SRN 6" Hovercraft

263 Windscale Reactor

(Des D. and A. Gillespie (4d., 6d.), A. Restall (others))

1966 (19 Sept). *British Technology. Chalk-surfaced paper.* W **179**. *P* 15 × 14.
701 **260** 4d. black and lemon 5 5
p. Three phosphor bands 5 5
702 **261** 6d. red, deep blue and orange 12 15
a. Red (Mini-cars) omitted £1750
b. Deep blue (Jaguar and inscr) omitted £1750
p. Three phosphor bands 15 15
703 **262** 1s. 3d. black, orange-red, slate and light greenish blue 30 60
p. Three phosphor bands 35 50
704 **263** 1s. 6d. black, yellow-green, bronze-green, lilac and deep blue 30 55
p. Three phosphor bands 35 60

264

265

266

267

268

269

All the above show battle scenes and they were issued together *se-tenant* in horizontal strips of six within the sheet.

NEW INFORMATION

The editor is always interested to correspond with people who have new information that will improve or correct the Catalogue.

270 Norman Ship

271 Norman Horsemen attacking Harold's Troops

(All the above are scenes from the Bayeux Tapestry)

(Des D. Gentleman. Photo, Queen's head die-stamped (6d., 1s. 3d.))

1966 (14 Oct). *900th Anniv of Battle of Hastings. Chalk-surfaced paper.* W **179** (*sideways on* 1s. 3d.). *P* 15 × 14.
705 **264** 4d. black, olive-green, bistre, deep blue, orange, mag, grn, blue and grey .. 10 10
a. Strip of 6. Nos. 705/10 .. .. 1·90
p. Three phosphor bands 10 50
pa. Strip of 6. Nos. 705p/10p .. .. 1·90
706 **265** 4d. black, olive-green, bistre, deep blue, orange, mag, grn, blue and grey .. 10 10
p. Three phosphor bands 10 50
707 **266** 4d. black, olive-green, bistre, deep blue, orange, mag, grn, blue and grey .. 10 10
p. Three phosphor bands 10 50
708 **267** 4d. black, olive-green, bistre, deep blue, magenta, green, blue and grey .. 10 10
p. Three phosphor bands 10 50
709 **268** 4d. black, olive-green, bistre, deep blue, orange, mag, grn, blue and grey .. 10 10
p. Three phosphor bands 10 50
710 **269** 4d. black, olive-green, bistre, deep blue, orange, mag, grn, blue and grey .. 10 10
p. Three phosphor bands 10 50
711 **270** 6d. black, olive-grn, vio, bl, grn & gold 15 25
p. Three phosphor bands 15 20
712 **271** 1s. 3d. black, lilac, bronze-green, rosine, bistre-brown and gold 20 30
p. Four phosphor bands 20 25
705/12 .. .. *Set of* 8 2·00 1·00
705p/12p .. .. *Set of* 8 2·00 3·00

Missing colours known on the 4d. are olive-green, bistre, deep blue, orange, magenta, green, blue and grey on ordinary paper and olive-green, bistre, deep blue, orange, magenta, green, blue and grey on phosphor. In addition the magenta and green are known both omitted on phosphor. On the 1s. 3d. the lilac is known omitted on ordinary and phosphor.

Nos. 705 and 709, with grey and blue omitted, have been seen commercially used, posted from Middleton-in-Teesdale.

MISSING GOLD HEADS. The 6d and 1s. 3d. were also issued with the die-stamped gold head omitted but as these can also be removed by chemical means we are not prepared to list them unless a way is found of distinguishing the genuine stamps from the fakes which will satisfy the Expert Committees.

The same remarks apply to Nos. 713/14.

272 King of the Orient **273** Snowman

(Des Tasveer Shemza (3d.), J. Berry (1s. 6d.) (winners of children's design competition). Photo, Queen's head die-stamped)

1966 (1 Dec). *Christmas. Chalk-surfaced paper.* W **179** (*sideways on* 3*d.*). *P* 14 × 15.
713 **272** 3d. black, blue, green, yell, red & gold 5 5
a. Queen's head double .. ..
p. One phosphor band 5 8
714 **273** 1s. 6d. blue, red, pink, black and gold 20 30
p. Two phosphor bands 20 35

Missing colours known are the green on the 3d. and the pink (snowman's hat) on the 1s. 6d., both on ordinary paper.

See note below Nos. 679/80 which also applies to No. 713p.

274 Sea Freight

275 Air Freight

(Des C. Abbott)

1967 (20 Feb). *European Free Trade Association (EFTA). Chalk-surfaced paper. W* **179.** *P* 15 × 14.

No.	Type	Description	Unused	Used
715	**274**	9d. deep blue, red, lilac, green, brown, new blue, yellow and black ..	10	15
		a. Black (Queen's head, etc.), brown, new blue and yellow omitted ..	£700	
		p. Three phosphor bands	10	20
716	**275**	1s. 6d. violet, red, deep blue, brown, green, blue-grey, new bl, yell & blk	20	25
		p. Three phosphor bands	20	25

The following missing colours are known:—9d. lilac, green, brown, new blue and yellow on ordinary paper and lilac, green, brown, new blue and yellow on phosphor.

1s. 6d. red, deep blue, brown, new blue, yellow and blue-grey on ordinary paper and red, deep blue, brown, new blue and blue-grey on phosphor.

276 Hawthorn and Bramble

277 Larger Bindweed and Viper's Bugloss

278 Ox-eye Daisy, Coltsfoot and Buttercup

279 Bluebell, Red Campion and Wood Anemone

The above were issued together *se-tenant* in blocks of four within the sheet.

280 Dog Violet

281 Primroses

(Des Rev. W. Keble Martin (T **276/9**), Mary Grierson (others))

1967 (24 Apr). *British Wild Flowers. Chalk-surfaced paper. W* **179.** *P* 15 × 14.

No.	Type	Description	Unused	Used
717	**276**	4d. grey, lemon, myrtle-green, red, agate and slate-purple	15	8
		a. Block of 4. Nos. 717/20	1·25	
		b. Grey double*		
		p. Three phosphor bands	10	10
		pa. Block of 4. Nos. 717p/20p	50	
718	**277**	4d. grey, lemon, myrtle-green, red, agate and violet	15	8
		b. Grey double*		
		p. Three phosphor bands	10	10
719	**278**	4d. grey, lemon, myrtle-green, red and agate	15	8
		b. Grey double*		
		p. Three phosphor bands	10	10
720	**279**	4d. grey, lemon, myrtle-green, reddish purple, agate and violet	15	8
		b. Grey double*		
		p. Three phosphor bands	10	10
721	**280**	9d. lavender-grey, green, reddish violet and orange-yellow	12	40
		p. Three phosphor bands	15	40
722	**281**	1s. 9d. lavender-grey, green, greenish yellow and orange	30	60
		p. Three phosphor bands	15	30
717/22		.. .. *Set of* 6	1·40	1·10
717p/22p		.. .. *Set of* 6	70	90

The following missing colours are known:— 4d. red and reddish purple on ordinary paper and agate, violet and slate-purple on phosphor.

* The double impression of the grey printing affects the Queen's head, value and inscription.

PHOSPHOR BANDS. Issues from No. 723 are normally with phosphor bands only, except for the high values. However, most stamps have appeared with the phosphor bands omitted in error, but they are outside the scope of this catalogue. They are listed in Volumes 3 and 4 of the Stanley Gibbons *Great Britain Specialised Catalogue*. See also further notes after No. X960.

PHOSPHORISED PAPER. Following the adoption of phosphor bands the Post Office started a series of experiments involving the addition of the phosphor to the paper coating before the stamps were printed. No. 743b was the first of these experiments to be issued for normal postal use. See also notes after No. X960.

PVA GUM. Polyvinyl alcohol was introduced by Harrisons in place of gum Arabic in 1968. It is almost invisible except that a small amount of pale yellowish colouring matter was introduced to make it possible to see that the stamps had been gummed. Although this can be distinguished from gum arabic in unused stamps there is, of course, no means of detecting it in used examples. Such varieties are outside the scope of this catalogue, but they are listed in the *Elizabethan Specialised Catalogue*. See further notes *re* gum after Nos. 744 and 762.

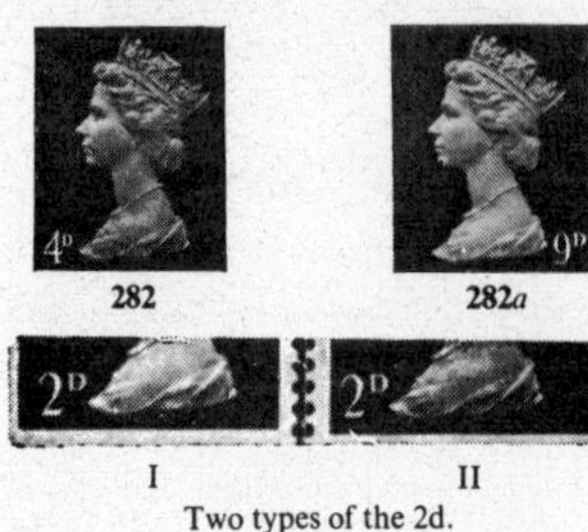

282 **282*a***

I II

Two types of the 2d.

I. Value spaced away from left side of stamp (cylinders 1 no dot and dot).

II. Value close to left side from new multipositive used for cylinders 5 no dot and dot onwards. The portrait appears in the centre, thus conforming to the other values.

(Des after plaster cast by Arnold Machin)

1967 (5 June)–**70.** *Chalk-surfaced paper. Two phosphor bands except where otherwise stated. No wmk. P* 15 × 14.

No.	Type	Description	Unused	Used
723	**282**	½d. orange-brown (5.2.68)	5	8
724		1d. lt olive (*shades*) (2 bands) (5.2.68)	5	5
		a. Imperf (coil strip)†	£350	
		b. Part perf pane*		
		c. Uncoated paper (1970)** ..	£120	
		l. Booklet pane. No. 724 × 2 *se-tenant* with 730 × 2 (6.4.68)	1·50	
		m. Booklet pane. No. 724 × 4 *se-tenant* with 734 × 2 (6.1.69)	3·00	
		n. Booklet pane. No. 724 × 6, 734 × 6 and 735 × 3 *se-tenant* (1.12.69) ..	12·00	
		na. Uncoated paper (1970)** ..	£1000	
725		1d. yellowish olive (1 centre band) (16.9.68)	30	70
		l. Booklet pane. No. 725 × 4 *se-tenant* with 732 × 2	1·75	
		m. Coil strip. No. 728 × 2 *se-tenant* with 729, 725 and 733 (27.8.69) ..	1·00	
726		2d. lake-brown (Type I) (2 bands) (5.2.68)	10	8
727		2d. lake-brown (Type II) (2 bands) (1969)	12	10
728		2d. lake-brown (Type II) (1 centre band) (27.8.69)	30	65
729		3d. violet (*shades*) (1 centre band) (8.8.67)	8	5
		a. Imperf (pair)	£450	
730		3d. violet (2 bands) (6.4.68)	30	10
		a. Uncoated paper**	£400	
731		4d. deep sepia (*shades*) (2 bands) ..	5	5
		a. Part perf pane*	80·00	
732		4d. deep olive-brown (*shades*) (1 centre band) (16.9.68)	5	5
		a. Part perf pane*	£125	
		l. Booklet pane. Two stamps plus two printed labels	75	
733		4d. brt verm (1 centre band) (6.1.69)	5	5
		a. *Tête-bêche* (horiz pair)	£1200	
		b. Uncoated paper (1970)** ..	20·00	
		l. Booklet pane. Two stamps plus two printed labels (3.3.69)	75	
734		4d. bright verm (1 side band) (6.1.69)	1·25	85
		a. Uncoated paper (1970)** ..	£150	
735		5d. royal blue (*shades*) (1.7.68) ..	8	5
		a. Imperf pane*	£250	
		b. Part perf pane*	£200	
		c. Imperf (pair)††	75·00	
		d. Uncoated paper (1970)** ..	30·00	
736		6d. brt reddish purple (*shades*) (5.2.68)	15	30
737	**282*a***	7d. bright emerald (1.7.68)	40	8
738		8d. bright vermilion (1.7.68)	8	45
739		8d. light turquoise-blue (6.1.69) ..	45	15
740		9d. myrtle-green (8.8.67)	60	8
741	**282**	10d. drab (1.7.68)	40	15
		a. Uncoated paper (1969)** ..	35·00	
742		1s. light bluish violet (*shades*) ..	35	5
743		1s. 6d. greenish blue and deep blue (*shades*) (8.8.67)	55	5
		a. Greenish blue omitted	70·00	
		b. Phosphorised paper (10.12.69) ..	1·00	1·25
		ba. Greenish blue omitted	£100	
744		1s. 9d. dull orange and black (*shades*)	60	20
723/44		.. .. *Set of* 16	3·00	1·25

*BOOKLET ERRORS. See note after No. 556. .

** Uncoated paper. This does not respond to the chalky test, and may be further distinguished from the normal chalk-surfaced paper by the fibres which clearly show on the surface, resulting in the printing impression being rougher, and by the screening dots which are not so evident. The 1d., 4d. and 5d. come from the £1 "Stamps for Cooks" Booklet; the 3d. and 10d. from sheets. The 20p. and 50p. high values (Nos. 830/1) exist with similar errors.

† No. 724a occurs in a vertical strip of four, top stamp perforated on three sides, bottom stamp imperf three sides and the two middle stamps completely imperf.

†† No. 735c comes from the original state of cylinder 15 which is identifiable by the screening dots which extend through the gutters of the stamps and into the margins of the sheet. This must not be confused with imperforate stamps from cylinder 10, a large quantity of which was stolen from the printers early in 1970.

The 1d. with centre band (725) only came in the September 1968 booklets (PVA gum) and the coil strip (725m) (gum arabic); the 2d. with centre band (728) was only issued in the coil strip (725m); the 3d. (No. 730) appeared in booklets on 6.4.68, from coils during December 1968 and from sheets in January 1969; and the 4d. with one side band (734) only in 10s. and £1 booklets.

Gum. The 1d. (725), 3d. (729), 4d. (731 and 733), 9d., 1s., 1s. 6d. and 1s. 9d. exist with gum arabic as well as the PVA gum; the 2d. (728) and coil strip (725m) exist only with gum arabic; and the remainder exist with PVA gum only.

The 4d. (731) in shades of washed-out grey are colour changelings which we understand are caused by the concentrated solvents used in modern dry cleaning methods.

For decimal issue, see Nos. X841/960.

283 "Master Lambton" (Sir Thomas Lawrence)

284 "Mares and Foals in a Landscape" (George Stubbs)

285 "Children Coming Out of School" (L. S. Lowry)

1967 (10 July). *British Paintings. Chalk-surfaced paper. Two phosphor bands. No wmk. P* 14 × 15 (*4d.*) *or* 15 × 14 (*others*).

No.	Type	Description	Unused	Used
748	**283**	4d. rose-red, lemon, brown, black, new blue and gold	5	5
		a. Gold (value and Queen's head) omitted	£120	
749	**284**	9d. Venetian red, ochre, grey-black, new blue, greenish yellow and black ..	15	20
		a. Black (Queen's head and value) omitted	£250	
750	**285**	1s. 6d. greenish yellow, grey, rose, new blue, grey-black and gold	15	20
		a. Gold (Queen's head) omitted ..	£150	

The 4d. is known with the new blue omitted, the 9d. with the greenish yellow omitted and the 1s. 6d. with the new blue, and grey omitted.

286 *Gypsy Moth IV*

(Des M. and Sylvia Goaman)

1967 (24 July). *Sir Francis Chichester's World Voyage. Chalk-surfaced paper. Three phosphor bands. No wmk. P* 15 × 14.

No.	Type	Description	Unused	Used
751	**286**	1s. 9d. black, brown-red, lt emer & blue	20	20

287 Radar Screen

288 Penicillin Mould

PRICES OF SETS

Set prices are given for many issues, generally those containing five stamps or more. Definitive sets include one of each value or major colour change, but do not cover different perforations, die types or minor shades. Where a choice is possible the set prices are based on the cheapest versions of the stamps included in the listings.

289 "VC-10" Jet Engines **290** Television Equipment

(Des C. Abbott (4d., 1s.), Negus-Sharland team (others))

1967 (19 Sept). *British Discovery and Invention. Chalk-surfaced paper. Three phosphor bands (4d.) or two phosphor bands (others). W* **179** *(sideways on* 1s. 9d.*). P* 14 × 15 *(*1s. 9d.*) or* 15 × 14 *(others).*

752	**287**	4d.	greenish yellow, black and vermilion	5	5
753	**288**	1s.	blue-green, light greenish blue, slate-purple and bluish violet	15	15
754	**289**	1s.	6d. black, grey, royal blue, ochre and turquoise-blue	15	15
755	**290**	1s.	9d. black, grey-blue, pale olive-grey, violet and orange	20	20

The 1s. 9d. exists with the grey-blue omitted.

WATERMARK. All issues from this date are on unwatermarked paper.

291 "The Adoration of the Shepherds" (School of Seville) **292** "Madonna and Child" (Murillo)

293 "The Adoration of the Shepherds" (Louis le Nain)

1967. *Christmas. Chalk-surfaced paper. One phosphor band (*3d.*) or two phosphor bands (others). P* 15 × 14 *(*1s. 6d.*) or* 14 × 15 *(others).*

756	**291**	3d.	ol-yell, rose, bl, blk & gold (27.11)	5	5
			a. Gold (value and Queen's head) omitted	40·00	
			b. Printed on the gummed side ..	£150	
757	**292**	4d.	bright purple, greenish yellow, new blue, grey-black and gold (18.10) ..	5	5
			a. Gold (value and Queen's head) omitted	45·00	
			b. Yellow (Child, robe and Madonna's face) omitted		
758	**293**	1s.	6d. brt purple, bistre, lemon, black, orange-red, ultramarine and gold	20	25
			a. Gold (value and Queen's head) omitted		

Distinct shades exist of the 4d. value but are not listable as there are intermediate shades. Stamps emanating from one machine show a darker background and give the appearance of the yellow colour being omitted but this is not so and these should not be confused with the true missing yellow No. 757b.

The 3d. is known with the rose colour omitted and the 1s. 6d. is known with the ultramarine colour omitted.

(Recess Bradbury, Wilkinson)

1967–68. *No wmk. White paper. P* 11 × 12.

759	**166**	2s.	6d. black-brown (1.7.68)	30	40
760	**167**	5s.	red (10.4.68)	1·00	75
761	**168**	10s.	bright ultramarine (10.4.68) ..	7·00	5·50
762	**169**	£1	black (4.12.67)	3·00	4·00

PVA GUM. All the following issues from this date have PVA gum *except where footnotes state otherwise.*

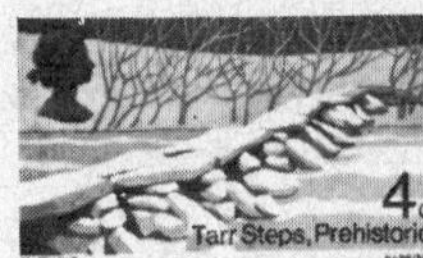

294 Tarr Steps, Exmoor

295 Aberfeldy Bridge

296 Menai Bridge

297 M4 Viaduct

(Des A. Restall (9d.), L. Rosoman (1s. 6d.), J. Matthews (others))

1968 (29 Apr). *British Bridges. Chalk-surfaced paper. Two phosphor bands. P* 15 × 14.

763	**294**	4d.	black, bluish violet, turq-bl & gold	5	5
			a. Printed on gummed side	20·00	
764	**295**	9d.	red-brown, myrtle-green, ultramarine, olive-brown, black and gold ..	15	15
			a. Gold (Queen's head) omitted ..	£120	
765	**296**	1s.	6d. olive-brown, red-orange, bright green, turquoise-green and gold ..	15	20
			a. Gold (Queen's head) omitted ..	£120	
766	**297**	1s.	9d. olive-brown, greenish yellow, dull green, deep ultramarine & gold	15	20
			a. Gold (Queen's head) omitted ..	£140	

The 9d. is known with ultramarine omitted and the 1s. 6d. with red-orange omitted.

298 "T U C" and Trades Unionists

299 Mrs. Emmeline Pankhurst (statute)

300 Sopwith "Camel" and "Lightning" Fighters

301 Captain Cook's *Endeavour* and Signature

(Des D. Gentleman (4d.), C. Abbott (others))

1968 (29 May). *British Anniversaries. Events described on stamps. Chalk-surfaced paper. Two phosphor bands. P* 15 × 14.

767	**298**	4d.	emerald, olive, blue and black ..	5	5
768	**299**	9d.	reddish violet, bluish grey and black	15	12
769	**300**	1s.	olive-brown, bl, red, slate-bl & blk	25	15
770	**301**	1s.	9d. yellow-ochre and blackish brown	25	25

302 "Queen Elizabeth I" (unknown artist) **303** "Pinkie" (Lawrence)

304 "Ruins of St. Mary Le Port" (Piper) **305** "The Hay Wain" (Constable)

1968 (12 Aug). *British Paintings. Queen's head embossed. Chalk-surfaced paper. Two phosphor bands. P* 15 × 14 *(*1s. 9d.*) or* 14 × 15 *(others).*

771	**302**	4d.	blk, verm, greenish yell, grey & gold	5	5
			a. Gold (value and Queen's head) omitted	£100	
772	**303**	1s.	mauve, new blue, greenish yellow, black, magenta and gold	15	15
			a. Gold (value and Queen's head) omitted	£150	
			b. Gold (value and Queen's head) and embossing omitted	£170	
773	**304**	1s.	6d. slate, orange, black, mauve, greenish yellow, ultramarine & gold	15	20
			a. Gold (value and Queen's head) omitted	£150	
774	**305**	1s.	9d. greenish yellow, black, new blue, red and gold	25	25
			a. Gold (value and Queen's head) and embossing omitted	£200	
			b. Red omitted	£600	

The 4d. is known with the vermilion omitted and the 4d. and 1s. with the embossing only omitted. Nos 772b and 774a are only known with the phosphor also omitted.

306 Boy and Girl with Rocking Horse

307 Girl with Doll's House **308** Boy with Train Set

(Des Rosalind Dease. Head printed in gold and then embossed)

1968 (25 Nov). *Christmas. Chalk-surfaced paper. One centre phosphor band (*4d.*) or two phosphor bands (others). P* 15 × 14 *(*4d.*) or* 14 × 15 *(others).*

775	**306**	4d.	black, orange, vermilion, ultramarine, bistre and gold	5	5
			a. Gold omitted	£350	
			b. Vermilion omitted*	75·00	
776	**307**	9d.	yellow-olive, black, brown, yellow, magenta, orange, turq-green & gold	12	20
777	**308**	1s.	6d. ultramarine, yellow-orange, brt purple, blue-green, black and gold	12	20

*The effect of the missing vermilion is shown on the rocking horse, saddle and faces which appear orange instead of red.

The 4d. is known with the ultramarine and phosphor omitted, the 9d. with the yellow omitted and all values with the embossing of Queen's head omitted.

309 R.M.S. *Queen Elizabeth 2*

310 Elizabethan Galleon

311 East Indiaman

312 *Cutty Sark*

313 S.S. *Great Britain*

314 R.M.S. *Mauretania*

(Des D. Gentleman)

1969 (15 Jan). *British Ships. Chalk-surfaced paper. Two vertical phosphor bands at right* (1*s*.), *one horizontal phosphor band* (5*d*.) *or two phosphor bands* (9*d*.). *P* 15 × 14.

No.	Type	Description	Unused	Used
778	**309**	5d. black, grey, red and turquoise ..	5	5
		a. Black (Queen's head, value, hull and inscr) omitted	£600	
		b. Grey (decks, etc.) omitted ..	80·00	
779	**310**	9d. red, blue, ochre, brown, blk & grey	20	50
		a. Strip of 3. Nos. 779/81	60	
		b. Red and blue omitted	£300	
		c. Blue omitted	£500	
780	**311**	9d. ochre, brown, black and grey ..	20	50
781	**312**	9d. ochre, brown, black and grey ..	20	50
782	**313**	1s. brn, black, grey, grn & greenish yell	25	35
		a. Pair. Nos. 782/3	50	
783	**314**	1s. red, black, brown, carmine and grey	25	35
		a. Carmine (hull overlay) omitted ..		
778/83		.. .. *Set of* 6	1·00	2·00

The 9d. and 1s. values were arranged in horizontal strips of three and pairs respectively throughout the sheet.

The 5d. is known with the red omitted and the 1s. (No. 782) with the greenish yellow omitted.

No. 779b is known only with the phosphor also omitted.

315 "Concorde" in Flight

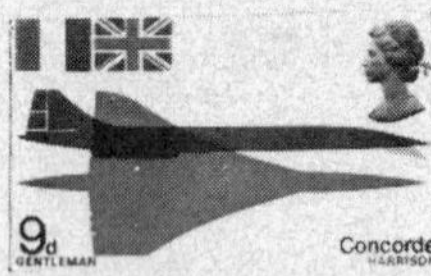

316 Plan and Elevation Views

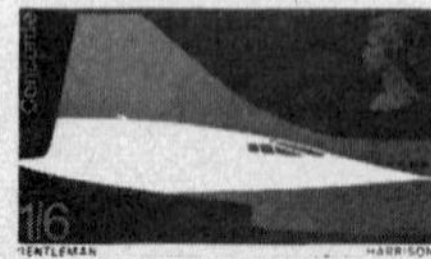

317 "Concorde's" Nose and Tail

(Des M. and Sylvia Goaman (4d.), D. Gentleman (9d., 1s. 6d.))

1969 (3 Mar). *First Flight of "Concorde". Chalk-surfaced paper. Two phosphor bands. P* 15 × 14.

No.	Type	Description	Unused	Used
784	**315**	4d. yellow-orange, violet, greenish blue, blue-green and pale green	5	5
		a. Violet (value, etc.) omitted ..	£180	
785	**316**	9d. ultramarine, emerald, red & grey-bl	15	20
786	**317**	1s. 6d. deep blue, silver-grey & lt blue	15	20
		a. Silver-grey omitted	£200	

No. 786a affects the Queen's head which appears in the light blue colour.

The 4d. is known with the yellow-orange omitted.

318 Queen Elizabeth II. (See also Type **357**)

(Des after plaster cast by Arnold Machin. Recess Bradbury, Wilkinson)

1969 (5 Mar). *P* 12.

No.	Type	Description	Unused	Used
787	**318**	2s. 6d. brown	60	30
788		5s. crimson-lake	3·75	50
789		10s. deep ultramarine	8·50	7·00
790		£1 bluish black	2·75	1·25

For decimal issue, see Nos. 829/31*a* and notes after No. 831*a*.

319 Page from *Daily Mail*, and Vickers "Vimy" Aircraft

320 Europa and CEPT Emblems

321 ILO Emblem

322 Flags of NATO Countries

323 Vickers "Vimy" Aircraft and Globe showing Flight

(Des P. Sharland (5d., 1s., 1s. 6d.), M. and Sylvia Goaman (9d., 1s. 9d.)

1969 (2 Apr). *Anniversaries. Events described on stamps. Chalk-surfaced paper. Two phosphor bands. P* 15 × 14.

No.	Type	Description	Unused	Used
791	**319**	5d. black, pale sage-grn, chest & new bl	5	5
792	**320**	9d. pale turq, dp bl, lt emer-green & blk	10	20
793	**321**	1s. bright purple, deep blue and lilac	15	15
794	**322**	1s. 6d. red, royal blue, yellow-green, black, lemon and new blue ..	15	20
795	**323**	1s. 9d. yellow-olive, greenish yellow and pale turquoise-green	25	20
		a. Uncoated paper*	£150	

*Uncoated paper. The second note after No. 744 also applies here.

The 1s. 6d. is known with black and also with yellow-green omitted.

324 Durham Cathedral

325 York Minster

326 St. Giles' Cathedral, Edinburgh

327 Canterbury Cathedral

328 St. Paul's Cathedral

329 Liverpool Metropolitan Cathedral

(Des P. Gauld)

1969 (28 May). *British Architecture. Cathedrals. Chalk-surfaced paper. Two phosphor bands. P* 15 × 14.

No.	Type	Description	Unused	Used
796	**324**	5d. grey-blk, orge, pale bluish vio & blk	10	5
		a. Block of 4. Nos. 796/9	90	
		b. Pale bluish violet omitted	£250	
797	**325**	5d. grey-black, pale bluish violet, new blue and black	10	5
		b. Pale bluish violet omitted	£250	
798	**326**	5d. grey-black, purple, green and black	10	5
799	**327**	5d. grey-black, green, new blue & black	10	5
800	**328**	9d. grey-blk, ochre, pale drab, vio & blk	15	25
		a. Black (value) omitted	50·00	
801	**329**	1s. 6d. grey-black, pale turquoise, pale reddish violet, pale yellow-ol & blk	15	25
		a. Black (value) omitted	£450	
		b. Black (value) double		
796/801		.. .. *Set of* 6	1·00	60

The 5d. values were issued together *se-tenant* in blocks of four throughout the sheet.

The 5d. (No. 798) is known with green omitted.

330 The King's Gate, Caernarvon Castle

331 The Eagle Tower, Caernarvon Castle

332 Queen Eleanor's Gate, Caernarvon Castle

333 Celtic Cross, Margam Abbey

334 H.R.H. The Prince of Wales (after photo by G. Argent)

(Des D. Gentleman)

1969 (1 July). *Investiture of H.R.H. The Prince of Wales. Chalk-surfaced paper. Two phosphor bands. P* 14 × 15.

No.	Type	Description	Unused	Used
802	**330**	5d. deep olive-grey, light olive-grey, deep grey, light grey, red, pale turquoise-green, black and silver ..	8	8
		a. Strip of 3. Nos. 802/4	40	
		b. Black (value and inscr) omitted ..	£150	
803	**331**	5d. deep olive-grey, light olive-grey, deep grey, light grey, red, pale turquoise-green, black and silver ..	8	8
		b. Black (value and inscr) omitted ..	£150	
804	**332**	5d. deep olive-grey, light olive-grey, deep grey, light grey, red, pale turquoise-green, black and silver ..	8	8
		b. Black (value and inscr) omitted ..	£150	
805	**333**	9d. deep grey, light grey, black and gold	12	30
806	**334**	1s. blackish yellow-olive and gold ..	15	20

The 5d. values were issued together *se-tenant* in strips of three throughout the sheet.

The 5d. values are known with red, pale turquoise-green and also deep grey omitted.

335 Mahatma Gandhi

(Des B. Mullick)

1969 (13 Aug). *Gandhi Centenary Year. Chalk-surfaced paper. Two phosphor bands. P* 15 × 14.

807 **335** 1s. 6d. black, green, red-orange & grey 20 20
a. Printed on the gummed side .. £225

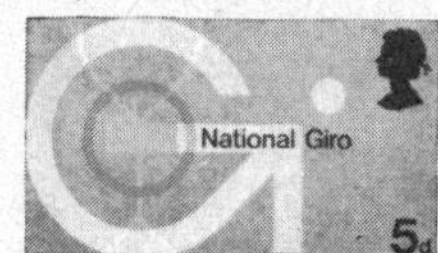

336 National Giro "G" Symbol

337 Telecommunications—International Subscriber Dialling

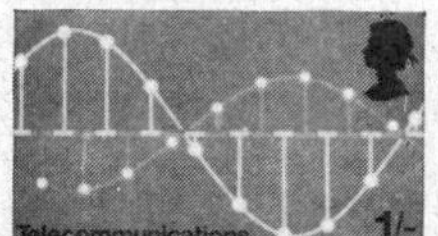

338 Telecommunications—Pulse Code Modulation

339 Postal Mechanisation—Automatic Sorting

(Des D. Gentleman. Litho De La Rue)

1969 (1 Oct). *Post Office Technology Commemoration. Chalk-surfaced paper. Two phosphor bands. P* 13½ × 14.

808 **336** 5d. new bl, greenish bl, lavender & blk 5 5
809 **337** 9d. emerald, violet-blue and black .. 15 20
810 **338** 1s. emerald, lavender and black .. 15 20
811 **339** 1s. 6d. brt purple, lt blue, grey-bl & blk 20 20

340 Herald Angel

341 The Three Shepherds

342 The Three Kings

(Des F. Wegner. Queen's head (and stars 4d., 5d. and scroll-work 1s. 6d.) printed in gold and then embossed)

1969 (26 Nov). *Christmas. Chalk-surfaced paper. Two phosphor bands (5d., 1s. 6d.) or one centre band (4d.). P* 15 × 14.

812 **340** 4d. vermilion, new blue, orange, bright purple, light green, bluish violet, blackish brown and gold 8 5
a. Gold (Queen's head etc.) omitted £300

813 **341** 5d. magenta, light blue, royal blue, olive-brown, green, greenish yellow, red and gold 8 5
a. Light blue (sheep, etc.) omitted .. 35·00
b. Red omitted* £170
c. Gold (Queen's head) omitted .. £120

814 **342** 1s. 6d. greenish yellow, bright purple, bluish violet, deep slate, orange, green, new blue and gold 15 30
a. Gold (Queen's head etc.) omitted 85·00
b. Deep slate (value) omitted .. £160

*The effect of the missing red is shown on the hat, leggings and purse which appear as dull orange.

The 5d. is known with the green omitted and the 1s. 6d. exists with either the greenish yellow, the bluish violet or the new blue missing. Both values are known with the embossing omitted.

Used copies of the 5d. have been seen with the olive-brown or greenish yellow omitted.

343 Fife Harling

344 Cotswold Limestone

345 Welsh Stucco

346 Ulster Thatch

(Des D. Gentleman (5d., 9d.), Sheila Robinson (1s., 1s. 6d.))

1970 (11 Feb). *British Rural Architecture. Chalk-surfaced paper. Two phosphor bands. P* 15 × 14.

815 **343** 5d. grey, grey-black, black, lemon, greenish bl, orge-brn, ultram & grn 8 5
a. Lemon omitted .. .. .. 30·00
b. Grey (Queen's head and cottage shading) omitted .. .. ..

816 **344** 9d. orange-brown, olive-yellow, bright green, black, grey-black and grey 20 25
817 **345** 1s. dp blue, reddish lilac, drab & new bl 30 30
818 **346** 1s. 6d. greenish yell, blk, turq-bl & lilac 30 45

The 1s is known with the new blue omitted, and the 1s. 6d. with the turquoise-blue omitted.

Used examples of the 5d. have been seen with the grey-black or greenish blue colours omitted.

347 Signing the Declaration of Arbroath

348 Florence Nightingale attending Patients

349 Signing of International Co-operative Alliance

350 Pilgrims and *Mayflower*

351 Sir William Herschel, Francis Baily, Sir John Herschel and Telescope

(Des F. Wegner (5d., 9d., and 1s. 6d.), Marjorie Saynor (1s., 1s. 9d.). Queen's head printed in gold and then embossed)

1970 (1 Apr). *Anniversaries. Events described on stamps. Chalk-surfaced paper. Two phosphor bands. P* 15 × 14.

819 **347** 5d. blk, yell-olive, blue, emer, greenish yellow, rose-red, gold & orange-red 5 5
a. Gold (Queen's head) omitted .. £190

820 **348** 9d ochre, deep blue, carmine, black, blue-green, yellow-olive, gold & bl 10 20

821 **349** 1s. green, greenish yellow, brown, black, cerise, gold and light blue .. 10 20
a. Gold (Queen's head) omitted .. 30·00

822 **350** 1s. 6d. greenish yellow, carmine, deep yellow-olive, emerald, black, blue, gold and sage-green 30 25
a. Gold (Queen's head) omitted .. 75·00

823 **351** 1s. 9d. blk, slate, lemon, gold & brt pur 30 55

The following missing colours are known: 5d. emerald, 9d. ochre, 1s. green, brown, 1s. 6d. emerald. The 9d., 1s. and 1s. 6d. are also known with the embossing omitted.

The 1s. 9d. with the lemon colour omitted has been seen used on a First Day Cover.

352 "Mr. Pickwick and Sam" (*Pickwick Papers*)

353 "Mr. and Mrs. Micawber" (*David Copperfield*)

354 "David Copperfield and Betsy Trotwood" (*David Copperfield*)

355 "Oliver asking for more" (*Oliver Twist*)

356 "Grasmere" (from engraving by J. Farrington, R.A.)

T **352/5** were issued together *se-tenant* in blocks of four throughout the sheet.

(Des Rosalind Dease. Queen's head printed in gold and then embossed)

1970 (3 June). *Literary Anniversaries. Death Centenary of Charles Dickens (novelist) (5d. × 4) and Birth Bicentenary of William Wordsworth (poet) (1s. 6d.). Chalk-surfaced paper. Two phosphor bands. P* 14 × 15.

824 **352** 5d. black, orange, silver, gold and mag 12 5
a. Block of 4. Nos. 824/7 80
ab. Imperf (block of four) £400

825 **353** 5d. black, magenta, silver, gold & orge 12 5

826 **354** 5d. black, light greenish blue, silver, gold and yellow-bistre 12 5
b. Yellow-bistre (value) omitted .. £300

827 **355** 5d. black, yellow-bistre, silver, gold and light greenish blue 12 5
b. Yellow-bistre (background) omitted £300
c. Light greenish blue (value) omitted* 70·00

828 **356** 1s. 6d. light yellow-olive, black, silver, gold and bright blue 15 30
a. Gold (Queen's head) omitted .. £140
b. Silver ("Grasmere") omitted .. 35·00

*No. 827c (unlike No. 826b) comes from a sheet on which the colour was only partially omitted so that, although No. 827 was completely without the light greenish blue colour, it was still partially present on No. 826.

The 1s. 6d. is known with embossing omitted.

357 (Value redrawn)

(Des after plaster cast by Arnold Machin. Recess B.W.)

1970 (17 June)–**72.** *Decimal Currency. Chalk-surfaced paper or phosphorised paper* (10p.). *P* 12.

829 **357** 10p. cerise .. .. 1·50 50
830 20p. olive-green 60 15
831 50p. deep ultramarine .. .. .. 1·25 30
831*b* £1 bluish black (6.12.72) .. .. 2·25 90

The 20p. and 50p. exist on thinner, uncoated paper and are listed in the *Elizabethan Catalogue.*

A whiter paper was introduced in 1973. The £1 appeared on 27 Sept. 1973, the 20p. on 30 Nov. 1973 and the 50p. on 20 Feb. 1974.

The 50p. was issued on 1 Feb. 1973 on phosphorised paper. This cannot be distinguished from No. 831 with the naked eye.

The £1, T **318**, was also issued, on 17 June 1970, in sheets of 100 (10 × 10) instead of panes of 40 (8 × 5) but it is not easy to distinguish from No. 790 in singles. It can be readily differentiated when in large strips or marginal pieces showing sheet markings or plate numbers.

358 Runners

359 Swimmers

360 Cyclists

(Des A. Restall. Litho D.L.R.)

1970 (15 July). *Ninth British Commonwealth Games. Chalk-surfaced paper. Two phosphor bands. P* 13½ × 14.

832 **358** 5d. pk, emer, greenish yell & dp yell-grn .. 8 5
a. Greenish yellow omitted .. ..
833 **359** 1s. 6d. light greenish blue, lilac, bistre-brown and Prussian blue 35 40
834 **360** 1s. 9d. yellow-orange, lilac, salmon and deep red-brown 35 50

361 1d. Black (1840)

362 1s. Green (1847)

363 4d. Carmine (1855)

(Des D. Gentleman)

1970 (18 Sept). "*Philympia 70*" *Stamp Exhibition. Chalk-surfaced paper. Two phosphor bands. P* 14 × 14½.

835 **361** 5d. grey-black, brownish bistre, black and dull purple 5 5
836 **362** 9d. light drab, bluish green, stone, black and dull purple 35 55
837 **363** 1s. 6d. carmine, lt drab, blk & dull pur 50 50

364 Shepherds and Apparition of the Angel

365 Mary, Joseph, and Christ in the Manger

366 The Wise Men bearing gifts

(Des Sally Stiff after De Lisle Psalter. Queen's head printed in gold and then embossed)

1970 (25 Nov). *Christmas. Chalk-surfaced paper. One centre phosphor band* (4*d.*) *or two phosphor bands* (*others*). *P* 14 × 15.

838 **364** 4d. brown-red, turquoise-green, pale chestnut, brn, grey-blk, gold & verm 5 5
839 **365** 5d. emerald, gold, blue, brown-red, ochre, grey-black and violet .. 5 5
a. Gold (Queen's head) omitted .. † —
b. Emerald omitted .. .. .. 45·00
c. Imperf (pair) £200
840 **366** 1s. 6d. gold, grey-black, pale turq-grn, salmon, ultram, ochre & yellow-grn 40 45
a. Salmon omitted .. .. .. 85·00

The 1s. 6d. exists with the ochre colour omitted. The 4d. and 5d. are known with embossing omitted, and the 1s. 6d. is known with embossing and phosphor omitted.

(New Currency. 100 new pence = £1)

"X" NUMBERS. The following definitive series has been allocated "X" prefixes to the catalogue numbers to avoid re-numbering all subsequent issues.

367

(Des from plaster cast by Arnold Machin)

1971 (15 Feb)–**85**. *Decimal Currency. T* **367**. *Chalk-surfaced paper.*

(*a*) *Photo Harrison* (*except for a printing of No.* X877 *in sheets produced by Enschedé in* 1979). *With phosphor bands. P* 15 × 14.

X841 ½p. turquoise-blue (2 bands) 5 5
a. Imperf (pair)† £200
l. Booklet pane. No. X841 × 2 *se-tenant* vert with X848 × 2 .. .. .. 3·50
la. Ditto. *se-tenant* horiz (14.7.71) 75
m. Booklet pane No. X841 × 5 plus label .. 2·75
n. Coil strip. No. X848, X841 × 2 and X844 × 2 .. .. 3·00
o. Booklet pane. No. X841 × 3, X850 × 3 and X851 × 6 (24.5.72) .. .. .. 25·00
p. Booklet pane. No. X841 × 3, X842 and X851 × 2 (24.5.72) .. .. .. 70·00
q. Coil strip. No. X868, X848, X844 and X841 × 2 (3.12.75) 35
r. Booklet pane. No. X841 × 2, X844 × 3 and X868 (10.3.76) .. .. .. 1·00
s. Booklet pane. No. X841 × 2, X844 × 2, X871 × 2 and X879 × 4 (8½p. values at right) (26.1.77) .. .. .. 4·00
sa. Ditto. 8½p. values at left.. .. .. 3·75
t. Booklet pane. Nos. X841, X844, X892 × 3 and X898 (14p. value at right) (26.1.81) .. 2·00
ta. Ditto. 14p. value at left .. .. 2·00
u. Booklet pane. Nos. X841, X856 × 4 and X895 × 3 (12½p. values at right) (1.2.82) 2·40
ua. Ditto. 12½p. values at left .. .. 2·40
X842 ½p. turquoise-blue (1 side band) (24.5.72) .. 60·00 30·00
X843 ½p. turquoise-blue (1 centre band) (14.12.77) 20 13
l. Coil strip. No. X843 × 2, X873 and X845 × 2 (14.12.77) 60
m. Booklet pane. No. X843 × 2, X845 × 2 and X873 plus label (8.2.78) 75
X844 1p. crimson (2 bands) 5 5
a. Imperf (vert coil) .. ..
b. Pair, one imperf 3 sides (vert coil) ..
c. Imperf (pair) .. .. ..
l. Booklet pane. No X844 × 2 *Se-tenant* vert with X847 × 2 .. .. .. 5·00
m. Ditto *Se-tenant* horiz (14.7.71) .. .. 1·50
n. Booklet pane. No. X844 × 2, X874 × 3 and X881 × 3 (9p. values at right) (13.6.77) 4·75
na. Ditto. 9p. values at left .. .. 2·50
X845 1p. crimson (1 centre band) (14.12.77) .. 5 5
l. Booklet pane. No. X877 and X845 × 2 plus label (17.10.79) 60
m. Coil strip. No. X877 and X845 × 2 plus 2 labels (16.1.80) 35
n. Booklet pane. No. X845 × 2, X859 and X894 each × 3 (5.4.83) .. .. 1·90
p. Booklet pane. Nos. X845 × 3, × 862 × 2, and X 896 × 3 (3.9.84) 75
X846 1p. crimson ("all-over") (10.10.79) .. 10 10
X847 1½p. black (2 bands) 10 5
a. Uncoated paper (1971)*.. .. .. £120
b. Imperf (pair) .. .. ..
c. Imperf 3 sides (horiz pair) ..
X848 2p. myrtle-green (2 bands) 5 5
l. Booklet pane. No. X848 × X878 × 2 and X888 × 3 plus label (10p. values at right) (28.8.79) .. .. 2·00
la. Ditto. 10p. values at left .. .. 2·00
m. Booklet pane. Nos. X848 × 3, X887 × 2 and X893 × 2 plus label (12p. values at right) (4.2.80) .. .. .. 3·00
ma. Ditto. 12p. values at left .. .. 3·00
n. Booklet pane. Nos. X848, X886 × 3, X887 and X893 × 4 with margins all round (16.4.80) .. .. 1·25
o. Booklet pane. No. X848 × 6 with margins all round (16.4.80) 25
p. Booklet pane. Nos. X848, X856, X894 and X895 × 6 with margins all round (19.5.82) 2·50
X849 2p. myrtle-green ("all-over") (10.10.79) .. 15 10
X850 2½p. magenta (1 centre and) 15 5
a. Imperf (pair)† £200
l. Booklet pane. No. X850 × 5 plus label .. 2·75
m. Booklet pane. No. X850 × 4 plus two labels .. .. 2·75
n. Booklet pane. No. X850 × 3, X851 × 3 and X854 × 6 (24.5.72) .. .. .. 16·00
X851 2½p. magenta (1 side band) .. .. 1·25 2·00
l. Booklet pane. No. X851 × 2 and X854 × 4 .. .. 12·00
X852 2½p. magenta (2 bands) (21.5.75) 20 50
X853 2½p. rose-red (2 bands) (26.8.81) 15 25
l. Booklet pane. Nos. X853 × 3, X861 × 2 and X892 × 3 (11½p. values at right) .. 3·75
la. Ditto. 11½p. values at left .. .. 3·75
X854 3p. ultramarine (2 bands) 15 5
a. Imperf (coil strip of 5) £600
b. Imperf (pair)† £250
c. Uncoated paper (1972)*.. .. .. 50·00
l. Booklet pane. No. X854 × 5 plus label .. 3·25
X855 3p. ultramarine (1 centre band) (10.9.73) .. 12 10
a. Imperf (pair)† £100
b. Imperf between (vert pair)† £110
c. Imperf horiz (vert pair)† £100
X856 3p. bright magenta (2 bands) (1.2.82) .. 15 20
X857 3½p. olive-grey (*shades*) (2 bands) .. 35 35
a. Imperf (pair) £200
X858 3½p. olive-grey (1 centre band) (24.6.74) .. 30 15
X859 3½p. purple-brown (1 centre band) (5.4.83) .. 20 20
X860 4p. ochre-brown (2 bands) 15 10
a. Imperf (pair)† £375
X861 4p. greenish blue (2 bands) (26.8.81) .. 50 60
X862 4p. greenish blue (1 centre band) (3.9.84) .. 8 8
X863 4p. greenish blue (1 side band) (8.1.85) .. 75 125
l. Booklet pane. No. X863 × 2, X897 × 4, X901 × 2 and X903 with margins all round 2·10
X864 4½p. grey-blue (2 bands) (24.10.73) .. 25 15
a. Imperf (pair) £170
X865 5p. pale violet (2 bands) 20 5
X866 5½p. violet (2 bands) (24.10.73) 30 35
X867 5½p. violet (1 centre band) (17.3.75) .. 30 25
a. Uncoated paper* £225
X868 6p. light emerald (2 bands) 20 8
a. Uncoated paper* .. .. .. 10·00
X869 6½p. greenish blue (2 bands) (4.9.74).. .. 50 60
X870 6½p. greenish blue (1 centre band) (24.9.75) .. 20 8
a. Imperf (vert pair) £300
b. Uncoated paper* £150
X871 6½p. greenish blue (1 side band) (26.1.77) .. 1·10 2·25
X872 7p. purple-brown (2 bands) (15.1.75) .. 25 10
a. Imperf (pair) £300
X873 7p. purple-brown (1 centre band) (13.6.77) .. 20 5
l. Booklet pane. No. X873 × 10 and X881 × 10 (15.11.78) .. .. .. 5·25
X874 7p. purple-brown (1 side band) (13.6.77) 75 75
X875 7½p. pale chestnut (2 bands) 25 10
X876 8p. rosine (2 bands) (24.10.73) 20 10
a. Uncoated paper* .. .. .. 6·00
X877 8p. rosine (1 centre band) (20.8.79).. .. 20 5
a. Uncoated paper* .. .. ..
b. Imperf (pair) £110
l. Booklet pane. Nos. X877 × 10 and X884 × 10 (14.11.79) .. .. .. 6·00
X878 8p. rosine (1 side band) (29.8.79) .. 40 75
X879 8½p. light yellowish green (*shades*) (2 bands) (24.9.75) 25 10
a. Imperf (pair) £325
X880 9p. yellow-orange and black (2 bands) 40 10
X881 9p. deep violet (2 bands) (25.2.76) .. 25 10
a. Imperf (pair) £250
X882 9½p. purple (2 bands) (25.2.76) .. 25 20
X883 10p. orange-brown and chestnut (11.8.71) 30 12
a. Orange-brown omitted .. .. 50·00
b. Imperf (horiz pair) £1200
X884 10p. orange-brown (2 bands) (25.2.76) 15 10
l. Booklet pane X884, X897 and X901 × 7, (4.9.84) with margins all round .. 2·10
X885 10p. orange-brown ("all-over") (3.10.79) 30 15
X886 10p. orange-brown (1 centre band) (4.2.80) .. 25 10
a. Imperf (pair) £200
l. Booklet pane. No. X886 × 9 with margins all round (16.4.80) .. .. 1·75
m. Booklet pane. Nos. X886 and X893, each × 10 (12.11.80) .. .. .. 6·00
X887 10p. orange-brown (1 side band) (4.2.80) 40 50
X888 10½p. yellow (2 bands) (25.2.76) .. 30 30
X889 10½p. deep dull blue (2 bands) (26.4.78) 30 15
X890 11p. brown-red (2 bands) (25.2.76) .. 45 30
a. Imperf (pair) £350
X891 11½p. drab (1 centre band) (14.1.81) .. 25 20
a. Imperf (pair) £200
l. Booklet pane. Nos. X891 and X898, each × 10 (11.11.81) .. .. .. 9·00
X892 11½p. drab (1 side band) (26.1.81) .. 45 45
l. Booklet pane. Nos. X892 × 4 and X898 × 6 (6.5.81) .. .. .. 4·75
X893 12p. yellowish green (2 bands) (4.2.80) 45 45
l. Booklet pane. No. X893 × 9 with margins all round (16.4.80) .. .. 1·50
X894 12½p. light emerald (1 centre band) (27.1.82) .. 20 20
a. Imperf (pair) £100
l. Booklet pane. Nos. X894 and X899 each × 10 (10.11.82) .. .. .. 9·00
X895 12½p. light emerald (1 side band) (1.2.82) 45 50
l. Booklet pane. Nos. X895 × 4 and X899 × 6 (1.2.82) .. .. .. 5·00
m. Booklet pane. No. X895 × 6 with margins all round (19.5.82) .. .. .. 1·25
n. Booklet pane. No. X895 × 4 and X900 × 6 (12½p. values at right) (5.4.83).. .. 5·50
na. Ditto. 12½p. values at left .. .. 5·50
X896 13p. pale chestnut (1 centre band) (28.8.84) 20 15
l. Booklet pane No. X896 × 9 with margins all round (8.1.85) .. .. .. 1·75
X897 13p. pale chestnut (1 side band) .. 20 20
l. Booklet pane. Nos. X897 × 4 and X901 × 6 (13p. values at right) (3.9.84) .. 2·40
la. Ditto. 13p. values at left.. .. 2·40
m. Booklet pane. No. X897 × 6 with margins all round (4.9.84) .. .. .. 1·25
X898 14p. grey-blue (2 bands) (26.1.81) .. 60 35
X899 15½p. pale violet (2 bands) (1.2.82) .. 60 60
l. Booklet pane. No. X899 × 6 with margins all round (19.5.82) .. .. .. 3·00
m. Booklet pane. No. X899 × 9 with margins all round (19.5.82) .. .. .. 5·00
X900 16p. olive-drab (2 bands) (5.4.83) .. 50 50
X901 17p. grey-blue (2 bands) (3.9.84) .. 30 30
X902 20p. dull purple (2 bands) (25.2.76) .. 50 25
X903 34p. ochre-brown (2 bands) (8.1.85) .. 2·00 2·00
X904 50p. ochre-brown (2 bands) (2.2.77) .. 1·00 70

(*b*) *Photo Harrison. On phosphorised paper. P* 15 × 14

X914 ½p. turquoise-blue (10.12.80) 5 5
a. Imperf (pair) £185

No.	Description	Unused	Used
	l. Coil strip. Nos. X914 and X920 × 3 (30.12.81)	1·25	
X915	1p. crimson (12.12.79)	5	5
	l. Coil strip. Nos. X915 and X920 × 3 (14.8.84)	20	
X916	2p. myrtle-green (12.12.79)	5	5
X917	2½p. rose-red (14.1.81)	10	8
	l. Coil strip. Nos. X917 and X918 × 3 (2.9.81)	65	
X918	3p. bright magenta (22.10.80)	5	5
	a. Imperf (horiz pair)		
	l. Booklet pane. Nos. X918, X919 × 2 and X932 × 6 with margins all round (14.9.83)	2·75	
X919	3½p. purple-brown (30.3.83)	8	8
X920	4p. greenish blue (30.12.81)	25	50
X921	5p. pale violet (10.10.79)	15	15
X922	8½p. yellowish green (24.3.76)	50	90
X923	10p. orange-brown (11.79)	15	20
X924	11p. brown-red (27.8.80)	50	60
X925	11½p. ochre-brown (15.8.79)	50	40
X926	12p. yellowish green (30.1.80)	40	40
X927	13p. olive-grey (15.8.79)	40	40
X928	13½p. purple-brown (30.1.80)	45	40
X929	14p. grey-blue (14.1.81)	45	30
X930	15p. ultramarine (15.8.79)	45	40
X931	15½p. pale violet (14.1.81)	50	30
	a. Imperf (pair)	£225	
X932	16p. olive-drab (30.3.83)	25	20
	a. Imperf (pair)	£175	
	l. Booklet pane. No. X932 × 9 with margins all round (14.9.83)	3·00	
X933	16½p. pale chestnut (27.1.82)	25	25
X934	17p. light emerald (30.1.80)	55	35
X935	17p. grey-blue (30.3.83)	30	25
	a. Imperf (pair)		
	l. Booklet pane. No. X935 × 6 with margins all round (4.9.84)	1·60	
X936	17½p. pale chestnut (30.1.80)	60	50
X937	18p. deep violet (14.1.81)	60	50
X938	18p. olive-grey (28.8.84)	30	25
X939	19½p. olive-grey (27.1.82)	60	50
X940	20p. purple (10.10.79)	60	45
X941	20½p. ultramarine (30.3.83)	35	40
X942	22p. blue (22.10.80)	60	50
X943	22p. bright green (28.8.84)	35	30
X944	23p. brown-red (30.3.83)	35	45
X945	24p. violet (28.8.84)	40	35
X946	25p. purple (14.1.81)	65	60
X947	26p. rosine (27.1.82)	40	40
X948	28p. deep violet (30.3.83)	45	50
X948	28p. deep violet (30.3.83)	45	50
	a. Imperf (pair)	£600	
X949	29p. ocre-brown (27.1.82)	75	70
X950	31p. purple (30.3.83)	50	55
X951	34p. ochre-brown (28.8.84)	55	50
	(*c*) *Photo Harrison. On ordinary paper. P* 15 × 14.		
X952	50p. ochre-brown (21.5.80)	75	70
	(*d*) *Litho J. W.* (*4p., 20p.*), *Questa* (*others*). *P* 13½ × 14		
X953	2p. emerald-green (*phosphorised paper*) (21.5.80)	5	10
	a. Perf 15 × 14 (10.7.84)	5	10
X954	4p. greenish blue (*2 phosphor bands*) (30.1.80)	15	30
X955	4p. greenish blue (*phosphorised paper*) (11.81)	8	5
X956	5p. light violet (*phosphorised paper*) (21.5.80)	20	20
X957	5p. claret (*phosphorised paper*) (27.1.82)	20	10
	a. Perf 15 × 14 (21.2.84)	8	5
X958	20p. purple (*2 phosphor bands*) (21.5.80)	55	40
X959	20p. purple (*phosphorised paper*) (11.81)	30	30
X960	75p. black (*ordinary paper*) (30.1.80)	1·50	1·00
	a. Perf 15 × 14 (21.2.84)	1·10	1·00

*See footnote after No. 744.

†These come from sheets with gum arabic.

Nos. X842, X851, X853, X856, X859, X863, X871, X874, X878, X887, X892/3, X895, X897, X900/1 and X903 come from booklets; Nos. X843 and X845 come from booklets or coils; No. X920 comes from coils. Nos. X871, X874, X878, X887, X892, X895 and X897 were each issued in equal quantities with the phosphor band at the right or the left.

Nos. X844a/b come from a strip of eight of the vertical coil. It comprises two normals, one imperforate at sides and bottom, one completely imperforate, one imperforate at top, left and bottom and partly perforated at right due to the bottom three stamps being perforated twice. No. X844b is also known from another strip having one stamp imperforate at sides and bottom.

Nos. X847b/c come from the same sheet, the latter having perforations at the foot of the stamps only.

No. X894l comes from the Christmas 1982 booklet and was printed with a blue Christmas star over the gum on the reverse of each stamp.

Coil strips Nos. X914l, X915l and X917l were produced by the Post Office for use by a large direct mail marketing firm. From 2 September 1981 No. X917l was available from the Philatelic Bureau, Edinburgh and, subsequently, from a number of other Post Office counters.

Nos. X914l and X915l were sold at the Philatelic Bureau and Post Office philatelic counters.

PART-PERFORATED SHEETS. Since the introduction of the "Jumelle" press in 1972 a number of part-perforated sheets, both definitive and commemoratives, have been discovered. It is believed that these occur when the operation of the press is interrupted. Such sheets invariably show a number of "blind" perforations, where the pins have failed to cut the paper. Our listings of imperforate errors from these sheets are for pairs showing no trace whatsoever of the perforations. Examples showing "blind" perforations are outside the scope of this catalogue.

In cases where perforation varieties affect *se-tenant* stamps fuller descriptions will be found in Vol. 4 of the *G.B. Specialised Catalogue*,

WHITE PAPER. From 1972 printings appeared on fluorescent white paper giving a stronger chalk reaction than the original ordinary cream paper.

GUM ARABIC. The following exist with gum arabic as well as PVA gum (with or without added dextrin): Nos. X841, X841n, X850, X854, X855, X860 and X868. See notes after No. 722.

DEXTRIN GUM. From 1973 printings appeared with PVA gum to which dextrin, a bluish green substance had been added, giving a very mottled appearance.

"ALL-OVER" PHOSPHOR. To improve mechanised handling most commemoratives from the 1972 Royal Silver Wedding 3p. value to the 1979 Rowland Hill Death Centenary set had the phosphor applied by printing cylinder across the entire surface of the stamp, giving a matt effect. Printing of the 1, 2 and 10p. definitives, released in October 1979, also had "all-over" phosphor, but these were purely a temporary expedient pending the adoption of phosphorised paper. Nos. X881, X888 and X904 have been discovered with "all-over" phosphor in addition to the normal phosphor bands. These errors are outside the scope of this catalogue.

PHOSPHORISED PAPER. Following the experiments on Nos. 743b and 829 a printing of the 4½p. definitive was issued on 13 November 1974, which had, in addition to the normal phosphor bands, phosphor included in the paper coating. Because of difficulties in identifying the phosphorised paper with the naked eye this printing is not listed separately in this catalogue.

No. X922 was the first value printed in phosphorised paper without phosphor bands and was a further experimental issue to test the efficacy of this system. From 15 August 1979 phosphorised paper was accepted for use generally, the paper replacing phosphor bands on values other than those required in the second-class rate.

Stamps on phosphorised paper show a shiny surface instead of the matt areas of those printed with phosphor bands.

VARNISH COATING. Nos. X841 and X881 exist with and without a varnish coating. This cannot easily be detected without the use of an ultra-violet lamp as it merely reduces the fluorescent paper reaction.

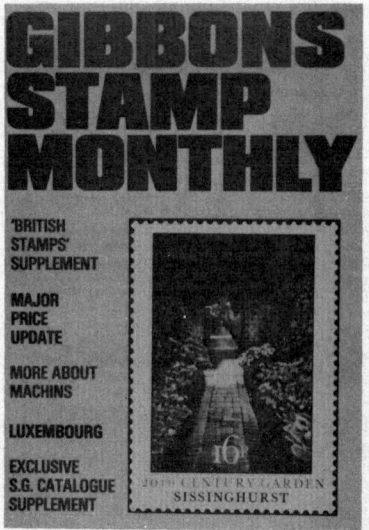

368 "A Mountain Road" (T. P. Flanagan)

369 "Deer's Meadow" (Tom Carr)

370 "Slieve na brock" (Colin Middleton)

(Layout des Stuart Rose)

1971 (16 June). *"Ulster* 1971" *Paintings. Chalk-surfaced paper. Two phosphor bands. P* 15 × 14.

881	**368**	3p.	yellow-buff, pale yellow, Venetian red, black, blue and drab ..	15	5
882	**369**	7½p.	olive-brown, brownish grey, pale olive-grey, dp bl, cobalt & grey-bl	80	85
883	**370**	9p.	greenish yellow, orange, grey, lavender-grey, bistre, black, pale ochre-brown, and ochre-brown ..	80	85

A used example of the 3p. has been seen with the Venetian red omitted.

The 7½p. is known with the pale olive-grey omitted (boulder in foreground), and the 9p. is known with orange omitted.

371 John Keats (150th Death Anniv)

372 Thomas Gray (Death Bicentenary)

373 Sir Walter Scott (Birth Bicentenary)

(Des Rosalind Dease. Queen's head printed in gold and then embossed)

1971 (28 July). *Literary Anniversaries. Chalk-surfaced paper. Two phosphor bands. P* 15 × 14.

884	**371**	3p.	black, gold and greyish blue ..	10	8
		a.	Gold (Queen's head) omitted ..	40·00	
885	**372**	5p.	black, gold and yellow-olive ..	35	60
		a.	Gold (Queen's head) omitted ..	90·00	
886	**373**	7½p.	black, gold and yellow-brown ..	1·10	1·00

The 7½p. exists with embossing omitted.

374 Servicemen and Nurse of 1921

375 Roman Centurion

376 Rugby Football, 1871

(Des F. Wegner)

1971 (25 Aug). *British Anniversaries. Events described on stamps. Chalk-surfaced paper. Two phosphor bands. P* 15 × 14.

887	**374**	3p.	red-orange, grey, deep blue, olive-grn, olive-brn, blk, rosine & vio-bl	10	5
		a.	Deep blue omitted*	£250	
		b.	Red-orange (nurse's cloak) omitted	£130	
		c.	Olive-brown (faces, etc.) omitted	45·00	
		d.	Black omitted	£750	
888	**375**	7½p.	grey, yellow-brown, vermilion, mauve, grey-black, black, silver, pale ochre and ochre	75	1·00
889	**376**	9p.	new blue, myrtle-green, grey-blk, lemon, olive-brown, mag & yell-ol	1·40	90
		a.	Olive-brown omitted	45·00	
		b.	New blue omitted		
		c.	Myrtle-green omitted		

*The effect of the missing deep blue is shown on the sailor's uniform, which appears as grey.

The 7½p. exists with grey omitted.

A used example has been seen of the 3p. with grey omitted.

377 Physical Sciences Building, University College of Wales, Aberystwyth

378 Faraday Building, Southampton University

379 Engineering Department, Leicester University

380 Hexagon Restaurant, Essex University

(Des N. Jenkins)

1971 (22 Sept). *British Architecture. Modern University Buildings. Chalk-surfaced paper. Two phosphor bands. P* 15 × 14.

890	**377**	3p.	olive-brn, ochre, lem, blk & yell-ol	15	8
891	**378**	5p.	rose, black, chestnut and lilac ..	60	80
892	**379**	7½p.	ochre, black and purple-brown ..	90	1·25
893	**380**	9p.	pale lilac, black, sepia-brn & dp bl	1·60	1·50

The 3p. exists with lemon omitted.

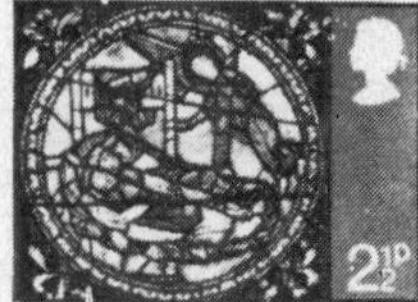

381 "Dream of the Wise Men"

382 "Adoration of the Magi"

383 "Ride of the Magi"

(Des Clarke-Clements-Hughes design team, from stained-glass windows, Canterbury Cathedral. Queen's head printed in gold and then embossed)

1971 (13 Oct). *Christmas. Ordinary paper. One centre phosphor band (2½p.) or two phosphor bands (others). P* 15 × 14.

894	**381**	2½p. new blue, black, lemon, emerald, reddish violet, carmine-red, carmine-rose and gold	15	5
		a. Imperf (pair)	£225	
895	**382**	3p. black, reddish violet, lemon, new bl, carm-rose, emer, ultram & gold	20	5
		a. Gold (Queen's head) omitted ..	£130	
		b. Carmine-rose omitted	£130	
896	**383**	7½p. black, lilac, lemon, emerald, new blue, rose, green and gold ..	2·00	1·60
		a. Gold (Queen's head) omitted ..	50·00	

The 3p. exists with lemon omitted and with embossing omitted; used copies have been seen with reddish violet and embossing omitted, with lemon and carmine-rose omitted, and with new blue omitted. The 7½p. is known with embossing omitted, embossing double, lilac omitted and emerald omitted.

WHITE CHALK-SURFACED PAPER. From No. 897 all issues, with the exception of Nos. 904/8, were printed on fluorescent white paper, giving a stronger chalk reaction than the original cream paper.

384 Sir James Clark Ross

385 Sir Martin Frobisher

386 Henry Hudson

387 Capt. Scott

(Des Marjorie Saynor. Queen's head printed in gold and then embossed)

1972 (16 Feb). *British Polar Explorers. Two phosphor bands. P* 14 × 15.

897	**384**	3p. yellow-brown, indigo, slate-black, flesh, lemon, rose, brt blue & gold	10	8
		a. Gold (Queen's head) omitted ..	30·00	
		b. Slate-black (hair, etc.) omitted ..	£500	
898	**385**	5p. salmon, flesh, purple-brown, ochre, black and gold	40	75
		a. Gold (Queen's head) omitted ..	60·00	
899	**386**	7½p. reddish violet, blue, deep slate, yellow-brown, buff, black and gold	90	75
		a. Gold (Queen's head) omitted ..	£100	
900	**387**	9p. dull blue, ultramarine, black, greenish yell, pale pink, rose-red & gold	90	75

The 3p. and 5p. are known with embossing omitted. The 3p. exists with lemon omitted and with gold and embossing omitted. An example of the 3p. is known used on piece with the flesh colour omitted.

388 Statuette of Tutankhamun

389 19th-century Coastguard

390 Ralph Vaughan Williams and Score

(Des Rosalind Dease (3p.), F. Wegner (7½p.), C. Abbott (9p.). Queen's head printed in gold and then embossed (7½p., 9p.))

1972 (26 Apr). *General Anniversaries. Events described on stamps. Two phosphor bands. P* 15 × 14.

901	**388**	3p. black, grey, gold, dull bistre-brown, blackish brn, pale stone & lt brn	10	5
902	**389**	7½p. pale yellow, new blue, slate-blue, violet-blue, slate and gold ..	95	85
903	**390**	9p. bistre-brown, black, sage-green, dp slate, yellow-ochre, brown & gold	95	85
		a. Gold (Queen's head) omitted ..	£200	
		b. Brown (facial features) omitted ..	£350	

The 7½p. exists with embossing omitted.

391 St. Andrew's, Greensted-juxta-Ongar, Essex

392 All Saints, Earls Barton, Northants

393 St. Andrew's, Letheringsett, Norfolk

394 St. Andrew's, Helpringham, Lincs

395 St. Mary the Virgin, Huish Episcopi, Somerset

(Des R. Maddox. Queen's head printed in gold and then embossed)

1972 (21 June). *British Architecture. Village Churches. Ordinary paper. Two phosphor bands. P* 14 × 15.

904	**391**	3p. violet-blue, black, lt yellow-olive, emerald-green, orange-verm & gold	15	15
		a. Gold (Queen's head) omitted ..	45·00	
905	**392**	4p. deep yellow-olive, black, emerald, violet-blue, orge-vermilion & gold	80	50
906	**393**	5p. deep emerald, black, royal blue, lt yellow-olive, orange-verm & gold	80	75
		a. Gold (Queen's head) omitted ..	£100	
907	**394**	7½p. orange-red, black, deep yellow-ol, royal blue, lt emerald & gold ..	1·50	1·50
908	**395**	9p. new blue, black, emerald-green, dp yellow-olive, orange-verm & gold	1·60	1·50

The 4p. exists with violet-blue omitted. The 3p., 4p., 5p. and 9p. exist with embossing omitted.

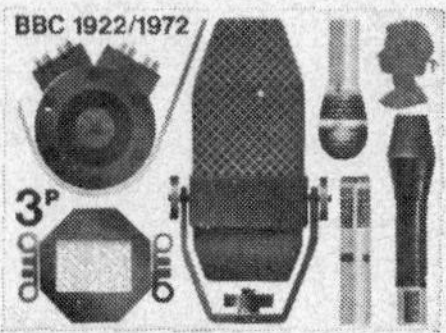

396 Microphones, 1924–69

MINIMUM PRICE

The minimum price quoted is 5p which represents a handling charge rather than a basis for valuing common stamps. For further notes about prices see introductory pages.

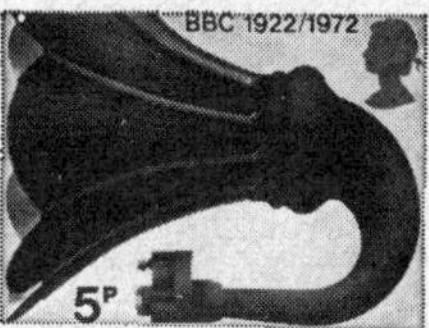

397 Horn Loudspeaker

398 T.V. Camera, 1972

399 Oscillator and Spark Transmitter, 1897

(Des D. Gentleman)

1972 (13 Sept). *Broadcasting Anniversaries. 75th Anniv of Marconi and Kemp's Radio Experiments (9p.), and 50th Anniv of Daily Broadcasting by the B.B.C. (others). Two phosphor bands. P* 15 × 14.

909	**396**	3p. pale brown, black, grey, greenish yellow and brownish slate ..	12	8
910	**397**	5p. brownish slate, lake-brown, salmon, lt brown, black & red-brn	60	50
911	**398**	7½p. light grey, slate, brownish slate, magenta and black	85	90
912	**399**	9p. lemon, brown, brownish slate, deep brownish slate, bluish slate & blk	95	90
		a. Brownish slate (Queen's head) omitted	£350	

The 3p. exists with greenish yellow omitted.

400 Angel holding Trumpet

401 Angel playing Lute

402 Angel playing Harp

(Des Sally Stiff. Photo and embossed)

1972 (18 Oct). *Christmas. One centre phosphor band (2½p.) or two phosphor bands (others). P* 14 × 15.

913	**400**	2½p. cerise, pale reddish brown, yellow-orange, orange-vermilion, lilac, gold, red-brown and deep grey ..	10	5
		a. Gold omitted	£170	
914	**401**	3p. ultramarine, lavender, light turquoise-blue, bright green, gold, red-brown and bluish violet ..	10	5
		a. Red-brown omitted	£200	
915	**402**	7½p. deep brown, pale lilac, light cinnamon, ochre, gold, red-brown and blackish violet	75	90

The 2½p. exists with deep grey omitted; the 3p. exists with bright green missing and bluish violet missing; the 7½p. exists with ochre omitted; the 2½p., 3p. and 7½p. exist with embossing omitted.

403 Queen Elizabeth and Duke of Edinburgh

404 "Europe"

(Des J. Matthews from photo by N. Parkinson)

1972 (20 Nov). *Royal Silver Wedding. "All-over" phosphor* (3*p.*) *or without phosphor* (20*p.*). *P* 14 × 15.

I. "REMBRANDT" Machine

916	**403**	3p.	brownish black, dp blue & silver	10	12
		a.	Silver omitted	£250	
917		20p.	brownish blk, reddish pur & silver	75	95

II. "JUMELLE" Machine

918	**403**	3p.	brownish black, deep blue & silver	15	20

The 3p. "JUMELLE" has a lighter shade of the brownish black than the 3p. "Rembrandt". It also has the brown cylinders less deeply etched, which can be distinguished in the Duke's face which is slightly lighter, and in the Queen's hair where the highlights are sharper.

3p. "REMBRANDT". Cyls. 3A-1B-11C no dot. Sheets of 100 (10 × 10).

3p. "JUMELLE". Cyls. 1A–1B–3C dot and no dot. Sheets of 100 (two panes 5 × 10, separated by gutter margin).

(Des P. Murdoch)

1973 (3 Jan). *Britain's Entry into European Communities. Two phosphor bands. P* 14 × 15.

919	**404**	3p.	dull orange, bright rose-red, ultramarine, light lilac and black ..	10	10
920		5p.	new blue, bright rose-red, ultramarine, cobalt-blue and black	40	55
		a.	Pair. Nos. 920/1	1·40	1·40
921		5p.	light emerald-green, bright rose-red, ultramarine, cobalt-blue and black	40	55

Nos. 920/1 were printed horizontally *se-tenant* throughout the sheet.

405 Oak Tree

(Des D. Gentleman)

1973 (28 Feb). *Tree Planting Year. British Trees* (1*st issue*). *Two phosphor bands. P* 15 × 14.

922	**405**	9p.	brownish black, apple-green, deep olive, sepia, blackish green and brownish grey	45	50
		a.	Brownish black (value and inscr) omitted	£275	
		b.	Brownish grey (Queen's head) omitted	£160	

See also No. 949.

CHALK-SURFACED PAPER. The following issues are printed on chalk-surfaced paper but where "all-over" phosphor has been applied there is no chalk reaction except in the sheet margins outside the phosphor area.

406 David Livingstone **407** H. M. Stanley

(T **406/7** were printed together, horizontally *se-tenant* within the sheet)

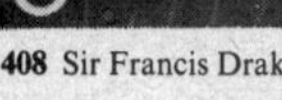

408 Sir Francis Drake **409** Walter Raleigh

410 Charles Sturt

(Des Marjorie Saynor. Queen's head printed in gold and then embossed)

1973 (18 Apr). *British Explorers. "All-over" phosphor. P* 14 × 15.

923	**406**	3p.	orange-yellow, light orange-brown, grey-black, light turquoise-blue, turquoise-blue and gold	25	20
		a.	Pair. Nos. 923/4	1·50	2·00
		b.	Gold (Queen's head) omitted ..	20·00	
		c.	Turquoise-blue (background and inscr) omitted	£300	
924	**407**	3p.	orange-yellow, light orange-brown, grey-black, light turquoise-blue, turquoise-blue and gold	25	20
		b.	Gold (Queen's head) omitted ..	20·00	
		c.	Turquoise-blue (background and inscr) omitted	£300	
925	**408**	5p.	light flesh, chrome-yellow, orange-yellow, sepia, brownish grey, grey-black, violet-blue and gold ..	50	30
		a.	Gold (Queen's head) omitted ..	60·00	
		b.	Grey-black omitted	£250	
926	**409**	7½p.	light flesh, reddish brown, sepia, ultram, grey-blk, brt lilac & gold	75	45
		a.	Gold (Queen's head) omitted ..		
927	**410**	9p.	flesh, pale stone, grey-blue, grey-black, brown-grey, Venetian red, brown-red and gold	75	55
		a.	Gold (Queen's head) omitted ..	50·00	
		b.	Brown-grey printing double *from*	75·00	

Caution is needed when buying missing gold heads in this issue as they can be removed by using a hard eraser, etc., but this invariably affects the "all-over" phosphor. Genuine examples have the phosphor intact. Used examples off cover cannot be distinguished as much of the phosphor is lost in the course of floating.

In the 5p. value the missing grey-black affects the doublet, which appears as brownish grey, and the lace ruff, which is entirely missing. The missing sepia affects only Drake's hair, which appears much lighter.

The double printing of the brown-grey (cylinder 1F) on the 9p. is a most unusual type of error to occur in a multicoloured photogravure issue. Two sheets are known and it is believed that they stuck to the cylinder and went through a second time. This would result in the following two sheets missing the colour but at the time of going to press this error has not been reported. The second print is slightly askew and more prominent in the top half of the sheets. Examples from the upper part of the sheet showing a clear double impression of the facial features are worth a substantial premium over the price quoted.

The 3p. values exist with the light orange-brown missing, the 5p. exists with the sepia omitted, the 7½p. with the ultramarine omitted and the 9p. with grey-black omitted; the 3p. values, the 5p. and the 9p. exist with embossing omitted.

411

412

413

(T **411/13** show sketches of W. G. Grace by Harry Furniss)

(Des E. Ripley. Queen's head printed in gold and then embossed)

1973 (16 May). *County Cricket* 1873–1973. *"All-over" phosphor. P* 14 × 15.

928	**411**	3p.	black, ochre and gold	10	10
		a.	Gold (Queen's head) omitted ..	£1200	
929	**412**	7½p.	black, light sage-green and gold ..	1·60	1·00
930	**413**	9p.	black, cobalt and gold	1·60	1·00

All three values exist with embossing omitted.

414 "Self-portrait" (Reynolds) **415** "Self-portrait" (Raeburn)

NEW INFORMATION

The editor is always interested to correspond with people who have new information that will improve or correct the Catalogue.

416 "Nelly O'Brien" (Reynolds) **417** "Rev. R. Walker (The Skater)" (Raeburn)

(Des S. Rose. Queen's head printed in gold and then embossed)

1973 (4 July). *British Paintings.* 250*th Birth Anniv of Sir Joshua Reynolds and* 150*th Death Anniv of Sir Henry Raeburn. "All-over" phosphor. P* 14 × 15.

931	**414**	3p.	rose, new blue, jet-black, magenta, greenish yellow, blk, ochre & gold	15	10
		a.	Gold (Queen's head) omitted ..	50·00	
932	**415**	5p.	cinnamon, greenish yellow, new blue, lt mag, blk, yell-olive & gold	75	45
		a.	Gold (Queen's head) omitted ..	50·00	
		b.	Greenish yellow omitted	£130	
933	**416**	7½p.	greenish yellow, new blue, light magenta, black, cinnamon and gold	80	60
		a.	Gold (Queen's head) omitted ..	50·00	
		b.	Cinnamon omitted	£400	
934	**417**	9p.	brownish rose, black, dull rose, pale yell, brownish grey, pale bl & gold	80	60

No. 931a is also known with the embossing also omitted or misplaced.

The 7½p. is known with the embossing omitted.

The 9p. is known with the brownish rose omitted. It is also known with the embossing and phosphor both omitted.

418 Court Masque Costumes

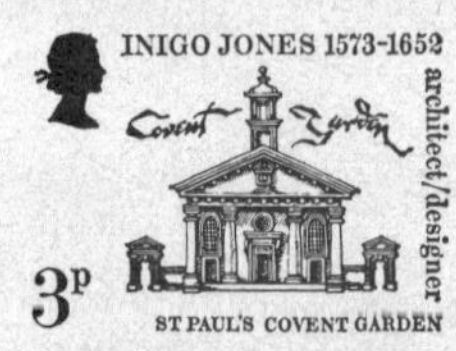

419 St. Paul's Church, Covent Garden

420 Prince's Lodging, Newmarket

421 Court Masque Stage Scene

T **418/19** and T **420/1** were printed horizontally *se-tenant* within the sheet

(Des Rosalind Dease. Litho and typo B.W.)

1973 (15 Aug). 400*th Birth Anniv of Inigo Jones* (*architect and designer*). *"All-over" phosphor. P* 15 × 14.

935	**418**	3p.	deep mauve, black and gold ..	60	20
		a.	Pair. Nos. 935/6	1·40	1·00
936	**419**	3p.	deep brown, black and gold ..	60	20
937	**420**	5p.	blue, black and gold ..	60	65
		a.	Pair. Nos. 937/8	1·75	2·00
938	**421**	5p.	grey-olive, black and gold	80	65

422 Palace of Westminster seen from Whitehall **423** Palace of Westminster seen from Millbank

(Des R. Downer. Recess and typo B.W.)

1973 (12 Sept). 19*th Commonwealth Parliamentary Conference. "All-over" phosphor. P* 15 × 14.

939	**422**	8p.	black, brownish grey and stone ..	40	55
940	**423**	10p.	gold and black	45	50

424 Princess Anne and Capt. Mark Phillips.

(Des C. Clements and E. Hughes from photo by Lord Litchfield)

1973 (14 Nov). *Royal Wedding. "All-over" phosphor. P* 15 × 14.

941	**424**	3½p.	dull violet and silver	15	5
		a.	Imperf (pair)	£450	
942		20p.	deep brown and silver	90	1·25
		a.	Silver omitted	£400	

425

426

427

428

429

T **425/9** depict the carol "Good King Wenceslas" and were printed horizontally *se-tenant* within the sheet.

430 "Good King Wenceslas, the Page and Peasant"

(Des D. Gentleman)

1973 (28 Nov). *Christmas. One centre phosphor band* (3*p*.) *or "all-over" phosphor* (3½*p*.). *P* 15 × 14.

943	**425**	3p.	grey-black, blue, brownish grey, light brown, bright rose-red, turq-green, salmon-pink and gold ..	40	15
		a.	Strip of 5. Nos. 943/7	3·25	
		b.	Imperf (horiz strip of 5)		
944	**426**	3p.	grey-black, violet-blue, slate, brown, rose-red, rosy mauve, turq-green, salmon-pink and gold ..	40	15
		a.	Rosy mauve omitted		
945	**427**	3p.	grey-black, violet-blue, slate, brown, rose-red, rosy mauve, turq-green, salmon-pink and gold ..	40	15
		a.	Rosy mauve omitted		
946	**428**	3p.	grey-black, violet-blue, slate, brown, rose-red, rosy mauve, turq-green, salmon-pink and gold ..	40	15
		a.	Rosy mauve omitted		
947	**429**	3p.	grey-black, violet-blue, slate, brown, rose-red, rosy mauve, turq-green, salmon-pink and gold ..	40	15
		a.	Rosy mauve omitted		
948	**430**	3½p.	salmon-pink, grey-black, red-brown, blue, turquoise-green, bright rose-red, rosy mauve, lavender-grey and gold	25	15
		a.	Imperf (pair)	£250	
		b.	Grey-black (value and inscr, etc) omitted	45·00	
		d.	Blue (leg, robes) omitted	50·00	
		e.	Rosy mauve (robe at right) omitted	45·00	
		f.	Blue and rosy mauve omitted ..	£150	
		g.	Bright rose-red (King's robe) omitted	45·00	
		h.	Red-brown (logs, basket etc) omitted		
943/8			.. .. *Set of* 6	3·25	50

The 3½p. also exists with salmon-pink omitted affecting the faces, hands and knees.

An example of the 3½p. with the gold background colour omitted has been seen used on cover; another has been seen with the turquoise-green omitted (used on piece); and a pair with the lavender-grey omitted (used on piece).

The 3p. and 3½p. are normally with PVA gum with added dextrin but the 3½p. also exists with normal PVA gum and the 3p. with gum arabic.

431 Horse Chestnut

(Des. D. Gentleman)

1974 (27 Feb). *British Trees* (*2nd issue*). *"All-over" phosphor. P* 15 × 14.

949	**431**	10p.	light emerald, bright green, greenish yellow, brown-olive, black and brownish grey	50	50

432 First Motor Fire-engine, 1904

433 Prize-winning Fire-engine, 1863

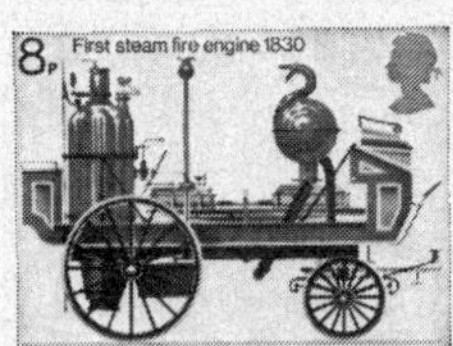

434 First Steam Fire-engine, 1830

435 Fire-engine, 1766

(Des D. Gentleman)

1974 (24 Apr). *Bicentenary of the Fire Prevention* (*Metropolis*) *Act. "All-over" phosphor. P* 15 × 14.

950	**432**	3½p.	grey-black, orange-yellow, greenish yellow, dull rose, ochre and grey	12	10
		a.	Imperf (pair)	£250	
951	**433**	5½p.	greenish yellow, deep rosy magenta, orange-yellow, light emerald, grey-black and grey	35	45
952	**434**	8p.	greenish yellow, light blue-green, light greenish blue, light chestnut, grey-black and grey	50	50
953	**435**	10p.	grey-black, pale reddish brown, lt brown, orange-yellow and grey ..	60	50

The 3½p. exists with ordinary PVA gum.

436 P & O Packet, *Peninsular*, 1888

437 Farman Biplane, 1911

438 Airmail-blue Van and Postbox, 1930

439 Imperial Airways "C" Class Flying-boat, 1937

(Des Rosalind Dease)

1974 (12 June). *Centenary of Universal Postal Union. "All-over" phosphor. P* 15 × 14.

954	**436**	3½p.	deep brownish grey, bright mauve, grey-black and gold	12	10
955	**437**	5½p.	pale orge, lt emer, grey-blk & gold	30	40
956	**438**	8p.	cobalt, brown, grey-black and gold	45	60
957	**439**	10p.	deep brownish grey, orange, grey-black and gold	50	55

440 Robert the Bruce

441 Owain Glyndŵr

442 Henry the Fifth

443 The Black Prince

(Des F. Wegner)

1974 (10 July). *Medieval Warriors. "All-over" phosphor. P* 15 × 14.

958	**440**	4½p.	greenish yellow, vermilion, slate-blue, red-brown, reddish brown, lilac-grey and gold	15	10
959	**441**	5½p.	lemon, vermilion, slate-blue red-brn, reddish brn, ol-drab & gold	60	70
960	**442**	8p.	deep grey, vermilion, greenish yellow, new blue, red-brown, deep cinnamon and gold	85	1·10
961	**443**	10p.	vermilion, greenish yellow, new blue, red-brown, reddish brown, light blue and gold	1·75	1·25

444 Churchill in Royal Yacht Squadron Uniform

445 Prime Minister, 1940

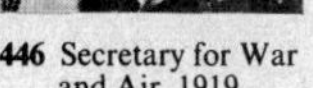

446 Secretary for War and Air, 1919 **447** War Correspondent, South Africa, 1899

(Des C. Clements and E. Hughes)

1974 (9 Oct). *Birth Centenary of Sir Winston Churchill. "All-over" phosphor. P* 14 × 15.

962	**444**	4½p.	Prussian blue, pale turquoise-green and silver	12	10
963	**445**	5½p.	sepia, brownish grey and silver ..	55	45
964	**446**	8p.	crimson, light claret and silver ..	45	45
965	**447**	10p.	light brown, stone and silver ..	50	40

448 "Adoration of the Magi" (York Minster, *circa* 1355)

449 "The Nativity" (St. Helen's Church, Norwich, *circa* 1480)

450 "Virgin and Child" (Ottery St. Mary Church, *circa* 1350)

451 "Virgin and Child" (Worcester Cathedral, *circa* 1224)

(Des Peter Hatch Partnership)

1974 (27 Nov). *Christmas. Church Roof Bosses. One phosphor band* (3½p.) *or "all-over" phosphor* (*others*). *P* 15 × 14.

966	**448**	3½p.	gold, light new blue, light brown, grey-black and light stone ..	8	8
967	**449**	4½p.	gold, yellow-orange, rose-red, light brown, grey-black, & lt new blue	10	12
968	**450**	8p.	blue, gold, light brown, rose-red, dull green and grey-black ..	45	60
969	**451**	10p.	gold, dull rose, grey-black, light new blue, pale cinnamon and light brown	65	50

The phosphor band on the 3½p. was first applied down the centre of the stamp but during the printing this was deliberately placed to the right between the roof boss and the value; however, intermediate positions, due to shifts, are known.

452 Invalid in Wheelchair

(Des P. Sharland)

1975 (22 Jan). *Health and Handicap Funds. "All-over" phosphor. P* 15 × 14.

970	**452**	4½p. + 1½p.	azure and grey-blue ..	15	20

453 "Peace—Burial at Sea"

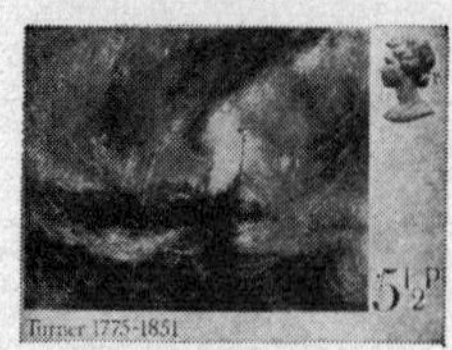

454 "Snowstorm—Steamer off a Harbour's Mouth"

455 "The Arsenal, Venice"

456 "St. Laurent"

(Des S. Rose)

1975 (19 Feb). *Birth Bicentenary of J. M. W. Turner* (*painter*). *"All-over" phosphor. P* 15 × 14.

971	**453**	4½p.	grey-blk, salmon, stone, bl & grey	10	12
972	**454**	5½p.	cobalt, greenish yellow, light yellow-brown, grey-black and rose	15	20
973	**455**	8p.	pale yellow-orange, greenish yellow, rose, cobalt and grey-black	25	35
974	**456**	10p.	deep blue, light yellow-ochre, light brown, deep cobalt and grey-black	30	35

457 Charlotte Square, Edinburgh

458 The Rows, Chester

T **457/8** were printed horizontally *se-tenant* within the sheet.

459 Royal Observatory, Greenwich

460 St. George's Chapel, Windsor

461 National Theatre, London

(Des P. Gauld)

1975 (23 Apr). *European Architectural Heritage Year. "All-over" phosphor. P* 15 × 14.

975	**457**	7p.	greenish yellow, bright orange, grey-black, red-brown, new blue, lavender and gold	25	25
		a.	Pair. Nos. 975/6	90	1·00
976	**458**	7p.	grey-black, greenish yellow, new blue, brt orange, red-brown & gold	25	25
977	**459**	8p.	magenta, deep slate, pale magenta, lt yellow-olive, grey-black & gold	20	30
978	**460**	10p.	bistre-brown, greenish yellow, deep slate, emer-green, grey-blk & gold	40	40
979	**461**	12p.	grey-blk, new bl, pale mag & gold	35	50

462 Sailing Dinghies

463 Racing Keel Yachts

464 Cruising Yachts

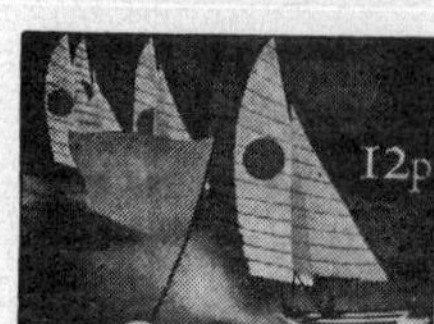

465 Multihulls

(Des A. Restall. Recess and photo)

1975 (11 June). *Sailing "All-over" phosphor. P* 15 × 14.

980	**462**	7p.	black, bluish violet, scarlet, orange-vermilion, orange and gold ..	20	15
981	**463**	8p.	black, orange-vermilion, orange, lavender, bright mauve, bright blue, deep ultramarine and gold ..	20	15
		a.	Black omitted	40·00	
982	**464**	10p.	black, orange, bluish emerald, light olive-drab, chocolate and gold ..	25	25
983	**465**	12p.	black, ultramarine, turquoise-blue, rose, grey, steel-blue and gold ..	45	75

On No. 981a the recess-printed black colour is completely omitted.

466 Stephenson's *Locomotion*, 1825

467 *Abbotsford*, 1876

468 *Caerphilly Castle*, 1923

469 High Speed Train, 1975

(Des B. Craker)

1975 (13 Aug). 150*th Anniv of Public Railways. "All-over" phosphor. P* 15 × 14.

984	**466**	7p.	red-brown, grey-black, greenish yellow, grey and silver	15	15
985	**467**	8p.	brown, orange-yellow, vermilion, grey-black, grey and silver ..	35	35
986	**468**	10p.	emerald-green, grey-black, yellow-orange, vermilion, grey and silver	40	40
987	**469**	12p.	grey-black, pale lemon, vermilion, blue, grey and silver	45	50

470 Palace of Westminster

(Des R. Downer)

1975 (3 Sept). 62*nd Inter-Parliamentary Union Conference. "All-over" phosphor. P* 15 × 14.

988	**470**	12p.	light new blue, black, brownish grey and gold	30	40

471 "Emma and Mr. Woodhouse" (*Emma*)

472 "Catherine Morland" (*Northanger Abbey*)

473 "Mr. Darcy" (*Pride and Prejudice*)

474 "Mary and Henry Crawford" (*Mansfield Park*)

(Des Barbara Brown)

1975 (22 Oct). *Birth Bicentenary of Jane Austen (novelist). "All-over" phosphor. P* 14 × 15.

989	**471**	8½p.	blue, slate, rose-red, light yellow, dull green, grey-black and gold ..	12	10
990	**472**	10p.	slate, bright magenta, grey, light yellow, grey-black and gold ..	25	30
991	**473**	11p.	dull blue, pink, olive-sepia, slate, pale greenish yell, grey-blk & gold	40	50
992	**474**	13p.	bright magenta, light new blue, slate, buff, dull blue-green, grey-black and gold	40	35

475 Angels with Harp and Lute

476 Angel with Mandolin

477 Angel with Horn

478 Angel with Trumpet

(Des R. Downer)

1975 (26 Nov). *Christmas. One phosphor band* (6½*p.*), *phosphor-inked* (8½*p.*) (*background*), *"all-over" phosphor* (*others*). *P* 15 × 14.

993	**475**	6½p.	bluish violet, bright reddish violet, light lavender and gold	15	15
994	**476**	8½p.	turquoise-green, bright emerald-green, slate, lt turq-green & gold	20	15
995	**477**	11p.	vermilion, cerise, pink and gold ..	45	55
996	**478**	13p.	drab, brn, brt orge, buff & gold ..	50	35

479 Housewife

480 Policeman

481 District Nurse

482 Industrialist

(Des P. Sharland)

1976 (10 Mar). *Telephone Centenary. "All-over" phosphor. P* 15 × 14.

997	**479**	8½p.	greenish blue, dp rose, black & bl	15	15
		a.	Deep rose omitted	£950	
998	**480**	10p.	greenish blue, black & yellow-ol	20	25
999	**481**	11p.	greenish blue, deep rose, black and bright mauve	40	55
1000	**482**	13p.	olive-brn, dp rose, blk & orge-red	50	35

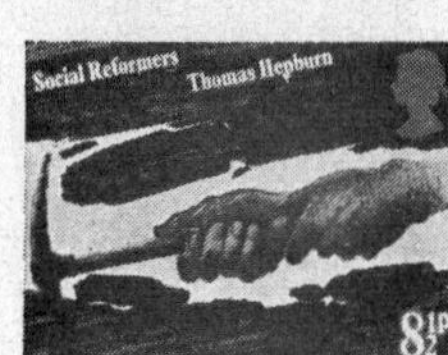

483 Hewing Coal (Thomas Hepburn)

484 Machinery (Robert Owen)

485 Chimney Cleaning (Lord Shaftesbury)

486 Hands clutching Prison Bars (Elizabeth Fry)

(Des D. Gentleman)

1976 (28 Apr). *Social Reformers. "All-over" phosphor. P* 15 × 14.

1001	**483**	8½p.	lavender-grey, grey-black, black and slate-grey	15	15
1002	**484**	10p.	lavender-grey, grey-black, grey and slate-violet	25	25
1003	**485**	11p.	black, slate-grey and drab ..	40	50
1004	**486**	13p.	slate-grey, black & deep dull grn	45	35

487 Benjamin Franklin (bust by Jean-Jacques Caffieri)

(Des P. Sharland)

1976 (2 June). *Bicentenary of American Revolution. "All-over" phosphor. P* 14 × 15.

1005	**487**	11p	pale bistre, slate-violet, pale blue-green, black and gold	30	35

488 "Elizabeth of Glamis"

489 "Grandpa Dickson"

490 "*Rosa Mundi*"

491 "Sweet Briar"

(Des Kristin Rosenberg)

1976 (30 June). *Centenary of Royal National Rose Society. "All-over" phosphor. P* 14 × 15.

1006	**488**	8½p.	bright rose-red, greenish yellow, emerald, grey-black and gold ..	20	15
1007	**489**	10p.	greenish yellow, bright green, red-dish brown, grey-black and gold	35	35
1008	**490**	11p.	bright magenta, greenish yellow, emerald, grey-blue, grey-black and gold	50	60
1009	**491**	13p.	rose-pink, lake-brown, yellow-green, pale greenish yellow, grey-black and gold	50	45
		a.	Value omitted*		

*The value was not etched in one position of the cylinder but the error was discovered before issue and most examples were removed from the sheets.

492 Archdruid

493 Morris Dancing

494 Scots Piper

495 Welsh Harpist

(Des Marjorie Saynor)

1976 (4 Aug). *British Cultural Traditions. "All-over" phosphor. P* 14 × 15.

1010	**492**	8½p.	yellow, sepia, bright rose, dull ultramarine, black and gold ..	15	15
1011	**493**	10p.	dull ultramarine, bright rose-red, sepia, greenish yellow, blk & gold	30	35
1012	**494**	11p.	bluish green, yellow-brown, yell-orge, blk, brt rose-red & gold ..	35	55
1013	**495**	13p.	dull violet-blue, yellow-orange, yell-brn, blk, bluish grn & gold	40	35

The 8½p. and 13p. commemorate the 800th Anniv of the Royal National Eisteddfod.

496 Woodcut from *The Canterbury Tales*

497 Extract from *The Tretyse of Love*

498 Woodcut from *The Game and Playe of Chesse*

499 Early Printing Press

(Des R. Gay. Queen's head printed in gold and then embossed)

1976 (29 Sept). *500th Anniv of British Printing. "All-over" phosphor. P* 14 × 15.

1014	**496**	8½p.	black, light new blue and gold ..	15	12
1015	**497**	10p.	black, olive-green and gold ..	25	25
1016	**498**	11p.	black, brownish grey and gold ..	30	50
1017	**499**	13p.	chocolate, pale ochre and gold ..	40	40

500 Virgin and Child

501 Angel with Crown

502 Angel appearing to Shepherds

503 The Three Kings

(Des Enid Marx)

1976 (24 Nov). *Christmas. English Medieval Embroidery. One phosphor band* (6½*p.*), *"all-over" phosphor* (*others*). *P* 15 × 14.

1018	**500**	6½p.	bl, bistre-yell, brn & brt orange	20	15
		a.	Imperf (pair)	£225	
1019	**501**	8½p.	sage-green, yellow, brown-ochre, chestnut and olive-black ..	25	20
1020	**502**	11p.	deep magenta, brown-orange, new blue, black and cinnamon ..	35	35
		a.	Uncoated paper*	45·00	
1021	**503**	13p.	bright purple, new blue, cinnamon, bronze-green and olive-grey	40	40

* See footnote after No. 744.

504 Lawn Tennis

505 Table Tennis

506 Squash

507 Badminton

(Des A. Restall)

1977 (12 Jan). *Racket Sports. Phosphorised paper. P* 15 × 14.

1022	**504**	8½p.	emer-grn, blk, grey & bluish grn	20	12
		a.	Imperf (horiz pair)	£650	
1023	**505**	10p.	myrtle-green, black, grey-black and deep blue-green	30	25
1024	**506**	11p.	orange, pale yellow, black, slate-black and grey	35	45
1025	**507**	13p.	brown, grey-black, grey and bright reddish violet	35	35

508

(Des after plaster cast by Arnold Machin)

1977 (2 Feb)–**84**. *P* 14 × 15.

1026	**508**		£1 brt yellow-green & blackish olive ..	1·50	35
			a. Imperf (pair)	£700	
1026*b*			£1.30, pale drab & dp blue-grn (3.8.83)	2·75	2·75
1026*c*			£1.33, pale mauve & grey-bl (28.8.84)	2·10	2·10
1027			£2 light emerald and purple-brown ..	3·00	40
1028			£5 salmon and chalky blue	7·50	3·00

509 Steroids—Conformational Analysis

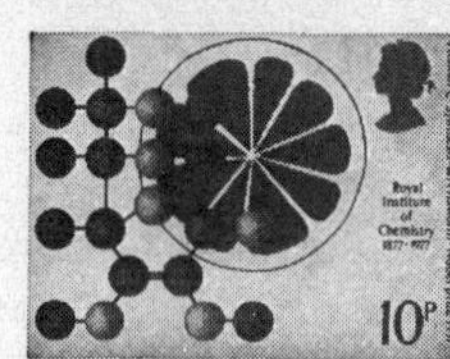

510 Vitamin C—Synthesis

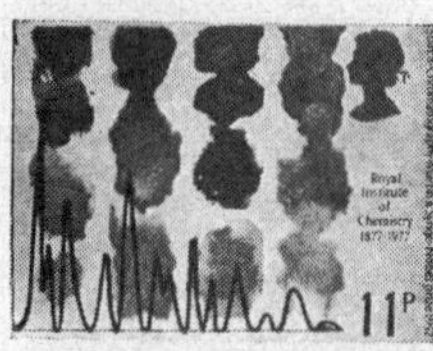

511 Starch—Chromatography

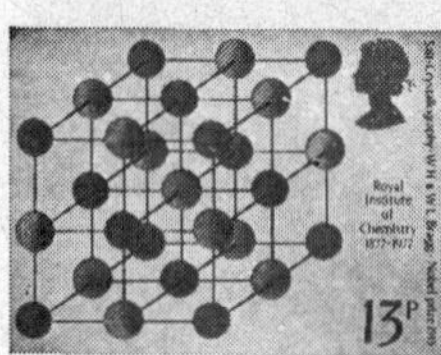

512 Salt—Crystallography

(Des J. Karo)

1977 (2 Mar). *Royal Institute of Chemistry Centenary. "All-over" phosphor. P* 15 × 14.

1029	**509**	8½p.	rosine, new blue, olive-yellow, brt mauve, yellow-brown, blk & gold	15	12
		a.	Imperf (horiz pair)	£550	
1030	**510**	10p.	bright orange, rosine, new blue, bright blue, black and gold ..	25	35
1031	**511**	11p.	rosine, greenish yellow, new blue, deep violet, black and gold ..	35	45
1032	**512**	13p.	new blue, brt green, black & gold	35	35

513

514

515

516

T **513/16** differ in the decorations of "ER".

(Des R. Guyatt)

1977 (11 May–15 June). *Silver Jubilee. "All-over" phosphor. P* 15 × 14.

No.	Type	Description		
1033	**513**	8½p. blackish green, black, silver, olive-grey and pale turquoise-green ..	15	15
		a. Imperf (pair)	£600	
1034		9p. maroon, black, silver, olive-grey and lavender (15 June)	25	30
1035	**514**	10p. blackish blue, black, silver, olive-grey and ochre	30	30
		a. Imperf (horiz pair)		
1036	**515**	11p. brown-purple, black, silver, olive-grey and rose-pink	35	30
		a. Imperf (horiz pair)	£850	
1037	**516**	13p. sepia, black, silver, olive-grey and bistre-yellow	35	35
		a. Imperf (pair)	£850	

517 "Gathering of Nations"

(Des P. Murdoch. Recess and photo)

1977 (8 June). *Commonwealth Heads of Government Meeting, London. "All-over" phosphor. P* 14 × 15.

No.	Type	Description		
1038	**517**	13p. black, blackish green, rose-car and silver	30	40

518 Hedgehog

519 Brown Hare

520 Red Squirrel

521 Otter

522 Badger

T **518/22** were printed horizontally *se-tenant* within the sheet.

(Des P. Oxenham)

1977 (5 Oct). *British Wildlife. "All-over" phosphor. P* 14 × 15.

No.	Type	Description		
1039	**518**	9p. reddish brown, grey-black, pale lemon, brt turq-bl, brt mag & gold	30	30
		a. Strip of 5. Nos. 1039/43 ..	1·50	
		b. Imperf (vert pair)		
		c. Imperf (horiz pair, Nos. 1039/40)		
1040	**519**	9p. reddish brown, grey-black, pale lemon, brt turq-bl, brt mag & gold	30	30
1041	**520**	9p. reddish brown, grey-black, pale lemon, brt turq-bl, brt mag & gold	30	30
1042	**521**	9p. reddish brown, grey-black, pale lemon, brt turq-bl, brt mag & gold	30	30
1043	**522**	9p. grey-black, reddish brown, pale lemon, brt turq-bl, brt mag & gold	30	30

523 "Three French Hens, Two Turtle Doves and a Partridge in a Pear Tree"

524 "Six Geese a-laying, Five Gold Rings, Four Colly Birds"

525 "Eight Maids a-milking, Seven Swans a-swimming"

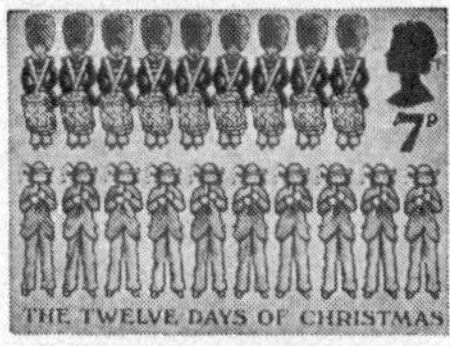

526 "Ten Pipers piping, Nine Drummers drumming"

527 "Twelve Lords a-leaping, Eleven Ladies dancing"

T **523/7** depict the carol "The Twelve Days of Christmas" and were printed horizontally *se-tenant* within the sheet.

528 "A Partridge in a Pear Tree"

(Des D. Gentleman)

1977 (23 Nov). *Christmas. One centre phosphor band* (7*p.*) *or "all-over" phosphor* (9*p.*). *P* 15 × 14.

No.	Type	Description		
1044	**523**	7p. slate, grey, bright yellow-green, new blue, rose-red and gold ..	20	20
		a. Strip of 5. Nos. 1044/8 ..	1·00	
		ab. Imperf (strip of 5. Nos. 1044/8) ..	£600	
1045	**524**	7p. slate, brt yellow-grn, new bl & gold	20	20
1046	**525**	7p. slate, grey, bright yellow-green, new blue, rose-red and gold ..	20	20
1047	**526**	7p. slate, grey, bright yellow-green, new blue, rose-red and gold ..	20	20
1048	**527**	7p. slate, grey, bright yellow-green, new blue, rose-red and gold ..	20	20
1049	**528**	9p. pale brown, pale orange, bright emerald, pale greenish yellow, slate-black and gold	20	20
		a. Imperf (pair)	£600	
1044/9		.. .. *Set of* 6	1·00	1·10

529 Oil—North Sea Production Platform

530 Coal—Modern Pithead

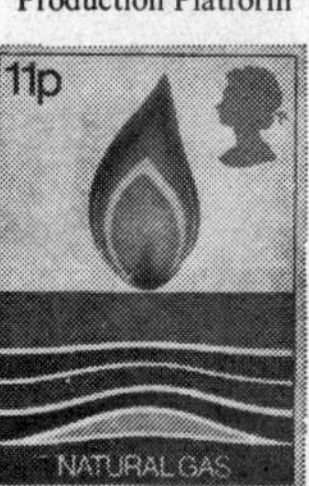

531 Natural Gas—Flame Rising from Sea

532 Electricity—Nuclear Power Station and Uranium Atom

(Des P. Murdoch)

1978 (25 Jan). *Energy Resources. "All-over" phosphor. P* 14 × 15.

No.	Type	Description		
1050	**529**	9p. deep brown, orange-vermilion, grey-black, greenish yellow, rose-pink, new blue and silver ..	15	20
1051	**530**	10½p. light emerald-green, grey-black, red-brown, slate-grey, pale apple-green and silver	25	30
1052	**531**	11p. greenish blue, bright violet, violet-blue, blackish brown, grey-black and silver	30	40
1053	**532**	13p. orange-vermilion, grey-black, deep brown, greenish yellow, light brown, light blue and silver ..	35	45

533 The Tower of London

534 Holyroodhouse

535 Caernarvon Castle

536 Hampton Court Palace

(Des R. Maddox (stamps), J. Matthews (miniature sheet))

1978 (1 Mar). *British Architecture. Historic Buildings. "All-over" phosphor. P* 15 × 14.

No.	Type	Description		
1054	**533**	9p. black, olive-brown, new blue, brt green, lt yellow-olive & rose-red	15	20
1055	**534**	10½p. black, brown-olive, orange-yell, brt grn, lt yell-olive & vio-bl ..	30	25
1056	**535**	11p. black, brown-olive, violet-blue, brt green, lt yellow-olive & dull bl	30	40
1057	**536**	13p. black, orange-yellow, lake-brown, bright green and light yellow-olive	35	35
MS1058		121 × 89 mm. Nos. 1054/7 (*sold at* 53½*p.*)	1·75	2·75
		a. Imperforate		
		b. Light yellow-olive (Queen's head) omitted		

The premium on No. **MS**1058 was used to support the London 1980 International Stamp Exhibition.

The miniature sheet also exists with either the rose-red (Union Jack on 9p.) or the orange-yellow omitted.

537 State Coach

538 St. Edward's Crown

539 The Sovereign's Orb

540 Imperial State Crown

(Des J. Matthews)

1978 (31 May). *25th Anniv of Coronation. "All-over" phosphor. P* 14 × 15.

1059	**537**	9p.	gold and royal blue	20	15
1060	**538**	10½p.	gold and brown-lake	30	25
1061	**539**	11p.	gold and deep dull green ..	30	30
1062	**540**	13p.	gold and reddish violet	35	30

541 Shire Horse

542 Shetland Pony

543 Welsh Pony

544 Thoroughbred

(Des P. Oxenham)

1978 (5 July). *Horses. "All-over" phosphor. P* 15 × 14.

1063	**541**	9p.	black, pale reddish brown, grey-black, greenish yellow, light blue, vermilion and gold	20	15
1064	**542**	10½p.	pale chestnut, magenta, brownish grey, greenish yellow, greenish blue, grey-black and gold ..	30	30
1065	**543**	11p.	reddish brown, black, light green, greenish yellow, bistre, grey-black and gold	30	40
1066	**544**	13p.	reddish brown, pale reddish brown, emerald, greenish yellow, grey-black and gold	35	40

545 "Penny-farthing" and 1884 Safety Bicycle

546 1920 Touring Bicycles

547 Modern Small-wheel Bicycles

ALTERED CATALOGUE NUMBERS

Any Catalogue numbers altered from the last edition are shown as a list in the introductory pages.

548 1978 Road-racers

(Des F. Wegner)

1978 (2 Aug). *Centenaries of Cyclists Touring Club and British Cycling Federation. "All-over" phosphor. P* 15 × 14.

1067	**545**	9p.	brown, deep dull blue, rose-pink, pale olive, grey-black and gold ..	20	15
		a.	Imperf (pair)	£250	
1068	**546**	10½p.	olive, pale yellow-orange, orange-vermilion, rose-red, light brown, grey-black and gold	30	30
1069	**547**	11p.	orange-vermilion, greenish blue, light brown, pale greenish yellow, deep grey, grey-black and gold ..	30	40
1070	**548**	13p.	new blue, orange-vermilion, light brn, olive-grey, grey-black & gold	35	40
		a.	Imperf (pair)	£500	

549 Singing Carols round the Christmas Tree

550 The Waits

551 18th-century Carol Singers

552 "The Boar's Head Carol"

(Des Faith Jaques)

1978 (22 Nov). *Christmas. One centre phosphor band* (7p.) *or "all-over" phosphor* (*others*). *P* 15 × 14.

1071	**549**	7p.	bright green, greenish yellow, magenta, new blue, black and gold	15	15
1072	**550**	9p.	magenta, greenish yellow, new blue, sage-green, black and gold	20	20
		a.	Imperf (horiz pair)		
1073	**551**	11p.	magenta, new blue, greenish yellow, yellow-brown, black and gold	35	40
		a.	Imperf (horiz pair)		
1074	**552**	13p.	salmon-pink, new blue, greenish yellow, magenta, black and gold	35	40

553 Old English Sheepdog

554 Welsh Springer Spaniel

555 West Highland Terrier

556 Irish Setter

(Des P. Barrett)

1979 (7 Feb). *Dogs. "All-over" phosphor. P* 15 × 14.

1075	**553**	9p.	grey-black, sepia, turquoise-green, pale greenish yellow, pale greenish blue and grey	20	20
1076	**554**	10½p.	grey-black, lake-brown, apple-green, pale greenish yellow, pale greenish blue and grey	25	30
1077	**555**	11p.	grey-black, claret, yellowish grn, pale greenish yell, cobalt & grey	40	40
		a.	Imperf (horiz pair)		
1078	**556**	13p.	grey-black, lake-brown, green, pale greenish yellow & dp turq-bl	45	40

557 Primrose

558 Daffodil

559 Bluebell

560 Snowdrop

(Des P. Newcombe)

1979 (21 Mar). *Spring Wild Flowers. "All-over" phosphor. P* 14 × 15.

1079	**557**	9p.	slate-black, deep brown, pale greenish yellow, deep olive, pale new blue and silver	20	20
		a.	Imperf (pair)	£200	
1080	**558**	10½p.	greenish yellow, grey-green, steel-blue, slate-blk, new blue & silver	30	30
1081	**559**	11p.	slate-black, deep brown, ultramarine, light greenish blue, pale greenish yellow and silver ..	30	30
		a.	Imperf (horiz pair)	£600	
1082	**560**	13p.	slate-black, indigo, grey-green, sepia, ochre and silver	35	35
		a.	Imperf (horiz pair)	£550	

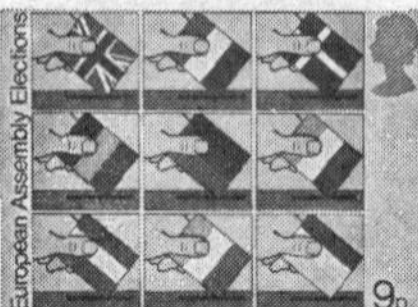

561

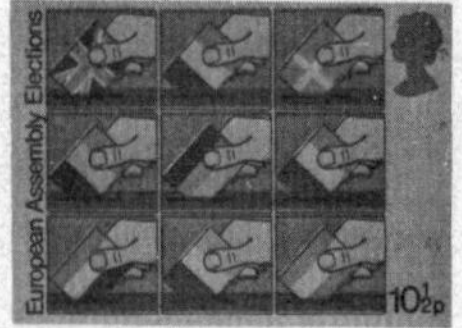

562

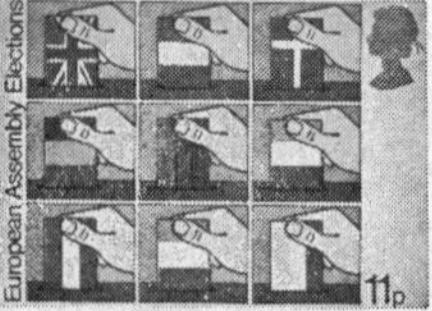

563

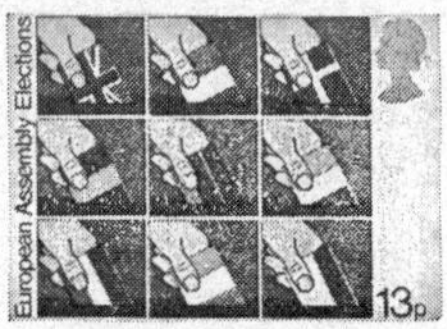

564

T **561/4** show Hands placing National Flags in Ballot Boxes.

(Des S. Cliff)

1979 (9 May). *First Direct Elections to European Assembly. Phosphorised paper. P* 15 × 14.

1083	**561**	9p.	grey-black, vermilion, cinnamon, pale greenish yellow, pale turq-green and dull ultramarine ..	20	20
1084	**562**	10½p.	grey-black, vermilion, cinnamon, pale greenish yellow, dull ultramarine, pale turq-grn & chestnut	25	25
1085	**563**	11p.	grey-black, vermilion, cinnamon, pale greenish yellow, dull ultramarine, pale turq-grn & grey-grn	35	35
1086	**564**	13p.	grey-black, vermilion, cinnamon, pale greenish yellow, dull ultramarine, pale turq-grn & brown	40	35

565 "Saddling 'Mahmoud' for the Derby, 1936" (Sir Alfred Munnings)

566 "The Liverpool Great National Steeple Chase, 1839" (aquatint by F. C. Turner)

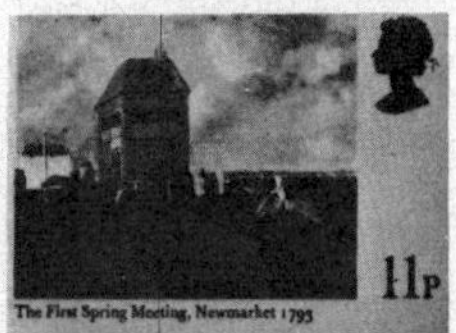

567 "The First Spring Meeting, Newmarket, 1793" (J. N. Sartorius)

568 "Racing at Dorsett Ferry, Windsor, 1684" (Francis Barlow)

(Des S. Rose)

1979 (6 June). *Horseracing Paintings. Bicentenary of the Derby* (9*p.*). *"All-over" phosphor. P* 15 × 14.

1087	**565**	9p.	light blue, red-brown, rose-pink, pale greenish yellow, grey-black and gold	20	20
1088	**566**	10½p.	bistre-yellow, slate-blue, salmon-pink, lt blue, grey-black and gold	25	25
1089	**567**	11p.	rose, vermilion, pale greenish yellow, new blue, grey-black and gold	30	30
1090	**568**	13p.	bistre-yellow, rose, turquoise, grey-black and gold	35	35

569 *The Tale of Peter Rabbit* (Beatrix Potter)

570 *The Wind in the Willows* (Kenneth Grahame)

571 *Winnie-the-Pooh* (A. A. Milne)

572 *Alice's Adventures in Wonderland* (Lewis Carroll)

(Des E. Hughes)

1979 (11 July). *International Year of the Child. Children's Book Illustrations. "All-over" phosphor. P* 14 × 15.

1091	**569**	9p.	deep bluish green, grey-black, bistre-brown, bright rose, greenish yellow and silver	20	20
1092	**570**	10½p.	dull ultramarine, grey-black, ol-brown, bright rose, yellow-orge, pale greenish yellow and silver ..	25	25
1093	**571**	11p.	drab, grey-black, greenish yellow, new bl, yell-orge, agate & silver	30	30
1094	**572**	13p.	pale greenish yellow, grey-black, bright rose, deep bluish green, olive-brown, new blue and silver	35	35

573 Sir Rowland Hill

574 Postman, *circa* 1839

575 London Postman, *circa* 1839

576 Woman and Young Girl with Letters, 1840

(Des E. Stemp)

1979 (22 Aug–24 Oct). *Death Centenary of Sir Rowland Hill. "All-over" phosphor. P* 14 × 15.

1095	**573**	10p.	grey-black, brown-ochre, myrtle-green, pale greenish yellow, rosine, bright blue and gold ..	20	20
1096	**574**	11½p.	grey-black, brown-ochre, bright blue, rosine, bistre-brown, pale greenish yellow and gold ..	25	20
1097	**575**	13p.	grey-black, brown-ochre, bright blue, rosine, bistre-brown, pale greenish yellow and gold ..	30	25
1098	**576**	15p.	grey-black, brown-ochre, myrtle-green, bistre-brown, rosine, pale greenish yellow and gold ..	40	35
MS1099			89 × 121 mm. Nos. 1095/8 (*sold at* 59½*p.*) (24 Oct)	95	90
			a. Imperforate	£1500	
			b. Brown-ochre (15p. background, etc) omitted	£800	
			c. Gold (Queen's head) omitted ..	£250	
			d. Brown-ochre, myrtle-green and gold omitted	£2000	
			e. Bright blue (13p. background, etc) omitted	£900	
			f. Myrtle-green (10p. (background), 15p.) omitted	£1500	

The premium on No. **MS**1099 was used to support the London 1980 International Stamp Exhibition.

Examples of No. **MS**1099 also exist with either the pale greenish yellow, the rosine or the bistre-brown omitted

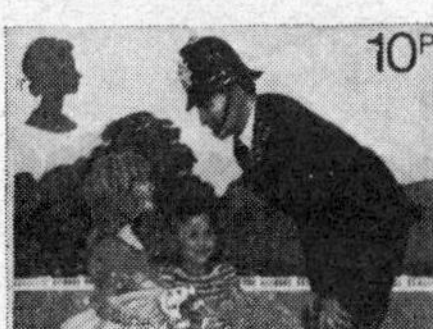

577 Policeman on the Beat

578 Policeman directing Traffic

579 Mounted Policeman

580 River Patrol Boat

(Des B. Sanders)

1979 (26 Sept). *150th Anniv of Metropolitan Police. Phosphorised paper. P* 15 × 14.

1100	**577**	10p.	grey-black, red-brown, emerald, greenish yellow, brt blue & mag	20	20
1101	**578**	11½p.	grey-black, bright orange, purple-brown, ultramarine, greenish yellow and deep bluish green ..	25	25
1102	**579**	13p.	grey-black, red-brown, magenta, ol-grn, greenish yell & dp dull bl	35	35
1103	**580**	15p.	grey-black, magenta, brown, slate-bl, dp brown & greenish blk	40	40

581 The Three Kings

582 Angel appearing to the Shepherds

583 The Nativity

584 Mary and Joseph travelling to Bethlehem

585 The Annunciation

(Des F. Wegner)

1979 (21 Nov). *Christmas. One centre phosphor band* (8*p.*) *or phosphorised paper* (*others*). *P* 15 × 14.

1104	**581**	8p.	blue, grey-black, ochre, slate-violet and gold	15	15
			a. Imperf (pair)	£250	
1105	**582**	10p.	bright rose-red, grey-black, chestnut, chrome-yell, dp vio & gold	20	20
			a. Imperf between (vert pair) ..	£350	
1106	**583**	11½p.	orange-vermilion, steel-bl, drab, grey-black, deep blue-grn & gold	25	25
1107	**584**	13p.	bright blue, orange-vermilion, bistre, grey-black and gold ..	35	35
1108	**585**	15p.	orange-vermilion, blue, bistre, grey-black, green and gold ..	40	40

586 Common Kingfisher **587** Dipper

588 Moorhen **589** Yellow Wagtails

(Des M. Warren)

1980 (16 Jan). *Centenary of Wild Bird Protection Act. Phosphorised paper. P* 14 × 15.

1109	**586**	10p.	bright blue, bright yellow-green, vermilion, pale greenish yellow, grey-black and gold	20	20
1110	**587**	11½p.	sepia, grey-black, dull ultramarine, vermilion, grey-green, pale greenish yellow and gold ..	30	20
1111	**588**	13p.	emerald-green, grey-black, bright bl, verm, pale greenish yell & gold	40	35
1112	**589**	15p.	greenish yellow, brown, light green, slate-bl, grey-blk & gold	45	35

590 "Rocket" approaching Moorish Arch, Liverpool

591 First and Second Class Carriages passing through Olive Mount cutting

592 Third Class Carriage and Cattle Truck crossing Chat Moss

593 Horsebox and Carriage Truck near Bridgewater Canal

594 Goods Truck and Mail-Coach at Manchester

T **590/4** were printed together, *se-tenant*, in horizontal strips of 5 throughout the sheet.

(Des D. Gentleman)

1980 (12 Mar). *150th Anniv of Liverpool and Manchester Railway. Phosphorised paper. P* 15 × 14.

1113	**590**	12p.	lemon, light brown, rose-red, pale blue and grey-black	30	30
		a.	Strip of 5. Nos. 1113/17 ..	1·75	
		ab.	Imperf (horiz strip of 5. Nos. 1113/17)	£900	
1114	**591**	12p.	rose-red, light brown, lemon, pale blue and grey-black	30	30
1115	**592**	12p.	pale blue, rose-red, lemon, light brown and grey-black	30	30
1116	**593**	12p.	light brown, lemon, rose-red, pale blue and grey-black	30	30
1117	**594**	12p.	light brown, rose-red, pale blue, lemon and grey-black	30	30

595 Montage of London Buildings

(Des J. Matthews. Recess)

1980 (9 Apr–7 May). *"London 1980" International Stamp Exhibition. Phosphorised paper. P* 14½ × 14.

1118	**595**	50p.	agate	1·00	1·00
MS1119			90 × 123 mm. No. 1118 (*sold at 75p.*) (7 May)	1·25	1·50
		a.	Error. Imperf	£650	

596 Buckingham Palace **597** The Albert Memorial

598 Royal Opera House **599** Hampton Court

600 Kensington Palace

(Des Sir Hugh Casson)

1980 (7 May). *London Landmarks. Phosphorised paper. P* 14 × 15.

1120	**596**	10½p.	grey, pale blue, rosine, pale greenish yell, yellowish green & silver	20	20
1121	**597**	12p.	grey-black, bistre, rosine, yellowish green, pale greenish yellow and silver	30	25
		a.	Imperf (vert pair)	£375	
1122	**598**	13½p.	grey-black, pale salmon, pale olgreen, slate-blue and silver ..	35	35
		a.	Imperf (pair)	£250	
1123	**599**	15p.	grey-black, pale salmon, slate-blue, dull yellowish green, olive-yellow and silver	40	35
1124	**600**	17½p.	grey, slate-blue, red-brown, sepia, yellowish green, pale greenish yellow and silver	45	40
		a.	Silver (Queen's head) omitted ..	£200	

No. 1124a shows the Queen's head in pale greenish yellow, this colour being printed beneath the silver for technical reasons.

601 Charlotte Brontë (*Jane Eyre*)

602 George Eliot (*The Mill on the Floss*)

603 Emily Brontë (*Wuthering Heights*)

604 Mrs. Gaskell (*North and South*)

T **601/4** show authoresses and scenes from their novels. T **601/2** also include the "Europa" C.E.P.T. emblem.

(Des Barbara Brown)

1980 (9 July). *Famous Authoresses. Phosphorised paper. P* 15 × 14.

1125	**601**	12p.	red-brown, bright rose, bright bl, greenish yellow, grey and silver	25	25
1126	**602**	13½p.	red-brown, dull vermilion, pale blue, pale greenish yellow, grey and silver	30	30
1127	**603**	15p.	red-brown, vermilion, blue, lemon, grey and silver	45	45
1128	**604**	17½p.	dull vermilion, slate blue, ultram, pale greenish yell, grey & silver	50	50
		a.	Imperf and slate-blue omitted (pair)		

The 13½p. value exists with the pale blue omitted.

605 Queen Elizabeth the Queen Mother

(Des J. Matthews from photograph by N. Parkinson)

1980 (4 Aug). *80th Birthday of Queen Elizabeth the Queen Mother. Phosphorised paper. P* 14 × 15.

1129	**605**	12p.	bright rose, greenish yellow, new blue, grey and silver	35	30

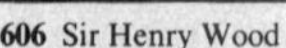

606 Sir Henry Wood **607** Sir Thomas Beecham

608 Sir Malcolm Sargent **609** Sir John Barbirolli

(Des P. Gauld)

1980 (10 Sept). *British Conductors. Phosphorised paper. P* 14 × 15.

1130	**606**	12p.	slate, rose-red, greenish yellow, bistre and gold	25	25
1131	**607**	13½p.	grey-black, vermilion, greenish yellow, pale carmine-rose and gold	30	30
1132	**608**	15p.	grey-black, bright rose-red, greenish yellow, turquoise-grn & gold	40	40
1133	**609**	17½p.	black, bright rose-red, greenish yellow, dull violet-blue and gold	45	45

610 Running　**611** Rugby

612 Boxing　**613** Cricket

(Des R. Goldsmith. Litho Questa)

1980 (10 Oct). *Sport Centenaries. Phosphorised paper. P* 14 × 14½.

1134	**610**	12p.	pale new blue, greenish yellow, magenta, light brown, reddish purple and gold	25	25
1135	**611**	13½p.	pale new blue, olive-yellow, bright purple, orange-vermilion, blackish lilac and gold	30	30
1136	**612**	15p.	pale new blue, greenish yellow, bright purple, chalky blue & gold	45	40
1137	**613**	17½p.	pale new blue, greenish yellow, magenta, dp ol, grey-brn & gold	50	50

Centenaries:—12p. Amateur Athletics Association; 13½p. Welsh Rugby Union; 15p. Amateur Boxing Association; 17½p. First England–Australia Test Match.

614 Christmas Tree

615 Candles

616 Apples and Mistletoe

617 Crown, Chains and Bell

618 Holly

(Des J. Matthews)

1980 (19 Nov). *Christmas. One centre phosphor band* (10*p.*) *or phosphorised paper* (*others*). *P* 15 × 14.

1138	**614**	10p.	black, turquoise-green, greenish yellow, vermilion and blue . .	20	20
1139	**615**	12p.	grey, magenta, rose-red, greenish grey and pale orange	25	25
1140	**616**	13½p.	grey-black, dull yellow-green, brown, greenish yellow and pale olive-bistre	35	35
1141	**617**	15p.	grey-black, bistre-yellow, bright orange, magenta and new blue . .	35	35
1142	**618**	17½p.	black, vermilion, dull yellowish green and greenish yellow . .	45	40

619 St. Valentine's Day

620 Morris Dancers

621 Lammastide

622 Medieval Mummers

T **619/20** also include the "Europa" C.E.P.T. emblem.

(Des F. Wegner)

1981 (6 Feb). *Folklore. Phosphorised paper. P* 15 × 14.

1143	**619**	14p.	cerise, green, yellow-orange, salmon-pink, black and gold . .	30	25
1144	**620**	18p.	dull ultramarine, lemon, lake-brown, brt green, black & gold	50	45
1145	**621**	22p.	chrome-yellow, rosine, brown, new blue, black and gold . .	60	60
1146	**622**	25p.	brt blue, red-brown, brt rose-red, greenish yellow, black and gold	65	65

623 Blind Man with Guide Dog

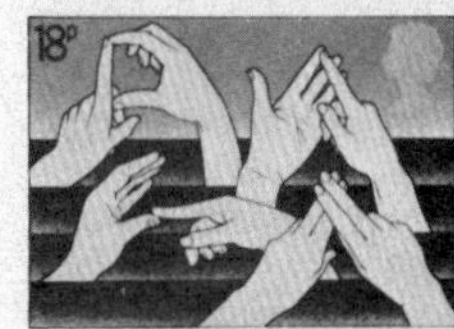

624 Hands spelling "Deaf" in Sign Language

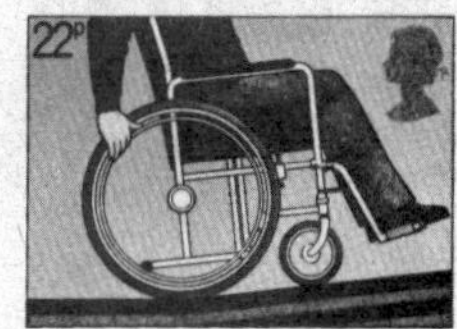

625 Disabled Man in Wheelchair

626 Disabled Artist painting with Foot

(Des J. Gibbs)

1981 (25 Mar). *International Year of the Disabled. Phosphorised paper. P* 15 × 14.

1147	**623**	14p.	drab, greenish yellow, bright rose-red, dull purple and silver . .	30	25
1148	**624**	18p.	deep blue-green, brt orange, dull vermilion, grey-black and silver	45	45
1149	**625**	22p.	brown-ochre, rosine, purple-brn, greenish blue, black and silver . .	60	60
1150	**626**	25p.	vermilion, lemon, pale salmon, olive-brn, new blue, blk & silver	65	65

627 Small Tortoiseshell　**628** Large Blue

629 Peacock　**630** Chequered Skipper

(Des G. Beningfield)

1981 (13 May). *Butterflies. Phosphorised paper. P* 14 × 15.

1151	**627**	14p.	greenish yellow, yellow-green, brt rose, brt blue, emerald & gold . .	30	25
1152	**628**	18p.	black, greenish yellow, dull yellowish green, bright mauve, bright blue, bright green and gold . .	45	45
1153	**629**	22p.	black, greenish yell, bronze-grn, rosine, ultramarine, lt grn & gold	60	60
1154	**630**	25p.	black, greenish yellow, bronze-green, bright rose-red, ultramarine, bright emerald and gold . .	65	65

631 Glenfinnan, Scotland

632 Derwentwater, England

633 Stackpole Head, Wales

634 Giant's Causeway, Northern Ireland

635 St. Kilda, Scotland

(Des M. Fairclough)

1981 (24 June). *50th Anniv of National Trust for Scotland. British Landscapes. Phosphorised paper. P* 15 × 14.

1155	**631**	14p.	lilac, dull blue, reddish brown, bistre-yellow, black and gold ..	30	25
1156	**632**	18p.	bottle green, bright blue, brown, bistre-yellow, black and gold ..	45	45
1157	**633**	20p.	deep turq-blue, dull blue, greenish yellow, reddish brn, black & gold	50	50
1158	**634**	22p.	chrome-yellow, reddish brn, new blue, yellow-brown, black & gold	55	60
1159	**635**	25p.	ultramarine, new blue, olive-green, olive-grey and gold ..	60	60

636 Prince Charles and Lady Diana Spencer

(Des J. Matthews from photograph by Lord Snowdon)

1981 (22 July). *Royal Wedding. Phosphorised paper. P* 14 × 15.

1160	**636**	14p.	grey-blk, greenish yellow, brt rose-red, ultram, pale bl, blue & silver	40	35
1161		25p.	drab, greenish yellow, bright rose-red, ultramarine, grey-brown, grey-black and silver	90	95

637 "Expeditions"

638 "Skills"

639 "Service"

640 "Recreation"

(Des P. Sharland. Litho J.W.)

1981 (12 Aug). *25th Anniv of Duke of Edinburgh Award Scheme. Phosphorised paper. P* 14.

1162	**637**	14p.	greenish yellow, magenta, pale new blue, black, emerald & silver	25	25
1163	**638**	18p.	greenish yellow, magenta, pale new blue, black, cobalt and gold	45	50
1164	**639**	22p.	greenish yellow, magenta, pale new blue, black, red-orge & gold	55	50
1165	**640**	25p.	bright orange, mauve, pale new blue, black, flesh and bronze ..	65	70

641 Cockle-dredging

642 Hauling in Trawl Net

643 Lobster Potting

644 Hoisting Seine Net

(Des B. Sanders)

1981 (23 Sept). *Fishing Industry. Phosphorised paper. P* 15 × 14.

1166	**641**	14p.	slate, greenish yellow, magenta, new blue, orange-brown, olive-grey and bronze-green	30	25
1167	**642**	18p.	slate, greenish yellow, brt crimson, ultramarine, blk & greenish slate	45	45
1168	**643**	22p.	grey, greenish yellow, bright rose, dull ultram, reddish lilac & black	55	55
1169	**644**	25p.	grey, greenish yellow, bright rose, cobalt and black	60	65

Nos. 1166/9 were issued on the occasion of the centenary of the Royal National Mission to Deep Sea Fishermen.

645 Father Christmas

646 Jesus Christ

647 Flying Angel

648 Joseph and Mary arriving at Bethlehem

NEW INFORMATION

The editor is always interested to correspond with people who have new information that will improve or correct the Catalogue.

649 Three Kings approaching Bethlehem

(Des Samantha Brown (11½p.), Tracy Jenkins (14p.), Lucinda Blackmore (18p.), Stephen Moore (22p.), Sophie Sharp (25p.))

1981 (18 Nov). *Christmas. Children's Pictures. One phosphor band* (11½p.) *or phosphorised paper* (*others*). *P* 15 × 14.

1170	**645**	11½p.	ultramarine, black, red, olive-bistre, bright green and gold ..	25	20
1171	**646**	14p.	bistre-yellow, brt magenta, blue, greenish blue, brt grn, blk & gold	35	25
1172	**647**	18p.	pale blue-green, bistre-yellow, brt magenta, ultramarine, blk & gold	45	45
1173	**648**	22p.	deep turquoise-blue, lemon, magenta, black and gold	55	55
1174	**649**	25p.	royal blue, lemon, bright magenta, black and gold	55	55

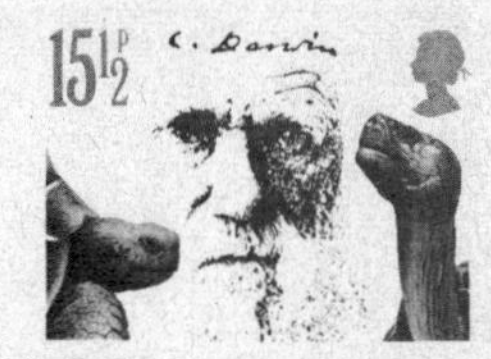

650 Charles Darwin and Giant Tortoises

651 Darwin and Marine Iguanas

652 Darwin, Cactus Ground Finch and Large Ground Finch

653 Darwin and Prehistoric Skulls

(Des D. Gentleman)

1982 (10 Feb). *Death Centenary of Charles Darwin. Phosphorised paper. P* 15 × 14.

1175	**650**	15½p.	dull purple, drab, bistre, black and grey-black	35	30
1176	**651**	19½p.	violet-grey, bistre-yellow, slate-black, red-brown, grey-blk & blk	50	50
1177	**652**	26p.	sage green, bistre-yellow, orange, chalky bl, grey-blk, red-brn & blk	65	65
1178	**653**	29p.	grey-brown, yellow-brn, brown-ochre, black and grey-black ..	70	70

654 Boys' Brigade

655 Girls' Brigade

656 Boy Scout Movement

657 Girl Guide Movement

(Des B. Sanders)

1982 (24 Mar). *Youth Organizations. Phosphorised paper. P* 15 × 14.

1179	**654**	15½p.	gold, greenish yellow, pale orange, mauve, dull blue and grey-black	35	30
1180	**655**	19½p.	gold, greenish yellow, pale orange, bright rose, deep ultramarine, olive-bistre and grey-black ..	50	50
1181	**656**	26p.	gold, greenish yellow, olive-sepia, rosine, deep blue, deep dull green and grey-black	65	65
1182	**657**	29p.	gold, yellow, dull orange, cerise, dull ultram, chestnut & grey-blk	70	70

Nos. 1179/82 were issued on the occasion of the 75th anniversary of the Boy Scout Movement; the 125th birth anniversary of Lord Baden-Powell and the centenary of the Boys' Brigade (1983).

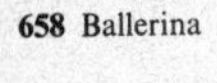
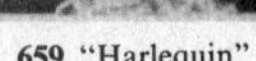

658 Ballerina

659 "Harlequin"

660 "Hamlet"

661 Opera Singer

(Des A. George)

1982 (28 Apr). *Europa. British Theatre. Phosphorised paper. P* 15 × 14.

1183	**658**	15½p.	carm-lake, greenish bl, greenish yell, grey-blk, bottle grn & silver	35	30
1184	**659**	19½p.	rosine, new blue, greenish yellow, black, ultramarine and silver ..	50	50
1185	**660**	26p.	carmine-red, bright rose-red, greenish yellow, black, dull ultramarine, lake-brown and silver ..	65	65
1186	**661**	29p.	rose-red, greenish yellow, bright blue, grey-black and silver ..	70	70

662 Henry VIII and *Mary Rose*

663 Admiral Blake and *Triumph*

664 Lord Nelson and H.M.S. *Victory*

665 Lord Fisher and H.M.S. *Dreadnought*

666 Viscount Cunningham and H.M.S *Warspite*

(Des Marjorie Saynor. Eng C. Slania. Recess and photo)

1982 (16 June). *Maritime Heritage. Phosphorised paper. P* 15 × 14.

1187	**662**	15½p.	black, lemon, bright rose, pale orange, ultramarine and grey ..	40	30
1188	**663**	19½p.	black, greenish yellow, bright rose-red, pale orange, ultram and grey	55	55
1189	**664**	24p.	black, orange-yellow, bright rose-red, lake-brown, dp ultram & grey	60	60
1190	**665**	26p.	black, orange-yellow, bright rose, lemon, ultramarine and grey ..	65	65
		a.	Imperf (pair)		
1191	**666**	29p.	black, olive-yellow, bright rose, orange-yellow, ultram & grey ..	80	80

Nos. 1187/91 were issued on the occasion of Maritime England Year, the Bicentenary of the Livery Grant by City of London to Worshipful Company of Shipwrights and the raising of *Mary Rose* from Portsmouth Harbour.

667 "Strawberry Thief" (William Morris)

668 Untitled (Steiner and Co)

669 "Cherry Orchard" (Paul Nash)

670 "Chevron" (Andrew Foster)

(Des Peter Hatch Partnership)

1982 (23 July). *British Textiles. Phosphorised paper. P* 14 × 15.

1192	**667**	15½p.	blue, olive-yellow, rosine, deep blue-green, bistre & Prussian blue	35	30
1193	**668**	19½p.	olive-grey, greenish yellow, bright magenta, dull grn, yell-brn & blk	45	50
1194	**669**	26p.	bright scarlet, dull mauve, dull ultramarine and bright carmine	60	60
1195	**670**	29p.	bronze-green, orange-yellow, turq-green, stone, chestnut & sage-grn	65	65

Nos. 1192/5 were issued on the occasion of the 250th birth anniversary of Sir Richard Arkwright (inventor of spinning machine).

671 Development of Communications

672 Modern Technological Aids

(Des Delaney and Ireland)

1982 (8 Sept). *Information Technology. Phosphorised paper. P* 14 × 15.

1196	**671**	15½p.	black, greenish yellow, bright rose-red, bistre-brn, new bl & lt ochre	50	35
		a.	Imperf (pair)	£200	
1197	**672**	26p.	black, greenish yellow, bright rose-red, ol-bistre, new bl & lt ol-grey	50	65
		a.	Imperf (pair)		

673 Austin "Seven" and "Metro"

674 Ford "Model T" and "Escort"

675 Jaguar "SS 1" and "XJ6"

676 Rolls-Royce "Silver Ghost" and "Silver Spirit"

(Des S. Paine. Litho Questa)

1982 (13 Oct). *British Motor Cars. Phosphorised paper. P* 14½ × 14.

1198	**673**	15½p.	slate, orange-vermilion, bright orange, drab, yellow-green, olive-yellow, bluish grey and black ..	40	30
1199	**674**	19½p.	slate, brt orange, olive-grey, rose-red, dull vermilion, grey & black	55	50
1200	**675**	26p.	slate, red-brown, bright orange, turquoise-green, myrtle-green, dull blue-green, grey and olive ..	70	65
1201	**676**	29p.	slate, bright orange, carmine-red, reddish purple, grey and black ..	75	70

677 "While Shepherds Watched"

678 "The Holly and the Ivy"

679 "I Saw Three Ships"

680 "We Three Kings"

681 "Good King Wenceslas"

(Des Barbara Brown)

1982 (17 Nov). *Christmas. Carols. One phosphor band* (12½*p.*) *or phosphorised paper* (*others*). *P* 15 × 14.

1202	**677**	12½p.	black, greenish yellow, bright scarlet, steel blue, red-brown and gold	30	25
1203	**678**	15½p.	black, bistre-yellow, bright rose-red, bright blue, brt green & gold	35	30
1204	**679**	19½p.	black, bistre-yellow, bright rose-red, dull blue, deep brown & gold	50	45
1205	**680**	26p.	black, bistre-yellow, brt magenta, brt blue, choc, gold & orange-red	75	70
1206	**681**	29p.	black, bistre-yellow, magenta, brt blue, chestnut, gold & brt mag ..	85	80

682 Salmon

683 Pike

684 Trout

685 Perch

(Des A. Jardine)

1983 (26 Jan). *British River Fishes. Phosphorised paper. P* 15 × 14.

1207	**682**	15½p.	grey-black, bistre-yellow, bright purple, new blue and silver ..	35	30
1208	**683**	19½p.	black, bistre-yellow, olive-bistre, dp claret, silver & dp bluish green	50	45
1209	**684**	26p.	grey-black, bistre-yellow, chrome-yellow, magenta, silver & pale bl	70	60
1210	**685**	29p.	black, greenish yellow, bright carmine, new blue and silver ..	75	65

686 Tropical Island

687 Desert

688 Temperate Farmland

689 Mountain Range

(Des D. Fraser)

1983 (9 Mar). *Commonwealth Day. Geographical Regions. Phosphorised paper. P* 14 × 15.

1211	**686**	15½p.	greenish blue, greenish yellow, bright rose, light brown, grey-black, deep claret and silver ..	35	30
1212	**687**	19½p.	brt lilac, greenish yell, mag, dull blue, grey-blk, dp dull-bl & silver	50	45
1213	**688**	26p.	lt blue, greenish yellow, brt mag, new blue, grey-blk, vio & silver	70	60
1214	**689**	29p.	dull vio-bl, reddish vio, slate-lilac, new blue, myrtle-grn, blk & silver	75	65

690 Humber Bridge

691 Thames Flood Barrier

692 *Iolair* (oilfield emergency support vessel)

(Des. M. Taylor)

1983 (25 May). *Europa. Engineering Achievements. Phosphorised paper. P* 15 × 14.

1215	**690**	16p.	silver, orange-yellow, ultramarine, black and grey	50	45
1216	**691**	20½p.	silver, greenish yellow, bright purple, blue, grey-black and grey ..	60	60
1217	**692**	28p.	silver, lemon, brt rose-red, chestnut, dull ultramarine, blk & grey	80	80

693 Musketeer and Pikeman, The Royal Scots (1633)

694 Fusilier and Ensign, The Royal Welch Fusiliers (mid-18th century)

695 Riflemen, 95th Rifles (The Royal Green Jackets) (1805)

696 Sergeant (khaki service uniform) and Guardsman (full dress), The Irish Guards (1900)

697 Paratroopers, The Parachute Regiment (1983)

(Des E. Stemp)

1983 (6 July). *British Army Uniforms. Phosphorised paper. P* 14 × 15.

1218	**693**	16p.	black, buff, deep brown, slate-black, rose-red, gold and new blue	40	35
1219	**694**	20½p.	black, buff, greenish yellow, slate-black, brown-rose, gold & brt bl	50	50
1220	**695**	26p.	black, buff, slate-purple, green, bistre and gold	65	65
1221	**696**	28p.	black, buff, light brown, grey, dull rose, gold and new blue ..	80	80
1222	**697**	31p.	black, buff, olive-yellow, grey, deep magenta, gold and new blue	90	90

Nos. 1218/22 were issued on the occasion of the 350th anniversary of the Royal Scots, the senior line regiment of the British Army.

698 20th-century Garden, Sissinghurst

699 19th-century Garden, Biddulph Grange

700 18th-century Garden, Blenheim

701 17th-century Garden, Pitmedden

(Des Liz Butler, Litho J.W.)

1983 (24 Aug). *British Gardens. Phosphorised paper. P* 14.

1223	**698**	16p.	greenish yellow, brt purple, new blue, black, bright green & silver	35	30
1224	**699**	20½p.	greenish yellow, brt purple, new blue, black, bright green & silver	45	45
1225	**700**	28p.	greenish yellow, brt purple, new blue, black, bright green & silver	65	60
1226	**701**	31p.	greenish yellow, brt purple, new blue, black, bright green & silver	75	70

Nos. 1223/6 were issued on the occasion of the death bicentenary of "Capability" Brown (landscape gardener)

702 Merry-go-round

703 Big Wheel, Helter-Skelter and Performing Animals

704 Side Shows

705 Early Produce Fair

(Des A. Restall)

1983 (5 Oct). *British Fairs. Phosphorised paper. P* 15 × 14.

1227	**702**	16p.	grey-black, greenish yellow, orge-red, ochre & turquoise-blue ..	35	30
1228	**703**	20½p.	grey-black, yellow-ochre, yellow-orange, brt magenta, violet & blk	45	45
1229	**704**	28p.	grey-black, bistre-yellow, orange-red, violet and yellow-brown ..	65	60
1230	**705**	31p.	grey-black, greenish yellow, red, dp turq-green, slate-violet & brn	75	70

706 "Christmas Post" (pillar-box)

707 "The Three Kings" (chimney-pots)

708 "World at Peace" (Dove and Blackbird)

709 "Light of Christmas" (street lamp)

710 "Christmas Dove" (hedge sculpture)

(Des T. Meeuwissen)

1983 (16 Nov). *Christmas. One phosphor band* (12½*p.*) *or phosphorised paper* (*others*). *P* 15 × 14.

No.	Type	Value	Description	Unused	Used
1231	**706**	12½p.	black, greenish yellow, bright rose-red, bright blue, gold and grey-black	30	30
		a.	Imperf (horiz pair)	£500	
1232	**707**	16p.	black, greenish yellow, bright rose, pale new blue, gold & brown-pur	40	40
1233	**708**	20½p.	black, greenish yellow, bright rose, new blue, gold and blue	55	55
1234	**709**	28p.	black, lemon, bright carmine, bluish violet, gold, deep turquoise-green and purple	70	70
1235	**710**	31p.	black, greenish yellow, brt rose, new blue, gold, green & brn-olive	80	80

711 Arms of the College of Arms

712 Arms of King Richard III (founder)

713 Arms of the Earl Marshal of England

714 Arms of the City of London

(Des J. Matthews)

1984 (17 Jan). *500th Anniv of College of Arms. Phosphorised paper. P* 14½.

No.	Type	Value	Description	Unused	Used
1236	**711**	16p.	black, chrome-yellow, reddish brown, scarlet-vermilion, bright blue and grey-black	40	35
1237	**712**	20½p.	black, chrome-yellow, rosine, bright blue and grey-black ..	60	55
1238	**713**	28p.	black, chrome-yellow, rosine, brt blue, dull green and grey-black ..	75	75
1239	**714**	31p.	black, chrome-yellow, rosine, bright blue and grey-black ..	80	80

715 Highland Cow

716 Chillingham Wild Bull

717 Hereford Bull

718 Welsh Black Bull

719 Irish Moiled Cow

(Des B. Driscoll)

1984 (6 Mar). *British Cattle. Phosphorised paper. P* 15 × 14.

No.	Type	Value	Description	Unused	Used
1240	**715**	16p.	grey-black, bistre-yellow, rosine, yellow-orge, new bl & pale drab	35	40
1241	**716**	20½p.	grey-black, greenish yellow, magenta, bistre, dull blue-green, pale drab and light green	45	50
1242	**717**	26p.	black, chrome-yellow, rosine, red-dish brown, new blue & pale drab	60	65
1243	**718**	28p.	black, greenish yellow, bright carmine, orange-brown, deep dull blue and pale drab	65	70
1244	**719**	31p.	grey-black, bistre-yellow, rosine, red-brown, light blue & pale drab	75	80

Nos. 1240/4 were issued on the occasion of the centenary of the Highland Cattle Society and the bicentenary of the Royal Highland and Agricultural Society of Scotland.

720 Liverpool Garden Festival Hall

721 Milburngate Centre, Durham

722 Bush House, Bristol

723 Commercial Street Development, Perth

(Des R. Maddox and Trickett and Webb Ltd)

1984 (10 Apr). *Urban Renewal. Phosphorised paper. P* 15 × 14.

No.	Type	Value	Description	Unused	Used
1245	**720**	16p.	bright emerald, greenish yellow, cerise, steel-bl, blk, silver & flesh	35	35
1246	**721**	20½p.	bright orange, greenish yellow, deep dull blue, yellowish green, azure, black and silver	50	55
		a.	Imperf (horiz pair)	£1000	
1247	**722**	28p.	rosine, greenish yellow, Prussian blue, pale blue-green, blk & silver	65	70
1248	**723**	31p.	blue, greenish yellow, cerise, grey-blue, bright green, black and silver	70	75

Nos. 1245/8 were issued on the occasion of 150th anniversaries of the Royal Institute of British Architects and the Chartered Institute of Building, and to commemorate the first International Gardens Festival, Liverpool.

ROYAL MAIL POSTAGE LABELS

These imperforate labels, printed in red on phosphorised paper with grey-green background design, were issued on 1 May 1984 as an experiment by the Post Office. Special microprocessor controlled machines were installed at post offices in Cambridge, London, Shirley, (Southampton) and Windsor to provide an after-hours sales service to the public. The machines printed and dispensed the labels according to the coins inserted and the buttons operated by the customer. Values were initially available in ½p steps to 16p and in addition, the labels were sold at philatelic counters in two packs containing either 3 values (3½, 12½, 16p) or 32 values (½p to 16p).

From 28 August 1984 the machines were adjusted to provide values up to 17p. After 31 December 1984 labels including ½p values were withdrawn. The machines were withdrawn from service on 30 April 1985.

724 C.E.P.T. 25th Anniversary Logo

725 Abduction of Europa

(Des J. Larrivière (T **724**), F. Wegner (T **725**))

1984 (15 May). *25th Anniv of C.E.P.T.* (*"Europa"*) (*T* **724**) *and Second Elections to European Parliament* (*T* **725**). *Phosphorised paper. P* 15 × 14.

No.	Type	Value	Description	Unused	Used
1249	**724**	16p.	greenish slate, deep blue and gold ..	35	35
		a.	Horiz pair. Nos. 1249/50	75	80
1250	**725**	16p.	greenish slate, deep blue, black and gold	35	35
1251	**724**	20½p.	Venetian red, deep magenta and gold	50	60
		a.	Horiz pair. Nos. 1251/2	1·00	1·20
1252	**725**	20½p.	Venetian, deep magenta, black and gold	50	60

Nos. 1249/50 and 1251/2 were each printed together, *se-tenant*, in horizontal pairs throughout the sheets.

726 Lancaster House

(Des P. Hogarth)

1984 (5 June). *London Economic Summit Conference. Phosphorised paper. P* 14 × 15.

1253 **726** 31p. silver, bistre-yellow, brown-ochre, black, rosine, bright blue and reddish lilac 65 70

727 View of Earth from "Apollo 11"

728 Navigational Chart of English Channel

729 Greenwich Observatory

730 Sir George Airy's Transit Telescope

1984 (26 June). *Centenary of the Greenwich Meridian. Phosphorised paper. P* 14 × 14½.

1254 **727** 16p. new blue, greenish yellow, magenta, black, scarlet and blue-black 35 35

1255 **728** 20½p. olive-sepia, light brown, pale buff, black and scarlet 45 45

1256 **729** 28p. new blue, greenish yellow, scarlet, black and bright purple 60 60

1257 **730** 31p. deep blue, cobalt, scarlet and black . . 65 65

On Nos. 1254/7 the Meridian is represented by a scarlet line.

731 Bath Mail Coach, 1784

732 Attack on Exeter Mail, 1816

733 Norwich Mail in Thunderstorm, 1827

734 Holyhead and Liverpool Mails leaving London, 1828

735 Edinburgh Mail Snowbound, 1831

(Des K. Bassford and S. Paine. Eng C. Slania. Recess and photo)

1984 (31 July). *Bicentenary of First Mail Coach Run Bath and Bristol to London. Phosphorised paper. P* 15 × 14.

1258 **731** 16p. pale stone, black, grey-black and bright scarlet 30 30

a. Horiz strip of 5 Nos. 1258/62 . . 1·75

1259 **732** 16p. pale stone, black, grey-black and bright scarlet 30 30

1260 **733** 16p. pale stone, black, grey-black and bright scarlet 30 30

1261 **734** 16p. pale stone, black, grey-black and bright scarlet 30 30

1262 **735** 16p. pale stone, black, grey-black and bright scarlet 30 30

Nos. 1258/62 were printed together, *se-tenant*, in horizontal strips of 5 throughout the sheet.

736 Nigerian Clinic

737 Violinist and Acropolis, Athens

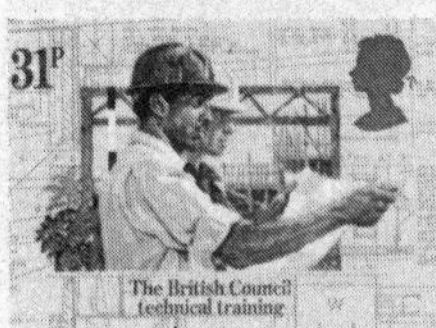

738 Building Project, Sri Lanka

739 British Council Library, Middle East

(Des F. Newell and J. Sorrell)

1984 (25 Sept). *50th Anniv of the British Council. Phosphorised paper. P* 15 × 14.

1263 **736** 17p. grey-green, greenish yellow, bright purple, dull blue, black, pale green and yellow-green 30 35

1264 **737** 22p. crimson, greenish yellow, bright rose-red, dull green, black, pale drab and slate-purple 35 40

1265 **738** 31p. sepia, olive-bistre, red, black, pale stone and olive-brown 50 55

1266 **739** 34p. steel blue, yellow, rose-red, new blue, black, azure and pale blue 55 60

740 The Holy Family

741 Arrival in Bethlehem

742 Shepherd and Lamb

743 Virgin and Child

744 Offering of Frankincense

(Des Yvonne Gilbert)

1984 (20 Nov). *Christmas. One phosphor band* (13*p.*) *or phosphorised paper* (*others*). *P* 15 × 14.

1267 **740** 13p. pale cream, grey-black, bistre-yellow, magenta, red-brown and lake-brown 20 25

1268 **741** 17p. pale cream, grey-black, yellow, magenta, dull blue and deep dull blue 30 35

1269 **742** 22p. pale cream, grey-black, olive-yellow, bright magenta, bright blue and brownish grey 35 40

1270 **743** 31p. pale cream, grey-black, bistre-yellow, magenta, dull blue and light brown 50 55

1271 **744** 34p. pale cream, olive-grey, bistre-yellow, magenta, turquoise-green and brown-olive 55 60

745 "The Flying Scotsman"

746 "The Golden Arrow"

747 "The Cheltenham Flyer"

748 "The Royal Scot"

749 "The Cornish Riviera"

(Des T. Cuneo)

1985 (22 Jan). *Famous Trains. Phosphorised paper. P* 15 × 14.
1272 **745** 17p. black, lemon, magenta, dull blue, grey-black and gold 30 35
1273 **746** 22p. black, greenish yellow, bright rose, deep dull blue, grey-black and gold .. 35 40
1274 **747** 29p. black, greenish yellow, magenta, blue, grey-black and gold 45 50
1275 **748** 31p. black, bistre-yellow, bright magenta, new blue slate-black and gold 50 55
1276 **749** 34p. black, greenish yellow, bright rose, blue, slate-black and gold 55 60

Nos. 1272/6 were issued on the occasion of the 150th anniversary of the Great Western Railway Company.

750 Buff-tailed Bumble Bee

751 Seven-spotted Ladybird

752 Wart-biter Bush-cricket

753 Stag Beetle

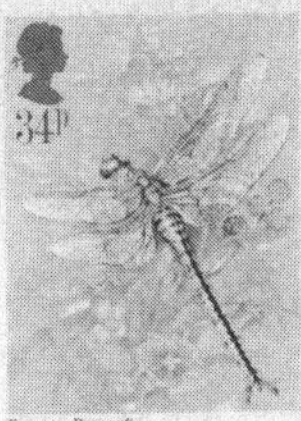

754 Emperor Dragonfly

(Des G. Beningfield)

1985 (12 Mar). *Insects. Phosphorised paper. P* 14 × 15.
1277 **750** 17p. black, greenish yellow, magenta, blue, azure, gold and slate-black 30 35
1278 **751** 22p. black, greenish yellow, bright rose-red, dull blue-green, slate-black and gold 35 40
1279 **752** 29p. black, greenish yellow, bright rose, greenish blue, grey-black, gold and bistre-yellow.. .. .. 45 50
1280 **753** 31p. black, greenish yellow, rose, pale new blue and gold 50 55
1281 **754** 34p. black, greenish yellow, magenta, greenish blue, grey-black and gold .. 55 60

Nos. 1277/81 were issued on the occasion of the centenaries of the Royal Entomological Society of London's Royal Charter, and of the Selborne Society.

755 "Water Music" (George Frideric Handel

756 "The Planets" Suite (Gustav Holst)

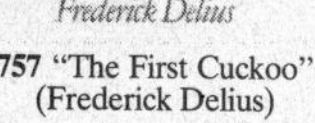

757 "The First Cuckoo" (Frederick Delius)

758 "Sea Pictures" (Edward Elgar)

(Des W. McLean)

1985 (14 May). *Europa. European Music Year. British Composers. Phosphorised paper. P* 14½.
1282 **755** 17p. black, bright yellow-green, deep magenta, new blue, grey-black and gold 30 35
1283 **756** 22p. black, greenish yellow, bright magenta, new blue, grey-black and gold 35 40
1284 **757** 31p. black, greenish yellow, magenta, greenish blue, grey-black and gold .. 50 55
1285 **758** 34p. black, olive-yellow, bistre, turquoise-blue, slate and gold 55 60

Nos. 1282/5 were issued on the occasion of the 300th birth anniversary of Handel.

759 R.N.L.I. Lifeboat and Signal Flags

760 Beachy Head Lighthouse and Chart

761 "Marecs A" Communications Satellite and Dish Aerials

762 Buoys

(Des F. Newell and J. Sorrel. Litho J.W.)

1985 (18 June). *Safety at Sea. Phosphorised paper. P* 14.
1286 **759** 17p. black, azure, emerald, ultramarine, orange-yellow, vermilion, bright blue, and chrome-yellow 30 35
1287 **760** 22p. black, azure, emerald, ultramarine, orange-yellow, vermilion, bright blue and chrome-yellow 35 40
1288 **761** 31p. black, azure, emerald, ultramarine, orange-yellow, vermillion, and bright blue 50 55
1289 **762** 34p. black, azure, emerald, ultramarine, orange-yellow, vermillion, bright blue and chrome-yellow 55 60

Nos. 1286/9 were issued on the occasion of the Bicentenary of the unimmersible lifeboat and the 50th anniversary of radar.

REGIONAL ISSUES

For Regional Issues of Guernsey, Jersey and the Isle of Man, *see* after Great Britain Postal Fiscals.

Printers (£ s. d. stamps of all regions):—Photo Harrison & Sons. Portrait by Dorothy Wilding Ltd.

DATES OF ISSUE. Conflicting dates of issue have been announced for some of the regional issues, partly explained by the stamps being released on different dates by the Philatelic Bureau in Edinburgh or the Philatelic Counter in London and in the regions. We have adopted the practice of giving the earliest known dates, since once released the stamps could have been used anywhere in the U.K.

I. NORTHERN IRELAND

N 1

N 2

N 3

(Des W. Hollywood (3d., 4d., 5d.), L. Pilton (6d., 9d.), T. Collins (1s. 3d., 1s. 6d.))

1958–67. *W* **179.** *P* 15 × 14.
NI1 **N 1** 3d. deep lilac (18.8.58) 10 5
p. One centre phosphor band (9.6.67) 5 5
NI2 4d. ultramarine (7.2.66) 10 5
p. Two phosphor bands (10.67) .. 10 5
NI3 **N 2** 6d. deep claret (29.9.58) 20 15
NI4 9d. bronze-green (2 phosphor bands) (1.3.67) 25 50
NI5 **N 3** 1s. 3d. green (29.9.58) 25 50
NI6 1s. 6d. grey-blue (2 phosphor bands) (1.3.67) 30 75

1968–69. *No wmk. Chalk-surfaced paper. One centre phosphor band (Nos.* NI8/9) *or two phosphor bands (others). P* 15 × 14.
NI 7 **N 1** 4d. deep bright blue (27.6.68) .. 10 20
NI 8 4d. olive-sepia (4.9.68) 8 8
NI 9 4d. bright vermilion (26.2.69) .. 20 15
NI10 5d. royal blue (4.9.68) 10 12
NI11 **N 3** 1s. 6d. grey-blue (20.5.69) .. .. 3·00 1·75

No. NI7 was only issued in Northern Ireland with gum arabic. After it had been withdrawn from Northern Ireland but whilst still on sale at the philatelic counters elsewhere, about fifty sheets with PVA gum were sold over the London Philatelic counter on 23 October 1968, and some were also on sale at the British Philatelic Exhibition Post Office in October, without any prior announcement. The other values exist with PVA gum only.

N 4

(Des J. Matthews after plaster cast by Arnold Machin)

1971 (7 July)–**84.** *Decimal Currency. Chalk-surfaced paper. Type* N **4.** (*a*) *Photo Harrison. With phosphor bands. P* 15 × 14.
NI12 2½p. bright magenta (1 centre band) .. 1·00 25
NI13 3p. ultramarine (2 bands) 50 25
NI14 3p. ultramarine (1 centre band) (23.1.74) 12 8
NI15 3½p. olive-grey (2 bands) (23.1.74) .. 15 15
NI16 3½p. olive-grey (1 centre band) (6.11.74) .. 15 35
NI17 4½p. grey-blue (2 bands) (6.11.74) .. 15 20
NI18 5p. reddish violet (2 bands) .. .. 1·75 1·50
NI19 5½p. violet (2 bands) (23.1.74) 25 20
NI20 5½p. violet (1 centre band) (21.5.75) .. 20 20
NI21 6½p. greenish blue (1 centre band) (14.1.76) 20 20
NI22 7p. purple-brown (1 centre band) (18.1.78) 20 15
NI23 7½p. chestnut (2 bands) .. .. .. 2·75 2·75
NI24 8p. rosine (2 bands) (23.1.74) 25 20
NI25 8½p. yellow-green (2 bands) (14.1.76) .. 25 20
NI26 9p. deep violet (2 bands) (18.1.78) .. 25 20
NI27 10p. orange-brown (2 bands) (20.10.76) .. 25 20
NI28 10p. orange-brown (1 centre band) (23.7.80) 15 20
NI29 10½p. steel-blue (2 bands) (18.1.78) .. 25 20
NI30 11p. scarlet (2 bands) (20.10.76) 25 20

(*b*) *Photo Harrison. On phosphorised paper. P* 15 × 14.
NI31 12p. yellowish green (23.7.80) 30 25
NI32 13½p. purple-brown (23.7.80) 35 35
NI33 15p. ultramarine (23.7.80) 30 30

(*c*) *Litho Questa. One side phosphor band* (11½*p*., 12½*p*, 13*p*.) *or on phosphorised paper* (*others*) *P* 15 × 14 (13*p*., 17*p*., 22*p*. (*No.* NI 45), 31*p*.) *or* 13½ × 14 (*others*)
NI34 11½p. ochre-brown (8.4.81) 30 25
NI35 12½p. light emerald (24.2.82) 25 25
a. Perf 15 × 14 (28.2.84) 20 15
NI36 13p. pale chestnut (23.10.84) 20 15
NI37 14p. grey-blue (8.4.81) 35 30
NI38 15½p. pale violet (24.2.82) 25 15
NI39 16p. drab (27.4.83) 35 30
a. Perf 15 × 14 (28.2.84) 25 30
NI40 17p. grey-blue (23.10.84) 30 25
NI41 18p. deep violet (8.4.81) 35 35
NI42 19½p. olive-grey (24.2.82) 50 40
NI43 20½p. ultramarine (27.4.83) 35 40
NI44 22p. blue (8.4.81) 50 45
NI45 22p. yellow-green (23.10.84) 35 30
NI46 26p. rosine (24.2.82) 40 40
NI47 28p. deep violet-blue (27.4.83) 45 50
NI48 31p. bright purple (23.10.84) 50 55

From 1972 printings were made on the fluorescent white paper and from 1973 printings had been added to the PVA gum (*see* notes after No. X960 of Great Britain).

II. SCOTLAND

S 1

S 2

S 3

(Des G. Huntly (3d., 4d., 5d), J. Fleming (6d., 9d.), A. Imrie (1s. 3d., 1s. 6d.))

1958–67. *W* **179.** *P* 15 × 14.

No.	Type	Description	Unused	Used
S1	S 1	3d. deep lilac (18.8.58)	8	5
		p. Two phosphor bands (29.1.63)	6·50	1·00
		pa. One side phosphor band (30.4.65)	10	30
		pb. One centre phosphor band (9.11.67)	10	15
S2		4d. ultramarine (7.2.66)	10	10
		p. Two phosphor bands	10	15
S3	S 2	6d. deep claret (29.9.58)	10	10
		p. Two phosphor bands (29.1.63)	15	40
S4		9d. bronze-green (2 phosphor bands) (1.3.67)	25	50
S5	S 3	1s. 3d. green (29.9.58)	25	40
		p. Two phosphor bands (29.1.63)	25	90
S6		1s. 6d. grey-blue (2 phosphor bands) (1.3.67)	35	60

The one phosphor band on No. S1pa was produced by printing broad phosphor bands across alternate vertical perforations. Individual stamps show the band at right or left (same prices either way).

1967–70. *No wmk. Chalk-surfaced paper. One centre phosphor band* (S7, S9/10) *or two phosphor bands* (*others*). *P* 15 × 14.

No.	Type	Description	Unused	Used
S 7	S 1	3d. deep lilac (16.5.68)	8	10
S 8		4d. deep bright blue (28.11.67)	8	10
S 9		4d. olive-sepia (4.9.68)	8	5
S10		4d. bright vermilion (26.2.69)	30	12
S11		5d. royal blue (4.9.68)	20	12
S12	S 2	9d. bronze-green (28.9.70)	7·00	7·50
S13	S 3	1s. 6d. grey-blue (12.12.68)	1·10	1·25

Nos. S7/8 exist with both gum arabic and PVA gum; others with PVA gum only.

S 4

(Des J. Matthews after plaster cast by Arnold Machin)

1971 (7 July)–**84.** *Decimal Currency. Chalk-surfaced paper. Type S* **4.**

(*a*) *Photo Harrison. With phosphor bands. P* 15 × 14

No.	Description	Unused	Used
S14	2½p. bright magenta (1 centre band)	35	35
S15	3p. ultramarine (2 bands)*	40	30
	Ega. Imperf (pair)	£170	
S16	3p. ultramarine (1 centre band) (23.1.74)	15	15
S17	3½p. olive-grey (2 bands) (23.1.74)	15	15
S18	3½p. olive-grey (1 centre band) (6.11.74)	15	15
S19	4½p. grey-blue (2 bands) (6.11.74)	15	20
S20	5p. reddish violet (2 bands)	1·75	1·25
S21	5½p. violet (2 bands) (23.1.74)	25	20
S22	5½p. violet (1 centre band) (21.5.75)	20	20
	a. Imperf (pair)	£225	
S23	6½p. greenish blue (1 centre band) (14.1.76)	20	15
S24	7p. purple-brown (1 centre band) (18.1.78)	20	15
S25	7½p. chestnut (2 bands)	2·50	2·75
S26	8p. rosine (2 bands) (23.1.74)	25	60
S27	8½p. yellow-green (2 bands) (14.1.76)	25	15
S28	9p. deep violet (2 bands) (18.1.78)	25	15
S29	10p. orange-brown (2 bands) (20.10.76)	25	20
S30	10p. orange-brown (1 centre band) (23.7.80)	15	25
S31	10½p. steel-blue (2 bands) (18.1.78)	25	20
S32	11p. scarlet (2 bands) (20.10.76)	25	20

(*b*) *Photo Harrison. On phosphorised paper. P* 15 × 14

No.	Description	Unused	Used
S33	12p. yellowish green (23.7.80)	25	25
S34	13½p. purple-brown (23.7.80)	35	35
S35	15p. ultramarine (23.7.80)	35	35

(*c*) *Litho J.W. One side phosphor band* (11½*p.*, 12½*p.*, 13*p.*) *or on phosphorised paper* (*others*). *P* 13½ × 14.

No.	Description	Unused	Used
S36	11½p. ochre-brown (8.4.81)	30	20
S37	12½p. light emerald (24.2.82)	20	20
S38	13p. pale chestnut (23.10.84)	20	15
S39	14p. grey-blue (8.4.81)	30	25
S40	15½p. pale violet (24.2.82)	25	15
S41	16p. drab (27.4.83)	25	30
S42	17p. grey-blue (23.10.84)	30	25
S43	18p. deep violet (8.4.81)	40	40
S44	19½p. olive-grey (24.2.82)	50	40
S45	20½p. ultramarine (27.4.83)	35	40
S46	22p. blue (8.4.81)	50	45
S47	22p. yellow-green (23.10.84)	35	30
S48	26p. rosine (24.2.82)	40	40
S49	28p. deep violet-blue (27.4.83)	45	50
S50	31p. bright purple (23.10.84)	50	55

†Exists only with gum arabic.

From 1972 printings were on fluorescent white paper. Nos. S14/15 exist with PVA and gum arabic and the remainder with PVA only. From 1973 printings had dextrin added (*see* notes after No. X960 of Great Britain).

III. WALES

From the inception of the Regional stamps, the Welsh versions were tendered to members of the public at all Post Offices within the former County of Monmouthshire but the English alternatives were available on request. Offices with a Monmouthshire postal address but situated outside the County, namely Beachley, Brockweir, Redbrook, Sedbury, Tutshill, Welsh Newton and Woodcroft, were not supplied with the Welsh Regional stamps.

With the re-formation of Counties, Monmouthshire became known as Gwent and was also declared to be part of Wales. From 1 July 1974, therefore, except for the offices mentioned above, only Welsh Regional stamps were available at the offices under the jurisdiction of Newport, Gwent.

W 1

W 2

W 3

(Des R. Stone)

1958–67. *W* **179.** *P* 15 × 14.

No.	Type	Description	Unused	Used
W1	W 1	3d. deep lilac (18.8.58)	8	5
		p. One centre phosphor band (16.5.67)	5	10
W2		4d. ultramarine (7.2.66)	10	5
		p. Two phosphor bands (10.67)	5	5
W3	W 2	6d. deep claret (29.9.58)	25	25
W4		9d. bronze-green (2 phosphor bands) (1.3.67)	25	45
W5	W 3	1s. 3d. green (29.9.58)	25	65
W6		1s. 6d. grey-blue (2 phosphor bands) (1.3.67)	35	40

1967–69. *No wmk. Chalk-surfaced paper. One centre phosphor band* (W7, W9/10) *or two phosphor bands* (*others*). *P* 15 × 14.

No.	Type	Description	Unused	Used
W 7	W 1	3d. deep lilac (6.12.67)	5	8
W 8		4d. deep bright blue (21.6.68)	8	10
W 9		4d. olive-sepia (4.9.68)	5	5
W10		4d. bright vermilion (26.2.69)	25	15
W11		5d. royal blue (4.9.68)	20	12
W12	W 3	1s. 6d. grey-blue (1.8.69)	4·00	2·75

The 3d. exists with gum arabic only; the remainder with PVA gum only.

W 4

(Des J. Matthews after plaster cast by Arnold Machin)

1971 (7 July)–**84.** *Decimal Currency. Chalk-surfaced paper. Type W* **4.** (*a*) *Photo Harrison. With phosphor bands. P* 15 × 14.

No.	Description	Unused	Used
W13	2½p. bright magenta (1 centre band)	15	20
	a. Imperf (pair)†	£250	
W14	3p. ultramarine (2 bands)	25	15
W15	3p. ultramarine (1 centre band) (23.1.74)	12	15
W16	3½p. olive-grey (2 bands) (23.1.74)	20	25
W17	3½p. olive-grey (1 centre band) (6.11.74)	20	25
W18	4½p. grey-blue (2 bands) (6.11.74)	20	25
W19	5p. reddish violet (2 bands)	1·75	90
W20	5½p. violet (2 bands) (23.1.74)	25	25
W21	5½p. violet (1 centre band) (21.5.75)	25	25
	a. Imperf (pair)		
W22	6½p. greenish blue (1 centre band) (14.1.76)	20	15
W23	7p. purple-brown (1 centre band) (18.1.78)	20	15
W24	7½p. chestnut (2 bands)	2·50	2·75
W25	8p. rosine (2 bands) (23.1.74)	25	20
W26	8½p. yellow-green (2 bands) (14.1.76)	25	15
W27	9p. deep violet (2 bands) (18.1.78)	25	15
W28	10p. orange-brown (2 bands) (20.10.76)	25	20
W29	10p. orange-brown (1 centre band) (23.7.80)	15	20
W30	10½p. steel-blue (2 bands) (18.1.78)	25	20
W31	11p. scarlet (2 bands) (20.10.76)	25	20

(*b*) *Photo Harrison. On phosphorised paper. P* 15 × 14

No.	Description	Unused	Used
W32	12p. yellowish green (23.7.80)	30	25
W33	13½p. purple-brown (23.7.80)	35	35
W34	15p. ultramarine (23.7.80)	35	30

(*c*) *Litho Questa. One side phosphor band* (11½*p.*, 12½*p*, 13*p.*) *or on phosphorised paper* (*others*). *P* 15 × 14 (13*p.*, 17*p.* 22*p.* (*No.* W46), 31*p.*) *or* 13½ × 14 (*others*)

No.	Description	Unused	Used
W35	11½p. ochre-brown (8.4.81)	30	25
W36	12½p. pale violet (24.2.82)	25	25
	a. Perf 15 + 14 (10.1.84)	20	15
W37	13p. pale chestnut (23.10.84)	20	15
W38	14p. grey-blue (8.4.81)	35	30
W39	15½p. pale violet (24.2.82)	35	30
W40	16p. drab (27.4.83)	35	30
	a. Perf 15 × 14 (10.1.84)	25	30
W41	17p. grey-blue (23.10.84)	30	25
W42	18p. deep violet (8.4.81)	35	35
W43	19½p. olive-grey (24.2.82)	50	40
W44	20½p. ultramarine (27.4.83)	35	40
W45	22p. blue (8.4.81)	50	45
W46	22p. yellow-green (23.10.84)	35	30
W47	26p. rosine (24.2.82)	40	40
W48	28p. deep violet-blue (27.8.83)	45	50
W49	31p. bright purple (23.10.84)	50	55

*Exists only with gum arabic.

From 1972 printings were on fluorescent white paper. Nos. W13/14 exist with PVA and gum arabic and the remainder with PVA only. From 1973 printings had dextrin added (*see* notes after No. X960 of Great Britain).

POSTAGE DUE STAMPS

PERFORATIONS. All postage due stamps are perf 14 × 15.

D 1

D 2

(Typo by Somerset House (early trial printings of ½d., 1d., 2d. and 5d.; all printings of 1s.) and by Harrison (later printings of all values except 1s.). Not easily distinguishable except by the control)

1914 (20 Apr)–**23.** *W* **100** (*Simple Cypher*) *sideways.*

No.	Type	Description	Unused	Used
D1	D 1	½d. emerald	30	30
D2		1d. carmine	30	20
		a. Pale carmine	1·00	10
D3		1½d. chestnut (1923)	28·00	12·00
D4		2d. agate	50	30
D5		3d. violet (1918)	2·00	1·25
		a. Bluish violet	2·25	2·50
D6		4d. dull grey-green (1921)	5·50	1·00
D7		5d. brownish cinnamon	2·50	75
D8		1s. bright blue (1915)	20·00	2·50
		a. Deep bright blue	20·00	2·50

The 1d. is known bisected and used to make up a 1½d. rate on understamped letters from Ceylon (1921) and the 2d. bisected and used as 1d. at West Kensington and at Streatham both in the same year.

1924. *As* 1914–23, *but on thick chalk-surfaced paper.*

No.	Type	Description	Unused	Used
D9	D 1	1d. carmine	3·25	3·25

(Typo Waterlow and (from 1934) Harrison)

1924–31. *W* **111** (*Block Cypher*) *sideways.*

No.	Type	Description	Unused	Used
D10	D 1	½d. emerald (6.25)	25	30
D11		1d. carmine (4.25)	50	20
D12		1½d. chestnut (10.24)	24·00	12·00
D13		2d. agate (7.24)	1·10	30
D14		3d. dull violet (10.24)	2·00	30
		a. Printed on gummed side	55·00	†
		b. Experimental paper W **111***a*	35·00	30·00
D15		4d. dull grey-green (10.24)	10·00	1·40
D16		5d. brownish cinnamon (1.31)	20·00	20·00
D17		1s. deep blue (9.24)	2·50	60
D18	D 2	2s. 6d. purple/*yellow* (10.24)	30·00	1·50

1936–37. *W* **125** (E 8 R) *sideways.*

No.	Type	Description	Unused	Used
D19	D 1	½d. emerald (6.37)	4·00	7·50
D20		1d. carmine (5.37)	1·00	1·25
D21		2d. agate (5.37)	4·00	2·50
D22		3d. dull violet (3.37)	1·50	1·50
D23		4d. dull grey-green (12.36)	8·00	15·00
D24		5d. brownish cinnamon (11.36)	25·00	15·00
		a. Yellow-brown (1937)	8·00	20·00
D25		1s. deep blue (12.36)	6·00	7·00
D26	D 2	2s. 6d. purple/*yellow* (5.37)	£160	12·00

The 1d. is known bisected (Solihull, 3 July 1937).

1937–38. *W* **127** (G VI R) *sideways.*

No.	Type	Description	Unused	Used
D27	D 1	½d. emerald (1938)	6·00	3·75
D28		1d. carmine (1938)	1·50	30
D29		2d. agate (1938)	1·40	30
D30		3d. violet (1938)	7·50	30
D31		4d. dull grey-green (1937)	30·00	7·00
D32		5d. yellow-brown (1938)	5·50	1·00
D33		1s. deep blue (1937)	20·00	60
D34	D 2	2s. 6d. purple/*yellow* (1938)	50·00	1·75

The 2d. is known bisected in June 1951 (Harpenden and St. Albans) and on 30 October 1954 (Harpenden).

DATES OF ISSUE. The dates for Nos. D35/68 are those on which stamps were first issued by the Supplies Department to postmasters.

1951–52. *Colours changed and new value* (1½*d.*). *W* **127** (G VI R) *sideways.*

No.	Type	Description	Unused	Used
D35	D 1	½d. orange (18.9.51)	1·75	6·00
D36		1d. violet-blue (6.6.51)	1·00	60
D37		1½d. green (11.2.52)	1·75	2·00
D38		4d. blue (14.8.51)	9·00	9·00
D39		1s. ochre (6.12.51)	18·00	3·25

The 1d. is known bisected (Dorking, 1952, and Camberley, 6 April 1954).

1954–55. *W* **153** (*Mult Tudor Crown and* E 2 R) *sideways.*

No.	Type	Description	Unused	Used
D40	D 1	½d. orange (8.6.55)	2·00	7·00
D41		2d. agate (28.7.55)	1·40	5·00
D42		3d. violet (4.5.55)	40·00	25·00
D43		4d. blue (14.7.55)	14·00	25·00
		a. Imperf (pair)	£170	
D44		5d. yellow-brown (19.5.55)	15·00	7·00
D45	D 2	2s. 6d. purple/*yellow* (11.54)	£100	4·50

1955–57. *W* **165** (*Mult St. Edward's Crown and* E 2 R) *sideways.*

No.	Type	Description	Unused	Used
D46	D 1	½d. orange (16.7.56)	1·75	6·00
D47		1d. violet-blue (7.6.56)	3·75	90
D48		1½d. green (13.2.56)	3·00	6·00
D49		2d. agate (22.5.56)	28·00	2·50
D50		3d. violet (5.3.56)	5·50	1·25
D51		4d. blue (24.4.56)	22·00	5·00
D52		5d. brown-ochre (23.3.56)	26·00	2·00
D53		1s. ochre (22.11.55)	45·00	1·50
D54	D 2	2s. 6d. purple/*yellow* (28.6.57)	£150	8·00
D55		5s. scarlet/*yellow* (25.11.55)	60·00	25·00

The 2d. is known bisected (June 1956), and also the 4d. (Poplar, London, April 1959).

1959–63. *W* **179** (*Mult St Edward's Crown*) *sideways.*

No.	Type	Description	Unused	Used
D56	D 1	½d. orange (18.10.61)	10	75
D57		1d. violet-blue (9.5.60)	10	15
D58		1½d. green (5.10.60)	80	2·75
D59		2d. agate (14.9.59)	1·25	25
D60		3d. violet (24.3.59)	40	10
D61		4d. blue (17.12.59)	40	35
D62		5d. yellow-brown (6.11.61)	40	60
D63		6d. purple (29.3.62)	70	12
D64		1s. ochre (11.4.60)	1·60	20

No.	Type	Description	Un	Used
D65	D 2	2s. 6d. purple/*yellow* (11.5.61)	1·25	40
D66		5s. scarlet/*yellow* (8.5.61)	3·00	60
D67		10s. blue/*yellow* (2.9.63)	9·50	3·50
D68		£1 black/*yellow* (2.9.63)	45·00	3·50

Whiter paper. The note after No. 586 also applies to Postage Due stamps.

The 1d. is known bisected (Newbury, Dec. 1962).

1968–69. *Typo. No wmk. Chalk-surfaced paper.*

No.	Type	Description	Un	Used
D69	D 1	2d. agate (11.4.68)	40	50
D70		3d. violet (9.9.68)	20	70
D71		4d. blue (6.5.68)	30	40
D72		5d. orange-brown (3.1.69)	4·50	12·00
D73		6d. purple (9.9.68)	70	80
D74		1s. ochre (19.11.68)	80	1·25

The 2d. and 4d. exist with gum arabic and PVA gum; remainder with PVA gum only.

1968–69. *Photo. No wmk. Chalk-surfaced paper. PVA gum. P* 14 × 15.

No.	Type	Description	Un	Used
D75	D 1	4d. blue (12.6.69)	5·00	7·00
D76		8d. red (3.10.68)	1·00	2·00

Nos. D75/6 are smaller, 21½ × 17½ mm.

D 3

D 4

(Des J. Matthews. Photo Harrison)

1970 (17 June)–**75.** *Decimal Currency. Chalk-surfaced paper. P* 14 × 15.

No.	Type	Description	Un	Used
D77	D 3	½p. turquoise-blue (15.2.71)	5	20
D78		1p. deep reddish purple (15.2.71)	5	10
D79		2p. myrtle-green (15.2.71)	5	10
D80		3p. ultramarine (15.2.71)	5	8
D81		4p. yellow-brown (15.2.71)	8	15
D82		5p. violet (15.2.71)	15	15
D83		7p. red-brown (21.8.74)	12	40
D84	D 4	10p. carmine	15	15
D85		11p. slate-green (18.6.75)	25	70
D86		20p. olive-brown	30	20
D87		50p. ultramarine	75	30
D88		£1 black	1·50	30
D89		£5 orange-yellow and black (2.4.73)	7·50	1·75

Later printings were on fluorescent white paper, some with dextrin added to the PVA gum (see notes after X944 of Great Britain).

D 5

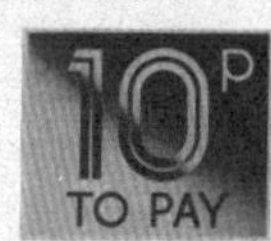
D 6

(Des Sedley Place Design Ltd. Photo Harrison)

1982 (9 June). *Chalk-surfaced paper. P* 14 × 15.

No.	Type	Description	Un	Used
D 90	D 5	1p. lake	5	5
D 91		2p. bright blue	5	5
D 92		3p. deep mauve	5	5
D 93		4p. deep blue	8	5
D 94		5p. sepia	8	10
D 95	D 6	10p. light brown	15	20
D 96		20p. olive-green	30	35
D 97		25p. deep greenish blue	40	40
D 98		50p. grey-black	75	75
D 99		£1 red	1·50	1·50
D100		£2 turquoise-blue	3·00	3·00
D101		£5 dull orange	7·50	3·50

OFFICIAL STAMPS

In 1840 the 1d. black (Type **1**), with "V R" in the upper corners, was prepared for official use, but never issued for postal purposes. Obliterated specimens are those which were used for experimental trials of obliterating inks, or those that passed through the post by oversight.

V 1

1840. *Prepared for use but not issued; "V" "R" in upper corners. Imperf.*

No.	Type	Description	Un	Used	Used on cover
V1	V 1	1d. black	£5500	£4000	£12000

The Official stamps would be more correctly termed Departmental stamps as they were exclusively for the use of certain government departments. Until 1882 official mail used ordinary postage stamps purchased at post offices, the cash being refunded once a quarter. Later the government departments obtained Official stamps by requisition.

Official stamps were on sale to the public for a short time at Somerset House but then withdrawn, it becoming an offence to deal in them in unused condition. This restriction was abandoned after all the Official stamps were withdrawn from use on 12 May 1904.

OVERPRINTS, PERFORATIONS, WATERMARKS. All Official stamps were overprinted by Thomas De La Rue & Co. and are perf 14. They are on Crown watermarked paper unless otherwise stated.

INLAND REVENUE

These stamps were used by revenue officials in the provinces, mail to and from Head Office passing without a stamp. The London Office used these stamps only for foreign mail.

I.R.
OFFICIAL
(O 1)

I. R.
OFFICIAL
(O 2)

Optd with Types O **1** (½*d. to* 1*s.*) *or* O **2** (*others*)

1882–1901. *Stamps of Queen Victoria. (a) Issues of* 1880–81.

No.	Description	Un	Used	★ Used on cover
O 1	½d. green (28.10.82)	7·50	1·60	15·00
O 3	1d. lilac (Die II) (27.9.82)	1·00	65	15·00
	a. Optd in blue-black	£100	18·00	
	b. "OFFICIAL" omitted	—	£2250	
O 4	6d. grey (30.10.82)	75·00	20·00	

No. O3 with the lines of the overprint transposed is an essay.

(*b*) *Issues of* 1884–88

No.	Description	Un	Used	Used on cover
O 5	½d. slate-blue (8.5.85)	11·00	8·00	
O 6	2½d. lilac (12.3.85)	55·00	25·00	
O 7	1s. green (12.3.85)	£2500	£450	
O 8	5s. rose (12.3.85)	£1300	£275	
	a. Raised stop after "R"	£1600	£325	
	b. Optd in blue-black	£2000	£450	
O 9	5s. rose (*blued paper*) (12.3.85)	£2750	£475	
O 9*a*	10s. cobalt (12.3.85)	£5000	£700	
O10	10s. ultramarine (12.3.85)	£2250	£475	
	a. Raised stop after "R"	£3000	£500	
	b. Optd in blue-black	£3500	£700	
O10*c*	10s. ultramarine (*blued paper*)	£5000	£1400	
O11	£1 brown-lilac (wmk Crowns) (12.3.85)	£18000	£3000	
	a. Frame broken	£20000	£3500	
O12	£1 brown-lilac (wmk Orbs) (1890)	£15000	£2750	
	a. Frame broken	£17000	£3000	

(*c*) *Issues of* 1887–92

No.	Description	Un	Used	Used on cover
O13	½d. vermilion (21.1.88)	1·10	40	12·00
	a. Without "I.R."	£1200		
	b. Imperf	£550		
	c. Opt double (imperf)	£650		
O14	2½d. purple/*blue* (20.10.91)	38·00	2·50	
O15	1s. green (15.3.89)	£180	20·00	
O16	£1 green (13.4.92)	£3500	£450	
	a. No stop after "R"	—	£700	
	b. Frame broken	£5500	£900	

Nos. O3, O13, O15 and O16 may be found with two varieties of overprint, namely, 1887 printings, *thin* letters, and 1894 printings, *thicker* letters.

(*d*) *Issues of* 1887 *and* 1900

No.	Description	Un	Used	Used on cover
O17	½d. blue-green (4.01)	3·00	85	15·00
O18	6d. purple/*rose-red* (14.6.01)	£100	12·00	
O19	1s. green and carmine (12.01)	£475	75·00	
★O1/19	**For well-centred, lightly used**		+35%	

1902–4. *Stamps of King Edward VII.*

No.	Description	Un	Used	Used on cover
O20	½d. blue-green, **O** (4.2.02)	6·50	1·25	50·00
O21	1d. scarlet, **O** (4.2.02)	10·00	70	20·00
O22	2½d. ultramarine, **O** (19.2.02)	£550	70·00	
O23	6d. dull purple, **O** (14.3.04)	£50000	£30000	
O24	1s. green and carmine, **O** (29.4.02)	£400	65·00	
O25	5s. carmine, **O** (29.4.02)	£4000	£1300	
	a. Raised stop after "R"	£4500	£1500	
O26	10s. ultramarine, **O** (29.4.02)	£15000	£9500	
	a. Raised stop after "R"	£17000	£11000	
O27	£1 dull blue-green, **O** (29.4.02)	£12000	£3750	

OFFICE OF WORKS

These were for use on official correspondence from the London Head Office and from departments in Birmingham, Bristol, Edinburgh, Glasgow, Leeds, Liverpool, Manchester and Southampton. They were also issued to the Clerks of Works at various embassies abroad.

O. W.
OFFICIAL
(O 3)

Optd with Type O **3**

Stamps of Queen Victoria

No.	Description	Un	Used	Used on cover
1896.				
O31	½d. vermilion (24.3.96)	50·00	15·00	75·00
O32	1d. lilac (Die II) (24.3.96)	50·00	12·00	£100
1901.				
O33	½d. blue-green (5.11.01)	50·00	20·00	
1902.				
O34	5d. purple and blue (II) (29.4.02)	£550	£120	
O35	10d. purple and carmine (28.5.02)	£950	£225	

1902–03. *Stamps of King Edward VII.*

No.	Description	Un	Used
O36	½d. blue-green, **O** (11.2.02)	£225	80·00
O37	1d. scarlet, **O** (11.2.02)	£225	80·00
O38	2d. green and carmine, **O** (29.3.02)	£400	75·00
O39	2½d. ultramarine, **O** (20.3.02)	£700	£100
O40	10d. purple and carm, **O** (18.5.03)	£3000	£900
★O31/40	**For well-centred, lightly used**		+25%

ARMY

Letters to and from the War Office in London passed without postage. The overprinted stamps were distributed to District and Station Paymasters for local correspondence.

ARMY
OFFICIAL
(O 4)

ARMY
OFFICIAL
(O 5)

ARMY
OFFICIAL
(O 6)

Optd with Type O **4** (½*d.*, 1*d.*) *or* O **5** (2½*d.*, 6*d.*)

Stamps of Queen Victoria

No.	Description	Un	Used	Used on cover
1896 (1 Sept).				
O41	½d. vermilion	1·10	50	20·00
	a. "OFFICIAI"	27·00	11·00	
	b. Lines of opt transposed	£1000		
O42	1d. lilac (Die II)	1·00	50	30·00
	a. "OFFICIAI"	27·00	11·00	
O43	2½d. purple/*blue*	4·00	2·00	
1900–1.				
O46	½d. blue-green (4.00)	1·75	3·00	
O47	6d. purple/*rose-red* (12.10.01)	13·00	8·00	

1902. *Stamps of King Edward VII optd with Type* O **4.**

No.	Description	Un	Used	Used on cover
O48	½d. blue-green, **O** (11.2.02)	1·75	65	30·00
O49	1d. scarlet, **O** (11.2.02)	1·25	55	30·00
	a. "ARMY" omitted			
O50	6d. dull purple, **O** (23.8.02)	60·00	30·00	

1903 (Sept). *Optd with Type* O **6.**

No.	Description	Un	Used
O52	6d. dull purple, **O**	£1000	£275

GOVERNMENT PARCELS

These stamps were issued to all departments, including the Head Office, for use on parcels weighing over 3 lb. Below this weight government parcels were sent by letter post to avoid the 55% of the postage paid from accruing to the railway companies, as laid down by parcel-post regulations. Most government parcels stamps suffered heavy postmarks in use.

GOVT
PARCELS
(O 7)

Optd as Type O **7**

Stamps of Queen Victoria

1883 (1 July)–**86.**

No.	Description	Un	★ Used
O61	1½d. lilac (30.4.86)	75·00	20·00
	a. No dot under "T"	£130	25·00
	b. Dot to left of "T"	£100	22·00
O62	6d. dull green (30.4.86)	£350	60·00
O63	9d. dull green (1.8.83)	£625	£175
O64	1s. brown (wmk Crown, Pl 13)	£425	60·00
	a. No dot under "T"	£475	70·00
	b. Dot to left of "T"	£475	70·00
O64*c*	1s. brown (Pl 14)	£725	85·00
	d. No dot under "T"	£825	90·00
1887–90.			
O65	1½d. purple and green (29.10.87)	12·00	1·60
	a. No dot under "T"	18·00	2·75
	b. Dot to right of "T"	16·00	1·75
	c. Dot to left of "T"	16·00	1·75
O66	6d. purple/*rose-red* (19.12.87)	25·00	10·00
	a. No dot under "T"	30·00	12·00
	b. Dot to right of "T"	30·00	12·00
	c. Dot to left of "T"	30·00	11·00
O67	9d. purple and blue (21.8.88)	55·00	15·00
O68	1s. dull green (25.3.90)	£120	70·00
	a. No dot under "T"	£140	75·00
	b. Dot to right of "T"	£140	75·00
	c. Dot to left of "T"	£160	80·00
	d. Optd in blue-black		
1891–1900.			
O69	1d. lilac (Die II) (6.97)	3·75	50
	a. No dot under "T"	11·00	3·75
	b. Dot to left of "T"	11·00	3·75
	c. Opt inverted	£800	£450
	d. Ditto. Dot to left of "T"	£900	£500
O70	2d. green and carmine (24.10.91)	45·00	3·75
	a. No dot under "T"	50·00	4·25
	b. Dot to left of "T"	50·00	5·00
O71	4½d. green and carmine (9.92)	60·00	60·00
O72	1s. green and carmine (11.00)	£160	50·00
	a. Opt inverted	—	£3750
★O61/72	**For well-centred lightly used**		+100%

1902. *Stamps of King Edward VII.*

No.	Description	Un	Used
O74	1d. scarlet, **O** (30.10.02)	10·00	5·00
O75	2d. green and carmine, **O** (29.4.02)	65·00	15·00
O76	6d. dull purple, **O** (19.2.02)	£100	15·00
O77	9d. purple and ultram (28.8.02)	£225	50·00
O78	1s. green and carmine, **O** (17.12.02)	£350	85·00

BOARD OF EDUCATION

BOARD
OF
EDUCATION
(O 8)

Optd with Type O **8**

1902 (19 Feb). *Stamps of Queen Victoria.*

No.	Description	Un	Used
O81	5d. purple and blue (II)	£475	65·00
O82	1s. green and carmine	£950	£375

1902–4. *Stamps of King Edward VII.*

O83	½d. blue-green, **O** (19.2.02)	16·00	5·00
O84	1d. scarlet, **O** (19.2.02)	16·00	5·00
O85	2½d. ultramarine, **O** (19.2.02)	£500	50·00
O86	5d. purple and blue, **O** (6.2.04)	£1500	£450
O87	1s. green and carmine, **O** (23.2.02) ..	£23000	£10000

ROYAL HOUSEHOLD

R.H.

OFFICIAL

(O 9)

1902. *Stamps of King Edward VII optd with Type* O **9.**

		Un	*Used*	*Used on cover*
O91	½d. blue-green, **O** (29.4.02)	£150	95·00	£250
O92	1d. scarlet, **O** (19.2.02)	£130	85·00	£350

ADMIRALTY

ADMIRALTY **ADMIRALTY**

OFFICIAL **OFFICIAL**

(O 10) (O 11)

1903 (3 Mar). *Stamps of King Edward VII optd with Type* O **10.**

O101	½d. blue-green, **O**	6·00	3·00	75·00
O102	1d. scarlet, **O**	5·00	2·50	50·00
O103	1½d. purple and green, **O**	60·00	40·00	
O104	2d. green and carmine, **O** ..	80·00	50·00	
O105	2½d. ultramarine, **O**	75·00	38·00	
O106	3d. purple/*yellow*, **O**	£100	35·00	

1903–4. *Stamps of King Edward VII optd with Type* O **11.**

O107	½d. blue-green, **O** (9.03)	7·00	4·00	90·00
O108	1d. scarlet, **O** (11.03)	6·50	3·50	50·00
O109	1½d. purple and green, **O** (2.04) ..	£150	50·00	
O110	2d. green and carmine, **O** (3.04)	£300	85·00	
O111	2½d. ultramarine, **O** (3.04) ..	£450	£225	
O112	3d. purple/*yellow*, **O** (2.04) ..	£300	50·00	

Stamps of various issues perforated with a Crown and initials ("H.M.O.W.", "O.W.", "B.T." or "S.O.") or with initials only ("H.M.S.O." or "D.S.I.R.") have also been used for official purposes, but these are outside the scope of the catalogue.

POSTAL FISCAL STAMPS

PRICES. Prices in the used column are for stamps with genuine postal cancellations dated from the time when they were authorised for use as postage stamps. Beware of stamps with fiscal cancellations removed and fraudulent postmarks applied.

VALIDITY. The 1d. Surface-printed stamps were authorised for postal use from 1 June 1881 and the 3d. and 6d. values, together with the Embossed issues, from 1 January 1883.

SURFACE-PRINTED ISSUES

(Typo Thomas De La Rue & Co)

F 1
Rectangular Buckle

F 2

F 3
Octagonal Buckle

F 4

F 5
Double-lined Anchor

F 6
Single-lined Anchor

1853–57. *P* 15½ × 15. (*a*) *Wmk* F **5** (*inverted*) (1853–55).

			Un	*Used*	*Used on cover*
F1	F **1**	1d. light blue (10.10.53) ..	8·50	11·00	£100
F2	F **2**	1d. ochre (10.53)	45·00	30·00	£130
		a. *Tête-bêche* (in block of four)	£8000		
F3	F **3**	1d. pale turquoise-blue (1854)	10·00	10·00	£100
F4		1d. light blue/*blue* (1854) ..	28·00	19·00	£120
F5	F **4**	1d. reddish lilac/*blue glazed paper* (25.3.55)	45·00	11·00	£100

Only one example is known of No. F2a outside the National Postal Museum and the Royal Collection.

(*b*) *Wmk* F **6** (1856–57)

F6	F **4**	1d. reddish lilac (*shades*) ..	5·50	4·00	80·00
F7		1d. reddish lilac/*bluish* (*shades*) (1857)	5·50	4·00	80·00

INLAND **REVENUE**

(F 7)

1860 (3 Apr). *No.* F7 *optd with Type* F **7,** *in red.*

F8	F **4**	1d. dull reddish lilac/*blue* ..	£325	£275	£450

BLUE PAPER. In the following issues we no longer distinguish between bluish and white paper. There is a range of papers from white or greyish to bluish.

F 8

F 9

F 10

1860–67. *Bluish to white paper. P* 15½ × 15. (*a*) *Wmk* F **6** (1860).

F 9	F **8**	1d. reddish lilac (May) ..	4·75	4·75	65·00
F10	F **9**	3d. reddish lilac (June) ..	£190	60·00	£120
F11	F **10**	6d. reddish lilac (Oct) ..	70·00	50·00	£150

(*b*) *W* **40.** (*Anchor* 16 *mm high*) (1864)

F12	F **8**	1d. pale reddish lilac (Nov)	4·75	4·75	65·00
F13	F **9**	3d. pale reddish lilac ..	60·00	45·00	
F14	F **10**	6d. pale reddish lilac ..	70·00	45·00	£150

(*c*) *W* **40** (*Anchor* 18 *mm high*) (1867)

F15	F **8**	1d. reddish lilac	13·00	6·00	£130
F16	F **9**	3d. reddish lilac	38·00	38·00	£110
F17	F **10**	6d. reddish lilac	70·00	35·00	£150

For stamps perf 14, see Nos. F24/7.

F 11

F 12

Four Dies of Type F 12

Die 1. Corner ornaments small and either joined or broken; heavy shading under chin

Die 2. Ornaments small and always broken; clear line of shading under chin

Die 3. Ornaments larger and joined; line of shading under chin extended half way down neck

Die 4. Ornaments much larger; straight line of shading continued to bottom of neck

1867–81. *White to bluish paper. P* 14. (*a*) *W* **47** (*Small Anchor*).

F18	F **11**	1d. purple (1.9.67)	6·00	4·00	50·00
F19	F **12**	1d. purple (Die 1) (6.68) ..	1·75	1·50	40·00
F20		1d. purple (Die 2) (6.76) ..	2·50	2·75	40·00
F21		1d. purple (Die 3) (3.77) ..	2·50	2·50	40·00
F22		1d. purple (Die 4) (7.78) ..	2·25	1·75	40·00

(*b*) *W* **48** (*Orb*)

F23	F **12**	1d. purple (Die 4) (1.81) ..	2·00	1·50	40·00

1881. *White to bluish paper. P* 14.

(*a*) *W* **40** (*Anchor* 18 *mm high*) (Jan)

F24	F **9**	3d. reddish lilac	£325	£200	£325
F25	F **10**	6d. reddish lilac	£170	50·00	£150

(*b*) *W* **40** (*Anchor* 20 *mm high*) (May)

F26	F **9**	3d. reddish lilac	£190	42·00	£110
F27	F **10**	6d. reddish lilac	90·00	60·00	£170

ISSUES EMBOSSED IN COLOUR

(Made at Somerset House)

The embossed stamps were struck from dies not appropriated to any special purpose on paper which had the words "INLAND REVENUE" previously printed, and thus became available for payment of any duties for which no special stamps had been provided.

The die letters are included in the embossed designs and holes were drilled for the insertion of plugs showing figures indicating dates of striking.

F 13

F 14

INLAND REVENUE INLAND REVENUE

(F 15) (F 16)

1860 (3 Apr)–**71.** *Types* F **13/14** *and similar types embossed on bluish paper. Underprint Type* F **15.** *No wmk. Imperf.*

		Un	*Used*
F28	2d. pink (Die A) (1.1.71)	90·00	90·00
F29	3d. pink (Die C)	60·00	55·00
	a. *Tête-bêche* (vert pair)	£900	
F30	3d. pink (Die D)	£250	
F31	6d. pink (Die T)	£650	
F32	6d. pink (Die U)	70·00	55·00
	a. *Tête-bêche* (vert pair)	£1000	
F33	9d. pink (Die C) (1.1.71)	£225	
F34	1s. pink (Die E) (28.6.61)	£325	£130
F35	1s. pink (Die F) (28.6.61)	85·00	65·00
	a. *Tête-bêche* (vert pair)	£400	
F36	2s. pink (Die K) (6.8.61)	£250	£150
F37	2s. 6d. pink (Die N) (28.6.61) ..	£500	
F38	2s. 6d. pink (Die O) (28.6.61) ..	60·00	50·00

1861–71. *As last but perf* 12½.

F39	2d. pink (Die A) (8.71)	£225	£110
F40	3d. pink (Die C)		
F41	3d. pink (Die D)		
F42	9d. pink (Die C) (8.71)	£250	£120
F43	1s. pink (Die E) (8.71)	£190	£110
F44	1s. pink (Die F) (8.71)	£170	85·00
F45	2s. 6d. pink (Die O) (8.71)	£100	50·00

1874 (Nov). *Types as before embossed on white paper. Underprint Type* F **16**, *in green. W* **47** (*Small Anchor*). *P* 12½.

F46	2d. pink (Die A)	—	£150
F47	9d. pink (Die C)		
F48	1s. pink (Die F)	£170	90·00
F49	2s. 6d. pink (Die O)	—	£130

1875 (Nov)–**80**. *As last but colour changed and on white or bluish paper.*

F50	2d. vermilion (Die A) (1880)	£250	85·00
F51	9d. vermilion (Die C) (1876)	£250	£120
F52	1s. vermilion (Die E)	£150	55·00
F53	1s. vermilion (Die F)	£150	55·00
F54	2s. 6d. vermilion (Die O) (1878)	£190	85·00

1882 (Oct). *As last but W* **48** (*Orbs*).

F55	2d. vermilion (Die A)		
F56	9d. vermilion (Die C)		
F57	1s. vermilion (Die E)		
F58	2s. 6d. vermilion (Die O)	£400	£190

The sale of Inland Revenue stamps up to the 2s. value ceased from 30 December 1882 and stocks were called in and destroyed. The 2s. 6d. value remained on sale until 2 July 1883 when it was replaced by the 2s. 6d. "Postage & Revenue" stamp. Inland Revenue stamps still in the hands of the public continued to be accepted for revenue and postal purposes.

CONTROLS. Since the 1967 edition of the Part 1 Catalogue the priced lists of stamps with control letters have been transferred to Volumes 1 and 2 of the Stanley Gibbons *Great Britain Specialised Catalogue*.

TELEGRAPH STAMPS. A priced listing of the Post Office telegraph stamps appears in Volume 1 of the Stanley Gibbons *Great Britain Specialised Catalogue*. The last listing for the private telegraph companies in the Part 1 Catalogue was in the 1940 edition and for military telegraphs the 1941 edition.

ISLAND ISSUES

Several islands off the coast of Great Britain have issued local stamps (usually termed British Private Local Issues or Local Carriage Labels) ostensibly to cover the cost of ferrying mail to the nearest mainland post office. No official post offices operate on most of these islands. As these stamps are not recognised as valid for national or international mail they are not listed here. The following islands are known to operate (or have operated) a local postal service and issued stamps from the dates shown:

Bardsey, Gwynedd (from 1979); *Bernera*, Hebrides (from 1977); *Brecqhou*, Channel Is. (1969); *Caldey*, Dyfed (from 1973); *Calf of Man*, Isle of Man (1962–73); *Calve*, Hebrides (from 1984); *Canna*, Hebrides (from 1958); *Carn Iar*, Hebrides (1961–62); *Davaar*, Argyllshire (from 1964; *Drake's Island*, Devon (1973–82); *Eynhallow*, Orkney (from 1973); *Gairsay*, Orkney (from 1980); *Grunay*, Shetland (from 1981); *Gugh*, Isles of Scilly (1962–80); *Herm*, Channel Is. (1949–69); *Heston*, Wigtownshire (1960s); *Hilbre*, Cheshire (1960s); *Inchcolm*, Fife (c. 1972); *Jethou*, Channel Is. (1960–69); *Lihou*, Channel Is. (1966–69); *Lundy*, Devon (from 1929); *Pabay*, Skye (1962–70 and 1972–79); *St Kilda*, Hebrides (1968–71); *Sanda*, Argyllshire (from 1962); *Shuna*, Argyllshire (from 1949); *Soay*, Skye (1965–67); *Staffa*, Hebrides (from 1969); *Steep Holm*, Avon (from 1980); *Stroma*, Caithness (1962–70) and *Summer Isles*, Hebrides (from 1970). Those issued for Soay have been declared bogus by a committee of the Philatelic Traders Society.

Issues of the *Commodore Shipping Co* (1950–69), the *Alderney Shipping Co* (1969–75) and the *Isle of Sark Shipping Co* (from 1969) were/ are for use on parcels carried by ship between Guernsey and Alderney and Sark. They are not valid for the carriage of letters and postcards.

Issues inscribed Alderney (1975–83) were issued in conjunction with an internal parcel delivery service. They were not valid for use on letters or postcards.

CHANNEL ISLANDS

GENERAL ISSUE

C **1** Gathering Vraic

C **2** Islanders gathering Vraic

(Des J. R. R. Stobie (1d.) or from drawing by E. Blampied (2½d.). Photo Harrison)

1948 (10 May). *Third Anniv of Liberation. W* **127** *of Great Britain. P* 15 × 14.

C1	C **1**	1d. scarlet	10	10
C2	C **2**	2½d. ultramarine	15	15

GUERNSEY

Further detailed information on the stamps of Guernsey will be found in the Stanley Gibbons *Channel Islands Specialised Catalogue*.

WAR OCCUPATION ISSUES

Stamps issued under British authority during the German Occupation

BISECTS. On 24 December 1940 authority was given, by Post Office notice, that prepayment of penny postage could be effected by using half a British 2d. stamp, diagonally bisected. Such stamps were first used on 27 December 1940.

The 2d. stamps generally available were those of the Postal Centenary issue, 1940 (S.G. 482) and the first colour of the King George VI issue (S.G. 465). These are listed under Nos. 482a and 465b. A number of the 2d. King George V, 1912–22, and of the King George V photogravure stamp (S.G. 442) which were in the hands of philatelists, were also bisected and used.

1

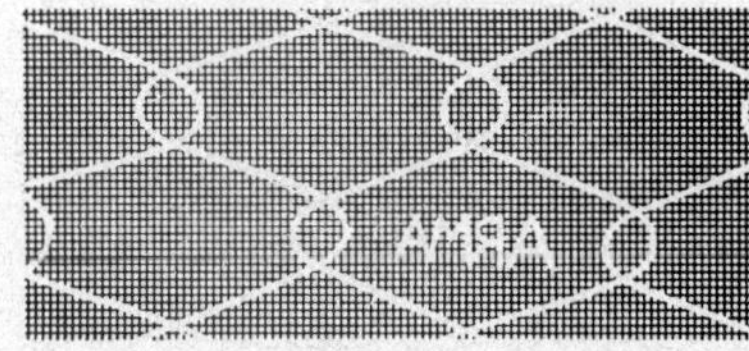

1*a* Loops (*half actual size*)

(Des E. W. Vaudin. Typo Guernsey Press Co Ltd)

1941–44. *Rouletted.* (*a*) *White paper. No wmk.*

1	**1**	½d. light green (7.4.41)	2·50	1·25
		a. Emerald-green (6.41)	2·50	2·50
		b. Bluish green (11.41)	32·00	12·00
		c. Bright green (2.42)	16·00	9·00
		d. Dull green (9.42)	4·00	1·75
		e. Olive-green (2.43)	21·00	12·00
		f. Pale yellowish green (7.43 and later) (*shades*)	2·50	2·00
		g. Imperf (pair)	£125	
		h. Imperf between (horiz pair)	£400	
		i. Imperf between (vert pair)	£500	
2		1d. scarlet (18.2.41)	£1·40	65
		a. Pale vermillion (7.43) (etc.)	2·75	1·75
		b. Carmine (1943)	4·50	3·00
		c. Imperf (pair)	£100	75·00
		d. Imperf between (horiz pair)	£400	
		da. Imperf vert (centre stamp of horiz strip of 3)		
		e. Imperf between (vert pair)	£500	
		f. Printed double (scarlet shade)	60·00	
3		2½d. ultramarine (12.4.44)	3·50	3·00
		a. Deep ultramarine (7.44)	3·50	3·00
		b. Imperf (pair)	£250	
		c. Imperf between (horiz pair)	£600	

(*b*) *Bluish French bank-note paper. W* **1a** (*sideways*)

4	**1**	½d. bright green (11.3.42)	11·00	18·00
5		1d. scarlet (9.4.42)	7·00	18·00

The dates given for the shades of Nos. 1 and 2 are the months in which they were printed as indicated on the printer's imprints. Others are issue dates.

REGIONAL ISSUES

DATES OF ISSUE. Conflicting dates of issue have been announced for some of the regional issues, partly explained by the stamps being released on different dates by the Philatelic Bureau in Edinburgh or the Philatelic Counter in London and in the regions. We have adopted the practice of giving the earliest known dates, since once released the stamps could have been used anywhere in the U.K.

2

3

(Des E. A. Piprell. Portrait by Dorothy Wilding Ltd. Photo Harrison & Sons)

1958 (18 Aug)–**67.** *W* **179** *of Great Britain. P* 15 × 14.

6	**2**	2½d. rose-red (8.6.64)	20	1·00
7	**3**	3d. deep lilac	20	15
		p. One centre phosphor band (24.5.67)	5	25
8		4d. ultramarine (7.2.66)	20	20
		p. Two phosphor bands (24.10.67)	10	10

1968–69. *No wmk. Chalk-surfaced paper. PVA gum**. *One centre phosphor band* (*Nos.* 10/11) *or two phosphor bands* (*others*). *P* 15 × 14.

9	**3**	4d. pale ultramarine (16.4.68)	8	60
10		4d. olive-sepia (4.9.68)	10	20
11		4d. bright vermilion (26.2.69)	10	40
12		5d. royal blue (4.9.68)	10	25

No. 9 was not issued in Guernsey until 22 April.

* PVA Gum. See note after No. 722 of Great Britain.

INDEPENDENT POSTAL ADMINISTRATION

4 Castle Cornet and Edward the Confessor

5 View of Sark

Two Types of 1d. and 1s. 6d.:

I. Latitude inscr "40° 30′ N".
II. Corrected to "49° 30′ N".

(Des R. Granger Barrett. Photo Harrison (½d. to 2s. 6d.); Delrieu (others))

1969 (1 Oct)–**70.** *Designs as T* **4**/**5.** *P* 14 (½*d. to* 2*s.* 6*d.*) *or* 12½ (*others*).

13	½d. deep magenta and black	10	15
14	1d. bright blue and black (I)	10	15
14*b*	1d. bright blue and black (II) (12.12.69)	50	50
	c. Booklet stamp with blank margins	55	55
15	1½d. yellow-brown and black	10	15
16	2d. gold, bright red, deep blue and black	20	15
17	3d. gold, pale greenish yellow, orge-red & blk	35	35
	a. Error. Wmk w **12**	£750	
18	4d. multicoloured	25	25
	a. Booklet stamp with blank margins (12.12.69)	45	45
	ab. Yellow omitted	£150	
19	5d. gold, brt vermilion, bluish violet & black	40	25
	a. Booklet stamp with blank margins (12.12.69)	50	50
	b. Gold (inscr etc.) omitted (booklets)	£300	
20	6d. gold, pale greenish yellow, light bronze-green and black	60	50
21	9d. gold, bright red, crimson and black	1·25	1·25
22	1s. gold, bright vermilion, bistre and black	1·00	1·00
23	1s. 6d. turquoise-green and black (I)	60	70
23*b*	1s. 6d. turquoise-green and black (II) (4.2.70)	6·50	2·50
24	1s. 9d. multicoloured	5·00	4·00
25	2s. 6d. bright reddish violet and black	14·00	6·00
26	5s. multicoloured	7·00	7·00
27	10s. multicoloured	50·00	35·00
	a. Perf 13 (4.3.70)	85·00	80·00
28	£1 multicoloured	10·00	11·00
	a. Perf 13 (4.3.70)	4·00	4·00
13/28	*Set of* 16	75·00	60·00

Designs: *Horiz as T* **4**—1d. (*both*), 1s. 6d. (*both*), Map and William I; 1½d. Martello Tower and Henry II; 2d. Arms of Sark and King John; 3d. Arms of Alderney and Edward III; 4d. Guernsey Lily and Henry V; 5d. Arms of Guernsey and Elizabeth I; 6d. Arms of Alderney and Charles II; 9d. Arms of Sark and George III; 1s. Arms of Guernsey and Queen Victoria; 1s. 9d. Guernsey Lily and Elizabeth I; 2s. 6d. Martello Tower and King John. *Horiz as T* **5**—10s. View of Alderney; £1, View of Guernsey.

The booklet panes consist of single perforated stamps with wide margins all round intended to fit automatic machines designed for the Great Britain 2s. booklets. They are therefore found with three margins when detached from booklets or four margins when complete.

There was no postal need for the ½d. and 1½d. values as the ½d. coin had been withdrawn prior to their issue in anticipation of decimalisation. These values were only on sale at the Philatelic Bureau and the Crown Agents as well as in the U.S.A.

Nos. 18a and 24 are known with blue-green omitted.

Nos. 14*b* and 23*b* are known only on thin paper and Nos. 13, 14, 16, 17, 20, 21, 22, 23, 24 and 25 also exist on thin paper.

19 Isaac Brock as Colonel **23** Landing Craft entering St. Peter's Harbour

(Litho Format)

1969 (1 Dec). *Birth Bicentenary of Sir Isaac Brock. T* **19** *and similar multicoloured designs. P* 13½ × 14 (*2s. 6d.*) *or* 14 × 13½ (*others*).

29 4d. Type **19** .. 25 25

30 5d. Sir Isaac Brock as Major-General .. 25 25

31 1s. 9d. Isaac Brock as Ensign .. 3·00 2·50

32 2s. 6d. Arms and flags (*horiz*) .. 3·00 2·50

(Des and photo Courvoisier)

1970 (9 May). *25th Anniv of Liberation. T* **23** *and similar designs. P* 11½.

33 4d. blue and pale blue .. 50 50

34 5d. brown-lake and pale grey .. 50 50

35 1s. 6d. bistre-brown and buff .. 5·50 3·50

Designs: *Horiz*—5d. British ships entering St. Peter's Port. *Vert*—1s. 6d. Brigadier Snow reading Proclamation.

26 Guernsey "Toms" **32** St. Peter Church, Sark

(Des and photo Courvoisier)

1970 (12 Aug). *Agriculture and Horticulture. T* **26** *and similar horiz designs. Multicoloured. P* 11½.

36 4d. Type **26** .. 50 30

37 5d. Guernsey Cow .. 50 30

38 9d. Guernsey Bull .. 7·00 3·75

39 1s. 6d. Freesias .. 8·00 4·25

(Des and photo Courvoisier)

1970 (11 Nov). *Christmas. T* **32** *and similar multicoloured designs. P* 11½.

40 4d. St. Anne's Church, Alderney (*horiz*) .. 40 20

41 5d. St. Peter's Church (*horiz*) .. 40 25

42 9d. Type **32** .. 2·40 1·75

43 1s. 6d. St. Tugual Chapel, Herm .. 3·25 1·90

INVALIDATION. The regional issues for Guernsey were invalidated for use in Guernsey and Jersey on 1 November 1969 but remained valid for use in the rest of the United Kingdom. Nos. 13/43 (except Nos. 28/a) and Nos. D1/7 were invalidated on 14 February 1972.

34 Martello Tower and King John

(Photo Harrison (½p. to 10p.), Delrieu (others))

1971 (6 Jan)–**73.** *Decimal Currency. Designs as Nos. 13/27 but values inscr in decimal currency as in T* **34.** *Chalk-surfaced paper. P* 14 (*½p. to 10p.*) *or* 13 (*20p., 50p.*).

44 ½p. deep magenta and black (15.2.71) .. 15 15

a. Booklet stamp with margins (*glazed, ordinary paper*) .. 15 25

ab. Ditto. Chalk-surfaced paper (2.4.73) .. 15 25

45 1p. bright blue and black (II) (15.2.71) .. 10 8

46 1½p. yellow-brown and black (15.2.71) .. 12 12

47 2p. multicoloured (15.2.71) .. 12 12

a. Booklet stamp with margins (*glazed, ordinary paper*) .. 25 15

ab. Ditto. Chalk-surfaced paper (2.4.73) .. 12 15

b. Glazed, ordinary paper (15.2.71) .. 30 30

48 2½p. gold, brt verm, bluish vio & blk (15.2.71) 15 5

a. Bright vermilion omitted .. £350

b. Booklet stamp with margins (*glazed, ordinary paper*) .. 20 20

ba. Ditto. Chalk-surfaced paper (2.4.73) .. 15 15

49 3p. gold, pale greenish yellow, orange-red and black (15.2.71) .. 20 20

50 3½p. mult (*glazed, ordinary paper*) (15.2.71) .. 25 25

51 4p. multicoloured (15.2.71) .. 30 25

52 5p. turquoise-green and black (II) (15.2.71) 25 25

53 6p. gold, pale greenish yellow, light bronze-green and black (15.2.71) .. 35 35

54 7½p. gold, brt verm, bistre & black (15.2.71) 45 45

55 9p. gold, brt red, crimson & black (15.2.71) 1·25 1·25

56 10p. bright reddish violet and black .. 2·50 2·25

a. Ordinary paper. *Bright reddish violet and deep black* (1.9.72) .. 1·50 1·50

57 20p. multicoloured (*glazed, ordinary paper*) .. 1·50 1·50

a. *Shade** (25.1.73) .. 75 75

58 50p. multicoloured (*glazed, ordinary paper*) .. 2·75 3·25

44/58 .. *Set of* 15 7·50 8·00

*No. 57 has the sky in a pale turquoise-blue; on No. 57*a* it is pale turquoise-green.

35 Hong Kong 2 c. of 1862

(Des and recess D.L.R.)

1971 (2 June). *Thomas De La Rue Commemoration. T* **35** *and similar horiz designs. P* 14 × 13½.

59 2p. dull purple to brown-purple* .. 50 25

60 2½p. carmine-red .. 50 25

61 4p. deep bluish green .. 7·50 3·50

62 7½p. deep blue .. 7·50 3·50

Designs: (each incorporating portraits of Queen Elizabeth II and Thomas De La Rue as in T 35)—2½p. Great Britain 4d. of 1855–7; 4p. Italian 5 c. of 1862; 7½p. Confederate States 5 c. of 1862.

* These colours represent the extreme range of shades of this value. The majority of the printing, however, is in an intermediate shade.

36 Ebenezer Church, St. Peter Port

(Des and photo Courvoisier)

1971 (27 Oct). *Christmas. T* **36** *and similar multicoloured designs. P* 11½.

63 2p. Type **36** .. 40 20

64 2½p. Church of St. Pierre du Bois .. 40 20

65 5p. St. Joseph's Church, St. Peter Port (*vert*) 2·75 2·50

66 7½d. Church of St. Philippe de Torteval (*vert*) 2·75 2·50

37 *Earl of Chesterfield* (1794)

(Des and photo Courvoisier)

1972 (10 Feb). *Mail Packet Boats* (*1st series*). *T* **37** *and similar horiz designs. Multicoloured. P* 11½.

67 2p. Type **37** .. 30 15

68 2½p. *Dasher* (1827) .. 30 15

69 7½p. *Ibex* (1891) .. 1·25 1·50

70 9p. *Alberta* (1900) .. 1·40 1·60

See also Nos. 80/3

38 Guernsey Bull

(Photo Courvoisier)

1972 (22 May). *World Conference of Guernsey Breeders, Guernsey. P* 11½.

71 **38** 5p. multicoloured .. 1·50 1·60

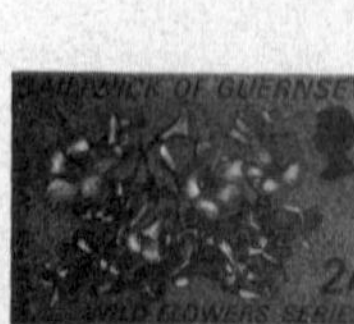

39 Bermuda Buttercup **40** Angels adoring Christ

(Des and photo Courvoisier)

1972 (24 May). *Wild Flowers. T* **39** *and similar multicoloured designs. P* 11½.

72 2p. Type **39** .. 15 20

73 2½p. Heath Spotted Orchid (*vert*) .. 15 20

74 7½p. Kaffir Fig .. 1·00 1·00

75 9p. Scarlet Pimpernel (*vert*) .. 1·40 1·50

(Des and photo Courvoisier)

1972 (20 Nov). *Royal Silver Wedding and Christmas. T* **40** *and similar vert designs showing stained-glass windows from Guernsey Churches. Multicoloured. P* 11½.

76 2p. Type **40** .. 10 10

77 2½p. The Epiphany .. 15 15

78 7½p. The Virgin Mary .. 50 70

79 9p. Christ .. 60 70

See also Nos. 89/92.

(Des and photo Courvoisier)

1973 (9 Mar). *Mail Packet Boats* (*2nd series*). *Multicoloured designs as T* **37.** *P* 11½.

80 2½p. *St. Julien* (1925) .. 10 10

81 3p. *Isle of Guernsey* (1930) .. 20 20

82 7½p. *St. Patrick* (1947) .. 50 60

83 9p. *Sarnia* (1961) .. 60 60

41 Supermarine "Sea Eagle" **42** "The Good Shepherd"

(Des and photo Courvoisier)

1973 (4 July). *50th Anniv of Air Service. T* **41** *and similar horiz designs. Multicoloured. P* 11½.

84 2½p. Type **41** .. 10 10

85 3p. Westland "Wessex" .. 12 15

86 5p. De Havilland "Rapide" .. 20 20

87 7½p. Douglas "Dakota" .. 40 45

88 9p. Vickers "Viscount" .. 40 50

(Des and photo Courvoisier)

1973 (24 Oct). *Christmas. T* **42** *and similar vert designs showing stained-glass windows from Guernsey Churches. Multicoloured. P* 11½.

89 2½p. Type **42** .. 8 8

90 3p. Christ at the well of Samaria .. 10 10

91 7½p. St. Dominic .. 25 25

92 20p. Mary and the Child Jesus .. 45 60

43 Princess Anne and Capt. Mark Phillips

(Des G. Anderson. Photo Courvoisier)

1973 (14 Nov). *Royal Wedding. P* 11½.

93 **43** 25p. multicoloured .. 75 80

44 *John Lockett*, 1875

(Des and photo Courvoisier)

1974 (15 Jan). *150th Anniv of Royal National Lifeboat Institution. T* **44** *and similar horiz designs. Multicoloured. P* 11½.

94 2½p. Type **44** .. 10 10

95 3p. *Arthur Lionel*, 1912 .. 10 10

96 8p. *Euphrosyne Kendal*, 1954 .. 25 30

97 10p. *Arun*, 1972 .. 25 30

45 Private, East Regt, 1815 **46** Driver, Field Battery, Royal Guernsey Artillery, 1848

(Photo Courvoisier (½ to 10p.) or Delrieu (others))

1974 (2 Apr)–**78.** *Designs as T* **45/6.** *Multicoloured.*

(*a*) *Vert designs as T* **45.** *P* 11½

98 ½p. Type **45** .. 5 5

a. Booklet strip of 8 (98 × 5 and 102 × 3)† 20

b. Booklet pane of 16 (98 × 4, 102 × 6 and 103 × 6)† .. 70

99 1p. Officer, 2nd North Regt, 1825 .. 5 5

a. Booklet strip of 8 (99 × 4, 103, 105 × 2 and 105*a*) (8.2.77)† .. 45

b. Booklet strip of 4 (99, 101 × 2 and 105*a*) (7.2.78)† .. 25

100 1½p. Gunner, Guernsey Artillery, 1787 .. 5 5

101 2p. Gunner, Guernsey Artillery, 1815 .. 10 5

102 2½p. Corporal, Royal Guernsey Artillery, 1868 .. 10 5

103 3p. Field Officer, Royal Guernsey Artillery, 1895 .. 10 5

104 3½p. Sergeant, 3rd Regt, 1867 .. .. 10 10
105 4p. Officer, East Regt, 1822 .. .. 15 10
105*a* 5p. Field Officer, Royal Guernsey Artillery, 1895 (29.5.76) 20 15
106 5½p. Colour-Sergeant of Grenadiers, East Regt, 1833 .. .. 20 15
107 6p. Officer, North Regt, 1832 .. .. 20 15
107*a* 7p. Officer, East Regt, 1822 (29.5.76) .. 30 20
108 8p. Field Officer, Rifle Company, 1868 .. 25 20
109 9p. Private, 4th West Regt, 1785 .. .. 30 25
110 10p. Field Officer, 4th West Regt, 1824 .. 30 25

(*b*) *Size as T* **46.** *P* 13 × 13½ (20, 50*p*.) *or* 13½ × 13 (£1)
111 20p. Type **46** (1.4.75) 60 55
112 50p. Officer, Field Battery, Royal Guernsey Artillery, 1868 (1.4.75) .. .. .. 1·40 1·25
113 £1 Cavalry Trooper, Light Dragoons, 1814 (*horiz*) (1.4.75) .. .. 3·00 3·00
98/113 .. .. *Set of* 18 6·50 6·00

The ½p. and 2½p. with the red colour omitted are chemically produced fakes.

† Nos. 98a/b come from special booklet sheets of 88 (8 × 11), and Nos. 99a/b from separate booklet sheets of 80 (2 panes 8 × 5). These sheets were put on sale in addition to the normal sheets. The strips and panes have the left-hand selvedge stuck into booklet covers, except for No. 99b which was loose, and then folded and supplied in plastic wallets.

47 Badge of Guernsey and U.P.U. Emblem

(Photo Courvoisier)

1974 (7 June). *U.P.U. Centenary.* *T* **47** *and similar horiz designs. Multicoloured. P* 11½.
114 2½p. Type **47** 5 5
115 3p. Map of Guernsey 8 8
116 8p. U.P.U. Building, Berne, and Guernsey flag 40 45
117 10p. "Salle des Etats" 40 45

48 "Cradle Rock"

49 Guernsey Spleenwort

(Des and photo Delrieu)

1974 (21 Sept). *Renoir Paintings.* *T* **48** *and similar multicoloured designs. P* 13.
118 3p. Type **48** 10 10
119 5½p. "Moulin Huet Bay" 15 15
120 8p. "Au Bord de la Mer" (*vert*) 30 35
121 10p. Self-portrait (*vert*) 35 40

(Des and photo Courvoisier)

1975 (7 Jan). *Guernsey Ferns.* *T* **49** *and similar vert designs. Multicoloured. P* 11½.
122 3½p. Type **49** 8 8
123 4p. Sand Quillwort 10 10
124 8p. Guernsey Quillwort 25 35
125 10p. Least Adder's Tongue 40 45

50 Victor Hugo House

51 Globe and Seal of Bailiwick

(Des and photo Courvoisier)

1975 (6 June). *Victor Hugo's Exile in Guernsey.* *T* **50** *and similar multicoloured designs. P* 11½.
126 3½p. Type **50** 8 8
127 4p. Candie Gardens (*vert*) 8 8
128 8p. United Europe Oak, Hauteville (*vert*) 30 35
129 10p. Tapestry Room, Hauteville 45 50
MS130 114 × 143 mm. Nos. 126/9 .. .. 1·00 1·10

(Des and photo Delrieu)

1975 (7 Oct). *Christmas. Multicoloured designs each showing Globe as T* **51.** *P* 13.
131 4p. Type **51** 8 10
132 6p. Guernsey flag 12 15
133 10p. Guernsey flag and Alderney shield (*horiz*) 25 25
134 12p. Guernsey flag and Sark shield (*horiz*) .. 35 40

52 Les Hanois

(Des and photo Courvoisier)

1976 (10 Feb). *Lighthouses.* *T* **52** *and similar horiz designs. Multicoloured. P* 11½.
135 4p. Type **52** 8 8
136 6p. Les Casquets 12 12
137 11p. Quesnard 40 50
138 13p. Point Robert 50 55

53 Milk Can

(Des and photo Courvoisier)

1976 (29 May). *Europa.* *T* **53** *and similar horiz design. P* 11½.
139 10p. chestnut and greenish black 50 50
140 25p. slate and deep dull blue 60 60
Design:—25p. Christening Cup.

54 Pine Forest, Guernsey

(Des and photo Courvoisier)

1976 (3 Aug). *Bailiwick Views.* *T* **54** *and similar multicoloured designs. P* 11½.
141 5p. Type **54** 15 15
142 7p. Herm and Jethou 15 15
143 11p. Grand Greve Bay, Sark (*vert*) 45 45
144 13p. Trois Vaux Bay, Alderney (*vert*) .. 45 45

55 Royal Court House, Guernsey

56 Queen Elizabeth II

(Des and photo Courvoisier)

1976 (14 Oct). *Christmas. Buildings.* *T* **55** *and similar horiz designs. Multicoloured. P* 11½.
145 5p. Type **55** 15 15
146 7p. Elizabeth College, Guernsey 15 15
147 11p. La Seigneurie, Sark 45 45
148 13p. Island Hall, Alderney 45 45

(Des R. Granger Barrett. Photo Courvoisier)

1977 (8 Feb). *Silver Jubilee.* *T* **56** *and similar vert design. Multicoloured. P* 11½.
149 7p. Type **56** 25 25
150 35p. Queen Elizabeth (half-length portrait) 85 85

57 Woodland, Talbot's Valley

58 Statue-menhir, Castel

(Des and photo Courvoisier)

1977 (17 May). *Europa.* *T* **57** *and similar horiz design. Multicoloured. P* 11½.
151 7p. Type **57** 15 15
152 25p. Pastureland, Talbot's Valley 70 70

(Des and photo Courvoisier)

1977 (2 Aug). *Prehistoric Monuments.* *T* **58** *and similar multicoloured designs. P* 11½.
153 5p. Type **58** 10 10
154 7p. Megalithic tomb, St. Saviour (*horiz*) .. 15 15
155 11p. Cist, Tourgis (*horiz*) 45 45
156 13p. Statue-menhir, St. Martin 45 45

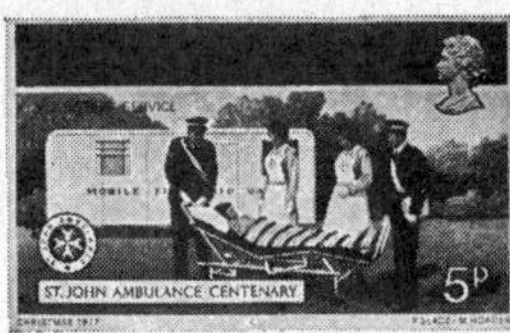

59 Mobile First Aid Unit

(Des P. Slade and M. Horder. Photo Courvoisier)

1977 (25 Oct). *Christmas and St. John Ambulance Centenary.* *T* **59** *and similar multicoloured designs. P* 11½.
157 5p. Type **59** 10 10
158 7p. Mobile radar unit 15 15
159 11p. Marine Ambulance *Flying Christine II* (*vert*) 45 45
160 13p. Cliff rescue (*vert*) 45 45

60 View from Clifton, *circa* 1830

(Des, recess and litho D.L.R.)

1978 (7 Feb). *Old Guernsey Prints* (1*st series*). *T* **60** *and similar horiz designs. P* 14 × 13½.
161 5p. black and pale apple-green 10 10
162 7p. black and stone 12 12
163 11p. black and light pink 45 45
164 13p. black and light azure 45 45
Designs:—7p. Market Square, St. Peter Port, *circa* 1838; 11p. Petit-Bo Bay, *circa* 1839; 13p. The Quay, St. Peter Port, *circa* 1830.
See also Nos. 249/52.

61 *Prosperity* Memorial

62 Queen Elizabeth II

(Des R. Granger Barrett. Litho Questa)

1978 (2 May). *Europa.* *T* **61** *and similar vert design. Multicoloured. P* 14½.
165 5p. Type **61** 15 15
166 7p. Victoria Monument 25 25

(Des R. Granger Barrett from bust by Arnold Machin. Photo Courvoisier)

1978 (2 May). *25th Anniv of Coronation. P* 11½.
167 **62** 20p. black, grey and bright blue 50 50

1978 (28 June). *Royal Visit. Design as No.* 167 *but inscr.* "VISIT OF H.M. THE QUEEN AND H.R.H. THE DUKE OF EDINBURGH JUNE 28–29, 1978 TO THE BAILIWICK OF GUERNSEY".
168 **62** 7p. black, grey and bright green 20 20

63 Northern Gannet

(Des J.W. Photo Courvoisier)

1978 (29 Aug). *Birds. T* **63** *and similar horiz designs. Multicoloured. P* 11½.

No.				
169	5p.	Type **63**	10	15
170	7p.	Firecrest	20	20
171	11p.	Dartford Warbler	35	35
172	13p.	Spotted Red-shank	35	35

64 Solanum

(Des and photo Courvoisier)

1978 (31 Oct). *Christmas. T* **64** *and similar designs. P* 11½.

No.				
173	5p.	multicoloured	10	15
174	7p.	multicoloured	20	30
175	11p.	multicoloured	35	35
176	13p.	dp blue-green, grey & greenish yellow	35	30

Designs: *Horiz*—7p. Christmas Rose. *Vert*—11p. Holly; 13p. Mistletoe.

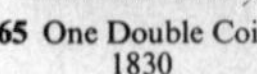

65 One Double Coin, 1830

66 Ten Shillings William I Commemorative Coin, 1966

66a Seal of the Bailiwick

(Des R. Reed and Courvoisier (£5). Photo Courvoisier)

1979 (13 Feb)–**83**. *Designs as T* **65/6***a*. *P* 11½.

No.				
177	½p.	multicoloured	5	5
		a. Booklet pane of 10. Nos. 177 × 2, 178 × 3, 179 × 2, 181, 183 and 187 (6.5.80)	55	
		b. Booklet pane of 10. Nos. 177 × 2, 178, 179 × 2, 183 × 2 and 187 × 3 (6.5.80)	85	
178	1p.	multicoloured	5	5
		a. Booklet strip of 4. Nos. 178 × 2, 179 and 182	25	
179	2p.	multicoloured	5	5
		a. Booklet strip of 5. Nos. 179, 182 × 2 and 184 × 2	55	
180	4p.	multicoloured	8	10
		a. Booklet pane of 10. Nos. 180 and 184, each × 5 (24.2.81)	1·10	
		b. Booklet pane of 15. Nos. 180, 184 and 190, each × 5 (24.2.81)	2·10	
		c. Booklet pane of 10. Nos. 180 × 2, 185 × 3 and 191 × 5 (14.3.83)	1·75	
		d. Booklet pane of 15. Nos. 180, 185 and 191 each × 5 (14.3.83)	2·25	
181	5p.	grey-black, silver & chestnut (*shades*)	8	10
		b. Booklet pane. Nos. 181 × 5, 184 × 4 and 191 (2.2.82)	1·25	
		c. Booklet pane. Nos. 181, 184 and 191 each × 5 (2.2.82)	2·25	
182	6p.	grey-black, silver and brown-red	10	12
183	7p.	grey-black, silver and green	12	15
184	8p.	grey-black, silver and brown	15	20
185	9p.	multicoloured	15	20
186	10p.	multicoloured (green background)	50	20
187	10p.	mult (orange background) (5.2.80)	20	25
188	11p.	multicoloured	20	25
189	11½p.	multicoloured (5.2.80)	20	25
190	12p.	multicoloured	20	25
191	13p.	multicoloured	25	30
192	14p.	grey-black, silver and dull blue	25	30
193	15p.	grey-black, silver and bistre	25	30
194	20p.	grey-black, silver and dull brown	35	40
195	50p.	grey-black, orange-red and silver (5.2.80)	90	1·00
196	£1	grey-blk, yellowish grn & silver (5.2.80)	1·75	1·90
197	£2	grey-black, new blue and silver (5.2.80)	3·50	3·75
198	£5	multicoloured (22.5.81)	9·00	9·50
177/98		*Set of* 22	16·50	17·50

Coins: *Vert as T* **65**—1p. Two doubles, 1899; 2p. Four doubles, 1902; 4p. Eight doubles 1959; 5p. Three pence, 1956; 6p. Five new pence, 1968; 7p. Fifty new pence, 1969; 8p. Ten new pence, 1970; 9p. Half new penny, 1971; 10p. (*both*), One new penny, 1971; 11p. Two new pence, 1971; 11½p. Half penny, 1979; 12p. One penny, 1977; 13p. Two pence, 1977; 14p. Five pence, 1977; 15p. Ten pence, 1977; 20p. Twenty-five pence, 1972. *Horiz as T* **66**—£1 Silver Jubilee commemorative crown, 1977; £2 Royal Silver Wedding crown, 1972.

Nos. 177a/b, 178a, 179a, 180a/d and 181b/c come from special booklet sheets of 40 (8 × 5) (Nos. 177a and 178a); 30 (6 × 5) (Nos. 177b, 180a/b, 180d and 181 b/c), 25 (5 × 5) (No. 179a) or 20 (4 × 5) No. 180c). These were put on sale in addition to the normal sheets, being first separated into strips, then folded and either affixed by the selvedge to booklet covers or supplied loose in plastic wallets.

67 Pillar-box and Postmark, 1853, Mail Van and Postmark, 1979

68 Steam Tram, 1879

(Des R. Granger Barrett. Photo Courvoisier)

1979 (8 May). *Europa. Communications. T* **67** *and similar vert design. Multicoloured. P* 11½.

No.				
201	6p.	Type **67**	20	15
202	8p.	Telephone, 1897 and telex machine, 1979	25	20

(Photo Courvoisier)

1979 (7 Aug). *History of Public Transport. T* **68** *and similar horiz designs. Multicoloured. P* 11½.

No.				
203	6p.	Type **68**	12	12
204	8p.	Electric tram, 1896	20	20
205	11p.	Motor bus, 1911	35	35
206	13p.	Motor bus, 1979	35	35

69 Bureau and Postal Headquarters

70 Major-General Le Marchant

(Des R. Granger Barrett. Photo Courvoisier)

1979 (1 Oct). *Christmas and* 10*th Anniv of Guernsey Postal Administration. T* **69** *and similar horiz designs. Multicoloured. P* 11½.

No.				
207	6p.	Type **69**	15	12
208	8p.	"Mails and telegrams"	25	20
209	13p.	"Parcels"	30	25
210	15p.	"Philately"	40	40
MS211		120 × 80 mm. Nos. 207/10	1·00	90

(Des and photo Courvoisier)

1980 (6 May). *Europa. Personalities. T* **70** *and similar vert design. Multicoloured. P* 11½.

No.				
212	10p.	Type **70**	25	25
213	13½p.	Admiral Lord De Saumarez	30	30

71 Policewoman with Lost Child

(Litho J.W.)

1980 (6 May). 60*th Anniv of Guernsey Police Force. T* **71** *and similar horiz designs. Multicoloured. P* 13½ × 14.

No.				
214	7p.	Type **71**	15	15
215	15p.	Police motorcyclist escorting lorry	40	35
216	17½p.	Police dog-handler	50	45

72 Golden Guernsey Goat

(Des P. Lambert. Photo Delrieu)

1980 (5 Aug). *Golden Guernsey Goats. T* **72** *and similar horiz designs showing goats. P* 13.

No.				
217	7p.	multicoloured	15	20
218	10p.	multicoloured	30	30
219	15p.	multicoloured	50	50
220	17½p.	multicoloured	50	50

NEW INFORMATION

The editor is always interested to correspond with people who have new information that will improve or correct the Catalogue.

73 "Sark Cottage"

(Photo Courvoisier)

1980 (15 Nov). *Christmas. Peter le Lievre Paintings. T* **73** *and similar multicoloured designs. P* 11½.

No.				
221	7p.	Type **73**	20	20
222	10p.	"Moulin Huet"	25	25
223	13½p.	"Boats at Sea"	30	30
224	15p.	"Cow Lane" (*vert*)	40	40
225	17½p.	"Peter le Lievre" (*vert*)	50	45

74 Common Blue

75 Sailors paying respect to "Le Petit Bonhomme Andriou" (rock resembling head of a man)

(Photo Harrison)

1981 (24 Feb). *Butterflies. T* **74** *and similar horiz designs. Multicoloured. P* 14.

No.				
226	8p.	Type **74**	20	20
227	12p.	Red Admiral	35	30
228	22p.	Small Tortoiseshell	60	55
229	25p.	Wall Brown	60	55

(Des C. Abbott. Litho Questa)

1981 (22 May). *Europa. Folklore. T* **75** *and similar vert design. P* 14½.

No.				
230	12p.	gold, red-brown and cinnamon	30	30
231	18p.	gold, indigo and azure	50	50

Design:—18p. Fairies and Guernsey Lily.

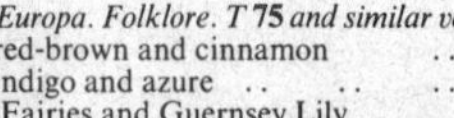

76 Prince Charles

77 Sark Launch

(Des C. Abbott. Litho Questa)

1981 (29 July). *Royal Wedding. T* **76** *and similar multicoloured designs. P* 14½.

No.				
232	8p.	Type **76**	20	20
		a. Horiz strip of 3. Nos. 232/4	65	
233	8p.	Prince Charles and Lady Diana Spencer	20	20
234	8p.	Lady Diana	20	20
235	12p.	Type **76**	30	30
		a. Horiz strip of 3. Nos. 235/7	1·00	
236	12p.	As No. 233	30	30
237	12p.	As No. 234	30	30
238	25p.	Royal family (49 × 32 *mm*)	75	85
MS239		104 × 127 mm. Nos. 232/8. P 14	2·50	2·50
232/8		*Set of* 7	2·25	2·25

The 8 and 12p. values were each printed together, *se-tenant*, in horizontal strips of 3 throughout the sheets.

(Des and photo Courvoisier)

1981 (25 Aug). *Inter-island Transport. T* **77** *and similar horiz designs. Multicoloured. P* 11½.

No.				
240	8p.	Type **77**	15	15
241	12p.	"Trislander" aeroplane	30	25
242	18p.	Hydrofoil	45	40
243	22p.	Herm catamaran	55	50
244	25p.	Alderney coaster	65	60

78 Rifle Shooting

79 Sir Edgar MacCulloch (founder-president) and Guille-Allès Library, St. Peter Port

(Des P. le Vasseur. Litho Questa)

1981 (17 Nov). *International Year for Disabled Persons. T* **78** *and similar horiz designs. Multicoloured. P* 14½.

No.				
245	8p.	Type **78**	15	15
246	12p.	Riding	40	40
247	22p.	Swimming	55	55
248	25p.	"Work"	60	60

(Des, recess and litho D.L.R.)

1982 (2 Feb). *Old Guernsey Prints (2nd series). Prints from sketches by T. Compton. Horiz designs as T* **60**. *P* 14 × 13½.

249	8p.	black and pale blue	15	15
250	12p.	black and pale turquoise-green	40	40
251	22p.	black and pale yellow-brown	55	55
252	25p.	black and pale rose-lilac	60	60

Designs:—8p. Jethou; 12p. Fermain Bay; 22p. The Terres; 25p. St. Peter Port.

(Des G. Drummond. Photo Courvoisier)

1982 (28 Apr). *Centenary of La Société Guernesiaise. T* **79** *and similar horiz designs. Multicoloured. P* 11½.

253	8p.	Type **79**	20	20
254	13p.	French invasion fleet crossing English Channel, 1066 ("History")	40	40
255	20p.	H.M.S. *Crescent* ("History")	50	50
256	24p.	Dragonfly ("Entomology")	65	65
257	26p.	Common Snipe caught for ringing ("Ornithology")	65	65
258	29p.	Samian Bowl, 160–200 A.D. ("Archaeology")	85	85
253/8		*Set of* 6	3·00	3·00

The 13 and 20p. values also include the Europa C.E.P.T. emblem in the designs.

80 "Sea Scouts" **81** Midnight Mass

(Des W.L.G. Creative Services Ltd. Litho Questa)

1982 (13 July). *75th Anniv of Boy Scout Movement. T* **80** *and similar vert designs. Multicoloured. P* 14½ × 14.

259	8p.	Type **80**	25	20
260	13p.	"Scouts"	30	35
261	26p.	"Cub Scouts"	60	60
262	29p.	"Air Scouts"	75	75

(Des Lynette Hemmant. Photo Harrison)

1982 (12 Oct). *Christmas. T* **81** *and similar horiz designs. Multicoloured. P* 14½.

263	8p.	Type **81**	20	15
	a.	Black (Queen's head, value and inscr) omitted		
264	13p.	Exchanging gifts	40	55
265	24p.	Christmas meal	65	65
266	26p.	Exchanging cards	65	65
267	29p.	Queen's Christmas message	75	75

82 Flute Player and Boats **83** Building Albert Pier Extension, 1850s

(Des Sally Stiff. Photo Harrison)

1983 (18 Jan). *Centenary of Boys' Brigade. T* **82** *and similar horiz designs. Multicoloured. P* 14.

268	8p.	Type **82**	20	20
269	13p.	Cymbal player and tug 'o' war	40	40
270	24p.	Trumpet player and bible class	65	65
271	26p.	Drummer and cadets marching	65	65
272	29p.	Boys' Brigade band	75	75

(Des C. Abbott. Photo Courvoisier)

1983 (14 Mar). *Europa. Development of St. Peter Port Harbour. T* **83** *and similar horiz designs. Multicoloured. P* 11½.

273	13p.	Type **83**	30	30
	a.	Horiz pair. Nos. 273/4	60	60
274	13p.	St. Peter Port Harbour, 1983	30	30
275	20p.	St. Peter Port, 1680	70	70
	a.	Horiz pair. Nos. 275/6	1·40	1·40
276	20p.	Artist's impression of future development scheme	70	70

The two designs of each value were issued together, *se-tenant*, in horizontal pairs throughout the sheets.

84 "View at Guernsey" (Renoir)

(Des and photo Courvoisier)

1983 (6 Sept). *Centenary of Renoir's Visit to Guernsey. T* **84** *and similar multicoloured designs, showing paintings. P* 11 × 11½ (13*p*.) *or* 11½ (*others*).

277	9p.	Type **84**	20	25
278	13p.	"Children on the Seashore" (25 × 39 *mm*)	30	35
279	26p.	"Marine, Guernesey"	55	60
280	28p.	"La Baie du Moulin Huet à travers les Arbres"	70	70
281	31p.	"Brouillard à Guernesey"	75	75

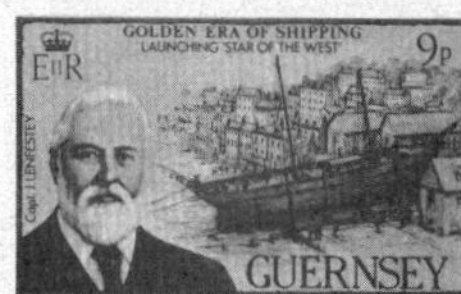

85 Launching *Star of the West*, 1869, and Capt. J. Lenfestey

(Des R. Granger Barrett. Litho Questa)

1983 (15 Nov). *Guernsey Shipping. "Star of the West". T* **85** *and similar horiz designs. Multicoloured. P* 14.

282	9p.	Type **85**	20	25
283	13p.	Leaving St. Peter Port	30	30
284	26p.	Off Rio Grande Bar	60	60
285	28p.	Off St. Lucia	75	75
286	31p.	Map of 1879–80 voyage	80	80

86 Dame of Sark as Young Woman

(Des Jennifer Toombs. Litho Questa)

1984 (7 Feb). *Birth Centenary of Sibyl Hathaway, Dame of Sark. T* **86** *and similar horiz designs. Multicoloured. P* 14½.

287	9p.	Type **86**	20	25
288	13p.	German occupation, 1940–45	30	30
289	26p.	Royal Visit, 1957	60	60
290	28p.	Chief Pleas	75	75
291	31p.	The Dame of Sark rose	80	80

87 C.E.P.T. 25th Anniversary Logo

(Des J. Larrivière and C. Abbott. Litho Questa)

1984 (10 Apr). *Europa. P* 15 × 14½.

292 **87**	13p.	cobalt, dull ultramarine and black	30	35
293	20½p.	emerald, deep dull green and black	50	50

88 The Royal Court and St. George's Flag **89** St. Apolline Chapel

(Des C. Abbott. Litho Questa)

1984 (10 Apr). *Links with the Commonwealth. T* **88** *and similar horiz design. Multicoloured. P* 14 × 14½.

294	9p.	Type **88**	25	25
295	31p.	Castle Cornet and Union flag	75	75

(Des C. Abbott. Litho Questa

1984 (18 Sept)–**85**. *Views. T* **89** *and similar multicoloured designs. P* 14½.

298	3p.	Type **89**	5	5
299	4p.	Petit Port (*horiz*)	8	10
	a.	Booklet pane. Nos. 299 × 2, 304 × 3 and 307 × 5	1·75	
	b.	Booklet pane. Nos. 299, 304 and 307, each × 5	2·25	
304	9p.	Cambridge Berth (*horiz*)	15	20
	a.	Booklet pane. Nos. 304 × 4 and 308 × 6 (19.3.85)	2·10	
	b.	Booklet pane. Nos. 304 × 2 and 308 × 8 (19.3.85)	2·25	
305	10p.	Belvior, Herm (*horiz*)	20	25
307	13p.	St. Saviours reservoir (*horiz*)	25	30
308	14p.	St. Peter Port	25	30
310	20p.	La Coupee, Sark (*horiz*)	35	40
312	40p.	Torteval church	70	75
313	50p.	Bordeaux (*horiz*)	90	1·00
314	£1	Albecq (*horiz*)	1·75	1·90
298/314		*Set of* 10	4·25	4·75

Booklet panes. Nos. 299a/b and 304a/b have margins all round and were issued, folded and loose, within the booklet covers.

Numbers have been reserved for future additions to this set.

90 "A Partridge in a Pear Tree" **91** Sir John Doyle and Coat of Arms

(Des R. Downer. Litho Questa)

1984 (20 Nov). *Christmas. "The Twelve Days of Christmas". T* **90** *and similar vert designs. Multicoloured. P* 14½.

316	5p.	Type **90**	10	12
	a.	Sheetlet of 12. Nos. 316/27	1·10	
317	5p.	"Two turtle doves"	10	12
318	5p.	"Three French hens"	10	12
319	5p.	"Four colly birds"	10	12
320	5p.	"Five gold rings"	10	12
321	5p.	"Six geese a-laying"	10	12
322	5p.	"Seven swans a-swimming"	10	12
323	5p.	"Eight maids a-milking"	10	12
324	5p.	"Nine drummers drumming"	10	12
325	5p.	"Ten pipers piping"	10	12
326	5p.	"Eleven ladies dancing"	10	12
327	5p.	"Twelve lords a-leaping"	10	12
316/27		*Set of* 12	1·10	1·25

Nos. 316/27 were issued, *se-tenant*, in sheetlets of 12.

(Des E. Stemp. Photo Courvoisier)

1984 (20 Nov). *150th Death Anniv of Lieut-General Sir John Doyle. T* **91** *and similar multicoloured designs. Granite paper. P* 11½.

328	13p.	Type **91**	25	30
329	29p.	Battle of Germantown, 1777 (*horiz*)	55	60
330	31p.	Reclamation of Braye du Valle, 1806 (*horiz*)	60	65
331	34p.	Mail for Alderney, 1812 (*horiz*)	70	75

92 Cuckoo Wrasse

(Des P. Barrett. Photo Courvoisier)

1985 (22 Jan). *Fishes. T* **92** *and similar horiz designs. Multicoloured. Granite paper. P* 11½.

332	9p.	Type **92**	20	25
333	13p.	Red Gurnard	25	30
334	29p.	Red Mullet	55	60
335	31p.	Mackerel	60	65
336	34p.	Sunfish	70	75

POSTAGE DUE STAMPS

D 1 Castle Cornet **D 2** St. Peter Port

(Des R. Granger Barrett. Photo Delrieu)

1969 (1 Oct). *Value in black; background colour given. No wmk. P* 12½ × 12.

D1	**D 1**	1d.	plum	2·50	1·00
D2		2d.	bright green	2·50	1·50
D3		3d.	vermilion	4·00	4·00
D4		4d.	ultramarine	5·00	5·00
D5		5d.	yellow-ochre	6·00	6·00
D6		6d.	turquoise-blue	9·00	10·00
D7		1s.	lake-brown	19·00	18·00
D1/7			*Set of* 7	42·00	40·00

1971 (15 Feb)–**76**. *As Type* D **1** *but values in decimal currency.*

D 8	**D 1**	½p.	plum	10	10
D 9		1p.	bright green	10	10
D10		2p.	vermilion	10	10
D11		3p.	ultramarine	10	12
D12		4p.	yellow-ochre	12	12
D13		5p.	turquoise-blue	15	15
D14		6p.	violet (10.2.76)	25	25
D15		8p.	light yellow-orange (7.10.75)	35	35
D16		10p.	lake-brown	40	40
D17		15p.	grey (10.2.76)	50	50
D8/17			*Set of* 10	2·00	2·00

(Photo Delrieu)

1977 (2 Aug)–**80**. *Face value in black; background colour given. P* 13.

D18	**D 2**	½p.	lake-brown	5	5
D19		1p.	bright purple	5	5
D20		2p.	bright orange	5	5
D21		3p.	vermilion	8	10
D22		4p.	turquoise-blue	10	12
D23		5p.	yellow-green	15	15
D24		6p.	turquoise-green	15	20
D25		8p.	brown-ochre	20	20
D26		10p.	ultramarine	25	25
D27		14p.	green (5.2.80)	35	35
D28		15p.	bright violet	35	35
D29		16p.	rose-red (5.2.80)	40	40
D18/29			*Set of* 12	2·10	2·10

D 3 Milking Cow

(Litho Questa)

1982 (13 July). *Guernsey Scenes, circa* 1900. *Horiz designs as Type* D 3. *P* 14½.

D30	1p. indigo, blue-black and bright green ..	5	5
D31	2p. sepia, yellow-brown and azure ..	5	5
D32	3p. blackish green, black and lilac ..	5	5
D33	4p. bottle-green, black and dull orange ..	8	10
D34	5p. dp violet-blue, blue-black & turq-grn ..	8	10
D35	16p. deep grey-blue, deep blue and cobalt ..	30	35
D36	18p. steel-blue, indigo and apple-green ..	30	35
D37	20p. brown-olive, agate and pale blue ..	35	40
D38	25p. Prussian blue, blue-black and rose-pink	45	50
D39	30p. dp bluish grn, blackish ol & bistre-yell	50	55
D40	50p. olive-brown, sepia and dull violet-blue	90	95
D41	£1 light brown, brown and pale brown ..	1·75	1·90
D30/41	.. .. *Set of* 12	4·25	4·75

Designs:—2p. Vale Mill; 3p. Sark cottage; 4p. Quay-side, St. Peter Port; 5p. Well, Water Lane, Moulin Huet; 16p. Seaweed gathering; 18p. Upper Walk, White Rock; 20p. Cobo Bay; 25p. Saint's Bay; 30p. La Coupee, Sark; 50p. Old Harbour, St. Peter Port; £1 Greenhouses, Doyle Road, St. Peter Port.

ALDERNEY

The following issues are provided by the Guernsey Post Office for use on Alderney. They are also valid for postal purposes throughout the rest of the Bailiwick of Guernsey.

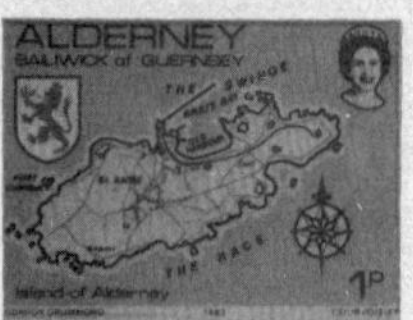

A **1** Island Map

(Des G. Drummond. Photo Courvoisier)

1983 (14 June). *Island Scenes. Type* A **1** *and similar horiz designs. Multicoloured. P* 11½.

A 1	1p. Type A **1**	5	5
A 2	4p. Hanging Rock	8	10
A 3	9p. States' Building, St. Anne	15	20
A 4	10p. St. Anne's Church	20	25
A 5	11p. Yachts in Braye Bay	20	25
A 6	12p. Victoria St., St. Anne	20	25
A 7	13p. Map of Channel	25	30
A 8	14p. Fort Clonque	25	30
A 9	15p. Corblets Bay and Fort	25	30
A10	16p. Old Tower, St. Anne	30	35
A11	17p. Golf course and Essex Castle	30	35
A12	18p. Old Harbour	30	35
A1/12	.. .. *Set of* 12	2·25	2·75

A2 Oystercatcher

(Des and photo Harrison)

1984 (12 June). *Birds. Type* **A2** *and similar horiz designs. Multicoloured. P* 14½.

A13	9p. Type **A2**	20	20
A14	13p. Turnstone	30	30
A15	26p. Ringed Plover	60	60
A16	28p. Dunlin	75	75
A17	31p. Curlew	80	80

A 3 Wessex Helicopter of the Queen's Flight

(Des A. Theobald. Photo Courvoisier)

1985 (19 Mar). *50th Anniv of Alderney Airport. Type* **A 3** *and similar horiz designs. Multicoloured. Granite paper. P* 11½.

A18	9p. Type A **3**	20	25
A19	13p. Britten-Norman "Trislander"	25	30
A20	29p. De Havilland "Heron"	60	65
A21	31p. De Havilland "Dragon Rapide"	60	65
A22	34p. Saro "Windhover"	70	75

ISLE OF MAN

REGIONAL ISSUES

Although specifically issued for use in the Isle of Man, these issues were also valid for use throughout Great Britain.

DATES OF ISSUE: The note at the beginning of Guernsey also applies here.

Nos. 8/11 and current stamps of Great Britain were withdrawn from sale on the island from 5 July 1973 when the independent postal administration was established but remained valid for use there for a time. They also remained on sale at the Philatelic Sales counters in the United Kingdom until 4 July 1974.

1

2

3

(Des J. Nicholson. Portrait by Dorothy Wilding Ltd. Photo Harrison)

1958 (18 Aug)–**68.** *W* **179.** *P* 15 × 14.

1	**1**	2½d. carmine-red (8.6.64)	50	1·50
2	**2**	3d. deep lilac	5	5
		a. Chalk-surfaced paper (17.5.63) ..	22·00	12·00
		p. One centre phosphor band (27.6.68)	5	35
3		4d. ultramarine (7.2.66)	70	75
		p. Two phosphor bands (5.7.67) ..	10	10

No. 2a was released in London sometime after 17 May 1963, this being the date of issue in Douglas.

1968–69. *No wmk. Chalk-surfaced paper. PVA gum. One centre phosphor band (Nos. 5/6) or two phosphor bands (others). P* 15 × 14.

4	**2**	4d. blue (24.6.68)	10	60
5		4d. olive-sepia (4.9.68)	10	40
6		4d. bright vermilion (26.2.69)	50	50
7		5d. royal blue (4.9.68)	50	40

(Des J. Matthews. Portrait after plaster cast by Arnold Machin. Photo Harrison)

1971 (7 July). *Decimal Currency. Chalk-surfaced paper. One centre phosphor band (2½p.) or two phosphor bands (others). P* 15 × 14.

8	**3**	2½p. bright magenta	10	10
9		3p. ultramarine	12	20
10		5p. reddish violet	70	1·50
11		7½p. chestnut	70	1·75

All values exist with PVA gum on ordinary cream paper and the 2½p. and 3p. also on fluorescent white paper.

INDEPENDENT POSTAL ADMINISTRATION

4 Castletown

5 Manx Cat

(Des J. Nicholson. Photo Courvoisier)

1973 (5 July)–**75.** *Horiz designs as T* **4** *(½p. to 9p., 11p. and 13p.) or vert designs as T* **5** *(others). Multicoloured. P* 11½.

12	½p. Type **4**	8	5
13	1p. Port Erin	8	5
14	1½p. Snaefell	8	5
15	2p. Laxey	8	5
16	2½p. Tynwald Hill	8	5
17	3p. Douglas Promenade	8	5
18	3½p. Port St. Mary	10	5
19	4p. Fairy Bridge	10	8
20	4½p. As 2½p. (8.1.75)	50	8
21	5p. Peel	20	8
22	5½p. As 3p. (28.5.75)	25	10
23	6p. Cregneish	20	12
24	7p. As 2p. (28.5.75)	25	15
25	7½p. Ramsey Bay	20	15
26	8p. As 7½p. (8.1.75)	60	20
27	9p. Douglas Bay	20	20
28	10p. Type **5**	25	30
29	11p. Monk's Bridge, Ballasalla (29.10.75) ..	45	30
30	13p. Derbyhaven (29.10.75)	45	40
31	20p. Manx Loaghtyn Ram	40	50
32	50p. Manx Shearwater	90	1·10
33	£1 Viking Longship	2·25	2·25
12/33	.. .. *Set of* 22	6·50	6·50

Some printings from late 1973 have invisible gum.

6 Viking landing on Man, A.D. 938

7 "Sutherland"

(Des J. Nicholson. Photo Harrison)

1973 (5 July). *Inauguration of Postal Independence. P* 14.

34	**6**	15p. multicoloured	80	90

(Des J. Nicholson. Photo Harrison)

1973 (4 Aug). *Steam Railway Centenary. T* **7** *and similar horiz designs. Multicoloured. P* 15 × 14.

35	2½p.	Type **7**	20	15
36	3p.	"Caledonia"	20	20
37	7½p.	"Kissack"	1·50	1·00
38	9p.	"Pender"	1·50	1·00

8 Leslie Randles, First Winner, 1923

(Des J. Nicholson. Litho J.W.)

1973 (4 Sept). *Golden Jubilee of the Manx Grand Prix. T* **8** *and similar horiz design. Multicoloured. P* 14.

39	3p.	Type **8**	20	20
40	3½p.	Alan Holmes, Double Winner, 1957 ..	20	20

9 Princess Anne and Capt. Mark Phillips

(Des A. Larkins. Recess and litho D.L.R.)

1973 (14 Nov). *Royal Wedding. P* 13½.

41 **9**	25p.	multicoloured	1·10	1·25

10 Badge, Citation and Sir William Hillary (Founder)

(Des J. Nicholson. Photo Courvoisier)

1974 (4 Mar). *150th Anniv of Royal National Lifeboat Institution. T* **10** *and similar horiz designs. Multicoloured. P* 11½.

42	3p.	Type **10**	10	10
43	3½p.	Wreck of *St. George*, 1830	12	12
44	8p.	R.N.L.B. *Manchester & Salford*, 1868–87	55	55
45	10p.	R.N.L.B. *Osman Gabriel*	55	55

11 Stanley Woods, 1935

(Des J. Nicholson. Litho D.L.R.)

1974 (29 May). *Tourist Trophy Motor-cycle Races* (*1st issue*). *T* **11** *and similar horiz designs. Multicoloured. P* 13 × 13½.

46	3p.	Type **11**	10	10
47	3½p.	Freddy Frith, 1937	10	10
48	8p.	Max Deubel and Emil Horner, 1961 ..	50	50
49	10p.	Mike Hailwood, 1961	50	50

See also Nos. 63/6.

12 Rushen Abbey and Arms

(Des J. Nicholson from ideas by G. Kneale. Litho Questa (3½p., 10p.) or J.W. (others))

1974 (18 Sept). *Historical Anniversaries. T* **12** *and similar horiz designs. Multicoloured. P* 14.

50	3½p.	Type **12**	12	10
51	4½p.	Magnus Haraldson rows King Edgar on the Dee	15	12
52	8p.	King Magnus and Norse fleet	40	40
53	10p.	Bridge at Avignon and bishop's mitre ..	40	40

Nos. 50 and 53 mark the 600th Death Anniv of William Russell, Bishop of Sodor and Man, and Nos. 51/2 the 1000th Anniv of the rule of King Magnus Haraldson.

13 Churchill and Bugler Dunne at Colenso, 1899

(Des G. Kneale. Photo Courvoisier)

1974 (22 Nov). *Birth Centenary of Sir Winston Churchill. T* **13** *and similar horiz designs. Multicoloured. P* 11½.

54	3½p.	Type **13**	10	10
55	4½p.	Churchill and Government Buildings, Douglas	10	10
56	8p.	Churchill and Manx ack-ack crew ..	50	50
57	20p.	Churchill as Freeman of Douglas ..	50	50
MS58		121 × 91 mm. Nos. 54/7	95	95

No. **MS**58 is inscribed "30th Nov. 1974".

14 Cabin School and Names of Pioneers

(Des J. Nicholson. Photo Courvoisier)

1975 (14 Mar). *Manx Pioneers in Cleveland, Ohio. T* **14** *and similar horiz designs. Multicoloured. P* 11½.

59	4½p.	Type **14**	10	10
60	5½p.	Terminal Tower Building, J. Gill and R. Carran	15	15
61	8p.	Clague House Museum, and Robert and Margaret Clague	35	35
62	10p.	S.S. *William T. Graves* and Thomas Quayle	45	45

15 Tom Sheard, 1923

(Des J. Nicholson. Litho J.W.)

1975 (28 May). *Tourist Trophy Motor-cycle Races* (*2nd issue*). *T* **15** *and similar horiz designs. Multicoloured. P* 13½.

63	5½p.	Type **15**	12	12
64	7p.	Walter Handley, 1925	25	20
65	10p.	Geoff Duke, 1955	30	30
66	12p.	Peter Williams, 1973	30	30

16 Sir George Goldie and Birthplace

17 Title Page of Manx Bible

(Des G. Kneale. Photo Courvoisier)

1975 (9 Sept). *50th Death Anniv of Sir George Goldie. T* **16** *and similar multicoloured designs. P* 11½.

67	5½p.	Type **16**	10	10
68	7p.	Goldie and map of Africa (*vert*) ..	20	20
69	10p.	Goldie as President of Geographical Society (*vert*)	30	30
70	12p.	River scene on the Niger	35	35

(Des J. Nicholson. Litho Questa)

1975 (29 Oct). *Christmas and Bicentenary of Manx Bible. T* **17** *and similar horiz designs. Multicoloured. P* 14.

71	5½p.	Type **17**	12	12
72	7p.	Rev. Philip Moore and Ballaugh Old Church	20	20
73	11p.	Bishop Hildesley and Bishops Court ..	40	40
74	13p.	John Kelly saving Bible manuscript ..	40	40

18 William Christian listening to Patrick Henry

19 First Horse Tram, 1876

(Des and litho J.W.)

1976 (12 Mar). *Bicentenary of American Revolution. T* **18** *and similar vert designs. Multicoloured. P* 13½.

75	5½p.	Type **18**	15	20
76	7p.	Conveying the Fincastle Resolutions ..	20	25
77	13p.	Patrick Henry and William Christian ..	35	35
78	20p.	Christian as an Indian fighter	50	50
MS79		153 × 89 mm. Nos. 75/8. P 14	2·25	2·75

(Des J. Nicholson. Photo Courvoisier)

1976 (26 May). *Douglas Horse Trams Centenary. T* **19** *and similar horiz designs. Multicoloured. P* 11½.

80	5½p.	Type **19**	10	12
81	7p.	"Toast-rack" tram, 1890	15	15
82	11p.	Horse-bus, 1895	30	30
83	13p.	Royal tram, 1972	40	40

20 Barroose Beaker

21 Diocesan Banner

(Des J. Nicholson. Photo Courvoisier)

1976 (28 July). *Europa. Ceramic Art. T* **20** *and similar multicoloured designs. P* 11½.

84	5p.	Type **20**	35	50
	a.	Strip of 3. Nos. 84/6	95	
85	5p.	Souvenir teapot	35	50
86	5p.	Laxey jug	35	50
87	10p.	Cronk Aust food vessel (*horiz*) ..	45	50
	a.	Strip of 3. Nos. 87/9	1·25	
88	10p.	Sansbury bowl (*horiz*)	45	50
89	10p.	Knox urn (*horiz*)	45	50
84/9		.. .. *Set of* 6	2·00	2·75

Nos. 84/6 and 87/9 were each printed in sheets of 9 (3 × 3) the three designs being horizontally and vertically *se-tenant*.

(Des G. Kneale. Litho Questa)

1976 (14 Oct). *Christmas and Centenary of Mothers' Union. T* **21** *and similar vert designs. Multicoloured. P* 14½.

90	6p.	Type **21**	15	15
91	7p.	Onchan banner	15	15
92	11p.	Castletown banner	35	35
93	13p.	Ramsey banner	45	45

22 Queen Elizabeth II

(Des A. Larkins. Litho and recess D.L.R.)

1977 (1 Mar). *Silver Jubilee. T* **22** *and similar multicoloured designs. P* 14 × 13 (*7p.*) *or* 13 × 14 (*others*).

94	6p.	Type **22**	20	20
95	7p.	Queen Elizabeth and Prince Philip (*vert*)	25	20
96	25p.	Queen Elizabeth	65	65

The 25p. is similar to T **22** but has the portrait on the right.

23 Carrick Bay from "Tom-the-Dipper"

(Des J. Nicholson. Litho Questa)

1977 (26 May). *Europa. Landscapes. T* **23** *and similar horiz design. Multicoloured. P* 13½ × 14.

97	6p.	Type **23**	20	20
98	10p.	View from Ramsey	20	20

24 F. A. Applebee, 1912

(Des J. Nicholson. Litho J.W.)

1977 (26 May). *Linked Anniversaries. T* **24** *and similar horiz designs. Multicoloured. P* 13½.

99	6p.	Type **24**	15	15
100	7p.	St. John Ambulance Brigade at Governor's Bridge, *c.* 1938	15	15
101	11p.	Scouts working scoreboard	40	40
102	13p.	John Williams, 1976	40	40

The events commemorated are: 70th Anniv of Manx TT; 70th Anniv of Boy Scouts; Centenary of St John Ambulance Brigade.

25 Old Summer House, Mount Morrison, Peel

(Des and photo Courvoisier)

1977 (19 Oct). *Bicentenary of the First Visit of John Wesley. T* **25** *and similar horiz designs. Multicoloured. P* 11½.

103	6p. Type **25**	15	15
104	7p. Wesley preaching in Castletown Square	20	20
105	11p. Wesley preaching outside Braddan Church	40	40
106	13p. New Methodist Church, Douglas ..	45	45

Nos. 104/5 are larger, 38 × 26 mm.

26 H.M.S. *Ben-My-Chree* and Short "Type 184" Seaplane, 1915

(Des A. Theobald. Litho J.W.)

1978 (28 Feb). *R.A.F. Diamond Jubilee. T* **26** *and similar horiz designs. Multicoloured. P* 13½ × 14.

107	6p. Type **26**	15	15
108	7p. H.M.S. *Vindex* and Bristol "Scout", 1915	25	25
109	11p. Boulton Paul "Defiant" over Douglas Bay, 1941	40	40
110	13p. "Jaguar" over Ramsey, 1977	45	45

27 Watch Tower, Langness

27a Queen Elizabeth II

(Des J. Nicholson (½p. to £1), G. Kneale (£2). Litho Questa (½p. to 16p.). Photo Courvoisier (20p. to £2))

1978 (28 Feb)–**81.** *Various multicoloured designs.*

(*a*) *As T* **27**. A. *P* 14. B. *P* 14½

		A		B	
111	½p. Type **27**	5	5	40	40
112	1p. Jurby Church	5	5	30	40
113	6p. Government Buildings	15	12	†	
114	7p. Tynwald Hill	15	15	1·00	1·00
115	8p. Milner's Tower ..	20	20	50	50
116	9p. Laxey Wheel	20	20	50	50
117	10p. Castle Rushen ..	20	20	50	50
118	11p. St. Ninian's Church ..	25	25	50	60
119	12p. Tower of Refuge ..	25	30	30	30
120	13p. St. German's Cathedral	55	55	30	40
121	14p. Point of Ayre Lighthouse	35	35	40	50
122	15p. Corrin's Tower ..	60	60	40	40
123	16p. Douglas Head Lighthouse	35	35	22·00	22·00
	(*b*) *As T* **27** *but size* 25 × 31 *mm. P* 11½ (18.10.78)				
124	20p. Fuchsia			50	50
125	25p. Manx cat			60	60
126	50p. Chough			1·10	1·10
127	£1 Viking warrior			2·25	2·25
	(*c*) *T* **27a**. *P* 11½ (29.9.81)				
128	£2 multicoloured			3·50	3·75
111/28	.. .. *Set of* 18			9·50	9·75

The 1p., 7p., 10p., 12p. to 16p. are horiz designs.

28 Queen Elizabeth in Coronation Regalia

29 Wheel-headed Cross-slab

(Des G. Kneale. Litho Questa)

1978 (24 May). *25th Anniv of Coronation. P* 14½ × 14.

132 **28**	25p. multicoloured	60	60

(Des J. Nicholson. Photo Courvoisier)

1978 (24 May). *Europa. Sculpture. T* **29** *and similar vert designs showing Celtic and Norse Crosses. Multicoloured. P* 11½.

133	6p. Type **29**	12	15
	a. Strip of 3. Nos. 133/5	35	
134	6p. Celtic wheel-cross	12	15
135	6p. Keeil Chiggyrt Stone	12	15
136	11p. Olaf Liotulfson Cross	25	30
	a. Strip of 3. Nos. 136/8	75	
137	11p. Odd's and Thorleif's Crosses	25	30
138	11p. Thor Cross	25	30
133/8	.. .. *Set of* 6	1·00	1·25

Nos. 133/5 and 136/8 were each printed together, *se-tenant*, in horizontal and vertical strips of 3 throughout the sheet.

30 J. K. Ward and Ward Library, Peel

31 Hunt the Wren

(Des J.W. (7p.), G. Kneale (11p.), J. Nicholson (others). Litho J.W.)

1978 (10 June). *Anniversaries and Events. T* **30** *and similar horiz designs. Multicoloured. Invisible gum. P* 13½.

139	6p. Type **30**	15	15
140	7p. Swimmer, cyclist and walker (42 × 26 *mm*)	20	20
141	11p. American Bald Eagle, Manx arms and maple leaf (42 × 26 *mm*)	40	40
142	13p. Lumber camp at Three Rivers, Quebec	40	40

Commemorations:—6, 13p. James Kewley Ward (Manx pioneer in Canada); 7p. Commonwealth Games, Edmonton; 11p. 50th anniversary of North American Manx Association.

(Des J. Nicholson. Litho J.W.)

1978 (18 Oct). *Christmas. P* 13.

143 **31**	5p. multicoloured	25	25

32 P. M. C. Kermode (founder) and *Nassa kermodei*

33 Postman, 1859

(Des J. Nicholson. Litho Questa)

1979 (27 Feb). *Centenary of Natural History and Antiquarian Society. T* **32** *and similar horiz designs. Multicoloured. P* 14.

144	6p. Type **32**	15	15
145	7p. Peregrine Falcon	20	20
146	11p. Fulmar	40	40
147	13p. *Epitriptus cowini*	45	45

(Des A. Theobald. Litho Questa)

1979 (16 May). *Europa. Communications. T* **33** *and similar vert design. Multicoloured. P* 14½.

148	6p. Type **33**	20	20
149	11p. Postman, 1979	25	25

34 Viking Longship Emblem

35 Viking Raid at Garwick

Two types of No. 150:

Type I. Wrongly inscribed "INSULAREM". "1979" imprint date.

Type II. Inscription corrected to "INSULARUM". "1980" imprint date.

(Des J. Nicholson. Litho Harrison (3, 4p.), J.W. (others))

1979 (16 May)–**80**. *Millenium of Tynwald. Multicoloured*

(*a*) *Vert designs as T* **34**. *P* 14½ × 14

150	3p. Type **34** (Type I)	10	5
	a. Booklet pane. Nos. 150 × 4, 151 × 2 (4p. stamps at top)	40	
	ab. Ditto (4p. stamps in centre)	40	
	b. Type II (29.9.80)	5	5
	ba. Booklet pane. Nos. 150b × 4, 151 × 2 (4p. stamps at bottom)	35	
151	4p. "Three Legs of Man" emblem	8	10
	(*b*) *Horiz designs as T* **35**. *P* 13		
152	6p. Type **35**	12	15
153	7p. 10th-century meeting of Tynwald ..	15	20
154	11p. Tynwald Hill and St. John's Church ..	30	25
155	13p. Procession to Tynwald Hill	35	30
150/5	.. .. *Set of* 6	1·00	1·00

See also Nos. 188/9.

The 3 and 4p. values were printed in sheets containing ten blocks of 6 and five blocks of 4 separated by blank margins. The blocks of 6 contained four 3p. values and two 4p., *se-tenant*, with the 4p. in either the top or centre rows. The blocks of 4 contain the 4p. value only.

For details of No. 150ba see after No. 189.

36 Queen and Court on Tynwald Hill

(Des G. Kneale. Litho Questa)

1979 (5 July). *Royal Visit. T* **36** *and similar horiz design. Multicoloured. P* 14½.

156	7p. Type **36**	20	20
157	13p. Queen and procession from St. John's Church to Tynwald Hill	30	30

37 *Odin's Raven*

(Des J. Nicholson. Litho Questa)

1979 (19 Oct). *Voyage of "Odin's Raven". P* 14 × 14½.

158 **37**	15p. multicoloured	40	40

38 John Quilliam seized by the Press Gang

39 Young Girl with Teddybear and Cat

(Des A. Theobald. Litho Questa)

1979 (19 Oct). *150th Death Anniv of Captain John Quilliam. T* **38** *and similar horiz designs. Multicoloured. P* 14.

159	6p. Type **38**	15	15
160	8p. Steering H.M.S. *Victory*, Battle of Trafalgar	20	20
161	13p. Capt. John Quilliam and H.M.S. *Spencer*	35	35
162	15p. Capt. John Quilliam (member of the House of Keys)	40	40

(Des Mrs E. Moore. Litho J.W.)

1979 (19 Oct). *Christmas. International Year of the Child. T* **39** *and similar vert design. Multicoloured. P* 13.

163	5p. Type **39**	12	12
164	7p. Father Christmas with young children	20	20

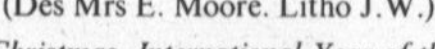

40 Conglomerate Arch, Langness

(Des J. Nicholson. Litho Questa)

1980 (5 Feb). *150th Anniv of Royal Geographical Society. T* **40** *and similar horiz designs. Multicoloured. P* 14½.

165 7p. Type **40** 20 20
166 8p. Braaid Circle 20 20
167 12p. Cashtal-yn-Ard 30 30
168 13p. Volcanic Rocks at Scarlett 35 30
169 15p. Sugar-loaf Rock 40 35

41 *Mona's Isle I*

(Des J. Nicholson. Photo Courvoisier)

1980 (6 May). *150th Anniv of Isle of Man Steam Packet Company. T* **41** *and similar horiz designs. Multicoloured. P* 11½.

170 7p. Type **41** 20 20
171 8p. *Douglas I* 20 20
172 11½p. *Mona's Queen II* sinking U-boat .. 30 30
173 12p. *King Orry* at surrender of German fleet 35 30
174 13p. *Ben-My-Chree IV* 35 30
175 15p. *Lady of Mann II* 40 35
170/5 .. .. *Set of* 6 1·60 1·60
MS176 180 × 125 mm. Nos. 170/5 .. .. 1·60 1·75

No. **MS**176 was issued to commemorate the "London 1980" International Stamp Exhibition.

42 Stained Glass Window, T. E. Brown Room, Manx Museum

(Des G. Kneale. Photo Courvoisier)

1980 (6 May). *Europa. Personalities. Thomas Edward Brown (poet and scholar) Commemoration. T* **42** *and similar horiz design. Multicoloured. P* 11½.

177 7p. Type **42** 20 20
178 13½p. Clifton College, Bristol 30 30

43 King Olav V

(Des J. Nicholson. Litho Questa)

1980 (13 June). *Visit of King Olav V of Norway. P* 14 × 14½.

179 **43** 12p. multicoloured 30 30
MS180 125 × 157 mm. Nos. 158 and 179 .. .. 90 90

44 Wren and View of Calf of Man

(Des J. Nicholson. Litho J.W.)

1980 (29 Sept). *Christmas and Wildlife Conservation Year. T* **44** *and similar horiz design. Multicoloured. P* 13½ × 14.

181 6p. Type **44** 15 20
182 8p. Robin and view of Port Erin Marine Biological Station 25 25

45 William Kermode and Brig *Robert Quayle*, 1819

46 Peregrine Falcon

(Des A. Theobald. Litho Questa)

1980 (29 Sept). *Kermode Family in Tasmania Commemoration. T* **45** *and similar horiz designs. Multicoloured. P* 14½.

183 7p. Type **45** 20 20
184 9p. "Mona Vale", Van Diemen's Land, 1834 25 25
185 13½p. Ross Bridge, Tasmania 30 30
186 15p. "Mona Vale", Tasmania (completed 1868) 35 35
187 17½p. Robert Q. Kermode and Parliament Buildings, Tasmania 40 40

(Des J. Nicholson. Litho Harrison)

1980 (29 Sept). *Booklet stamps. Vert designs as T* **46**. *Multicoloured. P* 14½ × 14.

188 1p. Type **46** 5 5
a. Booklet pane. Nos. 151, 188 and 189 each × 2 35
189 5p. Loaghtyn Ram 8 10

In addition to 40 and 80p. booklets Nos. 188/9 also come from special booklet sheets of 60. These sheets contained No. 150ba and 188a, each × 5.

47 Luggers passing Red Pier, Douglas

(Des J. Nicholson. Litho Questa)

1981 (24 Feb). *Centenary of Royal National Mission to Deep Sea Fishermen. T* **47** *and similar horiz designs. Multicoloured. P* 14.

190 8p. Type **47** 20 20
191 9p. Peel Lugger *Wanderer* rescuing survivors from the *Lusitania* 25 25
192 18p. Nickeys leaving Port St. Mary Harbour 40 40
193 20p. Nobby entering Ramsey Harbour .. 45 45
194 22p. Nickeys *Sunbeam* and *Zebra* at Port Erin 45 45

48 "Crosh Cuirn" Superstition

(Des J. Nicholson. Litho Questa)

1981 (22 May). *Europa. Folklore. T* **48** *and similar horiz design. Multicoloured. P* 14½.

195 8p. Type **48** 20 20
196 18p. "Bollan Cross" superstition 35 35

49 Lt. Mark Wilks (Royal Manx Fencibles) and Peel Castle

(Des A. Theobald. Litho Questa)

1981 (22 May). *150th Death Anniv of Colonel Mark Wilks. T* **49** *and similar horiz designs. Multicoloured. P* 14.

197 8p. Type **49** 20 20
198 20p. Ensign Mark Wilks and Fort St. George, Madras 55 55
199 22p. Governor Mark Wilks and Napoleon, St. Helena 70 70
200 25p. Col. Mark Wilks (Speaker of the House of Keys) and estate, Kirby 70 70

50 Miss Emmeline Goulden (Mrs. Pankhurst) and Mrs. Sophia Jane Goulden

(Des A. Theobald. Litho Questa)

1981 (22 May). *Centenary of Manx Women's Suffrage. P* 14.

201 **50** 9p. black, olive-grey and stone 25 25

51 Prince Charles and Lady Diana Spencer

(Des G. Kneale. Litho Harrison)

1981 (29 July). *Royal Wedding. P* 14.

202 **51** 9p. black, bright blue and pale blue .. 25 25
203 25p. black, bright blue and pink .. 75 65
MS204 130 × 183 mm. Nos. 202/3 × 2 .. .. 2·25 2·00

52 Douglas War Memorial, Poppies and Commemorative Inscription

(Des A. Theobald. Photo Courvoisier)

1981 (29 Sept). *60th Anniv of The Royal British Legion. T* **52** *and similar horiz designs. Multicoloured. P* 11½.

205 8p. Type **52** 25 25
206 10p. Major Robert Cain (war hero) 30 30
207 18p. Festival of Remembrance, Royal Albert Hall 45 45
208 20p. T.S.S. *Tynwald* at Dunkirk, May 1940 50 50

53 Nativity Scene (stained-glass window, St. George's Church)

(Des J.W. (7p.), G. Kneale (9p.). Litho J.W.)

1981 (29 Sept). *Christmas. T* **53** *and similar multicoloured design. P* 14.

209 7p. Type **53** 20 25
210 9p. Children from Special School performing nativity play (48 × 30 *mm*) 25 30

The 7p. value also commemorates the bicentenary of St. George's Church, Douglas and the 9p. the International Year for Disabled Persons.

54 Joseph and William Cunningham (founders of Isle of Man Boy Scout Movement) and Cunningham House Headquarters

(Des G. Kneale. Litho Questa)

1982 (23 Feb). *75th Anniv of Boy Scout Movement and 125th Birth Anniv of Lord Baden-Powell. T* **54** *and similar multicoloured designs. P* 14 × 14½ (19½*p*.) *or* 13½ × 14 (*others*).

211 9p. Type **54** 20 25
212 10p. Baden-Powell visiting Isle of Man, 1911 20 25
213 19½p. Baden-Powell and Scout emblem (40 × 31 *mm*) 50 50
214 24p. Scouts and Baden-Powell's last message 70 70
215 29p. Scout salute, handshake, emblem and globe 90 90

55 *The Principals and Duties of Christianity* (Bishop T. Wilson) (first book printed in Manx, 1707)

(Des A. Theobald. Photo Courvoisier)

1982 (1 June). *Europa. Historic Events. T* **55** *and similar horiz design. Multicoloured. Granite paper. P* 12 × 12½.

216 9p. Type **55** 30 30
217 19½p. Landing at Derbyhaven (visit of Thomas, 2nd Earl of Derby, 1507) .. 50 50

56 Charlie Collier (first TT race (single cylinder) winner) and Tourist Trophy Race, 1907

(Des J. Nicholson. Litho Questa)

1982 (1 June). *75th Anniv of Tourist Trophy Motorcycle Racing. T* **56** *and similar horiz designs. Multicoloured. P* 14.

218 9p. Type **56** 20 20
219 10p. Freddie Dixon (Sidecar and Junior TT winner) and Junior TT race, 1927 .. 20 20

220 24p. Jimmie Simpson (TT winner and first to lap at 60, 70 and 80 mph) and Senior TT, 1932 .. .. 65 65
221 26p. Mike Hailwood (winner of fourteen TT's) and Senior TT, 1961 .. .. 65 65
222 29p. Jock Taylor (Sidecar TT winner, 1978, 1980 and 1981) and Sidecar TT (with Benga Johansson), 1980 .. .. 75 75

57 *Mona I*

(Des J. Nicholson. Litho Questa)

1982 (5 Oct). *150th Anniv of Isle of Man Steam Packet Company Mail Contract. T* **57** *and similar horiz design. Multicoloured.* P 13½ × 14.
223 12p. Type **57** 30 30
224 19½p. *Manx Maid II* 50 55

58 Three Wise Men bearing Gifts

59 Princess Diana with Prince William

(Des and litho J.W.)

1982 (5 Oct). *Christmas. T* **58** *and similar multicoloured design.* P 13 × 13½ (8*p*.) *or* 13½ × 13 (11*p*.).
225 8p. Type **58** 25 25
226 11p. Christmas snow scene (*vert*) 30 35

(Des G. Kneale. Litho Questa)

1982 (12 Oct). *21st Birthday of Princess of Wales and Birth of Prince William. Sheet* 100 × 83 *mm.* P 14½ × 14.
MS227 **59** 50p. multicoloured .. .. .. 1·25 1·40

60 Opening of Salvation Army Citadel, and T.H. Cannell, J.P.

(Des A. Theobald. Photo Courvoisier)

1983 (15 Feb). *Centenary of Salvation Army in Isle of Man. T* **60** *and similar horiz designs. Multicoloured.* P 11½.
228 10p. Type **60** 20 20
229 12p. Early meeting place and Gen. William Booth 35 35
230 19½p. Salvation Army band 50 50
231 26p. Treating lepers and Lt.-Col. Thomas Bridson 70 70

61 Atlantic Puffins

61*a* "Queen Elizabeth II" (Ricardo Macarron)

(Des Colleen Corlett (£5), J. Nicholson (others). Litho Questa)

1983 (15 Feb)–**85**. *Sea Birds. T* **61** *and similar horiz designs. Multicoloured.* P 14 (20 *p. to* £1, 14 × 13½ (£5) *or* 14½ (*others*).
232 1p. Type **61** 5 5
233 2p. Northern Gannets 5 5
234 5p. Lesser Black-backed Gulls 8 10
235 8p. Common Cormorants 15 20
236 10p. Kittiwakes 20 25
237 11p. Shags 20 25
238 12p. Grey Herons 20 25
239 13p. Herring-gulls 25 30
240 14p. Razorbills 25 30
241 15p. Great Black-backed Gulls 25 30
242 16p. Common Shelducks 30 35
243 18p. Oystercatchers 30 35
244 20p. Arctic Terns (14.9.83) 35 40
245 25p. Common Guillemots (14.9.83) 45 50
246 50p. Redshanks (14.9.83) 90 95
247 £1 Mute Swans (14.9.83) .. .. 1·75 1·90
248 £5 Type **61*a*** (31.1.85) .. .. 9·00 9·50
232/48 .. .. *Set of* 17 14·00 15·00
Nos. 244/7 are larger, 39 × 26 mm.

62 Design Drawings by Robert Casement for the Great Laxey Wheel

(Des J. Nicholson. Litho Questa)

1983 (18 May). *Europa. The Great Laxey Wheel. T* **62** *and similar horiz design.* P 14.
249 10p. black, azure and buff 30 30
250 20½p. multicoloured 45 50
Design:—20½p. Robert Casement and the Great Laxey Wheel.

63 Nick Keig (international yachtsman) and Trimaran *Three Legs of Mann III*

64 New Post Office Headquarters, Douglas

(Des J. Nicholson (10p., 31p.), Colleen Corlett (12p., 28p.). Photo Courvoisier)

1983 (18 May). *150th Anniv of King William's College. T* **63** *and similar horiz designs. Multicoloured.* P 11½.
251 10p. Type **63** 20 20
252 12p. King William's College, Castletown .. 35 35
253 28p. Sir William Bragg (winner of Nobel Prize for Physics) and spectrometer .. 70 70
254 31p. General Sir George White V.C. and action at Charasiah .. .. .. 1·00 1·00

(Des Colleen Corlett (10p.), J. Nicholson (15p.). Litho Questa)

1983 (5 July). *World Communications Year and 10th Anniv of Isle of Man Post Office Authority. T* **64** *and similar vert design. Multicoloured.* P 14½.
255 10p. Type **64** 30 30
256 15p. As Type **6**, but inscr "POST OFFICE DECENNIUM 1983" 35 35

65 Shepherds

(Des Colleen Corlett. Litho J.W.)

1983 (14 Sept). *Christmas. T* **65** *and similar horiz design. Multicoloured.* P 13.
257 9p. Type **65** 20 20
258 12p. Three Kings 30 35

66 *Manx King*

67 C.E.P.T. 25th Anniversary Logo

(Des J. Nicholson (10p. to 31p.); Colleen Corlett, J. Nicholson and J. Smith (miniature sheet). Litho Questa)

1984 (14 Feb). *The Karran Fleet. T* **66** *and similar horiz designs. Multicoloured.* P 14.
259 10p. Type **66** 30 30
260 13p. *Hope* 35 35
261 20½p. *Rio Grande* 55 55
262 28p. *Lady Elizabeth* 70 70
263 31p. *Sumatra* 80 80
MS264 103 × 94 mm. 28p. As No. 262, 31p. *Lady Elizabeth* (as shown on Falkland Islands No. 417) (*sold at* 60p.) .. .. 1·10
No. **MS**264 was issued to commemorate links bewtween the Isle of Man and Falkland Islands.

(Des J. Larrivière, adapted Colleen Corlett. Photo Courvoisier)

1984 (27 Apr). *Europa.* P 12 × 11½.
265 **67** 10p. dull orange, deep reddish brown and pale orange 25 25
266 20½p. light blue, deep blue and pale blue 50 55

68 Railway Air Services "D.H.84"

69 Window from Glencrutchery House, Douglas

(Des A. Theobald. Litho Questa)

1984 (27 Apr). (27 Apr). *50th Anniv of First Official Airmail to the Isle of Man and 40th Anniv of International Civil Aviation Organization. T* **68** *and similar horiz designs. Multicoloured.* P 14.
267 11p. Type **68** 30 30
268 13p. West Coast Air Services "D.H.86" .. 35 35
269 26p. B.E.A. "DC-3" 70 70
270 28p. B.E.A. Vickers "Viscount" 75 75
271 31p. Telair "Islander" 80 80

(Des D. Swinton. Litho J.W.)

1984 (21 Sept). *Christmas. Stained-glass Windows. T* **69** *and similar vert design. Multicoloured.* P 14.
272 10p. Type **69** 20 25
273 13p. Window from Lonan Old Church 25 30

70 William Cain's Birthplace, Ballasalla

(Des J. Nicholson. Litho Questa)

1984 (21 Sept). *William Cain (civic leader, Victoria) Commemoration. T* **70** *and similar horiz designs. Multicoloured.* P 14½ × 14.
274 11p. Type **70** 20 25
275 22p. The *Anna* leaving Liverpool, 1852 .. 40 45
276 28p. Early Australian railway 55 60
277 30p. William Cain as Mayor of Melbourne, and Town Hall 60 65
278 33p. Royal Exhibition Building, Melbourne .. 65 70

71 Queen Elizabeth II and Commonwealth Parliamentary Association Badge

(Des and litho J.W.)

1984 (21 Sept). *Links with the Commonwealth. 30th Commonwealth Parliamentary Association Conference. T* **71** *and similar horiz design. Multicoloured.* P 14.
279 14p. Type **71** 30 35
280 33p. Queen Elizabeth II and Manx emblem .. 65 70

72 Cunningham House Headquarters, and Mrs. Willie Cunningham and Mrs. Joseph Cunningham (former Commissioners)

(Des Colleen Corlett. Photo Courvoisier)

1985 (31 Jan). *75th Anniv of Girl Guide Movement. T* **72** *and similar horiz designs. Multicoloured. Granite paper.* P 11½.
281 11p. Type **72** 20 25
282 14p. Princess Margaret, Isle of Man standard and guides 30 35
283 29p. Lady Olave Baden-Powell opening Guide Headquarters, 1955 .. .. .. 55 60
284 31p. Guide uniforms from 1910 to 1985 .. 60 65
285 34p. Guide handclasp, salute and early badge .. 70 75

POSTAGE DUE STAMPS

D 1

D 2

D 3

(Litho Questa)

1973 (5 July). *P* 13½ × 14.

No.	Type	Value	Description	Mint	Used
D1	**D 1**	½p.	red, black and bistre-yellow ..	2·25	1·25
D2		1p.	red, black and cinnamon	75	50
D3		2p.	red, black and light apple-green ..	15	15
D4		3p.	red, black and grey	25	20
D5		4p.	red, black and carmine-rose ..	35	25
D6		5p.	red, black and cobalt	40	30
D7		10p.	red, black and light lavender ..	50	40
D8		20p.	red, black and pale turquoise-green	90	60
D1/8			.. .. *Set of* 8	4·50	2·75

A second printing of all values was put on sale by the Philatelic Bureau from 1 September 1973. These can be distinguished by the addition of a small "A" after the date "1973" in the bottom left margin of the stamps. Spurious examples of the second printing exist with the "A" removed.

Prices quoted above are for the second printing. *Prices for set of* 8 *original printing* £45 *mint*, £30 *used*.

(Des and litho Questa)

1975 (8 Jan). *Arms and inscriptions in black and red; background colour given. P* 14 × 13½.

No.	Type	Value	Description	Mint	Used
D 9	**D 2**	½p.	greenish yellow	5	5
D10		1p.	flesh	5	5
D11		4p.	rose-lilac	10	10
D12		7p.	light greenish blue	20	20
D13		9p.	brownish grey	25	25
D14		10p.	bright mauve	30	30
D15		50p.	orange-yellow	1·40	1·40
D16		£1	turquoise-green	2·00	2·00
D9/16			.. .. *Set of* 8	3·75	3·75

(Litho B.D.T. International)

1982 (5 Oct). *P* 15 × 14.

No.	Type	Value	Description	Mint	Used
D17	**D 3**	1p.	multicoloured	5	5
D18		2p.	multicoloured	5	5
D19		5p.	multicoloured	8	10
D20		10p.	multicoloured	20	25
D21		20p.	multicoloured	35	40
D22		50p.	multicoloured	90	1·00
D23		£1	multicoloured	1·75	1·90
D24		£2	multicoloured	3·50	3·75
D17/24			.. .. *Set of* 8	6·00	6·75

JERSEY

Further detailed information on the stamps of Jersey will be found in the Stanley Gibbons *Channel Islands Specialised Catalogue*.

WAR OCCUPATION ISSUES

Stamps issued under British authority during the German Occupation

1

(Des Major N. V. L. Rybot. Typo *Evening Post*, Jersey)

1941–42. *White paper* (*thin to thick*). *No wmk. P* 11.

No.	Type	Value	Description	Mint	Used
1	**1**	½d.	bright green (29.1.42)	2·75	2·25
		a.	Imperf between (vert pair)	£500	
		b.	Imperf between (horiz pair) ..	£400	
		c.	Imperf (pair)	£100	
		d.	On greyish paper	4·00	4·25
2		1d.	scarlet (1.4.41)	3·25	2·25
		a.	Imperf between (vert pair)	£500	
		b.	Imperf between (horiz pair) ..	£400	
		c.	Imperf (pair)	£125	
		d.	On chalk-surfaced paper	38·00	40·00
		e.	On greyish paper	4·00	4·25

2 Old Jersey Farm

3 Portelet Bay

4 Corbière Lighthouse

5 Elizabeth Castle

6 Mont Orgueil Castle

7 Gathering Vraic (seaweed)

(Des E. Blampied. Eng H. Cortot. Typo French Govt Works, Paris)

1943–44. *No wmk. P* 13½.

No.	Type	Value	Description	Mint	Used
3	**2**	½d.	green (1 June)	7·00	2·25
		a.	Rough, grey paper (6.10.43) ..	10·00	7·50
4	**3**	1d.	scarlet (1 June)	60	15
		a.	On newsprint (28.2.44)	1·25	1·00
5	**4**	1½d.	brown (8 June)	1·40	1·75
6	**5**	2d.	orange-yellow (8 June)	1·75	1·25
7	**6**	2½d.	blue (29 June)	1·50	1·25
		a.	On newsprint (25.2.44)	60	1·00
		ba.	Thin paper*	£150	
8	**7**	3d.	violet (29 June)	80	2·50
D3/8			.. .. *Set of* 6	11·00	8·00

*On No. 7ba the design shows clearly through the back of the stamp.

REGIONAL ISSUES

DATES OF ISSUE. The note at the beginning of the Guernsey Regional Issues also applies here.

8

9

(Des E. Blampied (T **8**), W. Gardner (T **9**). Portrait by Dorothy Wilding Ltd. Photo Harrison & Sons)

1958 (18 Aug)–**67.** *W* **179** *of Great Britain. P* 15 × 14.

No.	Type	Value	Description	Mint	Used
9	**8**	2½d.	carmine-red (8.6.64)	20	1·00
		a.	Imperf three sides (pair)	£425	
10	**9**	3d.	deep lilac	40	20
		p.	One centre phosphor band (9.6.67)	5	30
11		4d.	ultramarine (7.2.66)	20	20
		p.	Two phosphor bands (5.9.67) ..	5	20

1968–69. *No wmk. Chalk-surfaced paper. PVA gum**. *One centre phosphor band* (*4d. values*) *or two phosphor bands* (*5d.*). *P* 15 × 14.

No.	Type	Value	Description	Mint	Used
12	**9**	4d.	olive-sepia (4.9.68)	10	15
13		4d.	bright vermilion (26.2.69)	10	25
14		5d.	royal blue (4.9.68)	10	15

*PVA Gum. See note after No. 722 of Great Britain.

INDEPENDENT POSTAL ADMINISTRATION

10 Elizabeth Castle

11 Queen Elizabeth II (after Cecil Beaton)

13 Queen Elizabeth II (after Cecil Beaton)

12 Jersey Airport

(Des V. Whiteley. Photo Harrison (½d. to 1s. 9d.); Courvoisier (others))

1969 (1 Oct). *T* **10/13** *and similar horiz designs as T* **10** (*½d. to* 1*s.* 6*d.*) *or T* **12** (5*s.*, 10*s.*, £1). *Multicoloured. P* 14 (*½d. to* 1*s.* 9*d.*) *or* 12 (*others*).

No.	Value	Description	Mint	Used
15	½d.	Type **10**	20	45
16	1d.	La Hougue Bie (prehistoric tomb) (*shades*)	25	20
	a.	Booklet stamp with blank margins ..	1·00	1·00
17	2d.	Portelet Bay	15	15
18	3d.	La Corbière Lighthouse	15	15
19	4d.	Mont Orgueil Castle by night	12	10
	a.	Booklet stamp with blank margins ..	50	50
20	5d.	Arms and Royal Mace	20	10
21	6d.	Jersey Cow	50	60
22	9d.	Chart of English Channel	1·00	1·25
23	1s.	Mont Orgueil Castle by day	1·75	1·25
24	1s.	6d. As 9d.	3·00	2·50
25	1s.	9d. Type **11**	3·00	3·00
26	2s.	6d. Type **12**	8·00	5·00
27	5s.	Legislative Chamber	24·00	14·00
28	10s.	The Royal Court	45·00	28·00
	a.	Error. Green border*	£3750	
29	£1	Type **13** (*shades*)	2·00	2·50
15/27		.. .. *Set of* 15	75·00	50·00

*During the final printing of the 10s. a sheet was printed in the colours of the 50p., No. 56, i.e. green border instead of slate.

The 3d. is known with the orange omitted.

There was no postal need for the ½d. value as the ½d. coin had been withdrawn prior to its issue in anticipation of decimalisation.

Nos. 16a and 19a come from 2s. booklets for the automatic machines formerly used for the Great Britain 2s. booklets (see also note after Guernsey No. 28).

Various papers were used by Harrisons. The ½d. and 1d. exist on much thicker paper from 2s. booklets and the 2d. to 1s. 9d. exist on thinner paper having white instead of creamy gum.

24 First Day Cover

25 Lord Coutanche, former Bailiff of Jersey

(Des R. Sellar. Photo Harrison)

1969 (1 Oct). *Inauguration of Post Office. P* 14.

No.	Type	Value	Description	Mint	Used
30	**24**	4d.	multicoloured	25	25
31		5d.	multicoloured	50	50
32		1s.	6d. multicoloured	2·75	5·00
33		1s.	9d. multicoloured	2·75	5·00

(Des Rosalind Dease. Photo Courvoisier)

1970 (9 May). *25th Anniv of Liberation. T* **25** *and similar multicoloured designs. P* 11½.

No.	Value	Description	Mint	Used
34	4d.	Type **25**	20	25
35	5d.	Sir Winston Churchill	30	25
36	1s.	6d. "Liberation" (Edmund Blampied) (*horiz*)	3·00	3·00
37	1s.	9d. S.S. *Vega* (*horiz*)	3·00	3·00

29 "A Tribute to Enid Blyton"

(Des Jennifer Toombs. Photo Courvoisier)

1970 (28 July). *"Battle of Flowers" Parade. T* **29** *and similar horiz designs. Multicoloured. P* 11½.

38 4d. Type **29** 25 25
39 5d. "Rags to Riches" (Cinderella and pumpkin) 30 25
40 1s. 6d. "Gourmet's Delight" (lobster and cornucopia) .. .. 15·00 4·25
41 1s. 9d. "We're the Greatest" (ostriches) .. 15·00 4·25

INVALIDATION. The regional issues for Jersey were invalidated for use in Jersey and Guernsey on 1 November 1969 but remained valid for use in the rest of the United Kingdom. Nos. 15/41 (except No. 29) and Nos. D1/6 were invalidated on 14 February 1972.

33 Jersey Airport

(Des V. Whiteley. Photo Harrison (½ to 9p.); Courvoisier (others))

1970 (1 Oct)–**74**. *Decimal Currency. Designs as Nos. 15/28, but with values inscr in decimal currency as in T* **33**, *and new horiz design as T* **10** (*6p.*).

42 ½p. Type **10** (15.2.71) 5 8
a. Booklet stamp with blank margins 60 60
43 1p. La Corbière Lighthouse (*shades*) (15.2.71) 5 5
44 1½p. Jersey Cow (15.2.71) 5 5
45 2p. Mont Orgueil Castle by night (15.2.71) .. 5 5
a. Booklet stamp with blank margins .. 1·00 1·00
46 2½p. Arms and Royal Mace (15.2.71) 5 8
a. Booklet stamp with blank margins 60 60
ab. Gold (Mace) omitted £250
ac. Gold (Mace) printed double £200
47 3p. La Hougue Bie (prehistoric tomb) (15.2.71) 10 10
a. Booklet stamp with blank margins (1.12.72) 40 40
48 3½p. Portelet Bay (15.2.71) 12 12
a. Booklet stamp with blank margins (1.7.74) 65 65
49 4p. Chart of English Channel (15.2.71) .. 12 12
49*a* 4½p. Arms and Royal Mace (1.11.74) 20 20
50 5p. Mont Orgueil Castle by day (15.2.71) .. 10 15
50*a* 5½p. Jersey Cow (1.11.74) 25 20
51 6p. Martello Tower, Archirondel (15.2.71) 25 20
52 7½p. Chart of English Channel (15.2.71) .. 25 20
52*a* 8p. Mont Orgueil Castle by night (1.11.74) 20 25
53 9p. Type **11** (15.2.71) 25 25
54 10p. Type **33** 35 30
55 20p. Legislative Chamber 85 50
56 50p. The Royal Court .. .. 1·50 1·50
42/56 .. .. *Set of* 18 4·25 4·00

Original printings of the ½p. to 4p., 5p. and 6p. to 9p. were with PVA gum; printings from 1974 (including original printings of the 4½p. and 5½p.) have dextrin added (see notes after No. X960. of Great Britain). The 10p. to 50p. have gum arabic.

The 1p. is known with the orange omitted.

The border of No. 56 has been changed from turquoise-blue to dull green.

34 White-eared Pheasant

(Des Jennifer Toombs. Photo Courvoisier)

1971 (12 Mar). *Wildlife Preservation Trust* (*1st series*). *T* **34** *and similar multicoloured designs. P* 11½.

57 2p. Type **34** 60 25
58 2½p. Thick-billed Parrot (*vert*) 60 25
59 7½p. Ursine Colobus Monkey (*vert*) .. .. 13·00 4·75
60 9p. Ring-tailed Lemur .. .. 13·00 4·75

See also Nos. 73/6, 217/21 and 324/9.

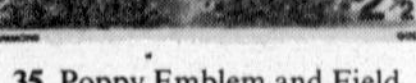

35 Poppy Emblem and Field **36** "Tante Elizabeth" (E. Blampied)

(Des G. Drummond. Litho Questa)

1971 (15 June). *50th Anniv of Royal British Legion. T* **35** *and similar horiz designs. Multicoloured. P* 14.

61 2p. Royal British Legion Badge 25 25
62 2½p. Type **35** 25 25
63 7½p. Jack Counter, V.C., and Victoria Cross 4·25 4·25
64 9p. Crossed Tricolour and Union Jack .. 4·25 4·25

(Des and photo Courvoisier)

1971 (5 Oct). *Paintings* (*1st series*). *T* **36** *and similar multicoloured designs. P* 11½.

65 2p. Type **36** 15 15
66 2½p. "English Fleet in the Channel" (P. Monamy) (*horiz*) 20 20
67 7½p. "The Boyhood of Raleigh" (Millais) (*horiz*) .. .. 4·50 4·50
68 9p. "The Blind Beggar" (W. W. Ouless) .. 4·50 4·50

See also Nos. 115/18 and 213/16.

37 Jersey Fern **38** Artillery Shako

(Des G. Drummond. Photo Courvoisier)

1972 (18 Jan). *Wild Flowers of Jersey. T* **37** *and similar vert designs. Multicoloured. P* 11½.

69 3p. Type **37** 15 15
70 5p. Jersey Thrift .. .. 1·00 1·00
71 7½p. Jersey Orchid .. .. 4·50 4·00
72 9p. Jersey Viper's Bugloss .. .. 4·50 4·00

(Des Jennifer Toombs. Photo Courvoisier)

1972 (17 Mar). *Wildlife Preservation Trust* (*2nd series*). *Multicoloured designs similar to T* **34**. *P* 11½.

73 2½p. Cheetah 50 15
74 3p. Rothschild's Mynah (*vert*) 30 20
75 7½p. Spectacled Bear .. .. 2·40 2·50
76 9p. Tuatara .. .. 2·40 2·50

(Des and photo Courvoisier)

1972 (27 June). *Royal Jersey Militia. T* **38** *and similar vert designs. Multicoloured. P* 11½.

77 2½p. Type **38** 15 15
78 3p. Shako (2nd North Regt) 15 20
79 7½p. Shako (5th South-West Regt) .. .. 1·40 1·25
80 9p. Helmet (3rd Jersey Light Infantry) .. 1·40 1·25

39 Princess Anne **40** Armorican Bronze Coins

(Des G. Drummond from photographs by D. Groves. Photo Courvoisier)

1972 (1 Nov). *Royal Silver Wedding. T* **39** *and similar multicoloured designs. P* 11½.

81 2½p. Type **39** 10 5
82 3p. Queen Elizabeth and Prince Philip (*horiz*) 10 5
83 7½p. Prince Charles 45 50
84 20p. The Royal Family (*horiz*) 45 50

(Des G. Drummond. Photo Courvoisier)

1973 (23 Jan). *Centenary of La Société Jersiaise. T* **40** *and similar multicoloured designs. P* 11½.

85 2½p. Silver cups 10 10
86 3p. Gold torque (*vert*) 10 10
87 7½p. Royal Seal of Charles II (*vert*) 45 45
88 9p. Type **40** 45 45

41 Balloon and Letter **42** "North Western"

(Des and photo Courvoisier)

1973 (16 May). *Jersey Aviation History. T* **41** *and similar horiz designs. Multicoloured. P* 11½.

89 3p. Type **41** 10 10
90 5p. Seaplane "Astra" 10 10
91 7½p. Supermarine "Sea Eagle" 45 45
92 9p. De Havilland "Express" 45 45

(Des G. Drummond. Photo Courvoisier)

1973 (6 Aug). *Centenary of Jersey Eastern Railway. T* **42** *and similar designs showing early locomotives. Multicoloured. P* 11½.

93 2½p. Type **42** 10 10
94 3p. "Calvados" 10 10
95 7½p. "Carteret" 45 45
96 9p. "Caesarea" 45 45

43 Princess Anne and Capt. Mark Phillips

(Des and photo Courvoisier)

1973 (14 Nov). *Royal Wedding. P* 11½.

97 **43** 3p. multicoloured 10 10
98 20p. multicoloured 70 70

44 Spider Crab **45** Freesias

(Des Jennifer Toombs. Photo Courvoisier)

1973 (15 Nov). *Marine Life. T* **44** *and similar horiz designs. Multicoloured. P* 11½.

99 2½p. Type **44** 8 5
100 3p. Conger eel 8 8
101 7½p. Lobster 30 35
102 20p. Ormer 40 40

(Des G. Drummond. Photo Courvoisier)

1974 (13 Feb). *Spring Flowers. T* **45** *and similar vert designs. Multicoloured. P* 11½.

103 3p. Type **45** 8 5
104 5½p. Anemones 10 10
105 8p. Carnations and Gladioli 20 20
106 10p. Daffodils and Iris 30 30

46 First Letter-Box and Contemporary Cover **47** John Wesley

(Des G. Drummond. Photo Courvoisier)

1974 (7 June). *U.P.U. Centenary. T* **46** *and similar horiz designs. Multicoloured. P* 11½.

107 2½p. Type **46** 5 5
108 3p. Postmen, 1862 and 1969 .. .. .. 5 5
109 5½p. Letter-box and letter, 1974 .. .. 35 35
110 20p. R.M.S. *Aquila* (1874) and aeroplane (1974) 60 65

(Des, recess and litho D.L.R.)

1974 (31 July). *Anniversaries. T* **47** *and similar vert designs. P* 13 × 14.

111 3p. light cinnamon and black 5 8
112 3½p. light azure and black 5 5
113 8p. light mauve and deep ultramarine .. 35 35
114 20p. pinkish stone and black 65 65

Portraits and events:—3p. Type **47** (Bicentenary of Methodism in Jersey); 3½p. Sir William Hillary, founder (150th Anniv of R.N.L.I.); 8p. Cannon Wace, poet and historian (800th Death Anniv); 20p. Sir Winston Churchill (Birth Centenary).

48 Royal Yacht **49** Potato Digger

(Des and photo Courvoisier)

1974 (22 Nov). *Paintings* (*2nd series*). *T* **48** *and similar multicoloured designs showing works by Peter Monamy. P* 11½.

115 3½p. Type **48** 8 5
116 5½p. French two-decker 12 12
117 8p. Dutch vessel (*horiz*) 35 35
118 25p. The Battle of Cap La Hague (55 × 27 *mm*) 65 70

(Des G. Drummond. Photo Courvoisier)

1975 (25 Feb). *19th-Century Farming. T* **49** *and similar horiz designs. Multicoloured. P* 11½.

119 3p. Type **49** 8 8
120 3½p. Cider crusher 10 8
121 8p. Six-horse plough 30 30
122 10p. Hay cart 35 35

50 H.M. Queen Elizabeth, the Queen Mother (photograph by Cecil Beaton)   **51** Shell

(Des and photo Courvoisier)

1975 (30 May). *Royal Visit. P* 11½.

123 **50** 20p. multicoloured 60 60

(Des A. Games. Photo Courvoisier)

1975 (6 June). *Jersey Tourism. T* **51** *and similar vert designs based on holiday posters. Multicoloured. P* 11½.

124 5p. Type **51** 10 10
125 8p. Parasol 15 15
126 10p. Deckchair 30 30
127 12p. Sandcastle with flags of Jersey and the U.K. 35 35
MS128 146 × 68 mm. Nos. 124/7 .. .. .. 1·10 1·25

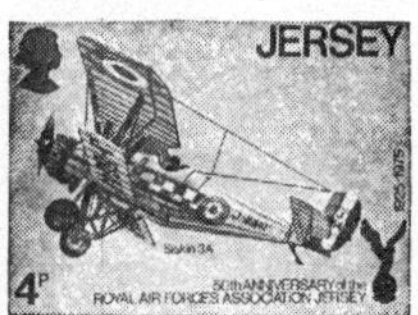

52 Common Tern   **53** Siskin "3-A"

(Des Jennifer Toombs. Photo Courvoisier)

1975 (28 July). *Sea Birds. T* **52** *and similar vert designs. Multicoloured. P* 11½.

129 4p. Type **52** 15 15
130 5p. British Storm Petrel 15 15
131 8p. Brent Geese 30 40
132 25p. Shag 50 65

(Des A. Theobald. Photo Courvoisier)

1975 (30 Oct). *50th Anniv of Royal Air Forces Association, Jersey Branch. T* **53** *and similar horiz designs. Multicoloured. P* 11½.

133 4p. Type **53** 10 10
134 5p. "Southampton" flying-boat 12 12
135 10p. Mk. I "Spitfire" 30 30
136 25p. Folland "Gnat" 60 60

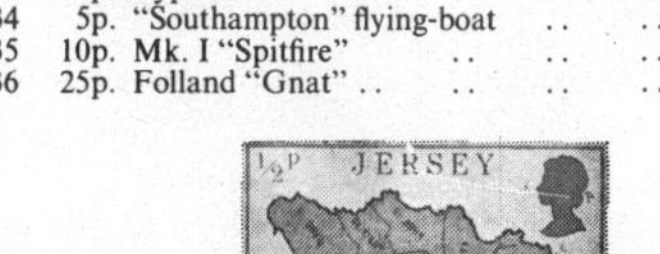

54 Map of Jersey Parishes

55 Parish Arms and Island Scene

(Des Courvoisier (£2). G. Drummond (others). Litho Questa (½ to 15p.). Photo Courvoisier (others))

1976–80. *Various multicoloured designs as T* **54/5**.

(*a*) *Parish Arms and Views as T* **54**. *P* 14½. (29 Jan)

137 ½p. Type **54** 5 5
138 1p. Zoological Park 5 5
a. Booklet pane of 2 plus 2 *se-tenant* labels (5.4.76) 80
b. Booklet pane of 4 (5.4.76) .. .. .. 1·00
139 5p. St. Mary's Church 10 10
a. Booklet pane of 4 (5.4.76) 60
140 6p. Seymour Tower 12 12
a. Booklet pane of 4 (28.2.78) 50
141 7p. La Corbière Lighthouse 15 15
a. Booklet pane of 4 (5.4.76) 50
142 8p. St. Saviour's Church 20 15
a. Booklet pane of 4 (28.2.78) 60
143 9p. Elizabeth Castle 20 20
a. Booklet pane of 4 (6.5.80) 65
144 10p. Gorey Harbour 20 20
145 11p. Jersey Airport 25 25
146 12p. Grosnez Castle 25 25
147 13p. Bonne Nuit Harbour 30 30
148 14p. Le Hocq Tower 30 30
149 15p. Morel Farm 30 30

(*b*) *Emblems as T* **55**. *P* 12 (20 Aug 1976–16 Nov 1977)

150 20p. Type **55** 40 40
151 30p. Flag and map 60 65
152 40p. Postal H.Q. and badge 80 80
153 50p. Parliament, Royal Court and arms .. 1·00 1·00
154 £1 Lieutenant-Governor's flag and Government House .. .. 2·00 2·00
155 £2 Queen Elizabeth II (photograph by Alex Wilson) (16.11.77) .. .. .. 3·50 3·75
137/55 .. .. *Set of* 19 9·50 9·50

Nos. 156/9 are vacant.

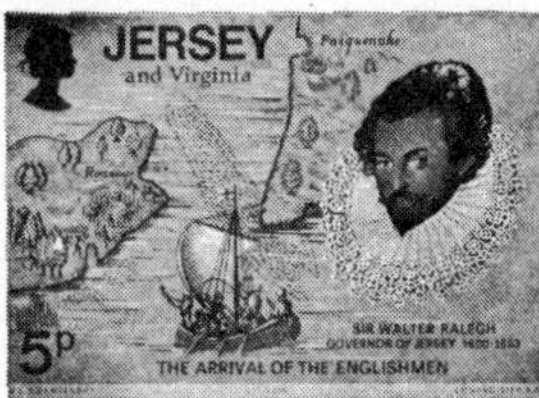

56 Sir Walter Ralegh and Map of Virginia

(Des M. Orbell. Photo Courvoisier)

1976 (29 May). *"Links with America". T* **56** *and similar horiz designs. Multicoloured. P* 11½.

160 5p. Type **56** 10 10
161 7p. Sir George Carteret and map of New Jersey 15 15
162 11p. Philippe Dauvergne and Long Island Landing 40 40
163 13p. John Copley and sketch 45 45

57 Dr. Grandin and Map of China   **58** Coronation, 1953 (photographed by Cecil Beaton)

(Des Jennifer Toombs. Photo Courvoisier)

1976 (25 Nov). *Birth Centenary of Dr. Lilian Grandin (medical missionary). T* **57** *and similar horiz designs. P* 11½.

164 5p. multicoloured 10 10
165 7p. light yellow, yellow-brown and black .. 15 15
166 11p. multicoloured 40 40
167 13p. multicoloured 45 45

Designs:—7p. Sampan on the Yangtze; 11p. Overland trek; 13p. Dr. Grandin at work.

(Des G. Drummond. Photo Courvoisier)

1977 (7 Feb). *Silver Jubilee. T* **58** *and similar vert designs. Multicoloured. P* 11½.

168 5p. Type **58** 12 12
169 7p. Visit to Jersey, 1957 .. .. .. 20 20
170 25p. Queen Elizabeth II (photo by Peter Grugeon) 90 90

59 Coins of 1871 and 1877

(Des D. Henley. Litho Questa)

1977 (25 Mar). *Centenary of Currency Reform. T* **59** *and similar horiz designs. Multicoloured. P* 14.

171 5p. Type **59** 10 12
172 7p. One-twelfth shilling, 1949 .. .. 15 15
173 11p. Silver Crown, 1966 .. .. .. 40 40
174 13p. £2 piece, 1972 .. .. 45 45

60 Sir William Weston and *Santa Anna*, 1530

(Des A. Theobald. Litho Questa)

1977 (24 June). *St. John Ambulance Centenary. T* **60** *and similar horiz designs each showing a Grand Prior of the Order. Multicoloured. P* 14 × 13½.

175 5p. Type **60** 10 12
176 7p. Sir William Drogo and ambulance, 1877 12 12
177 11p. Duke of Connaught and ambulance, 1917 .. .. 45 45
178 13p. Duke of Gloucester and stretcher-team, 1977 .. .. 45 45

61 Arrival of Queen Victoria, 1846

(Des R. Granger Barrett. Litho Questa)

1977 (29 Sept). *125th Anniv of Victoria College. T* **61** *and similar multicoloured designs. P* 14½.

179 7p. Type **61** 20 20
180 10½p. Victoria College, 1852 .. .. .. 20 20
181 11p. Sir Galahad statue, 1924 (*vert*) .. 35 35
182 13p. College Hall (*vert*) 35 35

62 Harry Vardon Statuette and Map of Royal Jersey Course

(Des Jennifer Toombs. Litho Questa)

1978 (28 Feb). *Centenary of Royal Jersey Golf Club. T* **62** *and similar horiz designs. Multicoloured. P* 14.

183 6p. Type **62** 15 15
184 8p. Harry Vardon's grip and swing .. 15 15
185 11p. Harry Vardon's putt 40 40
186 13p. Golf trophies and book by Harry Vardon 40 40

63 Mont Orgueil Castle   **64** "Gaspé Basin" (P. J. Ouless)

(Des from paintings by Thomas Phillips. Photo Courvoisier)

1978 (1 May). *Europa. Castles. T* **63** *and similar horiz designs. Multicoloured. P* 11½.

187 6p. Type **63** 15 15
188 8p. St. Aubin's Fort 20 20
189 10½p. Elizabeth Castle 30 30

(Des R. Granger Barrett. Litho Questa)

1978 (9 June). *Links with Canada. T* **64** *and similar horiz designs. Multicoloured. P* 14½.

190 6p. Type **64** 12 12
191 8p. Map of Gaspé Peninsula 15 15
192 10½p. Jersey sailing ship *Century* 25 25
193 11p. Early map of Jersey 30 30
194 13p. St. Aubin's Bay, town and harbour .. 35 35

65 Queen Elizabeth and Prince Philip   **66** Mail Cutter, 1778–1827

(Des and photo Courvoisier)

1978 (26 June). *25th Anniv of Coronation. T* **65** *and similar vert design. P* 11½.

195 8p. silver, black and cerise 15 15
196 25p. silver, black and new blue 65 65

Design:—25p. Hallmarks of 1953 and 1977.

(Des Jersey P.O. Litho Harrison)

1978 (18 Oct). *Bicentenary of England-Jersey Government Mail Packet Service. T* **66** *and similar horiz designs. P* 14½ × 14.

197 6p. black, yellow-brown and greenish yellow 12 12
198 8p. black, dull yellowish grn & pale yell-grn 15 15
199 10½p. black, ultramarine and cobalt 25 25
200 11p. black, purple and pale rose-lilac .. 30 30
201 13p. black, Venetian red and pink 40 40

Designs:—8p. *Flamer*, 1831–37; 10½p. *Diana*, 1877–90; 11p. *Ibex*, 1891–1925; 13p. *Caesarea*, 1960–75.

67 Jersey Calf   **68** Jersey Pillar Box, *circa* 1860

(Des Jersey P.O. and Questa. Litho Questa)

1979 (1 Mar). *9th World Jersey Cattle Bureau Conference. T* **67** *and similar horiz design. Multicoloured. P* 13½.
202 6p. Type **67** 20 15
203 25p. "Ansom Designette" (cow presented to the Queen, 27 June 1978) (46 × 29 *mm*) 70 65

(Des Jennifer Toombs. Litho Questa)

1979 (1 Mar). *Europa. T* **68** *and similar vert designs. Multicoloured.* A. *P* 14. B. *P* 14½.

			A		B	
204	8p.	Type **68**	20	20	30	30
	a.	Horiz pair. Nos. 204/5	40	40	60	60
205	8p.	Clearing a modern Jersey post box	20	20	30	30
206	10½p.	Telephone switchboard, *circa* 1900	60	60	30	30
	a.	Horiz pair, Nos. 206/7	1·25	1·25	60	60
207	10½p.	Modern S.P.C. telphone system	60	60	30	30

Nos. 204/5 and 206/7 were each printed together, *se-tenant*, in horizontal pairs throughout the sheets.

69 Percival "Mew Gull" **70** "My First Sermon"

(Des A. Theobald. Photo Courvoisier)

1979 (24 Apr). *25th Anniv of International Air Rally. T* **69** *and similar horiz designs. Multicoloured. P* 11½.
208 6p. Type **69** 15 15
209 8p. De Havilland "Chipmunk" 20 20
210 10½p. Druine "Turbulent" 25 25
211 11p. De Havilland "Tiger Moth" 30 30
212 13p. North American "Harvard" Mk. 4 .. 35 35

(Des Jersey P.O. and Courvoisier. Photo Courvoisier)

1979 (13 Aug). *International Year of the Child and 150th Birth Anniv of Millais. Paintings. T* **70** *and similar multicoloured designs. P* 12 × 12½ (25*p*.) *or* 12 × 11½ (*others*).
213 8p. Type **70** 25 20
214 10½p. "Orphans" 30 25
215 11p. "The Princes in the Tower" 40 30
216 25p. "Christ in the House of His Parents" (50 × 32 *mm*) 70 65

(Des Jennifer Toombs. Photo Courvoisier)

1979 (8 Nov). *Wildlife Preservation Trust* (*3rd series*). *Multicoloured designs as T* **34**. *P* 11½.
217 6p. Pink Pigeon (*vert*) 15 15
218 8p. Orang-Utan (*vert*) 20 20
219 11½p. Hermit Ibis 30 30
220 13p. Lowland Gorilla (*vert*) 35 35
221 15p. Rodrigues Fruit Bat (*vert*) 40 40

71 Plan of Mont Orgueil

(Litho Enschedé)

1980 (5 Feb). *Fortresses. T* **71** *and similar multicoloured designs showing drawings by Thomas Phillips. P* 13 × 13½ (25*p*.) *or* 13½ × 13 (*others*).
222 8p. Type **71** 30 30
223 11½p. Plan of La Tour de St. Aubin 35 35
224 13p. Plan of Elizabeth Castle 35 35
225 25p. Map of Jersey showing fortresses (38 × 27 *mm*) 70 70

72 Sir Walter Raleigh and Paul Ivy (engineer) discussing Elizabeth Castle

(Des Jersey Post Office and Questa. Litho Questa)

1980 (6 May). *Europa. Personalities. Links with Britain. T* **72** *and similar vert design. Multicoloured. P* 14.
226 9p. } Type **72** .. 20 20
227 9p. } .. 20 20
a. Horiz pair. Nos. 226/7 45
228 13½p. Sir George Carteret receiving rights to Smith's Island, Virginia from King .. 30 35
229 13½p. Charles II 30 35
a. Horiz pair. Nos. 228/9 65

Nos. 226/7 and 228/9 were each printed together, *se-tenant*, in horizontal pair throughout the sheet, forming composite designs.

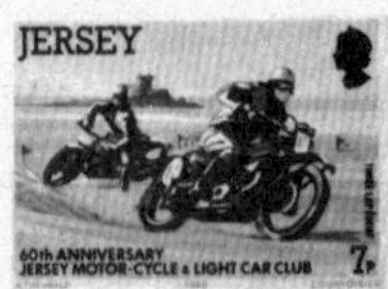

73 Planting **74** Three Lap Event

(Des R. Granger Barrett. Litho Questa)

1980 (6 May). *Centenary of Jersey Royal Potato. T* **73** *and similar vert designs. Multicoloured. P* 14.
230 7p. Type **73** 15 15
231 15p. Digging 40 45
232 17½p. Weighbridge 50 55

(Des A. Theobald. Photo Courvoisier)

1980 (24 July). *60th Anniv of Jersey Motor-cycle and Light Car Club. T* **74** *and similar horiz designs. Multicoloured. P* 11½.
233 7p. Type **74** 25 25
234 9p. Jersey International Road Race .. 25 25
235 13½p. Scrambling 40 40
236 15p. Sand racing (saloon cars) 40 40
237 17½p. National Hill Climb 40 40

75 *Eye of the Wind* **76** Detail of "The Death of Major Peirson"

(Des G. Drummond. Litho Questa)

1980 (1 Oct). *"Operation Drake" Round the World Expedition and 150th Anniv of Royal Geographical Society* (14*p*.). *P* 14.
238 7p. Type **75** 20 20
239 9p. Marine study from inflatable diving platform 25 25
240 13½p. Exploration of Papua New Guinea .. 35 35
241 14p. Captain Scott's ship *Discovery* .. 35 35
242 15p. Using aerial walkways, Conservation Project, Sulawesi 35 35
243 17½p. *Eye of the Wind* and Goodyear airship 40 40
238/43 .. .. *Set of* 6 1·75 1·75

(Photo Courvoisier)

1981 (6 Jan). *Bicentenary of Battle of Jersey. Painting "The Death of Major Peirson" by J. S. Copley. T* **76** *and similar vert designs showing details of the work. P* 12½ × 12.
244 7p. multicoloured 20 20
245 10p. multicoloured 20 20
246 15p. multicoloured 50 50
247 17½p. multicoloured 50 55
MS248 144 × 97 mm. Nos. 244/7 .. .. 1·25 1·50
Stamps from No. **MS**248 are without white margins.

77 De Bagot **78** Jersey Crest and Map of Channel

78a "Queen Elizabeth II" (Norman Hepple)

(Des and photo Courvoisier (£5). Des G. Drummond. Litho Questa (others))

1981 (24 Feb)–**84**. *Arms of Jersey Families. T* **77** *and similar designs in black, silver and mauve* (4*p*.), *black, silver and chrome-yellow* (20*p*.), *black and dull blue* (25*p*.) *or multicoloured* (*others*) *with T* **78**/*a*. *P* 12½ × 12 (£5) *or* 14 (*others*)
249 ½p. Type 77 .. .. 5 5
250 1p. De Carteret 5 5
a. Booklet pane of 6 10
251 2p. La Cloche 5 5
a. Booklet pane of 6 (1.12.81) 20
b. Perf 15 × 14 (15.11.84) 5 5
252 3p. Dumaresq 5 5
a. Booklet pane of 6 30
b. Perf. 15 × 14 (27.4.84) 5 5
ba. Booklet pane of 6 30
253 4p. Payn 8 10
254 5p. Janvrin 8 10
255 6p. Poingdestre 10 12
256 7p. Pipon 12 15
a. Booklet pane of 6 75
257 8p. Marett 15 20
a. Booklet pane of 6 (19.4.83) 85
258 9p. Le Breton 15 20
a. Perf 15 × 14 (27.4.84) 15 20
ab. Booklet pane of 6 90
259 10p. Le Maistre 20 25
a. Booklet pane of 6 .. .. 1·10
260 11p. Bisson (28.7.81) 20 25
a. Booklet pane of 6 (19.4.83) .. .. 1·25
261 12p. Robin (28.7.81) 20 25
a. Perf 15 × 14 (27.4.84) 20 25
ab. Booklet pane of 6 .. .. 1·25
262 13p. Herault (28.7.81) 25 30
a. Perf 15 × 14 (15.11.84) 25 30
263 14p. Messervy (28.7.81) 25 30
a. Perf 15 × 14 (15.11.84) 25 30
264 15p. Fiott (28.7.81) 25 30
265 20p. Badier (28.7.81) 35 40
266 25p. L'Arbalestier (23.2.82) 45 50
267 30p. Journeaux (23.2.82) 50 55
268 40p. Lempriere (23.2.82) 70 75
269 50p. D'Auvergne (23.2.82) 90 95
270 £1 Type **78** (23.2.82) .. .. 1·75 1·90
271 £5 Type **78a** (17.11.83) .. .. .. 9·00 9·50
249/71 .. .. *Set of* 23 14·50 15·00

Nos. 258a and 261a only come from the £2.16 stamp booklet issued 27 April 1984.

79 Knight of Hambye slaying Dragon

(Des Jennifer Toombs. Litho Questa)

1981 (7 Apr). *Europa. Folklore. T* **79** *and similar horiz designs. Multicoloured. P* 14½.
275 10p. Type **79** 25 25
276 10p. Servant slaying Knight of Hambye, and awaiting execution 25 25
a. Horiz pair. Nos. 275/6 .. .. .. 50 55
277 18p. St. Brelade celebrating Easter on island 45 45
278 18p. Island revealing itself as a huge fish .. 45 45
a. Horiz pair. Nos. 277/8 .. .. .. 1·00 1·00

Legends:—10p. (*both*), Slaying of the Dragon of Lawrence by the Knight of Hambye; 18p. (*both*), Voyages of St. Brelade.

Nos. 275/6 and 277/8 were each printed together, *se-tenant*, in horizontal pairs throughout the sheet.

80 The Harbour by Gaslight **81** Prince Charles and Lady Diana Spencer

(Des R. Granger Barrett. Photo Courvoisier)

1981 (22 May). *150th Anniv of Gas Lighting in Jersey. T* **80** *and similar horiz designs showing Jersey by gaslight. Multicoloured. P* 11½.
279 7p. Type **80** 20 20
280 10p. The Quay 25 25
281 18p. Royal Square 40 40
282 22p. Halkett Place 50 50
283 25p. Central Market 55 55

(Des Jersey P.O. and Courvoisier. Photo Courvoisier)

1981 (28 July). *Royal Wedding. P* 11½.
284 **81** 10p. multicoloured 50 70
285 25p. multicoloured .. .. .. 1·50 1·25

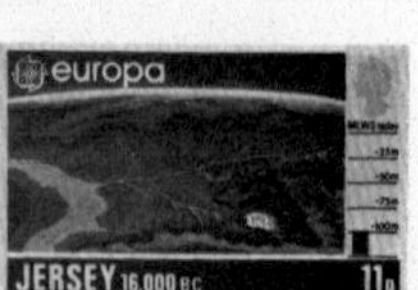

82 Christmas Tree in Royal Square **83** Jersey, 16,000 B.C.

(Des A. Copp. Litho Questa)

1981 (29 Sept). *Christmas. T* **82** *and similar vert designs. Multicoloured. P* 14½.
286 7p. Type **82** 20 20
287 10p. East window, Parish Church, St. Helier 35 35
288 18p. Boxing Day meet of Jersey Drag Hunt 55 60

(Des A. Copp. Litho Questa)

1982 (20 Apr). *Europa. Historic Events. Formation of Jersey. T* **83** *and similar multicoloured designs. P* 14½.
289 11p. Type **83** 25 25
290 11p. Jersey, 10,000 B.C. (*vert*) 30 30
291 19½p. 7,000 B.C. (*vert*) 50 50
292 19½p. 4,000 B.C. 50 50

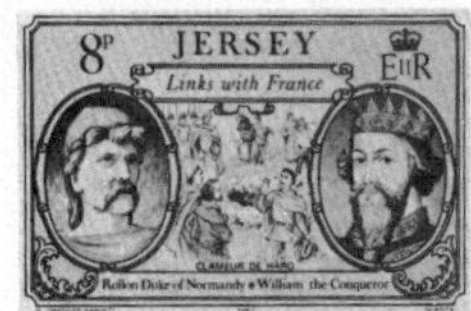

84 Duke Rollo of Normandy, William the Conqueror and "Clameur de Haro" (traditional procedure for obtaining justice)

(Des R. Granger Barrett. Litho Questa)

1982 (11 June–7 Sept). *Links with France. T* **84** *and similar horiz designs. Multicoloured. P* 14.

293	8p.	Type **84**	15	15
	a.	Horiz pair. Nos. 293/4	50	50
	b.	Booklet pane. Nos. 293 and 294 each × 2 (7 Sept)	75	
294	8p.	John of England, Philippe Auguste of France and Siege of Rouen	15	15
295	11p.	Jean Martell (brandy merchant), early still and view of Cognac	20	20
	a.	Horiz pair. Nos. 295/6	60	65
	b.	Booklet pane. Nos. 295 and 296 each × 2 (7 Sept)	90	
296	11p.	Victor Hugo, "Le Rocher des Proscrits" (rock where he used to meditate) and Marine Terrace	20	20
297	19½p.	Pierre Teilhard de Chardin (philosopher) and "Maison Saint Louis" (science institute)	40	40
	a.	Horiz pair. Nos. 297/8	1·10	1·25
	b.	Booklet pane. Nos. 297 and 298 each × 2 (7 Sept)	1·75	
298	19½p.	Père Charles Rey (scientist), anemotachymeter and The Observatory, St. Louis	40	40
293/8		.. .. *Set of* 6	1·90	2·00

The two designs of each value were printed together, *se-tenant*, in horizontal pairs throughout the sheet.

Nos. 293a, 295a and 297a were printed with either a French or an English inscription on the selvedge.

85 Sir William Smith, Founder of Boys' Brigade

86 *Tamar* with *Dolphin* at Port Egmont

(Des A. Theobald. Photo Courvoisier)

1982 (18 Nov). *75th Anniv of Boy Scout Movement (Nos.* 301/3) *and Centenary of Boys' Brigade (Nos.* 299/301). *T* **85** *and similar multicoloured designs. P* 11½.

299	8p.	Type **85**	15	15
300	11p.	Boys' Brigade "Old Boys" band, Liberation Parade, 1945 (*vert*)	30	30
301	24p.	William Smith and Lord Baden-Powell at Royal Albert Hall, 1903	60	60
302	26p.	Lord and Lady Baden-Powell in St. Helier, 1924 (*vert*)	65	65
303	29p.	Scouts at "Westward Ho" campsite, St. Ouen's Bay	75	75

(Des R. Granger Barrett. Litho Questa)

1983 (15 Feb). *Jersey Adventurers. 250th Birth Anniv of Philippe de Carteret. T* **86** *and similar horiz designs. Multicoloured. P* 14 × 14½.

304	8p.	Type **86**	15	20
305	11p.	*Dolphin* and *Swallow* off Magellan Strait	30	30
306	19½p.	Discovering Pitcairn Island	45	45
307	24p.	Carteret taking possession of English Cove, New Ireland	60	55
308	26p.	*Swallow* sinking a pirate, Macassar Strait	60	60
309	29p.	*Endymion* leading convoy from West Indies	65	65
304/9		.. .. *Set of* 6	2·50	2·50

87 1969 5s. Legislative Chamber Definitive

(Des G. Drummond. Litho Questa)

1983 (19 Apr). *Europa. T* **87** *and similar multicoloured designs. P* 14½.

310	11p.	Type **87**	20	25
	a.	Horiz pair. Nos. 310/11	55	
311	11p.	Royal Mace (23 × 32 *mm*)	25	25
312	19½p.	1969 10s. Royal Court definitive showing green border error	40	45
	a.	Horiz pair. Nos. 312/13	90	
313	19½p.	Bailiff's Seal (23 × 32 *mm*)	40	45

The two designs of each value were issued together, *se-tenant*, in horizontal pairs throughout the sheets.

88 Charles Le Geyt and Battle of Minden (1759)

(Des A. Copp. Litho Questa)

1983 (21 June). *World Communications Year and 250th Birth Anniv of Charles Le Geyt (first Jersey postmaster). T* **88** *and similar horiz designs. Multicoloured. P* 14.

314	8p.	Type **88**	25	25
315	11p.	London to Weymouth mail coach ..	35	35
316	24p.	P.O. Mail Packet *Chesterfield* attacked by French privateer	60	60
317	26p.	Mary Godfray and the Hue Street Post Office	65	65
318	29p.	Mail steamer leaving St. Helier harbour	70	70

89 Assembly Emblem

90 "Cardinal Newman"

(Des A. Copp. Litho Questa)

1983 (21 June). *13th General Assembly of the A.I.P.L.F. (Association Internationale des Parlementaires de Langue Francaise), Jersey. P* 14½.

319	**89**	19½p. multicoloured	50	60

(Des and photo Courvoisier)

1983 (20 Sept). *50th Death Anniv of Walter Ouless (artist). T* **90** *and similar multicoloured designs, showing paintings. P* 11½.

320	8p.	Type **90**	20	20
321	11p.	"Incident in the French Revolution" ..	35	35
322	20½p.	"Thomas Hardy"	60	60
323	31p.	"David with the head of Goliath" (38 × 32 *mm*)	85	90

91 Golden Lion Tamarin

92 C.E.P.T. 25th Anniversary Logo

(Des W. Oliver. Litho Questa)

1984 (17 Jan). *Wildlife Preservation Trust (4th series). T* **91** *and similar vert designs. Multicoloured. P* 13½ × 14.

324	9p.	Type **91**	20	25
325	12p.	Snow Leopard	30	30
326	20½p.	Jamaican Boa	55	50
327	26p.	Round Island Gecko	70	75
328	28p.	Coscoroba Swan	75	80
329	31p.	St. Lucia Amazon	80	90
324/9		.. .. *Set of* 6	3·00	3·25

(Des J. Larrivière. Litho Questa)

1984 (12 Mar). *Europa. P* 14½ × 15.

330	**92**	9p. cobalt, dull ultramarine and black	25	30
331		12p. light green, green and black ..	30	35
332		20½p. rose-lilac, deep magenta and black	50	55

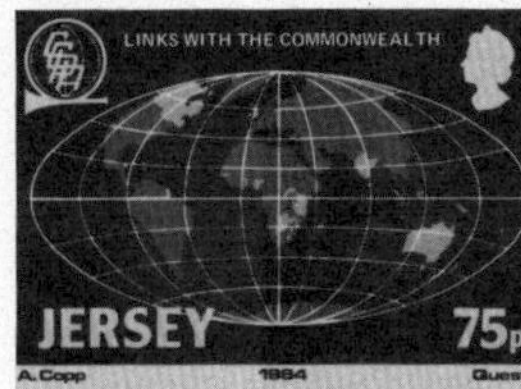

93 Map showing Commonwealth

(Des A. Copp. Litho Questa)

1984 (12 Mar). *Links with the Commonwealth. Sheet* 108 × 74 *mm. P* 15 × 14½.

MS333	**93**	75p. multicoloured	1·75	1·90

94 *Sarah Bloomshoft* at Demie de Pas Light, 1906

(Des G. Palmer. Litho Questa)

1984 (1 June). *Centenary of the Jersey R.N.L.I. Lifeboat Station T* **94** *and similar horiz designs showing famous rescues. Multicoloured. P* 14½.

334	9p.	Type **94**	30	30
335	9p.	*Hearts of Oak* and *Maurice Georges*, 1949	30	30
336	12p.	*Elizabeth Rippon* and *Hanna*, 1949 ..	35	35
337	12p.	*Elizabeth Rippon* and *Santa Maria*, 1951	35	35
338	20½p.	*Elizabeth Rippon and Bacchus*, 1973 ..	50	50
339	20½p.	*Thomas James King* and *Cythara*, 1983 ..	50	50
334/9		.. .. *Set of* 6	2·00	2·00

95 Bristol "Type 170" Freighter

(Des G. Drummond. Litho Questa)

1984 (24 July). *Aviation History. T* **95** *and similar horiz designs. Multicoloured. P* 14.

340	9p.	Type **95**	30	30
341	12p.	Airspeed "A.S.57 Ambassador 2" ..	35	35
342	26p.	De Havilland "D.H.14 Heron 1B" ..	75	75
343	31p.	De Havilland "D.H.89A Dragon Rapide"	90	90

96 "Robinson Crusoe leaves the Wreck"

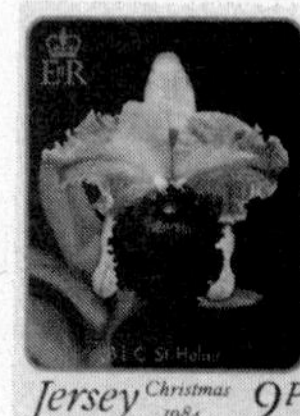

97 "B.L.C. St Helier" Orchid

(Des R. Granger Barrett. Photo Courvoisier)

1984 (21 Sept). *Links with Australia. Paintings by John Alexander Gilfillan. T* **96** *and similar horiz designs. Multicoloured. Granite paper. P* 11½ × 12.

344	9p.	Type **96**	20	25
345	12p.	"Edinburgh Castle"	25	30
346	20½p.	"Maori Village"	40	45
347	26p.	"Australian Landscape"	55	60
348	28p.	"Waterhouse's Corner, Adelaide" ..	55	60
349	31p.	"Captain Cook at Botany Bay" ..	60	65
344/9		.. .. *Set of* 6	2·25	2·50

(Photo Courvoisier)

1984 (15 Nov). *Christmas. Jersey Orchids. T* **97** *and similar vert design. Multicoloured. Granite paper. P* 12 × 11½.

350	9p.	Type **97**	20	25
351	12p.	"Oda Mt Bingham"	25	30

98 "*Hebe* off Corbiere, 1874"

(Photo Harrison)

1984 (26 Feb). *Death Centenary of Philip John Ouless (artist). T* **98** *and similar horiz designs. Multicoloured. P* 14 × 15.

352	9p.	Type **98**	20	25
353	12p.	"The *Gaspe* engaging the *Diomede*" ..	20	30
354	22p.	"The Paddle-steamer *London* entering Naples, 1856"	40	45
355	31p.	"The *Rambler* entering Cape Town, 1840"	60	65
356	34p.	"St. Aubin's Bay from Mount Bingham, 1872"	70	75

POSTAGE DUE STAMPS

D 1

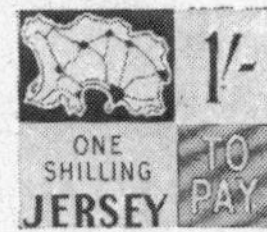

D 2 Map

(Des F. Guenier. Litho Bradbury, Wilkinson)

1969 (1 Oct). *P* 14 × 13½.

No.	Type	Description		Unused	Used
D1	D 1	1d. bluish violet		4·00	2·00
D2		2d. sepia		4·00	2·00
D3		3d. magenta		6·00	3·00
D4	D 2	1s. bright emerald		15·00	10·00
D5		2s. 6d. olive-grey		28·00	24·00
D6		5s. vermilion		40·00	45·00
D1/6			*Set of* 6	90·00	80·00

1971 (15 Feb)–**75**. *As Type* D **2** *but values in decimal currency.*

No.	Description		Unused	Used
D 7	½p. black		5	5
D 8	1p. violet-blue		5	5
D 9	2p. olive-grey		5	8
D10	3p. reddish purple		10	10
D11	4p. pale red		12	12
D12	5p. bright emerald		12	12
D13	6p. yellow-orange (12.8.74)		15	15
D14	7p. bistre-yellow (12.8.74)		15	15
D15	8p. light greenish blue (1.5.75)		25	25
D16	10p. pale olive-grey		35	35
D17	11p. ochre (1.5.75)		35	35
D18	14p. violet		40	40
D19	25p. myrtle-green (12.8.74)		80	80
D20	50p. dull purple (1.5.75)		1·40	1·40
D7/20		*Set of* 14	4·00	4·00

D **3** Arms of St. Clement and Dovecote at Samares

D **4** St. Brelade

(Des G. Drummond. Litho Questa)

1978 (17 Jan). *Type* D **3** *and similar horiz designs showing the Parish Arms given. P* 14.

No.	Description		Unused	Used
D21	1p. blue-green and black		5	5
D22	2p. orange-yellow and black (St. Lawrence)		5	5
D23	3p. lake-brown and black (St. John)		5	8
D24	4p. orange-vermilion and black (St. Ouen)		8	10
D25	5p. ultramarine and black (St. Peter)		10	12
D26	10p. brown-olive and black (St. Martin)		20	25
D27	12p. greenish blue and black (St. Helier)		25	30
D28	14p. red-orange and black (St. Saviour)		30	35
D29	15p. bright magenta and black (St. Brelade)		30	35
D30	20p. yellow-green and black (Grouville)		40	45
D31	50p. deep brown and black (St. Mary)		1·10	1·10
D32	£1 chalky blue and black (Trinity)		2·10	2·25
D21/32		*Set of* 12	4·75	5·00

Parish Views shown:—2p. Handois Reservoir; 3p. Sorel Point; 4p. Pinnacle Rock; 5p. Quetivel Mill; 10p. St. Catherine's Breakwater; 12p. St. Helier Harbour; 14p. Highlands College; 15p. Beauport Bay; 20p. La Hougue Bie; 50p. Perry Farm; £1 Bouley Bay.

1982 (7 Sept). *Type* D **4** *and similar vert designs depicting Jersey Harbours. P* 14.

No.	Description		Unused	Used
D33	1p. bright turquoise-green and black		5	5
D34	2p. chrome-yellow and black		5	5
D35	3p. lake-brown and black		5	5
D36	4p. red and black		8	10
D37	5p. bright blue and black		8	10
D38	6p. yellow-olive and black		10	12
D39	7p. bright reddish mauve and black		12	15
D40	8p. bright orange-red and black		15	20
D41	9p. bright green and black		15	20
D42	10p. turquoise-blue and black		20	25
D43	20p. apple-green and black		35	40
D44	30p. bright purple and black		50	55
D45	40p. dull orange and black		70	75
D46	£1 bright reddish violet and black		1·75	1·90
D33/46		*Set of* 14	4·75	4·25

Designs:—2p. St. Aubin; 3p. Rozel; 4p. Greve de Lecq; 5p. Bouley Bay; 6p. St. Catherine; 7p. Gorey; 8p. Bonne Nuit; 9p. La Roque; 10p. St. Helier; 20p. Ronez; 30p. La Collette; 40p. Elizabeth Castle; £1 Upper Harbour Marina.

British Post Offices Abroad

The origins of the network of Post Offices, Postal Agencies and Packet Agents can be recognised from the 18th century, but the system did not become established until the expansion of trade, following the end of the Napoleonic Wars in 1815.

Many offices were provided in newly acquired dependent territories, and were then, eventually, transferred from the control of the British Post Office to the evolving local administrations.

Those in foreign countries, nearly always based on existing British Consular appointments, were mostly connected to the network of British Packet lines which had been re-established in 1814. They tended to survive until the country in which they were situated established its own efficient postal service or joined the U.P.U. The term "Post Office Agent" was employed by the British G.P.O. and "Packet Agent" by the shipping lines to describe similar functions.

Listed in this section are the Crowned-circle handstamps and G.B. stamps used in the Post Offices and Agencies situated in foreign countries. Those for the territories within the scope of this volume will be found under the following headings:

	Page		Page
Antigua	11	Jamaica	372
Ascension	27	Lagos	396
Bahamas	53	Malta	449
Barbados	66	Mauritius	460
Bermuda	84	Montserrat	468
British Guiana	97	Newfoundland	484
British Honduras	101	New Zealand	503
British Levant	106	Niger Coast	528
British Virgin Islands	110	Niger Company Territories	529
Canada	125		
Cyprus	187	Nova Scotia	555
Dominica	199	St. Kitts-Nevis	604
Egypt	208	St. Lucia	614
Gibraltar	246	St. Vincent	623
Grenada	258	Seychelles	647
Hong Kong	291	Trinidad and Tobago	746
Ionian Islands	360	Turks Islands	760

Prices. Catalogue prices quoted in this section, and throughout the volume, covering Crowned-circle handstamps and stamps of Great Britain used abroad are for fine used examples with the cancellation or handstamp clearly legible. Poor impressions of the cancellations and handstamps are worth much less than the prices quoted.

CROWNED-CIRCLE HANDSTAMPS

Following the introduction, in 1840, of adhesive stamps in Great Britain there was considerable pressure from a number of the dependent territories for the British Post Office to provide something similar for their use.

Such suggestions were resisted, however, because of supposed operational problems, but the decision was taken, in connection with an expansion of the Packet Service, to issue a uniform series of handstamps and date stamps to the offices abroad, both in the dependent territories and in foreign countries.

Under the regulations circulated in December 1841, letters and packets forwarded through these offices to the United Kingdom or any of its territories were to be sent unpaid, the postage being collected on delivery. Where this was not possible, for example from a British colony to a foreign country or between two foreign ports, then a *crowned-circle handstamp* was to be applied with the postage, paid in advance, noted alongside in manuscript.

Examples of these handstamps were supplied over twenty years from 1842, but many continued to fulfil other functions long after the introduction of adhesive stamps in the colony concerned.

Our listings cover the use of these handstamps for their initial purpose and the prices quoted are for examples used on cover during the pre-adhesive period.

In most instances the dates quoted are those on which the handstamp appears in the G.P.O. Record Books, but it seems to have been normal for the handstamps to be sent to the office concerned immediately following this registration.

Many of the handstamps were individually cut by hand, so that each has its own characteristics, but for the purposes of the listing they have been grouped into nine Types as shown in the adjacent column. No attempt has been made to identify them by anything but the most major differences, so that minor differences in size and in the type of the crown have been ignored.

DOUBLE CIRCLE

CC 1 CC 1a

Curved "PAID"

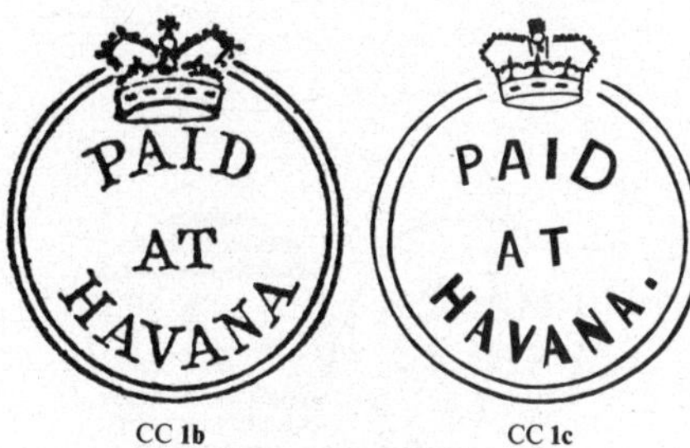

CC 1b CC 1c

Curved "PAID"

CC 2

Straight "PAID"

SINGLE CIRCLE

CC 3 CC 4

Straight "PAID"

CC 5

Curved "PAID"

CC 6 CC 7

Straight "PAID" Curved "PAID"

GREAT BRITAIN STAMPS USED ABROAD

Prices quoted are for single stamps not on cover unless otherwise stated. Stamps on cover are worth considerably more in most cases.

In many instances obliterators allocated to post offices abroad were, at a later date re-allocated to offices at home. Postmarks on issues later than those included in our lists can therefore safely be regarded as *not* having been "used abroad".

INDEX

		Page
A01	Kingston (Jamaica)	372
A02	St. John's (Antigua)	11
A03–A04	British Guiana	97
A05	Nassau (Bahamas)	53
A06	British Honduras	101
A07	Dominica	199
A08	Montserrat	468
A09	Nevis	604
A10	Kingstown (St. Vincent)	623
A11	Castries (St. Lucia)	614
A12	Basse-Terre (St. Christopher)	604
A13	Tortola (British Virgin Is)	110
A14	Scarborough (Tobago)	747
A15	St. George (Grenada)	258
A18	English Harbour (Antigua)	11
A25	Malta	449
A26	Gibraltar	246
A27–A78	Jamaica	372
A80–A99	See note on page	GB 67
Abutshi (Niger Company Territories)		529
Akassa (Niger Company Territories)		529
Ascension		27
B01	Alexandria	208
B02	Suez	209
B03, B12, B56, B57	See note on page	GB 67
B32	Buenos Ayres	GB 63
B53	See note on page	460
B62	See note on page	291
B64	See note on page	647
Benin and Benin River (Niger Coast Protectorate)		528
Bonny and Bonny River (Niger Coast Protectorate)		528
Brass River (Niger Coast Protectorate)		528
Burutu (Niger Company Territories)		530
C	Constantinople (British Levant)	106
C28	Montevideo	GB 67
C30	Valparaiso	GB 63
C35	Panama	GB 64
C36	Arica	GB 66
C37	Caldera	GB 63
C38	Callao	GB 66
C39	Cobija	GB 63
C40	Coquimbo	GB 63
C41	Guayaquil	GB 65
C42	Islay	GB 66
C43	Paita	GB 66
C51	St. Thomas (D.W.I.)	GB 64
C56 (or 65)	Carthagena	GB 63
C57	Greytown	GB 65
C58	Havana	GB 64
C59	Jacmel	GB 65
C60	La Guayra	GB 67
C61	San Juan	GB 67
C62	Santa Martha	GB 64
C63	Tampico	GB 65
C65 (see C56)		GB 63
C79	See note on page	GB 67
C81	Bahia	GB 63
C82	Pernambuco	GB 63
C83	Rio de Janeiro	GB 63
C86	Porto Plata	GB 65
C87	St. Domingo	GB 65
C88	St. Jago de Cuba	GB 64
Crimea (Army)		GB 67
D22	Ciudad Bolivar	GB 67
D26	Spanish Mail (St. Thomas)	GB 64
D47	Polymedia (Cyprus)	187
D48	Army H.Q. (Cyprus)	187
D65	Pisagua?	GB 66
D74	Pisco and Chincha Islands	GB 66
D87	Iquique	GB 66
E53	Port-au-Prince	GB 65
E88	Colon	GB 64
Egypt (Army)		GB 67
F69	Savanilla	GB 64
F83	Arroyo	GB 66
F84	Aguadilla	GB 66
F85	Mayaguez	GB 66
F87	Smyrna (British Levant)	106
F88	Ponce	GB 67
Forcados River (Niger Coast Protectorate)		528
G	Gibraltar	246
G06	Beyrout (British Levant)	106
Ionian Islands		360
Lokoja (Niger Company Territories)		530
M	Malta	449
Old Calabar River (Niger Coast Protectorate)		528
Opobo River (Niger Coast Protectorate		528
S	Stamboul (British Levant)	107
South Africa (Army)		GB 68
Salonica (British Levant)		106
Sudan (Army)		GB 68
247	Fernando Poo	GB 65
582	Naguabo	GB 67
942, 969, 974, 975, 981, 982	Cyprus	187
Wavy lines	Malta	449

TYPES OF OBLITERATOR FOR GREAT BRITAIN STAMPS USED ABROAD

HORIZONTAL OVAL

(1)

(2)

(3)

(4)

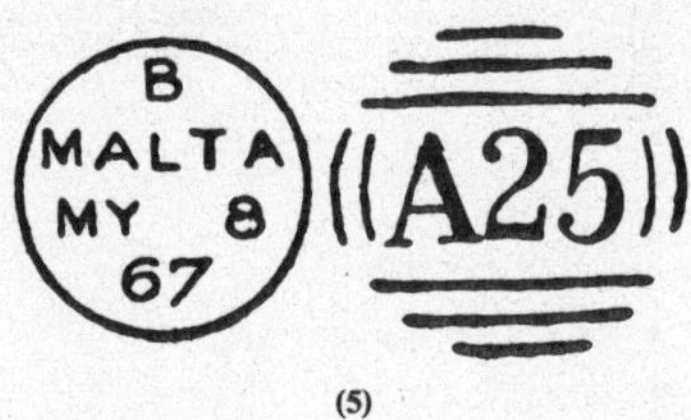

(5)

(6)

(7)

VERTICAL OVAL

(8)

(9)

(or with stop after "S")
(10)

(11)

(12)

(13)

(14)

(15)

CIRCULAR DATE STAMPS

(16)

(17)

(18)

(19)

(20)

ARGENTINE REPUBLIC

BUENOS AYRES

The first regular monthly British mail packet service was introduced in 1824, replacing a private arrangement which had previously existed for some years.

Great Britain stamps were used from 1860 until the office closed in 1873.

CROWNED-CIRCLE HANDSTAMPS

CC1 CC **7** BUENOS AYRES (R.) (5.1.1851) *Price on cover* £650

Stamps of GREAT BRITAIN *cancelled* "B 32" *as in Types* **2, 12** *or* **13.**

1860 *to* **1873.**

Z 1 1d. rose-red (1857)
Z 2 1d. rose-red (1864) *From* 10·00
Plate Nos. 71, 72, 73, 74, 76, 78, 79, 80, 81, 85, 87, 89, 90, 91, 92, 93, 94, 95, 96, 97, 99, 101, 103, 104, 107, 108, 110, 112, 113, 114, 117, 118, 119, 120, 121, 123, 125, 127, 129, 130, 131, 135, 136, 138, 139, 140, 142, 143, 145, 147, 149, 150, 151, 155, 159, 163, 164, 166, 169, 172.
Z 3 2d. blue (1858–69) *From* 18·00
Plate Nos. 8, 9, 12, 13, 14.
Z 4 3d. carmine-rose (1862) £150
Z 5 3d. rose (1865) (Plate No. 4) 45·00
Z 6 3d. rose (1867–73) *From* 18·00
Plate Nos. 4, 5, 6, 7, 8, 9, 10.
Z 7 4d. rose (1857) 38·00
Z 8 4d. red (1862) (Plate Nos. 3, 4) 48·00
Z 9 4d. vermilion (1865–73) *From* 22·00
Plate Nos. 7, 8, 9, 10, 11, 12, 13.
Z10 6d. lilac (1856) 50·00
Z11 6d. lilac (1862) (Plate Nos. 3, 4)
Z12 6d. lilac (1865–67) (Plate Nos. 5, 6) *From* 35·00
Z13 6d. lilac (1867) (Plate No. 6) 60·00
Z14 6d. violet (1867–70) (Plate Nos. 6, 8, 9) *From* 28·00
Z15 6d. buff (1872) (Plate No. 11) 60·00
Z16 6d. chestnut (1872) (Plate No. 11) 30·00
Z17 9d. bistre (1862) £200
Z18 9d. straw (1862) £140
Z19 9d. straw (1865) £250
Z20 9d. straw (1867) £150
Z21 10d. red-brown (1867) £175
Z22 1s. green (1856) 85·00
Z23 1s. green (1862) 60·00
Z24 1s. green (1865) (Plate No. 4) 38·00
Z25 1s. green (1867–73) (Plate Nos. 4, 5, 6, 7) *From* 15·00
Z26 1s. green (1873–77) (Plate No. 8)
Z27 2s. blue (1867) 90·00
Z28 5s. rose (1867) (Plate No. 1) £250

A "B 32" obliteration was later used by Mauritius on its own stamps.

AZORES

ST. MICHAELS (SAN MIGUEL)

A British Postal Agency existed at Ponta Delgada, the chief port of the island, to operate with the services of the Royal Mail Steam Packet Company.

CROWNED-CIRCLE HANDSTAMPS

CC1 CC **1b** ST. MICHAELS (27.5.1842)

BOLIVIA

COBIJA

It is believed that the British Postal Agency opened in 1852. The stamps of Great Britain were used between 1865 and 1878. The Agency closed in 1881, the town having been occupied by Chile in 1879.

CROWNED-CIRCLE HANDSTAMPS

CC1 CC **4** COBIJA (29.3.1862) *Price on cover* £3500

Stamps of GREAT BRITAIN *cancelled* "C 39" *as Types* **4, 8** *or* **12.**

1865 *to* **1878.**

Z 1 1d. rose-red (Plate Nos. 93, 95)
Z 2 2d. blue (1858–69) (Plate No. 14)
Z 3 3d. rose (1867–73) (Plate No. 6)
Z 4 3d. rose (1873–76) (Plate Nos. 16, 19)
Z 5 4d. sage-green (1877) (Plate No. 15)
Z 6 6d. violet (1867–79) (Plate No. 9) £275
Z 7 6d. buff (1872) (Plate No. 11)
Z 8 6d. grey (1874–76) (Plate Nos. 13, 14, 15, 16) £250
Z 9 1s. green (1867–73) (Plate Nos. 4, 5)
Z10 1s. green (1873–77) (Plate Nos. 10, 11, 12, 13) £250
Z11 2s. blue (1867) £350
Z12 5s. rose (1867–74) (Plate No. 2)

BRAZIL

The British Postal Agency at Rio de Janeiro opened in 1833, although the British Consulate had organised a limited postal service to Great Britain from 1810 onwards. The Agencies at Bahia and Pernambuco did not open until about 1850. All three agencies used the stamps of Great Britain from 1866, and were closed in 1874.

BAHIA

CROWNED-CIRCLE HANDSTAMPS

CC1 CC **7** BAHIA (B., G. *or* R.) (6.1.1851) *Price on cover* £1500

Stamps of GREAT BRITAIN *cancelled* "C 81" *as Type* **12.**

1866 *to* **1874.**

Z 1 1d. rose-red (1864–79) *From* 18·00
Plate Nos. 90, 96, 108, 113, 117, 135, 140, 147, 155.
Z 2 1½d. lake-red (1870–74) (Plate No. 3) 70·00
Z 3 2d. blue (1858–69) (Plate Nos. 9, 12, 13, 14) 40·00
Z 4 3d. rose (1865) (Plate No. 4)
Z 5 3d. rose (1867–73) (Plate Nos. 4, 6, 8, 9, 10) 30·00
Z 6 3d. rose (1873–79) (Plate No. 11)
Z 7 4d. vermilion (1865–73) *From* 25·00
Plate Nos. 8, 9, 10, 11, 12, 13.
Z 8 6d. lilac (1865–67) (Plate No. 5)
Z 9 6d. lilac (1867) (Plate No. 6) 45·00
Z10 6d. violet (1867–70) (Plate Nos. 6, 8, 9) *From* 35·00
Z11 6d. buff (1872–73) (Plate Nos. 11, 12) *From* 70·00
Z12 6d. chestnut (1872) (Plate No. 11)
Z13 6d. grey (1873) (Plate No. 12)
Z14 6d. grey (1874–76) (Plate No. 13)
Z15 9d. straw (1865) £250
Z16 9d. straw (1867) £110
Z17 1s. green (1865) (Plate No. 4) 40·00
Z18 1s. green (1867–73) (Plate Nos. 4, 5, 6, 7) *From* 20·00
Z19 1s. green (1873–77) (Plate Nos. 8, 9) *From* 25·00
Z20 2s. blue (1867) £140
Z21 5s. rose (1867) (Plate No. 1) £300

PERNAMBUCO

CROWNED-CIRCLE HANDSTAMPS

CC2 CC **7** PERNAMBUCO (Black *or* R.) (6.1.1851) *Price on cover* £1500

Stamps of GREAT BRITAIN *cancelled* "C 82" *as Type* **12.**

1866 *to* **1874.**

Z22 1d. rose-red (1864–79) *From* 30·00
Plate Nos. 85, 108, 111, 130, 131, 132, 149, 159, 160, 187.
Z23 2d. blue (1858–69) (Plate Nos. 9, 12, 13, 14) *From* 35·00
Z24 3d. rose (1867–73) (Plate Nos. 4, 5, 6, 7, 10) 35·00
Z25 3d. rose (1873–77) (Plate No. 11)
Z26 4d. vermilion (1865–73) *From* 26·00
Plate Nos. 9, 10, 11, 12, 13, 14.
Z27 6d. lilac (1865–67) (Plate Nos. 5, 6)
Z28 6d. lilac (1867) (Plate No. 6) 55·00
Z29 6d. violet (1867–70) (Plate Nos. 8, 9) *From* 40·00
Z30 6d. buff (1872–73) (Plate Nos. 11, 12) 50·00
Z31 6d. chestnut (1872) (Plate No. 11) 35·00
Z32 6d. grey (1873) (Plate No. 12)
Z33 9d. straw (1865) £250
Z34 9d. straw (1867) £150
Z35 10d. red-brown (1867) £200
Z36 1s. green (1865) (Plate No. 4) 70·00
Z37 1s. green (1867–73) (Plate Nos. 4, 5, 6, 7) 30·00
Z38 2s. blue (1867) £160
Z39 5s. rose (1867–74) (Plate Nos. 1, 2) £375

RIO DE JANEIRO

CROWNED-CIRCLE HANDSTAMPS

CC3 CC **7** RIO DE JANEIRO (Black, G. or R.) (6.1.1851) *Price on cover* £400

Stamps of GREAT BRITAIN *cancelled* "C 83" *as Type* **12.**

1866 *to* **1874.**

Z40 1d. rose-red (1857) 35·00
Z41 1d. rose-red (1864–79) *From* 17·00
Plate Nos. 71, 76, 80, 82, 86, 94, 113, 117, 119, 123, 132, 134, 135, 148, 159, 161, 166, 185, 200, 204.
Z42 2d. blue (1858–69) (Plate Nos. 9, 12, 13, 14) *From* 25·00
Z43 3d. rose (1867–73) (Plate Nos. 4, 5, 6, 7, 8) *From* 28·00
Z44 3d. rose (1873–77) (Plate No. 11)
Z45 4d. vermilion (1865–73) *From* 22·00
Plate Nos. 8, 9, 10, 11, 12, 13, 14.
Z46 6d. lilac (1865–67) (Plate No. 5)
Z47 6d. lilac (1867) (Plate No. 6) 45·00
Z48 6d. violet (1867–70) (Plate Nos. 6, 8, 9) *From* 28·00
Z49 6d. buff (1872) (Plate No. 11) 45·00
Z50 6d. chestnut (1872) (Plate No. 11) 40·00
Z51 6d. grey (1873) (Plate No. 12)
Z52 9d. straw (1865) £225
Z53 9d. straw (1867) £150
Z54 10d. red-brown (1867) £175
Z55 1s. green (1865) (Plate No. 4) 55·00
Z56 1s. green (1867–73) (Plate Nos. 4, 5, 6, 7) *From* 15·00
Z57 1s. green (1873–77) (Plate Nos. 8, 9) 22·00
Z58 2s. blue (1867) 80·00
Z59 5s. rose (1867–74) (Plate Nos. 1, 2) *From* £200

CAPE VERDE ISLANDS

Little is known concerning the British Postal Agency at St. Vincent, other than that which can be gleaned from the record books. No. CC1 was issued to the Agency in 1851, and it was still open four years later when a date stamp was sent out.

CROWNED-CIRCLE HANDSTAMPS

CC1 CC **6** ST. VINCENT C.DE.V. (6.1.1851) *Price on cover* £3500

CHILE

The British Postal Agency at Valparaiso opened in 1846, to be followed by further offices at Caldera (1862) and Coquimbo (1863). The stamps of Great Britain were introduced in 1865 and all three offices closed in 1881.

CALDERA

Stamps of GREAT BRITAIN *cancelled* "C 37" *as in Type* **4.**

1865 *to* **1881.**

Z 1 1d. rose-red (1864–79) *From* 20·00
Plate Nos. 71, 72, 88, 90, 95, 195.
Z 2 1½d. lake-red (1870–74) (Plate No. 3)
Z 3 2d. blue (1858–69) (Plate No. 9) 35·00
Z 4 3d. rose (1865) (Plate No. 4) 60·00
Z 5 3d. rose (1867–73) (Plate Nos. 5, 7)
Z 6 3d. rose (1873–76) *From* 22·00
Plate Nos. 11, 12, 16, 17, 18, 19.
Z 7 4d. red (1862) (Plate No. 4)
Z 8 4d. vermilion (1865–73) *From* 25·00
Plate Nos. 8, 12, 13, 14.
Z 9 4d. sage-green (1877) (Plate No. 16)
Z10 6d. lilac (1862) (Plate No. 4) 80·00
Z11 6d. lilac (1865–67) (Plate No. 6)
Z12 6d. violet (1867–70) (Plate Nos. 6, 8, 9) *From* 35·00
Z13 6d. buff (1872) (Plate No. 11)
Z14 6d. chestnut (1872) (Plate No. 11)
Z15 6d. grey (1873) (Plate No. 12)
Z16 6d. grey (1874–80) *From* 24·00
Plate Nos. 13, 14, 15, 16, 17.
Z17 8d. orange (1876) £200
Z18 9d. straw (1867) £150
Z19 10d. red-brown (1867) £190
Z20 1s. green (1865) (Plate No. 4)
Z21 1s. green (1867–73) (Plate Nos. 4, 5, 6) *From* 22·00
Z22 1s. green (1873–77) *From* 25·00
Plate Nos. 8, 10, 11, 12, 13.
Z23 2s. blue (1867) £140
Z24 2s. brown (1880) £1000
Z25 5s. rose (1867–74) (Plate No. 2) £325

COQUIMBO

Stamps of GREAT BRITAIN *cancelled* "C 40" *as in Type* **4.**

1865 *to* **1881.**

Z26 ½d. rose-red (1870–79) (Plate No. 14)
Z27 1d. rose-red (1857)
Z28 1d. rose-red (1864–79) (Plate Nos. 85, 204)
Z29 2d. blue (1858–69) (Plate Nos. 9, 14)
Z30 3d. rose (1865)
Z31 3d. rose (1872) (Plate No. 8)
Z32 3d. rose (1873–76) (Plate Nos. 18, 19) *From* 22·00
Z33 4d. red (1863) (Plate No. 4) 65·00
Z34 4d. vermilion (1865–73) (Plate Nos. 12, 14)
Z35 4d. sage-green (1877) (Plate Nos. 15, 16) £100
Z36 6d. lilac (1862) (Plate Nos. 3, 4) 65·00
Z37 6d. lilac (1865–67) (Plate No. 5)
Z38 6d. lilac (1867) (Plate No. 6) 50·00
Z39 6d. violet (1867–70) (Plate Nos. 6, 8, 9) *From* 35·00
Z40 6d. buff (1872–73) (Plate Nos. 11, 12) *From* 55·00
Z41 6d. chestnut (1872) (Plate No. 11)
Z42 6d. grey (1873) (Plate No. 12) 65·00
Z43 6d. grey (1874–76) (Plate Nos. 13, 14, 15, 16) *From* 22·00
Z44 8d. orange (1876)
Z45 9d. straw (1862) £175
Z46 9d. straw (1867) £150
Z47 10d. red-brown (1867)
Z48 1s. green (1865) (Plate No. 4) 60·00
Z49 1s. green (1867–73) (Plate Nos. 4, 5, 6) 22·00
Z50 1s. green (1873–77) *From* 26·00
Plate Nos. 8, 10, 11, 12, 13.
Z51 2s. blue (1867) £125
Z52 2s. brown (1880) £1200
Z53 5s. rose (1867–74) (Plate Nos. 1, 2) £300

VALPARAISO

CROWNED-CIRCLE HANDSTAMPS

CC1 CC **2** VALPARAISO (R.) (13.1.1846) *Price on cover* £500
CC2 CC **1** VALPARAISO (R.) (16.7.1846) *Price on cover* £650

Stamps of GREAT BRITAIN *cancelled* "C 30", *as in Types* **12** *and* **14** *or circular date stamp as Type* **16.**

1865 *to* **1881.**

Z54 ½d. rose-red (1870–79) *From* 50·00
Plate Nos. 6, 11, 12, 13, 14.
Z55 1d. rose-red (1864–79) *From* 18·00
Plate Nos. 80, 84, 85, 91, 122, 123, 138, 140, 148, 149, 152, 157, 158, 162, 167, 175, 178, 181, 185, 186, 187, 189, 190, 195, 197, 198, 199, 200, 201, 207, 209, 210, 211, 212, 213, 214, 215, 217.
Z56 1½d. lake-red (1870–74) (Plate Nos. 1, 3) *From* 55·00
Z57 2d. blue (1858–69) (Plate Nos. 9, 13, 14, 15) 35·00
Z58 2½d. rosy mauve (1875), white paper (Plate No. 2) 60·00
Z59 2½d. rosy mauve (1876) (Plate Nos. 4, 8) 50·00
Z60 3d. carmine-rose (1862)
Z61 3d. rose (1865) (Plate No. 4)
Z62 3d. rose (1867–73) *From* 20·00
Plate Nos. 5, 6, 7, 8, 9, 10.
Z63 3d. rose (1873–76) *From* 20·00
Plate Nos. 11, 12, 14, 16, 17, 18, 19.
Z64 4d. vermilion (1865–73) *From* 22·00
Plate Nos. 9, 10, 11, 12, 13, 14.
Z65 4d. vermilion (1876) (Plate No. 15) £160
Z66 4d. sage-green (1877) (Plate Nos. 15, 16) 90·00
Z67 4d. grey-brown (1880) *wmk* Large Garter
Plate No. 17.
Z68 6d. lilac (1862) (Plate Nos. 3, 4) *From* 45·00
Z69 6d. lilac (1865) (Plate Nos. 5, 6)
Z70 6d. lilac (1867) (Plate No. 6)
Z71 6d. violet (1867–70) (Plate Nos. 6, 8, 9) *From* 30·00
Z72 6d. buff (1872–73) (Plate Nos. 11, 12) *From* 40·00
Z73 6d. chestnut (1872) (Plate No. 11) 28·00
Z74 6d. grey (1873) (Plate No. 12) 40·00
Z75 6d. grey (1874–80) *From* 20·00
Plate Nos. 13, 14, 15, 16, 17.
Z76 6d. grey (1881) (Plate No. 17)
Z77 8d. orange (1876) £150
Z78 9d. straw (1862)
Z79 9d. straw (1865)
Z80 9d. straw (1867) £120
Z81 10d. red-brown (1867) £150
Z82 1s. geeen (1865) (Plate No. 4)
Z83 1s. green (1867–73) (Plate Nos. 4, 5, 6, 7) *From* 15·00
Z84 1s. green (1873–77) *From* 22·00
Plate Nos. 8, 9, 10, 11, 12, 13.
Z85 1s. orange-brown (1880) (Plate No. 13) £175
Z86 2s. blue (1867) 70·00
Z87 2s. brown (1880) £1000
Z88 5s. rose (1867–74) (Plate Nos. 1, 2) *From* £200
Z89 10s. grey-green (1878) (*wmk* Cross) £1700
Z90 £1 brown-lilac (1878) (*wmk* Cross) £3000

1880.

Z91 1d. Venetian red
Z92 1½d. Venetian red

COLOMBIA

The system of British Postal Agencies in the area was inaugurated by the opening of the Carthagena office in 1825. In 1842 agencies at Chagres, Panama and Santa Martha were added to the system. A further office opened at Colon in 1852, this port also being known as Aspinwall. During 1872 the system was further enlarged by an office at Savanilla, although this agency was later, 1878, transferred to Barranquilla.

Stamps of Great Britain were supplied to Carthagena, Panama and Santa Martha in 1865, Colon in 1870 and Savanilla in 1872.

All offices, except Chagres which had ceased to operate in 1855, closed for public business on 30 June 1881. Colon and Panama continued to exist as transit offices to deal with the mail across the isthmus. Both finally closed on 31 March 1921.

CARTHAGENA

CROWNED-CIRCLE HANDSTAMPS

CC1 CC **1b** CARTHAGENA (R.) (15.1.1841) *Price on cover* £750
CC2 CC **1** CARTHAGENA (1.7.1846) *Price on cover* £650

Stamps of GREAT BRITAIN *cancelled* "C 56" *as in Type* **4**.

1865 *to* **1881**.
Z 1 ½d. rose-red (1870–79) (Plate No. 10)
Z 2 1d. rose-red (1864–79) *From* 28·00
Plate Nos. 78, 87, 100, 111, 113, 117, 119, 125, 189, 217.
Z 3 2d. blue (1858–69) (Plate Nos. 9, 11, 14) *From* 25·00
Z 4 3d. *"Emblems"* (1865) (Plate No. 4)
Z 5 3d. rose (1865–68) (Plate Nos. 4, 5)
Z 6 3d. rose (1873–79) (Plate Nos. 12, 17, 18) *From* 35·00
Z 7 4d. vermilion (1865–73) *From* 25·00
Plate Nos. 7, 8, 9, 10, 11, 12, 13, 14.
Z 8 4d. vermilion (1876) (Plate No. 15) £150
Z 9 4d. sage-green (1877) (Plate Nos. 15, 16) *From* 90·00
Z10 6d. lilac (1865–67) (Plate Nos. 5, 6)
Z11 6d. violet (1867–70) (Plate Nos. 6, 8) *From* 40·00
Z12 6d. grey (1873) (Plate No. 12) 40·00
Z13 6d. grey (1874–76) (Plate Nos. 13, 14, 15, 16) *From* 28·00
Z14 8d. orange (1876) £150
Z15 9d. straw (1865)
Z16 1s. green (1865)
Z17 1s. green (1867–73) (Plate Nos. 4, 5, 7) 30·00
Z18 1s. green (1873–77) (Plate Nos. 8, 9, 10, 11, 12, 13) 30·00
Z19 1s. orange-brown (1880)
Z20 2s. blue (1867) £170
Z21 5s. rose (1867) (Plate No. 1) £300

Cancelled "C 65" (*incorrect handstamp, supplied in error*).

1866 *to* **1881**.
Z22 ½d. rose-red (1870–79) (Plate No. 10)
Z23 1d. rose-red (1864–79) (Plate Nos. 100, 111, 123) *From* 38·00
Z23*a* 1½d. lake-red (1870) (Plate No. 3)
Z24 2d. blue (1858–69) (Plate No. 9) 35·00
Z25 2d. rose (1880)
Z26 2½d. blue (1880) (Plate No. 19)
Z27 3d. rose (1867–73) (Plate No. 9)
Z28 3d. rose (1873–79) (Plate Nos. 14, 17, 19, 20)
Z29 4d. vermilion (1865–73) *From* 32·00
Plate Nos. 7, 9, 11, 12, 13, 14.
Z30 4d. vermilion (1876) (Plate No. 15) £175
Z31 4d. sage-green (1877) (Plate Nos. 15, 16) *From* £100
Z32 6d. violet (1867–70) (Plate Nos. 6, 8) 75·00
Z33 6d. pale buff (1872) (Plate No. 11)
Z34 6d. grey (1873) (Plate No. 12) 60·00
Z35 6d. grey (1874–80) (Plate Nos. 13, 15, 16, 17) 40·00
Z36 8d. orange (1876) £250
Z37 9d. straw (1865) £250
Z38 1s. green (1865) (Plate No. 4) 50·00
Z39 1s. green (1867) (Plate Nos. 4, 5, 6, 7) 25·00
Z40 1s. green (1873–77) (Plate Nos. 8, 11, 12, 13) *From* 30·00
Z41 1s. orange-brown (1880)
Z42 2s. blue (1867) £350
Z43 2s. brown (1880) £1200
Z44 5s. rose (1867) (Plate Nos. 1, 2) £350

CHAGRES

CROWNED-CIRCLE HANDSTAMPS

CC3 CC **1** CHAGRES (16.9.1846)

COLON

CROWNED-CIRCLE HANDSTAMPS

CC4 CC **5** COLON (R.) (21.6.1854) *Price on cover* £3000

Stamps of GREAT BRITAIN *cancelled* "E 88" *as in Type* **12**.

1870 *to* **1881**.
Z45 1d. rose-red (1864–79) *From* 22·00
Plate Nos. 107, 121, 122, 123, 125, 127, 130, 133, 136, 142, 150, 151, 152, 153, 155, 156, 157, 158, 160, 169, 171, 174, 176, 178, 179, 184, 187, 188, 194, 195, 201, 209, 213, 214, 217.
Z46 1d. Venetian red (1880)
Z47 1½d. lake-red (1870–74) (Plate No. 3) 85·00
Z48 2d. blue (1858–69) (Plate Nos. 14, 15) 28·00
Z49 2d. pale rose (1880)
Z50 3d. rose (1867–73) (Plate Nos. 6, 9)
Z51 3d. rose (1873–76) 35·00
Plate Nos. 11, 12, 16, 18, 19, 20.
Z52 4d. vermilion (1865–73) *From* 28·00
Plate Nos. 10, 11, 12, 13, 14.
Z53 4d. vermilion (1876) (Plate No. 15)
Z54 4d. sage-green (1877) (Plate Nos. 15, 16) 95·00
Z55 4d. grey-brown (1880) *wmk* Large Garter £120
Plate No. 17.
Z56 4d. grey-brown (1880) *wmk* Crown (Plate No. 17)
Z57 6d. violet (1867–70) (Plate Nos. 6, 8, 9)
Z58 6d. buff (1872) (Plate No. 11)
Z59 6d. chestnut (1872) (Plate No. 11) 50·00
Z60 6d. grey (1873) (Plate No. 12)
Z61 6d. grey (1874–80) *From* 25·00
Plate Nos. 13, 14, 15, 16, 17.
Z62 8d. orange (1876)
Z63 9d. straw (1867) £130
Z64 1s. green (1867–73) (Plate Nos. 4, 5, 6, 7) 25·00
Z65 1s. green (1873–77) *From* 25·00
Plate Nos. 8, 9, 10, 11, 12, 13.
Z66 1s. orange-brown (1880) (Plate 13) £180
Z67 1s. orange-brown (1881) (Plate 13) 55·00
Z68 2s. blue (1867) £120
Z69 2s. brown (1880) £1400
Z70 5s. rose (1867) (Plate Nos. 1, 2) £350

PANAMA

CROWNED-CIRCLE HANDSTAMPS

CC5 CC **1** PANAMA (R.) (24.8.1846) *Price on cover* £750

Stamps of GREAT BRITAIN *cancelled* "C 35" *as in Types* **4, 11** *or* **14**.

1865 *to* **1881**.
Z 71 ½d. rose-red (1870–79) *From* 25·00
Plate Nos. 10, 11, 12, 13, 14, 15, 19.
Z 72 1d. rose-red (1864–79) *From* 15·00
Plate Nos. 71, 72, 76, 81, 85, 87, 88, 89, 93, 95, 96, 101, 104, 114, 124, 130, 138, 139, 142, 159, 168, 171, 172, 174, 177, 179, 180, 184, 185, 187, 189, 191, 192, 193, 196, 200, 203, 204, 205, 207, 208, 209, 210, 211, 213, 214, 215, 218, 224.
Z 73 1½d. lake-red (1870–74) (Plate No. 3) 40·00
Z 74 2d. blue (1858–69) *From* 20·00
Plate Nos. 9, 12, 13, 14, 15.
Z 75 2½d. rosy mauve (1875) (Plate No. 1)
Z 76 2½d. rosy mauve (1876–80) (Plate Nos. 4, 12, 16)
Z 77 2½d. blue (1880) (Plate No. 19)
Z 78 2½d. blue (1881) (Plate Nos. 22, 23)
Z 79 3d. carmine-red (1862) 90·00
Z 80 3d. rose (1865) (Plate No. 4)
Z 81 3d. rose (1867–73) *From* 20·00
Plate Nos. 4, 5, 6, 7, 8, 9.
Z 82 3d. rose (1873–76) *From* 20·00
Plate Nos. 12, 14, 15, 16, 17, 18, 19, 20.
Z 83 3d. rose (1881) (Plate Nos. 20, 21)
Z 84 4d. red (1863) (Plate No. 4) 65·00
Z 85 4d. vermilion (1865–73) *From* 25·00
Plate Nos. 7, 8, 9, 10, 11, 12, 13, 14.
Z 86 4d. vermilion (1876) (Plate No. 15) £140
Z 87 4d. sage-green (1877) (Plate Nos. 15, 16) 80·00
Z 88 4d. grey-brown (1880) *wmk* Crown *From* 28·00
Plate Nos. 17, 18.
Z 89 6d. lilac (1862) (Plate Nos. 3, 4) *From* 55·00
Z 90 6d. lilac (1865–67) (Plate Nos. 5, 6) *From* 30·00
Z 91 6d. lilac (1867) (Plate No. 6)
Z 92 6d. violet (1867–70) (Plate Nos. 6, 8, 9) 28·00
Z 93 6d. buff (1872–73) (Plate Nos. 11, 12) *From* 42·00
Z 94 6d. chestnut (Plate No. 11) 25·00
Z 95 6d. grey (1873) (Plate No. 12) 40·00
Z 96 6d. grey (1874–80) *From* 25·00
Plate Nos. 13, 14, 15, 16, 17.
Z 97 6d. grey (1881) (Plate No. 17) 60·00
Z 98 8d. orange (1876) £140
Z 99 9d. straw (1862) £150
Z100 9d. straw (1867) £120
Z101 10d. red-brown (1867) £150
Z102 1s. green (1865) (Plate No. 4) 38·00
Z103 1s. green (1867–73) (Plate Nos. 4, 5, 6, 7) *From* 15·00
Z104 1s. green (1873–77) *From* 25·00
Plate Nos. 8, 9, 10, 11, 12, 13.
Z105 1s. orange-brown (1880) (Plate No. 13) £175
Z106 1s. orange-brown (1881) (Plate No. 13) 50·00
Z107 2s. blue (1867) 65·00
Z108 2s. brown (1880) £1200
Z109 5s. rose (1867–74) (Plate Nos. 1, 2) *From* £225

1880.
Z110 1d. Venetian red 15·00
Z111 2d. rose 25·00
Z112 5d. indigo 60·00

Later stamps cancelled "C 35" are believed to originate from sailors' letters or other forms of maritime mail.

SANTA MARTHA

CROWNED-CIRCLE HANDSTAMPS

CC6 CC **1b** SANTA MARTHA (R.) (15.12.1841) *Price on cover* £900

Stamps of GREAT BRITAIN *cancelled* "C 62" *as in Type* **4**.

1865 *to* **1881**.
Z113 ½d. rose-red (1870–79) (Plate No. 6) 65·00
Z114 1d. rose-red (1864–79) (Plate No. 106) 50·00
Z115 2d. blue (1858–69) (Plate No. 9) 65·00
Z116 4d. vermilion (1865–73) *From* 30·00
Plate Nos. 7, 8, 9, 11, 12, 13, 14.
Z117 4d. sage-green (1877) (Plate No. 15) £100
Z118 4d. grey-brown (1880) *wmk* Large Garter £100
Plate No. 17.
Z119 4d. grey-brown (1880) *wmk* Crown (Plate No. 17) 50·00
Z120 6d. lilac (1865–67) (Plate No. 5) 50·00
Z121 6d. grey (1873) (Plate No. 12)
Z122 6d. grey (1874–76) (Plate No. 14)
Z123 8d. orange (1876) £200
Z123*a* 9d. bistre (1862)
Z124 1s. green (1865) (Plate No. 4) 50·00
Z125 1s. green (1867–73) (Plate Nos. 5, 7) 40·00
Z126 1s. green (1873–77) (Plate No. 8)
Z127 2s. blue (1867) £275
Z128 5s. rose (1867) (Plate No. 2) £375

SAVANILLA (BARRANQUILLA)

Stamps of GREAT BRITAIN *cancelled* "F 69" *as in Type* **12**.

1872 *to* **1881**.
Z129 ½d. rose-red (1870–79) (Plate No. 6) 55·00
Z130 1d. rose-red (1864–79) (Plate Nos. 122, 171) 48·00
Z131 1½d. lake-red (1870–74) (Plate No. 3) 85·00
Z132 3d. rose (1867–73) (Plate No. 7)
Z133 3d. rose (1873–76) (Plate No. 20) 85·00
Z134 3d. rose (1881) (Plate No. 20) 85·00
Z135 4d. vermilion (1865–73) (Plate Nos. 12, 13, 14) 26·00
Z136 4d. vermilion (1876) (Plate No. 15) £150
Z137 4d. sage-green (1877) (Plate Nos. 15, 16) 50·00
Z138 4d. grey-brown (1880) *wmk* Large Garter 80·00
Plate No. 17.
Z139 4d. grey-brown (1880) *wmk* Crown (Plate No. 17) 50·00
Z140 6d. buff (1872) (Plate No. 11)
Z141 6d. grey (1878) (Plate No. 16) 60·00
Z142 8d. orange (1876) £200
Z143 1s. green (1867–73) (Plate Nos. 5, 7) 35·00
Z144 1s. green (1873–77) (Plate Nos. 8, 11, 12, 13) 38·00
Z145 1s. orange-brown (1880) £150
Z146 2s. blue (1867) £170
Z147 5s. rose (1867–74) (Plate No. 2) £350

CUBA

The British Postal Agency at Havana opened in 1762, the island then being part of the Spanish Empire. A further office, at St. Jago de Cuba, was added around 1840.

Great Britain stamps were supplied to these offices in 1865 and continued in use until they closed in 1877.

HAVANA

CROWNED-CIRCLE HANDSTAMPS

CC1 CC **1b** HAVANA (13.11.1841) *Price on cover* £850
CC2 CC **1c** HAVANA *Price on cover* £850
CC3 CC **2** HAVANA (14.7.1848) *Price on cover* £750

Stamps of GREAT BRITAIN *cancelled* "C 58" *as in Types* **4** *or* **14**.

1865 *to* **1877**.
Z 1 ½d. rose-red (1870) (Plate Nos. 6, 12) 50·00
Z 2 1d. rose-red (1864–79) 30·00
Plate Nos. 86, 90, 93, 115, 120, 123, 144, 146, 171, 174, 208.
Z 3 2d. blue (1858–69) (Plate Nos. 9, 14, 15) 35·00
Z 4 3d. rose (1867–73) (Plate No. 4) 75·00
Z 5 3d. rose (1873–76) (Plate Nos. 18, 19)
Z 6 4d. vermilion (1865–73) *From* 30·00
Plate Nos. 7, 10, 11, 12, 13, 14.
Z 7 4d. vermilion (1876) (Plate No. 15)
Z 8 6d. lilac (1865) (with hyphen) (Plate No. 5)
Z 9 6d. grey (1874–76) (Plate No. 15)
Z10 8d. orange (1876)
Z11 9d. straw (1867) £180
Z12 10d. red-brown (1867) £250
Z13 1s. green (1865) (Plate No. 4) 50·00
Z14 1s. green (1867–73) (Plate Nos. 4, 5, 7) *From* 32·00
Z15 1s. green (1873–77) (Plate Nos. 10, 12, 13) *From* 35·00
Z16 2s. blue (1867) £160
Z17 5s. rose (1867–74) (Plate Nos. 1, 2) £375

ST. JAGO DE CUBA

CROWNED-CIRCLE HANDSTAMPS

CC4 CC **1b** ST. JAGO-DE-CUBA (R.) (15.12.1841) *Price on cover* £3500

Stamps of GREAT BRITAIN *cancelled* "C 88" *as Type* **12**.

1865 *to* **1877**.
Z18 ½d. rose-red (1870–79) (Plate Nos. 4, 6, 14)
Z19 1d. rose-red (1864–79) *From* 50·00
Plate Nos. 100, 105, 106, 109, 120, 123, 138, 144, 146, 171, 208.
Z20 1½d. lake-red (1870–74) (Plate No. 3)
Z21 2d. blue (1858–69) (Plate Nos. 9, 12, 13, 14)
Z22 3d. rose (1867) (Plate No. 5)
Z23 4d. vermilion (1865–73) *From* 50·00
Plate Nos. 9, 10, 11, 12, 13, 14.
Z24 4d. vermilion (1876) (Plate No. 15) £160
Z25 6d. violet (1867–70) (Plate Nos. 6, 8, 9) *From* £170
Z26 6d. buff (Plate No. 11)
Z27 9d. straw (1865)
Z27*a* 9d. straw (1867)
Z28 10d. red-brown (1867) £250
Z29 1s. green (1867–73) (Plate Nos. 4, 5, 6) *From* £180
Z30 1s. green (1873–77) (Plate Nos. 9, 10, 12, 13)
Z31 2s. blue (1867)
Z32 5s. rose (1867) (Plate 1)

DANISH WEST INDIES

ST. THOMAS

The British Postal Agency at St. Thomas was opened *circa* 1843 and was the office around which many of the packet routes were organised.

Great Britain stamps were introduced on 3 July 1865, and the office closed in 1879.

CROWNED-CIRCLE HANDSTAMPS

CC1 CC **1** ST. THOMAS (R.) (*circa* 1850) *Price on cover* £500
CC2 CC **6** ST. THOMAS (R.) (1.5.1855) *Price on cover* £1000

Stamps of GREAT BRITAIN *cancelled* "C 51" *as in Types* **4, 12** *or* **14**.

1865 *to* **1879**.
Z 1 ½d. rose-red (1870–79) 30·00
Plate Nos. 5, 6, 8, 10, 11, 12.
Z 2 1d. rose-red (1857)
Z 3 1d. rose-red (1864–79) *From* 16·00
Plate Nos. 71, 72, 79, 81, 84, 85, 86, 87, 88, 89, 90, 93, 94, 95, 96, 97, 98, 99, 100, 101, 102, 105, 106, 107, 108, 109, 110, 111, 112, 113, 114, 116, 117, 118, 119, 120, 121, 122, 123, 124, 125, 127, 129, 130, 131, 133, 134, 136, 137, 138, 139, 140, 141, 142, 144, 145, 146, 147, 148, 149, 150, 151, 152, 154, 155, 156, 157, 158, 159, 160, 161, 162, 163, 164, 165, 166, 167, 169, 170, 171, 172, 173, 174, 175, 176, 177, 178, 179, 180, 181, 182, 184, 185, 186, 187, 189, 190, 197.
Z 4 1½d. lake-red (1870–74) (Plate Nos. 1, 3) 35·00
Z 5 2d. blue (1858–69) *From* 25·00
Plate Nos. 9, 12, 13, 14, 15.
Z 6 3d. rose (1865) (Plate No. 4) 50·00
Z 7 3d. rose (1867–73) *From* 20·00
Plate Nos. 4, 5, 6, 7, 8, 9, 10.
Z 8 3d. rose (1873–76) *From* 22·00
Plate Nos. 11, 12, 14, 15, 16, 17, 18, 19.
Z 9 4d. red (1862) (Plate Nos. 3, 4) 40·00
Z10 4d. vermilion (1865–73) *From* 25·00
Plate Nos. 7, 8, 9, 10, 11, 12, 13, 14.
Z11 4d. vermilion (1876) (Plate No. 15) £125
Z12 4d. sage-green (1877) (Plate Nos. 15, 16) *From* 90·00
Z13 4d. grey-brown (1880) *wmk* Large Garter £120
Plate No. 17.
Z14 6d. lilac (1864) (Plate No. 4) £100
Z15 6d. lilac (1865–67) (Plate Nos. 5, 6) *From* 35·00
Z16 6d. lilac (1867) (Plate No. 6) 32·00
Z17 6d. violet (1867–70) (Plate Nos. 6, 8, 9) *From* 30·00
Z18 6d. buff (1872–73) (Plate Nos. 11, 12) *From* 60·00
Z19 6d. chestnut (1872) (Plate No. 11) 26·00
Z20 6d. grey (1873) (Plate No. 12) 40·00
Z21 6d. grey (1874–76) (Plate Nos. 13, 14, 15, 16) 25·00
Z22 8d. orange (1876) £150
Z23 9d. straw (1862) £150
Z24 9d. bistre (1862) £140
Z25 9d. straw (1865) £250
Z26 9d. straw (1867) £100
Z27 10d. red-brown (1867) £150
Z28 1s. green (1865) (Plate No. 4) 38·00
Z29 1s. green (1867–73) (Plate Nos. 4, 5, 6, 7) *From* 15·00
Z30 1s. green (1873–77) *From* 22·00
Plate Nos, 8, 9, 10, 11, 12, 13.
Z31 2s. blue (1867) £120
Z32 5s. rose (1867–74) (Plate Nos. 1, 2) *From* £225

Stamps of GREAT BRITAIN *cancelled* "D 26" *as Type* **12** (*used in connection with the Spanish Mail Packets*).

1868 *to* **1871**.
Z33 1d. rose-red (1864)
Plate Nos. 98, 125.
Z34 4d. vermilion (1865–73) (Plate Nos. 9, 10, 11) £500
Z35 6d. violet (1867–70) (Plate No. 8)
Z36 1s. green (1867) (Plate No. 4)

DOMINICAN REPUBLIC

British Postal Agencies may have existed in the area before 1866, but it is only from that year that details can be found concerning offices at Porto Plata and St. Domingo.

Great Britain stamps were supplied in 1869, but both agencies did not operate between 1870 and 1876. Both finally closed in 1881.

PORTO PLATA

Stamps of GREAT BRITAIN *cancelled* "C 86" *or circular date stamp as in Types* **8** *or* **17**.

1869/70 *and* **1876** *to* **1881**.

Z 1 ½d. rose-red (1870–79) (Plate Nos. 10, 12, 14) *From* 50·00
Z 2 1d. rose-red (1864–79) *From* 30·00
Plate Nos. 123, 130, 136, 146, 151, 178, 199, 200, 205, 217.
Z 3 1½d. lake-red (1870–74) (Plate No. 3) 75·00
Z 4 2d. blue (1858–69) (Plate Nos. 14, 15) 35·00
Z 5 2½d. rosy mauve (1876–79) (Plate Nos. 13, 14) *From* £125
Z 6 3d. rose (1873–76) (Plate No. 18) 70·00
Z 7 4d. vermilion (1873) (Plate No. 14) 70·00
Z 8 4d. vermilion (1876) (Plate No. 15) £175
Z 9 4d. sage-green (1877) (Plate No. 15) £100
Z10 6d. violet (1867–70) (Plate No. 8)
Z11 6d. grey (1874–76) (Plate No. 15) 60·00
Z12 8d. orange (1876) £250
Z13 1s. green (1867–73) (Plate Nos. 4, 7) *From* 35·00
Z14 1s. green (1873–77) (Plate Nos. 11, 12, 13) *From* 30·00
Z15 2s. blue (1867) £180

ST. DOMINGO

Stamps of GREAT BRITAIN *cancelled* "C 87" *or circular date stamp as in Types* **12** *or* **16**.

1869/70 *and* **1876** *to* **1881**.

Z16 ½d. rose-red (1870–79) *From* 50·00
Plate Nos. 5, 6, 8, 10, 11, 13.
Z17 1d. rose-red (1864–79) *From* 35·00
Plate Nos. 146, 154, 171, 173, 174, 176, 178, 186, 190, 197, 220.
Z18 1½d. lake-red (1870–74) (Plate No. 3) 75·00
Z19 2d. blue (1858–69) (Plate Nos. 13, 14) 60·00
Z20 3d. rose (1873–76) (Plate No. 18)
Z21 4d. vermilion (1865–73) *From* 38·00
Plate Nos. 11, 12, 14.
Z22 4d. vermilion (1876) (Plate No. 15) £180
Z23 4d. sage-green (1877) (Plate No. 15) £125
Z24 6d. grey (1874–76) (Plate No. 15)
Z25 9d. straw (1867)
Z26 1s. green (1867) (Plate No. 4)
Z27 1s. green (1873–77) *From* 50·00
Plate Nos. 10, 11, 12, 13.
Z28 2s. blue (1867)

ECUADOR

GUAYAQUIL

The first British Postal Agent in Guayaquil was appointed during 1849.

Great Britain stamps were supplied in 1865 and continued to be used until the agency closed in 1880.

Stamps of GREAT BRITAIN *cancelled* "C 41" *as Type* **4**.

1865 *to* **1880**.

Z 1 ½d. rose-red (1870–79) (Plate Nos. 5, 6) 55·00
Z 2 1d. rose-red (1857)
Z 3 1d. rose-red (1864–79) *From* 25·00
Plate Nos. 74, 78, 85, 92, 94, 105, 110, 115, 133, 140, 145, 166, 174, 180, 216.
Z 4 1½d. lake-red (1870–74) (Plate No. 3) 75·00
Z 5 2d. blue (1858–69) (Plate Nos. 9, 13, 14) *From* 28·00
Z 6 3d. carmine-rose (1862) £150
Z 7 3d. rose (1865) (Plate No. 4) 40·00
Z 8 3d. rose (1867–73) (Plate Nos. 6, 7, 9, 10) *From* 20·00
Z 9 3d. rose (1873–76) *From* 20·00
Plate Nos. 11, 12, 15, 16, 17, 18, 19, 20.
Z10 4d. red (1862) (Plate Nos. 3, 4) 60·00
Z11 4d. vermilion (1865–73) *From* 25·00
Plate Nos. 7, 8, 9, 10, 11, 12, 13, 14.
Z12 4d. vermilion (1876) (Plate No. 15) £130
Z13 4d. sage-green (1877) (Plate Nos. 15, 16) 95·00
Z14 6d. lilac (1864) (Plate No. 4) 70·00
Z15 6d. lilac (1865–67) (Plate Nos. 5, 6) 32·00
Z16 6d. lilac (1867) (Plate No. 6)
Z17 6d. violet (1867–70) (Plate Nos. 6, 8, 9) *From* 30·00
Z18 6d. buff (1872–73) (Plate Nos. 11, 12) 70·00
Z19 6d. chestnut (1872)
Z20 6d. grey (1873) (Plate No. 12)
Z21 6d. grey (1874–76) (Plate Nos. 13, 14, 15, 16) *From* 25·00
Z22 8d. orange (1876) £175
Z23 9d. straw (1862) £190
Z24 9d. straw (1867) £120
Z25 10d. red-brown (1867) £150
Z26 1s. green (1865) (Plate No. 4) 40·00
Z27 1s. green (1867–73) (Plate Nos. 4, 5, 6, 7) *From* 22·00
Z28 1s. green (1873–77) *From* 30·00
Plate Nos. 8, 9, 10, 11, 12, 13.
Z29 2s. blue (1867) £120
Z30 2s. brown (1880) £1200
Z31 5s. rose (1867–74) (Plate Nos. 1, 2) *From* £350

FERNANDO PO

The British Consulate in this Spanish colony was a centre of British influence in the area before the growth of interest in Nigeria. The first British Post Office Agent (the resident Consul) was appointed in 1859.

Great Britain stamps were supplied in 1874 and the office remained open until 1877.

CROWNED-CIRCLE HANDSTAMPS

CC1 CC **4** FERNANDO-PO (R.) (19.2.1859) *Price on cover* £3500

Stamps of GREAT BRITAIN *cancelled* "247" *as Type* **9**.

1874 *to* **1877**.

Z1 4d. vermilion (1865–72) (Plate Nos. 13, 14) £650
Z2 4d. vermilion (1876) (Plate No. 15)
Z3 6d. grey (1874–76) (Plate Nos. 13, 14, 15, 16) £550

GUADELOUPE

A British Packet Agency was established on Guadeloupe around 1850 and appears to have remained active until sometime in the 1870s.

No. CC1 is often found used in conjunction with French Colonies (General Issues) adhesive stamps.

CROWNED-CIRCLE HANDSTAMPS

CC1 CC **1** GUADALOUPE (R., B. *or* Black) (9.3.1849) *Price on cover* £750

HAITI

The original British Postal Agencies in Haiti date from the 1830s, when it is known a Packet Agency was established at Jacmel. An office at Port-au-Prince followed in 1842, both these agencies remaining in operation until 30 June 1881.

During this period short-lived agencies also operated in the following Haitian towns: Aux Cayes (1859 to 1863), Cap Haitien (1842 to 1863), Gonaives (1849 to 1857) and St. Marc (1854 to 1861). A further agency may have operated at Le Mole around the year 1841.

Great Britain stamps were supplied to Jacmel in 1865 and to Port-au-Prince in 1869.

CAP HAITIEN

CROWNED-CIRCLE HANDSTAMPS

CC1 CC **1b** CAPE-HAITIEN (R.) (31.12.1841) *Price on cover* £2750

JACMEL

CROWNED-CIRCLE HANDSTAMPS

CC2 CC **1b** JACMEL (R.) (29.6.1843) *Price on cover* £900

Stamps of GREAT BRITAIN *cancelled* "C 59" *as Type* **4**.

1865 *to* **1881**.

Z 1 ½d. rose-red (1870–79) *From* 30·00
Plate Nos. 4, 5, 6, 10, 11, 12, 14, 15.
Z 2 1d. rose-red (1864–79) *From* 25·00
Plate Nos. 74, 87, 95, 106, 107, 109, 122, 136, 137, 139, 148, 150, 151, 152, 156, 157, 159, 160, 162, 164, 166, 167, 170, 171, 179, 181, 183, 184, 186, 187, 189, 192, 194, 198, 200, 204, 206, 215, 219.
Z 3 1½d. lake-red (1870–74) (Plate No. 3) 45·00
Z 4 2d. blue (1858–69) (Plate Nos. 9, 13, 14, 15) 28·00
Z 5 2½d. rosy mauve (1876) (Plate No. 4)
Z 6 3d. rose (1867–73) (Plate Nos. 5, 6, 7, 8, 9, 10) *From* 30·00
Z 7 3d. rose (1873–76) 30·00
Plate Nos. 11, 12, 14, 16, 17, 18, 19.
Z 8 4d. red (1863) (Plate No. 4) (*Hair lines*) 75·00
Z 9 4d. vermilion (1865–73) *From* 26·00
Plate Nos. 7, 8, 9, 10, 11, 12, 13, 14.
Z10 4d. vermilion (1876) (Plate No. 15) £145
Z11 4d. sage-green (1877) (Plate Nos. 15, 16) £100
Z12 4d. grey-brown (1880) *wmk* Large Garter 95·00
Plate No. 17.
Z13 4d. grey-brown (1880) *wmk* Crown (Plate No. 17) 25·00
Z14 6d. lilac (1867) (Plate Nos. 5, 6) 35·00
Z15 6d. violet (1867–70) (Plate Nos. 8, 9) 30·00
Z16 6d. buff (1872–73) (Plate Nos. 11, 12) *From* 55·00
Z17 6d. chestnut (1872) (Plate No. 11)
Z18 6d. grey (1873) (Plate No. 12)
Z19 6d. grey (1874–76) *From* 24·00
Plate Nos. 13, 14, 15, 16, 17.
Z20 8d. orange (1876) £180
Z21 9d. straw (1862) £130
Z22 9d. straw (1867) £125
Z23 10d. red-brown (1867) £125
Z24 1s. green (1865) (Plate No. 4) 50·00
Z25 1s. green (1867–73) (Plate Nos. 4, 5, 6, 7) *From* 20·00
Z26 1s. green (1873–77) *From* 25·00
Plate Nos. 8, 9, 10, 11, 12, 13.
Z27 1s. orange-brown (1880) (Plate No. 13) £150
Z28 2s. blue (1867) 80·00
Z29 2s. brown (1880) £1200
Z30 5s. rose (1867–74) (Plate Nos. 1, 2) *From* £250

1880.

Z31 ½d. green (1880) 22·00
Z32 1d. Venetian red 20·00
Z33 1½d. Venetian red 35·00
Z34 2d. rose 40·00

PORT-AU-PRINCE

CROWNED-CIRCLE HANDSTAMPS

CC3 CC **1b** PORT-AU-PRINCE (R.) (29.6.1843) *Price on cover* £1500

Stamps of GREAT BRITAIN *cancelled* "E 53" *as in Types* **8** *or* **12**.

1869 *to* **1881**.

Z35 ½d. rose-red (1870–79) *From* 35·00
Plate Nos. 5, 6, 10, 11, 12, 13.
Z36 1d. rose-red (1864–79) *From* 22·00
Plate Nos. 87, 134, 154, 167, 171, 174, 183, 187, 189, 193, 199, 200, 201, 202, 206, 209, 210, 218, 219.
Z37 1½d. lake-red (1870–74) (Plate No. 3) 45·00
Z38 2d. blue (1858–69) (Plate No. 9)
Z39 2d. blue (1855–69) (Plate Nos. 14, 15) 35·00
Z40 2½d. rosy mauve (1876–79) (Plate Nos. 3, 9) 70·00
Z41 3d. rose (1867–73) (Plate Nos. 6, 7)
Z42 3d. rose (1873–79) (Plate Nos. 17, 18, 20) 28·00
Z43 4d. vermilion (1865–73) *From* 25·00
Plate Nos. 11, 12, 13, 14.
Z44 4d. vermilion (1876) (Plate No. 15) £150
Z45 4d. sage-green (1877) (Plate Nos. 15, 16) *From* 90·00
Z46 4d. grey-brown (1880) *wmk* Large Garter 95·00
Plate No. 17.
Z47 4d. grey-brown (1880) *wmk* Crown (Plate No. 17) 25·00
Z48 6d. grey (1874–76) (Plate Nos. 15, 16)
Z49 8d. orange (1876) £170
Z50 1s. green (1867–73) (Plate Nos. 4, 5, 6, 7) *From* 20·00
Z51 1s. green (1873–77) *From* 30·00
Plate Nos. 8, 9, 10, 11, 12, 13.
Z52 1s. orange-brown (1880) (Plate No. 13) £150
Z53 1s. orange-brown (1881) (Plate No. 13) 50·00
Z54 2s. blue (1867) 90·00
Z55 2s. brown (1880) £1200
Z56 5s. rose (1867–74) (Plate Nos. 1, 2) £325
Z57 10s. greenish grey (1878) £1700

1880.

Z58 ½d. green 30·00
Z59 1d. Venetian red 24·00
Z60 1½d. Venetian red 35·00
Z61 2d. rose

MACAO

Some form of British Postal Agency was operating in this Portuguese territory as early as 1838, its existence being confirmed by a cover of that year. The Agency continued to function, in conjunction with the Hong Kong Post Office, until Portugal joined the U.P.U. in 1884.

CROWNED-CIRCLE HANDSTAMPS

CC1 CC **2** PAGO EM MACAO (1870) *Price on cover* £3250

What may be a locally-cut variation is known from the 1843–44 period. This shows a Crown over an oval 20 mm wide, inscribed "PAID AT MACAO". Three examples are said to exist, all struck in red.

MADEIRA

The British Postal Agency on this Portuguese island was operating at least as early as 1822, and perhaps some years before that.

It appears to have closed sometime in the 1850s.

CROWN-CIRCLE HANDSTAMPS

CC1 CC **1b** MADEIRA (R.) (28.2.1842) *Price on cover* £2000

MEXICO

The British Postal Agency at Vera Cruz opened in 1825, following the introduction of the Mexican Packet service. No handstamps were supplied, however, until 1842, when a similar agency at Tampico was set up.

Great Britain stamps were used at Tampico from 1865, but, apparently, were never sent to the Vera Cruz office. The Agency at Vera Cruz closed in 1874 and that at Tampico in 1876.

TAMPICO

CROWNED-CIRCLE HANDSTAMPS

CC1 CC **1b** TAMPICO (R.) (13.11.1841) *Price on cover* £1000

No. CC1 may be found on cover, used in conjunction with Mexico adhesive stamps.

Stamps of GREAT BRITAIN *cancelled* "C 63" *as Type* **4**.

1865 *to* **1876**.

Z 1 1d. rose-red (1864–79) *From* 60·00
Plate Nos. 81, 89, 103, 117, 139, 147.
Z 2 2d. blue (1858–69) (Plate Nos. 9, 14) 80·00
Z 3 4d. vermilion (1865–73) *From* 45·00
Plate Nos. 7, 8, 10, 11, 12, 13, 14.
Z 4 1s. green (1867–73) (Plate Nos. 4, 5, 7, 8) 60·00
Z 5 2s. blue (1867) £300

VERA CRUZ

CROWNED-CIRCLE HANDSTAMPS

CC2 CC **1b** VERA CRUZ (R.) (13.11.1841) *Price on cover* £1500
CC3 VERA CRUZ (Black) (*circa* 1845) *Price on cover* £700

No. CC3 can also be found used in conjunction with Mexico adhesive stamps.

NICARAGUA

GREYTOWN

British involvement on the Mosquito Coast of Nicaragua dates from 1655 when contacts were first made with the indigenous Misquito Indians. A formal alliance was signed in 1740 and the area was considered as a British dependency until the Spanish authorities negotiated a withdrawal in 1786.

The Misquitos remained under British protection, however, and, following the revolutionary period in the Spanish dominions, this eventually led to the appropriation, by the Misquitos with British backing, of the town of San Juan del Norte, later renamed Greytown.

The port was included in the Royal West Indian Mail Steam Packet Company's mail network from January 1842, forming part of the Jamaica District. This arrangement only lasted until September of that year, however, although packets were once again calling at Greytown by November 1844. Following the discovery of gold in California the office increased in importance, owing to the overland traffic, although the first distinctive postmark is not recorded in use until February 1856.

A subsidiary agency, without its own postmark, operated at Bluefields from 1857 to 1863.

The British Protectorate over the Misquitos ended in 1860, but the British Post Office at Greytown continued to operate, being supplied with Great Britain stamps in 1865. These are occasionally found used in combination with Nicaragua issues, which had only internal validity.

The British Post Office at Greytown closed in May 1882 when the Republic of Nicaragua joined the U.P.U.

CROWNED-CIRCLE HANDSTAMPS

Z 1

CC1 **Z 1** GREYTOWN (R.) (14.4.1859)

Z 2

Z 4

Z 3

Stamps of GREAT BRITAIN *cancelled* "C 57" *as in Types* **Z 2** *(issued* 1865), **Z 3** *(issued* 1875), *or with circular postmark as Type* **Z 4** *(issued* 1864).

1865 *to* **1882**.
Z 1 ½d. rose-red (1870–79) (Plate Nos. 5, 10, 11) 50·00
Z 2 1d. rose-red (1864–79) (Plate Nos. 180, 197, 210) 28·00
Z 3 1½d. lake-red (1870) (Plate No. 3) 35·00
Z 4 2d. blue (1858–69) (Plate Nos. 9, 14, 15)
Z 5 3d. rose (1873–76) (Plate Nos. 17, 18, 19, 20) 40·00
Z 6 3d. rose (1881) (Plate No. 20)
Z 7 4d. vermilion (1865–73) *From* 30·00
Plate Nos. 8, 10, 11, 12, 13, 14.
Z 8 4d. vermilion (1876) (Plate No. 15) £150
Z 9 4d. sage-green (1877) (Plate Nos. 15, 16) 80·00
Z10 4d. grey-brown (1880) *wmk* Large Garter 95·00
Plate No. 17.
Z11 4d. grey-brown (1880) *wmk* Crown (Plate No. 17) 80·00
Z12 6d. grey (1874–76) (Plate Nos. 14, 15, 16) 50·00
Z13 8d. orange (1876)
Z14 1s. green (1865) (Plate No. 4)
Z15 1s. green (1867–73) (Plate Nos. 6, 7)
Z16 1s. green (1873–77) (Plate Nos. 8, 12, 13) 28·00
Z17 1s. orange-brown (1880) (Plate No. 13) £130
Z18 1s. orange-brown (1881) (Plate No. 13) 45·00
Z19 2s. blue (1867) £100
Z20 2s. brown (1880) £1200
Z21 5s. rose (1867–74) (Plate Nos. 1, 2) £250
Z22 5s. rose (1882) (Plate No. 4), blue *paper* £900
Z23 10s. greenish grey (1878) £1300

1880.
Z24 1d. Venetian red
Z25 1½d. Venetian red 35·00

PERU

British Agencies in Peru date from 1846 when offices were established at Arica and Callao. The network was later expanded to include agencies at Paita and Pisco (both 1848), and Iquique and Islay (both 1869). This last office was transferred to Mollendo in 1871.

It is believed that a further agency existed at Pisagua, but no details exist.

Great Britain stamps were supplied from 1865. The Postal Agency at Pisco closed in 1870 and the remainder in 1879, the towns of Arica, Iquique and Pisagua passing to Chile by treaty in 1883.

ARICA

CROWNED-CIRCLE HANDSTAMPS

CC1 CC **1** ARICA (R.) (5.11.1850) *Price on cover* £2500

Stamps of GREAT BRITAIN *cancelled* "C 36" *as in Types* **4, 12** *or* **14**.

1865 *to* **1879**.
Z 1 ½d. rose-red (1870–79) *From* 40·00
Plate Nos. 5, 6, 10, 11, 13.
Z 2 1d. rose-red (1864–79) *From* 28·00
Plate Nos. 102, 139, 140, 163, 167.
Z 3 1½d. lake-red (1870–74) (Plate No. 3)
Z 4 2d. blue (1858–69) (Plate No. 14) 65·00
Z 5 3d. rose (1867–73) (Plate Nos. 5, 9)
Z 6 3d. rose (1873–76) *From* 22·00
Plate Nos. 11, 12, 17, 18, 19.
Z 7 4d. vermilion (1865–73) *From* 25·00
Plate Nos. 10, 11, 12, 13, 14.
Z 8 4d. vermilion (1876) (Plate No. 15)
Z 9 4d. sage-green (1877) (Plate Nos. 15, 16) 85·00
Z10 6d. lilac (1862) (Plate Nos. 3, 4)
Z11 6d. lilac (1865–67) (Plate No. 5)
Z12 6d. violet (1867–70) (Plate Nos. 6, 8, 9) 30·00
Z13 6d. buff (1872) (Plate No. 11) 75·00
Z14 6d. chestnut (1872) (Plate No. 11)
Z15 6d. grey (1873) (Plate No. 12) 45·00
Z16 6d. grey (1874–76) (Plate Nos. 13, 14, 15, 16) *From* 22·00
Z17 8d. orange (1876)
Z18 9d. straw (1862)
Z19 9d. straw (1865)
Z20 9d. straw (1867) £125
Z21 10d. red-brown (1867)
Z22 1s. green (1862)
Z23 1s. green (1865)
Z24 1s. green (1867–73) (Plate Nos. 4, 5, 6, 7) *From* 18·00
Z25 1s. green (1873–77) *From* 26·00
Plate Nos. 8, 9, 10, 11, 12, 13.
Z26 2s. blue (1867) £150
Z27 5s. rose (1867–74) (Plate Nos. 1, 2) £300

CALLAO

CROWNED-CIRCLE HANDSTAMPS

CC2 CC **2** CALLAO (R.) (13.1.1846) *Price on cover* £1200
CC3 CC **1** CALLAO (R.) (16.7.1846) *Price on cover* £700

Stamps of GREAT BRITAIN *cancelled* "C 38" *as in Types* **4, 12** *or with circular date stamp as Type* **5**.

1865 *to* **1879**.
Z28 ½d. rose-red (1870–79) *From* 28·00
Plate Nos. 5, 6, 10, 11, 12, 13, 14.
Z29 1d. rose-red (1864–79) *From* 12·00
Plate Nos. 74, 88, 89, 93, 94, 97, 108, 123, 127, 128, 130, 137, 139, 140, 141, 143, 144, 145, 146, 148, 149, 156, 157, 160, 163, 167, 171, 172, 173, 175, 180, 181, 182, 183, 185, 187, 190, 193, 195, 198, 199, 200, 201, 204, 206, 209, 210, 212, 213, 215.
Z30 1½d. lake-red (1870–74) (Plate No. 3)
Z31 2d. blue (1858–69) *From* 17·00
Plate Nos. 9, 12, 13, 14, 15.
Z32 3d. carmine-rose (1862)
Z33 3d. rose (1865) (Plate No. 4) 40·00
Z34 3d. rose (1867–73) *From* 20·00
Plate Nos. 5, 6, 7, 8, 9, 10.
Z35 3d. rose (1873–76) *From* 25·00
Plate Nos. 11, 12, 14, 15, 16, 17, 18, 19.
Z36 4d. red (1862) (Plate Nos. 3, 4)
Z37 4d. vermilion (1865–73) *From* 22·00
Plate Nos. 8, 10, 11, 12, 13, 14.
Z38 4d. vermilion (1876) (Plate No. 15) £130
Z39 4d. sage-green (1877) (Plate Nos. 15, 16) 80·00
Z40 6d. lilac (1862) (Plate Nos. 3, 4)
Z40*a* 6d. lilac (1865) (Plate No. 5)
Z41 6d. lilac (1867)
Z42 6d. violet (1867–70) (Plate Nos. 6, 8, 9) *From* 32·00
Z43 6d. buff (1872–73) (Plate Nos. 11, 12) *From* 45·00
Z44 6d. chestnut (1872) (Plate No. 11) 25·00
Z45 6d. grey (1873) (Plate No. 12) 40·00
Z46 6d. grey (1874–80) (Plate Nos. 13, 14, 15, 16) *From* 24·00
Z47 8d. orange (1876) £150
Z48 9d. straw (1862)
Z49 9d. straw (1865) £225
Z50 9d. straw (1867) £100
Z51 10d. red-brown (1867) £150
Z52 1s. green (1865)
Z53 1s. green (1867–73) (Plate Nos. 4, 5, 6, 7) *From* 15·00
Z54 1s. green (1873–77) *From* 22·00
Plate Nos. 8, 9, 10, 11, 12, 13.
Z55 2s. blue (1867) £100
Z56 5s. rose (1867–74) (Plate Nos. 1, 2) *From* £180

IQUIQUE

Stamps of GREAT BRITAIN *cancelled* "D 87" *as Type* **12**.

1865 *to* **1879**.
Z57 ½d. rose-red (1870–79) (Plate Nos. 5, 6, 13, 14) 55·00
Z58 1d. rose-red (1864–79) (Plate Nos. 76, 179, 185, 205) 35·00
Z59 2d. blue (1858–69) (Plate Nos. 9, 12, 13, 14)
Z60 3d. rose (1867–73) (Plate Nos. 5, 6, 7, 8, 9) *From* 35·00
Z61 3d. rose (1873–76) (Plate Nos. 12, 18, 19) 50·00
Z62 4d. vermilion (1865–73) (Plate Nos. 12, 13, 14) 32·00
Z63 4d. vermilion (1876) (Plate No. 15) £140
Z64 4d. sage-green (1877) (Plate Nos. 15, 16) *From* 95·00
Z65 6d. mauve (1869) (Plate Nos. 8, 9)
Z66 6d. buff (1872–73) (Plate Nos. 11, 12) *From* 75·00
Z67 6d. chestnut (1872) (Plate No. 11)
Z68 6d. grey (1873) (Plate No. 12) 50·00
Z69 6d. grey (1874–76) (Plate Nos. 13, 14, 15, 16)
Z70 8d. orange (1876) £200
Z71 9d. straw (1867) £110
Z72 10d. red-brown (1867)
Z73 1s. green (1867–73) (Plate Nos. 4, 6, 7) *From* 35·00
Z74 1s. green (1873–77) *From* 38·00
Plate Nos. 8, 9, 10, 11, 12, 13.
Z75 2s. blue (1867)

ISLAY (*later* MOLLENDO)

CROWNED-CIRCLE HANDSTAMPS

CC4 CC **1** ISLAY (R.) (23.10.1850)

Stamps of GREAT BRITAIN *cancelled* "C 42" *as Type* **4**.

1865 *to* **1879**.
Z76 1d. rose-red (1864–79) *From* 28·00
Plate Nos. 78, 84, 87, 88, 96, 103, 125, 134.
Z77 1½d. lake-red (1870–74) (Plate No. 3)
Z78 2d. blue (1858–69) (Plate Nos. 9, 13, 15) 22·00
Z79 3d. carmine-rose (1862)
Z80 3d. rose (1865) 60·00
Z81 3d. rose (1867–73) (Plate Nos. 4, 5, 6, 10) 30·00
Z82 4d. red (1862) (Plate Nos. 3, 4) 60·00
Z83 4d. vermilion (1867–73) *From* 28·00
Plate Nos. 9, 10, 11, 12, 13.
Z84 4d. vermilion (1876) (Plate No. 15)
Z85 4d. sage-green (1877) (Plate Nos. 15, 16) 85·00
Z86 6d. lilac (1862) (Plate Nos. 3, 4) 80·00
Z87 6d. lilac (1865) (Plate No. 5) 50·00
Z88 6d. violet (1867–70) (Plate Nos. 6, 8, 9) *From* 38·00
Z89 6d. buff (1873) (Plate No. 12)
Z90 6d. grey (1873) (Plate No. 12)
Z91 6d. grey (1874–76) (Plate Nos. 13, 14, 15, 16) *From* 25·00
Z92 9d. straw (1865) £225
Z93 9d. straw (1867) £120
Z94 10d. red-brown (1867) £160
Z95 1s. green (1865) (Plate No. 4)
Z96 1s. green (1867–73) (Plate Nos. 4, 5, 6, 7) *From* 25·00
Z97 1s. green (1873–77) (Plate Nos. 10, 12, 13) *From* 28·00
Z98 2s. blue (1867)
Z99 5s. rose (1867) (Plate No. 1)

PAITA

CROWNED-CIRCLE HANDSTAMPS

CC5 CC **1** PAITA (R.) (5.11.1850) *Price on cover* £3500

Stamps of GREAT BRITAIN *cancelled* "C 43" *as Type* **4**.

1865 *to* **1879**.
Z100 1d. rose-red (1864–79) (Plate Nos. 127, 147)
Z101 2d. blue (1858–69) (Plate Nos. 9, 14)
Z102 3d. rose (1867–73) (Plate Nos. 5, 6) 35·00
Z103 3d. rose (1876) (Plate Nos. 17, 18, 19) 35·00
Z104 4d. vermilion (1865–73) *From* 32·00
Plate Nos. 10, 11, 12, 13, 14.
Z105 4d. sage-green (1877) (Plate No. 15)
Z106 6d. lilac (1862) (Plate No. 3) 65·00
Z107 6d. lilac (1865–67) (Plate Nos. 5, 6) 45·00
Z108 6d. violet (1867–70) (Plate Nos. 6, 8, 9) 40·00
Z109 6d. buff (1872–73) (Plate Nos. 11, 12) *From* 55·00
Z110 6d. chestnut (Plate No. 11) 35·00
Z111 6d. grey (1873)
Z112 6d. grey (1874–76) (Plate Nos. 13, 14, 15)
Z113 9d. straw (1862)
Z114 10d. red-brown (1867) £200
Z115 1s. green (1865) (Plate No. 4)
Z116 1s. green (1867–73) (Plate No. 4) 35·00
Z117 1s. green (1873–77) (Plate Nos. 8, 9, 10, 13) 35·00
Z118 2s. blue (1867) £150
Z119 5s. rose (1867) (Plate No. 1) £350

PISAGUA(?)

Stamp of GREAT BRITAIN *cancelled* "D 65" *as Type* **12**.

Z120 2s. blue (1867)

PISCO AND CHINCHA ISLANDS

Stamps of GREAT BRITAIN *cancelled* "D 74" *as Type* **12**.

1865 *to* **1870**.
Z121 2d. blue (1858–69) (Plate No. 9)
Z122 4d. vermilion (1865–73) (Plate Nos. 10, 12) £135
Z123 6d. violet (1868) (Plate No. 6) £600
Z124 1s. green (1867) (Plate No. 4)
Z125 2s. blue (1867) £500

PORTO RICO

A British Postal Agency operated at San Juan from 1844. In 1872 further offices were opened at Aguadilla, Arroyo, Mayaguez and Ponce, with Naguabo added three years later.

Great Britain stamps were used during 1865–66 and from 1873 to 1877. All the British Agencies closed in 1877.

AGUADILLA

Stamps of GREAT BRITAIN *cancelled* "F 84" *as Type* **8**.

1873 *to* **1877**.
Z 1 ½d. rose-red (1870) (Plate No. 6) 70·00
Z 2 1d. rose-red (1864–79) 40·00
Plate Nos. 119, 122, 139, 156.
Z 3 2d. blue (1858–69) (Plate No. 14)
Z 4 3d. rose (1867–73) (Plate Nos. 7, 8, 9)
Z 5 3d. rose (1873–76) (Plate No. 12)
Z 6 4d. vermilion (1865–73) (Plate Nos. 12, 13, 14) 38·00
Z 7 4d. vermilion (1876) (Plate No. 15) £160
Z 8 6d. grey (1874–76) (Plate Nos. 13, 14)
Z 9 9d. straw (1867) £225
Z10 10d. red-brown (1867) £150
Z11 1s. green (1867–73) (Plate Nos. 4, 5, 6, 7) *From* 30·00
Z12 1s. green (1873–77) *From* 38·00
Plate Nos. 8, 9, 10, 11, 12.
Z13 2s. blue (1867) £225

ARROYO

Stamps of GREAT BRITAIN *cancelled* "F 83" *as Type* **8**.

1873 *to* **1877**.
Z14 ½d. rose-red (1870) (Plate No. 5) 55·00
Z15 1d. rose-red (1864–79) 45·00
Plate Nos. 149, 150, 151, 156, 164, 174, 175.
Z16 1½d. lake-red (1870) (Plate No. 1)
Z17 2d. blue (1858–69) (Plate No. 14)
Z18 3d. rose (1867–73) (Plate Nos. 7, 10) 40·00
Z19 3d. rose (1873–76) (Plate Nos. 11, 12, 14, 16, 18) 45·00
Z20 4d. vermilion (1865–73) (Plate Nos. 12, 13, 14) 38·00
Z21 4d. vermilion (1876) (Plate No. 15) £140
Z22 6d. chestnut (1872) (Plate No. 11) 50·00
Z23 6d. pale-buff (1872) (Plate No. 11) 55·00
Z23*a* 6d. grey (1873) (Plate No. 12)
Z24 6d. grey (1874–76) (Plate Nos. 13, 14, 15) 50·00
Z25 9d. straw (1867) £225
Z26 10d. red-brown (1867) £150
Z27 1s. green (1865) (Plate No. 4)
Z28 1s. green (1867–73) (Plate Nos. 4, 5, 6, 7) 38·00
Z29 1s. green (1873–77) 32·00
Plate Nos. 8, 9, 10, 11, 12, 13.
Z30 2s. blue (1867) £180
Z31 5s. rose (1867–74) (Plate No. 2)

MAYAGUEZ

Stamps of GREAT BRITAIN *cancelled* "F 85" *as Type* **8**.

1873 *to* **1877**.
Z32 ½d. rose-red (1870) *From* 40·00
Plate Nos. 4, 5, 6, 8, 10, 11.
Z33 1d. rose-red (1864–79) *From* 20·00
Plate Nos. 76, 120, 121, 122, 124, 134, 137, 140, 146, 149, 150, 151, 154, 155, 156, 160, 167, 170, 171, 174, 175, 176, 178, 180, 182, 185, 186, 189.
Z34 1½d. lake-red (1870–74) (Plate Nos. 1, 3) 38·00
Z35 2d. blue (1858–69) (Plate Nos. 13, 14, 15) 35·00
Z36 3d. rose (1867–73) (Plate Nos. 7, 8, 9, 10) 27·00
Z37 3d. rose (1873–76) 27·00
Plate Nos. 11, 12, 14, 15, 16, 17, 18, 19.
Z38 4d. vermilion (1865–73) (Plate Nos. 11, 12, 13, 14) 28·00
Z39 4d. vermilion (1876) (Plate No. 15) 80·00
Z40 4d. sage-green (1877) (Plate No. 15)
Z41 6d. mauve (1870) (Plate No. 9)
Z42 6d. buff (1872) (Plate No. 11) 65·00
Z43 6d. chestnut (1872) (Plate No. 11) 60·00
Z44 6d. grey (1873) (Plate No. 12)
Z45 6d. grey (1874–80) (Plate Nos. 13, 14, 15, 16) 32·00
Z46 8d. orange (1876) £150
Z47 9d. straw (1867) £125
Z48 10d. red-brown (1867) £125
Z49 1s. green (1867–73) (Plate Nos. 4, 5, 6, 7) 22·00
Z50 1s. green (1873–77) *From* 28·00
Plate Nos. 8, 9, 10, 11, 12.
Z51 2s. blue (1867) £160
Z52 5s. rose (1867–74) (Plate Nos. 1, 2)

NAGUABO

Stamps of GREAT BRITAIN *cancelled* "582" *as Type* **9**.

1875 *to* **1877**.
Z53 ½d. rose-red (1870–79) (Plate Nos. 5, 12, 14) .. ..
Z54 1d. rose-red (1864–70) (Plate Nos. 159, 165) .. ..
Z55 3d. rose (1873–76) (Plate Nos. 17, 18) £350
Z56 4d. vermilion (1872–73) (Plate Nos. 13, 14) *From* £300
Z57 4d. vermilion (1876) (Plate No. 15) .. ..
Z58 6d. grey (1874–76) (Plate Nos. 14, 15) .. ..
Z59 9d. straw (1867) .. ..
Z60 10d. red-brown (1867) £600
Z61 1s. green (1873–77) (Plate Nos. 11, 12) .. ..
Z62 2s. dull blue (1867) (Plate No. 1) £500

PONCE

Stamps of GREAT BRITAIN *cancelled* "F 88" *as Type* **8**.

1873 *to* **1877**.
Z63 ½d. rose-red (1870) (Plate Nos. 5, 10, 12) .. .. 45·00
Z64 1d. rose-red (1864–79) .. .. *From* 20·00
Plate Nos. 120, 121, 122, 123, 124, 146, 148, 154, 156, 157, 158, 160, 167, 171, 174, 175, 186, 187.
Z65 1½d. lake-red (1870–74) (Plate No. 3) £100
Z66 2d. blue (1858–69) (Plate Nos. 13, 14) .. .. 38·00
Z67 3d. rose (1867–73) (Plate Nos. 7, 8, 9) .. ..
Z68 3d. rose (1873–76) (Plate Nos. 12, 16, 17, 18, 19) .. 30·00
Z69 4d. vermilion (1865–73) .. .. .. *From* 30·00
Plate Nos. 8, 9, 12, 13, 14.
Z70 4d. vermilion (1876) (Plate No. 15) £110
Z71 4d. sage-green (1877) (Plate Nos. 15, 16) .. .. 80·00
Z72 6d. buff (1872–73) (Plate Nos. 11, 12) .. .. 60·00
Z73 6d. chestnut (1872) (Plate No. 11) .. .. .. 40·00
Z74 6d. grey (1873) (Plate No. 12) .. .. ..
Z75 6d. grey (1874–76) (Plate Nos. 13, 14, 15) .. *From* 32·00
Z76 9d. straw (1867) £175
Z77 10d. red-brown (1867) £130
Z78 1s. green (1867–73) (Plate Nos. 4, 6, 7) .. .. 26·00
Z79 1s. green (1873–77) .. .. *From* 25·00
Plate Nos. 8, 9, 10, 11, 12, 13.
Z80 2s. blue (1867) .. ..
Z81 5s. rose (1867–74) (Plate Nos. 1, 2) .. *From* £300

SAN JUAN

CROWNED-CIRCLE HANDSTAMPS

CC1 CC **1** SAN JUAN PORTO RICO (R. *or* Black) (25.5.1844) .. .. .. *Price on cover* £750

No. CC1 may be found on cover, used in conjunction with Spanish colonial adhesive stamps.

Stamps of GREAT BRITAIN *cancelled* "C 61" *as in Types* **4**, **8** *or* **14**.

1865 *to* **1866** *and* **1873** *to* **1877**.
Z 82 ½d. rose-red (1870) (Plate Nos. 5, 10, 15) .. *From* 30·00
Z 83 1d. rose-red (1857) .. ..
Z 84 1d. rose-red (1864–79) .. .. .. *From* 17·00
Plate Nos. 73, 81, 84, 90, 94, 100, 101, 102, 107, 117, 122, 124, 125, 127, 130, 137, 138, 139, 140, 145, 146, 149, 153, 156, 159, 160, 162, 163, 169, 171, 172, 173, 175, 179, 180, 182, 186.
Z 85 1½d. lake-red (1870–74) (Plate Nos. 1, 3) .. *From* 60·00
Z 86 2d. blue (1858–69) (Plate Nos. 9, 13, 14) .. *From* 24·00
Z 87 3d. rose (1865) (Plate No. 4) .. .. .. 35·00
Z 88 3d. rose (1867–73) .. .. *From* 24·00
Plate Nos. 5, 6, 7, 8, 9, 10.
Z 89 3d. rose (1873–76) .. .. *From* 24·00
Plate Nos. 11, 12, 14, 15, 16, 17, 18.
Z 90 4d. vermilion (1865–73) .. .. .. *From* 22·00
Plate Nos. 7, 8, 9, 10, 11, 12, 13, 14.
Z 91 4d. vermilion (1876) (Plate No. 15) .. .. 80·00
Z 92 6d. lilac (1865–67) (Plate Nos. 5, 6) .. *From* 32·00
Z 93 6d. lilac (1867) (Plate No. 6) .. .. .. 35·00
Z 94 6d. violet (1867–70) (Plate Nos. 6, 8, 9) .. *From* 27·00
Z 95 6d. buff (1872–73) (Plate Nos. 11, 12) .. .. 55·00
Z 96 6d. chestnut (1872) (Plate No. 11) .. .. 35·00
Z 97 6d. grey (1873) (Plate No. 12) .. .. ..
Z 98 6d. grey (1874–76) (Plate Nos. 13, 14, 15) .. *From* 22·00
Z 99 9d. straw (1862) £120
Z100 9d. straw (1865) £250
Z101 9d. straw (1867) .. .. 80·00
Z102 10d. red-brown (1867) £110
Z103 1s. green (1865) (Plate No. 4) .. .. .. 28·00
Z104 1s. green (1867–73) (Plate Nos. 4, 5, 6, 7) .. *From* 20·00
Z105 1s. green (1873–77) .. .. *From* 25·00
Plate Nos. 8, 9, 10, 11, 12, 13.
Z106 2s. blue (1867) .. .. 90·00
Z107 5s. rose (1867) (Plate Nos. 1, 2) .. .. *From* £250

SPAIN

Little is known about the operation of British Packet Agencies in Spain, other than the dates recorded for the various postal markings in the G.P.O. Proof Books. The Agency at Corunna is said to date from the early 18th century, and that at Teneriffe from the early 19th century.

Both appear to have closed by the late 1850s.

CORUNNA

CROWNED-CIRCLE HANDSTAMPS

CC1 CC **1b** CORUNNA (28.2.1842) .. .. ..

Although recorded in the G.P.O. Proof Books no example of No. CC1 on cover is known.

TENERIFFE (CANARY ISLANDS)

CROWNED-CIRCLE HANDSTAMPS

CC2 CC **7** TENERIFFE (6.1.1851) .. *Price on cover* £3000
CC3 CC **4** TENERIFFE (23.10.1857) .. *Price on cover* £3000

UNITED STATES OF AMERICA

The network of British Packet Agencies, to operate the trans-Atlantic Packet system, was re-established in 1814 after the War of 1812.

The New York Agency opened in that year to be followed by further offices at Boston, Charleston (South Carolina), New Orleans, Savannah (Georgia) (all in 1842), Mobile (Alabama) (1848) and San Francisco (1860). Of these agencies Charleston and Savannah closed the same year (1842) as did New Orleans, although the latter was re-activated from 1848 to 1850. Mobile closed 1850, Boston in 1865, New York in 1882 and San Francisco, for which no postal markings have been recorded, in 1883.

Although recorded in the G.P.O. Proof Books no actual examples of the Crowned-circle handstamps for Charleston, Mobile, New Orleans and Savannah are known on cover.

The G.P.O. proof books record, in error, a Crowned-circle handstamp for St. Michaels, Maryland. This handstamp was intended for the agency on San Miguel in the Azores.

CHARLESTON

CROWNED-CIRCLE HANDSTAMPS

CC1 CC **1b** CHARLESTON (15.12.1841) .. ..

MOBILE

CROWNED-CIRCLE HANDSTAMPS

CC2 CC **1b** MOBILE (15.12.1841) .. .. ..

NEW ORLEANS

CROWNED-CIRCLE HANDSTAMPS

CC3 CC **1b** NEW ORLEANS (15.12.1841) .. ..
CC4 CC **1** NEW ORLEANS (27.4.1848) .. ..

NEW YORK

CROWNED-CIRCLE HANDSTAMPS

CC5 CC **1b** NEW YORK (R.) (15.12.1841) *Price on cover* £7500

SAVANNAH

CROWNED-CIRCLE HANDSTAMPS

CC6 CC **1b** SAVANNAH (15.12.1841) .. ..

URUGUAY

MONTEVIDEO

The British Packet Agency opened around the year 1850 and continued to operate until 1873.

Great Britain stamps were in use from 1864.

CROWNED-CIRCLE HANDSTAMPS

CC1 CC **7** MONTEVIDEO (Black *or* R.) (6.1.1851) *Price on cover* £700

Stamps of GREAT BRITAIN *cancelled* "C 28" *as in Types* **4** *or* **12**.

1864 *to* **1873**.
Z 1 1d. rose-red (1864) .. .. 45·00
Plate Nos. 73, 92, 93, 94, 119, 148, 154, 157, 171.
Z 2 2d. blue (1858–69) (Plate Nos. 9, 13) .. .. 35·00
Z 3 3d. rose (1865) (Plate No. 4) .. .. ..
Z 4 3d. rose (1867–71) (Plate Nos. 4, 5, 7) .. .. 35·00
Z 5 3d. rose (1873–79) (Plate No. 19) .. ..
Z 6 4d. rose (1857) .. ..
Z 7 4d. red (1862) (Plate No. 4) .. .. ..
Z 8 4d. vermilion (1865–70) .. .. .. *From* 30·00
Plate Nos. 7, 8, 9, 10, 11, 12.
Z 9 6d. lilac (1856) .. ..
Z10 6d. lilac (1862) (Plate No. 4) .. .. ..
Z11 6d. lilac (1865–67) (Plate Nos. 5, 6) .. .. 45·00
Z12 6d. lilac (1867) (Plate No. 6) .. .. ..
Z13 6d. violet (1867–70) (Plate Nos. 8, 9) .. *From* 35·00
Z14 6d. buff (1872) .. ..
Z15 6d. chestnut (1872) .. ..
Z16 9d. straw (1862) .. ..
Z17 9d. straw (1865) .. ..
Z18 9d. straw (1867) £130
Z19 10d. red-brown (1867) £130
Z20 1s. green (1862) .. .. 75·00
Z21 1s. green (1865) (Plate No. 4) .. .. .. 35·00
Z22 1s. green (1867–73) (Plate Nos. 4, 5) .. .. 28·00
Z23 2s. blue (1867) .. .. 90·00
Z24 5s. rose (1867) (Plate No. 1) £250

VENEZUELA

British Postal Agencies were initially opened at La Guayra and Porto Cabello in 1841. Further offices were added at Maracaibo in 1842 and Ciudad Bolivar during 1868. All agencies closed in 1880.

Great Britain stamps were used at La Guayra from 1865 and at Ciudad Bolivar from its establishment in 1868.

CIUDAD BOLIVAR

Stamps of GREAT BRITAIN *cancelled* "D 22" *as Type* **12**, *or circular date stamp as Type* **17**.

1868 *to* **1880**.
Z 1 1d. rose-red (1864–79) (Plate No. 133) .. .. 70·00
Z 2 2d. blue (1858–69) (Plate No. 13) .. ..
Z 3 3d. rose (1867–73) (Plate No. 5) .. ..
Z 4 3d. rose (1873–79) (Plate No. 11) £125
Z 5 4d. vermilion (1865–73) (Plate Nos. 9, 12, 14) .. 42·00
Z 6 4d. sage-green (1877) (Plate Nos. 15, 16) .. *From* £125
Z 7 4d. grey-brown (1880) *wmk* Crown (Plate No. 17)
Z 8 9d. straw (1867) .. ..
Z 9 10d. red-brown (1867) .. ..
Z10 1s. green (1867–73) (Plate Nos. 4, 5, 7) .. *From* 90·00
Z11 1s. green (1873–77) (Plate Nos. 10, 12, 13) .. 65·00
Z12 2s. blue (1867) £275
Z13 5s. rose (1867–74) (Plate Nos. 1, 2) £375

LA GUAYRA

CROWNED-CIRCLE HANDSTAMPS

CC1 CC **1b** LA GUAYRA (R.) (15.12.1841) *Price on cover* £850

Stamps of GREAT BRITAIN *cancelled* "C 60" *as Type* **4**, *circular date stamp as Type* **16** *or with No.* CC1.

1865 *to* **1880**.
Z14 ½d. rose-red (1870) (Plate 6) .. ..
Z15 1d. rose-red (1864–79) .. .. .. *From* 35·00
Plate Nos. 81, 92, 96, 98, 111, 113, 115, 131, 138, 144, 145, 154, 177, 178, 180, 196.
Z16 1½d. lake-red (1870–74) (Plate No. 3) .. ..
Z17 2d. blue (1858–69) (Plate No. 14) .. .. .. 40·00
Z18 3d. rose (1873–76) .. .. *From* 45·00
Plate Nos. 14, 15, 17, 18, 19.
Z19 4d. vermilion (1865–73) .. .. .. *From* 28·00
Plate Nos. 7, 9, 11, 12, 13, 14.
Z20 4d. vermilion (1876) (Plate No. 15) £120
Z21 4d. sage-green (1877) (Plate Nos. 15, 16) .. .. 70·00
Z22 6d. lilac (1865) (Plate No. 5) .. .. ..
Z23 6d. violet (1867–70) (Plate Nos. 6, 8) .. ..
Z24 6d. buff (1872–73) (Plate Nos. 11, 12) .. *From* 80·00
Z25 6d. grey (1873) (Plate No. 12) .. .. .. 45·00
Z26 6d. grey (1874–76) (Plate Nos. 13, 14, 15, 16) .. 40·00
Z27 8d. orange (1876) £170
Z28 9d. straw (1862) .. ..
Z29 9d. straw (1867) .. ..
Z30 10d. red-brown (1867) .. ..
Z31 1s. green (1865) (Plate No. 4) .. .. .. 55·00
Z32 1s. green (1867–73) (Plate Nos. 4, 7) .. ..
Z33 1s. green (1873–77) .. .. *From* 30·00
Plate Nos. 8, 9, 10, 11, 12, 13.
Z34 2s. blue (1867) £200
Z35 5s. rose (1867–74) (Plate No. 1, 2) .. .. *From* £350

MARACAIBO

CROWNED-CIRCLE HANDSTAMPS

CC2 CC **1b** MARACAIBO (31.12.1841) .. ..

No examples of No. CC2 on cover have been recorded.

PORTO CABELLO

CROWNED-CIRCLE HANDSTAMPS

CC3 CC **1b** PORTO-CABELLO (R.) (15.12.1841) *Price on cover* £1500

MAIL BOAT OBLITERATIONS

For many years it was supposed that obliterations numbered A 80 to A 99, B 03, B 12, B 56, B 57 and C 79 were used on mail boats or at Naval Stations abroad (the whereabouts of which were not known), owing to the fact that they are almost invariably found on sailors' letters.

It is definitely known that these obliterations were allotted to mail boats and they are therefore omitted from this Catalogue.

ARMY FIELD OFFICES

1854 *to* **1857**. **CRIMEA.**

Crown between Stars
Z 1 1d. red-brown (1841), *imperf* £325
Z 2 1d. red-brown (1854), Die I, *wmk* Small Crown, *perf* 16 .. ..
Z 3 1d. red-brown (1855), Die II, *wmk* Small Crown, *perf* 16 .. .. 80·00
Z 4 1d. red-brown, Die I, *wmk* Small Crown, *perf* 14 ..
Z 5 1d. red-brown (1855), Die II, Small Crown, *perf* 14
Z 6 2d. blue (1841) *imperf* £625
Z 7 2d. blue, Small Crown (1854), *perf* 16 (Plate No. 4)
Z 8 1s. green (1847), embossed £850

Star between Cyphers
Z 9 1d. red-brown (1841), *imperf* .. ..
Z10 1d. red-brown (1854), Die I, *wmk* Small Crown, *perf* 16 .. .. 40·00
Z11 1d. red-brown (1855), Die II, *wmk* Small Crown, *perf* 16 .. .. 40·00
Z12 1d. red-brown (1855), Die I, *wmk* Small Crown, *perf* 14 .. .. 40·00
Z13 1d. red-brown (1855), Die II, *wmk* Small Crown, *perf* 14 .. .. 40·00
Z14 1d. red-brown (1855), Die II, *wmk* Large Crown, *perf* 16 .. .. 60·00
Z15 1d. red-brown (1855), Die II, *wmk* Large Crown, *perf* 14 .. .. 22·00
Z16 2d. blue (1841), *imperf* £600
Z17 2d. blue (1854) *wmk* Small Crown, *perf* 16 *From* 80·00
Plate Nos. 4, 5.
Z18 2d. blue (1855) *wmk* Small Crown, *perf* 14 .. £100
Plate No. 4.
Z19 2d. blue (1855), *wmk* Large Crown, *perf* 16 .. £150
Plate No. 5.
Z20 2d. blue (1855), *wmk* Large Crown, *perf* 14 .. 75·00
Plate No. 5.
Z21 4d. rose (1857) £500
Z22 6d. violet (1854), embossed £650
Z23 1s. green (1847), embossed £700

1882. **EGYPT.** *Tel-el-Kebir Campaign.*
Z24 ½d. rose-red (Plate No. 20) .. ..
Z25 ½d. green (1880) £200
Z26 1d. Venetian red (1880) .. ..
Z27 1d. lilac (1881) .. .. 90·00
Z28 2½d. blue (1881) (Plate Nos. 21, 22, 23) .. .. 45·00

1885. SUDAN. *Suakin Campaign.*

Z29	1d.	lilac (1881)	£250
Z30	2½d.	lilac (1884)	£150
Z31	5d.	green (1884)	£400

1899 *to* **1902. SOUTH AFRICA.**

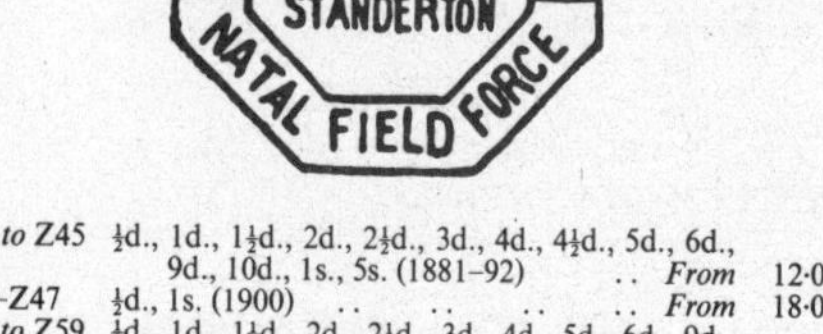

Z32 *to* Z45	½d., 1d., 1½d., 2d., 2½d., 3d., 4d., 4½d., 5d., 6d., 9d., 10d., 1s., 5s. (1881–92) .. *From*	12·00
Z46–Z47	½d., 1s. (1900) .. .. *From*	18·00
Z48 *to* Z59	½d., 1d., 1½d., 2d., 2½d., 3d., 4d., 5d., 6d., 9d., 10d., 1s. (1902) .. .. .. *From*	14·00

Many types of cancellation exist besides those shown.

ARMY OFFICIAL

Z60	½d.	vermilion	80·00
Z61	½d.	green	80·00
Z62	1d.	lilac	70·00
Z63	6d.	purple/*red*	

Abu Dhabi

Stamps of the BRITISH POSTAL AGENCIES IN EASTERN ARABIA were used by the British postal administration from 30 March 1963 until the introduction of Abu Dhabi issues in 1964. They can be found postmarked "ABU DHABI" or "DAS ISLAND".

An independent Arab Shaikhdom (one of the Trucial States), with a British postal administration until 31 December 1966.

1 Shaikh Shakhbut bin Sultan

3 Ruler's Palace

(Des M. Farrar Bell. Photo Harrison (5 n.p. to 75 n.p.). Des C. T. Kavanagh (1, 2 r.), Miss P. M. Goth (5, 10 r.). Recess B.W.)

1964 (30 Mar). *T* **1, 3** *and similar designs. P* 14½ (*5 to 75 n.p.*) *or* 13 × 13½ (*others*).

No.	Type	Value	Mint	Used
1	1	5 n.p. green	30	25
2		15 n.p. red-brown	40	25
3		20 n.p. ultramarine	45	30
4		30 n.p. red-orange	55	45
5	–	40 n.p. reddish violet	70	20
6	–	50 n.p. bistre	75	30
7	–	75 n.p. black	90	60
8	3	1 r. emerald	2·50	70
9		2 r. black	3·75	2·25
10	–	5 r. carmine-red	9·00	7·00
11	–	10 r. deep ultramarine	16·00	13·00
1/11		*Set of* 11	32·00	23·00

Designs: *As Type* **1** – 40, 50, 75 n.p. Arabian Gazelle. *As Type* **3** – 5, 10 r. Oil rig and camels.

5 — 6 — 7
Lanner Falcon

(Des V. Whiteley. Photo Harrison)

1965 (30 Mar). *Falconry. P* 14½.

No.	Type	Value	Mint	Used
12	**5**	20 n.p. light brown and grey-blue	2·25	80
13	**6**	40 n.p. light brown and blue	3·50	2·00
14	**7**	2 r. sepia and turquoise-green	8·50	8·50

(New Currency. 1,000 fils = 1 dinar)

Fils فلس

(8)

1966 (1 Oct). *Nos. 1/11 such as T* 8 ("FILS" *only on 40 f. to 70 f.*) *with new value expressed on remainder*), *by Arabian Printing and Publishing House, Bahrain. P* 13 × 13½ (*20 f.*), *others as before*.

No.	Type	Value	Mint	Used
15	1	5 f. on 5 n.p. green	65	90
16		15 f. on 15 n.p. red-brown	70	80
17		20 f. on 20 n.p. ultramarine	70	85
		a. Surch inverted	£100	£140
18		30 f. on 30 n.p. red-orange	1·25	2·50
		a. Arabic "2" for "3" in surch	£1300	
19	–	40 f. on 40 n.p. reddish violet	1·25	55
20	–	50 f. on 50 n.p. bistre	5·50	8·00
21	–	75 f. on 75 n.p. black	5·50	8·00
22	3	100 f. on 1 r. emerald	6·00	3·25
23		200 f. on 2 r. black	13·00	12·00
24	–	500 f. on 5 r. carmine-red	28·00	38·00
25	–	1 d. on 10 r. deep ultramarine	45·00	70·00
15/25		*Set of* 11	95·00	£130

The Abu Dhabi Post Department took over the postal services on 1 January 1967. Later stamp issues will be found in Part 19 (*Middle East*) of this Catalogue.

Aden

The first post office in Aden opened during January 1839, situated in what became known as the Crater district. No stamps were initially available, but, after the office was placed under the Bombay Postal Circle, Indian stamps were provided in 1857. Most Indian issues from the 1854 lithographs up to 1935 Silver Jubilee set can be found with Aden postmarks.

During 1857 a further office, Aden Steamer Point, was opened in the harbour area and much of the business transferred to it. The original Aden post office, in Crater, was renamed Aden Cantonment, later to be changed again to Aden Camp.

The first cancellation used with the Indian stamps was a plain diamond of dots. This type was also used elsewhere so that attribution to Aden is only possible when on cover. Aden was assigned "124" in the Indian postal number system and this formed the main feature of marks from 1857, either on its own or as part of a duplex.

1857 "124" Cancellation

1870 Aden Duplex

1872 Aden Steamer Point Duplex

Both post offices used this number until 1871 when Aden Cantonment was assigned "125", only to have this swiftly amended to "124A" in the same year.

1871 Aden Cantonment "125" Cancellation — 1871 Aden Cantonment "124A" Cancellation

Cancellations inscribed "Aden Steamer Point" disappear after 1876 and this office was then known simply as Aden. Just prior to this change the office was given number "B-22" under the revised Indian P.O. scheme and this number appears as a major part of the cancellations from 1875 to 1885, either on its own or as part of a duplex. Aden Camp, the alternative name for the Cantonment office, became "B-22/1".

1875 Aden Duplex

Squared-circle types for both offices were introduced in 1884 and were, in turn, replaced by standard Indian double and single circle marks until 1937.

A number of other post offices were opened between 1891 and 1937:

Dthali (*opened* 1903, *initially using* "EXPERIMENTAL P.O. B-84" *postmark; closed* 1907)
Karmaran (*opened c* 1915, *but no civilian postmarks known before* 1926)
Khormaksar (*opened* 1892)
Maalla (*open by* 1924; *closed* 1931)
Perim (*opened by* 1895; *closed* 1936)
Sheikh Othman (*opened* 1891; *closed* 1937)

PRICES FOR STAMPS ON COVER TO 1945
Nos. 1/12 *from* × 4
Nos. 13/15 *from* × 5
Nos. 16/27 *from* × 3

1 Dhow

2 King George VI and Queen Elizabeth

(Recess D.L.R.)

1937 (1 Apr). *Wmk Mult Script CA sideways. P* 13 × 12.

No.	Type	Value	Mint	Used
1	1	½ a. yellow-green	90	1·25
2		9 p. deep green	1·25	1·40
3		1 a. sepia	1·25	55
4		2 a. scarlet	1·60	2·50
5		2½ a. bright blue	1·75	2·50
6		3 a. carmine	3·75	4·75
7		3½ a. grey-blue	2·50	3·50
8		8 a. pale purple	4·50	6·50
9		1 r. brown	9·00	9·00
10		2 r. yellow	16·00	16·00
11		5 r. deep purple	60·00	60·00
12		10 r. olive-green	£130	£130
1/12		*Set of* 12	£200	£200
1/12 Perf "Specimen"		*Set of* 12	£300	

(Des and recess D.L.R.)

1937 (12 May). *Coronation. Wmk Mult Script CA. P* 14.

No.	Type	Value	Mint	Used
13	**2**	1 a. sepia	40	35
14		2½ a. light blue	55	65
15		3½ a. grey-blue	70	85
13/15 Perf "Specimen"		*Set of* 3	40·00	

3 Aidrus Mosque, Crater

9 Houses of Parliament, London

(Recess Waterlow)

1939 (19 Jan)–**48**. *Horiz designs as T* **3**. *Wmk Mult Script CA. P* 12½.

No.	Type	Value	Mint	Used
16		½ a. yellowish green	25	40
		a. Bluish green (9.48)	70	1·75
17		¾ a. red-brown	25	60
18		1 a. pale blue	30	25
19		1½ a. scarlet	60	75
20		2 a. sepia	25	25
21		2½ a. deep ultramarine	35	30
22		3 a. sepia and carmine	60	50
23		8 a. red-orange	60	40
23*a*		14 a. sepia and light blue (15.1.45)	1·50	2·00
24		1 r. emerald-green	1·00	1·00
25		2 r. deep blue and magenta	3·75	3·25
26		5 r. red-brown and olive-green	9·50	12·00
27		10 r. sepia and violet	14·00	16·00
16/27		*Set of* 13	29·00	35·00
16/27 Perf "Specimen"		*Set of* 13	£140	

Designs:—½ a., 2 a., Type **3**; ¾ a., 5 r. Adenese Camel Corps; 1 a., 2 r. The Harbour; 1½ a., 1 r. Adenese Dhow; 2½ a., 8 a. Mukalla; 3 a., 14 a., 10 r. "Capture of Aden, 1839" (Capt. Turnbull).

(Des and recess D.L.R.)

1946 (15 Oct). *Victory. Wmk Mult Script CA. P* 13½ × 14.

No.	Type	Value	Mint	Used
28	**9**	1½ a. carmine	35	45
29		2½ a. blue	45	45
28/9 Perf "Specimen"		*Set of* 2	40·00	

10 — 11
King George VI and Queen Elizabeth

(Des and photo Waterlow (T **10**). Design recess; name typo B. W. (T **11**))

1949 (17 Jan.). *Royal Silver Wedding. Wmk Mult Script CA.*

No.	Type	Value	Mint	Used
30	**10**	1½ a. scarlet (*p* 14 × 15)	40	50
31	**11**	10 r. mauve (*p* 11½ × 11)	22·00	30·00

1949 (10 Oct). *75th Anniv. of Universal Postal Union. As Nos. 114/17 of Antigua, surch with new values by Waterlow.*

No.	Value	Mint	Used
32	2½ a. on 20 c. ultramarine	50	75
33	3 a. on 30 c. carmine-red	1·00	1·25
34	8 a. on 50 c. orange	1·75	2·25
35	1 r. on 1s. blue	2·50	2·75

5
CENTS
(12)

13 Queen Elizabeth II

1951 (1 Oct). *Currency changed. Nos. 18 and 20/7 surch with new values, in cents or shillings, as T* **12**, *or in one line between bars (30 c.) by Waterlow.*
36 5 c. on 1 a. pale blue .. 20 40
37 10 c. on 2 a. sepia .. 20 45
38 15 c. on 2½ a. deep ultramarine .. 55 75
a. Surch double .. £350
39 20 c. on 3 a. sepia and carmine .. 30 40
40 30 c. on 8 a. red-orange (R.) .. 35 65
41 50 c. on 8 a. red-orange .. 35 50
42 70 c. on 14 a. sepia and light blue .. 45 60
43 1s. on 1 r. emerald-green .. 45 60
44 2s. on 2 r. deep blue and magenta .. 4·00 4·25
a. Surch albino .. £150
45 5s. on 5 r. red-brown and olive-green .. 10·00 11·00
46 10s. on 10 r. sepia and violet .. 16·00 19·00
36/46 .. *Set of* 11 30·00 35·00

(Des and eng B. W. Recess D.L.R.)

1953 (2 June). *Coronation. Wmk Mult Script CA. P* 13½ × 13.
47 **13** 15 c. black and green .. 30 75

14 Minaret

25 "Aden in 1572" (F. Hogenberg)

(Recess Waterlow, until 1961, then D.L.R.)

1953 (15 June)–**59**. *T* **14** *and similar designs, and T* **25**. *Wmk Mult Script CA. P* 13½ × 13 (20*s.*), 12 × 13½ (*Nos.* 57, 64, 66, 68) *or* 12 (*others*).
48 5 c. yellowish green .. 5 5
49 5 c. bluish green (1.6.55) .. 5 20
a. Perf 12 × 13½ (12.4.56) .. 5 10
50 10 c. orange .. 5 5
51 10 c. vermilion (1.2.55) .. 5 5
52 15 c. blue-green .. 10 5
53 15 c. greenish grey (26.4.59) (*shades*) .. 30 30
54 25 c. carmine-red .. 10 5
55 25 c. deep rose-red (15.3.56) (*shades*) .. 15 12
56 35 c. deep ultramarine .. 45 20
57 35 c. deep blue (15.10.58) (*shades*) .. 60 60
58 50 c. dull blue .. 20 10
59 50 c. deep blue (1.7.55) .. 25 40
a. Perf 12 × 13½ (12.4.56) .. 20 10
60 70 c. brown-grey .. 20 20
61 70 c. black (20.9.54) .. 25 45
a. Perf 12 × 13½ (12.4.56) .. 20 15
62 1s. sepia and reddish violet .. 30 10
63 1s. black and violet (1.7.55) .. 30 10
64 1s. 25, blue and black (16.7.56) (*shades*) .. 2·00 40
65 2s. sepia and rose-carmine .. 1·75 60
66 2s. black & carmine-red (1.3.56) (*shades*) .. 1·90 40
67 5s. sepia and dull blue .. 2·25 1·75
68 5s. black and deep dull blue (11.4.56) (*shades*) 2·00 90
69 10s. sepia and olive .. 3·25 12·00
70 10s. black and bronze-green (20.9.54) .. 3·50 1·90
71 20s. chocolate and reddish lilac .. 15·00 22·00
72 20s. black and deep lilac (7.1.57) (*shades*) .. 18·00 11·00
48/72 .. *Set of* 25 48·00 48·00
Designs: (*as Type* **14**). *Horiz*—10 c. Camel transport; 15 c. Crater; 25 c. Mosque; 1s. Dhow building. *Vert*—35 c. Dhow; 50 c. Map; 70c. Salt works; 1s. 25; Colony's badge; 2s. Aden Protectorate levy; 5s. Crater Pass; 10s. Tribesman.
On No. 70 the tribesman's skirt is shaded with cross-hatching instead of with mainly diagonal lines as in No. 69.

1954 (27 Apr). *Royal Visit. As No.* 62 *but inscr* "ROYAL VISIT 1954" *at top.*
73 1s. sepia and reddish violet .. 35 35

تعديل
الدستور
١٩٥٩
(26)

REVISED
CONSTITUTION
1959
(27)

1959 (26 Jan). *Revised Constitution. No.* 53 *optd with T* **26**, *and No.* 64 *optd with T* **27**, *in red, by Waterlow.*
74 15 c. slate-green .. 20 45
75 1s. 25, blue and black .. 45 85

28 Protein Foods

(Des M. Goaman. Photo Harrison)

1963 (4 June). *Freedom from Hunger. W w* **12**. *P* 14 × 14½.
76 **28** 1s. 25 c. bluish green .. 1·50 1·40

For Red Cross issue see under South Arabian Federation.

1964 (5 Feb)–**65**. *As Nos.* 48, *etc. but wmk.* w **12**. *P* 12 (10 *c.*, 15 *c.*, 25 *c.*, 1*s.*) *or* 12 × 13½ (*others*).
77 5 c. green (16.2.65) .. 20 60
78 10 c. bright orange .. 20 25
79 15 c. greenish grey .. 30 35
80 25 c. carmine-red .. 30 35
81 35 c. indigo-violet .. 75 80
82 50 c. indigo-blue (*shades*) .. 35 40
83 70 c. black (*shades*) .. 40 50
84 1s. black and violet (10.3.64) .. 80 90
85 1s. 25, ultramarine and black (10.3.64) .. 2·25 2·75
86 2s. black and carmine-rose (16.2.65) .. 2·50 9·00
77/86 .. *Set of* 10 7·50 14·00

The stamps of Aden were withdrawn on 31 March 1965 and superseded by the stamps of the SOUTH ARABIAN FEDERATION.

KATHIRI STATE OF SEIYUN

The stamps of ADEN were used in Kathiri State of Seiyun from 1937 until 1942.

PRICES FOR STAMPS ON COVER TO 1945
Nos. 1/11 *from* × 10

1 Sultan of Seiyun

2 Seiyun

(Recess D.L.R.)

1942 (July–Oct). *Designs as T* **1/2**. *Wmk Mult Script CA. T* **1**, *perf* 14; *others, perf* 12 × 13 (*vert*) *or* 13 × 12 (*horiz*).
1 ½ a. blue-green .. 15 35
2 ¾ a. brown .. 15 35
3 1 a. blue .. 15 35
4 1½ a. carmine .. 15 40
5 2 a. sepia .. 15 50
6 2½ a. blue .. 15 60
7 3 a. sepia and carmine .. 15 55
8 8 a. red .. 25 60
9 1 r. green .. 35 80
10 2 r. blue and purple .. 3·25 4·75
11 5 r. brown and green .. 7·00 9·00
1/11 .. *Set of* 11 10·50 16·00
1/11 Perf "Specimen" .. *Set of* 11 70·00
Designs:—½ to 1 a. Type **1**. *Vert as T* **2**—2 a. Tarim; 2½ a. Mosque, Seiyun; 1 r. South Gate, Tarim; 5 r. Mosque entrance, Tarim. *Horiz as T* **2**—3 a. Fortress, Tarim; 8 a. Mosque, Seiyun; 2 r. A Kathiri house.

VICTORY
ISSUE
8TH JUNE 1946
(10)

1946 (15 Oct). *Victory. No.* 4 *optd with T* **10**, *and No.* 6 *optd similarly but in four lines, by De La Rue.*
12 1½ a. carmine .. 15 12
13 2½ a. blue (R.) .. 15 15
a. Opt inverted .. £350
12/13 Perf "Specimen" .. *Set of* 2 50·00
No. 13 is known with surcharge double but the second impression is almost coincident with the first.

1949 (17 Jan). *Royal Silver Wedding. As Nos.* 30/1 *of Aden.*
14 1½ a. scarlet .. 20 30
15 5 r. green .. 7·50 13·00

1949 (10 Oct). *75th Anniv of U.P.U. As Nos.* 114/17 *of Antigua, but inscr* "ADEN KATHIRI STATE OF SEIYUN" *and surch with new values, by Waterlow.*
16 2½ a. on 20 c. ultramarine .. 30 70
17 3 a. on 30 c. carmine-red .. 60 90
18 8 a. on 50 c. orange .. 1·25 2·25
19 1 r. on 1s. blue .. 1·50 3·50

5 CTS (11)
50 CENTS (12)
5/- (13)

1951 (1 Oct). *Currency changed. Nos.* 3 *and* 5/11 *surch as T* **11** (5 *c.*), **12** (20 *c. and* 50 *c.*) *or* **13** (1*s. to* 5*s.*) 10 *c. and* 15 *c. are as T* **12**, *but abbrev* ("CTS"), *by Waterlow.*
20 5 c. on 1 a. blue (R.) .. 15 35
21 10 c. on 2 a. sepia .. 15 35
22 15 c. on 2½ a. blue .. 15 60
23 20 c. on 3 a. sepia and carmine .. 15 60
24 50 c. on 8 a. red .. 20 70
25 1s. on 1 r. green .. 35 90
26 2s. on 2 r. blue and purple .. 2·25 5·50
27 5s. on 5 r. brown and green .. 6·00 15·00
20/27 .. *Set of* 8 8·50 22·00

1953 (2 June). *Coronation. As No.* 47 *of Aden.*
28 15 c. black and deep green .. 25 85

14 Sultan Hussein

15 Tarim

(Des Freya Stark and H. Ingram. Recess D.L.R.)

1954 (15 Jan). *As Nos.* 1/11 (*but with portrait of Sultan Hussein as in T* **14/15**). *Wmk Mult Script CA. T* **14**, *perf* 12½; *others, perf* 12 × 13 (*vert*) *or* 13 × 12 (*horiz*).
29 5 c. sepia .. 5 12
30 10 c. deep blue .. 8 12
31 15 c. deep bluish green .. 12 15
32 25 c. carmine-red .. 12 15
33 35 c. deep blue .. 12 15
34 50 c. deep brown and carmine-red .. 15 15
35 1s. brown-orange .. 20 15
36 2s. deep yellow-green .. 90 90
37 5s. deep blue and violet .. 2·25 3·25
38 10s. yellow-brown and violet .. 3·75 8·50
29/38 .. *Set of* 10 7·00 12·00

16 Qarn Adh Dhabi

17 Seiyun

(Recess D.L.R.)

1964 (1 July). *Designs as T* **16/17**. *W w* **12**. *P* 12 × 13 (70 *c.*) *or* 13 × 12 (*others*).
39 70 c. black .. 35 75
40 1s. 25 c. blue-green .. 65 2·50
41 1s. 50 c. deep reddish violet .. 80 2·75
Design: *Horiz as T* **17**—1s. 50 c. Gheil Omer.

(New Currency. 1000 fils = 1 dinar)

SOUTH ARABIA الجنوب العربي 5 FILS (19)
SOUTH ARABIA الجنوب العربي 500 FILS (20)
SOUTH ARABIA الجنوب العربي 50 FILS (21)

1966 (1 Apr). *New Currency. Nos.* 29/41 *surch as T* **19/21**.
42 5 f. on 5 c. (**19**) .. 5 5
a. Surch quadruple, one inverted .. 45·00
43 5 f. on 10 c. (**19**) (R.) .. 5 5
44 10 f. on 15 c. (**21**) (R.) .. 5 5
a. Surch inverted .. 75·00
45 15 f. on 25 c. (**20**) .. 10 5
46 20 f. on 35 c. (**20**) (R.) .. 12 8
47 25 f. on 50 c. (**21**) (R.) .. 15 15
48 35 f. on 70 c. (**20**) (R.) .. 15 20
49 50 f. on 1s. (**21**) .. 15 15
50 65 f. on 1s. 25 (**21**) .. 15 20
51 75 f. on 1s. 50 (**21**) .. 20 30
52 100 f. on 2s. (**20**) (R.) .. 4·00 10·00
53 250 f. on 5s. (**21**) (R.) .. 1·50 3·50
54 500 f. on 10s. (**20**) .. 2·50 6·50
42/54 .. *Set of* 13 8·25 19·00

SOUTH ARABIA 5 FILS (22)
SOUTH ARABIA الجنوب العربي 50 FILS (23)
SOUTH ARABIA الجنوب العربي 15 FILS (24)

1966. *Nos. 29/41 surch with T* **22**/**4**.
55 5 f. on 5 c. (**22**) (B.) 5 5
a. Surch inverted .. .. 45·00
56 5 f. on 10 c. (**22**) (R.) 5 5
57 10 f. on 15 c. (**23**) (Y.) 5 5
a. Surch inverted .. ..
58 15 f. on 25 c. (**24**) (B.) 5 5
a. Surch inverted .. .. 45·00
59 20 f. on 35 c. (**24**) (Y.) 8 10
60 25 f. on 50 c. (**23**) (B.) 8 10
61 35 f. on 70 c. (**24**) (Br.) 10 12
62 50 f. on 1s. (**23**) (G.) 12 15
a. Stop after "FILS" .. .. 8·50
63 65 f. on 1s. 25 (**23**) (Y.) 20 45
64 75 f. on 1s. 50 (**23**) (G.) 25 50
65 100 f. on 2s. (**24**) (Y.) 50 95
a. Surch inverted .. .. 30·00
66 250 f. on 5s. (**23**) (Y.) .. .. 1·75 3·75
a. Surch inverted .. .. 75·00
67 500 f. on 10s. (**24**) (G.) .. .. 3·50 7·50
55/67 .. .. *Set of* 13 6·00 12·00

HELSINKI 1952
(**25**)

INTERNATIONAL COOPERATION THROUGH OLYMPICS
(**26**)

1966. *Nos. 57, 59, 61/7 optd as T* **25**/**6** *in red.*
68 10 f. on 15 c. deep bluish green (**25** ("LOS ANGELES 1932")) 5 5
69 20 f. on 35 c. deep blue (**25** ("BERLIN 1936")) 5 5
70 35 f. on 70 c. black (**26**) 8 8
a. Opt T **26** inverted .. ..
71 50 f. on 1s. brown-orange (**25** ("LONDON 1948")) 12 15
a. Stop after "FILS" .. .. 8·00
72 65 f. on 1s. 25, blue-green (**25**) 15 20
73 75 f. on 1s. 50, deep reddish violet (**25** ("MELBOURNE 1956")) 20 25
74 100 f. on 2s. deep yellow-green (**25** ("ROME 1960")) 30 40
75 250 f. on 5s. deep blue and violet (**25** ("TOKYO 1964")) .. .. 75 1·25
76 500 f. on 10s. yellow-brown and violet (**25** ("MEXICO CITY 1968")) .. .. .. 1·50 2·50
68/76 .. .. *Set of* 9 3·00 4·50

CHAMPION: ENGLAND
(**27**)

FOOTBALL 1966
(**28**)

1966 (19 Sept). *World Cup Football Championships. Nos.* 57, 59, 61/2, 65/7 *optd with T* **27**/**8**.
77 10 f. on 15 c. deep bluish green (**27**) 10 10
78 20 f. on 35 c. deep blue (**28**) 15 15
79 35 f. on 70 c. black (**28**) 20 20
80 50 f. on 1s. brown-orange (**27**) 25 25
a. Stop after "FILS" .. .. 8·50
81 100 f. on 2s. deep yellow-green (**28**) .. .. 1·00 1·00
82 250 f. on 5s. deep blue and violet (**27**) .. .. 3·25 3·25
83 500 f. on 10s. yellow-brown and violet (**28**) .. 5·00 5·00
77/83 .. .. *Set of* 7 9·00 9·00

29 "Telstar"

(Photo State Ptg Wks, Vienna)

1966 (25 Oct). *I.T.U. Centenary* (1965). *T* **29** *and similar vert designs. P* 13½.
84 5 f. blackish green, black and reddish violet 45 25
85 10 f. maroon, black and bright green 60 30
86 15 f. Prussian blue, black and orange .. 85 40
87 25 f. blackish green, black and orange-red .. 1·50 60
88 35 f. maroon, black and deep olive-yellow .. 2·00 85
89 50 f. Prussian blue, black and orange-brown 2·50 1·40
90 65 f. blackish green, black and orange-yellow 3·00 1·60
84/90 .. .. *Set of* 7 10·00 4·75
Designs:—10, 35 f. "Relay"; 15, 50 f. "Ranger"; others, Type **29**.

32 Churchill at Easel

(Photo State Ptg Wks, Vienna)

1966 (Dec). *Sir Winston Churchill's Paintings. T* **32** *and similar designs in black and gold (5 f.) or multicoloured (others). P* 13½.
91 5 f. Type **32** 60 12
92 10 f. "Antibes" 70 15
93 15 f. "Flowers" (*vert*) 80 20
94 20 f. "Tapestries" 90 35
95 25 f. "Village, Lake Lugano" .. .. .. 1·10 35
96 35 f. "Church, Lake Como" (*vert*) .. .. 1·50 40
97 50 f. "Flowers at Chartwell" (*vert*) .. .. 1·90 65
98 65 f. Type **32** .. .. 2·40 90
91/8 .. .. *Set of* 8 9·00 2·75

WORLD PEACE PANDIT NEHRU
(**39**)

40 "Master Crewe as Henry VIII" (Sir Joshua Reynolds)

1967. *"World Peace". Nos. 57, 59, 61/7 optd as T* **39** *in various sizes of type.*
99 10 f. on 15 c. dp bluish green (Type **39**) (R.) 10 10
100 20 f. on 35 c. deep blue ("WINSTON CHURCHILL") (R.) 35 20
101 35 f. on 70 c. black ("DAG HAMMARSKJOLD") (B.) 30 20
102 50 f. on 1s. brown-orange ("JOHN F. KENNEDY") (R.) 35 25
a. Stop after "FILS" .. .. 9·00
103 65 f. on 1s. 25, blue-green ("LUDWIG ERHARD") (Pk.) 50 35
104 75 f. on 1s. 50, deep reddish violet ("LYNDON JOHNSON") (B.) 60 40
105 100 f. on 2s. deep yellow-green ("ELEANOR ROOSEVELT") (B.) 80 80
106 250 f. on 5s. deep blue and violet ("WINSTON CHURCHILL") (R.) .. .. .. 3·25 3·25
107 500 f. on 10s. yellow-brown and violet ("JOHN F. KENNEDY") (R.) .. .. .. 3·50 3·50
99/107 .. .. *Set of* 9 9·00 8·00

(Photo State Ptg Wks, Vienna)

1967. *Paintings. T* **40** *and similar multicoloured designs. P* 13½.
108 5 f. Type **40** 12 10
109 10 f. "The Dancer" (Degas) 15 12
110 15 f. "The Fifer" (Manet) 20 15
111 20 f. "Stag at Sharkey's" (boxing match, G. Burrows) 25 20
112 25 f. "Don Manuel Osorio" (Goya) 30 25
113 35 f. "St. Martin distributing his Cloak" (A. van Dyck) 40 35
114 50 f. "The Blue Boy" (Gainsborough) 55 40
115 65 f. "The White Horse" (Gauguin) 70 50
116 75 f. "Mona Lisa" (Da Vinci) (45 × 62 *mm.*) .. 85 80
108/16 .. .. *Set of* 9 3·25 2·50

SCOTT CARPENTER
(**49**)

50 Churchill Crown

1967. *American Astronauts. Nos. 57, 59, 61/2 and 65/6 optd as T* **49** *in various sizes of type, in red.*
117 10 f. on 15 c. deep bluish green ("ALAN SHEPARD, JR.") 15 25
118 20 f. on 35 c. deep blue ("VIRGIL GRISSOM") 25 35
119 35 f. on 70 c. black ("JOHN GLENN, JR.") .. 40 55
120 50 f. on 1s. brown-orange (Type **49**) .. 45 65
a. Stop after "FILS" .. .. 9·50
121 100 f. on 2s. deep yellow-green ("WALTER SCHIRRA, JR.") .. .. 95 1·75
122 250 f. on 5s. deep blue and violet ("GORDON COOPER, JR.") .. .. 2·25 3·25
a. Opt (as T **49**) double .. .. .. 90·00
117/122 .. .. *Set of* 6 4·00 6·00

1967 (Mar). *Churchill Commemoration. Photo. P* 13½.
123 **50** 75 f. multicoloured .. .. 8·50 6·50

Later issues up to 1 October 1967 are recorded in the Appendix below.

Appendix

The following stamps have either been issued in excess of postal needs, or have not been made available to the public in reasonable quantities at face value. Miniature sheets, imperforate stamps etc., are excluded from this section.

1967

Hunting. 20 *f.*
Olympic Games, Grenoble. Postage 10, 25, 35, 50, 75 *f. Air* 100, 200 *f.*
Scout Jamboree, Idaho. Air 150 *f.*
Paintings by Renoir. Postage 10, 35, 50, 65, 75 *f. Air* 100, 200, 250 *f.*
Paintings by Toulouse-Lautrec. Postage 10, 35, 50, 65, 75 *f. Air* 100, 200, 250 *f.*

The National Liberation Front is said to have taken control on 1 October 1967 and full independence was granted by Great Britain on 30 November 1967. Stamps issued after independence will be found listed under YEMEN (PEOPLE'S DEMOCRATIC REPUBLIC) in Part 19 (*Middle East*) of this catalogue.

QU'AITI STATE IN HADHRAMAUT

The stamps of ADEN were used in Qu'aiti State in Hadhramaut from 1937 until 1942.

PRICES FOR STAMPS ON COVER TO 1945
Nos. 1/11 *from* × 6

I. Issues inscr "SHIHR and MUKALLA"

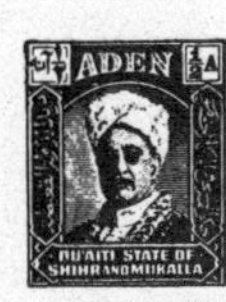

1 Sultan of Shihr and Mukalla

2 Mukalla Harbour

VICTORY ISSUE 8TH JUNE 1946
(**10**)

(Recess D.L.R.)

1942 (July)–**46**. *Wmk Mult Script CA. Designs as T* **1** (½ *to* 1 *a.*) *or T* **2** (*others*). *P* 14 (½ *to* 1 *a.*), 12 × 13 (1½, 2, 3 *a. and* 1 *r.*) *or* 13 × 12 (*others*).
1 ½ a. blue-green 15 30
a. Olive-green (12.46) .. .. 8·00 13·00
2 ¾ a. brown 15 30
3 1 a. blue 15 30
4 1½ a. carmine 15 55
5 2 a. sepia 15 65
6 2½ a. blue 15 55
7 3 a. sepia and carmine 15 55
8 8 a. red .. .. 25 1·75
9 1 r. green .. .. 35 1·00
10 2 r. blue and purple .. .. 3·25 4·50
11 5 r. brown and green .. .. 4·00 8·00
1/11 .. .. *Set of* 11 8·00 17·00
1/11 Perf "Specimen" .. .. *Set of* 11 70·00
Designs: *Vert*—2 a. Gateway of Shihr; 3 a. Outpost of Mukalla; 1 r. Du'an. *Horiz*—2½ a. Shibam; 8 a. 'Einat; 2 r. Mosque in Hureidha; 5 r. Meshhed.

1946 (15 Oct). *Victory. No.* 4 *optd. with T* **10** *and No.* 6 *optd similarly, but in three lines, by De La Rue.*
12 1½ a. carmine 15 15
13 2½ a. blue (R.) 15 15
12/13 Perf "Specimen" .. .. *Set of* 2 55·00

1949 (17 Jan). *Royal Silver Wedding. As Nos.* 30/1 *of Aden.*
14 1½ a. scarlet 20 30
15 5 r. green .. .. 7·50 13·00

1949 (10 Oct). *75th Anniv of Universal Postal Union. As Nos.* 114/17 *of Antigua, but surch with new values, by Waterlow.*
16 2½ a. on 20 c. ultramarine 30 70
17 3 a. on 30 c. carmine-red .. .. .. 1·25 1·50
18 8 a. on 50 c. orange .. .. 1·60 2·50
19 1 r. on 1s. blue .. .. 2·75 3·75
a. Surch omitted £750

1951 (1 Oct). *Currency changed. Surch with new values in cents or shillings as T* **11** *to* **13** *of Seiyun, by Waterlow.*
20 5 c. on 1 a. blue (R.) 15 25
21 10 c. on 2 a. sepia 15 25
22 15 c. on 2½ a. blue 15 25
23 20 c. on 3 a. sepia and carmine 15 30
a. Surch double, one albino .. .. ..
24 50 c. on 8 a. red 15 45
25 1s. on 1 r. green 35 80
26 2s. on 2 r. blue and purple .. .. .. 2·25 6·00
27 5s. on 5 r. brown and green .. .. .. 3·75 8·50
20/27 .. .. *Set of* 8 6·50 15·00

1953 (2 June). *Coronation. As No.* 47 *of Aden.*
28 15 c. black and deep blue 25 65

MINIMUM PRICE

The minimum price quoted is 5p which represents a handling charge rather than a basis for valuing common stamps. For further notes about prices see introductory pages.

II. Issues inscr "HADHRAMAUT"

11 Metal Work

22 Metal Work

(Des Mme M. de Sturler Raemaekers. Recess D.L.R.)

1955 (1 Sept). *T* **11** *and similar designs. Wmk Mult Script CA. P* 11½ × 13–13½ (*vert*) *or* 14 (*horiz*).
29 5 c. greenish blue 5 12
30 10 c. grey-black 10 12
31 15 c. deep green (*shades*) 10 15
32 25 c. carmine-red 12 12
33 35 c. blue 12 12
34 50 c. orange-red (*shades*) 15 15
35 90 c. sepia 20 15
36 1s. black and deep lilac 20 15
37 1s. 25, black and red-orange 35 50
38 2s. black and indigo 90 90
39 5s. black and bluish green .. .. .. 2·25 2·50
40 10s. black and lake .. .. 2·75 5·00
29/40 .. .. *Set of* 12 6·50 9·00
Designs: *Vert*—10 c. Mat-making; 15 c. Weaving; 25 c. Pottery; 35 c. Building; 50 c. Date cultivation; 90 c. Agriculture. *Horiz*—1s. Fisheries; 1s. 25, 10s. Lime-burning; 2s. Dhow building; 5s. Agriculture.

1963 (20 Oct). *As Nos.* 29/40 *but with inset portrait of Sultan Awadh bin Saleh el-Qu'aiti as in T* **22** *and wmk w* **12**.
41 5 c. greenish blue 5 5
42 10 c. grey-black 5 5
43 15 c. bronze-green 8 8
44 25 c. carmine-red 8 8
45 35 c. blue 8 10
46 50 c. red-orange 10 12
47 70 c. deep brown (as 90 c.) 15 20
48 1s. black and deep lilac 20 10
49 1s. 25, black and red-orange 45 65
50 2s. black and indigo-blue .. .. .. 1·50 1·50
51 5s. black and bluish green .. .. .. 3·50 6·00
52 10s. black and lake .. .. 3·75 8·50
41/52 .. .. *Set of* 12 9·00 16·00

(New Currency. 1000 fils = 1 dinar)

1966 (1 Apr). *New currency. Nos.* 41/52 *surch as T* **20/21** *of Kathiri State of Seiyun.*
53 5 f. on 5 c. greenish blue (**20**) (R.) 5 5
54 5 f. on 10 c. grey-black (**20**) (R.) 5 5
55 10 f. on 15 c. bronze-green (**20**) (R.) 8 5
56 15 f. on 25 c. carmine-red (**20**).. .. .. 8 10
57 20 f. on 35 c. blue (**20**) (R.) 8 12
58 25 f. on 50 c. red-orange (**20**) 8 12
59 35 f. on 70 c. deep brown (**20**) (R.) 10 15
60 50 f. on 1s. black and deep lilac (**21**) (R.) .. 12 15
61 65 f. on 1s. 25, black and red-orange (**21**) (R.) 25 35
62 100 f. on 2s. black and indigo-blue (**21**) (R.) .. 60 90
63 250 f. on 5s. black and bluish green (**21**) (R.) .. 1·50 2·50
64 500 f. on 10s. black and lake (**21**) (R.) .. 3·00 4·75
53/64 .. .. *Set of* 12 5·50 8·25

1874–1965 WINSTON CHURCHILL (23)

1917-1963 JOHN F. KENNEDY (24)

1966. *Churchill Commemoration. Nos.* 54/6 *optd with T* **23**.
65 5 f. on 10 c. grey-black (R.) 90 90
66 10 f. on 15 c. bronze-green (R.) .. .. .. 1·25 1·25
a. Opt T **23** inverted .. .. .. 75·00
67 15 f. on 25 c. carmine-red (B.).. .. .. 1·60 1·60

1966. *President Kennedy Commemoration. Nos.* 57/9 *optd with T* **24**.
68 20 f. on 35 c. blue (R.).. .. .. .. 80 1·25
69 25 f. on 50 c. red-orange (B.) .. .. .. 1·10 1·75
70 35 f. on 70 c. deep brown (B.) .. .. .. 1·60 2·25

25 World Cup Emblem

(Photo State Ptg Wks. Vienna)

1966. *World Cup Football Championship, England. T* **25** *and similar diamond-shaped designs. P* 13½.
71 5 f. maroon and yellow-orange 45 20
72 10 f. slate-violet and light green 55 20
73 15 f. maroon and yellow-orange 65 25
74 20 f. slate-violet and light green 80 35
75 25 f. blackish green and orange-red 90 45
76 35 f. blue and yellow .. .. 1·25 70
77 50 f. blackish green and orange-red .. .. 1·60 90
78 65 f. blue and yellow .. .. 2·00 1·25
71/78 .. .. *Set of* 8 7·50 3·75
Designs:—10, 35 f. Wembley Stadium; 15, 50 f. Footballers; 20 f. Jules Rimet Cup and football; 25, 65 f. Type **25**.

29 Mexican Hat and Blanket

(Photo State Ptg Wks, Vienna)

1966 (25 Oct). *Pre-Olympic Games, Mexico* (1968). *P* 13½.
79 **29** 75 f. sepia and light yellow-green .. 1·50 1·50

30 Telecommunications Satellite

(Photo State Ptg Wks, Vienna)

1966 (Dec). *International Co-operation Year* (1965). *T* **30** *and similar horiz designs. P* 13½.
80 5 f. maroon, bright purple and emerald .. 55 25
81 10 f. violet, orange, blue-green and new blue 70 25
82 15 f. maroon, new blue and red .. .. 1·10 30
83 20 f. Prussian blue, purple and red .. .. 1·25 35
84 25 f. violet, olive-yellow, red and emerald .. 1·50 40
85 35 f. maroon, rose-red and new blue .. .. 2·25 70
86 50 f. maroon, green and red .. .. .. 2·75 1·00
87 65 f. chocolate, bluish violet and red.. .. 3·25 1·50
80/87 .. .. *Set of* 8 12·00 4·25
Designs:—10, 25 f. Olympic runner (inscribed "ROME 1960"); 15 f. Fishes; 50 f. Tobacco plant; others, Type **30**.

Later issues up to 17 September 1967 are recorded in the Appendix below.

Appendix

The following stamps have either been issued in excess of postal needs, or have not been made available to the public in reasonable quantities at face value. Miniature sheets, imperforate stamps etc. are excluded from this section.

1967

Stampex Stamp Exhibition, London. Postage 5, 10, 15, 20, 25 *f. Air* 50, 65 *f.*
Amphilex International Stamp Exhibition, Amsterdam. Air 75 *f.*
Olympic Games, Mexico (1968), 75 *f.*
Paintings. Postage 5, 10, 15, 20, 25 *f. Air* 50, 65 *f.*
Scout Jamboree, Idaho. Air 35 *f.*
Space Research. Postage 10, 25, 35, 50, 75 *f. Air* 100, 250 *f.*

The National Liberation Front is said to have taken control on 17 September 1967 and full independence was granted by Great Britain on 30 November 1967. Stamps issued after independence, will be found listed under YEMEN (PEOPLE'S DEMOCRATIC REPUBLIC) in Part 19 (*Middle East*) of this catalogue.

MAHRA SULTANATE OF QISHN AND SOCOTRA

(Currency. 1000 fils = 1 dinar)

1 Mahra Flag

(Des and litho Harrison)

1967 (12 Mar). *Flag in green, black and vermilion; inscriptions in black; background colours given. P* 14 × 14½.
1 **1** 5 f. mauve 35 10
2 10 f. buff.. .. .. 45 15
3 15 f. sage-green 50 15
4 20 f. red-orange 60 20
5 25 f. yellow-brown 60 25
6 35 f. turquoise-green 60 25
7 50 f. new blue 60 25
8 65 f. blackish brown 65 25
9 100 f. violet 75 25
10 250 f. rose-red .. .. 1·00 40
11 500 f. grey-green .. .. 1·50 85
1/11 .. .. *Set of* 11 6·75 2·75

Later issues up to 1 October 1967 are recorded in the Appendix below.

Appendix

The following stamps have either been issued in excess of postal needs, or have not been made available to the public in reasonable quantities at face value. Miniature sheets, imperforate stamps etc., are excluded from this section.

1967

Scout Jamboree, Idaho. 15, 75, 100, 150 *f.*
President Kennedy Commemoration. Postage 10, 15, 25, 50, 75, 100, 150 *f. Air* 250, 500 *f.*
Olympic Games, Mexico (1968). *Postage* 10, 25, 50 *f. Air* 250, 500 *f.*

The National Liberation Front is said to have taken control on 1 October 1967 and full independence was granted by Great Britain on 30 November 1967. Stamps issued after independence, will be found listed under YEMEN (PEOPLE'S DEMOCRATIC REPUBLIC) in Part 19 (*Middle East*) of this catalogue.

Anguilla

St. Christopher, Nevis and Anguilla were granted Associated Statehood on 27 February 1967, but, following a referendum, Anguilla declared her independence on 30 May 1967 and the St. Christopher authorities withdrew. The following stamps were issued by the governing Council and have been accepted for international mail. On 7 July 1969 the Anguilla post office was officially recognised by the Government of St. Christopher, Nevis and Anguilla and normal postal communications via St. Christopher were resumed. By the Anguilla Act of 27 July 1971, Anguilla was restored to direct British control.

A degree of internal self-government with an Executive Council was introduced on 10 February 1976 and the links with St. Kitts-Nevis were officially severed on 18 December 1980.

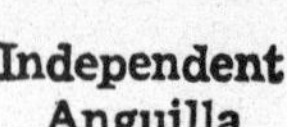
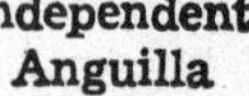

Independent Anguilla

(1)

2 Mahogany Tree, The Quarter

1967 (4 Sept). *Nos.* 129/44 *of St. Christopher, Nevis and Anguilla optd as T* **1**, *by Island Press Inc, St. Thomas, U.S. Virgin Islands.*
1 ½ c. New lighthouse, Sombrero .. .. 18·00 20·00
2 1 c. Loading sugar cane, St. Kitts .. .. 20·00 10·00
3 2 c. Pall Mall Square, Basseterre .. .. 22·00 7·00
4 3 c. Gateway, Brimstone Hill Fort, St. Kitts 22·00 8·50
5 4 c. Nelson's Spring, Nevis .. .. .. 22·00 8·50
6 5 c. Grammar School, St. Kitts .. .. 80·00 20·00
7 6 c. Crater, Mt. Misery, St. Kitts .. .. 35·00 12·00
8 10 c. Hibiscus .. .. 22·00 10·00
9 15 c. Sea Island cotton, Nevis.. .. .. 45·00 13·00
10 20 c. Boat building, Anguilla.. .. .. 75·00 15·00
11 25 c. White-crowned Pigeon .. .. .. 60·00 24·00
12 50 c. St. George's Church Tower, Basseterre — £400
13 60 c. Alexander Hamilton .. .. .. — £700
14 $1 Map of St. Kitts-Nevis .. .. .. — £400
15 $2.50, Map of Anguilla .. .. .. — £275
16 $5 Arms of St. Christopher, Nevis and Anguilla .. .. — £275
1/16 .. .. *Set of* 16 £6000 £2000
Owing to the limited stocks available for overprinting, the sale of the above stamps was personally controlled by the Postmaster and no orders from the trade were accepted.

(Des John Lister Ltd. Litho A. & M.)

1967 (27 Nov)–**68**. *T* **2** *and similar horiz designs. P* 12½ × 13.
17 1 c. dull green, bistre-brown and pale orange 5 5
18 2 c. bluish green and black (21.3.68).. .. 5 5
19 3 c. black and light emerald (10.2.68) .. 5 5
20 4 c. cobalt-blue and black (10.2.68) 8 8
21 5 c. multicoloured 8 8
22 6 c. light vermilion and black (21.3.68) .. 10 10
23 10 c. multicoloured 15 15
24 15 c. multicoloured (10.2.68) 30 30
25 20 c. multicoloured 40 30
26 25 c. multicoloured 50 30
27 40 c. apple green, light greenish blue and black 95 60
28 60 c. multicoloured (10.2.68) .. .. .. 1·75 1·50

29 $1 multicoloured (10.2.68) .. 2·50 2·25
30 $2.50, multicoloured (21.3.68) .. 4·50 3·00
31 $5 multicoloured (10.2.68) .. 8·50 6·50
17/31 .. *Set of* 15 18·00 14·00

Designs:—2 c. Sombrero Lighthouse; 3 c. St. Mary's Church; 4 c. Valley Police Station; 5 c. Old Plantation House, Mt. Fortune; 6 c. Valley Post Office; 10 c. Methodist Church, West End; 15 c. Wall-Blake Airport; 20 c. Aircraft over Sandy Ground; 25 c. Island Harbour; 40 c. Map of Anguilla; 60 c. Hermit Crab and Starfish; $1 Hibiscus; $2.50, Local scene; $5, Spiny Lobster.

On 9 January 1969 Anguilla reaffirmed her independence from St. Kitts and issued Nos. 17/31 overprinted in black "INDEPENDENCE JANUARY 1969" in two lines. These are outside the scope of this catalogue.

17 Yachts in Lagoon

18 Purple-throated Carib

(Des John Lister Ltd. Litho A. & M.)

1968 (11 May). *Anguillan Ships. T* **17** *and similar horiz designs. Multicoloured. P* 14.

32 10 c. Type **17** .. 40 30
33 15 c. Boat on beach .. 60 40
34 25 c. Schooner *Warspite* .. 75 50
35 40 c. *Atlantic Star* .. 1·00 80

(Des John Lister Ltd. Litho A. & M.)

1968 (8 July). *Anguillan Birds. T* **18** *and similar multicoloured designs. P* 14.

36 10 c. Type **18** .. 75 50
37 15 c. Bananaquit .. 95 60
38 25 c. Black-necked Stilt (*horiz*) .. 1·25 75
39 40 c. Royal Tern (*horiz*) .. 1·50 95

19 Guides' Badge and Anniversary Years

(Des John Lister Ltd. Litho A. & M.)

1968 (14 Oct). *35th Anniv of Anguillan Girl Guides. T* **19** *and similar multicoloured designs. P* 13 × 13½ (10, 25 c.) *or* 13½ × 13 (*others*).

40 10 c. Type **19** .. 20 20
41 15 c. Badge and silhouettes of Guides (*vert*) .. 30 30
42 25 c. Guides' badge and Headquarters .. 40 40
43 40 c. Association and Proficiency badges (*vert*) 60 50

20 The Three Kings

(Des John Lister Ltd. Litho A. & M.)

1968 (18 Nov). *Christmas. T* **20** *and similar designs. P* 13.

44 1 c. black and cerise .. 5 5
45 10 c. black and light greenish blue .. 30 20
46 15 c. black and chestnut .. 55 30
47 40 c. black and blue .. 75 50
48 50 c. black and dull green .. 80 70

Designs: *Vert*—10 c. The Wise Men; 15 c. Holy Family and manger. *Horiz*—40 c. The Shepherds; 50 c. Holy Family and donkey.

21 Bagging Salt

22 "The Crucifixion" (Studio of Massys)

(Des John Lister Ltd. Litho A. & M.)

1969 (4 Jan). *Anguillan Salt Industry. T* **21** *and similar horiz designs. Multicoloured. P* 13.

49 10 c. Type **21** .. 20 15
50 15 c. Packing salt .. 30 20
51 40 c. Salt pond .. 40 35
52 50 c. Loading salt .. 45 40

(Des John Lister Ltd. Litho Format)

1969 (31 Mar). *Easter Commemoration. T* **22** *and similar vert design. P.* 13½.

53 25 c. multicoloured .. 45 35
54 40 c. multicoloured .. 50 40

Design:—40 c. "The Last Supper" (ascribed to Roberti).

23 Amaryllis

(Des John Lister Ltd. Litho Format)

1969 (10 June). *Flowers of the Caribbean. T* **23** *and similar horiz designs. Multicoloured. P* 14.

55 10 c. Type **23** .. 25 15
56 15 c. Bougainvillea .. 35 20
57 40 c. Hibiscus .. 50 40
58 50 c. *Cattleya* orchid .. 70 45

24 Turbans and Star Shells

(Des John Lister Ltd. Litho A. & M.)

1969 (22 Sept). *Sea Shells. T* **24** *and similar horiz designs. Multicoloured. P* 14.

59 10 c. Type **24** .. 25 15
60 15 c. Spiny oysters .. 35 20
61 40 c. Scotch, Royal and Smooth Scotch bonnets 50 35
62 50 c. Triton trumpet .. 55 40

(25)

(26)

(27)

(28)

(29)

1969 (Oct). *Christmas. Nos.* 17, 25/8 *optd with T* **25/29**.

63 1 c. dull green, bistre-brown & light orange 10 5
64 20 c. multicoloured .. 60 40
65 25 c. multicoloured .. 70 40
66 40 c. apple-green, light greenish blue & black 1·50 75
67 60 c. multicoloured .. 1·90 1·50

30 Red Goatfish

31 "Morning Glory"

(Des John Lister Ltd. Litho A. & M.)

1969 (1 Dec). *Fishes. T* **30** *and similar horiz designs. Multicoloured. P* 14.

68 10 c. Type **30** .. 30 20
69 15 c. Blue Striped grunts .. 45 25
70 40 c. Mutton grouper .. 55 35
71 50 c. Banded Butterfly fish .. 65 40

(Des John Lister Ltd. Litho A. & M.)

1970 (23 Feb). *Flowers. T* **31** *and similar vert designs. Multicoloured. P* 14.

72 10 c. Type **31** .. 35 15
73 15 c. Blue Petrea .. 55 25
74 40 c. Hibiscus .. 90 60
75 50 c. "Flame Tree" .. 1·00 75

32 "Deposition" (Rosso Fiorentino)

33 Scout Badge and Map

(Des John Lister Ltd. Litho Format)

1970 (26 Mar). *Easter. T* **32** *and similar multicoloured designs. P* 13½.

76 10 c. "The Ascent to Calvary" (Tiepolo) (*horiz*) 25 15
77 20 c. "The Crucifixion" (Masaccio) .. 30 25
78 40 c. Type **32** .. 45 35
79 60 c. "The Ascent to Calvary" (Murillo) (*horiz*) 55 40

(Des John Lister Ltd. Litho A. & M.)

1970 (10 Aug). *40th Anniv of Scouting in Anguilla. T* **33** *and similar horiz designs. Multicoloured. P* 13.

80 10 c. Type **33** .. 25 15
81 15 c. Scout camp and cubs practising first-aid 35 25
82 40 c. Monkey Bridge .. 50 40
83 50 c. Scout H.Q. Building and Lord Baden-Powell .. 60 45

34 Boatbuilding

(Des John Lister Ltd. Litho Format)

1970 (23 Nov). *Various horiz designs as T* **34**. *Multicoloured. P* 14.

84 1 c. Type **34** .. 5 10
85 2 c. Road Construction .. 5 10
86 3 c. Quay, Blowing Point .. 5 10
87 4 c. Broadcaster, Radio Anguilla .. 8 12
88 5 c. Cottage Hospital Extension .. 8 12
89 6 c. Valley Secondary School .. 12 15
90 10 c. Hotel Extension .. 15 20
91 15 c. Sandy Ground .. 20 25
92 20 c. Supermarket and Cinema .. 25 30
93 25 c. Bananas and Mangoes .. 35 50
94 40 c. Wall Blake Airport .. 45 60
95 60 c. Sandy Ground Jetty .. 75 90
96 $1 Administration Buildings .. 1·40 1·60
97 $2.50, Livestock .. 3·00 3·75
98 $5 Sandy Hill Bay .. 6·00 7·00
84/98 .. *Set of* 15 12·00 14·00

35 "The Adoration of the Shepherds" (Reni)

36 "Ecce Homo" (detail, Correggio)

(Des John Lister Ltd. Litho Questa)

1970 (11 Dec). *Christmas. T* **35** *and similar vert designs. Multicoloured. P* 13½.

99 1 c. Type **35** .. 5 5
100 20 c. "The Virgin and Child" (Gozzoli) .. 35 30
101 25 c. "Mystic Nativity" (detail, Botticelli) .. 40 35
102 40 c. "The Santa Margherita Madonna" (detail, Mazzola) .. 50 45
103 50 c. "The Adoration of the Magi" (detail, Tiepolo) .. 60 50

(Des John Lister Ltd. Litho Format)

1971 (29 Mar). *Easter. T* **36** *and similar designs. P* 13½.

104 10 c. multicoloured .. 15 15
105 15 c. multicoloured .. 30 20
106 40 c. multicoloured .. 40 35
107 50 c. multicoloured .. 50 40

Designs: *Vert*—15 c. "Christ appearing to St. Peter" (detail, Carracci). *Horiz*—40 c. "Angels weeping over the Dead Christ" (detail, Guercino); 50 c. "The Supper at Emmaus" (detail, Caravaggio).

37 *Hypolimnas misippus*

38 *Magnanime* and *Amiable* in Battle

(Des John Lister Ltd. Litho Questa)

1971 (21 June). *Butterflies. T* **37** *and similar horiz designs. Multicoloured. P* 14 × 14½.

108 10 c. Type **37** 80 80
109 15 c. *Junonia lavinia* .. .. 1·00 1·00
110 40 c. *Agraulis vanillae* .. .. 1·60 1·60
111 50 c. *Danaus plexippus* .. .. 1·90 1·90

(Des John Lister Ltd. Litho Format)

1971 (30 Aug). *Sea-battles of the West Indies. T* **38** *and similar vert designs. Multicoloured. P* 14.

112 10 c. Type **38** 60 60
a. Horiz strip of 5. Nos. 112/16 .. .. 4·75
113 15 c. H.M.S. *Duke, Glorieux* and H.M.S. *Agamemnon* 75 75
114 25 c. H.M.S. *Formidable* and H.M.S. *Namur* against *Ville de Paris* .. .. 1·00 1·00
115 40 c. H.M.S. *Canada* .. .. 1·25 1·25
116 50 c. H.M.S. *St. Albans* and wreck of *Hector* 1·50 1·50

Nos. 112/16 were issued in horizontal *se-tenant* strips within the sheet, to form a composite design in the order listed.

ADMINISTRATION BY BRITISH COMMISSION

39 "The Ansidei Madonna" (detail, Raphael)

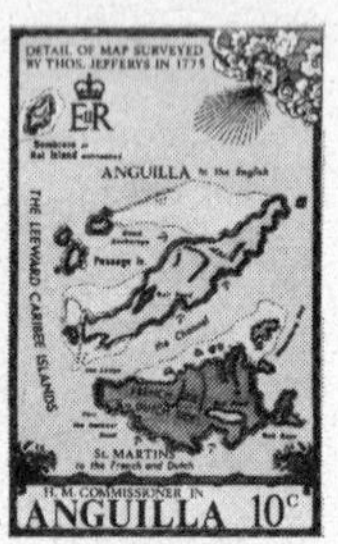

40 Map of Anguilla and St. Martins by Thomas Jefferys (1775)

(Des John Lister Ltd. Litho Questa)

1971 (29 Nov). *Christmas. T* **39** *and similar vert designs. P* 13½.

117 20 c. multicoloured 30 30
118 25 c. multicoloured 35 35
119 40 c. multicoloured 45 45
120 50 c. multicoloured 50 50

Designs:—25 c. "Mystic Nativity" (detail, Botticelli); 40 c. "Adoration of the Shepherds" (detail; ascr to Murillo); 50 c. "The Madonna of the Iris" (detail; ascr to Dürer).

(Litho Format)

1972 (24 Jan). *Maps. T* **40** *and similar multicoloured designs showing maps by the cartographers given. P* 14.

121 10 c. Type **40** 30 30
122 15 c. Samuel Fahlberg (1814) 40 40
123 40 c. Thomas Jefferys (1775) (*horiz*) 70 70
124 50 c. Capt. E. Barnett (1847) (*horiz*) 75 75

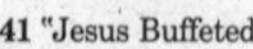

41 "Jesus Buffeted"

42 Loblolly Tree

(Des John Lister Ltd. Litho Format)

1972 (14 Mar). *Easter. Stained Glass Windows from Church of St. Michael, Bray, Berkshire. T* **41** *and similar vert designs. Multicoloured. P* 14 × 13½.

125 10 c. Type **41** 25 25
a. Horiz strip of 5. Nos. 125/9 .. .. 1·60
126 15 c. "The Way of Sorrows" 30 30
127 25 c. "The Crucifixion" 35 35
128 40 c. "Descent from the Cross" 40 40
129 50 c. "The Burial" 50 50

Nos. 125/9 were printed horizontally *se-tenant* within the sheet.

(Litho Questa ($10), Format (others))

1972 (30 Oct)–**75**. *T* **42** *and similar multicoloured designs (horiz, except 2, 4 and 6 c.). P* 13½.

130 1 c. Spear fishing 10 10
131 2 c. Type **42** 10 10
132 3 c. Sandy Ground 10 10
133 4 c. Ferry at Blowing Point 15 15
a. Gold (frame and ornaments) double ..
134 5 c. Agriculture 15 15
135 6 c. St. Mary's Church 25 15
136 10 c. St. Gerard's Church 25 25
137 15 c. Cottage Hospital extension 25 25
138 20 c. Public library 30 30
139 25 c. Sunset at Blowing Point 40 40
140 40 c. Boat building .. .. 1·50 1·50
141 60 c. Hibiscus .. .. 2·50 2·50
142 $1 Magnificent Frigate Bird .. .. .. 3·25 3·25
143 $2.50, Frangipani .. .. 6·00 6·50
144 $5 Brown Pelican .. .. 9·00 11·00
144*a* $10 Green-back turtle (20.5.75) .. .. 25·00 26·00
130/44*a* .. .. *Set of* 16 45·00 48·00

43 Schooner and Dolphin

(Des (from photograph by D. Groves) and photo Harrison)

1972 (20 Nov). *Royal Silver Wedding. Multicoloured; background colour given. W w* **12**. *P* 14 × 14½.

145 **43** 25 c. yellow-olive (*shades*) .. .. .. 1·50 2·25
146 40 c. chocolate .. .. 1·75 2·75

44 Flight into Egypt

45 "The Betrayal of Christ"

(Des John Lister Ltd. Litho Questa)

1972 (4 Dec). *Christmas. T* **44** *and similar vert designs. Multicoloured. P* 13½.

147 1 c. Type **44** 5 8
148 20 c. Star of Bethlehem 40 40
a. Vert strip of 4. Nos. 148/51 .. .. 1·75
149 25 c. Holy Family 45 45
150 40 c. Arrival of the Magi 50 50
151 50 c. Adoration of the Magi 55 55

Nos. 148/51 were printed vertically *se-tenant* within a sheet of 20 stamps.

(Des John Lister Ltd. Litho Questa)

1973 (26 Mar). *Easter. T* **45** *and similar vert designs. Multicoloured; bottom panel in gold and black. P* 13½.

152 1 c. Type **45** 5 5
153 10 c. "The Man of Sorrows" 12 12
a. Vert strip of 5. Nos. 153/7 .. .. 1·40
154 20 c. "Christ bearing the Cross" 25 30
155 25 c. "The Crucifixion" 30 35
156 40 c. "The Descent from the Cross" 40 45
157 50 c. "The Resurrection" 45 50
152/7 .. .. *Set of* 6 1·40 1·60
MS158 140 × 141 mm. Nos. 152/7. Bottom panel in gold and mauve .. .. 1·50 1·75

Nos. 153/7 were printed within one sheet, vertically *se-tenant*.

46 *Santa Maria*

47 Princess Anne and Captain Mark Phillips

(Des John Lister Ltd. Litho Questa)

1973 (10 Sept). *Columbus Discovers the West Indies. T* **46** *and similar horiz designs. Multicoloured. P* 13½.

159 1 c. Type **46** 5 5
160 20 c. Early map 75 75
a. Horiz strip of 4. Nos. 160/3 .. .. .. 5·00
161 40 c. Map of voyages 90 90
162 70 c. Sighting land .. .. 1·50 1·50
163 $1.20, Landing of Columbus .. .. .. 2·25 2·25
MS164 193 × 93 mm. Nos. 159/63 .. .. .. 6·00 7·00

Nos. 160/3 were printed horizontally *se-tenant* within the sheet.

(Des PAD Studio. Litho Questa)

1973 (14 Nov). *Royal Wedding. Centre multicoloured. W* w **12** (*sideways*). *P* 13½.

165 **47** 60 c. turquoise-green 35 20
166 $1.20, deep mauve 45 30

48 "The Adoration of the Shepherds" (Reni)

49 "The Crucifixion" (Raphael)

(Des John Lister Ltd. Litho Questa)

1973 (2 Dec). *Christmas. T* **48** *and similar horiz designs. Multicoloured. P* 13½.

167 1 c. Type **48** 5 5
168 10 c. "The Madonna and Child with Saints Jerome and Dominic" (Lippi) 20 20
a. Horiz strip of 5. Nos. 168/72 .. 1·50
169 20 c. "The Nativity" (Master of Brunswick) .. 30 30
170 25 c. "Madonna of the Meadow" (Bellini) .. 30 30
171 40 c. "Virgin and Child" (Cima) 40 40
172 50 c. "Adoration of the Kings" (Geertgen) .. 45 45
167/72 .. .. *Set of* 6 1·50 1·50
MS173 148 × 149 mm. Nos. 167/72 .. .. 1·75 1·75

Nos. 168/72 were printed within the sheet, horizontally *se-tenant*.

(Des John Lister Ltd. Litho Questa)

1974 (30 Mar). *Easter. T* **49** *and similar vert designs showing various details of Raphael's "Crucifixion". P* 13½.

174 1 c. multicoloured 5 5
175 15 c. multicoloured 15 15
a. Vert strip of 5. Nos. 175/9 .. .. 1·50
176 20 c. multicoloured 20 20
177 25 c. multicoloured 25 25
178 40 c. multicoloured 40 40
179 $1 multicoloured 70 70
174/9 .. .. *Set of* 6 1·50 1·50
MS180 123 × 141 mm. Nos. 174/9 .. .. 1·75 2·10

Nos. 175/9 were printed vertically *se-tenant* within one sheet.

50 Churchill making "Victory" Sign

(Des John Lister Ltd. Litho Questa)

1974 (24 June). *Birth Centenary of Sir Winston Churchill. T* **50** *and similar horiz designs. Multicoloured. P* 13½.

181 1 c. Type **50** 5 5
182 20 c. Churchill with Roosevelt 35 35
a. Horiz strip of 5. Nos. 182/6 .. .. 2·50
183 25 c. Wartime broadcast 40 40
184 40 c. Birthplace, Blenheim Palace 50 50
185 60 c. Churchill's statue 60 60
186 $1.20, Country residence, Chartwell .. 85 85
181/6 .. .. *Set of* 6 2·50 2·50
MS187 195 × 96 mm. Nos. 181/6 .. .. .. 3·25 3·25

Nos. 182/6 were printed horizontally *se-tenant* within the sheet.

51 U.P.U. Emblem

(Des John Lister Ltd. Litho Questa)

1974 (27 Aug). *Centenary of Universal Postal Union. P* 13½*.

188 **51** 1 c. black and bright blue 5 5
189 20 c. black and pale orange 12 12
a. Horiz strip of 5. Nos. 189/93 .. 1·90
190 25 c. black and light yellow 15 15
191 40 c. black and bright mauve 30 30
192 60 c. black and light emerald 50 50
193 $1.20, black and light blue 90 90
188/93 .. .. *Set of* 6 1·90 1·90
MS194 195 × 96 mm. Nos. 188/93 .. .. 2·25 2·50

Nos. 189/93 were printed horizontally *se-tenant* within the sheet.

*In No. **MS**194 the lower row of three stamps, 40 c., 60 c. and $1.20 values, are line-perforated 15 at foot, the remaining 3 stamps being comb-perforated 13½.

52 Anguillan pointing to Star

53 "Mary, John and Mary Magdalene" (Matthias Grünewald)

(Litho Questa)

1974 (16 Dec). *Christmas. T* **52** *and similar horiz designs. Multicoloured. P* 14.

195 1 c. Type **52** 5 5
196 20 c. Child in Manger 20 20
a. Horiz strip of 5. Nos. 196/200 .. .. 2·00
197 25 c. King's offering 25 25
198 40 c. Star over Map of Anguilla 35 35
199 60 c. Family looking at star 45 45
200 $1.20, Angels of Peace 90 90
195/200 .. .. *Set of* 6 2·00 2·00
MS201 177 × 85 mm. Nos. 195/200 .. .. 2·75 3·00

Nos. 196/200 were printed horizontally *se-tenant* within the sheet.

(Litho Questa)

1975 (25 Mar). *Easter. T* **53** *and similar multicoloured designs showing details of the Isenheim altarpiece. P* 14.

202 1 c. Type **53** 5 5
203 10 c. "The Crucifixion" 10 10
a. Horiz strip of 5. Nos. 203/7 .. .. 1·90
204 15 c. "St. John the Baptist" 12 12
205 20 c. "St. Sebastian and Angels" 15 15
206 $1 "The Entombment" 70 70
207 $1.50, "St. Anthony the Hermit" .. .. 1·00 1·00
202/7 .. .. *Set of* 6 1·90 1·90
MS208 134 × 127 mm. Nos. 202/7. Imperf. .. 2·40 2·50

Nos. 203/7 were printed horizontally *se-tenant* within the sheet.

54 Statue of Liberty

55 "Madonna, Child and the Infant John the Baptist" (Raphael)

(Des John Lister Ltd. Litho Questa)

1975 (10 Nov). *Bicentenary of American Revolution. T* **54** *and similar horiz designs. Multicoloured. P* 13½*.

209 1 c. Type **54** 5 5
210 10 c. The Capitol 12 12
a. Horiz strip of 5. Nos. 210/14 .. .. 2·25
211 15 c. "Congress voting for Independence" (Pine and Savage) 15 15
212 20 c. Washington and map 20 20
213 $1 Boston Tea Party 75 75
214 $1.50, Bicentenary logo .. .. .. 1·25 1·25
209/14 .. .. *Set of* 6 2·25 2·25
MS215 198 × 97 mm. Nos. 209/14 .. .. 3·00 3·25

Nos. 210/14 were printed horizontally *se-tenant* within the sheet.

*In No. **MS**215 the lower row of three stamps, 20 c., $1 and $1.50 values, are line-perforated 15 at foot, the remaining 3 stamps being comb-perforated 13½.

(Des John Lister Ltd. Litho Questa)

1975 (8 Dec). *Christmas. T* **55** *and similar vert designs showing the "Madonna and Child". Multicoloured. P* 13½.

216 1 c. Type **55** 5 5
217 10 c. Cima 20 20
a. Horiz strip of 5. Nos. 217/21 .. .. 2·10
218 15 c. Dolci 30 30
219 20 c. Dürer 35 35
220 $1 Bellini 70 70
221 $1.50, Botticelli 80 80
216/21 .. .. *Set of* 6 2·10 2·10
MS222 130 × 145 mm. Nos. 216/21 .. .. 2·10 2·50

Nos. 217/21 were printed horizontally *se-tenant* within the sheet.

EXECUTIVE COUNCIL

NEW CONSTITUTION 1976

(56)

57 Almond

1976 (10 Feb–1 July). *New Constitution. Nos.* 130 *etc. optd with T* **56** *or surch also.*

223 1 c. Spear fishing 15 15
224 2 c. on 1 c. Spear fishing 15 15
225 2 c. Type **42** (1.7.76) .. .. .. 1·25 90
226 3 c. on 40 c. Boat building 15 20
a. "3 c" omitted .. ..
b. Typo. "3 c"* .. .. 2·50 3·00
227 4 c. Ferry at Blowing Point 15 20
228 5 c. on 40 c. Boat building 15 20
229 6 c. St. Mary's Church 15 20
230 10 c. on 20 c. Public Library 15 20
231 10 c. St. Gerard's Church (1.7.76) .. .. 1·50 1·00
232 15 c. Cottage Hospital extension 25 35
233 20 c. Public Library 25 35
234 25 c. Sunset at Blowing Point 25 35
235 40 c. Boat building 45 60
236 60 c. Hibiscus 70 70
237 $1 Magnificent Frigate Bird .. .. 2·00 2·00
238 $2.50, Frangipani .. .. 2·25 2·25
239 $5 Brown Pelican .. .. 4·25 6·00
240 $10 Green-back turtle .. .. .. 9·00 10·00
223/40 .. .. *Set of* 18 21·00 23·00

*No. 226a/b occur on R. 5/2, the "3 c" having been omitted during the normal litho surcharging.

(Des John Lister Ltd. Litho Questa)

1976 (16 Feb). *Flowering Trees. T* **57** *and similar horiz designs. Multicoloured. P* 13½.

241 1 c. Type **57** 5 5
242 10 c. Autograph 12 12
a. Horiz strip of 5. Nos. 242/6 .. .. 1·75
243 15 c. Calabash 15 15
244 20 c. Cordia 20 20
245 $1 Papaya 65 75
246 $1.50, Flamboyant 70 90
241/6 .. .. *Set of* 6 1·75 2·00
MS247 194 × 99 mm. Nos. 241/6 .. .. 2·00 2·50

Nos. 242/6 were printed horizontally *se-tenant* within the sheet.

58 The Three Marys

59 French Ships approaching Anguilla

(Litho Questa)

1976 (5 Apr). *Easter. T* **58** *and similar multicoloured designs showing portions of the Altar Frontal Tapestry, Rheinau. P* 13½.

248 1 c. Type **58** 5 5
249 10 c. The Crucifixion 8 8
a. Horiz strip of 5. Nos. 249/53 .. .. 2·00
250 15 c. Two Soldiers 12 12
251 20 c. The Annunciation 15 15
252 $1 The complete tapestry (*horiz*) 75 75
253 $1.50, The Risen Christ .. .. .. 1·10 1·10
248/53 .. .. *Set of* 6 2·00 2·00
MS254 138 × 130 mm. Nos. 248/53. Imperf .. 2·25 2·40

Nos. 249/53 were printed horizontally *se-tenant* within the sheet.

(Des John Lister Ltd. Litho Questa)

1976 (8 Nov). *Battle for Anguilla,* 1796. *T* **59** *and similar horiz designs. Multicoloured. P* 13½.

255 1 c. Type **59** 5 5
256 3 c. Sailing boat leaving Anguilla 35 35
a. Horiz strip of 5. Nos. 256/60 .. .. 3·75
257 15 c. Capture of *Le Desius* 55 55
258 25 c. *La Vaillante* forced aground 80 80
259 $1 H.M.S. *Lapwing* .. .. .. 1·25 1·25
260 $1.50, *Les Desius* burning .. .. .. 1·75 1·75
255/60 .. .. *Set of* 6 4·25 4·25
MS261 205 × 103 mm. Nos. 255/60 .. .. 5·50 6·00

Nos. 256/60 were printed horizontally *se-tenant* within the sheet.

60 "Christmas Carnival" (A. Richardson)

(Litho Questa)

1976 (22 Nov). *Christmas. T* **60** *and similar horiz designs showing children's paintings. Multicoloured. P* 13½.

262 1 c. Type **60** 5 5
263 3 c. "Dreams of Christmas Gifts" (J. Connor) 10 10
a. Horiz strip of 5. Nos. 263/7 .. .. 1·75
264 15 c. "Carolling" (P. Richardson) 15 15
265 25 c. "Candle-light Procession" (A. Mussington) 25 25
266 $1 "Going to Church" (B. Franklin) .. 60 60
267 $1.50, "Coming Home for Christmas" (E. Gumbs) 80 80
262/7 .. .. *Set of* 6 1·75 1·75
MS268 232 × 147 mm. Nos. 262/7 .. .. 1·75 2·25

Nos. 263/7 were printed horizontally *se-tenant* within the sheet.

NEW INFORMATION

The editor is always interested to correspond with people who have new information that will improve or correct the Catalogue.

61 Prince Charles and H.M.S. *Minerva*

(Des John Lister Ltd. Litho Questa)

1977 (9 Feb). *Silver Jubilee. T* **61** *and similar horiz designs. Multicoloured. P* 13½.

269 25 c. Type **61** 25 25
270 40 c. Prince Philip landing at Road Bay, 1964 30 30
271 $1.20, Coronation scene 65 65
272 $2.50, Coronation regalia and map of Anguilla .. .. 1·25 1·25
MS273 145 × 96 mm. Nos. 269/72 .. .. 2·50 2·75

62 Yellow-crowned Night Heron

(Des John Lister Ltd. Litho Questa)

1977 (18 Apr)–**78**. *T* **62** *and similar horiz designs. Multicoloured. P* 13½.

274 1 c. Type **62** 10 10
275 2 c. Great Barracuda 15 10
276 3 c. Queen Conch 15 10
277 4 c. Spanish Bayonet 15 15
278 5 c. Trunkfish 15 10
279 6 c. Cable and Wireless Building 15 10
280 10 c. American Kestrel (20.2.78) 35 25
281 15 c. Ground orchid (20.2.78) 50 45
282 20 c. Parrotfish (20.2.78) 50 35
283 22 c. Lobster fishing boat (20.2.78) 35 35
284 35 c. Boat race (20.2.78) 40 35
285 50 c. Sea Bean (20.2.78) 55 35
286 $1 Sandy Island (20.2.78) 60 45
287 $2.50, Manchineel (20.2.78) .. .. .. 1·00 1·00
288 $5 Ground Lizard (20.2.78) .. .. .. 2·00 1·75
289 $10 Red-billed Tropic Bird .. .. .. 5·00 4·25
274/89 .. .. *Set of* 16 11·00 9·25

63 "The Crucifixion" (Massys)

(Des John Lister Ltd. Litho Questa)

1977 (25 Apr). *Easter. T* **63** *and similar horiz designs showing paintings by Castagno* ($1.50) *or Ugolino (others). Multicoloured. P* 13½.

291 1 c. Type **63** 5 5
292 3 c. "The Betrayal" 15 15
a. Horiz strip of 5. Nos. 292/6 .. .. 1·75
293 22 c. "The Way to Calvary" 25 25
294 30 c. "The Deposition" 30 30
295 $1 "The Resurrection" 60 60
296 $1.50, "The Crucifixion" 75 75
291/6 .. .. *Set of* 6 1·75 1·75
MS297 192 × 126 mm. Nos. 291/6 .. .. 1·90 2·00

Nos. 292/6 were printed horizontally *se-tenant* within the sheet.

ROYAL VISIT
TO WEST INDIES

(64)

65 "Le Chapeau de Paille"

1977 (26 Oct). *Royal Visit. Nos.* 269/**MS**273 *optd with T* **64**.

298 25 c. Type **61** 25 25
299 40 c. Prince Philip landing at Road Bay, 1964 30 35
300 $1.20, Coronation scene 70 75
301 $2.50, Coronation regalia and map of Anguilla .. .. 1·25 1·40
MS302 145 × 96 mm. Nos. 298/301 .. .. 2·25 2·50

(Des John Lister Ltd. Litho Questa)

1977 (1 Nov). 400*th Birth Anniv of Rubens. T* **65** *and similar vert designs. Multicoloured. P* 13½.

303 25 c. Type **65** 12 15
304 40 c. "Hélène Fourment and her Two Children" 20 25

305 $1.20, "Rubens and his Wife" 70 80
306 $2.50, "Marchesa Brigida Spinola-Doria" .. 1·00 1·25
MS307 93 × 145 mm. Nos. 303/6 .. .. .. 2·25 2·50
Each value was issued in sheets of 5 stamps and 1 label.

5c

EASTER 1978

(66) (67)

1977 (14 Nov). *Christmas. Nos. 262/8 with old date blocked out and additionally inscr* "1977", *some surch also as T* **66**.
308 1 c. Type **60** 5 5
309 5 c. on 3 c. "Dreams of Christmas Gifts" .. 12 12
a. Horiz strip of 5. Nos. 309/13 .. .. 2·25
310 12 c. on 15 c. "Carolling" 15 15
311 18 c. on 25 c. "Candle-light Procession" .. 20 20
312 $1 "Going to Church" 60 60
313 $2.50 on $1.50, "Coming Home for Christmas" 1·40 1·40
308/13 .. .. *Set of* 6 2·25 2·25
MS314 232 × 147 mm. Nos. 308/13 .. .. 3·50 3·75

1978 (6 Mar). *Easter. Nos.* 303/7 *optd with T* **67**, *in gold.*
315 25 c. Type **65** 20 20
316 40 c. "Hélène Fourment and her Two Children" 30 30
317 $1.20, "Rubens and his Wife" 65 65
318 $2.50, "Marchesa Brigida Spinola-Doria" .. 1·00 1·25
MS319 93 × 145 mm. Nos. 315/18 .. .. .. 2·25 2·50

68 Coronation Coach at Admiralty Arch

VALLEY SECONDARY SCHOOL 1953-1978

(69)

ROAD METHODIST CHURCH 1878-1978

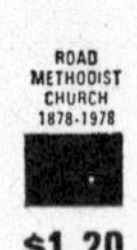

$1.20

(70)

(Des John Lister Ltd. Litho Questa)

1978 (6 Apr). *25th Anniv of Coronation. T* **68** *and similar horiz designs. Multicoloured. P* 14.
320 22 c. Buckingham Palace 20 20
321 50 c. Type **68** 30 30
322 $1.50, Balcony scene 60 70
323 $2.50, Royal coat of arms 80 90
MS324 138 × 92 mm. Nos. 320/3 .. .. .. 1·90 2·10

1978 (14 Aug). *Anniversaries. Nos.* 283/8 *optd as T* **69** *or surch as T* **70**.
325 22 c. Lobster fishing boat 20 20
a. Opt double £125
326 35 c. Boat race 30 30
327 50 c. Sea Bean 40 40
328 $1 Sandy Island 70 75
329 $1.20 on $5, Ground Lizard 85 90
330 $1.50 on $2.50, Manchineel .. .. .. 1·25 1·40
325/30 .. .. *Set of* 6 3·25 3·50
The 22, 35 c. and $1.50 values commemorate the 25th anniversary of Valley Secondary School; the other values commemorate the Centenary of Road Methodist Church.

71 Mother and Child

(Des and litho Questa)

1978 (11 Dec). *Christmas. Children's Paintings. T* **71** *and similar horiz designs. Multicoloured. P* 13½.
331 5 c. Type **71** 5 5
332 12 c. Christmas masquerade 5 5
333 18 c. Christmas dinner 10 10
334 22 c. Serenading 12 12
335 $1 Child in manger 45 45
336 $2.50, Family going to church .. .. 1·10 1·10
331/6 .. .. *Set of* 6 1·75 1·75
MS337 191 × 101 mm. Nos. 331/6 .. .. .. 1·90 2·00

1979 (15 Jan). *International Year of the Child. As Nos.* 331/7 *but additionally inscr with emblem and* "1979 INTERNATIONAL YEAR OF THE CHILD". *Borders in different colours.*
338 5 c. Type **71** 8 8
339 12 c. Christmas masquerade 10 10
340 18 c. Christmas dinner 15 15
341 22 c. Serenading 15 15
342 $1 Child in manger 60 60
343 $2.50, Family going to church .. .. 1·10 1·10
338/43 .. .. *Set of* 6 2·00 2·00
MS344 205 × 112 mm. Nos. 338/43 .. .. .. 2·25 2·50

12 CENTS

(72)

73 Valley Methodist Church

1979 (12 Feb). *Nos.* 274/7 *and* 279/80 *surch as T* **72**.
345 12 c. on 2 c. Great Barracuda 25 20
346 14 c. on 4 c. Spanish Bayonet 25 20
a. Surch inverted .. .. 70·00
347 18 c. on 3 c. Queen Conch 30 25
348 25 c. on 6 c. Cable and Wireless Building .. 35 30
349 38 c. on 10 c. American Kestrel 50 35
350 40 c. on 1 c. Type **62** 55 35
345/50 .. .. *Set of* 6 1·75 1·25

(Des John Lister Ltd. Litho Questa)

1979 (30 Mar). *Easter. Church Interiors. T* **73** *and similar horiz designs. Multicoloured. P* 14.
351 5 c. Type **73** 10 10
a. Horiz strip of 6. Nos. 351/6 .. .. 1·90
352 12 c. St. Mary's Anglican Church, The Valley 10 10
353 18 c. St. Gerard's Roman Catholic Church, The Valley 12 12
354 22 c. Road Methodist Church 15 15
355 $1.50, St. Augustine's Anglican Church, East End 70 70
356 $2.50, West End Methodist Church 95 95
351/6 .. .. *Set of* 6 1·90 1·90
MS357 190 × 105 mm. Nos. 351/6 .. .. .. 2·25 2·25
Nos. 351/6 were printed together horizontally *se-tenant*, within the sheet.

74 Cape of Good Hope 1d. "Woodblock" of 1881

(Des Stanley Gibbons Ltd. Litho Questa)

1979 (23 Apr). *Death Centenary of Sir Rowland Hill. T* **74** *and similar horiz designs showing stamps. Multicoloured. P* 14.
358 1 c. Type **74** 5 5
359 1 c. U.S.A. "inverted Jenny" of 1918 .. .. 5 5
360 22 c. Penny Black ("V.R. Official") 12 12
361 35 c. Germany 2 m. *Graf Zeppelin* of 1928 .. 20 20
362 $1.50, U.S.A. $5 Columbus of 1893 .. .. 60 60
363 $2.50, Great Britain £5 orange of 1882 .. 95 95
358/63 .. .. *Set of* 6 1·75 1·75
MS364 187 × 123 mm. Nos. 358/63 .. .. .. 2·00 2·10

75 Wright *Flyer I* (1st powered flight, 1903)

(Des John Lister Ltd. Litho Questa)

1979 (21 May). *History of Powered Flight. T* **75** *and similar horiz designs. Multicoloured. P* 14.
365 5 c. Type **75** 5 5
366 12 c. Louis Blériot at Dover after Channel crossing, 1909 .. .. 10 10
367 18 c. Vickers "Vimy" (1st non-stop crossing of Atlantic, 1919) 15 15
368 22 c. *Spirit of St. Louis* (1st solo Atlantic flight by Charles Lindbergh, 1927) 20 20
369 $1.50, "LZ 127" *Graf Zeppelin*, 1928 .. .. 70 70
370 $2.50, "Concorde", 1979 .. .. .. 1·10 1·10
365/70 .. .. *Set of* 6 2·10 2·10
MS371 200 × 113 mm. Nos. 365/70 .. .. .. 2·40 2·50

76 Sombrero Island

(Des John Lister Ltd. Litho Questa)

1979 (20 Aug). *Outer Islands. T* **76** *and similar horiz designs. Multicoloured. P* 14.
372 5 c. Type **76** 5 5
373 12 c. Anguillita Island 10 10
374 18 c. Sandy Island 15 15
375 25 c. Prickly Pear Cays 20 20
376 $1 Dog Island 60 60
377 $2.50, Scrub Island .. .. 1·00 1·00
372/7 .. .. *Set of* 6 1·90 2·00
MS378 180 × 91 mm. Nos. 372/7 .. .. .. 1·90 2·00

77 Red Poinsettia

(Des John Lister Ltd. Litho Format)

1979 (22 Oct). *Christmas. Flowers. T* **77** *and similar diamond-shaped designs. Multicoloured. P* 14½.
379 22 c. Type **77** 30 30
380 35 c. Kalanchoe 40 40
381 $1.50, Cream Poinsettia 80 80
382 $2.50, White Poinsettia .. .. .. 1·25 1·25
MS383 146 × 164 mm. Nos. 379/82 .. .. .. 3·00 3·25

78 Exhibition Scene

(Des R. Granger Barrett. Litho Format)

1979 (10 Dec). *"London 1980" International Stamp Exhibition (1st issue). T* **78** *and similar horiz designs. Multicoloured. A. P* 13 *(from sheets of* 20*). B. P* 14½ *(from booklets except* **MS**388B*)*

		A		B	
384	35 c. Type **78**	15	20	15	20
385	50 c. Earls Court Exhibition Centre	20	25	20	25
386	$1.50, Penny Black and Two-penny Blue stamps	55	60	55	60
387	$2.50, Exhibition logo	90	95	90	95
MS388	150 × 94 mm. Nos. 384/7	2·25	2·40	2·25	2·40

Nos. 384B/7B also exist from uncut booklet sheets of 10.
See also Nos. 407/10.

79 Games Site

(Des John Lister Ltd. Litho Format)

1980 (14 Jan). *Winter Olympic Games, Lake Placid, U.S.A. T* **79** *and similar horiz designs. Multicoloured. P* 13.
389 5 c. Type **79** 5 5
390 18 c. Ice-hockey 8 10
391 35 c. Ice-skating 15 20
392 50 c. Bobsleighing 20 25
393 $1 Skiing 40 45
394 $2.50, Luge-tobogganing 90 95
389/94 .. .. *Set of* 6 1·60 1·90
MS395 136 × 128 mm. Nos. 389/94 .. .. .. 1·90 2·00
Nos. 389/94 also exist perforated 14½ (*Price for set of 6 £1.60 mint, £1.90 used*) from additional sheetlets of 10. Stamps perforated 13 are from normal sheets of 40.

80 Salt ready for Reaping

50th Anniversary Scouting 1980

(81)

75th Anniversary Rotary 1980

(82)

(Des John Lister Ltd. Litho Questa)

1980 (14 Apr). *Salt Industry. T* **80** *and similar horiz designs. Multicoloured. P* 14.
396 5 c. Type **80** 5 5
397 12 c. Tallying salt 5 5
398 18 c. Unloading salt flats 5 5
399 22 c. Salt storage heap 10 10
400 $1 Salt for bagging and grinding 45 45
401 $2.50, Loading salt for export 95 95
396/401 .. .. *Set of* 6 1·50 1·50
MS402 180 × 92 mm. Nos. 396/401 .. .. .. 1·50 1·90
Nos. 396/7, 398/9 and 400/1 were each printed in the same sheet, but with the values in separate panes.

1980 (16 Apr). *Anniversaries. Nos.* 280, 282 *and* 287/8 *optd with T* **81** *(10 c., $2.50) or* **82** *(others).*
403 10 c. American Kestrel 10 10
404 20 c. Parrotfish 15 15
405 $2.50, Manchineel .. .. 1·00 1·00
406 $5 Ground Lizard .. .. 1·90 1·90
Commemorations:—10 c., $2.50, 50th anniversary of Anguilla Scout Movement; others, 75th anniversary of Rotary International.

83 Palace of Westminster and Great Britain 1970 9d. "Philympia" Commemorative

84 Queen Elizabeth the Queen Mother

(Des Stamp Magazine. Litho Rosenbaum Bros, Vienna)

1980 (6 May). *"London 1980" International Stamp Exhibition (2nd issue). T* **83** *and similar horiz designs showing famous landmarks and various international stamp exhibition commemorative stamps. Multicoloured. P* 13½.

407 50 c. Type **83** 20 25
408 $1.50, City Hall, Toronto and Canada 1978 $1.50, "CAPEX" 45 50
409 $2.50, Statue of Liberty and U.S.A. 1976 13 c. "Interphil" 75 85
MS410 157 × 130 mm. Nos. 407/9 .. .. .. 1·40 1·75

(Des R. Granger Barrett from photograph by N. Parkinson. Litho Rosenbaum Bros, Vienna)

1980 (4 Aug). *80th Birthday of Queen Elizabeth the Queen Mother. P* 13½.

411 **84** 35 c. multicoloured 15 20
412 50 c. multicoloured 20 25
413 $1.50, multicoloured 55 60
414 $3 multicoloured .. .. 1·25 1·40
MS415 160 × 110 mm. Nos. 411/14 .. .. .. 2·75 2·75

85 Brown Pelicans

SEPARATION 1980

(86)

(Des John Lister Ltd. Litho Questa)

1980 (13 Nov). *Christmas. Birds. T* **85** *and similar vert designs. Multicoloured. P* 13½.

416 5 c. Type **85** 10 10
417 22 c. Great Blue Heron 30 20
418 $1.50, Swallow 85 60
419 $3 Purple-throated Carib .. .. 1·50 1·40
MS420 126 × 160 mm. Nos. 416/19 .. .. .. 2·50 2·50

1980 (18 Dec). *Separation of Anguilla from St. Kitts-Nevis. Nos.* 274, 277, 279/89, 341 *and* 418/19 *optd as T* **86** *or surch also.*

421 1 c. Type **62** 5 5
422 2 c. on 4 c. Spanish Bayonet 10 10
423 5 c. on 15 c. Ground orchid 15 15
424 5 c. on $1.50, Swallow 15 15
425 5 c. on $3 Purple-throated Carib 15 15
426 10 c. American Kestrel 20 20
427 12 c. on $1 Sandy Island 20 20
428 14 c. on $2.50, Manchineel 20 20
429 15 c. Ground orchid 25 25
430 18 c. on $5 Ground Lizard 25 25
431 20 c. Parrotfish 25 25
432 22 c. Lobster fishing boat 25 25
433 25 c. on 15 c. Ground orchid 30 30
434 35 c. Boat race 30 30
435 38 c. on 22 c. Serenading 30 30
436 40 c. on 1 c. Type **62** 30 30
437 50 c. Sea Bean 35 35
438 $1 Sandy Island 50 50
439 $2.50, Manchineel .. .. 1·00 85
440 $5 Ground Lizard .. .. 2·25 1·75
441 $10 Red-billed Tropic Bird .. .. 5·00 3·75
442 $10 on 6 c. Cable and Wireless Building .. 5·00 3·75
421/42 .. .. *Set of* 22 16·00 13·00

87 First Petition for Separation, 1825

(Des John Lister Ltd. Litho Format)

1980 (18 Dec). *Separation of Anguilla from St. Kitts-Nevis. T* **87** *and similar horiz designs. Multicoloured. P* 14.

443 18 c. Type **87** 10 10
444 22 c. Referendum ballot paper, 1967 .. .. .. 12 12
445 35 c. Airport blockade, 1967 .. .. .. 20 20
446 50 c. Anguilla flag 25 25
447 $1 Separation celebrations, 1980 .. .. .. 45 45
MS448 178 × 92 mm. Nos. 443/7 .. .. .. 1·10 1·25

Nos. 443/4 and 445/6 were each printed in the same sheet with the two values in separate panes.

88 "Nelson's Dockyard" (R. Granger Barrett)

89 Minnie Mouse being chased by Bees

(Litho Rosenbaum Bros, Vienna)

1981 (2 Mar). *175th Death Anniv of Lord Nelson. Paintings. T* **88** *and similar horiz designs. Multicoloured. P* 14.

449 22 c. Type **88** 15 15
450 35 c. "Ships in which Nelson served" (Nicholas Pocock) 25 25
451 50 c. "H.M.S. *Victory*" (Monamy Swaine) .. 30 30
452 $3 "Battle of Trafalgar" (Clarkson Stanfield) 1·60 1·60
MS453 82 × 63 mm. $5 "Horatio Nelson" (L. F. Abbott) and coat of arms .. .. 2·75 2·75

(Litho Questa)

1981 (30 Mar). *Easter. Walt Disney Cartoon Characters. T* **89** *and similar vert designs. Multicoloured. P* 13½ × 14.

454 1 c. Type **89** 5 5
455 2 c. Pluto laughing at Mickey Mouse 5 5
456 3 c. Minnie Mouse tying ribbon round Pluto's neck 5 5
457 5 c. Minnie Mouse confronted by love-struck bird who fancies her bonnet 5 5
458 7 c. Dewey and Huey admiring themselves in mirror 5 5
459 9 c. Horace Horsecollar and Clarabelle Cow out for a stroll 5 5
460 10 c. Daisy Duck with hat full of Easter eggs 5 5
461 $2 Goofy unwrapping Easter hat .. .. 1·25 1·25
462 $3 Donald Duck in his Easter finery .. 1·60 1·60
454/62 .. .. *Set of* 9 2·75 2·75
MS463 134 × 108 mm. $5 Chip and Dale making off with hat .. .. 2·75 2·75

90 Prince Charles, Lady Diana Spencer and St. Paul's Cathedral

(Des R. Granger Barrett. Litho Rosenbaum Bros, Vienna)

1981 (15 June). *Royal Wedding. T* **90** *and similar horiz designs showing Prince Charles, Lady Diana Spencer and buildings. Multicoloured. P* 14. (a) *No wmk.*

464 50 c. Type **90** 35 35
465 $2.50, Althorp .. .. 1·25 1·25
466 $3 Windsor Castle .. .. 1·60 1·60
MS467 90 × 72 mm. $5 Buckingham Palace .. 2·75 3·00

(b) *Booklet stamps. W w* **15** *(sideways)*

468 50 c. Type **90** 30 35
a. Booklet pane of 4 .. .. 1·25
ab. Black ptg double .. .. 30·00
469 $3 As No. 466 .. .. 1·60 1·75
a. Booklet pane of 4 .. .. 6·00
ab. Black ptg double .. .. 35·00

Nos. 464/6 also exist from additional sheetlets of two stamps and one label with changed background colours (*Price for set of* 3 £6 *mint or used*).

Nos. 468/9 come from $14 stamp booklets.

Nos. 468ab and 469ab show the black features of the portraits strengthened by a further printing applied by typography. This is particularly visible on the Prince's suit and on the couple's hair.

91 Children playing in Tree

(Des Susan Csomer. Litho Rosenbaum Bros, Vienna)

1981 (31 July–30 Sept). *35th Anniv of U.N.I.C.E.F. T* **91** *and similar horiz designs. Multicoloured. P* 14.

470 5 c. Type **91** 5 5
471 10 c. Children playing by pool 5 5
472 15 c. Children playing musical instruments .. 10 10
473 $3 Children playing with pets (30 Sept) .. 1·60 1·60
MS474 78 × 106 mm. $4 Children playing football (*vert*) (30 Sept) .. .. 1·90 1·90

(Litho Questa)

1981 (2 Nov). *Christmas. Horiz designs as T* **89** *showing scenes from Walt Disney's cartoon film "The Night before Christmas". P* 13½.

475 1 c. multicoloured 5 5
476 2 c. multicoloured 5 5
477 3 c. multicoloured 5 5
478 5 c. multicoloured 5 5
479 7 c. multicoloured 5 5
480 10 c. multicoloured 5 5
481 12 c. multicoloured 5 5
482 $2 multicoloured .. .. 1·25 1·25
483 $3 multicoloured .. .. 1·60 1·60
475/83 .. .. *Set of* 9 2·75 2·75
MS484 130 × 105 mm. $5 multicoloured .. .. 2·75 2·75

92 Red Grouper

(93)

(Des R. Granger Barrett. Litho Questa)

1982 (1 Jan). *Horiz designs as T* **92**. *Multicoloured. P* 13½ × 14.

485 1 c. Type **92** 5 5
486 5 c. Ferry service, Blowing Point 5 5
487 10 c. Racing boats 5 5
488 15 c. Majorettes 8 5
489 20 c. Launching boat, Sandy Hill 10 10
490 25 c. Corals 12 12
491 30 c. Little Bay cliffs 15 15
492 35 c. Fountain Cave interior 35 35
493 40 c. Sunset over Sandy Island 20 20
494 45 c. Landing at Sombrero 25 30
495 60 c. Seine fishing 40 45
496 75 c. Boat race at sunset, Sandy Ground .. 40 45
497 $1 Bagging lobster at Island Harbour .. 55 60
498 $5 Brown Pelicans .. .. 3·25 3·50
499 $7.50, Hibiscus .. .. 4·50 4·75
500 $10 Queen Triggerfish .. .. 5·75 6·00
485/500 .. .. *Set of* 16 14·00 15·00

1982 (22 Mar). *No.* 494 *surch with T* **93**.

501 50 c. on 45 c. Landing at Sombrero 30 35

94 Anthurium and Zebra

95 Lady Diana Spencer in 1961

(Des R. Granger Barrett. Litho Questa)

1982 (5 Apr). *Easter. Flowers and Butterflies. T* **94** *and similar vert designs. Multicoloured. P* 14.

502 10 c. Type **94** 10 10
503 35 c. Bird of Paradise and Caribbean Buckeye 20 20
504 75 c. Allamanda and Monarch 40 40
505 $3 Orchid Tree and Red Rim .. .. 1·60 1·60
MS506 65 × 79 mm. $5 Amaryllis and Flambeau 2·75 2·75

(Des R. Granger Barrett. Litho C. Ueberreuter Security Printing, Vienna)

1982 (17 May–30 Aug). *21st Birthday of Princess of Wales. T* **95** *and similar vert designs. Multicoloured. P* 14.

507 10 c. Type **95** 10 10
a. Booklet pane of 4 (30 Aug) 40
508 30 c. Lady Diana Spencer in 1968 .. .. 20 20
509 40 c. Lady Diana in 1970 .. .. .. 25 25
a. Booklet pane of 4 (30 Aug) .. .. 1·00
510 60 c. Lady Diana in 1974 .. .. .. 35 35
a. Booklet pane of 4 (30 Aug) .. .. 1·40
511 $2 Lady Diana in 1981 .. .. .. 1·10 1·10
a. Booklet pane of 4 (30 Aug) .. .. 4·50
512 $3 Lady Diana in 1981 (*different*) .. 1·40 1·40
507/12 .. .. *Set of* 6 3·00 3·00
MS513 72 × 90 mm. $5 Princess of Wales .. .. 2·75 3·00
MS514 125 × 125 mm. As Nos. 507/12, but with buff borders .. .. 3·00 3·50

96 Pitching Tent

(Litho C. Ueberreuter Security Printing, Vienna)

1982 (5 July). *75th Anniv of Boy Scout Movement. T* **96** *and similar horiz designs. Multicoloured. P* 14.

515 10 c. Type **96** 10 10
516 35 c. Scout band 25 25
517 75 c. Yachting 45 45
518 $3 On parade .. .. 1·75 1·75
MS519 90 × 72 mm. $5 Cooking .. .. .. 2·75 2·75

(Litho Format)

1982 (3 Aug). *World Cup Football Championship, Spain. Horiz designs as T* **89** *showing scenes from Walt Disney's cartoon film "Bedknobs and Broomsticks". P* 11.

520 1 c. multicoloured 5 5
521 3 c. multicoloured 5 5

No.	Description		
522	4 c. multicoloured	5	5
523	5 c. multicoloured	5	5
524	7 c. multicoloured	5	5
525	9 c. multicoloured	5	5
526	10 c. multicoloured	5	5
527	$2.50 multicoloured	1·25	1·25
528	$3 multicoloured	1·50	1·50
520/8	*Set of* 9	2·75	2·75
MS529	126 × 101 mm. $5 multicoloured. P 14 × 13½	2·50	2·75

COMMONWEALTH
GAMES 1982

(97)

1982 (18 Oct). *Commonwealth Games, Brisbane. Nos.* 487, 495/6 *and* 498 *optd with T* **97**.

No.	Description		
530	10 c. Racing boats	10	10
	a. "S" omitted from "GAMES"	1·00	
531	60 c. Seine fishing	35	35
	a. "S" omitted from "GAMES"	2·00	
532	75 c. Boat race at sunset, Sandy Ground	45	45
	a. "S" omitted from "GAMES"	2·00	
533	$5 Brown Pelicans	2·75	2·75
	a. "S" omitted from "GAMES"	6·00	

The "S" omitted variety occurs on R.2/2 of the right-hand pane for all values.

(Litho Questa)

1982 (29 Nov). *Birth Centenary of A. A. Milne (author). Horiz designs as T* **89** *showing scenes from various "Winnie the Pooh" stories. P* 14 × 13½.

No.	Description		
534	1 c. multicoloured	5	5
535	2 c. multicoloured	5	5
536	3 c. multicoloured	5	5
537	5 c. multicoloured	5	5
538	7 c. multicoloured	5	5
539	10 c. multicoloured	10	10
540	12 c. multicoloured	10	10
541	20 c. multicoloured	15	15
542	$5 multicoloured	2·75	2·75
534/42	*Set of* 9	3·00	3·00
MS543	120 × 93 mm. $5 multicoloured	2·75	2·75

98 Culture

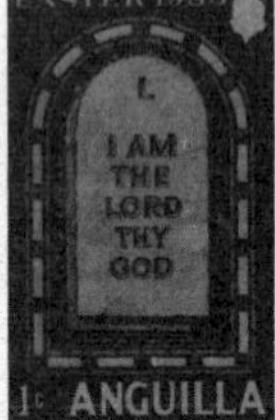

99 "I am the Lord Thy God"

(Des R. Granger Barrett. Litho Ueberreuter)

1983 (28 Feb). *Commonwealth Day. T* **98** *and similar horiz designs. Multicoloured. P* 14.

No.	Description		
544	10 c. Type **98**	10	10
545	35 c. Anguilla and British flags	30	30
546	75 c. Economic co-operation	60	50
547	$2.50, Salt industry (salt pond)	3·00	1·75
MS548	76 × 61 mm. $5 World map showing position of Commonwealth countries	4·00	3·00

(Litho Questa)

1983 (31 Mar). *Easter. The Ten Commandments. T* **99** *and similar vert designs. Multicoloured. P* 14.

No.	Description		
549	1 c. Type **99**	5	5
550	2 c. "Thou shalt not make any graven image"	5	5
551	3 c. "Thou shalt not take My Name in vain"	5	5
552	10 c. "Remember the Sabbath Day"	5	5
553	35 c. "Honour thy father and mother"	15	20
554	60 c. "Thou shalt not kill"	30	35
555	75 c. "Thou shalt not commit adultery"	35	40
556	$2 "Thou shalt not steal"	95	1·00
557	$2.50, "Thou shalt not bear false witness"	1·10	1·25
558	$5 "Thou shalt not covet"	2·50	2·50
549/58	*Set of* 10	5·25	5·50
MS559	126 × 102 mm. $5 "Moses receiving the Tablets" (16th-century woodcut)	2·50	2·50

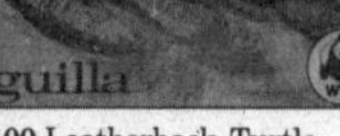

100 Leatherback Turtle

101 Montgolfier Hot Air Balloon, 1783

(Des R. Granger Barrett. Litho Questa)

1983 (10 Aug). *Turtles. T* **100** *and similar horiz designs. Multicoloured. A. P* 13½. *B. P* 12.

No.	Description	A		B	
560	10 c. Type **100**	5	10	10	15
561	35 c. Hawksbill Turtle	15	25	35	40
562	75 c. Green Turtle	35	40	65	70
563	$1 Loggerhead Turtle	50	60	80	85
MS564	93 × 72 mm. $5 Leatherback Turtle (*different*)	2·25	2·50	†	

(Des R. Granger Barrett. Litho Questa)

1983 (22 Aug). *Bicentenary of Manned Flight. T* **101** *and similar vert designs. Multicoloured. P* 13½.

No.	Description		
565	10 c. Type **101**	5	8
566	60 c. Blanchard and Jeffries crossing English Channel by balloon, 1785	30	35
567	$1 Henri Giffard's steam driven airship, 1852	45	50
568	$2.50, Otto Lilienthal and glider, 1890–96	1·10	1·25
MS569	72 × 90 mm. $5 Wilbur Wright flying round Statue of Liberty, 1909	2·50	2·75

102 Boys' Brigade Band and Flag

(Des R. Granger Barrett. Litho Questa)

1983 (12 Sept). *Centenary of Boys' Brigade. T* **102** *and similar horiz design. Multicoloured. P* 13½.

No.	Description		
570	10 c. Type **102**	5	8
571	$5 Brigade members marching	2·50	2·75
MS572	96 × 115 mm. Nos. 570/1	2·50	2·75

150TH ANNIVERSARY
ABOLITION OF SLAVERY ACT

(103)

1983 (24 Oct). *150th Anniv of the Abolition of Slavery. Nos.* 487, 493 *and* 497/8 *optd with T* **103**.

No.	Description		
573	10 c. Racing boats	5	8
	a. Opt inverted	35·00	
574	40 c. Sunset over Sandy Island	20	25
575	$1 Bagging lobster at Island Harbour	45	50
576	$5 Brown Pelicans	2·50	2·75

104 Jiminy on Clock (*Cricket on the Hearth*)

(Litho Format)

1983 (14 Nov). *Christmas. Walt Disney Cartoon Characters. T* **104** *and similar vert designs depicting scenes from Dickens' Christmas stories. Multicoloured. P* 13½.

No.	Description		
577	1 c. Type **104**	5	5
578	2 c. Jiminy with fiddle (*Cricket on the Hearth*)	5	5
579	3 c. Jiminy among toys (*Cricket on the Hearth*)	5	5
580	4 c. Mickey as Bob Cratchit (*A Christmas Carol*)	5	5
581	5 c. Donald Duck as Scrooge (*A Christmas Carol*)	5	5
582	6 c. Mini and Goofy in *The Chimes*	5	5
583	10 c. Goofy sees an imp appearing from bells (*The Chimes*)	5	8
584	$2 Donald Duck as Mr. Pickwick (*The Pickwick Papers*)	95	1·00
585	$3 Disney characters as Pickwickians (*The Pickwick Papers*)	1·40	1·50
577/85	*Set of* 9	2·40	2·75
MS586	130 × 104 mm. $5 Donald Duck as Mr. Pickwick with gifts (*The Pickwick Papers*)	2·50	2·75

105 100 Metres Race

(Litho Questa)

1984 (20 Feb–24 Apr). *Olympic Games, Los Angeles. T* **105** *and similar horiz designs showing Mickey Mouse in Decathlon events. Multicoloured. A. Inscr.* "1984 Los Angeles". *P* 14 × 13½. *B. Inscr.* "1984 Olympics Los Angeles" *and Olympic emblem. P* 14 × 13½ (**MS**596B) *or* 12 (*others*) (24 April).

No.	Description	A		B	
587	1 c. Type **105**	5	5	5	5
588	2 c. Long jumping	5	5	5	5
589	3 c. Shot-putting	5	5	5	5
590	4 c. High jumping	5	5	5	5
591	5 c. 400 metres race	5	5	5	5
592	6 c. Hurdling	5	5	5	5
593	10 c. Discus-throwing	5	5	5	5
594	$1 Pole-vaulting	45	50	45	50
595	$4 Javelin-throwing	1·90	2·00	1·90	2·00
587/95	*Set of* 9	2·50	2·75	2·50	2·75
MS596	117 × 93 mm. $5 1500 metres race	2·50	2·75	2·50	2·75

Nos. 587B/95B were each printed in small sheets of 6 stamps including one *se-tenant* stamp-size label in position 2.

106 "Justice"

35c

(107)

(Des and litho Questa)

1984 (19 Apr). *Easter. T* **106** *and similar vert designs showing details from "La Stanza della Segnatura" by Raphael. Multicoloured. P* 13½ × 14.

No.	Description		
597	10 c. Type **106**	8	10
598	25 c. "Poetry"	15	20
599	35 c. "Philosophy"	25	30
600	40 c. "Theology"	25	30
601	$1 "Abraham and Paul"	65	70
602	$2 "Moses and Matthew"	1·25	1·40
603	$3 "John and David"	2·00	2·10
604	$4 "Peter and Adam"	2·50	2·75
597/604	*Set of* 8	6·25	7·00
MS605	83 × 110 mm. $5 "Astronomy"	3·00	3·75

1984 (24 Apr–17 May). *Nos.* 485, 491 *and* 498/500 *surch as T* **107**.

No.	Description		
606	25 c. on $7.50, Hibiscus (17 May)	12	15
607	35 c. on 30 c. Little Bay cliffs	20	20
608	60 c. on 1 c. Type **92**	35	40
609	$2.50 on $5 Brown Pelicans	1·40	1·50
	a. Surch at left with decimal point*	18·00	
610	$2.50 on $10 Queen Triggerfish	1·40	1·50
	a. Surch at right without decimal point*	18·00	

*The surcharge on No. 609 shows the figures at right of the design and without a decimal point. On No. 610 they are to the left and include a decimal point. No 609a shows, in error, the surcharge for No. 610 and No. 610a that intended for No. 609.

108 Australia 1913 1d. Kangaroo Stamp

(Des K. Cato. Litho Leigh-Mardon Ltd, Melbourne)

1984 (16 July). *"Ausipex 84" International Stamp Exhibition, Melbourne. T* **108** *and similar horiz designs showing Australian stamps. Multicoloured. P* 13½ × 14.

No.	Description		
611	10 c. Type **108**	5	5
612	75 c. 1914 6d. Laughing Kookaburra	50	50
613	$1 1932 2d. Sydney Harbour Bridge	65	70
614	$2.50, 1938 10s. King George VI	1·75	2·00
MS615	95 × 86 mm. $5 £1 Bass and £2 Admiral King	3·50	3·75

109 Thomas Fowell Buxton

(Des R. Granger Barrett. Litho Questa)

1984 (1 Aug). *150th Anniv of Abolition of Slavery. T* **109** *and similar horiz designs. Multicoloured. P* 14.

No.	Description		
616	10 c. Type **109**	8	10
617	25 c. Abraham Lincoln	15	20
618	35 c. Henri Christophe	25	30
619	60 c. Thomas Clarkson	40	45
620	75 c. William Wilberforce	50	55
621	$1 Olaudah Equiano	65	70
622	$2.50, General Charles Gordon	1·75	2·00
623	$5 Granville Sharp	3·50	3·75
616/23	*Set of* 8	6·50	7·25
MS624	150 × 121 mm. Nos. 616/23. P 12	7·25	8·00

U.P.U. CONGRESS
HAMBURG 1984

(110)

PRINCE HENRY
BIRTH 15.9.84

(111)

1984 (13 Aug). *Universal Postal Union Congress, Hamburg. Nos. 486/7 and 498 optd as T* **110** *or surch also* (*No.* 626).
625 5 c. Ferry service, Blowing Point 5 5
626 20 c. on 10 c. Racing boats 12 15
627 $5 Brown Pelicans .. .. 3·50 3·75

1984 (31 Oct). *Birth of Prince Henry. Nos.* 507/14 *optd as T* **111**.
628 10 c. Type **95** 8 10
a. Booklet pane of 4 35
629 30 c. Lady Diana Spencer in 1968 .. .. 20 25
630 40 c. Lady Diana in 1970 .. .. .. 25 30
a. Booklet pane of 4 .. .. 1.00
631 60 c. Lady Diana in 1974 .. .. .. 40 45
a. Booklet pane of 4 .. .. 1.60
632 $2 Lady Diana in 1981 .. .. .. 1·25 1·40
a. Booklet pane of 4 .. .. 5.00
633 $3 Lady Diana in 1981 (*different*) .. .. 2·00 2·25
628/33 .. .. *Set of* 6 3·75 4·25
MS634 72 × 90 mm. $5 Princess of Wales .. .. 3·25 3·50
MS635 125 × 125 mm. As Nos. 628/33, but with buff borders .. .. 7·50 8·00

On No. **MS**634 the lines of overprint are larger, being placed vertically each side of the portrait.

Antigua

A branch office of the British G.P.O. was opened at St. John's, the capital, in 1850, to be followed by a second, at English Harbour, in 1857. Mail before 1850 was carried by packet or merchant ships often via Jamaica, and did not show local postal markings.

The stamps of Great Britain were used between May 1858 and March 1860, when the island postal service became the responsibility of the local colonial authorities. In the interim period, between the take-over and the appearance of Antiguan stamps, the crowned-circle handstamps were again utilised and can be found used as late as 1869.

For illustrations of the handstamp and postmark types see BRITISH POST OFFICES ABROAD notes, following GREAT BRITAIN.

ST. JOHN'S

CROWNED-CIRCLE HANDSTAMPS

CC1 CC **1** ANTIGUA (St. John's) (9.3.1850)(R.)
Price on cover £550

Stamps of GREAT BRITAIN *cancelled* "A 02" *as Type* **2**.

1858 *to* **1860**.
Z1 1d. rose-red (1857), *perf* 14 .. .. £375
Z2 2d. blue (1855), *perf* 14 (Plate 6) .. .. ..
Z3 2d. blue (1858) (Plate Nos. 7, 8, 9) £550
Z4 4d. rose (1857) £350
Z5 6d. lilac (1856) £160
Z6 1s. green (1856) £1400

ENGLISH HARBOUR

CROWNED-CIRCLE HANDSTAMPS

CC2 CC **3** ENGLISH HARBOUR (10.12.1857)
Price on cover £2250

Stamps of GREAT BRITAIN *cancelled* "A 18" *as Type* **2**.

1858 to **1860**.
Z7 6d. lilac £2000
Z8 1s. green (1856) .. ..

PRICES FOR STAMPS ON COVER TO 1945

No. 1	*from* × 4
Nos. 2/4	†
Nos. 5/30	*from* × 4
Nos. 31/51	*from* × 3
Nos. 52/4	*from* × 5
Nos. 55/61	*from* × 4
Nos. 62/80	*from* × 3
Nos. 81/90	*from* × 4
Nos. 91/4	*from* × 3
Nos. 95/7	*from* × 4
Nos. 98/109	*from* × 3

CROWN COLONY

1

3 (Die I)

(Des E. H. Corbould, probably eng C. H. Jeens. Recess P.B.)

1862 (Aug). *No wmk.* (*a*) *Rough perf* 14 *to* 16.
1 1 6d. blue-green £800 £500

(*b*) *P* 11 *to* 12½
2 1 6d. blue-green £3250

(*c*) *P* 14 *to* 16 × 11 *to* 12½
3 1 6d. blue-green £2250

(*d*) *P* 14 *to* 16 *compound with* 11 *to* 12½
4 1 6d. blue-green £2750

Nos. 2 to 4 have not been found used.

1863 (Jan)–**1867**. *Wmk Small Star. W w* **2**. *Rough perf* 14 *to* 16.
5 1 1d. rosy mauve .. .. 90·00 35·00
6 1d. dull rose (1864) .. .. .. 65·00 42·00
a. Imperf between (vert pair) £8000
7 1d. vermilion (1867) .. .. .. 50·00 32·00
a. Imperf between (pair) £8000
8 6d. green (*shades*) .. .. .. £225 32·00
9 6d. dark green .. .. .. £130 32·00
10 6d. yellow-green .. .. .. £2500 60·00

Caution is needed in buying No. 10 as some of the shades of No. 8 verge on yellow-green.

The 1d. rosy mauve exists perf compound of 11, 12 and 14 to 16. This is believed to be a trial perforation and it is not known used.

(Recess D.L.R. from P.B. plates)

1872. *Wmk Crown CC. P* 12½.
13 1 1d. lake .. .. 55·00 32·00
14 1d. scarlet .. .. 75·00 32·00
15 6d. blue-green .. .. £450 15·00

1876. *Wmk Crown CC. P* 14.
16 1 1d. lake .. .. 45·00 20·00
a. Bisected (½d.) (on cover) .. .. † £1100
17 1d. lake-rose .. .. 45·00 18·00
18 6d. blue-green .. .. £250 19·00

(Recess (T 1); typo (T 3) De La Rue & Co)

1879. *Wmk Crown CC. P* 14.
19 3 2½d. red-brown £450 £160
a. Large "2" in "2½" with slanting foot £5000 £1600
20 4d. blue .. .. £275 32·00

1882. *Wmk Crown CA. P* 14.
21 3 ½d. dull green .. .. 7·00 16·00
22 2½d. red-brown .. .. 90·00 35·00
a. Large "2" in "2½" with slanting foot £1300 £800
23 4d. blue .. .. £250 35·00

1884. *Wmk Crown CA. P* 12.
24 1 1d. carmine-red .. .. 27·00 24·00

The 1d. scarlet is a colour changeling.

1884–86. *Wmk Crown CA. P* 14.
25 1 1d. carmine-red .. .. .. 3·00 11·00
26 1d. rose .. .. 30·00 28·00
27 3 2½d. ultramarine .. .. 16·00 18·00
a. Large "2" in "2½" with slanting foot £160 £350
28 4d. chestnut .. .. 7·00 10·00
29 1 6d. deep green .. .. 38·00 £100
30 3 1s. mauve £200 £150
27/28, 30 Optd "Specimen" .. .. *Set of* 3 £130

Nos. 25 and 26 postmarked "A 12" in place of "A 02" were used in St. Christopher.

2½ 2½ 2½
A B C

The variety "Large '2' in '2½' with slanting foot" occurs on the first stamp of the seventh row in both left (A) and right (B) panes (in which positions the "NN" of "PENNY" have three vertical strokes shortened) and on the first stamp of the third row of the right-hand pane (C). The "2" varies slightly in each position.

From 31 October 1890 until 1903 Leeward Islands general issues were used. Subsequently both general issues and the following separate issues were in concurrent use, until 1 July 1956, when the general Leeward Island stamps were withdrawn.

4

5

(Typo D.L.R.)

1903–9. *T* **4** *and* **5** (5s.). *Wmk Crown CC. P* 14.
31 ½d. grey-black and grey-green, **O** .. .. 2·75 5·00
32 1d. grey-black and rose-red, **O** .. .. 5·50 1·75
a. Blue paper (1909) .. .. .. 60·00 60·00
33 2d. dull purple and brown, **O** .. .. 12·00 23·00
34 2½d. grey-black and blue, **OC** .. .. 14·00 18·00
35 3d. grey-green and orange-brown, **O** .. 17·00 26·00
36 6d. purple and black, **O** .. .. 28·00 32·00
37 1s. blue and dull purple, **OC** .. .. 28·00 29·00
38 2s. grey-green and pale violet, **O** .. 30·00 38·00
39 2s. 6d. grey-black and purple, **O** .. 28·00 32·00
40 5s. grey-green and violet, **OC** .. .. 80·00 80·00
31/40 .. .. *Set of* 10 £200 £250
31/40 Optd "Specimen" .. .. *Set of* 10 £180

1908–17. *T* **4**. *Wmk Mult Crown CA. P* 14.
41 ½d. green, **O** .. .. 1·50 3·25
42 ½d. blue-green, **O** (1917) .. .. 2·00 3·75
43 1d. red, **O** .. .. 3·50 2·00
44 1d. scarlet, **O** (5.8.15) .. .. 3·50 3·50
45 2d. dull purple and brown, **C** (1912) .. 6·50 10·00
46 2½d. ultramarine, **O** .. .. .. 9·00 13·00
a. Blue, **O** .. .. 13·00 20·00
47 3d. grey-green and orange-brown, **C** (1912) 11·00 18·00
48 6d. purple and black, **C** (1911) .. .. 16·00 25·00
49 1s. blue and dull purple, **C** .. .. 17·00 27·00
50 2s. grey-green and violet, **C** (1912) .. 42·00 55·00
41/50 .. .. *Set of* 8 £100 £140
41, 43, 46 Optd "Specimen" .. .. *Set of* 3 65·00

1913. *As T* **5**, *but portrait of King George V. Wmk Mult Crown CA. P* 14.
51 5s. grey-green and violet, **C** (Optd S. £80) 60·00 75·00

WAR STAMP
(7)

8

1916 (Sept)–**17**. *No.* 41 *optd in London with T* **7**.
52 4 ½d. deep green (Bk.) .. .. .. 50 1·10
53 ½d. green (R.) (1.10.17) .. .. .. 50 1·10

1918. *Optd with T* **7**. *Wmk Mult Crown CA. P* 14.
54 4 1½d. orange 35 90
52/4 Optd "Specimen" .. .. *Set of* 3 80·00

(Typo D.L.R.)

1921–29. *T* **8**. *P* 14. (*a*) *Wmk Mult Crown CA*.
55 3d. purple/*pale yellow*, **C** .. .. 4·50 10·00
56 4d. grey-black & red/*pale yellow*, **C** (Jan 1922) 4·50 10·00
57 1s. black/*emerald*, **C** .. .. .. 6·00 10·00
58 2s. purple and blue/*blue*, **C** .. .. 9·00 14·00
59 2s. 6d. black and red/*blue*, **C** .. .. 12·00 18·00

60		5s. green and red/*pale yellow*, C (Jan, 1922)	17·00	30·00
61		£1 purple and black/*red*, C (1922)	£225	£300
55/61		*Set of* 7	£250	£350
55/61 Optd "Specimen"		*Set of* 7	£325	

(*b*) *Wmk Mult Script CA*

62		½d. dull green, O	45	65
63		1d. carmine-red, O	1·40	45
64		1d. bright scarlet, O (1929)	90	70
65		1d. bright violet, O	2·50	3·50
66		1d. mauve, O	4·75	4·75
67		1½d. dull orange, O (1922)	5·00	9·50
68		1½d. carmine-red, O (1926)	1·25	2·50
69		1½d. pale red-brown, O (1929)	2·25	2·75
70		2d. grey, O	1·50	2·25
		a. Wmk sideways		
71		2½d. bright blue, O	9·00	13·00
72		2½d. ultramarine, O (1927)	6·50	7·50
73		2½d. orange-yellow, O	2·25	9·50
74		3d. purple/*pale yellow*, C (1925)	5·00	9·50
75		6d. dull and bright purple, C	3·50	7·50
76		1s. black/*emerald*, C (1929)	8·00	19·00
77		2s. purple and blue/*blue*, C (1927)	16·00	25·00
78		2s. 6d. black and red/*blue*, C (1927)	17·00	25·00
79		3s. green and violet, C (1922)	28·00	45·00
80		4s. grey-black and red, C (1922)	50·00	60·00
62/80		*Set of* 16	£150	£225
62/80 Optd/Perf "Specimen"		*Set of* 18	£250	

9 Old Dockyard, English Harbour

10 Government House, St. John's

(Des Mrs. J. Goodwin (5s.), Waterlow (others). Recess Waterlow)

1932 (27 Jan). *Tercentenary. T* **9/10** *and similar designs. Wmk Mult Script CA. P* 12½.

81	**9**	½d. green	1·40	2·50
82		1d. scarlet	1·75	2·00
83		1½d. brown	3·00	3·75
84	**10**	2d. grey	8·00	13·00
85		2½d. deep blue	8·00	13·00
86		3d. orange	10·00	18·00
87	–	6d. violet	18·00	23·00
88	–	1s. olive-green	30·00	40·00
89	–	2s. 6d. claret	75·00	95·00
90	–	5s. black and chocolate	£150	£180
81/90		*Set of* 10	£275	£350
81/90 Perf "Specimen"		*Set of* 10	£400	

Designs: *Horiz*—6d., 1s., 2s. 6d. Nelson's *Victory*. *Vert*—5s. Sir Thomas Warner's vessel.

13 Windsor Castle

(Des H. Fleury. Recess D.L.R.)

1935 (6 May). *Silver Jubilee. Wmk Mult Script CA. P* 13½ × 14.

91	**13**	1d. deep blue and carmine	1·75	2·00
		e. Horiz line from turret	17·00	
92		1½d. ultramarine and grey	2·50	2·25
93		2½d. brown and deep blue	5·50	8·50
94		1s. slate and purple	18·00	22·00
91/4 Perf "Specimen"		*Set of* 4	45·00	

For illustration of plate variety see Omnibus section following Zululand.

1937 (12 May). *Coronation. As Nos.* 13/15 *of Aden, but ptd by B.W. P* 11 × 11½.

95		1d. carmine	50	45
96		1½d. yellow-brown	60	55
97		2½d. blue	1·75	1·75
95/7 Perf "Specimen"		*Set of* 3	42·00	

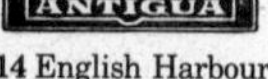

14 English Harbour

16 Nelson's Dockyard

(Recess Waterlow)

1938 (15 Nov)–**51**. *T* **14, 16** *and similar designs. Wmk Mult Script CA. P* 12½.

98	**14**	½d. green	25	35
99	**16**	1d. scarlet	70	60
		a. Red (8.42 and 11.47)	40	35
100		1½d. chocolate-brown	1·25	1·00
		a. Dull reddish brown (12.43)	60	75
		b. Lake-brown (7.49)	11·00	12·00
101	**14**	2d. grey	70	25
		a. Slate-grey (6.51)	1·25	1·25
102	**16**	2½d. deep ultramarine	40	40
103	–	3d. orange	40	40
104	–	6d. violet	50	40
105	–	1s. black and brown	1·50	75
		a. Black and red-brown (7.49)	12·00	9·50
		ab. Frame ptd double, once albino	£1200	
106	–	2s. 6d. brown-purple	12·00	6·00
		a. Maroon (8.42)	10·00	4·50
107	–	5s. olive-green	11·00	9·00
108	**16**	10s. magenta (April 1948)	25·00	30·00
109	–	£1 slate-green (April 1948)	35·00	42·00
98/109		*Set of* 12	75·00	80·00
98/109 Perf "Specimen"		*Set of* 12	£200	

Designs: *Horiz*—3d., 2s. 6d., £1 Fort James. *Vert*—6d., 1s., 5s. St. John's Harbour.

1946 (1 Nov). *Victory. As Nos.* 28/9 *of Aden.*

110		1½d. brown	25	30
111		3d. red-orange	25	30
110/111 Perf "Specimen"		*Set of* 2	32·00	

1949 (3 Jan). *Royal Silver Wedding. As Nos.* 30/1 *of Aden.*

112		2½d. ultramarine	20	30
113		5s. grey-olive	8·00	14·00

18 Hermes, Globe and Forms of Transport

19 Hemispheres, Aeroplane and Steamer

20 Hermes and Globe

21 U.P.U. Monument

(Recess, Waterlow (T **18, 21**). Design recess, name typo, B.W. (T **19, 20**))

1949 (10 Oct). *75th Anniv of Universal Postal Union. Wmk Mult Script CA.*

114	**18**	2½d. ultramarine (*p* 13½–14)	40	60
115	**19**	3d. orange (*p* 11 × 11½)	1·75	1·75
116	**20**	6d. purple (*p* 11 × 11½)	2·00	2·00
117	**21**	1s. red-brown (*p* 13½–14)	2·00	2·25

(New Currency. 100 cents = 1 dollar)

22 Arms of University

23 Princess Alice

(Recess Waterlow)

1951 (16 Feb). *Inauguration of B.W.I. University College. Wmk Mult Script CA. P* 14 × 14½.

118	**22**	3 c. black and brown	50	60
119	**23**	12 c. black and violet	70	80

1953 (2 June). *Coronation. As No.* 47 *of Aden.*

120		2 c. black and deep yellow-green	20	45

ALTERED CATALOGUE NUMBERS

Any Catalogue numbers altered from the last edition are shown as a list in the introductory pages.

24 Martello Tower

25 Federation Map

(Recess Waterlow until 1961, then D.L.R.)

1953 (2 Nov)–**61**. *Designs previously used for King George VI issue, but with portrait of Queen Elizabeth II, as in T* **24**. *Wmk Mult Script CA. P* 13 × 13½ (*horiz*) *or* 13½ × 13 (*vert*).

120*a*	–	½ c. brown (3.7.56)	5	20
121	–	1 c. slate-grey	10	15
		a. Slate (7.11.61)	20	20
122	–	2 c. green	10	5
123	–	3 c. black and orange-yellow	12	15
		a. Black and yellow-orange (5.12.61)	35	40
124	–	4 c. scarlet (*shades*)	12	10
125	–	5 c. black and slate-lilac	20	5
126	–	6 c. yellow-ochre (*shades*)	25	15
127	**24**	8 c. deep blue	35	10
128	–	12 c. violet	35	5
129	–	24 c. black and chocolate	60	15
130	**24**	48 c. purple and deep blue	2·50	1·50
131	–	60 c. maroon	3·50	1·75
132	–	$1.20, olive-green (*shades*)	3·25	2·25
133	–	$2.40, bright reddish purple	12·00	16·00
134	–	$4.80, slate-blue	17·00	24·00
120*a*/134		*Set of* 15	35·00	42·00

Designs: *Horiz*—½ c., 6 c., 60 c., $4.80, Fort James; 2 c., 3 c., 5 c., $2.40, Nelson's Dockyard. *Vert*—1 c., 4 c., English Harbour; 12 c., 24 c., $1.20, St. John's Harbour.

See also Nos. 149/58.

(Recess B.W.)

1958 (22 Apr). *Inauguration of British Caribbean Federation.* W w **12**. *P* 11½ × 11.

135	**25**	3 c. deep green	40	25
136		6 c. blue	75	70
137		12 c. scarlet	80	40

MINISTERIAL GOVERNMENT

COMMEMORATION
ANTIGUA
CONSTITUTION
1960

(26)

27 Nelson's Dockyard and Admiral Nelson

1960 (1 Jan). *New Constitution. Nos.* 123 *and* 128 *optd with T* **26**.

138		3 c. black and orange-yellow (R.)	15	20
139		12 c. violet	15	10

(Recess B.W.)

1961 (14 Nov). *Restoration of Nelson's Dockyard.* W w **12**. *P* 11½ × 11.

140	**27**	20 c. purple and brown	35	25
141		30 c. green and blue	40	40

28 Stamp of 1862 and R.M.S.P. *Solent* at English Harbour

(Des A. W. Morley. Recess B.W.)

1962 (1 Aug). *Stamp Centenary.* W w **12**. *P* 13½.

142	**28**	3 c. purple and deep green	12	5
143		10 c. blue and deep green	30	20
144		12 c. deep sepia and deep green	30	10
145		50 c. orange-brown and deep green	90	90

1963 (4 June). *Freedom from Hunger. As No.* 76 *of Aden.*

146		12 c. bluish green	45	50

29 Red Cross Emblem

(Des V. Whiteley. Litho B.W.)

1963 (2 Sept). *Red Cross Centenary.* W w **12**. *P* 13½.

147		3 c. red and black	60	50
148		12 c. red and blue	1·10	90

(Recess D.L.R.)

1963 (16 Sept)–**65**. *As* 1953—61 *but wmk* w **12**.

149	–	½ c. brown (13.4.65)	25	60
150	–	1 c. slate (13.4.65)	80	90
151	–	2 c. green	10	10
152	–	3 c. black and yellow-orange	12	12
153	–	4 c. brown-red	15	10

154 – 5 c. black and slate-lilac (*shades*) .. 15 5
155 – 6 c. yellow-ochre 30 30
156 **24** 8 c. deep blue 40 25
157 – 12 c. violet 50 25
158 – 24 c. black and deep chocolate (*shades*) 1·50 1·25
149/158 .. .. *Set of* 10 3·75 3·50

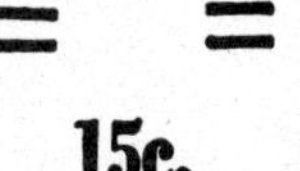

30 Shakespeare and Memorial Theatre, Stratford-upon-Avon

(**31**)

(Des R. Granger Barrett. Photo Harrison)

1964 (23 April). *400th Birth Anniv of William Shakespeare.* W w **12.** *P* 14 × 14½.
164 **30** 12 c. orange-brown 25 20

1965 (1 April). *No.* 157 *surch with T* **31.**
165 15 c. on 12 c. violet 15 15

32 I.T.U. Emblem

(Des M. Goaman. Litho Enschedé)

1965 (17 May). *I.T.U. Centenary.* W w **12.** *P* 11 × 11½.
166 **32** 2 c. light blue and light red 20 15
167 50 c. orange-yellow and ultramarine .. 2·50 1·75

33 I.C.Y. Emblem

(Des V. Whiteley. Litho Harrison)

1965 (25 Oct). *International Co-operation Year.* W w **12.** *P* 14½.
168 **33** 4 c. reddish purple and turquoise-green 20 15
169 15 c. deep bluish green and lavender .. 50 45

34 Sir Winston Churchill, and St. Paul's Cathedral in Wartime

(Des Jennifer Toombs. Photo Harrison)

1966 (24 Jan). *Churchill Commemoration. Printed in black, cerise and gold and with background in colours stated.* W w **12.** *P* 14.
170 **34** ½ c. new blue 5 5
171 4 c. deep green 50 30
172 25 c. brown .. .. 1·50 85
173 35 c. bluish violet .. .. 1·75 1·25

35 Queen Elizabeth II and Duke of Edinburgh

(Des H. Baxter. Litho B.W.)

1966 (4 Feb). *Royal Visit.* W w **12.** *P* 11 × 12.
174 **35** 6 c. black and ultramarine .. .. 1·75 1·25
175 15 c. black and magenta .. .. .. 2·00 1·25

36 Footballer's Legs, Ball and Jules Rimet Cup

(Des V. Whiteley. Litho Harrison)

1966 (1 July). *World Football Cup Championships.* W w **12** (*sideways*). *P* 14.
176 **36** 6 c. violet, yellow-green, lake & yell-brn 15 15
177 35 c. chocolate, blue-grn, lake & yell-brn 80 70

37 W.H.O. Building

(Des M. Goaman. Litho Harrison)

1966 (20 Sept). *Inauguration of W.H.O. Headquarters, Geneva.* W w **12** (*sideways*). *P* 14.
178 **37** 2 c. black, yellow-green and light blue 15 12
179 15 c. black, light purple and yellow-brown 90 70

38 Nelson's Dockyard

(Des, eng and recess B.W.)

1966 (1 Nov). *Horiz designs as T* **38.** W w **12.** *P* 11½ × 11.
180 ½ c. green and turquoise-blue 10 12
181 1 c. purple and cerise 10 10
182 2 c. slate-blue and yellow-orange 10 12
183 3 c. rose-red and black 10 12
184 4 c. slate-violet and brown 15 10
185 5 c. ultramarine and yellow-olive 12 5
186 6 c. salmon and purple 15 15
187 10 c. emerald and rose-red 20 10
188 15 c. brown and new blue 35 25
189 25 c. slate-blue and sepia 55 40
190 35 c. cerise and blackish brown .. .. 1·50 70
191 50 c. dull green and black .. .. .. 1·50 2·00
192 75 c. greenish blue and ultramarine .. .. 1·75 2·50
193 $1 cerise and yellow-olive (*shades*) .. .. 3·00 3·25
194 $2.50, black and cerise .. .. .. 3·50 6·00
195 $5 olive-green and slate-violet .. .. 7·50 9·50
180/195 .. .. *Set of* 16 19·00 23·00

Designs:—1 c. Old Post Office, St. John's; 2 c. Health Centre; 3 c. Teachers' Training College; 4 c. Martello Tower, Barbuda; 5 c. Ruins of Officers' Quarters, Shirley Heights; 6 c. Government House, Barbuda; 10 c. Princess Margaret School; 15 c. Air Terminal building; 25 c. General Post Office; 35 c. Clarence House; 50 c. Government House, St. John's; 75 c. Administration Building; $1, Courthouse, St. John's; $2.50, Magistrates' Court; $5, St. John's Cathedral.

See also Nos. 234/48.

54 "Education"

55 "Science"

56 "Culture"

(Des Jennifer Toombs. Litho Harrison)

1966 (1 Dec). *20th Anniv of U.N.E.S.C.O.* W w **12** (*sideways*). *P* 14.
196 **54** 4 c. slate-violet, red, yellow and orange 15 12
197 **55** 25 c. orange-yellow, violet and deep olive 45 30
198 **56** $1 black, bright purple and orange 3·50 3·25

NEW INFORMATION

The editor is always interested to correspond with people who have new information that will improve or correct the Catalogue.

ASSOCIATED STATEHOOD

57 State Flag and Maps

(Des W. D. Cribbs. Photo Harrison)

1967 (27 Feb). *Statehood. T* **57** *and similar horiz designs. Multicoloured.* W w **12** (*sideways*). *P* 14.
199 4 c. Type **57** 5 5
200 15 c. State Flag 10 5
201 25 c. Premier's Office and State Flag 15 15
202 35 c. As 15 c. 20 25

60 Gilbert Memorial Church

(Des G. Drummond (from sketches by W. D. Cribbs). Photo Harrison)

1967 (14 Dec). *300th Anniv of Barbuda Settlement. T* **64** *and similar horiz design.* W w **12.** *P* 11½ × 11.
208 **64** 4 c. deep ultramarine 10 5
209 – 6 c. purple 15 20
210 **64** 25 c. emerald 20 15
211 – 35 c. black 20 25
Design:—6, 35 c. Blaeu's map of 1665.

63 Coat of Arms

64 Settlers' Ship

(Des V. Whiteley (from sketches by W. D. Cribbs). Photo Harrison)

1967 (21 July). *300th Anniv of Treaty of Breda and Grant of New Arms.* W w **12** (*sideways*). *P* 14½ × 14.
206 **63** 15 c. multicoloured 12 10
207 35 c. multicoloured 20 15

(Des and recess B.W.)

1967 (14 Dec). *300th Anniv of Barbuda Settlement. T* **64** *and similar horiz design.* W w **12.** *P* 11½ × 11.
208 **64** 4 c. deep ultramarine 10 5
209 – 6 c. purple 15 20
210 **64** 25 c. emerald 20 15
211 – 35 c. black 20 25
Design:—6, 35 c. Blaeu's map of 1665.

66 Tracking Station

70 Limbo-dancing

(Des G. Vasarhelyi. Photo Harrison)

1968 (29 Mar). *N.A.S.A. Apollo Project. Inauguration of Dow Hill Tracking Station. T* **66** *and similar vert designs in deep blue, orange-yellow and black.* W w **12** (*sideways*). *P* 14½ × 14.
212 4 c. Type **66** 5 5
213 15 c. Antenna and spacecraft taking off .. 12 10
214 25 c. Spacecraft approaching Moon 15 10
215 50 c. Re-entry of space capsule 30 40

(Des and photo Harrison)

1968 (1 July). *Tourism. T* **70** *and similar horiz designs. Multicoloured.* W w **12.** *P* 14½ × 14.
216 ½ c. Type **70** 5 5
217 15 c. Water-skiing and bathers 15 10
218 25 c. Yachts and beach 25 35
219 35 c. Underwater swimming 30 35
220 50 c. Type **70** 50 60

74 Old Harbour in 1768

(Des R. Granger Barrett. Recess B.W.)

1968 (31 Oct). *Opening of St. John's Deep Water Harbour. T* **74** *and similar horiz designs. W* w **12.** *P* 13.

No.	Description		Unused	Used
221	2 c. light blue and carmine	..	5	5
222	15 c. light yellow-green and sepia	..	25	15
223	25 c. olive-yellow and blue	..	30	30
224	35 c. salmon and emerald	..	35	35
225	$1 black	..	80	90

Designs:—15 c. Old Harbour in 1829; 25 c. Freighter and chart of New Harbour; 35 c. New Harbour, 1968; $1, Type **74**.

78 Parliament Buildings

(Des R. Granger Barrett. Photo Harrison)

1969 (3 Feb). *Tercentenary of Parliament. T* **78** *and similar square designs. Multicoloured. W* w **12** *(sideways). P* 12½.

No.	Description		Unused	Used
226	4 c. Type **78**	..	8	8
227	15 c. Antigua Mace and bearer	..	15	12
228	25 c. House of Representatives' Room	..	20	15
229	50 c. Coat of arms and Seal of Antigua	..	45	60

82 Freight Transport

(Des Jennifer Toombs. Litho D.L.R.)

1969 (14 Apr). *1st Anniv of CARIFTA (Caribbean Free Trade Area). T* **82** *and similar design. W* w **12** *(sideways on 4 c., 15 c). P* 13.

No.	Description		Unused	Used
230	4 c. black and reddish purple	..	5	5
231	15 c. black and turquoise-blue	..	12	10
232	25 c. chocolate, black and yellow-ochre	..	20	15
233	35 c. chocolate, black and yellow-brown	..	35	35

Designs: *Horiz*—4, 15 c. Type **82**. *Vert*—25, 35 c. Crate of cargo.

1969–70. *As Nos.* 180/91 *and* 193/5 *but perf* 13½.
A. *Ordinary paper* (24.6.69).
B. *Glazed paper* (30.9.69 *or* 6.4.70 (4 *c.*))

No.	Description	A		B	
234	½ c. green and turquoise-blue ..	5	5	†	
235	1 c. purple and cerise ..	10	10	15	15
236	2 c. slate-blue & yellow-orange	12	12	15	15
237	3 c. rose-red and black ..	15	15	†	
238	4 c. slate-violet and brown ..	20	20	8·50	9·00
239	5 c. ultramarine & yellow-olive	25	25	25	25
240	6 c. salmon and purple ..	35	35	†	
241	10 c. emerald and rose-red ..	40	40	45	45
242	15 c. brown and new blue ..	†		65	70
243	25 c. slate-blue and sepia ..	†		60	75
244	35 c. cerise & blackish brown ..	†		70	1·00
245	50 c. dull green and black ..	†		90	1·60
246	$1 cerise and yellow-olive ..	†		2·75	3·75
247	$2.50, black and cerise ..	†		5·00	9·00
248	$5 olive-green & slate-violet ..	†		18·00	26·00
234/41A	*Set of* 8	1·50	1·50	†	
235/48B	*Set of* 12	†		35·00	48·00

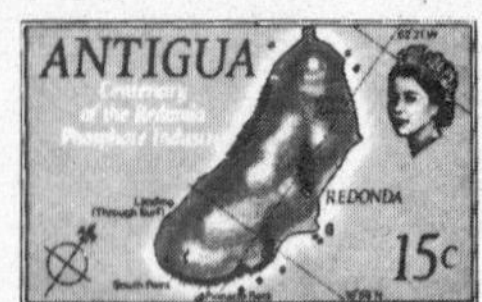

84 Island of Redonda (Chart)

(Des R. Granger Barrett. Photo Enschedé)

1969 (1 Aug). *Centenary of Redonda Phosphate Industry. T* **84** *and similar horiz design. W* w **12** *(sideways). P* 13 × 13½.

No.	Description		Unused	Used
249	15 c. Type **84**	..	25	15
250	25 c. Redonda from the sea	..	35	20
251	50 c. Type **84**	..	1·10	80

ALTERED CATALOGUE NUMBERS

Any Catalogue numbers altered from the last edition are shown as a list in the introductory pages.

86 "The Adoration of the Magi" (Marcillat)

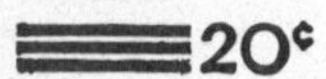

(88)

(Des adapted by V. Whiteley. Litho Enschedé)

1969 (15 Oct). *Christmas. Stained-glass Windows. T* **86** *and similar vert design. Multicoloured. W* w **12** *(sideways). P* 13 × 14.

No.	Description		Unused	Used
252	6 c. Type **86**	..	12	12
253	10 c. "The Nativity" (unknown German artist, 15th-century)	..	15	20
254	35 c. Type **86**	..	40	50
255	50 c. As 10 c.	..	50	60

1970 (2 Jan). *No.* 189 *surch with T* **88**.

No.	Description		Unused	Used
256	20 c. on 25 c. slate-blue and sepia	..	15	20

89 Coat of Arms

90 Sikorsky "S–38"

(Des and photo Harrison)

1970–73. *Coil Stamps. W* w **12.** *P* 14½ × 14.
A. *Chalk-surfaced paper. Wmk upright* (30.1.70).
B. *Glazed paper. Wmk sideways* (8.3.73).

No.	Type	Description	A.		B.	
257	**89**	5 c. blue ..	10	12	5	5
258		10 c. emerald ..	15	20	8	8
259		25 c. crimson ..	35	40	12	15

For 10 c. with watermark W w 14 (inverted), see No. 541*a*.

(Des R. Granger Barrett. Litho J.W.)

1970 (16 Feb). *40th Anniv of Antiguan Air Services. T* **90** *and similar designs. Multicoloured. W* w **12** *(sideways). P* 14½.

No.	Description		Unused	Used
260	5 c. Type **90**	..	15	5
261	20 c. Dornier "DO–X"	..	35	25
262	35 c. Hawker Siddeley "HS–748"	..	50	45
263	50 c. Douglas "C–124C Globemaster II"	..	65	75
264	75 c. Vickers "VC–10"	..	90	1·25

91 Dickens and Scene from *Nicholas Nickleby*

(Des Jennifer Toombs. Litho Walsall Security Printers Ltd)

1970 (19 May). *Death Centenary of Charles Dickens. T* **91** *and similar horiz designs. W* w **12** *(sideways). P* 14.

No.	Description		Unused	Used
265	5 c. bistre, sepia and black	..	10	5
266	20 c. light turquoise-blue, sepia and black	..	20	20
267	35 c. violet-blue, sepia and black	..	30	30
268	$1 rosine, sepia and black	..	80	1·25

Designs:—20 c. Dickens and Scene from *Pickwick Papers*; 35 c. Dickens and Scene from *Oliver Twist*; $1 Dickens and Scene from *David Copperfield*.

92 Carib Indian and War Canoe

93 "The Small Passion" (detail) (Dürer)

(Des J. W. Litho Questa)

1970 (19 Aug)–**75.** *Horiz designs as T* **92**. *Multicoloured. Toned paper. W* w **12** *(sideways). P* 14.

No.	Description		Unused	Used
269	½ c. Type **92**	..	10	20
270	1 c. Columbus and *Nina*	..	25	15
271	2 c. Sir Thomas Warner's emblem and ship	..	40	12
	a. Whiter paper (20.10.75)	..	2·00	2·50
272	3 c. Viscount Hood and H.M.S. *Barfleur*	..	40	20
273	4 c. Sir George Rodney and H.M.S. *Formidable*	..	40	25
274	5 c. Nelson and H.M.S. *Boreas*	..	50	20
275	6 c. William IV and H.M.S. *Pegasus*	..	50	25
276	10 c. "Blackbeard" and pirate ketch	..	65	35
277	15 c. Captain Collingwood and H.M.S. *Pelican*		1·75	1·00
278	20 c. Nelson and H.M.S. *Victory*	..	1·25	60
279	25 c. R.M.S.P. *Solent*	..	1·25	60
280	35 c. George V (when Prince George) and H.M.S. *Canada*	..	1·60	70
281	50 c. H.M.S. *Renown*	..	1·75	1·25
282	75 c. *Federal Maple*	..	2·75	2·50
283	$1 Yacht and Class Emblem	..	3·25	2·00
284	$2.50, H.M.S. *London*	..	5·50	7·50
285	$5 Tug *Pathfinder*	..	10·00	14·00
269/85		*Set of* 17	29·00	29·00

See also Nos. 323/34 and 426.

(Des G. Drummond. Recess and litho D.L.R.)

1970 (28 Oct). *Christmas. T* **93** *and similar vert design. W* w **12.** *P* 13½ × 14.

No.	Type	Description		Unused	Used
286	**93**	3 c. black and turquoise-blue	..	10	5
287	–	10 c. dull purple and pink	..	15	10
288	**93**	35 c. black and rose-red	..	40	35
289	–	50 c. black and lilac	..	50	65

Design:—10 c., 50 c. "Adoration of the Magi" (detail) (Dürer).

94 4th King's Own Regt, 1759

95 Market Woman casting Vote

1970 (14 Dec). *Military Uniforms* (1*st series*). *T* **94** *and similar vert designs. Multicoloured. W* w **12.** *P* 14 × 13½.

No.	Description		Unused	Used
290	½ c. Type **94**	..	5	5
291	10 c. 4th West India Regiment, 1804	..	50	50
292	20 c. 60th Regiment, The Royal American, 1809	..	90	90
293	35 c. 93rd Regiment, Sutherland Highlanders, 1826–34	..	1·50	1·50
294	75 c. 3rd West India Regiment, 1851	..	3·00	3·00
MS295	128 × 146 mm. Nos. 290/4	..	9·50	11·00

See also Nos. 303/8, 313/18, 353/8 and 380/5.

(Des Sylvia Goaman. Photo Harrison)

1971 (1 Feb). *20th Anniversary of Adult Suffrage. T* **95** *and similar vert designs. W* w **12** *(sideways). P* 14½ × 14.

No.	Description		Unused	Used
296	5 c. brown	..	5	5
297	20 c. deep olive	..	12	10
298	35 c. reddish purple	..	20	20
299	50 c. ultramarine	..	25	45

People voting:—20 c. Executive; 35 c. Housewife; 50 c. Artisan.

96 "The Last Supper"

97 "Madonna and Child" (detail, Veronese)

(Des Jennifer Toombs. Litho Questa)

1971 (7 Apr). *Easter. Works by Dürer. T* **96** *and similar vert designs. W* w **12.** *P* 14 × 13½.

No.	Description		Unused	Used
300	5 c. black, grey and scarlet	..	5	5
301	35 c. black, grey and bluish violet	..	20	25
302	75 c. black, grey and gold	..	55	70

Designs:—35 c. The Crucifixion; 75 c. The Resurrection.

(Des J. W. Litho Questa)

1971 (12 July). *Military Uniforms* (2*nd series*). *Multicoloured designs as T* **94**. *W* w **12.** *P* 13½.

No.	Description		Unused	Used
303	½ c. Private, 12th Regiment, The Suffolk (1704)	..	5	5
304	10 c. Grenadier, 38th Regiment, South Staffs (1751)	..	40	40
305	20 c. Light Company, 5th Regiment, Royal Northumberland Fusiliers (1778)	..	65	65
306	35 c. Private, 48th Regiment, The Northamptonshire (1793)	..	1·25	1·25
307	75 c. Private, 15th Regiment, East Yorks (1805)	..	2·75	2·75
MS308	127 × 144 mm. Nos. 303/7	..	7·50	7·50

(Des Jennifer Toombs. Litho Questa)

1971 (4 Oct). *Christmas. T* **97** *and similar vert design. Multicoloured. W* w **12**. *P* 13½.

309	3 c. Type **97**	10	5
310	5 c. "Adoration of the Shepherds" (detail, Veronese)	15	5
311	35 c. Type **97**	50	60
312	50 c. As 5 c.	70	80

(Des J. W. Litho Questa)

1972 (1 July). *Military Uniforms* (3*rd series*). *Multicoloured designs as T* **94**. *W* w **12** (*sideways*). *P* 14 × 13½.

313	½ c. Battalion Company Officer, 25th Foot, 1815	5	5
314	10 c. Sergeant, 14th Foot, 1837	40	40
315	20 c. Private, 67th Foot, 1853	65	65
316	35 c. Officer, Royal Artillery, 1854	1·25	1·25
317	75 c. Private, 29th Foot, 1870	2·50	2·50
MS318	125 × 141 mm. Nos. 313/17	8·00	8·00

98 Cowrie-Helmet

(Des J. W. Litho Questa)

1972 (1 Aug). *Shells. T* **98** *and similar horiz designs. Multicoloured. W* w **12** (*sideways*). *P* 14½.

319	3 c. Type **98**	20	15
320	5 c. Measled Cowrie	25	20
321	35 c. West Indian Fighting Conch	1·00	1·00
322	50 c. Hawk-wing Conch	1·40	1·40

1972–74. *As No.* 269 *etc., but W* w **12** (*upright*) *and whiter paper.*

323	½ c. Type **92**	15	25
324	1 c. Columbus and *Nina*	30	25
325	3 c. Viscount Hood and H.M.S. *Barfleur*	35	20
326	4 c. Sir George Rodney and H.M.S. *Formidable*	35	25
327	5 c. Nelson and H.M.S. *Boreas*	50	25
328	6 c. William IV and H.M.S. *Pegasus*	50	35
329	10 c. "Blackbeard" and pirate ketch	55	20
330	15 c. Collingwood and H.M.S. *Pelican*	1·50	55
331	75 c. *Federal Maple*	3·00	2·25
332	$1 Yacht and class emblem	3·50	1·75
333	$2.50, H.M.S. *London*	5·00	7·50
334	$5 Tug *Pathfinder*	9·50	15·00
323/34	*Set of* 12	23·00	26·00

Dates of issue:—2.11.72, ½ c., 15 c., 75 c., $1, $5; 2.1.74, 1 to 10 c.; 25.2.74, $2.50.

See also No. 426.

99 St. John's Cathedral, Side View

(Des J. W. Litho Format)

1972 (6 Nov). *Christmas and 125th Anniversary of St. John's Cathedral. T* **99** *and similar horiz designs. Multicoloured. W* w **12** (*sideways*). *P* 14.

335	35 c. Type **99**	50	45
336	50 c. Cathedral interior	65	65
337	75 c. St. John's Cathedral	80	1·00
MS338	165 × 102 mm. Nos. 335/7. P 15	2·75	3·25

100 Floral Pattern

(Des (from photograph by D. Groves) and photo Harrison)

1972 (20 Nov). *Royal Silver Wedding. Multicoloured; background colour given. W* w **12**. *P* 14 × 14½.

339	**100**	20 c. bright blue	20	25
340		35 c. turquoise-blue	25	30

101 Batsman and Map

(Des G. Vasarhelyi. Litho Questa)

1972 (15 Dec). *50th Anniv of Rising Sun Cricket Club. T* **101** *and similar horiz designs. Multicoloured. W* w **12**. *P* 13½.

341	5 c. Type **101**	45	25
342	35 c. Batsman and wicket-keeper	1·60	1·75
343	$1 Club badge	3·25	4·00
MS344	88 × 130 mm. Nos. 341/3	6·50	7·00

102 Yacht and Map **103** "Episcopal Coat of Arms"

(Des M. and G. Shamir. Litho Format)

1972 (29 Dec). *Sailing Week and Inauguration of Tourist Office, New York. T* **102** *and similar square designs. Multicoloured. W* w **12**. *P* 14½.

345	35 c. Type **102**	45	45
346	50 c. Yachts	60	60
347	75 c. St. John's G.P.O.	65	65
348	$1 Statue of Liberty	75	75
MS349	100 × 94 mm. Nos. 346, 348	2·25	2·50

(Des PAD Studio. Litho Format)

1973 (16 Apr). *Easter. T* **103** *and similar vert designs showing stained-glass windows from St. John's Cathedral. Multicoloured. W* w **12** (*sideways*). *P* 13½.

350	5 c. Type **103**	8	8
351	35 c. "The Crucifixion"	25	25
352	75 c. "Arms of 1st Bishop of Antigua"	55	70

(Des J. W. Litho Questa)

1973 (1 July). *Military Uniforms* (4*th series*). *Multicoloured designs as T* **94**. *W* w **12** (*sideways*). *P* 13½.

353	½ c. Private, Zacharia Tiffin's Regiment of Foot, 1701	5	5
354	10 c. Private, 63rd Regiment of Foot, 1759	30	30
355	20 c. Light Company Officer, 35th Regiment of Foot, 1828	40	40
356	35 c. Private, 2nd West India Regiment, 1853	70	70
357	75 c. Sergeant, 49th Regiment, 1858	1·50	1·50
MS358	127 × 145 mm. Nos. 353/7	3·00	3·25

104 Butterfly Costumes

(Des G. Vasarhelyi. Litho Format)

1973 (30 July). *Carnival. T* **104** *and similar horiz designs. Multicoloured. P* 13½.

359	5 c. Type **104**	10	12
360	20 c. Carnival street scene	30	30
361	35 c. Carnival troupe	45	45
362	75 c. Carnival Queen	1·00	1·00
MS363	134 × 95 mm. Nos. 359/62	2·25	2·50

105 "Virgin of the Milk Porridge" (Gerard David) **106** Princess Anne and Captain Mark Phillips

(Des G. Vasarhelyi. Litho Format)

1973 (15 Oct). *Christmas. T* **105** *and similar vert designs. Multicoloured. P* 14½.

364	3 c. Type **105**	10	10
365	5 c. "Adoration of the Magi" (Stomer)	12	10
366	20 c. "The Granducal Madonna" (Raphael)	25	25
367	35 c. "Nativity with God the Father and Holy Ghost" (Battista)	40	35
368	$1 "Madonna and Child" (Murillo)	1·25	1·50
MS369	130× 128 mm. Nos. 364/8	2·75	3·00

(Des G. Drummond. Litho Format)

1973 (14 Nov). *Royal Wedding. T* **106** *and similar horiz design. P* 13½.

370	**106**	35 c. multicoloured	25	25
371	–	$2 multicoloured	85	85
MS372		78 × 100 mm. Nos. 370/1	1·25	1·40

The $2 is as T **106** but has a different border.

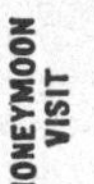

DECEMBER 16th
1973

(107)

1973 (15 Dec). *Honeymoon Visit of Princess Anne and Captain Phillips. Nos.* 370/**MS**372 *optd with T* **107** *by lithography.**

373	**106**	35 c. multicoloured	25	25
		a. Typo opt	95	95
374	–	$2 multicoloured	85	85
		a. Typo opt	2·75	2·75
MS375		78 × 100 mm. Nos. 373/4	1·25	1·40
		a. Typo opt	7·00	9·00

*The litho overprints can be distinguished from the typo by the latter being less clear, less intense, and showing through on the reverse.

108 Coats of Arms of Antigua and University

(Des PAD Studio. Litho D.L.R.)

1974 (18 Feb). *25th Anniv of University of West Indies. T* **108** *and similar horiz designs. Multicoloured. W* w **12**. *P* 13.

376	5 c. Type **108**	10	5
377	20 c. Extra-mural art	20	15
378	35 c. Antigua campus	30	25
379	75 c. Antigua chancellor	50	80

(Des J. W. Litho Questa)

1974 (1 May). *Military Uniforms* (5*th series*). *Multicoloured designs as T* **94**. *W* w **12** (*sideways*). *P* 13½.

380	½ c. Officer, 59th Foot, 1797	5	5
381	10 c. Gunner, Royal Artillery, 1800	25	25
	a. Error. Wmk T **55** of Malawi	£120	
382	20 c. Private, 1st West India Regiment, 1830	40	45
383	35 c. Officer, 92nd Foot, 1843	55	65
384	75 c. Private, 23rd Foot, 1846	1·00	1·40
MS385	127 × 145 mm. Nos. 380/4	2·25	2·50

109 English Postman, Mailcoach and Helicopter **110** Traditional Player

(Des G. Vasarhelyi. Litho Format)

1974 (15 July). *Centenary of Universal Postal Union. T* **109** *and similar horiz designs. Multicoloured. P* 14½.

386	½ c. Type **109**	5	5
387	1 c. Bellman, mailboat *Orinoco* and satellite	5	5
388	2 c. Train guard, post-bus and hydrofoil	5	5
389	5 c. Swiss messenger, Wells Fargo coach and "Concorde"	10	10
390	20 c. Postillion, Japanese postmen and carrier pigeon	30	30
391	35 c. Antiguan postman, flying-boat and tracking station	45	45
392	$1 Medieval courier, American express train and Boeing "747"	1·50	1·50
386/92	*Set of* 7	2·25	2·25
MS393	141 × 164 mm. Nos. 386/92 plus label. P 13	2·25	2·50

On the ½ c. "English" is spelt "Enlish", and on the 2 c. "Postal" is spelt "Fostal".

(Des C. Abbott. Litho Questa)

1974 (1 Aug). *Antiguan Steel Bands. T* **110** *and similar designs. W* w **12** (*sideways on* 5 *c.,* 75 *c. and* **MS**398). *P* 13.

394	5 c. rose-red, carmine and black	8	5
395	20 c. brown-ochre, chestnut and black	15	15
396	35 c. light sage-green, blue-green and black	25	25
397	75 c. dull blue, dull ultramarine and black	60	70
MS398	115 × 108 mm. Nos. 394/7	1·50	1·60

Designs: *Horiz*—20 c. Traditional band; 35 c. Modern band. *Vert*—75 c. Modern player.

111 Footballers

EARTHQUAKE RELIEF

(112)

(Des G. Vasarhelyi. Litho Format)

1974 (23 Sept). *World Cup Football Championships. T* **111** *and similar vert designs showing footballers. P* 14½.
399 **111** 5 c. multicoloured 5 5
400 – 35 c. multicoloured 20 20
401 – 75 c. multicoloured 45 65
402 – $1 multicoloured 75 90
MS403 135 × 130 mm. Nos. 399/402 plus two labels. P 13 .. .. 1·75 2·00

1974 (16 Oct). *Earthquake Relief Fund. Nos.* 400/2 *and* 397 *optd with T* **112**, *No.* 397 *surch also.*
404 35 c. multicoloured 35 35
405 75 c. multicoloured 60 60
406 $1 multicoloured 85 85
407 $5 on 75 c. dull blue, dull ultram & black 5·50 5·50

113 Churchill as Schoolboy and School College Building, Harrow **114** "Madonna of the Trees" (Bellini)

(Des V. Whiteley. Litho Format)

1974 (20 Oct). *Birth Centenary of Sir Winston Churchill. T* **113** *and similar horiz designs. Multicoloured. P* 14½.
408 5 c. Type **113** 10 5
409 35 c. Churchill and St. Paul's Cathedral .. 30 30
410 75 c. Coat of arms and catafalque 55 70
411 $1 Churchill, "reward" notice and South African escape route 70 90
MS412 1007 × 82 mm. Nos. 408/11. P 13.. .. 2·00 2·25

(Des M. Shamir. Litho Format)

1974 (18 Nov). *Christmas. T* **114** *and similar vert designs showing "Madonna and Child" by the artists given. Multicoloured. P* 14½.
413 ½ c. Type **114** 5 5
414 1 c. Raphael 5 5
415 2 c. Van der Weyden 5 5
416 3 c. Giorgione 5 5
417 5 c. Mantegna 8 8
418 20 c. Vivarini 20 20
419 35 c. Montagna 35 35
420 75 c. Lorenzo Costa 75 75
413/20 .. .. *Set of* 8 1·40 1·40
MS421 139 × 126 mm. Nos. 417/20. P 13.. .. 1·50 1·60

$10

(**115**)

116 Carib War Canoe, English Harbour, 1300

1975 (14 Jan). *Nos.* 331 *and* 390/2 *surch as T* **115**.
422 50 c. on 20 c. multicoloured .. .. .. 2·00 2·25
423 $2.50, on 35 c. multicoloured .. .. .. 6·50 7·50
424 $5 on $1 multicoloured .. .. .. 8·50 10·00
425 $10 on 75 c. multicoloured .. .. .. 9·50 13·00

1975 (21 Jan). *As No.* 334 *but W w* **14**.
426 $5 Tug *Pathfinder* .. .. 9·00 12·00

(Des G. Drummond. Litho Format)

1975 (17 Mar). *Nelson's Dockyard. T* **116** *and similar horiz designs. Multicoloured. P* 14½.
427 5 c. Type **116** 15 15
428 15 c. Ship of the line, English Harbour, 1770 30 30
429 35 c. H.M.S. *Boreas* at anchor, and Lord Nelson, 1787 .. .. 60 60
430 50 c. Yachts during "Sailing Week", 1974 .. 85 85
431 $1 Yacht Anchorage, Old Dockyard, 1970 .. 1·50 1·50
MS432 130 × 134 mm. As Nos. 427/31, but in larger format, 43 × 28 mm. P 13½ .. .. .. 3·75 4·00

117 Lady of the Valley Church

(Des R. Vigus. Litho Format)

1975 (19 May). *Antiguan Churches. T* **117** *and similar horiz designs. Multicoloured. P* 14½.
433 5 c. Type **117** 8 8
434 20 c. Gilbert Memorial 25 30
435 35 c. Grace Hill Moravian 40 45
436 50 c. St. Phillips 55 60
437 $1 Ebenezer Methodist .. .. .. 1·00 1·10
MS438 91 × 101 mm. Nos. 435/7. P 13 .. .. 2·10 2·25

118 Map of 1721 and Sextant of 1640

(Des PAD Studio. Litho Questa)

1975 (21 July). *Maps of Antigua. T* **118** *and similar horiz designs. Multicoloured. W w* **14** *(sideways). P* 14.
439 5 c. Type **118** 10 8
440 20 c. Map of 1775 and galleon.. .. .. 25 30
441 35 c. Maps of 1775 and 1955 .. .. .. 45 50
442 $1 1973 maps of Antigua and English Harbour .. .. 1·10 1·40
MS443 130 × 89 mm. Nos. 439/42 . .. .. 1·75 2·00

119 Scout Bugler

(Des G. Vasarhelyi. Litho Questa)

1975 (26 Aug). *World Scout Jamboree, Norway. T* **119** *and similar horiz designs. Multicoloured. P* 14.
444 15 c. Type **119** 25 25
445 20 c. Scouts in camp 30 30
446 35 c. "Lord Baden-Powell" (D. Jagger) .. 50 50
447 $2 Scout dancers from Dahomey .. .. 1·75 1·75
MS448 145 × 107 mm. Nos. 444/7. .. .. 2·75 3·00

120 *Eurema elathea* **121** "Madonna and Child" (Correggio)

(Des. G. Vasarhelyi. Litho Questa)

1975 (30 Oct). *Butterflies. T* **120** *and similar horiz designs. Multicoloured. P* 14.
449 ½ c. Type **120** 5 5
450 1 c. *Danaus plexippus* 8 5
451 2 c. *Phoebis philea* 10 8
452 5 c. *Hypolimnas misippus* 15 12
453 35c. *Eurema proterpia* 60 60
454 35 c. *Papilio polydamas* 90 90
455 $2 *Vanessa cardui* .. .. 4·00 4·00
449/55 .. .. *Set of* 7 5·50 5·50
MS456 147 × 94 mm. Nos. 452/5 .. .. .. 6·00 6·50
No. 452 is incorrectly captioned "Marpesia petreus thetys".

(Des G. Vasarhelyi. Litho Questa)

1975 (17 Nov). *Christmas. T* **121** *and similar vert designs showing "Madonna and Child". Multicoloured. P* 14.
457 ½ c. Type **121** 5 5
458 1 c. El Greco 5 5
459 2 c. Dürer 5 5
460 3 c. Antonello 5 5
461 5 c. Bellini 8 8
462 10 c. Dürer (*different*) 12 12
463 35 c. Bellini (*different*).. .. .. .. 30 30
464 $2 Dürer (*different*) .. .. 1·40 1·40
457/64 .. .. *Set of* 8 1·90 1·90
MS465 138 × 119 mm. Nos. 461/4 . .. .. 2·25 2·75

122 Vivian Richards **123** Antillean Crested Hummingbird

(Des G. Vasarhelyi. Litho Format)

1975 (15 Dec). *World Cup Cricket Winners. T* **122** *and similar multicoloured designs. P* 13½.
466 5 c. Type **122** 50 15
467 35 c. Andy Roberts .. .. 1·60 1·40
468 $2 West Indies team (*horiz*).. .. .. 4·50 4·50

(Des G. Vasarhelyi. Litho Format)

1976 (19 Jan)–**78**. *Various multicoloured designs as T* **123**. A *Without imprint* (19.1.76). B. *With imprint date at foot* (1978).

(*a*) *Size as T* **123**. *P* 14½

		A		B	
469	½ c. Type **123** ..	15	15	12	12
470	1 c. Imperial Amazon ..	15	15	12	12
471	2 c. Zenaida Dove	15	15	12	12
472	3 c. Loggerhead Kingbird	15	15	12	12
473	4 c. Red-necked Pigeon	15	15	12	12
474	5 c. Rufous-throated Solitaire	15	15	12	12
475	6 c. Orchid Tree	15	15	12	12
476	10 c. Bougainvillea	15	15	15	15
477	15 c. Geiger Tree	20	15	20	15
478	20 c. Flamboyant	20	15	20	15
479	25 c. Hibiscus	25	15	25	15
480	35 c. Flame of the Wood	30	20	25	20
481	50 c. Cannon at Fort James	45	30	40	30
482	75 c. Premier's Office	45	50	40	50
483	$1 Potworks Dam	70	70	60	65

(*b*) *Size* 44 × 28 *mm. P* 13½

		A		B	
484	$2.50, Irrigation Scheme, Diamond Estate ..	1·75	1·90	1·25	1·40
485	$5 Government House	3·00	3·25	2·50	2·75
486	$10 Coolidge Airport	4·50	5·50	4·50	5·50
469/86	*Set of* 18	11·50	12·50	10·50	11·50

124 Privates, Clark's Illinois Regt **125** High Jump

(Des J. W. Litho Format)

1976 (17 Mar). *Bicentenary of American Revolution. T* **124** *and similar vert designs. Multicoloured. P* 14½.
487 ½ c. Type **124** 5 5
488 1 c. Riflemen, Pennsylvania Militia 5 5
489 2 c. Powder horn 8 8
a. Imperf (pair) £180
490 5 c. Water bottle 12 12
491 35 c. American flags 45 45
492 $1 Privateer *Montgomery* .. .. .. 1·25 1·25
493 $5 Sloop *Ranger* .. .. 5·00 5·00
487/93 .. .. *Set of* 7 6·50 6·50
MS494 71 × 84 mm. $2.50 Congress flag. P 13 .. 4·00 4·00

(Des J. W. Litho Format)

1976 (26 Aug). *Water Sports. T* **126** *and similar horiz designs. Multicoloured. P* 14.
495 ½ c. orange-brown, bistre-yellow and black .. 5 5
496 1 c. light reddish violet and black 5 5
497 2 c. light green and black 5 5
498 15 c. bright blue and black 10 10
499 30 c. olive-brown, yellow-ochre and black .. 20 20
500 $1 red-orange, Venetian red and black .. 60 65
501 $2 rosine and black .. .. 1·40 1·50
495/501 .. .. *Set of* 7 2·25 2·40
MS502 88 × 138 mm. Nos. 498/501. P 13½ .. 2·75 3·00
Designs:—1 c. Boxing; 2 c. Pole vault; 15 c. Swimming; 30 c. Running; $1 Cycling; $2 Shot put.

126 Water Skiing

(Des J. W. Litho Questa)

1976 (26 Aug). *Water Sports. T* **126** *and similar horiz designs. Multicoloured. P* 14.
503 ½ c. Type **126** 5 5
504 1 c. Sailing 5 5
505 2 c. Snorkeling 5 5
506 20 c. Deep sea fishing 12 15
507 50 c. Scuba diving 35 35
508 $2 Swimming .. .. 1·25 1·25
503/8 .. .. *Set of* 6 1·60 1·60
MS509 89 × 114 mm. Nos. 506/8 .. .. .. 1·75 1·90

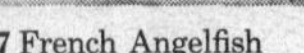

127 French Angelfish **128** The Annunciation

(Des G. Drummond. Litho Questa)

1976 (4 Oct). *Fishes. T* **127** *and similar horiz designs. Multicoloured. W w* **14** *(sideways). P* 13½.
510 15 c. Type **127** 25 25
511 30 c. Yellowfin Grouper 40 40
512 50 c. Yellowtail Snappers 55 65
513 90 c. Shy Hamlet 80 95

(Des J. W. Litho Walsall)

1976 (15 Nov). *Christmas. T* **128** *and similar vert designs. Multicoloured. P* 13½.
514 8 c. Type **128** 10 8
515 10 c. The Holy Family.. .. .. 12 10
516 15 c. The Magi 20 15
517 50 c. The Shepherds 40 40
518 $1 Epiphany scene 70 75

129 Mercury and U.P.U. Emblem

130 Royal Family

(Des BG Studio. Litho Questa)

1976 (28 Dec). *Special Events,* 1976. *T* **129** *and similar horiz designs. Multicoloured. P* 14.
519 ½ c. Type **129** 5 5
520 1 c. Alfred Nobel 5 5
521 10 c. Space satellite 20 12
522 50 c. Viv Richards and Andy Roberts.. .. 1·25 1·25
523 $1 Bell and telephones .. .. 1·75 1·75
524 $2 Yacht *Freelance* .. .. 2·75 2·75
519/24 .. .. *Set of* 6 5·50 5·50
MS525 127 × 101 mm. Nos. 521/4 .. .. 6·50 7·50
Events:—½ c. 25th Anniv of U.N. Postal Administration; 1 c. 75th Anniv of Nobel Prize; 10 c. "Viking" Space Mission; 50 c. Cricketing achievements; $1 Telephone Centenary; $2 "Operation Sail", U.S. Bicentennial.

(Des J. W. Litho Questa (Nos. 526/31); Manufactured by Walsall (Nos. 532/3))

1977. *Coil Stamps. W w* **14** *(inverted). P* 14½ × 14.
541*a* **89** 10 c. emerald .. .. — 15
526 10 c. Type **130** 10 10
527 30 c. Royal Visit, 1966.. .. .. .. 20 25
528 50 c. The Queen enthroned 40 35
529 90 c. The Queen after Coronation 55 50
530 $2.50, Queen and Prince Charles 85 90
MS531 116 × 78 mm. $5 Queen and Prince Philip 2·25 2·75
a. Error. Imperf £600

(b) Booklet stamps. Roul 5 × *imperf* (50 c.) *or imperf* ($5).* *Self-adhesive* (26 Sept)
532 50 c. Design as No. 529 (24 × 42 *mm*) .. 35 40
a. Booklet pane of 6.. .. .. .. 1·90
533 $5 Design as stamp from No. **MS**531 (24 × 42 *mm*) .. .. 2·25 3·00
a. Booklet pane of 1.. .. .. .. 2·25
*No. 532 was separated by various combinations of rotary knife (giving a straight edge) and roulette. No. 533 exists only with straight edges.
Stamps as Nos. 526/30 but perforated 11½ × 12, come from sheets of 5 stamps and 1 label. These were not placed on sale by the Antigua Post Office.

131 Making Camp

132 Carnival Costume

(Des J. W. Litho Questa)

1977 (23 May). *Caribbean Scout Jamboree, Jamaica. T* **131** *and similar horiz designs. Multicoloured. P* 14.
534 ½ c. Type **131** 5 5
535 1 c. Hiking 5 5
536 2 c. Rock-climbing 5 5
537 10 c. Cutting logs 8 8
538 30 c. Map and sign reading 20 20
539 50 c. First aid 35 35
540 $2 Rafting .. .. 2·00 2·00
534/40 .. .. *Set of* 7 2·50 2·50
MS541 127 × 114 mm. Nos. 538/40 .. .. 2·50 2·75

1977. *Coil Stamps. W w* **14** *(inverted). P* 14½ × 14.
541*a* **89** 10 c. emerald .. .. — 15

(Des C. Abbott. Litho Walsall)

1977 (18 July). *21st Anniv of Carnival. T* **132** *and similar vert designs. Multicoloured. P* 14.
542 10 c. Type **132** 8 8
543 30 c. Carnival Queen 20 20
544 50 c. Butterfly costume 35 35
545 90 c. Queen of the band 50 50
546 $1 Calypso King and Queen 55 55
MS547 140 × 120 mm. Nos. 542/6 .. .. 1·60 1·75

ROYAL VISIT
28th OCTOBER 1977
(133)

134 "Virgin and Child Enthroned" (Tura)

1977 (17 Oct). *Royal Visit. Nos.* 526/531 *optd with T* **133.** *P* 14.
548 10 c. Type **130** 5 5
549 30 c. Royal Visit, 1966.. .. .. .. 15 20
550 50 c. The Queen enthroned 25 30
551 90 c. The Queen after Coronation 45 50
552 $2.50, Queen and Prince Charles .. .. 90 1·00
MS553 116 × 78 mm. $5 Queen and Prince Philip 2·25 2·75
a. Opt double .. ..
Nos. 548/52 also exist perf 11½ × 12 *(Price for set of* 5 £1·90 *mint or used)* from additional sheetlets of five stamps and one label.

(Des M. Shamir. Litho Questa)

1977 (21 Nov). *Christmas. T* **134** *and similar vert designs showing "Virgin and Child" by the artists given. Multicoloured. P* 14.
554 ½ c. Type **134** 5 5
555 1 c. Crivelli 5 5
556 2 c. Lotto 5 5
557 8 c. Pontormo.. .. .. 8 8
558 10 c. Tura *(different)* 8 8
559 25 c. Lotto *(different)* 20 20
560 $2 Crivelli *(different)* .. .. .. 1·25 1·25
554/60 .. .. *Set of* 7 1·60 1·60
MS561 144 × 118 mm. Nos. 557/60 .. .. 1·75 2·00

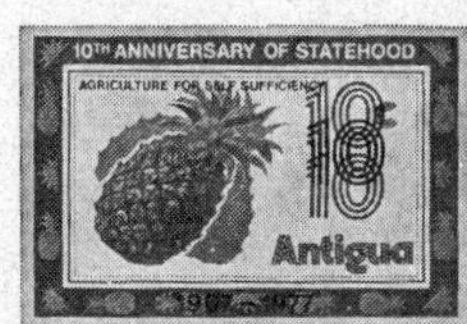

135 Pineapple

(Des and litho J.W.)

1977 (29 Dec). *Tenth Anniv of Statehood. T* **135** *and similar horiz designs. Multicoloured. P* 13.
562 10 c. Type **135** 8 8
563 15 c. State flag.. .. .. 10 10
564 50 c. Police band 30 30
565 90 c. Premier V. C. Bird 50 50
566 $2 State Coat of Arms .. .. .. 1·00 1·25
MS567 126 × 99 mm. Nos. 563/6. P 14 .. 2·25 2·50

136 *Glider III*, 1902

(Des PAD Studio. Litho Questa)

1978 (23 Mar). *75th Anniv of Powered Flight. T* **136** *and similar multicoloured designs. P* 14.
568 ½ c. Type **136** 5 5
569 1 c. *Flyer I*, 1903 .. .. 5 5
570 2 c. Launch system and engine 5 5
571 10 c. Orville Wright *(vert.)* 10 10
572 50 c. *Flyer III*, 1905 .. .. 35 35
573 90 c. Wilbur Wright *(vert)* 50 60
574 $2 Wright "Model B", 1910.. .. .. 1·00 1·25
568/74 .. .. *Set of* 7 1·90 2·10
MS575 90 × 75 mm. $2.50, *Flyer I* on launch system .. .. 1·60 1·75

137 Sunfish Regatta

(Des G. Drummond. Litho Format)

1978 (27 Apr). *Sailing Week. T* **137** *and similar horiz designs. Multicoloured. P* 15.
576 10 c. Type **137** 15 10
577 50 c. Fishing and work boat race 40 35
578 90 c. Curtain Bluff race 75 75
579 $2 Power boat rally.. .. .. .. 1·50 1·50
MS580 110 × 77 mm. $2.50, Guadeloupe–Antigua race .. .. 2·50 2·75

138 Queen Elizabeth and Prince Philip

139 Glass Coach

(Des J. W. Litho Questa (Nos. 581/6); Manufactured by Walsall (Nos. 587/9))

1978 (2 June). *25th Anniv of Coronation. Multicoloured. (a) Sheet stamps. Vert designs as T* **138.** *P* 14.
581 10 c. Type **138** 5 8
582 30 c. Crowning 15 20
583 50 c. Coronation procession 25 30
584 90 c. Queen seated in St. Edward's Chair .. 45 50
585 $2.50, Queen wearing Imperial State Crown 90 1·00
MS586 114 × 104 mm. $5 Queen and Prince Philip 2·00 2·40

(b) Booklet stamps. Horiz design as T **139** *showing State Coaches. Imperf* ($5) *or roul* 5 × *imperf*.* *Self-adhesive.*
587 25 c. Type **139** 12 15
a. Booklet pane. Nos. 587/8 × 3 .. .. 1·25
588 50 c. Irish State Coach 25 30
589 $5 Coronation Coach .. .. .. 2·50 2·75
a. Booklet pane of 1.. .. .. .. 2·50
Nos. 581/5 also exist perf 12 *(Price for set of* 5 £2 *mint or used)* from additional sheetlets of three stamps and one label. These stamps have changed background colours.
*Nos. 587/8 were separated by various combinations of rotary-knife (giving a straight edge) and roulette. No. 589 exists only with straight edges.

140 Player running with Ball

141 Petrea

(Des BG Studio. Litho Format)

1978 (17 Aug). *World Cup Football Championship, Argentina. T* **140** *and similar vert designs. Multicoloured. P* 14½.
590 10 c. Type **140** 5 5
591 15 c. Players in front of goal 5 5
592 $3 Referee and player .. .. .. 1·60 1·75
MS593 126 × 88 mm. 25 c. Player crouching with ball; 30 c. Players heading ball; 50 c. Players running with ball; $2 Goalkeeper diving. *(All horiz)* .. .. 1·90 2·00
Nos. 590/2 were each printed in small sheets of 6 including 1 *se-tenant* stamp-size label.

(Des G. Drummond. Litho Questa)

1978 (5 Oct). *Flowers. T* **141** *and similar vert designs. Multicoloured. P* 14.
594 25 c. Type **141** 20 20
595 50 c. Sunflower 40 40
596 90 c. Frangipani 60 60
597 $2 Passion Flower .. .. 1·40 1·40
MS598 118 × 85 mm. $2.50, Hibiscus .. .. 1·60 1·75

142 "St Ildefonso receiving the Chasuble from the Virgin" (Rubens)

143 1d. Stamp of 1863

(Des BG Studio. Litho Questa)

1978 (30 Oct). *Christmas Paintings. T* **142** *and similar horiz designs. Multicoloured. P* 14.
599 8 c. Type **142** 5 5
600 25 c. "The Flight of St. Barbara" (Rubens) .. 20 20
601 $2 "Madonna and Child, with St. Joseph, John the Baptist and Donor" (Sebastiano del Piombo*) .. .. 1·25 1·00
MS602 170 × 113 mm. $4 "The Annunciation" (Rubens) .. .. 4·00 4·00
*The work is incorrectly attributed to Rubens on the stamp.

(Des G. Vasarhelyi. Litho Questa)

1979 (12 Feb). *Death Centenary of Sir Rowland Hill. T* **143** *and similar vert designs. Multicoloured. P* 14.
603 25 c. Type **143** 12 12
604 50 c. Penny Black 25 25

605	$1 Stage-coach and woman posting letter, *circa* 1840	45	45
606	$2 Modern mail transport	1·00	1·00
MS607	108 × 82 mm. $2.50, Sir Rowland Hill ..	1·00	1·10

Nos. 603/6 also exist perf 12 (*Price for set of* 4 £1.60 *mint or used*) from additional sheetlets of four stamps and one label.

144 "The Deposition from the Cross" (painting)

145 Toy Yacht and Child's Hand

(Des BG Studio. Litho Questa)

1979 (15 Mar). *Easter. Works by Dürer. T* **144** *and similar vert designs. P* 14.

608	10 c. multicoloured	5	5
609	50 c. multicoloured	25	25
610	$4 black, magenta and greenish yellow ..	1·60	1·60
MS611	114 × 99 mm. $2.50, multicoloured ..	95	1·10

Designs:—50 c., $2.50, "Christ on the Cross—The Passion" (wood engravings) (*both different*); $4 "Man of Sorrows with Hands Raised" (wood engraving).

(Des M. Rubin. Litho Questa)

1979 (9 Apr). *International Year of the Child. T* **145** *and similar vert designs showing toys and hands of children of different races. Multicoloured. P* 14.

612	25 c. Type **145**	12	12
613	50 c. Rocket	25	25
614	90 c. Car	40	40
615	$2 Train	1·00	1·00
MS616	80 × 112 mm. $5 Aeroplane	1·90	2·25

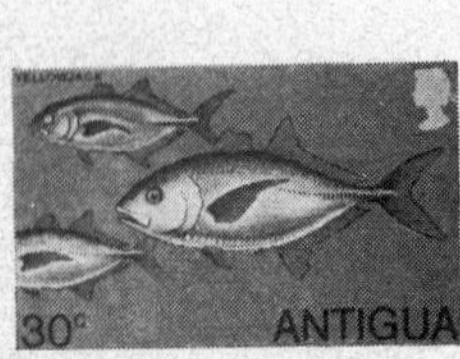

146 Yellowjack

147 Cook's Birthplace, Marton

(Des P. Powell. Litho Questa)

1979 (14 May). *Fishes. T* **146** *and similar horiz designs. Multicoloured. P* 14½ × 14.

617	30 c. Type **146**	15	15
618	50 c. Bluefin Tuna	25	25
619	90 c. Sailfish	40	40
620	$3 Wahoo	1·75	1·75
MS621	122 × 75 mm. $2.50, Barracuda ..	1·25	1·40

(Des J. W. Litho Questa)

1979 (2 July). *Death Bicentenary of Captain Cook. T* **147** *and similar vert designs. Multicoloured. P* 14.

622	25 c. Type **147**	45	30
623	50 c. H.M. Bark *Endeavour*	65	50
624	90 c. Marine chronometer	80	80
625	$3 Landing at Botany Bay	2·00	2·00
MS626	110 × 85 mm. $2.50, H.M.S. *Resolution* ..	1·90	2·25

148 The Holy Family

149 Javelin Throwing

(Des J.W. Litho Questa)

1979 (1 Oct). *Christmas. T* **148** *and similar vert designs. Multicoloured. P* 14.

627	8 c. Type **148**	5	5
628	25 c. Virgin and Child on Ass	10	12
629	50 c. Shepherd and star	20	25
630	$4 Wise Men with gifts	1·40	1·75
MS631	113 × 94 mm. $3 Angel with trumpet. P 12	1·25	1·50

(Des Design Images Inc. Litho Questa)

1980 (18 Feb). *Olympic Games, Moscow. T* **149** *and similar multicoloured designs. P* 14.

632	10 c. Type **149**	5	5
633	25 c. Running	15	15
634	$1 Pole vaulting	45	50
635	$2 Hurdling	80	90
MS636	127 × 96 mm. $3 Boxing (*horiz*)	1·25	1·50

150 Mickey Mouse and Aeroplane

LONDON 1980

(151)

(Litho Format)

1980 (24 Mar). *International Year of the Child* (1979). *Walt Disney Cartoon Characters. T* **150** *and similar multicoloured designs showing characters and transport. P* 11.

637	½ c. Type **150**	5	5
638	1 c. Donald Duck driving car	5	5
639	2 c. Goofy driving taxi	5	5
640	3 c. Mickey Mouse on motorcycle with Minnie Mouse in sidecar	5	5
641	4 c. Huey, Dewey and Louie riding cycle ..	5	5
642	5 c. Grandma Duck, chickens and pickup truck	5	5
643	10 c. Mickey Mouse driving jeep (*vert*) ..	5	5
644	$1 Chip and Dale in sailing boat	60	60
645	$4 Donald Duck riding toy train (*vert*) ..	2·25	2·25
637/45	.. .. *Set of* 9	2·75	2·75
MS646	101 × 127 mm. $2.50, Goofy flying biplane. P 14 × 13½	1·40	1·40

See also Nos. 671/80.

1980 (6 May). *"London 1980" International Stamp Exhibition. Nos.* 603/6 *optd with T* **151**. *P* 12.

647	25 c. Type **143**	15	15
648	50 c. Penny Black	25	25
649	$1 Stage-coach and woman posting letter, *circa* 1840	45	45
650	$2 Modern mail transport	90	90

152 "David" (statue, Donatello)

153 Rotary International 75th Anniversary Emblem and Headquarters, U.S.A.

(Des J.W. Litho Questa)

1980 (23 June). *Famous Works of Art. T* **152** *and similar multicoloured designs. P* 13½.

651	10 c. Type **152**	5	5
652	30 c. "The Birth of Venus" (painting, Sandro Botticelli) (*horiz*)	15	15
653	50 c. "Reclining Couple" (sarcophagus), Cerveteri (*horiz*)	25	25
654	90 c. "The Garden of Earthly Delights" (painting, Hieronymus Bosch) (*horiz*) ..	40	40
655	$1 "Portinari Altarpiece" (painting, Hugo van der Goes) (*horiz*)	45	45
656	$4 "Eleanora of Toledo and her Son Giovanni de'Medici" (painting, Agnolo Bronzino) ..	1·60	1·60
651/6	.. .. *Set of* 6	2·50	2·50
MS657	99 × 124 mm. $5 "The Holy Family" (painting, Rembrandt)	2·00	2·25

(Des G. Vasarhelyi. Litho Questa)

1980 (21 July). *75th Anniv of Rotary International. T* **153** *and similar horiz designs. Multicoloured. P* 14.

658	30 c. Type **153**	20	20
659	50 c. Rotary anniversary emblem and Antigua Rotary Club banner	25	25
660	90 c. Map of Antigua and Rotary emblem ..	40	40
661	$3 Paul P. Harris (founder) and Rotary emblem	1·40	1·50
MS662	102 × 78 mm. $5 Antiguan flags and Rotary emblems	2·00	2·50

154 Queen Elizabeth the Queen Mother

155 Ringed Kingfisher

(Des G. Vasarhelyi. Litho Questa)

1980 (4 Aug). *80th Birthday of Queen Elizabeth the Queen Mother. P* 14.

663	**154**	10 c. multicoloured	10	10
664		$2.50, multicoloured	1·50	1·50
MS665		68 × 90 mm. **154** $3 multicoloured. P 12 ..	1·75	1·90

(Des Jennifer Toombs. Litho Questa)

1980 (3 Nov). *Birds. T* **155** *and similar vert designs. Multicoloured. P* 14.

666	10 c. Type **155**	15	10
667	30 c. Plain Pigeon	30	25
668	$1 Green-throated Carib	80	60
669	$2 Black-necked Stilt	1·25	1·00
MS670	73 × 73 mm. $2.50, Roseate Tern	1·50	1·50

(Litho Format)

1980 (23 Dec). *Christmas. Scenes from Walt Disney's Cartoon Film "Sleeping Beauty". Horiz designs as T* **150**. *P* 11.

671	½ c. multicoloured	5	5
672	1 c. multicoloured	5	5
673	2 c. multicoloured	5	5
674	4 c. multicoloured	5	5
675	8 c. multicoloured	5	5
676	10 c. multicoloured	5	5
677	25 c. multicoloured	15	15
678	$2 multicoloured	1·25	1·25
679	$2.50, multicoloured	1·50	1·50
671/9	.. .. *Set of* 9	2·75	2·75
MS680	126 × 101 mm. $4 multicoloured (*vert*) P 13½ × 14	2·25	2·40

156 Diesel Locomotive No. 15

(Des G. Drummond. Litho Questa)

1981 (12 Jan). *Sugar Cane Railway Locomotives. T* **156** *and similar horiz designs. Multicoloured. P* 14.

681	25 c. Type **156**	15	15
682	50 c. Narrow-gauge steam locomotive ..	30	30
683	90 c. Diesel locomotives Nos. 1 and 10 ..	55	55
684	$3 Steam locomotive hauling sugar cane ..	2·00	2·00
MS685	82 × 111 mm. $2.50, Antigua sugar factory, railway yard and sheds	1·75	1·75

"INDEPENDENCE 1981"

(157)

158 "Pipes of Pan"

1981 (31 Mar). *Independence. Optd with T* **157**. A. *On Nos.* 475A, 478A, 480A *and* 484A/6A. B. *On Nos.* 475B/6B *and* 478B/86B.

		A		B	
686	6 c. Orchid Tree	25	25	5	5
687	10 c. Bougainvillea	†		5	5
688	20 c. Flamboyant	25	25	10	12
689	25 c. Hibiscus	†		15	15
690	35 c. Flame of the Wood ..	50	50	20	20
691	50 c. Cannon at Fort James ..	†		35	35
692	75 c. Premier's Office	†		40	40
693	$1 Potworks Dam	†		55	55
694	$2.50, Irrigation Scheme, Diamond Estate	1·50	1·60	1·25	1·25
695	$5 Government House ..	3·00	3·25	2·50	2·50
696	$10 Coolidge Airport	6·00	6·50	5·00	5·00
686A/96A	.. .. *Set of* 6	11·00	12·00	†	
686B/96B	.. .. *Set of* 11		†	9·50	9·50

(Des J.W. Litho Questa)

1981 (5 May). *Birth Centenary of Picasso. T* **158** *and similar vert designs. Multicoloured. P* 14.

697	10 c. Type **158**	5	5
698	50 c. "Seated Harlequin"	30	30
699	90 c. "Paulo as Harlequin"	55	55
700	$4 "Mother and Child"	2·50	2·50
MS701	115 × 140 mm. $5 "Three Musicians" (detail)	2·75	2·75

159 Prince Charles and Lady Diana Spencer

160 Prince of Wales at Investiture, 1969

(Des J.W. Litho Questa)

1981 (23 June). *Royal Wedding. T* **159** *and similar vert designs. Multicoloured. P* 14.
702 25 c. Type **159** 20 20
703 50 c. Glamis Castle 40 40
704 $4 Prince Charles skiing .. .. .. 2·10 2·10
MS705 96 × 82 mm. $5 Glass Coach .. .. 2·50 2·50
Nos. 702/4 also exist perforated 12 (*Price for set of* 3 £2.50 *mint or used*) from additional sheetlets of five stamps and one label. These stamps have changed background colours.

(Manufactured by Walsall)

1981 (23 June). *Royal Wedding. Booklet stamps. T* **160** *and similar vert designs. Multicoloured* ($5) *or black and flesh* (*others*). *Roul* 5 × *imperf**. *Self-adhesive*.
706 25 c. Type **160** 20 20
a. Booklet pane. Nos. 706/11 .. .. 3·25
707 25 c. Prince Charles as baby, 1948 .. .. 20 20
708 $1 Prince Charles at R.A.F. College, Cranwell, 1971 .. .. 55 55
709 $1 Prince Charles attending Hill House School, 1956 .. .. 55 55
710 $2 Prince Charles and Lady Diana Spencer 1·10 1·10
711 $2 Prince Charles at Trinity College, 1967 1·10 1·10
712 $5 Prince Charles and Lady Diana (*different*) 2·50 2·50
a. Booklet pane of 1 .. .. 2·50
706/12 .. .. *Set of* 7 5·50 5·50
*The 25 c. to $2 values were each separated by various combinations of rotary knife (giving a straight edge) and roulette. The $5 value exists only with straight edges.

161 Irene Joshua (founder)

162 Antigua and Barbuda Coat of Arms

(Des M. Diamond. Litho Format)

1981 (28 Oct). *50th Anniv of Antigua Girl Guide Movement. T* **161** *and similar horiz designs. Multicoloured. P* 14½.
713 10 c. Type **161** 5 5
714 50 c. Campfire sing-song 35 35
715 90 c. Sailing 65 65
716 $2.50, Animal tending .. .. .. 1·75 1·75
MS717 110 × 85 mm. $5 Raising the flag .. .. 3·00 3·25

INDEPENDENT

Nos. 718/22 and 733 onwards are inscribed "ANTIGUA & BARBUDA".

(Des E. Henry. Litho Format)

1981 (1 Nov). *Independence. T* **162** *and similar multicoloured designs. P* 14½.
718 10 c. Type **162** 5 5
719 50 c. Pineapple, Antigua flag and map .. 25 25
720 90 c. Prime Minister Vere Bird 50 50
721 $2.50, St. John's Cathedral (38 × 25 *mm*) .. 1·40 1·40
MS722 105 × 79 mm. $5 Map of Antigua and Barbuda (42 × 42 *mm*) .. .. 2·75 2·75

163 "Holy Night" (Jacques Stella)

164 Swimming

(Des Clover Mill. Litho Format)

1981 (16 Nov). *Christmas. Paintings. T* **163** *and similar vert designs. Multicoloured. P* 14½.
723 8 c. Type **163** 5 5
724 30 c. "Mary with Child" (Julius Schnorr von Carolfeld) 15 15
725 $1 "Virgin and Child" (Alonso Cano) .. 55 55
726 $3 "Virgin and Child" (Lorenzo di Credi) .. 1·75 1·75
MS727 77 × 111 mm. $5 "Holy Family" (Pieter von Avon) .. .. 2·50 2·50

(Des M. Diamond. Litho Format)

1981 (1 Dec). *International Year for Disabled Persons. Sport for the Disabled. T* **164** *and similar horiz designs. Multicoloured. P* 15.
728 10 c. Type **164** 5 5
729 50 c. Discus throwing 30 30
730 90 c. Archery 55 55
731 $2 Baseball .. .. 1·40 1·40
MS732 108 × 84 mm. $4 Basketball .. .. 2·50 2·50

NEW INFORMATION

The editor is always interested to correspond with people who have new information that will improve or correct the Catalogue.

165 Scene from Football Match

166 European "A-300 (Airbus)"

(Des Clover Mill. Litho Questa)

1982 (15 Apr). *World Cup Football Championship, Spain. T* **165** *and similar horiz designs showing scenes from different matches. P* 14.
733 10 c. multicoloured 5 5
734 50 c. multicoloured 30 30
735 90 c. multicoloured 55 55
736 $4 multicoloured .. .. 2·50 2·50
MS737 75 × 92 mm. $5 multicoloured .. .. 2·75 2·75
Nos. 733/6 also exist perforated 12 (*Price for set of* 4, £3 *mint or used*) from additional sheetlets of five stamps and one label. These stamps have changed inscription colours.

(Des Clover Mill. Litho Format)

1982 (17 June). *Coolidge International Airport. T* **166** *and similar multicoloured designs. P* 14½.
738 10 c. Type **166** 5 5
739 50 c. Hawker-Siddeley "748" 30 30
740 90 c. De Havilland "DCH6 (Twin Otter)" .. 55 55
741 $2.50, Britten-Norman "Islander" .. .. 1·50 1·50
MS742 99 × 73 mm. $5 Boeing "747 (Jumbo Jet)" (*horiz*) .. .. 2·75 2·75

167 Cordia

(Des G. Drummond. Litho Questa)

1982 (28 June). *Death Centenary of Charles Darwin. Fauna and Flora. T* **167** *and similar multicoloured designs. P* 15.
743 10 c. Type **167** 5 5
744 50 c. Golden Spotted Mongoose (*horiz*) .. 30 30
745 90 c. Corallita 55 55
746 $3 Bulldog Bat (*horiz*) .. .. .. 1·75 1·75
MS747 107 × 85 mm. $5 Caribbean Monk Seal 3·00 3·25

168 Queen's House, Greenwich

169 Princess of Wales

(Des PAD Studio. Litho Questa)

1982 (1 July). *21st Birthday of Princess of Wales. T* **168/9** *and similar vert design. Multicoloured. P* 14½ × 14.
748 90 c. Type **168** 45 45
749 $1 Prince and Princess of Wales 50 50
750 $4 Princess Diana (*different*) .. .. 2·00 2·00
MS751 102 × 75 mm. $5 Type **169** .. .. 2·40 2·50
Nos. 748/50 also exist in sheetlets of 5 stamps and 1 label.

170 Boy Scouts decorating Streets for Independence Parade

ROYAL BABY
21.6.82
(**171**)

(Des J. W. Litho Questa)

1982 (15 July). *75th Anniv of Boy Scout Movement. T* **170** *and similar horiz designs. Multicoloured. P* 14.
752 10 c. Type **170** 10 10
753 50 c. Boy Scout giving helping hand during street parade 35 35
754 90 c. Boy Scouts attending Princess Margaret at Independence Ceremony 65 65
755 $2.50, Cub Scout giving directions to tourists 1·75 1·75
MS756 102 × 72 mm. $5 Lord Baden-Powell .. 3·00 3·25

1982 (30 Aug). *Birth of Prince William of Wales. Nos.* 748/51 *optd with T* **171**.
757 90 c. Type **168** 45 45
758 $1 Prince and Princess of Wales 50 50
759 $4 Princess Diana (*different*) .. .. 2·00 2·00
MS760 102 × 75 mm. $5 Type **169** .. .. 2·40 2·50
Nos. 757/9 also exist in sheetlets of 5 stamps and 1 label.

172 Roosevelt in 1940

(Des PAD Studio. Litho Format)

1982 (20 Sept). *Birth Centenary of Franklin D. Roosevelt (Nos.* 761, 763, 765/6 *and* **MS**767) *and 250th Birth Anniv of George Washington (others). T* **172** *and similar multicoloured designs. P* 15.
761 10 c. Type **172** 5 5
762 25 c. Washington as blacksmith 15 15
763 45 c. Churchill, Roosevelt and Stalin at Yalta Conference 25 25
764 60 c. Washington crossing the Delaware (*vert*) 35 35
765 $1 "Roosevelt Special" train (*vert*) 55 55
766 $3 Portrait of Roosevelt (*vert*) .. .. 1·75 1·75
761/6 .. .. *Set of* 6 2·75 2·75
MS767 92 × 87 mm. $4 Roosevelt and Wife .. 2·00 2·10
MS768 92 × 87 mm. $4 Portrait of Washington (*vert*) .. .. 2·00 2·10

173 "Annunciation"

(Des Design Images. Litho Questa)

1982 (Nov). *Christmas. Religious Paintings by Raphael. T* **173** *and similar horiz designs. Multicoloured. P* 14 × 13½.
769 10 c. Type **173** 8 8
770 30 c. "Adoration of the Magi" 15 15
771 $1 "Presentation at the Temple" 50 50
772 $4 "Coronation of the Virgin" .. .. 2·10 2·25
MS773 95 × 124 mm. $5 "Marriage of the Virgin" 2·50 2·50

174 Tritons and Dolphins

175 Pineapple Produce

(Des Design Images. Litho Format)

1983 (28 Jan). *500th Birth Anniv of Raphael. Details from "Galatea" Fresco. T* **174** *and similar multicoloured designs. P* 14½.
774 45 c. Type **174** 20 25
775 50 c. Sea Nymph carried off by Triton .. 25 30
776 60 c. Winged angel steering Dolphins (*horiz*) 30 35
777 $4 Cupids shooting arrows (*horiz*) .. .. 1·90 2·00
MS778 101 × 125 mm. $5 Galatea pulled along by Dolphins .. .. 2·50 2·75

(Des Artists International. Litho Questa)

1983 (14 Mar). *Commonwealth Day. T* **175** *and similar horiz designs. Multicoloured. P* 14.
779 25 c. Type **175** 12 15
780 45 c. Carnival 20 25
781 60 c. Tourism 30 35
782 $3 Airport .. .. 1·40 1·50

176 T.V. Satellite Coverage of Royal Wedding

(Des PAD Studio. Litho Questa)

1983 (5 Apr). *World Communications Year. T* **176** *and similar horiz designs. Multicoloured. P* 14.
783 15 c. Type **176** 10 10
784 50 c. Police communications 35 35

785 60 c. House-to-train telephone call 40 40
786 $3 Satellite earth station with planets Jupiter and Saturn .. .. .. 1·60 1·75
MS787 100 × 90 mm. $5 "Comsat" satellite over West Indies .. .. 2·75 3·00

177 Bottlenose Dolphin

(Des D. Miller. Litho Format)

1983 (9 May). *Whales. T* **177** *and similar horiz designs. Multicoloured. P* 14½.

788 15 c. Type **177** 10 10
789 50 c. Finback Whale 35 35
790 60 c. Bowhead Whale 40 40
791 $3 Spectacled Porpoise .. .. 1·60 1·75
MS792 122 × 101 mm. $5 Unicorn Whale (Narwhal) 2·75 3·00

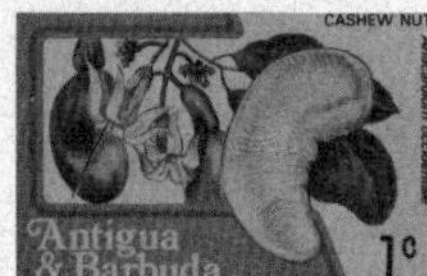

178 Cashew Nut

(Des J.W. Litho Questa)

1983 (11 July). *Fruits and Flowers. T* **178** *and similar horiz designs. Multicoloured. P* 14.

793 1 c. Type **178** 5 5
794 2 c. Passion Fruit 5 5
795 3 c. Mango 5 5
796 5 c. Grapefruit 5 5
797 10 c. Pawpaw 5 8
798 15 c. Breadfruit 8 10
799 20 c. Coconut 10 12
800 25 c. Oleander 12 15
801 30 c. Banana 15 20
802 40 c. Pineapple 20 25
803 45 c. Cordia 25 30
804 50 c. Cassia 30 35
805 60 c. Poui 35 40
806 $1 Frangipani 55 60
807 $2 Flamboyant .. .. 1·10 1·25
808 $2.50, Lemon .. .. 1·40 1·50
809 $5 Lignum Vitae .. .. 3·25 3·50
810 $10 National flag and coat of arms .. .. 5·75 6·00
793/810 .. .. *Set of* 18 12·00 13·50

179 Dornier "Do X" Flying Boat

(Des W. Wright. Litho Format)

1983 (15 Aug). *Bicentenary of Manned Flight. T* **179** *and similar horiz designs. Multicoloured. P* 14½.

811 30 c. Type **179** 15 20
812 50 c. Supermarine "S.6B" seaplane 25 30
813 60 c. Curtiss "9C" biplane and airship U.S.S. *Akron* 30 35
814 $4 *Pro Juventute* balloon .. .. .. 1·90 2·00
MS815 80 × 105 mm. $5 *Graf Zeppelin* .. .. 2·50 2·75

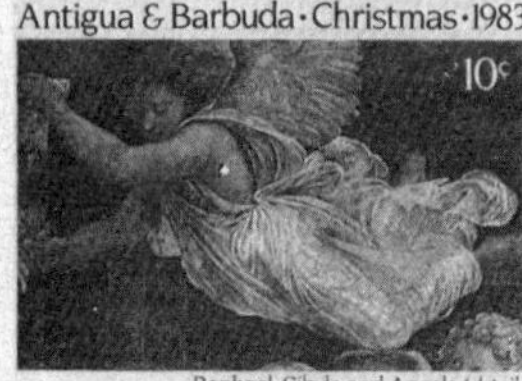

180 "Sibyls and Angels" (detail) (Raphael)

(Des W. Wright. Litho Format)

1983 (4 Oct). *Christmas. 500th Birth Anniv of Raphael. T* **180** *and similar horiz designs. P* 13½.

816 10 c. multicoloured 5 8
817 30 c. multicoloured 15 20
818 $1 multicoloured 45 50
819 $4 multicoloured .. .. 1·90 2·00
MS820 101 × 131 mm. $5 multicoloured .. .. 2·50 2·75

Designs: *Horiz*—10 c. to $4 Different details from "Sibyls and Angels". *Vert*—$5 "The Vision of Ezekiel".

181 John Wesley (founder)

182 Discus

(Des M. Diamond. Litho Questa)

1983 (7 Nov). *Bicentenary of Methodist Church* (1984). *T* **181** *and similar vert designs. Multicoloured. P* 14.

821 15 c. Type **181** 8 10
822 50 c. Nathaniel Gilbert (founder in Antigua) 25 30
823 60 c. St. John Methodist Church steeple .. 30 35
824 $3 Ebenezer Methodist Church, St. John's .. 1·60 1·75

(Des Artists International. Litho Format)

1984 (9 Jan). *Olympic Games, Los Angeles. T* **182** *and similar vert designs. Multicoloured. P* 14½.

825 25 c. Type **182** 12 15
826 50 c. Gymnastics 25 30
827 90 c. Hurdling 50 55
828 $3 Cycling .. .. 1·60 1·75
MS829 82 × 67 mm. $5 Volleyball .. .. 2·75 3·00

183 *Booker Vanguard*

184 Chenille

(Des Artists International. Litho Format)

1984 (14 June). *Ships. T* **183** *and similar multicoloured designs. P* 15.

830 45 c. Type **183** 30 35
831 50 c. S.S. *Canberra* 35 40
832 60 c. Sailing boats 40 45
833 $4 *Fairwind* .. .. 2·50 2·75
MS834 107 × 80 mm. $5 Eighteenth-century British man-of-war (*vert*) .. .. .. 3·25 3·50

(Des J.W. Litho Format)

1984 (19 June). *Universal Postal Union Congress, Hamburg. T* **184** *and similar vert designs showing flowers. Multicoloured. P* 15.

835 15 c. Type **184** 10 12
836 50 c. Shell Flower 35 40
837 60 c. Anthurium 40 45
838 $3 Angels Trumpet .. .. 2·00 2·25
MS839 100 × 75 mm. $5 Crown of Thorns .. 3·50 3·75

$2

$2

(185) (186)

1984 (25 June). (*a*) *Nos.* 702/5 *surch with T* **185**

840 $2 on 25 c. Type **159** .. .. 5·00 5·00
841 $2 on 50 c. Glamis Castle .. .. .. 5·00 5·00
842 $2 on $4 Prince Charles skiing .. .. 5·00 5·00
MS843 96 × 82 mm. $2 on $5 Glass Coach .. 12·00 12·00

(*b*) *Nos.* 748/51 *surch with T* **186**

844 $2 on 90 c. Type **168** (Gold)* .. .. 4·00 3·00
845 $2 on $1 Prince and Princess of Wales (Gold)* .. .. 4·00 3·00
846 $2 on $4 Princess Diana (*different*) (Gold)* 4·00 3·00
MS847 102 × 75 mm. $2 on $5 Type **169** (Gold) 10·00 8·00

(*c*) *Nos.* 757/60 *surch with T* **186**

848 $2 on 90 c. Type **168** (Gold)* .. .. 4·00 3·00
849 $2 on $1 Prince and Princess of Wales (Gold)* .. .. 4·00 3·00
850 $2 on $4 Princess Diana (*different*) (Gold)* 4·00 3·00
MS851 102 × 75 mm. $2 on $5 Type **169** (Gold) 10·00 8·00

(*d*) *Nos.* 779/82 *surch as T* **185**

852 $2 on 25 c. Type **175** .. .. 1·25 1·25
853 $2 on 45 c. Carnival .. .. 1·25 1·25
854 $2 on 60 c. Tourism .. .. 1·25 1·25
855 $2 on $3 Airport .. .. 1·25 1·25

*Nos. 844/6 and 848/50 also exist with similar surcharges in silver on the sheetlets of 5 stamps and 1 label (*price for set of* 3 *as Nos.* 844/6, *£*12 *mint or used*) (*price for set of* 3 *as Nos.* 848/50, *£*12 *mint or used*).

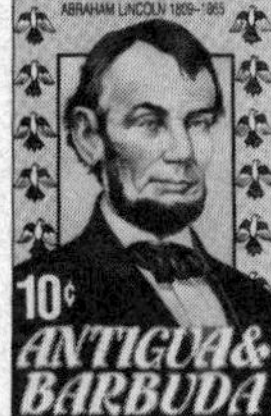

187 Abraham Lincoln

188 View of Moravian Mission

(Des Liane Fried. Litho Questa)

1984 (18 July). *Presidents of the United States of America. T* **18** *and similar vert designs. Multicoloured. P* 14.

856 10 c. Type **187** 8 1
857 20 c. Harry Truman 12 1
858 30 c. Dwight Eisenhower 20 2
859 40 c. Ronald Reagan 25 3
860 90 c. Gettysburg Address, 1863 .. .. 60 6
861 $1.10, Formation of N.A.T.O., 1949 .. .. 70 7
862 $1.50, Eisenhower during Second World War 1·00 1·1
863 $2 Reagan and Caribbean Basin Initiative 1·25 1·4
856/63 .. .. *Set of* 8 3·75 4·0

(Des and litho Questa)

1984 (1 Aug). *150th Anniv of Abolition of Slavery. T* **188** *and similar horiz designs. Multicoloured. P* 14.

864 40 c. Type **188** 25 30
865 50 c. Antigua Courthouse, 1823 .. .. 35 40
866 60 c. Planting sugar-cane, Monks Hill .. 40 45
867 $3 Boiling house, Delaps' estate .. .. 2·00 2·25
MS868 95 × 70 mm. $5 Loading sugar, Willoughby Bay .. .. 3·50 3·75

189 Rufous-sided Towhee

190 Grass-skiing

(Des Jennifer Toombs. Litho Format)

1984 (15 Aug). *Songbirds. T* **189** *and similar vert designs. Multicoloured. P* 15.

869 40 c. Type **189** 25 30
870 50 c. Parula Warbler 35 40
871 60 c. House-wren 40 45
872 $2 Ruby-crowned Kinglet .. .. .. 1·25 1·40
873 $3 Yellow-shafted Flicker .. .. .. 2·00 2·25
MS874 76 × 76 mm. $5 Yellow-breasted Chat .. 3·50 3·75

(Des Bonny Redecker. Litho Questa)

1984 (21 Sept). *"Ausipex" International Stamp Exhibition, Melbourne. Australian Sports. T* **190** *and similar vert designs. Multicoloured. P* 14½.

875 $1 Type **190** 65 70
876 $5 Australian Football .. .. .. 3·50 3·75
MS877 108 × 78 mm. $5 Boomerang-throwing .. 3·50 3·75

191 "The Virgin and Infant with Angels and Cherubs" (Correggio)

192 "The Blue Dancers" (Degas)

(Litho Format)

1984 (4 Oct). *450th Death Anniv of Correggio (painter). T* **191** *and similar vert designs. Multicoloured. P* 15.

878 25 c. Type **191** 15 20
879 60 c. "The Four Saints" 40 45
880 90 c. "St. Catherine" 60 65
881 $3 "The Campori Madonna" .. .. .. 2·00 2·25
MS882 90 × 60 mm. $5 "St. John the Baptist" .. 3·25 3·50

(Litho Format)

1984 (4 Oct). *150th Birth Anniv of Edgar Degas (painter). T* **192** *and similar multicoloured designs. P* 15.

883 15 c. Type **192** 10 12
884 50 c. "The Pink Dancers" 35 40
885 70 c. "Two Dancers" 45 50
886 $4 "Dancers at the Bar" .. .. .. 2·50 2·75
MS887 90 × 60 mm. $5 "The Folk Dancers" (40 × 27 *mm*) .. .. 3·25 3·50

BARBUDA

DEPENDENCY OF ANTIGUA

PRICES FOR STAMPS ON COVER TO 1945
Nos. 1/11 *from* × 2

BARBUDA

(1)

1922 (13 July). *Stamps of Leeward Islands optd with T* **1**. *All Die II.*

(*a*) *Wmk Mult Script CA*

1	**11**	½d. deep green, **O**	2·50	8·50
2		1d. bright scarlet, **O**	2·00	7·50
3	**10**	2d. slate-grey, **O**	2·50	8·00
4	**11**	2½d. bright blue, **O**	2·50	8·50
5		6d. dull and bright purple, **C**	5·00	16·00
6	**10**	2s. purple and blue/*blue*, **C**	14·00	40·00
7		3s. bright green and violet, **C**	38·00	60·00
8		4s. black and red, **C** (R.)	45·00	65·00

(*b*) *Wmk Mult Crown CA*

9	**10**	3d. dull purple/*pale yellow*, **C**	2·00	8·00
10	**12**	1s. black/*emerald*, **C** (R.)	5·00	13·00
11		5s. green and red/*pale yellow*, **C**	£140	£225
1/11		*Set of* 11	£225	£400
1/11 Optd "Specimen"		*Set of* 11	£400	

The postage stamps of Antigua were used in Barbuda until 1968.

The following issues of Barbuda were also valid for use in Antigua.

2 Map of Barbuda

3 Great Amberjack

(Des R. Granger Barrett. Litho Format)

1968 (19 Nov)–**70**. *Designs as T* **2/3**. *P* 14.

12	½ c. brown, black and pink	5	5
13	1 c. orange, black and flesh	5	5
14	2 c. blackish brown, rose-red and rose	5	5
15	3 c. blackish brown, orange-yellow and lemon	5	5
16	4 c. black, bright green and apple-green	8	8
17	5 c. blue-green, black and pale blue-green	10	10
18	6 c. black, bright purple and pale lilac	10	10
19	10 c. black, ultramarine and cobalt	12	12
20	15 c. black, blue-green and turquoise-green	15	15
20*a*	20 c. multicoloured (22.7.70)	1·50	2·00
21	25 c. multicoloured (5.2.69)	25	30
22	35 c. multicoloured (5.2.69)	30	35
23	50 c. multicoloured (5.2.69)	40	45
24	75 c. multicoloured (5.2.69)	70	80
25	$1 multicoloured (6.3.69)	1·25	2·00
26	$2.50, multicoloured (6.3.69)	3·50	6·50
27	$5 multicoloured (6.3.69)	7·50	12·00
12/27	*Set of* 17	15·00	23·00

Designs:—½ to 15 c. Type **2**. *Horiz as T* **3**—20 c. Great Barracuda; 35 c. French Angelfish; 50 c. Porkfish; 75 c. Striped Parrotfish; $1, Longspine Squirrelfish; $2.50, Catalufa; $5, Blue Chromis.

10 Sprinting and Aztec Sun-stone

14 "The Ascension" (Orcagna)

(Des R. Granger Barrett. Litho Format)

1968 (20 Dec). *Olympic Games, Mexico. T* **10** *and similar horiz designs. Multicoloured. P* 14.

28	25 c. Type **10**	45	65
29	35 c. High-jumping and Aztec statue	50	65
30	75 c. Yachting and Aztec lion mask	1·25	1·50
MS31	85 × 76 mm. $1 Football and engraved plate	3·50	4·00

(Des R. Granger Barret. Litho Format)

1969 (24 Mar). *Easter Commemoration. P* 14.

32	**14**	25 c. black and light blue	35	70
33		35 c. black and deep carmine	40	85
34		75 c. black and bluish lilac	60	1·25

OMNIBUS ISSUES

Details, together with prices for complete sets, of the various Omnibus issues from the 1935 Silver Jubilee series to date are included in a special section following Zululand at the end of the catalogue.

15 Scout Enrolment Ceremony

18 "Sistine Madonna" (Raphael)

(Des R. Granger Barrett. Litho Format)

1969 (7 Aug). *3rd Caribbean Scout Jamboree. T* **15** *and similar horiz designs. Multicoloured. P* 14.

35	25 c. Type **15**	35	70
36	35 c. Scouts around camp fire	45	85
37	75 c. Sea Scouts rowing boat	60	1·25

(Des. R. Granger Barrett. Litho Format)

1969 (20 Oct). *Christmas. P* 14.

38	**18**	½ c. multicoloured	5	5
39		25 c. multicoloured	25	60
40		35 c. multicoloured	35	85
41		75 c. multicoloured	45	1·25

19 William I (1066–87)

20c

(**20**)

(Des R. Granger Barrett. Litho Format (Nos. 42/9) or Questa (others))

1970–71. *English Monarchs. T* **19** *and similar vert designs. Multicoloured. P* 14½ × 14.

42	35 c. Type **19** (16.2.70)	90	45
43	35 c. William II (2.3.70)	60	45
44	35 c. Henry I (16.3.70)	60	45
45	35 c. Stephen (1.4.70)	60	45
46	35 c. Henry II (15.4.70)	60	45
47	35 c. Richard I (1.5.70)	60	45
48	35 c. John (15.5.70)	60	45
49	35 c. Henry III (1.6.70)	60	45
50	35 c. Edward I (15.6.70)	60	45
51	35 c. Edward II (1.7.70)	60	45
52	35 c. Edward III (15.7.70)	60	45
53	35 c. Richard II (1.8.70)	60	45
54	35 c. Henry IV (15.8.70	60	45
55	35 c. Henry V (1.9.70)	60	45
56	35 c. Henry VI (15.9.70)	60	45
57	35 c. Edward IV (1.10.70)	60	45
58	35 c. Edward V (15.10.70)	60	45
59	35 c. Richard III (2.11.70)	60	45
60	35 c. Henry VII (16.11.70)	60	45
61	35 c. Henry VIII (1.12.70)	60	45
62	35 c. Edward VI (15.12.70)	60	45
63	35 c. Lady Jane Grey (2.1.71)	60	45
64	35 c. Mary I (15.1.71)	60	45
65	35 c. Elizabeth I (1.2.71)	60	45
66	35 c. James I (15.2.71)	60	45
67	35 c. Charles I (1.3.71)	60	45
68	35 c. Charles II (15.3.71)	60	45
69	35 c. James II (1.4.71)	60	45
70	35 c. William III (15.4.71)	60	45
71	35 c. Mary II (1.5.71)	60	45
72	35 c. Anne (15.5.71)	60	45
73	35 c. George I (1.6.71)	60	45
74	35 c. George II (15.6.71)	60	45
75	35 c. George III (1.7.71)	60	45
76	35 c. George IV (15.7.71)	60	45
77	35 c. William IV (2.8.71)	60	45
78	35 c. Victoria (16.8.71)	60	45
42/78	*Set of* 37	20·00	15·00

See also Nos. 710/15.

1970 (26 Feb). *No. 12 surch with T* **20**.

79	**2**	20 c. on ½ c. brown, black and pink	30	60
		a. Surch inverted	50·00	

21 "The Way to Calvary" (Ugolino)

22 Oliver is introduced to Fagin (*Oliver Twist*)

(Des R. Granger Barrett. Litho Questa)

1970 (16 Mar). *Easter Paintings. T* **21** *and similar vert designs. Multicoloured P* 14.

80	25 c. Type **21**	30	60
	a. Horiz strip of 3. Nos. 80/2	1·10	
81	35 c. "The Deposition from the Cross" (Ugolino)	40	60
82	75 c. Crucifix (The Master of St. Francis)	50	75

Nos. 80/2 were printed together, *se-tenant*, in horizontal strips of 3 throughout the sheet.

(Des R. Granger Barrett. Litho Questa)

1970 (10 July). *Death Centenary of Charles Dickens. T* **22** *and similar horiz design. Multicoloured. P* 14.

83	20 c. Type **22**	45	50
84	75 c. Dickens and Scene from *The Old Curiosity Shop*	55	90

23 "Madonna of the Meadow" (Bellini)

24 Nurse with Patient in Wheelchair

(Des R. Granger Barrett. Litho Questa)

1970 (15 Oct). *Christmas. T* **23** *and similar horiz designs. Multicoloured. P* 14.

85	20 c. Type **23**	35	60
86	50 c. "Madonna, Child and Angels" (from Wilton diptych)	40	85
87	75 c. "The Nativity" (della Francesca)	50	95

(Des R. Granger Barrett. Litho Questa)

1970 (21 Dec). *Centenary of British Red Cross. T* **24** *and similar multicoloured designs. P* 14.

88	20 c. Type **24**	35	60
89	35 c. Nurse giving patient magazines (*horiz*)	60	90
90	75 c. Nurse and mother weighing baby (*horiz*)	75	1·60

25 Angel with Vases

26 Martello Tower

(Des R. Granger Barrett. Litho Questa)

1971 (7 Apr). *Easter. Details of the "Mond" Crucifixion by Raphael. T* **25** *and similar vert designs. Multicoloured. P* 14.

91	35 c. Type **25**	35	65
	a. Horiz strip of 3. Nos. 91/3	1·10	
92	50 c. Christ crucified	40	75
93	75 c. Angel with vase	45	90

Nos. 91/3 were issued horizontally *se-tenant* within the sheet.

(Des R. Granger Barrett. Litho Questa)

1971 (10 May). *Tourism. T* **26** *and similar horiz designs. Multicoloured. P* 14.

94	20 c. Type **26**	30	60
95	25 c. Sailing boats	40	70
96	50 c. Hotel bungalows	60	85
97	75 c. Government House and Mystery Stone	80	1·40

27 "The Granducal Madonna" (Raphael)

BARBUDA BARBUDA

(**28**)

(Des R. Granger Barrett. Litho Questa)

1971 (4 Oct). *Christmas. T* **27** *and similar vert designs. Multicoloured. P* 14.

98	½ c. Type **27**	5	5
99	35 c. "The Ansidei Madonna" (Raphael)	40	75
100	50 c. "The Madonna and Child" (Botticelli)	55	95
101	75 c. "The Madonna of the Trees" (Bellini)	65	1·10

The contract with the agency for the distribution of Barbuda stamps was cancelled by the Antiguan Government on 15 August 1971 but the above issue was duly authorised. Four stamps (20, 35, 50 and 70 c.) were prepared to commemorate the 500th anniversary of the birth of Albrecht Dürer but their issue was not authorised.

Barbuda ceased to have separate stamps issues in 1972 but again had stamps of her own on 14 November 1973 with the following issue.

1973 (14 Nov). *Royal Wedding. Nos.* 370/1 *of Antigua optd with T* **28**.
102 35 c. multicoloured .. 4·00 4·25
a. Opt inverted .. £100
103 $2 multicoloured .. 2·00 2·25
a. Opt inverted .. £120

No. **MS**372 of Antigua also exists with this overprint, but was not placed on sale at post offices. Examples of this sheet are known with "Specimen" overprint (*Price* £120).

BARBUDA (29) — BARBUDA (30) — BARBUDA (30*a*) — BARBUDA (31)

1973 (26 Nov)–**74**. *T* **92** *etc. of Antigua optd with T* **29**.

(*a*) *On Nos.* 270 *etc. W w* **12** (*sideways*)
104 1 c. Columbus and *Nina* .. 15 15
105 2 c. Sir Thomas Warner's emblem and ship 25 25
106 4 c. Sir George Rodney and H.M.S. *Formidable* .. 30 30
107 5 c. Nelson and H.M.S. *Boreas* .. 40 40
108 6 c. William IV and H.M.S. *Pegasus*.. 40 40
109 10 c. "Blackbeard" and pirate ketch .. 45 45
110 20 c. Nelson and H.M.S. *Victory* .. 60 60
111 25 c. R.M.S.P. *Solent* .. 60 60
112 35 c. George V (when Prince George) and H.M.S. *Canada* .. 70 70
113 50 c. H.M.S. *Renown* .. 70 70
114 75 c. *Federal Maple* .. 70 70
115 $2.50, H.M.S. *London* (18.2.74) .. 2·00 2·00

(*b*) *On Nos.* 323 *etc. W w* **12** (*upright*). *White paper*
116 ½ c. Type **92** (11.12.73) .. 15 20
117 3 c. Viscount Hood and H.M.S. *Barfleur* (11.12.73).. 25 25
118 15 c. Captain Collingwood and H.M.S. *Pelican* (11.12.73).. 50 50
119 $1 Yacht and Class Emblem (11.12.73) .. 75 80
120 $2.50, H.M.S. *London* (18.2.74) .. 13·00 11·00
121 $5 Tug *Pathfinder* (26.11.73) .. 4·00 4·50
104/21 .. *Set of* 18 23·00 22·00

1973 (26 Nov). *Commemorative stamps of Antigua optd.*

(*a*) *Nos.* 353, 355 *and* 357/8 *optd with T* **30**
122 ½ c. Private, Zacharia Tiffin's Regt of Foot, 1701 .. 5 5
123 20 c. Light Company Officer, 35th Regt of Foot, 1828 .. 30 30
a. Optd with T **30*a*** .. 1·75 1·75
124 75 c. Sergeant, 49th Regt, 1858 .. 65 75
MS125 127 × 145 mm .. 3·25 3·75

(*b*) *Nos* 360/3 *optd with T* **31**, *in red*
126 20 c. Carnival street scene .. 20 20
127 35 c. Carnival troupe .. 25 25
a. Opt inverted .. 30·00
128 75 c. Carnival Queen .. 45 50
MS129 134 × 95 mm .. 2·75 3·25
a. Albino opt
b. Opt double .. £275

Type **30*a*** is a typographical overprint, applied locally.

BARBUDA (32) — BARBUDA (33) — BARBUDA (34) — BARBUDA (35)

1973 (11 Dec). *Christmas. Nos.* 364/9 *of Antigua optd with T* **32**.
130 3 c. Type **105** (Sil.) .. 8 8
a. Opt inverted .. 40·00
b. "BABRUDA" (R.4/2) .. 5·50 5·50
131 5 c. "Adoration of the Magi" (Stomer) (Sil.) 10 10
a. "BABRUDA" (R.4/2) .. 7·00 7·00
132 20 c. "Granducal Madonna" (Raphael) (Sil.) .. 40 40
a. "BABRUDA" (R.4/2) .. 9·00 9·00
133 35 c. "Nativity with God the Father and Holy Ghost" (Battista) (R.) .. 55 55
134 $1 "Madonna and Child" (Murillo) (R.) .. 1·40 1·50
a. Opt inverted .. 45·00
MS135 130 × 128 mm. Nos. 130/4 (Sil.) .. 12·00 15·00

1973 (15 Dec). *Honeymoon Visit of Princess Anne and Capt. Phillips. Nos.* 373/5 *of Antigua further optd with T* **33**.
136 35 c. multicoloured .. 50 40
a. Opt double, one albino .. 65·00
b. Optd on Antigua No. 373a
137 $2 multicoloured .. 1·75 1·60
a. Optd on Antigua No. 374a
MS138 78 × 100 mm. Nos. 136/7 .. 6·50 7·50

1974 (18 Feb). *25th Anniv of University of West Indies. Nos.* 376/9 *of Antigua optd with T* **34**.
139 5 c. Coat of arms .. 8 8
140 20 c. Extra-mural art .. 15 15
141 35 c. Antigua campus .. 25 25
a. Opt double
142 75 c. Antigua Chancellor .. 55 60

1974 (1 May). *Military Uniforms. Nos.* 380/4 *of Antigua optd with T* **35**.
143 ½ c. Officer, 59th Foot, 1797 .. 5 5
144 10 c. Gunner, Royal Artillery, 1800 .. 15 15
a. Horiz pair, left-hand stamp without opt £120
145 20 c. Private, 1st West India Regt, 1830 .. 25 25
a. Horiz pair, left-hand stamp without opt £120
146 35 c. Officer, 92nd Foot, 1843 .. 40 40
a. Opt inverted .. 50·00
147 75 c. Private, 23rd Foot, 1846 .. 80 80

Nos. 144a and 145a come from sheets on which the overprint was so misplaced as to miss the first vertical row completely. Other stamps in these sheets show the overprint at left instead of right.

BARBUDA 13 JULY 1922 (**36**) — BARBUDA 15 SEPT. 1874 G.P.U. (**37** "General Postal Union") — BARBUDA (**38**)

1974 (15 July). *Centenary of Universal Postal Union* (*1st issue*). *Nos.* 386/92 *of Antigua optd with T* **36** (*Nos.* 148, 150, 152, 154, 156, 158 *and* 160) *or T* **37** (*others*), *in red.*
148 ½ c. English postman, mailcoach and helicopter .. 8 8
149 ½ c. English postman, mailcoach and helicopter .. 8 8
150 1 c. Bellman, mailboat *Orinoco* and satellite 8 8
151 1 c. Bellman, mailboat *Orinoco* and satellite 8 8
152 2 c. Train guard, post-bus and hydrofoil .. 8 8
153 2 c. Train guard, post-bus and hydrofoil .. 8 8
154 5 c. Swiss messenger, Wells Fargo coach and "Concorde" .. 10 12
155 5 c. Swiss messenger, Wells Fargo coach and "Concorde" .. 10 12
156 20 c. Postillion, Japanese postmen and carrier pigeon .. 60 70
157 20 c. Postillion, Japanese postmen and carrier pigeon .. 60 70
158 35 c. Antiguan postman, flying-boat and tracking station .. 1·25 1·50
159 35 c. Antiguan postman, flying-boat and tracking station .. 1·25 1·50
160 $1 Medieval courier, American express train and Boeing "747" .. 3·75 4·00
161 $1 Medieval courier, American express train and Boeing "747" .. 3·75 4·00
148/61 .. *Set of* 14 11·00 12·00
MS162 141 × 164 mm. No. **MS**393 of Antigua overprinted with T **38**, in red .. 5·00 6·00
a. Albino opt

Nos. 148/9, 150/1, 152/3, 154/5, 156/7, 158/9 and 160/1 were each printed together, *se-tenant*, in horizontal pairs throughout the sheet.

See also Nos. 177/80.

1974 (14 Aug). *Antiguan Steel Bands. Nos.* 394/8 *of Antigua optd with T* **38**.
163 5 c. rose-red, carmine and black .. 5 5
164 20 c. brown-ochre, chestnut and black .. 15 15
165 35 c. light sage-green, blue-green and black .. 25 25
166 75 c. dull blue, dull ultramarine and black .. 45 50
MS167 115 × 108 mm. Nos. 163/6 .. 1·25 1·25

39 Footballers

BARBUDA (**40**)

(Des G. Drummond. Litho Format)

1974 (2 Sept). *World Cup Football Championships* (*1st issue*). *Various horiz designs as T* **39** *each showing footballers in action. P* 14.
168 **39** 35 c. multicoloured .. 40 30
169 $1.20, multicoloured .. 70 65
170 $2.50, multicoloured .. 1·00 1·25
MS171 70 × 128 mm. Nos. 168/70 .. 2·25 2·75

1974 (23 Sept). *World Cup Football Championships* (*2nd issue*). *Nos.* 399/403 *of Antigua optd with T* **40**.
172 5 c. multicoloured .. 5 5
173 35 c. multicoloured .. 25 30
174 75 c. multicoloured .. 35 40
175 $1 multicoloured .. 40 50
MS176 135 × 130 mm. Nos. 172/5 .. 1·25 1·50

41 Ship Letter of 1833

42 Great Amberjack

(Des G. Drummond. Litho Questa)

1974 (30 Sept). *Centenary of Universal Postal Union* (*2nd issue*). *T* **41** *and similar vert designs. Multicoloured. P* 13½.
177 35 c. Type **41** .. 35 4[...]
178 $1.20, Stamps and postmark of 1922 .. 1·25 1·4[...]
179 $2.50, Mailplane over map of Barbuda 1·90 2·2[...]
MS180 128 × 97 mm. Nos. 177/9 .. 4·50 5·0[...]

(Des G. Drummond. Litho Questa)

1974 (15 Oct)–**75**. *Multicoloured designs as T* **42**. *P* 14 × 14½ (½ *c. to* 3 *c.,* 25 *c.*), 14½ × 14 (4 *c. to* 20 *c.,* 35 *c.*), 14 (50 *c. to* $1) *or* 13½ (*others*).
181 ½ c. Oleander, Rose Bay (6.1.75) .. 10 1[...]
182 1 c. Blue Petrea (6.1.75) .. 10 1[...]
183 2 c. Poinsettia (6.1.75) .. 10 1[...]
184 3 c. Cassia tree (6.1.75) .. 10 1[...]
185 4 c. Type **42** .. 10 1[...]
186 5 c. Holy Trinity School .. 15 1[...]
187 6 c. Snorkeling .. 15 1[...]
188 10 c. Pilgrim Holiness Church .. 15 1[...]
189 15 c. New Cottage Hospital .. 15 1[...]
190 20 c. Post Office and Treasury .. 15 1[...]
191 25 c. Island jetty and boats .. 30 2[...]
192 35 c. Martello Tower .. 30 2[...]
193 50 c. Warden's House (6.1.75).. 30 3[...]
194 75 c. Inter-island aircraft .. 75 8[...]
195 $1 Tortoise (6.1.75) .. 70 8[...]
196 $2.50, Spiny lobster (6.1.75).. 1·50 1·75
197 $5Magnificent Frigate Bird (6.1.75) .. 4·00 4·25
a.Perf 14 × 14½ (24.7.75)* .. 13·00 17·00
197*b* $10Hibiscus (19.9.75).. 9·00 9·50
181/97*b* .. *Set of* 18 16·00 17·00

*See footnote below Nos. 227/8.

The 50 c. to $1 are larger, 39 × 25 mm; the $2.50 and $5 are 45 × 29 mm; the $10 is 34 × 48 mm and the ½ c. to 3c. 25 c. and $10 are vert designs.

1974 (15 Oct). *Birth Centenary of Sir Winston Churchill* (*1st issue*). *Nos.* 408/12 *of Antigua optd with T* **38** *in red.*
198 5 c. Churchill as schoolboy, and school college building, Harrow .. 35 35
a. Opt inverted .. 60·00
199 35 c. Churchill and St. Paul's Cathedral .. 80 80
200 75 c. Coat of arms and catafalque .. 1·40 1·40
201 $1 Churchill, "reward" notice and South African escape route .. 1·90 1·90
a. Opt inverted .. 60·00
MS202 107 × 82 mm. Nos. 198/201 .. 11·00 12·00

43 Churchill making Broadcast

BARBUDA (**44**)

(Des G. Drummond. Litho Questa)

1974 (20 Nov). *Birth Centenary of Sir Winston Churchill* (*2nd issue*). *T* **43** *and similar horiz designs. Multicoloured. P* 13½ × 14.
203 5 c. Type **43** .. 15 15
204 35 c. Churchill and Chartwell .. 40 45
205 75 c. Churchill painting .. 60 65
206 $1 Churchill making "V" sign .. 75 80
MS207 146 × 95 mm. Nos. 203/6 .. 2·50 3·00

1974 (25 Nov). *Christmas. Nos.* 413/21 *of Antigua optd with T* **33**.
208 ½ c. Bellini .. 5 5
a. Opt inverted .. 45·00
209 1 c. Raphael .. 5 5
210 2 c. Van der Weyden .. 5 5
211 3 c. Giorgione .. 5 5
212 5 c. Mantegna .. 5 5
213 20 c. Vivarini .. 20 20
214 35 c. Montagna .. 30 30
215 75 c. Lorenzo Costa .. 60 60
208/15 .. *Set of* 8 1·25 1·25
MS216 139 × 126 mm. Nos. 208/15 .. 1·25 1·40

1975 (17 Mar). *Nelson's Dockyard. Nos.* 427/32 *of Antigua optd with T* **44**.
217 5 c. Carib war canoe, English Harbour, 1300 20 20
218 15 c. Ship of the line, English Harbour, 1770 35 35
219 35 c. H.M.S. *Boreas* at anchor, and Lord Nelson, 1787 .. 55 55
220 50 c. Yachts during "Sailing Week", 1974 .. 80 80
221 $1 Yacht Anchorage, Old Dockyard, 1970 .. 1·25 1·75
MS222 130 × 134 mm. As Nos. 217/21, but in larger format; 43 × 28 mm .. 3·25 3·50

45 Ships of the Line

(Des G. Vasarhelyi. Litho Format)

1975 (30 May). *Sea Battles. T* **45** *and similar horiz designs showing scenes from the Battle of the Saints,* 1782. *Multicoloured. P* 13½.
223 35 c. Type **45** .. 1·75 1·10
224 50 c. English three-masters .. 2·00 1·25
225 75 c. Ships firing broadsides .. 2·25 1·50
226 95 c. Sailors fleeing burning ship .. 2·50 1·75

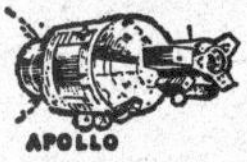

(46)

1975 (24 July). *"Apollo-Soyuz" Space Project. No.* 197a *optd with T* **46** *and similar ("Soyuz") opt.*

227	$5 Magnificent Frigate Bird ("Apollo")	6·50	9·00
	a. *Se-tenant* strip of 3. Nos. 227/8 and 197a	42·00	
228	$5 Magnificent Frigate Bird ("Soyuz")	6·50	9·00

Nos. 227/8 were issued together *se-tenant* in sheets of 25 (5 × 5), with the "Apollo" opts in the first and third vertical rows and the "Soyuz" opts in the second and fourth vertical rows, the fifth vertical row comprising five unoverprinted stamps (No. 197a).

47 Officer, 65th Foot, 1763

30TH ANNIVERSARY
UNITED NATIONS
1945 — 1975

(48)

(Des G. Drummond. Litho Questa)

1975 (17 Sept). *Military Uniforms. T* **47** *and similar vert designs. Multicoloured. P* 13½.

229	35 c. Type **47**	85	80
230	50 c. Grenadier, 27th Foot, 1701–10	1·10	1·10
231	75 c. Officer, 21st Foot, 1793–6	1·25	1·25
232	95 c. Officer, Royal Regt of Artillery, 1800	1·40	1·50

1975 (24 Oct). *30th Anniv of United Nations. Nos.* 203/6 *optd with T* **48**.

233	5 c. Churchill making broadcast	5	5
234	35 c. Churchill and Chartwell	30	30
235	75 c. Churchill painting	60	60
236	$1 Churchill making "V" sign	75	75

BARBUDA (49) BARBUDA (50)

1975 (17 Nov). *Christmas. Nos.* 457/65 *of Antigua optd with T* **49**.

237	½ c. Correggio	5	5
238	1 c. El Greco	5	5
239	2 c. Dürer	5	5
240	3 c. Antonello	5	5
241	5 c. Bellini	8	8
242	10 c. Dürer	10	10
243	25 c. Bellini	35	35
244	$2 Dürer	1·75	1·75
237/44	*Set of* 8	2·25	2·25
MS245	138 × 119 mm. Nos. 241/4	2·50	2·75

1975 (15 Dec). *World Cup Cricket Winners. Nos.* 466/8 *of Antigua optd with T* **50**.

246	5 c. Vivian Richards	75	75
247	35 c. Andy Roberts	1·50	1·50
248	$2 West Indies team	3·25	3·25

51 "Surrender of Cornwallis at Yorktown" (Trumbull)

(Des G. Vasarhelyi. Litho Format)

1976 (8 Mar). *Bicentenary of American Revolution. T* **51** *and similar horiz designs. Multicoloured. P* 13½ × 13.

249	15 c.	Type **51**	12	12
250	15 c.	Type **51**	12	12
251	15 c.	Type **51**	12	12
252	35 c.	"The Battle of Princeton"	30	30
253	35 c.	"The Battle of Princeton"	30	30
254	35 c.	"The Battle of Princeton"	30	30
255	$1	"Surrender of General Burgoyne at Saratoga" (W. Mercer)	80	80
256	$1	"Surrender of General Burgoyne at Saratoga" (W. Mercer)	80	80
257	$1	"Surrender of General Burgoyne at Saratoga" (W. Mercer)	80	80
258	$2	"The Declaration of Independence" (Trumbull)	1·40	1·40
259	$2	"The Declaration of Independence" (Trumbull)	1·40	1·40
260	$2	"The Declaration of Independence" (Trumbull)	1·40	1·40
249/60		*Set of* 12	7·00	7·00
MS261		140 × 70 mm. Nos. 249/54 and 255/60 (*two sheets*)	9·50	10·00

The three designs of each value were printed horizontally *se-tenant* within the sheet to form the composite designs listed. Type **51** shows the left-hand stamp of the 15 c. design.

MINIMUM PRICE

The minimum price quoted is 5p which represents a handling charge rather than a basis for valuing common stamps. For further notes about prices see introductory pages.

52 Bananaquits

(Des G. Drummond. Litho Format)

1976 (30 June). *Birds. T* **52** *and similar horiz designs. Multicoloured. P* 13½.

262	35 c. Type **52**	1·25	85
263	50 c. Blue-hooded Euphonia	1·50	90
264	75 c. Royal Tern	1·75	1·10
265	95 c. Killdeer Plover	2·00	1·40
266	$1.25, Common Cowbird	2·50	1·90
267	$2 Purple Gallinule	3·75	3·00
262/7	*Set of* 6	11·50	8·50

1976 (12 Aug). *Royal Visit to the U.S.A. As Nos.* 249/60 *but redrawn and inscr at top* "H.M. QUEEN ELIZABETH ROYAL VISIT 6TH JULY 1976 H.R.H. DUKE OF EDINBURGH".

268	15 c.	As Type **51**	12	12
269	15 c.	As Type **51**	12	12
270	15 c.	As Type **51**	12	12
271	35 c.	As Nos. 252/4	30	30
272	35 c.	As Nos. 252/4	30	30
273	35 c.	As Nos. 252/4	30	30
274	$1	As Nos. 255/7	80	80
275	$1	As Nos. 255/7	80	80
276	$1	As Nos. 255/7	80	80
277	$2	As Nos. 258/60	1·40	1·40
278	$2	As Nos. 258/60	1·40	1·40
279	$2	As Nos. 258/60	1·40	1·40
268/79		*Set of* 12	7·00	7·00
MS280		143 × 81 mm. Nos. 268/73 and 274/9 (*two sheets*)	8·00	8·50

The three designs of each value were printed horizontally *se-tenant*, imperf between.

BARBUDA (53) BARBUDA (54)

1976 (2 Dec). *Christmas. Nos.* 514/18 *of Antigua optd with T* **53**.

281	8 c. The Annunciation	12	12
282	10 c. The Holy Family	12	12
283	15 c. The Magi	20	20
284	50 c. The Shepherds	35	35
285	$1 Epiphany scene	60	60

1976 (28 Dec). *Olympic Games, Montreal. Nos.* 495/502 *of Antigua optd with T* **54**.

286	½ c. High-jump	5	5
287	1 c. Boxing	5	5
288	2 c. Pole-vault	5	5
289	15 c. Swimming	10	10
290	30 c. Running	20	20
291	$1 Cycling	80	70
292	$2 Shot put	1·25	1·50
286/92	*Set of* 7	2·25	2·40
MS293	88 × 138 mm. Nos. 289/92	2·75	3·00

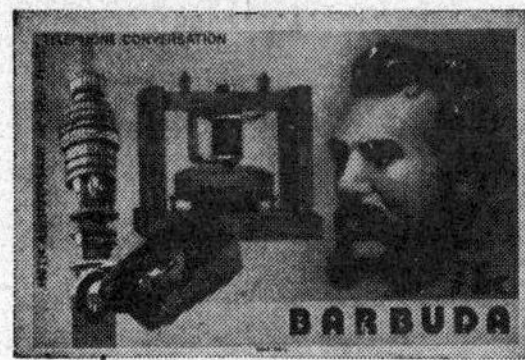

55 Post Office Tower, Telephones and Alexander Graham Bell

(Des G. Vasarhelyi. Litho Format)

1977 (31 Jan). *Telephone Centenary* (1976). *T* **55** *and similar horiz designs. Multicoloured. P* 13½.

294	75 c. Type **55**	70	65
295	$1.25, Dish aerial and television	1·00	90
296	$2 Globe and satellites	1·60	1·50
MS297	96 × 144 mm. Nos. 294/6. P 15	3·00	3·25

56 St. Margaret's Church, Westminster

1977 (7 Feb). *Silver Jubilee* (1*st issue*). *T* **56** *and similar horiz designs. Multicoloured. Litho. P* 13½ × 13.

298	75 c. Type **56**	45	50
299	75 c. Entrance, Westminster Abbey	45	50
300	75 c. Westminster Abbey	45	50
301	$1.25, Household Cavalry	55	60
302	$1.25, Coronation Coach	55	60
303	$1.25, Team of Horses	55	60
298/303	*Set of* 6	2·75	3·00
MS304	148 × 83 mm. Nos. 298/303. P 15	2·75	3·00

Nos. 298/300 and 301/3 were printed horizontally *se-tenant*, forming composite designs.

See also Nos. 323/30 and 375/8.

1977 (4 Apr). *Nos.* 469A/86A *of Antigua optd with T* **54**.

305	½ c. Antillean Crested Hummingbird	15	15
306	1 c. Imperial Parrot	20	20
307	2 c. Zenaida Dove	20	20
308	3 c. Loggerhead Kingbird	20	20
309	4 c. Red-necked Pigeon	20	20
310	5 c. Rufous-throated Solitaire	20	20
311	6 c. Orchid Tree	20	20
312	10 c. Bougainvillea	20	20
313	15 c. Geiger Tree	20	20
314	20 c. Flamboyant	25	25
315	25 c. Hibiscus	25	25
316	35 c. Flame of the Wood	30	30
317	50 c. Cannon at Fort James	40	35
318	75 c. Premier's Office	40	40
319	$1 Potworks Dam	50	50
320	$2.50, Irrigation scheme	1·25	1·40
321	$5 Government House	2·75	3·00
322	$10 Coolidge Airport	5·50	7·00
305/22	*Set of* 18	12·00	14·50

BARBUDA (57) B A R B U D A (58) BARBUDA (59)

1977 (4 Apr–20 Dec). *Silver Jubilee* (2*nd issue*).

(*a*) *Sheet stamps. Nos.* 526/31 *of Antigua optd with T* **57**

323	10 c. Royal Family	25	30
324	30 c. Royal Visit, 1966	55	60
325	50 c. Queen enthroned	85	90
326	90 c. Queen after Coronation	1·60	1·75
327	$2.50, Queen and Prince Charles	4·00	4·50
MS328	116 × 78 mm. $5 Queen Elizabeth and Prince Philip	6·00	7·00
	a. Error. Imperf	£600	
	b. Opt albino	25·00	
	c. Opt double		

(*b*) *Booklet stamps. Nos.* 532/3 *of Antigua optd with T* **58** *in silver* (50 *c.*) *or T* **59** *in gold* ($5) (20 Dec)

329	50 c. Queen after Coronation	80	1·25
	a. Booklet pane of 6	4·75	
330	$5 The Queen and Prince Philip	10·00	14·00
	a. Booklet pane of 1	10·00	

BARBUDA (60)

61 Royal Yacht *Britannia*

1977 (13 June). *Caribbean Scout Jamboree, Jamaica. Nos.* 534/41 *of Antigua optd with T* **60**.

331	½ c. Making camp	5	5
332	1 c. Hiking	5	5
333	2 c. Rock-climbing	5	5
334	10 c. Cutting logs	15	15
335	30 c. Map and sign reading	50	50
336	50 c. First aid	70	70
337	$2 Rafting	2·25	2·25
331/37	*Set of* 7	3·25	3·25
MS338	127 × 114 mm. Nos. 335/7	3·50	3·75

1977 (12 Aug). *21st Anniv of Carnival. Nos.* 542/7 *of Antigua optd with T* **60**.

339	10 c. Carnival costume	10	8
340	30 c. Carnival Queen	20	15
341	50 c. Butterfly costume	30	20
342	90 c. Queen of the band	50	40
343	$1 Calypso King and Queen	55	45
MS344	140 × 120 mm. Nos. 339/43	1·90	2·00

(Des G. Drummond. Litho Format)

1977 (27 Oct). *Royal Visit* (1*st issue*). *T* **61** *and similar horiz designs. Multicoloured. P* 14½.

345	50 c. Type **61**	50	40
346	$1.50, Jubilee emblem	1·10	85
347	$2.50, Union Jack and flag of Antigua	1·25	1·00
MS348	77 × 124 mm. Nos. 345/7	2·50	2·50

BARBUDA (62) BARBUDA (63)

64 Zeppelin "LZ1"

1977 (28 Nov–20 Dec). *Royal Visit* (2*nd issue*). *Nos.* 548/**MS**553 *of Antigua optd.* A. *With T* **57**. *P* 14 (28 Nov). B. *With T* **62**. *P* 11½ × 12 (20 Dec).

		A.		B.	
349	10 c. Royal Family	25	15	15	8
	a. Blue opt	†		35	35
350	30 c. Royal Visit, 1966	45	35	30	20
	a. Blue opt	†		90	95
351	50 c. Queen enthroned	65	55	40	30
	a. Blue opt	†		1·75	1·90

352 90 c. Queen after Coronation .. 1·25 1·00 70 50
a. Blue opt .. .. .. † 3·25 3·50
353 $2.50, Queen and Prince Charles .. .. .. 3·25 3·25 1·75 1·50
a. Blue opt .. .. .. † 9·00 9·50
MS354 116 × 78 mm. $5 Queen and Prince Philip .. .. .. 6·50 7·00 †

Nos. 349B/53B were each printed in small sheets of 6 including one *se-tenant* stamp-size label.

1977 (28 Nov). *Christmas. Nos. 554/61 of Antigua optd with T* **63**. *"Virgin and Child" paintings by the artists given.*

355 ½ c. Tura 5 5
356 1 c. Crivelli 5 5
357 2 c. Lotto 5 5
358 8 c. Pontormo 8 8
359 10 c. Tura 10 10
360 25 c. Lotto 20 20
361 $2 Crivelli .. .. 1·50 1·50
355/61 .. .. .. *Set of* 7 1·75 1·75
MS362 144 × 118 mm. Nos. 358/61 .. .. 2·25 2·40

(Des I. Oliver. Litho Format)

1977 (29 Dec). *Special Events*, 1977. *T* **64** *and similar horiz designs. Multicoloured. P* 14.

363 75 c. Type **64** 40 35
a. Nos 363/6 in *se-tenant* block .. 1·60
364 75 c. German battleship and naval airship "L 31" 40 35
365 75 c. *Graf Zeppelin* in hangar 40 35
366 75 c. Military airship gondola 40 35
367 95 c. "Sputnik 1" 50 40
a. Nos. 367/70 in *se-tenant* block .. 2·00
368 95 c. "Vostok" 50 40
369 95 c. "Voskhod" 50 40
370 95 c. Space walk 50 40
371 $1.25, Fuelling for flight 75 55
a. Nos. 371/4 in *se-tenant* block .. 3·00
372 $1.25, Leaving New York 75 55
373 $1.25, *Spirit of St. Louis* 75 55
374 $1.25, Welcome in England 75 55
375 $2 Lion of England .. .. .. 1·25 90
a. Nos. 375/8 in *se-tenant* block .. 5·00
376 $2 Unicorn of Scotland .. .. 1·25 90
377 $2 Yale of Beaufort .. .. .. 1·25 90
378 $2 Falcon of Plantagenets .. .. 1·25 90
379 $5 } .. 2·75 2·50
380 $5 } "Daniel in the Lion's Den" .. 2·75 2·50
381 $5 } (Rubens) .. 2·75 2·50
382 $5 } .. 2·75 2·50
a. Nos. 379/82 in *se-tenant* block .. 11·00
363/82 .. .. .. *Set of* 20 20·00 17·00
MS383 132 × 156 mm. Nos. 363/82 .. .. 20·00 20·00

Events:—75 c. 75th Anniv of Navigable Airships; 95 c. 20th Anniv of U.S.S.R. Space Programme; $1.25, 50th Anniv of Lindbergh's Transatlantic Flight; $2 Silver Jubilee of Queen Elizabeth II; $5 400th Birth Anniv of Rubens.

Nos. 363/66, 367/70, 371/74, 375/78 and 379/82 were printed in *se-tenant* blocks of four within the sheet.

BARBUDA

(65)

66 "Pieta" (sculpture) (detail)

1978 (15 Feb). *Tenth Anniv of Statehood. Nos. 562/7 of Antigua optd with T* **65**.

384 10 c. Pineapple 8 8
385 15 c. State flag 12 12
386 50 c. Police band 30 30
387 90 c. Premier V. C. Bird 60 55
388 $2 State Coat of Arms .. .. 1·40 1·25
MS389 126 × 99 mm. Nos. 385/88. P 14 .. 2·25 2·25

(Des G. Vasarhelyi. Litho Format)

1978 (23 Mar). *Easter. Works by Michelangelo. T* **66** *and similar horiz designs. Multicoloured. P* 13½ × 14.

390 75 c. Type **66** 50 55
391 95 c. "The Holy Family" (painting) .. 55 55
392 $1.25, "Libyan Sibyl" from Sistine Chapel, Rome 60 60
393 $2 "The Flood" from Sistine Chapel .. 80 80
MS394 117 × 85 mm. Nos. 390/3 .. .. 2·50 3·00

BARBUDA

(67)

68 St. Edward's Crown

1978 (28 Mar). *75th Anniv of Powered Flight. Nos. 568/75 of Antigua optd with T* **67**.

395 ½ c. *Glider III*, 1902 .. .. .. 5 5
396 1 c. *Flyer I*, 1903 .. .. .. 5 5
397 2 c. Launch system and engine 5 5
398 10 c. Orville Wright 5 5
399 50 c. *Flyer III*, 1905 .. .. .. 40 30
400 90 c. Wilbur Wright 60 45
401 $2 Wright "Model B", 1910 .. .. 1·25 95
395/401 .. .. .. *Set of* 7 2·25 1·75
MS402 90 × 75 mm. $2.50, *Flyer I* on launch system .. .. 1·50 1·60

1978 (22 May). *Sailing Week. Nos. 576/80 of Antigua optd with T* **67**.

403 10 c. Sunfish regatta 15 15
404 50 c. Fishing and work boat race 55 55
405 90 c. Curtain Bluff race 75 75
406 $2 Power boat rally .. .. .. 1·50 1·50
MS407 110 × 77 mm. $2.50, Guadeloupe–Antigua race .. .. 1·60 1·60
a. Albino opt .. .. † —

(Des J. Cooter. Litho)

1978 (2 June). *25th Anniv of Coronation* (1*st issue*). *T* **68** *and similar vert designs. Multicoloured. P* 15.

408 75 c. Type **68** 35 40
409 75 c. Imperial State Crown 35 40
410 $1.50, Queen Mary's Crown 65 75
411 $1.50, Queen Mother's Crown 65 75
412 $2.50, Queen Consort's Crown .. .. 90 1·00
413 $2.50, Queen Victoria's Crown .. .. 90 1·00
408/413 .. .. .. *Set of* 6 3·50 3·75
MS414 123 × 117 mm. Nos. 408/13. P 14½ .. 3·50 4·00

The two designs for each value were issued as two *se-tenant* pairs, together with 2 labels, in small sheets of 6.

1978 (2 June–12 Oct). *25th Anniv of Coronation* (*2nd issue*).

(*a*) *Sheet stamps. Nos. 581/6 of Antigua optd with T* **67**. *P* 14 (2.6)

415 10 c. Queen Elizabeth and Prince Philip .. 5 5
416 30 c. Crowning 15 20
417 50 c. Coronation procession 20 25
418 90 c. Queen seated in St. Edward's Chair .. 35 40
419 $2.50, Queen wearing Imperial State Crown 90 1·00
MS420 114 × 103 mm. $5 Queen and Prince Philip (17.7) .. .. 1·90 2·00

(*b*) *Booklet stamps. Horiz designs as Nos. 587/9 of Antigua but additionally inscr "BARBUDA". Multicoloured. Roul 5 × imperf*. Self-adhesive* (12.10)

421 25 c. Glass Coach 10 20
a. Booklet pane. Nos. 421/2 × 3 90
422 50 c. Irish State Coach 30 45
423 $5 Coronation Coach .. .. .. 1·90 2·40
a. Booklet pane of 1 .. .. .. 1·90

Nos. 415/19 also exist perf 12 (*Price for set of* 5 £2 *mint or used*) from additional sheetlets of three stamps and one label, issued 12 October 1978. These stamps have different background colours from Nos. 415/19.

*The 25 and 50 c. values were separated by various combinations of rotary knife (giving a straight edge) and roulette. The $5 value exists only with straight edges.

1978 (12 Sept). *World Cup Football Championship, Argentina. Nos. 590/3 of Antigua optd with T* **67**.

424 10 c. Player running with ball 5 5
425 15 c. Players in front of goal 5 5
426 $3 Referee and player .. .. .. 1·60 1·75
MS427 126 × 88 mm. 25 c. Player crouching with ball; 30 c. Players heading ball; 50 c. Players running with ball; $2 Goalkeeper diving .. .. 1·75 2·00

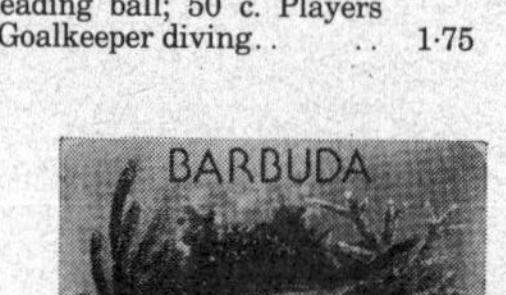

BARBUDA

(69)

70 Blackbar Soldierfish

1978 (20 Nov). *Flowers. Nos. 594/8 of Antigua optd with T* **69**.

428 25 c. Petrea 35 35
429 50 c. Sunflower 65 65
430 90 c. Frangipani 85 85
431 $2 Passion Flower .. .. .. 1·75 1·75
MS432 118 × 85 mm. $2.50, Hibiscus .. .. 2·00 2·25

1978 (20 Nov). *Christmas. Paintings. Nos. 599/602 optd with T* **69** *in silver.*

433 8 c. "St. Ildefonso receiving the Chasuble from the Virgin" 10 10
434 25 c. "The Flight of St. Barbara" 15 20
435 $2 "Madonna and Child, with St. Joseph, John the Baptist and Donor" .. .. 75 1·10
MS436 170 × 113 mm. $4 "The Annunciation" .. 1·75 2·00

(Litho Format)

1978 (20 Nov). *Flora and Fauna. T* **70** *and similar horiz designs. Multicoloured. P* 14½.

437 25 c. Type **70** 50 50
438 50 c. Painted Lady butterfly 90 90
439 75 c. Dwarf Poinciana .. .. .. 1·40 1·40
440 95 c. Zebra butterfly .. .. .. 1·75 1·75
441 $1.25, Bougainvillea .. .. .. 2·00 2·00

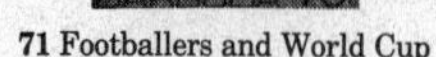

71 Footballers and World Cup

72 Sir Rowland Hill

(Des J. Cooter. Litho Format)

1978 (29 Dec). *Anniversaries and Events. T* **71** *and similar multicoloured designs. P* 14.

442 75 c. Type **71** 35 40
443 95 c. Wright brothers and *Flyer I* (*horiz*) .. 45 50
444 $1.25, *Double Eagle II* and map of Atlantic (*horiz*) 60 65
445 $2 Prince Philip paying homage to the newly crowned Queen 85 95
MS446 122 × 90 mm. Nos. 442/5. Imperf .. .. 2·25 2·50

Events:—75 c. Argentina—Winners of World Cup Football Championship; 95 c. 75th anniversary of powered flight; $1.25 1st Atlantic crossing by balloon; $2 25th anniversary of Coronation.

(Des J. Cooter. Litho Format)

1979 (4 Apr). *Death Centenary of Sir Rowland Hill* (1*st issue*). *T* **72** *and similar multicoloured designs. P* 14.

447 75 c. Type **72** 45 50
448 95 c. Mail coach, 1840 (*horiz*) 55 60
449 $1.25, London's first pillar box, 1855 (*horiz*) 60 70
450 $2 Mail leaving St. Martin's Le Grand Post Office, London 90 95
MS451 129 × 104 mm. Nos. 447/50 Imperf .. 2·50 2·75

Nos. 447/50 were each printed in small sheets of 4 including one *se-tenant* stamp-size label.

BARBUDA

(73)

74 Passengers alighting from British Airways Boeing "747"

1979 (4 Apr). *Death Centenary of Sir Rowland Hill* (*2nd issue*). *Nos. 603/7 of Antigua optd with T* **73** *in blue. P* 14.

452 25 c. Antigua 1863 1d. stamp 15 15
453 50 c. Penny Black stamp 25 25
454 $1 Stage-coach and woman posting letter, *circa* 1840 .. .. 50 50
455 $2 Modern mail transport .. .. 1·00 1·00
MS456 108 × 82 mm. $2.50, Sir Rowland Hill .. 1·10 1·25

Nos. 452/5 also exist perf 12 (*Price for set of* 4 £1.75 *mint or used*) from additional sheetlets of four stamps and one label, issued 28 December 1979.

1979 (12 Apr). *Easter. Works by Dürer. Nos. 608/11 of Antigua optd with T* **67**.

457 10 c. multicoloured 5 5
458 50 c. multicoloured 20 25
459 $4 black, magenta and greenish yellow .. 1·50 1·60
MS460 114 × 99 mm. $2.50, multicoloured .. 1·00 1·10

(Litho Format)

1979 (24 May). *30th Anniv of International Civil Aviation Organisation. T* **74** *and similar horiz designs. Multicoloured. P* 13½ × 14.

461 75 c. Type **74** 45 45
a. Block of 4. Nos. 461/3 plus label .. 1·40
462 95 c. Air traffic control 50 50
463 $1.25, Ground crew-man directing Boeing "707" on runway 60 60

Nos. 461/3 were either printed in separate sheets, or together with a stamp-size label, *se-tenant*, in blocks of 4, each block divided in the sheet by margins.

1979 (24 May). *International Year of the Child* (1*st issue*). *Nos. 612/16 of Antigua optd with T* **67**.

464 25 c. Yacht 25 25
465 50 c. Rocket 40 40
466 90 c. Car 65 65
467 $2 Train .. .. 1·25 1·25
MS468 80 × 112 mm. $5 Aeroplane .. .. 2·75 2·75

BARBUDA (75)

BARBUDA (76)

1979 (1 Aug). *Fishes. Nos. 617/21 of Antigua optd with T* **75**.

469 30 c. Yellowjack 20 20
470 50 c. Bluefin Tuna 30 30
471 90 c. Sailfish 40 40
472 $3 Wahoo .. .. 1·40 1·40
MS473 122 × 75 mm. $2.50, Barracuda (overprinted with T **73**) .. .. 1·00 1·25
a. Albino opt .. ..

1979 (1 Aug). *Death Bicentenary of Captain Cook. Nos. 622/6 of Antigua optd with T* **76**.

474 25 c. Cook's Birthplace, Marton 30 30
475 50 c. H.M. Bark *Endeavour* 50 50
476 90 c. Marine chronometer 65 65
477 $3 Landing at Botany Bay .. .. 1·75 1·75
MS478 110 × 85 mm. $2.50, H.M.S. *Resolution* (overprinted with T **82**) .. .. .. 1·25 1·50
a. Albino opt .. ..

PRICES OF SETS

Set prices are given for many issues, generally those containing five stamps or more. Definitive sets include one of each value or major colour change, but do not cover different perforations, die types or minor shades. Where a choice is possible the set prices are based on the cheapest versions of the stamps included in the listings.

77 "Virgin with the Pear"

BARBUDA
(78)

(Des G. Vasarhelyi. Litho Format)

1979 (24 Sept). *International Year of the Child (2nd issue). Details of Paintings by Dürer, showing the infant Jesus. T* **77** *and similar vert designs. Multicoloured. P* 14 × 13½.
479 25 c. Type **77** 15 15
480 50 c. "Virgin with the Pink" 25 30
481 75 c. "Virgin with the Pear" (*different*) .. 35 40
482 $1.25, "Nativity" 50 55
MS483 86 × 118 mm. Nos. 479/82 .. .. .. 1·25 1·40

1979 (21 Nov). *Christmas. Nos. 627/31 of Antigua optd with T* **78**.
484 8 c. The Holy Family.. .. .. .. 5 5
485 25 c. Virgin and Child on Ass.. .. .. 12 12
486 50 c. Shepherd and star 25 25
487 $4 Wise Men with gifts .. .. .. 1·75 2·00
MS488 113 × 94 mm. $3 Angel with trumpet .. 1·50 1·60

1980 (18 Mar). *Olympic Games, Moscow. Nos. 632/6 of Antigua optd with T* **67**.
489 10 c. Javelin throwing.. .. .. .. 10 10
490 25 c. Running 15 15
491 $1 Pole vaulting 40 45
492 $2 Hurdling 85 80
MS493 127 × 96 mm. $3 Boxing .. .. .. 1·25 1·40

LONDON 1980
(79)

80 "Apollo 11" Crew Badge

1980 (6 May). *"London 1980" International Stamp Exhibition. As Nos. 452/5 optd with T* **79** *in blue. P* 12.
494 25 c. Antigua 1863 1d. stamp.. .. .. 20 15
495 50 c. Penny Black stamp 30 30
496 $1 Mail coach and woman posting letter, *circa* 1840 .. .. 65 55
497 $2 Modern mail transport .. .. .. 1·50 1·10

(Litho Format)

1980 (21 May). *10th Anniv of Moon Landing. T* **80** *and similar horiz designs. Multicoloured. P* 13½ × 14.
498 75 c. Type **80** 40 40
499 95 c. Plaque left on Moon 50 50
500 $1.25, Rejoining mother ship 60 60
501 $2 Lunar Module .. .. 1·00 1·00
MS502 118 × 84 mm. Nos. 498/501 .. .. 2·50 2·50

81 American Wigeon

(Litho Questa)

1980 (16 June). *Birds. Multicoloured designs as T* **81**. *P* 14.
503 1 c. Type **81** 10 10
504 2 c. Snowy Plover 10 10
505 4 c. Rose-breasted Grosbeak 15 15
506 6 c. Mangrove Cuckoo 15 15
507 10 c. Adelaide's Warbler 15 15
508 15 c. Scaly-breasted Thrasher.. .. .. 20 20
509 20 c. Yellow-crowned Night Heron 20 20
510 25 c. Bridled Quail Dove 20 20
511 35 c. Carib Grackle 25 25
512 50 c. Pintail 35 35
513 75 c. Black-whiskered Vireo 45 45
514 $1 Blue-winged Teal 60 60
515 $1.50, Green-throated Carib (*vert*) 80 80
516 $2 Red-necked Pigeon (*vert*) .. .. 1·25 1·25
517 $2.50, Stolid Flycatcher (*vert*) .. .. 1·50 1·50
518 $5 Yellow-bellied Sapsucker (*vert*) .. .. 2·50 2·50
519 $7.50, Caribbean Elaenia (*vert*) .. .. 4·00 4·00
520 $10 Great Egret (*vert*) .. .. .. 5·00 5·00
503/20.. .. .. *Set of* 18 16·00 16·00

MINIMUM PRICE

The minimum price quoted is 5p which represents a handling charge rather than a basis for valuing common stamps. For further notes about prices see introductory pages.

1980 (29 July). *Famous Works of Art. Nos. 651/7 of Antigua optd with T* **67**.
521 10 c. "David" (statue, Donatello) 5 5
522 30 c. "The Birth of Venus" (painting, Sandro Botticelli) 20 20
523 50 c. "Reclining Couple" (sarcophagus), Cerveteri 30 30
524 90 c. "The Garden of Earthly Delights" (painting, Hieronymus Bosch) .. 50 50
525 $1 "Portinari Altarpiece" (painting, Hugo van der Goes) 55 55
526 $4 "Eleanora of Toledo and her Son Giovanni de' Medici" (painting, Agnolo Bronzino) 1·90 1·90
521/6 .. .. *Set of* 6 3·25 3·25
MS527 99 × 124 mm. $5 "The Holy Family" (painting, Rembrandt) .. .. 2·25 2·50

1980 (8 Sept). *75th Anniv of Rotary International. Nos. 658/62 of Antigua optd with T* **67**.
528 30 c. Rotary anniversary emblem and headquarters, U.S.A. 20 20
529 50 c. Rotary anniversary emblem and Antigua Rotary Club banner 30 30
530 90 c. Map of Antigua and Rotary emblem .. 50 50
531 $3 Paul P. Harris (founder) and Rotary emblem .. .. 1·60 1·60
MS532 102 × 77 mm. $5 Antigua flags and Rotary emblems .. .. 2·25 2·50

BARBUDA
(82)

BARBUDA
(83)

1980 (6 Oct). *80th Birthday of Queen Elizabeth the Queen Mother. Nos. 663/5 of Antigua optd with T* **82**.
533 10 c. multicoloured 15 15
a. Opt inverted .. .. 38·00
b. Opt double .. .. 40·00
534 $2.50, multicoloured .. .. .. 1·50 1·50
MS535 68 × 88 mm. $3 multicoloured .. .. 1·60 1·75

1980 (8 Dec). *Birds. Nos. 666/70 of Antigua optd with T* **83**.
536 10 c. Ringed Kingfisher 15 15
537 30 c. Plain Pigeon 25 25
538 $1 Green-throated Carib 70 70
539 $2 Black-necked Stilt .. .. .. 1·25 1·25
MS540 73 × 73 mm. $2.50, Roseate Tern.. .. 1·40 1·60

1981 (26 Jan). *Sugar Cane Railway Locomotives. Nos. 681/5 of Antigua optd with T* **67**.
541 25 c. Diesel Locomotive No. 15 .. .. 25 25
542 50 c. Narrow-gauge steam locomotive .. 35 35
543 90 c. Diesel locomotives Nos. 1 and 10 .. 55 55
544 $3 Steam locomotive hauling sugar cane .. 1·90 1·90
MS545 82 × 111 mm. $2.50, Antigua sugar factory, railway yard and sheds .. .. 1·60 1·75

84 Florence Nightingale

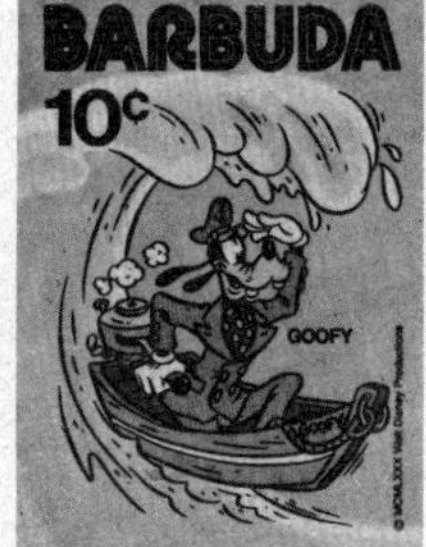

85 Goofy in Motor-boat

(Litho Format)

1981 (9 Mar). *Famous Women. T* **84** *and similar vert designs. P* 14 × 13½.
546 50 c. multicoloured 30 30
547 90 c. multicoloured 55 55
548 $1 multicoloured 60 60
549 $4 black, yellow-brown and rose-lilac .. 2·10 2·10
Designs:—90 c. Marie Curie; $1 Amy Johnson; $4 Eleanor Roosevelt.

(Litho Format)

1981 (15 May). *Walt Disney Cartoon Characters. T* **85** *and similar vert designs showing characters afloat. Multicoloured. P* 13½.
550 10 c. Type **85** 8 8
551 20 c. Donald Duck reversing car into sea .. 15 15
552 25 c. Mickey Mouse asking tug-boat to take on more than it can handle 20 20
553 30 c. Porpoise turning the tables on Goofy .. 25 25
554 35 c. Goofy in sailing boat 25 25
555 40 c. Mickey Mouse and boat being lifted out of water by fish 30 30
556 75 c. Donald Duck fishing for flying-fish with butterfly net 45 45
557 $1 Minnie Mouse in brightly decorated sailing boat 55 55
558 $2 Chip and Dale on floating ship-in-bottle 1·10 1·10
550/8 .. .. *Set of* 9 3·00 3·00
MS559 127 × 101 mm. $2.50, Donald Duck .. 1·50 1·60

BARBUDA
(86)

1981 (9 June). *Birth Centenary of Picasso. Nos. 697/701 of Antigua optd with T* **86**.
560 10 c. "Pipes of Pan" 5 5
561 50 c. "Seated Harlequin" 30 30
562 90 c. "Paulo as Harlequin" 55 55
563 $4 "Mother and Child" .. .. .. 2·10 2·10
MS564 115 × 140 mm. $5 "Three Musicians" (detail) .. .. 2·40 2·50

87 Buckingham Palace 88

(Des G. Drummond. Litho Format)

1981 (27 July). *Royal Wedding (1st issue). Buildings. T* **87/8** *and similar horiz designs. Each bicoloured*. P* 11 × 11½.
565 $1 Type **87** 70 70
566 $1 Type **88** 70 70
a. Sheetlet. Nos. 565/70 .. .. .. 6·50
b. Booklet pane. Nos. 565/6 × 2 in imperf between horiz pairs .. .. .. 2·50
567 $1.50 } Caernarvon Castle 85 85
568 $1.50 } 85 85
b. Booklet pane. Nos. 567/8 × 2 in imperf between horiz pairs .. .. .. 3·00
569 $4 } Highgrove House .. .. .. 1·75 1·75
570 $4 } .. .. 1·75 1·75
b. Booklet pane. Nos. 569/70 × 2 in imperf between horiz pairs .. .. .. 7·00
565/70 .. .. *Set of* 6 6·00 6·00
MS571 75 × 90 mm. $5 black and olive-yellow (St. Paul's Cathedral—26 × 32 *mm*). P 11½ × 11 2·25 2·50
*Nos. 565/70 each exist printed in black with three different background colours, rose-pink, turquoise-green and lavender.
No. 566b was printed only in black and rose-pink. No. 568b black and turquoise-green and No. 570b black and lavender.
Nos. 565/70 were printed together, *se-tenant*, in sheetlets of 6, the two versions of each value forming a composite design.

1981 (14 Aug). *Royal Wedding (2nd issue). Nos. 702/5 of Antigua optd with T* **86**.
572 25 c. Prince Charles and Lady Diana Spencer 25 25
573 50 c. Glamis Castle 35 35
a. Opt double .. .. 75·00
574 $4 Prince Charles skiing .. .. .. 1·90 1·90
a. Error. Optd on unissued Uganda 20s. as No. 343 .. .. £125
MS575 95 × 85 mm. $5 Glass Coach .. .. 2·50 2·50
Nos. 572/4 also exist perforated 12 (*Price for set of* 3 £2.50 *mint or used*) from additional sheetlets of five stamps and one label. These stamps have changed background colours. One sheetlet of the 25 c. is known with the overprints inverted.

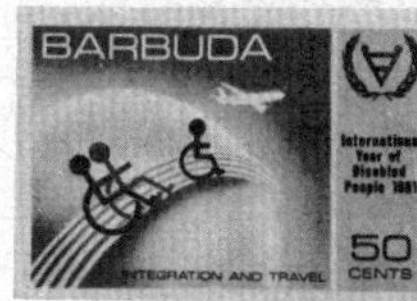

89 "Integration and Travel"

(Litho Format)

1981 (14 Sept). *International Year for Disabled Persons. T* **89** *and similar horiz designs. P* 14.
576 50 c. multicoloured 30 30
577 90 c. black, red-orange and blue-green .. 50 50
578 $1 black, light blue and bright green .. 55 55
579 $4 black, yellow-ochre and orange-brown .. 2·00 2·00
Designs:—90 c. Braille and sign language; $1 "Helping hands"; $4 "Mobility aids for disabled".

BARBUDA
(90)

1981 (12 Oct). *Royal Wedding (3rd issue). Booklet stamps. Nos. 706/12 of Antigua optd with T* **90** *in silver*.
580 25 c. Prince of Wales at Investiture, 1969 .. 25 25
a. Booklet pane. Nos. 580/5.. .. .. 4·00
581 25 c. Prince Charles as baby, 1948 .. .. 25 25
582 $1 Prince Charles at R.A.F. College, Cranwell, 1971 .. .. 75 75
583 $1 Prince Charles attending Hill House School, 1956 .. .. 75 75
584 $2 Prince Charles and Lady Diana Spencer 1·25 1·25
585 $2 Prince Charles at Trinity College, 1967 1·25 1·25
586 $5 Prince Charles and Lady Diana.. .. 3·00 3·00
a. Booklet pane of 1.. .. .. .. 3·00
580/6 .. .. *Set of* 7 7·00 7·00

1981 (1 Nov). *Independence. Nos. 686B/96B of Antigua additionally optd with T* **86**.
587 6 c. Orchid Tree 10 10
588 10 c. Bougainvillea 15 15
589 20 c. Flamboyant 20 20
590 25 c. Hibiscus 25 25
591 35 c. Flame of the Wood 30 30
592 50 c. Cannon at Fort James 35 35
593 75 c. Premier's Office 45 45
594 $1 Potworks Dam 55 55
595 $2.50, Irrigation scheme, Diamond Estate .. 1·50 1·50
596 $5 Government House .. .. .. 2·50 2·50
597 $10 Coolidge International Airport .. .. 4·75 4·75
587/97 .. .. *Set of* 11 10·00 10·00

BARBUDA (91) **BARBUDA** (92)

1981 (14 Dec). *50th Anniv of Antigua Girl Guide Movement. Nos. 713/17 of Antigua optd with T* **83** *(No.* **MS**602) *or T* **91** *(others).*

598 10 c. Irene Joshua (founder) 10 10
599 50 c. Campfire sing-song 30 30
600 90 c. Sailing 45 45
601 $2.50, Animal tending .. .. .. 1·40 1·40
MS602 110 × 85 mm. $5 Raising the flag .. .. 2·40 2·50

1981 (14 Dec). *International Year for Disabled Persons. Sport for the Disabled. Nos. 728/32 of Antigua optd with T* **83** *(No.* **MS**607) *or T* **91** *(others).*

603 10 c. Swimming 10 10
604 50 c. Discus throwing 30 30
605 90 c. Archery 45 45
606 $2 Baseball .. .. 1·25 1·25
MS607 108 × 84 mm. $4 Basketball .. .. 2·25 2·50

1981 (22 Dec). *Christmas. Paintings. Nos. 723/7 of Antigua optd with T* **92**.

608 8 c. "Holy Night" (Jacques Stella) 8 8
609 30 c. "Mary with Child" (Julius Schnorr von Carolfeld) 20 20
610 $1 "Virgin and Child" (Alonso Cano) (S.) .. 50 50
611 $3 "Virgin and Child" (Lorenzo di Credi) .. 1·50 1·50
MS612 77 × 111 mm. $5 "Holy Family" (Pieter von Avon) .. .. 2·40 2·50

93 Princess of Wales

S. Atlantic Fund + 50c. (94)

(Des G. Drummond. Litho Format)

1982 (21 June). *Birth of Prince William of Wales (1st issue). T* **93** *and similar vert portraits. W w* **15**. *P* 14.

613 $1 multicoloured 50 50
614 $2.50, multicoloured .. .. .. 1·10 1·10
a. Reddish violet (top inscr) omitted .. £175
615 $5 multicoloured .. .. 2·25 2·25
MS616 88 × 108 mm. $4 multicoloured. No wmk .. 2·00 2·10

Nos. 613/15 were issued in sheets of 10 stamps with 2 undenominated black prints, in positions 9 and 13, and 9 blank labels. These sheets exist in two different formats, with all stamps upright or with 6 stamps and one black print inverted.

1982 (28 June). *South Atlantic Fund. Booklet stamps. Nos. 580/6 surch as T* **94**.

617 25 c. +50 c. Prince of Wales at Investiture, 1969 .. .. 30 30
a. Booklet pane. Nos. 617/22 .. .. 3·75
b. Surch double .. .. 20·00
618 25 c. +50 c. Prince Charles as baby, 1948 .. 30 30
b. Surch double .. .. 20·00
619 $1 +50 c. Prince Charles at R.A.F. College, Cranwell, 1971 .. .. 60 60
b. Surch double .. .. 20·00
620 $1 +50 c. Prince Charles attending Hill House School, 1956 .. .. .. 60 60
b. Surch double .. .. 20·00
621 $2 +50 c. Prince Charles and Lady Diana Spencer .. .. 1·10 1·10
b. Surch double .. .. 20·00
622 $2 +50 c. Prince Charles at Trinity College, 1967 .. .. 1·10 1·10
b. Surch double .. .. 20·00
623 $5 +50 c. Prince Charles and Lady Diana 2·50 2·50
a. Booklet pane of 1 .. .. .. 2·50
b. Surch double £150
617/23 .. .. *Set of* 7 6·00 6·00

(Des G. Drummond. Litho Format)

1982 (1 July). *21st Birthday of Princess of Wales (1st issue). As Nos. 613/16 but inscribed* "Twenty First Birthday Greetings to H.R.H. The Princess of Wales". *W w* **15**. *P* 14.

624 $1 multicoloured 45 45
625 $2.50, multicoloured .. .. .. 1·25 1·25
626 $5 multicoloured .. .. 2·40 2·40
MS627 88 × 108 mm. $4 multicoloured. No wmk 2·10 2·25

See note beneath Nos. 613/16.

BARBUDA MAIL (95) **BARBUDA MAIL** (96)

1982 (30 Aug). *21st Birthday of Princess of Wales (2nd issue). Nos. 748/51 of Antigua optd as T* **95**, *in silver (No. 629) or black (others).*

628 90 c. Queen's House, Greenwich 45 45
629 $1 Prince and Princess of Wales 50 50
630 $4 Princess of Wales .. .. .. 2·10 2·25
MS631 102 × 75 mm. $5 Princess of Wales (*different*) .. .. 2·40 2·50

The overprint on No. **MS**631 measures 18 × 6 mm.

Nos. 628/30 also exist from additional sheetlets of 5 stamps and 1 label overprinted with a larger overprint, 18 × 6 mm long (*price for set of 3 £3 mint or used*). On the $1 and $4 values the second line of overprint aligns to left.

1982 (12 Oct). *Birth of Prince William of Wales (2nd issue). Nos. 757/60 of Antigua further optd with T* **95**, *in silver ($1, $4) or black (others).*

632 90 c. Queen's House, Greenwich 45 45
633 $1 Prince and Princess of Wales 50 50
634 $4 Princess of Wales .. .. .. 2·00 2·00
MS635 102 × 75 mm. $5 Princess of Wales (*different*) .. .. 2·40 2·50

The overprint on No. **MS**635 measures 18 × 6 mm.

1982 (6 Dec). *Birth Centenary of Franklin D. Roosevelt (Nos. 636, 638, 640/2) and 250th Birth Anniv of George Washington (others). Nos. 761/8 of Antigua optd as T* **95** *(second line ranged left on No.* **MS**642).

636 10 c. Roosevelt in 1940 .. .. .. 10 10
637 25 c. Washington as blacksmith 15 15
638 45 c. Churchill, Roosevelt and Stalin at Yalta conference 25 25
639 60 c. Washington crossing the Delaware .. 35 35
640 $1 "Roosevelt Special" train 55 55
641 $3 Portrait of Roosevelt .. .. 1·75 1·75
636/41 .. .. *Set of* 6 2·75 2·75
MS642 92 × 87 mm. $4 Roosevelt and wife .. 2·00 2·10
MS643 92 × 87 mm. $4 Portrait of Washington .. 2·00 2·10

1982 (6 Dec). *Christmas. Religious Paintings by Raphael. Nos. 769/73 of Antigua optd with T* **96**.

644 10 c. "Annunciation" 10 10
645 30 c. "Adoration of the Magi" 15 15
646 $1 "Presentation at the Temple" 50 50
647 $4 "Coronation of the Virgin" .. .. 2·10 2·25
MS648 95 × 124 mm. $5 "Marriage of the Virgin" 2·50 2·50

1983 (14 Mar). *500th Birth Anniv of Raphael. Details from "Galatea" Fresco. Nos. 774/8 of Antigua optd as T* **94** *(45, 50 c. and larger (18 × 6 mm) on* **MS**653) *or T* **96** *(others).*

649 45 c. Tritons and Dolphins 20 25
650 50 c. Sea Nymph carried off by Triton .. 25 30
651 60 c. Winged angel steering Dolphins (*horiz*) 30 35
652 $4 Cupids shooting arrows (*horiz*) .. .. 1·90 2·00
MS653 101 × 126 mm. $5 Galatea pulled along by Dolphins .. .. 2·50 2·75

1983 (14 Mar). *Commonwealth Day. Nos. 779/82 of Antigua optd as T* **96**.

654 25 c. Pineapple produce 12 15
655 45 c. Carnival 20 25
656 60 c. Tourism 30 35
657 $3 Airport .. .. 1·40 1·50

1983 (12 Apr). *World Communications Year. Nos. 783/7 of Antigua optd as T* **96** *(Nos. 658/61) or as T* **95** *with second line ranged left (No.* **MS**662).

658 15 c. T.V. satellite coverage of Royal Wedding 5 8
659 50 c. Police communications 25 30
660 60 c. House-to-train telephone call 30 35
661 $3 Satellite earth station with planets Jupiter and Saturn .. .. .. 1·40 1·50
MS662 100 × 90 mm. $5 "Comsat" satellite over West Indies .. .. 2·50 2·75

97 Vincenzo Lunardi's Balloon Flight, London, 1785

= 45c (98)

(Des G. Drummond. Litho)

1983 (13 June). *Bicentenary of Manned Flight (1st issue). T* **97** *and similar vert designs. Multicoloured. P* 14.

663 $1 Type **97** 45 50
664 $1.50, Montgolfier brothers' balloon flight, Paris, 1783 .. .. 70 75
665 $2.50, Blanchard and Jeffries' Cross-Channel balloon flight, 1785 .. .. .. 1·10 1·25
MS666 111 × 111 mm. $5 Maiden flight of *Graf Zeppelin*, 1928 .. .. 2·50 2·75

1983 (4 July). *Whales. Nos. 788/92 of Antigua optd as T* **95** *(Nos. 667/70) or larger, 17 × 5½ mm (No.* **MS**671), *each with the second line ranged left.*

667 15 c. Bottlenose Dolphin 5 8
668 50 c. Finback Whale 25 30
669 60 c. Bowhead Whale 30 35
670 $3 Spectacled Porpoise .. .. .. 1·40 1·50
MS671 122 × 101 mm. $5 Unicorn Whale (Narwhal) .. .. 2·50 2·75

1983 (12 Sept). *Bicentenary of Manned Flight (2nd issue). Nos. 811/15 of Antigua optd as T* **96**.

672 30 c. Dornier "Do X" flying boat 15 20
673 50 c. Supermarine "S.6B" seaplane 25 30
674 60 c. Curtiss "9C" biplane and airship U.S.S. *Akron* 30 35
675 $4 *Pro Juventute* balloon .. .. .. 1·90 2·00
MS676 80 × 105 mm. $5 *Graf Zeppelin* .. .. 2·50 2·75

1983 (21 Oct). *Nos. 565/70 surch as T* **98**. *A. P* 11 × 11½. *B. P* 14½.

		A		B	
677 45 c. on $1 Type **87** ..		45	45	2·25	2·25
a. Sheetlet. Nos. 677/82		3·00		12·00	
b. Error. 50 c. on $1 ..			†	7·50	—
c. Surch omitted ..			†	35·00	—
678 45 c. on $1 Type **88** ..		45	45	2·25	2·25
b. Error. 50 c. on $1 ..			†	7·50	—
c. Surch omitted ..			†	35·00	—
679 50 c. on $1.50, Caernarvon Castle (*left*) ..		50	50	2·25	2·25
b. Error. 45 c. on $1.50			†	7·50	—
c. Surch omitted ..			†	35·00	—
680 50 c. on $1.50, Caernarvon Castle (*right*) ..		50	50	2·25	2·25
b. Error. 45 c. on $1.50			†	7·50	—
c. Surch omitted ..			†	35·00	—
681 60 c. on $4 Highgrove House (*left*)		60	60	2·25	2·25
c. Surch omitted ..			†	35·00	—
682 60 c. on $4 Highgrove House (*right*)		60	60	2·25	2·25
c. Surch omitted ..			†	35·00	—
677/82 ..	*Set of* 6	3·00	3·00	12·00	12·00

Nos. 677b, 678b, 679b and 680b occur on the 14½ perforated sheetlets with rose-pink background.

1983 (28 Oct). *Nos. 793/810 of Antigua optd with T* **96**.

683 1 c. Cashew Nut 5 5
684 2 c. Passion Fruit 5 5
685 3 c. Mango 5 5
686 5 c. Grapefruit 5 5
687 10 c. Pawpaw 5 8
688 15 c. Breadfruit 8 10
689 20 c. Coconut 10 12
690 25 c. Oleander 12 15
691 30 c. Banana 15 20
692 40 c. Pineapple 20 25
693 45 c. Cordia 25 30
694 50 c. Cassia 30 35
695 60 c. Poui 35 40
696 $1 Frangipani 55 60
697 $2 Flamboyant .. .. 1·10 1·25
698 $2.50, Lemon .. .. 1·40 1·50
699 $5 Lignum Vitae .. .. 2·75 3·00
700 $10 National flag and coat of arms .. .. 5·75 6·00
683/700 .. .. *Set of* 18 12·00 13·00

BARBUDA MAIL (99)

100 Edward VII

1983 (28 Oct). *Christmas. 500th Birth Anniv of Raphael. Nos. 816/20 of Antigua optd with T* **99** *or slightly smaller (29 × 4 mm) (***MS**705).

701 10 c. multicoloured 5 8
702 30 c. multicoloured 15 20
703 $1 multicoloured 45 50
704 $4 multicoloured .. .. 1·90 2·00
MS705 101 × 131 mm. $5 multicoloured .. .. 2·50 2·75

1983 (14 Dec). *Bicentenary of Methodist Church (1984). Nos. 821/4 of Antigua optd with T* **94** *(in silver on 15 c. and 50 c.).*

706 15 c. John Wesley (founder) 10 12
707 50 c. Nathaniel Gilbert (founder in Antigua) 25 30
708 60 c. St. John Methodist Church steeple .. 30 35
709 $3 Ebenezer Methodist Church, St. John's 1·60 1·75

(Des G. Drummond. Litho Format)

1984 (14 Feb). *Members of British Royal Family. T* **100** *and similar vert portraits. Multicoloured. P* 14½.

710 $1 Type **100** 55 60
711 $1 George V 55 60
712 $1 George VI 55 60
713 $1 Elizabeth II 55 60
714 $1 Charles, Prince of Wales 55 60
715 $1 Prince William of Wales 55 60
710/15 .. .. *Set of* 6 3·00 3·25

1984 (26 Apr). *Olympic Games, Los Angeles (1st issue). Nos. 825/9 of Antigua optd as T* **99** *(23 × 3 mm in size on Nos. 716/19).*

716 25 c. Discus 15 20
717 50 c. Gymnastics 35 40
718 90 c. Hurdling 60 65
719 $3 Cycling .. .. 2·00 2·25
MS720 82 × 67 mm. $5 Volleyball .. .. 3·25 3·50

1984 (12 July). *Ships. Nos. 830/4 of Antigua optd with T* **95** *(***MS**725) *or T* **99** *(others).*

721 45 c. *Booker Vanguard* 30 35
722 50 c. S.S. *Canberra* 35 40
723 60 c. Sailing boats 40 45
724 $4 *Fairwind* .. .. 2·00 2·75
MS725 107 × 80 mm. $5 Eighteenth-century British man-of-war (*vert*) .. .. .. 3·25 3·50

1984 (12 July). *Universal Postal Union Congress, Hamburg. Nos. 835/9 of Antigua optd with T* **95**.

726 15 c. Chenille 10 12
727 50 c. Shell Flower 35 40
728 60 c. Anthurium 40 45
729 $3 Angels Trumpet .. .. .. 2·00 2·10
MS730 100 × 75 mm. $5 Crown of Thorns .. 3·25 3·50

101 Olympic Stadium, Athens, 1896

(Litho Format)

1984 (27 July). *Olympic Games, Los Angeles (2nd issue). T* 101 *and similar horiz designs. Multicoloured. P* 13½.

731	$1.50, Type **101**	1·00	1·10
732	$2.50, Olympic stadium, Los Angeles, 1984	1·75	2·00
733	$5 Athlete carrying Olympic torch	3·25	3·00
MS734	121 × 95 mm. No. 733. P 15	3·25	3·50

1984 (1 Oct). *Presidents of the United States of America. Nos.* 856/63 *of Antigua optd with T* **95** (*in silver on* 10, 90 *c.*, $1.10 *and* $1.50).

735	10 c. Abraham Lincoln	8	10
736	20 c. Harry Truman	12	15
737	30 c. Dwight Eisenhower	20	25
738	40 c. Ronald Reagan	25	30
739	90 c. Gettysburg Address, 1863	60	65
740	$1.10, Formation of N.A.T.O., 1949	70	75
741	$1.50, Eisenhower during Second World War	1·00	1·10
742	$2 Reagan and Caribbean Basin Initiative	1·25	1·40
735/42	*Set of* 8	3·75	4·25

1984 (1 Oct). 150*th Anniv of Abolition of Slavery. Nos.* 864/8 *of Antigua optd with T* **96** (*Nos.* 743/6) *or as T* **95**, *but* 18 × 6½ *mm* (*No.* **MS**747).

743	40 c. View of Moravian Mission	25	30
744	50 c. Antigua Courthouse, 1823	35	40
745	60 c. Planting sugar-cane, Monks Hill	40	45
746	$3 Boiling house, Delaps' Estate	2·00	2·10
MS747	95 × 70 mm. $5 Loading sugar, Willoughby Bay	3·25	3·50

1984 (21 Nov). *Songbirds. Nos.* 869/74 *of Antigua optd with T* **95** *or larger* (18 × 7 *mm*) (*No.* **MS**753).

748	40 c. Rufous-sided Towhee	30	35
749	50 c. Parula Warbler	35	40
750	60 c. House-wren	40	45
751	$2 Ruby-crowned Kinglet	1·40	1·50
752	$3 Yellow-shafted Flicker	2·00	2·25
MS753	76 × 76 mm. $5 Yellow-breasted Chat	3·50	3·75

1984 (21 Nov). 450*th Death Anniv of Correggio (painter). Nos.* 878/82 *of Antigua optd with T* **95** *or larger* (18 × 7 *mm*) *No.* **MS**758), *all in silver.*

754	25 c. "The Virgin and Infant with Angels and Cherubs"	15	20
755	60 c. "The Four Saints"	40	45
756	90 c. "St. Catherine"	60	65
757	$3 "The Campori Madonna"	2·00	2·75
MS758	90 × 60 mm. $5 "St. John the Baptist"	3·00	3·75

1984 (30 Nov). *"Ausipex" International Stamp Exhibition, Melbourne. Australian Sports. Nos.* 875/7 *of Antigua optd with T* **95** *or larger* (18 × 7 *mm*) (*No.* **MS**761).

759	$1 Grass-skiing	70	75
760	$5 Australian Football	3·50	3·75
MS761	108 × 78 mm. $5 Boomerang-throwing	3·50	3·75

REDONDA

DEPENDENCY OF ANTIGUA

Appendix

The following stamps were issued in anticipation of commercial and tourist development, philatelic mail being handled by a bureau in Antigua. Since at the present time the island is uninhabited, we do not list or stock these items. It is understood that the stamps are valid for the prepayment of postage in Antigua. Miniature sheets, imperforate stamps etc., are excluded from this section.

1979

Antigua 1976 *definitive issue optd* "REDONDA". 3, 5, 10, 25, 35, 50, 75 *c.*, $1, $2.50, $5, $10.
Antigua Coronation Anniversary issue optd "REDONDA". 10, 30, 50, 90 *c.*, $2.50.
Antigua World Cup Football Championship issue optd "REDONDA". 10, 15 *c.*, $3.
Death Centenary of Sir Rowland Hill. 50, 90 *c.*, $2.50, $3.
International Year of the Child. 25, 50 *c.*, $1, $2.
Christmas. Paintings. 8, 50, 90 *c.*, $3.

1980

Marine Life. 8, 25, 50 *c.*, $4.
75th Anniv of Rotary International. 25, 50 *c.*, $1, $2.
Birds of Redonda. 8, 10, 15, 25, 30, 50 *c.*, $1, $2, $5.
Olympic Medal Winners, Lake Placid and Moscow. 8, 25, 50 *c.*, $3.
80th Birthday of Queen Elizabeth the Queen Mother. 10 *c.*, $2.50.
Christmas. Paintings. 8, 25, 50 *c.*, $4.

1981

Royal Wedding. 25, 55 *c.*, $4.
Christmas. Walt Disney Cartoon Characters. ½, 1, 2, 3, 4, 5, 10 *c.*, $2.50, $3.
World Cup Football Championship, Spain (1982). 30 *c.* × 2, 50 *c.* × 2, $1 × 2, $2 × 2.

1982

Boy Scout Anniversaries. 8, 25, 50 *c.*, $3, $5.
Butterflies. 8, 30, 50 *c.*, $2.
21st Birthday of Princess of Wales. $2, $4.
Birth of Prince William of Wales. Optd on 21st Birthday of Princess of Wales issue. $2, $4.
Christmas. Walt Disney's "One Hundred and One Dalmatians". ½, 1, 2, 3, 4, 5, 10 *c.*, $2.50, $3.

1983

Easter. 500th Birth Anniv of Raphael. 10, 50, 90 *c.*, $4.
Bicentenary of Manned Flight. 10, 50, 90 *c.*, $2.50.
Christmas. Walt Disney Cartoon Characters. "Deck the Halls". ½, 1, 2, 3, 4, 5, 10 *c.*, $2.50, $3.

1984

Easter. Walt Disney Cartoon Characters. ½, 1, 2, 3, 4, 5, 10 *c.*, $2, $4.
Olympic Games, Los Angeles. 10, 50, 90 *c.*, $2.50.
Christmas. 50th Birthday of Donald Duck. 45, 60, 90 *c.*, $2, $4.

Ascension

DEPENDENCY OF ST. HELENA

Ascension, first occupied in 1815, was retained as a Royal Navy Establishment, under the control of the Admiralty from 1816 until 20 October 1922 when it became a dependency of St. Helena by Letters Patent.

A Post Office was established on the island in 1860. Stamps of Great Britain were first supplied to the island in 1867, but were, until 1887, often cancelled on arrival in the United Kingdom. The use of British stamps ceased in 1922.

Z 1

Z 2

Z 3

The original postmark type issued to Ascension, preceding the introduction of Great Britain stamps by several years, was as Type Z 1. This style, with "ASCENSION" extending over virtually half the circumference, continued to be used into the 1930's, appearing in different sizes with the diameter varying between 19 and 24½ mm. Type Z **2** was introduced *circa* 1921–22 and only occurs as a genuine usage on stamps current at that time.

Apparently similar postmarks on earlier issues, that is before 1921, are now generally recognised as forgeries, the accepted test being that, on genuine examples of Type Z **1**, a diameter passes through both the "A" and the last "N" of "ASCENSION".

Registered letters were cancelled with Type Z **3**, sent to the island in 1898, or with a scarce "hooded" type (a circular datestamp with curved label added at top) seen on covers between 1897 and 1903.

Stamps of GREAT BRITAIN *cancelled with Types* Z **1/3**.

1867 (3 Mar) *to* **1922**.

Z 1	1d. red-brown (1855)	£1100
Z 2	1d. rose-red (1864–79) *From*	£650
	Plate Nos. 71, 74, 78, 83, 85, 96, 100, 102, 103, 104, 122, 134, 138, 154, 155, 157, 160, 168, 178	
Z 3	6d. lilac (1865) (Plate No. 5)	£1300
Z 4	1s. green (1865) (Plate No. 4)	
Z 5	1s. green (1867) (Plate No. 7)	
Z 6	6d. grey (1880) (Plate Nos. 15, 17)	£1000
Z 7	1d. lilac (1881) (16 *dots*)	20·00
Z 8	½d. vermilion (1887–92)	20·00
Z 9	1½d. purple and green	45·00
Z10	2d. green and carmine	55·00
Z11	2½d. purple/*blue*	20·00
Z12	3d. purple/*yellow*	80·00
Z13	4d. green and brown	80·00
Z14	4½d. green and carmine	£250
Z15	5d. dull purple and blue	90·00
Z16	6d. purple/*rose-red*	85·00
Z17	9d. purple and blue	85·00
Z17*a*	10d. dull purple and carmine	£150
Z18	1s. green	95·00
Z19	½d. blue-green (1900)	13·00
Z20	1s. green and carmine	95·00
Z21	½d. green (1902 etc.)	13·00
Z22	1d. red (1902 etc.)	13·00
Z23	1½d. purple and green (1902 etc.)	38·00
Z24	2d. green and carmine (1902 etc.)	38·00
Z25	2½d. blue (1902 etc.)	38·00
Z26	3d. purple/*yellow* (1902 etc.)	45·00
Z27	4d. green and brown (1902 etc.)	£130
Z28	4d. orange (1902 etc.)	90·00
Z29	5d. purple and blue (1902 etc.)	85·00
Z30	6d. purple (1902 etc.)	90·00
Z31	7d. grey-black (1902 etc.)	£225
Z32	9d. purple and blue (1902 etc.)	90·00
Z32*a*	10d. dull purple and scarlet (1902 etc.)	£150
Z33	1s. green and carmine (1902 etc.)	55·00
Z33*a*	2s. 6d. dull reddish purple (1911)	£350
Z34	5s. carmine (1902 etc.)	£450
Z35	10s. ultramarine (1902 etc.)	£750
Z35*a*	£1 green (1902 etc.)	£1200
Z36	½d. yellow-green (1911–12)	20·00
Z37	½d. green (1911-12)	55·00
Z38	1d. scarlet (1911–12)	55·00
Z39	½d. green (1912–22)	13·00
Z40	1d. carmine (1912–22)	13·00
Z41	1½d. red-brown (1912–22)	13·00
Z42	2d. orange (1912–22)	13·00
Z43	2½d. blue (1912–22)	18·00
Z44	3d. violet (1912–22)	18·00
Z45	4d. grey-green (1912–22)	20·00
Z46	5d. brown (1912–22)	20·00
Z47	6d. purple (1912–22)	20·00
Z48	9d. agate (1912–22)	85·00
Z49	9d. olive-green (1912–22)	£120
Z50	10d. turquoise-blue (1912–22)	£120
Z51	1s. bistre (1912–22)	£110
Z52	2s. 6d. brown (1918–30)	£350

Supplies of some values do not appear to have been sent to the island, known examples originating from maritime or philatelic mail.

PRICES FOR STAMPS ON COVER TO 1945	
Nos. 1/34	*from* × 4
Nos. 35/7	*from* × 8
Nos. 38/47	*from* × 5

ASCENSION

(1)

2 Badge of St. Helena

1922 (2 Nov). *Stamps of St. Helena, optd with T* 1 *by D.L.R.*

(*a*) *Wmk Mult Script CA*

1	**14**	½d. black and green	2·50	7·00
2	**15**	1d. green	2·50	7·00
3		1½d. rose-scarlet	7·00	22·00
4	**14**	2d. black and grey	7·00	13·00
5		3d. bright blue	8·00	16·00
6	**15**	8d. black and dull purple	20·00	22·00
7		2s. black and blue/*blue*	£130	£150
8		3s. black and violet	£200	£225

(*b*) *Wmk Mult Crown CA*

9	**14**	1s. black/*green* (R.)	30·00	38·00
1/9		*Set of* 9	£375	£450
1/9 Optd "Specimen"		*Set of* 9	£700	

PLATE FLAWS ON THE 1924–33 ISSUE. Many constant plate varieties exist on both the vignette and duty plates of this issue.

The three major varieties are illustrated and listed below with prices for mint examples. Fine used stamps showing these flaws are worth a considerable premium over the mint prices quoted.

This issue utilised the same vignette plate as the St. Helena 1922–36 set so that these flaws occur there also.

Broken mainmast. Occurs on R.2/1 of all values.

Torn flag. Occurs on R.4/6 of all values except the 5d. Retouched on sheets of ½d. and 1d. printed after 1927.

Cleft rock. Occurs on R.5/1 of all values.

(Typo D.L.R.)

1924 (20 Aug)–**33.** *T* **2**. *Wmk Mult Script CA. P* 14.

10 ½d. grey-black and black, **C** .. .. 1·50 2·50
a. Broken mainmast .. .. 35·00
b. Torn flag .. .. 35·00
c. Cleft rock .. .. 35·00
11 1d. grey-black and deep blue-green, **C** .. 2·00 3·25
a. Broken mainmast .. .. 35·00
b. Torn flag .. .. 35·00
c. Cleft rock .. .. 35·00
11*d* 1d. grey-black & bt blue-green, **C** (1933) .. 65·00 £250
da. Broken mainmast £190
dc. Cleft rock £190
12 1½d. rose-red, **C** .. .. 4·00 7·50
a. Broken mainmast .. .. 50·00
b. Torn flag .. .. 50·00
c. Cleft rock .. .. 50·00
13 2d. grey-black and grey, **C** .. .. .. 4·00 4·00
a. Broken mainmast .. .. 55·00
b. Torn flag .. .. 55·00
c. Cleft rock .. .. 55·00
14 3d. blue, **C** .. .. 2·50 6·00
a. Broken mainmast .. .. 65·00
b. Torn flag .. .. 65·00
c. Cleft rock .. .. 65·00
15 4d. grey-black and black/*yellow*, **C** .. .. 23·00 30·00
a. Broken mainmast £110
b. Torn flag £110
c. Cleft rock £110
15*d* 5d. purple and olive-green, **C** (8.27) .. .. 13·00 17·00
da. Broken mainmast .. .. 90·00
dc. Cleft rock .. .. 90·00
16 6d. grey-black and bright purple, **C** .. .. 42·00 60·00
a. Broken mainmast £140
b. Torn flag £140
c. Cleft rock £140
17 8d. grey-black and bright violet, **C** .. .. 18·00 26·00
a. Broken mainmast .. .. 85·00
b. Torn flag .. .. 85·00
c. Cleft rock .. .. 85·00
18 1s. grey-black and brown, **C** .. .. .. 29·00 35·00
a. Broken mainmast £100
b. Torn flag £100
c. Cleft rock £100
19 2s. grey-black and blue/*blue*, **C** .. .. 80·00 90·00
a. Broken mainmast £250
b. Torn flag £250
c. Cleft rock £250
20 3s. grey-black and black/*blue*, **C** £120 £130
a. Broken mainmast £450
b. Torn flag £450
c. Cleft rock £450
10/20 .. .. *Set of* 12 £300 £350
10/20 Optd "Specimen" .. .. *Set of* 12 £650

3 Georgetown 4 Ascension Island

(Des and recess D.L.R.)

1934 (2 July). *T* **3/4** *and similar designs. Wmk Mult Script CA. P* 14.

21 **3** ½d. black and violet .. .. .. 45 1·00
22 **4** 1d. black and emerald .. .. .. 1·90 1·60
23 – 1½d. black and scarlet .. .. .. 1·90 1·90
24 **4** 2d. black and orange .. .. .. 1·90 1·90
25 – 3d. black and ultramarine .. .. 1·90 1·90
26 – 5d. black and blue .. .. .. 3·75 5·50
27 **4** 8d. black and sepia .. .. .. 10·00 11·00
28 – 1s. black and carmine .. .. .. 17·00 22·00
29 **4** 2s. 6d. black and bright purple .. .. 70·00 90·00
30 – 5s. black and brown £100 £120
21/30 .. .. *Set of* 10 £190 £250
21/30 Perf "Specimen" .. .. *Set of* 10 £275

Designs: *Horiz*—1½d. The Pier; 3d. Long Beach; 5d. Three Sisters; 1s. Sooty Tern and Wideawake Fair; 5s. Green Mountain.

1935 (6 May). *Silver Jubilee. As Nos.* 91/4 *of Antigua, but ptd by Waterlow. P* 11 × 12.

31 1½d. deep blue and scarlet .. .. .. 4·50 3·50
32 2d. ultramarine and grey .. .. .. 8·00 13·00
33 5d. green and indigo .. .. 11·00 14·00
34 1s. slate and purple .. .. 22·00 32·00
31/4 Perf "Specimen" .. .. .. *Set of* 4 85·00

1937 (19 May). *Coronation. As Nos.* 13/15 *of Aden. P* 14.

35 1d. green 50 90
36 2d. orange 90 70
37 3d. bright blue .. .. 2·00 2·00
35/7 Perf "Specimen" .. .. *Set of* 3 70·00

10 The Pier

(Recess D.L.R.)

1938 (12 May)–**53.** *Horiz designs as King George V issue, but modified and with portrait of King George VI as in T* **10**. *Wmk Mult Script CA. P* 13½.

38 **3** ½d. black and violet 45 65
a. Perf 13. *Black and bluish violet* (17.5.44) 30 65
39 – 1d. black and green .. .. .. 32·00 12·00
39*a* – 1d. black and yellow-orange (8.7.40) .. 6·00 9·50
b. Perf 13 (5.42) 35 70
c. Perf 14 (17.2.49) .. .. .. 65 4·00
39*d* – 1d. black and green, *p* 13 (1.6.49) .. 30 70
40 **10** 1½d. black and vermilion .. .. 1·25 1·60
a. Perf 13 (17.5.44) .. .. .. 70 1·25
b. Perf 14 (17.2.49) .. .. .. 3·00 13·00
40*c* 1½d. black and rose-carmine, *p* 14 (1.6.49) 45 1·25
ca. *Black and carmine* .. .. .. 2·75 6·00
d. Perf 13 (25.2.53) .. .. .. 1·75 6·50
41 – 2d. black and red-orange 55 70
a. Perf 13 (17.5.44) .. .. .. 80 1·00
b. Perf 14 (17.2.49) .. .. .. 9·00 20·00
41*c* – 2d. black and scarlet, *p* 14 (1.6.49) .. 60 70
42 – 3d. black and ultramarine .. .. 80·00 28·00
42*a* – 3d. black and grey (8.7.40) .. .. 1·25 90
b. Perf 13 (17.5.44) 80 70
42*c* – 4d. black and ultramarine (8.7.40) .. 1·00 1·25
d. Perf 13 (17.5.44) .. .. .. 80 1·00
43 – 6d. black and blue .. .. .. 1·10 1·25
a. Perf 13 (17.5.44) .. .. .. 1·90 1·25
44 **3** 1s. black and sepia .. .. .. 2·50 2·25
a. Perf 13 (17.5.44) .. .. .. 1·50 2·00
45 **10** 2s. 6d. black and deep carmine .. .. 11·00 13·00
a. Frame printed double, once albino
b. Perf 13 (17.5.44) .. .. .. 12·00 22·00
46 – 5s. black and yellow-brown .. .. 22·00 17·00
a. Perf 13 (17.5.44) .. .. .. 20·00 24·00
47 – 10s. black and bright purple .. .. 48·00 40·00
a. Perf 13 (17.5.44) .. .. .. 40·00 45·00
38/47a .. .. *Set of* 16 £170 £120
38/47 Perf "Specimen" .. .. *Set of* 13 £275

Designs: *Horiz*—1d. (Nos. 39/*c*), 2d., 4d. Green Mountain; 1d. (No. 39*d*), 6d., 10s. Three Sisters; 3d., 5s. Long Beach.

1946 (21 Oct). *Victory. As Nos.* 28/9 *of Aden.*

48 2d. red-orange 40 60
49 4d. blue 40 60
48/9 Perf "Specimen" .. .. *Set of* 2 42·00

1948 (20 Oct). *Royal Silver Wedding. As Nos.* 30/1 *of Aden.*

50 3d. black 60 70
51 10s. bright purple .. .. 42·00 48·00

1949 (10 Oct). *75th Anniv of Universal Postal Union. As Nos.* 114/17 *of Antigua.*

52 3d. carmine .. .. 1·40 1·40
53 4d. deep blue .. .. 3·00 2·50
54 6d. olive .. .. 4·50 4·50
55 1s. blue-black .. .. 5·50 6·00

1953 (2 June). *Coronation. As No.* 47 *of Aden.*

56 3d. black and grey-black .. .. .. 1·75 2·75

15 Water Catchment

(Recess B.W.)

1956 (19 Nov). *T* **15** *and similar horiz designs. Wmk Mult Script CA. P* 13.

57 ½d. black and brown 15 25
58 1d. black and magenta 40 25
59 1½d. black and orange 30 25
60 2d. black and carmine-red 50 40
61 2½d. black and orange-brown 50 45
62 3d. black and blue .. .. 1·50 1·00
63 4d. black and deep turquoise-green .. .. 1·25 1·25
64 6d. black and indigo 90 90
65 7d. black and deep olive .. .. .. 1·00 1·00
66 1s. black and vermilion .. .. .. 1·00 90
67 2s. 6d. black and deep dull purple .. .. 20·00 10·00
68 5s. black and blue-green .. .. .. 38·00 22·00
69 10s. black and purple .. .. 65·00 48·00
57/69 .. .. *Set of* 13 £120 80·00

Designs:—1d. Map of Ascension; 1½d. View of Georgetown; 2d. Map showing cable network; 2½d. Mountain road; 3d. White-tailed Tropic Bird; 4d. Long-finned Tunny; 6d. Rollers on the seashore; 7d. Young turtles; 1s. Land Crab; 2s. 6d. Sooty Tern; 5s. Perfect Crater; 10s. View of Ascension from North-west.

28 Brown Booby 42 Satellite Station

(Des after photos by N. P. Ashmole. Photo Harrison)

1963 (23 May). *T* **28** *and similar horiz designs. W* w **12**. *P* 14 × 14½.

70 1d. black, lemon and new blue 10 8
71 1½d. black, cobalt and ochre 15 10
72 2d. black, grey and bright blue 20 12
73 3d. black, magenta and turquoise-blue .. 20 15
74 4½d. black, bistre-brown and new blue .. 30 25
75 6d. bistre, black and yellow-green 30 30
76 7d. black, brown and reddish violet 35 35
77 10d. black, greenish yellow and blue-green .. 45 45
78 1s. multicoloured 50 50
79 1s. 6d. multicoloured .. .. 3·00 1·75
80 2s. 6d. multicoloured .. .. 4·50 2·75
81 5s. multicoloured .. .. 7·00 6·00
82 10s. multicoloured .. .. 15·00 13·00
83 £1 multicoloured .. .. 27·00 20·00
70/83 .. .. *Set of* 14 55·00 42·00

Designs:—1½d. White-capped Noddy; 2d. White Tern; 3d. Red-billed Tropic Bird; 4½d. Common Noddy; 6d. Sooty Tern; 7d. Ascension Frigate Bird; 10d. Blue-faced Booby; 1s. White-tailed Tropic Bird; 1s. 6d. Red-billed Tropic Bird; 2s. 6d. Madeiran Storm Petrel; 5s. Red-footed Booby (brown phase); 10s. Ascension Frigate Birds; £1 Red-footed Booby (white phase).

1963 (4 June). *Freedom from Hunger. As No.* 76 *of Aden.*

84 1s. 6d. carmine .. .. 5·00 2·50

1963 (2 Sept). *Red Cross Centenary. As Nos.* 147/8 *of Antigua.*

85 3d. red and black .. .. 2·75 1·50
86 1s. 6d. red and blue .. .. 7·00 5·50

1965 (17 May). *I.T.U. Centenary. As Nos.* 166/7 *of Antigua.*

87 3d. magenta and bluish violet .. .. 1·75 80
88 6d. turquoise-blue and light chestnut .. 2·00 1·10

1965 (25 Oct). *International Co-operation Year. As Nos.* 168/9 *of Antigua.*

89 1d. reddish purple and turquoise-green .. 65 30
90 6d. deep bluish green and lavender .. .. 2·25 1·50

1966 (24 Jan). *Churchill Commemoration. As Nos.* 170/3 *of Antigua.*

91 1d. new blue 75 30
92 3d. deep green .. .. 3·75 1·50
93 6d. brown .. .. 5·50 2·25
94 1s. 6d. bluish violet .. .. 7·50 3·00

1966 (1 July). *World Cup Football Championships. As Nos.* 176/7 *of Antigua.*

95 3d. violet, yellow-green, lake and yell-brn .. 1·75 60
96 6d. chocolate, blue-green, lake & yellow-brn 2·00 80

1966 (20 Sept). *Inauguration of W.H.O. Headquarters, Geneva. As Nos.* 178/9 *of Antigua.*

97 3d. black, yellow-green and light blue .. 2·25 65
98 1s. 6d. black, light purple and yellow-brown 4·75 1·90

(Des V. Whiteley. Photo Harrison)

1966 (7 Nov). *Opening of Apollo Communications Satellite Earth Station. W* w **12**. *(sideways). P* 14 × 14½.

99 **42** 4d. black and reddish violet 25 10
100 8d. black and deep bluish green 35 30
101 1s. 3d. black and olive-brown 45 35
102 2s. 6d. black and turquoise-blue 65 50

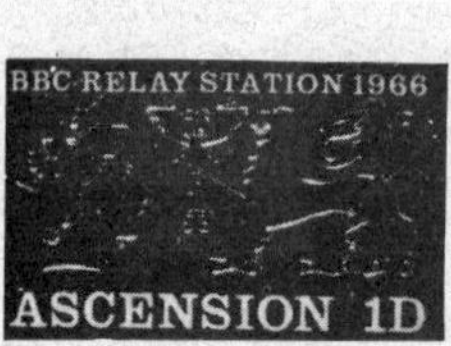

43 B.B.C. Emblem 44 Human Rights Emblem and Chain Links

(Des B.B.C. staff. Photo, Queen's head and emblem die-stamped, Harrison)

1966 (1 Dec). *Opening of B.B.C. Relay Station. W* w **12**. *P* 14½.

103 **43** 1d. gold and ultramarine 12 10
104 3d. gold and myrtle-green 20 10
105 6d. gold and reddish violet 25 15
106 1s. 6d. gold and red 30 35

1967 (1 Jan). *20th Anniv of U.N.E.S.C.O. As Nos.* 196/8 *of Antigua.*

107 3d. slate-violet, red, yellow and orange .. 3·00 1·00
108 6d. orange-yellow, violet and deep olive .. 4·25 1·50
109 1s. 6d. black, bright purple and orange .. 7·25 3·00

(Des and litho Harrison)

1968 (8 July). *Human Rights Year. W* w **12** *(sideways). P* 14½ × 14.

110 **44** 6d. light orange, red and black 50 30
111 1s. 6d. light grey-blue, red and black .. 65 40
112 2s. 6d. light green, red and black 75 60

45 Ascension Black-Fish 46 H.M.S. *Rattlesnake*

(Des M. Farrar Bell. Litho D.L.R.)

1968 (23 Oct). *Fishes (1st series). T* **45** *and similar horiz designs. W* w **12** *(sideways). P* 13.

113 4d. black, slate and turquoise-blue 85 45
114 8d. multicoloured .. .. 1·25 65
115 1s. 9d. multicoloured .. .. 1·90 1·00
116 2s. 3d. multicoloured .. .. 2·00 1·25

Designs:—8d. Leather-jacket; 1s. 9d. Tunny; 2s. 3d. Mako Shark.

See also Nos. 117/20 and 126/9.

(Des M. Farrar Bell. Litho D.L.R.)

1969 (3 Mar). *Fishes (2nd series). Horiz designs as T* **45**. *Multicoloured. W* w **12** *(sideways). P* 13.

117 4d. Sailfish .. .. 1·25 65
118 6d. Old Wife .. .. 1·75 85
119 1s. 6d. Yellowtail .. .. 2·75 1·75
120 2s. 11d. Jack .. .. 4·75 2·75

(Des L. Curtis. Photo Harrison)

1969 (1 Oct). *Royal Naval Crests (1st series). T* **46** *and similar vert designs. W* w **12** *(sideways). P* 14 × 14½.

121 4d. multicoloured 75 45
122 9d. multicoloured .. .. 1·25 55
123 1s. 9d. deep blue, pale blue and gold .. 2·25 80
124 2s. 3d. multicoloured .. .. 2·50 1·00
MS125 165 × 105 mm. Nos. 121/4. P 14½ .. 9·00 8·00

Designs:—9d. H.M.S. *Weston*; 1s. 9d. H.M.S. *Undaunted*; 2s. 3d. H.M.S. *Eagle*.

See also Nos. 130/4, 149/53, 154/8 and 166/70.

(Des M. Farrar Bell. Litho D.L.R.)

1970 (6 Apr). *Fishes (3rd series). Horiz designs as T* **45**. *Multicoloured. W* w **12** *(sideways). P* 14.

126 4d. Wahoo .. .. 2·00 1·25
127 9d. Coal-fish .. .. 2·25 1·75
128 1s. 9d. Dolphin .. .. 3·00 2·25
129 2s. 3d. Soldier Fish .. .. 3·25 2·50

(Des L. Curtis. Photo D.L.R.)

1970 (7 Sept). *Royal Naval Crests (2nd series). Designs as T* **46**. *Multicoloured. W* w **12**. *P* 12½.

130 4d. H.M.S. *Penelope* 90 55
131 9d. H.M.S. *Carlisle* .. .. 1·40 95
132 1s. 6d. H.M.S. *Amphion* .. .. .. 2·25 1·50
133 2s. 6d. H.M.S. *Magpie* .. .. .. 2·50 2·00
MS134 153 × 96 mm. Nos. 130/3 .. .. .. 9·00 8·00

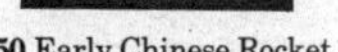

50 Early Chinese Rocket

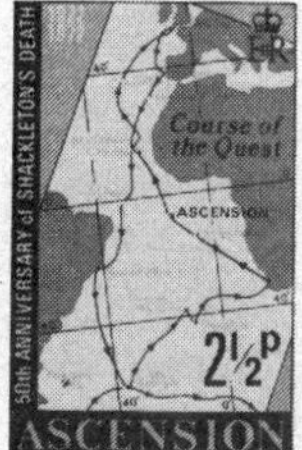

51 Course of the *Quest*

(Des V. Whiteley. Litho Format)

1971 (15 Feb). *Decimal Currency. The Evolution of Space Travel. T* **50** *and similar multicoloured designs. W* w **12** *(sideways on horiz designs). P* 14.

135 ½p. Type **50** 20 15
136 1p. Medieval Arab Astronomers 30 15
137 1½p. Tycho Brahe's Observatory, Quadrant and Supernova 45 25
138 2p. Galileo, Moon and Telescope 65 30
139 2½p. Isaac Newton, Instruments and Apple .. 70 40
140 3½p. Harrison's Chronometer and Ship .. 90 45
141 4½p. Space Rocket taking-off 95 50
142 5p. World's Largest Telescope, Palomar .. 1·25 60
143 7½p. World's largest Radio Telescope, Jodrell Bank .. .. 2·25 1·60
144 10p. Mariner VII and Mars .. .. .. 2·75 1·75
145 12½p. Sputnik II and Space Dog, Laika .. 3·50 2·25
146 25p. Walking in Space .. .. .. 4·75 3·25
147 50p. Apollo XI Crew on Moon .. .. 5·50 4·50
148 £1 Future Space Research Station .. .. 8·50 8·50
135/48 .. .. *Set of* 14 29·00 22·00

The ½p., 1p., 4½p. and 25p. are vertical, and the remainder are horizontal.

(Des L. Curtis. Photo D.L.R.)

1971 (15 Nov). *Royal Naval Crests (3rd series). Designs as T* **46**. *Multicoloured. W* w **12**. *P* 13.

149 2p. H.M.S. *Phoenix* 80 60
150 4p. H.M.S. *Milford* .. .. 1·40 1·10
151 9p. H.M.S. *Pelican* .. .. 1·75 1·60
152 15p. H.M.S. *Oberon* .. .. 2·25 2·25
MS153 151 × 104 mm. Nos. 149/52 .. .. 9·00 9·00

(Des L. Curtis. Litho Questa)

1972 (29 May). *Royal Naval Crests (4th series). Multicoloured designs as T* **46**. *W* w **12** *(sideways). P* 14.

154 1½p. H.M.S. *Lowestoft* 65 60
155 3p. H.M.S. *Auckland* 95 80
156 6p. H.M.S. *Nigeria* .. .. 1·10 1·40
157 17½p. H.M.S. *Bermuda* .. .. .. 2·50 2·75
MS158 157 × 93 mm. Nos. 154/7 .. .. 6·50 10·00

(Des J. Cooter. Litho Questa)

1972 (2 Aug). *50th Anniv of Shackleton's Death. T* **51** *and similar multicoloured designs. W* w **12** *(sideways on 4 and 7½p.). P* 14.

159 2½p. Type **51** .. .. 1·25 1·25
160 4p. Shackleton and *Quest* (*horiz*) .. .. 1·40 1·40
161 7½p. Shackleton's cabin and *Quest* (*horiz*) .. 1·60 1·60
162 11p. Shackleton's statue and memorial .. 1·75 1·75
MS163 139 × 114 mm. Nos. 159/62 (wmk sideways) 5·50 7·50

52 Land Crab and Mako Shark

(Des (from photograph by D. Groves) and photo Harrison)

1972 (20 Nov). *Royal Silver Wedding. Multicoloured; background colour given. W* w **12**. *P* 14 × 14½.

164 **52** 2p. bright bluish violet 30 30
165 16p. rose-carmine 65 75

(Des L. Curtis. Litho J.W.)

1973 (28 May). *Royal Naval Crests (5th series). Multicoloured designs as T* **46**. *W* w **12** *(sideways). P* 14.

166 2p. H.M.S. *Birmingham* .. .. .. 2·75 1·50
167 4p. H.M.S. *Cardiff* .. .. 3·50 2·25
168 9p. H.M.S. *Penzance* .. .. 4·50 2·50
169 13p. H.M.S. *Rochester* .. .. 4·75 3·25
MS170 109 × 152 mm. Nos. 166/9 .. .. 23·00 16·00

53 Green Turtle

(Des V. Whiteley Studio. Litho Enschedé)

1973 (28 Aug). *Turtles. T* **53** *and similar triangular designs. Multicoloured. W* w **12**. *P* 13½.

171 4p. Type **53** .. .. 3·25 2·00
172 9p. Loggerhead turtle .. .. 3·75 2·50
173 12p. Hawksbill turtle .. .. 4·00 2·75

54 Sergeant, R.M. Light Infantry, 1900

55 Letter and H.Q., Berne

(Des G. Drummond from paintings by C. Stadden. Litho Walsall)

1973 (31 Oct). *50th Anniv of Departure of Royal Marines from Ascension. T* **54** *and similar vert designs. Multicoloured. W* w **12** *(sideways). P* 14.

174 2p. Type **54** .. .. 2·75 1·75
175 6p. R.M. Private, 1816 .. .. .. 3·75 3·25
176 12p. R.M. Light Infantry Officer, 1880 .. 4·25 3·75
177 20p. R.M. Artillery Colour Sergeant, 1910 .. 4·75 4·50

1973 (14 Nov). *Royal Wedding. As Nos. 165/6 of Anguilla. Centre multicoloured. W* w **12** *(sideways). P* 13½.

178 2p. ochre 30 25
179 18p. dull blue-green 45 40

(Des PAD Studio. Litho Questa)

1974 (27 Mar). *Centenary of U.P.U. T* **55** *and similar horiz design. Multicoloured. W* w **12**. *P* 14½ × 14.

180 2p. Type **55** 40 40
181 9p. Hermes and U.P.U. monument 60 65

56 Churchill as a Boy, and Birthplace, Blenheim Palace

(Des J.W. Litho Questa)

1974 (30 Nov). *Birth Centenary of Sir Winston Churchill. T* **56** *and similar horiz design. Multicoloured. No wmk. P* 14.

182 5p. Type **56** 60 40
183 25p. Churchill as statesman, and U.N. Building .. .. 1·40 1·50
MS184 93 × 87 mm. Nos. 182/3 .. .. .. 2·25 2·50

57 "Skylab 3" and Photograph of Ascension

(Des PAD Studio. Litho Questa)

1975 (20 Mar). *Space Satellites. T* **57** *and similar horiz design. Multicoloured. W* w **12** *(sideways). P* 14.

185 2p. Type **57** 45 30
186 18p. "Skylab 4" command module and photograph 65 80

The date "11.1.73" given on the 2p. is incorrect, "Skylab 3" was launched in July 1973 and returned to Earth in September 1973.

The date on the 18p. is also incorrect. The photograph was taken on 16 January 1974, three days later than the date given in the caption.

58 U.S.A.F. "Starlifter"

APOLLO-SOYUZ
LINK
1975

(59)

(Des R. Granger Barrett. Litho Questa)

1975 (19 June). *Wideawake Airfield. T* **58** *and similar horiz designs. Multicoloured. W* w **12** *(sideways). P* 13½.

187 2p. Type **58** 70 55
188 5p. R.A.F. "Hercules" .. .. 1·00 75
189 9p. Vickers "VC-10" .. .. 1·40 1·25
190 24p. U.S.A.F. "Galaxy" .. .. 2·50 2·50
MS191 144 × 99 mm. Nos. 187/90 .. .. 8·50 9·00

1975 (18 Aug). *"Apollo–Soyuz" Space Link. Nos.* 141 *and* 145/6 *optd with T* **59**.

192 4½p. Space rocket taking-off 45 40
193 12½p. Sputnik II and Space Dog, Laika .. 60 85
194 25p. Walking in Space .. .. 75 1·25

60 Arrival of Royal Navy, 1815

(Des J.W. from paintings by Isobel McManus. Litho Walsall)

1975 (22 Oct). *160th Anniv of Occupation. T* **60** *and similar horiz designs. Multicoloured. W* w **14** *(sideways). P* 14.

195 2p. Type **60** 40 30
196 5p. Water Supply, Dampiers Drip 55 45
197 9p. First landing, 1815 .. .. .. 70 70
198 15p. The garden on Green Mountain .. .. 90 1·10

61 Yellow Canary

62 Boatswain Bird Island Sanctuary

(Des J.W. Litho Questa)

1976 (26 Apr). *Multicoloured designs as T* **61** *and T* **62**. *W* w **14** *(sideways on horiz designs). P* 13½ (£2) *or* 14 *(others)*.

199 1p. Type **61** 25 25
200 2p. White Tern 30 25
201 3p. Common Waxbill 40 30
202 4p. White-capped Noddy 40 30
203 5p. Common Noddy 40 30
204 6p. Common Mynah 45 35
205 7p. Madeiran Storm Petrel 55 55
206 8p. Sooty Tern 60 60
207 9p. Blue-faced Booby 65 65
208 10p. Red-footed Booby 70 70
209 15p. Bare-throated Francolin .. .. .. 1·50 1·50
210 18p. Brown Booby .. .. 1·50 1·50

211 25p. Red-billed Tropic Bird . . . . . . 1·75 1·75
212 50p. White-tailed Tropic Bird. . . . . . 2·75 3·00
213 £1 Ascension Frigate Bird . . . . . . 3·50 3·75
214 £2 Type **62** . . . . 6·50 7·50
199/214 . . . . . . *Set of* 16 20·00 21·00
The 2, 4, 7, 9, 15, 18p. and £1 are vertical designs.

63 G.B. Penny Red with Ascension Postmark

(Des C. Abbott. Litho J.W.)

1976 (4 May). *Festival of Stamps, London. T* **63** *and similar designs.* W w **14** (*sideways on* 5 *and* 25p.). *P* 13½.
215 5p. rose-red, black and cinnamon 30 30
216 9p. green, black and greenish stone. . . . 45 45
217 25p. multicoloured . . . . . . 85 1·00
MS218 133 × 121 mm. No. 217 with St. Helena 318 and Tristan da Cunha 206 (wmk sideways). P 13 2·50 3·00
Designs: *Vert*—9p. ½d. stamp of 1922. *Horiz*—25p. Cargo vessel *Southampton Castle.*
No. **MS**218 was postally valid on each island to the value of 25p.

64 U.S. Base, Ascension

65 Visit of Prince Philip, 1957

(Des V. Whiteley Studio. Litho J.W.)

1976 (4 July). *Bicentenary of American Revolution. T* **64** *and similar horiz designs. Multicoloured.* W w **14** (*sideways*). *P* 13.
219 8p. Type **64** 90 85
220 9p. NASA Station at Devils Ashpit . . . . 1·00 90
221 25p. "Viking" landing on Mars . . . . 2·00 1·75

(Des J. Cooter. Litho Walsall)

1977 (7 Feb). *Silver Jubilee. T* **65** *and similar horiz designs. Multicoloured.* W w **14** (*sideways on* 12 *and* 25p.). *P* 13½.
222 8p. Type **65** 50 55
223 12p. Coronation Coach leaving Buckingham Palace 60 65
224 25p. Coronation Coach 70 75

66 Tunnel carrying Water Pipe

67 Mars Bay Location, 1877

(Des G. Drummond. Litho Harrison)

1977 (27 June). *Water Supplies. T* **66** *and similar multicoloured designs.* W w **14** (*sideways on* 12 *and* 25p.). *P* 14.
225 3p. Type **66** 35 30
226 5p. Breakneck Valley wells 55 40
227 12p. Break tank (*horiz*) . . . . . . 1·25 95
228 25p. Water catchment (*horiz*) . . . . . . 1·75 1·40

(Des J.W. Litho Questa)

1977 (3 Oct). *Centenary of Visit of Professor Gill (astronomer). T* **67** *and similar horiz designs. Multicoloured.* W w **14** (*sideways*). *P* 13½.
229 3p. Type **67** 35 30
230 8p. Instrument sites, Mars Bay 65 60
231 12p. Sir David and Lady Gill . . . . . . 1·10 85
232 25p. Maps of Ascension . . . . . . 1·75 1·40

68 Lion of England

69 Queen Elizabeth II

(Des C. Abbott. Litho Questa)

1978 (2 June). *25th Anniv of Coronation. T* **68/9** *and similar vert design. P* 15.
233 **68** 25p. yellow, sepia and silver 70 75
a. Sheetlet. Nos. 233/5 × 2 . . . . 4·50
234 **69** 25p. multicoloured 70 75
235 – 25p. yellow, sepia and silver 70 75
Design:—No. 235, Green Turtle.
Nos. 233/5 were printed together in small sheets of 6, containing two *se-tenant* strips of 3 with horizontal gutter margin between.

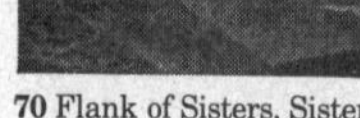

70 Flank of Sisters, Sisters' Red Hill and East Crater

71 "The Resolution" (H. Roberts)

(Des J.W. Litho Questa)

1978 (4 Sept). *Volcanic Rock Formations of Ascension. T* **70** *and similar horiz designs. Multicoloured.* W w **14**. *P* 14½.
236 3p. Type **70** 20 25
a. Horiz strip of 5. Nos. 236/40 . . . . 2·00
237 5p. Holland's Crater (Hollow Tooth) . . 30 35
238 12p. Street Crater, Lower Valley Crater and Bear's Back 45 50
239 15p. Butt Crater, Weather Post and Green Mountain 50 55
240 25p. Flank of Sisters, Thistle Hill and Two Boats Village 80 85
MS241 185 × 100 mm. Nos. 236/40, each × 2 . . 4·75 6·00
a. Blue ("Ascension Island") omitted . . £2500
Nos. 236/40 were printed together, *se-tenant*, in horizontal strips of 5 throughout the sheet forming a composite design.

(Des and litho (25p. also embossed) Walsall)

1979 (19 Feb*). *Bicentenary of Captain Cook's Voyages*, 1768–79. *T* **71** *and similar vert designs. Multicoloured. P* 11.
242 3p. Type **71** 45 30
243 8p. Chronometer 65 45
244 12p. Green Turtle 75 60
245 25p. Flaxman/Wedgwood medallion of Captain Cook . . . . 1·00 95
*This is the local date of issue; the stamps were released in London on 8 January.

72 St. Mary's Church, Georgetown

73 Landing Cable, Comfortless Cove

(Des Walsall. Litho Format)

1979 (24 May). *Ascension Day. T* **72** *and similar vert designs. Multicoloured.* W w **14**. *P* 14.
246 8p. Type **72** 50 45
247 12p. Map of Ascension 60 55
248 50p. "The Ascension" (painting by Rembrandt) 1·40 1·40

(Des G. Vasarhelyi. Litho Walsall)

1979 (15 Sept). *80th Anniv of Eastern Telegraph Company's Arrival on Ascension. T* **73** *and similar designs.* W w **14** (*inverted on* 12p. *or sideways on others*). *P* 14.
249 3p. black and carmine 12 12
250 8p. black and yellowish green 30 35
251 12p. black and yellow 40 45
252 15p. black and bright violet 45 50
253 25p. black and orange-brown 65 70
Designs: *Horiz*—8p. C.S. *Anglia*; 15p. C.S. *Seine*; 25p. Cable and Wireless earth station. *Vert*—12p. Map of Atlantic cable network.

74 1938 6d. Stamp

(Des BG Studio. Litho Questa)

1979 (12 Dec). *Death Centenary of Sir Rowland Hill. T* **74** *and similar designs.* W w **14** (*sideways on* 3 *and* 8p.). *P* 14.
254 3p. black, new blue and deep turquoise-blue 12 15
255 8p. black, blue-green and light green . . 30 35
256 12p. black, bright blue and turquoise-blue . . 35 40
257 50p. black, brownish grey and red . . . . 1·25 1·40
Designs: *Horiz*—8p. 1956 5s. definitive stamp. *Vert*—12p. 1924 3s. stamp; 50p. Sir Rowland Hill.

75 *Anogramma ascensionis*

76 17th-century Bottle Post

(Des J. Cooter. Litho Format)

1980 (18 Feb). *Ferns and Grasses. T* **75** *and similar multicoloured designs.* W w **14** (*sideways on* 12 *to* 24p.). *P* 14½ × 14 (3 *to* 8p.) *or* 14 × 14½ (12 *to* 24p.).
258 3p. Type **75** 10 8
259 6p. *Xiphopteris ascensionense* 20 20
260 8p. *Sporobolus caespitosus* 25 25
261 12p. *Sporobolus durus* (*vert*) 35 35
262 18p. *Dryopteris ascensionis* (*vert*) 45 45
263 24p. *Marattia purpurascens* (*vert*) 60 60
258/63 . . . . . . *Set of* 6 1·75 1·75

(Des L. Curtis. Litho Format)

1980 (1 May). *"London 1980" International Stamp Exhibition. T* **76** *and similar horiz designs. Multicoloured.* W w **14** (*sideways*). *P* 13½.
264 8p. Type **76** 25 25
265 12p. 19th-century chance calling ship . . 35 35
266 15p. Regular mail service from 1863 . . . . 40 40
267 50p. Mail services, 1980 . . . . . . 1·25 1·25
MS268 102 × 154 mm. Nos. 264/7 . . . . 2·25 2·40

77 Queen Elizabeth the Queen Mother

78 Lubbock's Yellowtail

(Des Harrison. Litho Questa)

1980 (11 Aug)*. *80th Birthday of Queen Elizabeth the Queen Mother.* W w **14** (*sideways*). *P* 14.
269 **77** 15p. multicoloured 55 55
*This was the local release date. The Crown Agents placed stocks on sale in London on 4 August.

(Des G. Drummond. Litho Enschedé)

1980 (15 Sept). *Fishes. T* **78** *and similar horiz designs. Multicoloured.* W w **14** (*sideways*). *P* 13 × 13½.
270 3p. Type **78** 20 15
271 10p. Resplendent Angelfish 45 35
272 25p. Hedgehog Butterflyfish 70 60
273 40p. Marmalade Razorfish 90 85

79 H.M.S. *Tortoise*

(Des D. Bowen. Litho Rosenbaum Bros, Vienna)

1980 (17 Nov). *150th Anniv of Royal Geographical Society. T* **79** *and similar multicoloured designs.* W w **14** (*sideways*). *P* 14 (60p.) *or* 13½ (*others*).
274 10p. Type **79** 45 40
275 15p. "Wideawake Fair" 55 45
276 60p. Mid-Atlantic Ridge (38 × 48 *mm*) . . 1·25 1·25

ALTERED CATALOGUE NUMBERS

Any Catalogue numbers altered from the last edition are shown as a list in the introductory pages.

80 Green Mountain Farm, 1881

(Des C. Abbott. Litho Format)

1981 (15 Feb). *Green Mountain Farm. T* **80** *and similar horiz designs. Multicoloured. W w* **14** *(sideways). P* 13½ × 14.

277	12p. Type **80**	45	35
278	15p. Two Boats, 1881	50	40
279	20p. Green Mountain and Two Boats, 1981 ..	60	50
280	30p. Green Mountain Farm, 1981	80	70

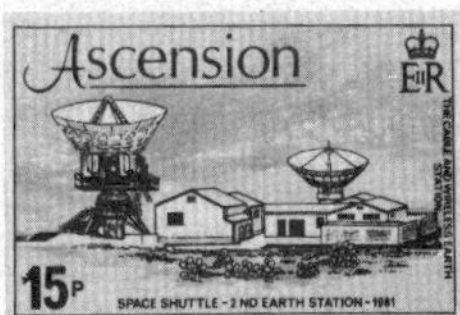

81 Cable and Wireless Earth Station

(Des G. Vasarhelyi and Walsall. Litho Walsall)

1981 (27 Apr). *"Space Shuttle" Mission and Opening of 2nd Earth Station. W w* **14** *(sideways). P* 14.

281	**81**	15p. black, bright blue and pale blue ..	45	35

82 Poinsettia

83 Solanum

(Des J. Cooter. Litho J.W.)

1981 (11 May)–**82**. *Flowers. Designs as T* **82** *(1 to 40p.) or vert as T* **83** *(50p. to £2). Multicoloured. W w* **14** *(sideways on 1, 2, 4, 5, 8, 15, 20, 40, 50p., £1 and £2). P* 13½. *A. Without imprint date. B. With imprint date* ("1982") (27.8.82).

		A		B	
282	1p. Type **82**	5	5	†	
283	2p. Clustered Wax Flower ..	5	5	5	5
284	3p. Kolanchoe (*vert*)	5	5	5	5
285	4p. Yellow Pops	8	10	†	
286	5p. Camels Foot Creeper ..	8	10	†	
287	8p. White Oleander	15	20	†	
288	10p. Ascension Lily (*vert*) ..	20	25	20	25
289	12p. Coral Plant (*vert*)	20	25	†	
290	15p. Yellow Allamanda ..	25	30	25	30
291	20p. Ascension Euphorbia ..	35	40	35	40
292	30p. Flame of the Forest (*vert*) ..	50	55	†	
293	40p. Bougainvillea "King Leopold"	70	75	†	
294	50p. Type **83**	90	1·10	†	
295	£1 Ladies Petticoat	1·75	1·90	1·75	1·90
296	£2 Red Hibiscus	3·50	3·75	†	
282A/96A	.. .. *Set of* 15	8·00	9·00	†	
283B/95B	.. .. *Set of* 6	†		2·40	2·75

Nos. 283B/95B had the imprint dates printed on the stamps by typography.

84 Map by Maxwell, 1793

(Des L. Curtis. Litho Walsall)

1981 (22 May). *Early Maps of Ascension. T* **84** *and similar horiz designs. W w* **14** *(sideways). P* 14 × 14½.

297	10p. black, gold and pale blue	40	35
298	12p. black, gold and apple-green	45	35
299	15p. black, gold and stone	50	40
300	40p. black, gold and pale greenish yellow ..	85	85
MS301	79 × 64 mm. 5p. × 4, multicoloured ..	60	60

Designs:—12p. Maxwell, 1793 (*different*); 15p. Ekeberg and Chapman, 1811; 40p. Campbell, 1819; miniature sheet, Linschoten, 1599.

Stamps from No. **MS**301 form a composite design.

85 Wedding Bouquet from Ascension

86 Prince Charles and Lady Diana Spencer

(Des J.W. Litho Questa)

1981 (22 July). *Royal Wedding. T* **85/6** *and similar vert design. Multicoloured. W w* **14**. *P* 14.

302	10p. Type **85**	40	40
303	15p. Prince Charles in Fleet Air Arm flying kit	55	45
304	50p. Type **86**	1·10	1·10

87 "Interest"

88 Scout crossing Rope Bridge

(Des BG Studio. Litho Questa)

1981 (14 Sept). *25th Anniv of Duke of Edinburgh Award Scheme. T* **87** *and similar vert designs. Multicoloured. W w* **14**. *P* 14.

305	5p. Type **87**	40	25
306	10p. "Physical activities"	45	35
307	15p. "Service"	50	45
308	40p. Duke of Edinburgh	1·00	80

(Des A. Theobald. Litho Format)

1982 (22 Feb). *75th Anniv of Boy Scout Movement. T* **88** *and similar designs. W w* **14** *(sideways). P* 14.

309	10p. black, bright blue and azure	45	35
310	15p. black, orange-brown and greenish yellow	55	50
311	25p. black, bright mauve and pale mauve ..	75	60
312	40p. black, rosine and pale orange	1·10	85
MS313	121 × 121 mm. 10p., 15p., 25p., 40p. As Nos. 309/12 (*each diamond*, 40 × 40 *mm*). P 14½	2·50	2·50

Designs:—15p. 1st Ascension Scout Group flag; 25p. Scouts learning to use radio; 40p. Lord Baden-Powell.

Stamps from No. **MS**313 have an overall design showing a flag printed on the reverse beneath the gum.

89 Charles Darwin

(Des L. Curtis. Litho Questa)

1982 (19 Apr). *150th Anniv of Charles Darwin's Voyage. T* **89** *and similar horiz designs. Multicoloured. W w* **14** *(sideways). P* 14.

314	10p. Type **89**	50	40
315	12p. Darwin's pistols	55	50
316	15p. Rock Crab	60	55
317	40p. H.M.S. *Beagle*	1·10	95

90 Fairey "Swordfish"

(Des A. Theobald. Litho Walsall)

1982 (15 June). *40th Anniv of Wideawake Airfield. T* **90** *and similar horiz designs. Multicoloured. W w* **14** *(sideways). P* 14.

318	5p. Type **90**	40	35
319	10p. North American "B-25C (Mitchell)" ..	60	40
320	15p. Boeing "EC-135N (Aria)"	75	55
321	50p. Lockheed "Hercules"	1·25	1·10

91 Ascension Coat of Arms

92 Formal Portrait

(Des Jennifer Toombs. Litho Questa)

1982 (1 July). *21st Birthday of Princess of Wales. T* **91/2** *and similar vert designs. Multicoloured. W w* **14**. *P* 14 × 14½.

322	12p. Type **91**	30	30
323	15p. Lady Diana Spencer in Music Room, Buckingham Palace	35	35
324	25p. Bride and Earl Spencer leaving Clarence House	55	55
325	50p. Type **92**	1·00	1·00

1st PARTICIPATION
COMMONWEALTH GAMES 1982

(**93**)

94 Bush House, London

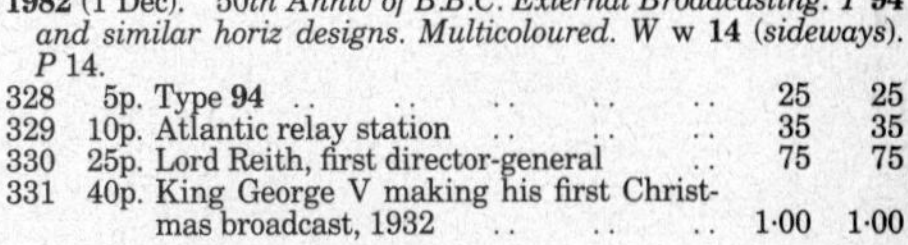

1982 (29 Oct). *Commonwealth Games, Brisbane. Nos.* 290B/1B *optd with T* **93**.

326	15p. Yellow Allamanda	40	40
327	20p. Ascension Euphorbia	50	50

(Des A. Theobald. Litho Questa)

1982 (1 Dec). *50th Anniv of B.B.C. External Broadcasting. T* **94** *and similar horiz designs. Multicoloured. W w* **14** *(sideways). P* 14.

328	5p. Type **94**	25	25
329	10p. Atlantic relay station	35	35
330	25p. Lord Reith, first director-general ..	75	75
331	40p. King George V making his first Christmas broadcast, 1932	1·00	1·00

95 *Manismius echinosphaerus*

96 Aerial View of Georgetown

(Des Harrison. Litho Questa)

1983 (1 Mar). *Fungi. T* **95** *and similar vert designs. Multicoloured. W w* **14**. *P* 14.

332	7p. Type **95**	25	25
333	12p. *Chlorophyllum molybditus*	35	35
334	15p. *Leucocoprinus cepaestipes*	40	40
335	20p. *Lycoperdon marginatum*	50	50
336	50p. *Marasmiellus distantifolius*	1·10	1·10

(Des Jennifer Toombs. Litho Format)

1983 (12 May). *Island Views (1st series) T* **96** *and similar horiz designs. Multicoloured. W w* **14** *(sideways). P* 14 × 13½.

337	12p. Type **96**	25	30
338	15p. Green Mountain farm	30	35
339	20p. Boatswain Bird Island	40	45
340	60p. Telemetry Hill by night	1·25	1·40

See also Nos. 367/70.

97 "Wessex 5" Helicopter of No. 845 Naval Air Squadron

(Des D. Hartley-Marjoram. Litho Questa)

1983 (1 Aug). *Bicentenary of Manned Flight. British Military Aircraft. T* **97** *and similar horiz designs. Multicoloured. W w* **14** *(sideways). P* 13½.

341	12p. Type **97**	30	35
342	15p. "Vulcan B2" of No. 44 Squadron ..	35	40
343	20p. "Nimrod MR2P" of No. 120 Squadron ..	45	50
344	60p. "Victor K2" of No. 55 Squadron	1·40	1·60

98 Iguanid

(Des D. Nockles. Litho Questa)

1983 (20 Sept). *Introduced Species. T* **98** *and similar horiz designs. Multicoloured. W w* **14** *(sideways). P* 14.

345	12p. Type **98**	25	30
346	15p. Rabbit	30	35
347	20p. Cat	40	45
348	60p. Donkey	1·25	1·40

99 *Tellina antonii philippi*

100 1922 1½d. Stamp

(Des G. Wilby. Litho Format)

1983 (28 Nov). *Sea Shells. T* **99** *and similar horiz designs. Multicoloured. W w* **14** *(sideways). P* 14½ × 14.

349	7p. Type **99**	15	20
350	12p. *Nodipecten nodosus (Linne)*	25	30
351	15p. *Cypraea lurida oceanica sch*	30	35
352	20p. *Nerita ascensionis gmelin*	40	45
353	50p. *Micromelo undatus (bruguiere)*	1·00	1·10

(Des C. Abbott. Litho Questa)

1984 (3 Jan). *150th Anniv of St. Helena as a British Colony. T* **100** *and similar vert designs showing stamps of the 1922 issue overprinted on St. Helena. Multicoloured. W w* **14**. *P* 14.

354	12p. Type **100**	30	35
355	15p. 1922 2d. stamp	35	40
356	20p. 1922 8d. stamp	40	45
357	60p. 1922 1s. stamp	1·25	1·40

101 Prince Andrew

102 Naval Semaphore

(Des L. Curtis. Litho Questa)

1984 (10 Apr). *Visit of Prince Andrew. Sheet,* 124 × 90 *mm, containing vert designs as T* **101**. *W w* **14** *(sideways). P* 14½ × 14.

MS358	12p. Type **101**; 70p. Prince Andrew in naval uniform	1·75	1·90

(Des D. Hartley-Marjoram. Litho Questa)

1984 (28 May). *250th Anniv of "Lloyd's List" (newspaper). T* **102** *and similar vert designs. Multicoloured. W w* **14**. *P* 14½ × 14.

359	12p. Type **102**	25	30
360	15p. *Southampton Castle*	30	35
361	20p. Pier Head	40	45
362	70p. *The Dane*	1·40	1·50

103 Penny Coin and Yellowfin Tuna

(Des G. Drummond. Litho Questa)

1984 (26 July). *New Coinage. T* **103** *and similar horiz designs. Multicoloured. W w* **14** *(sideways). P* 14.

363	12p. Type **103**	25	30
364	15p. Twopenny coin and donkey	30	35
365	20p. Fifty pence coin and Green Turtle	40	45
366	70p. Pound coin and Sooty Tern	1·40	1·50

(Des Jennifer Toombs. Litho B.D.T.)

1984 (26 Oct). *Island Views (2nd series). Horiz designs as T* **96**. *Multicoloured. W w* **14** *(sideways). P* 13½.

367	12p. The Devil's Riding-school	25	30
368	15p. St. Mary's Church	30	35
369	20p. Two Boats Village	40	45
370	70p. Ascension from the sea	1·40	1·50

Australia

AUSTRALIAN STATES. The following States combined to form the Commonwealth of Australia and their issues are listed in alphabetical order in this Catalogue:—

NEW SOUTH WALES

QUEENSLAND

SOUTH AUSTRALIA

TASMANIA

VICTORIA

WESTERN AUSTRALIA

PRICES FOR STAMPS ON COVER TO 1945

Nos. 1/27	*from* × 4
Nos. 29/34	*from* × 2
Nos. 35/50*d*	*from* × 3
Nos. 51/3	*from* × 4
Nos. 56/75	*from* × 3
Nos. 76/84	*from* × 4
Nos. 85/104	*from* × 3
Nos. 105/6	*from* × 4
Nos. 107/15	*from* × 3
No. 116	*from* × 5
Nos. 117/20	*from* × 4
Nos. 121/39*a*	*from* × 2
Nos. 140/*a*	*from* × 5
Nos. 141/4	*from* × 3
No. 146	*from* × 6
Nos. 147/53	*from* × 3
Nos. 153*a*/*b*	*from* × 2
Nos. 154/63	*from* × 3
Nos. 164/211	*from* × 2
Nos. D1/118	*from* × 8
Nos. O1/18	*from* × 5

PRINTERS. Except where otherwise stated, all Commonwealth stamps have been printed under Government authority at Melbourne. Until 1918 there were two establishments (both of the Treasury Dept)—the Note Printing Branch and the Stamp Printing Branch. The former printed T **3** and **4**.

In 1918 the Stamp Printing Branch was closed and all stamps were printed by the Note Printing Branch. In 1926 control was transferred from the Treasury to the Commonwealth Bank of Australia, and on 14 January 1960 the branch was attached to the newly established Reserve Bank of Australia.

Until 1942 stamps bore in the sheet margin the initials or names of successive managers and from 1942 to March 1952 the imprint "Printed by the Authority of the Government of the Commonwealth of Australia". Since November 1952 (or Nos. D129/31 for Postage Dues) imprints have been discontinued.

SPECIMEN OVERPRINTS. These come from Specimen sets, first produced in 1913. In these sets the lower values were cancelled-to-order, but stamps with a face value of 10s. or 75 c. were overprinted "Specimen" in different types. These overprints are listed as they could be purchased from the Australian Post Office.

1

2

Die I

Die II

Dies of Type **1** (mono-coloured values only):—

Die I. Break in inner frame line at lower left level with top of words of value.

Die II. Die repaired showing no break.

Die I was only used for the ½d., 1d., 2d. and 3d. Several plates were produced for each except the 3d. When the second plate of the 3d. was being prepared the damage became aggravated after making 105 out of the 120 units when the die was returned for repair. This gave rise to the *se-tenant* pairs showing the two states of the die.

Die II was used until 1945 and deteriorated progressively with damage to the frame lines and rounding of the corners.

Specialists recognise seven states of this die, but we only list the two most major of the later versions.

Die IIA. This state is as Die II, but, in addition, shows a break in the inner left-hand frame line, 9 mm from the top of the design.

Die IIB. As Die IIA, but now also showing break in outer frame line above "ST", and (not illustrated) an incomplete corner to the inner frame line at top right.

(Des B. Young. Eng S. Reading. Typo J. B. Cooke)

1913 (Jan–Apr). *W* **2**. *P* 12.

No.	Type	Description	Unused	Used
1	1	½d. green (Die I) (16 Jan)	7·00	1·50
2		1d. red (Die I) (2 Jan)	6·50	40
		a. Wmk sideways	£500	£120
		b. Carmine	6·50	40
		c. Die II. *Red*	6·50	40
		ca. Wmk sideways	£550	£120
		cb. Carmine	6·50	40
		d. Die IIA. *Red*	6·00	30
		da. Wmk sideways	£500	£120
		db. Carmine	6·00	30
3		2d. grey (Die I) (11 Jan)	24·00	2·75
4		2½d. indigo (Die II) (27 Jan)	32·00	10·00
5		3d. olive (Die I) (22 Jan)	32·00	5·50
		a. Imperf three sides (pair)	£9500	
		b. In pair with Die II	£300	£125
		c. Yellow-olive	32·00	6·00
		ca. In pair with Die II	£300	£125
		d. Die II. *Olive*	£140	35·00
		da. Yellow-olive	£140	35·00
6		4d. orange (Die II) (12 Feb)	75·00	27·00
		a. Orange-yellow	£170	48·00
8		5d. chestnut (Die II) (16 Jan)	60·00	28·00
9		6d. ultramarine (Die II) (11 Jan)	60·00	18·00
		a. Retouched "E"	£1500	£500
		b. Die IIA	£800	£225
10		9d. violet (Die II) (29 Jan)	60·00	16·00
11		1s. emerald (Die II) (21 Jan)	60·00	10·00
		a. Blue-green	60·00	10·00
12		2s. brown (Die II) (25 Jan)	£175	45·00
		a. Double print	†	—
13		5s. grey and yellow (20 March)	£325	£125
14		10s. grey and pink (20 March)	£650	£350
15		£1 brown and blue (20 March)	£1500	£1200
16		£2 black and rose (8 April)	£2750	£1750
1/16		*Set of* 15	£5000	£3250
14/16 Optd "Specimen"		*Set of* 3	£750	

No. 9a shows a badly distorted second "E" in "PENCE", which is unmistakable. It occurs on the last stamp in the sheet and was replaced by a substitute cliché in Type IIA (No. 9b).

No. 12a only exists on stamps perforated "O.S.".

See also Nos. 20/27 (*W* 5), 35/45*b* (*W* 6), 73/5 (*W* 6, new colours), 107/14 (*W* 7), 132/8 (*W* 15), 212 (2s. re-engraved).

INVERTED WATERMARKS are met with in some values in this and subsequent issues.

3

4 Laughing Kookaburra

(Des R. A. Harrison. Eng and recess T. S. Harrison)

1913 (8 Dec)–**14**. *No wmk. P* 11.

No.	Type	Description	Unused	Used
17	3	1d. red	4·00	6·50
		a. Pale rose-red	6·50	9·00
		b. Imperf horiz (vert pair)	£1500	
19	4	6d. claret (26.8.14)	£100	50·00

All printing from Plate 1 of the 1d. were in the shade of No. 17*a*. This plate shows many retouches.

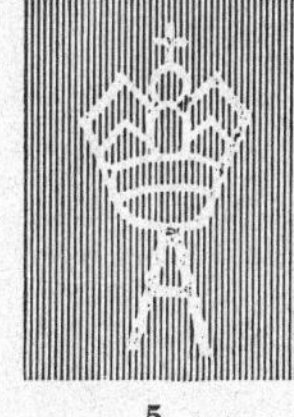

5

5*a*

(Typo J. B. Cooke)

1915. *W* **5**. *P* 12.

No.	Type	Description	Unused	Used
20	1	2d. grey (Die I) (2 Jan)	50·00	9·50
21		2½d. indigo (Die II) (July)	50·00	20·00
23		6d. ultramarine (Die II) (April)	£150	20·00
		a. Bright blue	£200	45·00
		b. Die IIA. *Ultramarine*	£900	£150
		ba. Bright blue	£1100	£200
24		9d. violet (Die II) (9 July)	£150	23·00
25		1s. blue-green (Die II) (Aug)	£150	20·00
26		2s. brown (Die II) (April)	£400	70·00
27		5s. grey and yellow (12 Feb)	£900	£175
		a. Yellow portion doubly printed	£5500	£1000
20/27		*Set of* 7	£1750	£300

The watermark in this issue is often misplaced as the paper was made for the portrait stamps.

Die II

Die III

Die II. The flaw distinguishing the so-called Die II is now known to be due to a defective roller-die and occurs in 18 impressions on one of the plates. It appears as a white upward projection to right of the base of figure "1" in the shield containing value at left, as shown in the illustration.

Die III. In 1918 a printing (in sheets of 120) was made on paper prepared for printing War Savings Stamps, with wmk T **5**. A special plate was made for this printing, differing in detail from those previously used. The shading round the head is even; the solid background of the words "ONE PENNY" is bounded at each end by a *white* vertical line; and there is a horizontal white line cutting the vertical shading lines at left on the King's neck. *See* No. 50c.

(Dies eng P. B. Typo J. B. Cooke until 1918, then T. S. Harrison)

1914–21. *W* **5**. *P* 14.

No.	Type	Description	Unused	Used
29	5*a*	½d. bright green (22.2.15)	3·00	60
		a. Green (13.5.16)	2·75	50
		b. Yellow-green (8.16)	20·00	5·00
		c. Thin "1" in fraction at right	£1000	£500
30		1d. carmine-red (*shades*) (I) (17.7.14)	6·50	25
		a. Rusted cliché (2 vars)*	£4000	£1000
		b. Substituted cliché	£1500	60·00
		c. Pale carmine (*shades*)	18·00	25
		d. Carmine-pink (1.18)	90·00	3·50
		e. Rose-red (3.18)	10·00	1·75
		f. Carmine (*aniline*) (1921)	13·00	1·90
31		1d. carmine-red (*shades*) (II) (1914)	£500	6·00
		a. Substituted cliché	£1500	60·00
		b. Pale red (*shades*)	£500	6·00
32		4d. orange (6.1.15)	35·00	4·00
		a. Yellow-orange	35·00	4·00
		b. Pale orange-yellow (10.15)	65·00	12·00
		c. Lemon-yellow (1916)	£160	25·00
		d. Dull orange	40·00	4·00
		e. Line through "FOUR PENCE" (*all shades*) *From*	£650	£140
34		5d. brown (22.2.15)	20·00	1·25
		a. Yellow-brown (1920)	25·00	1·50

The variety No. 29c was caused by the engraving of a new fraction in a defective electro.

*The two varieties listed under No. 30a were caused by rusting of the steel plate and show as white patches on the back of King's neck and on, and beside, the top of the right frame (upper left pane, No. 34); and on the left frame, wattles, head and ears of kangaroo (upper left pane, No. 35). These were noticed in late 1916 when the damaged impressions were removed and replaced by a pair of copper electros (Die II for No. 34 and Die I for No. 35), showing rounded corners and some frame damage, the former also showing a white spot under tail of emu. In time the tops of the crown quickly wore away. These substituted clichés (Nos. 30b and 31a) were formerly described as "Top of crown missing".

The 5d. is known printed on the gummed side of the paper.

Two machines were used for the 14 perforation, one an old single line, converted to that gauge, the other a new comb-machine. The former was used mainly for early printings of the 1d. and 5d. and very rarely for later printings of the ½d. and 1d.

See also Nos. 47/50*b* (*W* **5**, rough paper), 51/5*a* (*W* **6***a*), 56/66*b* and 76/84 (*W* **5**, new colours), 85/104 (*W* **7**), 124/31 (*W* **15**).

6

6*a*

Nos. 38ca and 73a
(R. 1/6, lower plate)

(Typo J. B. Cooke (to May 1918), T. S. Harrison (to February 1926), A. J. Mullett (to January 1927) and thereafter J. Ash)

1915–28. *W* **6** (*narrow Crown*). *P* 12.

No.	Type	Description	Unused	Used
35	1	2d. grey (Die I) (11.15)	22·00	3·25
		a. In pair with Die IIA (1917)*	£600	£170
		b. Silver-grey (shiny paper) (2.18)	20·00	3·50
		c. Die II. *Grey* (1918)	25·00	5·00
		ca. Silver-grey (shiny paper) (2.18)	24·00	5·00
36		2½d. deep blue (Die II) (9.17)	20·00	6·00
		a. Deep indigo (1920)	24·00	8·00
		ab. "1" of fraction omitted	£7000	£2750
37		3d. yellow-olive (Die I) (12.10.15)	22·00	2·75
		a. In pair with Die II	£200	70·00
		b. Olive-green (1917)	24·00	2·75
		ba. In pair with Die II	£200	70·00
		c. Die II. *Yellow-olive*	90·00	20·00
		ca. Olive-green	90·00	20·00
		d. Die IIB. *Light olive* (1923)	25·00	7·00
38		6d. ultramarine (Die II) (15.12.15)	45·00	7·50
		a. Die IIA (substituted cliché)	£600	£130
		b. Dull blue	65·00	8·00
		ba. Die IIA (substituted cliché)	£750	£140
		c. Die IIB. *Bright ultramarine* (23.7.21)	45·00	7·50
		ca. Leg of kangaroo broken	£2500	£500
39		9d. violet (Die II) (29.7.16)	35·00	4·75
		a. Die IIB. *Violet* (16.4.19)	32·00	4·00
40		1s. blue-green (Die II) (6.16)	32·00	2·75
		a. Die IIB (9.12.20)	32·00	2·75
		b. Wmk sideways (1927)	90·00	65·00
41		2s. brown (Die II) (6.16)	£150	25·00
		a. Imperf three sides (pair)	£12000	
		b. Red-brown	£175	30·00
42		5s. grey and yellow (4.18)	£175	48·00
		a. Grey and orange (1920)	£175	48·00
		b. Grey and deep yellow	£175	48·00
		ba. Wmk sideways	£2000	£1600
		c. Grey and pale yellow (1928)	£175	48·00
43		10s. grey and pink (5.2.17)	£500	£140
		a. Grey and bright aniline pink	£500	£140
		ab. Wmk sideways	£2500	£1800
		b. Grey and pale aniline pink (1928)	£500	£140
44		£1 chocolate and dull blue (7.16)	£1400	£600
		a. Chestnut and bright blue (1917)	£1400	£600
		b. Bistre-brown and bright blue	£1400	£600
		ba. Wmk sideways	£4000	£1800
45		£2 black and rose (12.19)	£2250	£1300
		a. Grey and crimson (1920)	£2250	£1300
		b. Purple-black and pale rose (1924)	£2000	£1300
35/45*b*		*Set of* 11	£4250	£2250
43/45 Optd "Specimen"		*Set of* 3	£850	

*The Die II of No. 35a is a substituted cliché introduced to replace a cracked plate which occurred on No. 55 of the upper left pane (Row 10, No. 1). The Die IIA characteristics are more pronounced in this cliché than on the sheet stamps from this die. The break at left, for instance, extends to the outer, in addition to the inner, frame line.

All values were printed by both Cooke and Harrison, and the 9d., 1s. and 5s. were also printed by Mullett and Ash.

1916–18. *W* **5**. *Rough paper, locally gummed. P* 14.

No.	Type	Description	Unused	Used
47	5*a*	1d. scarlet (I) (14.12.16)	20·00	70
48		1d. deep red (I) (1917)	20·00	50
49		1d. rose-red (I) (1918)	32·00	75
		a. Substituted cliché	£1600	£150
49*b*		1d. rosine (I) (1918)	£110	8·00
		c. Substituted cliché	£2000	£250
50		1d. rose-red (II) (1918)	£500	18·00
		aa. Substituted cliché	£1600	£150
50*a*		1d. rosine (II) (1918)	£750	60·00
		ab. Substituted cliché	£2000	£250
50*b*		5d. bright chestnut (1918)	£1100	95·00

For explanations of substituted cliché varieties, see 2nd paragraph of note below No. 34*a*.

For illustrations and descriptions of Dies II and III, see after T **5***a*.

No. 50*b* only comes perforated "O.S.".

1918 (June). *Printed from a new plate* (Die III) *on white unsurfaced paper, locally gummed. W* **5**. *P* 14.

No.	Type	Description	Unused	Used
50c	5*a*	1d. rose-red (III)	70·00	17·00
50*d*		1d. rose-carmine (III)	70·00	17·00

(Typo J. B. Cooke or T. S. Harrison)

1918–20. *W* **6***a* (*Mult*). *P* 14.

No.	Type	Description	Unused	Used
51	5*a*	½d. green (*shades*) (8.1.18)	3·25	1·50
		a. "1" in fraction at right thinner	£150	60·00
52		1d. carmine-pink (I) (23.1.18)	£180	40·00
		a. Deep red (I) (1918)	£850	£140
53		1d. carmine (I) (10.12.19)	30·00	4·50
		a. Deep red (*aniline*) (I) (1920)	£160	30·00
54		1½d. black-brown (30.1.19)	6·00	1·50
		a. Very thin paper (3.19)	35·00	12·00
55		1½d. red-brown (4.19)	7·00	1·25
		a. Chocolate	7·00	1·25

No. 51 was printed by Cooke and Harrison, Nos. 52/*a* by Cooke only and Nos. 53/55*a* by Harrison only. Nos. 52/*a* have rather yellowish gum, that of No. 53 being pure white.

(Typo T. S. Harrison and also A. J. Mullett for 1s. 4d. from March 1926)

1918–23. *W* **5**. *P* 14.

No.	Type	Description	Unused	Used
56	5*a*	½d. orange (9.11.23)	2·50	1·25
57		1d. violet (*shades*) (13.2.22)	4·00	60
		a. Imperf three sides (pair)	£7000	
		b. Red-violet	4·00	60
58		1½d. black-brown (9.11.18)	5·00	55
59		1½d. deep red-brown (6.19)	3·00	40
		a. Chocolate	4·00	40
60		1½d. bright red-brown (20.1.22)	14·00	1·50
61		1½d. green (7.3.23)	3·00	20
		a. Rough unsurfaced paper	90·00	45·00
62		2d. dull orange (5.10.20)	11·00	35
		a. Brown-orange	11·00	35
63		2d. bright rose-scarlet (17.2.22)	5·50	35
		a. Dull rose-scarlet	5·50	35
64		4d. violet (21.6.21)	18·00	15·00
		a. Line through "FOUR PENCE"	£7000	£3500
		b. "FOUR PENCE" in thinner letters	£700	£300

65 5a 4d. ultramarine (*shades*) (23.3.22) .. 60·00 9·50
a. "FOUR PENCE" in thinner letters £900 £200
b. Pale milky blue .. .. .. 65·00 15·00
66 1s. 4d. pale blue (2.12.20) .. .. 80·00 15·00
a. Dull greenish blue (1923) .. .. 80·00 15·00
b. Deep turquoise .. .. .. £650 70·00
56/66 .. .. *Set of* 11 £160 40·00

The 4d. ultramarine was originally printed by Cooke but the plates were worn in mid-1923 and Harrison prepared a new pair of plates. Stamps from these plates can only be distinguished by the minor flaws which are peculiar to them.

The variety of Nos. 64 and 65 with "FOUR PENCE" thinner, was caused by the correction of a defective cliché (No. 6, 2nd row, right-hand pane), which showed a line running through these words.

No. 61a was printed on a small residue of paper which had been employed for Nos. 47/50*d*.

(Typo T. S. Harrison (to February 1926), A. J. Mullett (to June 1927), thereafter J. Ash)

1923–24. *W* **6.** *P* 12.
73 1 6d. chestnut (Die IIB) (6.12.23) .. 15·00 2·50
a. Leg of kangaroo broken .. .. £200 90·00
74 2s. maroon (Die II) (1.5.24) .. .. 40·00 12·00
75 £1 grey (Die IIB) (1.5.24) (Optd S. £100) £700 £225

The 6d. and 2s. were printed by all three printers, but the £1 only by Harrison.

(Typo T. S. Harrison (to February 1926), thereafter A. J. Mullett)

1924. *P* 14. (*a*) *W* **5** (1 May).
76 5a 1d. sage-green .. .. 2·25 35
77 1½d. scarlet (*shades*) .. .. .. 2·00 30
a. Very thin paper .. .. .. 40·00 12·00
b. "HALEPENCE" .. .. .. 35·00 15·00
c. "RAL" of "AUSTRALIA" thin .. 35·00 15·00
d. Curved "1" and thin fraction at left 32·00 15·00
78 2d. red-brown .. .. 18·00 6·00
a. Bright red-brown .. .. .. 26·00 7·50
79 3d. dull ultramarine .. .. .. 22·00 1·50
a. Imperf three sides (pair) £6500
80 4d. olive-yellow .. .. 22·00 2·00
a. Olive-green .. .. 25·00 2·00
81 4½d. violet .. .. 24·00 2·75

(*b*) *W* **6a**
82 5a 1d. sage-green (20 May) .. .. 5·50 4·25

(*c*) *No wmk*
83 5a 1d. sage-green (18 August) .. .. 5·50 8·00
84 1½d. scarlet (14 August) .. .. .. 7·00 5·00
76/84 .. .. *Set of* 9 95·00 27·00

Nos. 78/*a* and 82/4 were printed by Harrison only but the remainder were printed by both Harrison and Mullett.

In the semi-transparent paper of Nos. 54a and 77a the watermark is almost indistinguishable. Nos. 77b, 77c and 77d are typical examples of retouching of which there are many others in these issues. In No. 77c the letters "RAL" differ markedly from the normal. There is a white stroke cutting the oval frame-line above the "L", and the right-hand outer line of the Crown does not cut the white frame-line above the "A". No. 77b is above No. 77c in the sheet, so that the varieties may be had *se-tenant*.

7

I

II

New Dies

1d. For differences see note after No. 34*a*.
1½d. From new steel plates made from a new die. Nos. 88 and 98 are the Ash printings, the ink of which is shiny.
2d. Die I. Height of frame 25.6 mm. Die II. Height 25.1 mm; lettering and figures of value bolder than Die I.
3d. Die II has bolder letters and figures than Die I, as illustrated above.
5d. Die II has a bolder figure "5" with flat top compared with Die I of the earlier issues.

(Typo by A. J. Mullett or J. Ash)

1926–30. *W* **7.** (*a*) *P* 14.
85 5a ½d. orange (10.3.27) .. .. .. 6·50 4·75
86 1d. sage-green (23.10.26) .. .. 2·50 75
87 1½d. scarlet (5.11.26) .. .. .. 5·00 70
88 1½d. golden scarlet (1927) .. .. 7·50 1·75
89 2d. red-brown (17.8.27) .. .. .. 28·00 18·00
90 3d. dull ultramarine (12.26) .. .. 22·00 5·50
91 4d. yellow-olive (17.1.28) .. .. 55·00 17·00
92 4½d. violet (26.10.27) .. .. .. 20·00 3·75
93 1s. 4d. pale greenish blue (6.9.27) .. £180 75·00
85/93 .. .. *Set of* 8 £275 £120

(*b*) *P* 13½ × 12½
94 5a ½d. orange (21.11.28) .. .. .. 1·75 90
95 1d. sage-green (Die I) (23.12.26) .. 1·75 25
96 5a 1d. sage-green (Die II) .. .. .. 50·00 70·00
97 1½d. scarlet (14.1.27) .. .. .. 2·00 35
98 1½d. golden scarlet .. .. .. 2·00 35
98*a* 1½d. red-brown (16.9.30) .. .. .. 5·50 4·50
99 2d. red-brown (28.4.28) .. .. .. 6·50 6·50
99*a* 2d. golden scarlet (Die I) (2.8.30) .. 5·50 80
99*b* 2d. golden scarlet (Die II) (9.9.30) .. 4·50 35
c. No wmk £1500 £800
d. Tête-bêche (pair) £28000
100 3d. dull ultramarine (Die I) (23.2.28) .. 35·00 4·00
101 3d. deep ultramarine (Die II) (28.9.29) 22·00 1·50
102 4d. yellow-olive (4.29) .. .. .. 23·00 2·00
103 4½d. violet (11.28) .. .. 55·00 12·00
103*a* 5d. orange-brown (Die II) (2.8.30) .. 20·00 2·25
104 1s. 4d. turquoise (30.9.28) .. .. £100 18·00
94/104 .. .. *Set of* 11 £225 45·00

Owing to defective manufacture, part of a sheet of the 2d. (Die II) escaped unwatermarked; while the watermark in other parts of the same sheet was faint or normal.

Only one example of No. 99d is known.

8 Parliament House, Canberra

9 "DH66" Biplane and Pastoral Scene

(Des R. A. Harrison. Die eng by Waterlow. Plates and printing by A. J. Mullett)

1927 (9 May). *Opening of Parliament House, Canberra. No wmk. P* 11.
105 8 1½d. brownish lake 60 60
a. Imperf between (pair) £2750 £1900

(Eng T. S. Harrison. Recess J. Ash)

1928 (29 Oct). *National Stamp Exhibition, Melbourne. As T* **4.** *No wmk. P* 11.
106 3d. blue .. .. 8·00 6·00
a. Pane of four with margins .. £200 £225
ab. Imperf (pane of four) £9500

No. 106a comes from special sheets of 60 stamps divided into 15 blocks of 4 (5 × 3) and separated by wide gutters perforated down the middle, printed and sold at the Exhibition.

(Typo J. Ash)

1929–30. *W* **7.** *P* 12.
107 1 6d. chestnut (Die IIB) (25.9.29) .. 18·00 4·00
108 9d. violet (Die IIB) (2.29) .. .. 28·00 7·00
109 1s. blue-green (Die IIB) (12.6.29) .. 32·00 4·00
110 2s. maroon (Die II) (3.29) .. .. 45·00 11·00
111 5s. grey and yellow (30.11.29) .. £275 70·00
112 10s. grey and pink (2.29) £450 £200
114 £2 black and rose (11.30) £2000 £350
107/114 .. .. *Set of* 7 £2500 £550
112/114 Optd "Specimen" .. .. *Set of* 2 £400

(Des R. A. Harrison and H. Herbert. Eng A. Taylor. Recess J. Ash)

1929 (20 May). *Air. No wmk. P* 11.
115 9 3d. green (*shades*) .. .. .. 13·00 4·75

10 Black Swan

11 Capt. Charles Sturt

(Des Pitt Morison. Eng F. D. Manley. Recess J. Ash)

1929 (28 Sept). *Centenary of Western Australia. No wmk. P* 11.
116 10 1½d. dull scarlet .. .. .. 1·00 1·00
a. Re-entry ("T" of "AUSTRALIA" clearly double) .. .. 65·00 35·00

(Des R. A. Harrison. Eng F. D. Manley. Recess J. Ash)

1930 (2 June). *Centenary of Exploration of River Murray by Capt. Sturt. No wmk. P* 11.
117 11 1½d. scarlet .. .. 1·00 40
118 3d. blue .. .. 5·00 6·00

No. 117 with manuscript surcharge of "2d. paid P M L H I" was issued by the Postmaster of Lord Howe Island during a shortage of 2d. stamps. A few copies of the 1½d. value No. 98 were also endorsed. These provisionals are not recognized by the Australian postal authorities. (*Price* £550 *un. or us., either stamp.*)

TWO

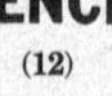

PENCE

(12)

13 The *Southern Cross* above hemispheres

1930 (1 Aug). *T* **5a** *surch as T* **12.** *W* **7.** *P* 13½ × 12½.
119 2d. on 1½d. golden scarlet 80 45
120 5d. on 4½d. violet .. .. .. 8·00 9·00

No. 120 is from a redrawn die in which the words "FOURPENCE HALFPENNY" are noticeably thicker than in the original die and the figure "4" has square instead of tapering serifs.

Stamps from the redrawn die without the surcharge were printed, but not issued thus. Some stamps, *cancelled to order*, were included in sets supplied by the post office. A few mint copies, which escaped the cancellation, were found and some may have been used postally. (*Price* £55 *used c.t.o.*)

(Des and eng F. D. Manley. Recess John Ash)

1931 (19 Mar). *Kingsford Smith's flights. No wmk. P* 11. (*a*) *Postage.*
121 13 2d. rose-red 75 35
122 3d. blue .. .. 5·00 5·00

(*b*) *Air. Inscr* "AIR MAIL SERVICE"
123 13 6d. violet .. .. 12·00 12·00
a. Re-entry ("FO" and "LD" double) .. 80·00 65·00

15

17 Superb Lyrebird

(Typo John Ash)

1931–36. *W* **15.** (*a*) *P* 13½ × 12½.
124 5a ½d. orange .. .. 3·00 3·75
125 1d. green (Die I) .. .. .. 1·25 10
126 1½d. red-brown (1936) .. .. .. 6·50 7·50
127 2d. golden scarlet (Die II) .. .. 1·75 5
128 3d. ultramarine (Die II) .. .. 20·00 55
129 4d. yellow-olive .. .. 22·00 75
130 5d. orange-brown (Die II) .. .. 18·00 30
131 1s. 4d. turquoise .. .. 80·00 5·50
124/131 .. .. *Set of* 8 £140 17·00

(*b*) *P* 12
132 1 6d. chestnut (Die IIB) (20.4.32) .. 18·00 17·00
133 9d. violet (Die IIB) (20.4.32) .. .. 18·00 1·75
134 2s. maroon (Die II) (6.8.35) .. .. 5·00 75
135 5s. grey and yellow (12.32) .. .. £175 17·00
136 10s. grey and pink (31.7.32) £450 £120
137 £1 grey (Die IIB) (11.35) £650 £225
138 £2 black and rose (6.34) £1800 £350
132/138 .. .. *Set of* 7 £2750 £650
136/138 Optd "Specimen" .. .. *Set of* 3 £130

Stamps as No. 127, without wmk and perf 11 are forgeries made in 1932 to defraud the P.O.

For re-engraved type of No. 134, see No. 212.

(Recess John Ash)

1931 (4 Nov). *Air Stamp. As T* **13** *but inscr* "AIR MAIL SERVICE" *in bottom tablet. No wmk. P* 11.
139 6d. sepia .. .. 20·00 15·00

1931 (17 Nov). *Air. No.* 139 *optd with Type* O **1.**
139*a* 6d. sepia .. .. 40·00 40·00

This stamp was not restricted to official use but was on general sale to the public.

(Des F. D. Manley. Recess John Ash)

1932 (15 Feb). *No wmk. P* 11.
140 17 1s. green .. .. 75·00 1·25
140*a* 1s. yellow-green .. .. .. 80·00 1·75

18 Sydney Harbour Bridge

19 Laughing Kookaburra

(Des R. A. Harrison. Eng F. D. Manley. Printed John Ash)

1932 (14 Mar). (*a*) *Recess. No wmk. P* 11.
141 18 2d. scarlet .. .. 2·50 1·25
142 3d. blue .. .. 10·00 9·00
143 5s. blue-green £450 £225

(*b*) *Typo. W* **15.** *P* 10½.
144 18 2d. scarlet .. .. 2·25 75

Stamps as No. 144 without wmk and perf 11 are forgeries made in 1932 to defraud the P.O.

(Typo John Ash)

1932 (1 June). *W* **15.** *P* 13½ × 12½.
146 19 6d. red-brown .. .. 22·00 55

20 Melbourne and R. Yarra

21 Merino Ram

(Des and eng F. D. Manley. Recess John Ash)

1934 (2 July). *Centenary of Victoria. W* **15.**

			I. *P* 10½.		II. *P* 11½.	
147	20	2d. orange-vermilion	1·75	70	2·50	70
148		3d. blue ..	9·00	6·50	9·00	6·50
149		1s. black ..	35·00	20·00	35·00	20·00

(Des and eng F. D. Manley. Recess John Ash)

1934 (1 Nov). *Capt. Macarthur Centenary. W* **15.** *P* 11½.

No.	Type	Description	Unused	Used
150	**21**	2d. carmine-red (A)	3·00	1·00
150*a*		2d. carmine-red (B)	28·00	2·75
151		3d. blue	10·00	8·00
152		9d. bright purple	35·00	28·00

Type A of the 2d. shows shading on the hill in the background varying from light to dark (as illustrated). Type B has the shading almost uniformly dark.

22 Hermes

23 Cenotaph, Whitehall

(Des F. D. Manley. Eng E. Broad and F. D. Manley. Recess John Ash until April 1940; W. C. G. McCracken thereafter)

1934–48. (*a*) *No wmk. P* 11.

No.	Type	Description	Unused	Used
153	**22**	1s. 6d. dull purple (1.12.34)	42·00	2·25
		(*b*) *W* **15.** *P* 13½ × 14		
153*a*	**22**	1s. 6d. dull purple (22.10.37)	8·00	50
		b. Thin rough paper (12.2.48)	7·00	50

(Des B. Cottier; adapted and eng F. D. Manley. Recess John Ash)

1935 (18 Mar). *20th Anniv of Gallipoli Landing. W* **15.** *P* 13½ × 12½ *or* 11 (1s.).

No.	Type	Description	Unused	Used
154	**23**	2d. scarlet	80	25
155		1s. black (*chalk-surfaced*)	48·00	38·00

24 King George V on "Anzac"

25 Amphitrite and Telephone Cable

(Des and eng F. D. Manley. Recess John Ash)

1935 (2 May). *Silver Jubilee. Chalk-surfaced paper. W* **15** (*sideways*). *P* 11½.

No.	Type	Description	Unused	Used
156	**24**	2d. scarlet	1·00	30
157		3d. blue	8·00	6·00
158		2s. bright violet	45·00	40·00

(Des and eng F. D. Manley. Recess John Ash)

1936 (1 Apr). *Opening of Submarine Telephone Link to Tasmania. W* **15.** *P* 11½.

No.	Type	Description	Unused	Used
159	**25**	2d. scarlet	80	25
160		3d. blue	6·00	5·00

26 Site of Adelaide, 1836; Old Gum Tree, Glenelg; King William St., Adelaide

(Des and eng F. D. Manley. Recess John Ash)

1936 (3 Aug). *Centenary of South Australia. W* **15** *P* 11½.

No.	Type	Description	Unused	Used
161	**26**	2d. carmine	90	25
162		3d. blue	5·00	4·50
163		1s. green	20·00	8·00

27 Kangaroo

28 Queen Elizabeth

29 King George VI

30 King George VI 31

32 Koala

Die I Die Ia Die II

33 Merino Ram

34 Laughing Kookaburra

35 Platypus

36 Superb Lyrebird

38 Queen Elizabeth

39 King George VI

40 King George VI and Queen Elizabeth

40*a*

40*b* (Background evenly shaded, lettering strengthened)

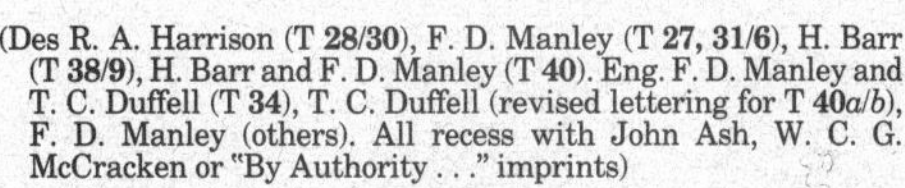

(Des R. A. Harrison (T **28/30**), F. D. Manley (T **27**, **31/6**), H. Barr (T **38/9**), H. Barr and F. D. Manley (T **40**). Eng. F. D. Manley and T. C. Duffell (T **34**), T. C. Duffell (revised lettering for T **40*a*/*b***), F. D. Manley (others). All recess with John Ash, W. C. G. McCracken or "By Authority . . ." imprints)

1937–49. *W* **15** (*sideways on* 5d., 9d., 5s. *and* 10s.).

No.	Type	Description	Unused	Used
		(*a*) *P* 13½ × 14 (*vert designs*) *or* 14 × 13½ (*horiz*)		
164	**27**	½d. orange (3.10.38)	1·75	60
165	**28**	1d. emerald-green (10.5.37)	35	10
166	**29**	1½d. maroon (20.4.38)	8·50	3·25
167	**30**	2d. scarlet (10.5.37)	35	10
167*a*	**31**	3d. blue (Die I, 1st ptg) (2.8.37)	£100	55·00
168		3d. blue (Die I) (2.8.37)	45·00	6·00
168*a*		3d. blue (Die Ia) (1937)	75·00	6·50
168*b*		3d. blue (Die II) (1938)	45·00	3·25
169		3d. bright blue, *thin paper* (Die II) (21.12.38)	45·00	2·50
170	**32**	4d. green (1.2.38)	10·00	45
171	**33**	5d. purple (1.12.38)	7·50	45
172	**34**	6d. purple-brown (2.8.37)	18·00	1·00
173	**35**	9d. chocolate (1.9.38)	12·00	1·25
174	**36**	1s. grey-green (2.8.37)	48·00	2·50
175	**31**	1s. 4d. deep magenta (3.10.38)	2·50	2·50
		a. Pale magenta	2·00	2·00
		(*b*) *P* 13½		
176	**38**	5s. claret **C** (1.4.38)	18·00	1·25
		a. Thin rough paper **O** (4.2.48)	18·00	2·50
177	**39**	10s. dull purple **C** (1.4.38) (Optd S. £45)	48·00	12·00
		a. Thin rough paper **O** (11.48)	70·00	30·00
178	**40**	£1 blue-slate **C** (1.11.38) (Optd S. £400)	£130	32·00
		a. Thin rough paper **O** (4.4.49)	£190	80·00
164/178		*Set of* 14	£300	55·00
		(*c*) *P* 15 × 14 (*vert designs*) *or* 14 × 15 (*horiz*)		
179	**27**	½d. orange (28.1.42)	35	5
		a. Coil pair	6·50	6·50
180	**40*a***	1d. emerald-green (1.8.38)	60	5
181		1d. maroon (10.12.41)	55	5
		a. Coil pair	8·00	8·00
182	**29**	1½d. maroon (21.11.41)	9·00	7·50
183		1½d. emerald-green (10.12.41)	50	25
184	**40*b***	2d. scarlet (11.7.38)	1·25	5
		a. Coil pair	£225	£225
185		2d. bright purple (10.12.41)	50	40
		a. Coil pair	15·00	15·00
186	**31**	3d. bright blue (10.40)	45·00	2·00
187		3d. purple-brown (10.1.42)	15	5
188	**32**	4d. green (10.42)	75	5
188*a*	**33**	5d. purple (5.46)	1·00	1·40
189	**34**	6d. red-brown (5.42)	1·50	10
		a. Purple-brown (1944)	1·25	5
190	**35**	9d. chocolate (1943)	1·50	5
191	**36**	1s. grey-green (3.41)	1·25	5
179/191		*Set of* 14	55·00	11·00

For unwmkd issue, see Nos. 228/30*d*.

Dies of the 3d. In Die I the letters "TA" of "POSTAGE" at right are joined by a white flaw; the outline of the chin consists of separate strokes.

Die Ia is similar, but "T" and "A" have been clearly separated by retouches made on the plate.

In Die II "T" and "A" are separate and a continuous line has been added to the chin. The outline of the cheek extends to about 1 mm above the lobe of the King's right ear.

No. 167*a* is a preliminary printing made with unsuitable ink and may be detected by the absence of finer details; the King's face appears whitish and the wattles are blank. The greater part of this printing was distributed to the Press with advance notices of the issue.

No. 186 is re-engraved and differs from Nos. 167*a* to 169 in the King's left eyebrow which is shaded downwards from left to right instead of from right to left.

Thin paper. Nos. 176a, 177a, 178a. In these varieties the watermark is more clearly visible on the back and the design is much less sharp. Early printings of No. 176a have tinted paper.

SPECIAL COIL PERFORATION. This special perforation of large and small holes on the narrow sides of the stamps is intended for stamps issued in coils, to facilitate separation. When they exist we list them as "Coil pairs".

The following with "special coil" perforation were placed on sale in *sheets*: Nos. 222*a* (1952), 228, 230, 237, 262 (1953), 309, 311, and 314. These are listed as "Coil blocks of four".

Coils with "normal" perforations also exist for some values.

41 "Governor Phillip at Sydney Cove" (J. Allcot)

42 A.I.F. and Nurse

(Des and eng E. Broad and F. D. Manley. Recess J. Ash)

1937 (1 Oct). *150th Anniv of Foundation of New South Wales. W* **15.** *P* 13½ × 14.

No.	Type	Description	Unused	Used
193	**41**	2d. scarlet	1·25	10
194		3d. bright blue	10·00	6·50
195		9d. purple	27·00	15·00

(Des and eng F. D. Manley from drawing by Virgil Reilly. Recess W. C. G. McCracken)

1940 (15 July). *Australian Imperial Forces. W* **15** (*sideways*). *P* 14 × 13½.

No.	Type	Description	Unused	Used
196	**42**	1d. green	1·25	60
197		2d. scarlet	1·25	15
198		3d. blue	10·00	8·00
199		6d. brown-purple	30·00	20·00

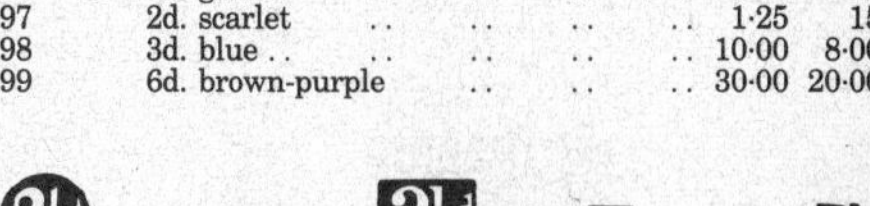

(**43**) (**44**) (**45**)

(Opts designed by F. D. Manley)

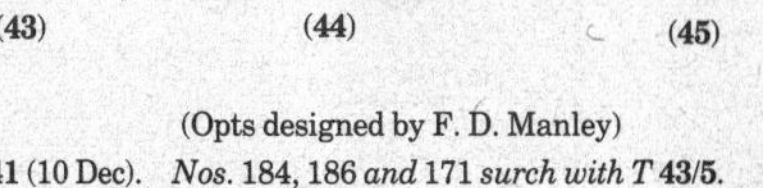

1941 (10 Dec). *Nos.* 184, 186 *and* 171 *surch with T* **43/5.**

No.	Type	Description	Unused	Used
200	**40*b***	2½d. on 2d. (V.)	90	20
201	**31**	3½d. on 3d. (Y. on Black)	1·25	1·00
202	**33**	5½d. on 5d. (V.)	8·00	4·75

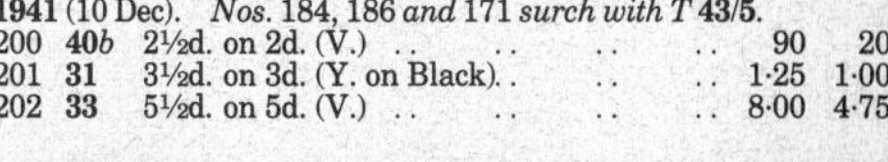

46 Queen Elizabeth

46*a*

47 King George VI

48 King George VI

49 King George VI

50 Emu

(Des and eng F. D. Manley)

1942–44. *Recess. W* **15.** *P* 15 × 14.

No.	Type	Description	Unused	Used
203	**46**	1d. brown-purple (1.1.43)	20	5
		a. Coil pair	5·50	5·50
204	**46*a***	1½d. green (1.12.42)	20	5
204*a*	**47**	2d. bright purple (4.12.44)	45	20
		b. Coil pair	35·00	35·00
		ba. Coil block of four		
205	**48**	2ud. scarlet (7.1.42)	20	5
		a. Imperf (pair)*	£1100	
206	**49**	3½d. bright blue (3.42)	20	5
		a. Deep blue	60	12
207	**50**	5½d. slate-blue (12.2.42)	45	5
203/207		*Set of* 6	1·50	40

*No. 205*a* is in pair with stamp which only has the right-hand side imperf.

For stamps as Nos. 204/*a* but without watermark see Nos. 229/30.

52 Duke and Duchess of Gloucester

(Des and eng F. D. Manley. Recess)

1945 (19 Feb). *Arrival of Duke and Duchess of Gloucester in Australia. W* **15.** *P* 14½.

No.	Type	Description	Unused	Used
209	**52**	2½d. lake	12	5
210		3½d. ultramarine	20	45
211		5½d. indigo	20	30

A

B

1946 (3 Jan). *Kangaroo type, as No.* 134, *but re-engraved as* B. *W* **15.** *P* 12.
212 **1** 2s. maroon .. .. 4·75 1·75
No. 134 has two background lines between the value circle and "TWO SHILLINGS"; No. 212 has only one line in this position. There are also differences in the shape of the letters.

53 Star and Wreath

56 Sir Thos. Mitchell and Queensland

(Des F. D. Manley (2½d.), F. D. Manley and G. Lissenden (3½d.), G. Lissenden (5½d.). Eng F. D. Manley. Recess)

1946 (18 Feb). *Victory Commemoration. T* **53** *and similar designs. W* **15** *(sideways on* 5½*d.). P* 14½.
213 2½d. scarlet 12 5
214 3½d. blue 25 45
215 5½d. green 30 40
Designs: *Horiz*—3½d. Flag and dove. *Vert*—5½d. Angel.

(Des and eng F. D. Manley. Recess)

1946 (14 Oct). *Centenary of Mitchell's Exploration of Central Queensland. W* **15.** *P* 14½.
216 **56** 2½d. scarlet 12 5
217 3½d. blue 25 65
218 1s. grey-olive 30 30

57 Lt. John Shortland R.N.

58 Steel Foundry

59 Coal Carrier Cranes

(Des G. Lissenden, eng G. Lissenden and F. D. Manley (5½d.); des and eng F. D. Manley (others). Recess)

1947 (8 Sept). *Sesquicentenary of City of Newcastle, New South Wales. W* **15** *(sideways on* 3½*d.). P* 14½ *or* 15 × 14 (2½*d.*).
219 **57** 2½d. lake 12 5
a. Imperf three sides .. .. ..
220 **58** 3½d. blue 25 65
221 **59** 5½d. green 25 45

The following items are understood to have been the subject of unauthorised leakages from the Commonwealth Note and Stamp Printing Branch and are therefore not listed by us.
It is certain that none of this material was distributed to post offices for issue to the public.
Imperforate all round. 1d. Princess Elizabeth; 1½d. Queen; 2½d. King; 4d. Koala; 6d. Kookaburra; 9d. Platypus; 1s. Lyrebird (small); 1s. 6d. Air Mail (Type **22**); 2½d. Newcastle.
Also 2½d. Peace, unwatermarked; 2½d. King, *tête-bêche*; 3½d. Newcastle, in dull ultramarine; 2½d. King on "toned" paper.

60 Queen Elizabeth II when Princess

(Des R. A. Harrison. Eng F. D. Manley. Recess)

1947 (20 Nov)–**48.** *Marriage of Princess Elizabeth. P* 14 × 15.
(a) W **15** *sideways*
222 **60** 1d. purple 15 5
(b) No wmk
222*a* **60** 1d. purple (8.48) 12 5
b. Coil pair .. .. 3·25 3·25
c. Coil block of four .. .. 6·00

PRICES OF SETS

Set prices are given for many issues, generally those containing five stamps or more. Definitive sets include one of each value or major colour change, but do not cover different perforations, die types or minor shades. Where a choice is possible the set prices are based on the cheapest versions of the stamps included in the listings.

61 Hereford Bull

61*a* Hermes and Globe

62 Aboriginal Art

62*a* Commonwealth Coat of Arms

(Des G. Sellheim (T **62**), F. D. Manley (others), Eng F. D. Manley and G. Lissenden (T **62**), F. D. Manley (others). Recess)

1948 (16 Feb)–**56.** *(a) W* **15** *(sideways). P* 14½.
223 **61** 1s. 3d. brown-purple .. .. .. 2·25 90
223*a* **61*a*** 1s. 6d. blackish brown (1.9.49) .. .. 3·75 10
224 **62** 2s. chocolate .. .. 4·00 5
(b) W **15.** *P* 14½ × 13½
224*a* **62*a*** 5s. claret (11.4.49) .. .. .. 12·00 15
224*b* 10s. purple (3.10.49) .. .. .. 35·00 45
224*c* £1 blue (28.11.49) .. .. .. 48·00 2·25
224*d* £2 green (16.1.50) .. .. .. £140 13·00
224*b/d* Optd "Specimen" .. .. *Set of* 3 £150
(c) No wmk. P 14½
224*e* **61*a*** 1s. 6d. blackish brown (6.12.56) .. 28·00 45
224*f* **62** 2s. chocolate (21.7.56) .. .. .. 30·00 45
223/224*f* .. .. *Set of* 9 £275 16·00

63 William J. Farrer

64 F. von Mueller

65 Boy Scout

(Des and eng F. D. Manley. Recess)

1948 (12 July). *William J. Farrer (wheat research). W* **15.** *P* 15 × 14.
225 **63** 2½d. scarlet 12 5

(Des and eng F. D. Manley. Recess)

1948 (13 Sept). *Sir Ferdinand von Mueller (botanist). W* **15.** *P* 15 × 14.
226 **64** 2½d. lake 12 5

(Des and eng F. D. Manley. Recess)

1948 (15 Nov). *Pan-Pacific Scout Jamboree Wonga Park. W* **15** *(sideways). P* 14 × 15.
227 **65** 2½d. lake 12 5
See also No. 254.

Sky retouch (normally unshaded near hill)

1948–56. *No wmk. P* 15 × 14 *or* 14 × 15 (9*d.*).
228 **27** ½d. orange (9.49) 20 5
aa. Sky retouch (Rt. pane, R. 6/8) .. 6·00
a. Coil pair .. .. 1·25 1·25
ab. Sky retouch (in pair) .. .. 60·00
b. Coil block of four .. .. .. 2·25
229 **46*a*** 1½d. green (29.8.49) 55 25
230 **47** 2d. bright purple (12.48) 60 20
aa. Coil pair .. .. 4·50 4·50
ab. Coil block of four .. .. .. 15·00
230*a* **32** 4d. green (18.8.56) .. .. .. 2·25 40
230*b* **34** 6d. purple-brown (18.8.56) .. .. 3·00 25
230*c* **35** 9d. chocolate (13.12.56) .. .. 18·00 80
230*d* **36** 1s. grey-green (13.12.56) .. .. 15·00 35
228/230*d* .. .. *Set of* 7 35·00 2·00

66 "Henry Lawson" (Sir Lionel Lindsay)

67 Mounted Postman and Aeroplane

(Des F. D. Manley. Eng E. R. M. Jones. Recess)

1949 (17 June). *Anniv of Birth of Henry Lawson (poet). P* 15 × 14.
231 **66** 2½d. maroon 15 5

(Des Sir Daryl Lindsay and F. D. Manley. Eng F. D. Manley. Recess)

1949 (10 Oct). *75th Anniv of Founding of U.P.U. P* 15 × 14.
232 **67** 3½d. ultramarine 20 30

68 Lord Forrest of Bunbury

69 King George VI

70 Queen Elizabeth

(Des and eng F. D. Manley. Recess)

1949 (28 Nov). *Lord Forrest of Bunbury (explorer and politician). W* **15.** *P* 15 × 14.
233 **68** 2½d. lake 15 5

(Des and eng F. D. Manley. Recess)

1950–51. *P* 15 × 14. *(a) W* **15.**
234 **69** 2½d. scarlet (12.4.50) 12 5
235 3d. scarlet (28.2.51) 20 10
aa. Coil pair .. .. 8·50 8·50
(b) No wmk
235*a* **69** 2½d. purple-brown (23.5.51) 20 15
235*b* 3d. grey-green (14.11.51) 20 5
c. Coil pair .. .. 16·00 16·00
On 1 December 1951 No. 235 was placed on sale in sheets of 144 originally intended for use in stamp booklets. These sheets contain 3 panes of 48 (16 × 3) with horizontal gutter margin between.

(Des and eng F. D. Manley. Recess)

1950–51. *P* 15 × 14.
236 **70** 1½d. green (19.6.50) 20 5
237 2d. yellow-green (28.3.51) 20 5
a. Coil pair .. .. 3·25 3·25
b. Coil block of four .. .. .. 6·00

71 Aborigine

72

73

Reproductions of First Stamps of New South Wales and Victoria

(Des F. D. Manley. Eng E. R. M. Jones. Recess)

1950 (14 Aug). *W* **15.** *P* 15 × 14.
238 **71** 8½d. brown 35 60
For T **71** in a larger size, see Nos. 253/*b*.

(Des and eng E. R. M. Jones (T **72**); des and eng G. Lissenden (T **73**). Recess)

1950 (27 Sept). *Centenary of First Adhesive Postage Stamps in Australia. P* 15 × 14.
239 **72** 2½d. maroon 15 5
a. Horiz pair. Nos. 239/40 .. .. 40 65
240 **73** 2½d. maroon 15 5
Nos. 239/40 were printed alternately in vertical columns throughout the sheet.

74 Sir Edmund Barton

75 Sir Henry Parkes

76 "Opening First Federal Parliament" (T. Roberts)

77 Federal Parliament House, Canberra

(Des and eng F. D. Manley. Recess)

1951 (1 May). *Golden Jubilee of Commonwealth of Australia. P* 15 × 14.
241 **74** 3d. lake 25 5
a. Horiz pair. Nos. 241/2 .. .. 1·00 1·40
242 **75** 3d. lake 25 5
243 **76** 5½d. blue .. .. 1·25 1·50
244 **77** 1s. 6d. purple-brown .. .. .. 1·75 70
Nos. 241/2 are printed alternately in vertical columns throughout the sheet.

78
E. H. Hargraves

79
C. J. Latrobe

80
King George VI

(Des and eng F. D. Manley. Recess)

1951 (2 July). *Centenary of Discovery of Gold in Australia. P* 15 × 14.
245 **78** 3d. maroon 20 5
a. Horiz pair. Nos. 245/6 .. .. 90 1·25

(Des and eng F. D. Manley. Recess)

1951 (2 July). *Centenary of Responsible Government in Victoria. P* 15 × 14.
246 **79** 3d. maroon 20 5
Nos. 245/6 are printed alternately in vertical columns throughout the sheet.

(Des and eng E. R. M. Jones. Recess)

1951 (31 Oct). *W* **15.** *P* 15 × 14.
247 **80** 7½d. blue 25 45
a. Imperf 3 sides (vert pr) £1000

81 King George VI

82 King George VI

(Des F. D. Manley. Eng G. Lissenden. Recess)

1951–52. *W* **15.** *P* 15 × 14.
248 **81** 3½d. brown-purple (28.11.51) 15 5
249 4½d. scarlet (20.2.52) 25 80
250 6½d. brown (20.2.52) 25 65
251 6½d. emerald-green (9.4.52) 20 20

(Des F. D. Manley. Eng D. Cameron (No. 252), E. R. M. Jones (Nos. 253/*b*). Recess)

1952 (19 Mar)–**65.** *P* 14½. (*a*) *W* **15** (*sideways*).
252 **82** 1s. 0½d. indigo .. .. .. 1·25 30
253 – 2s. 6d. deep brown .. .. .. 4·25 25
(*b*) *No wmk*
253*a* – 2s. 6d. deep brown (30.1.57) .. .. 15·00 30
b. Sepia (10.65) .. .. .. 20·00 8·50
Design:—2s. 6d. As T **71** but larger (21 × 25½ *mm*).
No. 253*b* was an emergency printing and can easily be distinguished from No. 253*a* as it is on white Harrison paper, No. 253*a* being on toned paper.

(Des and eng F. D. Manley. Recess)

1952 (19 Nov). *Pan-Pacific Scout Jamboree, Greystanes. As T* **65**, *but inscr* "1952–53". *W* **15** (*sideways*). *P* 14 × 15.
254 3½d. brown-lake 12 5

83 Butter

84 Wheat

85 Beef

(Des P.O. artists; adapted G. Lissenden. Typo)

1953 (11 Feb). *Food Production. P* 14½.
255 **83** 3d. emerald 60 10
a. Strip of 3. Nos. 255/7 .. .. 7·00
256 **84** 3d. emerald 60 10
257 **85** 3d. emerald 60 10
258 **83** 3½d. scarlet 60 5
a. Strip of 3. Nos. 258/60 .. .. 7·00
259 **84** 3½d. scarlet 60 5
260 **85** 3½d. scarlet 60 5
255/60 .. .. *Set of* 6 3·25 40
The three designs in each denomination appear in rotation, both horizontally and vertically, throughout the sheet.

86 Queen Elizabeth II

87 Queen Elizabeth II

(Des F. D. Manley from photograph by Dorothy Wilding Ltd. Eng D. Cameron. Recess)

1953–56. *P* 15 × 14. (*a*) *No wmk.*
261 **86** 1d. purple (19.8.53) 15 5
261*a* 2½d. blue (23.6.54) 20 5
262 3d. deep green (17.6.53) 20 5
aa. Coil pair .. .. .. 5·00 5·00
ab. Coil block of four .. .. .. 10·00
262*a* **86** 3½d. brown-red (2.7.56) 70 5
262*b* 6½d. orange (9.56) .. .. .. 3·50 60
(*b*) *W* **15**
263 **86** 3½d. brown-red (21.4.53) 20 5
263*a* 6½d. orange (23.6.54) 45 12

(Des and eng F. D. Manley. Recess)

1953 (25 May). *Coronation. P* 15 × 14.
264 **87** 3½d. scarlet 40 5
265 7½d. violet .. .. 1·75 1·75
266 2s. dull bluish green .. .. .. 4·50 80

88 Young Farmers and Calf

(Des P.O. artist; adapted P. E. Morriss. Eng E. R. M. Jones. Recess)

1953 (3 Sept). *25th Anniv of Australian Young Farmers' Clubs. P* 14½.
267 **88** 3½d. red-brown and deep green 15 5

89 Lt.-Gov. D. Collins

90 Lt.-Gov. W. Paterson

91 Sullivan Cove, Hobart, 1804

(Des E. R. M. Jones, eng D. Cameron (T **89**/**90**); des and eng G. Lissenden (T **91**). Recess)

1953 (23 Sept). *150th Anniv of Settlement in Tasmania. P* 15 × 14.
268 **89** 3½d. brown-purple 40 5
a. Horiz pair. Nos. 268/9 .. .. 1·50 2·25
269 **90** 3½d. brown-purple 40 5
270 **91** 2s. green .. .. 8·00 6·00
Nos. 268/9 were printed alternately in vertical columns throughout the sheet.

92 Stamp of 1853

(Des R. L. Beck; eng G. Lissenden. Recess)

1953 (11 Nov). *Tasmanian Postage Stamp Centenary. P* 14½.
271 **92** 3d. rose-red 20 10

93 Queen Elizabeth II and Duke of Edinburgh

94 Queen Elizabeth II

Re-entry

(Des and eng F. D. Manley; border and lettering on 7½d. des by R. M. Warner. Recess)

1954 (2 Feb). *Royal Visit. P* 14.
272 **93** 3½d. scarlet 45 5
a. Re-entry .. .. 25·00 3·75
273 **94** 7½d. purple .. .. 1·10 1·75
274 **93** 2s. dull bluish green .. .. .. 2·50 95

95 "Telegraphic Communications"

96 Red Cross and Globe

(Des R. M. Warner. Eng P. E. Morriss. Recess)

1954 (7 Apr). *Australian Telegraph System Centenary. P* 14.
275 **95** 3½d. brown-red 15 5

(Des B. Stewart. Eng P. E. Morriss. Design recess; cross typo)

1954 (9 June). *40th Anniv of Australian Red Cross Society. P* 14½.
276 **96** 3½d. ultramarine and scarlet 15 5

97 Black Swan

98 Locomotives of 1854 and 1954

(Des R. L. Beck. Eng G. Lissenden. Recess)

1954 (2 Aug). *Western Australian Postage Stamp Centenary. P* 14½.
277 **97** 3½d. black 15 5

(Des R. M. Warner. Eng G. Lissenden. Recess)

1954 (13 Sept). *Australian Railways Centenary. P* 14.
278 **98** 3½d. purple-brown 30 5

99 Territory Badge

100 Olympic Games Symbol

(Des F. D. Manley. Eng G. Lissenden. Recess)

1954 (17 Nov). *Australian Antarctic Research. P* 14½ × 13½.
279 **99** 3½d. grey-black 30 5

(Des R. L. Beck. Eng P. E. Morriss. Recess)

1954–55. *Olympic Games Propaganda. P* 14.
280 **100** 2s. deep bright blue (1.12.54) .. .. 2·75 1·75
280*a* 2s. deep bluish green (30.11.55) .. 3·00 2·00

101 Rotary Symbol, Globe and Flags

102 Queen Elizabeth II

(Des and eng D. Cameron. Recess)

1955 (23 Feb). *50th Anniv of Rotary International. P* 14 × 14½.
281 **101** 3½d. carmine 20 5

(Des F. D. Manley from bas-relief by W. L. Bowles. Eng G. Lissenden. Recess)

1955 (9 Mar)–**57.** *P* 14½. (*a*) *W* **15** (*sideways*).
282 **102** 1s. 0½d. deep blue .. .. .. 6·00 35
(*b*) *No wmk*
282*a* **102** 1s. 7d. red-brown (13.3.57) .. .. 8·50 20

103 American Memorial, Canberra

104 Cobb & Co. Coach (from dry-print by Sir Lionel Lindsay)

(Des R. L. Beck (head by F. D. Manley). Eng F. D. Manley. Recess)

1955 (4 May). *Australian–American Friendship. P* 14 × 14½.
283 **103** 3½d. violet-blue 15 5

(Design adapted and eng by F. D. Manley. Recess)

1955 (6 July). *Mail-coach Pioneers Commemoration. P* 14½ × 14.
284 **104** 3½d. blackish brown 35 5
285 2s. reddish brown .. .. 4·00 3·50

105 Y.M.C.A. Emblem and Map of the World

106 Florence Nightingale and Young Nurse

(Des E. Thake. Eng P. E. Morriss. Design recess; emblem typo)

1955 (10 Aug). *World Centenary of Y.M.C.A. P* 14½ × 14.
286 **105** 3½d. deep bluish green and red 20 5
a. Red (emblem) omitted £3500

(Des and eng F. D. Manley. Recess)

1955 (21 Sept). *Nursing Profession Commemoration. P* 14 × 14½.
287 **106** 3½d. reddish violet 20 5

107 Queen Victoria

108 Badges of New South Wales, Victoria and Tasmania

(Des and eng D. Cameron. Recess)

1955 (17 Oct). *Centenary of First South Australian Postage Stamps. P* 14½.
288 **107** 3½d. green 20 5

(Des and eng F. D. Manley. Recess)

1956 (26 Sept). *Centenary of Responsible Government in New South Wales, Victoria and Tasmania. P* 14½ × 14.
289 **108** 3½d. brown-lake 20 5

109 Arms of Melbourne

110 Olympic Torch and Symbol

111 Collins Street, Melbourne

112 Melbourne across R. Yarra

(Des P. E. Morriss; eng F. D. Manley (4d.). Des and eng F. D. Manley (7½d.). Recess. Des and photo Harrison from photographs by M. Murphy and sketches by L. Coles (1s.). Des and photo Courvoisier from photographs by M. Murphy (2s.))

1956 (31 Oct). *Olympic Games, Melbourne. P* 14½ (4d.), 14 × 14½ (7½d., 1s.) *or* 11½ (2s.).
290 **109** 4d. carmine-red 35 5
291 **110** 7½d. deep bright blue .. .. .. 1·00 1·75
292 **111** 1s. multicoloured .. .. .. 1·00 50
293 **112** 2s. multicoloured .. .. .. 1·50 2·00

PRICES OF SETS

Set prices are given for many issues, generally those containing five stamps or more. Definitive sets include one of each value or major colour change, but do not cover different perforations, die types or minor shades. Where a choice is possible the set prices are based on the cheapest versions of the stamps included in the listings.

113 Queen Elizabeth II

114 South Australia Coat of Arms

(Des F. D. Manley from bas-relief by W. L. Bowles. Eng G. Lissenden. Recess)

1957. *P* 15 × 14.
294 **113** 4d. lake (13 Mar) 30 5
295 10d. deep grey-blue (6 Mar) .. .. 2·25 30

The 4d. exists in booklet panes of six stamps, with imperf outer edges, producing single stamps with one or two adjacent sides imperf.

(Des and eng P. E. Morriss. Recess)

1957 (17 Apr). *Centenary of Responsible Government in South Australia. P* 14½.
296 **114** 4d. red-brown 15 5

115 Map of Australia and Caduceus

(Des J. E. Lyle; adapted B. Stewart. Eng D. Cameron. Recess)

1957 (21 Aug). *Flying Doctor Service. P* 14½ × 14.
297 **115** 7d. ultramarine 70 5

116 "The Spirit of Christmas"

Re-entry (Row 10/1)

(Des and eng D. Cameron from a painting by Sir Joshua Reynolds. Recess)

1957 (6 Nov). *Christmas. P* 14½ × 14.
298 **116** 3½d. scarlet 20 5
a. Re-entry .. .. 4·75 2·75
299 4d. purple 20 5

117 Queen Elizabeth II

118 Super-Constellation Airliner

(Des F. D. Manley from bas-relief by W. L. Bowles. Eng G. Lissenden. Recess)

1957 (13 Nov). *P* 15 × 14.
300 **117** 7½d. violet .. .. 2·25 75
a. Double print £375

(Des and eng P. E. Morriss. Recess)

1958 (6 Jan). *Inauguration of Australian "Round the World" Air Service. P* 14½ × 14.
301 **118** 2s. deep blue .. .. 3·00 1·50

119 Hall of Memory, Sailor and Airman

120 Sir Charles Kingsford Smith and *Southern Cross*

(Des and eng G. Lissenden. Recess)

1958 (10 Feb). *T* **119** *and similar horiz design. P* 14½ × 14.
302 **119** 5½d. brown-red 90 25
a. Horiz pair. Nos. 302/3 .. .. 7·00 8·50
303 – 5½d. brown-red 90 25

No. 303 shows a soldier and service-woman respectively in place of the sailor and airman. Nos. 302/3 are printed alternately in vertical columns throughout the sheet.

(Des J. E. Lyle. Eng F. D. Manley. Recess)

1958 (27 Aug). *30th Anniv of First Air Crossing of the Tasman Sea. P* 14 × 14½.
304 **120** 8d. deep ultramarine .. .. .. 1·75 1·00

121 Silver Mine, Broken Hill

122 The Nativity

(Des R. H. Evans; adapted and eng F. D. Manley. Recess)

1958 (10 Sept). *75th Anniv of Founding of Broken Hill. P* 14½ × 14.
305 **121** 4d. chocolate 15 5

(Des D. Cameron. Eng P. E. Morriss. Recess)

1958 (5 Nov). *Christmas. P* 14½ × 15.
306 **122** 3½d. deep scarlet 20 5
307 4d. deep violet 20 5

PHOSPHOR STAMPS ("Helecon"). "Helecon", a chemical substance of the zinc sulphide group, has been incorporated in stamps in two different ways, either in the ink with which the stamps are printed, or included in the surface coating of the stamp paper.

Owing to the difficulty of identification without the use of a U.V. lamp we do not list the helecon stamps separately but when in stock can supply them after testing under the lamp.

The first stamp to be issued was the 11d. Bandicoot from an experimental printing of four millions on helecon paper released to the public in December 1963. The next printing on ordinary paper was released in September 1964. The experimental printing was coarse, showing a lot of white dots and the colour is slate-blue, differing from both the ordinary and the later helecon paper.

The following helecon printings have been reported: 2d. and 3d. (sheets, coils and coil sheets) and 5d. (No. 354) Queen Elizabeth II; 8d. Tiger Cat; 11d. Bandicoot; 1s. Colombo Plan; 1s. 2d. Tasmanian Tiger; 2s. 3d. Wattle (No. 324*a*); and 6d. (No. 363*a*), 9d. and 1s. 6d. Birds (the 2s., 2s. 6d. and 3s. Birds were only issued on helecon paper). The 5d. Queen Elizabeth II in red (No. 354*b*) exists ordinary and with helecon ink. The coil pair was only issued with helecon ink; the booklet is normally with helecon ink but some were printed with ordinary ink by mistake. The Churchill stamp was printed on ordinary and helecon paper. The I.T.U. Centenary, Monash and later commemorative stamps were printed on helecon paper and all issues from No. 382 onwards were on helecon paper or paper coated with Derby Luminescence.

123

124

126

127

128

129

Queen Elizabeth II

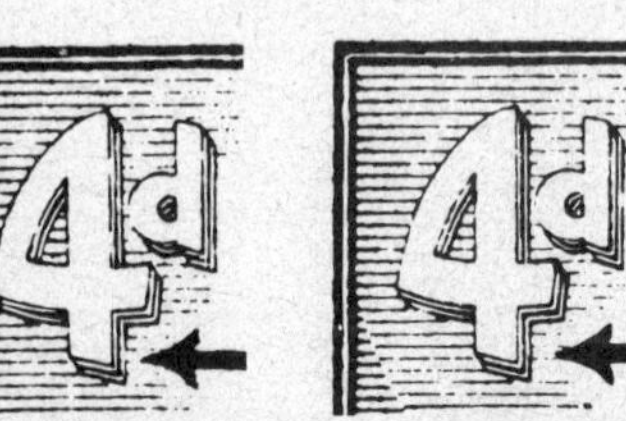

DIE I
Short break in outer line to bottom right of "4"

DIE II
Line unbroken

DIE A
Four short lines inside "5"

DIE B
Five short lines inside "5"

(Des G. Lissenden from photographs by Baron Studios. Eng F. D. Manley (2d.), D. Cameron (3d.). P. E. Morriss (others). Recess)

1959–62. *P* 14 × 15 (*horiz*), 15 × 14 (*vert*).
308 **123** 1d. deep slate-purple (*shades*) (2.2.59) .. 15 5
309 **124** 2d. brown (21.3.62) 25 5
a. Coil pair (1962) .. .. 3·75 3·75
b. Coil block of four .. .. .. 7·50
311 **126** 3d. blue-green (20.5.59) 25 5
a. Coil pair (8.60) .. .. 3·50 3·50
b. Coil block of four .. .. .. 7·00
312 **127** 3½d. deep green (18.3.59) 30 5
313 **128** 4d. carmine-lake (Die I) (*shades*) (2.2.59) 70 5
a. Die II (*shades*) 70 5
314 **129** 5d. deep blue (Die A or B) (1.10.59) .. 60 5
a. Vert *se-tenant* pair (A and B) .. 1·50 2·00
b. Coil pair (early 1960) .. .. 4·50 4·50
c. Coil block of four .. .. .. 9·00
308/14 .. .. *Set of* 6 2·10 25

No. 313. Die I occurs in the upper pane and Die II in the lower pane of the sheet.

No. 314. Both dies occur in alternate horizontal rows in the sheet (Die A in Row 1, Die B in Row 2, and so on), and their value is identical.

The Note after No. 295 also applies to Nos. 313/14.

131 Banded Ant-eater

137 Christmas Bells

142 Aboriginal Stockman

(Des Eileen Mayo (6d., 8d., 9d., 11d., 1s., 1s. 2d.), B. Stewart (5s.), Margaret Stones (others). Eng P. Morriss (11d.), F. D. Manley (1s.), B. Stewart (others). Recess)

1959–64. *T* **131, 137, 142** *and similar designs. W* **15** (5s.), *no wmk* (*others*). *P* 14 × 15 (1s. 2d.), 15 × 14 (6d. *to* 1s.), 14½ × 14 (5s.) *or* 14½ (*others*).
316 6d. brown (30.9.60) .. .. 1·75 5
317 8d. red-brown (*shades*) (11.5.60) .. .. 1·25 5
318 9d. deep sepia (21.10.59) .. .. .. 3·50 30
319 11d. deep blue (3.5.61) .. .. .. 1·75 15
320 1s. deep green (9.9.59) .. .. .. 4·75 20
321 1s. 2d. deep purple (21.3.62) .. .. .. 2·00 25
322 1s. 6d. crimson/*yellow* (3.2.60) .. .. 4·00 80
323 2s. grey-blue (8.4.59) .. .. .. 3·75 5
324 2s. 3d. green/*maize* (9.9.59) .. .. .. 4·75 5
324*a* 2s. 3d. yellow-green (28.10.64) .. .. 9·00 1·50
325 2s. 5d. brown/*yellow* (16.3.60) .. .. 11·00 35
326 3s. scarlet (15.7.59) .. .. 5·50 10
327 5s. red-brown (26.7.61) .. .. .. 38·00 75
a. White paper. *Brown-red* (17.6.64) .. £160 5·00
316/327 .. .. *Set of* 13 80·00 4·25

Designs: (*As T* **131**) *Vert*—8d. Tiger Cat (Dasyure); 9d. Kangaroos; 11d. Rabbit Bandicoot; 1s. Platypus. *Horiz*—1s. 2d. Tasmanian Tiger. (*As T* **137**) *Vert*—2s. Flannel Flower; 2s. 3d. Wattle; 2s. 5d. Banksia; 3s. Waratah.

No. 327 is on toned paper. No. 327a was a late printing on the white paper referred to in the note below No. 360.

See notes after No. 307 *re* helecon ink.

143 Postmaster Isaac Nichols boarding the brig *Experiment*

144 Parliament House, Brisbane, and Arms of Queensland

(Des R. Shackel; adapted and eng F. D. Manley. Recess)

1959 (22 Apr). *150th Anniv of the Australian Post Office. P* 14½ × 14.
331 **143** 4d. slate 30 5

(Des and eng G. Lissenden. Recess and typo)

1959 (5 June). *Centenary of Self-Government in Queensland. P* 14 × 14½.
332 **144** 4d. lilac and green 20 5

145 "The Approach of the Magi"

146 Girl Guide and Lord Baden-Powell

(Des and eng F. D. Manley. Recess)

1959 (4 Nov). *Christmas. P* 15 × 14.
333 **145** 5d. deep reddish violet 15 5

(Des and eng B. Stewart. Recess)

1960 (18 Aug). *Golden Jubilee of Girl Guide Movement. P* 14½ × 14.
334 **146** 5d. deep ultramarine 35 5

147 "The Overlanders" (Sir Daryl Lindsay)

148 "Archer" and Melbourne Cup

(Adapted and eng P. E. Morriss. Recess)

1960 (21 Sept). *Centenary of Northern Territory Exploration. P* 15 × 14½.
335 **147** 5d. magenta 25 5

There are two types in this issue. In Type I the horse's mane is rough and in Type II it is smooth. Type II occurs on 94 stamps in the Printer's sheet of 480.

(Des F. D. Manley. Eng G. Lissenden. Recess)

1960 (12 Oct). *100th Melbourne Cup Race Commemoration. P* 14½.
336 **148** 5d. sepia 20 5

149 Queen Victoria

150 Open Bible and Candle

(Des F. D. Manley. Eng B. Stewart. Recess)

1960 (2 Nov). *Centenary of First Queensland Postage Stamp. P* 14½ × 15.
337 **149** 5d. deep myrtle-green 20 5

(Des K. McKay. Adapted and eng B. Stewart. Recess)

1960 (9 Nov). *Christmas. P* 15 × 14½.
338 **150** 5d. carmine-red 15 5

151 Colombo Plan Bureau Emblem

152 Melba (after bust by Sir Bertram Mackennal)

(Des and eng G. Lissenden. Recess)

1961 (30 June). *Colombo Plan. P* 14 × 14½.
339 **151** 1s. red-brown 80 5

See notes after No. 307 *re* helecon ink.

(Des and eng B. Stewart. Recess)

1961 (20 Sept). *Centenary of Birth of Dame Nellie Melba (singer). P* 14½ × 15.
340 **152** 5d. blue 30 5

(Des G. Lissenden. Eng P. E. Morriss. Recess)

1961 (8 Nov). *Christmas. P* 14½ × 14.
341 **153** 5d. brown 15 5

154 J. M. Stuart

155 Flynn's Grave and Nursing Sister

(Des W. Jardine. Eng P. E. Morriss. Recess)

1962 (25 July). *Centenary of Stuart's Crossing of Australia from South to North. P* 14½ × 15.
342 **154** 5d. brown-red 20 5

(Des F. D. Manley. Photo)

1962 (5 Sept). *50th Anniv of Australian Inland Mission. P* 13½.
343 **155** 5d. multicoloured 30 10
a. Red omitted .. .. — £100

The note below No. 372b also applies to No. 343a.

156 "Woman"

157 "Madonna and Child"

(Des D. Dundas. Eng G. Lissenden. Recess)

1962 (26 Sept). *"Associated Country Women of the World" Conference, Melbourne. P* 14 × 14½.
344 **156** 5d. deep green 25 5

(Des and eng G. Lissenden. Recess)

1962 (17 Oct). *Christmas. P* 14½.
345 **157** 5d. violet 15 5

158 Perth and Kangaroo Paw (plant)

159 Arms of Perth and Running Track

(Des R. M. Warner (5d.), G. Hamori (2s. 3d.). Photo Harrison)

1962 (1 Nov). *Seventh British Empire and Commonwealth Games, Perth. P* 14 (5d.) *or* 14½ × 14 (2s. 3d.).
346 **158** 5d. multicoloured 40 10
a. Red omitted £200
347 **159** 2s. 3d. black, red, blue and green .. 10·00 8·50

160 Queen Elizabeth II.

161 Queen Elizabeth II and Duke of Edinburgh

(Des and eng after portraits by Anthony Buckley, P. E. Morriss (5d.), B. Stewart (2s. 3d.). Recess)

1963 (18 Feb). *Royal Visit. P* 14½.
348 **160** 5d. deep green 35 8
349 **161** 2s. 3d. brown-lake .. .. 8·00 6·50

162 Arms of Canberra and W. B. Griffin (architect)

163 Centenary Emblem

(Des and eng B. Stewart. Recess)

1963 (8 Mar). *50th Anniv of Canberra. P* 14½ × 14.
350 **162** 5d. deep green 20 5

(Des G. Hamori. Photo)

1963 (8 May). *Red Cross Centenary. P* 13½ × 13.
351 **163** 5d. red, grey-brown and blue 25 10

164 Blaxland, Lawson and Wentworth on Mt. York

(Des T. Alban. Eng P. E. Morriss. Recess)

1963 (28 May). *150th Anniv of First Crossing of Blue Mountains. P* 14½ × 14.
352 **164** 5d. ultramarine 25 5

165 "Export" **166** Queen Elizabeth II

(Des and eng B. Stewart. Recess)

1963 (28 Aug). *P* 14½ × 14.
353 **165** 5d. red 20 5

(Des and eng P. E. Morriss from photograph by Anthony Buckley. Recess)

1963 (9 Oct)–**65**. *P* 15 × 14.
354 **166** 5d. deep green 25 5
a. Imperf between (horiz pair) (31.7.64) 2·25 2·50
354*b* 5d. red (30.6.65) 40 5
c. Coil pair (30.6.65) .. .. .. 11·00 11·00

See notes after No. 307 *re* helecon ink.

The above exist in booklet panes of six stamps, with imperf outer edges, producing single stamps with one or two adjacent sides imperf.

No. 354a comes from sheets of uncut booklet panes containing 288 stamps (16 × 18) with wide margins intersecting the sheet horizontally below each third row, alternate rows of stamps imperforate between vertically and the outer left, right and bottom margins imperforate. This means that in each sheet there are 126 pairs of stamps imperf between vertically, plus a number with wide imperforate margins attached, as shown in the illustration.

167 Tasman and Ship **168** Dampier and *Roebuck*

(Des W. Jardine. Eng B. Stewart (4s., £1). E. R. M. Jones (10s.), P. E. Morriss (others). Recess)

1963–65. *T* **167/8** *and similar designs. No wmk* (4s.) *or W* **15** (*others*), (*sideways on* 5s., £1). *P* 14 *or* 14½ (5s., £1, £2).
355 4s. ultramarine (9.10.63) .. .. .. 8·00 60
356 5s. red-brown (25.11.64) .. .. .. 10·00 90
357 7s. 6d. olive (26.8.64) .. .. .. 40·00 30·00
358 10s. brown-purple (26.2.64) .. .. .. 60·00 5·00
a. White paper. *Deep brown-purple* (14.1.65) 90·00 6·00
359 £1 deep reddish violet (26.2.64) .. .. 85·00 20·00
a. White paper. *Deep bluish violet* (16.11.64) £120 22·00
360 £2 sepia (26.8.64) .. .. £120 80·00
355/360 .. .. *Set of* 6 £300 £130
357/60 Optd "Specimen" .. .. *Set of* 4 £425

Designs: *As T* **167**—7s. 6d. Captain Cook; 10s. Flinders and *Investigator*. *As T* **168**—£1 Bass and whaler; £2 Admiral King and *Mermaid*.

Nos. 358 and 359 were printed on a toned paper but all the other values are on white paper, the 4s. being on rather thicker paper.

173 "Peace on Earth . . ." **174** "Commonwealth Cable"

(Des R. M. Warner. Eng B. Stewart. Recess)

1963 (25 Oct). *Christmas*. *P* 14½.
361 **173** 5d. greenish blue 15 5

(Des P. E. Morriss. Photo)

1963 (3 Dec). *Opening of COMPAC* (*Trans-Pacific Telephone Cable*). *Chalky paper*. *P* 13½.
362 **174** 2s. 3d. red, blue, black and pale blue 10·00 10·00

175 Yellow-tailed Thornbill **176** Black-backed Magpie

(Des Mrs. H. Temple-Watts. Photo)

1964 (11 Mar)–**65**. *T* **175/6** *and similar designs showing birds. Chalky paper* (*except No.* 367*a*). *P* 13½.
363 6d. brown, yellow, black and bluish green (19.8.64) 75 25
a. Brown, yellow, black and emerald-green (12.65) .. .. 2·00 1·75
364 9d. black, grey and pale green .. .. 3·00 4·00
365 1s. 6d. pink, grey, dull purple and black .. 2·50 1·25
366 2s. yellow, black and pink (21.4.65).. .. 4·50 50
367 2s. 5d. deep royal blue, light violet-blue, yellow-orange, grey and black .. .. 15·00 4·00
367*a* 2s. 5d. deep blue, light blue, orange-brown, blue-grey and black (8.65) .. .. 38·00 12·00
368 2s. 6d. black, red, grey and green (21.4.65) .. 11·00 3·00
a. Red omitted (white breast) £550
369 3s. black, red, buff and yellow-green (21.4.65) 9·50 1·50
363/369 .. .. *Set of* 8 75·00 24·00

Designs: *Vert*—1s. 6d. Galah; 2s. Golden Whistler; 2s. 5d. Blue Wren; 3s. Straw-necked Ibis. *Horiz*—2s. 6d. Scarlet Robin.

No. 367*a* is from a printing on unsurfaced Wiggins Teape paper, the rest of the set being on chalk-surfaced Harrison paper. Apart from the differences in shade, the inscriptions, particularly "BLUE WREN", stand out very much more clearly on No. 367*a*. Although two colours are apparent in both stamps, the grey and black were printed from one plate.

See notes after No. 307 *re* helecon ink.

182 "Bleriot" Aircraft (type flown by M. Guillaux, 1914) Re-entry (upper plate, R. 4/4)

(Des K. McKay. Adapted and eng P. E. Morriss. Recess)

1964 (1 July). *50th Anniv of first Australian Airmail Flight*. *P* 14½ × 14.
370 **182** 5d. olive-green 40 10
a. Re-entry .. .. 90·00
371 2s. 3d. scarlet .. .. 7·00 4·50

183 Child looking at Nativity Scene **184** "Simpson and his Donkey"

(Des P. E. Morriss and J. Mason. Photo)

1964 (21 Oct). *Christmas*. *Chalky paper*. *P* 13½.
372 **183** 5d. red, blue, buff and black 15 5
a. Red omitted.. .. .. .. £200
b. Black omitted £200

The red ink is soluble and can be removed by bleaching and it is therefore advisable to obtain a certificate from a recognised expert committee before purchasing No. 372a.

(Des C. Andrew (after statue, Shrine of Remembrance, Melbourne). Eng E. R. M. Jones. Recess)

1965 (14 Apr). *50th Anniv of Gallipoli Landing*. *P* 14 × 14½.
373 **184** 5d. drab.. .. .. 40 10
374 8d. blue.. .. .. 3·00 4·00
375 2s. 3d. reddish purple .. .. .. 6·00 6·00

185 "Telecommunications" **186** Sir Winston Churchill

(Des J. McMahon and G. Hamori. Photo)

1965 (10 May). *I.T.U. Centenary*. *P* 13½.
376 **185** 5d. black, brown, orange-brown & bl .. 35 10
a. Black (value and pylon) omitted .. £400

(Des P. E. Morriss from photo by Karsh. Photo)

1965 (24 May). *Churchill Commemoration*. *Chalky paper*. *P* 13½.
377 **186** 5d. black, pale grey and light blue .. 30 10
a. Pale grey ("AUSTRALIA") omitted £300 £150

About half the printing was on helecon impregnated paper, differing slightly in the shade of the blue.

187 General Monash **188** Hargrave and "Seaplane" (1902)

(Des O. Foulkes and W. Walters. Photo)

1965 (23 June). *Birth Centenary of General Sir John Monash* (*engineer and soldier*). *Chalky paper*. *P* 13½.
378 **187** 5d. multicoloured 20 10

(Des G. Hamori. Photo)

1965 (4 Aug). *50th Death Anniv of Lawrence Hargrave* (*aviation pioneer*). *Chalky paper*. *P* 13½.
379 **188** 5d. purple-brown, blk, yell-ochre & pur 20 10
a. Purple (value) omitted £180

189 I.C.Y. Emblem **190** "Nativity Scene"

(Des H. Fallu from U.N. theme. Photo)

1965 (1 Sept). *International Co-operation Year*. *Chalky paper*. *P* 13½.
380 **189** 2s. 3d. emerald and light blue.. .. 7·50 6·50

(Des J. Mason. Photo)

1965 (20 Oct). *Christmas*. *P* 13½.
381 **190** 5d. multicoloured 15 5
a. Gold omitted £200
b. Blue omitted £180

No. 381a comes from the bottom row of a sheet in which the gold is completely omitted, the background appearing as black with "CHRISTMAS 1965" and "AUSTRALIA" omitted. The row above had the black missing from the lower two-fifths of the stamp.

(New Currency. 100 cents = 1 dollar)

191 Queen Elizabeth II **192** Blue-faced Honeyeater **193** Humbug Fish

(Des Mrs. H. Temple-Watts (6 c. (No. 387), 13 c., 24 c.), Eileen Mayo (7 c. (No. 388) to 10 c.). Recess (T **191**, 40 c. to $4). Photo Chalky paper (others))

1966 (14 Feb)–**73**. *Decimal currency*. *T* **191/3** *and similar designs, some reused from previous issues. No wmk*. *P* 14½ × 14 (*T* **191**), 14 (40 c., 75 c., $1), 14½ (50 c., $2, $4) *or* 13½ (*others*).
382 **191** 1 c. deep red-brown 35 5
383 2 c. olive-green .. .. .. 1·50 5
384 3 c. slate-green .. .. .. 1·50 5
385 4 c. red 20 5
a. Booklet pane. Five stamps plus one printed label .. .. .. 23·00
386 **175** 5 c. brown, yellow, black, & emer-green 80 10
a. Brown (plumage) omitted £200
b. Brown, yellow, black & bl-grn (1.67) 80 10
386*c* **191** 5 c. deep blue (29.9.67) .. .. .. 2·50 5
ca. Booklet pane. Five stamps plus one printed label .. .. .. 9·00
cb. Imperf in horiz strip of 3* £300
387 **192** 6 c. olive-yellow, blk, blue & pale grey .. 1·00 70
387*a* **191** 6 c. orange (28.9.70) 55 5
388 **193** 7 c. black, grey, salmon and brown .. 3·00 10
388*a* **191** 7 c. purple (1.10.71) 70 5
389 – 8 c. red, yell, bl-grn & blackish green .. 3·50 25
390 – 9 c. brown-red, purple-brown, black and light yellow-olive .. .. .. 3·50 10
391 – 10 c. orange, blackish brown, pale turquoise-blue and olive-brown .. 3·50 5
392 – 13 c. red, black, grey & light turq-green 5·00 40
a. Red omitted.. .. .. .. £200
b. Grey (plumage and legs) omitted .. £180
393 – 15 c. rose-carmine, black, grey and light bluish green .. .. .. 5·00 80
a. Rose-carmine omitted £750
394 – 20 c. yellow, black and pink .. .. 14·00 20
a. Yellow (plumage) omitted £200

395 – 24 c. ultramarine, yellow, blk & light brn 2·50 90
396 – 25 c. black, red, grey and green .. .. 10·00 30
a. Red omitted £425
397 – 30 c. black, red, buff & lt yellow-green .. 25·00 45
398 **167** 40 c. ultramarine .. .. 25·00 30
399 **168** 50 c. red-brown .. .. 32·00 20
400 – 75 c. olive .. .. 1·75 1·50
401 – $1 brown-purple (*shades*) .. .. 7·50 20
c. Perf 14½ × 14† (1973) .. .. £160 9·00
402 – $2 deep reddish violet .. .. .. 16·00 1·00
403 – $4 sepia .. .. 11·00 5·00
382/403 .. .. *Set of* 25 £160 11·00
400/3 Optd "Specimen" .. .. *Set of* 4 £120

Designs: *Vert* (*as T* **193**)—8 c. Coral Fish; 9 c. Hermit Crab; 10 c. Anemone Fish. (*as T* **192**)—13 c. Red-necked Avocet; 15 c. Galah; 20 c. Golden Whistler; 30 c. Straw-necked Ibis. *Horiz* (*as T* **192**)—24 c. Azure Kingfisher; 25 c. Scarlet Robin. *As T* **167**—75 c. Captain Cook; $1 Flinders and *Investigator*. *As T* **168**—$2 Bass and whaler; $4 Admiral King and *Mermaid*.

*This comprises two stamps imperf all round and one imperf on three sides.

†The note below No. 553 also applies to No. 401c, its exact gauge being 14·7 × 13·8. No. 401 is 14·25 × 13·95.

No. 385 is normally printed with helecon ink, the rest being on helecon paper. Early in 1967 experimental printings of No. 385 on different kinds of paper coated with helecon or Derby Luminescents phosphor were put on sale. They cannot be distinguished by the naked eye.

199 Queen Elizabeth II

200 "Saving Life"

1966 (14 Feb)–**67**. *Coil stamps. Photo. P* 14½ × *imperf.*
404 **199** 3 c. black, light brown and green .. 35 60
405 4 c. black, light brown & lt vermilion .. 70 15
405*a* 5 c. black, light brown and new blue (29.9.67) .. .. 1·00 5

(Des L. Mason. Photo)

1966 (6 July). *75th Anniv of Royal Life Saving Society. P* 13½.
406 **200** 4 c. black, bright blue and blue .. 15 5

201 "Adoration of the Shepherds"

202 Dutch Ship

(Des L. Stirling, after medieval engraving. Photo)

1966 (19 Oct). *Christmas. P* 13½.
407 **201** 4 c. black and yellow-olive 15 5

(Des F. Eidlitz. Photo)

1966 (24 Oct). *350th Anniv of Dirk Hartog's Landing in Australia. P* 13½.
408 **202** 4 c. multicoloured 25 5
a. Red (sphere) omitted £700

203 Open Bible

204 Ancient Keys and Modern Lock

(Des L. Stirling. Photo)

1967 (7 Mar). *150th Anniv of British and Foreign Bible Society in Australia. P* 13½.
409 **203** 4 c. multicoloured 20 5

(Des G. Andrews. Photo)

1967 (5 Apr). *150th Anniv of Australian Banking. P* 13½.
410 **204** 4 c. black, light blue and emerald .. 20 5

205 Lions Badge and 50 Stars

206 Y.W.C.A. Emblem

(Des M. Ripper. Photo)

1967 (7 June). *50th Anniv of Lions International. P* 13½.
411 **205** 4 c. black, gold and blue 25 5

(Des H. Williamson. Photo)

1967 (21 Aug). *World Y.W.C.A. Council Meeting. Monash University, Victoria. P* 13½.
412 **206** 4 c. dp blue, ultramarine, lt pur & lt bl 20 5

207 Anatomical Figures

5c
(**208**)

(Des R. Ingpen. Photo)

1967 (20 Sept). *Fifth World Gynaecology and Obstetrics Congress, Sydney. P* 13½.
413 **207** 4 c. black, blue and light reddish violet 20 5

1967 (29 Sept). *No.* 385 *surch with T* **208**.
414 **191** 5 c. on 4 c. red 60 10
a. Booklet pane. Five stamps plus one printed label .. .. .. 3·25

No. 414 was only issued in booklets and so only occurs with one or two adjacent sides imperforate. It only exists printed with helecon ink on normal paper.

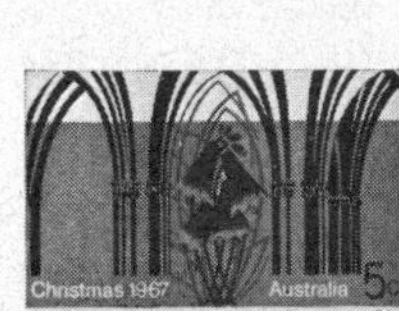

209 Christmas Bells and Gothic Arches

210 Religious Symbols

(Des M. Ripper (5 c.), Erica McGilchrist (25 c.). Photo)

1967. *Christmas. P* 13½.
415 **209** 5 c. multicoloured (18.10.67) 30 5
a. Imperf three sides .. .. ..
416 **210** 25 c. multicoloured (27.11.67) .. .. 3·25 3·00

211 Satellite in Orbit

212 World Weather Map

(Des J. Mason. Photo)

1968 (20 Mar). *World Weather Watch. P* 13 × 13½.
417 **211** 5 c. orange-brown, pl blue, black & ochre 35 10
418 **212** 20 c. orange-brown, blue and black .. 5·50 6·00

213 Radar Antenna

214 Kangaroo Paw (Western Australia)

(Des R. Ingpen. Photo)

1968 (20 Mar). *World Telecommunications Intelsat II. P* 13½ × 13.
419 **213** 25 c. greenish blue, black & lt blue-green 5·50 6·00

(Des Nell Wilson (6c., 30 c.); R. and P. Warner (13 c., 25 c.); Dorothy Thornhill (15 c., 20 c.). Photo)

1968 (10 July). *State Floral Emblems. T* **214** *and similar vert designs. Multicoloured. P* 13½.
420 6 c. Type **214** 80 60
421 13 c. Pink Heath (Victoria) .. .. 1·00 25
422 15 c. Tasmanian Blue Gum (Tasmania) .. 2·50 30
423 20 c. Sturt's Desert Pea (South Australia) .. 10·00 40
424 25 c. Cooktown Orchid (Queensland) .. .. 4·50 60
425 30 c. Waratah (New South Wales) (*shades*) .. 2·50 5
a. Green (leaves) omitted £350
420/5 .. .. *Set of* 6 19·00 2·00

No. 425 was reprinted in 1971, and this resulted in shade variations; particularly in the petals, which showed greater areas of white.

220 Soil Sample Analysis

(Des R. Ingpen. Photo)

1968 (6 Aug). *International Soil Science Congress and World Medical Association Assembly. P* 13 × 13½.
426 5 c. orange-brown, stone, greenish bl & blk 25 10
a. Nos. 426/7 *se-tenant* with gutter margin between .. .. 30·00 25·00
427 5 c. greenish blue, dull olive-yell, rose & blk 25 10

Design:—No. 427, Rubber-gloved hands, syringe and head of Hippocrates.

The above were printed in sheets of 100 containing a pane of 50 of each design.

The major shades formerly listed have been deleted as there is a range of intermediate shades.

222 Athlete carrying Torch, and Sunstone Symbol

223 Sunstone Symbol and Mexican Flag

(Des H. Williamson. Photo)

1968 (2 Oct). *Olympic Games. Mexico City. P* 13½ × 13 (5 c.) *or* 13 × 13½ (25 c.).
428 **222** 5 c. multicoloured 30 10
429 **223** 25 c. multicoloured .. .. .. 2·75 4·25

224 Houses and Dollar Signs

225 Church Window and View of Bethlehem

(Des Erica McGilchrist. Photo)

1968 (16 Oct). *Building and Savings Societies Congress. P* 13½ × 13.
430 **224** 5 c. multicoloured 15 25

(Des G. Hamori. Photo)

1968 (23 Oct). *Christmas. P* 13½ × 13.
431 **225** 5 c. multicoloured 12 5
a. Green window (gold omitted) .. £130

226 Edgeworth David (geologist)

(Des Note Ptg Branch (Nos. 432, 434), A. Cook (others). Recess, background litho)

1968 (6 Nov). *Famous Australians* (1*st series*). *T* **226** *and similar vert portraits. P* 14½ × 14.
432 5 c. myrtle-green/*pale green* .. .. 1·40 15
a. Booklet pane. Five stamps plus one printed label .. .. 7·00
433 5 c. black/*pale blue* .. .. .. 1·40 15
a. Booklet pane. Five stamps plus one printed label .. .. 7·00
434 5 c. blackish brown/*pale buff* .. .. 1·40 15
a. Booklet pane. Five stamps plus one printed label .. .. 7·00
435 5 c. deep violet/*pale lilac* .. .. 1·40 15
a. Booklet pane. Five stamps plus one printed label .. .. 7·00

Designs:—No. 432, Type **226**; No. 433, A. B. Paterson (poet); No. 434, Albert Namatjira (artist); No. 435, Caroline Chisholm (social worker).

Nos. 432/5 were only issued in booklets and only exist with one or two adjacent sides imperf.

See also Nos. 446/9, 479/82, 505/8, 537/40, 590/5, 602/7 and 637/40.

NEW INFORMATION

The editor is always interested to correspond with people who have new information that will improve or correct the Catalogue.

230 Macquarie Lighthouse

231 Pioneers and Modern Building, Darwin

(Des and eng Note Ptg Branch. Recess; background litho)

1968 (27 Nov). *150th Anniv of Macquarie Lighthouse. P* 14½ × 13½.
436 **230** 5 c. black/*pale yellow* 25 20
Used examples are known with the pale yellow background colour omitted.

(Des Mrs. M. Lyon. Photo)

1969 (5 Feb). *Centenary of Northern Territory Settlement. P* 13½.
437 **231** 5 c. blackish brown, yellow-olive and yellow-ochre 20 10

232 Melbourne Harbour

233 Concentric Circles (symbolising Management, Labour and Government)

(Des J. Mason. Photo)

1969 (26 Feb). *Sixth Biennial Conference of International Association of Ports and Harbours. P* 13½.
438 **232** 5 c. multicoloured 30 10

(Des G. Hamori. Photo.)

1969 (4 June). *50th Anniv of International Labour Organisation. P* 13½.
439 **233** 5 c. multicoloured 20 10
a. Gold (middle circle) omitted .. £350

234 Sugar Cane

(Des R. Ingpen. Photo)

1969 (17 Sept). *Primary Industries. T* **234** *and similar vert designs. Multicoloured. P* 13½ × 13.
440 7 c. Type **234** .. .. 2·75 3·25
441 15 c. Timber .. .. 9·50 7·00
a. Black ("Australia" and value) omitted .. £300
442 20 c. Wheat .. .. 3·25 80
443 25 c. Wool .. .. 4·00 2·25

238 "The Nativity" (stained-glass window)

240 Edmund Barton

(Des G. Hamori (5 c.), J. Coburn (25 c.). Photo)

1969 (15 Oct). *Christmas. T* **238** *and similar multicoloured designs. P* 13½ × 13 (5 c.) *or* 13 × 13½ (25 c.).
444 5 c. Type **238** 30 5
a. Magenta (robe) omitted £110
445 25 c. "Tree of Life", Christ in Crib and Christmas Star (abstract) .. .. .. 4·00 5·00

(Des from drawings by J. Santry. Recess, background litho)

1969 (22 Oct). *Famous Australians (2nd series). Prime Ministers. T* **240** *and similar vert designs each black on pale green. P* 14½ × 14.
446 5 c. Type **240** .. .. 1·25 15
a. Booklet pane. Five stamps plus one printed label .. .. 6·00
447 5 c. Alfred Deakin .. .. 1·25 15
a. Booklet pane. Five stamps plus one printed label .. .. 6·00
448 5 c. J. C. Watson .. .. 1·25 15
a. Booklet pane. Five stamps plus one printed label .. .. 6·00
449 5 c. G. H. Reid .. .. 1·25 15
a. Booklet pane. Five stamps plus one printed label .. .. 6·00
Nos. 446/9 were only issued in booklets and only exist with one or two adjacent sides imperf.

244 Capt. Ross Smith's Vickers "Vimy", 1919

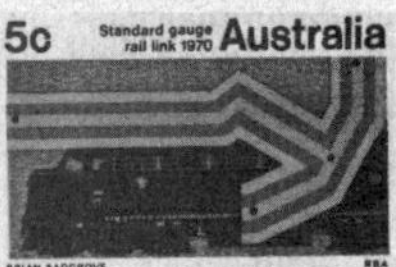
247 Symbolic Track and Diesel Locomotive

(Des E. Thake. Photo)

1969 (12 Nov). *50th Anniv of First England–Australia Flight. T* **244** *and similar horiz designs. P* 13½.
450 5 c. olive-green, pale blue, black and red .. 40 10
a. Strip of 3. Nos. 450/2 .. .. .. 6·00
451 5 c. black, red and olive-green 40 10
452 5 c. olive-green, black, pale blue and red .. 40 10
Designs:—No. 450, Type **244**; No. 451, Lt. H. Fysh and Lt. P. McGinness on 1919 survey with Ford car; No. 452, Capt. Wrigley and Sgt. Murphy in "BE 2E" taking off to meet the Smiths.
The three designs appear *se-tenant*, both horizontally and vertically, throughout the sheet.

(Des B. Sadgrove. Photo)

1970 (11 Feb). *Sydney–Perth Standard Gauge Railway Link. P* 13 × 13½.
453 **247** 5 c. multicoloured 25 10

248 Australian Pavilion, Osaka

251 Australian Flag

(Des J. Copeland (5 c.), A. Leydin (20 c.). Photo)

1970 (16 Mar). *World Fair, Osaka. T* **248** *and similar horiz design. P* 13½.
454 5 c. multicoloured 30 12
455 20 c. orange-red and black .. .. 1·75 1·75
Design:—20 c. "Southern Cross" and "from the Country of the South with warm feelings" (message).

(Des P.O. Artists (5 c.), J. Mason (30 c.). Photo)

1970 (31 Mar). *Royal Visit. T* **251** *and similar horiz design. P* 13 × 13½.
456 5 c. black and deep ochre 35 12
457 30 c. multicoloured .. .. 3·50 4·00
Design:—5 c. Queen Elizabeth II and Prince Philip.

252 Lucerne Plant, Bull and Sun

253 Captain Cook and H.M.S. *Endeavour*

(Des R. Ingpen. Photo)

1970 (13 Apr). *Eleventh International Grasslands Congress. P* 13 × 13½.
458 **252** 5 c. multicoloured 20 25

(Des R. Ingpen and "Team" (T. Keneally, A. Leydin, J. R. Smith). Photo)

1970 (20 Apr). *Bicentenary of Captain Cook's Discovery of Australia's East Coast. T* **253** *and similar vert designs. Multicoloured. P* 13½ × 13.
459 5 c. Type **253** 30 10
a. Strip of 5. Nos. 459/63 .. .. .. 4·50
460 5 c. Sextant and H.M.S. *Endeavour* 30 10
461 5 c. Landing at Botany Bay 30 10
462 5 c. Charting and exploring 30 10
463 5 c. Claiming possession 30 10
464 30 c. Captain Cook, H.M.S. *Endeavour*, sextant, aborigines and kangaroo (63 × 30 *mm*) .. .. 4·50 6·00
459/64 .. .. *Set of* 6 9·00 6·00
MS465 157 × 129 mm. Nos. 459/64. Imperf .. 16·00 15·00
The 5 c. stamps were issued horizontally *se-tenant* within the sheet, to form a composite design in the order listed.
50,000 miniature sheets were made available by the Post Office to the organisers of the Australian National Philatelic Exhibition which overprinted them in the white margin at each side of the 30 c. stamp with "Souvenir Sheet AUSTRALIAN NATIONAL PHILATELIC EXHIBITION" at left and "ANPEX 1970 SYDNEY 27 APRIL–1 MAY" at right in light red-brown and they were also serially numbered. These were put on sale at the exhibition on the basis of one sheet to each visitor paying 30 c. for admission. Although still valid for postage, since the stamps themselves had not been defaced, these sheets were not sold at post offices.
Subsequently further supplies were purchased and similarly overprinted and numbered by a private firm without the authority of the Post Office and ANPEX took successful legal action to stop their further sale to the public. This firm also had the unoverprinted sheets rouletted in colour between the stamps whilst further supplies of the normal sheets were overprinted with reproductions of old coins and others with an inscription commemorating the opening of Melbourne Airport on 1st July 1970, but all these are private productions. Further private productions have been reported.

259 Sturt's Desert Rose

AUSTRALIA AUSTRALIA
I. II.

Two types of 2 c.
I. "AUSTRALIA" thin: "2c" thin; flower name lightly printed.
II. Redrawn. "AUSTRALIA" thicker; "2c" much more heavily printed; flower name thicker and bolder.

(Des Note Ptg Branch. Photo)

1970–75. *Coil Stamps. Vert designs as T* **259**. *Multicoloured. Perf* 14½ × *imperf.*
465*a* 2 c. Type **259** (I) (1.10.71) 20 20
ab. Type II (1973) 5 5
466 4 c. Type **259** (27.4.70) .. .. 70 1·00
467 5 c. Golden Wattle (27.4.70) 20 10
468 6 c. Type **259** (28.9.70) .. .. 1·25 60
a. Green (leaves) omitted £180
468*b* 7 c. Sturt's Desert Pea (1.10.71) 30 15
c. Green (leaves) omitted .. .. .. 75·00
468*d* 10 c. As 7 c. (15.1.75) 10 5
465*a*/8*d* .. .. *Set of* 6 2·25 1·75
Nos. 465*a*/8*d* have horizontal coil perforations described after No. 191.
The 2 c. (No. 465*a*), 5 c. and 7 c. also exist on fluorescent paper; the 2 c. (No. 465ab) and 10 c. exist only on fluorescent paper (see note after No. 504).

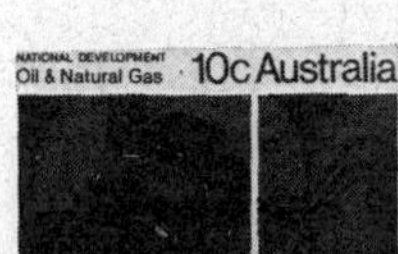
264 Oil and Natural Gas

265 Rising Flames

(Des L. Mason (7 c.), R. Ingpen (8 c., 9 c.), B. Sadgrove (10 c.). Photo)

1970 (31 Aug). *National Development (1st series). T* **264** *and similar horiz designs. Multicoloured. P* 13 × 13½.
469 7 c. Snowy Mountains Scheme .. .. .. 1·40 1·25
470 8 c. Ord River Scheme 60 25
471 9 c. Bauxite to aluminium 50 25
472 10 c. Type **264** .. .. 2·50 5
See also Nos. 541/4.

(Des G. Hamori. Photo)

1970 (2 Oct). *16th Commonwealth Parliamentary Association Conference, Canberra. P* 13½.
473 **265** 6 c. multicoloured 25 5

266 Milk Analysis and Dairy Herd

267 "The Nativity"

(Des R. Honisett. Photo)

1970 (7 Oct). *18th International Dairy Congress, Sydney. P* 13½.
474 **266** 6 c. multicoloured 30 8

(Des W. Beasley. Photo)

1970 (14 Oct). *Christmas. P* 13½.
475 **267** 6 c. multicoloured 15 5

268 U.N. "Plant" and Dove of Peace

269 Boeing "707" and Avro "504"

(Des Monad Ltd. Photo)

1970 (19 Oct). *25th Anniv of United Nations. P* 13½.
476 **268** 6 c. multicoloured 25 5

(Des G. Hamori. Photo)

1970 (2 Nov). *50th Anniv of QANTAS Airline. T* **269** *and similar horiz design. Multicoloured. P* 13½.
477 6 c. Type **269** 40 10
478 30 c. Avro "504" and Boeing "707" .. .. 3·25 2·25

270 The Duigan Brothers (Pioneer Aviators)

271 "Theatre"

(Des A. Cook (No. 480), T. Adams (No. 482), Note Ptg Branch (others). Recess (background litho))

1970 (16 Nov). *Famous Australians* (3*rd series*). *T* **270** *and similar vert designs. P* 14½ × 14.
479 6 c. blue .. .. 1·50 20
a. Booklet pane. Five stamps plus one printed label .. .. 7·50
480 6 c. black/*flesh* .. .. 1·50 20
a. Booklet pane. Five stamps plus one printed label .. .. 7·50
481 6 c. purple/*pink* .. .. 1·50 20
a. Booklet pane. Five stamps plus one printed label .. .. 7·50
482 6 c. brown-lake/*pink* .. .. 1·50 20
a. Booklet pane. Five stamps plus one printed label .. .. 7·50

Designs:—No. 479 Type **270**; No. 480 Lachlan Macquarie (Governor of N.S.W.); No. 481 Adam Lindsay Gordon (poet); No. 482 E. J. Eyre (explorer).

Nos. 479/82 were only issued in booklets and only exist with one or two adjacent sides imperf.

(Des D. Annand. Photo)

1971 (6 Jan). *"Australia–Asia". T* **271** *and similar horiz designs. Multicoloured. P* 13½ × 13.
483 7 c. Type **271** 90 80
484 15 c. "Music" .. .. 2·50 1·75
485 20 c. "Sea Craft" .. .. 2·75 1·50

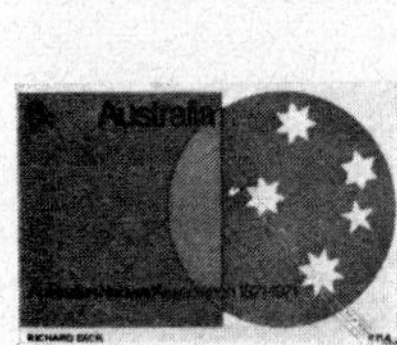

272 The Southern Cross

273 Market "Graph"

(Des R. Beck. Photo)

1971 (21 Apr). *Centenary of Australian Natives' Association. P* 13 × 13½.
486 **272** 6 c. black, vermilion and bright blue .. 20 5

(Des Monad Ltd. Photo)

1971 (5 May). *Centenary of Sydney Stock Exchange. P* 13½ × 13.
487 **273** 6 c. multicoloured 20 5

274 Rotary Emblem

275 "Mirage" Jets and "D.H.9a" Biplane

(Des H. Williamson. Photo)

1971 (17 May). *50th Anniv of Rotary International in Australia. P* 13 × 13½.
488 **274** 6 c. multicoloured 30 8

(Des R. Honisett. Photo)

1971 (9 June). *50th Anniv of R.A.A.F. P* 13½ × 13.
489 **275** 6 c. multicoloured 25 8
a. Black (face value and inscr) omitted £300

OMNIBUS ISSUES

Details, together with prices for complete sets, of the various Omnibus issues from the 1935 Silver Jubilee series to date are included in a special section following Zululand at the end of the catalogue.

276 Draught-horse, Cat and Dog

277 Bark Painting

(Des R. Ingpen. Photo)

1971 (5 July). *Animals. T* **276** *and similar vert designs. Multicoloured. P* 13½ × 13.
490 6 c. Type **276** 35 12
491 12 c. Vet and lamb ("Animal Science") .. 1·50 50
492 18 c. Red Kangaroo ("Fauna Conservation") .. 1·75 1·00
493 24 c. Guide-dog ("Animals Aid to Man") .. 2·50 2·25

The 6 c. commemorated the Centenary of the Australian R.S.P.C.A., and the others were short-term definitives.

(Des J. Mason. Photo)

1971 (29 Sept). *Aboriginal Art. T* **277** *and similar multicoloured designs. P* 13 × 13½ (20, 25 *c.*) *or* 13½ × 13 (*others*).
494 20 c. Type **277** 75 30
495 25 c. Body decoration 85 55
a. Black omitted* £200
496 30 c. Cave painting (*vert*) 90 45
497 35 c. Grave posts (*vert*) 90 40

*The omission of the black results in the stamp being without face-value and "AUSTRALIA".

Nos. 494/7 also exist on fluorescent paper and the 35 c. exists with both PVA gum and gum arabic.

278 The Three Kings and the Star

279 Andrew Fisher

(Des J. Lee. Photo)

1971 (13 Oct). *Christmas. Colours of star and colour of "AUSTRALIA" given. P* 13 × 13½.
498 **278** 7 c. royal blue, pl mauve & pl lake-brn 3·00 15
a. Block of 7. Nos. 498/504 .. .. 60·00
499 7 c. pale mauve, pl lake-brown & white 3·00 15
500 7 c. pale mauve, white and black .. 10·00 70
501 7 c. black, green and black .. .. 3·00 15
502 7 c. lilac, green and lilac .. .. 3·00 15
503 7 c. black, pale lake-brown and white .. 3·00 15
504 7 c. royal blue, pale mauve and green .. 27·00 1·75
498/504 .. .. *Set of* 7 48·00 3·00

Nos. 498/504, which also exist on fluorescent paper, were issued in sheets having two panes of 50 stamps. Each half pane had its stamps arranged thus:—

498	499	500	499	498
503	502	501	502	503
504	501	500	501	504
503	502	501	502	503
498	499	500	499	498

FLUORESCENT VERY WHITE CHALKY PAPER. As an experiment 10% of the above issue was printed on very white paper which fluoresces back and front under an ultraviolet lamp; it also has a strong coating of chalk on the surface. Late in 1972 this paper began to be introduced more generally and a number of stamps exist on both types of paper. The normal helecon paper does not fluoresce under the lamp but does react to the chalky test to a lesser degree.

Stamps reprinted on the white fluorescent paper are recorded below in footnotes and are listed in the *Elizabethan Catalogue*.

(Des J. Sandry. Recess)

1972 (8 Mar). *Famous Australians* (4*th series*). *Prime Ministers. T* **279** *and similar vert designs. P* 14½ × 14.
505 7 c. ultramarine (Type **279**) 90 15
a. Booklet pane. Five stamps plus one printed label .. .. 4·00
506 7 c. ultramarine. (W. M. Hughes) 90 15
a. Booklet pane. Five stamps plus one printed label .. .. 4·00
507 7 c. red (Joseph Cook) 90 15
a. Booklet pane. Five stamps plus one printed label .. .. 4·00
508 7 c. red (S. M. Bruce) 90 15
a. Booklet pane. Five stamps plus one printed label .. .. 4·00

Nos. 505/8 were issued only in booklets and exist with one or two adjacent sides imperf.

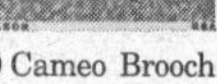

280 Cameo Brooch

281 Fruit

(Des Mrs. V. Mason. Photo)

1972 (18 Apr). *50th Anniv of Country Women's Association. P* 13½ × 13.
509 **280** 7 c. multicoloured 20 10

(Des D. Annand. Photo)

1972 (14 June). *Primary Industries. T* **281** *and similar horiz designs. Multicoloured. P* 13½.
510 20 c. Type **281** .. .. 7·00 7·50
511 25 c. Rice .. .. 7·00 7·50
512 30 c. Fish .. .. 7·00 6·50
513 35 c. Beef .. .. 14·00 4·50

282 Worker in Wheelchair

283 Telegraph Line

(Des from photographs by Barbara Ardizzone. Photo)

1972 (2 Aug). *Rehabilitation of the Disabled. T* **282** *and similar designs. P* 13½ × 13 (18 *c.*) *or* 13 × 13½ (*others*).
514 12 c. yellow-brown and emerald 25 10
515 18 c. sage-green and yellow-orange .. .. 1·60 35
516 24 c. blue and yellow-brown 40 35

Designs: *Horiz*—18 c. Patient and teacher. *Vert*—24 c. Boy playing with ball.

The 12 c. and 24 c. also exist on fluorescent paper.

(Des J. Copeland. Photo)

1972 (22 Aug). *Centenary of Overland Telegraph Line. P* 13 × 13½.
517 **283** 7 c. multicoloured 20 10

284 Athletics

285 Numerals and Computer Circuit

(Des B. Sadgrove. Photo)

1972 (28 Aug). *Olympic Games, Munich. T* **284** *and similar vert designs. Multicoloured. P* 13½ × 13.
518 7 c. Type **284** 35 20
519 7 c. Rowing 35 20
520 7 c. Swimming 35 20
521 35 c. Equestrian .. .. 4·75 4·75

(Des G. Andrews. Photo)

1972 (16 Oct). *Tenth International Congress of Accountants, Sydney. P* 13 × 13½.
522 **285** 7 c. multicoloured 25 10

286 Australian-build Harvester

(Des R. Ingpen. Photo)

1972 (15 Nov). *Pioneer Life. T* **286** *and similar multicoloured designs. P* 13½ × 13 (5, 10 *and* 60 *c.*) *or* 13 × 13½ (*others*).
523 5 c. Pioneer family (*vert*) 45 10
524 10 c. Water-pump (*vert*) .. .. 1·00 10
525 15 c. Type **286** 40 10
526 40 c. House 80 60
527 50 c. Stage-coach .. .. 2·50 40
528 60 c. Morse key (*vert*) .. .. 80 1·25
529 80 c. Paddle-steamer .. .. 1·00 1·25
a. Black (face-value and inscr) omitted .. £130
523/9 .. .. *Set of* 7 6·25 3·50

All values also exist on fluorescent paper and the 15 c. exists with both PVA gum and gum arabic.

287 Jesus with Children

288 "Length"

(Des from drawing by Wendy Tamlyn (7 c.), L. Stirling (35 c.). Photo)

1972 (29 Nov). *Christmas. T* **287** *and similar vert design. Multicoloured. P* 14½ × 14 (7 c.) *or* 13½ × 13 (35 c.).
530 7 c. Type **287** 30 5
a. Brown-red ("Australia 7c") omitted .. £170
b. Red-brown (inscr) omitted £170
531 35 c. Dove and spectrum motif .. .. 18·00 12·00

(Des Weatherhead & Stitt Pty. Ltd. Photo)

1973 (7 Mar). *Metric Conversion. T* **288** *and similar multicoloured designs. P* 14½ × 14 (*No.* 535) *or* 14 × 14½ (*others*).
532 7 c. Type **288** .. .. 1·50 45
533 7 c. "Volume" .. .. 1·50 45
a. Yellow-olive omitted* £175
534 7 c. "Mass" .. .. 1·50 45
535 7 c. "Temperature" (*horiz*) .. .. .. 1·50 45
*This results in the man's drink and shorts appearing white, and the colour of the stool being the same as the background.

289 Caduceus and Laurel Wreath **290** William Wentworth (statesman and explorer)

(Des H. Williamson. Photo)

1973 (4 Apr). *25th Anniv of W.H.O. P* 14½ × 14.
536 **289** 7 c. multicoloured 20 10

(Des J. Santry. Recess and litho)

1973 (16 May). *Famous Australians* (5*th series*). *T* **290** *and similar vert designs. P* 14½ × 14.
537 7 c. yellow-bistre and black 80 20
a. Block of 4. Nos. 537/40 .. .. .. 8·50
538 7 c. lilac and black 80 20
539 7 c. yellow-bistre and black 80 20
540 7 c. lilac and black 80 20
Designs:—No. 537, Type **290**; No. 538, Isaac Isaacs (first Australian-born Governor-General); No. 539, Mary Gilmore (writer); No. 540, Marcus Clarke (author).
Nos. 537/40 were printed in *se-tenant* blocks of four within the sheet. They also exist on fluorescent paper.

291 Shipping **292** Banded Coral Shrimp

(Des J. Copeland. Photo)

1973 (6 June). *National Development* (2*nd series*). *T* **291** *and similar vert designs. Multicoloured. P* 13½ × 13.
541 20 c. Type **291** .. .. 6·00 5·50
542 25 c. Iron ore and steel .. .. 7·00 4·00
543 30 c. Beef roads .. .. 10·00 5·50
544 35 c. Mapping .. .. 7·00 6·00

(Des Printing Bureau artists (1 to 4 c.), J. Mason (others). Photo)

1973 (11 July)–**74**. *Marine Life and Gemstones. T* **292** *and similar multicoloured designs. P* 14 × 14½ (1 *to* 4 *c.*) *or* 14½ × 14 (*others*).
545 1 c. Type **292** 5 5
a. Black (inscr and face value) omitted .. 50·00
546 2 c. Fiddler crab 8 5
547 3 c. Coral crab 10 5
548 4 c. Mauve stinger 20 12
a. Black (face value and inscr) omitted ..
549 6 c. Chrysoprase (*vert*) 20 5
550 7 c. Agate (*vert*) 20 5
a. Black (value and "agate") omitted .. 50·00
551 8 c. Opal (*vert*) 20 5
a. Black (face value and inscr) omitted ..
552 9 c. Rhodonite (*vert*) 25 10
552*a* 10 c. Star sapphire (*vert*) (16.10.74) 20 5
ab. Black (value, inscr, etc.) omitted .. 70·00
545/52*a* .. .. *Set of* 9 1·40 55
The 1, 3, 7 and 10 c. exist with PVA gum as well as gum arabic.

293 Children at Play **294** John Baptising Jesus

(Des G. Hamori. Photo)

1973 (5 Sept). *50th Anniv of Legacy* (*Welfare Organisation*). *P* 13 × 13½.
553 **293** 7 c. cinnamon, deep claret and emerald 20 10

PERFORATIONS. From 1973 to 1975 two different perforating machines were used for some issues, giving gauges of 14 or 14½ × 14 (on horizontal stamps), the exact measurement being 14.2 × 13.9 or 14.7 × 13.9. The latter gauge was also used for a reprint of the $1 definitive (No. 401c).

(Des G. Hamori. Photo)

1973 (3 Oct). *Christmas. T* **294** *and similar vert design. Multicoloured. P* 14 (7 c.) *or* 13½ × 13 (30 c.).
554 7 c. Type **294** 40 5
a. Perf 14 × 14½ .. .. 5·50 45
555 30 c. The Good Shepherd .. .. 4·50 5·00

295 Sydney Opera House **296** Wireless Receiver and Speaker

(Des A. Leydin. Photo)

1973 (17 Oct). *Architecture. T* **295** *and similar designs. P* 14 (7, 10 c.), 13 × 13½ (40 c.) *or* 13½ × 13 (50 c.).
556 7 c. pale turquoise-blue and new blue .. 60 5
a. Perf 14½ × 14 .. .. 9·00 1·50
557 10 c. light ochre and sepia .. .. .. 1·25 70
558 40 c. light grey, grey-brown and grey-black .. 2·25 2·25
559 50 c. multicoloured .. .. 3·50 3·75
Designs: *Horiz*—10 c. Buchanan's Hotel, Townsville; 40 c. Como House, Melbourne. *Vert*—50 c. St. James' Church, Sydney.

(Des E. Thake. Photo)

1973 (21 Nov). *50th Anniv of Regular Radio Broadcasting. P* 13 × 13½.
560 **296** 7 c. lt turquoise-blue, brown-red & blk 20 10

297 Wombat **298** "Sergeant of Light Horse" (G. Lambert)

(Des R. Bates. Photo)

1974 (13 Feb). *Animals. T* **297** *and similar vert designs. Multicoloured. P* 14 × 14½ (20, 30 c.) *or* 13½ × 13 (*others*).
561 20 c. Type **297** 40 5
562 25 c. Spiny Ant-eater .. .. 2·00 40
563 30 c. Brushtail Possum 70 10
a. Carmine-red (face-value, etc) omitted .. £190
564 75 c. Feather-tailed Glider .. .. .. 1·40 1·75
The 20 c. exists with gum arabic as well as PVA gum.

(Des P.O. artists. Litho Asher & Co, Melbourne ($5, $10). Photo R.B.A. (others))

1974 (24 Apr)–**79**. *Paintings. Multicoloured designs as T* **298**. *P* 13 × 13½ ($1), 13½ × 13 ($2, $4) *or* 14½ (*others*).
565 $1 Type **298** .. .. 1·50 15
566 $2 "Red Gums of the Far North" (H. Heysen) (*horiz*) .. .. 2·25 35
566*a* $4 "Shearing the Rams" (Tom Roberts) (*horiz*) .. .. 4·50 3·00
567 $5 "McMahon's Point" (Sir Arthur Streeton) (14.3.79) .. .. 6·25 4·00
567*a* $10 "Coming South" (Tom Roberts) (19.10.77) 12·50 10·00
567/*a*, 778 Optd "Specimen" .. .. *Set of* 3 9·00
The $1 and $2 exist with PVA gum as well as gum arabic.
Nos. 567/*a* and 778 optd "Specimen" come from a special "Ausipex 84" Presentation Pack issued on 9 February 1983.

299 Supreme Court Judge **300** Rugby Football

(Des T. Thompson. Photo)

1974 (15 May). *150th Anniv of Australia's Third Charter of Justice. P* 14 × 14½.
568 **299** 7 c. multicoloured 20 10
a. Perf 14 .. ..

(Des A. Leydin from drawings by D. O'Brien. Photo)

1974 (24 July). *Non-Olympic Sports. T* **300** *and similar multicoloured designs. P* 14½ × 14 (*Nos.* 569/70) *or* 14 × 14½ (*others*).
569 7 c. Type **300** 75 35
570 7 c. Bowls 75 35
571 7 c. Australian football (*vert*) 75 35
572 7 c. Cricket (*vert*) 75 35
573 7 c. Golf (*vert*) 75 35
574 7 c. Surfing (*vert*) 75 35
575 7 c. Tennis (*vert*) 75 35
569/75 .. .. *Set of* 7 4·75 2·25

301 "Transport of Mails" **302** Letter "A" and W. C. Wentworth (co-founder)

(Des J. Copeland. Photo)

1974 (9 Oct). *Centenary of Universal Postal Union. T* **301** *and similar vert design. Multicoloured. P* 14 (7 c.) *or* 13½ × 13 (30 c.).
576 7 c. Type **301** 90 25
a. Perf 14½ × 14 .. .. 50 15
577 30 c. Three-part version of Type **301** .. .. 1·75 1·75

(Des I. Dalton. Typo and litho)

1974 (9 Oct). *150th Anniv of First Independent Newspaper, "The Australian". P* 14.
578 **302** 7 c. black/*light cinnamon* .. .. 1·00 45
a. Perf 14 × 14½ 45 15

=
9c
(303)

304 "The Adoration of the Magi"

1974 (16 Oct). *No.* 551 *surch with T* **303**, *in red*.
579 9 c. on 8 c. Opal 25 15

(Des and recess R.B.A.)

1974 (13 Nov). *Christmas. Woodcuts by Dürer. T* **304** *and similar vert design. P* 14 × 14½.
580 10 c. black/*cream* 35 5
581 35 c. black/*cream* .. .. 1·75 1·75
Design:—35 c. "The Flight into Egypt".

PROCESS. All the following issues to No. 772 were printed in photogravure, *except where otherwise stated*.

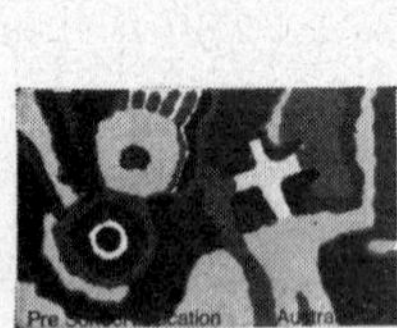

305 "Pre-School Education" **306** "Road Safety"

(Des Vivienne Binns (5 c.), Erica McGilchrist (11 c.), E. Tanner (15 c.), J. Meldrum (60 c.))

1974 (20 Nov). *Education in Australia. T* **305** *and similar multicoloured designs. P* 13½ × 13 (60 c.) *or* 13 × 13½ (*others*).
582 5 c. Type **305** 50 45
583 11 c. "Correspondence Schools" .. .. .. 1·00 20
584 15 c. "Science Education" .. .. 1·75 35
585 60 c. "Advanced Education" (*vert*) .. .. 3·25 3·25

(Des G. Andrews)

1975 (29 Jan). *Environment Dangers. T* **306** *and similar horiz designs. Multicoloured. P* 14.
586 10 c. Type **306** 80 25
587 10 c. "Pollution" 80 25
a. Perf 14½ × 14 .. .. 15·00 2·25
588 10 c. "Bush Fires" 80 25
a. Perf 14½ × 14 .. .. 2·75 75

307 Australian Women's Year Emblem

308 J. H. Scullin

(Des Leonora Howlett)

1975 (12 Mar). *International Women's Year. P* 14 × 14½.
589 **307** 10 c. dp violet-blue, green & bluish vio .. 30 15
This stamp exists with PVA gum as well as gum arabic.

(Des B. Dunlop)

1975 (26 Mar). *Famous Australians* (6*th series*). *Prime Ministers. T* **308** *and similar vert designs. Multicoloured. P* 14 × 15.
590 10 c. Type **308** 45 25
591 10 c. J. A. Lyons 45 25
592 10 c. Earle Page 45 25
593 10 c. Arthur Fadden 45 25
594 10 c. John Curtin 45 25
595 10 c. J. B. Chifley 45 25
590/5 .. .. *Set of* 6 2·40 1·40
Nos 591/2 and 594 exist with both PVA gum and gum arabic.

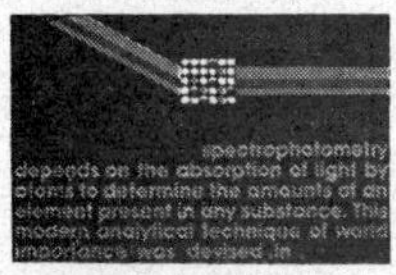

309 Atomic Absorption Spectrophotometry

310 Logo of Australian Postal Commission

(Des Weatherhead & Stitt)

1975 (14 May). *Scientific Development. T* **309** *and similar horiz designs. Multicoloured. P* 13 × 13½.
596 11 c. Type **309** 70 30
597 24 c. Radio astronomy .. .. 1·50 1·25
598 33 c. Immunology .. .. 2·00 1·75
599 48 c. Oceanography .. .. 2·50 2·00

(Des P. Huveneers)

1975 (1 July). *Inauguration of Australian Postal and Telecommunications Commissions. T* **310** *and similar horiz design. P* 14.
600 10 c. black, rosine and pale grey 25 10
a. Pair. Nos. 600/1 .. .. 2·00 2·00
b. Perf 14½ × 14 .. .. 25 10
ba. Pair. Nos. 600b/1b .. .. 1·75 1·75
601 10 c. black, orange-yellow and pale grey .. 25 10
b. Perf 14½ × 14 .. .. 25 10
Design:—No. 601, Logo of Australian Telecommunications Commission.
Nos. 600/1 were printed together, *se-tenant* in horizontal and vertical pairs throughout the sheet.

311 Edith Cowan

312 *Helichrysum thomsonii*

313 "Tambaran" House and Sydney Opera House

(Des D. and J. O'Brien)

1975 (6 Aug). *Famous Australians* (7*th series*). *Australian Women. T* **311** *and similar vert designs. Multicoloured.* A. *P* 14. B. *P* 14 × 14½.

		A.		B.	
602	10 c. Type **311**	75	45	1·00	45
603	10 c. Louisa Lawson	75	45	1·00	45
604	10 c. Ethel Richardson	75	45	1·00	45
605	10 c. Catherine Spence	75	45	1·00	45
606	10 c. Constance Stone	75	45	1·00	45
607	10 c. Truganini	75	45	1·00	45
602/7	*Set of* 6	4·00	2·50	5·50	2·50

No. 604 is inscribed with the *nom de plume* "Henry Handel Richardson".

(Des F. Knight)

1975 (27 Aug). *Wild Flowers. T* **312** *and similar multicoloured design. P* 14½ × 14 (18 *c.*) *or* 14 × 14½ (45 *c.*).
608 18 c. Type **312** 45 5
a. Black omitted .. .. 30·00
609 45 c. *Callistemon teretifolius* (*horiz*) 70 5
a. Black (face value and inscr) omitted .. £200
The 18 c. exists with both PVA gum and gum arabic.

(Des D. Annand (18 c.) or G. Hamori (25 c.))

1975 (16 Sept). *Papua New Guinea Independence. T* **313** *and similar horiz design. Multicoloured. P* 13½ (18 *c.*) *or* 13 × 13½ (25 *c.*).
610 18 c. Type **313** 30 10
611 25 c. "Freedom" (bird in flight) .. .. 1·25 1·50

314 Epiphany Scene

315 Australian Coat of Arms

(Des D. O'Brien (15 c.) or J. Milne (45 c.))

1975 (29 Oct). *Christmas. T* **314** *and similar horiz design. P* 14 × 14½ (15 *c.*) *or* 13 × 13½ (45 *c.*).
612 15 c. multicoloured 35 5
613 45 c. reddish violet, greenish blue and silver 2·25 3·25
Design:—45 c. "Shining Star".

(Des J. Spatchurst)

1976 (5 Jan). 75*th Anniv of Nationhood. P* 15 × 14.
614 **315** 18 c. multicoloured 50 30
a. Buff (supporters) omitted £250

316 Telephone-user, *circa* 1878

317 John Oxley

(Des R. Ingpen)

1976 (10 Mar). *Telephone Centenary. P* 13 × 13½.
615 **316** 18 c. multicoloured 30 15

(Des B. Dunlop)

1976 (9 June). 19*th Century Explorers. T* **317** *and similar horiz designs. Multicoloured. P* 13 × 13½.
616 18 c. Type **317** 50 40
617 18 c. Hume and Hovell 50 40
618 18 c. John Forrest 50 40
619 18 c. Ernest Giles 50 40
620 18 c. William Gosse 50 40
621 18 c. Peter Warburton 50 40
616/21 .. .. *Set of* 6 2·75 2·10

318 Measuring Stick, Graph and Computer Tape

319 Football

(Des R. Ingpen)

1976 (15 June). 50*th Anniv of Commonwealth Scientific and Industrial Research Organisation. P* 14½ × 14.
622 **318** 18 c. multicoloured 30 15

(Des A. Leydin)

1976 (14 July). *Olympic Games, Montreal. T* **319** *and similar multicoloured designs. P* 13 × 13½ (*Nos.* 623 *and* 626) *or* 13½ × 13 (*others*).
623 18 c. Type **319** 40 20
624 18 c. Gymnastics (*vert*) 40 20
625 25 c. Diving (*vert*) 70 75
626 40 c. Cycling 85 95
The 25 c. exists with gum arabic as well as PVA gum.

320 Richmond Bridge, Tasmania

321 Blamire Young (designer of first Australian stamp)

(Des O. Borchert)

1976 (23 Aug). *Australian Scenes. T* **320** *and similar designs. Multicoloured. P* 14 × 14½ (50 *c.*) *or* 14½ × 14 (*others*).
627 5 c. Type **320** 25 10
628 25 c. Broken Bay, N.S.W. 80 25
629 35 c. Wittenoom Gorge, W.A. 75 35
630 50 c. Mt. Buffalo, Victoria (*vert*) .. .. 1·25 35
631 70 c. Barrier Reef .. .. 1·50 1·50
632 85 c. Ayers Rock, N.T. .. .. 1·75 1·75
627/32 .. .. *Set of* 6 5·75 3·50

(Des R. Honisett)

1976 (27 Sept). *National Stamp Week. P* 13½ × 13.
633 **321** 18 c. multicoloured 30 15
MS634 101 × 112 mm. No. 633 × 4 .. .. 1·75 2·75

MS634 contains one stamp coloured as No. 633; the others, showing the different colour separations used in the printing, are each differently coloured.
The miniature sheet exists with "AUSTRALIAN STAMP PROMOTION COUNCIL" overprinted in red on the margin from a privately produced booklet.

322 "Virgin and Child" (detail, Simone Cantarini)

323 John Gould

(Des C. Medlycott (15 c.), Wendy Tamlyn (45 c.))

1976 (1 Nov). *Christmas. T* **322** *and similar horiz design. P* 14½ × 14 (15 *c.*) *or* 13 × 13½ (45 *c.*).
635 15 c. bright magenta and light azure 30 5
636 45 c. multicoloured .. .. 1·25 1·25
Design:—45 c. Toy koala bear and decorations.

(Des B. Weatherhead)

1976 (10 Nov). *Famous Australians* (8*th series*). *T* **323** *and similar horiz designs. Multicoloured. P* 14½ × 14.
637 18 c. Type **323** 40 35
638 18 c. Thomas Laby 40 35
a. Red-brown ("AUSTRALIA" etc.) omitted 80·00
639 18 c. Sir Baldwin Spencer 40 35
640 18 c. Griffith Taylor 40 35

324 "Music"

325 Queen Elizabeth II

1977 (19 Jan). *Performing Arts. T* **324** *and similar vert designs. Multicoloured. P* 14 × 14½.
641 20 c. Type **324** 60 20
642 30 c. Drama 85 25
643 40 c. Dance .. .. 1·25 30
644 60 c. Opera .. .. 1·75 1·75

(Des P.O. Artists. Litho Govt Printer, Sydney (2% of supplies) or by Norman J. Field, Melbourne)

1977 (2 Feb). *Silver Jubilee. T* **325** *and similar vert design. Multicoloured. P* 14 × 14½.
645 18 c. Type **325** 25 10
646 45 c. The Queen and Prince Philip .. .. 75 1·25

326 Fielder and Wicket Keeper

327 Parliament House

(Des B. Weatherhead)

1977 (9 Mar). *Australia–England Test Cricket Centenary. T* **326** *and similar vert designs. Multicoloured. P* 13½ × 13.
647 18 c. Type **326** 65 35
a. Horiz strip of 5. Nos. 647/51 .. .. 4·50
648 18 c. Umpire, batsman and scoreboard .. 65 35
649 18 c. Fielders 65 35
650 18 c. Batsman and umpire 65 35
651 18 c. Bowler and fielder 65 35
652 45 c. Batsman awaiting delivery .. .. 2·00 2·25
647/52 .. .. *Set of* 6 6·00 3·75
Nos. 647/51 were printed together, *se-tenant*, in horizontal strips of 5 throughout the sheet, forming a composite design.

(Des R.B.A.)

1977 (13 Apr). 50*th Anniv of Opening of Parliament House, Canberra. P* 14½ × 14.
653 **327** 18 c. multicoloured 30 10

328 Trade Unions Workers

329 Surfing Santa

(Des D. Lanyon; adapted B. Sadgrove)

1977 (9 May). *50th Anniv of Australian Council of Trade Unions. P* 13 × 13½.
654 **328** 18 c. multicoloured 30 10

(Des R. Roberts (15 c.), J. O'Brien (45 c.))

1977 (31 Oct). *Christmas. T* **329** *and similar vert design. Multicoloured. P* 14 × 14½ (15 c.) *or* 13½ × 13 (45 c.).
655 15 c. Type **329** 25 5
656 45 c. Madonna and Child . . . . . . 1·00 1·00

330 National Flag

331 Harry Hawker and Sopwith "Camel"

(Des Cato Hibberd Design)

1978 (26 Jan). *Australia Day. P* 13 × 13½.
657 **330** 18 c. multicoloured 40 25

(Litho Asher and Co, Melbourne)

1978 (19 Apr). *Early Australian Aviators. T* **331** *and similar horiz designs. Multicoloured. P* 15½.
658 18 c. Type **331** 40 35
a. Imperf (horiz pair) £160
659 18 c. Bert Hinkler and Avro "Avian" 40 35
a. Imperf (horiz pair) £250
660 18 c. Sir Charles Kingsford Smith and *Southern Cross* 40 35
a. Imperf (horiz pair) £170
661 18 c. Charles Ulm and *Southern Cross* . . 40 35
MS662 100 × 112 mm. Nos. 660/1 × 2. Imperf . . 1·50 1·75

332 Beechcraft "Baron" landing at Station Airstrip

333 Illawarra Flame Tree

1978 (15 May). *50th Anniv of Royal Flying Doctor Service. P* 13 × 13½.
663 **332** 18 c. multicoloured 30 15

(Des D. Rose)

1978 (1 June). *Trees. T* **333** *and similar vert designs. Multicoloured. P* 14 × 14½ (18 c.) *or* 13½ × 13 (*others*).
664 18 c. Type **333** 50 10
665 25 c. Ghost Gum . . . . 1·00 1·50
666 40 c. Grass Tree . . . . 1·60 1·50
667 45 c. Cootamundra Wattle . . . . . . 1·50 1·25

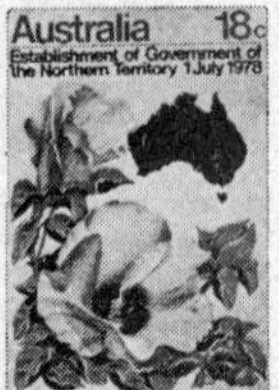

334 Sturt's Desert Rose and Map

335 Hooded Plover

(Des D. Pitt. Litho Asher and Co, Melbourne)

1978 (19 June). *Establishment of State Government for the Northern Territory. P* 15½.
668 **334** 18 c. multicoloured 30 15

(Des Kay Breeden-Williams. Photo)

1978 (3 July)–**80**. *Birds* (*1st series*). *Multicoloured designs as T* **335**. *P* 13½ × 13 (15, 40, 50 c.), 14½ × 14 (20 c. (*both*)), 14 × 14½ (22 c.), *or* 13 × 13½ (*others*).
669 1 c. Spotted-sided Finch (17.9.79) 5 5
670 2 c. Crimson Finch (17.9.79) 5 5
671 5 c. Type **335** (17.7.78) 15 5
672 15 c. Forest Kingfisher (*vert*) (17.9.79) . . 15 5
673 20 c. Australian Dabchick 45 20
674 20 c. Eastern Yellow Robin (17.9.79) 20 5
675 22 c. White-tailed Kingfisher (22 × 29 *mm*) (31.3.80) 65 5
676 25 c. Masked Plover (17.7.78) 80 15
677 30 c. Oystercatcher (17.7.78) 85 15
678 40 c. Variegated Wren (*vert*) (17.9.79) . . 45 15
679 50 c. Flame Robin (*vert*) (17.9.79) 70 50
680 55 c. Comb-crested Jacana . . . . . . 1·50 25
669/80 . . . . *Set of* 12 5·50 1·50
See also Nos. 734/40.

336 1928 3d. "National Stamp Exhibition" Commemorative

337 "The Madonna and Child" (after van Eyck)

(Des Cato Hibberd Design. Litho Asher and Co, Melbourne)

1978 (25 Sept). *National Stamp Week. 50th Anniv of National Stamp Exhibition, Melbourne. P* 15½.
694 **336** 20 c. multicoloured 35 15
MS695 78 × 113 mm. No. 694 × 4 . . . . 1·40 2·00

(Litho Asher and Co, Melbourne)

1978 (3 Oct–1 Nov). *Christmas. Paintings. T* **337** *and similar vert designs. Multicoloured. P* 14½ × 15.
696 15 c. Type **337** (1.11) 25 5
697 25 c. "The Virgin and Child" (Marmion) . . 90 1·00
698 55 c. "The Holy Family" (del Vaga) (1.11) . . 90 1·00

338 "Tulloch"

339 Raising the Flag, Sydney Cove, 26 January 1788

(Des B. Clinton)

1978 (18 Oct). *Race-horses. T* **338** *and similar multicoloured designs. P* 14½ × 14 (20 c.), 13 × 13½ (55 c.) *or* 13½ × 13 (*others*).
699 20 c. Type **338** 40 5
700 35 c. "Bernborough" (*vert*) 75 60
701 50 c. "Phar Lap" (*vert*) . . . . 1·10 1·00
702 55 c. "Peter Pan" . . . . 1·25 1·25

(Des B. Clinton. Litho Asher and Co, Melbourne)

1979 (26 Jan). *Australia Day. P* 15½.
703 **339** 20 c. multicoloured 30 15

340 P.S. *Canberra*

341 Port Campbell, Victoria

(Des O. Borchert)

1979 (14 Feb). *Ferries and Murray River Steamers. T* **340** *and similar horiz designs. Multicoloured. P* 14½ × 14 (20 c.) *or* 13 × 13½ (*others*).
704 20 c. Type **340** 30 5
705 35 c. M.V. *Lady Denman* 60 60
706 50 c. P.S. *Murray River Queen* 90 90
707 55 c. H.V. *Curl Curl* . . . . 1·00 1·00

(Des M. Robinson. Litho Asher and Co. Melbourne)

1979 (9 Apr). *National Parks. T* **341** *and similar multicoloured designs. P* 15½.
708 20 c. Type **341** 30 30
a. Horiz strip of 5. Nos. 708/12 . . 1·50
709 20 c. Uluru, Northern Territory 30 30
710 20 c. Royal, New South Wales 30 30
711 20 c. Flinders Ranges, South Australia . . 30 30
712 20 c. Nambung, Western Australia 30 30
713 20 c. Girraween, Queensland (*vert*) 30 30
a. Horiz pair. Nos. 713/14 . . . . 60 70
ab. Imperf (horiz pair)* £225
714 20 c. Mount Field, Tasmania (*vert*) 30 30
708/14 . . . . *Set of* 7 2·10 2·10
Nos. 708/14 were printed together, *se-tenant*; Nos. 708/12 in horizontal strips of 5 and Nos. 713/14 in horizontal pairs, throughout separate sheets.
*The imperforate error, No. 713ab, involves the two right-hand vertical columns of the sheet only, the left-hand stamp having vertical perforations at left.

342 "Double Fairlie" Type Locomotive, Western Australia

343 Symbolic Swan

(Des R. Honisett)

1979 (16 May). *Steam Railways. T* **342** *and similar horiz designs. Multicoloured. P* 14 × 14½ (20 c.) *or* 13 × 13½ (*others*).
715 20 c. Type **342** 30 5
716 35 c. Locomotive, "Puffing Billy" Line, Victoria 55 60
717 50 c. Locomotive, Pichi Richi Line, South Australia 80 85
718 55 c. Locomotive, Zig Zag Railway, New South Wales 90 95

(Des B. Weatherhead)

1979 (6 June). *150th Anniv of Western Australia. P* 13 × 13½.
719 **343** 20 c. multicoloured 30 15

344 Children playing on Slide

345 Letters and Parcels

(Des Wendy Tamlyn. Litho Asher and Co, Melbourne)

1979 (13 Aug). *International Year of the Child. P* 13½ × 13.
720 **344** 20 c. multicoloured 30 10

(Des A. Collins. Litho Asher and Co, Melbourne)

1979 (24 Sept–1 Nov). *Christmas. T* **345** *and similar vert designs. Multicoloured. P* 13 × 13½.
721 15 c. Christ's Nativity (Eastern European icon) (1.11.79) 20 5
722 25 c. Type **345** 60 60
723 55 c. "Madonna and Child" (Buglioni) (1.11.79) 85 70

346 Fly-fishing

347 Matthew Flinders

(Des B. Clinton)

1979 (24 Oct). *Fishing. T* **346** *and similar vert designs. P* 14 × 14½ (20 c.) *or* 13½ × 13 (*others*).
724 20 c. multicoloured 25 5
725 35 c. black, deep grey-blue and violet-blue . . 45 60
726 50 c. multicoloured 65 80
727 55 c. multicoloured 65 75
Designs:—35 c. Spinning; 50 c. Deep sea game-fishing; 55 c. Surf-fishing.

(Des B. Weatherhead. Litho Asher and Co, Melbourne)

1980 (23 Jan). *Australia Day. P* 13½ × 13.
728 **347** 20 c. multicoloured 25 10

348 Dingo

349 Queen Elizabeth II

(Des Marg Towt. Litho Asher and Co, Melbourne)

1980 (20 Feb). *Dogs. T* **348** *and similar horiz designs. Multicoloured. P* 13½ × 13.
729 20 c. Type **348** 35 5
730 25 c. Border Collie 35 35
731 35 c. Australian Terrier 55 65
732 50 c. Australian Cattle Dog . . . . . . 1·25 1·50
733 55 c. Australian Kelpie . . . . . . 1·00 1·25

(Des Kay Breeden-Williams. Litho Asher and Co, Melbourne)

1980 (31 Mar)–**83**. *Birds* (*2nd series*). *Multicoloured designs as T* **335**. *P* 12½.
734 10 c. Golden-shouldered Parrot (*vert*) (1.7.80) 30 5
a. Perf 14½ × 14 (5.83) 25 5
734*b* 18 c. Spotted Catbird (*vert*) (17.11.80) . . 35 35
735 28 c. Australian Bee Eater (*vert*) 60 20
736 35 c. Regent Bowerbird (*vert*) (1.7.80) . . 55 15
737 45 c. Masked Wood-swallow (1.7.80) 80 20
a. Perf 14 × 14½ (5.83) 60 20
738 60 c. Australian King Parrot (*vert*) . . . . 1·25 40
739 80 c. Rainbow Pitta (1.7.80) . . . . . . 1·25 45
740 $1 Black-backed Magpie (*vert*) (1.7.80) . . 1·40 50
734/40 . . . . *Set of* 8 5·75 2·10
Designs of Nos. 734/40 measure 22 × 29 mm (vert) or 29 × 22 mm (horiz).

(Des B. Weatherhead. Litho Asher and Co, Melbourne)

1980 (21 Apr). *Queen Elizabeth II's Birthday. P* 13 × 13½.
741 **349** 22 c. multicoloured 30 20

350 "Once a jolly Swagman camp'd by a Billabong" **351** High Court Buildings

(Des R. Roberts. Litho Asher and Co, Melbourne)

1980 (7 May). *Folklore. Scenes and Verses from the Folksong "Waltzing Matilda". T* **350** *and similar vert designs. Multicoloured. P* 13 × 13½.
742 22 c. Type **350** 40 10
a. Horiz strip of 5. Nos. 742/6 . . . . 1·75
743 22 c. "And he sang as he shoved that Jumbuck in his Tuckerbag" 40 10
744 22 c. "Up rode the Squatter, mounted on his Thoroughbred" 40 10
745 22 c. "Down came the Troopers one, two, three" 40 10
746 22 c. "And his Ghost may be heard as you pass by that Billabong" 40 10
Nos. 742/6 were printed together, *se-tenant*, in horizontal strips of 5 throughout the sheet, forming a composite design.

(Des Cato Hibberd Design. Litho Asher and Co, Melbourne)

1980 (19 May). *Opening of High Court Building, Canberra. P* 13 × 13½.
747 **351** 22 c. multicoloured 30 20

352 Salvation Army **353** Postbox, *circa* 1900

(Des J. Spatchurst. Litho Asher and Co, Melbourne)

1980 (11 Aug). *Community Welfare. T* **352** *and similar multicoloured designs. P* 13½ × 13 (*Nos.* 748, 751) *or* 13 × 13½ (*others*).
748 22 c. Type **352** 40 30
749 22 c. St. Vincent de Paul Society (*vert*) . . 40 30
750 22 c. Meals on Wheels (*vert*) 40 30
751 22 c. "Life. Be in it" 40 30

(Des B. Weatherhead. Litho Asher and Co, Melbourne)

1980 (29 Sept). *National Stamp Week. T* **353** *and similar vert designs showing postal history, circa* 1900. *Multicoloured. P* 13 × 13½.
752 22 c. Type **353** 35 10
a. Horiz strip of 5. Nos. 752/6 . . . . 1·60
753 22 c. Postman (facing left) 35 10
754 22 c. Mail van 35 10
755 22 c. Postman and postbox 35 10
756 22 c. Postman (facing right) 35 10
MS757 95 × 130 mm. Nos. 752, 754 and 756 . . 1·10 1·25
Nos. 752/6 were printed together, *se-tenant*, in horizontal strips of 5 throughout the sheet.
Stamps from No. **MS**757 have different backgrounds to the stamps from normal sheets.

354 "Holy Family" (painting, Prospero Fontana) **355** "Wackett", 1941

(Des B. Weatherhead. Litho Asher and Co, Melbourne)

1980 (1 Oct–3 Nov). *Christmas. Works of Art. T* **354** *and similar vert designs. Multicoloured. P* 13 × 13½.
758 15 c. "The Virgin Enthroned" (detail of painting by Justin O'Brien) (3.11) . . 20 5
759 28 c. Type **354** 40 40
760 60 c. "Madonna and Child" (sculpture by School of M. Zuern) (3.11) . . . . 90 1·25

NEW INFORMATION

The editor is always interested to correspond with people who have new information that will improve or correct the Catalogue.

(Des O. Borchert. Litho Victorian Government Printer, Melbourne (22 c.), Asher and Co, Melbourne (others))

1980 (19 Nov). *Aircraft. T* **355** *and similar horiz designs. Multicoloured. P* 13½ × 14 (22 *c.*) *or* 13½ × 13 (*others*).
761 22 c. Type **355** 35 5
762 40 c. "Winjeel", 1955 . . . . 60 65
763 45 c. "Boomerang", 1944 . . . . . . 70 75
764 60 c. "Nomad", 1975 . . . . 1·25 1·50

356 Flag in shape of Australia **357** Caricature of Darby Munro (jockey)

(Des B. Weatherhead. Litho Asher and Co, Melbourne)

1981 (21 Jan). *Australia Day. P* 13½ × 13.
765 **356** 22 c. multicoloured 30 20

(Des T. Rafty. Litho Cambec Press, Melbourne)

1981 (18 Feb). *Sports Personalities. T* **357** *and similar vert designs showing caricatures. Multicoloured. P* 14 × 13½.
766 22 c. Type **357** 30 5
767 35 c. Victor Trumper (cricketer) 60 60
768 55 c. Sir Norman Brookes (tennis player) . . 90 90
769 60 c. Walter Lindrum (billiards player) . . 1·00 1·00

358 1931 Kingsford Smith's Flights 6d. Commemorative **359** Apex Emblem and Map of Australia

(Des Cato Hibberd Design. Litho Asher and Co, Melbourne)

1981 (25 Mar). *50th Anniv of Official Australia–U.K. Airmail Service. T* **358** *and similar horiz design showing* 1931 *Kingsford Smith's Flights* 6d. *commemorative. P* 13 × 13½ (22 *c.*) *or* 13½ × 13 (60 *c.*).
770 22 c. blackish lilac, rosine and bright blue . . 30 10
771 60 c. blackish lilac, rosine and ultramarine . . 90 90

(Des P. Clark)

1981 (6 Apr). *50th Anniv of Apex (young men's service club). P* 13½.
772 **359** 22 c. multicoloured 30 30

ASHER AND CO. From April 1981 this firm was known as Leigh-Mardon Ltd, Melbourne.

360 Queen's Personal Standard for Australia **361** "Licence Inspected"

(Litho Leigh-Mardon Ltd, Melbourne)

1981 (21 Apr). *Queen Elizabeth II's Birthday. P* 13½ × 13.
773 **360** 22 c. multicoloured 30 30

(Des B. Weatherhead. Litho Leigh-Mardon Ltd, Melbourne)

1981 (20 May). *Gold Rush Era. Sketches by S. T. Gill. T* **361** *and similar vert designs. Multicoloured. P* 13 × 13½.
774 22 c. Type **361** 30 30
775 22 c. "Puddling" 30 30
776 22 c. "Quality of washing stuff" 30 30
777 22 c. "On route to deposit gold" 30 30

362 "On the Wallaby Track" (Fred McCubbin) **363** Tasmanian Tiger

(Litho Leigh-Mardon Ltd, Melbourne)

1981 (17 June)–**84.** *Paintings. T* **362** *and similar horiz design. Multicoloured. P* 15 × 14½.
778 $2 Type **362** . . . . 2·50 1·25
779 $5 "A Holiday at Mentone, 1888" (Charles Conder) (4.4.84) . . . . . . 6·25 5·00
For No. 778 overprinted "Specimen" see after No. 567*a*.
Numbers have been reserved for future additions to this series.

(Des C. McCubbin (4, 10, 20, 27 c. (No. 791), 30 c. (No. 792*a*), 35, 45, 60, 80 c., $1), F. Knight (5, 24, 25, 30 c. (No. 792), 50, 55 c.) or Beverley Bruen (others). Photo Note Ptg Branch, Reserve Bank of Australia and litho Leigh-Mardon (early ptgs of 24 c.), litho Leigh-Mardon (3, 5, 15, 24, 25, 27 c. (both), 30 c. (both), 40, 50, 55, 65, 75, 90 c.) or Cambec Press (others))

1981 (1 July)–**84.** *Wildlife. Multicoloured designs as T* **363.** *P* 13½ (1, 4, 10, 20, 24, 35, 45, 60, 70, 80, 85, 95 *c.*, $1), 14½ × 14 (27 *c.* (*No.* 791), 30 *c.* (*No.* 792*a*)) *or* 12½ (*others*).
781 1 c. Lace Monitor (2.2.83) 5 5
782 3 c. Corroboree Frog (19.4.82) 5 5
a. Perf 14 × 14½ (9.84) 5 5
783 4 c. Regent Skipper (butterfly) (*vert*) (15.6.83) 5 5
784 5 c. Queensland Hairy-nosed Wombat (*vert*) (15.7.81) 5 5
a. Perf 14½ × 14 (3.84) 5 5
785 10 c. Cairns Birdwing (butterfly) (*vert*) (15.6.83) 12 10
786 15 c. Eastern Snake-necked Tortoise (16.6.82) 20 15
a. Perf 14 × 14½ (3.84) 20 20
787 20 c. Macleay's Swallowtail (butterfly) (*vert*) (15.6.83) 25 20
788 24 c. Type **363** 35 30
789 25 c. Greater Bilby (*vert*) (15.7.81) . . 35 30
a. Perf 14½ × 14 (5.83) 35 30
790 27 c. Blue Mountain Tree Frog (19.4.82) . . 35 35
a. Perf 14 × 14½ (12.82) 35 35
791 27 c. Ulysses (butterfly) (*vert*) (15.6.83) . . 35 30
a. Imperf (pair) £275
792 30 c. Bridled Nail-tailed Wallaby (*vert*) (15.7.81) 40 30
792*a* 30 c. Chlorinda Hairstreak (butterfly) (*vert*) (24.10.83) 40 30
793 35 c. Blue Tiger (butterfly) (*vert*) (15.6.83) . . 40 35
794 40 c. Smooth Knob-tailed Gecko (16.6.82) . . 45 40
a. Perf 14 × 14½ (3.84) 45 50
795 45 c. Big Greasy (butterfly) (*vert*) (15.6.83) . . 55 45
796 50 c. Leadbeater's Possum (15.7.81) . . 60 50
a. Perf 14 × 14½ (1983) 60 50
797 55 c. Stick-nest Rat (*vert*) (15.7.81) . . 70 55
798 60 c. Wood White (butterfly) (*vert*) (15.6.83) . . 75 60
799 65 c. Yellow-faced Whip Snake (19.4.82) . . 80 65
a. Perf 14 × 14½ (3.84) 75 80
800 70 c. Crucifix Toad (2.2.83) 85 75
801 75 c. Eastern Water Dragon (19.4.82) . . 95 80
a. Perf 14 × 14½ (3.84) 95 80
802 80 c. Amaryllis Azure (butterfly) (*vert*) (15.6.83) . . . . . . 1·00 85
803 85 c. Centralian Blue-tongued Lizard (2.2.83) 1·10 90
804 90 c. Freshwater Crocodile (16.6.82) . . . . 1·10 95
805 95 c. Thorny Devil (2.2.83) . . . . . . 1·10 1·10
806 $1 Sword Grass Brown (butterfly) (*vert*) (15.6.83) . . . . . . 1·25 1·25
781/806 . . . . . . *Set of* 27 13·50 11·50
Numbers have been reserved for possible future additions to this series.

364 Prince Charles and Lady Diana Spencer **365** *Cortinarius cinnabarinus*

(Des B. Clinton. Litho Leigh-Mardon Ltd, Melbourne)

1981 (29 July). *Royal Wedding. P* 13½ × 13.
821 **364** 24 c. multicoloured 40 10
822 60 c. multicoloured . . . . . . 1·10 1·00

(Des Celia Rosser. Litho Leigh-Mardon Ltd, Melbourne)

1981 (19 Aug). *Australian Fungi. T* **365** *and similar vert designs. Multicoloured. P* 13 × 13½.
823 24 c. Type **365** 35 10
824 35 c. *Coprinus comatus* 60 60
825 55 c. *Armillaria luteobubalina* . . . . 1·00 90
826 60 c. *Cortinarius austro-venetus* . . . . 1·25 1·00

366 Disabled People playing Basketball **367** "Christmas Bush for His Adorning"

(Des J. Spatchurst. Litho Cambec Press, Melbourne)

1981 (16 Sept). *International Year for Disabled Persons. P* 14 × 13½.
827 **366** 24 c. multicoloured 35 30

(Des F. Beck. Litho Leigh-Mardon Ltd, Melbourne)

1981 (28 Sept–2 Nov). *Christmas. Scenes and Verses from Carols by W. James and J. Wheeler. T* **367** *and similar vert designs. Multicoloured. P* 13 × 13½.

828 18 c. Type **367** (2 Nov) 30 5
829 30 c. "The Silver Stars are in the Sky" .. 55 35
830 60 c. "Noeltime" (2 Nov) .. .. .. 1·00 80

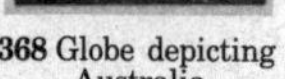

368 Globe depicting Australia   **369** Ocean Racer

(Des B. Weatherhead. Litho Leigh-Mardon Ltd, Melbourne)

1981 (30 Sept). *Commonwealth Heads of Government Meeting, Melbourne. P* 13 × 13½.

831 **368** 24 c. black, pale blue and gold 35 20
832 60 c. black, pale blue and silver .. .. 90 1·00

(Des R. Fletcher. Litho Leigh-Mardon Ltd, Melbourne)

1981 (14 Oct). *Yachts. T* **369** *and similar vert designs. Multicoloured. P* 13 × 13½.

833 24 c. Type **369** 35 10
834 35 c. Lightweight Sharpie 60 60
835 55 c. 12 Metre 95 95
836 60 c. Sabot .. .. 1·25 1·25

370 Aborigine, Governor Phillip (founder of N.S.W., 1788) and Post World War II Migrant   **371** Sperm Whale

(Des B. Clinton. Litho Cambec Press, Melbourne)

1982 (20 Jan). *Australia Day. "Three Great Waves of Migration". P* 13½ × 14.

837 **370** 24 c. multicoloured 35 30

(Des R. and Katrina Ingpen. Litho Cambec Press, Melbourne)

1982 (17 Feb). *Whales. T* **371** *and similar multicoloured designs. P* 13½ × 14 (24, 60 *c.*) *or* 14 × 13½ (*others*).

838 24 c. Type **371** 40 15
839 35 c. Southern Right Whale (*vert*) 60 60
840 55 c. Blue Whale (*vert*) .. .. .. 1·10 1·10
841 60 c. Humpback Whale .. .. .. 1·25 1·25

372 Queen Elizabeth II   **373** "Marjorie Atherton"

(Des R. Honisett. Litho Cambec Press, Melbourne)

1982 (21 Apr). *Queen Elizabeth II's Birthday. P* 14 × 13½.

842 **372** 27 c. multicoloured 35 30

(Des Betty Conabere. Litho Leigh-Mardon Ltd, Melbourne)

1982 (19 May). *Roses. T* **373** *and similar vert designs. Multicoloured. P* 13 × 13½.

843 27 c. Type **373** 40 15
844 40 c. "Imp" 65 60
845 65 c. "Minnie Watson" .. .. .. 1·25 1·00
846 75 c. "Satellite" .. .. 1·50 1·25

374 Radio Announcer and 1930-style Microphone   **375** Forbes Post Office

(Des Cato Hibberd Design. Litho Leigh-Mardon Ltd, Melbourne)

1982 (16 June). *50th Anniv of ABC (Australian Broadcasting Commission). T* **374** *and similar horiz design. Multicoloured. P* 13½ × 13.

847 27 c. Type **374** 35 10
a. Pair. Nos. 847/8 .. .. .. 70 60
848 27 c. ABC logo 35 10

Nos. 847/8 were printed together, *se-tenant*, in horizontal and vertical pairs throughout the sheet.

(Des F. Beck. Litho Cambec Press, Melbourne)

1982 (4 Aug). *Historic Australian Post Offices. T* **375** *and similar multicoloured designs. P* 14 × 13½ (*vert*) *or* 13½ × 14 (*horiz*).

849 27 c. Type **375** 40 30
850 27 c. Flemington Post Office 40 30
851 27 c. Rockhampton Post Office 40 30
852 27 c. Kingston S.E. Post Office (*horiz*) .. 40 30
853 27 c. York Post Office (*horiz*) 40 30
854 27 c. Launceston Post Office 40 30
855 27 c. Old Post and Telegraph Station, Alice Springs (*horiz*) 40 30
849/55 .. .. *Set of* 7 2·50 1·90

376 Early Australian Christmas Card   **377** Boxing

(Des B. Weatherhead. Litho Leigh-Mardon Ltd, Melbourne)

1982 (15 Sept–1 Nov). *Christmas. T* **376** *and similar multicoloured designs. P* 14½.

856 21 c. Bushman's Hotel, with Cobb's coach arriving (*horiz*) (1.11.82) 30 25
857 35 c. Type **376** 35 35
858 75 c. Little girl offering Christmas pudding to swagman (1.11.82) .. .. .. 1·10 1·10

(Des R. Carnielye. Litho Leigh-Mardon Ltd, Melbourne)

1982 (22 Sept). *Commonwealth Games, Brisbane. T* **377** *and similar horiz designs. P* 14½.

859 27 c. stone, lemon and bright carmine .. 35 30
860 27 c. lemon, stone and emerald 35 30
861 27 c. stone, lemon and yellow-brown .. 35 30
862 75 c. multicoloured .. .. .. 1·10 1·10
MS863 130 × 95 mm. Nos. 859/61. P 13½ × 13 .. 1·10 1·25

Designs:—No. 859, Type **377**; No. 860, Archery; No. 861, Weight-lifting; No. 862, Pole-vaulting.

378 Sydney Harbour Bridge 5s. Stamp of 1932   **379** "Yirawala" Bark Painting

(Des Cato Hibberd Design. Litho Cambec Press, Melbourne)

1982 (27 Sept). *National Stamp Week. P* 13½ × 14.

864 **378** 27 c. multicoloured 35 30

(Des Australia Post Graphic Design Section. Litho Leigh-Mardon Ltd, Melbourne)

1982 (12 Oct). *Opening of Australian National Gallery. P* 14½.

865 **379** 27 c. multicoloured 35 30

380 Mimi Spirits Dancing   **381** *Eucalyptus calophylla* "Rosea"

(Des D. Milaybuma (27 c.), L. Nabardayal (40 c.), J. Galareya (65 c.), D. Nguleingulei-Murrumurru (75 c.). Litho Cambec Press, Melbourne)

1982 (17 Nov). *Aboriginal Culture. Music and Dance. T* **380** *and similar horiz designs depicting Aboriginal Bark Paintings of Mimi Spirits. P* 13½ × 14.

866 27 c. multicoloured 35 30
867 40 c. multicoloured 55 60
868 65 c. multicoloured 90 95
869 75 c. multicoloured .. .. 1·10 1·25

(Des Elizabeth Conabere. Photo Enschedé)

1982 (17 Nov). *Eucalyptus Flowers. T* **381** *and similar horiz designs. Multicoloured. P* 12½ × 13½.

870 1 c. Type **381** 5 5
a. Booklet pane. Nos. 870/1 and 874 each × 2 60
b. Booklet pane. Nos. 870/1 each × 2, 872/3 and 874 × 3 .. .. 1·00
871 2 c. *Eucalyptus casia* 5 5
872 3 c. *Eucalyptus ficifolia* 5 8
873 10 c. *Eucalyptus globulus* 10 12
874 27 c. *Eucalyptus forrestiana* 25 30

Nos. 870/4 were only available from stamp booklets.

382 Shand Mason Steam Fire Engine, 1891   **383** H.M.S. *Sirius*

(Des A. Puckett. Litho Cambec Press, Melbourne)

1983 (12 Jan). *Historic Fire Engines. T* **382** *and similar horiz designs. Multicoloured. P* 13½ × 14.

875 27 c. Type **382** 30 35
876 40 c. Hotchkiss fire engine, 1914 .. .. 45 50
877 65 c. Ahrens-Fox PS2 fire engine, 1929 .. 80 85
878 75 c. Merryweather manual fire appliance, 1851 .. .. 90 95

(Des J. Spatchurst. Litho Leigh-Mardon Ltd, Melbourne)

1983 (26 Jan). *Australia Day. T* **383** *and similar horiz design. Multicoloured. P* 14½.

879 27 c. Type **383** 30 35
a. Pair. Nos. 879/80 .. .. .. 60 70
880 27 c. H.M. Brig *Supply* 30 35

Nos. 879/80 were printed together, *se-tenant*, in horizontal and vertical pairs throughout the sheet.

384 Stylised Kangaroo and Kiwi   **385** Equality and Dignity

(Des G. Emery. Litho Cambec Press, Melbourne)

1983 (2 Feb). *Closer Economic Relationship Agreement with New Zealand. P* 14 × 13½.

881 **384** 27 c. multicoloured 30 35

(Des G. Emery. Litho Leigh-Mardon Ltd, Melbourne)

1983 (9 Mar). *Commonwealth Day. T* **385** *and similar vert designs. Multicoloured. P* 14½.

882 27 c. Type **385** 30 35
883 27 c. Liberty and Freedom 30 35
884 27 c. Social Justice and Co-operation 30 35
885 75 c. Peace and Harmony 90 95

386 R.Y. *Britannia* passing Sydney Opera House   **387** "Postal and Telecommunications Services"

(Des J. Richards. Litho Leigh-Mardon Ltd, Melbourne)

1983 (20 Apr). *Queen Elizabeth II's Birthday. P* 14½.

886 **386** 27 c. multicoloured 40 35

(Des B. Sadgrove. Litho Cambec Press, Melbourne)

1983 (18 May). *World Communications Year. P* 13 × 13½.

887 **387** 27 c. multicoloured 30 35

388 Badge of the Order of St. John   **389** Jaycee Members and Badge

(Des T. McCauley. Litho Cambec Press, Melbourne)

1983 (8 June). *Centenary of St. John Ambulance in Australia. P* 14 × 13½.
388 **388** 27 c. black and deep turquoise-blue .. 30 35

(Des B. Clinton. Litho Cambec Press, Melbourne)

1983 (8 June). *50th Anniv of Australian Jaycees. P* 13½ × 14.
389 **389** 27 c. multicoloured 30 35

390 "The Bloke" **391** Nativity Scene

(Des B. Clinton. Litho Leigh-Mardon Ltd, Melbourne)

1983 (3 Aug). *"The Sentimental Bloke" (humorous poem by C. J. Dennis). T* **390** *and similar vert designs. Multicoloured. P* 14½.
890 27 c. Type **390** 30 35
a. Horiz strip of 5. Nos. 890/4 .. .. 1·50
891 27 c. "Doreen—The Intro" 30 35
892 27 c. "The Stror' at Coot" 30 35
893 27 c. "Hitched" 30 35
894 27 c. "The Mooch o'Life" 30 35
Nos. 890/4 were printed together, *se-tenant*, in horizontal strips of 5 throughout the sheet.

(Des Holly Alvarez (24 c.), Deanne Head (35 c.), Justine Jacobi (85 c.). Litho Cambec Press, Melbourne)

1983 (14 Sept–2 Nov). *Christmas. Children's Paintings. T* **391** *and similar horiz designs. Multicoloured. P* 13½ × 14.
895 24 c. Type **391** (2 November) 20 25
896 35 c. Kookaburra 40 45
897 85 c. Father Christmas in sleigh over beach (2 November) .. .. 1·00 1·10

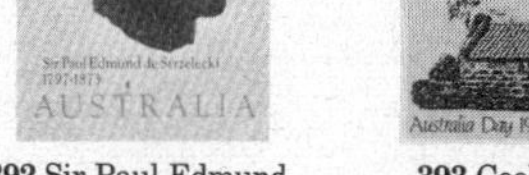

392 Sir Paul Edmund de Strzelecki **393** Cook Family Cottage, Melbourne

(Des Dianne Quinn. Litho Leigh-Mardon Ltd, Melbourne)

1983 (26 Sept). *Explorers of Australia. T* **392** *and similar vert designs. Multicoloured. P* 14½.
898 30 c. Type **392** 35 40
899 30 c. Ludwig Leichardt 35 40
900 30 c. William John Wills and Robert O'Hara Burke 35 40
901 30 c. Alexander Forrest 35 40

(Des J. Quinn. Litho Cambec Press, Melbourne)

1984 (26 Jan). *Australia Day. P* 13½ × 14.
902 **393** 30 c. black and stone 35 40

MACHINE LABELS. From 22 February 1984 gummed labels in the above design, ranging in value from 1 c. to $9.99, were available from seven automatic machines. The number at the top of the label indicates the location of the machine from which it was issued: 2000, Sydney; 2600, Canberra; 3000, Melbourne; 4000, Brisbane; 5000, Adelaide; 6000, Perth; 7000, Hobart.

394 Charles Ulm, *Faith in Australia* and Trans-Tasman Cover

(Des G. Beck and J. Quinn. Litho Cambec Press, Melbourne)

1984 (22 Feb). *50th Anniv of First Official Airmail Flights, New Zealand–Australia and Australia–Papua New Guinea. T* **394** *and similar horiz design. Multicoloured. P* 13½.
903 45 c. Type **394** 60 65
a. Horiz pair. Nos. 903/4 .. .. .. 1·25 1·25
904 45 c. As Type **394** but showing flown cover to Papua New Guinea 60 65
Nos. 903/4 were printed together, *se-tenant*, in horizontal pairs throughout the sheet.

395 Thomson "Steamer", 1898 **396** Queen Elizabeth II

(Des A. Puckett. Litho Leigh-Mardon Ltd, Melbourne)

1984 (14 Mar). *Veteran and Vintage Cars. T* **395** *and similar horiz designs. Multicoloured. P* 14½.
905 30 c. Type **395** 40 45
a. Vert strip of 5. Nos. 905/9 .. .. 1·90
906 30 c. Tarrant, 1906 .. .. 40 45
907 30 c. Gordon & Co "Australian Six", 1919 .. 40 45
908 30 c. Summit, 1923 .. .. 40 45
909 30 c. Chic, 1924 .. .. 40 45
Nos. 905/9 were printed together, *se-tenant*, in vertical strips of 5 throughout the sheet.

(Des B. Weatherhead. Litho Leigh-Mardon Ltd, Melbourne)

1984 (18 Apr). *Queen Elizabeth II's Birthday. P* 14½.
910 **396** 30 c. multicoloured 40 45

397 *Cutty Sark* **398** Freestyle

(Des J. Earl and J. Quinn. Litho Cambec Press, Melbourne)

1984 (23 May). *Clipper Ships. T* **397** *and similar multicoloured designs. P* 14 × 13½ (30 c., 85 c.) *or* 13½ × 14 (*others*).
911 30 c. Type **397** 40 45
912 45 c. *Orient* (*horiz*) 65 70
913 75 c. *Sabraon* (*horiz*) .. .. 1·10 1·25
914 85 c. *Thermopylae* .. .. 1·10 1·25

(Des B. Clinton. Litho Leigh-Mardon Ltd, Melbourne)

1984 (6 June). *Skiing. T* **398** *and similar multicoloured designs. P* 14½.
915 30 c. Type **398** 40 45
916 30 c. Downhill racer 40 45
917 30 c. Slalom (*horiz*) 40 45
918 30 c. Nordic (*horiz*) 40 45

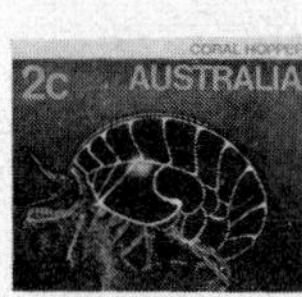

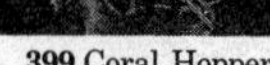

399 Coral Hopper **400** Before the Event

(Des G. Ryan and R. Fletcher. Litho Leigh-Mardon Ltd, Melbourne (30 c.) or Cambec Press, Melbourne (others))

1984 (18 June). *Marine Life. T* **399** *and similar horiz designs. Multicoloured. P* 14 × 14½ (30 c.) *or* 13½ (*others*).
919 2 c. Type **399** 5 5
920 25 c. Orange-tipped Cowrie 30 35
921 30 c. Choat's Wrasse 35 40
922 50 c. Blue-lined Surgeonfish 60 65
923 55 c. Bennett's Nudibranch 70 70
924 85 c. Regal Angelfish .. .. 1·00 1·00
919/24 .. .. *Set of* 6 2·75 3·00

(Des O. Schmidinger and Christine Stead. Litho Cambec Press, Melbourne)

1984 (25 July). *Olympic Games, Los Angeles. T* **400** *and similar multicoloured designs. P* 14 × 13½ (*No.* 943) *or* 13½ × 14 (*others*).
941 30 c. Type **400** 40 45
942 30 c. During the event 40 45
943 30 c. After the event (*vert*) 40 45

MINIMUM PRICE

The minimum price quoted is 5p which represents a handling charge rather than a basis for valuing common stamps. For further notes about prices see introductory pages.

401 Australian 1913 1d. Kangaroo Stamp **402** "Angel" (stained-glass window, St. Francis' Church, Melbourne)

(Des Ken Cato Design Studio. Litho Cambec Press, Melbourne)

1984 (22 Aug–21 Sept). *"Ausipex" International Stamp Exhibition, Melbourne. T* **401** *and similar vert designs. Multicoloured. P* 14½.
944 30 c. Type **401** 35 40
MS945 126 × 175 mm. 30 c. × 7, Victoria 1850 3d. "Half Length"; New South Wales 1850 1d. "Sydney View"; Tasmania 1853 1d.; South Australia 1855 1d.; Western Australia 1854 1d. "Black Swan"; Queensland 1860 6d.; Type **401** (21 Sept) .. .. 3·00 3·25
On No. **MS**945 the emblem and inscription on the sheet margin are embossed.

(Des Ken Cato Design Studio. Litho Cambec Press, Melbourne)

1984 (17 Sept–31 Oct). *Christmas. Stained-glass Windows. T* **402** *and similar vert designs. Multicoloured. P* 14 × 13½.
946 24 c. "Angel and Child" (Holy Trinity Church, Sydney) (31.10.84) 35 40
947 30 c. "Veiled Virgin and Child" (St. Mary's Catholic Church, Geelong) (31.10.84) .. 45 50
948 40 c. Type **402** 55 60
949 50 c. "Three Kings" (St. Mary's Cathedral, Sydney) (31.10.84) 75 80
950 85 c. "Madonna and Child" (St. Bartholomew's Church, Norwood) (31.10.84) .. .. 1·10 1·25

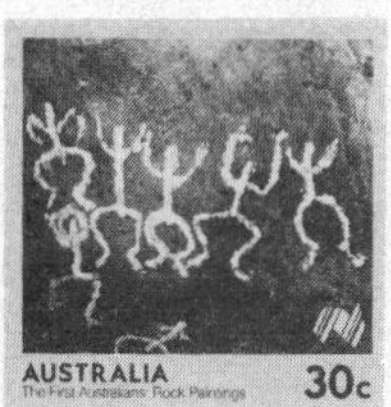

403 "Stick Figures" (Cobar Region) **404** Helmeted Honeyeater

(Des Elizabeth Innes. Litho Leigh-Mardon Ltd, Melbourne)

1984 (7 Nov). *Bicentenary of Australian Settlement (1988) (1st issue). The First Australians. T* **403** *and similar square designs showing aborigine rock paintings. Multicoloured. P* 14½.
951 30 c. Type **403** 45 50
952 30 c. "Bunjil" (large figure), Grampians .. 45 50
953 30 c. "Quikans" (tall figures), Cape York .. 45 50
954 30 c. "Wandjina Spirit and Baby Snakes" (Gibb River) 45 50
955 30 c. "Rock Python" (Gibb River) 45 50
956 30 c. "Silver Barramundi" (fish) (Kakadu National Park) 45 50
957 30 c. Bicentenary emblem 45 50
958 85 c. "Rock Possum" (Kakadu National Park) 1·10 1·25
951/8 .. .. *Set of* 8 3·75 4·25

(Des. G. Emery. Litho Leigh-Mardon Ltd, Melbourne)

1984 (19 Nov). *150th Anniv of Victoria. T* **404** *and similar vert design. Multicoloured. P* 14½.
959 30 c. Type **404** 45 50
a. Pair. Nos. 959/60 90
960 30 c. Leadbeater's Possum 45 50
Nos. 959/60 were issued together, *se-tenant*, in horizontal and vertical pairs throughout the sheet.

Index to Australian Stamp Designs from 1942

The following index is intended to facilitate the identification of all Australian stamps from 1942 onwards. Portrait stamps are usually listed under surnames only, views under the name of the town or city and other issues under the main subject or a prominent word and date chosen from the inscription. Simple abbreviations have occasionally been resorted to and when the same design or subject appears on more than one stamp, only the first of each series is indicated.

Aboriginal Art 224, 494, 865, 951
Aborigine 238
Accountants 522
Air Force 489
Aircraft 301, 304, 370, 450, 477, 489, 658, 761
Alice Springs 855
Animal Science 491
Animals 316, 490, 561, 729, 781
Animals Aid to Man 493
Antarctic Research 279
Anteater 316, 562
Anzac 373
Apex 772
"Ausipex" Int Stamp Exhib 944
"Australia Asia" 483
Australia Day 657, 703, 728, 765, 837, 879, 902
Australian Broadcasting 847
Australian Natives Association 486
Australian Settlement Bicent 951
Ayers Rock 632

Bandicoot 319
Banking 410
Barrier Reef 631
Barton 241, 446
Bass 359, 402
Beef 513
"Bernborough" (horse) 700
Bible Society 409
Bilby 789
Birds 363, 386, 392, 669, 734, 959
Black Swan 277
Blue Mountains 352
Britannia 886
British Empire Games 346
Broadcasting 560, 847
Broken Bay 628
Broken Hill 305
Brookes 768
Bruce 508
Buglioni 723
Building Societies 430
Bull 223
Butterflies 783

Cable 362
Canberra 244, 350, 653, 747
Canberra (ship) 704
Carols 828
Cars, Veteran and Vintage 905
Cattle Industry 327
Charles, Prince 821
Charter of Justice 568
Chic (car) 909
Chifley 595
Chisholm 435
Christmas 298, 306, 333, 338, 341, 345, 361, 372, 381, 407, 415, 431, 444, 475, 498, 530, 554, 580, 612, 635, 655, 696, 721, 758, 828, 856, 895, 946
Churchill 377
Clarke 540
Clipper ships 911
Coat of Arms 224*a*
Cobb 284
Collins 268
Colombo Plan 339
Commonwealth Day 882
Commonwealth Games 346, 859
Commonwealth Parliamentary Assn 473
Community Welfare 748
Conder 779
Cook, James 357, 400, 459
Cook, Joseph 507
Cook's Cottage 902
Coronation 264
Country Woman 344, 509
Cowan 602
Cricket 647
Crocodile 804
CSIRO 622
Curl Curl (ship) 707

Curtin 594
Cutty Sark (ship) 911

Dairy Congress 474
Dampier 356, 399
David 432
Deakin 447
Del Vaga 698
Dennis 890
Disabled 827
Dogs 493, 729
Duigan 479
Dürer 580

Economic Agreement 881
Education 582
Elizabeth II 222, 261, 272, 282, 294, 300, 308, 348, 354, 382, 404, 414, 645, 741, 842, 886, 910
Elizabeth II & Duke of Edinburgh 272, 349, 456, 646
Elizabeth, Queen Mother 203, 229, 236
Emu 207
"Encircling the Earth" 301
Environment Dangers 586
Eucalyptus 870
"Expo 70" 454
Export 353
Eyre 482

Fadden 593
Farrer 225
Fauna Conservation 492
Fire Engines 875
First Air Mails 370, 903
First England–Australia Flight 450, 770
Fish 388, 512, 545
Fisher 505
Fishing 724
Flemington 850
Flinders 358, 401, 728
Flowers 322, 420, 465*a*, 608, 668, 843, 870
Flying Doctor 297, 663
Fontana 759
Forbes 849
Forrest, A. 901
Forrest, J. 233, 618
"Foundation of Commonwealth" 241
Frog 782
Fruit 510
Fungi 823
Fysh 451

Gecko 794
Gemstones 549, 579
George VI 204*a*, 230, 234, 247
Giles 619
Gilmore 539
Girl Guides 334
Glider 564
Gloucester, Duke of 209
"Gold" 245
Gordon 481
Gordon and Co "Australian Six" (car) 907
Gosse 620
Gould 637
Grasslands Congress 458
Griffin 350
Guide-dog 493
Gynaecology 413

Hamori 554
Hargrave 379
Hargraves 245
Hartog 408
Hawker 658
Heads of Government 831
Hermes and Globe 223*a*
Heysen 566
Hinkler 659
Hobart Town 270
Horse, Cat and Dog 490
Hughes 506
Hume 617

Inland Mission 343
International Co-operation Year 380
International Labour Organization 439
International Women's Year 589
International Year of Child 720
Isaacs 538

Jaycee 889

Kangaroo 228, 318, 492
Koala 230*a*
King 360, 403

Kingston 852
Kookaburra 230*b*

Laby 638
Lady Denman (ship) 705
Lamb 491
Lambert 565
Latrobe 246
Launceston 854
Lawson, H. 231
Lawson, L. 603
Legacy 553
Leichardt 899
"Licence Inspected" 774
Life Saving 406
Lindrum 769
Lions 411
Lizard 803
Lyons 591
Lyrebird 230*d*

McCubbin 778
Macquarie 436, 480
Marine Life 545, 919
Marmion 697
Medical Association 427
Melba 340
Melbourne 558
Melbourne Cup 336
Mentone 779
Metric Conversion 532
Mitchell 216
Monash 378
Monitor 781
Mt Buffalo 630
Mueller 226
Munro 766
Murray River Queen (ship) 706

Namatjira 434
National Development 469, 541
National Gallery 865
National Parks 708
Nationhood 614
Newcastle 219
Newspaper 578
Northern Territory 335, 437, 668

O'Brien 758
Olympic Games, Los Angeles 941
Olympic Games, Melbourne 280, 290
Olympic Games, Mexico 428
Olympic Games, Montreal 623
Olympic Games, Munich 518
"On Route to deposit Gold" 777
"One Hundred Years" 239
Orient (ship) 912
Osaka Fair 454
Oxley 616

Page 592
Papua New Guinea 610, 904
Parkes 242
Paterson, A. B. 433
Paterson, W. 269
Peace 213
Performing Arts 641
"Peter Pan" (horse) 702
"Phar Lap" (horse) 701
Pioneer Life 523
Platypus 230*c*, 320
Ports and Harbours 438
Possum 563, 796, 960
Post Office 331
Postal Commission 600
Primary Industries 440, 510
"Produce Food" 255
"Puddling" 775

Qantas 477
"Quality of Washing Stuff" 776
Queensland 216, 332, 337

Railway 278, 453, 715
Rat 797
Red Cross 276, 351
Rehabilitation 514
Reid 449
Responsible Government 289, 296
Rice 511
Richardson 604
Richmond 627
Roberts 566*a*
Rockhampton 851
Roses 843
Rotary 281, 488
Royal Mail 284

R.S.P.C.A. 49
Royal Standard 77
Royal Visit 272, 45
Royal Wedding 82

Sabraon (ship) 91
St. John Ambulance 88
Scientific Development 59
Scout Jamboree 227, 25
Scullin 59
"Sentimental Bloke" 89
Silver Jubilee 64
Sirius (ship) 87
Skiing 91
Smith, Kingsford 66
Smith, Ross 45
Snake 79
Soil Science 42
South Australia 28
Spence 60
Spencer 63
Sports 56
Stained-glass windows 94
Stamp Week 633, 694, 75
Stamps 239, 271, 277, 288, 337, 633, 694 770, 864, 94
Standard Gauge 27
Stock Exchange 48
Stockman 32
Stone 60
Streeton 56
Strzelecki 89
Stuart 34
Sugar 44
Summit (car) 90
Supply (ship) 88
Sydney 55

Tarrant (car) 90
Tasman 355, 398
Tasman Flight 304, 903
Tasmania 268
Tasmanian Tiger 321, 788
Taylor 640
Telecommunication 376, 419
Telegraph 275, 517
Telephone 615
Thermopylae (ship) 914
Thomson "steamer" (car) 905
Thorny Devil 805
Tiger Cat 317
Timber 441
Toad 800
Tortoise 786
Townsville 557
Trade Unions 654
"Tradition of Service" 287
Trees 664
Truganini 607
Trumper 767
"Tulloch" (horse) 699

Ulm 661, 903
United Nations 476
U.P.U. 232, 576
U.S.A. Memorial 283

Van Diemen's Land 271
Van Eyck 696
Victoria 246, 959

Wallaby 792
"Waltzing Matilda" (song) 742
War Memorial 302
Warburton 621
Water Dragon 801
Watson 448
Weather 417
Wentworth 537
Western Australia 277, 719
Whales 838
Wheat 442
Wildlife 781
Wills 900
Wittenoom 629
Wombat 561, 784
Wool 443
World Communications Year 887
World Health Organization 536
Wrigley 452

Yachts 833
Y.M.C.A. 286
York 853
Young 633
Young Farmers 267
Y.W.C.A. 412

Zuern 760

POSTAGE DUE STAMPS

POSTAGE DUE PRINTERS. Nos. D1/62 were typographed at the New South Wales Government Printing Office, Sydney.

D 1

D 2

D 3

Type D **1** adapted from plates of New South Wales Type D **1**. No letters at foot.

1902 (From July). *Chalk-surfaced paper. Wmk Type* D **2**.

(*a*) *P* 11½, 12

D 1 D 1 ½d. emerald-green .. .. .. 3·25 3·00
D 2 1d. emerald-green .. .. .. 7·00 3·00
D 3 2d. emerald-green .. .. .. 11·00 3·50
D 4 3d. emerald-green .. .. .. 27·00 13·00
D 5 4d. emerald-green .. .. .. 25·00 8·50
D 6 6d. emerald-green .. .. .. 35·00 9·00
D 7 8d. emerald-green .. .. .. 95·00 48·00
D 8 5s. emerald-green .. .. .. £160 70·00

(*b*) *P* 11½, 12, *compound with* 11

D 9 D 1 1d. emerald-green .. .. .. 28·00 9·00
D10 2d. emerald-green .. .. .. 25·00 7·00

(*c*) *P* 11

D12 D 1 1d. emerald-green .. .. .. 90·00 32·00
D1/7 Optd "Specimen" .. .. *Set of* 7 £125

The ½d., 6d. and 8d. exist in dull green.

Stamps may be found showing portions of the letters "N S W" at foot.

1902–4. *Type* D **3**, *space at foot filled in. Chalky paper. Wmk Type* D **2**.

(*a*) *P* 11½, 12

D13 1d. emerald-green .. .. .. 26·00 9·00
D14 2d. emerald-green .. .. .. 24·00 11·00
D15 3d. emerald-green .. .. .. 30·00 11·00
D17 5d. emerald-green .. .. .. 22·00 7·00
D18 10d. emerald-green .. .. .. 45·00 11·00
D19 1s. emerald-green .. .. .. 45·00 8·00
D20 2s. emerald-green .. .. .. 60·00 16·00
D21 5s. emerald-green .. .. .. £275 70·00

(*b*) *P* 11½, 12, *compound with* 11

D22 ½d. emerald-green .. .. .. 3·00 1·50
D23 1d. emerald-green .. .. .. 3·50 1·50
D24 2d. emerald-green .. .. .. 8·00 1·50
D25 3d. emerald-green .. .. .. 20·00 3·75
D26 4d. emerald-green .. .. .. 22·00 4·00
D27 5d. emerald-green .. .. .. 35·00 8·00
D28 6d. emerald-green .. .. .. 32·00 8·00
D29 8d. emerald-green .. .. .. 50·00 20·00
D30 10d. emerald-green .. .. .. 55·00 16·00
D31 1s. emerald-green .. .. .. 55·00 8·00
D32 2s. emerald-green .. .. .. £100 20·00
D33 5s. emerald-green .. .. .. £120 14·00

(*c*) *P* 11

D34 ½d. emerald-green .. .. .. 32·00 20·00
D35 1d. emerald-green .. .. .. 22·00 3·50
D36 2d. emerald-green .. .. .. 27·00 4·00
D37 3d. emerald-green .. .. .. 25·00 7·50
D38 4d. emerald-green .. .. .. 35·00 8·00
D39 5d. emerald-green .. .. .. 45·00 9·00
D40 6d. emerald-green .. .. .. 35·00 11·00
D41 1s. emerald-green .. .. .. 55·00 16·00
D42 5s. emerald-green .. .. .. £175 35·00
D43 10s. emerald-green £1200 £650
D44 20s. emerald-green £2250 £1200
D13/44 Optd "Specimen" .. *Set of* 14 £500

Most values exist in dull green.

D 4

D 6

1906 (From Jan)–**08.** *Chalky paper. Wmk Type* D **4**.

(*a*) *P* 11½, 12, *compound with* 11

D45 D 3 ½d. green (1907) .. .. .. 5·00 2·50
D46 1d. green .. .. .. 6·00 2·25
D47 2d. green .. .. .. 12·00 3·25
D48 3d. green .. .. .. £110 48·00
D49 4d. green (1907) .. .. .. 40·00 20·00
D50 6d. green (1908) .. .. .. 50·00 20·00

(*b*) *P* 11

D51 D 3 1d. dull green .. .. .. 50·00 16·00
D52 4d. dull green .. .. .. £110 40·00

Shades exist.

1907 (From July). *Chalky paper. Wmk Type* w **11** (*see Introduction*). *P* 11½ × 11.

D53 D 3 ½d. dull green .. .. .. 15·00 15·00
D54 1d. dull green .. .. .. 25·00 12·00
D55 2d. dull green .. .. .. 50·00 30·00
D56 4d. dull green .. .. .. £110 45·00
D57 6d. dull green .. .. .. £130 45·00

1908 (Sept)–**09.** *Stroke after figure of value. Chalky paper. Wmk Type* D **4**.

(*a*) *P* 11½ × 11

D58 D 6 1s. dull green (1909) .. .. .. 70·00 14·00
D59 5s. dull green .. .. .. £200 48·00

(*b*) *P* 11

D60 D 6 2s. dull green £500 £325
D61 10s. dull green £1200 £500
D62 20s. dull green £3000 £1200

Nos. D1/62 were not for use in Victoria.

D 7

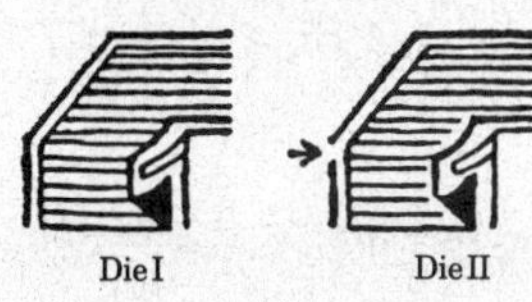
Die I Die II

1d.

Die I Die II

2d.

(Typo J. B. Cooke, Melbourne)

1909 (July)–**1911.** *Type* D **7**. *Wmk Crown over A, Type* w **11**.

(*a*) *P* 12 × 12½ (*comb*) *or* 12½ (*line*)

D63 ½d. rosine and yellow-green .. .. 8·50 6·00
D64 1d. rosine and yellow-green (I) .. .. 12·00 3·25
a. Die II (1911) .. .. .. 3·00 60
D65 2d. rosine and yellow-green (I) .. .. 17·00 3·25
a. Die II (7.10) .. .. .. 3·75 75
D66 3d. rosine and yellow-green .. .. 17·00 8·50
D67 4d. rosine and yellow-green .. .. 13·00 4·00
D68 6d. rosine and yellow-green .. .. 20·00 8·00
D69 1s. rosine and yellow-green .. .. 30·00 6·50
D70 2s. rosine and yellow-green .. .. 65·00 20·00
D71 5s. rosine and yellow-green .. .. 70·00 20·00
D72 10s. rosine and yellow-green .. .. £180 85·00
D73 £1 rosine and yellow-green £325 £140

(*b*) *P* 11

D74 1d. rose and yellow-green (II) (1911) £275 £150
D74*a* 2d. rose and yellow-green (II) (7.10)
D75 6d. rose and yellow-green £1100 £500

Only one example, unused without gum, is known of No. D74*a*.

The 1d. of this printing is distinguishable from No. D78 by the colours, the green being very yellow and the rose having less of a carmine tone. The paper is thicker and slightly toned, that of No. D78 being pure white; the gum is thick and yellowish, No. D78 having thin white gum.

All later issues of the 1d. and 2d. are Die II.

(Typo J. B. Cooke and T. S. Harrison (from May 1918))

1912–23. *Type* D **7**. *Thin paper. White gum. W* w **11**. (*a*) *P* 12½.

D76 ½d. scarlet and pale yellow-green (12.12) 16·00 12·00

(*b*) *P* 11

D77 ½d. rosine and bright apple-green (11.14) 2·50 1·50
a. Wmk sideways .. .. .. 2·25 1·50
D78 1d. rosine and bright apple-green (1913) 1·75 55
a. Wmk sideways .. .. .. 2·50 80

(*c*) *P* 14

D79 ½d. rosine and bright apple-green (1916) .. 40·00 17·00
a. Carmine and apple-green (Harrison) (1918) .. .. .. 9·00 4·50
D80 1d. rosine and bright apple-green (10.14) .. 35·00 10·00
a. Scarlet and pale yellow-green (1916) .. 12·00 3·25
b. Carmine and apple-green (Harrison) (1918) .. .. .. 6·50 2·00
D81 2d. scarlet and pale yellow-green (1915) .. 17·00 5·00
a. Carmine and apple-green (Harrison) (1918) .. .. .. 9·00 2·75
D82 3d. rosine and apple-green (5.16) .. 40·00 16·00
a. Wmk sideways £275 £200
D83 4d. rosine and apple-green (1916) .. 55·00 28·00
a. Wmk sideways £200 £130
b. Carmine and apple-green (Harrison) (1918) .. .. .. 35·00 24·00
c. Carmine and pale yellow-green (Harrison) (26.4.21) .. .. 30·00 22·00
D85 1s. scarlet and pale yellow-green (7.23) .. 25·00 10·00
D86 10s. scarlet and pale yellow-green (5.21) .. £300 £160
D87 £1 scarlet and pale yellow-green (5.21) .. £500 £200

Although printed by Cooke, the three higher values were not issued until some years later.

(Typo T. S. Harrison (to Feb. 1926), A. J. Mullet (to June 1927) and J. Ash (later))

1919–30. *Type* D **7**. *W* **6**. (*a*) *P* 14.

D91 ½d. carmine and yellow-green (7.23) .. 3·00 2·00
D92 1d. carmine and yellow-green (28.3.22) .. 1·60 65
D93 1½d. carmine and yellow-green (3.25) .. 5·50 8·50
D94 2d. carmine and yellow-green (20.3.22) .. 3·25 1·75
D95 3d. carmine and yellow-green (12.11.19) .. 8·00 3·50
D96 4d. carmine and yellow-green (13.2.22) .. 16·00 6·00
D97 6d. carmine and yellow-green (13.2.22) .. 25·00 9·50

(*b*) *P* 11

D98 4d. carmine and yellow-green (10.30) .. 6·00 3·00

All values perf 14 were printed by Harrison and all except the 4d. by Mullett and Ash. There is a wide variation of shades in this issue.

(Typo J. Ash)

1931–37. *Type* D **7**. *W* **15**. (*a*) *P* 14.

D100 1d. carmine and yellow-green (10.31) .. 8·50 6·50
D102 2d. carmine and yellow-green (19.10.31) .. 8·50 6·50

(*b*) *P* 11

D105 ½d. carmine and yellow-green (4.34) .. 7·50 8·50
D106 1d. carmine and yellow-green (1.33) .. 2·00 50
D107 2d. carmine and yellow-green (29.9.32) .. 2·00 60
D108 3d. carmine and yellow-green (4.37) .. 70·00 50·00
D109 4d. carmine and yellow-green (26.7.34) .. 3·75 2·50
D110 6d. carmine and yellow-green (4.36) .. £350 £200
D111 1s. carmine and yellow-green (8.34) .. 40·00 30·00

D 8

D 9

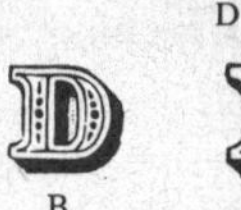
A B C

The differences are found in the middle of the "D"

D

E

Type E. Larger "1" with only three background lines above; hyphen more upright.

(Frame recess. Value typo J. Ash)

1938. *W* **15**. *P* 14½ × 14.

D112 D 8 ½d. carmine and green (A) .. .. 2·00 2·75
D113 1d. carmine and green (A) .. .. 2·00 40
D114 2d. carmine and green (A) .. .. 4·25 1·00
D115 3d. carmine and green (B) .. .. 9·00 5·00
D116 4d. carmine and green (A) .. .. 5·50 60
D117 6d. carmine and green (A) .. .. 25·00 18·00
D118 1s. carmine and green (D) .. .. 27·00 9·00

Shades exist.

1946–57. *Redrawn as Type* C *and* E (1s.). *W* **15**. *P* 14½ × 14.

D119 D 9 ½d. carmine and green (9.56) .. 1·50 2·00
D120 1d. carmine and green (11.1.47) .. 50 35
D121 2d. carmine and green (9.46) .. 2·00 60
D122 3d. carmine and green (25.9.46) .. 2·00 75
D123 4d. carmine and green (11.52) .. 2·75 1·25
D124 5d. carmine and green (12.48) .. 3·50 2·75
D125 6d. carmine and green (9.47) .. 8·00 1·25
D126 7d. carmine and green (26.8.53) .. 3·00 5·50
D127 8d. carmine and green (24.4.57) .. 25·00 18·00
D128 1s. carmine and green (9.47) .. 12·00 1·25
D119/28 .. .. .. *Set of* 10 55·00 30·00

There are many shades in this issue.

D 10

1953 (26 Aug)–**60.** *W* **15**. *P* 14½ × 14.

D129 D 10 1s. carmine & yellow-grn (17.2.54) 6·50 80
a. Carmine and deep green .. 9·00 2·50
D130 2s. carmine and yellow-green .. 18·00 5·50
a. Carmine and deep green .. 35·00 10·00
D131 5s. carmine and green .. 22·00 2·75
a. Carmine and deep green (1960) 22·00 6·00

A new die was introduced for No. D131*a*. This differs from the original in having a distinct gap between the two arms of the "S". On No. D131 these two features are joined.

I

II

Type I. Numeral, "D" and stop, generally unoutlined.

Type II. Clear white line separates numeral, etc. from background.

1958–60. *No wmk. P* 14½ × 14.
D132 **D 9** ½d. carmine and deep green (II) (27.2.58) .. .. 1·75 2·25
D133 1d. carmine and deep green (I) (25.2.58) .. .. 5·50 2·25
a. Type II (1959) 60 45
D134 3d. carmine and deep green (II) (25.5.60) .. .. 4·25 2·50
D135 4d. carmine and deep green (I) (27.2.58) .. .. 6·00 5·00
a. Type II (12.59) .. .. .. 14·00 13·00
D136 5d. carmine and deep green (I) (27.2.58) .. .. 14·00 6·50
a. Type II (10.59) .. .. .. 80·00 60·00
D137 6d. carmine and deep green (II) (25.5.60) .. .. 8·00 3·00
D138 8d. carmine and deep green (II) (25.2.58) .. .. 25·00 25·00
D139 10d. carmine and deep green (II) (9.12.59) .. .. 16·00 7·50
D140 **D 10** 1s. carmine and deep green (8.9.58) 7·50 4·00
a. Deep carmine & deep green (1960) 6·50 3·75
D141 2s. deep carmine and deep green (8.3.60) .. .. 30·00 20·00
D132/41 .. .. *Set of* 10 £100 70·00

Nos. D140*a* and D141. Value tablets are re-engraved and have thicker and sharper printed lines than before.

The use of Postage Due stamps ceased on 13 January 1963.

OFFICIAL STAMPS

Postage stamps perforated "O S" in either large or small letters were used for official purposes. We do not list such varieties.

(O 1)

1931 (4 May). *Optd with Type* O **1**.
O1 **13** 2d. rose-red .. .. 55·00 20·00
O2 3d. blue .. .. £200 60·00

For No. 139 overprinted with Type O **1**, see No. 139*a*.

1932–33. *Optd as Type* O **1**. (*a*) *W* **7**. (i) *P* 13½ × 12½.
O 4 **5a** 2d. golden-scarlet (No. 99*b*) .. .. 10·00 1·25
O 5 4d. yellow-olive (January 1932) 55·00 13·00
(ii) *P* 12
O 6 **1** 6d. chestnut .. .. £100 60·00
(*b*) *W* **15**. (i) *P* 13½ × 12½
O 7 **5a** ½d. orange .. .. 8·00 2·00
a. Overprint inverted £1800 £1000
O 8 1d. sage-green (February 1932) 4·00 1·50
O 9 2d. golden-scarlet (10.2.32) .. 8·00 1·40
a. Overprint inverted .. .. — £1500
O10 3d. ultramarine (March 1933) .. 20·00 14·00
O11 5d. orange-brown .. .. .. 70·00 35·00
(ii) *P* 12
O13 **1** 6d. chestnut .. .. 40·00 30·00
(*c*) *Recess. No wmk. P* 11
O16 **18** 2d. scarlet .. .. 11·00 8·00
O17 3d. blue .. .. 27·00 20·00
O18 **17** 1s. green .. .. 80·00 55·00

Issues of specially overprinted Official stamps became obsolete in 1933 when the various States reverted to the use of stamps with perforated initials.

BRITISH COMMONWEALTH OCCUPATION FORCE (JAPAN)

B.C.O.F. JAPAN 1946 (1)

B.C.O.F JAPAN 1946 (2)

1946 Wrong fount "6" (left pane R. 9/4)

1946 (11 Oct)–**48**. *Stamps of Australia optd as T* **1** (*1d., 3d.*) *or T* **2** (*others*) *at British Commonwealth Command Headquarters, Kure, Japan.*
B1 **27** ½d. orange (No. 179) .. .. .. 2·00 2·00
a. Wrong fount "6" .. .. .. 15·00 15·00
B2 **46** 1d. brown-purple (No. 203) .. .. 1·75 1·75
a. Error. Blue overprint .. .. 80·00 90·00
B3 **31** 3d. purple-brown (No. 187) .. .. 1·75 1·75
B4 **34** 6d. purple-brown (No. 189*a*) (8.5.47) .. 8·50 7·50
a. Wrong fount "6" .. .. .. 45·00 40·00
b. Stop after "JAPAN" (right pane R. 5/5) .. .. 45·00 40·00
B5 **36** 1s. grey-green (No. 191) (8.5.47) .. 14·00 12·00
a. Wrong fount "6" .. .. .. 75·00 65·00
b. Stop after "JAPAN" (right pane R. 5/5) .. .. 75·00 65·00
B6 **1** 2s. maroon (No. 212) (8.5.47) .. .. 45·00 45·00
B7 **38** 5s. claret (No. 176) (8.5.47) £180 £180
a. Thin rough paper (No. 176a) (1948) £200 £225
B1/B7 .. .. *Set of* 7 £225 £225

The ½d., 1d. and 3d. values were first issued on 11 October 1946, and withdrawn two days later, but were re-issued together with the other values on 8 May 1947.

The following values with T **2** opt in the colours given were from proof sheets which, however, were used for postage: ½d. (red), 1d. (red or black) and 3d. (gold, red or black). (*Price from* £450 *un.*)

The use of B.C.O.F. stamps ceased on 12 February 1949.

ALTERED CATALOGUE NUMBERS

Any Catalogue numbers altered from the last edition are shown as a list in the introductory pages.

AUSTRALIAN ANTARCTIC TERRITORY

VALIDITY. All Antarctic Territory stamps are also valid for use in Australia, where they are put on sale for a limited period when first issued.

DATES OF ISSUE. The dates given refer to release dates in Australia. Local release dates are usually later and where known they are given in footnotes.

1 1954 Expedition at Vestfold Hills and Map

(Des. T. Lawrence: adapted by artist of the Printing Branch. Recess)

1957 (27 Mar). *P* 14½.
1 **1** 2s. ultramarine .. .. 5·00 60

Issued Macquarie Island 11.12.57, Davis 6.2.58, Mawson 18.2.58, Wilkes 1.2.59.

2 Members of Shackleton Expedition at South Magnetic Pole, 1909

3 Weazel and Team

1959 (16 Dec). *T* **2** *and designs as T* **3**. *Recess; new values surch typo* (*5d., 8d.*). *P* 14½ (*5d.*), 14½ × 14 (*8d.*) *or* 14 × 14½ (*others*).
2 5d. on 4d. black and sepia .. .. 1·25 15
3 8d. on 7d. black and indigo .. .. .. 1·00 3·75
4 1s. deep green .. .. 6·00 2·75
5 2s. 3d. green .. .. 20·00 8·00

Designs: *Vert*—1s. Dog-team and iceberg; 2s. 3d. Map of Antarctica and Emperor Penguins. Issued Macquarie Island 26.12.59, Davis 30.1.60, Mawson 10.2.60, Wilkes 13.2.60.

6

7 Sir Douglas Mawson (Expedition leader)

1961 (5 July). *Recess. P* 14½.
6 **6** 5d. deep blue .. .. 2·25 15

Issued Macquarie Island 6.12.61, Wilkes 10.1.62, Davis 20.1.62, Mawson 30.1.62.

1961 (18 Oct). 50*th Anniv of* 1911–14 *Australasian Antarctic Expedition. Recess. P* 14½.
7 **7** 5d. myrtle-green .. .. 1·00 15

Issued Macquarie Island 6.12.61, Wilkes 10.1.62, Davis 20.1.62, Mawson 30.1.62.

(New Currency. 100 cents = 1 Australian dollar)

8 Aurora and Camera Dome

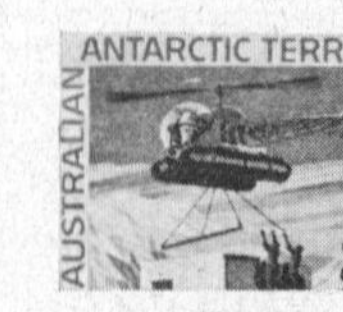

9 Helicopter

(Des J. Mason. Photo)

1966 (28 Sept)–**68**. *T* **8/10** *and similar multicoloured designs. P* 13½.
8 1 c. Type **8** (*shades*) 70 55
9 2 c. Banding penguins (*shades*) .. .. 1·60 70
10 4 c. Ship and iceberg 85 50
11 5 c. Banding elephant seals (25.9.68) .. 2·75 1·50
12 7 c. Measuring snow strata 90 45
13 10 c. Wind gauges .. .. 1·00 60
14 15 c. Weather balloon .. .. .. 3·50 2·50
15 20 c. Type **9** .. .. 5·00 3·00
16 25 c. Radio operator .. .. .. 6·00 5·00
17 50 c. Ice compression tests .. .. 22·00 13·00
18 $1 Parahelion ("mock sun") .. .. 48·00 25·00
8/18 .. .. *Set of* 11 85·00 48·00

The 1 c. to 15 c. are vert as Type **8**; the 25 c., 50 c. and $1 are horiz as Type **9**.

Nos. 8/10 and 12/18 placed on sale locally at Macquarie Island on 11.12.66, Wilkes 9.2.67 and Mawson 16.2.67.

No. 11 issued Macquarie Island 4.12.68, Mawson 13.1.69, Wilkes/Casey 9.2.69 and Davis 20.2.69.

11 Sastrugi (Snow Ridges)

12 Capt. Cook, Sextant and Compass

1971 (23 June). *Tenth Anniv of Antarctic Treaty. T* **11** *and similar horiz design.*
19 6 c. blue and black .. .. 2·50 1·2
20 30 c. multicoloured (Pancake ice) .. .. 8·50 7·0

Issued Macquarie Island 23.11.71, Mawson 27.12.71, Davis 13.1.72 and Casey 17.1.72.

(Des J. Mason. Photo)

1972 (13 Sept). *Bicentenary of Cook's Circumnavigation of Antarctica. T* **12** *and similar horiz design. Multicoloured. P* 13½
21 7 c. Type **12** .. .. 4·00 2·2
22 35 c. Chart and *Resolution* .. .. .. 12·00 9·0

Issued Macquarie Island 19.11.72, Mawson 24.12.72, Davis 3.1.73 and Casey 22.1.73.

13 Plankton

14 Admiral Byrd (expedition leader), Aircraft and Map of South Pole

(Des G. Browning (1, 7, 9, 10, 20 c., $1), R. Honisett (others). Photo)

1973 (5 Aug). *T* **13** *and similar multicoloured designs. P* 13 × 13½ (*horiz*) *or* 13½ × 13 (*vert*).
23 1 c. Type **13** 35 30
24 5 c. Mawson's "Gipsy Moth", 1931 .. .. 60 25
25 7 c. Adélie Penguin .. .. 2·00 55
26 8 c. Rymill's "Fox Moth", 1934–7 .. .. 45 30
27 9 c. Leopard seal (*horiz*) 45 30
28 10 c. Killer whale (*horiz*) .. .. .. 6·50 1·25
a. Buff (overlay on seals) omitted .. ..
29 20 c. Wandering Albatross (*horiz*) .. .. 1·50 90
30 25 c. Wilkins' Lockheed "Vega", 1928 (*horiz*) 1·25 1·00
31 30 c. Ellsworth's Northrop "Gamma", 1935 .. 1·40 1·25
32 35 c. Christensen's Avro "Avian", 1934 (*horiz*) 1·50 1·25
33 50 c. Byrd's "Tri-Motor", 1929 .. .. 1·00 1·25
34 $1 Sperm whale .. .. 3·75 2·75
23/34 .. .. *Set of* 12 19·00 10·00

Issued Macquarie Island 29.11.73, Mawson 30.12.73, Davis 10.1.74 and Casey 31.1.74.

(Des R. Honisett. Litho Asher and Co, Melbourne)

1979 (20 June). 50*th Anniv of First Flight over South Pole. T* **14** *and similar horiz design. Multicoloured. P* 15½.
35 20 c. Type 14 .. .. 50 40
36 55 c. Admiral Byrd, aircraft and Antarctic terrain .. .. 1·25 1·25

Issued Macquarie Island 24.10.79, Davis 3.1.80, Mawson 13.1.80 and Casey 9.2.80.

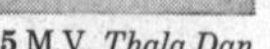

15 M.V. *Thala Dan*

16 Sir Douglas Mawson in Antarctic Terrain

(Des R. Honisett, Litho Asher and Co, Melbourne)

1979 (29 Aug)–**81**. *Ships. Multicoloured designs as T* **15**. *P* 13½ × 13 (*horiz*) *or* 13 × 13½ (*vert*).
37 1 c. S.Y. *Aurora* (*horiz*) (21.5.80) 5 5
38 2 c. R.Y. *Penola* (9.9.81) 5 5
39 5 c. Type **15** 10 5
40 10 c. H.M.S. *Challenger* (*horiz*) (9.9.81) .. 12 12
41 15 c. S.S. *Morning** (bow view) (*horiz*) (21.5.80) 1·25 1·50
42 15 c. S.Y. *Nimrod* (stern view) (*horiz*) (9.9.81) 20 20
43 20 c. R.R.S. *Discovery II* (*horiz*) 20 25
44 22 c. R.Y.S. *Terra Nova* (21.5.80) 30 25
45 25 c. S.S. *Endurance* 35 30
46 30 c. S.S. *Fram* (*horiz*) 40 35
47 35 c. M.S. *Nella Dan* (*horiz*) (21.5.80) 40 40
48 40 c. M.S. *Kista Dan* (9.9.81) 50 45
49 45 c. *L'Astrolabe* (*horiz*) (9.9.81) 60 50
50 50 c. S.S. *Norvegia* (*horiz*) (9.9.81) 60 55
51 55 c. S.Y. *Discovery* 70 60
52 $1 H.M.S. *Resolution* (21.5.80) .. .. 1·25 1·10
37/52 .. .. *Set of* 16 6·25 6·00

*No. 41 is incorrectly inscribed "S.Y. *Nimrod*".

On No. 46 the S.S. *Fram* is shown flying the Icelandic ensign, instead of the Norwegian.

Nos. 37, 41, 44, 47 and 52 issued Macquarie Island 27.10.80, Casey 1.12.80, Mawson 5.12.80 and Davis 11.12.80.
Nos. 38, 40, 42 and 48/50 issued Macquarie Island 21.10.81, Mawson 25.11.81, Davis 11.1.82 and Casey 25.1.82.
Nos. 39, 43, 45/6 and 51 issued Macquarie Island 24.10.79, Davis 3.1.80, Mawson 13.1.80 and Casey 9.2.80.

(Des R. Honisett. Litho Cambec Press, Melbourne)

1982 (5 May). *Birth Centenary of Sir Douglas Mawson (Antarctic explorer). T* **16** *and similar vert design. Multicoloured. P* 14 × 13½.
53 27 c. Type **16** 35 30
54 75 c. Sir Douglas Mawson and map of Australian Antarctic Territory .. .. 1·25 1·40
Issued Macquarie Island 26.10.82, Casey 16.1.83, Davis 10.2.83 and Mawson 2.3.83.

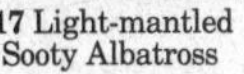

17 Light-mantled Sooty Albatross **18** Antarctic Scientist

(Des R. Honisett. Litho Leigh-Mardon Ltd, Melbourne)

1983 (6 Apr). *Regional Wildlife. T* **17** *and similar vert designs. Multicoloured. P* 14½.
55 27 c. Type **17** 40 40
a. Horiz strip of 5. Nos. 55/9 .. .. 1·75
56 27 c. King Cormorant 40 40
57 27 c. Elephant Seal 40 40
58 27 c. Royal Penguin 40 40
59 27 c. Dove Prion 40 40
Nos. 55/9 were issued together, *se-tenant*, in horizontal strips of five, forming a composite design.
Issued Macquarie Island 21.10.83, Mawson 9.12.83, Casey 1.1.84 and Davis 2.1.84.

(Des R. Honisett. Litho Leigh-Mardon Ltd, Melbourne)

1983 (17 Sept). *12th Antarctic Treaty Consultative Meeting, Canberra. P* 14½.
60 **18** 27 c. multicoloured 30 35

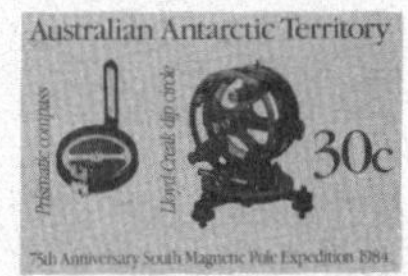

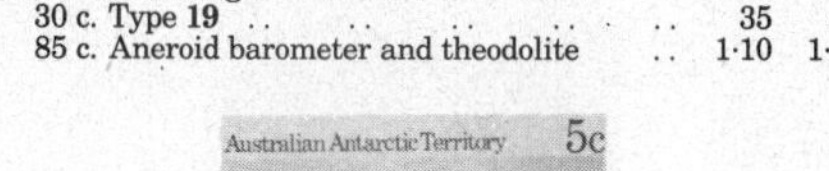

19 Prismatic Compass and Lloyd-Creak Dip Circle

(Des R. Fletcher. Litho Leigh-Mardon Ltd, Melbourne)

1984 (16 Jan). *75th Anniv of Magnetic Pole Expedition. T* **19** *and similar horiz design. Multicoloured. P* 14½.
61 30 c. Type **19** 35 40
62 85 c. Aneroid barometer and theodolite .. 1·10 1·25

20 Dog Team pulling Sledge

(Des G. Emery. Litho Cambec Press, Melbourne)

1984 (8 June). *Antarctic Scenes. T* **20** *and similar horiz designs. Multicoloured. P* 13½ × 14.
63 5 c. Type **20** 5 8
64 25 c. Sea-ice and iceberg 30 35
65 30 c. Mount Coates 35 40
66 75 c. Coastline .. .. 95 1·00
67 85 c. Landing strip .. .. 1·00 1·10

Baghdad
see Iraq

Bahamas

The British Post Office at Nassau was established during the early days of the West Indies packet system, and was certainly operating by 1733. The first known local postmark dates from 1802.
The crowned-circle handstamps Nos. CC1/2 were issued in 1846 and were replaced, for the public mails, by various stamps of Great Britain in 1858.
Local mail deliveries were rudimentary until 1859 when Nos. 1/2 were issued by the colonial authorities for interisland mails. Examples used for this purpose are usually cancelled in manuscript or with a "27" postmark. The "local" 1d. stamp became valid for overseas mails in May, 1860, when the colonial authorities took over this service from the British G.P.O.
For illustrations of the handstamp and postmark types see BRITISH POST OFFICES ABROAD notes, following GREAT BRITAIN.

NASSAU

CROWNED-CIRCLE HANDSTAMPS

CC1 CC1 BAHAMAS (Nassau) (1.6.1846) (R.)
Price on cover £1400
CC2 **CC2** BAHAMAS (Nassau) (1846)

Nos. CC1/2 were later struck in black and used as Official Paid marks between 1899 and 1935. Handstamps as Type CC **3**, struck in black, were used for the same purpose between 1933 and 1953, but it is believed that these were never employed during the pre-stamp period. *Price on cover from* £30.

Stamps of GREAT BRITAIN *cancelled* "A 05" *as Type* **2**.

1858 *to* **1860.**
Z1 1d. rose-red (1857), *perf* 14 .. .. £900
Z2 2d. blue (1858) (Plate Nos. 7, 8) £1200
Z3 4d. rose (1857) £400
Z4 6d. lilac (1856) £400
Z5 1s. green (1856) £1700

PRICES FOR STAMPS ON COVER TO 1945	
Nos. 1/44	*from* × 3
Nos. 45/57	*from* × 4
Nos. 58/99	*from* × 2
Nos. 100/36	*from* × 3
Nos. 137/8	*from* × 10
Nos. 139/44	*from* × 2
No. 145	*from* × 4
Nos. 146/8	*from* × 6
Nos. 149/57	*from* × 3
Nos. 158/60	*from* × 4
No. 161	*from* × 8
Nos. 162/75	*from* × 5
No. S1	*from* × 30
Nos. S2/3	*from* × 20

CROWN COLONY

1

2

3

(Eng and recess P.B.)

1859 (10 June). *No wmk. Imperf.* (a) *Thick paper.*
1 **1** 1d. reddish lake £4500 £2250
a. Brown-lake £2250 £1800
(b) *Thin paper*
2 **1** 1d. dull lake .. .. 30·00 £1200
Collectors are warned against false postmarks upon the remainder stamps of 1d., imperf, on thin paper.

1860 (Oct). *No wmk. Clean-cut perf* 14 *to* 16.
3 **1** 1d. lake £1100 £650

1861 (June–Dec). *No wmk.* (a) *Rough perf* 14 *to* 16.
4 **1** 1d. lake £750 £300
5 **2** 4d. dull rose (Dec, 1861) £1400 £325
a. Imperf between (pair) £6000
6 6d. grey-lilac (Dec, 1861) £2250 £400
a. Pale dull lilac £2250 £400
(b) *P* 11 *to* 12½
7 **1** 1d. lake £2000
No. 7 was not sent out to the Colony. It is also known part perforated.

(Recess D.L.R.)

1862. *No wmk.** (a) *P* 11½, 12.
8 **1** 1d. carmine-lake £500 £110
9 1d. lake £475 £120
10 **2** 4d. dull rose £1900 £200
11 6d. lavender-grey £2000 £300

(b) *P* 11½, 12, *compound with* 11
12 **1** 1d. carmine-lake £1300 £850
13 1d. lake £1300 £850
14 **2** 4d. dull rose £7500 £1700
15 6d. lavender-grey £8500 £1300

(c) *P* 13
16 **1** 1d. lake £500 £140
17 1d. brown-lake £500 £120
18 **2** 4d. dull rose £2000 £300
19 6d. lavender-grey £2250 £275
a. Lilac £2250 £500
*Stamps exist with part of papermaker's sheet wmk ("T. H. SAUNDERS" and date).

(T **3** Typo D.L.R.)

1863–80. *Wmk Crown CC.* (a) *P* 12½.
20 **1** 1d. brown-lake .. .. 80·00 80·00
21 1d. carmine-lake .. .. 85·00 85·00
22 1d. carmine-lake (aniline) .. .. 85·00 85·00
23 1d. rose-red .. .. 50·00 60·00
24 1d. red .. .. 55·00 60·00
25 1d. vermilion .. .. 55·00 60·00
26 **2** 4d. dull rose .. .. £350 85·00
27 4d. bright rose .. .. £120 75·00
28 4d. brownish rose £375 £100
28*a* 6d. rose-lilac £3250
29 6d. lilac (*shades*) .. .. .. £250 75·00
30 6d. deep violet .. .. £160 75·00
31 6d. violet (aniline) .. .. .. £225 90·00
32 **3** 1s. green (1865) £1600 £300
No. 28*a*, believed to be the shade of the first printing only, is a very rare stamp, not to be confused with No. 29.

(b) *P* 14
33 **1** 1d. scarlet-vermilion .. .. .. 35·00 25·00
34 1d. scarlet usual (or scarlet-vermilion) (aniline) .. .. £1400 †
35 **2** 4d. bright rose .. .. £600 80·00
36 4d. dull rose .. .. £1500 80·00
37 4d. rose-lake .. .. £600 80·00
38 **3** 1s. dark green (1863) .. .. .. 90·00 35·00
39 1s. green (thick paper) (1880?) .. .. 6·00 7·00
No. 34 is not known postally used, although manuscript fiscal cancellations are recorded on this shade.

1882 (March). *Wmk Crown CA.* (a) *P* 12.
40 **1** 1d. scarlet-vermilion .. .. .. 35·00 25·00
41 **2** 4d. rose .. .. £550 80·00

(b) *P* 14
42 **1** 1d. scarlet-vermilion .. .. .. £250 80·00
43 **2** 4d. rose .. .. £800 85·00
44 **3** 1s. green .. .. 30·00 26·00
See also No. 55.

FOURPENCE
(4)

5

Malformed "E"

(4) **5** Malformed "E"

1883. *No. 30 surch with T* **4**.
45 **2** 4d. on 6d. deep violet £500 £275
a. Surch inverted £2500 £2000
The surcharge is also found placed diagonally and in various other positions.
Caution is needed in buying Nos. 45 and 45a.

(Typo D.L.R.)

1884–98. *Wmk Crown CA. P* 14.
47 **5** 1d. pale rose .. .. 16·00 12·00
48 1d. carmine-rose .. .. 7·00 3·50
49 1d. bright carmine (aniline) .. .. 6·00 8·00
50 2½d. dull blue .. .. 20·00 20·00
51 2½d. blue .. .. 20·00 9·00
52 2½d. ultramarine .. .. 7·50 6·00
53 4d. deep yellow .. .. 10·00 8·00
54 6d. mauve .. .. 9·50 13·00
a. Malformed "E" (R.6/6) .. .. 80·00
55 **3** 1s. blue-green (1898) .. .. .. 32·00 22·00
56 **5** 5s. sage-green .. .. 65·00 65·00
57 £1 Venetian red £425 £325
47/57 .. .. *Set of* 7 £500 £400
50 & 54 Optd "Specimen" .. .. *Set of* 2 £140

6 Queen's Staircase, Nassau

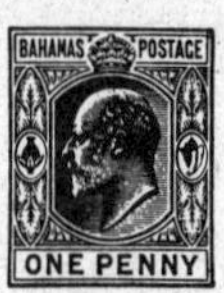

7

8

(Recess D.L.R.)

1901–10. *P* 14. (a) *Wmk Crown CC* (Sept 1901).
58 **6** 1d. black and red (Optd S. £35) .. .. 5·50 6·50
(b) *Wmk Mult Crown CA* (1910)
59 **6** 1d. black and red .. .. 6·50 4·50
For later shades, see Nos. 93/4 and 122.

(Typo D.L.R.)

1902 (Dec). *Wmk Crown CA. P* 14.
60 **7** 1d. carmine .. .. 3·50 2·00
61 2½d. ultramarine .. .. 7·50 5·50
62 4d. orange .. .. 11·00 16·00
63 4d. deep yellow .. .. 11·00 17·00

64 **7** 6d. brown .. .. 11·00 14·00
a. Malformed "E" (R.6/6) .. .. 95·00
65 1s. grey-black and carmine .. .. 13·00 17·00
66 1s. brownish grey and carmine .. 13·00 17·00
67 5s. dull purple and blue .. .. 55·00 60·00
68 £1 green and black £325 £375
60/8 .. .. *Set of* 7 £375 £450
60/68 Optd "Specimen" .. .. *Set of* 7 £500

1903. *Wmk Crown CC. P* 14.
69 **6** 5d. black and orange .. .. .. 15·00 28·00
70 2s. black and blue .. .. .. 17·00 35·00
71 3s. black and green .. .. .. 22·00 40·00
69/71 Optd "Specimen" .. *Set of* 3 £120

1906–11. *Wmk Mult Crown CA. P* 14.
72 **7** ½d. pale green (Optd S. £50) .. .. 6·00 1·75
73 1d. carmine-rose .. .. .. 7·00 1·40
74 2½d. ultramarine (1907) .. .. 24·00 30·00
75 6d. bistre-brown (1911) .. .. 70·00 £100
a. Malformed "E" (R.6/6) £450

(Typo D.L.R.)

1912–19. *Wmk Mult Crown CA. P* 14.
76 **8** ½d. green, **O** .. .. 80 1·25
77 ½d. yellow-green, **O** .. .. .. 1·50 1·25
78 1d. carmine (aniline), **O** 80 50
79 1d. deep rose, **O** .. .. .. 2·50 1·60
80 1d. rose, **O** .. .. 5·50 2·50
81 2d. grey, **O** (1919) .. .. .. 2·50 3·00
82 2½d. ultramarine, **O** .. .. .. 5·00 8·00
83 2½d. deep dull blue, **O** .. .. 8·50 12·00
84 4d. orange-yellow, **O** .. .. .. 5·00 10·00
85 4d. yellow, **O** .. .. 2·50 7·50
86 6d. bistre-brown, **O** .. .. .. 3·25 7·00
a. Malformed "E" (R.6/6) .. .. 32·00
87 1s. grey-black and carmine, **C** .. 3·50 7·50
88 1s. jet-black and carmine, **C** .. 9·50 15·00
89 5s. dull purple and blue, **C** .. 24·00 42·00
90 5s. pale dull purple and deep blue, **C** .. 32·00 42·00
91 £1 dull green and black, **C** £180 £225
92 £1 green and black, **C** £200 £225
76/91 .. .. *Set of* 9 £200 £250
76/91 Optd "Specimen" .. *Set of* 9 £425

1916–19. *Wmk Mult Crown CA. P* 14.
93 **6** 1d. grey-black and scarlet (1916) .. 4·50 6·00
94 1d. grey-black and deep carmine-red (1919) .. .. 4·25 6·50
95 3d. purple/*yellow* (*thin*) (1917) .. 11·00 13·00
96 3d. reddish purple/*buff* (*thick*) (1.19) .. 3·00 6·00
97 5d. black and mauve (18.5.17) .. 3·00 10·00
98 2s. black and blue (11.16) .. .. 20·00 30·00
99 3s. black and green (8.17) .. .. 38·00 48·00
95 & 97 Optd "Specimen" .. *Set of* 2 70·00

1.1.17. (9)   WAR TAX (10)

1917 (18 May). *No.* 59 *optd with T* **9**.
100 **6** 1d. black and red (R.) (Optd S. £60) .. 45 1·10
a. Long stroke to "7" .. .. 50·00 60·00
The above stamps were to have been on sale on 1 January 1917, but owing to delay in shipment they were not issued till May 1917.

1918 (21 Feb). *Optd at Nassau with T* **10**.
101 **8** ½d. green .. .. 4·50 6·00
a. Opt double £600 £600
b. Opt inverted £600
102 1d. carmine .. .. 1·25 1·75
a. Opt double £600 £600
b. Opt inverted £600
103 **6** 3d. purple/*yellow* .. .. .. 4·50 5·00
a. Opt double £600 £600
b. Opt inverted £700 £700
104 **8** 1s. grey-black and carmine .. .. 60·00 90·00
a. Opt double £1700

1918 (10 July). *Wmk Mult Crown CA. Optd with T* **10**.
105 **6** 1d. black and red .. .. .. 3·25 4·50
a. Opt double, one inverted £800
b. Opt double £850
c. Opt inverted £850 £900
No. 105a is from a sheet in which the top row was normal and the other four showed this error. No. 105 was on sale for ten days.

WAR TAX (11)   WAR TAX (12)   WAR CHARITY 3.6.18. (13)

1918 (1 June–20 July). *Optd in London with T* **11** *or* **12** (3d.).
106 **8** ½d. green .. .. 40 1·40
107 1d. carmine .. .. 40 1·25
a. Wmk sideways £550
108 **6** 3d. purple/*yellow* (20 July) .. .. 80 2·75
109 **8** 1s. grey-black and carmine (R.) .. 1·75 3·25
106/9 Optd "Specimen" .. *Set of* 4 £150

1919 (21 Mar). *Colour changed. Wmk Mult Crown CA. P* 14.
110 **6** 3d. black and brown (Optd S. £60) .. 1·50 6·50

1919 (21 Mar). *No.* 110 *optd with T* **12**.
111 **6** 3d. black and brown (Optd S. £60) .. 1·40 5·50

1919 (1 Jan). *No.* 59 *optd with T* **13**.
112 **6** 1d. black and red (R.) (Optd S. £60) .. 60 2·75
a. Opt double £1200
The date is that originally fixed for the issue of the stamp. The year 1918 was also the bicentenary of the appointment of the first Royal governor.

WAR TAX (14)   WAR TAX (15)

1919 (14 July). (*a*) *Optd with T* 14.
113 **8** ½d. green (R.) .. .. 40 1·50
114 1d. carmine .. .. 40 1·50
115 1s. grey-black and carmine (R.) .. 4·75 12·00
(*b*) *No.* 110 *optd with T* **15**
116 **6** 3d. black and brown .. .. .. 1·10 5·00
113/16 Optd "Specimen" .. .. *Set of* 4 £130

16   17

(Recess D.L.R.)

1920 (1 Mar). *Peace Celebration. Wmk Mult Crown CA* (*sideways*). *P* 14.
117 **16** ½d. green .. .. 70 3·00
118 1d. carmine .. .. 3·50 2·75
119 2d. slate-grey .. .. 4·50 7·00
120 3d. deep brown .. .. 4·50 12·00
121 1s. deep myrtle-green .. .. 35·00 48·00
117/21 Optd "Specimen" .. *Set of* 5 £200

1921–29. *Wmk Mult Script CA. P* 14. (*a*) *Staircase type.*
122 **6** 1d. grey and rose-red (29.3.21) .. 2·25 3·25
122*a* 5d. black and purple (1929) .. 6·00 14·00
123 2s. black and blue (1922) .. .. 20·00 30·00
123*a* 3s. black and green (1924) .. 38·00 48·00
122/123*a* Optd/Perf "Specimen" .. *Set of* 4 £160
(*b*) *King George V type*
124 **8** ½d. green, **O** (1924) 25 50
125 1d. carmine, **O** (8.9.21) 45 40
125*a* 2d. grey, **O** (1927) .. .. .. 90 2·75
126 2½d. ultramarine, **O** (1922) .. .. 1·00 2·75
127 4d. orange-yellow, **O** (1924) .. 1·50 5·50
128 6d. bistre-brown, **O** (1922) .. .. 1·25 5·00
a. Malformed "E" (R.6/6) .. .. 35·00
129 1s. black and carmine, **C** (1926) .. 4·00 10·00
130 5s. dull purple and blue, **C** (1924) .. 30·00 42·00
131 £1 green and black, **C** (1926) .. £200 £250
124/131 .. .. *Set of* 9 £225 £275
124/31 Optd "Specimen" .. *Set of* 9 £400

(Recess B. W.)

1930 (2 Jan). *Tercentenary of Colony. Wmk Mult Script CA. P* 12.
132 **17** 1d. black and scarlet .. .. 2·50 4·00
133 3d. black and deep brown .. .. 6·50 12·00
134 5d. black and deep purple .. .. 7·00 13·00
135 2s. black and deep blue .. .. 35·00 55·00
136 3s. black and green .. .. .. 50·00 75·00
132/6 Perf "Specimen" .. *Set of* 5 £200

18

(Recess B.W.)

1931. *Wmk Mult Script CA. P* 12.
137 **18** 2s. black and deep blue .. .. 1·25 80
a. Slate-purple and deep blue .. 16·00 17·00
138 3s. black and green .. .. .. 1·25 1·40
a. Slate-purple and green .. .. 17·00 16·00
137/8 Perf "Specimen" .. .. *Set of* 2 50·00

1931–7. *Wmk Mult Script CA. P* 14.
139 **8** 1½d. red-brown, **O** (1934) .. .. 95 2·00
140 3d. purple/*pale yellow*, **C** (1931) .. 6·00 12·00
a. *Purple/orange-yellow*, **C** (1937) .. 6·50 15·00
139/40 Perf "Specimen" .. *Set of* 2 45·00

1935 (6 May). *Silver Jubilee. As Nos.* 91/4 *of Antigua. P* 13½ × 14.
141 1½d. deep blue and carmine 70 70
f. Dash by turret .. .. .. 25·00
142 2½d. brown and deep blue .. .. 2·50 2·75
e. Horiz line from turret .. .. 25·00
143 6d. light blue and olive-green .. .. 6·00 9·00
144 1s. slate and purple .. .. .. 10·00 15·00
141/4 Perf "Specimen" .. *Set of* 4 42·00
For illustration of the plate variety see Omnibus section following Zululand.

19 Greater Flamingos in flight   **20** King George VI

(Recess Waterlow)

1935 (22 May). *Wmk Mult Script CA. P* 12½.
145 **19** 8d. ultramarine and scarlet .. .. 6·00 6·0
145 Perf "Specimen" .. .. 40·00

1937 (12 May). *Coronation. As Nos.* 13/15 *of Aden. P* 14.
146 ½d. green 35 40
147 1½d. yellow-brown 60 80
148 2½d. bright blue .. .. 1·50 1·50
146/8 Perf "Specimen" .. .. *Set of* 3 35·00

(Typo D.L.R.)

1938–52. *Wmk Mult Script CA. P* 14.
149 **20** ½d. bluish green (11.3.38) 30 60
a. Myrtle-green (12.46) 75 85
149*b* ½d. brown-purple (18.2.52) .. .. 30 2·75
ba. Error. Crown missing £1100
bb. Error. St. Edward's Crown .. £650
150 1d. carmine (11.3.38) .. .. .. 8·00 6·00
150*a* 1d. grey (17.9.41) 25 30
151 1½d. red-brown (19.4.38) 55 55
a. Pale red-brown (Apr 1948) .. 80 90
152 2d. grey (19.4.38) .. .. .. 19·00 22·00
152*a* 2d. scarlet (17.9.41) 30 70
ab. "TWO PENCE" printed double .. † £1600
152*b* 2d. green (1.5.51) .. .. .. 70 1·40
153 2½d. blue (11.3.38) .. .. .. 3·00 4·50
153*a* 2½d. violet (1943) 35 70
154 3d. violet (19.4.38) .. .. .. 8·00 12·00
154*a* 3d. blue (1943) 30 90
154*b* 3d. scarlet (1.2.52) .. .. .. 80 4·50
154*c* 10d. yellow-orange (18.11.46) .. .. 1·00 55
155 1s. black and carmine, **CO** (15.9.38) .. 1·00 70
156 5s. lilac and blue, **C** (19.4.38) .. 90·00 90·00
a. Purple and blue, **O** (1942) .. 30·00 15·00
b. Deep purple & br bl, **C** (1948) .. 30·00 15·00
157 £1 green and black, **C** (15.9.38) .. £100 £110
a. Blue-green and black, **O** (5.43) .. 55·00 50·00
149/157*a* .. .. *Set of* 17 £120 £110
149/57 Perf "Specimen" .. .. *Set of* 14 £350
No. 149bb occurs on a row in the watermark in which the crowns and letters "C A" alternate.
The ordinary paper of Nos. 155/7 is thick, smooth and opaque, and first appeared in 1942 as a substitute for chalk-surfaced paper.

21 Sea Garden, Nassau   **22** Fort Charlotte

23 Greater Flamingos in Flight

(Recess Waterlow)

1938 (1 July). *Wmk Mult Script CA. P* 12½.
158 **21** 4d. light blue and red-orange 80 55
159 **22** 6d. olive-green and light blue 60 35
160 **23** 8d. ultramarine and scarlet .. .. 85 1·25
158/60 Perf "Specimen" .. .. *Set of* 3 45·00

3d. (24)   1492 LANDFALL OF COLUMBUS 1942 (25)

1940 (28 Nov). *No.* 153 *surcharged with T* **24**.
161 **20** 3d. on 2½d. blue 15 70

1942 (12 Oct). 450*th Anniv of Landing of Columbus in New World. Optd locally with T* **25**.
162 **20** ½d. bluish green 20 60
163 1d. grey 20 60
164 1½d. red-brown 25 50
165 2d. scarlet 25 65
166 2½d. blue 25 65
167 3d. blue 25 65
168 **21** 4d. light blue and red-orange 50 90
a. "COIUMBUS" £170 £150
169 **22** 6d. olive-green and light blue .. .. 55 1·00
a. "COIUMBUS" £170 £150
170 **23** 8d. ultramarine and scarlet .. .. 55 1·25
a. "COIUMBUS" £300 £300
171 **20** 1s. black and carmine, **CO** .. .. 55 1·25

172 18 2s. black and deep blue 6·50 10·00
a. *Slate-purple and deep blue* 12·00 15·00
173 3s. black and green 16·00 22·00
a. *Slate-purple and green* 4·25 10·00
174 20 5s. purple and blue, CO 5·50 11·00
175 £1 green and black, C 30·00 38·00
a. *Blue-green and black, O* 32·00 38·00
162/175 *Set of* 14 42·00 65·00
162/75 Perf "Specimen" *Set of* 14 £300

The "COIUMBUS" error (Nos. 168a, 169a, 170a) occurs on R.5/2.

1946 (11 Nov). *Victory. As Nos.* 28/9 *of Aden.*
176 1½d. brown 12 20
177 3d. blue 20 25
176/7 Perf "Specimen" *Set of* 2 30·00

26 Infant Welfare Clinic

(Recess C.B.N.)

1948 (11 Oct). *Tercentenary of Settlement of Island of Eleuthera. T* **26** *and similar horiz designs. P* 12.
178 ½d. orange 20 60
179 1d. sage-green 20 40
180 1½d. yellow 25 80
181 2d. scarlet 30 60
182 2½d. brown-lake 40 85
183 3d. ultramarine 50 85
184 4d. black 50 1·25
185 6d. emerald-green 80 1·25
186 8d. violet 45 1·00
187 10d. carmine 45 55
188 1s. sepia 70 60
189 2s. magenta 7·00 12·00
190 3s. blue 8·00 12·00
191 5s. mauve 5·50 9·50
192 10s. grey 5·50 14·00
193 £1 vermilion 10·00 20·00
178/93 *Set of* 16 35·00 65·00

Designs:—1d. Agriculture (combine harvester); 1½d. Sisal; 2d. Straw work; 2½d. Dairy farm; 3d. Fishing fleet; 4d. Island settlement; 6d. Tuna fishing; 8d. Paradise Beach; 10d. Modern hotels; 1s. Yacht racing; 2s. Water sports (skiing); 3s. Shipbuilding; 5s. Transportation; 10s. Salt production; £1, Parliament Buildings.

1948 (1 Dec). *Royal Silver Wedding. As Nos.* 30/1 *of Aden.*
194 1½d. red-brown 15 35
195 £1 slate-green 35·00 48·00

1949 (10 Oct). *75th Anniv of Universal Postal Union. As Nos.* 114/17 *of Antigua.*
196 2½d. violet 35 60
197 3d. deep blue 1·00 1·25
198 6d. greenish blue 1·40 2·50
199 1s. carmine 2·25 3·75

1953 (3 June). *Coronation. As No.* 47 *of Aden.*
200 6d. black and pale blue 25 70

42 Infant Welfare Clinic **43** Queen Elizabeth II

(Recess B.W.)

1954 (1 Jan). *Designs previously used for King George VI issue, but with portrait of Queen Elizabeth II as in T* **42**, *and commemorative inscr omitted. Wmk Mult Script CA. P* 11 × 11½.
201 ½d. black and red-orange 12 45
202 1d. olive-green and brown 12 10
203 1½d. blue and black 12 45
204 2d. yellow-brown and myrtle-green (*shades*) 15 15
205 3d. black and carmine-red 25 25
206 4d. turquoise-green and deep reddish purple (*shades*) 30 25
207 5d. red-brown and deep bright blue 50 2·25
208 6d. light blue and black 30 20
209 8d. black and reddish lilac (*shades*) 40 30
210 10d. black and ultramarine (*shades*) 40 10
211 1s. ultramarine and olive-brown (*shades*) 65 15
212 2s. orange-brown and black (*shades*) 2·25 1·50
213 2s. 6d. black and deep blue 3·25 2·00
214 5s. bright emerald and orange (*shades*) 7·00 2·25
215 10s. black and slate-black 9·00 5·50
216 £1 slate-black and violet 18·00 14·00
201/216 *Set of* 16 38·00 27·00

Designs:—1d. Agriculture (combine harvester); 1½d. Island settlement; 2d. Straw work; 3d. Fishing fleet; 4d. Water sports (skiing); 5d. Dairy farm; 6d. Transportation; 8d. Paradise Beach; 10d. Modern hotels; 1s. Yacht racing; 2s. Sisal; 2s. 6d. Shipbuilding; 5s. Tuna fishing; 10s. Salt production; £1 Parliament Buildings.

See also No. 246.

(Recess Waterlow)

1959 (10 June). *Centenary of First Bahamas Postage Stamp. W w* **12**. *P* 13½.
217 43 1d. black and scarlet 10 10
218 2d. black and blue-green 15 30
219 6d. black and blue 20 20
220 10d. black and chocolate 25 45

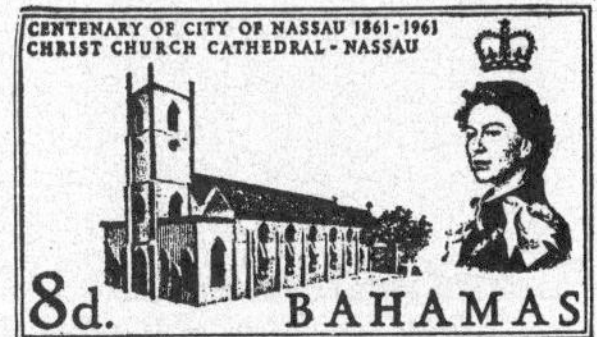

44 Christ Church Cathedral

(Photo Enschedé)

1962 (30 Jan). *Nassau Centenary. T* **44** *and similar horiz design. P* 14 × 13.
221 8d. green 25 35
222 10d. bluish violet 25 30

Design:—10d. Nassau Public Library.

1963 (4 June). *Freedom from Hunger. As No.* 76 *of Aden.*
223 8d. sepia 90 55
a. Name and value omitted £700

**BAHAMAS TALKS
1962**
(46)

**NEW CONSTITUTION
1964**
(47)

1963 (15 July). *Bahamas Talks,* 1962. *Nos.* 209/10 *optd with T* **46**.
224 8d. black and reddish lilac 50 60
225 10d. black and deep ultramarine 60 80

1963 (2 Sept). *Red Cross Centenary. As Nos.* 147/8 *of Antigua.*
226 1d. red and black 30 25
227 10d. red and blue 2·50 2·50

SELF GOVERNMENT

1964 (7 Jan). *New Constitution. As Nos.* 201/16 *but W w* **12**, *optd with T* **47**, *by B.W.*
228 ½d. black and red-orange 10 25
229 1d. olive-green and brown 10 15
230 1½d. blue and black 12 30
231 2d. yellow-brown and deep myrtle-green 15 20
232 3d. black and carmine-red 20 30
233 4d. turquoise-blue and deep reddish purple 25 45
234 5d. red-brown and deep bright blue 25 55
235 6d. light blue and black 30 30
236 8d. black and reddish lilac 40 60
237 10d. black and deep ultramarine 45 45
238 1s. ultramarine and olive-brown 70 55
239 2s. chestnut and black 2·00 2·75
240 2s. 6d. black and deep blue 2·50 3·75
241 5s. bright emerald and orange 5·60 6·00
242 10s. black and slate black 9·50 11·00
243 £1 slate-black and violet 16·00 19·00
228/243 *Set of* 16 35·00 42·00

1964 (23 April). *400th Birth Anniv of William Shakespeare. As No.* 164 *of Antigua.*
244 6d. turquoise 20 20

(48)

1964 (1 Oct). *Olympic Games, Tokyo. As No.* 211 *but W w* **12**, *surch with T* **48**.
245 8d. on 1s. ultramarine and olive-brown 20 20

1964 (6 Oct). *As No.* 204, *but wmk w* **12**.
246 2d. yellow-brown and deep myrtle-green 40 55

49 Colony's Badge (64)

(Queen's portrait by Anthony Buckley. Litho and recess (portrait and "BAHAMAS") B.W.)

1965 (7 Jan–14 Sept). *Horiz designs as T* **49**. *W w* **12**. *P* 13½.
247 ½d. multicoloured 12 20
248 1d. slate, light blue and orange 15 8
249 1½d. rose-red, green and brown 15 30
250 2d. slate, green and turquoise-blue 15 10
251 3d. red, light blue and purple 40 25
252 4d. green, blue and orange-brown 55 70
253 6d. dull green, light blue and rose 30 15
254 8d. reddish purple, light blue & bronze-green 70 60
255 10d. orange-brown, green and violet 30 10
256 1s. red, yellow, turquoise-blue & deep emer 80 10
a. *Red, yellow, dull blue & emer* (14.9.65) 60 10
257 2s. brown, light blue and emerald 1·75 1·25
258 2s. 6d. yellow-olive, blue and carmine 2·50 1·75
259 5s. orange-brown, ultramarine and green 3·25 2·00
260 10s. rose, blue and chocolate 6·50 4·75
261 £1 chestnut, blue and rose-red 9·50 8·00
247/261 *Set of* 15 24·00 18·00

Designs:—1d. Out Island Regatta; 1½d. Hospital; 2d. High School; 3d. Greater Flamingo; 4d. R.M.S. *Queen Elizabeth*; 6d. "Development"; 8d. Yachting; 10d. Public Square; 1s. Sea Garden; 2s. Old Cannons at Fort Charlotte; 2s. 6d. Sikorsky "S-38" seaplane, 1929 and Boeing "707" airliner; 5s. Williamson film project, 1914 and Undersea Post Office, 1939; 10s. Conch shell; £1, Columbus' flagship.

1965 (17 May). *I.T.U. Centenary. As Nos.* 166/7 *of Antigua.*
262 1d. light emerald and orange 20 15
263 2s. purple and yellow-olive 80 1·00

1965 (12 July). *No.* 254 *surch with T* **64**.
264 9d. on 8d. reddish purple, light blue and bronze-green 25 20

1965 (25 Oct). *International Co-operation Year. As Nos.* 168/9 *of Antigua.*
265 ½d. reddish purple and turquoise-green 5 10
266 1s. deep bluish green and lavender 45 45

1966 (24 Jan). *Churchill Commemoration. As Nos.* 170/3 *of Antigua.*
267 ½d. new blue 10 10
268 2d. deep green 55 30
269 10d. brown 1·00 85
270 1s. bluish violet 1·10 1·25

1966 (4 Feb). *Royal Visit. As Nos.* 174/5 *of Antigua, but inscr* "to the Caribbean" *omitted.*
271 6d. black and ultramarine 90 60
272 1s. black and magenta 1.75 1.50

(New Currency. 100 cents = 1 dollar.)

(65) (66)

1966 (25 May). *Decimal Currency. Nos.* 247/61 *variously surch as T* **65/6**, *by B.W.*
273 1 c. on ½d. multicoloured 5 5
274 2 c. on 1d. slate, light blue and orange 8 5
275 3 c. on 2d. slate, green and turquoise-blue 8 8
276 4 c. on 3d. red, light blue and purple 15 10
277 5 c. on 4d. green, blue and orange-brown 15 12
a. Surch omitted (vert strip of 10) £2750
278 8 c. on 6d. dull green, light blue and rose 20 20
279 10 c. on 8d. reddish purple, light blue and bronze-green 30 25
280 11 c. on 1½d. rose-red, green and brown 20 15
281 12 c. on 10d. orange-brown, green and violet 20 10
282 15 c. on 1s. multicoloured 40 15
283 22 c. on 2s. brown, light blue and emerald 90 80
284 50 c. on 2s. 6d. yellow-olive, blue and carmine 1·40 1·25
285 $1 on 5s. orange-brown, ultram & green 2·50 2·00
286 $2 on 10s. rose, blue and chocolate 4·75 3·75
287 $3 on £1 chestnut, blue and rose-red 8·00 7·50
273/287 *Set of* 15 17·00 15·00

The above were made on new printings some of which vary slightly in shade and in No. 273 the shield appears as vermilion and green instead of carmine and blue-green due to a different combination of the printing colours.

No. 277a. One sheet exists and the stamp can be distinguished from No. 252 when in a vertical strip of ten as these were printed in sheets of 100 whereas No. 252 was printed in sheets of 60 (six rows of ten across).

1966 (1 July). *World Cup Football Championships. As Nos.* 176/7 *of Antigua.*
288 8 c. violet, yellow-green, lake & yell-brown 25 20
289 15 c. chocolate, blue-green, lake & yell-brown 35 30

1966 (20 Sept). *Inauguration of W.H.O. Headquarters, Geneva. As Nos.* 178/9 *of Antigua.*
290 11 c. black, yellow-green and light blue 30 20
291 15 c. black, light purple and yellow-brown 35 25

1966 (1 Dec). *20th Anniv of U.N.E.S.C.O. As Nos.* 196/8 *of Antigua.*
292 3 c. slate-violet, red, yellow and orange 12 10
293 15 c. orange-yellow, violet and deep olive 45 30
294 $1 black, bright purple and orange 2·50 2·50

67 *Oceanic*

68 Conch Shell

(Portrait by Anthony Buckley. Litho and recess (portrait, "BAHAMAS" and value), B.W.)

1967 (25 May)–**71**. *T* **67/8** *or designs as Nos.* 247/51, 253/9 *and* 261 *but values in decimal currency and colours changed. Toned paper. W w* **12**. *P* 13½.
295 1 c. multicoloured (as ½d.) 10 20
a. Whiter paper (1970) 20 30
296 2 c. slate, light blue & deep emerald (as 1d.) 15 10
a. Whiter paper (1970) 50 50

297 3 c. slate, green and violet (as 2d.) 12 10
a. Whiter paper (1970) . . . . 26·00 3·00
298 4 c. red, light blue and ultramarine (as 3d.) 80 12
a. Whiter paper (9.70*) . . . . . . 9·00 9·00
299 5 c. black, greenish blue and purple . . 60 20
a. Whiter paper (1970) 95 80
300 8 c. dull green, light blue and sepia (as 6d.) 45 30
a. Whiter paper (1970) . . . . . . 70·00 14·00
301 10 c. reddish pur, greenish bl & carm (as 8d.) 50 15
a. Whiter paper (1970) 80 80
302 11 c. rose-red, green and blue (as 1½d.) . . 40 15
a. Whiter paper (1970) 80 80
303 12 c. orange-brown, green and olive (as 10d.) 40 15
a. Whiter paper (4.71) . . . . . . 12·00 18·00
304 15 c. red, yellow, turquoise-bl & carm (as 1s.) 65 15
a. Whiter paper (1970) . . . . . . £130 20·00
305 22 c. brown, new blue and rose-red (as 2s.) . . 1·25 1·00
a. Whiter paper (1970) . . . . . . 2·50 2·00
306 50 c. yellow-olive, new bl & emer (as 2s. 6d.) 2·25 1·25
a. Whiter paper (1970) . . . . . . 3·00 2·50
307 $1 orange-brown, ultram & slate-pur (as 5s.) 3·50 1·50
a. Whiter paper (4.71) . . . . . . 19·00 35·00
308 $2 multicoloured . . . . 6·50 3·00
a. Whiter paper (4.71) . . . . . . 30·00 45·00
309 $3 chestnut, new blue and purple (as £1) . . 7·50 5·50
a. Whiter paper (4.71) . . . . . . 35·00 45·00
295/309 . . . . *Set of* 15 22·00 12·00
295a/309a . . . . *Set of* 15 (whiter paper) £300 £180

*This is the earliest known date recorded in the Bahamas.

The 3 c. has the value at right instead of at left as on No. 250.

The 1970–71 printings on whiter paper were released as needed, the 12 c., $1, $2 and $3 only a week or two before the issue was withdrawn. Due to the marked difference in paper and the use of some new plates there are marked differences in shade in nearly all values.

69 Bahamas Crest

(Des R. Granger Barrett. Photo J. Enschedé)

1967 (1 Sept). *Diamond Jubilee of World Scouting. T* **69** *and similar horiz design. Multicoloured.* W **12** *(sideways). P* 14 × 13.

310 3 c. Type **69** 12 10
311 15 c. Scout badge 20 15

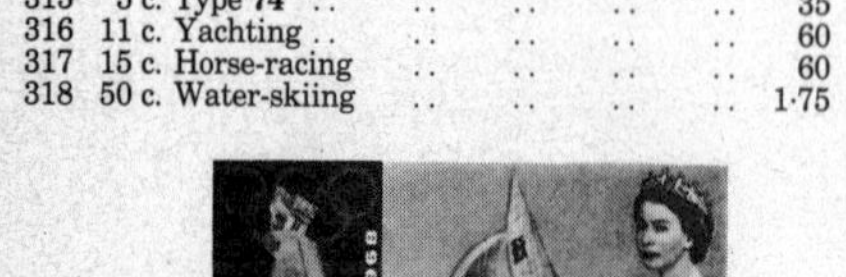

71 Globe and Emblem

74 Golf

(Des R. Granger Barrett, Litho D.L.R.)

1968 (13 May). *Human Rights Year. T* **71** *and similar horiz designs. Multicoloured.* W w **12** *(sideways). P* 14 × 13½.

312 3 c. Type **71** 10 5
313 12 c. Scales of Justice and emblem 25 25
314 $1 Bahamas Crest and emblem . . . . 1·00 1·60

(Litho B.W.)

1968 (20 Aug). *Tourism. T* **74** *and similar vert designs. Multicoloured. P* 13.

315 5 c. Type **74** 35 20
316 11 c. Yachting 60 30
317 15 c. Horse-racing 60 35
318 50 c. Water-skiing . . . . 1·75 2·25

78 Racing Yacht and Olympic Monument

(Photo Harrison)

1968 (29 Sept). *Olympic Games, Mexico City. T* **78** *and similar horiz designs. No wmk. P* 14½ × 13½.

319 5 c. red-brown, orange-yellow & blue-green 25 15
320 11 c. multicoloured 35 25
321 50 c. multicoloured . . . . 1·00 1·60
322 $1 olive-grey, greenish blue and violet . . 2·50 3·50

Designs:—11 c. Long-jumping and Olympic Monument; 50 c. Running and Olympic Monument; $1, Type **78**.

It is understood that the above were released by the Philatelic Agency in the U.S.A. on 1st September.

81 Legislative Building

(Des J. Cooter, Litho Format)

1968 (1 Nov). *14th Commonwealth Parliamentary Conference. T* **81** *and similar multicoloured designs. P* 14.

323 3 c. Type **81** 10 10
324 10 c. Bahamas Mace and Westminster Clock-Tower (*vert*) 15 15
325 12 c. Local straw market (*vert*) 20 20
326 15 c. Horse-drawn Surrey 30 30

85 Obverse and reverse of $100 Gold Coin

(Recess D.L.R.)

1968 (2 Dec). *Gold Coins commemorating the first General Election under the New Constitution. T* **85** *and similar "boomerang" shaped designs. P* 13½.

327 3 c. red/*gold* 20 25
328 12 c. blue-green/*gold* 45 60
329 15 c. dull purple/*gold* 55 75
330 $1 black/*gold* . . . . 3·75 4·50

Designs:—12 c. Obverse and reverse of $50 gold coin; 15 c. Obverse and reverse of $20 gold coin; $1, Obverse and reverse of $10 gold coin.

89 First Flight Postcard of 1919

90 Sikorsky "S–38" Seaplane of 1929

(Des V. Whiteley. Litho Format)

1969 (30 Jan). *50th Anniv of Bahamas Airmail Service. P* 14.

331 **89** 12 c. multicoloured 40 60
332 **90** 15 c. multicoloured 50 90

91 Game-fishing Boats

92 "The Adoration of the Shepherds" (Louis le Nain)

(Des J. Cooter. Litho Format)

1969 (26 Aug). *Tourism. One Millionth Visitor to Bahamas. T* **91** *and similar horiz designs. Multicoloured.* W w **12** *(sideways). P* 14½.

333 3 c. Type **91** 25 12
334 11 c. Paradise Beach 55 30
335 12 c. Sunfish sailing boats 55 40
336 15 c. Rawson Square and Parade 60 60
MS337 130 × 96 mm. Nos. 333/6 . . . . 4·50 5·00

(Des G. Drummond. Litho D.L.R.)

1969 (15 Oct). *Christmas. T* **92** *and similar vert designs.* W w **12**. *P* 12.

338 3 c. Type **92** 15 5
339 11 c. "The Adoration of the Shepherds" (Poussin) 30 30
340 12 c. "The Adoration of the Kings" (Gerard David) 30 30
341 15 c. "The Adoration of the Kings" (Vincenzo Foppa) 35 45

93 Badge of Girl Guides

(Des Mrs. R. Sands. Litho Harrison)

1970 (23 Feb). *Girl Guides Diamond Jubilee. T* **93** *and similar designs. Multicoloured.* W w **12**. *P* 14½.

342 3 c. Type **93** 15 10
343 12 c. Badge of Brownies 30 35
344 15 c. Badge of Rangers 40 55

94 U.P.U. Headquarters and Emblem

(Des L. Curtis, Litho J.W.)

1970 (20 May). *New U.P.U. Headquarters Building.* W w **12** *(sideways). P* 14.

345 **94** 3 c. multicoloured 15 12
346 15 c. multicoloured 30 45

95 Coach and Globe

(Des G. Drummond. Litho B.W.)

1970 (14 July). *"Goodwill Caravan". T* **95** *and similar horiz designs. Multicoloured.* W w **12** *(sideways). P* 13½ × 13.

347 3 c. Type **95** 20 12
348 11 c. Train and globe 70 45
349 12 c. Liner, Yacht and globe 70 60
350 15 c. Airliner and globe 70 80
MS351 165 × 125 mm Nos. 347/50 . . . . 8·00 9·50

96 Nurse, Patients and Greater Flamingo

97 "The Nativity" (detail, Pittoni)

(Photo Harrison)

1970 (1 Sept). *Centenary of British Red Cross. T* **96** *and similar horiz design. Multicoloured.* W w **12** *(sideways). P* 14½.

352 3 c. Type **96** 15 12
a. Gold ("EIIR", etc.) omitted £100
353 15 c. Hospital and Dolphin 25 40

(Des G. Drummond. Litho D.L.R.)

1970 (3 Nov). *Christmas. T* **97** *and similar vert designs. Multicoloured.* W w **12**. *P* 13.

354 3 c. Type **97** 15 5
355 11 c. "The Holy Family" (detail, Anton Raphael Mengs) 30 30
356 12 c. "The Adoration of the Shepherds" (detail, Giorgione) 35 35
357 15 c. "The Adoration of the Shepherds" (detail, School of Seville) 55 65
MS358 114 × 140 mm. Nos. 354/7 plus two labels 2·00 2·75

98 International Airport

(Des Mrs. W. Wasile. Litho Format)

1971 (27 Apr–1 Sept). *Multicoloured designs as T* **98**. W w **12** *(sideways on $1 to $3). P* 14½ × 14 *(1 to 50 c.) or* 14 × 14½ *($1 to $3).*

359 1 c. Type **98** 8 30
360 2 c. Breadfruit 12 35
361 3 c. Straw market 12 25
362 4 c. Hawksbill turtle . . . . 1·00 1·75

363 5 c. Grouper 35 35
364 6 c. As 4 c. (21.9.71) 25 25
365 7 c. Hibiscus (21.9.71) 40 50
366 8 c. Yellow Elder . . . . 70 1·10
367 10 c. Bahamian sponge boat 50 50
368 11 c. Greater Flamingos 50 45
369 12 c. As 7 c . . . . 2·00 2·75
370 15 c. Bonefish 50 55
371 18 c. Royal Poinciana (21.9.71) 55 65
372 22 c. As 18 c. . . . . 3·00 4·25
373 50 c. Post Office, Nassau . . . . 1·40 2·25
374 $1 Pineapple (*vert*) . . . . 4·25 3·50
375 $2 Crawfish (*vert*) . . . . 5·00 7·50
376 $3 Junkanoo (*vert*) . . . . 8·50 14·00
359/376 . . *Set of* 18 26·00 38·00

See also Nos. 395/400, 460/73 and 518/25.

99 Snowflake

(Litho (15 c. additionally die-stamped in gold) Walsall)

1971 (19 Oct). *Christmas. T* **99** *and similar horiz designs.* W w **12**. *P* 14 × 14½.

377 3 c. deep reddish purple, orange and gold . . 12 5
378 11 c. light ultramarine and gold . . 30 30
379 15 c. multicoloured . . 40 40
380 18 c. bluish green, royal blue and gold . . 45 45
MS381 126 × 95 mm. Nos. 377/80. P 15 . . 2·50 3·25

Designs:— 11 c. "Peace on Earth" (doves); 15 c. Arms of Bahamas and holly; 18 c. Starlit lagoon.

100 High jumping

(Des J. W. Litho B.W.)

1972 (11 July). *Olympic Games, Munich. T* **100** *and similar horiz designs. Multicoloured.* W w **12**. *P* 13½.

382 10 c. Type **100** 35 35
383 11 c. Cycling 40 40
384 15 c. Running 50 60
385 18 c. Sailing . . . . 80 1·00
MS386 127 × 95 mm. Nos. 382/5 . . . . 2·75 3·00

101 Shepherd

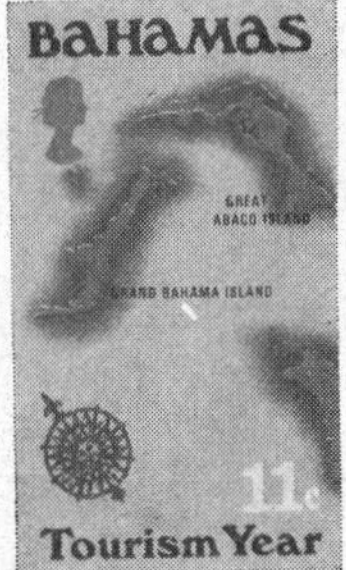

102 Northerly Bahama Islands

(Des Jennifer Toombs. Litho (15 c. additionally embossed) J.W.)

1972 (3 Oct). *Christmas. T* **101** *and similar vert designs. Multicoloured.* W w **12** (*sideways on* 6 *and* 20 *c.*) *P* 14.

387 3 c. Type **101** 10 10
388 6 c. Bells 20 20
389 15 c. Holly and Cross 45 45
390 20 c. Poinsettia 50 65
MS391 108 × 140 mm. Nos. 387/90 (wmk sideways) 2·00 2·75

(Des M. Shamir. Litho Format)

1972 (1 Nov). *Tourism Year of the Americas. Sheet* 133 × 105 *mm, containing T* **102** *and similar vert designs. P* 15.

MS392 11, 15, 18 and 50 c. multicoloured . . 3·50 4·00

The four designs are printed horizontally *se-tenant* in **MS**392, forming a composite map design of the Bahamas.

103 Mace and Galleon

(Des (from photograph by D. Groves) and photo Harrison)

1972 (13 Nov). *Royal Silver Wedding. Multicoloured; background colour given.* W w **12**. *P* 14 × 14½.

393 **103** 11 c. rose 20 25
394 18 c. bluish violet 20 30

1972 (23 Nov)–**73**. *As Nos.* 363, 366 *and* 373/6 *but wmk sideways on* 5 *to* 50 *c.; upright on* $1 *to* $3.

395 5 c. Grouper 60 45
396 8 c. Yellow Elder (25.7.73) . . . . 1·00 95
397 50 c. Post Office, Nassau (25.7.73) . . . . 1·90 2·75
398 $1 Pineapple (25.7.73) . . . . 3·25 4·00
399 $2 Crawfish (25.7.73) . . . . 6·00 8·00
400 $3 Junkanoo (1973) . . . . 12·00 18·00
395/400 . . *Set of* 6 22·00 30·00

Nos. 401/9 vacant.

104 Weather Satellite

(Des C. Abbott. Litho Questa)

1973 (3 Apr). *I.M.O./W.M.O. Centenary. T* **104** *and similar horiz design. Multicoloured.* W w **12**. *P* 14.

410 15 c. Type **104** 25 30
411 18 c. Weather radar 30 40

INDEPENDENT

105 C. A. Bain (national hero)

106 "The Virgin in Prayer" (Sassoferrato)

(Des PAD Studio. Litho Questa)

1973 (10 July–1 Aug). *Independence. T* **105** *and similar vert designs. Multicoloured.* W w **12** (*sideways*). *P* 14½ × 14.

412 3 c. Type **105** 10 10
413 11 c. Coat of arms 20 20
414 15 c. Bahamas flag 25 25
415 $1 Governor-General, M. B. Butler (1 Aug) 1·90 2·75
MS416 86 × 121 mm. Nos. 412/15 (1 Aug) . . 2·75 3·50

(Des C. Abbott. Litho Format)

1973 (16 Oct). *Christmas. T* **106** *and similar vert designs. Multicoloured.* W w **12** (*sideways*). *P* 14.

417 3 c. Type **106** 10 5
418 11 c. "Virgin and Child with St. John" (Filippino Lippi) 25 25
419 15 c. "A Choir of Angels" (Simon Marmion) . . 30 30
420 18 c. "The Two Trinities" (Murillo) . . 45 50
MS421 120 × 99 mm. Nos. 417/20 . . . . 2·00 2·50

107 "Agriculture and Sciences"

(Des C. Abbott. Litho Questa)

1974 (5 Feb). *25th Anniv of University of West Indies. T* **107** *and similar horiz design. Multicoloured.* W w **12**. *P* 13½.

422 15 c. Type **107** 45 45
423 18 c. "Arts, Engineering and General Studies" 45 45

108 U.P.U. Monument, Berne

(Des P. Powell. Litho Questa)

1974 (23 Apr). *Centenary of Universal Postal Union. Designs as T* **108** *showing different arrangements of the U.P.U. Monument.* W w **12** (*upright on* 3 *c.,* 14 *c. and* **MS**428; *sideways on others*). *P* 14.

424 **108** 3 c. multicoloured 10 10
425 – 13 c. multicoloured (*vert*) 35 35
426 – 14 c. multicoloured 40 40
427 – 18 c. multicoloured (*vert*) 55 60
MS428 128 × 95 mm. Nos. 424/7 . . . . 1·75 2·25

109 Roseate Spoonbills

(Des G. Drummond. Litho Questa)

1974 (10 Sept). *15th Anniv of Bahamas National Trust. T* **109** *and similar horiz designs. Multicoloured.* W w **12** (*sideways*). *P* 13½.

429 13 c. Type **109** 95 65
430 14 c. White-crowned Pigeon 95 65
431 21 c. White-tailed Tropic Birds . . . . 1·40 1·00
432 36 c. Cuban Amazon . . . . 1·75 1·60
MS433 123 × 120 mm. Nos. 429/32 . . . . 4·50 5·00

110 "The Holy Family" (Jacques de Stella)

(Des J. W. Litho Enschedé)

1974 (29 Oct). *Christmas. T* **110** *and similar horiz designs. Multicoloured.* W w **12** (*sideways*). *P* 13 × 13½.

434 8 c. Type **110** 20 15
435 10 c. "Madonna and Child" (16th-cent Brescian School) 30 30
436 12 c. "Virgin and Child with St. John the Baptist and St. Catherine" (Previtali) . . 30 30
437 21 c. "Virgin and Child with Angels" (Previtali) 60 60
MS438 126 × 105 mm. Nos. 434/7 . . . . 2·00 2·25

111 *Anteos maerula*

(Des PAD Studio. Litho D.L.R.)

1975 (4 Feb). *Butterflies. T* **111** *and similar horiz designs. Multicoloured.* W w **12**. *P* 14 × 13½.

439 3 c. Type **111** 25 15
440 14 c. *Eurema nicippe* 80 65
441 18 c. *Papilio andraemon bonhotei* 95 85
442 21 c. *Euptoieta hegesia* . . . . 1·10 1·00
MS443 119 × 94 mm. Nos. 439/42 . . . . 3·25 3·75

112 Sheep Husbandry

113 Rowena Rand (evangelist)

(Des Daphne Padden. Litho Questa)

1975 (27 May). *Economic Diversification. T* **112** *and similar multicoloured designs. P* 14.

444 3 c. Type **112** 10 10
445 14 c. Electric-reel fishing (*vert*) 30 30
446 18 c. Farming 35 35
447 21 c. Oil Refinery (*vert*) 50 50
MS448 127 × 94 mm. Nos. 444/7 . . . . 1·50 1·75

(Des Jennifer Toombs. Litho Questa)

1975 (22 July). *International Women's Year. T* **113** *and similar vert design.* W w **14** (*sideways*). *P* 14.

449 14 c. bistre-brown, lt turquoise-blue & ultram 25 30
450 18 c. lemon, bright yellow-green and sepia . . 30 40

Design:—18 c. I.W.Y. symbol and Harvest symbol.

114 "Adoration of the Shepherds" (Perugino)

(Des Jennifer Toombs. Litho J.W.)

1975 (2 Dec). *Christmas. T* **114** *and similar horiz design. Multicoloured. W* w **14** *(sideways). P* 13.

451 3 c. Type **114** 10 10
452 8 c. "Adoration of the Magi" (Ghirlandaio) .. 25 25
453 18 c. As 8 c. 50 55
454 21 c. Type **114** 65 75
MS455 142 × 107 mm. Nos. 451/4. P 13½ .. 1·90 2·50

115 Telephones, 1876 and 1976

(Des G. Vasarhelyi. Litho D.L.R.)

1976 (23 Mar). *Telephone Centenary. T* **115** *and similar horiz designs. Multicoloured. W* w **14** *(sideways). P* 14.

456 3 c. Type **115** 12 12
457 16 c. Radio-telephone link, Deleporte .. 40 40
458 21 c. Alexander Graham Bell 55 55
459 25 c. Satellite 70 70

1976 (30 Mar)–**79.** *Designs as Nos.* 359/63, 365/7 *and* 373/6 *(some with new face values).* W w **14** *(sideways on* $1 *to* $3). *Ordinary paper.*

460 1 c. Type **98** (1.11.76).. .. .. .. 20 25
a. Chalk-surfaced paper (1979) .. .. 1·50 1·50
461 2 c. Breadfruit 20 25
462 3 c. Straw market (1.11.76) 20 15
a. Chalk-surfaced paper (1979) 60 60
463 5 c. Grouper (1.11.76) 40 25
a. Chalk-surfaced paper (1979) 70 70
464 8 c. Yellow Elder 50 35
465 10 c. Bahamian sponge boat 50 35
466 16 c. As 7 c. (2.11.76) 50 35
a. Chalk-surfaced paper (1979) 90 90
467 21 c. As 2 c. (2.11.76) 50 40
a. Chalk-surfaced paper (1979) .. .. 1·25 1·50
468 25 c. As 4 c. (2.11.76) 50 40
a. Chalk-surfaced paper (1979) .. .. 1·75 2·00
469 40 c. As 10 c. (2.11.76).. .. .. 70 75
470 50 c. Post Office, Nassau .. .. .. 1·60 1·75
471 $1 Pineapple .. .. 2·25 2·50
472 $2 Crawfish (2.5.76).. .. .. .. 4·00 5·50
a. Chalk-surfaced paper (1979) .. .. 9·00 9·00
473 $3 Junkanoo (1.11.76) .. .. .. 6·50 9·00
460/73 .. .. *Set of* 14 17·00 20·00
460a72a .. .. *Set of* 7 14·00 14·00
No. 474 vacant.

116 Map of North America

(Des and litho Walsall)

1976 (1 June). *Bicentenary of American Revolution. T* **116** *and similar horiz design. Multicoloured. W* w **14** *(sideways). P* 14.

475 16 c. Type **116** 40 40
476 $1 John Murray, Earl of Dunmore .. .. 2·50 2·50
MS477 127 × 100 mm. No. 476 × 4 .. .. 10·00 11·00

117 Cycling

118 "Virgin and Child" (detail, Lippi)

1976 (13 July). *Olympic Games, Montreal. T* **117** *and similar vert designs. W* w **14**. *P* 14.

478 8 c. magenta, blue and pale cobalt 15 15
479 16 c. orange, brown and pale cobalt 30 30
480 25 c. blue, deep magenta and pale cobalt .. 60 70
481 40 c. brown, orange and pale cobalt .. .. 90 1·10
MS482 100 × 126 mm. Nos. 478/81 .. .. 2·00 2·50
Designs:—16 c. Jumping; 25 c. Sailing; 40 c. Boxing.

(Des G. Drummond. Litho Questa)

1976 (5 Oct). *Christmas. T* **118** *and similar vert designs. Multicoloured. W* w **14**. *P* 14.

483 3 c. Type **118** 10 10
484 21 c. "Adoration of the Shepherds" (School of Seville) 30 30
485 25 c. "Adoration of the Kings" (detail, Foppa) 50 50
486 40 c. "Virgin and Child" (detail, Vivarini) .. 75 85
MS487 107 × 127 mm. Nos. 483/6 .. .. 2·00 2·25

119 Queen beneath Cloth of Gold Canopy

(Des G. Vasarhelyi. Litho Cartor S.A., France)

1977 (7 Feb). *Silver Jubilee. T* **119** *and similar horiz designs. Multicoloured. No wmk. P* 12.

488 8 c. Type **119** 25 25
489 16 c. The Crowning 30 30
490 21 c. Taking the Oath 40 40
491 40 c. Queen with sceptre and orb 70 70
MS492 122 × 90 mm. Nos. 488/91 .. .. 2·25 2·50

120 Featherduster

(Des BG Studio. Litho J.W.)

1977 (24 May). *Marine Life. T* **120** *and similar designs. Multicoloured. W* w **14** *(sideways). P* 13½.

493 3 c. Type **120** 15 15
494 8 c. Pork Fish and cave 35 35
495 16 c. Elkhorn Coral 65 65
496 21 c. Soft Coral and sponge 75 75
MS497 119 × 93 mm. Nos. 493/6. P 14½ .. .. 2·50 3·00

121 Scouts around Campfire and Home-made Shower

Royal Visit
October 1977

(122)

(Des Harrison. Litho J.W.)

1977 (27 Sept). *Sixth Caribbean Scout Jamboree. T* **121** *and similar horiz design. Multicoloured. W* w **14** *(sideways). P* 13½.

498 16 c. Type **121** 35 35
499 21 c. Boating scenes 45 45
One used example of No. 498 is known with the mauve (face value and inscription) omitted.

1977 (19 Oct). *Royal Visit. As Nos.* 488/492, *but* W w **14** *(sideways), optd with T* **122**.

500 8 c. Type **119** 20 25
501 16 c. The Crowning 30 35
502 21 c. Taking the Oath 40 45
503 40 c. Queen with sceptre and orb 70 75
MS504 122 × 90 mm. Nos. 500/3 .. .. 1·50 1·75

123 Virgin and Child

124 Public Library, Nassau (Colonial)

(Des and litho J.W.)

1977 (25 Oct). *Christmas. T* **123** *and similar vert designs. Multicoloured. W* w **14**. *P* 13½.

505 3 c. Type **123** 10 10
506 16 c. The Magi 35 35
507 21 c. Nativity scene 45 45
508 25 c. The Magi and star 50 50
MS509 136 × 74 mm. Nos. 505/8. P 14 .. .. 1·40 1·60

(Des G. Drummond. Litho Questa)

1978 (28 Mar). *Architectural Heritage. T* **124** *and similar vert designs. W* w **14**. *P* 14½ × 14.

510 3 c. black and apple-green 10 10
511 8 c. black and pale greenish blue 15 15
512 6 c. black and mauve 30 30
513 18 c. black and salmon-pink 35 35
MS514 91 × 91 mm. Nos. 510/13 .. .. 1·00 1·10
Designs:—8 c. St. Matthew's Church (Gothic); 16 c. Government House (Colonial); 18 c. Hermitage, Cat Island (Spanish).

125 Sceptre, St. Edward's Crown and Orb

126 Coat of Arms within Wreath and Three Ships

(Des BG Studio. Litho Enschedé)

1978 (27 June). *25th Anniv of Coronation. T* **125** *and similar vert design. Multicoloured. W* w **14**. *P* 14 × 13½.

515 16 c. Type **125** 20 25
516 $1 Queen in Coronation regalia .. .. 1·25 1·50
MS517 147 × 96 mm. Nos. 515/16 .. .. 1·50 1·75

1978 (June). *As Nos.* 359/76, *but no wmk.*

518 1 c. Type **98** 25 35
519 5 c. Grouper 50 40
520 16 c. Hibiscus .. .. 1·00 80
521 25 c. Hawksbill Turtle .. .. 1·25 1·00
522 50 c. Post Office, Nassau .. .. .. 1·50 2·00
523 $1 Pineapple .. .. 2·75 3·25
524 $2 Crawfish .. .. 3·75 6·00
525 $3 Junkanoo .. .. 5·50 7·50
518/25 .. .. *Set of* 8 15·00 19·00
Nos. 526/31 vacant.

(Des Jennifer Toombs. Litho Questa)

1978 (14 Nov). *Christmas. T* **126** *and similar horiz design. W* w **14** *(sideways). P* 14 × 14½.

532 5 c. gold, bright crimson and bright rose .. 10 10
533 21 c. gold, deep ultramarine and violet-blue .. 25 25
MS534 95 × 95 mm. Nos. 532/3 .. .. .. 1·75 2·00
Design:—21 c. Three angels with trumpets.

127 Child reaching for Adult

128 Sir Rowland Hill and Penny Black

(Litho J.W.)

1979 (15 May). *International Year of the Child. T* **127** *and similar vert designs. Multicoloured. W* w **14**. *P* 13.

535 5 c. Type **127** 10 10
536 16 c. Boys playing leap-frog 25 25
537 21 c. Girls skipping 25 30
538 25 c. Bricks with I.Y.C. emblem 30 30
MS539 101 × 125 mm. Nos. 535/8. P 14 .. .. 90 1·00

(Des J. Cooter. Litho Walsall)

1979 (14 Aug). *Death Centenary of Sir Rowland Hill. T* **128** *and similar horiz designs. Multicoloured.* W w **14** *(sideways). P* 13½ × 14.

540 10 c. Type **128** 15 10
541 21 c. Printing press, 1840 and 6d. stamp of 1862 25 30
542 25 c. Great Britain 6d. stamp of 1856 with "A 05" (Nassau) cancellation and Two-penny blue 30 35
543 40 c. Early mailboat and 1d. stamp of 1859 .. 40 45
MS544 115 × 80 mm. Nos. 540/3 .. .. .. 1·25 1·60

129 Commemorative Plaque and Map of Bahamas

130 Goombay Carnival Headdress

(Des G. Drummond. Litho Secura, Singapore)

1979 (27 Sept). *250th Anniv of Parliament. T* **129** *and similar horiz designs. Multicoloured.* W w **14** *(sideways). P* 13½.

545 16 c. Type **129** 20 20
546 21 c. Parliament buildings 25 25
547 25 c. Legislative Chamber 30 30
548 $1 Senate Chamber .. .. 90 1·25
MS549 116 × 89 mm. Nos. 545/8 (wmk upright) 1·75 2·10

(Des BG Studio. Litho J.W.)

1979 (6 Nov). *Christmas. T* **130** *and similar vert designs showing Goombay Carnival headdresses. W* w **14**. *P* 13.

550 5 c. multicoloured 5 5
551 10 c. multicoloured 15 15
552 16 c. multicoloured 20 20
553 21 c. multicoloured 25 25
554 25 c. multicoloured 30 30
555 40 c. multicoloured 45 45
550/5 .. .. *Set of* 6 1·25 1·25
MS556 50 × 88 mm. Nos. 550/5 (wmk sideways). P 13½ .. .. 1·50 1·60

131 Landfall of Columbus, 1492

132 Virgin and Child

(Des J. W. Litho Format)

1980 (9 July). *Horiz designs as T* **131**. *Multicoloured. W w* **14**. *P* 14½.

557	1 c. Type **131**	5	5
558	3 c. Blackbeard the Pirate, 1718	5	5
559	5 c. Eleutheran Adventurers (Articles and Orders, 1647)	8	10
560	10 c. Ceremonial Mace	15	20
561	12 c. The Loyalists, 1783–88 (Colonel Andrew Deveaux)	20	25
562	15 c. Slave Trading, Vendue House	30	25
563	16 c. Wrecking in the 1800's	30	25
564	18 c. Blockade running (American Civil War)	35	30
565	21 c. Bootlegging, 1919–29	35	30
566	25 c. Pineapple cultivation	40	45
567	40 c. Sponge clipping	60	70
568	50 c. Tourist development	75	80
569	$1 Modern agriculture	1·50	1·75
570	$2 Modern air and sea transport	3·00	3·25
571	$3 Banking in the Bahamas (Central Bank)	4·50	4·75
572	$5 Independence, 10 July 1973 (Prince of Wales and Prime Minister L.O. Pindling)	7·75	8·00
557/72	*Set of* 16	18·00	19·00

(Des B. Malone. Litho Walsall)

1980 (28 Oct). *Christmas. Straw-work. T* **132** *and similar vert designs. Multicoloured. W w* **14**. *P* 14½ × 14.

573	5 c. Type **132**	5	5
574	21 c. Three Kings	25	25
575	25 c. Angel	30	30
576	$1 Christmas Tree	1·25	1·25
MS577	168 × 105 mm. Nos. 573/6	1·90	2·00

133 Disabled Person with Walking-stick

(Des and litho Walsall)

1981 (10 Feb). *International Year for Disabled Persons. T* **133** *and similar horiz design. Multicoloured. W w* **14** *(sideways). P* 14½ × 14.

578	5 c. Type **133**	5	5
579	$1 Disabled person in wheelchair	1·50	1·50
MS580	120 × 60 mm. Nos. 578/9	1·60	1·75

134 Grand Bahama Tracking Site

135 Prince Charles and Lady Diana Spencer

(Litho Enschedé)

1981 (21 Apr). *Space Exploration. T* **134** *and similar multi-coloured designs. W w* **14** *(sideways on 10 and 25 c.). P* 13½.

581	10 c. Type **134**	15	15
582	20 c. Satellite view of Bahamas (*vert*)	40	40
583	25 c. Satellite view of Eleuthera	45	45
584	50 c. Satellite view of Andros and New Providence (*vert*)	75	75
MS585	115 × 99 mm. Nos. 581/4 (wmk sideways)	1·60	1·75

(Des C. Abbott. Litho Questa)

1981 (22 July). *Royal Wedding. T* **135** *and similar horiz design. Multicoloured. W w* **14** *(sideways). P* 14 × 14½.

586	30 c. Type **135**	75	35
587	$2 Prince Charles and Prime Minister Pindling	3·75	2·40
MS588	142 × 120 mm. Nos. 586/7	5·00	3·25
	a. Upper stamp in miniature sheet imperf on 3 sides	£600	

No. **MS**588a shows the upper stamp in the miniature sheet perforated at foot only.

136 Bahama Pintail

(Des Walsall. Litho Questa)

1981 (25 Aug). *Wildlife* (1*st series*). *Birds. T* **136** *and similar horiz designs. Multicoloured. W w* **14** *(sideways). P* 14.

589	5 c. Type **136**	20	10
590	20 c. Reddish Egret	40	35
591	25 c. Brown Booby	45	40
592	$1 Black-billed Whistling Duck	1·40	1·40
MS593	100 × 74 mm. Nos. 589/92	2·50	2·75

See also Nos. 626/30, 653/7 and 690/4.

21 - 23 SEPTEMBER 1981

COMMONWEALTH FINANCE MINISTERS' MEETING

(137)

1981 (21 Sept). *Commonwealth Finance Ministers' Meeting. Nos.* 559/60, 566 *and* 568 *optd with T* **137**.

594	5 c. Eleutheran Adventurers (Articles and Orders, 1647)	10	15
595	10 c. Ceremonial Mace	15	20
596	25 c. Pineapple cultivation	40	50
597	50 c. Tourist development	75	90

138 Poultry

139 Father Christmas

(Des L. McCombie. Litho J.W.)

1981 (16 Oct). *World Food Day. T* **138** *and similar horiz designs. Multicoloured. W w* **14** *(sideways). P* 13.

598	5 c. Type **138**	5	5
599	20 c. Sheep	30	30
600	30 c. Lobsters	40	40
601	50 c. Pigs	75	90
MS602	115 × 63 mm. Nos. 598/601. P 14	1·50	1·75

(Des local artists. Litho Format)

1981 (24 Nov). *Christmas. T* **139** *and similar vert designs. Multi-coloured. W w* **14**. *P* 13½ × 14.

603	5 c. Type **139**	10	10
	a. Sheetlet of 9. Nos. 603/11	2·75	
604	5 c. Mother and child	10	10
605	5 c. St. Nicholas, Holland	10	10
606	25 c. Lussibruden, Sweden	30	30
607	25 c. Mother and child (*different*)	30	30
608	25 c. King Wenceslas, Czechoslovakia	30	30
609	30 c. Mother with child on knee	35	35
610	30 c. Mother carrying child	35	35
611	$1 Christkindl Angel, Germany	1·25	1·25
603/11	*Set of* 9	2·75	2·75

Nos. 603/11 were printed together, *se-tenant*, in a sheetlet of 9.

140 Robert Koch

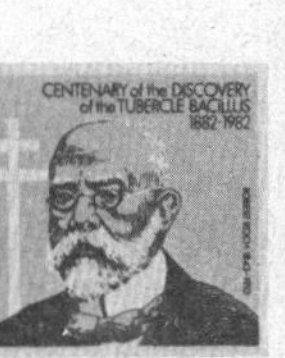

141 Male Flamingo (*Phoenicopterus ruber*)

(Des A. Theobald. Litho Harrison)

1982 (3 Feb). *Centenary of Discovery of Tubercle Bacillus by Robert Koch. T* **140** *and similar horiz designs. W w* **14** *(sideways). P* 14.

612	5 c. black, red-brown and rose-lilac	10	10
613	16 c. black, drab and dull orange	25	30
614	21 c. multicoloured	30	35
615	$1 multicoloured	1·50	1·75
MS616	94 × 97 mm. Nos. 612/15. P 14½	2·25	2·75

Designs:—16 c. Stylised infected person; 21 c. Early and modern microscopes; $1 Mantoux test.

(Des N. Arlott. Litho Questa)

1982 (28 Apr). *Greater Flamingos. T* **141** *and similar vert designs. Multicoloured. W w* **14**. *P* 14 × 13½.

617	25 c. Type **141**	45	45
	a. Horiz strip of 5. Nos. 617/21	2·00	
618	25 c. Female	45	45
619	25 c. Female with nestling	45	45
620	25 c. Juvenile	45	45
621	25 c. Immature bird	45	45

Nos. 617/21 were printed together, *se-tenant*, in horizontal strips of 5 throughout the sheet, forming a composite design.

142 Lady Diana Spencer at Ascot, June 1981

143 House of Assembly Plaque

(Des C. Abbott. Litho Format)

1982 (1 July). *21st Birthday of Princess of Wales. T* **142** *and similar vert designs. Multicoloured. W w* **14**. *P* 13½ × 14 (16 c., $1) *or* 13½ (*others*).

622	16 c. Bahamas coat of arms	20	20
	a. Perf 13½	1·00	1·00
623	25 c. Type **142**	35	35
624	40 c. Bride and Earl Spencer arriving at St. Paul's	50	55
625	$1 Formal portrait	1·25	1·50

(Des Walsall. Litho Questa)

1982 (18 Aug). *Wildlife* (2*nd series*). *Mammals. Horiz designs as T* **136**. *Multicoloured. W w* **14** *(sideways). P* 14.

626	10 c. Bat	15	15
627	16 c. Hutia	25	25
628	21 c. Racoon	35	35
629	$1 Dolphin	1·50	1·75
MS630	115 × 76 mm. Nos. 626/9	2·50	2·75

(Des and litho Walsall)

1982 (16 Oct). *28th Commonwealth Parliamentary Association Conference. T* **143** *and similar vert designs. Multicoloured. W w* **14**. *P* 14 × 13½.

631	5 c. Type **143**	10	10
632	25 c. Association coat of arms	35	35
633	40 c. Coat of arms	55	60
634	50 c. House of Assembly	70	75

144 Wesley Methodist Church, Baillou Hill Road

(Des Jennifer Toombs. Litho Format)

1982 (3 Nov). *Christmas. Churches. T* **144** *and similar horiz designs. Multicoloured. W w* **14** *(sideways). P* 14.

635	5 c. Type **144**	10	8
636	12 c. Centreville Seventh Day Adventist Church	20	20
637	15 c. The Church of God of Prophecy, East Street	25	25
638	21 c. Bethel Baptist Church, Meeting Street	30	30
639	25 c. St. Francis Xavier Catholic Church, Highbury Park	35	35
640	$1 Holy Cross Anglican Church, Highbury Park	1·50	1·75
635/40	*Set of* 6	2·50	2·75

145 Prime Minister Lynden O. Pindling

(Des Walsall. Litho Questa)

1983 (14 Mar). *Commonwealth Day T* **145** *and similar horiz designs. Multicoloured. W w* **14** *(sideways). P* 14.

641	5 c. Type **145**	5	8
642	25 c. Bahamian and Commonwealth flags	35	40
643	35 c. Map showing position of Bahamas	45	50
644	$1 Ocean liner	1·25	1·40

20c

(146)

1983 (5 Apr). *Nos.* 562/5 *surch as T* **146**.

645	20 c. on 15 c. Slave Trading, Vendue House	35	40
646	31 c. on 21 c. Bootlegging, 1919–29	55	60
647	35 c. on 16 c. Wrecking in the 1800's	60	65
648	80 c. on 18 c. Blockade running (American Civil War)	1·40	1·50

147 Customs Officers and Liner

148 Raising the National Flag

(Des Walsall. Litho Harrison)

1983 (31 May). *30th Anniv of Customs Co-operation Council. T* **147** *and similar vert design. Multicoloured.* W w **14**. *P* 13½ × 13.
649 31 c. Type **147** 40 45
650 $1 Customs officers and airliner .. .. 1·25 1·40

(Des L. Curtis. Litho Questa)

1983 (6 July). *10th Anniv of Independence.* W w **14**. *P* 14.
651 **148** $1 multicoloured .. .. .. 1·25 1·40
MS652 105 × 65 mm. No. 651. P 12 .. .. 1·25 1·40

(Des F. Solomon, adapted N. Arlott. Litho Harrison)

1983 (24 Aug). *Wildlife (3rd series). Butterflies. Horiz designs as T* **136**. W w **14** (*sideways*). *P* 14½ × 14.
653 5 c. multicoloured 5 8
654 25 c. multicoloured 35 40
655 31 c. black, bistre-yellow and bright rose-red 40 45
656 50 c. multicoloured 65 70
MS657 120 × 80 mm. Nos. 653/6 .. .. .. 1·40 1·60
a. Perf 14 .. .. 1·90 1·60
Designs:—5 c. Carter's Skipper; 25 c. Great Southern White; 31 c. Large Orange Sulphur; 50 c. The Flambeau.
No. **MS**657a was perforated by Questa, the remainder of the issue by Harrison.

149 "Loyalist Dreams"

150 Consolidated "Catalina"

(Des A. Lowe; adapted C. Abbott. Litho Questa)

1983 (28 Sept). *Bicentenary of Arrival of American Loyalists in the Bahamas. T* **149** *and similar multicoloured designs.* W w **14** (*sideways on* 31 c., 35 c.). *P* 14.
658 5 c. Type **149** 5 8
659 31 c. New Plymouth, Abaco (*horiz*) 45 50
660 35 c. New Plymouth Hotel (*horiz*) 50 55
661 50 c. "Island Hope" 65 70
MS662 111 × 76 mm. Nos. 658/61. Wmk sideways 1·50 1·60

(Des and litho Harrison)

1983 (13 Oct). *Air Bicentenary of Manned Flight. T* **150** *and similar horiz designs. Multicoloured.* W w **14** (*sideways*). *P* 14.
663 10 c. Type **150** 15 15
664 25 c. Avro "Tudor IV" 35 40
665 31 c. Avro "Lancastrian" 40 45
666 35 c. Consolidated "Commodore" 45 50

151 "Christmas Bells" (Monica Pinder)

152 1861 4d. Stamp

(Des local children, adapted G. Vasarhelyi. Litho Walsall)

1983 (1 Nov). *Christmas. Children's Paintings. T* **151** *and similar multicoloured designs.* W w **14** (*sideways on* 31 c. *and* 50 c.). *P* 14.
667 5 c. Type **151** 5 8
668 20 c. "Flamingo" (Cory Bullard) 25 30
669 25 c. "Yellow Hibiscus with Christmas Candle" (Monique Bailey) 35 40
670 31 c. "Santa goes a Sailing" (Sabrina Seiler) (*horiz*) 40 45
671 35 c. "Silhouette scene with Palm Trees" (James Blake) 45 50
672 50 c. "Silhouette scene with Pelicans" (Erik Russell) (*horiz*) 65 70
667/72 .. .. *Set of* 6 1·90 2·25

(Des D. Miller. Litho Format)

1984 (22 Feb). *125th Anniv of First Bahamas Postage Stamp. T* **152** *and similar vert design. Multicoloured.* W w **14**. *P* 14.
673 5 c. Type **152** 5 8
674 $1 1859 1d. stamp .. .. 1·40 1·50

153 R.M.S. *Trent*

154 Running

(Des L. Curtis. Litho Questa)

1984 (25 Apr). *250th Anniv of "Lloyd's List" (newspaper). T* **153** *and similar vert designs. Multicoloured.* W w **14**. *P* 14½ × 14.
675 5 c. Type **153** 8 10
676 31 c. R.M.S. *Orinoco* 55 60
677 35 c. Nassau harbour 60 65
678 50 c. M.V. *Oropesa* 90 95

(Des McCombie Skinner Studio. Litho Questa)

1984 (20 June). *Olympic Games, Los Angeles. T* **154** *and similar horiz designs.* W w **14** (*sideways*). *P* 14 × 14½.
679 5 c. green, black and gold 8 10
680 25 c. new blue, black and gold 45 50
681 31 c. brown-lake, black and gold 55 60
682 $1 sepia, black and gold .. .. .. 1·75 2·00
MS683 115 × 80 mm. Nos. 679/82 .. .. .. 2·75 3·00
Designs:— 25 c. Shot-putting; 31 c. Boxing; $1 Basketball.

155 Bahamas and Caribbean Community Flags

156 *Calliphlox evelynae*

(Des McCombie Skinner Studio. Litho Questa)

1984 (4 July). *5th Conference of Caribbean Community Heads of Government.* W w **14**. *P* 14.
684 **155** 50 c. multicoloured 90 95

(Des N. Arlott. Litho Questa)

1984 (15 Aug). *25th Anniv of National Trust. T* **156** *and similar vert designs. Multicoloured.* W w **14**. *P* 14.
685 31 c. Type **156** 55 60
a. Horiz strip of 5. Nos. 685/9 .. .. 2·50
686 31 c. *Megaceryle alcyon* and *Eleutherodactylus planirostris* 55 60
687 31 c. *Phoebis sennae, Phoenicopterus ruber* and *Himantopus himantopus* 55 60
688 31 c. *Urbanus proteus* and *Chelonia mydas* .. 55 60
689 31 c. *Pandion haliaetus* 55 60
Nos. 685/9 were printed together, *se-tenant*, in horizontal strips of 5 throughout the sheet, forming a composite design.

(Des N. Arlott. Litho Questa)

1984 (18 Sept). *Wildlife (4th series). Reptiles and Amphibians. Horiz designs as T* **136**. W w **14** (*sideways*). *P* 14.
690 5 c. Allen's Cay Iguana 8 10
691 25 c. Curly-tailed Lizard 45 50
692 35 c. Greenhouse Frog 60 65
693 50 c. Atlantic Green Turtle 90 95
MS694 112 × 82 mm. Nos. 690/3 .. .. .. 2·00 2·25

157 "The Holy Virgin with Jesus and Johannes" (19th-century porcelain plaque after Titian)

(Des D. Slater. Litho J.W.)

1984 (7 Nov). *Christmas. Religious Paintings. T* **157** *and similar vert designs. Multicoloured,* W w **14**. *P* 13½.
695 5 c. Type **157** 10 12
696 31 c. "Madonna with Child in Tropical Landscape" (aquarelle, Anais Colin) 55 60
697 35 c. "The Holy Virgin with the Child" (miniature on ivory, Elena Caula) 60 65
MS698 116 × 76 mm. Nos. 695/7. P 14. .. .. 1·25 1·40

SPECIAL DELIVERY STAMPS

SPECIAL
DELIVERY
(S 1)

1916 (1 May). *Wmk Crown CC. Opted locally with Type* S **1**.
S1 **6** 5d. black and orange .. .. .. 12·00 16·00
a. Opt double £1200 £1200
b. Opt double, one inverted £1300 £1300
c. Opt inverted £1200 £1200
d. Pair, one without opt £8000 £10000

There were three printings from similar settings of 30, and each sheet had to pass through the press twice. The first printing of 600 was on sale from 1 May 1916 in Canada at Ottawa, Toronto, Westmount (Montreal) and Winnipeg; and under an agreement with the Canadian P.O. were used in combination with Canadian stamps and were cancelled in Canada. The second printing (number unknown) was made about the beginning of December 1916, and the third of 6000, issued probably on 1 March 1917, were on sale only in the Bahamas. These printings caused the revocation, in mid-December 1916, of the agreement by Canada, which no longer accepted the stamps as payment of the special delivery fee and left them to be cancelled in the Bahamas.

It is not possible to identify the printings of the normal stamps without plating both the basic stamp and the overprint, though, in general, the word "SPECIAL" is further to the right in relation to "DELIVERY" in the third printing than in the first or second. Our prices for No. S1 are for the third printing and any stamps which can be positively identified as being from the first or second printings would be worth about eight times as much unused, and any on cover are very rare. All the errors appear to be from the third printing.

SPECIAL
DELIVERY
(S 2)

SPECIAL
DELIVERY
(S 3)

1917 (2 July). *Wmk Mult Crown CA. Optd in London with Type* S **2**.
S2 **6** 5d. black and orange (Optd S. £75) .. 1·75 4·00

1918. *Optd with Type* S **3**.
S3 **6** 5d. black and mauve (R.) (Optd S. £75) .. 85 2·40

Bahrain

An independent shaikhdom, with an Indian postal administration from 1884. A British postal administration operated from 1 April 1948 to 31 December 1965.

The first, and for 62 years the only, post office in Bahrain opened at the capital, Manama, on 1 August 1884 as a sub-office of the Indian Post Office at Bushire (Iran), both being part of the Bombay Postal Circle.

Unoverprinted postage stamps of India were supplied to the new office, continuing on sale there until 1933. Examples of the lower values can sometimes be found postmarked at Bahrain, but such cancellations on values over 4 a. are decidedly scarce. The occasional Official stamp can also be discovered, possibly used by the office of the Indian Political Agent.

The initial cancellation supplied showed a "B" against a circular background of horizontal lines, this being used in conjunction with a single ring date-stamp without any indication of the year of use.

1884 Cancellation and Date-stamp

This was followed by a squared-circle type, first seen in 1886, which was used into the early years of the 20th century. Its replacement was a single ring date-stamp, succeeded in turn by the first of a considerable number of Indian-style double-circle postmarks, all inscribed "BAHRAIN".

1886 Squared-circle

PRICES FOR STAMPS ON COVER TO 1945	
Nos. 1/4	*from* × 5
Nos. 15/19	*from* × 6
Nos. 20/37	*from* × 2
Nos. 38/50	*from* × 6

BAHRAIN (1) BAHRAIN (2)

Stamps of India overprinted with T 1 or T 2 (rupee values)

1933 (10 Aug–Dec). *King George V. Wmk Mult Star, T* **69**.

No.	Type	Description	Unused	Used
1	**55**	3 p. slate (12.33)	80	70
2	**56**	½ a. green	2·50	1·90
3	**80**	9 p. deep green	2·25	1·50
4	**57**	1 a. chocolate	1·60	1·25
5	**82**	1 a. 3 p. mauve	1·60	1·10
6	**70**	2 a. vermilion	3·00	3·00
7	**62**	3 a. blue	15·00	15·00
8	**83**	3 a. 6 p. ultramarine	1·60	1·25
9	**71**	4 a. sage-green	12·00	10·00
10	**65**	8 a. reddish purple	1·75	80
11	**66**	12 a. claret	2·75	1·25
12	**67**	1 r. chocolate and green	12·00	10·00
13		2 r. carmine and orange	35·00	32·00
14		5 r. ultramarine and purple	90·00	£110
1/14		*Set of* 14	£160	£170

The 9 p. exists both offset-litho and typo.

1934–37. *King George V. Wmk Mult Star, T* **69**.

No.	Type	Description	Unused	Used
15	**79**	½ a. green (1935)	1·25	60
16	**81**	1 a. chocolate (1935)	2·50	45
17	**59**	2 a. vermilion (1935)	9·50	3·75
17*a*		2 a. vermilion (*small die*) (1937)	14·00	90
18	**62**	3 a. carmine	4·25	35
19	**63**	4 a. sage-green (1935)	3·00	55

1938–41. *King George VI.*

No.	Type	Description	Unused	Used
20	**91**	3 p. slate (5.38)	1·40	80
21		½ a. red-brown (5.38)	20	12
22		9 p. green (5.38)	60	30
23		1 a. carmine (5.38)	40	15
24	**92**	2 a. vermilion (1939)	1·25	40
26	–	3 a. yellow-green (1941)	7·50	1·25
27	–	3½ a. bright blue (7.38)	2·00	2·00
28	–	4 a. brown (1941)	55·00	38·00
30	–	8 a. slate-violet (1940)	70·00	40·00
31	–	12 a. lake (1940)	65·00	55·00
32	**93**	1 r. grey and red-brown (1940)	2·25	1·25
33		2 r. purple and brown (1940)	13·00	3·25
34		5 r. green and blue (1940)	30·00	17·00
35		10 r. purple and claret (1941)	65·00	25·00
36		15 r. brown and green (1941)	32·00	32·00
37		25 r. slate-violet and purple (1941)	95·00	75·00
20/37		*Set of* 16	£400	£275

1942–45. *King George VI on white background.*

No.	Type	Description	Unused	Used
38	**100*a***	3 p. slate	15	20
39		½ a. purple	20	20
40		9 p. green	30	85
41		1 a. carmine	30	20
42	**101**	1 a. 3 p. bistre	50	1·60
43		1½ a. dull violet	65	35
44		2 a. vermilion	65	25
45		3 a. bright violet	90	1·40
46		3½ a. bright blue	2·25	2·50
47	**102**	4 a. brown	90	40
48		6 a. turquoise-green	5·50	3·50
49		8 a. slate-violet	55	70
50		12 a. lake	1·75	1·50
38/50		*Set of* 13	13·00	12·50

Stamps of Great Britain surcharged

For similar surcharges without the name of the country, see BRITISH POSTAL AGENCIES IN EASTERN ARABIA.

BAHRAIN 1 ANNA (3)

BAHRAIN 5 RUPEES (4)

1948 (1 Apr)–**49.** *Surch as T* **3**, **4** (*2 r. and 5 r.*) *or similar surch with bars at foot* (*10 r.*).

No.	Type	Description	Unused	Used
51	**128**	½ a. on ½d. pale green	20	35
52		1 a. on 1d. pale scarlet	20	35
53		1½ a. on 1½d. pale red-brown	20	70
54		2 a. on 2d. pale orange	20	35
55		2½ a. on 2½d. light ultramarine	50	80
56		3 a. on 3d. pale violet	20	35
57	**129**	6 a. on 6d. purple	20	25
58	**130**	1 r. on 1s. bistre-brown	90	90
59	**131**	2 r. on 2s. 6d. yellow-green	2·50	5·00
60		5 r. on 5s. red	8·50	17·00
60*a*	**132**	10 r. on 10s. ultramarine (4.7.49)	55·00	60·00
51/60*a*		*Set of* 11	60·00	75·00

BAHRAIN 2½ ANNAS (5)

BAHRAIN 15 RUPEES (6)

1948 (26 Apr). *Silver Wedding, surch as T* **5** *or* **6**.

No.	Type	Description	Unused	Used
61	**137**	2½ a. on 2½d. ultramarine	25	30
62	**138**	15 r. on £1 blue	45·00	70·00

1948 (29 July). *Olympic Games, surch as T* **5**, *but in one line* (*6 a.*) *or two lines* (*others*); *the 1 r. also has a square of dots as T* **7**.

No.	Type	Description	Unused	Used
63	**139**	2½ a. on 2½d. ultramarine	25	55
		a. Surch double	£325	£450
64	**140**	3 a. on 3d. violet	35	75
65	**141**	6 a. on 6d. bright purple	45	1·25
66	**142**	1 r. on 1s. brown	90	2·00

The only used copies seen of No. 63a were cancelled-to-order at Experimental P.O. K-121 (Muharraq) on 23 October 1948.

BAHRAIN 3 ANNAS

(7)

1949 (10 Oct). *75th Anniv of U.P.U., surch as T* **7**, *in one line* (*2½ a.*) *or in two lines* (*others*).

No.	Type	Description	Unused	Used
67	**143**	2½ a. on 2½d. ultramarine	40	55
68	**144**	3 a. on 3d. violet	60	95
69	**145**	6 a. on 6d. bright purple	80	1·50
70	**146**	1 r. on 1s. brown	1·40	2·00

BAHRAIN 2 RUPEES (7*a*) "2" level with "RUPEES". "BAHRAIN" sharp

BAHRAIN 2 RUPEES (7*b*) "2" raised "BAHRAIN" worn

The third type (No. 77b) is as Type II but the vertical distance between "BAHRAIN" and "2 RUPEES" is 16 mm. instead of 15 mm. and the value is set more to the left of "BAHRAIN".

1950 (2 Oct)–**55.** *Surch as T* **3** *or* **7a** (*rupee values*).

No.	Type	Description	Unused	Used
71	**128**	½ a. on ½d. pale orange (3.5.51)	20	40
72		1 a. on 1d. light ultramarine (3.5.51)	20	40
73		1½ a. on 1½d. pale green (3.5.51)	25	1·25
74		2 a. on 2d. pale red-brown (3.5.51)	25	35
75		2½ a. on 2½d. pale scarlet (3.5.51)	25	2·00
76	**129**	4 a. on 4d. light ultramarine	70	1·50
77	**147**	2 r. on 2s. 6d. yellow-green (3.5.51)	9·00	5·00
		a. Surch with Type **7b** (1955)	40·00	25·00
		b. Third type (1955)	£200	40·00
		ba. "I" inverted and raised	£450	£130
78	**148**	5 r. on 5s. red (3.5.51)	12·00	9·00
79	**149**	10 r. on 10s. ultramarine (3.5.51)	19·00	14·00
71/79		*Set of* 9	38·00	30·00

1952 (5 Dec)–**54.** *Q.E. II* (*W* **153**), *Surch as T* **3**.

No.	Type	Description	Unused	Used
80	**154**	½ a. on ½d. orange-red (31.8.53)	5	10
		a. Fraction "½" omitted	65·00	85·00
81		1 a. on 1d. ultramarine (31.8.53)	10	10
82	**154**	1½ a. on 1½d. green	12	10
83		2 a. on 2d. red-brown (31.8.53)	12	5
84	**155**	2½ a. on 2½d. carmine-red	20	10
85		3 a. on 3d. deep lilac (B.) (18.1.54)	20	5
86	**156**	4 a. on 4d. ultramarine (2.11.53)	95	30
87	**157**	6 a. on 6d. reddish purple (18.1.54)	60	5
88	**160**	12 a. on 1s. 3d. green (2.11.53)	2·50	60
89	**159**	1 r. on 1s. 6d. grey-blue (2.11.53)	2·75	10
80/89		*Set of* 10	6·75	1·40

The word BAHRAIN is in taller letters on the 1½ a., 2½a., 3 a. and 6 a.

2½ ANNAS BAHRAIN (8)

1953 (3 June). *Coronation. Surch as T* **8**, *or similarly.*

No.	Type	Description	Unused	Used
90	**161**	2½ a. on 2½d. carmine-red	80	85
91	**162**	4 a. on 4d. ultramarine	1·50	2·00
92	**163**	12 a. on 1s. 3d. deep yellow-green	2·00	2·00
93	**164**	1 r. on 1s. 6d. deep grey-blue	2·00	1·50

BAHRAIN 2 RUPEES I

BAHRAIN 2 RUPEES II

BAHRAIN 2 RUPEES III

(9)

BAHRAIN 5 RUPEES I

BAHRAIN 5 RUPEES II

(10)

BAHRAIN 10 RUPEES I

BAHRAIN 10 RUPEES II

(11)

TYPE I (T **9/11**). Type-set opt. Bold thick letters with sharp corners and straight edges.

TYPE II (T **9/11**). Plate-printed opt. Thinner letters, rounded corners and rough edges. Bars wider apart.

TYPE III (T **9**). Plate-printed opt. Similar to Type II as regards the position of the bars on all 40 stamps of the sheet, but the letters are thinner and with more rounded corners than in II, while the ink of the surcharge is less black.

The general characteristics of Type II of the 2 r. are less pronounced than in the other values, but a distinguishing test is in the relative position of the bars and the "U" of "RUPEES". In Type II (except for the 1st stamp, 5th row) the bars start immediately beneath the left-hand edge of the "U". In Type I they start more to the right.

In the 10 r. the "1" and the "0" are spaced 0.9 mm in Type I and only 0.6 mm in Type II.

1955 (23 Sept)–**60.** *T* **166/8** (*Waterlow ptgs*) *surch as T* **9/11**.

No.	Type	Description	Unused	Used
94	**166**	2 r. on 2s. 6d. black-brown (Type I)	6·50	1·25
		a. Type II (13.5.58)	10·00	8·00
		b. Type III (No. 536a, D.L.R.) (29.1.60)	30·00	45·00
95	**167**	5 r. on 5s. rose-red (Type I)	14·00	5·50
		a. Type II (19.8.57)	17·00	8·00
96	**168**	10 r. on 10s. ultramarine (Type I)	35·00	7·50
		a. Type II (13.5.58)	90·00	£100
		ab. Type II. Surch on No. 538a (D.L.R. ptg)	£200	

1956–7. *Q.E. II* (*W* **165**), *surch as T* **3**.

No.	Type	Description	Unused	Used
97	**154**	½ a. on ½d. orange-red (1.57)	10	15
98	**156**	4 a. on 4d. ultramarine (8.6.56)	6·50	12·00
99	**157**	6 a. on 6d. reddish purple (5.12.56)	50	40
100	**160**	12 a. on 1s. 3d. green (2.8.56)	8·50	13·00
101	**159**	1 r. on 1s. 6d. grey-blue (4.3.57)	1·75	10
		a. Surch double		

(New Currency. 100 naye paise = 1 rupee)

BAHRAIN NP 1 NP (12)

BAHRAIN 3 NP NP (13)

BAHRAIN 75 NP (14)

1957 (1 Apr)–**59.** *Q.E. II* (*W* **165**), *surch as T* **12** (*1 n.p., 15 n.p., 25 n.p., 40 n.p., and 50 n.p.*), *T* **14** (*75 n.p.*) *or T* **13** (*others*).

No.	Type	Description	Unused	Used
102	**157**	1 n.p. on 5d. brown	5	10
103	**154**	3 n.p. on ½d. orange-red	25	20
104		6 n.p. on 1d. ultramarine	25	20
105		9 n.p. on 1½d. green	25	12
106		12 n.p. on 2d. light red-brown	30	20

107	155	15 n.p. on 2½d. carmine-red (Type I)	25	15
		a. Type II (1959)	40	20
108		20 n.p. on 3d. deep lilac (B.)	20	5
109	156	25 n.p. on 4d. ultramarine	75	70
110	157	40 n.p. on 6d. reddish purple	40	5
		a. Deep claret (1959)	55	10
111	158	50 n.p. on 9d. bronze-green	3·25	2·00
112	160	75 n.p. on 1s. 3d. green	2·25	60
102/112		*Set of* 11	7·25	4·00

(15)

1957 (1 Aug). *World Scout Jubilee Jamboree. Surch in two lines as T* **15** *(15 n.p.), or in three lines (others).*

113	170	15 n.p. on 2½d. carmine-red	75	65
114	171	25 n.p. on 4d. ultramarine	90	85
115	172	75 n.p. on 1s. 3d. green	1·25	1·00

1960 (24 May). *Q.E. II (W* **179***), surch as T* **12**.

116	155	15 n.p. on 2½d. carmine-red (Type II)	6·50	11·00

16 17
Shaikh Sulman bin Hamed al-Khalifa

(Des M. Farrar Bell. Photo Harrison (T **16**). Des O. C. Meronti. Recess D.L.R. (T **17**))

1960 (1 July). *P* 15 × 14 *(T* **16***) or* 13½ × 13 *(T* **17***).*

117	16	5 n.p. bright blue	5	5
118		15 n.p. red-orange	10	5
119		20 n.p. reddish violet	10	5
120		30 n.p. bistre-brown	10	5
121		40 n.p. grey	15	5
122		50 n.p. emerald-green	15	12
123		75 n.p. chocolate	25	15
124	17	1 r. black	1·00	20
125		2 r. rose-red	2·75	40
126		5 r. deep blue	4·50	1·25
127		10 r. bronze-green	11·00	3·00
117/127		*Set of* 11	18·00	5·00

18 Shaikh Isa bin Sulman al-Khalifa

19 Air Terminal, Muharraq

20 Deep Water Harbour

(Des M. Farrar Bell. Photo Harrison (5 to 75 n.p.). Des D. C. Rivett. Recess B.W. (others))

1964 (22 Feb). *P* 15 × 14 *(T* **18***) or* 13½ × 13 *(T* **19/20***).*

128	18	5 n.p. bright blue	5	5
129		15 n.p. orange red	10	5
130		20 n.p. reddish violet	10	5
131		30 n.p. olive-brown	10	8
132		40 n.p. slate	15	8
133		50 n.p. emerald-green	15	8
134		75 n.p. brown	25	10
135	19	1 r. black	85	12
136		2 r. carmine-red	3·00	35
137	20	5 r. ultramarine	5·00	2·00
138		10 r. myrtle-green	10·00	4·75
128/138		*Set of* 11	18·00	7·00

LOCAL STAMPS

The following stamps were issued primarily for postage within Bahrain, but apparently also had franking value when used on external mail.

L 1 Shaikh Sulman bin Hamed al-Khalifa L 2

(Types L **1/2**. Recess D.L.R.)

1953–56. *P* 12 × 12½.

L1	L 1	½ a. deep green (1.10.56)	1·40	60
L2		1 a. deep blue (1.10.56)	1·40	60
L3		1½ a. carmine (15.2.53)	50	30

1957 (16 Oct). *As Nos.* L 1/3 *but values in new currency.*

L4		3 p. deep green	3·25	1·50
L5		6 p. carmine	3·25	1·50
L6		9 p. deep blue	3·25	1·50

1961 (20 Mar). *P* 12 × 12½.

L 7	L 2	5 p. green	1·00	40
L 8		10 p. carmine-red	80	40
L 9		15 p. grey	70	30
L10		20 p. blue	80	35
L11		30 p. sepia	75	30
L12		40 p. ultramarine	80	35
L7/12		*Set of* 6	4·25	1·90

The Bahrain Post Department took over the postal services on 1 January 1966. Later stamp issues will be found in Part 19 (*Middle East*) of the Stanley Gibbons catalogue.

Bangkok *see* British Post Office in Siam

Bangladesh

Prior to the issue of these stamps, various Pakistan issues were overprinted by local postmasters, mainly using handstamps. These are of philatelic interest, but are outside the scope of the catalogue.

1 Map of Bangladesh

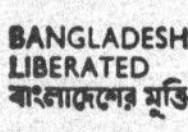

(2)

(Des B. Mullick. Litho Format)

1971 (29 July). *Vert designs as T* **1**. *P* 14 × 14½.

1	10 p. indigo-blue, red-orange and pale blue	5	5
2	20 p. multicoloured	5	5
3	50 p. multicoloured	8	8
4	1 r. multicoloured	15	15
5	2 r. deep greenish blue, light new blue and rose-magenta	30	30
6	3 r. apple-green, dull yellowish green and greenish blue	40	40
7	5 r. multicoloured	60	60
8	10 r. gold, rose-magenta & deep greenish blue	1·50	1·50
1/8	*Set of* 8	2·75	2·75

Designs:—20 p. "Dacca University Massacre"; 50 p. "75 Million People"; 1 r. Flag of Independence; 2 r. Ballot box; 3 r. Broken chain; 5 r. Shaikh Mujibur Rahman; 10 r. "Support Bangla Desh" and map.

1971 (20 Dec). *Liberation. Nos.* 1 *and* 7/8 *optd with T* **2**.

9	10 p. indigo-blue, red-orange and pale blue	5	5
10	5 r. multicoloured (O.)	1·00	1·00
11	10 r. gold, rose-magenta & deep greenish blue	1·75	2·00

The remaining values of the original issue were also overprinted and placed on sale in Great Britain but were not issued in Bangladesh. (*Price for the complete set £3 un.*)

On 1 February 1972 the Agency placed on sale a further issue in the flag, map and Shaikh Mujibur designs in new colours and new currency (100 paisas = 1 taka). This issue proved to be unacceptable to the Bangladesh authorities who declared them to be invalid for postal purposes, no supplies being sold within Bangladesh. The values comprise 1, 2, 3, 5, 7, 10, 15, 20, 25, 40, 50, 75 p. and 1, 2 and 5 t. (*Price for set of 14 un., £1.*)

(New Currency. 100 paisa = 1 taka)

3 "Martyrdom" **4** Flames of Independence

(Des and photo Indian Security Printing Press, Nasik)

1972 (21 Feb). *In Memory of the Martyrs. P* 13.

12	3	20 p. dull green and rose-red	5	5

(Photo Indian Security Printing Press, Nasik)

1972 (26 Mar). *First Anniv of Independence. P* 13.

13	4	20 p. brown-lake and red	5	5
14		60 p. dull ultramarine and red	8	10
15		75 p. reddish violet and red	10	12

5 Doves of Peace **6** "Homage to Martyrs"

(Litho B.W.)

1972 (16 Dec). *Victory Day. P* 13.

16	5	20 p. multicoloured	5	5
17		60 p. multicoloured	12	10
18		75 p. multicoloured	15	12

(Des K. G. Mustafa. Litho B.W.)

1973 (25 Mar). *In Memory of the Martyrs. P* 13.

19	6	20 p. multicoloured	5	5
20		60 p. multicoloured	8	10
21		1 t. 35, multicoloured	20	30

7 Embroidered Quilt **8** Court of Justice

(Litho B.W.)

1973 (30 Apr). *T* **7/8** *and similar designs. P* 14½ × 14 *(50 p., 1 t., 5 t., 10 t.) or* 14 × 14½ *(others).*

22	2 p. black	5	5
23	3 p. blue-green	5	5
	a. Imperf (pair)		
24	5 p. light brown	5	5
25	10 p. slate-black	5	5
26	20 p. yellow-green	10	5
27	25 p. bright reddish mauve	15	5
28	50 p. bright purple	15	5
29	60 p. greenish slate	15	5
30	75 p. yellow-orange	15	10
31	90 p. orange-brown	15	10
32	1 t. light violet	50	25
33	2 t. olive-green	75	40
34	5 t. grey-blue	1·25	90
35	10 t. rose	2·00	1·75
22/35	*Set of* 14	5·00	3·50

Designs: *As T* **7**—3 p. Jute field; 5 p. Jack fruit; 10 p. Bullocks ploughing; 20 p. Rakta jaba (flower); 25 p. Bengal tiger; 60 p. Bamboo grove; 75 p. Plucking tea; 90 p. Handicrafts. *Horiz (28 × 22 mm)*—50 p. Hilsa (fish). *Horiz as T* **8**—5 t. Fishing boat; 10 t. Sixty-dome mosque, Bagerhat. *Vert as T* **8**—2 t. Date tree.

See also Nos. 49/51*a* and 64/75.

9 Flame Emblem **10** Family, Map and Graph

(Des and litho Govt Printer, Dacca)

1973 (10 Dec). *5th Anniv of Declaration of Human Rights. P* 13½.

36	9	10 p. multicoloured	5	5
37		1 t. 25, multicoloured	15	15

(Des K. G. Mustafa. Litho B.W.)

1974 (10 Feb). *First Population Census. P* 13½.

38	10	20 p. multicoloured	5	5
39		25 p. multicoloured	5	5
40		75 p. multicoloured	12	12

11 Copernicus and Heliocentric System — 12 U.N. H.Q. and Bangladesh Flag

(Litho B.W.)

1974 (22 July). *500th Birth Anniv of Copernicus*. P 13 × 13½.

41 **11** 25 p. yellow-orange, bluish violet & blk . . 10 8
a. Imperf (pair) . . . . . . 22·00
42 75 p. orange, yellow-green and black . . 25 20

(Litho B.W.)

1974 (25 Sept). *Bangladesh's Admission to the U.N. Multi-coloured; frame colour given*. P 13.

43 **12** 25 p. light lilac 5 5
44 1 t. light greenish blue 15 20

13 U.P.U. Emblem — 14 Courts of Justice

(Des K. G. Mustafa. Litho B.W.)

1974 (9 Oct). *Centenary of Universal Postal Union*. T **13** *and similar vert design. Multicoloured; country-name on a yellow background* (Nos. 45/6) *or a blue background* (Nos. 47/8). P 13 × 13½.

45 25 p. Type **13** 5 5
46 1 t. 25, Mail runner 15 15
47 1 t. 75, Type **13** 20 20
48 5 t. As 1 t. 25 . . . . 80 1·10

The above exist imperforate in a miniature sheet from a restricted printing.

1974–76. *Nos. 32/5 redrawn with revised value inscriptions as* T **14**.

49 1 t. light violet 45 10
50 2 t. olive 65 45
51 5 t. grey-blue (1975) 90 70
51*a* 10 t. rose (1976) . . . . . . 1·75 1·10

15 Royal Bengal Tiger — 16 Symbolic Family

(Des and litho B.W.)

1974 (4 Nov). *Wildlife Preservation*. T **15** *and similar vert designs. Multicoloured*. P 13 × 13½.

52 25 p. Type **15** 35 10
53 50 p. Tiger whelp 80 45
54 2 t. Tiger in stream . . . . . . 2·50 3·00

(Litho B.W.)

1974 (30 Dec). *World Population Year. "Family Planning for All"*. T **16** *and similar multicoloured designs*. P 14.

55 25 p. Type **16** 15 5
56 70 p. Village family 25 25
57 1 t. 25, Heads of family (*horiz*) 40 55

The Bengali numerals on the 70 p. resemble "90".

17 Radar Antenna — 18 Woman's Head

(Des and litho B.W.)

1975 (14 June). *Inauguration of Betbunia Satellite Earth Station*. P 13½.

58 **17** 25 p. black, silver and dull red 5 5
59 1 t. black, silver and ultramarine . . 20 25

(Des A. F. Karim. Litho Asher & Co., Melbourne)

1975 (31 Dec). *International Women's Year*. P 15.

60 **18** 50 p. multicoloured 8 5
61 2 t. multicoloured 25 30

(Litho Asher & Co., Melbourne)

1976–77. *As Nos. 24/31 and 49/51a but redrawn in smaller size and colours changed* (5, 75 *p.*). P 14½ × 15 (50 *p.*), 14½ (1 *to* 10 *t.*) *or* 15 × 14½ (*others*). (*a*) 23 × 18 *mm* (50 *p.*) *or* 18 × 23 *mm* (*others*).

64 5 p. deep yellow-green (11.2.76) 5 5
a. Imperf (pair) . . . . . . 10·00
65 10 p. slate-black (28.4.76) 5 5
66 20 p. yellow-green (1.76) 5 5
a. Imperf (pair) . . . . . . 10·00
67 25 p. bright reddish mauve (1.76) 5 5
a. Imperf (pair) . . . . . . 10·00
68 50 p. light purple (8.6.76) 10 5
69 60 p. greenish slate (10.11.76) 5 5
70 75 p. yellow-olive (10.11.76) 5 5
71 90 p. orange-brown (10.11.76) 5 5

(*b*) 20 × 32 *mm* (2 *t.*) *or* 32 × 20 *mm* (*others*)

72 1 t. light violet (1.76) 30 8
73 2 t. olive-green (8.6.76) 20 15
a. Imperf (pair) . . . . . .
74 5 t. grey-blue (10.11.76) 30 35
75 10 t. rose (25.2.77) 60 65
64/75 . . . . . . *Set of* 12 1·60 1·40

19 Telephones, 1876 and 1976 — 20 Eye and Nutriments

(Des A. F. Karim. Litho Asher & Co., Melbourne)

1976 (10 Mar). *Telephone Centenary*. T **19** *and similar vert design*. P 15.

76 2 t. 25, multicoloured 20 20
77 5 t. dull vermilion, apple-green and black . . 50 65

Design:— 5 t. Alexander Graham Bell.

(Des A. F. Karim. Litho Asher & Co., Melbourne)

1976 (17 Apr). *Prevention of Blindness*. P 15.

78 **20** 30 p. multicoloured 5 5
79 2 t. 25, multicoloured 25 30

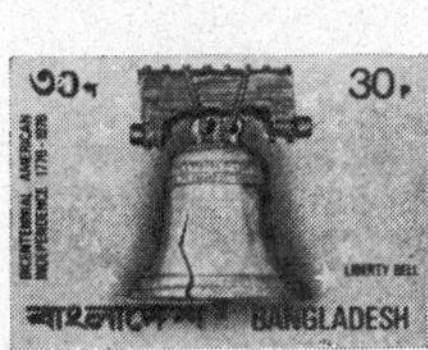

21 Liberty Bell — 22 Industry, Science, Agriculture and Education

(Des E. W. Roberts. Photo Heraclio Fournier)

1976 (29 May). *Bicentenary of American Revolution*. T **21** *and similar horiz designs. Multicoloured*. P 14.

80 30 p. Type **21** 5 5
81 2 t. 25, Statue of Liberty 25 25
82 5 t. *Mayflower* 60 60
83 10 t. Mount Rushmore . . . . . . 90 1·00
MS84 167 × 95 mm. Nos. 80/3 . . . . 3·00 3·00

No. **MS**84 also exists imperforate from a restricted printing.

(Des K. G. Mustafa. Litho Asher & Co., Melbourne)

1976 (29 July). *25th Anniv of the Colombo Plan*. P 15.

85 **22** 30 p. multicoloured 5 5
86 2 t. 25, multicoloured 25 30

23 Hurdling — 24 The Blessing

(Des K. G. Mustafa. Litho Asher & Co., Melbourne)

1976 (29 Nov). *Olympic Games, Montreal*. T **23** *and similar multi-coloured designs*. P 14½.

87 25 p. Type **23** 5 5
88 30 p. Running (*horiz*) 5 5
a. Imperf (pair) . . . . . .
89 1 t. Pole vault 10 10
90 2 t. 25, Swimming (*horiz*) 25 25
91 3 t. 50, Gymnastics 45 45
92 5 t. Football 60 60
87/92 . . . . . . *Set of* 6 1·40 1·40

(Des and litho Harrison)

1977 (7–17 Feb). *Silver Jubilee*. T **24** *and similar vert designs. Multicoloured*. P 14 × 14½.

93 30 p. Type **24** 10 8
94 2 t. 25, Queen Elizabeth II 35 40
95 10 t. Queen Elizabeth and Prince Philip . . 1·00 1·25
MS96 114 × 127 mm. Nos. 93/5. P 14½ (17 Feb) 2·00 2·50

25 Qazi Nazrul Islam (poet)

(Des K. G. Mustafa. Litho Harrison)

1977 (29 Aug). *Qazi Nazrul Islam Commemoration*. T **25** *and similar design*. P 14.

97 40 p. blue-green and black 5 5
98 2 t. 25, sepia, stone and chestnut 20 25

Design: *Horiz*—2 t. 25, Head and shoulders portrait.

26 Bird with Letter

(Des A. F. Karim. Litho Harrison)

1977 (29 Sept). *15th Anniv of Asian-Oceanic Postal Union*. P 14.

99 **26** 30 p. light rose, new blue and dull green 5 5
100 2 t. 25, light rose, new blue and light grey 20 25

27 Malayan Sun Bear — 28 Camp Fire and Tent

(Des K. G. Mustafa. Litho Harrison)

1977 (9 Nov). *Animals*. T **27** *and similar multicoloured designs*. P 13.

101 40 p. Type **27** 5 5
102 1 t. Spotted deer 15 10
103 2 t. 25, Leopard (*horiz*) 30 20
104 3 t. 50, Goyal (*horiz*) 45 35
105 4 t. Elephant (*horiz*) 55 40
106 5 t. Tiger (*horiz*) 70 65
101/6 . . . . . . *Set of* 6 2·00 1·60

The Bengali numerals on the 40 p. resemble "80", and that on the 4 t. resembles "8".

(Des A. F. Karim. Litho Harrison)

1978 (22 Jan). *First National Scout Jamboree*. T **28** *and similar designs*. P 13.

107 40 p. red, deep blue and light blue 5 5
108 3 t. 50, carmine, deep blue and green . . 45 30
109 5 t. reddish lilac, deep blue and bright green 55 45

Designs: *Horiz*—3 t. 50, Scout stretcher-team. *Vert*—5 t. Scout salute.

29 *Michelia champaca*

(Des and litho Harrison)

1978 (29 Apr). *Flowers. T* **29** *and similar horiz designs. Multicoloured. P* 14.

110	40 p. Type **29**	5	5
111	1 t. *Cassia fistula*	15	10
112	2 t. 25, *Delonix regia*	30	20
113	3 t. 50, *Nymphaea nouchali*	45	30
114	4 t. *Butea monosperma*	50	35
115	5 t. *Anthocephalus indicus*	55	45
110/15	*Set of* 6	1·75	1·25

30 St. Edward's Crown and Sceptres

31 Sir Alan Cobham's "DH50"

(Des and litho Harrison)

1978 (20 May). *25th Anniv of Coronation. T* **30** *and similar vert designs. Multicoloured. P* 14.

116	40 p. Type **30**	5	5
117	3 t. 50, Balcony scene	25	30
118	5 t. Queen Elizabeth and Prince Philip	40	45
119	10 t. Coronation portrait by Cecil Beaton	80	90
MS120	89 × 121 mm. Nos. 116/19. P 14½	1·60	2·00

(Des and litho Harrison)

1978 (15 June). *75th Anniv of Powered Flight. T* **31** *and similar horiz designs. P* 13.

121	40 p. multicoloured	5	5
122	2 t. 25, blackish brown and light new blue	30	30
123	3 t. 50, blackish brown and yellow	40	40
124	5 t. multicoloured	65	65

Designs:—2 t. 25, Captain Hans Bertram's seaplane *Atlantis*; 3 t. 50, Wright brothers' *Flyer I*, 5 t. "Concorde".

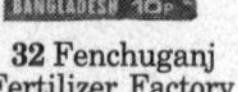

32 Fenchuganj Fertilizer Factory

33 Tawaf-E-Ka'aba, Mecca

(Des P. Mandal (5 p.), A. F. Karim (10 p.), Harrison (30, 50 p., 1 t.). Photo Harrison)

1978 (6 Nov)–**82.** *Designs as T* **32**. *P* 14½.

125	5 p. deep brown (25.3.79)	5	5
126	10 p. turquoise-blue	5	5
127	15 p. orange (1.8.80)	5	5
128	20 p. brown-red (15.12.79)	5	5
129	25 p. grey-blue (1982)	5	5
130	30 p. deep green (10.12.80)	5	5
131	40 p. maroon (15.12.79)	5	5
132	50 p. black (1981)	5	5
134	80 p. brown (1.8.80)	5	5
136	1 t. reddish violet (6.81)	5	5
137	2 t. dull ultramarine (21.10.81)	12	15
125/37	*Set of* 11	40	40

Designs: *Horiz*—5 p. Lalbag Fort; 25 p. Jute on a boat; 40 p., 50 p. Baital Mukarram Mosque; 1 t. Dotara (musical instrument); 2 t. Karnaphuli Dam. *Vert*—15 p. Pineapple; 20 p. Bangladesh gas; 30 p. Banana Tree; 80 p. Mohastan Garh.

(Des A. F. Karim. Litho J.W.)

1978 (9 Nov). *Holy Pilgrimage to Mecca. T* **33** *and similar multicoloured design. P* 13.

140	40 p. Type **33**	5	5
141	3 t. 50, Pilgrims in Wuquf, Arafat (*horiz*)	25	30

34 Jasim Uddin

(Des P. Mandal. Litho J.W.)

1979 (14 Mar). *3rd Death Anniv of Jasim Uddin (poet). P* 14.

142	**34**	40 p. multicoloured	5	5

35 Moulana Abdul Hamid Khan Bhashani

36 Sir Rowland Hill

(Des P. Mandal. Litho Harrison)

1979 (17 Nov). *3rd Death Anniv of Moulana Abdul Hamid Khan Bhashani (national leader). P* 12½.

143	**35**	40 p. multicoloured	5	5

(Des A. F. Karim. Litho Harrison)

1979 (26 Nov). *Death Centenary of Sir Rowland Hill. T* **36** *and similar designs. P* 14.

144	40 p. turquoise-blue, Venetian red and pale turquoise-blue	5	5
145	3 t. 50, multicoloured	35	30
146	10 t. multicoloured	80	1·00
MS147	176 × 96 mm. Nos. 144/6	1·25	1·40

Designs: *Horiz*—3 t. 50, 1971 10 p. definitive stamp and Sir Rowland Hill; 10 t. 1974 1 t. 25, Centenary of U.P.U. commemorative stamp and Sir Rowland Hill.

37 Children with Hoops

38 Rotary International Emblem

(Des P. Mandal. Litho Harrison)

1979 (17 Dec). *International Year of the Child. T* **37** *and similar vert designs. Multicoloured. P* 14 × 14½.

148	40 p. Type **37**	5	5
149	3 t. 50, Child with kite	30	35
150	5 t. Children playing	45	50
MS151	170 × 120 mm. Nos. 148/50. P 14½	1·90	1·90

(Des P. Mandal. Litho Rosenbaum Bros, Vienna)

1980 (23 Feb). *75th Anniv of Rotary International. T* **38** *and similar vert design showing club emblem. P* 13½.

152	40 p. black, vermilion and bistre-yellow	5	5
153	5 t. gold and bright blue	40	45

39 Canal Digging

40 A. K. Fazlul Huq

(Des A. F. Karim. Litho Rosenbaum Bros, Vienna)

1980 (27 Mar). *Mass Participation in Canal Digging. P* 13½.

154	**39**	40 p. multicoloured	5	5

(Des P. Mandal. Litho Rosenbaum Bros, Vienna)

1980 (27 Apr). *18th Death Anniv of A. K. Fazlul Huq (national leader). P* 13½.

155	**40**	40 p. multicoloured	5	5

On the face value the Bengali numerals resemble "80".

41 Early forms of Mail Transport

42 Dome of the Rock

(Des A. F. Karim. Litho Rosenbaum Bros, Vienna)

1980 (5 May). *"London 1980" International Stamp Exhibition. T* **41** *and similar horiz design. Multicoloured. P* 13½.

156	1 t. Type **41**	8	10
157	10 t. Modern forms of mail transport	80	85
MS158	140 × 95 mm. Nos. 156/7	1·00	1·00

(Des A. F. Karim. Litho Harrison)

1980 (21 Aug). *Palestinian Welfare. P* 14 × 14½.

159	**42**	50 p. deep mauve	5	5

43 Outdoor Class

(Des P. Mandal. Litho Rosenbaum Bros, Vienna)

1980 (23 Aug). *Education. P* 13½.

160	**43**	50 p. multicoloured	5	5

44 Beach Scene

45 Mecca

(Des A. F. Karim. Litho Rosenbaum Bros, Vienna)

1980 (27 Sept). *World Tourism Conference, Manila. T* **44** *and similar horiz design showing different beach scene. P* 14.

161	50 p. multicoloured	5	5
	a. Horiz pair. Nos. 161/2	55	55
162	5 t. multicoloured	50	50
MS163	140 × 88 mm. Nos. 161/2	75	75

Nos. 161/2 were printed together, *se-tenant*, in horizontal pairs throughout the sheet.

(Des A. F. Karim. Litho Rosenbaum Bros, Vienna)

1980 (11 Nov). *Moslem Year 1400 A.H. Commemoration. P* 14 × 13½.

164	**45**	50 p. multicoloured	5	5

46 Begum Roquiah

47 Deer and Scout Emblem

(Des A. F. Karim. Litho Rosenbaum Bros, Vienna)

1980 (9 Dec). *Birth Centenary of Begum Roquiah (campaigner for women's rights). P* 14.

165	**45**	50 p. multicoloured	5	5
166		2 t. multicoloured	15	20

(Des A. F. Karim. Litho Rosenbaum Bros, Vienna)

1981 (1 Jan). *5th Asia-Pacific/2nd Bangladesh Scout Jamboree. P* 13½.

167	**47**	50 p. multicoloured	5	5
168		5 t. multicoloured	40	45

2nd.
CENSUS
1981

(48)

49 Queen Elizabeth the Queen Mother

1981 (6 Mar). *Second Population Census. Nos. 38/40 optd with T* **48**.

169	**10**	20 p. multicoloured	5	5
170		25 p. multicoloured	5	5
171		75 p. multicoloured	5	5

(Des R. Granger Barrett. Litho Rosenbaum Bros, Vienna)

1981 (16 Mar). *80th Birthday of Queen Elizabeth the Queen Mother. P* 13½.

172	**49**	1 t. multicoloured	10	10
173		15 t. multicoloured	1·40	1·40
MS174		95 × 73 mm. Nos. 172/3	1·50	1·60

50 Revolutionary with Flag and Sub-machine-gun

51 Bangladesh Village and Farm Scenes

(Litho Rosenbaum Bros, Vienna)

1981 (26 Mar). *Tenth Anniv of Independence. T* **50** *and similar vert design. Multicoloured. P* 13½.

175	50 p. Type **50**	5	5
176	2 t. Figures on map symbolising Bangladesh life-style	15	20

(Des A. F. Karim. Litho Rosenbaum Bros, Vienna)

1981 (1 Sept). *U.N. Conference on Least Developed Countries, Paris. P* 14 × 13½.

177	**51**	50 p. multicoloured	5	5

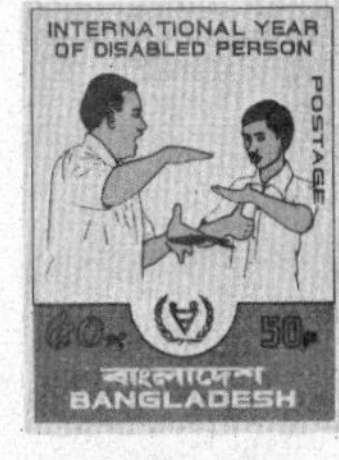

52 Kemal Atatürk in Civilian Dress

53 Deaf People using Sign Language

(Des F. Karim and P. Mandal. Litho Rosenbaum Bros, Vienna)

1981 (10 Nov). *Birth Centenary of Kemal Atatürk (Turkish statesman). T* **52** *and similar vert design. Multicoloured. P* 13½.

178	50 p. Type **52**	5	5
179	1 t. Kemal Atatürk in uniform	5	5

(Des F. Karim. Litho Ueberreuter, Austria)

1981 (26 Dec). *International Year for Disabled Persons. T* **53** *and similar multicoloured design. P* 13½ × 14 *(50 p.) or* 14 × 13½ *(2 t.).*

180	50 p. Type **53**	5	5
181	2 t. Disabled person writing *(horiz)*	12	15

54 Farm Scene and Wheat Ear

55 River Scene

(Des F. Karim. Litho Ueberreuter, Austria)

1981 (31 Dec). *World Food Day. P* 13½ × 14.

182	**54**	50 p. multicoloured	5	5

(Litho Rosenbaum Bros, Vienna)

1982 (22 May). *10th Anniv of Human Environment Conference. P* 13½ × 14.

183	**55**	50 p. multicoloured	5	5

56 Dr. M. Hussain

57 Knotted Rope surrounding Bengali "75"

(Litho Ueberreuter, Vienna)

1982 (9 Oct). *Dr. M. Hussain Commemoration. P* 13½.

184	**56**	50 p. multicoloured	5	5

(Litho Ueberreuter, Vienna)

1982 (21 Oct). *75th Anniv of Boy Scout Movement and 125th Birth Anniv of Lord Baden-Powell. T* **57** *and similar multicoloured design. P* 13½.

185	50 p. Type **57**	5	5
186	2 t. Lord Baden-Powell *(vert)*	10	12

58 Capt. Mohiuddin Jahangir

59 Metric Scales

(Litho Ueberreuter, Vienna)

1982 (16 Dec). *Heroes and Martyrs of the Liberation. T* **58** *and similar horiz designs. Multicoloured: background colours of commemorative plaque given. P* 13½.

187	50 p. Type **58** (pale orange)	5	5
	a. Horiz strip of 7. Nos. 187/93	25	
188	50 p. Sepoy Hamidur Rahman (apple-green)	5	5
189	50 p. Sepoy Mohammed Mustafa Kamal (dull claret)	5	5
190	50 p. Muhammed Ruhul Amin (bistre-yellow)	5	5
191	50 p. Flt. Lt. M. Matiur Rahman (olive-bistre)	5	5
192	50 p. Lance-Naik Munshi Abdur Rob (chestnut)	5	5
193	50 p. Lance-Naik Nur Mouhammad (bright green)	5	5
187/93	*Set of* 7	25	30

Nos. 187/93 were printed together, *se-tenant*, in horizontal strips of 7 throughout the sheet.

(Des F. Karim. Litho Ueberreuter, Vienna)

1983 (10 Jan). *Introduction of Metric Weights and Measures. T* **59** *and similar multicoloured design. P* 13½.

194	50 p. Type **59**	5	5
195	2 t. Weights, jug and tape measure *(horiz)*	12	15

60 Dr. Robert Koch

61 Open Stage Theatre

(Des F. Karim. Litho Ueberreuter, Vienna)

1983 (20 Feb). *Centenary (1982) of Robert Koch's Discovery of Tubercle Bacillus. T* **60** *and similar vert design. Multicoloured. P* 13½.

196	50 p. Type **60**	5	5
197	1 t. Microscope, slide and X-ray	8	10

(Des F. Karim and P. Mandal. Litho Ueberreuter, Vienna)

1983 (14 Mar). *Commonwealth Day. T* **61** *and similar horiz designs. Multicoloured. P* 13½.

198	1 t. Type **61**	8	10
199	3 t. Boat race	20	25
200	10 t. Snake dance	65	70
201	15 t. Picking tea	1·00	1·10

62 Dr. Muhammed Shahidulla

63 Magpie Robin

(Litho Ueberreuter, Vienna)

1983 (10 July). *Dr. Muhammed Shahidulla (Bengali scholar) Commemoration. P* 13½.

202	**62**	50 p. multicoloured	5	8

(Des F. Karim and P. Mandal. Litho Ueberreuter, Vienna)

1983 (17 Aug). *Birds of Bangladesh. T* **63** *and similar multicoloured designs. P* 13½.

203	50 p. Type **63**	5	8
204	2 t. White-breasted kingfisher *(vert)*	12	15
205	3 t. 75 Lesser Golden-backed Woodpecker *(vert)*	20	25
206	5 t. White-winged Wood Duck	35	40
MS207	165 × 110 mm. Nos. 203/6 *(sold at* 13 *t.)*	90	95

64 *Macrobrachium rosenbergii*

(Litho Ueberreuter, Vienna)

1983 (31 Oct). *Fishes. T* **64** *and similar horiz designs. Multicoloured. P* 13½.

208	50 p. Type **64**	5	5
209	2 t. *Stromateus cinereus*	12	15
210	3 t. 75, *Labeo rohita*	25	30
211	5 t. *Anabas testudineus*	35	40
MS212	119 × 98 mm. Nos. 208/11. Imperf *(sold at* 13 *t.)*	90	95

Visit of Queen
Nov. '83

(65)

1983 (14 Nov). *Visit of Queen Elizabeth II. No.* 95 *optd with T* **65** *in red.*

213	10 t. Queen Elizabeth and Prince Philip	60	65

66 Conference Hall, Dhaka

67 Early Mail Runner

(Litho Ueberreuter)

1983 (5 Dec). *14th Islamic Foreign Ministers' Conference, Dhaka. T* **66** *and similar horiz design. Multicoloured. P* 14 × 13½.

214	50 p. Type **66**	5	8
215	5 t. Old Fort, Dhaka	30	35

(Litho Ueberreuter, Vienna)

1983 (21 Dec). *World Communications Year. T* **67** *and similar multicoloured designs. P* 14.

216	50 p. Type **67**	5	5
217	5 t. Mail runner and dish aerial	35	40
218	10 t. Sailing ship, steam train and jet airliner *(horiz)*	70	75

প্রথম বাংলাদেশ জাতীয় ডাকটিকিট প্রদর্শনী - ১৯৮৪

68 Carrying Mail by Boat

(69)

(Litho State Ptg Wks, Moscow)

1983 (21 Dec). *Postal Communications. T* **68** *and similar designs. P* 11½ × 12½ *(5, 25 p.),* 12 × 11½ *(1, 2, 5 t.) or* 12½ × 11½ *(others).*

219	5 p. turquoise-blue	5	5
220	10 p. purple	5	5
221	15 p. new blue	5	5
222	20 p. grey-black	5	5
223	25 p. slate	5	5
224	30 p. brown	5	5
225	50 p. light brown	5	5
226	1 t. dull ultramarine	5	8
227	2 t. deep bluish green	12	15
228	5 t. bright purple	25	30
219/28	*Set of* 10	70	80

Designs: *Horiz* (22 × 17 *mm*)—10 p. Counter, Dhaka G.P.O.; 15 p. I.W.T.A. Terminal, Dhaka; 20 p. Inside railway travelling post office; 30 p. Emptying pillar box; 50 p. Mobile post office van. (30 × 19 *mm*)—1 t. Kamalapur Railway Station, Dhaka; 2 t. Zia International Airport; 5 t. Khulna G.P.O. *Vert* (17 × 22 *mm*)—25p. Delivering a letter.

1984 (1 Feb). *1st National Stamp Exhibition (1st issue). Nos.* 161/2 *optd with T* **69** *(5 t.) or* "First Bangladesh National Philatelic Exhibition–1984" *(50 p.), both in red.*

229	**44**	50 p. multicoloured	5	8
		a. Horiz pair. Nos. 229/30	35	
230	–	5 t. multicoloured	30	35

70 Girl with Stamp Album

(Des P. Mandal. Litho Harrison)

1984 (12 May). *1st National Stamp Exhibition (2nd issue). T* **70** *and similar triangular design. Multicoloured. P* 14.

231 50 p. Type **70** 5 8
a. Pair. Nos. 231/2 55
232 7 t. 50, Boy with stamp album 50 55

Nos. 231/2 were printed together, *se-tenant*, in pairs throughout the sheet.

71 Sarus Crane and Gavial

(Des P. Mandal and M. Akand. Litho Ueberreuter, Vienna)

1984 (17 July). *Dhaka Zoo. T* **71** *and similar vert design. Multicoloured. P* 14.

233 1 t. Type **71** 5 8
234 2 t. Peafowl and Royal Bengal Tiger 12 15

OFFICIAL STAMPS

SERVICE (O 1) SERVICE (O 2) **SERVICE** (O 3)

1973 (30 Apr). *Nos. 22/7, 29/30, 32 and 34 optd with Type* O 1.

O 1 **7** 2 p. black (R.) 5 5
O 2 – 3 p. blue-green 5 5
O 3 – 5 p. light brown 5 5
O 4 – 10 p. slate-black (R.) 5 5
O 5 – 20 p. yellow-green 5 5
O 6 – 25 p. bright reddish mauve 15 8
O 7 – 60 p. greenish slate (R.) 40 12
O 8 – 75 p. yellow-orange 20 10
O 9 **8** 1 t. light violet .. .. 2·75 1·75
O10 – 5 t. grey-blue .. .. 2·00 1·50
O1/10 .. .. *Set of* 10 5·00 3·25

1974–75. *Nos. 49/51 optd with Type* O 1.

O11 **14** 1 t. light violet 35 15
O12 – 2 t. olive 55 30
O13 – 5 t. grey-blue (1975) .. .. 1·50 1·10

1976. *Nos. 64/70 optd with Type* O **2** *and Nos. 72/4 optd with Type* O **3**.

O14 5 p. deep yellow-green (11.2.76) 5 5
O15 10 p. slate-black (R.) (28.4.76) 5 5
O16 20 p. yellow-green (1.76) 5 5
O17 25 p. bright reddish mauve (1.76) 5 5
O18 50 p. light purple (8.6.76) 5 5
O19 60 p. greenish slate (R.) (10.11.76) 5 5
O20 75 p. yellow-olive (10.11.76) 5 5
O21 1 t. ultramarine (1.76) 5 8
O22 2 t. olive-green (8.6.76) 12 15
O23 5 t. grey-blue (10.11.76) 30 35
O14/23 .. .. *Set of* 10 60 70

1979–82. *Nos. 128/37 optd with Type* O 1.

O24 20 p. brown-red 5 5
O25 25 p. grey-blue (1982) 5 5
O26 40 p. maroon 5 5
O27 50 p. black (24.9.81) 5 5
O28 80 p. brown 5 5
O29 1 t. reddish violet (24.9.81) 5 5
O30 2 t. dull ultramarine (21.10.81) 12 15
O24/30 .. .. *Set of* 7 25 30

Barbados

Regular mails between Barbados and Great Britain were established at an early date in the island's development and it is believed that the British Mail Packet Agency at Bridgetown was opened in 1688 as part of the considerable expansion of the Packet Service in that year.

From 1851 the colonial authorities were responsible for the internal postal system, but the British G.P.O. did not relinquish control of the overseas post until 1858.

For illustrations of the handstamp types see BRITISH POST OFFICES ABROAD notes, following GREAT BRITAIN.

CROWNED-CIRCLE HANDSTAMPS

CC1 CC **1** BARBADOS (3.10.1849) (R.) *Price on cover* £475

Combination covers exist with the local postage paid by a Barbados 1d. stamp and the overseas fee by an example of No. CC1.

During shortages of low value stamps in 1893 (17 February to 15 March) and 1896 (24 January to 28 April) No. CC1 was utilised, struck in black, on local mail. *Price on cover from* £60.

PRICES FOR STAMPS ON COVER TO 1945

Nos. 1/35	*from* × 5
Nos. 43/63	*from* × 4
Nos. 64/6	*from* × 10
Nos. 67/83	*from* × 5
Nos. 86/8	*from* × 3
Nos. 89/103	*from* × 4
No. 104	*from* × 20
Nos. 105/15	*from* × 4
Nos. 116/24	*from* × 8
Nos. 125/33	*from* × 5
Nos. 135/44	*from* × 4
Nos. 145/52	*from* × 6
No. 153	*from* × 8
Nos. 158/62	*from* × 5
Nos. 163/9	*from* × 3
Nos. 170/96	*from* × 4
Nos. 197/8	*from* × 10
Nos. 199/212	*from* × 6
Nos. 213/39	*from* × 3
No. 240	*from* × 10
Nos. 241/4	*from* × 5
Nos. 245/7	*from* × 6
Nos. 248/56*a*	*from* × 4
Nos. 257/61	*from* × 5
Nos. D1/3	*from* × 25

CROWN COLONY

1 Britannia 2

(Recess Perkins, Bacon & Co)

1852 (15 April)–**55.** *Paper blued. No wmk. Imperf.*

1 **1** (½d.) yellow-green .. .. — £700
2 (½d.) deep green .. .. 95·0 £300
3 (1d.) blue .. .. 21·00 £190
4 (1d.) deep blue .. .. 11·00 65·00
4*a* (2d.) greyish slate £300 £900
b. Bisected (1d.) (on cover) .. .. † £4750
5 (4d.) brownish red (1855) .. .. .. 27·00 £450

It has now been proved that the stamp in greyish slate was intended for issue as a 2d. stamp. As its use for this rate was extremely limited it was officially bisected and used for the penny rate in August and September, 1854.

Apart from the shade, which is distinctly paler, No. 4*a* can be distinguished from No. 5*b* by the smooth even gum, the gum of No. 5*b* being yellow and patchy, giving a mottled appearance to the back of the stamp. No. 5*a* also has the latter gum.

Prepared for use but not issued

5*a* **1** (No value), slate-blue (*shades*) .. .. 12·00
5*b* (No value), deep slate £400

1855–57. *White paper. No wmk. Imperf.*

7 **1** (½d.) yellow-green £475 £130
8 (½d.) green .. .. 95·00 £250
9 (1d.) pale blue .. .. 70·00 70·00
10 (1d.) deep blue .. .. 15·00 60·00

1858. *No wmk. Imperf.*

11 **2** 6d. pale rose-red £750 £140
11*a* 6d. deep rose-red £700 £250
12 1s. brown-black £200 £110
12*a* 1s. black .. .. £130 70·00

1860. *No wmk. (a) Pin-perf* 14.

13 **1** (½d.) yellow-green £1500 £375
14 (1d.) pale blue £1500 £150
15 (1d.) deep blue £1500 £150

(b) Pin-perf 12½

16 **1** (½d.) yellow-green £3750 £700
16*a* (1d.) blue .. .. — £1200

(c) Pin-perf 14 × 12½

16*b* **1** (½d.) yellow-green .. .. — £3000

1861. *No wmk. Clean-cut perf* 14 *to* 16.

17 **1** (½d.) deep green .. .. 45·00 12·00
18 (1d.) pale blue .. .. £500 22·00
19 (1d.) blue .. .. £650 22·00
a. Bisected (½d.) (on cover) .. .. † £2000

1861–70. *No wmk. (a) Rough perf* 14 *to* 16.

20 **1** (½d.) deep green .. .. 10·00 8·50
21 (½d.) green .. .. 6·00 5·50
21*a* (½d.) blue-green .. .. 45·00 75·00
b. Imperf (pair) £375
22 (½d.) grass-green .. .. 17·00 8·00
a. Imperf (pair) £375
23 (1d.) blue (1861) .. .. 26·00 5·50
a. Imperf (pair) £425
24 (1d.) deep blue .. .. 14·00 4·25
a. Bisected diag (½d.) (on cover) .. † £900
25 (4d.) dull rose-red (1861) .. .. .. 38·00 19·00
a. Imperf (pair) £525
26 (4d.) dull brown-red (1865) .. .. .. 70·00 27·00
a. Imperf (pair) £750
27 (4d.) lake-rose (1868) .. .. 45·00 40·00
a. Imperf (pair) £750
28 (4d.) dull vermilion (1869) .. .. .. £130 48·00
a. Imperf (pair) £750
29 **2** 6d. rose-red (1861) .. .. £160 11·00
30 6d. orange-red (1864) .. .. 55·00 13·00
31 6d. bright orange-vermilion (1868) .. 32·00 13·00
32 6d. dull orange-vermilion (1870) .. .. 32·00 11·00
a. Imperf (pair) £350
33 6d. orange (1870) .. .. 60·00 18·00
34 1s. brown-black (1863) .. .. .. 30·00 9·50
a. Error. Blue £12000
35 1s. black (1866) .. .. 17·00 11·00
a. Imperf between (horiz pair) £4000

(b) P 11 *to* 12

36 **1** (½d.) green £5500
37 (1d.) blue £2250

No. 34a only exists with manuscript corner to corner cross cleaned off.

Nos. 36 and 37 are only known unused.

1870. *Wmk Large Star, Type* w 1. *Rough perf* 14 *to* 16.

43 **1** (½d.) green .. .. 42·00 10·00
a. Imperf (pair) £450
43*b* (½d.) yellow-green .. .. 85·00 40·00
44 (1d.) blue .. .. £800 26·00
a. Blue paper .. .. — 48·00
45 (4d.) dull vermilion .. .. £600 29·00
46 **2** 6d. orange-vermilion .. .. £450 32·00
47 1s. black .. .. £180 21·00

1871. *Wmk Small Star, Type* w **2**. *Rough perf* 14 *to* 16.

48 **1** (1d.) blue .. .. 42·00 5·00
49 (4d.) dull rose-red .. .. £550 26·00
50 **2** 6d. orange-vermilion .. .. £250 20·00
51 1s. black .. .. 90·00 20·00

1872. *Wmk Small Star, Type* w **2**. *(a) Clean-cut perf* 14½ *to* 15½.

52 **1** (1d.) blue .. .. £160 4·00
a. Bisected diag (½d.) (on cover) .. † £850
53 **2** 6d. orange-vermilion .. .. £400 22·00
54 1s. black .. .. 70·00 8·00

(b) P 11 *to* 13 × 14½ *to* 15½

56 **1** (½d.) green .. .. £160 10·00
57 (4d.) dull vermilion .. .. £250 30·00

1873. *Wmk Large Star, Type* w **1**. *Clean-cut perf* 14½ *to* 15½.

58 **1** (½d.) green .. .. £140 11·00
59 (4d.) dull rose-red .. .. £550 75·00
60 **2** 6d. orange-vermilion .. .. £450 50·00
a. Imperf between (horiz pair) £2250
b. Imperf (pair) £120
61 1s. black .. .. 55·00 8·00
a. Imperf between (horiz pair)

Two used singles of No. 60b have been seen.

1873 (June). *Wmk Small Star, Type* w **2** *(two points upwards). P* 14.

63 **2** 3d. brown-purple £325 £110

3

1873. *Wmk Small Star, Type* w **2**. *P* 15½ × 15.

64 **3** 5s. dull rose £1200 £400

1874 (May). *Wmk Large Star, Type* w **1**. *(a) Perf* 14.

65 **2** ½d. deep green .. .. 9·50 7·00
66 1d. deep blue .. .. 42·00 2·75

(b) Clean-cut perf 14½ *to* 15½

66*a* **2** 1d. deep blue .. .. — £2250
b. Imperf (pair)

(Recess D.L.R.)

1875–78. *Wmk Crown CC (sideways on 6d. and 1s.). (a) P* 12½.

67 **2** ½d. bright green .. .. 9·00 4·00
68 4d. deep red .. .. £150 11·00
69 6d. bright yellow (aniline) .. .. .. £900 70·00
70 6d. chrome-yellow .. .. £550 65·00
71 1s. violet (aniline) .. .. £500 38·00

(b) P 14

72 **2** ½d. bright green (1876) .. .. .. 5·50 3·25
73 1d. dull blue .. .. 11·00 1·10
a. Bisected (½d.) (on cover) .. .. † £700
74 1d. grey-blue .. .. 12·00 1·25
a. Wmk sideways .. .. — £1400
75 3d. mauve-lilac (1878) .. .. .. 75·00 11·00
76 4d. red (1878) .. .. 70·00 14·00
77 4d. carmine .. .. £120 5·00
78 4d. crimson-lake .. .. £375 7·00
79 6d. chrome-yellow (1876) .. .. .. 90·00 5·00
80 6d. yellow .. .. £250 16·00
81 1s. purple (1876) .. .. £100 5·00
82 1s. violet (aniline) .. .. £1500 40·00
83 1s. dull mauve .. .. £250 4·25
a. Bisected (6d.) (on cover) .. .. † £3250

(c) P 14 × 12½

84 2 4d. red £8500

Very few specimens of No. 84 have been found unused. One used specimen is known.

1D. (A) 1D. (B) 1D. (C)

1878 (March). *No. 64, with lower label removed, divided vertically by perforation, and each half surch sideways in black.*

(A) *Large numeral "1", 7 mm high with curved serif, and large letter "D", 2¾ mm high.*

86 3 1d. on half 5s. dull rose £2750 £600
a. Unsevered pair (both No. 86) .. £9000 £1800
b. Ditto, Nos. 86 and 87 .. .. — £3500
c. Ditto, Nos. 86 and 88 .. ..
d. As 86b without dividing perf .. — £12000

(B) *As last, but numeral with straight serif.*

87 3 1d. on half 5s. dull rose £3000 £700
a. Unsevered pair .. .. .. — £2500

(C) *Smaller numeral "1", 6 mm high and smaller "D", 2½ mm high.*

88 3 1d. on half 5s dull rose £3500 £800
a. Unsevered pair £9500 £2500

All types of the surcharge are found reading upwards as well as downwards, and there are minor varieties of the type.

4

HALF-PENNY
(5)

(Typo D.L.R.)

1882–86. *Wmk Crown CA. P* 14.

89 4 ½d. dull green (1882) .. .. .. 2·75 1·25
90 ½d. green .. .. .. 2·75 1·25
91 1d. rose (1882) .. .. .. 7·50 1·25
a. Bisected (½d.) (on cover) .. .. † £500
92 1d. carmine .. .. .. 2·00 50
93 2½d. ultramarine (1882) .. .. 18·00 1·50
94 2½d. deep blue .. .. .. 22·00 1·25
95 3d. deep purple (1885) .. .. 65·00 20·00
96 3d. reddish purple .. .. 4·25 6·50
97 4d. grey (1882) .. .. .. £200 6·00
98 4d. pale brown (1885) .. .. 3·75 2·75
99 4d. deep brown .. .. .. 3·75 1·50
100 6d. olive-black (1886) .. .. 38·00 19·00
102 1s. chestnut (1886) .. .. 21·00 21·00
103 5s. bistre (1886) £190 £225
89/103 .. .. *Set of* 9 £425 £250
95/103, except 97, Optd "Specimen" *Set of* 5 £225

1892. *No.* 99 *surch with T* 5.

104 4 ½d. on 4d. deep brown .. .. 35 1·00
a. No hyphen .. .. .. 3·50 4·50
b. Surch double (R. + Bk.) £600 £900
ba. Do. No hyphen £1200 £1200
c. Surch "PENNY HALF" .. ..

6 Seal of Colony

7

(Typo D.L.R.)

1892–1903. *Wmk Crown CA. P* 14.

105 6 ¼d. slate-grey and carmine (1896) .. 35 40
106 ½d. dull green 25 35
107 1d. carmine 55 20
108 2d. slate-black and orange (1899) .. 6·00 3·00
109 2½d. ultramarine .. .. .. 4·75 80
110 5d. grey-olive .. .. .. 7·00 5·00
111 6d. mauve and carmine .. .. 7·00 5·50
112 8d. orange and ultramarine .. .. 3·25 9·50
113 10d. dull blue-green and carmine .. 8·00 10·00
114 2s. 6d. blue-black and orange .. 23·00 26·00
115 2s. 6d. violet and green (1903) .. 35·00 42·00
105/15 .. .. *Set of* 11 85·00 95·00
105/115 Optd "Specimen" .. .. *Set of* 11 £200

See also Nos. 135/44 and 163/9.

(Typo D.L.R.)

1897–98. *Diamond Jubilee. T* 7. *Wmk Crown CC. P* 14.

(a) *White paper* (1897)

116 ¼d. grey and carmine 50 60
117 ½d. dull green .. .. .. 1·50 60
118 1d. rose .. .. .. 2·50 85
119 2½d. ultramarine .. .. .. 5·50 1·50
120 5d. olive-brown .. .. .. 9·50 11·00
121 6d. mauve and carmine .. .. 11·00 11·00
122 8d. orange and ultramarine .. .. 9·00 11·00
123 10d. blue-green and carmine .. .. 20·00 23·00
124 2s. 6d. blue-black and orange .. .. 20·00 24·00
116/124 .. .. .. *Set of* 9 70·00 75·00
116/124 Optd "Specimen" .. .. *Set of* 9 £225

(b) *Paper blued* (1898)

125 ¼d. grey and carmine .. .. .. 26·00 30·00
126 ½d. dull green .. .. .. 27·00 30·00
127 1d. carmine .. .. .. 35·00 40·00
128 2½d. ultramarine .. .. .. 38·00 45·00
129 5d. olive-brown £225 £250
130 6d. mauve and carmine .. .. 95·00 £100
131 8d. orange and ultramarine .. .. 80·00 £100
132 10d. dull green and carmine £120 £140
133 2s. 6d. blue-black and orange .. .. 85·00 90·00

1904–5. *Wmk Mult Crown CA. P* 14.

135 6 ¼d. slate-grey and carmine 65 55
136 ½d. dull green .. .. .. 1·50 20
137 1d. carmine .. .. .. 1·00 20
139 2½d. blue .. .. .. 5·50 70
141 6d. mauve and carmine .. .. 12·00 12·00
142 8d. orange and ultramarine .. .. 19·00 24·00
144 2s. 6d. violet and green .. .. 28·00 40·00
135/144 .. .. *Set of* 7 60·00 70·00

See also Nos. 163/9.

8 Nelson Monument

(Des G. Goodman. Recess D.L.R.)

1906. *Nelson Centenary. Wmk Crown CC. P* 14.

145 8 ¼d. black and grey 75 90
146 ½d. black and pale green .. .. 3·50 80
147 1d. black and red .. .. .. 3·00 35
148 2d. black and yellow .. .. .. 4·00 7·50
149 2½d. black and bright blue .. .. 6·50 7·00
150 6d. black and mauve .. .. .. 21·00 21·00
151 1s. black and rose .. .. .. 22·00 24·00
145/151 .. .. .. *Set of* 7 55·00 55·00
145/51 Optd "Specimen" .. .. *Set of* 7 £190

Two sets may be made of the above: one on thick, opaque, creamy white paper; the other on thin, rather transparent, bluish white paper.

See also Nos. 158/62*a*.

9

Kingston Relief Fund. 1d.
(10)

(Des Lady Carter. Recess D.L.R.)

1906 (15 Aug). *Tercentenary of Annexation. Wmk Multiple Crown CA (sideways). P* 14.

152 9 1d. black, blue and green .. .. 10·00 1·75
152 Optd "Specimen" .. .. .. 85·00

1907 (25 Jan). *Kingston Relief Fund. No.* 108 *surch with T* 10.

153 6 1d. on 2d. slate-black and orange (R.) .. 3·00 4·00
a. Surch inverted (25.2.07) .. .. 3·00 4·50
b. Surch double £550 £600
c. Surch double, both inverted .. £550
d. Surch tête-bêche (pair) £600
e. No stop after "1d." .. .. .. 15·00 18·00
ea. Do., surch, inverted (25.2.07) .. 15·00 18·00

The above stamp was sold for 2d., of which 1d. was retained for the postal revenue, and the other 1d. given to a fund for the relief of the sufferers by the earthquake in Jamaica.

1907 (6 July). *Nelson Centenary. Wmk Mult Crown CA. P* 14.

158 8 ¼d. black and grey .. .. .. 1·90 2·25
161 2d. black and yellow .. .. .. 9·00 13·00
162 2½d. black and bright blue .. .. 14·00 17·00
a. Black and indigo £1000 £1100

1909–10. *Wmk Mult Crown CA. P* 14.

163 6 ¼d. brown 40 50
164 ½d. blue-green .. .. .. 1·75 90
165 1d. red 85 30
166 2d. greyish slate (1910) .. .. 4·50 6·50
167 2½d. bright blue (1910) .. .. 8·50 3·75
168 6d. dull and bright purple (1910) .. 9·00 13·00
169 1s. black/*green* (1910) .. .. 16·00 17·00
163/169 .. .. *Set of* 7 38·00 38·00
163, 165/6, 168/9 Optd "Specimen" *Set of* 5 £100

11

12

13

(Typo D.L.R.)

1912 (23 July–13 Aug). *Wmk Mult Crown CA. P* 14.

170 11 ¼d. brown (23 July) 15 25
a. Pale brown 60 55
171 ½d. green (23 July) 25 15
172 1d. red 90 30
a. Scarlet .. .. .. 4·75 90
173 2d. greyish slate .. .. .. 3·00 8·50
174 2½d. bright blue .. .. .. 1·75 1·10
175 12 3d. purple/*yellow* .. .. .. 2·25 5·00
176 4d. red and black/*yellow* .. .. 2·25 7·50
177 6d. purple and dull purple .. .. 5·00 6·50
178 13 1s. black/*green* .. .. .. 8·50 12·00
179 2s. blue and purple/*blue* .. .. 42·00 48·00
180 3s. violet and green .. .. .. 45·00 48·00
170/180 .. .. .. *Set of* 11 £100 £120
170/80 Optd "Specimen" .. .. *Set of* 11 £160

14

WAR TAX
(15)

(Recess D.L.R.)

1916 (16 June)–**20.** *Wmk Mult Crown CA. P* 14.

181 14 ¼d. deep brown 30 35
182 ¼d. chestnut-brown (4.18) 40 40
183 ¼d. sepia-brown (11.18) .. .. 1·00 1·50
184 ½d. green 75 50
185 ½d. deep green (4.18) 75 50
186 ½d. pale green (10.18) 90 80
187 1d. deep red .. .. .. 6·50 4·00
187*a* 1d. bright carmine-red .. .. 2·25 65
188 1d. pale carmine-red (7.17) .. .. 2·75 80
189 2d. grey .. .. .. 4·75 7·50
190 2½d. ultramarine .. .. .. 80 1·10
191 3d. purple/*yellow* (*thin paper*) .. 2·00 2·50
191*a* 3d. deep purple/*yellow* (*thick paper*) (1920) .. .. .. 13·00 15·00
192 4d. red/*yellow* (*thin paper*) (23.6.16) .. 1·60 6·00
193 6d. purple .. .. .. 2·00 3·25
194 1s. black/*green* .. .. .. 5·50 5·50
195 2s. purple/*blue* .. .. .. 20·00 21·00
196 3s. deep violet (23.6.16) .. .. 35·00 55·00
181/196 .. .. .. *Set of* 11 70·00 90·00
181/96 Optd "Specimen" .. .. *Set of* 11 £225

See also Nos. 199/200*a*.

1917 (10 Oct)–**18.** *War Tax. Optd in London with T* 15.

197 11 1d. bright red (Optd S. £55) 20 35
a. Imperf (pair) £2000
198 1d. pale red (*thicker bluish paper*) (4.18) 65 55

1918 (18 Feb). *Colours changed. Wmk Mult Crown CA. P* 14.

199 14 4d. black and red .. .. .. 75 3·50
200 3s. green and deep violet .. .. 17·00 23·00
200*a* 3s. green and bright violet £120 £140
199/200 Optd "Specimen" .. .. *Set of* 2 £150

The centres of these are from a new die having no circular border line.

16

17

(Recess D.L.R.)

1920 (9 Sept)–**21.** *Victory. P* 14.

(a) *Wmk Mult Crown CA* (*sideways on T* 17)

201 16 ¼d. black and bistre-brown 25 60
202 ½d. black and bright yellow-green .. 40 45
203 1d. black and vermilion 40 30
204 2d. black and grey .. .. .. 1·75 6·00
205 2½d. indigo and ultramarine .. .. 3·50 6·50
206 3d. black and purple .. .. .. 1·60 3·50
207 4d. black and blue-green .. .. 1·60 5·00
208 6d. black and brown-orange .. .. 2·50 6·00
209 17 1s. black and bright green .. .. 8·00 14·00
210 2s. black and brown .. .. .. 11·00 17·00
211 3s. black and dull orange .. .. 22·00 28·00

(b) *Wmk Mult Script CA*

212 16 1d. black and vermilion (22.8.21) .. 5·50 55
201/212 .. .. *Set of* 12 50·00 80·00
201/12 Optd "Specimen" .. .. *Set of* 12 £250

18

19

(Recess D.L.R.)

1921 (14 Nov)–**24.** *P* 14. (a) *Wmk Mult Crown CA.*

213 18 3d. purple/*pale yellow* .. .. .. 70 3·00
214 4d. red/*pale yellow* .. .. .. 1·60 3·00
215 1s. black/*emerald* .. .. .. 5·50 11·00

(b) *Wmk Mult Script CA*

217 18 ¼d. brown 30 12
219 ½d. green 30 40
220 1d. red 45 25
a. Bright rose-carmine .. .. 3·00 1·00
221 2d. grey .. .. .. 1·60 40
222 2½d. ultramarine .. .. .. 1·00 3·00

225 6d. reddish purple 2·00 4·50
226 1s. black/*emerald* (18.9.24) 20·00 22·00
227 2s. purple/*blue* 15·00 20·00
228 3s. deep violet 18·00 25·00
213/228 *Set of* 12 60·00 85·00
213/28 Optd "Specimen" *Set of* 12 £150

1925–35. *T* **19**. *Wmk Mult Script CA.* I. *P* 14. II. *P* 13½ × 12½ (1932).

		I.		II.	
229	¼d. brown	12	12	†	
230	½d. green	12	12	40	12
231	1d. scarlet	15	12	50	12
231*a*	1½d. orange	2·25	60	55	30
232	2d. grey	40	1·25	†	
233	2½d. blue	95	45	†	
233*a*	2½d. bright ultramarine	3·25	20	3·75	55
234	3d. purple/*pale yellow*	40	35	†	
234*a*	3d. reddish purple/*yell* (1935)	3·00	3·50	†	
235	4d. red/*pale yellow*	90	90	†	
236	6d. purple	1·40	1·40	†	
237	1s. black/*emerald*	2·75	5·00	10·00	14·00
237*a*	1s. brownish black/*bright yellow-green*	4·25	9·50	†	
238	2s. purple/*blue*	6·00	10·00	†	
238*a*	2s. 6d. carmine/*blue*	16·00	20·00	†	
239	3s. deep violet	11·00	13·00	†	
229/239	*Set of* 13	38·00	48·00	†	
229/39 Optd/Perf "Specimen"	*Set of* 13	£170			

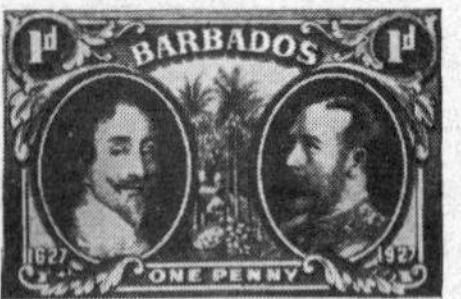

20 King Charles I and King George V

21 Badge of the Colony

(Recess B.W.)

1927 (17 Feb). *Tercentenary of Settlement of Barbados. Wmk Mult Script CA. P* 12½.
240 **20** 1d. carmine (Optd S. £50) 90 90

1935 (6 May). *Silver Jubilee. As Nos.* 91/4 *of Antigua, but ptd by Waterlow. P* 11 × 12.
241 1d. deep blue and scarlet 30 35
242 1½d. ultramarine and grey 60 65
243 2½d. brown and deep blue 2·25 1·75
244 1s. slate and purple 8·00 9·50
241/4 Perf "Specimen" *Set of* 4 55·00

1937 (14 May). *Coronation. As Nos.* 13/15 *of Aden. P* 14.
245 1d. scarlet 45 45
246 1½d. yellow-brown 65 65
247 2½d. bright blue 1·50 1·50
245/7 Perf "Specimen" *Set of* 3 45·00

(Recess D.L.R.)

1938 (3 Jan)–**48**. *Wmk Mult Script CA. P* 13½ × 13.
248 **21** ½d. green 70 35
a. Perf 14 (8.42) 35·00 2·50
248*b* ½d. yellow-bistre (16.10.42) 15 25
249 1d. scarlet (1941?) 55·00 2·50
a. Perf 14 (1938) 3·50 40
249*b* 1d. blue-green (16.10.42) 45 15
c. Perf 14 (11.42) 15 15
250 1½d. orange 25 15
a. Perf 14 (11.41) 1·25 25
250*b* 2d. claret (3.6.41) 60 80
250*c* 2d. carmine (20.9.43) 20 15
d. Perf 14 (9.44) 20 40
251 2½d. ultramarine 85 95
a. Blue (2.44) 65 2·25
252 3d. brown 35 65
a. Perf 14 (4.41) 30 40
252*b* 3d. blue (1.4.47) 35 35
253 4d. black 30 20
a. Perf 14 (10.44) 30 70
254 6d. violet 20 15
254*a* 8d. magenta (9.12.46) 60 80
255 1s. olive-green 6·00 1·75
a. Brown-olive (8.48) 90 35
256 2s. 6d. purple 3·50 1·10
256*a* 5s. indigo (3.6.41) 5·50 2·25
248/56*a* *Set of* 16 16·00 7·50
248/56*a* Perf "Specimen" *Set of* 16 £170

No. 249a was perforated by two machines, one gauging 13.8 × 14.1. (1938), the other 14.1 (1940).

Nos. 248, 248*b* and 249/*b* exist in coils constructed from normal sheets.

22 Kings Charles I, George VI, Assembly Chamber and Mace

ONE
PENNY

(23)

(Recess D.L.R.)

1939 (27 June). *Tercentenary of General Assembly. Wmk Mult Script CA. P* 13½ × 14.
257 **22** ½d. green 55 35
258 1d. scarlet 60 35
259 1½d. orange 1·60 1·25
260 2½d. bright ultramarine 2·40 2·50
261 3d. brown 2·40 4·75
257/61 Perf "Specimen" *Set of* 5 £170

1946 (18 Sept). *Victory. As Nos.* 28/9 *of Aden.*
262 1½d. red-orange 12 20
263 3d. brown 12 20
262/3 Perf "Specimen" *Set of* 2 48·00

(Surch by Barbados Advocate Co)

1947 (21 Apr). *Surch with T* **23**. (*a*) *P* 14.
264 **21** 1d. on 2d. carmine 45 90

(*b*) *P* 13½ × 13
264*a* **21** 1d. on 2d. carmine 70 1·60

1948 (24 Nov). *Royal Silver Wedding. As Nos.* 30/1 *of Aden.*
265 1½d. orange 15 12
266 5s. indigo 8·50 13·00

1949 (10 Oct). *75th Anniv of Universal Postal Union. As Nos.* 114/17 *of Antigua.*
267 1½d. red-orange 25 30
268 3d. deep blue 50 45
269 4d. grey 1·00 1·00
270 1s. olive 1·40 1·40

(New Currency. 100 cents = 1 Barbados dollar)

24 Dover Fort

27 Statue of Nelson

(Recess B.W.)

1950 (1 May). *T* **24**, **27** *and similar designs. Wmk Mult Script CA. P* 11 × 11½ (*horiz*), 13½ (*vert*).
271 1 c. indigo 20 60
272 2 c. emerald-green 15 30
273 3 c. reddish brown and blue-green 15 50
274 4 c. carmine 15 35
275 6 c. light blue 15 35
276 8 c. bright blue and purple-brown 55 45
277 12 c. greenish blue and brown-olive 90 65
278 24 c. scarlet and black 60 70
279 48 c. violet 3·25 3·00
280 60 c. green and claret 5·50 3·25
281 $1.20, carmine and olive-green 7·00 3·50
282 $2.40, black 12·00 11·00
271/282 *Set of* 12 28·00 22·00

Designs: *Horiz*—2 c. Sugar cane breeding; 3 c. Public buildings; 6 c. Casting net; 8 c. Inter-colonial schooner; 12 c. Flying fish; 24 c. Old Main Guard Garrison; 60 c. Careenage; $2.40, Seal of Barbados. *Vert*—48 c. The Cathedral; $1.20, Map of Barbados and wireless mast.

1951 (16 Feb). *Inauguration of B.W.I. University College. As Nos.* 118/19 *of Antigua.*
283 3 c. brown and blue-green 20 25
284 12 c. blue-green and brown-olive 45 50

36 King George VI and Stamp of 1852

(Recess Waterlow)

1952 (15 Apr). *Barbados Stamp Centenary. Wmk Mult Script CA. P* 13½.
285 **36** 3 c. green and slate-green 20 35
286 4 c. blue and carmine 20 40
287 12 c. slate-green and bright green 25 40
288 24 c. red-brown and brownish black 30 45

37 Harbour Police

(Recess B.W.)

1953 (13 Apr)–**57**. *Designs previously used for King George VI issue, but with portrait or cypher* ($2.40) *of Queen Elizabeth II, as in T* **37**. *Wmk Mult Script CA. P* 11 × 11½ (*horiz*) *or* 13½ (*vert*).
289 1 c. indigo 10 12
290 2 c. orange and deep turquoise (15.4.54) 12 5
291 3 c. black and emerald (15.4.54) 15 5
292 4 c. black and orange (*shades*) (15.4.54) 20 5
293 5 c. blue and deep carmine-red (4.1.54) 20 8
294 6 c. red-brown (15.4.54) 15 5
295 8 c. black and blue (15.4.54) 60 8
296 12 c. turquoise-blue and brown-olive (*shades*) (15.4.54) 75 5
297 24 c. rose-red and black (2.3.56) 45 10
298 48 c. deep violet (2.3.56) 2·25 90
299 60 c. blue-green and brown-purple (*shades*) (3.4.56) 5·50 1·75
300 $1.20, carmine and bronze-green (3.4.56) 9·00 3·25
301 $2.40, black (1.2.57) 10·00 3·50
289/301 *Set of* 13 27·00 9·00

Designs: *Horiz*—1 c. Dover Fort; 2 c. Sugar cane breeding; 3 c. Public buildings; 6 c. Casting net; 8 c. Inter-colonial schooner; 12 c. Flying fish; 24 c. Old Main Guard Garrison; 60 c. Careenage; $2.40, Seal of Barbados. *Vert*—4 c. Statue of Nelson; 48 c. The Cathedral; $1.20, Map of Barbados and wireless mast.

See also Nos. 312/19.

1953 (4 June). *Coronation. As No.* 47 *of Aden.*
302 4 c. black and red-orange 15 10

1958 (23 Apr). *Inauguration of British Caribbean Federation. As Nos.* 135/7 *of Antigua.*
303 3 c. deep green 20 15
304 6 c. blue 30 50
305 12 c. scarlet 35 15

38 Deep Water Harbour, Bridgetown

(Recess B.W.)

1961 (6 May). *Opening of Deep Water Harbour, Bridgetown. W* w **12**. *P* 11 × 12.
306 **38** 4 c. black and red-orange 10 5
307 8 c. black and blue 15 15
308 24 c. carmine-red and black 25 25

SELF-GOVERNMENT

39 Scout Badge and Map of Barbados

40 Deep Sea Coral

(Recess B.W.)

1962 (9 Mar). *Golden Jubilee of Barbados Boy Scout Association. W* w **12**. *P* 11½ × 11.
309 **39** 4 c. black and orange 15 8
310 12 c. blue and olive-brown 40 30
311 $1.20, carmine and olive-green 1·25 1·50

1964 (14 Jan)–**65**. *As Nos.* 289, *etc., but wmk* w **12**.
312 1 c. indigo (6.10.64) 50 75
313 4 c. black and orange 40 50
314 8 c. black and blue (29.6.65) 60 35
315 12 c. turquoise-blue and brown-olive (29.6.65) 60 50
316 24 c. rose-red and black (6.10.64) 50 35
317 48 c. deep violet 3·25 3·50
318 60 c. blue-green and brown-purple (6.10.64) 6·00 7·00
319 $2.40, black (29.6.65) 6·00 6·50
312/19 *Set of* 8 16·00 18·00

The above dates are for Crown Agents releases. The 14.1.64 printings were not released in Barbados until April 1964, the 6.10.64 printings until December 1964 and of the 29.6.65 printings the 8 c. and $2.40 were released from about 15 June 1965 but the 12 c. value was never put on sale in Barbados.

1965 (17 May). *I.T.U. Centenary. As Nos.* 166/7 *of Antigua.*
320 2 c. lilac and red 25 12
321 48 c. yellow and grey-brown 1·50 1·25

(Des V. Whiteley, from drawings by Mrs. J. Walker. Photo Harrison)

1965 (15 July). *Marine Life. Horiz designs as T* **40**. *W* w **12** (*upright*). *P* 14 × 13½.
322 1 c. black, pink and blue 8 15
323 2 c. olive-brown, yellow and magenta 12 15
324 3 c. olive-brown and orange 45 30
325 4 c. deep blue and olive-green 15 8
a. Imperf (pair) £200 90·00
326 5 c. sepia, rose and lilac 20 8
327 6 c. multicoloured 45 12
328 8 c. multicoloured 25 10
329 12 c. multicoloured 35 12
a. Grey printing double 32·00
330 15 c. black, greenish yellow and red 50 45
331 25 c. ultramarine and yellow-ochre 95 65
332 35 c. brown-red and deep green 1·25 65
333 50 c. bright blue and apple-green 2·25 1·40
334 $1 multicoloured 6·50 2·75
335 $2.50, multicoloured 7·50 4·00
322/335 *Set of* 14 19·00 10·00

Designs:—2 c. Lobster; 3 c. Sea Horse; 4 c. Sea Urchin; 5 c. Staghorn Coral; 6 c. Butterfly Fish; 8 c. File Shell; 12 c. Balloon Fish; 15 c. Angel Fish; 25 c. Brain Coral; 35 c. Brittle Star; 50 c. Flying Fish; $1 Queen Conch Shell; $2.50, Fiddler Crab.

The 3 c. value is wrongly inscribed "Hippocanpus", the correct spelling being Hippocampus.

See also Nos. 342, etc.

1966 (24 Jan). *Churchill Commemoration. As Nos.* 170/3 *of Antigua.*
336 1 c. new blue 5 10
337 4 c. deep green 40 15
338 25 c. brown 1·40 65
339 35 c. bluish violet 1·50 85

1966 (4 Feb). *Royal Visit. As Nos. 174/5 of Antigua.*

No.	Description	Unused	Used
340	3 c. black and ultramarine	45	25
341	35 c. black and magenta	2·00	1·00

41 Dolphin

54 Arms of Barbados

1966 (15 Mar)–**69**. *As Nos. 322/35 but wmk w* 12 *(sideways). New value and design (as T* 41).

No.	Description	Unused	Used
342	1 c. black, pink and blue	5	10
343	2 c. olive-brown, yellow and magenta (16.5.67)	10	5
344	3 c. olive-brown and orange (4.12.67) ..	30	20
345	4 c. deep blue and olive-green	20	5
346	5 c. sepia, rose and lilac (23.8.66)	25	5
347	6 c. multicoloured (31.1.67)	30	5
348	8 c. multicoloured (19.9.67)	25	10
349	12 c. multicoloured (31.1.67)	30	10
350	15 c. black, greenish yellow and red	65	10
351	25 c. ultramarine and yellow-ochre (*shades*) ..	90	25
352	35 c. brown-red and deep green (*shades*) (23.8.66)	1·25	25
353	50 c. bright blue and apple-green	1·40	70
354	$1 multicoloured (23.8.66)	3·25	1·50
355	$2.50, multicoloured (23.8.66)	7·00	4·75
355*a*	$5 multicoloured (9.1.69)	14·00	14·00
342/55*a*	.. .. *Set of* 15	27·00	20·00

The 3 c. value is correctly inscribed "Hippocampus".

All values except the 50 c. exist with PVA gum as well as gum arabic but the $5 exists with PVA gum only.

The $5 was released by the Crown Agents on 6 January but was not put on sale locally until 9 January.

INDEPENDENT

(Des. V. Whiteley. Photo Harrison)

1966 (2 Dec). *Independence. T* **54** *and similar multicoloured designs. P* 14.

No.	Description	Unused	Used
356	4 c. Type **54**	10	5
357	25 c. Hilton Hotel (*horiz*)	20	15
358	35 c. G. Sobers (Test cricketer)	75	45
359	50 c. Pine Hill Dairy (*horiz*)	80	60

1967 (6 Jan). *20th Anniv of U.N.E.S.CO. As Nos. 196/8 of Antigua.*

No.	Description	Unused	Used
360	4 c. slate-violet, red, yellow and orange ..	45	10
361	12 c. orange-yellow, violet and deep olive ..	1·25	55
362	25 c. black, bright purple and orange.. ..	1·90	1·25

58 Policeman and Anchor

62 Governor-General Sir Winston Scott, G.C.M.G.

(Des V. Whiteley. Litho D.L.R.)

1967 (16 Oct). *Centenary of Harbour Police. T* **58** *and similar multicoloured designs. P* 14.

No.	Description	Unused	Used
363	4 c. Type **58**	10	5
364	25 c. Policeman with telescope	35	15
365	35 c. Police launch (*horiz*)	45	25
366	50 c. Policeman outside H.Q.	55	35

(Des V. Whiteley. Photo Harrison)

1967 (4 Dec). *First Anniv of Independence. T* **62** *and similar multicoloured designs. P* 14½ × 14 (4 c.) *or* 14 × 14½ (*others*).

No.	Description	Unused	Used
367	4 c. Type **62**	5	5
368	25 c. Independence Arch (*horiz*)	15	15
369	35 c. Treasury Building (*horiz*)	20	20
370	50 c. Parliament Building (*horiz*)	30	30

66 U.N. Building, Santiago, Chile

67 Radar Antenna

(Des G. Vasarhelyi. Photo Harrison)

1968 (27 Feb). *20th Anniv of the Economic Commission for Latin America. P* 14½.

No.	Type	Description	Unused	Used
371	**66**	15 c. multicoloured	10	10

(Des G. Vasarhelyi. Photo Harrison)

1968 (4 June). *World Meteorological Day. T* **67** *and similar multi-coloured designs. P* 14 × 14½ (25 c.) *or* 14½ × 14 (*others*).

No.	Description	Unused	Used
372	3 c. Type **67**	5	5
373	25 c. Meteorological Institute (*horiz*)	15	15
374	50 c. Harp Gun and coat of arms	30	35

70 Lady Baden-Powell, and Guide at Camp Fire

(Des V. Whiteley (from local designs). Photo Harrison)

1968 (29 Aug). *50th Anniv of Girl Guiding in Barbados. T* **70** *and similar horiz designs. P* 14.

No.	Description	Unused	Used
375	3 c. ultramarine, black and gold	8	5
376	25 c. turquoise-blue, black and gold	40	25
377	35 c. orange-yellow, black and gold	50	40

Designs:—25 c. Lady Baden-Powell and Pax Hill; 35 c. Lady Baden-Powell and Guide badge.

73 Hands breaking Chain, and Human Rights Emblem

(Des V. Whiteley. Litho B.W.)

1968 (10 Dec).* *Human Rights Year. T* **73** *and similar horiz designs. P* 11 × 12.

No.	Description	Unused	Used
378	4 c. violet, brown and light green	5	5
379	25 c. black, blue and orange-yellow	15	15
380	35 c. multicoloured	25	25

Designs:—25 c. Human Rights emblem and family enchained; 35 c. Shadows of refugees beyond opening fence.

*This was the local release date but the Crown Agents issued the stamps on 29 October.

76 Racehorses in the Paddock

(Des J. Cooter. Litho Format)

1969 (20 Mar).* *Horse-Racing. T* **76** *and similar horiz designs. Multicoloured. P* 14.

No.	Description	Unused	Used
381	4 c. Type **76**	10	5
382	25 c. Starting-gate	25	5
383	35 c. On the flat	35	30
384	50 c. Winning post	50	45
MS385	117 × 85 mm. Nos. 381/4	2·50	3·00

*This was the local release date but the Crown Agents issued the stamps on 15 March.

80 Map showing "CARIFTA" Countries

81 "Strength in Unity"

(Des J. Cooter. Photo Harrison)

1969 (6 May). *First Anniv of CARIFTA (Caribbean Free Trade Area). W w* 12 *(sideways on T* **80**). *P* 14.

No.	Type	Description	Unused	Used
386	**80**	5 c. multicoloured	5	5
387	**81**	12 c. multicoloured	10	5
388	**80**	25 c. multicoloured	20	25
389	**81**	50 c. multicoloured	25	30

MINIMUM PRICE

The minimum price quoted is 5p which represents a handling charge rather than a basis for valuing common stamps. For further notes about prices see introductory pages.

82 I.L.O. Emblem and "1919-1969".

ONE CENT
(**83**)

(Des Sylvia Goaman. Litho Enschedé)

1969 (12 Aug). *50th Anniv of International Labour Organisation. P* 14 × 13.

No.	Type	Description	Unused	Used
390	**82**	4 c. black, emerald and turquoise-blue	5	5
391		25 c. black, cerise and brown-red ..	20	25

Although released by the Crown Agents on 5 August, the above were not put on sale in Barbados until 12 August.

1969 (30 Aug). *No. 363 surch with T* **83**.

No.	Description	Unused	Used
392	1 c. on 4 c. Type **58**	10	10
	a. Surch double	65·00	

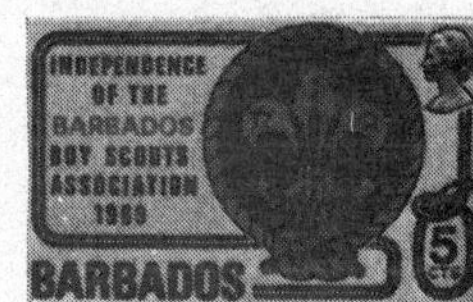

84 National Scout Badge

(Des J. Cooter. Litho Enschedé)

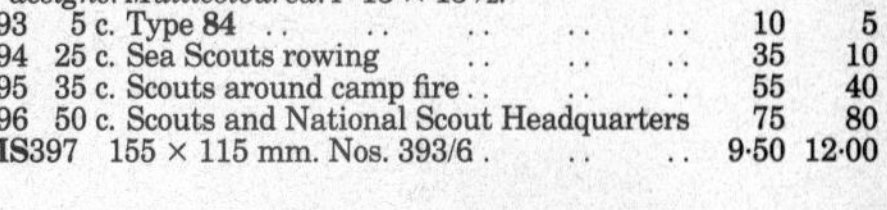

1969 (16 Dec). *Independence of Barbados Boy Scouts Association and 50th Anniv of Barbados Sea Scouts. T* **84** *and similar horiz designs. Multicoloured. P* 13 × 13½.

No.	Description	Unused	Used
393	5 c. Type **84**	10	5
394	25 c. Sea Scouts rowing	35	10
395	35 c. Scouts around camp fire	55	40
396	50 c. Scouts and National Scout Headquarters	75	80
MS397	155 × 115 mm. Nos. 393/6	9·50	12·00

4 X
(**88**)

89 Lion at Gun Hill

1970 (11 Mar). *No. 346 surch locally with T* **88**.

No.	Description	Unused	Used
398	4 c. on 5 c. sepia, rose and lilac	8	10
	a. Vert pair, one without surch	35·00	
	b. Surch double	25·00	
	c. Vert pair, one normal, one surch double		
	d. Surch triple		
	e. Surch normal on front, inverted on back	12·00	
	f. Surch omitted on front, inverted on back	16·00	

(Des J. W. Photo D.L.R.)

1970–71. *Multicoloured designs as T* **89**. *W w* **12** *(sideways on* 12 *c. to* $5). *P* 12½. *A. Chalk-surfaced paper* (4.5.70) *B. Glazed, ordinary paper* (13.12.71, 12 *c.,* 15 *c. and* $2.50; 15.3.71, *others*).

No.	Description	A		B	
399	1 c. Type **89**	5	5	5	10
400	2 c. Trafalgar Fountain ..	5	10	5	10
401	3 c. Montefiore Drinking Fountain	8	12	12	15
402	4 c. St. James' Monument ..	8	10	12	10
403	5 c. St. Anne's Fort	10	10	12	10
404	6 c. Old Sugar Mill, Morgan Lewis	35	50	†	
405	8 c. Cenotaph	12	12	12	12
406	10 c. South Point Lighthouse ..	30	15	30	15
407	12 c. Barbados Museum ..	20	20	30	25
408	15 c. Sharon Moravian Church	30	30	60	30
409	25 c. George Washington House	40	40	50	45
410	35 c. Nicholas Abbey	50	60	55	65
411	50 c. Bowmanston Pumping Station	70	85	70	95
412	$1 Queen Elizabeth Hospital	1·75	2·25	2·25	2·75
413	$2.50, Modern sugar factory ..	5·00	7·00	10·00	13·00
414	$5 Seawell International Air-port	9·00	12·00	12·00	15·00
399/414A	.. .. *Set of* 16	17·00	22·00		
399B/414B	.. .. *Set of* 15			25·00	30·00

The 2 to 10 c. values are vertical; the 12 c. to $5 horizontal.

See also Nos. 455/67.

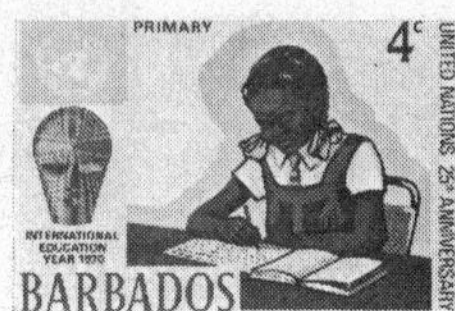

105 Primary Schoolgirl

(Des V. Whiteley. Litho J.W.)

1970 (26 June). *25th Anniv of United Nations. T* **105** *and similar horiz designs. Multicoloured.* W w **12.** P 14.

415	4 c. Type **106**	5	5
416	5 c. Secondary Schoolboy	5	5
417	25 c. Technical Student	25	25
418	50 c. University Buildings	50	50

106 Minnie Root

107 "Via Dolorosa" (Window, St. Margaret's Church, St. John)

(Des and litho J.W.)

1970 (24 Aug). *Flowers of Barbados. T* **106** *and similar designs. Multicoloured.* W w **12** (*sideways on horiz designs*). P 14½.

419	1 c. Barbados Easter Lily (*vert*)	5	5
420	5 c. Type **106**	20	10
421	10 c. Eyelash Orchid	35	20
422	25 c. Pride of Barbados (*vert*)	70	60
423	35 c. Christmas Hope	85	75
MS424	162 × 101 mm. Nos. 419/23. Imperf	1·75	1·90

(Des Jennifer Toombs. Litho J.W.)

1971 (7 Apr). *Easter. T* **107** *and similar vert design. Multicoloured.* W w **12.** P 14.

425	4 c. Type **107**	5	5
426	10 c. "The Resurrection" (Benjamin West)	10	8
427	35 c. Type **107**	45	40
428	50 c. As 10 c.	75	90

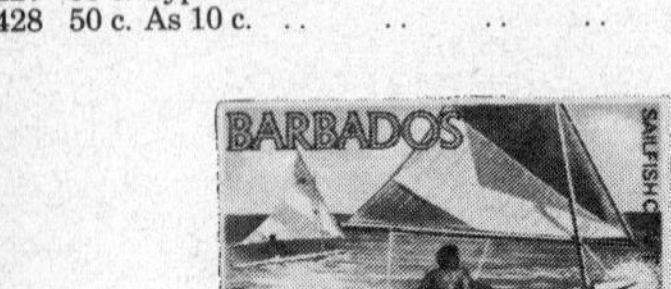

108 Sail-fish Craft

(Des and litho Harrison)

1971 (17 Aug). *Tourism. T* **108** *and similar horiz designs. Multicoloured.* W w **12** (*sideways on 5 c. and 25 c.*). P 14.

429	1 c. Type **108**	5	5
430	5 c. Tennis	15	5
431	12 c. Horse-riding	30	20
432	25 c. Water-skiing	40	40
433	50 c. Scuba-diving	65	65

109 S. J. Prescod (politician)

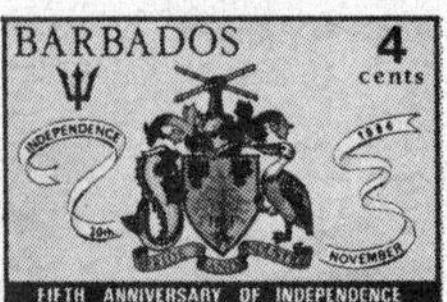

110 Arms of Barbados

(Des J.W. litho Questa)

1971 (28 Sept).* *Death Centenary of Samuel Jackman Prescod.* W w **12.** P 14.

434 **109**	3 c. multicoloured	5	5
435	35 c. multicoloured	30	40

*This is the local date but the Crown Agents released the stamps two days earlier.

(Des G. Drummond. Litho Questa)

1971 (23 Nov). *Fifth Anniv of Independence. T* **110** *and similar horiz design. Multicoloured.* W w **12** (*sideways*). P 14.

436	4 c. Type **110**	5	5
437	15 c. National flag and map	15	5
438	25 c. Type **110**	35	25
439	50 c. As 15 c.	65	85

111 Transmitting "Then and Now"

112 Map and Badge

(Des Cable & Wireless Ltd. Litho J.W.)

1972 (28 Mar). *Cable Link Centenary. T* **111** *and similar horiz designs. Multicoloured.* W w **12** (*sideways*). P 14.

440	4 c. Type **111**	5	5
441	10 c. Cable Ship *Stanley Angwin*	20	5
442	35 c. Barbados Earth Station and "Intelsat 4"	45	45
443	50 c. Mt. Misery and Tropospheric Scatter Station	65	1·00

(Des Mrs. C. Barrow (50 c.), Major L. Quintyne (others) and adapted by G. Drummond. Litho Questa)

1972 (1 Aug). *Diamond Jubilee of Scouts. T* **112** *and similar horiz designs. Multicoloured.* W w **12** (*sideways on 5 c.*). P 14.

444	5 c. Type **112**	8	5
445	15 c. Pioneers of scouting	25	15
446	25 c. Scouts	50	50
447	50 c. Flags	70	90

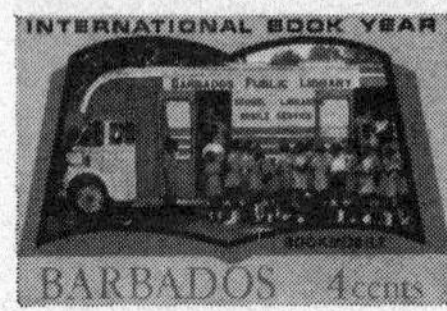

113 Mobile Library

(Des PAD Studio. Litho Harrison)

1972 (31 Oct). *International Book Year. T* **113** *and similar horiz designs. Multicoloured.* W w **12.** P 14.

448	4 c. Type **113**	5	5
449	15 c. Visual-aids van	20	12
450	25 c. Public library	25	10
451	$1 Codrington College	2·00	2·25

1972 (17 Nov)–**74**. *As Nos.* 402B/14B, *but* W w **12** (*sideways on* 4 *to* 10 c.; *upright on* 12 c. *to* $5).

455	4 c. St. James' Monument	45	35
456	5 c. St. Anne's Fort	50	35
457	6 c. Old Sugar Mill, Morgan Lewis	80	90
458	8 c. Cenotaph	50	40
459	10 c. South Point Lighthouse (21.1.74)	1·00	90
460	12 c. Barbados Museum	70	70
461	15 c. Sharon Moravian Church	60	45
462	25 c. George Washington House	1·50	65
463	35 c. Nicholas Abbey	2·00	70
464	50 c. Bowmanston Pumping Station	2·25	80
465	$1 Queen Elizabeth Hospital	3·50	2·00
466	$2.50, Modern sugar factory (2.10.73)	3·75	5·50
467	$5 Seawell International Airport (2.10.73)	6·50	7·00
455/67	*Set of* 13	22·00	19·00

114 Potter's Wheel

(Des PAD Studio. Litho Questa)

1973 (1 Mar). *Pottery in Barbados. T* **114** *and similar horiz designs. Multicoloured.* W w **12.** P 14.

468	5 c. Type **114**	8	5
469	15 c. Kilns	15	12
470	25 c. Finished products	25	15
471	$1 Market scene	1·40	1·90

115 First Flight, 1911

(Des C. Abbott. Litho Enschedé)

1973 (25 July). *Aviation. T* **115** *and similar horiz designs.* W w **12** (*sideways*). P 12½ × 12.

472	5 c. multicoloured	15	5
473	15 c. multicoloured	60	25
474	25 c. grey-blue, black and cobalt	85	45
475	50 c. multicoloured	1·50	1·60

Designs:—15 c. First flight to Barbados, 1928; 25 c. Passenger aircraft, 1939; 50 c. "VC-10" airliner, 1973.

116 University Chancellor (**117**)

(Des J. W. Litho Enschedé)

1973 (11 Dec). *25th Anniv of University of West Indies. T* **116** *and similar horiz designs. Multicoloured.* W w **12.** P 13 × 14.

476	5 c. Type **116**	5	5
477	25 c. Sherlock Hall	30	30
478	35 c. Cave Hill Campus	35	45

1974 (30 Apr). *No.* 462 *surch with T* **117.**

479	4 c. on 25 c. George Washington House	10	12
	a. "4c." omitted	15·00	

No. 479a occurs on R. 10/1, the overprint being applied to sheets consisting of two horizontal panes, 5 × 5. The variety occurs on plate 1A, and shows a clear albino impression of the "4c." on the reverse.

118 Old Sail Boat

(Des J. Cooter. Litho Questa)

1974 (11 June). *Fishing Boats of Barbados. T* **118** *and similar diamond-shaped designs. Multicoloured.* W w **12.** P 14.

480	15 c. Type **118**	20	20
481	35 c. Rowing-boat	45	40
482	50 c. Motor fishing-boat	60	60
483	$1 U.N.D.P. vessel, *Calamar*	1·00	1·10
MS484	140 × 140 mm. Nos. 480/3	2·50	3·00

119 *Cattleya Gaskelliana Alba*

(Des PAD Studio. Photo Harrison)

1974 (16 Sept)–**77**. *Orchids. T* **119** *and similar multicoloured designs.* W w **12** (*upright on* 1, 20, 25 c., $1 *and* $10; *sideways on others*). P 14½ × 14 ($1, $10) 14 × 14½ ($2.50, $5) *or* 14 (*others*).

485	1 c. Type **119**	15	15
486	2 c. *Renanthera storiei*	20	15
487	3 c. *Dendrobium* "Rose Marie"	20	10
488	4 c. *Epidendrum ibaguense*	60	25
489	5 c. *Schomburgkia humboldtii*	35	10
490	8 c. *Oncidium ampliatum*	45	25
491	10 c. *Arachnis maggie oei*	45	15
492	12 c. *Dendrobium aggregatum*	45	12
493	15 c. *Paphiopedilum puddle*	45	20
493*a*	20 c. *Spathoglottis* "The Gold" (3.5.77)	1·75	1·25
494	25 c. *Epidendrum ciliare* (Eyelash)	55	45
495	35 c. *Bletia patula*	1·00	45
495*a*	45 c. *Phalaenopsis schilleriana* "Sunset Glow" (3.5.77)	2·00	1·50
496	50 c. As 45 c.	1·25	70
497	$1 *Ascocenda* "Red Gem"	3·00	2·50
498	$2.50, *Brassolaeliocattleya* "Nugget"	3·25	3·25
499	$5 *Caularthron bicornutum*	5·00	7·00
500	$10 *Vanda* "Josephine Black"	9·50	13·00
485/500	*Set of* 18	28·00	28·00

The 1 c., 20 c., 25 c., $2.50 and $5 are horiz designs and the remainder are vert.

See also Nos. 510/24 and 543/51.

120 4d. Stamp of 1882, and U.P.U. Emblem

(Des Harrison. Litho Questa)

1974 (9 Oct). *Centenary of Universal Postal Union. T* **120** *and similar horiz designs.* W w **12** (*sideways*). P 14.

501	8 c. magenta, light orange & lt grey-green	12	12
502	35 c. dp rose-red, dull orange & bistre-brown	35	35
503	50 c. ultramarine, cobalt and silver	45	45
504	$1 bright blue, dull brown and grey-black	1·00	1·00
MS505	126 × 101 mm. Nos. 501/4	2·25	2·75

Designs:—35 c. Letters encircling the globe; 50 c. U.P.U. emblem and arms of Barbados; $1 Map of Barbados, sailing-ship and aeroplane.

121 Royal Yacht *Britannia*

(Des Jennifer Toombs. Litho Harrison)

1975 (18 Feb). *Royal Visit. T* **121** *and similar horiz design. Multicoloured.* W w **12** (*sideways on* 8 *and* 25 c.) P 14.

506	8 c. Type **121**	20	15
507	25 c. Type **121**	50	40
508	35 c. Sunset and palms	60	50
509	$1 As 35 c.	2·25	2·50

1975 (30 Apr)–**79**. *As Nos.* 485/9, 491/3, 494 *and* 495*a*/500 *but* W w **14** (*sideways on* 1, 25 *c.*, $1 *and* $10).
510 1 c. Type **119** 10 5
511 2 c. *Renanthera storiei* 12 5
512 3 c. *Dendrobium* "Rose Marie" 15 8
513 4 c. *Epidendrum ibaguense* 25 30
514 5 c. *Schomburgkia humboldtii* (19.10.77) 35 8
515 10 c. *Arachnis maggie oei* (19.10.77) 35 8
516 12 c. *Dendrobium aggregatum* (19.10.77) 40 15
517 15 c. *Paphiopedilum puddle* 70 15
518 25 c. *Epidendrum ciliare* (Eyelash) (27.3.79) 60 40
519 45 c. *Phalaenopsis schilleriana* "Sunset Glow" (25.5.78) 70 40
520 50 c. As 45 c. (23.8.79) 1·25 1·75
521 $1 *Ascocenda* "Red Gem" 3·50 3·50
522 $2.50, *Brassolaeliocattleya* "Nugget" 6·00 3·50
523 $5 *Caularthron bicornutum* 7·50 6·00
524 $10 *Vanda* "Josephine Black" 10·00 10·00
510/24 *Set of* 15 29·00 24·00
No. 525 vacant.

122 St. Michael's Cathedral

123 Pony Float

(Des R. Granger Barrett. Litho Questa)

1975 (29 July). *150th Anniv of Anglican Diocese. T* **122** *and similar square designs. Multicoloured.* W w **12** (*sideways*). *P* 13½.
526 5 c. Type **122** 5 5
527 15 c. Bishop Coleridge 15 12
528 50 c. All Saints' Church 50 65
529 $1 "Archangel Michael and Satan" (stained-glass window, St. Michael's Cathedral, Bridgetown) 80 1·10
MS530 95 × 96 mm. Nos. 526/9 (wmk upright) 2·25 2·25

(Des R. Granger Barrett. Litho Questa)

1975 (18 Nov). *Crop-over Festival. T* **123** *and similar horiz designs. Multicoloured.* W w **14** (*sideways*). *P* 14.
531 8 c. Type **123** 10 10
532 25 c. Man on stilts 25 25
533 35 c. Maypole dancing 40 40
534 50 c. Cuban dancers 50 50
MS535 127 × 85 mm. Nos. 531/4 1·75 1·90

124 Barbados Coat of Arms

125 17th-Century Sailing Ship

(Des and litho Harrison)

1975 (15 Dec). *Coil Definitives.* W w **12** *P* 15 × 14.
536 **124** 5 c. greenish blue 5 5
537 25 c. bluish violet 15 15
For 5 c. in this design, but watermarked W w **14**, see No. 743.

(Des PAD Studio. Litho J.W.)

1975 (17 Dec). *350th Anniv of First Settlement. T* **125** *and similar vert designs. Multicoloured.* W w **14**. *P* 13½.
538 4 c. Type **125** 20 5
539 10 c. Bearded fig tree and fruit 25 25
540 25 c. Ogilvy's 17th-century map 60 55
541 $1 Captain John Powell 2·25 2·75
MS542 105 × 115 mm. Nos. 538/41. P 14 × 14½ 3·25 3·50

1976 (20 Feb). *As Nos.* 485 *etc., but* W w **12** (*sideways on* 1 *c.*, 25 *c.*, $1) *or upright* (*others*).
543 1 c. Type **119** 25 25
544 2 c. *Rananthera storiei* 35 35
545 3 c. *Dendrobium* "Rose Marie" 40 45
546 4 c. *Epidendrum ibaguense* 45 60
547 10 c. *Arachnis maggie oei* 60 45
548 15 c. *Paphiopedilum puddle* 75 70
549 25 c. *Epidendrum ciliare* "Eyelash" 1·50 80
550 35 c. *Bletia patula* 1·60 1·25
551 $1 *Ascocenda* "Red Gem" 3·25 3·75
543/51 *Set of* 9 8·25 7·75
Nos. 552/8 vacant.

126 Map of the Caribbean

(Des PAD Studio. Litho Questa)

1976 (7 July). *West Indian Victory in World Cricket Cup. T* **126** *and similar design. No wmk. P* 14.
559 25 c. multicoloured 1·25 80
560 45 c. black and magenta 1·50 1·25
Design: *Vert*—45 c. The Prudential Cup.

127 Flag and Map of S. Carolina

(Des G. Vasarhelyi. Litho Walsall)

1976 (17 Aug). *Bicentenary of American Revolution. T* **127** *and similar horiz designs. Multicoloured.* W w **14** (*sideways*). *P* 13½.
561 15 c. Type **127** 35 35
562 25 c. George Washington and map of Bridgetown 45 45
563 50 c. Independence Declaration 85 85
564 $1 Prince Hall 1·60 1·60

128 Early Postman

(Des Jennifer Toombs. Litho Questa)

1976 (19 Oct). *125th Anniv of Post Office Act. T* **128** *and similar horiz designs. Multicoloured.* W w **14** (*sideways*) *P* 14.
565 8 c. Type **128** 10 10
566 35 c. Modern postman 30 30
567 50 c. Early letter 50 55
568 $1 Delivery van 1·10 1·10

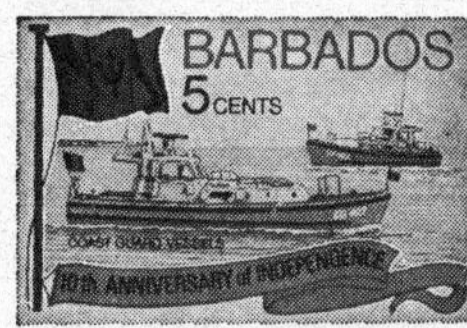

129 Coast Guard Vessels

(Des PAD Studio. Litho J.W.)

1976 (1 Dec).* *Tenth Anniv of Independence. T* **129** *and similar horiz designs. Multicoloured.* W w **14** (*sideways*). *P* 13 × 13½.
569 5 c. Type **129** 12 5
570 15 c. Reverse of currency note 20 15
571 25 c. National anthem 35 30
572 $1 Independence Day parade 1·00 1·10
MS573 90 × 125 mm. Nos. 569/72. P 14 2·00 2·10
*This is the local date of issue; the Crown Agents released the stamps a day earlier.

130 Arrival of Coronation Coach at Westminster Abbey

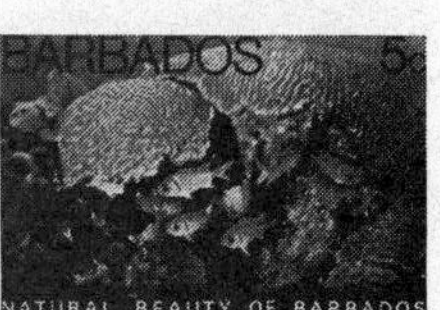

131 Underwater Park

(Des C. Abbott. Litho Walsall)

1977 (7 Feb). *Silver Jubilee. T* **130** *and similar vert designs. Multicoloured* W w **14**. *P* 13½.
574 15 c. Garfield Sobers being knighted, 1975 60 60
575 50 c. Type **130** 75 75
576 $1 Queen entering abbey 1·10 1·10
For the above with different inscription, see Nos. 590/2.

(Des R. Granger Barrett. Litho Questa)

1977 (3 May). *Natural Beauty of Barbados. T* **131** *and similar multicoloured designs.* W w **14** (*sideways on Nos.* 577 *and* 579). *P* 14.
577 5 c. Type **131** 15 8
578 35 c. Royal Palms (*vert*) 65 55
579 50 c. Underwater caves 85 70
580 $1 Stalagmite in Harrison's Cave (*vert*) 1·60 1·75
MS581 138 × 92 mm. Nos. 577/80 (wmk sideways) 3·50 3·75

NEW INFORMATION

The editor is always interested to correspond with people who have new information that will improve or correct the Catalogue.

132 Maces of the House of Commons

133 The Charter Scroll

(Des C. Abbott. Litho J. W.)

1977 (2 Aug). *13th Regional Conference of the Commonwealth Parliamentary Association. T* **132** *and similar designs.* W w **14** (*sideways on* $1). *P* 13½.
582 10 c. pale orange, yellow and lake-brown 10 8
583 25 c. apple-green, orange and deep green 25 25
584 50 c. multicoloured 50 50
585 $1 pale blue, orange and deep violet-blue 90 90
Designs: *Vert.*—25 c. Speaker's Chair; 50 c. Senate Chamber. *Horiz*—$1 Sam Lord's Castle.

(Des Walsall. Litho J.W.)

1977 (11 Oct). *350th Anniv of Granting of Charter to Earl of Carlisle. T* **133** *and similar multicoloured designs.* W w **14** (*sideways on* 45 *c. and* $1). *P* 13.
586 12 c. Type **133** 15 15
587 25 c. The earl receiving charter 30 30
588 45 c. The earl and Charles I (*horiz*) 60 60
589 $1 Ligon's map, 1657 (*horiz*) 1·25 1·25

(Des C. Abbott. Litho Walsall)

1977 (31 Oct). *Royal Visit. As Nos.* 574/6 *but inscr at top* "SILVER JUBILEE ROYAL VISIT". W w **14**. *Roul* 5. *Self-adhesive.*
590 15 c. Garfield Sobers being knighted, 1975 40 40
591 50 c. Type **130** 60 65
592 $1 Queen entering abbey 90 1·10

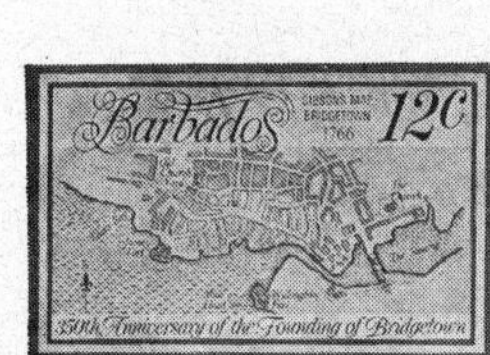

134 Gibson's Map of Bridgetown, 1766

135 Pelican

(Des J. W. Litho Questa)

1978 (1 Mar). *350th Anniv of Founding of Bridgetown. T* **134** *and similar horiz designs.* W w **14** (*sideways*). *P* 14.
593 12 c. multicoloured 12 12
594 25 c. black, light green and gold 30 30
595 45 c. multicoloured 50 50
596 $1 multicoloured 90 90
Designs:—25 c. "A Prospect of Bridgetown in Barbados" (engraving by S. Copens, 1695); 45 c. "Trafalgar Square, Bridgetown" (drawing by J. M. Carter, 1835); $1 The Bridges, 1978.

(Des C. Abbott. Litho Questa)

1978 (21 Apr). *25th Anniv of Coronation. T* **135** *and similar vert designs. P* 15.
597 50 c. yellow-olive, black and blue 30 35
a. Sheetlet. Nos. 597/9 × 2 1·75
598 50 c. multicoloured 30 35
599 50 c. yellow-olive, black and blue 30 35
Designs:—No. 597, Griffin of Edward III; No. 598, Queen Elizabeth II; No. 599, Type **135**.
Nos. 597/9 were printed together in small sheets of 6 containing two *se-tenant* strips of 3, with horizontal gutter margin between.

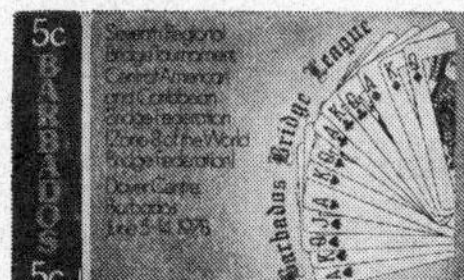

136 Barbados Bridge League Logo

(Des J. W. Litho Questa)

1978 (6 June). *7th Regional Bridge Tournament, Barbados. T* **136** *and similar horiz designs. Multicoloured.* W w **14** (*sideways*). *P* 14½.
600 5 c. Type **136** 10 10
601 10 c. Emblem of World Bridge Federation 15 15
602 45 c. Central American and Caribbean Bridge Federation emblem 45 45
603 $1 Playing cards on map of Caribbean 75 75
MS604 134 × 83 mm. Nos. 600/3 1·50 1·60

137 Camp Scene

(Des and litho Harrison)

1978 (1 Aug). *Diamond Jubilee of Guiding. T* **137** *and similar diamond-shaped designs. Multicoloured.* W w **14** (*sideways on* 12, 28 *c.*). *P* 13½.

605 12 c. Type **137** 15 15
606 28 c. Community work 30 30
607 50 c. Badge and "60" (*vert*) 50 50
608 $1 Guide badge (*vert*) 90 90

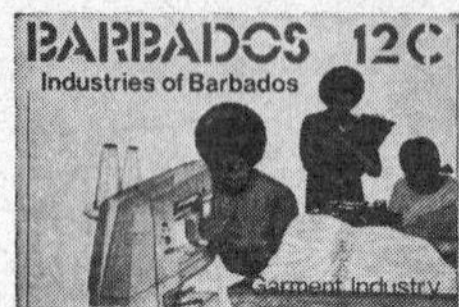

138 Garment Industry

(Des Walsall. Litho Harrison)

1978 (14 Nov). *Industries. T* **138** *and similar multicoloured designs.* W w **14** (*sideways on* 12 *and* 50 *c.*). *P* 14.

609 12 c. Type **138** 10 12
610 28 c. Cooper (*vert*) 20 25
611 45 c. Blacksmith (*vert*) 35 40
612 50 c. Wrought iron working 35 45

139 Early Mail Steamer

(Des J. Cooter. Litho J. W.)

1979 (8 Feb). *Ships. T* **139** *and similar horiz designs. Multicoloured.* W w **14** (*sideways*). *P* 13.

613 12 c. Type **139** 20 15
614 25 c. *Q.E.2* in Deep Water Harbour 35 30
615 50 c. *Ra* II nearing Barbados 50 50
616 $1 Early mail steamer (*different*) 90 90

140 1953 1 c. Definitive Stamp

(Des J.W. Litho Format)

1979 (8 May). *Death Centenary of Sir Rowland Hill. T* **140** *and similar multicoloured designs showing stamps.* W w **14** (*sideways on* 12 *c.*). *P* 14.

617 12 c. Type **140** 15 15
618 28 c. 1975 350th anniv of first settlement 25 c. commemorative (*vert*) 20 20
619 45 c. Penny Black with Maltese Cross postmark (*vert*) 30 30
MS620 137 × 90 mm 50 c. Unissued "Britannia" blue (wmk sideways) 35 40

All examples of No. 618 show anniversary spelt as "anniverary".

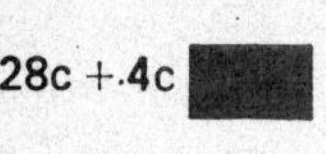

ST. VINCENT
RELIEF
FUND

(141)

142 Grassland Yellow Finch

1979 (29 May). *St Vincent Relief Fund. No.* 495 *surch with T* **141**.

621 28 c. + 4 c. on 35 c. *Bletia patula* 20 25

(Des J.W. Photo Harrison)

1979 (7 Aug)–**82**. *Birds. Vert designs as T* **142**. *Multicoloured.* W w **14** (*sideways on* 1, 5, 10, 12, 15, 20, 25, 28, 40, 50, 55, 60, 70 *c. and* $1). *P* 14.

622 1 c. Type **142** 5 5
623 2 c. Grey Kingbird 5 5
624 5 c. Lesser Antillean Bullfinch 5 5
625 8 c. Magnificent Frigate Bird 5 8
626 10 c. Cattle Egret (*shades*) 8 10
627 12 c. Green Heron 10 12
627*a* 15 c. Carib Grackle (1.3.82) 12 15
628 20 c. Antillean Crested Hummingbird 15 20
629 25 c. Scaly-breasted Ground Dove 20 25
630 28 c. As 15 c. 25 30
631 35 c. Green-throated Carib 30 35
631*a* 40 c. Red-necked Pigeon (1.3.82) 30 35
632 45 c. Zenaida Dove 35 40
633 50 c. As 40 c. 40 45
633*a* 55 c. American Golden Plover (1.9.81) 45 50
633*b* 60 c. Bananaquit (1.3.82) 45 50
634 70 c. As 60 c. 55 60
635 $1 Caribbean Elaenia 75 80
636 £2.50, American Redstart .. .. .. 2·00 2·25
637 $5 Belted Kingfisher .. .. 3·75 4·00
638 $10 Moorhen .. .. 7·50 8·00
622/38 .. .. *Set of* 21 16·00 17·00

143 Gun aboard Landing Craft at Foul Bay

144 Family

(Des G. Vasarhelyi. Litho Format)

1979 (9 Oct). *Space Project Commemorations. T* **143** *and similar multicoloured designs.* W w **14** (*sideways on* 10, 28 *and* 45 *c.*). *P* 14.

639 10 c. Type **143** 5 5
640 12 c. Transporting launcher through Barbados (*vert*) 12 12
641 20 c. Firing of 16" launcher in daylight (*vert*) 15 15
642 28 c. Bath Earth Station and "Intelsat IV A" 25 25
643 45 c. "Intelsat V" over the Caribbean.. .. 35 35
644 50 c. "Intelsat IV A" over Atlantic (*vert*) .. 35 35
639/44 .. .. *Set of* 6 1·10 1·10
MS645 118 × 90 mm. $1 Lunar module descending on to Moon (wmk sideways) 65 80

Commemorations:—10 to 20 c. H.A.R.P. Gun experiment: 28 to 50 c. First use of "Intelsat" satellites; $1, 10th anniversary of Moon landing.

(Des R. Granger Barrett. Litho Questa)

1979 (27 Nov). *International Year of the Child. T* **144** *and similar vert designs. Multicoloured.* W w **14**. *P* 14.

646 12 c. Type **144** 8 8
647 28 c. Ring of children and map of Barbados .. 20 20
648 45 c. Child with teacher 30 30
649 50 c. Children playing.. .. .. .. 30 30
650 $1 Children and kite 65 65

145 Map of Barbados

146 Private, Artillery Company, Barbados Volunteer Force, *circa* 1909

(Des G. Hutchins. Litho Security Printers (M), Malaysia)

1980 (19 Feb). *75th Anniv of Rotary International. T* **145** *and similar horiz designs. Multicoloured.* W w **14** (*sideways*). *P* 13.

651 12 c. Type **145** 10 10
652 28 c. Map of Caribbean 20 20
653 50 c. Rotary anniversary emblem 30 35
654 $1 Paul P. Harris (founder).. .. .. 60 75

(Des J.W. Litho Questa)

1980 (8 Apr). *75th Anniv of Barbados Regiment. T* **146** *and similar vert designs. Multicoloured.* W w **14**. *P* 14 × 14½.

655 12 c. Type **146** 10 10
656 35 c. Drum Major, Zouave Uniform 30 30
657 50 c. Sovereign's and Regimental colours .. 40 40
658 $1 Barbados Regiment Women's Corps .. 85 85

147 Early Postman

148 Underwater Scenery

(Des. V. Whiteley Studio. Litho Walsall)

1980 (6 May). *"London 1980" International Stamp Exhibition. Two sheets each* 122 × 125 *mm containing T* **147** *or similar vert design. Multicoloured.* W w **14**. *P* 14 × 13½.

MS659 (a) 28 c. × 6, Type **147** .. .. ..
(b) 50 c. × 6, Modern Postwoman and Inspector .. .. 3.00 } 3.50

The two sheets each contain the stamp in full colour and in five different colour separations.

(Des G. Drummond. Litho Security Printers (M), Malaysia)

1980 (30 Sept). *Underwater Scenery. T* **148** *and similar horiz designs.* W w **14** (*sideways*). *P* 13½.

660 12 c. multicoloured 5 5
661 28 c. multicoloured 25 25
662 50 c. multicoloured 35 35
663 $1 multicoloured 70 70
MS664 136 × 110 mm. Nos. 660/3 (wmk upright) 1·50 1·60

149 Bathsheba Railway Station

(Des J. W. Litho Questa)

1981 (13 Jan). *Early Transport. T* **149** *and similar horiz designs. Multicoloured.* W w **14** (*sideways*). *P* 14½ × 14.

665 12 c. Type **149** 10 10
666 28 c. Cab stand at The Green 25 25
667 45 c. Animal-drawn tram 35 35
668 70 c. Horse-drawn bus.. .. .. .. 60 60
669 $1 Railway station in Fairchild Street .. 75 75

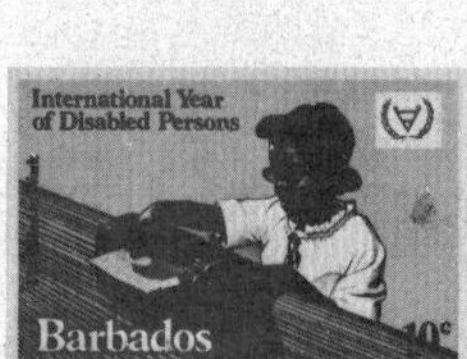

150 "The Blind at Work"

151 Prince Charles dressed for Polo

(Des BG Studio. Litho Walsall)

1981 (19 May). *International Year for Disabled Persons. T* **150** *and similar multicoloured designs.* W w **14** (*sideways on* 10 *c. and* $2.50). *P* 14.

670 10 c. Type **150** 5 5
671 25 c. Sign language (*vert*) 20 20
672 45 c. "Be alert to the white cane" (*vert*) .. 35 35
673 $2.50, Children at play .. .. .. 1·60 1·60

(Des and litho J.W.)

1981 (22 July). *Royal Wedding. T* **151** *and similar vert designs. Multicoloured.* W w **14**. *P* 13½ × 13.

674 28 c. Wedding bouquet from Barbados .. 25 25
675 50 c. Type **151** 35 35
676 $2.50, Prince Charles and Lady Diana Spencer .. .. 1·50 1·50

152 Landship Manoeuvre

(153)

(Des C. Abbott. Litho Harrison)

1981 (11 Aug). *Carifesta (Caribbean Festival of Arts), Barbados. T* **152** *and similar vert designs. Multicoloured. W w* **14**. *P* 14½ × 14.

677	15 c. Type **152**	12	12
678	20 c. Yoruba dancers	15	15
679	40 c. Tuk band	30	30
680	55 c. Sculpture of Frank Collymore	40	40
681	$1 Harbour scene	75	75

1981 (1 Sept). *Nos.* 630, 632 *and* 634 *surch as T* **153**.

682	15 c. on 28 c. Carib Grackle	12	12
683	40 c. on 45 c. Zenaida Dove	20	30
684	60 c. on 70 c. Bananaquit	40	40

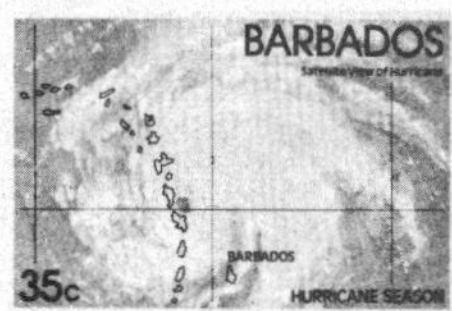

154 Satellite view of Hurricane

(Des A. Theobald. Litho Walsall)

1981 (29 Sept). *Hurricane Season. T* **154** *and similar horiz designs. W w* **14** *(sideways). P* 14.

685	35 c. black and blue	30	30
686	50 c. multicoloured	40	45
687	60 c. multicoloured	50	55
688	$1 multicoloured	75	90

Designs:—50 c. Hurricane "Gladys" from "Apollo 7"; 60 c. Police Department on hurricane watch; $1 Hurricane hunter (McDonnell "F2H-2P (Banshee)" jet aircraft).

155 Twin Falls

156 Black Belly Ram

(Des. L. Curtis. Litho Format)

1981 (1 Dec.) *Harrison's Cave. T* **155** *and similar vert designs. Multicoloured. W w* **14**. *P* 14 × 14½.

689	10 c. Type **155**	10	10
690	20 c. Stream in Rotunda Room	20	20
691	55 c. Formations in Rotunda Room	45	45
692	$2.50, Cascade Pool	1·60	1·60

(Des BG Studio. Litho Format)

1982 (9 Feb). *Black Belly Sheep. T* **156** *and similar horiz designs. Multicoloured. W w* **14** *(sideways). P* 14.

693	40 c. Type **156**	30	30
694	50 c. Black Belly ewe	40	40
695	60 c. Ewe with lambs	50	50
696	$1 Ram and ewe, with map of Barbados	75	75

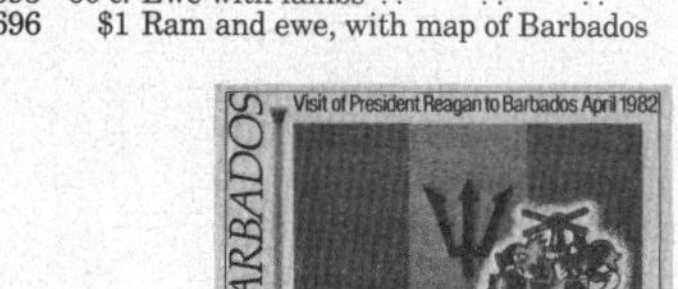

157 Barbados Coat of Arms and Flag

(Des Harrison. Litho Format)

1982 (8 Apr). *President Reagan's Visit. T* **157** *and similar horiz design. Multicoloured. W w* **14** *(sideways). P* 14.

697	20 c. Type **157**	30	35
	a. Pair. Nos. 697/8	60	70
698	20 c. U.S.A. coat of arms and flag	30	35
699	55 c. Type **157**	75	80
	a. Pair. Nos. 699/700	1·50	1·60
700	55 c. As No. 698	75	80

The two designs of each value were printed together, *se-tenant*, in horizontal and vertical pairs within small sheets of 8 stamps.

158 Lighter

159 Bride and Earl Spencer proceeding up Aisle

(Des J.W. Litho Harrison)

1982 (4 May). *Early Marine Transport. T* **158** *and similar horiz designs. Multicoloured. W w* **14** *(sideways). P* 14½.

701	20 c. Type **158**	20	25
702	35 c. Rowing boat	35	40
703	55 c. Speightstown schooner	50	55
704	$2.50, Inter-colonial schooner	2·50	2·75

(Des Jennifer Toombs. Litho Questa)

1982 (1 July). *21st Birthday of Princess of Wales. T* **159** *and similar vert designs. Multicoloured W w* **14**. *P* 14½ × 14.

705	20 c. Barbados coat of arms	20	25
706	60 c. Princess at Llanelwedd, October 1981	55	60
707	$1.20, Type **159**	1·25	1·40
708	$2.50, Formal portrait	2·25	2·40

160 "To Help other People"

161 Arms of George Washington

(Des G. Drummond. Litho Format)

1982 (7 Sept). *75th Anniv of Boy Scout Movement. T* **160** *and similar multicoloured designs. W w* **14** *(sideways on Nos.* 710/11). *P* 14.

709	15 c. Type **160**	15	15
710	40 c. "I Promise to do my Best" *(horiz)*	35	35
711	55 c. "To do my Duty to God, the Queen and my Country" *(horiz)*	50	50
712	$1 National and Troop flags	75	75
MS713	119 × 93 mm. $1.50, The Scout Law	1·25	1·40

(Des and litho J.W.)

1982 (2 Nov). *250th Birth Anniv of George Washington. T* **161** *and similar vert designs. Multicoloured. W w* **14**. *P* 13½ × 13.

714	10 c. Type **161**	10	8
715	55 c. Washington House, Barbados	45	45
716	60 c. Washington with troops	50	50
717	$2.50, Washington taking Oath	1·60	1·60

162 Gulf Fritillary

(Des I. Loe. Litho J.W.)

1983 (8 Feb). *Butterflies. T* **162** *and similar horiz designs. Multicoloured. W w* **14** *(sideways). P* 13 × 13½.

718	20 c. Type **162**	15	15
719	40 c. Monarch	30	30
720	55 c. Mimic	40	40
721	$2.50, Hanno Blue	1·60	1·60

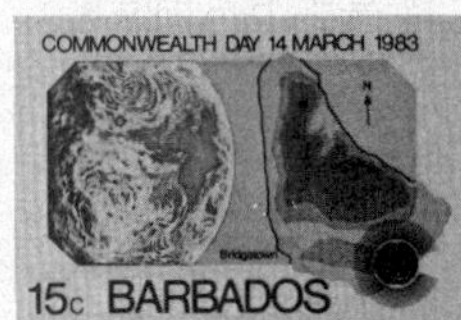

163 Map of Barbados and Satellite View

(Des D. Bowen. Litho J.W.)

1983 (14 Mar). *Commonwealth Day. T* **163** *and similar horiz designs. Multicoloured. W w* **14** *(sideways). P* 13.

722	15 c. Type **163**	15	15
723	40 c. Tourist beach	30	30
724	60 c. Sugar cane harvesting	50	50
725	$1 Cricket match	85	85

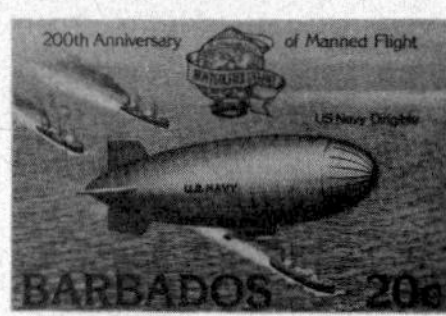

164 U.S. Navy Dirigible

(Des L. Curtis. Litho Format)

1983 (14 June). *Bicentenary of Manned Flight. T* **164** *and similar horiz designs. Multicoloured. W w* **14** *(sideways). P* 14.

726	20 c. Type **164**	15	20
727	40 c. Douglas "DC3"	25	30
728	55 c. Vickers "Viscount"	35	40
729	$1 Lockheed "Tristar"	70	75

165 Nash "600", 1941

166 Game in Progress

(Des and litho Harrison)

1983 (9 Aug). *Classic Cars. T* **165** *and similar horiz designs. Multicoloured. W w* **14** *(sideways). P* 14.

730	25 c. Type **165**	15	20
731	45 c. Dodge, 1938	25	30
732	75 c. Ford "Model AA", 1930	50	55
733	$2.50, Dodge "Four", 1918	1·75	1·75

(Des L. Curtis. Litho Questa)

1983 (30 Aug). *Table Tennis World Cup Competition. T* **166** *and similar vert designs. Multicoloured. W w* 14. *P* 14.

734	20 c. Type **166**	15	20
735	65 c. Map of Barbados	40	45
736	$1 World Table Tennis Cup	70	75

167 Angel playing Lute (detail "The Virgin and Child" (Masaccio))

168 Track and Field Events

(Des D. Miller. Litho Questa)

1983 (1 Nov). *Christmas. 50th Anniv of Barbados Museum. T* **167** *and similar multicoloured designs. W w* **14** *(sideways on* 45 *c.,* 75 *c. and* $2.50). *P* 14.

737	10 c. multicoloured	8	10
738	25 c. multicoloured	15	20
739	45 c. multicoloured	25	30
740	75 c. black and gold	50	55
741	$2.50, multicoloured	1·75	1·90
MS742	59 × 98 mm. $2 multicoloured	1·40	1·50

Designs: *Horiz*—45 c. "The Barbados Museum" (Richard Day); 75 c. "St. Ann's Garrison" (W. S. Hedges); $2.50, Needham's Point, Carlisle Bay. *Vert*—25 c., $2 Different details from "The Virgin and Child" (Masaccio).

1983 (Dec). *Coil Definitive. As No.* 536 *but W w* **14**.

743 **124**	5 c. greenish blue	5	5

No. 743 was also available from sheets.

(Des McCombie Skinner Studio. Litho Walsall)

1984 (28 Mar). *Olympic Games, Los Angeles. T* **168** *and similar horiz designs. W w* **14** *(sideways). P* 14.

745	50 c. bright green, black and olive-sepia	45	50
746	65 c. dull orange, black and drab	55	60
747	75 c. greenish blue, black and deep cobalt	65	70
748	$1 light brown, black and yellow-ochre	90	95
MS749	115 × 97 mm. Nos. 745/8	2·50	2·75

Designs:—65 c. Shooting; 75 c. Sailing; $1 Cycling.

169 Global Coverage

170 U.P.U. 1943 3d. Stamp and Logo

(Des C. Abbott. Litho Questa)

1984 (25 Apr). *250th Anniv of Lloyd's List (newspaper). T* **169** *and similar vert designs. Multicoloured. W w* **14**. *P* 14½ × 14.

750	45 c. Type **169**	40	45
751	50 c. Bridgetown harbour	45	50
752	75 c. *Philosopher*, 1857	65	70
753	$1 *Sea Princess*, 1984	90	95

(Des McCombie Skinner Studio. Litho J.W.)

1984 (6 June). *Universal Postal Union Congress, Hamburg. Sheet 90 × 75 mm. P 13½.*

MS754	**170**	$2 multicoloured	1·75	2·00

171 Local Junior Match

172 Poinsettia

(Des L. Curtis. Litho Walsall)

1984 (8 Aug). *60th Anniv of World Chess Federation. T* **171** *and similar horiz designs. Multicoloured. W* w **14** *(sideways). P* 14½.

755	25 c. Type **171**	20	25
756	45 c. Staunton and 19th-century Knight ..	40	45
757	65 c. Staunton and 18th-century Queen ..	55	60
758	$2 Staunton and 17th-century Castle ..	1·75	1·90

(Des I. Loe. Litho Questa)

1984 (24 Oct). *Christmas. Flowers. T* **172** *and similar vert designs. Multicoloured. W* w **14**. *P* 14.

759	50 c. Type **172**	45	50
760	65 c. Snow-on-the-Mountain	55	60
761	75 c. Christmas Candle	65	70
762	$1 Christmas Hope	90	95

PRICES OF SETS

Set prices are given for many issues, generally those containing five stamps or more. Definitive sets include one of each value or major colour change, but do not cover different perforations, die types or minor shades. Where a choice is possible the set prices are based on the cheapest versions of the stamps included in the listings.

POSTAGE DUE STAMPS

D 1

D 2

(Typo D.L.R.)

1934 (2 Jan)–**47**. *Wmk Mult Script CA. P* 14.

D1	D 1	½d. green (10.2.35)	50	90
D2		1d. black	90	70
		a. Bisected (½d.) (on cover)	†	£375
D3		3d. carmine (13.3.47)	14·00	16·00
D1/3		Perf "Specimen" .. .. *Set of* 3	48·00	

The use of the bisected 1d. stamp was officially authorised March 1934 pending the arrival of supplies of the ½d. received 1935. Some specimens had the value "½d." written across the half stamp in red or black ink (*Price on cover* £550).

(Typo D.L.R.)

1950 (8 Dec)–**53**. *Values in cents. Wmk Mult Script CA. P* 14.

D4	D 1	1 c. green, **O**	95	1·50
		a. Deep green, **C** (29.11.51)	30	45
		b. Error. Crown missing, W **9***a*, **C** ..	35·00	
		c. Error. St. Edward's Crown, W **9***b*, **C**	32·00	
D5		2 c. black, **O**	2·00	3·50
		a. Chalky paper (20.1.53)	40	75
		c. Error. St. Edward's Crown, W **9***b*, **C**	40·00	
D6		6 c. carmine, **O**	8·50	9·50
		a. Chalky paper (20.1.53)	2·25	5·00
		b. Error. Crown missing, W **9***a*, C ..	48·00	
		c. Error. St. Edward's Crown, W **9***b*, **C**	35·00	

The 1 c. stamps have no dot below "c".

1965 (3 Aug). *As Nos.* D4/6 *but wmk* w **12** *(upright). Chalky paper.*

D7	D 1	1 c. deep green (*shades*)	40	65
D8		2 c. black	40	80
D9		6 c. carmine (*shades*)	65	1·25

The 1 c. has no dot below "c".

1974 (4 Feb). *As No.* D9 *but W* w **12** *(sideways). Glazed, ordinary paper. P* 14 × 13½.

D10	D 1	6 c. carmine	3·75	5·50

1974 (4 Dec). *W* w **12** *(sideways). P* 13.

D12	D 1	2 c. black	2·25	3·50
D13		6 c. carmine	2·75	4·50

(Des Jennifer Toombs. Litho Questa)

1976 (12 May). *Different floral backgrounds as Type* D **2**. *W* w **14**. *P* 14.

D14	1 c. deep mauve and light pink	5	5
D15	2 c. ultramarine and light cobalt	5	5
D16	5 c. reddish brown and yellow	5	5
D17	10 c. royal blue and light lilac	8	10
D18	25 c. deep green and bright yellow-green ..	20	25
D19	$1 rose-carmine and rose	75	80
D14/19	.. .. *Set of* 6	1·00	1·10

Barbuda

(*see after* Antigua)

Basutoland

Stamps of CAPE OF GOOD HOPE were used in Basutoland from about 1876, initially cancelled by upright oval with framed number type postmarks of that colony. Cancellation numbers known to have been used in Basutoland are 133 (Quthing), 156 (Mafeteng), 210 (Mohaleshoek), 277 (Morija), 281 (Maseru), 317 (Thlotse Heights) and 688 (Teyateyaneng).

From 1910 until 1933 the stamps of SOUTH AFRICA were in use. Stamps of the Union provinces are also known used in Basutoland during the early years of this period and can also be found cancelled-to-order during 1932–33.

The following post offices and postal agencies existed in Basutoland before December 1933. Stamps of Cape of Good Hope or South Africa with recognisable postmarks from them are worth a premium. For a few of the smaller offices or agencies there are, as yet, no actual examples recorded. Dates given are those generally accepted as the year in which the office was first opened.

Bokong (1931)
Butha Buthe (1907)
Jonathan's (1927)
Khabos (1927)
Khetisas (1930)
Khukhune (1933)
Kolonyama (1914)
Kueneng (1914)
Leribe (1890)
Mafeteng (1874)
Majara (1912)
Makhoa (1932)
Makoalis (1927)
Mamathes (1919)
Mapoteng (1925)
Marakabeis (1932)
Maseru (1872)
Maseru Rail (1915?)
Mashai (1929)
Matsaile (1930)
Mekading (1914)
Mofokas (1915)
Mohaleshoek (1873)
Mokhotlong (1921)
Morija (1884)
Motsekuoa (1915)
Mount Morosi (1918)
Mphotos (1914)
Peka (1908)
Phamong (1932)
Pitseng (1921)
Qachasnek (1895)
Qalo (1923?)
Quthing (1882)
Rankakalas (1933)
Roma Mission (1913)
Sebapala (1930)
Seforong (1924)
Sehlabathebe (1921)
Sekake (1931)
Teyateyaneng (1886)
Thaba Bosigo (1913)
Thabana Morena (1922)
Thabaneng (1914)
Thaba Tseka (1929)
Thlotse Heights (1872)
Tsepo (1923)
Tsoelike (1927)
Tsoloane (1918)

For further details of the postal history of Basutoland see *The Cancellations and Postal Markings of Basutoland/Lesotho* by A. H. Scott, published by Collectors Mail Auctions (Pty) Ltd, Cape Town, from which the above has been, with permission, extracted.

PRICES FOR STAMPS ON COVER TO 1945

Nos. 1/19	*from* × 5
Nos. 11/14	*from* × 6
Nos. 15/17	*from* × 10
Nos. 18/28	*from* × 6
Nos. 29/31	*from* × 10
Nos. O1/4	*from* × 4
Nos. D1/2	*from* × 25

CROWN COLONY

1 King George V, Crocodile and Mountains

2 King George VI, Crocodile and Mountains

(Recess Waterlow)

1933 (1 Dec). *Wmk Mult Script CA. P* 12½.

1	**1**	½d. emerald	60	1·00
2		1d. scarlet	50	70
3		2d. bright purple	70	95
4		3d. bright blue	1·00	2·75
5		4d. grey	2·50	6·50
6		6d. orange-yellow	4·00	6·50
7		1s. red-orange	8·00	13·00
8		2s. 6d. sepia	24·00	45·00
9		5s. violet	90·00	£110
10		10s. olive-green	£200	£275
1/10		.. .. *Set of* 10	£300	£425
1/10		Perf "Specimen" .. .. *Set of* 10	£400	

1935 (4 May). *Silver Jubilee. As Nos.* 91/4 *of Antigua. P* 13½ × 14.

11	1d. deep blue and carmine	45	45
12	2d. ultramarine and grey	70	2·25

13 3d. brown and deep blue .. .. 3·25 3·75
14 6d. slate and purple .. .. 5·50 7·00
f. Dash by turret .. .. 20·00
11/14 Perf "Specimen" .. .. *Set of* 4 65·00

For illustration of plate variety see Omnibus section following Zululand.

1937 (12 May). *Coronation. As Nos 13/15 of Aden. P 14.*
15 1d. scarlet 35 35
16 2d. bright purple 40 55
17 3d. bright blue 55 90
15/17 Perf "Specimen" .. .. *Set of* 3 50·00

(Recess Waterlow)

1938 (1 Apr). *Wmk Mult Script CA. P 12½.*
18 **2** ½d. green 25 30
19 1d. scarlet 35 30
20 1½d. light blue 30 25
21 2d. bright purple 25 25
22 3d. bright blue 25 50
23 4d. grey .. .. 90 1·75
24 6d. orange-yellow 60 70
25 1s. red-orange 65 70
26 2s. 6d. sepia .. .. 5·50 5·50
27 5s. violet .. .. 10·00 11·00
28 10s. olive-green .. .. 14·00 20·00
18/28 .. .. *Set of* 11 30·00 38·00
18/28 Perf "Specimen" .. .. *Set of* 11 £120

Basutoland
(3)

1945 (3 Dec). *Victory. Stamps of South Africa, optd with T 3, inscr alternately in English and Afrikaans.*

				Un. pair	*Used pair*
29	**55**	1d. brown and carmine		40	25
30	**56**	2d. slate-blue and violet		40	35
31	**57**	3d. deep blue and blue		40	65

4 King George VI

5 King George VI and Queen Elizabeth

6 Queen Elizabeth II as Princess, and Princess Margaret

7 The Royal Family

(Recess Waterlow)

1947 (17 Feb). *Royal Visit. Wmk Mult Script CA. P 12½.*
32 **4** 1d. scarlet 10 10
33 **5** 2d. green 10 10
34 **6** 3d. ultramarine 10 10
35 **7** 1s. mauve 15 15
32/5 Perf "Specimen" .. .. *Set of* 4 £120

1948 (1 Dec). *Royal Silver Wedding. As Nos. 30/1 of Aden.*
36 1½d. ultramarine 15 15
37 10s. grey-olive .. .. 23·00 35·00

1949 (10 Oct). *75th Anniv of Universal Postal Union. As Nos. 114/17 of Antigua.*
38 1½d. blue 30 35
39 3d. deep blue 85 70
40 6d. orange 90 85
41 1s. red-brown .. .. 1·40 1·10

1953 (3 June). *Coronation. As No. 47 of Aden.*
42 2d. black and reddish purple 15 20

8 Qiloane

9 Mohair (Shearing Angora Goats)

(Recess D.L.R.)

1954 (18 Oct). *Designs as T8/9. Wmk Mult Script CA. P 11½ (10s.) or 13½ (others).*
43 ½d. grey-black and sepia 8 5
44 1d. grey-black and bluish green 8 5
45 2d. deep bright blue and orange 20 5
46 3d. yellow-green and deep rose-red (*shades*) 35 5
47 4½d. indigo and deep ultramarine 40 30
48 6d. chestnut and deep grey-green 40 25
49 1s. bronze-green and purple 50 30
50 1s. 3d. brown and turquoise-green .. .. 2·50 3·00
51 2s. 6d. deep ultramarine and crimson (*shades*) .. .. 4·25 6·00
52 5s. black and carmine-red .. .. .. 4·75 8·50
53 10s. black and maroon .. .. 14·00 20·00
43/53 .. .. *Set of* 11 25·00 35·00

Designs: *Horiz as T* 8—1d. Orange River; 2d Mosuto horseman; 3d. Basuto household; 4½d. Maletsunyane Falls; 6d. Herd-boy with Lesiba. 1s. Pastoral scene; 1s. 3d. Aeroplane over Lancers' Gap; 2s. 6d. Old Fort Leribe; 5s. Mission Cave House.

½d. ▬
(19)

20 "Chief Moshoeshoe I" (engraving by Delangle)

1959 (1 Aug). *No. 45 surch with T 19, by South African Govt Ptr, Pretoria.*
54 ½d. on 2d. deep bright blue and orange .. 10 10

(Des from drawings by James Walton. Recess Waterlow)

1959 (15 Dec). *Basutoland National Council. T 20 and similar vert designs. W w 12. P 13 × 13½.*
55 3d. black and yellow-olive 10 12
56 1s. carmine and yellow-green 20 30
57 1s. 3d. ultramarine and red-orange 30 60

Designs:—1s. Council house; 1s. 3d. Mosuto horseman.

(New Currency. 100 cents = 1 rand)

½c. (23) 1c. (24) 2c (25)

2½c (I) 2½c (II) 3½c (I) 3½c (II)

5c (I) 5c (II) 10c (I) 10c (II)

12½c (I) 12½c (II) 50c (I) 50c (II)

25c (I) 25c (II) 25c (III)

R1 (I) R1 (II) R1 (III)

1961 (14 Feb). *Nos. 43/53 surch with T 23 (½ c.), 24 (1 c.) or as T 25 (others) by South African Govt Printer, Pretoria*
58 ½ c. on ½d. grey-black and sepia 5 5
a. Surch double £160
59 1 c. on 1d. grey-black and bluish green .. 5 5
60 2 c. on 2d. deep bright blue and orange .. 10 5
a. Surch inverted .. .. 70·00
61 2½ c. on 3d. yellow-green and rose (Type I) .. 10 5
a. Type II 10 5
b. Type II inverted .. .. — £600
62 3½ c. on 4½d. indigo & deep ultram (Type I) .. 20 15
a. Type II .. .. 4·00 5·00
63 5 c. on 6d. chestnut & dp grey-green (Type I) 10 5
a. Type II 15 10
64 10 c. on 1s. bronze-green and purple (Type I) .. 15 5
a. Type II .. .. 48·00 48·00
65 12½ c. on 1s. 3d. brown & turq-green (Type I) .. 45 60
a. Type II 30 20
66 25 c. on 2s. 6d. bright ultramarine and crimson-lake (Type I) 45 65
a. Type II .. .. 16·00 15·00
b. Type III 55 80
67 50 c. on 5s. black and carmine-red (Type I) .. 2·75 6·00
a. Type II .. .. 1·75 2·00
68 1 r. on 10s. black and maroon (Type I) .. 17·00 12·00
a. Type II .. .. 14·00 23·00
b. Type III .. .. 3·25 4·75
58/68b .. .. *Set of* 11 6·00 7·50

There were two printings of the 2½ c. Type II, differing in the position of the surcharge on the stamps.

Examples of the 2 c. surcharge are known in a fount similar to Type **24**.

OMNIBUS ISSUES

Details, together with prices for complete sets, of the various Omnibus issues from the 1935 Silver Jubilee series to date are included in a special section following Zululand at the end of the catalogue.

26 Basuto Household

(Recess D.L.R.)

1961–63. *As Nos. 43/53 but values in cents as in T 26. Wmk Mult Script CA. P 13½ or 11½ (1 r.).*
69 ½ c. grey-black and sepia (as ½d). (25.9.62) .. 5 15
a. Imperf (pair) £150
70 1 c. grey-black and bluish green (as 1d.) (25.9.62) 8 15
71 2 c. deep bright blue and orange (as 2d.) (25.9.62) 12 25
72 2½ c. yellow-green and deep rose-red (*shades*) (14.2.61) 12 12
73 3½ c. indigo and deep ultramarine (as 4½d.) (25.9.62) 25 60
74 5 c. chestnut and deep grey-green (as 6d.) (10.8.62) 25 20
75 10 c. bronze-green and purple (as 1s.) (22.10.62) 25 25
76 12½ c. brown and turquoise-green (as 1s. 3d.) (17.12.62) .. .. 1·75 3·00
77 25 c. deep ultramarine and crimson (as 2s. 6d.) (25.9.62) .. .. 2·50 3·75
78 50 c. black and carmine-red (as 5s.) (22.10.62) 3·75 6·00
79 1 r. black and maroon (*shades*) (as 10s.) (4.2.63) .. .. 9·50 10·00
69/79 .. .. *Set of* 11 17·00 22·00

1963 (4 June). *Freedom from Hunger. As No. 76 of Aden.*
80 12½ c. reddish violet 60 25

1963 (2 Sept). *Red Cross Centenary. As Nos. 147/8 of Antigua.*
81 2½ c. red and black 20 10
82 12½ c. red and blue 90 65

1964. *As Nos. 70, 72, 74, 76 and 78, but W w 12.*
84 1 c. grey-black and bluish green (11.8.64) .. 10 12
86 2½ c. pale yellow-green and rose-red (10.3.64) 15 15
88 5 c. chestnut and deep grey-green (10.11.64) 35 45
90 12½ c. brown and turquoise-green (10.11.64) .. 2·00 1·50
92 50 c. black and carmine-red (29.9.64) .. 5·00 9·50

SELF-GOVERNMENT

27 Mosotho Woman and Child

28 Maseru Border Post

1965 (10 May). *New Constitution. T 27/28 and horiz designs similar to T 28. Multicoloured. W w 12. P 14 × 13½.*
94 2½ c. Type **27** 8 5
95 3½ c. Type **28** 10 5
96 5 c. Mountain scene 12 10
97 12½ c. Legislative Buildings 15 20

1965 (17 May). *I.T.U. Centenary. As Nos. 166/7 of Antigua.*
98 1 c. orange-red and bright purple 15 5
99 20 c. light blue and orange-brown 85 50

1965 (25 Oct). *International Co-operation Year. As Nos. 168/9 of Antigua.*
100 ½ c. reddish purple and turquoise-green 8 5
101 12½ c. deep bluish green and lavender 80 35

1966 (24 Jan). *Churchill Commemoration. As Nos. 170/3 of Antigua.*
102 1 c. new blue 20 10
103 2½ c. deep green 50 10
104 10 c. brown 75 35
105 22½ c. bluish violet .. .. 1·10 90

OFFICIAL STAMPS

1934 (4 May). *Nos. 1/3 and 6 optd "OFFICIAL".*
O1 **1** ½d. emerald £1600 £2000
O2 1d. scarlet £950 £1000
O3 2d. bright purple £600 £550
O4 6d. orange-yellow £10000 £4500
O1/4 .. .. *Set of* 4 £12000 £7000

Collectors are advised to buy these stamps only from reliable sources. They were not sold to the public.

POSTAGE DUE STAMPS

D 1

D 2

(Typo D.L.R.)

1933 (1 Dec)–**1952.** *Wmk Mult Script CA. P 14.*
D1 D 1 1d. carmine, O .. .. 1·10 2·00
a. Scarlet, O (1938) .. .. .. 6·50 8·00
b. Deep-carmine, C (24.10.51) 30 50
c. Error. Crown missing. W9*a*, C .. 40·00
d. Error. St. Edward's Crown, W9*b*, C 32·00

D2	D 1	2d. violet, O	1·50	2·50
		a. Chalky paper (6.11.52)	60	1·25
		b. Error. Crown missing. W9*a*, C	40·00	
		c. Error. St. Edward's Crown, W9*b*, C	32.00	
D1/2 Perf "Specimen"		*Set of* 2	28·00	

(Typo D.L.R.)

1956 (1 Dec). *Wmk Mult Script CA. P* 14.

D3	D 2	1d. carmine	20	50
D4		2d. deep reddish violet	30	75

5c 5c

(I) (II)

1961 (14 Feb). *Surch as T* **24**, *but without stop.*

D5	D 2	1 c. on 1d. carmine	12	35
D6		1 c. on 2d. deep reddish violet	12	35
D7		5 c. on 2d. deep reddish violet (Type I)	25	35
		a. Type II	22·00	30·00

1961 (June). *No.* D2*a surch as T* **24** (*without stop*).

D8	D 1	5 c. on 2d. violet	3·50	4·75
		a. Error. Missing Crown, W9*a*	£850	
		b. Error. St. Edwards Crown, W9*b*	£225	

1964. *As No.* D3/4 *but values in cents and W* w **12** (*sideways on* 1 *c.*).

D 9	D 2	1 c. carmine	45	85
D10		5 c. deep reddish violet	60	1·50

POSTAL FISCAL

In July 1961 the 10s. stamp, T **9**, surcharged "R1 Revenue", was used for postage at one post office at least, but such usage was officially unauthorised.

Basutoland attained independence on 4 October 1966, and her stamps were withdrawn on 31 October 1966. For later issues see LESOTHO.

Batum

BRITISH OCCUPATION

PRICES FOR STAMPS ON COVER	
Nos. 1/6	*from* × 40
Nos. 7/10	*from* × 10
Nos. 11/12	*from* × 12
Nos. 13/20	*from* × 60
Nos. 21/45	*from* × 10
Nos. 46/51	*from* × 20
Nos. 52/60	*from* × 60

1

БАТУМ. ОБ.

Руб 10 Руб

(2)

1919. *Litho. Imperf.*

1	1	5 k. green	1·00	1·50
2		10 k. ultramarine	1·00	1·50
3		50 k. yellow	35	45
4		1 r. chocolate	50	75
5		3 r. violet	2·50	3·00
6		5 r. brown	3·00	4·00

1919. *Russian stamps* (*Arms types*) *surch with T* **2**.

7	10 r. on 1 k. orange (*imperf*)	12·00	14·00
8	10 r. on 3 k. carmine-red (*imperf*)	6·00	8·00
9	10 r. on 5 k. brown-lilac (*perf*)	60·00	60·00
10	10 r. on 10 on 7 k. deep blue (*perf*)	70·00	70·00

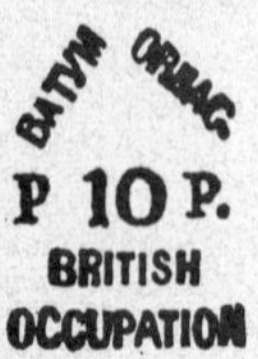

(3)

БАТУМЪ
BRITISH
Р.15 Р.
OCCUPATION
ОБЛ.

(4)

1919. *Russian stamps* (*Arms types*) *surch with T* **3** *or* **4**. *Imperf.*

11	10 r. on 3 k. carmine-red	5·00	6·00
12	15 r. on 1 k. orange	15·00	15·00
	a. Surch in red	13·00	13·00
	ab. Surch double		
	b. Surch in violet	15·00	15·00

BRITISH
OCCUPATION

(5)

БАТУМ.ОБЛ.
Р.50Р.
BRITISH
OCCUPATION

(6)

1919. *T* **1**, *new colours etc., optd with T* **5**.

13	5 k. yellow-green	2·00	3·00
14	10 k. bright blue	2·00	3·00
15	25 k. orange-yellow	2·00	3·00
16	1 r. pale blue	1·00	1·50
17	2 r. pink	35	45
18	3 r. bright violet	35	50
19	5 r. brown	45	65
	a. "CCUPATION"	†	†
20	7 r. brownish red	1·00	1·50

1920. *Russian stamps* (*Arms types*) *surch as T* **6**. (*a*) *Perf.*

21	25 r. on 5 k. brown-lilac	8·00	9·00
22	25 r. on 5 k. brown-lilac (B.)	9·00	10·00
23	25 r. on 10 on 7 k. deep blue	20·00	20·00
24	25 r. on 10 on 7 k. deep blue (B.)	15·00	15·00
25	25 r. on 20 on 14 k. deep carmine and blue	16·00	16·00
26	25 r. on 20 on 14 k. deep carmine and blue (B.)	15·00	15·00
27	25 r. on 25 k. deep violet and light green (B.)	21·00	21·00
28	25 r. on 25 k. deep violet and light green	20·00	20·00
29	25 r. on 50 k. green and copper-red	15·00	15·00
30	25 r. on 50 k. green and copper-red (B.)	16·00	16·00
31	50 r. on 2 k. yellow-green	21·00	21·00
32	50 r. on 3 k. carmine-red	21·00	21·00
33	50 r. on 4 k. red	20·00	20·00
34	50 r. on 5 k. brown-lilac	15·00	15·00
	(*b*) *Imperf*		
35	50 r. on 2 k. yellow-green	45·00	45·00
36	50 r. on 3 k. carmine-red	50·00	50·00
37	50 r. on 5 k. brown-lilac	£150	£150

1920. *Romanov issue, as T* **25** *of Russia, surch with T* **6**.

38	50 r. on 4 k. rose-carmine (B.)	15·00	15·00

1920. *Russian stamps* (*Arms types*) *surch as T* **3**. (*a*) *Imperf.*

39	50 r. on 1 k. orange	45·00	45·00
40	50 r. on 2 k. yellow-green	80·00	80·00
	(*b*) *Perf*		
41	50 r. on 2 k. yellow-green	60·00	60·00
42	50 r. on 3 k. carmine-red	120·00	120·00
43	50 r. on 4 k. red	80·00	80·00
44	50 r. on 5 k. brown-lilac	60·00	60·00
44*a*	50 r. on 10 k. deep blue (C.)	£200	£200
45	50 r. on 15 k. blue and red-brown	60·00	60·00

РУБ 25 ЛЕЙ

25 РУБ. 25

(7)

R.50R.
BRITISH
OCCUPATION
РУБ.

(8)

1920. *Nos.* 13 *and* 15 *surch with T* **7**.

46	25 r. on 5 k. yellow-green	8·00	8·00
47	25 r. on 5 k. yellow-green (B.)	8·00	8·00
48	25 r. on 25 k. orange-yellow	6·00	6·00
49	25 r. on 25 k. orange-yellow (B.)	20·00	20·00

1920. *No.* 3 *surch with T* **8**.

50	50 r. on 50 k. yellow	5·00	5·00
51	50 r. on 50 k. yellow (B.)	20·00	20·00

1920 (June). *T* **1** (*new colours etc.*) *optd with T* **5**. *Imperf.*

A. *Normal.* B. *Error* "BPITISH"

		A		B	
52	1 r. chestnut	12	12	—	—
53	2 r. pale blue	12	12	—	—
54	3 r. pink	12	12	—	—
55	5 r. black-brown	12	12	—	—
56	7 r. yellow	12	12	—	—
57	10 r. myrtle-green	15	20	—	—
58	15 r. violet	30	35	—	—
59	25 r. scarlet	40	45	—	—
60	50 r. deep blue	40	55	—	—

Bechuanaland

PRICES FOR STAMPS ON COVER TO 1945	
Nos. 1/8	*from* × 6
No. 9	*from* × 50
Nos. 10/21	*from* × 5
Nos. 22/8	*from* × 8
No. 29	*from* × 10
No. 30	*from* × 8
Nos. 31/2	*from* × 10
Nos. 33/7	*from* × 12
Nos. 38/9	*from* × 20
Nos. 40/51	*from* × 6
Nos. 52/8	*from* × 5
Nos. 59/71	*from* × 6
Nos. 72/82	*from* × 5
Nos. 83/98	*from* × 4
Nos. 99/110	*from* × 6
Nos. 111/17	*from* × 10
Nos. 118/28	*from* × 4
Nos. 129/31	*from* × 10
Nos. D1/3	*from* × 50
Nos. D4/6	*from* × 60
No. F1	*from* × 5
No. F2	–
No. F3	*from* × 5

A. BRITISH BECHUANALAND

CROWN COLONY

British Bechuanaland was proclaimed a Crown Colony on 30 September 1885.

British
Bechuanaland

(1)

BRITISH
BECHUANALAND

(2)

1885 (Dec)–**87**. *Stamps of Cape of Good Hope* ("*Hope*" *seated*) *optd with T* **1**, *by W. A. Richards & Sons, Cape Town.*

(*a*) *Wmk Crown CC* (*No.* 3) *or Crown CA* (*others*)

1	6	½d. slate (R.)	8·50	9·00
		a. Opt in lake		
		b. Opt double (Lake + Black)	£550	
2		3d. claret	20·00	26·00
3		4d. blue (12.86?)	45·00	48·00
		(*b*) *Wmk Anchor* (*Cape, T* 13)		
4	6	½d. grey-black (3.87?)	6·00	7·50
		a. Error "ritish"	£1300	
		b. Opt double	£400	£400
5		1d. pale rose-red	7·00	7·00
		a. Error "ritish"	£1300	£1200
		b. Opt double	—	£1500
6		2d. bistre	26·00	17·00
		a. Error "ritish"	£2750	£2750
		b. Opt double	—	£1000
7	4	6d. purple	32·00	28·00
8		1s. green (11.86?)	£200	£125
		a. Error "ritish"	£6000	£4250

Overprints with stop after "Bechuanaland" are forged.

1887 (1 Nov). *Stamp of Gt. Britain optd with T* **2**, *by D.L.R.*

9	71	½d. vermilion (H/S S. £120)	90	90
		a. Opt double	£1400	

3

4

5

(Typo D.L.R.)

1887 (1 Nov). *P* 13½, 14. (*a*) *Wmk Orb* (*G.B.T.* **48**).

10	3	1d. lilac and black	14·00	4·00
11		2d. lilac and black	20·00	4·00
		a. Pale dull lilac and black	32·00	19·00
12		3d. lilac and black	3·75	4·25
		a. Pale reddish lilac and black	32·00	9·00
13		4d. lilac and black	35·00	9·00
14		6d. lilac and black	42·00	25·00
		(*b*) *Wmk Script* "V R" *sideways, reading up*		
15	4	1s. green and black	48·00	11·00
16		2s. green and black	60·00	30·00
17		2s. 6d. green and black	65·00	32·00
18		5s. green and black	£140	£120
19		10s. green and black	£275	£275

(c) Wmk two orbs, sideways

20 **5** £1 lilac and black £1100 £1100
21 £5 lilac and black £3000 £1750
10/21 H/S "Specimen" .. .. *Set of* 12 £1500

Several values of the above series are known on blued paper. No. 11*a* is the first printing of the 2d. (on safety paper?) and has a faded appearance.

When purchasing Nos. 20/21 in used condition beware of copies with fiscal cancellations cleaned off and bearing forged postmarks.

For No. 15 surcharged "£5" see No. F2.

1d. (6) 1s. (7) One Half-Penny (8)

1888 (7 Aug). *Surch as T* **6** *or* **7**, *by P. Townshend & Co, Vryburg.*

22 **3** 1d. on 1d. lilac and black .. .. 7·00 5·50
23 2d. on 2d. lilac and black (R.) .. .. 9·00 5·50
a. *Pale dull lilac and black* .. .. 48·00 35·00
b. Curved foot to "2" £225 £190
24 2d. on 2d. lilac and black (G.) .. .. — £1200
25 4d. on 4d. lilac and black (R.) .. .. £125 90·00
26 6d. on 6d. lilac and black .. .. 60·00 30·00
27 6d. on 6d. lilac and black (B.) .. .. — £1400
28 **4** 1s. on 1s. green and black .. .. 90·00 55·00

1888 (Dec.) *No. 12a surch with T* **8**, *by P. Townshend & Co, Vryburg.*

29 **3** ½d. on 3d. pale reddish lilac and black 80·00 85·00
a. Broken "f" in "Half" .. .. ..

No. 29a shows the letter "f" almost completely missing. Two examples are known, one being in the Royal collection.

British Bechuanaland. (9) British Bechuanaland. (10) BRITISH BECHUANALAND (11)

1889 (Jan). *T* **6** *of Cape of Good Hope (wmk Anchor) optd with T* **9**, *by P. Townshend & Co, Vryburg.*

30 ½d. slate (G.) .. .. 5·50 9·00
b. Opt double, one inverted £350
c. Opt double, one vertical £350
ca. *Se-tenant* with stamp without opt .. £800
e. "British" omitted £1400

1891 (Nov). *T* **6** *of Cape of Good Hope (wmk Anchor), optd with T* **10**, *reading upwards.*

31 1d. rose-red .. .. 7·50 9·00
a. Pair, one without opt .. .. ..
b. "British" omitted .. .. .. — £170
c. "Bechuanaland" omitted £350
32 2d. bistre .. .. 3·25 3·75
a. No stop after "Bechuanaland" .. £130
31/32 H/S "Specimen" .. *Set of* 2 £325

See also Nos. 38 and 39.

1891 (Dec)–**1894**. *Stamps of Great Britain optd with T* **11**, *by D.L.R.*

33 **57** 1d. lilac .. .. 2·50 90
34 **73** 2d. green and carmine .. .. .. 1·60 2·50
35 **76** 4d. green and purple-brown .. .. 3·50 2·25
a. Bisected (2d.) (on cover) .. .. † £1000
36 **79** 6d. purple/*rose-red* .. .. 4·00 3·50
37 **82** 1s. green (July, 1894) .. .. .. 12·00 16·00
a. Bisected (6d.) (on cover) .. .. † —
33/36 H/S "Specimen" .. .. *Set of* 4 £250

1893–95. *As Nos. 31 and 32, but T* **10** *reads downwards.*

38 1d. rose-red (12.93) .. .. .. 1·60 1·90
a. Pair, one without opt .. ..
b. "British" omitted £225
c. Optd "Bechuanaland. British" .. ..
d. No dots to "i" of "British" .. .. 50·00 40·00
e. Opt reading up, no dots to "i" of "British" £225
39 2d. bistre (15.3.95) .. .. .. 2·75 2·00
a. Opt double £550 £550
b. "British" omitted £250 £250
c. Optd "Bechuanaland. British" .. .. — 90·00
d. No dots to "i" of British" .. .. 60·00 70·00

No. 38e was formerly listed as No. 31a but it does not occur on that setting and only exists from sheets fed the wrong way in the 1893 issue.

On 16 November 1895 British Bechuanaland was annexed to the Cape of Good Hope and ceased to have its own stamps, but they remained in use in the Protectorate until superseded in 1897.

B. BECHUANALAND PROTECTORATE

This large area north of the Molopo River was proclaimed a British Protectorate on 30 September 1885 at the request of the native chiefs.

A postal service using runners was inaugurated in August 1888 and Nos. 40 to 55 were issued as a temporary measure with the object of assessing the cost of this service.

Protectorate (12) 15½ mm Protectorate 1d (13)

(**Types 12/17** were applied by P. Townshend & Co. Vryburg)

1888 (7 Aug.). *No. 9 optd with T* **12** *and Nos. 10/19 surch or optd only as T* **13**.

40 **71** ½d. vermilion (H/S S. £120) .. .. 3·50 6·50
a. "Protectorate" double £250
41 **3** 1d. on 1d. lilac and black .. .. 4·00 7·50
a. Small figure "1" £225 £250
42 2d. on 2d. lilac and black .. .. 15·00 17·00
b. Curved foot to "2" £200 £200
43 3d. on 3d. pale reddish lilac and black 55·00 60·00
44 4d. on 4d. lilac and black £100 £100
a. Small figure "4" .. .. ..
45 6d. on 6d. lilac and black .. .. 38·00 40·00
46 **4** 1s. green and black (H/S S. £80) .. 50·00 38·00
a. First "o" omitted £2250 £2250
47 2s. green and black £250 £250
a. First "o" omitted £3000
48 2s. 6d. green and black £500 £475
a. First "o" omitted £3500
49 5s. green and black £1100 £1300
a. First "o" omitted £4000
50 10s. green and black £2750 £2750
a. First "o" omitted £7000

See also Nos. 54/5

1888 (Dec). *No. 25 optd with T* **12**.

51 **3** 4d. on 4d. lilac and black .. .. 45·00 32·00

Bechuanaland Protectorate. (14) Protectorate Fourpence (15)

1889 (Jan). *T* **6** *of Cape of Good Hope (wmk Anchor), optd with T* **14**.

52 ½d. slate (G.) .. .. 3·50 6·50
a. Opt double £275 £325
ab. Ditto, one reading "Protectorate Bechuanaland" .. .. ..
b. "Bechuanaland" omitted £450
c. Optd "Protectorate Bechuanaland" .. £110

1889 (Aug). *No. 9 surch with T* **15**.

53 **71** 4d. on ½d. vermilion (H/S S. £200) 5·00 6·00
a. Surch (T **15**) inverted .. .. — £2750

Protectorate (16) 15 mm Protectorate (17)

1890. *No. 9 optd.*

54 **16** ½d. vermilion .. .. .. 45·00 48·00
a. Type **16** inverted .. .. .. 45·00 55·00
b. Type **16** double .. .. .. 55·00 60·00
c. Type **16** double and inverted .. £400 £350
d. Error. "Portectorate" and opt inverted .. .. ..
55 **17** ½d. vermilion .. .. .. 50·00 60·00
a. Type **17** double £300
b. Error. "Protectorrte" .. .. ..

These were trial printings made in 1888 which were subsequently issued.

In June 1890 the Bechuanaland Protectorate and the Colony of British Bechuanaland came under one postal administration and the stamps of British Bechuanaland were used in the Protectorate until 1897.

BRITISH BECHUANALAND (18) BECHUANALAND PROTECTORATE (19)

1897. *T* **6** *of Cape of Good Hope (wmk Anchor), optd as T* **18**.

(*a*) *Lines 13 mm apart, bottom line 16 mm long, by Taylor & Marshall, Cape Town*

56 ½d. yellow-green (July?) .. .. 1·90 4·00

(*b*) *Lines 13½ mm apart, bottom line 15 mm long, by P. Townshend & Co, Vryburg*

57 ½d. yellow-green (April) .. .. 12·00 23·00

(*c*) *Lines 10½ mm apart, bottom line 15 mm long, by W. A. Richards & Sons, Cape Govt Printers*

58 ½d. yellow-green (July?) .. .. 6·50 11·00

Although issued only in the Protectorate, the above were presumably overprinted "BRITISH BECHUANALAND" because stamps bearing this inscription were in use there at the time.

1897 (Oct)–**1902**. *Stamps of Great Britain (Queen Victoria) optd with T* **19** *by D.L.R.*

59 **71** ½d. vermilion .. .. .. 60 1·50
60 ½d. blue-green (25.2.02) .. .. 1·25 2·25
61 **57** 1d. lilac .. .. 1·00 1·00
62 **73** 2d. green and carmine .. .. 3·25 4·50
63 **75** 3d. purple/*yellow* (12.97) .. .. 6·50 8·50
64 **76** 4d. green and purple-brown .. .. 11·00 11·00
65 **79** 6d. purple/*rose-red* .. .. .. 22·00 22·00
59/65 .. .. .. *Set of* 7 42·00 45·00
59/65 Optd "Specimen" .. .. *Set of* 7 £250

BECHUANALAND PROTECTORATE (20) BECHUANALAND PROTECTORATE (21)

1904–13. *Stamps of Great Britain (King Edward VII) optd with T* **20**, *by D.L.R.*

66 **83** ½d. blue-green (3.06) .. .. .. 2·75 3·00
67 ½d. yellow-green (11.08) .. .. 4·50 6·00
68 1d. scarlet (4.05) (S. £50) .. .. 3·75 1·50
69 **86** 2½d. ultramarine (29.11.04) .. .. 6·50 6·50
a. Stop after "P" in "PROTECTORATE" £950
70 **93** 1s. green and scarlet (10.12) (S. £60) 20·00 32·00
71 1s. green and carmine (1913) .. .. 24·00 35·00

Nos. 70 and 71 are the Somerset House printings.

1912 (Sept). *T* **102** *of Great Britain (King George V, wmk Crown) optd with T* **20**.

72 **102** 1d. scarlet .. .. 2·00 2·50
a. No cross on crown .. .. .. — 70·00
b. *Aniline scarlet* .. .. .. £120 80·00

1913 (July)–**24**. *Stamps of Great Britain (King George V) optd.*

(a) With T **20** *(wmk Script Cypher, T* **100**)

73 **105** ½d. green .. .. 85 1·25
74 **104** 1d. scarlet (*shades*) (4.15) .. .. 1·25 90
75 **105** 1½d. red-brown (12.20) .. .. .. 1·75 3·00
76 **106** 2d. reddish orange (Die I) .. .. 2·50 3·75
a. Orange (Die I) (1921) .. ..
77 2d. orange (Die II) (1924) .. .. 16·00 8·00
78 **104** 2½d. ultramarine .. .. .. 2·50 4·75
a. Blue (1915) .. .. ..
79 **106** 3d. blue-violet .. .. .. 5·50 9·00
80 4d. slate-green .. .. .. 4·50 8·00
81 **107** 6d. reddish purple (*shades*), **C** .. 5·50 7·50
a. Purple, **C** .. .. ..
82 **108** 1s. bistre-brown (S. £60) .. .. 7·00 10·00
a. Olive-bistre .. .. ..
73/82 .. .. .. *Set of* 9 28·00 45·00

(b) With T **21** *(wmk T* **110**)

(i) *Waterlow printings.* (1914–15)

83 **109** 2s. 6d. deep sepia-brown (1.15) £130 £160
a. Re-entry £650 £750
b. Opt double, one albino £180
84 5s. rose-carmine (1914) £180 £250
a. Opt double, one albino £250
83/84 Optd "Specimen" .. *Set of* 2 £250

(ii) *D.L.R. printings.* (1916–20)

85 **109** 2s. 6d. grey-brown (7.16) £130 £150
a. Re-entry £750
86 2s. 6d. deep brown (1920) £150 £170
a. Opt treble, two albino .. ..
87 5s. bright carmine (8.19) £250 £275
a. Opt double, one albino £300

(iii) *B.W. printings.* (1920–23)

88 **109** 2s. 6d. chocolate-brown (7.23) £150 £150
a. Major Re-entry £1500
b. Opt double, one albino .. ..
89 5s. rose-red (7.20) £180 £200
90 5s. deep carmine £180 £200
a. Opt treble, two albino £225

1925–27. *As 1913–24, but W* **111** *(block letters).*

91 **105** ½d. green (1927) .. .. .. 1·00 2·00
92 **104** 1d. scarlet (8.25) .. .. .. 1·25 2·00
93 **106** 2d. orange (Die II) (7.25) .. .. 1·75 2·50
94 3d. violet (10.26) .. .. .. 3·50 6·00
a. Opt double, one albino .. ..
95 4d. grey-green (10.26) .. .. 3·50 9·50
96 **107** 6d. purple, **C** (12.25) .. .. 6·50 11·00
97 6d. purple, **O** (1926) .. .. .. 11·00 17·00
98 **108** 1s. bistre-brown (10.26) .. .. 15·00 23·00
91/98 .. .. .. *Set of* 8 40·00 65·00

22 King George V, Baobab Tree and Cattle drinking

23 King George VI, Baobab Tree and Cattle drinking

(Des from photo by Resident Commissioner, Ngamiland, Recess Waterlow)

1932 (12 Dec). *Wmk Mult Script CA. P* 12½.

99 **22** ½d. green 40 70
100 1d. scarlet 50 95
101 2d. brown .. .. 1·60 1·60
102 3d. ultramarine .. .. .. 1·90 1·90
103 4d. orange .. .. 1·50 2·75
104 6d. purple .. .. 2·50 2·50
105 1s. black and olive-green .. .. 6·00 8·00
106 2s. black and orange .. .. .. 24·00 35·00
107 2s.6d. black and scarlet .. .. 27·00 38·00
108 3s. black and purple .. .. .. 38·00 48·00
109 5s. black and ultramarine .. .. 48·00 55·00
110 10s. black and brown £150 £170
99/110 .. .. .. *Set of* 12 £275 £325
99/110 Perf "Specimen" .. .. *Set of* 12 £350

1935 (4 May). *Silver Jubilee. As Nos. 91/4 of Antigua but ptd by B.W. P* 11 × 12.

No.	Description	Un.	Used
111	1d. deep blue and scarlet	30	60
	a. Extra flagstaff	80·00	
	b. Short extra flagstaff	50·00	
112	2d. ultramarine and grey-black	60	1·25
	a. Extra flagstaff	70·00	
	b. Short extra flagstaff	40·00	
	c. Lightning conductor	35·00	
113	3d. brown and deep blue	70	1·75
	a. Extra flagstaff	80·00	
	b. Short extra flagstaff	50·00	
	c. Lightning conductor	40·00	
114	6d. slate and purple	1·50	2·75
	a. Extra flagstaff	80·00	
	b. Short extra flagstaff	50·00	
	c. Lightning conductor	40·00	
111/14 Perf "Specimen"	*Set of* 4	60·00	

For illustrations of plate varieties see Omnibus section following Zululand.

1937 (12 May). *Coronation. As Nos.* 13/15 *of Aden. P* 14.

No.	Description	Un.	Used
115	1d. scarlet	30	40
116	2d. yellow-brown	35	40
117	3d. bright blue	35	65
115/17 Perf "Specimen"	*Set of* 3	50·00	

(Recess Waterlow)

1938 (1 Apr)–**52**. *Wmk Mult Script CA. P* 12½.

No.	Type	Description	Un.	Used
118	23	½d. green	1·10	1·25
		a. Light yellowish green (1941)	2·00	2·25
		b. Yellowish green (4.43)	1·00	1·00
		c. Deep green (4.49)	1·00	1·00
119		1d. scarlet	25	30
120		1½d. dull blue	1·75	1·25
		a. Light blue (4.43)	60	40
121		2d. chocolate-brown	25	40
122		3d. deep ultramarine	25	40
123		4d. orange	35	75
124		6d. reddish purple	3·50	2·50
		a. Purple (1944)	2·75	2·25
125		1s. black and brown-olive	90	1·40
		a. Grey-black and olive-green (21.5.52)	4·00	5·00
126		2s.6d. black and scarlet	4·50	7·00
127		5s. black and deep ultramarine	12·00	12·00
		a. Grey-black & dp ultramarine (10.46)	26·00	27·00
128		10s. black and red-brown	23·00	32·00
118/28		*Set of* 11	40·00	50·00
118/28 Perf "Specimen"		*Set of* 11	£160	

Bechuanaland

(24)

1945 (3 Dec). *Victory. Stamps of South Africa optd with T* **24**. *Inscr alternately in English and Afrikaans.*

No.	Type	Description	*Un. pair*	*Used pair*
129	55	1d. brown and carmine	20	25
130	56	2d. slate-blue and violet	25	35
131	57	3d. deep blue and blue	40	50
		a. Opt omitted (in vert pair with normal)	£3500	†

1947 (17 Feb). *Royal Visit. As Nos.* 32/5 *of Basutoland.*

No.	Description	Un.	Used
132	1d. scarlet	12	10
133	2d. green	12	10
134	3d. ultramarine	12	12
135	1s. mauve	25	15
132/5 Perf "Specimen"	*Set of* 4	90·00	

1948 (1 Dec). *Royal Silver Wedding. As Nos.* 30/1 *of Aden.*

No.	Description	Un.	Used
136	1½d. ultramarine	25	25
137	10s. black	16·00	27·00

1949 (10 Oct). *75th Anniv of Universal Postal Union. As Nos.* 114/17 *of Antigua.*

No.	Description	Un.	Used
138	1½d. blue	30	35
139	3d. deep blue	65	65
140	6d. magenta	90	90
141	1s. olive	1·40	1·40

1953 (3 June). *Coronation. As No.* 47 *of Aden.*

No.	Description	Un.	Used
142	2d. black and brown	20	30

25 Queen Elizabeth II, Baobab Tree and Cattle drinking

26 Queen Victoria, Queen Elizabeth II and Landscape

(Des from photo by Resident Commissioner, Ngamiland. Recess Waterlow)

1955 (3 Jan)–**58**. *Wmk Mult Script CA. P* 13½ × 14.

No.	Type	Description	Un.	Used
143	25	½d. green	10	12
144		1d. rose-red	12	5
145		2d. red-brown	15	12
146		3d. ultramarine (*shades*)	25	15
146*a*		4d. red-orange (1.12.58)	1·75	2·00
147		4½d. blackish blue	40	45
148		6d. purple	40	30
149		1s. black and brown-olive	45	40
150		1s.3d. black and lilac	3·00	3·50
151		2s.6d. black and rose-red	4·50	5·50
152		5s. black and violet-blue	5·50	6·50
153		10s. black and red-brown	12·00	15·00
143/153		*Set of* 12	26·00	30·00

(Photo Harrison)

1960 (21 Jan). *75th Anniv of Bechuanaland Protectorate. W w* **12**. *P* 14½ × 14.

No.	Type	Description	Un.	Used
154	26	1d. sepia and black	12	10
155		3d. magenta and black	20	10
156		6d. bright blue and black	25	35

New Currency. 100 cents = 1 rand

1c (27) — 1c (I) 1c (II) — 5c (I) 5c (II)

3 (I) 3 (II) 3 (III) (3½ c. on 4d.) — R1 (I) R1 (II)

1961 (14 Feb–June). *Nos.* 144/6*a and* 148/53 *surch as T* **27** *by South African Govt Printer, Pretoria.*

No.	Type	Description	Un.	Used
157	25	1 c. on 1d. rose-red (Type I)	5	5
		a. Type II (6.6)	12	15
158		2 c. on 2d. red-brown	5	5
159		2½ c. on 2d. red-brown (*two types*)	10	10
		b. Pair one without surch	£450	
160		2½ c. on 3d. bright ultramarine	90	1·25
161		3½ c. on 4d, red-orange (Type I)	40	40
		a. Type II	1·00	1·50
		b. Wide surch (I)	7·50	8·50
		c. Wide surch (II)	20·00	22·00
		d. Type III (6.6)	25	10
162		5 c. on 6d. purple (Type I)	40	40
		a. Type II (12.5)	20	15
163		10 c. on 1s. black and brown-olive	15	10
		a. Pair, one without surch	£450	
164		12½ c. on 1s. 3d. black and lilac	25	25
165		25 c. on 2s. 6d. black and rose-red	65	70
166		50 c. on 5s. black and violet-blue	1·50	1·00
167		1 r. on 10s. black & red-brown (Type I)	£200	90·00
		a. Type II (1st Ptg) (17.3)	7·50	8·50
		b. Type II (2nd Ptg)	3·75	4·25
157/167b		*Set of* 11	7·00	7·00

No. 161—3½ c. on 4d. Types I and II of "3" were mixed in the sheet of 60 stamps—38 of Type I, 22 of Type II. The "wide surcharge" measures 9½ mm overall (with "C" spaced 1½ mm from "½") and comes on 8 of the 10 stamps in the last vertical row (5 × Type I, 3 × Type II). The surcharge on the remainder of the sheet varies between 8½ and 9½ mm.

Type III was a later printing.

Nos. 167a/b—1 rand (Type II). The First Printing (No. 167a) had the surcharge at bottom left; in the Second Printing (No. 167b) it was placed towards the bottom of the stamp, either centrally or towards the right.

Later printings of the 2½ c. on 2d. and 12½ c. on 1s. 3d. were from fresh settings of type, but insufficiently different for separate listing here. Later printings of the 10 c. and 25 c. were identical with the originals.

28 African Golden Oriole

39 Bechuana Ox

(Des P. Jones. Photo Harrison)

1961 (2 Oct). *T* **28, 39** *and similar designs. W w* **12**. *P* 14½ × 14 (25, 50 *c.*) *or* 14 × 14½ (*others*).

No.	Description	Un.	Used
168	1 c. yellow, red, black and lilac	20	25
169	2 c. orange, black and yellow-olive	25	30
170	2½ c. carmine, green, black and bistre	25	12
171	3½ c. yellow, black, sepia and pink	35	35
172	5 c. yellow, blue, black and buff	50	25
173	7½ c. brown, red, black and apple-green	50	60
174	10 c. red, yellow, sepia & turquoise-green	75	50
175	12½ c. buff, blue, red and grey-black	4·75	2·25
176	20 c. yellow-brown and drab	60	70
177	25 c. deep brown and lemon	65	75
178	35 c. deep blue and orange	1·50	1·60
179	50 c. sepia and olive	1·40	2·25
180	1 r. black and cinnamon	4·50	4·50
181	2 r. brown and turquoise-blue	13·00	12·00
168/81	*Set of* 14	26·00	24·00

Designs: *Vert*—2 c. Hoopoe; 2½ c. Scarlet-chested Sunbird; 3½ c. Yellow-rumped Bishop; 5 c. Swallow-tailed Bee Eater; 7½ c. African Grey Hornbill; 10 c. Red-headed Weaver; 12½ c. Brown-headed Kingfisher; 20 c. Woman musician; 35 c. Woman grinding maize; 1 r. Lion; 2 r. Police camel patrol. *Horiz*—25 c. Baobab Tree.

1963 (4 June). *Freedom from Hunger. As No.* 76 *of Aden.*

No.	Description	Un.	Used
182	12½ c. bluish green	50	20

1963 (2 Sept). *Red Cross Centenary. As Nos.* 147/8 *of Antigua.*

No.	Description	Un.	Used
183	2½ c. red and black	30	20
184	12½ c. red and blue	80	70

1964 (23 April). *400th Birth Anniv of William Shakespeare. As No.* 164 *of Antigua.*

No.	Description	Un.	Used
185	12½c. light brown	20	15

NEW INFORMATION

The editor is always interested to correspond with people who have new information that will improve or correct the Catalogue.

C. BECHUANALAND

INTERNAL SELF-GOVERNMENT

42 Map and Gaberones Dam

(Des V. Whiteley. Photo Harrison)

1965 (1 Mar). *New Constitution. W w* **12**. *P* 14½ × 14.

No.	Type	Description	Un.	Used
186	42	2½ c. red and gold	10	5
187		5 c. ultramarine and gold	12	5
188		12½ c. brown and gold	25	15
189		25 c. green and gold	45	30

1965 (17 May). *I.T.U. Centenary. As Nos.* 166/7 *of Antigua.*

No.	Description	Un.	Used
190	2½ c. red and bistre-yellow	25	10
191	12½ c. mauve and brown	90	60

1965 (25 Oct). *International Co-operation Year. As Nos.* 168/9 *of Antigua.*

No.	Description	Un.	Used
194	1 c. new blue	15	12
195	2½ c. deep green	40	10
196	12½ c. brown	85	50
197	20 c. bluish violet	95	50

43 Haslar Smoke Generator

(Des V. Whiteley. Photo Harrison)

1966 (1 June). *Bechuanaland Royal Pioneer Corps. T* **43** *and similar horiz designs. W w* **12**. *P* 14½.

No.	Description	Un.	Used
198	2½ c. Prussian blue, red and light emerald	12	8
199	5 c. brown and light blue	20	15
200	15 c. Prussian blue, rosine and emerald	50	40
201	35 c. buff, blackish brown, red and green	85	90

Designs:—5 c. Bugler; 15 c. Gun-site; 35 c. Regimental cap badge.

POSTAGE DUE STAMPS

BECHUANALAND PROTECTORATE (D 1) — BECHUANALAND PROTECTORATE (D 2)

1926 (Jan). *Type* D 1 *of Great Britain, optd with Types* D **1** *or* D **2** (2*d.*).

No.	Description	Un.	Used
D1	½d. emerald (No. D10)	3·25	27·00
D2	1d. carmine (No. D9)	3·50	27·00
D3	2d. agate (No. D13)	7·50	50·00

D 3

1c 1c — I (Small) II (Large)

(Typo D.L.R.)

1932 (12 Dec)–**58**. *Wmk Mult Script CA. P* 14.

No.	Type	Description	Un.	Used
D4	D 3	½d. sage-green	2·00	4·25
D5		1d. carmine, O	2·00	3·00
		a. Chalky paper (27.11.58)	30	1·50
D6		2d. violet, O	3·75	7·50
		a. Chalky paper (27.11.58)	1·25	3·50
D4/6 Perf "Specimen"		*Set of* 3	60·00	

1961 (14 Feb). *Surch as T* **27**.

No.	Type	Description	Un.	Used
D7	D 3	1 c. on 1d., C (Type I)	40	85
		a. Type II (chalky paper)	12	40
		ab. Double surch (Type II)	70·00	
		b. Type II (ordinary paper)	16·00	
D8		2 c. on 2d., C (Type I)	40	90
		a. Type II (chalky paper)	25	45
		b. Type II (ordinary paper)	22·00	
D9		5 c. on ½d.	60	1·25

1961 (15 Nov). *As Type* D **3** *but values in cents. Chalky paper. Wmk Mult Script CA. P* 14.

No.	Description	Un.	Used
D10	1 c. carmine	20	55
D11	2 c. violet	20	70
D12	5 c. green	45	1·25

POSTAL FISCAL STAMPS

The following stamps issued for fiscal purposes were each allowed to be used for postal purposes for a short time. No. F2 was used by the public because the word "POSTAGE" had not been obliterated and No. F3 because the overprint did not include the words "Revenue only" as did the contemporary fiscal overprints for Basutoland and Swaziland.

Bechuanaland

Protectorate	£5	Bechuanaland Protectorate.
(F 1)	(F 2)	(F 3)

1910 (July). *No. 266 of Transvaal, optd with Type* **F 1.**
F1 6d. black and orange, C (B.) £100 £120

1918. *No. 15 surch with Type* F **2** *at top.*
F2 4 £5 on 1s. green and black £3250

1922. *No. 4b of South Africa optd with Type* **F 3**, *in varying positions.*
F3 1d. scarlet . . . . 40·00 42·00
a. Opt double, one albino . . . . . .

The stamps of Bechuanaland were withdrawn on independence, 29 September 1966. For later issues see BOTSWANA.

Belize
(*formerly* British Honduras)

✲BELIZE✲

(81)

1973 (11 June*). *As Nos. 277/b, 278, 256, 259, 262/6 and 338/40 of British Honduras with T* **81** *in silver and black by D.L.R. W w* **12** *(upright). P 13 × 12½.*
347 ½ c. Crana 5 5
348 1 c. Jew Fish 5 5
349 2 c. Warree 8 8
350 3 c. Grouper 8 8
351 4 c. Ant Bear 8 8
352 5 c. Bone Fish 10 10
353 10 c. Gibnut 15 15
a. Black (value etc.) omitted) £200
354 15 c. Dolphin 20 20
355 25 c. Night Walker 35 35
356 50 c. Mutton Snapper 55 55
357 $1 Bush Dog . . . . 90 1·25
358 $2 Great Barracuda . . . . 2·25 3·00
359 $5 Mountain Lion . . . . 4·50 7·00
347/59 . . . . *Set of* 13 8·50 12·00
*This is the local date of issue: the Crown Agents released the stamps on 1 June.

1973 (14 Nov). *Royal Wedding. As Nos. 165/6 of Anguilla. Centre multicoloured. W w* **12** *(sideways). P 13½.*
360 26 c. light turquoise-blue 20 20
361 50 c. ochre 25 25

82 Crana

1974 (1 Jan). *Designs as Nos. 256/67 and 277 of British Honduras inscr. "BELIZE" as in T* **82**. *W w* **12**. *P 13½.*
362 ½ c. Type **82** 5 5
363 1 c. Jew Fish 5 5
364 2 c. Warree 5 5
365 3 c. Grouper 5 5
366 4 c. Ant Bear 8 8
367 5 c. Bone Fish 10 10
368 10 c. Gibnut 15 15
369 15 c. Dolphin 20 20
370 25 c. Night Walker 35 35
371 50 c. Mutton Snapper 60 70
372 $1 Bush Dog . . . . 1·50 1·90
373 $2 Great Barracuda . . . . 3·00 3·75
374 $5 Mountain Lion . . . . 6·50 8·00
362/74 . . . . *Set of* 13 11·00 14·00

83 Deer

(Des Mrs. Hosek; adapted PAD Studio, Litho Questa)

1974 (1 May). *Mayan Artefacts (1st series). T* **83** *and similar horiz designs showing pottery motifs. Multicoloured. W w* **12**. *P 14½.*
375 3 c. Type **83** 5 5
376 6 c. Jaguar deity 8 5
377 16 c. Sea monster 15 15
378 26 c. Cormorant 25 25
379 50 c. Scarlet macaw 40 40
See also Nos. 398/402.

84 *Parides arcas*

(Des J. Cooter from the collection of P. T. Hill. Litho Harrison)

1974 (2 Sept)–**75**. *Butterflies. Horiz designs as T* **84**. *Multicoloured. W w* **12** *(sideways). P 14 (½, 1, 2, 3, 4, 5, 10, 26 c.) or 14 × 14½ (others).*
380 ½ c. Type **84** 15 5
381 1 c. *Thecla regalis* 20 5
382 2 c. *Colobura dirce* 20 8
383 3 c. *Catonephele numilia* 20 8
384 4 c. *Battus belus* 20 8
385 5 c. *Callicore patelina* 20 10
386 10 c. *Callicore astala* 35 15
387 15 c. *Nessaea aglaura* 75 40
388 16 c. *Prepona pseudojoiceyi* 75 25
389 25 c. *Papilio thoas* 80 35
390 26 c. *Hamadryas arethusa* . . . . . . 4·00 4·75
391 50 c. *Thecla bathildis* . . . . 1·25 50
392 $1 *Caligo uranus* . . . . 1·50 60
393 $2 *Heliconius sapho* . . . . 2·50 1·25
394 $5 *Eurytides philolaus* . . . . . . 3·75 4·75
395 $10 *Philaethria dido* (2.1.75) . . . . . . 10·00 5·50
380/95 . . . . *Set of* 16 24·00 17·00
See also Nos. 403/13 and 426/33.

85 Churchill when Prime Minister, and Coronation Scene

86 The Actun Balam Vase

(Des J.W. Litho Questa)

1974 (30 Nov). *Birth Centenary of Sir Winston Churchill. T* **85** *and similar horiz design. Multicoloured. W w* **14** *(sideways). P* 14.
396 50 c. Type **85** 35 35
397 $1 Churchill in stetson, and Williamsburg Liberty Bell 50 50

(Des Mrs. Hosek; adapted P. Powell. Litho Questa)

1975 (2 June). *Mayan Artefacts (2nd series). T* **86** *and similar vert designs showing decorated vessels. Multicoloured. W w* **14**. *P* 14.
398 3 c. Type **86** 5 5
399 6 c. Seated figure 8 5
400 16 c. Costumed priest 15 15
401 26 c. Head with headdress 25 25
402 50 c. Layman and priest 40 40

1975–78. *As Nos. 380, 382/7 and 389 and new value (35 c.), but W w* **14** *(sideways on ½, 2, 3, 4, 5, 10 and 35 c.). P 14 × 14½ (15, 25 c.) or 14 (others).*
403 ½ c. Type **84** (11.6.75) 20 30
405 2 c. *Colobura dirce* (17.5.77) 25 10
406 3 c. *Catonephele numilia* (17.5.77) 30 10
407 4 c. *Battus belus* (7.3.77) 35 10
408 5 c. *Callicore patelina* (11.2.77) 40 15
409 10 c. *Callicore astala* (11.2.77) 50 15
410 15 c. *Nessaea aglaura* (17.5.77) 65 35
412 25 c. *Papilio thoas* (27.1.78) 75 40
413 35 c. Type **84** (25.7.77) . . . . 1·25 1·25
403/13 . . . . *Set of* 9 4·25 2·50

1975–77. *As Nos. 387, 389, 391 and 394 but W w* **12** *upright.*
426 15 c. *Nessaea aglaura* (20.10.75) 55 60
428 25 c. *Papilio thoas* (7.3.77) 55 50
429 50 c. *Thecla bathildis* (7.3.77) 95 60
433 $5 *Eurytides philolaus* (20.10.75) . . . . 7·00 7·00

87 Musicians

(Des PAD Studio. Litho Harrison)

1975 (17 Nov). *Christmas. T* **87** *and similar multicoloured designs. W w* **12** *(upright on 6 c. 26 c.) or sideways (others). P 14 × 14½ (horiz) or 14½ × 14 (vert).*
435 6 c. Type **87** 8 5
436 26 c. Children and "crib" 20 10
437 50 c. Dancer and drummers (*vert*) 30 30
a. Imperf (pair) . . . . 95·00
438 $1 Family and map (*vert*) 50 55

OMNIBUS ISSUES

Details, together with prices for complete sets, of the various Omnibus issues from the 1935 Silver Jubilee series to date are included in a special section following Zululand at the end of the catalogue.

88 William Wrigley Jr. and Chicle Tapping

(Des PAD Studio. Litho Questa)

1976 (29 Mar). *Bicentenary of American Revolution. T* **88** *and similar horiz designs. Multicoloured. W w* **14** *(sideways). P* 14.
439 10 c. Type **88** 12 10
440 35 c. Charles Lindbergh and *Spirit of St. Louis* 40 50
441 $1 J. L. Stephens (archaeologist) . . . . 1·00 1·40

89 Cycling

(Des J.W. Litho Walsall)

1976 (17 July). *Olympic Games. Montreal. T* **89** *and similar horiz designs. Multicoloured. W w* **14** *(sideways). P* 14.
442 35 c. Type **89** 25 25
443 45 c. Running 30 30
444 $1 Shooting 55 55

(90) (91)

1976 (30 Aug). *As No. 390, but W w* **14** *(sideways), surch with T* **90** *by Harrison.*
445 20 c. on 26 c. *Hamadryas arethusa* 25 40

1976 (18 Oct). *West Indian Victory in World Cricket Cup. As Nos. 559/60 of Barbados.*
446 35 c. Map of the Caribbean 70 60
447 $1 The Prudential Cup . . . . 1·40 1·40

1976 (2 Dec). *No. 426 surch with T* **91** *by the Govt Printery, Belize.*
448 5 c. on 15 c. *Nessaea aglaura* 30 30

92 Queen and Bishops

(Des R. Granger Barrett. Litho Enschedé)

1977 (7 Feb). *Silver Jubilee. T* **92** *and similar horiz designs. Multicoloured. W w* **14** *(sideways). P 13 × 13½.*
449 10 c. Royal Visit, 1975 . . . . 10 10
450 35 c. Queen and Rose Window 30 30
451 $2 Type **92** . . . . 1·25 1·50

93 Red-capped Manakin 94 Laboratory Workers

(Des and litho J.W.)

1977 (3 Sept). *Birds (1st series). T* **93** *and similar vert designs. Multicoloured. W w* **14**. *P* 14.
452 8 c. Type **93** 20 15
453 10 c. Hooded Oriole 25 20
454 25 c. Blue-crowned Motmot 55 55
455 35 c. Slaty-breasted Tinamou 75 75
456 45 c. Ocellated Turkey . . . . 1·60 2·00
457 $1 White Hawk . . . . 1·60 2·00
452/7 . . . . *Set of* 6 3·75 4·00
MS458 110 × 133 mm. Nos. 452/7 . . . . . . 3·75 4·25
See also Nos. 467/73, 488/94 and 560/6.

(Des G. Hutchins. Litho J.W.)

1977 (2 Dec). *75th Anniv of Pan-American Health Organisation. T* **94** *and similar horiz design. Multicoloured. W w* **14** *(sideways). P* 13½.
459 35 c. Type **94** 25 25
460 $1 Mobile medical unit 50 65
MS461 126 × 95 mm. Nos. 459/60. P 13 .. .. 1·25 1·25

BELIZE DEFENCE FORCE
1ST JANUARY 1978

(95)

1978 (15 Feb). *Establishment of Belize Defence Force. Nos.* 409 *and* 413 *optd with T* **95** *in gold by Govt Printery, Belize.*
462 10 c. *Callicore astala* 15 10
463 35 c. *Parides arcas* 30 30

96 White Lion of Mortimer

97 *Russelia sarmentosa*

(Des. C. Abbott. Litho Questa)

1978 (21 Apr). *25th Anniv of Coronation (1st issue). T* **96** *and similar vert designs. P* 15.
464 75 c. bistre, carmine and silver 40 40
a. Sheetlet. Nos. 464/6 × 2 .. .. .. 2·40
465 75 c. multicoloured 40 40
466 75 c. bistre, carmine and silver 40 40
Designs:—No. 464, Type **96**; No. 465, Queen Elizabeth II; No 466, Jaguar (Maya god of Day and Night).
Nos. 464/6 were printed together in small sheets of 6, containing two *se-tenant* strips of 3 with horizontal gutter margin between.
See also Nos. 495/503.

(Des. J.W. Litho Questa)

1978 (31 July). *Birds (2nd series). Vert designs as T* **93**. *Multicoloured. W w* **14**. *P* 14½.
467 10 c. White-capped Parrot 20 20
468 25 c. Crimson-collared Tanager 55 45
469 35 c. Citreoline Trogon 70 55
470 45 c. American Finfoot 90 70
471 50 c. Muscovy Duck 95 80
472 $1 King Vulture .. .. 1·50 2·00
467/72 .. .. *Set of* 6 4·25 4·25
MS473 111 × 133 mm. Nos. 467/72 .. .. 4·25 4·75

(Des J. Cooter. Litho Questa)

1978 (16 Oct). *Christmas. Wild Flowers and Ferns. T* **97** *and similar vert designs. Multicoloured. W w* **14**. *P* 14 × 13½.
474 10 c. Type **97** 8 5
475 15 c. *Lygodium polymorphum* 12 10
476 35 c. *Heliconia aurantiaca* 20 15
477 45 c. *Adiantum tetraphyllum* 25 25
478 50 c. *Angelonia ciliaris* 25 25
479 $1 *Thelypteris obliterata* 45 50
474/79 .. .. *Set of* 6 1·25 1·10

98 Internal Airmail Service, 1937

(Des D. Bowen. Litho Questa)

1979 (15 Jan). *Centenary of U.P.U. Membership. T* **98** *and similar horiz designs. Multicoloured. W w* **14** *(sideways). P* 13½ × 14.
480 5 c. Type **98** 5 5
481 10 c. M.V. *Heron H* on mail service, 1949 .. 5 5
482 35 c. Internal mail service, 1920 (canoe) .. 20 20
483 45 c. Internal mail service, 1910 (railway) .. 25 25
484 50 c. Mounted mail courier, 1882 .. .. 30 30
485 $2 R.M.S. *Eagle*, 1856 .. .. .. 1·00 1·25
480/5 .. .. *Set of* 6 1·60 1·90

15¢

(99)

15c

(100)

1979. *No.* 413 *surch. (a) By typography, locally, with T* **99**.
486 15 c. on 35 c. Type **84** (March).. .. .. 28·00

(b) By lithography, in Great Britain, with T **100**
487 15 c. on 35 c. Type **84** (June) 25 35

(Des J.W. Litho Questa)

1979 (16 Apr). *Birds (3rd series). Vert designs as T* **93**. *Multicoloured. P* 14.
488 10 c. Boat-billed Heron 15 8
489 25 c. Grey-necked Wood Rail 35 20
490 35 c. Lineated Woodpecker 45 30
491 45 c. Blue-grey Tanager 50 40
492 50 c. Laughing Falcon.. .. .. .. 50 50
493 $1 Long-tailed Hermit .. .. .. 90 1·00
488/93 .. .. *Set of* 6 2·50 2·25
MS494 113 × 136 mm. Nos. 488/93 .. .. 2·50 2·75

PRINTER. The following issues to No. 734 were printed in lithography by Lito Nacional, Porto, Portugal.

AVAILABILITY. Certain values of some issues to No. 734 were only available in restricted quantities in Belize.

101 Paslow Building, Belize G.P.O.

(Des A. Medina)

1979 (31 May). *25th Anniv of Coronation (2nd issue). T* **101** *and similar multicoloured designs. P* 14.
495 25 c. Type **101** 20 5
496 50 c. Houses of Parliament 30 5
497 75 c. Coronation State Coach 45 5
498 $1 Queen on horseback (*vert*) 60 8
499 $2 Prince of Wales (*vert*) .. .. .. 1·25 15
500 $3 Queen and Duke of Edinburgh (*vert*) .. 1·90 20
501 $4 Portrait of Queen (*vert*) .. .. .. 2·50 25
502 $5 St. Edward's Crown (*vert*) .. .. 3·00 30
495/502 .. .. *Set of* 8 9·00 1·00
MS503 Two sheets, both 126 × 95 mm: (a) $5 Princess Anne on horseback at Montreal Olympics (*vert*), $10 Queen at Montreal Olympics (*vert*); (b) $15 As Type **101** .. .. .. *Set of* 2 *sheets* 18·00
Nos. 495/502 also exist imperforate from a restricted printing (*price for set of* 8 £40 *mint*).

102 Safety Aeroplane (1909)

(Des A. Medina)

1979 (30 July). *Death Centenary of Sir Rowland Hill and 75th Anniv of I.C.A.O. (International Civil Aviation Organization). T* **102** *and similar horiz designs. Multicoloured. P* 14.
504 4 c. Type **102** 5 5
505 25 c. Boeing "707-720" 20 5
506 50 c. "Concorde" 30 5
507 75 c. Handley Page "W86" (1922) 45 8
508 $1 Avro "F" (1912) 60 10
509 $1.50, Cody (1910) 95 15
510 $2 Triplane II (1909) .. .. 1·25 25
511 $3 Santos Dumont's aeroplane (1906) .. 1·90 35
512 $4 First motorized flight, Wright brothers (1903) .. .. 2·50 50
504/12 .. .. *Set of* 9 7·00 1·25
MS513 Two sheets: (a) 115 × 95 mm. $5 Dunne "D5" (1910), $5 G.B. 1969 "Concorde" stamp; (b) 130 × 95 mm. $10 Boeing "707–720" (*different*). *Set of* 2 *sheets* 18·00
Nos. 504/12 also exist imperforate from a restricted printing (*price for set of* 9 £55 *mint*).

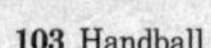
103 Handball

104 Olympic torch

(Des A. Medina)

1979 (10 Oct). *Olympic Games. Moscow* (1980). *T* **103** *and similar vert designs. Multicoloured. P* 14.
514 25 c. Type **103** 20 5
515 50 c. Weightlifting 30 5
516 75 c. Athletics 45 5
517 $1 Football 60 8
518 $2 Yachting .. .. 1·25 15
519 $3 Swimming .. .. 1·90 20
520 $4 Boxing .. .. 2·50 25
521 $5 Cycling .. .. 3·00 30
514/21 .. .. *Set of* 8 9·00 1·00
MS522 Two sheets: (a) 126 × 92 mm. $5 Athletics (*different*), $10 Boxing (*different*); (b) 92 × 126 mm. $15 As $5 .. .. *Set of* 2 *sheets* 18·00
Nos. 514/21 also exist imperforate from a restricted printing (*price for set of* 8 £55 *mint*).

(Des A. Medina)

1979 (4 Dec). *Winter Olympic Games. Lake Placid* (1980). *T* **104** *and similar vert designs. Multicoloured. P* 14.
523 25 c. Type **104** 20 5
524 50 c. Giant slalom 30 5
525 75 c. Figure-skating 45 5
526 $1 Slalom skiing 60 8
527 $2 Speed-skating .. .. 1·25 15
528 $3 Cross-country skiing .. .. .. 1·90 20
529 $4 Shooting .. .. 2·50 25
530 $5 Gold, Silver and Bronze medals.. .. 3·00 30
523/30 .. .. *Set of* 8 9·00 1·00
MS531 Two sheets: (a) 127 × 90 mm. $5 Lighting the Olympic Flame, $10 Gold, Silver and Bronze medals (*different*); (b) 90 × 127 mm. $15 Olympic Torch (*different*) .. .. .. *Set of* 2 *sheets* 18·00
Nos. 523/30 also exist imperforate from a restricted printing (*price for set of* 8 £55 *mint*).

105 *Cypraea zebra*

106 Girl and Flower Arrangement

(Des C. Abbott)

1980 (7 Jan). *Shells. Multicoloured designs as T* **105**. *P* 14.
532 1 c. Type **105** 5 5
533 2 c. *Macrocallista maculata* 5 5
534 3 c. *Arca zebra* (*vert*) 5 5
535 4 c. *Chama macerophylla* (*vert*) 10 5
536 5 c. *Latirus cariniferus* 10 5
537 10 c. *Conus spurius* (*vert*) 15 5
538 15 c. *Murex cabritii* (*vert*) 20 5
539 20 c. *Atrina rigida* 20 5
540 25 c. *Chlamys imbricata* (*vert*) 20 5
541 35 c. *Conus granulatus* 30 5
542 45 c. *Tellina radiata* (*vert*) 35 8
543 50 c. *Leucozonia nassa leucozonalis* 35 8
544 85 c. *Tripterotyphis triangularis* 65 12
545 $1 *Strombus gigas* (*vert*) 75 12
546 $2 *Strombus gallus* (*vert*) .. .. .. 1·40 30
547 $5 *Fasciolaria tulipa* .. .. .. 3·25 75
548 $10 *Arene cruentata* .. .. .. 5·50 1·25
532/548 .. .. *Set of* 17 12·00 2·50
MS549 Two sheets, each 125 × 90 mm: (a) Nos. 544 and 547; (b) Nos. 546 and 548 .. .. 12·00 13·00
Some of the above exist with a different date in the imprint at the foot of each stamp.

(Des A. Medina ($5), C. Mullin (others))

1980 (15 Mar). *International Year of the Child. T* **106** *and similar vert designs. Multicoloured. P* 14.
550 25 c. Type **106** 20 5
551 50 c. Boy holding football 30 5
552 75 c. Boy with butterfly 45 5
553 $1 Girl holding doll 60 8
554 $1.50, Boy carrying basket of fruit 95 15
555 $2 Boy holding shell .. .. 1·25 20
556 $3 Girl holding posy.. .. .. .. 1·90 25
557 $4 Boy and girl wrapped in blanket .. 2·50 30
550/7 .. .. *Set of* 8 7·00 1·00
MS558 130 × 95 mm. $5 Three children of different races, $5 "Madonna with Cat" (A. Dürer) (*each* 35 × 53 *mm*). P 13.. .. .. 6·00
MS559 111 × 151 mm. $10 Children and Christmas tree (73 × 110 *mm*). P 13 .. .. 6·00
Nos. 550/7 also exist imperforate from a restricted printing (*price for set of* 8 £35 *mint*).

107 Jabiru

10¢

(108)

(Des J.W. Litho Questa)

1980 (16 June). *Birds* (4*th series*). *T* **107** *and similar vert designs. Multicoloured. P* 13.
560 10 c. Type **107** 20 10
a. Sheetlet. Nos. 560/5 .. .. 4·00
561 25 c. Barred Antshrike 40 15
562 35 c. Royal Flycatcher 55 25
563 45 c. White-necked Puffbird 75 30
564 50 c. Ornate Hawk-eagle 80 30
565 $1 Golden Masked Tanager .. .. .. 1·60 55
560/5 .. .. *Set of* 6 4·00 1·50
MS566 85 × 90 mm. $2 Type **107**, $3 As $1 .. 5·00 5·00
Nos. 560/5 were printed together, *se-tenant* in sheetlets of 6 or in "double" sheetlets of 12.

1980 (July). *No.* 412 *surch with T* **108**.
567 10 c. on 25 c. *Papilio thoas* 15 20

109 Speed Skating

40c
(110)

1980 (20 Aug). *Medal Winners, Winter Olympic Games, Lake Placid. T* **109** *and similar vert designs. Multicoloured. P* 14.
568 25 c. Type **109** 20 5
569 50 c. Ice hockey 30 5
570 75 c. Figure-skating 45 5
571 $1 Alpine skiing 60 8
572 $1.50, Giant slalom (women) 95 15
573 $2 Speed-skating (women) .. .. .. 1·25 20
574 $3 Cross-country skiing .. .. .. 1·90 25
575 $5 Giant slalom .. .. 3·00 30
568/75 .. .. *Set of* 8 7·50 1·00
MS576 Two sheets: (a) 126 × 91 mm. $5 Type **109**; $10 Type **109**; (b) 91 × 126 mm. $10 As 75 c. *Set of* 2 *sheets* 15·00
Nos. 568/75 also exist imperforate from a restricted printing (*price for set of* 8 £55 *mint*)

1980 (3 Oct). *"ESPAMER" International Stamp Exhibition, Madrid. Nos.* 560/5 *optd* (*Nos.* 577/9) *or surch as T* **110**.
577 10 c. Type **107** 30 15
a. Sheetlet. Nos. 577/82 .. .. .. 6·00
578 25 c. Barred Antshrike 70 35
579 35 c. Royal Flycatcher .. .. 1·10 55
580 40 c. on 45 c. White-necked Puffbird .. .. 1·50 75
581 40 c. on 50 c. Ornate Hawk-eagle .. .. 1·50 75
582 40 c. on $1 Golden Masked Tanager .. .. 1·50 75
577/82 .. .. *Set of* 6 6·00 3·00

111 Witch in Sky

112 Queen Elizabeth The Queen Mother

(Des C. Mullin)

1980 (24 Nov). *Fairy Tales. Sleeping Beauty. T* **111** *and similar vert designs illustrating the story. P* 14.
583 25 c. multicoloured 20 5
584 40 c. multicoloured 25 5
585 50 c. multicoloured 30 5
586 75 c. multicoloured 45 8
587 $1 multicoloured 60 15
588 $1.50, multicoloured 95 20
589 $3 multicoloured .. .. 1·90 25
590 $4 multicoloured .. .. 2·50 30
583/90 .. .. *Set of* 8 6·50 1·00
MS591 Two sheets: (a) 82 × 110 mm. $8 "Paumgartner Altar-piece" (Dürer); (b) 110 × 82 mm. $5 Marriage ceremony, $5 Sleeping Beauty and Prince on horseback .. .. *Set of* 2 *sheets* 11·00
Nos. 583/90 also exist imperforate from a restricted printing (*price for set of* 8 £55 *mint*).

(Des C. Mullen)

1980 (12 Dec). *80th Birthday of Queen Elizabeth the Queen Mother. P* 13.
592 **112** $1 multicoloured 80 30
MS593 82 × 110 mm, $5 As Type **112** (41 × 32 *mm*) 4·00 4·00
No. 592 exists imperforate from a restricted printing (*price* £4.50 *mint*).

113 The Annunciation

$1

(114)

(Des C. Mullin)

1980 (30 Dec). *Christmas. T* **113** *and similar vert designs. Multicoloured. P* 14.
594 25 c. Type **113** 20 5
595 50 c. Bethlehem 30 5
596 75 c. The Holy Family 45 5
597 $1 The Nativity 60 8
598 $1.50,The flight into Egypt 95 15
599 $2 Shepherds following the Star .. .. 1·25 20
600 $3 Virgin, Child and Angel .. .. .. 1·90 25
601 $4 Adoration of the Kings .. .. .. 2·50 30
594/601 .. .. *Set of* 8 7·00 1·00
MS602 Two sheets, each 82 × 111 mm: (a) $5 As $1; (b) $10 As $3 .. .. .. *Set of* 2 *sheets* 9·00

1981 (22 May). *"WIPA" International Stamp Exhibition. Vienna. Nos.* 598 *and* 601/2b *surch with T* **114**.
603 $1 on $1.50, The flight into Egypt 60 65
604 $2 on $4 Adoration of the Kings .. .. 1·25 1·40
MS605 82 × 111 mm. $2 on $10 Virgin, Child and Angel .. .. 1·25 1·50

115 Paul Harris (founder)

116 Prince of Wales Coat of Arms

1981 (26 May). *75th Anniv of Rotary International. T* **115** *and similar multicoloured designs. P* 14.
606 25 c. Type **115** 20 25
607 50 c. Emblems of Rotary activities 30 35
608 $1 75th Anniversary emblem 60 65
609 $1·50, Educational scholarship programme (*horiz*) .. .. 95 1·00
610 $2 "Project Hippocrates" .. .. .. 1·25 1·40
611 $3 Emblems (*horiz*) .. .. 1·90 2·00
612 $5 Emblem and handshake (*horiz*) .. .. 3·00 3·25
606/12 .. .. *Set of* 7 7·00 8·00
MS613 Two sheets: (a) 95 × 130 mm. $10 As 50 c.; (b) 130 × 95 mm, $5 As $1, $10 As $2 *Set of* 2 *sheets* 15·00
*Nos. 606/13, together with a 75 c. value showing a map, were originally issued on 30 March 1981, but were withdrawn from sale after two hours as there were objections to the colours used on the map. The stamps, without the offending 75 c., were reissued on 26 May. First Day covers carry the later date and there are no reports of examples used before 26 May.

(Des C. Mullin)

1981 (16 July). *Royal Wedding. T* **116** *and similar vert designs. Multicoloured.* (*a*) *Size* 22 × 38 *mm* (*from sheets of* 27). *P* 13½ × 14.
614 50 c. Type **116** 60 65
a. Horiz pair. Nos. 614/15 .. .. .. 1·90
615 $1 Prince Charles in military uniform .. 1·25 1·40
a. Horiz pair. Nos. 615/16 .. .. .. 3·25
616 $1.50, Royal couple .. .. 1·90 2·00
(*b*) *Size* 25 × 42 *mm with gold borders* (*sheets of* 6 *stamps and* 3 *labels*). *P* 13.
617 50 c. Type **116** 60 15
618 $1 As No. 615 .. .. 1·25 35
619 $1.50, As No. 616 .. .. 1·90 45
614/19 .. .. *Set of* 6 6·50 4·50
MS620 145 × 85 mm. $3 × 3 As Nos 614/16, but 30 × 47 mm. P 14 .. .. 8·00 8·50
Nos. 614/16 were each printed in blocks of 9 (3 × 3), the blocks *se-tenant* within the sheet.
Nos. 614/16 also exist imperforate from a restricted printing (*price for set of* 3 £25 *mint*)

10c
■
(117)

1981 (22 Aug). *No.* 538 *surch with T* **117**.
621 10 c. on 15 c. *Murex cabritii* 10 15
For a similar surcharge, but with rectangular obliterating panel see No. 728.

118 Athletics

(Des C. Mullin)

1981 (14 Sept). *History of the Olympic Games. T* **118** *and similar vert designs. Multicoloured. P* 14.
622 85 c. Type **118** 55 5
623 $1 Cycling 60 8
624 $1.50, Boxing 95 12
625 $2 1984 Games–Los Angeles and Sarajevo 1·25 20
626 $3 Baron Pierre de Coubertin .. .. 1·90 30
627 $5 Olympic Flame .. .. 3·00 40
622/7 .. .. *Set of* 6 7·50 1·00
MS628 Two sheets, each 175 × 123 mm: (a) $5 As $3, $10 As $5 (*each* 35 × 53 *mm*). P 13½; (b) $15 As $2 (45 × 67 *mm*). P 14½. .. *Set of* 2 *sheets* 18·00

Independence
21 Sept.,1981
(119)

$1

(120)

1981 (21 Sept). *Independence Commemoration* (1*st issue*). *Optd as T* **119** (*a*) *On Nos.* 532/44 *and* 546/9.
629 1 c. Type **119** 5 5
630 2 c. *Macrocallista maculata* 5 5
631 3 c. *Arca zebra* (*vert*) 5 5
632 4 c. *Chama macerophylla* (*vert*) 5 5
633 5 c. *Latirus cariniferus* 5 5
634 10 c. *Conus spurius* (*vert*) 5 5
635 15 c. *Murex cabritii* (*vert*) 10 12
636 20 c. *Atrina rigida* 12 15
637 25 c. *Chlamys imbricata* (*vert*) 20 25
638 35 c. *Conus granulatus* 25 30
639 45 c. *Tellina radiata* (*vert*) 30 35
640 50 c. *Leucozonia nassa leucozonalis* 30 35
641 85 c. *Tripterotyphis triangularis* 55 60
642 $2 *Strombus gallus* (*vert*) .. .. .. 1·25 1·40
643 $5 *Fasciolaria tulipa* .. .. .. 3·00 3·25
a. Opt inverted .. .. † —
644 $10 *Arene cruentata* .. .. 6·00 6·50
629/44 .. .. *Set of* 16 11·00 12·00
MS645 Two sheets, each 126 × 91 mm: (a) Nos. 641 and 643; (b) Nos. 642 and 644 .. *Set of* 2 *sheets* 11·00
On the vertical designs and the miniature sheets the overprint is in roman type.

(*b*) *On Nos.* 606/13
646 25 c. Type **115** (Gold) 20 25
647 50 c. Emblems of Rotary activities 30 35
648 $1 75th Anniversary emblem 60 65
649 $1.50, Educational scholarship programme 95 1·00
650 $2 "Project Hippocrates" (Gold) .. .. 1·25 1·40
651 $3 Emblems .. .. 1·90 2·00
652 $5 Emblems and handshake .. .. .. 3·00 3·25
646/52 .. .. *Set of* 7 *sheets* 7·00 8·00
MS653 Two sheets: (a) 95 × 130 mm. $10 As 50 c.; (b) 130 × 95 mm. $5 As $1, $10 As $2 (Gold) *Set of* 2 *sheets* 15·00
See also Nos. 657/63.

1981 (13 Nov). *"ESPAMER" International Stamp Exhibition, Buenos Aires. Nos.* 609 *and* **MS**613b *surch with T* **120**.
654 $1 on $1.50, Educational scholarship programme .. .. 1·00 1·00
MS655 95 × 130 mm. $1 on $5 75th anniversary emblem, $1 on $10 "Project Hippocrates" .. .. 3·50 3·75

(121)

1981 (14 Nov). *"Philatelia 81" International Stamp Exhibition, Frankfurt. No.* **MS**549 *surch with T* 121 *in red*.
MS656 Two sheets, each 125 × 90 mm: (a) $1 on 85 c. *Tripterotyphis triangularis*, $1 on $5 *Fasciolaria tulipa*; (b) $1 on $2 *Strombus gallus*. $1 on $10 *Arene cruentata* .. .. *Set of* 2 *sheets* 18·00

ALTERED CATALOGUE NUMBERS

Any Catalogue numbers altered from the last edition are shown as a list in the introductory pages.

122 Black Orchid

123 Uruguayan Footballer

(Des C. Mullin)

1981 (18 Dec)–**82**. *Independence Commemoration (2nd issue) T* **122** *and similar multicoloured designs. P* 14.

657 10 c. Belize Coat of Arms (*horiz*) (10.2.82) .. 5 5
658 35 c. Map of Belize (10.2.82) .. 25 30
659 50 c. Type **122** .. 30 35
660 85 c. Tapir (*horiz*) .. 55 60
661 $1 Mahogany Tree .. 60 65
662 $2 Keel-billed Toucan (*horiz*) .. 1·25 1·40
657/62 .. *Set of* 6 2·50 3·00
MS663 130 × 98 mm. $5 As 10 c. P 14½ (10.2.82) 3·00 3·25

(Des C. Mullin)

1981 (28 Dec). *World Cup Football Championship, Spain (1st issue). T* **123** *and similar vert designs. Multicoloured. P* 14.

664 10 c. Type **123** .. 5 5
665 25 c. Italian footballer .. 20 5
666 50 c. German footballer .. 30 8
667 $1 Brazilian footballer .. 60 15
668 $1.50, Argentinian footballer .. 95 25
669 $2 English footballer .. 1·25 35
664/9 .. *Set of* 6 3·00 80
MS670 Two sheets: (a) 145 × 115 mm. $2 "SPAIN '82" logo; (b) 155 × 115 mm. $3 Footballer (46 × 76 *mm*) .. *Set of 2 sheets* 3·00

124 British 19th-century Man o' War

(Des C. Mullin)

1982 (15 Mar). *Sailing Ships. T* **124** *and similar horiz designs. Multicoloured. P* 14.

671 10 c. Type **124** .. 5 5
672 25 c. *Madagascar* (1837) .. 20 5
673 35 c. Brig *Whitby* (1838) .. 25 8
674 50 c. *China* (1838) .. 30 12
675 85 c. *Swiftsure* (1850) .. 55 20
676 $2 *Windsor Castle* (1857) .. 1·25 40
671/6 .. *Set of* 6 2·25 80
MS677 110 × 87 mm. $5 Ships in battle .. 3·00 3·25

(125)

126 Princess Diana

1982 (28 Apr). *"ESSEN '82" International Stamp Exhibition, West Germany. Nos. 662 and 669 surch with T* **125**.

678 $1 on $2 Keel-billed Toucan .. 1·00 65
679 $1 on $2 English footballer .. 1·00 65

(Des C. Mullin)

1982 (20 May). *21st Birthday of Princess of Wales. T* **126** *and similar vert designs showing portrait of Princess of Wales with different backgrounds. (a) Size 22 × 38 mm (from sheets of 25). P* 13½ × 14.

680 50 c. multicoloured .. 30 35
a. *Tête-bêche* (pair) .. 60
681 $1 multicoloured .. 60 65
a. *Tête-bêche* (pair) .. 1·25
682 $1.50, multicoloured .. 95 1·00
a. *Tête-bêche* (pair) .. 1·90

(*b*) *Size 25 × 43 mm (from sheets of 6 stamps and 3 labels). P* 13

683 50 c. multicoloured .. 30 10
684 $1 multicoloured .. 60 20
685 $1.50, multicoloured .. 95 30
680/5 .. *Set of* 6 3·25 2·25
MS686 145 × 85 mm. $3 × 3 As Nos. 680/2, but 30 × 47 mm. P 14 .. 5·50 6·00

127 Lighting Camp-fire

(Des C. Mullin)

1982 (31 Aug). *125th Birth Anniv of Lord Baden-Powell. T* **127** *and similar horiz designs. Multicoloured. P* 14.

687 10 c. Type **127** .. 5 5
688 25 c. Bird watching .. 20 25
689 35 c. Three scouts, one playing guitar .. 25 30
690 50 c. Hiking .. 30 35
691 85 c. Scouts with flag .. 55 60
692 $2 Saluting .. 1·25 1·40
687/92 .. *Set of* 6 2·25 2·50
MS693 Two sheets: each 85 × 115 mm: (a) $2 Scout with flag; (b) $3 Portrait of Lord Baden-Powell .. *Set of 2 sheets* 3·50

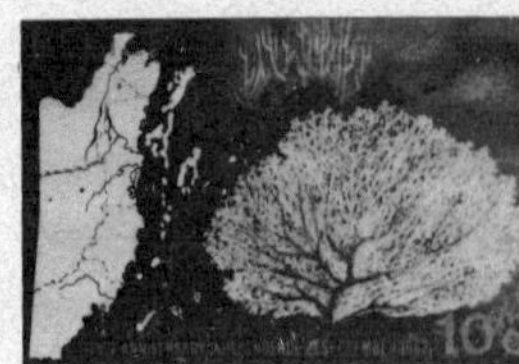

128 *Gorgonia ventalina*

(Des C. Mullin)

1982 (20 Sept). *First Anniv of Independence. Marine Life. T* **128** *and similar horiz designs. P* 14.

694 10 c. Type **128** .. 5 5
695 35 c. *Carpiuis corallinus* .. 25 8
696 50 c. *Plexaura flexuasa* .. 30 10
697 85 c. *Candylactis gigantea* .. 55 15
698 $1 *Stenopus hispidus* .. 60 20
699 $2 *Abudefduf saxatilis* .. 1·25 35
694/9 .. *Set of* 6 2·75 80
MS700 130 × 98 mm. $5 *Schyllarides aequinocialis*. P 14½ .. 3·25 3·50

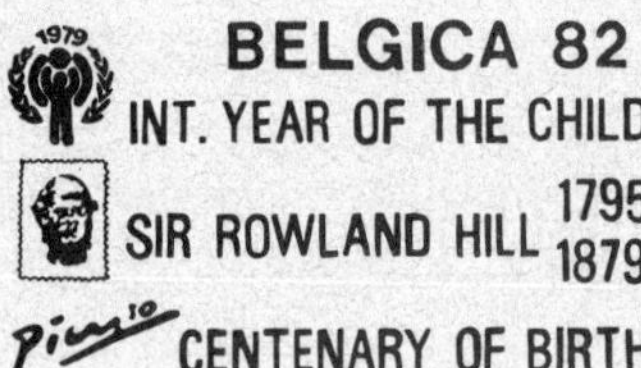

(129)

1982 (1 Oct). *"BELGICA 82" International Stamp Exhibition, Brussels. Nos 687/92 optd as T* **129** *in gold.*

701 10 c. Type **127** ..
702 25 c. Bird watching ..
703 35 c. Three scouts, one playing guitar ..
704 50 c. Hiking ..
705 85 c. Scouts with flag ..
706 $2 Saluting ..
701/6 .. *Set of* 6 25·00 25·00

BIRTH OF H.R.H.

PRINCE
WILLIAM ARTHUR
PHILIP LOUIS
21ST JUNE 1982

(130)

131 Scotland v New Zealand

1982 (21 Oct). *Birth of Prince William of Wales (1st issue). Nos. 680/6 optd as T* **130** *in silver. (a) Size 22 × 38 mm.*

707 50 c. multicoloured .. 30 35
a. *Tête-bêche* (pair) .. 65
b. Opt double .. £100
708 $1 multicoloured .. 60 65
a. *Tête-bêche* (pair) .. 1·40
709 $1.50, multicoloured .. 95 1·00
a. *Tête-beche* (pair) .. 2·00

(*b*) *Size 25 × 43 mm*

710 50 c. multicoloured .. 30 35
711 $1 multicoloured .. 60 65
712 $1.50, multicoloured .. 95 1·00
707/12 .. *Set of* 6 3·25 3·50
MS713 145 × 85 mm. $3 × 3 As Nos. 707/9, but 30 × 47 mm .. 5·50 6·00

1982 (25 Oct). *Birth of Prince William of Wales (2nd issue). Nos 614/20 optd as T* **130** *in gold (a) Size 22 × 38 mm.*

714 50 c. Type **116** .. 2·50 1·00
a. Horiz pair. Nos. 714/15 .. 7·50
715 $1 Prince Charles in military uniform .. 5·00 2·00
a. Horiz pair. Nos. 715/16 .. 12·50
716 $1.50, Royal couple .. 7·50 3·00

(*b*) *Size 25 × 42 mm*

717 50 c. Type **116** .. 2·00 1·00
718 $1 As No. 715 .. 4·00 1·50
719 $1.50, As No. 716 .. 6·00 2·50
714/9 .. *Set of* 6 25·00 10·00
MS720 145 × 85 mm. $3 × 3 As Nos. 714/16 but 30 × 47 mm .. 11·00 11·00

No. **MS**720 occurs with two different sizes of overprint. On the normal version the top line of the overprint, "BIRTH OF H.R.H." measures 19½ mm in length. On examples with the larger overprint this measures 22 mm. (*Price for miniature sheet with larger overprint £35 mint.*)

(Des Baumann)

1982 (10 Dec). *World Cup Football Championship, Spain (2nd issue). T* **131** *and similar horiz designs. Multicoloured. P* 14.

721 20 c. + 10 c. Type **131** .. 20 5
722 30 c. + 15 c. Scotland v New Zealand (*different*) 30 5
723 40 c. + 20 c. Kuwait v France .. 40 8
724 60 c. + 30 c. Italy v Brazil .. 60 15
725 $1 + 50 c. France v Northern Ireland .. 1·00 25
726 $1.50 + 75 c. Austria v Chile .. 1·50 35
721/6 .. *Set of* 6 3·50 80
MS727 Two sheets: (a) 91 × 137 mm. $1 + 50 c. Germany v Italy (50 × 70 *mm*); (b) 122 × 116 mm. $2 + $1 England v France (50 × 70 *mm*) .. *Set of 2 sheets* 3·00 3·25

10c

(132)

133 Belize Cathedral

1983 (28 Jan). *No. 538 surch with T* **132**.

728 10 c. on 15 c. *Murex cabritii* ..

No. 728 differs from the previous provisional, No. 621, in the size of the obliterating panel over the original face value. On No. 621 this measures 4½ × 4½ mm, but No. 728 shows it larger, 7 × 5½ mm.

1983 (7 March). *Visit of Pope John Paul II. P* 13½.

729 **133** 50 c. multicoloured .. 35 35
MS730 135 × 110 mm. $2.50, Pope John Paul II (30 × 47 *mm*). P 14 .. 1·75 2·00

134 Map of Belize

10c

(135)

1983 (14 Mar). *Commonwealth Day. T* **134** *and similar multicoloured designs. P* 13.

731 35 c. Type **134** .. 25 30
732 50 c. "Maya Stella" from Lamanai Indian church (*horiz*) .. 30 35
733 85 c. Supreme Court Building (*horiz*) .. 55 60
734 $2 University Centre, Belize (*horiz*) .. 1·25 1·40

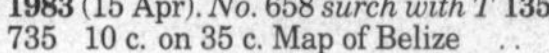

1983 (15 Apr). *No. 658 surch with T* **135**.

735 10 c. on 35 c. Map of Belize ..

136 Lana's "Flying boat" 1670

(Des C. Mullin)

1983 (16 May). *Bicentenary of Manned Flight. T* **136** *and similar horiz designs. Multicoloured. P* 14.

736 10 c. Type **136** .. 5 5
737 25 c. Barthelemy Lourenco's flying machine, 1709 .. 20 25
738 50 c. Guyton de Morveau's airship .. 30 35
739 85 c. Early dirigible .. 55 60
740 $1 The *Clement Bayard* .. 60 65
741 $1.50, *R-34* airship .. 95 1·00
736/41 .. *Set of* 6 2·25 2·50
MS742 Two sheets: (a) 125 × 84 mm. $3 Night scene from the *Nassau* balloon; (b) 115 × 128 mm. $3 Montgolfier balloon (*vert*) .. *Set of 2 sheets* 3·50 3·75

$1.25

$1.25

(137) (138)

1983 (9 June). *Nos.* 662 *and* 699 *surch with T* **137/8**.

743 $1.25 on $2 Keel-billed Toucan (surch T **137**) 2·00 2·25
744 $1.25 on $2 *Abudefduf saxatilis* (surch T **138**) 3·00 2·25

10C 10C

(139) (140)

1983 (28 Sept). *No.* 541 *surch with T* **139/40**.

745 10 c. on 35 c. *Conus granulatus* (surch T **139**)
a. Surch inverted
b. Vert pair, lower stamp without surch
746 10 c. on 35 c. *Conus granulatus* (surch T **140**)

141 Altun Ha

(Des G. Vasarhelyi. Litho Format)

1983 (14 Nov). *Maya Monuments. T* **141** *and similar horiz designs. Multicoloured. P* 13½ × 14.

747 10 c. Type **141** 8 10
748 15 c. Xunantunich 10 12
749 75 c. Cerros 55 60
750 $2 Lamanai 1·40 1·50
MS751 102 × 72 mm. $3 Xunantunich (*different*) 2·10 2·25

142 Belmopan Earth Station

(Des G. Vasarhelyi. Litho Format)

1983 (28 Nov). *World Communications Year. T* **142** *and similar horiz designs. Multicoloured. P* 14.

752 10 c. Type **142** 8 10
753 15 c. *Telstar* 2 10 12
754 75 c. U.P.U. logo 55 60
755 $2 M.V. *Heron H* mail service 1·40 1·50

143 Jaguar Cub

(Des G. Vasarhelyi. Litho Format)

1983 (9 Dec). *The Jaguar. T* **143** *and similar horiz designs. Multicoloured. P* 14.

756 5 c. Type **143** 5 5
757 10 c. Adult Jaguar 8 10
758 85 c. Jaguar in river 60 65
759 $1 Jaguar on rock 70 75
MS760 102 × 72 mm. $3 Jaguar in tree (44 × 28 *mm*). P 13½ × 14 2·10 2·25

144 Pope John Paul II

(Des G. Vasarhelyi. Litho Format)

1983 (22 Dec). *Christmas. T* **144** *and similar designs showing Pope John Paul II at Papal Mass on 11 March 1983 in Belize. P* 13½ × 14.

761 10 c. multicoloured 8 10
762 15 c. multicoloured 10 12
763 75 c. multicoloured 55 60
764 $2 multicoloured 1·40 1·50
MS765 102 × 72 mm. $3 multicoloured 2·10 2·25

145 Foureye Butterflyfish

(Des G. Drummond. Litho Format)

1984 (27 Feb). *Marine Life from the Belize Coral Reef. T* **145** *and similar horiz designs. Multicoloured. P* 15.

766 1 c. Type **145** 5 5
767 2 c. Cushion Star 5 5
768 3 c. Flower Coral 5 5
769 4 c. Fairy Basslet 5 5
770 5 c. Spanish Hogfish 5 5
771 6 c. Star-eyed Hermit Crab 5 5
712 10 c. Sea Fans and Fire Sponge 8 10
773 15 c. Blueheads 12 15
774 25 c. Blue-striped Grunt 20 25
775 50 c. Coral Crab 40 45
776 60 c. Tube Sponge 45 50
777 75 c. Brain Coral 60 65
778 $1 Yellow-tail Snapper 75 80
779 $2 Common Lettuce Slug 1·50 1·60
780 $5 Yellow Damselfish 3·75 4·00
781 $10 Rock Beauty 7·75 8·00
766/81 *Set of* 16 14·00 15·00

VISIT OF THE LORD
ARCHBISHOP OF CANTERBURY
8th–11th MARCH 1984

(146)

1984 (8 Mar). *Visit of the Archbishop of Canterbury. Nos.* 772 *and* 775 *optd with T* **146**.

782 10 c. Sea Fans and Fire Sponge 8 10
783 50 c. Coral Crab 45 50

147 Shooting

(Des G. Vasarhelyi. Litho Format)

1984 (30 Apr). *Olympic Games, Los Angeles*, (a) *Sheet stamps. T* **147** *and similar horiz designs. Multicoloured. P* 13½ × 14.

784 25 c. Type **147** 20 25
785 75 c. Boxing 65 70
786 $1 Marathon 90 95
787 $2 Cycling 1·75 1·90
MS788 101 × 72 mm. $3 Statue of Discus-thrower 2·75 3·00

(*b*) *Booklet stamps. Similar designs to T* **147** *but Royal cypher replaced by Queen's head. P* 14½.

789 5 c. 1896 Marathon 5 5
a. Booklet pane. No. 789 × 4 20
790 20 c. Sprinting 15 20
a. Booklet pane. No. 790 × 4 60
791 25 c. Shot-putting 20 25
a. Booklet pane. No. 791 × 4 80
792 $2 Olympic torch 1·75 1·90
a. Booklet pane. No. 792 × 4 7·00

148 British Honduras 1866 1s. Stamp

149 Prince Albert

(Des G. Vasarhelyi. Litho Format)

1984 (26 Sept). *"Ausipex" International Stamp Exhibition, Melbourne. T* **148** *and similar horiz designs. Multicoloured. P* 14 × 13½ ($2) *or* 15 (*others*).

793 15 c. Type **148** 10 20
794 30 c. Bath mail coach, 1784 25 30
795 65 c. Sir Rowland Hill and Penny Black 60 65
796 75 c. British Honduras railway, 1910 65 70
797 $2 Royal Exhibition Buildings, Melbourne (46 × 28 *mm*) 1·75 1·90
MS798 103 × 73 mm. $3 Australia 1932 Sydney Harbour Bridge 5s. and British Honduras 1866 1s. stamps (44 × 28 *mm*). P 13½ × 14 2·75 3·00

(Des G. Vasarhelyi. Litho Format)

1984 (15 Oct). *500th Anniv of British Royal House of Tudor* (1985). *T* **149** *and similar vert designs showing members of the Royal Family. Multicoloured. P* 14.

799 50 c. Type **149** 45 50
a. Sheetlet. Nos. 799/800 × 2 1·75
800 50 c. Queen Victoria 45 50
801 75 c. King George VI 65 70
a. Sheetlet. Nos. 801/2 × 2 2·50
802 75 c. Queen Elizabeth the Queen Mother 65 70
803 $1 Princess of Wales 90 95
a. Sheetlet. Nos. 803/4 × 2 3·50
804 $1 Prince of Wales 90 95
799/804 *Set of* 6 3·50 4·00
MS805 147 × 97 mm. $1.50, Prince Phillip; $1.50, Queen Elizabeth II 2·75 3·00

Nos. 799/804 were only issued in sheetlets of four stamps of one value, two of each design, with an illustrated vertical gutter margin

150 White-fronted Parrot

151 Effigy Censer, 1450 (Santa Rita Site)

(Des. G. Vasarhelyi. Litho Format)

1984 (1 Nov). *Parrots. T* **150** *and similar multicoloured designs. P* 11

806 $1 Type **150** 90 95
a. Block of 4. Nos. 806/9 1·40
807 $1 White-capped Parrot (*horiz*) 90 95
808 $1 Mealy Parrot (*horiz*) 90 95
809 $1 Red-lored Parrot 90 95
MS810 102 × 73 mm. $3 Scarlet Macaw. P 13½ × 14 2·75 3·00

Nos. 806/9 were issued together, *se-tenant*, in blocks of 4 throughout the sheet, each block forming a composite design.

(Des G. Vasarhelyi. Litho Format)

1984 (30 Nov). *Maya Artefacts. T* **151** *and similar vert designs. Multicoloured. P* 15

811 25 c. Type **151** 20 25
812 75 c. Vase, 675 (Actun Chapat) 65 70
813 $1 Tripod Vase, 500 (Santa Rita site) 90 95
814 $2 Sun god Kinich Ahau, 600 (Altun Ha site) 1·75 1·90

POSTAGE DUE STAMPS

D 2

(Des P. Powell. Litho Questa)

1976 (1 July). *Type* D **2** *and similar vert designs, but with different frames. W* w **14** (*sideways*). *P* 13½ x 14.

D 6 D 2 1 c. red and dull green 5 10
D 7 – 2 c. light magenta and bluish violet 5 10
D 8 – 5 c. dull green and orange-brown 10 15
D 9 – 15 c. apple-green and dull vermilion 15 20
D10 – 25 c. orange and olive-green 20 30

CAYES OF BELIZE

A chain of several hundred islands, coral atolls, reefs and sand-banks stretching along the eastern seaboard of Belize.

Appendix

The following issues for the Cayes of Belize fall outside the criteria for full listing as detailed on page viii

1984

Marine Life, Map and Views. 1, 2, 5, 10, 15, 25, 75 c., $3, $5
250th Anniv of Lloyd's List (*newspaper*). 25, 75 c., $1, $2.
Olympic Games, Los Angeles. 10, 15, 75 c., $2
90th Anniv of "Caye Service" Local Stamps. 10, 15, 75 c., $2

Bermuda

The first internal postal system for Bermuda was organised by the proprietor of the *Bermuda Gazette* in 1784. This service later competed with that of the Bermuda Post Office, set up in 1812.

The British G.P.O. retained control of the overseas posts, however, until this service passed to the Bermuda authorities in 1859.

For illustrations of the handstamp types see BRITISH POST OFFICES ABROAD notes, following GREAT BRITAIN.

CROWNED-CIRCLE HANDSTAMPS

CC1 CC1 ST. GEORGES BERMUDA (R.) (1.8.1845) *Price on cover* £4750
CC2 IRELAND ISLE BERMUDA (R.) (1.8.1845) *Price on cover* £3750
CC3 HAMILTON BERMUDA (R.) (13.11.1846) *Price on cover* £3250

For Nos. CC1 and CC3 used as adhesive Postmasters' Stamps see Nos. O7 and O6.

PRICES FOR STAMPS ON COVER TO 1945	
Nos. 1/11	*from* × 5
Nos. 12/17	*from* × 10
Nos. 19/29*a*	*from* × 8
Nos. 30/*a*	*from* × 10
Nos. 31/4	*from* × 4
Nos. 34*a*/55	*from* × 3
Nos. 56/8	*from* × 10
Nos. 59/76	*from* × 4
Nos. 76*a*/93	*from* × 3
Nos. 94/7	*from* × 4
Nos. 98/106	*from* × 3
Nos. 107/15	*from* × 4
Nos. 116/21	*from* × 5
No. 122	*from* × 20

COLONY

O 1

O 2

1848–61. *Postmasters' Stamps. Adhesives prepared and issued by the postmasters at Hamilton and St. Georges. Dated as given in brackets.*

(*a*) *By W. B. Perot at Hamilton*

O1 O 1 1d. black/*bluish grey* (1848) — £70000
O2 1d. black/*bluish grey* (1849) — £85000
O3 1d. red/*thick white* (1853) — £70000
O4 1d. red/*bluish laid* (1854) — £100000
O5 1d. red/*bluish wove* (1856) — £100000
O6 O 2 (1d.) carmine-red/*bluish laid* (1861) — £70000

(*b*) *By J. H. Thies at St. Georges*
As Type O 2 *but inscr* "ST. GEORGES"

O7 – (1d.) carmine-red/*buff* (1860) — £60000

Stamps of Type O 1 bear manuscript value and signature, the dates being those shown on the eleven known examples. The stamps are distributed between the dates as follows: 1845 three examples, 1849 two examples, 1853 three examples, 1854 two examples, 1856 one example.

It is believed that the franking value of Nos. O6/7 was 1d., although this is not shown on the actual stamps. Five examples are known of this type from Hamilton, including one unused, and five from St. Georges.

Prices shown reflect our estimation of value based on known copies. For instance of the two copies known of No. O4, one is in the Royal collection and the other is on entire.

1 2 3 4 5

(Typo D.L.R.)

1865–1903. *Wmk Crown CC.* (*a*) *P* 14.

1 1 1d. rose-red (25.9.65) 27·00 3·25
2 1d. pale rose 32·00 5·00
3 2 2d. dull blue (14.3.66) 55·00 15·00
4 2d. bright blue 75·00 9·00
5 3 3d. yellow-buff (10.3.73) £400 60·00
5*a* 3d. orange £500 55·00
6 4 6d. dull purple (25.9.65) £900 75·00
7 6d. dull mauve 22·00 16·00
8 5 1s. green (25.9.65) £130 28·00

(*b*) *Imperf*

9 1 1d. rose-red £11000 £8000

(*c*) *P* 14 × 12½

10 3 3d. yellow-buff (1882) £160 42·00
10*a* 4 6d. bright mauve (1903) 21·00 22·00
11 5 1s. green (1894) 28·00 £100
a. Vert strip of 3, two stamps imperf horiz £8000

Though manufactured early in 1880, stamps *P* 14 × 12½ were not issued until the dates given above.

THREE PENCE (6) THREE PENCE (6*a*)

THREE PENCE (7) One Penny. (8)

1874 (12 Mar–19 May). *Nos.* 1 *and* 8 *surch diagonally.*

(*a*) *With T* **6** ("P" *and* "R" *different type*)

12 1 3d. on 1d. rose-red £6000
13 5 3d. on 1s. green £1300 £850

(*b*) *With T* **6a** ("P" *same type as* "R")

13*b* 5 3d. on 1s. green £1700 £800

(*c*) *With T* **7** (19 May)

14 5 3d. on 1s. green £750 £650

The 3d. on 1d. was not regularly issued, though a few specimens were used later. Nos. 13, 13*b* and 14, being handstamped, are found with double or partial double surcharges.

(Surch by Queen's Printer, Donald McPhee Lee)

1875 (March–May). *Surch with T* **8**.

15 2 1d. on 2d. (No. 4) (23 Apr) £650 £375
a. No stop after "Penny" £5500 £3750
16 3 1d. on 3d. (No. 5) (8 May) £475 £450
17 5 1d. on 1s. (No. 8) (11 Mar) £400 £275
a. Surch inverted — £6000
b. No stop after "Penny"

Our prices for Nos. 12/17 are for stamps in average condition; fine examples, which are seldom available, are worth a substantial premium.

9

10

11

(Typo D.L.R.)

1880 (23 Mar). *Wmk Crown CC. P* 14.

19 9 ½d. stone 1·90 3·00
20 10 4d. orange-red 5·25 2·75

(Typo D.L.R.)

1883–98. *Wmk Crown CA. P* 14.

21 9 ½d. dull green (Oct, 1892) 1·90 1·90
21*a* ½d. deep grey-green (1893) 1·90 1·10
22 1 1d. dull rose (Dec. 1883) 55·00 5·00
23 1d. rose-red 38·00 2·25
24 1d. carmine-rose (1886) 16·00 1·50
24*a* 1d. aniline carmine (1889) 1·50 35
25 2 2d. blue (Dec. 1886) 20·00 3·00
26 2d. aniline purple (July, 1893) 10·00 5·50
26*a* 2d. brown-purple (1898) 2·75 3·00
27 11 2½d. deep ultramarine (10.11.84) 8·00 1·00
27*a* 2½d. pale ultramarine 7·00 1·00
28 3 3d. grey (Jan, 1886) 17·00 5·50
29 5 1s. yellow-brown (1893) 27·00 22·00
29*a* 1s. olive-brown 27·00 22·00
21/29*a* *Set of* 7 70·00 32·00
21, 26 & 29 Optd "Specimen" *Set of* 3 £375

1893 PROVISIONAL POSTCARD. During a shortage of 1d. stamps a limited supply of September 1880 postcard, franked with Nos. 19 and 22, was surcharged "One Penny" across the two stamps. This surcharge was applied by the *Royal Gazette* press. It is generally believed that an individual in the Post Office acquired all the examples, but provisional postcards are known used to Europe and, one example only, locally. *Price from* £550 *unused,* £1400 *used.*

ONE FARTHING
(12)

13 Dry Dock

1901. *As Nos.* 29/*a but colour changed, surch with T* **12** *by D.L.R.*

30 5 ¼d. on 1s. dull grey (11.1.01) (Optd S. £70) 30 40
30*a* ¼d. on 1s. bluish grey (3.01) 40 45
ab. "F" in "FARTHING" inserted by handstamp

Two examples of No. 30ab are known, one being in the Royal Collection. It would appear that the "F" in position one of an unspecified horizontal row was either weak or missing and an additional impression of the letter was then inserted by a separate handstamp.

(Typo D.L.R.)

1902 (Nov)–**04.** *Wmk Crown CA. P* 14.

31 13 ½d. black and green (12.03) 7·00 4·5
32 1d. brown and carmine 7·00 3
33 3d. magenta and sage-green (9.03) 3·00 5·0
34 10 4d. orange-brown (18.1.04) 25·00 32·0
31/33 Optd "Specimen" *Set of* 3 £110

1906–09. *Wmk Mult Crown CA. P* 14.

34*a* 13 ¼d. brown and violet (9.08) 1·50 2·7
35 ½d. black and green (12.06) 6·50 3·7
36 1d. brown and carmine (4.06) 7·50 6
37 2d. grey and orange (10.07) 7·50 11·0
38 2½d. brown and ultramarine (12.06) 9·00 20·0
39 4d. blue and chocolate (11.09) 6·50 12·0
34*a*/39 *Set of* 6 35·00 45·0
34*a*. 37/39 Optd "Specimen" *Set of* 4 £170

1908–10. *Wmk Mult Crown CA. P* 14.

41 13 ½d. green (3.09) 3·75 3·0
42 1d. red (5.08) 7·00 6
43 2½d. blue (14.2.10) 20·00 16·0
41/43 Optd "Specimen" *Set of* 3 £150

14

15

(Recess (**14**), Typo (**15**) D.L.R.)

1910–25. *Wmk Mult Crown CA. P* 14.

44 14 ¼d. brown (26.3.12) 1·50 2·25
a. Pale brown 90 2·00
45 ½d. green (4.6.10) 1·10 55
a. Deep green 3·25 1·50
46 1d. red (I) (15.10.10) 2·50 60
a. Rose-red 4·50 60
b. Carmine (12.19) 10·00 4·50
47 2d. grey (1.13) 2·75 4·75
48 2½d. blue (27.3.12) 3·00 2·50
49 3d. purple/*yellow* (1.13) 3·25 5·25
49*a* 4d. red/*yellow* (1.9.19) 3·50 5·50
50 6d. purple (26.3.12) 11·00 16·00
a. Pale claret (2.6.24) 10·00 11·00
51 1s. black/*green* (26.3.12) 8·50 9·50
a. Jet-black/olive (1925) 8·00 12·00
51*b* 15 2s. purple and blue/*blue*, **C** (19.6.20) 10·00 28·00
52 2s. 6d. black and red/*blue*, **C** (1.4.18) 23·00 40·00
52*a* 4s. black and carmine, **C** (19.6.20) 60·00 80·00
53 5s. deep green and deep red/*yellow*, **C** (1.4.18) 65·00 90·00
a. Green and carmine-red/pale yellow, **C** (1920) 45·00 60·00
54 10s. green and carmine/*pale bluish green*, **C** (1.4.18) £225 £300
a. Green and red/pale bluish green, **C** (1922) £170 £250
55 £1 purple and black/*red*, **C** (1.4.18) £550 £800
44/55 *Set of* 15 £800 £1200
44/55 Optd "Specimen" *Set of* 15 £900

Nos. 44 to 51*a* are comb-perf 13.8 × 14. No. 45 exists also line-perf 13.75.

Beware of cleaned copies of the 10s. with faked postmarks.

See also Nos. 76*a*/93.

WAR TAX (16) WAR TAX (17)

1918 (4 May). *Nos.* 46 *and* 46*a optd locally with T* **16**.

56 14 1d. red 35 65
a. Rose-red 30 65

1920 (5 Feb). *No.* 46*b optd with T* **17**.

58 14 1d. carmine 50 1·10

The War Tax stamps represented a compulsory levy in addition to normal postal fees until 31 Dec 1920. Subsequently they were valid for ordinary postage.

18

19

(Des by the Governor (Gen. Sir James Willcocks). Typo D.L.R.)

1920 (11 Nov)–**21.** *Tercentenary of Representative Institutions* (1*st issue*). *P* 14. (*a*) *Wmk Mult Crown CA* (*sideways*) (19.1.21).

59 18 ¼d. brown, **O** 80 2·25
60 ½d. green, **O** 1·10 3·75
61 2d. grey, **O** 6·50 12·00
62 3d. dull and deep purple/*pale yellow*, **C** 6·50 15·00
63 4d. black and red/*pale yellow*, **C** 11·00 18·00
64 1s. black/*blue-green*, **C** 18·00 28·00

(*b*) *Wmk Mult Script CA* (*sideways*)

65 18 1d. carmine, **O** 1·00 1·10
66 2½d. bright blue, **O** 6·50 13·00
67 6d. dull and bright purple, **C** (19.1.21) 18·00 28·00
59/67 *Set of* 9 60·00 £110

(Des. H. J. Dale. Recess D.L.R.)

21 (12 May). *Tercentenary of Representative Institutions* (2nd *issue*). *P* 14. (*a*) *Wmk Crown CA* (*sideways*).
19 2d. slate-grey .. .. 6·50 9·00
2½d. bright ultramarine .. .. .. 6·00 6·00
3d. purple/*pale yellow* .. .. .. 6·00 9·00
4d. red/*pale yellow* .. .. .. 8·00 9·50
6d. purple .. .. 9·50 19·00
1s. black/green .. .. 23·00 27·00

(*b*) *Wmk Mult Script CA* (*sideways*)
19 ¼d. brown .. .. 75 1·60
½d. green .. .. 3·75 4·50
1d. deep carmine .. .. .. 2·25 1·00
/76 .. .. *Set of* 9 60·00 80·00
/76 Optd "Specimen" .. .. *Set of* 9 £325

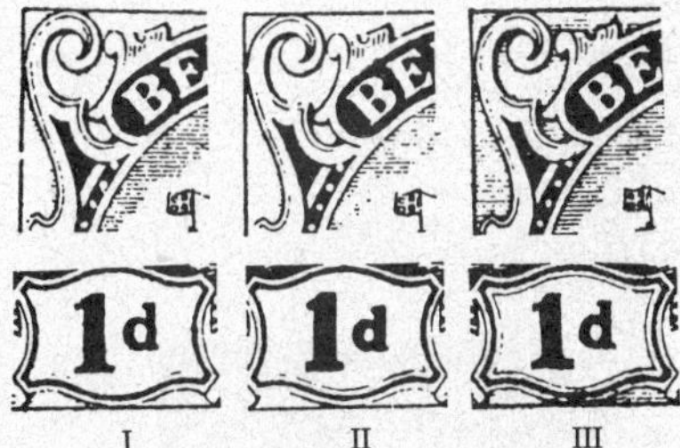

I II III

Three Types of the 1d.
I. Scroll at top left very weak and figure "1" has pointed serifs.
II. Scroll weak. "1" has square serifs and "1d" is heavy.
III. Redrawn. Scroll is completed by a strong line and "1" is thinner with long square serifs.

I II

Two Types of the 2½d.
I. Short, thick figures, especially of the "1", small "d".
II. Figures taller and thinner, "d" larger.

922–34. *Wmk Mult Script CA. P* 14.
6*a* **14** ¼d. brown (7.28) .. .. .. 50 1·25
7 ½d. green (11.22) 30 30
8 1d. scarlet (I) ((11.22) .. .. .. 2·25 60
a. Carmine (6.24) .. .. .. 4·50 60
8*b* 1d. carmine (II) (12.25) .. .. .. 4·75 1·25
c. Scarlet (8.27) .. .. .. 4·50 80
9 1d. scarlet (III) (10.28) 75 50
a. Carmine-lake (1934) .. .. 2·00 60
9*b* 1½d. red-brown (27.3.34) .. .. .. 3·50 1·10
0 2d. grey (12.23) .. .. 1·00 2·00
1 2½d. pale sage-green (12.22) .. .. 7·50 8·50
a. Deep sage-green (1924) .. .. 3·00 3·75
2 2½d. ultramarine (I) (1.12.26) .. .. 2·25 85
2*a* 2½d. ultramarine (II) (3.32) .. .. 2·75 85
3 3d. ultramarine (12.24) .. .. 20·00 27·00
4 3d. purple/*yellow* (10.26) .. .. 1·10 1·50
5 4d. red/*yellow* (8.24) .. .. .. 1·25 2·25
6 6d. purple (8.24) .. .. .. 2·25 2·50
7 1s. black/*emerald* (10.27) .. .. 10·00 12·00
a. Brownish black/yellow-green (1934) 35·00 45·00
8 **15** 2s. purple and bright blue/*pale blue*, **C** (1.9.27) .. .. 32·00 45·00
a. Purple and blue/grey, **C** (1931) .. 32·00 45·00
9 2s. 6d. black and carmine/*pale blue*, **C** (4.27) .. .. 45·00 55·00
a. Black and red/blue to deep blue, **C** (1929) .. .. 45·00 55·00
b. Grey-black and pale orange-vermilion/grey-blue, **C** (8.30) .. £2500 £2500
c. Black and vermilion/deep blue, **C** (1931) .. .. 45·00 55·00
d. Black and bright orange-vermilion/deep blue, **C** (20.7.32) £1500 £1500
92 10s. green and red/*pale emerald*, **C** (12.24) £200 £275
a. Green and red/deep emerald, **C** (1931) £200 £275
93 12s. 6d. grey and orange, **CO** (8.32) .. £450 £500
76*a*/93 .. .. *Set of* 16 £700 £850
76*a*/93 Optd/Perf "Specimen" .. *Set of* 16 £800

Nos. 76*a* to 87 exist both line-perf 13.75 and comb-perf 13.8 × 14 except Nos. 79*b*, 82*a* and 87*a* which are line-perf only.

The true No. 89*b* is the only stamp on grey-blue paper; other deeper orange-vermilion shades exist on different papers.

No. 93 on ordinary paper would seem to be an error. Our prices are for the chalky paper.

Beware of fiscally used 2s. 6d. 10s. and 12s. 6d. stamps cleaned and bearing faked postmarks. Large quantities were used for a "head tax" levied on travellers leaving the country.

For 12s. 6d. design inscribed "Revenue" at both sides see No. F1 under POSTAL FISCAL.

(Recess Waterlow)

1935 (6 May). *Silver Jubilee. As T* **13** *of Antigua. Wmk Mult Script CA. P* 11 × 12.
94 1d. deep blue and scarlet 45 55
95 1½d. ultramarine and grey 70 75
96 2½d. brown and deep blue .. .. .. 1·60 3·25
97 1s. slate and purple .. .. 11·00 13·00
94/7 Perf "Specimen" .. .. *Set of* 4 60·00

ALTERED CATALOGUE NUMBERS

Any Catalogue numbers altered from the last edition are shown as a list in the introductory pages.

20 Hamilton Harbour

21 South shore near Spanish Rock

22 The *Lucie*

23 Grape Bay, Paget Parish

24 Point House, Warwick Parish

25 House at Par-la-Ville, Hamilton

(Recess B.W.)

1936 (14 Apr)–**47**. *Wmk Mult Script CA* (*sideways on horiz designs*). *P* 12.
98 **20** ½d. bright green 25 20
99 **21** 1d. black and scarlet 35 20
100 1½d. black and chocolate 75 40
101 **22** 2d. black and pale blue .. .. .. 7·00 6·00
102 **23** 2½d. light and deep blue .. .. .. 1·00 1·10
103 **24** 3d. black and scarlet .. .. .. 3·50 4·00
104 **25** 6d. carmine-lake and violet 55 50
a. Claret and dull violet (6.47) .. 65 25
105 **23** 1s. green .. .. 10·00 12·00
106 **20** 1s. 6d. brown 55 60
98/106 .. .. *Set of* 9 21·00 22·00
98/106 Perf "Specimen" .. .. *Set of* 9 £140

All are line-perf 11.9, except printings of the 6d. from July 1951 onwards, which are comb-perf 11.9 × 11.75.

1937 (14 May). *Coronation Issue. As T* **2** *of Aden. P* 14.
107 1d. scarlet 50 40
108 1½d. yellow-brown 70 30
109 2½d. bright blue .. .. 1·50 1·75
107/9 Perf "Specimen" .. .. *Set of* 3 45·00

26 Ships in Hamilton Harbour

27 St. David's Lighthouse

28 White-tailed Tropic Bird, Arms of Bermuda and Native Flower

(Des Miss Higginbotham (T **28**). Recess B.W.)

1938 (20 Jan)–**1952**. *T* **22**, *T* **23** (*but with portrait of King George VI*) *and T* **26** *to* **28**. *Wmk Mult Script CA. P* 12.
110 **26** 1d. black and rose-red (*a*) (*b*) .. .. 22·00 3·00
a. Black and dull red (*a*) (*b*) (5.44) .. 55 35
111 1½d. deep blue and purple-brown (*a*)(*b*) .. 1·00 70
a. Blue and brown (*a*) (3.43) .. .. 1·50 1·25
b. Light blue and purple-brown (*a*) (*b*) (9.45) 70 35
112 **22** 2d. light blue and sepia (*a*) .. .. 30·00 15·00
112*a* 2d. ultramarine and scarlet (*a*) (*b*) (12.11.40) .. .. 3·25 2·00
113 **23** 2½d. light and deep blue (*a*) .. .. 6·50 1·40
113*a* 2½d. light blue and sepia-black (*a*) (18.12.41) .. .. 1·25 80
b. Pale blue and sepia-black (*a*) (3.43) 1·50 1·10
c. Bright blue and deep sepia-black (*b*) (23.9.52) 85 70
114 **27** 3d. black and rose-red (*a*) .. .. 8·00 2·25
114*a* 3d. black and deep blue (*a*) (*b*) (16.7.41) 90 40
114*b* **28** 7½d. black, blue and bright green (*a*) (18.12.41) .. .. 3·00 2·50
c. Black, blue and yellow green (*a*) (3.43) .. .. 3·25 3·25
115 **23** 1s. green (*a*) (*b*) .. .. 1·25 90
a. Bluish green (*b*) (20.6.52) .. .. 2·50 2·75

Perforations. Two different perforating machines were used on the various printings of these stamps: (*a*) the original 11.9 line perforation; (*b*) 11.9 × 11.75 comb perforation, introduced in July 1950. These perforations occur as indicated above.

29 King George VI

HALF
PENNY

X X

(**30**)

(Typo D.L.R.)

1938 (20 Jan)–**1953**. *T* **29**. *P* 14 (*a*) *Wmk Mult Script CA*.
116 2s. deep purple & ultramarine/*grey-blue*, **C** 50·00 30·00
a. Purple and blue/deep blue, **O** (1942) .. 7·50 6·00
b. Purple and deep blue/pale blue, **O** (5.3.43) 6·50 4·00
c. Perf 13. *Dull purple and blue/pale blue*, **O** (15.2.50) .. .. 16·00 17·00
d. Perf 13. *Purple and deep blue/pale blue*, **O** (10.50) .. .. 7·50 5·00
117 2s. 6d. black and red/*grey-blue*, **C** .. .. 35·00 14·00
a. Black and red/pale blue, **O** (1942) .. 10·00 9·00
b. Perf 13. *Black and orange-red/pale blue*, **O** (10.10.50) .. .. 10·00 8·00
c. Perf 13. *Black and red/pale blue*, **O** (18.6.52) .. .. 9·50 14·00
118 5s. green and red/*yellow*, **C** .. .. .. 55·00 28·00
a. Pale green and red/yellow, **C** (1939) .. £100 50·00
b. Pale bluish green and carmine-red/pale yellow, **O** (3.43) .. .. £100 90·00
c. Green and red/pale yellow, **O** (4.44) .. 15·00 13·00
d. Perf 13. *Pale green and red/pale yellow (shades)*, **OC** (15.2.50) .. .. .. 11·00 12·00
119 10s. green and deep lake/*pale emerald*, **C** .. £150 £150
a. Bluish green and deep red/green, **O** (7.39) £160 £140
b. Yellowish green and deep carmine-red/green, **O** (1941–44) .. .. .. 65·00 65·00
c. Deep green and dull red/green, **O** (5.2.47) 75·00 75·00
d. Perf 13. *Green and vermilion/green*, **O** (21.9.51) .. .. 30·00 30·00
e. Perf 13. *Green and dull red/green*, **O** (16.4.53) .. .. 20·00 30·00
120 12s. 6d. deep grey and brownish orange (*shades*), **C** £350 £300
a. Grey and pale orange, **CO** (7.39) .. .. 70·00 55·00
*b. Grey and yellow**, **O** (?1947) £600 £600
c. Perf 13. *Grey & pale orange*, **C** (10.10.50) 65·00 60·00

(*b*) *Wmk Mult Crown CA*
121 £1 purple and black/*red*, **C** £180 £120
a. Pale purple and black/salmon, **C** (1941) .. 60·00 55·00
b. Plum and black/salmon, **C** (1943) .. 55·00 55·00
c. Perf 13. *Violet and black/scarlet*, **C** (7.12.51) .. .. 38·00 40·00
d. Perf 13. *Brt violet & black/scarlet* (6.52) 90·00 £100
110*b*/121c .. .. *Set of* 16 £180 £160
110/121 Perf "Specimen" .. .. *Set of* 16 £800

In No. 116*a* the coloured surfacing of the paper is mottled with white specks sometimes accompanied by very close horizontal lines.

In Nos. 116*b*, 117*a* and 118*a* the surfacing is the same colour as the back, sometimes applied in widely spaced horizontal lines giving the appearance of laid paper.

Printings of the 2s, 2s. 6d., 5s. and 10s., from dispatches in 1941, exist perf 14.2 line. The normal comb perforation measures 13.9 × 13.8. These line perforations are comparatively rare.

No. 120 can be easily identified from the chalk-surfaced printings of No. 120*a* by the deep centre shade and by the paper, which is very stout for the 1938 printings.

*No. 120*b* is the so-called "lemon" shade.

1940 (20 Dec). *No.* 110 *surch with T* **30**.
122 **26** ½d. on 1d. black and red (*shades*) .. 40 60

The spacing between "PENNY" and "X" varies from 12½ mm to 14 mm.

1946 (6 Nov). *Victory. As Nos.* 28/9 *of Aden.*
123 1½d. brown 25 35
124 3d. blue 40 40
123/4 Perf "Specimen" .. .. *Set of* 2 40·00

1948 (1 Dec). *Royal Silver Wedding. As Nos.* 30/1 *of Aden.*
125 1½d. red-brown 40 50
126 £1 carmine .. .. 60·00 70·00

31 Postmaster Perot's Stamp

(Recess B.W.)

1949 (11 Apr). *Centenary of Postmaster Perot's Stamp. Wmk Mult Script CA. P* 13½.
127 **31** 2½d. blue and brown 20 20
128 3d. black and blue 20 25
129 6d. violet and green 20 25

1949 (10 Oct). *75th Anniv of Universal Postal Union. As Nos.* 114/17 *of Antigua.*
130 2½d. blue-black 90 65
131 3d. deep blue .. .. 1·75 1·25
132 6d. purple .. .. 1·90 1·25
133 1s. blue-green .. .. 2·50 2·00

1953 (4 June). *Coronation. As No.* 47 *of Aden, but ptd by B.W.*
134 1½d. black and blue 25 15

32 Easter Lilies

34 Easter Lily

37 Map of Bermuda

Die I "Sandy's" Die II "Sandys"

(Des C. Deakins (½d., 3d., 1s.3d., 5s.), J. Berry (1d., 1½d., 2½d., 1s.). B. Brown (2d., 6d., 8d.), D. Haig (4½d., 9d.), Pamela Braley-Smith (2s. 6d.) and E. C. Leslie (10s.) Recess (except £1, centre typo), B.W.)

1953 (9 Nov)–**62**. *T* **32, 34, 37,** *and similar designs. Wmk Mult Script CA. P* 13½.

No.	Type	Description		
135	32	½d. olive-green (*shades*)	12	15
136	–	1d. black and red (*shades*)	12	15
137	34	1½d. green	20	12
138	–	2d. ultramarine and brown-red	40	15
139	–	2½d. rose-red	50	50
140	37	3d. deep purple (I)	30	12
140*a*	–	3d. deep purple (II) (2.1.57)	35	10
141	–	4d. black and bright blue	25	40
142	–	4½d. emerald	45	90
143	–	6d. black and deep turquoise	70	50
143*a*	–	8d. black and red (16.5.55)	1·25	45
143*b*	–	9d. violet (6.1.58)	2·50	1·50
144	–	1s. orange	45	15
145	37	1s. 3d. blue (I) (*shades*)	1·00	20
145*b*		1s. 3d. blue (II) (2.1.57)	1·00	30
		c. Bright blue (II) (14.8.62)	1·00	40
146	–	2s. brown	2·00	85
147	–	2s. 6d. scarlet	1·25	65
148	–	5s. carmine	6·50	1·50
149	–	10s. deep ultramarine (*shades*)	10·00	6·50
150	–	£1 brown, blue, red, grn & bronze-grn	25·00	22·00
135/150		*Set of* 18	48·00	32·00

Designs: *Horiz*—1d., 4d. Postmaster Perot's stamp; 2d. Bermuda racing dinghy; 2½d. Sir George Somers and *Sea Venture*; 4½d., 9d. *Sea Venture*, inter-island boat, coin and Perot stamp; 6d., 8d. White-tailed Tropic Bird; 1s. Early Bermudian coinage; 2s. Arms of St. Georges; 5s. Hog coin; 10s. Obverse and reverse of hog coin; £1 Arms of Bermuda. *Vert*.—2s. 6d. Warwick Fort.

Nos. 136, 138 and 143 exist in coils, constructed from normal sheets.

1953 (26 Nov). *Royal Visit. As No.* 143 *but inscr* "ROYAL VISIT 1953" *in top left corner.*

No.	Description		
151	6d. black and deep turquoise	20	25

Three Power Talks
December, 1953.
(46)

50TH ANNIVERSARY
U S – BERMUDA
OCEAN RACE 1956
(47)

1953 (8 Dec). *Three Power Talks. Nos.* 140 *and* 145 *optd with T* 46.

No.	Type	Description		
152	37	3d. deep purple (B.)	12	10
153		1s. 3d. blue (R.)	20	20

There are two settings of this overprint.

1956 (22 June). *50th Anniv United States–Bermuda Yacht Race. Nos.* 143*a and* 145 *optd with T* 47 *by The Bermuda Press.*

No.	Description		
154	8d. black and red (Bk.)	20	15
155	1s. 3d. greenish blue (R.)	20	30

48 Perot's Post Office

(Des W. Harrington. Recess B.W.)

1959 (1 Jan.) *Wmk Mult Script CA. P* 13½.

No.	Type	Description		
156	48	6d. black and deep mauve	20	15

MINIMUM PRICE

The minimum price quoted is 5p which represents a handling charge rather than a basis for valuing common stamps. For further notes about prices see introductory pages.

49 Arms of King James I and Queen Elizabeth II

(Des W. Harrington. Recess; arms litho D.L.R.)

1959 (29 July). *350th Anniv of First Settlement. Arms, red, yellow and blue; frame colours below.* W w **12**. *P* 13.

No.	Type	Description		
157	49	1½d. grey-blue	15	10
158		3d. drab-grey	25	30
159		4d. reddish purple	35	50
160		8d. slate-violet	50	30
161		9d. olive-green	65	1·25
162		1s. 3d. brown	65	60
157/162		*Set of* 6	2·25	2·75

50 The Old Rectory, St. George's, *circa* 1730

67 Finn Boat

(Des W. Harrington. Photo Harrison)

1962 (26 Oct)–**65**. *Horiz designs as T* **50**. W w **12** (*upright*). *P* 12½.

No.	Description		
163	1d. reddish purple, black and orange	8	12
164	2d. lilac, indigo, yellow and green (*shades*)	8	8
	a. Lilac omitted	£400	85·00
	b. Green omitted		
	c. Imperf (pair)		
165	3d. yellow-brown and light blue	12	5
	a. Yellow-brown omitted	£700	
166	4d. red-brown and magenta	20	20
167	5d. grey-blue and rose	80	90
168	6d. grey-blue emerald and light blue	20	10
169	8d. bright blue, bright green and orange	30	10
170	9d. light blue and brown	35	25
170*a*	10d. violet and ochre (8.2.65)	1·00	1·00
171	1s. black, emerald, bright blue and orange	30	10
172	1s. 3d. lake, grey and bistre	50	15
173	1s. 6d. violet and ochre	2·50	3·00
174	2s. red-brown and orange	2·00	90
175	2s. 3d. bistre-brown and yellow-green	3·00	4·00
176	2s. 6d. bistre-brown, bluish grn & olive-yell	90	70
177	5s. brown-purple and blue-green	1·50	1·50
178	10s. magenta, deep bluish green and buff	5·00	6·00
179	£1 black, yellow-olive and yellow-orange	12·00	14·00
163/79	*Set of* 18	28·00	30·00

Designs:—2d. Church of St. Peter, St. Georges; 3d. Government House, 1892; 4d. The Cathedral, Hamilton, 1894; 5d. H.M. Dockyard, 1811; 6d. Perot's Post Office, 1848; 8d. G.P.O. Hamilton; 9d. Library, Par-la-Ville; 10d., 1s. 6d. Bermuda Cottage, *circa* 1705; 1s. Christ Church, Warwick, 1719; 1s. 3d. City Hall, Hamilton, 1960; 2s. Town of St. George; 2s 3d. Bermuda House, *circa* 1710; 2s. 6d. Bermuda House, early 18th-century; 5s. Colonial Secretariat, 1833; 10s. Old Post Office, Somerset, 1890; £1 The House of Assembly, 1815.

A single copy of No. 164b is known, used on piece.

See also Nos. 195/200 and 246a.

1963 (4 June). *Freedom from Hunger. As No.* 76 *of Aden.*

No.	Description		
180	1s. 3d. sepia	3·00	1·50

1963 (2 Sept). *Red Cross Centenary. As Nos.* 147/8 *of Antigua.*

No.	Description		
181	3d. red and black	1·25	30
182	1s. 3d. red and blue	4·25	3·50

(Des V. Whiteley. Photo D.L.R.)

1964 (28 Sept). *Olympic Games, Tokyo.* W w **12**. *P* 14 × 13½.

No.	Type	Description		
183	67	3d. red, violet and blue	15	10

1965 (17 May). *I.T.U. Centenary. As Nos.* 166/7 *of Antigua.*

No.	Description		
184	3d. light blue and emerald	1·25	45
185	2s. yellow and ultramarine	3·25	2·75

68 Scout Badge and St. Edward's Crown

(Des W. Harrington. Photo Harrison)

1965 (24 July). *50th Anniv of Bermuda Boy Scouts Association.* W w **12**. *P* 12½.

No.	Type	Description		
186	68	2s. multicoloured	45	50

1965 (25 Oct). *International Co-operation Year. As Nos.* 168/9 *of Antigua.*

No.	Description		
187	4d. reddish purple and turquoise-green	80	25
188	2s. 6d. deep bluish green and lavender	2·50	1·75

1966 (24 Jan). *Churchill Commemoration. As Nos.* 170/3 *of Antigua.*

No.	Description		
189	3d. new blue	70	25
190	6d. deep green	1·40	6
191	10d. brown	1·60	1·4
192	1s. 3d. bluish violet	1·90	1·9

1966 (1 July). *World Cup Football Championships. As Nos.* 176 *of Antigua.*

No.	Description		
193	10d. violet, yellow-green, lake & yellow-brn	70	3
194	2s. 6d. chocolate, blue-grn, lake & yell-brn	1·40	1·4

1966 (25 Oct)–**69**. *Designs as Nos.* 164, 167 (1s. 6d.), 169, 170*a and* 174 *but W* w **12** (*sideways*).

No.	Description		
195	2d. lilac, indigo, yellow and green (20.5.69)	1·40	1·7
196	8d. bright blue, bright green and orange (14.2.67)	50	4
197	10d. violet and ochre (1.11.66)	75	6
198	1s. black, emerald, bright blue and orange (14.2.67)	50	2
199	1s. 6d. grey-blue and rose (1.11.66)	3·00	1·7
200	2s. red-brown and orange	3·00	3·5
195/200	*Set of* 6	8·00	7·5

The 2d. value exists with PVA gum only, and the 8d. exists wit PVA gum as well as gum arabic.

1966 (1 Dec). *20th Anniv of U.N.E.S.C.O. As Nos.* 196/8 *Antigua.*

No.	Description		
201	4d. slate-violet, red, yellow and orange	1·00	2
202	1s. 3d. orange-yellow, violet and deep olive	2·75	1·5
203	2s. black, bright purple and orange	3·50	2·0

69 G.P.O. Building

(Des G. Vasarhelyi. Photo Harrison)

1967 (23 June). *Opening of New General Post Office. Hamilton* W w **12**. P 14½.

No.	Type	Description		
204	69	3d. multicoloured	10	5
205		1s. multicoloured	20	10
206		1s. 6d. multicoloured	25	25
207		2s. 6d. multicoloured	30	35

70 Cable Ship and Chain Links

(Des V. Whiteley. Photo Harrison)

1967 (14 Sept). *Inauguration of Bermuda–Tortola Telephone Service. T* **70** *and similar horiz designs. Multicoloured.* W w **12**. *P* 14½ × 14.

No.	Description		
208	3d. Type **70**	15	5
209	1s. Map, telephone and microphone	25	10
210	1s. 6d. Telecommunications media	30	25
211	2s. 6d. Cable ship and marine fauna	45	35

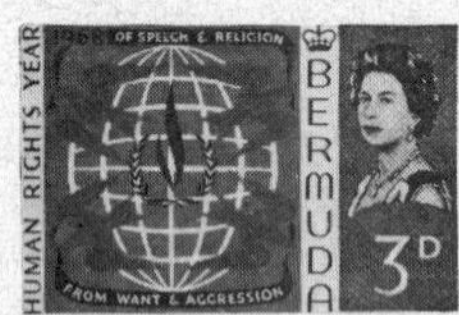

74 Human Rights Emblem and Doves

(Des M. Farrar Bell. Litho Harrison)

1968 (1 Feb). *Human Rights Year.* W w **12**. *P* 14 × 14½.

No.	Type	Description		
212	74	3d. indigo, blue and dull green	10	5
213		1s. yellow-brown, blue and light blue	15	10
214		1s. 6d. black, blue and rose	20	15
215		2s. 6d. grey-green, blue and yellow	30	25

REPRESENTATIVE GOVERNMENT

75 Mace and Queen's Profile

(Des R. Granger Barrett. Photo Harrison)

1968 (1 July). *New Constitution. T* **75** *and similar horiz design.* W w **12**. *P* 14.

No.	Type	Description		
216	75	3d. multicoloured	10	5
217		1s. multicoloured	15	10
218	–	1s. 6d. greenish yellow, black & turq-bl	20	20
219	–	2s. 6d. lilac, black and orange-yellow	25	25

Design:—1s. 6d., 2s. 6d. Houses of Parliament and House of Assembly, Bermuda.

77 Football, Athletics and Yachting

(Des V. Whiteley. Photo Harrison)

1968 (24 Sept). *Olympic Games, Mexico.* W w **12**. *P* 12½.

No.	Type	Description	Unused	Used
220	77	3d. multicoloured	10	5
		a. Red-brown ("BERMUDA" and value) omitted	£1100	
221		1s. multicoloured	15	10
222		1s. 6d. multicoloured	35	25
223		2s. 6d. multicoloured	95	55

78 Brownie and Guide

79 Guides and Badge

(Des Harrison. Litho Format)

1969 (17 Feb). *50th Anniv of Bermuda Girl Guides. P* 14.

No.	Type	Description	Unused	Used
224	78	3d. multicoloured	10	5
225		1s. multicoloured	20	10
226	79	1s. 6d. multicoloured	35	25
227		2s. 6d. multicoloured	75	70

80 Emerald-studded Gold Cross and Seaweed

1c

(82)

(Des K. Giles adapted by V. Whiteley. Photo Harrison)

1969 (29 Sept). *Underwater Treasure. T* **80** *and similar vert design. Multicoloured. W* w **12** (*sideways*). *P* 14½ × 14.

No.	Description	Unused	Used
228	4d. Type **80**	25	15
229	1s. 3d. Emerald-studded gold cross and seabed	60	45
230	2s. Type **80**	80	70
231	2s. 6d. As 1s. 3d.	90	90

(New Currency. 100 cents = 1 dollar)

1970 (6 Feb). *Decimal Currency. As Nos.* 163, 165/6, 168, 170, 172, 175/9 *and* 195/200 *surch as T* **82**. *W* w **12** (*sideways on* 2, 5, 10, 12, 15, 18, 24, 30, 60 *c.*, $1.20 *and* $2.40).

No.	Description	Unused	Used
232	1 c. on 1d. reddish purple, black and orange	5	5
233	2 c. on 2d. lilac, indigo, yellow and green	10	10
	a. Lilac omitted	£400	
	b. Pair, one without surch		
	c. Wmk upright	75	90
234	3 c. on 3d. yellow-brown and light blue	10	10
235	4 c. on 4d. red-brown and magenta (Br.)	12	12
236	5 c. on 8d. bright blue, brt green & orange	15	15
237	6 c. on 6d. grey-blue, emerald and light blue	15	12
	a. Horiz pair, one with albino surch, the other with albino bar		
238	9 c. on 9d. light blue and brown (Br.)	25	35
239	10 c. on 10d. violet and ochre	25	25
240	12 c. on 1s. black, emerald, brt blue & orange	25	15
241	15 c. on 1s. 3d. lake, grey and bistre	1·25	1·00
242	18 c. on 1s. 6d. grey-blue and rose	80	65
243	24 c. on 2s. red-brown and orange	85	75
244	30 c. on 2s. 6d. bistre-brown, bluish green and olive-yellow	80	90
245	36 c. on 2s. 3d. bistre-brown and yellow-green	1·50	2·00
246	60 c. on 5s. brown-purple and blue-green	2·25	2·75
	a. Surch omitted†	£190	
247	$1.20, on 10s. mag., dp bluish grn & buff	5·00	9·00
248	$2.40, on £1 black, yellow-olive & yell-orge	9·00	13·00
232/48	*Set of* 17	20·00	28·00

†No. 246a differs from the normal No. 177 by its watermark, which is sideways, and its gum, which is PVA.

83 Spathiphyllum

(Des W. Harrington. Photo D.L.R.)

1970 (6 July). *Flowers. Multicoloured designs as T* **83**. *W* w **12** (*sideways on horiz designs*). *P* 14.

No.	Description	Unused	Used
249	1 c. Type **83**	5	12
250	2 c. Bottlebrush	20	25
251	3 c. Oleander (*vert*)	10	10
252	4 c. Bermudiana	12	10
253	5 c. Poinsettia	30	20
254	6 c. Hibiscus	30	30
255	9 c. Cereus	20	20
256	10 c. Bougainvillea (*vert*)	20	15
257	12 c. Jacaranda	1·00	60
258	15 c. Passion-Flower	90	1·40
258*a*	17 c. As 15 c. (2.6.75)	1·25	1·00
259	18 c. Coralita	1·50	2·25
259*a*	20 c. As 18 c. (2.6.75)	1·25	1·00
260	24 c. Morning Glory	1·75	2·75
260*a*	25 c. As 24 c. (2.6.75)	1·25	1·25
261	30 c. Tecoma	1·00	1·25
262	36 c. Angel's Trumpet	1·50	2·50
262*a*	40 c. As 36 c. (2.6.75)	1·50	1·50
263	60 c. Plumbago	2·50	3·00
263*a*	$1 As 60 c. (2.6.75)	2·50	2·25
264	$1.20, Bird of Paradise flower	4·50	4·50
264*a*	$2 As $1.20 (2.6.75)	4·25	4·50
265	$2.40, Chalice Cup	9·50	10·00
265*a*	$3 As $2.40 (2.6.75)	7·50	9·00
249/65*a*	*Set of* 24	40·00	45·00

See also Nos. 303/6 and 340/1.

84 The State House, St. George's

(Des G. Drummond. Litho Questa)

1970 (12 Oct). *350th Anniv of Bermuda Parliament. T* **84** *and similar horiz designs. Multicoloured. W* w **12** (*sideways*). *P* 14.

No.	Description	Unused	Used
266	4 c. Type **84**	15	5
267	15 c. The Sessions House, Hamilton	45	40
268	18 c. St. Peter's Church, St George's	60	60
269	24 c. Town Hall, Hamilton	70	90
MS270	131 × 95 mm. Nos. 266/9	4·00	4·25

85 Street Scene, St. George's

(Des G. Drummond. Litho Questa)

1971 (8 Feb). *"Keep Bermuda Beautiful". T* **85** *and similar horiz designs. Multicoloured. W* w **12** (*sideways*). *P* 14.

No.	Description	Unused	Used
271	4 c. Type **85**	30	12
272	15 c. Horseshoe Bay	75	55
273	18 c. Gibb's Hill Lighthouse	1·40	1·00
274	24 c. Hamilton Harbour	1·50	1·75

86 Building of the *Deliverance*

(Des E. Amos. Adapted C. Abbott. Litho Questa)

1971 (10 May). *Voyage of the "Deliverance". T* **86** *and similar multicoloured designs. W* w **12** (*sideways on* 4 *c. and* 24 *c.*). *P* 14.

No.	Description	Unused	Used
275	4 c. Type **86**	50	20
276	15 c. *Deliverance* and *Patience* at Jamestown	1·50	1·75
277	18 c. Wreck of the *Sea Venture*	1·75	2·25
278	24 c. *Deliverance* and *Patience* on the high seas	1·90	2·75

The 15 c. and 18 c. are vert designs.

87 Green overlooking Ocean View

(Des G. Drummond. Litho D.L.R.)

1971 (1 Nov). *Golfing in Bermuda. T* **87** *and similar horiz designs. Multicoloured. W* w **12** (*sideways*). *P* 13.

No.	Description	Unused	Used
279	4 c. Type **87**	30	15
280	15 c. Golfers at Port Royal	85	1·10
281	18 c. Castle Harbour	95	1·10
282	24 c. Belmont	1·25	1·50

HEATH - NIXON
DECEMBER 1971

(88)

1971 (20 Dec). *Anglo-American Talks. Nos.* 252, 258, 259 *and* 260 *optd with T* **88** *by Format.*

No.	Description	Unused	Used
283	4 c. Bermudiana	10	10
284	15 c. Passion Glory	15	15
285	18 c. Coralita	20	50
286	24 c. Morning Glory	30	65

89 Bonefish

(Des Maynard Reece. Litho B.W.)

1972 (21 Aug). *World Fishing Records. T* **89** *and similar horiz designs. Multicoloured. W* w **12**. *P* 13½ × 14.

No.	Description	Unused	Used
287	4 c. Type **89**	30	10
288	15 c. Wahoo	60	55
289	18 c. Yellowfin Tuna	65	85
290	24 c. Greater Amberjack	80	1·50

90 "Admiralty Oar" and Mace

(Des (from photograph by D. Groves) and photo Harrison)

1972 (20 Nov). *Royal Silver Wedding. Multicoloured; background colour given. W* w **12**. *P* 14 × 14½.

No.	Type	Description	Unused	Used
291	90	4 c. bright bluish violet	8	5
292		15 c. rose-carmine	35	45

91 Palmetto

92 Bernard Park, Pembroke, 1973

(Des Jennifer Toombs. Litho J.W.)

1973 (3 Sept). *Tree Planting Year. T* **91** *and similar vert designs. Multicoloured. W* w **12** (*sideways*). *P* 14.

No.	Description	Unused	Used
293	4 c. Type **91**	25	10
294	15 c. Olivewood Bark	90	75
	a. Brown (Queen's head and value) omitted	£550	
295	18 c. Bermuda Cedar	1·00	1·25
296	24 c. Mahogany	1·10	1·75

1973 (21 Nov*). *Royal Wedding. As Nos.* 165/6 *of Anguilla. Centre multicoloured. W* w **12** (*sideways*). *P* 13½.

No.	Description	Unused	Used
297	15 c. bright mauve	20	20
298	18 c. steel blue	25	30

*This is the local date of issue. The Crown Agents released the stamps on the 14 November.

(Des J.W. Litho Questa)

1973 (17 Dec). *Lawn Tennis Centenary. T* **92** *and similar horiz designs. Multicoloured. W* w **12**. *P* 14.

No.	Description	Unused	Used
299	4 c. Type **92**	30	10
300	15 c. Clermont Court, 1873	80	60
301	18 c. Leamington Spa Court, 1872	1·00	1·25
302	24 c. Staten Island Courts, 1874	1·25	1·60

1974 (13 June)–**76**. *As Nos.* 253/4, 257 *and* 261, *but wmk upright.*

No.	Description	Unused	Used
303	5 c. Poinsettia	90	90
304	6 c. Hibiscus	1·25	1·25
305	12 c. Jacaranda	1·40	1·75
306	30 c. Tecoma (11.6.76)	2·75	3·25

Nos. 307/19 vacant.

93 Weather Vane, City Hall

94 Jack of Clubs and "good bridge hand"

(Des G. Drummond. Litho Questa)

1974 (24 June). *50th Anniv of Rotary in Bermuda. T* **93** *and similar horiz designs. Multicoloured. W* w **12** (*sideways*). *P* 14.

No.	Value	Description	Unused	Used
320	5 c.	Type **93**	25	10
321	17 c.	St. Peter's Church, St George's	75	60
322	20 c.	Somerset Bridge	95	1·50
323	25 c.	Map of Bermuda, 1626	1·10	1·90

(Des J.W. Litho Format)

1975 (27 Jan). *World Bridge Championships, Bermuda. T* **94** *and similar vert designs. Multicoloured. W* w **12**. *P* 14.

No.	Value	Description	Unused	Used
324	5 c.	Type **94**	25	10
325	17 c.	Queen of Diamonds and Bermuda Bowl	75	60
326	20 c.	King of Hearts and Bermuda Bowl ..	85	1·50
327	25 c.	Ace of Spaces and Bermuda Bowl ..	95	1·60

95 Queen Elizabeth II and the Duke of Edinburgh

(Des and photo Harrison)

1975 (17 Feb). *Royal Visit. W* w **14**. *P* 14 × 14½.

No.	Type	Description	Unused	Used
328	**95**	17 c. multicoloured	70	80
329		20 c. multicoloured	80	1·10

96 "Cavalier" Flying-boat, 1937

(Des R. Granger Barrett. Litho Questa)

1975 (28 Apr). *50th Anniv of Air-mail Service to Bermuda. T* **96** *and similar horiz designs. Multicoloured. W* w **14** (*sideways*). *P* 14.

No.	Value	Description	Unused	Used
330	5 c.	Type **96**	40	10
331	17 c.	Airship *Los Angeles*, 1925	1·40	85
332	20 c.	Lockheed "Constellation", 1946	1·60	1·75
333	25 c.	Boeing "747", 1970	1·90	2·25
MS334		128 × 85 mm. Nos. 330/3	6·50	7·50

97 Supporters of American Army raiding Royal Magazine

98 Launching Bathysphere

(Des J. Cooter. Litho J.W.)

1975 (27 Oct). *Bicentenary of Gunpowder Plot. St. George's. T* **97** *and similar horiz designs. Multicoloured. W* w **14** (*sideways*). *P* 13 × 13½.

No.	Value	Description	Unused	Used
335	5 c.	Type **97**	30	10
336	17 c.	Setting off for raid	80	65
337	20 c.	Loading gunpowder aboard American ship	95	1·40
338	25 c.	Gunpowder on beach	1·25	1·75
MS339		165 × 138 mm. Nos. 335/8. P 14 (*sold for* 75 c.)	3·50	4·50

1975 (8 Dec)–**76**. *As Nos.* 250 *and* 254 *but W* w **14** (*sideways*).

No.	Value	Description	Unused	Used
340	2 c.	Bottlebrush	60	80
341	6 c.	Hibiscus (11.6.76)	85	1·25

Nos. 342/56 vacant.

(Des G. Drummond. Litho Questa)

1976 (29 Mar). *50th Anniv of Bermuda Biological Station. T* **98** *and similar multicoloured designs. W* w **14** (*sideways on* 17 *and* 20 *c.*). *P* 14.

No.	Value	Description	Unused	Used
357	5 c.	Type **98**	35	10
358	17 c.	View from the sea (*horiz*)	90	80
359	20 c.	H.M.S. *Challenger*, 1873 (*horiz*)	1·00	1·75
360	25 c.	Beebe's bathysphere descent, 1934 ..	1·25	2·25

99 *Christian Radich.*

(Des R. Granger Barrett. Litho J.W.)

1975 (15 June). *Tall Ships Race, 1976. T* **99** *and similar horiz designs. Multicoloured. W* w **12** (*sideways*). *P* 13.

No.	Value	Description	Unused	Used
361	5 c.	Type **99**	50	15
362	12 c.	*Juan Sebastian de Elcano*	95	95
363	17 c.	U.S.C.G. *Eagle*	1·40	1·10
364	20 c.	*Winston S. Churchill*	1·75	1·90
365	40 c.	*Kruzenshtern*	2·25	2·75
366	$1	*Cutty Sark* trophy	3·75	5·50
361/16		.. .. *Set of* 6	9·50	11·00

100 Silver Trophy and Club Flags

(Des C. Abbott. Litho Questa)

1976 (16 Aug). *75th Anniv of the St. George's v. Somerset Cricket Cup Match. T* **100** *and similar horiz designs. Multicoloured. W* w **14** (*sideways*). *P* 14½ × 14.

No.	Value	Description	Unused	Used
367	5 c.	Type **100**	35	10
368	17 c.	Badge and Pavilion, St. George's Club ..	95	75
369	20 c.	Badge and Pavilion Somerset Club ..	1·25	1·75
370	25 c.	Somerset playing field	1·75	2·50

101 Royal Visit, 1975

102 Stockdale House, St. George's 1784–1812

(Des Harrison. Litho Walsall)

1977 (7 Feb). *Silver Jubilee. T* **101** *and similar vert designs. Multicoloured. W* w **14**. *P* 13½.

No.	Value	Description	Unused	Used
371	5 c.	Type **101**	15	10
372	20 c.	St. Edward's Crown	35	35
373	$1	Queen in Chair of Estate	1·25	1·50

(Des G. Drummond. Litho J.W.)

1977 (20 June). *Centenary of U.P.U. Membership. T* **102** *and similar horiz designs. Multicoloured. W* w **14** (*sideways*). *P* 13.

No.	Value	Description	Unused	Used
374	5 c.	Type **102**	20	10
375	15 c.	Perot Post Office and stamp	60	50
376	17 c.	St. George's P.O. *circa* 1860	60	50
377	20 c.	Old G.P.O., Hamilton, *circa* 1935 ..	65	60
378	40 c.	New G.P.O., Hamilton, 1967	1·25	1·10

103 17th-Century Ship approaching Castle Island

104 Great Seal of Queen Elizabeth I

(Des R. Granger Barrett. Litho Questa)

1977 (26 Sept). *Piloting. T* **103** *and similar horiz designs. Multicoloured. W* w **14** (*sideways*). *P* 13½.

No.	Value	Description	Unused	Used
379	5 c.	Type **103**	20	10
380	15 c.	Pilot leaving ship, 1795	45	45
381	17 c.	Pilots rowing out to paddle-steamer ..	50	50
382	20 c.	Pilot gigs and brig *Harvest Queen* ..	65	70
383	40 c.	Modern pilot cutter and R.M.S. *Queen Elizabeth 2*	1·25	1·40

(Des BG Studio. Litho Questa)

1978 (28 Aug). *25th Anniv of Coronation. T* **104** *and similar ve*[rt] *designs. Multicoloured. W* w **14**. *P* 14 × 13½.

No.	Value	Description	Unused	Used
384	8 c.	Type **104**	15	
385	50 c.	Great Seal of Queen Elizabeth II ..	65	
386	$1	Queen Elizabeth II	1·00	1·

105 White-tailed Tropic Bird

(Des G. Drummond. Photo Harrison)

1978 (15 Nov)–**83**. *Wildlife. Horiz designs as T* **105**. *Multi-coloured. W* w **14** (*sideways on* 8, 15, 20, 40 *c. and* $1). *P* 14 × 14½ (4, 5 *c.*, $2, 5) *or* 14 (*others*).

No.	Value	Description	Unused	Used
387	3 c.	Type **105**	5	
	a.	Perf 14 × 14½ (3.8.83)*	5	
388	4 c.	White-eyed Vireo	5	
389	5 c.	Eastern Bluebird	5	
390	7 c.	Whistling Frog (19.2.79)	10	1
391	8 c.	Common Cardinal	12	1
392	10 c.	Spiny Lobster (19.2.79)	15	2
393	12 c.	Land Crab (19.2.79)	15	2
394	15 c.	Lizard (Skink) (19.2.79)	20	2
395	20 c.	Foureye Butterfly Fish (12.3.79) ..	30	3
396	25 c.	Red Hind (12.3.79)	40	4
	a.	Greenish blue omitted		
397	30 c.	Monarch Butterfly (19.2.79)	45	5
398	40 c.	Rock Beauty (12.3.79)	60	6
399	50 c.	Banded Butterfly Fish (12.3.79)	80	8
400	$1	Blue Angelfish (12.3.79)	1·50	1·6
401	$2	Humpback Whale (12.3.79)	3·00	3·2
402	$3	Green Turtle (19.2.79)	4·50	4·7
403	$5	Cahow	7·75	8·0
387/403		.. .. *Set of* 17	18·00	19·0

*Earliest known postmark date.

106 Map by Sir George Somers, 1609

107 Policeman and Policewoman

(Des J. Cooter. Litho Questa)

1979 (14 May). *Antique Maps. T* **106** *and similar multicoloured designs. W* w **14** (*sideways on* 8, 15, 25 *and* 50 *c.*) *P* 14 × 13½ (20 *c.*) *or* 13½ × 14 (*others*).

No.	Value	Description	Unused	Used
404	8 c.	Type **106**	15	12
405	15 c.	Map by John Seller, 1685	20	20
406	20 c.	Map by H. Moll, 1729–40 (*vert*)	30	30
407	25 c.	Map by Desbruslins, 1740	35	35
408	50 c.	Map by Speed, 1626	70	90

(Des L. Curtis. Litho Questa)

1979 (26 Nov). *Centenary of Police Force. T* **107** *and similar multicoloured designs. W* w **14** (*sideways on* 20 *and* 25 *c.*). *P* 14.

No.	Value	Description	Unused	Used
409	8 c.	Type **107**	15	10
410	20 c.	Policeman directing traffic (*horiz*) ..	40	45
411	25 c.	Police patrol launch (*horiz*)	45	50
412	50 c.	Police car and motorcycle	80	1·00

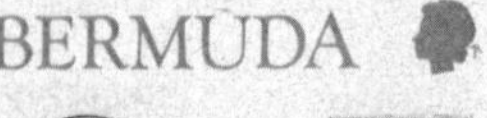

8 cents

ROWLAND HILL AND THE PENNY POST

108 1848 1d. "Perot" and Penny Black Stamps

(Des J.W. Litho Enschedé)

1980 (25 Feb). *Death Centenary of Sir Rowland Hill* (1979). *T* **108** *and similar horiz designs. Multicoloured. W* w **14** (*sideways*). *P* 13 × 13½.

No.	Value	Description	Unused	Used
413	8 c.	Type **108**	10	10
414	20 c.	1848 1d. "Perot" stamp and Sir Rowland Hill	25	30
415	25 c.	1848 1d. "Perot" stamp and early letter	30	35
416	50 c.	1848 1d. "Perot" stamp and "Paid 1" cancellation	55	60

109 British Airways "Tristar 500" Airliner approaching Bermuda

110 Gina Swainson with Rose

(Des R. Granger Barrett. Litho Harrison)

1980 (6 May). *"London 1980" International Stamp Exhibition. Mail-carrying Transport. T* **109** *and similar horiz designs. Multi-coloured.* W w **14** *(sideways).* P 13 × 13½.

417 25 c. Type **109** 30 30
418 50 c. S.S. *Orduna* in Grassy Bay 60 60
419 $1 *Delta* at St. George's Harbour .. .. 1·25 1·25
420 $2 *Lord Sidmouth* in Old Ship Channel, St. George's .. .. 2·25 2·25

(Des Walsall. Litho Questa)

1980 (8 May). *"Miss World 1979–80" (Gina Swainson) Commemoration. T* **110** *and similar vert designs. Multicoloured.* W w **14**. P 14 × 13½.

421 8 c. Type **110** 15 10
422 20 c. After crowning ceremony 40 40
423 50 c. On Peacock Throne at "Welcome Home" party 75 75
424 $1 In Bermuda carriage .. .. .. 1·40 1·60

111 Queen Elizabeth the Queen Mother

(Des and litho Harrison)

1980 (4 Aug). *80th Birthday of Queen Elizabeth the Queen Mother.* W w **14** *(sideways).* P 14.

425 **111** 25 c. multicoloured 30 40

112 Bermuda from Satellite

113 Kitchen, 18th-century

(Des. L. Curtis. Litho Questa)

1980 (24 Sept). *Commonwealth Finance Ministers Meeting. T* **112** *and similar horiz designs. Multicoloured.* W w **14** *(sideways).* P 14.

426 8 c. Type **112** 15 10
427 20 c. "Camden" 30 35
428 25 c. Princess Hotel, Hamilton 35 45
429 50 c. Government House 60 80

(Des J.W. Litho Questa)

1981 (21 May). *Heritage Week. T* **113** *and similar horiz designs. Multicoloured.* W w **14** *(sideways).* P 14.

430 8 c. Type **113** 15 10
431 25 c. Gathering Easter lilies, 20th-century .. 40 40
432 30 c. Fishing, 20th-century 50 50
433 40 c. Stone cutting, 19th-century 55 55
434 50 c. Onion shipping, 19th-century 65 65
435 $1 Privateering, 17th-century .. .. 1·50 1·50
430/5 .. .. *Set of* 6 3·25 3·25

114 Wedding Bouquet from Bermuda

115 "Service", Hamilton

(Des J.W. Litho Questa)

1981 (22 July). *Royal Wedding. T* **114** *and similar vert designs. Multicoloured.* W w **14**. P 14.

436 30 c. Type **114** 50 50
437 50 c. Prince Charles as Royal Navy Commander 65 65
438 $1 Prince Charles and Lady Diana Spencer 1·25 1·25

(Des L. Curtis. Litho Questa)

1981 (28 Sept). *25th Anniv of Duke of Edinburgh Award Scheme. T* **115** *and similar vert designs. Multicoloured.* W w **14**. P 14.

439 10 c. Type **115** 15 10
440 25 c. "Outward Bound", Paget Island 40 40
441 30 c. "Expedition", St. David's Island 45 45
442 $1 Duke of Edinburgh .. .. .. 1·50 1·50

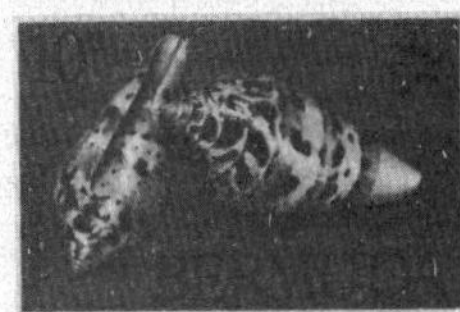

116 *Conus species*

(Des Walsall. Litho Questa)

1982 (22 Apr). *Sea-shells. T* **116** *and similar horiz designs. Multi-coloured.* W w **14** *(sideways).* P 14.

443 10 c. Type **116** 15 10
444 25 c. *Bursa finlayi* 40 40
445 30 c. *Sconsia striata* 45 45
446 $1 *Murex pterynotus lightbourni* .. .. 1·50 1·50

117 Regimental Colours and Colour Party

118 Charles Fort

(Des G. Drummond. Litho Questa)

1982 (17 June). *Bermuda Regiment. T* **117** *and similar horiz designs. Multicoloured.* W w **14** *(sideways).* P 14.

447 10 c. Type **117** 15 10
448 25 c. Queen's Birthday Parade 40 40
449 30 c. Governor inspecting Guard of Honour .. 50 50
450 40 c. Beating the Retreat 55 55
451 50 c. Ceremonial gunners 65 65
452 $1 Guard of Honour, Royal visit, 1975 .. 1·50 1·50
447/52 .. .. *Set of* 6 3·25 3·25

(Des L. Curtis. Litho Questa)

1982 (18 Nov) *Historic Bermuda Forts. T* **118** *and similar multi-coloured designs.* W w **14** *(sideways on 30 c. and $1).* P 14.

453 10 c. Type **118** 15 12
454 25 c. Pembroks Fort 40 40
455 30 c. Southampton Fort *(horiz)* 45 45
456 $1 Smiths Fort and Pagets Fort *(horiz)* .. 1·50 1·50

119 Arms of Sir Edwin Sandys

120 Early Fitted Dinghy

(Des Harrison. Litho J.W.)

1983 (14 Apr). *Coats of Arms (1st series). T* **119** *and similar vert designs. Multicoloured.* W w **14**. P 13.

457 10 c. Type **119** 15 15
458 25 c. Arms of the Bermuda Company 40 40
459 50 c. Arms of William Herbert, Earl of Pembroke 70 70
460 $1 Arms of Sir George Somers .. .. 1·50 1·50
See also Nos. 482/5.

(Des L. Curtis. Litho Harrison)

1983 (23 June). *Fitted Dinghies. T* **120** *and similar vert designs. Multicoloured.* W w **14** *(sideways).* P 14.

461 12 c. Type **120** 20 20
462 30 c. Modern dinghy inshore 45 45
463 40 c. Early dinghy *(different)* 60 60
464 $1 Modern dinghy with red and white spinnaker .. .. 1·50 1·50

ALTERED CATALOGUE NUMBERS

Any Catalogue numbers altered from the last edition are shown as a list in the introductory pages.

121 Curtiss "Jenny" Seaplane (First Flight over Bermuda)

122 Joseph Stockdale

(Des A. Theobald. Litho Walsall)

1983 (13 Oct). *Bicentenary of Manned Flight. T* **121** *and similar horiz designs. Multicoloured.* W w **14** *(sideways).* P 14.

465 12 c. Type **121** 20 15
466 30 c. *Pilot Radio*, Stinson seaplane (First completed flight between U.S.A. and Bermuda) 45 45
467 40 c. Short "Empire" flying boat *Cavalier* (First scheduled passenger flight) .. 60 60
468 $1 U.S.S. *Los Angeles* (airship) moored to U.S.S. *Patoka* .. .. .. 1·50 1·50

(Des L. Curtis. Litho Harrison)

1984 (26 Jan). *Bicentenary of Bermuda's First Newspaper and Postal Service. T* **122** *and similar multicoloured designs.* W w **14** *(sideways on 40 c. and $1).* P 14.

469 12 c. Type **122** 20 25
470 30 c. *The Bermuda Gazette* 50 55
471 40 c. Stockdale's postal service *(horiz)* .. 70 75
472 $1 *Lady Hammond* (mail boat) *(horiz)* .. 1·75 1·90

123 Sir Thomas Gates and Sir George Somers

124 Swimming

(Des R. Granger Barrett. Litho Walsall)

1984 (3 May). *375th Anniv of First Settlement. T* **123** *and similar horiz designs. Multicoloured.* W w **14** *(sideways).* P 14.

473 12 c. Type **123** 20 25
474 30 c. Jamestown, Virginia 50 55
475 40 c. Wreck of *Sea Venture* 70 75
476 $1 Fleet leaving Plymouth, Devon .. .. 1·75 1·90
MS477 130 × 73 mm. Nos. 474 and 476 .. .. 2·25 2·50

(Des C. Collins. Litho J.W.)

1984 (19 July). *Olympic Games, Los Angeles. T* **124** *and similar multicoloured designs.* W w **14** *(sideways on 30 c., $1).* P 14.

478 12 c. Type **124** 20 25
479 30 c. Track and field events *(horiz)* 50 55
480 40 c. Equestrian competition 70 75
481 $1 Sailing *(horiz)* .. .. 1·75 1·90

(Des Harrison. Litho J.W.)

1984 (27 Sept). *Coats of Arms (2nd series). Vert designs as T* **119**. *Multicoloured.* W w **14**. P 13.

482 12 c. Arms of Henry Wriothesley, Earl of Southampton 20 25
483 30 c. Arms of Sir Thomas Smith 50 55
484 40 c. Arms of William Cavendish, Earl of Devonshire 70 75
485 $1 Town arms of St. George .. .. .. 1·75 1·90

POSTAL FISCAL

1937 (1 Feb). *As T* **15**, *but inscr* "REVENUE" *at each side. Wmk Mult Script CA.* P 14.

F1 12s. 6d. grey and orange, C £250 £350

No. F1 was issued for fiscal purposes during 1936. Its use as a postage stamp was authorised from 1 February to April 1937. The used price quoted above is for examples postmarked during this period. Later in the same year postmarks with other dates were obtained by favour.

Botswana
(*formerly* Bechuanaland)

INDEPENDENCE

47 National Assembly Building

(Des R. Granger Barrett. Photo Harrison)

1966 (30 Sept). *Independence. T* **47** *and similar horiz designs. Multicoloured. P* 14½.

202 2½ c. Type **47** 10 8
a. Imperf (pair) £170
203 5 c. Abattoir, Lobatsi 12 10
204 15 c. National Airways "Dakota" 35 15
205 35 c. State House, Gaberones 50 35

REPUBLIC OF BOTSWANA

(**51**)

52 Golden Oriole

1966 (30 Sept). *Nos.* 168/81 *of Bechuanaland optd as T* **51**.

206 1 c. yellow, red, black and lilac 15 5
207 2 c. orange, black and yellow-olive 20 5
208 2½ c. carmine, green, black and bistre .. 25 5
209 3½ c. yellow, black, sepia and pink 40 15
210 5 c. yellow, blue, black and buff 40 20
211 7½ c. brown, red, black and apple-green .. 40 30
212 10 c. red, yellow, sepia & turquoise-green .. 70 20
213 12½ c. buff, blue, red and grey-black .. .. 1·50 50
214 20 c. yellow-brown and drab 45 45
215 25 c. deep brown and lemon 50 50
216 35 c. deep blue and orange .. .. .. 85 1·00
217 50 c. sepia and olive .. .. 1·00 1·25
218 1 r. black and cinnamon .. .. .. 2·25 3·50
219 2 r. brown and turquoise-blue .. .. 4·25 7·00
206/219 .. .. *Set of* 14 12·00 14·00

(Des D. M. Reid-Henry. Photo Harrison)

1967 (3 Jan). *Birds. Vert designs as T* **52**. *Multicoloured. P* 14 × 14½.

220 1 c. Type **52** 20 12
a. Error. Wmk **105** of Malta .. .. † £700
221 2 c. Hoopoe 40 10
222 3 c. Groundscraper Thrush 55 10
223 4 c. Cordon-bleu 55 10
224 5 c. Secretary Bird 55 10
225 7 c. Yellow-billed Hornbill 60 30
226 10 c. Burchell's Gonolek 60 15
227 15 c. Malachite Kingfisher .. .. .. 2·25 45
228 20 c. African Fish Eagle .. .. .. 2·00 65
229 25 c. Go-away Bird .. .. 1·75 60
230 35 c. Scimitar-bill .. .. 3·00 70
231 50 c. Comb Duck .. .. 3·00 2·25
232 1 r. Levaillant's Barbet .. .. .. 5·50 4·50
233 2 r. Didric Cuckoo .. .. 12·00 14·00
220/33 .. .. *Set of* 14 30·00 22·00

A used copy of the 20 c. has been seen with the pale brown colour missing, resulting in the value (normally shown in white) being omitted.

The 1, 2, 4, 7 and 10 c. values exist with PVA gum as well as gum arabic.

66 Students and University

(Des V. Whiteley. Photo Harrison)

1967 (7 Apr). *First Conferment of University Degrees. P* 14 × 14½.

234 **66** 3 c. sepia, ultramarine & lt orange-yell 5 5
235 7 c. sepia, ultram & lt greenish bl .. 10 10
236 15 c. sepia, ultramarine and rose .. 20 25
237 35 c. sepia, ultramarine and light violet 25 30

NEW INFORMATION

The editor is always interested to correspond with people who have new information that will improve or correct the Catalogue.

67 Chobe Bush-buck

(Des G. Vasarhelyi. Photo Harrison)

1967 (2 Oct). *Chobe Game Reserve. T* **67** *and similar horiz designs. Multicoloured. P* 14.

238 3 c. Type **67** 5 5
239 7 c. Sable antelope 15 15
240 35 c. Fishing on Chobe River 80 45

70 Arms of Botswana and Human Rights Emblem

(Litho D.L.R.)

1968 (8 Apr). *Human Rights Year. T* **70** *and similar horiz designs showing Arms of Botswana and Human Rights emblem arranged differehtly. P* 13½ × 13.

241 3 c. multicoloured 5 5
242 15 c. multicoloured 15 15
243 25 c. multicoloured 25 30

73 Eland and Giraffe Rock Paintings, Tsodilo Hills

75 "Baobab Trees" (Thomas Baines)

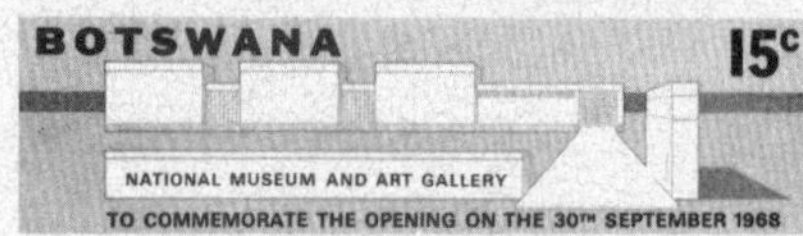

76 National Museum and Art Gallery

(Litho D.L.R.)

1968 (30 Sept). *Opening of National Museum and Art Gallery. T* **73/6** *and similar multicoloured design. P* 12½ (7 *c.*), 12½ × 13½ (15 *c.*), *or* 13 × 13½ (*others*).

244 3 c. Type **73** 5 5
245 7 c. Girl wearing ceremonial beads (30 × 48 *mm*) 20 20
246 10 c. Type **75** 30 30
247 15 c. Type **76** 45 45
MS248 132 × 82 mm. Nos. 244/7. P 13 .. .. 2·00 2·75

77 African Family, and Star over Village

(Des Mrs M. E. Townsend and J. Cooter. Litho Enschedé)

1968 (11 Nov). *Christmas. P* 13 × 14.

249 **77** 1 c. multicoloured 5 5
250 2 c. multicoloured 5 5
251 5 c. multicoloured 5 5
252 25 c. multicoloured 35 45

78 Scout, Lion and Badge in Frame

(Des D.L.R. Litho Format)

1969 (21 Aug). *22nd World Scout Conference, Helsinki. T* **78** *and similar multicoloured designs. P* 13½.

253 3 c. Type **78** 30 5
254 15 c. Scouts cooking over open fire (*vert*) .. 95 65
255 25 c. Scouts around camp fire .. .. .. 1·25 85

81 Woman, Child and Christmas Star

82 Diamond Treatment Plant, Orapa

(Des V. Whiteley. Litho Harrison)

1969 (6 Nov). *Christmas. P* 14½ × 14.

256 **81** 1 c. pale blue and chocolate 5 5
257 2 c. pale yellow-olive and chocolate .. 8 8
258 4 c. yellow and chocolate 10 10
259 35 c. chocolate and bluish violet 40 45
MS260 86 × 128 mm. Nos. 256/9. P 14½ (*shades*) 1·60 1·75

(Des J.W. Litho Harrison)

1970 (23 Mar). *Developing Botswana. T* **82** *and similar designs. Multicoloured. P* 14½ × 14 (3 *c.*, 7 *c.*) *or* 14 × 14½ (*others*).

261 3 c. Type **82** 10 5
262 7 c. Copper-nickel mining 25 25
263 10 c. Copper-nickel mine, Selebi-Pikwe (*horiz*) 35 35
264 35 c. Orapa diamond mine, and diamonds (*horiz*) .. .. 1·10 75

83 Mr. Micawber (*David Copperfield*)

(Des V. Whiteley. Litho Walsall)

1970 (6 July). *Death Centenary of Charles Dickens. T* **83** *and similar horiz designs. Multicoloured. P* 11.

265 3 c. Type **83** 12 5
266 7 c. Scrooge (*A Christmas Carol*) 25 20
267 15 c. Fagin (*Oliver Twist*) 50 50
268 25 c. Bill Sykes (*Oliver Twist*) 80 80
MS269 114 × 81 mm. Nos. 265/8 .. .. .. 3·75 4·25

84 U.N. Building and Emblem

(Des J. Cooter. Litho Walsall)

1970 (24 Oct). *25th Anniv of United Nations. P* 11.

270 **84** 15 c. bright blue, chestnut and silver .. 30 30

85 Crocodile

(Des A. Vale. Litho Questa)

1970 (3 Nov). *Christmas. T* **85** *and similar horiz designs. Multicoloured. P* 14.

271 1 c. Type **85** 5 5
272 2 c. Giraffe 5 5
273 7 c. Elephant 15 15
274 25 c. Rhinoceros 35 40
MS275 128 × 90 mm. Nos. 271/4 .. .. .. 2·00 2·50

86 Sorghum

(Des J.W. Litho Questa)

1971 (6 April). *Important Crops. T* **86** *and similar horiz designs. Multicoloured. P* 14.

276 3 c. Type **86** 8 5
277 7 c. Millet 15 10
278 10 c. Maize 20 15
279 35 c. Groundnuts 50 60

87 Map and Head of Cow

88 King bringing Gift of Gold

(Des L. Curtis. Litho Harrison)

1971 (30 Sept). *Fifth Anniv of Independence. T* **87** *and similar vert designs inscr* "PULA" (local greeting). *P* 14½ × 14.

280 3 c. black, brown and apple-green 12 5
281 4 c. black, new blue and pale blue 15 10
282 7 c. black and red-orange 35 35
283 10 c. multicoloured 35 35
284 20 c. multicoloured .. .. 95 1·25

Designs:—4 c. Map and cogs; 7 c. Map and zebra; 10 c. Map and sorghum stalk crossed by tusk; 20 c. Arms and map of Botswana.

(Des A. Vale. Litho Questa)

1971 (11 Nov). *Christmas. T* **88** *and similar vert designs. Multicoloured. P* 14.

285 2 c. Type **88** 8 5
286 3 c. King bearing frankincense 8 5
287 7 c. King bearing myrrh 15 15
288 20 c. Three Kings behold the star 40 50
MS289 85 × 128 mm. Nos. 285/8 .. .. .. 2·00 2·50

89 Orion

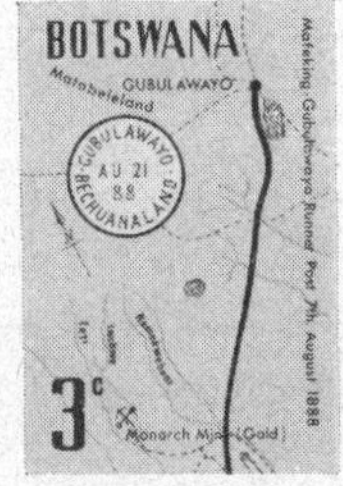

90 Postmark and Map

(Des R. Granger Barrett. Litho Questa)

1972 (24 Apr). *"Night Sky". T* **89** *and similar vert designs. P* 14.

290 3 c. turquoise-blue, black and red 20 5
291 7 c. dull blue, black and yellow 45 60
292 10 c. dull green, black and orange 55 75
293 20 c. deep violet-blue, black and blue-green .. 1·00 1·25

Constellations:—7 c. The Scorpion; 10 c. The Centaur; 20 c. The Cross.

(Des M. Bryan; adapted G. Drummond. Litho A. & M.)

1972 (21 Aug). *Mafeking-Gubulawayo Runner Post. T* **90** *and similar vert designs. Multicoloured. P* 13½ × 13.

294 3 c. Type **90** 25 5
295 4 c. Bechuanaland stamp and map 30 45
296 7 c. Runners and map 50 65
297 20 c. Mafeking postmark and map .. .. 1·25 1·60
MS298 84 × 216 mm. Nos. 294/7 vertically *se-tenant*, forming a composite map design .. .. 6·00 8·50

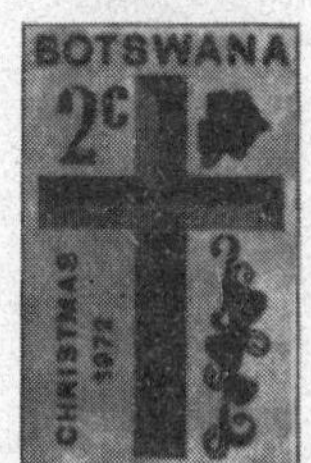

91 Cross, Map and Bells

92 Thor

(Des locally; adapted J. Cooter. Litho Questa)

1972 (6 Nov). *Christmas. Vert designs each with Cross and Map as T* **91**. *Multicoloured. P* 14.

299 2 c. Type **91** 5 5
300 3 c. Cross, map and candle 8 5
301 7 c. Cross, map and Christmas tree 20 20
302 20 c. Cross, map, star and holly 45 60
MS303 96 × 119 mm. Nos. 299/302 .. .. 2·75 3·75

(Des Mrs. E. Elphick; adapted Jennifer Toombs. Litho Questa)

1973 (23 Mar). *I.M.O./W.M.O. Centenary. T* **92** *and similar designs showing Norse myths. Multicoloured. P* 14.

304 3 c. Type **92** 10 5
305 4 c. Sun God's chariot (*horiz*). 15 15
306 7 c. Ymir, the frost giant 25 15
307 20 c. Odin and Sleipnir (*horiz*) 45 60

NEW INFORMATION

The editor is always interested to correspond with people who have new information that will improve or correct the Catalogue.

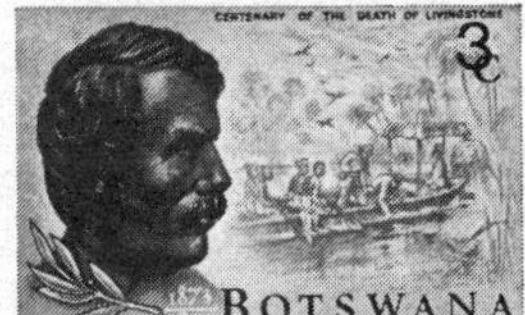

93 Livingstone and River Scene

(Des G. Vasarhelyi. Litho Walsall Security Printers, Ltd)

1973 (10 Sept). *Death Centenary of Dr. Livingstone. T* **93** *and similar horiz design. Multicoloured. P* 13½.

308 3 c. Type **93** 10 5
309 20 c. Livingstone meeting Stanley 70 80

94 Donkey and Foal at Village Trough

95 Gaberone Campus

(Des locally; adapted G. Vasarhelyi. Litho Questa)

1973 (3 Dec). *Christmas. T* **94** *and similar multicoloured designs. P* 14.

310 3 c. Type **94** 10 5
311 4 c. Shepherd and flock (*horiz*) 12 10
312 7 c. Mother and child.. .. .. .. 20 25
313 20 c. Kgotla meeting (*horiz*) 45 75

(Des locally; adapted P. Powell. Litho Questa)

1974 (8 May). *Tenth Anniv of University of Botswana, Lesotho and Swaziland. T* **95** *and similar horiz designs. Multicoloured. P* 14.

314 3 c. Type **95** 10 5
315 7 c. Kwaluseni Campus 20 15
316 20 c. Roma Campus 50 45
317 35 c. Map and flags of the three countries .. 85 75

96 Methods of Mail Transport

(Des locally; adapted G. Vasarhelyi. Litho J.W.)

1974 (29 May). *Centenary of Universal Postal Union. T* **96** *and similar horiz designs. Multicoloured. P* 14.

318 2 c. Type **96** 45 35
319 3 c. Post Office, Palapye, *circa* 1889 .. .. 45 35
320 7 c. Bechuanaland Police Camel Post, *circa* 1900 .. .. 95 75
321 20 c. Mail-planes of 1920 and 1974 .. .. 2·75 2·40

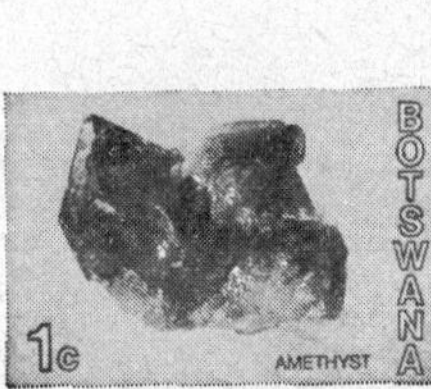

97 Amethyst

98 *Stapelia variegata*

(Des locally; adapted PAD Studio. Photo Enschedé)

1975 (1 July). *Botswana Minerals. T* **97** *and similar horiz designs. Multicoloured. P* 14 × 13.

322 1 c. Type **97** 20 10
323 2 c. Agate—"Botswana Pink" 20 12
324 3 c. Quartz 25 15
325 4 c. Copper nickel 30 20
326 5 c. Moss agate 30 20
327 7 c. Agate 35 25
328 10 c. Stilbite 45 30
329 15 c. Moshaneng Banded Marble 75 50
330 20 c. Gem diamonds 90 60
331 25 c. Chrysotile 90 70
332 35 c. Jasper .. .. 1·75 1·25
333 50 c. Moss quartz .. .. 2·25 1·75
334 1 r. Citrine .. .. 5·00 4·50
335 2 r. Chalcopyrite .. .. 12·00 11·00
322/35 .. .. *Set of* 14 23·00 19·00

(Des M. Bryan. Litho Questa)

1974 (4 Nov). *Christmas. T* **98** *and similar vert designs showing flowers. Multicoloured. P* 14.

336 2 c. Type **98** 15 10
337 7 c. *Hibiscus lunarifolius* 45 35
338 15 c. *Ceratotheca triloba* 95 60
339 20 c. *Nerine laticoma* .. .. 1·10 75
MS340 85 × 130 mm. Nos. 336/9 .. .. .. 2·50 3·00

99 President Sir Seretse Khama

100 Ostrich

(Des M. Bryan: adapted G. Vasarhelyi. Photo Enschedé)

1975 (24 Mar). *Tenth Anniv of Self-Government. P* 13½ × 13.

341 **99** 4 c. multicoloured 12 10
342 10 c. multicoloured 25 25
343 20 c. multicoloured 50 50
344 35 c. multicoloured 80 80
MS345 93 × 130 mm. Nos. 341/4 .. .. 1·75 1·90

(Des M. Bryan. Litho Questa)

1975 (23 June). *Rock Paintings, Tsodilo Hills. T* **100** *and similar horiz designs. Multicoloured. P* 14.

346 4 c. Type **100** 35 10
347 10 c. Rhinoceros 80 35
348 25 c. Hyena .. .. 2·00 85
349 35 c. Scorpion .. .. 2·25 1·40
MS350 150 × 150 mm. Nos. 346/9 .. .. 5·00 5·50

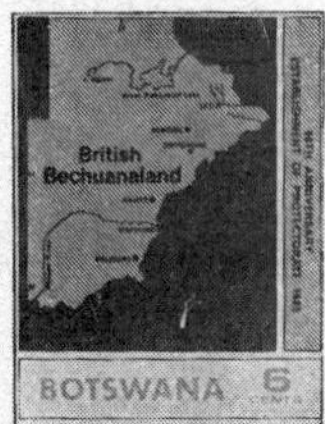

101 Map of British Bechuanaland, 1885

102 *Aloe marlothii*

(Des M. Bryan and G. Vasarhelyi. Litho Harrison)

1975 (13 Oct). *Anniversaries. T* **101** *and similar multicoloured designs. P* 14 × 14½ (25 *c.*) *or* 14½ × 14 (*others*).

351 6 c. Type **101** 30 30
352 10 c. Chief Khama, 1875 .. .. .. 45 40
353 25 c. Chiefs Sebele, Bathoen and Khama, 1895 (*horiz*) .. .. 1·00 80

Events:—6 c. 90th Anniv of Protectorate; 10 c. Centenary of Khama's Accession; 25 c. 80th Anniv of Chiefs' visit to London.

(Des M. Bryan. Litho Questa)

1975 (3 Nov). *Christmas. T* **102** *and similar vert designs showing aloes. Multicoloured. P* 14½.

354 3 c. Type **102** 35 10
355 10 c. *Aloe lutescens* 90 35
356 15 c. *Aloe zebrina* .. .. 1·25 85
357 25 c. *Aloe littoralis* .. .. 1·75 1·40

103 Drum

(Des M. Bryan. Litho Questa)

1976 (1 Mar). *Traditional Musical Instruments. T* **103** *and similar horiz designs. Multicoloured. P* 14.

358 4 c. Type **103** 20 10
359 10 c. Hand Piano 50 30
360 15 c. Segankuru (violin) 65 55
361 25 c. Kudu Signal Horn 85 85

104 One Pula Note

(Des M. Bryan from banknotes by D.L.R. Litho Questa)

1976 (28 June). *First National Currency. T* **104** *and similar horiz designs. Multicoloured. P* 14.

362 4 c. Type **104** 15 10
363 10 c. Two pula note 45 30
364 15 c. Five pula note 70 55
365 25 c. Ten pula note 90 85
MS366 163 × 107 mm. Nos. 362/5 .. .. 2·25 2·50

(New Currency. 100 thebe = 1 pula)

1t (105) (Type I) 1t (105) (Type II) 2t (I) 2t (II)

4t (I) 4t (II) 5t (I) 5t (II)

15t (I) 15t (II) 20t (I) 20t (II)

(Surch in letterpress by Govt Printer, Pretoria (Type I), or in lithography by Enschedé (Type II))

1976 (23 Aug)–77. *Nos.* 322/35 *surch as T* **105.**

367 1 t. on 1 c. Type **97** (I) 10 5
  a. Type II Surch (15.7.77) 15 10
368 2 t. on 2 c. Agate—"Botswana Pink" (I) .. 12 8
  a. Type II Surch (15.7.77) 20 15
369 3 t. on 3 c. Quartz (Gold) 15 10
370 4 t. on 4 c. Copper nickel (I) 20 12
  a. Type II Surch (15.7.77) 35 25
371 5 t. on 5 c. Moss agate (I) 20 12
  a. Type II Surch (15.7.77) 35 25
372 7 t. on 7 c. Agate 30 20
373 10 t. on 10 c. Stilbite 35 25
374 15 t. on 15 c. Moshaneng Banded Marble (I) (Gold) 60 55
  a. Type II Surch (15.7.77) 80 80
375 20 t. on 20 c. Gem diamonds (I) 75 55
  a. Type II Surch (15.7.77) .. .. 1·00 90
376 25 t. on 25 c. Chrysotile 80 70
377 35 t. on 35 c. Jasper .. .. 1·00 1·00
378 50 t. on 50 c. Moss quartz .. .. 1·50 1·50
379 1 p. on 1 r. Citrine .. .. 3·25 3·25
380 2 p. on 2 r. Chalcopyrite (Gold) .. .. .. 7·00 7·00
367/80 .. .. *Set of* 14 15·00 14·00
367a/75a .. .. *Set of* 6 2·50 2·25

106 Botswanan Cattle

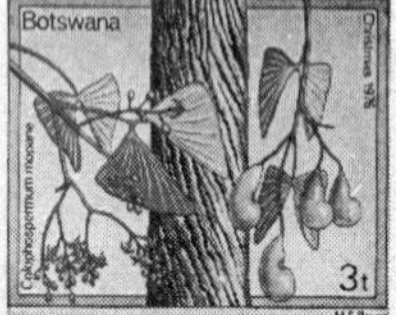

107 *Colophospermum mopane*

(Des M. Bryan. Litho Questa)

1976 (30 Sept). *Tenth Anniv of Independence. T* **106** *and similar multicoloured designs. P* 14.

381 4 t. Type **106** 15 10
382 10 t. Deer, Okavango Delta (*vert*) 40 35
383 15 t. Schools and pupils 50 45
384 25 t. Rural weaving (*vert*) 75 65
385 35 t. Miner (*vert*) 95 85

Nos. 381/5 were printed on sand-grained paper which has an uneven surface.

(Des M. Bryan. Litho J.W.)

1976 (1 Nov). *Christmas. T* **107** *and similar horiz designs showing trees. Multicoloured. P* 13.

386 3 t. Type **107** 15 10
387 4 t. *Baikiaea plurijuga* 15 10
388 10 t. *Sterculia rogersii* 40 30
389 25 t. *Acacia nilotica* .. .. 1·00 70
390 40 t. *Kigelia africana* .. .. 1·75 1·00

108 Coronation Coach

(Des M. Bryan and G. Vasarhelyi. Litho Cartor S.A., France)

1977 (7 Feb). *Silver Jubilee. T* **108** *and similar horiz designs. Multicoloured. P* 12.

391 4 t. Queen and Sir Seretse Khama 10 10
392 25 t. Type **108** 40 40
393 40 t. The Recognition 60 65

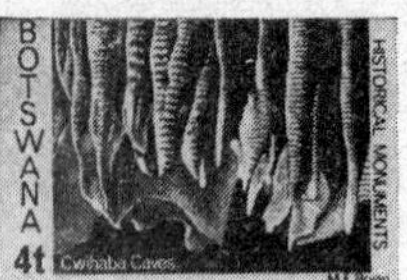

109 Clawless Otter **110** Cwihaba Caves

(Des M. Bryan. Litho Questa)

1977 (6 June). *Diminishing Species. T* **109** *and similar horiz designs. Multicoloured. P* 14.

394 3 t. Type **109** 25 20
395 4 t. Serval 25 20
396 10 t. Bat-eared fox 60 40
397 25 t. Pangolin .. .. 1·60 1·10
398 40 t. Brown hyena .. .. 2·75 1·90

(Des M. Bryan. Litho J.W.)

1977 (12 Aug). *Historical Monuments. T* **110** *and similar horiz designs. Multicoloured. P* 14.

399 4 t. Type **110** 20 15
400 5 t. Khama Memorial 20 15
401 15 t. Green's Tree 60 60
402 20 t. Mmajojo Ruins 65 65
403 25 t. Ancient morabaraba board 70 70
404 35 t. Matsieng's footprint 95 95
399/404 .. .. *Set of* 6 3·00 3·00
MS405 154 × 105 mm. Nos. 399/404 .. .. 3·00 3·75

111 *Hypoxis nitida*

112 Little Black Bustard

(Des M. Bryan. Litho Questa)

1977 (7 Nov*). *Christmas. T* **111** *and similar vert designs showing lilies. Multicoloured. P* 14.

406 3 t. Type **111** 15 8
407 5 t. *Haemanthus magnificus* 20 12
408 10 t. *Boophane disticha* 40 25
409 25 t. *Vellozia retinervis* 80 55
410 40 t. *Ammocharis coranica* .. .. .. 1·25 95

*This is the local release date. The Crown Agents released the stamps on 31 October.

(Des M. Bryan. Photo Harrison)

1978 (3 July). *Birds. Vert designs as T* **112**. *Multicoloured. P* 14 × 14½ (1 *to* 20 *t.*) *or* 14 (25*t to* 5 *p.*).

411 1 t. Type **112** 20 15
412 2 t. Marabou Stork 20 15
413 3 t. Green Wood Hoopoe 20 15
414 4 t. Carmine Bee Eater 25 15
415 5 t. African Jacana 25 15
416 7 t. African Paradise Flycatcher 35 15
417 10 t. Bennett's Woodpecker 50 15
418 15 t. Red Bishop 60 35
419 20 t. Crowned Plover 60 45
420 25 t. Giant Kingfisher 60 50
421 30 t. White-faced Whistling Duck 60 50
422 35 t. Striated Heron 60 50
423 45 t. Black-headed Heron 65 65
424 50 t. Spotted Eagle Owl 65 65
425 1 p. Gabar Goshawk .. .. 1·00 1·00
426 2 p. Martial Eagle .. .. 2·00 2·75
427 5 p. Saddle-bill Stork .. .. 6·00 6·50
411/27 .. .. *Set of* 17 14·00 13·00

113 Tawana making Karos

(Des M. Bryan. Litho Questa)

1978 (11 Sept). *Okavango Delta. T* **113** *and similar horiz designs. Multicoloured. P* 14.

428 4 t. Type **113** 10 8
429 5 t. Tribe localities 10 8
430 15 t. Bushmen collecting roots 35 35
431 20 t. Herero woman milking 40 40
432 25 t. Yei poling "mokoro" (canoe) 50 50
433 35 t. Mbukushu fishing 65 65
428/33 .. .. *Set of* 6 1·90 1·90
MS434 150 × 98 mm. Nos. 428/33 .. .. 1·90 2·00

Nos. 428/34 were printed on sand-grained paper which has an uneven surface.

114 *Caralluma lutea* **115** Sip Well

(Des M. Bryan. Litho J.W.)

1978 (6 Nov). *Christmas. Flowers. T* **114** *and similar vert designs. Multicoloured. P* 14.

435 5 t. Type **114** 20 10
436 10 t. *Hoodia lugardii* 35 25
437 15 t. *Ipomoea transvaalensis* 60 40
438 25 t. *Ansellia gigantea* 80 55

(Des M. Bryan. Litho Questa)

1979 (12 Feb). *Water Development. T* **115** *and similar vert designs. Multicoloured. P* 14.

439 3 t. Type **115** 10 5
440 5 t. Watering pit 15 8
441 10 t. Hand dug well 25 15
442 25 t. Windmill 55 40
443 40 t. Modern drilling rig 90 70

116 Pottery **117** 1885 British Bechuanaland 1d. Stamp and Sir Rowland Hill

(Des M. Bryan. Litho Questa)

1979 (11 June). *Handicrafts. T* **116** *and similar vert designs. Multicoloured. P* 14½ × 14.

444 5 t. Type **116** 15 5
445 10 t. Clay modelling 30 15
446 25 t. Basketry 55 35
447 40 t. Beadwork 90 75
MS448 123 × 96 mm. Nos. 444/7 .. .. .. 1·75 1·90

(Des M. Bryan. Litho Secura, Singapore)

1979 (27 Aug). *Death Centenary of Sir Rowland Hill. T* **117** *and similar horiz designs showing stamps and Sir Rowland Hill. Multicoloured. P* 13½.

449 5 t. Type **117** 10 10
450 25 t. 1932 Bechuanaland Protectorate 2d .. 45 45
451 45 t. 1967 2 c. definitive 65 65

118 Children Playing

119 *Ximenia caffra*

(Des K. Mosenyi (5 t.), M. Bryan (10 t.). Litho Questa)

1979 (24 Sept). *International Year of the Child. T* **118** *and similar multicoloured design. P* 14.

452 5 t. Type **118** 8 8
453 10 t. Child playing with doll (*vert*) 20 20

(Des M. Bryan. Litho Questa)

1979 (12 Nov). *Christmas. Fruit. T* **119** *and similar vert designs. Multicoloured. P* 14.

454 5 t. Type **119** 10 8
455 10 t. *Sclerocarya caffra* 20 20
456 15 t. *Hexalobus monopetalus* 35 35
457 25 t. *Ficus soldanella* 45 45

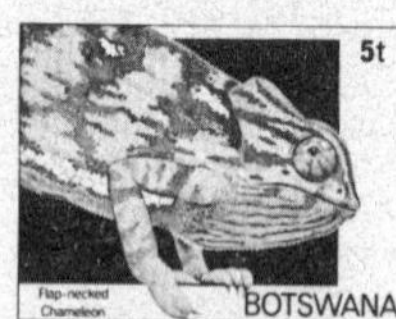

120 Flap-necked Chameleon

121 Rock Breaking

(Des M. Bryan. Litho Security Printers (M), Malaysia)

1980 (3 Mar). *Reptiles. T* **120** *and similar horiz designs. Multicoloured. P* 13½.

458 5 t. Type **120** 8 8
459 10 t. Leopard Tortoise 15 15
460 25 t. Puff Adder 40 40
461 40 t. White-throated Monitor 60 60

(Des M. Bryan. Litho Secura, Singapore)

1980 (7 July). *Early Mining. T* **121** *and similar horiz designs. Multicoloured. P* 13½.

462 5 t. Type **121** 5 5
463 10 t. Ore hoisting 15 15
464 15 t. Ore transport 30 30
465 20 t. Ore crushing 35 35
466 25 t. Smelting 40 40
467 35 t. Tools and products 55 55
462/7 .. .. *Set of* 6 1·60 1·60

122 "Chiwele and the Giant"

(Des W. Battiss. Litho Questa)

1980 (8 Sept). *Folktales. T* **122** *and similar multicoloured designs. P* 14 (5 *t.*), 14 × 13½ (45 *t.*) *or* 14½ × 14 (*others*).

468 5 t. Type **122** (35 × 22 *mm*) 5 5
469 10 t. "Kgori is not deceived" (28 × 37 *mm*) .. 15 12

470 30 t. "Nyambi's wife and Crocodile" (28 × 37 *mm*) 45 45
471 45 t. "Clever Hare" (44 × 27 *mm*) 60 60

123 Game watching. Makgadikgadi Pans

(Des M. Bryan. Litho Govt Printer, Pretoria)

1980 (6 Oct). *World Tourism Conference, Manila. P* 14.
472 **123** 5 t. multicoloured 10 10

124 *Acacia gerrardii*

125 Heinrich von Stephan with Bechuanaland 1949 3d. and Botswana 1974 3 c. U.P.U. Anniversary Commemoratives

(Des M. Bryan. Litho Govt Printer, Pretoria)

1980 (3 Nov). *Christmas. Flora. T* **124** *and similar vert designs. Multicoloured. P* 14 × 13½.
473 5 t. Type **124** 5 5
474 10 t. *Acacia nilotica* 15 12
475 25 t. *Acacia erubescens* 45 35
476 40 t. *Dichrostachys cinerea* 80 75

(Des M. Bryan. Litho Govt Printer, Pretoria)

1981 (7 Jan). *150th Birth Anniv of Heinrich von Stephan (founder of U.P.U.). T* **125** *and similar horiz design showing Von Stephan and U.P.U. anniversary commemoratives. Multicoloured. P* 14.
477 6 t. Type **125** 10 10
478 20 t. Bechuanaland 1949 6d. and Botswana 1974 7 c. 35 35

126 Emperor Dragonfly

127 Camphill Community Ramkoromane, Otse

(Des M. Bryan. Litho Govt Printer, Pretoria)

1981 (23 Feb). *Insects. T* **126** *and similar vert designs. Multicoloured. P* 14.
479 6 t. Type **126** 15 10
480 7 t. Praying Mantis 15 12
481 10 t. Elegant Grasshopper 20 15
482 20 t. Dung Beetle 35 35
483 30 t. Citrus Swallowtail Butterfly 50 50
484 45 t. Mopane Worm 65 65
479/84 .. .. *Set of* 6 1·75 1·75
MS485 180 × 89 mm. Nos. 479/84 .. .. .. 1·75 2·00

(Des M. Bryan. Litho Govt Printer, Pretoria)

1981 (6 Apr). *International Year for Disabled Persons. T* **127** *and similar horiz designs. Multicoloured. P* 14.
486 6 t. Type **127** 10 10
487 20 t. Resource Centre for the Blind, Mochudi 35 35
488 30 t. Tlamelong Rehabilitation Centre, Tlokweng 45 45

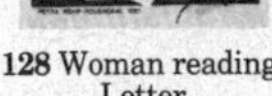

128 Woman reading Letter

129 Sir Seretse Khama and Building

(Des Petra Rouendaal. Litho Govt Printer, Pretoria)

1981 (8 June). *Literacy Programme. T* **128** *and similar vert designs. Multicoloured. P* 14.
489 6 t. Type **128** 10 10
490 7 t. Man filling in form 12 12
491 20 t. Boy reading newspaper 35 35
492 30 t. Child being taught to read 45 45

(Des G. Vasarhelyi. Litho Format)

1981 (13 July). *First Death Anniv of President Sir Seretse Khama. T* **129** *and similar horiz designs. Multicoloured. P* 14.
493 6 t. Type **129** 10 10
494 10 t. Seretse Khama and building (*different*) 15 15
495 30 t. Seretse Khama and Botswana flag .. 45 45
496 45 t. Seretse Khama and building (*different*) 70 70

25t

(130)

131 Traditional Ploughing

1981 (1 Sept). *Nos.* 417 *and* 422 *surch as T* **130**.
497 25 t. on 35 t. Striated Heron 45 50
498 30 t. on 10 t. Bennett's Woodpecker 45 50

(Des K. Mosinyi. Litho Format)

1981 (21 Sept). *Cattle Industry. T* **131** *and similar horiz designs. Multicoloured. P* 14½.
499 6 t. Type **131** 10 5
500 20 t. Agricultural show 35 35
501 30 t. Botswana Meat Commission 45 45
502 45 t. Vaccine Institute, Botswana 70 70

132 *Nymphaea caerulea*

133 "Cattle Post Scene" (Boitumelo Golaakwena)

(Des M. Bryan. Litho Govt Printer, Pretoria)

1981 (11 Nov). *Christmas. Flowers. T* **132** *and similar vert designs. Multicoloured. P* 14.
503 6 t. Type **132** 15 5
504 10 t. *Nymphoides indica* 20 15
505 25 t. *Nymphaea lotus* 50 50
506 40 t. *Ottelia kunenensis* 80 80

(Litho Govt Printer, Pretoria)

1982 (15 Feb). *Children's Art. T* **133** *and similar horiz designs. Multicoloured. P* 14.
507 6 t. Type **133** 10 5
508 10 t. "Kgotla Meeting" (Reginald Klinck) .. 15 15
509 30 t. "Village Water Supply" (Keromemang Matswiri) 45 45
510 45 t. "With the Crops" (Kennedy Balemoge) .. 70 70

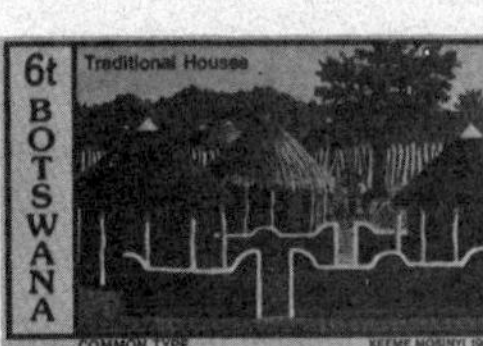

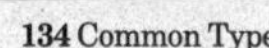

134 Common Type

135 African Masked Weaver

(Des K. Mosinyi and V. Moremi. Litho Govt Printer, Pretoria)

1982 (3 May). *Traditional Houses. T* **134** *and similar horiz designs. Multicoloured. P* 14.
511 6 t. Type **134** 10 5
512 10 t. Kgatleng type 15 15
513 30 t. North Eastern type 45 45
514 45 t. Sarwa type 70 70

(Des M. Bryan. Photo Harrison)

1982 (1 July). *Birds. T* **135** *and similar multicoloured designs. P* 14 × 14½ (1 *t. to* 10 *t.*) *or* 14½ × 14 (*others*).
515 1 t. Type **135** 5 5
516 2 t. Lesser Double-collared Sunbird 5 5
517 3 t. Red-throated Bee Eater 5 5
518 4 t. Ostrich 5 5
519 5 t. Grey-headed Gull 5 5
520 6 t. African Pygmy Goose 5 5
521 7 t. Cattle Egret 5 8
522 8 t. Lanner Falcon 8 10
523 10 t. Yellow-billed Stork 8 10
524 15 t. Red-billed Pintail (*horiz*) 15 20
525 20 t. Barn Owl (*horiz*) 15 20
526 25 t. Hammerkop (*horiz*) 20 25
527 30 t. South African Stilt (*horiz*) 25 30
528 35 t. Blacksmith Plover (*horiz*) 30 35
529 45 t. Senegal Wattled Plover (*horiz*) 40 45
530 50 t. Helmet Guineafowl (*horiz*) 40 45
531 1 p. Cape Vulture (*horiz*) 80 85
532 2 p. Augur Buzzard (*horiz*) .. .. .. 1·75 1·90
515/32 .. .. *Set of* 18 4·50 5·00

136 *Coprinus comatus*

137 President Quett Masire

(Des G. Condy. Litho Mardon Printers Ltd, Zimbabwe)

1982 (2 Nov). *Christmas. Fungi. T* **136** *and similar vert designs. Multicoloured. P* 14.
533 7 t. Type **136** 10 10
534 15 t. *Lactarius delicosus* 20 15
535 35 t. *Amanita pantherina* 55 55
536 50 t. *Boletus edulis* 75 75

(Des G. Vasarhelyi. Litho Questa)

1983 (14 Mar). *Commonwealth Day. T* **137** *and similar horiz designs. Multicoloured. P* 14.
537 7 t. Type **137** 5 8
538 15 t. Native dancers 15 20
539 35 t. Melbourne conference centre 45 50
540 45 t. Meeting of Heads of State, Melbourne .. 55 60

138 Wattled Crane

139 Wooden Spoons

(Des Petra Rouendaal (50 t.), G. Condy (others). Litho Mardon Printers Ltd, Zimbabwe)

1983 (19 Apr). *Endangered Species. T* **138** *and similar vert designs. Multicoloured. P* 14.
541 7 t. Type **138** 5 8
542 15 t. *Aloe lutescens* 15 20
543 35 t. Roan Antelope 45 50
544 50 t. Ivory Palm (*Hyphaene ventricosa*) .. 55 60

(Des M. Bryan. Litho Mardon Printers Ltd, Zimbabwe)

1983 (20 July). *Traditional Artifacts. T* **139** *and similar vert designs. Multicoloured. P* 14.
545 7 t. Type **139** 8 10
546 15 t. Personal ornaments 15 20
547 35 t. Ox-hide milk bag 45 50
548 50 t. Decorated knives 55 60
MS549 115 × 102 mm. Nos. 545/8 .. .. .. 1·10 1·25

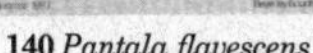

140 *Pantala flavescens*

141 Sorting Diamonds

(Des Beverley Boudreau. Litho Mardon Printers Ltd, Zimbabwe)

1983 (7 Nov). *Christmas. Dragonflies. T* **140** *and similar horiz designs. Multicoloured. P* 14.
550 6 t. Type **140** 5 8
551 15 t. *Anex imperator* 15 20
552 25 t. *Trithemis arteriosa* 30 35
553 45 t. *Chlorolestes elegans* 55 60

(Des M. Khan. Litho Mardon Printers Ltd, Zimbabwe)

1984 (19 Mar). *Mining Industry. T* **141** *and similar multicoloured designs. P* 14½.
554 7 t. Type **141** 8 10
555 15 t. Lime kiln 15 20
556 35 t. Copper-nickel smelter plant (*vert*) .. 35 40
557 50 t. Stockpiled coal (*vert*) 50 55

142 Riding Cattle

143 Avro "504" Aircraft

(Des S. Mogotsi. Litho Mardon Printers Ltd, Zimbabwe)

1984 (18 June). *Traditional Transport.* **T 142** *and similar horiz designs. Multicoloured. P* 14½ × 14.

558	7 t. Type **142**	8	10
559	25 t. Sledge	25	30
560	35 t. Wagon	35	40
561	50 t. Two wheeled donkey cart	50	55

(Des V. Larsson. Litho Mardon Printers Ltd, Zimbabwe)

1984 (8 Oct). *40th Anniv of International Civil Aviation Organization.* **T 143** *and similar horiz designs, each with I.C.A.O. emblem. Multicoloured. P* 14½ × 14.

562	7 t. Type **143**	8	10
563	10 t. Westland "Wessex"	10	12
564	15 t. Junkers "Ju 52/3M"	20	25
565	25 t. De Havilland "Dragon Six"	25	30
566	35 t. Douglas "DC3 Dakota"	35	40
567	50 t. Fokker "F27 Friendship"	50	55
562/7	*Set of* 6	1·25	1·50

144 *Papilio demodocus*

(Des Dr. M. Kahn. Litho Mardon Printers Ltd, Zimbabwe)

1984 (5 Nov). *Christmas. Butterflies.* **T 144** *and similar horiz designs. Multicoloured. P* 14½ × 14.

568	7 t. Type **144**	8	10
569	25 t. *Byblia acheloia*	25	30
570	35 t. *Hypolimnas missipus*	35	40
571	50 t. *Graphium taboranus*	50	55

POSTAGE DUE STAMPS

REPUBLIC OF

BOTSWANA

(D 4)

D **5** Elephant

D **6** Zebra

1967 (1 Mar). *Nos.* D10/12 *of Bechuanaland optd with Type* D **4**.

D13	1 c. carmine	20	65
D14	2 c. violet	25	80
D15	5 c. green	40	1·00

(Des and litho B.W.)

1971 (9 June). *P* 13½.

D16	D **5**	1 c. carmine	35	60
D17		2 c. bluish violet	45	70
D18		6 c. sepia	70	1·25
D19		14 c. blue-green	1·25	2·25

(Des M. Bryan. Litho Govt Printer, Pretoria)

1977 (18 Apr)–**84**. *P* 12½.

D20	D **6**	1 t. black and vermilion (1978)	5	5
		a. Perf 14 (1.84)	5	5
D21		2 t. black and emerald	5	5
		a. Perf 14 (1.84)	5	5
D22		4 t. black and red	5	5
		a. Perf 14 (1.84)	5	5
D23		10 t. black and deep ultramarine	10	12
		a. Perf 14 (1.84)	8	10
D24		16 t. black and chestnut	15	30
		a. Perf. 14 (1.84)	12	15

Nos. D20a/4a are on whiter paper.

British Antarctic Territory

1 M.V. *Kista Dan*

(Des B.W. (No. 15*a*), M. Goaman (others). Recess B.W.)

1963 (1 Feb)–**69**. *Horiz designs as T* **1**, *W* w **12**. *P* 11 × 11½.

1	½d. deep blue	35	45
2	1d. brown	25	25
3	1½d. orange-red and brown-purple	25	25
4	2d. purple	30	30
5	2½d. myrtle-green	40	40
6	3d. deep blue	85	45
7	4d. sepia	60	60
8	6d. olive and deep ultramarine	1·25	90
9	9d. olive-green	1·25	1·00
10	1s. deep turquoise-blue	1·25	1·00
11	2s. deep violet and orange-sepia	12·00	10·00
12	2s. 6d. blue	12·00	10·00
13	5s. red-orange and rose-red	18·00	18·00
14	10s. deep ultramarine and emerald	48·00	48·00
15	£1 black and light blue	85·00	65·00
15*a*	£1 red and brownish black (1.12.69)	£200	£200
1/15*a*	*Set of* 6	£350	£325

Designs:—1d. Manhauling; 1½d. Muskeg (tractor); 2d. Skiing; 2½d. Beaver (aircraft); 3d. R.R.S. *John Biscoe*; 4d. Camp scene; 6d. H.M.S. *Protector*; 9d. Sledging; 1s. Otter (aircraft); 2s. Huskies; 2s. 6d. Helicopter; 5s. Snocat (tractor); 10s. R.R.S. *Shackleton*; £1 (No. 15) Antarctic Map; £1 (No. 15*a*) H.M.S. *Endurance*.

1966 (24 Jan). *Churchill Commemoration. As Nos.* 170/3 *of Antigua.*

16	½d. new blue	80	35
17	1d. deep green	3·00	1·00
18	1s. brown	23·00	7·00
19	2s. bluish violet	26·00	11·00

17 Lemaire Channel and Icebergs

(Des R. Granger Barrett. Litho Format)

1969 (6 Feb). *25th Anniv of Continuous Scientific Work.* **T 17** *and similar horiz designs. W* w **12** (*sideways*). *P* 14.

20	3½d. black, pale blue and ultramarine	3·50	2·50
21	6d. multicoloured	3·50	2·75
22	1s. black, pale blue and vermilion	3·50	3·25
23	2s. black, orange and turquoise-blue	4·75	5·00

Designs:—6d. Radio Sonde balloon; 1s. Muskeg pulling tent equipment; 2s. Surveyors with theodolite.

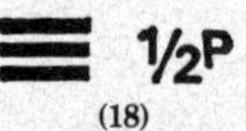

(18)

19 Setting up Camp

1971 (15 Feb). *Decimal Currency. As Nos.* 1/14, *but glazed paper, colours changed and surch as T* **18**.

24	½p. on ½d. blue	70	70
25	1p. on 1d pale brown	60	35
26	1½p. on 1½d. red and pale brown-purple	60	40
27	2p. on 2d. bright purple	65	40
28	2½p. on 2½d. green	80	50
29	3p. on 3d. blue	1·40	1·00
30	4p. on 4d. bistre-brown	1·50	1·25
31	5p. on 6d. olive and ultramarine	2·50	2·00
32	6p. on 9d. dull green	6·50	3·75
33	7½p. on 1s. turquoise-blue	6·50	4·00
34	10p. on 2s. violet and orange-sepia	15·00	13·00
35	15p. on 2s. 6d. pale blue	16·00	18·00
36	25p. on 5s. orange and pale rose-red	25·00	28·00
37	50p. on 10s. ultramarine and emerald	75·00	75·00
24/37	*Set of* 14	£140	£130

(Des M. Goaman. Recess and litho Enschedé)

1971 (23 June). *10th Anniv of Antarctic Treaty. Vert designs each including Antarctic Map and Queen Elizabeth, as T* **19**. *Multicoloured. W* w **12** (*sideways*). *P* 14 × 13.

38	1½p. Type **19**	5·00	2·50
39	4p. Snow petrels	7·00	4·00
40	5p. Weddell seals	7·50	4·75
41	10p. Adelie penguins	8·50	6·50

Owing to the difficulty of access at the time of issue, the above were not put on sale in British Antarctic Territory until early 1972.

20 Seals and Emperor Penguins

21 James Cook and *Resolution*

(Des (from photograph by D. Groves) and photo Harrison)

1972 (13 Dec*). *Royal Silver Wedding. Multicoloured; background colour given. W* w **12**. *P* 14 × 14½.

42	**20**	5p. red-brown	2·25	1·50
43		10p. brown-olive	2·25	1·50

*This is the local release date; they were issued by the Crown Agents on 20 November.

(Des J.W. Litho Questa)

1978 (14 Feb). *T* **21** *and similar vert designs. Multicoloured. W* w **12** (*sideways*). *P* 14 × 14½.

44	½p. Type **21** (*shades*)	2·00	2·00
45	1p. Thaddeus Von Bellingshausen and *Vostok*	2·50	2·50
46	1½p. James Weddell and *Jane*	3·75	3·75
47	2p. John Biscoe and *Tula*	90	90
48	2½p. J. S. C. Dumont d'Urville and *Astrolabe*	90	90
49	3p. James Clark Ross and *Erebus*	95	95
50	4p. C. A. Larsen and *Jason*	95	95
51	5p. Adrien de Gerlache and *Belgica*	1·00	1·00
52	6p. Otto Nordenskjöld and *Antarctic*	1·00	1·00
53	7½p. W. S. Bruce and *Scotia*	1·50	1·50
54	10p. Jean-Baptiste Charcot and *Pourquoi Pas?*	1·75	1·75
55	15p. Ernest Shackleton and *Endurance*	3·00	3·00
56	25p. Hubert Wilkins and *San Francisco*	3·25	3·25
57	50p. Lincoln Ellsworth and *Polar Star*	3·50	5·50
58	£1 John Rymill and *Penola*	10·00	14·00
44/58	*Set of* 15	32·00	35·00

The 25 and 50p. show aircraft; the rest show ships.
See also Nos. 64/78.

1973 (23 Dec*). *Royal Wedding. As Nos.* 165/6 *of Anguilla. Centre multicoloured. W* w **12** (*sideways*). *P* 13½.

59	5p. ochre	50	40
60	15p. light turquoise-blue	90	60

*This is the local date of issue: the Crown Agents released the stamps on 14 November.

22 Churchill and Churchill Peninsula, B.A.T.

(Des G. Vasarhelyi. Litho Format)

1974 (10 Dec*). *Birth Centenary of Sir Winston Churchill. T* **22** *and similar horiz design. Multicoloured. W* w **12** (*sideways on* 5p). *P* 14.

61	5p. Type **22**	1·50	1·50
62	15p. Churchill and *Trepassey* ("Operation Tabarin", 1943)	2·00	2·00
MS63	114 × 88 mm. Nos. 61/2	6·00	6·00

*This is the local date of issue: the Crown Agents released the stamps on 30 November.

1975 (11 June)–**81**. *As Nos.* 44/58 *but W* w **14**. *Ordinary paper* (½p) *or chalk-surfaced paper* (*others*). *P* 12 (4, 6, 7½p.) *or* 14 × 14½ (*others*).

64	½p. Type **21**	90	95
	a. Chalk-surfaced paper (14.3.78)	30	30
65	1p. Thaddeus Von Bellingshausen and *Vostok* (14.3.78)	25	30
66	1½p. James Weddell and *Jane* (14.3.78)	25	30
67	2p. John Biscoe and *Tula* (11.12.79)	50	55
68	2½p. J. S. C. Dumont d'Urville and *Astrolabe* (11.12.79)	40	50
69	3p. James Clark Ross and *Erebus* (11.12.79)	50	60
70	4p. C. A. Larsen and *Jason* (5.12.80)	30	40
71	5p. Adrien de Gerlache and *Belgica* (11.12.79)	90	1·00
72	6p. Otto Nordenskjöld and *Antarctic* (5.12.80)	70	90
73	7½p. W. S. Bruce and *Scotia* (5.12.80)	80	1·00
74	10p. Jean-Baptiste Charcot and *Pourquoi Pas?* (11.12.79)	1·00	1·10
	a. Perf 12 (25.11.81)	1·00	1·50
75	15p. Ernest Shackleton and *Endurance* (11.12.79)	1·00	1·25
	a. Perf 12 (25.11.81)	1·25	1·75
76	25p. Hubert Wilkins and *San Francisco* (11.12.79)	1·25	1·50
	a. Perf 12 (25.11.81)	1·75	2·25
77	50p. Lincoln Ellsworth and *Polar Star* (11.12.79)	4·25	4·50
	a. Perf 12 (5.12.80)	1·10	1·60
78	£1 John Rymill and *Penola* (14.3.78)	8·50	4·75
	a. Perf 12 (5.12.80)	2·00	2·50
64a/78a	*Set of* 15	10·00	12·50

NEW INFORMATION

The editor is always interested to correspond with people who have new information that will improve or correct the Catalogue.

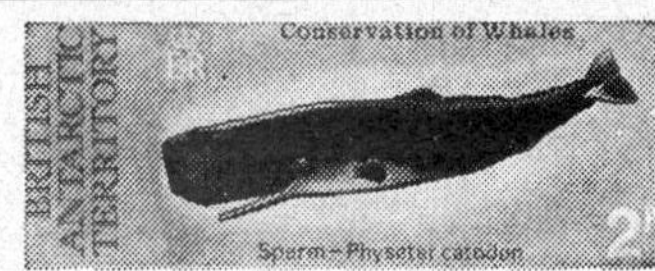

23 Sperm Whale

(Des J. Cooter. Litho Questa)

1977 (4 Jan). *Whale Conservation. T* **23** *and similar horiz designs. W w* **14** *(sideways). P* 13½.

79	2p. brownish black, slate and bright blue ..	2·50	1·90
80	8p. grey, brownish black and rosine.. ..	3·50	2·75
81	11p. multicoloured	3·50	2·50
82	25p. grey-blue, brownish blk & lt blue-green	4·50	3·25

Designs:—8p. Fin Whale; 11p. Humpback Whale; 25p. Blue Whale.

24 The Queen before Taking the Oath **25** Emperor Penguin

(Des J.W. Litho Questa)

1977 (7 Feb). *Silver Jubilee. T* **24** *and similar horiz designs. Multicoloured. W w* **14** *(sideways). P* 13½.

83	6p. Prince Philip's visit, 1956/7	85	40
84	11p. Coronation Oath..	1·10	65
85	33p. Type **24**	1·40	75

(Des C. Abbott. Litho Questa)

1978 (2 June). *25th Anniv of Coronation. T* **25** *and similar vert designs. P* 15.

86	25p. green, deep bluish green and silver ..	1·00	85
	a. Sheetlet Nos. 86/8 × 2	5·50	
87	25p. multicoloured	1·00	85
88	25p. green, deep bluish green and silver ..	1·00	85

Designs:— No. 86. Black Bull of Clarence; No. 87, Queen Elizabeth II; No. 88, Type **25**.

Nos. 86/8 were printed together in small sheets of 6, containing two *se-tenant* strips of 3 with a horizontal gutter margin between.

26 Macaroni Penguins

(Des G. Drummond. Litho Walsall)

1979 (14 Jan). *Penguins. T* **26** *and similar horiz designs. Multicoloured. W w* **14** *(sideways). P* 13½.

89	3p. Type **26**	6·50	3·00
90	8p. Gentoo penguins..	2·50	1·25
91	11p. Adelie penguins	2·75	1·50
92	25p. Emperor penguins	4·00	2·00

27 Sir John Barrow

(Des A. Theobald. Litho Secura, Singapore)

1980 (14 Dec†). *150th Anniv of Royal Geographical Society. Former Presidents. T* **27** *and similar horiz designs. Multicoloured. W w* **14** *(sideways). P* 13½.

93	3p. Type **27**	15	8
94	7p. Sir Clement Markham	25	25
95	11p. Lord Curzon	35	35
96	15p. Sir William Goodenough	40	40
97	22p. Sir James Wordie	60	60
98	30p. Sir Raymond Priestley	70	70
93/8	.. .. *Set of* 6	2·25	2·25

†This is the local date of issue; the Crown Agents released the stamps on 1 December.

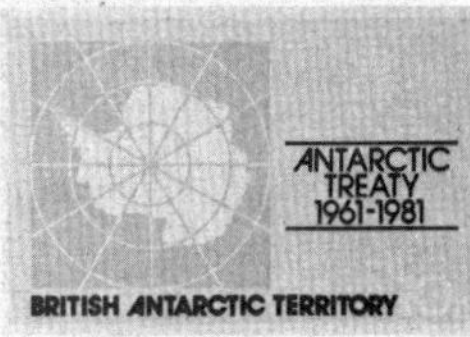

28 Map of Antarctic

(Des Walsall. Litho Questa)

1981 (1 Dec). *20th Anniv of Antarctic Treaty. T* **28** *and similar horiz designs. W w* **14** *(sideways). P* 13½ × 14.

99	10p. black, new blue and azure	40	40
100	13p. black, new blue and apple green . ..	45	45
101	25p. black, new blue and mauve	60	60
102	26p. black, brown-ochre and rose-red. ..	60	60

Designs:—13p. Conservation research ("scientific co-operation"); 25p. Satellite image mapping ("technical co-operation"); 26p. Global geophysics ("scientific co-operation").

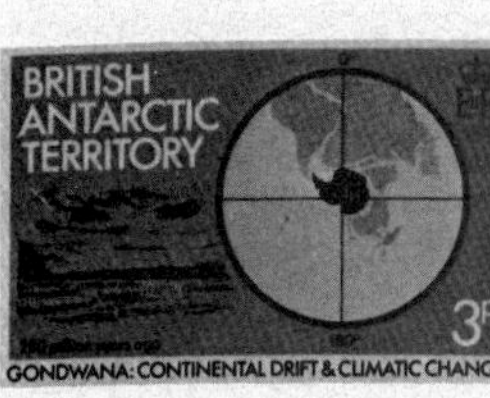

29 Map of Gondwana showing position of Continents 280 million years ago, and Contemporary Landscape Scene

30 British Antarctic Territory Coat of Arms

(Des C. Abbott. Litho Walsall)

1982 (8 Mar). *Gondwana—Continental Drift and Climatic Change. T* **29** *and similar horiz designs depicting maps of Gondwana showing position of continents, and contemporary landscape scenes. Multicoloured. W w* **14** *(sideways). P* 13½ × 14.

103	3p. Type **29**	20	20
104	6p. 260 million years ago	25	25
105	10p. 230 million years ago	30	30
106	13p. 175 million years ago	35	35
107	25p. 50 million years ago	60	60
108	26p. Present day	60	60
103/8	.. .. *Set of* 6	2·10	2·10

(Des Jennifer Toombs. Litho Questa)

1982 (1 July). *21st Birthday of Princess of Wales. T* **30** *and similar vert designs. Multicoloured. W w* **14**. *P* 14½ × 14.

109	5p. Type **30**	12	20
110	17p. Princess of Wales (detail of painting by Bryan Organ)	35	50
111	37p. Wedding ceremony	75	1·00
112	90p. Formal portrait	95	1·40

31 Leopard Seal

(Des R. Granger Barrett. Litho Walsall)

1983 (3 Jan). *10th Anniv* (1982) *of Antarctic Seal Conservation Convention. T* **31** *and similar horiz designs. Multicoloured. W w* **14** *(sideways). P* 11.

113	5p. Type **31**	10	12
114	10p. Weddell Seals	20	25
115	13p. Elephant Seals	25	30
116	17p. Fur Seals..	35	40
117	25p. Ross Seal..	50	55
118	34p. Crabeater Seals	65	70
113/18	.. .. *Set of* 6	1·75	2·10

32 De Havilland "Twin Otter"

(Des Harrison. Litho Questa)

1983 (20 Dec). *Bicentenary of Manned Flight. T* **32** *and similar horiz designs. Multicoloured. W w* **14** *(sideways). P* 14.

119	5p. Type **32**	10	12
120	13p. De Havilland "Single Otter"	25	30
121	17p. Consolidated "Canso"	35	40
122	50p. Lockheed "Vega"..	1·00	1·10

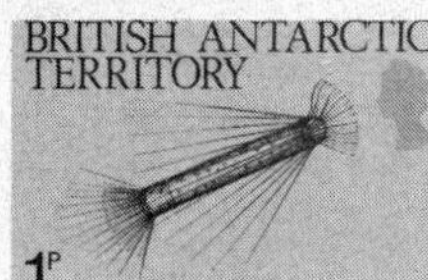

33 *Corethron criophilum*

(Des I. Loe. Litho Walsall)

1984 (15 Mar). *Marine Life. T* **33** *and similar horiz designs. Multicoloured. W w* **14** *(sideways). P* 14.

123	1p. Type **33**	5	5
124	2p. *Desmonena gaudichaudi*	5	5
125	3p. *Tomopteris carpenteri*	5	5
126	4p. *Pareuchaeta antarctica*	8	10
127	5p. *Antarctomysis maxima*	8	10
128	6p. *Antarcturus signiensis*	10	12
129	7p. *Serolis cornuta*	12	15
130	8p. *Parathemisto gaudichaudii*	15	20
131	9p. *Bovallia gigantea*	15	20
132	10p. *Euphausia superba*	20	25
133	15p. *Colossendeis australis*	25	30
134	20p. *Todarodes sagittatus*	35	40
135	25p. *Notothenia neglecta*	45	50
136	50p. *Chaenocephalus aceratus*	90	95
137	£1 *Lobodon carcinophagus*	1·75	1·90
138	£3 Antarctic marine food chain	5·50	5·75
123/38	.. .. *Set of* 16	9·50	10·00

British Central Africa *see* Nyasaland Protectorate

British Columbia & Vancouver Island

PRICES FOR STAMPS ON COVER

No. 1	—
Nos. 2/3	*from* × 6
Nos. 11/12	—
Nos. 13/14	*from* × 6
Nos. 21/2	*from* × 10
Nos. 23/7	*from* × 6
Nos. 28/33	*from* × 10

1

(Typo D.L.R.)

1860. *No Wmk. Imperf.*
1 1 2½d. pale dull red £2000

1860. *No wmk. P* 14.
2 1 2½d. deep reddish rose £275 £200
3 2½d. pale reddish rose £275 £200

From 20 June 1864 to 1 November 1865, the 2½d. was sold for 3d., and did duty as a 3d. provisional. No 1 was never actually issued.

VANCOUVER ISLAND

2 3

(Typo D.L.R.)

1865 (19 Sept). *Wmk Crown CC.* (*a*) *Imperf.*
11 2 5c. rose £18000 £8000
12 3 10 c. blue £1800 £1300

(*b*) *P* 14
13 2 5 c. rose £180 £130
14 3 10 c. blue £190 £140

Medium or poor copies of Nos. 11 and 12 can be supplied at much lower prices, when in stock.

BRITISH COLUMBIA

4

(Typo D.L.R.)

1865 (1 Nov)–**67.** *Wmk Crown CC. P* 14.
21 4 3d. deep blue . . . . . . 70·00 60·00
22 3d. pale blue (1867) . . . . . . 70·00 60·00

On 19 November 1866, British Columbia and Vancouver Island were consolidated as one territory called British Columbia, after which date the current stamps of each colony were distributed and used throughout the combined territory.

Though bearing the names of both colonies the 2½d. of 1860 was mainly used for inland postage in British Columbia.

TWO CENTS (5) **5.CENTS.5** (6)

1868–71. *T* 4 *in various colours. Wmk Crown CC. Surch as T* **5** *or* **6.**

(*a*) *P* 12½ (3.69)
23 5 c. red (Bk.) £600 £600
24 10 c. lake (B.) £550 £550
25 25 c. yellow (V.) £500 £500
26 50 c. mauve (R.) £500 £500
27 $1 green (G.) £900 £900

(*b*) *P* 14
28 2 c. brown (Bk.) (1.68) . . . . . . 90·00 90·00
29 5 c. pale red (Bk.) (5.69) £110 £100
30 10 c. lake (B.) £1000
31 25 c. yellow (V.) (7.69) £130 £120
32 50 c. mauve (R.) (2.71) £850
33 $1 green (G.) £900

Nos. 30 and 33 were not issued.

The stamps of British Columbia were withdrawn from use on 20 July 1871, when the Colony joined the Dominion of Canada.

British East Africa

The area which became British East Africa had been part of the domain of the Zanzibari Sultans since 1794. In 1887 the administration of the province was granted to the British East Africa Association, incorporated as the Imperial British East Africa Company the following year.

Company post offices were established at Lamu and Mombasa in May 1890, British mails having been previously sent via the Indian post office on Zanzibar, opened in 1875.

A German postal agency opened at Lamu on 22 November 1888 and continued to operate until 31 March 1891, using German stamps. These can be identified by the "LAMU/OSTAFRIKA" cancellations and are listed under German East Africa in our *Part* 7 (*Germany*) catalogue.

PRICES FOR STAMPS ON COVER

Nos. 1/3	*from* × 6
Nos. 4/19	*from* × 20
Nos. 20/6	*from* × 3
Nos. 27/8	*from* × 6
Nos. 29/30	*from* × 10
Nos. 31/2	*from* × 4
Nos. 33/47	*from* × 10
No. 48	*from* × 10
Nos. 49/63	*from* × 6
No. 64	*from* × 5
Nos. 65/79	*from* × 10
Nos. 80/91	*from* × 5
Nos. 92/9	*from* × 10

BRITISH EAST AFRICA COMPANY ADMINISTRATION

BRITISH EAST AFRICA COMPANY

HALF ANNA (1)

BRITISH EAST AFRICA COMPANY

1 ANNA (2)

(Surch D.L.R.)

1890 (May). *Stamps of Great Britain* (*Queen Victoria*) *surch as T* **1** *or* **2** (1 *a. and* 4 *a.*).
1 57 ½ a. on 1d. deep purple £500 £300
2 73 1 a. on 2d. green and carmine £550 £350
3 78 4 a. on 5d. dull purple and blue £600 £350

A copy of the ½ a. with the short crossbar of "F" in "HALF" omitted exists in the Royal Collection but is the only known example.

Stamps of INDIA were used in British East Africa during August and September 1890 being postmarked "MOMBASA" or "LAMU".

3

4

5 ANNAS. (5)

(Litho B.W.)

1890 (Oct)–**1894.** *P* 14.
4 3 ½ a. dull brown . . . . 1·50 1·50
a. Imperf (pair) £425 £350
b. Deep brown (9.93) . . . . . . 1·25 1·25
ba. Imperf (pair) £375 £300
bb. Imperf between (horiz pair) . . £1400 £750
bc. Imperf between (vert pair) . . £475 £450
c. Pale brown (12.94) 70 70
5 1 a. blue-green . . . . 2·75 2·75
aa. "ANL" (broken "D") (R.6/3) . . 75·00 85·00
a. Imperf (pair) £425 £350
ab. "ANL" (broken "D") (R.6/3) . .
b. Deep blue-green (12.94) 75
ba. Imperf (pair) £425 £350
6 2 a. vermilion . . . . 2·75 3·25
a. Imperf (pair) £800 £400
7 2½ a. black/*yellow-buff* (7.91) . . . . 24·00 9·50
a. Black/pale buff (7.92) . . . . 18·00 2·50
b. Black/bright yellow (9.93) . . . . 3·75 2·50
bb. Imperf (pair) £500 £400
bc. Imperf between (horiz pair) . . £450 £400
bd. Imperf between (vert pair) . . £750 £400
8 3 3 a. black/*dull red* (2.91) . . . . 6·00 6·50
a. Black/bright red (9.93) . . . . 1·10 1·50
ab. Imperf (pair) £425 £350
ac. Imperf between (horiz pair) . . £425 £350
ad. Imperf between (vert pair) . . £400 £325
9 4 a. yellow-brown . . . . . . 2·50 4·50
a. Imperf (pair) £850 £400
10 4 a. grey (*imperf*) £1200 £1400
11 4½ a. dull violet (2.91) . . . . . . 17·00 13·00
a. Brown-purple (9.93) . . . . 2·50 12·00
ab. Imperf (pair) £650 £375
ac. Imperf between (horiz pair) . . £1200 £1100
ad. Imperf between (vert pair) . . £500 £400
12 8 a. blue . . . . 5·50 6·50
a. Imperf (pair) £850 £400
13 8 a. grey £250 £250
14 1 r. carmine . . . . 6·00 9·00
a. Imperf (pair) £1700 £450
15 1 r. grey £200 £250
16 4 2 r. brick-red . . . . 11·00 14·00
17 3 r. slate-purple . . . . 8·00 14·00
18 4 r. ultramarine . . . . 12·00 19·00
19 5 r. grey-green . . . . 35·00 30·00
4/19 . . . . *Set of* 15 (*perf*) £325 £350

For the 5 a. and 7½ a. see Nos. 29/30.

The paper of Nos. 7, 7*a*, 7*b*, 8 and 8*a* is coloured on the surface only.

Printings of 1890/92 are on thin paper having the outer margins of the sheets imperf and bearing sheet watermark "PURE LINEN WOVE BANK" and "W. C. S. & Co." in a monogram, the trademark of the makers, Messrs. William Collins, Sons & Co.

1893/94 printings are on thicker coarser paper with outer margins perforated through the selvedge and without watermark. Single specimens cannot always be distinguished by lack of watermark alone. Exceptions are the 1893 printings of the 2½ a. and 3 a. which were on Wiggins Teape paper showing a sheet watermark of "1011" in figures 1 centimetre high.

Nos. 7 (coloured through) and 16/19 on thick unwatermarked paper are from a special printing made for presentation purposes.

The printings of the 4 a., 8 a. and 1 r. values in grey were intended for fiscal purposes, but in the event, were made available for postal use.

Forgeries of the 4 a., 8 a., 1 r., grey and 2 to 5 r. exist. The latter are common and can be distinguished by the scroll above "LIGHT" where there are five vertical lines of shading in the forgeries and seven in the genuine stamps. Forged cancellations exist on the commoner stamps. Beware of "imperf" stamps made by trimming margins of stamps from marginal rows.

1891. *Mombasa Provisionals.* (*a*) *New value handstamped in dull violet, and manuscript initials in black.*
20 3 "½ Anna' on 2 a. vermilion ("A.D.") (January) £1400 £650
a. "½ Anna" double . . . . — £1100
21 "1 Anna' on 4 a. brown ("A.B.") (February) £2500 £1000

(*b*) *Manuscript value and initials in black*
22 3 "½ Anna" on 2 a. vermilion ("A.D.") (January) . . . . — £450
a. Error. "½ Annas" ("A.D.") . . . . — £1200
23 "½ Anna" on 2 a. vermilion ("A.B.") (February) £1700 £450
a. Error. "½ Annas" ("A.B.") . . . . — £750
24 "½ Anna" on 3 a. black/*dull red* ("A.B.") (May) £1800 £750
25 "1 Anna" on 3 a. black/*dull red* ("V.H.M.") (June) £1800 £800
26 "1 Anna" on 4 a. brown ("A.B.") (March) £1500 £600

A.D. = Andrew Dick, Chief Accountant.
A.B. = Archibald Brown, Cashier of the Company.
V.H.M. = Victor H. Mackenzie, Bank Manager.

(Surch B.W.)

1894 (1 Nov). *Surch as T* **5**.
27 3 5 a. on 8 a. blue . . . . . . 50·00 85·00
28 7½ a. on 1 r. carmine . . . . . . 50·00 85·00
27/28 Handstamped "Specimen" . . *Set of* 2 £150

Forgeries exist.

1894 (Dec). *No wmk. P* 14.
29 3 5 a. black/*grey-blue* . . . . . . 1·75 9·50
30 7½ a. black . . . . 1·75 9·50
29/30 Handstamped "Specimen" . . *Set of* 2 £100

These two stamps have "LD" after "COMPANY" in the inscription.

The paper of No. 29 is coloured on the surface only.

1895 (Feb.). *Surch with manuscript value and initials* ("T.E.C.R.").
31 3 "½ anna" on 3 a. black/*dull red* (19.2) £130 45·00
32 "1 anna" on 3 a. black/*dull red* (22.2) £1600 £950

T.E.C.R. = T. E. C. Remington, Postmaster at Mombasa.

The Company experienced considerable financial problems during 1894 with the result that the British Government agreed to assume the administration of the territory, as a protectorate, on 1 July 1895.

IMPERIAL ADMINISTRATION

BRITISH EAST AFRICA (6)

2½ (7)

(Handstamped at Mombasa)

1895 (1 July). *Handstamped with T* **6**.
33 3 ½ a. deep brown . . . . . . 30·00 18·00
a. Pale brown
b. Double £110 £110
34 1 a. blue-green . . . . . . 42·00 45·00
a. Double . . . . 95·00 95·00
35 2 a. vermilion . . . . . . 80·00 80·00
a. Double £140 £140
36 2½ a. black/*bright yellow* . . . . 75·00 48·00
a. Double £140 £140
37 3 a. black/*dull red* . . . . . . 32·00 32·00

38 **3** 4 a. yellow-brown 32·00 32·00
a. Double £140 £140
39 4½ a. dull violet 85·00 80·00
a. Double £180 £180
b. Brown-purple £250 £200
ba. Double
40 5 a. black/*grey-blue* £110 85·00
a. Double £425 £425
41 7½ c. black 60·00 60·00
a. Double £180 £180
42 8 a. blue 65·00 65·00
a. Double £225 £225
b. Inverted £1200
43 1 r. carmine 38·00 42·00
a. Double £180 £200
44 **4** 2 r. brick-red 90·00 95·00
45 3 r. slate-purple 85·00 90·00
a. Double £350 £350
b. Inverted
46 4 r. ultramarine 95·00 90·00
a. Double £350 £350
47 5 r. grey-green £250 £300
a. Double £600 £600
33/47 *Set of* 15 £1000 £1100
Forgeries exist.

1895 (1 Oct). *No. 39 surch locally with T* **7**.
48 **3** 2½ a. on 4½ a. dull violet (R.) 60·00 55·00
a. Opt (T **6**) double £375 £325

British East Africa
(8)

British East Africa
(9)

SETTING OF TYPE 8. This consisted of 120 impressions in 10 horizontal rows of 12 stamps. This matched the size of the pane for all the Indian issues to 1 r. with the exception of the 6 a. The sheets of this value contained four panes, each 8 × 10, which meant that the outer vertical margins also received the overprint.
The setting of Type **9** is not known.
Although only the one setting was used for the low values it is known that some of the overprint errors occurred, or were corrected, during the course of the various printings.

(Overprinted at the offices of *The Zanzibar Gazette*)

1895 (11 Nov)–**96**. *Stamps of India (Queen Victoria) optd with T* **8** *or* **9** *(2 r. to 5 r.).*
49 **23** ½ a. deep green 2·00 2·25
a. "Brltish" for "British" £1100 £1000
b. "Brltish" for "British" (R.10/12) £150
c. "Afrlca" for "Africa" (R.1/11) £150
d. Opt double, one albino £750
50 **25** 1 a. plum 2·25 2·75
a. "Brltish" for "British" £1000 £900
b. "Brltish" for "British" (R.10/12) £150
c. "Afrlca" for "Africa" (R.1/11) £200
51 **26** 1½ a. sepia (23.11.95) 3·75 3·75
a. "Brltish" for "British" (R.10/12) £160
b. "Afrlca" for "Africa" (R.1/11) £200
52 **27** 2 a. ultramarine 2·00 2·75
a. "Brltish" for "British" £850
b. "Brltish" for "British" (R.10/12) £160
c. "Afrlca" for "Africa" (R.1/11) £150 £140
53 **36** 2½ a. green 6·50 3·50
a. "Biitish" for "British" £1600
b. "Bpitish" for "British" £1600
c. "Brltish" for "British" † £900
d. "Eas" for "East" (R.2/12) £475 £500
e. "Brltish" for "British" (R.10/12) £200 £180
f. "Afrlca" for "Africa" (R.1/11) £160
54 **28** 3 a. brown-orange (18.12.95) 7·50 7·50
a. "Brltish" for "British" (R.10/12) £150 £140
b. "Afrlca" for "Africa" (R.1/11) £180
55 **29** 4 a. olive-green (18.12.95) 12·00 12·00
a. *Slate-green* 12·00 12·00
b. "Brltish" for "British" (R.10/12) £160 £140
c. "Afrlca" for "Africa" (R.1/11) £190
56 **21** 6 a. pale brown (18.12.95) 20·00 23·00
a. "Brltish" for "British" (R.10/12) £325
b. "Afrlca" for "Africa" (R.1/11) £225
c. Opt double, one albino £750
57 **31** 8 a. dull mauve (18.12.95) 40·00 45·00
a. "Brltish" for "British" (R.10/12) £225
b. "Afrlca" for "Africa" (R.1/11) £225
c. Magenta (1896) 28·00 35·00
ca. Inverted "a" for "t" of "East" (R.2/12) † £1000
58 **32** 12 a. purple/*red* (18.12.95) 19·00 26·00
a. "Brltish" for "British" (R.10/12) £225 £180
b. "Afrlca" for "Africa" (R.1/11) £225
59 **33** 1 r. slate (18.12.95) 42·00 48·00
a. "Brltish" for "British" (R.10/12) £225
b. "Afrlca" for "Africa" (R.1/11) £225
60 **37** 1 r. green and carmine (1896) 20·00 26·00
a. Inverted "a" for "t" of "East" (R.2/12) £1200
b. "Brltish" for "British" (R.10/12) £225
c. "Afrlca" for "Africa" (R.1/11) £225
d. Opt double, one sideways £225 £250
61 **38** 2 r. carmine and yellow-brown (18.12.95) 48·00 65·00
62 3 r. brown and green (18.12.95) 60·00 75·00
63 5 r. ultramarine and violet (18.12.95) 75·00 80·00
a. Opt double £1200
49/63 *Set of* 15 £300 £350
The 2½ a. is known on cover used on 31 October but was probably from a trial printing released in error.
The relative horizontal positions of the three lines of the overprint vary considerably but the distance vertically between the lines of the overprint is constant.
There are other varieties, such as inverted "s" in "British", wide and narrow "B", and inverted "V" for "A" in "Africa" (R.1/1 and R.6/7).
The 2, 3, and 5 r., normally overprinted in larger type than the lower values, are also known with a smaller overprint, for use as specimen stamps for the U.P.U. These were not issued for postal purposes (*price* £250 *un per set*).
Forgeries exist.

2½
(10)

11

1895 (Dec). *No. 51 surch locally with T* **10**, *in bright red.*
64 **26** 2½ on 1½ a. sepia 32·00 35·00
a. Inverted "1" in fraction (R.5/7, R.10/7) £300
The setting of Type **10** was in 5 horizontal rows of 12 stamps, repeated twice for each pane.
No. 51 also exists surcharged with T **12**, **13** and **14** in *brown-red*. These stamps were sent to the Postal Union authorities at Berne, but were never issued to the public (*Price* £40 *each un*).

(Recess D.L.R.)

1896 (19 May)–**1901**. *Wmk Crown CA. P* 14.
65 **11** ½ a. yellow-green 45 45
66 1 a. carmine-rose 75 25
a. Bright rose-red 1·00 25
b. Rosine (1901) 12·00 2·25
67 2 a. chocolate 1·50 1·25
68 2½ a. deep blue 3·25 1·75
a. Violet-blue 3·25 1·10
69 3 a. grey 2·50 3·75
70 4 a. deep green 6·50 1·50
71 4½ a. orange-yellow 3·75 5·00
72 5 a. yellow-bistre 6·50 4·50
73 7½ a. mauve 6·00 12·00
74 8 a. grey-olive 2·50 4·50
75 1 r. pale dull blue 18·00 17·00
a. Ultramarine 18·00 14·00
76 2 r. orange 50·00 24·00
77 3 r. deep violet 50·00 24·00
78 4 r. carmine-lake 50·00 40·00
79 5 r. sepia 50·00 40·00
a. Thin "U" in "RUPEES" (R.3/2) £950 £900
65/79 *Set of* 15 £225 £150
65/79 Optd "Specimen" *Set of* 15 £375

(Overprinted at the offices of *The Zanzibar Gazette*)

1897 (Jan). *Stamps of Zanzibar (1896 issue) optd with T* **8**. *Wmk Single Rosette.*
80 **13** ½ a. green and red 38·00 25·00
81 1 a. indigo and red 85·00 85·00
82 2 a. red-brown and red 38·00 25·00
83 4½ a. orange and red 42·00 25·00
84 5 a. bistre and red 42·00 28·00
85 7½ a. mauve and red 55·00 45·00
80/85 *Set of* 6 £275 £225
The above six stamps exist with an overprint similar to T **8** but normally showing a stop after "Africa". These overprints (in red on the 1 a.) were made officially to supply the U.P.U. However, the stop does not always show. Pieces are known showing overprints with and without stop *se-tenant* (including the red overprint on the 1 a.).
Stamps of Zanzibar, wmk. "Multiple Rosettes" and overprinted with T **8** are forgeries.

2½ **(12)** 2½ **(13)** 2½ **(14)**

SETTING OF TYPES 12/14. The panes of 120 were surcharged by two applications of a setting of 60 (6 × 10). This contained 26 examples of Type **12**, 10 of Type **13** and 24 of Type **14**.

1897 (Jan). *Nos. 157 and 162 of Zanzibar optd with T* **8** *and further surch locally, in red.*
86 **12** 2½ on 1 a. indigo and red 50·00 40·00
b. Opt Type **8** double £4000
87 **13** 2½ on 1 a. indigo and red 65·00 55·00
88 **14** 2½ on 1 a. indigo and red 50·00 42·00
a. Opt Type **8** double £4500
89 **12** 2½ on 3 a. grey and red 50·00 40·00
90 **13** 2½ on 3 a. grey and red 65·00 55·00
91 **14** 2½ on 3 a. grey and red 50·00 40·00
86/91 *Set of* 6 £300 £250
Both the notes after No. 85 also apply here.
A special printing for U.P.U. requirements was made with the 2½ surcharge on the 1 a. and 3 a. stamps overprinted as T **8** but *with stop* after "Africa". It also included a "2" over "1" error in T **14**.

15

(Recess D.L.R.)

1897 (Nov)–**1903**. *Wmk Crown CC. P* 14.
92 **15** 1 r. grey-blue 21·00 21·00
a. Dull blue (1901) 11·00 10·00
b. Bright ultramarine (1903) 75·00 60·00
93 2 r. orange 40·00 40·00
94 3 r. deep violet 40·00 50·00
95 4 r. carmine 60·00 75·00
96 5 r. deep sepia 70·00 £110
97 10 r. yellow-bistre (S. £80) £150 £200
98 20 r. pale green (S. £175) £700 £850
99 50 r. mauve (S. £400) £2250 £2250
92/96 Optd "Specimen" *Set of* 5 £250

In 1903 stamps of British East Africa were superseded by those of East Africa and Uganda Protectorate (*See* KENYA, UGANDA and TANGANYIKA).

British Forces in Egypt *see* Egypt

British Guiana

The postal service from what was to become British Guiana dates from the last years of the 18th-century, being placed on a more regular basis after the final British occupation.
An inland postal system was organised in 1850, using the adhesive stamps of British Guiana, but, until 1 May 1860, overseas mails continued to be the province of the British G.P.O. The stamps of Great Britain being supplied for use on such letters from 11 May 1858.
For illustration of the handstamp and postmark type see BRITISH POST OFFICES ABROAD notes, following GREAT BRITAIN.

CROWNED-CIRCLED HANDSTAMPS

The provision of a handstamp, probably as Type CC **1**, inscribed "DEMERARA", is recorded in the G.P.O. proof book under 1 March 1856. No examples have been reported. A further handstamp, as Type CC **6**, recorded in the proof book on 17 February 1866, is known used as a cancellation in at least two instances, *circa* 1868.

GEORGETOWN (DEMERARA)

Stamps of GREAT BRITAIN *cancelled* "A 03" *as Type* **2**.

1858 to **1860**.
Z1 1d. rose-red (1857), *perf* 14 £120
Z2 4d. rose (1857) £110
Z3 6d. lilac (1856) £100
a. Azure paper
Z4 1s. green (1856) £900

NEW AMSTERDAM (BERBICE)

Stamps of GREAT BRITAIN *cancelled* "A 04" *as Type* **2**.

1858 to **1860**.
Z5 1d. rose-red (1857), *perf* 14
Z6 2d. blue (1858) (Plate Nos. 7, 8) £350
Z7 4d. rose (1857) £175
Z8 6d. lilac (1856) £175
Z9 1s. green (1856) £1000

PRICES FOR STAMPS ON COVER TO 1945

Nos. 1/10	*from* × 3
Nos. 11/17	*from* × 2
Nos. 18/21	*from* × 3
No. 23	†
Nos. 24/7	*from* × 3
Nos. 29/115	*from* × 4
Nos. 116/125	*from* × 5
Nos. 126/36	*from* × 3
Nos. 137/59	*from* × 4
Nos. 162/5	*from* × 6
Nos. 170/4	*from* × 3
Nos. 175/89	*from* × 6
No. 192	*from* × 20
Nos. 193/210	*from* × 4
Nos. 213/15	*from* × 5
Nos. 216/21	*from* × 3
Nos. 222/4	*from* × 8
Nos. 233/50	*from* × 3
No. 251	—
Nos. 252/7	*from* × 3
Nos. 259/82	*from* × 4
Nos. 283/7	*from* × 5
Nos. 288/300	*from* × 4
Nos. 301/4	*from* × 5
Nos. 305/7	*from* × 6
Nos. 308/19	*from* × 5
Nos. D1/4	*from* × 12
Nos. O1/12	*from* × 10

CROWN COLONY

1

2

(Set up and printed at the office of the *Royal Gazette*, Georgetown, British Guiana)

1850 (1 July)–**51**. *Type-set. Black impression. (a) Medium wove paper. Prices are for—*I. *Cut square.* II. *Cut round.*
I *Used* II *Used*
1 **1** 2 c. *rose* (1.3.51) — £55000
2 4 c. *orange* £15000 £2500
3 4 c. *lemon-yellow* £20000 £3000
4 8 c. *green* £8500 £2000

5	1	12 c. *blue*	£4000	£1700
6		12 c. *indigo*	£8500	£1700
7		12 c. *pale blue*	£8000	£2250
		a. "2" of "12" with straight foot	—	£3500
		b. "1" of "12" omitted	†	£24000

(b) Pelure paper

8	1	4 c. *pale yellow*	£25000	£3000

These stamps were initialled by the postmaster, or the Post Office clerks, before they were issued. The initials are—E. T. E. D(alton), E. D. W(ight), J. B. S(mith), H. A. K(illikelley), and W. H. L(ortimer). There are several types of each value and it has been suggested that the setting contained one horizontal row of four slightly different impressions.

Only ten examples of No. 1 have been recorded.

(Litho Waterlow)

1852 (1 Jan). *Surface-coloured paper Imperf.*

			Un	*Used*
9	2	1 c. black/*magenta*	£8500	£4250
10		4 c. black/*deep blue*	£10000	£4250

There are two types of each value.

Reprints, on thicker paper and perf 12½, were made in 1865 (*Price £8 either value*).

Reprints with the perforations removed are sometimes offered as genuine originals.

CONDITION. Prices for Nos. 9 to 21 are for fine copies. Poor to medium specimens can be supplied when in stock at much lower rates.

3

4

5

(Dies eng and stamps litho Waterlow)

1853–59. *Imperf. (a) Original printing.*

11	3	1 c. vermilion	£3000	£1000

This 1 c. in *reddish brown* is probably a proof.

A B C D

A. "O" large and 1 mm from left corner.
B. "O" small and ¾ mm from left corner.
C. "O" small and ¾ mm from left corner. "NT" widely spaced.
D. "ONE" close together, "O" 1¼ mm from left corner.

(b) Fresh lithographic transfers with varying labels of value. White line above value (1858–59).

12	3	1 c. dull red (A)	£1800	£650
13		1 c. brownish red (A)	£4000	£650
14		1 c. dull red (B)	£2250	£700
15		1 c. brownish red (B)	£4000	£700
16		1 c. dull red (C)	£2250	£700
17		1 c. dull red (D)	£3500	£2250

1853–59. *Imperf.*

18	4	4 c. deep blue	£900	£400
		a. Retouched	£1900	£800
19		4 c. blue (1855)	£750	£400
20		4 c. pale blue (1859)	£650	£300
		a. Retouched	£1500	£550

These stamps are generally found with a white line or traces of it above the label of value and lower corner figures. In some stamps on the sheet this line is missing, owing to having been retouched, and in these cases a line of colour usually appears in its place.

The 1 c. and 4 c stamps were reprinted in 1865 from fresh transfers of five varieties. These are on thin paper and perf 12½.

1860 (May). *Figures in corners framed. Imperf.*

21	5	4 c. blue	£2500	£425

6

(Type-set and printed at the *Official Gazette* by Baum and Dallas, Georgetown).

1856. *(a) Surface-coloured paper.*

23	6	1 c. black/*magenta*		
24		4 c. black/*magenta* (Feb)	—	£5500
25		4 c. black/*rose-carmine* (Sept)	—	£7500
26		4 c. black/*blue* (Oct)	—	£30000

(b) Paper coloured through

27	6	4 c. black/*deep blue* (Aug)	—	£40000

Since only one example of No. 23 is known, no market price can be given. This celebrated stamp frequently termed "the world's rarest", was last on the market in 1980.

These stamps, like those of the first issue, were initialled before being issued; the initials are—E.T.E.D., E.D.W., C.A. W(atson), and W.H.L.

The 4 c is known in eight types, differing in the position of the inscriptions.

PAPERMAKERS' WATERMARKS. Seven different papermakers' watermarks were used in the period 1860 to 1875 and stamps bearing portions of these are worth a premium.

7

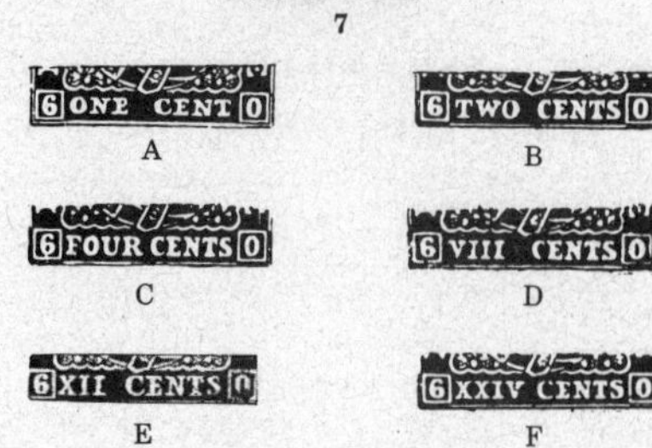

A B C D E F

(Dies eng and litho Waterlow)

1860 (July)–**63**. *Tablets of value as illustrated. Thick paper. P* 12.

29	7	1 c. pale rose	£750	£140
30		2 c. deep orange (8.60)	80·00	26·00
31		2 c. pale orange	80·00	26·00
32		4 c. deep blue (8.60)	£180	30·00
33		4 c. blue	£140	26·00
34		8 c. brownish rose	£200	32·00
35		8 c. pink	£170	30·00
36		12 c. lilac (11.61)	£300	26·00
37		12 c. grey-lilac	£250	26·00
38		24 c. deep green (6.63)	£700	55·00
39		24 c. green	£700	55·00

The 1 c. was reprinted in 1865 on *thin* paper, P 12½—13, and in a different shade. *Price* £3.75.

The 12 c. in both shades is frequently found surcharged with a large "5d" in *red*; this is to denote the proportion of postage repayable by the colony to Great Britain for overseas letters.

1861 (1 Nov). *Colour changed. Thick paper P* 12.

40	7	1 c. reddish brown	£170	60·00

1862–66. *(a) Thin paper. P* 12 (1862).

41	7	1 c. brown	£275	£130
42		1 c. black	45·00	20·00
43		2 c. orange	45·00	16·00
44		4 c. blue	50·00	17·00
45		4 c. pale blue	45·00	13·00
46		8 c. pink	55·00	25·00
47		12 c. dull purple	55·00	14·00
48		12 c. purple	55·00	15·00
49		12 c. lilac	65·00	24·00
50		24 c. green	£400	48·00

(b) Thin paper. P 12½ × 13 (1863)

51	7	1 c. black	23·00	8·00
52		2 c. orange	45·00	11·00
53		4 c. blue	50·00	13·00
54		8 c. pink	95·00	35·00
55		12 c. brownish lilac	£300	45·00
56		24 c. green	£400	45·00

Copies are found on *pelure* paper.

(c) Medium paper. P 12½–13 (1863)

57	7	1 c. black	23·00	11·00
58		2 c. deep orange	23·00	11·00
59		2 c. orange	25·00	9·50
60		4 c. greyish blue	38·00	8·50
61		4 c. blue	38·00	16·00
62		8 c. pink	85·00	23·00
63		12 c. brownish lilac	£170	35·00
64		24 c. green	85·00	38·00
65		24 c. deep green	£200	38·00

(d) Medium paper. P 10 (March 1866)

65*a*	7	12 c. grey-lilac	£200	35·00

8

9

G H

I

K

New transfers for the 1 c., 2 c., 8 c., and 12 c. with the spaces between values and the word "CENTS" about 1 mm.

1863–75. *Medium paper (a) P* 12½–13 (1863–64).

66	8	1 c. black	16·00	12·00
67		2 c. orange-red	20·00	3·25
68		2 c. orange	16·00	3·25
69	9	6 c. blue	45·00	22·00
70		6 c. greenish blue	45·00	26·00
71		6 c. deep blue	45·00	23·00
72		6 c. milky blue	50·00	22·00
73	8	8 c. pink	55·00	9·00
74		8 c. carmine	55·00	9·00
75	8	12 c. grey-lilac	£225	12·00
76		12 c. brownish purple	£275	15·00
77	9	24 c. green (*perf* 12)	£150	15·00
78		24 c. yellow-green (*perf* 12)	55·00	8·00
79		24 c. yellow-green (*perf* 12½–13)	55·00	7·50
80		24 c. green (*perf* 12½–13)	55·00	9·00
81		24 c. blue-green (*perf* 12½–13)	85·00	17·00
82		48 c. pale red	70·00	28·00
83		48 c. deep red	70·00	30·00
84		48 c. carmine-rose	£150	28·00

The 4 c. corresponding to this issue can only be distinguished from that of the previous issue by minor plating flaws.

There is a variety of the 6 c. with stop before "VICISSIM".

Varieties of most of the values of issues of 1863–64 and 1866 are to be found on both very thin and thick papers.

(b) P 10 (1866)

85	8	1 c. black	7·50	3·00
86		1 c. grey-black	8·50	4·00
87		2 c. orange	5·00	2·75
88		2 c. reddish orange	12·00	2·75
89		4 c. slate-blue	30·00	8·00
90		4 c. blue	32·00	5·00
		a. Bisected (on cover)	†	£3000
		b. Ditto Imperf (on cover)	†	—
91		4 c. pale blue	38·00	7·50
92	9	6 c. milky blue	55·00	14·00
93		6 c. ultramarine	55·00	23·00
94		6 c. dull blue	55·00	20·00
95	8	8 c. pink	55·00	11·00
96		8 c. brownish pink	55·00	11·00
96*a*		8 c. carmine	55·00	13·00
97		12 c. pale lilac	£130	11·00
98		12 c. grey-lilac	55·00	11·00
99		12 c. brownish grey	55·00	12·00
100		12 c. lilac	55·00	12·00
101	9	24 c. deep green	£120	9·00
102		24 c. bluish green	—	8·00
103		24 c. yellow-green	75·00	7·50
104		48 c. crimson	£225	24·00
105		48 c. red	£225	24·00
104 Handstamped "Specimen"			£120	
104 Perf "Specimen"			80·00	

(c) P 15 (1875)

106	8	1 c. black	13·00	5·50
107		2 c. orange-red	70·00	8·00
108		2 c. orange	70·00	8·00
109		4 c. bright blue	£150	60·00
111	9	6 c. ultramarine	£170	38·00
112	8	8 c. deep rose	90·00	38·00
113		12 c. lilac	£275	38·00
114	9	24 c. yellow-green	£400	35·00
115		24 c. deep green	£400	35·00

There is a variety of the 48 c. with stop after "P" in "PETIMUSQUE".

Imperforate stamps of this and of the previous issue are considered to be proofs.

PRICES for stamps of the 1862 issue are for good average copies. Copies with roulettes on all sides very seldom occur and do not exist in marginal positions.

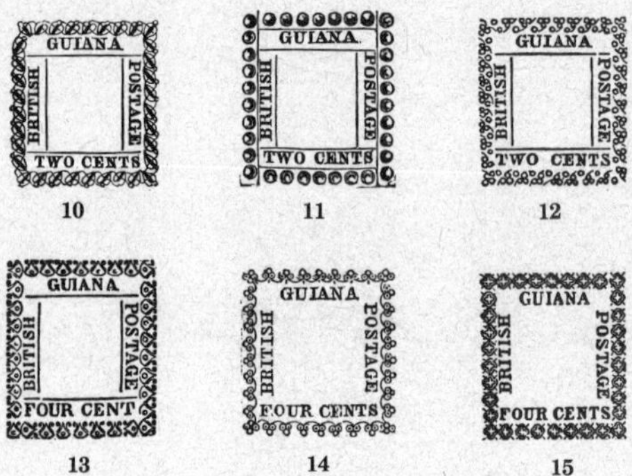

10 11 12 13 14 15

(Type-set and printed by George Melville at the Office of the *Royal Gazette*, Georgetown)

1862 (Sept). *Black on coloured paper. Roul* 6.

116	10	1 c. *rose* (*12 in sheet*)	£1000	£180
		a. Unsigned	£100	
		b. "1" for "I" in "BRITISH"	—	£190
		c. Wrong ornament on left	—	£190
117		2 c. *yellow* (*12 in sheet*)	£1000	£160
		a. Unsigned	£100	
		b. "1" for "I" in "BRITISH"	—	£190
		c. Wrong ornament on left	—	£140
118	11	1 c. *rose* (*8 in sheet*)	£1100	£180
		a. Unsigned	£100	
		b. "1" for "I" in "BRITISH"	—	£190
		c. "1" for "I" in "GUIANA"	—	£190
		d. Italic "S" in "POSTAGE"	—	£160
		e. Narrow "T" in "CENTS"	—	£160
		f. Wrong ornament in top frame	—	£160
		g. Wrong ornament in left frame	—	£160
119		2 c. *yellow* (*8 in sheet*)	£1300	£190
		a. Unsigned	£100	£160
		b. "1" for "I" in "British"	—	£190
		c. "1" for "I" in "GUIANA"	—	£190
		d. Italic "S" in "POSTAGE"	—	£190
		e. "C" for "O" in "TWO" and narrow "T" in "CENTS"	—	£190
		f. Wrong ornament in top frame	—	£160
		g. Italic "T" in "TWO"	—	£160
120	12	1 c. *rose* (*4 in sheet*)	£1800	£275
		a. Unsigned	£250	
		b. "1" for "I" in "GUIANA"	—	£250
		c. "C" for "O" in "POSTAGE"	—	£250
121		2 c. *yellow* (*4 in sheet*)	£2000	£300
		a. Unsigned		
		b. "1" for "I" in "GUIANA"	—	£250
		c. "C" for "O" in "POSTAGE"	—	£250

122 **13** 4 c. *blue* (10 *in sheet*) £900 £140
a. Unsigned
b. Ornament omitted on right — £190
123 **14** 4 c. *blue* (6 *in sheet*) £1100 £200
a. Unsigned £200
124 **15** 4 c. *blue* (6 *in sheet*) £1000 £250
a. Unsigned £200
b. "1" for "I" in "BRITISH" — £250
125 – 4 c. *blue* (2 *in sheet*) £2250 £1200
a. Unsigned

No. 125 is as Type **15**, but with four thin inner lines.

Each value was printed in sheets of 24, comprising 24 varieties of type. Stamps were initialled in the centre before use by the Acting Receiver-General of the colony, Robert Mather.

16

(17)

(Typo D.L.R.)

1876 (1 July)–**79**. *Wmk Crown CC. (a) P* 14.
126 **16** 1 c. slate 2·75 1·40
127 2 c. orange 15·00 1·25
128 4 c. blue 45·00 7·50
129 6 c. brown 35·00 7·50
130 8 c. rose 35·00 3·50
131 12 c. pale violet 40·00 5·00
132 24 c. emerald-green 40·00 8·50
133 48 c. red-brown 70·00 11·00
134 96 c. olive-bistre £350 £225
126/134 *Set of* 9 £550 £250
126/132, 134 Handstamped/Perf "Specimen" *Set of* 8 £275

(b) P 12½ (1877)
135 **16** 4 c. blue £1200 £200

(c) Perf compound of 14 × 12½ (1879)
136 **16** 1 c. slate — £200

1878. *Provisionals. Various stamps with old values ruled through with thick bars, in black ink, the bars varying in depth of colour.*

(a) With two horiz bars (17 Apr)
137 **16** (1 c.) on 6 c. brown 30·00 35·00

(b) Official stamps with horiz bars across "OFFICIAL" *(end Aug)*
138 **8** 1 c. black 55·00 35·00
139 **16** 1 c. slate 55·00 24·00
140 2 c. orange 60·00 35·00

(c) With horiz and vert bars as T **17** (6 Nov)
141 **9** (1 c.) on 6 c. ultramarine (93) 70·00 28·00
142 **16** (1 c.) on 6 c. brown 75·00 32·00

(d) Official stamps with bars across "OFFICIAL" (23 Nov)

(i) With two horiz bars and one vert
144 **16** (1 c.) on 4 c. blue 55·00 32·00
145 (1 c.) on 6 c. brown 60·00 32·00
146 **8** (2 c.) on 8 c. rose 60·00 38·00

(ii) With one horiz bar and one vert
148 **16** (2 c.) on 8 c. rose 75·00 40·00

1 2 2
(18) (19) (20)

1881 (21 Dec). *No.* 134 *with old value ruled through with bar in black ink and surch.*
149 **18** 1 on 96 c. olive-bistre 4·00 4·50
a. Bar in red
b. Bar omitted
150 **19** 2 on 96 c. olive-bistre 4·50 8·00
a. Bar in red
b. Bar omitted
151 **20** 2 on 96 c. olive-bistre 15·00 15·00

1 1 OFFICIAL 2 2
(21) (22) (23) (24)

1881 (28 Dec). *Various stamps with old value ruled with bar and surch. (a) On No.* 105.
152 **21** 1 on 48 c. red 14·00 4·25
a. Bar omitted

(b) On No. 133
153 **22** 1 on 48 c. red-brown 48·00 35·00

(c) On Official stamps
154 **21** 1 on 12 c. brownish purple (O4) 38·00 26·00
155 **23** 2 on 12 c. pale violet (O11) 25·00 15·00
a. Surch double £425 £350
b. Do. T **23** and **24**
c. Extra bar through "OFFICIAL"
156 **24** 2 on 12 c. pale violet (O11) 70·00 55·00
157 **23** 2 on 24 c. emerald-green (O12) 38·00 15·00
a. Surch double £550
158 **24** 2 on 24 c. emerald-green (O12) 13·00 5·50
159 **19** 2 on 24 c. green (O5) 70·00 55·00

On Nos. 149/59 the bar is found in various thicknesses ranging from 1 to 4 mm.

26

27

(Type-set, Baldwin & Co. Georgetown)

1882. *Black impression. P* 12. *Perforated with the word* "SPECIMEN" *diagonally.*
162 **26** 1 c. *magenta* 25·00 20·00
a. Imperf between (*pair*)
b. Without "SPECIMEN" 55·00 50·00
c. "1" with foot 42·00 40·00
163 2 c. *yellow* 32·00 20·00
a. Without "SPECIMEN" 55·00 50·00
b. Small "2" 35·00 30·00
164 **27** 1 c. *magenta* 25·00 17·00
a. Without "SPECIMEN" 55·00 50·00
b. "1" with foot 35·00 32·00
165 2 c. *yellow* 35·00 30·00
a. Bisected diagonally (1 c.)
b. Without "SPECIMEN" 55·00 50·00
c. Small "2" 45·00 40·00

These stamps were perforated "SPECIMEN" as a precaution against fraud. Stamps are known with "SPECIMEN" double.

The 1 c. and 2 c. stamps were printed in separate sheets; but utilising the same clichés, these being altered according to the face value required. Two settings were used, common to both values:—

1st setting. Four rows of three, T **26** being Nos. 5, 6, 7, 8, 11 and 12, and T **27** the remainder.

From this setting there were two printings of the 2 c., but only one of the 1 c.

2nd setting. Six rows of two, T **26** being Nos. 3, 7, 8, 9, 11 and 12, and T **27** the remainder.

There were two printings of each value from this setting.

Se-tenant pairs are worth about 20% more.

The "1" with foot occurs on T **27** on No. 9 in the first setting and on T **26** on No. 7 in the first printing only of the second setting.

The small "2" appears on T **26** in the first setting on Nos. 6, 7, 8 and 12 in the first printing and on Nos. 7, 8 and 12 only in the second printing: in the second setting it comes on Nos. 3, 9 and 12 in the first printing and on Nos. 9, 11 and 12 in the second printing. On T **27** the variety occurs in the first setting on No. 9 of the second printing only and in the second setting on No. 10 in both printings.

(Typo D.L.R.)

1882. *Wmk Crown C.A. P* 14.
170 **16** 1 c. slate (27 Jan) 2·75 55
171 2 c. orange (27 Jan) 9·00 95
a. Value doubly printed
172 4 c. blue 26·00 9·50
173 6 c. brown 5·50 6·00
174 8 c. rose 35·00 1·75

INLAND 4 CENTS 4 CENTS
(a) (b)
Two types of "4"

2 CENTS
REVENUE
(28)

6 6
(c) (d)
Two types of "6"

1888–89. *T* **16** *(without value in lower label) optd.* "INLAND REVENUE", *and surch with value as T* **28**, *by D.L.R. Wmk Crown CA. P* 14.
175 1 c. dull purple (8.89) 65 65
176 2 c. dull purple (25.5.89) 75 65
177 3 c. dull purple 65 65
178 4 c. dull purple *(a)* 1·60 90
a. Larger figure "4" *(b)* 17·00 9·00
179 6 c. dull purple *(c)* 2·25 1·40
a. Figure 6 with straight top *(d)* 5·50 3·25
180 8 c. dull purple (8.89) 1·25 90
181 10 c. dull purple 3·50 2·50
182 20 c. dull purple 8·00 6·00
183 40 c. dull purple 8·00 8·00
184 72 c. dull purple (1.10.88) 12·00 9·50
185 $1 green (1.10.88) £200 £140
186 $2 green (1.10.88) 95·00 70·00
187 $3 green (1.10.88) 48·00 42·00
188 $4 green *(a)* (1.10.88) £175 £150
a. Larger figure "4" *(b)* £500 £500
189 $5 green (1.10.88) 85·00 70·00
175/189 *Set of* 15 £550 £450

2
(29)

30

INLAND
One
Cent
~~1 DOLLAR~~
REVENUE
(31)

1889 (6 June). *No.* 176 *surch locally as T* **29**.
192 "2" on 2 c. dull purple (R.) 55 55

The varieties with figure "2" *inverted* or *double* were made privately by a postal employee in Demerara.

1889 (Sept). *Wmk Crown CA. P* 14.
193 **30** 1 c. dull purple and slate-grey 90 90
194 2 c. dull purple and orange 80 50
195 4 c. dull purple and ultramarine 2·75 2·50
196 4 c. dull purple and cobalt 8·50 2·25
197 6 c. dull purple and brown 15·00 6·50
198 6 c. dull purple and maroon 6·00 3·25
199 8 c. dull purple and rose 4·00 2·25
200 **30** 12 c. dull purple and bright purple 8·50 1·25
200*a* 12 c. dull purple and mauve 7·00 2·00
201 24 c. dull purple and green 7·00 3·00
202 48 c. dull purple and orange-red 13·00 8·00
203 72 c. dull purple and red-brown 19·00 16·00
204 72 c. dull purple and yellow-brown 35·00 40·00
205 96 c. dull purple and carmine 48·00 50·00
206 96 c. dull purple and rosine 60·00 60·00
193/205 *Set of* 10 £100 80·00
193/205 Optd "Specimen" *Set of* 10 £250

1890 (15 July). *Stamps of* 1888–89 *surch locally* "One Cent", *in red, as in T* **31**.
207 1 c. on $1 (No. 185) 1·25 1·00
a. Surch double — 40·00
208 1 c. on $2 (No. 186) 70 1·25
a. Surch double 70·00
209 1 c. on $3 (No. 187) 1·40 1·25
a. Surch double 55·00
210 1 c. on $4 (No. 188) 3·00 4·25
a. Surch double 60·00
b. Larger figure "4" *(b)* 14·00 15·00

1890–91. *Colours changed. Wmk Crown CA. P* 14
213 **30** 1 c. sea-green (12.90) 30 30
214 5 c. ultramarine (1.91) 2·75 40
215 8 c. dull purple and greenish black (10.90) 3·25 5.00
213/215 Optd "Specimen" *Set of* 3 80·00

32 Mount Roraima

33 Kaieteur Falls

(Recess D.L.R.)

1898 (18 July). *Queen Victoria's Jubilee. Wmk Crown CC (sideways on T* **32**). *P* 14.
216 **32** 1 c. blue-black and carmine 3·50 75
217 **33** 2 c. brown and indigo 4·75 1·25
a. Imperf between (pair) £2500
218 2 c. brown and blue 10·00 1·10
219 **32** 5 c. green and sepia 15·00 5·50
a. Imperf between (pair)
220 **33** 10 c. blue-black and orange-red 18·00 16·00
221 **32** 15 c. red-brown and blue 18·00 17·00
216/221 Optd "Specimen" *Set of* 5 £130

A second plate was later used for the 1 c. on which the lines of shading on the mountains in the background are strengthened, and those along the ridge show distinct from each other, whereas, in the original, they are more or less blurred. In the second plate the shading of the sky is less pronounced.

TWO CENTS.
(34)

35

(Surch at Printing Office of the *Daily Chronicle*, Georgetown)

1899 (22 Feb). *Surch with T* **34**
222 **32** 2 c. on 5 c. (No. 219) 1·90 2·25
a. No stop after "CENTS" 24·00 24·00
223 **33** 2 c. on 10 c. (No. 220) 90 1·25
a. No stop after "CENTS" 20·00 20·00
b. "GENTS" for "CENTS" 45·00 45·00
c. Surch inverted £180 £200
224 **32** 2 c. on 15 c. (No. 221) 2·50 2·75
a. No stop after "CENTS" 45·00 45·00
b. Surch double £325
c. Surch double, one without stop
d. Surch inverted £250 £250

The "no stop" variety occurs on the 53rd stamp in sheets of No. 222 and of the first setting of No. 223 and on the 21st stamp in the second setting of No. 223.

The "GENTS" error is on the 55th stamp in the sheet.

Of No. 224c. only one specimen exists.

1900–7. *T* **30**. *Wmk Crown CA. P* 14
233 1 c. grey-green (1907) 2·25 1·40
234 2 c. dull purple and carmine 2·75 45
235 2 c. dull purple and black/*red* 80 25
236 6 c. grey-black and ultramarine (1902) 7·50 9·50
237 48 c. grey and purple-brown (1901) 26·00 30·00
a. Brownish grey and brown (1907) 20·00 28·00
238 60 c. green and rosine (1903) 48·00 60·00
233/238 *Set of* 6 75·00 90·00
233/238 Optd "Specimen" *Set of* 6 £130

No. 233 is a reissue of No. 213 in non-fugitive ink.

1905–7. *T* **30**. *Wmk Multiple Crown CA. P* 14.
240 1 c. grey-green 30 30
241 2 c. purple and black/*red* **OC** 50 25
242 4 c. dull purple and ultramarine, **OC** 7·00 6·50
243 5 c. dull purple and blue/*blue*, **OC** (Optd S. £30) 4·00 3·50
244 6 c. grey-black and ultramarine, **OC** 9·50 11·00
245 12 c. dull and bright purple, **OC** 17·00 18·00
246 24 c. dull purple and green, **OC** (1906) 5·50 5·50
247 48 c. grey and purple-brown, **OC** 15·00 20·00
248 60 c. green and rosine, **OC** 15·00 24·00
249 72 c. purple and orange-brown, **C** (1907) 24·00 32·00
250 96 c. black and vermilion/*yellow*, **C** (1906) (Optd S. £30) 30·00 42·00
240/250 *Set of* 11 £120 £150

1905. *Optd* "POSTAGE AND REVENUE". *Wmk Multiple Crown CA. P* 14.
251 **35** $2.40, green and violet, **C** (S. £130) £180 £200

1907–10. *Colours changed. Wmk Mult Crown CA. P 14*

No.	Type	Description	Unused	Used
252	**30**	1 c. blue-green, **O** (1910)	1·10	1·25
253		2 c. rose-red, **O**	3·00	40
		a. Redrawn (1910)	2·00	40
254		4 c. brown and purple, **O**	3·25	1·75
255		5 c. ultramarine, **O**	1·50	75
256		6 c. grey and black, **O**	11·00	7·00
257		12 c. orange and mauve, **O**	5·50	3·75
252/257		*Set of* 6	22·00	13·50
253/257 Optd "Specimen"		*Set of* 5	£140	

In No. 253a the flag at the main truck is close to the mast, whereas in the original type it appears to be flying loose from halyards. There are two background lines above the value "2 CENTS" instead of three and the "S" is further away from the end of the tablet.

37

War
Tax

(38)

(Typo D.L.R.)

1913–21. *Wmk Mult Crown CA. P 14.*

No.	Type	Description	Unused	Used
259	**37**	1 c. yellow-green, **O**	90	70
		a. Blue-green, **O** (1917)	70	30
260		2 c. carmine, **O**	60	15
		a. Scarlet, **O** (1916)	50	10
		b. Wmk sideways		
261		4 c. brown and bright purple, **C** (1914)	2·00	95
		a. Deep brown and purple, **C**	2·50	85
262		5 c. bright blue, **O**	1·00	1·25
263		6 c. grey and black, **O**	1·00	1·00
264		12 c. orange and violet, **C**	1·25	1·10
265		24 c. dull purple and green, **O** (1915)	3·25	3·75
266		48 c. grey and purple-brown, **C** (1914)	8·00	10·00
267		60 c. green and rosine, **C** (1915)	16·00	23·00
268		72 c. purple and orange-brown, **C** (1915)	24·00	32·00
269		96 c. black and vermilion/*yellow*, **C** (1915)	25·00	35·00
		a. White back (1913)	18·00	26·00
		b. On lemon (1916) (Optd S. £20)	20·00	28,00
		c. On pale yellow (1921) (Optd S. £20)	22·00	35·00
259/269*a*		*Set of* 11	70·00	90·00
259/69*a* Optd "Specimen"		*Set of* 11	£200	

1918 (4 Jan). *No. 260a optd with T* **38**, *by D.L.R.*

No.	Type	Description	Unused	Used
271	**37**	2 c. scarlet	30	30

The relative position of the words "WAR" and "TAX" vary considerably in the sheet.

1921–27. *Wmk Mult Script CA. P 14*

No.	Type	Description	Unused	Used
272	**37**	1 c. green, **O** (1922)	50	30
273		2 c. rose-carmine, **O**	50	35
274		2 c. bright violet, **O** (1923)	30	15
275		4 c. brown and bright purple, **O** (1922)	1·10	25
276		6 c. bright blue, **O** (1922)	1·25	60
277		12 c. orange and violet, **O**(1922)	1·60	1·50
278		24 c. dull purple and green, **C**	2·75	3·75
279		48 c. black and purple, **C** (1926)	7·50	7·50
280		60 c. green and rosine, **C** (1926)	9·00	14·00
281		72 c. dull purple & orange-brn, **C** (1923)	11·00	15·00
282		96 c. black and red/*yellow*, **C** (1927)	16·00	24·00
272/282		*Set of* 11	45·00	60·00
272/82 Optd "Specimen"		*Set of* 11	£225	

39 Ploughing a Rice Field

40 Indian shooting Fish

(Recess Waterlow)

1931 (21 July). *Centenary of County Union T* **39/40** *and similar designs. Wmk Mult Script CA. P* 12½.

No.	Type	Description	Unused	Used
283		1 c. emerald-green	60	1·00
284		2 c. brown	90	30
285		4 c. carmine	3·25	1·50
286		6 c. blue	5·50	6·00
287		$1 violet	35·00	45·00
283/7 Perf "Specimen"		*Set of* 5	£120	

Designs: *Vert*—4 c., $1 Kaieteur Falls. *Horiz*—6 c. Public buildings, Georgetown.

43 Ploughing a Rice Field

44 Gold Mining

(Recess Waterlow)

1934 (1 Oct)–**51**. *T* **40** (*without dates at top of frame*), **43/4** *and similar designs. Wmk Mult Script CA (sideways on horiz designs). P* 12½.

No.	Type	Description	Unused	Used
288	**43**	1 c. green	30	30
289	**40**	2 c. red-brown	30	12
290	**44**	3 c. scarlet	12	12
		aa. Wmk error. Crown missing		
		a. Perf 12½ × 13½ (30.12.43)	8	5
291	–	4 c. slate-violet	1·10	45
		a. Imperf between (vert pair)	†	£5000
292	–	6 c. deep ultramarine	3·00	2·00
293	–	12 c. red-orange	12	12
		a. Perf 13½ × 12½ (16.4.51)	12	30
294	–	24 c. purple	4·75	4·75
295	–	48 c. black	10·00	12·00
296	–	50 c. green	12·00	15·00
297	–	60 c. red-brown	32·00	32·00
298	–	72 c. purple	2·75	2·75
299	–	96 c. black	28·00	35·00
300	–	$1 bright violet	38·00	42·00
288/300		*Set of* 13	£120	£130
288/300 Perf "Specimen"		*Set of* 13	£170	

Designs: *Vert*—4 c., 50 c. Kaieteur Falls (as No. 285, but with dates omitted); 96 c. Sir Walter Raleigh and his son. *Horiz*—6 c. Shooting logs over falls; 12 c. Stabroek Market 24 c. Sugar cane in punts; 48 c. Forest road; 60 c. Victoria Regia Lilies; 72 c. Mount Roraima; $1 Botanical Gardens.

No. 290a was first line-perforated, but from 28.4.49 printings appeared comb-perforated.

1935 (6 May). *Silver Jubilee. As T* **13** *of Antigua.*

No.	Type	Description	Unused	Used
301		2 c. ultramarine and grey	15	15
		e. Horiz line from turret	2·00	
302		6 c. brown and deep blue	1·10	1·00
		e. Horiz line from turret	10·00	
303		12 c. green and indigo	1·75	2·25
		e. Horiz line from turret	12·00	
304		24 c. slate and purple	3·75	4·50
301/4 Perf "Specimen'		*Set of* 4	55·00	

For illustration of plate variety see Omnibus section following Zululand.

1937 (12 May). *Coronation. As T* **2** *of Aden.*

No.	Type	Description	Unused	Used
305		2 c. yellow-brown	15	12
306		4 c. grey-black	35	35
307		6 c. bright blue	50	75
305/7 Perf "Specimen"		*Set of* 3	45·00	

53 South America

54 Victoria Regia Lilies

(Recess Waterlow)

1938 (1 Feb)–**1952**. *As earlier types but with portrait of King George VI as in T* **53/4**. *Wmk Mult Script CA. P* 12½

No.	Type	Description	Unused	Used
308	**43**	1 c. yellow-green	2·25	45
		aa. Green (1944)	15	10
		a. Perf 13½ × 12½ (1949)	10	10
309	–	2 c. slate-violet	20	10
		a. Perf 12½ × 13½ (28.4.49)	20	10
310	**53**	4 c. scarlet and black	30	10
		a. Imperf horiz (vert pair)	£3000	£1500
		b. Perf 12½ × 13½ (1952)	25	12
311	**40**	6 c. deep ultramarine	35	12
		a. Perf 12½ × 13½ (24.10.49)	30	12
312	–	24 c. blue-green	12·00	6·00
		a. Wmk sideways	2·50	40
313	–	36 c. bright violet (7.3.38)	1·25	40
		a. Perf 12½ × 13½ (13.12.51)	1·75	50
314	–	48 c. orange	1·00	30
		a. Perf 13½ × 12½ (14.6.51)	1·25	1·00
315	–	60 c. red-brown	2·50	1·25
316	–	96 c. purple	4·00	2·75
		a. Perf 12½ × 13½ (1944)	2·50	3·00
317	–	$1 bright violet	4·00	1·25
		a. Perf 13½ × 12½ (1951)	£200	£225
318	–	$2 purple (11.6.45)	6·50	8·50
		a. Perf 13½ × 12½ (9.8.50)	6·50	8·50
319	**54**	$3 red-brown (2.7.45)	18·00	18·00
		a. Bright red-brown (Dec.1946)	22·00	26·00
		b. Perf 13½ × 12½. *Red-brown* (29.10.52)	16·00	25·00
308a/319		*Set of* 12	35·00	32·00
308/19 Perf "Specimen"		*Set of* 12	£160	

Designs: *Vert*—2 c., 36 c. Kaieteur Falls; 96 c. Sir Walter Raleigh and his son. *Horiz*—24 c. Sugar cane in punts; 48 c. Forest road; 60 c. Shooting logs over falls; $1 Botanical Gardens; $2 Mount Roraima.

No. 316a was first line-perforated, but from 8.2.51 printings appeared comb-perforated.

1946 (21 Oct). *Victory. As Nos.* 28/9 *of Aden.*

No.	Type	Description	Unused	Used
320		3 c. carmine	15	15
321		6 c. blue	15	15
320/1 Perf "Specimen"		*Set of* 2	45·00	

1948 (20 Dec). *Royal Silver Wedding. As Nos.* 30/1 *of Aden; (recess $3).*

No.	Type	Description	Unused	Used
322		3 c. scarlet	12	12
323		$3 red-brown	12·00	20·00

1949 (10 Oct). *75th Anniv of Universal Postal Union. As Nos.* 114/17 *of Antigua.*

No.	Type	Description	Unused	Used
324		4 c. carmine	40	35
325		6 c. deep blue	65	65
326		12 c. orange	80	75
327		24 c. blue-green	1·25	1·25

1951 (16 Feb). *University College of B.W.I. As Nos.* 118/19 *of Antigua.*

No.	Type	Description	Unused	Used
328		3 c. black and carmine	30	25
329		6 c. black and blue	45	40

1953 (2 June). *Coronation. As No.* 47 *of Aden.*

No.	Type	Description	Unused	Used
330		4 c. black and scarlet	15	8

55 G.P.O. Georgetown

62 Felling Greenheart.

(Centre litho, frame recess ($1); recess (others). Waterlow (until 1961), then D.L.R.)

1954 (1 Dec)–**62**. *T* **55, 62** *and similar designs. Wmk Mult Script CA. P* 12½ × 13* (*horiz*) *or* 13 (*vert*).

No.	Type	Description	Unused	Used
331		1 c. black	5	5
332		2 c. myrtle-green	5	5
333		3 c. brown-olive and red-brown	40	5
334		4 c. violet	10	5
		a. D.L.R. ptg (*shades*) (5.12.61)	1·50	80
335		5 c. scarlet and black	10	10
336		6 c. yellow-green (*shades*)	10	5
337		8 c. ultramarine (*shades*)	15	10
338		12 c. black and reddish brown (*shades*)	15	5
339		24 c. black and brownish orange (*shades*)	90	5
340		36 c. rose-carmine and black	70	25
341		48 c. ultramarine and brown-lake (*shades*)	70	45
		ab. D.L.R. ptg. *Bright ultramarine and pale brown-lake* (19.9.61)	9·50	5·50
342		72 c. carmine and emerald	4·50	3·25
		a. D.L.R. ptg (17.7.62)	13·00	12·00
343		$1 pink, yellow, green and black	5·50	80
344		$2 deep mauve (*shades*)	6·50	1·25
345		$5 ultramarine and black	13·00	8·00
		a. D.L.R. ptg (19.9.61)	20·00	13·00
331/345		*Set of* 15	29·00	13·00

Designs: *Horiz*—2 c. Botanical Gardens; 3 c. Victoria Regia Lilies; 5 c. Map of Caribbean; 6 c. Rice combine-harvester; 8 c. Sugar cane entering factory; 24 c. Mining for bauxite; 36 c. Mount Roraima; $1 Channel-billed Toucan; $2 Dredging gold. *Vert*—4 c. Amerindian shooting fish; 48 c. Kaieteur Falls; 72 c. Arapaima; $5 Arms of British Guiana.

The separately listed De La Rue printings (Nos. 334a, 341ab, 342a and 345a) are identifiable as singles by the single wide-tooth perfs at each side at the *bottom* of the stamps. In the Waterlow these wide teeth are at the *top*.

*All the Waterlow printing and early De La Rue printings of the horizontal designs measure 12.3 × 12.8, but De La Rue printings of 22 May 1962 and all later printings (including those on the Block CA watermark) measure 12.3 × 12.6.

See also Nos. 354/65.

SELF-GOVERNMENT

70

(Photo Harrison)

1961 (23 Oct). *History and Culture Week. W* w **12** *P* 14½ × 14.

No.	Type	Description	Unused	Used
346	**70**	5 c. sepia and orange-red	5	5
347		6 c. sepia and blue-green	5	5
348		30 c. sepia and yellow-orange	25	25

1963 (14 July). *Freedom from Hunger. As No.* 76 *of Aden.*

No.	Type	Description	Unused	Used
349		20 c. reddish violet	40	25

1963 (2 Sept). *Red Cross Centenary. As Nos.* 147/8 *of Antigua.*

No.	Type	Description	Unused	Used
350		5 c. red and black	10	5
351		20 c. red and blue	60	50

1963–65. *As Nos.* 333/44, *but wmk* w **12**.

No.	Type	Description	Unused	Used
354		3 c. brown-olive and red-brown (12.65)	1·50	1·50
356		5 c. scarlet and black (28.5.64)	15	5
359		12 c. black and yellowish brown (6.10.64)	15	5
360		24 c. black and bright orange (10.12.63)	80	5
361		36 c. rose-carmine and black (10.12.63)	60	10
362		48 c. bright ultramarine and Venetian red (25.11.63)	1·25	1·50
363		72 c. carmine and emerald (25.11.63)	4·25	8·00
364		$1 pink, yellow, green and black (10.12.63)	3·50	2·25
365		$2 reddish mauve (10.12.63)	8·50	15·00
354/365		*Set of* 9	19·00	26·00

There was no London release of No. 354.

For 1 c. value, see No. 393aA of Guyana.

71 Weightlifting

(Photo D.L.R.)

1964 (1 Oct). *Olympic Games, Tokyo. W* w **12**. *P* 13 × 13½.

No.	Type	Description	Unused	Used
367	**71**	5 c. orange	5	5
368		8 c. blue	8	5
369		25 c. magenta	20	25

1965 (17 May). *I.T.U. Centenary. As Nos.* 166/7 *of Antigua.*
370 5 c. emerald and yellow-olive 15 5
371 25 c. light blue and magenta 50 25

1965 (25 Oct). *International Co-operation Year. As Nos.* 168/9 *of Antigua.*
372 5 c. reddish purple and turquoise-green 15 5
373 25 c. deep bluish green and lavender 45 35

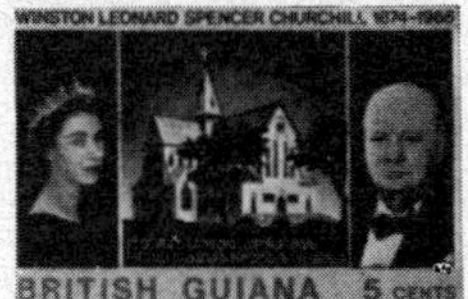

72 St. George's Cathedral, Georgetown

(Des Jennifer Toombs, Photo Harrison)

1966 (24 Jan). *Churchill Commemoration.* W w **12**. *P* 14 × 14½.
374 **72** 5 c. black, crimson and gold 30 15
375 25 c. black, blue and gold 1·10 65

1966 (3 Feb). *Royal Visit. As Nos.* 174/5 *of Antigua.*
376 3 c. black and ultramarine 60 15
377 25 c. black and magenta 2·00 75

POSTAGE DUE STAMPS

D 1

(Typo D.L.R.)

1940 (Mar)–**55**. *Wmk Mult Script CA. P* 14.
D 1 D 1 1 c. green, **O** 60 85
a. Deep green, **C** (30.4.52) 15 35
b. W9*a* (Crown missing), **C** 30·00
c. W9*b* (St. Edward's Crown), **C** 21·00
D 2 2 c. black, **C** 75 80
aa. Chalky paper (30.4.52) 15 35
a. W9*a* (Crown missing), **C** 30·00
b. W9*b* (St. Edward's Crown), **C** 20·00
D 3 4 c. bright blue, **C** (1.5.52) 40 1·00
a. W9*a* (Crown missing), **C** 25·00
b. W9*b* (St. Edward's Crown), **C** 20·00
D 4 12 c. scarlet, **O** 1·60 2·25
a. Chalky paper (19.7.55) 1·25 3·00
D1, D2 and D4 Perf "Specimen" *Set of* 3 50·00

OFFICIAL STAMPS

OFFICIAL (O 1) **OFFICIAL** (O 2)

1875. *Optd with Type* O 1 (1 c), *or* O **2** (*others*) *P*.10.
O1 **8** 1 c. black (R.) 15·00 10·00
a. Imperf between (pair) — £1100
O2 2 c. orange 55·00 10·00
O3 8 c. rose £130 55·00
O4 **7** 12 c. brownish purple £500 £225
O5 **9** 24 c. green £275 90·00

Two types of the word "OFFICIAL" are found on each value. On the 1 c., the word is either 16 or 17 mm long. On the other values the chief difference is in the shape and position of the letter "o" in "OFFICIAL". In one case the "o" is upright, in the other it slants to the left.

1877. *Optd with Type* O **2**. *Wmk Crown CC. P* 14.
O 6 **16** 1 c. slate £100 45·00
a. Imperf between (vert pair) — £3000
O 7 2 c. orange 38·00 10·00
O 8 4 c. blue 50·00 20·00
O 9 6 c. brown £1400 £300
O10 8 c. rose £1400 £250

Prepared for use, but not issued

O11 **16** 12 c. pale violet £600
O12 24 c. green £750

The "OFFICIAL" overprints have been extensively forged.
The use of Official stamps was discontinued in June 1878.

British Guiana attained independence on 25 May 1966. For later issues see GUYANA.

PRICES OF SETS

Set prices are given for many issues, generally those containing five stamps or more. Definitive sets include one of each value or major colour change, but do not cover different perforations, die types or minor shades. Where a choice is possible the set prices are based on the cheapest versions of the stamps included in the listings.

British Honduras

It is recorded that the first local post office was established by the inhabitants in 1809, but Belize did not become a regular packet port of call until 1829. A branch office of the British G.P.O. was established in 1857 and the stamps of Great Britain were supplied for use on overseas mail from 1858.

The colonial authorities took over the postal service on 1 April, 1860, the Great Britain stamps being withdrawn the following month. There was no inland postal service until 1862.

For illustrations of the handstamp and postmark types see BRITISH POST OFFICES ABROAD notes, following GREAT BRITAIN.

BELIZE

CROWNED-CIRCLE HANDSTAMPS

CC1 CC 1*b* BELIZE (R.)(13.11.1841) *Price on cover* £1900

Stamps of GREAT BRITAIN *cancelled* "A 06" *as Type* **2**.

1858 *to* **1860**.
Z1 1d. rose-red (1857), *perf* 14 £850
Z2 4d. rose (1857) £350
Z3 6d. lilac (1856) £350
Z4 1s. green (1856) £800

PRICES FOR STAMPS ON COVER TO 1945

Nos. 1/4	*from* × 15
Nos. 5/16	*from* × 10
Nos. 17/22	*from* × 8
Nos. 23/6	*from* × 6
Nos. 27/30	*from* × 4
Nos. 35/42	*from* × 10
Nos. 43/4	*from* × 15
Nos. 49/50	*from* × 12
Nos. 51/69	*from* × 10
Nos. 80/100	*from* × 5
Nos. 101/10	*from* × 4
Nos. 111/20	*from* × 10
Nos. 121/2	*from* × 5
No. 123	*from* × 6
Nos. 124/37	*from* × 5
Nos. 138/42	*from* × 10
Nos. 143/6	*from* × 5
Nos. 147/9	*from* × 8
Nos. 150/61	*from* × 5
Nos. D1/3	*from* × 25

CROWN COLONY

1

(Typo D.L.R.)

1866 (Jan.) *No wmk. P* 14.
1 1 1d. pale blue 38·00 35·00
a. Imperf between (pair)
2 1d. blue 38·00 35·00
3 6d. rose £150 90·00
4 1s. green £180 85·00
a. In horiz pair with 6d. £15000
b. In vert pair with 1d. £22000

In the first printing all three values were printed in the same sheet separated by horizontal and vertical gutter margins. The sheet comprised two panes of 60 of the 1d. at the top with a pane of 60 of the 1s. at bottom left and another of 6d. at bottom right. Copies of 1d. *se-tenant* with the 6d. are not known. There were two later printings of the 1d. but they were in sheets without the 6d. and 1s.

1872–79. *Wmk Crown CC.* (*a*) *P* 12½.
5 1 1d. pale blue 50·00 16·00
6 1d. deep blue (1874) 45·00 16·00
7 3d. red-brown 85·00 65·00
8 3d. chocolate (1874) 95·00 75·00
9 6d. rose £130 25·00
9*a* 6d. bright rose-carmine (1874) £225 35·00
10 1s. green £225 28·00
10*a* 1s. deep green (1874) £180 20·00
b. Imperf between (pair) — £13000

(*b*) *P* 14 (1877–79)
11 1 1d. pale blue (1878) 35·00 15·00
12 1d. blue 27·00 10·00
a. Imperf between (pair) £2500
13 3d. chestnut 70·00 14·00
14 4d. mauve (1879) £100 11·00
15 6d. rose (1878) £225 £150
16 1s. green £130 16·00
a. Imperf between (pair)

1882–87. *Wmk Crown CA. P* 14.
17 1 1d. blue (4.84) 22·00 13·00
18 1d. rose (1884) 15·00 11·00
a. Bisected (½d.) (on cover)
19 1d. carmine (1887) 24·00 13·00
20 4d. mauve (7.82) 55·00 5·50
21 6d. yellow (1885) £200 £140
22 1s. grey (1.87) £225 £120
18,22 Optd "Specimen" *Set of* 2 £170

2 CENTS (2) **TWO** (3) **2 CENTS** (4)

1888 (1 Jan.). *Stamps of* 1872–79 (*wmk Crown CC*), *surch locally as T* **2**. (*a*) *P* 12½.
23 1 2 c. on 6d. rose 90·00 90·00
24 3 c. on 3d. chocolate £8500 £3500

(*b*) *P* 14
25 1 2 c. on 6d. rose 65·00 65·00
a. Surch double £1000
b. Bisected (1 c.) (on cover) † £110
c. Slanting "2" with curved foot £500
26 3 c. on 3d. chestnut 55·00 55·00

There are very dangerous forgeries of these surcharges.

1888. *Stamps of* 1882–87 (*wmk Crown CA*), *surch locally as T* **2**, *P* 14.
27 1 2 c. on 1d. rose 6·50 14·00
a. Surch inverted £1000 £900
b. Surch double £900 £850
c. Bisected (1 c.) (on cover) † £160
28 10 c. on 4d. mauve 28·00 14·00
29 20 c. on 6d. yellow 28·00 22·00
30 30 c. on 1s. grey £325 £450
a. Error. "5" for "50" £6000

Various settings were used for the surcharges on Nos. 23/30, the most common of which was of 36 (6 × 6) impressions. For No. 29 this setting was so applied that an albino surcharge occurs in the margin above each stamp in the first horizontal row.

The same setting was subsequently amended, by altering the "2" to "1", to surcharge the 4d. value. As this was in sheets of 30 it was only necessary to alter the values on the bottom five rows of the setting. Albino surcharges once again occur in the top margin of the sheet, but, as the type in the first horizontal row remained unaltered, these read "20 CENTS" rather than the "10 CENTS" on the actual stamps.

1888 (July). *No.* 30 *further surch locally with T* **3**.
35 1 "TWO" on 50c. on 1s. grey (R.) 32·00 50·00
a. Bisected (1 c.) (on cover) † £190
b. Surch in black £9000 £7500
c. Surch double (R. + Blk.) £7000 £6500

1888 (July)–**91**. *Surch in London as T* **4**. *Wmk Crown CA. P* 14.
36 1 1 c. on 1d. dull green (?12.91) 55 70
37 2 c. on 1d. carmine 55 1·25
a. Bisected (1 c.) (on cover) † £130
38 3 c. on 3d. red-brown 70 1·40
39 6 c. on 3d. ultramarine (?4.91) 1·40 5·00
40 10 c. on 4d. mauve 1·40 1·40
a. Surch double £950
41 20 c. on 6d. yellow (2.89) 6·00 14·00
42 50 c. on 1s. grey (11.88) 16·00 32·00
36/42 Optd "Specimen" *Set of* 7 £400

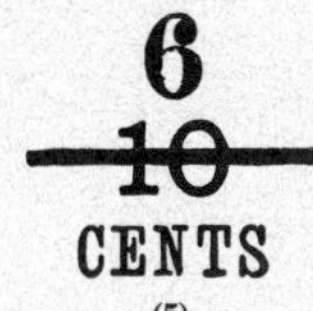

(5)

FIVE (6) **15** (7)

1891. *Stamps of* 1888–9 *surch locally.* (*a*) *With T* **5** (May).
43 1 6 c. on 10 c. on 4d. mauve (R.) 85 3·75
a. "6" and bar inverted £375 £375
b. "6" only inverted — £2250
44 6 c. on 10 c. on 4d. mauve (Blk.) 1·10 3·50
a. "6" and bar inverted £2250 £650
b. "6" only inverted — £2250

Of variety (b) only six copies of each can exist, as one of each of these errors came in the first six sheets, and the mistake was then corrected. Of variety (a) more copies exist.

Essays are known with "SIX" in place of "6", both with and without bars (*price* £70 *and* £375 *respectively*). Although not issued, we mention them, as two contemporary covers franked with them are known.

(*b*) *With T* **6/7** (23 Oct)
49 1 5 c. on 3 c. on 3d. red-brown 1·60 3·75
a. Wide space between "I" and "V" 35·00 42·00
b. "FIVE" and bar double £160
50 15 c. on 6 c. on 3d. ultramarine (R.) 8·00 14·00
a. Surch double

8

9

10

11

(Typo D.L.R.)

1891 (July)–**1901**. *Wmk Crown CA. P* 14.
51 **8** 1 c. dull green (4.95) 50 85
52 2 c. carmine-rose 55 40
53 3 c. brown .. .. .. 1·25 2·50
54 5 c. ultramarine (4.95) .. .. 12·00 1·25
55 **11** 5 c. grey-black & ultram/*blue* (10.00) .. 2·00 1·50
56 **8** 6 c. ultramarine .. .. .. 2·25 1·40
57 **9** 10 c. mauve and green (4.95) .. 8·00 7·50
58 **10** 10 c. dull purple and green (1901) .. 3·75 7·00
59 **9** 12 c. pale mauve and green .. .. 20·00 4·50
a. Violet and green .. .. 5·00 7·00
60 24 c. yellow and blue .. .. 7·00 13·00
a. Orange and blue .. .. 15·00 26·00
61 25 c. red-brown and green (4.95) .. 16·00 25·00
62 **10** 50 c. green and carmine (3.98) .. .. 15·00 23·00
63 **11** $1 green and carmine (12.99) .. .. 22·00 30·00
64 $2 green and ultramarine (12.99) .. 45·00 55·00
65 $5 green and black (12.99) £225 £275
51/65 .. .. *Set of* 15 £300 £400
51/65 Optd "Specimen" .. .. *Set of* 15 £425

1899 (1 July). *Optd* "REVENUE" A. *Opt* 12 *mm long*. B. *Opt* 11 *mm long*.

		A		B	
66	5 c. (No. 54)	2·75	3·75	4·00	5·50
	a. "BEVENUE"	42·00	55·00	†	
67	10 c. (No. 57)	5·00	8·00	9·50	13·00
	a. "BEVENUE"	£160	—	†	
	b. "REVENU"	—	—	£325	£350
68	25 c. (No. 61)	3·25	7·50	5·00	9·00
	a. "BEVENUE"	75·00	£100	†	
	b. "REVE UE"	—	—	—	†
69	50 c. No. 42)	£110	£150	£140	£190
	a. "BEVENUE"	£2500	—	†	

Two minor varieties, a small "U" and a tall, narrow "U" are found in the word "REVENUE".

The overprint setting of 60 (6 × 10) contained 43 examples of the 12 mm size and 17 of the 11 mm. The smaller size overprints occur on R.8/1, R8/3 to 6 and on all positions in Rows 9 and 10.

The "BEVENUE" error appears on R.6/4 and, it is believed, "REVE UE" comes from R.6/6. Both occur on parts of the printing only. The missing "E" developed during the overprinting and damage to this letter can be observed on at least eight positions in the setting. Examples of No. 67b are now known to exist on both sizes of the overprint.

14 15

(Typo D.L.R.)

1902 (10 Oct)–**04**. *Wmk Crown CA. P* 14.
80 **14** 1 c. grey-green and green (28.4.04) .. 4·00 8·50
81 2 c. purple and black/*red* (18.3.03) .. 60 60
82 5 c. grey-black and blue/*blue* .. .. 2·75 2·25
83 **15** 20 c. dull and bright purple (28.4.04) .. 12·00 18·00
80/3 Optd "Specimen" .. .. *Set of* 4 95·00

1904–07. *Wmk Mult Crown CA. P* 14.
84 **14** 1 c. grey-green and green, **OC** .. .. 60 1·25
85 2 c. purple and black/*red*, **OC** 60 30
86 5 c. grey-black and blue/*blue*, **C** .. 1·75 1·00
87 **15** 10 c. dull purple and emerald-green, **C** .. 6·00 8·50
89 25 c. dull purple and orange, **C** .. .. 7·50 13·00
90 50 c. grey-green and carmine, **C**.. .. 15·00 23·00
91 **14** $1 grey-green and carmine, **C**.. .. 25·00 35·00
92 $2 grey-green and blue, **C** .. .. 55·00 70·00
93 $5 grey-green and black, **C** £250 £300
84/93 .. .. *Set of* 9 £325 £400
87/93 Optd "Specimen" .. .. *Set of* 6 £275
Dates of issue:—1 c. 8.05; 2 c. 12.04; 5 c. 5.2.06; others 20.9.07

1908 (7 Dec)–**11**. *Colours changed. Wmk Mult Crown CA. P* 14.
95 **14** 1 c. blue-green, **O** (1.7.10) .. .. 1·25 1·00
96 2 c. carmine, **O** 90 50
97 5 c. ultramarine, **O** (1.6.09) .. .. 2·25 1·25
100 **15** 25 c. black/*green*, **C** (14.10.11) .. .. 9·50 20·00
96/100 Optd "Specimen" .. .. *Set of* 3 95·00

16 17 (18)

(Typo D.L.R.)

1913–21. *Wmk Mult Crown CA. P* 14.
101 **16** 1 c. blue-green, **O** 30 30
a. Yellow-green (13.3.17) 65 75
102 2 c. red, **O** 70 75
a. Bright scarlet (1915) 60 90
b. Dull scarlet (8.17) .. .. 1·75 1·25
c. Red/bluish .. .. .. 4·50 4·50
103 3 c. orange, **O** (16.4.17).. .. .. 30 45
104 5 c. bright blue, **O** .. .. .. 1·50 1·60
105 **17** 10 c. dull purple and yellow-green, **C** .. 3·25 5·00
a. Dull purple and bright green (1917) 4·50 6·50
106 25 c. black/*green*, **C** .. .. .. 3·25 5·50
a. On blue-green, olive back (8.17) .. 3·50 7·00
b. On emerald back (1921) .. .. 3·50 10·00
107 50 c. purple and blue/*blue*, **C** .. .. 7·50 9·00
108 **16** $1 black and carmine, **C** .. .. 8·00 11·00
109 $2 purple and green, **C** .. .. 38·00 45·00
110 $5 purple and black/*red*, **C** £200 £300
101/110 .. .. *Set of* 10 £225 £350
101/10 Optd "Specimen" .. .. *Set of* 10 £300

1915–16. *Optd with T* **18**, *in violet.*
111 **16** 1 c. green (30.12.15) .. .. .. 90 4·00
a. Yellow-green (6.6.16) .. .. 50 3·00
112 2 c. scarlet (3.11.15) 60 75
113 5 c. bright blue (29.7.15) .. .. 60 4·00
111/13 Optd "Specimen" .. .. *Set of* 3 £140

These stamps were shipped early in the 1914–18 war, and were thus overprinted, so that if seized by the enemy, they could be distinguished and rendered invalid.

WAR WAR
(19) (20) 21

1916 (23 Aug). *No.* 111 *optd locally with T* **19**.
114 **16** 1 c. green 20 45
a. Opt inverted £175 £190

1917. *Nos.* 101 *and* 103 *optd with T* **19**.
116 **16** 1 c. blue-green .. .. 35 1·25
a. Yellow-green .. .. .. 35 1·25
118 3 c. orange .. .. 60 1·50
a. Overprint double £325

1918. *Nos.* 101 *and* 103 *optd with T* **20**.
119 **16** 1 c. blue-green 25 80
a. Yellow-green .. .. .. 1·40 2·50
120 3 c. orange .. .. 35 1·25
119/20 Optd "Specimen" .. .. *Set of* 2 £130

(Recess D.L.R.)

1921 (28 Apr). *Peace Commemoration. Wmk Mult Crown CA* (*sideways*). *P* 14.
121 **21** 2 c. rose-red (Optd S. £60) .. .. 2·25 1·75

1921 (26 Nov). *Wmk Mult Script CA. P* 14.
122 **16** 1 c. green, **O** (Optd S. £55) .. .. 2·00 4·00

1922 (4 Jan). *As T* **21** *but with words* "PEACE" *omitted. Wmk Mult Script CA* (*sideways*). *P* 14.
123 4 c. slate (Optd S. £60).. .. .. .. 4·00 2·00

BELIZE RELIEF FUND PLUS 3 CENTS

22 (23)

(Typo D.L.R.)

1922 (1 Aug)–**33**. *Ordinary paper* (1 c. *to* 5 c.) *or chalk-surfaced paper* (*others*). *P* 14 (*a*) *Wmk Mult Crown CA*.
124 **22** 25 c. black/*emerald* .. .. .. 7·00 16·00
125 $5 purple and black/*red* (1.10.24) .. £200 £300

(*b*) *Wmk Mult Script CA*
126 **22** 1 c. green (2.1.29) .. .. .. 45 1·00
127 2 c. brown (1.3.23) 25 35
128 2 c. rose-carmine (10.12.26) 30 25
129 3 c. orange (1933) .. .. .. 2·50 2·50
130 4 c. grey (1.10.29) .. .. .. 1·40 70
131 5 c. ultramarine .. .. .. 1·40 1·00
a. Milky blue (1923) .. .. .. 2·25 3·00
132 10 c. dull purple and sage-green (1.12.22) 1·10 90
133 25 c. black/*emerald* (1.10.24) .. .. 2·25 3·25
134 50 c. purple and blue/*blue* (1.11.23) .. 7·00 9·50
136 $1 black and scarlet (2.1.25) .. .. 10·00 15·00
137 $2 yellow-green and bright purple .. 38·00 45·00
124/137 .. .. *Set of* 13 £225 £350
124/137 Opted/Perf "Specimen" .. *Set of* 13 £300

1932 (2 May). *Belize Relief Fund. Surch as T* **23**. *Wmk Mult Script CA. P* 14.
138 **22** 1 c. + 1 c. green .. .. 1·10 5·50
139 2 c. + 2 c. rose-carmine .. .. .. 1·60 5·50
140 3 c. + 3 c. orange .. .. 2·25 6·50
141 4 c. + 4 c. grey (R.) .. .. .. 3·75 9·50
142 5 c. + 5 c. ultramarine .. .. .. 7·50 16·00
138/42 Perf "Specimen" .. .. *Set of* 5 £160

1935 (6 May). *Silver Jubilee. As Nos.* 91/4 *of Antigua, but ptd by B. W. & Co. P* 11 × 12.
143 3 c. ultramarine and grey-black 50 65
a. Extra flagstaff .. .. 40·00
b. Short extra flagstaff .. .. .. 20·00
c. Lightning conductor .. .. .. 15·00
144 4 c. green and indigo 75 80
a. Extra flagstaff £170
c. Lightning conductor .. .. .. 50·00
d. Double flagstaff .. .. 50·00
145 5 c. brown and deep blue .. .. .. 2·00 2·25
146 25 c. slate and purple .. .. 3·75 5·00
a. Extra flagstaff £250
b. Short extra flagstaff £120
c. Lightning conductor .. .. .. 75·00
d. Double flagstaff .. .. 75·00
143/6 Perf "Specimen" .. .. *Set of* 4 55·00

For illustrations of plate varieties see Omnibus section following Zululand.

1937 (12 May). *Coronation. As Nos.* 13/15 *of Aden.*
147 3 c. orange 30 40
148 4 c. grey-black 40 45
149 5 c. bright blue 40 55
147/9 Perf "Specimen" .. .. *Set of* 3 50·00

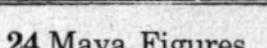

24 Maya Figures. **25** Chicle Tapping

(Recess B.W.)

1938 (10 Jan)–**47**. *T* **24/5** *and similar designs. Wmk Mult Script CA* (*sideways on horizontal stamps*). *P* 11½ × 11 (*horiz designs*) *or* 11 × 11½ (*vert designs*).
150 1 c. bright magenta and green (14.2.38) .. 15 30
151 2 c. black and scarlet (14.2.38) 15 30
a. Perf 12 (1947) .. .. 1·25 1·00
152 3 c. purple and brown 15 25
153 4 c. black and green 20 25
154 5 c. mauve and dull blue 25 35
155 10 c. green and reddish brown (14.2.38) .. 50 35
156 15 c. brown and light blue (14.2.38) .. 60 55
157 25 c. blue and green (14.2.38).. .. 1·00 75
158 50 c. black and purple (14.2.38) .. .. 2·25 1·60
159 $1 scarlet and olive (28.2.38) .. .. 7·00 3·25
160 $2 deep blue and maroon (28.2.38).. .. 12·00 12·00
161 $5 scarlet and brown (28.2.38) .. .. 26·00 21·00
150/161 .. .. *Set of* 12 45·00 38·00
150/61 Perf "Specimen" .. .. *Set of* 12 95·00

Designs: *Vert*—3 c. Cohune palm; $1 Court House, Belize. $2 Mahogany felling; $5 Arms of Colony. *Horiz*—4 c. Local products; 5 c. Grapefruit; 10 c. Mahogany logs in river; 15 c. Sergeant's Cay; 25 c. Dorey; 50 c. Chicle industry.

1946 (9 Sept). *Victory. As Nos.* 28/9 *of Aden.*
162 3 c. brown 20 20
163 5 c. blue 20 20
162/3 Perf "Specimen" .. .. *Set of* 2 28·00

1948 (1 Oct). *Royal Silver Wedding. As Nos.* 30/1 *of Aden.*
164 4 c. green 20 15
165 $5 brown .. .. 23·00 35·00

36 Island of St George's Cay **37** H. M. Sloop, *Merlin*

(Recess Waterlow)

1949 (10 Jan). 150*th Anniv of Battle of St. George's Cay. Wmk Mult Script CA. P* 12½.
166 **36** 1 c. ultramarine and green 15 30
167 3 c. blue and yellow-brown 15 30
168 4 c. olive and violet 15 45
169 **37** 5 c. brown and deep blue 30 30
170 10 c. green and red-brown 50 40
171 15 c. emerald and ultramarine 55 75
166/171 .. .. *Set of* 6 1·60 2·25

1949 (10 Oct). *75th Anniv of U.P.U. As Nos.* 114/17 *of Antigua.*
172 4 c. blue-green 30 30
173 5 c. deep blue 50 50
174 10 c. red-brown .. .. 1·25 1·50
175 25 c. blue .. .. 1·75 2·00

1951 (16 Feb). *Inauguration of B.W.I. University College. As Nos.* 118/19 *of Antigua.*
176 3 c. reddish violet and brown 45 40
177 10 c. green and brown.. .. .. .. 65 60

1953 (2 June). *Coronation. As No.* 47 *of Aden.*
178 4 c. black and green 15 40

38 Arms of British Honduras **46** Maya Indian

(Recess Waterlow (until 20.6.1961), then D.L.R.)

1953 (2 Sept)–**57**. *T* **38, 46** *and similar designs. Wmk Mult Script CA. P* 13½.
179 1 c. green and black 5 12
a. Perf 13½ × 13 (3.10.61).. .. .. 10 15
180 2 c. yellow-brown and black 12 45
a. Perf 14 (18.9.57) 12 5
b. Perf 13½ × 13 (20.6.61).. .. .. 15 20
181 3 c. reddish violet and bright purple (*shades*) 12 5
a. Perf 14 (18.9.57) 12 5
b. Perf 13½ × 13 (20.6.61).. .. .. 1·25 1·75
182 4 c. brown and green.. .. .. .. 15 15
183 5 c. deep olive-green and scarlet 15 10
a. Perf 14 (15.5.57) 15 5
184 10 c. slate and bright blue 15 5
a. Perf 13½ × 13 (19.1.62).. .. .. 35 65
185 15 c. green and violet 20 20
186 25 c. bright blue and yellow-brown .. .. 1·75 65

187 50 c. yellow-brown and reddish purple (*shades*) 1·00 1·25
188 $1 slate-blue and red-brown 3·50 3·50
189 $2 scarlet and grey 7·00 7·00
190 $5 purple and slate 22·00 17·00
179/190 *Set of* 12 32·00 27·00

Designs: *Horiz*—2 c. Mountain Cow; 3 c. Mace and Legislative Council Chamber; 4 c. Pine industry; 5 c. Spiny Lobster, 10 c. Stanley Field Airport; 15 c. Maya frieze; 25 c. Blue Butterfly; $1 Armadillo; $2 Hawkesworth Bridge. *Vert*—$5 Mountain Orchid.

Nos. 179/90 were released a day earlier by the Crown Agents in London.

Stamps from the Waterlow printings perforated 13½ × 13 or 14 have a very fine perforation tooth at the *top* of each vertical side. On the De La Rue printings this tooth is at the *bottom*.

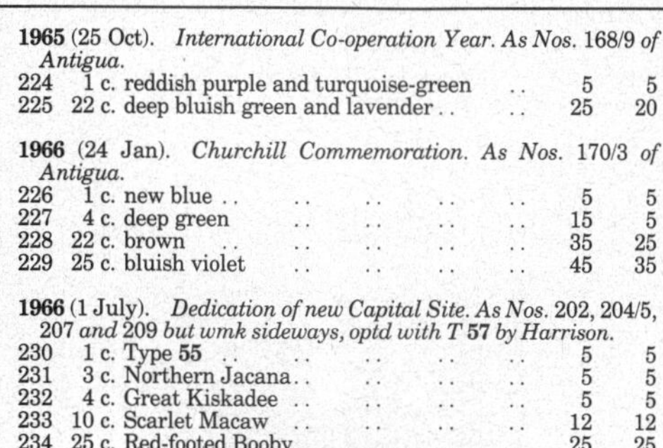

50 "Belize from Fort George, 1842" (C. J. Hullmandel)

51 Public Seals, 1860 and 1960.

52 Tamarind Tree, Newtown Barracks.

(Recess B.W.)

1960 (1 July). *Post Office Centenary.* W w **12**. *P* 11½ × 11.
191 **50** 2 c. green 10 10
192 **51** 10 c. deep carmine 15 5
193 **52** 15 c. blue 25 30

NEW CONSTITUTION
1960
(53)

HURRICANE
HATTIE
(54)

1961 (1 Mar). *New Constitution. Nos.* 180a, 181a *and* 184/5 *optd with T* **53** *by Waterlow.*
194 2 c. yellow-brown and black 8 10
195 3 c. reddish violet and bright purple 8 8
196 10 c. slate and bright blue 12 12
197 15 c. green and violet 20 30

1962 (15 Jan). *Hurricane Hattie Relief Fund. Nos.* 179a, 184a, 186 *and* 187 *optd with T* **54** *by D.L.R.*
198 1 c. green and black 5 10
199 10 c. slate and bright blue 10 12
200 25 c. bright blue and yellow-brown 25 25
201 50 c. yellow-brown and reddish purple 30 40

55 Great Curassow

(Des D. R. Eckelberry. Photo Harrison)

1962 (2 Apr). *Horiz designs on T* **55**. *Multicoloured.* W w **12** *(upright). P* 14 × 14½.
202 1 c. Type **55** 20 12
203 2 c. Red-legged Honey-creeper 30 12
204 3 c. Northern Jacana 30 12
a. Blue-green (legs) omitted 90·00
205 4 c. Great Kiskadee 35 12
206 5 c. Scarlet-rumped Tanager 40 12
207 10 c. Scarlet Macaw 40 20
a. Blue omitted 80·00
208 15 c. Slaty-tailed Trogon 45 25
209 25 c. Red-footed Booby 70 40
210 50 c. Keel-billed Toucan 1·75 80
211 $1 Magnificent Frigate Bird 4·00 2·00
212 $2 Rufous-tailed Jacamar (*shades*) 9·00 7·50
213 $5 Montezuma Oropendola 20·00 15·00
202/213 *Set of* 12 35·00 24·00

See also Nos. 239/45.

1963 (4 June). *Freedom from Hunger. As No.* 76 *of Aden.*
214 22 c. bluish green 45 30

1963 (2 Sept). *Red Cross Centenary. As Nos.* 147/8 *of Antigua.*
215 4 c. red and black 20 10
216 22 c. red and blue 70 60

SELF-GOVERNMENT

SELF GOVERNMENT
1964
(56)

DEDICATION OF SITE
NEW CAPITAL
9th OCTOBER 1965
(57)

1964. *New Constitution. Nos.* 202, 204/5, 207 *and* 209 *optd with T* **56**.
217 1 c. Type **55** (20.4) 5 5
a. Opt inverted 70·00
218 3 c. Northern Jacana (20.4) 5 5
219 4 c. Great Kiskadee (3.2) 5 5
220 10 c. Scarlet Macaw (20.4) 15 15
221 25 c. Red-footed Booby (3.2) 20 20

1965 (17 May). *I.T.U. Centenary. As Nos.* 166/7 *of Antigua.*
222 2 c. orange-red and light green 5 5
223 50 c. yellow and light purple 45 40

1965 (25 Oct). *International Co-operation Year. As Nos.* 168/9 *of Antigua.*
224 1 c. reddish purple and turquoise-green 5 5
225 22 c. deep bluish green and lavender 25 20

1966 (24 Jan). *Churchill Commemoration. As Nos.* 170/3 *of Antigua.*
226 1 c. new blue 5 5
227 4 c. deep green 15 5
228 22 c. brown 35 25
229 25 c. bluish violet 45 35

1966 (1 July). *Dedication of new Capital Site. As Nos.* 202, 204/5, 207 *and* 209 *but wmk sideways, optd with T* **57** *by Harrison.*
230 1 c. Type **55** 5 5
231 3 c. Northern Jacana 5 5
232 4 c. Great Kiskadee 5 5
233 10 c. Scarlet Macaw 12 12
234 25 c. Red-footed Booby 25 25

58 Citrus Grove

(Des V. Whiteley. Photo Harrison)

1966 (1 Oct). *Stamp Centenary. T* **58** *and similar horiz designs. Multicoloured.* W w **12**. *P* 14 × 14½.
235 5 c. Type **58** 5 5
236 10 c. Half Moon Cay 10 10
237 22 c. Hidden Valley Falls 20 10
238 25 c. Maya Ruins, Xunantunich 25 25

1967. *As Nos.* 202, *etc, but wmk sideways.*
239 1 c. Type **55** (16.2) 8 8
240 2 c. Red-legged Honey-creeper (28.11) 15 15
241 4 c. Great Kiskadee (16.2) 20 15
242 5 c. Scarlet-rumped Tanager (16.2) 30 10
243 10 c. Scarlet Macaw (28.11) 50 15
244 15 c. Slaty-tailed Trogon (28.11) 70 30
245 50 c. Keel-billed Toucan (16.2) 3·75 2·50
239/245 *Set of* 7 5·00 3·00

The 15 c. value exists with PVA gum as well as gum arabic.

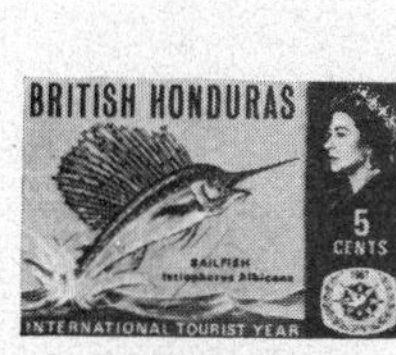

59 Sailfish

60 *Schomburgkia tibicinis*

(Des R. Granger Barrett. Photo Harrison)

1967 (1 Dec). *International Tourist Year. T* **59** *and similar horiz designs.* W w **12**. *P* 12½.
246 5 c. deep violet-blue, black and light yellow 5 5
247 10 c. brown, black and orange-red 10 10
248 22 c. yellow-orange, black and bright green 15 10
249 25 c. lt greenish blue, black & greenish yellow 20 20

Designs:—10 c. Deer; 22 c. Jaguar; 25 c. Tarpon.

(Des Sylvia Goaman, Photo Harrison)

1968 (16 Apr). *20th Anniv of Economic Commission for Latin America. T* **60** *and similar vert designs. Multicoloured.* W w **12** *(sideways). P* 14½ × 14.
250 5 c. Type **60** 10 5
251 10 c. *Maxillaria tenuifolia* 20 10
252 22 c. *Bletia purpurea* 35 10
253 25 c. *Sobralia macrantha* 45 40

61 Monument to Belizean Patriots

62 Monument at Site of New Capital

(Des G. Vasarhelyi. Litho B.W.)

1968 (15 July). *Human Rights Year.* W w **12**. *P* 13½.
254 **61** 22 c. multicoloured 15 5
255 **62** 50 c. multicoloured 20 25

63 Jew Fish

(Des J. W. Litho D.L.R.)

1968 (15 Oct). *Wildlife. Horiz designs as T* **63**. *Multicoloured. No wmk. P* 13 × 12½.
256 1 c. Type **63** 5 5
257 2 c. Warree 8 5
258 3 c. Grouper 10 5
259 4 c. Ant Bear 10 15
260 5 c. Bonefish 12 15
261 10 c. Gibnut 15 15
262 15 c. Dolphin 30 25
263 25 c. Night Walker 30 30
264 50 c. Mutton Snapper 70 70
265 $1 Bush Dog 2·00 1·60
266 $2 Great Barracuda 3·00 2·75
267 $5 Mountain Lion 9·50 6·50
256/67 *Set of* 12 15·00 11·00

See also Nos. 276/8 and 338/40

64 *Rhyncholaelia digbyana*

65 Ziricote Tree

(Des Sylvia Goaman. Photo Harrison)

1969 (9 Apr). *Orchids of Belize* (1st series). *T* **64** *and similar vert designs. Multicoloured.* W w **12** *(sideways). P* 14½ × 14.
268 5 c. Type **64** 15 5
269 10 c. *Cattleya bowringiana* 25 20
270 22 c. *Lycaste cochleatum* 50 10
271 25 c. *Coryanthes speciosum* 60 45

See also Nos. 287/90.

(Des V. Whiteley. Litho D.L.R.)

1969 (1 Sept). *Indigenous Hardwoods* (1st series). *T* **65** *and similar vert designs. Multicoloured.* W w **12**. *P* 14.
272 5 c. Type **65** 5 5
273 10 c. Rosewood 10 10
274 22 c. Mayflower 20 10
275 25 c. Mahogany 20 30

See also Nos. 291/4 and 315/18.

1969–72. *As Nos.* 257/8, 261, 267 *and new value and design* (½ c.), *but* W w **12** *(sideways).*
276 ½ c. Crana Fish (ultramarine background) (1.9.69) 10 10
277 ½ c. Crana Fish (yellow-olive background) (1.2.71) 10 8
a. Black (inscr and value) omitted 70·00
277*c* 2 c. Waree (5.5.72) 90 90
277*d* 3 c. Grouper (5.5.72) 90 90
277*e* 10 c. Gibnut (5.5.72) 1·75 1·50
278 $5 Mountain Lion (12.5.70) 13·00 13·00
276/78 *Set of* 6 15·00 15·00

66 "The Virgin and Child" (Bellini

POPULATION
CENSUS 1970
(68

(Des adapted by G. Drummond. Litho Format)

1969 (1 Nov). *Christmas. Paintings. T* **66** *and similar vert design. Multicoloured.* W w **12**. *P* 14× 14½.
279 5 c. Type **66** 5 5
280 15 c. Type **66** 10 10
281 22 c. "The Adoration of the Kings" (Veronese) 15 10
282 25 c. As 22 c. 20 25

Although released by the Crown Agents on 1 October this issue was not put on sale locally until 1 November.

1970 (2 Feb). *Population Census. As Nos.* 260 *and* 262/3 *but* W w **12** *(sideways) and No.* 277*e optd with T* **68**.
283 5 c. Bonefish 5 5
284 10 c. Gibnut 10 10
285 15 c. Dolphin 10 10
286 25 c. Night Walker 15 20

(Des G. Drummond. Litho Format)

1970 (2 Apr). *Orchids of Belize* (2nd series). *As T* **64**. *Multicoloured.* W w **12**. *P* 14.
287 5 c. Black Orchid 15 5
288 15 c. White Butterfly Orchid 30 15
289 22 c. Swan Orchid 40 10
290 25 c. Butterfly Orchid 45 35

69 Santa Maria

70 "The Nativity" (A. Hughes).

(Des Jennifer Toombs, Litho Questa)

1970 (7 Sept). *Indigenous Hardwoods (2nd series). T* **69** *and similar vert designs. Multicoloured. W w* **12** *(sideways). P* 14 × 14½.

291	5 c. Type **69**	5	5
292	15 c. Nargusta	15	10
293	22 c. Cedar	30	15
294	25 c. Sapodilla	40	35

(Des J. Cooter Litho J.W.)

1970 (7 Nov*). *Christmas. T* **70** *and similar vert design. Multicoloured. W w* **12.** *P* 14.

295	½ c. Type **70**	5	5
296	5 c. "The Mystic Nativity" (Botticelli)	5	5
297	10 c. Type **70**	8	8
298	15 c. As 5 c	12	12
299	22 c. Type **70**	15	10
300	50 c. As 5 c.	40	50
295/300	*Set of* 6	75	80

*These stamps were released by the Crown Agents in London on 2 November.

71 Legislative Assembly House

(Des. G. Drummond. Litho Enschedé)

1971 (30 Jan). *Establishment of New Capital, Belmopan. T* **71** *and similar horiz designs. Multicoloured. W w* **12** *upright* (5 *c.,* 10 *c.*) *or sideways (others). P* 13 × 13½.

301	5 c. Old Capital, Belize	10	10
302	10 c. Government Plaza	15	15
303	15 c. Type **71**	20	30
304	22 c. Magistrates' Court	30	30
305	25 c. Police H.Q.	30	40
306	50 c. New G.P.O.	55	75
301/306	*Set of* 6	1·40	1·75

The 5 c. and 10 c. are larger, 60 × 22 mm.

72 *Tabebuia chrysantha*

(Des Sylvia Goaman. Litho Questa)

1971 (27 Mar). *Easter. T* **72** *and similar horiz designs showing flowers. Multicoloured. W w* **12** *(sideways). P* 14.

307	½ c. Type **72**	5	5
308	5 c. *Hymenocallis littorallis*	5	5
309	10 c. *Hippeastrum equestre*	8	8
310	15 c. Type **72**	12	12
311	22 c. As 5 c.	25	15
312	25 c. As 10 c.	30	35
307/12	*Set of* 6	75	70

RACIAL EQUALITY
YEAR - 1971

(73)

74 Tubroos

1971 (14 June). *Racial Equality Year. As No.* 264, *but W w* **12** *(sideways) and No.* 277e *optd with T* **73**.

313	10 c. Gibnut	10	5
314	50 c. Mutton Snapper	25	30

(Des Jennifer Toombs, Litho Questa)

1971 (16 Aug). *Indigenous Hardwoods (3rd series). T* **74** *and similar vert designs. Multicoloured. W w* **12.** *P* 13½.

315	5 c. Type **74**	12	12
316	15 c. Yemeri	25	35
317	26 c. Billywebb	35	40
318	50 c. Logwood	90	1·40
MS319	96 × 171 mm. Nos. 315/18	5·50	6·50
	a. Silver (Queen's head) omitted	£1100	

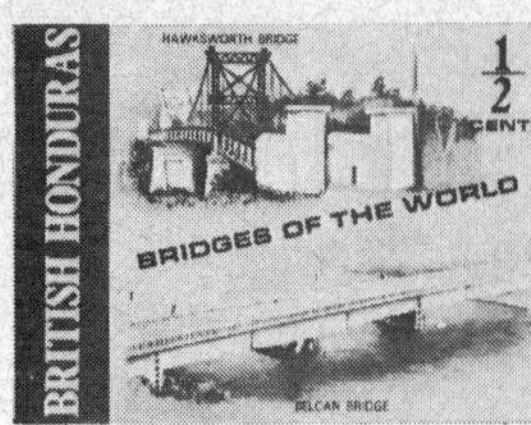

75 Hawksworth and Belcan Bridges

(Des and litho J.W.)

1971 (23 Sept). *Bridges of the World. T* **75** *and similar horiz designs. Multicoloured. W w* **12** *(sideways). P* 13½.

320	½ c. Type **75**	5	5
321	5 c. Narrows Bridge, N.Y. and Quebec Bridge	5	5
322	26 c. London Bridge (1871) and reconstructed, Arizona (1971)	30	40
323	50 c. Belize Mexican Bridge and Swing Bridge	50	70

76 *Petrae volubis*

77 Seated Figure

(Des G. Drummond. Litho Format)

1972 (28 Feb). *Easter. T* **76** *and similar vert designs showing wild flowers. Multicoloured. W w* **12.** *P* 14½.

324	6 c. Type **76**	10	10
325	15 c. Yemeri	30	30
326	26 c. Mayflower	45	45
327	50 c. Tiger's Claw	70	70

(Des Jennifer Toombs. Litho Questa)

1972 (22 May). *Mayan Artefacts. T* **77** *and similar multicoloured designs. W w* **12** *(sideways except* 16 *c.). P* 13½ × 13 (16 *c.) or* 13 × 13½ *(others).*

328	3 c. Type **77**	5	5
329	6 c. Priest in "dancing" pose	10	10
330	16 c. Sun God's head (*horiz*)	20	20
331	26 c. Priest and Sun God	30	30
332	50 c. Full-front figure	60	80

Nos. 328/32 are inscribed on the reverse with information about the artefacts depicted.

78 Banak

79 Orchids of Belize

(Des Jennifer Toombs. Litho Questa)

1972 (21 Aug). *Indigenous Hardwoods (4th series). T* **78** *and similar vert designs. Multicoloured. W w* **12** *(sideways). P* 14½.

333	3 c. Type **78**	8	8
334	5 c. Quamwood	10	10
335	16 c. Waika Chewstick	25	25
336	26 c. Mamee-Apple	40	40
337	50 c. My Lady	70	70

1972 (17 Nov). *As Nos.* 258 *and* 260/1, *but W w* **12** *(upright).*

338	3 c. Grouper	45	50
339	5 c. Bonefish	50	55
340	10 c. Gibnut	70	1·10

(Des (from photograph by D. Groves) and photo Harrison)

1972 (20 Nov). *Royal Silver Wedding. Multicoloured; background colour given. W w* **12.** *P* 14 × 14½.

341	**79**	26 c. deep myrtle-green	30	35
342		50 c. bright bluish violet	45	50

OMNIBUS ISSUES

Details, together with prices for complete sets, of the various Omnibus issues from the 1935 Silver Jubilee series to date are included in a special section following Zululand at the end of the catalogue.

80 Baron Bliss Day

(Des J.W. Litho Questa)

1973 (9 Mar). *Festivals of Belize. T* **80** *and similar horiz designs. Multicoloured. W w* **12.** *P* 14½ × 14.

343	3 c. Type **80**	5	5
344	10 c. Labour Day	15	15
345	26 c. Carib Settlement Day	25	25
346	50 c. Pan American Day	60	70

POSTAGE DUE STAMPS

D 1

(Typo D.L.R.)

1923–64. *Wmk Mult Script CA. P* 14.

D1	**D 1**	1 c. black, **O**	65	1·75
		a. Chalky paper (25.9.56)	90	2·00
		b. White uncoated paper (9.4.64)	12·00	15·00
D2		2 c. black, **O**	75	1·75
		a. Chalky paper (25.9.56)	75	2·00
D3		4 c. black, **O**	2·75	7·50
		a. Chalky paper (25.9.56)	2·75	6·00
D1/3 Optd "Specimen"		*Set of* 3	42·00	

The early ordinary paper printings were yellowish and quite distinct from No. D1b.

1965 (3 Aug)–**72.** *As Nos.* D2a *and* D3a, *but Wmk* w **12** *(sideways on* 2 *c.). P* 13½ × 13 (2 *c.) or* 13½ × 14 (4 *c.).*

D4	**D 1**	2 c. black (10.1.72)	65	1·75
D5		4 c. black	1·00	2·25

On 1 June 1973, British Honduras was renamed BELIZE.

British Indian Ocean Territory

This Crown Colony was created on 8 November 1965 and comprised the Chagos Archipelago, previously administered by Mauritius, together with the islands of Aldabra, Farquhar and Desroches, previously administered by Seychelles.

(Currency. 100 cents=1 rupee)

B.I.O.T.

(1)

1968 (17 Jan). *As Nos.* 196/200, 202/4 *and* 206/12 *of Seychelles, optd with T* 1. *W w* **12** *(sideways on* 5, 10, 15, 20, 25, 50, 75 *c. and* 10 *r.).*

1	5 c. multicoloured	10	10
2	10 c. multicoloured	12	12
3	15 c. multicoloured	12	12
4	20 c. multicoloured	15	15
5	25 c. multicoloured	20	20
6	40 c. multicoloured	35	35
7	45 c. multicoloured	60	60
8	50 c. multicoloured	60	60
9	75 c. multicoloured	80	80
10	1 r. multicoloured	90	90
11	1 r. 50, multicoloured	2·50	2·50
12	2 r. 25, multicoloured	6·00	6·00
13	3 r. 50, multicoloured	7·00	8·00
14	5 r. multicoloured	12·00	14·00
15	10 r. multicoloured	25·00	32·00
1/15	*Set of* 15	50·00	60·00

These were issued by the Crown Agents on 15 January but owing to shipping delays they were not put on sale locally until 17 January.

"Missing stop" varieties occur as follows: after "O" twice in each sheet on the 5, 10, 15, 20, 25, 40, 45 and 50 c. and 1, 1.50, 2.25, 3.50, 5 and 10 r.; after "I" once in the sheet on the same values; after "B" once in the sheet on the 45 c. and 10 r. only. Prices, for pairs with and without stop after "O" are from three times the normal price for a single and for the other varieties, from four times normal.

We have seen a sheet of the 5 c. and of the 10 c. with all stops in place so either the no stop varieties developed during printing or they were discovered and inserted during the printing.

2 Lascar

(Des G. Drummond, based on drawings by Mrs. W. Veevers-Carter. Litho D.L.R.)

1968 (23 Oct)–**70**. *Marine Life. Multicoloured designs as T* **2**. *White paper (Nos. 20a, 23a, 24a) or cream paper (others).* W w **12** *(sideways on horiz, inverted on vert designs).* P 14.

16 5 c. Type **2** 30 20
17 10 c. Hammerhead Shark (*vert*) 30 20
18 15 c. Tiger Shark 30 20
19 20 c. Bat Ray.. .. .. 30 25
20 25 c. Butterfly Fish (*vert*) .. .. .. 1·00 1·25
20*a* 30 c. Robber Crab (7.12.70) .. .. .. 1·50 2·25
21 40 c. Caranx 40 40
22 45 c. Garfish (*vert*) .. .. 4·50 5·00
23 50 c. Barracuda 45 25
23*a* 60 c. Spotted Pebble Crab (7.12.70) .. .. 2·00 3·00
24 75 c. Parrot Fish .. .. 6·00 6·50
24*a* 85 c. Dorade (*Elegatis bipinnulatus*) (7.12.70) 2·25 3·25
25 1 r. Giant Hermit Crab .. .. 1·00 75
26 1 r. 50, Humphead .. .. 2·75 2·75
27 2 r. 25, Rock Cod .. .. 20·00 24·00
28 3 r. 50, Black Marlin .. .. 6·00 8·00
29 5 r. black, blue-green and greenish blue (Whale Shark) (*vert*) .. .. .. 9·00 11·00
30 10 r. Lion Fish .. .. 14·00 18·00
a. Imperf (pair) £175
16/30 .. .. *Set of* 18 65·00 80·00

See also No. 52.

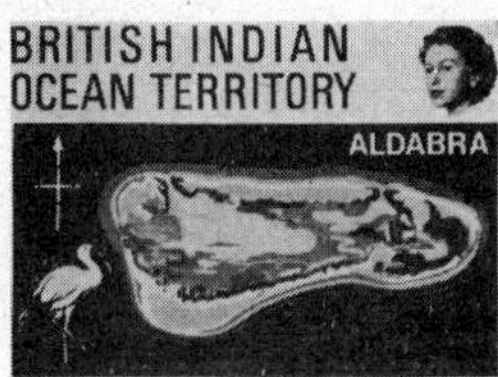

3 Sacred Ibis and Aldabra Coral Atoll

(Des and litho D.L.R.)

1969 (10 July). *Coral Atolls.* W w **12** *(sideways).* P 13½ × 13.

31 **3** 2 r. 25, multicoloured .. .. 3·00 2·75

4 Out-rigger

(Des Mrs. M. Hayward adapted by V. Whiteley. Litho D.L.R.)

1969 (15 Dec.) *Ships of the Islands. T* **4** *and similar horiz designs. Multicoloured.* W w **12** *(sideways).* P 13½ × 14.

32 45 c. Type **4** .. .. 1·25 1·25
33 75 c. Pirogue .. .. 1·40 1·75
34 1 r. M. V. *Nordvaer* .. .. 1·60 2·25
35 1 r. 50, *Isle of Farquhar* .. .. 1·75 2·50

5 Giant Land Tortoise

(Des G. Drummond. Litho Format)

1971 (1 Feb). *Aldabra Nature Reserve. T* **5** *and similar horiz designs. Multicoloured.* W w **12** *(sideways).* P 13½.

36 45 c. Type **5** .. .. 3·50 3·50
37 75 c. Aldabra Lily .. .. 4·00 4·00
38 1 r. Aldabra Snail .. .. 4·50 4·50
39 1 r. 50, Western Reef Herons .. .. .. 6·50 6·50

6 Arms of Royal Society and White-throated Rail

(Des V. Whiteley. Litho J.W.)

1971 (30 June). *Opening of Royal Society Research Station on Aldabra.* W w **12** *(sideways).* P 13½.

40 **6** 3 r. 50, multicoloured .. .. 9·00 11·00

7 Staghorn Coral

(Des V. Whiteley. Litho A. & M.)

1972 (1 Mar). *Coral. T* **7** *and similar horiz designs. Multicoloured.* W w **12** *(sideways).* P 13½.

41 40 c. Type **7** .. .. 3·00 3·00
42 60 c. Brain coral .. .. 3·50 3·50
43 1 r. Mushroom coral.. .. .. 4·00 4·00
44 1 r. 75, Organ Pipe coral .. .. 5·00 5·00

On some sheets of No. 43 the inks have been applied in a different order, resulting in an almost total absence of blue.

8 White-throated Rail and Sacred Ibis

9 "Christ on the Cross"

(Des (from photograph by D. Groves) and photo Harrison)

1972 (20 Nov.). *Royal Silver Wedding. Multicoloured; background colour given.* W w **12**. P 14 × 14½.

45 **8** 95 c. deep dull green (*shades*) 80 90
46 1 r. 50, bright bluish violet 80 90

(Des Jennifer Toombs. Litho Questa)

1973 (9 Apr). *Easter. T* **9** *and similar vert design showing illustrations from 17th-century Ethiopian manuscript. Multicoloured.* W w **12** *(sideways).* P 14.

47 45 c. Type **9** 65 90
48 75 c. Joseph and Nicodemus burying Jesus 75 1·25
49 1 r. Type **9** .. .. 80 1·40
50 1 r. 50. As 75 c. .. .. 90 1·50
MS51 126 × 110 mm. Nos. 47/50 .. .. .. 2·75 5·00

1973 (2 Oct). *As No. 16 but white paper and wmk upright.*

52 5 c. Type **2** .. .. 50 1·75

No. 52 differs in shade from No. 16 because of the change of paper.

10 Upsidedown Jellyfish

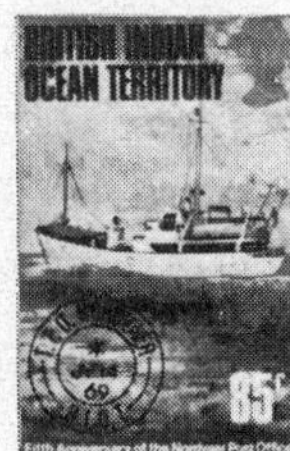

11 M.V. *Nordvaer*

(Des G. Drummond. Litho Walsall)

1973 (12 Nov). *Wildlife (1st series). T* **10** *and similar vert designs. Multicoloured.* W w **12** *(sideways).* P 14.

53 50 c. Type **10** .. .. 2·50 3·00
54 1 r. Butterflies .. .. 2·50 3·00
55 1 r. 50, Spider .. .. 2·75 3·00

See also Nos. 58/61, 77/80 and 86/9.

(Des C. Abbott. Litho Walsall)

1974 (14 July). *Fifth Anniv of "Nordvaer" Travelling Post Office. T* **11** *and similar vert design. Multicoloured.* W w **12** *(sideways).* P 14.

56 85 c. Type **11** 75 75
57 2 r. 50, *Nordvaer* off shore .. .. .. 1·50 1·75

12 Auger Shells

(Des PAD Studio. Litho J.W.)

1974 (12 Nov). *Wildlife (2nd series). T* **12** *and similar horiz designs showing shells. Multicoloured.* W w **12**. P 13½ × 14.

58 45 c. Type **12** .. .. 1·00 1·25
59 75 c. Green Turban .. .. 1·10 1·40
60 1 r. Drupe Snail .. .. 1·40 1·60
61 1 r. 50, Helmet Shell .. .. 1·50 1·90

13 Aldabra Drongo

14 *Grewia salicifolia*

(Des R. Granger Barrett. Litho Questa)

1975 (28 Feb). *Birds. Multicoloured designs as T* **13**. W w **12** *(sideways on horiz designs).* P 14.

62 5 c. Type **13** 35 40
63 10 c. Black Coucal 35 45
64 20 c. Mascarene Fody 50 60
65 25 c. White Tern 60 75
66 30 c. Crested Tern 60 75
67 40 c. Brown Booby 60 80
68 50 c. Common Noddy (*horiz*) 65 85
69 60 c. Grey Heron .. .. 80 1·00
70 65 c. Blue-faced Booby (*horiz*) .. .. .. 80 1·00
71 95 c. Madagascar White Eye (*horiz*) .. .. 1·00 1·50
72 1 r. Striated Heron (*horiz*) .. .. .. 1·25 1·75
73 1 r. 75, Lesser Frigate Bird (*horiz*) .. .. 1·75 3·00
74 3 r. 50, White-tailed Tropic Bird (*horiz*) .. 2·75 3·75
75 5 r. Souimanga Sunbird (*horiz*) .. .. 4·00 5·00
76 10 r. Madagascar Turtle Dove (*horiz*) .. .. 7·50 9·00
62/76 .. .. *Set of* 15 21·00 28·00

(Des Sylvia Goaman. Litho Questa)

1975 (10 July). *Wildlife (3rd series). T* **14** *and similar vert designs showing seashore plants. Multicoloured.* W w **12** *(sideways).* P 14.

77 50 c. Type **14** 45 65
78 65 c. *Cassia aldabrensis* 50 75
79 1 r. *Hypoestes aldabrensis* .. .. .. 70 1·00
80 1 r. 60, *Euphorbia pyrifolia* .. .. .. 85 1·25

15 Map of Aldabra

(Des L. Curtis. Litho Questa)

1975 (8 Nov). *10th Anniv of Territory. Maps. T* **15** *and similar horiz designs. Multicoloured.* W w **12**. P 13½.

81 50 c. Type **15** 60 85
82 1 r. Desroches .. .. 70 1·00
83 1 r. 50, Farquhar .. .. 1·00 1·50
84 2 r. Diego Garcia .. .. 1·25 1·75
MS85 147 × 147 mm. Nos. 81/4 (wmk sideways) 4·25 6·00

16 Crimson Speckled Moth

(Des PAD Studio. Litho Questa)

1976 (22 Mar). *Wildlife (4th series). T* **16** *and similar horiz designs. Multicoloured.* W w **12** *(sideways).* P 13½.

86 65 c. Type **16** 65 90
87 1 r. 20, *Dysdercus fasciatus* (weevil) .. .. 75 1·10
88 1 r. 50, *Sphex torridus* (wasp).. .. .. 80 1·25
89 2 r. *Oryctes rhinoceros* (beetle) .. .. .. 85 1·25

When the Seychelles achieved independence on 29 June 1976 the islands of Aldabra, Farquhar and Desroches reverted to its administration. The British Indian Ocean Territory at the present time thus consists only of the Chagos Archipelago, an island group, the largest of whose five main atolls is Diego Garcia. There is no indigenous population and the Commissioner for the Territory resides in London. The last definitive issue was withdrawn in August 1979.

OMNIBUS ISSUES

Details, together with prices for complete sets, of the various Omnibus issues from the 1935 Silver Jubilee series to date are included in a special section following Zululand at the end of the catalogue.

British Levant

The term "British Levant" is used by stamp collectors to describe the issues made by various British Post Offices within the former Turkish Empire.

Arrangements for the first such service were included amongst the terms of a commercial treaty between the two countries in 1832, but the system did not start operations until September 1857 when a post office for civilian use was opened in Constantinople, replacing the Army Post Office which had existed there since November 1854.

Eventually the number of British Post Offices grew to five:

Beyrout (Beirut, Lebanon). Opened 1873, closed 30 September 1914.

Constantinople (Istanbul). Opened 1 September 1857, closed 30 September 1914, re-opened 4 February 1919, finally closed 27 September 1923.

Salonica (Thessalonika, Greece). Opened 1 May 1900, closed October 1914. The city was captured by Greek troops on 7 November 1912 and incorporated into Greece by the Treaty of London (July 1913).

Smyrna (Izmir). Opened 1872, closed 30 September 1914, re-opened 1 March 1919, finally closed September 1922. Between May 1919 and September 1922 the city was under Greek occupation.

Stamboul (a sub-office of Constantinople). Opened 1 April 1884, closed 25 August 1896, re-opened 10 February 1908, finally closed 30 September 1914.

Stamps from the two British Post Offices in Egypt, still technically part of the Turkish Empire, are listed under EGYPT.

A. BRITISH POST OFFICES IN TURKISH EMPIRE, 1873–1914

For illustrations of the postmark types see BRITISH POST OFFICES ABROAD notes, following GREAT BRITAIN.

After 15 August 1905 the post offices were supplied with Great Britain stamps overprinted "LEVANT". Subsequent examples of unoverprinted stamps with Levant postmarks did not originate from the post offices and are now omitted from the listing. The use of such stamps during 1919–22 at Constantinople and Smyrna is, however, covered by a later note.

BEYROUT (BEIRUT)

Stamps of GREAT BRITAIN *cancelled* "G 06" *or circular postmark as in Types* **8**, **18** *or* **20**.

1873.

Z 1 ½d. rose-red (1870–90) .. .. .. *From* 14·00
Plate Nos. 12, 13, 14, 19, 20.

Z 2 1d. rose-red (1864–79) .. .. .. *From* 8·00
Plate Nos. 107, 118, 130, 140, 145, 148, 155, 157, 162, 167, 177, 179, 180, 184, 185, 186, 195, 198, 200, 203, 204, 211, 213, 215, 218, 220, 222.

Z 3 1½d. lake-red (1870–74) (Plate 3) £200

Z 4 2d. blue (1858–69) .. .. .. *From* 14·00
Plate Nos. 13, 14, 15.

Z 5 2½d. rosy mauve (1875) (*blued paper*) .. 70·00
Plate No. 1.

Z 6 2½d. rosy mauve (1875–76) .. .. *From* 30·00
Plate Nos. 1, 2, 3.

Z 7 2½d. rosy mauve (1876–79) .. .. *From* 25·00
Plate Nos. 3, 4, 5, 6, 7, 8, 9, 10, 11, 12, 13, 14, 15, 16, 17.

Z 8 2½d. blue (1880) .. .. .. *From* 15·00
Plate Nos. 17, 18, 19, 20.

Z 9 2½d. blue (1881) .. .. .. *From* 8·00
Plate Nos. 21, 22, 23.

Z10 3d. rose (1867–73) (Plate No. 10) .. ..

Z11 3d. rose (1873–76) .. .. ..
Plate Nos. 12, 15, 16, 18, 19, 20.

Z12 3d. rose (1881) (Plate Nos. 20, 21) .. ..

Z13 4d. vermilion (1865–73) .. .. *From* 32·00
Plate Nos. 11, 12, 13, 14.

Z14 4d. vermilion (1876) (Plate No. 15) £160

Z15 4d. sage-green (1877) .. .. ..
Plate Nos. 15, 16.

Z16 4d. grey-brown (1880) *wmk* Large Garter (Plate No. 17) .. .. ..

Z17 4d. grey-brown (1880) *wmk* Crown .. ..
Plate Nos. 17, 18.

Z18 6d. mauve (1870) (Plate Nos. 8, 9) .. ..

Z19 6d. buff (1872–73) .. .. *From* 75·00
Plate Nos. 11, 12.

Z20 6d. chestnut (1872) (Plate No. 11) .. .. 32·00

Z21 6d. grey (1873) (Plate No. 12) .. .. ..

Z22 6d. grey (1874–80) .. .. *From* 25·00
Plate Nos. 13, 14, 15, 16, 17.

Z23 8d. orange (1876) .. .. ..

Z24 10d. red-brown (1867) £160

Z25 1s. green (1867–73) .. .. .. 17·00
Plate Nos. 6, 7.

Z26 1s. green (1873–77) .. .. *From* 32·00
Plate Nos. 8, 9, 10, 12, 13.

Z27 1s. orange-brown (1880) (Plate No. 13)

Z28 1s. orange-brown (1881) .. .. .. 40·00
Plate Nos. 13, 14.

Z29 2s. blue (1867) £125

Z30 5s. rose (1867) (Plate Nos. 1, 2) .. *From* £600

1880.

Z31 ½d. deep green .. .. .. 4·00
Z32 ½d. pale green .. .. .. 3·75
Z33 1d. Venetian red .. .. .. 6·25
Z34 1½d. Venetian red £125
Z35 2d. pale rose .. .. .. 27·00
Z36 2d. deep rose .. .. .. 27·00
Z37 5d. indigo .. .. .. 55·00

1881.

Z38 1d. lilac (14 *dots*) .. .. ..
Z39 1d. lilac (16 *dots*) .. .. ..

1884.

Z40–46 ½d., 1½d., 2d., 2½d., 4d., 5d., 1s. .. *From* 3·25

1887.

Z47–55 ½d., 1½d., 2d., 2½d., 3d., 4½d., 5d., 6d., 1s. .. .. *From* 2·75

1900.

Z56–57 ½d., 1s. .. .. .. *From* 2·75

1902–04. *De La Rue ptgs.*

Z58–64 ½d. blue-green, ½d. yellow-green, 1d., 2½d., 5d., 10d., 1s. .. .. *From* 1·50

POSTAL FISCALS

Z65 1d. purple (*wmk* Anchor) .. .. ..
Z66 1d. purple (*wmk* Orb) .. .. ..

CONSTANTINOPLE

Stamps of GREAT BRITAIN *cancelled* "C" *or circular postmark as in Types* **1**, **10** *or* **19**.

1857.

Z 68 ½d. rose-red (1870–79) .. .. *From* 14·00
Plate Nos. 5, 6, 10, 11, 12, 13, 14, 15, 20.

Z 69 1d. red-brown (1854), Die I, *wmk* Small Crown, *perf* 16 .. .. ..

Z 70 1d. red-brown (1855), Die II, *wmk* Small Crown, *perf* 14 .. .. ..

Z 71 1d. red-brown, (1855), Die II, *wmk* Large Crown, *perf* 14 .. .. .. 16·00

Z 72 1d. rose-red (1857) .. .. .. 6·00

Z 73 1d. rose-red (1861) Alphabet IV .. ..

Z 74 1d. rose-red (1864–79) .. .. *From* 3·75
Plate Nos. 71, 72, 73, 74, 76, 78, 79, 80, 81, 83, 85, 87, 89, 90, 92, 93, 94, 95, 96, 97, 99, 101, 102, 105, 106, 108, 109, 110, 113, 116, 118, 119, 120, 121, 122, 123, 124, 125, 127, 129, 130, 131, 134, 135, 136, 137, 138, 140, 141, 143, 144, 145, 146, 147, 148, 149, 150, 151, 152, 155, 156, 157, 158, 159, 160, 161, 162, 163, 164, 166, 167, 170, 171, 172, 173, 174, 175, 176, 177, 178, 179, 180, 181, 183, 184, 186, 187, 188, 189, 190, 191, 192, 193, 194, 195, 196, 197, 198, 200, 201, 203, 204, 205, 206, 207, 208, 210, 212, 214, 215, 216, 220, 222, 224.

Z 75 1½d. rose-red (1870) (Plate 1) £180

Z 76 2d. blue (1855), *wmk* Large Crown, *perf* 14. (Plate Nos. 5, 6) .. .. ..

Z 77 2d. blue (1858–69) .. .. *From* 7·50
Plate Nos. 8, 9, 12, 13, 14, 15.

Z 78 2½d. rosy mauve (1875–76) (*blued paper*) (Plate Nos. 1, 2) .. .. *From* 50·00

Z 79 2½d. rosy mauve (1875–76) .. *From* 25·00
Plate Nos. 1, 2, 3.

Z 80 2½d. rosy mauve (*Error of Lettering*) ..

Z 81 2½d. rosy mauve (1876–79) .. *From* 23·00
Plate Nos. 3 to 17.

Z 82 2½d. blue (1880–81) .. .. *From* 11·00
Plate Nos. 17, 18, 19, 20.

Z 83 2½d. blue (1881) (Plate Nos. 21, 22, 23) .. 6·00
Z 84 3d. carmine-rose (1862) (Plate No. 2) .. £110
Z 85 3d. rose (1865) (Plate No. 4) .. .. 65·00
Z 86 3d. rose (1867–73) (Plate Nos. 4 to 10) .. 65·00

Z 87 3d. rose (1873–76) .. .. .. 20·00
Plates, 11, 12, 15, 16, 17, 18, 19.

Z 88 3d. rose (1881) (Plate No. 21) .. ..
Z 89 3d. on 3d. lilac (1883) (Plate No. 21) .. ..
Z 90 4d. rose (1857) .. .. .. 40·00
a. Rose-carmine .. .. ..
Z 91 4d. red (1862) (Plate Nos. 3, 4) .. *From* 35·00

Z 92 4d. vermilion (1865–73) .. .. *From* 26·00
Plate Nos. 7 to 14.

Z 93 4d. vermilion (1876) (Plate No. 15) .. £140

Z 94 4d. sage-green (1877) .. .. .. 75·00
Plate Nos. 15, 16.

Z 95 4d. grey-brown (1880) *wmk* Large Garter (Plate No. 17) .. .. ..

Z 96 4d. grey-brown (1880) *wmk* Crown (Plate Nos. 17, 18) .. .. *From* 17·00

Z 97 6d. lilac (1856) .. .. .. 50·00
Z 98 6d. lilac (1862) (Plate Nos. 3, 4) .. *From* 35·00

Z 99 6d. lilac (1865–67) .. .. .. 32·00
Plate Nos. 5, 6.

Z100 6d. lilac (1867) (Plate No. 6) .. .. 40·00

Z101 6d. violet (1867–70) .. .. *From* 32·00
Plate Nos. 6, 8, 9.

Z102 6d. buff (1872–73) .. .. .. 48·00
Plate Nos. 11, 12.

Z103 6d. chestnut (1872) (Plate No. 11) .. 26·00
Z104 6d. grey (1873) (Plate No. 12) .. .. 50·00

Z105 6d. grey (1874–76) .. .. *From* 20·00
Plate Nos. 13, 14, 15, 16.

Z106 6d. grey (1881–82) (Plate Nos. 17, 18) .. 15·00
Z107 6d. on 6d. lilac (1883) .. .. .. 65·00
a. Dots slanting (Letters MI or SJ) .. £110
Z108 8d. orange (1876) £275
Z109 10d. red-brown (1867), *wmk* Emblems .. £10000
Z110 10d. red-brown (1867) £160
Z111 1s. green (1856) .. .. .. 70·00
Z112 1s. green (1862) .. .. .. 60·00
Z113 1s. green (1862) ("K" *variety*) .. ..
Z114 1s. green (1862) (*thick paper*) .. ..
Z115 1s. green (1865) (Plate No. 4) .. .. 35·00

Z116 1s. green (1867–73) .. .. *From* 10·00
Plate Nos. 4, 5, 6, 7.

Z117 1s. green (1873–77) .. .. *From* 26·00
Plate Nos. 8, 9, 10, 11, 12, 13.

Z118 1s. orange-brown (1880) (Plate No. 13) £175

Z119 1s. orange-brown (1881) .. .. *From* 32·00
Plate Nos. 13, 14.

Z120 2s. blue (1867) .. .. .. 85·00

Z121 5s. rose (1867–74) .. .. *From* £200
Plate Nos. 1, 2.

Z122 5s. rose (1882) (*white paper*) £850
Z123 5s. rose (1882) (*blued paper*) £1000

1880.

Z124 ½d. deep green .. .. .. 3·50
Z125 ½d. pale green .. .. .. 4·25
Z126 1d. Venetian red .. .. .. 2·50
Z127 2d. pale rose .. .. .. 26·00
Z128 2d. deep rose .. .. .. 32·00
Z129 5d. indigo .. .. ..

1881.

Z130 1d. lilac (14 *dots*) .. .. ..
Z131 1d. lilac (16 *dots*) .. .. .. 2·25

1883 *to* **1884.**

Z132 ½d. slate 3.75
Z133–136 1½d., 2d., 2½d., 3d. .. .. *From* 6·00
Z137–141 4d., 5d., 6d., 9d., 1s. .. .. *From* 65·00
Z142 2s. 6d. lilac (*blued paper*) .. ..
Z143 2s. 6d. lilac (*white paper*) .. .. 80·00
Z144 5s. rose (*blued paper*) .. ..
Z145 5s. rose (*white paper*) .. ..

1887.

Z146–157 ½d., 1½d., 2d., 2½d., 3d., 4d., 4½d., 5d., 6d., 9d., 10d., 1s. .. .. *From* 2·25

1900.

Z158–159 ½d., 1s. .. .. .. *From* 2·25

1902–04. *De La Rue ptgs.*

Z160–174 ½d. blue-green, ½d. yellow-green, 1d., 1½d., 2d., 2½d., 3d., 4d. brown and green, 5d., 6d., 9d., 10d., 1s., 2s. 6d., 5s. .. *From* 2·25

POSTAL FISCAL

Z175 1d. purple (No. F19) (1868) .. .. ..

SALONICA

Stamps of GREAT BRITAIN *cancelled with circular postmark as in Type* **18** *or double-circle datestamp.*

1900.

Z202 ½d. vermilion (1887) .. .. .. 8·50
Z203 ½d. green (1900) .. .. .. 10·00
Z204 1d. lilac (1881) .. .. .. 12·00
Z205 6d. purple/*red* (1887) .. .. .. 14·00
Z206 1s. green and carmine (1900) .. .. 70·00
Z207 5s. rose (*white paper*) (1883) £175

1902.

Z208 ½d. blue-green .. .. .. 14·00
Z209 ½d. yellow-green .. .. .. 8·50
Z209*a* 1d. scarlet .. .. .. 8·50
Z209*b* 2½d. blue .. .. .. 12·00
Z209*c* 1s. green and carmine .. .. 25·00

SMYRNA (IZMIR)

Stamps of GREAT BRITAIN *cancelled* "F 87" *or circular postmark as in Type* **8**, **16** *or* **18**.

1872.

Z210 ½d. rose-red (1870–79) .. .. *From* 14·00
Plates 11, 12, 13, 14, 15.

Z211 1d. rose-red (1864–79) .. .. *From* 6·00
Plate Nos. 120, 124, 134, 137, 138, 139, 140, 142, 143, 145, 146, 148, 149, 150, 151, 152, 153, 155, 156, 157, 158, 159, 160, 161, 162, 163, 164, 166, 167, 168, 169, 170, 171, 172, 173, 174, 175, 176, 177, 178, 183, 184, 185, 186, 187, 188, 191, 193, 195, 196, 198, 200, 201, 204, 210, 215, 217, 218.

Z212 1½d. lake-red (1870–74) (Plate Nos. 1, 3) *From* £200
Z213 2d. blue (1858) *wmk* Large Crown, *perf* 16

Z214 2d. blue (1858–69) .. .. *From* 11·00
Plate Nos. 13, 14, 15.

Z215 2½d. rosy mauve (1875) (*blued paper*) .. 55·00
Plate No. 1.

Z216 2½d. rosy mauve (1875–76) .. *From* 26·00
Plate Nos. 1, 2, 3.

Z217 2½d. rosy mauve (*Error of lettering*) ..

Z218 2½d. rosy mauve (1876–79) .. *From* 22·00
Plate Nos. 3, 4, 5, 6, 7, 8, 9, 10, 11, 12, 13, 14, 15, 16, 17.

Z219 2½d. blue (1880) .. .. *From* 8·50
Plate Nos. 17, 18, 19, 20.

Z220 2½d. blue (1881) .. .. .. 7·00
Plate Nos. 21, 22, 23.

Z221 3d. rose (1867–73) .. .. .. 25·00
Plate Nos. 5, 7, 9, 10.

Z222 3d. rose (1873–76) (Plate No. 14) .. ..

Z223 4d. vermilion (1865–73) .. .. 26·00
Plate Nos. 12, 13, 14.

Z224 4d. vermilion (1876) (Plate No. 15) .. £130

Z225 4d. sage-green (1877) .. .. .. 85·00
Plate Nos. 15, 16.

Z226 4d. grey-brown (1880) *wmk* Large Garter (Plate No. 17) .. ..

Z227 4d. grey-brown (1880) *wmk* Crown (Plate Nos. 17, 18) .. .. *From* 15·00

Z228 6d. buff (1872–73) .. .. *From* 70·00
Plate Nos. 11, 12.

Z229 6d. chestnut (1872) (Plate No. 11) .. ..
Z230 6d. grey (1873) (Plate No. 12) .. .. 65·00

Z231 6d. grey (1874–80) .. .. *From* 22·00
Plate Nos. 13, 14, 15, 16, 17.

Z232 6d. grey (1881–82) (Plate Nos. 17, 18) ..
Z233 6d. on 6d. lilac (1883) .. .. .. 70·00
Z234 8d. orange (1876) .. .. ..
Z235 9d. straw (1867) £175
Z236 10d. red-brown (1867) £130
Z237 1s. green (1867–73) (Plate Nos. 6, 7) ..

Z238 1s. green (1873–77) .. .. *From* 27·00
Plate Nos. 8, 9, 10, 11, 12, 13.

Z239 1s. orange-brown (1880) (Plate No. 13) £160
Z240 1s. orange-brown (1881) (Plate Nos. 13, 14) .. 40·00
Z241 5s. rose (1867–74) (Plate No. 2) ..

1880.

Z242 ½d. deep green .. .. .. 4·00
Z243 ½d. pale green .. .. .. 3·75
Z244 1d. Venetian red .. .. .. 6·50
Z245 1½d. Venetian red .. .. .. 70·00

Z246 2d. pale rose .. .. 24·00
Z247 2d. deep rose .. .. 26·00
Z248 5d. indigo .. .. 48·00

1881.
Z249 1d. lilac (16 *dots*) .. .. 3·75

1884.
Z250 ½d. slate-blue .. .. 6·00
Z251–252 2d., 2½d. .. .. *From* 6·00
Z253–255 4d., 5d., 1s. .. .. *From* 70·00

1887.
Z256–264 ½d., 1½d., 2d., 2½d., 3d., 4d., 5d., 6d., 1s... .. .. *From* 2·75

1900.
Z265–266 ½d., 1s. .. .. *From* 3·00

1902–04. *De La Rue ptgs.*
Z267–281 ½d. blue-green, ½d. yellow-green, 1d., 1½d., 2d., 2½d., 3d., 4d. brown and green, 5d., 6d., 9d., 10d., 1s., 2s. 6d., 5s.. . *From* 3·75

STAMBOUL (CONSTANTINOPLE)

Stamps of GREAT BRITAIN *cancelled* "S" *as Type* **10**, *or circular postmarks inscribed either* "BRITISH POST OFFICE CONSTANTINOPLE S" *or* "BRITISH POST OFFICE STAMBOUL" *as Type* **18**.

1884.
Z296 ½d. slate .. .. 15·00
Z297 1d. lilac .. .. 7·00
Z298 2d. lilac .. ..
Z299 2½d. lilac .. .. 9·00
Z300 5d. green .. .. 70·00

1887.
Z306–317 ½d., 1½d., 2d., 2½d., 3d., 4d., 4½d., 5d., 6d., 9d., 10d., 1s. .. .. .. *From* 3·00

The "S" cancellation was in use from 1885 to 1892 and the "Stamboul" mark from 1892 to 1896, when the office was closed, and from its reopening in 1908 to 1914. The "CONSTANTINOPLE S" handstamp was normally used as a back stamp, but can be found cancelling stamps in the period 1885 to 1892.

PRICES FOR STAMPS ON COVER

Nos. 1/40	*from* × 3
Nos. L1/4	*from* × 3
Nos. L5/10	*from* × 5
Nos. L11/17	*from* × 3

I. TURKISH CURRENCY

Following the depreciation of the Turkish piastre against sterling in 1884 it was decided to issue stamps surcharged in Turkish currency to avoid speculation. During the early period unsurcharged stamps of Great Britain remained on sale from the British Post Offices at the current rate of exchange until replaced by "LEVANT" overprints.

80 PARAS (1) **4 PIASTRES** (2) **12 PIASTRES** (3)

***Stamps of Great Britain (Queen Victoria) surch as T* 1 *to* 3**

PRINTERS. Nos. 1/24 were surcharged or overprinted by De La Rue, *unless otherwise stated.*

1885 (1 Aug).
1 **64** 40 pa. on 2½d. lilac .. .. .. 27·00 4·00
2 **62** 80 pa. on 5d. green .. .. .. £225 9·50
3 **58** 12 pi. on 2s. 6d. lilac/*bluish* £250 £160
a. On white paper (S. £120) .. .. 38·00 22·00

1877 (June)–**96.**
4 **74** 40 pa. on 2½d. purple/*blue* .. .. 1·90 60
a. Surch double £1700 £2500
5 **78** 80 pa. on 5d. purple and blue (6.90) .. 6·00 1·00
a. Small "0" in "80" .. .. .. 75·00 55·00
6 **81** 4 pi. on 10d. dull purple and carmine (10.10.96) .. .. 26·00 10·00
a. Dull purple and deep bright carmine .. .. .. 24·00 9·50
b. Large, wide "4" .. .. .. 38·00 40·00

No. 5a occurs twice on each sheet in positions R.4/2 and R.4/8 of both the upper and the lower pane.

1893 (25 Feb). *Roughly handstamped at Constantinople, as T* **1**.
7 **71** 40 pa. on ½d. vermilion £450 £170

This provisional was in use for five days only at the Constantinople and Stamboul offices. As fraudulent copies were made with the original handstamp, and can be found "used" on piece cancelled by fraudulent use of the usual canceller, this stamp should only be purchased from undoubted sources. It is also known with genuine handstamp inverted.

1902–5. *Stamps of King Edward VII surch as T* **1** *to* **3**.
8 **86** 40 pa. on 2½d. ultramarine, **O** (6.2.02) .. 2·75 70
a. Pale ultramarine .. .. .. 2·75 65
9 **89** 80 pa. on 5d. purple and ultramarine, **O** (5.6.02) .. .. 3·25 3·25
a. Small "0" in "80" £160 £130
10 **92** 4 pi. on 10d. dull purple and carmine, **O** (6.9.02) .. .. 12·00 5·00
a. No cross on crown £120 £130
b. Chalky paper .. .. .. 13·00 9·50
ba. Chalky. No cross on crown £140 £175
11 **94** 12 pi. on 2s. 6d. lilac, **O** (29.8.03) .. 27·00 32·00
a. Pale dull purple, **C** .. .. 55·00 65·00
b. Dull purple, **C** .. .. .. 27·00 32·00
12 **95** 24 pi. on 5s. carmine, **O** (15.8.05) .. 65·00 75·00
9/11 H/S "Specimen" .. .. .. *Set of* 3 £180

No. 9a only occurs on the first printing of 80 pa. on 5d.

1 PIASTRE
(4)

1905–08. *Surch in* "PIASTRES" *instead of* "PARAS" *as T* **4** *and* **2**.
13 **86** 1 pi. on 2½d. ultramarine, **O** (19.4.06) 3·25 45
14 **89** 2 pi. on 5d. dull purple and ultramarine, **O** (11.11.05) .. .. 9·50 3·50
a. Chalky paper (1.08) .. .. .. 9·50 3·50
b. Slate-purple and ultramarine, **C** 17·00 7·00

1 Piastre (5) **1 PIASTRE 10 PARAS** (6)

1906 (2 July). *Issued at Beyrout. No. L4 surch with T* **5** *by American Press, Beyrout.*
15 **85** 1 pi. on 2d. grey-green and carmine, **O** £1500 £800

1909 (16 Nov–Dec). *Stamps of King Edward VII surch as T* **1** (30 *pa.*), **6**, *and* **2** (5 *pi.*).
16 **84** 30 pa. on 1½d. pale dull purple and green, **C** .. .. 2·50 2·00
a. Surch double, one albino ..
17 **87** 1 pi. 10 pa. on 3d. dull purple/*orange-yellow*, **C** .. .. 9·50 16·00
18 **88** 1 pi. 30 pa. on 4d. green and chocolate-brown, **C** .. .. 9·50 14·00
19 1 pi. 30 pa. on 4d. pale orange, **O** (16.12.09) .. .. 12·00 15·00
20 **83** 2 pi. 20 pa. on 6d. dull purple, **C** .. 23·00 35·00
21 **93** 5 pi. on 1s. dull green and carmine, **C** 10·00 16·00
16/21 .. .. *Set of* 6 60·00 90·00

1¾ PIASTRE (7)

Normal "4"

Pointed "4"

1910 (24 Jan). *Stamps of King Edward VII surch as T* **7**.
22 **87** 1¼ pi. on 3d. dull purple/*orange-yellow*, **C** 1·25 2·50
23 **88** 1¾ pi. on 4d. pale orange, **O** .. .. 1·40 2·25
a. Orange-red, **O** .. .. .. 1·75 3·00
b. Thin, pointed "4" in fraction .. 35·00 45·00
24 **83** 2½ pi. on 6d. dull purple, **C** .. .. 3·00 3·25

No. 23b occurs in the first and seventh vertical rows of the sheet. The variety also occurs on No. 38, but not on No. 38b.

1 PIASTRE (8) **1 PIASTRE** (9)

TYPE DIFFERENCES. In T **4** the letters are tall and narrow and the space enclosed by the upper part of the "A" is small.

In T **8** the opening of the "A" is similar but the letters are shorter and broader, the "P" and the "E" being particularly noticeable.

In T **9** the letters are short and broad, but the "A" is thin and open.

1911–13. *Stamps of King Edward VII, Harrison or Somerset House ptgs, surch at Somerset House.*

(*a*) *Surch with T* **4** (20 *July*)
25 **86** 1 pi. on 2½d. bright blue (*perf* 14) .. 3·25 5·00
26 1 pi. on 2½d. bright blue (*perf* 15 × 14) (14.10.11) .. .. 7·00 2·75
a. Dull blue .. .. 7·00 2·75
b. Surch double, one albino .. ..

(*b*) *Surch with T* **8**
27 **86** 1 pi. on 2½d. brt blue (*perf* 15 × 14) (3.12) .. .. 12·00 5·00
a. Dull blue .. .. 12·00 5·00

(*c*) *Surch with T* **9** (7.12)
28 **86** 1 pi. on 2½d. bright blue (*perf* 15 × 14) 15·00 1·00
a. Dull blue .. .. 15·00 1·00

(*d*) *Surch as T* **1** *to* **3** (1911–13)
29 **84** 30 pa. on 1½d. reddish purple and bright green (22.8.11) .. .. .. 4·00 1·40
a. Slate-purple and green .. .. 4·00 3·00
b. Surch double, one albino ..
30 **89** 2 pi. on 5d. dull reddish purple and bright blue (13.5.12) .. .. 3·00 2·75
a. Deep dull reddish purple and bright blue .. .. 3·00 2·75
31 **92** 4 pi. on 10d. dull purple and scarlet (26.6.12) .. .. 11·00 13·00
a. Dull reddish purple and aniline pink .. ..
b. Dull reddish purple and carmine 12·00 14·00
c. No cross on crown ..
32 **93** 5 pi. on 1s. green and carmine (1913) 11·00 11·00
33 **94** 12 pi. on 2s. 6d. dull reddish purple (3.2.12) .. .. 80·00 80·00
a. Dull greyish purple .. .. 27·00 32·00
b. Pale dull reddish purple .. .. 27·00 32·00
34 **95** 24 pi. on 5s. carmine (1913) .. .. 60·00 65·00
a. Surch double, one albino ..
29/34 .. .. *Set of* 6 £100 £110

1913 (Apr)–**14.** *Stamps of King George V, wmk Royal Cypher, surch as T* **1** (30 *pa.*), **9** (1 *pi.*), **7** *or* **2** (4 *and* 5 *pi.*).
35 **105** 30 pa. on 1½d. red-brown (4.13) .. 2·75 4·50
36 **104** 1 pi. on 2½d. cobalt-blue (6.13) .. 50 35
a. Bright blue 50 35
37 **106** 1¼ pi. on 3d. dull reddish violet (9.13) .. 1·50 4·25
a. Violet .. .. 1·50 4·25
38 1¾ pi. on 4d. deep grey-green (7.13) .. 2·50 5·00
a. Thin, pointed "4" in fraction .. 75·00 85·00
b. Grey-green .. .. .. 2·25 5·00
39 **108** 4 pi. on 10d. turquoise-blue (12.13) .. 11·00 12·00
40 5 pi. on 1s. bistre-brown (1.14) .. .. 21·00 35·00
35/40 .. .. *Set of* 6 35·00 55·00

II. BRITISH CURRENCY

Stamps overprinted "LEVANT", were for use on parcels, newspapers and printed matter. The face values were left in sterling to simplify accounting with the steamship and railway companies involved in the transmission of these classes of mail. They replaced those unoverprinted Great Britain stamps which had remained on sale from the Levant Post Offices after the introduction of the Turkish currency surcharges.

LEVANT
(L 1)

1905 (15 Aug)–**12.** *Stamps of King Edward VII optd with Type* L **1**.

(*a*) *De La Rue ptgs*
L 1 **83** ½d. pale yellowish green, **O** .. .. 1·25 45
a. Yellowish green, **O** .. .. 1·25 45
L 2 1d. scarlet, **O** .. .. 1·25 45
a. Bright scarlet, **O** .. .. .. 2·00 1·50
L 3 **84** 1½d. dull purple and green, **O** .. 6·00 5·00
a. Chalky paper .. .. .. 10·00 6·50
L 4 **85** 2d. grey-green and carmine, **O** .. 6·50 8·50
a. Chalky paper .. .. .. 4·00 6·00
b. Pale blue-green and carmine, **C** .. 4·00 6·00
L 5 **86** 2½d. ultramarine, **O** .. .. .. 12·00 16·00
L 6 **87** 3d. purple/*orange-yellow*, **O** .. .. 9·00 15·00
L 7 **88** 4d. grey-green and brown, **O** .. .. 7·00 13·00
a. Green and chocolate-brown, **O** .. 7·00 13·00
L 8 **89** 5d. dull purple and ultramarine, **O** .. 18·00 26·00
L 9 **83** 6d. pale dull purple, **O** .. .. 15·00 26·00
L10 **93** 1s. dull green and carmine, **O** .. 25·00 30·00
a. Chalky paper .. .. .. 25·00 30·00
L1/10 .. .. *Set of* 10 90·00 £120

(*b*) *Harrison ptgs optd at Somerset House*
L11 **83** ½d. dull yellow-green (*p.* 14) (2.12) .. 4·00 9·00
a. Dull green .. .. 4·00 9·00
b. Deep dull green .. .. .. 4·00 9·00

On 28 December 1909 all values, except for the ½d., 1d. and 2d. stamps, were withdrawn from sale. Subsequent dated cancellations on the withdrawn values are philatelic, being worth only a fraction of the used prices quoted.

1911–13. *Stamps of King George V optd with Type* L **1** *at Somerset House.* (*a*) *Die A. Wmk Crown.*
L12 **98** ½d. green (No. 322) (12.9.11) .. .. 1·50 2·25
L13 **99** 1d. carmine-red (No. 327) (1.1.12) .. 1·50 3·00
a. No cross on crown .. .. ..
b. Opt double, one albino .. .. 70·00

(*b*) *Redrawn types. Wmk Crown*
L14 **101** ½d. green (No. 339) (21.3.12) 50 30
a. Yellow-green 60 30
L15 **102** 1d. bright scarlet (No. 341) (24.2.12) .. 50 30
a. Scarlet (No. 342) 60 30
b. Opt triple, two albino .. ..

(*c*) *New types. Wmk Royal Cypher* (7.13)
L16 **105** ½d. green (No. 351) 30 50
a. Yellow-green 40 50
L17 **104** 1d. scarlet (No. 357) .. .. .. 50 1·75
a. Vermilion .. .. 70 1·75

Similar overprints were issued when the British Post Offices reopened in 1919, and are listed below.

B. BRITISH POST OFFICES IN CONSTANTINOPLE AND SMYRNA, 1919–1923

CONSTANTINOPLE

Following the occupation of Constantinople by Allied forces a British Military Post Office was opened for civilian use on 4 February 1919. During the period of its existence stamps of Great Britain with face values to 10s. were available and such use can be identified by the following cancellations:

"FIELD POST OFFICE H12" (4 February 1919 to March 1919)
"ARMY POST OFFICE Y" (March 1919 to July 1919)
"ARMY POST OFFICE S.X.3" (April 1919 to July 1919)
"BRITISH A.P.O. CONSTANTINOPLE" (July 1919 to Sept 1920).

Of these four marks the first two types were also used for military mail.

The office reverted to civilian control in July 1920, Nos. 41/50 and L18/24 being intended for its use.

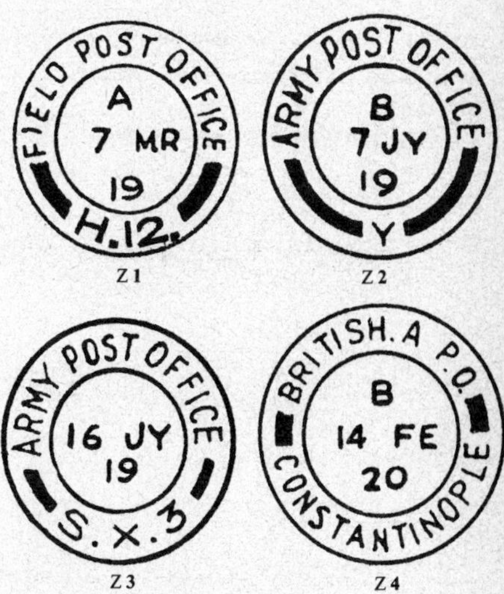

Z 1 Z 2 Z 3 Z 4

1919–20. *Used at the Army Post Office. Stamps of* GREAT BRITAIN *cancelled with Types* Z 1, Z 2, Z 3, Z 4.

Z176–187	½d., 1d., 1½d., 2d. Die I, 2½d., 4d., 6d., 9d. agate, 1s., 2s. 6d., 5s., 10s.	*From*	3·00

1920–21. *Used at the Civilian Post Office. Stamps of* GREAT BRITAIN *cancelled with Type* 18 *or double-circle datestamp.*

Z188–201	½d., 1d., 1½d., 2d. Die I, 2½d., 3d., 4d., 5d., 6d., 10d., 1s, 2s. 6d., 5s., 10s	*From*	2·50

SMYRNA

When the office re-opened on 1 March 1919 existing stocks of surcharged or overprinted issues were utilised until they were exhausted in mid-1920. During this period examples of Nos. 24, 30*a*, 35, 36, L4*b*, L14/17 are known with commercial postmarks. These stamps were supplemented and replaced by ordinary stamps of Great Britain.

Stamps of GREAT BRITAIN *cancelled with circular postmark as Type* 18 *or with* "REGISTERED" *oval.*

Z282–293	½d., 1d., 1½d., 2d. Die I, 2d. Die II, 2½d. blue, 2½d. Prussian blue, 4d., 6d., 10d., 1s., 2s. 6d., 5s.	*From*	4·50

PRICES FOR STAMPS ON COVER

Nos. 41/50	*from* × 2
Nos. L18/24	*from* × 5

Stamps of Great Britain surch at Somerset House

I. TURKISH CURRENCY

1½ PIASTRES (10) 15 PIASTRES (11)

1921 (Aug). *Stamps of King George V, wmk Royal Cypher, surch as T* 1 *(30 pa.),* 10 *and* 11 *(15 and 18¾ pi.).*

No.	Type		Unused	Used
41	**105**	30 pa. on ½d. green	30	1·75
		a. Yellow-green	30	1·75
42	**104**	1½ pi. on 1d. bright scarlet	30	40
		a. Vermilion	30	50
		b. Scarlet-vermilion	30	60
43		3¾ pi. on 2½d. blue	50	1·25
		a. Dull Prussian blue	6·00	2·00
44	**106**	4½ pi. on 3d. violet	95	2·75
		a. Bluish violet	1·00	2·50
45	**107**	7½ pi. on 5d. brown	40	40
		a. Yellow-brown	40	75
46	**108**	15 pi. on 10d. turquoise-blue	70	50
47		18¾ pi. on 1s. bistre-brown	5·00	4·00
		a. Olive-bistre	5·00	5·00

45 PIASTRES (12)

1921. *Stamps of King George V (Bradbury, Wilkinson printing) surch as T* 12.

No.	Type		Unused	Used
48	**109**	45 pi. on 2s. 6d. chocolate-brown	27·00	40·00
		a. Olive-brown	42·00	55·00
49		90 pi. on 5s. rose-red	50·00	45·00
50		180 pi. on 10s. dull grey-blue	80·00	60·00
		a. Opt double, one albino		
41/50		*Set of* 10	£150	£130
47/50 H/S "Specimen"		*Set of* 4	£375	

II. BRITISH CURRENCY

1921. *Stamps of King George V optd as Type* L 1.

No.	Type		Unused	Used
L18	**106**	2d. reddish orange (Die I)	2·00	11·00
		a. Bright orange	2·00	11·00
L19		3d. bluish violet	4·75	8·50
L20		4d. grey-green	3·25	9·00
L21	**107**	5d. yellow-brown	7·50	13·00
L22		6d. dull purple, C	8·00	13·00
		a. Reddish purple, C	6·50	6·50
L23	**108**	1s. bistre-brown (H/S/S. £110)	6·50	6·50
		a. Olive-bistre	6·50	6·50
L24	**109**	2s. 6d. chocolate-brown (H/S S. £200)	45·00	65·00
		a. Olive-brown	65·00	95·00
L18/24		*Set of* 7	70·00	£110

On No. L24 the letters of the overprint are shorter, being only 3 mm high.

Nos. 41/50 and L18/24 were used at the Constantinople office only.

C. BRITISH FIELD OFFICE IN SALONICA

These overprints were originally prepared for use by a civilian post office to be set up on Mt Athos, Northern Greece. When the project was abandoned they were placed on sale at the Army Field Office in Salonica.

PRICES FOR STAMPS ON COVER

Nos. S1/8	*from* × 3

Levant (S 1)

1916 (end Feb–9 Mar). *Stamps of Gt. Britain, optd with Type* S 1 *by Army Printing Office, Salonica.*

No.	Type		Unused	Used
S 1	**105**	½d. green	15·00	22·00
		a. Opt double	£375	£375
		b. Vert pair, one without opt	£350	£375
S 2	**104**	1d. scarlet	15·00	22·00
		a. Opt double	£500	£500
S 3	**106**	2d. reddish orange (Die I)	55·00	80·00
S 4		3d. bluish violet	42·00	65·00
		a. Opt double		
S 5		4d. grey-green	65·00	80·00
S 6	**107**	6d. reddish purple, C	55·00	80·00
		a. Vert pair, one without opt	£450	£575
S 7	**108**	9d. agate	£170	£250
		a. Opt double	£2750	£1750
		ab. Opt double, one albino (inverted and reversed)	£1000	
S 8		1s. bistre-brown	£160	£325
S 1/8		*Set of* 8	£550	£800

There are numerous forgeries of this overprint.

British New Guinea
see Papua

British Occupation of Iraq
see Iraq

British Occupation of Italian Colonies

PRICES FOR STAMPS ON COVER TO 1945

Nos. M1/21	*from* × 4
Nos. MD1/5	*from* × 10
Nos. S1/9	*from* × 4

The above prices refer to covers from the territories concerned, not examples used in Great Britain.

MIDDLE EAST FORCES

For use in territory occupied by British Forces in Eritrea (1942), Italian Somaliland (1942), Cyrenaica (1943), Tripolitania (1943), and some of the Dodecanese Islands (1945).

PRICES. Our prices for used stamps with "M.E.F." overprints are for specimens with identifiable postmarks of the territories in which they were issued. These stamps were also used in the United Kingdom with official sanction, from the summer of 1950 onwards, and with U.K. postmarks are worth about 25 per cent less.

M.E.F. (M 1) Opt. 14 mm long. Regular lettering and upright oblong stops.

M.E.F. (M 2) Opt. 13½ mm long. Regular lettering and square stops.

M.E.F. (M 2*a*) Opt. 13½ mm long. Rough lettering and round stops.

(Illustrations twice actual size)

1942 (2 Mar). *Stamps of Great Britain optd.* W **127**. *P* 15 × 14.

(*a*) *With Type* M 1 *by Harrison & Sons*

No.	Type		Unused	Used
M 1	**128**	1d. scarlet (No. 463)	20	50
M 2		2d. orange (No. 465)	25	50
M 3	**128**	2½d. ultramarine (No. 466)	20	40
M 4		3d. violet (No. 467)	25	35
		a. Opt double		
M 5	**129**	5d. brown	30	50

(*b*) *With Type* M **2** *by Army Printing Services, Cairo*

No.	Type		Unused	Used
M 6	**128**	1d. scarlet (No. 463)	12·00	6·50
		a. Optd. with Type M 2*a*	10·00	6·00
		b. Nos. M6/a *se-tenant* vert	30·00	30·00
M 7		2d. orange (No. 465)	25·00	20·00
		a. Optd with Type M 2*a*	20·00	17·00
		b. Nos. M7/a *se-tenant* vert	60·00	60·00
M 8		2½d. ultramarine (No. 466)	11·00	6·50
		a. Optd with Type M 2*a*	9·00	5·00
		b. Nos. M8/a *se-tenant* vert	30·00	30·00
M 9		3d. violet (No. 467)	16·00	14·00
		a. Optd with Type M 2*a*	13·00	11·00
		b. Nos. M9/a *se-tenant* vert	50·00	50·00
M10	**129**	5d. brown	95·00	40·00
		a. Optd with Type M 2*a*	85·00	35·00
		b. Nos. M10/a *se-tenant* vert	£275	£225

See note after No. M21.

Nos. M6/10 were issued in panes of 60 (6 × 10), rows 2, 3, and 7 being overprinted with Type M **2** and the other seven rows with Type M 2*a*.

M.E.F. (M 3)

Optd 13½ mm long. Regular lettering and upright oblong stops.

(Illustration twice actual size)

1943 (1 Jan)–**1947.** *Stamps of Great Britain optd with Type* M 3 *by Harrison & Sons.* W **127**, *P* 15 × 14 *(1d. to 1s.);* W **133**, *P* 14 *(others).*

No.	Type		Unused	Used
M11	**128**	1d. pale scarlet (No. 486)	35	15
M12		2d. pale orange (No. 488)	35	15
M13		2½d. light ultramarine (No. 489)	30	15
M14		3d. pale violet (No. 490)	30	15
M15	**129**	5d. brown	40	20
M16		6d. purple	30	30
M17	**130**	9d. deep olive-green	1·25	90
M18		1s. bistre-brown	90	65
M19	**131**	2s. 6d. yellow-green	7·00	2·50
M20		5s. red (1947)	16·00	18·00
M21	**132**	10s. ultramarine (1947)	22·00	20·00
M11/21		*Set of* 11	45·00	38·00
M18/21 H/S "Specimen"		*Set of* 4	£600	

The overprint on No. M15 should not be confused with the other overprints on the 5d. value. It can be distinguished from No. M5 by the ½ mm difference in length; and from No. M10 by the more intense colour, thicker lettering and larger stops.

POSTAGE DUE STAMPS

M.E.F. (MD 1)

1942. *Postage Due Stamps of Great Britain optd with Type* MD 1, *in blue-black.* W **127** *(sideways). P* 14 × 15.

No.	Type		Unused	Used
MD1	D 1	½d. emerald	40	2·00
MD2		1d. carmine	40	2·00
MD3		2d. agate	2·25	4·00
MD4		3d. violet	1·10	4·00
MD5		1s. deep blue (H/S S. £150)	6·50	10·00

ERITREA

BRITISH MILITARY ADMINISTRATION

B. M. A. ERITREA 10 CENTS (E 1) B. M. A. ERITREA 5 SHILLINGS (E 2)

1948–9. *Stamps of Great Britain surch as Types* E 1 *or* E **2**.

No.	Type		Unused	Used
E 1	**128**	5 c. on ½d. pale green	30	55
E 2		10 c. on 1d. pale scarlet	50	1·75
E 3		20 c. on 2d. pale orange	80	2·25
E 4		25 c. on 2½d. light ultramarine	30	95
E 5		30 c. on 3d. pale violet	1·40	2·50
E 6	**129**	40 c. on 5d. brown	35	1·75
E 7		50 c. on 6d. purple	45	1·10
E 7*a*	**130**	65 c. on 8d. bright carmine (1.2.49)	1·50	2·25
E 8		75 c. on 9d. deep olive-green	85	1·50
E 9		1 s. on 1s. bistre-brown	85	1·25
E10	**131**	2 s. 50 c. on 2s. 6d. yellow-green	7·00	12·00
E11		5 s. on 5s. red	12·00	19·00
E12	**132**	10 s. on 10s. ultramarine	20·00	27·00
E1/12		*Set of* 13	42·00	65·00

BRITISH ADMINISTRATION

1950 (6 Feb). *As Nos.* E1/12, *but surch* "B.A. ERITREA" *and new values instead of* "B.M.A." *etc.*

No.	Type		Unused	Used
E13	**128**	5 c. on ½d. pale green	25	90
E14		10 c. on 1d. pale scarlet	25	80
E15		20 c. on 2d. pale orange	25	1·00
E16		25 c. on 2½d. light ultramarine	25	1·00
E17		30 c. on 3d. pale violet	25	1·00
E18	**129**	40 c. on 5d. brown	40	1·00

E19	129	50 c. on 6d. purple	55	80
E20	130	65 c. on 8d. bright carmine	80	1·75
E21		75 c. on 9d. deep olive-green	50	90
E22		1 s. on 1s. bistre-brown	55	80
E23	131	2 s. 50 c. on 2s. 6d. yellow-green	5·00	8·50
E24		5 s. on 5s. red	15·00	15·00
E25	132	10 s. on 10s. ultramarine	30·00	35·00
E13/25		*Set of* 13	48·00	60·00

1951 (3 May). *Nos.* 503/4, 506/7 *and* 509/11 *of Great Britain surch* "B.A. ERITREA" *and new values.*

E26	128	5 c. on ½d. pale orange	25	80
E27		10 c. on 1d. light ultramarine	25	70
E28		20 c. on 2d. pale red-brown	35	90
E29		25 c. on 2½d. pale scarlet	25	70
E30	147	2 s. 50 c. on 2s. 6d. yellow-green	7·00	9·00
E31	148	5 s. on 5s. red	18·00	21·00
E32		10 s. on 10s. ultramarine	27·00	23·00
E26/32		*Set of* 7	48·00	50·00

POSTAGE DUE STAMPS

B. M. A.
ERITREA
10 CENTS

(ED 1)

1948. *Postage Due stamps of Great Britain surch as Type* ED 1.

ED1	D 1	5 c. on ½d. emerald	9·00	20·00
ED2		10 c. on 1d. carmine	8·00	19·00
ED3		20 c. on 2d. agate	8·00	20·00
ED4		30 c. on 3d. violet	10·00	20·00
ED5		1 s. on 1s. deep blue	20·00	30·00

1950 (6 Feb). *As Nos.* ED1/5, *but surch* "B.A. ERITREA" *and new values instead of* "B.M.A." *etc.*

ED6	D 1	5 c. on ½d. emerald	14·00	20·00
ED7		10 c. on 1d. carmine	10·00	17·00
		a. "C" of "CENTS" omitted	£800	
ED8		20 c. on 2d. agate	12·00	14·00
ED9		30 c. on 3d. violet	13·00	15·00
ED10		1 s. on 1s. deep blue	17·00	22·00

Stamps of Ethiopia were used in Eritrea after 15 September 1952 following federation with Ethiopia.

SOMALIA

BRITISH OCCUPATION

E.A.F.

(S 1. "East Africa Forces")

1943 (15 Jan)–**46.** *Stamps of Great Britain optd with Type* S 1, *in blue.*

S1	128	1d. pale scarlet	25	70
S2		2d. pale orange	25	80
S3		2½d. light ultramarine	25	1·50
S4		3d. pale violet	25	50
S5	129	5d. brown	25	65
S6		6d. purple	30	90
S7	130	9d. deep olive-green	70	2·75
S8		1s. bistre-brown	70	50
S9	131	2s. 6d. yellow-green (1946)	8·00	8·00
S1/9		*Set of* 9	10·00	14·50
S8/9 H/S "Specimen"		*Set of* 2	£250	

The note *re* used prices above Type M 1 of Middle East Forces also applies to the above issue.

BRITISH MILITARY ADMINISTRATION

1948 (27 May). *Stamps of Great Britain surch* "B.M.A./SOMALIA" *and new values, as Types* E 1 *and* E 2 *of Eritrea.*

S10	128	5 c. on ½d. pale green	20	90
S11		15 c. on 1½d. pale red-brown	1·25	4·50
S12		20 c. on 2d. pale orange	20	1·75
S13		25 c. on 2½d. light ultramarine	20	75
S14		30 c. on 3d. pale violet	1·40	9·00
S15	129	40 c. on 5d. brown	25	1·25
S16		50 c. on 6d. purple	50	2·00
S17	130	75 c. on 9d. deep olive-green	1·60	7·50
S18		1 s. on 1s. bistre-brown	1·00	1·25
S19	131	2 s. 50 c. on 2s. 6d. yellow-green	6·50	16·00
S20		5 s. on 5s. red	15·00	27·00
S10/20		*Set of* 11	25·00	65·00

BRITISH ADMINISTRATION

1950 (2 Jan). *As Nos.* S10/20, *but surch* "B.A./SOMALIA" *and new values, instead of* "B.M.A." *etc.*

S21	128	5 c. on ½d. pale green	20	75
S22		15 c. on 1½d. pale red-brown	70	5·00
S23		20 c. on 2d. pale orange	75	2·50
S24		25 c. on 2½d. light ultramarine	40	1·25
S25		30 c. on 3d. pale violet	1·25	3·00
S26	129	40 c. on 5d. brown	85	1·25
S27		50 c. on 6d. purple	50	1·25
S28	130	75 c. on 9d. deep olive-green	1·25	4·50
S29		1 s. on 1s. bistre-brown	90	2·00
S30	131	2 s. 50 c. on 2s. 6d. yellow-green	8·50	18·00
S31		5 s. on 5s. red	15·00	22·00
S21/31		*Set of* 11	27·00	55·00

Somalia reverted to Italian Administration on 1 April 1950 later becoming independent. Later issues will be found listed in Part 8 (*Italy and Switzerland*) of this catalogue.

MINIMUM PRICE

The minimum price quoted is 5p which represents a handling charge rather than a basis for valuing common stamps. For further notes about prices see introductory pages.

TRIPOLITANIA

BRITISH MILITARY ADMINISTRATION

1948 (1 July). *Stamps of Great Britain surch* "B.M.A./TRIPOLITANIA" *and new values, as Types* E 1 *and* E 2 *of Eritrea, but expressed in M(ilitary) A(dministration) L(ire).*

T 1	128	1 l. on ½d. pale green	25	1·25
T 2		2 l. on 1d. pale scarlet	20	90
T 3		3 l. on 1½d. pale red-brown	20	1·25
T 4		4 l. on 2d. pale orange	25	1·00
T 5		5 l. on 2½d. light ultramarine	25	1·10
T 6		6 l. on 3d. pale violet	20	1·10
T 7	129	10 l. on 5d. brown	20	1·00
T 8		12 l. on 6d. purple	25	90
T 9	130	18 l. on 9d. deep olive-green	90	2·25
T10		24 l. on 1s. bistre-brown	1·10	3·00
T11	131	60 l. on 2s. 6d. yellow-green	3·25	10·00
T12		120 l. on 5s. red	10·00	25·00
T13	132	240 l. on 10s. ultramarine	17·00	50·00
T1/13		*Set of* 13	30·00	90·00

BRITISH ADMINISTRATION

1950 (6 Feb). *As Nos.* T1/13, *but surch.* "B.A. TRIPOLITANIA" *and new values, instead of* "B.M.A." *etc.*

T14	128	1 l. on ½d. pale green	35	2·00
T15		2 l. on 1d. pale scarlet	30	1·10
T16		3 l. on 1½d. pale red-brown	50	2·00
T17		4 l. on 2d. pale orange	25	1·50
T18		5 l. on 2½d. light ultramarine	25	1·50
T19		6 l. on 3d. pale violet	25	1·50
T20	129	10 l. on 5d. brown	25	1·25
T21		12 l. on 6d. purple	25	1·25
T22	130	18 l. on 9d. deep olive-green	55	1·60
T23		24 l. on 1s. bistre-brown	75	2·25
T24	131	60 l. on 2s. 6d. yellow-green	7·00	13·00
T25		120 l. on 5s. red	14·00	27·00
T26	132	240 l. on 10s. ultramarine	28·00	40·00
T14/26		*Set of* 13	48·00	85·00

1951 (3 May). *Nos.* 503/7 *and* 509/11 *of Great Britain surch* "B.A. TRIPOLITANIA" *and new values.*

T27	128	1 l. on ½d. pale orange	20	1·75
T28		2 l. on 1d. light ultramarine	20	1·60
T29		3 l. on 1½d. pale green	65	1·75
T30		4 l. on 2d. pale red-brown	40	1·60
T31		5 l. on 2½d. pale scarlet	25	1·60
T32	147	60 l. on 2s. 6d. yellow-green	6·00	17·00
T33	148	120 l. on 5s. red	14·00	25·00
T34	149	240 l. on 10s. ultramarine	25·00	35·00
T27/34		*Set of* 8	42·00	75·00

POSTAGE DUE STAMPS

1948. *Postage Due stamps of Great Britain surch.* "B.M.A./TRIPOLITANIA" *and new values, as Type* ED 1 *of Eritrea, but expressed in M(ilitary) A(dministration) L(ire).*

TD1	D 1	1 l. on ½d. emerald	2·75	11·00
TD2		2 l. on 1d. carmine	2·75	11·00
TD3		4 l. on 2d. agate	5·50	15·00
TD4		6 l. on 3d. violet	9·00	22·00
TD5		24 l. on 1s. deep blue	28·00	48·00

1950 (6 Feb). *As Nos.* TD1/5, *but surch* "B.A. TRIPOLITANIA" *and new values, instead of* "B.M.A." *etc.*

TD 6	D 1	1 l. on ½d. emerald	4·50	15·00
TD 7		2 l. on 1d. carmine	2·50	12·00
TD 8		4 l. on 2d. agate	2·75	12·00
TD 9		6 l. on 3d. violet	12·00	35·00
TD10		24 l. on 1s. deep blue	28·00	48·00

Tripolitania is now part of the independent republic of Libya.

British P.Os in Crete

BRITISH ADMINISTRATION (CANDIA PROVINCE (NOW IRAKLION))

During the provisional Joint Administration by France, Great Britain, Italy, and Russia.

PRICES FOR STAMPS ON COVER

No. 1	*from* × 10
Nos. 2/5	—

1

2

1898 (25 Nov). *Handstruck locally. Imperf.*

1	1	20 pa. bright violet	£550	£375

1898 (3 Dec). *Litho by M. Grundmann, Athens. P* 11½.

2	2	10 pa. blue	8·00	12·00
		a. Imperf (pair)	£250	
3		20 pa. green	8·00	12·00
		a. Imperf (pair)	£250	

1899. *P* 11½.

4	2	10 pa. brown	8·00	13·00
		a. Imperf (pair)	£250	
5		20 pa. rose	14·00	15·00
		a. Imperf (pair)	£250	

The British postal service closed at the end of 1899.

British P.O. in Siam
(Bangkok)

PRICES FOR STAMPS ON COVER

The issues of the British Post Office in Siam are worth from × 40 the prices quoted for used stamps when on cover.

B

(1)

1882–85. *Stamps of Straits Settlements optd with T* 1.

(*a*) *On issue of* 1867

1	–	32 c. on 2 a. yellow (No. 9)	£4500	£4500

(*b*) *On issues of* 1867–82. *Wmk Crown CC*

2	5	2 c. brown	£350	£475
3		4 c. rose	£350	£350
		a. Opt double	—	£3500
4	18	5 c. purple-brown	38·00	38·00
5	5	6 c. lilac	30·00	30·00
6	6	8 c. orange	£525	38·00
7	19	10 c. slate	48·00	30·00
8	6	12 c. blue	£225	£100
9	7	24 c. green	£100	30·00
10	8	30 c. claret	£5500	£2750
11	9	96 c. grey	£550	£600

(*c*) *On issue of April* 1883

12	9	2 c. on 32 c. pale red (*Wide* "E" (No. 59))	£400	£500
13		2 c. on 32 c. pale red (*Wide* "S" (No. 60))	£450	£550

(*d*) *On issues of* 1882–84. *Wmk Crown CA*

14	5	2 c. brown	30·00	30·00
15		2 c. rose	11·00	10·00
		a. Opt inverted	—	£1500
		b. Opt double	£600	
16		4 c. rose	55·00	50·00
17		4 c. brown	17·00	17·00
18	18	5 c. blue	50·00	30·00
19	5	6 c. lilac	30·00	20·00
20	6	8 c. orange	20·00	15·00
		a. Opt inverted	—	£1800
21	19	10 c. slate	30·00	20·00
22	6	12 c. dull purple	45·00	30·00
23	7	24 c. green	£700	£600

The use of these stamps ceased on 1 July 1885.

British Postal Agencies in Eastern Arabia

Certain Arab States in Eastern Arabia, whilst remaining independent, had British postal administrations.

Bahrain and Kuwait (from 1948) and Qatar (from 1957) used British stamps overprinted and surcharged in local currency. Abu Dhabi (from 1964) and Trucial States (from 1961 and used only in Dubai) had definitive issues made under the auspices of the British Agencies.

In addition, British stamps were surcharged with value only for use in Muscat and certain other states. They were formerly listed under Muscat as they were first put on sale there, but in view of their more extended use, the list has been transferred here, retaining the same numbering.

The stamps were used in Muscat from 1 April 1948 to 29 April 1966; in Dubai from 1 April 1948 to 6 January 1961; in Qatar: Doha from August 1950, Umm Said from February 1956, to 31 March 1957; and in Abu Dhabi from 30 March 1963 (Das Island from December 1960) to 29 March 1964.

Certain of them were placed on sale in Kuwait Post Offices in 1951 and in 1953 due to shortages of stamps with "KUWAIT" overprint; and they can all be found commercially used from that state and from Bahrain.

Stamps of Great Britain surcharged

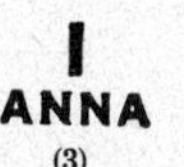

1 ANNA

(3)

2 RUPEES

(4)

1948 (1 Apr). *Surch with T* **3** (½ *a. to* 1 *r.*) *or* **4** (2 *r.*).

No.	Type	Description	Unused	Used
16	**128**	½ a. on ½d. pale green	30	45
17		1 a. on 1d. pale scarlet	30	25
18		1½ a. on 1½d. pale red-brown	30	25
19		2 a. on 2d. pale orange	50	60
20		2½ a. on 2½d. light ultramarine	35	1·10
21		3 a. on 3d. pale violet	35	20
22	**129**	6 a. on 6d. purple	40	20
23	**130**	1 r. on 1s. bistre-brown	1·75	1·90
24	**131**	2 r. on 2s. 6d. yellow-green	12·00	18·00
16/24		*Set of* 9	15·00	21·00

One example of No. 22 is known with the surcharge almost completely omitted from position R. 20/2 in the sheet.

2½ ANNAS (5)

15 RUPEES (6)

1948 (26 Apr). *Royal Silver Wedding. Nos.* 493/4 *surch with T* **5** *or* **6**.

No.	Type	Description	Unused	Used
25	**137**	2½ a. on 2½d. ultramarine	40	40
26	**138**	15 r. on £1 blue	45·00	70·00

1948 (29 July). *Olympic Games. Nos.* 495/8 *surch with new values in* "ANNAS" *or* "1 RUPEE", *as T* **5/6**, *but in one line on* 2½ *a. (vert) or* 6 *a. and* 1 *r. (horiz) and grills obliterating former values of all except* 2½ *a.*

No.	Type	Description	Unused	Used
27	**139**	2½ a. on 2½d. ultramarine	35	60
28	**140**	3 a. on 3d. violet	45	80
29	**141**	6 a. on 6d. bright purple	55	85
30	**142**	1 r. on 1s. brown	1·00	1·40
		a. Surch double	£400	

1949 (10 Oct). *75th Anniv of Universal Postal Union. Nos.* 499/502 *surch with new values in* "ANNAS" *or* "1 RUPEE" *as T* **3/4**, *but all in one line, with grills obliterating former values.*

No.	Type	Description	Unused	Used
31	**143**	2½ a. on 2½d. ultramarine	50	1·00
32	**144**	3 a. on 3d. violet	50	1·25
33	**145**	6 a. on 6d. bright purple	60	1·10
34	**146**	1 r. on 1s. brown	1·25	1·75

2 RUPEES (6*a*)

2 RUPEES (6*b*)

Type **6***a*. "2" and "RUPEES" level and in line with lower of the two bars.

Type **6***b*. "2" raised in relation to "RUPEES" and whole surcharge below the lower bar.

1950 (2 Oct)–**55**. *Nos.* 503/8 *surch as T* **3** *and No.* 509 *with T* **6***a*.

No.	Type	Description	Unused	Used
35	**128**	½ a. on ½d. pale orange (3.5.51)	35	1·25
36		1 a. on 1d. light ultramarine (3.5.51)	35	1·25
37		1½ a. on 1½d. pale green (3.5.51)	2·00	2·75
38		2 a. on 2d. pale red-brown (3.5.51)	35	2·00
39		2½ a. on 2½d. pale scarlet (3.5.51)	1·00	2·75
40	**129**	4 a. on 4d. light ultramarine	1·00	2·00
41	**147**	2 r. on 2s. 6d. yellow-green (3.5.51)	24·00	14·00
		a. Surch with Type **6***b* (1955)	85·00	65·00
35/41		*Set of* 7	26·00	23·00

1952 (10 Dec)–**54**. *Stamps of Queen Elizabeth II wmk Tudor Crown, surch as T* **3**.

No.	Type	Description	Unused	Used
42	**154**	½ a. on ½d. orange-red (31.8.53)	8	5
43		1 a. on 1d. ultramarine (31.8.53)	10	5
44		1½ a. on 1½d. green	12	8
45		2 a. on 2d. red-brown (31.8.53)	12	5
46	**155**	2½ a. on 2½d. carmine-red	20	5
47		3 a. on 3d. deep lilac (B.) (18.1.54)	20	5
48	**156**	4 a. on 4d. ultramarine (2.11.53)	60	60
49	**157**	6 a. on 6d. reddish purple (18.1.54)	35	5
50	**160**	12 a. on 1s. 3d. green (2.11.53)	2·50	80
51	**159**	1 r. on 1s. 6d. grey-blue (2.11.53)	2·75	25
42/51		*Set of* 10	6·25	1·90

1953 (10 June). *Coronation. Nos.* 532/5 *surch with new values.*

No.	Type	Description	Unused	Used
52	**161**	2½ a. on 2½d. carmine-red	1·00	1·00
53	**162**	4 a. on 4d. ultramarine	1·25	1·40
54	**163**	12 a. on 1s. 3d. deep yellow-green	2·25	2·75
55	**164**	1 r. on 1s. 6d. deep grey-blue	3·00	2·00

2 RUPEES I

2 RUPEES II

2 RUPEES III

(7)

5 RUPEES I

5 RUPEES II

(8)

Types of surcharges

2 rupees.

Type I. *On Waterlow ptg.* Top of "R" level with top of "2" and other letters of "RUPEES". Bars 7 mm long.

Type II. *On Waterlow ptg.* "R" dropped out of alignment with "2" and other letters of "RUPEES". Bars 6½ mm long.

Type III. *On De La Rue ptg.* Top of "R" below level of top of "2". Bars 7–7¼ mm long and with left sides aligned with "S".

5 rupees.

Type I. *On Waterlow ptg.* Ends of letters square and sharp. There were two printings made in March and May 1957.

Type II. *On De La Rue ptg.* Type is thicker and ends of letters are relatively rounded.

For differences between Waterlow and De La Rue printings of the basic stamps see notes in Great Britain after No. 539.

1955–60. *T* **166/7** *(Waterlow ptgs) (W* **165**, *St. Edward's Crown) surch with T* **7/8**.

No.	Type	Description	Unused	Used
56	**166**	2 r. on 2s. 6d. black-brown (Type I) (23.9.55)	5·00	1·25
		a. Type II (2.57)	5·00	2·75
		b. Type III (No. 536a D.L.R.) (6.60)	32·00	45·00
57	**167**	5 r. on 5s. rose-red (Type I) (1.3.57)	12·00	3·50
		a. Wide surcharge	£200	£180
		b. Type II (No. 537a D.L.R.) (27.1.60)	30·00	42·00

No. 57a ("5" and "R" spaced 2¼ mm instead of 1¼ mm) occurred on the last stamp of Row 8 of the first "Waterlow" issue.

1956–57. *Stamps of Queen Elizabeth II, W* **165**, *St. Edward's Crown, surch as T* **3**.

No.	Type	Description	Unused	Used
58	**154**	1 a. on 1d. ultramarine (4.3.57)	35	60
58*a*		1½ a. on 1½d. green (1956)	—	£150
59		2 a. on 2d. red-brown (8.6.56)	60	70
60	**155**	2½ a. on 2½d. carmine-red (8.6.56)	70	80
61		3 a. on 3d. deep lilac (B.) (3.2.57)	1·60	1·90
62	**156**	4 a. on 4d. ultramarine (9.12.56)	5·50	8·00
63	**157**	6 a. on 6d. red-purple (10.2.57)	1·90	2·00
64	**159**	1 r. on 1s. 6d. grey-blue (2.8.56)	2·00	30
58/64 (*ex* 58*a*)		*Set of* 7	11·00	13·00

NP 1 NP (9)

3 NP NP (10)

75 NP (11)

1957 (1 Apr)–**59**. *Value in naye paise. Stamps of Queen Elizabeth II, W* **165**, *St. Edward's Crown, surch as T* **9** (1, 15, 25, 40, 50 *n.p.*), **11** (75 *n.p.*) *or* **10** *(others).*

No.	Type	Description	Unused	Used
65	**157**	1 n.p. on 5d. brown	5	20
66	**154**	3 n.p. on ½d. orange-red	20	25
67		6 n.p. on 1d. ultramarine	20	30
68		9 n.p. on 1½d. green	20	25
69		12 n.p. on 2d. light red-brown	40	50
70	**155**	15 n.p. on 2½d. carmine-red (Type I)	40	45
		a. Type II (4.59)	35	60
71		20 n.p. on 3d. deep lilac (B.)	20	5
72	**156**	25 n.p. on 4d. ultramarine	90	1·25
73	**157**	40 n.p. on 6d. reddish purple	35	5
		a. Deep claret (3.59)	45	10
74	**158**	50 n.p. on 9d. bronze-green	1·50	60
75	**160**	75 n.p. on 1s. 3d. green	2·50	70
65/75		*Set of* 11	6·00	4·25

15 NP

(12)

1957 (1 Aug). *World Scout Jubilee Jamboree. Nos.* 557/9 *surch in one line as T* **12** (15 *n.p.*), *or in two lines (others).*

No.	Description	Unused	Used
76	15 n.p. on 2½d. carmine-red	1·00	90
77	25 n.p. on 4d. ultramarine	1·10	1·10
78	75 n.p. on 1s. 3d. green	1·25	1·40

1960–61. *Stamps of Queen Elizabeth II, W* **179**, *Mult Crown, surch as T* **9** (1, 15, 30, 40, 50 *n.p.*), **11**, (75 *n.p.*), **3** (1 *r.*), **7** (2 *r.*, 5 *r.*) *or* **10** *(others).*

No.	Type	Description	Unused	Used
79	**157**	1 n.p. on 5d. brown	5	20
80	**154**	3 n.p. on ½d. orange-red	90	1·25
81		5 n.p. on 1d. ultramarine	50	40
82		6 n.p. on 1d. ultramarine	2·00	2·00
83		10 n.p. on 1½d. green	50	40
84		12 n.p. on 2d. light red-brown	4·50	4·75
85	**155**	15 n.p. on 2½d. carmine-red (Type II)	35	5
86		20 n.p. on 3d. deep lilac (B.)	35	5
87	**156**	30 n.p. on 4½d. chestnut	60	55
88	**157**	40 n.p. on 6d. deep claret	60	15
89	**158**	50 n.p. on 9d. bronze-green	90	1·00
90	**160**	75 n.p. on 1s. 3d. green	1·25	1·25
91	**159**	1 r. on 1s. 6d. grey-blue	1·50	1·75
92	**166**	2 r. on 2s. 6d. black-brown (No. 595)	8·00	13·00
93	**167**	5 r. on 5s. rose-red (No. 596)	22·00	30·00
70/93		*Set of* 15	40·00	50·00

Dates of issue: 1960—1 n.p., 15 n.p., June, 3 n.p., 6 n.p., 12n.p.; Oct, 20 n.p., 40 n.p. 1961—8 April, others.

British Solomon Islands *see* Solomon Islands

British Somaliland *see* Somaliland Protectorate

British South Africa Company *see* Rhodesia

British Virgin Islands

CROWN COLONY

Apart from the 1951 Legislative Council issue, the word "BRITISH" did not appear regularly on the stamps until 1968 when it was introduced to avoid confusion with the nearby Virgin Islands of the United States (the former Danish West Indies).

Most mail from the early years of the islands' history was sent via the Danish island of St. Thomas.

It is not known exactly when the first post office, or agency, was established on Tortola, but an entry in a G.P.O. account book suggests that it was operating by 1787. Correspondence is known from the postmaster in 1791. The stamps of Great Britain were used there from 1858 to May 1860, when the colonial authorities assumed responsibility for the overseas mails from the British G.P.O.

For illustrations of the handstamp and postmark types see BRITISH POST OFFICES ABROAD notes, following GREAT BRITAIN.

TORTOLA

CROWNED-CIRCLE HANDSTAMPS

CC1 CC 1 TORTOLA (R.) (15.12.1842) *Price on cover* £3500

CC2 CC 3 TORTOLA (R.) (21.6.1854) *Price on cover* —

No. CC2 is known used as an Official Paid mark during the years 1900 to 1918. *Price on cover* £900.

Stamps of GREAT BRITAIN *cancelled* "A 13" *as Type* **2**.

1858 *to* **1860**.

No.	Description	Price
Z1	1d. rose-red (1857), *perf* 14	£3000
Z2	4d. rose (1857)	£2750
Z3	6d. lilac (1856)	£1100
Z4	1s. green (1856)	

PRICES FOR STAMPS ON COVER TO 1945

Nos.	
Nos. 1/7	*from* × 10
Nos. 8/22	*from* × 6
Nos. 24/31	*from* × 4
Nos. 32/41	*from* × 5
No. 42	*from* × 10
Nos. 43/50	*from* × 4
Nos. 54/77	*from* × 3
Nos. 78/81	*from* × 6
Nos. 82/101	*from* × 3
Nos. 103/6	*from* × 4
Nos. 107/9	*from* × 6
Nos. 110/21	*from* × 2

1 St. Ursula 2

(Litho Nissen & Parker. Original dies by Waterlow)

1866. *No wmk. P* 12 *(a) White wove paper.*

No.	Type	Description	Unused	Used
1	**1**	1d. green	40·00	55·00
2		1d. deep green	40·00	55·00
3	**2**	6d. rose	90·00	£110
4		6d. deep rose	£130	£140
		a. Large "V" in "VIRGIN"	£450	£550

(b) Toned paper

5 1 1d. green .. .. 40·00 55·00
a. Perf 15 × 12 .. .. £4250 £5500
6 1d. deep green £100 £120
7 2 6d. rose-red .. .. 60·00 90·00
a. Large "V" in "VIRGIN" £350 £425

The above were printed in sheets of 25.

6d. stamps showing part of the papermaker's watermark ("A. Cowan & Sons Extra Superfine A. C. & S.") are worth 50% more.

Beware of fakes of No. 5a made from perf 12 stamps.

3

4

Normal Variety

1s. Long-tailed "S" in "ISLANDS"

1867–70. *No wmk. P 15. 1s. with double-lined frame.*

(a) White wove paper

8 1 1d. blue-green (1870) .. .. .. 65·00 70·00
9 1d. yellow-green (1868) .. .. 80·00 80.00
10 2 6d. pale rose £450 £450
11 4 1s. black and rose-carmine £200 £275
a. Long-tailed "S" £525 £575

(b) Toned paper

12 1 1d. yellow-green (1868) .. .. 85·00 80·00
13 2 6d. dull rose (1868) £225 £275
14 4 1s. black and rose-carmine (*blued*) .. £200 £275
aa. Long-tailed "S" £525 £575
14*a* 1s. black and rose-carmine £275 £300
b. Long-tailed "S" £550 £600

(c) Pale rose paper

15 3 4d. lake-red .. .. 50·00 70·00

(d) Buff paper

16 3 4d. lake-red .. .. 40·00 60·00
17 4d. lake-brown .. .. 40·00 60·00

The thin lines of the frame on the 1s. are close together and sometimes merge into one.

The 1d. was originally in sheets of 20, but from 1870 was in sheets of 12; the 4d. was in sheets of 25; the 6d. and 1s. were in sheets of 20.

1867. *As T 4, but with crimson frames superimposed with bands extending through margins. P 15.*

18 4 1s. black and rose-carmine (*white paper*) 45·00 55·00
a. Long-tailed "S" £100 £120
b. Figure of Virgin omitted £55000
19 1s. black and rose-carmine (*toned paper*) 45·00 55·00
a. Long-tailed "S" £100 £120
20 1s. black and rose-carmine (*blued paper*) £700 £850
a. Long-tailed "S" £1600 £1400

1868. *Nos. 11 and 14a with frame lines retouched so as to make them single lines. Margins remain white. P 15.*

21 4 1s. black and rose-carmine (*white paper*) £130 £160
aa. Long-tailed "S" £275 £350
21*a* 1s. black and rose-carmine (*toned paper*) £130 £160
b. Long-tailed "S" £275 £350

(Litho D.L.R.)

1878. *Wmk Crown CC (sideways). P 14.*

22 1 1d. green .. .. 65·00 75·00
a. Yellow-green £170 £120
b. Wmk upright .. .. .. 80·00 £100

6 (Die I)

4D

(7)

(Typo D.L.R.)

1880. *Wmk Crown CC. P 14.*

24 6 1d. emerald-green .. .. .. 35·00 50·00
25 2½d. red-brown .. .. 55·00 75·00

1883–84. *Wmk Crown CA. P 14.*

26 6 ½d. yellow-buff .. .. 60·00 70·00
27 ½d. yellow-green .. .. 4·00 8·00
28 ½d. dull bluish green .. .. .. 8·00 13·00
29 1d. pale rose .. .. 15·00 18·00
30 1d. deep rose .. .. 38·00 50·00
31 2½d. ultramarine (1884) .. .. .. 4·50 8·00

Nos. 25, 27 and 31 exist imperf but it is not known whether they were issued (*Price* £1000 *in pairs, each*).

(Litho D.L.R.)

1887–89. *Wmk Crown CA. P 14.*

32 1 1d. red .. .. 6·00 8·00
33 1d. rose-red .. .. 6·00 8·00
34 1d. rose .. .. 6·00 16·00
35 3 4d. chestnut .. .. 65·00 85·00
36 4d. pale chestnut .. .. 65·00 85·00
37 4d. brown-red .. .. 80·00 90·00
38 2 6d. dull violet .. .. 26·00 55·00
39 6d. deep violet .. .. 26·00 55·00
40 4 1s. sepia £100 £120
41 1s. brown (light *to* deep) .. .. 80·00 95·00
41*a* 1s. very light brown £650
33/41 Optd "Specimen" .. .. *Set of* 4 £350

The De La Rue transfers of T 1 to 4 are new transfers and differ from those of Messrs. Nissen and Parker, particularly T 4

1888 (July). *No. 19 surch with T 7, in violet.*

42 4 4d. on 1s. black and rose-carmine/*toned* £110 £150
a. Surch double £6000
b. Surch inverted (in pair with normal) £25000
c. Long-tailed "S" £250 £400

The special issues for Virgin Islands were superseded on 31 October 1890, by the general issue for Leeward Islands. In 1899, however, a new special issue (given below) appeared; it did not supersede the general issue for Leeward Islands, but was used concurrently, as were all subsequent issues, until 1 July 1956, when the general Leeward Islands stamps were withdrawn.

8

9

10

(Recess D.L.R.)

1899. *Wmk Crown CA. P 14.*

43 8 ½d. yellow-green .. .. .. 80 1·90
a. Error. "HALFPFNNY" .. .. 80·00 £100
b. Error. "HALFPENNY" .. .. 80·00 £100
c. Imperf between (horiz pair) .. £6500
44 1d. brick-red .. .. 3·25 3·25
45 2½d. ultramarine .. .. 15·00 14·00
46 4d. brown .. .. 8·00 12·00
a. Error. "FOURPENCF" £1300 £1200
47 6d. dull violet .. .. 7·00 9·50
48 7d. deep green .. .. 8·50 10·00
49 1s. brown-yellow .. .. .. 20·00 29·00
50 5s. indigo .. .. 75·00 85·00
43/50 .. .. *Set of* 8 £120 £150
43/50 Optd "Specimen" .. .. *Set of* 8 £275

(Typo D.L.R.)

1904 (1 June). *Wmk Mult Crown CA. P 14.*

54 9 ½d. dull purple and green 60 65
55 1d. dull purple and scarlet .. .. 1·25 1·10
56 10 2d. dull purple and ochre .. .. 5·50 9·00
57 9 2½d. dull purple and ultramarine .. 3·75 6·00
58 10 3d. dull purple and black .. .. 4·50 7·00
59 9 6d. dull purple and brown .. .. 5·00 7·00
60 10 1s. green and scarlet .. .. 6·00 8·00
61 2s. 6d. green and black .. .. 24·00 38·00
62 9 5s. green and blue .. .. .. 45·00 60·00
54/62 .. .. *Set of* 9 85·00 £120
54/62 Optd "Specimen" .. .. *Set of* 9 £300

11

12

(Typo D.L.R.)

1913–19. *Wmk Mult Crown CA. P 14.*

63 11 ½d. green, **O** .. .. 75 1·60
64 ½d. yellow-green, **O** (1916) .. .. 1·75 2·50
65 ½d. blue-green and deep green, **O** (1919) 85 1·90
66 1d. deep red, **O** .. .. 7·50 9·00
67 1d. deep red and carmine, **O** .. .. 5·50 8·00
68 1d. scarlet, **O** (1917) .. .. .. 3·00 5.25
69 1d. carmine-red, **O** (1919) .. .. 19·00 12·00
70 12 2d. grey, **O** .. .. 3·75 6·50
71 2d. slate-grey, **O** (1919) .. .. 4·00 8·50
72 11 2½d. bright blue, **O** .. .. .. 4·00 7·50
73 12 3d. purple/*yellow*, **C** .. .. 1·75 6·50
74 11 6d. dull and bright purple, **C** .. 3·00 6·00
75 12 1s. black/*green*, **C** .. .. .. 5·50 7·50
76 2s. 6d., black and red/*blue*, **C** .. 25·00 30·00
77 11 5s. green and red/*yellow*, **C** .. 48·00 60·00
63/77 .. .. *Set of* 9 85·00 £120
63/77 Optd "Specimen" .. .. *Set of* 9 £300

WAR STAMP

(13)

14

1917. *Optd with T 13.*

78 11 1d. carmine .. .. 1·75 4·00
a. Watermark sideways £600
b. Pale red/bluish .. .. .. 30 1·00
c. Scarlet .. .. 35 1·40
79 12 3d. purple/*yellow* .. .. .. 75 2·75
a. Purple/lemon .. .. .. 3·50 5·50
b. Purple/pale yellow .. .. .. 2·00 4·25
78/79 Optd "Specimen" .. .. *Set of* 2 £110

1921 (18 Nov). *As 1913–19, but wmk Mult Script CA.*

80 11 ½d. green, **O** .. .. 85 3·50
81 1d. scarlet and deep carmine, **O** .. 1·60 3·50
80/1 Optd "Specimen" .. .. *Set of* 2 £100

(Typo D.L.R.)

1922 (15 June)–**29.** *T 14. P 14. (a) Wmk Mult Crown CA.*

82 3d. purple/*pale yellow*, **C** .. .. .. 40 2·00
83 1s. black/*emerald*, **C** .. .. .. 1·40 6·00
84 2s. 6d. black and red/*blue*, **C** .. .. 6·00 10·00
85 5s. green and red/*pale yellow*, **C** .. 26·00 42·00
82/5 Optd "Specimen" .. .. *Set of* 4 £140

(b) Wmk Mult Script CA

86 ½d. dull green, **O** 20 55
87 1d. rose-carmine, **O** 25 60
88 1d. bright violet, **O** (1927) .. .. 1·40 2·25
89 1d. scarlet, **O** (1929) .. .. .. 3·00 3·75
90 1½d. carmine-red, **O** (1927) .. .. 2·50 3·00
91 1½d. Venetian red, **O** (1928) .. .. 3·00 3·25
92 2d. grey, **O** .. .. 90 1·75
93 2½d. pale bright blue, **O** .. .. .. 3·25 7·50
94 2½d. dull orange, **O** (1.9.23) .. .. 2·00 1·40
95 2½d. bright blue, **O** (1927) .. .. 3·00 6·50
96 3d. purple/*pale yellow*, **O** (1928) .. 1·50 3·25
97 5d. dull purple and olive, **C** .. .. 8·50 18·00
98 6d. dull and bright purple, **C** .. .. 1·40 4·25
99 1s. black/*emerald*, **C** (1928) .. .. 3·25 5·50
100 2s. 6d. black and red/*blue*, **C** (1928) .. 11·00 17·00
101 5s. green and red/*yellow*, **C** (1.9.23) .. 19·00 30·00
86/101 .. .. *Set of* 14 50·00 90·00
86/101 Optd/Perf "Specimen" .. *Set of* 16 £450

In the 1½d. stamps the value is in colour on a white ground.

1935 (6 May). *Silver Jubilee. As Nos. 91/4 of Antigua but printed by Waterlow. P 11 × 12.*

103 1d. deep blue and scarlet 45 80
104 1½d. ultramarine and grey .. .. .. 45 1·00
105 2½d. brown and deep blue .. .. .. 65 1·25
106 1s. slate and purple .. .. .. 4·00 7·50
103/6 Perf "Specimen" .. .. *Set of* 4 70·00

1937 (12 May). *Coronation. As T 2 of Aden. Recess B.W. Wmk Mult Script CA. P 11 × 11½.*

107 1d. carmine 25 40
108 1½d. yellow-brown 55 75
109 2½d. blue 60 85
107/9 Perf "Specimen" .. .. *Set of* 3 55·00

15 King George VI and Badge of Colony

16 Map

(Photo Harrison)

1938 (1 Aug)–**47.** *Wmk Mult Script CA. P 14.*

110 15 ½d. green, **CO** 15 15
111 1d. scarlet, **CO** 15 15
112 1½d. red-brown, **CO** 15 15
113 2d. grey, **CO** 35 15
114 2½d. ultramarine, **CO** 40 25
115 3d. orange, **CO** 30 25
116 6d. mauve, **CO** 65 35
117 1s. olive-brown, **CO** 90 60
118 2s. 6d. sepia, **CO** .. .. .. 5·50 3·00
119 5s. carmine, **CO** .. .. .. 8·00 3·50
120 10s. blue **C** (1.12.47) .. .. .. 10·00 14·00
121 £1 black, **C** (1.12.47) .. .. .. 22·00 38·00
110/121 .. .. *Set of* 12 45·00 55·00
110/21 Perf "Specimen" .. .. *Set of* 12 £250

In substitution for the original chalky paper, the ordinary paper of Nos. 110/19 is thick, smooth and opaque and first appeared in August 1942 (1s. to 5s.) and in October 1943 (pence values).

1946 (1 Nov). *Victory. As Nos. 28/9 of Aden.*

122 1½d. lake-brown 15 15
123 3d. orange 20 15
122/3 Perf "Specimen" .. .. *Set of* 2 55·00

1949 (3 Jan). *Royal Siver Wedding. As Nos. 30/1 of Aden.*

124 2½d. ultramarine 15 15
125 £1 black .. .. 13·00 22·00

1949 (10 Oct). *75th Anniv of U.P.U. As Nos. 114/17 of Antigua.*

126 2½d. ultramarine 35 20
127 3d. orange 55 30
128 6d. magenta 85 55
129 1s. olive .. .. 1·60 1·40

(New Currency. 100 cents = 1 B.W.I. dollar)

1951. *Inauguration of B.W.I. University College. As Nos. 118/19 of Antigua.*

130 3 c. black and brown-red (10.4) 30 55
131 12 c. black and redish violet (16.2) .. .. 60 2·00

(Recess Waterlow)

1951 (2 Apr). *Restoration of Legislative Council. Wmk Mult Script CA. P 14½ x 14.*

132 16 6 c. orange 20 50
133 12 c. purple 20 85
134 24 c. olive .. .. 45 1·25
135 $1.20 carmine .. .. 1·25 3·50

PRICES OF SETS

Set prices are given for many issues, generally those containing five stamps or more. Definitive sets include one of each value or major colour change, but do not cover different perforations, die types or minor shades. Where a choice is possible the set prices are based on the cheapest versions of the stamps included in the listings.

17 Sombrero Lighthouse

18 Map of Jost Van Dyke

(Recess D.L.R.)

1952 (15 Apr). *T* **17/18** *and similar designs. Wmk Mult Script CA. P* 12½ × 13 (*vert*) *or* 13 × 12½ (*horiz*).

136 1 c. black 25 40
137 2 c. deep green 40 65
138 3 c. black and brown 25 70
139 4 c. carmine-red 45 70
140 5 c. claret and black 60 1·25
141 8 c. bright blue 35 70
142 12 c. dull violet 45 1·00
143 24 c. deep brown 55 1·25
144 60 c. yellow-green and blue 2·50 8·50
145 $1.20, black and bright blue 4·25 8·50
146 $2.40, yellowish green and red-brown 12·00 14·00
147 $4.80, bright blue and carmine 16·00 32·00
136/147 *Set of* 12 35·00 65·00

Designs: *Horiz*—3 c. Sheep industry; 4 c. Map of Anegada; 5 c. Cattle industry; 8 c. Map of Virgin Gorda; 12 c. Map of Tortola; 60 c. Dead Man's Chest; $1.20, Sir Francis Drake Channel; $2.40, Road Town; $4.80, Map of Virgin Islands. *Vert*—24 c. Badge of the Presidency.

1953 (2 June). *Coronation. As No.* 47 *of Aden.*

148 2 c. black and green 15 45

29 Map of Tortola

30 Brown Pelican

(Recess D.L.R.)

1956 (1 Nov). *Designs as T* **29/30**. *Wmk Mult Script CA. P* 13 × 12½ (½ *c. to* $1.20) *or* 12 × 11½ ($2.40 *and* $4.80).

149 ½ c. black and reddish purple (*shades*) 5 5
150 1 c. turquoise-blue and slate (*shades*) 20 10
151 2 c. vermilion and black 15 10
152 3 c. blue and deep olive 20 15
153 4 c. deep brown and turquoise-green 15 10
154 5 c. grey-black 15 10
155 8 c. yellow-orange and deep blue 15 40
156 12 c. ultramarine and rose-red 60 35
157 24 c. myrtle-green and brown-orange 35 25
158 60 c. indigo and yellow-orange 3·50 3·50
159 $1.20, deep yellow-green and carmine-red 2·75 4·50
160 $2.40, lemon and deep dull purple 12·00 14·00
161 $4.80, blackish brown and turquoise-blue 24·00 25·00
149/161 *Set of* 13 40·00 45·00

Designs: *Size as T* **29**—1 c. Virgin Islands Sloop; 2 c. Nelthrop Red Poll Bull; 3 c. Road Harbour; 4 c. Mountain travel; 5 c. Badge of the Presidency; 8 c. Beach scene; 12 c. Boat launching; 24 c. White Cedar tree; 60 c. Bonito; $1.20, Treasury Square. *Size as T* **30**—$4.80, Magnificent Frigate Bird.

(New Currency. 100 cents = 1 U.S. dollar)

(42)

1962 (10 Dec). *Nos.* 149/53 *and* 155/61 *surch in U.S. currency as T* **42** *by D.L.R. W w* **12**.

162 1 c. on ½ c. black and deep reddish purple 15 5
163 2 c. on 1 c. turquoise and slate-violet 15 8
164 3 c. on 2 c. vermilion and black 15 8
165 4 c. on 3 c. black and deep olive 15 10
166 5 c. on 4 c. deep brown and turquoise-green 15 10
167 8 c. on 8 c. yellow-orange and deep blue 20 10
168 10 c. on 12 c. ultramarine and rose-red 25 10
169 12 c. on 24 c. myrtle-green and brown-orange 25 10
170 25 c. on 60 c. indigo and yellow-orange 75 80
171 70 c. on $1.20, dp yellow-green & carmine-red 1·00 1·40
a. Stop to right of C in surcharge instead of beneath it (in pair with normal) 5·50 7·50
172 $1.40 on $2.40, lemon and deep dull purple 4·50 6·00
173 $2.80 on $4.80, blackish brown and turquoise-blue 9·00 10·00
162/173 *Set of* 12 15·00 17·00

No. 171a occurs on the first stamp on Rows 1 to 10.

1963 (4 June). *Freedom from Hunger. As No.* 76 *of Aden.*

174 25 c. reddish violet 40 25

1963 (2 Sept). *Red Cross Centenary. As Nos.* 147/8 *of Antigua.*

175 2 c. red and black 15 15
176 25 c. red and blue 60 60

1964 (23 Apr). 400*th Birth Anniv of William Shakespeare. As No.* 164 *of Antigua.*

177 10 c. bright blue 15 12

43 Bonito

44 Map of Tortola

45 Badge of the Colony

(Des and recess D.L.R.)

1964 (2 Nov). *Designs as T* **43/5**. *W w* **12**. *P* 11½ × 12 ($2.80), 13 × 13½ (70 *c.*, $1, $1.40), *or* 13 × 12½ (*others*).

178 1 c. blue and olive-green 10 5
179 2 c. yellow-olive and rose-red 10 5
180 3 c. sepia and turquoise-blue 20 5
181 4 c. black and carmine-red 10 8
182 5 c. black and deep bluish green 15 10
183 6 c. black and brown-orange 10 12
184 8 c. black and magenta 12 10
185 10 c. lake and deep lilac (*shades*) 30 10
186 12 c. deep bluish green and deep violet-blue 60 55
187 15 c. yellow-green and grey-black 35 60
188 25 c. green and purple 90 40
189 70 c. black and yellow-brown 2·25 1·75
190 $1 yellow-green and chestnut 3·25 2·25
191 $1.40, light blue and rose 6·50 5·50
192 $2.80, black and bright purple 10·00 8·00
178/192 *Set of* 15 22·00 18·00

Designs: *Horiz as T* **43**—2 c. Soper's Hole; 3 c. Brown Pelican; 4 c. Dead Man's Chest; 5 c. Road Harbour; 6 c. Fallen Jerusalem; 8 c. The Baths, Virgin Gorda; 10 c. Map of Virgin Islands; 12 c. Tortola-St. Thomas Ferry; 15 c. The Towers, Tortola; 25 c. Beef Island Airfield. *Vert as T* **44**—$1 Virgin Gorda; $1.40, Yachts at anchor.

1965 (17 May). *I.T.U. Centenary. As Nos.* 166/7 *of Antigua.*

193 4 c. yellow and turquoise 15 10
194 25 c. light blue and orange-buff 60 35

1965 (25 Oct). *International Co-operation Year. As Nos.* 168/9 *of Antigua.*

195 1 c. reddish purple and turquoise-green 5 5
196 25 c. deep bluish green and lavender 40 30

1966 (24 Jan). *Churchill Commemoration. As Nos.* 170/3 *of Antigua.*

197 1 c. new blue 5 5
198 2 c. deep green 5 5
199 10 c. brown 30 20
200 25 c. bluish violet 60 45

1966 (22 Feb). *Royal Visit. As Nos.* 174/5 *of Antigua.*

201 4 c. black and ultramarine 25 15
202 70 c. black and magenta 1·25 65

58 R.M.S. *Atrato*, 1866

(Des R. Granger Barrett. Litho B.W.)

1966 (25 Apr). *Stamp Centenary. T* **58** *and similar horiz designs. W w* **12** (*sideways*). *P* 13.

203 5 c. black, red, yellow and emerald 10 10
204 10 c. black, green and rose-red/*cream* 20 15
205 25 c. black, rose-red and blue/*pale green* 35 25
206 60 c. black, red and green/*pale blue* 75 50

Design:—10 c. 1d. and 6d. stamps of 1866; 25 c. Air mail transport, Beef Island, and 6d. stamp of 1866; 60 c. Landing mail at Roadtown, 1866 and 1d. stamp of 1866.

50c.

(62)

1966 (15 Sept). *As Nos.* 189 *and* 191/2 *but wmk sideways, surch as T* **62**.

207 50 c. on 70 c. black and yellow-brown 1·00 1·25
208 $1.50 on $1.40, light blue and rose 3·75 3·75
209 $3 on $2.80, black and bright purple 5·50 6·00

1966 (1 Dec). 20*th Anniv of U.N.E.S.C.O. As Nos.* 196/8 *of Antigua.*

210 2 c. slate-violet, red, yellow and orange 5 5
211 12 c. orange-yellow, violet and deep olive 25 10
212 60 c. black, bright purple and orange 70 50

63 Map of Virgin Islands

(Des G. Vasarhelyi. Photo Harrison)

1967 (18 Apr). *New Constitution. W w* **12**. *P* 14½.

213 **63** 2 c. multicoloured 5 5
214 10 c. multicoloured 10 10
215 25 c. multicoloured 20 15
216 $1 multicoloured 75 90

64 Cable Ship and Bermuda-Tortola Link

(Des G. Drummond, Photo Harrison)

1967 (14 Sept). *Inauguration of Bermuda-Tortola Telephone Service. T* **64** *and similar horiz designs. Multicoloured. W w* **12**. *P* 14½.

217 4 c. Type **64** 10 5
218 10 c. Chalwell Telecommunications Station 10 10
219 50 c. Cable Ship *Mercury* 60 35

67 Blue Marlin

(Des V. Whiteley. Photo Enschedé)

1968 (2 Jan). *Game Fishing. T* **67** *and similar horiz designs. W w* **12** (*sideways*). *P* 12½ × 12.

220 2 c. multicoloured 10 5
221 10 c. multicoloured 25 10
222 25 c. black, blue and bright violet 40 25
223 40 c. multicoloured 75 50

Designs:—10 c. Cobia; 25 c. Wahoo; 50 c. Fishing launch and map.

1968
INTERNATIONAL
YEAR FOR
HUMAN RIGHTS

(71)

72 Dr. Martin Luther King, Bible, Sword and Armour Gauntlet

1968 (29 July). *Human Rights Year. Nos.* 185 *and* 188 *optd with T* **71**.

224 10 c. lake and deep lilac 10 10
225 25 c. green and purple 15 15

29 July was the date of issue in the islands. The Crown Agents supplies went on sale in London on 1 July, the local consignment being delayed in transit.

(Des V. Whiteley. Litho Format)

1968 (15 Oct). *Martin Luther King Commemoration. W w* **12** (*sideways*). *P* 14.

226 **72** 4 c. multicoloured 5 5
227 25 c. multicoloured 15 15

73 DHC-6 "Twin Otter"

(Des R. Granger Barrett. Litho Format)

1968 (16 Dec). *Opening of Beef Island Airport Extension. T* **73** *and similar horiz designs. Multicoloured. P* 14.

228 2 c. Type **73** 8 8
229 10 c. HS "748" Airliner 12 8
230 25 c. HS "Heron" 20 15
231 $1 Royal Engineers cap badge 80 70

NEW INFORMATION

The editor is always interested to correspond with people who have new information that will improve or correct the Catalogue.

77 Long John Silver and Jim Hawkins

78 Jim Hawkins escaping from the Pirates

(Des Jennifer Toombs. Photo Enschedé)

1969 (18 Mar). *75th Death Anniv of Robert Louis Stevenson. Scenes from "Treasure Island". T* **77/8** *and similar designs.* W w **12** (*sideways on* 10 c., $1). *P* 13½ × 13 (4 c., 40 c.) *or* 13 × 13½ (*others*).

232 4 c. indigo, pale yellow and carmine-red .. 30 15
233 10 c. multicoloured 45 10
234 40 c. brown, black and blue .. .. .. 1·00 65
235 $1 multicoloured .. .. 1·50 75

Designs: *Vert*—40 c. The fight with Israel Hands. *Horiz*—$1 Treasure trove.

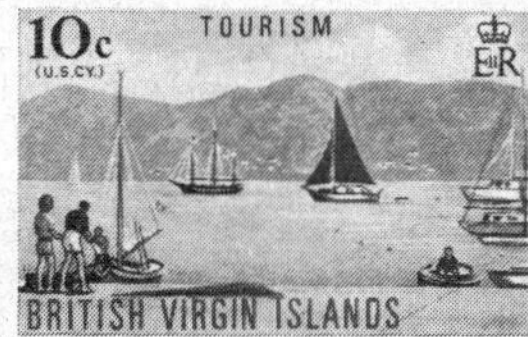

82 Yachts in Road Harbour, Tortola

(Des J. Cooter, Litho P.B.)

1969 (20 Oct). *Tourism. T* **82** *and similar multicoloured designs.* W w **12** (*sideways on* 2 c., $1). *P* 12½.

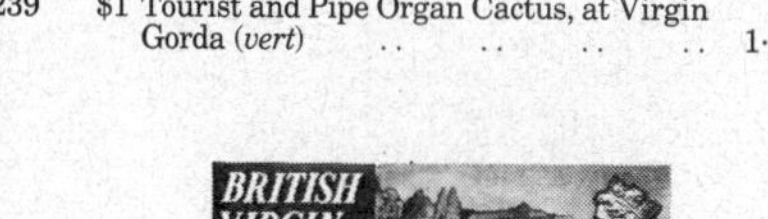

236 2 c. Tourist and Rock Grouper (fish) (*vert*) .. 15 10
237 10 c. Type **82** 20 10
238 20 c. Sun-bathing at Virgin Gorda National Park 30 20
239 $1 Tourist and Pipe Organ Cactus, at Virgin Gorda (*vert*) .. .. 1·50 1·00

85 Carib Canoe

(Des and litho J.W.)

1970 (16 Feb)–74. *Horiz designs as T* **85**. W w **12** (*sideways*). *P* 14.

240 ½ c. buff, red-brown and sepia 10 10
241 1 c. new blue, apple-green and chalky blue .. 15 15
a. Perf 13½ (12.11.74) 55 70
242 2 c. yellow-orange, red-brown and slate .. 25 20
243 3 c. orange-red, cobalt and sepia 25 20
244 4 c. greenish blue, chalky blue & bistre-brn 25 20
245 5 c. emerald, pink and black 30 12
246 6 c. reddish violet, mauve and myrtle-green 40 25
247 8 c. apple-green, greenish yellow and sepia .. 50 50
248 10 c. greenish blue, yellow-brown & red-brown 50 15
a. Perf 13½ (12.11.74) .. .. .. 1·25 1·50
249 12 c. yellow, crimson and brown 65 35
a. Perf 13½ (12.11.74) .. .. .. 1.50 2·00
250 15 c. turquoise-green, orange & bistre-brown 90 65
a. Perf 13½ (12.11.74) .. .. .. 1·75 2·00
251 25 c. grey-green, steel-blue and plum .. .. 1·50 90
252 50 c. magenta, dull green and purple-brown .. 2·25 1·50
253 $1 salmon, olive-green and red-brown .. 2·75 3·25
254 $2 buff, slate and grey .. .. .. 4·50 6·00
255 $3 ochre, deep blue and sepia .. .. 6·00 6·50
256 $5 violet and grey .. .. 11·00 12·00
240/256 .. .. *Set of* 17 29·00 30·00

Designs:—1 c. *Santamariagallante* (Columbus' flagship). 2 c. *Elizabeth Bonaventure* (Drake's flagship); 3 c. Dutch Buccaneer, *circa* 1660; 4 c. *Thetis*, 1827 (after etching by E. W. Cooke); 5 c. Henry Morgan's ship (17th-century); 6 c. H.M. Frigate *Boreas* (Captain Nelson, 1784); 8 c. H.M. Schooner *Eclair*, 1804; 10 c. H.M.S. *Formidable*, 1782; 12 c. H.M. Sloop *Nymph*, 1778; 15 c. *Windsor Castle*, Post Office Packet, 1807; 25 c. H.M. Frigate *Astrea*, 1808; 50 c. Wreck of R.M.S. *Rhone*, 1860; $1 Tortola Sloop; $2 H.M. Cruiser *Frobisher*; $3 Merchant Tanker *Booker Viking*, 1967; $5 Hydrofoil *Sun Arrow*.

See also Nos. 295/300.

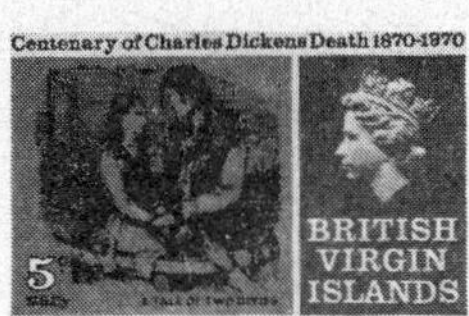

102 *A Tale of Two Cities*

(Des W. G. Brown. Litho D.L.R.)

1970 (4 May). *Death Centenary of Charles Dickens. T* **102** *and similar horiz designs showing original book illustrations.* W w **12** (*sideways*). *P* 14.

257 5 c. black, light rose and grey 15 10
258 10 c. black, light blue and pale green 35 15
259 25 c. black, light green and pale yellow .. 60 45

Designs:—10 c. *Oliver Twist*; 25 c. *Great Expectations*.

103 Hospital Visit

(Des R. Granger Barrett. Litho Questa)

1970 (10 Aug). *Centenary of British Red Cross. T* **103** *and similar horiz designs. Multicoloured.* W w **12** (*sideways*). *P* 14.

260 4 c. Type **103** 8 5
261 10 c. First Aid Class 12 10
262 25 c. Red Cross and Coat of Arms 35 30

104 Mary Read

105 Children and "UNICEF"

(Des and litho J.W.)

1970 (16 Nov). *Pirates. T* **104** *and similar vert designs. Multicoloured.* W w **12**. *P* 14 × 14½.

263 ½ c. Type **104** 5 5
264 10 c. George Lowther 45 10
265 30 c. Edward Teach (Blackbeard) .. .. 1·00 60
266 60 c. Henry Morgan .. .. 1·75 1·00

(Des L. Curtis. Litho Format)

1971 (13 Dec). *25th Anniv of UNICEF.* W w **12** (*sideways*). *P* 13½ × 14.

267 **106** 15 c. multicoloured 20 25
268 30 c. multicoloured 50 55

VISIT OF
H.R.H.
THE
PRINCESS MARGARET
1972 1972

(**106**)

1972 (7 Mar). *Royal Visit of Princess Margaret. Nos.* 244 *and* 251 *optd with T* **106**.

269 4 c. greenish blue, chalky blue & bistre-brn 12 12
270 25 c. grey-green, steel-blue and plum 45 50

107 Seaman of 1800

108 Sailfish and the Yacht *Sir Winston Churchill*

(Des J. W. Litho Questa)

1972 (17 Mar). *"Interpex" Stamp Exhibition, New York. T* **107** *and similar vert designs showing Naval Uniforms. Multicoloured.* W w **12** (*sideways*). *P* 13½.

271 ½ c. Type **107** 5 5
272 10 c. Boatswain, 1787–1807 .. .. .. 30 25
273 30 c. Captain, 1795–1812 .. .. .. 90 70
274 60 c. Admiral, 1787–95. .. .. .. 1·75 1·50

(Des (from photograph by D. Groves) and photo Harrison)

1972 (24 Nov). *Royal Silver Wedding. Multicoloured; background colour given.* W w **12**. *P* 14 × 14½.

275 **108** 15 c. bright blue 25 20
276 25 c. turquoise-blue 35 20
a. Blue omitted* £225

*The omission of the blue colour results in the Duke's suit appearing sepia instead of deep blue.

109 Blue Marlin

(Des G. Drummond. Litho Questa)

1972 (12 Dec). *Game Fish. T* **109** *and similar horiz designs. Multicoloured.* W w **12**. *P* 13½.

277 ½ c. Type **109** 5 10
a. Pair. Nos. 277/8 .. .. 10 20
278 ½ c. Wahoo 5 10
279 15 c. Allison Tuna 40 45
280 25 c. White Marlin 60 65
281 50 c. Sailfish .. .. 1·40 1.60
282 $1 Dolphin .. .. 2·75 3·00
277/82 .. .. *Set of* 6 4·75 5·50
MS283 194 × 158 mm. Nos. 277/82 .. .. 6·50 7·00

Nos. 277/8 were printed horizontally and vertically *se-tenant* within the sheet.

110 J. C. Lettsom

111 Green-throated Carib and Antillean Crested Hummingbird

(Des J. Cooter. Litho Questa)

1973 (9 Mar). *"Interpex 1973" (Quakers). T* **110** *and similar multicoloured designs.* W w **12** (*sideways on* ½ c. *and* 15 c.). *P* 13½.

284 ½ c. Type **110** 5 8
285 10 c. Lettsom House (*horiz*) 30 30
286 15 c. Dr. W. Thornton 40 40
287 30 c. Dr. Thornton and Capitol, Washington (*horiz*) 70 75
288 $1 William Penn (*horiz*) .. .. .. 1·90 2·10

(Des G. Drummond. Litho Questa)

1973 (30 June). *First Issue of Coinage. T* **111** *and similar horiz designs showing coins and local scenery. Multicoloured.* W w **12**. *P* 14.

289 1 c. Type **111** 8 8
290 5 c. Zenaida Dove 40 40
291 10 c. Ringed Kingfisher 50 50
292 25 c. Mangrove Cuckoo 75 90
293 50 c. Brown Pelican .. .. 1·00 1·40
294 $1 Magnificent Frigatebird .. .. .. 2·00 2·50
289/94 .. .. *Set of* 6 4·25 5·00

1973 (17 Oct). *As Nos.* 240, 243/5 *and* 248/9, *but wmk upright.*

295 ½ c. buff, red-brown and sepia 25 40
296 3 c. orange-red, cobalt and sepia .. .. 85 1·25
297 4 c. greenish blue, chalky blue & bistre-brn 85 1·25
298 5 c. emerald, pink and black .. .. .. 85 1·25
299 10 c. greenish blue, yellow-brown & red-brown 1·25 2·00
300 12 c. yellow, dull crimson and light brown .. 2·00 3·00
295/300 .. .. *Set of* 6 5·50 8·25

1973 (14 Nov). *Royal Wedding. As Nos.* 165/6 *of Anguilla. Centre multicoloured.* W w **12** (*sideways*). *P* 13½.

301 5 c. brown-ochre 10 10
302 50 c. light turquoise-blue 25 25

112 "The Virgin and Child" (Pintoricchio)

113 Crest of the *Canopus* (French)

(Des G. Drummond. Litho Questa)

1973 (7 Dec). *Christmas. T* **112** *and similar vert designs Multicoloured.* W w **12**. *P* 14.

303 ½ c. Type **112** 5 5
304 3 c. "Virgin and Child" (Lorenzo di Credi) .. 10 5
305 25 c. "Virgin and Child" (Crivelli) 35 45
306 50 c. "Virgin and Child with St. John" (Luini) 60 85

(Des J. Cooter. Litho Questa)

1974 (22 Mar). *"Interpex 1974" (Naval Crests). T* **113** *and similar vert designs. Multicoloured. W w* **12**. *P* 14.

307 5 c. Type **113** 10 10
308 18 c. U.S.S. *Saginaw* 25 35
309 25 c. H.M.S. *Rothesay* 40 50
310 50 c. H.M.C.S. *Ottawa* 60 85
MS311 196 × 128 mm. Nos. 307/10 .. .. 2·75 3·25

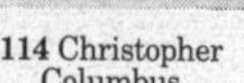

114 Christopher Columbus

115 Trumpet Triton

(Des J. W. Litho Format)

1974 (19 Aug). *Historical Figures. T* **114** *and similar vert designs. W w* **12**. *P* 14.

312 5 c. orange and black 15 10
313 10 c. greenish blue and black 30 30
314 25 c. reddish violet and black 60 60
315 40 c. yellow-brown and sepia 90 95
MS316 84 × 119 mm. Nos. 312/15 .. .. 2·40 2·50

Portraits:—10 c. Sir Walter Raleigh; 25 c. Sir Martin Frobisher; 40 c. Sir Francis Drake.

(Des G. Drummond. Litho Harrison)

1974 (30 Sept). *Seashells. T* **115** *and similar horiz designs. Multicoloured. W w* **12**. *P* 13 × 13½.

317 5 c. Type **115** 20 20
a. Wmk T **53** of Lesotho (sideways) .. £140
318 18 c. West Indian Murex 60 60
319 25 c. Bleeding Tooth 75 75
320 75 c. Virgin Islands Latirus .. .. .. 2·00 2·25
MS321 146 × 95 mm. Nos. 317/20 .. .. 4·25 5·00

116 Churchill and St. Mary, Aldermanbury, London

117 H.M.S. *Boreas*

(Des J. W. Litho Questa)

1974 (30 Nov). *Birth Centenary of Sir Winston Churchill. T* **116** *and similar horiz design. Multicoloured. W w* **14** *(sideways). P* 14.

322 10 c. Type **116** 30 30
323 50 c. St. Mary, Fulton, Missouri 80 80
MS324 141 × 108 mm. Nos. 322/3 .. .. 1·40 1·50

(Des J. Cooter. Litho J. W.)

1975 (14 Mar). *"Interpex 1975" Stamp Exhibition, New York. Ships' Figureheads. T* **117** *and similar vert designs. Multicoloured. W w* **12**. *P* 13.

325 5 c. Type **117** 25 25
326 18 c. *Golden Hind* 60 60
327 40 c. H.M.S. *Superb* .. .. 1·00 1·10
328 85 c. H.M.S. *Formidable* .. .. .. 1·75 1·90
MS329 192 × 127 mm. Nos. 325/8. (Wmk inverted). P 14 .. .. 3·50 3·75

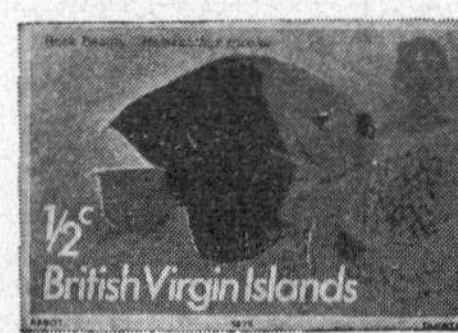

118 Rock Beauty

(Des C. Abbott. Litho Questa)

1975 (16 June–15 Aug). *Fishes. Horiz designs as T* **118**. *Multicoloured. W w* **14** *(sideways). P* 14.

330 ½ c. Type **118** 10 10
331 1 c. Squirrelfish 15 15
332 3 c. Queen Triggerfish 15 15
333 5 c. Blue Angelfish 20 20
334 8 c. Stoplight Parrotfish 25 25
335 10 c. Queen Angelfish 25 25
336 12 c. Nassau Grouper 30 30
337 13 c. Blue Tang 30 30
338 15 c. Sergeant Major 35 35
339 18 c. Jewfish 45 60
340 20 c. Bluehead Wrasse 50 50
341 25 c. Grey Angelfish 50 60
342 60 c. Glasseye Snapper .. .. 1·00 1·25
343 $1 Blue Chromis .. .. 1·50 1·75
344 $2.50, French Angelfish .. .. .. 3·50 3·75
345 $3 Queen Parrotfish .. .. 4·25 4·75
346 $5 Four-eye Butterfly Fish (15.8) .. .. 9·50 9·50
330/46 .. .. *Set of* 17 21·00 22·00

The original imprint at foot has the date "1975". Some values were later reprinted with the date altered to "1977".

The imprints on all the stamps show the designer's name as "Abbot".

119 St. George's Parish School (First meeting-place, 1950)

(Des R. Granger Barrett. Litho Questa)

1975 (27 Nov). *25th Anniv of Restoration of Legislative Council. T* **119** *and similar horiz designs. Multicoloured. W w* **14** *(sideways). P* 14.

347 5 c. Type **119** 10 10
348 25 c. Legislative Council Building 35 35
349 40 c. Mace and gavel 55 55
350 75 c. Commemorative scroll .. .. .. 90 1·00

120 Copper Mine Point

(Des PAD Studio. Litho Walsall)

1976 (12 Mar). *Historic Sites. T* **120** *and similar horiz designs. Multicoloured. W w* **14** *(sideways). P* 14½.

351 5 c. Type **120** 10 10
352 18 c. Pleasant Valley 25 30
353 50 c. Callwood Distillery 75 80
354 75 c. The Dungeon .. .. 1·00 1·25

121 Massachusetts Brig *Hazard*

(Des J. W. Litho Questa)

1976 (29 May). *Bicentenary of American Revolution. T* **121** *and similar horiz designs. Multicoloured, W w* **14** *(sideways). P* 14.

355 8 c. Type **121** 50 45
356 22 c. American Privateer *Spy* .. .. .. 1·10 95
357 40 c. Continental Navy frigate *Raleigh* .. 1·75 1·40
358 75 c. Frigate *Alliance* and H.M.S. *Trepasy* .. 2·25 1·90
MS359 114 × 89 mm. No. 355/8 .. .. .. 7·50 8·00

122 Government House, Tortola

123 Royal Visit, 1966

(Des Walsall. Litho Questa)

1976 (29 Oct). *Fifth Anniv of Friendship Day with U.S. Virgin Is. T* **122** *and similar multicoloured designs. W w* **14** *(sideways on 8 and 75 c.). P* 14.

360 8 c. Type **122** 10 10
361 15 c. Government House, St. Croix (*vert*) .. 20 20
362 30 c. Flags (*vert*) 35 35
363 75 c. Government seals 75 85

(Des J. Cooter. Litho Walsall)

1977 (7 Feb). *Silver Jubilee. T* **123** *and similar vert designs (inscr "SILVER JUBILEE" at top). Multicoloured. W w* **14**. *P* 13½.

364 8 c. Type **123** 10 15
365 30 c. The Holy Bible 40 60
366 60 c. Presentation of Holy Bible 60 85

For stamps with different inscription, see Nos. 371/3.

The imprint at the stamp's foot gives the designer (wrongly) as "Waddington Studio".

124 Chart of 1739

(Des J. Cooter. Litho Walsall)

1977 (13 June). *18th-Century Maps. T* **124** *and similar horiz designs. Multicoloured. W w* **14**. *P* 13½.

367 8 c. Type **124** 40 25
368 22 c. French Map, 1758 .. .. 75 80
369 30 c. Map from English and Danish surveys, 1775 .. .. 95 1·00
370 75 c. Map of 1779 .. .. 2·00 2·00

1977 (26 Oct). *Royal Visit. Designs as Nos. 364/6 but inscr. "SILVER JUBILEE ROYAL VISIT" at top, and face-values changed.*

371 5 c. Type **123** 10 10
372 25 c. The Holy Bible 30 35
373 50 c. Presentation of Holy Bible 50 55

The above also differ from Nos. 364/6 in having the silver frame removed and the silver lettering replaced by white. The imprint at foot now has the designer's name correctly given as "J. E. Cooter".

125 Divers checking Equipment

126 Fire Coral

(Des J. W. Litho Rosenbaum Bros, Vienna)

1978 (10 Feb). *Tourism. T* **125** *and similar vert designs. Multicoloured. W w* **14**. *P* 13½.

374 ½ c. Type **125** 5 5
375 5 c. Cup coral on wreck 15 15
376 8 c. Sponge formation on wreck 25 20
377 22 c. Cup coral and sponges 60 50
378 30 c. Sponges inside cave 75 60
379 75 c. Marine life .. .. 1·50 1·25
374/9 .. .. *Set of* 6 3·00 2·50

(Des G. Drummond. Litho Harrison)

1978 (27 Feb). *Corals. T* **126** *and similar horiz designs. Multicoloured. W w* **14** *(sideways). P* 14.

380 8 c. Type **126** 35 25
381 15 c. Staghorn coral 60 50
382 40 c. Brain coral .. .. 1·25 1·10
383 75 c. Elkhorn coral .. .. 2·25 1·75

127 Iguana

128 Lignum Vitae

(Des Jennifer Toombs. Litho Questa)

1978 (2 June). *25th Anniv of Coronation. T* **127** *and similar vert designs. P* 15.

384 50 c. brown-ochre, green and silver 55 65
a. Sheetlet. Nos. 384/6 × 2 .. .. .. 3·50
385 50 c. multicoloured 55 65
386 50 c. brown-ochre, green and silver 55 65

Designs:—No. 384, Plantagenet Falcon; No. 385, Queen Elizabeth II; No. 386, Type **127**.

(Des and litho J.W.)

1978 (4 Sept). *Flowering Trees. T* **128** *and similar horiz designs. Multicoloured. W w* **14** *(sideways). P* 13.

387 8 c. Type **128** 25 20
388 22 c. Ginger Thomas 55 55
389 40 c. Dog Almond 70 70
390 75 c. White Cedar .. .. 1·25 1·40
MS391 131 × 95 mm. Nos. 387/90. P 14 .. .. 2·75 3·00

129 *Eurema lisa*

(Des G. Hutchins. Litho Questa)

1978 (4 Dec). *Butterflies. T* **129** *and similar horiz designs. Multicoloured. W w* **14** *(sideways). P* 14.

392 5 c. Type **129** . . 25 12
393 22 c. *Dione vanillae* . . 75 45
394 30 c. *Heliconius charitonius* . . 85 50
395 75 c. *Hemiargus hanno* . . 1·25 1·25
MS396 159 × 113 mm. No. 392 × 6 and 393 × 3 3·00 3·50

130 Spiny Lobster

(Des Picton Print. Litho Harrison)

1979 (10 Feb). *Wildlife Conservation. T* **130** *and similar multicoloured designs. W w* **14** *(sideways on 5 and 22 c.). P* 14.

397 5 c. Type **130** . . 20 10
398 15 c. Large Iguana (*vert*) . . 50 30
399 22 c. Hawksbill Turtle . . 70 40
400 75 c. Black Coral (*vert*) . . 2·00 1·50
MS401 130 × 153 mm. Nos. 397/400 (wmk sideways) . . 3·25 3·50

131 Strawberry Cactus 132 West Indian Girl

(Des BG Studio. Litho Format)

1979 (7 May). *Cacti. T* **131** *and similar vert designs. Multicoloured. W w* **14**. *P* 14.

402 ½ c. Type **131** . . 5 5
403 5 c. Snowy Cactus . . 15 15
404 13 c. Barrel Cactus . . 25 25
405 22 c. Tree Cactus . . 45 45
406 30 c. Prickly Pear . . 50 50
407 75 c. Dildo Cactus . . 1·00 1·00
402/7 . . *Set of* 6 2·25 2·25

(Des R. Granger Barrett. Litho Questa)

1979 (9 July). *International Year of the Child. T* **132** *and similar vert designs. Multicoloured. W w* **14** *(inverted). P* 14½ × 14.

408 5 c. Type **132** . . 8 8
409 10 c. African boy . . 15 15
410 13 c. Asian girl . . 20 20
411 $1 European boy . . 1·00 1·25
MS412 91 × 114 mm. Nos. 408/11 . . 1·75 1·90

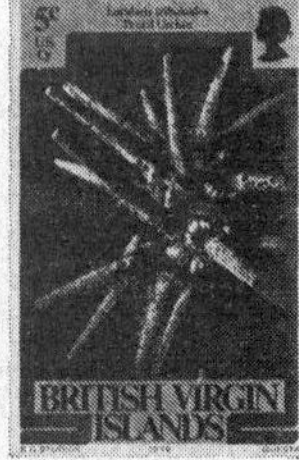

133 1956 Road Harbour 3 c. Definitive Stamp 134 Pencil Urchin

(Des J. W. Photo Heraclio Fournier)

1979 (1 Oct). *Death Centenary of Sir Rowland Hill. T* **133** *and similar designs showing stamps. P* 13½.

413 5 c. deep blue, new blue and brown-olive . . 10 5
414 13 c. deep blue and claret . . 20 15
415 75 c. deep blue and bright purple . . 75 90
MS416 37 × 91 mm. $1 deep blue & carm-red. P 13 1·25 1·60

Designs: (39 × 27 *mm*)—13 c. 1889 2½d.; 75 c. Great Britain unissued 1910 2d. Tyrian plum. (40 × 28 *mm*)—$1. 1867 1s. "Missing Virgin" error.

(Des BG Studio. Litho Questa)

1979 (17 Dec)–**82**. *Marine Life. Vert designs as T* **134**. *Multicoloured. W w* **14**. *Ordinary paper. P* 14.

417 ½ c. Calcified Algae (1.4.80) . . 5 5
418 1 c. Purple-tipped Sea Anemone (1.4.80) . . 5 5
419 3 c. Common Starfish (1.4.80) . . 5 5
420 5 c. Type **134** . . 5 5
 a. Chalk-surfaced paper (27.8.82) . . 5 5
421 8 c. Triton's Trumpet (shell) . . 15 20
 a. Chalk-surfaced paper (27.8.82) . . 12 15
422 10 c. Christmas Tree Worms . . 15 20
423 13 c. Flamingo Tongue Snail (1.4.80) . . 20 25
 a. Chalk-surfaced paper (27.8.82) . . 20 25
424 15 c. Spider Crab . . 20 25
 a. Chalk-surfaced paper (27.8.82) . . 20 25
425 18 c. Sea Squirts (1.4.80) . . 25 30
426 20 c. True Tulip (shell) . . 30 35
 a. Chalk-surfaced paper (27.8.82) . . 30 35
427 25 c. Rooster Tail Conch (shell) . . 40 45
428 30 c. Fighting Conch (shell) (1.4.80) . . 45 50
 a. Chalk-surfaced paper (27.8.82) . . 45 50
429 60 c. Mangrove Crab (1.4.80) . . 90 95
430 $1 Coral Polyps (1.4.80) . . 1·50 1·60
431 $2.50, Peppermint Shrimp . . 3·75 4·00
432 $3 West Indian Murex (shell) . . 4·50 4·75
433 $5 Carpet Anemone (1.4.80) . . 7·75 8·00
417/33 . . *Set of* 17 18·50 19·50

Nos. 420a/28a were printed with a changed imprint date, "1982".

135 Rotary Athletics Meeting, Tortola 136 Brown Booby

(Des J. W. Litho Enschedé)

1980 (23 Feb). *75th Anniv of Rotary International. T* **135** *and similar horiz designs. Multicoloured. W w* **14** *(sideways). P* 13½ × 14.

434 8 c. Type **135** . . 12 12
435 22 c. Paul P. Harris (founder) and Rotary emblem . . 30 30
436 60 c. "Creation of a National Park", Mount Sage, Tortola . . 85 85
437 $1 Rotary anniversary emblem . . 1·40 1·40
MS438 149 × 148 mm. Nos. 434/7 . . 2·40 2·75

(Des K. Penny. Litho Secura, Singapore)

1980 (6 May). *"London 1980" International Stamp Exhibition. Birds. T* **136** *and similar horiz designs. Multicoloured. W w* **14** *(sideways). P* 13½.

439 20 c. Type **136** . . 35 35
 a. Wmk upright . . 50 50
440 25 c. Magnificent Frigate Bird . . 45 45
 a. Wmk upright . . 1·75 1·75
441 50 c. White-tailed Tropic Bird . . 65 65
 a. Wmk upright . . 80 80
442 75 c. Brown Pelican . . 90 95
MS443 152 × 130 mm. Nos. 439/42 . . 2·25 2·50

CARIBBEAN
COMMONWEALTH
PARLIAMENTARY
ASSOCIATION
MEETING
TORTOLA 11-19 JULY 1980

(137)

138 Sir Francis Drake

1980 (7 July). *Caribbean Commonwealth Parliamentary Association Meeting, Tortola. Nos. 414/15 optd wth T* **137**.

444 13 c. deep blue and claret . . 12 15
445 75 c. deep blue and bright blue . . 80 90

(Des Franklin Mint. Litho Questa)

1980 (26 Sept). *Sir Francis Drake Commemoration. T* **138** *and similar vert designs. Multicoloured. W w* **14** *(inverted on 75 c.). P* 14 × 14½.

446 8 c. Type **138** . . 12 10
447 15 c. Queen Elizabeth I . . 20 20
448 30 c. Drake receiving knighthood . . 40 40
449 75 c. *Golden Hinde* and coat of arms . . 1·10 1·10
MS450 171 × 121 mm. Nos. 446/9. Wmk inverted 1·75 1·90
 a. 75 c. value in miniature sheet imperf . . £150

139 Jost van Dyke

(Des Jennifer Toombs. Litho Rosenbaum Bros, Vienna)

1980 (1 Dec). *Island Profiles. T* **139** *and similar horiz designs. Multicoloured. W w* **14** *(sideways). P* 13½.

451 2 c. Type **139** . . 5 5
452 5 c. Peter Island . . 10 10
453 13 c. Virgin Gorda . . 20 20
454 22 c. Anegada . . 30 30
455 30 c. Norman Island . . 45 45
456 $1 Tortola . . 1·25 1·25
451/6 . . *Set of* 6 2·10 2·10
MS457 95 × 88 mm. No. 456 (wmk upright) . . 1·25 1·50
 a. Error. Imperf . . £325
 b. Gold and black omitted . . £325

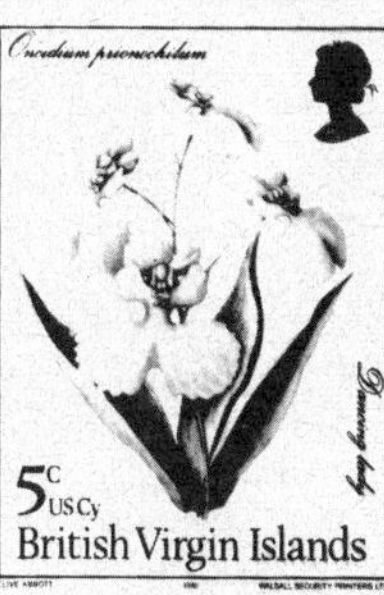

140 Dancing Lady 141 Wedding Bouquet from British Virgin Islands

(Des C. Abbott. Litho Walsall)

1981 (3 Mar). *Flowers. T* **140** *and similar vert designs. Multicoloured. W w* **14** *(sideways). P* 11.

458 5 c. Type **140** . . 10 10
459 20 c. Love in the Mist . . 35 35
460 22 c. *Pitcairnia angustifolia* . . 35 35
461 75 c. Dutchman's Pipe . . 1·25 1·25
462 $1 Maiden Apple . . 1·50 1·50

(Des J. W. Litho Harrison)

1981 (22 July). *Royal Wedding. T* **141** *and similar vert designs. Multicoloured. W w* **14**. *P* 14.

463 10 c. Type **141** . . 15 15
464 35 c. Prince Charles and Queen Elizabeth the Queen Mother in Garter robes . . 45 45
465 $1.25, Prince Charles and Lady Diana Spencer . . 1·25 1·25

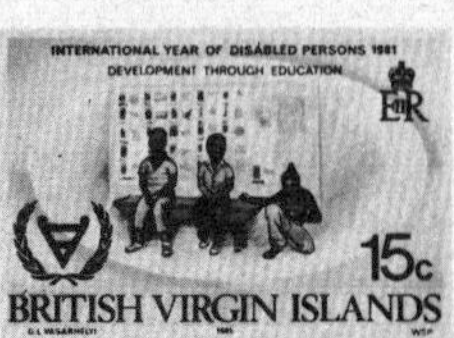

142 Stamp Collecting 143 "Development through Education"

(Des BG Studio. Litho Questa)

1981 (10 Oct). *25th Anniv of Duke of Edinburgh Award Scheme. T* **142** *and similar vert designs. Multicoloured. W w* **14**. *P* 14.

466 10 c. Type **142** . . 15 15
467 15 c. Athletics . . 20 20
468 50 c. Camping . . 75 75
469 $1 Duke of Edinburgh . . 1·50 1·50

(Des G. Vasarhelyi. Litho Walsall)

1981 (19 Oct). *International Year for Disabled Persons. T* **143** *and similar horiz designs. Multicoloured. W w* **14** *(sideways). P* 14.

470 15 c. Type **143** . . 20 20
471 20 c. Fort Charlotte Children's Centre . . 30 30
472 30 c. "Developing cultural awareness" . . 40 40
473 $1 Fort Charlotte Children's Centre (*different*) . . 1·50 1·50

144 Detail from "The Adoration of the Shepherds" (Rubens) 145 Green-throated Caribs and Erythrina

(Des J. W. Litho Questa)

1981 (30 Nov). *Christmas. T* **144** *and similar designs showing details from "The Adoration of the Shepherds" by Rubens. W w* **14**. *P* 14.

474 5 c. multicoloured . . 5 5
475 15 c. multicoloured . . 20 20
476 30 c. multicoloured . . 40 40
477 $1 multicoloured . . 1·50 1·50
MS478 117 × 90 mm. 50 c. multicoloured (*horiz*) (wmk sideways) . . 75 85

(Des Walsall. Litho Format)

1982 (5 Apr). *Hummingbirds. T* **145** *and similar vert designs. Multicoloured. W w* **14** *(sideways). P* 14 × 14½.

479 15 c. Type **145** . . 25 15
480 30 c. Green-throated Carib and Bougainvillea 45 45
481 35 c. Antillean Crested Hummingbirds and *Granadilla passiflora* . . 55 55
482 $1.25, Antillean Crested Hummingbird and Hibiscus . . 1·90 1·90

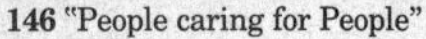

146 "People caring for People"

147 Princess at Victoria and Albert Museum, November 1981

(Des Harrison. Litho Format)

1982 (3 May). *Tenth Anniv of Lions Club of Tortola. T* **146** *and similar horiz designs. Multicoloured. W* w **14** *(sideways). P* 13½ × 14.

483 10 c. Type **146** 15 15
484 20 c. Tortola Headquarters 30 30
485 30 c. "We Serve" 40 40
486 $1.50, "Lions" symbol .. .. 1·90 1·90
MS487 124 × 102 mm. Nos. 483/6 .. .. 2·75 3·00

(Des C. Abbott. Litho Harrison)

1982 (2 July*). *21st Birthday of Princess of Wales. T* **147** *and similar vert designs. Multicoloured.* W w **14**. *P* 14½ × 14.

488 10 c. British Virgin Islands coat of arms .. 15 15
489 35 c. Type **147** 40 40
490 50 c. Bride and groom proceeding into Vestry 60 60
491 $1.50, Formal portrait .. .. 1·50 1·75

*This is the local release date. The Crown Agents released the stamps on 1 July.

148 Douglas "DC-3"

(Des A. Theobald. Litho Questa)

1982 (10 Sept). *10th Anniv of Air BVI. T* **148** *and similar horiz designs. Multicoloured.* W w **14** *(sideways). P* 14.

492 10 c. Type **148** 15 15
493 15 c. Britten-Norman "Islander" .. 25 25
494 60 c. Hawker Siddeley "748" 90 90
495 75 c. Runway scene .. .. 1·10 1·10

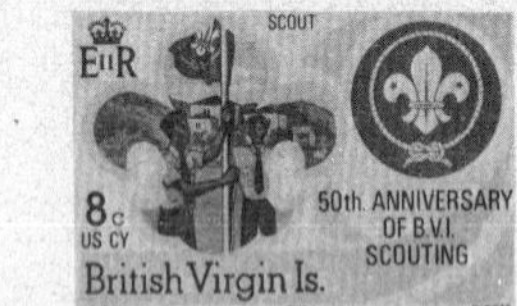

149 Scouts raising Flag

(Des R. Vigurs. Litho Questa)

1982 (18 Nov). *75th Anniv of Boy Scout Movement* ($1) *and 50th Anniv of Scouting in B.V.I. (others). T* **149** *and similar horiz designs. Multicoloured.* W w **14** *(sideways). P* 14.

496 8 c. Type **149** 15 15
497 20 c. Cub Scout 35 35
498 50 c. Sea Scout 75 75
499 $1 First camp, Brownsea Island, and portrait of Lord Baden-Powell .. .. 1·50 1·50

150 Legislature in Session

151 Florence Nightingale

(Des G. Vasarhelyi. Litho Enschedé)

1983 (10 Mar). *Commonwealth Day. T* **150** *and similar horiz designs. Multicoloured.* W w **14** *(sideways). P* 13 × 13½.

500 10 c. Type **150** 12 15
501 30 c. Tourism 40 45
502 35 c. Satellite view of Earth showing Virgin Islands 45 50
503 75 c. B.V.I. and Commonwealth flags .. 1·00 1·10

(Des L. Curtis. Litho Questa)

1983 (9 May). *Nursing Week. T* **151** *and similar multicoloured designs.* W w **14** *(sideways on* 60 *c. and* 75 *c.). P* 14.

504 10 c. Type **151** 12 15
505 30 c. Staff nurse and assistant nurse .. 40 45
506 60 c. Public Health nurses testing blood pressure (*horiz*) 80 85
507 75 c. Peebles Hospital (*horiz*) .. .. 1·00 1·10

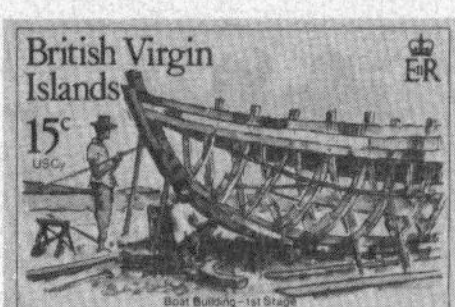

152 Frame Construction

(Des R. Burnett. Litho Harrison)

1983 (25 July). *Traditional Boat-building. T* **152** *and similar horiz designs. Multicoloured.* W w **14** *(sideways). P* 14.

508 15 c. Type **152** 20 25
509 25 c. Planking 35 40
510 50 c. Launching 65 70
511 $1 Maiden voyage .. .. 1·25 1·40
MS512 127 × 101 mm. Nos. 508/11 .. .. 2·40 2·75

153 Grumman "Goose" Seaplane

154 "Madonna and Child with the Infant Baptist"

(Des Walsall. Litho Questa)

1983 (15 Sept). *Bicentenary of Manned Flight. T* **153** *and similar horiz designs. Multicoloured.* W w **14** *(sideways). P* 14.

513 10 c. Type **153** 12 15
514 30 c. De Havilland "Heron" 40 45
515 60 c. EMB "110P1 Bandeirante" .. 80 85
516 $1.25, British Aerospace "HS 748" .. 1·50 1·60

(Des M. Joyce. Litho Questa)

1983 (7 Nov). *Christmas. 500th Birth Anniv of Raphael. T* **154** *and similar vert designs showing details of different paintings. Multicoloured.* W w **14**. *P* 14½ × 14.

517 8 c. Type **154** 10 12
518 15 c. "La Belle Jardiniére" 20 25
519 50 c. "Madonna Del Granduca" 65 70
520 $1 "The Terranuova Madonna" .. 1·25 1·40
MS521 108 × 101 mm. Nos. 517/20 .. .. 2·10 2·25

155 Local Tournament

156 Port Purcell

(Des L. Curtis. Litho Questa)

1984 (20 Feb). *60th Anniv of World Chess Federation. T* **155** *and similar multicoloured designs.* W w **14** *(sideways on* 10 *c. and* $1, *inverted on* 35 *c.). P* 14.

522 10 c. Type **155** 15 20
523 35 c. "Staunton" chess pieces (*vert*) .. 45 50
524 75 c. Winning position, 1980 Chess Olympiad (*vert*) .. .. 1·10 1·25
525 $1 B.V.I. Gold Medal from 1980 Chess Olympiad .. .. 1·40 1·50

(Des L. Curtis. Litho Questa)

1984 (16 Apr). *250th Anniv of "Lloyd's List" (newspaper). T* **156** *and similar vert designs. Multicoloured.* W w **14**. *P* 14½ × 14.

526 15 c. Type **156** 25 30
527 25 c. Boeing "747" 45 50
528 50 c. Loss of R.M.S. *Rhone* 90 95
529 $1 M.S. *Booker Viking* .. .. 1·75 1·90

157 Steam Ship, Aeroplane and U.P.U. Logo

(Des L. Curtis. Litho Walsall)

1984 (16 May). *Universal Postal Union Congress, Hamburg. Sheet* 90 × 69 *mm.* W w **14** *(sideways). P* 14.

MS530 **157** $1 pale blue and black .. .. 1·75 1·90

158 Running

159 Steel Band

(Des R. Granger Barrett. Litho Walsall)

1984 (3 July). *Olympic Games, Los Angeles. T* **158** *and similar horiz designs. Multicoloured.* W w **14** *(sideways). P* 14.

531 15 c. Type **158** 25 30
a. Pair. Nos. 531/2 50
532 15 c. Runner 25 30
533 20 c. Wind-surfing 35 40
a. Pair. Nos. 533/4 70
534 20 c. Surfer 35 40
535 30 c. Sailing 50 55
a. Pair. Nos. 535/6 .. .. 1·00
536 30 c. Yacht 50 55
531/6 .. .. *Set of* 6 2·00 2·25
MS537 97 × 69 mm. $1 Torch bearer. Wmk upright 1·75 1·90

Nos. 531/2, 533/4 and 535/6 were printed together, *se-tenant*, in horizontal and vertical pairs throughout the sheets.

(Des D. Miller. Litho Format)

1984 (14 Aug). *150th Anniv of Abolition of Slavery. T* **159** *and similar vert designs showing various aspects of Emancipation Festival. Multicoloured.* W w **14**. *P* 14.

538 10 c. Type **159** 20 25
a. Horiz strip of 5. Nos. 538/42 .. 1·00
539 10 c. Dancing girls 20 25
540 10 c. Men in traditional costumes .. 20 25
541 10 c. Girl in traditional costume .. 20 25
542 10 c. Festival Queen 20 25
543 30 c. Green and yellow dinghies .. 50 55
a. Horiz strip of 5. Nos. 543/7 .. 2·25
544 30 c. Blue and red dinghies 50 55
545 30 c. White and blue dinghies .. 50 55
546 30 c. Red and yellow dinghies .. 50 55
547 30 c. Blue and white dinghies .. 50 55
538/47 .. .. *Set of* 10 3·00 3·25

Nos. 538/42 and 543/7 were each printed together, *se-tenant*, in horizontal strips of 5 throughout the sheet, forming composite designs. On Nos. 543/7 the sail colours of the dinghies are described to assist identification.

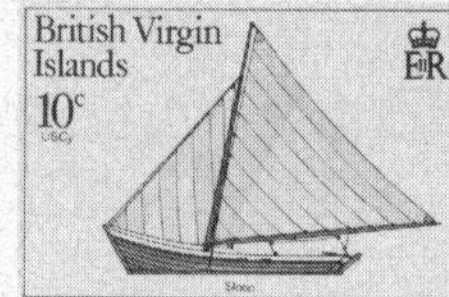

160 Sloop

(Des R. Burnett. Litho J.W.)

1984 (15 Nov). *Boats. T* **160** *and similar horiz designs. Multicoloured.* W w **14** *(sideways). P* 13 × 13½.

548 10 c. Type **160** 15 20
549 35 c. Fishing boat 60 65
550 60 c. Schooner .. .. 1·00 1·10
551 75 c. Cargo boat .. .. 1·25 1·40
MS552 125 × 90 mm. Nos. 548/51. P 14 .. 3·00 3·25

161 One Cent Coin and Aerial View

(Litho Walsall)

1985 (15 Jan). *New Coinage. T* **161** *and similar horiz designs showing coins and local scenery. Multicoloured.* W w **14** *(sideways). P* 14½.

553 1 c. Type **161** 5 5
554 5 c. Five cent coin and boulders on beach .. 8 10
555 10 c. Ten cent coin and scuba diving .. 15 20
556 25 c. Twenty-five cent coin and yachts .. 40 45
557 50 c. Fifty cent coin and jetty 85 90
558 $1 One dollar coin and beach at night .. 1·60 1·75
553/8 .. .. *Set of* 6 2·75 3·00
MS559 103 × 156 mm. Nos. 553/8 .. .. 3·00 3·25

Brunei

Sultan Hashim Jalil-ul-alam Akamudin, 1885–1906

For many years the status of the 1895 issue remained uncertain to such an extent that the 1906 provisionals on Labuan were taken to be the first issue of Brunei.

The 1895 "Star and Crescent" design stamps were, from their first appearance, considered bogus or, at best, as an issue made purely for philatelic purposes. Research into the background of the events surrounding the set led to the publication, in 1933, of the original agreement between Sultan Hashim and J. C. Robertson dated 20 August 1894 which made clear that the stamps fulfilled a genuine postal purpose. Although Robertson and his partners intended to exploit the philatelic sales for their own benefit the agreement testifies, as does other evidence, to the use of the stamps by the Sultan for his postal service. As Brunei did not, at that time, belong to any local or international postal union the stamps were only valid within the state or on mail to Labuan or Sarawak. Items for further afield required franking with Labuan stamps in addition. Although most covers surviving are addressed to Robertson's associates enough commercial covers and cards exist to show that there was, indeed, a postal service.

PRICES FOR STAMPS ON COVER TO 1945

Nos. 1/10 are rare used on cover.
Nos. 11/22 *from* × 30
Nos. 23/33 *from* × 25
Nos. 34/50 *from* × 10
Nos. 51/9 *from* × 12
Nos. 60/78 *from* × 8

The Sarawak Government maintained a post office at the coal mining centre of Brooketon, and the stamps of SARAWAK were used there from 1893 until the office was handed over to Brunei in February 1907.

1 Star and Local Scene

(Litho in Glasgow)

1895 (22 July). *P* 13–13½.

No.	Type	Description	Unused	Used
1	1	½ c. brown	30	6·50
2		1 c. brown-lake	30	6·50
3		2 c. grey-black	2·50	6·50
4		3 c. deep blue	2·50	6·50
5		5 c. deep blue-green	4·50	6·50
6		8 c. plum	5·50	6·50
7		10 c. orange-red	7·00	9·50
		a. Imperf (pair)	£350	
8		25 c. turquoise-green	8·00	13·00
9		50 c. yellow-green	18·00	27·00
10		$1 yellow-olive	20·00	45·00
1/10		*Set of* 10	60·00	£120

BRUNEI. (2)

BRUNEI. TWO CENTS. (3)

BRUNEI. 25 CENTS. (4)

(Optd by Govt Printer, Singapore)

1906 (11–17 Oct). *Stamps of Labuan, T* 18 (*Nos.* 116c, *etc.*), *optd with T* 2, *or surch as T* 3 *or* 4 (25 c.), *in red. P* 13½ *or* 14 (1 c.).

No.	Description	Unused	Used
11	1 c. black and purple	14·00	18·00
	a. Error. Opt in black	£2000	£2500
12	2 c. on 3 c. black and sepia	2·75	4·50
	a. "BRUNEI" double	£3500	£2500
13	2 c. on 8 c. black and vermilion	27·00	32·00
	a. "TWO CENTS" double	£4500	
	b. "TWO CENTS" omitted in vert pair with normal	£6000	
14	3 c. black and sepia	27·00	32·00
15	4 c. on 12 c. black and yellow (17.10.06)	2·00	6·00
16	5 c. on 16 c. green and brown (17.10.06)	27·00	26·00
17	8 c. black and vermilion	9·50	18·00
18	10 c. on 16 c. green and brown (17.10.06)	8·50	17·00
19	25 c. on 16 c. green and brown (17.10.06)	£110	£150
20	30 c. on 16 c. green and brown (17.10.06)	£100	£140
21	50 c. on 16 c. green and brown (17.10.06)	£100	£140
22	$1 on 8 c. black and vermilion (17.10.06)	£100	£140
11/22	*Set of* 12	£500	£650

Sultan Mohamed Jemal-ul-Alam, 1906–1924

PRINTERS. All Brunei stamps from Nos. 13 to 113 were recess-printed by De La Rue.

OMNIBUS ISSUES

Details, together with prices for complete sets, of the various Omnibus issues from the 1935 Silver Jubilee series to date are included in a special section following Zululand at the end of the catalogue.

5 View on Brunei River

1907–10. *Wmk Mult Crown CA. P* 14.

No.	Type	Description	Unused	Used
23	5	1 c. grey-black and pale green	2·00	4·75
24		2 c. grey-black and scarlet	2·50	4·50
25		3 c. grey-black and chocolate	15·00	18·00
26		4 c. grey-black and mauve	11·00	15·00
		a. Grey-black and reddish purple (1910)	50·00	70·00
27		5 c. grey-black and blue	45·00	70·00
28		8 c. grey-black and orange	8·50	28·00
29		10 c. grey-black and deep green	12·00	26·00
30		25 c. pale blue and ochre-brown	24·00	40·00
31		30 c. violet and black	24·00	40·00
32		50 c. green and deep brown	24·00	40·00
33		$1 red and grey	90·00	£150
23/33		*Set of* 11	£225	£400
23/33 Optd "Specimen"		*Set of* 11	£325	

I

II

I Double plate. Lowest line of shading on water is dotted.
II Single plate. Dotted line of shading removed.

Stamps printed in two colours are as I.

1908 (12 June)–**20.** *Colours changed. Double or single plates. Wmk Mult Crown CA. P* 14.

No.	Type	Description	Unused	Used
34	5	1 c. green (I)	65	2·00
35		1 c. green (II) (1911)	40	75
36		2 c. black and brown (5.4.11)	75	1·25
37		3 c. scarlet (I)	1·40	2·00
38		3 c. scarlet (II) (1916)	12·00	24·00
39		4 c. claret (II)	70	85
40		5 c. black and orange	7·50	7·50
41		8 c. blue and indigo-blue (10.08)	6·50	9·50
42		10 c. purple/*yellow* (II) (1912)	1·60	1·60
		a. On pale yellow (Optd S. £6)	1·25	2·75
43		25 c. deep lilac (II) (30.5.12)	2·25	4·50
44		30 c. purple and orange-yellow (18.3.12)	8·50	12·00
45		50 c. black/*green* (II) (1912)	16·00	30·00
		a. On blue-green (1920)	9·50	16·00
46		$1 black and red/*blue* (18.3.12)	30·00	48·00
47		$5 carmine/*green* (I) (1910)	80·00	£130
48		$25 black/*red* (I) (1910)	£600	
34/47		*Set of* 12	£130	£200
34/48 Optd "Specimen"		*Set of* 13	£550	

Retouch Normal

MALAYA-
BORNEO
EXHIBITION,
1922.

(6)

RETOUCHES. We list the very distinctive 5 c. Retouch (top left value tablet, 1st row, 8th stamp) but there are others of interest, notably in the clouds.

1916. *Colours changed. Single plates. Wmk Mult Crown CA. P* 14.

No.	Type	Description	Unused	Used
49	5	5 c. orange	2·50	3·25
		a. "5 c." retouch	£110	£140
50		8 c. ultramarine	4·25	12·00
49/50 Optd "Specimen"		*Set of* 2	£120	

MALAYA-BORNEO EXHIBITION OVERPRINTS. These were produced from a setting of 30 examples, applied twice to overprint the complete sheet of 60 stamps. Three prominent overprint flaws exist, each occurring on all the stamps in two vertical rows of the sheet.

HI	EX	NE
Short "I" (all stamps in 2nd and 8th vertical rows)	Broken "E" (all stamps in 4th and 10th vertical rows)	Broken "N" (all stamps in 6th and 12th vertical rows)

(Optd by Govt Printer, Singapore)

1922 (31 Mar). *Optd with T* 6, *in black.*

No.	Type	Description	Unused	Used
51	5	1 c. green (II)	2·75	14·00
		a. Short "I"	8·00	
		b. Broken "E"	8·00	
		c. Broken "N"	8·00	
52		2 c. black and brown	5·50	14·00
		a. Short "I"	14·00	
		b. Broken "E"	14·00	
		c. Broken "N"	14·00	
53	5	3 c. scarlet (II)	6·50	23·00
		a. Short "I"	16·00	
		b. Broken "E"	16·00	
		c. Broken "N"	16·00	
54	5	4 c. claret (II)	5·50	32·00
		a. Short "I"	14·00	
		b. Broken "E"	14·00	
		c. Broken "N"	14·00	
55		5 c. orange (II)	9·00	48·00
		a. "5 c." retouch	£180	£400
		b. Short "I"	20·00	
		c. Broken "E"	20·00	
		d. Broken "N"	20·00	
56		10 c. purple/*yellow* (II)	13·00	55·00
		a. Short "I"	28·00	
		b. Broken "E"	28·00	
		c. Broken "N"	28·00	
57		25 c. purple (II)	29·00	95·00
		a. Short "I"	50·00	
		b. Broken "E"	50·00	
		c. Broken "N"	50·00	
58		50 c. black/*blue-green* (II)	90·00	£225
		a. Short "I"	£160	
		b. Broken "E"	£160	
		c. Broken "N"	£160	
59		$1 black and red/*blue*	£125	£225
		a. Short "I"	£225	
		b. Broken "E"	£225	
		c. Broken "N"	£225	
51/9		*Set of* 9	£250	£650

Sultan Ahmed Tajudin Akhazul Khairi Wadin, 1924–1950

7 Native houses, Water Village

1924 (Feb)–**37.** *Printed from single plates as Type* II, *except* 30 c. *and* $1 *as Type* I. *Wmk Mult Script CA. P* 14.

No.	Type	Description	Unused	Used
60	5	1 c. black (9.26)	30	55
61		2 c. brown (3.24)	95	2·75
62		2 c. green (3.33)	40	75
63		3 c. green (3.24)	95	4·00
64		4 c. maroon (3.24)	2·25	2·25
65		4 c. orange (1929)	1·25	85
66		5 c. orange-yellow* (3.24)	80	1·25
		a. "5 c." retouch	£120	£150
67		5 c. grey (1931)	4·75	4·75
		a. "5 c." retouch	£225	£275
68		5 c. chocolate (1933)	50	55
		a. "5 c." retouch	60·00	80·00
69	7	6 c. intense black** (3.24)	6·00	7·50
70		6 c. scarlet (1931)	3·75	9·00
71	5	8 c. ultramarine (9.27)	4·50	5·00
72		8 c. grey-black (1933)	2·50	1·75
73		10 c. purple/*yellow* (3.37)	8·00	13·00
74	7	12 c. blue	7·00	9·50
		a. Pale greenish blue (1927)	£130	£200
75	5	25 c. slate-purple (1931)	6·00	8·00
76		30 c. purple and orange-yellow (1931)	4·50	8·50
77		50 c. black/*emerald* (1931)	8·00	19·00
78		$1 black and red/*blue* (1931)	32·00	50·00
60/78		*Set of* 19	80·00	£130
60/72, 74/8 Optd/Perf "Specimen"		*Set of* 18	£400	

*For 5 c. orange, see No. 82. No. 66 is a "Wet" printing and No. 82 a "Dry".

**For 6 c. black, see No. 83. Apart from the difference in shade there is a variation in size, No. 69 being 37¾ mm long and No. 83 39 mm.

The 2 c. orange in Type 5 and the 6 c. greenish black, 8 c. red and 15 c. ultramarine in Type 7 were not issued without the Japanese Occupation overprint, although unoverprinted copies exist.

During the life of this issue De La Rue changed the method of production from a "Wet" to a "Dry" process. Initially the stamps were printed on ungummed paper which was dampened before being put on the press. Once the paper had dried, and contracted in the process, the gum was then applied. "Dry" printings, introduced around 1934, were on pre-gummed paper. The contraction of the "Wet" printings was considerable and usually involves a difference of between 0.5 mm and 1 mm when compared with the larger "Dry" printings. The following stamps occur from both "Wet" and "Dry" versions: 1 c., 2 c. green, 4 c. orange, 5 c. chocolate, 6 c. scarlet, 8 c. grey-black, 10 c. and 25 c.

Stamps of this issue can be found either line or comb perforated.

After the cessation of hostilities with the Japanese postal services were re-introduced by the British Military Administration. Post offices under B.M.A. control were opened at Brunei Town and Kuala Belait on 17 December 1945 where B.M.A. overprints on the stamps of NORTH BORNEO and SARAWAK were used until the reappearance of Brunei issues on 2 January 1947.

1947 (2 Jan)–**51.** *Colours changed and new values. Wmk Mult Script CA. P* 14.

No.	Type	Description	Unused	Used
79	5	1 c. chocolate	35	25
80		2 c. grey	30	75
		a. Perf 14½ × 13½ (25.9.50)	1·25	1·40
		ab. Black (27.6.51)	45	1·75
81	7	3 c. green	75	1·50
82	5	5 c. orange*	50	80
		a. "5 c." retouch	50·00	55·00
		b. Perf 14½ × 13½ (25.9.50)	4·00	5·00
		c. Ditto. "5 c." retouch	60·00	60·00
83	7	6 c. black*	1·25	2·00
84	5	8 c. scarlet	30	25
		a. Perf 13 (25.1.51)	25	1·75
85		10 c. violet	30	5
		a. Perf 14½ × 13½ (25.9.50)	1·50	2·25
86		15 c. ultramarine	55	20
87		25 c. purple	25	40
		a. Perf 14½ × 13½ (25.1.51)	40	2·75
88		30 c. black and orange	40	55
		a. Perf 14½ × 13½ (25.1.51)	40	3·00

89 **5** 50 c. black 40 60
a. Perf 13 (25.9.50) .. .. .. 1·50 8·00
90 $1 black and scarlet .. .. .. 1·10 80
91 $5 green and red-orange (2.2.48) .. 20·00 18·00
92 $10 black and purple (2.2.48) .. .. 25·00 40·00
79/92 .. .. *Set of* 14 45·00 60·00
79/92 Perf "Specimen" .. .. *Set of* 14 £180

*See also Nos. 66 and 69.

Nos. 79/80, 82, 85 and 87 utilised the plates of the pre-war issue and were line perforated until the introduction of the comb perforation 14½ × 13½ in September 1950.

8 Sultan Ahmed Tajudin and Water Village

1949 (22 Sept). *Sultan's Silver Jubilee. Wmk Mult Script CA. P* 13.
93 **8** 8 c. black and carmine .. .. .. 1·25 1·75
94 25 c. purple and red-orange .. .. 1·25 80
95 50 c. black and blue .. .. .. 2·00 2·25

1949 (10 Oct). *75th Anniv of Universal Postal Union. As Nos.* 114/17 *of Antigua.*
96 8 c. carmine .. .. 65 1·25
97 15 c. deep blue .. .. 1·50 1·50
98 25 c. magenta .. .. 1·60 1·60
99 50 c. blue-black .. .. 2·00 2·25

Sutan Sir Omar Ali Saifuddin-Wasa'adul Khairi Wadin, 1950–1967

9 Sultan Omar Ali Saifuddin

10 Native houses, Water Village

1952 (1 Mar). *Wmk Mult Script CA. P* 13.
100 **9** 1 c. black 5 12
101 2 c. black and orange 8 12
102 3 c. black and lake-brown 10 10
103 4 c. black and green 10 5
104 6 c. black and grey 12 5
105 8 c. black and crimson (*shades*) .. 15 12
106 10 c. black and sepia 15 5
107 12 c. black and violet 15 5
108 15 c. black and pale blue.. .. .. 25 5
109 25 c. black and purple (*shades*) 30 5
110 50 c. black and ultramarine (*shades*) .. 40 5
111 **10** $1 black and green (*shades*) .. .. 1·25 60
112 $2 black and scarlet .. .. .. 7·50 2·50
113 $5 black and maroon (*shades*).. .. 13·00 4·00
100/13 .. .. *Set of* 14 22·00 7·00

No. 106 exists in coils constructed from normal sheets.

See also Nos. 118/31 and 202/9.

11 Brunei Mosque and Sultan Omar

(Recess B.W.)

1958 (24 Sept). *Opening of Brunei Mosque. W* w **12**. *P* 13½.
114 **11** 8 c. black and myrtle-green 25 70
115 15 c. black and carmine 25 20
116 35 c. black and deep lilac 50 75

12 "Protein Foods"

(Des M. Goaman. Photo Harrison)

1963 (4 June). *Freedom from Hunger. W* w **12**. *P* 14 × 14½.
117 **12** 12 c. sepia .. .. 1·75 1·25

1964–71. *As Nos.* 100/13, *but W* w **12**. *Glazed paper* ($2, 5) *or ordinary paper* (*others*).
118 **9** 1 c. black (17.3.64) 5 5
a. Glazed paper. *Grey* (*shades*) (28.11.69) 5 5
119 2 c. black and orange (17.3.64).. .. 5 5
a. Glazed paper (27.5.70) 10 5
120 3 c. black and lake-brown (10.11.64) .. 8 5
a. Glazed paper (27.5.70) 10 8
121 4 c. black and green (12.5.64) 8 5
a. Glazed paper (*shades*) (22.4.70) .. 10 10
122 6 c. black and grey (12.5.64) 12 5
a. Glazed paper (*shades*) (28.11.69) .. 15 8
b. Black (28.11.69) .. .. .. 1·50 1·75
123 **9** 8 c. black and crimson-lake (12.5.64) .. 20 5
a. Glazed paper (*shades*) (27.5.70) .. 20 25
124 10 c. black and sepia (12.5.64) 15 5
a. Glazed paper (*shades*) (31.3.70) .. 20 5
125 12 c. black and violet (12.5.64) 20 5
a. Glazed paper (5.11.70) 20 15
126 15 c. black and pale blue (12.5.64) .. 20 5
a. Glazed paper (28.11.69) 20 12
127 25 c. black and purple (12.5.64) 25 5
a. Glazed paper (18.5.70) 70 45
b. Glazed paper. *Black and reddish violet* (30.4.71) 85 25
128 50 c. black and ultramarine (*shades*) (10.11.64) 40 10
b. Glazed paper (*shades*) (5.11.70) .. 50 40
129 **10** $1 black and bronze-green (14.5.68) .. 1·25 1·25
a. Glazed paper (5.11.70) .. .. 1·75 1·60
130 $2 black and scarlet (5.11.70) .. .. 12·00 10·00
131 $5 black and maroon (5.11.70) .. 19·00 15·00
118/29 .. .. *Set of* 12 2·75 1·60
118a/29a, 130/1 .. .. .. *Set of* 14 32·00 25·00

Printings of the 6 and 15 c. issued on 28 November 1969 were on both ordinary and glazed paper, the 6 c. on ordinary producing a distinct shade.

No. 124a exists in coils constructed from normal sheets.

13 I.T.U. Emblem

(Des M. Goaman. Litho Enschedé)

1965 (17 May). *I.T.U. Centenary. W* w **12**. *P* 11 × 11½.
132 **13** 4 c. mauve and orange-brown 35 10
133 75 c. orange-yellow and light emerald .. 1·25 65

14 I.C.Y. Emblem

(Des V. Whiteley. Litho Harrison)

1965 (25 Oct). *International Co-operation Year. W* w **12**. *P* 14.
134 **14** 4 c. reddish purple and turquoise-green 20 8
135 15 c. deep bluish green and lavender .. 55 40

15 Sir Winston Churchill and St. Paul's Cathedral in Wartime

(Des Jennifer Toombs. Photo Harrison)

1966 (24 Jan). *Churchill Commemoration. W* w **12**. *P* 14.
136 **15** 3 c. black, cerise, gold and new blue .. 30 12
137 10 c. black, cerise, gold and deep green .. 1·00 25
138 15 c. black, cerise, gold and brown .. 1·25 45
139 75 c. black, cerise, gold and bluish violet 2·75 2·25

16 Footballer's Legs, Ball and Jules Rimet Cup

(Des V. Whiteley. Litho Harrison)

1966 (4 July). *World Cup Football Championships. W* w **12** (*sideways*). *P* 14.
140 **16** 4 c. violet, yellow-green, lake & yell-brn 20 12
141 75 c. chocolate, blue-grn, lake & yell-brn 75 65

17 W.H.O. Building

(Des M. Goaman. Litho Harrison)

1966 (20 Sept). *Inauguration of W.H.O. Headquarters, Geneva. W* w **12** (*sideways*). *P* 14.
142 **17** 12 c. black, yellow-green and light blue 30 15
143 25 c. black, light purple and yellow-brown 45 30

18 "Education"

19 "Science"

20 "Culture"

(Des Jennifer Toombs. Litho Harrison)

1966 (1 Dec). *20th Anniv of U.N.E.S.C.O. W* w **12** (*sideways*). *P* 14.
144 **18** 4 c. slate-violet, red, yellow and orange 35 15
145 **19** 15 c. orange-yellow, violet and deep olive 85 30
146 **20** 75 c. black, bright purple and orange 2·50 1·90

Sultan Sir Hassanal Bolkiah Mu'izzadin Waddaulah, 1967

21 Religious Headquarters Building

(Des and photo Harrison)

1967 (19 Dec). *1400th Anniv of Revelation of the Koran. W* w **12** (*sideways*). *P* 12½.
147 **21** 4 c. multicoloured 10 8
148 10 c. multicoloured 15 10
149 – 25 c. multicoloured 20 20
150 – 50 c. multicoloured 40 35

Nos. 149/50 are as T **21** but have sprigs of laurel flanking the main design (which has a smaller circle) in place of flagpoles.

22 Sultan of Brunei, Mosque and Flags

(Des V. Whiteley. Photo Enschedé)

1968 (9 July). *Installation of Y.T.M. Seri Paduka Duli Pengiran Temenggong. T* **22** *and similar multicoloured design. P* 14 × 13 (12 *c.*) *or* 13 × 14 (*others*).
151 4 c. Type **22** 25 20
152 12 c. Sultan of Brunei, Mosque and Flags (*horiz*) 45 45
153 25 c. Type **22** 60 70

23 Sultan of Brunei

24 Sultan of Brunei

(Des V. Whiteley. Litho D.L.R.)

1968 (15 July). *Sultan's Birthday.* W w **12** (*sideways*). P 12.

154	**23**	4 c. multicoloured	12	10
155		12 c. multicoloured	20	20
156		25 c. multicoloured	35	35

(Des V. Whiteley. Photo Harrison)

1968 (1 Aug). *Coronation of the Sultan of Brunei.* W w **12** (*sideways*). P 14½ × 14.

157	**24**	4 c. multicoloured	15	10
158		12 c. multicoloured	25	25
159		25 c. multicoloured	40	35

25 New Building and Sultan's Portrait

26 New Building and Sultan's Portrait

(Photo Enschedé)

1968 (29 Sept). *Opening of Language and Literature Bureau.* W w **12** (*sideways*). P 13½ (10 c.) or 12½ × 13½ (*others*).

160	**25**	10 c. multicoloured	15	15
		a. Tête-bêche (pair)	30	30
161	**26**	15 c. multicoloured	25	25
162		30 c. multicoloured	45	45

The above were scheduled for release in 1967, and when finally issued had the year altered by overprinting.

27 Human Rights Emblem and struggling Man

28 Sultan of Brunei and W.H.O. Emblem

(Des V. Whiteley. Litho Harrison)

1968 (16 Dec). *Human Rights Year.* W w **12**. P 14.

163	**27**	12 c. black, yellow and green	20	10
164		25 c. black, yellow and blue	30	25
165		75 c. black, yellow and dull purple ..	70	80

(Des V. Whiteley. Litho Format)

1968 (19 Dec). *20th Anniv of World Health Organization.* P 14.

166	**28**	4 c. yellow, black and cobalt	15	8
167		15 c. yellow, black and deep bluish violet	25	15
168		25 c. yellow, black and pale yellow-olive	40	35

29 Deep Sea Oil-Rig, Sultan of Brunei and inset portrait of Pengiran Di-Gadong

(Des adapted by V. Whiteley. Photo Enschedé)

1969 (10 July). *Installation (9th May, 1968) of Pengiran Shahbandar as Y.T.M. Seri Paduka Duli Pengiran Di-Gadong Sahibol Mal.* W w **12**. P 14 × 13.

169	**29**	12 c. multicoloured	35	20
170		40 c. multicoloured	70	55
171		50 c. multicoloured	80	65

30 Aerial View of Parliament Buildings

(Des Harrison. Litho D.L.R.)

1969 (23 Sept). *Opening of Royal Audience Hall and Legislative Council Chamber.* P 15.

172	**30**	12 c. multicoloured	25	15
173		25 c. multicoloured	45	30
174	–	50 c. rose-red and bluish violet	75	50

Design:—50 c. Elevation of new buildings.

32 Youth Centre and Sultan's Portrait

(Des V. Whiteley. Litho D.L.R.)

1969 (20 Dec). *Opening of the New Youth Centre.* W w **12**. P 15 × 14½.

175	**32**	6 c. flesh, slate-lilac and black	20	10
176		10 c. olive-yellow, grey-green and blackish brown	25	10
177		30 c. yellow-olive, yellow-brown & black	60	45

33 Soldier, Sultan and Badge

34 Badge, and Officer in Full-dress Uniform

(Des Maj. M. A. Bowman. Adapted V. Whiteley. Litho Questa)

1971 (3 May). *Tenth Anniv of Royal Brunei Malay Regiment. Multicoloured designs, each with Badge and Sultan's portrait as* T **33**. W w **12** (*sideways on* 15 *and* 75 c.). P 14½.

178	10 c. Type **33**	45	30
179	15 c. Helicopter (*horiz*)	55	40
180	75 c. Patrol boat (*horiz*)	3·00	3·50

(Des Supt. T. Swan. Litho Format)

1971 (14 Aug). *50th Anniv of Royal Brunei Police Force.* T **34** *and similar vert designs. Multicoloured.* W w **12**. P 14½.

181	10 c. Type **34**	50	30
182	15 c. Badge and Patrol Constable ..	70	50
183	50 c. Badge and Traffic Constable ..	2·50	3·00

35 Perdana Wazir, Sultan of Brunei and view of Water Village

(Des and litho Harrison)

1971 (27 Aug). *Installation of the Yang Teramat Mulia as the Perdana Wazir* (1970). T **35** *and similar horiz designs showing different views of Brunei Town.* W w **12**. P 14.

184	**35**	15 c. multicoloured	50	35
185	–	25 c. multicoloured	80	75
186	–	50 c. multicoloured	1·50	2·00

36 Pottery

(Des C. Abbott. Litho Questa)

1972 (29 Feb). *Opening of Brunei Museum.* T **36** *and similar horiz designs. Multicoloured.* W w **12** (*sideways*). P 13½.

187	10 c. Type **36**	20	12
188	12 c. Straw-work	25	20
189	15 c. Leather-work	30	20
190	25 c. Gold-work	1·00	1·10
191	50 c. Museum Building (58 × 21 *mm*) ..	2·00	2·50

37 Brunei Museum, Queen Elizabeth and Sultan of Brunei

(Des locally. Photo Enschedé)

1972 (29 Feb). *Royal Visit.* T **37** *and similar horiz designs each with portraits of Queen and Sultan. Multicoloured.* W w **12** (*sideways*). P 13 × 13½.

192	10 c. Type **37**	20	20
193	15 c. Native houses	30	30
194	25 c. Mosque	75	90
195	50 c. Royal Assembly Hall	2·25	2·75

38 Secretariat Building

(Des Harrison. Litho J.W.)

1972 (4 Oct). *Renaming of Brunei Town as Bandar Seri Begawan.* T **38** *and similar horiz designs.* W w **12** (*sideways*). P 13½.

196	10 c. multicoloured	15	15
197	15 c. green, light yellow and black	25	20
198	25 c. ultramarine, lemon and black	50	65
199	50 c. rosine, pale turquoise-blue and black ..	95	1·40

Views:—15 c. Darul Hana Palace; 25 c. Old Brunei Town; 50 c. Town and Water Village.

39 Blackburn "Beverley" parachuting Supplies

(Des Trident Artists. Litho Questa)

1972 (15 Nov). *Opening of R.A.F. Museum, Hendon.* T **39** *and similar horiz design. Multicoloured.* W w **12** (*sideways on* 75 c.). P 14 × 13½ (25 c.) or 13½ × 14 (75 c.).

200	25 c. Type **39**	1·25	1·25
201	75 c. Blackburn "Beverley" landing	2·75	3·25

1972 (17 Nov)–**73**. *As Nos. 119/26, but* W w **12** (*sideways*). *Glazed paper.*

202	**9**	2 c. black and orange (9.5.73)	15	50
203		3 c. black and lake-brown	25	40
204		4 c. black and green	40	35
205		6 c. black and grey	30	25
206		8 c. black and brown-red (9.5.73) ..	25	60
207		10 c. black and sepia (*shades*)	30	25
208		12 c. black and violet	1·50	1·75
209		15 c. black and pale blue	1·25	1·50
202/9		.. .. *Set of* 8	4·00	5·00

40 Girl with Traditional Flower-pot, and Boy with Bowl and Pipe

(Des (from photograph by D. Groves) and photo Harrison)

1972 (20 Nov). *Royal Silver Wedding. Multicoloured; background colour given.* W w **12**. P 14 × 14½.

210	**40**	12 c. carmine-red	15	5
211		75 c. deep myrtle-green	40	50

OMNIBUS ISSUES

Details, together with prices for complete sets, of the various Omnibus issues from the 1935 Silver Jubilee series to date are included in a special section following Zululand at the end of the catalogue.

41 Interpol H.Q., Paris

(Des Shamir Bros. Litho Harrison)

1973 (7 Sept). *50th Anniv of Interpol. T* **41** *and similar horiz design. W* w **12** *(inverted on 50 c.). P* 14 × 14½.

212 25 c. bright green, purple and dull blue-black .. 1·25 1·50
213 50 c. pale greenish blue, ultramarine & carm .. 1·25 1·50

The 50 c. shows a different view of the H.Q.

42 Sultan, Princess Anne and Capt. Phillips

(Des PAD Studio. Litho Format)

1973 (14 Nov). *Royal Wedding. W* w **12**. *P* 14.

214 **42** 25 c. multicoloured 20 15
215 50 c. multicoloured 30 25

43 Churchill Painting

44 Sultan Sir Hassanal Bolkiah Mu'izzaddin Waddaulah

(Des C. Abbott. Litho Questa)

1973 (31 Dec). *Opening of Churchill Memorial Building. T* **43** *and similar vert design. Multicoloured. W* w **12** *(sideways). P* 14 × 13½.

216 12 c. Type **43** 10 5
217 50 c. Churchill Statue 30 35

(Des Staff Artists, Dept of Language and Literature. Photo Harrison)

1974 (15 July*). *Multicoloured; background colour given. W* w **12** *(sideways). P* 13½ × 14½.

218 **44** 4 c. turquoise-green 10 10
219 5 c. pale blue 10 10
220 6 c. olive 12 15
221 10 c. lavender 15 10
222 15 c. light brown 20 15
223 20 c. stone 20 20
224 25 c. sage-green 25 25
225 30 c. bright blue 25 30
226 35 c. grey 35 30
227 40 c. bright purple 35 35
228 50 c. cinnamon 40 30
229 75 c. light yellow-green 60 60
230 $1 pale salmon .. .. 1·25 90
231 $2 greenish yellow .. .. 2·25 2·00
232 $5 silver .. .. 5·50 5·00
233 $10 gold .. .. 11·00 12·00
218/33 .. .. *Set of* 16 21·00 21·00

*This was the London release date. The stamps were not put on sale locally until 29 August 1974, but First Day Covers were cancelled with the 15 July date.

See also Nos. 244/59 and 260/2.

45 Aerial View of Airport

(Des Harrison. Litho B.W.)

1974 (18 July). *Inauguration of Brunei International Airport. T* **45** *and similar horiz design. Multicoloured. W* w **12**. *P* 14 × 14½ (50 c.) *or* 12½ × 13 (75 c.).

234 50 c. Type **45** .. .. 95 1·25
235 75 c. Sultan in Army uniform, and airport (48 × 36 *mm*) .. .. 1·40 1·75

46 U.P.U. Emblem and Sultan

(Des J.W. Litho Harrison)

1974 (28 Oct). *Centenary of Universal Postal Union. W* w **12** *(sideways). P* 14½.

236 **46** 12 c. multicoloured 30 20
237 50 c. multicoloured 75 90
238 75 c. multicoloured .. .. 1·00 1·25

47 Sir Winston Churchill

(Des C. Abbott. Litho Questa)

1974 (30 Nov). *Birth Centenary of Sir Winston Churchill. T* **47** *and similar horiz design. Multicoloured. W* w **14** *(sideways). P* 14.

239 12 c. Type **47** 30 20
240 75 c. Churchill smoking cigar (profile) .. 80 1·10

48 Boeing "737" and R.B.A. Crest

(Des PAD Studio. Litho Enschedé)

1975 (14 May). *Inauguration of Royal Brunei Airlines. T* **48** *and similar horiz designs. Multicoloured. No wmk. P* 12½ × 12.

241 12 c. Type **48** 30 25
242 35 c. "737" over Bandar Seri Begawan Mosque 80 1·00
243 75 c. "737" in flight .. .. 1·90 2·25

1975 (13 Aug). *As Nos.* 218/33 *but W* w **14** *(sideways).*

244 **44** 4 c. turquoise-green 5 5
245 5 c. pale blue 5 5
246 6 c. olive 5 5
247 10 c. lavender *(shades)* 5 5
248 15 c. light brown 10 12
249 20 c. stone 12 15
250 25 c. sage-green *(shades)* 15 20
251 30 c. bright blue 20 25
252 35 c. grey 25 30
253 40 c. bright purple 25 30
254 50 c. cinnamon 35 40
255 75 c. light yellow-green 50 55
256 $1 pale salmon 65 70
257 $2 greenish yellow .. .. 1·25 1·40
258 $5 silver .. .. 3·25 3·50
259 $10 gold .. .. 6·50 7·00
244/59 .. .. *Set of* 16 13·00 14·00

1976 (12 Apr). *As Nos.* 221 *and* 223/4 *but W* w **12** *(upright).*

260 **44** 10 c. lavender 15 10
261 20 c. stone 30 25
262 25 c. sage-green 35 30

10
sen

(49)

50 Royal Coat of Arms

(Surchd by Govt Printer, Brunei)

1976 (16 Aug). *No.* 246 *surch with T* **49** *in silver.*

263 **44** 10 c. on 6 c. olive 20 20
a. Surch on No. 220 .. ..

(Des C. Abbott. Litho D.L.R.)

1977 (7 June). *Silver Jubilee. T* **50** *and similar vert designs. Multicoloured. W* w **14**. *P* 13½ × 14.

264 10 c. Type **50** 15 20
265 20 c. Imperial State Crown 25 35
a. Silver omitted £300
266 75 c. Queen Elizabeth (portrait by Annigoni) 65 1·00

51 The Moment of Crowning

52 Royal Crest

(Des J. Cooter. Litho Enschedé)

1978 (2 June). *25th Anniv of Coronation. T* **51** *and similar vert designs. Multicoloured. W* w **14**. *P* 13½ × 13.

267 10 c. Type **51** 15 10
268 20 c. Queen in Coronation regalia 20 20
269 75 c. Queen's departure from Abbey 70 90

(Des local artist; adapted BG Studio. Litho Cartor S.A., France)

1978 (1 Aug). *10th Anniv of Sultan's Coronation. T* **52** *and similar vert designs. W* w **14** *(inverted). P* 12.

270 10 c. black, scarlet and greenish yellow .. 15 12
271 20 c. multicoloured 30 30
272 75 c. multicoloured .. .. 80 1·00
MS273 182 × 77 mm. Nos. 270/2 .. .. .. 3·75 5·00

Designs:—20 c. Coronation ceremony; 75 c. Royal Crown.

53 Human Rights Emblem and struggling Man

54 Smiling Children

(Des V. Whiteley; adapted L. McCombie. Litho Questa)

1978 (10 Dec). *Human Rights Year. W* w **14**. *P* 14½.

274 **53** 10 c. black, yellow and scarlet 10 10
275 20 c. black, yellow and violet 25 25
276 75 c. black, yellow and bistre 75 85

Type **53** is similar to the design used for the 1968 Human Rights Year issue.

(Des L. Curtis. Litho Harrison)

1979 (30 June). *International Year of the Child. T* **54** *and similar horiz design. W* w **14** *(sideways). P* 14.

277 10 c. multicoloured 10 10
278 $1 black and dull green .. .. .. 1·00 1·25

Design:—$1 I.Y.C. emblem.

55 Earth Satellite Station

56 Hegira Symbol

(Des A. Theobald. Litho Questa)

1979 (23 Sept). *Telisai Earth Satellite Station. T* **55** *and similar horiz designs. Multicoloured. W* w **14** *(sideways). P* 14.

279 10 c. Type **55** 15 10
280 20 c. Satellite and antenna 25 15
281 75 c. Television camera, telex machine and telephone 70 85

(Litho Secura, Singapore)

1979 (21 Nov). *Moslem Year 1400 AH Commemoration. W* w **14**. *P* 13 × 13½.

282 **56** 10 c. black, yellow and emerald 10 10
283 20 c. black, yellow and light blue .. 20 15
284 75 c. black, yellow and violet 60 75
MS285 178 × 200 mm. Nos. 282/4 .. .. 1·00 1·25

ALTERED CATALOGUE NUMBERS

Any Catalogue numbers altered from the last edition are shown as a list in the introductory pages.

57 Installation Ceremony

58 Royal Umbrella and Sash

(Des BG Studio. Litho Questa)

1980 (8 Nov). *Installation of Prince Sufri Bolkiah as First Wazir. T* **57** *and similar vert design. Multicoloured.* W w **14**. *P* 13½.
286 10 c. Type **57** 10 5
287 75 c. Prince Sufri 50 40
Nos. 286/7 have blue borders.

(Des BG Studio. Litho Secura, Singapore)

1980 (6 Dec). *Installation of Prince Jefri Bolkiah as Second Wazir. Vert designs as T* **57**. *Multicoloured.* W w **14**. *P* 13½.
288 10 c. Installation ceremony 15 5
289 75 c. Prince Jefri 70 60
Nos. 288/9 have green borders.

(Des BG Studio. Litho Security Printers (M), Malaysia)

1981 (18 Jan*). *Royal Regalia* (*1st series*). *T* **58** *and similar multi-coloured designs. P* 13½ × 13 (50 c.) *or* 12 × 11½ (*others*).
290 10 c. Type **58** 15 15
291 15 c. Sword and Shield 20 20
292 20 c. Lance and Sheath 25 30
293 30 c. Betel-leaf Container 35 45
294 50 c. Coronation Crown (23 × 40 *mm*) .. 60 80
MS295 98 × 142 mm. Nos. 290/4 .. .. .. 1·75 2·25
*This is the local release date. The Crown Agents released the stamps on 19 January.
See also Nos. 298/303, 314/19 and 320/5.

59 I.T.U. and W.H.O. Emblems

60 Shield and Broadsword

(Litho Security Printers (M), Malaysia)

1981 (17 May). *World Telecommunications and Health Day. P* 13 × 13½.
296 **59** 10 c. black and bright crimson 10 5
297 75 c. black, chalky blue & pale violet-bl 65 80

(Des BG Studio. Litho Security Printers (M), Malaysia)

1981 (15 July). *Royal Regalia* (*2nd series*). *T* **60** *and similar multicoloured designs. P* 12.
298 10 c. Type **60** 10 10
299 15 c. Blunderbuss and Pouch 15 15
300 20 c. Crossed Lances and Sash 20 20
301 30 c. Sword, Shield and Sash 30 30
302 50 c. Forked Lance 50 50
303 75 c. Royal Drum (29 × 45 *mm*) 70 85
298/303 .. .. *Set of* 6 1·60 1·75

61 Prince Charles as Colonel of the Welsh Guards

62 Fishing

(Des J.W. Litho Format)

1981 (29 July). *Royal Wedding. T* **61** *and similar vert designs. Multicoloured.* W w **14**. *P* 14.
304 10 c. Wedding bouquet from Brunei 15 15
305 $1 Type **61** 65 70
306 $2 Prince Charles and Lady Diana Spencer 1·25 1·40

(Des local artist. Litho Secura, Singapore)

1981 (16 Oct). *World Food Day. T* **62** *and similar vert design. Multicoloured. P* 12 × 11½.
307 10 c. Type **62** 10 5
308 $1 Farm produce and machinery 75 80

63 Blind Man and Braille Alphabet

64 Drawing of Infected Lungs

(Des local artist. Litho Security Printers (M), Malaysia)

1981 (16 Dec). *International Year for Disabled Persons. T* **63** *and similar vert designs. Multicoloured.* W w **14**. *P* 12.
309 10 c. Type **63** 5 5
310 20 c. Deaf people and sign language 15 15
a. Wmk sideways 20 20
311 75 c. Disabled person and wheelchairs .. 60 75

(Des local artist. Litho Security Printers (M), Malaysia)

1982 (24 May). *Centenary of Robert Koch's Discovery of Tubercle Bacillus. T* **64** *and similar horiz design. Multicoloured.* W w **14**. *P* 12 (10 c.) *or* 13½ (75 c.).
312 10 c. Type **64** 10 5
313 75 c. Magnified tubercle bacillus and microscope 60 75

(Des PAD Studio. Litho Security Printers (M), Malaysia)

1982 (31 May). *Royal Regalia* (*3rd series*). *Multicoloured designs as T* **60**. W w **14** (*sideways*). *P* 13½ (75 c.) *or* 12 × 11½ (*others*).
314 10 c. Ceremonial Ornament 10 10
315 15 c. Silver Betel Caddy 15 15
316 20 c. Traditional Flower-pot 20 20
317 30 c. Solitary Candle 30 30
318 50 c. Golden Pipe 50 50
319 75 c. Royal Chin Support (28 × 45 *mm*) .. 70 80
314/19 .. .. *Set of* 6 1·75 1·90

(Des BG Studio. Litho Security Printers (M), Malaysia)

1982 (15 July). *Royal Regalia* (*4th series*). *Multicoloured designs as T* **60**. W w **14** (*sideways*). *P* 12 (75 c.) *or* 12 × 11½ (*others*).
320 10 c. Royal Mace 10 10
321 15 c. Ceremonial Shield and Spears 15 15
322 20 c. Embroidered Ornament 20 20
323 30 c. Golden-tasselled Cushion 30 30
324 50 c. Ceremonial Dagger and Sheath 50 50
325 75 c. Religious Mace (28 × 45 *mm*) 70 80
320/5 .. .. *Set of* 6 1·75 1·90

65 Brunei Flag

(Des Siti Zaleha Haji Kaprawi. Litho Secura, Singapore)

1983 (14 Mar). *Commonwealth Day. T* **65** *and similar horiz designs. P* 13 × 13½.
326 10 c. multicoloured 5 8
a. Horiz strip of 4. Nos. 326/9 .. .. 1·75
327 20 c. bright blue, black and buff 12 15
328 75 c. bright blue, black and bright green .. 45 50
329 $2 bright blue, black and lemon .. .. 1·40 1·50
Designs:—20 c. Brunei Mosque; 75 c. Machinery; $2 Sultan of Brunei.
Nos. 326/9 were printed together, *se-tenant*, in horizontal strips of four throughout the sheet.

66 "Postal Service"

67 Football

(Litho Secura, Singapore)

1983 (15 Aug). *World Communications Year. T* **66** *and similar horiz designs. P* 13½.
330 10 c. multicoloured 10 8
331 75 c. yellow, orange-brown and black .. 45 50
332 $2 multicoloured .. .. 1·25 1·40
Designs:—75 c. "Telephone Service"; $2 "Communications".

(Litho Security Printers (M), Malaysia)

1983 (23 Sept). *Official Opening of the Negara Hassanal Bolkiah Stadium. T* **67** *and similar multicoloured designs. P* 12.
333 10 c. Type **67** 5 8
334 75 c. Athletics 50 55
335 $1 View of stadium (44 × 27 *mm*) 70 75

68 Fishermen and Crustacea

(Litho Secura, Singapore)

1983 (23 Sept). *Fishery Resources. T* **68** *and similar horiz designs. Multicoloured. P* 13½ × 14.
336 10 c. Type **68** 5 8
337 50 c. Fishermen with net 35 40
338 75 c. Fishing trawler 50 55
339 $1 Fishing with hook and tackle 70 75

INDEPENDENCE

69 Royal Assembly Hall

(Des Haji Salleh Bin Haji Ibrahim (No. 346) Pengiran Haji Muhammed Bin Pengiran Duraman (No. **MS**348) or Siti Zaleha Haji Kaprawi (others). Litho Cartor, France)

1984 (1 Jan). *Independence. T* **69** *and similar designs. P* 13.
340 10 c. pale stone and bright orange 8 10
341 20 c. flesh and brown-red 15 20
342 35 c. rose-pink and plum 30 35
343 50 c. pale blue and new blue 40 45
344 75 c. bright yellow-green and emerald .. 55 60
345 $1 light brownish grey and light brown .. 75 80
346 $3 multicoloured .. .. 2·25 2·50
340/6 .. .. *Set of* 7 4·00 4·50
MS347 150 × 120 mm. Nos. 340/6 .. .. 4·50 4·75
MS348 Two sheets each 150 × 120 mm. containing 4 stamps (34 × 69 *mm.*). (a) 25 c. × 4 grey-black and new blue (Signing of the Brunei Constitution). (b) 25 c. × 4 multicoloured (Signing of Brunei-U.K. Friendship Agreement) .. .. *Set of* 2 *sheets* 1·50 1·60
Designs:—34 × 25 *mm*. 20 c. Government Secretariat Building; 35 c. New Supreme Court; 50 c. Natural gas well; 75 c. Omar Ali Saifuddin Mosque; $1 Sultan's Palace; 68 × 29 *mm*. $3 Brunei flag and map of South-East Asia.

70 Natural Forests and Enrichment Planting

(Des Awang Nor Ariffin bin Md. Yassin. Litho Secura, Singapore)

1984 (21 Apr). *Forestry Resources. T* **70** *and similar horiz designs. Multicoloured. P* 13½ × 14.
349 10 c. Type **70** 8 10
350 50 c. Forests and water resources 40 45
351 75 c. Recreation forests 55 60
352 $1 Forests and wildlife 75 80

71 Sultan Omar Saifuddin 50 c. Stamp of 1952

(Recess and litho D.L.R.)

1984 (22 Oct). *"Philakorea" International Stamp Exhibition, Seoul. T* **71** *and similar vert designs. Multicoloured. P* 13.
353 10 c. Type **71** 8 10
354 75 c. Brunei River view 10 c. stamp of 1907 .. 55 60
355 $2 Star and view ½ c. stamp of 1895 .. 1·50 1·60
MS356 Three sheets, 117 × 100 mm., each containing one stamp as Nos. 353/5 .. *Set of* 3 *sheets* 2·25

JAPANESE OCCUPATION OF BRUNEI

Stamps listed under this heading were valid in Brunei, Labuan, North Borneo and Sarawak.

PRICES FOR STAMPS ON COVER	
Nos. J1/16	*from* × 5
Nos. J17/20	—

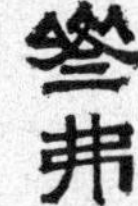

(1) ("Imperial Japanese Government")

(2) ("Imperial Japanese Postal Service $3")

1942 (Oct)–**44.** *Stamps of Brunei handstamped with T* **1** *in violet to blue. Wmk Mult Script CA* (*except Nos.* J18/19, *Mult Crown CA*). *P* 14.

No.	Type	Description	Unused	Used
J 1	5	1 c. black	5·00	10·00
J 2		2 c. green	25·00	80·00
J 3		2 c. orange (9.44)	2·50	5·00
J 4		3 c. green	20·00	60·00
J 5		4 c. orange	3·00	7·50
J 6		5 c. chocolate	3·00	7·50
		a. "5 c." retouch	£200	£250
J 7	7	6 c. greenish grey (*p* 14 × 11½) (9.44)	55·00	90·00
J 8		6 c. scarlet	£375	£500
J 9	5	8 c. grey-black	£375	£650
J10	7	8 c. red	3·00	7·00
J11	5	10 c. purple/*yellow* (9.44)	7·00	13·00
J12	7	12 c. blue (9.44)	7·00	13·00
J13		15 c. ultramarine (9.44)	7·00	13·00
J14	5	25 c. slate-purple (9.44)	16·00	25·00
J15		30 c. purple and orange-yellow	£120	£225
J16		50 c. black/*emerald* (9.44)	29·00	38·00
J17		$1 black and red/*blue* (9.44)	45·00	55·00
J18		$5 carmine/*green* (9.44)	£750	
J19		$25 black/*red* (9.44)	£1000	

The overprint varies in shade from violet to blue, and, being handstamped, exists double and treble.

Nos. J3, J7, J10 and J13 were not issued without the overprint.

1944 (May). *No. 60 of Brunei surch with T* **2** *in orange-red.*

No.	Type	Description	Unused	Used
J20	5	$3 on 1 c. black	£1800	£1400

Burma

Stamps of India were used in Burma from 1854 and, after 1856, individual examples can be identified by the use of the concentric octagonal postmarks of the Bengal Postal Circle of which the following were supplied to Burmese post offices:

Type A
No. B 156
(Rangoon)

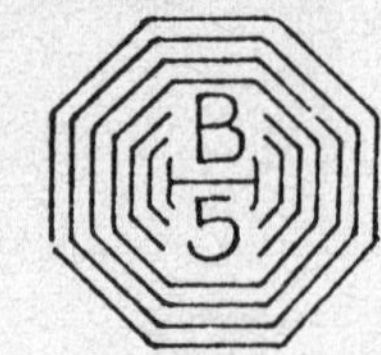

Type B
No. B 5
(Akyab)

B5	Akyab	B146	Pegu
B12*	Bassein	B150	Prome
B22	Nga Thine Khyoung	B156*	Rangoon
B56	Amherst	B159	Sandoway
B108	Kyouk Phyoo	B165	Sarawah (*to* 1860)
B111	Meeaday	B165	Henzada (*from* 1861)
B112	Mengyee	B171	Shoay Gyeen
B127	Moulmein	B173	Sittang
B128	Mergui	B179	Thayetmyo
B129	Tavoy	B181	Toungoo
B133	Myanoung	B227	Port Blair
B136	Namayan		

*Exists in black or blue. Remainder in black only.

Akyab, Moulmein and Rangoon used postmarks as both Type A and Type B, Port Blair as Type B only and the remainder as Type A only.

From 1860 various types of duplex cancellations were introduced and Burmese examples can be identified when sufficient of the left-hand portion is visible on the stamp. Such marks were issued for the following offices:

Akyab	Rangoon
Bassein	Rangoon C.R.H.
Mandalay	(Cantonment Receiving House)
Moulmein	Thayetmyo
Port Blair	Toungoo
Prome	

1862 Duplex from
Toungoo

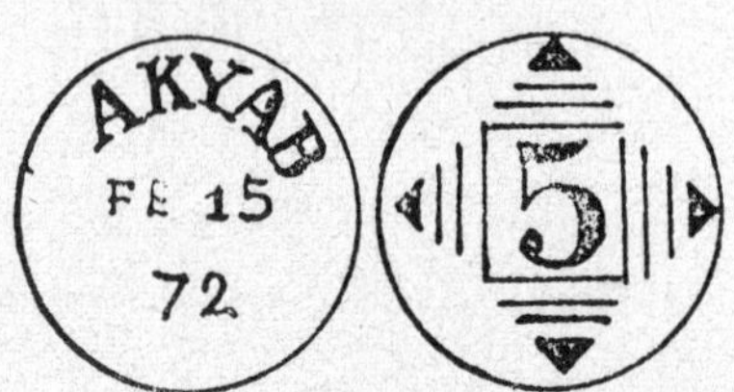

1865 Duplex from
Akyab

During 1875, a further series of duplex marks was introduced in which the right-hand portion of the cancellation included the office code number, prefixed by the letter "R" for Rangoon:

R–1	Rangoon	1/R–8	Amherst
R–1/1	Rangoon Cantonment	R–9	Myanoung
R–2	Akyab	R–10	Port Blair
R–3	Bassein	R–11	Prome
R–4	Henzada	R–12	Sandoway
R–5	Kyouk Phyoo	R–13	Shwegyeen
R–6	Mandalay	R–14	Tavoy
R–7	Mergui	R–15	Thayetmyo
R–8	Moulmein	R–16	Tounghoo

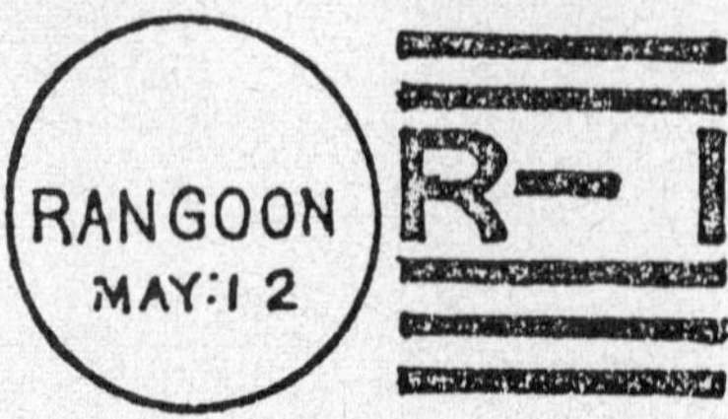

1875 type from
Rangoon

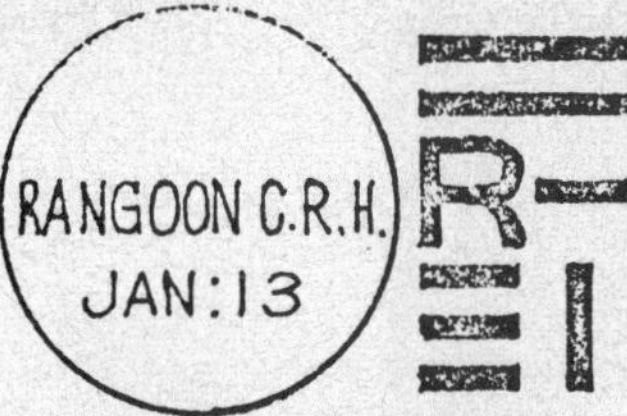

1875 type from Rangoon
Cantonment Receiving House

From 1886 the whole of Burma was united under the Crown and the post offices were supplied with circular date stamps giving the name of the town.

Most Indian stamps, both postage and official, issued during the period were supplied to post offices in Burma. None of the imperforates printed by De La Rue have been seen however, and from the later issues the following have not been recorded with Burma postmarks:

Nos. 39a, 66a, 68, 85a, 92a, 110a/b, 148a, 155a, 165, 192a/c, 195a/b, O15, O38, O40b, O50a/b, O76a, O101a, O102, O103/a, O104/5 and O142.

The value of most India stamps used in Burma coincides proportionately with the used prices quoted for India, but some, especially the provisional surcharges, are extremely rare with Burmese postmarks. Stamps of the face value of 2 r. and above from the reigns of Victoria and Edward VII are more common with telegraph cancellations than with those of the postal service.

PRICES FOR STAMPS ON COVER TO 1945	
Nos. 1/18	*from* × 6
Nos. 18*a*/33	*from* × 4
No. 34	*from* × 5
Nos. 35/50	*from* × 8
Nos. O1/27	*from* × 15

BRITISH ADMINISTRATION

From 1 January 1886 Burma was a province of the Indian Empire but was separated from India and came under direct British administration on 1 April 1937.

BURMA (1) **BURMA** (1*a*)

1937 (1 April). *Stamps of India* (*King George V inscr* "INDIA POSTAGE") *optd with T* **1** *or* **1***a* (*rupee values*). *W* **69**. *P* 14.

No.	Description	Unused	Used
1	3 p. slate	25	12
2	½ a. green	25	12
3	9 p. deep green	30	12
4	1 a. chocolate	30	25
5	2 a. vermilion (*small die*)	30	25
6	2½ a. orange	40	30
7	3 a. carmine	80	70
8	3½ a. deep blue	80	55
	a. Dull blue	6·00	8·00
9	4 a. sage-green	70	25
10	6 a. bistre	70	70
11	8 a. reddish purple	1·25	55
12	12 a. claret	1·50	1·25
13	1 r. chocolate and green	1·75	65
14	2 r. carmine and orange	4·00	1·40
15	5 r. ultramarine and purple	8·50	7·00
16	10 r. green and scarlet	18·00	9·00
17	15 r. blue and olive	90·00	55·00
18	25 r. orange and blue	£170	£130
1/18	.. .. *Set of* 18	£275	£180

The opt is at top on all values except the 3 a.

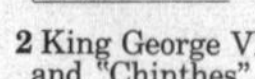

2 King George VI and "Chinthes"

3 King George VI and "Nagas"

4 Royal Barge

8 King George VI and Peacock

10 Elephants' Heads

(Des Maung Kyi (2 a. 6 p.), Maung Hline (3 a.), Maung Ohn Pe (3 a. 6 p.) and N. K. D. Naigamwalla (8 a.). Litho Security Ptg Press, Nasik)

1938 (15 Nov)–**40**. *T* **2/4, 8** *and similar designs. W* **10**. *P* 14 (*vert*) *or* 13½ × 13 (*horiz*).

No.	Type	Description	Unused	Used
18*a*	2	1 p. red-orange (1.8.40)	20	35
19		3 p. bright violet	12	25
20		6 p. bright blue	10	10
21		9 p. yellow-green	45	80
22	3	1 a. purple-brown	10	5
23		1½ a. turquoise-green	20	45
24		2 a. carmine	30	20
25	4	2 a. 6 p. claret	65	40
26	–	3 a. dull violet	1·50	60
27	–	3 a. 6 p. light blue and blue	1·75	2·75
28	3	4 a. greenish blue	35	35
29	–	8 a. myrtle-green	1·40	90
30	8	1 r. purple and blue	1·75	90
31		2 r. brown and purple	5·00	1·50
32	–	5 r. violet and scarlet	21·00	7·00
33	–	10 r. brown and myrtle	42·00	30·00
18*a*/33		*Set of* 16	70·00	42·00

Designs: *Horiz* (*as T* **4**)—3 a. Burma teak; 3 a. 6 p. Burma rice; 8 a. River Irrawaddy. *Vert* (*as T* **8**)—5 r., 10 r. King George VI and "Nats".

The 1 a. exists lithographed and typographed, the latter having a "Jubilee" line in the sheet margin.

COMMEMORATION
POSTAGE STAMP
6th MAY 1840

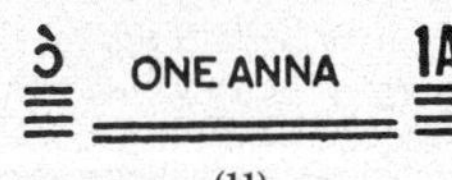

(11)

1940 (6 May) *Centenary of First Adhesive Postage Stamps. No.* 25 *surch with T* **11**.

No.	Type	Description	Unused	Used
34	4	1 a. on 2 a. 6 p. claret	1·25	1·00

For stamps issued in 1942–45 see under Japanese Occupation.

CHIN HILLS DISTRICT. This area, in the far north-west of the country, remained in British hands when the Japanese overran Burma in May 1942.

During the period July to December 1942 the local officials were authorised to produce provisional stamps and the letters "OHMS" are known overprinted by typewriter on Nos. 3, 20, 22, 23, 24, 28 and 31 of Burma or handstamped, in violet, on Nos. 25, 27 and 29. The two types can also occur together or in combination with a handstamped "Service".

From early in 1943 ordinary postage stamps of India were used from the Chin Hills post offices of Falam, Haka, Fort White and Tiddim, this expedient continuing until the fall of Falam to the Japanese on 7 November 1943.

The provisional stamps should only be collected on Official cover where dates and the sender's handwriting can be authenticated.

BRITISH MILITARY ADMINISTRATION

MILY ADMN (12) MILY ADMN (13)

1945 (from 16 June). *Nos.* 18*a to* 33, *optd with T* **12** (*small stamps*) *or* **13** (*others*).

No.	Type	Description	Unused	Used
35	2	1 p. red-orange	8	10
		a. Opt omitted (in pair with normal)		
36		3 p. bright violet	8	25
37		6 p. bright blue	8	20
38		9 p. yellow-green	8	15
39	3	1 a. purple-brown (16.6)	8	12
40		1½ a. turquoise-green (16.6)	8	15
41		2 a. carmine	8	15
42	4	2 a. 6 p. claret	12	35
43	–	3 a. dull violet	20	20
44	–	3 a. 6 p. light blue and blue	8	40
45	3	4 a. greenish blue	8	25
46	–	8 a. myrtle-green	12	25
47	8	1 r. purple and blue	20	45
48		2 r. brown and purple	30	70
49	–	5 r. violet and scarlet	50	1·40
50	–	10 r. brown and myrtle	1·50	2·50
35/50		*Set of* 16	3·25	7·00

BRITISH CIVIL ADMINISTRATION

1946 (1 Jan). *As Nos.* 19/33, *but colours changed.*

No.	Type	Description	Unused	Used
51	2	3 p. brown	8	20
52		6 p. deep violet	8	8
53		9 p. green	10	25
54	3	1 a. blue	10	10
55		1½ a. orange	8	8
56		2 a. claret	20	25
57	4	2 a. 6 p. greenish blue	10	20
57*a*	–	3 a. blue-violet	35	30
57*b*	–	3 a. 6 p. black and ultramarine	10	30
58	3	4 a. purple	10	30
59	–	8 a. maroon	30	30
60	8	1 r. violet and maroon	30	25
61		2 r. brown and orange	85	85
62	–	5 r. green and brown	1·75	2·00
63	–	10 r. claret and violet	3·50	3·75
51/63		*Set of* 15	7·00	8·00

MINIMUM PRICE

The minimum price quoted is 5p which represents a handling charge rather than a basis for valuing common stamps. For further notes about prices see introductory pages.

14 Burman

(Des A. G. I. McGeogh. Litho Nasik)

1946 (2 May). *Victory. T* **14** *and similar vert designs. W* **10** (*sideways*). *P* 13.

No.	Description	Unused	Used
64	9 p. turquoise-green	10	8
65	1½ a. violet	10	8
66	2 a. carmine	10	8
67	3 a. 6 p. ultramarine	12	15

Designs:—1½ a. Burmese woman; 2 a. Chinthe; 3 a. 6 p. Elephant.

INTERIM BURMESE GOVERNMENT

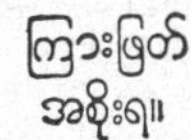

(**18** *Trans.* "Interim Government")

1947 (1 Oct). *Stamps of* 1946 *optd with T* **18** (*small stamps*) *or larger opt* (*others*).

No.	Type	Description	Unused	Used
68	2	3 p. brown	25	20
69		6 p. deep violet	8	25
70		9 p. green	8	25
		a. Opt inverted	10·00	10·00
71	3	1 a. blue	8	25
72		1½ a. orange	30	12
73		2 a. claret	10	15
74	4	2 a. 6 p. greenish blue	30	30
75	–	3 a. blue-violet	20	25
76	–	3 a. 6 p. black and ultramarine	10	25
77	3	4 a. purple	25	30
78	–	8 a. maroon	35	35
79	8	1 r. violet and maroon	55	40
80		2 r. brown and orange	90	80
81	–	5 r. green and brown	1·40	1·40
82	–	10 r. claret and violet	2·00	2·25
68/82		*Set of* 15	6·00	6·75

The 3 p., 6 p., 2 a., 2 a. 6 p., 3 a. 6 p. and 1 r. are also known with overprint inverted.

OFFICIAL STAMPS

BURMA BURMA

SERVICE (O 1) SERVICE (O 1a)

1937 (Apr–June). *Stamps of India* (*King George V inscr* "INDIA POSTAGE") *optd with Type* O **1** *or* O **1a** (*rupee values*). *W* **69**. *P* 14.

No.	Description	Unused	Used
O 1	3 p. slate	10	25
O 2	½ a. green	35	30
O 3	9 p. deep green	30	45
O 4	1 a. chocolate	30	30
O 5	2 a. vermilion (*small die*)	30	45
O 6	2½ a. orange	45	55
O 7	4 a. sage-green	45	40
O 8	6 a. bistre	80	1·25
O 9	8 a. reddish purple (1.4.37)	55	55
O10	12 a. claret (1.4.37)	90	90
O11	1 r. chocolate and green (1.4.37)	1·75	90
O12	2 r. carmine and orange	3·00	3·75
O13	5 r. ultramarine and purple	8·50	11·00
O14	10 r. green and scarlet	35·00	38·00
O1/14	*Set of* 14	48·00	55·00

The bulk of the above issue was overprinted "BURMA" and "SERVICE" by lithography at one operation; but a certain quantity of some values was overprinted at two operations.

SERVICE (O 2) SERVICE (O 3)

1939. *Nos.* 19/24 *and* 28 *optd with Type* O **2** (*typo*) *and Nos.* 25 *and* 29/33 *optd with Type* O **3** (*litho*).

No.	Type	Description	Unused	Used
O15	2	3 p. bright violet	10	20
O16		6 p. bright blue	10	20
O17		9 p. yellow-green	35	40
O18	3	1 a. purple-brown	12	15
O19		1½ a. turquoise-green	75	40
O20		2 a. carmine	20	30
O21	4	2 a. 6 p. claret	90	90
O22	3	4 a. greenish blue	1·40	45
O23	–	8 a. myrtle-green	2·25	1·25
O24	8	1 r. purple and blue	2·50	1·50
O25		2 r. brown and purple	5·50	2·50
O26	–	5 r. violet and scarlet	20·00	8·50
O27	–	10 r. brown and myrtle	42·00	18·00
O15/27		*Set of* 13	70·00	30·00

1946. *British Civil Administration. Nos.* 51/6 *and* 58 *optd with Type* O **2** (*typo*) *and Nos.* 57 *and* 59/63 *optd with Type* O **3** (*litho*).

No.	Type	Description	Unused	Used
O28	2	3 p. brown	10	35
O29		6 p. deep violet	20	25
O30		9 p. green	10	35
O31	3	1 a. blue	10	35
O32		1½ a. orange	12	15
O33		2 a. claret	10	35
O34	4	2 a. 6 p. greenish blue	10	35
O35	3	4 a. purple	10	35
O36	–	8 a. maroon	15	35
O37	8	1 r. violet and maroon	50	65
O38		2 r. brown and orange	2·50	3·00
O39	–	5 r. green and brown	5·50	8·00
O40	–	10 r. claret and violet	7·00	13·00
O28/40		*Set of* 13	15·00	25·00

1947. *Interim Burmese Government. Nos.* O28/40 *optd with T* **18** (*small stamps*) *or larger opt* (*others*).

No.	Type	Description	Unused	Used
O41	2	3 p. brown	10	30
O42		6 p. deep violet	15	10
O43		9 p. green	15	20
O44	3	1 a. blue	40	35
O45		1½ a. orange	50	20
O46		2 a. claret	50	20
O47	4	2 a. 6 p. greenish blue	50	45
O48	3	4 a. purple	50	30
O49	–	8 a. maroon	60	40
O50	8	1 r. violet and maroon	1·50	1·00
O51		2 r. brown and orange	4·00	3·00
O52	–	5 r. green and brown	7·50	8·50
O53	–	10 r. claret and violet	13·00	15·00
O41/53		*Set of* 13	26·00	27·00

Later stamp issues will be found listed in Part 21 (*South-East Asia*) of this catalogue.

JAPANESE OCCUPATION OF BURMA

PRICES FOR STAMPS ON COVER

Nos. J1/44	—
Nos. J45/71	*from* × 4
No. J72	*from* × 6
Nos. J73/94	*from* × 10
Nos. J95/101	—
Nos. J102/8	*from* × 12

BURMA INDEPENDENCE ARMY ADMINISTRATION

The Burma Independence Army, formed by Aung San in 1941, took control of the Delta area of the Irrawaddy in May 1942. They reopened a postal service in the area and were authorised by the Japanese to overprint local stocks of stamps with the Burmese emblem of a peacock.

Postage and Official stamps with the peacock overprints or handstamps were used for ordinary postal purposes with the probable exception of No. J44.

DISTINGUISHING FEATURES. Type 1. Body and head of Peacock always clearly outlined by broad uncoloured band. There are four slightly different sub-types of overprint Type **1**.

Type **2**. Peacock with slender neck and more delicately detailed tail. Clear spur on leg at right. Heavy fist-shaped blob of ink below and parallel to beak and neck.

Type **4**. No basic curve. Each feather separately outlined. Straight, short legs.

Type **5**. Much fine detail in wings and tail in clearly printed overprints. Thin, long legs ending in claws which, with the basic arc, enclose clear white spaces in well-printed copies. Blob of colour below beak shows shaded detail and never has the heavy fist-like appearance of this portion in Type **2**.

Two sub-types may be distinguished in Type **5**, the basic arc of one having a chord of 14–15 mm and the other 12½–13 mm.

Type **6**. Similar to Type **5**, but with arc deeply curved and reaching nearly to the top of the wings. Single diagonal line parallel to neck below beak.

Collectors are warned against forgeries of these overprints, often in the wrong colours or on the wrong values.

(1)

(2)

(3)

1942 (May). *Stamps of Burma overprinted with the national device of a Peacock.*

I. *Overprinted at Myaungmya*

A. *With Type* **1** *in black*

On Postage Stamps of King George V

No.	Type	Description	Unused
J 1		9 p. deep green (No. 3)	28·00
J 2		3½ a. deep blue (No. 8)	15·00

On Official Stamp of King George V

No.	Type	Description	Unused
J 3		6 a. bistre (No. O8)	28·00

On Postage Stamps of King George VI

No.	Type	Description	Unused
J 4	2	9 p. yellow-green	65·00
J 5	3	1 a. purple-brown	£120
J 6		4 a. greenish blue (opt black on red)	75·00
		a. Triple opt, black on double red	£160

On Official Stamps of King George VI

J 7 2 3 p. bright violet 6·50 8·50
J 8 6 p. bright blue 4·00 6·50
J 9 3 1 a. purple-brown 3·50 5·00
J 9*a* 1½ a. turquoise-green £275
J10 2 a. carmine 7·00 9·00
J11 4 a. greenish blue 6·00 7·50

The overprint on No. J6 was apparently first done in red in error, and then corrected in black. Some stamps have the black overprint so accurately superimposed that the red hardly shows. These are rare.

Nos. J5 and J9 exist with the Peacock overprint on both the typographed and the litho printings of the original stamps.

B. *With Types* **2** *or* **3** (*rupee values*), *in black*

On Postage Stamps of King George VI

J12 2 3 p. bright violet 5·50 12·00
J13 6 p. bright blue 12·00 12·00
J14 9 p. yellow-green 5·50 8·00
J15 3 1 a. purple-brown 4·00 5·00
J16 2 a. carmine 4·50 6·00
J17 4 a. greenish blue 7·50 10·00
a. Opt double
b. Opt inverted
c. Opt double, one inverted £200
d. Opt double, both inverted £200
J18 1 r. purple and blue £120
J19 2 r. brown and purple 90·00

The Myaungmya overprints (including No. J44) are usually clearly printed.

(4)

(5)

(6)

Type **5** generally shows the details of the peacock much less clearly and, due to heavy inking, or careless impression, sometimes appears as almost solid colour.

Type **6** was officially applied only to postal stationery. However, the handstamp remained in the possession of a postal official who used it on postage stamps after the war. These stamps are no longer listed.

II. *Handstamped (at Pyapon?) with T* **4**, *in black (so-called experimental type)*

On Postage Stamps of King George VI

J19*a* 3 1 a. purple-brown 60·00
J20 2 a. carmine 32·00
J21 4 a. greenish blue £120

Unused specimens of these stamps are usually in poor condition.

III. *Overprinted at Henzada with T* **5** *in blue, or blue-black*

On Postage Stamps of King George V

J22 3 p. slate (No. 1) 2·00 3·50
a. Opt double 7·50 12·00
J23 9 p. deep green (No. 3) 11·00 15·00
a. Opt double 32·00
J24 2 a. vermilion (No. 5) 35·00 50·00

On Postage Stamps of King George VI

J25 2 1 p. red-orange 40·00 55·00
J26 3 p. bright violet 11·00 20·00
J27 6 p. bright blue 9·00 18·00
a. Opt double 38·00
b. Clear opt, on back and front 75·00
J28 9 p. yellow-green £110
J29 3 1 a. purple-brown 3·00 5·00
a. Opt inverted 75·00
J30 1½ a. turquoise-green 5·50 9·00
a. Opt omitted (in pair with normal)
J31 2 a. carmine 5·50 8·50
J32 4 a. greenish blue 16·00 20·00
a. Opt double 40·00
b. Opt inverted

On Official Stamps of King George VI

J33 2 3 p. bright violet 35·00 45·00
J34 6 p. bright blue 32·00 42·00
J35 3 1½ a. turquoise-green 40·00 60·00
J35*a* 2 a. carmine 95·00 95·00
J36 4 a. greenish blue £200

(6*a*)

("Yon Thon" = "Office use")

V. *Official Stamp of King George VI optd at Myaungmya with Type* **6a** *in black*

J44 7 8 a. myrtle-green 32·00

No. J44 was probably for official use.

There are two types of T **6***a*, one with base of peacock 8 mm long and the other with base about 5 mm long. The neck and other details also vary. The two types are found *se-tenant* in the sheet.

Stocks of the peacock types were withdrawn when the Japanese Directorate-General took control of the postal services in the Delta in August 1942.

JAPANESE ARMY ADMINISTRATION

7

8 Farmer

1942 (1 June). *Impressed by hand. Thick yellowish paper. P* 12 × 11. *No gum.*

J45 7 (1 a.) red 20·00 28·00

This device was the personal seal of S. Yano, the Japanese official in charge of the Posts and Telegraphs department of the Japanese Army Administration. It was impressed on paper already perforated by a line machine. Some stamps show part of the papermaker's watermark, either "ABSORBO DUPLICATOR" or "ELEPHANT BRAND", each with an elephant.

Other impressions of this seal on different papers, and showing signs of wear, were not valid for postal purposes.

(Des T. Kato. Typo *Rangoon Gazette* Press)

1942 (15 June). *Value in annas. P* 11 *or* 11 × 11½. *Laid bâtonné paper. No gum.*

J46 8 1 a. scarlet 11·00 11·00

Some stamps show part of the papermaker's watermark, either "ELEPHANT BRAND" or "TITAGHUR SUPERFINE", each with an elephant.

½A. (9)   1R. (10)

1942 (22 Sept). (*a*) *Contemporary Japanese definitive stamps* (*Cat. Nos. in brackets*) *surch as T* **9/10**.

J47 9 ¼ a. on 1 s. chestnut (317) 7·00 8·00
a. Surch inverted 38·00 38·00
J48 ½ a. on 2 s. scarlet (318) 7·00 8·00
a. Surch inverted 18·00
b. Surch double, inverted 38·00
J49 ¾ a. on 3 s. green (319) 15·00 15·00
a. Surch inverted 38·00 38·00
b. Surch double, one inverted — 48·00
J50 1 a. on 5 s. claret (396) 12·00 13·00
a. Surch inverted 38·00 38·00
b. Surch double, one inverted — 48·00
c. Surch omitted (in pair with normal) — 35·00
J51 3 a. on 7 s. green (323) 22·00 22·00
a. Surch inverted 40·00
J52 4 a. on 4 s. green (320) 18·00 18·00
a. Surch inverted 50·00
J53 8 a. on 8 s. violet (324) 65·00 75·00
a. Surch inverted 75·00 85·00
b. Surch double, one inverted £150
c. Surch in red £150 £160
d. Red surch inverted £250
J54 10 1 r. on 10 s. lake (325) 9·00 10·00
a. Surch inverted — 30·00
b. Surch double
c. Surch double (black and red) 45·00
d. Surch omitted (in pair with normal) — 40·00
J55 2 r. on 20 s. ultramarine (328) 25·00 25·00
a. Surch inverted 50·00 60·00
b. Surch double, inverted 50·00
c. Surch omitted (in pair with normal black surch) 60·00 60·00
d. Surch in red 25·00 22·00
e. Red surch inverted 50·00
f. Red surch double 70·00
g. Surch omitted (in pair with normal red surch) — 55·00
J56 9 5 r. on 30 s. blue-green (330) 7·50 7·50
a. Surch inverted £110
b. Surch double
c. Surch in red 14·00 14·00
d. Red surch inverted 35·00 30·00
e. J56a and J56d *se-tenant* — £130
f. Surch omitted (in pair with normal red surch) — 40·00

(*b*) *Japanese stamp commemorating the fall of Singapore similarly surch*

J56*g* 9 4 a. on 4 + 2 s. green and red (386) 50·00 50·00
h. Surch omitted (in pair with normal) £350
i. Surch inverted

(New Currency. 100 cents = 1 rupee)

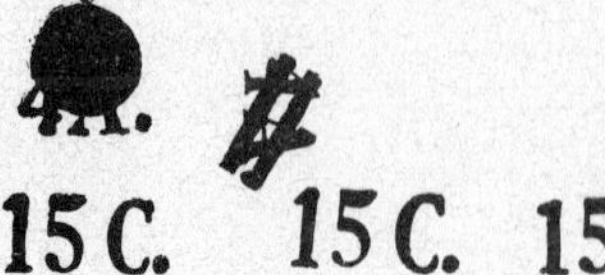

(11) (12) (13)

1942 (15 Oct). *Previous issues, with "anna" surcharges obliterated, and handstamped with new value in cents, as T* **11** *and* **12** (*No. J57 handstamped with new value only*). (*a*) *T* **8** (*Farmer*).

J57 5 c. on 1 a. scarlet 4·00 6·50

(*b*) *Contemporary Japanese issues*

J58 1 c. on ¼ a. on 1 s. (J47) 18·00 18·00
a. "1 c." omitted in pair with normal
J59 2 c. on ½ a. on 2 s. (J48) 18·00 18·00
J60 3 c. on ¾ a. on 3 s. (J49) 20·00 20·00
a. Surch in blue
J61 5 c. on 1 a. on 5 s. (J50) 25·00 25·00
J62 10 c. on 3 a. on 7 s. (J51) 42·00 42·00
J63 15 c. on 4 a. on 4 s. (J52) 15·00 15·00
J64 20 c. on 8 a. on 8 s. (J53) 85·00 70·00
a. 20 c. on 8 a. (R.) on 8 s. (J53a) — 75·00

The "anna" surcharges were obliterated by any means available, in some cases by a bar or bars, and in others by the butt of a pencil dipped in ink. In the case of the fractional surcharges, the letter "A" and one figure of the fraction, were sometimes barred out, leaving the remainder of the fraction to represent the new value, e.g. the "1" of "½" deleted to create the 2 c. surcharge or the "4" of "¾" to create the 3 c. surcharge.

1942. *Contemporary stamps of Japan* (*Cat. Nos. in brackets*) *surcharged in cents only, as T* **13**.

J65 1 c. on 1 s. chestnut (317) 7·50 7·50
a. Surch inverted 20·00 20·00
J66 2 c. on 2 s. scarlet (318) 14·00 15·00
J67 3 c. on 3 s. green (319) 13·00 15·00
a. Pair, with and without surch — 45·00
b. Surch inverted 30·00
c. Surch in blue 45·00 55·00
d. Surch in blue inverted 95·00 £110
J68 5 c. on 5 s. claret (396) 13·00 15·00
a. Surch in violet 65·00
b. Surch in violet inverted — 60·00
J69 10 c. on 7 s. green (323) 18·00 22·00
J70 15 c. on 4 s. green (320) 7·50 8·50
a. Surch inverted 32·00 38·00
b. Pair, with and without surch — 38·00
J71 20 c. on 8 s. violet (324) 42·00 40·00

Nos. J67c and J68a were issued for use in the Shan States.

BURMESE GOVERNMENT

On 1 November 1942 the Japanese Army Administration handed over the control of the postal department to the Burmese Government. On 1 August 1943 Burma was declared by the Japanese to be independent.

14 Burma State Crest

15 Farmer

(Des U Tun Tin and Maung Tin from drawing by U Ba Than. Typo Rangoon)

1943 (15 Feb). *P* 11. *No gum.*

J72 14 5 c. scarlet 7·00 8·00
a. Imperf 8·00 8·00
b. Printed on both sides 60·00

No. J72 was usually sold affixed to envelopes, particularly those with the embossed 1 a. King George VI stamp, which it covered. Unused specimens off cover are rarely met with and blocks are very rare.

1943. *P* 11½. *Typo. No gum.*

J73 15 1 c. orange (22 March) 50 70
a. Brown-orange 60 90
J74 2 c. yellow-green (24 March) 50 80
a. Blue-green 2·00
J75 3 c. light blue (25 March) 50 60
a. On laid paper 6·00 7·00
J76 5 c. carmine (small "c") (17 March) 2·75 3·25
J77 5 c. carmine (large "C") 40 50
a. Imperf (pair)
b. "G" for "C"
J78 10 c. grey-brown (25 March) 70 1·00
a. Imperf (pair)
J79 15 c. magenta (26 March) 15 55
a. On laid paper 6·00 7·50
b. Inverted "C" in value 45·00 60·00
J80 20 c. grey-lilac (29 March) 15 50
J81 30 c. deep blue-green (29 March) 15 55

The 1 c., 2 c. and 3 c. have large "C" in value as illustrated. The 10 c. and higher values have small "c". Owing to hurried printing and the method of make-up (the different values being plugged in individually to the same basic plate) numerous varieties may be found in the values, e.g. missing stops and different types of figure or "c".

There are marked varieties of shade in this issue.

16 Soldier carving word "Independence"

17 Rejoicing Peasant

18 Boy with National Flag

(Des Maung Ba Thit (**16**), Naung Ohn Maung (**17**), and Maung Soi Yi (**18**). Typo State Press, Rangoon)

1943 (1 Aug). *Independence Day.* (*a*) *P* 11.

J82	**16**	1 c. orange	2·00	2·75
J83	**17**	3 c. light blue	2·25	3·00
J84	**18**	5 c. carmine	2·25	3·00
		(*b*) *Rouletted*		
J82*a*	**16**	1 c. orange	60	90
		b. Perf × roul		
		c. Imperf (pair)	30·00	35·00
J83*a*	**17**	3 c. light blue	60	90
		b. Perf × roul		
		c. Imperf (pair)	30·00	35·00
J84*a*	**18**	5 c. carmine	60	90
		aa. Horiz roulette omitted (vert pair)		
		b. Perf × roul		
		c. Imperf (pair)	30·00	35·00

The stamps perf × rouletted may have one, two, or three sides perforated.

The rouletted stamps often appear to be roughly perforated owing to failure to make clean cuts. These apparent perforations are very small and quite unlike the large, clean holes of the stamps perforated 11.

A few imperforate sets, mounted on a special card folder and cancelled with the commemorative postmark were presented to officials. These are rare.

19 Burmese Woman

20 Elephant carrying Log

21 Watch Tower, Mandalay

(Typo G. Kolff & Co, Batavia)

1943 (1 Oct). *P* 12½.

J85	**19**	1 c. red-orange	2·50	3·50
J86		2 c. yellow-green	10	40
J87		3 c. deep violet	12	25
		a. Bright violet	20	25
J88	**20**	5 c. carmine	10	25
J89		10 c. blue	15	15
J90		15 c. red-orange	10	25
J91		20 c. yellow-green	10	50
J92		30 c. olive-brown	10	50
J93	**21**	1 r. red-orange	12	55
J94		2 r. bright violet	15	1·00

22 Bullock Cart

23 Shan Woman

ဗမာနိုင်ငံတော်

၂၀ ဆင့်။

(**24** "Burma State" and value)

(Typo G. Kolff & Co, Batavia)

1943. *Issue for Shan States. P* 12½.

J 95	**22**	1 c. olive-brown	15·00
J 96		2 c. yellow-green	15·00
J 97		3 c. bright violet	12·00
J 98		5 c. ultramarine	2·00
J 99	**23**	10 c. blue	15·00
J100		20 c. carmine	15·00
J101		30 c. olive-brown	15·00

The Shan States were placed under the administration of the Burmese Government on 24 December 1943, and these stamps were later overprinted as T **24** for use throughout Burma.

1944 (1 Nov). *Optd as T* **24** (*the lower characters differ for each value*).

J102	**22**	1 c. olive-brown	90	1·25
J103		2 c. yellow-green	10	30
		a. Opt inverted	£130	
J104		3 c. bright violet	75	1·25
J105		5 c. ultramarine	45	55
J106	**23**	10 c. blue	70	1·25
J107		20 c. carmine	15	55
J108		30 c. olive-brown	15	55

The British 14th Army recaptured Mandalay on 20 March 1945 and Rangoon on 6 May.

PRICES OF SETS

Set prices are given for many issues, generally those containing five stamps or more. Definitive sets include one of each value or major colour change, but do not cover different perforations, die types or minor shades. Where a choice is possible the set prices are based on the cheapest versions of the stamps included in the listings.

Bushire

BRITISH OCCUPATION

PRICES FOR STAMPS ON COVER

Nos. 1/14	*from* × 10
Nos. 15/30	*from* × 5

BUSHIRE
Under British
Occupation.

(1)

Stamps of Iran (*Persia*) *overprinted with T* **1**

1915 (15 Aug). *Nos.* 361, *etc.* (*Ahmed Mirza*).

1	1 ch. orange and green	11·00	14·00
	a. No stop	32·00	42·00
2	2 ch. sepia and carmine	11·00	14·00
	a. No stop	32·00	42·00
3	3 ch. green and grey	11·00	14·00
	a. No stop	32·00	42·00
4	5 ch. carmine and brown	£170	£200
5	6 ch. brown-lake and green	11·00	14·00
	a. No stop	32·00	42·00
6	9 ch. indigo-lilac and brown	16·00	21·00
	a. No stop	50·00	65·00
	b. Opt double		
7	10 ch. brown and carmine	16·00	21·00
	a. No stop	50·00	65·00
8	12 ch. blue and green	22·00	28·00
	a. No stop	70·00	80·00
9	24 ch. green and purple	22·00	28·00
	a. No stop	70·00	75·00
10	1 kr. carmine and blue	21·00	21·00
	a. Double overprint	£4500	
	b. No stop	70·00	70·00
11	2 kr. claret and green	50·00	55·00
	a. No stop	£200	
12	3 kr. black and lilac	£130	£150
	a. No stop	£250	
13	5 kr. blue and red	48·00	50·00
	a. No stop	£190	
14	10 kr. rose and bistre-brown	42·00	45·00
	a. No stop	£175	

Nos. 1/14 were overprinted in strips of 10, five different settings having been identified. The "No stop" variety occurs on the second setting stamp 10 (where the gap between "Under" and "British" measures 2 mm) and stamp 9 of the third, fourth and fifth settings (on which position the gap is 3 mm).

1915 (Sept). *Nos.* 426, *etc.* (*Coronation of Shah Ahmed*) *optd in strips of* 5.

15	1 ch. deep blue and carmine	£275	£300
16	2 ch. carmine and deep blue	£5000	
17	3 ch. deep green	£350	£400
18	5 ch. vermilion	£3500	
19	6 ch. carmine and green	£2750	
20	9 ch. deep violet and brown	£450	£500
21	10 ch. brown and deep green	£750	£800
22	12 ch. ultramarine	£850	£950
23	24 ch. sepia and brown	£350	£400
24	1 kr. black, brown and silver	£325	£375
25	2 kr. carmine, slate and silver	£275	£300
26	3 kr. sepia, dull lilac and silver	£400	£425
27	5 kr. slate, sepia and silver	£375	£425
	a. Overprint inverted		
28	1 t. black, violet and gold	£325	£400
29	3 t. red, crimson and gold	£1400	

1915. *No.* 414 ("1 CH 1915" *provisional*).

30	1 ch. on 5 ch. carmine and brown		

Bushire, a seaport town of Persia, was occupied by the British on 8 August 1915. The Persian postal authorities resumed control on 16 October 1915.

Cameroons

BRITISH OCCUPATION

PRICES FOR STAMPS ON COVER

The stamps of British Occupation of Cameroons are rare used on cover.

(A)

(B)

The above ((A) and (B)) are the types of German Colonial stamps that have been surcharged.

C.E.F.
1d.
(1)

C.E.F.
1s.
(2)

1915. *German Colonial issues of Cameroons, Type* A *surch as T* **1** *and Type* B *as T* **2**, *in black or blue.*

1	A	½d. on 3 pf. (No. 7) (B.)	4·00	5·00
2		½d. on 5 pf. (No. 21) (B.)	1·25	2·25
		a. Surch double	£300	£150
		b. Surch in black	10·00	14·00
3		1d. on 10 pf. (No. 22) (B.)	1·25	2·25
		a. Thin serif and foot to "1"	10·00	12·00
		b. Surch double	£100	
		c. Surch double with thin serif and foot to "1"	£1700	
		d. "1d" double, but "C.E.F." not double	£1200	
		e. Surch in black	15·00	20·00
		f. Surch in black with thin serif and foot to "1"	50·00	
		g. "C.E.F. omitted"	£1500	
4		2d. on 20 pf. (No. 23)	3·00	4·50
5		2½d. on 25 pf. (No. 11)	8·00	9·00
		a. Surch double	£2000	
6		3d. on 30 pf. (No. 12)	8·00	9·50
		a. Surch treble, two albino		
7		4d. on 40 pf. (No. 13)	8·00	9·50
		a. Shorter "4"	£300	
		b. Surch treble, two albino		
8		6d. on 50 pf. (No. 14)	8·00	9·50
		a. Surch double, one albino		
9		8d. on 80 pf. (No. 15)	8·00	9·50
10	B	1s. on 1 m. (No. 16)	90·00	£100
		a. "s" inverted	£325	£350
11		2s. on 2 m. (No. 17)	90·00	£100
		a. "s" inverted	£325	£350
12		3s. on 3 m. (No. 18)	90·00	£100
		a. "s" inverted	£325	£350
		b. Surch double	£2500	
		c. Surch double and "s" inverted		
13		5s. on 5 m. (No. 25a)	£120	£120
		a. "s" inverted	£400	£425
1/13		*Set of* 13	£375	£425

The letters "C.E.F." signify "Cameroons Expeditionary Force." British Cameroons was later incorporated in Nigeria and used Nigerian stamps.

For stamps optd "CAMEROONS U.K.T.T.", see under SOUTHERN CAMEROONS.

Canada

CANADIAN PROVINCES. The following Provinces issued their own stamps before joining the Confederation of Canada, whilst the former Dominion of Newfoundland became part of Canada in 1949. Their issues are listed in alphabetical order in this Catalogue:

BRITISH COLUMBIA and VANCOUVER ISLAND
NEW BRUNSWICK
NEWFOUNDLAND
NOVA SCOTIA
PRINCE EDWARD ISLAND

NEW CARLISLE, GASPÉ

POSTMASTER'S PROVISIONAL ENVELOPE

1

1851 (7 April).

1	1	3d. black	† £60000

Only one example is known, with the impression cancelled by the signature of the postmaster, R. W. Kelly.

COLONY OF CANADA

The first British post offices in what was to become the colony of Canada were opened at Quebec, Montreal and Trois Rivières during 1763. These, and subsequent, offices remained part of the British G.P.O. system until 6 April 1851.

For illustration of the handstamp types see BRITISH POST OFFICES ABROAD notes, following GREAT BRITAIN.

QUEBEC

CROWNED-CIRCLE HANDSTAMPS

CC1 CC 1c QUEBEC L.C. (R.) (13.1.1842) *Price on cover* £150

PRICES FOR STAMPS ON COVER TO 1945

Nos. 1/22*a*	*from* × 2
Nos. 23/8*a*	*from* × 3
Nos. 29/43*a*	*from* × 3
Nos. 44/5	*from* × 8
Nos. 46/65	*from* × 2
Nos. 66/8	*from* × 10
Nos. 69/73	*from* × 3
Nos. 74/6	*from* × 2
Nos. 77/90	*from* × 3
Nos. 90*a*/9	*from* × 2
Nos. 101/2	*from* × 5
Nos. 103/14	*from* × 3
Nos. 115/20	*from* × 6
Nos. 121/49	*from* × 3
Nos. 150/65	*from* × 2
Nos. 166/72	*from* × 3
Nos. 173/87	*from* × 5
Nos. 188/95	*from* × 2
Nos. 196/215	*from* × 3
Nos. 219/224*b*	*from* × 4
Nos. 225/45	*from* × 2
Nos. 246/55	*from* × 8
Nos. 256/310	*from* × 2
No. 312	*from* × 20
No. 313	*from* × 10
Nos. 315/18	*from* × 2
Nos. 319/28	*from* × 3
Nos. 329/40	*from* × 2
Nos. 341/400	*from* × 1
Nos. R1/11	*from* × 5
Nos. S1/3	*from* × 8
No. S4	*from* × 6
No. S5	*from* × 5
Nos. S6/11	*from* × 3
Nos. S12/14	*from* × 5
Nos. D1/8	*from* × 4
Nos. D9/13	*from* × 5
Nos. D14/24	*from* × 4

1 Beaver (Designed by Sir Sandford Fleming)

2 Prince Albert

3

Major re-entry: Line though "EE PEN"

(T 1/6. Eng and recess Rawdon, Wright, Hatch and Edson, New York)

1851. *Imperf. Laid paper.*

No.	Type	Description	Unused	Used
1	1	3d. red (23 April)	£7000	£500
1*a*		3d. orange-vermilion	£7000	£500
		b. Major re-entry	—	£1600
2	2	6d. slate-violet (15 May)	£7500	£1300
3		6d. brown-purple	£8000	£1600
		a. Bisected (3d.) on cover	†	£20000
4	3	12d. black (14 June)	£42000	£38000

There are several re-entries on the plate of the 3d. in addition to the major re-entry listed. All re-entries occur in this stamp on all papers.

1852–57. *Imperf.*

No.	Type	Description	Unused	Used
		A. *Thin wove paper*		
6	1	3d. red	£1300	£160
		a. Bisected, on cover	†	£22000
7		3d. deep red	£1300	£160
7*a*		3d. scarlet-vermilion	£1400	£170
		b. Major re-entry	—	£1200
9*a*	3	12d. black	—	£38000
		B. *Medium hard wove paper*		
10	1	3d. red	£750	£140
11		3d. deep red	£750	£140
11*a*		3d. brown-red	£750	£140
		b. Major re-entry	—	£600
		c. Bisected (1½d.) on cover	†	—
12	2	6d. slate-violet	£7500	£900
		a. Bisected (3d.), on cover	†	£12000
13		6d. greenish grey	£7500	£950
14		6d. brownish grey	£8000	£1000
14*a*	3	12d. black	—	£38000
		C. *Thick hard wove paper*		
15	1	3d. red	£1200	£450
		a. Bisected, on cover	—	£15000
16	2	6d. grey-lilac	£12000	£2000
		D. *Very thick soft wove paper*		
17	2	6d. purple (reddish)	£11000	£2500
		a. Bisected (3d.), on cover	†	£18000

We no longer list the 6d. on thin wove paper as there is no record of a printing on this paper. The 12d. exists and comes from a proof sheet. The laid lines on thin paper are often difficult to see, having been pressed out, and these are sometimes mistaken for wove paper.

No.	Type	Description	Unused	Used
		E. *Thin soft ribbed paper* (1857)		
18	1	3d. red	£2500	£750
		F. *Thin brittle wove paper* (1857)		
19	1	3d. red	£4250	£1400

4 Jacques Cartier

5

6

1855 (Jan)–**57.** *Imperf.*

No.	Type	Description	Unused	Used
		A. *Thin wove paper*		
20	4	10d. bright blue	£6500	£1000
20*a*		10d. dull blue	£6500	£1000
		aa. Major re-entry*	—	£2000
		B. *Medium wove paper, semi-transparent*		
20*b*	4	10d. bright blue	£7000	£1100
20*c*		10d. Prussian blue	£7000	£1100
		d. Major re-entry*	—	£2250
		C. *Stout hard wove paper* (1857)		
21	4	10d. blue	£6500	£1200
		a. Major re-entry*	—	£2500

These stamps may be divided into "wide" and "narrow," due to the shrinkage of the paper, which was wetted before printing, and which contracted unevenly when drying. The width varies from 17 mm to 18 mm, the narrower being the commoner.

*The 10d. Major Re-entry listed shows strong doubling of top frame line and left-hand "8d. stg.", and line through lower parts of "ANAD" and "ENCE". There are other, lesser re-entries.

1857 (2 June). *Imperf.*

No.	Type	Description	Unused	Used
22	5	7½d. pale yellow-green	£7000	£1600
22*a*		7½d. deep yellow-green	£7500	£1500

There are several re-entries in these stamps.

The same remarks apply to this stamp as to the 10d. blue. The width varies less, being generally 18 to 18½ mm.

1857 (1 Aug). *Imperf.*

No.	Type	Description	Unused	Used
		A. *Stout hard wove paper*		
23	6	½d. deep rose	£650	£400
		B. *Thin soft ribbed paper*		
24	6	½d. deep rose (*horiz*)	£2750	£1600
24*a*		½d. deep rose (*vert*)	£4000	£2000

1858–59. *P* 11¾. A *Stout wove paper.*

No.	Type	Description	Unused	Used
25	6	½d. deep rose (12.58)	£1000	£400
		a. Lilac-rose	£1200	£500
26	1	3d. red (1.59)	£1700	£400
27	2	6d. brownish grey (1.59)	£5000	£1900
		a. Slate-violet	£5000	£1700
		B. *Thin ribbed paper*		
27*b*	6	½d. deep rose-red	—	£3000
28	1	3d. red	—	£1100
		C. *Thick hard paper*		
28*a*	1	3d. red	—	£1200

The 3d. is known perf 14, and also *percé en scie* 13, both being unofficial, but used at the period of issue.

(New Currency. 100 cents = 1 dollar)

7

8 Beaver

9 Prince Albert

10

11 Jacques Cartier

(Recess A.B.N. Co)

(On 1 May 1858, Messrs. Rawdon, Wright, Hatch and Edson joined with six other firms to form "The American Bank Note Co" and the "imprint" on sheets of the following stamps has the new title of the firm with "New York" added.)

1859 (1 July). *P* 12.

No.	Type	Description	Unused	Used
29	7	1 c. pale rose (to rose-red)	£130	22·00
30		1 c. deep rose (to carmine-rose)	£140	35·00
		a. Imperf (pair)	£2250	
		b. Imperf × perf		
31	8	5 c. pale red	£140	10·00
32		5 c. deep red	£140	10·00
		a. Re-entry* (R.3/8)	—	£700
		b. Imperf (pair)	£5500	
		c. Bisected (2½ c.) with 10 c. on cover	†	£3250
33	9	10 c. black-brown	£4000	£1100
		a. Bisected (5 c.), on cover	†	£5000
33*b*		10 c. deep red-purple	£2000	£650
		ba. Bisected (5 c.), on cover	†	£3500
34		10 c. purple (*shades*)	£600	35·00
		a. Bisected (5 c.), on cover	†	£3500
35		10 c. brownish purple	£550	35·00
36		10 c. brown (to pale)	£550	35·00
		a. Bisected (5 c.), on cover	†	£4250
37		10 c. dull violet	£450	35·00
38		10 c. bright red-purple	£450	35·00
		a. Imperf (pair)	£3000	
39	10	12½ c. deep yellow-green	£325	35·00
40		12½ c. pale yellow-green	£300	35·00
41	10	12½ c. blue-green	£300	35·00
		a. Imperf (pair)	£2250	
		b. Imperf between (vert pair)		
42	11	17 c. deep blue	£450	55·00
		a. Imperf (pair)	£2500	
43		17 c. slate-blue	£500	75·00
43*a*		17 c. indigo	£450	55·00
		b. Imperf (pair)	£2500	

*The price of No. 32a is for the very marked re-entry showing oval frame line doubled above "CANADA". Slighter re-entries are worth from £25 upwards in used condition.

As there were numerous P.O. Dept. orders for the 10 c., 12½ c. and 17 c. and some of these were executed by more than one separate printing, with no special care to ensure uniformity of colour, there is a wide range of shade, especially in the 10 c., and some shades recur at intervals after periods during which other shades predominated. The colour-names given in the above list therefore represent groups only.

It has been proved by leading Canadian specialists that the perforations may be an aid to the approximate dating of a particular stamp, the gauge used measuring 11¾ × 11¾ from mid-July, 1859 to late 1862, 12 × 11¾ from mid-1862 to early 1865 and 12 × 12 from April, 1865 to 1868. Exceptionally in the 5 c. value many sheets were perforated 12 × 12 between May and October, 1862, whilst the last printings of the 12½ c. and 17 c. perf 11¾ × 11¾ were in July 1863, the perf 12 × 11¾ starting towards the end of 1863.

12

(Recess A.B.N. Co)

1864 (1 Aug). *P* 12.

No.	Type	Description	Unused	Used
44	12	2 c. rose-red	£350	90·00
45		2 c. bright rose	£350	90·00
		a. Imperf (pair)	£1700	

DOMINION OF CANADA

13

14

20

Large types

On 1 July 1867, Canada, Nova Scotia, and New Brunswick were united, the combined territory being termed "The Dominion of Canada". Under the Act of Union provision was made for the admission of Newfoundland, Prince Edward Island, British Columbia, Rupert's Land, and North-Western Territory.

(Recess British American Bank Note Co, at Ottawa or Montreal)

T 13 *and* 14 (*various frames*)

1868 (March). *Ottawa printings. Thin rather transparent crisp paper. P* 12.

No.	Type	Description	Unused	Used
46	13	½ c. black	90·00	75·00
47	14	1 c. red-brown	£350	75·00
48		2 c. grass-green	£400	60·00
49		3 c. red-brown	£600	45·00
50		6 c. blackish brown	£1200	£275
51		12½ c. bright blue	£800	£225
52		15 c. deep reddish purple	£1300	£275

In these first printings the impression is generally blurred and the lines of the background are less clearly defined than in later printings.

1868–71. *Ottawa printings. Medium to stout wove paper. P* 12.

No.	Type	Description	Unused	Used
53	13	½ c. black	32·00	30·00
54		½ c. grey-black	32·00	30·00
		a. Imperf between (pair)		
		b. Watermarked	£8750	£5500
55	14	1 c. red-brown	£275	35·00
		a. Laid paper	£6500	£1600
		b. Watermarked (1868)	£1800	£275
56		2 c. deep green	£300	22·00
57		2 c. pale emerald-green (1871)	£350	28·00
		aa. Bisected (1 c. with 2 c. to make 3 c. rate) on cover	†	£4000
		a. Laid paper	—	£45000
57*b*		2 c. bluish green	£250	22·00
		c. Watermarked (1868)	£1400	£275
58		3 c. brown-red	£500	15·00
		a. Laid paper	£6000	£300
		b. Watermarked (1868)	£2000	£180
59		6 c. blackish brown (to chocolate)	£600	28·00
		a. Watermarked (1868)	£1900	£650
60		6 c. yellow-brown (1870)	£550	28·00
		a. Bisected (3 c.), on cover	†	£2000
61		12½ c. bright blue	£350	42·00
		a. Imperf horiz (vert pair)	†	—
		b. Watermarked (1868)	£1900	£200
62		12½ c. pale dull blue (milky)	£350	42·00
63		15 c. deep reddish purple	£450	70·00
63*a*		15 c. pale reddish purple	£400	70·00
		b. Watermarked (1868)	—	£1500
64		15 c. dull violet-grey	£200	28·00
		a. Watermarked (1868)	—	£850
65		15 c. dull grey-purple	£300	28·00

For 1 c. orange see Nos. 74/6

1879–88. *Montreal printings. Medium to stout wove paper. P* 12.

No.	Type	Description	Unused	Used
66	44	15 c. clear deep violet	£2750	£650
67		15 c. deep slate	£190	32·00
68		15 c. slaty blue	£190	32·00

The watermark on the stout paper stamps consists of the words "E & G BOTHWELL CLUTHA MILLS," in large double-lined capitals. Portions of one or two letters only may be found on these stamps, which occur in the early printings of 1868.

The papers may, in most cases, be easily divided if the stamps are laid face downwards and carefully compared. The thin hard paper is more or less transparent and shows the design through the stamp; the thicker paper is softer to the feel and more opaque.

The paper of this issue may be still further subdivided in several values into sets on—(a) *Medium to stout wove*. (b) *Thin, soft, very white*: and (c) *Thinner and poorer quality, sometimes greyish or yellowish (from* 1878 *to end of issue)*.

Of the 2 c. laid paper No. 57*a* two examples only are known.

1875–78. *Montreal printings. Medium to stout wove paper. P* 11½ × 12 *or* 11¾ × 12.

69 **13** ½ c. black .. .. 35·00 32·00
70 **20** 5 c. olive-green (1 Oct, 1875) .. .. £1100 80·00
a. Perf 12 .. .. — £4500
71 **14** 15 c. dull grey-purple £750 £225
72 15 c. lilac-grey (Mar, 1877) £950 £225
a. Script Wmk* £11000 £2750
b. "BOTHWELL" watermark† .. † —
73 15 c. slate £1100 £450

*The watermark on No. 72*a* is part of the words "Alexr. Pirie & Sons" in script lettering, a very small quantity of paper thus watermarked having been used for printing this stamp.

†For description of this watermark see below No. 68.

One used copy of the 12½ c. has been reported in this perforation.

See also No. 113/14.

1869. *Ottawa printings. Colour changed. Stout wove paper. P* 12.

74 **14** 1 c. deep orange (Jan, 1869) .. .. £800 90·00
75 1 c. orange-yellow (May (?), 1869) .. £800 75·00
76 1 c. pale orange-yellow .. .. .. £800 75·00
a. Imperf .. ..

21 *Small types* 27

(Nos. 77–114 and 117–120. Recess British American Bank Note Co, at Montreal or Ottawa)

1870–88. *T* **21** *(various frames). P* 12 *(or slightly under).*

Montreal printings

Papers (a) 1870–80. *Medium to stout wove*
(b) 1870–72. *Thin, soft, very white*
(c) 1878–97. *Thinner and poorer quality*

77 **21** 1 c. bright orange (*a, b*) (1870–73) £110 25·00
78 1 c. orange-yellow (*a*) (1876–79) .. 30·00 85
79 1 c. pale dull yellow (*a*) (1877–79) .. 20·00 30
80 1 c. bright yellow (*a, c*) (1878–97) .. 14·00 5
a. Imperf (pair) (*c*) £300
b. Bisected (½ c.) (on *Railway News*) † £3000
c. Printed both sides £1400
81 2 c. dp green (*a, b*) (1872–73 & 1876–78) 70·00 50
82 2 c. grass-green (*c*) (1878–88) .. .. 30·00 15
a. Imperf (pair) (1891–93?) £325
b. Bisected (1 c.) on cover .. † £1300
83 3 c. Indian red (*a*) (1.70).. .. .. £800 70·00
a. Perf 12½ £1700 £1100
83*b* 3 c. pale rose-red (*a*) (9.70) .. .. £225 8·00
84 3 c. deep rose-red (*a, b*) (1870–73) .. £250 8·50
84*a* 3 c. deep rose-red (*thick soft paper*) (Jan, 1871) .. .. — £300
85 3 c. dull red (*a*) (1876–88) .. 35·00 50
86 3 c. orange-red (*a, c*) (1876–88) (*shades*) 25·00 30
87 5 c. olive-grey (*a, c*) (February, 1876–88) £100 1·00
88 6 c. yellowish brown (*a, b, c*) (1872–73 and 1876–90) .. .. .. £120 6·50
a. Bisected (3 c.) on cover .. † £1600
89 10 c. pale lilac-magenta (*a*) (1876–?) .. £400 55·00
90 10 c. deep lilac-magenta (*a, c*) (March 1876–88) .. .. £400 55·00

One used copy of the 10 c. perf 12½ has been reported.

1873–77. *P* 11½ × 12. *Medium to stout wove paper.*

90*a* **21** 1 c. bright orange .. .. .. £150 16·00
91 1 c. orange-yellow (1873–79) .. .. £140 8·00
92 1 c. pale dull yellow (1877–79) .. .. £130 13·00
93 2 c. deep green (1873–78) .. .. £180 8·00
94 3 c. dull red (1875–79) .. .. .. £190 9·00
95 3 c. orange-red (1873–79) .. .. £190 9·00
96 5 c. olive-grey (1876–79) .. .. £375 20·00
97 6 c. yellowish brown (1876–79).. .. £375 15·00
98 10 c. very pale lilac-magenta (1874–79) £800 £250
99 10 c. deep lilac-magenta (1876–79) £450 £150

1882–97. *P* 12. *Thinnish paper often toned.*

101 **27** ½ c. black (July, 1882–97) .. .. 4·00 3·75
102 ½ c. grey-black .. .. .. 4·00 3·75
a. Imperf (pair) (1891–93?) £400
b. Imperf between (pair) £750

1888–97. *As T* **14** *and* **21** *(various frames). P* 12.

Ottawa printings

Thinnish paper of poor quality, often toned grey or yellowish

103 **21** 2 c. dull sea-green (Jan, 1888) .. .. 25·00 12
104 2 c. blue-green (July, 1889–91).. .. 17·00 15
105 3 c. rose-carm (Oct, 1888–April, 1889).. £300 11·00
106 3 c. bright vermilion (April, 1889–97).. 10·00 5
a. Imperf (pair) (1891–93?) £300
107 5 c. brownish grey (May, 1888).. .. 22·00 5
a. Imperf (pair) (1891–93) £325
108 6 c. deep chestnut (Oct, 1890) .. .. 50·00 7·00
a. "5 c." re-entry* £1900 £1300
109 6 c. pale chestnut .. .. .. 50·00 5·00
a. Imperf (pair) (1891–93?) £375
110 10 c. lilac-pink (March, 1888) .. £130 19·00
110*a* 10 c. salmon-pink £200 £110
111 **21** 10 c. carmine-pink (April, 1890).. .. £130 12·00
a. Imperf (pair) (1891–93?) £300
112 10 c. brownish red (1894?) £110
a. Imperf (pair) £275
113 **14** 15 c. slate-purple (*shades*) (July, 1888) .. 60·00 16·00
114 15 c. slate-violet (*shades*) (May, 1890) .. 60·00 16·00
a. Imperf (brown-purple) (pair) .. £500

*No. 108a show traces of the 5 c. value 2½ mm lower than the 6 c. design.

The 1 c. showed no change in the Ottawa printings, so is not included. The 2 c. reverted to its previous grass-green shade in 1891. The 15 c. stamps are generally found with yellowish streaky gum; about 1895 remainders of this value were used concurrently with the 1888 and 1890 shades. They vary from grey and slate to a nearly true blue.

28 29

(Recess B.A.B.N.)

1893 (17 Feb). *P* 12.

115 **28** 20 c. vermilion .. .. £225 65·00
a. Imperf (pair) £1200
116 50 c. blue .. .. £325 45·00
a. Imperf (Prussian blue) (pair) .. £1200

1893 (1 Aug). *P* 12.

117 **29** 8 c. pale bluish grey .. .. .. 55·00 3·00
a. Imperf (pair) £450
118 8 c. bluish slate .. .. 55·00 3·00
119 8 c. slate-purple.. .. .. .. 55·00 3·00
120 8 c. blackish purple .. .. .. 55·00 3·00

PRINTERS. The following stamps to No. 287 were recess-printed by the American Bank Note Co, Ottawa, which in 1923 became the Canadian Bank Note Co.

30

(Des L. Pereira and F. Brownell)

1897 (19 June). *Jubilee issue. P* 12.

121 **30** ½ c. black .. .. 50·00 50·00
122 1 c. orange .. .. 6·00 4·00
123 1 c. orange-yellow .. .. .. 6·00 4·00
a. Bisected (½ c.) on cover ..
124 2 c. green .. .. 9·00 7·00
125 2 c. deep green .. .. 10·00 7·50
126 3 c. carmine .. .. 4·50 1·50
127 5 c. slate-blue .. .. 25·00 20·00
128 5 c. deep blue .. .. 20·00 18·00
129 6 c. brown .. .. £100 90·00
130 8 c. slate-violet .. .. 30·00 28·00
131 10 c. purple .. .. 50·00 50·00
132 15 c. slate £120 £100
133 20 c. vermilion £120 £100
134 50 c. pale ultramarine £120 £100
135 50 c. bright ultramarine.. .. .. £120 £100
136 $1 lake £400 £350
137 $2 deep violet £750 £300
138 $3 bistre £900 £650
139 $4 violet £900 £650
140 $5 olive-green £900 £650
121/140 .. .. .. *Set of* 16 £4250 £3000
133/40 Optd "Specimen" .. *Set of* 7 £2750

No 123*a* was used on issues of the *Railway News* of 5, 6 and 8 November 1897 and must be on a large part of the original newspaper with New Glasgow postmark.

31 32

(From photograph by W. & D. Downey, London)

1897–98. *P* 12.

141 **31** ½ c. grey-black (9.11.97) .. .. 3·00 4·00
142 ½ c. black .. .. 5·00 6·00
a. Imperf (pair) £350
143 1 c. blue-green (12.97) .. .. 7·50 50
a. Imperf (pair) £350
144 2 c. violet (12.97) .. .. .. 9·00 75
a. Imperf (pair) £350
145 3 c. carmine (1.98) .. .. .. 9·50 20
a. Imperf (pair) £650
146 5 c. deep blue/*bluish* (12.97) .. .. 35·00 2·50
a. Imperf (pair) £350
147 6 c. brown (12.97) .. .. .. 40·00 16·00
a. Imperf (pair) £650
148 8 c. orange (12.97) .. .. .. 48·00 6·00
a. Imperf (pair) £350
149 10 c. brownish purple (1.98) .. .. 95·00 45·00
a. Imperf (pair) £350
141/149 .. .. .. *Set of* 8 £200 70·00

IMPERF SIDES. Stamps with one side, or two adjacent sides imperf come from booklet panes.

Two types of the 2 c.

Die Ia. Frame consists of four fine lines.

Die Ib. Frame has one thick line between two fine lines.

The die was retouched in 1900 for Plates 11 and 12 producing weak vertical frame lines and then retouched again in 1902 for Plates 15 to 20 resulting in much thicker frame lines. No. 155*b* covers both states of the retouching.

1898–1902. *P* 12.

150 **32** ½ c. black (9.98) .. .. 1·75 1·50
a. Imperf (pair) £350
151 1 c. blue-green (6.98) .. .. .. 14·00 20
152 1 c. deep green/*toned paper* .. .. 14·00 20
a. Imperf (pair) £650
153 2 c. dull purple (Die Ia) (9.98) .. .. 14·00 25
a. Thick paper (6.99) .. .. .. 70·00 10·00
154 2 c. violet (Die Ia) .. .. .. 14·00 20
154*a* 2 c. reddish purple (Die Ia) .. .. 23·00 60
155 2 c. rose-carmine (Die Ia) (20.8.99) .. 15·00 12
a. Imperf (pair) £275
155*b* 2 c. rose-carmine (Die Ib) (1900) .. 17·00 25
c. Booklet pane of 6 (11.6.00).. .. £750
156 3 c. rose-carmine (6.98).. .. .. 15·00 40
157 5 c. slate-blue/*bluish* .. .. .. 48·00 70
a. Imperf (pair) £700
158 5 c. Prussian blue/*bluish* .. .. 48·00 70
159 6 c. brown (9.98) .. .. .. 55·00 15·00
a. Imperf (pair) £600
160 7 c. greenish yellow (23.12.02).. .. 40·00 8·00
161 8 c. orange-yellow (10.98) (Optd S. £130) 60·00 12·00
162 8 c. brownish orange .. .. .. 60·00 12·00
a. Imperf (pair) £600
163 10 c. pale brownish purple (11.98) .. £110 10·00
164 10 c. deep brownish purple .. .. £110 10·00
a. Imperf (pair) £600
165 20 c. olive-green (29.12.00) .. .. £300 60·00
150/165 .. .. .. *Set of* 11 £575 95·00

The 7 c. and 20 c. also exist imperf but unlike the values listed in this condition, they have no gum. (*Price,* 7 c. £300, 20 c. £1200 *pair, un.*)

33

(Des Postmaster-General Mulock; frame, recess; colours, typo)

1898 (7 Dec). *Imperial Penny Postage. Design in black. British possessions in red. Oceans in colours given. P* 12.

166 **33** 2 c. lavender .. .. 35·00 9·00
167 2 c. greenish blue .. .. .. 18·00 5·00
168 2 c. blue .. .. 18·00 5·00
a. Imperf (pair) £350

1899 (5 Jan). *Provisionals used at Port Hood. No.* 156 *divided vertically and handstamped.*

169 **32** "1" in blue, on ⅓ of 3 c.. .. .. — £3500
170 "2" in violet, on ⅔ of 3 c. .. .. — £3000

2 CENTS

(34)

35 King Edward VII

1899. *Surch with T* **34**, *by Public Printing Office.*

171 **31** 2 c. on 3 c. carmine (8 Aug) .. .. 5·50 3·25
a. Surch inverted £250
172 **32** 2 c. on 3 c. rose-carmine (28 July) .. 6·50 3·00
a. Surch inverted £250

(Des King George V when Prince of Wales and J. A. Tilleard)

1903 (1 July)–**12.** *P* 12.

173 **35** 1 c. pale green .. .. 8·50 10
174 1 c. deep green .. .. 8·00 10
175 1 c. green .. .. 8·00 10
176 2 c. rose-carmine .. .. .. 8·00 10
a. Booklet pane of 6 .. .. .. £900
177 2 c. pale rose-carmine .. .. .. 12·00 10
a. Imperf (pair) (18.7.09) .. .. 24·00 24·00
178 5 c. blue/*bluish* .. .. .. 40·00 1·75
179 5 c. indigo/*bluish* .. .. .. 40·00 1·75
180 7 c. yellow-olive.. .. .. .. 35·00 1·75
181 7 c. greenish bistre .. .. .. 50·00 2·00
181*a* 7 c. straw (1.12).. .. .. .. 90·00 35·00
182 10 c. brown-lilac .. .. 55·00 3·00
183 10 c. pale dull purple .. .. .. 55·00 3·00
184 10 c. dull purple .. .. 55·00 3·00
185 20 c. pale olive-green (27.9.04) .. .. £200 12·00
186 20 c. deep olive-green (S. £70) .. .. £200 12·00
187 50 c. deep violet (19.11.08) .. .. £250 35·00
173/187 .. .. .. *Set of* 7 £550 50·00

The 1 c., 5 c., 7 c. and 10 c. exist imperforate but are believed to be proofs.

IMPERFORATE AND PART-PERFORATED SHEETS. Prior to 1946 many Canadian issues exist imperforate, or with other perforation varieties, in the colours of the issued stamps and, usually, with gum. In the years before 1927 such examples are believed to come from imprimatur sheets, removed from the Canadian Post Office archives. From 1927 until 1946 it is known that the printers involved in the production of the various issues submitted several imperforate plate proof sheets of each stamp to the Post Office authorities for approval. Some of these sheets or part sheets were retained for record purposes, but the remainder found their way onto the philatelic market.

Part-perforated sheets also occur from 1927–29 issues.

From 1908 until 1946 we now only list and price such varieties of this type which are known to be genuine errors, sold from post offices. Where other imperforate or similar varieties are known they are recorded in footnotes.

It is possible, and in some cases probable, that some imperforate varieties listed before 1908 may have also been removed from the archives as mentioned above, but it is far harder to be explicit over the status of this earlier material.

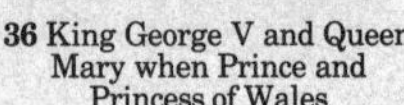

36 King George V and Queen Mary when Prince and Princess of Wales

37 Jacques Cartier and Samuel Champlain

(Des Machado)

1908 (16 July). *Quebec Tercentenary T* **36/7** *and similar horiz designs. P* 12.

188		½ c. sepia	3·00	4·00
189		1 c. blue-green	6·00	4·00
190		2 c. carmine	7·00	80
191		5 c. indigo	40·00	22·00
192		7 c. olive-green	45·00	28·00
193		10 c. violet	65·00	40·00
194		15 c. brown-orange	90·00	50·00
195		20 c. dull brown	£120	70·00
188/195		*Set of* 8	£325	£190

Designs:—2 c. King Edward VII and Queen Alexandra; 5 c. Champlain's House in Quebec; 7 c. Generals Montcalm and Wolfe; 10 c. Quebec in 1700; 15 c. Champlain's departure for the West; 20 c. Cartier's arrival before Quebec.

Some values exist on both *toned* and *white* papers.

Nos. 188/95 exist imperforate.

WET AND DRY PRINTINGS. Until the end of December 1922 all Canadian stamps were produced by the "wet" method of recess-printing in which the paper was dampened before printing, dried and then gummed.

In late December 1922 the Canadian Bank Note Co. began to use the "dry" process in which the paper was gummed before printing. Late printings of the 3 c. brown were the first stamps to be produced by this method, but the changeover was not completed until January 1926.

"Dry" printings have a sharper appearance and can often be found with a degree of embossing showing on the reverse. Stamps from "wet" printings shrink during drying and are narrower than "dry" examples. In many cases the difference can be as great as 0.5 mm. On some early booklet panes the difference is in the vertical, rather than the horizontal, measurement.

On Nos. 196/205 all values only exist from "wet" printings, except the 3 c., 20 c. and 50 c. which come from both types of printing.

44

1912–22. *P* 12.

196	44	1 c. yellow-green (22.12.11)	2·50	5
		a. With fine horiz lines across stamp	18·00	6·00
197		1 c. bluish green	2·50	20
		a. Booklet pane of 6 (1.5.13)	28·00	
198		1 c. deep bluish green	2·50	20
199		1 c. deep yellow-green	2·50	20
		a. Booklet pane of 6	28·00	
200		2 c. rose-red (22.12.11)	2·50	5
201		2 c. deep rose-red	2·75	10
		a. Booklet pane of 6 (1.12)	28·00	
202		2 c. pale rose-red	2·50	10
		a. With fine horiz lines across stamp	14·00	4·00
203		2 c. carmine	2·50	10
204		3 c. brown (6.8.18)	6·00	10
205		3 c. deep brown	3·00	5
		a. Booklet pane of 4 + 2 labels (2.22)	45·00	
205*b*		5 c. deep blue (1.12)	40·00	50
206		5 c. indigo	45·00	60
206*a*		5 c. grey-blue	37·00	50
206*b*		7 c. straw (12.1.12)	55·00	9·00
207		7 c. pale sage-green (1914)	£200	25·00
208		7 c. olive-yellow (1915)	18·00	1·00
209		7 c. yellow-ochre (1916)	12·00	1·00
210		10 c. brownish purple (12.1.12)	70·00	95
211		10 c. reddish purple	55·00	95
212		20 c. olive-green (23.1.12)	28·00	85
213		20 c. olive	28·00	85
214		50 c. grey-black (26.1.12)	£100	6·00
215		50 c. sepia	25·00	2·25
196/215		*Set of* 8	£170	6·00

The 20 c. and 50 c. values exist imperforate.

1912 (Nov)–**1921.** *For use in coil-machines.* (a) *P* 12 × *imperf.*

216	44	1 c. yellow-green (1914)	4·00	4·25
217		1 c. blue-green	9·00	11·00
		a. Two large holes at top and bottom (pair) (7.18)	50·00	40·00
218		2 c. deep rose-red (1914)	12·00	10·00
218*a*		3 c. brown (1921)	3·50	4·00

No. 217a has two large holes about 3½ mm in diameter in the top and bottom margins. They were for experimental use in a vending machine at Toronto in July 1918 and were only in use for two days.

The 1 c. and 2 c. also exist with two small "V" shaped holes about 9.5 mm apart at top which are gripper marks due to modifications made in vending machines in 1917.

(b) *Imperf* × *perf* 8

219	44	1 c. yellow-green (9.12)	6·00	60
220		1 c. blue-green	6·50	60
		a. With fine horiz lines across stamp	42·00	
221		2 c. carmine (9.12)	6·50	25
222		2 c. rose-red	9·00	40
223		2 c. scarlet	11·00	3·50
224		3 c. brown (8.18)	2·50	30

(c) *P* 8 × *imperf*

224*a*	44	1 c. blue-green (15.2.13)	45·00	30·00
224*b*		2 c. carmine (15.2.13)	45·00	30·00

The stamps imperf × perf 8 were sold in coils over the counter; those perf 8 × imperf were on sale in automatic machines. Varieties showing perf 12 on 2 or 3 adjacent sides and 1 or 2 sides imperf are from booklets, or the margins of sheets.

(45)

46

47

1915 (12 Feb). *Optd with T* **45**.

225	44	5 c. blue	£125	£150
226		20 c. olive-green	38·00	38·00
227		50 c. sepia (R.)	70·00	70·00

These stamps were intended for tax purposes, but owing to ambiguity in an official circular dated 16 April 1915, it was for a time believed that their use for postal purposes was authorised. The position was clarified by a further circular on 20 May 1916 which made clear that Nos. 225/7 were for fiscal use only.

1915. *P* 12.

228	46	1 c. green (15.4.15)	2·00	20
229		2 c. carmine-red (16.4.15)	2·00	20
230		2 c. rose-carmine	3·75	2·00

Die I

Die II

In Die I there is a long horizontal coloured line under the foot of the "T", and a solid bar of colour runs upwards from the "1" to the "T".

In Die II this solid bar of colour is absent, and there is a short horizontal line under the left side of the "T", with two short vertical dashes and a number of dots under the right-hand side.

1916 (1 Jan). *P* 12.

231	47	2 c. + 1 c. rose-red (Die I)	4·50	75
232		2 c. + 1 c. bright carmine (Die I)	4·50	75
233		2 c. + 1 c. scarlet (Die I)	4·50	75

1916 (Feb). *Imperf* × *perf* 8 *(coils).*

234	47	2 c. + 1 c. rose-red (Die I)	40·00	3·00

1916 (July). *P* 12 × 8.

235	47	2 c. + 1 c. carmine-red (Die I)	11·00	18·00
236		2 c. + 1 c. bright rose-red (Die I)	11·00	18·00

1916 (Aug). *P* 12.

237	47	2 c. + 1 c. carmine-red (Die II)	70·00	6·50

1916 (Aug). *Colour changed.* (a) *P* 12.

238	47	2 c. + 1 c. brown (Die I)	90·00	8·50
239		2 c. + 1 c. yellow-brown (Die II)	2·00	15
		a. Imperf (pair)		
240		2 c. + 1 c. deep brown (Die II)	7·50	15

(b) *Imperf* × *perf* 8

241	47	2 c. + 1 c. brown (Die I)	60·00	3·00
		a. Pair, 241 and 243		
243		2 c. deep brown (Die II)	11·00	60

This value also exists p 12 × imperf or imperf × p 12, but was not issued with these perforations.

48 Quebec Conference, 1864, from painting "The Fathers of Confederation", by Robert Harris

1917 (15 Sept). *50th Anniv of Confederation. P* 12.

244	48	3 c. bistre-brown	16·00	75
245		3 c. deep brown	18·00	75

No. 244 exists imperforate.

Die I. Space between top of "N" and oval frame line and space between "CENT" and lower frame line.

Die II. "ONE CENT" appears larger so that "N" touches oval and "CENT" almost touches frame line. There are other differences but this is the most obvious one.

Die I. The lowest of the three horizontal lines of shading below the medals does not touch the three heavy diagonal lines; three complete white spaces over both "E's" of "THREE"; long centre bar to figures "3". Vertical spandrel lines fine.

Die II. The lowest horizontal line of shading touches the first of the three diagonal lines; two and a half spaces over first "E" and spaces over second "E" partly filled by stem of maple leaf; short centre bar to figures "3". Vertical spandrel lines thick. There are numerous other minor differences.

WET AND DRY PRINTINGS. See notes above No. 196.

On Nos. 246/63 all listed items occur from both "wet" and "dry" printings except Nos. 246aa/ab, 248aa, 256, 259, 260 and 262 which come "wet" only, and Nos. 246a, 248/a, 252/4*a*, 256b and 263 which are "dry" only.

1922–31. *As T* **44**. (a) *P* 12.

246	44	1 c. chrome-yellow (Die I) (7.6.22)	2·50	15
		aa. Booklet pane of 4 + 2 labels (7.22)	35·00	
		ab. Booklet pane of 6 (12.22)	20·00	
		a. Die II (1925)	2·25	10
247		2 c. deep green (6.6.22)	2·75	5
		aa. Booklet pane of 4 + 2 labels (7.22)	22·00	
		ab. Booklet pane of 6 (12.22)	£350	
		b. Thin paper (9.24)	2·50	4·50
248		3 c. carmine (Die I) (18.12.23)	2·50	5
		aa. Booklet pane of 4 + 2 labels (12.23)	22·00	
		a. Die II (11.24)	5·00	20
249		4 c. olive-yellow (7.7.22)	7·00	1·50
		a. Yellow-ochre	7·00	1·50
250		5 c. violet (2.2.22)	5·00	45
		a. Thin paper (9.24)	5·00	8·00
		b. Reddish violet (1925)	5·00	55
251		7 c. red-brown (12.12.24)	8·00	7·00
		a. Thin paper		
252		8 c. blue (1.9.25)	11·00	7·00
253		10 c. blue (20.2.22)	12·00	90
254		10 c. bistre-brown (1.8.25)	12·00	90
		a. Yellow-brown	14·00	1·25
255		$1 brown-orange (22.7.23)	60·00	5·00
246/255		*Set of* 10	£100	20·00

The $1 differs from T **44** in that the value tablets are oval.

Nos. 249/55 exist imperforate.

(b) *Imperf* × *perf* 8

256	44	1 c. chrome-yellow (Die I) (1922)	5·00	3·00
		a. Imperf horiz (vert pair) (1924)	£300	
		b. Die II (1925)	6·00	4·00
		c. Do. Imperf horiz (vert pair) (1927)	9·00	
257		2 c. deep green (7.22)	6·00	50
		b. Imperf horiz (vert pair) (1927)	9·00	
258		3 c. carmine (Die I) (9.4.24)	30·00	3·00
		a. Imperf horiz (vert pair) (1924)	£350	
		b. Die II (1925)	35·00	12·00

Nos. 256a, 256c, 257b and 258a come from coil printings sold in sheet form. Those issued in 1924 were from "wet" printings and those in 1927 from "dry". A "wet" printing of No. 257b, issued in 1924, also exists (*Price* £300 *mint*), but cannot be identified from that issued in 1927 except by the differences between "wet" and "dry" stamps.

(c) *Imperf (pairs)*

259	44	1 c. chrome-yellow (Die I) (6.10.24)	65·00	65·00
260		2 c. deep green (6.10.24)	65·00	65·00
261		3 c. carmine (Die I) (31.12.23)†	40·00	40·00

(d) *P* 12 × *imperf*

262	44	2 c. deep green (9.24)	65·00	75·00

(e) *P* 12 × 8

263	44	3 c. carmine (Die II) (24.6.31)	4·00	3·00

Nos. 259 to 261 were on sale only at the Philatelic Branch P.O. Dept, Ottawa.

†Earliest known postmark.

(49)

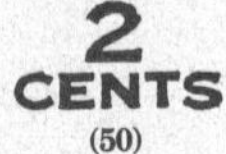

(50)

1926. *No.* 248 *surch.*

(a) *With T* **49**, *by the Govt Printing Bureau*

264	44	2 c. on 3 c. carmine (12.10.26)	25·00	30·00
		a. Pair, one without surch	£300	
		b. On Die II		

(b) *With T* **50**, *by the Canadian Bank Note Co*

265	44	2 c. on 3 c. carmine (4.11.26)	12·00	12·00
		a. Surch double (partly treble)	£175	

PRICES OF SETS

Set prices are given for many issues, generally those containing five stamps or more. Definitive sets include one of each value or major colour change, but do not cover different perforations, die types or minor shades. Where a choice is possible the set prices are based on the cheapest versions of the stamps included in the listings.

51 Sir J. A. Macdonald

52 "The Fathers of Confederation"

53 Parliament Buildings, Ottawa

54 Sir W. Laurier

55 Canada, Map 1867–1927

1927 (29 June). *60th Anniv of Confederation. P* 12. I. *Commemorative Issue. Inscr* "1867–1927 CANADA CONFEDERATION".

266 **51** 1 c. orange .. .. 1·10 65
267 **52** 2 c. green 75 15
268 **53** 3 c. carmine .. .. 3·00 2·50
269 **54** 5 c. violet .. .. 2·00 1·75
270 **55** 12 c. blue .. .. 4·00 2·25

Nos. 266/70 exist imperforate, imperf × perf or perf × imperf.

56 Darcy McGee

57 Sir W. Laurier and Sir J. A. Macdonald

58 R. Baldwin and L. H. Lafontaine

II. *Historical Issue*

271 **56** 5 c. violet .. .. 1·25 1·25
272 **57** 12 c. green .. .. 2·50 2·25
273 **58** 20 c. carmine .. .. 5·50 3·75

Nos. 271/3 exist imperforate, imperf × perf or perf × imperf.

59

1928 (21 Sept). *Air. P* 12.

274 **59** 5 c. olive-brown .. .. 2·50 1·00

No. 274 exists imperforate, imperf × perf or perf × imperf.

60 King George V

61 Mt Hurd and Indian Totem Poles

62 Quebec Bridge

63 Harvesting with Horses

64 Fishing smack *Bluenose*

65 Parliament Buildings, Ottawa

1928–29. (*a*) *P* 12.

275 **60** 1 c. orange (25.10.28) .. .. .. 1·60 15
a. Booklet pane of 6 .. .. 16·00
276 2 c. green (16.10.28) 65 10
a. Booklet pane of 6 .. .. 16·00
277 3 c. lake (12.12.28) .. .. 10·00 6·50
278 4 c. olive-bistre (16.8.29) .. .. .. 9·50 3·25
279 5 c. violet (12.12.28) .. .. 3·50 1·90
a. Booklet pane of 6 (6.1.29) .. .. 75·00
280 8 c. blue (21.12.28) .. .. 4·00 1·50
281 **61** 10 c. green (5.11.28) .. .. 3·00 50
282 **62** 12 c. grey-black (6.1.29) .. .. .. 8·00 2·50
283 **63** 20 c. lake (6.1.29) .. .. 14·00 3·25
284 **64** 50 c. blue (6.1.29) .. .. £125 19·00
285 **65** $1 olive-green (6.1.29) .. .. .. £150 30·00
a. Brown-olive £350 £100
275/285 .. .. *Set of* 11 £275 50·00

(*b*) *Imperf* × *perf* 8 (5.11.28)

286 **60** 1 c. orange .. .. 6·50 8·00
287 2 c. green .. .. 4·00 70

Slight differences in the size of many Canadian stamps, due to paper shrinkage, are to be found.

Nos. 275/85 exist imperforate, imperf × perf or perf × imperf. *Tête-bêche* horizontal pairs of the 1 c., 2 c. and 5 c. are also known from uncut booklet sheets.

PRINTERS. The following stamps to No. 334 were recess-printed by the British American Bank Note Co, Ottawa.

66

67 Parliamentary Library, Ottawa

68 The Old Citadel, Quebec

69 Harvesting with Tractor

70 Acadian Memorial Church and Statue of "Evangeline", Grand Pre, Nova Scotia

71 Mt Edith Cavell, Canadian Rockies

Die I 1 c. Die II

Die I 2 c. Die II

1 c. Die I. Three thick coloured lines and one thin between "P" and ornament, at right. Curved line in ball-ornament short.
Die II. Four thick lines. Curved line longer.

2 c. Die I. Three thick coloured lines between "P" and ornament, at left. Short line in ball.
Die II. Four thick lines. Curved line longer.

1930–31. (*a*) *P* 11.

288 **66** 1 c. orange (I) (17.7.30) 30 30
289 2 c. green (I) (6.7.30) 40 10
a. Booklet pane of 6 (6.7.30) .. .. 22·00
290 4 c. yellow-bistre (5.11.30) .. .. 3·00 2·25
291 5 c. violet (18.6.30) .. .. .. 1·60 1·60
292 8 c. blue (13.8.30) .. .. .. 5·50 6·50
293 **67** 10 c. olive-green (15.9.30) .. .. 2·50 60
a. Imperf (pair) £1000
294 **68** 12 c. grey-black (4.12.30) .. .. 4·50 3·00
295 **69** 20 c. red (4.12.30) .. .. .. 8·00 40
296 **70** 50 c. blue (4.12.30) .. .. .. £100 8·00
297 **71** $1 olive-green (4.12.30) .. .. £125 12·00
288/297 .. .. .. *Set of* 10 £225 25·00

Nos. 294/7 exist imperforate.

(*b*) *Imperf* × *perf* 8½

298 **66** 1 c. orange (I) .. .. 7·50 5·00
299 2 c. green (I) .. .. 3·00 1·25

Colours changed and new value. (*a*) *P* 11

300 **66** 1 c. green (I) (6.12.30) 70 5
a. Imperf (pair) .. ..
b. Booklet pane of 6 (5.12.30) .. .. 22·00
c. Booklet pane of 4 + 2 labels (13.11.31) £110
d. Die II 75 5
301 2 c. scarlet (I) (17.11.30) 70 5
a. Booklet pane of 6 (17.11.30) .. .. 12·00
b. Die II .. .. 1·25 5
302 2 c. deep brown (I) (4.7.31) .. .. 2·00 1·90
a. Booklet pane of 6 (13.7.31) .. .. 22·00
b. Die II 70 12
ba. Booklet pane of 4 + 2 labels (13.11.31) £120
303 3 c. scarlet (13.7.31) .. .. .. 1·25 5
a. Booklet pane of 4 + 2 labels (13.11.31) .. .. 22·00
304 **66** 5 c. deep slate-blue (13.11.30) .. .. 3·00 5
a. Dull blue .. .. 6·00 30
305 8 c. red-orange (5.11.30) .. .. 3·50 4·00
300/305 .. .. *Set of* 6 9·00 4·00

(*b*) *Imperf* × *perf* 8½

306 **66** 1 c. green (I) .. .. 4·50 4·75
307 2 c. scarlet (I) .. .. 6·50 2·25
308 2 c. deep brown (I) (4.7.31) .. .. 6·00 40
309 3 c. scarlet (13.7.31) .. .. .. 7·50 25

Some low values in the above and subsequent issues have been printed by both Rotary and "Flat plate" processes. The former can be distinguished by the gum, which has a striped appearance.

For 13 c. bright violet, T **68**, see No. 325.

72 Mercury and Western Hemisphere

73 Sir Georges Etienne Cartier

1930 (4 Dec). *Air. P* 11.

310 **72** 5 c. deep brown .. .. 12·00 8·00

1931 (30 Sept). *P* 11.

312 **73** 10 c. olive-green .. .. 2·50 12

No. 312 exists imperforate.

(74) (75)

1932 (22 Feb). *Air. No.* 274 *surch with T* 74.

313 **59** 6 c. on 5 c. olive-brown .. .. .. 4·00 2·00

Examples of this stamp with surcharge inverted, surcharge double, surcharge triple or surcharge omitted in pair with normal are not now believed to have been regularly issued. Such "errors" have also been forged and collectors are warned against forged examples, some of which bear unauthorized markings which purport to be the guarantee of Stanley Gibbons Ltd.

1932 (21 June). *Nos.* 301/*b surch with T* 75.

314 **66** 3 c. on 2 c. scarlet (I) .. .. .. 1·40 1·40
314*a* 3 c. on 2 c. scarlet (II) 50 8

76 King George V

77 Duke of Windsor when Prince of Wales

78 Allegory of British Empire

6 6

OTTAWA CONFERENCE
1932

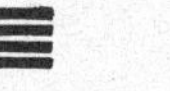

(79)

1932 (12 July). *Ottawa Conference. P* 11. (*a*) *Postage stamps.*

315 **76** 3 c. scarlet 50 50
316 **77** 5 c. blue .. .. 4·00 1·75
317 **78** 13 c. green .. .. 5·00 5·00

(*b*) *Air. No.* 310 *surch with T* 79

318 **72** 6 c. on 5 c. deep brown (B.) .. .. 10·00 8·50

80 King George V

"3" level Die I

"3" raised Die II

1932 (1 Dec)–**33.** (*a*) *P* 11.

319 **80** 1 c. green 45 5
a. Booklet pane of 6 .. .. .. 15·00
b. Booklet pane of 4 + 2 labels (19.9.33) 75·00
320 2 c. sepia 50 5
a. Booklet pane of 6 .. .. .. 15·00
b. Booklet pane of 4 + 2 labels (19.9.33) 75·00
321 3 c. scarlet (Die I) 90 12
a. Booklet pane of 4 + 2 labels .. 22·00
b. Die II (29.11.32) 75 5
ba. Booklet pane of 4 + 2 labels (19.9.33) 20·00
322 4 c. yellow-brown .. .. .. 28·00 4·00
323 5 c. blue .. .. 3·00 5
a. Imperf vert (horiz pair) .. ..
324 8 c. red-orange .. .. 7·00 2·50

325 **68** 13 c. bright violet .. 12·00 2·00
319/325 .. *Set of* 7 48·00 8·00
Nos. 319/25 exist imperforate.

(*b*) *Imperf* × *perf* 8½ (1933)

326 **80** 1 c. green .. 12·00 1·50
327 2 c. sepia .. 12·00 45
328 3 c. scarlet (Die II) .. 7·00 20

81 Parliament Buildings, Ottawa

1933 (18 May). *U.P.U. Congress Preliminary Meeting. P* 11.
329 **81** 5 c. blue .. 3·00 1·75
No. 329 exists imperforate.

WORLD'S
GRAIN EXHIBITION &
CONFERENCE

REGINA 1933

(82)

1933 (24 July). *World's Grain Exhibition and Conference, Regina. Optd with T* **82**. *P* 11.
330 **69** 20 c. red (B.) .. 20·00 6·00
No. 330 exists imperforate.

83 S.S. *Royal William* (after S. Skillett) — **84** Jacques Cartier approaching Land

1933 (17 Aug). *Centenary of First Trans-Atlantic Steamboat Crossing. P* 11.
331 **83** 5 c. blue .. 3·00 1·75
No. 331 exists imperforate.

1934 (1 July). *Fourth Centenary of Discovery of Canada. P* 11.
332 **84** 3 c. blue .. 2·00 60
No. 332 exists imperforate.

85 U.E.L. Statue, Hamilton — **86** Seal of New Brunswick

1934 (1 July). *150th Anniv of Arrival of United Empire Loyalists. P* 11.
333 **85** 10 c. olive-green .. 12·00 4·00
No. 333 exists imperforate.

1934 (16 Aug). *150th Anniv of Province of New Brunswick. P* 11.
334 **86** 2 c. red-brown .. 1·00 85
No. 334 exists imperforate.

PRINTERS. The following stamps were recess-printed (except where otherwise stated) by the Canadian Bank Note Co, Ottawa, until No. 616.

87 Queen Elizabeth II when Princess — **89** King George V and Queen Mary

1935 (4 May). *Silver Jubilee. T* **87**, **89** *and similar designs. P* 12.
335 1 c. green .. 40 30
336 2 c. brown .. 50 20
337 3 c. carmine-red .. 1·40 15
338 5 c. blue .. 3·00 2·00
339 10 c. green .. 2·50 2·00
340 13 c. blue .. 5·00 3·25
335/340 .. *Set of* 6 11·50 7·00
Designs: *Vert* (*as T* **87**)—2 c. King George VI when Duke of York; 5 c. King Edward VIII when Prince of Wales. *Horiz* (*as T* **89**)—10 c. Windsor Castle; 13 c. Royal Yacht *Britannia*.
Nos. 335/40 exist imperforate.

93 King George V — **94** Royal Canadian Mounted Policeman

99 Daedalus

1935 (1 June–5 Nov). *T* **93/4**, **99** *and similar designs.* (*a*) *Postage.* (i) *P* 12.
341 **93** 1 c. green .. 25 5
a. Booklet pane of 6 .. 18·00
b. Booklet pane of 4 + 2 labels .. 50·00
342 2 c. brown .. 45 5
a. Booklet pane of 6 .. 18·00
b. Booklet pane of 4 + 2 labels .. 50·00
343 3 c. scarlet .. 60 5
a. Booklet pane of 4 + 2 labels .. 18·00
344 4 c. yellow .. 1·00 60
345 5 c. blue .. 1·00 10
a. Imperf vert (horiz pair) .. £300
346 8 c. orange .. 1·00 1·60
347 **94** 10 c. carmine .. 2·50 10
348 – 13 c. purple .. 2·50 65
349 – 20 c. olive-green .. 11·00 45
350 – 50 c. deep violet .. 24·00 3·00
351 – $1 bright blue .. 45·00 9·00
341/351 .. *Set of* 11 80·00 14·00

(ii) *Coil stamps. Imperf* × *perf* 8

352 **93** 1 c. green (5.11.35) .. 13·00 1·75
353 2 c. brown (14.10.35) .. 11·00 55
354 3 c. scarlet (20.7.35) .. 7·00 25

(*b*) *Air. P* 12

355 **99** 6 c. red-brown .. 2·50 1·25
a. Imperf vert (horiz pair) ..
Designs: *Horiz* (*as T* **94**)—13 c. Confederation Conference, Charlottetown, 1864; 20 c. Niagara Falls; 50 c. Parliament Buildings, Victoria, British Columbia; $1 Champlain Monument, Quebec.
Nos. 341/51 and 355 exist imperforate.

100 King George VI and Queen Elizabeth

1937 (10 May). *Coronation. P* 12.
356 **100** 3 c. carmine .. 60 12
No. 356 exists imperforate.

101 King George VI — **102** Memorial Chamber Parliament Buildings, Ottawa

107 Seaplane over S.S. *Distributor* on River Mackenzie

(T **101**. Photograph by Bertram Park)

1937–38. *T* **101/2**, **107** *and similar designs.* (*a*) *Postage.* (i) *P* 12.
357 **101** 1 c. green (1.4.37) .. 35 5
a. Booklet pane of 6 .. 3·50
b. Booklet pane of 4 + 2 labels .. 16·00
358 2 c. brown (1.4.37) .. 35 5
a. Booklet pane of 6 .. 10·00
b. Booklet pane of 4 + 2 labels .. 14·00
359 3 c. scarlet (1.4.37) .. 50 5
a. Booklet pane of 4 + 2 labels .. 4·25
360 4 c. yellow (10.5.37) .. 2·00 40
361 5 c. blue (10.5.37) .. 2·00 5
362 8 c. orange (10.5.37) .. 2·25 40
363 **102** 10 c. rose-carmine (15.6.38) .. 6·00 5
a. Red .. 6·00 5
364 – 13 c. blue (15.11.38) .. 11·00 50
365 – 20 c. red-brown (15.6.38) .. 15·00 40
366 – 50 c. green (15.6.38) .. 38·00 10·00
367 – $1 violet (15.6.38) .. 90·00 10·00
a. Imperf horiz (vert pair) ..
357/367 .. *Set of* 11 £150 20·00
Nos. 357/67 exist imperforate.

(ii) *Coil stamps. Imperf* × *perf* 8

368 **101** 1 c. green (15.6.37) .. 2·00 1·50
369 2 c. brown (18.6.37) .. 3·00 1·50
370 3 c. scarlet (15.4.37) .. 6·00 50

(*b*) *Air. P* 12

371 **107** 6 c. blue (15.6.38) .. 1·25 25
Designs: *Horiz* (*as T* **107**)—13 c. Entrance to Halifax Harbour; 20 c. Fort Garry Gate, Winnipeg; 50 c. Entrance, Vancouver Harbour; $1 Chateau de Ramezay, Montreal.

108 Queen Elizabeth II when Princess and Princess Margaret — **109** National War Memorial, Ottawa

110 King George VI and Queen Elizabeth

1939 (15 May). *Royal Visit. P* 12.
372 **108** 1 c. black and green .. 30 12
373 **109** 2 c. black and brown .. 30 12
374 **110** 3 c. black and carmine .. 30 8
Nos. 372/4 exist imperforate.

111 King George VI in Naval uniform — **112** King George VI in Military uniform — **113** King George VI in Air Force uniform

114 Grain Elevator — **116** Parliament Buildings

117 Ram Tank — **121** Air Training Camp

1942 (1 July)–**1948.** *War Effort. T* **111/14**, **116/17**, **121** *and similar designs.* (*a*) *Postage.* (i) *P* 12.
375 **111** 1 c. green .. 25 5
a. Booklet pane of 6 .. 2·75
b. Booklet pane of 4 + 2 labels .. 8·50
376 **112** 2 c. brown .. 35 5
a. Booklet pane of 6 .. 8·50
b. Booklet pane of 4 + 2 labels .. 9·50
377 **113** 3 c. carmine-lake .. 45 5
a. Booklet pane of 4 + 2 labels .. 3·50
378 3 c. purple (30.6.43) .. 45 5
a. Booklet pane of 6 .. 6·50
b. Booklet pane of 4 + 2 labels .. 3·50
379 **114** 4 c. slate .. 1·40 60
380 **112** 4 c. carmine-lake (9.4.43) .. 35 5
a. Booklet pane of 6 .. 3·25
381 **111** 5 c. blue .. 1·00 5
382 – 8 c. red-brown .. 2·25 40
383 **116** 10 c. brown .. 5·00 5
384 **117** 13 c. dull green .. 5·00 4·00
385 14 c. dull green (16.4.43) .. 7·50 45
386 – 20 c. chocolate .. 6·00 15
387 – 50 c. violet .. 20·00 1·50
388 – $1 blue .. 70·00 7·00
375/388 .. *Set of* 14 £110 13·00
Nos. 375/88 exist imperforate.

(ii) *Coil stamps. Imperf* × *perf* 8

389 **111** 1 c. green (9.2.43) .. 60 80
390 **112** 2 c. brown (24.11.42) .. 1·50 2·00
391 **113** 3 c. carmine-lake (23.9.42) .. 1·50 2·50
392 3 c. purple (19.8.43) .. 4·00 2·00
393 **112** 4 c. carmine-lake (13.5.43) .. 3·00 1·25

(iii) *Booklet stamps. Imperf* × *perf* 12

394 **111** 1 c. green (24.11.42) .. 60 60
395 **113** 3 c. purple (20.8.42) .. 80 90
396 **112** 4 c. carmine-lake (3.5.43) .. 1·00 1·25
Nos. 394/6 are from booklets in which the stamps are in strips of three, imperforate at top and bottom and right-hand end.

(iv) *Coil stamps. Imperf × perf* 9½

397 **111** 1 c. green (13.7.48) .. .. .. 4·00 4·50
397*a* **112** 2 c. brown (1.10.48) .. .. .. 10·00 13·00
398 **113** 3 c. purple (2.7.48) .. .. .. 6·00 5·00
398*a* **112** 4 c. carmine-lake (22.7.48) .. .. 7·00 5·00

(*b*) *Air. P* 12

399 **121** 6 c. blue (1.7.42) .. .. .. 3·00 1·00
400 7 c. blue (16.4.43 .. .. .. 70 12

Designs: *Horiz* (*as T* 114)—8 c. Farm scene. (*as T* 117)—20 c. Launching of Corvette H.M.C.S. *La Malbaie*, Sorel; 50 c. Munitions factory; $1 Destroyer.

122 Ontario Farm Scene **129** Alexander Graham Bell and "Fame"

1946 (16 Sept). *Peace Re-conversion. T* **122** *and similar horiz designs. P* 12 (*a*). *Postage.*

401 8 c. brown .. .. 1·25 1·00
402 10 c. olive-green .. .. 1·75 5
403 14 c. sepia .. .. 3·00 40
404 20 c. slate .. .. 3·75 5
405 50 c. green .. .. 17·00 1·50
406 $1 purple .. .. 40·00 1·50

(*b*) *Air*

407 7 c. blue .. .. 1·50 12
a. Booklet pane of 4 .. .. 5·50
401/407 .. .. *Set of* 7 60·00 4·00

Designs:—7 c. Canada Geese in flight; 10 c. Great Bear Lake; 14 c. St. Maurice River Power Station; 20 c. Combine Harvester; 50 c. Lumbering in British Columbia; $1 Train Ferry, Prince Edward Is.

1947 (3 Mar). *Birth Centenary of Bell* (*inventor of telephone*). *P* 12.

408 **129** 4 c. blue 15 8

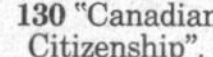

130 "Canadian Citizenship". **131** Queen Elizabeth II when Princess

1947 (1 July). *Advent of Canadian Citizenship and Eightieth Anniv of Confederation. P* 12.

409 **130** 4 c. blue 15 8

(From photograph by Dorothy Wilding)

1948 (16 Feb). *Princess Elizabeth's Marriage. P* 12.

410 **131** 4 c. blue 15 8

132 Queen Victoria, Parliament Building, Ottawa, and King George VI **133** Cabot's Ship *Matthew*

1948 (1 Oct). *One Hundred Years of Responsible Government. P* 12.

411 **132** 4 c. grey 15 5

1949 (1 Apr). *Entry of Newfoundland into Canadian Confederation. P* 12.

412 **133** 4 c. green 15 8

134 "Founding of Halifax, 1749" (C. W. Jefferys)

1949 (21 June). *Bicentenary of Halifax, Nova Scotia. P* 12.

413 **134** 4 c. violet 15 8

OMNIBUS ISSUES

Details, together with prices for complete sets, of the various Omnibus issues from the 1935 Silver Jubilee series to date are included in a special section following Zululand at the end of the catalogue.

135 **136** **137**

138 King George VI **139**

(From photographs by Dorothy Wilding)

1949 (15 Nov)–**51.** (i) *P* 12.

414 **135** 1 c. green 8 5
415 **136** 2 c. sepia 15 10
415*a* 2 c. olive-green (25.7.51) 30 5
416 **137** 3 c. purple 15 5
a. Booklet pane of 4 + 2 labels .. 1·75
417 **138** 4 c. carmine-lake 30 5
a. Booklet pane of 6 .. .. .. 13·00
417*b* 4 c. vermilion (25.7.51) 40 5
c. Booklet pane of 6 .. .. .. 4·00
418 **139** 5 c. blue 90 5

(ii) *Imperf × perf* 9½ (*coil stamps*)

419 **135** 1 c. green (18.5.50) .. .. .. 90 1·00
420 **136** 2 c. sepia (18.5.50) .. .. .. 2·75 3·25
420*a* 2 c. olive-green (9.10.51) .. .. .. 1·00 1·25
421 **137** 3 c. purple (18.5.50) .. .. .. 1·50 2·00
422 **138** 4 c. carmine-lake (20.4.50) .. .. 7·00 5·00
422*a* 4 c. vermilion (27.11.51) .. .. .. 1·50 1·50

(iii) *Imperf × perf* 12 (*booklets*)

422*b* **135** 1 c. green (18.5.50) 25 40
423 **137** 3 c. purple (12.4.50) 60 70
423*a* **138** 4 c. carmine-lake (5.4.50) .. .. 7·00 6·00
423*b* 4 c. vermilion (2.6.51) .. .. .. 2·50 1·75

These booklet stamps come from strips of three, imperforate at top and bottom and right-hand end.

140 King George VI **141** Oil Wells in Alberta

(From photograph by Dorothy Wilding)

1950 (19 Jan). *As T* **135/9** *but without* "POSTES POSTAGE", *as T* **140**. (i) *P* 12.

424 1 c. green 8 10
425 2 c. sepia 20 30
426 3 c. purple 15 25
427 4 c. carmine-lake 20 5
428 5 c. blue .. .. 75 1·00

(ii) *Imperf × perf* 9½ (*coil stamps*)

429 1 c. green 40 75
430 3 c. purple .. .. 80 1·50

1950 (1 Mar). *P* 12.

431 **141** 50 c. green .. .. 14·00 1·50

142 Drying Furs **143** Fisherman

1950 (2 Oct). *P* 12.

432 **142** 10 c. brown-purple 85 5

1951 (1 Feb). *P* 12.

433 **143** $1 ultramarine .. .. .. 65·00 10·00

144 Sir R. L. Borden **145** W. L. Mackenzie King

1951 (25 June). *Prime Ministers* (*1st issue*). *P* 12.

434 **144** 3 c. blue-green 20 5
435 **145** 4 c. rose-carmine 20 5

See also Nos. 444/5, 475/6 and 483/4.

146 Mail Trains, 1851 and 1951 **147** SS. *City of Toronto* and SS. *Prince George*

148 Mail Coach and Aeroplane **149** Reproduction of 3d., 1851

1951 (24 Sept). *Canadian Stamp Centenary. P* 12.

436 **146** 4 c. black 50 10
437 **147** 5 c. violet .. .. 2·00 2·50
438 **148** 7 c. blue 75 70
439 **149** 15 c. scarlet 90 12

150 Queen Elizabeth II when Princess and Duke of Edinburgh **151** Forestry Products

1951 (26 Oct). *Royal Visit. P* 12.

440 **150** 4 c. violet 15 5

(Des A. L. Pollock)

1952 (1 Apr). *P* 12.

441 **151** 20 c. grey .. .. 1·10 5

152 Red Cross Emblem

1952 (26 July). *18th International Red Cross Conference, Toronto. Design recess; cross litho. P* 12.

442 **152** 4 c. scarlet and blue 15 5

153 Canada Goose **154** Pacific Coast Indian House and Totem Pole

(Des E. Hahn)

1952 (3 Nov). *P* 12.

443 **153** 7 c. blue 30 5

1952 (3 Nov). *Prime Ministers* (*2nd issue*). *Various portraits as T* **144**. *P* 12.

444 3 c. reddish purple 15 5
445 4 c. orange-red 15 5

Portraits:—3 c. Sir John J. C. Abbott; 4 c. A. Mackenzie.

(Des E. Hahn)

1953 (2 Feb). *P* 12.

446 **154** $1 black .. .. 15·00 45

155 Polar Bear **156** Moose **157** Bighorn Sheep

(Des J. Crosby (2 c.), E. Hahn (others))

1953 (1 Apr). *National Wild Life Week. P* 12.

447 **155** 2 c. blue 15 5
448 **156** 3 c. sepia 15 5
449 **157** 4 c. slate 20 5

158 Queen Elizabeth II **159**

(From photograph by Karsh, Ottawa)

1953 (1 May–3 Sept). (*a*) *Sheet stamps. P* 12.

450	**158**	1 c. purple-brown	5	5
451		2 c. green	8	5
452		3 c. carmine	12	5
		a. Booklet pane of 4 + 2 labels (6.7) ..	1·25	
453		4 c. violet	15	5
		a. Booklet pane of 6	2·25	
454		5 c. ultramarine	15	5
		(*b*) *Coil stamps. Imperf × perf* 9½		
455	**158**	2 c. green (30.7)	1·25	1·10
456		3 c. carmine (27.7)	1·50	1·25
457		4 c. violet (3.9)	1·50	1·25
		(*c*) *Booklet stamps. Imperf × perf* 12		
458	**158**	1 c. purple-brown (12.8)	1·40	1·75
		a. Booklet pane of 3	3·75	
459		3 c. carmine (17.7)	1·40	1·75
		a. Booklet pane of 3	3·75	
460		4 c. violet (6.7)	1·40	1·75
		a. Booklet pane of 3	3·75	

These booklet stamps have top and bottom or top, bottom and right-hand sides imperforate.

(Des E. Hahn)

1953 (1 June). *Coronation. P* 12

461 **159** 4 c. violet 15 5

160 Textile Industry **161** Queen Elizabeth II

(Des A. L. Pollock)

1953 (2 Nov). *P* 12.

462 **160** 50 c. deep bluish green .. .. .. 3·75 10

(From photograph by Dorothy Wilding)

1954–62. (i) *P* 12.

463	**161**	1 c. purple-brown (10.6.54)	5	5
		a. Booklet pane. Five stamps plus printed label (1.6.56)	55	
		p. Two phosphor bands (13.1.62) ..	80	85
464		2 c. green (10.6.54)	8	5
		a. Pack. Two blocks of 25	4·75	
		p. Two phosphor bands (13.1.62) ..	80	85
465		3 c. carmine (10.6.54)	15	5
		a. Imperf vert (horiz pair)	£1000	
		p. Two phosphor bands (13.1.62) ..	1·00	1·00
466		4 c. violet (10.6.54)	20	5
		a. Booklet pane. Five stamps plus printed label (1.6.56)	1·50	
		b. Booklet pane of 6 (7.7.55)	4·00	
		p. One phosphor band (13.1.62) ..	3·75	5·50
467		5 c. bright blue (1.4.54)	20	5
		a. Booklet pane. Five stamps plus printed label (14.7.54)	1·75	
		b. Pack. One block of 20	5·00	
		p. Two phosphor bands (13.1.62) ..	3·75	5·50
468		6 c. red-orange (10.6.54)	30	30
463/8 ..		.. .. *Set of* 6	90	45
		(ii) *Imperf × perf* 9½ (*coil stamps*)		
469	**161**	2 c. green (9.9.54)	50	70
470		4 c. violet (23.8.54)	90	65
471		5 c. bright blue (6.7.54)	1·40	30

Nos. 464a and 467b are blocks with the outer edges imperf. These come from "One Dollar Plastic Packages" sold at post offices.

WINNIPEG PHOSPHOR BANDS. In 1962 facer-cancelling machines were introduced in Winnipeg which were activated by phosphor bands on the stamps. Under long or short wave ultra-violet light the phosphor glows and there is also a short after-glow when the lamp is turned off. This should not be confused with the fluorescent bands introduced in Ottawa in 1971.

162 Walrus **163** Beaver **164** Northern Gannet

(Des E. Hahn)

1954 (1 Apr). *National Wild Life Week. P* 12.

472	**162**	4 c. slate-black	15	5
473	**163**	5 c. ultramarine	15	5
		a. Booklet pane. Five stamps plus one printed label	1·75	

(Des L. Hyde)

1954 (1 Apr). *P* 12.

474 **164** 15 c. black 75 5

1954 (1 Nov). *Prime Ministers* (3rd *issue*). *Various portraits as T* **144**. *P* 12.

475	4 c. violet	15	5
476	5 c. bright blue	15	5

Portraits:—4 c. Sir John Thompson; 5 c. Sir Mackenzie Bowell.

165 Eskimo Hunter

(Des H. Beament)

1955 (21 Feb). *P* 12.

477 **165** 10 c. purple-brown 30 5

166 Musk-ox **167** Whooping Cranes

(Des E. Hahn (4 c.), Dr. W. Rowan (5 c.))

1955 (4 Apr). *National Wild Life Week. P* 12.

478	**166**	4 c. violet	20	5
479	**167**	5 c. ultramarine	25	10

168 Dove and Torch **169** Pioneer Settlers

(Des W. Lohse)

1955 (1 June). *Tenth Anniv of International Civil Aviation Organisation. P* 12.

480 **168** 5 c. ultramarine 20 10

(Des L. Hyde)

1955 (30 June). *50th Anniv of Alberta and Saskatchewan Provinces. P* 12.

481 **169** 5 c. ultramarine 20 10

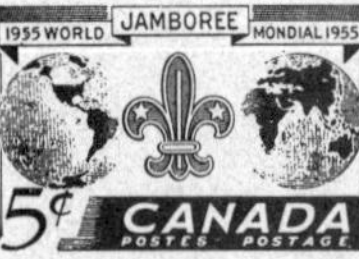

170 Scout Badge and Globe **173** Ice-hockey Players

(Des L. Hyde)

1955 (20 Aug). *Eighth World Scout Jamboree, Niagara-on-the-Lake. P* 12.

482 **170** 5 c. orange-brown and green 25 5

1955 (8 Nov). *Prime Ministers* (4*th issue*). *Various portraits as T* **144**. *P* 12.

483	4 c. violet	15	5
484	5 c. bright blue	15	5

Portraits:—4 c. R. B. Bennett; 5 c. Sir Charles Tupper.

(Des J. Simpkins)

1956 (23 Jan). *Ice-hockey Commemoration. P* 12.

485 **173** 5 c. ultramarine 25 5

174 Caribou **175** Mountain Goat

(Des E. Hahn)

1956 (12 Apr). *National Wild Life Week. P* 12.

486	**174**	4 c. violet	15	5
487	**175**	5 c. bright blue	15	5

OMNIBUS ISSUES

Details, together with prices for complete sets, of the various Omnibus issues from the 1935 Silver Jubilee series to date are included in a special section following Zululand at the end of the catalogue.

176 Pulp and Paper Industry **177** Chemical Industry

(Des A. J. Casson (20 c.), A. L. Pollock (25 c.))

1956 (7 June). *P* 12.

488	**176**	20 c. green	90	5
489	**177**	25 c. red	1·50	5

178

(Des A. Price)

1956 (9 Oct). *Fire Prevention Week. P* 12

490 **178** 5 c. red and black 15 5

179 Fishing **180** Swimming

(Des L. Hyde)

1957 (7 Mar). *Outdoor Recreation. T* **179**/**180** *and similar horiz designs. P* 12.

491	**179**	5 c. ultramarine	25	12
		a. Block of 4. Nos. 491/4	1·60	
492	**180**	5 c. ultramarine	25	12
493	–	5 c. ultramarine	25	12
494	–	5 c. ultramarine	25	12

Designs:— No. 493, Hunting. No. 494, Skiing.

No. 491/4 are printed together in sheets of 50 (5 × 10). In the first, second, fourth and fifth vertical rows the four different designs are arranged in *se-tenant* blocks, whilst the central row is made up as follows (reading downwards):—Nos. 491/4, 491/2 (or 493/4), 491/4.

183 Great Northern Diver **184** Thompson with Sextant, and North American Map

(Des L. Hyde)

1957 (10 Apr). *National Wild Life Week. P* 12.

495 **183** 5 c. black 20 5

(Des G. A. Gundersen)

1957 (5 June). *Death Centenary of David Thompson* (*explorer*). *P* 12.

496 **184** 5 c. ultramarine 30 10

185 Parliament Buildings, Ottawa **186** Globe within Posthorn

(Des Carl Mangold)

1957 (14 Aug). 14*th U.P.U. Congress, Ottawa. P* 12.

497	**185**	5 c. grey-blue	35	5
498	**186**	15 c. blackish blue	1·25	1·25

187 Miner **188** Queen Elizabeth II and Duke of Edinburgh

(Des A. J. Casson)

1957 (5 Sept). *Mining Industry. P* 12.

499 **187** 5 c. black 20 5

(From photographs by Karsh, Ottawa)

1957 (10 Oct). *Royal Visit. P* 12.

500 **188** 5 c. black 20 5

189 "A Free Press"

190 Microscope

(Des A. L. Pollock)

1958 (22 Jan). *The Canadian Press. P* 12.
501 **189** 5 c. black 20 15

(Des A. L. Pollock)

1958 (5 Mar). *International Geophysical Year. P* 12.
502 **190** 5 c. blue 25 5

191 Miner panning for Gold

192 La Verendrye (statue)

(Des J. Harman)

1958 (8 May). *Centenary of British Columbia. P* 12.
503 **191** 5 c. deep turquoise-green 25 5

(Des G. Trottier)

1958 (4 June). *La Verendrye (explorer) Commemoration. P* 12.
504 **192** 5 c. ultramarine 20 5

193 Samuel de Champlain and the Heights of Quebec

194 Nurse

(Des G. Trottier)

1958 (26 June). *350th Anniv of Founding of Quebec. P* 12.
505 **193** 5 c. brown-ochre and deep green .. 25 5

(Des G. Trottier)

1958 (30 July). *National Health. P* 12.
506 **194** 5 c. reddish purple 25 5

195 "Petroleum 1858–1958"

196 Speaker's Chair and Mace

(Des A. L. Pollock)

1958 (10 Sept). *Centenary of Canadian Oil Industry. P* 12.
507 **195** 5 c. scarlet and olive 25 5

(Des G. Trottier and C. Dair)

1958 (2 Oct). *Bicentenary of First Elected Assembly. P* 12.
508 **196** 5 c. deep slate 20 5

197 The "Silver Dart"

198 Globe showing N.A.T.O. Countries

1959 (23 Feb). *50th Anniv of First Flight of the "Silver Dart" in Canada. P* 12.
509 **197** 5 c. black and ultramarine 20 5

(Des P. Weiss)

1959 (2 Apr). *Tenth Anniv of North Atlantic Treaty Organisation. P* 12.
510 **198** 5 c. ultramarine 25 5

199

200 Queen Elizabeth II

(Des Helen Fitzgerald)

1959 (13 May). *"Associated Country Women of the World" Commemoration. P* 12.
511 **199** 5 c. black and yellow-olive 15 5

(Des after painting by Annigoni)

1959 (18 June). *Royal Visit. P* 12.
512 **200** 5 c. lake-red 25 5

201 Maple Leaf linked with American Eagle

202 Maple Leaves

(Des A. L. Pollock, G. Trottier (of Canada); W. H. Buckley, A. J. Copeland, E. Metzl (of the United States))

1959 (26 June). *Opening of St. Lawrence Seaway. P* 12.
513 **201** 5 c. ultramarine and red 25 5
a. Centre inverted £12000 £8500

(Des P. Weiss)

1959 (10 Sept). *Bicentenary of Battle of Plains of Abraham (Quebec). P* 12.
514 **202** 5 c. deep green and red 25 5

203

204 Dollard des Ormeaux

(Des Helen Fitzgerald)

1960 (20 Apr). *Golden Jubilee of Canadian Girl Guides Movement. P* 12.
515 **203** 5 c. ultramarine and orange-brown .. 25 5

(Des P. Weiss)

1960 (19 May). *Tercentenary of Battle of the Long Sault. P* 12.
516 **204** 5 c. ultramarine and light brown .. 25 5

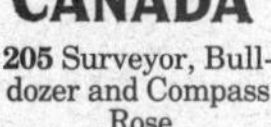

205 Surveyor, Bulldozer and Compass Rose

206 E. Pauline Johnson

(Des B. J. Reddie)

1961 (8 Feb). *Northern Development. P* 12.
517 **205** 5 c. emerald and red 20 5

(Des B. J. Reddie)

1961 (10 Mar). *Birth Centenary of E. Pauline Johnson (Mohawk poetess). P* 12.
518 **206** 5 c. green and red 25 5

207 Arthur Meighen (statesman)

208 Engineers and Dam

1961 (19 Apr). *Arthur Meighen Commemoration. P* 12.
519 **207** 5 c. ultramarine 20 5

(Des B. J. Reddie)

1961 (28 June). *Tenth Anniv of Colombo Plan. P* 12.
520 **208** 5 c. blue and brown 25 5

209 "Resources for Tomorrow"

210 "Education"

(Des A. L. Pollock)

1961 (12 Oct). *Natural Resources. P* 12.
521 **209** 5 c. blue-green and brown 20 5

(Des Helen Fitzgerald)

1962 (28 Feb). *Education Year. P* 12.
522 **210** 5 c. black and orange-brown 20 5

211 Lord Selkirk and Farmer

212 Talon bestowing Gifts on Married Couple

(Des Phillips-Gutkin Ltd)

1962 (3 May). *150th Anniv of Red River Settlement. P* 12.
523 **211** 5 c. chocolate and green 20 5

(Des P. Weiss)

1962 (13 June). *Jean Talon Commemoration. P* 12.
524 **212** 5 c. blue 20 5

213 Br Columbia & Vancouver Is 2½d. stamp of 1860, and Parliament Buildings, B.C.

214 Highway (map version) and Provincial Arms

(Des Helen Bacon)

1962 (22 Aug). *Centenary of Victoria, B.C. P* 12.
525 **213** 5 c. red and black 20 5

(Des A. L. Pollock)

1962 (31 Aug). *Opening of Trans-Canada Highway. P* 12.
526 **214** 5 c. black and orange-brown 20 5

215 Queen Elizabeth II and Wheat (agriculture) Symbol

216 Sir Casimir Gzowski

(From drawing by Ernst Roch)

1962–64. *Horiz designs as T* **215** *showing Queen Elizabeth II and industry symbols.* (i) *P* 12.
527 1 c. chocolate (4.2.63) 5 5
a. Booklet pane. Five stamps plus one printed label (15.5.63) .. .. 2·00
p. Two phosphor bands (15.5.63) 15 12
528 2 c. green (2.5.63) 10 5
a. Pack. Two blocks of 25 .. .. .. 5·50
p. Two phosphor bands (15.5.63) 25 12
529 3 c. reddish violet† (2.5.63) 20 5
p. Two phosphor bands (15.5.63) 35 15
530 4 c. carmine-red (4.2.63) 15 5
a. Booklet pane. Five stamps plus one printed label (15.5.63) .. .. 2·50
b. Pack. One block of 25 .. .. .. 3·75
p. One centre phosphor band (*narrow*)* (2.63) 90 80
pa. One centre phosphor band (*wide*) (8.64) 2·50 3·25
pb. One side phosphor band (12.64) .. 55 70
531 5 c. ultramarine (3.10.62) 20 5
a. Booklet pane. Five stamps plus one printed label (1963) .. .. .. 2·50
b. Pack. One block of 20 .. .. .. 4·75
c. Imperf horiz (vert pair) .. .. ..
p. Two phosphor bands (31.1.63?) 45 15
pa. Pack. One block of 20 .. .. .. 14·00

(ii) *P 9½ × imperf coil stamps*)

532 2 c. green (1963) .. .. 3·75 4·75
532*a* 3 c. reddish violet (1964) .. .. .. 3·25 2·50
533 4 c. carmine-red (15.5.63) .. .. .. 1·75 1·75
534 5 c. ultramarine (15.5.63) .. .. .. 1·75 45

Symbols:–1 c. Crystals (Mining); 2 c. Tree (Forestry); 3 c. Fish (Fisheries); 4 c. Electricity pylon (Industrial power).

Nos. 528a, 530b, 531b and 531pa are blocks with the outer edges imperf. These come from "One Dollar Plastic Packages" sold at post offices.

†This is a fugitive colour which tends to become reddish on drying. In successive printings the violet colour became more and more reddish as the printer tried to match the shade of each previous printing instead of referring back to the original shade. A deep reddish violet is also known from Plate 3. As there is such a range of shades it is not practical to list them.

*On No. 530p the band is 4 mm wide as against 8 mm on No. 530pa. No. 530pb exists with the band at either left or right side of the stamp, the bands being applied across alternate vertical perforations.

(Des P. Weiss)

1963 (5 Mar). *150th Birth Anniv of Gzowski (engineer). P* 12.
535 **216** 5 c. reddish purple 20 5

217 "Export Trade" **218** Frobisher and barque *Gabriel*

(Des A. L. Pollock)

1963 (14 June). *P* 12.
536 **217** $1 carmine .. .. 20·00 2·00

(Des P. Weiss)

1963 (21 Aug). *Sir Martin Frobisher Commemoration. P* 12.
537 **218** 5 c. ultramarine 25 5

219 Horseman and Map **220** Canada Geese

(Des B. J. Reddie)

1963 (25 Sept). *Bicentenary of Quebec–Trois-Rivieres–Montreal Postal Service. P* 12.
538 **219** 5 c. red-brown and deep green 25 5

(Des A. Short and P. Arthur)

1963 (30 Oct). *P* 12.
539 **220** 15 c. blue .. .. 3·00 5

221 Jet Airliner (composite) and Uplands Airport, Ottawa **222** "Peace on Earth"

1964. *P* 12.
540 **221** 7 c. blue (11 Mar) 40 60
540*a* 8 c. blue (18 Nov) 50 45

1964 (8 Apr). *"Peace". Litho and recess. P* 12.
541 **222** 5 c. ochre, blue and turquoise-blue 20 5

223 Maple Leaves

1964 (14 May). *"Canadian Unity". P* 12.
542 **223** 5 c. lake-red and light blue 25 5

224 White Trillium and Arms of Ontario **236** Maple Leaf and Arms of Canada

1964–66. *Provincial Emblems. T* **224, 236** *and similar horiz designs. Recess (No. 555) or litho and recess (others). P* 12.
543 5 c. green, brown and orange (30.6.64) .. 35 20
544 5 c. green, orange-brown and yellow (30.6.64) 35 20
545 5 c. carmine-red, green and bluish violet (3.2.65) 35 20
546 5 c. blue, red and green (3.2.65) 35 20
547 5 c. purple, green and yellow-brown (28.4.65) 35 20
548 5 c. red-brown, deep bluish green and mauve (28.4.65) 35 20
549 5 c. slate-lilac, green and light reddish purple (21.7.65) 35 20
550 5 c. green, yellow and rose-red (19.1.66) .. 35 20
551 5 c. sepia, orange and green (19.1.66) .. 35 20
552 5 c. black, green and red (23.2.66) 35 20
553 5 c. drab, green and yellow (23.3.66) 35 20
554 5 c. blue, green and rose-red (23.3.66) .. 35 20
555 5 c. red and blue (30.6.66) 35 20
543/55 .. .. *Set of* 13 4·00 2·40

Designs:—No. 543, Type **224**; No. 544, Madonna Lily and Arms of Quebec; No. 545, Purple Violet and Arms of New Brunswick; No. 546, Mayflower and Arms of Nova Scotia; No. 547, Dogwood and Arms of British Columbia; No. 548, Prairie Crocus and Arms of Manitoba; No. 549, Lady's Slipper and Arms of Prince Edward Island; No. 550, Wild Rose and Arms of Alberta; No. 551, Prairie Lily and Arms of Saskatchewan; No. 552, Pitcher Plant and Arms of Newfoundland; No. 553, Mountain Avens and Arms of Northwest Territories; No. 554, Fireweed and Arms of Yukon Territory; No. 555, Type **236**.

8 ═

(**237**) **238** Fathers of the Confederation Memorial, Charlottetown

1964 (15 July). *No. 540 surch with T* **237**.
556 **221** 8 c. on 7 c. blue 30 50

(Des P. Weiss)

1964 (29 July). *Centenary of Charlottetown Conference. P* 12.
557 **238** 5 c. black 20 5

239 Maple Leaf and Hand with Quill Pen **240** Queen Elizabeth II

(Des P. Weiss)

1964 (9 Sept). *Centenary of Quebec Conference. P* 12.
558 **239** 5 c. light red and chocolate 20 5

(Portrait by Anthony Buckley)

1964 (5 Oct). *Royal Visit. P* 12.
559 **240** 5 c. reddish purple 20 5

241 "Canadian Family" **242** "Co-operation"

1964 (14 Oct). *Christmas. P* 12.
560 **241** 3 c. scarlet 10 5
a. Pack. Two blocks of 25 .. .. 6·00
p. Two phosphor bands 75 80
pa. Pack. Two blocks of 25 .. .. 12·00
561 5 c. ultramarine 15 5
p. Two phosphor bands .. .. 2·25 2·25

Nos. 560a and 560pa are blocks with the outer edges imperf. These come from "$1.50 Plastic Packages" sold at post offices.

1965 (3 Mar). *International Co-operation Year. P* 12.
562 **242** 5 c. grey-green 25 8

ALTERED CATALOGUE NUMBERS

Any Catalogue numbers altered from the last edition are shown as a list in the introductory pages.

243 Sir W. Grenfell **244** National Flag

1965 (9 June). *Birth Centenary of Sir Wilfred Grenfell (missionary). P* 12.
563 **243** 5 c. deep bluish green 20 5

1965 (30 June). *Inauguration of National Flag. P* 12.
564 **244** 5 c. red and blue 20 5

245 Sir Winston Churchill **246** Peace Tower, Parliament Buildings, Ottawa

(Des P. Weiss from photo by Karsh. Litho)

1965 (12 Aug). *Churchill Commemoration. P* 12.
565 **245** 5 c. purple-brown 25 8

(Des Philips-Gutkin)

1965 (8 Sept). *Inter-Parliamentary Union Conference, Ottawa. P* 12.
566 **246** 5 c. deep green 20 8

247 Parliament Buildings, Ottawa, 1865 **248** "Gold, Frankincense and Myrrh"

(Des G. Trottier)

1965 (8 Sept). *Centenary of Proclamation of Ottawa as Capital. P* 12.
567 **247** 5 c. brown 20 5

(Des Helen Fitzgerald)

1965 (13 Oct). *Christmas. P* 12.
568 **248** 3 c. olive-green 10 5
a. Pack. Two blocks of 25 .. .. 5·00
p. Two phosphor bands 25 25
pa. Pack. Two blocks of 25 .. .. 6·00
569 5 c. ultramarine 15 5
p. Two phosphor bands 40 40

Nos. 568a and 568pa are blocks with the outer edges imperf. These come from "$1.50 Plastic Packages" sold at post offices.

249 "Alouette 2" over Canada **250** La Salle

1966 (5 Jan). *Launching of Canadian Satellite, "Alouette 2". P* 12.
570 **249** 5 c. ultramarine 20 5

(Des Brigdens Ltd., Toronto)

1966 (13 Apr). *300th Anniv of La Salle's Arrival in Canada. P* 12.
571 **250** 5 c. deep bluish green 20 5

251 Road Signs **252** Canadian Delegation and Houses of Parliament

(Des Helen Fitzgerald)

1966 (2 May). *Highway Safety. Invisible gum. P* 12.
572 **251** 5 c. yellow, blue and black 20 5

(Des P. Pederson (Brigdens Ltd))

1966 (26 May). *London Conference Centenary. P* 12.
573 **252** 5 c. red-brown 20 5

253 Douglas Point Nuclear Power Station — **254** Parliamentary Library, Ottawa

(Des A. L. Pollock)

1966 (27 July). *Peaceful Uses of Atomic Energy. P* 12.

574 **253**	5 c. ultramarine	20	5

(Des Brigdens Ltd)

1966 (8 Sept). *Commonwealth Parliamentary Association Conference, Ottawa. P* 12.

575 **254**	5 c. purple	20	5

255 "Praying Hands", after Dürer — **256** Flag and Canada on Globe

(Des G. Holloway)

1966 (12 Oct). *Christmas. P* 12.

576 **255**	3 c. carmine	10	5
	a. Pack. Two blocks of 25	4·50	
	p. Two phosphor bands	20	20
	pa. Pack. Two blocks of 25	9·00	
577	5 c. orange	12	5
	p. Two phosphor bands	30	50

Nos. 576a and 576pa are blocks with the outer edges imperf. These come from "$1.50 Plastic Packages" sold at post offices.

(Des Brigdens Ltd)

1967 (11 Jan). *Canadian Centennial. Invisible gum. P* 12.

578 **256**	5 c. scarlet and blue	20	5
	p. Two phosphor bands	25	40

257 Northern Lights and Dog-team — **263** "The Jack Pine" (T. Thomson)

1967 (8 Feb)–**72**. *T* **257, 263** *and similar horiz designs.*

A. *Recess C.B.N.*

(i) *P* 12

579	1 c. brown	5	5
	a. Booklet pane. Five stamps plus one printed label (2.67)	50	
	p. Two phosphor bands	40	30
	pa. Centre phosphor band (12.68)	40	25
580	2 c. green	5	5
	b. Booklet pane. No. 580 × 4 *se-tenant* with No. 581 × 4 with gutter margin between (26.10.70)	2·50	
	p. Two phosphor bands	40	25
	pa. Centre phosphor band (12.68)	30	20
581	3 c. slate-purple	10	5
	p. Two phosphor bands	40	30
582	4 c. red	15	5
	a. Booklet pane. Five stamps plus one printed label (2.67)	1·75	
	b. Pack. One block of 25 (2.67)	10·00	
	p. One side phosphor band	60	45
	pa. Centre phosphor band (3.69)	35	25
583	5 c. blue	15	5
	a. Booklet pane. Five stamps plus one printed label (2.67)	6·00	
	b. Pack. One block of 20 (2.67)	25·00	
	p. Two phosphor bands	60	25
	pa. Pack. One block of 20 (2.67)	45·00	
	pb. Centre phosphor band (12.68)	40	20
583*c*	6 c. black (2.72)	60	20
	cp. Centre phosphor band (2.72)	75	40
584	8 c. purple-brown	70	25
585	10 c. olive-green	45	5
	p. Two phosphor bands (9.12.69)	1·25	35
586	15 c. dull purple	60	5
	p. Two phosphor bands (9.12.69)	1·10	60
587	20 c. deep blue	1·25	5
	p. Two phosphor bands (9.12.69)	1·50	90
588	25 c. myrtle-green	1·25	5
	p. Two phosphor bands (9.12.69)	2·50	1·75
589	50 c. cinnamon	4·75	25
590	$1 scarlet	12·00	80
579/90	*Set of* 13	20·00	1·60
579pa/588p	*Set of* 10	8·00	4·75

(ii) *Perf* 9½ × *imperf* (*coil stamps*)

591	3 c. slate-purple (3.67)	1·25	1·50
592	4 c. red (3.67)	1·25	1·50
593	5 c. blue (2.67)	1·25	75

(iii) *Perf* 10 × *imperf* (*coil stamps*)

594	6 c. orange-red (1.69)	40	45
	a. Imperf (vert pair)	£200	
595	6 c. black (8.70)	35	30
	a. Imperf (vert pair)	£350	
596	7 c. green (30.6.71)	40	30
	a. Imperf (vert pair)	£350	
597	8 c. black (30.12.71)	30	20
	a. Imperf (vert pair)	£175	

B. *Recess B.A.B.N.*

(i) *P* 10 (*sheets* (601/p) *or booklets*)

598	1 c. brown (9.68)	12	30
	a. Booklet pane. No. 598 × 5 *se-tenant* with No. 599 × 5 (9.68)	2·25	
	b. Booklet pane. No. 601 × 4 *se-tenant* with No. 598 plus one printed label (10.68)	2·50	
599	4 c. red (9.68)	25	40
	a. Booklet pane. 25 stamps plus two printed labels	9·00	
600	5 c. blue (9.68)	25	40
	a. Booklet pane of 20	6·50	
601	6 c. orange-red (10.68)	45	30
	a. Booklet pane. 25 stamps plus two printed labels (1.69)	12·00	
	p. Two phosphor bands (1.11.68)	50	45
602	6 c. black (1.70)	50	40
	a. Booklet pane. 25 stamps plus two printed labels	14·00	
603	6 c. black (*re-engraved die*) (8.70)	3·25	1·40
	a. Booklet pane of 4	12·00	

(ii) *P* 12½ × 12 (*sheets* (606/10) *or booklets*)

604	1 c. brown (30.6.71)	20	20
	a. Booklet pane. Nos. 604 × 4,605 × 4 and 609 × 12 *se-tenant*	9·00	
	b. Booklet pane. No. 604 × 3, No. 608 and No. 610 × 2 *se-tenant* (30.12.71)	2·00	
	c. Booklet pane. No. 604 × 6, No. 608 and No. 610 × 11 *se-tenant* (30.12.71)	6·00	
	d. Booklet pane. No. 604, No. 605 and No. 609 × 3 *se-tenant* plus one printed label	5·00	
	e. Booklet pane. No. 604 × 4, No. 608 and No. 610 × 5 *se-tenant* (8.72)	2·50	
605	3 c. slate-purple (30.6.71)	45	30
606	6 c. orange-red (3.69)	45	25
	p. Two phosphor bands	75	15
607	6 c. black (7.1.70)	25	5
	a. Booklet pane. 25 stamps plus two printed labels (8.70)	16·00	
	p. Two phosphor bands	60	60
608	6 c. black (*re-engraved die*) (9.70)	35	5
	a. Booklet pane of 4 (11.70)	5·00	
	p. One centre phosphor band (9.71)	80	45
609	7 c. myrtle-green (30.6.71)	30	10
	p. Two phosphor bands	60	35
610	8 c. slate-black (30.12.71)	30	10
	p. Two phosphor bands	60	35

Designs: (*as T* **257**)—2 c. Totem pole; 3 c. Combine-harvester and oil derrick; 4 c. Ship in lock; 5 c. Harbour scene; 6 c., 7 c. "Transport"; 8 c. (Nos. 597, 610) Library of Parliament. (*as T* **263**)—8 c. (No. 584) "Alaska Highway" (A. Y. Jackson); 15 c. "Bylot Island" (L. Harris); 20 c. "Quebec Ferry" (J. W. Morrice); 25 c. "The Solemn Land" (J. E. H. MacDonald); 50 c. "Summer's Stores" (grain elevators) (J. Ensor); $1 "Oilfield" (near Edmonton) (H. G. Glyde).

Nos. 582b, 583b and 583pa are blocks with the outer edges imperf. These come from "One Dollar Plastic Packages" sold at post offices.

No. 582p comes with the band to the left or right of the stamp, the phosphor having been applied across alternate vertical perforations.

Normal

Re-engraved

When the basic postal rate was changed to 6 c. the C.B.N. lent their die to B.A.B.N. who made a duplicate die from it by transfer. Parts of this proved to be weak, but it was used for Nos. 601/2 and 606/7. B.A.B.N. later re-engraved their die to make fresh plates which were used for Nos. 603 and 608. No. 608 first appeared on sheets from Plate 4.

There are no records of dates of issue of the booklets, packs and coils, but supplies of these were distributed to depots in the months indicated.

IMPERF BETWEEN PAIRS FROM COIL STAMPS. Nos. 595/6 (and possibly others) are known in blocks or horizontal pairs imperf between vertically. Coils are supplied to post offices in batches of ten coils held together by roulettes between every fourth stamp so that they can easily be split apart. If two or more unsplit coils are purchased it is possible to obtain blocks or pairs imperf between vertically.

Vertical coil stamps are also known imperf between horizontally or with some stamps apparently completely imperf. These can result from blind perforations identifiable by slight indentations.

WHITE FLUORESCENT PAPER. Different papers with varying degrees of whiteness have been used for Canadian stamps, but during 1968–70 a distinctive very white and highly fluorescent paper was used known as "hybrite"; this fluoresces on the back and front. This paper has also been employed for commemorative issues, some of which exist on more than one type of paper. The white fluorescent papers are recorded in the Stanley Gibbons *Elizabethan Catalogue.*

FLUORESCENT BANDS. During the second half of 1971 new sorting machines were installed in the Ottawa area which were activated by stamps bearing fluorescent bands. These differ from the Winnipeg phosphor bands in that there is no after-glow and they are hardly visible to the naked eye and so can only be distinguished by using an ultra-violet lamp. For this reason they are outside the scope of this catalogue but instead are recorded in footnotes. They are, however, fully listed in the Stanley Gibbons *Elizabethan Catalogue.*

In the 1967–72 definitive issue fluorescent bands occur on some printings of Nos. 579, 580, 581, 582, 583*c*, 585, 586, 597, 604, 608 and 610.

The experiments were successful and what was at first called "Ottawa tagging" has since come into more general use and the Winnipeg phosphor was phased out. However, the substance at first used (known as OP–4) was found to migrate to envelopes, documents, album pages, etc. as well as to adjoining stamps. Late in 1972 this fault was cured by using another substance (called OP–2). The migrating bands were used on early printings of Nos. 604, 608 and 610 as well as certain stamps referred to in a footnote after No. 692. It is most advisable to use plastic mounts for housing stamps with migrating bands or else clear acetate should be affixed to the album leaves.

269 Canadian Pavilion — **270** Allegory of "Womanhood" on Ballot-box

(Des C.B.N.)

1967 (28 Apr). *World Fair, Montreal. P* 12.

611 **269**	5 c. blue and red	20	5

(Des Helen Fitzgerald. Litho)

1967 (24 May). *50th Anniv of Women's Franchise. P* 12.

612 **270**	5 c. reddish purple and black	20	5

271 Queen Elizabeth II and Centennial Emblem — **272** Athlete

(Portrait from photo by Anthony Buckley)

1967 (30 June). *Royal Visit. P* 12.

613 **271**	5 c. plum and orange-brown	20	5

(Des Brigdens Ltd)

1967 (19 July). *Fifth Pan-American Games, Winnipeg. P* 12.

614 **272**	5 c. rose-red	20	5

273 "World News" — **274** Governor-General Vanier

(Des W. McLauchlan)

1967 (31 Aug). *50th Anniv of the Canadian Press. P* 12.

615 **273**	5 c. blue	20	5

(Des from photo by Karsh)

1967 (15 Sept). *Vanier Commemoration. P* 12.

616 **274**	5 c. black	20	5

PRINTERS. The following were printed either by the Canadian Bank Note Co, Ottawa (C.B.N.) or the British American Bank Note Co, Ottawa (B.A.B.N.), *except where otherwise stated.*

275 People of 1867 and Toronto, 1967 — **276** Carol Singers

(Des and recess C.B.N.)

1967 (28 Sept). *Centenary of Toronto as Capital City of Ontario. P* 12.

617 **275**	5 c. myrtle-green and vermilion	20	5

(Des and recess B.A.B.N.)

1967 (11 Oct). *Christmas. P* 12.

618 **276**	3 c. scarlet	10	5
	a. Pack. Two blocks of 25	4·25	
	p. Two phosphor bands	15	15
	pa. Pack. Two blocks of 25	5·00	
619	5 c. emerald-green	15	5
	p. Two phosphor bands	30	40

Nos. 618a and 618pa are blocks with the outer edges imperf. These come from "$1.50 Plastic Packs" sold at post offices.

277 Grey Jays **278** Weather Map and Instruments

(Des M. G. Loates. Litho C.B.N.)

1968 (15 Feb). *Wild Life. P* 12.
620 **277** 5 c. multicoloured 30 10
See also Nos. 638/40.

(Des and litho B.A.B.N.)

1968 (13 Mar). *Bicentenary of First Meteorological Readings. P* 11.
621 **278** 5 c. multicoloured 25 8

279 Narwhal **280** Globe, Maple Leaf and Rain Gauge

(Des J. A. Crosby. Litho B.A.B.N.)

1968 (10 Apr). *Wildlife. P* 11.
622 **279** 5 c. multicoloured 25 8
No. 622 has a background of yellow-green and pale blue but copies are known with the yellow-green apparently missing. This "yellow-green" is produced by an overlay of yellow on the blue but we have not come across any copies where the yellow is completely missing and the wide range of colour variation is due to technical dificulties in maintaining an exact blend of the two colours.

(Des I. von Mosdossy. Litho B.A.B.N.)

1968 (8 May). *International Hydrological Decade. P* 11.
623 **280** 5 c. multicoloured 25 8

IMPERF EDGES. On Nos. 624/54, 657 and 659 (stamps printed by the B.A.B.N. Co.) the outer edges of the sheets were guillotined to remove the imprints for P.O. stock so that single stamps may, therefore, be found with either one, or two adjacent sides imperforate.

281 *Nonsuch* **282** Lacrosse Players

(Recess and photo B.A.B.N.)

1968 (5 June). *300th Anniv of Voyage of the "Nonsuch". P* 10.
624 **281** 5 c. multicoloured 25 10

(Des J. E. Aldridge. Recess and photo B.A.B.N.)

1968 (3 July). *Lacrosse. P* 10.
625 **282** 5 c. black, red and lemon 20 10

283 Front Page of *The Globe*, George Brown and Legislative Building **284** H. Bourassa

(Des N. Sabolotny. Recess and photo B.A.B.N.)

1968 (21 Aug). *150th Birth Anniv of George Brown (politician and journalist). P* 10.
626 **283** 5 c. multicoloured 20 10

(Des, recess and litho C.B.N.)

1968 (4 Sept). *Birth Centenary of Henri Bourassa (journalist and politician). P* 12.
627 **284** 5 c. black, red and pale cream 20 10

285 John McCrae, Battlefield and First Lines of "In Flanders Fields" **286** Armistice Monument, Vimy

(Des I. von Mosdossy. Litho C.B.N.)

1968 (15 Oct). *50th Death Anniv of John McCrae (soldier and poet). P* 12.
628 **285** 5 c. multicoloured 20 10

(Des and recess C.B.N.)

1968 (15 Oct). *50th Anniversary of 1918 Armistice. P* 12.
629 **286** 15 c. slate-black .. .. 1·00 1·25

287 Eskimo Family (carving) **288** "Mother and Child" (carving)

(Designs from Eskimo carvings by Munamee (6 c.) and unknown carver (5 c.). Photo C.B.N.)

1968. *Christmas. P* 12.
630 **287** 5 c. black and new blue (1.11.68) .. 12 5
a. Booklet pane of 10 .. .. 2·25
p. One centre phosphor band 15 15
pa. Booklet pane of 10 .. .. 2·50
631 **288** 6 c. black and ochre (15.11.68) .. 15 5
p. Two phosphor bands 30 40

289 Curling **290** Vincent Massey

(Des D. Eales. Recess and photo B.A.B.N.)

1969 (15 Jan). *Curling. P* 10.
632 **289** 6 c. black, new blue and scarlet .. 20 10

(Des I. von Mosdossy. Recess and litho C.B.N.)

1969 (20 Feb). *Vincent Massey, First Canadian-born Governor-General. P* 12.
633 **290** 6 c. sepia and yellow-ochre 20 10

291 "Return from the Harvest Field" (Suzor-Côté) **292** Globe and Tools

(Photo C.B.N.)

1969 (14 Mar). *Birth Centenary of Marc Aurèle de Foy Suzor-Côté (painter). P* 12.
634 **291** 50 c. multicoloured .. .. .. 3·00 4·25

(Des J. Hébert. Recess B.A.B.N.)

1969 (21 May). *50th Anniv of International Labour Organisation. P* 12½ × 12.
635 **292** 6 c. bronze-green 20 10

PHILATELIC TERMS ILLUSTRATED

293 Vickers "Vimy" Aircraft over Atlantic Ocean **294** "Sir William Osler" (J. S. Sargent)

(Des R. W. Bradford. Recess and photo B.A.B.N.)

1969 (13 June). *50th Anniv of First Non-stop Transatlantic Flight. P* 12 × 12½.
636 **293** 15 c. chocolate, bright green & pale blue 1·25 1·75

(Des, recess and photo B.A.B.N.)

1969 (23 June). *50th Death Anniv of Sir William Osler (physician). P* 12½ × 12.
637 **294** 6 c. deep blue, light blue and chestnut 20 10

295 White-throated Sparrows **298** Flags of Winter and Summer Games

(Des M. G. Loates. Litho C.B.N.)

1969 (23 July). *Birds. T* **295** *and similar multicoloured designs. P* 12.
638 6 c. Type **295** 25 10
639 10 c. Savannah Sparrow (*horiz*) 65 80
640 25 c. Hermit Thrush (*horiz*) .. .. .. 1·90 2·75

(Des C. McDiarmid. Recess and litho C.B.N.)

1969 (15 Aug). *Canadian Games. P* 12.
641 **298** 6 c. emerald, scarlet and blue 20 10

299 Outline of Prince Edward Island showing Charlottetown **300** Sir Isaac Brock and Memorial Column

(Des L. Fitzgerald. Recess and photo B.A.B.N.)

1969 (15 Aug). *Bicentenary of Charlottetown as Capital of Prince Edward Island. P* 12 × 12½.
642 **299** 6 c. yellow-brown, black and blue 25 10

(Des I. von Mosdossy. Recess and litho C.B.N.)

1969 (12 Sept). *Birth Bicentenary of Sir Isaac Brock. P* 12.
643 **300** 6 c. orange, bistre and bistre-brown 20 8

301 Children of the World in Prayer **302** Stephen Butler Leacock, Mask and "Mariposa"

(Des Rapid Grip and Batten Ltd. Litho C.B.N.)

1969 (8 Oct). *Christmas. P* 12.
644 **301** 5 c. multicoloured 10 5
a. Booklet pane of 10 .. .. .. 1·75
p. One centre phosphor band 20 20
pa. Booklet pane of 10 .. .. .. 2·50
645 6 c. multicoloured 12 5
a. Black (inscr value and frame) omitted £1000
p. Two phosphor bands 25 30

(Des, recess and photo B.A.B.N.)

1969 (12 Nov). *Birth Centenary of Stephen Butler Leacock (humorist). P* 12 × 12½.
646 **302** 6 c. multicoloured 20 8

303 Symbolic Cross-roads

304 "Enchanted Owl" (Kenojuak)

(Des K. C. Lochhead. Litho C.B.N.)

1970 (27 Jan). *Centenary of Manitoba. P* 12.

647	**303**	6 c. ultramarine, lemon and vermilion	20	8
		p. Two phosphor bands	20	25

(Des N. E. Hallendy and Miss S. Van Raalte. Recess C.B.N.)

1970 (27 Jan). *Centenary of Northwest Territories. P* 12.

648	**304**	6 c. carmine-red and black	15	10

305 Microscopic View of Inside of Leaf

306 Expo 67 Emblem and Stylized Cherry Blossom

(Des I. Charney. Recess and photo B.A.B.N.)

1970 (18 Feb). *International Biological Programme. P* 12 × 12½.

649	**305**	6 c. emerald, orange-yellow & ultram ..	20	10

(Des E. R. C. Bethune. Litho C.B.N.)

1970 (18 Mar). *World Fair, Osaka. T* **306** *and similar horiz designs. Multicoloured; colour of Cherry Blossom given. P* 12.

650	25 c. red	1·75	1·50
	a. Block of 4. Nos. 650/3	7·00	
	p. Two phosphor bands	2·25	2·50
	pa. Block of 4. Nos. 650p/3p	9·00	
651	25 c. violet	1·75	1·50
	p. Two phosphor bands	2·25	2·50
652	25 c. green	1·75	1·50
	p. Two phosphor bands	2·25	2·50
653	25 c. blue	1·75	1·50
	p. Two phosphor bands	2·25	2·50

Designs:—No. 650, Type **306**; No. 651, Dogwood and stylized cherry blossom; No. 652, White Trillium and stylized cherry blossom; No. 653, White Garden Lily and stylized cherry blossom.

Nos. 650/3 and 650p/3p are printed together in sheets of 50 (5 × 10). In the first, second, fourth and fifth vertical rows the four different designs are arranged in *se-tenant* blocks, whilst the centre row is composed as follows (reading downwards:—650(p)/3(p), 650(p) × 2, 653(p), 651(p), 652(p) and 650(p).

310 Henry Kelsey

311 "Towards Unification"

(Des D. Burton. Recess and photo B.A.B.N.)

1970 (15 Apr). *300th Birth Anniv of Henry Kelsey (explorer). P* 12 × 12½.

654	**310**	6 c. multicoloured	20	10

(Des B. Fisher. Litho B.A.B.N.)

1970 (13 May). *25th Anniv of United Nations. P* 11.

655	**311**	10 c. blue	55	50
		p. Two phosphor bands	1·25	1·75
656		15 c. magenta and bluish lilac	70	70
		p. Two phosphor bands	1·50	2·00

312 Louis Riel (Métis leader)

313 Mackenzie's Inscription, Dean Channel

(Des R. Derreth. Photo B.A.B.N.)

1970 (19 June). *Louis Riel Commemoration. P* 12½ × 12.

657	**312**	6 c. greenish blue and vermilion ..	15	10

(Design from Government Archives photo. Recess C.B.N.)

1970 (25 June). *Sir Alexander Mackenzie (explorer). P* 12 × 11½.

658	**313**	6 c. bistre-brown	15	10

ALTERED CATALOGUE NUMBERS

Any Catalogue numbers altered from the last edition are shown as a list in the introductory pages.

314 Sir Oliver Mowat (statesman)

315 "Isles of Spruce" (A. Lismer)

(Des E. Roch. Recess and photo B.A.B.N.)

1970 (12 Aug). *Sir Oliver Mowat Commemoration. P* 12.

659	**314**	6 c. vermilion and black	15	10

(Litho Ashton-Potter)

1970 (18 Sept). *50th Anniv of "Group of Seven" (artists). P* 11.

660	**315**	6 c. multicoloured	15	10

316 "Horse-drawn Sleigh" (D. Niskala)

317 "Christ in Manger" (C. Fortier)

(Des from children's drawings. Litho C.B.N.)

1970 (7 Oct). *Christmas. Horiz designs as T* **316/17**, *showing children's drawings. Multicoloured. P* 12.

661	5 c. Type **316**	20	5
	a. Strip of 5. Nos. 661/5	1·50	
	p. One centre phosphor band	25	15
	pa. Strip of 5. Nos. 661p/5p	1·50	
662	5 c. "Stable" and Star of Bethlehem" (L. Wilson) (26 × 21 *mm*)	20	5
	p. One centre phosphor band	25	15
663	5 c. "Snowmen" (M. Lecompte) (26 × 21 *mm*)	20	5
	p. One centre phosphor band	25	15
664	5 c. "Skiing" (D. Durham) (26 × 21 *mm*) ..	20	5
	p. One centre phosphor band	25	15
665	5 c. "Santa Claus" (A. Martin) (26 × 21 *mm*)	20	5
	p. One centre phosphor band	25	15
666	6 c. "Santa Claus" (E. Bhattacharya) (26 × 21 *mm*)	25	5
	a. Strip of 5. Nos. 666/70		
	p. Two phosphor bands	30	20
	pa. Strip of 5. Nos. 666p/70p..	2·00	
667	6 c. "Christ in Manger" (J. McKinney) (26 × 21 *mm*)	25	5
	p. Two phosphor bands	30	20
668	6 c. "Toy Shop" (N. Whateley) (26 × 21 *mm*) ..	25	5
	p. Two phosphor bands	30	20
669	6 c. "Christmas Tree" (J. Pomperleau) (26 × 21 *mm*)	25	5
	p. Two phosphor bands	30	20
670	6 c. "Church" (J. McMillan) (26 × 21 *mm*) ..	25	5
	p. Two phosphor bands	30	20
671	10 c. Type **317**	30	25
	p. Two phosphor bands	55	60
672	15 c. "Trees and Sledge" (J. Dojcak) (35 × 21 mm)	45	60
	p. Two phosphor bands	70	75
661/72	.. .. *Set of* 12	3·25	1·25
661p/672p	.. .. *Set of* 12	4·25	2.75

The designs of the 5 c. and 6 c. were each issued with the various designs *se-tenant* in a diamond shaped arrangement within the sheet. This generally results in *se-tenant* pairs both vert and horiz, but due to the sheet arrangement vert and horiz pairs of the same design exist from the two centre vert and horiz rows.

328 Sir Donald A. Smith

329 "Big Raven" (E. Carr)

(Des Dora de Pédery-Hunt. Litho C.B.N.)

1970 (4 Nov). *150th Birth Anniv of Sir Donald Alexander Smith. P* 12.

673	**328**	6 c. yellow, brown and bronze-green	15	10

(Litho C.B.N.)

1971 (12 Feb). *Birth Centenary of Emily Carr (painter). P* 12.

674	**329**	6 c. multicoloured	20	10

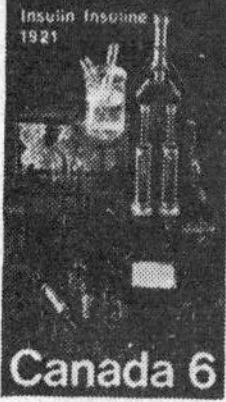
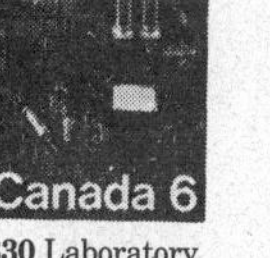

330 Laboratory Equipment

331 "The Atom"

(Des R. Webber. Litho B.A.B.N.)

1971 (3 Mar). *50th Anniv of Discovery of Insulin. P* 10½.

675	**330**	6 c. multicoloured	20	10

(Des R. Webber. Litho B.A.B.N.)

1971 (24 Mar). *Birth Centenary of Lord Rutherford (scientist). P* 11.

676	**331**	6 c. yellow, red and deep chocolate	25	10

332 Maple "Keys"

333 Louis Papineau

(Des Alma Duncan. Litho Ashton-Potter)

1971. *"The Maple Leaf in Four Seasons". T* **332** *and similar vert designs. Multicoloured. P* 11.

677	6 c. Type **332** (Spring) (14.4)	25	12
	a. Imperf (pair)	£750	
678	6 c. Green leaves (Summer) (16.6)	25	12
679	7 c. Autumn leaves (3.9)	25	12
	a. Grey (inscr and value) omitted	£1500	
680	7 c. Withered leaves and snow (Winter) (19.11)	25	12

(Des L. Marquart. Recess and photo B.A.B.N.)

1971 (7 May). *Death Centenary of Louis-Joseph Papineau (politician). P* 12½ × 12.

681	**333**	6 c. multicoloured	20	15

334 Chart of Coppermine River

335 "People" and Computer Tapes

(Des L. Marquart. Recess and photo B.A.B.N.)

1971 (7 May). *Bicentenary of Samuel Hearne's Expedition to Coppermine. P* 12 × 12½.

682	**334**	6 c. red, sepia and pale buff	20	15

(Des H. Kleefeld. Litho C.B.N.)

1971 (1 June). *Centennial of Census. P* 11½.

683	**335**	6 c. blue, red and black	20	10

336 Maple Leaves

(Des B. Kramer. Litho C.B.N.)

1971 (1 June). *Radio Canada International. P* 12.

684	**336**	15 c. red, yellow and black	1·50	1·75
		p. Two phosphor bands	2·25	2·75

337 "BC"

(Des E. R. C. Bethune. Litho C.B.N.)

1971 (20 July). *Centenary of British Columbia's Entry into the Confederation. P* 12.

685	**337**	7 c. multicoloured	20	12

338 "Indian Encampment on Lake Huron" (Kane)

339 "Snowflake"

(Des and litho B.A.B.N.)

1971 (11 Aug). *Death Centenary of Paul Kane (painter). P* 12½.

686	**338**	7 c. multicoloured	30	15

(Des Lisl Levinsohn. Recess (6 c., 7 c.) or recess and litho (others) C.B.N.)

1971 (6 Oct). *Christmas. T* **379** *and similar design. P* 12.

687	**339**	6 c. deep blue	12	5
		p. One centre phosphor band ..	15	15
688		7 c. deep emerald	15	5
		p. Two phosphor bands	25	20
689	–	10 c. silver and cerise	40	45
		p. Two phosphor bands	60	70

690 – 15 c. silver, brown-purple and lavender .. 55 55
 p. Two phosphor bands 75 90

Design:—10 c., 15 c. "Snowflake" design similar to T **339** but square (26 × 26 mm).

340 Pierre Laporte (Quebec Cabinet Minister)

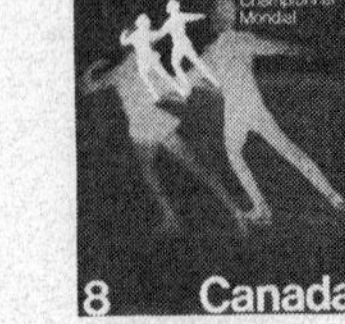

341 Skaters

(Des G. Gundersen. Recess and litho B.A.B.N.)

1971 (20 Oct). *First Anniv of the Assassination of Pierre Laporte. P* 12½ × 12.
691 **340** 7 c. black/*pale buff* 20 10

(Des Design Workshop, Toronto. Litho C.B.N.)

1972 (1 Mar). *World Figure Skating Championships. Calgary. P* 11½ × 12.
692 **341** 8 c. purple 20 10

MIGRATING FLUORESCENT BANDS. These are referred to in the notes after No. 610. In the following issues they exist on Nos. 719/20 and 731/2 and on early printings only of Nos. 702/6.

342 J. A. MacDonald

343 Forest, Central Canada

344 Vancouver

(Des D. Annesley (1 to 10 c. (701)), R. Derreth (others))

1972–77. *Various designs as T* **342/4**.

(a) *T* **342** *and similar vert portraits. Recess C.B.N. (1 to 6 c. and last ptgs of 7 and 8 c. (No. 700), B.A.B.N. (7, 8, 10 c. and booklet panes). Two fluorescent bands. P* 12 × 12½ (1 *to* 8 c.) *or* 13 (10 c.). (17.10.73)

693 1 c. orange 5 5
 a. Booklet pane. Nos. 693 × 3, 698 and 700 × 2 (10.4.74) 55
 b. Booklet pane. Nos. 693 × 6, 698 and 700 × 11 (17.1.75) .. .. .. 1·90
 c. Booklet pane Nos. 693 × 2, 694 × 4 and 701a × 4 (1.9.76) .. .. .. 1·10
694 2 c. deep green 5 5
695 3 c. agate 8 5
696 4 c. black 10 5
697 5 c. deep magenta 10 5
698 6 c. Indian red 12 5
699 7 c. reddish brown (8.4.74) 12 5
700 8 c. dull ultramarine 20 5
 a. Perf 13 (12.76) 60 30
701 10 c. brown-lake (1.9.76) 20 5
 a. Perf 12 × 12½ (*booklets*) 25 25

(b) *T* **343** *and similar vert designs. Recess and photo B.A.B.N. Two fluorescent bands. P* 12½ × 12 (8.9.72)

702 10 c. deep green, blue-green & yellow-orange 30 10
 b. Perf 13 (2.76) 30 15
 p. Two phosphor bands 90 50
703 15 c. dull ultramarine and orange-brown .. 45 10
 b. Perf 13 (2.76) 40 20
 p. Two phosphor bands 95 90
704 20 c. pale orange, reddish violet & ultramarine 45 15
 a. Perf 13 (2.76) 45 20
 p. Two phosphor bands .. .. .. 1·25 1·25
705 25 c. deep ultramarine and pale blue .. 50 12
 b. Perf 13 (2.76) 45 15
 p. Two phosphor bands .. .. .. 2·25 1·50
706 50 c. blue-green, royal blue and buff (*shades*) 80 15
 b. Perf 13 (2.76) 75 30

(c) *T* **344** *and similar horiz design. Recess B.A.B.N. and litho Ashton-Potter. No fluorescent bands. P* 11 (17.3.72)

707 $1 multicoloured .. .. 7·00 3·00
708 $2 multicoloured .. .. 2·50 1·75

(d) *T* **344**. *Recess and photo B.A.B.N. Two fluorescent bands. P* 12½ × 12 (24.10.73)

709 $1 multicoloured .. .. 1·75 80
 a. Perf 13 (4.77) .. .. 1·25 70

(e) *As Nos.* 700/1. *Recess C.B.N. Imperf × perf* 10 (*coil stamps*)

710 8 c. dull ultramarine (10.4.74) 20 10
 a. Imperf (horiz pair) £100
711 10 c. brown-lake (1.9.76) 20 15
 a. Imperf (horiz pair) £130

Designs (1 to 7c. show Canadian Prime Ministers):—2 c. W. Laurier; 3 c. R. Borden; 4 c. W. L. Mackenzie King; 5 c. R. B. Bennett; 6 c. L. B. Pearson; 7 c. Louis St. Laurent; 8 and 10 c. (Nos. 701/a, 711), Queen Elizabeth II; 15 c. Mountain sheep; 20 c. Prairie landscape from the air; 25 c. Polar Bears; 50 c. Seashore, Eastern Canada; $2 Quebec.

Stamps from booklets exist with one or two adjacent sides imperforate.

345 Heart

1972 (7 Apr). *Heart Disease* (*World Health Day*). *P* 12 × 12½.
719 **345** 8 c. carmine 25 10

This stamp exists on two kinds of paper, with or without fluorescent bands.

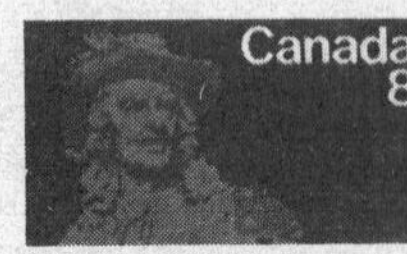

346 Frontenac and Fort Saint-Louis, Quebec

(Des L. Marquart. Recess and photo B.A.B.N.)

1972 (17 May). *300th Anniv of Governor Frontenac's Appointment to New France. P* 12 × 12½.
720 **346** 8 c. brown-red, orange-brn & dp ultram 25 10

This exists with or without fluorescent bands.

347 Plains Indians' Artefacts

347a Buffalo Chase

(Des G. Beaupré. Litho Ashton-Potter (721/2, 725/6 and 729/30), B.A.B.N. (723/4), C.B.N. (727/8))

1972–76. *Canadian Indians. P* 12 × 12½ (721/2, 725/6), 12 (723/4), 13 (727/30), 12½ × 12 (731/6) *or* 12½ (737/40).

(a) *Horiz designs issued in se-tenant pairs, the first showing Artefacts as T* **347**, *the second showing Scenes from Indian Life as T* **347a**

721 8 c. multicoloured (6.7.72) 40 10
 a. Pair. Nos. 721/2 .. .. 85 85
722 8 c. deep brown, yellow & grey-black (6.7.72) 40 10
723 8 c. multicoloured (21.2.73) 40 10
 a. Pair. Nos. 723/4 .. .. 85 85
724 8 c. multicoloured (21.2.73) 40 10
725 8 c. multicoloured (16.1.74) 40 10
 a. Pair. Nos. 725/6 .. .. 85 85
726 8 c. dp brown, yellow & grey-black (16.1.74) 40 10
727 8 c. multicoloured (4.4.75) 40 10
 a. Pair. Nos. 727/8 .. .. 85 85
 ab. Imperf between (horiz pair) £375
728 8 c. multicoloured (4.4.75) 40 10
729 10 c. multicoloured (17.9.76) 40 20
 a. Pair. Nos. 729/30 .. .. 85 85
730 10 c. light stone and black (17.9.76) .. 40 20

Designs show the following tribes: Nos. 721/2 (T **347/a**), Plains Indians; 723/4, Algonkians; 725/6, Pacific Coast Indians; 727/8, Subarctic Indians; 729/30, Iroquoians.

348 Thunderbird and Tribal Pattern

348a Dancer in Ceremonial Costume

(Des G. Beaupré. Recess and photo B.A.B.N. (731/6). Litho and embossed Ashton-Potter (737, 739). Litho Ashton-Potter (738, 740))

(b) *Vert designs issued in se-tenant pairs, the first showing Thunderbird and pattern as T* **348**, *the second Costumes as T* **348a**

731 8 c. light yellow-orange, rose-red and black (4.10.72) 40 15
 a. Pair. Nos. 731/2 .. .. 85 85
732 8 c. multicoloured (4.10.72) 40 15
733 8 c. light rose-red, violet and black (28.11.73) 40 10
 a. Pair. Nos. 733/4 .. .. 85 85
734 8 c. turquoise-green, lake-brown and black (28.11.73) 40 10
735 8 c. rose-red and black (22.2.74) 40 10
 a. Pair. Nos. 735/6 .. .. 85 85
736 8 c. multicoloured (22.2.74) 40 10
737 8 c. myrtle-green, grey-brown and black (4.4.75) 40 10
 a. Pair. Nos. 737/8 .. .. 85 85
738 8 c. multicoloured (4.4.75) 40 10
739 10 c. olive-bistre, reddish orange and black (17.9.76) 40 20
 a. Pair. Nos. 739/40 .. .. 85 85
740 10 c. multicoloured (17.9.76) 40 20
721/40 .. .. *Set of* 20 7·50 2·10

Designs show the following tribes: Nos. 731/2 (T **348/a**), Plains Indians; 733/4, Algonkians; 735/6, Pacific Coast Indians; 737/8, Subarctic Indians; 739/40, Iroquoians.

Nos. 721/2 and 731/2 exist with or without fluorescent bands and the remainder only with fluorescent bands.

349 Photogrammetric Surveying

350 Candles

(Des Gottschalk and Ash Ltd. Litho Ashton-Potter)

1972 (2 Aug). *Earth Sciences. T* **349** *and similar square designs. P* 12.

741 15 c. multicoloured .. .. 1·50 1·50
 a. Block of 4. Nos. 741/4 .. .. .. 6·00
742 15 c. pale grey, dull ultramarine and black .. 1·50 1·50
743 15 c. multicoloured .. .. 1·50 1·50
744 15 c. light emerald, red-orange and black .. 1·50 1·50

Designs and Events:—No. 741, Type **349** (12th Congress of International Society of Photogrammetry); No. 742, "Siegfried" lines (6th Conference of International Cartographic Association); No. 743, Earth's crust (24th International Geological Congress); No. 744, Diagram of village at road-intersection (22nd International Geographical Congress).

Nos. 741/4 were issued in sheets of 64, made up of 4 panes of 16, each pane having a marginal commemorative inscription. Within a pane are 4 copies of each design, arranged in *se-tenant* blocks of 4.

This issue exists with or without fluorescent bands.

(Des R. Webber. Litho Ashton-Potter)

1972 (1 Nov). *Christmas. T* **350** *and similar designs. P* 12½ × 12 (6 *and* 8 c.) *or* 11 × 10½ (*others*).

745 **350** 6 c. multicoloured 12 5
 p. One centre phosphor band 25 20
746 8 c. multicoloured 20 5
 p. Two phosphor bands 30 35
747 – 10 c. multicoloured 40 25
 p. Two phosphor bands 70 70
748 – 15 c. multicoloured 50 40
 p. Two phosphor bands .. .. .. 80 1·00

Designs: *Horiz* (36 × 20 *mm*)—10 c. Candles with fruits and pine boughs; 15 c. Candles with prayer-book, caskets and vase.

This issue also exists with fluorescent bands.

351 "The Blacksmith's Shop" (Krieghoff)

352 François de Montmorency-Laval

(Des and litho B.A.B.N. and Saults & Pollard Ltd., Winnipeg)

1972 (29 Nov). *Death Centenary of Cornelius Krieghoff* (*painter*). *P* 12½.
749 **351** 8 c. multicoloured 20 10

This stamp exists with or without fluorescent bands.

FLUORESCENT BANDS. Stamps from No. 750 onwards were issued only with two fluorescent bands, *unless otherwise stated.* Examples are known with the bands omitted in error, but such varieties are outside the scope of the catalogue.

(Des M. Fog and G. Lorange. Litho Ashton-Potter)

1973 (31 Jan). *350th Birth Anniv of Monsignor de Laval* (*First Bishop of Quebec*). *P* 11.
750 **352** 8 c. ultramarine, gold and silver .. 25 12

353 Commissioner French and Route of the March West

(Des Dallaire Morin DeVito Inc. Litho Ashton-Potter)

1973 (9 Mar). *Centenary of Royal Canadian Mounted Police. T* **353** *and similar horiz designs. Multicoloured* (*except* 8 c.). *P* 11.

751 8 c. Type **353** (deep reddish brown, dull orange and orange-vermilion) 25 10
752 10 c. Spectrograph 70 90
753 15 c. Mounted policeman .. .. .. 95 1·10

MINIMUM PRICE

The minimum price quoted is 5p which represents a handling charge rather than a basis for valuing common stamps. For further notes about prices see introductory pages.

354 Jeanne Mance

(Des R. Bellemare. Litho Ashton-Potter)

1973 (18 Apr). *300th Death Anniv of Jeanne Mance (nurse). P* 11.
754 **354** 8 c. multicoloured 25 12

355 Joseph Howe

356 "Mist Fantasy" (MacDonald)

(Des A. Fleming. Litho Ashton-Potter)

1973 (16 May). *Death Centenary of Joseph Howe (Nova Scotian politician). P* 11.
755 **355** 8 c. gold and black 25 12

(Des and litho Ashton-Potter)

1973 (8 June). *Birth Centenary of J. E. H. MacDonald (artist). P* 12½.
756 **356** 15 c. multicoloured 65 90

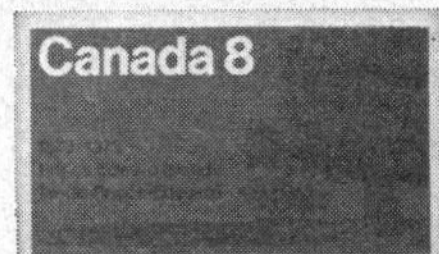

357 Oaks and Harbour

(Des A. Mann. Recess and photo B.A.B.N.)

1973 (22 June). *Centenary of Prince Edward Island's Entry into the Confederation. P* 12.
757 **357** 8 c. pale orange and brown-red .. 25 12

358 Scottish Settlers

359 Queen Elizabeth II

(Des P. Swan. Litho Ashton-Potter)

1973 (20 July). *Bicentennial of Arrival of Scottish Settlers at Pictou, Nova Scotia. P* 12 × 12½.
758 **358** 8 c. multicoloured 25 12

(Des A. Fleming from photograph by Anthony Buckley. Eng G. A. Gundersen. Recess and photo B.A.B.N.)

1973 (2 Aug). *Royal Visit and Commonwealth Heads of Government Meeting, Ottawa. P* 12 × 12½.
759 **359** 8 c. multicoloured 25 15
760 15 c. red, black and bright gold (*shades*) 1·40 1·50

360 Nellie McClung

361 Emblem of 1976 Olympics

(Des S. Mennie. Litho Ashton-Potter)

1973 (29 Aug). *Birth Centenary of Nellie McClung (feminist). P* 10½ × 11.
761 **360** 8 c. multicoloured 25 12

(Des Wallis and Matanovic. Litho Ashton-Potter)

1973 (20 Sept). *Olympic Games, Montreal* (1976) (*1st issue*). *P* 12 × 12½.
762 **361** 8 c. multicoloured 15 10
763 15 c. multicoloured 40 60
See also Nos. 768/71, 772/4, 786/9, 798/802, 809/11, 814/16, 829/31, 833/7 and 842/4.

362 Ice-skate

363 Diving

(Des A. Maggs. Litho Ashton-Potter)

1973 (7 Nov). *Christmas. T* **362** *and similar vert designs. Multicoloured. P* 12½ × 12 (6, 8 *c.*) *or* 11 (*others*).
764 6 c. Type **362** 12 5
765 8 c. Bird decoration 15 5
766 10 c. Santa Claus (20 × 36 *mm*) 60 75
767 15 c. Shepherd (20 × 36 *mm*) 70 80

(Des Hunter, Straker, Templeton Ltd. Recess C.B.N.)

1974 (22 Mar). *Olympic Games, Montreal* (1976) (*2nd issue*). *"Summer Activities". T* **363** *and similar vert designs. Each deep blue. P* 12.
768 8 c. Type **363** 20 10
a. Block of 4. Nos. 768/71 75
769 8 c. "Jogging" 20 10
770 8 c. Cycling 20 10
771 8 c. Hiking 20 10
Nos. 768/71 were printed in *se-tenant* blocks of four throughout the sheet. Each design has a second (latent) image—the Canadian Olympic Games symbol—which appears when the stamp is viewed obliquely to the light.
See also Nos. 786/9.

(Des Wallis and Matanovic. Litho Ashton-Potter)

1974 (17 Apr). *Olympic Games, Montreal* (1976) (*3rd issue*). *As T* **361** *but smaller* (20 × 36½ *mm*). *P* 12½.
772 **361** 8 c. + 2 c. multicoloured 25 25
773 10 c. + 5 c. multicoloured 40 60
774 15 c. + 5 c. multicoloured 50 80

364 Winnipeg Signpost, 1872

365 Postmaster and Customer

(Des J. R. MacDonald. Litho and embossed Ashton-Potter)

1974 (3 May). *Winnipeg Centennial. P* 12½ × 12.
775 **364** 8 c. multicoloured 20 12

(Des S. Mennie. Litho Ashton-Potter)

1974 (11 June). *Centenary of Canadian Letter Carrier Delivery Service. T* **365** *and similar horiz designs. Multicoloured. P* 13½.
776 8 c. Type **365** 25 20
a. Block of 6. Nos. 776/81 .. .. .. 2·25
777 8 c. Postman collecting mail 25 20
778 8 c. Mail handler 25 20
779 8 c. Mail sorters 25 20
780 8 c. Postman making delivery 25 20
781 8 c. Rural delivery by car 25 20
776/81 .. .. *Set of* 6 2·25 1·10
Nos. 776/81 were printed in *se-tenant* combinations throughout a sheet of 50, giving 6 blocks of 6 and 14 single stamps.

366 "Canada's Contribution to Agriculture"

367 Telephone Development

(Des M. Brett, P. Cowley-Brown, and A. McAllister. Litho Ashton-Potter)

1974 (12 July). *"Agricultural Education". Centenary of Ontario Agricultural College. P* 12½ × 12.
782 **366** 8 c. multicoloured 20 12

(Des R. Webber. Litho Ashton-Potter)

1974 (26 July). *Centenary of Invention of Telephone by Alexander Graham Bell. P* 12½.
783 **367** 8 c. multicoloured 20 12

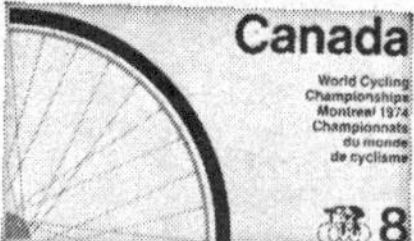

368 Bicycle Wheel

(Des Burns and Cooper. Recess and photo B.A.B.N.)

1974 (7 Aug). *World Cycling Championships, Montreal. P* 12 × 12½.
784 **368** 8 c. black, rosine and silver 20 12

369 Mennonite Settlers

(Des W. Davies. Litho Ashton-Potter)

1974 (28 Aug). *Centenary of Arrival of Mennonites in Manitoba. P* 12½.
785 **369** 8 c. multicoloured 20 10

(Des Hunter, Straker, Templeton Ltd. Recess C.B.N.)

1974 (23 Sept). *Olympic Games, Montreal* (1976) (*4th issue*). *"Winter Activities". Horiz designs as T* **363**, *each rosine. P* 13½ × 13.
786 8 c. Snow-shoeing 25 10
a. Block of 4. Nos. 786/9 90
787 8 c. Skiing 25 10
788 8 c. Skating 25 10
789 8 c. Curling 25 10

370 Mercury, Winged Horses and U.P.U. Emblem

(Des G. Gundersen. Recess and photo B.A.B.N.)

1974 (9 Oct). *Centenary of Universal Postal Union. P* 12 × 12½.
790 **370** 8 c. violet, red-orange and cobalt .. 15 10
791 15 c. red-orange, violet and cobalt .. 65 1·25

371 "The Nativity" (J. P. Lemieux)

372 Marconi and St. John's Harbour, Newfoundland

(Des Wallis and Matanovic. Litho Ashton-Potter)

1974 (1 Nov). *Christmas. T* **371** *and similar horiz designs showing paintings. Multicoloured. P* 13½.
792 6 c. Type **371** 12 5
793 8 c. "Skaters in Hull" (H. Masson) (34 × 31 *mm*) 15 5
794 10 c. "The Ice Cone, Montmorency Falls" (R. C. Todd) 45 65
795 15 c. "Village in the Laurentian Mountains" (C. A. Gagnon) 55 85

(Des J. Boyle. Litho Ashton-Potter)

1974 (15 Nov). *Birth Centenary of Guglielmo Marconi (radio pioneer). P* 13.
796 **372** 8 c. multicoloured 20 12

373 Merritt and Welland Canal

374 Swimming

(Des W. Rueter. Recess (B.A.B.N.) and litho (C.B.N.))

1974 (29 Nov). *William Merritt Commemoration. P* 13 × 13½.
797 **373** 8 c. multicoloured 20 12

(Des Wallis and Matanovic. Litho C.B.N.)

1975 (5 Feb). *Olympic Games, Montreal* (1976) (*5th issue*). *T* **374** *and similar horiz designs. Multicoloured.*
798 8 c. + 2 c. Type **374** 20 15
799 10 c. + 5 c. Rowing 30 60
800 15 c. + 5 c. Sailing 45 75

OMNIBUS ISSUES

Details, together with prices for complete sets, of the various Omnibus issues from the 1935 Silver Jubilee series to date are included in a special section following Zululand at the end of the catalogue.

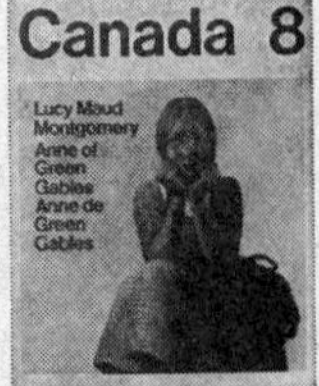

375 "The Sprinter" **376** "Anne of Green Gables" (Lucy Maud Montgomery)

(Des A. R. Fleming. Litho and embossed Ashton-Potter)

1975 (14 Mar). *Olympic Games, Montreal* (1976) (*6th issue*). *T* **375** *and similar multicoloured design showing sculpture by R. T. McKenzie. P* 12½ × 12 ($1) *or* 12 × 12½ ($2).
801 $1 Type **375** . . . . 2·75 3·50
802 $2 "The Diver" (*vert*) . . . . 3·25 5·50

(Des P. Swan (No. 803), C. Gagnon (No. 804). Litho Ashton-Potter)

1975 (15 May). *Canadian Writers* (*1st series*). *T* **376** *and similar vert design. Multicoloured. P* 13½.
803 8 c. Type **376** 20 5
a. Pair. Nos. 803/4 . . . . 40 70
804 8 c. "Maria Chapdelaine" (Louis Hémon) . . 20 5
Nos. 803/4 were printed horizontally and vertically *se-tenant* throughout the sheet.
See also Nos. 846/7, 940/1 and 1085/6.

377 Marguerite Bourgeoys (founder of the Order of Notre Dame) **378** S. D. Chown (founder of United Church of Canada)

(Des Design and Communication, Montreal. Litho Ashton-Potter (Nos. 805/6). Des W. Southern. Eng G. Gundersen. Recess and photo B.A.B.N. (Nos. 807/8))

1975 (30 May). *Canadian Celebrities. T* **377/8** *and similar vert designs.*

(*a*) *As T* **377.** *P* 12½ × 12
805 8 c. multicoloured 20 12
806 8 c. multicoloured 20 12

(*b*) *As T* **378.** *P* 12 × 12½
807 8 c. sepia, flesh and light yellow 20 5
a. Pair. Nos. 807/8 . . . . 45 70
808 8 c. sepia, flesh and light yellow 20 5
Designs:—No. 805, Type **377**; No. 806, Alphonse Desjardins (leader of Credit Union movement); No. 807, Type **378**; No. 808, Dr. J. Cook (first moderator of Presbyterian Church in Canada).
Nos. 807/8 were printed together in the sheet horizontally and vertically *se-tenant*.

379 Pole-vaulting **380** "Untamed" (photo by Walt Petrigo)

(Des P. Swan. Litho Ashton-Potter)

1975 (11 June). *Olympic Games, Montreal* (1976) (*7th issue*). *T* **379** *and similar vert designs. Multicoloured. P* 12 × 12½.
809 20 c. Type **379** 35 50
810 25 c. Marathon-running 45 75
811 50 c. Hurdling . . . . 65 1·10

(Des B. Reilander. Litho C.B.N.)

1975 (3 July). *Centenary of Calgary. P* 12 × 12½.
812 **380** 8 c. multicoloured 20 12

381 I.W.Y. Symbol **382** Fencing

(Des Susan McPhee. Recess and photo B.A.B.N.)

1975 (14 July). *International Women's Year. P* 13.
813 **381** 8 c. lt grey-brown, bistre-yellow & blk 20 12

(Des J. Hill. Litho C.B.N.)

1975 (6 Aug). *Olympic Games, Montreal* (1976) (*8th issue*). *T* **382** *and similar vert designs showing combat sports. Multicoloured. P* 13.
814 8 c. + 2 c. Type **382** 25 15
815 10 c. + 5 c. Boxing 35 70
816 15 c. + 5 c. Judo 45 85

383 "Justice-Justitia" (statue by W. S. Allward) **384** *William D. Lawrence*

(Des A. Fleming. Litho Ashton-Potter)

1975 (2 Sept). *Centenary of Canadian Supreme Court. P* 12½.
817 **383** 8 c. multicoloured 20 12

(Des T. Bjarnason. Recess and photo B.A.B.N.)

1975 (24 Sept). *Canadian Ships* (*1st series*). *T* **384** *and similar horiz designs showing coastal ships. P* 13.
818 8 c. yellow-brown and black 45 15
a. Block of 4. Nos. 818/21 . . . . . . 2·50
819 8 c. blue-green and black 45 15
820 8 c. yellow-green and black 45 15
821 8 c. yellow-brown and black 45 15
Designs:—No. 819, *Neptune*; No. 820, *Beaver*; No. 821, *Quadra*.
Nos. 818/21 were printed in *se-tenant* combinations throughout a sheet of 50 giving 10 blocks of 4 and 10 single stamps.
See also Nos. 851/4, 902/5 and 931/4.

385 "Santa Claus" (G. Kelly) **386** Text, Badge and Bugle

(Des B. Reilander from children's paintings. Litho Ashton-Potter)

1975 (22 Oct). *Christmas. T* **385** *and similar multicoloured designs. P* 13.
822 6 c. Type **385** 10 5
a. Pair. Nos. 822/3 . . . . 20 30
823 6 c. "Skater" (Bill Cawsey) 10 5
824 8 c. "Child" (D. Hébert) 12 5
a. Pair. Nos. 824/5 . . . . 25 35
825 8 c. "Family" (L. Caldwell) 12 5
826 10 c. "Gift" (D. Lovely) 25 40
827 15 c. "Trees" (R. Kowalski) (*horiz*) 40 65
822/7 . . . . *Set of* 6 1·00 1·50
Nos. 822/3 and 824/5 were respectively issued together *se-tenant* in an alternate arrangement within the sheet.

(Des R. Kavach. Recess and photo B.A.B.N.)

1975 (10 Nov). *50th Anniv of Royal Canadian Legion. P* 12½ × 13.
828 **386** 8 c. multicoloured 20 12

387 Basketball

(Des J. Hill. Litho Ashton-Potter)

1976 (7 Jan). *Olympic Games, Montreal* (*9th issue*). *T* **387** *and similar vert designs. Multicoloured. P* 13.
829 8 c. + 2 c. Type **387** 25 15
830 10 c. + 5 c. Gymnastics 40 70
831 20 c. + 5 c. Soccer 50 90

388 Games Symbol and Snow Crystal **389** "Communications Arts"

(Des R. Harder. Litho Ashton-Potter)

1976 (6 Feb). *12th Winter Olympic Games. Innsbruck. P* 12½.
832 **388** 20 c. multicoloured 40 60

(Des R. Webber. Litho C.B.N.)

1976 (6 Feb). *Olympic Games, Montreal* (*10th issue*). *T* **389** *and similar vert designs. Multicoloured. P* 12 × 12½.
833 20 c. Type **389** 30 15
834 25 c. "Handicrafts" 35 60
835 50 c. "Performing Arts" . . . . 60 1·00

390 Place Ville Marie and Notre-Dame Church

(Des J. and P. Mercier. Recess and photo B.A.B.N.)

1976 (12 Mar). *Olympic Games, Montreal* (*11th issue*). *T* **390** *and similar horiz design. Multicoloured. P* 13.
836 $1 Type **390** . . . . 3·50 5·50
837 $2 Olympic Stadium and flags . . . . . . 4·50 6·50

391 Flower and Urban Sprawl **392** Benjamin Franklin and Map

(Des I. McLeod. Litho Ashton-Potter)

1976 (12 May). *U.N. Conference on Human Settlements* (*HABITAT*), *Vancouver. P* 12 × 12½.
838 **391** 20 c. multicoloured 30 45

(Des B. Reilander. Recess and photo B.A.B.N.)

1976 (1 June). *Bicentenary of American Revolution. P* 13.
839 **392** 10 c. multicoloured 35 30

393 Wing Parade before Mackenzie Building **394** Transfer of Olympic Flame by Satellite

(Des W. Davies. Litho C.B.N.)

1976 (1 June). *Royal Military College Centenary. T* **393** *and similar vert design. Multicoloured. P* 12 × 12½.
840 8 c. Colour party and Memorial Arch . . 20 5
a. Pair. Nos. 840/1 . . . . 40 60
ab. Printed double (pair) . . . . . .
841 8 c. Type **393** 20 5
Nos. 840/1 were printed horizontally and vertically *se-tenant* throughout the sheet.

(Des P. Swan. Litho Ashton-Potter)

1976 (18 June). *Olympic Games, Montreal* (*12th issue*). *T* **394** *and similar horiz designs. Multicoloured. P* 13½.
842 8 c. Type **394** 15 10
843 20 c. Carrying the Olympic flag 30 55
844 25 c. Athletes with medals 45 80

395 Archer

(Des T. Bjarnason. Litho C.B.N.)

1976 (3 Aug). *Olympiad for the Physically Disabled. P* 12 × 12½.
845 **395** 20 c. multicoloured 30 40

396 "Sam McGee" (Robert W. Service) **397** "Nativity" (F. Mayer)

(Des D. Bierk (No. 846), A. Dumas (No. 847). Litho Ashton-Potter)

1976 (17 Aug). *Canadian Writers* (2*nd series*). *T* **396** *and similar vert design. Multicoloured. P* 13.
846 8 c. Type **396** 20 5
a. Pair. Nos. 846/7 .. .. 40 65
847 8 c. "Le Survenant" (Germaine Guèvremont) 20 5
Nos. 846/7 were printed horizontally and vertically *se-tenant* throughout the sheet.

(Des B. Reilander. Litho Ashton-Potter)

1976 (3 Nov). *Christmas. T* **397** *and similar vert designs showing stained-glass windows. Multicoloured. P* 13½.
848 8 c. Type **397** 12 5
849 10 c. "Nativity" (G. Maile & Son) 12 5
850 20 c. "Nativity" (Yvonne Williams) 35 60

398 *Northcote* **399** Queen Elizabeth II

(Des T. Bjarnason. Recess and litho C.B.N.)

1976 (19 Nov). *Canadian Ships* (2*nd series*). *T* **398** *and similar horiz designs showing inland vessels. P* 12 × 12½.
851 10 c. ochre, chestnut and black 30 12
a. Block of 4. Nos. 851/4 .. .. .. 1·10
852 10 c. violet-blue and black 30 12
853 10 c. bright blue and black 30 12
854 10 c. apple-green, olive-green and black .. 30 12
Designs:—No. 851, Type **398**; No. 852, *Passport*; No. 853, *Chicora*; No. 854, *Athabasca*.
Nos. 851/4 were printed in *se-tenant* combinations throughout a sheet of 50, giving 10 blocks of 4 and 10 single stamps.

(Des K. Rodmell from photograph by P. Grugeon. Litho ("25" die-stamped) Ashton-Potter)

1977 (4 Feb). *Silver Jubilee. P* 12½ × 12.
855 **399** 25 c. multicoloured 40 65

400 Bottle Gentian **401** Queen Elizabeth II (bas-relief by J. Huta) **402** Houses of Parliament

403 Trembling Aspen **404** Prairie Town Main Street

405 Fundy National Park

(Des R. Derreth (Nos. 870/4). T. Bjarnason (880/3*a*), R. Bolt (884), B. Laycock and W. Tibbles (884*b*), B. Laycock (884*c*), A. Collier (885), W. Terry and W. Tibbles (885*a*), Heather Cooper (others). Eng Y. Baril (880/3*a*))

1977 (1 Mar)–**83.** (*a*) *Vert designs as T* **400** *showing flowers. Multicoloured.* (i) *Recess and litho C.B.N. Sheet stamps. P* 12 × 12½.
856 1 c. Type **400** (22.4.77) 5 5
857 2 c. Red Columbine (22.4.77) 5 5
858 3 c. Canada Lily (22.4.77) 5 5
859 4 c. Hepatica (22.4.77) 10 5
860 5 c. Shooting Star (22.4.77) 10 5
861 10 c. Franklin's Lady's Slipper Orchid (22.4.77) 25 5
a. Perf 13 (8.78) 25 10

(ii) *Recess and photo B.A.B.N. Booklet stamps* (1, 2 c.) *or sheet stamps* (*others*). *P* 12 × 12½ (1, 2 c.) *or* 13 (*others*)
862 1 c. Type **400** (10.77) 20 25
a. Booklet pane. Nos. 862 × 2 and 867a × 4 1·90
b. Perf 13 (from sheets) (16.8.79) 5 5
863 2 c. Red Columbine (17.5.78) 20 25
a. Booklet pane. Nos. 863 × 4 and 868a × 3 plus one printed label .. .. .. 2·10
b. Perf 13 (from sheets) (2.8.79) 5 5
864 3 c. Canada Lily (11.4.79) 5 5
864*a* 4 c. Hepatica (3.7.79) 10 5
865 5 c. Shooting Star (23.1.79) 10 5
865*a* 10 c. Franklin's Lady's Slipper Orchid (4.10.79) 15 5
866 12 c. Jewelweed (6.7.78) 25 12
866*a* 15 c. Canada Violet (16.8.79) 25 5

(*b*) *T* **401.** *Recess and photo B.A.B.N. P* 13
867 12 c. black, grey and cobalt (1.3.77) 30 5
a. Perf 12 × 12½ (from booklets) (10.77) .. 40 50
868 14 c. black, grey and rose-red (7.3.78) .. 35 5
a. Perf 12 × 12½ (from booklets) (17.5.78) 45 50
ab. Booklet pane. No. 868a × 25, plus two printed labels (11.78) .. .. .. 8·00
869 17 c. black, grey and yellowish green (8.3.79) 25 5
a. Perf 12 × 12½ (from booklets) (28.3.79) 25 10
ab. Booklet pane. No. 869a × 25, plus two printed labels (3.7.79) .. .. .. 5·50
869*b* 30 c. maroon, grey & reddish pur (11.5.82) .. 40 35
869*c* 32 c. black, grey and light blue (24.5.83) .. 35 30

(*c*) *T* **402.** (i) *Recess C.B.N.* (*Nos.* 872*a*, 873/4) *or B.A.B.N.* (*others*). *Booklet stamps* (*Nos.* 870/1) *or sheet stamps* (*others*). *P* 12 × 12½ (1, 5 *c.*) *or* 13 (*others*)
870 1 c. indigo (28.3.79) 40 40
a. Booklet pane. Nos. 869a × 2, 870 and 871 × 3 .. .. 1·40
871 5 c. deep rose-lilac (28.3.79) 25 15
872 12 c. blue (chalk-surfaced paper) (3.5.77) .. 25 5
a. New blue (ordinary paper) (4.78) 25 10
873 14 c. scarlet (7.3.78) 35 5
874 17 c. deep green (8.3.79) 30 10

(ii) *Recess C.B.N. Coil stamps. Imperf* × *perf* 10
874*a* 12 c. new blue (3.5.77) 25 25
ab. Imperf (horiz pair) .. .. .. 80·00
874*b* 14 c. scarlet (7.3.78) 30 30
ba. Imperf (horiz pair) .. .. .. 80·00
874*c* 17 c. deep green (8.3.79) 30 15
ca. Imperf (horiz pair) £100

(*d*) *Vert designs as T* **403** *showing leaves. Multicoloured. Recess and photo B.A.B.N. P* 13
875 15 c. Type **403** (8.8.77) 25 15
876 20 c. Douglas Fir (8.8.77) 25 15
877 25 c. Sugar Maple (8.8.77) 30 15
878 30 c. Red Oak (7.3.78) 35 20
879 35 c. White Pine (8.3.79) 35 20

(*e*) *Horiz designs as T* **404** *showing city streets. Multicoloured. P* 13
(i) *Recess and photo B.A.B.N. No fluorescent bands* (75, 80 *c.*) (6.7.78)
880 50 c. Type **404** .. .. 1·50 80
881 75 c. Eastern city street 90 55
882 80 c. Maritimes street 95 60

(ii) *Recess and litho C.B.N.*
883 50 c. Type **404** (13.12.78) 50 35
883*a* 60 c. Ontario city street (11.5.82) 60 45

(*f*) *Horiz designs as T* **405** *showing national parks. Multicoloured. Recess and litho C.B.N.* ($1 *with or without fluorescent bands, others only exist without*). *P* 13½.
884 $1 Type **405** (24.1.79) .. .. .. 1·25 80
884*b* $1 Glacier (15.8.84) .. .. 1·10 1·25
884*c* $1.50, Waterton Lakes (18.6.82) .. .. 1·75 1·50
885 $2 Kluane (27.4.79) .. .. 2·25 1·50
885*a* $5 Point Pelee (10.1.83) .. .. .. 5·75 3·50

The main differences between No. 861a and the earlier No. 865 are in the background. On No. 861a this is toned and has the blurred edges typical of photogravure. No. 865 has a background of solid appearance with the edges clean. The B.A.B.N. version also has stronger lines on the recess part of the design.

No. 883 can be identified from 880 in that the brown printing from the recess plate of the former is deeper and the detail more defined; the registration plate of the car in the foreground can clearly be seen under a glass as "1978". The "hidden date" (1977) occurs alongside the grain elevator door on No. 880. Also the colours from the lithographic plates of No. 883 are much bolder than those from the photogravure cylinders of 880. In addition the paper of No. 883 has a shiny appearance.

Stamps with one or two adjacent sides imperforate come from booklets.

406 Eastern Cougar **407** "April in Algonquin Park"

(Des R. Bateman. Litho Ashton-Potter)

1977 (30 Mar). *Endangered Wildlife* (1*st series*). *P* 12½.
886 **406** 12 c. multicoloured 20 20
See also Nos. 906, 936/7, 976/7 and 1006/7.

(Litho Ashton-Potter)

1977 (26 May). *Birth Centenary of Tom Thomson* (*painter*). *T* **407** *and similar square design. Multicoloured. P* 12.
887 12 c. Type **407** 20 5
a. Pair. Nos. 887/8 .. .. 45 70
888 12 c. "Autumn Birches" 20 5
Nos. 887/8 were printed horizontally and vertically *se-tenant* throughout the sheet.

408 Crown and Lion **409** Peace Bridge, Niagara River

(Des A. Hobbs. Litho (No. 890 also embossed) Ashton-Potter)

1977 (30 June). *Anniversaries. T* **408** *and similar horiz design. Multicoloured. P* 12½.
889 12 c. Type **408** 15 15
890 12 c. Order of Canada 15 15
Events:—No. 889, 25th Anniv of first Canadian-born Governor-General; No. 890, Tenth Anniv of Order of Canada.

(Des R. Harder. Litho Ashton-Potter)

1977 (4 Aug). 50*th Anniv of Opening of Peace Bridge. P* 12½.
891 **409** 12 c. multicoloured 20 20

410 Sir Sandford Fleming (engineer)

(Des W. Davies. Recess B.A.B.N.)

1977 (16 Sept). *Famous Canadians. T* **410** *and similar horiz design. P* 13.
892 12 c. grey-blue 20 5
a. Pair. Nos. 892/3 .. .. 45 55
893 12 c. reddish brown 20 5
Design:—No. 892, Joseph E. Bernier (explorer) and C. G. S. *Arctic*.
The above were printed together, horizontally and vertically *se-tenant* throughout the sheet.

411 Peace Tower, Parliament Buildings, Ottawa **412** Hunter Braves following Star

(Des S. Ash. Litho Ashton-Potter)

1977 (19 Sept). 23*rd Commonwealth Parliamentary Conference. P* 12½.
894 **411** 25 c. multicoloured 40 45

(Des R. G. White. Litho C.B.N.)

1977 (26 Oct). *Christmas. T* **412** *and similar horiz designs depicting Canada's first Christmas carol "Jesous Ahatonhia". Multicoloured. P* 13½ × 13.
895 10 c. Type **412** 12 5
896 12 c. Angelic choir and the Northern Lights .. 12 5
a. Imperf (vert pair) £500
897 25 c. Christ Child and chiefs 45 70

413 Seal Hunter (soapstone sculpture) **414** Pinky (fishing boat)

(Des R. Derreth. Litho Ashton-Potter)

1977 (18 Nov). *Canadian Eskimos* ("*Inuits*") (1*st series*). *Hunting. T* **413** *and similar horiz designs. Multicoloured. P* 12 × 12½.
898 12 c. Type **413** 15 5
a. Pair. Nos. 898/9 .. .. 35 50
899 12 c. Fishing with spear 15 5
900 12 c. Disguised archer 15 5
a. Pair. Nos. 900/1 .. .. 35 50
901 12 c. Walrus hunting 15 5
Nos. 898/9 and 900/1 were each printed together, *se-tenant*, in horizontal and vertical pairs throughout the sheet.
See also Nos. 924/7, 958/61 and 989/92.

(Des T. Bjarnason. Recess and litho C.B.N.)

1977 (18 Nov). *Canadian Ships* (3*rd series*). *T* **414** *and similar horiz designs, showing sailing craft. Multicoloured. P* 12 × 12½.
902 12 c. Type **414** 20 10
a. Block of 4. Nos. 902/5 75
903 12 c. Five-masted schooner 20 10
904 12 c. Tern schooner 20 10
905 12 c. Mackinaw boat 20 10
Nos. 902/5 were printed in *se-tenant* combinations throughout a sheet of 50, giving 10 blocks of 4 and 10 single stamps.

415 Peregrine Falcon

416 Pair of 1851 12d. Black Stamps

(Des R. Bateman. Litho Ashton-Potter)

1978 (18 Jan). *Endangered Wildlife (2nd series). P* 12½.
906 **415** 12 c. multicoloured 20 20

(Des C. Brett. Recess and photo B.A.B.N.)

1978 (18 Jan). *"CAPEX 78" International Stamp Exhibition, Toronto (1st issue). P* 13.
907 **416** 12 c. black and brownish grey 15 15
See also Nos. 914/17.

417 Games Emblem

418 "Captain Cook" (Nathaniel Dance)

(Des S. Ash. Litho Ashton-Potter)

1978 (31 Mar). *Commonwealth Games. Edmonton (1st issue). T* **417** *and similar horiz design. Multicoloured. P* 12½.
908 14 c. Type **417** 15 10
909 30 c. Badminton 40 60
See also Nos. 918/21.

(Des W. Rueter. Litho Ashton-Potter)

1978 (26 Apr). *Bicentenary of Cook's Third Voyage. T* **418** *and similar vert design. Multicoloured. P* 13½.
910 14 c. Type **418** 20 5
a. Pair. Nos. 910/11 .. .. 50 65
911 14 c. "Nootka Sound" (J. Webber) 20 5
Nos. 910/11 were printed together, *se-tenant*, in horizontal and vertical pairs throughout the sheet.

419 Hardrock Silver Mine, Cobalt, Ontario

420 Prince's Gate (Exhibition entrance)

(Des W. Davies. Litho Ashton-Potter)

1978 (19 May). *Resource Development. T* **419** *and similar horiz design. Multicoloured. P* 12½.
912 14 c. Type **419** 20 5
a. Pair. Nos. 912/13 .. .. 60 75
913 14 c. Giant excavators, Athabasca Tar Sands 20 5
Nos. 912/13 were printed together, *se-tenant*, in horizontal and vertical pairs throughout the sheet.

(Des C. Brett. Eng R. Couture. Recess and photo B.A.B.N.)

1978 (10 June). *"CAPEX 78" International Stamp Exhibition, Toronto (2nd issue). Horiz designs as T* **416**. *Two fluorescent bands (none on $1.25 from miniature sheet). P* 13.
914 14 c. Prussian blue, pale grey and brownish grey 20 10
915 30 c. deep rose, pale grey and brownish grey 35 45
916 $1.25, slate-violet, pale grey & brnish grey 90 1·40
MS917 101 × 76 mm. Nos. 914/16 .. .. .. 1·50 2·25
Designs:—14 c. Pair of 1855 10d. Cartier stamps; 30 c. Pair of 1857 ½d. deep rose stamps; $1.25, Pair of 1851 6d. Prince Albert stamps.

(Des S. Ash. Litho Ashton-Potter)

1978 (3 Aug). *Commonwealth Games, Edmonton (2nd issue). Horiz designs as T* **417**. *Multicoloured. P* 12½.
918 14 c. Games stadium 15 5
a. Pair. Nos. 918/19 .. .. 35 45
919 14 c. Running 15 5
920 30 c. Alberta Legislature building 35 20
a. Pair. Nos. 920/1 .. .. 75 1·10
921 30 c. Bowls 35 20
Nos. 918/19 and 920/1 were each printed together, *se-tenant*, in horizontal and vertical pairs throughout the sheet.

(Des T. Dimson, Litho Ashton-Potter)

1978 (16 Aug). *Centenary of National Exhibition. P* 12½.
922 **420** 14 c. multicoloured 15 15

MINIMUM PRICE

The minimum price quoted is 5p which represents a handling charge rather than a basis for valuing common stamps. For further notes about prices see introductory pages.

421 Marguerite d'Youville

422 "Madonna of the Flowering Pea" (Cologne School)

(Des A. Dumas. Litho C.B.N.)

1978 (21 Sept). *Marguerite d'Youville (founder of Grey Nuns) Commemoration. P* 13.
923 **421** 14 c. multicoloured 15 15

(Des R. Derreth. Litho Ashton-Potter)

1978 (27 Sept). *Canadian Eskimos ("Inuits") (2nd series). Travel. Horiz designs as T* **413**. *Multicoloured. P* 13½.
924 14 c. Woman on foot (painting by Pitseolak) .. 15 5
a. Pair. Nos. 924/5 .. .. 50 65
925 14 c. "Migration" (soapstone sculpture of sailing umiak by Joe Talurinili) 15 5
926 14 c. Aeroplane (stonecut and stencil print by Pudlo) 15 5
a. Pair. Nos. 926/7 .. .. 50 65
927 14 c. Dogteam and dogsled (ivory sculpture by Abraham Kingmeatook) 15 5
Nos. 924/5 and 926/7 were each printed together, *se-tenant*, in horizontal and vertical pairs throughout the sheet.

(Des J. Morin. Litho Ashton-Potter)

1978 (20 Oct). *Christmas. Paintings. T* **422** *and similar vert designs. Multicoloured. P* 12½.
928 12 c. Type **422** 15 5
929 14 c. "The Virgin and Child with St. Anthony and Donor" (detail, Hans Memling) .. 15 5
930 30 c. "The Virgin and Child" (Jacopo di Cione) 40 55

423 *Chief Justice Robinson*

424 Carnival Revellers

(Des T. Bjarnason. Recess and litho C.B.N.)

1978 (15 Nov). *Canadian Ships (4th series). T* **423** *and similar horiz designs showing ice vessels. Multicoloured. P* 13.
931 14 c. Type **423** 20 12
a. Block of 4. Nos. 931/4 85
932 14 c. *St. Roch* 20 12
933 14 c. *Northern Light* 20 12
934 14 c. *Labrador* 20 12
Nos. 931/4 were printed in *se-tenant* combinations throughout a sheet of 50, giving 10 blocks of 4 and 10 single stamps.

(Des A. Dumas. Litho Ashton-Potter)

1979 (1 Feb). *Quebec Carnival. P* 13.
935 **424** 14 c. multicoloured 20 15

425 Eastern Spiny Soft-shelled Turtle (*Trionyx spinifera*)

426 Knotted Ribbon round Woman's Finger

(Des G. Lowe (17 c.), R. Bateman (35 c.). Litho Ashton-Potter)

1979 (10 Apr). *Endangered Wildlife (3rd series). T* **425** *and similar horiz design. Multicoloured. P* 12½.
936 17 c. Type **425** 20 12
937 35 c. Bowhead Whale (*Balaena mysticetus*) .. 40 60

(Des D. Haws. Litho Ashton-Potter)

1979 (27 Apr). *Postal Code Publicity. T* **426** *and similar vert design. Multicoloured. P* 13.
938 17 c. Type **426** 20 5
a. Pair. Nos. 938/9 .. .. 40 50
939 17 c. Knotted string round man's finger .. 20 5
Nos. 938/9 were printed together, *se-tenant*, in horizontal and vertical pairs throughout the sheet.

427 Scene from "Fruits of the Earth" by Frederick Philip Grove

428 Charles-Michel de Salaberry (military hero)

(Des Rosemary Kilbourne (No. 940), Monique Charbonneau (941). Litho C.B.N.)

1979 (3 May). *Canadian Writers (3rd series). T* **427** *and similar horiz design. Multicoloured. P* 13.
940 17 c. Type **427** 20 5
a. Pair. Nos. 940/1 .. .. 40 50
941 17 c. Scene from "Le Vaisseau d'Or" by Émile Nelligan 20 5
Nos. 940/1 were printed together, *se-tenant*, in horizontal and vertical pairs throughout the sheet.

(Des T. Dimson. Litho and embossed Ashton-Potter)

1979 (11 May). *Famous Canadians. T* **428** *and similar vert design. Multicoloured. P* 13.
942 17 c. Type **428** 20 5
a. Pair. Nos. 942/3 .. .. 40 50
943 17 c. John By (engineer) 20 5
Nos. 942/3 were printed together, *se-tenant*, in horizontal and vertical pairs throughout the sheet.

429 Ontario

430 Paddling Kayak

(Des R. Bellemare. Litho Ashton-Potter)

1979 (15 June). *Canada Day. Flags. Sheet* 128 × 140 *mm containing T* **429** *and similar horiz designs. Multicoloured. P* 13.
MS944 17 c. × 12; Type **429**; Quebec; Nova Scotia; New Brunswick; Manitoba; British Columbia; Prince Edward Island; Saskatchewan; Alberta; Newfoundland; Northwest Territories; Yukon Territory .. .. 3·50

(Des J. Eby. Litho Ashton-Potter)

1979 (3 July). *Canoe-Kayak Championships. P* 12½.
956 **430** 17 c. multicoloured 25 20

431 Hockey Players

432 Toy Train

(Des J. Eby. Litho Ashton-Potter)

1979 (16 Aug). *Women's Field Hockey Championships, Vancouver. P* 12½.
957 **431** 17 c. black, yellow and emerald 25 20

(Des R. Derreth. Litho Ashton-Potter)

1979 (13 Sept). *Canadian Eskimos ("Inuits") (3rd series). "Shelter" (Nos. 958/9) and "Community" (Nos. 960/1). Horiz designs as T* **413**. *Multicoloured. P* 13.
958 17 c. "Summer Tent" (print by Kiakshuk) .. 15 5
a. Pair. Nos. 958/9 .. .. 45 60
959 17 c. "Five Eskimos building an Igloo" (soapstone sculpture by Abraham) 15 5
960 17 c. "The Dance" (print by Kalvak) 15 5
a. Pair. Nos. 960/1 .. .. 45 60
961 17 c. "Inuit drum dance" (soapstone sculptures by Madeleine Isserkut and Jean Mapsalak) 15 5
Nos. 958/9 and 960/1 were each printed together, *se-tenant*, in horizontal and vertical pairs throughout the sheet.

(Des A. Maggs. Litho C.B.N.)

1979 (17 Oct). *Christmas. T* **432** *and similar multicoloured designs showing toys. Fluorescent frame (35 c.) or two fluorescent bands (others). P* 13.
962 15 c. Type **432** 15 5
963 17 c. Hobby-horse 15 5
964 35 c. Rag-doll (*vert*) 45 70

433 "Child watering Tree of Life" (painting by Marie-Annick Viatour)

434 Canadair "CL-215"

(Des J. Morin. Litho Ashton-Potter)

1979 (24 Oct). *International Year of the Child. P* 13.
965 **433** 17 c. multicoloured 20 20

(Des R. Bradford and J. Charette. Litho Ashton-Potter)

1979 (15 Nov). *Canadian Aircraft* (1*st series*). *Flying Boats. T* **434** *and similar horiz designs. Multicoloured. P* 12½.
966 17 c. Type **434** 15 5
a. Pair. Nos. 966/7 .. .. 35 45
967 17 c. Curtiss "HS-2L" 15 5
968 35 c. Vickers "Vedette" 30 10
a. Pair. Nos. 968/9 .. .. 65 75
969 35 c. Consolidated "Canso" 30 10
Nos. 966/7 and 968/9 were each printed together, *se-tenant*, in horizontal and vertical pairs throughout the sheet.
See also Nos. 996/9, 1026/9 and 1050/3.

435 Map of Arctic Islands

436 Skiing

(Des Gottschalk and Ash Ltd. Litho Ashton-Potter)

1980 (23 Jan). *Centenary of Arctic Islands Acquisition. P* 13.
970 **435** 17 c. multicoloured 20 20

(Des C. Malenfant. Litho C.B.N.)

1980 (23 Jan). *Winter Olympic Games, Lake Placid, U.S.A. P* 13.
971 **436** 35 c. multicoloured 40 50

437 "A Meeting of the School Trustees" (painting by Robert Harris)

438 Atlantic Whitefish (*Coregonus canadensis*)

(Des J. Morin. Litho Ashton-Potter)

1980 (6 Mar). *Centenary of Royal Canadian Academy of Arts. T* **437** *and similar horiz designs. Multicoloured. P* 13.
972 17 c. Type **437** 15 5
a. Pair. Nos. 972/3 .. .. 30 30
973 17 c. "Inspiration" (sculpture by Philippe Hébert) 15 5
974 35 c. "Sunrise on the Saguenay" (painting by Lucius O'Brien) 35 10
a. Pair. Nos. 974/5 .. .. 70 90
975 35 c. Sketch of design for original Parliament Buildings by Thomas Fuller 35 10
Nos. 972/3 and 974/5 were each printed together, *se-tenant*, in horizontal and vertical pairs throughout the sheet.

(Des M. Dumas (No. 976), R. Bateman (No. 977). Litho Ashton-Potter)

1980 (6 May). *Endangered Wildlife* (4*th series*). *T* **438** *and similar horiz design. Multicoloured. P* 12½.
976 17 c. Type **438** 20 20
977 17 c. Prairie Chicken (*Tympanuchus cupido pinnatus*) 20 20

439 Garden Flowers

440 "Helping Hand"

(Des Heather Cooper. Litho Ashton-Potter)

1980 (29 May). *International Flower Show, Montreal. P* 13.
978 **439** 17 c. multicoloured 20 20

(Des R. Harder. Litho and embossed Ashton-Potter)

1980 (29 May). *Rehabilitation. P* 12½.
979 **440** 17 c. gold and ultramarine 20 20

441 Opening Bars of "O Canada"

442 John G. Diefenbaker

(Des F. Peter. Litho Ashton-Potter)

1980 (6 June). *Centenary of "O Canada" (national song). T* **441** *and similar horiz design. Multicoloured. P* 12½.
980 17 c. Type **441** 20 5
a. Pair. Nos. 980/1 .. .. 40 45
981 17 c. Galixa Lavallee (composer), Adolphe-Basile Routhier (original writer) and Robert Stanley Wier (writer of English version) 20 5
Nos. 980/1 were printed together, *se-tenant*, in horizontal and vertical pairs throughout.

(Des B. Reilander. Eng Y. Baril. Recess C.B.N.)

1980 (20 June). *John G. Diefenbaker (former Prime Minister) Commemoration. P* 13½ × 13.
982 **442** 17 c. deep ultramarine 20 20

443 Emma Albani (singer)

444 Alberta

(Des C. Webster (No. 985), H. Brown (others). Litho Ashton-Potter)

1980 (4 July). *Famous Canadians. T* **443** *and similar multi-coloured designs. P* 13.
983 17 c. Type **443** 20 5
a. Pair. Nos. 983/4 .. .. 40 40
984 17 c. Healey Willan (composer) 20 5
985 17 c. Ned Hanlan (oarsman) (*horiz*) 20 20
Nos. 983/4 were printed together, *se-tenant*, in horizontal and vertical pairs throughout the sheet.

(Des G. Hunter and C. Yaneff. Litho Ashton-Potter)

1980 (27 Aug). *75th Anniv of Alberta and Saskatchewan Provinces. T* **444** *and similar horiz design. Multicoloured. P* 13.
986 17 c. Type **444** 20 20
987 17 c. Saskatchewan 20 20

445 Uraninite Molecular Structure

446 "Christmas Morning" (J. S. Hallam)

(Des J. Charette. Litho C.B.N.)

1980 (3 Sept). *Uranium Resources. P* 13.
988 **445** 35 c. multicoloured 40 40

(Des R. Derreth. Litho C.B.N.)

1980 (25 Sept). *Canadian Eskimos ("Inuits") (4th series). Spirits. Horiz designs as T* **413**. *Multicoloured. P* 13½.
989 17 c. "Return of the Sun" (print by Kenojouak) 15 5
a. Pair. Nos. 989/90 .. .. 30 40
990 17 c. "Sedna" (sculpture by Ashoona Kiawak) 15 5
991 35 c. "Shaman" (print by Simon Tookoome) .. 30 10
a. Pair. Nos. 991/2 .. .. 60 70
992 35 c. "Bird Spirit" (sculpture by Doris Hagiolok) 30 10
Nos. 989/90 and 991/2 were each printed together, *se-tenant*, in horizontal and vertical pairs throughout the sheet.

(Des Yvon Laroche. Litho Ashton-Potter)

1980 (22 Oct). *Christmas. Paintings. T* **446** *and similar vert designs. Multicoloured. P* 12½ × 12.
993 15 c. Type **446** 15 5
994 17 c. "Sleigh Ride" (Frank Hennessy) 20 5
995 35 c. "McGill Cab Stand" (Kathleen Morris) .. 40 55

447 Avro Canada "CF-100"

(Des R. Bradford and J. Charette. Litho C.B.N.)

1980 (10 Nov). *Canadian Aircraft* (2*nd series*). *T* **447** *and similar horiz designs. Multicoloured. P* 13.
996 17 c. Type **447** 20 5
a. Pair. Nos. 996/7 .. .. 40 50
997 17 c. Avro "Lancaster" 20 5
998 35 c. Curtiss "JN-4 (Canuck)" 40 10
a. Pair. Nos. 998/9 .. .. 80 90
999 35 c. Hawker "Hurricane" 40 10
Nos. 996/7 and 998/9 were each printed together, *se-tenant*, in horizontal and vertical pairs throughout the sheet.

NEW INFORMATION

The editor is always interested to correspond with people who have new information that will improve or correct the Catalogue.

448 Emmanuel-Persillier Lachapelle

449 Mandora Instrument (18th-century)

(Des J. Morin. Litho Ashton-Potter)

1980 (5 Dec). *Dr. Emmanuel-Persillier Lachapelle (founder of Notre-Dame Hospital, Montreal) Commemoration. P* 13½.
1000 **448** 17 c. cobalt, chocolate and brown .. 20 20

1981 (19 Jan). *"The Look of Music" Exhibition, Vancouver. P* 12½.
1001 **449** 17 c. multicoloured 20 20

450 Henrietta Edwards

451 Vancouver Island Marmot (*Marmota vancouverensis*)

(Des Muriel Wood and D. Goddard. Litho C.B.N.)

1981 (4 Mar). *Feminists. T* **450** *and similar horiz designs. Multi-coloured. P* 13.
1002 17 c. Type **450** 20 20
a. Block of 4. Nos. 1002/5 70
1003 17 c. Louise McKinney 20 20
1004 17 c. Idola Saint-Jean 20 20
1005 17 c. Emily Stowe 20 20
Nos. 1002/5 were printed together, *se-tenant*, in different combinations throughout the sheet, giving ten blocks of 4 and ten single stamps.

(Des M. Dumas (17 c.), R. Bateman (35 c.). Litho C.B.N.)

1981 (6 Apr). *Endangered Wildlife* (5*th series*). *T* **451** *and similar horiz design. Multicoloured. P* 13.
1006 17 c. Type **451** 20 20
1007 35 c. Wood Bison (*Bison bison athabascae*) .. 40 40

452 Kateri Tekakwitha

453 "Self Portrait" (Frederick H. Varley)

(Des L. Marquart. Litho Ashton-Potter)

1981 (24 Apr). *17th-century Canadian Catholic Women. Statues by Emile Brunet. T* **452** *and similar vert design. P* 12½.
1008 17 c. red-brown and pale grey-olive 20 5
a. Pair. Nos. 1008/9 .. .. 40 50
1009 17 c. steel blue and new blue 20 5
Designs:—No. 1008, Type **452**; No. 1009, Marie de l'Incarnation.
Nos. 1008/9 were printed together, *se-tenant*, in horizontal and vertical pairs throughout the sheet.

(Des P. Fontaine. Litho Ashton-Potter (17 c. (*both*)), B.A.B.N. (35 c.))

1981 (22 May). *Canadian Paintings. T* **453** *and similar multi-coloured designs. P* 12½ (17 c. (*both*)) *or* 13 × 13½ (35 c.).
1010 17 c. Type **453** 20 20
1011 17 c. "At Baie Saint-Paul" (Marc-Aurele Fortin) (*horiz*) 20 20
1012 35 c. "Untitled No. 6" (Paul-Emile Borduas) .. 40 40

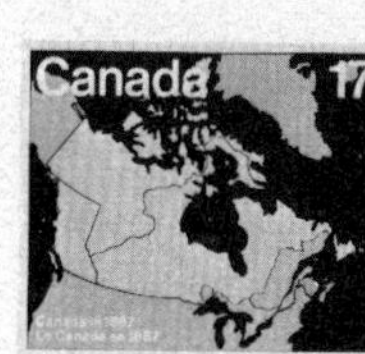

454 Canada in 1867

455 Frère Marie-Victorin

(Des R. Bellemare. Litho B.A.B.N.)

1981 (30 June). *Canada Day. Maps showing evolution of Canada from Confederation to present day. T* **454** *and similar horiz designs. Multicoloured. P* 13½.
1013 17 c. Type **454** 20 15
a. Horiz strip of 4. Nos. 1013/16 70
1014 17 c. Canada in 1873 .. .. 20 15

1015 17 c. Canada in 1905 .. 20 15
1016 17 c. Canada since 1949 .. 20 15
Nos. 1013/16 were printed together, *se-tenant*, in horizontal strips of 4 throughout the sheet.

(Des R. Hill. Litho and embossed Ashton-Potter)

1981 (22 July). *Canadian Botanists. T* **455** *and similar vert design. Multicoloured. P* 12½ × 12.
1017 17 c. Type **455** .. 20 5
a. Pair. Nos. 1017/18 .. 40 40
1018 17 c. John Macoun .. 20 5
Nos. 1017/18 were printed together, *se-tenant*, in horizontal and vertical pairs throughout the sheet.

456 The Montreal Rose

457 Drawing of Niagara-on-the-Lake

(Des J.-P. Beaudin, J. Morin and T. Yakobina. Litho C.B.N.)

1981 (22 July). *Montreal Flower Show. P* 13½.
1019 **456** 17 c. multicoloured .. 20 15

(Des J. Mardon. Recess and litho B.A.B.N.)

1981 (31 July). *Bicentenary of Niagara-on-the-Lake (town). P* 13 × 13½.
1020 **457** 17 c. multicoloured .. 20 15

458 Acadian Community

459 Aaron R. Mosher

(Des N. DeGrâce. Litho Ashton-Potter)

1981 (14 Aug). *Centenary of first Acadia (community) Convention. P* 13½.
1021 **458** 17 c. multicoloured .. 20 15

(Des R. Hill. Litho Ashton-Potter)

1981 (8 Sept). *Birth Centenary of Aaron R. Mosher (founder of Canadian Labour Congress). P* 13½.
1022 **459** 17 c. multicoloured .. 20 15

460 Christmas Tree, 1781

461 De Havilland "Tiger Moth"

(Des Anita Kunz and W. Tibbles. Litho Ashton-Potter)

1981 (16 Nov). *Christmas. Bicentenary of First Illuminated Christmas Tree in Canada. T* **460** *and similar vert designs. Multicoloured. P* 13½.
1023 15 c. Type **460** .. 15 5
1024 15 c. Christmas Tree, 1881 .. 15 5
1025 15 c. Christmas Tree, 1981 .. 15 5

(Des R. Bradford and J. Charette. Litho Ashton-Potter)

1981 (24 Nov). *Canadian Aircraft (3rd series). T* **461** *and similar horiz designs. Multicoloured. P* 12½.
1026 17 c. Type **461** .. 20 5
a. Pair. Nos. 1026/7 .. 40 40
1027 17 c. Canadair "CL-41 (Tutor)" .. 20 5
1028 35 c. Avro "Canada" jetliner .. 35 25
a. Pair. Nos. 1028/9 .. 70 70
1029 35 c. De Havilland Canada "Dash 7" .. 35 25
The two designs of each value were printed together, *se-tenant*, in horizontal and vertical pairs throughout the sheet.

462 Canadian Maple Leaf Emblem

463 1851 3d. Stamp

(Des R. Bellemare. Recess B.A.B.N. (No. 1030*a*), C.B.N. (others))

1981 (29 Dec). *Ordinary paper. (a) Sheet stamp. P* 13 × 13½.
1030 **462** A (30 c.), bright scarlet .. 25 25
a. Carmine-red, chalk-surfaced paper 25 25
(b) Coil stamp. Imperf × perf 10
1031 **462** A (30 c.), bright scarlet .. 25 25
a. Imperf (pair) ..
Nos. 1030/1 were printed before a new first class domestic letter rate had been agreed, "A" representing the face value of the stamp later decided at 30 c. Because of U.P.U. regulations these stamps were only intended for use within Canada.

(Recess, or recess and photo (Nos. 1032/*b*), B.A.B.N. (Nos. 1032/5*b*) or C.B.N. (Nos. 1036/*a*))

1982 (1 Mar)–**83**. *Designs as Nos.* 1030/1 *but including face values.*
(a) Sheet stamps (Nos. 1032, 1032*b) or from booklets (Nos.* 1032a, 1032ba). *P* 13 × 13½
1032 **462** 30 c. verm, slate-blue & azure (11.5.82) 30 25
a. Perf 12 × 12½ (from booklets) (30.6.82) .. 30 40
ab. Booklet pane. No. 1032a × 20 plus one printed label .. 5·00
1032*b* 32 c. verm, orge-brn & stone (10.2.83) 35 40
ba. Perf 12 × 12½ (from booklets) (8.4.83) .. 35 40
bb. Booklet pane. No. 1032ba × 25 plus two printed labels .. 9·50
(b) Booklet stamps. Ordinary paper. P 12 × 12½*
1033 **462** 5 c. maroon .. 5 5
a. Booklet pane. Nos. 1033 × 2, 1034 and 1035 plus two printed labels in bottom row .. 45
ab. Ditto. Printed labels in top row (10.82) .. 65
b. Chalk-surfaced paper .. 10 10
ba. Booklet pane. Nos. 1033*b* × 2, 1034a and 1035a plus two printed labels in bottom row .. 70
bb. Ditto. Printed labels in top row (10.82) .. 70
c. Booklet pane. Nos. 1033 × 2, 1033*d* and 1035*b* plus two printed labels (15.2.83) .. 60
1033*d* 8 c. indigo (15.2.83) .. 10 10
1034 10 c. bottle green .. 15 15
a. Chalk-surfaced paper .. 15 15
1035 30 c. carmine-red .. 30 30
a. Chalk-surfaced paper .. 30 30
1035*b* 32 c. Indian red (15.2.83) .. 35 40
(c) Coil stamps. Imperf × perf 10
1036 **462** 30 c. bright scarlet (20.5.82)† .. 35 25
1036*a* 32 c. Indian red (10.2.83) .. 35 40
*The 30 c. and 32 c. values are perforated on two sides, the other values on three.
†The 30 c. coil stamp was originally intended for release on 11 May, but, due to production difficulties, it was not placed on sale until 20 May; F.D.C.s, however, carry the 11 May postmark.

(Des Gottschalk and Ash Ltd. Litho C.B.N.)

1982 (11 Mar–20 May). *"Canada 82" International Philatelic Youth Exhibition, Toronto. Stamps on Stamps. T* **463** *and similar horiz designs. Multicoloured. P* 13½.
1037 30 c. Type **463** .. 25 25
1038 30 c. 1908 Centenary of Quebec 15 c. commemorative (20.5.82) .. 25 25
1039 35 c. 1935 10 c. .. 30 30
1040 35 c. 1928 10 c. (20.5.82) .. 30 30
1041 60 c. 1929 50 c. (20.5.82) .. 50 45
MS1042 159 × 108 mm. Nos. 1037/41 (20.5.82) .. 1·75 2·00

464 Jules Léger

465 Stylised Drawing of Terry Fox

(Des P. Fontaine from photograph by M. Bedford. Litho Ashton-Potter)

1982 (2 Apr). *Jules Léger (politician) Commemoration. P* 13½.
1043 **464** 30 c. multicoloured .. 30 20

(Des F. Peter. Litho Ashton-Potter)

1982 (13 Apr). *Cancer-victim Terry Fox's "Marathon of Hope" (Trans-Canada fund-raising run) Commemoration. P* 12½.
1044 **465** 30 c. multicoloured .. 30 20

466 Stylised Open Book

(Des F. Peter. Litho Ashton-Potter)

1982 (16 Apr). *Patriation of Constitution. P* 12 × 12½.
1045 **466** 30 c. multicoloured .. 30 20

467 1880's Male and Female Salvationists with Street Scene

468 "The Highway near Kluane Lake" (Yukon Territory) (Jackson)

(Des T. Dimson. Litho C.B.N.)

1982 (25 June). *Centenary of the Salvation Army in Canada. P* 13½.
1046 **467** 30 c. multicoloured .. 30 25

(Des J. Morin and P. Sasseville. Litho Ashton-Potter)

1982 (30 June). *Canada Day. Paintings of Canadian Landscapes. Sheet,* 139 × 139 *mm, containing T* **468** *and similar horiz designs. Multicoloured. P* 12½ × 12.
MS1047 30 c. × 12, Type **468**; "Street Scene, Montreal" (Quebec) (Hébert); "Breakwater" (Newfoundland) (Pratt); "Along Great Slave Lake" (Northwest Territories) (Richard); "Till Hill" (Prince Edward Island) (Lamb); "Family and Rainstorm" (Nova Scotia) (Colville); "Brown Shadows" (Saskatchewan) (Knowles); "The Red Brick House" (Ontario) (Milne); "Campus Gates" (New Brunswick) (Bobak); "Prairie Town—Early Morning" (Alberta) (Kerr); "Totems at Ninstints" (British Columbia) (Plaskett); "Doc Snider's House" (Manitoba) (FitzGerald) .. 2·75

469 Regina Legislature Building

470 Finish of Race

(Des Kim Martin and R. Russell. Litho Ashton-Potter)

1982 (3 Aug). *Regina Centenary. P* 13½ × 13.
1048 **469** 30 c. multicoloured .. 30 25

(Des B. Reilander. Litho Ashton-Potter)

1982 (4 Aug). *Centenary of Royal Canadian Henley Regatta. P* 12½.
1049 **470** 30 c. multicoloured .. 30 25

471 Fairchild "FC-2W1"

472 Decoy

(Des R. Bradford. Litho Ashton-Potter)

1982 (5 Oct). *Canadian Aircraft (4th series). Bush Aircraft. T* **471** *and similar horiz designs. Multicoloured. P* 12½.
1050 30 c. Type **471** .. 30 15
a. Pair. Nos. 1050/1 .. 60 60
1051 30 c. De Havilland Canada "Beaver" .. 30 15
1052 60 c. Fokker "Super Universal" .. 55 60
a. Pair. Nos. 1052/3 .. 1·10 1·25
1053 60 c. Noorduyn "Norseman" .. 55 60
Nos. 1050/1 and 1052/3 were each printed together, *se-tenant*, in horiz and vert pairs throughout the sheet.

(Des J. P. Beaudin and J. Morin. Litho C.B.N. (Nos. 1055a, 1057a) or Ashton-Potter (others))

1982 (19 Oct)–**84**. *Heritage Artifacts. T* **472** *and similar designs. No fluorescent bands* (1 c. *to* 5 c.). *P* 12 × 12½ (37 c., 48 c., 64 c.) *or* 14 × 13½ *(others).*
1054 1 c. black, grey-brown and brown .. 5 5
1055 2 c. black, pale turquoise-blue & dp bl-green 5 5
a. Perf 13 × 13½ (10.2.84) .. 5 5
1056 3 c. black, dull violet-blue and chalky blue .. 5 5
1057 5 c. black, flesh and chestnut .. 10 5
a. Perf 13 × 13½ (6.7.84) .. 5 5
1058 10 c. black, light blue & deep turquoise-blue .. 10 5
1059 20 c. black, brownish grey and sepia .. 20 25
1060 37 c. grey-black, deep yellow-green and sage-green (8.4.83) .. 45 40
1061 48 c. blackish brown, red-brown and pale pink (8.4.83) .. 60 55
1062 64 c. grey-black, black and pale grey (8.4.83) 70 65
1054/62 .. *Set of* 9 2·00 1·75
Designs: *Vert (as T* **472**)—2 c. Fishing spear; 3 c. Stable lantern; 5 c. Bucket; 10 c. Weathercock; 20 c. Skates. *Horiz* (26 × 20 *mm*)—37 c. Plough; 48 c. Cradle; 64 c. Kitchen stove.

PRICES OF SETS

Set prices are given for many issues, generally those containing five stamps or more. Definitive sets include one of each value or major colour change, but do not cover different perforations, die types or minor shades. Where a choice is possible the set prices are based on the cheapest versions of the stamps included in the listings.

475 Mary, Joseph and Baby Jesus

476 Globes forming Symbolic Designs

(Des J. Eby. Litho C.B.N.)

1982 (3 Nov). *Christmas. Nativity Scenes. T* **475** *and similar vert designs. Multicoloured. P* 13.

1080 30 c. Type **475** 30 35
1081 35 c. The Shepherds 35 40
1082 60 c. The Three Wise Men 55 60

(Des R. Bellemare. Litho Ashton-Potter)

1983 (10 Mar). *World Communications Year. Fluorescent frame. P* 12 × 12½.

1083 **476** 32 c. multicoloured 30 35

477 Map of World showing Canada

(Des R. Harder. Litho Ashton-Potter)

1983 (10 Mar). *World Communications Year. Fluorescent frame. P* 12 × 12½.

1083 **476** 32 c. multicoloured 30 35

478 Scene from Novel "Angéline de Montbrun" by Laure Conan (Félicité Angers)

479 St. John Ambulance Badge and "100"

(Des R. Milot (No. 1085), Claire Pratt (No. 1086), adapted W. Tibbles. Litho C.B.N.)

1983 (22 Apr). *Canadian Writers* (4*th series*). *T* **478** *and similar horiz design. Multicoloured. P* 13.

1085 32 c. Type **478** 30 35
a. Pair. Nos. 1085/6 60
1086 32 c. Woodcut illustrating "Sea-gulls" (poem by E. J. Pratt) 30 35

Nos. 1085/6 were printed together, *se-tenant*, in horizontal and vertical pairs throughout the sheet.

(Des L. Fishauf. Litho Ashton-Potter)

1983 (3 June). *Centenary of St. John Ambulance in Canada. P* 13.

1087 **479** 32 c. brt rose-red, gold & dp chocolate 30 35

480 Victory Pictogram

481 Fort William, Ontario

(Des Krista Huebner, D. Kilvert and P.-Y. Pelletier. Litho C.B.N.)

1983 (28 June). *"Universiade 83" World University Games, Edmonton. P* 13.

1088 **480** 32 c. multicoloured 30 35
1089 64 c. multicoloured 65 70

(Des R. Harder. Litho Ashton-Potter)

1983 (30 June). *Canada Day. Forts. T* **481** *and similar horiz designs. Multicoloured. P* 12½ × 13.

1090 32 c. Fort Henry, Ontario (44 × 22 *mm*) .. 35 35
a. Booklet pane. Nos. 1090/9 .. .. 3·25
1091 32 c. Type **481** 35 35
1092 32 c. Fort Rodd Hill, British Columbia .. 35 35
1093 32 c. Fort Wellington, Ontario (28 × 22 *mm*) .. 35 35
1094 32 c. Fort Prince of Wales, Manitoba (28 × 22 *mm*) 35 35
1095 32 c. Halifax Citadel, Nova Scotia (44 × 22 *mm*) 35 35
1096 32 c. Fort Chambly, Quebec 35 35
1097 32 c. Fort No. 1, Point Levis, Quebec 35 35
1098 32 c. Coteau-du-Lac Fort, Quebec (28 × 22 *mm*) 35 35
1099 32 c. Fort Beauséjour, New Brunswick (28 × 22 *mm*) 35 35
1090/9 .. .. *Set of* 10 3·25 3·25

Nos. 1090/9 were only available from $3.20 stamp booklets containing the *se-tenant* pane, No. 1090a.

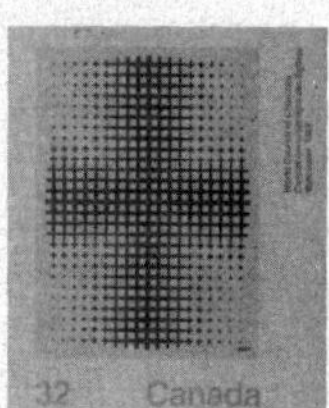

482 Scouting Poster by Marc Fournier (aged 12)

483 Cross Symbol

(Des F. Dallaire. Litho Ashton-Potter)

1983 (6 July). *75th Anniv of Scouting in Canada and 15th World Scout Jamboree, Alberta. P* 13.

1100 **482** 32 c. multicoloured 30 35

(Des G. Tsetsekas. Recess and photo B.A.B.N.)

1983 (22 July). *6th Assembly of the World Council of Churches, Vancouver. P* 13.

1101 **483** 32 c. blue-green and grey-lilac 30 35

484 Sir Humphrey Gilbert (founder)

485 "NICKEL" Deposits

(Des R. Hill. Litho C.B.N.)

1983 (3 Aug). *400th Anniv of Newfoundland. P* 13.

1102 **484** 32 c. multicoloured 30 35

(Des J. Capon. Litho ("NICKEL" die-stamped)ƒ C.B.N.)

1983 (12 Aug). *Centenary of Discovery of Sudbury Nickel Deposits. P* 13.

1103 **485** 32 c. multicoloured 30 35

486 Josiah Henson and Escaping Slaves

487 Type 0-4-0, *Dorchester* Locomotive

(Des T. Kew and J. Hamel. Litho B.A.B.N.)

1983 (16 Sept). *Nineteenth-century Social Reformers. T* **486** *and similar horiz design. Multicoloured. P* 13 × 13½ (*No.* 1104) *or* 13 (*No.* 1105).

1104 32 c. Type **486** 30 35
1105 32 c. Father Antoine Labelle and rural village (32 × 26 *mm*) 30 35

(Des E. Roch. Litho Ashton-Potter)

1983 (3 Oct). *Railway Locomotives.* (1*st series*). *T* **487** *and similar horiz designs. Multicoloured. P* 12½ × 13.

1106 32 c. Type **487** 30 35
a. Pair. Nos. 1106/7 .. .. 60 70
1107 32 c. Type 4-4-0, *Toronto* 30 35
1108 37 c. Type 0-6-0, *Samson* 40 40
1109 64 c. Type 4-4-0, *Adam Brown*.. .. .. 65 70

Nos. 1106/7 were printed together, *se-tenant*, in horizontal and vertical pairs throughout the sheet.

See also 1132/6.

488 School Coat of Arms

489 City Church

(Des Denise Saulnier. Litho C.B.N.)

1983 (28 Oct). *Centenary of Dalhousie Law School. P* 13.

1110 **488** 32 c. multicoloured 30 35

(Des C. Simard. Litho Ashton-Potter)

1983 (3 Nov). *Christmas. Churches. T* **489** *and similar horiz designs. Multicoloured. P* 13.

1111 32 c. Type **489** 30 35
1112 37 c. Family walking to church 40 45
1113 64 c. Country chapel 65 70

490 Royal Canadian Regiment and British Columbia Regiment

(Des W. Southern and R. Tibbles. Litho C.B.N.)

1983 (10 Nov). *Canadian Army Regiments. T* **490** *and similar vert design. Multicoloured. P* 13.

1114 32 c. Type **490** 30 35
a. Pair. Nos. 1114/15 .. .. .. 60 70
1115 32 c. Royal Winnipeg Rifles and Royal Canadian Dragoons 30 35

Nos. 1114/15 were printed together, *se-tenant*, in horizontal and vertical pairs throughout the sheet.

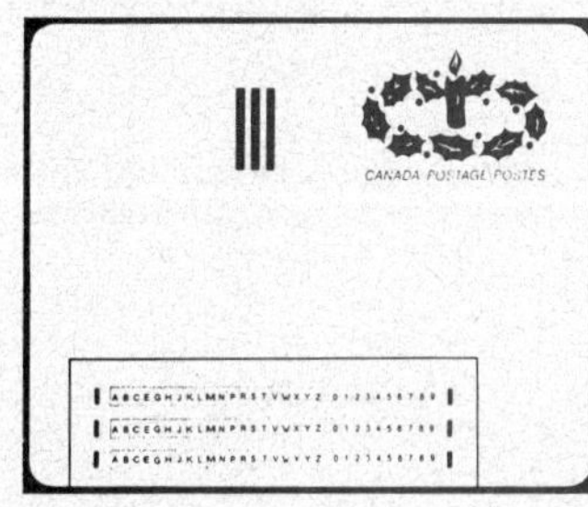

(*Illustration reduced: actual size* 112 × 88 mm)

"STICK 'N TICK" POSTAGE LABELS. Prepaid labels in the above design, printed in a combination of red, green and black, were tested by the Canadian Post Office in Winnipeg, Manitoba, between 21 November and 17 December 1983. These self-adhesive labels were sold to the public in kits of 12 or 25, at a saving of 35 c. or $1.11 on the normal postage. They were primarily intended for use on Christmas cards and were only valid on mail posted to Canadian addresses.

The label was affixed to normally addressed envelopes, but the user was then required to mark the postal code on the three lines at the foot. It was hoped that this incentive would increase the use of the postal codes and so speed automatic mail sorting.

The system was extended to seven other cities in 1984. The second version had separate postage paid and Postal Code labels, being available from 5 November until 17 December 1984.

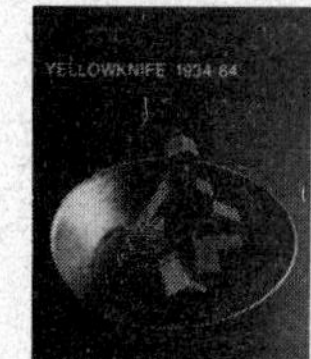

491 Gold Mine in Prospecting Pan

492 Montreal Symphony Orchestra

(Des K. Hughes. Litho Ashton-Potter)

1984 (15 Mar). *50th Anniv of Yellowknife. P* 13½.

1116 **491** 32 c. multicoloured 40 45

(Des J. Delisle and P. Kohler. Litho Ashton-Potter)

1984 (24 Mar). *50th Anniv of Montreal Symphony Orchestra. P* 12½.

1117 **492** 32 c. multicoloured 40 45

493 Jacques Cartier

494 Class "A" Square-rigged Ship

(Des Y. Paquir, Engraved C. Haley. Recess French Govt Ptg Wks, Perigueux)

1984 (20 Apr). *450th Anniv of Jacques Cartier's Voyage to Canada. P* 13.

1118 **493** 32 c. multicoloured 40 45

(Des O. Schenk. Litho Ashton-Potter)

1984 (18 May). *Tall Ships Visit. P* 12 × 12½.
1119 **494** 32 c. multicoloured 40 45

495 Service Medal **496** Oared Galleys

(Des W. Tibbles and C. Webster. Litho Ashton-Potter)

1984 (28 May). *75th Anniv of Canadian Red Cross Society. P* 13½.
1120 **495** 32 c. multicoloured 40 45

(Des P. Dorn. Photo and recess B.A.B.N.)

1984 (18 June). *Bicentenary of New Brunswick. P* 13½.
1121 **496** 32 c. multicoloured 40 45

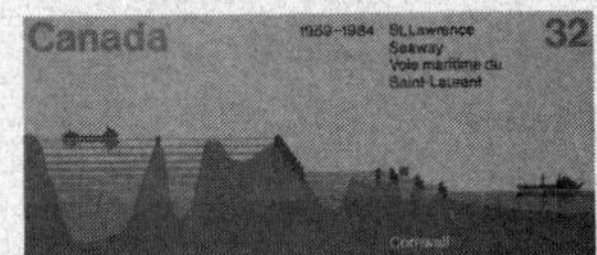

497 St. Lawrence Seaway

(Des E. Barenscher. Litho C.B.N.)

1984 (26 June). *25th Anniv of St. Lawrence Seaway. P* 13.
1122 **497** 32 c. multicoloured 40 45

498 New Brunswick **499** Loyalists of 1784

(Des J. Morin and T. Yakobina. Litho C.B.N.)

1984 (29 June). *Canada Day. Paintings by Jean Paul Lemieux. Sheet,* 138 × 122 *mm, containing T* **498** *and similar multi-coloured designs. P* 13.
MS1123 32 c. × 12, Type **498**; British Columbia; Northwest Territories; Quebec; Manitoba; Alberta; Prince Edward Island; Saskatchewan; Nova Scotia (*vert*); Yukon Territory, Newfoundland; Ontario (*vert*) .. .. 5·00

The captions on the Northwest Territories and Yukon Territory paintings were transposed at the design stage.

(Des W. Davies. Litho B.A.B.N.)

1984 (3 July). *Bicentenary of Arrival of United Empire Loyalists. P* 13 × 13½.
1124 **499** 32 c. multicoloured 40 45

500 St. John's Basilica **501** Coat of Arms of Pope John Paul II

(Des J. Morin and R. Ethier. Litho C.B.N.)

1984 (17 Aug). *Bicentenary of Roman Catholic Church in Newfoundland. P* 13½.
1125 **500** 32 c. multicoloured 40 45

(Des L. Rivard. Litho Ashton-Potter)

1984 (31 Aug). *Papal Visit. P* 12½.
1126 **501** 32 c. multicoloured 40 45
1127 64 c. multicoloured 85 90

502 Louisbourg Lighthouse, 1734

(Des D. Noble and K. Rodmell. Litho Ashton-Potter)

1984 (21 Sept). *Canadian Lighthouses. T* **502** *and similar horiz designs. Multicoloured. P* 12½.
1128 32 c. Type **502** 40 45
a. Block of 4. Nos. 1128/31 .. .. .. 1·50
1129 32 c. Fisgard Lighthouse, 1860 .. .. 40 45
1130 32 c. Ile Verte Lighthouse, 1809 .. .. 40 45
1131 32 c. Gibraltar Point Lighthouse, 1808 .. 40 45

Nos. 1128/31 were printed in *se-tenant* combinations throughout a sheet of 50, giving 10 blocks of 4 and 10 single stamps.

503 Type 0-6-0, *Scotia* Locomotive

(Des E. Roch. Litho Ashton-Potter)

1984 (25 Oct). *Railway Locomotives (2nd series). T* **503** *and similar horiz designs. Multicoloured. P* 12½ × 13.
1132 32 c. Type **503** 40 45
a. Pair. Nos. 1132/3 .. .. 80 90
1133 32 c. Type 4-4-0, *Countess of Dufferin* .. 40 45
1134 37 c. Type 2-6-0, GT Class E3 .. .. .. 50 55
1135 64 c. Type 4-6-0, CP Class D10a 85 90
MS1136 153 × 104 mm. As Nos. 1132/5, but with background colour changed from pale green to pale grey-blue .. .. 2·25 2·50

Nos. 1132/3 were issued together, *se-tenant*, in horizontal and vertical pairs throughout the sheet.

No. **MS**1136 commemorates "CANADA 84" National Stamp Exhibition, Montreal.

504 "The Annunciation" (Jean Dallaire) **505** Pilots of 1914–18, 1939–45 and 1984

(Des J. Morin and T. Yakobina. Litho Ashton-Potter)

1984 (2 Nov). *Christmas. Religious Paintings. T* **504** *and similar horiz designs. Multicoloured. P* 13½.
1137 32 c. Type **504** 40 45
1138 37 c. "The Three Kings" (Simone Bouchard) .. 50 55
1139 64 c. "Snow in Bethlehem" (David Milne) .. 85 90

(Des W. Southern and R. Tibbles. Litho Ashton-Potter)

1984 (9 Nov). *60th Anniv of Royal Canadian Air Force. P* 12 × 12½.
1140 505 32 c. multicoloured 40 45

506 Treffle Berthiaume (editor)

(Des P.-Y. Pelletier. Litho Ashton-Potter)

1984 (16 Nov.) *Centenary of La Presse (newspaper). P* 13 × 13½.
1141 **506** 32 c. agate, vermilion and pale grey-brown 40 45

Index to Canada Stamp Designs from 1952

The following index is intended to facilitate the identification of Canadian issues from 1942. Portrait stamps are usually listed under surnames only, views under the name of the town or city and other issues under the main subject or a prominent word and date chosen from the inscription. Simple abbreviations have occasionally been resorted to and when the same design or subject appears on more than one stamp, only the first of each series is indicated.

Abbott 444
Academy of Arts 972
Acadia 1021
Adam Brown (loco) 1109
"Agricultural Education" 782
Air Force 1140
Air Training camp 399
Aircraft 399, 438, 509, 540, 556, 636, 966, 996, 1026, 1050
Albani 983
Alberta and Saskatchewan 481
Algonkians 723
"Alouette" 570
Antique instruments 1001
Archer 845
Arctic Islands 970
Arms and flowers 543
Artifacts 1054
Athabasca (ship) 854
Autumn 679
Avro-Canada (aircraft) 996, 1028
Avro "Lancaster" (aircraft) 997

Basketball 829
"Be Prepared" 515
Beaver 473
Beaver (ship) 820
Bell 408
Bennett 483, 697
Bernier 893
Berthiaume 1141
Biological programme 649
Bird decoration 765
Birds 407, 443, 474, 479, 495, 539, 620, 638, 906
Bison 1007
Bobak **MS**1047
Borden 434, 695
Borduas 1012
Bouchard 1137
Bourassa 627
Bourgeoys 805
Bowell 476
Bowls 921
Boxing 815
British Columbia 503, 685
Brock 643
Brown 626
By 943

Cabot 412
Calgary 812
Canada Day **MS**944, 1013, **MS**1047, 1090, **MS**1123
Canada Games 641
Canada Geese 407, 443, 539
Canadair (aircraft) 966, 1027
Canadian Indians 721
Canadian Press 615
Candles 745
"Capex '78" 907, 914
Caribou 486
Carr 674
Cartier 1118
Cartography 742
Census 683
Chair and mace 508
Charlottetown 642
Charlottetown Conference 557
Chemical industry 489
Cherry blossom 650
Chicora (ship) 853
Chief Justice Robinson (ship) 931
Child 824
Children's paintings 661, 822
Chown 807
Christ in manger 667
Christmas 560, 568, 576, 618, 630, 644, 661, 687, 745, 764, 792, 822, 848, 895, 928, 962, 993, 1023, 1080, 1111, 1137
Christmas tree 669, 1023
Church 670, 1111
Churchill 565
Citizenship 409
City streets 880
City view 708
Civil aviation 480
Coat of arms and flowers 543
Colombo Plan 520
Coteau-du-Lac 1098
Colville **MS**1047
Combine harvester 404
Commonwealth Day 1084
Commonwealth Games 908, 918
Commonwealth Parliamentary Assn 575
Commonwealth Parliamentary Conf 894
Conan 1085
Congresses 741
Consolidated "Canso" (aircraft) 969
Constitution 1045
Cook, Dr. J. 808
Cook, James 910
Cougar 886
Countess of Dufferin (loco) 1133
Country women 511
CP Class D10a (loco) 1135
Cradle 1061
Crate 536
Curling 632, 789

Curtiss (aircraft) 967, 998
Cycling 770

Dalhousie Law School 1110
Dallaire 1137
De Havilland (aircraft) 1026, 1051
Desjardins 806
Destroyer 388
Diefenbaker 982
Diving 768
Dollard des Ormeaux 516
Dorchester (loco) 1106
Drying furs 432
Duck 495

Education 522
Edwards 1002
Elizabeth II 410, 450, 463, 512, 527, 559, 579, 613, 700, 759, 855, 867
Elizabeth II and Duke of Edinburgh 440, 500
Eskimo hunter 477
Excavators 913
Expo '67 611

Fairchild (aircraft) 1050
Family group 785, 825
Farm scene 382, 401
Fencing 814
Ferry 587
"First Land Route" 538
First Non-stop Flight 636
Fisgard 1129
Fish 976
Fisherman 433
Fishing 491
FitzGerald **MS**1047
Flag and Canada 578
Flags **MS**944
Fleming 892
Flower and buildings 838
Flowers 543, 650, 856, 978, 1019
Fokker (aircraft) 1052
Football 831
Forest 702
Forestry 441
Fort Beauséjour 1099
Fort Chambly 1096
Fort Henry 1090
Fortin 1011
Fort No. 1, Point Levis 1097
Fort Prince of Wales 1094
Fort Rodd Hill 1092
Fort Wellington 1093
Fort William 1091
Fox 1044
Franklin 839
Free Press 501
French 751
Frobisher 537
Frontenac 720
Fuller 975
Fundy 884

Gagnon 795
Games, flags 641
Gannet 474
Gateway 922
Geography 744
Geology 743
George VI 375, 389, 414
Gibraltar Point 1131
Gilbert 1102
Girl Guides 515
Glacier 884*b*
Globe 510
Grain elevator 379, 589
Great Bear Lake 402
Grey Jay 620
Grenfell 563
Group of Seven 660
Grove 940
GT Class E3 (loco) 1134
Guevremont 847
Gymnastics 830
Gzowski 535

Halifax 413, 1095
Hanlan 985
Harris 972
Hawker "Hurricane" (aircraft) 999
Hearne 682
Hébert 973, **MS**1047
Hémon 804
Hens 977
Henson 1104
Heritage 1054
Highway 584
Highway safety 572
Hiking 771
Hockey 957
Horse-drawn sleigh 661
Houses of Parliament 870
Howe 755
Hunting 898
Hurdling 811
Hydrological Decade 623

"I remember" 650
Ice hockey 485
Iceberg and boatman 477
Ice-skate 764
Ile Verte 1130
Indians of the Pacific Coast 725
Indians of the Plains 721
Insulin 675
International Co-operation Year 562
International Labour Organisation 635
International Women's Year 813
Interparliamentary Union 566
Inuits 898, 924, 958, 989

Iroquoians 729, 739

Jackson **MS**1047
Jamboree 482
"Jesous Ahatonhia" 895
Jet airliner 540, 556, 1028
Jogging 769
Johnson 518
Judo 816

Kane 686
Kayak 956
Kelsey 654
Kerr **MS**1047
King 435, 696
Kluane 885
Knowles **MS**1047
Krieghoff 749

Labelle 1105
Labrador (ship) 934
Lachapelle 1000
Lacrosse 625
Lake 402
Lake Placid 971
Lamb **MS**1047
Landscapes 584, 704, **MS**1047
Laporte 691
"La Presse" 1141
La Salle 571
Launching 386
Laurier 694
La Verendrye 504
Leacock 646
Leaves 875
Leger 1043
Lemieux 792, **MS**1123
Lighthouses 1128
London Conference 573
Louisbourg 1128
Loyalists 1124
Lumbering 405

McClung 761
McCrae 628
MacDonald, J. A. 693
MacDonald, J. E. H. 756
Mackenzie, A. 445, 658
McKenzie, R. T. 801
McKinney 1003
Macoun 1018
Mail coach 438
Mail trains 436
Mance 754
Manitoba 647
Map 536, 970, 1013
Maple leaf 555, 1030
Maple leaf and hand 558
Maple leaves 542, 677, 684
"Marathon of Hope" 1044
Marconi 796
Marie 1009
Marie-Victorin 1017
Marmot 1006
Massey 633, 889
Masson 793
Matthew (ship) 412
Meighen 519
Merritt 797
"Merry Christmas" 993, 1023
Meteorology 621
Microscope 502
Milne **MS**1047, 1139
Miner 499, 912
Montgomery 803
Montmorency-Laval 750
Montreal Symphony Orchestra 1117
Moose 448
Mosher 1022
Mountain Goat 487
Mounted Police 751
Mowat 659
Munitions factory 387
Musical instrument 1001
Musk Ox 478

Narwhal 622
National flag 564, 578
Nativity 848, 1080
N.A.T.O. 510
Nelligan 941
Neptune (ship) 819
New Brunswick 1121
Newfoundland 1102, 1125
Niagara-on-the-Lake 1020
Nickel 1103
Nonsuch (ship) 624
Noorduyn "Norseman" (aircraft) 1053
Northcote (ship) 851
Northern development 517
Northern Light (ship) 933
Northwest Territories 648
Nova Scotia 508
Nurse 506

O'Brien 974
"O Canada" 980
Oil wells 431, 590
Olympic Games, Innsbruck 832
Olympic Games, Montreal 762, 768, 786, 798, 809, 814, 829, 833, 842
Order of Canada 890
"OSM 50 MSO" 1117
Osler 637

"Pacem in Terris" 541
Paintings **MS**1123, 1137
Pan American Games 614
Papal Visit 1126
Papineau 681
Parliament Buildings 383, 567, 870

Passport (ship) 852
Peace Bridge 891
"Peaceful Uses" 574
Pearson 698
Peregrine Falcon 906
Petroleum 507
Philatelic Exhibition 1037
Photogrammetry 741
Pine tree 585
Pinky (boat) 902
Plains of Abraham 514
Plaskett **MS**1047
Plough 1060
Point Pelée 885*a*
Polar Bear 447, 705
Pole-vaulting 809
Postman 777
Post Office 776
Postal Code 938
Power station 403
Pratt, C. **MS**1047
Pratt, E. 1086
Praying hands 576
"Prevent Fires" 490
Prince Edward Island 757
Pulp and paper 488

Quadra (ship) 821
Quebec 505
Quebec Carnival 935

Radio Canada 684
Railway locomotive 1106, 1132
Red Cross 442, 1120
Red River Settlement 523
Regatta 1049
Regiments 1114
Regina 1048
Rehabilitation 979
Reservoir 403
"Resources for Tomorrow" 521
Responsible Government 411
Richard **MS**1047
Riel 657
River scene 588
Roman Catholic Church (Newfoundland) 1125
Rose 1019
Rowing 799
Royal Canadian Academy 972
Royal Canadian Legion 828
Royal Military College 840
Royal Visit 440, 512
Running 810, 919
Rutherford 676

Sailing 800
Saint-Jean 1004
St. John Ambulance 1087
St. John's 1125
St. Laurent 699
St. Lawrence Seaway 513, 1122
St. Roch (ship) 932
Salaberry 942
Salvation Army 1046
Samson (loco) 1108
Santa Claus 665, 766, 822
Saskatchewan 987
Satellite 570
Scotia (loco) 1132
Scottish settlers 758
Scouting 1100
"SERVICE" 1120
Service, R. 846
Sheep 449, 703
Shelter 958
Shepherd 767
Ships 386, 406, 412, 437, 818, 851, 902, 931, 1119
Shooting 493
"Silver Dart" (aircraft) 509
Skating 692, 788, 823
Skiing 494, 664, 787
Skyscrapers 707
Smith 673
Snow-shoeing 786
Snowflake 687
Snowmen 663
Spirits 989
Spring 677
Stable and star 662
Stadium 918
Stained glass windows 848
Stamps 439, 525, 907, 914, 1037
Steam ships 437
Stove 1062
Stowe 1005
Sub-Arctic Indians 727
Summer 678
Supreme Court 817
Suzor Côté 634
Swimming 492, 798

Tall Ships' visit 1119
Talon 524
Tank 384
Tekakwitha 1008
Telephone 783
Textile industry 462
"The Globe" 626
Thompson, D. 496
Thompson, J. 475
Thomson 887
Todd 794
Toronto (loco) 1107
Toronto Centenary 617
Totem pole 446
Toys 962
Toyshop 668
Train ferry 406
Trains 436

Index to Canada Stamp Designs from 1942—*Continued*

Transatlantic Flight 636
Trans-Canada Highway 526
Travel 924
Trees 827
Trees and sledge 672
Tupper 484
Turtle 936

United Empire Loyalists 1124
United Nations 655

"Universiade 83" 1088
U.P.U. 497, 790
Uranium 988

Vanier 616
Varley 1010
Vickers "Vedette" (aircraft) .. 968
Victoria B. C. 525
Vimy Monument 629
Virgin and Child 928

"Votes for Women" 612

Walrus 472
Waterton Lakes 884*b*
Whale 622, 937
Whooping Cranes 479
Wigwam and furs 432
Willan 984
William D. Lawrence (ship) .. 818
Winnipeg 775

Winter 680
Winter landscape 586
World Communications Year .. 1083
World Council of Churches .. 1101
World Cycling Championships .. 784
World Figure Skating Championships 692
World Health Day 719

Year of Child 695
Yellowknife 1116
Youville 923

REGISTRATION STAMPS

R 1

(Eng and recess – printed British-American Bank Note Co, Montreal and Ottawa)

1875 (15 Nov)–**92.** *White wove paper.* (*a*) *P* 12 (*or slightly under*).

R 1	R 1	2 c. orange	45·00	3·00
R 2		2 c. orange-red (1889)	50·00	6·00
R 3		2 c. vermilion	65·00	7·00
		a. Imperf (pair)		
R 4		2 c. rose-carmine (1888)	£110	30·00
R 5		5 c. yellow-green (1878)	60·00	2·25
R 6		5 c. deep green	50·00	2·50
		a. Imperf (pair)	£2500	
R 7		5 c. blue-green (1888)	65·00	2·50
R 7*a*		5 c. dull sea-green (1892)	80·00	4·50
R 8		8 c. bright blue	£350	£275
R 9		8 c. dull blue	£350	£275
		(*b*) *P* 12 × 11½ *or* 12 × 11¾		
R10	R 1	2 c. orange	—	40·00
R11		5 c. green (*shades*)	£250	£150

SPECIAL DELIVERY STAMPS

PRINTERS. The following Special Delivery and Postage Due Stamps were recess-printed by the American Bank Note Co (to 1928), the British American Bank Note Co (to 1934), and the Canadian Bank Note Co (1935 onwards).

S 1

1898–1920. *P* 12.

S1	S 1	10 c. blue-green (28.6.98)	70·00	8·00
S2		10 c. deep green (12.13)	45·00	6·00
S3		10 c. yellowish green (8.20)	45·00	6·00

The differences between Types I and II (figures "10" with and without shading) formerly illustrated were due to wear of the plate. There was only one die.

S 2

S 3 Mail-carrying, 1867 and 1927

1922 (21 Aug). *P* 12.

S4	S 2	20 c. carmine-red	40·00	7·00

No. S4 exists in two slightly different sizes due to the use of "wet" or "dry" printing processes. See note below No. 195.

1927 (29 June). *60th Anniversary of Confederation. P* 12.

S5	S 3	20 c. orange	8·00	7·50

No. S5 exists imperforate, imperf × perf or perf × imperf.

S 4

1930 (2 Sept). *P* 11.

S6	S 4	20 c. brown-red	40·00	13·00

1932 (24 Dec). *Type as* S 4, *but inscr* "CENTS" *in place of* "TWENTY CENTS". *P* 11.

S7		20 c. brown-red	32·00	15·00

S 5 Allegory of Progress

(Des A. Foringer)

1935 (1 June). *P* 12.

S8	S 5	20 c. scarlet	5·50	4·50

No. S8 exists imperforate.

S 6 Canadian Coat of Arms

1938–39. *P* 12.

S 9	S 6	10 c. green (1.4.39)	7·00	2·25
S10		20 c. scarlet (15.6.38)	22·00	22·00

Nos. S9/10 exist imperforate.

≡10 10≡

(S 7)

1939 (1 Mar). *Surch with Type* **S 7.**

S11	S 6	10 c. on 20 c. scarlet	6·50	6·50

S 8 Coat of Arms and Flags

S 9 Trans-Canada Plane

1942 (1 July)–**1943.** *War Effort. P* 12. (*a*) *Postage.*

S12	S 8	10 c. green	2·50	85
		(*b*) *Air*		
S13	S 9	16 c. ultramarine	2·25	1·25
S14		17 c. ultramarine (1.4.43)	2·50	1·75

Nos. S12/14 exist imperforate.

S 10 Arms of Canada and Peace Symbols

S 11 Transatlantic Plane over Quebec

1946 (16 Sept)–**1947.** *P* 12. (*a*) *Postage.*

S15	S 10	10 c. green	2·25	60
		(*b*) *Air.* (i) *Circumflex accent in* "EXPRÊS"		
S16	S 11	17 c. ultramarine	4·50	4·75
		(ii) *Grave accent in* "EXPRÈS"		
S17	S 11	17 c. ultramarine (1947)	4·50	4·50

POSTAGE DUE STAMPS

PRINTERS. See note under "Special Delivery Stamps".

D 1

D 2

1906 (1 July)–**28.** *P* 12.

D1	D 1	1 c. dull violet	6·00	2·75
D2		1 c. red-violet	7·00	2·75
		a. Thin paper (10.24)	12·00	12·00
D3		2 c. dull violet	8·00	80
D4		2 c. red-violet	8·00	80
		a. Thin paper (10.24)	15·00	9·00
D5		4 c. violet (3.7.28)	40·00	24·00
D6		5 c. dull violet	9·00	1·00
D7		5 c. red-violet	9·00	1·00
		a. Thin paper (10.24)	15·00	9·00
D8		10 c. violet (3.7.28)	28·00	12·00

The 1 c., 2 c. and 5 c. values exist imperforate.

Printings up to December 1922 used the "wet" method, those from December 1922 onwards the "dry".

1930–2. *P* 11.

D 9	D 2	1 c. bright violet (14.7.30)	8·00	6·50
D10		2 c. bright violet (21.8.30)	7·00	1·10
D11		4 c. bright violet (14.10.30)	15·00	8·00
D12		5 c. bright violet (12.12.31)	11·00	8·00
D13		10 c. bright violet (24.8.32)	85·00	23·00

Nos. D9/11 and D13 exist imperforate.

D 3

D 4

D 5

1933–4. *P* 11.

D14	D 3	1 c. violet (5.5.34)	10·00	8·50
D15		2 c. violet (20.12.33)	4·75	2·00
D16		4 c. violet (12.12.33)	10·00	8·50
D17		10 c. violet (20.12.33)	15·00	9·50

No. D14 exists imperforate.

1935–65. *P* 12.

D18	D 4	1 c. violet (14.10.35)	40	15
D19		2 c. violet (9.9.35)	40	15
D20		3 c. violet (4.65)	4·00	6·50
D21		4 c. violet (2.7.35)	80	12
D22		5 c. violet (12.48)	70	25
D23		6 c. violet (1957)	2·50	4·00
D24		10 c. violet (16.9.35)	80	15
D18/24		.. .. *Set of* 7	8·50	11·00

The 1 c., 2 c., 4 c. and 10 c., exist imperforate.

1967–78. *Litho. P* 12½ × 12 (20 *c.*, 24 *c.*, 50 *c.*) *or* 12 (*others*).

		(*a*) *Size* 20 × 17½ *mm*		
D25	D 5	1 c. scarlet (3.67)	60	50
D26		2 c. scarlet (3.67)	60	50
D27		3 c. scarlet (3.67)	90	55
D28		4 c. scarlet (2.67)	2·25	95
D29		5 c. scarlet (3.67)	3·50	2·75
D30		6 c. scarlet (2.67)	1·60	1·75
D31		10 c. scarlet (1.67)	2·00	2·00
D25/31		.. .. *Set of* 7	10·00	8·00
		(*b*) *Size* 19½ × 16 *mm*		
D32	D 5	1 c. scarlet (12.70)	35	15
		a. Perf 12½ × 12 (11.77)	15	20
D33		2 c. scarlet (1972)	20	25
D34		3 c. scarlet (1.74)	25	35
D35		4 c. scarlet (4.69)	85	60
		a. Perf 12½ × 12 (11.77)	40	45
D36		5 c. scarlet (2.69)	20·00	25·00
		a. Perf 12½ × 12 (11.77)	45	50
D37		6 c. scarlet (1972)	60	60
D38		8 c. scarlet (1.69)	75	60
		a. Perf 12½ × 12 (28.6.78)	65	75
D39		10 c. scarlet (4.69)	1·00	70
		a. Perf 12½ × 12 (9.77)	60	75
D40		12 c. scarlet (1.69)	1·25	1·00
		a. Perf 12½ × 12 (9.77)	1·50	2·00
D41		16 c. scarlet (1.74)	60	75
D42		20 c. scarlet (10.77)	60	75
D43		24 c. scarlet (10.77)	70	85
D44		50 c. scarlet (10.77)	1·25	1·50
D32/44		.. .. *Set of* 13	6·50	7·50

There are no records of dates of issue of the above but supplies were distributed to depots in the months indicated.

Both white and ordinary papers have been used for Nos. D32/41. These are listed in Stanley Gibbons *Elizabethan Catalogue.*

OFFICIAL STAMPS

We do not list stamps perforated "O.H.M.S.".

O.H.M.S.

(O 1)

1949. *Nos.* 375/6, 378, 380 *and* 402/6 *optd as Type* O 1.

(a) Postage

O1 **111** 1 c. green 2·00 1·90
a. Missing stop after "S" 40·00 25·00
O2 **112** 2 c. brown 9·00 10·00
a. Missing stop after "S" 50·00 42·00
O3 **113** 3 c. purple 2·25 1·10
O4 **112** 4 c. carmine-lake 2·25 50
O5 – 10 c. olive-green 3·50 65
a. Missing stop after "S" 40·00 20·00
O6 – 14 c. sepia 5·00 1·60
a. Missing stop after "S" 50·00 25·00
O7 – 20 c. slate 9·00 2·25
a. Missing stop after "S" 60·00 35·00
O8 – 50 c. green £160 £120
a. Missing stop after "S" £300 £200
O9 – $1 purple 45·00 40·00
a. Missing stop after "S" £550 £550

(b) Air

O10 – 7 c. blue 6·00 2·25
a. Missing stop after "S" 50·00 45·00
O1/10 *Set of* 10 £225 £150

MISSING STOP VARIETIES. These occur on R.6/2 of the lower left pane (Nos. O1a, O2a and O15a) or R.10/2 of the lower left pane (Nos. O5a, O6a, O7a, O8a, O9a and O10a).

1949–50. *Nos.* 414/15, 416/17, 418 *and* 431 *optd as Type* O 1.

O11 **135** 1 c. green 20 20
O12 **136** 2 c. sepia 50 45
O13 **137** 3 c. purple 65 25
O14 **138** 4 c. carmine-lake 80 12
O15 **139** 5 c. blue (1949) 1·25 85
a. Missing stop after "S" 35·00 25·00
O16 **141** 50 c. green (1950) 27·00 20·00

G (O 2) **G** (O 3) **G** (O 4)

Type O 4 differs from Type O 3 in having a thinner appearance and an upward sloping left serif to the lower arm. It results from a new plate introduced in 1961/62. Variations in thickness are known in Type O 2 but these are due to wear and subsequent cleaning of the plate.

1950 (2 Oct)–**52.** *Nos.* 402/4, 406/7, 414/18 *and* 431 *optd with Type* O **2** (1 *to* 5 *c.*) *or* O **3** (7 *c. to* $1). *(a) Postage.*

O17 **135** 1 c. green 10 10
O18 **136** 2 c. sepia 50 30
O19 2 c. olive-green (11.51) 30 8
O20 **137** 3 c. purple 50 10
O21 **138** 4 c. carmine-lake 55 8
O22 4 c. vermilion (1.5.52) 55 8
O23 **139** 5 c. blue 1·25 55
O24 – 10 c. olive-green 2·00 45
O25 – 14 c. sepia 4·50 1·75
O26 – 20 c. slate 11·00 1·00
O27 **141** 50 c. green 7·50 6·50
O28 – $1 purple 65·00 45·00

(b) Air

O29 – 7 c. blue 7·50 6·50
O17/29 *Set of* 13 90·00 55·00

1950–51. *Nos.* 432/3 *optd with Type* O **3**.

O30 **142** 10 c. brown-purple 1·40 12
a. Opt omitted in pair with normal £425 £450
O31 **143** $1 ultramarine (1.2.51) 80·00 60·00

1952–53. *Nos.* 441, 443 *and* 446 *optd with Type* O **3**.

O32 **153** 7 c. blue (3.11.52) 1·25 75
O33 **151** 20 c. grey (1.4.52) 1·25 12
O34 **154** $1 black (2.2.53) 15·00 10·00

1953 (1 Sept)–**61.** *Nos.* 450/4 *and* 462 *optd with Type* O **2** (1 *to* 5 *c.*) *or* O **3** (50 *c.*).

O35 **158** 1 c. purple-brown 15 10
O36 2 c. green 25 5
O37 3 c. carmine 25 5
O38 4 c. violet 35 5
O39 5 c. ultramarine 40 5
O40 **160** 50 c. deep bluish green (2.11.53) 3·50 75
a. Opt Type O **4** (24.4.61*) 3·75 1·50
* Earliest recorded date.

1955–56. *Nos.* 463/4 *and* 466/7 *optd with Type* O **2**.

O41 **161** 1 c. purple-brown (12.11.56) 35 20
O42 2 c. green (19.1.56) 35 5
O43 4 c. violet (23.7.56) 75 5
O44 5 c. bright blue (11.1.55) 35 5

1955–62. *Nos.* 477 *and* 488 *optd with Type* O **3**.

O45 **165** 10 c. purple-brown (21.2.55) 45 5
a. Opt Type O **4** (28.3.62*) 50 30
O46 **176** 20 c. green (4.12.56) 1·10 10
a. Opt Type O **4** (10.4.62*) 4·75 30
* Earliest recorded date.

1963 (15 May). *Nos.* 527/8 *and* 530/1 *optd as Type* O **2**.

O47 1 c. chocolate 50 2·00
O48 2 c. green 50 2·00
a. Type O 2 omitted (vert pair with normal) £475
O49 4 c. carmine-red 50 2·00
O50 5 c. ultramarine 35 75

No. O48a comes from the top row of an upper pane on which the overprint was misplaced downwards by one row. Owing to the margin between the panes the top row of the bottom pane had the overprint at the top of the stamp.

The use of official stamps was discontinued on 31 December 1963.

OFFICIAL SPECIAL DELIVERY STAMPS

1950. *No.* S15 *optd as Type* O 1, *but larger.*

OS1 **S 10** 10 c. green 22·00 18·00

1950 (2 Oct). *No.* S15 *optd as Type* O **2**, *but larger.*

OS2 **S 10** 10 c. green 40·00 35·00

Cape of Good Hope

PRICES FOR STAMPS ON COVER

Nos. 1/4	*from* × 3
Nos. 5/8	*from* × 2
Nos. 9/12	*from* × 3
Nos. 13/21	*from* × 2
Nos. 23/6	*from* × 3
Nos. 27/31	*from* × 6
Nos. 32/3	*from* × 5
No. 34	*from* × 8
No. 35	*from* × 15
No. 36	*from* × 5
Nos. 37/8	*from* × 10
Nos. 39/40	*from* × 8
Nos. 41/2	*from* × 6
Nos. 43/54	*from* × 10
Nos. 55/6	*from* × 20
No. 57	*from* × 40
Nos. 58/69	*from* × 10
Nos. 70/8	*from* × 6

PRICES. Our prices for early Cape of Good Hope are for stamps in very fine condition. Exceptional copies are worth more, poorer copies considerably less.

1 Hope

2

(Des Charles Bell, Surveyor-General. Eng W. Humphrys. Recess P.B.)

1853 (1 Sept). *W* **2**. *Imperf. (a) Paper deeply blued.*

1 **1** 1d. pale brick-red £3500 £275
a. Deep brick-red £4500 £300
2 4d. deep blue £1800 £160

Beware of proofs with faked watermarks offered as originals of No. 2.

(b) Paper slightly blued (blueing not so pronounced at back)

3 **1** 1d. brick-red £2500 £200
a. Brown-red £2750 £225
4 4d. deep blue £1200 £110
a. Pale blue £1300 £150

Both values are known with wmk sideways.

1855–8. *White or cream toned paper without blueing (No. 5).* **W 2.**

(a) Imperf.

5 **1** 1d. brick-red/*cream toned paper* (1857) £4250 £800
a. Rose (1858) £450 £200
b. Deep rose-red £550 £225
6 4d. deep blue (1855) £400 45·00
a. Blue £250 45·00
7 6d. slate-lilac (18.2.58) £4250 £450
a. Blued paper £4250 £500
b. Pale rose-lilac £700 £200
c. Deep rose-lilac £1700 £300
d. Slate-purple. Blued paper £3500 £550
8 1s. bright yellow-green (18.2.58) £2250 £160
a. Deep dark green £225 £600

The method adopted for producing the plate of the 4d., 6d., and 1s. stamps involved the use of two dies, so that there are two types of each of these values, differing slightly in detail, but produced in equal numbers.

All values of this issue are known with watermark sideways. The 6d. is known bisected and used with 1d. for 4d. rate.

The paper of No. 5 is similar to that of Nos. 1/4, but is without the blueing. It is much thicker than the white paper used for later printings of the 1d. The evolution of the paper on these Cape of Good Hope stamps is similar to that on the line-engraved issues of Great Britain.

The 4d. value is known printed in black on white watermarked paper. Eleven authenticated copies have been recorded, the majority of which show cancellations or, at least, some indication that they have been used.

It was, at one time, believed that these stamps came from a small supply printed in black to mark the death of the Prince Consort, but references to examples can be found in the philatelic press before news of this event reached Cape Town.

It is now thought that these stamps represent proof sheets, possibly pressed into service during a shortage of stamps in 1861.

There is, however, no official confirmation of this theory. (*Price un.* £25000.)

(b) Unofficially rouletted

9 **1** 1d. brick-red — £2750
10 4d. blue — £2250
11 6d. rose-lilac — £1500
12 1s. bright yellow-green — £2750
a. Deep dark green — £3000

These rouletted stamps are best collected on cover.

3 Hope

(Local provisional (so-called "wood-block") issue. Engraved on steel by C. J. Roberts. Printed from stereotyped plates by Saul Solomon & Co, Cape Town)

1861 (Feb–April). *Laid paper. Imperf.*

13 **3** 1d. vermilion (27 February) £13000 £2000
a. Carmine (7 March) £18000 £3000
b. Brick-red (10 April) £19000 £2750
c. Error. Pale milky blue — £22000
ca. Pale bright blue — £22000
14 4d. pale milky blue (23 February) £5500 £1500
aa. Retouch or repair to rt-hand corner — £5500
a. Pale grey-blue (March?) £6500 £1500
b. Pale bright blue (March?) £6500 £1900
ba. Retouch or repair to rt-hand corner — £5500
c. Deep bright blue (12 April) — £4500
d. Blue £8500 £2750
e. Error. Vermilion £50000 £25000
ea. Carmine — £28000

Both values were officially reprinted in March, 1883, on wove paper. The 1d. is in deep red, and the 4d. in a deeper blue than that of the deepest shade of the issued stamp.

Specimens of the reprints have done postal duty, but their use thus was not intended. There are no reprints of the errors or of the retouched 4d.

Further reprints were made privately but with official permission, in 1940/41, in colours much deeper than those of any of the original printings, and on thick carton paper.

Early in 1863, Perkins Bacon Ltd handed over the four plates used for printing the triangular Cape of Good Hope stamps to De La Rue & Co, Ltd, who made all the subsequent printings.

(Printed from the P.B. plates by D.L.R.)

1863–4. *Imperf. (a) W* **2**.

18 **1** 1d. deep carmine-red £120 £275
a. Deep brown-red £350 £275
b. Brownish red £350 £275
19 4d. deep blue £100 42·00
a. Blue £120 60·00
b. Slate-blue £2000 £550
c. Steel-blue £1800 £425
20 6d. bright mauve £175 £550
21 1s. bright emerald-green £400 £475
a. Pale emerald-green £1100

(b) Wmk Crown CC (sideways)

22 **1** 1d. deep carmine-red £15000

No. 22 was a trial printing, and is only known unused.

Our prices for the 4d. blue are for stamps which are blue by comparison with the other listed shades. An exceptionally pale shade is recognised by specialists and is rare.

All values of this issue are known with watermark lying sideways.

With the exception of the 4d., these stamps may be easily distinguished from those printed by Perkins Bacon by their colours, which are quite distinct.

The De La Rue stamps of all values are less clearly printed, the figure of Hope and the lettering of the inscriptions standing out less boldly, while the fine lines of the background appear blurred and broken when examined under a glass. The background as a whole often shows irregularity in the apparent depth of colour, due to wear of the plates.

For note regarding the two dies of the 4d., 6d., and 1s. values, see after No. 8.

All the triangular stamps were demonetised as from 1 October 1900.

4 "Hope" seated, with vine and ram. (With outer frame-line)

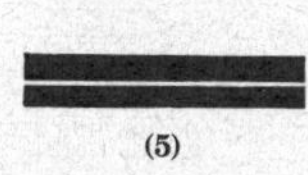

(5)

(Des Charles Bell; die engraved on steel and stamps typo by D.L.R.)

1864–77. *With outer frame-line surrounding the design. Wmk Crown CC. P* 14.

23 **4** 1d. carmine-red (5.65) 40·00 6·50
a. Rose-red 40·00 6·75
24 4d. pale blue (8.65) 50·00 2·00
a. Blue 60·00 2·00
b. Ultramarine £140 50·00
c. Deep blue (1872) 80·00 2·00
25 6d. pale lilac (before 21.3.64) 60·00 12·00
a. Deep lilac £130 6·50
b. Violet (to bright) (1877) 60·00 2·00
26 1s. deep green (1.64) £350 11·00
a. Green 45·00 2·50
b. Blue-green 50·00 3·00

The 1d. rose-red, 6d. lilac, and 1s. blue-green are known imperf, probably from proof sheets.

The 1d. and 4d. stamps of this issue may be found with side and/or top outer frame-lines missing, due to wear of the plates.

(Surch by Saul Solomon & Co, Cape Town)

1868 (17 Nov). *No.* 25*a surch with T* **5**.

27 **4** 4d. on 6d. deep lilac (R.) 60·00 10·00
a. "Peuce" for "Pence" £1500
b. "Fonr" for "Four" — £550

Specimens may also be found with bars omitted or at the top of the stamp, due to misplacement of the sheet.

The space between the words and bars varies from 12½ to 16 mm, stamps with spacing 15½ and 16 mm being rare. There were two printings, one of 120,000 in November 1868 and another of 1,000,000 in December. Stamps showing widest spacings are probably from the earlier printing.

6 (No outer frame-line)

(Die re-engraved. Typo D.L.R.)

1871–6. *Outer frame-line removed. Wmk Crown CC. P 14.*
28 **6** ½d. pale grey-black (12.75) .. .. 2·50 2·10
a. Deep grey-black .. .. 2·25 2·00
29 1d. pale carmine-red (2.72) .. .. 4·50 35
a. Deep carmine-red .. .. 5·00 35
30 4d. dull blue (12.76) .. .. .. 40·00 50
a. Deep blue .. .. .. 40·00 80
b. Ultramarine .. .. .. £130 28·00
31 5s. yellow-orange (25.8.71) .. .. 65·00 6·50

The ½d., 1d. and 5s. are known imperf, probably from proof sheets.

For the 3d. of this issue see Nos. 36 and 39.

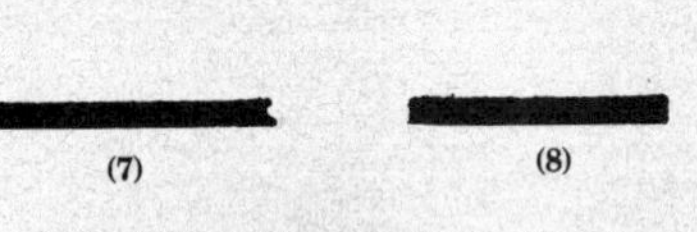

(7) (8)

(Surch by Saul Solomon & Co, Cape Town)

1874–6. *Nos. 25a and 26a surch with T 7.*
32 **4** 1d. on 6d. deep lilac (R.) (1.9.74) .. £180 19·00
a. "E" of "PENNY" omitted .. .. — £350
33 1d. on 1s. green (11.76) .. .. 12·00 12·00

These provisionals are found with the bar only, either across the centre of the stamp or at top, with value only; or with value and bar close together, either at top or foot. Such varieties are due to misplacement of sheets during surcharging.

1879 (1 Nov). *No. 30 surch with T 8.*
34 **6** 3d. on 4d. blue (R.) .. .. .. 30·00 3·50
a. "PENCB" for "PENCE" £1200 £275
b. "THE.EE" for "THREE" £1500 £350
c. Surch double .. .. .. — £1500
d. Variety b. double .. .. ..

The double surcharge must also have existed showing variety a. but only variety b. is known.

There are numerous minor varieties, including letters broken or out of alignment, due to defective printing and use of poor type.

The spacing between the bar and the words varies from 16½ to 18 mm.

THREEPENCE (9) 3 (10) 3 (11)

(Surch by D.L.R.)

1880 (Feb). *Special printing of the 4d. in new colour, surch, with T 9. Wmk Crown CC.*
35 **6** 3d. on 4d. pale dull rose .. .. 11·00 2·00

A minor constant variety exists with foot of "P" in "PENCE" broken off, making the letter appear shorter.

1880 (1 July). *Wmk Crown CC. P 14.*
36 **6** 3d. pale dull rose .. .. .. 60·00 5·00

(Surch by Saul Solomon & Co, Cape Town)

1880 (Aug). *No. 36 surch.*
37 **10** "3" on 3d. pale rose .. .. .. 10·00 1·00
a. Surch inverted .. .. .. £375 40·00
38 **11** "3" on 3d. pale dull rose .. .. 35·00 3·00
a. Surch inverted .. .. .. — £900

The "3" (T **10**) is sometimes found broken. Vertical pairs are known showing the two types of surcharge *se-tenant*, and vertical strips of three exist, the top stamp having surcharge T **10**, the middle stamp being without surcharge, and the lower stamp having surcharge T **11** (*price for strip of 3 un.* £3000).

1881 (Jan). *Wmk Crown CC. P 14.*
39 **6** 3d. pale claret .. .. .. 14·00 1·75
a. Deep claret .. .. .. 18·00 1·50

This was a definite colour change made at the request of the Postmaster-General owing to the similarity between the colours of the 1d. stamp and the 3d. in pale dull rose. Imperf copies are probably from proof sheets.

Proofs of this value were printed in brown, on unwatermarked wove paper and imperf, but the colour was rejected as unsuitable.

1882 (July). *Wmk Crown CA. P 14.*
40 **6** 3d. pale claret .. .. .. 2·25 1·00
a. Deep claret .. .. .. 2·75 90

One Half-penny. (12)

13 "Cabled Anchor"

(Surch by Saul Solomon & Co, Cape Town)

1882 (July). *Nos. 39a and 40a surch with T 12.*
41 **6** ½d. on 3d. deep claret (Wmk CC) .. £1300 £100
a. Hyphen omitted .. .. — £3000
42 ½d. on 3d. deep claret (Wmk CA) .. 2·50 1·60
a. "p" in "penny" omitted £1500 £700
b. "y" in "penny" omitted £650
c. Hyphen omitted £350 £300

Varieties also exist with broken and defective letters, and with the obliterating bar omitted or at the top of the stamp.

1882–83. *Wmk Crown CA. P 14.*
43 **6** ½d. black (1.9.82) .. .. .. 3·00 20
a. Grey-black .. .. .. 1·50 15
44 1d. rose-red (7.82) .. .. .. 7·50 12
a. Deep rose-red .. .. .. 5·50 12
45 2d. pale bistre (1.9.82) .. .. 14·00 15
a. Deep bistre .. .. .. 23·00 12
46 **4** 6d. mauve (to bright) (8.82) .. .. 20·00 70
47 **6** 5s. orange (8.83) £700 £200

Imperf pairs of the ½d., 1d., and 2d. are known, probably from proof sheets.

For the 3d. stamp with this watermark see No. 40.

1884–90. *W 13. P 14.*
48 **6** ½d. black (1.86) 15 12
a. Grey-black 15 12
49 1d. rose-red (12.85) 20 12
a. Carmine-red 15 12
50 2d. pale bistre (12.84) .. .. 1·00 12
a. Deep bistre 40 12
51 4d. blue (6.90) 65 15
a. Deep blue 70 15
52 **4** 6d. reddish purple (12.84) .. .. 11·00 1·60
a. Purple (shades) .. .. .. 1·25 20
b. Bright mauve .. .. .. 6·50 40
53 1s. yellow-green (12.85) .. .. 22·00 1·90
a. Blue-green (1889) .. .. .. 9·00 30
54 **6** 5s. orange (7.87) .. .. .. 25·00 1·50
48/54 .. .. *Set of* 7 32·00 1·90

All the above stamps are known in imperf pairs, probably from proof sheets.

For later shade and colour changes, etc., see Nos. 59, etc.

2½d (14)

15

ONE PENNY. (16)

(Surch by D.L.R.)

1891 (Mar). *Special printing of the 3d. in new colour, surch with T 14.*
55 **6** 2½d. on 3d. pale magenta .. .. 2·10 70
a. Deep magenta 65 20
b. "1" with horiz serif .. .. 35·00 30·00

No. 55b occurs on two stamps (Nos. 8 and 49) of the pane of 60.

Two types of "d" are found in the surcharge, one with square end to serif at top, and the other with pointed serif.

1892 (June). *W 13. P 14.*
56 **15** 2½d. sage-green 75 15
a. Olive-green .. .. .. 3·50 70

(Surch by W. A. Richards & Sons, Cape Town)

1893 (Mar). *Nos. 50/a surch with T 16.*
57 **6** 1d. on 2d. pale bistre .. .. .. 1·10 12
a. Deep bistre 40 12
b. No stop after "PENNY" .. .. 16·00 10·00
c. Surch double .. .. .. — £400

No. 57b occurs on stamp No. 42 of the upper left-hand pane, and on No. 6 of the lower right-hand pane.

Minor varieties exist showing broken letters and letters out of alignment or widely spaced. Also with obliterating bar omitted, due to misplacement of the sheet during surcharging.

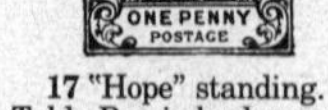

17 "Hope" standing. Table Bay in background

18 Table Mountain and Bay with Arms of the Colony

(Des Mr. Mountford. Typo D.L.R.)

1883 (Oct). *W 13. P 14.*
58 **17** 1d. rose-red 15 12
a. Carmine 15 12

The above stamp is known in imperf pairs, probably from proof sheets.

1893–98. *New colours, etc. W 13. P 14.*
59 **6** ½d. pale yellow-green (12.96) 15 12
a. Green .. .. .. 1·90 20
60 2d. chocolate-brown (3.97) 30 12
61 **15** 2½d. pale ultramarine (3.96) 45 20
a. Ultramarine 30 12
62 **6** 3d. bright magenta (9.98) 70 30
63 4d. sage-green (3.97) .. .. 1·00 30
64 1s. blue-green (12.93) .. .. 5·50 45
a. Deep blue-green .. .. 22·00 4·00
65 1s. yellow-ochre (5.96) .. .. 2·00 35
66 5s. brown-orange (6.96) .. .. 9·50 1·50
59/66 .. .. *Set of* 8 16·00 2·10

1898–1902. *W 13. P 14.*
67 **17** ½d. green (10.98) 15 12
68 3d. magenta (3.02) .. .. .. 1·50 50

(Des E. Sturman. Typo D.L.R.)

1900 (Jan). *W 13. P 14.*
69 **18** 1d. carmine 15 12

19 20 21 22 23 24 25 26 27

(Typo D.L.R.)

1902 (Dec)–**04.** *W 13. P 14.*
70 **19** ½d. green 15 12
71 **20** 1d. carmine 20 12
72 **21** 2d. brown (10.04) 55 30
73 **22** 2½d. ultramarine (3.04) .. .. 1·75 3·25
74 **23** 3d. magenta (4.03) 70 12
75 **24** 4d. olive-green (2.03) .. .. 1·50 30
76 **25** 6d. bright mauve (3.03) .. .. 1·50 30
77 **26** 1s. yellow-ochre .. .. .. 2·75 35
78 **27** 5s. brown-orange (2.03) .. .. 15·00 5·00
70/8 .. .. *Set of* 9 20·00 7·00

All values exist in imperf pairs, from proof sheets.

When the Union of South Africa came into being in 1910 the stamps of the Cape of Good Hope (except the already demonetised triangulars) became available for postal use throughout the Union, until 31 December 1937, from which date the stamps of the four provinces of the Union were demonetised. For Union issues see under SOUTH AFRICA.

BRITISH KAFFRARIA

The history of the Cape eastern frontier was punctuated by a series of armed conflicts with the native population, known as the Kaffir Wars. After a particularly violent outbreak in 1846 the Governor, Sir Harry Smith, advanced the line of the Cape frontier to the Keikama and Tyumie Rivers. In the area between the new frontier and the Kei River a buffer state, British Kaffraria, was established on 17 December 1847. This area was not annexed to the Cape, but was administered as a separate Crown dependency by the Governor of Cape Colony in his capacity as High Commissioner for South Africa.

The territory, with its administration based on King William's Town, used the stamps of the Cape of Good Hope from 1853 onwards, the mail being sent via Port Elizabeth or overland from the Cape. Covers from British Kaffraria franked with the triangular issues are rare.

The first postal marking known from British Kaffraria is the 1849 type octagonal numeral No. 47 from Port Beaufort. Oval postmarks of the 1853 type were used at Alice, Aliwal North, Bedford, Fort Beaufort, King William's Town and Queenstown. In 1864 numeral cancellations were issued to all post offices within the Cape system and it is known that the following numbers were initially assigned to post towns in Kaffraria: 4 (King William's Town), 7 (Bedford), 11 (Queenstown), 29 (East London), 32 (Fort Beaufort), 38 (Aliwal North) and 104 (Cathcart).

It is believed that post offices may have also existed at Adelaide, Barkly East, Sterkstoom and Stutterheim, but, to date, no examples of handstamps or cancellations are known from them during the British Kaffraria period.

Following the decimation by famine of the Xhosa tribes in 1857 British Kaffraria was annexed to Cape Colony in 1865. The area eventually formed the basis of the Ciskei independent "homeland".

MAFEKING SIEGE STAMPS

PRICES FOR STAMPS ON COVER	
Nos. 1/16	*from* × 3
Nos. 17/22	*from* × 2

24 MARCH to 17 MAY 1900

There are numerous forgeries of the Mafeking overprints, many of which were brought home by soldiers returning from the Boer War.

MAFEKING, 3d. BESIEGED. (1)

MAFEKING 3d. BESIEGED. (2)

(Surcharged by Townsend & Co, Mafeking)

1900 (24 Mar–25 Apr). *Various stamps surch as T* **1** *and* **2**.

(A) *Cape of Good Hope stamps surch as T* **1** (24 Mar)

No.	Type	Description	Unused	Used
1	**6**	1d. on ½d. green	£150	48·00
2	**17**	1d. on ½d. green	£175	55·00
3		3d. on 1d. carmine	£150	48·00
4	**6**	6d. on 3d. magenta	£3500	£325
5		1s. on 4d. sage-green	£3000	£325

A variety in the setting of each value exists without comma after "MAFEKING".

(B) *Nos. 59 and 61/3 of Bechuanaland Protectorate surch as T* **1**

No.	Type	Description	Unused	Used
6		1d. on ½d. vermilion (28.3)	£150	48·00
		a. Surch inverted	—	£3500
		b. Vert pair, surch tête-bêche	—	£6000
7		3d. on 1d. lilac (4.4)	£850	65·00
		a. Surch double	—	£4500
8		6d. on 2d. green and carmine (6.4.)	£1000	65·00
9		6d. on 3d. purple/*yellow* (4.4)	£2500	£250
		a. Surch inverted	—	£6000
		b. Surch double		

(C) *Nos. 12 and 35 of British Bechuanaland surch as T* **1**

No.	Type	Description	Unused	Used
10		6d. on 3d. lilac and black (27.3)	£400	60·00
11		1s. on 4d. green and purple-brown (29.3)	£1200	65·00
		a. Surch double	—	£6000
		b. Surch treble	—	£7000
		c. Surch double, one inverted	—	£7000

(D) *Nos. 61/2 and 65 of Bechuanaland Protectorate surch as T* **2** (25 Apr)

No.	Type	Description	Unused	Used
12		3d. on 1d. lilac	£900	55·00
		a. Surch double	—	£6000
13		6d. on 2d. green and carmine	£1100	60·00
14		1s. on 6d. purple/*rose-red*	£2500	80·00

(E) *Nos. 36/7 of British Bechuanaland surch as T* **2**

No.	Type	Description	Unused	Used
15		1s. on 6d. purple/*rose-red* (3.5)	£4500	£700
16		2s. on 1s. green (25.4)	£3500	£300

No. 11a has both surcharges T **1**. Copies exist with normal surcharge T **1** and the second surcharge T **2** but are believed to be trials.

In the stamps overprinted "BECHUANALAND PROTECTORATE" and "BRITISH BECHUANALAND" the local surcharge is so adjusted as not to overlap the original overprint.

3 Cadet Sergt.-major Goodyear

4 General Baden-Powell

(Des Dr. W. A. Hayes (T **3**), Capt. H. Greener (T **4**))

1900 (9–11 Apr). *Produced photographically by Dr. D. Taylor. Horiz laid paper with sheet wmk "OCEANA FINE". P* 12.

(*a*) 18½ *mm wide.* (*b*) 21 *mm wide*

No.	Type	Description	Unused	Used
17	**3**	1d. pale blue/*blue*	£950	£250
18		1d. deep blue/*blue*	£950	£275
19	**4**	3d. pale blue/*blue* (*a*)	£1300	£475
		a. Reversed design	£15000	£12000
20		3d. deep blue/*blue* (*a*)	£1400	£400
		a. Imperf between (horiz pair)	—	£11000
		b. Double print	—	£9500
21		3d. pale blue/*blue* (*b*) (11.4)	£5500	£900
22		3d. deep blue/*blue* (*b*) (11.4)	£6000	£1200

These stamps vary a great deal in colour from deep blue to pale grey.

No. 18 in an imperforate pair is now believed to be a proof. The only known example is untrimmed and without gum.

VRYBURG

PRICES FOR STAMPS ON COVER

Nos. 1/4	*from* × 5
Nos. 11/12	*from* × 2

TEMPORARY BOER OCCUPATION

½ PENCE

Z.A.R.

(1)

1899 (Nov). *Cape stamps surch as T* **1**. *A. Surch* 10 *mm high. B. Surch* 12 *mm high.*

No.	Type	Description	A. Unused	A. Used	B. Unused	B. Used
1	**6**	½ PENCE, green	£200	90·00	—	£600
2	**17**	1 PENCE, rose	£250	£110	—	£700
3	**4**	2 PENCE on 6d. mauve	†		£3000	£500
4	**15**	2½ pence, blue	£2250	£425	—	—

Nos. 1A, 2A, 4A, and 3B are known with italic "Z" in the surcharge. *Prices from 4 times normal.*

BRITISH REOCCUPATION

V. R. SPECIAL POST

(2)

1900 (May). *Provisionals issued by the Military Authorities. Stamps of Transvaal optd with T* **2**.

No.	Type	Description	Unused	Used
11	**30**	½d. green	—	£1000
12		1d. carmine and green	£3500	£1500
13		2d. deep brown and green		
14		2½d. blue and green		

Cayman Islands

Stamps of Jamaica were used in Cayman Islands from April 1889 until 19 February 1901.

PRICES OF NOS. Z1/27. These are for a single stamp showing a clear impression of the postmark. Examples used on cover are worth considerably more.

GEORGETOWN, GRAND CAYMAN

Z 1

Z 2

Z 3

Stamps of JAMAICA *cancelled with Type* Z 1.

1889 *to* **1894**.

No.	Description	Price
Z1	½d. yellow-green (No. 16)	£250
Z2	1d. purple and mauve (No. 27)	£250
Z3	2d. green (No. 28)	£650
Z4	2½d. dull purple and blue (No. 29)	£750
Z5	4d. red-orange (No. 22)	£950

Stamps of JAMAICA *cancelled with Type* Z 2.

1895 *to* **1898**.

No.	Description	Price
Z6	½d. yellow-green (No. 16)	£300
Z7	1d. purple and mauve (No. 27)	£225
Z8	2½d. dull purple and blue (No. 29)	£350
Z9	3d. sage-green (No. 21)	£1300

Stamps of JAMAICA *cancelled with Type* Z 3.

1898 *to* **1901**.

No.	Description	Price
Z10	½d. yellow-green (No. 16)	£225
	a. Green (No. 16*a*)	£225
Z11	1d. purple and mauve (No. 27)	£250
Z12	1d. red (No. 31)	£250
Z13	2½d. dull purple and blue (No. 29)	£325

OFFICIAL STAMPS

Stamps of JAMAICA *cancelled with Type* Z 1.

1889 *to* **1894**.

No.	Description	Price
Z14	½d. green (No. O1)	£550
Z15	½d. green (No. O3)	£650
Z16	1d. rose (No. O4)	£650
Z17	2d. grey (No. O5)	£950

Stamps of JAMAICA *cancelled with Type* Z 2.

1895 *to* **1898**.

No.	Description	Price
Z18	½d. green (No. O3)	£850
Z19	1d. rose (No. O4)	£1300
Z20	2d. grey (No. O5)	£1300

STAKE BAY, CAYMAN BRAC

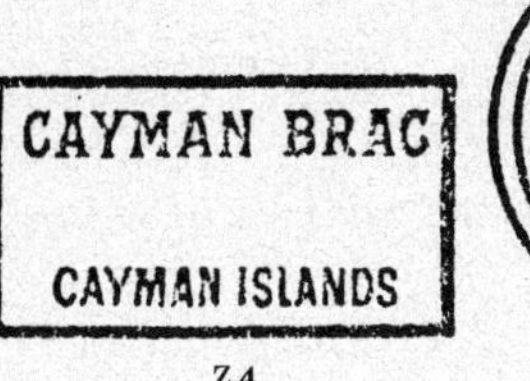

Z 4

Z 5

Stamps of JAMAICA *cancelled with Type* Z 4.

1898 *to* **1900**.

No.	Description	Price
Z21	½d. yellow-green (No. 16)	£950
Z22	1d. purple and mauve (No. 27)	£2500
Z23	2d. green (No. 28)	£1300
Z24	2½d. dull purple and blue (No. 29)	£950

Stamps of JAMAICA *cancelled with Type* Z 5.

1900 *to* **1901**.

No.	Description	Price
Z25	1d. purple and mauve (No. 27)	£950
Z26	1d. red (No. 31)	£1300
Z27	2½d. dull purple and blue (No. 29)	£950

PRICES FOR STAMPS ON COVER TO 1945

Nos. 1/2	*from* × 20
Nos. 3/12	*from* × 5
Nos. 13/24	*from* × 3
Nos. 25/34	*from* × 5
Nos. 38/52*b*	*from* × 3
Nos. 53/67	*from* × 4
Nos. 69/83	*from* × 3
Nos. 84/95	*from* × 5
Nos. 96/9	*from* × 4
Nos. 100/11	*from* × 3
Nos. 112/14	*from* × 5
Nos. 115/26	*from* × 2

DEPENDENCY OF JAMAICA

1

2

3

(T **1/9** and **12/13** typo D.L.R.)

1900 (Nov). *Wmk Crown CA. P* 14.

No.	Type	Description	Unused	Used
1	**1**	½d. deep green	3·75	5·00
		a. Pale green	1·50	3·75
2		1d. rose-carmine	4·00	2·25
		a. Pale carmine	7·00	8·00
1/2 Optd "Specimen"		*Set of* 2	£130	

1901 (20 Dec)–**03**. *Wmk Crown CA. P* 14.

No.	Type	Description	Unused	Used
3	**2**	½d. green (15.9.02)	3·50	7·50
4		1d. carmine (6.3.03)	7·50	7·50
5		2½d. bright blue	7·50	11·00
6		6d. brown	22·00	28·00
7	**3**	1s. orange	65·00	75·00
3/7 Optd "Specimen"		*Set of* 5	£275	

1905 (Mar–18 Oct). *Wmk Mult Crown CA. P* 14.

No.	Type	Description	Unused	Used
8	**2**	½d. green	80	3·00
9		1d. carmine (18.10)	11·00	17·00
10		2½d. bright blue	4·25	9·50
11		6d. brown	28·00	40·00
12	**3**	1s. orange	50·00	60·00

1907 (13 Mar). *Wmk Mult Crown CA. P* 14.

No.	Type	Description	Unused	Used
13	**3**	4d. brown and blue	24·00	32·00
14	**2**	6d. olive and rose	24·00	32·00
15	**3**	1s. violet and green	35·00	45·00
16		5s. salmon and green	£170	£250
13/16 Optd "Specimen"		*Set of* 4	£375	

One Halfpenny. (4)

½D (5)

1D (6)

1907 (30 Aug). *No. 9 surch at Govt Printing Office, Kingston, with T* **4**.

No.	Type	Description	Unused	Used
17	**2**	½d. on 1dd. carmine	32·00	48·00

1907 (Nov). *No. 16 handstamped at Georgetown P.O. with T* **5** *or* **6**.

No.	Type	Description	Unused	Used
18	**3**	½d. on 5s. salmon and green (26.11)	£250	£350
		a. Surch inverted	£12000	
		b. Surch double	£8000	£9000
		c. Surch double, one inverted		
		d. Surch omitted (in pair with normal)	£16000	
19		1d. on 5s. salmon and green (23.11)	£225	£300
		a. Surch double	£11000	

The ½d. on 5s. may be found with the figures "1" or "2" omitted, owing to defective handstamping.

8

9

2½D

(10)

1907 (27 Dec)–**09**. *Ordinary paper* (½*d. to* 2½*d.*) *or chalk-surfaced papers* (*others*). *P* 14. (*a*) *Wmk Mult Crown CA.*

No.	Type	Description	Unused	Used
25	**8**	½d. green	1·40	2·00
26		1d. carmine	1·40	1·75
27		2½d. ultramarine (30.3.08)	6·50	12·00
28	**9**	3d. purple/*yellow* (30.3.08)	6·50	12·00
29		4d. black and red/*yellow* (30.3.08)	55·00	65·00
30	**8**	6d. dull and bright purple (2.10.08)	10·00	22·00
		a. Dull purple and violet-purple	13·00	22·00

No.	Type	Description	Unused	Used
31	9	1s. black/*green* (5.4.09)	9·50	20·00
32		5s. green and red/*yellow* (30.3.08)	45·00	55·00
		(*b*) *Wmk Crown CA* (30.3.08)		
33	9	1s. black/*green*	28·00	48·00
34	8	10s. green and red/*green*	£250	£375
25/34		*Set of* 10	£375	£550
25/34 (*except* 31) Optd "Specimen"		*Set of* 9	£475	

1908 (12 Feb). *No. 13 handstamped locally with T* **10**.

No.	Type	Description	Unused	Used
35		2½d. on 4d. brown and blue	£1800	£2500
		a. Surch double	£20000	£15000

The 1d. on 4d. (No. 29) is a revenue stamp and was never authorised for postal use (*price* £225 *un.*). Exists with surcharge inverted (*price* £2000 *un.*).

MANUSCRIPT PROVISIONALS. During May 1908 supplies of ½d. and 1d. stamps became exhausted, and the payment of postage was indicated by a manuscript endorsement. Such endorsements were in use from 12 to 23 May.

No.	Description	*Price on cover*
MP1	"Postage Paid G.A.P." (12, 18 and 23 May)	£1500
MP1*a*	"½ Postage Paid G.A.P." (23 May)	£2250

In October of the same year there was a further shortage of ¼d. stamps and the manuscript endorsements were again introduced.

No.	Description	*Price on cover*
MP2	"Pd ¼d. W. J. McC." (4 to 27 October)	£190
MP3	"Paid" (7 October)	£3250
MP4	"Pd ¼d" (8 October)	£2500
MP5	"Paid ¼ GAP. asst." (15 October)	£2500

No. MP2 exists in different inks and formats.

Manuscript endorsement for the 2½d. rate is also known, but this is thought to have been done by oversight.

11 12 13

1908 (30 June)–**09**. *Wmk Mult Crown CA. Litho. P* 14.

No.	Type	Description	Unused	Used
38	11	¼d. brown, **O** (Optd S. £65)	25	50
		a. Grey-brown (2.09)	90	1·40

1912 (24 Apr)–**20**. *Wmk Mult Crown CA. Ordinary paper* (¼*d. to* 2½*d.*) *or chalk-surfaced paper* (*others*). *P* 14.

No.	Type	Description	Unused	Used
40	13	¼d. brown (10.2.13)	30	60
41	12	½d. green	60	2·25
42		1d. red (25.2.13)	1·00	1·75
43	13	2d. pale grey	1·00	3·00
44	12	2½d. bright blue (26.8.14)	5·50	8·50
		a. Deep bright blue (9.11.17)	7·50	11·00
45	13	3d. purple/*yellow* (26.11.14)	11·00	14·00
		a. White back (19.11.13) (Optd S. £50)	3·00	5·50
		b. On lemon (12.3.18)	3·00	8·50
		c. On orange-buff (1920)	6·00	12·00
		d. On pale yellow (1920)	5·00	11·00
46		4d. black and red/*yellow* (25.2.13)	1·75	4·50
47	12	6d. dull and bright purple (25.2.13)	3·75	7·00
48	13	1s. black/*green* (15.5.16)	8·50	12·00
		a. White back (19.11.13) (Optd S. £65)	7·00	9·00
49		2s. purple and bright blue/*blue*	12·00	23·00
50		3s. green and violet	17·00	26·00
51		5s. green and red/*yellow* (26.8.14)	48·00	70·00
52	12	10s. deep green and red/*green* (26.11.14)	£110	£140
		a. White back (19.11.13) (Optd S. £100)	£110	£140
		b. On blue-green, olive back (5.10.18)	£100	£160
40/52*b*		*Set of* 13	£180	£275
40/52 Optd "Specimen"		*Set of* 13	£500	

WAR STAMP. 1½d (14) WAR STAMP. 1½d (15)

1917 (26 Feb). *T* **12**, *surch with T* **14** *or* **15**.

No.	Type	Description	Unused	Used
53	14	1½d. on 2½d. deep blue	1·75	4·50
		a. No fraction bar	40·00	55·00
		b. Missing stop after "STAMP" (R.1/4)	£170	
54	15	1½d. on 2½d. deep blue	70	3·00
		a. No fraction bar	27·00	42·00

In No. 53 the spacing between the word "STAMP" and the top of the figure "1" varies between 1½ mm and 5 mm.

WAR STAMP 1½d (16) WAR STAMP 1½d (17) WAR STAMP 1½d. (18)

1917 (4 Sept). *T* **12** *surch with T* **16** *or* **17**.

No.	Type	Description	Unused	Used
55	16	1½d. on 2½d. deep blue	£950	£1400
56	17	1½d. on 2½d. deep blue (Optd S.£100)	30	50

1919–20. *T* **12** *and* **13** (2½*d. special printing*), *optd only, or surch in addition.*

No.	Type	Description	Unused	Used
57	16	½d. green (4.2.19)	35	90
58	18	1½d. on 2d. grey (10.3.20)	1·50	3·75
59	17	1½d. on 2½d. orange (4.2.19)	1·25	2·50
57, 59 Optd "Specimen"		*Set of* 2	£120	

In T **16** the "R" of "WAR" has a curved foot and the other letters vary slightly from T **17**. "1½d." is in thin type. In T **17** the "R" has a straight foot, and the "1½d." differs.

The ½d. stamps on *buff* paper, and later consignments of the 2d. T **13** on *pinkish*, derived their colour from the paper in which they were packed for despatch from England.

19

20 King William IV and King George V

(Recess D.L.R.)

1921 (4 Apr)–**26**. *P* 14. (*a*) *Wmk Mult Crown CA.*

No.	Type	Description	Unused	Used
60	19	3d. purple/*orange-buff*	2·75	8·00
		a. Purple/pale yellow	60·00	70·00
62		4d. red/*yellow* (1.4.22)	1·40	6·00
63		1s. black/*green*	5·00	11·00
64		5s. yellow-green/*pale yellow*	22·00	40·00
		a. Deep green/pale yellow	30·00	55·00
		b. Blue-green/pale yellow	35·00	55·00
		c. Deep green/orange-buff (19.11.21)	30·00	55·00
67		10s. carmine/*green* (19.11.21)	70·00	90·00
60/7 Optd "Specimen"		*Set of* 5	£375	
		(*b*) *Wmk Mult Script CA*		
69	19	¼d. yellow-brown (1.4.22)	30	65
70		½d. pale grey-green (1.4.22)	50	75
71		1d. deep carmine-red (1.4.22)	50	1·25
72		1½d. orange-brown	90	1·25
73		2d. slate-grey (1.4.22)	1·50	3·00
74		2½d. bright blue (1.4.22)	1·40	2·00
75		3d. purple/*yellow* (29.6.23)	1·40	2·00
76		4½d. sage-green (29.6.23)	2·50	6·00
77		6d. claret (1.4.22)	5·50	11·00
		a. Deep claret	14·00	20·00
79		1s. black/*green* (15.5.25)	4·50	11·00
80		2s. violet/*blue* (1.4.22)	8·50	13·00
81		3s. violet (1.4.22)	17·00	30·00
82		5s. green/*yellow* (15.2.25)	28·00	40·00
83		10s. carmine/*green* (5.9.26)	60·00	90·00
69/83		*Set of* 14	£120	£190
69/83 Optd "Specimen"		*Set of* 14	£600	

(Recess Waterlow)

1932 (5 Dec). *Centenary of the "Assembly of Justices and Vestry". Wmk Mult Script CA. P* 12½.

No.	Type	Description	Unused	Used
84	20	¼d. brown	1·00	1·50
85		½d. green	2·25	3·75
86		1d. scarlet	2·25	2·75
87		1½d. red-orange	2·50	3·00
88		2d. grey	3·00	3·50
89		2½d. ultramarine	3·00	3·50
90		3d. olive-green	6·00	14·00
91		6d. purple	15·00	23·00
92		1s. black and brown	24·00	30·00
93		2s. black and ultramarine	60·00	65·00
94		5s. black and green	£225	£250
95		10s. black and scarlet	£600	£800
84/95		*Set of* 12	£850	£1000
84/95 Perf "Specimen"		*Set of* 12	£1000	

1935 (6 May). *Silver Jubilee. As Nos.* 91/4 *of Antigua.*

No.	Type	Description	Unused	Used
96		½d. black and green	30	55
		e. Horiz line from turret	5·00	
97		2½d. brown and deep blue	1·75	3·50
98		6d. light blue and olive-green	4·00	5·50
99		1s. slate and purple	6·00	7·50
96/9 Perf "Specimen"		*Set of* 4	75·00	

For illustration of plate variety see Omnibus section following Zululand.

21 Cayman Islands

24 Conch Shells and Coconut Palms

(Recess Waterlow)

1935 (1 May)–**36**. *T* **21**, **24** *and similar designs. Wmk Mult Script CA. P* 12½.

No.	Type	Description	Unused	Used
100	21	¼d. black and brown	15	15
101	–	½d. ultramarine & yellow-green (1.1.36)	40	45
102	–	1d. ultramarine and scarlet	3·50	1·40
103	24	1½d. black and orange	1·50	1·00
104	–	2d. ultramarine and purple	1·75	1·25
105	–	2½d. blue and black (1.1.36)	8·00	1·60
106	21	3d. black and olive-green	3·00	1·75
107	–	6d. bright purple and black (1.1.36)	13·00	12·00
108	–	1s. ultramarine and orange (1.1.36)	7·00	8·50
109	–	2s. ultramarine and black	40·00	45·00
110	–	5s. green and black	50·00	70·00
111	24	10s. black and scarlet	95·00	£150
100/11		*Set of* 12	£200	£250
100/11 Perf "Specimen"		*Set of* 12	£400	

Designs: *Horiz*—½d., 2d., 1s. Cat boat; 1d., 2s. Red-footed Booby; 2½d., 6d. 5s. Hawksbill Turtles.

1937 (13 May). *Coronation Issue. As Nos.* 13/15 *of Aden but ptd by B.W. P* 11 × 11½.

No.	Type	Description	Unused	Used
112		½d. green	55	30
113		1d. carmine	70	45
114		2½d. blue	1·50	1·50
112/14 Perf "Specimen"		*Set of* 3	50·00	

26 Beach View

27 Dolphin fish (*Coryphaena hippurus*)

(Recess D.L.R. (½d., 2d., 6d., 1s., 10s.), Waterlow (others))

1938 (5 May)–**48**. *T* **26/7** *and similar designs. Wmk Mult Script CA* (*sideways on* ¼*d.*, 1*d.*, 1½*d.*, 2½*d.*, 3*d.*, 2*s.*, 5*s.*). *Various perfs.*

No.	Type	Description	Unused	Used
115	26	¼d. red-orange (*p* 12½)	10	30
		a. Perf 13½ × 12½ (16.7.43)	15	45
116	27	½d. green (*p* 13 × 11½)	30	25
		a. Perf 14 (16.7.43)	30	55
117	–	1d. scarlet (*p* 12½)	12	30
118	26	1½d. black (*p* 12½)	15	20
119	–	2d. violet (*p* 11½ × 13)	50	50
		a. Perf 14 (16.7.43)	25	75
120	–	2½d. bright blue (*p* 12½)	15	60
120*a*	–	2½d. orange (*p* 12½) (25.8.47)	2·00	65
121	–	3d. orange (*p* 12½)	30	85
121*a*	–	3d. bright blue (*p* 12½) (25.8.47)	1·75	80
122	–	6d. olive-green (*p* 11½ × 13)	2·50	3·25
		a. Perf 14 (16.7.43)	1·60	75
		b. Brownish olive (*p* 11½ × 13) (8.7.47)	1·10	2·00
123	27	1s. red-brown (*p* 13 × 11½)	2·75	3·00
		a. Perf 14 (16.7.43)	2·00	1·50
124	26	2s. yellow-green (*shades*) (*p* 12½)	18·00	19·00
		a. Deep green (16.7.43)	13·00	13·00
125	–	5s. carmine-lake (*p* 12½)	11·00	9·00
		a. Crimson (1948)	16·00	16·00
126	–	10s. chocolate (*p* 11½ × 13)	20·00	16·00
		a. Perf 14 (16.7.43)	20·00	17·00
115/126*a*		*Set of* 14	48·00	40·00
115/26 Perf "Specimen"		*Set of* 14	£225	

Designs: *Horiz* (*as T* **26**)—1d., 3d. Cayman Islands map; 2½d., 5s. Cayman schooner. *Vert* (*as T* **27**)—2d., 6d., 10s. Hawksbill Turtles.

1946 (26 Aug). *Victory. As Nos.* 28/9 *of Aden.*

No.	Type	Description	Unused	Used
127		1½d. black	20	20
128		3d. orange-yellow	20	15
127/8 Perf "Specimen"		*Set of* 2	45·00	

1948 (29 Nov). *Royal Silver Wedding. As Nos.* 30/1 *of Aden.*

No.	Type	Description	Unused	Used
129		½d. green	20	20
130		10s. violet-blue	16·00	24·00

1949 (10 Oct). *75th Anniv of Universal Postal Union. As Nos.* 114/17 *of Antigua.*

No.	Type	Description	Unused	Used
131		2½d. orange	50	45
132		3d. deep blue	85	60
133		6d. olive	1·25	1·50
134		1s. red-brown	1·75	2·00

31 Cat Boat

32 Coconut Grove, Cayman Brac

(Recess B.W.)

1950 (2 Oct). *T* **31/2** *and similar horiz designs. Wmk Mult Script CA. P* 11½ × 11.

No.	Type	Description	Unused	Used
135		¼d. bright blue and pale scarlet	30	85
136		½d. reddish violet and emerald-green	30	80
137		1d. olive-green and deep blue	1·00	1·25
138		1½d. green and brown	70	95
139		2d. reddish violet and rose-carmine	1·40	1·75
140		2½d. turquoise and black	1·40	1·60
141		3d. bright green and light blue	2·25	1·50
142		6d. red-brown and blue	1·90	2·00
143		9d. scarlet and grey-green	4·00	4·00
144		1s. brown and orange	3·50	4·00
145		2s. violet and reddish purple	7·50	12·00
146		5s. olive-green and violet	12·00	14·00
147		10s. black and scarlet	18·00	24·00
135/47		*Set of* 13	48·00	60·00

Designs:—1d. Green Turtle; 1½d. Thatch rope industry; 2d. Cayman seamen; 2½d. Map of Cayman Islands; 3d. Parrot Fish; 6d. Bluff, Cayman Brac; 9d. Georgetown harbour; 1s. Turtle in "crawl"; 2s. Cayman schooner; 5s. Boat-building; 10s. Government Offices, Grand Cayman.

44 South Sound Lighthouse, Grand Cayman

45 Queen Elizabeth II

(Recess B.W.)

1953 (2 Mar)–**59**. *Designs previously used for King George VI issue but with portrait of Queen Elizabeth II as in T* **44/5**. *Wmk Mult Script CA. P* 11½ × 11 *or* 11 × 11½ (4*d.*, £1).

No.	Type	Description	Unused	Used
148		¼d. dp brt blue & rose-red (*shades*) (21.2.55)	20	15
149		½d. purple and bluish green (7.7.54)	8	15

150 1d. brown-olive and indigo (7.7.54) .. 60 20
151 1½d. deep green and red-brown (7.7.54) .. 15 20
152 2d. reddish violet and cerise (2.6.54) .. 80 30
153 2½d. turquoise-blue and black (2.6.54) .. 60 40
154 3d. bright green and blue (21.2.55) .. .. 1·50 60
155 4d. black and deep blue (*shades*) 80 30
156 6d. lake-brown and deep blue (7.7.54) .. 70 25
157 9d. scarlet and bluish green (2.6.54) .. 1·00 30
158 1s. brown and red-orange (21.2.55) .. 1·00 20
159 2s. slate-violet and reddish purple (21.2.55) 7·00 5·50
160 5s. olive-green and slate-violet (21.2.55) .. 9·00 8·00
161 10s. black and rose-red (21.2.55) .. .. 9·00 12·00
161*a* £1 blue (6.1.59) .. .. 29·00 18·00
148/161*a* .. .. *Set of* 15 55·00 42·00

Designs: *Horiz*—¼d. Cat boat; ½d. Coconut grove, Cayman Brac; 1d. Green Turtle; 1½d. Thatch rope industry; 2d. Cayman seamen; 2½d. Map of Cayman Islands; 3d. Parrot Fish; 6d. Bluff, Cayman Brac; 9d. Georgetown harbour; 1s. Turtle in "crawl"; 2s. Cayman schooner; 5s. Boat-building; 10s. Government Offices, Grand Cayman.

1953 (2 June). *Coronation. As No.* 47 *of Aden but ptd by B.W.*
162 1d. black and emerald 15 30

46 Arms of the Cayman Islands

(Photo D.L.R.)

1959 (4 July). *New Constitution. Wmk Mult Script CA. P* 12.
163 **46** 2½d. black and light blue 15 25
164 1s. black and orange 25 20

CROWN COLONY

47 Cuban Amazon

48 Cat Boat

(Recess B.W.)

1962 (28 Nov). *T* **47/8** *and similar designs. W w* **12.** *P* 11 × 11½ (*vert*) *or* 11½ × 11 (*horiz*).
165 ¼d. emerald and red (*shades*) 15 20
166 1d. black and yellow-olive 20 12
167 1½d. yellow and purple 12 12
168 2d. blue and deep brown 15 15
169 2½d. violet and bluish green 15 15
170 3d. bright blue and carmine 20 20
171 4d. deep green and purple 70 40
172 6d. bluish green and sepia 75 45
173 9d. ultramarine and purple 75 55
174 1s. sepia and rose-red 60 30
175 1s. 3d. bluish green and orange-brown .. 1·75 1·90
176 1s. 9d. deep turquoise and violet .. .. 2·25 2·00
177 5s. plum and deep green .. .. .. 3·50 3·75
178 10s. olive and blue .. .. 9·00 11·00
179 £1 carmine and black .. .. .. 17·00 19·00
165/79 .. .. *Set of* 15 32·00 35·00

Designs: *Horiz*—1½d. *Schomburgkia thomsoniana* (orchid); 2d. Map of Cayman Islands; 2½d. Fisherman casting net; 3d. West Bay Beach; 4d. Green Turtle; 6d. Cayman schooner; 1s. Iguana; 1s. 3d. Swimming Pool, Cayman Brac; 1s. 9d. Water sports; 5s. Fort George. *Vert*—9d. Angler with Kingfish; 10s. Coat of Arms; £1 Queen Elizabeth II.

1963 (4 June). *Freedom from Hunger. As No.* 76 *of Aden.*
180 1s. 9d. carmine 80 55

1963 (2 Sept). *Red Cross Centenary. As Nos.* 147/8 *of Antigua.*
181 1d. red and black 20 12
182 1s. 9d. red and blue .. .. 1·40 1·00

1964 (23 April). *400th Birth Anniv of William Shakespeare. As No.* 164 *of Antigua.*
183 6d. magenta 20 12

1965 (17 May). *I.T.U. Centenary. As Nos.* 166/7 *of Antigua.*
184 1d. blue and light purple 30 10
185 1s. 3d. bright purple and green .. .. 1·25 55

1965 (25 Oct). *International Co-operation Year. As Nos.* 168/9 *of Antigua.*
186 1d. reddish purple and turquoise-green .. 10 10
187 1s. deep bluish green and lavender 50 40

1966 (24 Jan). *Churchill Commemoration. As Nos.* 170/3 *of Antigua.*
188 ¼d. new blue 5 5
189 1d. deep green 20 10
190 1s. brown 70 35
191 1s. 9d. bluish violet 90 60

1966 (4 Feb). *Royal Visit. As Nos.* 174/5 *of Antigua.*
192 1d. black and ultramarine 20 10
193 1s. 9d. black and magenta 65 40

1966 (1 July). *World Cup Football Championships. As Nos.* 176/7 *of Antigua.*
194 1½d. violet, yellow-green, lake & yellow-brn 12 10
195 1s. 9d. chocolate, blue-grn, lake & yell-brn 40 40

1966 (20 Sept). *Inauguration of W.H.O. Headquarters, Geneva. As Nos.* 178/9 *of Antigua.*
196 2d. black, yellow-green and light blue .. 20 10
197 1s. 3d. black, light purple and yellow-brown 45 40

62 Telephone and Map

(Des V. Whiteley. Litho Harrison)

1966 (5 Dec). *International Telephone Links. W w* **12.** *P* 14½ × 14.
198 **62** 4d. red, black, greenish blue & ol-grn .. 10 10
199 9d. violet-blue, black, brown-red & lt grn 15 15

1966 (12 Dec*). *20th Anniv of U.N.E.S.C.O. As Nos.* 196/8 *of Antigua.*
200 1d. slate-violet, red, yellow and orange .. 15 10
201 1s. 9d. orange-yellow, violet and deep olive 55 30
202 5s. black, bright purple and orange .. 1·60 1·50

*This is the local date of issue; the Crown Agents released the stamps on 1 December.

63 BAC 1-11 Airliner over Cayman Schooner

(Des V. Whiteley. Photo Harrison)

1966 (17 Dec). *Opening of Cayman Jet Service. W w* **12.** *P* 14½.
203 **63** 1s. black, new blue and olive-green .. 20 12
204 1s. 9d. deep purple-brown, ultramarine and emerald 30 20

64 Water-skiing

(Des G. Vasarhelyi. Photo Harrison)

1967 (1 Dec). *International Tourist Year. T* **64** *and similar horiz designs. Multicoloured. W w* **12.** *P* 14½ × 14.
205 4d. Type **64** 12 5
a. Gold omitted .. .. 90·00 45·00
206 6d. Skin diving 12 10
207 1s. Sport fishing 15 10
208 1s. 9d. Sailing 25 20

A used copy of No. 207 is known with yellow omitted.

68 Former Slaves and Emblem

(Des and photo Harrison)

1968 (3 June). *Human Rights Year. W w* **12.** *P* 14½ × 14.
209 **68** 3d. deep bluish green, black and gold .. 5 5
210 9d. brown, gold and myrtle-green .. 10 10
211 5s. ultramarine, gold and myrtle-green 50 50

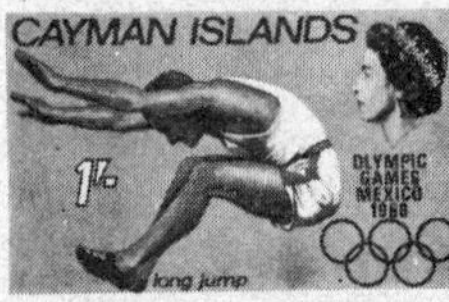

69 Long-jumping

(Des R. Granger Barrett. Litho P.B.)

1968 (1 Oct). *Olympic Games, Mexico. T* **69** *and similar multi-coloured designs. W w* **12.** *P* 13½.
212 1s. Type **69** 15 12
213 1s. 3d. High jumping 20 20
214 2s. Pole vaulting (*vert*) 30 30

MINIMUM PRICE

The minimum price quoted is 5p which represents a handling charge rather than a basis for valuing common stamps. For further notes about prices see introductory pages.

72 "The Adoration of the Shepherds" (Fabritius)

(Des and photo Harrison)

1968–69. *Christmas. T* **72** *and similar horiz design. Centres multicoloured; country name and frames in gold; value and background in colours given. P* 14 × 14½.

(*a*) *W w* **12.** (18.11.68)
215 **72** ¼d. brown 5 5
a. Gold omitted £130
216 – 1d. bluish violet 5 5
217 **72** 6d. bright blue 10 10
218 – 8d. cerise 12 12
219 **72** 1s. 3d. bright green 15 15
220 – 2s. grey 15 20

(*b*) *No wmk* (8.1.69)
221 **72** ¼d. bright purple 5 5
215/21 .. .. *Set of* 7 60 65

Design:—1d., 8d., 2s. "The Adoration of the Shepherds" (Rembrandt).

74 Grand Cayman Thrush

76 Arms of the Cayman Islands

(Des G. Vasarhelyi. Litho Format)

1969 (5 June). *Designs as T* **74** *and T* **76** *in black, ochre and red* (£1) *or multicoloured* (*others*). *No wmk. P* 14.
222 ¼d. Type **74** 5 5
223 1d. Brahmin Cattle (*horiz*) 10 5
224 2d. Blowholes on the coast (*horiz*) 10 5
225 2½d. Map of Grand Cayman (*horiz*) 15 5
226 3d. Georgetown scene (*horiz*) 15 5
227 4d. Royal Poinciana (*horiz*) 30 5
228 6d. Cayman Brac and Little Cayman on Chart (*horiz*) 30 10
229 8d. Motor vessels at berth (*horiz*) 30 12
230 1s. Basket-making (*horiz*) 25 12
231 1s. 3d. Beach scene (*horiz*) 40 70
232 1s. 6d. Straw-rope making (*horiz*) 50 80
233 2s. Barracuda (*horiz*) .. .. .. 1·00 1·00
234 4s. Government House (*horiz*) .. .. 90 1·25
235 10s. Type **76** .. .. 1·75 2·50
236 £1 Queen Elizabeth II (*vert*) .. .. 3·50 4·50
222/36 .. .. *Set of* 15 9·00 10·00

1969 (11 Aug). *As No.* 222, *but wmk w* **12** (*sideways*).
237 **74** ¼d. multicoloured 10 15

(New Currency. 100 cents = 1 dollar.)

C-DAY
8th September 1969 ¼C=

(89)

1969 (8 Sept). *Decimal Currency. No.* 237, *and as Nos.* 223/36, *but wmk w* **12** (*sideways on horiz designs*), *surch as T* **89.**
238 ¼ c. on ¼d. Type **74** 5 5
239 1 c. on 1d. Brahmin Cattle 5 5
240 2 c. on 2d. Blowholes on the coast 5 5
241 3 c. on 4d. Royal Poinciana 5 5
242 4 c. on 2½d. Map of Grand Cayman 8 8
243 5 c. on 6d. Cayman Brac and Little Cayman on Chart 8 10
244 7 c. on 8d. Motor vessels at berth 12 10
245 8 c. on 3d. Georgetown scene 15 10
246 10 c. on 1s. Basket-making 25 12
247 12 c. on 1s. 3d. Beach scene 35 40
248 15 c. on 1s. 6d. Straw-rope making 45 50
249 20 c. on 2s. Barracuda .. .. 1·25 1·25
250 40 c. on 4s. Government House .. .. 1·00 1·25
251 $1 on 10s. Type **76** .. .. 2·25 2·75
252 $2 on £1 Queen Elizabeth II .. .. 4·25 7·50
238/52 .. .. *Set of* 15 9·50 13·00

90 "Virgin and Child" (Vivarini)

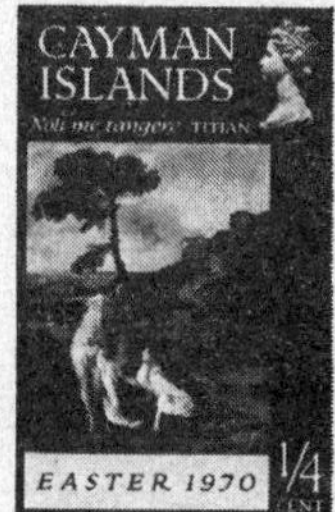

92 "Noli me tangere" (Titian)

(Des adapted by G. Drummond. Photo Harrison)

1969 (14 Nov*). *Christmas. Multicoloured; background colours given. W w* **12** *(sideways on 1, 7 and 20 c.). P* 14½.

253	**90**	¼ c. orange-red	5	5
254		¼ c. magenta	5	5
255		¼ c. emerald	5	5
		a. Gold frame omitted	£120	
256		¼ c. new blue	5	5
257	–	1 c. ultramarine	5	5
258	**90**	5 c. orange-red	8	8
259	–	7 c. myrtle-green	10	10
260	**90**	12 c. emerald	15	15
261	–	20 c. brown-purple	25	30
253/61		*Set of* 9	60	80

Design:—1, 7, 20 c. "The Adoration of the Kings" (Gossaert).

*This is the local release date. The Crown Agents released the stamps on 4 November.

(Des L. Curtis. Litho D.L.R.)

1970 (23 Mar). *Easter. Paintings multicoloured; frame colours given. P* 14.

262	**92**	¼ c. carmine-red	5	5
263		¼ c. deep green	5	5
264		¼ c. yellow-brown	5	5
265		¼ c. pale violet	5	5
266		10 c. chalky blue	15	15
267		12 c. chestnut	15	15
268		40 c. plum	35	45
262/8		*Set of* 7	65	75

93 Barnaby (*Barnaby Rudge*)

97 Cayman Red-legged Thrush

(Des Jennifer Toombs. Photo Harrison)

1970 (17 June). *Death Centenary of Charles Dickens. T* **93** *and similar vert designs. W w* **12** *(sideways). P* 14½ × 14.

269	1 c. black, olive-green and greenish yellow	5	5
270	12 c. black, lake-brown and red	20	20
271	20 c. black, ochre-brown and gold	30	35
272	40 c. black, bright ultramarine and new blue	70	80

Designs:—12 c. Sairey Gamp (*Martin Chuzzlewit*); 20 c. Mr. Micawber and David (*David Copperfield*); 40 c. The "Marchioness" (*The Old Curiosity Shop*).

1970 (8 Sept). *Decimal Currency. Designs as Nos. 223/37, but with values inscr in decimal currency as T* **97**. *W w* **12** *(sideways on cent values).*

273	¼ c. Type **97**	10	5
274	1 c. Brahmin Cattle	10	8
275	2 c. Blowholes on the coast	10	10
276	3 c. Royal Poinciana	20	10
277	4 c. Map of Grand Cayman	20	12
278	5 c. Cayman Brac and Little Cayman on Chart	35	10
279	7 c. Motor vessels at berth	30	10
280	8 c. Georgetown scene	30	15
281	10 c. Basket-making	30	15
282	12 c. Beach scene	90	45
283	15 c. Straw-rope making	2·00	1·00
284	20 c. Barracuda	2·75	1·75
285	40 c. Government House	2·00	2·00
286	$1 Type **76**	4·50	4·75
287	$2 Queen Elizabeth II	7·50	8·50
273/87	*Set of* 15	19·00	17·00

98 The Three Wise Men

(Des G. Drummond. Litho Format)

1970 (8 Oct). *Christmas. T* **98** *and similar horiz design. W w* **12** *(sideways). P* 14.

288	**98**	¼ c. apple-green, grey and emerald	5	5
289	–	1 c. black, lemon and turquoise-green	5	5
290	**98**	5 c. grey, red-orange and crimson	10	10
291	–	10 c. black, lemon and orange-red	15	15
292	**98**	12 c. grey, pale turquoise & ultram	15	15
293	–	20 c. black, lemon and green	25	30
288/93		*Set of* 6	65	70

Design:—1, 10, 20 c. Nativity scene and Globe.

PRICES OF SETS

Set prices are given for many issues, generally those containing five stamps or more. Definitive sets include one of each value or major colour change, but do not cover different perforations, die types or minor shades. Where a choice is possible the set prices are based on the cheapest versions of the stamps included in the listings.

100 Grand Cayman Terrapin

(Des V. Whiteley. Photo Harrison)

1971 (28 Jan). *Turtles. T* **100** *and similar diamond-shaped designs. W w* **12** *(sideways, reading from inscr to "ISLANDS"). P* 14½ × 14.

294	5 c. Type **100**	45	45
295	7 c. Green Turtle	50	50
296	12 c. Hawksbill Turtle	80	90
297	20 c. Turtle Farm	1·50	1·75

101 *Dendrophylax fawcettii*

102 "Adoration of the Kings" (French, 15th Cent)

(Des Sylvia Goaman. Litho Questa)

1971 (7 Apr). *Orchids. T* **101** *and similar vert designs. Multicoloured. W w* **12**. *P* 14.

298	¼ c. Type **101**	5	5
299	2 c. *Schomburgkia thomsoniana*	40	30
300	10 c. *Vanilla claviculata*	90	90
301	40 c. *Oncidium variegatum*	2·75	3·50

(Des Jennifer Toombs. Litho Questa)

1971 (15 Oct*). *Christmas. T* **102** *and similar vert designs. Multicoloured. W w* **12**. *P* 14.

302	¼ c. Type **102**	5	5
303	1 c. "The Nativity" (Parisian, 14th Cent.)	5	5
304	5 c. "Adoration of the Magi" (Burgundian, 15th Cent.)	10	10
305	12 c. Type **102**	25	30
306	15 c. As 1 c.	30	35
307	20 c. As 5 c.	40	60
302/7	*Set of* 6	1·00	1·25
MS308	113 × 115 mm. Nos. 302/7	2·00	2·75

*This is the local date of issue. The Crown Agents released the stamps on 27 September.

103 Turtle and Telephone Cable

(Des Anglo Arts Associates. Litho Walsall)

1972 (10 Jan). *Co-Axial Telephone Cable. W w* **12** *(sideways). P* 14.

309	**103**	2 c. multicoloured	5	5
310		10 c. multicoloured	25	25
311		40 c. multicoloured	75	1·25

104 Court House Building

(Des C. Abbott. Litho Questa)

1972 (15 Aug). *New Government Buildings. T* **104** *and similar horiz design. Multicoloured. W w* **12**. *P* 13½.

312	5 c. Type **104**	10	10
313	15 c. Legislative Assembly Building	30	40
314	25 c. Type **104**	45	55
315	40 c. As 15 c.	65	1·00
MS316	121 × 108 mm. Nos. 312/15	1·50	2·40

105 Hawksbill Turtle and Conch Shell

(Des (from photograph by D. Groves) and photo Harrison)

1972 (20 Nov). *Royal Silver Wedding. Multicoloured; background colour given. W w* **12**. *P* 14 × 14½.

317	**105**	12 c. deep slate-violet	20	20
318		30 c. yellow-olive	30	30
		a. Blue omitted*	£250	

*The omission of the blue colour results in the Duke's suit appearing sepia instead of deep blue.

106 $1 Coin and Note

107 "The Way of Sorrow"

(Des and photo D.L.R.)

1973 (15 Jan). *First Issue of Currency. T* **106** *and similar horiz designs. Multicoloured. W w* **12** *(sideways). P* 13.

319	3 c. Type **106**	10	10
320	6 c. $5 Coin and note	20	20
321	15 c. $10 Coin and note	45	50
322	25 c. $25 Coin and note	60	75
MS323	128 × 107 mm. Nos. 319/22	2·50	2·75

(Des G. Drummond. Litho Questa)

1973 (11 Apr*). *Easter. T* **107** *and similar multicoloured designs showing stained-glass windows. W w* **12** *(sideways on 10 and 12 c.). P* 14½.

324	10 c. Type **107**	15	15
325	12 c. "Christ Resurrected"	25	25
326	20 c. "The Last Supper" (*horiz*)	40	40
327	30 c. "Christ on the Cross" (*horiz*)	60	60
MS328	122 × 105 mm. Nos. 324/7. Imperf	2·25	2·75

*This is the local date of issue; the Crown Agents released the stamps on 15 March.

108 "The Nativity" (Sforza Book of Hours)

109 White-winged Dove

(Des J. Cooter. Litho Questa)

1973 (2 Oct). *Christmas. T* **108** *and similar vert design. W w* **12** *(sideways). P* 14.

329	**108**	3 c. multicoloured	8	8
330	–	5 c. multicoloured	12	12
331	**108**	9 c. multicoloured	20	20
332	–	12 c. multicoloured	25	25
333	**108**	15 c. multicoloured	30	30
334	–	25 c. multicoloured	50	50
329/34		*Set of* 6	1·25	1·25

Design:—5, 12, 25 c. "The Adoration of the Magi" (Breviary of Queen Isabella).

1973 (14 Nov). *Royal Wedding. As Nos.* 165/6 *of Anguilla. Centre multicoloured. W w* **12** *(sideways). P* 13½.

335	10 c. sage-green	15	20
336	30 c. bright mauve	30	30

(Des M. Goaman. Litho Walsall)

1974 (2 Jan). *Birds (1st series). T* **109** *and similar vert designs. Multicoloured. W w* **12** *(sideways). P* 14.

337	3 c. Type **109**	75	30
338	10 c. Vitelline Warbler	1·40	80
339	12 c. Antillean Grackle	1·40	80
340	20 c. West Indian Red-bellied Woodpecker	2·10	1·75
341	30 c. Stripe-headed Tanager	3·50	3·00
342	50 c. Yucatan Vireo	5·00	4·25
337/42	*Set of* 6	13·00	10·00

See also Nos. 383/8.

110 Old School Building

(Des PAD Studio. Litho Questa)

1974 (1 May). *25th Anniv of University of West Indies. T* **110** *and similar horiz designs. Multicoloured.* W w **12** *(sideways). P* 14.

343 12 c. Type **110** 15 15
344 20 c. New Comprehensive School 25 30
345 30 c. Creative Arts Centre, Mona 40 55

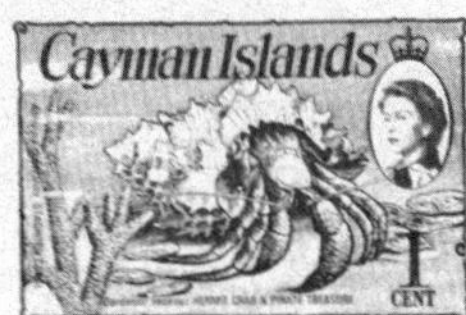

111 Hermit Crab and Staghorn Coral

(Des J.W. Litho Kynoch Press)

1974 (1 Aug). *Multicoloured designs as T* **111** *(size* 41½ × 27 *mm).* W w **12** *(sideways on* $1 *and* $2*). P* 14.

346 1 c. Type **111** 45 35
347 3 c. Treasure-chest and Lion's Paw 75 50
348 4 c. Treasure and Spotted Scorpion-fish .. 60 55
349 5 c. Flintlock pistol and Brain Coral .. 80 50
350 6 c. Blackbeard and Green Turtle 45 60
351 9 c. Jewelled pomander and Pork-fish .. 3·50 3·50
352 10 c. Spiny Lobster and treasure 85 50
353 12 c. Jewelled sword and dagger, and Sea-fan 65 45
354 15 c. Cabrit's Murex and treasure 70 60
355 20 c. Queen Conch and treasure .. .. 2·50 1·75
356 25 c. Hogfish and treasure .. .. 1·00 1·00
357 40 c. Gold chalice and sea-whip .. .. 1·75 1·50
358 $1 Coat of arms *(vert)* .. .. 4·00 4·25
359 $2 Queen Elizabeth II *(vert)*.. .. .. 7·50 9·00
346/59 .. .. *Set of* 14 23·00 23·00

See also Nos. 364/6, 412/19 and 445/51.

112 Sea Captain and Ship (Shipbuilding)

(Des G. Vasarhelyi. Litho D.L.R.)

1974 (7 Oct). *Local Industries. T* **112** *and similar horiz designs. Multicoloured.* W w **12** *(inverted on* 8 c. *and* 12 c.*). P* 14 × 13½.

360 8 c. Type **112** 15 15
361 12 c. Thatcher and cottages 25 25
362 20 c. Farmer and plantation 35 45
MS363 92 × 132 mm. Nos. 360/2 .. .. .. 1·00 1·25

1974–75. *As Nos.* 346/7 *and design of* 351, *but wmk sideways.*

364 1 c. Type **111** (29.9.75) 80 90
365 3 c. Treasure-chest and Lions-paw (12.11.74) 1·75 1·75
366 8 c. Jewelled pomander and Pork-fish (16.12.74).. .. .. 1·75 2·50

Nos. 367/79 vacant.

113 Arms of Cinque Ports and Lord Warden's Flag

114 "The Crucifixion"

(Des P. Powell. Litho D.L.R.)

1974 (30 Nov). *Birth Centenary of Sir Winston Churchill. T* **113** *and similar vert design. Multicoloured.* W w **12** *(sideways). P* 13½ × 14.

380 12 c. Type **113** 25 25
381 50 c. Churchill's coat of arms .. .. .. 1·00 1·25
MS382 98 × 86 mm. Nos. 380/1 .. .. .. 1·75 1·90

(Des M. Goaman. Litho Questa)

1975 (1 Jan). *Birds (2nd series). Multicoloured designs as T* **109**. W w **12** *(sideways). P* 14.

383 3 c. Common Flicker 35 20
384 10 c. Black-billed Whistling Duck 60 45
385 12 c. Yellow Warbler 70 55
386 20 c. White-bellied Dove .. .. .. 1·25 1·25
387 30 c. Magnificent Frigate Bird .. .. 1·90 1·90
388 50 c. Cuban Amazon .. .. 2·50 2·50
a. Error. Wmk Lesotho T **53** (inverted) .. £550
383/8 .. .. *Set of* 6 6·50 6·25

(Des PAD Studio. Litho D.L.R.)

1975 (24 Mar). *Easter. French Pastoral Staffs. T* **114** *and similar vert design showing "The Crucifixion" (different). Multicoloured.* W w **12** *(sideways). P* 13½ × 14.

389 **114** 15 c. multicoloured 25 30
390 – 35 c. multicoloured 40 55
MS391 128 × 98 mm. Nos. 389/90. W w **12** *(upright)* 1·25 1·50
a. Error. Imperf .. .. ..

See also Nos. 396/**MS**398.

115 Israel Hands

(Des J.W. Litho Harrison)

1975 (25 July). *Pirates. T* **115** *and similar horiz designs. Multicoloured.* W w **12** *(sideways). P* 14.

392 10 c. Type **115** 30 20
393 12 c. John Fenn 40 25
394 20 c. Thomas Anstis 75 60
395 30 c. Edward Low .. .. 1·00 75

(Des PAD Studio. Litho Questa)

1975 (31 Oct). *Christmas. Vert designs as T* **114** *showing "Virgin and Child with Angels" (both different).* W w **14**. *P* 14.

396 12 c. multicoloured 20 20
397 50 c. multicoloured .. .. 90 1·00
MS398 113 × 85 mm. Nos. 396/7 .. .. .. 1·40 1·75

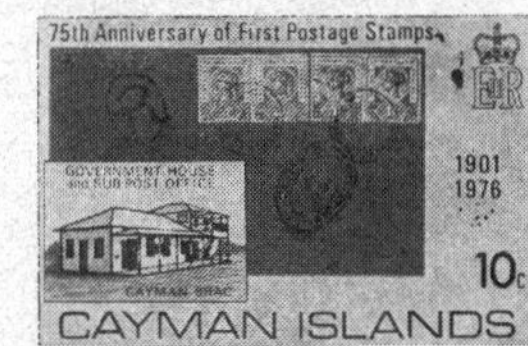

116 Registered Cover, Government House and Sub-Post Office

(Des J. Cooter. Litho Questa)

1976 (12 Mar). *75th Anniv of First Cayman Is. Postage Stamp. T* **116** *and similar horiz designs. Multicoloured.* W w **14** *(sideways). P* 13½.

399 10 c. Type **116** 20 15
400 20 c. ½d. stamp and 1890–94 postmark .. 40 45
401 30 c. 1d. stamp and 1908 surcharge 60 60
402 50 c. ½d. and 1d. stamps .. .. .. 1·00 1·00
MS403 117 × 147 mm. Nos. 399/402 .. .. 2·40 3·00

117 Seals of Georgia, Delaware and New Hampshire

(Des P. Powell. Litho J.W.)

1976 (29 May). *Bicentenary of American Revolution. T* **117** *and similar horiz designs showing seals of the States given. Multicoloured.* W w **14** *(sideways). P* 13½ × 14.

404 10 c. Type **117** 40 30
405 15 c. S. Carolina, New Jersey and Maryland .. 60 45
406 20 c. Virginia, Rhode Is. and Massachusetts .. 70 55
407 25 c. New York, Connecticut and N. Carolina 80 60
408 30 c. Pennsylvania seal, Liberty Bell and U.S. Great Seal 90 70
MS409 166 × 124 mm. Nos. 404/8. P 14 .. .. 6·00 6·00

118 Racing Dinghies

119 Queen Elizabeth II and Westminster Abbey

(Des C. Abbott. Litho D.L.R.)

1976 (16 Aug). *Olympic Games, Montreal. T* **118** *and similar vert design. Multicoloured.* W w **14**. *P* 14.

410 20 c. Type **118** 40 45
411 50 c. Racing dinghy .. .. 1·10 1·00

1976 (3 Sept)–**78**. *As Nos.* 347/9, 352, 355, 358/9 *and* 366, *but* W w **14** *(upright on* $1, *inverted on* $2, *sideways on others). Chalk-surfaced paper (*4, 5 c. *and* $1*) or ordinary paper (others).*

412 3 c. Treasure-chest and Lion's Paw 75 45
a. Chalk-surfaced paper (19.10.77).. .. 1·25 90
413 4 c. Treasure and Spotted Scorpion-fish (19.10.77).. .. .. 90 40
414 5 c. Flintlock pistol and Brain Coral (19.10.77).. .. .. 1·25 40
415 8 c. Jewelled pomander and Pork-fish .. 1·75 60
a. Chalk-surfaced paper (19.10.77).. .. 2·25 1·50
416 10 c. Spiny Lobster and treasure .. .. 1·00 65
a. Chalk-surfaced paper (27.1.78) .. .. 1·75 80
417 20 c. Queen Conch and treasure .. .. 3·00 2·50
a. Chalk-surfaced paper (27.1.78) .. .. 3·50 2·50
418 $1 Coat of arms (19.10.77) .. .. .. 6·50 5·50
419 $2 Queen Elizabeth II .. .. .. 7·50 6·50
a. Chalk-surfaced paper (19.10.77).. .. 11·00 12·00
412/19 .. .. *Set of* 8 20·00 15·00

Nos. 420/6 vacant.

(Des BG Studio. Litho Questa)

1977 (7 Feb). *Silver Jubilee. T* **119** *and similar multicoloured designs.* W w **14** *(sideways on* 50 c.*). P* 13½.

427 8 c. Prince of Wales' visit, 1973 .. .. 20 30
428 30 c. Type **119** 45 65
429 50 c. Preparation for the Anointing *(horiz)* .. 70 90

120 Scuba Diving

(Des Jennifer Toombs. Litho J.W.)

1977 (25 July). *Tourism. T* **120** *and similar horiz designs. Multicoloured.* W w **14** *(sideways). P* 13½.

430 5 c. Type **120** 20 20
431 10 c. Exploring a wreck 30 30
432 20 c. Fairy Basslet (fish) 75 75
433 25 c. Sergeant majors (fish) 85 85
MS434 146 × 89 mm. Nos. 430/3. P 14½.. .. 2·00 2·25

121 *Composia fidelissima*

(Des J. Cooter. Litho Enschedé)

1977 (2 Dec). *Butterflies. T* **121** *and similar horiz designs. Multicoloured.* W w **14** *(sideways). P* 14 × 13.

435 5 c. Type **121** 25 15
436 8 c. Passion-flower Butterfly.. .. .. 35 25
437 10 c. Monarch Butterfly 35 25
438 15 c. *Agraulis vanillae* 60 50
439 20 c. Nymphalid Butterfly 75 65
440 30 c. *Anartia jatrophae* 95 80
435/40 .. .. *Set of* 6 3·00 2·40

122 Cruise Ship *Southward*

123 "The Crucifixion" (Dürer)

(Des G. Hutchins. Litho Questa)

1978 (23 Jan). *New Harbour and Cruise Ships. T* **122** *and similar multicoloured designs.* W w **14** *(sideways on* 3, 5 c.*). P* 14 × 14½ (3, 5 c.) *or* 14½ × 14 *(others).*

441 3 c. Type **122** 15 10
442 5 c. Cruise ship *Renaissance* 20 10
443 30 c. New harbour *(vert)* 90 80
444 50 c. Cruise ship *Daphne (vert)* .. .. 1·50 1·25

(Litho Walsall)

1978 (16 Mar)–**80**. *Designs as Nos.* 346/7, 349, 352, 355 *and* 357/9 *but smaller,* 40 × 26 *or* 26 × 40 *mm.* W w **14** *(sideways on* 1 *to* 40 c.*). Chalk-surfaced paper.*

445 1 c. Type **111** 75 40
446 3 c. Treasure-chest and Lion's Paw 80 35
447 5 c. Flintlock pistol and Brain Coral (11.12.79).. .. .. 1·25 1·00
448 10 c. Spiny Lobster and treasure (25.5.78) .. 1·60 45
449 20 c. Queen Conch and treasure (25.5.78) .. 3·25 1·25
450 40 c. Gold chalice and sea-whip (1979*) .. 8·00 8·50
451 $1 Coat of arms (30.7.80) .. .. .. 5·50 7·00
452 $2 Queen Elizabeth II (3.4.80) .. .. 9·00 11·00
445/52 .. .. *Set of* 8 27·00 27·00

*Supplies of No. 450 were sent to Cayman Islands on 7 May 1979. It is not known when these stamps were first placed on sale.

Nos. 453/8 vacant.

(Des Jennifer Toombs. Litho Cartor S.A., France)

1978 (20 Mar). *Easter and 450th Death Anniv of Dürer. T* **123** *and similar vert designs. W w* **14** (*inverted on* 20 c.). *P* 12.

No.	Value	Description	Unused	Used
459	10 c.	magenta and black	20	20
460	15 c.	yellow and black	35	35
461	20 c.	turquoise-green and black	45	45
462	30 c.	lilac and black	65	65
MS463		120 × 108 mm. Nos. 459/62	1·60	1·75

Designs:—15 c. "Christ at Emmaus"; 20 c. "The Entry into Jerusalem"; 30 c. "Christ washing Peter's Feet".

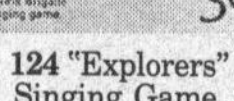

124 "Explorers" Singing Game

125 Yale of Beaufort

(Des Walsall. Litho Questa)

1978 (25 Apr). *3rd International Council Meeting of Girls' Brigade. T* **124** *and similar vert designs. Multicoloured. W w* **14.** *P* 14.

No.	Value	Description	Unused	Used
464	3 c.	Type **124**	15	15
465	10 c.	Colour party	45	45
466	20 c.	Girls and Duke of Edinburgh Award interests	70	70
467	50 c.	Girls using domestic skills	1·50	1·50

(Des C. Abbott. Litho Questa)

1978 (2 June). *25th Anniv of Coronation. T* **125** *and similar vert designs. P* 15.

No.	Value	Description	Unused	Used
468	30 c.	apple-green, deep magenta and silver	35	55
		a. Sheetlet. Nos. 468/70 × 2	2·25	
469	30 c.	multicoloured	35	55
470	30 c.	apple-green, deep magenta and silver	35	55

Designs:—No. 468, Type **125**; No. 469, Queen Elizabeth II; No. 470, Screech Owl.

Nos. 468/70 were printed together in small sheets of 6, containing two *se-tenant* strips of 3, with horizontal gutter margin between.

126 Four Eyed Butterfly Fish

(Des G. Hutchins. Litho Walsall)

1978 (29 Aug). *Fish (1st series). T* **126** *and similar horiz designs. Multicoloured. W w* **14** (*sideways*). *P* 14.

No.	Value	Description	Unused	Used
471	3 c.	Type **126**	15	10
472	5 c.	Grey Angel Fish	20	12
473	10 c.	Squirrel Fish	35	25
474	15 c.	Parrot Fish	50	45
475	20 c.	Spanish Hogfish	60	55
476	30 c.	Queen Angel Fish	75	70
471/6		*Set of* 6	2·25	2·00

Examples of the 15 c. value inscribed "SERGEANT MAJOR FISH" and 20 c. inscribed "PARROT FISH" were prepared, but not issued for postal purposes.

See also Nos. 483/8.

127 Lockheed "Lodestar"

(Des A. Theobald. Litho Format)

1979 (5 Feb). *25th Anniv of Owen Roberts Airfield. T* **127** *and similar horiz designs. Multicoloured. W w* **14** (*sideways*). *P* 14½ × 14.

No.	Value	Description	Unused	Used
477	3 c.	Type **127**	15	10
478	5 c.	Consolidated "PBY"	15	10
479	10 c.	Vickers "Viking"	30	25
480	15 c.	B.A.C. "1-11" on tarmac	45	40
481	20 c.	Piper "Cheyenne", H.S. "125" and Bell "47" (helicopter)	50	45
482	30 c.	B.A.C. "1-11" over airfield	75	65
477/82		*Set of* 6	2·10	1·75

128 Trumpetfish

(Des R. Granger Barrett. Litho Questa)

1979 (20 Apr). *Fish (2nd series). T* **128** *and similar horiz designs. Multicoloured. W w* **14** (*sideways*). *P* 14.

No.	Value	Description	Unused	Used
483	1 c.	Type **128**	5	5
484	3 c.	Nassau Grouper	15	10
485	5 c.	French Angelfish	15	10
486	10 c.	Schoolmaster Snappers	30	30
487	20 c.	Banded Butterflyfish	50	50
488	50 c.	Blackbar Soldierfish	95	95
483/8		*Set of* 6	1·90	1·90

129 1900 1d. Stamp

(Des J.W. Litho Walsall)

1979 (15 Aug). *Death Centenary of Sir Rowland Hill. T* **129** *and similar horiz designs showing stamps and Sir Rowland Hill. W w* **14** (*sideways*). *P* 13½.

No.	Value	Description	Unused	Used
489	5 c.	black, rose-carmine and grey-blue	10	10
490	10 c.	multicoloured	20	25
491	20 c.	multicoloured	35	35
MS492		138 × 90 mm. 50 c. multicoloured	80	90

Designs:—10 c. Great Britain 1902 3d.; 20 c. 1955 £1 definitive; 50 c. 1908 2½d.

130 Holy Family and Angels

(Des G. Vasarhelyi. Litho Secura, Singapore)

1979 (20 Nov). *Christmas. T* **130** *and similar horiz designs. Multicoloured. W w* **14** (*sideways*). *P* 13½ × 13.

No.	Value	Description	Unused	Used
493	10 c.	Type **130**	15	15
494	20 c.	Angels appearing before shepherds	30	30
495	30 c.	Nativity scene	45	45
496	40 c.	Wise men following star	65	65

131 Local Rotary Project

(Des Walsall. Litho Secura, Singapore)

1980 (14 Feb). *75th Anniv of Rotary International. T* **131** *and similar designs in black, bistre-yellow and deep ultramarine. W w* **14** (*sideways on* 20 c.). *P* 13½ × 13 (20 c.) *or* 13 × 13½ (*others*).

No.	Value	Description	Unused	Used
497	20 c.	Type **131**	45	45
498	30 c.	Paul P. Harris (founder) (*vert*)	65	65
499	50 c.	Rotary anniversary emblem (*vert*)	80	80

132 Walking Mail Carrier (late 19th-century)

(Des J.W. Litho Walsall)

1980 (6 May). *"London 1980" International Stamp Exhibition. T* **132** *and similar horiz designs. Multicoloured. W w* **14** (*sideways*). *P* 14.

No.	Value	Description	Unused	Used
500	5 c.	Type **132**	12	12
501	10 c.	Delivering mail by cat boat (late 19th-century)	20	20
502	15 c.	Mounted mail carrier (early 20th-century)	30	30
503	30 c.	Horse-drawn waggonette (early 20th-century)	55	55
504	40 c.	Postman on bicycle (mid 20th-century)	60	60
505	$1	Motor transport (late 20th-century)	1·50	1·50
500/5		*Set of* 6	3·00	3·00

133 Queen Elizabeth the Queen Mother

134 Atlantic Spiny Oyster

(Des and litho Harrison)

1980 (4 Aug). *80th Birthday of Queen Elizabeth the Queen Mother. W w* **14** (*sideways*). *P* 14.

No.	Type	Value	Description	Unused	Used
506	**133**	20 c.	multicoloured	35	35

(Des J.W. Litho Walsall)

1980 (12 Aug). *Shells (1st series). T* **134** *and similar horiz designs. Multicoloured. W w* **14** (*sideways*). *P* 14½ × 14.

No.	Value	Description	Unused	Used
507	5 c.	Type **134**	15	15
508	10 c.	West Indian Murex	25	25
509	30 c.	Triton	60	60
510	50 c.	Murex-line vase shell	80	80

See also Nos. 565/8 and 582/5.

135 Lantana

136 Juvenile Tarpon and Fire Sponge

(Des G. Hutchins. Litho Rosenbaum Bros, Vienna)

1980 (21 Oct). *Flowers (1st series). T* **135** *and similar horiz designs. Multicoloured. W w* **14** (*sideways*). *P* 13½.

No.	Value	Description	Unused	Used
511	5 c.	Type **135**	10	10
512	15 c.	Bauhinia	25	25
513	30 c.	Hibiscus Rosa	45	45
514	$1	Milk and Wine Lily	1·75	1·75

See also Nos. 541/4.

(Des G. Drummond. Litho J.W.)

1980 (9 Dec)–**82.** *Flora and Fauna of the Mangrove Swamp. Vert designs as T* **136**. *Multicoloured. W w* **14.** *P* 13.

A. *Without imprint date.*

B. *Printed with imprint date at foot of designs* (14.6.82).

No.	Value	Description	A		B	
515	3 c.	Type **136**	10	10	5	8
516	5 c.	Mangrove Root Oyster	12	12	8	10
517	10 c.	Mangrove Crab	15	20	15	20
518	15 c.	Lizard and Crescent Spot Butterfly	30	30	25	30
519	20 c.	Louisiana Heron	45	45	35	40
520	30 c.	Red Mangrove Flower	55	60	55	60
521	40 c.	Red Mangrove Seeds	75	80	75	80
522	50 c.	Waterhouse's Leaf-nosed Bat	1·10	1·25	90	95
523	$1	Black-crowned Night Heron	2·00	2·00	1·90	2·00
524	$2	Cayman Islands coat of arms	3·25	3·50	3·75	4·00
525	$4	Queen Elizabeth II	6·50	6·75	7·50	7·75
515/25		*Set of* 11	14·00	14·50	14·50	15·50

137 Eucharist

138 Wood Slave

(Des Jennifer Toombs. Litho Questa)

1981 (17 Mar). *Easter. T* **137** *and similar vert designs. Multicoloured. W w* **14.** *P* 14.

No.	Value	Description	Unused	Used
526	3 c.	Type **137**	10	10
527	10 c.	Crown of thorns	20	15
528	20 c.	Crucifix	35	35
529	$1	Lord Jesus Christ	1·60	1·60

(Des R. Granger Barrett. Litho Rosenbaum Bros, Vienna)

1981 (16 June). *Reptiles and Amphibians. T* **138** *and similar horiz designs. Multicoloured. W w* **14** (*sideways*). *P* 13½.

No.	Value	Description	Unused	Used
530	20 c.	Type **138**	35	35
531	30 c.	Cayman Iguana	55	55
532	40 c.	Lion Lizard	70	70
533	50 c.	Terrapin ("Hickatee")	80	80

139 Prince Charles

140 Disabled Scuba Divers

(Des J.W. Litho Walsall)

1981 (22 July). *Royal Wedding. T* **139** *and similar vert designs. Multicoloured. W w* **14.** *P* 14.

No.	Value	Description	Unused	Used
534	20 c.	Wedding bouquet from Cayman Islands	25	25

535	30 c. Type **139**	40	40
536	$1 Prince Charles and Lady Diana Spencer	1·50	1·50

(Des J.W. Litho Walsall)

1981 (29 Sept). *International Year for Disabled Persons. T* **140** *and similar horiz designs. Multicoloured.* W w **14** *(sideways). P* 14.

537	5 c. Type **140**	10	10
538	15 c. Old School for the Handicapped	30	30
539	20 c. New School for the Handicapped	35	35
540	$1 Disabled people in wheelchairs, by the sea	1·60	1·60

(Des G. Hutchins. Litho Questa)

1981 (20 Oct). *Flowers (2nd series). Horiz designs as T* **135.** *Multicoloured.* W w **14** *(sideways). P* 13½.

541	3 c. Bougainvillea	10	10
542	10 c. Morning Glory	30	30
543	20 c. Wild Amaryllis	50	50
544	$1 Cordia	1·75	1·75

141 Dr. Robert Koch and Microscope

142 Bride and Groom walking down Aisle

(Des and litho Walsall)

1982 (24 Mar). *Centenary of Robert Koch's Discovery of Tubercle Bacillus. T* **141** *and similar multicoloured designs.* W w **14** *(sideways on* 15 c.). *P* 14½.

545	15 c. Type **141**	25	25
546	30 c. Koch looking through microscope *(vert)*	45	45
547	40 c. Microscope *(vert)*	70	70
548	50 c. Dr. Robert Koch *(vert)*	80	80

(Des Jennifer Toombs. Litho J.W.)

1982 (1 July). *21st Birthday of Princess of Wales. T* **142** *and similar vert designs. Multicoloured.* W w **14.** *P* 13.

549	20 c. Cayman Islands coat of arms	35	35
550	30 c. Lady Diana Spencer in London, June 1981	45	45
551	40 c. Type **142**	55	55
552	50 c. Formal portrait	65	70

143 Pitching Tent

144 "Madonna and Child with the Infant Baptist"

(Des L. Walker. Litho Questa)

1982 (24 Aug). *75th Anniv of Boy Scout Movement. T* **143** *and similar horiz designs. Multicoloured.* W w **14** *(sideways). P* 14.

553	3 c. Type **143**	10	10
554	20 c. Scouts camping	40	40
555	30 c. Cub Scouts and Leaders	55	55
556	50 c. Boating skills	85	85

(Des PAD Studio. Litho Questa)

1982 (26 Oct). *Christmas. Raphael Paintings. T* **144** *and similar vert designs. Multicoloured.* W w **14.** *P* 14½ × 14.

557	3 c. Type **144**	8	8
558	10 c. "Madonna of the Tower"	20	20
559	20 c. "Ansidei Madonna"	35	35
560	30 c. "Madonna and Child"	50	50

145 Mace

(Des and litho Walsall)

1982 (9 Nov). *150th Anniv of Representative Government. T* **145** *and similar horiz designs. Multicoloured.* W w **14** *(sideways). P* 14½ × 14.

561	3 c. Type **145**	8	8
562	10 c. Old Courthouse	20	20
563	20 c. Commonwealth Parliamentary Association coat of arms	35	35
564	30 c. Legislative Assembly building	50	60

(Des J.W. Litho Format)

1983 (11 Jan). *Shells (2nd series). Horiz designs as T* **134.** *Multicoloured.* W w **14** *(sideways). P* 13½ × 13.

565	5 c. *Natica canrena*	10	10
566	10 c. *Cassis tuberosa*	20	20
567	20 c. *Strombus gallus*	35	40
568	$1 *Cypraecassis testiculus*	1·60	1·60

146 Legislative Building, Cayman Brac

(Des C. Abbott. Litho Questa)

1983 (15 Feb). *Royal Visit. T* **146** *and similar multicoloured designs.* W w **14** *(sideways on* 20 c., 30 c.). *P* 14.

569	20 c. Type **146**	30	35
570	30 c. Legislative Building, Grand Cayman	45	50
571	50 c. Duke of Edinburgh *(vert)*	80	85
572	$1 Queen Elizabeth II *(vert)*	1·60	1·75
MS573	113 × 94 mm. Nos. 569/72 (wmk sideways)	3·00	3·25

147 Satellite View of Earth

(Des J.W. Litho Questa)

1983 (14 Mar). *Commonwealth Day. T* **147** *and similar horiz designs. Multicoloured.* W w **14** *(sideways). P* 14.

574	3 c. Type **147**	5	8
575	15 c. Cayman Islands and Commonwealth flags	25	30
576	20 c. Fishing	30	35
577	40 c. Portrait of Queen Elizabeth II	60	65

148 MRCU "Cessna" Aircraft

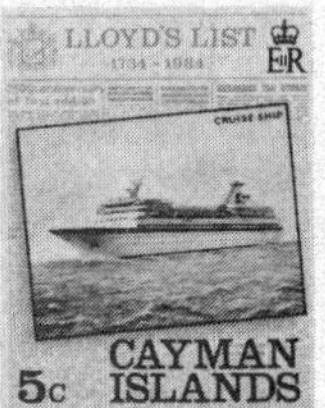

149 Cruise Ship

(Des Harrison. Litho Questa)

1983 (10 Oct). *Bicentenary of Manned Flight. T* **148** *and similar horiz designs. Multicoloured.* W w **14** *(sideways). P* 14.

578	3 c. Type **148**	5	8
579	10 c. Consolidated "PBY Catalina"	15	20
580	20 c. Boeing "727-200"	30	35
581	40 c. Hawker-Siddeley "HS 748"	60	65

(Des J.W. Litho Questa)

1984 (18 Jan). *Shells (3rd series). Horiz designs as T* **134.** *Multicoloured.* W w **14** *(sideways). P* 14 × 14½.

582	3 c. *Natica floridana*	5	8
583	10 c. *Conus austini*	20	25
584	30 c. *Colubraria obscura*	55	60
585	50 c. *Turbo cailletii*	90	95

(Des G. Vasarhelyi and L. Curtis. Litho Questa)

1984 (18 June). *250th Anniv of "Lloyd's List" (newspaper). T* **149** *and similar vert designs. Multicoloured.* W w **14.** *P* 14½ × 14.

586	5 c. Type **149**	10	12
587	10 c. View of old harbour	20	25
588	25 c. Wreck of R.M.S. *Ridgefield*	50	55
589	50 c. Schooner *Goldfield*	1·00	1·10
MS590	105 × 75 mm. $1 Schooner *Goldfield* *(different)*	2·10	2·25

U.P.U. CONGRESS
HAMBURG 1984

(150)

151 Snowy Egret

1984 (18 June). *Universal Postal Union Congress, Hamburg. No.* 589 *optd with T* **150.**

591	50 c. Schooner *Goldfield*	1·00	1·10

(Des Josephine Martin. Litho Questa)

1984 (15 Aug). *Birds of the Cayman Islands. T* **151** *and similar horiz designs. Multicoloured.* W w **14** *(sideways). P* 14 × 14½.

592	5 c. Type **151**	10	12
593	10 c. Bananaquit	20	25
594	35 c. Kingfisher	75	80
595	$1 Brown Booby	2·10	2·25

152 Couple on Beach at Sunset

(Des G. Wilby. Litho Questa)

1984 (17 Oct). *Christmas. Local Festivities. T* **152** *and similar vert designs. Multicoloured.* W w **14** *(sideways). P* 14.

596	5 c. Type **152**	10	12
	a. Horiz strip of 4. Nos. 596/9	40	
597	5 c. Family and schooner	10	12
598	5 c. Carol singers	10	12
599	5 c. East End bonfire	10	12
600	25 c. Yachts	50	55
	a. Horiz strip of 4. Nos. 600/3	2·00	
601	25 c. Father Christmas in power-boat	50	55
602	25 c. Children on beach	50	55
603	25 c. Beach party	50	55
596/603	*Set of* 8	2·25	2·40
MS604	59 × 79 mm. $1 As No. 600, but larger, 27 × 41 mm	2·10	2·25

Nos. 597/600 and 601/4 were each printed together, *se-tenant*, in horizontal strips of 4 throughout the sheets, the four designs of each value forming a composite picture of a beach scene at night (5 c.) or in the daytime (25 c.).

Ceylon

PRICES FOR STAMPS ON COVER TO 1945

Nos. 1/4	*from* × 5
Nos. 5/67	*from* × 4
Nos. 68/117	*from* × 6
Nos. 118/20	*from* × 12
Nos. 121/38	*from* × 4
Nos. 139/41	†
Nos. 142/3	*from* × 6
Nos. 146/51	*from* × 4
Nos. 151*a*/2	†
Nos. 153/93	*from* × 5
Nos. 194/201	*from* × 10
Nos. 202/43	*from* × 4
Nos. 245/9	*from* × 4
Nos. 250/5	*from* × 5
Nos. 256/64	*from* × 4
Nos. 265/76	*from* × 3
Nos. 277/88	*from* × 4
Nos. 289/300	*from* × 8
Nos. 301/25	*from* × 2
Nos. 326/9*a*	—
Nos. 330/7*a*	*from* × 4
Nos. 338/52	*from* × 2
Nos. 353/4	—
Nos. 355/9	*from* × 2
No. 360	—
Nos. 360*a*/*g*	*from* × 2
Nos. 361/2	*from* × 5
Nos. 363/71	*from* × 3
Nos. 372/82	*from* × 2
Nos. 383/5	*from* × 3
Nos. 386/97	*from* × 2
Nos. 398/9	*from* × 8
Nos. O1/17	*from* × 20

CROWN COLONY

PRICES. The prices of the imperf stamps of Ceylon vary greatly according to condition. The following prices are for fine copies with four margins.

Poor to medium specimens can be supplied at much lower prices.

1

2

(Recess P.B.)

1857 (1 April). *Blued paper. Wmk Star W w* **1**. *Imperf.*

1	**1**	6d. purple-brown	£7500	£550

Collectors should beware of proofs with faked watermark, often offered as originals.

(Typo D.L.R.)

1857 (Oct)–**58.** *No wmk. Imperf. (a) Blue glazed paper.*

3	**2**	½d. lilac	£3000	£550
		(b) White glazed paper		
4	**2**	½d. lilac (1858)	£140	80·00

3

4

NOTE. Beware of stamps of Type **3** which are often offered with corners added.

(Recess P.B.)

1857–9. *White paper. Wmk Star, W w* **1**. *(a) Imperf.*

5	**1**	1d. blue (24.8.57)	£450	18·00
6		1d. deep blue	£550	18·00
		a. Blued paper	—	85·00
7		2d. deep green (24.8.57)	£150	50·00
8		2d. yellow-green	£600	£110
9	**3**	4d. dull rose (23.4.59)	£50000	£4500
10	**1**	5d. chestnut (2.7.57)	£2000	£200
11		6d. purple-brown	£1300	£175
12		6d. brown	£4000	£500
12*a*		6d. deep brown	£4500	£1200
13	**3**	8d. brown (23.4.59)	£12000	£1800
14		9d. purple-brown (23.4.59)	£20000	£1300
15	**4**	10d. orange-vermilion (2.7.57)	£1000	£325
16		1s. dull violet (2.7.57)	£4000	£275
17	**3**	1s. 9d. green (23.4.59)	£600	£1000
18		1s. 9d. pale yellow-green	£1800	£1800
19		2s. blue (23.4.59)	£5000	£1500
		(b) "Unofficial" P 7½ (No. 22a) or rouletted (Nos. 20/2)		
20	**2**	½d. lilac (*No wmk*)	£5000	
21	**1**	1d. blue (*Wmk Star*)	£5000	
22		2d. deep green (*Wmk Star*)	£1800	£1000
22*a*		1s. 9d. green (*Wmk Star*)	£4000	

These stamps are believed to have been made by a Ceylon firm, or firms, for their own convenience.

(Recess P.B.)

1861. *Wmk Star, W w* **1**. *(a) Clean-cut perf 14 to 15½.*

23	**1**	1d. deep blue	70·00	12·00
24		1d. pale blue	£125	18·00
25		2d. green	£175	30·00
27		5d. chestnut	70·00	12·00
29	**4**	1s. dull violet	70·00	19·00
30	**3**	2s. deep full blue	£1000	£275
		(b) Intermediate perf 14 to 15½		
31	**1**	1d. deep blue	45·00	12·00
32		1d. blue	45·00	13·00
33		2d. green	45·00	27·00
34	**3**	4d. dull rose	£1600	£175
34*a*	**1**	5d. chestnut	£275	£125
35		6d. brown	£900	50·00
36		6d. yellowish brown	—	80·00
36*a*		6d. olive-brown	—	50·00
37	**3**	8d. brown	£1000	£250
38		9d. dull purple-brown	£2250	£700
40	**4**	1s. bright violet	60·00	14·00
41		1s. dull violet	60·00	13·00
		(c) Rough perf 14 to 15½		
42	**1**	1d. blue	38·00	6·00
43		1d. blue (*bleuté paper*)	£160	20·00
44	**3**	4d. rose-red	95·00	30·00
45		4d. deep rose-red	95·00	30·00
47	**1**	6d. yellowish brown	£900	80·00
48		6d. blackish brown	£200	40·00
48*a*		6d. olive-brown	£250	35·00
49	**3**	8d. brown	£1100	£175
50		8d. yellow-brown	£850	£175
51		9d. olive-brown	£250	25·00
52		9d. yellowish brown	£300	40·00
53		9d. deep brown	50·00	20·00
53*a*	**4**	10d. orange-vermilion	£110	20·00
		b. Imperf between (pair)		
54		1s. dull violet	£200	8·00
55	**3**	2s. blue	£500	80·00
56		2s. deep blue	£500	90·00
		(d) Rough perf 14 to 15½. Prepared for use, but not issued		
57	**3**	1s. 9d. green	£425	

No. 33 is known imperf between (vert pair), used.

No. 34 is distinguished from Nos. 44/5 with fraudulently altered perfs by its colour.

(Recess or typo (T **2**). D.L.R.)

1862–64. *No wmk. (a) Smooth paper. P* 13.

58	**1**	1d. blue	45·00	6·00
59		5d. deep red-brown	£800	£150
60		6d. reddish brown	55·00	20·00
61		6d. deep brown	65·00	20·00
62	**3**	9d. brown	£350	50·00
63	**4**	1s. cold violet	£1500	70·00
		(b) Smooth paper. P 11½, 12		
64	**1**	1d. blue	£400	70·00
		(c) Glazed paper. P 12½ (1864)		
65	**2**	½d. pale lilac	£110	85·00

The 1s. is known imperf, but not used. The "no wmk" stamps were printed on paper having the papermaker's name and date, "T H SAUNDERS 1862" across the sheets, and one or more of these letters or figures are often found on the stamps.

(Recess P.B., perforated by D.L.R.)

1864 (Sept). *Wmk Star, W w* **1**. *P* 12½.

66	**4**	10d. vermilion	£300	20·00
67		10d. orange-red	£300	20·00

5

6

T **5.** 23 mm high. "CC" oval.
T **6.** 21½ mm high. "CC" round and smaller.

(Recess or typo (T **2**) D.L.R.)

1863–6. *Paper medium thin and slightly soft.* **W 5.** *Wmks arranged in four panes, each of 60, with the words* "CROWN COLONIES" *between the panes. Portions of these letters often appear on the stamps.*

		(a) P 11½, 12		
68	**1**	1d. blue	£700	35·00
		(b) P 13		
69	**1**	6d. brown	£1200	50·00
70	**3**	9d. brown	£2000	£250
		(c) P 12½		
71	**2**	½d. mauve	12·00	5·00
72		½d. lilac	14·00	5·00
73		½d. deep lilac	14·00	6·00
74	**1**	1d. dark blue	16·00	4·00
75		1d. blue	16·00	4·00
76		2d. yellow-green	£4000	£225
77		2d. deep bottle-green	—	£3000
78		2d. grey-green	40·00	6·00
79		2d. emerald-green	80·00	55·00
80		2d. maize	£225	30·00
81	**3**	4d. lake-rose	£170	17·00
82	**3**	4d. rose	55·00	12·00
83	**1**	5d. reddish brown	95·00	40·00
84		5d. deep sage-green	£1100	£150
84*a*		5d. olive-green	60·00	13·00
85		6d. brown	21·00	8·00
86		6d. reddish brown	22·00	8·00
87		6d. deep brown	17·00	4·75
88	**3**	8d. light carmine-brown	22·00	11·00
89		8d. dark carmine-brown	22·00	11·00
90		9d. brown	£160	18·00
91	**4**	10d. vermilion	£600	12·00
91*a*		10d. orange	£100	18·00
92	**3**	2s. dark blue	£110	25·00

The ½d. lilac; 1d. blue; 2d. grey-green; 2d. maize; and 5d. deep sage-green and olive-green, are known imperf.

1867. *Paper hand-made. Prepared and used only for these Ceylon stamps.* **W 6.** *Wmks arranged in one pane of 240 in 20 rows of 12, with the words* "CROWN COLONIES" *twice in each side margin. P* 12½.

93	**1**	1d. pale blue	15·00	4·00
94		1d. Prussian blue	14·00	4·25
95		2d. maize	28·00	6·00
96		2d. olive-yellow	17·00	5·00
97		2d. greenish yellow	£125	42·00
98		2d. orange-yellow	15·00	4·00
99	**3**	4d. pale rose	25·00	11·00
100		4d. rose	14·00	6·00
101	**1**	5d. pale sage-green	17·00	6·00
102		5d. deep olive-green	38·00	6·00
103		5d. deep myrtle-green	16·00	12·00
104		6d. deep brown	18·00	5·00
105		6d. blackish brown	24·00	5·00
106		6d. red-brown	18·00	4·25
107	**3**	8d. pale carmine-brown	35·00	18·00
108		8d. deep carmine-brown	25·00	10·00
109		9d. bistre-brown	£125	25·00
110		9d. deep brown	16·00	7·00
111	**4**	10d. vermilion	£650	£140
111*a*		10d. red-orange	24·00	5·00
112		10d. orange	26·00	5·50
113		1s. lilac	£250	12·00
114		1s. violet	60·00	5·50
115	**3**	2s. pale blue	75·00	14·00
116		2s. blue	55·00	11·00
117		2s. Prussian blue	55·00	11·00

The 1d. pale blue, 6d. deep brown, 9d. deep brown and 10d. orange are known imperf but only unused.

PRINTERS. All stamps from No. 118 to 367 were typographed by De La Rue & Co, Ltd, London.

7

8

1866. *Wmk Crown CC. P* 12½.

118	**7**	3d. rose	£100	35·00

1867–8. *Wmk Crown CC. P* 14.

119	**8**	1d. blue	8·50	4·50
120	**7**	3d. pale rose (1867)	27·00	12·00
		a. Deep rose	32·00	12·00

(New Currency. 100 cents = 1 rupee)

9

10

11

12

13

14

15

16

17

18

19

1872–80. *Wmk Crown CC. (a) P 14.*

121 **9** 2 c. pale brown (*shades*) .. .. 2·50 80
122 **10** 4 c. grey .. .. .. 8·00 60
123 4 c. rosy-mauve (1880) .. .. 18·00 1·50
124 **11** 8 c. orange-yellow .. .. 18·00 4·00
a. Yellow .. .. 13·00 4·00
126 **12** 16 c. pale violet .. .. .. 24·00 3·25
127 **13** 24 c. green .. .. .. 16·00 3·25
128 **14** 32 c. slate (1877) .. .. .. 35·00 7·50
129 **15** 36 c. blue .. .. .. 35·00 7·50
130 **16** 48 c. rose .. .. .. 35·00 7·50
131 **17** 64 c. red-brown (1877) .. .. 80·00 28·00
132 **18** 96 c. drab .. .. .. 45·00 14·00
121/132 .. .. *Set of* 11 £275 70·00

(b) P 14 × 12½

133 **9** 2 c. brown .. .. .. £100 12·00
134 **10** 4 c. grey .. .. .. £100 8·00
135 **11** 8 c. orange-yellow .. .. 80·00 14·00

(c) P 12½

136 **9** 2 c. brown .. .. .. £600 20·00
137 **10** 4 c. grey .. .. .. £300 75·00

(d) P 12½ × 14

138 **19** 2 r. 50 c. dull-rose £250 £100

(e) Prepared for use and sent out to Ceylon, but not issued unsurcharged

139 **14** 32 c. slate (*p* 14 × 12½) £500
140 **17** 64 c. red-brown (*p* 14 × 12½) .. £800
141 **19** 2 r. 50, dull rose (*p* 12½) .. £700

FORGERIES.—Beware of forged overprint and surcharge varieties on Victorian issues.

SIXTEEN

16

CENTS
(20)

1882. *Nos.* 127 *and* 131 *surch as T* **20**.

142 **13** 16 c. on 24 c. green .. .. 12·00 6·50
a. Surch inverted
143 **17** 20 c. on 64 c. red-brown .. .. 8·00 3·00
a. Surch double .. .. — £425

1883–98. *Wmk Crown CA. (a) P 14.*

146 **9** 2 c. pale brown .. .. 12·00 1·25
147 2 c. dull green (1884) (Optd S. £50) .. 65 15
148 **10** 4 c. rosy mauve 70 20
149 4 c. rose (1884) (Optd S. £70) .. 2·50 5·00
150 **11** 8 c. orange .. .. .. 3·25 5·00
a. Yellow (1898) .. .. 3·25 5·00
151 **12** 16 c. pale violet .. .. .. £400 95·00

(b) Trial perforation. P 12

151*a* **9** 2 c. dull green £475
151*b* **10** 4 c. rose £1200
151*c* **13** 24 c. brown-purple £800

(c) Prepared for use and sent out to Ceylon, but not issued unsurcharged. P 14

152 **13** 24 c. brown-purple (Optd S.£160) .. £425

Postage &

FIVE
CENTS

Revenue
(21)

TEN
CENTS
(22)

Twenty
Cents
(23)

One Rupee
Twelve
Cents
(24)

1885. *T* 10/19 *surch locally as T* **21/24**.

I. *Wmk Crown CC. (a) P 14*

153 **21** 5 c. on 16 c. pale violet .. .. — £700
154 5 c. on 24 c. green .. .. £425 30·00
155 5 c. on 32 c. slate .. .. 17·00 8·00
a. Surch inverted .. .. — £225
b. Dark grey .. .. 14·00 8·00
156 5 c. on 36 c. blue .. .. 22·00 3·25
a. Surch inverted .. .. — £110
157 5 c. on 48 c. rose .. .. 80·00 12·00
158 5 c. on 64 c. red-brown .. .. 19·00 3·25
a. Surch double .. .. — £110
159 5 c. on 96 c. drab .. .. 65·00 18·00
161 **22** 10 c. on 16 c. pale violet £650 £325
162 10 c. on 24 c. green .. .. £225 40·00
163 10 c. on 36 c. blue .. .. 85·00 55·00
164 10 c. on 64 c. red-brown .. .. 40·00 22·00
165 20 c. on 24 c. green .. .. 21·00 9·50
166 **23** 20 c. on 32 c. slate .. .. 14·00 8·50
a. Dark grey .. .. 14·00 9·50
167 25 c. on 32 c. slate .. .. 8·00 4·25
a. Dark grey .. .. 8·00 3·25
168 28 c. on 48 c. rose .. .. 12·00 4·25
a. Surch double .. .. — £250
169 **22** 30 c. on 36 c. blue .. .. 6·50 6·50
a. Surch inverted .. .. 75·00 38·00
170 56 c. on 96 c. drab .. .. 11·00 7·50

(b) P 14 × 12½

172 **21** 5 c. on 32 c. slate .. .. 38·00 9·50
173 5 c. on 64 c. red-brown .. .. 42·00 13·00
174 **22** 10 c. on 64 c. red-brown .. .. 24·00 23·00
a. Imperf between (vert pair) .. £850
175 **24** 1 r. 12 c. on 2 r. 50 c. dull rose (*p* 12½) 85·00 30·00
176 1 r. 12 c. on 2 r. 50 c. dull rose (*p* 12½ × 14) .. 21·00 18·00

II. *Wmk Crown CA. P 14*

177 **21** 5 c. on 4 c. rosy mauve £160 £110
178 5 c. on 4 c. rose .. .. 4·75 45
a. Surch inverted £125 £100
179 5 c. on 8 c. orange-yellow .. .. 9·50 3·00
a. Surch double .. .. — 75·00
b. Surch inverted .. .. — £150
180 5 c. on 16 c. pale violet .. .. 15·00 7·50
a. Surch inverted .. .. — 55·00
181 5 c. on 24 c. green .. .. — £3500
182 5 c. on 24 c. brown-purple .. .. £150 75·00
184 **22** 10 c. on 16 c. pale violet .. .. — £350
185 10 c. on 24 c. brown-purple .. .. 7·00 4·25
186 15 c. on 16 c. pale violet .. .. 7·00 5·50

REVENUE AND POSTAGE

5 CENTS
(25)

10 CENTS
(26)

1 R. 12 C.
(27)

1885–87. *T* 11/15, 18 *and* 19 *surch with T* **25/7** *by D.L.R. P* 14.

(a) Wmk Crown CA

187 **25** 5 c. on 8 c. lilac .. .. 3·50 70
188 **26** 10 c. on 24 c. brown-purple .. .. 7·50 3·50
189 15 c. on 16 c. orange-yellow .. .. 13·00 4·75
190 28 c. on 32 c. slate .. .. 7·50 2·25
191 30 c. on 36 c. olive-green .. .. 13·00 11·00
192 56 c. on 96 c. drab .. .. 13·00 7·00

(b) Wmk Crown CC (sideways)

193 **27** 1 r. 12 c. on 2 r. 50, dull rose .. 25·00 25·00
187/93 Optd "Specimen" .. *Set of* 7 £150

28

29

5 c. Type (*a*) has thicker lines in the background and masses of solid colour under the chin, in front of the throat, at the back of the neck, and at the base. Type (*b*) has thinner lines in the background, and coil and pendant curl clearer.

1886. *Wmk Crown CA. P* 14.

194 **28** 5 c. dull purple (*a*) .. .. 4·00 15
195 5 c. dull purple (*b*) 65 10
196 **29** 15 c. sage-green .. .. 1·40 75
197 15 c. olive-green .. .. 1·50 45
198 25 c. yellow-brown .. .. 1·10 1·25
a. Value in yellow .. .. 48·00 35·00
199 28 c. slate .. .. 3·25 1·40
194, 197/9 Optd "Specimen" .. *Set of* 4 95·00

30

1887. *Wmk Crown CC. P* 14.

201 **30** 1 r. 12, dull rose (Optd S. £80) .. .. 12·00 12·00

This stamp comes on both white and bluish paper with wmk sideways, and, in a different shade, with upright wmk.

TWO CENTS
(31)

Two
(32)

2 Cents
(33)

Two Cents
(34)

2 Cents
(35)

1888–90. *Nos.* 148/9 *surch with T* **31/5**.

202 **31** 2 c. on 4 c. rosy mauve 30 20
a. Surch inverted .. .. 3·50 3·50
b. Surch double, one inverted .. — 18·00
203 2 c. on 4 c. rose 30 30
a. Surch inverted .. .. 4·50 4·00
b. Surch double .. .. — 16·00
204 **32** 2 (c.) on 4 c. rosy mauve 60 20
a. Surch inverted .. .. 9·00 8·00
b. Surch double .. .. 14·00 11·00
c. Surch double, one inverted .. 7·00 6·00
205 **32** 2 (c.) on 4 c. rose 55 20
a. Surch inverted .. .. 32·00
b. Surch double .. .. 14·00 11·00
c. Surch double, one inverted .. 14·00 14·00
206 **33** 2 c. on 4 c. rosy mauve .. .. 14·00 10·00
a. Surch inverted .. .. — 12·00
b. Surch double, one inverted .. 18·00
207 2 c. on 4 c. rose 85 90
a. Surch inverted .. .. 6·50 6·50
b. Surch double
c. Surch double, one inverted .. 4·50 4·25
208 **34** 2 c. on 4 c. rosy mauve .. .. 14·00 14·00
a. Surch inverted .. .. 27·00 11·00
209 2 c. on 4 c. rose 85 45
a. Surch inverted .. .. 4·50 4·50
b. Surch double .. .. 13·00 13·00
c. Surch double, one inverted .. 4·50 4·25
210 **35** 2 c. on 4 c. rosy mauve .. .. 14·00 13·00
a. Surch inverted .. .. 22·00 20·00
b. Surch double, one inverted .. 22·00 20·00
c. Surch double .. .. — 17·00
d. "s" of "Cents" inverted
e. As d. Whole surch inverted
211 2 c. on 4 c. rose .. .. 1·50 50
a. Surch inverted .. .. 3·25 3·25
b. Surch double .. .. 20·00 18·00
c. Surch double, one inverted .. 7·00 6·50
d. "s" of "Cents" inverted .. — 25·00
209, 211 Optd "Specimen" .. *Set of* 2 95·00

The 4 c. rose and the 4 c. rosy mauve are found surcharged "Postal Commission 3 (or "Three") Cents". They denote the extra commission charged by the Post Office on postal orders which had not been cashed within three months of the date of issue. For a short time the Post Office did not object to the use of these stamps on letters.

POSTAGE

Five Cents

REVENUE
(36)

FIFTEEN
CENTS
(37)

1890. *No.* 197 *surch with T* **36**.

233 5 c. on 15 c. olive-green (Optd S. £30) .. 55 75
a. Surch inverted .. .. 7·50 7·50
b. Surch double .. .. 48·00 38·00
c. "Flve" for "Five" .. .. 48·00 38·00
d. Variety as c, inverted
e. "REVENUE" omitted .. .. 48·00 38·00
f. Inverted "s" in "Cents" .. .. 7·50 7·50
g. Variety as f, and whole surch inverted £300
h. "REVENUE" omitted and inverted "s" in "Cents" .. 85·00
i. "POSTAGE" spaced between "T" and "A" 20·00

1891. *Nos.* 198/9 *surch with T* **37**.

239 **29** 15 c. on 25 c. yellow-brown .. .. 5·50 5·00
240 15 c. on 28 c. slate .. .. 5·50 5·00

3 Cents
(38)

39

1892. *Nos.* 148/9 *and* 199 *surch with T* **38**.

241 **10** 3 c. on 4 c. rosy mauve 45 55
242 3 c. on 4 c. rose (Optd S. £40) .. 70 2·00
243 **28** 3 c. on 28 c. slate 45 65
a. Surch double .. .. 22·00

1893–99. *Wmk Crown CA. P* 14.

245 **39** 3 c. terracotta and blue-green .. 85 45
246 **10** 4 c. carmine-rose (1898) .. 3·75 3·75
247 **29** 30 c. bright mauve and chestnut .. 3·75 1·40
a. Bright violet and chestnut .. 2·50 1·40
249 **19** 2 r. 50, purple/*red* (1899) .. 21·00 20·00
245, 247/9 Optd "Specimen" .. *Set of* 3 75·00

Six Cents
(40)

2 R. 25 C.
(41)

1899. *(a) No.* 196 *surch with T* **40**.

250 **29** 6 c. on 15 c. sage-green 45 40

(b) As No. 138 *but colour changed and perf* 14, *surch as T* **41**.

254 **19** 1 r. 50 c. on 2 r. 50, slate .. 19·00 15·00
255 2 r. 25 c. on 2 r. 50, yellow .. 24·00 22·00
250/5 Optd "Specimen" .. *Set of* 3 £120

43

1899–1900. *Wmk Crown CA* (1 *r.* 50, 2 *r.* 25 *wmk Crown CC*). *P* 14.

256 **9** 2 c. pale orange-brown 70 30
257 **39** 3 c. deep green 70 45
258 **10** 4 c. yellow .. .. 70 1·50
259 **29** 6 c. rose and black 70 45

260 39 12 c. sage-green and rose .. .. 2·00 3·25
261 29 15 c. blue .. .. 2·75 1·50
262 39 75 c. black and red-brown .. .. 4·00 3·50
263 43 1 r. 50, rose .. .. .. 24·00 24·00
264 2 r. 25, dull blue .. .. .. 32·00 32·00
256/64 .. .. .. *Set of* 9 60·00 60·00
256/64 Optd "Specimen" .. .. *Set of* 9 £150

44 45 46

47 48

1903–5. *Wmk Crown CA. P* 14.
265 44 2 c. red-brown 70 25
266 45 3 c. green 80 60
267 4 c. orange-yellow and blue .. 1·50 1·50
268 46 5 c. dull purple .. .. .. 1·25 30
269 47 6 c. carmine .. .. .. 2·00 1·25
270 45 12 c. sage-green and rosine .. 4·25 4·75
271 48 15 c. blue .. .. .. 6·50 2·25
272 25 c. bistre .. .. .. 5·50 7·00
273 30 c. dull violet and green .. 4·50 4·75
274 45 75 c. dull blue and orange (1905) .. 4·25 12·00
275 48 1 r. 50, greyish slate (1904) .. 38·00 38·00
276 2 r. 25, brown and green (1904) .. 38·00 35·00
265/276 .. .. *Set of* 12 95·00 95·00
265/76 Optd "Specimen" .. *Set of* 12 £225

1904–5. *Wmk Mult Crown CA. P* 14.
277 44 2 c. red-brown, O 45 10
278 45 3 c. green, O 65 15
279 4 c. orange and ultramarine, O .. 35 50
280 46 5 c. dull purple, OC .. .. 1·75 60
281 47 6 c. carmine, O 80 25
282 45 12 c. sage-green and rosine, O .. 1·75 1·75
283 48 15 c. blue, O 70 50
284 25 c. bistre, O (1905) .. .. 7·00 3·75
285 30 c. violet and green, O (1905) .. 2·50 1·50
286 45 75 c. dull blue and orange, O (1905) .. 5·25 8·00
287 48 1 r. 50, grey, O (1905) .. .. 15·00 19·00
288 2 r. 25, brown and green, O .. 22·00 25·00
277/88 .. .. *Set of* 12 50·00 55·00

50

51

1908. *Wmk Mult Crown CA. P* 14.
289 50 5 c. deep purple, O 60 10
290 5 c. dull purple, O .. .. 1·25 30
291 51 6 c. carmine, O 70 20
289, 291 Optd "Specimen" .. *Set of* 2 55·00

1910–11. *Wmk Mult Crown CA. P* 14.
292 44 2 c. brown-orange, O (1911) .. 1·00 1·25
293 48 3 c. green, O (1911) 85 50
294 10 c. sage-green and maroon, O .. 1·50 70
295 25 c. grey, O .. .. .. 2·75 85
296 50 c. chocolate, O .. .. 5·50 7·50
297 1 r. purple/*yellow*, O .. .. 7·50 10·00
298 2 r. red/*yellow*, O .. .. 15·00 25·00
299 5 r. black/*green*, O .. .. 40·00 60·00
300 10 r. black/*red*, O .. .. 75·00 £110
292/300 .. .. *Set of* 9 £130 £190
292/300 Optd "Specimen" .. *Set of* 9 £275

52

53

(A)

(B)

Most values in Type **52** were produced by two printing operations, using "Key" and "Duty" plates. Differences in the two Dies of the Key plate are described in the introduction to this catalogue.

In the Ceylon series, however, the 1 c. and 5 c. values, together with later printings of the 3 c. and 6 c., were printed from special plates at one operation. These plates can be identified by the large "C" in the value tablet (see illustration A). Examples of these values from Key and Duty plates printing have value tablet as illustration B. The 3 c. and 5 c. stamps from the single plates *resemble* Die I, and the 1 c. and 6 c. Die II, although in the latter case the inner top corners of the side panels are square and not curved.

1912–25. *T* **52** *and* **53** (50 *r. to* 1000 *r.*). *Wmk Mult Crown CA. P* 14.

(*a*) *Printed from single plates. Value tablet as* A
301 1 c. brown, O 12 20
302 3 c. blue-green, O 70 45
303 5 c. purple, O 70 35
304 5 c. bright magenta, O 25 25
a. Wmk sideways .. .. .. 2·00
305 6 c. pale scarlet, O 85 60
306 6 c. carmine, O .. .. .. 1·40 75
a. Wmk sideways .. .. .. 2·50

(*b*) *Printed from Key and Duty plates at two operations. Die I.* 3 *c. and* 6 *c. have value tablet as* B
307 2 c. brown-orange, O 35 25
308 2 c. deep orange-brown, O 35 25
309 3 c. yellow-green, O .. .. 1·25 90
310 3 c. deep green, O 70 70
311 6 c. scarlet, O .. .. .. 1·10 45
312 6 c. bright scarlet, O .. .. 1·10 45
313 10 c. sage-green, O .. .. .. 2·50 1·40
314 10 c. deep sage-green, O .. .. 2·25 1·25
315 15 c. ultramarine, O .. .. 2·00 1·25
316 15 c. deep bright blue, O .. .. 2·00 1·25
317 25 c. yellow and blue, O .. .. 1·75 1·25
318 25 c. orange and blue, O .. .. 2·50 1·75
319 30 c. blue-green and violet, C .. 2·75 1·90
320 30 c. yellow-green and violet, C .. 2·75 2·75
a. Wmk sideways .. .. .. 1·60
321 50 c. black and scarlet, C .. .. 1·60 1·90
322 1 r. purple/*yellow*, C .. .. 2·25 2·75
a. White back (1914) (Optd S. £32) 1·60 2·50
b. On lemon (1916) (Optd S. £32) 5·00 5·00
c. On orange-buff .. .. .. 11·00 13·00
d. On pale yellow (Optd S. £32) .. 5·50 7·50
323 2 r. black and red/*yellow*, C .. 7·00 8·00
a. White back (Optd S. £32) .. 3·50 6·50
b. On lemon (Optd S. £32) .. 14·00 18·00
c. On orange-buff .. .. .. 19·00 22·00
d. On pale yellow .. .. .. 19·00 22·00
324 5 r. black/*green*, C .. .. 14·00 18·00
a. White back (Optd S. £35) .. 12·00 16·00
b. On blue-green, olive back (1921) (Optd S. £40) .. .. .. 13·00 20·00
c. On emerald back (Die II) (Optd S. £50) 55·00 60·00
325 10 r. purple and black/*red*, C .. 29·00 30·00
a. Die II .. .. .. 32·00
326 20 r. black and red/*blue*, C .. .. 65·00 60·00
327 50 r. dull purple, C (S. £100) .. £250
328 100 r. grey-black, C (S. £350) .. £1200
329 500 r. dull green, C (S. £400) .. £3500
329*a* 1000 r. purple/*red*, C (1925) (S. £700) .. £10000
301/25 .. .. *Set of* 14 50·00 55·00
301/26 Optd "Specimen" .. *Set of* 15 £250

WAR STAMP
(54)

WAR STAMP ONE CENT
(55)

1918 (18 Nov). (*a*) *Optd with T* **54**.
330 52 2 c. brown-orange 15 40
a. Opt inverted .. .. .. 24·00 24·00
b. Opt double .. .. .. 24·00 24·00
c. Opt omitted in pair with opt inverted
331 3 c. blue-green (No. 302) 10 30
332 3 c. yellow-green (No. 309) 35 90
a. Opt double .. .. .. 40·00 40·00
333 5 c. purple 10 30
a. Opt double .. .. .. 24·00 24·00
334 5 c. bright magenta 45 85
a. Opt inverted .. .. .. 24·00 24·00
b. Opt double .. .. .. 23·00 23·00

(*b*) *Surch with T* **55**
335 52 1 c. on 5 c. purple 5 25
336 1 c. on 5 c. bright magenta 12 25
330/1, 333, 335 Optd "Specimen" .. *Set of* 4 80·00

Collectors are warned against forgeries of the errors in the "WAR STAMP" overprints.

1918. *Surch as T* **55**, *but without* "WAR STAMP".
337 52 1 c. on 5 c. purple (Optd S. £30) .. 15 30
337*a* 1 c. on 5 c. bright magenta .. 35 60

1921–34. *Wmk Mult Script CA. P* 14.

A. **1921–27.** *The original issue.*

(*a*) *Printed from single plates. Value tablet as* A
338 52 1 c. brown, O (1927) 12 35
339 3 c. green, O (5.5.22) .. .. 65 1·00
340 5 c. bright magenta, O (1927) .. 10 20
341 6 c. carmine-red, O (3.8.21) .. 35 60

(*b*) *Printed from Key and Duty plates at two operations. Die I* (10 *c. to* 30 *c. and* 1 *r.*) *or Die II* (2*c.,* 50 *c.,* 2 *r. to* 20 *r.*)
342 52 2 c. brown-orange, O (1927) .. 30 45
343 10 c. sage-green, O (16.9.21) .. 75 40
344 15 c. ultramarine, O (30.5.22) .. 2·75 3·50
345 20 c. bright blue, O (1922) .. 3·25 2·25
346 25 c. yellow and blue, O (17.10.21) .. 80 1·50
347 30 c. yellow-green and violet, C (15.3.22) 1·75 2·50
348 50 c. black and scarlet, C (1922) .. 2·50 1·50
349 1 r. purple/*pale yellow*, C (1923) .. 15·00 13·00
350 2 r. black and red/*pale yellow*, C (1923) 6·00 8·00
351 5 r. black/*emerald*, C (1925) .. 22·00 27·00
352 20 r. black and red/*blue*, C (1924) .. 55·00 60·00
353 53 50 r. dull purple, C (1924) (S. £90) .. £300
354 100 r. grey-black, C (1924) (S. £225) .. £1400
338/51 .. .. *Set of* 14 50·00 55·00
338/52 Optd "Specimen" .. *Set of* 15 £225

B. **1922–27.** *New values and colour changed.*

(*a*) *Printed from single plates. Value tablet as* A
355 52 3 c. slate-grey, O (1923) 10 20
a. Wmk sideways .. ..
356 6 c. bright violet, O 15 25

(*b*) *Printed from Key and Duty plates at two operations. Die I* (12 *c.,* 15 *c.*) *or Die II* (9 *c.*)
357 52 9 c. red/*yellow*, O (1926) 30 50
358 12 c. rose-scarlet, O (1924) .. .. 2·75 3·50
359 15 c. green/*pale yellow*, O .. .. 1·75 1·90
360 53 100 r. dull purple and blue, C (24.10.27) (S.£300) £1100
355/9 Optd "Specimen" .. *Set of* 5 £120

C. **1924–25.** *Key and Duty plates. Change to Die II.*
360*a* 52 10 c. sage green, O 60 80
360*b* 12 c. rose-scarlet, O (1924) .. 1·75 2·50
360*c* 15 c. green/*pale yellow*, O .. 2·50 2·50
360*d* 20 c. bright blue, O 55 70
360*e* 25 c. yellow and blue, O .. .. 1·60 2·25
360*f* 30 c. yellow-green and violet, C .. 1·60 2·00
360*g* 1 r. purple/*pale yellow*, C .. .. 10·00 11·00

D. **1934.** *Key and Duty plates. Reappearance of Die I* (*Key Plate* 23).
360*h* 52 50 c. black and scarlet, C .. .. 26·00 35·00

The 30 c. value also reappeared in Die I from Plate 23 but this was identical with No. 347.

2 Cents.
(56)

57

(Surch at Ceylon Govt Printing Works)

1926 (27 Nov). *Surch as T* **56**.
361 52 2 c. on 3 c. slate-grey 50 70
a. Surch double .. .. 45·00
b. Bar omitted .. .. .. 38·00
362 5 c. on 6 c. bright violet 50 40
361/2 Optd "Specimen" .. *Set of* 2 60·00

1927 (27 Nov)–**29.** *Wmk Mult Script CA. P* 14.
363 57 1 r. dull and bright purple, C (1928) .. 3·75 1·75
364 2 r. green and carmine, C (1929) .. 8·00 4·75
365 5 r. green and dull purple, C (1928) .. 22·00 17·00
366 10 r. green and brown-orange, C .. 32·00 38·00
367 20 r. dull purple and blue, C .. 65·00 70·00
363/7 Optd "Specimen" .. *Set of* 5 £160

No. 364. Collectors are warned against faked 2 r. stamps, showing what purports to be a double centre.

58 Tapping Rubber

60 Adam's Peak

(Recess D.L.R. (2, 3, 20, 50 c.), B.W. (others))

1935 (1 May)–**36.** *T* **58, 60** *and similar designs. Wmk Mult Script CA* (*sideways on* 10, 15, 25, 30 *c. and* 1 *r.*). *Various perfs.*
368 2 c. black and carmine (*p* 12 × 13) .. 20 20
a. Perf 14 .. .. .. 2·50 50
369 3 c. blk & ol-green (*p* 13 × 12) (1.10.35) 35 20
a. Perf 14 .. .. .. 3·25 50
370 6 c. black & blue (*p* 11 × 11½) (1.1.36) 40 30
371 9 c. green & orange (*p* 11 × 11½) (1.1.36) 50 25
372 10 c. black & purple (*p* 11½ × 11) (1.6.35) 80 70
373 15 c. red-brown and green (*p* 11½ × 11) 1·25 60
374 20 c. black & grey-blue (*p* 12 × 13) (1.1.36) 1·75 75
375 25 c. deep blue & chocolate (*p* 11½ × 11) 1·25 60
376 30 c. carm & green (*p* 11½ × 11) (1.8.35) 3·00 1·50
377 50 c. black and mauve (*p* 14) (1.1.36) .. 5·00 65
378 1 r. vio-bl & chocolate (*p* 11½ × 11) (1.7.35) .. 8·50 7·00
368/78 .. .. *Set of* 11 21·00 11·50
368/78 Perf "Specimen" .. *Set of* 11 £100

Designs: *Vert*—6 c. Colombo Harbour; 9 c. Plucking tea; 20 c. Coconut Palms. *Horiz*—10 c. Hill paddy (rice); 15 c. River scene; 25 c. Temple of the Tooth, Kandy; 30 c. Ancient irrigation tank; 50 c. Wild elephants; 1 r. Trincomalee.

1935 (6 May). *Silver Jubilee. As Nos.* 91/4 *of Antigua.*
379 6 c. ultramarine and grey 30 30
380 9 c. green and indigo 70 80
381 20 c. brown and deep blue .. .. 1·50 1·75
e. Horiz line from turret .. .. 8·00
382 50 c. slate and purple .. .. 5·00 4·50
379/82 Perf "Specimen" .. *Set of* 4 40·00

For illustration of plate variety, see Omnibus section following Zululand.

1937 (12 May). *Coronation. As Nos.* 13/15 *of Aden but ptd by B.W. & Co. P* 11 × 11½.
383 6 c. carmine 40 12
384 9 c. green 50 75
385 20 c. blue .. .. .. 1·50 1·60
383/5 Perf "Specimen" .. *Set of* 3 50·00

69 Tapping Rubber

70 Sigiriya (Lion Rock)

71 Ancient Guard-stone, Anuradhapura

72 King George VI

(Recess B.W. (stamps perf 11 × 11½ or 11½ × 11), D.L.R. (all others) T **72** typo D.L.R.)

1938–49. *T* **69/72** *and designs as* 1935–36, *but with portrait of King George VI instead of King George V and* "POSTAGE & REVENUE" *omitted. Wmk Mult Script CA* (*sideways on* 10, 15, 25, 30 *c. and* 1 *r.*). *Various perfs.*

No.	Type	Description	Unused	Used
386	**69**	2 c. blk & carm (*p* 11½ × 13) (25.4.38)	2·50	60
		a. Perf 13½ × 13 (1938)	14·00	95
		b. Perf 13½ (25.4.38)	20	12
		c. Perf 11 × 11½ (17.2.44)	10	20
		d. Perf 12 (22.4.49)	15	60
387	**60**	3 c. black and deep blue-green (*p* 13 × 11½) (21.3.38)	7·00	50
		a. Perf 13 × 13½ (1938)	£130	4·00
		b. Perf 13½ (21.3.38)	30	12
		c. Perf 14 (7.41)	25·00	75
		d. Perf 11½ × 11 (14.5.42)	10	10
		e. Perf 12 (14.1.46)	10	10
387*f*	–	5 c. sage-grn & orge (*p* 13½) (1.1.43) ..	25	20
		g. Perf 12 (1947)	20	20
388	–	6 c. black and blue (*p* 11 × 11½) (1.1.38)	10	5
389	**70**	10 c. blk & light bl (*p* 11½ × 11) (1.2.38)	35	15
		a. Wmk upright (1.6.44)	20	12
390	–	15 c. grn & red-brn (*p* 11½ × 11) (1.1.38)	35	12
		a. Wmk upright (23.7.45)	20	12
391	–	20 c. blk & grey-bl (*p* 11½ × 11) (15.1.38)	40	10
392	–	25 c. deep bl & choc (*p* 11 × 11½) (15.1.38)	45	25
		a. Wmk upright (1944)	20	10
393	–	30 c. carm & grn (*p* 11½ × 11) (1.2.38) ..	3·50	1·50
		a. Wmk upright (16.4.45)	3·00	1·25
394	–	50 c. blk & mve (*p* 13 × 11½) (25.4.38) ..	70·00	35·00
		a. Perf 13 × 13½ (1938)	85·00	2·75
		b. Perf 13½ (25.4.38)	3·00	50
		c. Perf 14 (4.42)	26·00	11·00
		d. Perf 11½ × 11 (14.5.42)	1·25	15
		e. Perf 12 (14.1.46)	1·00	20
395	–	1 r. blue-violet and chocolate (*p* 11½ × 11) (1.2.38)	3·25	80
		a. Wmk upright (1944)	3·25	80
396	**71**	2 r. blk and carm (*p* 11 × 11½) (1.2.38)	2·25	80
396*a*		2 r. blk & vio (*p* 11 × 11½) (15.3.47) ..	2·00	60
397	**72**	5 r. green & purple (*shades*), **C** (*p* 14) (10.10.38)	9·00	1·50
		a. Green and pale purple, **O** (19.2.43) ..	8·00	1·00
386/97*a* (*cheapest*)		.. .. .. *Set of* 14	19·00	5·00
387/97 Perf "Specimen"		.. .. *Set of* 14	£150	

Designs: *Vert*—5 c. Coconut Palms; 6 c. Colombo Harbour; 20 c. Plucking tea. *Horiz*—15 c. River scene; 25 c. Temple of the Tooth, Kandy; 30 c. Ancient irrigation tank; 50 c. Wild elephants; 1 r. Trincomalee.

3 CENTS

(73)

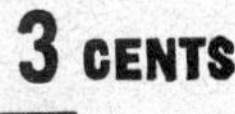

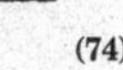

(74)

1940–41. *Nos.* 388 *and* 391 *surch.*

No.	Type	Description	Unused	Used
398	**73**	3 c. on 6 c. (10.5.41)	20	10
399	**74**	3 c. on 20 c. (5.11.40)	40	30

1946 (10 Dec). *Victory. As Nos.* 28/9 *of Aden.*

No.	Description	Unused	Used
400	6 c. blue	20	12
401	15 c. brown	20	15
400/1	Perf "Specimen" .. .. *Set of* 2	30·00	

75 Parliament Building

76 Adam's Peak

(Des R. Tenison and M. S. V. Rodrigo. Recess B.W.)

1947 (25 Nov). *Inauguration of New Constitution. T* **75/6** *and similar designs. Wmk Mult Script CA. P* 11 × 12 (*horiz*) *or* 12 × 11 (*vert*).

No.	Description	Unused	Used
402	6 c. black and blue	12	15
403	10 c. black, orange and carmine	12	25
404	15 c. green and purple	12	25
405	25 c. ochre and emerald-green	12	25
402/5	Perf "Specimen" .. .. *Set of* 4	£120	

Designs: *Horiz*—15 c. Temple of the Tooth. *Vert*—25 c. Anuradhapura.

DOMINION

79 Lion Flag of Dominion

80 D. S. Senanayake

81 Lotus Flowers and Sinhalese Letters "Sri"

(Recess (flag typo) B.W.)

1949 (4 Feb–Apr). *First Anniv of Independence.* (*a*) *Wmk Mult Script CA* (*sideways on* 4 *c.*). *P* 12½ × 12 (4 *c.*) *or* 12 × 12½ (5 *c.*).

No.	Type	Description	Unused	Used
406	**79**	4 c. yellow, carmine and brown ..	5	10
407	**80**	5 c. brown and green	5	5

(*b*) **W 81** (*sideways on* 15 *c.*). *P* 13 × 12½ (15 *c.*) *or* 12 × 12½ (25 *c.*) (5 April)

No.	Type	Description	Unused	Used
408	**79**	15 c. yellow, carmine and vermilion ..	15	20
409	**80**	25 c. brown and blue	15	30

The 15 c. is larger, measuring 28 × 12 mm.

82 Globe and Forms of Transport

83

84

(Recess D.L.R.)

1949 (10 Oct). *75th Anniv of Universal Postal Union.* **W 81**. *P* 13 (25 *c.*) *or* 12 (*others*).

No.	Type	Description	Unused	Used
410	**82**	5 c. brown and bluish green	35	5
411	**83**	15 c. black and carmine	1·25	60
412	**84**	25 c. black and ultramarine	1·40	25

85 Kandyan Dancer

88 Sigiriya (Lion Rock)

89 Octagon Library, Temple of the Tooth

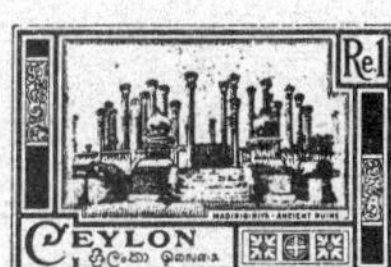

90 Ruins at Madirigiriya

(Recess B.W.)

1950 (4 Feb). *T* **85, 88/90** *and similar designs.* **W 81**. *P* 11 × 11½ (75 *c.*), 11½ × 11 (1 *r.*), 12 × 12½ (*others*).

No.	Description	Unused	Used
413	4 c. purple and scarlet	10	5
414	5 c. green	12	5
415	15 c. blue-green and violet	40	5
416	30 c. carmine and yellow	25	15
417	75 c. ultramarine and orange	60	20
418	1 r. deep blue and brown	75	10
413/18	.. .. *Set of* 6	2·00	50

Designs: *Vert* (*as T* **88**)—5 c. Kiri Vehera, Polonnaruwa; 15 c. Vesak Orchid.

91 Ruhuna National Park

92 Ancient Guard-stone, Anuradhapura

96 Star Orchid

97 Rubber Plantation

99 Tea Plantation

I. No. 424

II. No. 424a (Dot added)

(Photo Courvoisier)

1951 (1 Aug)–**54.** *T* **91/2, 96/7, 99** *and similar designs. No wmk. P* 11½.

No.	Description	Unused	Used
419	2 c. brown and blue-green (15.5.54)	5	5
420	3 c. black and slate-violet (15.5.54)	5	5
421	6 c. brown-black & yellow-green (15.5.54) ..	5	5
422	10 c. green and blue-grey	60	5
423	25 c. orange-brown & bright blue (15.3.54) ..	10	5
424	35 c. red and deep green (I) (1.2.52)	40	10
	a. Type II (1954)	50	5
425	40 c. deep brown (15.5.54)	25	20
426	50 c. indigo and slate-grey (15.3.54)	30	5
427	85 c. black and deep blue-green (15.5.54) ..	50	10
428	2 r. blue and deep brown (15.5.54)	2·75	20
429	5 r. brown and orange (15.3.54)	4·75	50
430	10 r. red-brown and buff (15.3.54)	13·00	3·25
419/30	.. .. *Set of* 12	21·00	4·00

Designs: *Vert* (*as T* **91**)—6 c. Harvesting rice; 10 c. Coconut trees; 25 c. Sigiriya fresco. (*As T* **99**)—5 r. Bas-relief, Anuradhapura; 10 r. Harvesting rice. *Horiz* (*as T* **97**)—50 c. Outrigger canoe; (*as T* **99**)—2 r. River Gal Dam.

103 Ceylon Mace and Symbols of Progress

(Photo Harrison)

1952 (23 Feb). *Colombo Plan Exhibition. Chalk-surfaced paper.* **W 81** (*sideways*). *P* 14½ × 14.

No.	Type	Description	Unused	Used
431	**103**	5 c. green	10	5
432		15 c. ultramarine	30	30

104 Queen Elizabeth II

105 Ceremonial Procession

(Recess B.W.)

1953 (2 June). *Coronation.* **W 81**. *P* 12 × 13.

No.	Type	Description	Unused	Used
433	**104**	5 c. green	15	5

(Recess D.L.R.)

1954 (10 Apr). *Royal Visit.* **W 81** (*sideways*). *P* 13 × 12½.

No.	Type	Description	Unused	Used
434	**105**	10 c. deep blue	15	5

106 King Coconuts

107 Farm Produce

(Photo Courvoisier)

1954 (1 Dec). *No wmk. P 11½.*
435 **106** 10 c. orange, bistre-brown and buff .. 5 5

(Photo Harrison)

1955 (10 Dec). *Royal Agricultural and Food Exhibition. W* **81** *(sideways). P 14 × 14½.*
436 **107** 10 c. brown and orange 5 5

108 Sir John Kotelawala and House of Representatives

(Photo Courvoisier)

1956 (26 Mar). *Prime Minister's 25 Years of Public Service. P 11½.*
437 **108** 10 c. deep bluish green 5 5

109 Arrival of Vijaya in Ceylon

110 Lampstand and Dharmachakra

111 Hand of Peace and Dharmachakra

112 Dharmachakra encircling the Globe

(Photo Courvoisier)

1956. *Buddha Jayanti. P 11½.*
438 **109** 3 c. blue and brownish grey (23 May) .. 20 10
439 **110** 4 c. + 2 c. grnish yell & dp bl (10 May) 25 25
440 **111** 10 c. + 5 c. carm, yellow & grey (10 May). 30 30
441 **112** 15 c. bright blue (23 May) 30 5

113 Mail Transport

114 Stamp of 1857

(Photo Enschedé (4 c., 10 c.), Courvoisier (others))

1957 (1 Apr). *Centenary of First Ceylon Postage Stamp. P 12½ × 13 (4 c., 10 c.) or 11½ (others).*
442 **113** 4 c. orange-red and deep bluish green 25 5
443 10 c. vermilion and blue 30 5
444 **114** 35 c. brown, yellow and blue 45 20
445 85 c. brown, yellow and grey-green .. 90 75

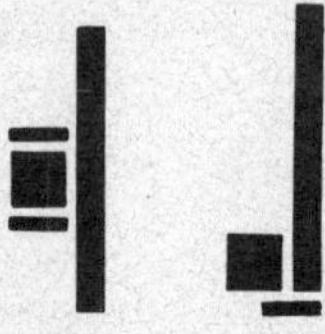

(115) (116)

117 Kandyan Dancer

1958 (15 Jan). *Nos. 439/40 with premium obliterated as T* **115** *(4 c.) or T* **116** *(10 c.).*
446 **110** 4 c. greenish yellow and deep blue .. 5 5
a. Opt inverted .. .. 8·00
b. Opt double .. .. 10·00
447 **111** 10 c. carmine, yellow and grey 5 5
a. Opt inverted .. .. 13·00

The 4 c. exists with opt misplaced to right so that some stamps show the vertical bar on the left (*Price £18 un.*).

(Recess B.W. (4 c., 5 c., 15 c., 30 c., 75 c., 1 r.). Photo Courvoisier (others))

1958 (14 May)–**59**. *As earlier types, but inscriptions redrawn as in T* **117**. *W* **81**; *P 11 × 11½ (75 c.), 11½ × 11 (1 r.) or 12 × 12½ (4 c., 5 c., 15 c., 30 c.). No wmk; P 11½ (others).*
448 **91** 2 c. brown and blue-green 5 5
449 **92** 3 c. black and slate-violet 5 5
450 **117** 4 c. purple and scarlet 5 5
451 – 5 c. green (*shades*) (1.10.58) 5 5
452 – 6 c. brown-black and yellow-green .. 5 5
453 **106** 10 c. orge, bistre-brown & buff (1.10.58).. 5 5
454 – 15 c. blue-green and violet (1.10.58) .. 35 5
455 – 25 c. orange-brown and bright blue .. 10 5
456 **88** 30 c. carmine and yellow (1.5.59) .. 15 5
457 **96** 35 c. red and deep green (II) (15.7.58) .. 45 5
459 – 50 c. indigo and slate-grey (15.7.58) .. 30 5
460 **89** 75 c. ultram & orange (*shades*) (1.5.59) .. 25 10
461 **99** 85 c. black and deep blue-green (1.5.59).. 3·00 90
462 **90** 1 r. deep blue and brown (1.10.58) .. 40 8
463 – 2 r. blue and deep brown 60 10
464 – 5 r. brown and orange .. .. .. 1·25 20
465 – 10 r. red-brown and buff.. .. .. 2·50 80
448/65 .. .. *Set of* 17 8·50 2·25

Designs: *Vert* (*as T* **117**)—5 c. Kiri Vehera Polonnaruwa; 6 c. Harvesting rice; 15 c. Vesak Orchid; 25 c. Sigiriya fresco. (*as T* **99**)—5 r. Bas-relief, Anuradhapura; 10 r. Harvesting rice. *Horiz* (*as T* **97**)—50 c. Outrigger canoe. (*as T* **99**)—2 r. River Gal Dam.

118 "Human Rights"

119 Portraits of Founders and University Buildings

(Photo Enschedé)

1958 (10 Dec). *Tenth Anniv of Declaration of Human Rights. P 13 × 12½.*
466 **118** 10 c. vermilion and dull purple 5 5
467 85 c. vermilion and deep blue-green .. 40 50

(Photo Enschedé)

1959 (31 Dec). *Institution of Pirivena Universities. P 13 × 12½.*
468 **119** 10 c. red-orange and ultramarine .. 5 5

120 Uprooted Tree

121 S.W.R.D. Bandaranaike

(Des W. A. Ariyasena. Photo Courvoisier)

1960 (7 Apr). *World Refugee Year. P 11½.*
469 **120** 4 c. red-brown and gold.. .. .. 5 5
470 25 c. blackish violet and gold 15 25

(Photo Courvoisier)

1961 (8 Jan). *Prime Minister Bandaranaike Commemoration. P 11½.*
471 **121** 10 c. deep blue and greenish blue .. 5 5
a. Portrait redrawn 12 5

No. 471a can be identified by Mr. Bandaranaike's dark hair at temples.

122 Ceylon Scout Badge

123 Campaign Emblem

(Des W. A. Ariyasena. Photo Courvoisier)

1962 (26 Feb). *Golden Jubilee of Ceylon Boy Scouts Association. P 11½.*
472 **122** 35 c. buff and blue 25 10

(Photo Harrison)

1962 (7 Apr). *Malaria Eradication. W* **81**. *P 14½ × 14.*
473 **123** 25 c. red-orange and sepia 10 10

124 Moth and Comet Aircraft

125 "Produce" and Campaign Emblem

(Photo Courvoisier)

1963 (26 Feb). *25th Anniv of Airmail. P 11½.*
474 **124** 50 c. black and light blue 25 30

(Photo Courvoisier)

1963 (21 Mar). *Freedom from Hunger. P 11½.*
475 **125** 5 c. vermilion and blue 20 5
476 25 c. brown and yellow-olive 65 25

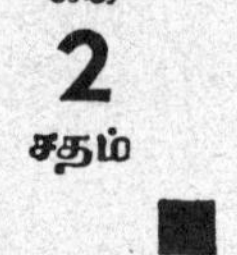

(126)

127 "Rural Life"

1963 (1 June). *No. 450 surch with T* **126**.
477 **117** 2 c. on 4 c. purple and scarlet 5 5
a. Surch inverted .. .. .. 16·00
b. Surch double .. .. .. 13·00

(Photo Harrison)

1963 (5 July). *Golden Jubilee of Ceylon Co-operative Movement (1962). W* **81**. *P 14 × 14½.*
478 **127** 60 c. rose-red and black 20 20

128 S. W. R. D. Bandaranaike

129 Terrain, Elephant and Tree

(Recess Courvoisier)

1963 (26 Sept). *P 11½.*
479 **128** 10 c. light blue 5 5

(Photo Harrison)

1963 (2 Dec). *National Conservation Week. W* **81** *(sideways). P 14 × 14½.*
480 **129** 5 c. sepia and blue 5 5

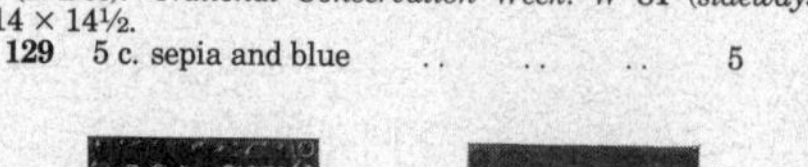

130 S. W. R. D. Bandaranaike

131 Anagarika Dharmapala (Buddhist missionary)

(T **130/1**. Photo Courvoisier)

1964 (1 July). *P 11½.*
481 **130** 10 c. deep violet-blue and greenish grey 5 5

1964 (16 Sept). *Birth Centenary of Anagarika Dharmapala (founder of Maha Bodhi Society). P 11½.*
482 **131** 25 c. sepia and olive-yellow 5 5

134 Southern Grackle

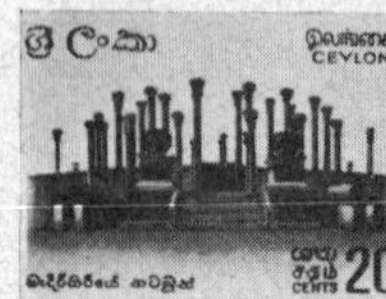

138 Ruins at Madirigiriya

135 D. S. Senanayake **136**

146 Tea Plantation

149 Map of Ceylon

(Des A. Dharmasiri (5 r.); P. A. Miththapala (10 r.). Photo Courvoisier (10 c. (486), 20 c.), Harrison (10 c. (487), 60 c., 1 r., 5 r., 10 r.), D.L.R. (others incl sheet))

1964 (1 Oct)–**69**. *T* **134/6, 138, 146, 149** *and similar designs. No wmk (Nos.* 486, 489), *W* **81** *(others; sideways on Nos.* 487, 494, 499). *P* 11½ *(Nos.* 486, 489), 14½ × 14 *(No.* 494) *or* 14 *(others).*

485	**134**	5 c. multicoloured (5.2.66)	5	5
486	**135**	10 c. myrtle-green (22.3.66)	5	5
487	**136**	10 c. myrtle-green (23.9.68)	5	5
		a. Imperf (pair)	38·00	
488	–	15 c. multicoloured (5.2.66)	35	5
489	**138**	20 c. brown-purple and buff	8	5
494	–	60 c. multicoloured (5.2.66)	45	5
		a. Red omitted	30·00	
		b. Blue and green omitted*	30·00	
495	–	75 c. multicoloured (5.2.66)	45	5
497	**146**	1 r. brown and bluish green	30	5
		a. Brown omitted	85·00	
		b. Bluish green omitted	£130	
499	–	5 r. multicoloured (15.8.69)	1·25	70
500	**149**	10 r. multicoloured (1.10.69)	4·50	1·75
485/500		*Set of* 10	6·75	2·50

MS500*a* 148 × 174 mm. As Nos. 485, 488, 494 and 495. Imperf. . . 1·75 2·50

Designs: *Horiz (as T* **134**)—15 c. Common Peafowl; 60 c. Ceylon Jungle-fowl; 75 c. Asian Black-headed Oriole. *(as T* **138**)—5 r. Girls transplanting rice.

The 5 c., 75 c. and 1 r. exist with PVA gum as well as gum arabic.

In the miniature sheet the inscriptions on the 60 c. have been rearranged to conform with the style of the other values.

*Actually only the blue printing is omitted on this sheet, but where this was printed over the yellow to form the leaves it appeared as green.

150 Exhibition Buildings and Cogwheels

151 Trains of 1864 and 1964

(Photo State Printing Works, Budapest)

1964 (1 Dec). *Industrial Exhibition. T* **150** *and similar horiz design. No wmk. P* 11.

501	–	5 c. multicoloured	5	5
		a. Pair. Nos. 501/2	10	15
502	**150**	5 c. multicoloured	5	5

No. 501 is inscribed "INDUSTRIAL EXHIBITION" in Sinhala and Tamil, No. 502 in Sinhala and English. The stamps were issued together *se-tenant* in alternate vertical rows, producing horizontal pairs.

(Photo Harrison)

1964 (21 Dec). *Centenary of Ceylon Railways. T* **151** *and similar horiz design. W* **81** *(sideways). P* 14 × 14½.

503	–	60 c. blue, reddish purple & yellow-grn	80	25
		a. Pair. Nos. 503/4	1·60	1·10
504	**151**	60 c. blue, reddish purple & yellow-grn	80	25

No. 503 is inscribed "RAILWAY CENTENARY" in Sinhala and Tamil, No. 504 in Sinhala and English. The stamps were issued together *se-tenant* in alternate horizontal rows, producing vertical pairs.

152 I.T.U. Emblem and Symbols

153 I.C.Y. Emblem

(Photo Harrison)

1965 (16 May). *I.T.U. Centenary. W* **81** *(sideways). P* 14½.

505	**152**	2 c. bright blue and red	15	25
506		30 c. brown and red	80	45

(Photo Courvoisier)

1965 (26 June). *International Co-operation Year. T* **153** *and similar horiz design. P* 11½.

507	3 c. deep blue and rose-carmine	15	20
508	50 c. black, rose-carmine and gold	80	50

No. 508 is similar to T **153** but has the multilingual inscription "CEYLON" rearranged.

154 Town Hall, Colombo

5 ■
(155)

(Photo Courvoisier)

1965 (29 Oct). *Centenary of Colombo Municipal Council. P* 11 × 11½.

509	**154**	25 c. myrtle-green and sepia	8	5

1965 (18 Dec). *No.* 481 *surch with T* **155**.

510	**130**	5 c. on 10 c. dp vio-bl & greenish grey	5	5

157 Kandy and Council Crest

158 W.H.O. Building

(Photo Harrison)

1966 (15 June). *Kandy Municipal Council Centenary. W* **81**. *P* 14 × 13½.

512	**157**	25 c. multicoloured	5	5

(Litho D.L.R.)

1966 (8 Oct). *Inauguration of W.H.O. Headquarters. Geneva. P* 14.

513	**158**	4 c. multicoloured	15	15
514		1 r. multicoloured	70	60

159 Rice Paddy and Map of Ceylon

160 Rice Paddy and Globe

(Photo Courvoisier)

1966 (25 Oct). *International Rice Year. P* 11½.

515	**159**	6 c. multicoloured	10	10
516	**160**	30 c. multicoloured	15	15

161 U.N.E.S.C.O. Emblem

162 Water-resources Map

(Litho State Ptg Wks, Vienna)

1966 (3 Nov). *20th Anniv of U.N.E.S.C.O. P* 12.

517	**161**	3 c. multicoloured	15	15
518		50 c. multicoloured	60	30

(Litho D.L.R.)

1966 (1 Dec). *International Hydrological Decade. P* 14.

519	**162**	2 c. orange-brown, greenish yellow & bl	5	10
520		2 r. orge-brn, grnish yell, bl & yell-grn	50	65

163 Devotees at Buddhist Temple

167 Galle Fort and Clock Tower

(Photo State Ptg Wks, Vienna)

1967 (2 Jan). *Poya Holiday System. T* **163** *and similar horiz designs. Multicoloured. P* 12.

521	5 c. Type **163**	5	5
522	20 c. Mihintale	5	5
523	35 c. Sacred Bo-tree, Anuradhapura	5	5
524	60 c. Adam's Peak	10	8

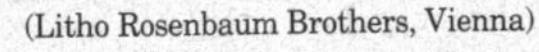

(Litho Rosenbaum Brothers, Vienna)

1967 (5 Jan). *Centenary of Galle Municipal Council. P* 13½.

525	**167**	25 c. multicoloured	5	5

168 Field Research

(Litho Rosenbaum Bros, Vienna)

1967 (1 Aug). *Centenary of Ceylon Tea Industry. T* **168** *and similar horiz designs. Multicoloured. P* 13½.

526	4 c. Type **168**	5	10
527	40 c. Tea-tasting equipment	15	5
528	50 c. Leaves and bud	15	5
529	1 r. Shipping tea	40	20

172 Elephant Ride

173 Ranger, Jubilee Emblem and Flag

(Litho Rosenbaum Bros, Vienna)

1967 (15 Aug). *International Tourist Year. P* 13½.

530	**172**	45 c. multicoloured	35	10

1967 (15 Sept). *1st National Stamp Exhibition. No.* **MS**500*a optd* "FIRST NATIONAL STAMP EXHIBITION 1967".

MS531 148 × 174 mm. Nos. 485, 488, 494/5. Imperf 2·75 3·25

(Litho D.L.R.)

1967 (19 Sept). *Golden Jubilee of Ceylon Girl Guides Association. P* 12½ × 13.

532	**173**	3 c. multicoloured	10	5
533		25 c. multicoloured	25	20

174 Col. Olcott and Buddhist Flag

(Litho Rosenbaum Bros, Vienna)

1967 (8 Dec). *60th Death Anniv of Colonel H. S. Olcott (theosophist). P* 13½.

534	**174**	15 c. multicoloured	10	5

175 Independence Hall

176 Lion Flag and Sceptre

(Photo Harrison)

1968 (2 Feb). *20th Anniv of Independence. W* **81** *(sideways). P* 14.

535	**175**	5 c. multicoloured	5	5
536	**176**	1 r. multicoloured	25	10

177 Sir D. B. Jayatilleke

178 Institute of Hygiene

(Litho D.L.R.)

1968 (14 Feb). *Birth Centenary of Sir Baron Jayatilleke (scholar and statesman). P* 14.

537	**177**	25 c. yellow-brown and sepia	5	5

(Litho B.W.)

1968 (7 Apr). *20th Anniv of World Health Organization. W* **81**. *P* 12.

538	**178**	50 c. multicoloured	15	10

179 Aircraft over Terminal Building

181 Open Quran and "1400"

(Des and litho B.W.)

1968 (5 Aug). *Opening of Colombo Airport. W* **81**. *P* 13½.
539 **179** 60 c. grey-blue, chestnut, red and yellow .. 10 5

(Des M. I. M. Mohideen. Photo Harrison)

1968 (14 Oct). *1400th Anniv of the Holy Quran. W* **81**. *P* 14.
541 **181** 25 c. multicoloured 8 5

182 Human Rights Emblem

183 All Ceylon Buddhist Congress Headquarters

(Photo Pakistan Security Printing Corp)

1968 (10 Dec). *Human Rights Year. P* 12½ × 13½.
542 **182** 2 c. multicoloured 5 5
543 20 c. multicoloured 5 5
544 40 c. multicoloured 15 15
545 2 r. multicoloured .. .. .. 55 1·25

(Des A. Dharmasiri. Litho Rosenbaum Bros, Vienna)

1968 (19 Dec). *Golden Jubilee of All Ceylon Buddhist Congress. P* 13½.
546 **183** 5 c. multicoloured 5 5

A 50 c. value showing a footprint was prepared but its release was stopped the day before it was due for issue. However, some are known to have been released in error at rural offices.

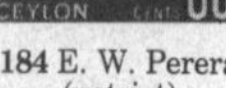

184 E. W. Perera (patriot)

185 Symbols of Strength in Savings

(Photo Harrison)

1969 (17 Feb). *E. W. Perera Commemoration. W* **81**. *P* 14 × 13½.
547 **184** 60 c. brown 10 10

(Des A. Dharmasiri. Photo Harrison)

1969 (20 Mar). *Silver Jubilee of National Savings Movement. W* **81**. *P* 14.
548 **185** 3 c. multicoloured 5 5

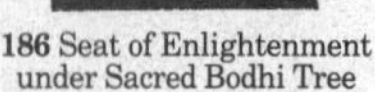
186 Seat of Enlightenment under Sacred Bodhi Tree

187 Buduresmala (Six fold Buddha-Rays)

(Des L. T. P. Manjusree. Litho D.L.R.)

1969 (10 Apr). *Vesak Day (inscr "Wesak"). W* **81** *(sideways). P* 15.
549 **186** 4 c. multicoloured 5 5
550 **187** 6 c. multicoloured 5 5
551 **186** 35 c. multicoloured 10 10

No. 549 exists with the gold apparently omitted. Normally the gold appears (without a separate plate number) over an underlay of olive-green on carmine. In one sheet we have seen, the gold only shows as tiny specks under a strong magnifying glass and as there may be intermediate stages of faint printing we do not list this.

188 A. E. Goonesinghe

189 I.L.O. Emblem

(Des and photo Harrison)

1969 (29 Apr). *Commemoration of Goonesinghe (founder of Labour Movement in Ceylon). W* **81**. *P* 14.
522 **188** 15 c. multicoloured 10 5

(Photo Harrison)

1969 (4 May). *50th Anniv of International Labour Organisation. W* **81** *(sideways). P* 14.
553 **189** 5 c. black and turquoise-blue 5 5
554 25 c. black and carmine-red 10 10

190 Convocation Hall, University of Ceylon

192 Uranium Atom

(Des Ahangama Edward (35 c.); L. D. P. Jayawardena (50 c.); A. Dharmasiri (60 c.); 4 c. from photograph. Litho Rosenbaum Bros, Vienna)

1969 (1 Aug). *Educational Centenary. T* **190**, **192** *and similar multicoloured designs. P* 13½.
555 4 c. Type **190** 5 5
556 35 c. Lamp of Learning, Globe and flags *(horiz)* 10 5
557 50 c. Type **192** 15 12
558 60 c. Symbols of Scientific education 15 15

194 Ath Pana (Elephant Lamp)

195 Rock Fortress of Sigiriya

(Des from photographs. Litho Rosenbaum Bros, Vienna)

1969 (1 Aug). *Archaeological Centenary. P* 13½.
559 **194** 6 c. multicoloured 10 10
560 **195** 1 r. multicoloured 25 20

196 Leopard

197 Emblem and Symbols

(Litho Rosenbaum Bros, Vienna)

1970 (11 May). *Wildlife Conservation. T* **196** *and similar horiz designs. Multicoloured. P* 13½.
561 5 c. Wild Buffalo 5 10
562 15 c. Slender Loris 25 15
a. Brown-black and orange-brown colours omitted .. .. 35·00
563 50 c. Spotted Deer 60 70
a. Imperf (in vert pair with stamp perf 3 sides) .. .. 75·00
564 1 r. Type **196** .. .. 90 1·50

In No. 562a the sky is blue instead of violet and the animal is in green and yellow only.

(Des A. Dharmasiri. Litho Rosenbaum Bros, Vienna)

1970 (17 June). *Asian Productivity Year. P* 13½.
565 **197** 60 c. multicoloured 12 12

198 New U.P.U. H.Q. Building

199 Oil Lamp and Caduceus

(Litho Rosenbaum Bros, Vienna)

1970 (14 Aug). *New U.P.U. Headquarters Building. P* 13½.
566 **198** 50 c. yellow-orange, black and new blue 12 10
a. New blue (Building) omitted .. 50·00
567 1 r. 10, vermilion, black and new blue 25 30

(Des A. Dharmasiri. Litho Rosenbaum Bros, Vienna)

1970 (1 Sept). *Centenary of Colombo Medical School. P* 13½.
568 **199** 5 c. multicoloured 8 10
a. Vert pair, bottom stamp imperf .. 90·00
569 45 c. multicoloured 20 35

200 Victory March and S. W. R. D. Bandaranaike

201 U.N. Emblem and Dove of Peace

(Des A. Dharmasiri. Litho D.L.R.)

1970 (25 Sept). *Definitive issue marking establishment of United Front Government. P* 13½.
570 **200** 10 c. multicoloured 5 5

(Des A. Dharmasiri. Photo Pakistan Security Printing Corp)

1970 (24 Oct). *25th Anniv of United Nations. P* 12½ × 13½.
571 **201** 2 r. multicoloured 40 55

202 Keppetipola Dissawa

203 Ola Leaf Manuscript

(Des A. Dharmasiri. Litho Harrison)

1970 (26 Nov). *152nd Death Anniv of Keppetipola Dissawa (Kandyan patriot). P* 14 × 14½.
572 **202** 25 c. multicoloured 10 10

(Des A. Dharmasiri. Photo Pakistan Security Printing Corp)

1970 (21 Dec). *International Education Year. P* 13.
573 **203** 15 c. multicoloured 10 10

204 C. H. de Soysa

205 D. E. H. Pedris (patriot)

206 Lenin

(Des L. D. P. Jayawardena. Litho Pakistan Security Printing Corp)

1971 (3 Mar). *135th Birth Anniv of C. H. de Soysa (philanthropist). P* 13½.
574 **204** 20 c. multicoloured 8 12

(Des L. D. P. Jayawardena. Litho Harrison)

1971 (8 July). *D. E. H. Pedris Commemoration. P* 14 × 14½.
575 **205** 25 c. multicoloured 10 15

(Des L. D. P. Jayawardena. Litho Harrison)

1971 (31 Aug). *Lenin Commemoration. P* 14½.
576 **206** 40 c. multicoloured 20 15

207 Ananda Rajakaruna

(208)

(Des A. Dharmasiri (Nos. 577 and 579), P. A. Miththapala (Nos. 578 and 580), L. D. P. Jayawardena (No. 581). Litho Harrison)

1971 (29 Oct). *Poets and Philosophers. T* **207** *and similar vert designs. P* 14 × 13½.
577 5 c. royal blue 5 5
578 5 c. lake-brown 5 5
579 5 c. red-orange 5 5
580 5 c. deep slate-blue 5 5
581 5 c. brown 5 5

Portraits: No. 577, Type **207**; No. 578, Arumuga Navalar; No. 579, Rev. S. Mahinda; No. 580, Ananda Coomaraswamy; No. 581, Cumaratunga Munidasa.

1971. *Nos.* 549/50, 555, 559 *and* 570 *surch as T* **208** *(obliterating shape differs).*
582 **186** 5 c. on 4 c. multicoloured 8 8
a. Surch inverted, reading "ᘓ X" .. 10·00
b. Pair, one with "X" omitted .. 25·00
c. Surch double, one inverted ..
d. Ditto. Pair, one with "X" omitted ..
583 **190** 5 c. on 4 c. multicoloured 8 8
a. Surch inverted .. .. .. 9·00
b. Surch double, one inverted .. .. 9·00
584 **200** 15 c. on 10 c. multicoloured 10 8
a. Surch inverted .. .. .. 9·00
b. Surch double .. .. .. 10·00

585 **187** 25 c. on 6 c. multicoloured 15 12
a. Surch double, one inverted .. .. 15·00
b. Surch inverted .. .. .. 12·00
586 **194** 25 c. on 6 c. multicoloured 15 12
a. Surch inverted .. .. .. 11·00
Dates of issue:—No. 584, 2.12.71; others, 26.11.71.

209 Colombo Plan Emblem and Ceylon   **210** Globe and CARE Package

(Des P. A. Miththapala. Litho Harrison)

1971 (28 Dec). *20th Anniv of Colombo Plan. P* 14 × 14½.
587 **209** 20 c. multicoloured 15 15

(Des A. Dharmasiri. Litho Harrison)

1971 (28 Dec). *20th Anniv of CARE (Co-operative for American Relief Everywhere). P* 14 × 13½.
588 **210** 50 c. new blue, lilac and violet 12 15

211 W.H.O. Emblem and Heart   **212** Map of Asia and U.N. Emblem

(Des A. Miththapala. Litho D.L.R.)

1972 (2 May). *World Health Day. P* 13 × 13½.
589 **211** 25 c. multicoloured 10 15

(Des L. D. P. Jayawardena. Litho B.W.)

1972 (2 May). *25th Anniv of ECAFE (Economic Commission for Asia and the Far East). P* 13.
590 **212** 85 c. multicoloured 30 30

OFFICIAL STAMPS

1869. *Issues of* 1863–68 *overprinted* "SERVICE" *in block letters.*
Although these stamps were prepared for use and sent out to the colony, they were never issued.

Prices:

Narrow "SERVICE"		Wide "SERVICE"	
No. 98. 2d.	35·00	No. 119. 1d.	35·00
104. 6d.	45·00	120. 3d.	50·00
108. 8d.	50·00		
113. 1s.	60·00		
116. 2s.	65·00		
116. 2s. *imp.*	£250		

On

Service

(O 3)

Contemporary issues overprinted with Type O **3**

1895–96.
O1 **9** 2 c. green .. .. 2·50 15
O2 **39** 3 c. terracotta and blue-green .. .. 2·75 80
O3 **28** 5 c. dull purple (*b*) 80 10
O4 **29** 15 c. sage-green .. .. 3·50 30
O5 25 c. yellow-brown .. .. .. 3·50 70
O6 30 c. bright mauve and brown .. .. 3·50 30
O7 **30** 1 r. 12, dull rose .. .. .. 26·00 16·00
The varieties of the 1 r. 12 mentioned in note after No. 201 all exist with the "On Service" overprint.

1899–1900.
O 8 **9** 2 c. pale orange-brown 85 30
O 9 **39** 3 c. deep green .. .. 2·50 50
O10 **29** 15 c. blue .. .. 3·00 60
O11 **39** 75 c. black and red-brown (R.) (1899) .. 3·00 3·00

1903. *King Edward VII.*
O12 **44** 2 c. orange-brown .. .. .. 2·50 1·25
O13 **45** 3 c. green .. .. 2·25 2·25
O14 **46** 5 c. dull purple .. .. 2·50 55
O15 **48** 15 c. blue .. .. 5·00 2·50
O16 25 c. bistre .. .. 14·00 14·00
O17 30 c. dull violet and green .. .. 6·00 2·00
About half a dozen sheets of the 15 c. were overprinted with a space of 3 mm instead of 4 mm between the words "On" and "Service".

POSTAL FISCAL

1952 (1 Dec). *As T* **72** *but inscr* "REVENUE" *at sides.*
F1 10 r. dull green and yellow-orange, **C** .. 45·00 28·00
This revenue stamp was on sale for postal use from 1 December 1952, until 14 March 1954.

On 22 May 1972, Ceylon became the Republic of SRI LANKA.

Channel Islands

These issues are now listed under GREAT BRITAIN after the Postal Fiscal Issues.

China—British Post Offices

***see after* Hong Kong**

Christmas Island

Formerly a part of the Straits Settlements and then of the Colony of Singapore, Christmas Island became an Australian territory on 15 October 1958.

Stamps of the STRAITS SETTLEMENTS and later SINGAPORE were used on Christmas Island from 1901 until 1942 and subsequently from 1946 to 1958.

(Currency. 100 cents = 1 dollar (Malayan))

1 Queen Elizabeth II

(Des G. Lissenden. Recess with name and value typo in black. Note Printing Branch, Commonwealth Bank, Melbourne)

1958 (15 Oct). *No wmk. P* 14½.
1 **1** 2 c. yellow-orange 90 20
2 4 c. brown .. .. 1·00 25
3 5 c. deep mauve .. .. 1·00 25
4 6 c. grey-blue .. .. 2·25 40
5 8 c. black-brown .. .. 2·75 90
6 10 c. violet .. .. 2·75 90
7 12 c. carmine .. .. 4·75 2·50
8 20 c. blue .. .. 8·00 4·50
9 50 c. yellow-green .. .. 17·00 8·00
10 $1 deep bluish green .. .. .. 18·00 8·00
1/10 .. .. *Set of* 10 50·00 23·00

PRINTERS. Nos. 11/32 were printed by the Note Printing Branch, Reserve Bank of Australia, Melbourne. Nos. 33/82 were printed in photogravure by Harrison and Sons, Ltd, London.

2 Map   11 White-tailed Tropic Bird

(Des G. Lissenden (2, 8c.), P. Morriss (4, 5, 10, 20 c.), B. Stewart (others). Recess)

1963 (28 Aug). *T* **2** *and similar designs and T* **11.** *P* 14½ × 14 ($1) *or* 14½ (*others*).
11 2 c. orange 60 30
12 4 c. red-brown 80 30
13 5 c. purple 85 40
14 6 c. indigo 60 40
15 8 c. black .. .. 1·60 60
16 10 c. violet 60 30
17 12 c. brown-red 80 35
18 20 c. blue .. .. 3·00 1·75
19 50 c. green .. .. 4·00 2·25
20 $1 yellow .. .. 7·00 3·00
11/20 .. .. *Set of* 10 18·00 9·00
Designs: *Vert*—4 c. Moonflower; 5 c. Robber Crab; 8 c. Phosphate train; 10 c. Raising phosphate. *Horiz*—6 c. Island scene; 12 c. Flying Fish Cove; 20 c. Loading cantilever; 50 c. Christmas Island Frigate Bird.

I Thick lettering

II Thinner lettering

1965. *50th Anniv of Gallipoli Landing. As T* **184** *of Australia, but slightly larger* (22 × 34½ *mm*) *and colour changed. Photo.*
21 10 c. sepia, black and emerald (I) (14.4) .. 1·25 65
a. Black-brown, black and light emerald (II) (24.4) .. .. 1·75 1·25

(New Currency. 100 cents = 1 dollar (Australian))

12 Golden Striped Grouper   **13** "Angel" (mosaic)

(Des G. Hamori. Photo)

1968 (6 May)–**70.** *Fishes. T* **12** *and similar horiz designs. Multicoloured. P* 13½.
22 1 c. Type **12** 25 15
23 2 c. Moorish Idol 90 30
24 3 c. Forceps Fish 90 30
25 4 c. Queen Triggerfish 90 30
a. Deep blue (face value) omitted £300
26 5 c. Regal Angelfish .. .. 1·00 30
27 9 c. Surgeon Fish .. .. 3·50 1·00
28 10 c. Scorpion Fish .. .. 2·25 60
28*a* 15 c. Saddleback Butterfly (fish) (14.12.70) .. 15·00 13·00
29 20 c. Clown Butterfly (fish) .. .. .. 6·50 2·00
29*a* 30 c. Ghost Pipefish (14.12.70) .. .. 15·00 13·00
30 50 c. Blue Lined Surgeon .. .. .. 17·00 9·00
31 $1 Meyers Butterfly (fish) .. .. .. 28·00 13·00
22/31 .. .. *Set of* 12 80·00 48·00

(Des G. Hamori. Photo)

1969 (10 Nov). *Christmas. P* 13½.
32 **13** 5 c. red, deep blue and gold 20 15

14 "The Ansidei Madonna" (Raphael)   **15** "The Adoration of the Shepherds" (ascr to the School of Seville)

(Des Harrison)

1970 (26 Oct). *Christmas. Paintings. T* **14** *and similar vert design. Multicoloured. P* 14 × 14½.
33 3 c. Type **14** 20 20
34 5 c. "The Virgin and Child, St. John the Baptist and an Angel" (Morando) .. 20 20

(Des Harrison)

1971 (4 Oct). *Christmas. T* **15** *and similar vert design. Multicoloured. W* w **12.** *P* 14.
35 6 c. Type **15** .. .. 1·25 90
36 20 c. "The Adoration of the Shepherds" (Reni) 2·25 1·75

16 H.M.S. *Flying Fish*, 1887

17 Angel of Peace

(Des V. Whiteley)

1972 (7 Feb)—**73.** *Ships. Horiz designs as T* **16.** *Multicoloured. P* 14 × 13½.

No.	Description		
37	1 c. *Eagle*, 1714 (5.6.72)	20	10
38	2 c. H.M.S. *Redpole*, 1890 (5.6.72)	25	15
39	3 c. M.V. *Hoi Houw*, 1959 (5.6.72)	25	15
40	4 c. *Pigot*, 1771 (6.2.73)	25	15
41	5 c. S.S. *Valetta*, 1968 (6.2.73)	25	15
42	6 c. Type **16**	30	20
43	7 c. *Asia*, 1805	30	20
44	8 c. T.S.S. *Islander*, 1929–60	35	25
45	9 c. H.M.S. *Imperieuse**, 1888 (6.2.73)	55	40
46	10 c. H.M.S. *Egeria*, 1887 (4.6.73)	55	40
47	20 c. *Thomas*, 1615	85	70
48	25 c. H.M.S. *Gordon*, 1864 (4.6.73)	95	85
49	30 c. *Cygnet*, 1688 (4.6.73)	95	95
50	35 c. S.S. *Triadic*, 1958 (4.6.73)	1·10	1·10
51	50 c. H.M.S. *Amethyst*, 1857 (6.2.73)	4·00	4·00
52	$1 *Royal Mary*, 1643 (5.6.72)	4·75	6·50
37/52	*Set of* 16	14·00	15·00

*The design is wrongly inscribed "H.M.S. *Imperious*".

(Des Jennifer Toombs)

1972 (2 Oct). *Christmas. T* **17** *and similar vert design. Multicoloured. P* 14.

No.	Description		
53	3 c. Type **17**	90	90
	a. Pair. Nos. 53/4	1·75	1·75
54	3 c. Angel of Joy	90	90
55	7 c. Type **17**	1·25	1·25
	a. Pair. Nos. 55/6	2·50	2·50
56	7 c. As No. 54	1·25	1·25

Nos. 53/4 and 55/6 have the two designs printed horizontally *se-tenant* within the sheet.

18 Virgin and Child, and Map

19 Mary and Holy Child within Christmas Star

(Des P. L. S. Cheong)

1973 (2 Oct). *Christmas. P* 14 × 13.

No.	Type	Description		
57	18	7 c. multicoloured	2·50	1·75
58		25 c. multicoloured	7·00	5·00

(Des Jennifer Toombs)

1974 (2 Oct). *Christmas. P* 13 × 14½.

No.	Type	Description		
59	19	7 c. mauve and grey-black	1·50	1·50
60		30 c. light orange, bright yell & grey-blk	5·00	5·00

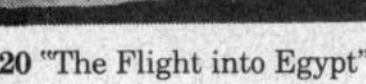

20 "The Flight into Egypt"

21 Dove of Peace and Star of Bethlehem

(Des Jennifer Toombs)

1975 (2 Oct). *Christmas. P* 14 × 13.

No.	Type	Description		
61	20	10 c. light greenish yellow, agate and gold	1·00	1·00
62		35 c. bright rose, deep blue and gold	2·00	2·25

(Des R. Bates)

1976 (2 Oct). *Christmas. P* 13½.

No.	Type	Description		
63	21	10 c. cerise, lemon and bright mauve	1·00	1·00
		a. Pair. Nos. 63/4	2·00	2·00
64	–	10 c. cerise, lemon and bright mauve	1·00	1·00
65	21	35 c. reddish violet, light greenish blue and light yellow-green	1·40	1·40
		a. Pair. Nos. 65/6	2·75	2·75
66	–	35 c. reddish violet, light greenish blue and light yellow-green	1·40	1·40

Nos. 64 and 66 are "mirror-images" of T **21**, the two designs of each value being printed horizontally *se-tenant* throughout the sheet.

22 William Dampier (explorer)

23 Australian Coat of Arms on Map of Christmas Island

(Des V. Whiteley Studio)

1977 (30 Apr)–**78.** *Famous Visitors. Horiz designs as T* **22** *in black, vermilion and greenish yellow* (45 c.) *or multicoloured* (*others*). *P* 14 × 13.

No.	Description		
67	1 c. Type **22**	10	5
68	2 c. Capt. de Vlamingh (explorer) (22.2.78)	15	5
69	3 c. Vice-Admiral MacLear (22.2.78)	15	5
70	4 c. Sir John Murray (oceanographer) (22.2.78)	15	5
71	5 c. Admiral Aldrich (31.5.78)	15	5
72	6 c. Andrew Clunies-Ross (first settler)	15	5
73	7 c. J. J. Lister (naturalist) (31.5.78)	20	8
74	8 c. Admiral of the Fleet Sir William May (1.9.78)	20	10
75	9 c. Henry Ridley (botanist)	20	10
76	10 c. George Clunies-Ross (phosphate miner) (1.9.78)	20	15
77	20 c. Capt. Joshua Slocum (yachtsman) (1.9.78)	40	25
78	45 c. Charles Andrews (naturalist) (31.5.78)	85	45
79	50 c. Richard Hanitsch (biologist) (31.5.78)	95	50
80	75 c. Victor Purcell (scholar) (1.9.78)	85	70
81	$1 Fam Choo Beng (educator)	1·25	95
82	$2 Sir Harold Spencer-Jones (astronomer) (22.2.78)	2·50	2·00
67/82	*Set of* 16	7·50	5·50

(Des Mrs S. Muir. Litho Harrison)

1977 (2 June). *Silver Jubilee. P* 14½ × 13½.

No.	Type	Description		
83	23	45 c. multicoloured	1·00	1·25

24 "A Partridge in a Pear Tree"

25 Abbott's Booby

(Des Jennifer Toombs. Litho Questa)

1977 (20 Oct)–**78.** *Christmas. T* **24** *and similar vert designs depicting the carol "The Twelve Days of Christmas". Multicoloured. P* 14.

A. *No wmk.* B. *W w* **14** (27.1.78)

No.	Description	A.		B.	
84	10 c. Type **24**	25	25	20	20
	a. Sheetlet. Nos. 84/95	2·75	—	2·10	—
85	10 c. "Two turtle doves"	25	25	20	20
86	10 c. "Three French hens"	25	25	20	20
87	10 c. "Four calling birds"	25	25	20	20
88	10 c. "Five gold rings"	25	25	20	20
89	10 c. "Six geese a-laying"	25	25	20	20
90	10 c. "Seven swans a-swimming"	25	25	20	20
91	10 c. "Eight maids a-milking"	25	25	20	20
92	10 c. "Nine ladies dancing"	25	25	20	20
93	10 c. "Ten lords a-leaping"	25	25	20	20
94	10 c. "Eleven pipers piping"	25	25	20	20
95	10 c. "Twelve drummers drumming"	25	25	20	20
84/95	*Set of* 12	2·75	2·75	2·10	2·10

Nos. 84/95 were printed as a *se-tenant* block within a sheetlet 142 × 170 mm.

(Des Jennifer Toombs. Litho Questa)

1978 (21 Apr). *25th Anniv of Coronation. T* **25** *and similar vert designs. P* 15.

No.	Description		
96	45 c. black and bright ultramarine	60	75
	a. Sheetlet. Nos. 96/8 × 2	4·50	
97	45 c. multicoloured	60	75
98	45 c. black and bright ultramarine	60	75

Designs:—No. 96, White Swan of Bohun; No. 97, Queen Elizabeth II; No. 98, Type **25**.

Nos. 96/8 were printed together in small sheets of 6, containing two *se-tenant* strips of 3 with horizontal gutter margin between.

26 "Christ Child"

27 Chinese Children

(Des Jennifer Toombs. Litho J.W.)

1978 (2 Oct). *Christmas. Scenes from "The Song of Christmas". T* **26** *and similar horiz designs. Multicoloured. P* 14.

No.	Description		
99	10 c. Type **26**	20	20
	a. Sheetlet. Nos. 99/107	1·60	
100	10 c. "Herald Angels"	20	20
101	10 c. "Redeemer"	20	20
102	10 c. "Israel"	20	20
103	10 c. "Star"	20	20
104	10 c. "Three Wise Men"	20	20
105	10 c. "Manger"	20	20
106	10 c. "All He Stands For"	20	20
107	10 c. "Shepherds Came"	20	20
99/107	*Set of* 9	1·60	1·60

Nos. 99/107 were printed together, *se-tenant*, in a small sheet of 9.

(Des Jennifer Toombs. Litho Questa)

1979 (20 Apr). *International Year of the Child. T* **27** *and similar vert designs showing children of different races. Multicoloured, colour of inscr given. P* 14.

No.	Description		
108	20 c. apple-green (Type **27**)	70	70
	a. Horiz strip of 5. Nos. 108/12	3·25	
109	20 c. turquoise-green (Malay children)	70	70
110	20 c. lilac (Indian children)	70	70
111	20 c. rose (European children)	70	70
112	20 c. orange-yellow ("Oranges and Lemons")	70	70

Nos. 108/12 were printed together, *se-tenant*, in horizontal strips of 5 throughout the sheet, forming a composite design.

28 1958 2 c. Definitive

29 Wise Men following Star

(Des J.W. Litho Questa)

1979 (27 Aug). *Death Centenary of Sir Rowland Hill. T* **28** *and similar horiz designs showing stamps and Sir Rowland Hill. Multicoloured. P* 13½.

No.	Description		
113	20 c. Type **28**	30	35
	a. Horiz strip of 5. Nos. 113/17	1·40	
114	20 c. 1963 2 c. Map definitive	30	35
115	20 c. 1965 50th anniversary of Gallipoli Landing 10 c. commemorative	30	35
116	20 c. 1968 4 c. Queen Triggerfish definitive	30	35
117	20 c. 1969 5 c. Christmas issue	30	35

Nos. 113/17 were printed together, *se-tenant*, in horizontal strips of 5 throughout the sheet.

(Des L. Curtis. Litho Walsall)

1979 (22 Oct). *Christmas. T* **29** *and similar horiz design. Multicoloured. P* 14 × 14½.

No.	Description		
118	20 c. Type **29**	40	35
119	55 c. Virgin and Child	60	50

30 9th Green

31 Surveying

(Des R. Granger Barrett. Litho Format)

1980 (12 Feb). *25th Anniv of Christmas Island Golf Club. T* **30** *and similar horiz design. Multicoloured. P* 14½ × 14.

No.	Description		
120	20 c. Type **30**	40	40
121	55 c. Clubhouse	70	65

(Des L. Curtis. Litho Walsall)

1980 (6 May). *Phosphate Industry* (1st issue). *T* **31** *and similar horiz designs. Multicoloured. P* 14.

No.	Description		
122	15 c. Type **31**	25	25
123	22 c. Drilling for samples	35	35
124	40 c. Sample analysis	50	50
125	55 c. Mine planning	70	70

See also Nos. 126/9, 136/9 and 140/3.

(Des L. Curtis. Litho Walsall)

1980 (14 July). *Phosphate Industry* (2nd issue). *Horiz designs as T* **31.** *Multicoloured. P* 14.

No.	Description		
126	15 c. Jungle clearing	25	25
127	22 c. Overburden removal	30	30
128	40 c. Open cut mining	50	50
129	55 c. Restoration	60	60

32 Angel with Harp

33 *Cryptoblepharus egeriae*

(Des Jennifer Toombs. Litho Walsall)

1980 (6 Oct). *Christmas. T* **32** *and similar vert designs. Multicoloured. P* 13½ × 13.

130 15 c. Type **32** 20 20
 a. Sheetlet. Nos. 130/5 .. .. .. 2·00
131 15 c. Angel with wounded soldier 20 20
132 22 c. Virgin and Child.. .. .. .. 30 30
133 22 c. Kneeling couple 30 30
134 60 c. Angel with harp (*different*) 65 65
135 60 c. Angel with children 65 65
130/5 .. .. *Set of* 6 2·00 2·00

Nos. 130/5 were printed together in small sheets of 6, containing two *se-tenant* strips of 3 (Nos. 130, 132, 134 and 131, 133, 135) with horizontal gutter margin between.

(Des L. Curtis. Litho Walsall)

1981 (9 Feb). *Phosphate Industry (3rd issue). Horiz designs as T* **31**. *Multicoloured. P* 14.

136 22 c. Screening and stockpiling 35 35
137 28 c. Train loading 40 40
138 40 c. Railing 50 50
139 60 c. Drying 75 75

(Des L. Curtis. Litho Walsall)

1981 (4 May). *Phosphate Industry (4th issue). Horiz designs as T* **31**. *Multicoloured. P* 14.

140 22 c. Crushing 35 35
141 28 c. Conveying 40 40
142 40 c. Bulk storage 50 50
143 60 c. Ship loading 75 75

(Des L. Curtis. Litho Walsall)

1981 (10 Aug). *Reptiles. T* **33** *and similar horiz designs. Multicoloured. P* 13.

144 24 c. Type **33** 35 30
145 30 c. *Emoia nativitata* 40 40
146 40 c. *Lepidodactylus listeri* 50 50
147 60 c. *Cyrtodactylus sp. nov.* 75 75

34 Scene from Carol "Away in a Manger"

35 Eastern Reef Heron

(Des Jennifer Toombs. Litho Questa)

1981 (19 Oct). *Christmas. T* **34** *and similar horiz designs showing scenes from carol "Away in a Manger". P* 14½ × 14.

148 18 c. silver, deep blue and turquoise-blue .. 30 30
 a. Sheetlet. Nos. 148/51 .. .. .. 1·75
149 24 c. multicoloured 40 40
150 40 c. multicoloured 50 50
151 60 c. multicoloured 70 70

Nos. 148/51 were printed together, *se-tenant*, in sheetlets of 4.

(Des N. Arlott. Litho Questa)

1982 (8 Mar)–**83**. *Birds. Multicoloured designs as T* **35**. *P* 14.

152 1 c. Type **35** 5 5
153 2 c. Common Noddy 5 5
154 3 c. White-bellied Swiftlet (14.6.82) 5 5
155 4 c. Christmas Island Imperial Pigeon (14.6.82) 5 5
156 5 c. Christmas Island White Eye (21.2.83) .. 5 8
157 10 c. Island Thrush (14.6.82) 12 15
158 25 c. Red-tailed Tropic Bird 30 35
159 30 c. Emerald Dove (21.2.83) 35 40
160 40 c. Brown Booby (23.8.82) 50 55
161 50 c. Red-footed Booby (23.8.82) 60 65
162 65 c. Christmas Island Frigate Bird (23.8.82) 80 85
163 75 c. White-tailed Tropic Bird (23.8.82) .. 95 1·00
164 80 c. Australian Kestrel (*vert*) (21.2.83) .. 1·10 1·25
165 $1 Christmas Island Hawk Owl (*vert*) (21.2.83) .. .. 1·25 1·40
166 $2 Australian Goshawk (*vert*) (14.6.82) .. 2·50 2·75
167 $4 Abbott's Booby (*vert*) .. .. .. 5·00 5·50
152/67 .. .. *Set of* 16 12·00 13·00

36 Joseph

37 "Mirror" Dinghy and Club House

(Des Jennifer Toombs. Litho and embossed Walsall)

1982 (18 Oct). *Christmas. Origami Paper Sculptures. T* **36** *and similar vert designs. Multicoloured. P* 14½ × 14.

168 27 c. Type **36** 40 40
 a. Horiz strip of 3. Nos. 168/70 .. .. 1·75
169 50 c. Angel 55 55
170 75 c. Mary and baby Jesus 90 90

Nos. 168/70 were printed together, *se-tenant*, in horiz strips of 3 throughout the sheet.

(Des L. McCombie. Litho Format)

1983 (2 May). *25th Anniv of Christmas Island Boat Club. T* **37** *and similar multicoloured designs. P* 14 × 14½ (27, 35 *c.*) *or* 14½ × 14 (*others*).

171 27 c. Type **37** 45 40
172 35 c. Ocean-going yachts 50 45
173 50 c. Fishing launch and cargo ship (*horiz*) .. 70 65
174 75 c. Dinghy-racing and cantilever (*horiz*) .. 1·10 95

38 Maps of Christmas Island and Australia, Kangaroo and White-tailed Tropic Bird

39 Candle and Holly

(Des A. Theobald. Litho Questa)

1983 (1 Oct). *25th Anniv of Christmas Island as an Australian Territory. T* **38** *and similar horiz designs. Multicoloured. P* 14.

175 24 c. Type **38** 20 25
176 30 c. Christmas Island and Australian flag .. 35 40
177 85 c. Maps of Christmas Island and Australia, with Boeing "727" .. .. 1·00 1·10

(Des J.W. Litho Walsall)

1983 (31 Oct). *Christmas. Candles. T* **39** *and similar vert designs. Multicoloured. P* 13.

178 24 c. Type **39** 20 25
179 30 c. Six gold candles 35 40
180 85 c. Candles .. .. 1·00 1·10

40 Feeding on Leaf

41 *Leucocoprinus fragilissimus*

(Des L. Curtis. Litho Questa)

1984 (20 Feb). *Red Land Crab. T* **40** *and similar horiz designs showing various aspects of crab's life. Multicoloured. P* 14 × 14½.

181 30 c. Type **40** 40 45
182 40 c. Migration 55 60
183 55 c. Development stages 70 75
184 85 c. Adult female and young .. .. .. 1·10 1·25

(Des I. Loe. Litho Format)

1984 (30 Apr). *Fungi. T* **41** *and similar vert designs. Multicoloured. P* 14 × 14½.

185 30 c. Type **41** 40 45
186 40 c. *Microporus xanthopus* 55 60
187 45 c. *Trogia anthidepas* 65 70
188 55 c. *Haddowia longipes* 80 85
189 85 c. *Phillipsia domingensis* .. .. .. 1·10 1·25

42 Run-out

43 Arrival of Father Christmas

(Des A. Theobald. Litho J.W.)

1984 (23 July). *25th Anniversary of Cricket on Christmas Island. T* **42** *and similar horiz designs. Multicoloured. P* 14.

190 30 c. Type **42** 40 45
191 40 c. Bowled-out 55 60
192 55 c. Batsman in action 80 85
193 85 c. Fielder diving for catch .. .. .. 1·10 1·25

(Des D. Slater. Litho B.D.T.)

1984 (21 Sept). *Christmas and "Ausipex" International Stamp Exhibition, Melbourne. Sheet* 100 × 100 *mm containing T* **43** *and similar horiz designs. Multicoloured. P* 13½.

MS194 30 c. Type **43**; 55 c. Distribution of presents; 85 c. Departure of Father Christmas .. .. 2·40

No. **MS**194 also contains three labels horizontally *se-tenant* with the stamps and forming composite designs with them.

Cocos (Keeling) Is.

Formerly incorporated with Singapore: an Australian territory since 23 November 1955.

The stamps of the STRAITS SETTLEMENTS were used by a postal agency operating on Cocos (Keeling) Islands from 1 April 1933 until 1 March 1937. The postal agency reopened on 2 September 1952 and used the stamps of SINGAPORE until the islands were transferred to Australia in 1955. From 1955 until 1963 stamps of AUSTRALIA were in use.

PRINTERS. All the following stamps to No. 31 were printed by the Note Printing Branch, Reserve Bank of Australia, Melbourne.

1 Copra Industry

2 "Super Constellation"

1963 (11 June). *T* **1/2** *and similar designs. Recess. P* 14½ × 14 (*5d., 2s. 3d.*) *or* 14½ (*others*).

1 3d. chocolate .. .. 5·50 2·50
2 5d. ultramarine .. .. 4·50 90
3 8d. scarlet .. .. 14·00 3·00
4 1s. green .. .. 10·00 1·75
5 2s. deep purple .. .. 25·00 12·00
6 2s. 3d. deep green .. .. 45·00 25·00
1/6 .. .. *Set of* 6 90·00 40·00

Designs: *Vert (as T* **1**)—8d. Map of islands; 2s. Dukong (sailboat). *Horiz (as T* **1**)—1s. Palms. (*as T* **2**)—2s. 3d. White Tern.

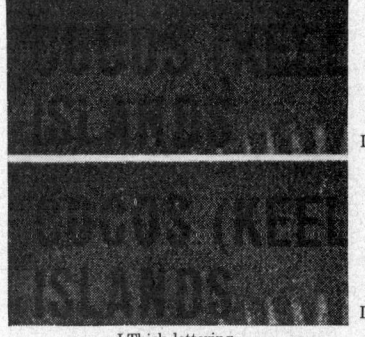

I Thick lettering

II Thinner lettering

1965. *50th Anniv of Gallipoli Landing. As T* **184** *of Australia, but slightly larger* (22 × 34½ *mm*) *and colour changed. Photo.*

7 5d. sepia, black and emerald (I) (14.4) .. 2·00 1·25
 a. *Black-brown, black and light emerald* (II) (24.4) .. .. 2·50 1·50

With the introduction of decimal currency on 14 February 1966, Australian stamps were used in Cocos Islands, until the appearance of the new definitives on 9 July 1969.

7 Reef Clam

8 Great Frigate Bird

(Des L. Annois (1 c. to 6 c.); P. Jones (10 c. to $1). Photo)

1969 (9 July). *Decimal Currency. T* **8** *or designs as T* **7**. *Multicoloured. P* 13½ × 13 (*1 c., 2 c., 50 c., $1*) *or* 13 × 13½ (*others*).

8 1 c. Turban Shell (*vert*) 60 20
9 2 c. Burrowing clam (*vert*) .. .. .. 1·25 45
10 3 c. Type **7** 50 15
11 4 c. Blenny (fish) 50 15
 a. Salmon-pink omitted £450
12 5 c. Coral 55 15
13 6 c. Flying Fish .. .. 1·00 35
14 10 c. Banded Rail .. .. 2·50 90
15 15 c. Java Sparrow .. .. 2·25 70
16 20 c. Red-tailed Tropic Bird .. .. .. 2·25 70
17 30 c. Sooty Tern .. .. 2·75 1·00
18 50 c. Eastern Reef Heron (*vert*) .. .. 3·50 1·75
19 $1 Type **8** .. .. 7·50 7·50
8/19 .. .. *Set of* 12 23·00 12·50

9 *Dragon*, 1609

10 Map of Cocos (Keeling) Islands Union Flag, Stars and Trees

(Des R. Honisett. Photo)

1976 (29 Mar). *Multicoloured designs as T* **9.** *P* 13½ × 13 (1, 25, 30, 50 *c.*, $1) *or* 13 × 13½ (*others*).

20	1 c. Type **9**	12	12
21	2 c. H.M.S. *Juno*, 1857	20	20
22	5 c. H.M.S. *Beagle*, 1836	30	20
23	10 c. H.M.A.S. *Sydney*, 1914	45	30
24	15 c. S.M.S. *Emden*, 1914	80	50
25	20 c. *Ayesha*, 1907	1·00	65
26	25 c. T.S.S. *Islander*, 1927	1·00	75
27	30 c. M.V. *Cheshire*, 1951	1·00	90
28	35 c. Jukung (sailboat)	1·25	1·10
29	40 c. C.S. *Scotia*, 1900	1·50	1·40
30	50 c. R.M.S. *Orontes*, 1929	1·75	1·50
31	$1 Royal Yacht *Gothic*, 1954	3·50	3·00
20/31	*Set of* 12	11·50	9·50

The 2 c. to 20 c., 35 c. and 40 c. are horizontal designs.

(Des Marg Towt. Litho Asher and Co, Melbourne)

1979 (3 Sept). *Inauguration of Independent Postal Service* (20 *c.*) *and Establishment of First Statutory Council* (50 *c.*). *T* **10** *and similar horiz design. Multicoloured. P* 15½ × 15.

32	20 c. Type **10**	50	40
33	50 c. Council seal and sailing-boat	75	70

11 Bright Yellow Long-nosed Butterfly Fish

12 "Peace on Earth"

(Des Marg Towt. Litho Asher and Co, Melbourne)

1979 (3 Sept)–**80.** *Fishes. Horiz designs as T* **11.** *Multicoloured. P* 13½ × 13 (22 *c.*, 28 *c.*, 60 *c.*) *or* 15½ × 15 (*others*).

34	1 c. Type **11**	10	15
35	2 c. Clown Butterfly Fish (19.11.79)	15	15
36	5 c. *Anthias sp.*	15	20
37	10 c. Meyer's Butterfly Fish (18.2.80)	20	20
38	15 c. Wrasse (19.11.79)	25	25
39	20 c. Charles' Clown Fish (19.11.79)	30	30
39*a*	22 c. Yellow-striped Emerald Triggerfish (1.7.80)	30	30
40	25 c. *Cheilinus fasciatus* (18.2.80)	35	35
40*a*	28 c. *Macropharyngodon meleagris* (1.7.80)	35	35
41	30 c. *Chaetodon madagascariensis* (19.11.79)	45	45
42	35 c. Angel Fish	45	50
43	40 c. Hog Fish (19.11.79)	60	60
44	50 c. Wrasse (*different*) (19.11.79)	75	75
45	55 c. *Anampses meleagrides* (18.2.80)	75	75
45*a*	60 c. Grouper (1.7.80)	75	75
46	$1 Surgeon Fish	1·25	1·50
47	$2 Three-banded Butterfly Fish (18.2.80)	2·50	2·50
34/47	*Set of* 17	8·75	9·00

(Des D. Pitt. Litho Asher & Co, Melbourne)

1979 (22 Oct). *Christmas. T* **12** *and similar multicoloured design. P* 15 × 15½ (25 *c.*) *or* 15½ × 15 (55 *c.*).

48	25 c. Type **12**	50	35
49	55 c. "Goodwill Toward Men" (*horiz*)	75	90

13 Star, Map of Cocos (Keeling) Islands and Island Landscape

14 "Administered by the British Government, 1857"

(Des P. Arnold. Litho Asher and Co, Melbourne)

1980 (22 Oct). *Christmas. T* **13** *and similar horiz designs. Multicoloured. P* 13.

50	15 c. Type **13**	20	20
51	28 c. Map and Wise Men following star	35	35
52	60 c. Map and Nativity scene	80	80

(Des Sue Wilson. Litho Asher and Co, Melbourne)

1980 (24 Nov). *25th Anniv of Cocos (Keeling) Islands as an Australian Territory. T* **14** *and similar horiz designs. Multicoloured. P* 13½ × 13.

53	22 c. Type **14**	30	30
	a. Horiz strip of 5. Nos. 53/7	1·40	
54	22 c. "Administered by the Government of Ceylon, 1878, 1942–6"	30	30
55	22 c. "Administered by the Straits Settlements, 1886"	30	30
56	22 c. "Administered by the Colony of Singapore, 1946"	30	30
57	22 c. "Administered by the Australian Government, 1955"	30	30

Nos. 53/7 were printed together, *se-tenant*, in horizontal strips of 5 throughout the sheet, forming a composite design.

15 *Eye of the Wind* and Map of Cocos (Keeling) Islands

16 Aerial View of Animal Quarantine Station

(Des Sue Wilson. Litho Asher and Co, Melbourne)

1980 (18 Dec). *"Operation Drake" (round the world expedition) and 400th Anniv of Sir Francis Drake's Circumnavigation of the World. T* **15** *and similar multicoloured designs. P* 13.

58	22 c. Type **15**	30	30
59	28 c. Map of the World showing voyage routes (*horiz*)	40	40
60	35 c. Sir Francis Drake and *Golden Hind*	45	45
61	60 c. Prince Charles and *Eye of the Wind*	80	80

(Des Cato Hibberd Design. Litho Leigh-Mardon Ltd, Melbourne)

1981 (12 May). *Opening of Animal Quarantine Station. T* **16** *and similar horiz designs. Multicoloured. P* 13½ × 13.

62	22 c. Type **16**	35	35
63	45 c. Unloading livestock	65	65
64	60 c. Livestock in pen	80	80

17 Consolidated "Catalina" *Guba II* Flying Boat

18 Prince Charles and Lady Diana Spencer

(Des R. Honisett. Litho Leigh-Mardon Ltd, Melbourne)

1981 (23 June). *Aircraft. T* **17** *and similar horiz designs. Multicoloured. P* 13½ × 13.

65	22 c. Type **17**	30	30
	a. Horiz strip of 5. Nos. 65/9	1·40	
66	22 c. Consolidated "Liberator" and Avro "Lancastrian"	30	30
67	22 c. Douglas "DC4 (Skymaster)" and Lockheed "Constellation"	30	30
68	22 c. Lockheed "Electra"	30	30
69	22 c. Boeing "727" airliners	30	30

Nos. 65/9 were printed together, *se-tenant*, in horizontal strips of 5 throughout the sheet.

(Des B. Clinton. Litho Leigh-Mardon Ltd, Melbourne)

1981 (29 July). *Royal Wedding. P* 13½ × 13.

70	**18**	24 c. multicoloured	60	40
71		60 c. multicoloured	1·00	85

19 "Angels we have heard on High"

20 *Pachyseris speciosa* and *Heliofungia actiniformis* (corals)

(Des B. Weatherhead. Litho Leigh-Mardon Ltd, Melbourne)

1981 (22 Oct). *Christmas. Scenes and Lines from Carol "Angels we have heard on High". T* **19** *and similar horiz designs. Multicoloured. P* 13½ × 13.

72	18 c. Type **19**	30	30
73	30 c. "Shepherds why this Jubilee?"	45	45
74	60 c. "Come to Bethlehem and see Him"	80	80

(Des B. Weatherhead. Litho Leigh-Mardon Ltd, Melbourne)

1981 (28 Dec). *150th Anniv of Charles Darwin's Voyage. T* **20** *and similar horiz designs. Multicoloured. P* 13½ × 13.

75	24 c. Type **20**	40	40
76	45 c. Charles Darwin in 1853 and *Pavona cactus* (coral)	65	65
77	60 c. H.M.S. *Beagle*, 1832, and *Lobophyllia hemprichii* (coral)	80	80
MS78	130 × 95 mm. 24 c. Cross-section of West Island; 24 c. Cross-section of Home Island	75	85

21 Queen Victoria

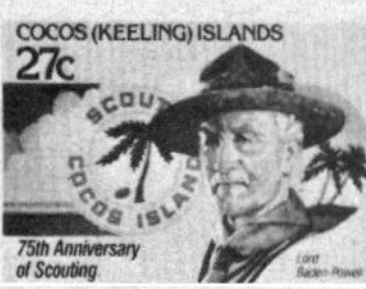

22 Lord Baden-Powell

(Des B. Weatherhead. Litho Cambec Press, Melbourne)

1982 (31 Mar). *125th Anniv of Annexation of Cocos (Keeling) Islands to British Empire. T* **21** *and similar horiz designs. Multicoloured. P* 13½ × 14.

79	24 c. Type **21**	30	30
80	45 c. Union flag	60	60
81	60 c. Capt. S. Fremantle (annexation visit, 1857)	80	80

(Des B. Clinton. Litho Cambec Press, Melbourne)

1982 (21 July). *75th Anniv of Boy Scout Movement. T* **22** *and similar multicoloured design. P* 13½ × 14 (27 *c.*) *or* 14 × 13½ (75 *c.*).

82	27 c. Type **22**	40	40
83	75 c. "75" and map of Cocos (Keeling) Islands (*vert*)	1·10	1·10

23 *Precis villida*

24 "Call His Name Immanuel"

(Des B. Hargreaves. Litho Harrison)

1982 (6 Sept)–**83.** *Butterflies and Moths. T* **23** *and similar multicoloured designs. P* 14.

84	1 c. Type **23**	5	5
85	2 c. *Cephonodes picus* (*horiz*) (6.1.83)	5	5
86	5 c. *Macroglossum corythus* (*horiz*)	5	8
87	10 c. *Chasmina candida* (6.1.83)	12	15
88	20 c. *Nagia linteola* (*horiz*) (6.4.83)	20	25
89	25 c. *Eublemma rivula* (1.7.83)	30	35
90	30 c. *Eurrhyparodes tricoloralis* (6.4.83)	35	40
91	35 c. *Hippotion boerhaviae* (*horiz*)	40	45
92	40 c. *Euploea core corinna* (6.4.83)	50	55
93	45 c. *Psara hipponalis* (*horiz*) (6.4.83)	55	60
94	50 c. *Danaus chrysippus* (*horiz*) (1.7.83)	60	65
95	55 c. *Hypolimas misippus* (6.1.83)	70	75
96	60 c. *Spodoptera litura* (1.7.83)	75	80
97	$1 *Achaea janata*	1·25	1·40
98	$2 *Hippotion velox* (*horiz*) (1.7.83)	2·50	2·75
99	$3 *Utetheisa pulchelloides* (*horiz*) (6.1.83)	3·75	4·00
84/99	*Set of* 16	11·00	12·00

(Des G. Hamori. Litho Cambec Press, Melbourne)

1982 (25 Oct). *Christmas. T* **24** *and similar horiz designs. Multicoloured. P* 13½ × 14.

100	21 c. Type **24**	25	25
101	35 c. "I bring you good tidings"	40	40
102	75 c. "Arise and flee into Egypt"	1·00	1·00

25 "God will look after us" (*Matt.* 1:20)

26 Hari Raya Celebrations

(Des R. Roberts. Litho Cambec Press, Melbourne)

1983 (25 Oct). *Christmas. Extracts from the New Testament. T* **25** *and similar vert designs. Multicoloured. P* 14 × 13½.

103	24 c. Type **25**	25	30
	a. Horiz strip of 5. Nos. 103/7	1·25	
104	24 c. "Our baby King, Jesus" (*Matthew* 2:2)	25	30
105	24 c. "Your Saviour is born" (*Luke* 2:11)	25	30
106	24 c. "Wise men followed the Star" (*Matthew* 2:9–10)	25	30
107	24 c. "And worship the Lord" (*Matthew* 2:11)	25	30

Nos. 103/7 were printed together, *se-tenant*, in horizontal strips of 5 throughout the sheet.

(Des Marg Towt. Litho Cambec Press, Melbourne)

1984 (24 Jan). *Cocos-Malay Culture.* (*1st series*). *Festivals. T* **26** *and similar vert designs. Multicoloured. P* 13½ × 13.

108	45 c. Type **26**	60	65
109	75 c. Melenggok dancing	90	95
110	85 c. Cocos-Malay wedding	1·00	1·10

See also Nos. 126/8.

OMNIBUS ISSUES

Details, together with prices for complete sets, of the various Omnibus issues from the 1935 Silver Jubilee series to date are included in a special section following Zululand at the end of the catalogue.

27 Unpacking Barrel

28 Captain William Keeling

(Des R. Honisett. Litho Cambec Press, Melbourne)

1984 (20 Apr). *75th Anniv of Cocos Barrel Mail. T* **27** *and similar horiz designs. Multicoloured. P* 13½ × 14.
111 35 c. Type **27** 45 50
112 55 c. Jukong awaiting mail ship 80 85
113 70 c. P. & O. mail ship *Omar* .. .. .. 1·00 1·10
MS114 125 × 95 mm. $1 Retrieving barrel .. 1·40 1·50

(Des B. Clinton. Litho Cambec Press, Melbourne)

1984 (10 July). *375th Anniv of Discovery of Cocos (Keeling) Islands. T* **28** *and similar vert designs. Multicoloured. P* 14.
115 30 c. Type **28** 40 45
116 65 c. Keeling's ship *Hector* 90 95
117 95 c. Mariner's astrolabe .. .. .. 1·25 1·40
118 $1. 10, Map *circa* 1666 .. .. .. 1·50 1·60

29 Malay Settlement, Home Island

30 "Rainbow" Fish

(Des E. Roberts. Litho Cambec Press, Melbourne)

1984 (21 Sept). *"Ausipex" International Stamp Exhibition, Melbourne. T* **29** *and similar horiz designs. Multicoloured. P* 13½ × 14.
119 45 c. Type **29** 65 70
120 55 c. Airstrip, West Island 80 85
MS121 130 × 95 mm. $2 Jukongs (native craft) racing .. .. 2·75 3·00

(Des R. Roberts. Litho Cambec Press, Melbourne)

1984 (31 Oct). *Christmas. T* **30** *and similar horiz designs. Multicoloured. P* 13½ × 14.
122 24 c. Type **30** 35 40
123 35 c. "Rainbow" butterfly 45 50
124 55 c. "Rainbow" bird 80 85

31 Cocos Islanders

32 Jukong building

(Des B. Weatherhead. Litho Cambec Press, Melbourne)

1984 (30 Nov). *Integration of Cocos (Keeling) Islands with Australia. Sheet* 90 × 52 *mm. containing T* **31** *and similar horiz design. Multicoloured. P* 13½ × 14.
MS125 30 c. Type **31**: 30 c. Australian flag on island 65 70

(Des Marg Towt. Litho Cambec Press, Melbourne)

1985 (30 Jan). *Cocos-Malay Culture (2nd series). Handicrafts. T* **32** *and similar vert designs. Multicoloured. P* 14 × 13½.
126 30 c. Type **32** 35 40
127 45 c. Blacksmithing 50 55
128 55 c. Woodcarving 60 65

Cook Islands

(Rarotonga)

These are also known as the Hervey Islands. The islands of Manikiki, Rakahanga, and Pukapuka were annexed to the group in October 1890, and use the same stamps.

PRICES FOR STAMPS ON COVER TO 1945

Nos. 1/4 *from* × 5
Nos. 5/74 *from* × 4
Nos. 75/145 *from* × 3

BRITISH PROTECTORATE

1

2 Queen Makea Takau

3 Torea or Wry-bill

(Des F. Moss. Typo Govt Printing Office, Wellington)

1892 (19 Apr). *No wmk. P* 12½.

A. *Toned paper.* B. *White paper.*

			A.		B.	
1	1	1d. black	26·00	30·00	26·00	30·00
		a. Imperf between (vert pair)	£8000	—	†	
2		1½d. mauve	32·00	38·00	32·00	38·00
		a. Imperf (pair) ..	—	—	£8000	—
3		2½d. blue	38·00	38·00	38·00	38·00
4		10d. carmine	£140	£130	£160	£130

(Eng A. E. Cousins. Typo Govt Printing Office, Wellington)

1893 (28 July)–**1900**. *W* **12b** *of New Zealand* (N Z *and Star wide apart*) (*sideways on T* **3**). (*a*) *P* 12 × 11½.
5 **2** 1d. brown .. .. 24·00 30·00
6 1d. blue (3.4.94) .. .. 6·50 6·00
a. Perf 12 × 11½ and 12½ mixed ..
7 1½d. mauve .. .. 7·00 9·00
8 2½d. rose .. .. 25·00 26·00
a. Rose-carmine .. .. .. 55·00 55·00
ab. Perf 12 × 11½ and 12½ mixed ..
9 5d. olive-black .. .. 11·00 15·00
10 10d. green .. .. 48·00 55·00
5/10 .. .. *Set of* 6 £110 £130

(*b*) *P* 11 (July 1896–1900)
11 **3** ½d. blue (11.99) .. .. 3·50 4·75
12 **2** 1d. blue .. .. 3·00 4·50
13 1d. brown/*cream* (4.99) .. .. .. 5·00 12·00
a. Wmk sideways .. .. ..
14 1½d. deep lilac .. .. 4·00 6·00
a. Deep mauve (1900) .. .. .. 3·75 6·00
15 **3** 2d. brown/*thin toned* (7.98) .. .. 4·50 6·50
a. Deep brown (1900) .. .. .. 3·75 6·50
16 **2** 2½d. pale rose .. .. 25·00 38·00
a. Deep rose (1900) .. .. .. 5·50 9·00
17 5d. olive-black .. .. 16·00 17·00
18 **3** 6d. purple/*thin toned* (7.98) .. .. 20·00 25·00
a. Bright purple (1900) .. .. .. 13·00 19·00
19 **2** 10d. green .. .. 13·00 19·00
20 **3** 1s. red/*thin toned* (7.98) .. .. 50·00 70·00
a. Deep carmine (1900) .. .. .. 35·00 48·00
11/20a .. .. *Set of* 10 90·00 £130

ONE
HALF
PENNY
(4)

(5)

1899 (24 Apr). *No. 12 surch with T* **4** *by Govt Printer, Rarotonga.*
21 **2** ½d. on 1d. blue .. .. 38·00 45·00
a. Surch inverted £800 £825
b. Surch double £900 £750

NEW ZEALAND TERRITORY

1901 (8 Oct). *No. 13 optd with T* **5** *by Govt Printer, Rarotonga.*
22 **2** 1d. brown £130 £125
a. Crown inverted £1300 £1300
c. Optd with crown twice £1400 £1500

1902. *No wmk. P* 11.

(*a*) *Medium white Cowan paper* (Feb)
23 **3** ½d. blue-green .. .. 5·50 6·50
24 **2** 1d. dull rose .. .. 9·00 9·50

(*b*) *Thick white Pirie paper* (May)
25 **3** ½d. yellow-green .. .. 3·25 3·50
a. Imperf between (horiz pair) .. £800
26 **2** 1d. rose-red .. .. 7·00 10·00
a. Rose-lake .. .. 6·50 6·50
27 2½d. dull blue .. .. 12·00 18·00

1902 (Sept). *W* **14** *of New Zealand* (*single-lined* NZ *and Star, close together; sideways on T* **2**). *P* 11.
28 **3** ½d. yellow-green .. .. 1·40 2·50
a. Grey-green .. .. 13·00 17·00
29 **2** 1d. rose-pink .. .. 1·75 6·50
30 1½d. deep mauve .. .. 3·00 6·50
31 **3** 2d. deep brown .. .. 3·50 7·50
a. No figures of value £1500 £1400
b. Perf 11 × 14 .. .. ..
32 **2** 2½d. deep blue .. .. 3·75 6·50
33 5d. olive-black .. .. 20·00 25·00
34 **3** 6d. purple .. .. 20·00 25·00
35 **2** 10d. green .. .. 48·00 55·00
36 **3** 1s. carmine .. .. 48·00 55·00
a. Perf 11 × 14 .. .. .. £325
28/36 .. .. *Set of* 9 £130 £170

1909–11. *W* **41** *of New Zealand.*
37 **3** ½d. green (*p* 14½ × 14) (1911) .. .. 4·50 6·00
38 **2** 1d. deep red (*p* 14) .. .. .. 6·50 9·00

1913–19. *W* **41** *of New Zealand* (*sideways on T* **3**). *Chalk-surfaced paper.*
39 **3** ½d. deep green (*p* 14) (1915) .. .. 80 2·75
a. Wmk upright .. .. .. 90 3·25
40 **2** 1d. red (*p* 14) (7.13) .. .. .. 2·00 4·75
41 1d. red (*p* 14 × 14½) (1914) .. .. 3·00 4·75
42 1½d. deep mauve (*p* 14) (1915) .. .. 35·00 38·00
43 1½d. deep mauve (*p* 14 × 15) (1916) .. 3·00 3·25
44 **3** 2d. deep brown (*p* 15 × 14) (1919) .. 12·00 23·00
45 **2** 10d. green (*p* 14 × 15) (1918) .. .. 20·00 32·00
46 **3** 1s. carmine (*p* 15 × 14) (1919) .. .. 20·00 32·00
39/46 .. .. *Set of* 6 50·00 90·00

RAROTONGA

APA PENE
(8)

1919 (Apr–July). *Contemporary stamps of New Zealand surch as T* **8**.

(*a*) *Typographed. P* 14 × 15
50 **60b** ½d. green (R.) (June) 15 35
51 **51** 1d. carmine (B.) (June) 20 35
52 **60b** 1½d. orange-brown (R.) (June) 45 85
53 2d. yellow (R.) 55 80
54 3d. chocolate (B.) (July) .. .. .. 1·25 1·75

(*b*) *Recess.* (*a*) *P* 14 × 14½. (*b*) *P* 14 × 13½
55 **60** 2½d. blue (R.) (*a*) (June) .. .. 1·60 2·00
a. Vert pair. Nos. 55/6 .. .. 25·00 29·00
56 2½d. blue (R.) (*b*) .. .. .. 1·60 5·00
57 3d. chocolate (B.) (*a*) .. .. .. 80 2·25
a. Vert pair. Nos. 57/8 .. .. 29·00 42·00
58 3d. chocolate (B.) (*b*) .. .. .. 1·25 4·00
59 4d. violet (B.) (*a*) .. .. .. 1·25 3·50
a. Vert pair. Nos. 59/60 .. .. 22·00 25·00
60 4d. violet (B.) (*b*) .. .. .. 1·75 5·50
61 4½d. deep green (B.) (*a*) .. .. .. 1·40 4·25
a. Vert pair. Nos. 61/2 .. .. 29·00 35·00
62 4½d. deep green (B.) (*b*) .. .. .. 1·40 4·75
63 6d. carmine (B.) (*a*) (June) .. .. 1·75 5·00
a. Vert pair. Nos. 63/4 .. .. 50·00 55·00
64 6d. carmine (B.) (*b*) .. .. .. 2·00 5·50
65 7½d. red-brown (B.) (*b*) .. .. .. 2·00 5·50
66 9d. sage-green (R.) (*a*) .. .. .. 3·00 6·50
a. Vert pair. Nos. 66/7 .. .. 50·00 55·00
67 9d. sage-green (R.) (*b*) .. .. .. 3·50 6·50
68 1s. vermilion (B.) (*a*) (June) .. .. 3·75 11·00
a. Vert pair. Nos. 68/9 .. .. 65·00 80·00
69 1s. vermilion (B.) (*b*) .. .. .. 5·00 11·00
50/69 (*cheapest*) .. .. .. *Set of* 12 17·00 38·00

9 Capt. Cook landing

10 Wharf at Avarua

11 "Capt. Cook" (Dance)

12 Palm Tree

13 Huts at Arorangi

14 Avarua Harbour

(Des, eng and recess Perkins, Bacon & Co)

1920 (23 Aug). *No wmk. P* 14.
70 **9** ½d. black and green .. .. .. 1·75 5·00
71 **10** 1d. black and carmine-red .. .. 1·40 3·75
72 **11** 1½d. black and dull blue .. .. .. 5·25 7·50
73 **12** 3d. black and chocolate .. .. .. 4·25 7·50

74 **13** 6d. brown and yellow-orange .. .. .. 5·50 8·50
75 **14** 1s. black and violet .. .. .. 11·00 20·00
70/5 .. .. *Set of* 6 26·00 48·00

RAROTONGA
(15)

1921 (Oct). *Postal Fiscal stamps as Type* F **4** *of New Zealand optd with T* **15**. *W* **41** *(sideways). Chalk-surfaced "De La Rue" paper. P* 14½ × 14.
76 2s. deep blue (R.) .. .. 26·00 35·00
a. Carmine opt £140 £150
77 2s. 6d. grey-brown (B.) .. .. 18·00 30·00
78 5s. yellow-green (R.) .. .. 26·00 35·00
79 10s. maroon (B.) .. .. 42·00 48·00
80 £1 rose-carmine (B.) .. .. 75·00 80·00
See also Nos. 85/9.

16 Te Po, Rarotongan Chief

17 Harbour, Rarotonga and Mt Ikurangi

(2½d. from a print; 4d. des A. H. Messenger. Plates by P.B. Recess Govt Ptg Office, Wellington)

1924–27. *W* **41** *of New Zealand. P* 14.
81 **9** ½d. black and green (13.5.26) .. .. 2·75 3·50
82 **10** 1d. black and deep carmine (10.11.24) 2·75 1·50
83 **16** 2½d. red-brown and steel blue (15.10.27) 4·00 7·50
84 **17** 4d. green and violet (15.10.27) .. .. 6·00 11·00

1926 (Feb–May). *As Nos. 76/80, but thick, opaque white chalk-surfaced "Cowan" paper.*
85 2s. blue (C.) £100 £110
86 2s. 6d. deep grey-brown (B.) .. .. .. 45·00 55·00
87 5s. yellow-green (R.) (May) .. .. .. 35·00 45·00
88 10s. brown-red (B.) (May) .. .. .. 45·00 60·00
89 £1 rose-pink (B.) (May) .. .. .. 70·00 75·00

1926–28. *T* **72** *("Admiral" Type) of New Zealand, overprinted with T* **15**. *(a) "Jones" chalk-surfaced paper.*
90 2s. deep blue (R.) (10.26) .. .. .. 18·00 38·00
(b) "Cowan" thick chalk-surfaced paper
91 2s. light blue (R.) (18.6.27) .. .. .. 20·00 35·00
92 3s. bright mauve (R.) (30.1.28) .. .. 27·00 42·00

TWO PENCE
(18)

COOK ISLANDS.
(19)

1931. *Surch with T* **18**. *P* 14. *(a) No wmk.*
93 **11** 2d. on 1½d. black and blue (R.) .. 3·50 3·00
(b) W **41** *of New Zealand*
94 **11** 2d. on 1½d. black and blue (R.) .. 1·50 2·00

1931 (12 Nov)–**32.** *Postal Fiscal stamps as Type* F **6** *of New Zealand. W* **41**. *Thick, opaque, white chalk-faced "Cowan" paper. P* 14.
(a) Optd with T **15**
95 2s. 6d. deep brown (B.) .. .. .. 9·00 11·00
96 5s. green (R.) .. .. 15·00 22·00
97 10s. carmine-lake (B.) .. .. .. 30·00 42·00
98 £1 pink (B.) .. .. 48·00 55·00
(b) Optd with T **19** *(3.32)*
98*a* £3 green (R.) .. .. 50·00 75·00
98*b* £5 blue (R.) £130 £150
The £3 and £5 values were mainly used for fiscal purposes.

20 Capt. Cook landing

21 Capt. Cook

22 Double Maori Canoe

23 Natives working Cargo

24 Port of Avarua

25 R.M.S. *Monowai*

26 King George V

(Des L. C. Mitchell. Recess P.B.)

1932 (16 Mar). *No wmk. P* 13.
99 **20** ½d. black and deep green .. .. 1·75 1·90
a. Perf 14 .. .. 26·00 30·00
100 **21** 1d. black and lake .. .. .. 1·90 2·50
a. Centre inverted £1500 £1400
b. Perf 14 .. .. 15·00 16·00
101 **22** 2d. black and brown .. .. .. 2·50 3·50
a. Perf 14 .. .. 7·50 8·00
102 **23** 2½d. black and deep blue .. .. 7·00 11·00
a. Perf 14 .. .. 10·00 11·00
103 **24** 4d. black and bright blue .. .. 11·00 15·00
a. Perf 14 .. .. 8·00 14·00
b. Perf 14 × 13 .. .. .. 48·00 60·00
c. Perf comp of 14 and 13 .. ..
104 **25** 6d. black and orange .. .. .. 18·00 24·00
a. Perf 14 .. .. 4·50 8·50
105 **26** 1s. black and violet (*p* 14) .. .. 11·00 15·00
99/105 .. .. *Set of* 7 32·00 50·00

(Recess from P.B. plates at Govt Printing Office, Wellington)

1933–36. *Wmk T* **41** *of New Zealand (Single N Z and Star). P* 14.
106 **20** ½d. black and deep green 40 70
107 **21** 1d. black and scarlet (1935) 55 70
108 **22** 2d. black and brown (1936) 55 40
109 **23** 2½d. black and deep blue 55 80
110 **24** 4d. black and bright blue 55 60
111 **25** 6d. black and orange-yellow (1936) .. 1·50 2·25
112 **26** 1s. black and violet (1936) .. .. 12·00 16·00
106/12 .. .. *Set of* 7 14·50 19·00

SILVER JUBILEE OF KING GEORGE V. 1910 - 1935.
(27)

Normal letters
B K E N
B K E N
Narrow letters

COOK IS'DS.
(28)

1935 (7 May). *Silver Jubilee. Optd with T* **27** *(wider vertical spacing on 6d.). Colours changed. W* **41** *of New Zealand. P* 14.
113 **21** 1d. red-brown and lake 50 85
a. Narrow "K" in "KING" .. .. 4·00
b. Narrow "B" in "JUBILEE" .. .. 4·50
114 **23** 2½d. dull and deep blue (R.) .. .. 1·25 1·40
a. Narrow first "E" in "GEORGE" .. 6·00 6·50
115 **25** 6d. green and orange .. .. .. 4·00 6·50
a. Narrow "N" in "KING" .. .. 22·00

1936 (15 July)–**44.** *Stamps of New Zealand optd with T* **19**. *W* **41**.
(a) Thick, white, opaque chalk-surfaced "Cowan" paper. P 14
(i) As T **72** *("Admiral" type)*
116 2s. blue .. .. 17·00 32·00
117 3s. mauve .. .. 25·00 35·00
(ii) As Type F **6** *("Arms" type)*
118 2s. 6d. deep brown .. .. 18·00 25·00
119 5s. green (R.) .. .. 18·00 27·00
120 10s. carmine-lake .. .. 35·00 55·00
121 £1 pink .. .. 55·00 70·00
(b) Thin, hard, chalk-surfaced "Wiggins, Teape" paper
122 2s. 6d. dull brown (12.40) .. .. .. 35·00 38·00
123 5s. green (R.) (10.40) .. .. .. 70·00 75·00
123*a* 10s. pale carmine-lake (11.44) .. .. 55·00 70·00
123*b* £3 green (R.) (date?) £170 £275

1937 (1 June). *Coronation. Nos. 599/601 of New Zealand optd with T* **28**.
124 **106** 1d. carmine 25 15
125 2½d. Prussian blue 25 40
126 6d. red-orange 45 45

29 King George VI

30 Native Village

31 Native Canoe

32 Tropical Landscape

(Des J. Berry (2s., 3s., and frame of 1s.). Eng B.W. Recess Govt Ptg. Office, Wellington)

1938 (2 May). *W* **41** *of New Zealand. P* 14.
127 **29** 1s. black and violet .. .. .. 4·00 2·00
128 **30** 2s. black and red-brown .. .. .. 6·50 4·00
129 **31** 3s. light blue and emerald-green .. 12·00 8·00

(Recess B.W.)

1940 (2 Sept). *Surch as in T* **32**. *W* **98** *of New Zealand. P* 13½ × 14.
130 **32** 3d. on 1½d. black and purple 12 20
Type **32** was not issued without surcharge.

1943–50. *Postal Fiscal stamps as Type* F **6** *of New Zealand optd with T* **19**. *W* **98**. *"Wiggins, Teape" chalk-surfaced paper. P* 14.
131 2s. 6d. dull brown (3.46) .. .. .. 5·00 9·00
132 5s. green (R.) (11.43) .. .. .. 9·00 12·00
133 10s. carmine-lake (10.48) .. .. .. 24·00 30·00
134 £1 pink (11.47) .. .. 27·00 35·00
135 £3 green (R.) (1946?) £130 £200
136 £5 blue (R.) (25.10.50) £250 £300
131/6 .. .. *Set of* 6 £400 £550
The £3 and £5 were mainly used for fiscal purposes.
All values were later printed with the watermark inverted for technical reasons and the prices quoted are for the cheapest form. They are fully listed in the *Elizabethan Specialised Catalogue*.

(Recess Govt Ptg Office, Wellington)

1944–46. *W* **98** *of New Zealand (sideways on ½d. 1d., 1s., and 2s.). P* 14.
137 **20** ½d. black and deep green (11.44) .. 85 60
138 **21** 1d. black and scarlet (3.45) .. .. 2·00 45
139 **22** 2d. black and brown (2.46) .. .. 1·25 70
140 **23** 2½d. black and deep blue (5.45) .. 75 60
141 **24** 4d. black and blue (4.44) 80 95
142 **25** 6d. black and orange (6.44) .. .. 1·10 60
143 **29** 1s. black and violet (9.44) 90 85
144 **30** 2s. black and red-brown (8.45) .. .. 5·00 8·50
145 **31** 3s. light blue and emerald-green (6.45) 12·00 15·00
137/45 .. .. *Set of* 9 22·00 25·00

COOK ISLANDS
(33)

1946 (1 June). *Peace. Nos. 668, 670, 674/5 of New Zealand optd with T* **33** *(reading up and down at sides on 2d.).*
146 1d. green 10 5
147 2d. purple (B.) 10 15
148 6d. chocolate and vermilion 15 15
149 8d. black and carmine (B.) 15 20

34 Ngatangiia Channel, Rarotonga

41 Map and Statue of Capt. Cook

(Des J. Berry. Recess Waterlow)

1949 (1 Aug)–**61.** *T* **34, 41** *and similar designs. W* **98** *of New Zealand (sideways on shilling values). P* 13½ × 13 *(horiz) or* 13 × 13½ *(vert).*
150 ½d. violet and brown 10 45
151 1d. chestnut and green 95 85
152 2d. reddish brown and scarlet 70 80
153 3d. green and ultramarine 45 80
a. Wmk sideways (white opaque paper) (22.5.61) .. .. 2·00 2·50
154 5d. emerald-green and violet .. .. 1·25 1·25
155 6d. black and carmine .. .. .. 1·00 1·00
156 8d. olive-green and orange .. .. .. 80 2·00
157 1s. light blue and chocolate .. .. 3·75 2·75
158 2s. yellow-brown and carmine .. .. 4·50 7·50
159 3s. light blue and bluish green .. .. 7·50 11·00
150/59 .. .. *Set of* 10 19·00 26·00
Designs: *Horiz*—1d. Capt. Cook and map of Hervey Islands; 2d. Rarotonga and Revd. John Williams; 3d. Aitutaki and Palm trees; 5d. Rarotonga airfield; 6d. Penrhyn village; 8d. Native hut. *Vert*—2s. Native hut and palms; 3s. M.V. *Matua*.
See note on white opaque paper below No. 736 of New Zealand.

1953 (25 May). *Coronation. As Nos. 715 and 717 of New Zealand, but inscr "COOK ISLANDS".*
160 3d. brown 50 45
161 6d. slate-grey 75 80

1/6

(44)

1960 (1 Apr). *No. 154 surch with T* **44**.
162 1s. 6d. on 5d. emerald-green and violet .. 30 65

OMNIBUS ISSUES

Details, together with prices for complete sets, of the various Omnibus issues from the 1935 Silver Jubilee series to date are included in a special section following Zululand at the end of the catalogue.

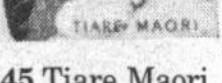

45 Tiare Maori

48 White Tern

52 Queen Elizabeth II

53 Island Scene

(Des J. Berry. Recess (1s. 6d.), litho (others) B.W.)

1963 (4 June). *T* **45, 48, 52/3** *and similar designs. Wmk T* **98** *of New Zealand (sideways). P* 13½ × 13 (*1d., 2d., 8d.*), 13 × 13½ (*3d., 5d., 6d., 1s.*) *or* 13½ (*others*).

163	1d. emerald-green and yellow	15	10
164	2d. brown-red and yellow	8	10
165	3d. yellow, yellow-green & reddish violet ..	15	12
166	5d. blue and black	1·60	35
167	6d. red, yellow and green	65	25
168	8d. black and blue	75	45
169	1s. orange-yellow and yellow-green.. ..	40	30
170	1s. 6d. bluish violet	3·50	3·50
171	2s. bistre-brown and grey-blue	1·75	1·90
172	3s. black and yellow-green	2·25	2·50
173	5s. bistre-brown and blue	11·00	9·50
163/73	.. .. *Set of* 11	20·00	17·00

Designs: *Vert* (*as T* **45**)—2d. Fishing god; 8d. Skipjack Tuna. *Horiz* (*as T* **48**)—3d. Frangipani; 6d. Hibiscus; 1s. Oranges. (*As T* **53**)—3s. Administration Centre, Mangaia; 5s. Rarotonga.

56 Eclipse and Palm

57 N.Z. Ensign and Map

(Des L. C. Mitchell. Litho B.W.)

1965 (31 May). *Solar Eclipse Observation, Manuae Island. W* **98** *of New Zealand. P* 13½.

174	**56**	6d. black, yellow and light blue ..	15	12

SELF-GOVERNMENT

(Des R. M. Conly (4d.), L. C. Mitchell (10d., 1s.), J. Berry (1s. 9d.). Litho B.W.)

1965 (16 Sept). *Internal Self-Government. T* **57** *and similar horiz designs. W* **98** *of New Zealand (sideways). P* 13½.

175	4d. red and blue	15	5
176	10d. multicoloured	20	25
177	1s. multicoloured	20	20
178	1s. 9d. multicoloured	70	70

Designs:—10d. London Missionary Society Church; 1s. Proclamation of Cession, 1900; 1s. 9d. Nikao School.

In Memoriam
SIR WINSTON CHURCHILL
1874 - 1965
(61)

Airmail
(62)

1966 (24 Jan). *Churchill Commemoration. Nos.* 171/3 *and* 175/7 *optd with T* **61**, *in red.*

179	4d. red and blue	85	30
180	10d. multicoloured	2·50	1·25
	a. Opt inverted	£200	
181	1s. multicoloured	2·50	1·50
	a. Opt inverted	£150	
182	2s. bistre-brown and grey-blue	3·25	3·00
183	3s. black and yellow-green	3·25	3·00
184	5s. bistre-brown and blue	4·00	4·00
179/84	.. .. *Set of* 6	15·00	12·00

1966 (22 Apr). *Air. Various stamps optd with T* **62** *or surch also.*

185	6d. red, yellow and green (No. 167) ..	1·50	60
186	7d. on 8d. black and blue (No. 168) ..	1·50	60
187	10d. on 3d. yellow, yellow-green and reddish violet (No. 165)	1·25	25
188	1s. orange-yellow and yellow-green (No. 169)	1·25	40
189	1s. 6d. bluish violet (No. 170)	1·75	1·75
190	2s. 3d. on 3s. black and yellow-green (No. 172)	1·50	1·50
191	5s. bistre-brown and blue (No. 173).. ..	4·50	4·50
192	10s. on 2s. bistre-brown and grey-blue (No. 171)	6·50	8·00
193	£1 pink (No. 134)	15·00	20·00
	a. Aeroplane omitted	24·00	27·00
185/93	.. .. *Set of* 9	32·00	35·00

No. 193a occurred in all stamps of the last vertical row as insufficient aeroplane symbols were available. There are also numerous other varieties on all values, notably aeroplanes of different sizes and broken first "i" with dot missing owing to damaged type.

PRINTERS. The following stamps were printed in photogravure by Heraclio Fournier, Spain *except where otherwise stated.*

63 "Adoration of the Magi" (Fra Angelico)

1966 (28 Nov). *Christmas. T* **63** *and similar multicoloured designs.*
A. *P* 13 × 12 (*horiz*) *or* 12 × 13 (*vert*).
B. *P* 13 × 14½ (*horiz*) *or* 14½ × 13 (*vert*).

		A		B	
194	1d. Type **63**	25	15	5	5
195	2d. "The Nativity" (Memling) (*vert*)	10·00	5·50	12	10
196	4d. "Adoration of the Magi" (Velazquez) (*horiz*) ..	60	40	15	15
197	10d. "Adoration of the Magi" (Bosch) (*horiz*)	1·75	1·25	25	15
198	1s. 6d. "Adoration of the Shepherds" (J. de Ribera) (*vert*)	3·50	2·50	40	50

68 Tennis, and Queen Elizabeth II

(Des V. Whiteley)

1967 (12 Jan). *2nd South Pacific Games, Nouméa. T* **68** *and similar horiz designs in orange-brown, black and new blue (1d.) or multicoloured (others). P* 13½. (*a*) *Postage.*

199	½d. Type **68**	5	5
200	1d. Netball and Games emblem	5	5
201	4d. Boxing and Cook Islands' team badge ..	12	10
202	7d. Football and Queen Elizabeth II ..	20	15
	(*b*) *Air*		
203	10d. Running and Games emblem	20	20
204	2s. 3d. Running and Cook Islands' team badge	30	30
199/204	.. .. *Set of* 6	80	75

(New Currency, 100 cents = 1 dollar)

1c (74) — **2½c** (I) — **2½c** (II)

These occur on alternative vertical rows within the sheet.

1967 (3 Apr–6 June). *Decimal Currency. Nos.* 134/6, 163/70 *and* 172/5 *surch as T* **74** *by the Government Printer. Sterling values unobliterated except No.* 218.

205	1 c. on 1d. emerald-green & yellow (4.5) ..	1·25	1·25
206	2 c. on 2d. brown-red & yellow	10	10
207	2½ c. on 3d. yellow, yellow-green and reddish violet (I)	20	12
208	2½ c. on 3d. yellow, yellow-green and reddish violet (II)	20	12
209	3 c. on 4d. red and blue	20	12
210	4 c. on 5d. blue and black (4.5)	80	35
211	5 c. on 6d. red, yellow and green	25	12
212	5 c. on 6d. black, yellow and light blue ..	1·50	65
213	7 c. on 8d. black and blue	30	15
214	10 c. on 1s. orange-yellow & yellow-green ..	20	20
215	15 c. on 1s. 6d. bluish violet (R.) (4.5.67) ..	3·75	2·25
216	30 c. on 3s. black and yellow-green (R.) (4.5.67)	14·00	9·00
217	50 c. on 5s. bistre-brown and blue (R.) (4.5.67)	9·00	3·75
218	$1 and 10s. on 10d. multicoloured (R.) (4.5.67)	18·00	12·00
219	$2 on £1 pink (R.) (6.6.67)	£140	£140
220	$6 on £3 green (R.) (6.6.67)	£200	£200
221	$10 on £5 blue (R.) (6.6.67)	£300	£300
205/18	.. .. *Set of* 14	45·00	27·00

The surcharge on No. 218 is $1 and its equivalent of 10s. in the old currency. The "10d." is obliterated by three bars.

A large number of minor varieties exist in these surcharges, such as wrong fount letter "C" and figures.

ALTERED CATALOGUE NUMBERS

Any Catalogue numbers altered from the last edition are shown as a list in the introductory pages.

75 Village Scene. Cook Islands 1d. Stamp of 1892 and Queen Victoria (from "Penny Black")

(Des V. Whiteley)

1967 (3 July). *75th Anniv of First Cook Islands Stamps. T* **75** *and similar horiz designs. Multicoloured. P* 13½.

222	1 c. (1d.) Type **75**	5	5
223	3 c. (4d.) Post Office, Avarua, Rarotonga and Queen Elizabeth II	15	10
224	8 c. (10d.) Avarua, Rarotonga and Cook Islands 10d. stamp of 1892	30	20
225	18 c. (1s. 9d.) S.S. *Moana Roa*, "DC-3" aircraft, map and Captain Cook	50	35
MS226	134 × 109 mm. Nos. 222/5	2·00	2·25

The face values are expressed in decimal currency and in the sterling equivalent.

Each value was issued in sheets of 8 stamps and 1 label.

79 Hibiscus

80 Queen Elizabeth II

81 Queen Elizabeth and Flowers

Two types of $4

I. Value 32½ mm long. Coarse screen.
II. Value 33½ mm long. Finer screen.

(Floral designs from paintings by Mrs. Kay W. Billings)

1967–71. *Multicoloured designs as T* **79/81**. *P* 14 × 13½. A. *Without fluorescent security markings.* B. *With fluorescent security markings.*

		A		B	
227	½ c. Type **79**	5	5	5	5
228	1 c. *Hibiscus syriacus* (27 × 37 *mm*)	5	5	5	5
229	2 c. Frangipani (27 × 37 *mm*)	8	5	5	5
230	2½ c. *Clitoria ternatea* (27 × 37 *mm*)	12	5	12	5
231	3 c. "Suva Queen" (27 × 37 *mm*)	12	5	12	5
232	4 c. Water Lily ("WALTER LILY") (27 × 37 *mm*) ..	40	40	†	
233	4 c. Water Lily (27 × 37 *mm*)	15	8	15	8
234	5 c. *Bauhinia bipinnata rosea* (27 × 37 *mm*)	15	8	15	8
235	6 c. Hibiscus (27 × 37 *mm*)	15	8	15	8
236	8 c. *Allamanda cathartica* (27 × 37 *mm*)	20	10	20	10
237	9 c. Stephanotis (27 × 37 *mm*)	20	10	20	10
238	10 c. *Poinciana regia flamboyant* (27 × 37 *mm*)	25	10	25	10
239	15 c. Frangipani (27 × 37 *mm*)	40	20	40	20
240	20 c. Thunbergia (27 × 37 *mm*)	45	25	45	25
241	25 c. Canna Lily (27 × 37 *mm*)	45	30	45	30
242	30 c. *Euphorbia pulcherrima poinsettia* (27 × 37 *mm*) ..	50	50	50	50
243	50 c. *Gardinia taitensis* (27 × 37 *mm*)	90	70	90	70
244	$1 Type **80**	1·75	1·50	1·75	1·50
245	$2 Type **80**	3·50	2·75	3·50	2·75
246	$4 Type **81** (I)	9·00	9·00	45·00	48·00
246*c*	$4 Type **81** (II)	†		10·00	9·50
247	$6 Type **81**	11·00	13·00	13·00	11·00
247*c*	$8 Type **81**	17·00	19·00	17·00	15·00
248	$10 Type **81**	18·00	19·00	19·00	17·00
227A/243A	.. .. *Set of* 17	4·25	2·75		
227B/243B	.. .. *Set of* 16			3·75	2·50

Dates of issue:—Nos. 227/238A, 31.7.67; Nos. 239/243A, 11.8.67; Nos. 244/245A, 31.8.67; Nos. 246/247A, 30.4.68; No. 248A, 12.7.68; No. 247*c*A, 21.4.69; Nos. 227/243B, 9.2.70; Nos. 244/245B, 12.10.70; No. 246*c*B, 14.7.71; No. 246B, 11.11.70; No. 247B, 12.2.71; No. 247*c*B, 3.5.71; No. 248B, 14.6.71.

The "WALTER" spelling error occurred on all stamps in one of the four post office sheets which went to make up the printing sheet and this was corrected in later supplies.

FLUORESCENT PAPER. This is on paper treated with fluorescent security markings, in the form of faint multiple coats of arms. Stamps exist with these markings inverted. In addition an invisible synthetic gum has been used which prevents curling and is suitable for use in the tropics without interleaving the sheets.

Some of the above are known with these markings omitted and can be distinguished when in unused condition from the original printings without markings by their synthetic invisible gum.

97 "Ia Orana Maria"

1967 (24 Oct). *Gauguin's Polynesian Paintings. T* **97** *and similar designs. Multicoloured. P* 13.

No.	Description	Unused	Used
249	1 c. Type **97**	5	5
250	3 c. "Riders on the Beach"	5	5
251	5 c. "Still Life with Flowers"	8	5
252	8 c. "Whispered Words"	15	10
253	15 c. "Maternity"	20	20
254	22 c. "Why are you angry?"	30	20
249/54	*Set of* 6	75	60
MS255	156 × 132 mm. Nos. 249/54	1·50	1·50

The 5 c. includes an inset portrait of Queen Elizabeth.

98 "The Holy Family" (Rubens)

HURRICANE
RELIEF
PLUS 5c

(99)

1967 (4 Dec). *Christmas. Renaissance Paintings. T* **98** *and similar designs. Multicoloured. P* 12 × 13.

No.	Description	Unused	Used
256	1 c. Type **98**	5	5
257	3 c. "Adoration of the Magi" (Dürer)	8	8
258	4 c. "The Lucca Madonna" (J. van Eyck)	10	8
259	8 c. "The Adoration of the Shepherds" (J. da Bassano)	15	12
260	15 c. "Adoration of the Shepherds" (El Greco)	20	15
261	25 c. "Madonna and Child" (Correggio)	20	15
256/61	*Set of* 6	70	55

1968 (12 Feb). *Hurricane Relief. Nos.* 231A, 233A, 251, 238A, 241A *and* 243/4A *surch as T* **99** *by Govt Printer, Rarotonga.*

No.	Description	Unused	Used
262	3 c. + 1 c. "Suva Queen"	15	12
263	4 c. + 1 c. Water Lily	15	12
264	5 c. + 2 c. "Still Life with Flowers"	15	15
265	10 c. + 2 c. *Poinciana regia flamboyant*	25	25
266	25 c. + 5 c. Canna Lily	35	30
267	50 c. + 10 c. *Gardinia taitensis*	65	55
268	$1 + 10 c. Type **80**	1·00	75
262/8	*Set of* 7	2·40	2·00

The surcharge on No. 268 is as T **99**, but with seriffed letters. On No. 264 silver blocking obliterates the design area around the lettering.

100 "Matavai Bay, Tahiti" (J. Barralet)

101 *"Resolution* and *Discovery"* (J. Webber)

(Des J. Berry)

1968 (12 Sept). *Bicentenary of Captain Cook's First Voyage of Discovery. Multicoloured. Invisible gum. P* 13.

(*a*) *Postage. Vert. designs as T* **100**

No.	Description	Unused	Used
269	½ c. Type **100**	5	5
270	1 c. "Island of Huaheine" (John Cleveley)	15	10
271	2 c. "Town of St. Peter and St. Paul, Kamchatka" (J. Webber)	40	35
272	4 c. "The Ice Islands" (Antarctica: W. Hodges)	40	35

(*b*) *Air. Horiz designs as T* **101**

No.	Description	Unused	Used
273	6 c. Type **101**	90	65
274	10 c. "The Island of Tahiti" (W. Hodges)	1·25	75
275	15 c. "Karakakooa, Hawaii" (J. Webber)	1·50	90
276	25 c. "The Landing at Middleburg" (J. Sherwin)	1·75	1·25
269/76	*Set of* 8	6·00	4·00

Each value was issued in sheets of 10 stamps and 2 labels.

FLUORESCENT PAPER. From No. 277, *unless otherwise stated*, all issues are printed on paper treated with fluorescent security markings with invisible synthetic gum. These markings may be inverted or omitted in error.

102 Sailing

103 "Madonna and Child" (Titian)

1968 (21 Oct). *Olympic Games, Mexico. T* **102** *and similar horiz designs. Multicoloured. P* 13.

No.	Description	Unused	Used
277	1 c. Type **102**	5	5
278	5 c. Gymnastics	10	5
279	15 c. High-jumping	25	20
280	20 c. High-diving	30	20
281	30 c. Cycling	30	25
282	50 c. Hurdling	30	30
277/82	*Set of* 6	1·10	95

Each value was issued in sheets of 10 stamps and 2 labels.

1968 (2 Dec). *Christmas. Paintings. T* **103** *and similar vert designs. Multicoloured. P* 13½.

No.	Description	Unused	Used
283	1 c. Type **103**	5	5
284	4 c. "The Holy Family with Lamb" (Raphael)	10	10
285	10 c. "The Virgin of the Rosary" (Murillo)	15	12
286	20 c. "Adoration of the Kings" (Memling)	20	15
287	30 c. "Adoration of the Magi" (Ghirlandaio)	25	20
MS288	114 × 177 mm. Nos. 283/7 plus label	1·60	1·60

104 Camp-fire Cooking

1969 (6 Feb). *Diamond Jubilee of New Zealand Scout Movement and Fifth National (New Zealand) Jamboree. T* **104** *and similar square designs. Multicoloured. P* 13½.

No.	Description	Unused	Used
289	½ c. Type **104**	5	5
290	1 c. Descent by rope	5	5
291	5 c. Semaphore	10	10
292	10 c. Tree-planting	15	12
293	20 c. Constructing a shelter	25	15
294	30 c. Lord Baden-Powell and island scene	40	30
289/94	*Set of* 6	90	70

Each value was issued in sheets of 10 stamps and 2 labels.

105 Pole-vaulter

1969 (7 July). *Third South Pacific Games, Port Moresby. T* **105** *and similar triangular designs. Multicoloured. Without fluorescent security markings. P* 13 × 13½.

No.	Description	Unused	Used
295	½ c. Type **105**	5	5
296	½ c. Footballer	5	5
297	1 c. High Jumping	5	5
298	1 c. Weightlifter	5	5
299	4 c. Tennis-player	5	5
300	4 c. Hurdler	5	5
301	10 c. Javelin-thrower	25	20
302	10 c. Basketball	25	20
303	15 c. Golfer	35	25
304	15 c. Boxer	35	25
295/304	*Set of* 10	1·25	1·00
MS305	174 × 129 mm. Nos. 295/304 plus two labels	1·75	1·75

Each value was issued in sheets containing 5 *se-tenant* pairs of both designs and 2 labels.

106 Flowers, Map and Captain Cook

1969 (8 Oct). *South Pacific Conference, Nouméa. T* **106** *and similar horiz designs. Multicoloured. Without fluorescent security markings. P* 13.

No.	Description	Unused	Used
306	5 c. Flowers, map and Premier Albert Henry	35	10
307	10 c. Type **106**	65	45
308	25 c. Flowers, map and N.Z. arms	75	60
309	30 c. Queen Elizabeth II, map and flowers	85	65

107 "Virgin and Child with Saints Jerome and Dominic" (Lippi)

108 "The Resurrection of Christ" (Raphael)

1969 (21 Nov). *Christmas. Paintings. T* **107** *and similar designs. Multicoloured. Without fluorescent security markings. P* 13.

No.	Description	Unused	Used
310	1 c. Type **107**	5	5
311	4 c. "The Holy Family" (Fra Bartolomeo)	8	8
312	10 c. "The Adoration of the Shepherds" (A. Mengs)	15	12
313	20 c. "Madonna and Child with Saints" (R. Campin)	25	20
314	30 c. "The Madonna of the Basket" (Correggio)	25	20
MS315	132 × 97 mm. Nos. 310/14	1·40	1·40

Each value was issued in sheets of 9 stamps and 1 label.

1970 (12 Mar). *Easter. Paintings. T* **108** *and similar vert designs showing "The Resurrection of Christ" by the artists named. Multicoloured. P* 13.

No.	Description	Unused	Used
316	4 c. Type **108**	10	10
317	8 c. Dirk Bouts	15	12
318	20 c. Altdorfer	25	20
319	25 c. Murillo	30	25
MS320	132 × 162 mm. Nos. 316/19	1·25	1·60

Each value was issued in sheets of 8 stamps and 1 label.

KIA ORANA
APOLLO 13
ASTRONAUTS
Te Atua to
Tatou Irinakianga

(109)

1970 (17–30 Apr). *Apollo* 13. *Nos.* 233, 236, 239/40, 242 *and* 245/6 *optd with T* **109** (4 c. *to* $2) *or with first three lines only in larger type* ($4), *by Govt Printer. A. Without fluorescent security markings. B. With fluorescent security markings.*

No.	Description	A Unused	A Used	B Unused	B Used
321	4 c. Water Lily	8	8	†	
	a. Opt albino	35·00	—	†	
322	8 c. *Allamanda cathartica*	12	12	†	
323	15 c. Frangipani	25	25	†	
324	20 c. Thunbergia	30	30	†	
325	30 c. *Euphorbia pulcherrima poinsettia*	40	40	†	
326	$2 Type **80**	2·25	2·50	†	
327	$4 Type **81** (30.4)	65·00	65·00	4·00	6·00
321/6A, 327B	*Set of* 7	6·50	8·50		

110 The Royal Family

(Des V. Whiteley (5 c.), J. Berry ($1))

1970 (12 June). *Royal Visit to New Zealand. T* **110** *and similar horiz designs. Multicoloured. P* 13.

No.	Description	Unused	Used
328	5 c. Type **110**	85	50
329	30 c. Captain Cook and H.M.S. *Endeavour*	3·50	2·75
330	$1 Royal Visit commemorative coin	5·00	4·50
MS331	145 × 97 mm. Nos. 328/30	10·00	10·00

Each value was issued in sheets of 8 stamps and 1 label.

FOUR
DOLLARS

FIFTH ANNIVERSARY
SELF-GOVERNMENT
AUGUST 1970

$4.00

(113) (114)

1970 (27 Aug). *5th Anniv of Self-Government Nos.* 328/30 *optd with T* **113** (30 *c. and* $1), *or in single line in silver around frame of stamp* (5 *c.*).

332 5 c. Type **110** 50 35
333 30 c. Captain Cook and H.M.S. *Endeavour* .. 2·50 2·50
334 $1 Royal Visit commemorative coin .. 3·50 3·50

1970 (11 Nov). *Nos.* 247*c and* 248 *surch with T* **114** *by Govt Printer, Rarotonga. A. Without fluorescent security markings. B. With fluorescent security markings.*

			A		B	
335	**81**	$4 on $8 multicoloured	35·00	35·00	16·00	13·00
336		$4 on $10 multicoloured	55·00	48·00	7·50	7·50

There are variations in the setting of this surcharge and also in the rule.

115 Mary, Joseph and Christ in Manger

PLUS 20c

UNITED
KINGDOM

SPECIAL
MAIL SERVICE

(116)

(Des from De Lisle Psalter)

1970 (30 Nov). *Christmas. T* **115** *and similar square designs. Multicoloured. P* 13.

337 1 c. Type **115** 5 5
338 4 c. Shepherds and Apparition of the Angel 10 8
339 10 c. Mary showing Child to Joseph .. 20 15
340 20 c. The Wise Men bearing Gifts 25 20
341 30 c. Parents wrapping Child in swaddling clothes 30 25
MS342 100 × 139 mm. Nos. 337/41 plus label .. 1·60 1·75

Each value was issued in sheets of 5 stamps and 1 label. Stamps from the miniature sheet are smaller, since they do not have the buff parchment border as on the stamps from the sheets.

1971. *Nos.* 242B *and* 243B *surch as T* **116**.

343 30 c. + 20 c. *Euphorbia pulcherrima poinsettia* (25.2) .. .. 1·25 1·50
344 50 c. + 20 c. *Gardinia taitensis* (8.3) .. .. 4·25 4·50

The premium of 20 c. was to prepay a private delivery service fee in Great Britain during the postal strike. The mail was sent by air to a forwarding address in the Netherlands. No. 343 was intended for ordinary airmail ½ oz letters, and No. 344 included registration fee.

The postal strike ended on 8 March and both stamps were withdrawn on 12 March.

117 Wedding of Princess Elizabeth and Prince Philip

(Des from photographs. Litho Format)

1971 (11 Mar). *Royal Visit of H.R.H. The Duke of Edinburgh. T* **117** *and similar horiz designs. Multicoloured. P* 13½.

345 1 c. Type **117** 30 50
346 4 c. Queen Elizabeth, Prince Philip, Princess Anne and Prince Charles at Windsor .. 75 1·25
347 10 c. Prince Philip sailing .. .. .. 1·25 1·50
348 15 c. Prince Philip in polo gear .. .. 1·25 1·50
349 25 c. Prince Philip in naval uniform, and the royal yacht *Britannia* .. .. .. 2·00 2·25
MS350 168 × 122 mm. Nos 345/9 plus printed labels in positions 1, 3, 4, and 6 .. .. .. 5·50 7·50

Each value was issued in sheets of 7 stamps and 2 labels.

(118)

(119)

1971 (8 Sept). *Fourth South Pacific Games, Tahiti. Nos.* 238B, 241B *and* 242B *optd with T* **118** *in black, or surch as T* **119** *in blue.*

351 10 c. *Poinciana regia flamboyant* 20 20
352 10 c. + 1 c. *Poinciana regia flamboyant* .. 20 20
353 10 c. + 3 c. *Poinciana regia flamboyant* .. 20 20
354 25 c. Canna Lily 35 25
355 25 c. + 1 c. Canna Lily 35 25
356 25 c. + 3 c. Canna Lily 35 25
357 30 c. *Euphorbia pulcherrima poinsettia* .. 35 25
358 30 c. + 1 c. *Euphorbia pulcherrima poinsettia* 35 25
359 30 c. + 3 c. *Euphorbia pulcherrima poinsettia* 35 25
351/9 .. .. *Set of* 9 2·40 1·90

The stamps additionally surcharged 1 c. or 3 c. helped to finance the Cook Islands' team at the games.

10c ≡

(120)

121 "Virgin and Child" (Bellini)

1971 (20 Oct). *Nos.* 230B, 233B, 236B/7B *and* 239B *surch with T* **120**.

360 10 c. on 2½ c. *Clitoria ternatea* 25 30
361 10 c. on 4 c. Water Lily 25 30
362 10 c. on 8 c. *Allamanda cathartica* 25 30
a. Surch inverted £130
363 10 c. on 9 c. Stephanotis 25 30
364 10 c. on 15 c. Frangipani 25 30
a. Surch double .. .. 90·00

1971 (30 Nov). *Christmas. T* **121** *and similar vert designs showing different paintings of the "Virgin and Child", by Bellini. P* 13.

365 1 c. multicoloured 8 8
366 4 c. multicoloured 8 8
367 10 c. multicoloured 25 15
368 20 c. multicoloured 50 30
369 30 c. multicoloured 65 50
MS370 135 × 147 mm. Nos. 365/9 .. .. 2·50 2·75
MS371 92 × 98 mm. 50 c. + 5 c. "The Holy Family in a Garland of Flowers (Jan Brueghel and Pieter van Avont) (41 × 41 *mm*) .. .. 1·75 1·90

Each value was issued in sheets of 8 stamps and 1 label.

SOUTH PACIFIC
COMMISSION
FEB. 1947 - 1972

(122)

123 St. John

1972 (17 Feb). *25th Anniv of South Pacific Commission. No.* 244B *optd with T* **122**.

372 **80** $1 multicoloured .. .. 1·25 1·75

(Des from De Lisle Psalter)

1972 (6 Mar). *Easter. T* **123** *and similar vert designs. Multicoloured. P* 13.

373 5 c. Type **123** 15 12
374 10 c. Christ on the Cross 25 20
375 30 c. Mary, Mother of Jesus 45 35
MS376 79 × 112 mm. Nos. 373/5 forming triptych of "The Crucifixion" .. .. 2·50 2·75

Stamps from the miniature sheet do not have a border around the perforations, and are therefore smaller than stamps from sheets.

HURRICANE
RELIEF
PLUS 2c

(124)

Hurricane
Relief
Plus 5c

(125)

1972 (30 Mar). *Hurricane Relief. Nos.* 373/5 *surch as T* **124**, *and Nos.* 239B, 241B *and* 243B *surch as T* **125**, *by Govt Printer, Rarotonga.*

377 5 c. + 2 c. Type **123** (R.) 12 12
a. Albino surch .. .. 40·00
378 10 c. + 2 c. Christ on the Cross (R.) .. 25 25
379 15 c. + 5 c. Frangipani 25 40
380 25 c. + 5 c. Canna Lily 65 65
381 30 c. + 5 c. Mary, Mother of Jesus 70 70
a. Albino surch .. ..
382 50 c. + 10 c. *Gardinia taitensis* 90 90
377/82 .. .. *Set of* 6 2·75 2·75

126 Rocket heading for Moon 127

1972 (17 Apr). *Apollo Moon Exploration Flights. T* **126/7** *and similar horiz designs. Multicoloured. P* 13.

383 5 c. Type **126** 15 15
384 5 c. Type **127** 15 15
385 10 c. } Astronauts on Moon 30 30
386 10 c. } .. 30 30
387 25 c. } Moon Rover and astronauts working .. 60 60
388 25 c. } .. 60 60
389 30 c. } Splashdown and helicopter 60 60
390 30 c. } .. 60 60
383/90 .. .. *Set of* 8 3·00 3·00
MS391 83 × 205 mm. Nos. 383/90 .. .. 5·00 5·50

These were issued in horizontal *se-tenant* pairs of each value, forming one composite design.

HURRICANE
RELIEF
Plus 2c

(128)

129 High-jumping

1972 (24 May). *Hurricane Relief. Nos.* 383/91 *surch as T* **128**.

392 5 c. + 2 c. Type **126** 12 12
393 5 c. + 2 c. Type **127** 12 12
394 10 c. + 2 c. } Astronauts on Moon 20 20
395 10 c. + 2 c. } .. 20 20
396 25 c. + 2 c. } Moon Rover and astronauts .. 35 35
397 25 c. + 2 c. } .. 35 35
398 30 c. + 2 c. } Splashdown and astronauts .. 40 40
399 30 c. + 2 c. } .. 40 40
392/9 .. .. *Set of* 8 1·90 1·90
MS400 83 × 205 mm. **MS**391 surch 3 c. on each stamp .. .. 3·50 3·50

1972 (26 June). *Olympic Games, Munich. T* **129** *and similar vert designs. Multicoloured. P* 13½.

401 10 c. Type **129** 25 20
402 25 c. Running 80 70
403 30 c. Boxing 90 80
MS404 88 × 78 mm. 50 c. + 5 c. Pierre de Coubertin 2·75 3·00
MS405 84 × 133 mm. Nos. 401/3 plus *se-tenant* label 3·50 3·75

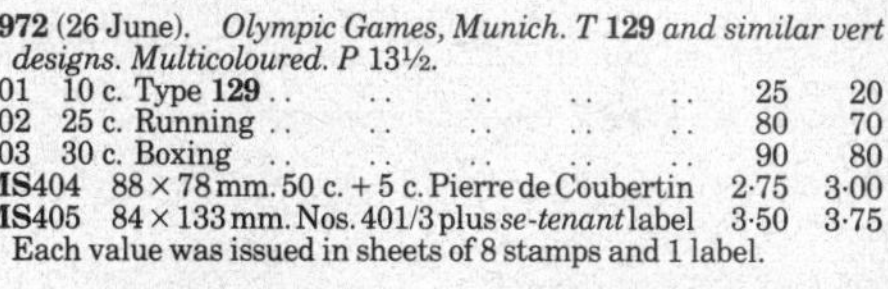

Each value was issued in sheets of 8 stamps and 1 label.

130 "The Rest on the Flight into Egypt" (Caravaggio)

131 Marriage Ceremony

1972 (11 Oct). *Christmas T* **130** *and similar vert designs. Multicoloured. P* 13.

406 1 c. Type **130** 5 5
407 5 c. "Madonna of the Swallow" (Guercino) 12 12
408 10 c. "Madonna of the Green Cushion" (Solario) 25 20
409 20 c. "Madonna and Child" (di Credi) .. 50 35
410 30 c. "Madonna and Child" (Bellini) 75 55
MS411 141 × 152 mm. Nos. 406/10 plus *se-tenant* label in position 1 .. .. 2·25 2·50
MS412 101 × 82 mm. 50 c + 5 c. "The Holy Night" (Correggio) (31 × 43 *mm*) .. .. .. 2·00 2·25

Each value was issued in sheets of 9 stamps and 1 label.

1972 (20 Nov). *Royal Silver Wedding. T* **131** *and similar black and silver designs. P* 13.

413 5 c. Type **131** 15 15
414 10 c. Leaving Westminster Abbey 40 40
415 15 c. Bride and Bridegroom (40 × 41 *mm*) .. 50 50
416 30 c. Family Group (67 × 40 *mm*) .. .. 80 1·00

The 5, 10 and 15 c. values were each issued in sheets of 8 stamps and 1 label.

132 Taro Leaf

133 "Noli me Tangere" (Titian)

1973 (15 Mar). *Silver Wedding Coinage. T* **132** *and similar designs showing coins. P* 13.

No.	Description		
417	1 c. black, rosy carmine and gold	5	5
418	2 c. black, bright blue and gold	5	5
419	5 c. black, green and silver	12	5
420	10 c. black, royal blue and silver	25	15
421	20 c. black, deep blue-green and silver	50	35
422	50 c. black, carmine and silver	1·25	1·00
423	$1 black, bright blue and silver	2·25	1·75
417/23	*Set of* 7	4·00	3·25

Designs: *As T* **132**—2 c. Pineapple; 5 c. Hibiscus. 46 × 30 *mm*—10 c. Oranges; 20 c. White Tern; 50 c. Skipjack Tuna. 32 × 55 *mm*—$1 Tangaroa.

Each value was issued in sheets of 20 stamps and 1 label.

1973 (9 Apr). *Easter. T* **133** *and similar vert designs. Multicoloured. P* 13.

No.	Description		
424	5 c. Type **133**	12	10
425	10 c. "The Descent from the Cross" (Rubens)	20	15
426	30 c. "The Lamentation of Christ" (Dürer)	50	45
MS427	132 × 67 mm. Nos. 424/6	1·75	2·00

Each value was issued in sheets of 15 stamps and 1 label.

1973 (30 Apr). *Easter. Children's Charity. Designs as Nos. 424/6 in separate Miniature Sheets 67 × 87 mm, each with a face value of* 50 c. + 5 c. *P* 13 × 14.

No.	Description		
MS428	As Nos. 424/6 . . *Set of 3 sheets*	3·50	3·75

134 Queen Elizabeth II in Coronation Regalia

TENTH ANNIVERSARY
CESSATION OF
NUCLEAR TESTING
TREATY

(**135**)

1973 (1 June). *20th Anniv of Queen Elizabeth's Coronation. P* 14 × 13½.

No.	Description		
429	**134** 10 c. multicoloured	2·25	2·40
MS430	64 × 89 mm. 50 c. as 10 c. P 13 × 14	9·00	9·00

The perforated portion of **MS**430 is similar to No. 429, but has no borders.

No. 429 was issued in sheets of 5 papers and 1 label.

1973 (25 July). *Tenth Anniv of Treaty Banning Nuclear Testing. Nos. 234B, 236B, 238B, and 240B/242B optd with T* **135**.

No.	Description		
431	5 c. *Bauhinia bi-pinnata rosea*	15	15
432	8 c. *Allamanda cathartica*	20	20
433	10 c. *Poinciana regia flamboyant*	25	25
434	20 c. Thunbergia	35	35
435	25 c. Canna Lily	40	40
436	30 c. *Euphorbia pulcherrima poinsettia*	45	45
431/6	*Set of* 6	1·60	1·60

136 Tipairua

1973 (17 Sept). *Maori Exploration of the Pacific. T* **136** *and similar horiz designs showing sailing craft. Multicoloured. P* 13.

No.	Description		
437	½ c. Type **136**	5	5
438	1 c. Wa'a Kaulua	10	5
439	1½ c. Tainui	15	8
440	5 c. War canoe	40	15
441	10 c. Pahi	60	30
442	15 c. Amastasi	85	45
443	25 c. Vaka	1·10	60
437/443	*Set of* 7	3·00	1·50

137 The Annunciation

138 Princess Anne

1973 (30 Oct). *Christmas. T* **137** *and similar vert designs showing scenes from a 15th-century Flemish "Book of Hours". Multicoloured. P* 13.

No.	Description		
444	1 c. Type **137**	5	5
445	5 c. The Visitation	12	12
446	10 c. Annunciation to the Shepherds	30	25
447	20 c. Epiphany	45	40
448	30 c. The Slaughter of the Innocents	60	60
MS449	121 × 128 mm. Nos. 444/8 plus *se-tenant* label	1·60	1·60

Each value was issued in sheets of 14 stamps and 1 label.

See also No. **MS**454.

1973 (14 Nov). *Royal Wedding. T* **138** *and similar vert designs. Multicoloured. P* 14 × 13½.

No.	Description		
450	25 c. Type **138**	35	30
451	30 c. Capt. Mark Phillips	40	35
452	50 c. Princess Anne and Capt. Phillips	50	45
MS453	119 × 100 mm. No. 450/2 plus *se-tenant* label. P 13	1·50	1·75

Each value was issued in sheets of 8 stamps and 1 label.

1973 (3 Dec). *Christmas. Children's Charity. Designs as Nos. 444/8 in separate Miniature Sheets 50 × 70 mm, each with a face value of* 50 c. + 5 c.

No.	Description		
MS454	As Nos. 444/8 . . *Set of 5 sheets*	4·25	4·25

139 Running

140 "Jesus carrying the Cross" (Raphael)

1974 (24 Jan). *Commonwealth Games, Christchurch. T* **139** *and similar multicoloured designs. P* 14 × 13½ (1 *and* 3 c.) *or* 13½ × 14 (*others*).

No.	Description		
455	1 c. Diving (*vert*)	5	5
456	3 c. Boxing (*vert*)	10	10
457	5 c. Type **139**	12	12
458	10 c. Weightlifting	25	20
459	30 c. Cycling	70	55
MS460	115 × 90 mm. 50 c. Discobolus	1·25	1·25

Each value was issued in sheets of 15 stamps and 1 label.

1974 (25 Mar). *Easter. T* **140** *and similar vert designs. Multicoloured. P* 13½.

No.	Description		
461	5 c. Type **140**	10	10
462	10 c. "The Holy Trinity" (El Greco)	20	20
463	30 c. "The Deposition of Christ" (Caravaggio)	50	55
MS464	130 × 70 mm. Nos. 461/3	1·25	1·40

Each value was issued in sheets of 20 stamps and 1 label.

1974 (22 Apr). *Easter. Children's Charity. Designs as Nos. 461/3 in separate Miniature Sheets 59 × 87 mm, each with a face value of* 50 c. + 5 c.

No.	Description		
MS465	As Nos. 461/3 . . *Set of 3 sheets*	2·75	3·00

141 Helmet Shell

142 Queen Elizabeth II

1974 (17 May)–**75**. *Sea-shells. Horiz designs as T* **141** (½ *to* 60 c.), *T* **142** *or larger horiz design* ($4 *to* $10). *Multicoloured. P* 14 × 13½ ($4 *to* $10) *or* 13½ (*others*).

No.	Description		
466	½ c. Type **141**	5	5
467	1 c. Vase shell	10	5
468	1½ c. Cockle shell	15	5
469	2 c. *Terebellum terebellum*	15	5
470	3 c. Bat volutes	20	5
471	4 c. Conch shell	20	5
472	5 c. Triton shell	20	5
473	6 c. Shake-head couries	25	8
474	8 c. Helmet shell (*different*)	30	10
475	10 c. Auger shell	30	10
476	15 c. Metre shell	50	15
477	20 c. Naticacid shell	55	20
478	25 c. Scallop shell	60	25
479	30 c. Soldier Cone shell	75	35
480	50 c. Cloth of Gold Cone shell (26.8.74)	1·40	1·25
481	60 c. Olive shell (26.8.74)	1·75	1·50
482	$1 Type **142** (26.8.74)	2·00	1·90
483	$2 Type **142** (27.1.75)	2·50	2·10
484	$4 Queen Elizabeth II and seashells (17.3.75)	3·75	4·50
485	$6 As $4 (29.4.75)	8·00	7·00
486	$8 As $4 (30.5.75)	8·50	9·00
487	$10 As $4 (30.6.75)	9·50	10·00
466/82	*Set of* 17	8·50	5·50

Nos. 484/7 are larger, 60 × 39 mm.

143 Footballer and Australasian Map

144 Obverse and Reverse of Commemorative $2·50 Silver Coin

1974 (5 July). *World Cup Football Championships, West Germany. T* **143** *and similar horiz designs. Multicoloured. P* 13.

No.	Description		
488	25 c. Type **143**	50	50
489	50 c. Map and Munich Stadium	85	85
490	$1 Footballer, stadium and World Cup	1·40	1·40
MS491	89 × 100 mm. Nos. 488/90	3·25	3·75

Each value was issued in sheets of 8 stamps and 1 label.

1974 (22 July). *Bicentenary of Capt. Cook's Second Voyage of Discovery. T* **144** *and similar vert design. P* 14.

No.	Description		
492	$2.50, silver, black and violet	12·00	12·00
493	$7.50, silver, black and deep turquoise-green	26·00	26·00
MS494	73 × 73 mm. Nos. 492/3	55·00	55·00

Design:—$7.50. As T **144** but showing $7.50 coin.

Each value was issued in sheets of 5 stamps and 1 label.

145 Early Stamps of Cook Islands

146 "Madonna of the Goldfinch" (Raphael)

1974 (16 Sept). *Centenary of Universal Postal Union. T* **145** *and similar horiz designs. Multicoloured. P* 13½ × 14.

No.	Description		
495	10 c. Type **145**	25	25
496	25 c. Old landing strip, Rarotonga, and stamp of 1898	55	55
497	30 c. Post Office, Rarotonga, and stamp of 1920	60	60
498	50 c. U.P.U. emblem and stamps	75	75
MS499	118 × 79 mm. Nos. 495/8. P 13	2·25	2·50

Each value was issued in sheets of 8 stamps and 1 label.

1974 (15 Oct). *Christmas. T* **146** *and similar vert designs. Multicoloured. P* 13.

No.	Description		
500	1 c. Type **146**	5	5
501	5 c. "The Sacred Family" (Andrea del Sarto)	15	12
502	10 c. "The Virgin adoring the Child" (Correggio)	30	25
503	20 c. "The Holy Family" (Rembrandt)	40	35
504	30 c. "The Virgin and Child" (Rogier Van Der Weyden)	55	45
500/504	*Set of* 5	1·25	1·10
MS505	114 × 133 mm. Nos. 500/4 plus *se-tenant* label	1·50	1·75

Each value was issued in sheets of 15 stamps and 1 label.

See also No. **MS**512.

147 Churchill and Blenheim Palace

1974 (20 Nov). *Birth Centenary of Sir Winston Churchill. T* **147** *and similar horiz designs. Multicoloured. P* 13 × 14.

No.	Description		
506	5 c. Type **147**	40	40
507	10 c. Churchill and Houses of Parliament	60	60
508	25 c. Churchill and Chartwell	1·10	1·10
509	30 c. Churchill and Buckingham Palace	1·40	1·40
510	50 c. Churchill and St. Paul's Cathedral	1·75	1·75
506/10	*Set of* 5	4·75	4·75

MS511 108 × 114 mm. Nos. 506/10 plus *se-tenant* label .. .. 5·50 5·50
Each value was issued in sheets of 5 stamps and 1 label.

1974 (9 Dec). *Christmas. Children's Charity. Designs as Nos. 500/504 in separate miniature sheets* 53 × 69 *mm, each with a face value of* 50 c. + 5 c.
MS5122 As Nos. 500/4 .. .. *Set of* 5 *sheets* 4·25 4·25

148 Vasco Nuñez de Balboa and Discovery of Pacific Ocean (1513).

1975 (3 Feb). *Pacific Explorers. T* **148** *and similar horiz designs. Multicoloured. P* 13.
513 1 c. Type **148** 8 8
514 5 c. Fernando de Magellanes and map (1520) 35 35
515 10 c. Juan Sebastian de Elcano and *Vitoria* (1520) 60 50
516 25 c. Friar de Urdaneta and ship (1564–67) .. 1·50 1·25
517 30 c. Miguel Lopez de Legazpi and ship (1564–67) .. .. 1·60 1·50
513/17 .. .. *Set of* 5 3·75 3·25

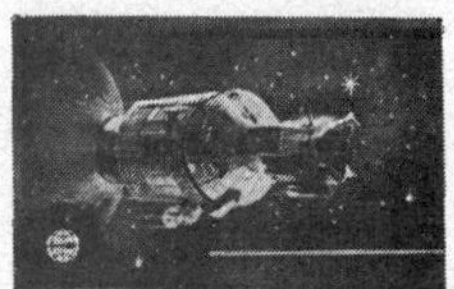
149 "Apollo" Capsule

1975 (15 July). *"Apollo-Soyuz" Space Project. T* **149** *and similar horiz designs. Multicoloured. P* 13½.
518 25 c. Type **149** 50 35
519 25 c. "Soyuz" capsule 50 35
520 30 c. "Soyuz" crew 55 40
521 30 c. "Apollo" crew 55 40
522 50 c. Cosmonaut within "Soyuz" 65 50
523 50 c. Astronauts within "Apollo" 65 50
518/23 .. .. *Set of* 6 3·00 2·25
MS524 119 × 119 mm. Nos. 518/23. P 13 × 14 .. 4·25 4·75
Each value was issued in sheets containing 9 horizontal *se-tenant* pairs of the two designs, together with 2 labels.

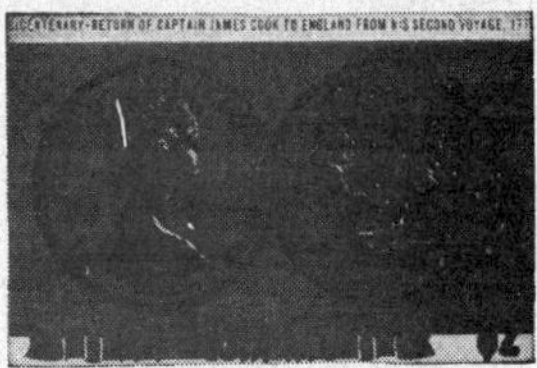
150 $100 Commemorative Gold Coin

1975 (8 Aug). *Bicentenary of Captain Cook's Second Voyage. P* 13.
525 **150** $2 brown, gold and bluish violet .. 11·00 7·50
No. 525 was issued in sheets of 5 stamps and 1 label.

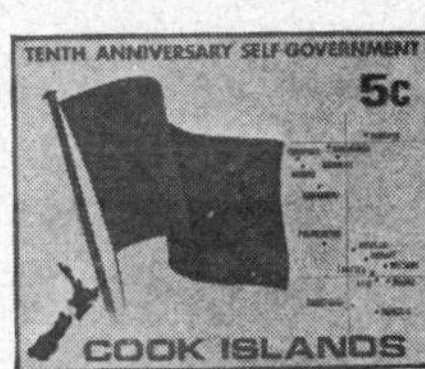

151 Cook Islands' Flag and Map

1975 (8 Aug). *Tenth Anniv of Self-Government. T* **151** *and similar multicoloured designs. P* 13.
526 5 c. Type **151** 30 15
527 10 c. Premier Sir Albert Henry and flag (*vert*) 45 20
528 25 c. Rarotonga and flag .. .. 1·00 65

152 "Madonna by the Fireside" (R. Campin)

153 "Entombment of Christ" (Raphael)

1975 (1 Dec). *Christmas. T* **152** *and similar vert designs. Multicoloured. P* 13½.
529 6 c. Type **152** 12 12
530 10 c. "Madonna in the Meadow" (Raphael) .. 20 20
531 15 c. "Madonna of the Oak" (attrib Raphael) .. 30 25
532 20 c. "Adoration of the Shepherds" (J. B. Maino) 35 25
533 35 c. "The Annunciation" (Murillo) 45 35
529/33 .. .. *Set of* 5 1·25 1·10
MS534 110 × 124 mm. Nos. 529/33 .. .. 1·60 1·75

1975 (15 Dec). *Christmas. Children's Charity. Designs as Nos. 529/33 in separate miniature sheets* 53 × 71 *mm, each with a face value of* 75 c. + 5 c.
MS535 As Nos. 529/33 .. .. *Set of* 5 *sheets* 6·00 6·00
a. Error. Miniature sheet as No. 531 imperf £250

1976 (29 Mar). *Easter. T* **153** *and similar square designs. Multicoloured. P* 13.
536 7 c. Type **153** 25 25
537 15 c. "Pietà" (Veronese) 40 40
538 35 c. "Pietà" (El Greco) 70 70
MS539 144 × 57 mm. Nos. 536/8 .. .. .. 1·50 1·60
Each value was issued in sheets of 20 stamps and 1 label.

1976 (3 May). *Easter. Children's Charity. Designs as Nos. 536/8 in separate miniature sheets* 69 × 69 *mm. each with a face value of* 60 c. + 5 c.
MS540 As Nos. 536/8 .. .. *Set of* 3 *sheets* 3·50 3·50

154 Benjamin Franklin and *Resolution*

1976 (29 May). *Bicentenary of American Revolution. T* **154** *and similar horiz designs. Multicoloured. P* 13.
541 $1 Type **154** .. .. 6·00 5·00
542 $2 Captain Cook and *Resolution* .. .. 8·00 7·00
MS543 118 × 58 mm. $3 Cook, Franklin and *Resolution* (74 × 31 *mm*) .. .. 14·00 13·00
Each value was issued in sheets of 5 stamps and 1 label.

1976 (9 July). *Visit of Queen Elizabeth to the U.S.A. Nos.* 541/3 *optd.* "ROYAL VISIT JULY 1976".
544 $1 Type **154** .. .. 5·00 4·25
545 $2 Captain Cook and *Resolution* .. .. 6·50 6·00
MS546 $3 Cook, Franklin and *Resolution* .. 12·00 11·00

156 Hurdling

157 "The Visitation"

1976 (22 July). *Olympic Games, Montreal. T* **156** *and similar square designs. Multicoloured. P* 13.
547 7 c. } Type **156** 15 10
548 7 c. } .. 15 10
549 15 c. } Hockey 30 20
550 15 c. } .. 30 20
551 30 c. } Fencing 60 50
552 30 c. } .. 60 50
553 35 c. } Football 70 60
554 35 c. } .. 70 60
547/54 .. .. *Set of* 8 3·25 2·50
MS555 104 × 146 mm. Nos. 547/54 .. .. 3·50 3·75
Each value was issued in sheets containing 5 horizontal *se-tenant* pairs and 2 labels. In each pair the first stamp has the face-value on the right, the second has it on the left. Illustrated is the left-hand stamp of the 7 c. design.

1976 (12 Oct). *Christmas. T* **157** *and similar vert designs showing Renaissance sculptures. Multicoloured. P* 14 × 13½.
556 6 c. Type **157** 12 10
557 10 c. "Adoration of the Shepherds" 25 20
558 15 c. "Adoration of the Shepherds" (*different*) 35 30
559 20 c. "The Epiphany" 40 35
560 35 c. "The Holy Family" 60 50
556/60 .. .. *Set of* 5 1·50 1·25
MS561 116 × 110 mm. Nos. 556/60. P 13 .. .. 1·75 1·90
Each value was issued in sheets of 20 stamps and 1 label.

1976 (2 Nov.) *Christmas. Children's Charity. Designs as Nos. 556/60 in separate miniature sheets* 66 × 80 *mm, each with a face value of* 75 c. + 5 c.
MS562 As Nos. 556/60 .. .. *Set of* 5 *sheets* 7·00 7·00

158 Obverse and Reverse of $5 Mangaia Kingfisher Coin

1976 (15 Nov). *National Wildlife and Conservation Day. P* 13.
563 **158** $1 multicoloured .. .. 3·75 2·75
No. 563 was issued in sheets of 5 stamps and 1 label.

159 Imperial State Crown

160 "Christ on the Cross"

1977 (7 Feb). *Silver Jubilee. T* **159** *and similar vert designs. Multicoloured. P* 13.
564 25 c. Type **159** 90 75
565 25 c. Queen with regalia 90 75
566 50 c. Westminster Abbey .. .. 2·00 1·75
567 50 c. Coronation Coach .. .. 2·00 1·75
568 $1 Queen and Prince Philip .. .. .. 4·25 3·50
569 $1 Royal Visit, 1974 .. .. 4·25 3·50
564/9 .. .. *Set of* 6 13·00 11·00
MS570 130 × 136 mm. As Nos. 564/9 (borders and "COOK ISLANDS" in a different colour) .. .. 12·00 12·00
The two designs of each value are printed horizontally *se-tenant* throughout the sheet, and stamps from **MS**570 have borders and "COOK ISLANDS" in a different colour.

1977 (28 Mar). *Easter and 400th Birth Anniv of Rubens. T* **160** *and similar vert designs. Multicoloured. P* 14 × 13½.
571 7 c. Type **160** 30 15
572 15 c. "Christ on the Cross" 50 20
573 35 c. "The Deposition of Christ" 85 55
MS574 118 × 65 mm. Nos. 571/3. P 13 .. .. 1·60 1·75
Each value was issued in sheets of 24 stamps and 1 label.

1977 (18 Apr). *Easter. Children's Charity. Designs as Nos. 571/3 in separate miniature sheets* 60 × 79 *mm, each with a face value of* 60 c. + 5 c. *P* 13 × 14.
MS575 As Nos. 571/3 .. .. *Set of* 3 *sheets* 3·50 3·50

161 "Virgin and Child" (Memling)

162 Obverse and Reverse of $5 Atiu Swiftlet Coin

1977 (3 Oct). *Christmas. T* **161** *and similar vert designs. Multicoloured. P* 14.
576 6 c. Type **161** 15 10
577 10 c. "Madonna and Child with Saints and Donors" (Memling) 20 15
578 15 c. "Adoration of the Kings" (Geertgen) .. 35 25
579 20 c. "Virgin and Child with Saints" (Crivelli) 40 35
580 35 c. "Adoration of the Magi" (16th-cent Flemish School) 60 55
576/80 .. .. *Set of* 5 1·50 1·25
MS581 118 × 111 mm. Nos. 576/80. P 13½ .. 1·60 1·75
Each value was issued in sheets of 24 stamps and 1 label.

1977 (31 Oct). *Christmas. Children's Charity. Designs as Nos. 576/80 in separate miniature sheets* 69 × 69 *mm, each with a face value of* 75 c. + 5 c.
MS582 As Nos. 576/80 .. .. *Set of* 5 *sheets* 6·00 6·00

1977 (15 Nov). *National Wildlife and Conservation Day. P* 13.
583 **162** $1 multicoloured .. .. 4·00 2·50
No. 583 was issued in sheets containing 10 stamps and 2 labels.

163 Captain Cook and H.M.S. *Resolution* (from paintings by N. Dance and H. Roberts)

1978 (20 Jan). *Bicentenary of Discovery of Hawaii. T* **163** *and similar horiz designs. Multicoloured. P* 13½.
584 50 c. Type **163** .. .. 1·75 85
585 $1 Earl of Sandwich, and Cook landing at Owhyhee (from paintings by Thomas Gainsborough and J. Cleveley) .. .. 2·50 1·90
586 $2 Obverse and reverse of $200 coin and Cook monument, Hawaii .. .. .. 4·50 3·25
MS587 118 × 95 mm. Nos. 584/86 .. .. .. 8·00 7·00
Each value was issued in sheets of 5 stamps and 1 label.

164 "Pieta" (Van der Weyden)

165 Queen Elizabeth II

1978 (20 Mar). *Easter. Paintings from National Gallery, London. T* **164** *and similar horiz designs. Multicoloured. P* 13.
588 15 c. Type **164** 20 20
589 35 c. "The Entombment" (Michelangelo) .. 45 45
590 75 c. "The Supper at Emmaus" (Caravaggio) 85 85
MS591 114 × 96 mm. Nos. 588/90 .. .. 1·90 2·00
Each value was issued in sheets of 5 stamps and 1 label.

1978 (10 Apr). *Easter. Children's Charity. Designs as Nos.* 588/90 *in separate miniature sheets*, 85 × 72 *mm, each with a face value of* 60 *c.* + 5 *c. P* 13½.
MS592 As Nos. 588/90 .. . . *Set of* 3 *sheets* 2·75 2·75

1978 (6 June). 25*th Anniv of Coronation. T* **165** *and similar vert designs. Multicoloured. P* 13.
593 50 c. Type **165** 70 80
594 50 c. The Lion of England 70 80
595 50 c. Imperial State Crown 70 80
596 50 c. Statue of Tangaroa (god) 70 80
597 70 c. Type **165** 75 85
598 70 c. Sceptre with Cross 75 85
599 70 c. St. Edward's Crown 75 85
600 70 c. Rarotongan staff god 75 85
593/600 .. .. .. *Set of* 8 5·00 6·00
MS601 103 × 142 mm. Nos. 593/600*. .. .. 5·00 6·50
Each value was issued in sheets containing the 4 designs and 2 labels.
* In No **MS**601 the designs of Nos. 595 and 599 are transposed.

5c 
(166)

1978 (10 Nov). *Nos.* 466, 468, 473/4 *and* 478/81 *surch as T* **166**.
602 5 c. on 1½ c. *Corculum cardissa* (Silver) .. 15 10
603 7 c. on ½ c. Type **141** 20 12
604 10 c. on 6 c. *Cypraea caputserpentis* (Gold) .. 25 15
605 10 c. on 8 c. *Bursa granularis* (Gold) 25 15
606 15 c. on ½ c. Type **141** 30 25
607 15 c. on 25 c. *Gloripallium pallium* (Silver) .. 30 25
608 15 c. on 30 c. *Conus miles* 30 25
609 15 c. on 50 c. *Conus textile* (Silver) 30 25
610 15 c. on 60 c. *Oliva sericea* (Gold) 30 25
611 17 c. on ½ c. Type **141** 35 30
612 17 c. on 50 c. *Conus textile* (Silver) 35 30
602/12 .. .. *Set of* 11 2·75 2·10

1728 · 250th ANNIVERSARY OF COOK'S BIRTH · 1978
(167)

1978 (13 Nov). 250*th Birth Anniv of Captain Cook. Nos.* 584/7 *optd with T* **167** *on silver.*
613 50 c. Type **163** .. .. 1·75 1·25
614 $1 Earl of Sandwich, and Cook landing at Owhyhee (from paintings by Thomas Gainsborough and J. Cleveley) .. 2·50 2·00
615 $2 Obverse and reverse of $200 coin and Cook monument, Hawaii .. .. 4·00 4·00
MS616 Nos. 613/15 .. .. 8·50 7·50

168 Obverse and Reverse of $5 Polynesian Warblers Coin

1978 (15 Nov). *National Wildlife and Conservation Day. P* 13.
617 **168** $1 multicoloured .. .. .. 2·50 1·75

169 "The Virgin and Child" (Van der Weyden)

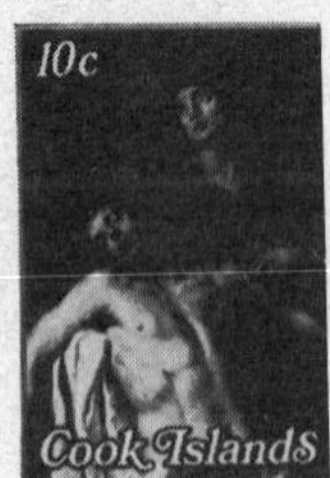

170 Virgin with Body of Christ

1978 (8 Dec). *Christmas. Paintings. T* **169** *and similar vert designs. Multicoloured. P* 13.
618 15 c. Type **169** 30 20
619 17 c. "The Virgin and Child" (Crivelli) .. 35 30
620 35 c. "The Virgin and Child" (Murillo) .. 60 50
MS621 107 x 70 mm. Nos. 618/20.. .. .. 1·25 1·25

1979 (12 Jan). *Christmas. Children's Charity. Designs as Nos.* 618/20 *in separate miniature sheets* 57 x 87 *mm. each with a face value of* 75 *c.* + 5 *c. P* 13½
MS622 As Nos. 618/20 .. . . *Set of* 3 *sheets* 3·00 3·75

1979 (5 Apr). *Easter. Details of Painting "Descent" by Gaspar de Crayar. T* **170** *and similar vert designs. Multicoloured. P* 13.
623 10 c. Type **170** 12 12
624 12 c. St. John 15 15
625 15 c. Mary Magdalene 25 25
626 20 c. Weeping angels 25 25
MS627 83 × 100 mm. As Nos. 623/6, but each with charity premium of 2 c. 85 90
Stamps from No. **MS**627 are slightly smaller, 32 × 40 mm, and are without borders.

171 "Captain Cook" (James Weber)

172 Post-Rider

1979 (23 July). *Death Bicentenary of Captain Cook. T* **171** *and similar vert designs. Multicoloured. P* 14 × 13.
628 20 c. Type **171** 25 25
629 30 c. *Resolution* 45 45
630 35 c. *Endeavour* 55 55
631 50 c. "Death of Captain Cook" (George Carter) 70 70
MS632 78 × 112 mm. Nos. 628/31 .. .. 1·90 2·00
Stamps from No. **MS**632 have black borders.

1979 (10 Sept). *Death Centenary of Sir Rowland Hill. History of Mail Transport. T* **172** *and similar square designs. Multicoloured. P* 14.
633 30 c. Type **172** 35 40
634 30 c. Mail coach 35 40
635 30 c. Automobile 35 40
636 30 c. Railway train 35 40
637 35 c. *Cap-Horniers* (sailing ship) 40 45
638 35 c. River steamer 40 45
639 35 c. *Deutschland* (liner) 40 45
640 35 c. *United States* (liner) 40 45
641 50 c. Balloon *Neptune* 55 60
642 50 c. Junkers "F13" (aeroplane) 55 60
643 50 c. *Graf Zeppelin* 55 60
644 50 c. "Concorde" 55 60
633/44 .. .. .. *Set of* 12 4·75 5·00
MS645 132 × 104 mm. Nos. 633/44 .. .. 5·00 5·50
Nos. 633/6, 637/40 and 641/4 were each printed together, *se-tenant*, in blocks of 4 throughout the sheets.

6c 
(173)

1979 (12 Sept). *Nos.* 466, 468 *and* 481 *surch as T* **173**.
646 6 c. on ½ c. Type **141** (Gold) 15 15
647 10 c. on 1½ c. *Corculum cardissa* (Silver) .. 20 20
648 15 c. on 60 c. *Oliva sericea* (Gold) 30 30

174 Brother and Sister

175 "Apollo 11" Emblem

1979 (10 Oct). *International Year of the Child. T* **174** *and similar horiz designs. Multicoloured. P* 13.
649 30 c. Type **174** 40 40
650 50 c. Boy with tree drum 55 55
651 65 c. Children dancing 70 70
MS652 102 × 75 mm. As Nos. 649/51, but each with charity premium of 5 c. P 13½ × 13 .. .. 1·90 2·00
Designs for stamps from No. **MS**652 are as Nos. 649/51 but have I.Y.C. emblem in red.

1979 (7 Nov). 10*th Anniv of Moon Landing. T* **175** *and similar vert designs. Multicoloured. P* 14.
653 30 c. Type **175** 35 40
654 50 c. Crew of "Apollo 11" 50 60
655 60 c. Astronaut on Moon 60 70
656 65 c. Command module after splashdown .. 65 75
MS657 119 × 105 mm. Nos. 653/6. P 13½ .. 2·10 2·25

OMNIBUS ISSUES

Details, together with prices for complete sets, of the various Omnibus issues from the 1935 Silver Jubilee series to date are included in a special section following Zululand at the end of the catalogue.

176 Obverse and Reverse of $5 Rarotonga Fruit Dove Coin.

177 Glass Christmas Tree Ornaments

1979 (15 Nov). *National Wildlife and Conservation Day. P* 13 × 14.
658 **176** $1 multicoloured .. .. .. 1·75 1·75

1979 (14 Dec). *Christmas. T* **177** *and similar vert designs. Multicoloured. P* 13½. (*a*) *Postage.*
659 6 c. Type **177** 5 5
660 10 c. Hibiscus flower and star.. .. .. 12 12
661 12 c. Poinsettia flower, bells and candle .. 15 15
662 15 c. Poinsettia leaves and Tiki (god).. .. 20 20

(*b*) *Air*
663 20 c. Type **177** 25 25
664 25 c. As 10 c. 30 30
665 30 c. As 12 c. 35 35
666 35 c. As 15 c. 40 40
659/66 .. .. *Set of* 8 1·40 1·60

1980 (15 Jan). *Christmas. Children's Charity. Designs as Nos.* 659/66 *with additional premiums.* (*a*) *Postage.*
667 6 c. + 2 c. Type **177** 8 10
668 10 c. + 2 c. Hibiscus flower and star 12 15
669 12 c. + 2 c. Poinsettia flower, bells and candle 15 20
670 15 c. + 2 c. Poinsettia leaves and Tiki (god) .. 20 25

(*b*) *Air*
671 20 c. + 4 c. Type **177** 25 30
672 25 c. + 4 c. As 10 c. 30 35
673 30 c. + 4 c. As 12 c. 35 40
674 35 c. + 4 c. As 15 c. 40 45
667/74 .. .. *Set of* 8 1·60 2·00

178 "Flagellation"

179 Dove with Olive Twig

1980 (31 Mar). *Easter. Illustrations by Gustave Doré. T* **178** *and similar vert designs in sepia and gold. P* 13.
675 20 c. Type **178** 20 25
676 20 c. "Crown of Thorns" 20 25
677 30 c. "Jesus Insulted" 30 35
678 30 c. "Jesus Falls" 30 35
679 35 c. "The Crucifixion" 35 40
680 35 c. "The Descent from the Cross" 35 40
675/80 .. .. *Set of* 6 1·50 1·75
MS681 120 × 110 mm. As Nos. 675/80, but each with charity premium of 2 c. .. .. 1·75 1·90
Nos. 675/6, 677/8 and 679/80 were each printed together, *se-tenant*, in vertical pairs throughout the sheet.

1980 (23 Apr). *Easter. Children's Charity. Designs as Nos.* 675/80 *in separate miniature sheets* 60 × 71 *mm, each with a face value of* 75 *c.* + 5 *c. P* 13.
MS682 As Nos. 675/80 .. . . *Set of* 6 *sheets* 4·75 5·00

1980 (27 May). 75*th Anniv of Rotary International. T* **179** *and similar horiz designs. Multicoloured. P* 14.
683 30 c. Type **179** 45 45
684 35 c. Hibiscus flower 50 50
685 50 c. Ribbons 60 60
MS686 72 × 113 mm. Nos. 683/5 but each with premium of 3 c. P 13½ .. .. .. 1·40 1·50

ZEAPEX STAMP EXHIBITION–AUCKLAND 1980

(180)

181 Queen Elizabeth the Queen Mother

1980 (22 Aug). *"Zeapex 80" International Stamp Exhibition, Auckland. Nos.* 633/45 *optd with T* **180** *in black on silver background.*
687 30 c. Type **172** 25 30
688 30 c. Mail coach 25 30
689 30 c. Automobile 25 30
690 30 c. Railway train 25 30

691 35 c. *Cap-Horniers* (sailing ship) 30 35
692 35 c. River steamer 30 35
693 35 c. *Deutschland* (liner) 30 35
694 35 c. *United States* (liner) 30 35
695 50 c. Balloon *Neptune* 50 45
696 50 c. Junkers "F13" (aeroplane) . . 50 45
697 50 c. *Graf Zeppelin* 50 45
698 50 c. "Concorde" 50 45
687/98 . . . . . . *Set of* 12 4·00 4·00
MS699 132 × 104 mm. Nos. 687/98 . . . . 4·50 4·25

1980 (22 Aug). *"Zeapex 80" International Stamp Exhibition, Auckland. As No.* **MS**681 *but containing stamps without charity premium of* 2 c. *optd* "Zeapex '80 Auckland + 10 c" *in black on gold background.*
MS700 120 × 110 mm. Nos. 675/80 (*sold at* $1.80) 1·50 1·60
Stamps from No. **MS**700 are unaffected by the overprint which appears on the sheet margin.

1980 (23 Sept). *80th Birthday of Queen Elizabeth the Queen Mother. P* 13.
701 **181** 50 c. multicoloured . . . . . . 1·25 90
MS702 64× 78 mm. **181** $2 multicoloured . . 2·50 2·25

182 Satellites orbiting Moon

183 Scene from novel *From the Earth to the Moon*

1980 (7 Nov). *350th Death Anniv of Johannes Kepler (astronomer). T* **182** *and similar horiz designs. Multicoloured. P* 13.
703 12 c. Type **182** 35 35
704 12 c. Space-craft orbiting Moon 35 35
705 50 c. Space-craft orbiting Moon (*different*) . . 80 80
706 50 c. Astronaut and Moon vehicle 80 80
MS707 122 × 122 mm. Nos. 703/6 . . . . 2·10 2·40
Nos. 703/4 and 705/6 were each printed together, *se-tenant*, in horizontal pairs throughout the sheet.

1980 (7 Nov). *75th Death Anniv of Jules Verne (author). T* **183** *and similar vert designs showing scenes from the novel "From the Earth to the Moon". P* 13.
708 20 c. multicoloured (green background) . . 35 35
709 20 c. multicoloured (brown background) . . 35 35
710 30 c. multicoloured (mauve background) . . 45 45
711 30 c. multicoloured (blue background) . . 45 45
MS712 121 × 122 mm. Nos. 708/11 . . . . 1·40 1·40
Nos. 708/9 and 710/11 were each printed together, *se-tenant*, in horizontal pairs throughout the sheet.

184 *Siphonogorgia*

185 Annunciation

1980 (21 Nov)–**82**. *Corals. Multicoloured designs as T* **184**. *P* 13 (1 c. *to* $1) *or* 14 × 13½ ($2 *to* $10).
713 1 c. Type **184** 10 5
714 1 c. *Pavona praetorta* 10 5
715 1 c. *Stylaster echinatus* 10 5
716 1 c. *Tubastraea* 10 5
717 3 c. *Millepora alcicornis* 15 5
718 3 c. *Junceella gemmacea* 15 5
719 3 c. *Fungia fungites* 15 5
720 3 c. *Heliofungia actiniformis* 15 5
721 4 c. *Distichopora violacea* 15 5
722 4 c. *Stylaster* 15 5
723 4 c. *Gonipora* 15 5
724 4 c. *Caulastraea echinulata* 15 5
725 5 c. *Ptilosarcus gurneyi* 20 5
726 5 c. *Stylophora pistillata* 20 5
727 5 c. *Melithaea squamata* 20 5
728 5 c. *Porites andrewsi* 20 5
729 6 c. *Lobophyllia bemprichii* 20 10
730 6 c. *Palauastrea ramosa* 20 10
731 6 c. *Bellonella indica* 20 10
732 6 c. *Pectinia alcicornis* 20 10
733 8 c. *Sarcophyton digitatum* 20 10
734 8 c. *Melithaea albitincta* 20 10
735 8 c. *Plerogyra sinuosa* 20 10
736 8 c. *Dendrophyllia gracilis* 20 10
737 10 c. Type **184** (19.12.80) 25 15
738 10 c. As No. 714 (19.12.80) 25 15
739 10 c. As No. 715 (19.12.80) 25 15
740 10 c. As No. 716 (19.12.80) 25 15
741 12 c. As No. 717 (19.12.80) 25 15
742 12 c. As No. 718 (19.12.80) 25 15
743 12 c. As No. 719 (19.12.80) 25 15
744 12 c. As No. 720 (19.12.80) 25 15
745 15 c. As No. 721 (19.12.80) 30 20
746 15 c. As No. 722 (19.12.80) 30 20
747 15 c. As No. 723 (19.12.80) 30 20
748 15 c. As No. 724 (19.12.80) 30 20
749 20 c. As No. 725 (19.12.80) 35 25
750 20 c. As No. 726 (19.12.80) 35 25
751 20 c. As No. 727 (19.12.80) 35 25
752 20 c. As No. 728 (19.12.80) 35 25
753 25 c. As No. 729 (19.12.80) 35 25
754 25 c. As No. 730 (19.12.80) 35 25
755 25 c. As No. 731 (19.12.80) 35 25
756 25 c. As No. 732 (19.12.80) 35 25
757 30 c. As No. 733 (19.12.80) 40 30
758 30 c. As No. 734 (19.12.80) 40 30
759 30 c. As No. 735 (19.12.80) 40 30
760 30 c. As No. 736 (19.12.80) 40 30
761 35 c. Type **184** (16.3..81) 45 35
762 35 c. As No. 714 (16.3.81) 45 35
763 35 c. As No. 715 (16.3.81) 45 35
764 35 c. As No. 716 (16.3.81) 45 35
765 50 c. As No. 717 (16.3.81) 65 55
766 50 c. As No. 718 (16.3.81) 65 55
767 50 c. As No. 719 (16.3.81) 65 55
768 50 c. As No. 720 (16.3.81) 65 55
769 60 c. As No. 721 (16.3.81) 75 65
770 60 c. As No. 722 (16.3.81) 75 65
771 60 c. As No. 723 (16.3.81) 75 65
772 60 c. As No. 724 (16.3.81) 75 65
773 70 c. As No. 725 (13.4.81) 85 75
774 70 c. As No. 726 (13.4.81) 85 75
775 70 c. As No. 727 (13.4.81) 85 75
776 70 c. As No. 728 (13.4.81) 85 75
777 80 c. As No. 729 (13.4.81) 90 80
778 80 c. As No. 730 (13.4.81) 90 80
779 80 c. As No. 731 (13.4.81) 90 80
780 80 c. As No. 732 (13.4.81) 90 80
781 $1 As No. 733 (20.5.81) . . . . 1·00 1·00
782 $1 As No. 734 (20.5.81) . . . . 1·00 1·00
783 $1 As No. 735 (20.5.81) . . . . 1·00 1·00
784 $1 As No. 736 (20.5.81) . . . . 1·00 1·00
785 $2 As No. 723 (27.11.81) . . . . 1·40 1·50
786 $3 As No. 720 (27.11.81) . . . . 2·00 2·10
787 $4 As No. 726 (11.1.82) . . . . 2·50 2·75
788 $6 As No. 715 (11.1.82) . . . . 3·75 4·00
789 $10 As No. 734 (5.3.82) . . . . 6·50 6·75
713/89 . . . . . . *Set of* 77 42·00 35·00
Nos. 761/84 are 30 × 40 mm and Nos. 785/9, which include a portrait of Queen Elizabeth II in each design, are 55 × 35 mm in size.
The four designs of each value to the $1 were printed together, *se-tenant*, in horizontal strips of 4 (Nos. 713/60) or in blocks of 4 (Nos. 761/84) throughout the sheet.
For similar designs with redrawn frames and inscriptions see Nos. 966/92.

1980 (1 Dec). *Christmas. Illustrations from 13th-century French Prayer Book. T* **185** *and similar vert designs. Multicoloured. P* 14 × 13½.
801 15 c. Type **185** 15 15
802 30 c. Visitation 30 30
803 40 c. Nativity 35 35
804 50 c. Epiphany 50 50
MS805 89 × 114 mm. Nos. 801/4. P 13½ . . . . 1·40 1·50

1981 (9 Jan). *Christmas. Children's Charity. Designs as Nos.* 801/4 *in separate miniature sheets* 55 × 68 *mm, each with a face value of* 75 c. + 5 c. *Imperf.*
MS806 As Nos. 801/4 . . . . *Set of* 4 *sheets* 3·50 4·00

186 "The Crucifixion" (from book of Saint-Amand)

187 Prince Charles

1981 (10 Apr). *Easter. Illustrations from 12th-century French Prayer Books. T* **186** *and similar horiz designs. Multicoloured. P* 13½ × 14.
807 15 c. Type **186** 20 20
808 25 c. "Placing in Tomb" (from book of Ingeburge) 30 30
809 40 c. "Mourning at the Sepulchre" (from book of Ingeburge) 40 40
MS810 72 × 116 mm. As Nos. 807/9 but each with charity premium of 2 c. P 13½ . . . . 1·10 1·10

1981 (28 Apr). *Easter. Children's Charity. Designs as Nos.* 807/9 *in separate miniature sheets* 64 × 53 *mm, each with a face value of* 75 c. +5 c. *Imperf.*
MS811 As Nos. 807/9 . . . . *Set of* 3 *sheets* 2·75 2·75

1981 (29 July). *Royal Wedding. T* **187** *and similar vert design. Multicoloured. P* 14.
812 $1 Type **187** . . . . 1·50 1·50
813 $2 Prince Charles and Lady Diana Spencer 3·50 3·50
MS814 106 × 59 mm. Nos. 812/13. P 13½ . . 5·00 5·00
Nos. 812/13 were each printed in small sheets of 4.

190 "Holy Virgin with Child"

191 Princess of Wales (inscr "21st Birthday)

WORLD CUP CHAMPIONSHIP · ESPANA '82
COOK ISLANDS
188 Footballers

+
5
c
(189)

1981 (20 Oct). *World Cup Football Championship, Spain* (1982). *T* **188** *and similar horiz designs showing footballers. Multicoloured. P* 13½ × 14.
815 20 c. Type **188** 20 20
816 20 c. Figures to right of stamp 20 20
817 30 c. Figures to left 30 30
818 30 c. Figures to right 30 30
819 35 c. Figures to left 35 35
820 35 c. Figures to right 35 35
821 50 c. Figures to left 45 45
822 50 c. Figures to right 45 45
815/22 . . . . . . *Set of* 8 2·40 2·40
MS823 180 × 94 mm. As Nos. 815/22, but each stamp with a charity premium of 3 c. P 13½ . . 2·75 3·00
The two designs of each value were printed together, *se-tenant*, in horizontal pairs throughout the sheet, forming composite designs.

1981 (10 Nov). *International Year for Disabled Persons. Nos.* 812/14 *surch as T* **189**.
824 $1 + 5 c. Type **187** . . . . . . 3·00 2·50
825 $2 + 5 c. Prince Charles and Lady Diana Spencer . . . . 6·00 5·00
MS826 106 × 59 mm. $1 + 10 c., $2 + 10 c. As Nos. 824/5 . . . . 9·00 9·00
Nos. 824/6 have commemorative inscriptions overprinted on the sheet margins.

1981 (14 Dec). *Christmas. Details from Paintings by Rubens. T* **190** *and similar vert designs. Multicoloured. P* 14 × 13½.
827 8 c. Type **190** 10 8
828 15 c. "Coronation of St. Catherine" 15 12
829 40 c. "Adoration of the Shepherds" 35 35
830 50 c. "Adoration of the Magi" 45 45
MS831 86 × 110 mm. As Nos. 827/30, but each with a charity premium of 3 c. P 13½ . . . . 1·25 1·40

1982 (18 Jan). *Christmas. Children's Charity. Designs as Nos.* 827/30 *in separate miniature sheets* 62 × 78 *mm, each with a face value of* 75 c. + 5 c.
MS832 As Nos. 827/30 . . . . *Set of* 4 *sheets* 2·75 3·00

1982 (21 June). *21st Birthday of Princess of Wales. T* **191** *and similar horiz designs. Multicoloured. P* 14.
833 $1.25, Type **191** . . . . 1·25 1·25
a. Pair. Nos. 833/4 . . . . . . 2·50 2·50
834 $1.25, As Type **191**, but inscr "1 July 1982" . . 1·25 1·25
835 $2.50, Princess (*different*) (inscr "21st Birthday") . . . . 1·75 1·75
a. Pair. Nos. 835/6 . . . . . . 3·50 3·50
836 $2·50, As No. 835, but inscr "1 July 1982" . . 1·75 1·75
MS837 92 × 72 mm. $1.25, Type **191**; $2.50, As No. 835. Both inscribed "21st Birthday 1 July 1982". P 13½ . . . . 2·75 2·75
The two designs for each value were printed together, *se-tenant*, in small sheets of 4.

ROYAL BIRTH · 21 JUNE 1982
(192)

1982 (12 July). *Birth of Prince William of Wales (1st issue). Nos.* 812/14 *optd as T* **192**.
838 $1 Type **187** (optd with T **192**) . . . . 3·50 2·25
a. Pair. Nos. 838/9 . . . . . . 7·00 4·50
839 $1 Type **187** (optd "PRINCE WILLIAM OF WALES") . . . . 3·50 2·25
840 $2 Prince Charles and Lady Diana Spencer (optd with T **192**) . . . . . . 6·00 5·00
a. Pair. Nos. 840/1 . . . . . . 12·00 10·00
841 $2 Prince Charles and Lady Diana Spencer (optd. "PRINCE WILLIAM OF WALES") 6·00 5·00
MS842 106 × 59mm. Nos. 812/13 optd "21 JUNE 1982. ROYAL BIRTH" . . . . . . 9·00 8·50

1982 (3 Aug). *Birth of Prince William of Wales (2nd issue). Designs as Nos.* 833/7 *but with changed inscriptions. Multicoloured. P*14.
843 $1.25, As Type **191** (inscr "Royal Birth") . . 1·25 1·25
a. Pair. Nos. 843/4 . . . . . . 2·50 2·50
844 $1.25, As Type **191** (inscr "21 June 1982") . . 1·25 1·25
845 $2.50, As No. 835 (inscr "Royal Birth") . . 1·75 1·75
a. Pair. Nos. 845/6 . . . . . . 3·50 3·50
846 $2.50, As No. 835 (inscr "21 June 1982") . . 1·75 1·75
MS847 92 × 73 mm. $1.25, As Type **191**; $2.50, As No. 835. Both inscribed "Royal Birth 21 June 1982". P 13½ . . . . 2·75 2·75

193 "Serenade"

194 Franklin D. Roosevelt

(Litho Format)

1982 (10 Sept). *Norman Rockwell (painter) Commemoration. T* **193** *and similar vert designs. Multicoloured. P* 13½ × 14.
848 5 c. Type **193** 10 10
849 10 c. "The Hikers" 12 12
850 20 c. "The Doctor and the Doll" 25 25
851 30 c. "Home from Camp" 30 30

1982 (30 Sept). *Air. American Anniversaries. T* **194** *and similar vert designs. Multicoloured. P* 14.
852 60 c. Type **194** 70 70
853 80 c. Benjamin Franklin 80 80
854 $1.40, George Washington . . . . 1·25 1·25
MS855 116 × 60 mm. Nos. 852/4. P 13½ . . . . 2·75 3·00
Anniversaries:—60 c. Roosevelt birth centenary; 80 c. "Articles of Peace" negotiations bicentenary; $1.40, Washington 250th birth anniv.

195 "Virgin with Garlands" (detail) (Rubens) and Princess Diana with Prince William

196 Princess Diana and Prince William

1982 (30 Nov). *Christmas. T* **195** *and similar horiz designs depicting different details from Rubens' painting "Virgin with Garlands". P* 13½ × 14.
856 35 c. multicoloured 35 35
857 48 c. multicoloured 55 55
858 60 c. multicoloured 65 65
859 $1.70, multicoloured . . . . 1·60 1·60
MS860 104 × 83 mm. 60 c × 4. Designs, each 27 × 32 mm, forming complete painting "Virgin with Garlands". P 13 × 13½ . . . . 2·50 2·75

1982 (30 Nov). *Christmas. Birth of Prince William of Wales. Children's Charity. Sheet* 73 × 59 *mm. P* 13.
MS861 **196** 75 c. + 5 c. multicoloured 85 95
No. **MS**861 comes with 4 different background designs showing details from painting "Virgin with Garlands" (Rubens).

197 Statue of Tangaroa

198 Scouts using Map and Compass

1983 (14 Mar). *Commonwealth Day. T* **197** *and similar vert designs. Multicoloured. P* 14 × 13½.
862 60 c. Type **197** 55 60
863 60 c. Rarotonga oranges 55 60
864 60 c. Rarotonga airport 55 60
865 60 c. Prime Minister Sir Thomas Davis . . 55 60
Nos. 862/5 were issued together, *se-tenant*, in blocks of four throughout the sheet.

1983 (5 Apr). *75th Anniv of Boy Scout Movement and 125th Birth Anniv of Lord Baden-Powell. T* **198** *and similar vert designs. Multicoloured. P* 13.
866 12 c. Type **198** 10 12
867 12 c. Hiking 10 12
868 36 c. Campfire cooking 30 35
869 36 c. Erecting tent 30 35
870 48 c. Hauling on rope 40 45
871 48 c. Using bos'n's chair 40 45
872 60 c. Digging hole for sapling 55 60
873 60 c. Planting sapling 55 60
866/73 . . . . *Set of* 8 2·50 2·75
MS874 161 × 132 mm. As Nos. 866/73, but each with a premium of 2 c. . . . . 2·50 2·75
The two designs of each value were printed together, *se-tenant*, in horizontal pairs throughout the sheets.

XV WORLD JAMBOREE
(199)

1983 (4 July). *15th World Scout Jamboree, Alberta, Canada. Nos.* 866/74 *optd with T* **199** *(Nos.* 875, 877, 879, 881*) or with* "ALBERTA, CANADA 1983" *(others).*
875 12 c. Type **198** 10 15
876 12 c. Hiking 10 15
877 36 c. Campfire cooking 30 35
878 36 c. Erecting tent 30 35
879 48 c. Hauling on rope 40 45
880 48 c. Using bos'n chair 40 45
881 60 c. Digging hole for sapling 55 60
882 60 c. Planting sapling 55 60
875/82 . . . . *Set of* 8 2·50 2·75
MS883 161 × 132 mm. As Nos. 875/82, but each with a premium of 2 c. . . . . 2·50 2·75
The two designs of each value were printed together, *se-tenant*, in horizontal pairs throughout the sheet. In each such pair the left-hand design is overprinted with Type **199** and the right-hand with "ALBERTA, CANADA 1983".

18c
(200)

$5.60
(201)

1983 (12–30 Aug). *Various stamps surch. (a) Nos.* 733/6, 745/8, 753/ 64 *and* 773/6 *as T* **200.**
884 18 c. on 8 c. multicoloured (No. 733) . . 15 15
885 18 c. on 8 c. multicoloured (No. 734) . . 15 15
886 18 c. on 8 c. multicoloured (No. 735) . . 15 15
887 18 c. on 8 c. multicoloured (No. 736) . . 15 15
888 36 c. on 15 c. multicoloured (No. 745) . . 30 30
889 36 c. on 15 c. multicoloured (No. 746) . . 30 30
890 36 c. on 15 c. multicoloured (No. 747) . . 30 30
891 36 c. on 15 c. multicoloured (No. 748) . . 30 30
892 36 c. on 30 c. multicoloured (No. 757) . . 30 30
893 36 c. on 30 c. multicoloured (No. 758) . . 30 30
894 36 c. on 30 c. multicoloured (No. 759) . . 30 30
895 36 c. on 30 c. multicoloured (No. 760) . . 30 30
896 36 c. on 35 c. multicoloured (No. 761) (30.8.83) . . 30 30
897 36 c. on 35 c. multicoloured (No. 762) (30.8.83) . . 30 30
898 36 c. on 35 c. multicoloured (No. 763) (30.8.83) . . 30 30
899 36 c. on 35 c. multicoloured (No. 764) (30.8.83) . . 30 30
900 48 c. on 25 c. multicoloured (No. 753) . . 45 45
901 48 c. on 25 c. multicoloured (No. 754) . . 45 45
902 48 c. on 25 c. multicoloured (No. 755) . . 45 45
903 48 c. on 25 c. multicoloured (No. 756) . . 45 45
904 72 c. on 70 c. multicoloured (No. 773) . . 65 65
905 72 c. on 70 c. multicoloured (No. 774) . . 65 65
906 72 c. on 70 c. multicoloured (No. 775) . . 65 65
907 72 c. on 70 c. multicoloured (No. 776) . . 65 65

(b) Nos. 788/9, 813, 835/6 *and* 854, *as T* **201** *in gold*
908 96 c. on $1.40, George Washington . . 1·25 1·25
909 96 c. on $2 Prince Charles and Lady Diana Spencer . . . . 7·50 5·00
a. Surch double £125
b. Error. Surch on No. 840 . . . . 15·00
ba. Pair, Nos. 909 b/c . . . . 30·00
c. Error. Surch on No. 841 . . . . 15·00
910 96 c. on $2·50 Princess Diana (inscr "21st Birthday") (30.8.83) . . . . 2·50 2·50
911 96 c. on $2.50. As No. 910 but inscr "1 July 1982" (30.8.83) . . . . 2·50 2·50
912 $5.60 on $6 *Stylaster echinatus* . . . . 5·50 5·00
913 $5.60 on $10 *Melithaea albitincta* (30.8.83) . . 4·50 4·50
884/913 . . . . *Set of* 30 30·00 27·00
The surcharge on No. 908 is printed in gold, on a black background, over the old value.

202 Union Flag

203 Dish Aerial, Satellite Earth Station

1983 (9 Sept). *Cook Islands Flags and Ensigns. T* **202** *and similar horiz designs. Multicoloured. P* 13½ × 14. *(a) Postage. Gold frames.*
914 6 c. Type **202** 5 5
915 6 c. Group Federal flag 5 5
916 12 c. Raratonga ensign 10 12
917 12 c. Flag of New Zealand 10 12
918 15 c. Cook Islands' flag (1973–79) . . 12 15
919 15 c. Cook Islands' National flag . . 12 15

(b) Air. Silver frames and backgrounds changed
920 20 c. Type **202** 20 25
921 20 c. Group Federal flag 20 25
922 30 c. Raratonga ensign 25 30
923 30 c. Flag of New Zealand 25 30
924 35 c. Cook Islands' flag (1973–79) . . 30 35
925 35 c. Cook Islands' National flag . . 30 35
914/25 . . . . *Set of* 12 1·75 2·00
MS926 Two sheets, each 132 × 120 mm. (a) Nos. 914/19; (b) Nos. 920/5. P 13 . . . . 1·90 2·25
The two designs of each value were issued as *se-tenant* horizontal pairs within the sheets.

1983 (10 Oct). *World Communications Year. T* **203** *and similar vert designs showing satellites. P* 13.
927 36 c. multicoloured 30 35
928 48 c. multicoloured 45 45
929 60 c. multicoloured 55 60
930 96 c. multicoloured 85 90
MS931 90 × 65 mm. $2 multicoloured . . . . 1·75 1·90

204 "La Belle Jardinière"

205 Montgolfier Balloon 1783

1983 (14 Nov). *Christmas. 500th Birth Anniv of Raphael. T* **204** *and similar vert designs. Multicoloured. P* 14 × 13½.
932 12 c. Type **204** 10 12
933 18 c. "Madonna and Child with Five Saints" . . 20 25
934 36 c. "Madonna and Child with St. John" . . 30 35
935 48 c. "Madonna of the Fish" 40 45
936 60 c. "The Madonna of the Baldacchino" . . 55 60
MS937 139 × 113 mm. As Nos. 932/6 but each with a premium of 3 c. . . . . 1·60 1·75
Nos. 932/6 were each printed in small sheets of 5 stamps and 1 label.

1983 (9 Dec). *Christmas. 500th Birth Anniv of Raphael. Children's Charity. Designs as Nos.* 932/6 *in separate miniature sheets* 66 × 82 *mm., each with a face value of* 85 c. + 5 c. *P* 13.
MS938 As Nos. 932/6 . . *Set of* 5 *sheets* 4·00

1984 (16 Jan). *Bicentenary of Manned Flight* (1983). *T* **205** *and similar vert designs. Multicoloured. P* 13.
939 36 c. Type **205** 30 35
940 48 c. Adorne's ascent, Strasbourg, 1784 . . 40 45
941 60 c. Balloon driven by sails, 1785 . . 55 60
942 72 c. Ascent of man on horse, 1798 . . 70 75
943 96 c. Godard's aerial acrobatics, 1850 . . 85 90
MS944 104 × 85 mm. $2.50, Blanchard and Jeffries crossing Channel, 1785 . . . . 2·25
MS945 122 × 132 mm. As Nos. 939/43 but each with a premium of 5 c. . . . . 3·00
Nos. 939/43 were each printed in small sheets of 5 stamps and 1 label.

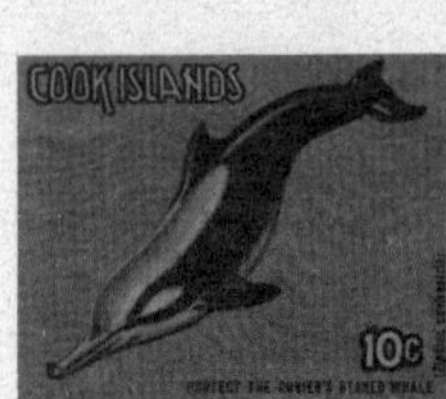

206 Cuvier's Beaked Whale

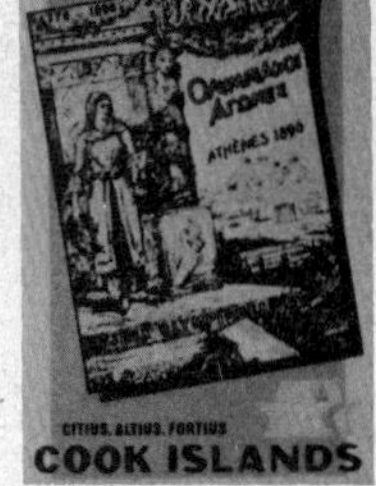

207 Athens, 1896

1984 (10 Feb). *Save the Whales. T* **206** *and similar horiz designs. Multicoloured. P* 13.
946 10 c. Type **206** 8 10
947 18 c. Risso's Dolphin 20 25
948 20 c. True's Beaked Whale 20 25
949 24 c. Long-finned Pilot Whale 20 25
950 30 c. Narwhal 25 30
951 36 c. Beluga 30 35
952 42 c. Common Dolphin 35 40
953 48 c. Commerson's Dolphin 45 50
954 60 c. Bottle-nosed Dolphin 55 60
955 72 c. Sowerby's Whale 70 75
956 96 c. Common Porpoise 90 95
957 $2 Boutu . . . . 1·75 1·90
946/57 . . . . *Set of* 12 5·50 6·00

1984 (8 Mar). *Olympic Games, Los Angeles. T* **207** *and similar vert designs showing official posters of earlier Games. Multicoloured. P* 13½.
958 18 c. Type **207** 15 20
959 24 c. Paris, 1900 . . . . 20 25
960 36 c. St. Louis, 1904 . . . . 30 35
961 48 c. London, 1948 . . . . 40 45
962 60 c. Tokyo, 1964 . . . . 45 50
963 72 c. Berlin, 1936 . . . . 55 60
964 96 c. Rome, 1960 . . . . 75 80
965 $1.20 Los Angeles, 1930 . . . . 90 95
958/65 . . . . *Set of* 8 3·50 3·75

208 *Siphonogorgia*

$3.60
(209)

1984 (23 Mar–10 Aug). *Corals (2nd series). (a) Designs as No.* 713 *etc, but with redrawn frames and inscriptions as in T* **208**. *Multicoloured. P* 13.
966 1 c. Type **208** 5 5
967 2 c. *Millepora alcicornis* 5 5
968 3 c. *Distichopora violacea* 5 5
969 5 c. *Ptilosarcus gurneyi* 5 5
970 10 c. *Lobophyllia bemprichii* 8 10
971 12 c. *Sarcophyton digitatum* 8 10
972 14 c. *Pavona praetorta* 10 12
973 18 c. *Junceella gemmacea* 12 15
974 20 c. *Stylaster* 15 20

975 24 c. *Stylophora pistillata* 20 25
976 30 c. *Palauastrea ramosa* 20 25
977 36 c. *Melithaea albitincta* 25 30
978 40 c. *Stylaster echinatus* 30 35
979 42 c. *Fungia fungites* 30 35
980 48 c. *Gonipora* 35 40
981 50 c. *Melithaea squamata* (15 May) 35 40
982 52 c. *Bellonella indica* (15 May) 35 40
983 55 c. *Plerogyra sinuosa* (15 May) 45 50
984 60 c. *Tubastraea* (15 May) 45 50
985 70 c. *Heliofungia actiniformis* (15 May) .. 50 55
986 85 c. *Caulastraea echinulata* (15 May) .. 60 65
987 96 c. *Porites andrewsi* (15 May) 70 75
988 $1.10, *Pectinia alcicornis* (15 May) .. 80 85
989 $1.20, *Dendrophyllia gracilis* (15 May) .. 90 95

(b) Nos. 785/9 surch as T **209** *in gold on black*
990 $3.60, on $2 *Gonipora* (28 June) .. .. 2·60 2·75
991 $4.20 on $3 *Heliofungia actiniformis* (28 June) .. .. 3·00 3·25
992 $5 on $4 *Stylophora pistillata* (28 June) .. 3·75 4·00
993 $7.20 on $6 *Stylaster echinatus* (20 July) 5·25 5·50
994 $9.60 on $10 *Melithaea albitincta* (10 Aug) 7·00 7·25
966/94 .. .. *Set of* 29 25·50 27·50

Equestrian
Team Dressage
Germany

(210)

1984 (24 Aug). *Olympic Gold Medal Winners. Nos.* 963/5 *optd as T* **210**.
995 72 c. Berlin, 1936 (optd T **210**) 60 65
996 96 c. Rome, 1960 (optd "Decathlon Daley Thompson Great Britain") 80 85
997 $1.20 Los Angeles, 1930 (optd "Four Gold Medals Carl Lewis U.S.A." .. .. 1·00 1·10

211 Capt. Cook's Cottage, Melbourne

1984 (20 Sept). *"Ausipex" International Stamp Exhibition, Melbourne. T* **211** *and similar horiz designs. Multicoloured. P* 13.
998 36 c. Type **211** 30 35
999 48 c. "The *Endeavour* careened for Repairs" (Sydney Parkinson) 40 45
1000 60 c. "Cook's landing at Botany Bay" (E. Phillips Fox) 50 55
1001 $2 "Capt. James Cook" (John Webber) .. 1·75 1·90
MS1002 140 × 100 mm. As Nos. 998/1001, but each stamp with a face value of 90 c. .. .. 3·00 3·25

OFFICIAL STAMPS

O.H.M.S. (O 1) O.H.M.S. (O 2)

1975 (17 Mar–19 May). *Nos.* 228/31, 233, 235/7, 239/40, 243/5 *and* 246c/7 *optd with Type* O 1 *(5, 10, 18, 25 and 30 c. surch also), in black and silver*
O 1 1 c. *Hibiscus syriacus* .. ..
O 2 2 c. Frangipani .. ..
O 3 3 c. "Suva Queen" .. ..
O 4 4 c. Water Lily .. ..
O 5 5 c. on 2½ c. *Clitoria ternatea* .. .. ..
O 6 8 c. *Allamanda cathartica* .. .. ..
O 7 10 c. on 6 c. Hibiscus .. ..
O 8 18 c. on 20 c. Thunbergia .. .. ..
O 9 25 c. on 9 c. Stephanotis .. .. ..
O10 30 c. on 15 c. Frangipani .. .. ..
O11 50 c. *Gardinia taitensis* .. .. ..
O12 $1 Type **80** .. ..
O13 $2 Type **80** .. ..
O14 $4 Type **81** (19 May) .. .. ..
O15 $6 Type **81** (19 May) .. .. ..
O1/15 .. .. *Set of* 15 † 30·00
These stamps were only sold to the public cancelled-to-order and not in unused condition.

1978 (19 Oct)–**79**. *Nos.* 466/7, 474, 478/81, 484/5, 542 *and* 568/9 *optd or surch (2, 5, 10, 15, 18 and 35 c.) as Type* O **2**.
O16 1 c. *Vasum tubinellus* (Silver) 5 5
O17 2 c. on ½ c. Type **141** 5 5
O18 5 c. on ½ c. Type **141** 5 5
O19 10 c. on 8 c. *Bursa granularis* (Silver) .. 8 10
O20 15 c. on 50 c. *Conus textile* (Silver) .. 10 12
O21 18 c. on 60 c. *Oliva sericea* (Silver) .. 12 15
O22 25 c. *Gloripallium pallium* 15 20
O23 30 c. *Conus miles* (Silver) 20 25
O24 35 c. on 60 c. *Oliva sericea* (Silver) .. 25 30
O25 50 c. *Conus textile* (Silver) 30 35
O26 60 c. *Oliva sericea* (Silver) 40 45
O27 $1 Queen and Prince Philip (Silver) .. 2·00 1·00
O28 $1 Royal Visit, 1974 (Silver) .. .. 2·00 1·00
O29 $2 Captain Cook and *Resolution* .. 3·50 2·50
O30 $4 Queen Elizabeth II and seashells (15.2.79) .. .. 3·00 2·75
O31 $6 As $4 (15.2.79) .. .. .. 4·50 4·00
O16/31 .. .. *Set of* 16 15·00 12·00
These stamps were originally only sold to the public cancelled-to-order and not in unused condition. They were made available to overseas collectors in mint condition during 1980.

AITUTAKI

Stamps of COOK ISLANDS were used in Aitutaki from 1892 until 1903.

PRICES FOR STAMPS ON COVER TO 1945
Nos. 1/8 *from* × 4
Nos. 9/14 *from* × 3
Nos. 15/29 *from* × 4
Nos. 30/2 *from* × 6

A. NEW ZEALAND DEPENDENCY

The island of Aitutaki, previously under British protection, was annexed by New Zealand on 11 June 1901.

Stamps of New Zealand overprinted or surcharged.

AITUTAKI. (1) Ava Pene. (2) ½d.
Tai Pene. (3) 1d. Rua Pene Ma Te Ava. (4) 2½d.
Toru Pene. (5) 3d. Ono Pene. (6) 6d.
Tai Tiringi. (7) 1s.

1903 (June)–**11**. 1902 *issue surch with T* 1 *at top, and T* 2 *to* 7 *at foot. W* **41**. *(a) P* 14.
1 **23** ½d. green (R.) .. .. 3·00 6·00
2 **40** 1d. carmine (B.) .. .. 4·00 7·00
3 **27** 2½d. deep blue (R.)(9.11) .. .. .. 4·50 8·50
a. "Ava" without stop £130 £160

(b) P 11
4 **27** 2½d. blue (R.) .. .. 5·50 8·50
5 **28** 3d. yellow-brown (B.) .. .. .. 5·50 13·00
6 **31** 6d. rose-red (B.) .. .. .. 12·00 23·00
7 **34** 1s. bright red (B.) .. .. .. 55·00 70·00
a. "Tiringi" without stop £250 £325
8 1s. orange-red (B.) .. .. .. 65·00 80·00
a. "Tiringi" without stop £350 £375
b. Orange-brown £120 £130
c. Do. "Tiringi" without stop £700 £750
With the exception of No. 3, the above were issued in Auckland on 12 June and in Aitutaki on 29 June 1903.

AITUTAKI.

Ono Pene.

(8)

1911–16. ½d. *and* 1d. *surch as on Nos.* 1/2, 6d. *and* 1s. *as T* 8.
9 **50** ½d. green (R.) (9.11) .. .. .. 55 2·25
10 **51** 1d. carmine (B.) (2.13) .. .. .. 1·25 3·25
11 **52** 6d. carmine (B.) (*p* 14 × 14½)(23.5.16) 35·00 55·00
12 1s. vermilion (B.) (*p* 14 × 14½) (9.14) 55·00 90·00

1916–17. *King George V stamps surch as T* **8**. *P* 14 × 14½.
13 **60** 6d. carmine (B.) (6.6.16) .. .. 7·50 16·50
a. Perf 14 × 13½ .. .. .. 17·00 35·00
b. Vert pair. Nos. 13/13a .. .. 48·00 65·00
14 1s. vermilion (B.) (3.17) .. .. 30·00 50·00
a. Perf 14 × 13½ .. .. .. 28·00 50·00
b. Vert pair. Nos. 14/14a £130 £170
c. "Tai" without dot £200 £190
d. "Tiringi" no dot on second "i" .. £200 £200
e. "Tiringi" no dot on third "i" £250 £275

1917–18. *King George V stamps optd* "AITUTAKI", *only, as in T* **8**. *W* **41**. *P* 14 × 14½.
15 **60** 2½d. deep blue (R.) (12.18) .. .. 1·50 5·50
a. Perf 14 × 13½ .. .. .. 2·00 5·50
b. Vert pair. Nos. 15/15a .. .. 70·00 95·00
16 3d. chocolate (B.)(1.18) .. .. 1·50 6·50
a. Perf 14 × 13½ .. .. .. 2·50 8·00
b. Vert pair. Nos. 16/16a .. .. 65·00 90·00
17 6d. carmine (B.)(11.17) .. .. 4·50 8·00
a. Perf 14 × 13½ .. .. .. 8·50 18·00
b. Vert pair. Nos. 17/17a .. .. 70·00 95·00
18 1s. vermilion (B.)(11.17) .. .. 9·00 17·00
a. Perf 14 × 13½ .. .. .. 12·00 22·00
b. Vert pair. Nos. 18/18a .. .. 80·00 £110

1917–20. *Optd* "AITUTAKI" *as in T* **8**. *Typo. W* **41**. *P* 14 × 15.
19 **60*b*** ½d. green (R.) (2.20) .. .. .. 85 1·75
20 **51** 1d. carmine (B.)(5.20) .. .. .. 1·25 2·50
21 **60*b*** 1½d. slate (R.)(11.17) .. .. .. 2·25 7·00
22 1½d. orange-brown (R.) (2.19) .. 1·25 6·00
23 3d. chocolate (B.)(6.19) .. .. 4·25 9·50

(Des and recess Perkins, Bacon & Co)

1920 (23 Aug). *As Types of Cook Islands, but inscr* "AITUTAKI". *No wmk. P* 14.
24 **9** ½d. black and green .. .. .. 2·00 4·00
25 **10** 1d. black and dull carmine .. .. 1·50 3·50
26 **11** 1½d. black and sepia .. .. .. 3·00 5·00
27 **12** 3d. black and deep blue .. .. 2·00 6·50
28 **13** 6d. red-brown and slate .. .. 5·00 13·00
29 **14** 1s. black and purple .. .. .. 7·50 15·00
24/29 .. .. *Set of* 6 19·00 42·00

(Recess Govt Printing Office, Wellington)

1924–27. *As Types of Cook Islands, but inscr* "AITUTAKI". *W* **41**. *P* 14.
30 **9** ½d. black and green (5.27) .. .. 1·75 4·00
31 **10** 1d. black and deep carmine (10.24) .. 1·40 3·00
32 **16** 2½d. black and dull blue (10.27) .. .. 6·00 14·00

Cook Islands stamps superseded those of Aitutaki on 15 March 1932. Separate issues were resumed in 1972.

B. PART OF COOK ISLANDS

On 9 August 1972, Aitutaki became a Port of Entry into the Cook Islands, and at the close of business on the previous day, Cook Islands stamps were withdrawn from sale there. Whilst remaining part of the Cook Islands, Aitutaki has a separate postal service.

PRINTERS. Stamps of Aitutaki were printed in photogravure by Heraclio Fournier, Spain, *unless otherwise stated*. All issues are on paper treated with fluorescent security markings, and with synthetic gum. The fluorescent markings can be found inverted or omitted.

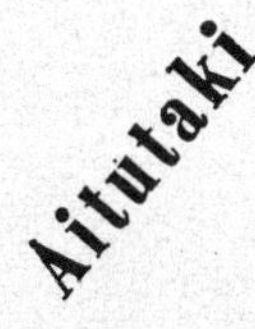

(9) Aitutaki (10)

(Optd by Govt Printer, Wellington)

1972 (9 Aug). *Nos.* 227B *etc. of Cook Is. optd with T* **9** *(applied horizontally on $1), by New Zealand Govt Printer*.
33 ½ c. Type **79** .. .. 50 1·00
34 1 c. *Hibiscus syriacus* .. .. .. 1·00 2·00
35 2½ c. *Clitoria ternatea* .. .. .. 6·00 9·00
36 4 c. Water Lily (No. 233B) .. .. 1·00 1·00
37 5 c. *Bauhinia bi-pinnata rosea* .. .. 7·50 10·00
38 10 c. *Poinciana regia flamboyant* .. .. 7·50 7·50
39 20 c. Thunbergia .. .. 1·25 1·25
40 25 c. Canna Lily .. .. 1·25 1·25
41 50 c. *Gardinia taitensis* .. .. .. 7·00 4·50
42 $1 Type **80** .. .. 9·50 8·50
*a. Shade** .. ..
33/42 .. .. *Set of* 10 38·00 42·00
* No. 42*a* has the border flowers predominantly in a carmine colour instead of scarlet, and may be due to a missing yellow colour.

1972 (27 Oct). *Christmas. Nos.* 406/8 *of Cook. Is. optd in silver with T* **10**.
43 **130** 1 c. multicoloured 5 5
44 – 5 c. multicoloured 20 30
45 – 10 c. multicoloured 30 35

1972 (20 Nov). *Royal Silver Wedding. As Nos.* 413 *and* 415 *of Cook Is., but inscr* "COOK ISLANDS Aitutaki".
46 **131** 5 c. black and silver .. .. .. 3·50 2·75
47 – 15 c. black and silver .. .. .. 2·00 1·50

AITUTAKI (11) AITUTAKI (12)

1972 (24 Nov). *No.* 245B *of Cook Is. optd with T* **11** *by Govt Printer, Rarotonga*.
48 **80** $2 multicoloured .. .. .. 2·50 2·50
a. Optd "AJTUTAKI" for "AITUTAKI" (R.2/4) .. .. 18·00
b. On No. 245A (gum arabic printing) .. 50·00

1972 (11 Dec). *Nos.* 227B *etc of Cook Is. optd with T* **12**, *by Heraclio Fournier*.
49 ½ c. Type **79** 5 5
50 1 c. *Hibiscus syriacus* 8 8
51 2½ c. *Clitoria ternatea* 10 10
52 4 c. Water Lily (No. 233B) 12 12
53 5 c. *Bauhinia bi-pinnata rosea* 12 12
54 10 c. *Poinciana regia flamboyant* 25 25
55 20 c. Thunbergia 45 50
56 25 c. Canna Lily 55 65
57 50 c. *Gardinia taitensis* .. .. .. 1·25 1·40
58 $1 Type **80** .. .. 2·75 3·00
49/58 .. .. *Set of* 10 5·00 5·50

13 "Christ Mocked" (Grünewald) AITUTAKI (14)

1973 (6 Apr). *Easter. T* **13** *and similar vert designs. Multicoloured. P* 13.

No.	Description		
59	1 c. Type **13**	5	5
60	1 c. "St. Veronica" (Van der Weyden)	5	5
61	1 c. "The Crucified Christ with Virgin Mary, Saints and Angels" (Raphael)	5	5
62	1 c. "Resurrection" (Piero della Francesca)	5	5
63	5 c. "The Last Supper" (Master of Amiens)	15	15
64	5 c. "Condemnation" (Holbein)	15	15
65	5 c. "Christ on the Cross" (Rubens)	15	15
66	5 c. "Resurrection" (El Greco)	15	15
67	10 c. "Disrobing of Christ" (El Greco)	25	25
68	10 c. "St. Veronica" (Van Oostsanen)	25	25
69	10 c. "Christ on the Cross" (Rubens)	25	25
70	10 c. "Resurrection" (Bouts)	25	25
59/70	*Set of* 12	1·60	1·60

Nos. 59/62, 63/6 and 67/70 were each printed together, *se-tenant*, in blocks of 4 throughout the sheet.

1973 (14 May). *Silver Wedding Coinage. Nos.* 417/23 *of Cook Is. optd in silver and black as T* **14**.

No.	Description		
71	1 c. black, rosy carmine and gold	5	5
72	2 c. black, bright blue and gold	8	8
73	5 c. black, green and silver	15	15
74	10 c. black, royal blue and silver	25	25
75	20 c. black, deep blue-green and silver	50	50
76	50 c. black, carmine and silver	1·25	1·25
77	$1 black, bright blue and silver	2·00	2·00
71/7	*Set of* 7	3·75	3·75

TENTH ANNIVERSARY
CESSATION
OF
NUCLEAR TESTING
TREATY

(15)

16 Red Hibiscus and Princess Anne

1973 (13 Aug). *Tenth Anniv of Treaty Banning Nuclear Testing. Nos.* 236B, 238B, 240B *and* 243B *of Cook Is. optd with T* **15** *and T* **12** *together.*

No.	Description		
78	8 c. *Allamanda cathartica*	25	25
79	10 c. *Poinciana regia flamboyant*	30	30
80	20 c. Thunbergia	65	65
81	50 c. *Gardinia taitensis*	1·50	1·50

1973 (14 Nov). *Royal Wedding. T* **16** *and similar horiz design. Multicoloured. P* 13½ × 14.

No.	Description		
82	25 c. Type **16**	30	35
83	30 c. Capt. Phillips and Blue Hibiscus	35	35
MS84	114 × 65 mm. Nos. 82/3. P 13	1·25	1·25

17 "Virgin and Child" (Montagna)

18 *Murex ramosus*

1973 (10 Dec). *Christmas. T* **17** *and similar vert designs showing "The Virgin and Child" by the artists listed. Multicoloured. P* 13½.

No.	Description		
85	1 c. Type **17**	5	5
86	1 c. Crivelli	5	5
87	1 c. Van Dyck	5	5
88	1 c. Perugino	5	5
89	5 c. Veronese	20	20
90	5 c. Veronese	20	20
91	5 c. Cima	20	20
92	5 c. Memling	20	20
93	10 c. Memling	25	25
94	10 c. Del Colle	25	25
95	10 c. Raphael	25	25
96	10 c. Lotto	25	25
85/96	*Set of* 12	1·75	1·75

Nos. 85/8, 89/92 and 93/6 were each printed together, *se-tenant*, in blocks of 4 throughout the sheet.

1974 (31 Jan)–**75**. *T* **18** *and similar horiz designs showing sea-shells. Multicoloured. P* 13.

No.	Description		
97	½ c. Type **18**	5	5
98	1 c. *Nautilus macromphallus*	10	5
99	2 c. *Harpa major*	12	5
100	3 c. *Phalium strigatum*	15	5
101	4 c. *Cypraea talpa*	15	5
102	5 c. *Mitra stictica*	15	5
103	8 c. *Charonia tritonis*	20	8
104	10 c. *Murex triremis*	20	10
105	20 c. *Oliva sericea*	40	20
106	25 c. *Tritonalia rubeta*	45	25
107	60 c. *Strombus latissimus*	80	70
108	$1 *Biplex perca*	1·25	1·10
109	$2 Queen Elizabeth II and *Terebra maculata* (20.1.75)	3·00	3·75
110	$5 Queen Elizabeth II and *Cypraea hesitata* (28.2.75)	7·00	7·00
97/110	*Set of* 14	12·50	12·00

Nos. 109/110 are larger, 53 × 25 mm.

19 Bligh and *Bounty*

(Des G. Vasarhelyi)

1974 (11 Apr). *William Bligh's Discovery of Aitutaki. T* **19** *and similar horiz designs. Multicoloured. P* 13½.

No.	Description		
114	1 c. Type **19**	25	20
115	1 c. *Bounty*	25	20
116	5 c. Bligh, and *Bounty* at Aitutaki	60	50
117	5 c. Aitutaki chart of 1856	60	50
118	8 c. Capt. Cook and *Resolution*	75	75
119	8 c. Map of Aitutaki and inset location map	75	75
114/119	*Set of* 6	3·00	2·50

Nos. 114/15, 116/17 and 118/19 were each printed together, *se-tenant*, in horizontal and vertical pairs throughout the sheet.

See also Nos. 123/8.

20 Aitutaki Stamps of 1903, and Map

21 "Virgin and Child" (Hugo van der Goes)

1974 (15 July). *Centenary of Universal Postal Union. T* **20** *and similar horiz design. Multicoloured. P* 13½ × 14.

No.	Description		
120	25 c. Type **20**	75	75
121	50 c. Stamps of 1903 and 1920, and map	1·00	1·00
MS122	66 × 75 mm. Nos. 120/1. P 13	2·50	2·75

Each value was issued in sheets of 5 stamps and 1 label.

1974 (9 Sept). *Air. As Nos.* 114/119, *but larger* (46 × 26 *mm*), *denominations changed, and inscr* "AIR MAIL".

No.	Description		
123	10 c. Type **19**	80	60
124	10 c. *Bounty*	80	60
125	25 c. Bligh, and *Bounty* at Aitutaki	1·10	90
126	25 c. Aitutaki chart of 1856	1·10	90
127	30 c. Capt. Cook and *Resolution*	1·10	1·00
128	30 c. Map of Aitutaki and inset location map	1·10	1·00
123/8	*Set of* 6	5·50	4·50

Nos. 123/4, 125/6 and 127/8 were each printed together, *se-tenant*, in horizontal and vertical pairs throughout the sheet.

1974 (11 Oct). *Christmas. T* **21** *and similar vert designs showing "Virgin and Child" by the artists listed. Multicoloured. P* 13.

No.	Description		
129	1 c. Type **21**	5	5
130	5 c. Bellini	15	15
131	8 c. Gerard David	25	25
132	10 c. Antonello da Messina	30	30
133	25 c. Joos van Cleve	45	45
134	30 c. Master of the Life of St. Catherine	50	50
129/34	*Set of* 6	1·50	1·50
MS135	127 × 134 mm. Nos. 129/34	1·90	2·00

Each value was issued in sheets of 15 stamps and 1 label.

22 Churchill as Schoolboy

+1c

(23)

1974 (29 Nov). *Birth Centenary of Sir Winston Churchill. T* **22** *and similar vert designs. Multicoloured. P* 13½.

No.	Description		
136	10 c. Type **22**	30	25
137	25 c. Churchill as young man	60	50
138	30 c. Churchill with troops	75	60
139	50 c. Churchill painting	1·50	1·25
140	$1 Giving "V" sign	2·75	2·25
MS141	115 × 108 mm. Nos. 136/40 plus *se-tenant* label. P 13	7·00	7·00

Each value was issued in sheets of 5 stamps and 1 label.

1974 (2 Dec). *Children's Christmas Fund. Nos.* 129/34 *surch with T* **23**.

No.	Description		
142	1 c. + 1 c. multicoloured	5	5
143	5 c. + 1 c. multicoloured	15	15
144	8 c. + 1 c. multicoloured	20	20
145	10 c. + 1 c. multicoloured	30	30
146	25 c. + 1 c. multicoloured	45	45
147	30 c. + 1 c. multicoloured	50	50
142/7	*Set of* 6	1·50	1·50

24 Soviet and U.S. Flags

25 "Madonna and Child with Saints Francis and John" (Lorenzetti)

1975 (24 July). *"Apollo-Soyuz" Space Project. T* **24** *and similar horiz design. Multicoloured. P* 13 × 14.

No.	Description		
148	25 c. Type **24**	70	70
149	50 c. Daedalus and space capsule	1·25	1·25
MS150	123 × 61 mm. Nos. 148/9	2·25	2·25

Each value was issued in sheets of 8 stamps and 1 label.

1975 (24 Nov). *Christmas. T* **25** *and similar vert designs. Multicoloured. P* 13½.

No.	Description		
151	6 c.	20	20
152	6 c. } Type **25**	20	20
153	6 c.	20	20
154	7 c.	20	20
155	7 c. } "Adoration of the Kings" (Van der Weyden)	20	20
156	7 c.	20	20
157	15 c.	30	30
158	15 c. } "Madonna and Child Enthroneth with Saints Onufrius and John the Baptist" (Montagna)	30	30
159	15 c.	30	30
160	20 c.	35	35
161	20 c. } "Adoration of the Shepherds" (Reni)	35	35
162	20 c.	35	35
151/62	*Set of* 12	2·75	2·75
MS163	104 × 201 mm. Nos. 151/62. P 13	3·50	3·50

Nos. 151/3, 154/6, 157/9 and 160/2 were each printed together, *se-tenant*, in horizontal strips of 3 throughout the sheet, forming composite designs. Type **25** shows the left-hand stamp of the 6 c. design.

1975 (19 Dec). *Children's Christmas Fund. Nos.* 151/62 *surch as T* **23**, *in silver.*

No.	Description		
164	6 c. + 1 c.	20	20
165	6 c. + 1 c. } Type **25**	20	20
166	6 c. + 1 c.	20	20
167	7 c. + 1 c.	20	20
168	7 c. + 1 c. } "Adoration of the Kings" (Van der Weyden)	20	20
169	7 c. + 1 c.	20	20
170	15 c. + 1 c.	30	30
171	15 c. + 1 c. } "Madonna and Child" (Montagna)	30	30
172	15 c. + 1 c.	30	30
173	20 c. + 1 c.	35	35
174	20 c. + 1 c. } "Adoration of the Shepherds" (Reni)	35	35
175	20 c. + 1 c.	35	35
164/75	*Set of* 12	2·75	2·75

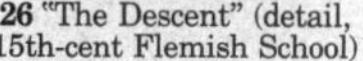

26 "The Descent" (detail, 15th-cent Flemish School)

27 "The Declaration of Independence" (detail)

1976 (5 Apr). *Easter. Various vert designs showing portions of "The Descent" as in T* **26**. *P* 13.

No.	Type	Description		
176	**26**	15 c. multicoloured	35	35
177	–	30 c. multicoloured	55	55
178	–	35 c. multicoloured	60	60
MS179		87 × 67 mm. Nos. 176/8 forming a complete picture of "The Descent". P 12½ × 13	1·90	2·00

Stamps from No. **MS**179 have no borders and are therefore smaller than stamps from the sheets.

Each value was issued in sheets of 8 stamps and 1 label.

1976 (1 June). *Bicentenary of American Revolution. T* **27** *and similar vert designs showing paintings by John Trumbull. Multicoloured. P* 13.

No.	Description		
180	30 c.	90	90
181	30 c. } Type **27**	90	90
182	30 c.	90	90
183	35 c.	1·00	1·00
184	35 c. } "The Surrender of Lord Cornwallis at Yorktown"	1·00	1·00
185	35 c.	1·00	1·00
186	50 c.	1·25	1·25
187	50 c. } "The Resignation of General Washington"	1·25	1·25
188	50 c.	1·25	1·25
180/8	*Set of* 9	8·50	8·50
MS189	132 × 120 mm. Nos. 180/8. P 13	9·00	9·50

Nos. 180/2, 183/5 and 186/8 were each printed together, *se-tenant*, in horizontal strips of 3 throughout the sheet, forming composite designs. Each sheet includes 3 stamp-size labels. Type **27** shows the left-hand stamp of the 30 c. design.

Stamps from No. **MS**189 have their borders in a different colour and come with a different inscription.

28 Cycling

1976 (15 July). *Olympic Games, Montreal. T* **28** *and similar horiz designs. Multicoloured. P* 13 × 14.

No.	Description		
190	15 c. Type **28**	35	35
191	35 c. Sailing	65	65
192	60 c. Hockey	85	85
193	70 c. Sprinting	95	95
MS194	107 × 97 mm. Nos. 190/3	3·25	3·25

Stamps from No. **MS**194 have borders of a different colour.

Each value was issued in sheets of 5 stamps and 1 label.

ROYAL VISIT JULY 1976

(29)

30 "The Visitation"

1976 (30 July). *Visit of Queen Elizabeth to the U.S.A. Nos.* 190/**MS**194 *optd with T* **29**.

195 15 c. Type **28** 40 35
196 35 c. Sailing 70 65
197 60 c. Hockey .. .. 1·25 1·10
198 70 c. Sprinting .. .. 1·40 1·25
MS199 107 × 97 mm. Nos. 195/8 .. .. .. 3·25 3·50

1976 (18 Oct). *Christmas. T* **30** *and similar vert designs. Figures in gold; background colours given. P* 13.

200 6 c. } deep bluish green 15 15
201 6 c. } .. 15 15
202 7 c. } dull brown-purple 20 20
203 7 c. } .. 20 20
204 15 c. } deep blue 30 30
205 15 c. } .. 30 30
206 20 c. } reddish violet 35 35
207 20 c. } .. 35 35
200/207 .. .. *Set of* 8 1·75 1·75
MS208 128 × 96 mm. As Nos. 200/207 but with borders on three sides .. .. 1·75 1·90

Designs:—7 c. "Angel and Shepherds"; 15 c. "The Holy Family"; 20 c. "The Magi".

Nos. 200/1, 202/3, 204/5 and 206/7 were each printed together, *se-tenant*, in horizontal pairs throughout the sheet, forming composite designs. Type **30** shows the left-hand stamp of the 6 c. design.

+1c

(31)

32 Alexander Graham Bell and First Telephone

1976 (19 Nov). *Children's Christmas Fund. Nos.* 200/**MS**208 *surch in silver as T* **31**.

209 6 c. + 1 c. } "The Visitation" 15 15
210 6 c. + 1 c. } .. 15 15
211 7 c. + 1 c. } "Angel and Shepherds" 20 20
212 7 c. + 1 c. } .. 20 20
213 15 c. + 1 c. } "The Holy Family" 30 30
214 15 c. + 1 c. } .. 30 30
215 20 c. + 1 c. } "The Magi" 35 35
216 20 c. + 1 c. } .. 35 35
209/16 .. .. *Set of* 8 1·75 1·75
MS217 128 × 96 mm. As Nos. 209/216 but with a premium of "+ 2 c." and borders on three sides .. 2·00 2·25

1977 (3 Mar). *Telephone Centenary* (1976). *T* **32** *and similar horiz design. P* 13.

218 25 c. black, gold and dull scarlet 45 45
219 70 c. black, gold and lilac .. .. .. 1·25 1·25
MS220 116 × 59 mm. As Nos. 218/19 but with different colours .. .. 1·75 1·90

Design:—70 c. Earth Station and satellite.

33 "Christ on the Cross" (detail)

1977 (31 Mar). *Easter and 400th Birth Anniv of Rubens. T* **33** *and similar horiz designs. Multicoloured. P* 13½ × 14.

221 15 c. Type **33** 50 35
222 20 c. "Lamentation for Christ" 55 40
223 35 c. "Christ with Straw" 65 60
MS224 115 × 57 mm. Nos. 221/3. P 13 × 12½ .. 1·60 1·75

Each value was issued in sheets of 8 stamps and 1 label.

34 Capt. Bligh, George III and H.M.S. *Bounty*

1977 (21 Apr). *Silver Jubilee. T* **34** *and similar horiz designs. Multicoloured. P* 13.

225 25 c. Type **34** 85 85
226 35 c. Rev. Williams, George IV and Aitutaki Church .. .. 1·10 1·10
227 50 c. Union Jack, Queen Victoria and island map .. .. 1·75 1·75
228 $1 Balcony scene, 1953 .. .. .. 3·50 3·50
MS229 130 × 87 mm. Nos. 225/8 but with gold borders. P 13½ × 13 .. .. 7·00 7·00

Each value was issued in sheets of 5 stamps and 1 label.

35 The Shepherds

+1c

(36)

1977 (14 Oct). *Christmas. T* **35** *and similar vert designs. Multicoloured. P* 13½ × 14.

230 6 c. } Type **35** 10 10
231 6 c. } .. 10 10
232 7 c. } The Holy Family 10 10
233 7 c. } .. 10 10
234 15 c. } The Three Kings with Virgin and 25 25
235 15 c. } Child 25 25
236 20 c. } Flight into Egypt 30 30
237 20 c. } .. 30 30
230/7 .. .. *Set of* 8 1·40 1·40
MS238 130 × 95 mm. Nos. 230/7 .. .. 1·50 1·60

Each design covers two stamps; Type **35** shows the left-hand stamp of the 6 c. design.

1977 (15 Nov). *Children's Christmas Fund. Nos.* 230/7 *surch with T* **36**.

239 6 c. + 1 c. } Type **35** 10 10
240 6 c. + 1 c. } .. 10 10
241 7 c. + 1 c. } The Holy Family 10 10
242 7 c. + 1 c. } .. 10 10
243 15 c. + 1 c. } The Three Kings with Virgin 25 25
244 15 c. + 1 c. } and Child 25 25
245 20 c. + 1 c. } Flight into Egypt 30 30
246 20 c. + 1 c. } .. 30 30
239/46 .. .. *Set of* 8 1·40 1·40
MS247 130 × 95 mm. As Nos. 239/46 but each with premium of "+ 2 c." .. .. 1·75 1·90

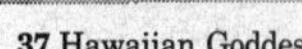

37 Hawaiian Goddess

38 "Christ on the Way to Calvary" (Martini)

1978 (19 Jan). *Bicentenary of Discovery of Hawaii. T* **37** *and similar multicoloured designs. P* 13½.

248 35 c. Type **37** 70 70
249 50 c. Figurehead of H.M.S. *Resolution* (*horiz*) 95 95
250 $1 Hawaiian temple figure .. .. .. 1·60 1·60
MS251 168 × 75 mm. Nos. 248/50 .. .. 3·50 3·50

1978 (17 Mar). *Easter. Details of Paintings from Louvre, Paris. T* **38** *and similar horiz designs. Multicoloured. P* 13½ × 14.

252 15 c. Type **38** 25 25
253 20 c. "Piéta of Avignon" (E. Quarton) .. 30 30
254 35 c. "Pilgrims at Emmaus" (Rembrandt) .. 50 50
MS255 108 × 83 mm. Nos. 252/4 .. .. 1·25 1·50

Each value was printed in two panes of 9 within the sheet, both panes including one *se-tenant* stamp-size label.

1978 (17 Mar). *Easter. Children's Charity. Designs as Nos.* 252/4, *but smaller* (34 × 26 *mm*) *and without margins, in separate miniature sheets* 75 × 58 *mm, each with a face value of* 50 c. + 5 c. *P* 14.

MS256 As Nos. 252/4 .. .. *Set of* 3 *sheets* 2·25 2·25

39 Yale of Beaufort

40 "Adoration of the Infant Jesus"

1978 (15 June). *25th Anniv of Coronation. T* **39** *and similar vert designs. Multicoloured. P* 13½ × 13.

257 $1 Type **39** .. .. 1·50 1·90
258 $1 Queen Elizabeth II .. .. .. 1·50 1·90
259 $1 Aitutaki ancestral statue .. .. .. 1·50 1·90
MS260 98 × 127 mm. Nos. 257/9 × 2 .. .. 8·00 10·00

Stamps from No. **MS**260 have coloured borders, the upper row in lavender and the lower in apple-green.

Nos. 257/9 were printed together, *se-tenant*, in small sheets of 6, containing two horizontal strips of 3.

1978 (4 Dec). *Christmas. 450th Death Anniv. of Dürer. T* **40** *and similar vert designs. Multicoloured. P* 13 × 14.

261 15 c. Type **40** 30 25
262 17 c. "The Madonna with Child" 35 25
263 30 c. "The Madonna with the Iris" 50 40
264 35 c. "The Madonna of the Siskin" 55 45
MS265 101 × 109 mm. As Nos. 261/4 but each with premium of "+ 2 c." .. .. 1·60 1·75

Nos. 261/4 were each printed in small sheets of 6, including 1 *se-tenant* stamp-size label.

41 "Captain Cook" (Nathaniel Dance)

42 Girl with Flowers

1979 (20 July). *Death Bicentenary of Captain Cook. Paintings. T* **41** *and similar vert designs. Multicoloured. P* 14 × 13½.

266 50 c. Type **41** 80 80
267 75 c. "*Resolution* and *Adventure* at Matavai Bay" (William Hodges) 95 95
MS268 94 × 58 mm. Nos. 266/7. P 13½ .. .. 2·00 2·50

1979 (1 Oct). *International Year of the Child. T* **42** *and similar vert designs. Multicoloured. P* 14 × 13½.

269 30 c. Type **42** 45 45
270 35 c. Boy playing guitar 70 70
271 65 c. Children in canoe 90 90
MS272 104 × 80 mm. As Nos. 269/71, but each with a premium of "+ 3 c." .. .. 2·25 2·40

43 "Man writing a Letter" (painting by G. Metsu)

44 "The Burial of Christ" (detail, Quentin Metsys)

1979 (14 Nov). *Death Centenary of Sir Rowland Hill. T* **43** *and similar horiz designs. Multicoloured. P* 13.

273 50 c. Type **43** 70 70
274 50 c. Sir Rowland Hill with Penny Black, 1903 ½d. and 1911 1d. stamps 70 70
275 50 c. "Girl in Blue reading a Letter" (painting by J. Vermeer) 70 70
276 65 c. "Woman writing a Letter" (painting by G. Terborch) 75 75
277 65 c. Sir Rowland Hill with Penny Black, 1903 3d. and 1920 ½d. stamps 75 75
278 65 c. "Lady writing a Letter" (painting by J. Vermeer) 75 75
273/8 .. .. *Set of* 6 4·00 4·00
MS279 151 × 85 mm. 30 c. × 6. As Nos. 273/8 .. 2·25 2·40

Nos. 273/5 and 276/8 were printed together, *se-tenant*, in horizontal strips of 3, the sheet having two panes separated by margin, one containing 273/5 × 3, the other containing 276/8 × 3.

1980 (3 Apr). *Easter. T* **44** *and similar vert designs showing different details of painting "The Burial of Christ" by Quentin Metsys. P* 13.

280 20 c. multicoloured 25 30
281 30 c. multicoloured 35 40
282 35 c. multicoloured 40 40
MS283 93 × 71 mm. As Nos. 280/2, but each with premium of "+ 2 c." .. .. 1·00 1·10

45 Einstein as Young Man

46 Ancestor Figure, Aitutaki

1980 (21 July). *25th Death Anniv of Albert Einstein (physicist). T* **45** *and similar vert designs. Multicoloured. P* 14 × 13½.

284 12 c. Type **45** 25 25
285 12 c. Atom and "E=mc²" equation 25 25
286 15 c. Einstein as middle-aged man 30 30
287 15 c. Cross over nuclear explosion (Nuclear Test Ban Treaty, 1963) 30 30
288 20 c. Einstein as old man 40 40
289 20 c. Hand over bomb explosion (Nuclear Test Ban Treaty, 1963) 40 40
284/9 .. .. *Set of* 6 1·75 1·75
MS290 113 × 118 mm. Nos. 284/9. P 13½ .. 1·75 1·90

Nos. 284/5, 286/7 and 288/9 were each printed together, *se-tenant*, in horizontal pairs throughout the sheet.

1980 (26 Sept). *South Pacific Festival of Arts. T* **46** *and similar vert designs. Multicoloured. P* 13½.

291 6 c. Type **46** 5 5
292 6 c. Staff god image, Rarotonga 5 5
293 6 c. Trade adze, Mangaia 5 5
294 6 c. Carved image of Tangaroa, Rarotonga .. 5 5
295 12 c. Wooden image, Aitutaki 12 12
296 12 c. Hand club, Rarotonga 12 12
297 12 c. Carved mace "god", Mangaia 12 12
298 12 c. Fisherman's god, Rarotonga 12 12
299 15 c. Ti'i image, Aitutaki 15 15
300 15 c. Fisherman's god, Rarotonga (*different*) .. 15 15
301 15 c. Carved mace "god", Cook Islands .. 15 15
302 15 c. Carved image of Tangaroa, Rarotonga (*different*) 15 15
303 20 c. Chief's headdress, Aitutaki 20 20
304 20 c. Carved "mace" god, Cook Islands (*different*) 20 20
305 20 c. Staff god image, Rarotonga (*different*) .. 20 20
306 20 c. Carved image of Tangaroa, Rarotonga (*different*) 20 20
291/306 .. .. *Set of* 16 1·90 1·90
MS307 134 × 194 mm. Nos. 291/306 .. .. 1·90 2·00

The four designs of each value were printed together, *se-tenant*, in blocks of 4 throughout the sheet.

47 Virgin and Child (13th-century)

48 "Mourning Virgin"

1980 (21 Nov). *Christmas. Sculptures. T* **47** *and similar vert designs showing various Virgin and Child works from the periods given. Multicoloured. P* 13.

308 15 c. Type **47** 15 15
309 20 c. 14th-century 20 20
310 25 c. 15th-century 25 25
311 35 c. 15th-century (*different*) 35 40
MS312 82 × 120 mm. As Nos. 306/11 but each with premium of 2 c. .. .. 1·10 1·25

1981 (31 Mar). *Easter. Details of Sculpture "Burial of Christ" by Pedro Roldan. T* **48** *and similar vert designs. P* 14.

313 30 c. gold and myrtle-green 40 40
314 40 c. gold and deep reddish lilac 45 45
315 50 c. gold and Prussian blue 55 55
MS316 107 × 60 mm. As Nos. 313/15 but each with premium of 2 c. .. .. 1·40 1·50

Designs:—40 c. "Christ"; 50 c. "Saint John".

49 Gouldian Finch (*Poephila gouldiae*)

50 Prince Charles

1981 (6 Apr)–**82**. *Birds.* (*1st series*) *Multicoloured designs as T* **49**. *P* 14 × 13½ (1 *to* 10 c.), 13 ½ × 14 (15 *to* 70 c.) *or* 13 ($1 *to* $4).

317 1 c. Type **49** 5 5
318 1 c. Common Starling (*Sturnus vulgaris*) .. 5 5
319 2 c. Golden Whistler (*Pachycephala pectoralis*) 5 5
320 2 c. Scarlet Robin (*Petroica multicolor*) .. 5 5
321 3 c. Rufous Fantail (*Rhipidura rufifrous*) .. 10 10
322 3 c. Peregrine Falcon (*Falco peregrinus*) .. 10 10
323 4 c. Java Sparrow (*Padda oryzivora*) .. 10 10
324 4 c. Barn Owl (*Tyto alba*) 10 10
325 5 c. Tahitian Lory (*Vini peruviana*) 10 10
326 5 c. White-breasted Wood Swallow (*Artamus leucorhynchus*) 10 10
327 6 c. Purple Swamphen (*Porphyrio porphyrio*) 10 10
328 6 c. Rock Dove (*Columba livia*) 10 10
329 10 c. Chestnut-breasted Mannikin (*Lonchura castaneothorax*) 15 10
330 10 c. Zebra Dove (*Geopelia striata*) 15 10
331 12 c. Eastern Reef Heron (*Egretta sacra*) .. 15 12
332 12 c. Common Mynah (*Acridotheres tristis*) .. 15 12
333 15 c. Whimbrel (*Numenius phaeopus*) (*horiz*) (8.5.81) 20 15
334 15 c. Black-browed Albatross (*Diomeda melanophris*) (*horiz*) (8.5.81) 20 15
335 20 c. American Golden Plover (*Pluvialis dominica*) (*horiz*) (8.5.81) 25 20
336 20 c. White Tern (*Gygis alba*) (*horiz*) (8.5.81) 25 20
337 25 c. Spotbill Duck (*Anas superciliosa*) (*horiz*) (8.5.81) 30 25
338 25 c. Brown Booby (*Sula leucogaster*) (*horiz*) (8.5.81) 30 25
339 30 c. Great Frigate Bird (*Fregata minor*) (*horiz*) (8.5.81) 35 30
340 30 c. Pintail (*Anas acuta*) (*horiz*) (8.5.81) .. 35 30
341 35 c. Long-billed Reed Warbler (*Conopoderas caffra caffra*) (14.1.82) 35 35
342 35 c. Pomarine Skua (*Stercorarius pomarinus*) (14.1.82) 35 35
343 40 c. Banded Rail (*Gallirallus philippensis goodsoni*) (14.1.82) 40 40
344 40 c. Spotted Triller (*Lalage maculosa pumila*) (14.1.82) 40 40
345 50 c. Royal Albatross (*Diomedea epomophora*) (14.1.82) 55 55
346 50 c. Stephen's Lory (*Vini stepheni*) (14.1.82) 55 55
347 70 c. Red-headed Parrot Finch (*Erythrura cyaneovirens*) (14.1.82) 70 70
348 70 c. Orange Dove (*Ptilinopus victor victor*) (14.1.82) 70 70
349 $1 Blue-headed Flycatcher (*Myiagra azureocapilla whitneyi*) (15.2.82) .. .. 1·00 1·00
350 $2 Red-bellied Flycatcher (*Myiagra vanikorensis rufiventris*) (15.5.82) .. .. 2·00 2·00
351 $4 Red Munia (*Amandava amandava*) (19.3.82) .. .. 3·75 3·75
352 $5 Flat-headed Kingfisher (*Halcyon recurvirostris*) (19.3.82) .. .. .. 4·75 4·75
317/52 .. .. *Set of* 36 17·00 17·00

The two designs of each value (1 c. to 70 c.) were printed together, *se-tenant*, in horizontal and vertical pairs throughout the sheet.

Nos. 341/8 are 35 × 27 mm and Nos. 349/52, which include a portrait of Queen Elizabeth II, 35 × 48 mm in size.

See also Nos. 475/94 for redrawn designs as Type **65**.

Nos. 353/90 are vacant.

1981 (10 June). *Royal Wedding. T* **50** *and similar multicoloured designs. P* 14 ($1.40) *or* 13 × 13½ (*others*).

391 60 c. Type **50** .. .. 1·00 1·00
392 80 c. Lady Diana Spencer .. .. .. 1·25 1·25
393 $1.40, Prince Charles and Lady Diana (87 × 70 *mm*) .. .. 2·25 2·25

(**51**) **52** Footballers

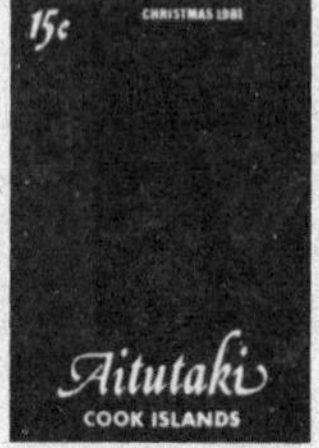

53 "The Holy Family"

1981 (23 Nov). *International Year for Disabled Persons. Nos.* 391/3 *surch with T* **51** *on gold background.*

394 60 c. + 5 c. Type **50** .. .. 1·50 1·50
395 80 c. + 5 c. Lady Diana Spencer .. .. 2·00 2·00
396 $1. 40 + 5 c.Prince Charles and Lady Diana .. .. 4·00 3·50

Nos. 394/6 have commemorative inscriptions overprinted on the sheet margins.

1981 (30 Nov). *World Cup Football Championship, Spain* (1982). *T* **52** *and similar horiz designs showing footballers. Multicoloured. P* 14.

397 12 c. Ball to left of stamp 15 15
398 12 c. Ball to right 15 15
399 15 c. Ball to right 20 20
400 15 c. Ball to left 20 20
401 20 c. Ball to left 25 25
402 20 c. Ball to right 25 25
403 25 c. Type **52** 30 30
404 25 c. "ESPANA 82" inscr on printed background 30 30
397/404 .. .. *Set of* 8 1·60 1·60
MS405 100 × 137 mm. 12 c. + 2 c., 15 c. + 2 c., 20 c. + 2 c., 25 c. + 2 c., each × 2. As Nos. 397/404 1·75 2·00

The two designs of each value were printed together, *se-tenant*, in horizontal pairs throughout the sheet.

1981 (10 Dec). *Christmas. Details from Etchings by Rembrandt. T* **53** *and similar designs in purple-brown and gold. P* 14.

406 15 c. Type **53** 20 15
407 30 c. "Virgin with Child" 35 30
408 40 c. "Adoration of the Shepherds" (*horiz*) .. 50 50
409 50 c. "The Holy Family" (*horiz*) 60 60
MS410 Designs as Nos. 406/9 in separate miniature sheets, 65 × 82 mm or 82 × 65 mm, each with a face value of 80 c. + 5 c. P 14 × 13½ .. *Set of* 4 *sheets* 2·75 3·00

54 Princess of Wales

(**55**)

1982 (24 June). *21st Birthday of Princess of Wales. T* **54** *and similar vert designs. Multicoloured. P* 14.

411 70 c. Type **54** 70 70
412 $1 Prince and Princess of Wales 85 85
413 $2 Princess Diana (*different*) .. .. 1·60 1·75
MS414 82 × 91 mm. Nos. 411/13 .. .. 2·75 2·75

Nos. 411/13 were each printed in small sheets of 6 including two *se-tenant* stamp-size labels. The silver markings in the margins of the individual stamps differ for each position in the sheetlet.

1982 (13 July). *Birth of Prince William of Wales* (*1st issue*). *Nos.* 391/3 *optd as T* **55**.

415 60 c. Type **50** (optd with T **55**) .. .. .. 2·00 1·50
a. Pair. Nos. 415/16 .. .. .. 4·00 3·00
416 60 c. Type **50** (optd "COMMEMORATING THE ROYAL BIRTH") .. .. .. 2·00 1·50
417 80 c. Lady Diana Spencer (optd with T **55**) .. 2·50 1·75
a. Pair. Nos. 417/18 .. .. .. 5·00 3·50
418 80 c. Lady Diana Spencer (optd "COMMEMORATING THE ROYAL BIRTH") .. 2·50 1·75
419 $1.40, Prince Charles and Lady Diana (87 × 70 *mm*) (optd as T **55**) .. .. 4·50 3·75
a. Pair. Nos. 419/20 .. .. 9·00 6·50
420 $1.40, Prince Charles and Lady Diana (87 × 70 *mm*) (optd "COMMEMORATING THE ROYAL BIRTH") .. .. .. 4·50 3·75
415/20 .. .. *Set of* 6 16·00 13·00

Nos. 415/16, 417/18 and 419/20 were each printed together in *se-tenant* pairs, horiz and vert, throughout the sheets.

1982 (5 Aug). *Birth of Prince William of Wales (2nd issue). As Nos.* 411/14, *but inscr* "ROYAL BIRTH 21 JUNE 1982 PRINCE WILLIAM OF WALES". *Multicoloured. P* 14.

421 70 c. Type **54** 70 70
422 $1 Prince and Princess of Wales 85 85
423 $2 Princess Diana (*different*) .. .. 1·60 1·60
MS424 81 × 91 mm. Nos. 421/3 .. .. .. 2·75 3·00

56 "Virgin and Child" (12th-century sculpture)

57 Aitutaki Bananas

1982 (10 Dec). *Christmas. Religious Sculptures. T* **56** *and similar vert designs. Multicoloured. P* 13.

425 18 c. Type **56** 20 20
426 36 c. "Virgin and Child" (12th-century) .. 30 30
427 48 c. "Virgin and Child" (13th-century) .. 50 50
428 60 c. "Virgin and Child" (15th-century) .. 65 65
MS429 99 × 115 mm. As Nos. 425/8 but each with 2 c. charity premium .. .. 1·60 1·75

Nos. 425/8 were each printed in small sheets of 6 including one *se-tenant*, stamp size, label, depicting the Prince and Princess of Wales with Prince William.

1983 (14 Mar). *Commonwealth Day. T* **57** *and similar horiz designs. Multicoloured. P* 13.

430 48 c. Type **57** 50 50
431 48 c. Ancient Ti'i image 50 50
432 48 c. Tourist canoeing 50 50
433 48 c. Captain William Bligh and chart .. 50 50

Nos. 430/3 were issued together, *se-tenant*, in blocks of four throughout the sheet.

58 Scouts around Campfire

15th WORLD SCOUT JAMBOREE

(**59**)

1983 (18 Apr). *75th Anniv of Boy Scout Movement, T* **58** *and similar horiz designs. Multicoloured. P* 13½ × 14.

434 36 c. Type **58** 40 40
435 48 c. Scout saluting 50 50
436 60 c. Scouts hiking 65 65
MS437 78 × 107 mm. As Nos. 434/6 but each with premium of 3 c. P 13 .. .. 1·50 1·60

1983 (11 July). *15th World Scout Jamboree, Alberta, Canada. Nos.* 434/7 *optd with T* **59**.

438 36 c. Type **58** 40 40
439 48 c. Scout saluting 50 50
440 60 c. Scouts hiking 65 65
MS441 78 × 107 mm. As Nos. 438/40 but each with a premium of 3 c. .. .. 1·50 1·60

60 Modern Sport Balloon

18c

(**61**)

$1.20

(**62**)

1983 (22 July). *Bicentenary of Manned Flight. T* **60** *and similar vert designs showing different modern sport balloons. P* 14 × 13.

442 18 c. multicoloured 12 15
443 36 c. multicoloured 30 40

444 48 c. multicoloured 40 50
445 60 c. multicoloured 55 60
MS446 64 × 80 mm. $2.50, multicoloured (48½ × 28½ *mm*) .. .. 2·00 2·25
Nos. 442/5 were each issued in small sheets of 4 stamps.

1983 (22 Sept). *Various stamps surch.*

(a) Nos. 335/48 *and* 352 *as T* **61**
447 18 c. on 20 c. American Golden Plover (*Pluvialis dominica*) 12 15
448 18 c. on 20 c. White Tern (*Gygis alba*) .. 12 15
449 36 c. on 25 c. Spotbill Duck (*Anas superciliosa*) 25 30
450 36 c. on 25 c. Brown Booby (*Sula leucogaster*) 25 30
451 36 c. on 30 c. Great Frigate Bird (*Fregata minor*) 25 30
452 36 c. on 30 c. Pintail (*Anas acuta*) 25 30
453 36 c. on 35 c. Long-billed Reed Warbler (*Conopoderas caffra caffra*) 25 30
454 36 c. on 35 c. Pomarine Skua (*Stercorarius pomarinus*) 25 30
455 48 c. on 40 c. Banded Rail (*Gallirallus philippensis goodsoni*) 35 40
456 48 c. on 40 c. Spotted Triller (*Lalage maculosa pumila*) 35 40
457 48 c. on 50 c. Royal Albatross (*Diomedea epomophora*) 35 40
458 48 c. on 50 c. Stephen's Lory (*Vini stepheni*) 35 40
459 72 c. on 70 c. Red-headed Parrot Finch (*Erythrura cyaneovirens*) 55 60
460 72 c. on 70 c. Orange Dove (*Ptilinopus victor victor*) 55 60
461 $5.60 on $5 Flat-headed Kingfisher (*Halcyon recurvirostris*) .. .. .. 4·50 4·75

(b) Nos. 392/3 *and* 412/13 *as T* **62**
462 96 c. on 80 c. Lady Diana Spencer (Gold) .. 4·00 2·50
a. Error. Surch on No. 417 .. .. .. 12·00
ab. Pair. Nos. 462/a/b .. .. .. 28·00
b. Error. Surch on No. 418 .. .. .. 12·00
463 96 c. on $1 Prince and Princess of Wales .. 3·50 2·00
464 $1.20 on $1.40, Prince Charles and Lady Diana (Gold) .. .. 4·00 2·50
a. Error. Surch on No. 419 .. .. .. 12·00
ab. Pair. Nos. 464a/b .. .. .. 25·00
b. Error. Surch on No. 420 .. .. .. 12·00
465 $1.20 on $2, Princess Diana .. .. 3·50 2·00
447/65 .. .. .. *Set of* 19 21·00 17·00
On Nos. 462 and 464 the gold surcharge is printed on a black obliterating panel over the original face value.

63 International Mail

64 "Madonna of the Chair"

1983 (29 Sept). *World Communications Year. T* **63** *and similar vert designs. Multicoloured. P* 14 × 13½.
466 48 c. Type **63** 40 45
467 60 c. Telecommunications 55 60
468 96 c. Space satellites 85 90
MS469 126 × 53 mm. Nos. 466/8. P 13 .. .. 1·75 1·90

1983 (21 Nov). *Christmas. 500th Birth Anniv of Raphael. T* **64** *and similar horiz designs. Multicoloured. P* 13½ × 14.
470 36 c. Type **64** 30 35
471 48 c. "The Alba Madonna" 40 45
472 60 c. "Conestabile Madonna" 55 60
MS473 95 × 116 mm. As Nos. 470/2, but each with a premium of 3 c. P 13 .. .. .. 1·40 1·50

1983 (15 Dec). *Christmas. 500th Birth Anniv of Raphael. Children's Charity. Designs as Nos.* 470/2 *in separate miniature sheets* 46 × 47 *mm, but each with different frames and a face value of* 85 *c.* + 5 *c. Imperf.*
MS474 As Nos. 470/2 .. .. *Set of* 3 *sheets* 2·40 2·50

65 Gouldian Finch

66 Javelin-throwing

1984 (13 Feb–2 July). *Birds (2nd series). Designs as Nos.* 317 *etc. but with redrawn frames and inscriptions as in T* **65**. *Multicoloured. P* 13 × 13½ *($3 to $9.60) or* 14 *(others).*
475 2 c. Type **65** 5 5
476 3 c. Common Starling 5 5
477 5 c. Scarlet Robin 5 5
478 10 c. Golden Whistler 8 10
479 12 c. Rufous Fantail 8 10
480 18 c. Peregrine Falcon 12 15
481 24 c. Barn Owl 15 20
482 30 c. Java Sparrow 20 25
483 36 c. White-breasted Wood Swallow 25 30
484 48 c. Tahitian Lory 35 40
485 50 c. Rock Dove (26 Mar) 40 45
486 60 c. Purple Swamphen (26 Mar) 45 50
487 72 c. Zebra Dove (26 Mar) 55 60
488 96 c. Chestnut-breasted Mannikin (26 Mar) .. 70 75
489 $1.20, Common Mynah (26 Mar) 90 95
490 $2.10, Eastern Reef Heron (30 Apr) .. 1·50 1·60
491 $3 Blue-headed Flycatcher (29 × 42 *mm*) (30 Apr) .. .. 2·25 2·50
492 $4.20, Red-bellied Flycatcher (30 × 42 *mm*) (5 June) .. .. 3·00 3·25
493 $5.60, Red Munia (30 × 42 *mm*) (5 June) .. 4·00 4·25
494 $9.60, Flat-headed Kingfisher (30 × 42 *mm*) (2 July) .. .. 7·00 7·25
475/94 .. .. *Set of* 20 19·50 20·50

1984 (24 July). *Olympic Games, Los Angeles. T* **66** *and similar vert designs showing Memorial Coliseum and various events. Multicoloured. P* 13 × 13½.
495 36 c. Type **66** 30 35
496 48 c. Shot-putting 40 45
497 60 c. Hurdling 50 55
498 $2 Basketball .. .. 1·75 1·90
MS499 88 × 117 mm. As Nos. 495/8, but each with a charity premium of 5 c. .. .. .. 3·00 3·25

1984 (21 Aug). *Olympic Gold Medal Winners. Nos.* 495/8 *optd as T* **209** *of Cook Islands in gold on black background.*
500 36 c. Type **66** (optd "Javelin Throw Tessa Sanderson Great Britain") 30 35
501 48 c. Shot-putting (optd "Shot Put Claudia Losch Germany") 40 45
502 60 c. Hurdling (optd "Heptathlon Glynis Nunn Australia") 50 55
503 $2 Basketball (optd "Team Basketball United States") .. .. 1·75 1·90

67 Capt. William Bligh and Chart

1984 (14 Sept). *"Ausipex" International Stamp Exhibition, Melbourne. T* **67** *and similar horiz designs. Multicoloured. P* 14.
504 60 c. Type **67** 50 55
505 96 c. H.M.S. *Bounty* and map 80 85
506 $1.40, Aitutaki stamps of 1974, 1979 and 1981 with map .. .. 1·25 1·40
MS507 85 × 113 mm. As Nos. 504/6, but each with a premium of 5 c. P 13½ .. .. .. 2·35 3·00

15.9.84 Birth
Prince Henry
$3

(68)

69 The Annunciation

1984 (10 Oct). *Birth of Prince Henry (1st issue). No.* 391 *surch with T* **68** *in gold.*
508 $3 on 60 c. Type **50** .. .. .. 4·00 3·00
On No. 508 the gold surcharge is printed on a black obliterating panel over the original face value.

1984 (16 Nov). *Christmas. Details from Altarpiece, St. Paul's Church, Palencia, Spain. T* **69** *and similar vert designs. Multicoloured. P* 13½ × 13.
509 36 c. Type **69** 30 35
510 48 c. The Nativity 40 45
511 60 c. The Epiphany 45 50
512 96 c. The Flight into Egypt 75 80
MS513 Designs as Nos. 509/12 in separate miniature sheets, each 45 × 53 mm and with a face value of 90 c. + 7 c. Imperf. .. .. *Set of* 4 *sheets* 3·00

OFFICIAL STAMPS

O H.M.S.

(O 1)

1978 (3 Nov)–**79**. *Nos.* 98/105, 107/10 *and* 227/8 *optd or surch (Nos.* O8/9 *and* O15) *as Type* O 1.
O 1 1 c. *Nautilus macromphallus* 12 5
O 2 2 c. *Harpa major* 15 5
O 3 3 c. *Phalium strigatum* 15 5
O 4 4 c. *Cypraea talpa* 15 5
O 5 5 c. *Mitra stictica* 15 5
O 6 8 c. *Charonia tritonis* 20 8
O 7 10 c. *Murex triremis* 25 10
O 8 15 c. on 60 c. *Strombus latissimus* .. 40 12
O 9 18 c. on 60 c. *Strombus latissimus* .. 40 15
O10 20 c. *Oliva sericea* (Gold) 40 15
O11 50 c. Union Jack, Queen Victoria and island map 85 55
O12 60 c. *Strombus latissimus* 95 70
O13 $1 *Biplex perca* .. .. 1·60 1·25
O14 $2 Queen Elizabeth II and *Terebra maculata* (20.2.79) .. .. 2·50 2·00
O15 $4 on $1 Balcony scene, 1953 (Sil.) (20.2.79) 4·75 4·25
O16 $5 Queen Elizabeth II and *Cypraea hesitata* (20.2.79) .. .. 5·50 5·50
O1/16 .. .. .. *Set of* 16 17·00 14·00
These stamps were originally only sold to the public cancelled-to-order and not in unused condition.
They were made available to overseas collectors in mint condition during 1980.

PENRHYN ISLAND

Stamps of COOK ISLANDS were used on Penrhyn Island from late 1901 until the issue of the surcharged stamps in May 1902.

PRICES FOR STAMPS ON COVER TO 1945

Nos. 1/8	*from* × 4
Nos. 9/10	*from* × 50
Nos. 11/13	—
Nos. 14/18	*from* × 3
Nos. 19/23	*from* × 2
Nos. 24/37	*from* × 3
Nos. 38/40	*from* × 5

A. NEW ZEALAND DEPENDENCY

The island of Penrhyn, previously under British protection, was annexed by New Zealand on 11 June 1901.

Stamps of New Zealand overprinted or surcharged

PENRHYN ISLAND.
½ PENI.
(1)

PENRHYN ISLAND.
TAI PENI.
(2) 1d.

PENRHYN ISLAND.
2½ PENI.
(3)

1902 (5 May). *1902 issue surch with T* **1**, **2** *and* **3**.

(1) Waterlow paper. No wmk. P 11
1 **27** 2½d. blue (R.) .. .. 85 2·00
a. "½" and "P" spaced .. .. .. 8·50 13·00

(2) Basted Mills paper. Wmk double-lined "NZ" and Star. T **36a**

(a) P 11
3 **40** 1d. carmine (Br.) .. .. .. 80·00 90·00

(b) P 14
4 **23** ½d. green (R.) .. .. 1·10 1·75
a. No stop after "ISLAND" .. .. 85·00 90·00
5 **40** 1d. carmine (Br.) .. .. .. 1·50 3·00
a. *Pale carmine* .. .. .. 1·50 3·00

(c) P 11 × 14
7 **40** 1d. carmine (Br.) .. .. .. £100 90·00

(d) Mixed perfs
8 **40** 1d. carmine (Br.) £170

(3) Cowan paper. Wmk single-lined "N Z" and Star, T **41**. *(a) P* 14
9 **23** ½d. green (R.) 65 85
a. No stop after "ISLAND" .. .. 60·00 65·00
10 **40** 1d. carmine (B.) 65 85
a. No stop after "ISLAND" .. .. 35·00 42·00

(b) P 11 × 14
11 **40** 1d. carmine (B.) .. .. ..

(c) Mixed perfs
12 **23** ½d. green (R.) £150 £170
13 **40** 1d. carmine (B.) .. .. .. 55·00 70·00

PENRHYN ISLAND.
(4)

Toru Pene.
(5) 3d.

Ono Pene.
(6) 6d.

Tahi Silingi.
(7) 1s.

1903 (28 Feb). *1902 issue surch with name at top, T* **4**, *and values at foot, T* **5/7**. *W* **41**. *P* 11.
14 **28** 3d. yellow-brown (B.) .. .. .. 6·50 9·00
15 **31** 6d. rose-red (B.) .. .. .. 11·00 17·00
16 **34** 1s. brown-red (B.) .. .. .. 30·00 42·00
17 1s. bright red (B.) .. .. .. 30·00 42·00
18 1s. orange-red (B.) .. .. .. 38·00 50·00

1914–15. *Surch with T* **1** *(½d.) or optd with T* **4** *at top and surch with T* **6/7** *at foot.*
19 **50** ½d. yellow-green (C.)(5.14) .. .. 90 2·50
a. No stop after "ISLAND" .. .. 32·00 45·00
b. No stop after "PENI" .. .. 70·00 75·00
20 ½d. yellow-green (V.)(1.15) .. .. 65 2·00
a. No stop after "ISLAND" .. .. 15·00 20·00
b. No stop after "PENI" .. .. 35·00 45·00
22 **52** 6d. carmine (B.) (8.14) .. .. 30·00 45·00
23 1s. vermilion (B.)(8.14) .. .. 42·00 60·00

1917–20. *King George V stamps optd with name only. T* **4**. *P* 14 × 14½.
24 2½d. blue (R.)(10.20) .. .. .. 1·25 2·75
a. No stop after "ISLAND" .. .. 55·00 70·00
b. Perf 14 × 13½ .. .. .. 2·50 4·75
c. Vert pair. Nos. 24/4b .. .. 50·00 60·00
25 3d. chocolate (B.)(6.18) .. .. 8·50 14·00
a. Perf 14 × 13½ .. .. .. 8·50 18·00
b. Vert pair. Nos. 25/5a .. .. 70·00 80·00
26 6d. carmine (B.)(1.18) .. .. .. 5·00 9·50
a. No stop after "ISLAND" .. .. 85·00 95·00
b. Perf 14 × 13½ .. .. .. 7·00 12·00
c. Vert pair. Nos. 26/6b .. .. 55·00 65·00

27		1s. vermilion (B.)(12.17)	12·00	20·00
		a. No stop after "ISLAND"	85·00	95·00
		b. Perf 14 × 13½	15·00	26·00
		c. Vert pair. Nos. 27/7b	£110	£110

1917–20. *Optd as T* 4. *Typo. W* **41.** *P* 14 × 15.

28	**60b**	½d. green (R.)(2.20)	65	85
		a. No stop after "ISLAND"	16·00	25·00
		b. Narrow spacing	5·00	6·00
29		1½d. slate (R.)(11.17)	2·25	4·00
		a. Narrow spacing	15·00	22·00
30		1½d. orange-brown (R.)(2.19)	60	2·50
		a. Narrow spacing	5·00	10·00
31		3d. chocolate (B.)(6.19)	1·75	5·50
		a. Narrow spacing	14·00	25·00

The overprint was applied in a setting of 30 (6 × 5) in which positions 22 to 24 had "PENRHYN ISLANDS" spaced approximately ½ mm apart instead of 1¼ mm.

(Recess P.B.)

1920 (23 Aug). *As Types of Cook Islands but inscr* "PENRHYN". *No wmk. P* 14.

32	**9**	½d. black and emerald	90	2·00
		a. Imperf between (vert pair)*	£550	
		b. Imperf vert (horiz pair)*	£550	
33	**10**	1d. black and deep red	1·25	2·50
34	**11**	1½d. black and deep violet	4·00	6·50
35	**12**	3d. black and red	2·00	4·25
36	**13**	6d. red-brown and sepia	3·25	9·50
37	**14**	1s. black and slate-blue	9·50	17·00
32/37		*Set of* 6	19·00	38·00

*Nos. 32a/b occur from a sheet on which the top two rows were imperf between horizontally and the second row additionally imperf vertically.

(Recess Govt Printing Office, Wellington)

1927–29. *As Types of Cook Islands, but inscr* "PENRHYN". *W* **41.** *P* 14.

38	**9**	½d. black and green (5.29)	1·25	4·00
39	**10**	1d. black and deep carmine (14.3.28)	1·50	2·75
40	**16**	2½d. red-brown and dull blue (10.27)	1·75	7·00

Cook Islands stamps superseded those of Penrhyn Islands on 15 March 1932. Separate issues were resumed in 1973.

B. PART OF COOK ISLANDS

The following issues are for use in all the islands of the Northern Cook Islands group.

PRINTERS. The note at the beginning of Aitutaki concerning printers and gum also applies here. All issues except Nos. 41A/52A are on paper treated with fluorescent security markings. The markings can be found inverted or omitted.

PENRHYN

NORTHERN

(8)

PENRHYN
NORTHERN

(9)

1973 (24 Oct–14 Nov). *Nos.* 228/45 *of Cook Is optd with T* **8** (*without* "NORTHERN" *on* $1, $2).
A. *Without fluorescent security markings. Gum arabic*
B. *With fluorescent security markings. PVA gum*

		A.		B.	
41	1 c. multicoloured	60	—	5	8
42	2 c. multicoloured	90	—	5	8
43	3 c. multicoloured	1·25	—	8	10
44	4 c. multicoloured (No. 233)	1·50	—	8	10
	a. Optd on Cook Is No. 232	60·00	—	†	
45	5 c. multicoloured	1·75	—	10	12
46	6 c. multicoloured	2·00	—	20	30
47	8 c. multicoloured	2·25	—	30	40
48	15 c. multicoloured	4·25	—	45	50
49	20 c. multicoloured	†		75	80
50	50 c. multicoloured	15·00	—	2·25	2·50
51	$1 multicoloured	28·00	—	3·00	3·75
52	$2 multicoloured (14.11)	55·00	—	5·00	7·00
41A/52A	*Set of* 11	£100	—	†	
41B/52B	*Set of* 12	†		11·00	14·00

1973 (14 Nov). *Royal Wedding. Nos.* 450/2 *of Cook Is optd as T* **9**, *in silver.*

53	**138**	25 c. multicoloured	85	80
54	–	30 c. multicoloured	85	80
55	–	50 c. multicoloured	85	80

10 *Ostracion sp* **11** Penrhyn Stamps of 1902

1974 (15 Aug)–**75.** *Fishes. T* **10** *and similar horiz designs. Multicoloured. P* 13½ (½ *c. to* $1) *or* 13 × 12½ ($2, $5).

56	½ c. Type **10**	5	5
57	1 c. *Monodactylus argenteus*	10	5
58	2 c. *Pomacanthus imperator*	15	5
59	3 c. *Chelmon rostratus*	15	5
60	4 c. *Chaetodon ornatissimus*	15	5
61	5 c. *Chaetodon melanotus*	15	5
62	8 c. *Chaetodon raffessi*	20	10
63	10 c. *Chaetodon ephippium*	25	10
64	20 c. *Pygoplites diacanthus*	45	25
65	25 c. *Heniochus acuminatus*	50	25
66	60 c. *Plectorhynchus chaetodonoides*	1·25	75
67	$1 *Balistipus undulatus*	1·50	1·10
68	$2 Birds-eye view of Penrhyn (12.2.75)	3·00	2·75
69	$5 Satellite view of Australasia (12.3.75)	6·50	6·50
56/69	*Set of* 14	13·00	11·00

Nos. 68/9 are larger, 63 × 25 mm.

1974 (27 Sept). *Centenary of Universal Postal Union. T* **11** *and similar vert design. Multicoloured. P* 13.

70	25 c. Type **11**	60	55
71	50 c. Stamps of 1920	65	70

Each value was issued in sheets of 8 stamps and 1 label.

12 "Adoration of the Kings" (Memling)

1974 (30 Oct). *Christmas. T* **12** *and similar horiz designs. Multicoloured. P* 13.

72	5 c. Type **12**	15	12
73	10 c. "Adoration of the Shepherds" (Hugo van der Goes)	30	25
74	25 c. "Adoration of the Magi" (Rubens)	65	60
75	30 c. "The Holy Family" (Borgianni)	75	70

13 Churchill giving "V" Sign (**14**)

1974 (30 Nov.) *Birth Centenary of Sir Winston Churchill. T* **13** *and similar vert design. P* 13.

76	30 c. agate and gold	90	90
77	50 c. myrtle-green and gold	1·10	1·10

Design:—50 c. Full-face portrait.

1975 (24 July). *"Apollo-Soyuz" Space Project. No.* 69 *optd with T* **14.**

78	$5 Satellite view of Australasia	7·50	7·50

15 "Virgin and Child" (Bouts) **16** "Pietà"

1975 (21 Nov). *Christmas. T* **15** *and similar vert designs showing the "Virgin and Child". Multicoloured. P* 14 × 13.

79	7 c. Type **15**	25	15
80	15 c. Leonardo da Vinci	50	35
81	35 c. Raphael	85	70

1976 (19 Mar). *Easter and 500th Birth Anniv of Michelangelo. T* **16** *and similar vert designs. P* 14 × 13.

82	15 c. sepia and gold	50	30
83	20 c. blackish purple and gold	60	40
84	35 c. myrtle-green and gold	85	70
MS85	112 × 72 mm. Nos. 82/4	2·25	2·50

Each value was issued in sheets of 8 stamps and 1 label.

17 "Washington crossing the Delaware" (E. Leutze) **18** Running

1976 (20 May). *Bicentenary of American Revolution. T* **17** *and similar vert designs. Multicoloured. P* 13.

86	30 c.	Type **17**	90	55
87	30 c.	Type **17**	90	55
88	30 c.	Type **17**	90	55
89	50 c.	"The Spirit of '76" (A. M. Willard)	1·10	70
90	50 c.	"The Spirit of '76" (A. M. Willard)	1·10	70
91	50 c.	"The Spirit of '76" (A. M. Willard)	1·10	70
86/91		*Set of* 6	5·50	4·00
MS92		103 × 103 mm. Nos. 86/91. P 13	7·00	7·00

Nos. 86/8 and 89/91 were each printed together, *se-tenant*, in horizontal strips of 3 throughout the sheet, forming composite designs. Each sheet includes 3 stamp-size labels. Type **17** shows the left-hand stamp of the 30 c. design.

1976 (9 July). *Olympic Games, Montreal. T* **18** *and similar horiz designs. Multicoloured. P* 14.

93	25 c. Type **18**	65	40
94	30 c. Long Jumping	70	45
95	75 c. Throwing the Javelin	1·50	1·00
MS96	86 × 128 mm. Nos. 93/5. P 14 × 13	3·00	3·25

19 "The Flight into Egypt" **20** The Queen in Coronation Robes

1976 (20 Oct). *Christmas. Dürer Engravings. T* **19** *and similar horiz designs. P* 13.

97	7 c. black and silver	20	15
98	15 c. steel blue and silver	35	30
99	35 c. violet and silver	65	60

Designs:—15 c. "Adoration of the Magi"; 35 c. "The Nativity".

1977 (24 Mar). *Silver Jubilee. T* **20** *and similar vert designs. Multicoloured. P* 13.

100	50 c. Type **20**	1·90	1·75
101	$1 Queen and Prince Philip	2·40	2·25
102	$2 Queen Elizabeth II	4·00	3·25
MS103	128 × 87 mm. Nos. 100/2. P 13	7·50	7·00

Stamps from the miniature sheet have silver borders.

21 "The Annunciation" **22** Iiwi

1977 (23 Sept). *Christmas. T* **21** *and similar designs showing illustrations by J. S. von Carolsfeld. P* 13.

104	7 c. light stone, purple-brown and gold	25	20
105	15 c. pale rose, deep maroon and gold	40	30
106	35 c. blackish green, pale green and gold	70	55

Designs:—15 c. "The Announcement to the Shepherds"; 35 c. "The Nativity".

1978 (19 Jan). *Bicentenary of Discovery of Hawaii. T* **22** *and similar vert designs showing extinct Hawaiian birds or artefacts. Multicoloured. P* 13.

107	20 c. Type **22**	40	40
108	20 c. Elgin cloak	40	40
109	30 c. Apapane	50	50
110	30 c. Feather image of a god	50	50
111	35 c. Moorhen	60	60
112	35 c. Feather cape, helmet and staff	60	60
113	75 c. Yellow-tufted Bee-eater	1·25	1·25
114	75 c. Feather image and cloak	1·25	1·25
107/114	*Set of* 8	5·00	5·00
MS115	Two sheets each 78 × 119 mm containing (a) Nos. 107, 109, 111, 113; (b) Nos. 108, 110, 112, 114	6·50	7·00

Nos. 107/8, 109/10, 111/12 and 113/14 were each printed together, *se-tenant*, in horizontal and vertical pairs throughout the sheet.

23 "The Road to Calvary" **24** Royal Coat of Arms

1978 (10 Mar). *Easter and 400th Birth Anniv of Rubens. T* **23** *and similar vert designs. Multicoloured. P* 13.

116	10 c. Type **23**	25	20
117	15 c. "Christ on the Cross"	35	30
118	35 c. "Christ with Straw"	60	55
MS119	87 × 138 mm. Nos. 116/18	1·25	1·40

Stamps from No. **MS**119 are slightly larger (28 × 36 mm.)

1978 (17 Apr). *Easter. Children's Charity. Designs as Nos.* 116/18 *in separate miniature sheets.* 49 × 68 *mm, each with a face value of* 60 *c.* + 5 *c. P* 12½–13.

MS120	As Nos. 116/18 *Set of* 3 *sheets*	3·25	3·50

1978 (24 May). *25th Anniv of Coronation. T* **24** *and similar vert designs. P* 13.
121 90 c. black, gold and deep lilac .. .. 1·40 1·25
122 90 c. multicoloured .. .. 1·40 1·25
123 90 c. black, gold and deep bluish green .. 1·40 1·25
MS124 75 × 122 mm. Nos. 121/3 .. .. .. 3·75 3·75
Designs:—No. 122, Queen Elizabeth II; No. 123, New Zealand coat of arms.
Nos. 121/3 were printed together in small sheets of 6, containing two *se-tenant* strips of 3, with horizontal gutter margin between.

25 "Madonna of the Pear"

26 Sir Rowland Hill and G.B. Penny Black Stamp

1978 (29 Nov). *Christmas. 450th Death Anniv of Dürer. T* **25** *and similar vert design. Multicoloured. P* 14.
125 30 c. Type **25** 50 45
126 35 c. "The Virgin and Child with St. Anne" .. 50 45
MS127 101 × 60 mm. Nos. 125/6. P 13½ .. .. 1·10 1·25
Nos. 125/6 were each printed in small sheets of 6.

1979 (26 Sept). *Death Centenary of Sir Rowland Hill. T* **26** *and similar vert designs. Multicoloured. P* 13½ × 14.
128 75 c. Type **26** 75 80
129 75 c. 1974 Centenary of Universal Postal Union 25 c. and 50 c. commemoratives .. 75 80
130 90 c. Sir Rowland Hill 90 95
131 90 c. 1978 25th anniv of Coronation 90 c. (Queen Elizabeth II) commemorative .. 90 95
MS132 116 × 58 mm. Nos. 128/31 .. .. .. 3·25 3·50
Stamps from No. **MS**132 have cream backgrounds.
Nos. 128/9 and 130/1 were each printed together, *se-tenant*, in horizontal and vertical pairs throughout small sheets of 8.

27 Max and Moritz

28 "Christ carrying Cross" (Book of Ferdinand II)

1979 (20 Nov). *International Year of the Child. Illustrations from Max and Moritz stories by Wilhelm Busch. T* **27** *and similar horiz designs. Multicoloured. P* 13.
133 12 c. Type **27** 15 15
134 12 c. Max and Moritz looking down chimney .. 15 15
135 12 c. Max and Moritz making off with food .. 15 15
136 12 c. Cook about to beat dog 15 15
137 15 c. Max sawing through bridge 20 20
138 15 c. Pursuer approaching bridge 20 20
139 15 c. Bridge collapsing under pursuer 20 20
140 15 c. Pursuer in river 20 20
141 20 c. Baker locking shop 25 25
142 20 c. Max and Moritz coming out of hiding .. 25 25
143 20 c. Max and Moritz falling in dough .. 25 25
144 20 c. Max and Moritz after being rolled into buns by baker 25 25
133/44 .. .. *Set of* 12 2·10 2·10
Nos. 133/6, 137/40 and 141/4 were each printed together, *se-tenant*, in sheets of 4, either with or without labels containing extracts from the books on the top and bottom selvedge.

1980 (28 Mar). *Easter. Scenes from 15th-century Prayer Books. T* **28** *and similar vert designs. Multicoloured. P* 13.
145 12 c. Type **28** 20 20
146 20 c. "The Crucifixion" (William Vrelant, Book of Duke of Burgundy) 25 25
147 35 c. "Descent from the Cross" (Book of Ferdinand II) 40 40
MS148 111 × 65 mm. Nos. 145/7 .. .. .. 75 80
Stamps from No. **MS**148 have cream borders.

1980 (28 Mar). *Easter. Children's Charity. Designs as Nos. 145/7 in separate miniature sheets 54 × 85 mm, each with a face value of* 70 c. + 5 c.
MS149 As Nos. 145/7 .. .. *Set of 3 sheets* 2·25 2·50

29 Queen Elizabeth the Queen Mother in 1937

30 Falk Hoffman, D.D.R. (platform diving) (gold)

1980 (17 Sept). *80th Birthday of Queen Elizabeth the Queen Mother. P* 13.
150 **29** $1 multicoloured .. .. 1·75 1·50
MS151 55 × 84 mm. **29** $2.50 multicoloured .. 3·00 2·75

1980 (14 Nov). *Olympic Games, Moscow. Medal Winners. T* **30** *and similar vert designs. Multicoloured. P* 13½.
152 10 c. Type **30** 12 12
153 10 c. Martina Jaschke, D.D.R. (platform diving) (gold) 12 12
154 20 c. Tomi Polkolainen, Finland (archery) (gold) 20 20
155 20 c. Kete Losaberidse, U.S.S.R. (archery) (gold) 20 20
156 30 c. Czechoslovakia (football) (gold) 30 30
157 30 c. D.D.R. (football) (silver) 30 30
158 50 c. Barbel Wockel, D.D.R. (200-metre dash) (gold) 45 45
159 50 c. Pietro Mennea, Italy (200-metre dash) (gold) 45 45
152/9 .. .. *Set of* 8 1·90 1·90
MS160 150 × 106 mm. Nos. 152/9. P 13 .. .. 2·00 2·10
Stamps from No. **MS**160 have gold borders.
Nos. 152/3, 154/5, 156/7 and 158/9 were each printed together, *se-tenant*, in horizontal pairs throughout the sheet.

31 "The Virgin of Counsellors" (Luis Dalmau)

32 Amatasi

1980 (5 Dec). *Christmas. Paintings. T* **31** *and similar vert designs. Multicoloured. P* 13.
161 20 c. Type **31** 20 20
162 35 c. "Virgin and Child" (Serra brothers) .. 35 35
163 50 c. "The Virgin of Albocacer" (Master of the Porciuncula) 50 50
MS164 135 × 75 mm. Nos. 161/3 .. .. .. 1·10 1·25

1980 (5 Dec). *Christmas. Children's Charity. Designs as Nos. 161/3 in separate miniature sheets, 54 × 77 mm, each with a face value of* 70 c. + 5 c.
MS165 As Nos. 161/3 .. .. *Set of 3 sheets* 2·25

1981 (16 Feb–21 Sept). *Sailing Craft and Ships (1st series). Multicoloured designs as T* **32**. *P* 14 *(Nos. 166/85),* 13 × 14½ *(Nos. 186/205) or* 13½ *(Nos. 206/8).*
166 1 c. Type **32** 8 8
167 1 c. Ndrua 8 8
168 1 c. Waka 8 8
169 1 c. Tongiaki 8 8
170 3 c. Va'a Teu'ua 12 10
171 3 c. *Victoria*, 1500 .. .. 12 10
172 3 c. *Golden Hind*, 1560 .. .. .. 12 10
173 3 c. *Boudeuse*, 1760 .. .. 12 10
174 4 c. *Bounty*, 1787 .. .. 12 10
175 4 c. *Astrolabe*, 1811 .. .. 12 10
176 4 c. *Star of India*, 1861 .. .. .. 12 10
177 4 c. *Great Republic*, 1853 .. .. .. 12 10
178 6 c. *Balcutha*, 1886 .. .. 15 10
179 6 c. *Coonatto*, 1863 .. .. 15 10
180 6 c. *Antiope*, 1866 .. .. 15 10
181 6 c. *Teaping*, 1863 .. .. 15 10
182 10 c. *Preussen*, 1902 .. .. 15 10
183 10 c. *Pamir*, 1921 .. .. 15 10
184 10 c. *Cap Hornier*, 1910 .. .. .. 15 10
185 10 c. *Patriarch*, 1869 .. .. 15 10
186 15 c. As Type **32** (16 Mar) 25 25
187 15 c. As No. 167 (16 Mar) 25 25
188 15 c. As No. 168 (16 Mar) 25 25
189 15 c. As No. 169 (16 Mar) 25 25
190 20 c. As No. 170 (16 Mar) 25 25
191 20 c. As No. 171 (16 Mar) 25 25
192 20 c. As No. 172 (16 Mar) 25 25
193 20 c. As No. 173 (16 Mar) 25 25
194 30 c. As No. 174 (16 Mar) 35 35
195 30 c. As No. 175 (16 Mar) 35 35
196 30 c. As No. 176 (16 Mar) 35 35
197 30 c. As No. 177 (16 Mar) 35 35
198 50 c. As No. 178 (16 Mar) 60 60
199 50 c. As No. 179 (16 Mar) 60 60
200 50 c. As No. 180 (16 Mar) 60 60
201 50 c. As No. 181 (16 Mar) 60 60
202 $1 As No. 182 (15 May) 95 95
203 $1 As No. 183 (15 May) 95 95
204 $1 As No. 184 (15 May) 95 95
205 $1 As No. 185 (15 May) 95 95
206 $2 *Cutty Sark*, 1869 (26 June) .. .. 2·00 2·00
207 $4 *Mermerus*, 1872 (26 June) .. .. 3·50 3·75
208 $6 *Resolution* and *Discovery*, 1776–80 (21 Sept) .. .. 5·50 5·50
166/208 .. .. *Set of* 43 21·00 21·00
Nos. 186/205 are 41 × 25 mm and Nos. 206/8 47 × 33 mm in size.
On Nos. 166/205 the four designs of each value were printed together, *se-tenant*, in blocks of 4 throughout the sheet.
For redrawn versions of these designs in other face values see Nos. 337/55.

33 "Jesus at the Grove" (Veronese)

34 Prince Charles as Young Child

1981 (5 Apr). *Easter. Paintings. T* **33** *and similar vert designs. Multicoloured. P* 14.
218 30 c. Type **33** 25 25
219 40 c. "Christ with Crown of Thorns" (Titian) .. 35 35
220 50 c. "Pietá" (Van Dyck) 50 50
MS221 110 × 68 mm. Nos. 218/20. P 13½ .. .. 1·25 1·25

1981 (5 Apr). *Easter. Children's Charity. Designs as Nos. 218/20 in separate miniature sheets 70 × 86 mm., each with a face value of* 70 c. + 5 c. *P* 13½.
MS222 As Nos. 218/20 .. .. *Set of 3 sheets* 2·50 2·50

1981 (10 July). *Royal Wedding. T* **34** *and similar vert designs. Multicoloured. P* 14.
223 40 c. Type **34** 65 65
224 50 c. Prince Charles as schoolboy 75 75
225 60 c. Prince Charles as young man 85 85
226 70 c. Prince Charles in ceremonial Naval uniform .. .. 1·00 1·00
227 80 c. Prince Charles as Colonel-in-Chief, Royal Regiment of Wales .. .. .. 1·25 1·25
MS228 99 × 89 mm. Nos. 223/7 .. .. .. 4·50 4·50
Nos. 223/7 were each printed in small sheets of 6 including one *se-tenant* stamp-size label.

1981 (30 Nov). *International Year for Disabled Persons. Nos. 223/8 surch as T* **51** *of Aitutaki.*
229 40 c.+ 5 c. Type **34** .. .. 1·25 1·25
230 50 c.+ 5 c. Prince Charles as schoolboy .. 1·40 1·40
231 60 c.+ 5 c. Prince Charles as young man .. 1·50 1·50
232 70 c.+ 5 c. Prince Charles in ceremonial Naval uniform .. .. 1·75 1·75
233 80 c.+ 5 c. Prince Charles as Colonel-in-Chief, Royal Regiment of Wales .. .. .. 2·25 2·25
MS234 99 × 89 mm. As Nos. 229/33, but 10 c. premium on each stamp .. .. 8·00 8·00
Nos. 229/34 have commemorative inscriptions overprinted on the sheet margins.

35 Footballer

36 "The Virgin on a Crescent"

1981 (7 Dec). *World Cup Football Championship, Spain (1982). T* **35** *and similar vert designs showing footballers. Multicoloured. P* 13.
235 15 c. Type **35** 15 15
236 15 c. Footballer wearing orange jersey with black and mauve stripes 15 15
237 15 c. Player in blue jersey 15 15
238 35 c. Player in blue jersey 30 30
239 35 c. Player in red jersey 30 30
240 35 c. Player in yellow jersey with green stripes 30 30
241 50 c. Player in orange jersey 45 45
242 50 c. Player in mauve jersey 45 45
243 50 c. Player in black jersey 45 45
235/43 .. .. *Set of* 9 2·50 2·50
MS244 113 × 151 mm. As Nos. 235/43, but each stamp with a premium of 3 c. .. .. .. 3·50 3·75
The three designs of each value were printed together, *se-tenant*, in horizontal strips of 3 throughout the sheet.

1981 (15 Dec). *Christmas. Details from Engravings by Dürer. T* **36** *and similar vert designs in violet, deep reddish purple and stone. P* 13 × 13½.
245 30 c. Type **36** 30 30
246 40 c. "The Virgin at the Fence" 40 40
247 50 c. "The Holy Virgin and Child" 50 50
MS248 134 × 75 mm. As Nos. 245/7, but each stamp with a premium of 2 c. .. .. .. 1·25 1·40
MS249 Designs as Nos. 245/7 in separate miniature sheets, 58 × 85 mm, each with a face value of 70 c. + 5 c. P 14 × 13½ .. *Set of 3 sheets* 2·00 2·25

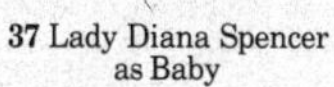

37 Lady Diana Spencer as Baby

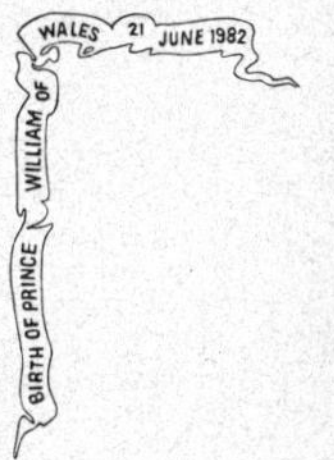

(38)

1982 (1 July). *21st Birthday of Princess of Wales. T* **37** *and similar vert designs. Multicoloured. P* 14.
250 30 c. Type **37** .. 30 30
251 50 c. As young child .. 45 45
252 70 c. As schoolgirl .. 60 60
253 80 c. As teenager .. 80 80
254 $1.40, As young lady .. 1·25 1·25
MS255 87 × 110 mm. Nos. 250/4 .. 3·00 3·25

1982 (30 July). *Birth of Prince William of Wales. Nos. 223/8 optd with T* **38**.
256 40 c. Type **34** .. 1·25 1·25
257 50 c. Prince Charles as schoolboy .. 1·50 1·50
258 60 c. Prince Charles as young man .. 1·75 1·75
259 70 c. Prince Charles in ceremonial Naval uniform .. 2·25 2·25
260 80 c. Prince Charles as Colonel-in-Chief, Royal Regiment of Wales .. 2·75 2·75
MS261 99 × 89 mm. Nos. 256/60 .. 9·50 9·50

1982 (6 Sept). *Birth of Prince William of Wales. As Nos. 250/5 but with changed inscriptions. Multicoloured. P* 13½ × 14.
262 30 c. As Type **37** (inscr "21 JUNE 1982. BIRTH OF PRINCE WILLIAM OF WALES") .. 25 30
263 30 c. As Type **37** (inscr "COMMEMORATING THE BIRTH OF PRINCE WILLIAM OF WALES") .. 25 30
264 50 c. As No. 251 (inscr. "21 JUNE 1982. BIRTH OF PRINCE WILLIAM OF WALES") .. 40 45
265 50 c. As No. 251 (inscr "COMMEMORATING THE BIRTH OF PRINCE WILLIAM OF WALES") .. 40 45
266 70 c. As No. 252 (inscr "21 JUNE 1982. BIRTH OF PRINCE WILLIAM OF WALES") .. 60 65
267 70 c. As No. 252 (inscr "COMMEMORATING THE BIRTH OF PRINCE WILLIAM OF WALES") .. 60 65
268 80 c. As No. 253 (inscr "21 JUNE 1982. BIRTH OF PRINCE WILLIAM OF WALES") .. 60 65
269 80 c. As No. 253 (inscr "COMMEMORATING THE BIRTH OF PRINCE WILLIAM OF WALES") .. 60 65
270 $1.40, As No. 254 (inscr "21 JUNE 1982. BIRTH OF PRINCE WILLIAM OF WALES") .. 1·10 1·25
271 $1.40, As No. 254 (inscr "COMMEMORATING THE BIRTH OF PRINCE WILLIAM OF WALES") .. 1·10 1·25
262/71 .. *Set of* 10 5·50 6·00
MS272 88 × 109 mm. As **MS**255 (stamps inscr "21 JUNE 1982. ROYAL BIRTH PRINCE WILLIAM OF WALES" .. 2·75 2·75
Nos. 262/3, 264/5, 266/7, 268/9 and 270/1 were printed together, *se-tenant*, in sheets of 5 stamps and 1 label, there being three examples of the "21 JUNE 1982 . . ." and two of the "COMMEMORATING . . ." in each sheet.

39 "Virgin and Child" (detail, Joos Van Cleve)

40 Red Coral

1982 (10 Dec). *Christmas. Details from Renaissance Paintings of "Virgin and Child". T* **39** *and similar vert designs. Multicoloured. P* 14 × 13½.
273 35 c. Type **39** .. 30 30
274 48 c. "Virgin and Child" (Filippino Lippi) .. 45 45
275 60 c. "Virgin and Child" (Cima da Conegliano) .. 60 60
MS276 134 × 73 mm. As Nos. 273/5 but each with 2 c. charity premium. P 13 .. 1·60 1·75
Nos. 273/5 were each printed in small sheets of 6 including one *se-tenant*, stamp size, label, depicting the Prince and Princess of Wales with Prince William.

1982 (10 Dec). *Christmas. Children's Charity. Designs as Nos. 273/5, but without frames, in separate miniature sheets,* 60 × 85 *mm, each with a face value of* 70 c. + 5 c. *P* 13.
MS277 As Nos. 273/5 .. *Set of* 3 *sheets* 1·75 1·90

1983 (14 Mar). *Commonwealth Day. T* **40** *and similar vert designs. Multicoloured. P* 13.
278 60 c. Type **40** .. 55 60
279 60 c. Aerial view of Penrhyn atoll .. 55 60
280 60 c. Eleanor Roosevelt on Penrhyn during Second World War .. 55 60
281 60 c. Map of South Pacific .. 55 60
Nos. 278/81 were issued together, *se-tenant*, in blocks of four throughout the sheet.

41 Scout Emblem and Blue Tropical Flower

XV
WORLD
JAMBOREE
CANADA
1983
(**42**)

1983 (5 Apr). *75th Anniv of Boy Scout Movement. T* **41** *and similar horiz designs. Multicoloured. P* 13 × 14.
282 36 c. Type **41** .. 30 35
283 48 c. Emblem and pink flower .. 40 45
284 60 c. Emblem and orange flower .. 55 60
MS285 86 × 46 mm. $2 As 48 c., but with elements of design reversed .. 1·75 1·90

1983 (8 July). *15th World Scout Jamboree, Alberta, Canada. Nos. 282/5 optd with T* **42**.
286 36 c. Type **41** .. 30 35
287 48 c. Emblem and pink flower .. 40 45
288 60 c. Emblem and orange flower .. 55 60
MS289 86 × 46 mm. $2 As 48 c., but with elements of design reversed .. 1·75 1·90

43 School of Whales

44 Cable-laying Ship

1983 (29 July). *Whale Conservation. T* **43** *and similar vert designs. Multicoloured. P* 13.
290 8 c. Type **43** .. 5 8
291 15 c. Harpooner preparing to strike .. 12 15
292 35 c. Whale attacking boat .. 30 35
293 60 c. Dead whales marked with flags .. 55 60
294 $1 Dead whales on slipway .. 90 95

1983 (23 Sept). *World Communications Year. T* **44** *and similar horiz designs. Multicoloured. P* 13.
295 36 c. Type **44** .. 30 35
296 48 c. Men watching cable being laid .. 40 45
297 60 c. Cable-laying ship (*different*) .. 55 60
MS298 115 × 90 mm. As Nos. 295/7 but each with charity premium of 3 c. .. 1·25
On No. **MS**298 the values are printed in black and have been transposed with the World Communications Year logo.

1983 (26 Sept). *Various stamps surch as T* **200** *of Cook Islands.*

(a) Nos. 182/5, 190/7 and 206
299 18 c. on 10 c. *Preussen*, 1902 .. 15 20
300 18 c. on 10 c. *Pamir*, 1921 .. 15 20
301 18 c. on 10 c. *Cap Hornier*, 1910 .. 15 20
302 18 c. on 10 c. *Patriarch*, 1869 .. 15 20
303 36 c. on 20 c. Va'a Teu'ua .. 30 35
304 36 c. on 20 c. *Victoria*, 1500 .. 30 35
305 36 c. on 20 c. *Golden Hind*, 1560 .. 30 35
306 36 c. on 20 c. *Boudeuse*, 1760 .. 30 35
307 36 c. on 30 c. *Bounty*, 1787 .. 30 35
308 36 c. on 30 c. *Astrolabe*, 1811 .. 30 35
309 36 c. on 30 c. *Star of India*, 1861 .. 30 35
310 36 c. on 30 c. *Great Republic*, 1853 .. 30 35
311 $1.20 on $2 *Cutty Sark*, 1869 .. 1·25 1·40

(b) Nos. 252/3
312 72 c. on 70 c. Princess Diana as schoolgirl .. 2·00 1·50
313 96 c. on 80 c. Princess Diana as teenager .. 2·25 1·75
299/313 .. *Set of* 15 8·00 7·00

1983 (28 Oct). *Nos. 208, 225/6, 254 and 268/9 surch as T* **200** *of Cook Islands.*
314 48 c. on 60 c. Prince Charles as young man (Gold) .. 2·75 2·00
a. Error. Surch on No. 258 .. 4·50 4·50
315 72 c. on 70 c. Prince Charles in ceremonial Naval uniform .. 3·25 2·25
a. Error. Surch on No. 259 .. 4·50 4·50
316 96 c. on 80 c. As No. 253 (inscr "21 JUNE 1982 . . .") .. 2·00 1·50
a. Error. Surch on No. 260 .. 5·00 5·00
317 96 c. on 80 c. As No. 253 (inscr "COMMEMORATING. . .") .. 1·50 1·50
318 $1.20 on $1.40, Princess Diana as young lady 2·50 2·00
319 $5.60 on $6 *Resolution* and *Discovery*, 1776–80 .. 4·50 4·50
314/19 .. *Set of* 6 15·00 12·00

45 George Cayley's Airship Design, 1837

1983 (31 Oct). *Bicentenary of Manned Flight. T* **45** *and similar horiz designs. Multicoloured. P* 13. *A. Inscr "NORTHERN COOK ISLANS". B. Corrected spelling optd in black on silver over original inscription.*

		A		B	
320	36 c. Type **45**	75	60	30	35
321	48 c. Dupuy De Lome's man-powered airship, 1872	1·00	70	40	45
322	60 c. Santos Dumont's sixth airship, 1901	1·25	1·00	45	50
323	96 c. Lebaudy's practical airship, 1902	2·00	1·50	75	80
324	$1.32 LZ 127 *Graf Zeppelin*, 1929				
		3·00	2·00	1·00	1·10
MS325	113 × 138 mm. Nos. 320/4	8·00		2·75	

46 "Madonna in the Meadow"

47 Waka

1983 (30 Nov). *Christmas. 500th Birth Anniv of Raphael. T* **46** *and similar vert designs. Multicoloured. P* 13.
326 36 c. Type **46** .. 35 40
327 42 c. "Tempi Madonna" .. 35 40
328 48 c. "The Smaller Cowper Madonna" .. 45 50
329 60 c. "Madonna della Tenda" .. 55 60
MS330 87 × 115 mm. As Nos. 326/9 but each with a charity premium of 3 c. .. 1·75

1983 (1 Dec). *Nos. 266/7, 227 and 270/1 surch as T* **200** *of Cook Islands.*
331 72 c. on 70 c. As No. 252 (inscr "21 JUNE 1982. . .") .. 2·00 1·75
332 72 c. on 70 c. As No. 252 (inscr "COMMEMORATING. . .") .. 1·50 1·25
333 96 c. on 80 c. Prince Charles as Colonel-in-Chief, Royal Regiment of Wales .. 2·00 1·50
334 $1.20 on $1.40, As No. 254 (inscr "21 JUNE 1982. . .") .. 2·25 1·75
335 $1.20 on $1.40, As No. 254 (inscr "COMMEMORATING. . .") .. 1·75 1·50

1983 (28 Dec). *Christmas. 500th Birth Anniv of Raphael. Children's Charity. Designs as Nos. 326/9 in separate miniature sheets,* 65 × 84 *mm, each with a face value of* 75 c. + 5 c. *P* 13.
MS336 As Nos. 326/9 .. *Set of* 4 *sheets* 2·90

1984 (8 Feb–15 June). *Sailing Craft and Ships (2nd series). Designs as Nos. 166, etc. but with redrawn frames, inscriptions and compass rose at top right as in T* **47**. *Multicoloured. P* 13 × 13½ ($9.60), 13 ($3, $5) *or* 11 (*others*).
337 2 c. Type **47** .. 5 5
338 4 c. Amatasi .. 5 5
339 5 c. Ndrua .. 5 5
340 8 c. Tongiaki .. 8 10
341 10 c. *Victoria* .. 8 10
342 18 c. *Golden Hind* .. 15 20
343 20 c. *Boudeuse* .. 15 20
344 30 c. *Bounty* .. 25 30
345 36 c. *Astrolabe* .. 30 35
346 48 c. *Great Republic* .. 35 40
347 50 c. *Star of India* (21 Mar) .. 40 45
348 60 c. *Coonatto* (21 Mar) .. 45 50
349 72 c. *Antiope* (21 Mar) .. 55 60
350 80 c. *Balcutha* (21 Mar) .. 60 65
351 96 c. *Cap Hornier* (21 Mar) .. 70 75
352 $1.20, *Pamir* (21 Mar) .. 90 95
353 $3 *Mermerus* (41 × 31 *mm*) (4 May) .. 2·25 2·40
354 $5 *Cutty Sark* (41 × 31 *mm*) (4 May) .. 3·75 4·00
355 $9.60 *Resolution* and *Discovery* (40 × 32 *mm*) (15 June) .. 7·00 7·25
337/55 .. *Set of* 19 15·50 16·50

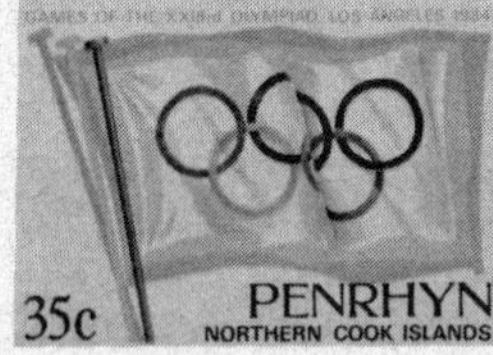

48 Olympic Flag

1984 (20 July). *Olympic Games, Los Angeles. T* **48** *and similar horiz designs. Multicoloured. P* 13½ × 13.
356 35 c. Type **48** .. 30 35
357 60 c. Olympic torch and flags .. 50 55
358 $1.80, Ancient athletes and Coliseum .. 1·50 1·60
MS359 103 × 86 mm. As Nos. 356/8 but each with a charity premium of 5 c. .. 2·40 2·50

49 Penrhyn Stamps of 1978, 1979 and 1981

1984 (20 Sept). *"Ausipex" International Stamp Exhibition, Melbourne. T* **49** *and similar horiz design. Multicoloured. P* 13½ × 13.
360 60 c. Type **49** .. 50 55
361 $1.20, Location map of Penrhyn .. 1·00 1·10
MS362 90 × 90 mm. As Nos. 360/1, but each with a face value of 96 c. .. 1·75 2·00

$2

Birth of
Prince Henry
15 Sept. 1984

(**50**)

51 "Virgin and Child" (Giovanni Bellini)

1984 (18 Oct). *Birth of Prince Henry. Nos. 223/4 and 250/1 surch as T* **50**.
363 $2 on 30 c. Type **37** .. .. 2·25 1·50
364 $2 on 40 c. Type **34** .. .. 2·75 1·75
365 $2 on 50 c. Prince Charles as schoolboy .. 2·75 1·75
366 $2 on 50 c. Lady Diana as young child (Gold) 2·25 1·50

1984 (15 Nov). *Christmas. Paintings of the Virgin and Child by different artists. T* **51** *and similar vert designs. Multicoloured. P* 13 × 13½.
367 36 c. Type **51** 30 35
368 48 c. Lorenzo di Credi 40 45
369 60 c. Palma the Older 45 50
370 96 c. Raphael 75 80
MS371 93 × 118 mm. As Nos. 367/70, but each with a charity premium of 5 c. .. .. 2·00

1984 (10 Dec). *Christmas. Children's Charity. Designs as Nos. 367/70, but without frames, in separate miniature sheets* 67 × 81 *mm, each with a face value of* 96 c. + 10 c. *P* 13½.
MS372 As Nos. 367/70 .. .. *Set of* 4 *sheets* 3·00

OFFICIAL STAMPS

O.H.M.S.

(O 1)

1978 (14 Nov). *Nos.* 57/66, 89/91 *and* 101/2 *optd or surch (Nos.* O8/9 *and* O12) *as Type* O 1.
O 1 1 c. *Mondactylus argenteus* 10 5
O 2 2 c. *Pomacanthus imperator*.. .. .. 10 5
O 3 3 c. *Chelmon rostratus* 10 5
O 4 4 c. *Chaetodon ornatissimus* 10 5
O 5 5 c. *Chaetodon melanotus* 10 5
O 6 8 c. *Chaetodon raffessi* 10 8
O 7 10 c. *Chaetodon ephippium* 15 10
O 8 15 c. on 60 c. *Plectorhynchus chaetodonoides* 15 12
O 9 18 c. on 60 c. *Plectorhynchus chaetodonoides* 20 15
O10 20 c. *Pygoplites diacanthus* 20 15
O11 25 c. *Heniochus acuminatus* (Silver) 25 20
O12 30 c. on 60 c. *Plectorhynchus chaetodonoides* 30 25
O13 50 c. } 45 35
O14 50 c. } "The Spirit of '76" (A. M. Willard) (Gold) 45 35
O15 50 c. } 45 35
O16 $1 Queen and Prince Philip (Silver) .. 2·25 1·00
O17 $2 Queen Elizabeth II (Gold) .. .. 4·50 2·25
O1/17 .. .. *Set of* 17 9·00 5·00

These stamps were originally only sold to the public cancelled-to-order and not in unused condition. They were made available to overseas collectors in mint condition during 1980.

Cyprus

Cyprus was part of the Turkish Ottoman Empire from 1571.

The first records of an organised postal service date from 1871 when a post office was opened at Nicosia (Lefkosa) under the jurisdiction of the Damascus Head Post Office. Various stamps of Turkey from the 1868 issue onwards are known used from this office, cancelled "KIBRIS", in Arabic, within a double-lined oblong. Manuscript cancellations have also been reported. The records report the opening of a further office at Larnaca (Tuzla) in 1873, but no cancellation for this office has been identified.

To provide an overseas postal service the Austrian Empire opened a post office in Larnaca during 1846. Stamps of the Austrian Post Offices in the Turkish Empire were placed on sale there from 1 June 1864 and were cancelled with an unframed straight-line mark or circular date stamp. This Austrian post office closed in 1879.

BRITISH ADMINISTRATION

Following the convention with Turkey, Great Britain assumed the administration of Cyprus on 11 July 1878 and the first post office, as part of the British G.P.O. system, was opened at Larnaca on 27 July 1878. Further offices at Famagusta, Kyrenia, Limassol, Nicosia and Paphos followed in September 1878. In addition two Camp post offices, mainly for the use of the administration, were established at Nicosia (Headquarters Camp) and Polymedia (Polemidhia) (near Limassol). These were supplied with numeral postmarks in January 1881, which can be found cancelling Great Britain stamps for a short period after that date.

The stamps of Great Britain were supplied to the various offices as they opened and continued to be used until the Cyprus Administration assumed responsibility for the postal service on 1 April 1880, although scattered examples are known dating from 1881.

For illustrations of the postmark types see BRITISH POST OFFICES ABROAD notes, following GREAT BRITAIN.

FAMAGUSTA

Stamps of GREAT BRITAIN *cancelled* "982" *as Type* **9**

1878 *to* **1880–81**.
Z1 ½d. rose-red (1870–79) (Plate Nos. 11, 13).. .. £450
Z2 1d. rose-red (1864–70) .. ..
Plate Nos. 145, 174, 181, 193, 202, 206, 215.
Z3 2d. blue (1858–69) (Plate Nos. 13, 14, 15).. .. £900
Z4 2½d. rosy mauve (1876) (Plate Nos. 13, 16).. .. £800
Z5 6d. grey (1874–80) (Plate No. 15) .. .. ..
Z6 1s. green (1873–77) (Plate No. 12).. .. .. £1400
Z7 1s. orange-brown (1881) (Plate No. 14) £2000

KYRENIA

Stamps of GREAT BRITAIN *cancelled* "974" *as Type* **9**

1878 *to* **1880**.
Z 8 ½d. rose-red (1870–79) (Plate No. 1) .. ..
Z 9 1d. rose-red (1864–79) .. .. .. *From* £190
Plate Nos. 168, 171, 193, 196, 206, 207, 209, 220.
Z10 2d. blue (1858–69) (Plate Nos. 13, 15) .. *From* £550
Z11 2½d. rosy mauve (1876–79) .. .. .. *From* £130
Plate Nos. 12, 13, 14, 15.
Z12 4d. sage-green (1877) (Plate No. 16) .. ..
Z13 6d. grey (1874–80) (Plate No. 16) .. .. ..

LARNACA

Stamps of GREAT BRITAIN *cancelled* "942" *as Type* **9**

1878 *to* **1880–81**.
Z14 ½d. rose-red (1870–79) .. .. .. *From* £250
Plate Nos. 11, 12, 13, 14, 15, 19, 20.
Z15 1d. rose-red (1864–79) .. .. .. *From* 95·00
Plate Nos. 129, 131, 146, 154, 170, 171, 174, 175, 176, 177, 178, 179, 181, 182, 183, 184, 187, 188, 190, 191, 192, 193, 194, 195, 196, 197, 198, 199, 200, 201, 202, 203, 204, 205, 206, 207, 208, 209, 210, 212, 213, 214, 215, 216, 217, 218, 220, 221, 222, 225.
Z16 1½d. lake-red (1870) (Plate No. 3) £1200
Z17 2d. blue (1858–69 (Plate Nos. 9, 13, 14, 15) .. 55·00
Z18 2½d. rosy mauve (1876–79) .. .. .. *From* 25·00
Plate Nos. 4, 5, 6, 8, 10, 11, 12, 13, 14, 15, 16, 17.
Z19 2½d. blue (1880–81) (Plate Nos. 17, 18, 19, 20) .. £400
Z20 2½d. blue (1881) (Plate No. 21) £400
Z21 4d. sage-green (1877) (Plate Nos. 15, 16) .. £500
Z22 6d. grey (1874–76) (Plate No. 15, 16, 17) .. £250
Z23 6d. pale buff (1872–73) (Plate No. 11) £1100
Z24 8d. orange (1876) £3000
Z25 1s. green (1873–77) (Plate Nos. 12, 13) £350
Z26 1s. orange-brown (1881) (Plate No. 14) £1500
Z27 5s. rose (1874) (Plate No. 2) £3000

LIMASSOL

Stamps of GREAT BRITAIN *cancelled* "975" *as Type* **9**

1878 *to* **1880**.
Z28 ½d. rose-red (1870–79) (Plate Nos. 11, 13, 15, 19) £200
Z29 1d. rose-red (1864–79) .. .. .. *From* 65·00
Plate Nos. 160, 171, 173, 174, 177, 179, 184, 187, 190, 193, 195, 196, 197, 198, 200, 202, 206, 207, 208, 209, 210, 213, 215, 216, 218, 220, 221, 222, 225.
Z30 1½d. lake-red (1870–74) (Plate No. 3) £1500
Z31 2d. blue (1858–69) (Plate Nos. 14, 15) .. *From* 95·00
Z32 2½d. rosy-mauve (1876–80) .. .. .. *From* 65·00
Plate Nos. 11, 12, 13, 14, 15, 16.
Z33 2½d. blue (1880) (Plate Nos. 17, 19, 20) .. *From* £1200
Z34 4d. sage-green (Plate No. 16) £275

NICOSIA

Stamps of GREAT BRITAIN *cancelled* "969" *as Type* **9**

1878 *to* **1880–81**.
Z35 ½d. rose-red (1870–79) £250
Plate Nos. 12, 13, 14, 15, 20.
Z36 1d. rose-red (1864–79) .. .. .. *From* 60·00
Plate Nos. 170, 171, 174, 189, 190, 192, 193, 195, 196, 198, 200, 202, 203, 205, 206, 207, 210, 212, 214, 215, 218, 221, 222, 225.
Z37 2d. blue (1858–69) (Plate Nos. 14 and 15).. ..
Z38 2½d. rosy mauve (1876–79) .. .. .. *From* 90·00
Plate Nos. 10, 11, 12, 13, 14, 15, 16.
Z39 2½d. blue (1880) (Plate No. 20) .. .. ..
Z40 2½d. blue (1881) (Plate No. 21) .. .. ..
Z41 4d. vermilion (1876) (Plate No. 15) .. ..
Z42 4d. sage-green (1877) (Plate No. 16) £500
Z43 6d. grey (1873) (Plate No. 16) £500

PAPHOS

Stamps of GREAT BRITAIN *cancelled* "981" *as Type* **9**

1878 *to* **1880**.
Z44 ½d. rose-red (1870–79) (Plate No. 13, 15) .. ..
Z45 1d. rose-red (1864–79) .. .. .. *From* £225
Plate Nos. 196, 201, 202, 204, 206, 213, 217.
Z46 2d. blue (1858–69) (Plate No. 15) £600
Z47 2½d. rosy mauve (1876–79) .. .. .. *From* £300
Plate Nos. 13, 14, 15.

HEADQUARTER CAMP, NICOSIA

Stamps of GREAT BRITAIN *cancelled* "D 48" *as Type* **8**

1881.
Z48 ½d. rose-red (1870–79) (Plate Nos. 13, 20).. .. £1200
Z49 1d. rose-red (1864–79) .. .. .. *From* £550
Plate Nos. 123, 171, 174, 177, 201, 204, 205, 214, 218.
Z50 2d. blue (1858–69) (Plate No. 15) £1200

POLYMEDIA (POLEMIDHIA) CAMP, LIMASSOL

Stamps of GREAT BRITAIN *cancelled* "D 47" *as Type* **8**

1881.
Z51 ½d. rose-red (1870–79) (Plate No. 11) £1300
Z52 1d. rose-red (1864–79) .. .. .. *From* £550
Plate Nos. 78, 99, 110, 132, 175, 192, 197, 205, 206, 207, 208, 209.
Z53 2d. blue (1858–69) (Plate No. 15) £1100

"D 48" differs from Type **8** in that the "D" is taller and narrower and the "4" has pronounced serifs. Stamps with "D 47" and "D 48" having four bars instead of three were used in Great Britain before the altered postmarks were sent to Cyprus.

PRICES FOR STAMPS ON COVER TO 1945	
Nos. 1/10	*from* × 5
Nos. 11/49	*from* × 4
Nos. 50/122	*from* × 3
Nos. 123/43	*from* × 4
Nos. 144/50	*from* × 3
Nos. 151/63	*from* × 5

PERFORATION. Nos. 1/122 are perf 14.

Stamps of Great Britain overprinted

CYPRUS (1) CYPRUS (2)

(Optd by D.L.R.)

1880 (1 Apr).
1 **1** ½d. rose .. .. 70·00 80·00
a. Opt double (Plate 15) .. .. .. — £3000

Plate No.	*Un.*	*Used*	*Plate No.*	*Un.*	*Used*
12.	90·00	£170	19.	£2750	£1200
15.	70·00	80·00			

2 **2** 1d. red .. .. 7·50 20·00
a. Opt double (Plate 208) £6000
aa. Opt double (Plate 218) £2500
b. Pair, one without opt (Plate 208) £6500

174.	£800	£850	208.	55·00	26·00
181.	80·00	90·00	215.	9·00	20·00
184.	£5500	£1800	216.	11·00	23·00
193.	£500	†	217.	9·00	23·00
196.	£500	†	218.	11·00	23·00
201.	7·50	20·00	220.	£700	£450
205.	16·00	22·00			

3 **2** 2½d. rosy mauve .. .. 2·00 3·25
a. Large thin "C" (Plate 14) .. .. 15·00 24·00
b. Large thin "C" (Plate 15) .. .. 17·00 30·00

14.	2·00	3·25	15.	2·50	9·00

4 **2** 4d. sage-green (Plate 16) £120 £130
5 6d. grey (Plate 16) £500 £550
6 1s. green (Plate 13) £600 £450

HALF-PENNY (3) 18 mm HALF-PENNY (4) 16 or 16½ mm

HALF-PENNY (5) 13 mm 30 PARAS (6)

(Optd by Govt Ptg Office, Nicosia)

1881 (Feb–June). *No. 2 surch.*
7 **3** ½d. on 1d. red (Feb) .. .. .. 35·00 40·00
a. "HALFPENN" (*all plates*).. *From* £600 £600

Plate No.	*Un.*	*Used*	*Plate No.*	*Un.*	*Used*
174.	55·00	£160	215.	£200	£400
181.	55·00	70·00	216.	35·00	40·00
201.	35·00	40·00	217.	£350	£300
205.	45·00	45·00	218.	£250	£300
208.	90·00	£130	220.	95·00	£110

8 4 ½d. on 1d. red (Apr) .. .. .. 70·00 85·00
a. Surch double (Plates 201 and 216) £1500

201 .. .. 70·00 85·00 | 218 .. .. — —
216 .. .. £175 £275

9 5 ½d. on 1d. red (June) .. .. .. 25·00 35·00
a. Surch double (Plate 201) .. ..
aa. Surch double (Plate 205) £500
ab. Surch double (Plate 215) £425 £425
b. Surch treble (Plate 205) .. ..
ba. Surch treble (Plate 215) £500
bb. Surch treble (Plate 217) .. ..
bc. Surch treble (Plate 218) £750
c. Surch quadruple (Plate 205) .. £1500
ca. Surch quadruple (Plate 215) .. £1400
d. "CYPRUS" double (Plate 218) ..

201 .. .. — — | 217 .. .. 35·00 40·00
205 .. .. 85·00 — | 218 .. .. 35·00 40·00
215 .. .. 25·00 35·00

10 6 30 paras on 1d. red (June) .. .. 60·00 85·00
a. Surch double, one invtd (Plate 216) £1600
aa. Surch double, one invtd (Plate 220) £1100 £1300

201 .. .. 70·00 85·00 | 217 .. .. 90·00 £100
216 .. .. 60·00 85·00 | 220 .. .. 95·00 £110

(New Currency: 40 paras = 1 piastre. 180 piastres = £1)

7 (8) (9)

(Typo D.L.R.)

1881 (1 July). *Die I. Wmk Crown CC.*
11 7 ½ pi. emerald-green .. .. .. £225 65·00
12 1 pi. rose .. .. £300 65·00
13 2 pi. blue .. .. £500 65·00
14 4 pi. pale olive-green £950 £275
15 6 pi. olive-grey £1200 £400

Stamps of Queen Victoria initialled "J.A.B." or overprinted "POSTAL SURCHARGE" with or without the same initials were employed for accounting purposes between the Chief Post Office and sub-offices, the initials are those of the then Postmaster, Mr. J. A. Bulmer.

1882 (May)–**86**. *Die I*. Wmk Crown CA.*
16 7 ½ pi. emerald-green (5.82) £4000 £300
a. Dull green (4.83) .. .. 4·00 60
17 30 pa. pale mauve (7.6.82) .. .. 30·00 15·00
18 1 pi. rose (5.83) .. .. .. 35·00 3·00
19 2 pi. blue (9.83) .. .. .. 60·00 3·00
20 4 pi. deep olive-green (1883) .. .. £275 28·00
a. Pale olive-green .. .. £225 25·00
21 6 pi. olive-grey (1.83) .. .. 42·00 15·00
22 12 pi. orange-brown (1886) (Optd S. £250) £175 32·00
16*a*/22 .. .. *Set of* 7 £550 80·00

* For description and illustrations of Dies I and II see Introduction.
See also Nos. 31/7.

1882. *Surch locally with T* **8/9**. *(a) Wmk Crown CC.*
23 7 ½ on ½ pi. emerald-green (6.82) .. .. £180 35·00
24 30 pa. on 1 pi. rose (22.5.82) £1200 £170

(b) Wmk Crown CA
25 7 ½ on ½ pi. emerald-green (6.82) .. .. 55·00 10·00
a. Surch double .. .. .. — £1400

Two varities of T **10**:
(a) Fractions approx 6 mm apart
(b) Fractions approx 8 mm apart

(10) 11

1886 (Apr). *Surch with T* **10** *(a) by De La Rue.*

(a) Wmk Crown CC
26 7 ½ on ½ pi. emerald-green £3250

(b) Wmk Crown CA
27 7 ½ on ½ pi. emerald-green .. .. £140 55·00
The status of No. 26 remains in doubt as it is not known used.

1886 (May). *Surch with T* **10** *(b) by De La Rue.*

(a) Wmk Crown CC
28 7 ½ on ½ pi. emerald-green £3250 £425
a. Large "1" at left .. .. .. — £1200
b. Small "1" at right £5500 £1900

(b) Wmk Crown CA
29 7 ½ on ½ pi. emerald-green .. .. £125 10·00
a. Large "1" at left £850 £200
b. Small "1" at right £1300 £275

A third type of this surcharge is known with the fraction spaced approximately 10 mm apart on CA paper with postmarks from August 1886. This may be due to the shifting of type.

1892–94. *Die II. Wmk Crown CA.*
31 7 ½ pi. dull green .. .. .. 2·75 85
32 30 pa. mauve .. .. 2·50 2·25
33 1 pi. carmine .. .. 7·00 2·25
34 2 pi. ultramarine .. .. .. 12·00 1·25
35 4 pi. olive-green .. .. .. 50·00 9·00
a. Pale olive-green .. .. 22·00 8·50
36 6 pi. olive-grey (1894) £120 £180
37 12 pi. orange-brown £110 £140
31/37 .. .. *Set of* 7 £250 £300

1894 (14 Aug)–**96**. *Colours changed and new values. Die II. Wmk Crown CA.*
40 7 ½ pi. green and carmine (1896) .. .. 3·00 45
41 30 pa. bright mauve and green (1896) .. 2·25 70
42 1 pi. carmine and blue (1896) .. .. 3·75 50
43 2 pi. blue and purple (1896) .. .. 4·25 60
44 4 pi. sage-green and purple (1896) .. 10·00 3·75
45 6 pi. sepia and green (1896) .. .. 7·50 7·50
46 9 pi. brown and carmine .. .. .. 17·00 8·50
47 12 pi. orange-brown and black (1896) .. 17·00 28·00
48 18 pi. greyish slate and brown .. .. 55·00 40·00
49 45 pi. grey-purple and blue £130 £130
40/49 .. .. *Set of* 10 £225 £200
40/49 Optd "Specimen" .. .. *Set of* 10 £450

(Typo D.L.R.)

1902–04. *Wmk Crown CA.*
50 11 ½ pi. green and carmine (12.02) .. .. 3·00 80
51 30 pa. violet and green (2.03) .. .. 1·75 1·50
a. Mauve and green .. .. 2·75 2·50
52 1 pi. carmine and blue (9.03) .. .. 9·00 2·75
53 2 pi. blue and purple (2.03) .. .. 14·00 8·00
54 4 pi. olive-green and purple (9.03) .. 20·00 11·00
55 6 pi. sepia and green (9.03) .. .. 40·00 48·00
56 9 pi. brown and carmine (5.04) .. .. 75·00 £120
57 12 pi. chestnut and black (4.03) .. .. 10·00 14·00
58 18 pi. black and brown (5.04) .. .. 60·00 70·00
59 45 pi. dull purple and ultramarine (10.03) £250 £275
50/59 .. .. *Set of* 10 £450 £500
50/59 Optd "Specimen" .. .. *Set of* 10 £550

1904–10. *Wmk Mult Crown CA.*
60 11 5 pa. bistre and black (14.1.08) 40 75
61 10 pa. orange and green (12.06) .. .. 1·50 1·25
a. Yellow and green .. .. 22·00 11·00
62 ½ pi. green and carmine (1.7.04) .. .. 2·00 30
63 30 pa. purple and green (1.7.04) .. .. 6·00 1·75
a. Violet and green (1910) .. .. 7·50 2·00
64 1 pi. carmine and blue (11.04) .. .. 1·75 50
65 2 pi. blue and purple (11.04) .. .. 3·50 85
66 4 pi. olive-green and purple (2.05) .. 11·00 8·00
67 6 pi. sepia and green (17.7.04) .. .. 9·50 8·00
68 9 pi. brown and carmine (30.5.04) .. .. 9·00 11·00
a. Yellow-brown and carmine .. 10·00 13·00
69 12 pi. chestnut and black (4.06) .. .. 24·00 13·00
70 18 pi. black and brown (16.6.04) .. .. 28·00 12·00
71 45 pi. dull purple and ultram (15.6.04) .. 55·00 55·00
60/71 .. .. *Set of* 12 £140 £100
60/61 Optd "Specimen" .. .. *Set of* 2 £180

12 13

(Typo D.L.R.)

1912 (July)–**15**. *Wmk Mult Crown CA.*
74 12 10 pa. orange and green (11.12) .. .. 2·25 1·25
a. Wmk sideways .. ..
b. Orange-yellow and bright green (8.15) .. .. .. 2·00 1·25
75 ½ pi. green and carmine .. .. .. 1·50 1·10
a. Yellow-green and carmine .. .. 3·00 1·40
76 30 pa. violet and green (8.13) .. .. 1·50 1·00
77 1 pi. rose-red and blue (9.12) .. .. 3·00 2·75
a. Carmine and blue (8.15?) .. .. 10·00 4·75
78 2 pi. blue and purple (7.13) .. .. 4·50 2·00
79 4 pi. olive-green and purple .. .. 3·50 2·40
80 6 pi. sepia and green .. .. .. 3·50 3·25
81 9 pi. brown and carmine (3.15) .. .. 17·00 14·00
a. Yellow-brown and carmine .. .. 17·00 17·00
82 12 pi. chestnut and black (7.13) .. .. 7·50 12·00
83 18 pi. black and brown (3.15) .. .. 15·00 17·00
84 45 pi. dull purple and ultramarine (3.15) 60·00 65·00
74/84 .. .. *Set of* 11 £110 £110
74/84 Optd "Specimen" .. .. *Set of* 11 £375

1921–23. *(a) Wmk Mult Script CA.*
85 12 10 pa. orange and green .. .. .. 1·50 2·00
86 10 pa. grey and yellow (1923) .. .. 6·00 8·00
87 30 pa. violet and green .. .. .. 2·00 1·00
88 30 pa. green (1923) .. .. .. 3·25 2·00
89 1 pi. carmine and blue .. .. .. 7·00 11·00
90 1 pi. violet and red (1922) .. .. 4·00 5·50
91 1½ pi. yellow and black (1922) .. .. 3·50 4·75
92 2 pi. blue and purple .. .. .. 7·50 8·50
93 2 pi. carmine and blue (1922) .. .. 8·50 12·00
94 2¾ pi. blue and purple (1922) .. .. 9·50 15·00
95 4 pi. olive-green and purple .. .. 6·50 10·00
96 6 pi. sepia and green (1923) .. .. 9·50 16·00
97 9 pi. brown and carmine (1922) .. .. 17·00 22·00
a. Yellow-brown and carmine .. .. 23·00 30·00
98 18 pi. black and brown (1923) .. .. 60·00 75·00
99 45 pi. dull purple and ultramarine (1923) £150 £190
85/99 .. .. *Set of* 15 £275 £350
85/99 Optd "Specimen" .. .. *Set of* 15 £550

(b) Wmk Mult Crown CA (1923)
100 12 10s. green and red/*pale yellow* £500 £550
101 £1 purple and black/*red* £1100 £1200
100/101 Optd "Specimen" .. .. *Set of* 2 £700

1924. *Chalk-surfaced paper. (a) Wmk Mult Crown CA.*
102 13 £1 purple and black/*red* £450 £500

(b) Wmk Mult Script CA
103 13 ¼ pi. grey and chestnut 55 45
104 ½ pi. black .. .. 1·25 2·25
105 ¾ pi. green .. .. 1·40 75
106 1 pi. purple and chestnut 65 45
107 1½ pi. orange and black .. .. .. 1·40 2·75
108 2 pi. carmine and green .. .. .. 2·75 4·50
109 2¾ pi. bright blue and purple .. .. 1·60 3·25
110 4 pi. sage-green and purple .. .. 3·75 4·00
111 4½ pi. black and orange/*emerald* .. .. 3·75 5·00
112 6 pi. olive-brown and green .. .. 4·00 7·50
113 13 9 pi. brown and purple .. .. .. 4·25 6·50
114 12 pi. chestnut and black .. .. .. 7·00 18·00
115 18 pi. black and orange .. .. .. 18·00 16·00
116 45 pi. purple and blue .. .. .. 28·00 35·00
117 90 pi. green and red/*yellow* .. .. 60·00 80·00
117*a* £5 black/*yellow* (1928) (Optd S. £1300) £4000 £6500

CROWN COLONY

1925–28. *Wmk Mult Script CA.*
118 13 ½ pi. green, **C** .. .. .. 1·50 2·00
119 ¾ pi. brownish black, **C** .. .. 1·75 20
120 1½ pi. scarlet, **O** .. .. .. 1·90 90
121 2 pi. yellow and black, **C** .. .. 5·00 6·00
122 2½ pi. bright blue, **O** .. .. .. 2·75 80
102/122 .. .. .. *Set of* 21 *to* £1 £550 £600
102/22 Optd "Specimen" .. .. *Set of* 21 £700

In the above set the fraction bar in the value is horizontal. In Nos. 91, 94, 107 and 109 it is diagonal.

14 Silver Coin of Amathus **16** Map of Cyprus

(Recess B.W.)

1928 (1 Feb). *50th Anniv of British Rule. T* **14**, **16** *and similar designs. Wmk Mult Script CA. P* 12.
123 ¾ pi. deep dull purple .. .. .. 1·25 70
124 1 pi. black and greenish blue .. .. 1·60 2·00
125 1½ pi. scarlet .. .. 4·25 4·50
126 2½ pi. light blue .. .. 2·00 3·75
127 4 pi. deep brown .. .. 7·50 13·00
128 6 pi. blue .. .. 9·50 15·00
129 9 pi. maroon .. .. 8·50 11·00
130 18 pi. black and brown .. .. .. 20·00 26·00
131 45 pi. violet and blue .. .. .. 45·00 48·00
132 £1 blue and bistre-brown £400 £450
123/132 .. .. *Set of* 10 £450 £500
123/32 Optd "Specimen" .. .. *Set of* 10 £900

Designs: *Vert*—1 pi. Zeno (philosopher); 2½ pi. Discovery of body of St Barnabas; 4 pi. Cloister, Abbey of Bella Paise; 9 pi. Tekke of Umm Haram; 18 pi. Statue of Richard I, London; 45 pi. St Nicholas, Famagusta; £1 King George V. *Horiz*—6 pi. Badge of Cyprus.

24 Vouni Palace **25** Salamis

30 St. Sophia, Nicosia **31** Bairakdar Mosque

(Recess Waterlow)

1934 (1 Dec). *T* **24/5**, **30/31** *and similar designs. Wmk Mult Script CA (sideways on ½ pi., 1½ pi, 2½ pi., 4½ pi., 6 pi., 9 pi., and 18 pi.), P 12½.*
133 ¼ pi. ultramarine and orange-brown .. 40 75
a. Imperf between (vert pair) £9000
134 ½ pi. green 50 90
a. Imperf between (vert pair) £7500 £8000
135 ¾ pi. black and violet 60 30
a. Imperf between (pair) £7000
136 1 pi. black and red-brown .. .. .. 1·40 1·75
a. Imperf between (vert pair) £7500 £8000
b. Imperf between (horiz pair) £5500
137 1½ pi. carmine .. .. 90 1·00
138 2½ pi. ultramarine .. .. .. 1·25 1·75
139 4½ pi. black and crimson .. .. .. 5·50 3·25
140 6 pi. black and blue .. .. .. 7·50 10·00
141 9 pi. sepia and violet .. .. .. 5·50 6·00
142 18 pi. black and olive-green .. .. 23·00 22·00
143 45 pi. green and black .. .. .. 60·00 55·00
133/143 .. .. *Set of* 11 95·00 90·00
133/43 Perf "Specimen" .. .. *Set of* 11 £350

Designs: *Horiz.*—¾ pi. Peristerona Church; 1 pi. Soli Theatre; 1½ pi. Kyrenia Harbour; 2½ pi. Kolossi Castle; 45 pi. Forest scene. *Vert*—9 pi. Queen's Window, St. Hilarion Castle; 18 pi. Buyuk Khan, Nicosia.

1935 (6 May). *Silver Jubilee. As Nos. 91/4 of Antigua, but ptd by Waterlow & Sons. P* 11 × 12.
144 ¾ pi. ultramarine and grey 40 25
145 1½ pi. deep blue and scarlet .. .. 2·25 2·25
146 2½ pi. brown and deep blue .. .. 7·00 7·50
147 9 pi. slate and purple .. .. .. 13·00 14·00
144/7 Perf "Specimen" .. .. *Set of* 4 75·00

1937 (12 May). *Coronation. As Nos. 13/15 of Aden, but ptd by B.W. & Co. P* 11 × 11½.
148 ¾ pi. grey 55 20
149 1½ pi. carmine 95 60
150 2½ pi. blue .. .. 2·00 1·75
148/50 Perf "Specimen" .. .. *Set of* 3 45·00

35 Vouni Palace

36 Map of Cyprus

37 Citadel (Othello's Tower), Famagusta

38 King George VI

(Recess Waterlow)

1938 (12 May)–**1951**. *T* **35** *to* **38** *and other designs as* 1934, *but with portrait of King George VI. Wmk Mult Script CA. P* 12½.
151 **35** ¼ pi. ultramarine and orange-brown .. 20 20
152 **25** ½ pi. green 15 12
152*a* – ½ pi. violet (2.7.51) 85 25
153 – ¾ pi. black and violet .. .. .. 2·50 15
154 – 1 pi. orange 40 15
a. Perf 13½ × 12½ (1944) .. .. £250 20·00
155 – 1½ pi. carmine .. .. 1·50 1·00
155*a* – 1½ pi. violet (15.3.43) 30 25
155*ab* – 1½ pi. green (2.7.51) .. .. .. 1·50 30
155*b* – 2 pi. black and carmine (30.1.42) .. 25 15
c. Perf 12½ × 13½ (1944) .. .. 1·25 3·00
156 – 2½ pi. ultramarine .. .. 7·50 4·25
156*a* – 3 pi. ultramarine (30.1.42) 30 12
156*b* – 4 pi. ultramarine (2.7.51) .. .. 3·25 30
157 **36** 4½ pi. grey 25 12
158 **31** 6 pi. black and blue 80 60
159 **37** 9 pi. black and purple 50 15
160 – 18 pi. black and olive-green .. .. 2·50 85
a. Black and sage-green (19.8.47) .. 5·00 2·50
161 – 45 pi. green and black .. .. .. 9·00 2·50
162 **38** 90 pi. mauve and black .. .. .. 32·00 10·00
163 – £1 scarlet and indigo .. .. .. 65·00 35·00
151/163 .. .. *Set of* 19 £120 50·00
151/63 Perf "Specimen" .. .. *Set of* 16 £250

Designs: *Horiz*—¾ pi., 2 pi. Peristerona Church; 1 pi. Soli Theatre; 1½ pi. Kyrenia Harbour; 2½ pi., 3 pi., 4 pi. Kolossi Castle; 45 pi. Forest scene. *Vert*—18 pi. Buyuk Khan, Nicosia.

1946 (21 Oct). *Victory. As Nos.* 28/9 *of Aden.*
164 1½ pi. deep violet 20 20
165 3 pi. blue 25 20
164/5 Perf "Specimen" .. .. *Set of* 2 60·00

1948 (20 Dec). *Royal Silver Wedding. As Nos.* 30/1 *of Aden.*
166 1½ pi. violet 25 25
167 £1 indigo .. .. 60·00 60·00

1949 (10 Oct). *75th Anniv of Universal Postal Union. As Nos.* 114/17 *of Antigua but inscr* "CYPRUS" *(recess).*
168 1½ pi. violet 60 65
169 2 pi. carmine-red .. .. 1·00 1·25
170 3 pi. deep blue .. .. 1·75 2·50
171 9 pi. purple .. .. 3·75 4·00

1953 (2 June). *Coronation. As No.* 47 *of Aden, but ptd by* B.W.
172 1½ pi. black and emerald 30 10

(New Currency. 1000 mils. = £1)

39 Carobs

42 Copper Pyrites Mine

49 St. Hilarion Castle

52 Coins of Salamis, Paphos, Citium and Idalium

(Recess B.W.)

1955 (1 Aug)–**60**. *T* **39, 42, 49, 52** *and similar designs. Wmk Mult Script CA. P* 13½ *(Nos.* 183/5) *or* 11½ *(others).*
173 2 m. blackish brown 12 40
174 3 m. blue-violet 15 12
175 5 m. brown-orange (*shades*) 15 5
176 10 m. deep brown and deep green 25 5
177 15 m. olive-green and indigo 75 25
aa. Yellow-olive and indigo (17.9.58) .. 4·00 1·25
a. Bistre and indigo (14.6.60) .. .. 6·00 2·25
178 20 m. brown and deep bright blue 40 15
179 25 m. deep turquoise-blue (*shades*) 65 40
180 30 m. black and carmine-lake 60 5
181 35 m. orange-brown & deep turquoise-blue .. 60 35
182 40 m. deep green and sepia .. .. .. 1·00 55
183 50 m. turquoise-blue and reddish brown .. 80 30
184 100 m. mauve and bluish green .. .. 4·25 75
185 250 m. deep grey-blue and brown .. .. 9·50 3·50
186 500 m. slate and purple .. .. 30·00 12·00
187 £1 brown-lake and slate .. .. .. 30·00 22·00
173/87 .. .. *Set of* 15 70·00 38·00

Designs: *Vert (as T* **40**)—3 m. Grapes; 5 m. Oranges. *(as T* **52**)—£1 Arms of Byzantium, Lusignan, Ottoman Empire and Venice. *Horiz* (as *T* **42**)—15 m. Troodos Forest; 20 m. Beach of Aphrodite; 25 m. Ancient coin of Paphos; 30 m. Kyrenia; 35 m. Harvest in Mesaoria; 40 m. Famagusta Harbour. *(as T* **50**)—100 m. Hala Sultan Tekke; 250 m. Kanakaria Church.

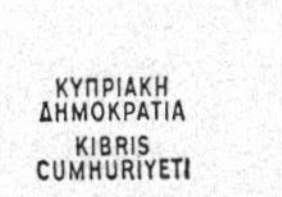

(**54** "Cyprus Republic")

55 Map of Cyprus

1960 (16 Aug). *Nos.* 173/87 *optd as T* **54**, *in blue by B.W. Opt larger on Nos.* 191/7 *and in two lines on Nos.* 198/202.
188 2 m. blackish brown 25 70
189 3 m. blue-violet 25 40
190 5 m. brown-orange (*shades*) 25 10
191 10 m. deep brown and deep green 40 10
192 15 m. yellow-bistre and indigo (*shades*) .. 90 45
a. Olive-green and indigo .. .. .. 85·00 15·00
193 20 m. brown and deep bright blue 65 45
a. Opt double .. .. † £4000
194 25 m. deep turquoise-blue (*shades*) .. .. 1·25 55
195 30 m. black and carmine-lake .. .. .. 2·00 10
a. Opt double .. .. † £4000
196 35 m. orange-brown & dp turquoise-blue .. 1·50 75
197 40 m. deep green and sepia .. .. .. 2·50 90
198 50 m. turquoise-blue and reddish brown .. 2·25 70
199 100 m. mauve and bluish green .. .. 8·50 2·00
200 250 m. deep grey-blue and brown .. .. 32·00 5·00
201 500 m. slate and purple .. .. 55·00 22·00
202 £1 brown-lake and slate .. .. .. 85·00 48·00
188/202 .. .. *Set of* 15 £170 70·00

Only a single used example of No. 195a is known.

(Recess B.W.)

1960 (16 Aug). *Constitution of Republic. W w* **12.** *P* 11½.
203 **55** 10 m. sepia and deep green 35 10
204 30 m. ultramarine and deep brown .. 1·25 80
205 100 m. purple and deep slate .. .. 3·50 3·25

PRINTERS. All the following were lithographed by Aspioti-Elka, Athens, *unless otherwise stated.*

56 Doves

(Des T. Kurpershoek)

1962 (19 Mar). *Europa. P* 14 × 13.
206 **56** 10 m. purple and mauve 10 5
207 40 m. ultramarine and cobalt 35 45
208 100 m. emerald and pale green 45 60

57 Campaign Emblem

1962 (14 May). *Malaria Eradication. P* 14 × 13½.
209 **57** 10 m. black and olive-green 30 15
210 30 m. black and brown 40 20

58 Mult K C K Δ and Map

WATERMARK VARIETIES. The issues printed by Aspioti-Elka with W **58** are known with the vertical stamps having the watermark normal or inverted and the horizontal stamps with the watermark reading upwards or downwards.

62 St. Sophia Church

63 St. Barnabas's Church

1962 (17 Sept). *T* **62/3** *and similar designs. W* **58** *(sideways on* 25, 30, 40, 50, 250 *m.,* £1). *P* 13½ × 14 *(vert) or* 14 × 13½ *(horiz).*
211 3 m. deep brown and orange-brown 10 5
212 5 m. purple and grey-green 10 5
213 10 m. black and yellow-green 15 5
214 15 m. black and reddish purple 25 15
215 25 m. deep brown and chestnut 40 35
216 30 m. deep blue and light blue 35 5
217 35 m. light green and blue 55 10
218 40 m. black and violet-blue .. .. .. 1·50 90
219 50 m. bronze-green and bistre .. .. .. 1·25 5
220 100 m. deep brown and yellow-brown .. .. 4·25 80
221 250 m. black and cinnamon .. .. .. 15·00 3·50
222 500 m. deep brown and light green .. .. 32·00 15·00
223 £1 bronze-green and grey .. .. .. 40·00 25·00
211/23 .. .. *Set of* 13 85·00 42·00

Designs: *Vert*—3 m. Iron Age jug; 5 m. Grapes; 10 m. Bronze head of Apollo; 35 m. Head of Aphrodite; 100 m. Hala Sultan Tekke; 500 m. Cyprus Moufflon. *Horiz*—30 m. Temple of Apollo Hylates; 40 m. Skiing at Troodos; 50 m. Salamis Gymnasium; 250 m. Bella Paise Abbey; £1 St. Hilarion Castle.

72 Europa "Tree"

(Des Lex Weyer)

1963 (28 Jan). *Europa. W* **58** *(sideways). P* 14 × 13½.
224 **72** 10 m. bright blue and black 50 15
225 40 m. carmine-red and black .. .. 2·50 1·50
226 150 m. emerald-green and black .. .. 6·00 6·00

73 Harvester

75 Wolf Cub in Camp

1963 (21 Mar). *Freedom from Hunger. T* **73** *and similar vert design. W* **58.** *P* 13½ × 14.
227 25 m. ochre, sepia and bright blue 60 25
228 75 m. grey, black and lake .. .. .. 5·00 3·50

Design:— 75 m. Demeter, Goddess of Corn.

1963 (21 Aug). *50th Anniv of Cyprus Scout Movement and Third Commonwealth Scout Conference, Platres. T* **75** *and similar vert designs. Multicoloured. W* **58.** *P* 13½ × 14.
229 3 m. Type **75** 20 15
230 20 m. Sea Scout .. .. 1·00 60
231 150 m. Scout with Moufflon .. .. .. 3·50 3·25
MS231*a* 110 × 90 mm. Nos. 229/31 *(sold at* 250 *m.).*
Imperf £160 £180

78 Nurse tending Child

79 Children's Home, Kyrenia

1963 (9 Sept). *Centenary of Red Cross. W* **58** *(sideways on* 100 *m.). P* 13½ × 14 (10 *m.) or* 14 × 13½ (100 *m.).*
232 **78** 10 m. red, black, grey-bl, chestnut & black .. 50 15
233 **79** 100 m. red, green, black and blue .. 4·50 4·25

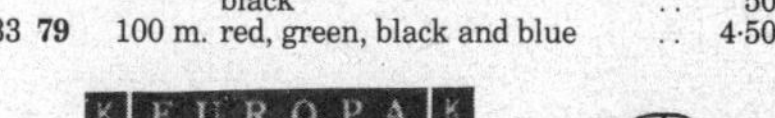

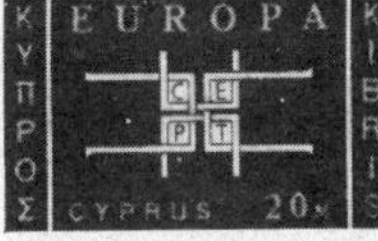

80 "Co-operation" (emblem)

(**81**)

(Des A. Holm)

1963 (4 Nov). *Europa. W* **58** *(sideways). P* 14 × 13½.

234	**80**	20 m. buff, blue and violet	90	40
235		30 m. grey, yellow and blue	1·25	40
236		150 m. buff, blue and orange-brown	6·50	8·00

1964 (5 May). *U.N. Security Council's Cyprus Resolutions, March,* 1964. *Nos.* 213, 216, 218/20, *optd with T* **81** *in blue.*

237	10 m. black and yellow-green	20	10
238	30 m. deep blue and light blue	35	12
239	40 m. black and violet-blue	45	55
240	50 m. bronze-green and bistre	45	55
241	100 m. deep brown and yellow-brown	60	1·25

82 Soli Theatre

1964 (15 June). *400th Birth Anniv of Shakespeare. T* **82** *and similar horiz designs. Multicoloured. W* **58**. *P* 13½ × 13.

242	15 m. Type **82**	20	10
243	35 m. Curium Theatre	25	10
244	50 m. Salamis Theatre	30	10
245	100 m. Othello Tower and scene from *Othello*	1·00	1·40

86 Running

89 Europa "Flower"

1964 (6 July). *Olympic Games, Tokyo. T* **86** *and similar designs. W* **58** *(sideways,* 25 *m.* 75 *m.). P* 13½ × 14 (10 *m.) or* 14 × 13½ *(others)*

246	10 m. brown, black and yellow	15	10
247	25 m. brown, blue and blue-grey	45	20
248	75 m. brown, black and orange-red	90	1·40
MS248*a*	110 × 90 mm. Nos. 246/8 *(sold at* 250 *m.).* Imperf	9·50	14·00

Designs: *Horiz*—25 m. Boxing; 75 m. Charioteers.

(Des G. Bétemps)

1964 (14 Sept). *Europa. W* **58**. *P* 13½ × 14.

249	**89**	20 m. chestnut and light ochre	60	25
250		30 m. ultramarine and light blue	70	25
251		150 m. olive and light blue-green	5·50	4·50

90 Dionysus and Acme

91 Silenus (satyr)

1964 (26 Oct). *Cyprus Wines. T* **90/1** *and similar multicoloured designs. W* **58** *(sideways,* 10 *m., or* 100 *m.). P* 14 × 13½ *(horiz)* 13½ × 14 *(vert).*

252	10 m. Type **90**	40	15
253	40 m. Type **91**	1·00	45
254	50 m. Commandaria Wine *(vert)*	1·25	30
255	100 m. Wine factory *(horiz)*	3·00	2·50

94 President Kennedy

1965 (15 Feb). *President Kennedy Commemoration. W* **58** *(sideways). P* 14 × 13½.

256	**94**	10 m. ultramarine	15	10
257		40 m. green	60	60
258		100 m. carmine-lake	80	90
MS258*a*		110 × 90 mm. Nos. 256/8 *(sold at* 250 *m.).* Imperf	3·50	7·00

MINIMUM PRICE

The minimum price quoted is 5p which represents a handling charge rather than a basis for valuing common stamps. For further notes about prices see introductory pages.

95 "Old Age"

96 "Maternity"

1965 (12 Aug). *Social Insurance Law. T* **95/6** *and similar design. W* **58**. *P* 13½ × 12 (75 *m.) or* 13½ × 14 *(others).*

259	30 m. drab and dull green	40	25
260	45 m. light grey-green, blue & dp ultramarine	75	55
261	75 m. red-brown and flesh	2·75	2·75

Design: *Vert as T* **95**—45 m. "Accident".

98 I.T.U. Emblem and Symbols

1965 (17 May). *I.T.U. Centenary, W* **58** *(sideways). P* 14 × 13½.

262	**98**	15 m. black, brown and yellow	75	20
263		60 m. black, green and light green	3·75	3·00
264		75 m. black, indigo and light blue	4·00	4·25

99 I.C.Y. Emblem

1965 (17 May). *International Co-operation Year. W* **58** *(sideways). P* 14 × 13½.

265	**99**	50 m. brown, dp green & lt yellow-brown	2·25	50
266		100 m. purple, dp green & lt purple	3·00	1·00

100 Europa "Sprig"

U. N.
Resolution
on Cyprus
18 Dec. 1965

(101)

(Des. H. Karlsson)

1965 (27 Sept). *Europa. W* **58** *(sideways). P* 14 × 13½.

267	**100**	5 m. black, orange-brown and orange	15	10
268		40 m. black, orange-brown & lt emerald	1·60	1·25
269		150 m. black, orange-brown & lt grey	3·50	3·25

1966 (31 Jan). *U.N. General Assembly's Cyprus Resolution,* 18 *December* 1965. *Nos.* 211, 213, 216 *and* 221 *optd with T* **101**, *in blue.*

270	3 m. deep brown and orange-brown	12	20
271	10 m. black and yellow-green	30	10
272	30 m. deep blue and light blue	70	35
273	250 m. black and cinnamon	1·75	4·00

102 Discovery of St. Barnabas's Body

104 St. Barnabas (icon)

103 St. Barnabas's Chapel

105 "Privileges of Cyprus Church"
(Actual size 102 × 82 *mm)*

1966 (25 Apr). *1900th Death Anniv of St. Barnabas. W* **58** *(sideways on* 15 *m.,* 100 *m.,* 250 *m.). P* 14 × 13 (25 *m). or* 13 × 14 *(others).*

274	**102**	15 m. multicoloured	20	5
275	**103**	25 m. drab, black and blue	40	15
276	**104**	100 m. multicoloured	1·10	1·90
MS277		110 × 91 mm. **105** 250 m. mult. Imperf	9·00	20·00

5 M

Ξ

(106)

107 General K. S. Thimayya and U. N. Emblem

1966 (30 May). *No.* 211 *surch with T* **106**

278	5 m. on 3 m. deep brown & orange-brown	5	5

1966 (6 June) *General Thimayya Commemoration. W* **58** *(sideways). P* 14 × 13.

279	**107**	50 m. black and light orange-brown	20	10

108 Europa "Ship"

(Des G. and J. Bender)

1966 (26 Sept). *Europa. W* **58**. *P* 13½ × 14.

280	**108**	20 m. green and blue	25	15
281		30 m. bright purple and blue	25	15
282		150 m. bistre and blue	2·00	2·50

110 Church of St. James (Tricomo)

119 Vase of 7th Century B.C.

120 Bronze Ingot-stand

1966 (21 Nov). *T* **110, 119/20** *and similar designs. W* **58** *(sideways on* 3, 15, 25, 50, 250, 500 *m., £*1). *P* 12 × 13 (3 *m.),* 13 × 12 (5, 10 *m.),* 14 × 13½ (15, 25, 50 *m.),* 13½ × 14 (20, 30, 35, 40, 100 *m.) or* 13 × 14 *(others).*

283	3 m. grey-green, buff, black & light blue	10	20
284	5 m. bistre, black & steel-blue *(shades)*	10	5
285	10 m. black and bistre	12	10
286	15 m. black, chestnut & lt orange-brown	15	5
287	20 m. black, slate and brown	35	20
288	25 m. black, drab and lake-brown	30	10
289	30 m. black, yellow-ochre and turquoise	40	20

290 35 m. yellow, black and carmine-red 50 30
291 40 m. black, grey and new blue 70 20
a. Grey background omitted .. ..
292 50 m. black, slate and brown 90 5
293 100 m. black, red, pale buff and grey .. .. 3·00 25
294 250 m. olive-green, black and light yellow-ochre 4·50 70
295 500 m. multicoloured .. .. 9·00 3·50
296 £1 black, drab and slate .. .. .. 20·00 12·00
283/96 .. .. *Set of* 14 35·00 16·00

Designs: *Horiz* (*as T* **110**)—3 m. Stavrovouni Monastery. (*As T* **119**)—15 m. Ancient ship (painting); 25 m. Sleeping Eros (marble statue); 50 m. Silver coin of Alexander the Great. *Vert* (*as T* **110**)—10 m. Zeno of Cibium (marble bust). (*As T* **119**)—20 m. Silver coin of Evagoras I; 30 m. St. Nicholas Cathedral, Famagusta; 35 m. Gold sceptre from Curium; 40 m. Silver disc from 7th century. (*As T* **120**)—500 m. "The Rape of Ganymede" (mosaic); £1 Aphrodite (marble statue).

123 Power Station, Limassol

124 Cogwheels

1967 (10 Apr). *First Development Programme. T* **123** *and similar designs but horiz. Multicoloured. W* **58** (*sideways on* 15 *to* 100 *m.*). *P* 13½ × 14 (10 *m.*) *or* 14 × 13½ (*others*).
297 10 m. Type **123** 12 10
298 15 m. Arghaka-Maghounda Dam 15 10
299 35 m. Troodos Highway 20 25
300 50 m. Hilton Hotel, Nicosia 20 10
301 100 m. Famagusta Harbour .. .. .. 75 1·00

(Des O. Bonnevalle)

1967 (2 May). *Europa. W* **58**. *P* 13½ × 14.
302 **124** 20 m. olive-green, green & pale yell-grn 35 15
303 30 m. reddish violet, lilac and pale lilac 35 15
304 150 m. brown, light reddish brown and pale yellow-brown .. .. 1·50 2·00

125 Throwing the Javelin

126 Running (amphora) and Map of Eastern Mediterranean
(*Actual size* 97 × 77 *mm*)

(Des Aspioti-Elka, Athens)

1967 (4 Sept). *Athletic Games, Nicosia. T* **125** *and similar designs and T* **126**. *Multicoloured. W* **58**. *P* 13½ × 13.
305 15 m. Type **125** 15 10
306 35 m. Running.. .. .. 30 50
307 100 m. High-jumping 40 65
MS308 110 × 90 mm. 250 m. Type **126** (wmk sideways). Imperf .. .. 1·90 3·50

127 Ancient Monuments

128 St. Andrew Mosaic

1967 (16 Oct). *International Tourist Year. T* **127** *and similar horiz designs. Multicoloured. W* **58**. *P* 13 × 13½.
309 10 m. Type **127** 15 10
310 40 m. Famagusta Beach 30 75
311 50 m. "Comet" at Nicosia Airport 30 10
312 100 m. Skier and youth hostel .. .. .. 50 1·00

1967 (8 Nov). *Centenary of St. Andrew's Monastery. W* **58** (*sideways*). *P* 13 × 13½.
313 **128** 25 m. multicoloured 15 12

129 The Crucifixion

130 The Three Magi

(Photo French Govt Ptg Wks, Paris)

1967 (8 Nov). *Cyprus Art Exhibition, Paris. P* 12½ × 13½.
314 **129** 50 m. multicoloured 15 12

1967 (8 Nov). *20th Anniv of U.N.E.S.C.O. W* **58** (*sideways*). *P* 13 × 13½.
315 **130** 75 m. multicoloured 50 30

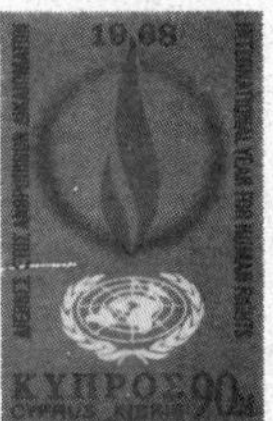

131 Human Rights Emblem over Stars

132 Human Rights and U.N. Emblems

133 Scroll of Declaration
(*Actual size* 95 × 75½ *mm*)

1968 (18 Mar). *Human Rights Year. W* **58**. *P* 13 × 14.
316 **131** 50 m. multicoloured 20 10
317 **132** 90 m. multicoloured 50 70
MS318 95 × 75½ mm. **133** 250 m. multicoloured. W **58** (sideways). Imperf. .. .. 1·75 3·00

134 Europa "Key"

(Des H. Schwarzenbach)

1968 (29 Apr). *Europa. W* **58** (*sideways*). *P* 14 × 13.
319 **134** 20 m. multicoloured 15 12
320 30 m. multicoloured 20 15
321 150 m. multicoloured .. .. .. 1·25 1·60

135 U.N. Children's Fund Symbol and Boy drinking Milk

136 Aesculapius

(Des A. Tassos)

1968 (2 Sept). *21st Anniv of U.N.I.C.E.F. W* **58** (*sideways*). *P* 14 × 13.
322 **135** 35 m. yellow-brown, carmine-red & blk 15 20

(Des A. Tassos)

1968 (2 Sept). *20th Anniv of W.H.O. W* **58**. *P* 13 × 14.
323 **136** 50 m. black, green and light olive .. 15 10

137 Throwing the Discus

138 I.L.O. Emblem

1968 (24 Oct). *Olympic Games, Mexico. T* **137** *and similar designs. Multicoloured. W* **58** (*sideways on* 100 *m.*). *P* 14 × 13 (100 *m.*) *or* 13 × 14 (*others*).
324 10 m. Type **137** 10 5
325 25 m. Sprint finish 20 12
326 100 m. Olympic Stadium (*horiz*) .. .. 45 1·10

(Des Aspioti-Elka)

1969 (3 Mar). *50th Anniv of International Labour Organization. W* **58**. *P* 12 × 13½.
327 **138** 50 m. yellow-brown, blue and light blue 20 12
328 90 m. yellow-brown, black and pale grey 45 60

139 Mercator's Map of Cyprus, 1554

140 Blaeu's Map of Cyprus, 1635

(Des Aspioti-Elka)

1969 (7 Apr). *First International Congress of Cypriot Studies. W* **58** (*sideways*). *P* 14 × 14½.
329 **139** 35 m. multicoloured 25 30
330 **140** 50 m. multicoloured 25 10
a. Wmk upright .. .. .. — 2·00

141 Europa Emblem

142 Common Roller

(Des L. Gasbarra and G. Belli)

1969 (28 Apr). *Europa. W* **58** (*sideways*). *P* 14 × 13½.
331 **141** 20 m. multicoloured 20 20
332 30 m. multicoloured 25 12
333 150 m. multicoloured .. .. .. 1·25 1·75

(Des Aspioti-Elka)

1969 (7 July). *Birds of Cyprus. T* **142** *and similar designs. Multicoloured. W* **58** (*sideways on horiz designs*). *P* 13½ × 12 (*horiz designs*) *or* 12 × 13½ (*vert designs*).
334 5 m. Type **142** 12 10
335 15 m. Audouin's Gull 20 10
336 20 m. Cyprus Warbler.. .. .. .. 25 10
337 30 m. Jay (*vert*) 30 10
338 40 m. Hoopoe (*vert*) 40 20
339 90 m. Eleanora's Falcon (*vert*).. .. .. 2·00 3·25
334/9 .. .. *Set of* 6 3·00 3·50

The above were printed on glazed Samuel Jones paper with very faint watermark.

143 "The Nativity" (12th-century Wall Painting)

145 "Virgin and Child between Archangels Michael and Gabriel" (6th–7th-century Mosaic) (*Actual size 102 × 81 mm*)

1969 (24 Nov). *Christmas. T* **143** *and similar horiz design, and T* **145**. *Multicoloured. W* **58** (*sideways*). *P* 13½ × 13.

340 20 m. Type **143** 15 10
341 45 m. "The Nativity" (14th-century wall painting) 20 20
MS342 110 × 90 mm. 250 m. Type **145**. Imperf .. 3·50 6·50

146 Mahatma Gandhi

(Des Aspioti-Elka)

1970 (26 Jan). *Birth Centenary of Mahatma Gandhi. W* **58** (*sideways*). *P* 14 × 13½.

343 **146** 25 m. ultramarine, drab and black .. 25 10
344 75 m. yellow-brown, drab and black .. 50 50

147 "Flaming Sun" 148 Gladioli

(Des L. le Brocquy)

1970 (4 May). *Europa. W* **58** (*sideways*). *P* 14 × 13.

345 **147** 20 m. brown, greenish yellow & orange 25 12
346 30 m. new blue, greenish yellow & orge 25 12
347 150 m. bright purple, greenish yell & orge 1·50 1·60

1970 (3 Aug). *European Conservation Year. T* **148** *and similar vert designs. Multicoloured. W* **58**. *P* 13 × 13½.

348 10 m. Type **148** 12 8
349 50 m. Poppies 35 8
350 90 m. Giant fennel .. .. 80 1·50

149 I.E.Y. Emblem 150 Mosaic

151 Globe, Dove and U.N. Emblem

1970 (7 Sept). *International Events. W* **58** (*sideways on horiz designs*). *P* 13 × 14 (5 *m.*), *or* 14 × 13 (*others*).

351 **149** 5 m. black, red-brown & lt yellow-brn 5 5
352 **150** 15 m. multicoloured 12 5
353 **151** 75 m. multicoloured 30 45

Events:—5 m. International Education Year; 15 m. 50th General Assembly of International Vine and Wine Office; 75 m. 25th Anniv of United Nations.

152 Virgin and Child 153 Cotton Napkin

(Des from Wall Painting in 16th-cent Church. Photo Harrison)

1970 (23 Nov). *Christmas. T* **152** *and similar multicoloured designs. P* 14 × 14½.

354 25 m. Archangel (facing right) 15 5
a. Horiz strip of 3. Nos. 354/6 45
355 25 m. Type **152** 15 5
356 25 m. Archangel (facing left) 15 5
357 75 m. Virgin and Child between Archangels 25 45

The 75 m. is horiz, size 42 × 30 mm, and the 25 m. values are vert, size as T **152**.

Nos. 354/6 were issued in *se-tenant* strips of three, throughout the sheet. The triptych thus formed is depicted in its entirety on the 75 m. value.

1971 (22 Feb). *Multicoloured designs as T* **153**. *W* **58** (*sideways on horiz designs*). (*a*) *Vert designs* 23 × 33 *mm. P* 12 × 13½.

358 3 m. Type **153** 10 12
359 5 m. St. George and Dragon (19th-cent bas-relief) 10 5

(*b*) *Vert* (10, 20, 25, 40, 50, 75 *m.*) *or horiz* (15, 30, 90 *m.*) *designs, each* 24 × 37 *or* 37 × 24 *mm. P* 13 × 14 (15, 30, 90 *m*) *or* 14 × 13 (*others*)

360 10 m. Woman in festival costume 15 5
361 15 m. Archaic Bichrome Kylix (cup) (*shades*) 20 5
362 20 m. A pair of donors (St. Mamas Church) .. 20 5
363 25 m. "The Creation" (6th-cent mosaic) .. 25 5
364 30 m. Athena and horse-drawn chariot (4th-cent B.C. terracotta) 30 5
365 40 m. Shepherd playing pipe (14th-cent fresco) 50 25
366 50 m. Hellenistic head (3rd cent B.C.) .. 50 5
367 75 m. Detail of Apse mosaic .. .. .. 1·75 50
368 90 m. Mycenaean silver bowl .. .. .. 1·40 60

(*c*) *Horiz* (250, 500 *m.*) *or vert* (£1) *designs, each* 41 × 28 *or* 28 × 41 *mm. P* 13½ × 13 (250, 500 *m.*) *or* 13 × 13½ (£1)

369 250 m. Moufflon (detail of 3rd-cent mosaic) (*shades*) .. .. 7·00 3·00
370 500 m. Ladies and sacred tree (detail, 6th-cent amphora) .. .. 6·00 4·00
371 £1 Horned god from Enkomi (12th-cent bronze statue) .. .. .. 9·00 6·00
358/71 .. .. *Set of* 14 25·00 13·00

154 Europa Chain 155 Archbishop Kyprianos

(Des H. Haflidason)

1971 (3 May). *Europa, W* **58** (*sideways*). *P* 14 × 13

372 **154** 20 m. pale blue, ultramarine and black 20 12
373 30 m. apple green, myrtle-green & blk. 20 12
374 150 m. lemon, bright green and black .. 1·25 2·10

The above were printed on glazed paper with very faint watermark.

1971 (9 July). *150th Anniv. of Greek War of Independence. T* **155** *and similar multicoloured designs. W* **58** (*sideways on* 30 *m.*). *P* 13½ × 12½ (30 *m.*) *or* 12½ × 13½ (*others*).

375 15 m. Type **155** 10 5
376 30 m. "Taking the Oath" (*horiz*) 20 15
377 100 m. Bishop Paleon Patron Germanos, flag and freedom-fighters .. .. .. 55 1·00

156 Harbour Castle 157 Madonna and Child in Stable

1971 (20 Sept). *Tourism. T* **156** *and similar multicoloured designs. W* **58** (*sideways on* 15 *and* 100 *m.*). *P* 13½ × 13 (15 *m.*, 100 *m.*) *or* 13 × 13½ (*others*).

378 15 m. Type **156** 10 5
379 25 m. Gourd on sunny beach 15 5
380 60 m. Mountain scenery 40 75
381 100 m. Church and blue sky 45 80

The 25 and 60 m. are vert designs.

(Des A. Tassos)

1971 (22 Nov). *Christmas. T* **157** *and similar vert designs. Multicoloured. W* **58**. *P* 13 × 14.

382 10 m. Type **157** 5 5
a. Horiz strip of 3. Nos. 382/4 65
383 50 m. The Three Wise Men 30 30
384 100 m. The Shepherds 35 35

The 10 m. was issued in sheets of 100, and all three values were printed horizontally *se-tenant* in sheets of 36, the order being 50, 10 and 100 m.

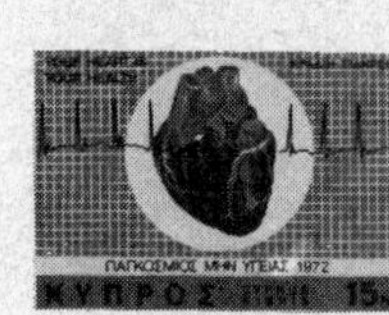

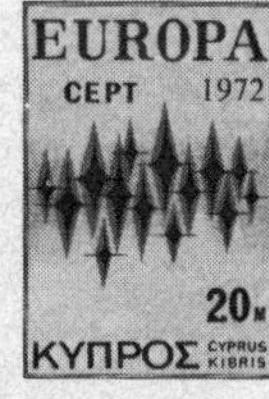

158 Heart 159 "Communications"

1972 (11 Apr). *World Health Month. W* **58** (*sideways*). *P* 13½ × 12.

385 **158** 15 m. multicoloured 15 10
386 50 m. multicoloured 25 40

(Des P. Huovinen)

1972 (22 May). *Europa. W* **58**. *P* 12½ × 13½.

387 **159** 20 m. yellow-orge, sepia & pale grey-brn 15 12
388 30 m. yell-orge, brt dp ultram & cobalt 20 15
389 150 m. yellow-orange, myrtle-green and pale-turquoise-green .. .. 2·50 3·00

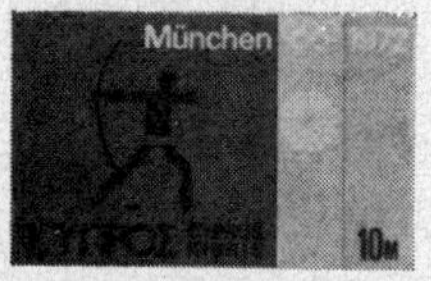

160 Archery

1972 (24 July). *Olympic Games. T* **160** *and similar horiz designs. Multicoloured. W* **58** (*sideways*). *P* 14 × 13.

390 10 m. Type **160** 5 5
391 40 m. Wrestling 20 20
392 100 m. Football .. .. 75 1·25

161 Stater of Marion 162 Bathing the Child Jesus

1972 (25 Sept). *Ancient Coins of Cyprus* (1*st series*), *T* **161** *and similar horiz designs. W* **58** (*sideways*), *P* 14 × 13.

393 20 m. pale turquoise-blue, black and silver .. 15 12
394 30 m. pale violet-blue, black and silver .. 20 5
395 40 m. brownish stone, black and silver .. 25 25
396 100 m. light salmon-pink, black and silver .. 1·25 1·75

Coins:—30 m. Stater of Paphos; 40 m. Stater of Lapithos, 100 m. Stater of Idalion.

See also Nos. 486/9.

(Des A. Tassos)

1972 (20 Nov). *Christmas. T* **162** *and similar vert designs showing portions of a mural in the Church of the Holy Cross of Agiasmati. Multicoloured. W* **58** (*sideways on* **MS**400). *P* 13 × 14.

397 10 m. Type **162** 5 5
398 20 m. The Magi 12 5
399 100 m. The Nativity 40 75
MS400 100 × 90 mm. 250 m. Showing the mural in full. Imperf .. .. 1·25 2·50

163 Snow-covered Landscape

1973 (13 Mar). *29th Internation Ski Federation Congress. T* **163** *and similar horiz design. Multicoloured. W* **58** (*sideways*). *P* 14 × 13.

401 20 m. Type **163** 15 10
402 100 m. Congress emblem 55 90

164 Europa "Posthorn"

(Des I. F. Anisdahl)

1973 (7 May). *Europa. W* **58** (*sideways*). *P* 14 × 13.

403 **164** 20 m. multicoloured 25 12
404 30 m. multicoloured 25 15
405 150 m. multicoloured .. .. 1·75 2·25

165 Archbishopric Palace, Nicosia

20M
(166)

1973 (23 July). *Traditional Architecture. T* **165** *and similar multicoloured designs. W* **58** (*sideways on* 20 *and* 100 *m.*). *P* 14 × 13 (20 *and* 100 *m.*) *or* 13 × 14 (*others*).

406 20 m. Type **165** 15 10
407 30 m. Konak of Hajigeorgajis Cornessios, Nicosia (*vert*) 20 10
408 50 m. House at Gourri, 1850 (*vert*) 30 5
409 100 n. House at Rizokarpaso, 1772 .. .. 1·00 1·50

1973 (24 Sept). *No.* 361 *surch with T* **166**.

410 20 m. on 15 m. Archaic Bichrome Kylix (cup) (*shades*) 15 15

167 Scout Emblem

168 Archangel Gabriel

1973 (24 Sept). *Anniversaries. T* **167** *and similar designs. W* **58** (*sideways on* 25 *and* 35 *m.*). *P* 13 × 14 (10, 50 *and* 100 *m.*) *or* 14 × 13 (*others*).

411 10 m. yellow-olive and deep brown 5 5
412 25 m. deep blue, and slate-lilac 12 5
413 35 m. light brown-olive, stone and sage-green 20 30
414 50 m. dull blue and indigo 30 5
415 100 m. brown and sepia.. .. .. 85 1·25

Designs and Events: *Vert*—10 m. Type **167** (60th Anniv of Cyprus Boy Scouts); 50 m. Airline emblem (25th Anniv of Cyprus Airways); 100 m. Interpol emblem (50th Anniv of Interpol). *Horiz*—25 m. Outline of Cyprus and E.E.C. nations (Association of Cyprus with the E.E.C.); 35 m. F.A.O. emblem (Tenth Anniv of F.A.O.).

1973 (26 Nov). *Christmas. T* **168** *and similar multicoloured designs. W* **58** (*sideways on* 100 *m.*). *P* 14 × 13 (100 *m.*) *or* 13 × 14 (*others*).

416 10 m. Type **168** 5 5
417 20 m. Madonna and Child 12 10
418 100 m. Arakas Church (*horiz*) .. .. .. 60 1·25

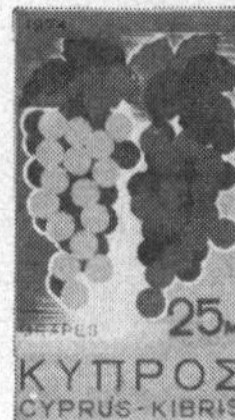

169 Grapes

170 "The Rape of Europa" (Silver Stater of Marion)

1974 (18 Mar). *Products of Cyprus. T* **169** *and similar vert designs. Multicoloured. W* **58**. *P* 13 × 14.

419 25 m. Type **169** 20 12
420 50 m. Grapefruit 30 30
a. Horiz strip of 3, Nos. 420/2 90
421 50 m. Oranges 30 30
422 50 m. Lemons 30 30

Nos. 420/2 were printed together, horizontally *se-tenant* throughout the sheet.

1974 (29 Apr). *Europa. W* **58**. *P* 13½ × 14.

423 **170** 10 m. multicoloured 15 10
424 40 m. multicoloured 30 25
425 150 m. multicoloured .. .. 1·50 2·10

171 Title Page of A. Kyprianos' "History of Cyprus" (1788)

REFUGEE
FUND
ΤΑΜΕΙΟΝ
ΠΡΟΣΦΥΓΩΝ
GÖÇMENLER
FONU
10M
(172)

1974 (22 July*). *Second International Congress of Cypriot Studies. T* **171** *and similar multicoloured designs. W* **58** (*sideways on* 25 *m. and* **MS**429). *P* 14 × 13½ (25 *m.*) *or* 13½ × 14 (*others*).

426 10 m. Type **171** 5 5
427 25 m. Solon (philosopher) in mosaic (*horiz*) .. 25 15
428 100 m. "St. Neophytos" (wall painting).. .. 60 1·00
MS429 111 × 90 mm. 250 m. Ortelius' map of Cyprus and Greek Islands, 1584. Imperf .. .. 2·25 3·50

*Although this is the date appearing on first day covers, it is reported that the stamps were not put on sale until the 24th.

1974 (1 Oct). *Obligatory Tax. Refugee Fund No.* 359 *surch with T* **172**.

430 10 m. on 5 m. St. George and Dragon.. .. 8 5

SECURITY
COUNCIL
RESOLUTION
353
20 JULY 1974
(173)

174 "Refugees"

1974 (14 Oct). *U.N. Security Council Resolution* 353. *Nos.* 360, 365, 366 *and* 369 *optd as T* **173**.

431 10 m. Woman in festival costume 12 5
432 40 m. Shepherd playing pipe 40 45
433 50 m. Hellenistic head.. .. .. .. 40 5
434 250 m. Moufflon (*shades*) .. .. 1·90 3·00

1974 (2 Dec). *Obligatory Tax. Refugee Fund. W* **58** (*sideways*). *P* 12 × 12½.

435 **174** 10 m. black and light grey 5 5

175 "Virgin and Child between Two Angels"

1974 (2 Dec). *Christmas. T* **175** *and similar multicoloured designs showing wall-paintings. W* **58** (*sideways on* 10 *m. and* 100 *m.*). *P* 13 × 14 (50 *m.*) *or* 14 × 13 (*others*).

436 10 m. Type **175** 10 5
437 50 m. "Adoration of the Magi" (*vert*) 35 35
438 100 m. "Flight into Egypt" 45 55

176 First Cyprus Mail-coach

177 "The Distaff" (M. Kashalos)

(Des and photo Harrison)

1975 (17 Feb). *International Events. T* **176** *and similar designs. No wmk. P* 14.

439 **176** 20 m. multicoloured 15 5
440 – 30 m. ultramarine, slate-blk & dull orge 25 30
441 **176** 50 m. multicoloured 30 15
442 – 100 m. multicoloured 40 60

Designs and Events:—20 m., 50 m. Centenary of Universal Postal Union. *Vert*.—30 m. "Disabled Persons" (Eighth European Meeting of International Society for the Rehabilitation of Disabled Persons); 100 m. Council flag (25th Anniv of Council of Europe).

(Des and photo Harrison)

1975 (28 Apr). *Europa. T* **177** *and similar vert designs. Multicoloured. P* 13½ × 14½.

443 20 m. Type **177** 15 12
a. Horiz strip of 3. Nos. 443/5 85
444 30 m. "Nature Morte" (C. Savva) 25 25
445 150 m. "Virgin and Child of Liopetri" (G. P. Georghiou) .. .. 50 1·75

Nos. 443/5 were printed horizontally *se-tenant* throughout the sheet.

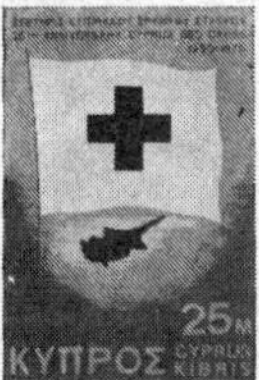

178 Red Cross Flag over Map

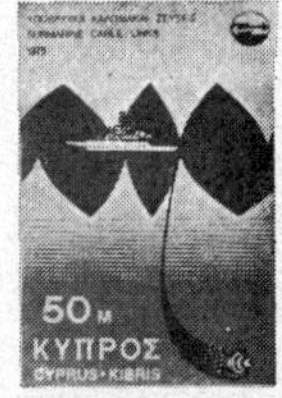

179 Submarine Cable Links

(Des Aspioti-Elka)

1975 (4 Aug). *International Events. T* **178** *and similar horiz designs. P* 12½ × 13½ (25 *m.*) *or* 13½ × 12½ (*others*).

446 25 m. multicoloured 10 5
447 30 m. turquoise-green and greenish blue .. 15 10
448 75 m. red-brown, orge-brn & pale blue-grey .. 35 45

Designs and events: *Vert*—25 m. Type **178** (25th Anniversary of Cyprus Red Cross). *Horiz*—30 m. Nurse and lamp (International Nurses' Day); 75 m. Woman's Steatite Idol (International Women's Year).

1975 (13 Oct). *Telecommunications Achievements. T* **179** *and similar design. W* **58** (*sideways on* 100 *m.*). *P* 12 × 13½ (50 *m.*) *or* 13½ × 12 (100 *m.*).

449 50 m. multicoloured 25 5
450 100 m. orange-yellow, dull violet and lilac .. 65 80

Design: *Horiz*—100 m. International subscriber dialling.

10M
(180)

181 Human-figured Vessel, 19th-Century

1976 (5 Jan). *No.* 358 *surch with T* **180**.

451 10 m. on 3 m. Cotton napkin 10 10

1976 (3 May). *Europa. T* **181** *and similar vert designs. Multicoloured. W* **58**. *P* 13 × 14.

452 20 m. Type **181** 15 10
453 60 m. Composite vessel, 2100–2000 B.C. .. 55 60
454 100 m. Byzantine goblet .. .. .. 70 1·10

182 Self-help Housing

183 Terracotta Statue

1976 (3 May). *Economic Reactivation. T* **182** *and similar horiz designs. Multicoloured. W* **58** (*sideways*). *P* 14 × 13.

455 10 m. Type **182** 5 5
456 25 m. Handicrafts 15 15
457 30 m. Reafforestation 20 15
458 60 m. Air Communications 35 20

1976 (7 June). *Cypriot Treasures. T* **183** *and similar designs. W* **58** (*sideways on horiz designs, upright on vert designs*). *P* 12 × 13½ (5, 10 *m.*), 13 × 14 (20, 25, 30 *m*), 14 × 13 (40, 50, 60 *m.*), 13½ × 12 (100 *m.*) *or* 13 × 13½ (250 *m. to* £1).

459 5 m. multicoloured 10 5
460 10 m. multicoloured 10 5
461 20 m. red, yellow and black 20 5
462 25 m. multicoloured 20 5
463 30 m. multicoloured 25 5
464 40 m. grey-green, light olive-bistre and black 30 5
465 50 m. buff, brown and black 35 5
466 60 m. multicoloured 45 10
467 100 m. multicoloured 50 20
468 250 m. deep dull blue, grey and black .. 1·40 65
469 500 m. black, stone and deep blue-green .. 2·25 1·40
470 £1 multicoloured .. .. 3·00 3·50
459/70 .. .. *Set of* 12 8·00 5·50

Sizes:—23 × 34 *mm*, 5 m., 10 m.; 34 × 23 *mm*, 100 m.; 24 × 37 *mm*, 20, 25, 30 m.; 37 × 24 *mm*, 40, 50, 60 m.; 28 × 41 *mm*, others.

Designs:—10 m. Limestone head; 20 m. Gold necklace; 25 m. Terracotta warrior; 30 m. Statue of a priest; 40 m. Bronze tablet; 50 m. Mycenaean crater; 60 m. Limestone sarcophagus; 100 m. Gold bracelet; 250 m. Silver dish; 500 m. Bronze stand; £1 Statue of Artemis.

PRICES OF SETS

Set prices are given for many issues, generally those containing five stamps or more. Definitive sets include one of each value or major colour change, but do not cover different perforations, die types or minor shades. Where a choice is possible the set prices are based on the cheapest versions of the stamps included in the listings.

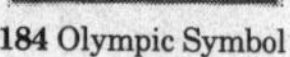

184 Olympic Symbol

185 "George Washington" (G. Stuart)

(Litho Harrison)

1976 (5 July). *Olympic Games, Montreal. T* **184** *and similar designs. P* 14.
471 20 m. carmine-red, black and yellow 12 10
472 60 m. multicoloured 25 25
473 100 m. multicoloured 35 40
Designs: *Horiz*—60, 100 m. Olympic symbols (*different*).

1976 (5 July). *Bicentenary of American Revolution. W* **58**. *P* 13 × 13½.
474 **185** 100 m. multicoloured 55 65

186 Children in Library

187 Archangel Michael

1976 (27 Sept). *International Events. T* **186** *and similar vert designs. W* **58**. *P* 13½ × 12½ (50 *m.*) *or* 13½ (*others*).
475 40 m. multicoloured 25 15
476 50 m. yellow-brown and black 25 10
477 80 m. multicoloured 45 60
Designs and Events:—40 m. Type **186** (Promotion of Children's Books); 50 m. Low-cost housing (HABITAT Conference, Vancouver); 80 m. Eye protected by hands (World Health Day).

(Litho Harrison)

1976 (15 Nov). *Christmas. T* **187** *and similar vert designs, showing icons from Ayios Neophytis Monastery. Multicoloured. P* 12½.
478 10 m. Type **187** 12 5
479 15 m. Archangel Gabriel 15 5
480 150 m. The Nativity 60 70

188 "Cyprus 74" (wood-engraving by A. Tassos)

189 "Landscape" (A. Diamantis)

1977 (10 Jan.) *Obligatory Tax. Refugee Fund. W* **58**. *P* 13 × 12½.
481 **188** 10 m. grey-black 5 5
For 1 c. value, see No. 634.

1977 (2 May). *Europa. T* **189** *and similar horiz designs. Multi-coloured. No wmk. P* 13½ × 13.
482 20 m. Type **189** 15 10
483 60 m. "Trees and Meadows" (T. Kanthos) .. 40 50
484 120 m. "Harbour Scene" (V. Ioannides) .. 55 75

190 Overprinted 500 m. Stamp of 1960

191 Bronze Coin of Emperor Trajan

1977 (13 June). *Silver Jubilee. W* **58**. *P* 13 × 13½.
485 **190** 120 m. multicoloured 35 60

(Litho Harrison)

1977 (13 June). *Ancient Coins of Cyprus* (2*nd series*). *T* **191** *and similar horiz designs. P* 14.
486 10 m. brownish black, gold and ultramarine .. 10 5
487 40 m. brownish black, silver and pale blue .. 30 20
488 60 m. brownish black, silver and dull orange .. 35 35
489 100 m. brownish black, gold and blue-green .. 45 75
Designs:—40 m. Silver tetradrachm of Demetrios Poliorcetes; 60 m. Silver tetradrachm of Ptolemy VIII; 100 m. Gold Octadrachm of Arsinoe II.

192 Archbishop Makarios in Ceremonial Robes

193 Embroidery, Pottery and Weaving

1977 (10 Sept). *Death of Archbishop Makarios. T* **192** *and similar vert designs. Multicoloured. P* 13 × 13½.
490 20 m. Type **192** 12 10
491 60 m. Archbishop and doorway 30 20
492 250 m. Head and shoulders portrait .. .. 80 1·40

1977 (17 Oct). *Anniversaries and Events. T* **193** *and similar horiz designs. Multicoloured. W* **58** (*sideways*). *P* 13½ × 13.
493 20 m. Type **193** 10 8
494 40 m. Map of Mediterranean 20 15
495 60 m. Gold medals 30 25
496 80 m. "Sputnik" 30 45
Designs commemorate: 20 m. Revitalisation of handicrafts; 40 m. "Man and the Biosphere" Programme in the Mediterranean region; 60 m. Gold medals won by Cypriot students in the Orleans Gymnasiade; 80 m. 60th Anniv of Russian October Revolution.

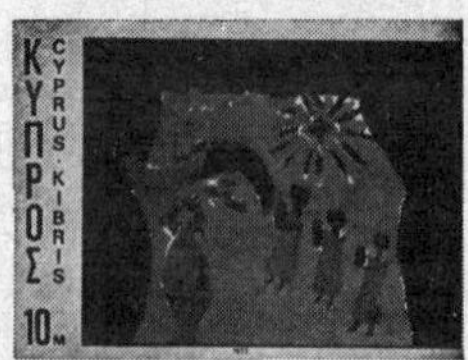

194 "Nativity"

(Litho Harrison)

1977 (21 Nov). *Christmas. T* **194** *and similar horiz designs showing children's paintings. Multicoloured. P* 14 × 13½.
497 10 m. Type **194** 10 5
498 40 m. "The Three Kings" 30 25
499 150 m. "Flight into Egypt" 60 70

195 Demetrios Libertis

196 Chrysorrhogiatissa Monastery Courtyard

(Des A. Ioannides)

1978 (6 Mar). *Cypriot Poets. T* **195** *and similar horiz design. W* **58** (*sideways*). *P* 14 × 13.
500 40 m. dull brown and olive-bistre 30 20
501 150 m. grey, grey-black and light red 55 55
Design:—150 m. Vasilis Michaelides.

(Litho Harrison)

1978 (24 Apr). *Europa. Architecture. T* **196** *and similar horiz designs. Multicoloured. P* 14 × 13½.
502 25 m. Type **196** 10 5
503 75 m. Kolossi Castle 30 10
504 125 m. Municipal Library, Paphos 55 75

197 Archbishop of Cyprus, 1950–77

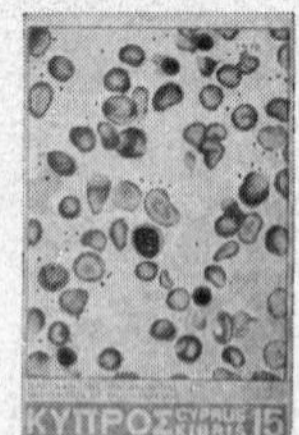

198 Affected Blood Corpuscles (Prevention of Thalassaemia)

(Photo Harrison)

1978 (3 Aug). *Archbishop Makarios Commemoration. T* **197** *and similar vert designs. Multicoloured. P* 14 × 15.
505 15 m. Type **197** 20 20
    b. Horiz strip of 5. Nos. 505/9 .. .. 1·10
    ba. Imperf (horiz strip of 5) .. .. ..
506 25 m. Exiled in Seychelles, 9 March 1956–28 March 1957 .. .. 20 20
507 50 m. President of the Republic, 1960–77 .. 25 25
508 75 m. "Soldier of Christ" 30 35
509 100 m. "Fighter for Freedom" 35 45
MS510 110 × 80 mm. 300 m. "The Great Leader". Imperf .. .. 3·00 4·50
Nos. 505/9 were printed together, *se-tenant*, in horizontal strips of 5 throughout the sheet.

1978 (23 Oct). *Anniversaries and Events. T* **198** *and similar designs. P* 13½ × 14 (15, 35 *m.*) *or* 14 × 13½ (*others*).
511 15 m. multicoloured 5 5
512 35 m. multicoloured 20 15
513 75 m. black and grey 30 12
514 125 m. multicoloured 55 80
Designs and commemorations: *Vert*—35 m. Aristotle (sculpture) (2300th death anniversary). *Horiz*—75 m. "Heads" (Human Rights); 125 m. Wright brothers and *Flyer* (75th anniversary of powered flight).

199 Icon Stand

200 Aphrodite (statue from Soloi)

(Litho Harrison)

1978 (4 Dec). *Christmas. T* **199** *and similar vert designs showing icon stands. P* 14 × 14½.
515 15 m. multicoloured 10 5
516 35 m. multicoloured 25 10
517 150 m. multicoloured .. .. 75 1·00

(Litho Harrison)

1979 (12 Mar). *Aphrodite* (*Greek goddess of love and beauty*) *Commemoration. T* **200** *and similar horiz design showing Aphrodite emerging from the sea at Paphos* (*legendary birth-place*). *Multicoloured. P* 14 × 13½.
518 75 m. Type **200** 30 25
519 125 m. Aphrodite on a shell (detail from "Birth of Venus" by Botticelli) 40 35

201 Van, Mail-coach and Envelope

202 Peacock Wrasse (*thalassoma pavo*)

(Des G. Simonis)

1979 (30 Apr). *Europa. Communications. T* **201** *and similar horiz designs. Multicoloured. W* **58** (*sideways*). *P* 14 × 13.
520 25 m. Type **201** 10 5
521 75 m. Radar, satellite and early telephone .. 30 15
522 125 m. Aircraft, ship and envelopes 45 40

(Des A. Tassos)

1979 (25 June). *Flora and Fauna. T* **202** *and similar multi-coloured designs. W* **58** (*sideways on* 25 *and* 125 *m.*). *P* 13½ × 12 (25, 125 *m.*) *or* 12 × 13½ (*others*).
523 25 m. Type **202** 10 5
524 50 m. Black Partridge (*Francolinus francolinus*) (*vert*) 35 20
525 75 m. Cedar (*Cedar brevifolia*) (*vert*) 35 25
526 125 m. Mule (*Equus mulus*) 40 45

203 I.B.E. and U.N.E.S.C.O. Emblems

204 "Jesus" (from Church of the Virgin Mary of Arakas, Lagoudhera)

(Des A. Kalathia (25 m.), A. Ioannides (others). Litho Harrison)

1979 (1 Oct). *Anniversaries and Events. T* **203** *and similar designs in black, yellow-brown and yellow-ochre* (50 *m.*) *or multi-coloured* (*others*). *P* 12½.
527 15 m. Type **203** 8 5
528 25 m. Graphic design of dove and stamp album (*horiz*) 12 5
529 50 m. Lord Kitchener and map of Cyprus (*horiz*) 25 20
530 75 m. Child's face (*horiz*) 30 15
531 100 m. Graphic design of footballers (*horiz*) .. 40 25
532 125 m. Rotary International emblem and "75" .. 55 40
527/32 .. .. *Set of* 6 1·50 1·00
Commemorations:—15 m. 50th anniversary of International Bureau of Education; 25 m. 20th anniversary of Cyprus Philatelic Society; 50 m. Centenary of Cyprus Survey; 75 m. International Year of the Child; 100 m. 25th anniv of U.E.F.A. (European Football Association); 125 m. 75th anniv of Rotary International.

1979 (5 Nov). *Christmas. Icons. T* **204** *and similar vert designs. Multicoloured. W* **58**. *P* 13 × 13½ (35 *m.*) *or* 13½ × 14 (*others*).
533 15 m. Type **204** 10 5
534 35 m. "Nativity" (from the Iconostasis of the Church of St. Nicholas, Famagusta District) (29 × 41 *mm*) 20 10
535 150 m. "Holy Mary" (from Church of the Virgin Mary of Arakas, Lagoudhera) 60 60

205 1880 ½d. Stamp with "969" (Nicosia) Postmark

206 St. Barnabas (Patron Saint of Cyprus)

(Des A. Tassos)

1980 (17 Mar). *Cyprus Stamp Centenary. T* **205** *and similar horiz designs. Multicoloured. W* **58** (*sideways*). *P* 13½ × 13.
536 40 m. Type **205** 20 15
537 125 m. 1880 2½d. stamp with "974" (Kyrenia) postmark 40 40
538 175 m. 1880 1s. stamp with "942" (Larnaca) postmark 45 65
MS539 105 × 85 mm. 500 m. 1880 1d. ½d., 2½d., 4d., 6d. and 1s. stamps (90 × 75 *mm*). Imperf .. 2·00 2·50

(Photo Harrison)

1980 (28 Apr). *Europa. Personalities. T* **206** *and similar vert design. Multicoloured. P* 12½.
540 40 m. Type **206** 20 12
541 125 m. Zeno of Citium (founder of the Stoic philosophy) 50 50

207 Sailing

208 Gold Necklace, Arsos (7th-century BC)

(Des A. Ioannides)

1980 (23 June). *Olympic Games, Moscow. T* **207** *and similar horiz designs. Multicoloured. W* **58** (*sideways*). *P* 13½ × 13.
542 40 m. Type **207** 15 12
543 125 m. Swimming 35 35
544 200 m. Gymnastics 60 65

1980 (15 Sept). *Archaeological Treasures. Multicoloured designs as T* **208**. *W* **58** (*sideways on* 15, 40, 150 *and* 500 *m.*). *P* 14 × 13 (15, 40, 150 *and* 500 *m.*) *or* 13 × 14 (*others*).
545 10 m. Type **208** 5 5
546 15 m. Bronze cow, Vouni Palace (5th-century B.C.) (*horiz*) 10 5
547 25 m. Amphora, Salamis (6th-century B.C.) .. 15 5
548 40 m. Gold finger-ring, Enkomi (13th-century B.C.) (*horiz*) 20 5
549 50 m. Bronze cauldron, Salamis (8th-century B.C.) 20 5
550 75 m. Funerary stele, Marion (5th-century B.C.) 35 10
551 100 m. Jug (15–14th-century B.C.) 40 15
552 125 m. Warrior (Terracotta) (6–5th-century B.C.) 40 20
553 150 m. Lions attacking bull (bronze relief), Vouni Palace (5th-century B.C.) (*horiz*) 50 20
554 175 m. Faience rhyton, Kition (13th-century B.C.) 60 25
555 200 m. Bronze statue of Ingot God, Enkomi (12th-century B.C.) 65 30
556 500 m. Stone bowl, Khirokitia (6th-millennium B.C.) (*horiz*) .. .. 1·40 70
557 £1 Ivory plaque, Salamis (7th-century B.C.) 2·25 1·50
558 £2 "Leda and the Swan" (mosaic), Kouklia (3rd-century A.D.) .. .. .. 4·50 3·25
545/58 .. .. *Set of* 14 10·50 6·00

209 Cyprus Flag

210 Peace Dove and Head Silhouettes

1980 (1 Oct). *20th Anniv of Republic. T* **209** *and similar multicoloured designs. P* 13½ × 13 (125 *m.*) *or* 13 × 14 (*others*).
559 40 m. Type **209** 15 12
560 125 m. Signing Treaty of Establishment (41 × 29 *mm*) 40 40
561 175 m. Archbishop Makarios 55 55

1980 (29 Nov). *International Palestinian Solidarity Day. T* **210** *and similar horiz design showing Peace Dove and head silhouettes. W* **58** (*sideways*). *P* 13½ × 13.
562 40 m. grey and black 30 30
a. Horiz pair. Nos. 562/3 .. .. .. 65 65
563 125 m. grey and black 35 35
Nos. 562/3 were printed together, *se-tenant*, in horizontal pairs throughout the sheet.

211 Pulpit, Tripiotis Church, Nicosia

212 Folk-dancing

1980 (29 Nov). *Christmas. T* **211** *and similar vert designs. Multicoloured. W* **58**. *P* 13 × 14.
564 25 m. Type **211** 10 5
565 100 m. Holy door of the Iconostasis, Panayia Church, Paralimni (24 × 37 *mm*) .. 40 35
566 125 m. Pulpit, Ayios Lazaros Church, Larnaca 45 40

(Litho Harrison)

1981 (4 May). *Europa. Folklore. T* **212** *and similar vert design showing folk-dancing. P* 14.
567 40 m. multicoloured 15 12
568 175 m. multicoloured 55 60

213 Self-portrait

214 *Ophrys kotschyi*

1981 (15 June). *500th Anniv of Leonardo da Vinci's Visit. T* **213** *and similar multicoloured designs. W* **58** (*sideways on* 125 *m.*). *P* 12 × 14 (125 *m.*) *or* 13½ × 14 (*others*).
569 50 m. Type **213** 20 15
570 125 m. "The Last Supper" (50 × 25 *mm*) .. 40 40
571 175 m. "Lefkaritiko" (Cyprus Lace) and Milan Cathedral 60 60

1981 (6 July). *Cypriot Wild Orchids. T* **214** *and similar vert designs. Multicoloured. W* **58**. *P* 13½ × 14.
572 25 m. Type **214** 15 15
a. Block of 4. Nos. 572/5 95
573 50 m. *Orchis punctulata* 20 20
574 75 m. *Orphrys argolica elegans* 25 25
575 150 m. *Epipactis veratrifolia* 40 45
Nos. 572/5 were printed together, *se-tenant*, in blocks of 4 throughout the sheet.

215 Heinrich von Stephan

216 "The Lady of the Angels" (from Church of the Transfiguration of Christ, Palekhori)

1981 (28 Sept). *Commemorations. T* **215** *and similar horiz designs. W* **58** (*sideways*). *P* 13½ × 13.
576 25 m. brown-olive, dp yellow-green & brt bl .. 10 5
577 40 m. multicoloured 15 10
578 125 m. black, vermilion and deep yellow-green 35 35
579 150 m. multicoloured 40 40
580 200 m. multicoloured 70 70
Designs and commemorations:—25 m. Type **215** (150th birth anniversary of Henrich von Stephan (founder of U.P.U.)); 40 m. Stylised man holding dish of food (World Food Day); 125 m. Stylised hands (International Year for Disabled Persons); 150 m. Stylised building and flower (European Campaign for Urban Renaissance); 200 m. Prince Charles, Lady Diana Spencer and St. Paul's Cathedral (Royal Wedding).

1981 (16 Nov). *Christmas. Paintings from Nicosia District Churches. T* **216** *and similar multicoloured designs. W* **58** (*sideways on* 25 *and* 125 *m.*). *P* 12½.
581 25 m. Type **216** 10 5
582 100 m. "The Almighty" (from Church of Madonna of Arakas, Lagoudera) (*vert*) 35 35
583 125 m. "Baptism of Christ" (from Church of Our Lady of Assinou, Nikitari) 45 45

NEW INFORMATION

The editor is always interested to correspond with people who have new information that will improve or correct the Catalogue.

217 "Louomene" (statue of Aphrodite bathing, 250 B.C.)

218 Liberation of Cyprus by Emperor Nicephorus II Phocas, 965 A.D.

1982 (12 Apr). *Aphrodite (Greek, goddess of love and beauty) Commemoration. T* **217** *and similar vert design. Multicoloured. W* **58**. *P* 13½ × 14.
584 125 m. Type **217** 40 40
585 175 m. "Anadyomene" (Aphrodite emerging from the waters) (Titian) 50 50

(Photo Harrison)

1982 (3 May). *Europa. Historic Events. T* **218** *and similar horiz design. Multicoloured. P* 12½.
586 40 m. Type **218** 15 10
587 175 m. Conversion of Roman Proconsul Sergius Paulus to Christianity, Paphos, 45 A.D. 50 55

219 Monogram of Christ (mosaic)

100 =

(220)

1982 (5 July). *World Cultural Heritage. T* **219** *and similar multicoloured designs. W* **58** (*sideways on* 50 *and* 225 *m.*). *P* 13½ × 14 (125 *m.*) *or* 12½ (*others*).
588 50 m. Type **219** 20 10
589 125 m. Head of king of Palaepaphos (sculpture) (24 × 37 *mm*) 40 40
590 225 m. Theseus (Greek god) (mosaic) 70 70

1982 (6 Sept). *No.* 550 *surch with T* **220**.
591 100 m. on 75 m. Funerary stele, Marion (5th-century B.C.) 25 15

221 Cyprus and Stylised "75"

222 Holy Communion—The Bread

1982 (8 Nov). *75th Anniv of Boy Scout Movement. T* **221** *and similar multicoloured designs. W* **58** (*sideways on* 100 *m. and* 175 *m.*). *P* 12½ × 13½ (125 *m.*) *or* 13½ × 12½ (*others*).
592 100 m. Type **221** 35 25
593 125 m. Lord Baden-Powell (*vert*) 40 40
594 175 m. Camp-site 50 60

1982 (6 Dec). *Christmas. T* **222** *and similar designs. W* **58** (*sideways on* 25 *and* 250 *m.*). *P* 12½ × 12 (25 *and* 250 *m.*) *or* 13½ × 14 (100 *m.*).
595 25 m. multicoloured 10 8
596 100 m. gold and black 35 30
597 250 m. multicoloured 80 85
Designs: *Vert*—100 m. Holy Chalice. *Horiz*—250 m. Holy Communion—The Wine.

223 Cyprus Forest Industries' Sawmill

1983 (14 Mar). *Commonwealth Day. T* **223** *and similar horiz designs. Multicoloured. W* **58** (*sideways*). *P* 14 × 13½.
598 50 m. Type **223** 12 15
599 125 m. "Ikarios and the Discovery of Wine" (3rd-cent mosaic) 30 35
600 150 m. Folk-dancers, Commonwealth Film and Television Festival, 1980 .. .. 40 45
601 175 m. Royal Exhibition Building, Melbourne (Commonwealth Heads of Government Meeting, 1981) 45 50

224 Cyprosyllabic Inscription (6th-cent B.C.)

225 *Pararge aegeria*

(Des G. Simonis. Photo Harrison)

1983 (3 May). *Europa. T* **224** *and similar horiz design. Multicoloured. P* 14½ × 14.
602 50 m. Type **224** 12 15
603 200 m. Copper ore, ingot (Enkomi 1400-1250 B.C.) and bronze jug (2nd-cent A.D.) .. 50 55

1983 (28 June). *Butterflies. T* **225** *and similar horiz designs. Multicoloured. W* w **58**. *P* 12½.
604 60 m. Type **225** 15 20
605 130 m. *Aricia medon* 30 35
606 250 m. *Glaucopsyche paphos* 65 70

(New Currency: 100 cents = £1 (Cyprus))

1c

=

(226)

227 View of Power Station

1983 (3 Oct). *Nos.* 545/56 *surch as T* **226**.
607 1 c. on 10 m. Type **208** 5 5
608 2 c. on 15 m. Bronze cow, Vouni Palace (5th-century B.C.) 5 5
609 3 c. on 25 m. Amphora, Salamis (6th-century B.C.) 5 8
610 4 c. on 40 m. Gold finger-ring, Enkomi (13th-century B.C.) 8 10
611 5 c. on 50 m. Bronze cauldron, Salamis (8th-century B.C.) 12 15
612 6 c. on 75 m. Funerary stele, Marion (5th-century B.C.) 12 15
613 10 c. on 100 m. Jug (15–14th-century B.C.) 20 25
614 13 c. on 125 m. Warrior (Terracotta) (6–5th-century B.C.) 30 35
615 15 c. on 150 m. Lions attacking bull (bronze relief), Vouni Palace (5th-century B.C.) 35 40
616 20 c. on 200 m. Bronze statue of Ingot God, Enkomi (12th-century B.C.) 45 50
617 25 c. on 175 m. Faience rhyton, Kition (13th-century B.C.) 55 65
618 50 c. on 500 m. Stone bowl, Khirokitia (6th-millennium B.C.) .. .. .. 1·10 1·25
607/18 .. .. *Set of* 12 3·00 3·75

1983 (27 Oct). *Anniversaries and Events. T* **227** *and similar vert designs. Multicoloured. W* **58**. *P* 13 × 14.
619 3 c. Type **227** 8 10
620 6 c. W.C.Y. logo 15 20
621 13 c. Cruise liner and cargo ship 30 35
622 15 c. Human Rights emblem and map of Europe 40 45
623 20 c. Nicos Kazantzakis (poet) 50 55
624 25 c. Archbishop Makarios in church 65 70
619/24 .. .. *Set of* 6 1·75 2·10
Commemorations:—3 c. 30th anniv of the Cyprus Electricity Authority; 6 c. World Communications Year; 13 c. 25th anniv of International Maritime Organization; 15 c. 35th anniv of Universal Declaration of Human Rights; 20 c. Birth centenary; 25 c. 70th birth anniv.

228 St. Lazaros Church, Larnaca

229 Waterside Cafe, Larnaca

1983 (12 Dec). *Christmas. T* **228** *and similar vert designs. Multicoloured. W* **58**. *P* 12 × 13½.
625 4 c. Type **228** 10 12
626 13 c. St. Varvara Church, Kaimakli, Nicosia 30 35
627 20 c. St. Ioannis Church, Larnaca 50 55

(Litho Harrison)

1984 (6 Mar). *Old Engravings. T* **229** *and similar horiz designs. Each pale stone and black. P* 14½ × 14 (6 *c.*) *or* 14 (*others*).
628 6 c. Type **229** 15 20
629 20 c. Bazaar at Larnaca (30 × 25 *mm*) .. 50 55
630 30 c. East Gate, Nicosia (30 × 25 *mm*) .. 80 85
MS631 110 × 85 mm. 75 c. Interior of St. Lazarus Church, Larnaca .. .. 1·90 2·00

230 C.E.P.T. 25th Anniversary Logo

(Des J. Larrivière. Litho Harrison)

1984 (30 Apr). *Europa. W* **58**. *P* 12½.
632 **230** 6 c. apple-green, deep bl-green & blk .. 15 20
633 15 c. light blue, dull ultram & blk .. 40 45

(Des A. Tassos. Litho J.W.)

1984 (18 June). *Obligatory Tax. Refugee Fund. Design as T* **188** *but new value and* "1984" *date. W* **58**. *P* 13 × 12½.
634 1 c. grey-black 5 5

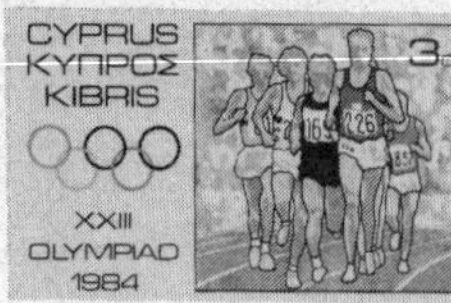

231 Running

(Des. K. Haine. Litho Harrison)

1984 (18 June). *Olympic Games. Los Angeles. T* **231** *and similar horiz designs. Multicoloured. W* **58** (*sideways*). *P* 14.
635 3 c. Type **231** 8 10
636 4 c. Olympic column 10 12
637 13 c. Swimming 35 40
638 20 c. Gymnastics 50 55

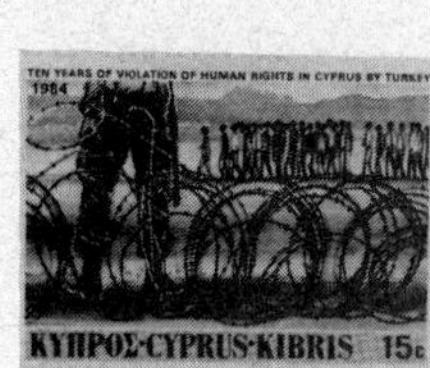

232 Prisoners-of-War

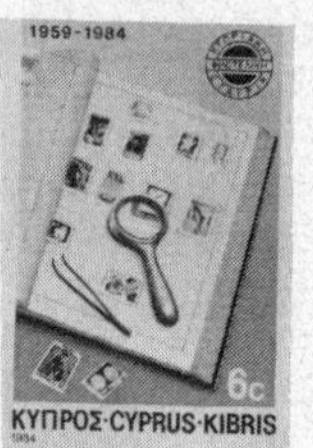

233 Open Stamp Album (25th Anniv of Cyprus Philatelic Society)

(Des A. Tassos)

1984 (20 July). *10th Anniv of Turkish Landings in Cyprus. T* **232** *and similar horiz design. Multicoloured. P* 14 × 13½.
639 15 c. Type **232** 40 45
640 20 c. Map and burning buildings 50 55

(Des and litho Harrison)

1984 (15 Oct). *Anniversaries and Events. T* **233** *and similar multicoloured designs. W* **58** (*sideways on horiz designs*). *P* 12½.
641 6 c. Type **233** 15 20
642 10 c. Football in motion (*horiz*) (50th anniv of Cyprus Football Association) 25 30
643 15 c. "Dr. George Papanicolaou" (medical scientist – birth cent) 40 45
644 25 c. Antique map of Cyprus and ikon (*horiz*) (International Symposia on Cartography and Medieval Paleography) 65 70

(Des and litho Harrison)

1984 (26 Nov). *Christmas. Illuminated Gospels. T* **234** *and similar vert designs. Multicoloured. W* **58**. *P* 12½.
645 4 c. Type **234** 10 12
646 13 c. Beginning of St. Mark's Gospel 35 40
647 20 c. St. Luke (miniature from 11th-century Gospel) 50 55

TURKISH CYPRIOT POSTS

After the inter-communal clashes during December 1963, a separate postal service was established on 6 January 1964 between some of the Turkish Cypriot areas, using handstamps inscribed "KIBRIS TURK POSTALARI". During 1964, however, an agreement was reached between representatives of the two communities for the restoration of postal services. This agreement, to which the United Nations representatives were a party, was ratified in November 1966 by the Republic's Council of Ministers. Under the scheme postal services were provided for the Turkish Cypriot communities in Famagusta, Larnaca, Limassol, Lefka, Nicosia and Paphos staffed by Turkish Cypriot employees of the Cypriot Department of Posts.

On 8 April 1970 5 m. and 15 m. locally-produced labels, originally designated "Social Aid Stamps", were issued by the Turkish Cypriot community and these can be found on commercial covers. These local stamps are outside the scope of this catalogue.

On 29 October 1973 Nos. 1/7 were placed on sale, but were used only on mail between the Turkish Cypriot areas.

Following the intervention by the Republic of Turkey on 20 July 1974 these stamps replaced issues of the Republic of Cyprus in that part of the island, north and east of the Attila Line, controlled by the Autonomous Turkish Cypriot Administration.

1 50th Anniversary Emblem

KIBRIS
TÜRK
FEDERE
DEVLETİ
13.2.1975

30M

(2)

(Des F. Direkoglu, Miss E. Ata and G. Pir. Litho)

1974 (27 July*). *50th Anniv of Republic of Turkey. T* 1 *and similar designs in vermilion and black* (15 *m.*) *or multicoloured* (*others*). *P* 12 × 11½ (*vert*) *or* 11½ × 12 (*horiz*).
1 3 m. Woman sentry (*vert*) .. .. .. 30·00 30·00
2 5 m. Military Parade, Nicosia 60 40
3 10 m. Man and woman with Turkish flags (*vert*) 50 20
4 15 m. Type **1** .. .. 2·50 1·50
5 20 m. Atatürk statue, Kyrenia Gate, Nicosia (*vert*) 70 20
6 50 m. "The Fallen" (*vert*) .. .. .. 2·00 1·50
7 70 m. Turkish flag and map of Cyprus .. 16·00 16·00
1/7 .. .. *Set of* 7 48·00 48·00
*This is the date on which Nos. 1/7 became valid for international mail.

On 13 February 1975 a Turkish Cypriot Federated State was proclaimed in that part of Cyprus under Turkish occupation and later 9,000 Turkish Cypriots were transferred from the South to the North of the island.

1975 (3 Mar). *Proclamation of the Turkish Federated State of Cyprus. Nos.* 3 *and* 5 *surch as T* **2**.
8 30 m. on 20 m. Atatürk statue, Kyrenia Gate, Nicosia .. .. 1·50 1·75
9 100 m. on 10 m. Man and woman with Turkish flags .. .. 2·40 4·00
On No. 9 the surcharge appears at the top of the stamp and the inscription at the bottom.

3 Namik Kemal's Bust, Famagusta

4 Map of Cyprus

(Des Işil Özişik. Litho Güzel Sanatlar Matbaasi, Ankara)

1975 (21 Apr). *Multicoloured designs as T* **3**. *Imprint at foot with date* "1975". *P* 13.
10 3 m. Type **3** 12 12
11 10 m. Atatürk Statue, Nicosia 15 15
12 15 m. St. Hilarion Castle 25 25
13 20 m. Atatürk Square, Nicosia 35 30
14 25 m. Famagusta Beach 35 35
15 30 m. Kyrenia Harbour 45 15
16 50 m. Lala Mustafa Pasha Mosque, Famagusta (*vert*) 70 15
17 100 m. Interior, Kyrenia Castle .. .. 1·50 1·50
18 250 m. Castle walls, Kyrenia .. .. .. 2·75 3·75
19 500 m. Othello Tower, Famagusta (*vert*) .. 5·50 7·50
10/19 .. .. *Set of* 10 11·00 13·00
See also Nos. 37/8.

(Des B. Erkmen (30 m.), S. Tuga (50 m.), N. Güneş (150 m.). Litho Ajans-Türk Matbaacilik Sanayii, Ankara)

1975 (20 July). *"Peace in Cyprus". T* **4** *and similar multicoloured designs. P* 13.
20 30 m. Type **4** 60 40
21 50 m. Map, laurel and broken chain 70 50
22 150 m. Map and laurel-sprig on globe (*vert*) .. 2·00 3·00

5 "Pomegranates" (I. V. Guney)

(Litho Güzel Sanatlar Matbaasi, Ankara)

1975 (29 Dec). *Europa. Paintings. T* **5** *and similar horiz design. Multicoloured. P* 13.

23 90 m. Type **5** .. .. 80 1·25
24 100 m. "Harvest Time" (F. Direkoglu) .. .. 80 1·25

10 M ———

(**6**)

7 "Expectation"

1976 (28 Apr). *Nos.* 16/17 *surch as T* **6** *at Govt Printing House, Nicosia in horizontal clichés of* 10.

25 10 m. on 50 m. Lala Mustafa Pasha Mosque, Famagusta .. .. 1·25 1·75
26 30 m. on 100 m. Interior, Kyrenia Castle .. 1·25 2·00

(Litho Ajans-Türk Matbaacilik Sanayii, Ankara)

1976 (3 May). *Europa. T* **7** *and similar vert design showing ceramic statuette. Multicoloured. P* 13.

27 60 m. Type **7** 35 60
28 120 m. "Man in Meditation" 45 80

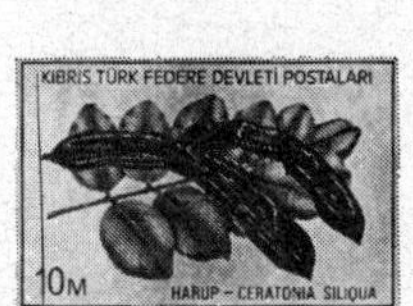

8 Carob

9 Olympic Symbol "Flower"

(Des Sadettin Atlihan. Litho Güzel Sanatlar Matbaasi, Ankara)

1976 (28 June). *Export Products—Fruits. T* **8** *and similar horiz designs. Multicoloured. P* 13.

29 10 m. Type **8** 12 12
30 25 m. Mandarin 20 5
31 40 m. Strawberry 25 5
32 60 m. Orange 35 15
33 80 m. Lemon 55 80

(Des C. Mutver (60 m.), A. B. Kocamanoglu (100 m.). Litho Güzel Sanatlar Matbaasi, Ankara)

1976 (17 July). *Olympic Games. Montreal. T* **9** *and similar horiz design. Multicoloured. P* 13.

34 60 m. Type **9** 40 60
35 100 m. Olympic symbol and doves 50 80

10 Kyrenia Harbour

11 Liberation Monument, Karaeglanoglu (Ay. Georghios)

(Des Işil Özişik. Litho Ajans-Türk Matbaacilik Sanayii, Ankara)

1976 (2 Aug). *New design* (5 *m.*) *or as Nos.* 12/13 *but redrawn with lettering altered and new imprint at foot with date* "1976". *P* 13.

36 5 m. Type **10** 15 15
37 15 m. St. Hilarion Castle 20 12
38 20 m. Atatürk Square, Nicosia 20 12

Nos. 39/46 vacant.

(Des Dincer Erimez and Cahit Gizer. Litho Ajans-Türk Matbaacilik Sanayii, Ankara)

1976 (1 Nov). *Liberation Monument. T* **11** *and similar vert design. P* 13.

47 **11** 30 m. lt turquoise-blue, lt flesh & black 20 20
48 – 150 m. light verm, light flesh & blk .. 70 1·25

No. 48 shows a different view of the Monument.

12 Hotel, Salamis Bay

(Litho Türk Tarih Kurumu)

1977 (2 May). *Europa. T* **12** *and similar horiz design. Multicoloured. P* 13.

49 80 m. Type **12** 35 60
50 100 m. Kyrenia Port 35 60

13 Earthenware

14 Arap Ahmet Pasha Mosque

(Litho Güzel Sanatlar Matbaasi, Ankara)

1977 (27 June). *Handicrafts. T* **13** *and similar designs. Multicoloured. P* 13.

51 15 m. Type **13** 12 8
52 30 m. Pottery (*vert*) 20 12
53 125 m. Basketware 60 90

(Litho APA Ofset Basimevi, Istanbul)

1977 (2 Dec). *Turkish Buildings in Cyprus. T* **14** *and similar horiz designs. Multicoloured. P* 13.

54 20 m. Type **14** 10 10
55 40 m. Paphos Castle 20 25
56 70 m. Bekir Pasha aqueducts 30 35
57 80 m. Sultan Mahmut library 30 35

15 Namik Kemal (bust) and House, Famagusta

16 Old Man and Woman

(Des B. Ozak. Litho Ticaret Matbaacilik T.A.S., Izmir)

1977 (21 Dec). *Namik Kemal (patriotic poet). T* **15** *and similar multicoloured design. P* 12½ × 13 (30 *m.*) *or* 13 × 12½ (140 *m.*)

58 30 m. Type **15** 15 15
59 140 m. Namik Kemal (portrait) (*vert*) 40 50

(New Currency. 100 kurus = 1 lira)

(Litho Ajans-Türk, Ankara)

1978 (17 Apr). *Social Security. T* **16** *and similar vert designs. P* 13 × 13½.

60 150 k. black, yellow and blue 12 10
61 275 k. black, red-orange and green 25 25
62 375 k. black, blue and red-orange 35 35

Designs:—275 k. Injured man with crutch; 375 k. Woman with family.

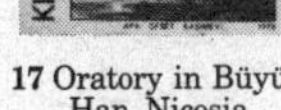

17 Oratory in Büyük Han, Nicosia

18 "Land Transport"

(Des I. Özisik. Litho APA Ofset Basimevi, Istanbul)

1978 (2 May). *Europa. T* **17** *and similar horiz design. Multicoloured. P* 13.

63 225 k. Type **17** 30 30
64 450 k. Cistern in Selimiye Mosque, Nicosia .. 45 45

(Litho APA Ofset Basimevi, Istanbul)

1978 (10 July). *Communications. T* **18** *and similar horiz designs. Multicoloured. P* 13.

65 75 k. Type **18** 5 5
66 100 k. "Sea transport" 10 10
67 650 k. "Air transport" 40 40

19 Dove with Laurel Branch

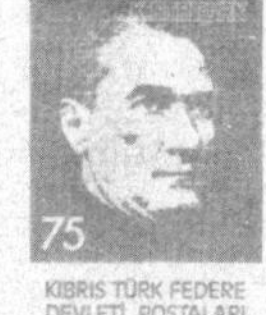

20 Kemal Atatürk

(Des E. Kaya (725 k.), C. Kirkbesoglu (others). Litho APA Ofset Basimevi, Istanbul)

1978 (13 Sept). *National Oath. T* **19** *and similar designs. P* 13.

68 150 k. orange-yellow, violet and black.. .. 10 10
69 225 k. black, Indian red and orange-yellow .. 15 15
70 725 k. black, cobalt and orange-yellow .. 35 45

Designs: *Vert*—225 k. "Taking the Oath". *Horiz*—725 k. Symbolic dove.

(Des C. Mutver. Litho Türk Tarih Kurumu)

1978 (10 Nov). *Kemal Atatürk Commemoration. P* 13.

71 **20** 75 k. pale turquoise-grn & turq-grn .. 15 15
72 450 k. pale flesh and light brown .. 25 40
73 650 k. pale blue and light blue 30 45

50 Krs.

(**21**)

22 Gun Barrel with Olive Branch and Map of Cyprus

1979 (4 June). *Nos.* 30/3 *surch as T* **21**, *by Govt Printing Office, Lefkosa*

74 50 k. on 25 m. Mandarin 5 5
75 1 l. on 40 m. Strawberry 5 5
76 3 l. on 60 m. Orange 15 15
77 5 l. on 80 m. Lemon 30 40

(Des N. E. Dündar. Litho Ajans-Türk, Ankara)

1979 (20 July). *5th Anniv of Turkish Peace Operation in Cyprus. Sheet* 72 × 52 *mm. Imperf.*

MS78 **22** 15 l. black, deep turquoise-blue and pale green .. .. 2·00 2·50

23 Postage Stamp and Map of Cyprus

24 Symbolised Microwave Antenna

(Des S. Mumcu. Litho Ajans-Türk, Ankara)

1979 (20 Aug). *Europa. Communications. T* **23** *and similar horiz designs. Multicoloured. P* 13.

79 2 l. Type **23** 15 12
80 3 l. Postage stamps, building and map .. 25 25
81 8 l. Telephones, Earth and satellite 45 50

(Litho Ticaret Matbaacilik TAS, Izmir)

1979 (24 Sept). *50th Anniv of International Consultative Radio Committee. P* 13 × 12½.

82 **24** 2 l. multicoloured 20 20
83 5 l. multicoloured 20 20
84 6 l. multicoloured 25 25

25 School Children

26 Lala Mustafa Pasha Mosque, Magusa

(Des H. Hastürk (1½ l.), G. Akansel (4½ l.), P. Yalyali (6 l.). Litho APA Ofset Basimevi, Istanbul)

1979 (29 Oct). *International Year of the Child. Children's Drawings. T* **25** *and similar multicoloured designs. P* 13.

85 1½ l. Type **25** 15 15
86 4½ l. Children and globe (*horiz*) 25 25
87 6 l. College children.. .. .. 30 30

(Des S. Mumcu (20 l.), I. Ozisik (others). Litho Ajans-Türk, Ankara)

1980 (23 Mar). *Islamic Commemorations. T* **26** *and similar vert designs. Multicoloured. P* 13.

88 2½ l. Type **26** 10 10
89 10 l. Arap Ahmet Pasha Mosque, Lefkosa .. 30 30
90 20 l. Mecca and Medina 50 60

Commemorations:—2½ l. 1st Islamic Conference in Turkish Cyprus; 10 l. General Assembly of World Islam Congress; 20 l. Moslem Year 1400AH.

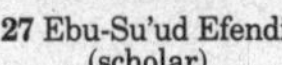
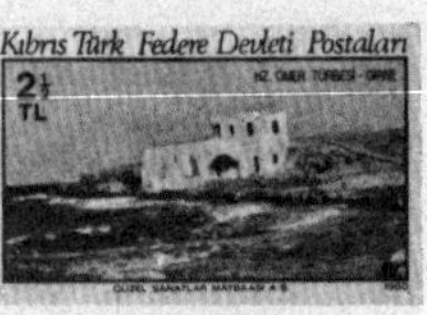

27 Ebu-Su'ud Efendi (scholar)   **28** Omer's Shrine, Kyrenia

(Litho Ajans-Türk, Ankara)

1980 (23 May). *Europa. Personalities. T* **27** *and similar vert. design. Multicoloured. P* 13.
91 5 l. Type **27** 20 20
92 30 l. Sultan Selim II .. .. 1·10 1·25

(Litho Guzel Sanatlar Matbaasi, Ankara)

1980 (25 June). *Ancient Monuments, T* **28** *and similar horiz designs. P* 13.
93 2½ l. new blue and stone 5 5
94 3½ l. grey-green and pale rose-pink 10 10
95 5 l. lake and pale blue-green 15 15
96 10 l. deep mauve and pale green 30 30
97 20 l. dull ultramarine and pale greenish yell .. 55 55
Designs:—3½ l. Entrance gate, Famagusta; 5 l. Funerary monuments (16th-century), Famagusta; 10 l. Bella Paise Abbey, Kyrenia; 20 l. Selimiye Mosque, Nicosia.

29 Cyprus 1880 6d.   **30** Dome of the Rock   **31** Extract from World Muslim Congress Statement in Turkish

(Litho Ajans-Türk, Ankara)

1980 (16 Aug). *Cyprus Stamp Centenary. T* **29** *and similar designs showing stamps. P* 14.
98 7½ l. black, drab and grey-olive 25 25
99 15 l. brown, grey-blue and blue 50 45
100 50 l. black, rose and grey .. .. .. 1·50 1·75
Designs: *Horiz*:—15 l. Cyprus 1960 Constitution of the Republic 30 m. commemorative. *Vert*—50 l. Social Aid local, 1970.

(Litho Guzel Sanatlar Matbaasi, Ankara)

1980 (16 Oct). *Palestinian Solidarity. T* **30** *and similar multicoloured design. P* 13.
101 15 l. Type **30** 50 45
102 35 l. Dome of the Rock (*horiz*) .. .. .. 1·00 95

(Des S. Mumcu. Litho Turk Tarih Kurumu Basimevi, Ankara)

1981 (24 Mar). *Solidarity with Islamic Countries Day. T* **31** *and similar vert design showing extract from World Muslim Congress statement. P* 13.
103 1 l. rosine, stone and olive-sepia 25 30
104 35 l. black, pale blue-green and myrtle-green 90 95
Design:—35 l. Extract in English

32 Atatürk   **33** Folk-dancing

(Des F. Duran, Litho Ajans-Türk, Ankara)

1981 (19 May). *Atatürk Stamp Exhibition, Lefkosa. P* 13.
105 **32** 20 l. multicoloured 60 65
No. 105 was printed in sheets of 100, including 50 *se-tenant* stamp-size labels.

(Litho Ticaret Matbaacilik TAS, Izmir)

1981 (29 June). *Europa, Folklore. T* **33** *and similar horiz design showing folk-dancing. P* 12½ × 13.
106 10 l. multicoloured 25 30
107 30 l. multicoloured 60 65

34 Kemal Atatürk   **35** *Convolvulus althaeoides*

(Litho Basin Ofset, Ankara)

1981 (23 July). *Birth Centenary of Kemal Atatürk. Sheet* 70 × 95 *mm. Imperf.*
MS108 **34** 150 l. multicoloured .. .. .. 3·00 3·00

(Litho Turk Tarih Kurumu)

1981 (28 Sept)–**82**. *Flowers, Multicoloured designs as T* **35**. *P* 13.
109 1 l. Type **35** 5 5
110 5 l. *Cyclamen persicum mill (horiz)* (22.1.82) 5 5
111 10 l. *Mandragora officinarum (horiz)* .. 5 8
112 25 l. *Papaver rhoeas L.* 8 10
113 30 l. *Arum dioscoridis sibth* (22.1.82) .. 10 12
114 50 l. *Chrysanthemum segetem L.* (*horiz*) (22.1.82) 15 20
115 100 l. *Cistus salviaefolius L.* (22.1.82) 30 40
116 150 l. *Ferula communis L. (horiz)* 50 55
109/16 .. .. *Set of* 8 1·10 1·40

36 Stylized Disabled Person in Wheelchair   **37** Turkish Cypriot and Palestinian Flags

(Des H. Ulucam (7½ l.), N. Kozal (others). Litho Türk Tarih Kurumu)

1981 (16 Oct). *Commemorations. T* **36** *and similar multicoloured designs. P* 13.
117 7½ l. Type **36** 20 20
118 10 l. Heads of people of different races, peace dove and barbed wire (*vert*) 30 35
119 20 l. People of different races reaching out from globe, with dishes (*vert*) 40 50
Commemorations:—7½ l. International Year for Disabled Persons; 10 l. Anti-apartheid Publicity; 20 l. World Food Day.

(Des H. Ulucam. Litho Türk Tarih Kurumu)

1981 (29 Nov). *Palestinian Solidarity. P* 13.
120 **37** 10 l. multicoloured 25 30

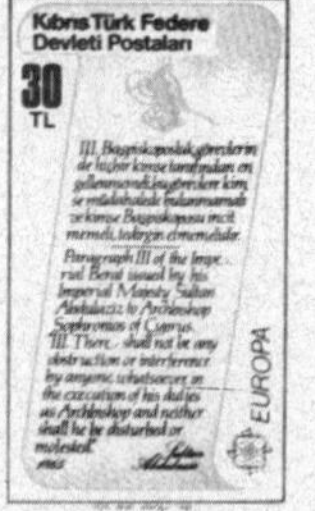

38 Prince Charles and Lady Diana Spencer   **39** Berat issued by Sultan Abdul Aziz to Archbishop Sophronios

(Des. H. Ulucam. Litho Türk Tarih Kurumu, Ankara)

1981 (30 Nov). *Royal Wedding. P* 13
121 **38** 50 l. multicoloured .. .. 1·00 1·10

(Des H. Ulucam, Litho Tezel Ofset, Lefkosa)

1982 (30 July). *Europa (CEPT). Sheet* 83 × 124 *mm containing T* **39** *and similar vert design. Multicoloured. P* 12½ × 13.
MS122 30 l. × 2. Type **39**; 70 l. × 2, Painting of Turkish forces landing at Tuzla, 1571 .. .. 4·00 4·25

40 Buffavento Castle   **41** "Wedding" (A. Örek)

(Des H. Ulucam, Litho Tezel Ofset, Lefkosa)

1982 (20 Aug). *Tourism. T* **40** *and similar multicoloured designs. P* 12.
123 5 l. Type **40** 5 5
124 10 l. Windsurfing (*horiz*) 10 10
125 15 l. Kantara Castle (*horiz*) 12 12
126 30 l. Shipwreck (300 B.C.) (*horiz*) 25 30

(Litho Ajans-Türk, Ankara)

1982 (3 Dec). *Paintings* (1*st series*). *T***41** *and similar multicoloured design. P* 13.
127 30 l. Type **41** 15 20
128 50 l. "Carob Pickers" (O. Nazim) (*vert*) .. 30 35
See also Nos. 132/3 and 157/8.

42 Cross of Lorraine, Koch and Bacillus (Cent of Koch's Discovery of Tubercle Bacillus)   **43** "Calloused Hands" (Salih Oral)

(Des H. Ulucam. Litho Tezel Ofset, Lefkosa)

1982 (15 Dec.) *Anniversaries and Events. T* **42** *and similar multicoloured designs. P* 12.
129 10 l. Type **42** 5 8
130 30 l. Spectrum on football pitch (World Cup Football Championships, Spain) .. 15 20
131 70 l. "75" and Lord Baden-Powell (75th anniv of Boy Scout movement and 125th birth anniv) (*vert*) 40 45

(Litho Ajans-Türk, Ankara)

1983 (16 May). *Paintings* (2*nd series*). *T* **43** *and similar vert design. Multicoloured. P* 13.
132 30 l. Type **43** 15 20
133 35 l. "Malya—Limassol Bus" (Emin Cizenel) 15 20

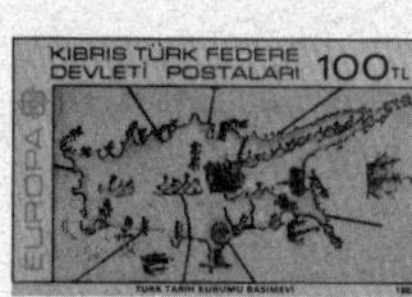

44 Old Map of Cyprus by Piri Reis   **45** First Turkish Cypriot 10 m. Stamp

(Litho Türk Tarih Kurumu, Ankara)

1983 (30 June). *Europa. Sheet* 82 × 78 *mm, containing T* **44** *and similar horiz design. Multicoloured. P* 13.
MS134 100 l. Type **44**; 100 l. Cyprus as seen from "Skylab" .. .. 1·10 1·25

(Des E. Ata (15 l.), A. Hasan (20 l.), G. Pir (25 l.), H. Ulucam (others). Litho Ajans-Türk, Ankara)

1983 (1 Aug). *Anniversaries and Events. T* **45** *and similar multicoloured designs commemorating World Communications Year (30, 50 l.) or 25th Anniv. of T.M.T. (Turkish Cypriot Resistance Organization). P* 13.
135 15 l. Type **45** 8 10
136 20 l. "Turkish Achievements in Cyprus" (*horiz*)) 12 15
137 25 l. "Liberation Fighters" 15 20
138 30 l. Dish aerial and telegraph pole (*horiz*) .. 15 20
139 50 l. Dove and envelopes (*horiz*) 30 35

Kuzey Kıbrıs
Türk Cumhuriyeti
15.11.1983

46 European Bee Eater   (**47**)

(Des E. Cizenel. Litho Ajans-Türk, Ankara)

1983 (10 Oct). *Birds of Cyprus. T* **46** *and similar horiz designs. Multicoloured. P* 13.
140 10 l. Type **46** 5 8
a. Block of 4. Nos. 140/3 75
141 15 l. Goldfinch 8 10
142 50 l. European Robin 30 35
143 65 l. Golden Oriole 35 40
Nos. 140/3 were printed together, *se-tenant*, in blocks of 4 throughout the sheet.

1983 (7 Dec). *Establishment of the Republic. Nos.* 109, 111/12 *and* 116 *surch as T* 47 (No. 145) *or optd only.*

144		10 l. *Mandragara officinarum*	5	5
145		15 l. on 1 l. Type **35**	5	5
146		25 l. *Papaver rhoeas L*	12	15
147		100 l. *Ferula communis L*	65	70

48 C.E.P.T. 25th Anniversary Logo.

49 Olympic Flame

(Des J. Larrivière. Litho Tezel Ofset, Lefkosa)

1984 (30 May). *Europa. P* 12 × 12½.

148	**48**	50 l. lemon, chestnut and black	20	25
149		100 l. pale blue, bright blue and black	40	45

(Des H. Ulucam. Litho Tezel Ofset, Lefkosa)

1984 (19 June). *Olympic Games, Los Angeles. T* **49** *and similar multicoloured designs. P* 12½ × 12 (10 *l.*) *or* 12 × 12½ (*others*).

150		10 l. Type **49**	5	8
151		20 l. Olympic events within rings (*horiz*)	8	10
152		70 l. Martial arts event (*horiz*)	25	30

50 Atatürk Cultural Centre

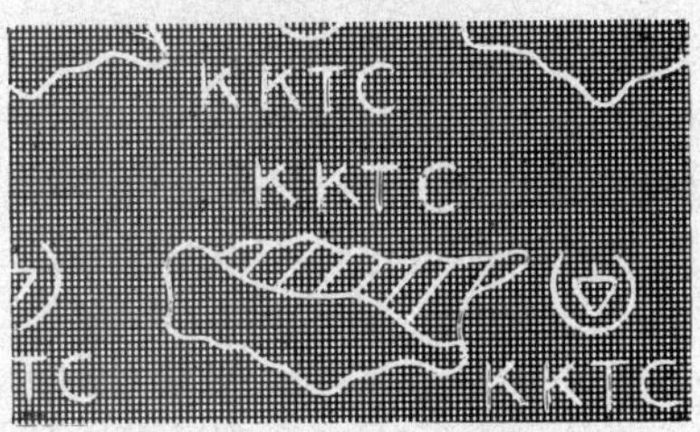

(51)

(Des H. Ulucam. Litho Tezel Ofset, Lefkosa)

1984 (20 July). *Opening of Atatürk Cultural Centre, Lefkosa. W* **51**. *P* 12 × 12½.

153	**50**	120 l. stone, black and chestnut	50	55

52 Turkish Cypriot Flag and Map

(Des C. Guzeloglu and M. Gozbebek. Litho Tezel Ofset, Lefkosa)

1984 (20 July). *10th Anniv of Turkish Landings in Cyprus. T* **52** *and similar horiz design. W* **51**. *Multicoloured. P* 12 × 12½.

154		20 l. Type **52**	8	10
155		70 l. Turkish Cypriot flag within book	25	30

53 Burnt and Replanted Forests

(Des H. Ulucam. Litho Tezel Ofset, Lefkosa)

1984 (20 Aug). *World Forestry Resources. W* **51**. *P* 12 × 12½.

156	**53**	90 l. multicoloured	35	40

54 "Old Turkish Houses, Nicosia" (Cevdet Cagdas)

(Litho Tezel Ofset, Lefkosa)

1984 (21 Sept). *Paintings* (*3rd series*). *T* **54** *and similar horiz design. Multicoloured. W* **51**. *P* 13 × 12½.

157		20 l. Type **54**	8	10
158		70 l. "Scenery" (Olga Lauf)	25	30

Cyrenaica

The Italian colony of Cyrenaica was occupied by Allied forces in 1943 and placed under British Military Administration. Stamps of Great Britain overprinted "M.E.F." (see BRITISH OCCUPATION OF ITALIAN COLONIES) were introduced in that year.

In June 1949 the British authorities recognised the leader of the Senussi, Amir Mohammed Idris Al-Senussi, as Amir of Cyrenaica with autonomy in internal affairs.

(Currency. 1000 millièmes = 1 Egyptian pound)

24 Mounted Warrior 25

(Recess Waterlow)

1950 (16 Jan). *P* 12½.

136	**24**	1 m brown	8	8
137		2 m. carmine	8	8
138		3 m. orange-yellow	8	8
139		4 m. blue-green	90	1·00
140		5 m. grey-black	25	25
141		8 m. orange	30	30
142		10 m. violet	35	35
143		12 m. scarlet	35	35
144		20 m. blue	40	40
145	**25**	50 m. ultramarine and purple-brown	1·90	1·90
146		100 m. carmine and black	6·00	6·00
147		200 m. violet and deep blue	8·00	9·00
148		500 m. orange-yellow and green	30·00	35·00
136/148		*Set of* 13	45·00	48·00

POSTAGE DUE STAMPS

D 26

(Recess Waterlow)

1950 (16 Jan). *P* 12½

D149	**D 26**	2 m. brown	25·00	32·00
D150		4 m. blue-green	25·00	32·00
D151		8 m. scarlet	25·00	32·00
D152		10 m. orange	25·00	32·00
D153		20 m. orange-yellow	25·00	32·00
D154		40 m. blue	25·00	32·00
D155		100 m. grey-brown	25·00	32·00
D149/155		*Set of* 7	£160	£200

On 24 December 1951 Cyrenaica became part of the independent Kingdom of Libya, whose issues are listed in Part 13 (*Africa since Independence F—M*) of this catalogue.

Dominica

CROWN COLONY

A branch office of the British G.P.O. was opened at Roseau by 1845, using the crowned-circle handstamp supplied in that year. The stamps of Great Britain were used between May 1858 and March 1860, after which the colonial authorities assumed responsibility for the postal service. Until the introduction of Nos. 1/3 in 1874 No. CC1 and later handstamps were utilized.

For illustrations of handstamp and postmark types see BRITISH POST OFFICES ABROAD notes, following GREAT BRITAIN.

ROSEAU

CROWNED/CIRCLE HANDSTAMPS

CC1 CC 1 DOMINICA (R.) (17.5.1845) *Price on cover* £500

No. CC1 is also known struck in black on various adhesive stamps.

Stamps of GREAT BRITAIN *cancelled* "A 07" *as Type* **2**.

1858 *to* **1860**

Z1	1d. rose-red (1857), *perf* 14	£125
Z2	2d. blue (1858) (Plate No. 7)	
Z3	4d. rose (1857)	£275
Z4	6d. lilac (1856)	£275
Z5	1s. green	£1000

PRICES FOR STAMPS ON COVER TO 1945

Nos. 1/3	*from* × 8
Nos. 4/26	*from* × 4
Nos. 27/95	*from* × 3
Nos. 96/8	*from* × 4
Nos. 99/109	*from* × 3
Nos. R1/6	*from* × 5

1

½ (2) 1/2 (3) HALF PENNY (4)

(Typo D.L.R.)

1874 (4 May). *Wmk Crown CC. P* 12½.

1	**1**	1d. lilac	£225	38·00
2		6d. green	£400	85·00
3		1s. dull magenta	£300	65·00

NCE — Normal
NCE — Malformed "CE"

1877–79. *Wmk Crown CC. P* 14.

4	**1**	½d. olive-yellow (1879)	9·00	14·00
5		1d. lilac	5·00	4·00
		a. Bisected vert or diag (½d.) (on cover or card)	†	£1400
6		2½d. red-brown (1879)	£150	25·00
7		4d. blue (1879)	95·00	8·50
		a. Malformed "CE" in "PENCE"	£2000	£300
8		6d. green	£140	25·00
9		1s. magenta	£120	42·00

1882 (25 Nov)–**83.** *No.* 5 *bisected and surch.*

10	**2**	½(d.), in *black*, on half 1d.	£140	35·00
		a. Surch inverted	£800	£800
		b. Surcharges *tête-bêche* (pair)	£1400	
11	**3**	½(d.), in *red*, on half 1d.	28·00	28·00
		a. Surch inverted	£800	£300
		c. Surch double	£1600	
14	**4**	½d. in *black*, on half 1d. (3.83)	35·00	40·00
		a. Unsevered pair	£120	£130
		b. Surch double	£800	

Type 4 is found reading up or down.

1883–84. *Wmk Crown CA. P* 14.

15	**1**	½d. olive-yellow	4·00	7·00
16		2½d. red-brown (1884)	£130	11·00

Half Penny (5) One Penny (6)

1886 (Mar). *Nos.* 8 *and* 9 *surch.*

17	**5**	½d. on 6d. green	9·00	14·00
18	**6**	1d. on 6d. green	£13000	£11000
		a. Thick bar (approx 1 mm)	—	£13000
19		1d. on 1s. magenta	14·00	16·00
		a. Surch double	£4750	£2750

There are variations in the spacing of the letters of "One Penny" in the surcharge of No. 19

1886–88. *Wmk Crown CA. P* 14.

20	**1**	½d. dull green	1·25	6·00
21		1d. lilac	14·00	12·00
		a. Bisected (½d.) (on cover)	†	£1600
22		1d. rose (1887)	6·50	7·00
		a. Deep carmine	2·25	3·50
		b. Bisected (½d.) (on cover)	†	£1600
23		2½d. ultramarine (1888)	6·00	5·50
24		4d. grey	4·50	5·00
		a. Malformed "CE" in "PENCE"	£150	£175
25		6d. orange (1888)	16·00	28·00
26		1s. dull magenta (1888)	£225	£275
20/26		*Set of* 7	£250	£300
20, 22/25 Optd "Speciment"		*Set of* 5	£275	

The stamps of Dominica were superseded by the general issue for Leeward Islands on 31 October 1890, but the sets following were in concurrent use with the stamps inscribed "LEEWARD ISLANDS" until 31 December 1939, when the island came under the administration of the Windward Islands.

WATERMARKS. Nos. 27/91 all have the watermark *sideways* except Nos. 36, 46 and 54.

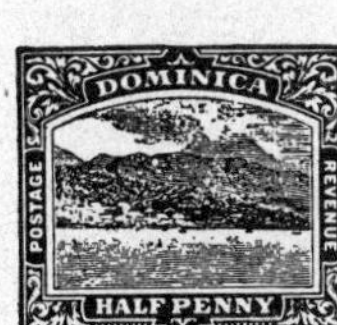

9 View of Roseau from the Sea

10

(T **9** to **11** typo D.L.R.)

1903. *T* **9** *and* **10** (5s.). *Wmk Crown CC. P* 14.

27	½d. green and grey-green, **OC**	3·00	3·25
28	1d. grey and red, **OC**	3·75	1·40
29	2d. green and brown, **OC**	6·50	7·50
30	2½d. grey and bright blue, **OC**	8·00	7·50
31	3d. dull purple and grey-black, **OC**	9·00	9·00
32	6d. grey and chestnut, **O**	10·00	12·00
33	1s. magenta and grey-green, **OC**	18·00	20·00
34	2s. grey-black and purple, **O**	22·00	28·00
35	2s. 6d. grey-green and maize, **O**	24·00	35·00
36	5s. black and brown, **O**	£140	£170
27/36	*Set of* 10	£225	£275
27/36 Optd "Specimen"	*Set of* 10	£350	

1907–8. *T* **9** *and* **10** (5s.). *Wmk Multiple Crown CA. P* 14

37	½d. green, **OC**	2·00	2·25
38	1d. grey and red, **C**	2·00	80
39	2d. green and brown, **C**	8·00	12·00

40 2½d. grey and bright blue, C 11·00 17·00
41 3d. dull purple and grey-black, C 11·00 16·00
42 6d. black and chestnut, C (1908) 42·00 60·00
43 1s. magenta and grey-green, C 14·00 24·00
44 2s. grey-black and purple, C (1908) 27·00 35·00
45 2s. 6d. grey-green and maize, C (1908) 27·00 42·00
46 5s. black and brown, C (1908) 90·00 95·00
37/46 *Set of* 10 £200 £275

11

WAR TAX

ONE HALFPENNY

(12)

1908–21. *T* 9 *and* 11 *(5s.). Wmk Mult Crown CA. P* 14.
47 9 ½d. blue-green, O 1·40 2·50
a. Deep green, O (1918) 1·75 2·00
48 1d. carmine-red, O 1·75 1·00
a. Scarlet, O 1·40 1·40
49 2d. grey, O (1909) 6·00 11·00
a. Slate, O 6·00 11·00
50 2½d. blue, O 7·00 11·00
a. Bright blue, O 5·50 8·50
51 3d. purple *yellow,* OC (1909) 5·00 8·50
a. On pale yellow 12·00 18·00
52 6d. dull and bright purple, C (1909) 17·00 23·00
a. Dull purple, O 6·00 11·00
53 1s. black/*green,* OC (1910) 8·00 11·00
53*a* 2s. purple and deep blue/*blue,* C (1919) 16·00 27·00
53*b* 2s. 6d. black and red/*blue,* C (1921) 24·00 42·00
54 11 5s. red and green/*yellow,* C (1914) 55·00 70·00
47/54 *Set of* 10 £110 £170
48/54 Optd "Specimen" *Set of* 9 £350
53 Optd "Specimen" in black instead of red 85·00

1916. *No.* 47 *surch with T* 12
55 9 ½d. on ½d. blue-green (R.) 30 1·40
a. Small "O" in "ONE" 8·50 15·00

1918 (18 Mar). *No.* 47 *optd locally with T* 12 *but with* "ONE HALF-PENNY" *blanked out.*
56 9 ½d. blue-green (Blk.) 85 4·00

The blanking out of the surcharge was not completely successful so that it almost always appears as an albino to a greater or lesser extent.

WAR TAX

(14)

1918 (June). *Nos.* 47 *and* 51 *optd in London with T* 14.
57 9 ½d. blue-green 15 80
58 3d. purple/*yellow* (R.) 25 2·00

WAR TAX
=1½D.=

(15)

1 ½D.

Short Fraction Bar (R.6/4)

1919. *Special printing of T* 9, *surch with T* 15.
59 9 1½d. on 2½d. orange (R.) 15 1·40
a. Short fraction bar

1920. *As No.* 59, *but without* "WAR TAX".
60 9 1½d. on 2½d. orange (Blk.) 2·00 5·00
a. Short fraction bar
55/60 Optd "Specimen" *Set of* 6 £275

1921. *Wmk Mult Script CA. P* 14
62 9 ½d. blue-green 2·00 4·25
63 1d. carmine-red 1·40 2·50
64 1½d. orange 5·50 8·50
65 2d. grey 7·00 9·00
66 2½d. bright blue 2·00 9·00
67 6d. purple, C 7·00 13·00
69 2s. purple and blue/*blue* 30·00 55·00
70 2s. 6d. black and red/*blue* 30·00 50·00
62/70 *Set of* 8 75·00 £140
62/70 Optd "Specimen" *Set of* 8 £275

The 1½d. has figures of value, in the lower corner and no ornamentation below words of value.

16

(Typo D.L.R.)

1923 (Feb)–33. *Chalk-surfaced paper. P* 14.

(a) Wmk Multi Script CA
71 16 ½d. black and green 75 65
72 1d. black and bright violet 1·50 1·50
73 1d. black and scarlet (1933) 3·00 2·25
74 1½d. black and scarlet 1·25 1·10
75 1½d. black and red-brown (1933) 3·50 2·50
76 2d. black and grey 1·25 1·90
77 2½d. black and orange-yellow 2·00 4·50
78 2½d. black and ultramarine (1927) 2·50 3·50
79 3d. black and ultramarine 2·50 4·50
80 3d. black and red/*yellow* (1927) 1·50 2·25
81 4d. black and brown 1·50 6·50
82 6d. black and bright magenta 3·00 6·00
83 16 1s. black/*emerald* 5·00 6·00
84 2s. black and blue/*blue* 7·00 13·00
85 2s. 6d. black and red/*blue* 10·00 15·00
86 3s. black and purple/*yellow* (1927) 7·00 15·00
87 4s. black and red/*emerald* 11·00 22·00
88 5s. black and green/*yellow* (1927) 17·00 28·00

(b) Wmk Mult Crown CA
89 16 3s. black and purple/*yellow* 10·00 26·00
90 5s. black and green/*yellow* 15·00 28·00
91 £1 black and purple/*red* £350 £500
71/91 *Set of* 21 £400 £600
71/91 Optd/Perf "Specimen" *Set of* 21 £700

1935 (6 May). *Silver Jubilee. As Nos.* 91/4 *of Antigua.*
92 1d. deep blue and carmine 75 75
e. Horiz line from turret 4·00
93 1½d. ultramarine and grey 1·00 90
e. Horiz line from turret 6·00
94 2½d. brown and deep blue 3·75 5·00
95 1s. slate and purple 7·00 11·00
92/5 Perf "Specimen" *Set of* 4 65·00

For illustration of plate variety see Omnibus section following Zululand.

1937 (12 May). *Coronation. As Nos.* 13/15 *of Aden, but printed by B.W. P* 11 × 11½.
96 1d. carmine 30 45
97 1½d. yellow-brown 30 30
98 2½d. blue 60 1·40
96/8 Perf "Specimen" *Set of* 3 45·00

17 Fresh Water Lake

18 Layou River

(Recess Waterlow)

1938 (15 Aug)–47. *T* 17/18 *and similar horiz designs. Wmk Mult Script CA. P* 12½.
99 17 ½d. brown and green 15 15
100 18 1d. grey and scarlet 20 20
101 – 1½d. green and purple 30 30
102 2d. carmine and grey-black 30 35
103 – 2½d. purple and bright blue 4·00 1·50
a. Purple & brt ultram (1942) 40 45
104 18 3d. olive-green and brown 30 40
104*a* – 3½d. ultramarine and purple (15.10.47) 70 45
105 17 6d. emerald-green and violet 50 50
105*a* 7d. green and yellow-brown (15.10.47) 50 50
106 – 1s. violet and olive-green 90 65
106*a* 18 2s. slate and purple (15.10.47) 2·00 3·50
107 17 2s. 6d. black and vermilion 3·75 3·50
108 18 5s. light blue and sepia 7·00 5·50
108*a* – 10s. black and brown-orange (15.10.47) 12·00 18·00
99/108*a* *Set of* 14 26·00 30·00

Designs:–1½d., 2½d., 3½d. Picking limes; 2d., 1s., 10s. Boiling Lake.

21 King George VI

(Photo Harrison)

1940 (15 Apr). *Wmk Mult Script CA. P* 15 × 14.
109 21 ¼d. chocolate, CO 10 10
99/109 Perf "Specimen" *Set of* 15 £250

1946 (14 Oct). *Victory. As Nos.* 28/9 *of Aden.*
110 1d. carmine 20 12
111 3½d. blue 20 15
110/11 Perf "Specimen" *Set of* 2 48·00

1948 (1 Dec.) *Royal Silver Wedding. As Nos.* 30/1 *of Aden.*
112 1d. scarlet 15 12
113 10s. red-brown 9·00 20·00

(New Currency. 100 cents = 1 dollar)

1949 (10 Oct). *75th Anniv of Universal Postal Union. As Nos.* 114/17 *of Antigua.*
114 5 c. blue 25 35
115 6 c. brown 45 50
116 12 c. purple 85 1·25
117 24 c. olive 1·00 1·25

1951 (16 Feb). *Inauguration of B.W.I. University College. As Nos.* 118/19 *of Antigua.*
118 3 c. yellow-green and reddish violet 30 25
119 12 c. deep green and carmine 45 35

22 King George VI

23 Drying Cocoa

(Photo Harrison (½ c.). Recess B.W. (others))

1951 (1 July). *T* 22 *and designs as T* 23. *Wmk Mult Script CA. P* 15 × 14 (½ c.), 13½ × 13 ($2.40), 13 × 13½ *(others).*
120 ½ c. chocolate 20 25
121 1 c. black and vermilion 20 20
122 2 c. red-brown and deep green 15 45
123 3 c. green and reddish violet 20 45
124 4 c. brown-orange and sepia 25 40
125 5 c. black and carmine 30 40
a. "C" of "CA" missing from wmk
126 6 c. olive and chestnut 25 40
127 8 c. blue-green and blue 30 65
128 12 c. black and bright green 30 70
129 14 c. blue and violet 30 60
130 24 c. reddish violet and rose-carmine 45 65
131 48 c. bright green and red-orange 1·75 3·50
132 60 c. carmine and black 1·60 2·75
133 $1.20, emerald and black 5·00 6·00
134 $2.40, orange and black 23·00 30·00
120/134 *Set of* 15 30·00 42·00

Designs: *Horiz*—2 c., 60 c. Making Carib baskets; 3 c., 48 c. Lime plantation; 4 c. Picking oranges; 5 c. Bananas; 6 c. Botanical Gardens; 8 c. Drying vanilla beans; 12 c., $1.20, Fresh Water Lake; 14 c. Layou River; 24 c. Boiling Lake. *Vert*—$2.40, Picking oranges.

NEW
CONSTITUTION
1951

(34)

1951 (15 Oct). *New Constitution. Nos.* 123, 125, 127 *and* 129 *optd with T* 34 *by B.W.*
135 3 c. green and reddish violet 15 40
136 5 c. black and carmine 15 30
137 8 c. blue-green and blue (R.) 35 25
138 14 c. blue and violet (R.) 30 30

1953 (2 June). *Coronation. As No.* 47 *of Aden.*
139 2 c. black and deep green 12 10

35 Queen Elizabeth II

36 Mat Making

37 Picking Oranges

38 Canoe Making

(Photo Harrison (½ c.). Recess B.W. (others))

1954 (1 Oct)–57. *Designs previously used for King George VI issue, but with portrait of Queen Elizabeth II as in T* 35/8. *Wmk Mult Script CA. P* 15 × 14 (½ c.), 13½ × 13 ($2.40), 13 × 13½ *(others).*
140 35 ½ c. brown 5 5
141 – 1 c. black and vermilion 5 5
142 – 2 c. chocolate and myrtle-green *(shades)* 10 5
143 – 3 c. green and purple 10 10
144 36 3 c. black and carmine (15.10.57) 15 10
145 37 4 c. brown-orange and sepia 10 5
146 – 5 c. black and carmine-red 10 10
147 38 5 c. light blue and sepia-brown *(shades)* (15.10.57) 1·25 20
148 – 6 c. bronze-green and red-brown 10 5
149 – 8 c. deep green and deep blue 12 5
150 – 10 c. green and brown *(shades)* (15.10.57) 20 10
151 – 12 c. black and emerald 25 5
152 – 14 c. blue and purple 15 5
153 – 24 c. purple and carmine 20 5
154 – 48 c. green and red-orange 1·75 6·00
155 36 48 c. deep brown and violet (15.10.57) 3·50 3·50
156 – 60 c. rose-red and black 75 95
157 – $1.20, emerald and black 6·00 5·50
158 – $2.40, yellow-orange and black 8·50 11·00
140/158 *Set of* 19 21·00 25·00

Designs: *Horiz*—1 c. Drying cocoa; 2 c., 60 c. Making Carib baskets; 3 c. (No. 143), 48 c. (No. 154) Lime plantation; 5 c. (No. 146) Bananas; 6 c. Botanical Gardens; 8 c. Drying vanilla beans; 10 c. Bananas *(different)*; 12 c., $1.20, Fresh Water Lake; 14 c. Layou River; 24 c. Boiling Lake. *Vert*—$2.40, Picking oranges.

1958 (22 Apr). *Inauguration of British Caribbean Federation. As Nos.* 135/7 *of Antigua.*
159 3 c. deep green 10 10
160 6 c. blue 15 15
161 12 c. scarlet 15 10

40 Seashore at Rosalie

48 Traditional Costume

Two types of 14 c.

I. Eyes of model looking straight ahead.
II. Eyes looking to her right.

(Des S. Scott. Photo Harrison)

1963 (16 May)–65. *T* 40, 48 *and similar designs. W w* 12 *(upright). P* 14 × 14½ *(vert)* or 14½ × 14 *(horiz).*
162 1 c. green, blue and sepia 5 10
163 2 c. bright blue 5 5

164 3 c. blackish brown and blue 5 5
165 4 c. green, sepia and slate-violet 5 5
166 5 c. magenta 8 5
167 6 c. green, bistre and violet 8 8
168 8 c. green, sepia and black 10 10
169 10 c. sepia and pink 10 12
170 12 c. green, blue and blackish brown .. 12 15
171 14 c. multicoloured (I) 20 15
171a 14 c. multicoloured (II) (1.4.65) 20 12
172 15 c. yellow, green and brown 15 15
173 24 c. multicoloured 60 20
174 48 c. green, blue and black 80 35
175 60 c. orange, green and black 85 80
176 $1.20, multicoloured .. .. .. 3·00 1·60
177 $2.40, blue, turquoise and brown .. .. 3·50 3·50
178 $4.80, green, blue and brown .. .. 9·00 10·00
162/78 .. .. *Set of* 17 17·00 16·00

Designs: *Vert*—2 c., 5 c. Queen Elizabeth II; 24 c. Imperial Amazon; $2.40, Trafalgar Falls; $4.80, Coconut Palm. *Horiz*—3 c. Sailing canoe; 4 c. Sulphur springs; 6 c. Road making; 8 c. Dug-out canoe; 10 c. Crapaud; 12 c. Scott's Head; 15 c. Bananas; 48 c. Good-will; 60 c. Cocoa tree; $1.20, Coat of Arms.

See also Nos. 200/4.

1963 (4 June). *Freedom from Hunger. As No.* 76 *of Aden.*
179 15 c. reddish violet 25 15

1963 (2 Sept). *Red Cross Centenary. As Nos.* 147/8 *of Antigua.*
180 5 c. red and black 15 10
181 15 c. red and blue 40 40

1964 (23 April). 400*th Birth Anniv of William Shakespeare. As No.* 164 *of Antigua.*
182 15 c. bright purple 20 15

1965 (17 May). *I.T.U. Centenary. As Nos.* 166/7 *of Antigua.*
183 2 c. light emerald and blue 10 5
184 48 c. turquoise-blue and grey 35 30

1965 (25 Oct). *International Co-operation Year. As Nos.* 168/9 *of Antigua.*
185 1 c. reddish purple and turquoise-green .. 5 5
186 15 c. deep bluish green and lavender 25 25

1966 (24 Jan). *Churchill Commemoration. As Nos.* 170/3 *of Antigua.*
187 1 c. new blue 5 5
a. Gold omitted £350
188 5 c. deep green 10 8
189 15 c. brown 30 25
190 24 c. bluish violet 40 50

1966 (4 Feb). *Royal Visit. As Nos.* 174/5 *of Antigua.*
191 5 c. black and ultramarine 25 12
192 15 c. black and magenta 35 25

1966 (1 July). *World Cup Football Championships. As Nos.* 176/7 *of Antigua.*
193 5 c. violet, yellow-green, lake & yellow-brown 10 5
194 24 c. chocolate, blue-green, lake & yell-brown 25 20

1966 (20 Sept). *Inauguration of W.H.O. Headquarters, Geneva. As Nos.* 178/9 *of Antigua.*
195 5 c. black, yellow-green and light blue .. 10 5
196 24 c. black, light purple and yellow-brown .. 20 25

1966 (1 Dec). 20*th Anniv of U.N.E.S.C.O. As Nos.* 196/8 *of Antigua.*
197 5 c. slate-violet, red, yellow and orange .. 10 5
198 15 c. orange-yellow, violet and deep olive .. 25 25
199 24 c. black, bright purple and orange 25 30

1966 (30 Dec)–**67**. *As Nos.* 165, 167/9 *and* 172 *but wmk* w **12** *sideways.*
200 4 c. green, sepia and slate-violet (16.5.67) .. 12 12
201 6 c. green, bistre and violet 15 12
202 8 c. green, sepia and black 30 30
203 10 c. sepia and pink (16.5.67) 20 20
204 15 c. yellow, green and brown (16.5.67) .. 35 50

ASSOCIATED STATEHOOD

56 Children of Three Races

(Des and photo Harrison)

1967 (2 Nov). *National Day. T* **56** *and similar horiz designs. Multicoloured. W* w **12**. *P* 14½.
205 5 c. Type **56** 5 5
206 10 c. The *Santa Maria* and motto 8 8
207 15 c. Hands holding motto ribbon 8 8
208 24 c. Belaire dancing 10 10

57 John F. Kennedy

(Des G. Vasarhelyi. Litho D.L.R.)

1968 (20 Apr). *Human Rights Year. T* **57** *and similar horiz designs. Multicoloured. W* w **12** *(sideways). P* 14 × 13½.
209 1 c. Type **57** 5 5
210 10 c. Cecil A. E. Rawle 10 10
a. Imperf (pair) £130
211 12 c. Pope John XXIII 10 10
212 48 c. Florence Nightingale 20 25
213 60 c. Albert Schweitzer 30 35

ASSOCIATED STATEHOOD (58)

NATIONAL DAY 3 NOVEMBER 1968 (59)

1968 (8 July). *Associated Statehood. As Nos.* 162, 170 *and* 174, *but wmk sideways, or Nos.* 163/4, 166, 170, 171*a*, 173, 175/8 *and* 200/4 *optd with T* **58**.
214 1 c. green, blue and sepia (Sil.) 5 5
215 2 c. bright blue (Sil.) 5 5
216 3 c. blackish brown and blue (Sil.) 5 5
217 4 c. green, sepia and slate-violet (Sil.) .. 5 5
218 5 c. magenta (Sil.) 5 5
219 6 c. green, bistre and violet 5 5
220 8 c. green, sepia and black 5 5
221 10 c. sepia and pink (Sil.) 8 5
222 12 c. green, blue and blackish brown (Sil.) (wmk sideways) 10 5
a. Wmk upright 10 10
224 14 c. multicoloured (II) (Sil.) 10 10
225 15 c. yellow, green and brown (Sil.) 12 10
226 24 c. multicoloured (Sil.) 25 10
227 48 c. green, bl & blk (Sil.) (wmk sideways) .. 70 70
a. Wmk upright .. .. 1·00 1·25
228 60 c. orange, green and black 70 70
229 $1.20, multicoloured .. .. .. 1·25 1·75
230 $2.40, blue, turquoise and brown (Sil.) .. 2·75 3·25
231 $4.80, green, blue and brown (Sil.) .. 3·25 4·25
214/31 .. .. *Set of* 17 8·50 10·00

The 2, 5, 6, 8 and 10 c. values exist with PVA gum as well as gum arabic.

1968 (3 Nov). *National Day. Nos.* 162/4, 171 *and* 176 *optd with T* **59**.
232 1 c. green, blue and sepia 5 5
a. Opt inverted .. .. 45·00
233 2 c. bright blue 5 5
a. Opt double .. .. 30·00
234 3 c. blackish brown and blue 5 5
a. Opt inverted .. .. 30·00
235 14 c. multicoloured (I) 10 10
236 $1.20, multicoloured 35 55
a. Opt double .. .. 30·00
b. Vert pair, one opt omitted, other opt double £150

The above set was put on sale by the New York Agency on 1 November but not sold locally until the 3 November.

60 Forward shooting at Goal

(Des M. Shamir (1 c., 60 c.), K. Plowitz (5 c., 48 c.). Litho B.W.)

1968 (25 Nov). *Olympic Games, Mexico. T* **60** *and similar horiz designs. Multicoloured. P* 11½ × 11.
237 1 c. Type **60** 5 5
a. Horiz pair. Nos. 237/8 .. .. .. 10 10
238 1 c. Goalkeeper trying to save goal 5 5
239 5 c. Swimmers about to dive 5 5
a. Horiz pair. Nos. 239/40 .. .. .. 10 10
240 5 c. Swimmers diving 5 5
241 48 c. Javelin-throwing 20 20
a. Horiz pair. Nos. 241/2 .. .. .. 40 40
242 48 c. Hurdling 20 20
243 60 c. Basketball 25 30
a. Horiz pair. Nos. 243/4 .. .. .. 50 60
244 60 c. Basketball players 25 30
237/44 .. .. *Set of* 8 1·00 1·10

Nos. 237/44 were issued in sheets of 40 containing two panes of *se-tenant* pairs.

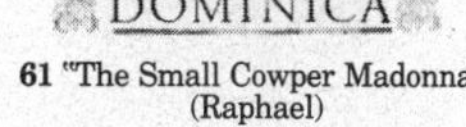

61 "The Small Cowper Madonna" (Raphael)

62 "Venus and Adonis" (Rubens)

(Photo Delrieu, Paris)

1968 (23 Dec). *Christmas. P* 12½ × 12.
245 **61** 5 c. multicoloured 10 10

Three other values were issued: 12 c. "Madonna of the Chair" (Raphael); 24 c. "Madonna and Child" (Italo-Byzantine, XVI century); $1.20 "Madonna and Child" (Byzantine, XIII century). Sizes as T **61**.

These only come from miniature sheets, containing two *se-tenant* strips of each value.

(Litho D.L.R.)

1969 (30 Jan). 20*th Anniv of World Health Organisation. Paintings. T* **62** *and similar vert designs. Multicoloured. W* w **12**. *P* 15.
246 5 c. Type **62** 5 5
247 15 c. "The Death of Socrates" (J.-L. David) .. 8 8
248 24 c. "Christ and the Pilgrims of Emmaus" (Velasquez) 12 12
249 50 c. "Pilate washing his Hands" (Rembrandt) 25 30

66 Picking Oranges

67 "Strength in Unity" Emblem and Fruit Trees

(Des K. Plowitz. Litho Harrison)

1969 (10 Mar). *Tourism. T* **66** *and similar horiz designs. Multicoloured. W* w **12**. *P* 14½.
250 10 c. Type **66** 8 8
a. Horiz pair. Nos. 250/1 .. .. .. 15 15
251 10 c. Woman, child and ocean scene 8 8
252 12 c. Fort Yeoung Hotel 10 10
a. Horiz pair. Nos. 252/3 .. .. .. 20 20
253 12 c. Red-necked Amazons 10 10
254 24 c. Calypso band 15 15
a. Horiz pair. Nos. 254/5 .. .. .. 30 30
255 24 c. Women dancing 15 15
256 48 c. Underwater life 35 35
a. Horiz pair. Nos. 256/7 .. .. .. 70 70
257 48 c. Skin-diver and turtle 35 35
250/7 .. .. *Set of* 8 1·25 1·25

Each denomination was printed *se-tenant* throughout the sheet. The 12 c. values are on cream coloured paper.

(Litho B.W.)

1969 (July). *First Anniv of CARIFTA (Caribbean Free Trade Area). T* **67** *and similar horiz designs. Multicoloured. P* 13½ × 13.
258 5 c. Type **67** 5 5
259 8 c. "HS 748" aircraft, emblem and island .. 8 5
260 12 c. Chart of Caribbean Sea and emblem .. 10 8
261 24 c. Steamship unloading, tug and emblem .. 20 15

71 "Spinning"

72 Mahatma Gandhi Weaving and Clock Tower, Westminster

(Litho B.W.)

1969 (10 July). 50*th Anniv of International Labour Organisation. T* **71** *and similar vert designs showing paintings of people at work by J. Millet, bordered by flags of member-nations of the I.L.O. Multicoloured. No wmk. P* 13 × 13½.
262 15 c. Type **71** 10 8
263 30 c. "Threshing" 15 15
264 38 c. "Flax-pulling" 20 20

(Des G. Vasarhelyi. Litho Format)

1969 (20 Oct). *Birth Centenary of Mahatma Gandhi. T* **72** *and similar horiz designs. Multicoloured. P* 14½.
265 6 c. Type **72** 30 12
266 38 c. Gandhi, Nehru and Mausoleum 70 60
267 $1.20, Gandhi and Taj Mahal .. .. 1·75 1·60

Nos. 265/7 are incorrectly inscribed "Ghandi".

75 "Saint Joseph"

(Des G. Vasarhelyi. Litho Govt Printer, Jerusalem)

1969 (3 Nov). *National Day. Stained Glass Windows. T* **75** *and similar vert designs. Multicoloured. P* 14.
268 6 c. Type **75** 10 8
269 8 c. "Saint John" 10 10
270 12 c. "Saint Peter" 12 12
271 60 c. "Saint Paul" 55 80

Nos. 268/71 were printed in sheets of 16 (4 × 4) containing 12 stamps and four printed labels in the top row. The labels each contain two lines of a patriotic poem by W. O. M. Pond, the first letter from each line spelling "DOMINICA".

79 Queen Elizabeth II 80 Purple-throated Carib and Flower

81 Government Headquarters

82 Coat of Arms

(Photo D.L.R.)

1969–72. *T* **79/82** *and similar horiz designs. Multicoloured. W* **41** *of Singapore* (60 *c. to* $4.80) *or no wmk* (*others*). *P* 13½ × 14 (½ c.), 14 × 13½ (1 *to* 50 *c.*) *or* 14 (60 *c. to* $4.80).

A. *Chalk-surfaced paper* (26.11.69)
B. *Glazed paper* (1972)

		A		B	
272	½ c. Type **79**	5	5	5	5
273	1 c. Type **80**	15	8	20	10
274	2 c. Poinsettia	15	10	20	10
275	3 c. Red-necked Pigeon ..	25	12	30	20
276	4 c. Imperial Amazon	25	12	30	20
277	5 c. Swallowtail Butterfly ..	30	20	40	25
278	6 c. Julia Butterfly ..	30	20	40	25
279	8 c. Shipping Bananas ..	20	15	25	20
280	10 c. Portsmouth Harbour ..	30	15	35	20
281	12 c. Copra Processing Plant ..	30	20	35	20
282	15 c. Straw Workers	30	20	35	30
283	25 c. Timber Plant	35	30	40	35
284	30 c. Pumice Mine	1·25	70	1·25	70
285	38 c. Grammar School and Playing Field	3·00	2·25	4·50	4·50
286	50 c. Roseau Cathedral	1·00	60	1·00	90
287	60 c. Type **81**	1·00	1·25	†	
288	$1.20, Melville Hall Airport (40 × 27 *mm*)	2·50	2·25	†	
289	$2.40, Type **82**	4·75	6·50	†	
290	$4.80, Type **79** (26 × 39 *mm*)	9·00	12·00	†	
272A/90A	.. .. *Set of* 19	23·00	25·00		
272B/90B	.. .. *Set of* 15			9·00	7·50

99 "Virgin and Child with St. John" (Perugino) 101 Astronaut's First Step onto the Moon

(Des G. Vasarhelyi. Litho B.W.)

1969 (19 Dec). *Christmas. Paintings. T* **99** *and similar vert designs. Multicoloured. P* 14 × 14½.
291 6 c. "Virgin and Child with St. John" (Lippi) 10 10
292 10 c. "Holy Family with the Lamb" (Raphael) 12 12
293 15 c. Type **99** 20 20
294 $1.20, "Madonna of the Rose Hedge" (Botticelli) .. .. .. 80 1·00
MS295 89 × 76 mm. Nos. 293/4. Imperf .. .. 1·25 1·60

(Des G. Vasarhelyi. Photo Banknote Printing Office, Helsinki)

1970 (6 Feb*). *Moon Landing. T* **101** *and similar horiz designs. Multicoloured. P* 12½.
296 ½ c. Type **101** 5 5
297 5 c. Scientific Experiment on the Moon, and Flag 15 15
298 8 c. Astronauts collecting Rocks 20 20
299 30 c. Module over the Moon 40 40
300 50 c. Moon Plaque 60 60
301 60 c. Astronauts 75 75
296/301 .. .. .. *Set of* 6 1·90 1·90
MS302 116 × 112 mm. Nos. 298/301. Imperf .. 1·75 1·90

*This is the date of release in Dominica, but the above were released by the Philatelic Agency in the U.S.A. on 2 February.

107 Giant Green Turtle

(Des G. Drummond. Litho Kyodo Printing Co, Tokyo)

1970 (7 Sept). *Flora and Fauna. T* **107** *and similar horiz designs. Multicoloured. P* 13.
303 6 c. Type **107** 40 25
304 24 c. Flying fish 70 60
305 38 c. Anthurium lily 80 70
306 60 c. Imperial and Red-necked Amazons .. 1·75 1·50
MS307 160 × 111 mm. Nos. 303/6 .. .. .. 6·00 7·50

108 18th-Century National Costume 109 Scrooge and Marley's Ghost

(Des G. Drummond from local designs. Litho Questa)

1970 (30 Oct). *National Day. T* **108** *and similar horiz designs. Multicoloured. P* 14.
308 5 c. Type **108** 8 8
309 8 c. Carib Basketry 10 10
310 $1 Flag and Chart of Dominica 60 75
MS311 150 × 85 mm. Nos. 308/10 plus three labels 1·00 1·50

(Des R. Granger Barrett. Litho Questa)

1970 (23 Nov). *Christmas and Charles Dickens' Death Centenary. T* **109** *and similar vert designs showing scenes from "A Christmas Carol". Multicoloured. P* 14 × 14½.
312 2 c. Type **109** 8 8
313 15 c. Fezziwig's Ball 20 20
314 24 c. Scrooge and his Nephew's Party 30 30
315 $1.20, Scrooge and the Ghost of Christmas Present .. .. 1·10 1·50
MS316 142 × 87 mm. Nos. 312/15 .. .. 3·50 4·25

110 "The Doctor" (Sir Luke Fildes)

(Des G. Vasarhelyi. Litho Questa)

1970 (28 Dec). *Centenary of British Red Cross. T* **110** *and similar horiz designs. Multicoloured. P* 14½ × 14.
317 8 c. Type **110** 10 10
318 10 c. Hands and Red Cross 10 10
319 15 c. Flag of Dominica and Red Cross Emblem 15 15
320 50 c. "The Sick Child" (E. Munch) 75 75
MS321 108 × 76 mm. Nos. 317/20 .. .. 2·00 2·50

111 Marigot School

(Des G. Vasarhelyi. Litho Questa)

1971 (1 Mar). *International Education Year* (1970). *T* **111** *and similar horiz designs. Multicoloured. P* 13½.
322 5 c. Type **111** 5 5
323 8 c. Goodwill Junior High School 8 8
324 14 c. University of West Indies (Jamaica) .. 15 15
325 $1 Trinity College, Cambridge 50 65
MS326 85 × 85 mm. Nos. 324/5 .. .. .. 90 1·25

112 Waterfall

(Des O. Bonnevalle. Litho Questa)

1971 (22 Mar). *Tourism. T* **112** *and similar horiz designs. Multicoloured. P* 13½.
327 5 c. Type **112** 10 10
328 10 c. Boat-building 20 20
329 30 c. Sailing 35 35
330 50 c. Yacht and motor launch 55 55
MS331 130 × 86 mm. Nos. 327/30 .. .. 1·25 1·75

113 UNICEF Symbol in "D" 114 German Boy Scout

(Des G. Drummond. Litho Questa)

1971 (14 June). *25th Anniv of UNICEF. P* 14.
332 **113** 5 c. bluish violet, black and gold .. 8 8
333 10 c. yellow, black and gold 10 10
334 38 c. green, black and gold 25 25
335 $1.20 orange, black and gold 55 75
MS336 84 × 79 mm. Nos. 333 and 335 .. .. 75 1·10

(Litho Format)

h8**1971** (18 Oct). *World Scout Jamboree, Asagiri, Japan. T* **114** *and similar vert designs showing Boy Scouts from the nations listed. Multicoloured. W* w **12**. *P* 11.
337 20 c. Type **114** 20 20
338 24 c. Great Britain 25 25
339 30 c. Japan 35 35
340 $1 Dominica 80 95
MS341 114 × 102 mm. Nos. 339/40 .. .. 1·75 2·25

The above were printed on thick paper and the watermark is very faint.

"Dominica" on the scout's shirt pocket is omitted on the $1 value from the miniature sheet.

115 Groine at Portsmouth

(Des V. Whiteley. Litho Format)

1971 (15 Nov). *National Day. T* **115** *and similar multicoloured designs. P* 13½.
342 8 c. Type **115** 8 8
343 15 c. Carnival scene 10 10
344 20 c. Carifta Queen (*vert*) 15 15
345 50 c. Rock of Atkinson (*vert*) 40 50
MS346 63 × 89 mm. $1.20, As 20 c. P 15 .. .. 1·00 1·25

116 Eight Reals Piece, 1761

(Des G. Drummond. Litho Questa)

1972 (7 Feb). *Coins. T* **116** *and similar designs. P* 14.
347 10 c. black, silver and violet 10 10
348 30 c. black, silver and yellowish green .. 30 35
349 35 c. black, silver and bright blue 35 40
350 50 c. black, silver and vermilion 65 80
MS351 86 × 90 mm. Nos. 349/50 .. .. .. 1·40 1·75

Designs: *Horiz*—30 c. Eleven and three bitt pieces, 1798. *Vert*—35 c. Two reals and two bitt pieces, 1770; 50 c. Mocos, Pieces-of-eight and eight reals-eleven bitts piece, 1798.

117 Manicou

(Des R. Granger Barrett. Litho Questa)

1972 (3 June). *U.N. Conference on the Human Environment, Stockholm. T* **117** *and similar horiz designs. Multicoloured. W* w **12** (*sideways*). *P* 14.
352 ½ c. Type **117** 5 5
353 35 c. Agouti (rodent) 40 25
354 60 c. Orchid 95 60
355 $1.20, Hibiscus .. .. 1·60 1·60
MS356 139 × 94 mm. Nos. 352/5 .. .. .. 5·50 7·00

118 Sprinter

(Des R. Granger Barrett. Litho Format)

1972 (16 Oct*). *Olympic Games, Munich. T* **118** *and similar multicoloured designs. P* 14.

357	30 c. Type **118**	20	25
358	35 c. Hurdler	25	30
359	58 c. Hammer-thrower (*vert*)	45	50
360	72 c. Long-jumper (*vert*)	65	70
MS361	98 × 96 mm. Nos. 359/60. P 15	1·50	1·90

*This is the local release date; the American philatelic agency released the stamps on 9 October.

119 General Post Office

(Des G. Vasarhelyi. Litho Format)

1972 (1 Nov). *National Day. T* **119** *and similar horiz designs. Multicoloured. P* 13½.

362	10 c. Type **119**	10	8
363	20 c. Morne Diablotin	15	15
364	30 c. Rodney's Rock	25	30
MS365	83 × 96 mm. Nos. 363/4. P 15	65	70

120 Bananas and Imperial Amazon

(Des (from photograph by D. Groves) and photo Harrison)

1972 (20 Nov). *Royal Silver Wedding. Multicoloured; background colour given. W* w **12**. *P* 14 × 14½.

366	**120**	5 c. yellow-olive (*shades*)	8	10
367		$1 myrtle-green	50	65

121 "The Adoration of the Shepherds" (Caravaggio) **122** Launching of Weather Satellite

(Des G. Vasarhelyi. Litho Format)

1972 (4 Dec*). *Christmas. T* **121** *and similar vert designs. Multicoloured. P* 13½.

368	8 c. Type **121**	10	8
369	14 c. "The Myosotis Virgin" (Rubens)	15	12
370	30 c. "Madonna and Child with St. Francesca Romana" (Gentileschi)	30	20
371	$1 "Adoration of the Kings" (Mostaert)	70	1·00
MS372	102 × 79 mm. Nos. 370/1. Imperf.	1·25	1·50

* This is the date of release in Dominica; the stamps were put on sale by the Philatelic agency in the U.S.A. on 27 November.

No. 368 is wrongly attributed to Boccaccino in the design.

(Des G. Vasarhelyi. Litho Format)

1973 (16 July). *I.M.O./W.M.O. Centenary. T* **122** *and similar multicoloured designs. P* 14½.

373	½ c. Type **122**	5	5
374	1 c. Nimbus satellite	5	5
375	2 c. Radiosonde balloon	5	5
376	30 c. Radarscope (*horiz*)	20	20
377	35 c. Diagram of pressure zones (*horiz*)	25	25
378	50 c. Hurricane shown by satellite (*horiz*)	35	40
379	$1 Computer weather-map (*horiz*)	65	70
373/9	*Set of* 7	1·40	1·50
MS380	90 × 105 mm. Nos. 378/9	1·25	1·40

NEW INFORMATION

The editor is always interested to correspond with people who have new information that will improve or correct the Catalogue.

123 Going to Hospital **124** Cyrique Crab

(Des G. Vasarhelyi. Litho Format)

1973 (20 Aug). *25th Anniv of W.H.O. T* **123** *and similar horiz designs. Multicoloured. P* 14½.

381	½ c. Type **123**	5	5
382	1 c. Maternity care	5	5
383	2 c. Smallpox inoculation	5	5
384	30 c. Emergency service	30	30
385	35 c. Waiting for the doctor	35	35
386	50 c. Medical examination	40	40
387	$1 Travelling doctor	65	65
381/7	*Set of* 7	1·60	1·60
MS388	112 × 110 mm. Nos. 386/7. P 14 × 14½	1·40	1·50
	a. Perf 14½	65·00	45·00

(Des G. Drummond. Litho Format)

1973 (15 Oct). *Flora and Fauna. T* **124** *and similar vert designs. Multicoloured. P* 14½.

389	½ c. Type **124**	5	5
390	22 c. Blue Land-crab	35	35
391	25 c. Bread Fruit	35	35
392	$1.20, Sunflower	1·75	2·25
MS393	91 × 127 mm. Nos. 389/92	3·75	4·75

125 Princess Anne and Captain Mark Phillips

(Des G. Drummond. Litho Format)

1973 (14 Nov). *Royal Wedding. P* 13½.

394	**125**	25 c. multicoloured	15	15
395	–	$2 multicoloured	80	80
MS396		79 × 100 mm. 75 c. as 25 c. and $1.20 as $2	90	90

No. 395 is as T **125**, but the portrait has a different frame.

126 "Adoration of the Kings" (Brueghel)

(Des M. Shamir. Litho Format)

1973 (26 Nov). *Christmas. T* **126** *and similar horiz designs. Multicoloured. P* 14½.

397	½ c. Type **126**	5	5
398	1 c. "Adoration of the Magi" (Botticelli)	5	5
399	2 c. "Adoration of the Magi" (Dürer)	5	5
400	12 c. "Mystic Nativity" (Botticelli)	10	10
401	22 c. "Adoration of the Magi" (Rubens)	15	15
402	35 c. "The Nativity" (Dürer)	20	20
403	$1 "Adoration of the Shepherds" (Giorgione)	50	65
397/403	*Set of* 7	90	1·10
MS404	122 × 98 mm. Nos. 402/3	1·00	1·40

127 Carib Basket-weaving

(Des G. Drummond. Litho Format)

1973 (17 Dec). *National Day. T* **127** *and similar multicoloured designs. P* 13½.

405	5 c. Type **127**	5	5
406	10 c. Staircase of the Snake	8	8
407	50 c. Miss Caribbean Queen (*vert*)	35	35
408	50 c. Miss Carifta Queen (*vert*)	35	40
409	$1 Dance group	60	60
MS410	95 × 127 mm. Nos. 405/6 and 409	80	1·00

128 University Centre, Dominica

(Des G. Drummond. Litho Format)

1974 (21 Jan). *25th Anniv of West Indies University. T* **128** *and similar horiz designs. Multicoloured. P* 14½.

411	12 c. Type **128**	8	8
412	30 c. Graduation ceremony	12	15
413	$1 University coat of arms	40	65
MS414	97 × 131 mm. Nos. 411/13	80	95

129 Dominicia 1d. Stamp of 1874 and Map **130** Footballer and Flag of Brazil

(Des G. Drummond. Litho Format)

1974 (27 May). *Stamp Centenary. T* **129** *and similar horiz designs. Multicoloured. P* 14½.

415	½ c. Type **129**	5	5
416	1 c. 6d. stamp of 1874 and posthorn	5	5
417	2 c. 1s. stamp of 1874 and arms	5	5
418	10 c. Type **129**	30	30
419	50 c. As 1 c.	65	65
420	$1.20, As 2 c.	90	90
415/20	*Set of* 6	1·75	1·75
MS421	105 × 121 mm. Nos. 418/20	1·75	2·00

(Des V. Whiteley. Litho Format)

1974 (12 Aug). *World Cup Football Championship, West Germany. T* **130** *and similar vert designs, showing footballers and flags of the countries given. Multicoloured. P* 14½.

422	½ c. Type **130**	5	5
423	1 c. West Germany	5	5
424	2 c. Italy	5	5
425	30 c. Scotland	15	15
426	40 c. Sweden	20	20
427	50 c. Netherlands	25	25
428	$1 Yugoslavia	50	65
422/8	*Set of* 7	1·10	1·25
MS429	89 × 87 mm. Nos. 427/8	85	1·10

131 Indian Hole

(Des G. Vasarhelyi. Litho Format)

1974 (1 Nov). *National Day. T* **131** *and similar horiz designs. Multicoloured. P* 13½.

430	10 c. Type **131**	5	5
431	40 c. Teachers' Training College	15	15
432	$1 Bay Oil distillery plant, Petite Savanne	50	70
MS433	96 × 143 mm. Nos. 430/2	80	1·00

132 Churchill with "Colonist"

(Des G. Drummond. Litho Format)

1974 (25 Nov). *Birth Centenary of Sir Winston Churchill. T* **132** *and similar horiz designs. Multicoloured. P* 14½.

434	½ c. Type **132**	5	5
435	1 c. Churchill and Eisenhower	5	5
436	2 c. Churchill and Roosevelt	5	5
437	20 c. Churchill and troops on assault-course	20	20
438	45 c. Painting at Marrakesh	35	35
439	$2 Giving the "V" sign	1·25	1·50
434/9	*Set of* 6	1·75	2·00
MS440	126 × 100 mm. Nos. 438/9. P 13	1·75	2·25

133 Mailboats *Orinoco* (1851) and *Geesthaven* (1974) **134** "The Virgin and Child" (Tiso)

(Des G. Drummond. Litho Format)

1974 (4 Dec). *Centenary of Universal Postal Union. T* **133** *and similar horiz designs. Multicoloured. P* 13.

441 10 c. Type **133** .. 15 15
442 $2 De Havilland "4" (1918) and Boeing "747" (1974) .. 1·25 1·50
MS443 107 × 93 mm. $1.20 as 10 c. and $2.40 as $2 2·25 2·75

Nos. 442 and **MS**443 are inscr "De Haviland".

(Des M. Shamir. Litho Questa)

1974 (16 Dec). *Christmas. T* **134** *and similar vert designs. Multicoloured. P* 14.

444 ½ c. Type **134** .. 5 5
445 1 c. "Madonna and Child with Saints" (Costa) 5 5
446 2 c. "The Nativity" (School of Rimini, 14th-cent) .. 5 5
447 10 c. "The Rest on the Flight into Egypt" (Romanelli) .. 8 8
448 25 c. "Adoration of the Shepherds" (da Sermoneta) .. 15 15
449 45 c. "The Nativity" (Guido Reni) .. 20 25
450 $1 "The Adoration of the Magi" (Caselli) .. 45 60
444/50 .. *Set of* 7 90 1·10
MS451 114 × 78 mm. Nos. 449/50 .. 80 1·00

135 Trigger Fish

(Des G. Vasarhelyi. Litho Format)

1975 (2 June). *Fishes. T* **135** *and similar horiz designs. Multicoloured. P* 14.

452 ½ c. Type **135** .. 5 5
453 1 c. Cola .. 5 5
454 2 c. Sailfish .. 10 10
455 3 c. Vayway .. 10 10
456 20 c. Bechine .. 90 75
457 $2 Grouper .. 4·00 3·25
452/7 .. *Set of* 6 4·75 4·00
MS458 104 × 80 mm. No. 457. P 13 .. 4·00 4·25

136 *Myscelia antholia*

(Des J. W. Litho Format)

1975 (28 July). *Dominican Butterflies. T* **136** *and similar horiz designs. Multicoloured. P* 14½.

459 ½ c. Type **136** .. 5 5
460 1 c. *Lycorea ceres* .. 5 5
461 2 c. *Siderone nemesis* .. 5 5
462 6 c. *Battus polydamas* .. 20 20
463 30 c. *Anartia lytrea* .. 70 70
464 40 c. *Morpho peleides* .. 75 75
465 $2 *Dryas julia* .. 3·00 3·00
459/65 .. *Set of* 7 4·50 2·50
MS466 108 × 80 mm. No. 465. P 13 .. 3·00 3·25

137 R.M.S. *Yare*

(Des J. W. Litho Questa)

1975 (1 Sept). *"Ships Tied to Dominica's History". T* **137** *and similar horiz designs. Multicoloured. P* 14.

467 ½ c. Type **137** .. 5 5
468 1 c. R.M.S. *Thames* .. 5 5
469 2 c. S.S. *Lady Nelson* .. 5 5
470 20 c. S.S. *Lady Rodney* .. 45 35
471 45 c. M.V. *Statesman* .. 70 55
472 50 c. M.V. *Geestecape* .. 80 65
473 $2 M.V. *Geestestar* .. 4·50 3·25
467/73 .. *Set of* 7 6·00 4·50
MS474 78 × 103 mm. Nos. 472/3 .. 5·00 5·00

138 "Women in Agriculture" **139** Miss Caribbean Queen, 1975

(Litho Questa)

1975 (20 Oct). *International Women's Year. T* **138** *and similar horiz design. Multicoloured. P* 14.

475 10 c. Type **138** .. 15 15
476 $2 "Women in Industry and Commerce" .. 1·25 1·50

(Litho Format)

1975 (6 Nov). *National Day. T* **139** *and similar multicoloured designs. P* 14 × 13½ (*vert*) *or* 13½ × 14 (*horiz*).

477 5 c. Type **139** .. 5 5
478 10 c. Public Library (*horiz*) .. 10 10
479 30 c. Citrus Factory (*horiz*) .. 20 20
480 $1 National Day Trophy .. 50 75
MS481 130 × 98 mm. Nos. 478/80. Imperf .. 1·00 1·40

140 "Virgin and Child" (Mantegna) **141** Hibiscus

(Des M. Shamir. Litho Questa)

1975 (24 Nov). *Christmas. T* **140** *and similar vert designs showing "Virgin and Child". Multicoloured. P* 14.

482 ½ c. Type **140** .. 5 5
483 1 c. Fra Filippo Lippi .. 5 5
484 2 c. Bellini .. 5 5
485 10 c. Botticelli .. 15 10
486 25 c. Bellini .. 25 20
487 45 c. Correggio .. 35 30
488 $1 Dürer .. 1·00 90
482/88 .. *Set of* 7 1·75 1·40
MS489 139 × 85 mm. Nos. 487/88 .. 1·50 2·00

(Des J.W. Litho Format)

1975 (8 Dec)–**78**. *T* **141** *and similar multicoloured designs.*

(*a*) *Size as T* **141**. *P* 14½

490 ½ c. Type **141** .. 10 5
491 1 c. African Tulip .. 15 5
492 2 c. Castor Oil Tree .. 15 5
493 3 c. White Cedar Flower .. 15 5
494 4 c. Egg Plant .. 15 5
495 5 c. Gare .. 20 5
496 6 c. Ochro .. 20 5
497 8 c. Zenaida Dove .. 40 10
498 10 c. Screw Pine .. 20 10
a. Perf 13½ (1978) .. 25·00
499 20 c. Mango Longue .. 25 15
500 25 c. Crayfish .. 35 15
501 30 c. Manicou .. 40 20

(*b*) *Size* 28 × 44 *mm* ($10) *or* 44 × 28 *mm* (*others*). *P* 13½

502 40 c. Bay Leaf Groves .. 45 25
503 50 c. Tomatoes .. 50 30
504 $1 Lime Factory .. 75 55
505 $2 Rum Distillery .. 1·75 1·50
506 $5 Bay Oil Distillery .. 4·25 4·50
507 $10 Queen Elizabeth II .. 10·00 11·00
490/507 .. *Set of* 18 18·00 17·00

142 American Infantry **143** Rowing

(Des J.W. Litho Format)

1976 (12 Apr). *Bicentenary of American Revolution. T* **142** *and similar vert designs. Multicoloured. P* 14½.

508 ½ c. Type **142** .. 5 5
509 1 c. English three-decker, 1782 .. 5 5
510 2 c. George Washington .. 5 5
511 45 c. British sailors .. 90 70
512 75 c. British ensign .. 1·50 1·00
513 $2 Admiral Hood .. 3·50 2·50
508/13 .. *Set of* 6 5·50 4·00
MS514 105 × 92 mm. Nos. 512/13. P 13 .. 5·00 5·50

(Des J.W. Litho Format)

1976 (24 May). *Olympic Games, Montreal. T* **143** *and similar vert designs. Multicoloured. P* 14½.

515 ½ c. Type **143** .. 5 5
516 1 c. Shot putting .. 5 5
517 2 c. Swimming .. 5 5
518 40 c. Relay .. 30 30
519 45 c. Gymnastics .. 35 35
520 60 c. Sailing .. 55 55
521 $2 Archery .. 1·50 1·50
515/21 .. *Set of* 7 2·50 2·50
MS522 90 × 104 mm. Nos. 520/1. P 13 .. 2·25 2·40

144 Ringed Kingfisher **145** Viking Spacecraft System

(Des G. Drummond. Litho Format)

1976 (28 June). *Wild Birds. T* **144** *and similar multicoloured designs. P* 14½.

523 ½ c. Type **144** .. 5 5
524 1 c. Mourning Dove .. 5 5
525 2 c. Green Heron .. 10 8
526 15 c. Broad-winged Hawk .. 70 60
527 30 c. Blue-headed Hummingbird .. 1·25 95
528 45 c. Bananaquit .. 1·90 1·50
529 $2 Imperial Amazon .. 8·50 7·50
523/9 .. *Set of* 7 11·00 9·50
MS530 133 × 101 mm. Nos. 527/9. P 13 .. 11·00 11·00

1976 (26 July). *West Indian Victory in World Cricket Cup. As Nos.* 559/60 *of Barbados.*

531 15 c. Map of the Caribbean .. 1·00 90
532 25 c. Prudential Cup .. 1·25 1·00

(Des PAD Studio. Litho Format)

1976 (20 Sept). *Viking Space Mission. T* **145** *and similar multicoloured designs. P* 14½.

533 ½ c. Type **145** .. 5 5
534 1 c. Launching pad (*horiz*) .. 5 5
535 2 c. Titan IIID and Centaur DII .. 5 5
536 3 c. Orbiter and lander capsule .. 5 5
537 45 c. Capsule, parachute unopened .. 30 25
538 75 c. Capsule, parachute opened .. 50 40
539 $1 Lander descending (*horiz*) .. 60 50
540 $2 Space vehicle on Mars (*horiz*) .. 1·25 90
533/40 .. *Set of* 8 2·50 2·00
MS541 104 × 78 mm. Nos. 539/40. P 13 .. 2·00 2·50

146 "Virgin and Child with Saints Anthony of Padua and Roch" (Giorgione) **147** Island Craft Co-operative

(Des M. Shamir. Litho Questa)

1976 (1 Nov). *Christmas. T* **146** *and similar vert designs showing "Virgin and Child" by the artists named. Multicoloured. P* 14.

542 ½ c. Type **146** .. 5 5
543 1 c. Bellini .. 5 5
544 2 c. Mantegna .. 5 5
545 6 c. Mantegna (*different*) .. 10 10
546 25 c. Memling .. 25 25
547 45 c. Correggio .. 35 35
548 $3 Raphael .. 1·75 1·75
542/8 .. *Set of* 7 2·25 2·25
MS549 140 × 85 mm. 50 c. as No. 547 and $1 as No. 548 .. 1·25 1·60

(Des G. Drummond. Litho Questa)

1976 (22 Nov). *National Day. T* **147** *and similar horiz designs. Multicoloured. P* 13½.

550 10 c. Type **147** .. 8 8
551 50 c. Harvesting bananas .. 30 35
552 $1 Boxing plant .. 55 70
MS553 96 × 122 mm. Nos. 550/2 .. 95 1·00

148 Common Sundial **149** The Queen Crowned and Enthroned

(Des J.W. Litho Questa)

1976 (20 Dec). *Shells. T* **148** *and similar vert designs. Multicoloured. P* 14.

554 ½ c. Type **148** .. 5 5
555 1 c. Flame Helmet .. 5 5
556 2 c. Mouse Cone .. 5 5
557 20 c. Caribbean vase .. 45 45
558 40 c. West Indian Fighting Conch .. 70 70
559 50 c. Short Coral Shell .. 70 70

560 $3 Apple Murex .. .. 3·50 3·50
554/60 .. .. *Set of* 7 5·00 5·00
MS561 101 × 55 mm. $2 Long-spined Star Shell 3·00 3·50

(Des J.W. Litho Questa)

1977 (7 Feb). *Silver Jubilee. T* **149** *and similar horiz designs. Multicoloured. P* 14 × 13½.

562 ½ c. Type **149** 5 5
563 1 c. Imperial State Crown 5 5
564 45 c. Queen Elizabeth and Princess Anne .. 40 30
565 $2 Coronation Ring 90 80
566 $2.50, Ampulla and Spoon .. .. .. 1·25 1·10
MS567 104 × 79 mm. $5 Queen Elizabeth and Prince Philip .. .. 1·90 2·00

Nos. 562/6 also exist perf 12 × 11½ (*Price for set of* 5 £3.50 *mint or used*) from additional sheetlets of 5 stamps and one label. Stamps perforated 14 × 13½ are from normal sheets of 40. Stamps from the sheets of 5 have the arch at left in a different colour.

150 Joseph Haydn

151 Hiking

(Des J.W. Litho Questa)

1977 (25 Apr). *150th Death Anniv of Ludwig van Beethoven. T* **150** *and similar vert designs. Multicoloured. P* **14**.

568 ½ c. Type **150** 5 5
569 1 c. Scene from "Fidelio" 5 5
570 2 c. Maria Casentini (dancer) 5 5
571 15 c. Beethoven and pastoral scene 15 10
572 30 c. "Wellington's Victory" 25 20
573 40 c. Henriette Sontag (singer) 35 30
574 $2 The young Beethoven .. .. .. 2·00 1·75
568/74 .. .. *Set of* 7 2·50 2·25
MS575 138 × 93 mm. Nos. 572/4 .. .. .. 2·75 3·00

(Des J.W. Litho Questa)

1977 (8 Aug). *Caribbean Scout Jamboree, Jamaica. T* **151** *and similar horiz designs. Multicoloured. P* 14.

576 ½ c. Type **151** 5 5
577 1 c. First-aid 5 5
578 2 c. Camping 5 5
579 45 c. Rock climbing 35 35
580 50 c. Canoeing 40 40
581 $3 Sailing .. .. 2·50 2·00
576/81 .. .. *Set of* 6 3·00 2·50
MS582 111 × 113 mm. 75 c. Map reading and $2 Campfire singsong .. .. 2·00 2·25

152 Holy Family

ROYAL VISIT
W.I. 1977

(153)

(Des G. Vasarhelyi. Litho Questa)

1977 (17 Nov). *Christmas. T* **152** *and similar horiz designs showing book miniatures from Foix Book of Hours* ($3) *or De Lisle Psalter (others). Multicoloured. P* 14.

583 ½ c. Type **152** 5 5
584 1 c. Angel and Shepherds 5 5
585 2 c. Holy Baptism 5 5
586 6 c. Flight into Egypt 10 10
587 15 c. Three Kings with gifts 20 20
588 45 c. Holy Family in the Temple 40 40
589 $3 Flight into Egypt (*different*) .. .. 1·25 1·60
583/9 .. .. *Set of* 7 1·90 2·25
MS590 113 × 85 mm. 50 c. Virgin and Child; $2 Flight into Egypt (*different*) .. .. .. 1·25 1·75

1977 (28 Nov). *Royal Visit. Nos.* 562/7 *optd with T* **153**. *A. In top left-hand corner**. *P* 14 × 13½. *B. Above* "JUBILEE". *P* 12 × 11½.

		A.		B.	
591	½ c. Type **149**	†		5	5
592	1 c. Imperial State Crown ..	†		8	5
593	45 c. Queen Elizabeth and Princess Anne	30	20	25	20
594	$2 Coronation Ring	95	70	90	70
595	$2.50, Ampulla and Spoon ..	1·25	80	1·10	80
MS596	104 × 79 mm. $5 Queen Elizabeth and Prince Philip ..	2·25	1·90	†	
	a. Optd "W.I. 1977" only on stamp	18·00	18·00	†	

*Stamp from No. **MS**596 has the overprint to left of face-value.

No. **MS**596a is overprinted "W.I. 1977" beneath "ROYAL VISIT" inscription to left of stamp design. Overprint as T **153**, but in one line, appears at top left of *miniature sheet*.

154 "Sousouelle Souris"

(Des L. Honychurch and J.W. Litho Questa)

1978 (9 Jan). *"History of Carnival". T* **154** *and similar horiz designs. Multicoloured. P* 14.

597 ½ c. Type **154** 5 5
598 1 c. Sensay costume 5 5
599 2 c. Street musicians 5 5
600 45 c. Douiette band 20 20
601 50 c. Pappy Show wedding 20 20
602 $2 Masquerade band .. .. .. 75 1·00
597/602 .. .. *Set of* 6 1·10 1·40
MS603 104 × 88 mm. $2.50 as No. 602 .. .. 1·00 1·25

155 Col. Charles Lindbergh and *Spirit of St. Louis*

156 Queen receiving Homage

(Des G. Drummond. Litho Format)

1978 (13 Mar). *Aviation Anniversaries. T* **155** *and similar horiz designs. Multicoloured. P* 14½.

604 6 c. Type **155** 5 8
605 10 c. *Spirit of St. Louis*, New York, 20 May 1927 .. .. 5 8
606 15 c. Lindbergh and map of Atlantic 8 10
607 20 c. Lindbergh reaches Paris, 21 May 1927 .. 10 12
608 40 c. *LZ1*, Lake Constance, 1900 .. .. 20 20
609 60 c. Count F. von Zeppelin and *LZ2*, 1906 .. 30 30
610 $3 *LZ127* (*Graf Zeppelin*), 1928 .. .. 1·40 1·40
604/10 .. .. *Set of* 7 2·00 2·00
MS611 139 × 108 mm. 50 c. *Spirit of St. Louis* in mid-Atlantic; $2 *Graf Zeppelin*, 1928 .. .. 1·25 1·50

The 6, 10, 15, 20 and 50 c. values commemorate the 50th anniversary of first solo transatlantic flight by Col. Charles Lindbergh; the other values commemorate anniversaries of various Zeppelin airships.

(Des J.W. Litho Questa)

1978 (2 June). *25th Anniv of Coronation. T* **156** *and similar vert designs. Multicoloured. P* 14.

612 45 c. Type **156** 35 25
613 $2 Balcony scene 85 75
614 $2.50, Queen and Prince Philip 95 85
MS615 76 × 107 mm. $5 Queen Elizabeth II .. 2·00 1·60

Nos. 612/14 also exist perf 12 (*Price for set of* 3 £2·00 *mint or used*) from additional sheetlets of 3 stamps and 1 label. Stamps perforated 14 come from sheets of 50. The stamps from sheetlets have changed background or inscription colours.

157 Wilbur Wright's Aeroplane

158 "Two Apostles" (Rubens)

(Des G. Vasarhelyi. Litho Format)

1978 (10 July). *75th Anniv of Powered Flight. T* **157** *and similar horiz designs. Multicoloured. P* 14½.

616 30 c. Type **157** 15 15
617 40 c. *Flyer*, 1908 .. .. 20 20
618 60 c. *Flyer* 1 .. .. 30 30
619 $2 *Flyer* 1 (*different*) .. .. .. 1·00 1·00
MS620 116 × 89 mm. $3 Wilbur and Orville Wright .. .. 1·40 1·60

(Des BG Studio. Litho Questa)

1978 (16 Oct). *Christmas. Paintings. T* **158** *and similar vert designs. Multicoloured. P* 14.

621 20 c. Type **158** 10 10
622 45 c. "The Descent from the Cross" (Rubens) 20 20
623 50 c. "St Ildefonso receiving the Chasuble" (Rubens) 25 20
624 $3 "The Assumption of the Virgin" (Rubens) 1·10 1·50
MS625 113 × 83 mm. $2 "The Holy Family" (Sebastiano del Piombo*) .. .. 80 1·10

*This painting was incorrectly attributed to Rubens on the stamp.

PRICES OF SETS

Set prices are given for many issues, generally those containing five stamps or more. Definitive sets include one of each value or major colour change, but do not cover different perforations, die types or minor shades. Where a choice is possible the set prices are based on the cheapest versions of the stamps included in the listings.

INDEPENDENT

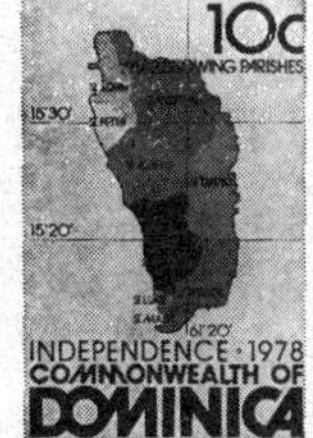

159 Map showing Parishes

INDEPENDENCE
3rd NOVEMBER
1978

(160)

(Des J.W. Litho Questa)

1978 (3 Nov). *Independence. T* **159** *and similar vert designs. Multicoloured. P* 14.

626 10 c. Type **159** 5 5
627 25 c. *Sabinea carinalis* (National flower) .. 12 12
628 45 c. New National flag 25 25
629 50 c. Coat of arms 25 25
630 $2 Patrick John (Prime Minister) 70 70
MS631 113 × 90 mm. $2.50, Type **159** .. .. 4·00 4·00

1978 (3 Nov)–**79**. *Independence. Nos.* 490/507 (10 *c. now perf* 13½) *optd as T* **160** *by typography*.

632 ½ c. Type **141** 10 10
633 1 c. African Tulip 10 10
634 2 c. Castor Oil Tree 10 10
635 3 c. White Cedar Flower 15 15
636 4 c. Egg Plant 15 15
637 5 c. Gare 15 15
638 6 c. Ochro 15 15
639 8 c. Zenaida Dove 30 20
640 10 c. Screw Pine 15 15
 a. Perf 14½. Litho opt (7.79) 15 15
641 20 c. Mango Longue 20 15
642 25 c. Crayfish 25 20
643 30 c. Manicou 25 20
644 40 c. Bay Leaf Groves 25 25
 a. Litho opt (7.79) 25 25
645 50 c. Tomatoes 30 30
646 $1 Lime Factory 70 65
647 $2 Rum Distillery .. .. 1·25 1·00
648 $5 Bay Oil Distillery .. .. .. 2·50 2·25
649 $10 Queen Elizabeth II .. .. .. 5·50 4·50
 a. Litho opt (7.79) .. .. .. 5·50 4·50
632/49 .. .. *Set of* 18 11·00 10·00

For History of Aviation gold foil stamps see Appendix at the end of the Dominica listing.

161 Sir Rowland Hill

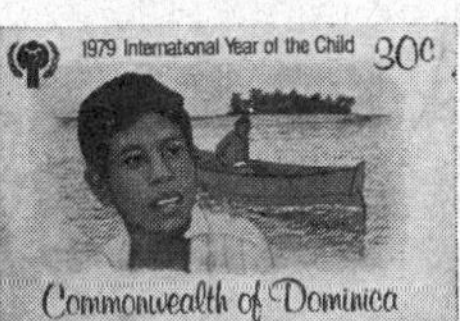

162 Children and Canoe

(Des BG Studio. Litho Questa)

1979 (19 Mar). *Death Centenary of Sir Rowland Hill. T* **161** *and similar vert designs. P* 14.

650 25 c. multicoloured 15 15
651 45 c. multicoloured 25 25
652 50 c. black, reddish violet and magenta .. 30 30
653 $2 black, magenta and yellow .. .. 85 1·10
MS654 186 × 96 mm. $5 black and vermilion .. 2·75 3·00

Designs:—45 c. Great Britain 1840 2d. blue; 50 c. 1874 1d. stamp; $2 Maltese Cross cancellations; $5 Penny Black.

Nos. 650/3 also exist perf 12 (*Price for set of* 4 £1·40 *mint or used*) from additional sheetlets of 5 stamps and 1 label. Shades of these stamps differ from those perforated 14 which come from sheets of 40.

(Des BG Studio. Litho Questa)

1979 (23 Apr). *International Year of the Child. T* **162** *and similar horiz designs. Multicoloured. P* 14.

655 30 c. Type **162** 25 25
656 40 c. Children with bananas 35 35
657 50 c. Children playing cricket 50 50
658 $3 Child feeding rabbits .. .. .. 1·75 1·75
MS659 117 × 85 mm. $5 Child with catch of fish .. 2·25 2·50

163 Grouper

(Des G. Drummond. Litho Questa)

1979 (21 May). *Marine Wildlife. T* **163** *and similar horiz designs. Multicoloured. P* 14.

660 10 c. Type **163** 10 5
661 30 c. Spotted Dolphin 25 15
662 50 c. White-tailed Tropic Bird 40 25

663 60 c. Brown Pelican 50 30
664 $1 Pilot Whale 70 45
665 $2 Brown Booby .. .. 1·10 80
660/5 .. .. *Set of* 6 2·75 1·75
MS666 120 × 94 mm. $3 Elkhorn Coral .. .. 1·60 1·75

164 H.M. Bark *Endeavour*

(Des J.W. Litho Questa)

1979 (16 July). *Death Bicentenary of Captain Cook. T* **164** *and similar horiz designs. Multicoloured. P* 14.
667 10 c. Type **164** 20 10
668 50 c. H.M.S. *Resolution* 45 45
669 60 c. H.M.S. *Discovery* 55 55
670 $2 Detail of Cook's chart of New Zealand, 1770 .. .. 1·10 1·10
MS671 97 × 90 mm. $5 Captain Cook and signature .. .. 2·50 3·00

165 Cooking at Camp-fire

166 Colvillea

(Des M. Diamond. Litho Questa)

1979 (30 July). *50th Anniv of Girl Guide Movement in Dominica. T* **165** *and similar horiz designs. Multicoloured. P* 14.
672 10 c. Type **165** 10 5
673 20 c. Pitching emergency rain tent 20 10
674 50 c. Raising Dominican flag 40 25
675 $2.50, Singing and dancing to accordion .. 1·25 1·50
MS676 110 × 86 mm. $3 Guides of different age-groups .. .. 1·60 1·75

(Des J.W. Litho Questa)

1979 (3 Sept). *Flowering Trees. T* **166** *and similar vert designs. Multicoloured. P* 14.
677 20 c. Type **166** 10 10
678 40 c. Lignum Vitae 20 20
679 60 c. Dwarf Poinciana 30 30
680 $2 Fern Tree 95 95
MS681 114 × 89 mm. $3 Perfume Tree .. .. 1·25 1·40

167 Cathedral of the Assumption, Roseau

(Des W. Grout. Litho Questa)

1979 (11 Oct). *Christmas. Cathedrals. T* **167** *and similar multi-coloured designs. P* 14.
682 6 c. Type **167** 5 5
683 45 c. St. Paul's, London (*vert*) 20 20
684 60 c. St. Peter's, Rome 25 25
685 $3 Notre Dame, Paris (*vert*) .. .. .. 1·00 1·00
MS686 113 × 85 mm. 40 c. St. Patrick's, New York; $2 Cologne Cathedral (*both vert*) .. .. .. 85 1·25

HURRICANE RELIEF

(168)

169 Mickey Mouse and Octopus playing Xylophone

1979 (29 Oct). *Hurricane Relief. Nos.* 495, 502 *and* 506/7 *optd as T* **168**.
687 5 c. Gare 5 5
688 40 c. Bay Leaf Groves 12 15
689 $5 Bay Oil Distillery .. .. 1·90 2·00
690 $10 Queen Elizabeth II .. .. 3·75 4·00

(Litho Format)

1979 (2 Nov). *International Year of the Child. Walt Disney Cartoon Characters. T* **169** *and similar vert designs showing characters playing musical instruments. Multicoloured. P* 11.
691 ½ c. Type **169** 5 5
692 1 c. Goofy playing guitar on rocking-horse .. 5 5
693 2 c. Mickey Mouse playing violin and Goofy playing bagpipes 5 5
694 3 c. Donald Duck playing drum with pneumatic drill 5 5
695 4 c. Minnie Mouse playing saxophone on roller-skates 5 5
696 5 c. Goofy as one-man-band 5 5
697 10 c. Dale being blown from French horn by Horace Horsecollar 5 5
698 $2 Huey, Dewey and Louie playing bass .. 1·50 1·25
699 $2.50, Donald Duck playing piano and Huey playing trumpet .. .. 1·75 1·50
691/9 .. .. *Set of* 9 3·25 2·75
MS700 127 × 102 mm. $3 Mickey Mouse playing piano. P 13½ .. .. 1·75 1·75

170 Hospital Ward

(Des BG Studio. Litho Questa)

1980 (31 Mar). *75th Anniv of Rotary International. T* **170** *and similar horiz designs. Multicoloured. P* 14.
701 10 c. Type **170** 5 5
702 20 c. Electric-cardiogram 15 15
703 40 c. Site for mental hospital 25 25
704 $2.50, Paul P. Harris (founder) .. .. 1·40 1·40
MS705 128 × 113 mm. $3 Interlocking cogs of Rotary emblem and globe .. .. 1·40 1·60

1980 (6 May). *"London 1980" International Stamp Exhibition. As Nos.* 650/3 *optd with T* **262** *of Grenada. P* 12.
706 25 c. multicoloured 15 15
707 45 c. multicoloured 20 20
708 50 c. olive-brown, blue and rose-red 30 30
709 $2 olive-brown, vermilion and yellow .. 95 95

171 Shot Putting

(Des J.W. Litho Questa)

1980 (27 May). *Olympic Games, Moscow. T* **171** *and similar horiz designs. Multicoloured. P* 14.
710 30 c. Type **171** 12 15
711 40 c. Basketball 15 20
712 60 c. Swimming 25 30
713 $2 Gymnastics .. .. 90 1·00
MS714 114 × 86 mm. $3 The Marathon .. .. 1·25 1·50

172 "Supper at Emmaus" (Caravaggio)

(Des J.W. Litho Questa)

1980 (22 July). *Famous Paintings. T* **172** *and similar multi-coloured designs. P* 13½.
715 20 c. Type **172** 10 10
716 25 c. "Portrait of Charles I Hunting" (Van Dyck) (*vert*) 12 12
717 30 c. "The Maids of Honour" (Velasquez) (*vert*) 15 15
718 45 c. "The Rape of the Sabine Women" (Poussin) 20 20
719 $1 "Embarkation for Cythera" (Watteau) .. 45 45
720 $5 "Girl before a Mirror" (Picasso) (*vert*) .. 2·00 2·00
715/20 .. .. *Set of* 6 2·75 2·75
MS721 114 × 111 mm. $3 "The Holy Family" (Rembrandt) (*vert*) .. .. 1·40 1·50

173 Scene from "Peter Pan"

(Litho Walsall)

1980 (1 Oct). *Christmas. Scenes from Walt Disney's Cartoon Film "Peter Pan". T* **173** *and similar horiz designs. P* 11.
722 ½ c. multicoloured 5 5
723 1 c. multicoloured 5 5
724 2 c. multicoloured 5 5
725 3 c. multicoloured 5 5
726 4 c. multicoloured 5 5
727 5 c. multicoloured 5 5
728 10 c. multicoloured 5 5
729 $2 multicoloured 90 80
730 $2.50, multicoloured .. .. .. 1·00 95
722/30 .. .. *Set of* 9 2·00 1·90
MS731 124 × 98 mm. $4 multicoloured (*vert*) .. 2·00 2·25

174 Queen Elizabeth the Queen Mother in Doorway

(Litho Questa)

1980 (20 Oct). *80th Birthday of Queen Elizabeth the Queen Mother. P* 12.
732 **174** 40 c. multicoloured 35 35
733 $2.50, multicoloured .. .. .. 1·40 1·40
MS734 85 × 66 mm. **174** $3 multicoloured .. 1·75 1·75
Nos. 732/3 also exist perforated 14 (*price for pair* £1·75 *mint or used*) from additional sheetlets of 9. Stamps perforated 12 are from normal sheets of 50.

175 Douglas Bay

(Des G. Drummond. Litho Questa)

1981 (12 Feb). *Dominica Safari. T* **175** *and similar multicoloured designs. P* 14.
735 20 c. Type **175** 10 10
736 30 c. Valley of Desolation 15 15
737 40 c. Emerald Pool (*vert*) 20 20
738 $3 Indian River (*vert*) .. .. .. 1·60 1·60
MS739 84 × 104 mm. $4 Trafalgar Falls (*vert*) .. 2·40 2·50

(Litho Format)

1981 (30 Apr). *50th Anniv of Walt Disney's Cartoon Character, Pluto. Vert designs as T* **169**. *Multicoloured. P* 13½ × 14.
740 $2 Pluto and Fifi .. .. 1·25 1·25
MS741 128 × 102 mm. $4 Pluto in scene from film *Pluto's Blue Note* .. .. 2·40 2·50

176 Forest Thrush

177 Windsor Castle

(Des P. Barrett. Litho Questa)

1981 (30 Apr). *Birds. T* **176** *and similar horiz designs. Multi-coloured. P* 14.
742 20 c. Type **176** 15 10
743 30 c. Stolid Flycatcher 25 15
744 40 c. Blue-hooded Euphonia 30 20
745 $5 Lesser Antillean Pewee .. .. .. 3·00 3·00
MS746 121 × 95 mm. $3 Imperial Amazon .. 1·75 1·75

(Des J.W. Litho Questa)

1981 (23 June). *Royal Wedding. T* **177** *and similar vert designs. Multicoloured. A. P* 14. *B. P* 12.

		A		B	
747	45 c. Prince Charles and Lady Diana Spencer	25	25	7·00	7·00
748	60 c. Type **177**	35	35	7·00	7·00
749	$4 Prince Charles as helicopter pilot	1·75	1·75	7·00	7·00
MS750	96 × 82 mm. $5 Helicopter of Queen's Flight	2·50	2·50	†	

Nos. 747B/9B also exist from additional sheetlets of five stamps and one label with changed background colours.

OMNIBUS ISSUES

Details, together with prices for complete sets, of the various Omnibus issues from the 1935 Silver Jubilee series to date are included in a special section following Zululand at the end of the catalogue.

178 Lady Diana Spencer

179 Ixora

(Manufactured by Walsall)

1981 (23 June). *Royal Wedding. Booklet stamps. T* **178** *and similar vert designs. Multicoloured. Roul* 5 × *imperf*. Self-adhesive.*

751 25 c. Type **178** 30 30
a. Booklet pane. Nos. 751/2, each × 3 .. 5·00
752 $2 Prince Charles .. .. 1·50 1·50
753 $5 Prince Charles and Lady Diana Spencer 3·75 3·75
a. Booklet pane of 1.. .. .. .. 3·75

*The 25 c. and $2 values were separated by various combinations of rotary knife (giving a straight edge) and roulette. The $5 value exists only with straight edges.

(Litho Questa)

1981 (2 Nov). *Christmas. Horiz designs as T* **169** *showing scenes from Walt Disney's cartoon film "Santa's Workshop". P* 13½.

754 ½ c. multicoloured 5 5
755 1 c. multicoloured 5 5
756 2 c. multicoloured 5 5
757 3 c. multicoloured 5 5
758 4 c. multicoloured 5 5
759 5 c. multicoloured 5 5
760 10 c. multicoloured 5 5
761 45 c. multicoloured 30 30
762 $5 multicoloured .. .. 2·50 2·50
754/62 .. .. *Set of* 9 2·75 2·75
MS763 129 × 103 mm. $4 multicoloured.. .. 2·25 2·50

(Des P. Barrett. Litho Questa)

1981 (1 Dec)–**84**. *Plant Life. Horiz designs as T* **179**. *Multi-coloured. A. Without imprint date. P* 14. *B. With imprint date ("1984") at foot of design. P* 12 (1984).

		A.		B.	
764	1 c. Type **179**	5	5	†	
765	2 c. Flamboyant	5	5	†	
766	4 c. Poinsettia	5	5	†	
767	5 c. Bois Caribe (national flower of Dominica)	5	5	†	
768	8 c. Annatto or Roucou ..	5	5	†	
769	10 c. Passion Fruit	5	5	5	5
770	15 c. Breadfruit or Yampain ..	8	10	†	
771	20 c. Allamanda or Buttercup ..	10	12	†	
772	25 c. Cashew Nut	12	15	†	
773	35 c. Soursop or Couassol ..	20	25	†	
774	40 c. Bougainvillea	20	25	†	
775	45 c. Anthurium	25	30	†	
776	60 c. Cacao or Cocoa	35	40	†	
777	90 c. Pawpaw Tree or Papay ..	50	60	†	
778	$1 Coconut Palm	55	60	55	60
779	$2 Coffee Tree or Café ..	1·10	1·25	†	
780	$5 Heliconia or Lobster Claw	3·25	3·50	3·25	3·50
781	$10 Banana/Fig	5·75	6·00	5·75	6·00
764A/81A	.. .. *Set of* 18	11·50	12·50	†	

180 Curb slope for Wheelchairs

181 "Olga Picasso in an Armchair"

(Des BG Studio. Litho Format)

1981 (22 Dec). *International Year for Disabled Persons. T* **180** *and similar vert designs. Multicoloured. P* 14½.

782 45 c. Type **180** 30 25
783 60 c. Bus with invalid step 40 35
784 75 c. Motor car controls adapted for handicapped 50 40
785 $4 Bus with wheelchair ramp .. .. 2·25 2·25
MS786 82 × 96 mm. $5 Specially designed elevator control panel .. .. 2·50 2·75

(Des J.W. Litho Format)

1981 (30 Dec). *Birth Centenary of Picasso. T* **181** *and similar vert designs. Multicoloured. P* 14½.

787 45 c. Type **181** 30 25
788 60 c. "Bathers".. .. .. 40 35
789 75 c. "Woman in Spanish Costume" 50 40
790 $4 "Detail of Dog and Cock" .. .. 2·25 2·25
MS791 140 × 115 mm. $5 "Sleeping Peasants" (detail) .. .. 2·50 2·75

(Litho Questa)

1982 (29 Jan). *World Cup Football Championship, Spain. Walt Disney Cartoon Characters. Horiz designs as T* **169**. *Multi-coloured. P* 14 × 13½.

792 ½ c. Goofy chasing ball with butterfly net .. 5 5
793 1 c. Donald Duck with ball in beak 5 5
794 2 c. Goofy as goalkeeper 5 5
795 3 c. Goofy looking for ball 5 5
796 4 c. Goofy as park attendant puncturing ball with litter spike 5 5
797 5 c. Pete and Donald Duck playing 5 5
798 10 c. Donald Duck after kicking rock instead of ball 10 10
799 60 c. Donald Duck feeling effects of a hard game and Daisy Duck dusting ball .. 55 55
800 $5 Goofy hiding ball under his jersey from Mickey Mouse .. .. 2·75 2·75
792/800 .. .. *Set of* 9 3·25 3·25
MS801 132 × 105 mm. $4 Dale making off with ball 2·25 2·25

182 "Golden Days"

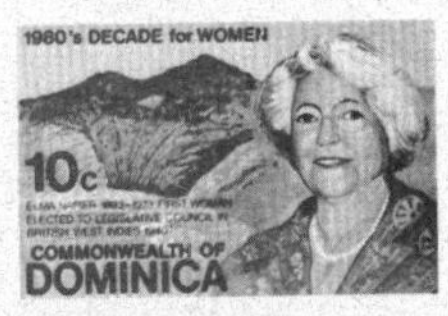

183 Elma Napier (first woman elected to B.W.I. Legislative Council)

(Des M.B.I. Studios. Litho Questa)

1982 (10 Mar). *Norman Rockwell (painter) Commemoration. T* **182** *and similar vert designs. Multicoloured. P* 14 × 13½.

802 10 c. Type **182** 8 8
803 25 c. "The Morning News" 12 12
804 45 c. "The Marbles Champ" 30 30
805 $1 "Speeding Along" 55 55

(Des BG Studio. Litho Questa)

1982 (15 Apr). *Decade for Women. T* **183** *and similar horiz designs. Multicoloured. P* 14.

806 10 c. Type **183** 8 8
807 45 c. Margaret Mead (anthropologist) .. 30 30
808 $1 Mabel ("Cissy") Caudeiron (folk song composer and historian).. .. .. 55 55
809 $4 Eleanor Roosevelt .. .. .. 2·25 2·25
MS810 92 × 63 mm. $3 Florence Nightingale .. 1·75 1·90

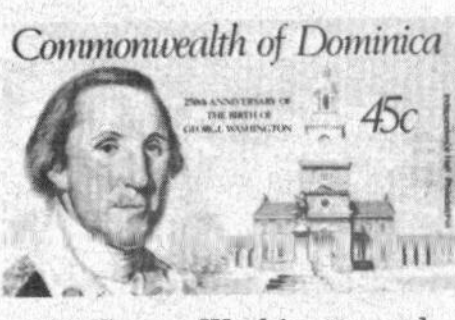

184 George Washington and Independence Hall, Philadelphia

185 Godman's Leaf Butterfly

(Des J.W. Litho Format)

1982 (1 May). *250th Birth Anniv of George Washington* (45, 90 c.) *and Birth Centenary of Franklin D. Roosevelt* (60 c., $2). *T* **184** *and similar horiz designs. Multicoloured. P* 14½.

811 45 c. Type **184** 30 25
812 60 c. Franklin D. Roosevelt and Capitol, Washington D.C. 40 35
813 90 c. Washington at Yorktown (detail, "The Surrender of Cornwallis" by Trumbull) 55 50
814 $2 Construction of dam (from W. Gropper's mural commemorating Roosevelt's "New Deal") .. .. 1·40 1·40
MS815 115 × 90 mm. $5 Washington and Roosevelt with U.S.A. flags of 1777 and 1933 .. .. 2·50 2·75

(Des P. Barrett. Litho Questa)

1982 (1 June). *Butterflies. T* **185** *and similar vert designs. Multi-coloured. P* 14.

816 15 c. Type **185** 20 10
817 45 c. Zebra 45 30
818 60 c. Mimic 55 40
819 $3 Red Rim .. .. 2·25 2·50
MS820 77 × 105 mm. $5 Southern Dagger Tail .. 2·75 3·00

186 Prince and Princess of Wales

187 Scouts around Campfire

(Des PAD Studio. Litho Questa)

1982 (1 July). *21st Birthday of Princess of Wales. T* **186** *and similar vert designs. Multicoloured. P* 14½ × 14.

821 45 c. Buckingham Palace 30 30
822 $2 Type **186** .. .. 1·10 1·10
823 $4 Princess of Wales .. .. 1·90 1·90
MS824 103 × 75 mm. $5 Princess Diana (*different*) 2·25 2·50

Nos. 821/3 also exist in sheetlets of 5 stamps and 1 label.

(Des R. Sauber. Litho Questa)

1982 (3 Aug). *75th Anniv of Boy Scout Movement. T* **187** *and similar multicoloured designs. P* 14.

825 45 c. Type **187** 30 25
826 60 c. Temperature study, Valley of Desolation 45 35
827 75 c. Learning about native birds 50 45
828 $3 Canoe trip along Indian River .. .. 1·90 1·90
MS829 99 × 70 mm. $5 Dominican scouts saluting the flag (*vert*) .. .. 2·40 2·75

1982 (30 Aug). *Birth of Prince William of Wales. Nos. 821/4 optd with T* **171** *of Antigua.*

830 45 c. Buckingham Palace 30 30
831 $2 Type **186** .. .. 1·10 1·10
832 $4 Princess of Wales .. .. 1·90 1·90
MS833 103 × 75 mm. $5 Princess Diana (*different*) 2·25 2·50

Nos. 830/2 also exist in sheetlets of 5 stamps and 1 label.

188 "Holy Family of Francis I"

189 Goosebeak Whale

(Des Design Images. Litho Questa)

1982 (3 Nov). *Christmas. Raphael Paintings. T* **188** *and similar vert designs. Multicoloured. P* 13½ × 14.

834 25 c. Type **188** 15 10
835 30 c. "Holy Family of the Pearl" 20 15
836 90 c. "Canigiani Holy Family" 55 55
837 $4 "Holy Family of the Oak Tree" .. .. 1·90 1·90
MS838 95 × 125 mm. $5 "Holy Family of the Lamb" .. .. 2·40 2·50

(Des J. Cooter. Litho Questa)

1983 (15 Feb). *Save the Whales. T* **189** *and similar horiz designs. Multicoloured. P* 14.

839 45 c. Type **189** 30 30
840 60 c. Humpback Whale 35 35
841 75 c. Great Right Whale 40 40
842 $3 Melonhead Whale .. .. .. 1·75 2·00
MS843 99 × 72 mm. $5 Pygmy Sperm Whale .. 3·00 3·25

190 Banana Export

(Des R. Vigurs. Litho Questa)

1983 (14 Mar). *Commonwealth Day. T* **190** *and similar horiz designs. Multicoloured. P* 14.

844 25 c. Type **190** 12 15
845 30 c. Road building 15 20
846 90 c. Community nursing 40 45
847 $3 Tourism—handicrafts .. .. .. 1·40 1·50

191 Map and Satellite Picture of Hurricane

(Des G. Vasarhelyi. Litho Questa)

1983 (18 Apr). *World Communications Year. T* **191** *and similar horiz designs. Multicoloured. P* 14.

848 45 c. Type **191** 20 25
849 60 c. Aircraft-to-ship transmission 30 35
850 90 c. Satellite communications 40 45
851 $2 Shortwave radio .. .. 95 1·00
MS852 110 × 85 mm. $5 Communications satellite 2·50 2·75

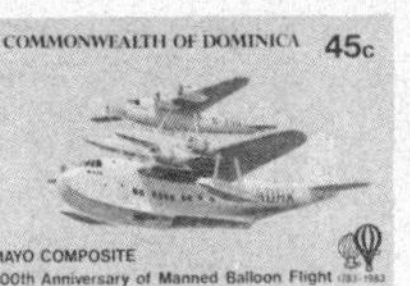

192 *Mayo-Mercury* Composite

(Des W. Wright. Litho Format)

1983 (19 July). *Bicentenary of Manned Flight. T* **192** *and similar horiz designs. Multicoloured. P* 14½.

853	45 c. Type **192**	20	25
854	60 c. Macchi "M.39" seaplane	30	35
855	90 c. Fairey "Swordfish" biplane	40	45
856	$4 Zeppelin "*LZ3*"	1·90	2·00
MS857	105 × 79 mm. $5 *Double Eagle II* (balloon)	2·50	2·75

193 Duesenberg "SJ", 1935

(Des R. Sauber. Litho Questa)

1983 (1 Sept). *Classic Motor Cars. T* **193** *and similar horiz designs. Multicoloured. P* 14.

858	10 c. Type **193**	5	5
859	45 c. Studebaker "Avanti", 1962	20	25
860	60 c. Cord "812", 1936	30	35
861	75 c. MG "TC", 1945	35	40
862	90 c. Camaro "350 SS", 1967	40	45
863	$3 Porsch "356", 1948	1·40	1·50
858/63	*Set of* 6	2·40	2·50
MS864	110 × 75 mm. $5 Ferrari "312 T", 1975	2·50	2·60

194 "Charity"

(Des Design Images. Litho Format)

1983 (4 Oct). *Christmas. 500th Birth Anniv of Raphael. T* **194** *and similar horiz designs. Multicoloured. P* 13½.

865	45 c. Type **194**	20	25
866	60 c. "Hope"	30	35
867	90 c. "Faith"	40	45
868	$4 "The Cardinal Virtues"	1·90	2·00
MS869	101 × 127 mm. $5 "Justice"	2·50	2·75

195 Plumbeous Warbler **196** Donald Duck

(Des Jennifer Toombs. Litho Questa)

1984 (24 Apr). *Birds. T* **195** *and similar horiz designs. Multicoloured. P* 14.

870	5 c. Type **195**	5	5
871	45 c. Imperial Parrot	30	35
872	60 c. Blue-headed Hummingbird	40	45
873	90 c. Red-necked parrot	60	65
MS874	72 × 72 mm. $5 Roseate Flamingos	3·25	3·50

(Litho Format)

1984 (1 May). *Easter. T* **196** *and similar vert designs showing Disney cartoon characters and eggs. Multicoloured. P* 11.

875	½ c. Type **196**	5	5
876	1 c. Mickey Mouse	5	5
877	2 c. Tortoise and Hare	5	5
878	3 c. Brer Rabbit and Brer Bear	5	5
879	4 c. Donald Duck (*different*)	5	5
880	5 c. White Rabbit	5	5
881	10 c. Thumper	8	10
882	$2 Pluto	1·25	1·40
883	$4 Pluto (*different*)	2·50	2·75
875/83	*Set of* 9	3·50	4·00
MS884	126 × 100 mm. $5 Chip and Dale. P 13½ × 14	3·25	3·50

197 Gymnastics **198** *Atlantic Star*

(Des R. Sauber. Litho Questa)

1984 (14 May). *Olympic Games, Los Angeles. T* **197** *and similar vert designs. Multicoloured. P* 14.

885	30 c. Type **197**	20	25
886	45 c. Javelin-throwing	30	35
887	60 c. High diving	40	45
888	$4 Fencing	2·50	2·75
MS889	104 × 85 mm. $5 Equestrian event	3·25	3·50

(Des W. Wright. Litho Questa)

1984 (14 June). *Shipping. T* **198** *and similar horiz designs. Multicoloured. P* 14.

890	45 c. Type **198**	30	35
891	60 c. Liner *Atlantic*	40	45
892	90 c. Carib fishing boat	60	65
893	$4 Liner *Norway*	2·00	2·75
MS894	106 × 79 mm. $5 *Santa Maria*	3·25	3·50

19th UPU
CONGRESS HAMBURG

(199)

200 *Guzmania lingulata*

1984 (19 June). *Universal Postal Union Congress, Hamburg. Nos.* 769A *and* 780A *optd with T* **199**.

895	10 c. Passion Fruit	8	10
896	$5 Heliconia or Lobster Claw	3·25	3·50

(Des P. Barrett. Litho Questa)

1984 (13 Aug). *"Ausipex" International Stamp Exhibition, Melbourne. Bromilaids. T* **200** *and similar vert designs. Multicoloured. P* 14.

897	45 c. Type **200**	30	35
898	60 c. *Pitcairnia angustifolia*	40	45
899	75 c. *Tillandsia fasciculata*	50	55
900	$3 *Aechmea smithiorum*	2·00	2·25
MS901	75 × 105 mm. $5 *Tillandsia utriculata*	3·25	3·50

201 "The Virgin and Child with Young St John" (Correggio) **202** "Before the Start" (Edgar Degas)

(Litho Format)

1984 (30 Oct). *450th Death Anniv of Correggio (painter). T* **201** *and similar vert designs. Multicoloured. P* 15.

902	25 c. Type **201**	15	20
903	60 c. "Christ bids Farewell to the Virgin Mary"	35	40
904	90 c. "Do not Touch Me"	55	60
905	$4 "The Mystical Marriage of St Catherine"	2·40	2·50
MS906	89 × 60 mm. $5 "The Adoration of the Magi"	3·00	3·50

(Litho Format)

1984 (30 Oct). *150th Birth Anniv of Edgar Degas (painter). T* **202** *and similar multicoloured designs. P* 15.

907	30 c. Type **202**	20	25
908	45 c. "Race on the Racecourse"	30	35
909	$1 "Jockeys at the Flagpole"	60	65
910	$3 "Racehorses at Longchamp"	1·75	1·90
MS911	89 × 60 mm. $5 "Self-portrait" (*vert*)	3·00	3·50

POSTAL FISCALS

REVENUE Revenue

(R 1) **(R 2)**

1879–86. *Optd with Type* R **1**. (*a*) *Wmk Crown CC.*

R1	1	1d. lilac	24·00	7·00
		a. Bisected vert (½d.) on cover		
R2		6d. green	2·75	7·50
R3		1s. magenta	8·50	14·00
		(*b*) *Wmk Crown CA*		
R4	1	1d. lilac (1886)	75	1·00

1888. *Optd with Type* R **2**. *Wmk Crown CA.*

R6	1	1d. carmine	25·00	22·00

Appendix

The following stamps have either been issued in excess of postal needs, or have not been made available to the public in reasonable quantities at face value. Miniature sheets, imperforate stamps etc., are excluded from this section.

1978–79

History of Aviation. $16 × 30, each embossed on gold foil.

East Africa

For the issues of the combined East African Postal Administration from 1933 until 1976 *see* KENYA, UGANDA AND TANZANIA.

East Africa and Uganda Protectorates *see* Kenya, Uganda and Tanganyika

East Africa (G.E.A.) *see* Tanzania

Egypt

TURKISH SUZERAINTY

In 1517 Sultan Selim I added Egypt to the Ottoman Empire, and it stayed more or less under Turkish rule until 1805, when Mohammed Ali became governor. He established a dynasty of governors owing nominal allegiance to the Sultan of Turkey until 1914.

Khedive Ismail

18 January 1863–26 June 1879

He obtained the honorific title of Khedive (viceroy) from the Sultan in 1867.

The operations of British Consular Post Offices in Egypt date from 1839 when the first office, at Alexandria, was opened. Further offices at Suez (1847) and Cairo (1859) followed.

Great Britain stamps were issued to Alexandria and Suez offices in 1860 and continued to be used there until the three offices closed in 1882, following the British Military Occupation.

Stamps issued after 1877 can be found with the Egyptian cancellation "Port Said", but these are on letters posted from British ships.

For cancellations used during the 1882 campaign see ARMY FIELD OFFICES at the end of the BRITISH POST OFFICES ABROAD section, following GREAT BRITAIN.

For illustrations of the handstamp and postmark types see BRITISH POST OFFICES ABROAD NOTES, following GREAT BRITAIN.

ALEXANDRIA

CROWNED-CIRCLE HANDSTAMPS

CC1 CC1b ALEXANDRIA (R. *or* Black) (5.1843) *Price on cover* £1100

Stamps of **GREAT BRITAIN** *cancelled* "B 01" *as in Types* **2**, **8**, **12** *or* **15**.

1860 *to* **1879.**

Z 1	½d. rose-red (1870–79) *From*	12·00
	Plate Nos. 5, 6, 8, 10, 13, 14, 15, 19, 20.	
Z 2	1d. rose-red (1857)	6·00
Z 3	1d. rose-red (1861) (Alph IV)	
Z 4	1d. rose-red (1864–79) *From*	6·00
	Plate Nos. 71, 72, 73, 74, 76, 78, 79, 80, 81, 82, 83, 84, 85, 86, 87, 88, 89, 90, 91, 92, 93, 94, 95, 96, 97, 98, 99, 101, 102, 103, 104, 106, 107, 108, 109, 110, 111, 112, 113, 114, 115, 117, 118, 119, 120, 121, 122, 123, 124, 125, 127, 129, 130, 131, 133, 134, 136, 137, 138, 139, 140, 142, 143, 144, 145, 146, 147, 148, 149, 150, 152, 154, 156, 157, 158, 159, 160, 162, 163, 165, 168, 169, 170, 171, 172, 174, 175, 177, 179, 180, 181, 182, 183, 185, 188, 190, 198, 200, 203, 206, 210, 220.	

Z 5	2d. blue (1858–69)	*From* 6·00
	Plate Nos. 7, 8, 9, 13, 14, 15.	
Z 6	2½d. rosy mauve (1875) (blued *paper*) ..	*From* 60·00
	Plate Nos. 1, 2.	
Z 7	2½d. rosy mauve (1875–6) (Plate Nos. 1, 2, 3) ..	27·00
Z 8	2½d. rosy mauve (*Error of Lettering*)	£1250
Z 9	2½d. rosy mauve (1876–79)	*From* 21·00
	Plate Nos. 3, 4, 5, 6, 7, 8, 9.	
Z10	3d. carmine-rose (1862)	£110
Z11	3d. rose (1865) (Plate No. 4)	55·00
Z12	3d. rose (1867–73) (Plate Nos. 4, 5, 6, 7, 8, 9)	*From* 21·00
Z13	3d. rose (1875–76)	*From* 21·00
	Plate Nos. 11, 12, 14, 15, 16, 18, 19.	
Z14	3d. rose (1881) (Plate No. 20)	
Z15	4d. rose (1857)	40·00
Z16	4d. red (1862) (Plate Nos. 3, 4)	*From* 40·00
Z17	4d. vermilion (1865–73)	23·00
	Plate Nos. 7, 8, 9, 10, 11, 12, 13, 14.	
Z18	4d. vermilion (1876) (Plate No. 15)	£120
Z19	4d. sage-green (1877) (Plate No. 15)	75·00
Z20	6d. lilac (1856)	45·00
Z21	6d. lilac (1862) (Plate Nos. 3, 4)	*From* 40·00
Z22	6d. lilac (1865–67) (Plate Nos. 5, 6) ..	*From* 30·00
Z23	6d. lilac (1867) (Plate No. 6)	42·00
Z24	6d. violet (1867–70) (Plate Nos. 6, 8, 9) ..	*From* 30·00
	a. Imperf (Plate No. 8)	£1200
Z25	6d. buff (1872–73) (Plate Nos. 11, 12) ..	*From* 55·00
Z26	6d. chestnut (1872) (Plate No. 11)	27·00
Z27	6d. grey (1873) (Plate No. 12)	45·00
Z28	6d. grey (1874–76) (Plate Nos. 13, 14, 15) ..	*From* 21·00
Z29	9d. straw (1862)	£120
Z30	9d. bistre (1862)	
Z31	9d. straw (1865)	
Z32	9d. straw (1867)	
Z33	10d. red-brown (1867)	£120
Z34	1s. green (1856)	60·00
Z35	1s. green (1862)	50·00
Z36	1s. green (1862) ("K" *variety*)	
Z37	1s. green (1865) (Plate No. 4)	30·00
Z38	1s. green (1867–73) (Plate Nos. 4, 5, 6, 7) ..	*From* 10·00
Z39	1s. green (1873–77)	*From* 25·00
	Plate Nos. 8, 9, 10, 11, 12, 13.	
Z40	2s. blue (1867)	75·00
Z41	5s. rose (1867–74) (Plate Nos. 1, 2) ..	*From* £180

CAIRO

CROWNED-CIRCLE HANDSTAMPS

CC2 CC6 CAIRO (R.) (23.3.1859).. .. *Price on cover* £1300

SUEZ

CROWNED-CIRCLE HANDSTAMPS

CC3 CC1 SUEZ (R., B. *or* Black) (16.7.1847) *Price on cover* £1800

Stamps of GREAT BRITAIN *cancelled "B 02" as in Types* **2** *and* **8**, *or with circular date stamp as Type* **5**.

1860 *to* **1879.**

Z42	½d. rose-red (1870–79)	23·00
	Plate Nos. 6, 10, 11, 12, 13, 14.	
Z43	1d. rose-red (1857)	7·50
Z44	1d. rose-red (1864–79)	*From* 7·00
	Plate Nos. 73, 74, 79, 80, 81, 83, 84, 86, 87, 90, 91, 93, 94, 97, 100, 101, 106, 107, 108, 110, 113, 118, 119, 120, 121, 122, 123, 124, 125, 129, 130, 131, 134, 137, 138, 140, 142, 143, 144, 145, 147, 148, 149, 150, 151, 152, 153, 154, 156, 158, 159, 160, 161, 162, 163, 164, 165, 166, 167, 168, 170, 174, 176, 177, 178, 179, 180, 181, 182, 184, 185, 186, 187, 189, 190, 205.	
Z45	2d. blue (1858–69)	*From* 12·00
	Plate Nos. 8, 9, 13, 14, 15.	
Z46	2½d. rosy mauve (1875) (blued *paper*) ..	*From* 55·00
	Plate Nos. 1, 2, 3.	
Z47	2½d. rosy mauve (1875–76) (Plate Nos. 1, 2, 3)	*From* 30·00
Z48	2½d. rosy mauve (*Error of Lettering*)	£1250
Z49	2½d. rosy mauve (1876–79)	*From* 24·00
	Plate Nos. 3, 4, 5, 6, 7, 8, 9, 10.	
Z50	3d. carmine-rose (1862)	£120
Z51	3d. rose (1865) (Plate No. 4)	60·00
Z52	3d. rose (1867–73) (Plate Nos. 5, 6, 7, 8, 10)	
Z53	3d. rose (1873–76) (Plate Nos. 12, 16) ..	*From* 24·00
Z54	4d. rose (1857)	50·00
Z55	4d. red (1862) (Plate Nos. 3, 4)	*From* 42·00
Z56	4d. vermilion (1865–73)	*From* 27·00
	Plate Nos. 7, 8, 9, 10, 11, 12, 13, 14.	
Z57	4d. vermilion (1876) (Plate No. 15)	
Z58	4d. sage-green (1877) (Plate No. 15)	75·00
Z59	6d. lilac (1856)	45·00
Z60	6d. lilac (1862) (Plate Nos. 3, 4)	*From* 40·00
Z61	6d. lilac (1865–67) (Plate Nos. 5, 6) ..	*From* 32·00
Z62	6d. lilac (1867) (Plate No. 6)	42·00
Z63	6d. violet (1867–70) (Plate Nos. 6, 8, 9) ..	*From* 32·00
Z64	6d. buff (1872–73) (Plate Nos. 11, 12) ..	*From* 60·00
Z65	6d. pale chestnut (Plate No. 12)	£2250
Z66	6d. chestnut (1872) (Plate No. 11)	27·00
Z67	6d. grey (1873) (Plate No. 12)	50·00
Z68	6d. grey (1874–76) (Plate Nos. 13, 14, 15, 16)	*From* 23·00
Z69	8d. orange (1876)	
Z70	9d. straw (1862)	£150
	a. Thick paper	
Z71	9d. bistre (1862)	
Z72	9d. straw (1867)	
Z73	10d. red-brown (1867)	£150
Z74	1s. green (1856)	65·00
Z75	1s. green (1862)	55·00
Z76	1s. green (1862) ("K" *variety*)	
Z77	1s. green (1865) (Plate No. 4)	40·00
Z78	1s. green (1867–73) (Plate Nos. 4, 5, 6, 7) ..	*From* 11·00
Z79	1s. green (1873–77)	*From* 27·00
	Plate Nos. 8, 9, 10, 11, 12.	
Z80	2s. blue (1867)	£120
Z81	5s. rose (1867–74) (Plate Nos. 1, 2) ..	*From* £250

PRICES FOR STAMPS ON COVER

Nos. 1/7	*from* × 8
Nos. 11/41	*from* × 6
Nos. 42/3	*from* × 30
Nos. 44/83	*from* × 5
Nos. 84/97	*from* × 2
Nos. D57/70	*from* × 10
Nos. D71/86	*from* × 5
Nos. D84/103	*from* × 2
Nos. O64/87	*from* × 5
Nos. O88/101	*from* × 2

(Currency: 40 paras = 1 piastre)

1

2

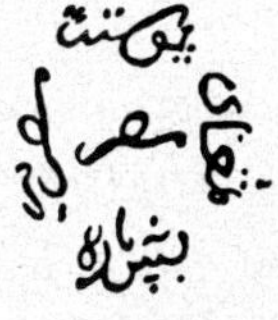
(3)

(Printed by Pellas Bros, Genoa. Litho, except for 1 pi. (typo). Black inscription (T **3**) litho, except on 1 pi. and 2 pi. (typo))

1866 (1 Jan). *Various designs as T* **1** *with black inscription as T* **3**. *The lowest group of characters indicates the value.* 1 *pi. no wmk, others W* **2** *(usually inverted). P* 12½.

1	5 pa. grey	20·00	18·00
	a. *Greenish grey*	20·00	18·00
	b. Imperf (pair)	£150	
	c. Imperf between (pair)	£250	
	d. Perf 12½ × 13 and compound..	30·00	30·00
	e. Perf 13	£200	£250
2	10 pa. brown	35·00	22·00
	a. Imperf (pair)	£110	
	b. Imperf between (pair)	£300	
	c. Perf 12½ × 13 and compound..	50·00	35·00
	d. Perf 12½ × 15	£225	£250
	e. Perf 13	£150	£170
3	20 pa. pale blue	50·00	22·00
	a. *Greenish blue*	50·00	22.00
	b. Imperf (pair)	£200	
	c. Imperf between (pair)	£350	
	d. Perf 12½ × 13 and compound..	70·00	70·00
	e. Perf 13	£350	£200
4	1 pi. mauve	38·00	4·00
	a. Imperf (pair)	£100	
	b. Imperf between (pair)	£275	
	c. Perf 12½ × 13 and compound..	70·00	20·00
	d. Perf 13	£250	£180
5	2 pi. yellow	60·00	30·00
	a. *Orange-yellow*	60·00	30·00
	b. Imperf	90·00	
	c. Imperf between (pair)	£300	£300
	d. Bisected diag (1 pi.) (on cover)..	†	£1200
	e. Perf 12½ × 13 and compound..	90·00	40·00
	f. Perf 12½ × 15	£120	
6	5 pi. rose	£200	£150
	a. Imperf	£250	
	b. Imperf between (pair)	£800	
	c. Perf 12½ × 13 and compound..	£225	
	d. Error. Inscr 10 pi., perf 12½ × 15	£600	£650
	e. Do. but imperf	£400	
7	10 pi. slate	£225	£225
	a. Imperf	£250	
	b. Imperf between (pair)	£1500	
	c. Perf 12½ × 13 and compound..	£350	£350
	d. Perf 13	£1200	

The 2 pi. bisected was authorised for use between 16 and 31 July 1867.

Stamps perforated 13 all round occurred only in the corner of a sheet and so are very rare. Of the 10 pi. only 1 copy has been recorded unused.

Specialists distinguish two types of each value which differ in the ornamentation.

Proofs of all values exist in smooth paper, without watermark. Beware of forgeries.

4

5

6

(Des F. Hoff, Hirschberg, Silesia. Litho V. Penasson, Alexandria)

1867 (1 Aug)–**69**. *W* **6**. *P* 15 × 12½.

11	4	5 pa. orange-yellow	15·00	7·00
		a. Imperf	35·00	35·00
		b. Imperf between (horiz pair)	£120	
12		10 pa. dull lilac	32·00	8·00
		a. Bisected diag (5 pa.) (on cover) (7.69)	†	£500
		b. Bright mauve (7.69)	25·00	8·00
		ba. Bisected diag (5 pa.) (on cover) (7.69)	†	£500
13	4	20 pa. deep blue-green	35·00	12·00
		a. Pale blue-green	35·00	12·00
		b. Yellow-green (7.69)	38·00	12·00
14	5	1 pi. dull rose-red *to* rose	8·00	1·25
		a. Lake	70·00	20·00
		b. Imperf	40·00	
		c. Imperf between (horiz pair) ..	£120	
		d. Bisected diag (20 pa.) (on cover)	†	£600
		e. Rouletted	30·00	
15		2 pi. bright blue	60·00	10·00
		a. Pale blue	60·00	10·00
		b. Imperf	£100	
		c. Imperf between (pair) ..	£350	
		d. Bisected diag (1 pi.) (on cover) ..	†	—
		e. Perf 12½	£200	
16		5 pi. brown	£250	£150

Specialists distinguish four types of each value.

Stamps printed both sides, both imperf and perf, come from printers' waste. The 1 pi. rose without watermark is a proof.

7

8 (Side panels transposed and inverted)

1872 (1 Jan). *T* **7** *(the so-called "Penasson" printing*). Thick opaque paper. W* **6**. I. *P* 12½ × 13½. II. *P* 13½.

A. LITHOGRAPHED

			I		II	
26	7	20 pa. blue (*shades*) ..	75·00	25·00	£130	40·00
		a. Imperf	—	£100	†	
		b. Imperf between (pair)	—	£1500	†	
27		1 pi. red (*shades*) ..	£150	2·50	—	4·00

B. TYPOGRAPHED

			I		II	
28	7	5 pa. brown (*shades*) ..	7·00	4·00	11·00	7·00
29		10 pa. mauve	6·00	3·00	6·00	2·50
30		20 pa. blue (*shades*) ..	18·00	3·50	28·00	10·00
31		1 pi. rose-red	16·00	1·00	28·00	3·00
		a. Bisected (20 pa.) (on cover)	†	£250	†	
32		2 pi. chrome-yellow ..	30·00	3·50	15·00	3·00
		a. Bisected (1 pi.) (on cover)	†	£425	†	
33		2½ pi. violet	30·00	6·00	£600	£170
34		5 pi. yellow-green ..	£180	35·00	£250	50·00
		a. Tête-bêche (pair) ..	—	—	†	

*The lithographed stamps are now believed to have been printed by Penasson, but the typographed by the Government Printing Works at Bûlâq, Cairo.

The lithographed and typographed stamps each show the characteristic differences between these two processes:—

The typographed stamps show the coloured lines of the design impressed into the paper and an accumulation of ink along the margins of the lines.

The lithographed stamps are essentially flat in appearance, without the heaping of the ink. Many of the 20 pa. show evidence of retouching, particularly of the outer frame lines.

The 2 p. vertically bisected was used at Gallipoli.

1874 (Oct)–**75.** *Typo from new stereos at Bûlâq, on thinner paper. W* **6**. I. *P* 12½. II. *P* 13½ × 12½.

			I		II	
35	8	5 pa. brown (4.75) ..	4·50	2·50	3·00	2·50
		a. Tête-bêche (vert pair)	30·00	30·00	45·00	45·00
		ab. Tête-bêche (horiz pair)	£250	£250	£275	£275
		b. Imperf	—	50·00	†	
		c. Imp between (pair)	£100	£120	†	
36	7	10 pa. lilac (*shades*) ..	4·00	3·00	4·50	2·25
		a. Tête-bêche (pair) ..	£120	£120	£120	£120
		b. Imperf	—	30·00	†	
37		20 pa. bluish grey (*shades*)	32·00	3·00	4·00	2·50
		a. Imp between (pair)	†		£250	—
		b. Bisected diag (10 pa.) (on cover)	†	—	†	
38		1 pi. red (*shades*) ..	3·00	80	12·00	1·00
		a. Tête-bêche (vert pair)	60·00	60·00	£300	£300
		ab. Tête-bêche (horiz pair)	£250	£250	—	—
		b. Imperf	6·00	6·00	†	
		c. Imp between (pair)..	—	60·00	†	
39		2 pi. yellow	22·00	4·00	5·00	3·50
		a. Tête-bêche (pair) ..	£350	£350	£350	£350
		aa. Bisected diag (1 pi.) (on cover)	†		†	£2000
		b. Perf 12½ × 13½ ..	†		16·00	6·00
		ba. Tête-bêche (pair) ..	†		£750	—
40		2½ pi. violet	7·00	5·00	†	
		a. Tête-bêche (pair) ..	£275	—	†	
		b. Perf 12½ × 13½ ..	†		18·00	12·00
		ba. Tête-bêche (pair) ..	†		†	£750
41		5 pi. green	35·00	14·00	†	
		a. Perf 12½ × 13½ ..	†		£300	£275
		b. Imperf (pair) ..	—	—	†	

The 1872 printings have a thick line of colour in the top margin of the sheet and the other margins are all plain, an exception being the 5 pa., which on the majority of the sheets has the line at the righthand side of the sheet. The 1874–75 printings have a wide fancy border all round every sheet.

The 1872 printings are on thick opaque paper, with the impressions sharp and clear. The 1874–75 printings are on thinner paper, often semi-transparent and oily in appearance, and having the impressions very blurred and badly printed. These are only general distinctions and there are a number of exceptions.

The majority of the 1874–75 stamps have blind or defective perforations, while the 1872 stamps have clean-cut perfs.

There seem to be many different compositions of the sheets, containing the *tête-bêche* varieties, settings being known with 1, 3, 9 and 10 inverted stamps in various sheets. Sheets of the 5 pa. are known with 9 of the 20 horizontal rows inverted, giving vertical *tête-bêche* pairs; four stamps were inverted within their row giving four horizontal *tête-bêche* pairs.

(9)

1879 (1 Jan). *Stamps of* 1874 *surch as T* **9**, *at Bûlâq.*

I. *P* 12½. II. *P* 12½ × 13½

			I		II	
42	**7**	5 pa. on 2½ pi. violet	6·00	6·00	6·50	6·50
		a. Surch inverted	70·00	70·00	£140	£140
		b. Tête-bêche (pair)	£3000	—	—	—
		c. Imperf	40·00	—	†	
43		10 pa. on 2½ pi. violet	6·00	6·00	12·00	12·00
		a. Surch inverted	75·00	75·00	£110	£110
		b. Tête-bêche (pair)	£1300	—	£1300	—
		c. Imperf	—	—	†	

10

11

12

13 14

15

(Typo De La Rue)

1879 (1 Apr). *Ordinary paper. W* **6**. *P* 14.

44	**10**	5 pa. deep brown	20	15
		a. Pale brown	30	15
45	**11**	10 pa. mauve	18·00	3·00
46	**12**	20 pa. pale blue	35·00	1·50
47	**13**	1 pi. rose	13·00	20
		a. Pale rose	12·00	20
48	**14**	2 pi. orange	13·00	40
		a. Orange-yellow	12·00	50
49	**15**	5 pi. green	55·00	6·00
		a. Blue-green	55·00	5·00

Khedive Tewfik

26 June 1879–7 January 1892

British troops were landed in Egypt in 1882 to secure the Suez Canal against a nationalist movement led by Arabi Pasha. Arabi was defeated at Tel-el-Kebir and British troops remained in Egypt until 1954. A British resident and consul-general advised the Khedive. Holders of this post were Sir Evelyn Baring (Lord Cromer), 1883–1907; Sir Eldon Gorst, 1907–11; and Lord Kitchener, 1911–14.

1881–84. *Colours changed. Ordinary paper. W* **6**. *P* 14.

50	**11**	10 pa. lilac-rose (1.81)	30·00	4·00
51		10 pa. bluish grey (25.1.82)	5·00	70
52		10 pa. green (15.12.84)	20	10
53	**12**	20 pa. rose-carmine (15.12.84)	3·00	50
		a. Bright rose	3·00	40
54	**13**	1 pi. blue (15.12.84)	1·50	10
		a. Deep ultramarine	4·50	20
		b. Pale ultramarine	1·50	10
55	**15**	5 pi. pale grey (15.12.84)	12·00	50
		a. Slate	11·00	40

See also Nos. 63 and 69/71.

(16)

1884 (1 Feb). *Surch with T* **16**, *at Bûlâq.*

56	**15**	29 pa. on 5 pi. green	6·00	1·25
		a. Surch inverted	35·00	30·00

(New Currency: 1000 milliemes = 100 piastres = £1 Egyptian)

18

19

20

21

(Typo De La Rue)

1888 (1 Jan). *Ordinary paper. W* **6**. *P* 14.

57	**18**	1 m. pale brown	25	8
		a. Deep brown	30	8
58	**19**	2 m. blue-green	50	8
		a. Green	50	8
59	**20**	5 m. rose-carmine	90	5
		a. Bright rose	1·10	5
		b. Aniline rose	1·10	5
60	**21**	10 p. mauve	15·00	80
		a. Aniline mauve	17·00	80

Khedive Abbas Hilmi

7 January 1892–19 December 1914

24

1892–93. *New design and colours changed. Ordinary paper. W* **6**. *P* 14.

61	**24**	3 m. maroon (1.1.92)	2·00	1·00
62		3 m. yellow (1.8.93)	1·25	20
		a. Orange-yellow	1·10	20
63	**14**	2 p. orange-brown (1.8.93)	12·00	40

1902–6. *Chalk-surfaced paper. W* **6**. *P* 14.

64	**18**	1 m. pale brown	15	5
		a. Deep brown	15	5
65	**19**	2 m. green	50	5
66	**24**	3 m. orange-yellow	80	8
67	**20**	4 m. vermilion (1906)	60	8
68		5 m. pale rose	1·00	5
		a. Deep aniline rose	1·00	5
69	**13**	1 p. ultramarine	2·00	8
		a. Blue	1·50	10
70	**14**	2 p. orange-brown	10·00	15
		a. Orange	11·00	60
71	**15**	5 p. slate-grey	12·00	20
72	**21**	10 p. mauve	18·00	70
64/72		*Set of* 9	40·00	1·25

29 Native Boats on the Nile

30 Cleopatra with Head-dress of Isis

31 Ras-el-Tin Palace, Alexandria

35 Pylon of Karnak Temple, Luxor

37 Rock Temples of Abu Simbel

(Typo De La Rue)

1914 (8 Jan). *W* **6**. *P* 14.

73	**29**	1 m. sepia	10	5
74	**30**	2 m. green	25	8
75	**31**	3 m. orange-yellow	40	20
		a. Double impression		
76	–	4 m. vermilion	80	40
77	–	5 m. lake	60	5
		a. Wmk sideways (booklets)	6·00	1·50
78	–	10 m. dull blue	1·25	5
79	**35**	20 m. olive	3·00	10
80	–	50 m. purple	5·00	40
81	**37**	100 m. slate	10·00	60
82	–	200 m. maroon	22·00	1·00
73/82		*Set of* 10	40·00	2·75

Designs: *As T* **29**—4 m. Pyramids at Giza; 5 m. Sphinx; 10 m. Colossi of Thebes. *As T* **37**—50 m. Cairo Citadel; 200 m. Aswân Dam.

All the above exist imperforate, but imperforate stamps without watermark are proofs.

BRITISH PROTECTORATE

On 18 December 1914, after war with Turkey had begun, Egypt was declared to be a British protectorate. Abbas Hilmi was deposed, and his uncle, Hussein Kamil, was proclaimed Sultan of Egypt.

Sultan Hussein Kamil

19 December 1914–9 October 1917

(39)

1915 (15 Oct). *Surch with T* **39**, *at Bûlâq.*

83	**31**	2 m. on 3 m. orange-yellow	30	30
		a. Surch inverted	£120	£120

Sultan Ahmed Fuad

9 October 1917–15 March 1922

40

(A)

(B)

(Typo Harrison & Sons)

1921–22. *W* **40**. *(a) As Nos.* 73/82. (i) *P* 13½ × 14.

84	**29**	1 m. sepia (A)	15	10
		a. Two dots omitted (B)	10·00	10·00
85	**30**	2 m. green	1·25	75
		a. Imperf between (pair)		
86		2 m. vermilion (1922)	30	20
87	**31**	3 m. orange-yellow (12.21)	1·00	30
88	–	4 m. green (1922)	1·50	1·00
89	–	5 m. lake (1.21)	60	5
		a. Imperf between (pair)		
90	–	5 m. pink (11.21)	1·00	5
91	–	10 m. dull blue	2·00	8
92	–	10 m. lake (9.22)	1·50	15
		(ii) *P* 14		
93	**35**	20 m. olive	5·00	12
94	–	50 m. purple	10·00	20
95	**37**	100 m. slate (1922)	25·00	3·00
84/95		*Set of* 12	45·00	4·50

41 Statue of Rameses II

42

In T **42** the Arabic inscription at right is corrected

(b) New design. P 13½ × 14

96	**41**	15 m. indigo (3.22)	1·50	15
97	**42**	15 m. indigo	7·00	80

POSTAGE DUE STAMPS

D 1

D 2

D 3

(Des L. Barkhausen. Litho V. Penasson, Alexandria)

1884 (1 Feb). *W* **6**. *P* 10½.

D57	D 1	10 pa. red	9·00	2·50
		a. Imperf	40·00	
		b. Imperf between (pair)	50·00	
D58		20 pa. red	20·00	3·50
D59		1 pi. red	35·00	8·00
D60		2 pi. red	50·00	4·00
D61		5 pi. red	10·00	10·00

1886 (1 Aug). *No wmk. P* 10½.

D62	D 1	10 pa. rose-red	4·00	1·00
		a. Imperf between (pair)	30·00	
D63		20 pa. rose-red	70·00	12·00
		a. Imperf between (pair)		
D64		1 pi. rose-red	3·00	1·00
		a. Imperf between (pair)	50·00	50·00
D65		2 pi. rose-red	3·50	50
		a. Imperf between (pair)	50·00	

Specialists distinguish four types of each value in both these issues.

(Litho V. Penasson, Alexandria)

1888 (1 Jan). *No wmk. P* 11½.

D66	D 2	2 m. green	1·50	1·00
		a. Imperf between (pair)	80·00	75·00
D67		5 m. rose-carmine	2·50	1·00
D68		1 p. blue	22·00	10·00
		a. Imperf between (pair)	80·00	
D69		2 p. orange	20·00	4·00
D70		5 p. grey	70·00	50·00
		a. With stop after "PIASTRES."	£100	65·00

Specialists distinguish four types of each value.

Beware of forgeries of the 5 p.

(Typo De La Rue)

1889 (Apr). *Ordinary or chalk-surfaced paper. W* **6** *(upright). P* 14.

D71	D 3	2 m. green	1·00	10
		a. Bisected (1 m.) (on cover with unbisected 2 m.)	—	£100
D72		4 m. maroon	60	10
D73		1 p. ultramarine	2·00	10
D74		2 p. orange	1·75	40
		a. Bisected diagonally (1 p.) (on cover)		

See also Nos. D84/6 for stamps with watermark sideways.

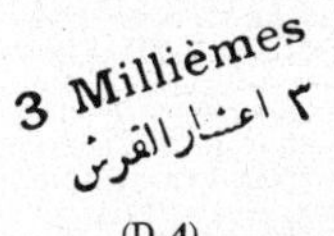

(D 4)

3 Millièmes

(D 5)

Type D 4

The Arabic figure at right is less than 2 mm from the next character, which consists of a straight stroke only.

Type D 5

The distance is 3 mm and the straight character has a comma-like character above it. There are other minor differences.

1898 (June)–**1905.** *No.* D74 *surch, at Bûlâq.*

(*a*) *With Type* D 4. *Ordinary paper*

D75	D 3	3 m. on 2 p. orange	25	25
		a. Surch inverted	32·00	25·00

A variety exists in which an Arabic figure "٢ (2)" has been inserted in the surcharge in error and a correct figure "٣ (3)" printed immediately above it.

(*b*) *With Type* D 5. *Ordinary or chalk-surfaced paper* (1905)

D76	D 3	3 m. on 2 p. orange	30	25
		a. Surch inverted	28·00	22·00
		b. Surch double	£100	

1918. *As Nos.* D71/3 *but wmk sideways.*

D84	D 3	2 m. bright green	1·50	15
D85		4 m. maroon	1·50	50
D86		1 p. dull ultramarine	4·00	50

D 6

D 7

(Typo Harrison)

1921 (Oct)–**22.** *Chalk-surfaced paper.* W **40.** P 14 × 13½.

D 98	D 6	2 m. green	20	12
D 99		2 m. scarlet (1922)	12	8
D100		4 m. scarlet	1·40	70
D101		4 m. green	25	10
D102	D 7	10 m. deep slate-blue (11.21)	1·25	1·00
D103		10 m. lake (1922)	30	12
D98/103		*Set of* 6	3·00	1·75

OFFICIAL STAMPS

O 1

O.H.H.S.
اميري

(O 2)

O.H.H.S.
اميرى

(O 3)

(Typo De La Rue)

1893 (1 Jan). *Ordinary or chalk-surfaced paper.* W **6.** P 14.

O64	O 1	(–) chestnut	15	5
		a. Wmk sideways	75	25

This stamp, with overprint 3 P.T. and Arabic equivalent, is a fiscal.

1907. *As Nos.* 67/71 *but optd with Type* O **2,** *by De La Rue.*

O73	**18**	1 m. brown	10	5
O74	**19**	2 m. green	15	5
		a. Opt double		
O75	**24**	3 m. orange-yellow	15	5
O76	**20**	5 m. rose-carmine	15	5
O77	**13**	1 p. blue	40	8
O78	**15**	5 p. slate-grey	2·00	15
O73/8		*Set of* 6	2·50	35

1913 (Nov). *As No.* 68 *but optd* "O.H.H.S." *only as in Type* O **3,** *at Bûlâq.*

O79	**20**	5 m. rose-carmine	50	10
		a. No stop after "S"	6·00	4·00
		b. Opt inverted	80·00	40·00
		c. Opt between inverted commas	—	£100

1914 (Dec)–**15.** *Stamps of* 1902–6 *and* 1914 *optd with Type* O **3,** *at Bûlâq.*

O83	**29**	1 m. sepia (1.15)	15	12
		a. No stop after "S"	3·00	3·00
O84	**19**	2 m. green (3.15)	20	20
		a. No stop after "S"	5·00	5·00
		b. Opt inverted	15·00	15·00
		c. Opt double	£200	
O85	**31**	3 m. orange-yellow (3.15)	15	12
		a. No stop after "S"	5·00	5·00
O86	**20**	4 m. vermilion (12.14)	25	15
		a. Opt inverted	£110	80·00
O87	–	5 m. lake (1.15)	30	8
		a. No stop after "S"	5·00	5·00

O.H.H.S.
أميرى

(O 4)

O.H.H.S.
أميرى

(O 5)

1915 (Oct). *Nos.* 65, 67 *and* 77 *optd lithographically with Type* O 4, *at Bûlâq.*

O88	**19**	2 m. green	15	12
		a. Opt inverted	8·00	8·00
		b. Opt double	10·00	
O89	**20**	4 m. vermilion	20	12
O90	–	5 m. lake	25	15
		a. Pair, one without opt	£170	

1922. *Nos.* 84, *etc. optd lithographically with Type* O **5,** *at Bûlâq.*

O 98	**29**	1 m. sepia (A) (28.6)	1·50	1·25
		a. Two dots omitted (B)	£200	
O 99	**30**	2 m. vermilion (16.6)	1·50	1·25
O100	**31**	3 m. orange-yellow (28.6)	50·00	50·00
O101	–	5 m. pink (13.3)	1·50	1·10

Egypt was declared to be an independent kingdom on 15 March 1922, and Sultan Ahmed Fuad became king.

Later stamp issues will be found listed in Part 19 (*Middle East*) of this catalogue.

BRITISH FORCES IN EGYPT

From 1 November 1932, to 29 February 1936 members of the British Forces in Egypt and their families were allowed to send letters to the British Isles at reduced rates. Special seals which were on sale in booklets at N.A.A.F.I. Institutes and Canteens were used instead of Egyptian stamps, and were stuck on the back of the envelopes, letters bearing the seals being franked on the front with a hand-stamp inscribed "EGYPT POSTAGE PREPAID" in a double circle surmounted by a crown.

PRICES FOR STAMPS ON COVER

Nos. A1/9	*from* × 5
No. A10	*from* × 3
No. A11	*from* × 5
No. A12	*from* × 100
No. A13	*from* × 10
No. A14	*from* × 400
No. A15	*from* × 10

A 1

A 2

(Des Lt.-Col. C. Fraser. Typo Hanbury, Tomsett & Co, London)

1932 (1 Nov)–**33.** P 11. (*a*) *Inscr* "POSTAL SEAL".

A1	A 1	1 p. deep blue and red	17·00	8·00

(*b*) *Inscr* "LETTER SEAL"

A2	A 1	1 p. deep blue and red (8.33)	14·00	5·50

(Des Sgt. W. F. Lait. Litho Walker & Co, Amalgamated Press, Cairo)

1932 (26 Nov)–**35.** *Christmas Seals.* P 11½.

A3	A 2	3 m. black/*azure*	22·00	27·00
A4		3 m. brown-lake (13.11.33)	8·00	9·00
A5		3 m. deep blue (17.11.34)	6·00	7·00
A6		3 m. vermilion (23.11.35)	2·50	3·25
		a. Pale vermilion (19.12.35)	6·50	8·00

A 3

(Des Miss Waugh. Photo Harrison)

1934 (1 June)–**35.** (*a*) P 14½ × 14.

A7	A 3	1 p. carmine	22·00	4·00
A8		1 p. green (5.12.34)	4·00	2·75

(*b*) P 13½ × 14

A9	A 3	1 p. carmine (24.4.35)	1·40	85

JUBILEE
COMMEMORATION
1935

(A 4)

1935 (6 May). *Silver Jubilee. As No.* A9, *but colour changed and optd with Type* A 4, *in red.*

A10	A 3	1 p. ultramarine	£200	£200

Xmas 1935
3 Milliemes

(A 5)

1935 (16 Dec). *Provisional Christmas Seal. No.* A9 *surch with Type* A 5.

A11	A 3	3 m. on 1 p. carmine	28·00	25·00

The seals and letter stamps were replaced by the following Army Post stamps issued by the Egyptian Postal Administration.

NEW INFORMATION

The editor is always interested to correspond with people who have new information that will improve or correct the Catalogue.

A 6 King Fuad I

A 7 King Farouk

(Types A 6/A 7. Photo Survey Dept, Cairo)

1936. W **48** *of Egypt* (*Mult Crown and Arabic* "F"). P 13½ × 14.

A12	A 6	3 m. green (9.11.36)	50	50
A13		10 m. carmine (1.3.36)	90	20

1939 (12 Dec). W **48** *of Egypt* (*Mult Crown and Arabic* "F"). P 13 × 13½.

A14	A 7	3 m. green	45	40
A15		10 m. carmine	45	20

These stamps were withdrawn in April 1941 but the concession, without the use of special stamps, continued until October 1951 when the postal agreement was abrogated.

Falkland Islands

PRICES FOR STAMPS ON COVER TO 1945

Nos. 1/4	*from* × 6
Nos. 5/12	*from* × 8
Nos. 13/14	*from* × 10
Nos. 15/38	*from* × 8
Nos. 41/2	*from* × 5
Nos. 43/59	*from* × 4
Nos. 60/114	*from* × 3
No. 115	*from* × 2
Nos. 116/26	*from* × 3
Nos. 127/38	*from* × 4
Nos. 139/42	*from* × 5
Nos. 143/5	*from* × 8
Nos. 146/63	*from* × 3

CROWN COLONY

(1) (2)

1869–76. *The Franks.*

FR1	1	In black, *on cover*	£6500
FR2	2	In red, *on cover* (1876)	£9500

On *piece*, No. FR1 on white or coloured papers £65; No. FR2 on white £90. The use of these franks ceased when the first stamps were issued.

3

½d.

(4)

In the ½d., 2d., 2½d. and 9d. the figures of value in the lower corners are replaced by small rosettes and the words of value are in colour.

NOTE. Nos. 1, 2, 3, 4, 8, 10, 11 and 12 exist with one or two sides imperf from the margin of the sheets.

(Recess B.W.)

1878–79. *No wmk.* P 14, 14½.

1	3	1d. claret (19.6.78)	£550	£375
2		4d. grey-black (Sept 1879)	£1000	£130
		a. On wmkd paper	£1800	£375
3		6d. blue-green (19.6.78)	35·00	42·00
4		1s. bistre-brown (1878)	35·00	42·00

No. 2a shows portions of the papermaker's watermark—"R. TURNER, CHAFFORD MILLS"—in ornate double-lined capitals.

1882 (22 Nov). *Wmk Crown CA* (*upright*). P 14, 14½.

5	3	1d. dull claret	£300	85·00
		a. Imperf between (horiz pair)	£20000	
6		4d. grey-black	40·00	42·00

1885 (23 Mar)–**87.** *Wmk Crown CA* (*sideways to left or right*). *P* 14, 14½.

No.	Type	Description	Unused	Used
7	**3**	1d. pale claret	40·00	32·00
8		1d. brownish claret (3.10.87)	35·00	30·00
		a. Bisected (on cover) (1891)*.. ..	†	£2000
9		4d. pale grey-black	£225	30·00
10		4d. grey-black (3.10.87)	£225	30·00

*See note below No. 14.

1889 (26 Sept)–**91.** *Wmk Crown CA* (*upright*). *P* 14, 14½.

No.	Type	Description	Unused	Used
11	**3**	1d. red-brown (21.5.91)..	50·00	50·00
		a. Bisected (on cover)*	†	£2000
12		4d. olive grey-black	40·00	42·00

*See note below No. 14.

1891. *Nos.* 8 *and* 11 *bisected diagonally and each half handstamped with T* **4**.

No.	Type	Description	Unused	Used
13	**3**	½d. on half of 1d. brownish claret (No. 8)	£300	£275
		a. Unsevered pair	£1000	£950
		b. Unsevered pair *se-tenant* with unsurcharged whole stamp ..	£6500	
14		½d. on half 1d. red-brown (No. 11) ..	£200	£130
		a. Unsevered pair	—	£450
		b. Unsevered pair *se-tenant* with unsurcharged whole stamp ..		

1891 PROVISIONALS. In 1891 the postage to the United Kingdom and Colonies was reduced from 4d. to 2½d. per half ounce. As no ½d. or 2½d. stamps were available the bisection of the 1d. was authorised from 1 January 1891. This authorisation was withdrawn on 11 January 1892, although bisects were accepted for postage until July of that year. The ½d. and 2½d. stamps were placed on sale from 10 September 1891.

Cork Cancel used in 1891

The Type 4 surcharge was not used regularly; unsurcharged bisects being employed far more frequently. Genuine bisects should be cancelled with the cork cancel illustrated above. The use of any other postmark, including a different cork cancel, requires date evidence linked to known mail ship sailings to prove authenticity.

Posthumous strikes of the surcharge on "souvenir" bisects usually show a broken "2" and/or a large full stop. These are known on bisected examples of No. 18 and on varieties such as surcharge inverted, double or sideways. Forgeries exist of all these provisionals.

1891 (May)–**1902.** *Wmk Crown CA* (*upright*). *P* 14, 14½.

No.	Type	Description	Unused	Used
15	**3**	½d. blue-green (May–Nov 1891) ..	14·00	20·00
16		½d. green (20.5.92)	14·00	16·00
		a. Deep dull green (15.4.96) ..	22·00	25·00
17		½d. deep yellow-green (1894–95) ..	14·00	20·00
		a. Yellow-green (19.6.99)	2·00	2·50
		b. Dull yellowish green (13.1.1902) ..	2·00	2·50
18		1d. orange red-brown (14.10.91) ..	38·00	42·00
		a. Brown (1891?)	35·00	40·00
19		1d. reddish chestnut (20.4.92)	35·00	40·00
20		1d. orange-brn (*Wmk reversed*) (18.1.94)	25·00	27·00
21		1d. claret (23.7.94)	27·00	30·00
22		1d. Venetian red (pale to deep) (1895–96)	6·00	6·00
		a. Venetian claret (1898?)	8·00	8·00
23		1d. pale red (19.6.99)	4·25	3·75
24		1d. orange-red (13.1.1902)	6·00	6·00
25		2d. purple (pale to deep) (1895–98)	7·50	14·00
26		2d. reddish purple (15.4.96)	6·50	14·00
27		2½d. pale chalky ultram (May–Aug 1891)	65·00	35·00
28		2½d. dull blue (19.11.91)..	24·00	25·00
29		2½d. Prussian blue (18.1.94)	£200	£180
30		2½d. ultramarine (1894–96)	8·50	15·00
		a. Pale ultramarine (10.6.98)	9·00	14·00
		b. Deep ultramarine (18.9.1901) ..	9·50	20·00
32		4d. olive-black (11.5.95)	17·00	25·00
33		6d. orange-yellow (19.11.91)	22·00	32·00
34		6d. yellow (15.4.96)	20·00	32.00
35		9d. pale reddish orange (15.11.95)	20·00	48·00
36		9d. salmon (15.4.96)	25·00	48·00
37		1s. grey-brown (15.11.95)	25·00	35·00
38		1s. yellow-brown (15.4.96)	23·00	35·00
15/38		.. .. *Set of* 8	90·00	£160
½d., 2d., 2½d., 6d., 9d. Optd "Specimen"		*Set of* 5	£950	

NOTES. The dates shown above are those on which the printer delivered the various printings to the Crown Agents. Several months could elapse before the stamps went on sale in the Colony, depending on the availability of shipping.

The plates used for these stamps did not fit the paper so that the watermark appears in all sorts of positions on the stamp. Well centred examples are scarce. Examples can also be found showing parts of the marginal watermarks, either CROWN AGENTS horizontally in letters 12 mm high or "CROWN AGENTS FOR THE COLONIES" vertically in 7 mm letters. Both are in double-lined capitals.

Many stamps between Nos. 5 and 38 can be found with the watermark reversed, inverted or both, in addition to those noted above where such variations are a constant feature.

The 2½d. ultramarine printing can sometimes be found in a violet shade, but the reason for this is unknown.

5 6

(Recess B.W.)

1898 (June). *Wmk Crown CC. P* 14, 14½.

No.	Type	Description	Unused	Used
41	**5**	2s. 6d. deep blue	£250	£300
42	**6**	5s. red	£250	£275
41/2 Optd "Specimen"		.. .. *Set of* 2	£600	

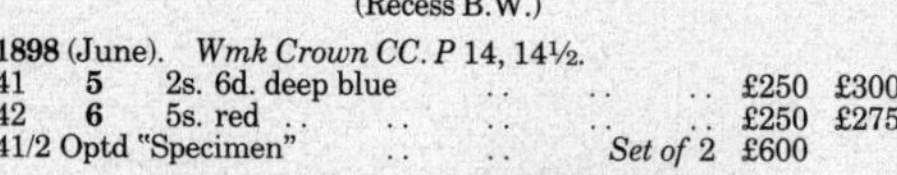

7 8

(Recess D.L.R.)

1904–12. *Wmk Mult Crown CA. P* 14.

No.	Type	Description	Unused	Used
43	**7**	½d. yellow-green (1904)	1·50	1·90
44		½d. pale yell-grn on thick paper (1907)	4·50	7·50
45		½d. deep yellow-green (1911)	2·75	3·00
46		1d. vermilion (1904)	3·75	1·90
47		1d. vermilion, thick paper (1907) ..	3·25	2·00
48		1d. dull coppery red (1907)	£200	48·00
49		1d. orange-vermilion (1911)	3·00	1·60
50		2d. purple (1904)	7·00	24·00
51		2d. reddish purple (1912)	£450	£475
52		2½d. ultramarine (*shades*)	23·00	20·00
53		2½d. deep blue (1912)	£400	£350
54		6d. orange (1904)	32·00	42·00
55		1s. brown (1904)	30·00	40·00
56	**8**	3s. green (1904)	£130	£120
57		3s. deep green (1906)	£120	£130
58		5s. red (1904)	£140	£140
43/58		.. .. *Set of* 8	£325	£350
43/58 Optd "Specimen"		.. .. *Set of* 8	£600	

1906. *Wmk Mult Crown CA, sideways. P* 14.

No.	Type	Description	Unused	Used
59	**7**	1d. vermilion	1·25	2·50

SOUTH GEORGIA UNDERPRINT. The Post Office on South Georgia opened on 3 December 1909, a stock of Falkland Islands stamps with values from ½d. to 5s. being supplied, together with a straight-line handstamp inscribed "South Georgia". It was intended that this mark should be struck on covers, below the stamps, as an indication of the origin of the mail, the stamps themselves being cancelled with a Falkland Islands postmark. Examples are known on the Edward VII stamps and on some values of the Victorian issue. This underprint can, on occasion, be found struck across the stamps, rather than below them.

Its use continues after the introduction of the South Georgia cancellation in July 1910, but no example has been reported after June 1912. (*Price for example of underprint on cover* (a) *In conjunction with* "FALKLAND ISLANDS" *postmark* (December 1909 *to* June 1910) *from* £1600 (b) *In conjunction with* "SOUTH GEORGIA" *postmark* (July 1910 *to* June 1912) *from* £1200)

SOUTH GEORGIA PROVISIONAL HANDSTAMPS. During October 1911 the arrival of the German South Polar Expedition at Grytviken, South Georgia, resulted in the local supply of stamps becoming exhausted. The Acting Magistrate, Mr. E. B. Binnie, who was also responsible for the postal facilities, produced a handstamp reading "Paid At SOUTH GEORGIA" which, together with a manuscript indication of the postage paid and his signature, was used on mail from October 1911 to January 1912.

PH1 "Paid 1 At SOUTH GEORGIA EBB" *Price on cover* £4000
PH2 "Paid 2½ At SOUTH GEORGIA EBB" *Price on cover* £4750

9 10

(Recess D.L.R.)

1912–20. *Wmk Mult Crown CA. P* 14.

No.	Type	Description	Unused	Used
60	**9**	½d. yellow-green (1912)	2·00	2·50
61		½d. deep yellow-green (1914)	18·00	27·00
62		½d. pale green (1918)	5·00	9·00
63		½d. green (1919)	2·75	4·00
64		½d. green on thick greyish paper (1920)	3·75	11·00
65		1d. vermilion (1912)	3·25	2·75
66		1d. orange-vermilion (1914, 1916) ..	4·50	2·50
66*a*		1d. pale scarlet* (1918)..	†	—
67		1d. scarlet (1919)	3·00	2·75
68		1d. scarlet on thick greyish paper (1920)	4·75	2·25
69		2d. deep purple (1912)	7·00	13·00
69*a*		2d. deep reddish purple (1914).. ..	25·00	22·00
69*b*		2d. purple (1918)	25·00	32·00
70		2d. pale purple (1919)	4·75	9·50
71		2½d. dark blue (1912)	8·50	15·00
72		2½d. bright blue (1914)	10·00	15·00
73		2½d. milky blue (1916)	£300	£375
74		2½d. blue (1919)	6·50	13·00
75		6d. yellow-orange (1912)	8·50	20·00
76		6d. brown-orange (1919)	7·50	14·00
77		1s. yellow-brown (1912)	22·00	27·00
78		1s. pale bistre-brown (1919)	25·00	35·00
79		1s. brown on thick greyish paper (1920)	30·00	42·00
80		1s. deep brown on thick greyish paper (1920)	42·00	55·00
81	**10**	3s. deep green (1912)	60·00	70·00
82		5s. red (1912)	65·00	85·00
83		5s. reddish maroon (1914)	90·00	95·00
83*a*		5s. maroon (1916)	65·00	85·00
84		10s. red/*green* (1913)	£190	£250
85		£1 black/*red* (1913)	£500	£550
60/85		.. .. *Set of* 11	£850	£950
60/85 (incl two 5s.) Optd "Specimen"..		*Set of* 11	£2000	

As there was considerable variation in shade in the war-time printings it is useful to know that 1914, 1916 and 1918 printings of Type **9** were all line perforated instead of comb, i.e. Nos. 61/2, 66*a*, 69*a*/*b*, and 72/3. The majority of stamps from the 1916 2½d. printing and all of the printing produced in 1918 are similar in shade to No. 71. Unused examples from these printings can be identified by the white paper and gum used.

*It was previously believed that all examples of the 1d. pale scarlet from the 1918 printing were overprinted to form No. 90, but it has now been established that some unoverprinted sheets of this shade were used during 1919.

SOUTH GEORGIA BISECTS. The 2½d. No. 74 and 6d. No. 76 were bisected and used as 1d. and 2½d. respectively in S. Georgia in 1923. This procedure was not authorised from Port Stanley. (*Prices on cover*: 2½d. £4000, 6d. £10000.)

PORT FOSTER HANDSTAMP. Postal facilities at Port Foster, Deception Island, South Shetlands were first provided during the 1912–13 whaling season. Permission was given for stamps on cover to be cancelled with a straight-line "PORT FOSTER" handstamp as an indication of origin. The handstamp is known to have been applied to Edward VII 1d. and George V ½d. and 1d. Falkland Islands issues. It is sometimes used in conjunction with a "FALKLAND ISLANDS" circular postmark.

Unused stamps and higher values with this handstamp were, it is believed, subsequently "made to order".

WAR STAMP

(11)

2½D

(12)

1918–20. *Optd by Govt Printing Press, Stanley, with T* **11**.

No.	Type	Description	Unused	Used
86	**9**	½d. pale yellow-green (No. 62) (7.10.18)	1·50	6·50
87		½d. yellow-green (No. 60) (3.19) ..	7·50	13·00
		a. Albino impression only	£1000	
88		½d. green (No. 63) (3.19)	75	3·50
89		½d. green on thick greyish paper (No. 64) (5.20)	15·00	42·00
90		1d. pale scarlet (7.10.18)	4·50	8·00
		a. Opt double, one albino	£375	
91		1d. bright orange-verm (No. 66) (3.19)	6·50	15·00
92		1d. scarlet (No. 67) (3.19)	75	3·00
		a. Opt double	£1400	
93		1d. scarlet on thick greyish paper (No. 68) (5.20)	38·00	70·00
94		1s. yellow-brown (No. 77) (7.10.18) ..	35·00	45·00
95		1s. pale bistre-brown (No. 78) (3.19) ..	7·50	28·00
		a. Opt double, one albino	£1000	£500
96		1s. brown on thick greyish paper (No. 79) (5.20)	14·00	32·00
		a. Opt double, one albino	£1000	£650
97		1s. deep brown on thick greyish paper (No. 80) (5.20)	18·00	40·00

Nos. 86, 90 and 91 are line perf, the rest being comb.

There were five printings of the "WAR STAMP" overprint, but all, except that in May 1920, used the same setting. Composition of the five printings was as follows:

October 1918. Nos. 86, 90 and 94
January 1919. Nos. 86, 90 and 94
March 1919. Nos. 87/8, 91/2 and 95
October 1919. Nos. 88, 92 and 95
May 1920. Nos. 89, 93 and 96/7.

1921–29. *Wmk Mult Script CA. P* 14.

No.	Type	Description	Unused	Used
98	**9**	½d. bright yellow-green	2·00	2·75
99		½d. green (1925)	1·60	2·75
100		1d. scarlet-vermilion (1924)	1·50	1.25
101		1d. scarlet (1925)	3·00	1·25
102		1d. deep scarlet (1928)	3·25	1·50
103		2d. reddish purple (1923)	3·50	3·50
104		2d. purple (1927)	3·00	3·00
105		2½d. indigo	7·50	10·00
106		2½d. deep purple/*lemon* (1923)	4·75	9·50
107		2½d. pale purple/*yellow* (1925)	5·00	12·00
108		2½d. dark blue (1927)	10·00	17·00
109		2½d. steel blue (Jan 1928)	5·00	13·00
110		2½d. Prussian blue (1929)	£375	£550
111		6d. orange (*shades*) (1925)	6·50	14·00
113		1s. bistre-brown	18·00	35·00
114	**10**	3s. green (1923)	90·00	£120
98/114..		.. .. *Set of* 9	£120	£190
98/114 Optd "Specimen"		.. .. *Set of* 9	£650	

1928 (7 Feb). *No.* 104 *surch with T* **12**.

No.	Type	Description	Unused	Used
115	**9**	2½d. on 2d. purple	£750	£800
		a. Surch double	£30000	

No. 115 was produced on South Georgia during a shortage of 2½d. stamps. The provisional was withdrawn on 22 February 1928.

13 Whale and Penguins 14

(Recess P.B.)

1929 (2 Sept)–**36.** *P* 14. (*a*) *Wmk Mult Script CA.*

No.	Type	Description	Unused	Used
116	**13**	½d. green	55	85
117		1d. scarlet	75	50
		a. Deep red (1.35)	7·00	12·00
118		2d. grey	80	1·10
119		2½d. blue	85	1·50
120	**14**	4d. orange (1931)	4·50	9·50
		a. Deep orange..	20·00	32·00
121	**13**	6d. purple	5·50	7·00
		a. Reddish purple (1936)	32·00	40·00
122		1s. black/*emerald*	9·50	14·00
		a. On bright emerald (1936)	32·00	45·00
123		2s. 6d. carmine/*blue*	25·00	32·00
124		5s. green/*yellow*	42·00	48·00
125		10s. carmine/*emerald*	55·00	90·00

(b) *Wmk Mult Crown CA*

No.	Type	Description		Unused	Used
126	13	£1 black/*red*		£450	£550
116/126			*Set of* 11	£550	£700
116/26 Perf "Specimen"			*Set of* 11	£1300	

Two kinds of perforation exist:
A. Comb perf 13.9:—original values of 1929.
B. Line perf 13.9, 14.2 or compound:—4d. and 1936 printings of ½d., 1d., 6d. and 1s.

15 Romney Marsh Ram

26 King George V

(Des (except 6d.) by G. Roberts. Eng and recess B.W.)

1933 (2 Jan). *Centenary of British Administration. T* **15, 26** *and similar designs. Wmk Mult Script CA. P* 12.

No.	Description		Unused	Used
127	½d. black and green		3·00	4·25
128	1d. black and scarlet		2·50	2·75
129	1½d. black and blue		3·25	8·00
130	2d. black and brown		6·00	9·50
131	3d. black and violet		7·50	12·00
132	4d. black and orange		9·50	15·00
133	6d. black and slate		32·00	42·00
134	1s. black and olive-green		35·00	55·00
135	2s. 6d. black and violet		£100	£120
136	5s. black and yellow		£550	£700
	a. Black and yellow-orange		£1000	£1200
137	10s. black and chestnut		£700	£850
138	£1 black and carmine		£2000	£2250
127/138		*Set of* 12	£3250	£3750
127/38 Perf "Specimen"		*Set of* 12	£3000	

Designs: *Horiz*—1d. Iceberg; 1½d. Whale-catcher *Bransfield*; 2d. Port Louis; 3d. Map of Falkland Islands; 4d. South Georgia; 6d. Whale; 1s. Government House, Stanley. *Vert*—2s. 6d. Battle Memorial; 5s. King Penguin; 10s. Coat of Arms.

Examples of all values are known with forged Port Stanley postmarks, dated 6 January 1933.

1935 (7 May). *Silver Jubilee. As Nos. 91/4 of Antigua, but printed by B.W. P* 11 × 12.

No.	Description		Unused	Used
139	1d. deep blue and scarlet		1·25	65
	b. Short extra flagstaff		60·00	
	d. Double flagstaff		38·00	
140	2½d. brown and deep blue		3·00	3·50
	b. Short extra flagstaff		70·00	
	d. Double flagstaff		45·00	
	g. Re-entry on value tablet (R. 8/1)		£150	
141	4d. green and indigo		3·50	4·50
	b. Short extra flagstaff		60·00	
	d. Double flagstaff		30·00	
142	1s. slate and purple		5·00	6·50
	a. Extra flagstaff		£2250	£2250
	b. Short extra flagstaff		50·00	
	c. Lightning conductor		50·00	
	d. Double flagstaff		30·00	
139/42 Perf "Specimen"		*Set of* 4	£110	

For illustrations of plate varieties see Omnibus section following Zululand.

1937 (12 May). *Coronation. As Nos. 13/15 of Aden, but printed by B.W. P* 11 × 11½.

No.	Description		Unused	Used
143	½d. green		50	30
144	1d. carmine		50	30
145	2½d. blue		1·10	75
143/5 Perf "Specimen"		*Set of* 3	75·00	

27 Whales' Jaw Bones

(Des G. Roberts (½d., 2d., 1s., 2s. 6d. to £1). Recess B.W.)

1938 (3 Jan)–**50.** *Horiz designs as T* **27**. *Wmk Mult Script CA. P* 12.

No.	Description		Unused	Used
146	½d. black and green (*shades*)		25	25
147	1d. black and carmine		6·50	5·00
	a. Black and scarlet		2·75	70
148	1d. black and violet (14.7.41)		75	35
	a. Black and purple-violet (1.43)		1·00	70
149	2d. black and deep violet		2·00	1·25
150	2d. black and carmine-red (14.7.41)		75	2·25
	a. Black and red (1.43)		55	30
151	2½d. black and bright blue		70	75
152	2½d. black and blue (15.6.49)		1·90	3·50
153	3d. black and blue (14.7.41)		1·50	2·00
	a. Black and deep blue (1.43)		2·00	2·50
154	4d. black and purple		1·50	1·25
155	6d. black and brown		5·50	5·00
156	6d. black (15.6.49)		2·50	9·00
157	9d. black and grey-blue		2·25	1·25
158	1s. pale blue		35·00	22·00
	a. Deep blue (1941)		5·50	4·25
159	1s. 3d. black and carmine-red (10.12.46)		1·25	2·00
160	2s. 6d. slate		40·00	27·00
161	5s. bright blue and pale brown		45·00	35·00
	a. Blue and buff-brown (9.2.50)		48·00	35·00
	b. Indigo and yellow-brown (1939?)		£275	£130
162	10s. black and orange		45·00	38·00
163	£1 black and violet		80·00	55·00
146/163		*Set of* 18	£225	£170
146/63 Perf "Specimen"		*Set of* 16	£700	

Designs:—Nos. 147 and 150, Black-necked Swan; Nos. 148/9, Battle Memorial; Nos. 151 and 153, Flock of sheep; Nos. 152 and 154, Magellan Goose; No. 155/6, R.R.S. *Discovery II*; No. 157, R.R.S. *William Scoresby*; No. 158, Mount Sugar Top; No. 159; Turkey Vultures; No. 160, Gentoo Penguins; No. 161, Sea Lion; No. 162, Deception Island; No. 163, Arms of Falkland Islands.

1946 (7 Oct). *Victory. As Nos. 28/9 of Aden.*

No.	Description		Unused	Used
164	1d. dull violet		35	35
165	3d. blue		35	45
164/5 Perf "Specimen"		*Set of* 2	90·00	

1948 (1 Nov). *Royal Silver Wedding. As Nos. 30/1 of Aden.*

No.	Description	Unused	Used
166	2½d. ultramarine	1·00	70
167	£1 mauve	90·00	90·00

1949 (10 Oct). *75th Anniv of Universal Postal Union. As Nos. 114/17 of Antigua.*

No.	Description	Unused	Used
168	1d. violet	1·40	75
169	3d. deep blue	3·00	1·50
170	1s. 3d. deep blue-green	4·25	3·50
171	2s. blue	4·50	6·00

39 Sheep

43 Arms of the Colony

(Recess Waterlow)

1952 (2 Jan). *T* **39, 43** *and similar designs. Wmk Mult Script CA. P* 13 × 13½ (*vert*) *or* 13½ × 13 (*horiz*).

No.	Description		Unused	Used
172	½d. green		65	80
173	1d. scarlet		80	60
174	2d. violet		2·25	2·50
175	2½d. black and light ultramarine		85	95
176	3d. deep ultramarine		1·00	90
177	4d. reddish purple		1·75	2·75
178	6d. bistre-brown		6·00	2·00
179	9d. orange-yellow		6·00	6·00
180	1s. black		6·50	2·00
181	1s. 3d. orange		3·25	10·00
182	2s. 6d. olive-green		7·00	12·00
183	5s. purple		7·00	7·50
184	10s. grey		19·00	30·00
185	£1 black		32·00	38·00
172/185		*Set of* 14	85·00	£100

Designs: *Horiz*—1d. R.M.S. *Fitzroy*; 2d. Magellan Goose; 2½d. Map of Falkland Islands; 4d. Auster aircraft; 6d. M.S.S. *John Biscoe*; 9d. View of the Two Sisters; 1s. 3d. Kelp goose and gander; 10s. Sea-lion and female (Clapmatch); £1 Hulk of *Great Britain*. *Vert*—1s. Gentoo Penguins; 2s. 6d. Sheep-shearing; 5s. Battle Memorial.

1953 (4 June). *Coronation. As No. 47 of Aden.*

No.	Description	Unused	Used
186	1d. black and scarlet	1·00	1·25

53 M.S.S. *John Biscoe*

54 Austral Thrush

(Recess Waterlow)

1955–57. *Designs previously used for King George VI issue but with portrait of Queen Elizabeth II as in T* **53**. *Wmk Mult Script CA. P* 13 × 13½ (*vert*) *or* 13½ × 13 (*horiz*).

No.	Description		Unused	Used
187	½d. green (2.9.57)		80	1·75
188	1d. scarlet (2.9.57)		1·50	65
189	2d. violet (3.9.56)		3·75	4·50
190	6d. deep yellow-brown (1.6.55)		4·25	1·75
191	9d. orange-yellow (2.9.57)		20·00	20·00
192	1s. black (15.7.55)		4·25	2·50
187/92		*Set of* 6	32·00	28·00

Designs: *Horiz*—½d. Sheep; 1d. R.M.S. *Fitzroy*; 2d. Magellan Goose; 9d. View of Two Sisters. *Vert*—1s. Gentoo Penguins.

(Recess Waterlow, then D.L.R. (from 9.1.62 onwards))

1960 (10 Feb). *T* **54** *and similar horiz designs. W w* **12** (*upright*). *P* 13½.

No.	Description		Unused	Used
193	½d. black and myrtle-green (*shades*)		70	70
194	1d. black and scarlet (*shades*)		75	35
195	2d. black and blue (*shades*)		95	60
196	2½d. black and yellow-brown		1·00	35
197	3d. black and olive		60	20
198	4d. black and carmine		80	50
199	5½d. black and violet		80	80
200	6d. black and sepia		80	20
201	9d. black and orange-red		1·00	1·00
202	1s. black and maroon		80	20
203	1s. 3d. black and ultramarine		5·50	6·50
204	2s. black and brown-red (*shades*)		14·00	2·25
205	5s. black and turquoise		18·00	12·00
206	10s. black and purple		35·00	19·00
207	£1 black and orange-yellow		60·00	42·00
193/207		*Set of* 15	£130	80·00

Designs:—1d. Southern Black-backed Gull; 2d. Gentoo Penguins; 2½d. Long-tailed Meadowlark; 3d. Magellan Geese; 4d. Falkland Islands Flightless Steamer Ducks; 5½d. Rockhopper Penguin; 6d. Black-browed Albatross; 9d. Silvery Grebe; 1s. Magellanic Oyster-catchers; 1s. 3d. Chilean Teal: 2s. Kelp Geese; 5s. King Cormorants; 10s. Common Caracara; £1 Black-necked Swan.

See also No. 227.

69 Morse Key

70 One-valve Receiver

(Des M. Goaman. Photo Enschedé)

1962 (5 Oct). *50th Anniv of Establishment of Radio Communications. T* **69/70** *and similar vert design. W w* **12**. *P* 11½ × 11.

No.	Type	Description	Unused	Used
208	69	6d. carmine-lake and orange	1·75	75
209	70	1s. deep bluish green and yellow-olive	2·25	90
210	–	2s. deep violet and ultramarine	2·25	1·40

Design;—2s. Rotary Spark Transmitter.

1963 (4 June). *Freedom from Hunger. As No. 76 of Aden.*

No.	Description	Unused	Used
211	1s. ultramarine	14·00	4·75

1963 (2 Sept). *Red Cross Centenary. As Nos. 147/8 of Antigua.*

No.	Description	Unused	Used
212	1d. red and black	3·50	80
213	1s. red and blue	17·00	9·00

1964 (23 April). *400th Birth Anniv of William Shakespeare. As No. 164 of Antigua.*

No.	Description	Unused	Used
214	6d. black	1·00	50

72 H.M.S. *Glasgow*

(Recess D.L.R.)

1964 (8 Dec) *50th Anniv of the Battle of the Falkland Islands. T* **72** *and similar designs. W w* **12**. *P* 13 × 14 (2*s*.) *or* 13 (*others*).

No.	Description	Unused	Used
215	2½d. black and red	5·50	2·25
216	6d. black and light blue	1·25	40
	a. Centre Type **72**	£10000	
217	1s. black and carmine-red	1·90	1·00
218	2s. black and blue	4·75	2·50

Designs: *Horiz*—6d. H.M.S. *Kent*; 1s. H.M.S. *Invincible*. *Vert*—2s. Battle Memorial.

It is believed that No. 216a came from a sheet which was first printed with the centre of the 2½d. and then accidentally included among the supply of the 6d. value and thus received the wrong frame. Sixteen copies of the error have been reported.

1965 (26 May). *I.T.U. Centenary. As Nos. 166/7 of Antigua.*

No.	Description	Unused	Used
219	1d. light blue and deep blue	85	30
220	2s. lilac and bistre-yellow	12·00	3·75

1965 (25 Oct). *International Co-operation Year. As Nos. 168/9 of Antigua.*

No.	Description	Unused	Used
221	1d. reddish purple and turquoise-green	1·00	30
222	1s. deep bluish green and lavender	7·50	2·75

1966 (24 Jan). *Churchill Commemoration. As Nos. 170/3 of Antigua.*

No.	Description	Unused	Used
223	½d. new blue	65	25
224	1d. deep green	2·25	60
225	1s. brown	6·50	1·75
226	2s. bluish violet	8·00	3·25

1966 (25 Oct). *As No. 193 but wmk w* **12** *sideways.*

No.	Type	Description	Unused	Used
227	54	½d. black and myrtle-green	30	30

76 Globe and Human Rights Emblem

77 Dusty Miller

(Des M. Farrar Bell. Photo Harrison)

1968 (4 July). *Human Rights Year. W w* **12**. *P* 14 × 14½.

No.	Type	Description	Unused	Used
228	76	2d. multicoloured	60	30
		a. Yellow omitted ("1968" white)	£475	
229		6d. multicoloured	70	50
230		1s. multicoloured	80	60
231		2s. multicoloured	90	70

(Des Sylvia Goaman. Photo Harrison)

1968 (9 Oct). *Flowers. Designs as T* **77**. *Chalk-surfaced paper. W w* **12** (*sideways on vert designs*). *P* 14.

No.	Description	Unused	Used
232	½d. multicoloured	12	15
233	1½d. multicoloured	20	15
234	2d. multicoloured	20	15
235	3d. multicoloured	25	20
236	3½d. multicoloured	30	25
237	4½d. multicoloured	35	30
238	5½d. olive-yellow, brown and yellow-green	40	40
239	6d. carmine, black and yellow-green	50	40
240	1s. multicoloured	60	60
241	1s. 6d. multicoloured	5·50	8·00

242 2s. multicoloured .. .. 6·50 8·50
243 3s. multicoloured .. .. 9·00 8·50
244 5s. multicoloured .. .. 20·00 11·00
245 £1 multicoloured .. .. 14·00 8·00
232/245 .. .. *Set of* 14 50·00 42·00

Designs: *Horiz*—1½d. Pig Vine; 3½d. Sea Cabbage; 5½d. Arrowleaf Marigold; 6d. Diddle Dee; 1s. Scurvy Grass; 5s. Felton's Flower. *Vert*—2d. Pale Maiden; 3d. Dog Orchid; 4½d. Vanilla Daisy; 1s. 6d. Prickly Burr; 2s. Fachine; 3s. Lavender; £1 Yellow Orchid.

For stamps inscribed in decimal currency see Nos. 276/88, 293/5 and 315.

91 DHC-2 Beaver Floatplane

(Des V. Whiteley. Litho Format)

1969 (8 Apr). *21st Anniv of Government Air Services. T* **91** *and similar horiz designs. Multicoloured. W w* 12 *sideways). P* 14.

246 2d. Type **91** 45 25
247 6d. "Norseman" 50 50
248 1s. "Auster" 60 80
249 2s. Falkland Islands Arms .. .. .. 2·25 2·75

92 Holy Trinity Church, 1869

(Des G. Drummond. Litho Format)

1969 (30 Oct). *Centenary of Bishop Stirling's Consecration. T* **92** *and similar horiz designs. W w* 12 *(sideways). P* 14.

250 2d. black, grey and apple-green 55 30
251 6d. black, grey and orange-red 60 45
252 1s. black, grey and lilac 65 80
253 2s. multicoloured .. .. 1·25 1·75

Designs:—6d. Christ Church Cathedral, 1969; 1s. Bishop Stirling; 2s. Bishop's Mitre.

96 Mounted Volunteer

97 S.S. *Great Britain* (1843)

(Des R. Granger Barrett. Litho B.W.)

1970 (30 Apr). *Golden Jubilee of Defence Force. T* **96** *and similar designs. Multicoloured. W w* 12 *(sideways on 2d. and 1s.). P* 13.

254 2d. Type **96** .. .. 1·90 85
255 6d. Defence Post *(horiz)* .. .. .. 2·00 95
256 1s. Corporal in Number One Dress Uniform 2·75 1·10
257 2s. Defence Force Badge *(horiz)* .. .. 5·50 2·75

(Des V. Whiteley. Litho J.W.)

1970 (30 Oct). *Restoration of S.S. "Great Britain". T* **97** *and views of the ship at different dates. Multicoloured. W w* 12 *(sideways). P* 14½ × 14.

258 2d. Type **97** .. .. 2·50 90
259 4d. In 1845 .. .. 2·75 2·00
260 9d. In 1876 .. .. 3·00 2·50
261 1s. In 1886 .. .. 3·25 3·00
262 2s. In 1970 .. .. 3·50 3·75

½p
(98)

99 Dusty Miller

1971 (15 Feb). *Decimal Currency. Nos.* 232/44 *surch as T* **98**. *W w* 12 *(sideways on vert designs). P* 14.

263 ½p. on ½d. multicoloured 35 45
264 1p. on 1½d. multicoloured 25 25
a. Error. Surch 5p. £250
b. Do. but surch at right £500
c. Surch albino .. .. 75·00
d. Surch albino in pair with normal .. £700
265 1½p. on 2d. multicoloured 30 35
266 2p. on 3d. multicoloured 30 40
267 2½p. on 3½d. multicoloured 30 40
268 3p. on 4½d. multicoloured 30 40
269 4p. on 5½d. olive-yellow, brown & yell-grn 40 50
270 5p. on 6d. carmine, black and yellow-green 40 50
271 6p. on 1s. multicoloured .. .. .. 4·00 4·00
272 7½p. on 1s. 6d. multicoloured .. .. .. 6·00 6.00
273 10p. on 2s. multicoloured .. .. .. 6·50 7·00
274 15p. on 3s. multicoloured .. .. .. 7·00 7·50
275 25p. on 5s. multicoloured .. .. .. 7·50 11·00
263/75 .. .. *Set of* 13 30·00 35·00

1972 (1 June). *As Nos. 232/44, but Glazed, ordinary paper and with values inscr in decimal currency as T* **99**. *W w* 12 *(sideways on* ½, 1½, 2, 3, 7½, 10 *and* 15p.). *P* 14.

276 ½p. multicoloured 65 80
277 1p. multicoloured (as 1½d.) 40 30
278 1½p. multicoloured (as 2d.) 45 35
279 2p. multicoloured (as 3d.) .. .. .. 3·25 1·50
280 2½p. multicoloured (as 3½d.) 55 55
281 3p. multicoloured (as 4½d.) 55 55
282 4p. olive-yellow, brown & yell-grn (as 5½d.) 60 45
283 5p. carmine, black and yellow-green (as 6d.) 60 60
284 6p. multicoloured (as 1s.) .. .. .. 15·00 9·50
285 7½p. multicoloured (as 1s. 6d.) .. .. 2·25 4·00
286 10p. multicoloured (as 2s.) .. .. .. 4·50 5·00
287 15p. multicoloured (as 3s.) .. .. .. 3·75 5·00
288 25p. multicoloured (as 5s.) .. .. .. 4·50 6·50
276/88 .. .. *Set of* 13 32·00 32·00

See also Nos. 293/5 and 315.

100 Romney Marsh Sheep and Giant Sea Lions

(Des (from photograph by D. Groves) and photo Harrison)

1972 (20 Nov). *Royal Silver Wedding. Multicoloured; background colour givn. W w* **12**. *P* 14 × 14½.

289 **100** 1p. grey-green 50 25
290 10p. bright blue .. .. 1·00 85

1973 (14 Nov). *Royal Wedding. As Nos.* 165/6 *of Anguilla. Centre multicoloured. W w* 12 *(sideways). P* 13½.

291 5p. bright mauve 45 25
292 15p. brown-ochre 55 35

1974 (25 Feb–18 Oct). *As Nos.* 276, 279 *and* 284, *but wmk upright on* ½p. *and* 2p. *and sideways on* 6p. *P* 14.

293 ½p. multicoloured (18.10.74) .. .. .. 9·00 10.00
294 2p. multicoloured .. .. 4·00 2·75
295 6p. multicoloured (28.3.74) .. .. .. 2·00 2·25

101 Fur Seal

102 19th-Century Mail-coach

(Des J. Cooter. Litho Walsall)

1974 (6 Mar). *Tourism. T* **101** *and similar horiz designs. Multicoloured. W w* **12**. *P* 14.

296 2p. Type **101** .. .. 2.00 1·00
297 4p. Trout-fishing .. .. 2·75 1·75
298 5p. Rockhopper penguins .. .. .. 3·50 2·50
299 15p. Long-tailed Meadowlark .. .. .. 6·50 4·00

(Des PAD Studio. Litho Questa)

1974 (31 July). *Centenary of Universal Postal Union. T* **102** *and similar vert designs. Multicoloured. W w* **12** *(sideways). P* 14.

300 2p. Type **102** 25 25
301 5p. Packet ship, 1841 .. .. 50 60
302 8p. First U.K. aerial post, 1911 .. .. 60 70
303 16p. Ship's catapult mail, 1920's .. .. 90 1·00

103 Churchill and Houses of Parliament

(Des G. Vasarhelyi. Litho Enschedé)

1974 (30 Nov). *Birth Centenary of Sir Winston Churchill. T* **103** *and similar horiz designs. Multicoloured. W w* **12**. *P* 13½.

304 16p. Type **103** .. .. 1·25 1·40
305 20p. Churchill and warships .. .. .. 1·75 1·60
MS306 108 × 83 mm. Nos. 304/5 .. .. .. 6·50 7·00

MINIMUM PRICE

The minimum price quoted is 5p which represents a handling charge rather than a basis for valuing common stamps. For further notes about prices see introductory pages.

104 H.M.S. *Exeter*

105 Seal and Flag Badge

(Des J.W. Litho Harrison)

1974 (13 Dec). *35th Anniv of the Battle of the River Plate. T* **104** *and similar horiz designs. Multicoloured. W w* **12** *(sideways). P* 14.

307 2p. Type **104** .. .. 2·25 1·40
308 6p. H.M.N.Z. *Achilles* .. .. 3·50 2·75
309 8p. *Admiral Graf Spee* .. .. 4·00 3·75
310 16p. H.M.S. *Ajax* .. .. 7·00 8·50

(Des PAD Studio. Litho Walsall)

1975 (28 Oct). *50th Anniv of Heraldic Arms. T* **105** *and similar vert designs. Multicoloured. W w* **14** *(inverted). P* 14.

311 2p. Type **105** 35 35
312 7½p. Coat of arms, 1925 .. .. .. 75 1·00
313 10p. Coat of arms, 1948 .. .. .. 85 1·25
314 16p. Arms of the Dependencies, 1952 .. 1·40 1·75

1975 (8 Dec). *As No.* 276 *but W w* 14 *(sideways). P* 14.

315 **99** ½p. multicoloured .. .. .. 1·10 1·75

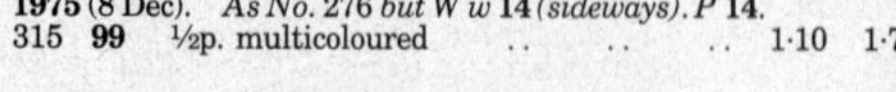

106 ½p. Coin and Trout

(Des G. Drummond. Litho Questa)

1975 (31 Dec). *New Coinage. T* **106** *and similar horiz designs each showing coin as T* **106**. *Multicoloured. W w* **12** *(sideways). P* 14.

316 2p. Type **106** 70 45
317 5½p. Gentoo Penguin and 1p. coin 80 90
318 8p. Magellan Goose and 2p. coin .. .. 1·40 2·00
319 10p. Black-browed Albatross and 5p. coin .. 1·50 2·25
320 16p. Sea lion and 10p. coin .. .. .. 1·75 2·75

107 Gathering Sheep

(Des PAD Studio. Litho J.W.)

1976 (28 Apr). *Sheep Farming Industry. T* **107** *and similar horiz designs. Multicoloured. W w* **14** *(sideways). P* 13½.

321 2p. Type **107** 35 20
322 7½p. Shearing 80 70
323 10p. Dipping .. .. 1·00 90
324 20p. Shipping .. .. 1·75 2·00

108 The Queen awaiting Anointment

(Des M. and G. Shamir; adapted J.W. Litho Questa)

1977 (7 Feb–1 Nov). *Silver Jubilee. T* **108** *and similar horiz designs. Multicoloured. P* 13½. *(a) W w* **14** *(sideways).*

325 6p. Visit of Prince Philip, 1957 .. .. 1·00 80
326 11p. Queen Elizabeth, ampulla and anointing spoon 80 65
a. Booklet pane of 4 with blank margins (1.11.77) .. .. 2·75
327 33p. Type **108** .. .. 1·00 1·40
a. Booklet pane of 4 with blank margins (1.11.77) .. .. 3·25

(b) W w 12 *(sideways)* (1.11.77)

327*b* 6p. Visit of Prince Philip,1957 .. .. 2·50 3·00
ba. Booklet pane of 4 with blank margins 9·00

109 Map of Falkland Islands

(Des K. Penny. Litho Questa)

1977 (24 Oct). *Telecommunications. T* **109** *and similar horiz designs. Multicoloured.* W w **14** (*sideways*). *P* 14½.

328	3p. Type **109**	35	20
329	11p. Ship to shore communications	60	65
330	40p. Telex and telephone service	2·50	2·50

110 *A.E.S.*, 1957–74

(Des J. Smith; adapted R. Granger Barrett. Litho Questa)

1978 (25 Jan)–**82**. *Mail Ships. Horiz designs as T* **110**. *Multicoloured.* W w **14** (*sideways*). *P* 14. *A. Printed without imprint date. B. With imprint date* ("1982") *at foot of designs* (13.7.82*).

		A		B	
331	1p. Type **110**	10	15	15	25
332	2p. *Darwin*, 1957–73	15	15	20	25
333	3p. *Merak-N.*, 1951–2	15	15	20	25
334	4p. *Fitzroy*, 1936–57	25	20	25	30
335	5p. *Lafonia*, 1936–41	25	20	30	30
336	6p. *Fleurus*, 1924–33	30	20	30	30
337	7p. S.S. *Falkland*, 1914–34 ..	30	30	35	40
338	8p. *Oravia*, 1900–12	35	35	45	55
339	9p. *Memphis*, 1890–97 ..	35	35	45	55
340	10p. *Black Hawk*, 1873–80 ..	35	35	45	55
341	20p. *Foam*, 1863–72	70	90	70	95
342	25p. *Fairy*, 1857–61	1·00	1·60	95	1·40
343	50p. *Amelia*, 1852–54	2·25	3·00	1·75	2·50
344	£1 *Nautilus*, 1846–48 ..	4·00	5·50	3·00	4·25
345	£3 *Hebe*, 1842–46	12·00	15·00	7·00	9·00
331/45	.. .. .. *Set of* 15	20·00	25·00	15·00	20·00

*Nos. 331B/45B were not available locally until 1 December 1982.

111 Short "Hythe" at Stanley

(Des L. McCombie. Litho Walsall)

1978 (28 Apr). *26th Anniv of First Direct Flight, Southampton–Port Stanley. T* **111** *and similar horiz design. Multicoloured.* W w **14** (*sideways*). *P* 14.

346	11p. Type **111**	1·25	1·25
347	33p. Route map and Short "Hythe"	1·75	1·75

112 Red Dragon of Wales

113 First Fox Bay P.O. and 1d. Stamp of 1878

(Des C. Abbott. Litho Questa)

1978 (2 June). *25th Anniv of Coronation. T* **112** *and similar vert designs. P* 15.

348	25p. bistre, bright blue and silver	1·00	1·00
	a. Sheetlet. Nos. 348/50 × 2	6·00	
349	25p. multicoloured	1·00	1·00
350	25p. bistre, bright blue and silver	1·00	1·00

Designs:—No. 348, Type **112**; No. 349, Queen Elizabeth II; No. 350, Hornless Ram.

Nos. 348/50 were printed together in small sheets of 6, containing two *se-tenant* strips of 3, with horizontal gutter margin between.

(Des J. Cooter. Litho B.W.)

1978 (8 Aug). *Centenary of First Falkland Is Postage Stamps. T* **113** *and similar vert designs. Multicoloured.* W w **14**. *P* 13½ × 13.

351	3p. Type **113**	30	20
352	11p. Second Stanley P.O. and 4d. stamp of 1879	60	60
353	15p. New Island P.O. and 6d. stamp of 1878 ..	70	70
354	22p. First Stanley P.O. and 1s. stamp of 1878	95	95

114 *Macrocystis pyrifera*

115 Britten-Norman "Islander" over Falkland Islands

(Des I. Strange. Litho Questa)

1979 (19 Feb). *Kelp and Seaweed. T* **114** *and similar multi-coloured designs.* W w **14** (*sideways on* 11 *and* 15p.). *P* 14.

355	3p. Type **114**	25	15
356	7p. *Durvillea* sp	40	40
357	11p. *Lessonia* sp (*horiz*)	55	55
358	15p. *Callophyllis* sp (*horiz*)	60	60
359	25p. *Iradaea* sp	85	85

(Des G. Hutchins. Litho Rosenbaum Bros, Vienna)

1979 (1 May). *Opening of Stanley Airport. T* **115** *and similar horiz designs showing diagrammatic drawings. Multicoloured.* W w **14** (*sideways*). *P* 13½.

360	3p. Type **115**	30	20
361	11p. Fokker "F27" over South Atlantic ..	70	70
362	15p. Fokker "F28" over Airport	80	85
363	25p. Cessna "172 (Skyhawk)", Britten-Norman "Islander", Fokker "F27" and "F28" over runway	1·25	1·25

116 Sir Rowland Hill and 1953 Coronation 1d. Commemorative

(Des J.W. Litho Questa)

1979 (27 Aug). *Death Centenary of Sir Rowland Hill. T* **116** *and similar multicoloured designs showing stamps and portrait.* W w **14** (*sideways on* 3 *and* 25p.). *P* 14.

364	3p. Type **116**	25	25
365	11p. 1878 1d. stamp (*vert*)	50	70
366	25p. Penny Black	75	85
MS367	137 × 98 mm. 33p. 1916 5s. stamp (*vert*) ..	1·40	1·75

117 Mail Drop by "Beaver" Aircraft **118** Peale's Porpoise

(Des A. Peake; adapted J.W. Litho Questa)

1979 (26 Nov). *Centenary of U.P.U. Membership. T* **117** *and similar horiz designs. Multicoloured.* W w **14** (*sideways*). *P* 14.

368	3p. Type **117**	25	20
369	11p. Mail by horseback	55	55
370	25p. Mail by schooner *Gwendolin*	1·00	1·00

(Des I. Strange. Litho Harrison)

1980 (25 Feb). *Dolphins and Porpoises. T* **118** *and similar designs.* W w **14** (*sideways on* 6, 7, 15 *and* 25p.). *P* 14.

371	3p. black, chestnut and blue	25	25
372	6p. multicoloured	35	40
373	7p. multicoloured	35	40
374	11p. black, new blue and rose-red	60	65
375	15p. black, chestnut and greyish blue ..	75	75
376	25p. multicoloured	1·00	1·25
371/6	.. .. *Set of* 6	3·00	3·25

Designs: *Horiz*—6p. Commerson's Dolphin; 7p. Hour-glass Dolphin; 15p. Dusky Dolphin; 25p. Killer Whale. *Vert*—11p. Spectacled Porpoise.

119 1878 Falkland Islands Postmark

(Des G. Hutchins. Litho Walsall)

1980 (6 May). *"London 1980" International Stamp Exhibition. T* **119** *and similar horiz designs showing postmarks.* W w **14** (*sideways*). *P* 14.

377	11p. black, gold and light blue	35	35
	a. Block of 6. Nos. 377/82	1·90	
378	11p. black, gold and greenish yellow	35	35
379	11p. black, gold and blue-green	35	35
380	11p. black, gold and pale violet	35	35
381	11p. black, gold and claret	35	35
382	11p. black, gold and flesh	35	35
377/82	.. .. .. *Set of* 6	1·90	1·90

Designs:—No. 377, Type **119**; No. 378, 1915 New Island; No. 379, 1901 Falkland Islands; No. 380, 1935 Port Stanley; No. 381, 1952 Port Stanley first overseas airmail; No. 382, 1934 Fox Bay.

Nos. 377/82 were printed together, *se-tenant*, as a sheetlet, containing one of each design.

120 Queen Elizabeth the Queen Mother

(Des Harrison. Litho Questa)

1980 (4 Aug). *80th Birthday of Queen Elizabeth the Queen Mother.* W w **14** (*sideways*). *P* 14.

383	**120**	11p. multicoloured	40	55

121 Forster's Caracara

(Des I. Strange. Litho Secura, Singapore)

1980 (11 Aug). *Birds of Prey. T* **121** *and similar horiz designs. Multicoloured.* W w **14** (*sideways*). *P* 13 × 13½.

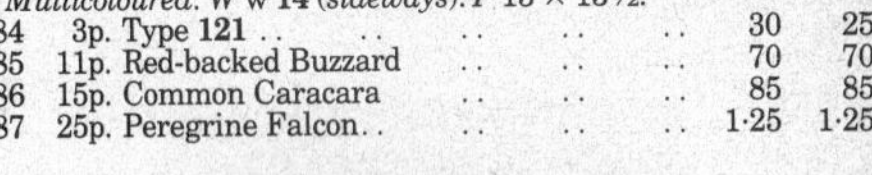

384	3p. Type **121**	30	25
385	11p. Red-backed Buzzard	70	70
386	15p. Common Caracara	85	85
387	25p. Peregrine Falcon	1·25	1·25

122 Stanley

(Des C. Abbott. Litho Rosenbaum Bros, Vienna)

1980 (22 Dec). *Early Settlements. T* **122** *and similar horiz designs. Multicoloured.* W w **14** (*sideways*). *P* 14.

388	3p. Type **122**	30	25
389	11p. Port Egmont	60	55
390	25p. Port Louis	1·25	1·10
391	33p. Mission House, Keppel Island	1·50	1·40

123 Sheep

(Des P. Oxenham. Litho Questa)

1981 (9 Jan). *Farm Animals. T* **123** *and similar horiz designs. Multicoloured.* W w **14** (*sideways*). *P* 14.

392	3p. Type **123**	25	25
393	11p. Cattle	45	45
394	25p. Horse	90	90
395	33p. Dogs	1·25	1·25

124 Bowles and Carver, 1779 **125** Wedding Bouquet from Falkland Islands

(Des I. Strange. Litho Walsall)

1981 (22 May). *Early Maps. T* **124** *and similar horiz designs in black, dull rose and stone* (26p.) *or multicoloured* (*others*). *W* w **14** (*sideways*). *P* 14.

No.	Description	Unused	Used
396	3p. Type **124**	20	20
397	10p. J. Hawkesworth, 1773	40	50
398	13p. Eman, Bowen, 1747	55	65
399	15p. T. Boutflower, 1768	60	70
400	25p. Philippe de Pretot, 1771	1·00	1·10
401	26p. Bellin *Petite Atlas Maritime*, Paris, 1764	1·00	1·10
396/401	.. .. *Set of* 6	3·25	3·75

(Des and litho J.W.)

1981 (22 July). *Royal Wedding. T* **125** *and similar vert designs. Multicoloured. W* w **14**. *P* 13½ × 13.

No.	Description	Unused	Used
402	10p. Type **125**	45	50
403	13p. Prince Charles riding	55	60
404	52p. Prince Charles and Lady Diana Spencer	1·00	1·00

126 "Handicrafts"

127 "The Adoration of the Holy Child" (16th-century Dutch artist)

(Des BG Studio. Litho Questa)

1981 (14 Sept). *25th Anniv of Duke of Edinburgh Award Scheme. T* **126** *and similar vert designs. Multicoloured. W* w **14**. *P* 14.

No.	Description	Unused	Used
405	10p. Type **126**	50	45
406	13p. "Camping"	60	55
407	15p. "Canoeing"	70	65
408	26p. Duke of Edinburgh	1·00	90

(Des BG Studio. Litho Walsall)

1981 (2 Nov). *Christmas. Paintings. T* **127** *and similar vert designs. Multicoloured. W* w **14**. *P* 14.

No.	Description	Unused	Used
409	3p. Type **127**	20	20
410	13p. "The Holy Family in an Italian Landscape" (17th-century Genoan artist) ..	35	55
411	26p. "The Holy Virgin" (Reni)	55	90

128 Falkland Herring

(Des I. Strange. Litho Questa)

1981 (7 Dec). *Shelf Fishes. T* **128** *and similar multicoloured designs. W* w **14** (*sideways on* 5, 15 *and* 25*p.*). *P* 14 × 13½ (13, 26*p.*) *or* 13½ × 14 (*others*).

No.	Description	Unused	Used
412	5p. Type **128**	15	15
413	13p. Rock Cod (*vert*)	30	35
414	15p. Patagonian Hake	35	40
415	25p. Southern Blue Whiting	60	70
416	26p. Grey-tailed Skate (*vert*)	60	70

129 *Lady Elizabeth*, 1913

(Des J. Smith. Litho Questa)

1982 (15 Feb). *Shipwrecks. T* **129** *and similar horiz designs. Multicoloured. W* w **14** (*sideways*). *P* 14½.

No.	Description	Unused	Used
417	5p. Type **129**	20	30
418	13p. *Capricorn*, 1882	35	50
419	15p. *Jhelum*, 1870	40	60
420	25p. *Snowsquall*, 1864	75	1·00
421	26p. *St. Mary*, 1890	75	1·00

ARGENTINE OCCUPATION

2 April to 15 June 1982

Following incidents, involving the illegal presence of Argentine scrap-metal workers on the dependency of South Georgia during March 1982, Argentine forces attacked Port Stanley, the capital of the Falkland Islands early in the morning of 2 April. The small garrison of Royal Marines was overwhelmed and the Governor forced to agree to a cease-fire, before being deported.

South Georgia was occupied by the Argentines on the following day.

British forces, dispatched from the United Kingdom, recaptured South Georgia on 25 April, and, after landing at various points on East Falkland, forced the surrender of the Argentine troops throughout the islands on 15 June.

The last mail to be dispatched from the Falkland Islands prior to the invasion left on 31 March. The Port Stanley Post Office was closed on 2 April, when all current issues were withdrawn. From 5 April an Argentine post office operated in the town, initially accepting mail without stamps, which was then cancelled by a postmark inscribed "ISLAS MALVINAS". Any letters tendered franked with Falkland Islands issues had these cancelled by ball-point pen. A limited range of Argentine stamps was placed on sale from 8 April. The Argentine definitive overprinted "LAS MALVINAS SON ARGENTINAS" for use throughout the country, was also available.

Following the Argentine surrender a rudimentary mail service was operating by 17 June, but the Port Stanley Post Office did not re-open until 24 June.

The last mail from South Georgia before the invasion was sent out on 16 March, although items remaining in the post office there were evacuated by the Deputy Postmaster when he was deported to the United Kingdom by the Argentines. The first mail left after recapture by the British on 2 May.

BRITISH ADMINISTRATION RESTORED

130 Charles Darwin

131 Falkland Islands Coat of Arms

(Des L. Curtis. Litho Questa)

1982 (5 July*). *150th Anniv of Charles Darwin's Voyage. T* **130** *and similar horiz designs. Multicoloured. W* w **14** (*sideways*). *P* 14.

No.	Description	Unused	Used
422	5p. Type **130**	20	20
423	17p. Darwin's microscope	50	55
424	25p. Warrah (wild dog)	65	75
425	34p. H.M. *Beagle*	85	95
	a. Pale brown (background to side panels) omitted	£550	

*It was initially intended that these stamps were to be issued on 19 April. First Day covers were prepared, postmarked with this date, but, because of the Argentine invasion, the stamps were not actually released until 5 July. A postmark showing the actual date of issue was struck alongside the stamps on the First Day covers.

(Des C. Abbott. Litho J.W.)

1982 (16 Aug). *21st Birthday of Princess of Wales. T* **131** *and similar vert designs. Multicoloured. W* w **14**. *P* 13.

No.	Description	Unused	Used
426	5p. Type **131**	15	15
427	17p. Princess at Royal Opera House, Covent Garden, November 1981 ..	40	40
428	37p. Bride and groom in doorway of St Paul's	75	85
429	50p. Formal portrait	1·00	1·10

132 Map of Falkland Islands

(Des PAD Studio. Litho Format)

1982 (13 Sept). *Rebuilding Fund. W* w **14** (*sideways*). *P* 11.

No.	Description	Unused	Used
430	**132** £1 + £1 multicoloured	4·00	4·75

1st PARTICIPATION
COMMONWEALTH GAMES 1982

(**133**)

134 Blackish Cinclodes

1982 (7 Oct). *Commonwealth Games, Brisbane. Nos.* 335B *and* 342B *optd with T* **133**.

No.	Description	Unused	Used
431	5p. *Lafonia*, 1936–41	15	15
432	25p. *Fairy*, 1857–61	60	70

(Des I. Strange. Litho W. S. Cowells Ltd)

1982 (6 Dec). *Birds of the Passerine Family. T* **134** *and similar vert designs. Multicoloured. W* w **14** (*inverted on* 10*p.*). *P* 15 × 14½.

No.	Description	Unused	Used
433	5p. Type **134**	10	10
434	10p. Black-chinned Siskin	20	20
435	13p. Short-billed Marsh Wren	25	25
436	17p. Black-throated Finch	35	35
437	25p. Correndera Pipit	50	50
438	34p. Dark-faced Ground Tyrant	65	65
433/8	.. .. *Set of* 6	1·90	1·90

135 Raising Flag, Port Louis, 1833

136 1933 British Administration Centenary 3d. Commemorative

(Des I. Strange and J. Sheridan. Litho Questa)

1983 (3 Jan). *150th Anniv of British Administration. T* **135** *and similar multicoloured designs. W* w **14** (*sideways on* 2, 10, 15, 25 *and* 50*p.*). *P* 14 × 13½ (1, 5, 20, 40*p.*, £1, £2) *or* 13½ × 14 (*others*).

No.	Description	Unused	Used
439	1p. Type **135**	5	5
440	2p. Chelsea pensioners and barracks, 1849 (*horiz*)	8	8
441	5p. Development of wool trade, 1874 ..	12	12
442	10p. Ship-repairing trade, 1850–1890 (*horiz*)	30	30
443	15p. Government House, early 20th century (*horiz*)	35	35
444	20p. Battle of Falkland Islands, 1914 ..	45	45
445	25p. Whalebone Arch, 1933	55	55
446	40p. Contribution to War effort, 1939–45 ..	80	80
447	50p. Duke of Edinburgh's visit, 1957 (*horiz*) ..	1·10	1·10
448	£1 Royal Marine uniforms	2·00	2·00
449	£2 Queen Elizabeth II	3·75	4·00
439/49	.. .. *Set of* 11	8·50	8·75

(Des L. Curtis. Litho Questa)

1983 (14 Mar). *Commonwealth Day. T* **136** *and similar multicoloured designs. W* w **14** (*sideways on* 5*p.*, 17*p.*). *P* 14.

No.	Description	Unused	Used
450	5p. Type **136**	12	15
451	17p. 1933 British Administration Centenary ½d. commemorative	35	45
452	34p. 1933 British Administration Centenary 10s. commemorative (*vert*)	70	80
453	50p. 1983 British Administration 150th anniversary £2 commemorative (*vert*) ..	1·00	1·25

137 British Army advancing across East Falkland

(Des A. Theobald. Litho Questa)

1983 (14 June). *First Anniv of Liberation. T* **137** *and similar horiz designs. Multicoloured. W* w **14** (*sideways*). *P* 14.

No.	Description	Unused	Used
454	5p. Type **137**	15	20
455	13p. S.S. *Canberra* and M.V. *Norland* at San Carlos	30	35
456	17p. R.A.F. Hawker "Harrier" fighter ..	35	50
457	50p. Aircraft carrier H.M.S. *Hermes*	1·00	1·10
MS458	169 × 130 mm. Nos. 454/7. P 12	1·75	2·00

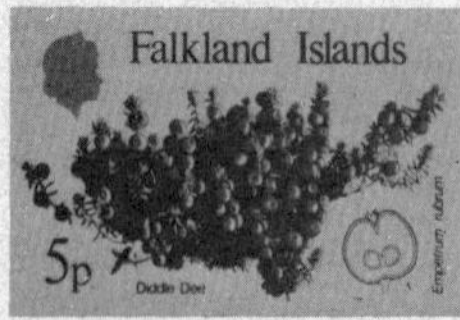

138 Diddle Dee

(Des A. Chater. Litho Questa)

1983 (10 Oct). *Native Fruits. T* **138** *and similar horiz designs. Multicoloured. W* w **14** (*sideways*). *P* 14.

No.	Description	Unused	Used
459	5p. Type **138**	10	15
460	17p. Tea Berry	35	50
461	25p. Mountain Berry	50	65
462	34p. Native Strawberry	70	80

139 Britten-Norman "Islander"

(Des Harrison. Litho Questa)

1983 (14 Nov). *Bicentenary of Manned Flight. T* **139** *and similar horiz designs. Multicoloured. W* w **14** (*sideways*). *P* 14.

No.	Description	Unused	Used
463	5p. Type **139**	10	15
464	13p. "DHC-2 Beaver"	30	40
465	17p. Noorduyn "Norseman"	35	45
466	50p. Auster	1·00	1·25

17 p

(140)

1984 (3 Jan). *Nos.* 443 *and* 445 *surch as T* **140** *by Govt Printer, Port Stanley.*

467 17p. on 15p. Government House, early 20th century 35 40
468 22p. on 25p. Whalebone Arch, 1933 .. .. .. 45 50

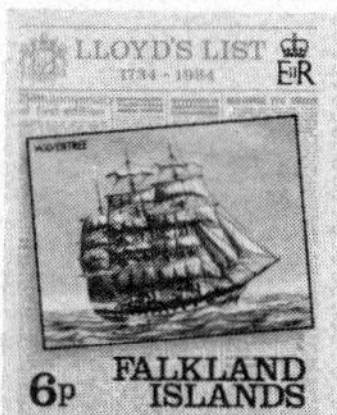

141 Green Spider (juvenile) **142** *Wavertree*

(Des I. Strange. Litho Questa)

1984 (3 Jan). *Insects and Spiders. T* **141** *and similar horiz designs. Multicoloured. W* w **14** (*sideways*). *P* 14.

469 1p. Type **141** 5 5
470 2p. Ichneumon Fly (*Alophophion occidentalis*) 5 5
471 3p. Brocade Moth 5 5
472 4p. Black Beetle 8 10
473 5p. "The Queen of the Falklands" 8 10
474 6p. Green Spider 10 12
475 7p. Ichneumon Fly (*Trachysphyrus penai*) .. 12 15
476 8p. Ochre Spider 15 20
477 9p. Clocker Weevil 15 20
478 10p. Hover Fly 20 25
479 20p. Weevil 35 40
480 25p. Metallic Beetle 45 50
481 50p. Camel Cricket 90 95
482 £1 Beauchene Spider .. .. 1·75 1·90
483 £3 Southern Painted Lady .. .. 5·00 5·50
469/83 .. .. *Set of* 15 8·50 9·50

(Des A. Theobald. Litho Questa)

1984 (7 May). 250*th Anniv of "Lloyd's List"* (*newspaper*). *T* **142** *and similar vert designs. Multicoloured. W* w **14**. *P* 14½ × 14.

484 6p. Type **142** 15 20
485 17p. Port Stanley 40 50
486 22p. R.M.S. *Oravia* stranded 45 55
487 52p. *Cunard Countess* .. .. 1·10 1·25

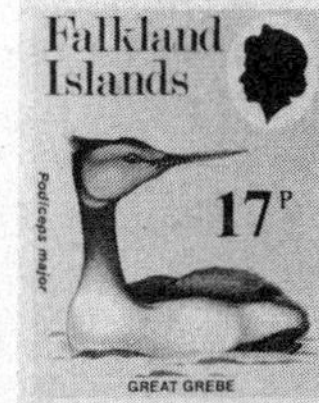

143 Ship, Aircraft and U.P.U. Logo **144** Great Grebe

(Des E. Nisbet, adapted L. Curtis. Litho Questa)

1984 (25 June). *Universal Postal Union Congress, Hamburg. W* w 14 (*sideways*). *P* 14.

488 **143** 22p. multicoloured 45 50

(Des I. Strange. Litho Questa)

1984 (6 Aug). *Grebes. T* **144** *and similar vert designs. Multicoloured. W* w **14**. *P* 14½.

489 17p. Type **144** 35 40
490 22p. Silver Grebe 45 50
491 52p. Rolland's Grebe .. .. 1·10 1·25

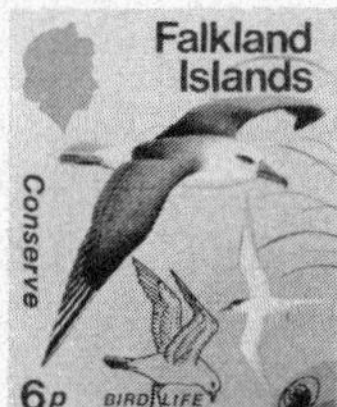

145 Black-browed Albatross

(Des I. Strange. Litho Questa)

1984 (5 Nov). *Nature Conservation. T* **145** *and similar vert designs. Multicoloured. W* w **14**. *P* 14½ × 14.

492 6p. Type **145** 12 15
493 17p. Tussock grass 35 40
494 22p. Dusky Dolphin and Sea Lion 40 45
495 52p. *Notothenia* (fish) and krill .. .. .. 1·00 1·10
MS496 130 × 90 mm. Nos. 492/5 .. .. .. 1·90 2·10

FALKLAND ISLANDS DEPENDENCIES

The stamps of FALKLAND ISLANDS were used on South Georgia (Grytviken) from 3 December 1909 until 1944 and at Port Foster, Deception Island in the South Shetlands group from 1912 to 1931, both offices operating during the whaling season only.

PRICES FOR STAMPS ON COVER TO 1945
Nos. A1/D8 *from* × 10

A. GRAHAM LAND

GRAHAM LAND

DEPENDENCY OF

(A 1)

1944 (12 Feb)–**45.** *Falkland Islands Nos.* 146, 148, 150, 153/5, 157 *and* 158*a optd with Type* A 1, *in red.*

A1 ½d. black and green 40 85
a. Blue-black and green .. .. .. 80·00
A2 1d. black and violet 40 85
A3 2d. black and carmine-red .. .. 40 1·00
A4 3d. black and blue .. .. 45 1·10
A5 4d. black and purple .. .. 90 1·40
A6 6d. black and brown .. .. 4·00 3·00
a. Blue-black and brown (1945) .. .. 20·00
A7 9d. black and grey-blue .. .. 2·50 2·50
A8 1s. deep blue .. .. 2·50 2·50
A1/8 Perf "Specimen" .. .. *Set of* 8 £300

B. SOUTH GEORGIA

1944 (3 Apr)–**45.** *Falkland Islands Nos.* 146, 148, 150, 153/5, 157 *and* 158*a optd* "SOUTH GEORGIA/DEPENDENCY OF", *in red, as Type* A 1, *of Graham Land.*

B1 ½d. black and green 40 85
B2 1d. black and violet 40 85
B3 2d. black and carmine-red .. .. 40 1·00
B4 3d. black and blue .. .. 45 1·10
B5 4d. black and purple .. .. 90 1·40
B6 6d. black and brown .. .. 4·00 3·00
a. Blue-black and brown (1945) .. .. 20·00
B7 9d. black and grey-blue .. .. 2·50 2·50
B8 1s. deep blue .. .. 2·50 2·50
B1/8 Perf "Specimen" .. .. *Set of* 8 £300

For later issues, see after No. G44.

C. SOUTH ORKNEYS

1944 (21 Feb)–**45.** *Falkland Islands Nos.* 146, 148, 150, 153/5, 157 *and* 158*a optd* "SOUTH ORKNEYS/DEPENDENCY OF", *in red as Type* A 1 *of Graham Land.*

C1 ½d. black and green 40 85
C2 1d. black and violet 40 85
C3 2d. black and carmine-red .. .. 40 1·00
C4 3d. black and blue .. .. 45 1·10
C5 4d. black and purple .. .. 90 1·40
C6 6d. black and brown .. .. 4·00 3·00
a. Blue-black and brown (1945) .. .. 20·00
C7 9d. black and grey-blue .. .. 2·50 2·50
C8 1s. deep blue .. .. 2·50 2·50
C1/8 Perf "Specimen" .. .. *Set of* 8 £300

D. SOUTH SHETLANDS

1944–45. *Falkland Islands Nos.* 146, 148, 150, 153/5, 157 *and* 158*a optd* "SOUTH SHETLANDS/DEPENDENCY OF", *in red, as Type* A 1 *of Graham Land.*

D1 ½d. black and green 40 85
D2 1d. black and violet 40 85
D3 2d. black and carmine-red .. .. 40 1·00
D4 3d. black and blue .. .. 45 1·10
D5 4d. black and purple .. .. 90 1·40
D6 6d. black and brown .. .. 4·00 3·00
a. Blue-black and brown (1945) .. .. 20·00
D7 9d. black and grey-blue .. .. 2·50 2·50
D8 1s. deep blue .. .. 2·50 2·50
D1/8 Perf "Specimen" .. .. *Set of* 8 £300
A1/D8 .. .. *Set of* 32 42·00 45·00

From 1 February 1946 to 16 July 1963, Graham Land, South Georgia, South Orkneys and South Shetlands used FALKLAND ISLANDS DEPENDENCIES stamps.

E. FALKLAND ISLANDS DEPENDENCIES

For use in all four dependencies.

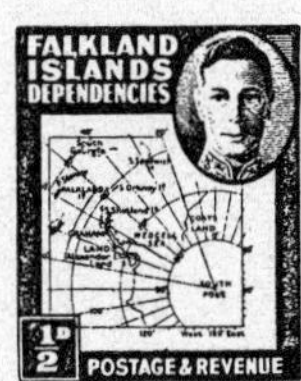

G 1

(Map litho, frame recess D.L.R.)

1946 (1 Feb)–**49.** *Wmk Mult Script CA, sideways. P* 12.

(*a*) *Map thick and coarse*

G 1 G 1 ½d. black and green .. .. 80 1·75
G 2 1d. black and violet .. .. 80 1·75
G 3 2d. black and carmine .. .. 1·00 3·00
G 4 G 1 3d. black and blue .. .. 1·25 3·00
G 5 4d. black and claret .. .. 2·00 4·25
G 6 6d. black and orange .. .. 5·00 6·50
a. Black and ochre .. .. 42·00 90·00
G 7 9d. black and brown .. .. 2·50 4·50
G 8 1s. black and purple .. .. 3·25 7·00
G1/8 .. .. *Set of* 8 15·00 28·00
G1/8 Perf "Specimen" .. .. *Set of* 8 £550

(*b*) *Map thin and clear* (16.2.48)

G 9 G 1 ½d. black and green .. .. 2·00 6·50
G10 1d. black and violet .. .. 1·25 6·50
G11 2d. black and carmine .. .. 3·50 7·00
G11*a* 2½d. black and deep blue (6.3.49) .. .. 9·00 7·00
G12 3d. black and blue .. .. 1·50 4·50
G13 4d. black and claret .. .. 4·50 9·00
G14 6d. black and orange .. .. 6·50 9·00
G15 9d. black and brown .. .. 6·50 9·00
G16 1s. black and purple .. .. 9·00 17·00
G9/16 .. .. *Set of* 9 40·00 70·00

In Nos. G1/8 a variety with a gap in the 80th parallel occurs six times in each sheet of all values in positions 4, 9, 24, 29, 44, and 49.

In Nos. G9 to G16 the map is redrawn; the "o°" meridian does not touch the "S" of "COATS", the "n" of "Alexander" is not joined to the "L" of "Land" below, and the loops of letters "s" and "t" are generally more open.

1946 (4 Oct). *Victory. As Nos.* 28/9 *of Aden.*

G17 1d. deep violet 90 80
G18 3d. blue 90 90
G17/18 Perf "Specimen" .. .. *Set of* 2 £100

1948 (6 Dec). *Royal Silver Wedding. As Nos.* 30/1 *of Aden but inscr* "FALKLAND ISLANDS DEPENDENCIES" (*recess* 1s.).

G19 2½d. ultramarine .. .. 1·00 1·00
G20 1s. violet-blue .. .. 10·00 10·00

1949 (10 Oct). 75*th Anniv of U.P.U. As Nos.* 114/17 *of Antigua.*

G21 1d. violet .. .. 2·75 2·50
G22 2d. carmine-red .. .. 7·50 6·00
G23 3d. deep blue .. .. 9·00 6·00
G24 6d. red-orange .. .. 14·00 12·00

1953 (4 June). *Coronation. As No.* 47 *of Aden.*

G25 1d. black and violet .. .. 2·00 2·40

G 2 *John Biscoe*, 1947–52 **G 3** *Trepassey*, 1945–47

(Recess Waterlow, then D.L.R. (from 27.3.62))

1954 (1 Feb). *Types* G **2/3** *and similar designs showing ships. Wmk Mult Script CA. P* 12½.

G26 ½d. black and bluish green (*shades*) 25 25
G27 1d. black and sepia-brown (*shades*) 40 30
G28 1½d. black and olive (*shades*) 25 25
G29 2d. black and rose-red 40 35
G30 2½d. black and yellow-ochre 40 35
G31 3d. black and deep bright blue 40 35
G32 4d. black and bright reddish purple 65 65
G33 6d. black and deep lilac 85 85
G34 9d. black .. .. 1·00 1·00
G35 1s. black and brown .. .. 1·00 90
G36 2s. black and carmine .. .. 13·00 8·00
G37 2s. 6d. black and pale turquoise .. .. 13·00 8·00
G38 5s. black and violet .. .. 32·00 20·00
G39 10s. black and blue .. .. 70·00 45·00
G40 £1 black .. .. £150 80·00
G26/40 .. .. *Set of* 15 £250 £150

Designs: *Horiz*—1½d. *Wyatt Earp*, 1934–36; 2d. *Eagle*, 1944–45; 2½d. *Penola*, 1934–37; 3d. *Discovery II*, 1929–37; 4d. *William Scoresby*, 1926–46; 1s. *Deutschland*, 1910–12; 2s. *Pourquoi-Pas?*, 1908–10; 10s. *Antarctic*, 1901–03. *Vert*—6d. *Discovery*, 1925–27; 9d. *Endurance*, 1914–16; 2s. 6d. *Français*, 1903–05; 5s. *Scotia*, 1902–04; £1 *Belgica*, 1897–99.

TRANS-ANTARCTIC
EXPEDITION 1955-1958

(G 4)

1956 (30 Jan). *Trans-Antarctic Expedition. Nos.* G27, G30/1 *and* G33 *optd with Type* G 4.

G41 1d. black and sepia-brown 20 45
G42 2½d. black and yellow-ochre 85 95
G43 3d. black and deep bright blue 85 95
G44 6d. black and deep lilac .. .. 85 1·00

The stamps of Falkland Islands Dependencies were withdrawn on 16 July 1963 after Graham Land, South Orkneys and South Shetlands had become a separate colony, BRITISH ANTARCTIC TERRITORY. From 17 July 1963 to 4 May 1980 South Georgia and South Sandwich Islands used SOUTH GEORGIA stamps.

F. SOUTH GEORGIA

1 Reindeer **2** South Sandwich Islands

(Des D.L.R. (No. 16), M. Goaman (others). Recess D.L.R.)

1963 (17 July)–**69**. *T 1/2 and similar designs. Ordinary or glazed paper (No. 16). W w* **12**. *P* 15.
1 ½d. brown-red 65 50
a. Perf 14 × 15 (13.2.67) .. .. 1·25 1·75
2 1d. violet-blue 70 25
3 2d. turquoise-blue 70 30
4 2½d. black .. .. 1·25 65
5 3d. bistre 90 35
6 4d. bronze-green 90 50
7 5½d. deep violet 90 50
8 6d. orange 90 40
9 9d. blue .. .. 2·00 1·25
10 1s. purple .. .. 1·00 70
11 2s. yellow-olive and light blue .. .. 10·00 9·00
12 2s. 6d. blue .. .. 12·00 9·00
13 5s. orange-brown .. .. 22·00 16·00
14 10s. magenta .. .. 40·00 30·00
15 £1 ultramarine £130 £100
16 £1 grey-black (1.12.69) .. .. .. 28·00 35·00
1/16 .. .. *Set of* 16 £225 £180

Designs: *Vert*—2d. Sperm Whale; 3d. Fur Seal; 6d. Light-mantled Sooty Albatross; 10s. Plankton and krill; £1 (No. 16) King Penguins. *Horiz*—2½d. Bearded and King Penguin; 4d. Fin Whale; 5½d. Elephant Seal; 9d. Whale-catcher; 1s. Leopard Seal; 2s. Shackleton's Cross; 2s. 6d. Wandering Albatross; 5s. Elephant and Fur Seal; £1 (No. 15) Blue Whale.

1970 (22 Jan). *As No. 1, but wmk w* **12** *sideways and on glazed paper.*
17 ½d. brown-red .. .. 1·25 2·50

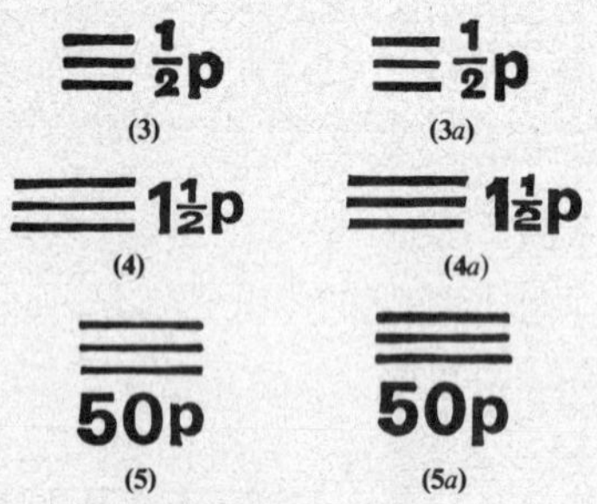

(3) (3*a*) (4) (4*a*) (5) (5*a*)

1971 (15 Feb)–**76**. *Decimal Currency. Nos. 17 and 2/14 surch as T* **3/4**. *Nos. 18/a wmk sideways, glazed paper. Others wmk upright, ordinary paper.*
18 ½p. on ½d. brown-red (T **3**) .. .. .. 95 1·60
a. Surch with T **3***a* (16.6.72) .. .. 1·00 90
b. Do. Wmk upright (24.8.73) .. .. 90 1·25
19 1p. on 1d. violet-blue.. .. .. .. 1·50 55
a. Glazed paper (1.12.72) .. .. .. 2·25 2·25
b. Do. but wmk sideways (9.3.76) .. .. 3·25 5·00
20 1½p. on 5½d. deep violet (T **4**) .. .. 1·50 1·75
a. Surch with T **4***a*. Glazed paper (24.8.73) 2·50 2·75
21 2p. on 2d. turquoise-blue 70 40
22 2½p. on 2½d. black .. .. 1·00 60
23 3p. on 3d. bistre 80 60
24 4p. on 4d. bronze-green 90 65
25 5p. on 6d. orange 90 50
26 6p. on 9d. blue .. .. 1·50 90
27 7½p. on 1s. purple .. .. 1·25 1·00
28 10p. on 2s. yellow-olive and light blue .. 15·00 14·00
29 15p. on 2s. 6d. blue .. .. 17·00 17·00
30 25p. on 5s. orange-brown .. .. .. 15·00 14·00
31 50p. on 10s. magenta (Type **5**) .. .. 35·00 30·00
a. Surch with Type **5***a*. Glazed paper (1.12.72) .. .. 30·00 35·00
b. Do. but wmk sideways (9.3.76) .. .. 35·00 42·00
18/31 .. .. *Set of* 14 80·00 75·00

The surcharge on No. 19b shows a larger "p".
See also Nos. 53/66.

6 *Endurance* beset in Weddell Sea

(Des R. Granger Barrett. Litho A. & M.)

1972 (5 Jan). *50th Death Anniv of Sir Ernest Shackleton. T* **6** *and similar horiz designs. Multicoloured. W w* **12** *(sideways). P* 13½.
32 1½p. Type **6** .. .. 1·50 1·60
33 5p. Launching the longboat *James Caird* .. 2·00 2·10
34 10p. Route of the *James Caird* .. .. 2·25 2·50
35 20p. Sir Ernest Shackleton and the *Quest* .. 3·00 3·75

7 Elephant Seal and King Penguins

(Des (from photograph by D. Groves) and photo Harrison)

1972 (20 Nov). *Royal Silver Wedding. Multicoloured; background colour given. W w* **12**. *P* 14 × 14½.
36 **7** 5p. slate-green .. .. 1·10 90
37 10p. bluish violet .. .. 1·25 90

1973 (1 Dec*). *Royal Wedding. As Nos. 165/6 of Anguilla. Centre multicoloured. W w* **12** *(sideways). P* 13½.
38 5p. brown-ochre 60 40
39 15p. bright lilac 65 60

*This is the local date of issue: the Crown Agents released the stamps on 14 November.

8 Churchill and Westminster Skyline

9 Captain Cook

(Des L. Curtis. Litho Questa)

1974 (14 Dec*). *Birth Centenary of Sir Winston Churchill. T* **8** *and similar horiz design. Multicoloured. W w* **12** *(sideways). P* 14½.
40 15p. Type **8** .. .. 1·75 1·60
41 25p. Churchill and warship .. .. .. 1·75 1·60
MS42 122 × 98 mm. Nos. 40/1 .. .. 5·50 6·00

*This is the local date of issue: the Crown Agents released the stamps on 30 November.

(Des J. Cooter. Litho Questa)

1975 (26 Apr). *Bicentenary of Possession by Captain Cook. T* **9** *and similar horiz designs. Multicoloured. W w* **12** *(sideways on 8 and 16p.). P* 13.
43 2p. Type **9** .. .. 1·75 1·00
44 8p. H.M.S. *Resolution* .. .. .. 2·50 2·00
45 16p. Possession Bay .. .. .. 3·50 2·50

10 *Discovery* and Biological Laboratory

11 Queen and Retinue after Coronation

(Des J. W. Litho Format)

1976 (21 Dec). *50th Anniv of "Discovery" Investigations. T* **10** *and similar vert designs. Multicoloured. W w* **14**. *P* 14.
46 2p. Type **10** 95 55
47 8p. *William Scoresby* and water-sampling bottles .. .. 1·25 90
48 11p. *Discovery II* and plankton net .. .. 1·50 1·25
49 25p. Biological Station and krill .. .. 2·50 2·50

(Des G. Drummond. Litho Questa)

1977 (7 Feb). *Silver Jubilee. T* **11** *and similar horiz designs. Multicoloured. W w* **14** *(sideways). P* 13½.
50 6p. Visit by Prince Philip, 1957 .. .. 65 65
51 11p. Queen Elizabeth and Westminster Abbey 75 75
52 33p. Type **11** .. .. 1·10 1·40

1977 (17 May)–**78**. *As Nos. 18a etc., but W w* **14** *(inverted on 1p.; upright on 3p., 5p. and 50p.; sideways on others). Glazed paper.*
53 ½p. on ½d. brown-red 80 80
54 1p. on 1d. violet-blue (16.8.77) .. .. 1·00 1·25
55 1½p. on 5½d. deep violet (16.8.77) .. .. 1·40 1·60
57 2½p. on 2½d. black (16.8.77) .. .. 2·75 2·00
58 3p. on 3d. bistre (16.8.77) .. .. 2·50 2·00
59 4p. on 4d. bronze-green (16.8.77) .. .. 10·00 8·00
60 5p. on 6d. orange .. .. .. 3·25 2·75
62 7½p. on 1s. purple (16.8.77) .. .. 9·00 10·00
63 10p. on 2s. yellow-olive and light blue (16.8.77) 8·50 8·50
64 15p. on 2s. 6d. blue (16.8.77) .. .. 8·00 12·00
65 25p. on 5s. orange-brown (16.8.77) .. .. 9·00 12·00
66 50p. on 10s. pale magenta (12.78) .. .. 5·50 13·00
53/66 .. .. *Set of* 12 55·00 65·00

Surcharges on the above differ from those on Nos. 18a/30 by having straight outlines and being slightly more slender. The change in paper also results in the colours appearing brighter.

12 Fur Seal

13 *Resolution*

(Des C. Abbott. Litho Questa)

1978 (2 June). *25th Anniv of Coronation. T* **12** *and similar vert designs. P* 15.
67 25p. indigo, ultramarine and silver 85 95
a. Sheetlet. Nos. 67/9 × 2 .. .. .. 4·75
68 25p. multicoloured 85 95
69 25p. indigo, ultramarine and silver 85 95

Designs:—No. 67, Panther of Henry VI; No. 68, Queen Elizabeth II; No. 69, Type **12**.

Nos. 67/9 were printed together in small sheets of 6, containing two *se-tenant* strips of 3, with horizontal gutter margin between.

(Des and litho (25p. also embossed) Walsall)

1979 (14 Feb). *Bicentenary of Captain Cook's Voyages, 1768–79. T* **13** *and similar vert designs. Multicoloured. P* 11.
70 3p. Type **13** .. .. 1·10 75
71 6p. *Resolution* and map of South Georgia and S. Sandwich Isles showing route .. 90 55
72 11p. King Penguin (based on drawing by George Forster) .. .. .. 1·60 1·90
73 25p. Flaxman/Wedgwood medallion of Captain Cook.. .. .. .. 1·90 2·00

From 5 May 1980 South Georgia and South Sandwich Islands used stamps inscribed FALKLAND ISLANDS DEPENDENCIES.

G. FALKLAND ISLANDS DEPENDENCIES

For use in South Georgia and South Sandwich Islands.

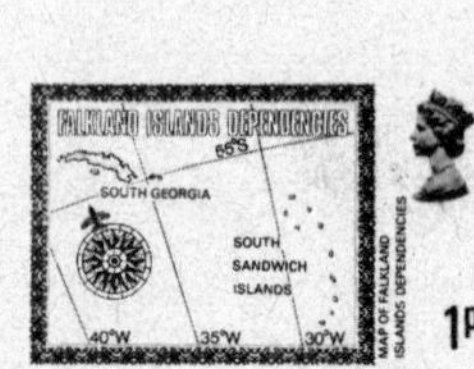

14 Map of Falkland Islands Dependencies

15 Magellanic Clubmoss

(Des and litho J.W.)

1980 (5 May)–**84**. *Horiz designs as T* **14**. *Multicoloured. W w* **14** *(sideways). P* 13½. *A. Without imprint date. B. With imprint date ("1984") at foot of design* (3.5.84).

		A		B	
74	1p. Type **14**	15	20	5	5
75	2p. Shag Rocks	15	25	5	5
76	3p. Bird and Willis Islands ..	15	25	5	8
77	4p. Gulbrandsen Lake ..	20	30	8	10
78	5p. King Edward Point ..	20	30	8	10
79	6p. Sir Ernest Shackleton's Memorial Cross, Hope Point	20	30	10	12
80	7p. Sir Ernest Shackleton's Grave, Grytviken	30	40	12	15
81	8p. Grytviken Church ..	30	40	15	20
82	9p. Coaling Hulk *Louise* at Grytviken	30	45	15	20
83	10p. Clerke Rocks	30	45	20	25
84	20p. Candlemas Island.. ..	90	1·25	35	40
85	25p. Twitcher Rock and Cook Island, Southern Thule ..	1·10	1·50	45	50
86	50p. R.R.S. *John Biscoe* in Cumberland Bay	1·40	2·00	90	95
87	£1 R.R.S. *Bransfield* in Cumberland Bay	2·00	2·75	†	
88	£3 H.M.S. *Endurance* in Cumberland Bay	5·00	6·50	†	
74/88	.. .. .. *Set of* 15	11·50	16·00		
74B/86B	.. .. *Set of* 13			2·50	2·75

(Des L. McCombie. Litho Rosenbaum Bros, Vienna)

1981 (5 Feb). *Plants. T* **15** *and similar vert designs. Multicoloured. W w* **14** *(inverted on 25p.). P* 14.
89 3p. Type **15** 25 25
90 6p. Alpine Cat's-tail 30 30
91 7p. Greater Burnet 30 30
92 11p. Antarctic Bedstraw 50 50
93 15p. Brown Rush 70 70
a. Light brown (Queen's head and territory inscr) omitted £1750
94 25p. Antarctic Hair Grass .. .. .. 1·25 1·25
89/94 .. .. *Set of* 6 3·00 3·00

16 Wedding Bouquet from Falkland Islands Dependencies

17 Introduced Reindeer during Calving, Spring

(Des J.W. Litho Format)

1981 (22 July). *Royal Wedding. T* **16** *and similar vert designs. Multicoloured. W w* **14**. *P* 14.
95 10p. Type **16** 55 55
96 13p. Prince Charles dressed for skiing .. 65 65
97 52p. Prince Charles and Lady Diana Spencer 1·25 1·25

(Des A. Theobald. Litho Format)

1982 (29 Jan). *Reindeer. T* **17** *and similar horiz designs. Multicoloured. W w* **14** *(sideways). P* 14.

98	5p. Type **17**	40	50
99	13p. Bull at rut, Autumn	60	70
100	25p. Reindeer and mountains, Winter	1·00	1·25
101	26p. Reindeer feeding on tussock grass, late Winter	1·00	1·25

18 Mite (*Gamasellus racovitzai*) **19** Lady Diana Spencer at Tidworth, Hampshire, July 1981

(Des I. Loe. Litho Questa)

1982 (16 Mar). *Insects. T* **18** *and similar vert designs. Multicoloured. W w* **14**. *P* 14.

102	5p. Type **18**	20	25
103	10p. Mite (*Alaskozetes antarcticus*)	30	35
104	13p. Ubiquitous Springtail (*Cryptopygus antarcticus*)	35	40
105	15p. Spider (*Notiomaso australis*)	40	45
106	25p. Beetle (*Hydromedion sparsutum*)	75	80
107	26p. Midge (*Parochlus steinenii*)	75	80
102/7	*Set of* 6	2·50	2·75

(Des C. Abbott. Litho Format)

1982 (7 Sept). *21st Birthday of Princess of Wales. T* **19** *and similar vert designs. Multicoloured. W w* **14**. *P* 13½ × 14.

108	5p. Falklands Islands Dependencies coat of arms	10	15
109	17p. Type **19**	30	35
	a. Perf 13½	22·00	22·00
110	37p. Bride and groom on steps of St Paul's	75	80
111	50p. Formal portrait	1·00	1·10

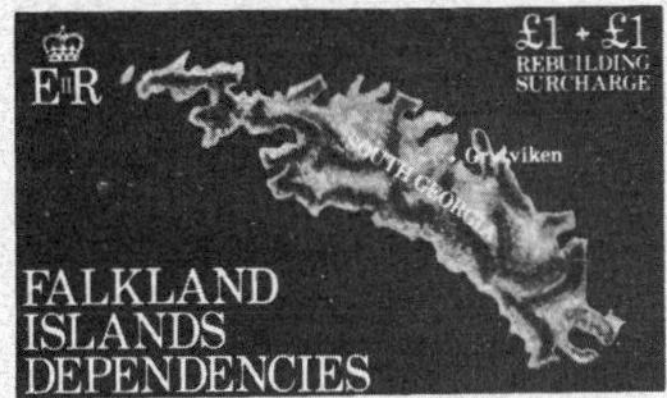

20 Map of South Georgia

(Des PAD Studio. Litho Format)

1982 (13 Sept). *Rebuilding Fund. W w* **14** *(sideways). P* 11.

112	**20**	£1 + £1 multicoloured	4·00	4·75

21 Westland "Whirlwind" **22** *Euphausia superba*

(Des Harrison. Litho Questa)

1983 (23 Dec). *Bicentenary of Manned Flight. T* **21** *and similar horiz designs. Multicoloured. W w* **14** *(sideways). P* 14.

113	5p. Type **21**	10	15
114	13p. Westland "Wasp"	30	40
115	17p. Saunders-Roe "Walrus"	35	45
116	50p. Auster	1·00	1·25

(Des N. Weaver. Litho Questa)

1984 (23 Mar). *Crustacea. T* **22** *and similar vert designs. Multicoloured. W w* **14**. *P* 14½ × 14.

117	5p. Type **22**	10	15
118	17p. *Glyptonotus antarcticus*	35	45
119	25p. *Epimeria monodon*	50	60
120	34p. *Serolis pagenstecheri*	70	80

NEW INFORMATION

The editor is always interested to correspond with people who have new information that will improve or correct the Catalogue.

Fiji

PRICES FOR STAMPS ON COVER TO 1945

Nos. 1/9	*from* × 6
Nos. 10/34	*from* × 5
Nos. 35/59	*from* × 8
Nos. 60/3	—
Nos. 64/9	*from* × 20
Nos. 70/5	*from* × 5
Nos. 76/103	*from* × 8
Nos. 104/14	*from* × 5
Nos. 115/24	*from* × 4
Nos. 125/37	*from* × 3
Nos. 138/241	*from* × 4
Nos. 242/5	*from* × 3
Nos. 246/8	*from* × 8
Nos. 249/66*b*	*from* × 2
No. 267	*from* × 8
Nos. D1/5*c*	*from* × 4
Nos. D6/10	*from* × 15
Nos. D11/18	*from* × 20

TIMES
FIJI 1 EXPRESS.
PENNY.

1

(Type-set and printed at the office of *The Fiji Times*, Levuka, Ovalau, Fiji, in sheets of twenty-four stamps arranged in four rows of six stamps of each value in the following order: 6d., 1s., 1d., 3d.)

1870 (1 Nov)–**71**. *Rouletted in the printing.* (a) *Quadrillé paper.*

1	**1**	1d. black/*rose*	£1700	£2000
2		3d. black/*rose*	£1000	£1600
3		6d. black/*rose*	£1500	£1900
4		1s. black/*rose*	£1300	£1700
		(b) *Laid bâtonné paper* (1871)		
5	**1**	1d. black/*rose*	£600	£650
6		3d. black/*rose*	£900	£1100
7		6d. black/*rose*	£650	£650
8		9d. black/*rose*	£900	£1100
9		1s. black/*rose*	£700	£700

The stamps of the last group were printed from the same plate as the first, but the values of the last three stamps in the bottom row of the sheet were altered to "9d." by inserting figures "9" in place of the figures "3".

There are no reprints of these stamps, but the 1d., 3d., 6d. and 1s. are known in the correct type on *yellow wove* paper and are believed to be proofs.

There are also three different sets of imitations made by the proprietors of *The Fiji Times* to meet the demands of collectors:—

The first was produced in 1876 on *white wove* or *vertically laid* paper, rouletted on dotted lines and arranged in sheets of 40 (5 rows of 8) comprising 1d., 3d., 6d., 9d. and 1s.; the horizontal frame lines are continuous and the vertical ones broken.

The second was produced later on *thick rosy mauve wove* paper, rouletted on dotted lines and arranged in sheets of 30 (5 rows of 6) comprising 1s., 9d., 6d., 3d. and 1d.; the vertical frame lines are continuous and the horizontal ones broken.

The third only came to light in the 1960s and is rare, only one complete sheet being known. The sheet arrangement is the same as Nos. 1/4, which suggests that this was the first imitation to be produced. It is on *off-white wove* paper, rouletted on closely dotted or solid lines, with vertical frame lines continuous and the horizontal ones broken, as in the originals. These differ from the proofs mentioned above in that the lettering is slightly larger and the figures also differ.

King Cakobau, June 1871–Oct 1874

2 **3** **(4)**

(Eng and electrotyped by A. L. Jackson. Typo Govt Printing Office, Sydney)

1871 (Nov). *Wove paper. Wmk* "FIJI POSTAGE" *in small sans-serif capitals across the middle row of stamps in the sheet. P* 12½.

10	**2**	1d. blue	70·00	£100
11		3d. pale yellow-green	£130	£225
12	**3**	6d. rose	£150	£225

The 3d. differs from T **2** in having a white circle containing square dots surrounding the centre.

All three values are known *imperf*, but were not issued in that condition.

See notes after No. 33b.

1872 (13 Jan). *Surch as T* **4**, *at Govt Ptg Office, Sydney.*

13	**2**	2 c. on 1d. pale blue	18·00	24·00
		a. Deep blue	19·00	24·00
14		6 c. on 3d. yellow-green	25·00	35·00
15	**3**	12 c. on 6d. carmine-rose	40·00	40·00

CROWN COLONY

Ceded to Great Britain, 10 October 1874

V.R. **(5)** V.R. **(6)** 2d. **(7)**

Varieties:—

V.R.✠ V.R.

(*Enlarged*)

Cross pattée stop Inverted "A"

Cross pattée stop after "R" (No. 26).
Round raised stop after "V" (No. 28).
Round raised stops after "V" and "R" (No. 29).
Inverted "A" for "V" (No. 30).
No stop after "R" (No. 13 on T **5**, No. 43 on T **6**).

(Optd at *Polynesian Gazette* Office, Levuka)

1874 (10 Oct). *Nos.* 13/15 *optd.* (a) *With T* **5**.

16	**2**	2 c. on 1d. blue	£275	85·00
		a. No stop after "R"	—	£850
		b. Cross pattée stop after "R"	—	£850
		c. Round raised stop after "V"	—	£850
		d. Round raised stops after "V" and "R"	—	£850
		e. Inverted "A" for "V"	—	£850
17		6 c. on 3d. green	£500	£300
		a. No stop after "R"		
		b. Cross pattée stop after "R"		
		c. Round raised stop after "V"		
		d. Round raised stops after "V" and "R"		
		e. Inverted "A" for "V"	£1500	
18	**3**	12 c. on 6d. rose	£250	85·00
		a. No stop after "R"	—	£850
		b. Cross pattée stop after "R"	—	£850
		c. Round raised stop after "V"	—	£850
		d. Round raised stops after "V" and "R"	—	£850
		e. Inverted "A" for "V"	—	£850
		f. Opt inverted	—	£2000
		(b) *With T* **6**		
19	**2**	2 c. on 1d. blue	£325	95·00
		a. No stop after "R"	£1000	£850
20		6 c. on 3d. green	£700	£500
		a. No stop after "R"	£1500	
21	**3**	12 c. on 6d. rose	£300	£130
		a. No stop after "R"	—	£850
		b. Opt inverted	£2000	

1875. *Stamps of* 1874 *surch in Levuka with T* **7**.

		(a) *In red* (May?)		
22	**2**	2d. on 6 c. on 3d. green (No. 17)	£125	60·00
		a. No stop after "R"	£900	£500
		b. Cross pattée stop after "R"	£900	£500
		c. Round raised stop after "V"	£900	£500
		d. Round raised stops after "V" and "R"	£900	£500
		e. Inverted "A" for "V"	£900	£500
		f. No stop after "2d"	£900	£500
23		2d. on 6 c. on 3d. green (No. 20)	£200	£120
		a. No stop after "R"	£900	£500
		b. Stop between "2" and "d"	£1000	£500
		(b) *In black* (30 Sept)		
24	**2**	2d. on 6 c. on 3d. green (No. 17)	£450	£200
		a. No stop after "R"	£1300	£700
		b. Cross pattée stop after "R"	£1300	£700
		c. Round raised stop after "V"	£1300	£700
		d. Round raised stops after "V" and "R"	£1300	£700
		e. Inverted "A" for "V"	£1300	£700
		f. No stop after "2d"	£1300	£700
25		2d. on 6 c. on 3d. green (No. 20)	£650	£300
		a. No stop after "R"	£1300	£700
		b. Stop between "2" and "d"	£1300	
		c. "V.R." double	—	£2000

1875 (20 Nov). *No.* 15 *surch in Levuka with T* **7** *and* "V.R." *at one operation.* (a) "V.R." *T* **5**.

26	**3**	2d. on 12 c. on 6d. rose	£450	£250
		aa. Round raised stop after "R"		
		a. Inverted "A" for "V"	£550	£425
		b. Do. and round raised stop after "V"	£600	£475
		c. As "a" and round raised stops after "R" and "V"	£550	£425
		d. Surch double	—	£1100
		(b) "V.R." *T* **6**		
27	**3**	2d. on 12 c. on 6d. rose	£450	£250
		a. Surch double	—	£1500

The position of No. 26aa is not known.

VR **(8)** Two Pence **(9)**

(Typo Govt Printing Office, Sydney, from plates of 1871)

1876–77. *On paper previously lithographed* "VR" *as T* **8**, *the 3d. surch with T* **9**. *P* 12½. (a) *Wove paper* (31.1.76).

28	**2**	1d. grey-blue	22·00	22·00
		a. Dull blue	22·00	22·00
		b. Doubly printed		
		c. Void corner		
		d. Imperf between (pair)		
29		2d. on 3d. pale green	26·00	26·00
		a. Deep green	26·00	26·00
30	**3**	6d. pale rose	45·00	40·00
		a. Dull rose	42·00	26·00
		b. Carmine-rose	42·00	26·00
		c. Doubly printed		
		(b) *Laid paper* (5.1.77)		
31	**2**	1d. blue	8·50	11·00
		a. Deep blue	10·00	11·00
		b. Void corner	70·00	40·00
		c. Imperf between (pair)	£850	

32 2 2d. on 3d. yellow-green .. .. .. 48·00 48·00
a. Deep yellow-green .. .. .. 48·00 48·00
b. Perf 10 .. .. £225
c. Imperf between (pair) £850
d. Perf 11 .. .. £275
33 3 6d. rose .. .. 26·00 26·00
a. Carmine-rose .. .. .. 26·00 26·00
b. Imperf between (pair) £850

The 3d. *green* is known without the surcharge T **9** on wove paper and also without the surcharge and the monogram. In this latter condition it can only be distinguished from No. 11 by its colour, which is a fuller, deeper yellow-green.

Stamps on both wove and laid paper *imperf* are from printer's trial or waste sheets and were not issued.

All values are known on laid paper without the monogram "VR" and the 3d. stamp also without the surcharge but these are also believed to be from printer's trial sheets and were never issued. Being on laid paper they are easily distinguishable from Nos. 10/12.

1877 (12 Oct). *Optd with T* **8** *and surch as T* **9**. *Laid paper. P* 12½.
34 2 4d. on 3d. mauve .. .. .. 40·00 30·00
a. Imperf between (pair) £850

10

11

A
B
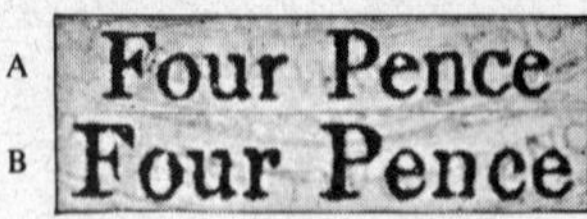

Type A: Length 12½ mm
Type B: Length 14 mm
Note also the different shape of the two "e"s.

(Typo from new plates made from original dies of 1871 with "CR" altered to "VR" at Govt Printing Office, Sydney. 2d. and 4d. made from old 3d. die.)

1878–1900. *Surcharges as T* **9** *or as Types* A *or* B *for 4d. value. Wove paper with paper-maker's name* "T. H. SAUNDERS" *or* "SANDERSON" *in double-lined capitals extending over seven stamps in each full sheet. (a) P* 12½ *(1878–80).*
35 10 1d. pale ultramarine .. .. .. 4·50 4·50
a. Ultramarine .. .. .. 6·50 6·50
36 2d. on 3d. green .. .. .. 4·00 5·00
37 2d. yellow-green .. .. .. 8·50 7·00
a. Blue-green .. .. .. 8·50 7·00
b. Error. Ultramarine £15000
38 11 6d. rose .. .. 48·00 12·00

(b) P 10 (1881–90)
39 10 1d. dull blue .. .. .. 15·00 4·50
a. Ultramarine .. .. .. 5·50 3·75
b. Cambridge blue (12.7.83) .. 10·00 3·75
40 2d. yellow-green .. .. .. 4·25 2·25
a. Blue-green .. .. .. 4·25 3·00
41 4d. on 1d. mauve .. .. .. 8·50 7·50
42 4d. on 2d. pale mauve (A) .. .. 22·00 7·50
a. Dull purple .. .. .. 22·00 7·50
43 4d. on 2d. dull purple (B) .. .. — £100
44 4d. mauve .. .. 26·00
a. Deep purple .. .. .. 26·00 28·00
45 11 6d. pale rose .. .. .. 32·00 9·00
a. Bright rose .. .. .. 12·00 12·00

(c) P 10 × 12½ (1882)
46 10 1d. ultramarine .. .. .. 26·00 17·00
47 2d. green .. .. 90·00 22·00
48 11 6d. rose .. .. £200 30·00

(d) P 12½ × 10 (1890)
49 10 1d. ultramarine .. .. ..

(e) P 12 × 10 *or* 10 × 12 (1885)
50 10 1d. ultramarine .. .. .. 26·00 6·50
a. Dull blue .. .. ..
51 2d. yellow-green .. .. .. 26·00 6·50
52 11 6d. rose .. ..

(f) P 11 × 10 (1893)
53 10 1d. ultramarine .. .. .. 2·75 3·00
54 4d. pale mauve .. .. .. 6·00 5·50
55 11 6d. pale rose .. .. .. 6·50 5·50
a. Rose .. .. 8·50 5·50

(g) P 11 (1897–99)
56 10 4d. mauve .. .. 7·00 7·00
57 11 6d. dull rose .. .. .. 22·00 22·00
a. Printed both sides (12.99) .. £350 £300
b. Bright rose .. .. .. 25·00 13·00

(h) P 11 × *nearly* 12 (1900)*
58 10 4d. deep purple .. .. .. 14·00
a. *Bright purple* .. .. .. 6·00 6·00
59 11 6d. rose .. .. 26·00
a. Bright rose .. .. .. 6·00 4·50

(i) Imperf (1882–90)
60 10 1d. ultramarine .. .. ..
61 2d. yellow-green .. .. ..
62 4d. on 2d. pale mauve .. ..
63 11 6d. rose .. ..

*Under this heading are included all the stamps formerly catalogued as *perfs* 12 × 11; 11 × 12; 11 × 11½; or 11½ × 11. They are all compounds of *perf* 11 with that of the machine gauging *nearly* 12, which has sometimes been measured as 11½ and sometimes as 12.

12

13

(Typo Govt Printing Office, Sydney)

1881–99. *Paper-maker's name wmkd as previous issue.*

(a) P 10 (19.10.81)
64 12 1s. pale brown .. .. .. 25·00 11·00
a. Deep brown .. .. .. 25·00 13·00

(b) P 11 × 10 (1894)
65 12 1s. pale brown .. .. .. 35·00 25·00

(c) P 11 (1897)
66 12 1s. pale brown .. .. .. 27·00 14·00

(d) P 11 × *nearly* 12 (5.99)
67 12 1s. pale brown .. .. .. 23·00 8·50
a. Brown .. .. 23·00 8·50
b. Deep brown .. .. .. 27·00 32·00

(e) P nearly 12 × 11 (3.97)
68 12 1s. brown .. .. 35·00 20·00

Dates given of earliest known use.
Forgeries exist.

(Centre typo, frame litho Govt Printing Office, Sydney)

1882 (23 May). *Toned paper wmkd with paper-maker's name* "Cowan" *in old English outline type once in each sheet. P* 10.
69 13 5s. dull red and black .. .. 60·00 60·00

In July 1900, an electrotyped plate of a 5s. stamp was made and stamps were printed from it with pale orange-red centre and grey-black frame; these are known *perf* 10, *perf nearly* 12, and *imperf.* These stamps were sold as remainders with a special obliteration dated "15 Dec., 00," but were not issued for postal use. The design differs in many particulars from the issued stamp.

2½d. (14) 2½d. (15)

T **14**. Fraction bar 1 mm from "2".
T **15**. Fraction bar 2 mm from "2".

(Stamps typo in Sydney and surch at Govt Printing Office, Suva)

1891 (1 Jan). *T* **10** *surch. P* 10.
70 14 2½d. on 2d. green .. .. .. 38·00 38·00
71 15 2½d. on 2d. green £110 £100

½d. (16) 5d (17)

FIVE PENCE (18) 2 mm spacing FIVE PENCE (19) 3 mm spacing

1892. *P* 10. *(a) Surch on T* **10**.
72 16 ½d. on 1d. dull blue (1.3) .. .. 40·00 40·00
a. Ultramarine .. .. .. 25·00 25·00
73 17 5d. on 4d. deep purple (25.7) .. 45·00 45·00
a. Dull purple .. .. .. 45·00 45·00

(b) Surch on T **11**
74 18 5d. on 6d. brownish rose (30.11) .. 45·00 45·00
a. Bright rose .. .. .. 38·00 38·00
b. Perf 10 × 12½ .. .. ..
75 19 5d. on 6d. rose (31.12) .. .. 55·00
a. Deep rose .. .. .. 42·00
b. Brownish rose .. .. .. 38·00

20

21 Native Canoe

22

(Typo in Sydney)

1891–1902. *Wmk in sheet, either* "SANDERSON" *or* "NEW SOUTH WALES GOVERNMENT" *in outline capitals.*

(a) P 10 (1891–93)
76 20 ½d. slate-grey .. .. .. 3·50 3·00
77 21 1d. black .. .. 4·00 3·00
78 2d. pale green .. .. .. 50·00 8·00
79 22 2½d. chocolate .. .. .. 20·00 9·50
80 21 5d. ultramarine .. .. .. 27·00 9·50

(b) P 11 × 10 (1893–97)
81 20 ½d. slate-grey .. .. .. 4·50 10·00
82 21 1d. black .. .. 4·75 2·50
83 2d. green .. .. 4·75 2·50
84 22 2½d. chocolate .. .. .. 16·00 8·50
a. Brown .. .. 6·50 5·50
b. Yellowish brown .. ..
85 21 5d. ultramarine .. .. .. 7·00 7·50

(c) P 11 (1893–98)
86 20 ½d. slate-grey .. .. .. 2·75 4·00
a. Greenish slate .. .. .. 3·50 5·00
87 21 1d. black .. .. 2·50 2·50
88 21 1d. pale mauve .. .. .. 2·75 1·75
a. Rosy mauve .. .. .. 2·75 1·75
89 2d. dull green .. .. .. 4·25 2·00
a. Emerald-green .. .. .. 4·25 2·00
90 22 2½d. brown .. .. 7·50 6·00
a. Yellowish brown .. .. 10·00 10·00
91 21 5d. ultramarine .. .. ..

(d) P 10 × 12 *or* 12 × 10 (1894–98)
92 20 ½d. pale grey .. .. ..
93 21 1d. black .. .. 5·00 4·25
94 2d. dull green .. .. .. — £200

(e) Perf nearly 12 (1895–97)
95 20 ½d. greenish slate .. .. .. 3·25 4·00
a. Grey .. .. 11·00
96 21 1d. black .. .. £130 7·50
97 1d. rosy mauve .. .. .. 4·50 3·50
98 2d. dull green .. .. .. 50·00 17·00

(f) P 11 *and nearly* 12, *compound* (1897–1902)
99 20 ½d. greenish slate .. .. .. 1·75 2·25
100 21 1d. black £130
101 1d. rosy mauve .. .. .. 3·00 90
a. Pale rosy mauve .. .. .. 3·00 2·00
102 2d. dull green .. .. .. 13·00 4·00
103 22 2½d. brown .. .. 11·00 11·00
a. Yellow-brown .. .. .. 6·50 6·50

The 2½d. brown is known *doubly printed*, but only occurs in the remainders and with the special obliteration. It was never issued for postal use.

23

24

(Typo D.L.R.)

1903 (1 Feb). *Wmk Crown CA. P* 14.
104 23 ½d. green and pale green .. .. 65 1·25
105 1d. dull purple and black/*red* .. 4·00 1·50
106 24 2d. dull purple and orange .. 1·00 2·00
107 23 2½d. dull purple and blue/*blue* .. 14·00 20·00
108 3d. dull purple and purple .. 3·50 5·50
109 24 4d. dull purple and black .. 3·50 5·00
110 23 5d. dull purple and green .. 3·50 7·50
111 24 6d. dull purple and carmine .. 5·50 8·50
112 23 1s. green and carmine .. .. 13·00 20·00
113 24 5s. green and black .. .. 30·00 45·00
114 23 £1 grey-black and ultramarine .. £500 £550
104/14 .. .. *Set of* 11 £550 £600
104/14 Optd "Specimen" .. .. *Set of* 11 £600

1904–9. *Wmk Mult Crown CA. P* 14.
115 23 ½d. green and pale green, **O** .. 2·25 1·50
116 1d. purple and black/*red*, **O** .. 2·75 35
117 1s. green and carmine, **C** (1909) .. 29·00 35·00

1906–12. *Colours changed. Wmk Mult Crown CA. P* 14.
118 23 ½d. green, **O** (1908) .. .. 1·25 1·60
119 1d. red, **O** (1906) .. .. .. 1·40 50
120 2½d. bright blue, **O** (1910) .. .. 2·50 5·50
121 24 6d. dull purple, **C** (1910) .. .. 5·00 9·00
122 23 1s. black/*green*, **C** (1911) .. .. 8·00 13·00
123 24 5s. green and red/*yellow*, **C** (1911) .. 38·00 48·00
124 23 £1 purple and black/*red*, **C** (1912) .. £325 £350
118/124 .. .. *Set of* 7 £350 £375
119/24 Optd "Specimen" .. .. *Set of* 6 £650

25

26

WAR STAMP
(27)

(Typo D.L.R.)

1912 (Oct)–**23**. *Ordinary paper (¼d. to 4d.) or chalk-surfaced paper (others). Wmk Mult Crown CA. P* 14.
125 26 ¼d. brown (1916) 30 60
a. Deep brown 60 60
126 25 ½d. green 60 50
a. Yellow-green (1915) .. .. 4·00 4·00
b. Blue-green (1917) .. .. 1·00 1·00
127 1d. carmine .. .. 1·90 20
a. Bright scarlet (2.16) .. .. 1·50 90
b. Deep rose (1919) .. .. 3·00 60
128 26 2d. greyish slate (5.14) .. .. 1·25 40
a. Wmk sideways .. ..
129 25 2½d. bright blue (5.14) .. .. 4·00 5·50
130 3d. purple/*yellow* (5.14) .. .. 3·25 4·50
a. Wmk sideways £650
b. On lemon (1915) .. .. .. 4·50 7·00
c. On pale yellow (Die I) .. .. 3·00 6·50
d. On pale yellow (Die II) (1923) .. 5·00 7·00
131 26 4d. black and red/*yellow* (5.14) .. 6·00 9·50
a. On lemon .. .. 6·00 11·00
b. On orange-buff (1.21) .. .. 27·00 38·00
c. On pale yellow (Die I) (1921) .. 10·00 14·00
d. On pale yellow (Die II) (1923) (Optd S. £25) .. .. .. 7·00 15·00
132 25 5d. dull purple and olive-green (5.14) 8·00 9·00
133 26 6d. dull and bright purple (5.14) .. 3·50 5·50
134 25 1s. black/*green* (10.13) .. .. 5·50 12·00
a. White back (4.14) .. .. .. 4·50 8·00
b. On blue-green, olive back (1917) .. 8·00 10·00
c. On emerald back (Die I) (1921) .. 5·50 11·00
d. On emerald back (Die II) (1923) .. 6·00 11·00
135 26 2s. 6d. black and red/*blue* (29.1.16) .. 20·00 27·00
136 5s. green and red/*yellow* .. .. 32·00 42·00
137 25 £1 purple and black/*red* (Die I) (5.14) £325 £375
a. Die II £325 £375
125/37a .. .. *Set of* 13 £350 £425
125/37 Optd "Specimen" .. .. *Set of* 13 £650

1915 (Dec)–**19.** *Optd locally with T* **27**.
138 **25** ½d. blue-green . . . . 25 1·00
a. *Yellow-green* . . . . 30 1·50
b. Opt inverted £550
c. Opt double . . . .
139 1d. carmine . . . . 12·00 20·00
a. *Bright scarlet* . . . . 80 1·75
b. Do. Strip of 12, one without opt . . £7500
c. Opt inverted £550
d. *Deep rose* (1919) . . . . 1·50 1·75
138, 139 H/S "Specimen" . . *Set of* 2 £100

No. 139b occurred on one pane of 120 only, the overprint being so misplaced that all the stamps of the last vertical row escaped it entirely.

Nos. 140/227 no longer used.

1922–27. *Wmk Mult Script CA. P* 14.
228 **26** ¼d. deep brown, **O** (1923) . . 1·50 6·00
229 **25** ½d. green, **O** (1923) . . 50 1·60
230 1d. carmine-red, **O** . . 2·25 2·75
231 1d. violet, **O** (1927) . . 90 20
232 **26** 1½d. scarlet, **O** (1927) . . 3·75 3·75
233 2d. grey, **O** . . 1·00 15
234 **25** 3d. bright blue, **O** (1924) . . 1·40 2·50
235 **26** 4d. black and red/*lemon*, **O** (1924) . . 4·50 6·50
a. *On orange-buff* (1927) . . 6·00 8·00
236 **25** 5d. dull purple and sage-green, **O** . . 1·75 2·75
237 **26** 6d. dull and bright purple, **O** . . 2·00 2·25
238 **25** 1s. black/*emerald*, **C** (1924) . . 3·50 8·00
239 **26** 2s. purple and blue/*blue*, **C** (1927) . . 26·00 45·00
240 2s. 6d. black and red/*blue*, **C** (1925) . . 17·00 35·00
241 5s. green and red/*yellow*, **C** (1926) . . 48·00 60·00
228/241 . . *Set of* 14 £100 £160
228/41 Optd "Specimen" . . *Set of* 14 £450

The 2d. imperforate with watermark Type **10** of Ireland came from a trial printing and was not issued.

1935 (6 May). *Silver Jubilee. As Nos.* 91/4 *of Antigua.*
242 1½d. deep blue and carmine . . 45 1·75
a. *Deep blue and aniline red* . . 3·50 8·00
243 2d. ultramarine and grey . . 80 1·00
e. Horiz line from turret . . 8·00
244 3d. brown and deep blue . . 2·75 4·50
245 1s. slate and purple . . 6·00 8·50
242/5 Perf "Specimen" . . *Set of* 4 70·00

For illustration of plate variety see Omnibus section following Zululand.

1937 (12 May). *Coronation. As Nos.* 13/15 *of Aden, but ptd by B.W. P* 11 × 11½.
246 1d. purple . . 70 70
247 2d. grey-black . . 80 70
248 3d. Prussian blue . . 80 70
246/8 Perf "Specimen" . . *Set of* 3 55·00

28 Native sailing Canoe

29 Native Village

30 Native Canoe

31 Map of Fiji Islands

Two Dies of Type **30**:

Die I
Empty Canoe

Die II
Native in Canoe

Two Dies of Type **31**:

Die I
Without "180°"

Die II
With "180°"

(Des V. E. Ousey (½d., 1s., 2s. 6d.), C. D. Lovejoy (1d., 1½d., 5d.), I. Stinson (3d., 5s.) and A. V. Guy (2d. (Nos. 253/4), 2½d., 6d., 2s.). Recess De La Rue (½d., 1½d., 2d., (Nos. 253/5a), 2½d., 6d., 8d., 1s. 5d., 1s. 6d.), Waterlow (others))

1938 (5 Apr)–**1955.** *T* **28/31** *and similar designs. Wmk Mult Script CA. Various perfs.*
249 **28** ½d. green (*p* 13½) . . 35 25
a. Perf 14 (1941) . . 6·50 4·00
b. Perf 12 (1948) . . 35 40
250 **29** 1d. brown and blue (*p* 12½) . . 35 15
251 **30** 1½d. carmine (Die I) (*p* 13½) . . 7·50 1·25
252 1½d. carmine (Die II) (*p* 13½) (1.10.40) . . 1·75 1·00
a. *Deep carmine* (10.42) . . 4·50 3·75
b. Perf 14 (1942) . . 9·50 22·00
c. Perf 12 (21.7.49) . . 1·10 1·50
253 **31** 2d. brown and green (Die I) (*p* 13½) . . 12·00 45

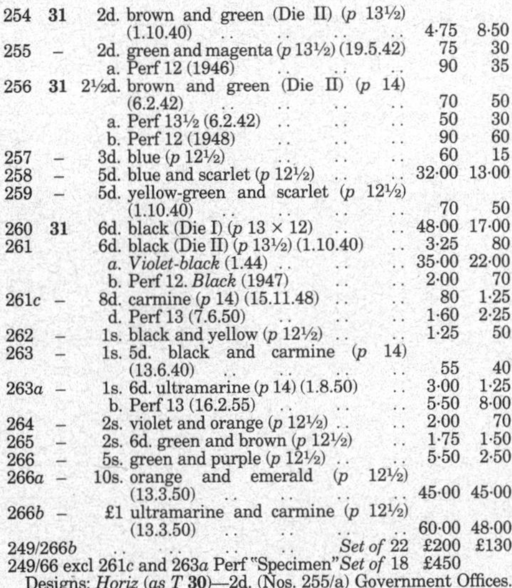

254 **31** 2d. brown and green (Die II) (*p* 13½) (1.10.40) . . 4·75 8·50
255 – 2d. green and magenta (*p* 13½) (19.5.42) 75 30
a. Perf 12 (1946) . . 90 35
256 **31** 2½d. brown and green (Die II) (*p* 14) (6.2.42) . . 70 50
a. Perf 13½ (6.2.42) . . 50 30
b. Perf 12 (1948) . . 90 60
257 – 3d. blue (*p* 12½) . . 60 15
258 – 5d. blue and scarlet (*p* 12½) . . 32·00 13·00
259 – 5d. yellow-green and scarlet (*p* 12½) (1.10.40) . . 70 50
260 **31** 6d. black (Die I) (*p* 13 × 12) . . 48·00 17·00
261 6d. black (Die II) (*p* 13½) (1.10.40) . . 3·25 80
a. *Violet-black* (1.44) . . 35·00 22·00
b. Perf 12. *Black* (1947) . . 2·00 70
261*c* – 8d. carmine (*p* 14) (15.11.48) . . 80 1·25
d. Perf 13 (7.6.50) . . 1·60 2·25
262 – 1s. black and yellow (*p* 12½) . . 1·25 50
263 – 1s. 5d. black and carmine (*p* 14) (13.6.40) . . 55 40
263*a* – 1s. 6d. ultramarine (*p* 14) (1.8.50) . . 3·00 1·25
b. Perf 13 (16.2.55) . . 5·50 8·00
264 – 2s. violet and orange (*p* 12½) . . 2·00 70
265 – 2s. 6d. green and brown (*p* 12½) . . 1·75 1·50
266 – 5s. green and purple (*p* 12½) . . 5·50 2·50
266*a* – 10s. orange and emerald (*p* 12½) (13.3.50) . . 45·00 45·00
266*b* – £1 ultramarine and carmine (*p* 12½) (13.3.50) . . 60·00 48·00
249/266*b* . . *Set of* 22 £200 £130
249/66 excl 261*c* and 263*a* Perf "Specimen" *Set of* 18 £450

Designs: *Horiz* (*as T* **30**)—2d. (Nos. 255/a) Government Offices. (*As T* **29**)—3d. Canoe and arms of Fiji; 8d., 1s. 5d., 1s. 6d. Arms of Fiji; 2s. Suva Harbour; 2s. 6d. River scene; 5s. Chief's hut. *Vert* (*as T* **29**)—5d. Sugar cane; 1s. Spearing fish by torchlight; 10s. Paw-paw Tree; £1 Police bugler.

2½d.

(**42**)

1941 (10 Feb). *No.* 254 *surch with T* **42**.
267 **31** 2½d. on 2d. brown and green . . 25 12

1946 (17 Aug). *Victory. As Nos.* 28/9 *of Aden.*
268 2½d. green . . 25 15
a. Printed double, one albino . . £175
269 3d. blue . . 30 15
268/9 Perf "Specimen" . . *Set of* 2 60·00

1948 (17 Dec). *Royal Silver Wedding. As Nos.* 30/1 *of Aden.*
270 2½d. green . . 50 20
271 5s. violet-blue . . 18·00 15·00

1949 (10 Oct). *75th Anniv of U.P.U. As Nos.* 114/17 *of Antigua.*
272 2d. bright reddish purple . . 55 40
273 3d. deep blue . . 1·25 90
274 8d. carmine-red . . 1·40 1·50
275 1s. 6d. blue . . 2·75 1·75

43 Children Bathing

44 Rugby Football

(Recess B.W.)

1951 (17 Sept). *Health Stamps. Wmk Mult Script CA. P* 13½.
276 **43** 1d. + 1d. brown . . 15 35
277 **44** 2d. + 1d. green . . 20 35

1953 (2 June). *Coronation. As No.* 47 *of Aden.*
278 2½d. black and green . . 70 70

45 Arms of Fiji

(Recess D.L.R.)

1953 (16 Dec). *Royal Visit. Wmk Mult Script CA. P* 13.
279 **45** 8d. deep carmine-red . . 25 15

46 Queen Elizabeth II (after Annigoni)

47 Government Offices

48 Loading Copra

49 Sugar Cane Train

50 Preparing Bananas for Export

51 Gold Industry

(Des V. E. Ousey (½d., 1s., 2s. 6d.), A. V. Guy (6d.). Recess D.L.R. (½d., 2d., 6d., 8d.), Waterlow (1s., 2s. 6d., 10s., £1) B.W. (others))

1954 (1 Feb)–**56.** *T* **46/51** *and similar designs previously used for King George VI issue (but with portrait of Queen Elizabeth II as in T* **47**). *Wmk Mult Script CA. P* 12 (2*d.*) 13 (8*d.*), 12½ (1*s.*, 2*s.*, 6*d.*, 10*s.*, £1), 11½ × 11 (3*d.*, 1*s.* 6*d.*, 2*s.*, 5*s.*) *or* 11½ (½*d.*, 1*d.*, 1½*d.*, 2½*d.*).
280 – ½d. myrtle-green (1.7.54) . . 8 12
281 **46** 1d. turquoise-blue (1.6.56) . . 15 5
282 1½d. sepia (1.10.56) . . 25 10
283 **47** 2d. green and magenta . . 1·00 30
284 **46** 2½d. blue-violet (1.10.56) . . 80 10
285 **48** 3d. brown and reddish violet (*shades*) (1.10.56) . . 70 10
287 – 6d. black (1.7.54) . . 1·00 12
288 – 8d. deep carmine-red (*shades*) (1.7.54) . . 1·25 90
289 – 1s. black and yellow . . 1·00 10
290 **49** 1s. 6d. blue and myrtle-green (1.10.56) 8·00 1·40
291 **50** 2s. black and carmine (1.10.56) . . 6·50 30
292 – 2s. 6d. bluish green and brown (*shades*) 2·25 20
293 **51** 5s. ochre and blue (1.10.56) . . 22·00 1·50
294 – 10s. orange and emerald (1.7.54) . . 19·00 30·00
295 – £1 ultramarine and carmine (1.7.54) 48·00 17·00
280/95 . . *Set of* 15 £100 48·00

Designs: *Vert* (22½ × 36 *mm*)—½d. Fijians sailing canoe. (25 × 31 *mm*)—1s. Spearing fish by torchlight; 10s. Paw-paw tree; £1 Police bugler. *Horiz* (36 × 22½ *mm*)—6d. Map of Fiji. (31 × 25 *mm*)—8d. Arms of Fiji; 2s. 6d. River scene.

52 River Scene

53 Cross of Lorraine

(Recess B.W.)

1954 (1 Apr). *Health Stamps. Wmk Mult Script CA. P* 11 × 11½.
296 **52** 1½d. + ½d. bistre-brown and green . . 15 15
297 **53** 2½d. + ½d. orange and black . . 15 10

54 Queen Elizabeth II (after Annigoni)

55 Fijian beating Lali

56 Hibiscus

60 Red Shining Parrot

(Des M. Goaman: Photo Harrison (8d., 4s.). Recess. B.W. (others))

1959–63. *T* **54/6**, **60** *and similar designs. Wmk Mult Script CA. P* 11½ (*T* **46** *and* **54**), 11½ × 11 (6*d.*, 10*d.*, 1*s.*, 2*s.* 6*d.*, 10*s.*, £1), 14½ × 14 (8*d.*) *or* 14 × 14½ (4*s*).
298 **46** ½d. emerald-green (14.11.61) . . 15 30
299 **54** 1d. deep ultramarine (3.12.62) . . 90 60
300 1½d. sepia (3.12.62) . . 90 45
301 **46** 2d. rose-red (14.11.61) . . 60 45
302 2½d. orange-brown (3.12.62) . . 1·50 1·25
303 **55** 6d. carmine and black (14.11.61) . . 1·00 10
304 **56** 8d. scarlet, yellow, green & blk (1.8.61) 70 65
305 – 10d. brown and carmine (1.4.63) . . 3·00 2·50
306 – 1s. light blue and blue (14.11.61) . . 1·75 10
307 – 2s. 6d. black and purple (14.11.61) . . 7·50 70
308 **60** 4s. red, green, blue & slate-grn (13.7.59) 3·75 7·50
309 – 10s. emerald and deep sepia (14.11.61) . . 10·00 12·00
310 – £1 black and orange (14.11.61) . . 35·00 17·00
298/310 . . *Set of* 13 60·00 38·00

Designs: *Horiz* (*as T* **55**)—10d. Yaqona ceremony; 1s. Location map; 2s. 6d. Nadi Airport; 10s. Cutting sugar-cane; £1 Arms of Fiji.
Nos. 299 and 311 have turtles either side of "Fiji" instead of shells.

63 Queen Elizabeth II

64 International Dateline

65 White Orchid

66 Orange Dove

(Des M. Goaman. Photo Harrison (3d., 9d. 1s. 6d., 2s., 4s., 5s.). Recess B.W. (others))

1962 (3 Dec)–**66**. W w **12** (*upright*). *P* 11½ (*1d., 2d.*), 12½ (*3d.*), 11½ × 11 (*6d., 10d., 2s. 6d., 10s., £1*), 14½ × 14 (*9d., 2s.*) *or* 14 × 14½ (*1s. 6d., 4s., 5s.*).

311 **54** 1d. deep ultramarine (14.1.64) 70 50
312 **46** 2d. rose-red (3.8.65) 45 40
313 **63** 3d. multicoloured 25 8
314 **55** 6d. carmine and black (9.6.64) 95 15
315 **56** 9d. scarlet, yellow, green & ultram (1.4.63) .. .. 1·00 65
316 – 10d. brown and carmine (14.1.64) .. 90 40
317 – 1s. light blue and blue (24.1.66*) .. 2·25 30
318 **64** 1s. 6d. red, yellow, gold, black and blue 3·50 1·50
319 **65** 2s. yellow-green, green & copper (*shades*) .. .. 6·00 1·75
320 – 2s. 6d. black and purple (*shades*) (3.8.65) 2·75 80
321 **60** 4s. red, yellow-green, bl & grn (1.4.64) 3·50 6·00
322 4s. red, green, blue & slate-grn (1.3.66) 5·50 8·00
323 **66** 5s. red, yellow and grey .. .. 10·00 85
324 – 10s. emerald and deep sepia (14.1.64) .. 14·00 11·00
325 – £1 black and orange (9.6.64) .. .. 23·00 18·00
311/25 .. .. *Set of* 15 65·00 45·00

Designs: *Horiz* (*as T* **55**)—10d. Yaqona Ceremony; 1s. Location map; 2s. 6d. Nadi Airport; 10s. Cutting sugar-cane; £1 Arms of Fiji.
*This is the earliest known used date in Fiji and it was not released by the Crown Agents until 1 November.
See also No. 359.

ROYAL VISIT
1963
(67)

ROYAL VISIT 1963
(68)

1963 (1 Feb). *Royal Visit. Nos.* 313 *and* 306 *optd with T* **67**/**8**.
326 **67** 3d. multicoloured 20 10
327 **68** 1s. light blue and blue 40 20

1963 (4 June). *Freedom from Hunger. As No.* 76 *of Aden.*
328 2s. ultramarine .. .. 9·00 3·50

69 Running

(**73** Cable-laying ship, *Retriever*.)

(Des M. Goaman. Photo Harrison)

1963 (6 Aug). *First South Pacific Games, Suva. T* **69** *and similar designs.* W w **12**. *P* 14½.
329 3d. red-brown, yellow and black 30 10
330 9d. red-brown, violet and black 90 60
331 1s. red-brown, green and black 90 35
332 2s. 6d. red-brown, light blue and black .. 3·00 1·40

Designs: *Vert*—9d. Throwing the discus; 1s. Hockey. *Horiz*—2s. 6d. High-jumping.

1963 (2 Sept). *Red Cross Centenary. As Nos.* 147/8 *of Antigua.*
333 2d. red and black 70 25
334 2s. red and blue .. .. 6·00 2·50

1963 (3 Dec). *Opening of COMPAC (Trans-Pacific Telephone Cable). No.* 317 *optd with T* **73** *by B.W.*
335 1s. light blue and blue 75 30

74 Jamborette Emblem

75 Scouts of Three Races

(Des V. Whiteley assisted by Norman L. Joe, Asst. D.C., Fiji Scouts for Jamboree emblem. Photo Harrison)

1964 (4 Aug). *50th Anniv of Fijian Scout Movement.* W w **12**. *P* 12½;
336 **74** 3d. red, gold, ultramarine and deep green 20 10
337 **75** 1s. violet and yellow-brown 40 20

76 Flying-boat *Aotearoa*

78 *Aotearoa* and Map

(Des V. Whiteley. Photo Harrison)

1964 (24 Oct). *25th Anniv of First Fiji-Tonga Airmail Service. T* **76**, **78** *and similar design.* W w **12**. *P* 14½ × 14 (*1s.*) *or* 12½ (*others*).
338 3d. black and vermilion 20 10
339 6d. vermilion and bright blue 40 20
340 1s. black and turquoise-blue 75 30

Design: *Vert* (*as T* **76**)—6d. Fiji Airways "Heron".

1965 (17 May). *I.T.U. Centenary. As Nos.* 166/7 *of Antigua.*
341 3d. blue and rose-carmine 75 12
342 2s. orange-yellow and bistre .. .. 3·00 80

1965 (25 Oct). *International Co-operation Year. As Nos.* 168/9 *of Antigua.*
343 2d. reddish purple and turquoise-green .. 65 20
344 2s. 6d. deep bluish green and lavender .. 2·25 70

1966 (24 Jan). *Churchill Commemoration. As Nos.* 170/3 *of Antigua.*
345 3d. new blue 80 15
346 9d. deep green .. .. 1·40 1·10
347 1s. brown .. .. 1·25 35
348 2s. 6d. bluish violet .. .. .. 3·00 2·50

1966 (1 July). *World Cup Football Championships. As Nos.* 176/7 *of Antigua.*
349 2d. violet, yellow-green, lake & yellow-brn .. 35 10
350 2s. chocolate, blue-green, lake & yellow-brn 1·50 65

79 H.M.S. *Pandora* approaching Split Island, Rotuma

(Des V. Whiteley. Photo Enschedé)

1966 (29 Aug). *175th Anniv of Discovery of Rotuma. T* **79** *and similar horiz designs. Multicoloured.* W w **12** (*sideways*). *P* 14 × 13.
351 3d. Type **79** 30 5
352 10d. Rotuma Chiefs 40 20
353 1s. 6d. Rotumans welcoming H.M.S. *Pandora* 90 30

1966 (20 Sept). *Inauguration of W.H.O. Headquarters, Geneva. As Nos.* 178/9 *of Antigua.*
354 6d. black, yellow-green and light blue .. 1·00 30
355 2s. 6d. black, light purple and yellow-brown 4·50 2·50

LEGISLATIVE ASSEMBLY

82 Running

(Des V. Whiteley. Photo Harrison)

1966 (5 Dec*). *2nd South Pacific Games, Nouméa. T* **82** *and similar designs.* W w **12** (*sideways on 9d.*). *P* 14½ × 14 (*9d.*) *or* 14 × 14½ (*others*).
356 3d. black, chestnut and yellow-olive .. 10 10
357 9d. black, chestnut and greenish blue .. 20 20
358 1s. multicoloured 20 15

Designs: *Vert*—9d. Putting the shot. *Horiz*—1s. Diving.
*These were not released in London until 8.12.66.

1967 (16 Feb). *As No.* 321 *but wmk* w **12** *sideways.*
359 **60** 4s. red, yellow-green, blue and green .. 3·75 3·75

85 Military Forces Band

(Des G. Vasarhelyi. Photo Enschedé)

1967 (20 Oct). *International Tourist Year. T* **85** *and similar horiz designs. Multicoloured.* W w **12** (*sideways*). *P* 14 × 13.
360 3d. Type **85** 20 10
361 9d. Reef diving 35 20
362 1s. Beqa fire walkers 35 15
363 2s. Cruise liner at Suva 90 40

89 Bligh (bust), H.M.S. *Providence* and Chart

91 Bligh's Tomb

90 "*Bounty*'s longboat being chased in Fiji waters"

(Des V. Whiteley. Photo Harrison)

1967 (11 Dec). *150th Death Anniv of Admiral Bligh.* W w **12** (*sideways on 1s.*). *P* 12½ × 13 (*1s.*) *or* 15 × 14 (*others*).
364 **89** 4d. multicoloured 20 10
365 **90** 1s. multicoloured 60 20
366 **91** 2s. 6d. multicoloured 75 35

92 Simmonds "Spartan" Seaplane

(Des V. Whiteley. Photo Harrison)

1968 (5 June). *40th Anniv of Kingsford Smith's Pacific Flight via Fiji. T* **92** *and similar horiz designs.* W w **12**. *P* 14 × 14½.
367 2d. black and green 20 15
368 6d. greenish blue, black and lake 30 15
369 1s. deep violet and turquoise-green 40 15
370 2s. orange-brown and blue 70 45

Designs—6d. H.S. "748" and airline insignias; 1s. *Southern Cross* and crew; 2s. Lockheed "Altair" monoplane.

96 Bure Huts

97 Eastern Reef Heron (after Belcher)

98 Sea Snake

99 Queen Elizabeth and Arms of Fiji

(Des G. Hamori (½d., 1d., 9d.), W. O. Cernohorsky (2d., 4s.) H. S. Robinson (4d., 10d.), D. W. Blair (6d., 5s.), P. D. Clarke (1s.), G. Vasarhelyi (2s. 6d.), W. O. Cernohorsky and E. Jones (3s.), E. Jones and G. Hamori (10s.), E. Jones (£1). Adapted V. Whiteley. Photo D.L.R.)

1968 (15 July). *T* **96**/**9** *and similar designs.* W w **12** (*sideways on all vert designs*). *P* 14 × 13½ (*2s., 2s. 6d., 5s., £1*), 13½ × 14 (*3d., 1s., 1s. 6d., 4s., 10s.*) *or* 13½ × 13 (*others*).
371 ½d. multicoloured 5 5
372 1d. deep greenish blue, red and yellow .. 8 5
373 2d. new blue, brown and ochre 10 5
374 3d. blackish green, blue and ochre 35 5
375 4d. multicoloured 40 5
376 6d. multicoloured 25 5
377 9d. multicoloured 25 15
378 10d. royal blue, orange and blackish brown .. 60 15
379 1s. Prussian blue and brown-red 35 15
380 1s. 6d. multicoloured .. .. .. 5·00 3·50
381 2s. turquoise, black and rosine .. .. 2·25 3·00
382 2s. 6d. multicoloured .. .. .. 2·25 1·75
383 3s. multicoloured .. .. .. 5·00 6·00
384 4s. yellow-ochre, black and olive .. .. 2·75 4·00
385 5s. multicoloured .. .. .. 5·00 4·50
386 10s. lake-brown, black and ochre .. .. 5·00 7·50
387 £1 multicoloured .. .. .. 6·00 12·00
371/87 .. .. *Set of* 17 32·00 38·00

Designs: *Horiz* (*as T* **96**)—1d. Passion Flowers; 2d. Pearly Nautilus; 4d. Hawk Moth; 6d. Angel Fish; 9d. Bamboo raft; 10d. Tiger Moth; 3s. Golden Cowrie Shell. *Vert* (*as T* **97**)—1s. Black Marlin; 1s. 6d. Orange-breasted Honeyeaters (after Belcher); 4s. Mining industry; 10s. Ceremonial Whale's Tooth. *Horiz as T* **98**—2s. 6d. Outrigger canoes; 5s. Bamboo Orchids.

113 Map of Fiji, W.H.O. Emblem and Nurses

(Des V. Whiteley. Litho D.L.R.)

1968 (9 Dec). *20th Anniv of World Health Organization. T* **113** *and similar horiz designs. Multicoloured. W* w **12** *(sideways). P* 14.

388 3d. Type **113** 15 8
389 9d. Transferring patient to Medical Ship *Vuniwai* 40 30
390 3s. Recreation .. .. 1·00 1·00

(New Currency. 100 cents = 1 dollar.)

116 Passion Flowers 117 Fijian Soldiers overlooking the Solomon Islands

1969 (13 Jan)–**70**. *Decimal Currency. Designs as Nos.* 371/87, *but with values inscr in decimal currency as T* **116**. *W* w **12** *(sideways on vert designs) Chalk-surfaced paper. P* 14 × 13½ (20, 25, 50 c. $2) 13½ × 14 (3, 10, 15, 40 c., $1) *or* 13½ × 13 *(others)*.

391 **116** 1 c. deep greenish blue, red and yellow.. 5 5
392 – 2 c. new blue, brown and ochre (as 2d.).. 12 5
393 **97** 3 c. blackish green, blue and ochre .. 25 5
394 – 4 c. multicoloured (as 4d.) 40 10
395 – 5 c. multicoloured (as 6d.) 20 5
396 **96** 6 c. multicoloured 20 10
397 – 8 c. multicoloured (as 9d.) 25 10
398 – 9 c. royal blue, orange and blackish brown (as 10d.) 55 35
399 – 10 c. Prussian blue and brown-red (as 1s.) 30 25
400 – 15 c. multicoloured (as 1s. 6d.) .. .. 6·00 2·25
401 **98** 20 c. turquoise, black and rosine .. 1·40 1·00
402 – 25 c. multicoloured (as 2s. 6d.) .. .. 1·60 50
403 – 30 c. multicoloured (as 3s.) .. .. 6·50 3·25
404 – 40 c. yellow-ochre, black and olive (as 4s.) 2·75 4.00
405 – 50 c. multicoloured (as 5s.) .. .. 6·00 1·00
a. Glazed, ordinary paper (3.9.70) .. 9·00 2·75
406 – $1 lake-brown, black and ochre (as 10s.) 6·00 2·50
a. Glazed, ordinary paper (3.9.70) .. 10·00 4·75
407 **99** $2 multicoloured .. .. .. 6·50 11·00
391/407 .. .. *Set of* 17 35·00 24·00

(Des G. Drummond. Photo Harrison)

1969 (23 June). *25th Anniv of Fijian Military Forces' Solomons Campaign. T* **117** *and similar horiz designs. W* w **12**. *P* 14.

408 3 c. yellow-brown, black and bright emerald 20 10
409 10 c. multicoloured 25 10
410 25 c. multicoloured 45 35

Designs:—10 c. Regimental Flags and Soldiers in full dress and battledress; 25 c. Cpl. Sefanaia Sukanaivalu and Victoria Cross.

120 Javelin Thrower 123 Map of South Pacific and "Mortar-board"

(Des L. Curtis. Photo Harrison)

1969 (18 Aug). *3rd South Pacific Games, Port Moresby. T* **120** *and similar vert designs. W* w **12** *(sideways). P* 14½ × 14.

411 4 c. black, brown and vermilion 15 10
412 8 c. black, grey and new blue 20 10
413 20 c. multicoloured 30 20

Designs:—8 c. Yachting; 20 c. Games medal and winners' rostrum.

(Des G. Drummond. Photo Harrison)

1969 (10 Nov). *Inauguration of University of the South Pacific. T* **123** *and similar horiz designs. Multicoloured. W* w **12**. *P* 14 × 15.

414 2 c. Type **123** 10 5
415 8 c. R.N.Z.A.F. badge and "Sunderland" flying-boat over Laucala Bay (site of University) 25 10
416 25 c. Science students at work 35 35

ALTERED CATALOGUE NUMBERS

Any Catalogue numbers altered from the last edition are shown as a list in the introductory pages.

ROYAL VISIT
1970

(126)

127 Chaulmugra Tree, Makogai

1970 (4 Mar). *Royal Visit. Nos.* 392, 399 *and* 402 *optd with T* **126**.

417 2 c. new blue, brown and ochre 20 25
418 10 c. Prussian blue and brown-red 40 35
419 25 c. multicoloured .. .. 1·00 65

(Des G. Drummond. Photo Harrison)

1970 (25 May). *Closing of Leprosy Hospital Makogai. T* **127** *and similar designs. W* w **12** *(sideways on* 10 c.*). P* 14 × 14½.

420 2 c. multicoloured 10 8
421 10 c. pale turquoise-green and black 30 30
a. Pair. Nos. 421/2 .. .. 60 60
422 10 c. turquoise-blue, black and magenta .. 30 30
423 30 c. multicoloured 90 90

Designs: *Vert*—No. 421, "Cascade" (Semisi Maya); No. 422, "Sea Urchins" (Semisi Maya). *Horiz*—No. 423, Makogai Hospital.

Nos. 421/2 were printed together *se-tenant* throughout the sheet.

131 Abel Tasman and Log, 1643

(Des V. Whiteley. Litho D.L.R.)

1970 (18 Aug). *Explorers and Discoverers. T* **131** *and similar horiz designs. W* w **12** *(sideways). P* 13 × 12½.

424 2 c. black, brown and turquoise 75 30
425 3 c. multicoloured .. .. 1·75 90
426 8 c. multicoloured .. .. 1·90 1·00
427 25 c. multicoloured .. .. 2·25 1·50

Designs:—3 c. Captain Cook and *Endeavour*, 1774; 8 c. Captain Bligh and longboat, 1789; 25 c. Fijian and ocean-going canoe.

INDEPENDENT

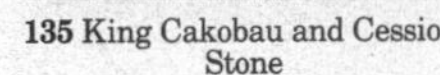

135 King Cakobau and Cession Stone 139 1d. and 6d. Stamps of 1870

(Des J.W. Litho Format)

1970 (10 Oct). *Independence. T* **135** *and similar horiz designs. Multicoloured. W* w **12** *(sideways). P* 14.

428 2 c. Type **135** 12 10
429 3 c. Children of the World 12 10
430 10 c. Prime Minister and Fijian flag 20 15
431 25 c. Dancers in costume 60 60

The design for the 10 c. value does not incorporate the Queen's head profile.

(Des V. Whiteley. Photo Harrison)

1970 (2 Nov). *Stamp Centenary. T* **139** *and similar horiz designs. Multicoloured. W* w **12** *(sideways on* 15 c.*). P* 14½ × 14.

432 4 c. Type **139** 20 10
433 15 c. Fijian Stamps of all Reigns 40 50
434 20 c. *Fiji Times* Office and modern G.P.O. .. 50 60

The 15 c. is larger, 61 × 21 mm.

140 Grey-backed White Eye 141 Masked Shining Parrot

(Des G. Drummond. Litho Questa)

1971 (6 Aug)–**72**. *Birds and Flowers. Vert designs as T* **140/1**. *Multicoloured. W* w **12** *(upright)*.

(*a*) *Size as T* **140**. *P* 13½ × 14

435 1 c. *Cirrhopetalum umbellatum* (4.1.72) .. 10 20
436 2 c. Cardinal Honeyeater (22.11.71) 12 12
437 3 c. *Calanthe furcata* (23.6.72) 20 20
438 4 c. *Bulbophyllum sp nov* (23.6.72) 20 20
439 5 c. Type **140** 25 25
440 6 c. *Phaius tancarvilliae* (23.6.72) 35 40
441 8 c. Blue-headed Flycatcher (22.11.71) .. 35 35
442 10 c. *Acanthephippium vitiense* (4.1.72) .. 40 15
443 15 c. *Dendrobium tokai* (23.6.72) .. .. 1·50 90
444 20 c. Slaty Flycatcher 90 80

(*b*) *Size as T* **141**. *P* 14

445 25 c. Yellow-faced Honeyeater (22.11.71) .. 1·25 50
446 30 c. *Dendrobium gordonii* (4.1.72) .. .. 2·75 1·25
447 40 c. Type **141** .. .. 2·25 1·25
448 50 c. White-throated Pigeon .. .. .. 3·00 1·75
449 $1 Collared Lory (22.11.71).. .. .. 6·00 4·50
450 $2 *Dendrobium platygastrium* (4.1.72) .. 13·00 15·00
435/50 .. .. *Set of* 16 29·00 25·00

See also Nos. 459/73 and 505/20.

142 Women's Basketball 143 Community Education

(Des R. Granger Barrett. Litho Questa)

1971 (6 Sept). *Fourth South Pacific Games, Tahiti. T* **142** *and similar vert designs. W* w **12**. *P* 14.

451 8 c. multicoloured 25 15
452 10 c. cobalt, black and brown 35 20
453 25 c. pale turquoise-green, black and brown .. 90 65

Designs:—10c. Running; 25 c. Weightlifting.

(Des V. Whiteley. Litho Questa)

1972 (7 Feb). *25th Anniv of South Pacific Commission. T* **143** *and similar vert designs. Multicoloured. W* w **12**. *P* 14.

454 2 c. Type **143** 10 5
455 4 c. Public Health 25 25
456 50 c. Economic Growth .. .. .. 1·75 1·75

144 "Native Canoe" 145 Flowers, Conch and Ceremonial Whale's Tooth

(Des locally and adapted by A. B. New. Litho Questa)

1972 (10 Apr). *South Pacific Festival of Arts, Suva. W* w **12**. *P* 14.

457 **144** 10 c. black, orange and new blue .. 20 20

1972 (17 Nov)–**74**. *As Nos.* 436/41, 443/5 *and* 447/50 *but W* w **12** *sideways*.

459 2 c. Cardinal Honey-eater (12.12.73) .. 25 30
460 3 c. *Calanthe furcata* (8.3.73) 70 55
461 4 c. *Bulbophyllum sp nov* (11.4.73) 70 45
462 5 c. Type **140** (8.3.73).. .. .. .. 70 40
463 6 c. *Phaius tancarvilliae* (11.4.73) .. .. 1·50 1·00
464 8 c. Blue-crested Broadbill (11.4.73).. .. 1·50 75
466 15 c. *Dendrobium tokai* (11.4.73) .. .. 3·00 2·00
467 20 c. Slaty Flycatcher .. .. 2·75 2·00
468 25 c. Kandavu Honey-eater (11.4.73).. .. 1·50 1·75
470 40 c. Type **141** (15.3.74) .. .. .. 2·50 3·00
471 50 c. White-throated Pigeon (15.3.74) .. 2·75 3·00
472 $1 Collared Lory .. .. 5·00 7·50
473 $2 *Dendrobium platygastrium* .. .. 11·00 14·00
459/73 .. .. *Set of* 13 30·00 32·00

(Des (from photograph by D. Groves) and photo Harrison)

1972 (20 Nov). *Royal Silver Wedding. Multicoloured; background colour given. W* w **12**. *P* 14 × 14½.

474 10 c. slate-green 20 15
475 25 c. bright purple 30 20
a. Blue printing omitted* £140

*The omission of the blue colour results in the Duke's suit appearing brown instead of deep blue.

HURRICANE
RELIEF
+10c

(146)

147 Line Out

1972 (4 Dec). *Hurricane Relief. Nos.* 400 *and* 403 *surch as T* **146**, *by the Reserve Bank of Australia*.

476 15 c. + 5 c. multicoloured 60 70
477 30 c. + 10 c. multicoloured 65 80

(Des J.W. Litho Questa)

1973 (9 Mar). *Diamond Jubilee of Fiji Rugby Union. T* **147** *and similar vert designs. Multicoloured. W* w **12** *(sideways). P* 14.

478 2 c. Type **147** 15 10

479 8 c. Body tackle 40 15
480 25 c. Conversion .. .. 1·00 85

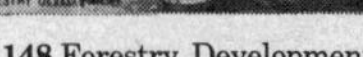

148 Forestry Development

149 Christmas

(Des J.W. from local ideas. Litho Questa)

1973 (23 July). *Development Projects. T* **148** *and similar horiz designs. Multicoloured. W* w **12**. *P* 14.
481 5 c. Type **148** 15 5
482 8 c. Rice irrigation scheme 30 20
483 10 c. Low income housing 30 15
484 25 c. Highway construction 75 70

(Des L. Curtis. Litho Questa)

1973 (26 Oct). *Festivals of Joy. T* **149** *and similar vert designs. Multicoloured. W* w **12** (*sideways*). *P* 14.
485 3 c. Type **149** 12 5
486 10 c. Diwali 20 15
487 20 c. Id-ul-Fitar 50 55
488 25 c. Chinese New Year 60 65

150 Athletics

151 Bowler

(Des G. Drummond. Litho Questa)

1974 (7 Jan). *Commonwealth Games, Christchurch. T* **150** *and similar vert designs. Multicoloured. W* w **12** (*sideways*). *P* 14.
489 3 c. Type **150** 12 5
490 8 c. Boxing 30 30
491 50 c. Bowling .. .. 3·25 3·75

(Des Hon. P. Snow. Adapted J.W. Litho Questa)

1974 (21 Feb). *Cricket Centenary. T* **151** *and similar multi-coloured designs. W* w **12** (*sideways on* 3 *and* 25 *c.*). *P* 14.
492 3 c. Type **151** 40 25
493 25 c. Batsman and wicketkeeper .. .. .. 2·50 2·00
494 40 c. Fielder (*horiz*) .. .. 3·25 3·25

152 Fijian Postman

(Des L. Curtis. Litho Format)

1974 (22 May). *Centenary of the Universal Postal Union. T* **152** *and similar horiz designs. Multicoloured. W* w **12**. *P* 14.
495 3 c. Type **152** 15 5
496 8 c. Loading mail onto ship 50 35
497 30 c. Fijian post office and mail bus .. .. 1·50 1·25
498 50 c. Modern aircraft .. .. 2·00 1·75

153 Cubs lighting Fire

154 Cakobau Club and Flag

(Des E. W. Roberts. Litho Questa)

1974 (30 Aug). *First National Scout Jamboree, Lautoka. T* **153** *and similar multicoloured designs. W* w **12** (*sideways on* 40 *c.*). *P* 14.
499 3 c. Type **153** 15 5
500 10 c. Scouts reading map 50 45
501 40 c. Scouts and Fijian flag (*vert*) .. .. 1·90 1·90

(Des J.W. Litho Enschedé)

1974 (9 Oct). *Centenary of Deed of Cession and Fourth Anniv of Independence. T* **154** *and similar horiz designs. Multicoloured. W* w **12** (*sideways on* 8 *and* 50 *c.*). *P* 13½ × 13 (3 *c.*) *or* 13 × 13½ (*others*).
502 3 c. Type **154** 10 5
503 8 c. King Cakobau and Queen Victoria .. 30 30
504 50 c. Raising the Royal Standard at Nasova Ovalau .. .. 1·50 1·60

1975 (9 Apr)–**77**. *As Nos.* 435/44 *and* 446/50, *but W* w **14** (*sideways on* 1 *and* 10 *c*).
505 1 c. *Cirrhopetalum umbellatum* 10 20
506 2 c. Cardinal Honey-eater 15 20
507 3 c. *Calanthe furcata* 20 20
508 4 c. *Bulbophyllum sp nov* (3.9.76) 20 10
509 5 c. Type **140** 20 10
510 6 c. *Phaius tancarvilliae* (3.9.76) 30 10
511 8 c. Blue-crested Broadbill (3.9.76) 35 12
512 10 c. *Acanthephippium vitiense* 40 25
513 15 c. *Dendrobium tokai* (3.9.76) .. .. 1·50 60
514 20 c. Slaty Flycatcher (15.7.77) .. .. 3·00 75
516 30 c. *Dendrobium gordonii* (3.9.76) .. .. 2·50 1·50
517 40 c. Type **141** (3.9.76) .. .. .. 2·00 1·75
518 50 c. White-throated pigeon (3.9.76) .. .. 2·25 2·00
519 $1 Collared Lory (3.9.76) .. .. .. 4·50 4·25
520 $2 *Dendrobium platygastrium* (3.9.76) .. 9·00 7·00
505/20 .. .. *Set of* 15 24·00 17·00

155 "Diwali" (Hindu Festival)

156 Steam Loco No. 21

(Des Jennifer Toombs. Litho Walsall)

1975 (31 Oct). *Festivals of Joy. T* **155** *and similar vert designs. Multicoloured. W* w **14** (*inverted*). *P* 14.
521 3 c. Type **155** 15 5
522 15 c. "Id-Ul-Fitar" (Muslim Festival) 40 30
523 25 c. Chinese New Year 60 50
524 30 c. Christmas 75 70
MS525 121 × 101 mm. Nos. 521/4. *W* w **14** (sideways) .. .. 5·00 6·00
a. Imperf between (vert) £1000

(Des R. Granger Barrett. Litho Questa)

1976 (26 Jan). *Sugar Trains. T* **156** *and similar horiz designs. Multicoloured. W* w **14** (*sideways*). *P* 14.
526 4 c. Type **156** 30 5
527 15 c. Diesel Loco No. 8 .. .. 85 55
528 20 c. Diesel Loco No. 1 .. .. 90 60
529 30 c. Free Passenger Train .. .. .. 1·25 1·00

157 Fiji Blind Society and Rotary Symbols

(Des V. Whiteley Studio. Litho J.W.)

1976 (26 Mar). *40th Anniv of Rotary in Fiji. T* **157** *and similar horiz design. W* w **14** (*sideways*). *P* 13.
530 10 c. ultramarine, pale sage-green and black .. 25 25
531 25 c. multicoloured 70 80
Design:—25 c. Ambulance and Rotary symbol.

158 D. H. "Drover"

(Des P. Powell. Litho Questa)

1976 (1 Sept). *25th Anniv of Air Services. T* **158** *and similar horiz designs. Multicoloured. W* w **14**. *P* 13½ × 14.
532 4 c. Type **158** 30 20
533 15 c. B.A.C. "1–11" .. .. 1·00 75
534 25 c. H.S. "748" .. .. 1·90 1·10
535 30 c. Britten-Norman "Trislander" .. .. 2·00 1·40

159 The Queen's Visit to Fiji, 1970

160 Map of the World

(Des L. Curtis. Litho Questa)

1977 (7 Feb). *Silver Jubilee. T* **159** *and similar vert designs. Multicoloured. W* w **14**. *P* 13½.
536 10 c. Type **159** 20 25
537 25 c. King Edward's Chair 40 55
538 30 c. Queen wearing cloth-of-gold supertunica 50 65

(Des J.W. Litho Walsall)

1977 (12 Apr). *E.E.C./A.C.P.* Council of Ministers Conference, Fiji. T* **160** *and similar horiz design. Multicoloured. W* w **14** (*sideways*). *P* 14.
539 4 c. Type **160** 15 12
540 30 c. Map of Fiji group .. .. 1·25 1·00
*A.C.P. = African, Caribbean, Pacific Group.

161 *Hibiscus rosa-sinensis*

(Des V. Whiteley Studio. Litho Walsall)

1977 (27 Aug). *21st Anniv of Fiji Hibiscus Festival. T* **161** *and similar horiz designs. W* w **14** (*sideways*). *P* 14.
541 **161** 4 c. multicoloured 15 5
542 – 15 c. multicoloured 50 50
543 – 30 c. multicoloured 85 85
544 – 35 c. multicoloured .. .. 1·00 1·00
Nos. 542/44 show different varieties of *H rosa-sinensis*.

162 Drua

163 White Hart of Richard II

(Des P. Powell. Litho Questa)

1977 (7 Nov). *Canoes. T* **162** *and similar horiz designs. Multi-coloured. W* w **14** (*sideways*). *P* 14.
545 4 c. Type **162** 15 5
546 15 c. Tabilai 45 45
547 25 c. Takai 65 65
548 40 c. Camakua .. .. 90 1·10

(Des C. Abbott. Litho Questa)

1978 (21 Apr). *25th Anniv of Coronation. T* **163** *and similar vert designs. P* 15.
549 25 c. bistre, blue-green and silver 55 55
a. Sheetlet. Nos. 549/51 × 2 .. .. 3·50
550 25 c. multicoloured 55 55
551 25 c. bistre, blue-green and silver 55 55
Designs:—No. 549, Type **163**; No. 550, Queen Elizabeth II; No. 551, Banded Iguana.
Nos. 549/51 were printed together in small sheets of 6, containing two *se-tenant* strips of 3, with horizontal gutter margin between.

164 Defence Force surrounding Plane, Suva

(Des A. Theobald. Litho Harrison)

1978 (26 June). *Aviation Anniversaries. T* **164** *and similar horiz designs. Multicoloured. W* w **14** (*sideways*). *P* 14.
552 4 c. Type **164** 20 5
553 15 c. *Southern Cross* prior to leaving Naselai Beach 55 50
554 25 c. Wright *Flyer* 90 80
555 30 c. Bristol "F2B" .. .. 1·00 90
Anniversaries:—25 c. 75th of powered flight; 30 c. 60th of R.A.F.; others. 50th of first trans-Pacific flight by Kingsford-Smith.

165 Shallow Wooden Oil Dish in shape of Human Figure

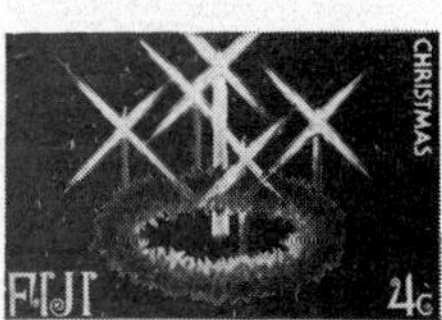

166 Advent Crown with Candles (Christmas)

(Des J. Cooter. Litho Questa)

1978 (14 Aug). *Fijian Artifacts. T* **165** *and similar multicoloured designs. W* w **14** *(sideways on* 15 *and* 25 *c.). P* 14.

556	4 c. Type **165**	10	5
557	15 c. Necklace of cachalot teeth (*horiz*)	30	25
558	25 c. Double water bottle (*horiz*)	45	50
559	30 c. Finely carved Ula or throwing club	50	55

(Des Jennifer Toombs. Litho Harrison)

1978 (30 Oct). *Festivals. T* **166** *and similar horiz designs. Multicoloured. W* w **14** *(sideways). P* 14.

560	4 c. Type **166**	8	5
561	15 c. Lamps (Diwali)	25	25
562	25 c. Coffee pot, cups and fruit (Id-Ul-Fitr)	45	45
563	40 c. Lion (Chinese New Year)	60	65

167 Banded Iguana

(Des L. Curtis and G. Drummond. Litho Questa)

1979 (19 Mar). *Endangered Wildlife. T* **167** *and similar horiz designs. Multicoloured. W* w **14** *(sideways). P* 14.

564	4 c. Type **167**	10	5
565	15 c. Tree Frog	40	40
566	25 c. Long-legged Warbler	65	65
567	30 c. Pink-billed Parrot Finch	75	75

168 Women with Dholak

(Des J.W. Litho Questa)

1979 (11 May). *Centenary of Arrival of Indians. T* **168** *and similar horiz designs. Multicoloured. W* w **14** *(sideways). P* 14.

568	4 c. Type **168**	8	5
569	15 c. Men sitting round tanoa	30	25
570	30 c. Farmer and sugar cane plantation	50	50
571	40 c. Sailing ship *Leonidas*	70	70

169 Soccer

(Des BG Studio. Litho Questa)

1979 (2 July). *6th South Pacific Games. T* **169** *and similar horiz designs. Multicoloured. W* w **14** *(sideways). P* 14.

572	4 c. Type **169**	10	5
573	15 c. Rugby Union	35	25
574	30 c. Lawn tennis	65	50
575	40 c. Weightlifting	70	65

170 Indian Child and Map of Fiji

(Des D. Bowen. Litho Walsall)

1979 (17 Sept). *International Year of the Child. T* **170** *and similar horiz designs showing children and map of Fiji. Multicoloured. W* w **14** *(sideways). P* 14½ × 14.

576	4 c. + 1 c. Type **170**	15	15
577	15 c. + 2 c. European child	35	30
578	30 c. + 3 c. Chinese child	55	40
570	40 c. + 4 c. Fijian child	65	50

171 Old Town Hall, Suva

(Des J.W. Litho Questa (1, 2, 3, 10, 15, 20, 30 c., $5) or Harrison (others))

1979 (11 Nov)–**84**. *Architecture. Multicoloured designs as T* **171**. *W* w **14** *(sideways on horiz designs). P* 13½ × 13 ($1), 13 × 13½ ($2), 13½ × 14 ($5) *or* 14 *(others).*

A. *Without imprint date at foot.* B. *With imprint date* ("1983").

		A		B	
580	1 c. Type **171**	5	5	†	
581	2 c. Dudley Church, Suva	5	5	5	5
582	3 c. Fiji International Telecommunications Building, Suva	5	5	†	
583	5 c. Lautoka Mosque	5	5	5	5
584	6 c. General Post Office, Suva	5	5	8	5
585	10 c. Fiji Visitors Bureau, Suva	12	15	†	
586	12 c. Public School, Levuka	15	20	†	
587	15 c. Colonial War Memorial Hospital, Suva	20	25	†	
588	18 c. Labasa Sugar Mill	25	30	†	
589	20 c. Rewa Bridge, Nausori	25	30	†	
590	30 c. Sacred Heart Cathedral, Suva (*vert*)	40	45	†	
591	35 c. Grand Pacific Hotel, Suva	45	50	†	
592	45 c. Shiva Temple, Suva	55	60	†	
593	50 c. Serua Island Village	65	70	†	
594	$1 Solo Lighthouse (30 × 46 *mm*)	1·25	1·40	†	
595	$2 Baker Memorial Hall, Nausori (46 × 30 *mm*)	2·50	2·75	†	
595*a*	$5 Government House (46 × 30 *mm*)	6·50	6·75	†	
580/95*a*	*Set of* 17	12·00	13·00		

Dates of issue:—11.11.79 Nos. 580A/82A, 585A, 587A, 589A/90A, 595aA, 22.12.80 Nos. 583A/84A, 586A, 588A, 591A/95A, 15.6.83 No. 584B, 1.84 No. 583B; 2.84 581B.

172 *Southern Cross*, 1873

(Des L. Dunn. Litho Secura, Singapore)

1980 (28 Apr). *"London 1980" International Stamp Exhibition. Mail-carrying Ships. T* **172** *and similar horiz designs. Multicoloured. W* w **14** *(sideways). P* 13½.

596	6 c. Type **172**	15	10
597	20 c. *Levuka*, 1910	30	25
598	45 c. *Matua*, 1936	60	50
599	50 c. *Oronsay*, 1951	65	55

173 Sovi Bay

(Des BG Studio. Litho Questa)

1980 (18 Aug). *Tourism. T* **173** *and similar horiz designs. Multicoloured. W* w **14** *(sideways). P* 13½ × 14.

600	6 c. Type **173**	10	10
601	20 c. Evening scene, Yanuca Island	30	30
602	45 c. Dravuni Beach	65	65
603	50 c. Wakaya Island	70	70

174 Official Opening of Parliament, 1979

(Des J. Cooter. Litho J.W.)

1980 (6 Oct). *10th Anniv of Independence. T* **174** *and similar multicoloured designs. W* w **14** *(sideways on* 6 *and* 45 *c.). P* 13.

604	6 c. Type **174**	10	10
605	20 c. Fiji coat of arms (*vert*)	25	30
606	45 c. Fiji flag	50	60
607	50 c. Queen Elizabeth II (*vert*)	50	65

175 "Coastal Scene" (painting, Semisi Maya)

176 Prince Charles Sailing

(Des J.W. Litho Questa)

1981 (21 Apr). *International Year for Disabled Persons. T* **175** *and similar multicoloured designs. W* w **14** *(sideways on* 6 *and* 35 *c.). P* 14.

608	6 c. Type **175**	10	5
609	35 c. "Underwater Scene" (painting, Semisi Maya)	55	60
610	50 c. Semisi Maya (disabled artist) at work (*vert*)	70	75
611	60 c. "Peacock" (painting, Semisi Maya) (*vert*)	75	80

(Des J.W. Litho Questa)

1981 (22 July). *Royal Wedding. T* **176** *and similar vert designs. Multicoloured. W* w **14**. *P* 14.

612	6 c. Wedding bouquet from Fiji	10	10
613	45 c. Type **176**	60	60
614	$1 Prince Charles and Lady Diana Spencer	1·25	1·40

177 Operator Assistance Centre

178 "Eat Fiji Foods"

(Des A. Theobald. Litho Format)

1981 (17 Aug). *Telecommunications. T* **177** *and similar horiz designs. Multicoloured. W* w **14** *(sideways). P* 14.

615	6 c. Type **177**	10	5
616	35 c. Microwave station	55	50
617	50 c. Satellite earth station	75	75
618	60 c. Cable ship *Retriever*	90	90

(Des J.W. Litho Format)

1981 (21 Sept). *World Food Day. W* w **14**. *P* 14½ × 14.

619	**178** 20 c. multicoloured	35	35

179 Ratu Sir Lala Sukuna (first Speaker, Legislative Council)

(Des A. Theobald. Litho Format)

1981 (19 Oct). *Commonwealth Parliamentary Association Conference, Suva. T* **179** *and similar horiz designs. W* w **14** *(sideways). P* 14.

620	6 c. black, buff and orange-brown	10	10
621	35 c. multicoloured	55	55
622	50 c. multicoloured	70	70
MS623	73 × 53 mm. 60 c. multicoloured	80	90

Designs:—35 c. Mace of the House of Representatives; 50 c. Suva Civic Centre; 60 c. Flags of C.P.A. countries.

180 Bell "P-39 Airacobra"

(Des A. Theobald. Litho Walsall)

1981 (7 Dec). *World War II Aircraft. T* **180** *and similar horiz designs. Multicoloured. W* w **14** *(sideways). P* 14.

624	6 c. Type **180**	15	10
625	18 c. Consolidated "PBY-5 Catalina"	45	35
626	35 c. Curtiss "P-40 Warhawk"	60	60
627	60 c. Short "Singapore"	85	85

6c FIJI

181 Scouts constructing Shelter

(Des B. Melton. Litho Questa)

1982 (22 Feb). *75th Anniv of Boy Scout Movement. T* **181** *and similar multicoloured designs. W* w **14** (*sideways on* 6 *and* 45 *c.*). *P* 14½.

628 6 c. Type **181** 10 10
629 20 c. Scouts sailing (*vert*) 40 40
630 45 c. Scouts by campfire 75 75
631 60 c. Lord Baden-Powell (*vert*) 90 90

182 Fiji Soldiers at U.N. Checkpoint

(Des J.W. Litho Format)

1982 (3 May). *Disciplined Forces. T* **182** *and similar horiz designs. Multicoloured. W* w **14** (*sideways*). *P* 14.

632 12 c. Type **182** 20 12
633 30 c. Soldiers engaged in rural development 45 45
634 40 c. Police patrol 60 60
635 70 c. Naval patrol-boat 90 90

183 Footballers and Fiji Football Association Logo

184 Bride and Groom leaving St. Paul's

(Des A. Theobald. Litho Walsall)

1982 (15 June). *World Cup Football Championship, Spain. T* **183** *and similar horiz designs. W* w **14** (*sideways*). *P* 14.

636 6 c. rosine, black and lemon 10 8
637 18 c. multicoloured 30 25
638 50 c. multicoloured 80 70
639 90 c. multicoloured . . . . 1·40 1·40

Designs:—18 c. Footballers and World Cup emblem; 50 c. Footballer and Bernabeu Stadium; 90 c. Footballers and Naranjito (mascot).

(Des C. Abbott. Litho Harrison)

1982 (1 July). *21st Birthday of Princess of Wales. T* **184** *and similar vert designs. Multicoloured. W* w **14**. *P* 14½ × 14.

640 20 c. Fiji coat of arms 25 25
641 35 c. Lady Diana Spencer at Broadlands, May 1981 . . . . 35 35
642 45 c. Type **184** 50 50
643 $1 Formal portrait . . . . 1·25 1·25

185 Prince Philip

186 Baby Jesus with Mary and Joseph

(Des C. Abbott. Litho Format)

1982 (1 Nov). *Royal Visit. T* **185** *and similar multicoloured designs. W* w **14**. *P* 14.

644 6 c. Type **185** 10 8
645 45 c. Queen Elizabeth II 65 70

MS646 128 × 88 mm. Nos. 644/5 and $1 Royal Yacht *Britannia* (*horiz*). Wmk sideways . . . . 2·10 2·25

(Des G. Wilby. Litho Questa)

1982 (22 Nov). *Christmas. T* **186** *and similar horiz designs. Multicoloured. W* w **14** (*sideways*). *P* 14 × 14½.

647 6 c. Type **186** 10 8
648 20 c. Three Wise Men presenting gifts . . 30 30
649 35 c. Carol-singing 45 45

MS650 94 × 42 mm. $1 "Faith" (from the "Three Virtues" by Raphael) . . . . 1·25 1·50

187 Red-throated Lorikeet

188 Bure in Traditional Village

(Des N. Arlott. Litho Questa)

1983 (14 Feb). *Parrots. T* **187** *and similar vert designs. Multicoloured. W* w **14**. *P* 14.

651 20 c. Type **187** 35 25
652 40 c. Blue-crowned Lory 60 60
653 55 c. Masked Shining Parrot 80 80
654 70 c. Red Shining Parrot . . . . 1·10 1·10

(Des B. Melton. Litho Questa)

1983 (14 Mar). *Commonwealth Day. T* **188** *and similar horiz designs. Multicoloured. W* w **14** (*sideways*). *P* 14.

655 8 c. Type **188** 10 12
656 25 c. Barefoot firewalkers 35 40
657 50 c. Sugar industry 65 70
658 80 c. Kava "Yagona" ceremony . . . . . . 1·00 1·10

189 First Manned Balloon Flight, 1783

190 Nawanawa

(Des Harrison. Litho Questa)

1983 (18 July). *Bicentenary of Manned Flight. T* **189** *and similar horiz designs. Multicoloured. W* w **14** (*sideways*). *P* 14.

659 8 c. Type **189** 10 12
660 20 c. Wright brothers' *Flyer* 25 30
661 25 c. Douglas "Super DC3" 35 40
662 40 c. De Havilland "Comet" 55 60
663 50 c. Boeing "747" 65 70
664 58 c. Space Shuttle 75 80
659/64 . . . . *Set of* 6 2·40 2·50

(Des Harrison. Litho Format)

1983 (26 Sept). *Flowers* (*1st series*). *T* **190** *and similar vert designs. Multicoloured. W* w **14**. *P* 14 × 14½.

665 8 c. Type **190** 10 12
666 25 c. Rosawa 35 40
667 40 c. Warerega 55 60
668 $1 Saburo . . . . 1·25 1·40

See also Nos. 680/3.

191 Fijian beating Lali and Earth Satellite Station

192 *Dacryopinax spathularia*

(Des Garden Studio. Litho Questa)

1983 (7 Nov). *World Communications Year. W* w **14**. *P* 13½.

669 **191** 50 c. multicoloured 65 70

(Des Jennifer Toombs. Litho Enschedé)

1984 (9 Jan). *Fungi. T* **192** *and similar multicoloured designs. W* w **14** (*sideways on* 50 *c. and* $1). *P* 13½ × 13 (8 *c. to* 40 *c.*) *or* 13 × 13½ (*others*).

670 8 c. Type **192** 10 12
671 15 c. *Podoscypha involuta* 20 25
672 40 c. *Lentinus squarrosulus* 55 60
673 50 c. *Scleroderma flavidum* (*horiz*) 65 70
674 $1 *Phillipsia domingensis* (*horiz*) . . . . 1·25 1·40

193 *Tui Lau* on Reef

(Des L. Curtis. Litho Questa)

1984 (7 May). *250th Anniv of "Lloyd's List"* (*newspaper*). *T* **193** *and similar vert designs. Multicoloured. W* w **14**. *P* 14½ × 14.

675 8 c. Type **193** 10 12
676 40 c. S.S. *Tofua* 60 65
677 55 c. S.S. *Canberra* 80 85
678 60 c. Suva wharf 90 95

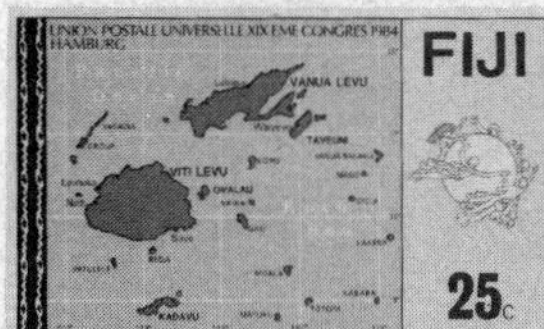

194 Map of Fijian Islands

(Des J. Cooter. Litho Questa)

1984 (14 June). *Universal Postal Union Congress, Hamburg. Sheet* 77 × 65 *mm. W* w **14** (*sideways*). *P* 14½.

MS679 **194** 25 c. multicoloured 35 40

(Des Harrison. Litho Format)

1984 (9 July). *Flowers* (*2nd series*). *Horiz designs as T* **190**. *W* w **14**. *P* 14 × 14½.

680 15 c. Drividrivi 20 25
681 20 c. Vesida 30 35
682 50 c. Vuga 75 80
683 70 c. Qaiqi . . . . 1·00 1·10

195 Prize Bull, Yalavou Cattle Scheme

(Des D. Hartley-Marjoram. Litho Walsall)

1984 (17 Sept). *"Ausipex" International Stamp Exhibition, Melbourne. T* **195** *and similar multicoloured designs. W* w **14** (*sideways on* 8, 40 *c. and* $1). *P* 14½ × 14 (25 *c.*) *or* 14 × 14½ (*others*).

684 8 c. Type **195** 10 12
685 25 c. Wailoa Power Station (*vert*) 35 40
686 40 c. Air Pacific Boeing "737" airliner . . 60 65
687 $1 Container ship *Fua Kavenga* . . . . 1·50 1·60

196 The Stable at Bethlehem

(Des G. Vasarhelyi. Litho Format)

1984 (5 Nov). *Christmas. Children's Paintings. T* **196** *and similar multicoloured designs. W* w **14** (*sideways on horiz designs*). *P* 14.

688 8 c. Type **196** 10 12
689 20 c. Outrigger canoe 30 35
690 25 c. Father Christmas and Christmas tree . . 35 40
691 40 c. Going to church 60 65
692 $1 Decorating Christmas tree (*vert*) . . 1·50 1·60

197 Monarch

(Des Annette Robinson. Litho Questa)

1985 (4 Feb). *Butterflies. T* **197** *and similar multicoloured designs. W* w **14** (*sideways on* 8 *c. and* 25 *c.*). *P* 14.

693 8 c. Type **197** 10 12
694 25 c. Common Eggfly 35 40
695 40 c. Long-tailed Blue (*vert*) 55 60
696 $1 Meadow Argus (*vert*) . . . . 1·25 1·40

POSTAGE DUE STAMPS

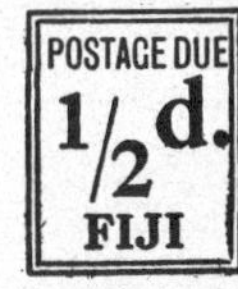

D 1 D 2

1917 (1 Jan). *Typo locally, on thick yellowish white laid paper. No gum. P* 11.

D1 D 1 ½d. black £375 £325
a. *Se-tenant* strip of 8: 1d. (×3) + ½d. + 4d. + 3d. (×3) £3750
D2 1d. black .. .. £100 65·00
D3 2d. black .. .. £110 55·00
D4 3d. black .. .. £150 70·00
D5 4d. black £400 £325

No. D2a derives from sheets of 96 (8 × 12). The 2d. was printed separately in sheets of 84 (7 × 12). On all these sheets marginal copies were imperforate on the outer edge.

1917 (April)–**18**. *Narrower setting, value in ½d. as Type* D **2**.

D5*a* ½d. black £475 £200
D5*b* 1d. black £175 £100
D5*c* 2d. black (4.18) £550 £500

1d. and 2d. stamps must have wide margins (3½ to 4 mm) on the vertical sides to be Nos. D2 or D3. Stamps with narrow margins of approximately the same width on all four sides are Nos. D5*b* or D5*c*.

Nos. D5*a/c* were printed in separate sheets of 84 (7 × 12). The marginal copies are perforated on all sides.

D 3 D 4

(Typo D.L.R.)

1917–18 (1 June). *Wmk Mult Crown CA. P* 14.

D 6 D 3 ½d. black .. .. 3·00 5·50
D 7 1d. black .. .. 3·00 3·75
D 8 2d. black .. .. 3·25 5·50
D 9 3d. black .. .. 5·00 9·00
D10 4d. black .. .. 8·50 14·00
D6/10 Optd "Specimen" .. .. *Set of* 5 £190

(Typo Waterlow)

1940. *Wmk Mult Script CA. P* 12½.

D11 D 4 1d. emerald-green .. .. .. 2·50 11·00
D12 2d. emerald-green .. .. .. 3·50 14·00
D13 3d. emerald-green .. .. .. 4·00 14·00
D14 4d. emerald-green .. .. .. 6·00 16·00
D15 5d. emerald-green .. .. .. 7·00 23·00
D16 6d. emerald-green .. .. .. 10·00 30·00
D17 1s. carmine-lake .. .. .. 15·00 50·00
D18 1s. 6d. carmine-lake .. .. .. 32·00 £100
D11/18 .. .. *Set of* 8 70·00 £225
D11/18 Perf "Specimen" .. .. *Set of* 8 £180

Gambia

PRICES FOR STAMPS ON COVER TO 1945

Nos. 1/8	*from* × 10
Nos. 10/20	*from* × 5
Nos. 21/36	*from* × 8
Nos. 37/44	*from* × 6
Nos. 45/56	*from* × 4
Nos. 57/68	*from* × 5
Nos. 69/70	*from* × 4
Nos. 72/142	*from* × 5
Nos. 143/6	*from* × 4
Nos. 147/9	*from* × 8
Nos. 150/61	*from* × 3

WEST AFRICAN SETTLEMENT

PRICES. The prices of Nos. 1 to 8 are for fine copies, with good margins and embossing. Brilliant or poor copies can be supplied at prices consistent with their condition.

DOUBLE EMBOSSING. The majority of the stamps of T 1 with so-called "double embossing" are merely specimens in which the printing and embossing do not register accurately and have no special value. We no longer list "twice embossed" or "twice embossed, once inverted" varieties as they are considered to be outside the scope of this catalogue.

1

(Typo and embossed by D.L.R.)

1869–72. *No wmk. Imperf.*

1 1 4d. brown £475 £150
2 4d. pale brown £400 £200
3 6d. deep blue (19.4.69) £400 £175
3*a* 6d. blue (30.4.69) £500 £150
4 6d. pale blue (17.2.72) £2000 1000

Our prices for the 6d., pale blue, No. 4, are for stamps which are pale by comparison with specimens of the "deep blue" and "blue" colour groups listed under Nos. 3 and 3*a*. An exceptionally pale shade is recognized by specialists and this is rare. The dates given for the 6d. are those of the earliest known postmarks.

1874 (Aug). *Wmk Crown CC. Imperf.*

5 1 4d. brown £400 £200
6 4d. pale brown £400 £200
7 6d. deep blue £350 £225
8 6d. blue £350 £200
a. Sloping label .. ..

SLOPING LABEL VARIETY. Traces of this flaw first occur in the 6d. imperforate on R.1/1 and R.1/5. In the perforated printings the variety on R.1/5 is much more pronounced and appears as illustrated above. Our listings are these examples from R.1/5, less noticeable varieties of this type from R.1/1, which slope from right to left, being worth less. These varieties continued to appear until the introduction of a new 6d. plate in 1893, used for No. 34.

1880 (June). *Wmk Crown CC. P* 14 (*comb*).

10 1 ½d. orange .. .. 4·25 8·50
11 ½d. dull orange .. .. 4·25 8·50
12 1d. maroon .. .. 6·00 6·00
13 2d. rose .. .. 18·00 9·50
14 3d. pale dull ultramarine .. .. 40·00 30·00
14*b* 3d. bright ultramarine .. .. .. 50·00 30·00
15 4d. brown .. .. £175 14·00
16 4d. pale brown .. .. £160 15·00
17 6d. deep blue .. .. 80·00 50·00
a. Sloping label £275 £175
18 6d. blue .. .. 80·00 50·00
a. Sloping label £275 £175
19 1s. green £250 £130
20 1s. deep green £250 £150
10/20 .. .. *Set of* 7 £550 £225

The watermark in this issue is found sideways as well as upright. These stamps also exist in line perf 14, believed to have come from the first delivery to the Colony. All are worth at least 50% more than the comb perforations and some of them are rare.

1883–93. *Wmk Crown CA, sideways. P* 14.

21 1 ½d. myrtle-green (1887) .. .. 80 1·00
22 ½d. grey-green .. .. 1·10 1·60
22*b* 1d. maroon .. .. — £15000
23 1d. crimson (1887) .. .. .. 2·50 3·00
23*a* 1d. aniline crimson .. .. .. 9·00 9·50
23*b* 1d. pale carmine .. .. .. 9·00 9·00
24 2d. orange (1887) .. .. .. 6·00 6·50
25 2d. deep orange .. .. 4·50 6·00
26 2½d. ultramarine (1886) .. .. .. 4·50 5·50
27 2½d. deep bright blue .. .. .. 4·50 5·00
28 1 3d. slate-grey (1883) .. .. .. 4·50 9·00
29 3d. grey .. .. 3·00 8·00
30 4d. brown (1887) .. .. 4·00 4·00
31 4d. deep brown .. .. 4·00 4·00
32 6d. yellowish olive-green (1886) .. 45·00 38·00
a. Sloping label £150 £130
32*b* 6d. olive-green .. .. 70·00 50·00
ba. Sloping label £225 £160
33 6d. bronze-green .. .. 17·00 24·00
a. Sloping label .. .. 55·00 65·00
33*b* 6d. deep bronze-green .. .. .. 17·00 24·00
ba. Sloping label .. .. 55·00 60·00
34 6d. slate-green (1893) .. .. .. 9·00 20·00
35 1s. violet (1887) .. .. 9·00 15·00
36 1s. deep violet .. .. 11·00 20·00
36*b* 1s. aniline violet £1000
21/36 .. .. *Set of* 8 35·00 55·00
21/24, 32 Optd "Specimen" .. .. *Set of* 4 £400

The above were printed in panes of 15 on paper intended for larger panes. Hence the watermark is sometimes misplaced or omitted and letters from "CROWN AGENTS FOR THE COLONIES" from the margin may appear on the stamps.

The ½d., 2d., 3d., 4d., 6d. (No. 32) and 1s. with watermark Crown CA are known imperf (*price from* £1500).

The previously listed 3d. "pearl-grey" shade has been deleted as it is impossible to distinguish from other 3d. shades when it occurs on a single stamp. Sheets from this late printing can be identified by three coloured dots in the left sheet margin and one in the right, this being the reverse of the normal arrangement.

CROWN COLONY

2 3 4

(Typo D.L.R.)

1898 (Jan)–**1902.** *Wmk Crown CA. P* 14.

37 2 ½d. dull green (*shades*) .. .. .. 2·00 2·00
38 1d. carmine (*shades*) .. .. .. 2·50 2·00
39 2d. orange and mauve .. .. .. 3·50 6·50
40 2½d. ultramarine .. .. 3·25 4·50
41 3d. reddish purple and blue .. .. 7·00 11·00
a. Deep purple and ultramarine (1902) 70·00 £100
42 4d. brown and blue .. .. .. 8·00 15·00
43 6d. olive-green and carmine .. .. 14·00 20·00
44 1s. violet and green .. .. .. 20·00 32·00
37/44 .. .. *Set of* 8 55·00 85·00
37/44 Optd "Specimen" .. .. *Set of* 8 £275

1902 (13 Mar)–**05.** *Wmk Crown CA. P* 14.

45 3 ½d. green (19.4.02) .. .. .. 60 1·75
46 1d. carmine .. .. 1·50 1·10
47 2d. orange and mauve (14.6.02) .. 3·50 4·50
48 2½d. ultramarine (14.6.02) .. .. 9·00 14·00
49 3d. purple and ultramarine (19.4.02) .. 9·00 7·00
50 4d. brown and ultramarine (14.6.02) .. 6·50 12·00
51 6d. pale sage-green & carmine (14.6.02) 7·50 12·00
52 1s. violet and green (14.6.02) .. .. 48·00 60·00
53 4 1s. 6d. green and carmine/*yellow* (6.4.05) 14·00 17·00
54 2s. deep slate and orange (14.6.02) .. 27·00 38·00
55 2s. 6d. purple and brown/*yellow* (6.4.05) 32·00 48·00
56 3s. carmine and green/*yellow* (6.4.05) .. 35·00 48·00
45/56 .. .. *Set of* 12 £170 £225
45/56 Optd "Specimen" .. .. *Set of* 12 £450

1904 (Aug)–**06.** *Wmk Mult Crown CA. P* 14.

57 3 ½d. green (23.2.06) 80 50
58 1d. carmine .. .. 2·00 35
59 2d. orange and mauve (23.2.06) .. .. 8·50 7·00
60 2½d. bright blue (23.2.06) .. .. 2·75 3·75
a. Bright blue and ultramarine .. 7·50 11·00
61 3d. purple and ultramarine (23.2.06) .. 6·50 6·50
62 4d. brown and ultramarine (23.2.06) .. 8·50 13·00
63 4 5d. grey and black (6.4.05) .. .. 8·00 11·00
64 3 6d. olive-green and carmine (23.2.06) .. 6·50 12·00
65 4 7½d. green and carmine (6.4.05) .. .. 6·50 12·00
66 10d. olive and carmine (6.4.05) .. .. 9·50 14·00
67 3 1s. violet and green (23.2.06) .. .. 24·00 32·00
68 4 2s. deep slate and orange (23.2.06) .. 45·00 55·00
57/68 .. .. *Set of* 12 £110 £150
63, 65/6 Optd "Specimen" .. .. *Set of* 3 £110

See also Nos. 72/85.

(5) (6)

1906 (10 April). *Nos.* 55 *and* 56 *surch locally with T* **5** *and* **6** *respectively.*

69 ½d. on 2s. 6d. purple and brown/*yellow* .. 32·00 45·00
70 1d. on 3s. carmine and green/*yellow*. .. 42·00 48·00
a. Surch double £2250 £5000

No. 69 was surcharged in a setting of 30 (6 × 5), the spacing between the words and the bars being 5 mm on rows 1, 2 and 5; and 4 mm on rows 3 and 4. Constant varieties occur on R.2/1 (broken "E") and R.5/1 (dropped "Y") of the setting.

No. 70 was surcharged in a setting of 60 (6 × 10) and a similar dropped "Y" variety occurs on R.6/3 and R.8/5.

1909. *Colours changed. Wmk Mult Crown CA. P* 14.

72 3 ½d. blue-green .. .. 75 1·40
73 1d. red 80 35
74 2d. greyish slate .. .. 1·60 3·25
75 3d. purple/*yellow* .. .. 3·75 3·00
a. Purple/lemon-yellow .. .. .. 6·00 5·00
76 4d. black and red/*yellow* .. .. .. 1·50 1·60
77 4 5d. orange and purple .. .. .. 3·50 3·25
78 3 6d. dull and bright purple .. .. 2·75 3·50
79 4 7½d. brown and blue .. .. .. 3·50 4·50
80 10d. pale sage-green and carmine .. 5·00 6·50

81 3 1s. black/*green* 3·75 6·50
82 4 1s. 6d. violet and green 14·00 20·00
83 2s. purple and bright blue/*blue* 12·00 19·00
84 2s. 6d. black and red/*blue* 24·00 25·00
85 3s. yellow and green 42·00 45·00
72/85 *Set of* 14 £110 £130
73/85 Optd "Specimen" *Set of* 13 £350

7

8

Split "A"

The split "A" variety occurs on No. 45 in the left-hand pane in printings to 1918 of all values up to 3s. (*Prices about six to ten times normal.*)

(Typo D.L.R.)

1912 (1 Sept)–**22.** *Wmk Mult Crown CA. P* 14.
86 7 ½d. pale green, **O** 65 65
a. Green 55 65
b. Deep green 65 90
87 1d. red, **O** 45 30
a. Rose-red 65 40
b. Scarlet (1916) 90 50
88 8 1½d. olive-green and blue-green, **O** 60 1·00
89 7 2d. greyish slate, **O** 50 75
90 2½d. deep bright blue, **O** 4·00 3·00
a. Bright blue 4·25 2·25
91 3d. purple/*yellow*, **O** 60 90
a. On lemon (1917) 12·00 16·00
b. On orange-buff (1920) 13·00 6·50
c. On pale yellow 70 1·10
92 4d. black and red/*yellow*, **O** 2·75 7·00
a. On lemon 2·00 7·00
b. On orange-buff 5·50 10·00
c. On pale yellow 3·00 5·50
93 8 5d. orange and purple, **O** 90 2·25
94 7 6d. dull and bright purple, **O** 1·10 1·75
95 8 7½d. brown and blue, **O** 1·40 3·25
96 10d. pale sage-green and carmine, **O** 6·50 13·00
a. Deep sage-green and carmine 3·75 10·00
97 7 1s. black/*green*, **O** 1·25 3·00
a. On emerald back 2·50 7·00
98 8 1s. 6d. violet and green, **O** 7·50 10·00
99 2s. purple and blue/*blue*, **O** 7·50 10·00
100 2s. 6d. black and red/*blue*, **O** 10·00 14·00
101 3s. yellow and green, **O** 16·00 20·00
102 5s. green and red/*pale yellow*, **C** (1922) 38·00 50·00
86/102 *Set of* 17 85·00 £120
86/102 Optd "Specimen" *Set of* 17 £450

1921–22. *Wmk Mult Script CA. P* 14.
108 7 ½d. dull green, **O** 50 2·25
109 1d. carmine-red, **O** 1·00 1·25
110 8 1½d. olive-green and blue-green, **O** 2·50 7·00
111 7 2d. grey, **O** 1·75 3·00
112 2½d. bright blue, **O** 1·00 4·50
113 8 5d. orange and purple, **O** 2·75 8·00
114 7 6d. dull and bright purple, **O** 3·50 7·50
115 8 7½d. brown and blue, **O** 3·75 11·00
116 10d. pale sage-green and carmine, **O** 5·50 14·00
117 4s. black and red, **C** (1922) 38·00 50·00
108/117 *Set of* 10 55·00 £100
108/17 Optd "Specimen" *Set of* 10 £275

9

10

(Recess D.L.R.)

1922 (1 Sept)–**27.** *Portrait and shield in black. P* 14*.

(*a*) *Wmk Mult Crown CA*
118 9 4d. red/*yellow* (*a*) 80 1·75
119 7½d. purple/*yellow* (*a*) 2·25 6·50
120 10 1s. purple/*yellow* (*a*) 6·50 14·00
121 5s. green/*yellow* (*c*) 30·00 40·00
118/121 Optd/H/S "Specimen" *Set of* 4 £180

(*b*) *Wmk Mult Script CA*
122 9 ½d. green (*abd*) 45 30
123 ½d. deep green (*abd*) 65 50
124 1d. brown (*abd*) 60 15
125 1½d. bright rose-scarlet (*abd*) 70 20
126 2d. grey (*ab*) 70 60
127 2½d. orange-yellow (*b*) 70 3·75
128 3d. bright blue (*abd*) 75 20
129 4d. red/*yellow* (*b*) (1927) 95 4·00
130 5d. sage-green (*a*) 2·00 5·50
131 6d. claret (*ad*) 1·25 70
132 7½d. purple/*yellow* (*ab*) (1927) 3·25 9·50
133 10d. blue (*a*) 3·50 8·50
134 10 1s. purple/*yellow* (*aef*) (9.24) 3·00 1·40
a. Blackish purple/yellow-buff (*c*) 24·00 30·00
135 1s. 6d. blue (*af*) 7·00 10·00
136 2s. purple/*blue* (*ac*) 8·00 7·00
137 2s. 6d. deep green (*a*) 10·00 13·00
138 3s. bright aniline violet (*a*) 13·00 22·00
139 3s. slate-purple (*c*) £225 £500
140 4s. brown (*ace*) 10·00 18·00
141 5s. green/*yellow* (*acf*) (9.26) 17·00 25·00
142 10s. sage-green (*ce*) 60·00 75·00
118/142 *Set of* 23 £160 £250
122/42 Optd "Specimen" *Set of* 19 £700

Perforations. A number of different perforating machines were used for the various printings of these stamps and the following varieties are known: (*a*) the original 14 line perforation; (*b*) 14 × 13.8 comb perforation used for Type **9**; (*c*) 13.8 × 13.7 comb perforation used for Type **10**; (*d*) 13.7 line perforation used for Type **9**; (*e*) 14 × 13.8 compound line perforation used for Type **10**; (*f*) 13.8 × 14 compound line perforation used for Type **10**. The occurrence of these perforations on the individual values is indicated by the letters shown after the colour descriptions above.

No. 139 has been faked, but note that this stamp is comb perf 13.8 × 13.7 whereas No. 138 is line perf 14 exactly. There are also shades of the slate-purple.

1935 (6 May). *Silver Jubilee. As T* **13** *of Antigua. Recess B.W. Wmk Mult Script CA. P* 11 × 12.
143 1½d. deep blue and scarlet 65 50
a. Extra flagstaff 90·00
b. Short extra flagstaff 35·00
c. Lightning conductor 30·00
d. Double flagstaff 20·00
144 3d. brown and deep blue 1·75 1·75
a. Extra flagstaff £170
b. Short extra flagstaff 60·00
c. Lightning conductor 50·00
145 6d. light blue and olive-green 2·25 3·50
a. Extra flagstaff £170
c. Lightning conductor 50·00
146 1s. slate and purple 2·50 3·50
a. Extra flagstaff £300
b. Short extra flagstaff £100
c. Lightning conductor 90·00
143/6 Perf "Specimen" *Set of* 4 55·00

For illustrations of plate varieties see Omnibus section following Zululand.

Examples of Nos 145a and 146a are known with the extra flagstaff erased from the stamp with a sharp point.

1937 (12 May). *Coronation. As T* 2 *of Aden. Recess B.W. Wmk Mult Script CA. P* 11 × 11½.
147 1d. yellow-brown 20 30
148 1½d. carmine 20 30
149 3d. blue 55 65
147/9 Perf "Specimen" *Set of* 3 45·00

11 Elephant (from Colony Badge)

(Recess B.W.)

1938 (1 Apr)–**46.** *Wmk Mult Script CA. P* 12.
150 11 ½d. black and emerald-green 35 25
151 1d. purple and brown 40 15
152 1½d. lake and carmine 23·00 7·00
a. Lake and scarlet (1942) 40 25
152*b* 1½d. blue and black (2.1.45) 75 75
153 2d. blue and black 70 1·25
153*a* 2d. lake and scarlet (1943) 50 40
154 3d. light blue and grey-blue 30 15
154*a* 5d. sage-green & purple-brn (13.3.41) 60 50
155 6d. olive-green and claret 75 40
156 1s. slate-blue and violet 1·50 30
156*a* 1s. 3d. chocolate & lt blue (28.11.46) 1·25 65
157 2s. carmine and blue 3·75 3·50
158 2s. 6d. sepia and dull green 4·50 2·50
159 4s. vermilion and purple 10·00 8·50
160 5s. blue and vermilion 9·00 9·50
161 10s. orange and black 16·00 12·00
150/161 *Set of* 16 45·00 38·00
150/61 Perf "Specimen" *Set of* 16 £140

1946 (6 Aug). *Victory. As Nos. 28/9 of Aden.*
162 1½d. black 45 20
163 3d. blue 45 25
162/3 Perf "Specimen" *Set of* 2 55·00

1948 (24 Dec). *Royal Silver Wedding. As Nos. 30/1 of Aden.*
164 1½d. black 25 25
165 £1 mauve 14·00 23·00

1949 (10 Oct). *75th Anniv of Universal Postal Union. As Nos. 114/17 of Antigua.*
166 1½d. blue-black 45 60
167 3d. deep blue 1·00 1·10
168 6d. magenta 1·25 1·25
169 1s. violet 1·50 1·75

1953 (2 June). *Coronation. As No. 47 of Aden, but ptd by B.W.*
170 1½d. black and deep bright blue 15 40

12 Tapping for Palm Wine

13 Cutter

(Des Mrs O. W. Meronti. Recess D.L.R.)

1953 (2 Nov). *T* **12**/**13** *and similar horiz designs. Wmk Mult Script CA. P* 13½.
171 12 ½d. carmine-red & bluish grn (*shades*) 12 20
172 13 1d. dp ultramarine & dp brown (*shades*) 30 10
173 – 1½d. deep brown and grey-black 12 10
174 – 2½d. black and carmine-red 35 30
175 – 3d. deep blue and slate-lilac 30 15
176 – 4d. black and deep blue 45 60
177 12 6d. brown and reddish purple 30 12
178 – 1s. yellow-brown and yellow-green 30 15
179 13 1s. 3d. ultramarine & pale bl (*shades*) 2·50 15
180 – 2s. indigo and carmine 3·00 2·25
181 13 2s. 6d. deep bluish green and sepia 2·00 1·75
182 – 4s. grey-blue and Indian red 2·00 2·50
183 – 5s. chocolate and bright blue 2·00 2·00
184 – 10s. deep blue and myrtle-green 8·50 9·00
185 – £1 green and black 13·00 16·00
171/85 *Set of* 15 32·00 32·00

Designs:—1½d., 5s. Wollof woman; 2½d., 2s. Barra canoe; 3d., 10s. S.S. *Lady Wright*; 4d., 4s. James Island; 1s., 2s. 6d. Woman hoeing; £1 Elephant and palm (from Colony Badge).

20 Queen Elizabeth II and Palm

21 Queen Elizabeth II and West African Map

(Des J. R. F. Ithier (T **20**), A. W. Morley (T **21**). Recess B.W.)

1961 (2 Dec). *Royal Visit. W w* **12**. *P* 11½.
186 20 2d. green and purple 10 8
187 21 3d. turquoise-blue and sepia 15 8
188 6d. blue and cerise 20 15
189 20 1s. 3d. violet and myrtle-green 25 45

1963 (4 June). *Freedom from Hunger. As No. 76 of Aden.*
190 1s. 3d. carmine 60 25

1963 (2 Sept). *Red Cross Centenary. As Nos. 147/8 of Antigua.*
191 2d. red and black 20 10
192 1s. 3d. red and blue 75 35

SELF-GOVERNMENT

22 Beautiful Sunbird

SELF GOVERNMENT
1963
(**35**)

(Des V. Whiteley. Photo Harrison)

1963 (4 Nov). *Birds. Horiz designs as T* **22**. *Multicoloured. W w* **12**. *P* 12½ × 13.
193 ½d. Type **22** 15 15
194 1d. Yellow-mantled Whydah 20 10
195 1½d. Cattle Egret 40 50
196 2d. Senegal Parrot 25 15
197 3d. Rose-ringed Parakeet 25 12
198 4d. Violet Starling 40 35
199 6d. Village Weaver 50 15
200 1s. Rufous-crowned Roller 60 15
201 1s. 3d. Red-eyed Dove 3·25 1·40
202 2s. 6d. Double-spurred Francolin 4·50 3·75
203 4s. Palm-nut Vulture 5·50 4·50
204 10s. Orange-cheeked Waxbill 11·00 10·00
205 £1 African Emerald Cuckoo 23·00 20·00
193/205 *Set of* 13 45·00 38·00

1963 (7 Nov). *New Constitution. Nos. 194, 197, 200/1 optd with T* **35**.
206 1d. Yellow-mantled Whydah 5 5
207 3d. Rose-ringed Parakeet 8 8
208 1s. Rufous-crowned Roller 15 10
a. Opt double † —
209 1s. 3d. Red-eyed Dove 20 15

1964 (23 Apr). *400th Birth Anniv of William Shakespeare. As No. 164 of Antigua.*
210 6d. greenish blue 15 10

INDEPENDENT

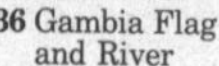
36 Gambia Flag and River

37 Arms

(Des V. Whiteley. Photo Harrison)

1965 (18 Feb). *Independence. P* 14½.
211 36 ½d. multicoloured 5 5
212 37 2d. multicoloured 5 5
213 36 7½d. multicoloured 15 15
214 37 1s. 6d. multicoloured 15 15

(38) **39** I.T.U. Emblem and Symbols

1965 (18 Feb). *Nos.* 193/205 *optd with T* **38** *or with date centred (1d., 2d., 3d., 4d., 1s., 5s.).*

No.	Description		Unused	Used
215	½d. Type **22**		10	15
216	1d. Yellow-mantled Whydah		10	10
217	1½d. Cattle Egret		15	25
218	2d. Senegal Parrot		15	15
219	3d. Rose-ringed Parakeet		20	15
220	4d. Violet Starling		20	30
221	6d. Village Weaver		20	20
222	1s. Rufous-crowned Roller		30	20
223	1s. 3d. Red-eyed Dove		60	30
224	2s. 6d. Double-spurred Francolin		70	35
225	5s. Palm-nut Vulture		1·00	1·25
226	10s. Orange-cheeked Waxbill		2·50	5·00
227	£1 African Emerald Cuckoo		5·50	10·00
215/27		*Set of* 13	11·00	17·00

(Des V. Whiteley. Photo Harrison)

1965 (17 May). *I.T.U. Centenary. P* 14½.

No.	Type	Description	Unused	Used
228	**39**	1d. silver and Prussian blue	20	5
229		1s. 6d. gold and bluish violet	80	35

THE GAMBIA. From this point onwards stamps are inscribed "The Gambia".

40 Sir Winston Churchill and Houses of Parliament

(Des Jennifer Toombs. Photo Harrison)

1966 (24 Jan). *Churchill Commemoration. P* 14 × 14½.

No.	Type	Description	Unused	Used
230	**40**	1d. multicoloured	15	10
231		6d. multicoloured	40	20
232		1s. 6d. multicoloured	1·00	80

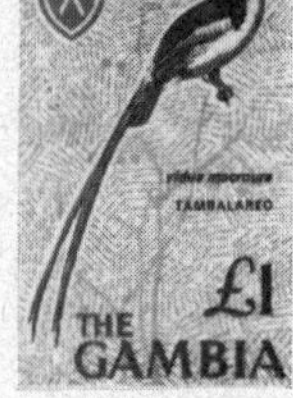

41 Red-cheeked Cordon Bleu **42** Pin-tailed Whydah

(Des V. Whiteley. Photo Harrison)

1966 (18 Feb). *Birds. Horiz designs as T* **41**, *and T* **42**. *Multicoloured. P* 14 × 14½ (£1) *or* 12 × 13 (*others*).

No.	Description		Unused	Used
233	½d. Type **41**		20	15
234	1d. White-faced Whistling Duck		25	8
235	1½d. Red-throated Bee Eater		30	15
236	2d. Lesser Pied Kingfisher		75	15
237	3d. Golden Bishop		40	12
238	4d. African Fish Eagle		60	30
239	6d. Yellow-bellied Green Pigeon		60	15
240	1s. Blue-bellied Roller		60	15
241	1s. 6d. African Pygmy Kingfisher		85	50
242	2s. 6d. Spur-winged Goose		1·25	80
243	5s. Cardinal Woodpecker		1·50	2·00
244	10s. Violet Turaco		2·00	3·50
245	£1 Type **42**		2·75	8·00
233/45		*Set of* 13	11·00	14·50

The ½d., 1d. and 2d. to 1s. values exist with PVA gum as well as gum arabic.

54 Arms, Early Settlement and Modern Buildings

(Photo, arms die-stamped Harrison)

1966 (24 June). *150th Anniv of Bathurst. P* 14½ × 14.

No.	Type	Description	Unused	Used
246	**54**	1d. silver, brown and yellow-orange	8	5
247		2d. silver, brown and light blue	10	5
248		6d. silver, brown and light emerald	15	10
249		1s. 6d. silver, brown and light magenta	20	25

55 I.T.Y. Emblem and Hotels

(Des and photo (emblem die-stamped) Harrison)

1967 (20 Dec). *International Tourist Year. P* 14½ × 14.

No.	Type	Description	Unused	Used
250	**55**	2d. silver, brown and apple-green	10	5
251		1s. silver, brown and orange	12	10
252		1s. 6d. silver, brown and magenta	15	25

56 Handcuffs

(Des V. Whiteley. Photo Enschedé)

1968 (15 July). *Human Rights Year. T* **56** *and similar horiz designs. Multicoloured. P* 14 × 13.

No.	Description	Unused	Used
253	1d. Type **56**	5	5
254	1s. Fort Bullen	15	10
255	5s. Methodist Church	45	60

59 Queen Victoria, Queen Elizabeth II and 4d. Stamp of 1869

(Des G. Drummond. Photo and embossing (cameo head) Harrison)

1969 (20 Jan). *Gambia Stamp Centenary. P* 14½ × 13½.

No.	Type	Description	Unused	Used
256	**59**	4d. sepia and yellow-ochre	25	20
257		6d. Prussian blue and deep yellow-green	30	25
258	–	2s. 6d. multicoloured	90	1·00

Design:—2s. 6d. Queen Elizabeth II with 4d. and 6d. stamps of 1869.

In the 6d. value the stamp illustrated is the 6d. of 1869.

61 Catapult-Ship *Westfalen* launching Dornier "Wal"

(Des L. Curtis. Litho Format International)

1969 (15 Dec). *35th Anniv of Pioneer Air Services. T* **61** *and similar horiz designs showing various forms of transport, map of South Atlantic and Lufthansa emblem. Multicoloured. P* 13½ × 14.

No.	Description	Unused	Used
259	2d. Type **61**	15	12
260	1s. Dornier "Wal" flying-boat	40	20
261	1s. 6d. *Graf Zeppelin* airship	80	45

REPUBLIC

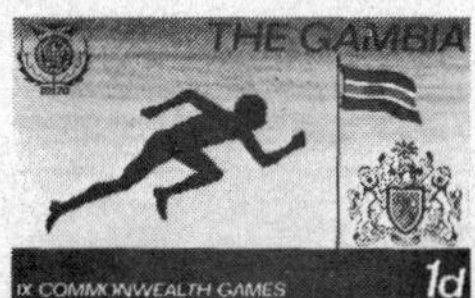

63 Athlete and Gambian Flag

(Des Jennifer Toombs. Litho Format)

1970 (16 July). *Ninth British Commonwealth Games, Edinburgh. P* 14.

No.	Type	Description	Unused	Used
262	**63**	1d. multicoloured	10	5
263		1s. multicoloured	20	20
264		5s. multicoloured	55	65

64 President Sir Dawda Kairaba Jawara and State House

(Des G. Vasarhelyi. Litho Questa)

1970 (2 Nov). *Republic Day. T* **64** *and similar multicoloured designs. P* 14.

No.	Description	Unused	Used
265	2d. Type **64**	8	8
266	1s. President Sir Dawda Jawara	12	12
267	1s. 6d. President and flag of Gambia	20	25

The 1s. and 1s. 6d. are both vertical designs.

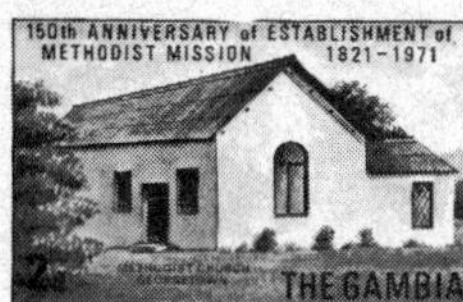

65 Methodist Church, Georgetown

(Des J. Cooter. Litho Questa)

1971 (16 Apr). *150th Anniv of Establishment of Methodist Mission. T* **65** *and similar multicoloured designs. P* 14.

No.	Description	Unused	Used
268	2d. Type **65**	8	5
269	1s. Map of Africa and Gambian flag (*vert*)	15	15
270	1s. 6d. John Wesley and scroll (*horiz*)	30	40

(New Currency. 100 bututs = 1 dalasy)

66 Yellowfin Tunny

(Des J.W. Litho Format)

1971 (1 July). *New Currency. Fishes. Horiz designs as T* **66**. *Multicoloured. P* 14.

No.	Description		Unused	Used
271	2 b. Type **66**		8	10
272	4 b. Peters' Mormyrid		12	10
273	6 b. Tropical Flying Fish		15	15
274	8 b. African Sleeper Goby		15	15
275	10 b. Yellowtail Snapper		20	12
276	13 b. Rock Hind		20	25
277	25 b. Gymnallabes		35	25
278	38 b. Tiger Shark		45	45
279	50 b. Electric Catfish		60	55
280	63 b. Black Synbranchus		70	90
281	1 d. 25, Smalltooth Sawfish		1·50	1·75
282	2 d. 50, Barracuda		4·25	4·50
283	5 d. Brown Bullhead		7·00	8·50
271/83		*Set of* 13	14·00	15·00

67 Mungo Park in Scotland

(Des J.W. from ideas by P. J. Westwood. Litho Questa)

1971 (10 Sept). *Birth Bicentenary of Mungo Park (explorer). T* **67** *and similar horiz designs. Multicoloured. W w* **12** *(sideways). P* 13½ × 13.

No.	Description	Unused	Used
284	4 b. Type **67**	10	10
285	25 b. Dug-out canoe	50	40
286	37 b. Death of Mungo Park, Busa Rapids	75	60

68 Radio Gambia

(Des G. Drummond. Litho Questa)

1972 (1 July). *Tenth Anniv of Radio Gambia. T* **68** *and similar horiz design. P* 14.

No.	Type	Description	Unused	Used
287	**68**	4 b. orange-ochre and black	10	5
288	–	25 b. light new blue, red-orange and black	20	20
289	**68**	37 b. bright green and black	30	30

Design:—25 b. Broadcast-area map.

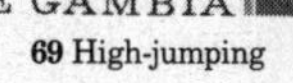

69 High-jumping **70** Manding Woman

(Des and litho D.L.R.)

1972 (31 Aug). *Olympic Games, Munich. P* 13.

No.	Type	Description	Unused	Used
290	**69**	4 b. multicoloured	8	5
291		25 b. multicoloured	15	15
292		37 b. multicoloured	20	30

(Des C. Abbott. Litho Questa)

1972 (16 Oct). *International Conference on Manding Studies, London. T* **70** *and similar vert designs. Multicoloured. P* 14 × 14½.
293 2 b. Type **70** 5 5
294 25 b. Musician playing the Kora 30 25
295 37 b. Map of Mali Empire 40 35

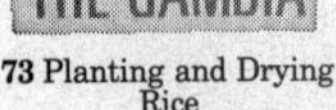

71 Children carrying Fanal

72 Groundnuts

(Des L. Curtis. Litho Enschedé)

1972 (1 Dec). *Fanals (Model Boats). T* **71** *and similar horiz design. Multicoloured. P* 13 × 13½.
296 2 b. Type **71** 5 5
297 1 d. 25, Fanal with lanterns . . . . . . 1·25 1·25

(Des locally; adapted G. Drummond. Litho Harrison)

1973 (31 Mar). *Freedom from Hunger Campaign. P* 14½ × 14.
298 **72** 2 b. multicoloured 12 12
299 25 b. multicoloured 30 20
300 37 b. multicoloured 40 30

73 Planting and Drying Rice

74 Oil Palm

(Des PAD Studio. Litho J.W.)

1973 (30 Apr). *Agriculture* (1st series). *T* **73** *and similar vert designs. Multicoloured. P* 14.
301 2 b. Type **73** 12 15
302 25 b. Guinea Corn 55 40
303 37 b. Rice 70 50

(Des PAD Studio. Litho Format)

1973 (16 July). *Agriculture* (2nd series). *T* **74** *and similar vert designs. Multicoloured. P* 12.
304 2 b. Type **74** 12 15
305 25 b. Limes 50 40
306 37 b. Oil palm (fruits) 60 50

75 Cassava

(Des PAD Studio. Litho Questa)

1973 (15 Oct). *Agriculture* (3rd series). *T* **75** *and similar horiz design. Multicoloured. P* 14.
307 2 b. Type **75** 12 12
308 50 b. Cotton 70 50

76 O.A.U. Emblem

(Des and litho D.L.R.)

1973 (1 Nov). *Tenth Anniv of O.A.U. P* 13½ × 13.
309 **76** 4 b. multicoloured 5 5
310 25 b. multicoloured 15 20
311 37 b. multicoloured 20 25

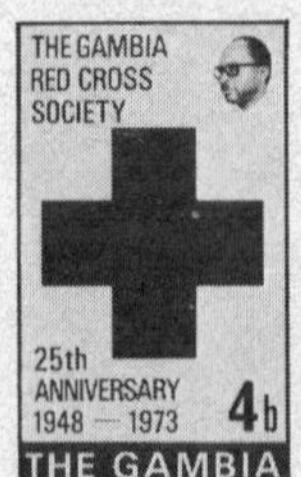

77 Red Cross

78 Arms of Banjul

(Des J. Cooter. Litho Questa)

1973 (30 Nov). *25th Anniv of Gambian Red Cross. P* 14 × 14½.
312 **77** 4 b. dull orange-red, and black 10 5
313 25 b. dull orange-red, black and new blue 35 20
314 37 b. dull orange-red, black & lt yell-grn 45 35

(Des and litho D.L.R.)

1973 (17 Dec). *Change of Bathurst's Name to Banjul. P* 13½ × 13.
315 **78** 4 b. multicoloured 5 5
316 25 b. multicoloured 15 20
317 37 b. multicoloured 30 35

79 U.P.U. Emblem

(Des and litho D.L.R.)

1974 (24 Aug). *Centenary of Universal Postal Union. P* 13½.
318 **79** 4 b. multicoloured 10 10
319 37 b. multicoloured 45 55

80 Churchill as Harrow Schoolboy

81 "Different Races"

(Des and litho J.W.)

1974 (30 Nov). *Birth Centenary of Sir Winston Churchill. T* **80** *and similar vert designs. Multicoloured. P* 13½.
320 4 b. Type **80** 10 5
321 37 b. Churchill as 4th Hussars officer 40 25
322 50 b. Churchill as Prime Minister 50 40

(Des G. Vasarhelyi. Litho Questa)

1974 (16 Dec). *World Population Year. T* **81** *and similar horiz designs. Multicoloured. P* 14.
323 4 b. Type **81** 8 5
324 37 b. "Multiplication and Division of Races" . . 25 30
325 50 b. "World Population" 40 45

82 Dr. Schweitzer and River Scene

(Des G. Vasarhelyi. Litho Walsall)

1975 (14 Jan). *Birth Centenary of Dr. Albert Schweitzer. T* **82** *and similar horiz designs. Multicoloured. P* 14.
326 10 b. Type **82** 15 5
327 50 b. Surgery scene 70 50
328 1 d. 25, River journey . . . . 1·60 1·10

83 Dove of Peace

84 Development Graph

(Des and litho D.L.R.)

1975 (18 Feb). *Tenth Anniv of Independence. T* **83** *and similar horiz designs. Multicoloured. P* 13.
329 4 b. Type **83** 5 5
330 10 b. Gambian flag 10 10
331 50 b. Gambian arms 30 35
332 1 d. 25, Map of The Gambia 65 85

(Des PAD Studio. Litho Questa)

1975 (31 Mar). *Tenth Anniv of African Development Bank. T* **84** *and similar vert designs. Multicoloured. P* 14½.
333 10 b. Type **84** 10 10
334 50 b. Symbolic plant 30 30
335 1 d. 25, Bank emblem and symbols . . . . 80 1·10

85 "Statute of David" (Michelangelo)

86 School Building

(Des C. Abbott. Litho Walsall)

1975 (14 Nov). *500th Birth Anniv of Michelangelo. T* **85** *and similar multicoloured designs. P* 14½ × 14 (1 d. 25) *or* 14 × 14½ (*others*).
336 10 b. Type **85** 10 10
337 50 b. "Madonna of the Steps" 30 35
338 1 d. 25, "Battle of the Centaurs" (*horiz*) . . 80 95

(Des G. Vasarhelyi. Litho Format)

1975 (17 Nov). *Centenary of Gambia High School. T* **86** *and similar horiz designs. Multicoloured. P* 14½.
339 10 b. Type **86** 10 10
340 50 b. Pupil with scientific apparatus 30 35
341 1 d. 50, School crest 80 90

87 "Teaching"

(Des A. B. Oliver; adapted by Jennifer Toombs. Litho Questa)

1975 (15 Dec). *International Women's Year. T* **87** *and similar horiz designs. Multicoloured. P* 14½.
342 4 b. Type **87** 5 5
343 10 b. "Planting rice" 15 10
344 50 b. "Nursing" 60 35
345 1 d. 50, "Directing traffic" . . . . . . 1·75 1·00

88 Woman playing Golf

89 American Militiaman

(Des R. Granger Barrett. Litho J.W.)

1976 (18 Feb). *11th Anniv of Independence. T* **88** *and similar horiz designs. Multicoloured. P* 14½ × 14.
346 10 b. Type **88** 35 15
347 50 b. Man playing golf . . . . 1·25 60
348 1 d. 50, President playing golf . . . . . . 2·50 2·00

(Des C. Abbott. Litho Questa)

1976 (15 May). *Bicentenary of American Revolution. T* **89** *and similar vert designs. Multicoloured. P* 14 × 13½.
349 25 b. Type **89** 50 25
350 50 b. Soldier of the Continental Army 80 45
351 1 d. 25, Independence Declaration . . . . 2·00 1·40
MS352 110 × 80 mm. Nos. 349/51 . . . . . . 4·00 4·50

MINIMUM PRICE

The minimum price quoted is 5p which represents a handling charge rather than a basis for valuing common stamps. For further notes about prices see introductory pages.

90 Mother and Child   91 Serval Cat

(Des G. Vasarhelyi. Litho Questa)

1976 (28 Oct). *Christmas. P* 14.

353 **90** 10 b. multicoloured 10 5
354 50 b. multicoloured 35 30
355 1 d. 25, multicoloured 65 75

(Des G. Drummond. Litho Questa)

1976 (29 Nov). *Abuko Nature Reserve* (1*st series*). *T* **91** *and similar horiz designs. Multicoloured. P* 13½.

356 10 b. Type **91** 30 10
357 25 b. Harnessed Antelope 90 50
358 50 b. Sitatunga (deer) .. .. 1·40 75
359 1 d. 25, Leopard .. .. 3·00 1·75
MS360 137 × 110 mm. Nos. 356/9 .. .. .. 7·00 6·50

See also Nos. 400/3, 431/5 and 460/3.

92 Festival Emblem and Gambian Weaver

(Des E. N. Sillah; adapted C. Abbott. Litho Walsall)

1977 (12 Jan). *Second World Black and African Festival of Arts and Culture, Nigeria. P* 14.

361 **92** 25 b. multicoloured 40 30
362 50 b. multicoloured 65 50
363 1 d. 25, multicoloured .. .. 1·75 1·60
MS364 118 × 114 mm. Nos. 361/3 .. .. .. 3·75 3·75

93 The Spurs and Jewelled Sword

(Des PAD Studio. Litho Questa)

1977 (7 Feb). *Silver Jubilee. T* **93** *and similar horiz designs. Multicoloured. P* 13½.

365 25 b. Queen's visit, 1961 .. .. .. 2·50 2·25
366 50 b. Type **93** .. .. 1·50 1·50
367 1 d. 25, Oblation of the sword .. .. .. 2·50 2·25

94 Stone Circles, Kuntaur

(Des J.W. Litho Questa)

1977 (18 Feb). *Tourism. T* **94** *and similar horiz designs. Multicoloured. P* 14.

368 25 b. Type **94** 25 25
369 50 b. Ruined fort, James Island 60 60
370 1 d. 25, Mungo Park Monument .. .. .. 1·50 1·50

95 Widow of Last Year   96 Endangered Animals

(Des PAD Studio. Litho Questa)

1977 (1 July)–**79**. *Flowers and Shrubs. Multicoloured designs as T* **95**. *Chalk-surfaced paper* (*No.* 376*a*) *or ordinary paper* (*others*). *P* 14.

371 2 b. Type **95** 5 10
a. Chalk-surfaced paper (23.11.79).. .. 15 10
372 4 b. White Water-lily.. .. .. 8 12
a. Chalk-surfaced paper (23.11.79).. .. 15 10
373 6 b. Fireball Lily 8 12
a. Chalk-surfaced paper (22.6.79) 15 10
374 8 b. Cocks-comb 10 15
a. Chalk-surfaced paper (23.11.79).. .. 15 15
375 10 b. Broad Leaved Ground Orchid 15 15
a. Chalk-surfaced paper (23.11.79).. .. 20 15
376 13 b. Fibre Plant (pale yellow background) .. 12 20
376*a* 13 b. Fibre Plant (pale olive-grey background) (*chalk-surfaced paper*) (25.7.79) 70 80
377 25 b. False Kapok 15 15
a. Chalk-surfaced paper (16.3.78) 30 20
378 38 b. Baobab 25 30
a. Chalk-surfaced paper (23.11.79).. .. 30 30
379 50 b. Coral Tree 35 35
a. Chalk-surfaced paper (16.3.78) 50 40
380 63 b. Gloriosa Lily 40 50
a. Chalk-surfaced paper (23.11.79).. .. 50 50
381 1 d. 25, Bell-flowered Mimosa 70 80
a. Chalk-surfaced paper (23.11.79).. .. 85 85
382 2 d. 50, Kindin Dolo .. .. 1·10 1·25
383 5 d. African Tulip Tree .. .. 2·25 2·50
371/83 .. .. *Set of* 14 5·75 6·75

The 6 to 38 b., 1 d. 25 and 2 d. 50 are vertical designs.

(Des N. Fortey (10, 50 b.), D. J. Thorp (25 b.), M. Langley (1 d. 25). Litho Questa)

1977 (15 Oct). *Banjul Declaration. T* **96** *and similar vert designs. P* 14.

384 10 b. black and light new blue.. .. .. 15 10
385 25 b. multicoloured 50 30
386 50 b. multicoloured 85 45
387 1 d. 25, black and light vermilion .. .. 2·00 95

Designs:—25 b. Extract from Declaration; 50 b. Declaration in full; 1 d. 25, Endangered insects and flowers.

97 "Flight into Egypt"   98 Dome of the Rock, Jerusalem

(Des BG Studio and Enschedé. Litho Enschedé)

1977 (15 Dec). *400th Birth Anniv of Rubens. T* **97** *and similar vert designs. Multicoloured. P* 13½ × 14.

388 10 b. Type **97** 10 10
389 25 b. "The Education of the Virgin" 30 20
390 50 b. "Clara Serena Rubens" 60 45
391 1 d. "Madonna with Saints" .. .. .. 1·00 80

Nos. 388/91 were each printed in small sheets of 6 including 1 *se-tenant* stamp-size label.

(Des J. Cooter. Litho Questa)

1978 (3 Jan). *Palestinian Welfare. P* 14½ × 14.

392 **98** 8 b. multicoloured 50 15
393 25 b. multicoloured .. .. 2·50 85

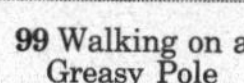

99 Walking on a Greasy Pole   100 Lion

(Des J.W. Litho Harrison)

1978 (18 Feb). *13th Anniv of Independence. T* **99** *and similar vert designs showing scenes from the Independence Regatta. Multicoloured. P* 14.

394 10 b. Type **99** 10 10
395 50 b. Pillow fighting 35 35
396 1 d. 25, Long rowing boat 90 90

(Des Jennifer Toombs. Litho Questa)

1978 (15 Apr). *25th Anniv of Coronation. T* **100** *and similar vert designs. P* 15.

397 1 d. black, agate and orange-yellow 50 70
a. Sheetlet. Nos. 397/9 × 2 .. .. .. 3·00
398 1 d. multicoloured 50 70
399 1 d. black, agate and orange-yellow 50 70

Designs:—No. 397, White Greyhound of Richmond; No. 398, Queen Elizabeth II; No. 399, Type **100**.

Nos. 397/9 were printed together in small sheets of 6, containing two *se-tenant* strips of 3, with horizontal gutter margin between.

NEW INFORMATION

The editor is always interested to correspond with people who have new information that will improve or correct the Catalogue.

101 Verreaux's Eagle Owl   102 M.V. *Lady Wright* (previous vessel)

(Des M. Bryan. Litho Questa)

1978 (28 Oct). *Abuko Nature Reserve* (2*nd series*). *T* **101** *and similar vert designs. Multicoloured. P* 14 × 13½.

400 20 b. Type **101** 35 35
401 25 b. Lizard Buzzard 40 40
402 50 b. African Harrier Hawk 85 85
403 1 d. 25, Long-crested Eagle .. .. .. 2·00 2·00

(Des A. Theobald. Litho Questa)

1978 (1 Dec). *New River Vessel "Lady Chilel Jawara" Commemoration. T* **102** *and similar horiz designs. Multicoloured. P* 14.

404 8 b. Type **102** 15 10
405 25 b. *Lady Chilel Jawara* (sectional view) .. 50 25
406 1 d. *Lady Chilel Jawara* .. .. .. 1·60 1·10

25b

103 Police Service   (104)

(Des G. Vasarhelyi. Litho Questa)

1979 (18 Feb). *14th Anniv of Independence. T* **103** *and similar horiz designs. Multicoloured. P* 14.

407 10 b. Type **103** 15 8
408 50 b. Fire service 60 40
409 1 d. 25, Ambulance service .. .. .. 1·40 1·10

1979 (5–26 Mar). *Nos.* 376 *and* 380/1 *surch as T* **104**.

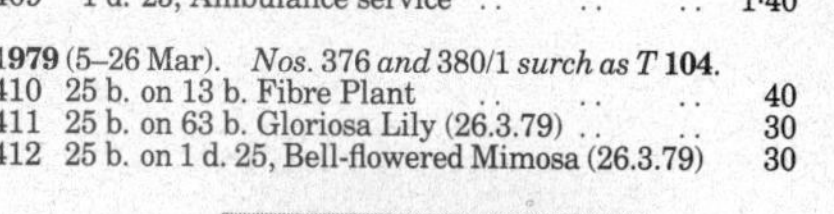

410 25 b. on 13 b. Fibre Plant 40 55
411 25 b. on 63 b. Gloriosa Lily (26.3.79) 30 35
412 25 b. on 1 d. 25, Bell-flowered Mimosa (26.3.79) 30 35

105 "Ramsgate Sands" (detail showing Children playing on Beach)

(Des C. Abbott. Litho Questa)

1979 (25 May). *International Year of the Child. T* **105** *and similar multicoloured designs showing the painting "Ramsgate Sands" by William Powell Frith. P* 14 × 13½ (25 *b.*) *or* 13½ × 14 (*others*).

413 10 b. Type **105** 8 8
414 25 b. Detail showing child paddling (*vert*) .. 20 20
415 1 d. Complete painting (60 × 23 *mm*) .. 60 60

106 1883 2½d. Stamp

(Des J.W. Litho Questa)

1979 (16 Aug). *Death Centenary of Sir Rowland Hill. T* **106** *and similar horiz designs showing stamps. Multicoloured. P* 14.

416 10 b. Type **106** 12 12
417 25 b. 1869 4d. 20 15
418 50 b. 1965 7½d. Independence commemorative 30 25
419 1 d. 25, 1935 1½d. Silver Jubilee commemorative 60 60
MS420 109 × 83 mm. No. 419 .. .. .. 65 70

107 Satellite Earth Station under Construction   108 "Apollo 11" leaving Launch Pad

(Des A. Theobald. Litho Questa)

1979 (20 Sept). *Abuko Satellite Earth Station. T* **107** *and similar horiz designs. Multicoloured. P* 14.

421 25 b. Type **107** 25 20
422 50 b. Satellite Earth Station (completed) .. 50 45
423 1 d. "Intelsat" satellites 90 70

(Des and litho Walsall)

1979 (17 Oct). *10th Anniv of Moon Landing. T* **108** *and similar vert designs. Multicoloured. (a) Sheet stamps. P* 14.

424 25 b. Type **108** 25 25
425 38 b. "Apollo 11" in Moon orbit 35 45
426 50 b. Splashdown 50 55

(b) Booklet stamps. Roul 5 × imperf. Self-adhesive*

427 25 b. Type **108** 25 30
a. Booklet pane. Nos. 427/9, each × 2 .. 1·60
428 38 b. As No. 425 .. .. 30 35
429 50 b. As No. 426 .. .. 30 40
430 2 d. Lunar module on Moon .. .. .. 1·50 1·75
a. Booklet pane of 1 .. .. 1·50

*Nos. 427/9 are separated by various combinations of rotary-knife (giving a straight edge) and roulette. No. 430 exists only with straight edges.

109 Large Spotted Acraea

(Des J. Cooter. Litho Questa)

1980 (3 Jan). *Abuko Nature Reserve (3rd series). Butterflies. T* **109** *and similar horiz designs. Multicoloured. P* 13½.

431 25 b. Type **109** 25 20
432 50 b. Yellow Pansy 45 40
433 1 d. Veined Swallowtail 75 80
434 1 d. 25, Foxy Charaxes 80 85
MS435 145 × 122 mm. Nos. 431/4 .. .. .. 2·00 2·10

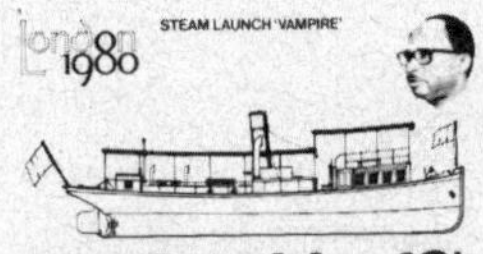

110 Steam Launch *Vampire*

(Des C. Abbott. Litho Harrison)

1980 (6 May). *"London 1980" International Stamp Exhibition. Mail Boats. T* **110** *and similar multicoloured designs. P* 14 (10, 25 b.) *or* 13 × 14 *(others).*

436 10 b. Type **110** 15 10
437 25 b. T.S.S. *Lady Denham* 25 15
438 50 b. T.S.C.M.Y. *Mansa Kila Ba* (49 × 26 *mm*) 40 35
439 1 d. 25, T.S.S. *Prince of Wales* (49 × 26 *mm*) .. 70 80

111 Queen Elizabeth the Queen Mother

(Des and litho Harrison)

1980 (4 Aug). *80th Birthday of Queen Elizabeth the Queen Mother. P* 14.

440 **111** 67 b. multicoloured 35 40

112 Phoenician Trading Vessel

113 "Madonna and Child" (Francesco de Mura)

(Des A. Theobald. Litho Walsall)

1980 (2 Oct). *Early Sailing Vessels. T* **112** *and similar horiz designs. Multicoloured. P* 14½ × 14.

441 8 b. Type **112** 10 5
442 67 b. Egyptian sea-going vessel 40 40
443 75 b. Portuguese caravel 45 45
444 1 d. Spanish vessel 70 70

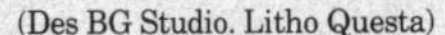

(Des BG Studio. Litho Questa)

1980 (23 Dec). *Christmas. Paintings. T* **113** *and similar vert designs. Multicoloured. P* 14.

445 8 b. Type **113** 5 5
446 67 b. "Praying Madonna with Crown of Stars" (workshop of Correggio) 45 45
447 75 b. "La Zingarella" (workshop replica of Correggio painting) 45 50

114 New Atlantic Hotel

(Des BG Studio. Litho Format)

1981 (18 Feb). *World Tourism Conference, Manila. T* **114** *and similar horiz designs. Multicoloured. P* 14.

448 25 b. Type **114** 20 15
449 75 b. Ancient stone circle 55 55
450 85 b. Conference emblem 70 70

115 1979 Abuko Satellite Earth Station 50 b. Commemorative

116 Prince Charles in Naval Uniform

(Des BG Studio. Litho Questa)

1981 (17 May). *World Telecommunications Day. T* **115** *and similar horiz designs. P* 14.

451 50 b. multicoloured 55 55
452 50 b. multicoloured 55 55
453 85 b. black and brown-ochre 80 80

Designs:—No. 452, 1975 Birth Centenary of Dr. Albert Schweitzer 50 b. commemorative; No. 453, I.T.U. and W.H.O. emblems.

(Des and litho J.W.)

1981 (22 July). *Royal Wedding. T* **116** *and similar vert designs. Multicoloured. P* 13½ × 13.

454 75 b. Wedding bouquet from Gambia 45 45
455 1 d. Type **116** 60 60
456 1 d. 25, Prince Charles and Lady Diana Spencer 70 70

117 Planting-out Seedlings

(Des Jennifer Toombs. Litho Format)

1981 (4 Sept). *10th Anniv of West African Rice Development Association. T* **117** *and similar horiz designs. Multicoloured. P* 14.

457 10 b. Type **117** 5 5
458 50 b. Care of the crops 35 35
459 85 b. Winnowing and drying 55 55

118 Bosc's Monitor

(Des J. Cooter. Litho Format)

1981 (17 Nov). *Abuko Nature Reserve (4th series). Reptiles. T* **118** *and similar horiz designs. Multicoloured. P* 14.

460 40 b. Type **118** 30 30
461 60 b. Dwarf Crocodile 50 50
462 80 b. Royal Python 60 60
463 85 b. Chameleon 65 65

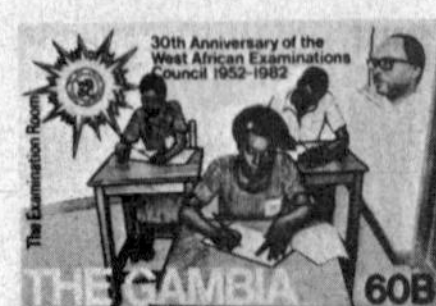

119 Examination Room

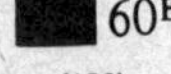

(120)

(Des PAD Studio. Litho Walsall)

1982 (16 Mar). *30th Anniv of West African Examinations Council. T* **119** *and similar horiz designs. Multicoloured. P* 14.

464 60 b. Type **119** 40 40
465 85 b. First High School 55 55
466 1 d. 10, Council's office 70 70

1982 (19 Apr). *No. 454 surch with T* **120**.

467 60 b. on 75 b. Wedding bouquet from Gambia 3·50 2·50

121 Tree-planting ("Conservation")

(Des L. Curtis. Litho Harrison)

1982 (16 May). *75th Anniv of Boy Scout Movement. T* **121** *and similar horiz designs. Multicoloured. P* 14.

468 85 b. Type **121** 60 60
469 1 d. 25, Woodworking 80 80
470 1 d. 27, Lord Baden-Powell 80 80

122 Gambia Football Team

123 Gambia Coat of Arms

(Des A. Theobald. Litho Questa)

1982 (13 June). *World Cup Football Championship, Spain. T* **122** *and similar horiz designs. Multicoloured. P* 14.

471 10 b. Type **122** 5 5
472 1 d. 10, Gambian team practice 70 70
473 1 d. 25, Bernabéu Stadium, Madrid 75 75
474 1 d. 55, FIFA World Cup 80 80
MS475 114 × 85 mm. Nos. 471/4 .. .. .. 2·25 2·50

(Des C. Abbott. Litho Walsall)

1982 (1 July). *21st Birthday of Princess of Wales. T* **123** *and similar vert designs. Multicoloured. P* 14½ × 14.

476 10 b. Type **123** 5 5
477 85 b. Princess at Cardiff City Hall, October 1981 .. .. 40 50
478 1 d. 10, Bride and groom returning to Buckingham Palace 50 55
479 2 d. 50, Formal portrait .. .. .. 1·25 1·40

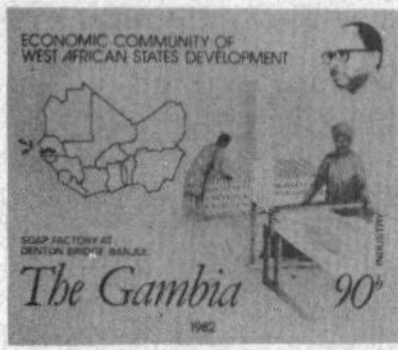

124 Vegetable Garden at Yundum Experimental Farm

(Des Harrison. Litho Questa)

1982 (5 Nov). *Economic Community of West African States Development. T* **124** *and similar horiz designs. Multicoloured. P* 14 × 14½.

480 10 b. Type **124** 8 8
481 60 b. Banjul/Kaolack microwave tower .. 40 40
482 90 b. Soap factory, Denton Bridge, Banjul .. 50 50
483 1 d. 25, Control tower, Yundum Airport .. 60 60

125 *Kassina cassinoides*

(Des PAD Studio. Litho Questa)

1982 (2 Dec). *Frogs. T* **125** *and similar horiz designs. Multicoloured. P* 14.

484 10 b. Type **125** 10 8
485 20 b. *Hylarana galamensis* 20 10
486 85 b. *Euphlyctis occipitalis* 50 50
487 2 d. *Kassina senegalensis* .. .. .. 1·40 1·40

OMNIBUS ISSUES

Details, together with prices for complete sets, of the various Omnibus issues from the 1935 Silver Jubilee series to date are included in a special section following Zululand at the end of the catalogue.

126 Satellite View of Gambia

127 Blessed Anne Marie Javouhey (foundress of the Order)

(Des Walsall. Litho Questa)

1983 (14 Mar). *Commonwealth Day. T* **126** *and similar horiz designs. Multicoloured. P* 14.

488 10 b. Type **126** 5 8
489 60 b. Batik cloth 40 45
490 1 d. 10, Bagging groundnuts 60 65
491 2 d. 10, Gambia flag .. .. 1·10 1·25

(Des G. Vasarhelyi. Litho Format)

1983 (8 Apr). *Centenary of Sisters of St. Joseph of Cluny's Work in Gambia. T* **127** *and similar multicoloured design. P* 13½.

492 10 b. Type **127** 5 8
493 85 b. Bathurst Hospital, nun and schoolchildren (*horiz*) 45 50

128 Canoes

(Des A. Theobald. Litho Walsall)

1983 (11 July). *River Craft. T* **128** *and similar horiz designs. Multicoloured. P* 14.

494 1 b. Type **128** 5 5
495 2 b. Upstream ferry 5 5
496 3 b. Dredging vessel 5 5
497 4 b. *Sir Dawda* (harbour launch) 5 5
498 5 b. Cargo liner 5 5
499 10 b. *Lady Dale* (60 ft launch) 5 8
500 20 b. Multi-purpose "Combo" ship 8 10
501 30 b. Large sailing canoe 10 12
502 40 b. *Lady Wright* (passenger and cargo ferry) 15 20
503 50 b. Cargo liner (*different*) 20 25
504 75 b. Fishing boats 25 30
505 1 d. Tug with groundnut barges 35 40
506 1 d. 25, Groundnut canoe 45 50
507 2 d. 50, *Banjul* (car ferry) 85 90
508 5 d. *Bintang Bolong* (ferry) .. .. .. 1·75 1·90
509 10 d. *Lady Chilel Jawara* (passenger and cargo ferry) .. .. 3·50 3·75
494/509 .. .. *Set of* 16 6·50 8·00

Nos. 494/509 come with a pattern of blue fluorescent security markings, resembling rosettes, printed on the reverse beneath the gum.

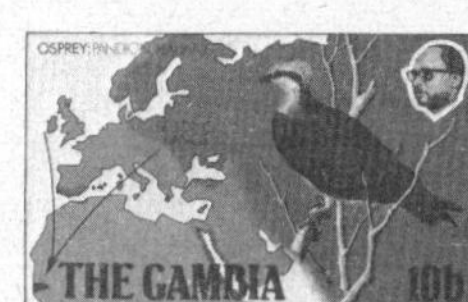

129 Osprey in Tree

(Des N. Arlott. Litho Questa)

1983 (12 Sept). *The Osprey. T* **129** *and similar horiz designs. Multicoloured. P* 14.

510 10 b. Type **129** 10 8
511 60 b. Osprey 40 40
512 85 b. Osprey with catch 50 50
513 1 d. 10, In flight 65 65

130 Local Ferry

(Des L. Curtis. Litho Questa)

1983 (10 Oct). *World Communications Year. T* **130** *and similar horiz designs. Multicoloured. P* 14.

514 10 b. Type **130** 5 8
515 85 b. Telex operator 45 50
516 90 b. Radio Gambia 45 50
517 1 d. 10, Loading mail onto aircraft 60 65

131 "St. Paul preaching at Athens" (detail) (Raphael)

(Des C. Abbott. Litho Questa)

1983 (1 Nov). *500th Birth Anniv of Raphael. T* **131** *and similar designs. P* 14.

518 60 b. multicoloured 35 40
519 85 b. multicoloured 45 50
520 1 d. multicoloured 50 55
MS521 105 × 83 mm. 2 d. multicoloured .. .. 1·00

Nos. 519/21 show different details of "St. Paul preaching at Athens", the 85 b. and 1 d. being horizontal and the 2 d. vertical.

132 Early Balloon and Siege of Paris Cover

133 Shot-putting

(Des Harrison. Litho Questa)

1983 (12 Dec). *Bicentenary of Manned Flight. T* **132** *and similar horiz designs. Multicoloured. P* 14.

522 60 b. Type **132** 35 40
a. Booklet pane. Nos. 522/3, each × 2 .. 1·60
523 85 b. Lufthansa aircraft and flown cover .. 45 50
524 90 b. Junkers aircraft and Hans Bertram cover 45 50
a. Booklet pane. Nos. 524/5, each × 2 .. 2·25
525 1 d. 25, Lunar module and H. E. Sieger's space cover 65 70
526 4 d. *Graf Zeppelin* (airship) .. .. .. 2·00 2·25
a. Booklet pane of 1 .. .. 2·00

Nos. 522/6 come with a pattern of blue fluorescent security markings, resembling rosettes, printed on the reverse beneath the gum.

No. 526 only exists from booklets.

On 14 December 1983 four provisional surcharges, 1 d. 50 on 1 d. 25 (No. 439), 1 d. 50 on 1 d. 25 (No. 473), 2d. on 1 d. 25 (No. 456) and 2 d. on 1 d. 10 (No. 478), were issued in very limited quantities, there being, it is believed, no more than 600 complete sets (*Price for set of* 4 £110 *mint*).

(Des G. Vasarhelyi. Litho Questa)

1984 (30 Mar). *Olympic Games, Los Angeles (1st issue). T* **133** *and similar multicoloured designs. P* 11.

527 60 b. Type **133** 25 30
528 85 b. High jumping (*horiz*) 35 40
529 90 b. Wrestling 35 40
530 1 d. Gymnastics 40 45
531 1 d. 25, Swimming (*horiz*) 50 55
532 2 d. Diving 80 85
527/32 .. .. *Set of* 6 2·40 2·75
MS533 100 × 80 mm. 5 d. Yachting. P 13½ × 14 2·00 2·25

See also Nos. 555/8.

134 Goofy

(Litho Format)

1984 (27 Apr). *Easter. T* **134** *and similar vert designs showing Walt Disney cartoon characters painting eggs. P* 11.

534 1 b. Type **134** 5 5
535 2 b. Mickey Mouse 5 5
536 3 b. Huey, Dewey and Louie 5 5
537 4 b. Goofy (*different*) 5 5
538 5 b. Donald Duck 5 5
539 10 b. Chip 'n Dale 5 5
540 60 b. Pluto 25 30
541 90 b. Scrooge McDuck 35 40
542 5 d. Morty and Ferdie .. .. 2·00 2·10
534/42 .. .. *Set of* 9 2·75 3·00
MS543 125 × 100 mm. 5 d. Donald Duck (*different*). P 13½ × 14 .. .. 2·00 2·25

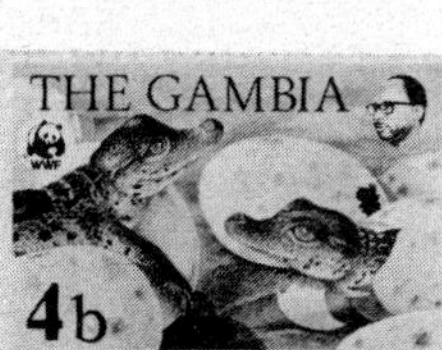

135 Young Crocodiles Hatching

136 Port Banjul

(Des Doreen McGuinness. Litho Format)

1984 (23 May). *The Nile Crocodile. T* **135** *and similar horiz designs. Multicoloured. P* 14.

544 4 b. Type **135** 5 5
545 6 b. Adult carrying young 5 5
546 90 b. Adult 30 35
547 1 d. 50, Crocodile at riverbank 60 65
MS548 126 × 94 mm. Nos. 544/7 .. .. .. 1·00 1·25

Nos. 544/8 come with a pattern of blue fluorescent security markings, resembling rosettes, printed on the reverse beneath the gum.

(Des C. Collins. Litho Questa)

1984 (1 June). *250th Anniv of "Lloyd's List" (newspaper). T* **136** *and similar vert designs. Multicoloured. P* 14½ × 14.

549 60 b. Type **136** 25 30
550 85 b. Cargo ship 35 40
551 90 b. Sinking of the *Dagomba* 35 40
552 1 d. 25, 19th century frigate 50 55

Nos. 549/52 come with a pattern of blue fluorescent security markings, resembling rosettes, printed on the reverse beneath the gum.

19th UPU
CONGRESS HAMBURG
(137)

138 Sprinting

1984 (19 June). *Universal Postal Union Congress, Hamburg. Nos.* 507/8 *optd with T* **137**.

553 2 d. 50, *Banjul* (car ferry) .. .. .. 1·00 1·10
554 5 d. *Bintang Bolong* (ferry) .. .. .. 2·00 2·25

(Des G. Vasarhelyi. Litho Walsall)

1984 (27 July). *Olympic Games, Los Angeles (2nd issue). T* **138** *and similar horiz designs. Multicoloured. P* 14.

555 60 b. Type **138** 25 30
556 85 b. Long jumping 35 40
557 90 b. Long-distance running 35 40
558 1 d. 25, Triple jumping 50 55

Nos. 555/8 come with a pattern of blue fluorescent security markings, resembling rosettes, printed on the reverse beneath the gum.

60b
THE GAMBIA

139 *Graf Zeppelin*

(Des D. Hartley-Marjoram. Litho Questa)

1984 (1 Nov). *50th Anniv of Gambia–South America Trans-atlantic Flights. T* **139** *and similar horiz designs. Multicoloured. P* 14.

559 60 b. Type **139** 25 30
560 85 b. Dornier "Wal" on S.S. *Westfalen* .. 35 40
561 90 b. Dornier "DO.18" 35 40
562 1 d. 25, Dornier "Wal" 50 55

Nos. 559/62 come with a pattern of blue fluorescent security markings, resembling rosettes, printed on the reverse beneath the gum.

Ghana

(*formerly* Gold Coast)

DOMINION

***CANCELLED REMAINDERS.** In 1961 remainders of some issues of 1957 to 1960 were put on the market cancelled-to-order in such a way as to be indistinguishable from genuine postally used copies for all practical purposes. Our used quotations which are indicated by an asterisk are the same for cancelled-to-order or postally used copies.

29 Dr. Kwame Nkrumah, Palm-nut Vulture and Map of Africa

GHANA
INDEPENDENCE
6TH MARCH.
1957.

(30)

(Photo Harrison)

1957 (6 Mar). *Independence. Wmk Mult Script CA. P* 14 × 14½.

No.	Type	Description	Unused	Used
166	**29**	2d. scarlet	10	5*
167		2½d. green	10	5*
168		4d. brown	15	5*
169		1s. 3d. deep blue	30	5*

1957 (6 Mar)–**58.** *Nos.* 153/64 *of Gold Coast optd as T* **30**.

No.	Description	Unused	Used
170	½d. bistre-brown and scarlet (*shades*)	5	5*
171	1d. deep blue (R.)	5	5*
172	1½d. emerald-green	10	5*
173	2d. chocolate (26.5.58)	20	10
174	2½d. scarlet (26.5.58)	75	90
175	3d. magenta	10	5*
176	4d. blue (26.5.58)	1·50	1·75
177	6d. black and orange (R.)	8	5*
178	1s. black and orange-red	12	5*
179	2s. brown-olive and carmine	25	5*
180	5s. purple and black	75	10*
181	10s. black and olive-green	1·25	30*
170/181	*Set of* 12	4·75	2·75*

The 6d. (No. 177) exists with double overprint.

Nos. 173/4 and 176 were officially issued on 26 May 1958 although, in error, small quantities were sold at certain post offices when the rest of the set appeared.

Nos. 170 and 171 exist in coils constructed from normal sheets.

31 Viking Ship

(Des W. Wind. Recess E. A. Wright Bank Note Co., Philadelphia)

1957 (27 Dec). *Inauguration of Black Star Shipping Line. T* **31** *and similar horiz designs. No wmk. P* 12.

No.	Description	Unused	Used
182	2½d. emerald-green	20	10
	a. Imperf between (vert pair)	£200	
	b. Imperf between (horiz pair)	£200	
183	1s. 3d. deep blue	45	90
	a. Imperf horiz (vert pair)	£200	
184	5s. bright purple	1·25	2·50
	a. Imperf vert (horiz pair)	£275	

Designs:—1s. 3d. Galleon; 5s. M.V. *Volta River*.

PRINTERS. Nos. 185/**MS**568 were printed in photogravure by Harrison & Sons *except where otherwise stated.*

34 Ambassador Hotel, Accra

35 Ghana Coat of Arms

1958 (6 Mar). *First Anniv of Independence. T* **34/5** *and similar designs. Wmk Mult Script CA. P* 14½ × 14 (2*s.*) *or* 14 × 14½ (*others*).

No.	Description	Unused	Used
185	½d. black, red, yellow, green and carmine	5	5
186	2½d. black, red, green and yellow	5	5
187	1s. 3d. black, red, yellow, green and blue	15	20
188	2s. red, yellow, blue, green, brown and black	20	35

Designs: *Horiz as T* 34—2½d. State Opening of Parliament; 1s. 3d. National Monument.

MINIMUM PRICE

The minimum price quoted is 5p which represents a handling charge rather than a basis for valuing common stamps. For further notes about prices see introductory pages.

38 Map showing the Independent African States

39 Map of Africa and Flaming Torch

(Des R. Milton)

1958 (15 Apr). *First Conference of Independent African States, Accra. Wmk Mult Script CA. P* 13½ × 14½ (2½*d.*, 3*d*) *or* 14½ × 13½ (*others*).

No.	Type	Description	Unused	Used
189	**38**	2½d. black, bistre and bright carmine-red	5	5
190		3d. black, bistre, brown and bright green	8	8
191	**39**	1s. black, yellow, red and dull blue	15	15
192		2s. 6d. black, yellow, red and dull violet	25	30

40 Palm-nut Vulture over Globe

41 "Britannia" Airliner

(Des M. Goaman (2½d., 2s. 6d.), R. Milton (1s. 3d.), W. Wind (2s.))

1958 (15 July). *Inauguration of Ghana Airways. T* **40/1** *and similar designs. Wmk Mult Script CA. P* 15 × 14 (2*s.* 6*d.*) *or* 14 × 15 (*others*).

No.	Description	Unused	Used
193	2½d. black, yellow-bistre & rose-carmine	8	5
194	1s. 3d. multicoloured	20	20
195	2s. multicoloured	25	35
196	2s. 6d. black and bistre	35	40

Designs: *Horiz* (*as T* 41)—2s. "Stratocruiser" and White-faced Storm Petrel. (*As T* 40)—2s. 6d. Palm-nut Vulture and jet aircraft.

PRIME
MINISTER'S
VISIT,
U.S.A. AND
CANADA

(44)

45

1958 (18 July). *Prime Minister's Visit to the United States and Canada. Nos.* 166/9 *optd with T* **44**.

No.	Type	Description	Unused	Used
197	**29**	2d. scarlet	5	5
198		2½d. green	5	5
199		4d. brown	8	8
200		1s. 3d. deep blue	10	10

(Des W. Wind)

1958 (24 Oct). *United Nations Day. Wmk Mult Script CA. P* 14 × 14½.

No.	Type	Description	Unused	Used
201	**45**	2½d. purple-brown, green and black	5	5
202		1s. 3d. purple-brown, blue and black	15	10
203		2s. 6d. purple-brown, violet and black	20	25

46 Dr. Nkrumah and Lincoln Statue, Washington

47

(Des M. Goaman)

1959 (12 Feb). *150th Birth Anniv of Abraham Lincoln.* W **47**. *P* 14 × 14½.

No.	Type	Description	Unused	Used
204	**46**	2½d. pink and deep purple	5	5
205		1s. 3d. light blue and blue	15	10
206		2s. 6d. orange-yellow & dp olive-green	20	25
MS206*a*		102 × 77 mm. Nos. 204/6. Imperf	1·00	1·50

48 Kente Cloth and Traditional Symbols

(Des Mrs. T. Sutherland (½d.), M. Karoly (2½d.), K. Antubam (1s. 3d.), A. M. Medina (2s.))

1959 (6 Mar). *Second Anniv of Independence. T* **48** *and similar multicoloured designs. W* **47**. *P* 14½ × 14 (2*s.*) *or* 14 × 14½ (*others*).

No.	Description	Unused	Used
207	½d. Type **48**	5	5
208	2½d. Talking drums and elephant-horn blower	5	5
209	1s. 3d. "Symbol of Greeting" (*vert*)	15	15
210	2s. Map of Africa, Ghana flag and palms	25	50

52 Globe and Flags

(Des Mrs. H. Potter)

1959 (15 Apr). *Africa Freedom Day. W* **47** (*sideways*). *P* 14½ × 14.

No.	Type	Description	Unused	Used
211	**52**	2½d. multicoloured	5	5
212		8½d. multicoloured	15	15

53 "God's Omnipotence"

54 Nkrumah Statue, Accra

55 Ghana Timber

56 Volta River

65a Leaping Antelope

Two Types of ½d. and 3d:

I. Inscr "GOD'S OMNIPOTENCE"
II. Inscr "GYE NYAMA"

(Des Mrs. T. Sutherland (½d., 3d.), Ghana Information Bureau (source of 1d. and 2d.), O. Haulkland (1½d.), A. Medina (2½d., 4d.), M. Goaman (6d., 1s. 3d., 2s. 6d.), W. Wind (11d., 1s., 2s., 5s.), W. H. Brown (10s.), M. Shamir (£1)).

1959 (5 Oct)–**61.** *T* **53/6**, **65***a*, *and similar multicoloured designs. W* **47** (*sideways on horiz designs*). *P* 11½ × 12 (½*d.*), 12 × 11½ (1*d.*), 14 × 14½ (1½*d.*, 11*d.*, 1*s.*, 2*s. and* 5*s.*), 14 × 15 (10*s.*) *or* 14½ × 14 (*others*). (*a*) *Postage.*

No.	Description	Unused	Used
213	½d. Type **53** (I)	5	5
	a. Type II (29.4.61)	30	5
214	1d. Type **54**	5	5
215	1½d. Type **55**	5	5
216	2d. Type **56**	5	5
217	2½d. Cocoa bean	5	5
218	3d. "God's Omnipotence" (I)	5	5
	a. Type II (29.4.61)	35	5
219	4d. Diamond and Mine	25	5
220	6d. Red-crowned Bishop	25	5
221	11d. Golden Spider Lily	25	5
222	1s. Shell Ginger	25	5
223	2s. 6d. Great Blue Turaco	1·00	20
224	5s. Tiger Orchid	3·00	50
225	10s. Tropical African Cichlid	2·75	90
225*a*	£1 Type **65***a* (29.4.61)	9·00	4·75
	(*b*) *Air*		
226	1s. 3d. Pennant-winged Nightjar	70	5
227	2s. Crowned Cranes	80	5
213/27	*Set of* 16	17·00	6·00

Nos. 217/224 and 226/7 are as Types **55/6**, the 11d., 1s., 5s. and 2s. (air) being vertical and the remainder horizontal. No. 225 is as Type **65***a*.

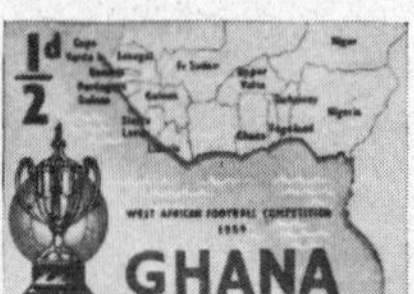

68 Gold Cup and West African Map

(Des K. Lehmann (½d., 3d.), M. & G. Shamir (1d.), W. Wind (8d.), and K. Antubam (2s. 6d.))

1959 (15 Oct). *West African Football Competition, 1959. T* **68** *and similar multicoloured designs. W* **47** *(sideways on horiz designs). P* 14 × 14½ *(1d., 2s. 6d) or* 14½ × 14 *(others).*

228 ½d. Type **68** 5 5*
229 1d. Footballers (*vert*) 5 5*
230 3d. Goalkeeper saving ball 8 5*
231 8d. Forward attacking goal 20 10*
232 2s. 6d. "Kwame Nkrumah" Gold Cup (*vert*) 55 20*

73 The Duke of Edinburgh and Arms of Ghana

(Des A. S. B. New)

1959 (24 Nov). *Visit of the Duke of Edinburgh to Ghana. W* **47** *(sideways). P* 15 × 14.

233 **73** 3d. black and magenta 5 5*

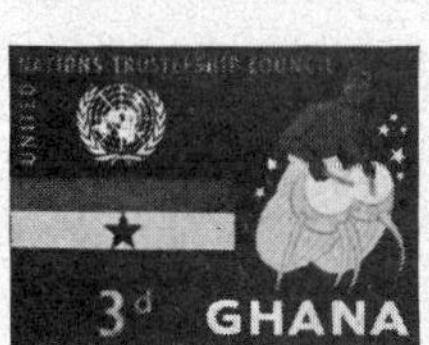

74 Ghana Flag and Talking Drums **75** Ghana Flag and U.N. Emblem

(Des K. Antubam (2s. 6d.), A. Medina (others))

1959 (10 Dec). *United Nations Trusteeship Council. T* **74/5** *and similar multicoloured designs. W* **47** *(sideways on 3d.). P* 14½ × 14 *(3d.) or* 14 × 14½ *(others).*

234 3d. Type **74** 5 5*
235 6d. Type **75** 8 5*
236 1s. 3d. Ghana flag and U.N. emblem (*vert*) 15 10*
237 2s. 6d. "Totem Pole" (*vert*) 20 20*

78 Eagles in Flight **79** Fireworks

(Des A. Medina (½d.), M. Goaman (3d.), W. Wind (1s. 3d., 2s.))

1960 (6 Mar). *Third Anniv of Independence. T* **78/9** *and similar vert designs. Multicoloured. W* **47**. *P* 14 × 14½.

238 ½d. Type **78** 5 5*
239 3d. Type **79** 5 5*
240 1s. 3d. "Third Anniversary" 20 12*
241 2s. "Ship of State" 30 20*

82

(Des W. Wind)

1960 (15 Apr). *Africa Freedom Day. T* **82** *and similar horiz designs. Multicoloured. W* **47** *(sideways). P* 14½ × 14.

242 3d. Type **82** 5 5*
243 6d. Letter "f" 8 5*
244 1s. Letter "d" 15 10*

REPUBLIC

85 President Nkrumah

(Des A. Medina (3d., 10s.), W. Wind (1s. 3d., 2s.))

1960 (1 July). *Republic Day. T* **85** *and similar multicoloured designs. W* **47**. *P* 14½ × 14 *(10s.) or* 14 × 14½ *(others).*

245 3d. Type **85** 5 5
246 1s. 3d. Ghana flag 15 12
247 2s. Torch of Freedom 25 25
248 10s. Arms of Ghana (*horiz*) 75 75
MS248*a* 102 × 77 mm. Nos. 245/8. Imperf .. 80 1·25

89 Olympic Torch **90** Athlete

(Des A. Medina (T **89**), W. Wind (T **90**))

1960 (15 Aug). *Olympic Games. W* **47** *(sideways on T* **90**). *P* 14 × 14½ *(T* **89**) *or* 14½ × 14 *(T* **90**).

249 **89** 3d. multicoloured 5 5
250 6d. multicoloured 10 5
251 **90** 1s. 3d. multicoloured 15 20
252 2s. 6d. multicoloured 30 35

91 President Nkrumah **94** U.N. Emblem and Ghana Flag

(Des M. Goaman (3d., 6d.), W. Wind (1s. 3d.))

1960 (21 Sept). *Founder's Day. T* **91** *and similar multicoloured designs. W* **47** *(sideways on 3d.). P* 14½ × 14 *(3d.) or* 14 × 14½ *(others).*

253 3d. Type **91** 5 5
254 6d. President Nkrumah (*vert*) 8 5
255 1s. 3d. Flag-draped column over map of African (*vert*) 20 15

(Des M. Goaman (3d., 1s. 3d.), W. Wind (6d.))

1960 (10 Dec). *Human Rights Day. T* **94** *and similar vert designs. W* **47**. *P* 14 × 14½.

256 3d. multicoloured 5 5
257 6d. yellow, black and blue 8 5
258 1s. 3d. multicoloured 20 20

Designs:—6d. U.N. emblem and Torch; 1s. 3d. U.N. emblem.

97 Talking Drums **100** Eagle on Column

(Des M. Goaman (3d.), A. S. B. New (6d.), W. Wind (2s.))

1961 (15 Apr). *Africa Freedom Day. T* **97** *and similar designs. W* **47** *(sideways on 2s.). P* 14½ × 14 *(2s.) or* 14 × 14½ *(others).*

259 3d. multicoloured 5 5
260 6d. red, black and green 8 5
261 2s. multicoloured 30 35

Designs: *Vert.*—6d. Map of Africa. *Horiz*—2s. Flags and map.

(Des A. S. B. New (3d.), M. Shamir (1s. 3d.), W. Wind (2s.))

1961 (1 July). *First Anniv of Republic. T* **100** *and similar vert designs. Multicoloured. W* **47**. *P* 14 × 14½.

262 3d. Type **100** 5 5
263 1s. 3d. "Flower" 15 12
264 2s. Ghana flags 30 35

103 Dove with Olive Branch **106** Pres. Nkrumah and Globe

(Des V. Whiteley)

1961 (1 Sept). *Belgrade Conference. T* **103** *and similar designs. W* **47** *(sideways on 1s. 3d., 5s.). P* 14 × 14½ *(3d.) or* 14½ × 14 *(others).*

265 3d. yellow-green 5 5
266 1s. 3d. deep blue 20 20
267 5s. bright reddish purple .. .. 85 1·10

Designs: *Horiz.*—1s. 3d. World map, chain and olive branch; 5s. Rostrum, conference room.

(Des A. Medina (3d.), M. Goaman (1s. 3d.), Miriam Karoly (5s.))

1961 (21 Sept). *Founder's Day. T* **106** *and similar multicoloured designs. W* **47** *(sideways on 3d.). P* 14½ × 14 *(3d.) or* 14 × 14½ *(others).*

268 3d. Type **106** 5 5
269 1s. 3d. President and Kente Cloth (*vert*) 25 20
270 5s. President in national costume (*vert*) .. 95 1·40
MS270*a* Three sheets 106 × 86 mm (3d.) or 86 × 106 mm (others) each with Nos. 268/70 in block of four. Imperf .. .. *Three sheets* 11·00 12·00

The 1s. 3d. Miniature Sheet is known with the brown colour omitted.

109 Queen Elizabeth II and African Map

(Des M. Goaman)

1961 (9 Nov). *Royal Visit. W* **47**. *P* 14½ × 14.

271 **109** 3d. multicoloured 5 5
272 1s. 3d. multicoloured 30 20
273 5s. multicoloured .. .. 1·00 1·25
MS273*a* 106 × 84 mm. No. 273 in block of four. Imperf .. .. 7·00 7·50

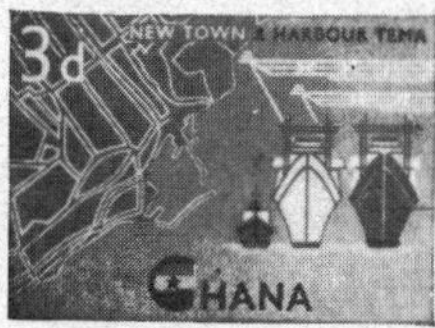

110 Ships in Tema Harbour

(Des C. Bottiau. Litho Enschedé & Sons)

1962 (10 Feb). *Opening of Tema Harbour. T* **110** *and similar horiz designs. Multicoloured. No wmk. P* 14 × 13. *(a) Postage.*

274 3d. Type **110** 10 5

(b) Air

275 1s. 3d. Aircraft and ships at Tema 35 20
276 2s. 6d. As 1s. 3d. 70 55

112 Africa and Peace Dove **113** Compass over Africa

(Des R. Hegeman. Litho Enschedé)

1962 (6 Mar). *First Anniv of Casablanca Conference. No wmk. P* 13 × 14. *(a) Postage.*

277 **112** 3d. multicoloured 5 5

(b) Air

278 **112** 1s. 3d. multicoloured 20 20
279 2s. 6d. multicoloured 25 35

(Des R. Hegeman)

1962 (24 Apr). *Africa Freedom Day. W* **47**. *P* 14 × 14½.

280 **113** 3d. sepia, blue-green and reddish purple 5 5
281 6d. sepia, blue-green and orange-brown 8 5
282 1s. 3d. sepia, blue-green and red .. 15 15

114 Ghana Star and "Five Continents" **115** Atomic Bomb-burst "Skull"

(Des M. Goaman (3d.), M. Shamir (6d.), W. Wind (1s. 3d.))

1962 (21 June). *Accra Assembly, T* **114/15** *and similar vert design. W* **47**. *P* 14 × 14½.
283 3d. black and lake-red .. 8 5
284 6d. black and scarlet .. 12 10
285 1s. 3d. turquoise .. 30 30
Design:—1s. 3d. Dove of Peace.

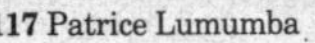

117 Patrice Lumumba

118 Star over Two Columns

(Des A. S. B. New)

1952 (30 June). *1st Death Anniv of Lumumba. W* **47**. *P* 14½ × 14.
286 **117** 3d. black and orange-yellow .. 8 5
287 6d. black, green and lake .. 10 5
288 1s. 3d. black, pink and black-green .. 20 20

(Des A. S. B. New (3d.), A. Medina (6d.), M. Goaman (1s. 3d.) Litho Enschedé)

1962 (1 July). *2nd Anniv of Republic. T* **118** *and similar multi-coloured designs. P* 14 × 13½ *(1s. 3d.) or* 13½ × 14 *(others).*
289 3d. Type **118** .. 5 5
290 6d. Flaming torch .. 10 5
291 1s. 3d. Eagle trailing flag (*horiz*) .. 15 20

121 President Nkrumah

125 Campaign Emblem

(Litho Enschedé)

1962 (21 Sept). *Founder's Day. T* **121** *and similar vert designs. P* 13 × 14½.
292 1d. multicoloured .. 5 5
293 3d. multicoloured .. 5 5
294 1s. 3d. black and bright blue .. 15 10
295 2s. multicoloured .. 20 25
Designs:—3d. Nkrumah medallion; 1s. 3d. President Nkrumah and Ghana Star; 2s. Laying "Ghana" Brick.

1962 (3 Dec). *Malaria Eradication. W* **47**. *P* 14 × 14½.
296 **125** 1d. cerise .. 5 5
297 4d. yellow-green .. 10 5
298 6d. bistre .. 10 5
299 1s. 3d. bluish violet .. 20 25
MS299*a* 90 × 115 mm. Nos. 296/9. Imperf .. 65 85

126 Campaign Emblem

129 Map of Africa

1963 (21 Mar). *Freedom from Hunger. T* **126** *and similar designs. W* **47** *(sideways on 4d., 1s. 3d.). P* 14 × 14½ *(1d.) or* 14½ × 14 *(others).*
300 1d. multicoloured .. 10 5
301 4d. sepia, yellow and orange .. 40 5
302 1s. 3d. ochre, black and green .. 1·25 55
Designs: *Horiz*—4d. Emblem in hands; 1s. 3d. World map and emblem.

1963 (15 Apr). *Africa Freedom Day. T* **129** *and similar designs. W* **47** *(sideways on 4d.). P* 14½ × 14 *(4d.) or* 14 × 14½ *(others).*
303 1d. gold and red .. 5 5
304 4d. red, black and yellow .. 10 5
305 1s. 3d. multicoloured .. 20 20
306 2s. 6d. multicoloured .. 40 50
Designs: *Horiz*—4d. Carved stool. *Vert*—1s. 3d. Map and bowl of fire; 2s. 6d. Antelope and flag.

OMNIBUS ISSUES

Details, together with prices for complete sets, of the various Omnibus issues from the 1935 Silver Jubilee series to date are included in a special section following Zululand at the end of the catalogue.

133 Red Cross

137 "3rd Anniversary"

(Des R. Hegeman (4d.), M. Shamir (others))

1963 (28 May). *Red Cross Centenary. T* **133** *and similar multi-coloured designs. W* **47** *(sideways on 1½d., 4d.). P* 14½ × 14 *(1d., 1s. 3d.) or* 14 × 14½ *(others).*
307 1d. Type **133** .. 10 5
308 1½d. Centenary emblem (*horiz*) .. 20 15
309 4d. Nurses and child (*horiz*) .. 35 5
310 1s. 3d. Emblem, globe and laurel .. 75 55
MS310*a* 102 × 127 mm. Nos. 307/10. Imperf .. 1·10 1·40

(Des M. Goaman (1d., 4d.), R. Hegeman (others))

1963 (1 July). *3rd Anniv of Republic. T* **137** *and similar multi-coloured designs. W* **47** *(sideways on 1d., 4d.). P* 14½ × 14 *(horiz) or* 14 × 14½ *(vert).*
311 1d. Type **137** .. 5 5
312 4d. Three Ghanaian flags .. 10 5
313 1s. 3d. Map, flag and star (*vert*) .. 15 20
314 2s. 6d. Flag and torch (*vert*) .. 25 35

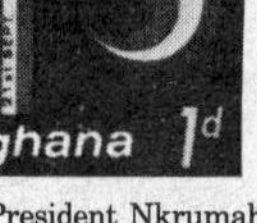

141 President Nkrumah and Ghana Flag

145 Rameses II, Abu Simbel

(Des R. Hegeman (1d., 4d.), M. Shamir (1s. 3d.), G. Rose (5s.))

1963 (21 Sept). *Founder's Day. T* **141** *and similar designs. W* **47** *(sideways on 1s. 3d., 5s.). P* 14 × 14½ *(vert) or* 14½ × 14 *(horiz).*
315 1d. multicoloured .. 5 5
316 4d. multicoloured .. 8 5
317 1s. 3d. multicoloured .. 20 10
318 5s. yellow and bright reddish purple .. 60 75
Designs: *Vert*—4d. Nkrumah and flag. *Horiz*—1s. 3d. Nkrumah and fireworks; 5s. Symbol of Wisdom.

(Des M. Farrar Bell and R. Hegeman. Litho (1½d., 2d.) or photo (others) Enschedé)

1963 (1 Nov). *Nubian Monuments Preservation. T* **145** *and similar multicoloured designs. No wmk. P* 11½ × 11 *(vert) or* 11 × 11½ *(horiz).*
319 1d. Type **145** .. 5 5
320 1½d. Rock paintings (*horiz*) .. 10 15
321 2d. Queen Nefertari (*horiz*) .. 10 5
322 4d. Sphinx, Sebua .. 20 12
323 1s. 3d. Rock Temple, Abu Simbel (*horiz*) .. 70 80

150 Steam and Diesel Locomotives

151 Eleanor Roosevelt and "Flame of Freedom"

(Des H. L. W. Stevens)

1963 (1 Dec). *60th Anniv of Ghana Railway. W* **47** *(sideways). P* 14½ × 14.
324 **150** 1d. multicoloured .. 10 5
325 6d. multicoloured .. 50 10
326 1s. 3d. multicoloured .. 1·00 60
327 2s. 6d. multicoloured .. 2·25 2·25

(Des R. Hegeman and F. H. Savage. Photo Enschedé)

1963 (10 Dec). *15th Anniv of Declaration of Human Rights. T* **151** *and similar multicoloured designs. No wmk. P* 11 × 11½ *(1s. 3d.) or* 11½ × 11 *(others).*
328 1d. Type **151** .. 5 5
329 4d. Type **151** .. 8 5
330 6d. Eleanor Roosevelt .. 10 5
331 1s. 3d. Eleanor Roosevelt and emblems (*horiz*) .. 15 15
No. 329 differs from No. 328 in the arrangement of the trailing "flame" and of the background within the circular emblem.

154 Sun and Globe Emblem

155 Harvesting Corn on State Farm

1964 (15 June). *International Quiet Sun Years. W* **47** *(sideways). Each blue, yellow, red and green; background colours given. P* 14½.
332 **154** 3d. pale brown .. 5 5
333 6d. pale grey .. 8 5
334 1s. 3d. mauve .. 12 15
MS334*a* 90 × 90 mm. No. 334 in block of four. Imperf .. 1·25 1·60
Nos. 332/4 each exist in a miniature sheet of 12 in different colours (i.e. 3d. in colours of 6d.; 6d. in colours of 1s. 3d.; 1s. 3d. in colours of 3d.) but these were not generally available to the public.

(Des M. Shamir. Photo Govt Printer, Israel)

1964 (1 July). *4th Anniv of Republic. T* **155** *and similar horiz designs. P* 13 × 14.
335 3d. olive, brown and yellow-olive .. 5 5
336 6d. bluish green, brown and turquoise-green .. 10 5
337 1s. 3d. brown-red, brown and salmon-red .. 20 10
338 5s. multicoloured .. 60 90
MS338*a* 126 × 100 mm. Nos. 335/8. Imperf .. 1·00 1·25
Designs:—6d. Oil refinery, Tema; 1s. 3d. "Communal Labour"; 5s. Procession headed by flag.

159 Globe and Dove

163 Pres. Nkrumah and Hibiscus Flowers

(Des M. Shamir. Litho Lewin-Epstein Ltd, Bat Yam, Israel)

1964 (15 July). *1st Anniv of African Unity Charter. T* **159** *and similar designs. P* 14.
339 3d. multicoloured .. 5 5
340 6d. deep bronze-green and red .. 10 5
341 1s. 3d. multicoloured .. 15 10
342 5s. multicoloured .. 55 80
Designs: *Vert*—6d. Map of Africa and quill pen; 5s. Planting flower. *Horiz*—1s. 3d. Hitched rope on map of Africa.

1964 (21 Sept). *Founder's Day. W* **47** *(sideways). P* 14 × 14½.
343 **163** 3d. sepia, red, deep green and light blue .. 5 5
344 6d. sepia, red, deep green and yellow .. 10 5
345 1s. 3d. sepia, red, deep green and grey .. 15 10
346 2s. 6d. sepia, red, dp grn & light emerald .. 25 35
MS346*a* 90 × 122 mm. No. 346 in block of four. Imperf .. 1·50 2·50

IMPERFORATE STAMPS. Many issues, including miniature sheets, from here onwards exist imperforate, but these were not sold at post offices.

164 Hurdling

(Des A. S. B. New (No. 352))

1964 (25 Oct). *Olympic Games, Tokyo. T* **164** *and similar multicoloured designs. W* **47** *(sideways on 1d., 2½d., 6d., 5s.). P* 14½ × 14 *(horiz) or* 14 × 14½ *(vert).*
347 1d. Type **164** .. 5 5
348 2½d. Running .. 8 5
349 3d. Boxing (*vert*) .. 10 5
350 4d. Long-jumping (*vert*) .. 12 5
351 6d. Football (*vert*) .. 12 5
352 1s. 3d. Athlete holding Olympic Torch (*vert*) .. 35 25
353 5s. Olympic Rings and flags .. 1·40 1·75
347/53 .. *Set of* 7 2·00 2·00
MS353*a* 128 × 102 mm. Nos. 351/3. Imperf .. 2·00 2·50

171 G. Washington Carver (botanist) and Plant

173 African Elephant

(Des M. Shamir)

1964 (7 Dec). *U.N.E.S.C.O. Week.* *W* **47**. *P* 14½.
354 **171** 6d. deep blue and green 10 5
355 – 1s. 3d. reddish purple and greenish blue 25 20
356 **171** 5s. sepia and orange-red .. .. 1·50 2·00
MS356*a* 127 × 77 mm. Nos. 354/6. Imperf .. 2·10 2·40
Designs:—1s. 3d. Albert Einstein (scientist) and atomic symbol.

(Des A. S. B. New (No. 360). Photo Enschedé)

1964 (14 Dec). *Multicoloured designs as T* **173**. *P* 11½ × 11 (*vert*) *or* 11 × 11½ (*horiz*).
357 1d. Type **173** 15 10
358 1½d. Secretary Bird (*horiz*) 25 50
359 2½d. Purple Wreath (flower) 30 60
360 3d. Grey Parrot 30 30
361 4d. Blue-naped Mousebird (*horiz*) 40 40
362 6d. African Tulip Tree (*horiz*) 45 20
363 1s. 3d. Violet Starling (*horiz*) .. .. 90 1·25
364 2s. 6d. Hippopotamus (*horiz*) .. .. 2·25 4·00
357/64 .. .. *Set of* 8 4·50 6·50
MS364*a* (*a*) 150 × 86 mm. Nos. 357/9, (*b*) 150 × 110 mm. Nos. 360/4. Both Imperf .. *Two sheets* 8·00 10·00

181 I.C.Y. Emblem

182 I.T.U. Emblem and Symbols

(Litho Enschedé)

1965 (22 Feb). *International Co-operation Year.* *P* 14 × 12½.
365 **181** 1d. multicoloured 15 5
366 4d. multicoloured 45 20
367 6d. multicoloured 55 15
368 1s. 3d. multicoloured .. .. .. 1·40 1·00
MS368*a* 100 × 100 mm. No. 368 in block of four. Imperf .. .. 2·25 2·25

(Litho Enschedé)

1965 (12 Apr). *I.T.U. Centenary.* *P* 13½.
369 **182** 1d. multicoloured 15 5
370 6d. multicoloured 30 10
371 1s. 3d. multicoloured 65 40
372 5s. multicoloured .. .. .. 2·75 2·75
MS372*a* 132 × 115 mm. Nos. 369/72. Imperf .. 4·75 5·50

183 Lincoln's Home

(Des M. Farrar Bell (6d.), A. S. B. New (1s. 3d., 5s.), R. Hegeman (2s.))

1965 (17 May). *Death Centenary of Abraham Lincoln. T* **183** *and similar square-shaped designs. W* **47** (*sideways*). *P* 12½.
373 6d. multicoloured 15 5
374 1s. 3d. black, red and blue 40 25
375 2s. black, orange-brown and greenish yellow 55 55
376 5s. black and red .. .. 1·25 2·00
MS376*a* 115 × 115 mm. Nos. 373/6. Imperf .. 2·25 3·50
Designs:—1s. 3d. Lincoln's Inaugural Address; 2s. Abraham Lincoln; 5s. Adaptation of U.S. 90 c. Lincoln Stamp of 1869.

(New Currency. 100 pesewas = 1 cedi)

187 Obverse (Pres. Nkrumah) and Reverse of 5 p. Coin

(Photo Enschedé)

1965 (19 July). *Introduction of Decimal Currency. T* **187** *and similar horiz designs. Multicoloured. P* 11 × 13 (5 *p*., 10 *p*.), 13 × 12½ (25 *p*.) *or* 13½ × 14 (50 *p*.).
377 5 p. Type **187** 15 8
378 10 p. As Type **187** 30 15
379 25 p. Size 63 × 39 mm 80 80
380 50 p. Size 71 × 43½ mm .. .. .. 1·50 1·75
The coins in Nos. 378/80 are all circular and express the same denominations as on the stamps.

NEW INFORMATION

The editor is always interested to correspond with people who have new information that will improve or correct the Catalogue.

₵2·40
Ghana New Currency
19th July. 1965.

(188)

1965 (19 July). *Nos.* 214, 216 *and* 218*a*/27 *surch as T* **188** *diagonally upwards,* (D) *or horizontally,* (H), *by Govt Printer, Accra.*

(*a*) *Postage*
381 1 p. on 1d. multicoloured (R.) (D) 5 5
a. Surch inverted .. .. 15·00
b. Surch double
382 2 p. on 2d. multicoloured (Ultram.) (H) .. 5 5
a. Surch inverted
b. Surch double .. .. 10·00
c. Surch on back only
d. Surch on back and face
e. Red surch .. .. 26·00
f. Orange surch .. .. 26·00
g. Indigo surch
383 3 p. on 3d. multicoloured (II) (Br.) (H) .. 95 1·00
a. Surch inverted .. .. 18·00
b. Indigo surch
384 4 p. on 4d. multicoloured (B.) (H) 12 5
a. Surch inverted .. .. 14·00
b. Surch double
c. Red surch
385 6 p. on 6d. multicoloured (Blk.) (H) 15 5
a. Surch inverted .. .. 8·50
b. Surch double .. .. 15·00
c. Horiz pair, one without surch .. .. 40·00
386 11 p. on 11d. multicoloured (W.) (D) 25 12
a. Surch inverted .. .. 11·00
387 12 p. on 1s. multicoloured (B.) (D) 25 10
a. Surch double
b. Black surch .. .. 9·00
ba. Surch inverted .. .. 9·00
388 30 p. on 2s. 6d. multicoloured (B.) (H) .. .. 1·50 1·25
389 60 p. on 5s. multicoloured (B.) (D) .. .. 2·50 1·25
a. Surch double (G. + B.) .. .. .. 20·00
390 ₵1.20 on 10s. multicoloured (B.) (D) .. 2·75 4·00
a. Surch double (G. + B.)
391 ₵2.40 on £1 multicoloured (B.) (D) .. .. 5·50 9·00

(*b*) *Air*
392 15 p. on 1s. 3d. multicoloured (W.) (H) .. 90 20
a. Surch inverted
393 24 p. on 2s. multicoloured (G.) (D) .. .. 1·00 40
381/93 .. .. *Set of* 13 14·00 16·00
On the diagonal surcharges the values are horizontal.
The 30 p. was not released in Ghana until 30 July and the 3 p. sometime later.
Numerous minor varieties exist.

189 "OAU" and Flag

190 "OAU", Heads and Flag

191 "OAU" Emblem and Flag

192 African Map and Flag

1965 (21 Oct). *O.A.U. Summit Conference, Accra. T* **189/92** *and similar horiz designs. Multicoloured. W* **47** (*sideways, except on* 6 *p*.). *P* 14 (*T* **189/91**) *or* 14½ × 14 (*others*).
394 1 p. Type **189** 5 5
395 2 p. Type **190** 5 5
396 5 p. Type **191** 12 8
397 6 p. Type **192** 12 8
398 15 p. "Sunburst", map and flag 35 35
399 24 p. "O.A.U." on map, and flag 60 70
394/9 .. .. *Set of* 6 1·10 1·25

195 Goalkeeper saving Ball

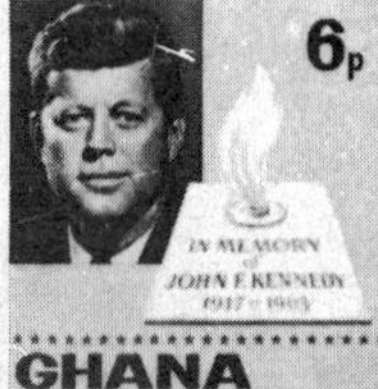

198 Pres. Kennedy and Grave Memorial

(Photo Enschedé)

1965 (15 Nov). *African Soccer Cup Competition. T* **195** *and similar multicoloured designs. P* 13 × 14 (15 *p*.) *or* 14 × 13 (*others*).
400 6 p. Type **195** 15 8
401 15 p. Player with ball (*vert*) 35 30
402 24 p. Players, ball and soccer cup 60 60

(Des A. S. B. New (No. 405))

1965 (15 Dec)–**66**. *2nd Anniv of President Kennedy's Death. T* **198** *and similar square-shaped designs. W* **47** (*sideways*). *P* 12½.
403 6 p. multicoloured 25 10
404 15 p. violet, red and green 55 35
405 24 p. black and reddish violet 75 60
406 30 p. dull purple and black 90 75
MS407 114½ × 114 mm. Nos. 403/6. Imperf (21.3.66) .. .. 3·50 4·75
Designs:—15 p. Pres. Kennedy and Eternal Flame; 24 p. Pres. Kennedy and memorial inscription; 30 p. President Kennedy.

202 Section of Dam and Generators

Black Stars Retain Africa Cup
21st Nov. 1965

(206)

(Des A. S. B. New (No. 411). Photo Enschedé)

1966 (22 Jan). *Volta River Project. T* **202** *and similar horiz designs. P* 11 × 11½.
408 6 p. multicoloured 15 5
409 15 p. multicoloured 40 35
410 24 p. multicoloured 50 55
411 30 p. black and new blue 70 85
Designs:—15 p. Dam and Lake Volta; 24 p. Word "GHANA" as dam; 30 p. "Fertility".

1966 (7 Feb). *"Black Stars" Victory in African Soccer Cup Competition. Nos.* 400/2 *optd with T* **206**, *in black.*
412 6 p. Type **195** 15 15
a. Green opt .. .. 20·00
b. Green opt double, one inverted
413 15 p. Player with ball 30 30
414 24 p. Players, ball and cup 45 45
a. Opt inverted* .. .. 26·00
ab. Vert pair, one without opt, the other with opt inverted
b. Error. Opt for 15 p. on 24 p. inverted.*
*In No. 414a the overprint reads downwards (top right to bottom left), but in No. 414b it reads upwards (bottom right to top left).

DATES OF ISSUE of miniature sheets are approximate as they are generally released some time after the related ordinary stamps, but it known that the G.P.O. sometimes apply first-day cancellations months after the dates shown on the cancellations.

207 W.H.O. Building and Ghana Flag

1966 (1 July). *Inauguration of W.H.O. Headquarters, Geneva. T* **207** *and similar horiz design. Multicoloured. W* **47**. *P* 14½ × 14.
415 6 p. Type **207** 15 8
416 15 p. Type **207** 35 25
417 24 p. W.H.O. Building and emblem 65 65
418 30 p. As 24 p. 85 85
MS419 120 × 101 mm. Nos. 415/18. Imperf (11.66) 4·25 5·50

209 Herring

214 African "Links" and Ghana Flag

(Des O. Hamann. Photo Enschedé)

1966 (10 Aug). *Freedom from Hunger. T* **209** *and similar horiz designs. Multicoloured. P* 14 × 13.
420 6 p. Type **209** 20 10
421 15 p. Flat Fish 45 25
422 24 p. Spade Fish 75 55
423 30 p. Red Snapper .. .. 1·00 85
424 60 p. Tuna .. .. 2·50 2·75
MS425 126 × 109 mm. No. 423 in block of four. Imperf (Nov) .. .. 6·50 7·00

(Photo Enschedé)

1966 (11 Oct). *Third Anniv of African Charter. T* **214** *and similar multicoloured designs. P* 13½.
426 6 p. Type **214** 10 8
427 15 p. Flags as "Quill", and diamond (*horiz*) .. 35 35
428 24 p. Ship's wheel, map and cocoa bean (*horiz*) 45 45

217 Player heading Ball, and Jules Rimet Cup

1966 (14 Nov). *World Cup Football Championships, England. T* **217** *and similar horiz designs. Multicoloured. W* **47.** *P* 14½ × 14.
429 5 p. Type **217** 12 5
430 15 p. Goalkeeper clearing ball.. .. .. .. 30 25
431 24 p. Player and Jules Rimet Cup (replica) .. 50 40
432 30 p. Players and Jules Rimet Cup (replica) .. 65 55
433 60 p. Players with ball.. .. .. 1·60 1·40
MS434 120 × 102 mm. 60 p. (block of four). Imperf 5·00 7·50

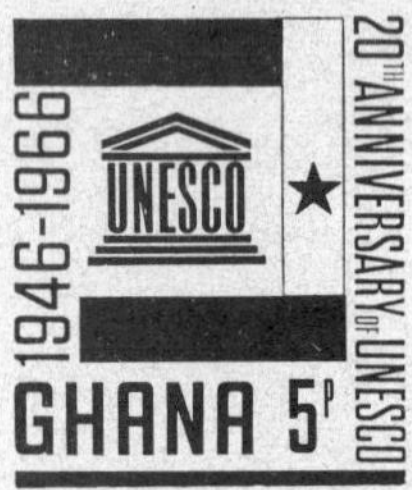

222 U.N.E.S.C.O. Emblem

1966 (23 Dec). *20th Anniv of U.N.E.S.C.O. W* **47** *(sideways). P* 14½.
435 **222** 5 p. multicoloured 12 10
436 15 p. multicoloured 35 35
437 24 p. multicoloured 60 60
438 30 p. multicoloured .. .. 90 1·25
439 60 p. multicoloured .. .. 2·00 2·50
MS440 140 × 115 mm. Nos. 435/9. Imperf .. 6·50 8·50

223 Fair Emblem and Crates

1967 (1 Feb). *Ghana Trade Fair, Accra. T* **223** *and similar multicoloured designs. W* **47** *(sideways on 24 p.). P* 14 × 14½ *(24 p.) or* 14½ × 14 *(others).*
441 5 p. Type **223** 10 8
442 15 p. Fair emblem and world map 30 20
443 24 p. Shipping and flags (*vert*).. .. .. 50 45
444 36 p. Fair emblem and hand-held hoist .. 65 65

(New Currency. 100 new pesewas = 1 new cedi (1·2 old cedi))

1½Np N₵2.00
(227) (228)

229 Ghana Eagle and Flag

1967 (23 Feb). *Nos.* 216, 219/23, 225/6 *and* 393 *surch as T* **227/8.**

(*a*) *Postage*
445 1½ n.p. on 2d. multicoloured (Blk.) .. .. 7·00 3·00
446 3½ n.p. on 4d. multicoloured (R.) 20 5
447 5 n.p. on 6d. multicoloured (R.) 20 5
448 9 n.p. on 11d. multicoloured (W.) 30 15
449 10 n.p. on 1s. multicoloured (W.) 30 15
450 25 n.p. on 2s. 6d. multicoloured (R.) .. 2·25 1·75
451 1 n.c. on 10s. multicoloured (R.) .. .. 9·50 13·00
452 2 n.c. on £1 multicoloured (R.) .. .. 20·00 26·00

(*b*) *Air*
453 12½ n.p. on 1s. 3d. multicoloured (W.) .. 1·25 70
454 20 n.p. on 24 p. on 2s. multicoloured (R.) 2·00 1·50
445/54.. .. .. *Set of* 10 38·00 42·00
Inverted surcharges in a different type face on the 3½, 5 and 25 n.p. are fakes.

(Des M. Shamir)

1967 (24 Feb). *First Anniv of February 24 Revolution. W* **47** *(sideways). P* 14 × 14½.
455 **229** 1 n.p. multicoloured 5 5
456 4 n.p. multicoloured 15 5
457 12½ n.p. multicoloured 60 45
458 25 n.p. multicoloured .. .. .. 1·25 1·50
MS459 89 × 108 mm. Nos. 455/8. Perf or imperf .. 3·50 5·00

230 Maize

231 Forest Kingfisher

235 Rufous-crowned Roller

236 Akosombo Dam

1967 (1 June–4 Sept). *T* **230/1, 235/6** *and similar designs. W* **47** *(1½, 2, 4, 50 n.p. and 1 n.c.) or sideways (others). P* 11½ × 12 *(1, 8 n.p.),* 12 × 11½ *(4 n.p.),* 14 × 14½ *(1½, 2, 2½, 20 n.p., 2 n.c. 50) or* 14½ × 14 *(others).*
460 1 n.p. multicoloured 5 5
461 1½ n.p. multicoloured 20 5
a. Blue omitted* .. .. 65·00
b. Green printed double, once inverted†
462 2 n.p. multicoloured (4.9) 10 5
463 2½ n.p. multicoloured (4.9) 30 5
a. Wmk upright .. .. 30·00
464 3 n.p. multicoloured 15 5
465 4 n.p. multicoloured 15 5
466 6 n.p. multicoloured 15 5
467 8 n.p. multicoloured 15 5
468 9 n.p. multicoloured (4.9) 20 5
469 10 n.p. multicoloured 15 5
470 20 n.p. deep blue and new blue (4.9) 20 5
471 50 n.p. multicoloured 55 15
472 1 n.c. multicoloured (4.9) 70 50
473 2 n.c. multicoloured (4.9) .. .. .. 1·40 1·25
474 2 n.c. 50, multicoloured .. .. .. 1·60 1·50
460/74 .. .. *Set of* 15 5·50 3·25
Designs: *Vert* (*as T* **231**)—2 n.p. The Ghana Mace; 2½ n.p. Commelina; 20 n.p. Hare; 2 n.c. Frangipani; 2 n.c. 50, Seat of State. *Horiz* (*as T* **236**)—3 n.p. Mud-fish; 9 n.p. Chameleon; 10 n.p. Tema Harbour; 50 n.p. Black-winged Stilt; 1 n.c. Wooden Stool. (*As T* **230**)—8 n.p. Adomi Bridge.
*In this stamp the blue not only affects the bird but is printed over the yellow background to give the value in green, so that its omission results in the value also being omitted.
†This affects the feather-tips and the flag.
The 2 n.p. and 20 n.p. were officially issued on 4 September but small quantities of both were released in error on 1 June. The 2½ n.p. is also known to have been released in error in June.

245 Kumasi Fort

249 "Luna 10"

(Des O. Hamann)

1967 (1 July). *Castles and Forts. T* **245** *and similar designs. Multicoloured. W* **47** *(diagonal). P* 14½.
475 4 n.p. Type **245** 30 5
476 12½ n.p. Christiansborg Castle and British galleon .. .. 1·50 1·25
477 20 n.p. Elmina Castle and Portuguese galleon .. .. 1·75 1·75
478 25 n.p. Cape Coast Castle and Spanish galleon .. .. 2·00 2·25

(Des M. Shamir. Photo Enschedé)

1967 (16 Aug). *"Peaceful Use of Outer Space". T* **249** *and similar square designs. Multicoloured. P* 13½ × 14.
479 4 n.p. Type **249** 10 5
480 10 n.p. "Orbiter 1" 25 25
481 12½ n.p. Man in Space 35 35
MS482 140 × 90 mm. Nos. 479/81. Imperf .. 95 1·40

252 Scouts and Camp-fire

(Photo Enschedé)

1967 (18 Sept). *50th Anniv of Ghanaian Scout Movement. T* **252** *and similar horiz designs. Multicoloured. P* 14½ × 13.
483 4 n.p. Type **252** 25 5
484 10 n.p. Scout on march 85 40
485 12½ n.p. Lord Baden-Powell .. .. .. 1·10 90
MS486 167 × 95 mm. Nos. 483/5. Imperf .. .. 2·50 3·25

255 U.N. Headquarters Building **256** General View of U.N. H.Q., Manhattan

(Litho D.L.R.)

1967 (20 Nov). *United Nations Day (24 October). P* 13½.
487 **255** 4 n.p. multicoloured 15 5
488 10 n.p. multicoloured 30 20
489 **256** 50 n.p. multicoloured 70 90
490 2 n.c. 50, multicoloured .. .. 5·00 8·00
MS491 76 × 75 mm. No. 490. Imperf (4.12.67) .. 7·00 9·00

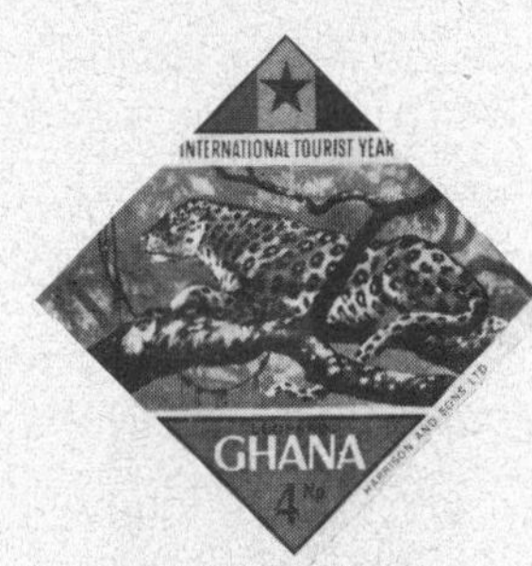

257 Leopard

1967 (28 Dec). *International Tourist Year. T* **257** *and similar diamond-shaped designs. Multicoloured. W* **47** *(diagonal). P* 12½.
492 4 n.p. Type **257** 25 10
493 12½ n.p. Citrus Swallowtail Butterfly .. 75 90
494 20 n.p. Carmine Bee Eater .. .. .. 1·50 1·75
495 50 n.p. Water Buck .. .. 3·00 4·25
MS496 126 × 126 mm. Nos. 493/5. Imperf .. 7·50 8·00

261 Revolutionaries entering Accra

(Litho D.L.R.)

1968 (24 Feb). *2nd Anniv of February Revolution. T* **261** *and similar horiz designs. Multicoloured. P* 14.
497 4 n.p. Type **261** 15 5
498 12½ n.p. Marching troops 50 35
499 20 n.p. Cheering people 80 70
500 40 n.p. Victory celebrations .. .. 1·40 1·75

265 Microscope and Cocoa Beans

1968 (18 Mar). *Cocoa Research. T* **265** *and similar horiz design. Multicoloured. W* **47** *(sideways). P* 14½ × 14.
501 2½ n.p. Type **265** 8 5
502 4 n.p. Microscope and cocoa tree, beans and pods 12 5
503 10 n.p. Type **265** 40 30
504 25 n.p. As 4 n.p. .. .. 1·25 1·40
MS505 102 × 102 mm. Nos. 501/4. Imperf .. 1·75 1·90

267 Kotoka and Flowers

271 Tobacco

(Des A. S. B. New (No. 508) and F. Mate (others) Litho D.L.R.)

1968 (17 Apr). *1st Death Anniv of Lt.-Gen. E. K. Kotoka. T* **267** *and similar multicoloured designs. P* 14.

506 4 n.p. Type **267** 12 5
507 12½ n.p. Kotoka and wreath 45 30
508 20 n.p. Kotoka in civilian clothes 70 80
509 40 n.p. Lt.-Gen. Kotoka (*vert*) .. .. 1·00 1·25

(Des A. S. B. New (5 n.p.))

1968 (19 Aug). *T* **271** *and similar vert designs. Multicoloured. W* **47** *(sideways). P* 14 × 14½.

510 4 n.p. Type **271** 15 8
511 5 n.p. Porcupine 15 8
512 12½ n.p. Rubber 50 50
513 20 n.p. *Cymothoe sangaris* (butterfly) .. 80 1·25
514 40 n.p. *Charaxes ameliae* (butterfly) .. 1·75 2·25
MS515 88 × 114 mm. Nos. 510, 512/14. Imperf 3·00 4·00

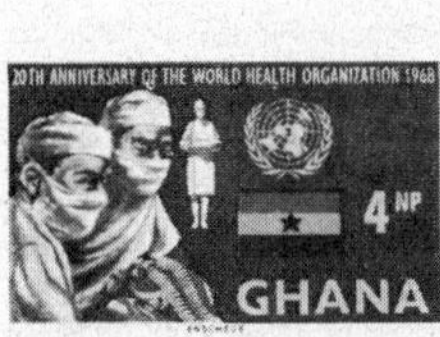

276 Surgeons, Flag and W.H.O. Emblem

277 Hurdling

(Photo Enschedé)

1968 (11 Nov). *20th Anniv of World Health Organization. P* 14 × 13.

516 **276** 4 n.p. multicoloured 12 5
517 12½ n.p. multicoloured 40 35
518 20 n.p. multicoloured 70 70
519 40 n.p. multicoloured .. .. .. 1·25 1·50
MS520 132 × 110 mm. Nos. 516/19. Imperf .. 2·75 3·25

1969 (10 Jan). *Olympic Games, Mexico* (1968). *T* **277** *and similar vert designs. Multicoloured. W* **47** *(sideways). P* 14 × 14½.

521 4 n.p. Type **277** 12 5
522 12½ n.p. Boxing 40 40
523 20 n.p. Torch, Olympic Rings and flags .. 70 80
524 40 n.p. Football .. .. 1·50 1·75
MS525 89 × 114 mm. Nos. 521/4. Imperf (17.1.69) 3·50 4·00

281 U.N. Building

285 Dr. J. B. Danquah

(Litho D.L.R.)

1969 (1 Feb). *United Nations Day* (1968). *T* **281** *and similar square-shaped designs. Multicoloured. P* 13½.

526 4 n.p. Type **281** 12 5
527 12½ n.p. Native stool, staff and U.N. emblem 35 35
528 20 n.p. U.N. building and emblem over Ghanaian flag 70 70
529 40 n.p. U.N. emblem encircled by flags .. 1·60 1·75
MS530 127 × 117 mm. No. 526/9. Imperf .. 3·00 3·25

1969 (7 Mar). *Human Rights Year. T* **285** *and similar horiz design. Multicoloured. W* **47** *(sideways on* **MS**535). *P* 14½ × 14.

531 4 n.p. Type **285** 10 5
532 12½ n.p. Dr. Martin Luther King 30 25
533 20 n.p. As 12½ n.p. 45 50
534 40 n.p. Type **285** .. .. 80 1·00
MS535 116 × 50 mm. Nos. 531/4. Imperf (17.4.69) 1·75 1·90

287 Constituent Assembly Building

1969 (10 Sept). *Third Anniv of the Revolution. T* **287** *and similar horiz design. W* **47** *(sideways on* **MS**540). *P* 14½ × 14.

536 4 n.p. Type **287** 12 5
537 12½ n.p. Arms of Ghana 35 20
538 20 n.p. Type **287** 40 55
539 40 n.p. As 12½ n.p. .. .. 90 1·25
MS540 114 × 89 mm. Nos. 536/9. Imperf .. .. 1·75 1·90

NEW CONSTITUTION
1969
(289)

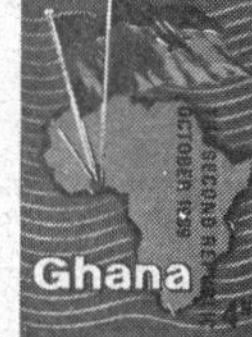

290 Map of Africa and Flags

1969 (1 Oct). *New Constitution. Nos. 460/74 optd with T* **289** *in various positions by Government Press, Accra.*

541 1 n.p. multicoloured (Horiz) 5 12
542 1½ n.p. multicoloured (Vert down) 15 20
a. Opt vert up .. .. 6·00
543 2 n.p. multicoloured (Vert up) 8 15
a. Opt vert down .. .. 5·00
b. Opt double .. .. 12·00
544 2½ n.p. multicoloured (Vert up) 8 15
545 3 n.p. multicoloured (Horiz) 15 15
a. Opt inverted .. .. 15·00
546 4 n.p. multicoloured (Y.) (Vert down) .. 30 15
a. Black opt (vert down) .. .. .. 6·00 1·00
b. Black opt (vert up) .. .. .. 10·00
c. Red opt (vert down) .. .. .. 18·00
d. Opt double (White vert down + yellow vert up) .. .. 27·00
547 6 n.p. multicoloured (Horiz) 12 20
548 8 n.p. multicoloured (Horiz) 15 20
549 9 n.p. multicoloured (Horiz) 15 20
550 10 n.p. multicoloured (Horiz) 20 20
551 20 n.p. deep blue and new blue (Vert up) .. 35 40
a. Opt vert down .. .. 20·00
552 50 n.p. multicoloured (Horiz) .. .. .. 3·00 3·00
a. Opt double .. ..
553 1 n.c. multicoloured (Horiz) .. .. .. 2·25 3·25
554 2 n.c. multicoloured (R.) (Vert up) .. .. 5·50 7·50
a. Opt double (vert up and down) ..
555 2 n.c. 50, multicoloured (Vert down) .. 5·50 8·50
541/55 .. .. *Set of* 15 16·00 22·00

The 1 n.p. is known with the overprint inverted, "NEW CONSTITUTION" appearing between the stamps across the perforations.

(Litho D.L.R.)

1969 (4 Dec). *Inauguration of Second Republic. T* **290** *and similar vert designs. Multicoloured. P* 14.

556 4 n.p. Type **290** 10 5
557 12½ n.p. Figure "2", branch and Ghanaian colours 30 20
558 20 n.p. Hands receiving egg 45 50
559 40 n.p. Type **290** .. .. 90 1·00

293 I.L.O. Emblem and Cog-wheels

1970 (5 Jan). *50th Anniv of International Labour Organisation. W* **47** *(sideways). P* 14½ × 14.

560 **293** 4 n.p. multicoloured 15 5
561 12½ n.p. multicoloured 40 25
562 20 n.p. multicoloured 55 45
MS563 117 × 89 mm. Nos. 560/2. Imperf .. .. 1·50 1·75

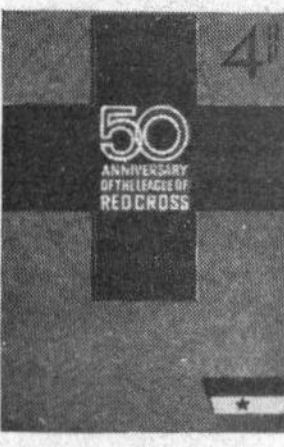

294 Red Cross and Globe

298 General Kotoka, "VC-10" and Airport

1970 (2 Feb). *50th Anniv of League of Red Cross Societies. T* **294** *and similar multicoloured designs. W* **47** *(sideways on 4 n.p.). P* 14 × 14½ *(4 n.p.) or* 14½ × 14 *(others).*

564 4 n.p. Type **294** 15 5
565 12½ n.p. Henri Dunant and Red Cross emblem (*horiz*) 45 25
566 20 n.p. Patient receiving medicine (*horiz*) .. 80 60
567 40 n.p. Patient having arm bandaged (*horiz*) 1·75 1·40
MS568 114 × 89 mm. Nos. 564/7. Imperf .. .. 6·50 7·00

(Des G. Vasarhelyi. Litho D.L.R.)

1970 (17 Apr). *Inauguration of Kotoka Airport. T* **298** *and similar horiz designs. Multicoloured. P* 13 × 13½.

569 4 n.p. Type **298** 12 5
570 12½ n.p. Control tower and tail of "VC-10" .. 35 35
571 20 n.p. Aerial view of airport 60 75
572 40 n.p. Airport and flags .. .. .. 1·00 1·60

302 Lunar Module landing on Moon

306 Adult Education

(Des A. Medina (4 n.p., 12½ n.p.), G. Vasarhelyi (others). Litho D.L.R.)

1970 (15 June). *Moon Landing. T* **302** *and similar multicoloured designs. P* 12½.

573 4 n.p. Type **302** 30 5
574 12½ n.p. Astronaut's first step onto the Moon .. 85 75
575 20 n.p. Astronaut with equipment on Moon (*horiz*) .. .. 1·75 1·50
576 40 n.p. Astronauts (*horiz*) .. .. .. 3·25 3·25
MS577 142 × 142 mm. Nos. 573/6. Imperf (with or without simulated perfs) .. .. 7·00 9·00

On 18 September 1970 Nos. 573/6 were issued overprinted "PHILYMPIA LONDON 1970" but it is understood that only 900 sets were made available for sale in Ghana and we do not consider that this is sufficient to constitute normal postal use. The miniature sheet was also overprinted but not issued in Ghana.

(Litho D.L.R.)

1970 (10 Aug). *International Education Year. T* **306** *and similar horiz designs. Multicoloured. P* 13.

578 4 n.p. Type **306** 10 5
579 12½ n.p. International education 30 20
580 20 n.p. "Ntesie" and I.E.Y. symbols 45 40
581 40 n.p. Nursery schools .. .. 80 1·00

310 Saluting March-Past

314 *Crinum ornatum*

(Litho D.L.R.)

1970 (1 Oct). *First Anniv of the Second Republic. T* **310** *and similar horiz designs. Multicoloured. P* 13 × 13½.

582 4 n.p. Type **310** 10 5
583 12½ n.p. Busia declaration 30 20
584 20 n.p. Doves symbol 45 40
585 40 n.p. Opening of Parliament .. .. .. 80 1·00

(Des G. Vasarhelyi. Photo Harrison)

1970 (2 Nov). *Flora and Fauna. T* **314** *and similar horiz designs. Multicoloured. W* **47** *(sideways). P* 14½ × 14.

586 4 n.p. Type **314** 50 5
587 12½ n.p. Lioness 85 45
588 20 n.p. *Ansellia africana* (flower) .. .. 1·40 1·25
589 40 n.p. Elephant .. .. 2·75 3·00

315 Kuduo Brass Casket

(Des G. Vasarhelyi. Photo Harrison)

1970 (7 Dec). *Monuments and Archaeological Sites in Ghana. T* **315** *and similar horiz designs. Multicoloured. W* **47**. *P* 14½ × 14.

590 4 n.p. Type **315** 15 5
591 12½ n.p. Akan Traditional House 55 45
592 20 n.p. Larabanga Mosque 85 85
593 40 n.p. Funerary Clay Head .. .. .. 1·50 1·90
MS594 89 × 71 mm. Nos. 590, 592 and 12½ n.p. Basilica of Pompeii; 40 n.p. Pistrinum of Pompeii. (wmk sideways). Imperf (2.71) .. .. .. 3·00 4·25

316 Trade Fair Building

(Des G. Drummond (4 n.p., 50 n.p.), A. Larkins (others). Photo Harrison)

1971 (5 Feb). *International Trade Fair, Accra. T* **316** *and similar multicoloured designs. W* **47** *(sideways, except 50 n.p.). P* 14 × 14½ *(50 n.p.) or* 14½ × 14 *(others).*

595 4 n.p. Type **316** 12 5
596 12½ n.p. Cosmetics and Pharmaceutical Goods 30 30

597	20 n.p. Vehicles	50	50
598	40 n.p. Construction Equipment	90	1·25
599	50 n.p. Transport and Packing Case (*vert*)	1·00	1·40

317 Christ on the Cross

318 Corn Cob

(Des from stained-glass windows. Litho D.L.R.)

1971 (19 May). *Easter. T* **317** *and similar square designs. Multicoloured. P* 13.

600	4 n.p. Type **317**	10	5
601	12½ n.p. Christ and Disciples	40	45
602	20 n.p. Christ blessing Disciples	60	85

(Photo Harrison)

1971 (15 June). *Freedom from Hunger Campaign. W* **47**. *P* 14 × 14½.

603	**318** 4 n.p. multicoloured	15	5
604	12½ n.p. multicoloured	70	75
605	20 n.p. multicoloured	1·25	1·10

Remainder stocks of the above were overprinted on the occasion of the death of Lord Boyd Orr and the 4 n.p. surcharged 60 n.p.

It is understood that 8,070 sets from the New York Agency were overprinted locally and returned to the Agency. Limited remainders of these stamps (only 330 of the 60 n.p.) were sold at the G.P.O. We do not list these as they were not freely on sale in Ghana.

319 Guides Emblem and Ghana Flag

320 Child-care Centre

(Des and litho Questa)

1971 (22 July). *Ghana Girl Guides Golden Jubilee. T* **319** *and similar horiz designs each with Guides Emblem. Multicoloured. P* 14.

606	4 n.p. Type **319**	20	5
607	12½ n.p. Mrs. E. Ofuatey-Kodjoe (founder) and guides with flags	50	50
608	20 n.p. Guides laying stones	80	80
609	40 n.p. Camp-fire and tent	1·25	1·60
610	50 n.p. Signallers	1·50	1·90
MS611	133 × 105 mm. Nos. 606/10. Imperf	5·50	6·50

(Des and litho D.L.R.)

1971 (7 Aug). *Y.W.C.A. World Council Meeting, Accra. T* **320** *and similar horiz designs. Multicoloured. P* 13.

612	4 n.p. Type **320**	10	5
613	12½ n.p. Council meeting	30	30
614	20 n.p. School typing-class	50	60
615	40 n.p. Building Fund Day	90	1·40
MS616	84 × 83 mm. Nos. 612/15. Imperf	1·90	2·50

321 Firework Display

322 Weighing Baby

(Photo Harrison)

1971 (22 Nov). *Christmas. T* **321** *and similar horiz designs. Multicoloured. W* **47** *(sideways on* 3 *and* 6 *n.p.). P* 14 × 14½ *(*1 *n.p.) or* 14½ × 14 *(others).*

617	1 n.p. Type **321**	5	5
618	3 n.p. African Nativity	12	15
619	6 n.p. The flight into Egypt	20	25

(Litho D.L.R.)

1971 (20 Dec). *25th Anniv of U.N.I.C.E.F. T* **322** *and similar multicoloured designs, each showing the U.N.I.C.E.F. symbol. No wmk* (**MS**624) *or W* **47** *(sideways on* 5 *and* 30 *n.p.). P* 13.

620	5 n.p. Type **322**	10	8
621	15 n.p. Mother and child (*horiz*)	40	40
622	30 n.p. Nurse	60	70
623	50 n.p. Young boy (*horiz*)	1·00	1·40
MS624	111 × 120 mm. Nos. 620/3. Imperf	3·00	4·25

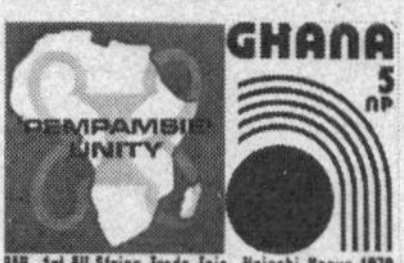

323 Unity Symbol and Trade Fair Emblem

(Litho Questa)

1972 (23 Feb). *All-Africa Trade Fair. T* **323** *and similar horiz designs. Multicoloured. W* **47**. *P* 14.

625	5 n.p. Type **323**	12	8
626	15 n.p. Horn of Plenty	40	40
627	30 n.p. Fireworks on map of Africa	70	95
628	60 n.p. "Participating Nations"	1·40	2·00
629	1 n.c. As No. 628	2·25	3·25

All designs include the Trade Fair Emblem as in T **323**.

On 24 June 1972, on the occasion of the Belgian International Philatelic Exhibition, Nos. 625/9 were issued overprinted '"BELGICA 72"' in red. Only very limited supplies were sent to Ghana (we understand not more than 900 sets), and for this reason we do not list them.

(New Currency. 100 pesewas = 1 cedi = 0.8 (1967) new cedi)

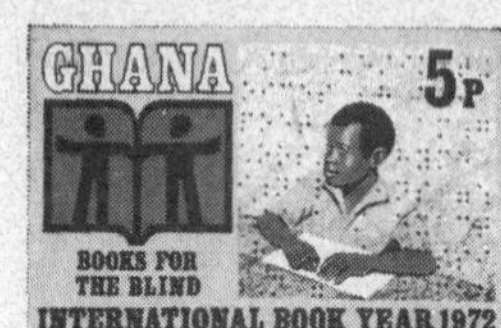

324 Books for the Blind

(Des and litho D.L.R.)

1972 (21 Apr). *International Book Year. T* **324** *and similar multicoloured designs. P* 13.

630	5 p. Type **324**	15	10
631	15 p. Children's books	35	40
632	30 p. Books for recreation	60	75
633	50 p. Books for students	1·00	1·60
634	1 c. Book and flame of knowledge (*vert*)	2·00	3·00
MS635	99 × 106 mm. Nos. 630/4. Imperf.	7·50	9·50

325 *Hypoxis urceolata*

(Litho D.L.R.)

1972 (3 July). *Flora and Fauna. T* **325** *and similar horiz designs. Multicoloured. P* 13½.

636	5 p. Type **325**	25	10
637	15 p. *Cercopithecus mona* (monkey)	55	65
638	30 p. *Crinum ornatum*	1·75	1·90
639	1 c. *Funisciurus substriatus* (squirrel)	3·75	5·00

326 Football

(Litho D.L.R.)

1972 (5 Sept). *Olympic Games, Munich. T* **326** *and similar horiz designs. Multicoloured. P* 13.

640	5 p. Type **326**	10	8
641	15 p. Running	25	30
642	30 p. Boxing	50	65
643	50 p. Long-jumping	90	1·40
644	1 c. High-jumping	1·90	2·75
MS645	86 × 43 mm. 40 p. as No. 642 *se-tenant* with 60 p. as No. 640	3·00	5·00

327 Senior Scout and Cub

(Litho Questa)

1972 (2 Oct). *65th Anniv of Boy Scouts. T* **327** *and similar diamond-shaped designs. Multicoloured. P* 13½.

646	5 p. Type **327**	20	10
647	15 p. Scout and tent	45	45
648	30 p. Sea scouts	90	90
649	50 p. Leader with cubs	1·40	1·60
650	1 c. Training school	2·75	3·00
MS651	110 × 110 mm. 40 p. as 30 p.; 60 p. as 1 c.	3·25	4·00

328 "The Holy Night" (Correggio)

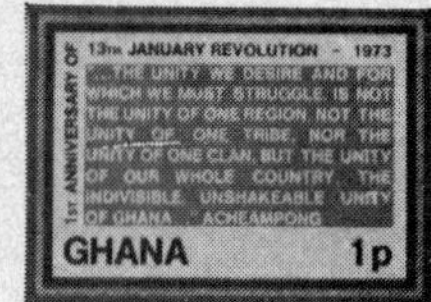

329 Extract from Speech

(Des G. Vasarhelyi and L. Apelt. Litho Questa)

1972 (1 Dec). *Christmas. T* **328** *and similar vert designs. Multicoloured. P* 13½.

652	1 p. Type **328**	5	5
653	3 p. "Adoration of the Kings" (Holbein)	5	5
654	15 p. "Madonna of the Passion" (School of Ricco)	30	30
655	30 p. "King Melchior"	55	55
656	60 p. "King Gaspar, Mary and Jesus"	1·10	1·40
657	1 c. "King Balthasar"	1·75	2·25
652/7	*Set of* 6	3·50	4·25
MS658	139 × 90 mm. Nos. 655/7. Imperf.	5·00	6·50

Nos. 655/7 are from a 16th-cent. Norman stained-glass window.

(Des and litho. D.L.R.)

1973 (10 Apr). *First Anniv of January 13 Revolution. T* **329** *and similar multicoloured designs. P* 13 × 14 *(*5, 15 *p.) or* 14 × 13 *(others).*

659	1 p. Type **329**	5	5
660	3 p. Market scene	5	5
661	5 p. Selling bananas (*vert*)	10	5
662	15 p. Farmer with hoe and produce (*vert*)	30	30
663	30 p. Market traders	55	55
664	1 c. Farmer cutting palm-nuts	1·60	1·75
659/64	*Set of* 6	2·40	2·50
MS665	90 × 55 mm. 40 p. as 1 c. and 60 p. Miners	1·75	2·00

330 Under 5's Clinic

(Litho D.L.R.)

1973 (24 July). *25th Anniv of W.H.O. T* **330** *and similar square designs. Multicoloured. P* 13½.

666	5 p. Type **330**	10	5
667	15 p. Radiography	30	30
668	30 p. Immunisation	55	60
669	50 p. Starving child	90	1·25
670	1 c. W.H.O. H.Q., Geneva	1·75	2·25

1st WORLD SCOUTING CONFERENCE IN AFRICA

(331)

1973 (14 Aug). *First World Scouting Conference, Nairobi/Addis Ababa. Nos.* 646/51 *optd with T* **331**.

671	5 p. Type **327**	10	15
672	15 p. Scout and tent	35	55
673	30 p. Sea scouts	60	95
674	50 p. Leader with cubs	90	1·75
675	1 c. Training school	1·90	2·75
MS676	110 × 110 mm. 40 p. as 30 p.; 60 p. as 1 c.	2·50	4·00

332 Poultry Farming

(Litho Questa)

1973 (11 Sept). *Tenth Anniv of World Food Programme. T* **332** *and similar horiz designs. Multicoloured. P* 14.

677	5 p. Type **332**	10	5
678	15 p. Mechanisation	25	25
679	50 p. Cocoa harvest	90	1·10
680	1 c. F.A.O. H.Q., Rome	1·75	2·25
MS681	92 × 104 mm. 40 p. as 15 p.; 60 p. as 1 c.	1·90	2·25

333 "Green Alert"

(Litho D.L.R.)

1973 (1 Oct). *50th Anniv of Interpol. T* **333** *and similar horiz designs. Multicoloured. P* 13.

682 5 p. Type **333** 15 10
683 30 p. "Red Alert" .. .. 1·00 1·00
684 50 p. "Blue Alert" .. .. 1·75 1·90
685 1 c. "Black Alert" .. .. 3·75 4·25

334 Handshake

(Litho Format)

1973 (22 Oct). *Tenth Anniv of O.A.U. T* **334** *and similar horiz designs. Multicoloured. P* 14 × 14½.

686 5 p. Type **334** 10 5
687 30 p. Africa Hall, Addis Ababa 55 70
688 50 p. O.A.U. emblem .. .. 90 1·50
689 1 c. "X" in colours of Ghana flag .. .. .. 1·75 2·50

335 Weather Balloon

CHRISTMAS 1973 1p GHANA

336 Epiphany Scene

(Des G. Vasarhelyi. Litho Format)

1973 (16 Nov). *I.M.O./W.M.O. Centenary. T* **335** *and similar horiz designs. Multicoloured. P* 14 × 14½.

690 5 p. Type **335** 8 5
691 15 p. Satellite "Tiros" 20 25
692 30 p. Computer weather map 45 80
693 1 c. Radar .. .. 1·60 2·50
MS694 120 × 95 mm. 40 p. as 15 p.; 60 p. as 30 p. 2·00 2·50

(Litho D.L.R.)

1973 (10 Dec). *Christmas. T* **336** *and similar vert designs. Multicoloured. P* 14.

695 1 p. Type **336** 5 5
696 3 p. Madonna and Child 5 5
697 30 p. "Madonna and Child" (Murillo) .. .. 70 1·10
698 50 p. "Adoration of the Magi" (Tiepolo) .. 1·10 1·90
MS699 77 × 103 mm. Nos. 695/8. Imperf. .. .. 2·00 2·75

337 "Christ carrying the Cross" (Thomas de Kolozsvar)

338 Letters

(Des M. Shamir and A. Larkins. Litho D.L.R.)

1974 (17 Apr). *Easter. T* **337** *and similar vert designs. P* 14.

700 5 p. multicoloured 12 5
701 30 p. bright blue, silver and sepia 55 65
702 50 p. light orange-vermilion, silver and sepia 90 1·40
703 1 c. dull yellow-green, silver and sepia .. 1·75 2·50
MS704 111 × 106 mm. 15 p. as No. 700, 20 p. as No. 701, 25 p. as No. 702. Imperf .. .. .. 1·75 2·00

Designs (from 15th-century English carved alabaster):—30 p. "The Betrayal"; 50 p. "The Deposition"; 1 c. "The Risen Christ and Mary Magdalene".

(Des A. Larkins. Litho Questa)

1974 (21 May). *Centenary of Universal Postal Union. T* **338** *and similar horiz designs. Multicoloured. P* 14½.

705 5 p. Type **338** 5 5
706 9 p. U.P.U. Monument and H.Q. 15 15
707 50 p. Airmail letter .. .. 70 1·25
708 1 c. U.P.U. Monument and Ghana stamp .. 1·25 1·90
MS709 108 × 90 mm. 20 p. as No. 705, 30 p. as No. 706, 40 p. as No. 707, 60 p. as No. 708 .. .. 2·00 2·50

1974 (7 June). *"Internaba 1974" Stamp Exhibition, Basle. Nos. 705/9 additionally inscribed* "INTERNABA 1974".

710 5 p. Type **338** 5 10
711 9 p. U.P.U. Monument and H.Q. 15 15
712 50 p. Airmail letter .. .. 70 1·00
713 1 c. U.P.U. Monument and Ghana stamp .. 1·25 1·75
MS714 108 × 90 mm. 20 p. as No. 710; 30 p. as No. 711; 40 p. as No. 712; 60 p. as No. 713 .. .. 2·25 2·75

339 Footballers

(Des G. Vasarhelyi. Litho Format)

1974 (17 June). *World Cup Football Championships, West Germany. T* **339** *and similar horiz designs showing footballers. P* 14½.

715 **339** 5 p. multicoloured 10 5
716 – 30 p. multicoloured 45 60
717 – 50 p. multicoloured 65 95
718 – 1 c. multicoloured .. .. 1·00 1·75
MS719 148 × 94 mm. 25, 40, 55 and 60 p. as Nos. 715/18 .. .. 2·00 2·25

Nos. 715/18 also exist perf 13 (*Price for set of 4 £2·25 mint or used*) from additional sheetlets of 5 stamps and 1 label. Stamps perforated 14½ are from normal sheets of 25.

340 Roundabout

WEST GERMANY WINNERS

(341)

(Des and litho B.W.)

1974 (16 July). *Change to Driving on the Right. T* **340** *and similar designs. P* 13½ (*5 and 15 p.*) *or* 14½ × 14 (*others*).

720 5 p. bright yellow-grn, rose-vermilion & blk 12 12
721 15 p. lavender, dull red and black 35 45
722 30 p. multicoloured 60 70
723 50 p. multicoloured .. .. 90 1·25
724 1 c. multicoloured .. .. 1·75 2·25

Designs: *Horiz*—15 p. Warning triangle sign. *Vert* (29 × 42 *mm*)—30 p. Highway arrow and slogan; 50 p. Warning hands; 1 c. Car on symbolic hands.

1974 (30 Aug). *West Germany's Victory in World Cup. Nos. 715/19 optd with T* **341**. *P* 14½.

725 **339** 5 p. multicoloured 8 10
726 – 30 p. multicoloured 35 45
727 – 50 p. multicoloured 55 65
728 – 1 c. multicoloured .. .. 90 1·50
MS729 148 × 94 mm. 25, 40, 55, 60 p. as Nos. 725/8 .. .. 1·75 2·50

This overprint also exists on the stamps perforated 13 mentioned below No. **MS**719 (*Price for set of 4 £1·75 mint or used*).

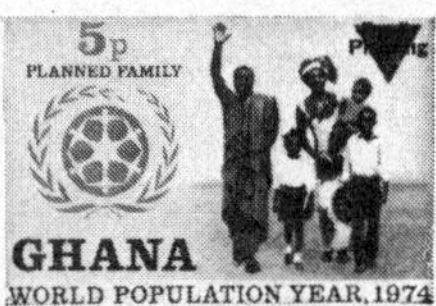

342 "Planned Family"

(Des and litho D.L.R.)

1974 (12 Sept). *World Population Year. T* **342** *and similar horiz designs. Multicoloured. P* 12½.

730 5 p. Type **342** 10 8
731 30 p. Family planning clinic 50 45
732 50 p. Immunization 85 90
733 1 c. Population census enumeration .. .. 1·60 1·75

343 Angel

APOLLO
SOYUZ
JULY 15, 1975

(344)

(Des A. Medina (5 and 7 p.), A. Larkins (others). Litho D.L.R.)

1974 (19 Dec). *Christmas. T* **343** *and similar multicoloured designs. P* 13½.

734 5 p. Type **343** 8 8
735 7 p. The Magi (*diamond* 47 × 47 *mm*) .. 10 10
736 9 p. The Nativity 12 12
737 1 c. The Annunciation .. .. 1·40 1·75
MS738 128 × 128 mm. 15 p. Type **343**; 30 p. as 7 p.; 45 p. as 9 p.; 60 p. as 1 c. Imperf .. .. .. 1·50 2·25

1975 (15 Aug). *"Apollo–Soyuz" Space Link. Nos. 715/19 optd with T* **344**. *P* 14½.

739 5 p. multicoloured 10 10
740 30 p. multicoloured 40 45
741 50 p. multicoloured 75 80
742 1 c. multicoloured .. .. 1·00 1·40
MS743 148 × 94 mm. 25, 40, 55, 60 p. as Nos. 739/42 .. .. 2·75 3·00

This overprint also exists on the stamps perforated 13 mentioned below No. **MS**719 (*Price for set of 4 £4·50 mint or used*).

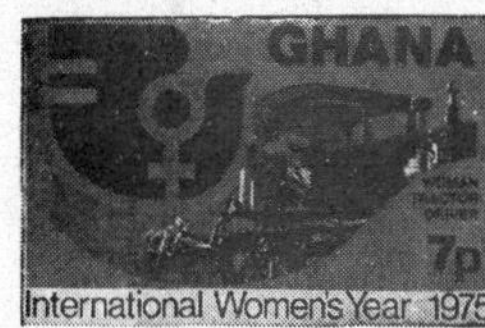

345 Tractor Driver

(Des and litho D.L.R.)

1975 (3 Sept). *International Women's Year. T* **345** *and similar horiz designs each showing I.W.Y. emblem. Multicoloured. P* 14 × 13½.

744 7 p. Type **345** 15 12
745 30 p. Motor mechanic 45 45
746 60 p. Factory workers 90 90
747 1 c. Cocoa research .. .. 1·50 1·50
MS748 136 × 110 mm. 15, 40, 65 and 80 p. as Nos. 744/7. Imperf .. .. 3·75 4·25

346 Angel

(Litho D.L.R.)

1975 (31 Dec). *Christmas. T* **346** *and similar horiz designs. P* 14 × 13½.

749 2 p. multicoloured 8 8
750 5 p. greenish yellow and light green 10 10
751 7 p. greenish yellow and light green 12 12
752 30 p. greenish yellow and light green 45 50
753 1 c. greenish yellow and light green .. .. 1·25 1·50
MS754 98 × 87 mm. 15, 40, 65 and 80 p. as Nos. 750/3. Imperf .. .. 3·00 3·50

Designs:—5 p. Angel with harp; 7 p. Angel with lute; 30 p. Angel with viol; 1 c. Angel with trumpet.

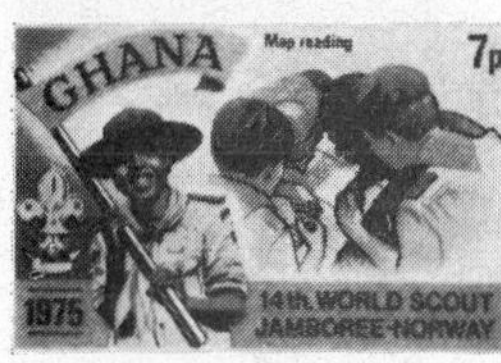

347 Map Reading

(Litho Format)

1976 (5 Jan). *14th World Scout Jamboree, Norway. T* **347** *and similar horiz designs. Multicoloured. P* 13½ × 14.

755 7 p. Type **347** 20 12
756 30 p. Sailing 70 75
757 60 p. Hiking .. .. 1·40 1·50
758 1 c. Life-saving .. .. 1·75 2·00
MS759 133 × 99 mm. 15, 40, 65 and 80 p. as Nos. 755/8 .. .. 3·75 4·00

348 Bottles (litre)

(Litho D.L.R.)

1976 (5 Jan). *Metrication Publicity. T* **348** *and similar horiz designs. Multicoloured. P* 14.

760 7 p. Type **348** 15 12
761 30 p. Scales (kilogramme) 50 50
762 60 p. Tape measure and bale of cloth (metre) 1·10 1·25
763 1 c. Ice, thermometer and kettle (temperature) .. .. 1·60 1·90

349 Fair Site

(Litho Format)

1976 (6 Apr). *International Trade Fair, Accra. T* **349** *and similar horiz designs. P* 13½.

764 **349** 7 p. multicoloured 15 12
765 – 30 p. multicoloured 50 50
766 – 60 p. multicoloured .. .. 1·10 1·10
767 – 1 c. multicoloured .. .. 1·60 1·90

Nos. 765/7 are as T **349** but show different views of the Fair.

'INTERPHIL' 76
BICENTENNIAL
EXHIBITION

(350)

351 Shot-put

1976 (28 May). *Interphil Stamp Exhibition, Philadelphia. Nos. 755/9 optd with T* **350** *in blue.*

768 7 p. Type **347** 15 15
769 30 p. Sailing 60 60
770 60 p. Hiking .. .. 1·00 1·00
771 1 c. Life-saving .. .. 1·75 1·90
MS772 133 × 99 mm. 15, 40, 65 and 80 p. as Nos. 768/71 .. .. 3·25 3·50

(Des PAD Studio. Litho Format)

1976 (9 Aug). *Olympic Games, Montreal. T* **351** *and similar vert designs. Multicoloured. P* 13½.

773 7 p. Type **351** 12 12
774 30 p. Football 55 55
775 60 p. Women's 1500 metres 85 90
776 1 c. Boxing .. .. 1·25 1·40
MS777 103 × 135 mm. 15, 40, 65 and 80 p. as Nos. 773/6 .. .. 2·50 3·25

Nos. 773/6 also exist perf 15 (*Price for set of* 4 *£3 mint or used*) from additional sheetlets of 5 stamps and 1 label. Stamps perforated 13½ are from normal sheets of 30.

352 Supreme Court

(Litho D.L.R.)

1976 (7 Sept). *Centenary of Supreme Court. T* **352** *and similar horiz designs. P* 14.

778 **352** 8 p. multicoloured 15 12
779 – 30 p. multicoloured 45 45
780 – 60 p. multicoloured 85 85
781 – 1 c. multicoloured .. .. 1·40 1·40

Nos. 779/81 show different views of the Court Building.

353 Examination for River Blindness

(Des and litho D.L.R.)

1976 (28 Oct). *Prevention of Blindness. T* **353** *and similar horiz designs. Multicoloured. P* 14 × 13½.

782 7 p. Type **353** 25 15
783 30 p. Entomologist 90 90
784 60 p. Normal vision .. .. 1·60 1·60
785 1 c. Blackfly eradication .. .. 2·50 2·50

354 Fireworks Party, Christmas Eve

(Des A. Adom & A. Larkins. Litho D.L.R.)

1976 (15 Dec). *Christmas. T* **354** *and similar horiz designs. Multicoloured. P* 13.

786 6 p. Type **354** 20 12
787 8 p. Children and gifts 25 15
788 30 p. Christmas feast 85 90
789 1 c. As 8 p. .. .. 2·50 3·25
MS790 122 × 98 mm. 15, 40, 65 and 80 p. as Nos. 786/9. Imperf .. .. 4·00 4·25

1876
A. Graham Bell
GHANA 8p
CENTENARY OF FIRST TELEPHONE TRANSMISSION 1976

355 "Gallows Frame" Telephone and Alexander Graham Bell

EAST GERMANY
WINNERS

(356)

(Des A. Larkins. Litho Format)

1976 (17 Dec). *Telephone Centenary. T* **355** *and similar horiz designs showing telephones and Alexander Graham Bell. Multicoloured. P* 13.

791 8 p. Type **355** 20 15
792 30 p. 1895 telephone 65 65
793 60 p. 1929 telephone .. .. 1·25 1·25
794 1 c. 1976 telephone .. .. 1·75 1·75
MS795 125 × 92 mm. 15, 40, 65 and 80 p. as Nos. 791/4 .. .. 4·50 5·00

1977 (22 Feb). *Olympic Winners. Nos. 773/7 optd with the name of the country given, as T* **356**. *P* 13½.

796 7 p. East Germany 15 15
797 30 p. East Germany 55 55
798 60 p. U.S.S.R. .. .. 1·00 1·00
799 1 c. U.S.A. .. .. 1·90 1·90
MS800 103 × 135 mm. 15, 40, 65 and 80 p. as Nos. 796/9 .. .. 4·00 4·25

357 Dipo Dancers and Drum Ensemble

(Des A. Larkins. Litho Format)

1977 (24 Mar). *Second World Black and African Festival of Arts and Culture, Nigeria. T* **357** *and similar horiz designs. Multicoloured. P* 13½.

801 8 p. Type **357** 25 20
802 30 p. Arts and Crafts 90 80
803 60 p. Acon music and dancing priests .. .. 1·90 1·60
804 1 c. African huts .. .. 2·50 2·50
MS805 164 × 120 mm. 15, 40, 65 and 80 p. as Nos. 801/4 .. .. 6·00 6·50

PRINCE CHARLES
VISITS GHANA
17th TO 25th
MARCH, 1977

(358)

1977 (2 June). *Prince Charles's Visit to Ghana. Nos.* 791/5 *optd with T* **358**.

806 8 p. Type **355** 50 35
807 30 p. 1895 telephone .. .. 1·60 1·25
808 60 p. 1929 telephone .. .. 2·50 2·25
809 1 c. 1976 telephone .. .. 3·25 2·75
MS810 125 × 92 mm. 15, 40, 65 and 80 p. as Nos. 806/9 .. .. 5·50 6·50

359 Olive Colobus Monkey

360 "Le Chapeau de Paille" (Rubens—400th Birth Anniv)

(Des PAD Studio. Litho Format)

1977 (22 June). *Wildlife. T* **359** *and similar horiz designs. Multicoloured. P* 13½.

811 8 p. Type **359** 45 15
812 20 p. Ebien Palm Squirrel .. .. 1·25 80
813 30 p. African Wild Dog .. .. 1·75 1·25
814 60 p. West African Manatee (sea cow) .. .. 3·00 2·25
MS815 140 × 101 mm. 15, 40, 65 and 80 p. as Nos. 811/14 .. .. 5·50 5·50

(Des PAD Studio. Litho Format)

1977 (Sept). *Painters' Anniversaries. T* **360** *and similar vert designs. Multicoloured. P* 14 × 13½.

816 8 p. Type **360** 20 10
817 30 p. "Isabella of Portugal" (Titian—500th Birth Anniv) 50 40
818 60 p. "Duke and Duchess of Cumberland" (Gainsborough—250th Birth Anniv) .. 85 75
819 1 c. "Rubens and Isabella Brandt" .. .. 1·50 1·60
MS820 99 × 149 mm. 15, 40, 65 and 80 p. as Nos. 816/19 .. .. 2·50 3·50

361 The Magi, Madonna and Child

REFERENDUM 1978
VOTE EARLY

(362)

(Litho De La Rue, Colombia)

1977 (30 Dec). *Christmas. T* **361** *and similar multicoloured designs. P* 14 (1 *p.*, 8 *p.*) *or* 14 × 13½ (*others*).

821 1 p. Type **361** 5 5
822 2 p. Choir from Abossey Okai (45 × 27 *mm*) 5 5
823 6 p. Methodist Church, Wesley, Accra (45 × 27 *mm*) 10 10
824 8 p. Madonna and Child 15 12
825 30 p. Holy Spirit Cathedral, Accra (45 × 27 *mm*) 65 50
826 1 c. Ebeneezer Presbyterian Church, Accra (45 × 27 *mm*) .. .. 1·75 1·60
821/6 .. .. *Set of* 6 2·40 2·25
MS827 122 × 97 mm. 15, 40, 65 and 80 p. as Nos. 822/3 and 825/6. Imperf .. .. 3·75 4·25

Nos. 822/3 and 825/6 all have as a background the score to the carol "Hark the Herald Angels Sing".

1978 (Mar). 1978 *Referendum. Nos. 821/7 optd with T* **362** *by De La Rue, Colombia.*

828 1 p. Type **361** 5 5
829 2 p. Choir from Abossey Okai 5 5
830 6 p. Methodist Church, Wesley, Accra 12 12
831 8 p. Madonna and Child 12 12
832 30 p. Holy Spirit Cathedral, Accra 50 60
833 1 c. Ebeneezer Presbyterian Church, Accra 1·60 2·00
828/33 .. .. *Set of* 6 2·25 2·75
MS834 122 × 97 mm. 15, 40, 65, 80 p. as Nos. 829/30 and 832/3 .. .. 20·00 15·00

363 Cutting Bananas

(Litho De La Rue, Colombia)

1978 (15 May). *Operation "Feed Yourself". T* **363** *and similar horiz designs. Multicoloured. P* 14.

835 2 p. Type **363** 5 5
836 8 p. Home produce 15 15
837 30 p. Market 40 45
838 60 p. Fishing 75 80
839 1 c. Mechanisation .. .. 1·40 1·60

364 Wright Biplane

"CAPEX 78
JUNE 9-18 1978"

(365)

(Des J.W. Litho Format)

1978 (6 June). *75th Anniv of Powered Flight. T* **364** *and similar vert designs. P* 14 × 13½.

840 8 p. black, deep brown and brown-ochre .. 20 12
841 30 p. black, deep brown and blue-green .. 40 40
842 60 p. black, deep brown and rosine 75 75
843 1 c. black, deep brown and ultramarine .. 1·10 1·40
MS844 167 × 100 mm. 15, 40, 65, 80 p. as Nos. 840/3 .. .. 2·50 3·00

Designs:—30 p. "Heracles"; 60 p. D.H. "Comet"; 1 c. "Concorde".

1978 (9 June). *"CAPEX 1978" International Stamp Exhibition, Toronto. Nos.* 840/4 *optd with T* **365**.

845 8 p. black, deep brown and brown-ochre .. 20 20
846 30 p. black, deep brown and blue-green .. 40 40
847 60 p. black, deep brown and rosine 75 75
848 1 c. black, deep brown and ultramarine .. 1·40 1·40
MS849 167 × 100 mm. 15, 40, 65, 80 p. as Nos. 845/8 .. .. 2·50 3·00

366 Players and African Cup Emblem

(Litho Format)

1978 (1 July). *Football Championships. T* **366** *and similar horiz designs. Multicoloured. P* 13½ × 14.

850 8 p. Type **366** 20 15
851 30 p. Players and African Cup emblem (*different*) 40 40
852 60 p. Players and World Cup emblem 75 75
853 1 c. Goalkeeper and World Cup emblem .. 1·25 1·25
MS854 111 × 105 mm. 15, 40, 65, 80 p. as Nos. 850/3 .. .. 2·50 3·00

The 8 and 30 p. values commemorate the African Nations Cup; the other values the World Cup Football Championship, Argentina.

367 "The Betrayal"

"GHANA WINNERS"

(368)

(Litho Format)

1978 (15 July). *Easter. Details from drawings by Dürer. T* **367** *and similar vert designs. P* 14 × 13½.

855 11 p. black and bright reddish violet 10 10
856 39 p. black and flesh 35 35
857 60 p. black and orange-yellow 55 55
858 1 c. black and pale yellow-green 75 75

Designs:—39 p. "The Crucifixion"; 60 p. "The Deposition"; 1 c. "The Resurrection".

1978 (21 Aug). *Ghana—Winners of African Nations Football Cup and Argentina—Winners of World Cup Football Championship. Nos.* 850/1 *and* **MS**854 *optd with T* **368** *and Nos.* 852/3 *optd* "ARGENTINA WINS".

859 8 p. Type **366** 20 20
860 30 p. Players and African Cup emblem (*different*) 40 40
861 60 p. Players and World Cup emblem 65 75
862 1 c. Goalkeeper and World Cup emblem .. 1·00 1·25
MS863 111 × 105 mm. 15, 40, 65, 80 p. as Nos. 859/62 but all opt with T **368** .. .. 2·25 2·50

369 *Bauhinia purpurea*

(Litho Format)

1978 (20 Nov). *Flowers. T* **369** *and similar vert designs. Multicoloured. P* 14 × 13½.

864 11 p. Type **369** 20 10
865 39 p. *Cassia fistula* 65 65
866 60 p. *Plumeria acutifolia* 85 85
867 1 c. *Jacaranda mimosifolia* .. .. 1·25 1·25

370 Mail Van

(Litho Format)

1978 (4 Dec). *75th Anniv of Ghana Railways. T* **370** *and similar horiz designs. Multicoloured. P* 13½ × 14.

868 11 p. Type **370** 40 10
869 39 p. Pay and bank car .. .. 1·00 65
870 60 p. Locomotive, 1922 .. .. 1·40 1·00
871 1 c. Diesel locomotive 1960 .. .. 1·90 1·40

371 "Orbiter" Spacecraft

(Litho Format)

1979 (5 July). *"Pioneer" Venus Space Project. T* **371** *and similar horiz designs. Multicoloured. P* 14 × 13½.

872 11 p. Type **371** 10 10
873 39 p. "Multiprobe" spacecraft 30 30
874 60 p. "Orbiter" and "Multiprobe" spacecraft in Venus orbit 45 45
875 3 c. Radar chart of Venus .. .. 1·40 1·60
MS876 135 × 94 mm. 15, 40, 65 p., 2 c. as Nos. 872/5. Imperf .. .. 1·50 1·60

372 "O Come All Ye Faithful"

373 Dr. J. B. Danquah (lawyer and nationalist)

(Litho D.L.R.)

1979 (20 Dec). *Christmas. Opening Lines and Scenes from well known Carols. T* **372** *and similar horiz designs. Multicoloured. P* 14 × 14½.

877 8 p. Type **372** 8 10
878 10 p. "O Little Town of Bethlehem" 8 10
879 15 p. "We Three Kings of Orient Are" 10 12
880 20 p. "I Saw Three Ships come Sailing By" .. 12 15
881 2 c. "Away in a Manger" .. .. 1·00 1·25
882 4 c. "Ding Dong Merrily on High" .. .. 2·00 2·50
877/82 .. .. *Set of* 6 3·00 3·75
MS883 110 × 95 mm. 25, 65 p., 1, 2 c. as Nos. 877, 879 and 881/2 .. .. 2·25 2·75

(Litho D.L.R.)

1980 (21 Jan). *Great Ghanaians. T* **373** *and similar vert designs. Multicoloured. P* 14 × 13½.

884 20 p. Type **373** 12 15
885 65 p. John Mensah Sarbah (nationalist) .. 45 50
886 80 p. Dr. J. E. K. Aggrey (educationalist) .. 55 60
887 2 c. Dr. Kwame Nkrumah (nationalist) .. 1·25 1·40
888 4 c. G. E. (Paa) Grant (lawyer) .. .. 2·50 2·75

374 Tribesman ringing Clack Bells

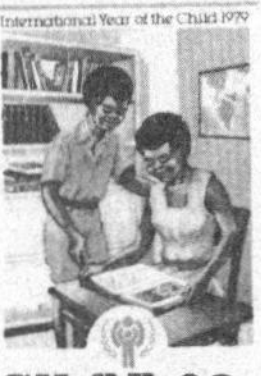

375 Children in Classroom

(Des G. Vasarhelyi. Litho Format)

1980 (12 Mar). *Death Centenary of Sir Rowland Hill* (1979). *T* **374** *and similar horiz designs. Multicoloured.* (a) *P* 14½.

889 20 p. Type **374** 12 15
890 65 p. Chieftain with Golden Elephant staff .. 45 50
891 2 c. Tribesman banging drums .. .. 1·25 1·40
892 4 c. Chieftain with ivory and gold staff .. 2·50 2·75

(*b*) *P* 13½

893 25 p. Type **374** 15 20
894 50 p. As 65 p. 35 40
895 1 c. As 2 c. 70 75
896 5 c. As 4 c. .. .. 3·50 3·75
889/96 .. .. *Set of* 8 8·00 9·00
MS897 115 × 86 mm. Nos. 893/6. P 14½ .. 4·50 5·50

Nos. 893/6 were each printed in small sheets of 6 including one *se-tenant* stamp-size label.

(Des J.W. Litho Questa)

1980 (2 Apr). *International Year of the Child* (1979). *T* **375** *and similar vert designs. Multicoloured. P* 14½.

898 20 p. Type **375** 15 15
899 65 p. Children playing football 55 60
900 2 c. Children playing in boat .. .. .. 1·10 1·40
901 4 c. Mother and child .. .. 2·00 2·50
MS902 156 × 94 mm. 25, 50 p., 1, 3 c. as Nos. 898/901 .. .. 2·75 3·25

"LONDON 1980"
6th - 14th May 1980

(376)

"PAPAL VISIT"
8th - 9th May
1980

(377)

1980 (6 May). *"London 1980" International Stamp Exhibition. Nos.* 889/97 *optd with T* **376**. (a) *P* 14½.

903 20 p. Type **374** 12 15
904 65 p. Chieftain with Golden Elephant staff .. 45 50
905 2 c. Tribesman banging drums .. .. 1·25 1·40
906 4 c. Chieftain with ivory and gold staff .. 2·50 2·75

(*b*) *P* 13½

907 25 p. Type **374** 15 20
908 50 p. As 65 p. 35 40
909 1 c. As 2 c. 70 75
910 5 c. As 4 c. .. .. 3·50 3·75
903/10 .. .. *Set of* 8 8·00 9·00
MS911 115 × 86 mm. Nos. 907/10. P 14½ .. 5·00 5·50

1980 (8 May). *Papal Visit. Nos.* 898/902 *optd with T* **377**.

912 20 p. Type **375** 20 25
913 65 p. Children playing football 55 60
914 2 c. Children playing in boat .. .. .. 1·40 1·60
915 4 c. Mother and child .. .. 2·50 2·75
MS916 156 × 94 mm. 25, 50 p., 1, 3 c. as Nos. 912/15 .. .. 3·75 4·25

378 Parliament House

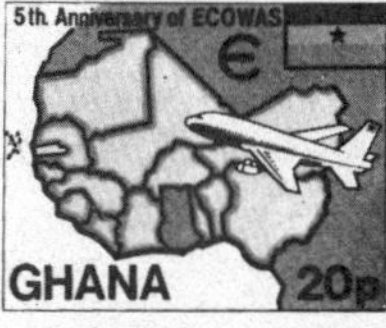

379 Airliner and Map of West Africa

(Litho Questa)

1980 (4 Aug). *Third Republic Commemoration. T* **378** *and similar horiz designs. Multicoloured. P* 14.

917 20 p. Type **378** 15 15
918 65 p. Supreme Court 50 60
919 2 c. The Castle .. .. 1·00 1·40
MS920 72 × 113 mm. 25 p., 1, 3 c. As Nos. 917/19 2·50 2·75

(Litho Questa)

1980 (5 Nov). *Fifth Anniv of E.C.O.W.A.S. (Economic Community of West African States). T* **379** *and similar horiz designs showing symbols named and map of West Africa. Multicoloured. P* 14.

921 20 p. Type **379** 15 15
922 65 p. Radio antenna 50 50
923 80 p. Cog-wheels 60 60
924 2 c. Corn ear .. .. 1·25 1·50

380 "O.A.U."

381 "The Adoration of the Magi"

(Litho Questa)

1980 (26 Nov). *Organisation of African Unity First Economic Summit, Nigeria. T* **380** *and similar vert designs. Multicoloured. P* 14½ × 14.

925 20 p. Type **380** 15 15
926 65 p. Banner with maps of Africa and Ghana 50 55
927 80 p. Map of Africa 60 70
928 2 c. Ghana flag, banner and map of Africa .. 1·25 1·40

(Litho Format)

1980 (10 Dec). *Christmas. Paintings by Fra Angelico. T* **381** *and similar vert designs. Multicoloured. P* 14.

929 15 p. Type **381** 15 12
930 20 p. "The Virgin and Child enthroned with four Angels" 15 15
931 2 c. "The Virgin and Child enthroned with eight Angels" .. .. 1·40 1·50
932 4 c. "The Annunciation" .. .. 2·50 2·75
MS933 77 × 112 mm. 25, 50 p., 1, 3 c. As Nos. 929/32 .. .. 3·25 3·50

382 "Health"

383 Narina's Trogon

(Litho Format)

1980 (18 Dec). *75th Anniv of Rotary International. T* **382** *and similar horiz designs. Multicoloured. P* 14.

934 20 p. Type **382** 15 15
935 65 p. Rotary emblem and motto with maps of World and Ghana 55 55
936 2 c. Rotary emblem, globe and outstretched hands .. .. 1·40 1·50
937 4 c. "Eradication of Hunger" .. .. 2·50 2·75
MS938 121 × 93 mm. 25, 50 p., 1, 3 c. As Nos. 934/7 .. .. 3·25 3·50

(Des G. Drummond. Litho Harrison)

1981 (12 Jan). *Birds. T* **383** *and similar vert designs. Multicoloured. P* 14.

939 20 p. Type **383** 15 15
940 65 p. White-crowned Robin 50 50
941 2 c. Swallow-tailed Bee Eater .. .. .. 1·40 1·50
942 4 c. Rose-ringed Parakeet .. .. 2·75 3·00
MS943 89 × 121 mm. 25, 50 p., 1, 3 c. As Nos. 939/42. P 14½ .. .. 3·50 4·00

384 Pope John Paul II and Archbishop of Canterbury with President Limann during Papal Visit

385 Royal Yacht *Britannia*

(Litho Format)

1981 (3 Mar). *First Anniv of Papal Visit. P* 14 × 13½.

944 **384** 20 p. multicoloured .. 20 15
945 65 p. multicoloured .. 55 55
946 80 p. multicoloured .. 70 70
947 2 c. multicoloured .. 1·60 1·60

(Des J.W. Litho Questa)

1981 (8 July–16 Sept). *Royal Wedding. T* **385** *and similar vert designs. Multicoloured.* (i) *Sheet stamps* (8 July). (*a*) *P* 14.

948 20 p. Prince Charles and Lady Diana Spencer 15 5
949 80 p. Prince Charles on visit to Ghana .. 45 45
950 4 c. Type **385** .. 2·00 2·00
MS951 95 × 85 mm. 7 c. St. Paul's Cathedral .. 3·50 3·50

(*b*) *P* 12

952 65 p. As 20 p. .. 40 40
953 1 c. As 80 p. .. 75 75
954 3 c. Type **385** .. 2·00 2·00

(ii) *Booklet stamps. P* 14 (16 Sept)

955 2 c. Type **385** .. 1·25 1·25
a. Booklet pane. Nos. 955/6 each × 2 .. 7·50
956 5 c. As 20 p. .. 2·50 2·50

The 65 p., 1 and 3 c. values were each printed in small sheets of 6 including one *se-tenant* stamp-size label.

The above exist imperforate from a restricted printing (*Price for Nos.* 948/50 *set of* 3 £20, **MS**951 £20, *Nos.* 952/4 *set of* 3 £20 *and booklet pane No.* 955a £30, *all mint*).

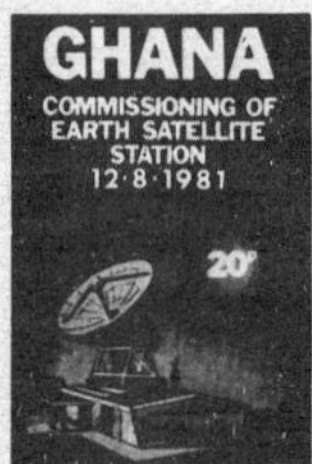

386 Earth Satellite Station

387 Pounding Fufu

(Litho Questa)

1981 (28 Sept). *Commissioning of Earth Satellite Station. T* **386** *and similar vert designs. Multicoloured. P* 14.

957 20 p. Type **386** .. 10 10
958 65 p. Satellites beaming signals to Earth .. 35 35
959 80 p. Satellite .. 45 45
960 4 c. Satellite orbiting Earth .. 2·25 2·25
MS961 112 × 100 mm. 25 p., 50 p., 1 c., 3 c. As Nos. 957/60 .. 2·50 2·75

(Des BG Studio. Litho Format)

1981 (16 Oct). *World Food Day. T* **387** *and similar horiz designs. Multicoloured. P* 13½ × 14.

962 20 p. Type **387** .. 10 10
963 65 p. Plucking Cocoa .. 35 35
964 80 p. Preparing Banku .. 45 45
965 2 c. Garri processing .. 1·25 1·25
MS966 131 × 99 mm. 25 p., 50 p., 1 c., 3 c. As Nos. 962/5 .. 2·50 2·75

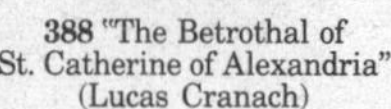

388 "The Betrothal of St. Catherine of Alexandria" (Lucas Cranach)

389 Blind Person

(Des Clover Mill. Litho Format)

1981 (26 Nov). *Christmas. Details from Paintings. T* **388** *and similar vert designs. Multicoloured. P* 15.

967 15 p. Type **388** .. 10 5
968 20 p. "Angelic Musicians play for Mary and Child" (Aachener Altares) .. 10 5
969 65 p. "Child Jesus embracing his Mother" (Gabriel Metsu) .. 35 35
970 80 p. "Madonna and Child" (Fra Filippo Lippi) 45 45
971 2 c. "The Madonna with Infant Jesus" (Barnaba da Modena) .. 1·25 1·25
972 4 c. "The Immaculate Conception" (Murillo) 2·10 2·10
967/72 .. *Set of* 6 4·00 4·00
MS973 82 × 102 mm. 6 c. "Madonna and Child with Angels" (Hans Memling) .. 2·75 3·00

(Des G. Vasarhelyi. Litho Questa)

1982 (8 Feb). *International Year for Disabled Persons. T* **389** *and similar horiz designs. Multicoloured. P* 14.

974 20 p. Type **389** .. 10 10
975 65 p. Disabled person with crutches .. 35 35
976 80 p. Blind child reading braille .. 45 45
977 4 c. Disabled people helping one another .. 2·25 2·25
MS978 109 × 85 mm. 6 c. Group of disabled people 2·75 2·75

390 Clawless Otter

391 Blue-spot Commodore

(Des G. Drummond. Litho Harrison)

1982 (22 Feb). *Flora and Fauna. T* **390** *and similar vert designs. Multicoloured. P* 14.

979 20 p. Type **390** .. 15 15
980 65 p. Bushbuck .. 40 40
981 80 p. Aardvark .. 50 50
982 1 c. Scarlet Bell Tree .. 60 60
983 2 c. Glory-Lilies .. 1·25 1·25
984 4 c. Blue-Pea .. 2·25 2·25
979/84 .. *Set of* 6 4·75 4·75
MS985 76 × 100 mm. 5 c. Chimpanzee .. 2·50 3·25

(Litho Harrison)

1982 (3 May). *Butterflies. T* **391** *and similar vert designs. Multicoloured. P* 14.

986 20 p. Type **391** .. 10 10
987 65 p. Emperor Swallowtail .. 35 35
988 2 c. Orange Admiral .. 1·25 1·25
989 4 c. Giant Charaxes .. 2·25 2·25
MS990 98 × 123 mm. 25 p., 50 p., 1 c., 3 c. As Nos. 986/9. P 14½ .. 3·50 4·00

392 Scouts planting Tree

(Des M. Diamond. Litho Format)

1982 (1 June). *75th Anniv of Boy Scout Movement. T* **392** *and similar multicoloured designs. P* 14½ × 15.

991 20 p. Type **392** .. 10 10
992 65 p. Scouts cooking on camp-fire .. 35 35
993 80 p. Sea Scouts sailing .. 45 45
994 3 c. Scouts observing elephant .. 1·60 1·60
MS995 101 × 71 mm. 5 c. Lord Baden-Powell (*vert*). P 15 × 14½ .. 2·40 2·50

393 Initial Stages of Construction

(Des C. Tetteh. Litho Questa)

1982 (28 June). *Kpong Hydro-Electric Project. T* **393** *and similar horiz designs. Multicoloured. P* 14.

996 20 p. Type **393** .. 10 8
997 65 p. Truck removing rubble .. 35 35
998 80 p. Hydro-electric turbines .. 45 45
999 2 c. Aerial view of completed plant .. 1·25 1·25

394 Footballers

(Des M. and S. Gerber Studio. Litho Format)

1982 (19 July). *World Cup Football Championship, Spain. T* **394** *and similar horiz designs showing footballers.* (*a*) *P* 14½.

1000 **394** 20 p. multicoloured .. 10 8
1001 – 65 p. multicoloured .. 35 35
1002 – 80 p. multicoloured .. 45 45
1003 – 4 c. multicoloured .. 2·00 2·00
MS1004 110 × 90 mm. 6 c. multicoloured .. 2·75 2·75

(*b*) *P* 14 × 14½

1005 **394** 30 p. multicoloured .. 20 20
1006 – 80 p. multicoloured (as No. 1001) .. 45 45
1007 – 1 c. multicoloured (as No. 1002) .. 55 55
1008 – 3 c. multicoloured (as No. 1003) .. 1·60 1·60

Nos. 1005/8 were each printed in small sheets including one *se-tenant*, stamp-size, label.

395 The Fight against Tuberculosis

396 The Shepherds worship Jesus

(Des M. Diamond. Litho Harrison)

1982 (9 Aug). *Centenary of Robert Koch's Discovery of Tubercle Bacillus. T* **395** *and similar horiz designs. Multicoloured. P* 14.

1009 20 p. Type **395** .. 10 10
1010 65 p. Robert Koch .. 35 35
1011 80 p. Robert Koch in Africa .. 45 45
1012 1 c. Centenary of discovery of Tuberculosis .. 55 55
1013 2 c. Robert Koch and Nobel Prize, 1905 .. 1·10 1·10

(Des E. Oimensah. Litho Format)

1982 (22 Dec). *Christmas. T* **396** *and similar vert designs. Multicoloured. P* 14½.

1014 15 p. Type **396** .. 8 8
1015 20 p. Mary, Joseph and baby Jesus .. 10 10
1016 65 p. The Three Kings sight star .. 30 30
1017 4 c. Winged Angel .. 1·90 2·00
MS1018 90 × 110 mm. 6 c. The Three Kings with Jesus .. 2·75 3·00

397 Ghana and Commonwealth Flags with Coat of Arms

WINNER ITALY
3–1
(**398**)

(Des J.W. Litho Format)

1983 (14 Mar). *Commonwealth Day. T* **397** *and similar vert designs. Multicoloured. P* 14½.

1019 20 p. Type **397** .. 10 10
1020 55 p. Satellite view of Ghana .. 25 30
1021 80 p. Minerals of Ghana .. 35 40
1022 3 c. African Fish Eagle .. 1·50 1·50

1983 (30 May). *Italy's Victory in World Cup Football Championship* (1982). *Nos.* 1000/8 *optd with T* **398**, *in gold.* (*a*) *P* 14½.

1023 **394** 20 p. multicoloured .. 8 10
1024 – 65 p. multicoloured .. 25 30
1025 – 80 p. multicoloured .. 35 40
1026 – 4 c. multicoloured .. 1·75 1·90
MS1027 110 × 90 mm. 6 c. multicoloured .. 2·50 2·75

(*b*) *P* 14 × 14½

1028 **394** 30 p. multicoloured .. 12 15
1029 – 80 p. multicoloured .. 35 40
1030 – 1 c. multicoloured .. 40 45
1031 – 3 c. multicoloured .. 1·25 1·40
1023/31 .. *Set of* 8 4·00 4·50

No. **MS**1027 has an additional overprint, "FINAL: ITALY V. W. GERMANY", on the sheet margin.

INFLATION HANDSTAMPS. During 1983 the value of the Ghanaian currency fell drastically and as a result, there was a considerable rise in postal rates.

To cope with this situation supplies of past commemorative issues were made available from the post offices, many being handstamped "NOT FOR PHILATELIC USE" in one line within a frame. These handstamps were usually applied in blue, haphazardly across the sheet with examples so far reported on Nos. 656/7, 664, 670, 680, 689, 703, 708, 718, 747, 753, 757, 762/3, 766, 775, 780/1, 814, 817, 846, 860, 865, 867, 869, 875 and 882.

(**398***a*)

399 Short Fin Pilot Whale

1983 (Oct). *No.* 470 *surch with T* **398***a*.

1031*a* 1 c. on 20 p. deep blue and new blue .. 5 5
ab. Surch triple

(Des J. Iskowitz. Litho Format)

1983 (15 Nov). *Coastal Marine Mammals. T* **399** *and similar horiz designs. Multicoloured. P* 14½.

1032 1 c. Type **399** .. 5 5
1033 1 c. 40, Risso's Grey Dolphin .. 5 5

1034 2 c. 30, False Killer Whale 8 10
1035 3 c. Spinner Dolphin 12 15
1036 5 c. Atlantic Humpback 20 25
MS1037 117 × 76 mm. 6 c. As 5 c. 25 30

400 *Hemichramis fasciatus* 401 Communication Devices

(Des and litho De La Rue)

1983 (12 Dec). *T* **400** *and similar designs. P* 14.
1038 5 p. multicoloured 5 5
1039 10 p. multicoloured 5 5
1040 20 p. multicoloured 5 5
1041 50 p. deep grey-green, yellow-orange and black 5 5
1042 1 c. yellow-orange, violet-blue and black 5 5
1043 2 c. multicoloured 8 10
1044 3 c. multicoloured 12 15
1045 4 c. multicoloured 15 20
1046 5 c. multicoloured 20 25
1047 10 c. multicoloured 40 45
1038/47 *Set of* 10 1·10 1·40
Designs: *Horiz*—10 p. *Hemichramis fasciatus (different)*; 2 c. Jet airliner. *Vert*—20 p. *Haemanthus rupestris*; 50 p. Mounted warrior; 1 c. Scorpion; 3 c. *Cercocebus torquatus*; 4 c. *Galagiodes demidovi*; 5 c. *Kaemferia nigerica*; 10 c. *Camaroptera brevicaudata*.

(Des PAD Studio. Litho Questa)

1983 (13 Dec). *World Communications Year. T* **401** *and similar vert designs. Multicoloured. P* 14.
1048 1 c. Type **401** 5 5
1049 1 c. 40, Satellite dish aerial 5 5
1050 2 c. 30, Cable and cable-laying ship 10 12
1051 3 c. Switchboard operators 12 15
1052 5 c. Aircraft cockpit and air traffic controllers 20 25
MS1053 95 × 70 mm. 6 c. Space satellite 25 30

402 Children receiving Presents 403 Soldiers with Rifles

1983 (28 Dec). *Christmas. T* **402** *and similar multicoloured designs. P* 14 × 13½ *(70 p. and 3 c.) or* 14½ × 14 *(others)*.
1054 70 p. Type **402** 5 5
1055 1 c. Nativity and Star of Bethlehem (28 × 36 *mm*) 5 5
1056 1 c. 40, Children celebrating (28 × 36 *mm*) 5 5
1057 2 c. 30, Family praying (28 × 36 *mm*) 10 12
1058 3 c. Dancing to bongo drum 12 15
MS1059 70 × 90 mm. 6 c. As 2 c. 30 25 30

(Des and litho B.D.T.)

1984 (26 Jan). *Namibia Day. T* **403** *and similar vert designs. P* 14.
1060 50 p. blue-green and black 5 5
1061 1 c. multicoloured 5 5
1062 1 c. 40, new blue, bright blue and black 5 5
1063 2 c. 30, multicoloured 10 12
1064 3 c. multicoloured 12 15
Designs:—1 c. Soldiers supported by tank; 1 c. 40, Machete cutting chains; 2 c. 30, Peasant woman; 3 c. Soldiers and artillery support.

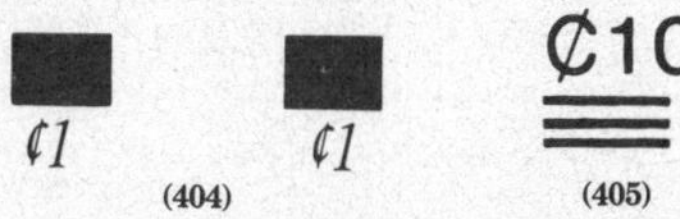

(404) (405)

1984 (8 Feb). (*a*) *Nos.* 948/51 *surch as T* **404**
1065 1 c. on 20 p. Prince Charles and Lady Diana Spencer 4·00 3·00
1066 9 c. on 80 p. Prince Charles on visit to Ghana 5·00 4·00
a. Imperf (pair) with surch inverted £275
1067 20 c. on 4 c. Type **385** 6·00 6·00
MS1068 95 × 85 mm. 60 c. on 7 c. St. Paul's Cathedral 15·00 15·00

(*b*) *Nos.* 991/2 *and* 994/5 *surch as T* **405**
1069 10 c. on 20 p. Type **392** 40 45
1070 19 c. on 65 p. Scouts cooking on camp-fire 80 85
1071 30 c. on 3 c. Scouts observing elephant 1·25 1·40
MS1072 101 × 71 mm. 60 c. on 5 c. Lord Baden-Powell 2·50 2·75

(*c*) *Nos.* 1000/6 *and* 1008 *surch as T* **405**
1073 **394** 1 c. on 20 p. multicoloured 5 5
1074 – 9 c. on 65 p. multicoloured 40 45
1075 – 9 c. on 3 c. multicoloured 40 45
1076 **394** 10 c. on 30 p. multicoloured 40 45
1077 – 10 c. on 80 p. multicoloured (No. 1002) 40 45
1078 – 20 c. on 80 p. multicoloured (No. 1006) 85 90
1079 – 20 c. on 4 c. multicoloured 85 90
MS1080 110 × 90 mm. 60 c. on 6 c. multicoloured 2·50 2·75

(*d*) *Nos.* 1019/22 *surch as T* **405**
1081 1 c. on 20 p. Type **397** 5 5
1082 9 c. on 55 p. Satellite view of Ghana 40 45
1083 30 c. on 80 p. Minerals of Ghana 1·25 1·40
1084 50 c. on 3 c. African Fish Eagle 2·10 2·25

(*e*) *Nos.* 1023/9 *and* 1031 *surch as T* **405**
1085 **394** 1 c. on 20 p. multicoloured 5 5
1086 – 9 c. on 65 p. multicoloured 40 45
1087 – 9 c. on 3 c. multicoloured 40 45
1088 **394** 10 c. on 30 p. multicoloured 40 45
1089 – 10 c. on 80 p. multicoloured (No. 1025) 40 45
1090 – 20 c. on 80 p. multicoloured (No. 1029) 80 85
1091 – 20 c. on 4 c. multicoloured 80 85
MS1092 110 × 90 mm. 60 c. on 6 c. multicoloured 2·50 2·75
1065/7, 1064/71, 1073/9, 1081/91 *Set of* 24 25·00 23·00

c 10

19TH U.P.U CONGRESS - HAMBURG

(406)

1984 (19 June). *Universal Postal Union Congress, Hamburg. Nos.* 1035/7 *surch as T* **406**.
1093 10 c. on 3 c. Spinner Dolphin 40 45
1094 50 c. on 5 c. Atlantic Humpback 2·10 2·25
MS1095 117 × 76 mm. 60 c. on 6 c. As No. 1094 2·50 2·75

407 Cross and Crown of Thorns 408 Women's 400 Metre Race

(Litho Format)

1984 (26 June). *Easter. T* **407** *and similar vert designs. Multicoloured. P* 15.
1096 1 c. Type **407** 5 8
1097 1 c. 40, Christ praying 5 8
1098 2 c. 30, The Resurrection 10 12
1099 3 c. Palm Sunday 12 15
1100 50 c. Christ on the road to Emmaus 2·10 2·25
MS1101 102 × 86 mm. 60 c. Type **407** 2·50 2·75

(Des P. Cox and J. Iskowitz. Litho Format)

1984 (13 Aug). *Olympic Games, Los Angeles. T* **408** *and similar vert designs. Multicoloured. P* 15.
1102 1 c. Type **408** 5 8
1103 1 c. 40, Boxing 5 8
1104 2 c. 30, Hockey 10 12
1105 3 c. Men's 400 metre race 12 15
1106 50 c. Rhythmic gymnastics 2·10 2·25
MS1107 103 × 78 mm. 70 c. Football 3·00 3·25

409 *Amorphophallus johnsonii* 410 Young Bongo

(Litho Harrison)

1984 (24 Aug). *Flowers. T* **409** *and similar vert designs. Multicoloured. P* 14.
1108 1 c. Type **409** 5 5
1109 1 c. 40, *Pancratium trianthum* 5 8
1110 2 c. 30, *Eulophia cucullata* 10 12
1111 3 c. *Amorphophallus abyssinicus* 12 15
1112 50 c. *Chlorophytum togoense* 2·10 2·25
MS1113 70 × 96 mm. 60 c. Type **409** 2·50 2·75

(Des Susan David. Litho B.D.T.)

1984 (7 Sept). *Endangered Antelopes. T* **410** *and similar horiz designs. Multicoloured. P* 14.
1114 1 c. Type **410** 5 5
1115 2 c. 30, Bongo bucks fighting 10 12
1116 3 c. Bongo family 12 15
1117 20 c. Bongo herd in high grass 80 85
MS1118 100 × 71 mm. 70 c. Head of Kob. P 14½ × 14 3·00 3·25

OMNIBUS ISSUES

Details, together with prices for complete sets, of the various Omnibus issues from the 1935 Silver Jubilee series to date are included in a special section following Zululand at the end of the catalogue.

411 Dipo Girl 412 The Three Wise Men Bringing Gifts

(Des and litho B.D.T.)

1984 (3 Oct). *Ghanaian Culture. T* **411** *and similar vert designs. Multicoloured. P* 14.
1119 1 c. Type **411** 5 5
1120 1 c. 40, Adowa dancer 5 8
1121 2 c. 30, Agbadza dancer 10 12
1122 3 c. Damba dancer 12 15
1123 50 c. Dipo dancer 1·75 1·90
MS1124 70 × 84 mm. 70 c. Mandolin player. P 14 × 15 2·00 2·75

(Litho D.L.R.)

1984 (19 Nov). *Christmas. T* **412** *and similar vert designs. Multicoloured. P* 12 × 12½.
1125 70 p. Type **412** 5 5
1126 1 c. Choir of angels 5 5
1127 1 c. 40, Mary and shepherds at manger 5 8
1128 2 c. 30, The flight into Egypt 10 12
1129 3 c. Simeon blessing Jesus 12 15
1130 50 c. Holy Family and angels 1·75 1·90
1125/30 *Set of* 6 1·90 2·10
MS1131 70 × 90 mm. 70 c. Type **412** 2·50 2·75

POSTAGE DUE STAMPS

GHANA

(D 2)

D 3

1958 (25 June). *Postage Due stamps of Gold Coast. Chalk-surfaced paper. Optd with Type* D **2**, *in red*.
D 9 D 1 1d. black 5 20
D10 2d. black 8 25
D11 3d. black 12 30
D12 6d. black 25 50
D13 1s. black 45 95

(Typo De La Rue)

1958 (1 Dec). *Chalk-surfaced paper. Wmk Mult Script CA. P* 14.
D14 D 3 1d. carmine 5 20
D15 2d. green 8 20
D16 3d. orange 12 30
D17 6d. bright ultramarine 20 55
D18 1s. reddish violet 45 1·00

3p.
Ghana New Currency
19th July, 1965.

(D 4)

1½Np

(D 5)

1965 (19 July). *Nos.* D14/18 *surch as Type* D **4** *diagonally upwards* (D) *or horiz* (H), *by Govt Printer, Accra.*
D19 D 3 1 p. on 1d. (D) 5 20
a. Surch inverted 4·50
b. Surch double
D20 2 p. on 2d. (B.) (H) 8 30
a. Surch inverted 4·50
D21 3 p. on 3d. (Indigo) (H) 12 35
a. Surch inverted
b. Ultramarine surch
ba. Ditto. Surch inverted 6·50
bb. Ditto. Surch on back and face
c. Black surch
D22 6 p. on 6d. (R.) (H) 25 60
a. Surch inverted
b. Purple-brown surch
ba. Ditto. Surch double 19·00
c. Green surch 13·00
D23 12 p. on 1s. (B.) (D) 50 1·40
On the diagonal surcharges the figures of value are horizontal.

1968 (Feb)–**70**. *Nos.* D20/2 *additionally surch as Type* D **5**, *in red* (1½ *n.p.*, 5 *n.p.*) *or black* (2½ *n.p.*).
D24 D 3 1½ n.p. on 2 p. on 2d. 4·00 3·50
a. Type D 4 double, one albino
b. Albino surch (Type D 4)
D25 2½ n.p. on 3 p. on 3d. (4.70?) 1·00 3·00
a. Type D 4 double, one albino 5·00
D26 5 n.p. on 6 p. on 6d. (1970) 1·00
The above were three in a series of surcharges, the others being 1 n.p. on 1 p. and 10 n.p. on 12 p., which were prepared, but owing to confusion due to the two surcharges in similar currency it was decided by the authorities not to issue the stamps, however, Nos. D24/6 were issued in error.

(Litho D.L.R.)

1970. *Inscr in new currency. P* 14¼ × 14.
D27 D 3 1 n.p. carmine-red 10 20
D28 1½ n.p. green 10 25
D29 2½ n.p. yellow-orange 15 30
D30 5 n.p. ultramarine 20 35
D31 10 n.p. reddish violet 30 55

(Litho D.L.R.)

1980–81. *Currency described as "p". P* 14½ × 14.
D32 D 3 2 p. reddish orange 5 5
D33 3 p. brown 5 5

Gibraltar

CROWN COLONY

Early details of postal arrangements in Gibraltar are hard to establish, although it is known that postal facilities were provided by the Civil Secretary's Office from the early 1760s. Gibraltar became a packet port in 1806, the first official Packet Agent being appointed three years later, although the Civil Secretary's Office continued to be responsible for other mail. The two services were amalgamated on 1 January 1857 as a Branch Office of the British G.P.O., the control of the postal services not reverting to Gibraltar until 1 January 1886.

Stamps of Great Britain were issued for use in Gibraltar from 3 September 1857 to the end of 1885.

For illustrations of the postmark types see BRITISH POST OFFICES ABROAD notes, following GREAT BRITAIN.

Stamps of GREAT BRITAIN *cancelled* "G" *as Type* **1** (3 Sept 1857 *to* 19 Feb 1859).

Z 1 1d. red-brown (1854) Die I £300
Z 2 1d. red-brown (1855), Die II, *wmk* Small Crown, *perf* 16 .. .. £550
Z 3 1d. red-brown (1855), Die II, *wmk* Small Crown, *perf* 14 .. .. £250
Z 4 1d. red-brown (1855), Die II, *wmk* Large Crown, *perf* 14 .. .. 60·00
Z 5 1d. rose-red (1857), Die II, *wmk* Large Crown, *perf* 14 .. .. 20·00
Z 6 2d. blue (1855), *wmk* Small Crown, *perf* 14 .. £275
Z 7 2d. blue (1855–58), *wmk* Large Crown, *perf* 16 .. £275
Z 8 2d. blue (1855), *wmk* Large Crown, *perf* 14 *From* 55·00
Plate Nos. 5, 6.
Z 9 2d. blue (1858) (Plate No. 7) £200
Z10 4d. rose (1857) .. .. 42·00
a. Thick glazed paper
Z11 6d. lilac (1856) .. .. 40·00
Z12 6d. lilac (1856) (blued *paper*) £750
Z13 1s. green (1856) .. .. 75·00
a. Thick paper
Z14 1s. green (1856) (blued *paper*) £1300

Stamps of GREAT BRITAIN *cancelled* "A 26" *as in Types* **2, 5, 11** *or* **14** (20 Feb 1859 *to* 31 Dec 1885).

Z15 ½d. rose-red (1870–79) .. *From* 12·00
Plate Nos. 4, 5, 6, 8, 10, 11, 12, 13, 14, 15, 19, 20.
Z16 1d. red-brown (1841), *imperf*
Z17 1d. red-brown (1855), *wmk* Large Crown, *perf* 14 .. £150
Z18 1d. rose-red (1857), *wmk* Large Crown, *perf* 14 .. 12·00
Z19 1d. rose-red (1864–79) .. *From* 16·00
Plate Nos. 71, 72, 73, 74, 76, 78, 79, 80, 81, 82, 83, 84, 85, 86, 87, 88, 89, 90, 91, 92, 93, 94, 95, 96, 97, 98, 99, 100, 101, 102, 103, 104, 105, 106, 107, 108, 109, 110, 111, 112, 113, 114, 115, 116, 117, 118, 119, 120, 121, 122, 123, 124, 125, 127, 129, 130, 131, 132, 133, 134, 135, 136, 137, 138, 139, 140, 141, 142, 143, 144, 145, 146, 147, 148, 149, 150, 151, 152, 153, 154, 155, 156, 157, 158, 159, 160, 161, 162, 163, 164, 165, 166, 167, 168, 169, 170, 171, 172, 173, 174, 175, 176, 177, 178, 179, 180, 181, 182, 183, 184, 185, 186, 187, 188, 189, 190, 191, 192, 193, 194, 195, 196, 197, 198, 199, 200, 201, 202, 203, 204, 205, 206, 207, 208, 209, 210, 211, 212, 213, 214, 215, 216, 217, 218, 219, 220, 221, 222, 223, 224, 225.
Z20 1½d. lake-red (1870) (Plate No. 3)
Z21 2d. blue (1855), *wmk* Large Crown, *perf* 14 .. 95·00
Plate No. 6.
Z22 2d. blue (1858–69) .. *From* 16·00
Plate Nos. 7, 8, 9, 12, 13, 14, 15.
Z23 2½d. rosy mauve (1875) (blued *paper*) .. *From* £100
Plate Nos. 1, 2, 3.
Z24 2½d. rosy mauve (1875–76) (Plate Nos. 1, 2, 3) *From* 24·00
Z25 2½d. rosy mauve (*Error of Lettering*)..
Z26 2½d. rosy mauve (1876–79) .. *From* 20·00
Plate Nos. 3, 4, 5, 6, 7, 8, 9, 10, 11, 12, 13, 14, 15, 16, 17.
Z27 2½d. blue (1880–81) (Plate Nos. 17, 18, 19, 20) *From* 12·00
Z28 2½d. blue (1881) (Plate Nos. 21, 22, 23) .. *From* 10·00
Z29 3d. carmine-rose (1862) .. £150
Z30 3d. rose (1865) (Plate No. 4).. .. 45·00
Z31 3d. rose (1867–73) .. *From* 18·00
Plate Nos. 4, 5, 6, 7, 8, 9, 10.
Z32 3d. rose (1873–76) .. *From* 22·00
Plate Nos. 11, 12, 14, 15, 16, 17, 18, 19, 20.
Z33 3d. rose (1881) (Plate Nos. 20, 21) ..
Z34 3d. lilac (1883) (3d. *on* 3d) .. 70·00
Z35 4d. rose (1857) .. 42·00
Z36 4d. red (1862) (Plate Nos. 3, 4) .. *From* 45·00
Z37 4d. vermilion (1865–73) .. *From* 30·00
Plate Nos. 7, 8, 9, 10, 11, 12, 13, 14.
Z38 4d. vermilion (1876) (Plate No. 15).. .. £225
Z39 4d. sage-green (1877) (Plate Nos. 15, 16) .. 80·00
Z40 4d. grey-brown (1880) *wmk* Large Garter .. £130
Plate No. 17.
Z41 4d. grey-brown (1880) *wmk* Crown.. .. *From* 16·00
Plate Nos. 17, 18.
Z42 6d. lilac (1856) .. 42·00
Z43 6d. lilac (1862) (Plate Nos. 3, 4) .. *From* 38·00
Z44 6d. lilac (1865–67) (Plate Nos. 5, 6).. *From* 32·00
Z45 6d. lilac (1867) (Plate No. 6).. .. 42·00
Z46 6d. violet (1867–70) (Plate Nos. 6, 8, 9) *From* 32·00
Z47 6d. buff (1872–73) (Plate Nos. 11, 12) *From* £180
Z48 6d. chestnut (1872) (Plate No. 11) .. 28·00
Z49 6d. grey (1873) (Plate No. 12) .. 60·00
Z50 6d. grey (1874–80) .. *From* 24·00
Plate Nos. 13, 14, 15, 16, 17.
Z51 6d. grey (1881) (Plate Nos. 17, 18) ..
Z52 6d. lilac (1883) (6d. *on* 6d.) .. 80·00
Z53 8d. orange (1876) .. £170
Z54 9d. bistre (1862) .. £160
Z55 9d. straw (1862) .. £600
Z56 9d. straw (1865) .. £550
Z57 9d. straw (1867) .. £120
Z58 10d. red-brown (1867) .. £150
Z59 1s. green (1856) .. 70·00
Z60 1s. green (1862) .. 60·00
Z61 1s. green (1862) ("K" *variety*) .. £2000
Z62 1s. green (1865) (Plate No. 4) .. 35·00
Z63 1s. green (1867–73) (Plate Nos. 4, 5, 6, 7) .. *From* 12·00
Z64 1s. green (1873–77).. .. *From* 36·00
Plate Nos. 8, 9, 10, 11, 12, 13.
Z65 1s. orange-brown (1880) (Plate No. 13) .. £180
Z66 1s. orange-brown (1881) (Plate Nos. 13, 14) *From* 38·00
Z67 2s. blue (1867) .. £120
Z68 5s. rose (1867) (Plate No. 1).. .. £600

1880.
Z69 ½d. deep green .. 12·00
Z70 ½d. pale green .. 12·00
Z71 1d. Venetian red .. 12·00
Z72 1½d. Venetian red
Z73 2d. pale rose .. .. 60·00
Z74 2d. deep rose..
Z75 5d. indigo

1881.
Z76 1d. lilac (14 *dots*) .. 17·00
Z77 1d. lilac (16 *dots*) .. 7·50

1884.
Z78–81 ½d. slate blue; 2d., 2½d., 3d. .. *From* 11·00
Z82–83 4d., 6d. .. *From* 70·00

POSTAL FISCAL

Z84 1d. purple (1881), *wmk* Orb.. .. £1100

PRICES FOR STAMPS ON COVER TO 1945

Nos. 1/7	*from* × 5
Nos. 8/21	*from* × 4
Nos. 22/33	*from* × 5
Nos. 39/45	*from* × 4
Nos. 46/109	*from* × 3
Nos. 110/13	*from* × 4
Nos. 114/17	*from* × 3
Nos. 118/20	*from* × 5
Nos. 121/31	*from* × 3

GIBRALTAR
(1)

1886 (1 Jan). *Contemporary types of Bermuda optd with T* **1** *by D.L.R. Wmk Crown CA. P* 14.

1 9 ½d. dull green .. 7·00 7·00
2 1 1d. rose-red .. 20·00 10·00
3 2 2d. purple-brown .. 55·00 50·00
4 11 2½d. ultramarine .. 60·00 8·00
a. Optd in blue-black .. £475 £200
5 10 4d. orange-brown .. 75·00 75·00
6 4 6d. deep lilac .. £200 £180
7 5 1s. yellow-brown .. £500 £450
1/7 .. *Set of* 7 £800 £700
1/7 Optd "Specimen" .. *Set of* 7 £1600

PRINTER. All Gibraltar stamps to No. 109 were typographed by De La Rue & Co, Ltd.

2

3

4

5

1886 (Nov)–**87**. *Wmk Crown CA. P* 14.

8 2 ½d. dull green (1.87) .. 2·75 2·75
9 3 1d. rose (12.86) .. 10·00 2·75
10 4 2d. brown-purple (12.86) .. 28·00 25·00
11 5 2½d. blue.. .. 28·00 8·00
12 4 4d. orange-brown (16.4.87) .. 55·00 45·00
13 6d. lilac (16.4.87) .. 80·00 70·00
14 1s. bistre (2.87).. .. £225 £200
8/14 .. *Set of* 7 £350 £300
8/14 Optd "Specimen" .. *Set of* 7 £500

See also Nos. 39 to 45.

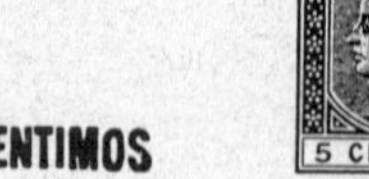
(6) 7

1889 (July). *Surch as T* **6**.

15 2 5 c. on ½d. green .. 8·00 9·50
16 3 10 c. on 1d. rose .. 7·00 6·50
17 4 25 c. on 2d. brown-purple .. 6·50 8·00
a. Small "I" (R.6/2) .. £275 £300
b. Broken "N" (R.10/5) .. £350 £350
18 5 25 c. on 2½d. bright blue .. 16·00 5·00
a. Small "I" (R.6/2) .. £160 £140
b. Broken "N" (R.10/5) .. £190 £170
19 4 40 c. on 4d. orange-brown .. 38·00 42·00
20 50 c. on 6d. bright lilac .. 38·00 50·00
21 75 c. on 1s. bistre.. .. 45·00 60·00
15/21 .. *Set of* 7 £140 £160
15/21 Optd "Specimen" .. *Set of* 7 £500

10 c., 40 c. and 50 c. values from this issue and that of 1889–96 are known bisected and used for half their value from various post offices in Morocco (*price on cover from* £2250). These bisects were never authorised by the Gibraltar Post Office.

Two varieties of the figure "5" of the 5 c., 25 c., 50 c. and 75 c. may be found.

1889 (Nov)–**96**. *Issue in Spanish currency. Wmk Crown CA. P* 14.

22 7 5 c. green .. 1·00 60
23 10 c. carmine .. 1·00 60
b. Value omitted .. £4500
24 20 c. olive-green and brown (2.1.96) 7·50 12·00
25 20 c. olive-green (8.7.96).. .. 4·75 10·00
26 25 c. ultramarine .. 4·50 1·25
a. Deep ultramarine .. 7·00 1·25
27 40 c. orange-brown .. 3·50 5·50
28 50 c. bright lilac (1890) .. 4·50 5·50
29 75 c. olive-green (1890) .. 30·00 35·00
30 1 p. bistre (11.89) .. 42·00 42·00
31 1 p. bistre and ultramarine (6.95) 6·50 8·00
32 2 p. black and carmine (2.1.96).. 18·00 27·00
33 5 p. slate-grey (12.89) .. 55·00 65·00
22/33 .. *Set of* 12 £160 £190
22/33 (excluding No. 25). Optd "Specimen" *Set of* 11 £425

1898 (1 Oct). *Reissue in Sterling currency. Wmk Crown CA. P* 14.

39 2 ½d. grey-green .. 80 1·25
40 3 1d. carmine .. 1·25 85
41 4 2d. brown-purple and ultramarine .. 6·50 6·50
42 5 2½d. bright ultramarine.. .. 8·00 2·00
43 4 4d. orange-brown and green .. 15·00 15·00
44 6d. violet and red .. 24·00 28·00
45 1s. bistre and carmine .. 24·00 30·00
39/45 .. *Set of* 7 70·00 75·00
39/45 Optd "Specimen" .. *Set of* 7 £275

No. 39 is greyer than No. 8, No. 40 brighter and deeper than No. 9 and No. 42 much brighter than No. 11.

8

9

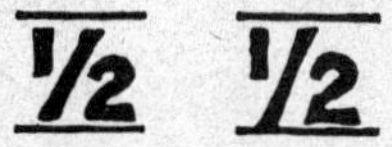

½ Normal ½ Large "2"
2½d.

This occurs on R.10/1 in each pane of 60 above Plate No. 1 & 2. The diagonal stroke is longer.

1903 (1 May). *Wmk Crown CA. P* 14.

46 8 ½d. grey-green and green .. 2·25 4·25
47 1d. dull purple/*red* .. 6·50 1·60
48 2d. grey-green and carmine .. 9·50 9·50
49 2½d. dull purple and black/*blue* .. 1·60 3·25
a. Large "2" in "½" .. 28·00 38·00
50 6d. dull purple and violet .. 12·00 18·00
51 1s. black and carmine .. 17·00 23·00
52 9 2s. green and blue .. 42·00 55·00
53 4s. dull purple and green .. 48·00 65·00
54 8s. dull purple and black/*blue* .. 80·00 90·00
55 £1 dull purple and black/*red* .. £600 £700
46/55 .. *Set of* 10 £750 £850
46/55 Optd "Specimen" .. *Set of* 10 £650

1904–8. *Wmk Mult Crown CA. P* 14.

56 8 ½d. dull and bright green, **OC** (1.6.04).. 1·25 1·75
57 1d. dull purple/*red*, **OC** (10.10.04) .. 1·25 70
a. Bisected (½d.) (on card) .. † £1500
58 2d. grey-green and carmine, **OC** (9.1.05) 5·50 5·50
59 2½d. purple and black/*blue*, **C** (4.5.07) .. 14·00 30·00
a. Large "2" in "½" .. 90·00 £130
60 6d. dull purple and violet, **OC** (19.4.06) 4·75 10·00
61 1s. black and carmine, **OC** (13.10.05) .. 13·00 13·00
62 9 2s. green and blue, **OC** (2.2.05) .. 40·00 55·00
63 4s. deep purple and green, **C** (6.08) .. 70·00 80·00
64 £1 dp purple & black/*red*, **C** (15.3.08) £500 £600
56/64 .. *Set of* 9 £600 £700

1907–12. *Colours changed. Wmk Mult Crown CA. P* 14.

66 8 ½d. blue-green, **O** (1907) .. 90 1·00
67 1d. carmine, **O** (1.07) .. 75 60
a. Wmk sideways
68 2d. greyish slate, **O** (5.10) .. 4·25 8·00
69 2½d. ultramarine, **O** (6.07) .. 2·75 4·25
a. Large "2" in "½" .. 24·00 38·00
70 6d. dull and bright purple, **C** (3.12) .. 85·00 £250
71 1s. black/*green*, **C** (1910) .. 12·00 16·00
72 9 2s. purple and bright blue/*blue*, **C** (4.10) 30·00 42·00
73 4s. black and carmine, **C** (4.10) .. 48·00 60·00
74 8s. purple and green, **C** (1911).. .. £225 £180
66/74 .. *Set of* 9 £375 £550
67/74 Optd "Specimen" .. *Set of* 8 £650

NEW INFORMATION

The editor is always interested to correspond with people who have new information that will improve or correct the Catalogue.

10

11

WAR TAX

(12)

1912 (17 July)–**24.** *Wmk Mult Crown CA. P* 14.
76 10 ½d. blue-green, **O** 60 45
a. Yellow-green (4.17) .. .. 1·25 35
77 1d. carmine-red, **O** .. .. 1·75 55
a. Scarlet (6.16) .. .. 2·75 55
78 2d. greyish slate, **O** .. .. 3·00 1·75
79 2½d. deep bright blue, **O** .. .. .. 3·25 1·75
a. Large "2" in "½" .. .. .. 26·00 22·00
b. Pale ultramarine (1917) .. .. .. 7·00 2·00
ba. Large "2" in "½" .. .. .. 50·00 26·00
80 6d. dull purple and mauve, **C** .. .. 9·00 7·00
81 1s. black/*green*, **OC** .. .. .. 5·50 5·50
a. On blue-green, olive back (1919) .. 12·00 12·00
b. On emerald surface (12.23) (Optd S. £35) .. .. 18·00 22·00
c. On emerald back, **C** (3.24) .. .. 8·50 22·00
82 11 2s. dull purple and blue/*blue*, **C** .. 16·00 7·50
83 4s. black and carmine, **C** .. .. 30·00 42·00
84 8s. dull purple and green, **C** .. .. 45·00 55·00
85 £1 dull purple and black/*red*, **C** .. £225 £250
76/85 .. .. *Set of* 10 £300 £325
76/85 Optd "Specimen" .. .. *Set of* 10 £500

1918 (15 Apr). *Optd with T* **12** *by Beanland, Malin & Co, Gibraltar.*
86 10 ½d. green .. .. 50 1·00
Two printings of this overprint exist, the second being in slightly heavier type on a deeper shade of green.

3 PENCE (I) THREE PENCE (II)

1921–27. *Wmk Mult Script CA. P* 14.
89 10 ½d. green, **O** (25.4.27) 30 30
90 1d. carmine-red, **O** (2.21) .. .. .. 1·00 70
91 1½d. chestnut, **O** (1.12.22) 75 50
a. Pale chestnut (7.24) 75 40
93 2d. grey, **O** (17.2.21) .. .. .. 1·60 1·25
94 2½d. bright blue, **O** (2.21) .. .. .. 9·50 9·50
a. Large "2" in "½" .. .. .. 55·00 55·00
95 3d. bright blue, **O** (I) (1.1.22) .. .. 2·50 4·25
a. Ultramarine .. .. 1·60 3·00
97 6d. dull purple and mauve, **C** (1.23) .. 6·00 7·00
a. Bright purple and magenta (22.7.26) 1·90 4·50
98 1s. black/*emerald*, **C** (20.6.24) .. .. 8·00 9·50
99 11 2s. grey-purple & blue/*blue*, **C** (20.6.24) 20·00 35·00
a. Reddish purple and blue/blue (1925) 6·50 22·00
100 4s. black and carmine, **C** (20.6.24) .. 32·00 42·00
101 8s. dull purple and green, **C** (20.6.24) .. £160 £250
89/101 .. .. *Set of* 11 £200 £300
89/101 Optd "Specimen" .. .. *Set of* 11 £550
The ½d. exists in coils constructed from normal sheets.

1925 (15 Oct)–**32.** *New values and colours changed. Wmk Mult Script CA. P* 14.
102 10 1s. sage-green and black, **C** (8.1.29) .. 8·00 10·00
a. Olive and black (1932) .. .. 8·00 10·00
103 11 2s. red-brown and black, **C** (8.1.29) .. 14·00 25·00
104 2s. 6d. green and black, **C** .. .. 8·00 14·00
105 5s. carmine and black, **C** .. .. 18·00 35·00
106 10s. deep ultramarine and black, **C** .. 32·00 48·00
107 £1 red-orange and black, **C** (16.11.27) .. £180 £200
108 £5 violet and black, **C** (S. £1200) .. £2250 £3000
102/7 .. .. *Set of* 6 £250 £300
102/7 Optd/Perf "Specimen" .. .. *Set of* 6 £600

1930 (12 Apr). *T* **10** *inscribed* "THREE PENCE". *Wmk Mult Script CA. P* 14.
109 3d. ultramarine (II) (Perf S. £70) .. .. 11·00 6·00

13 The Rock of Gibraltar

(Des Capt. H. St. C. Garrod. Recess D.L.R.)

1931–33. *T* **13.** *Wmk Mult Script CA.* A. *P* 14. B. *P* 13½ × 14.

		A		B	
110	1d. scarlet (1.7.31)	1·75	2·00	7·50	3·25
111	1½d. red-brown (1.7.31)	2·25	2·50	4·25	2·50
112	2d. pale grey (1.11.32)	2·50	2·00	9·50	2·25
113	3d. blue (1.6.33)	3·50	5·50	15·00	14·00
110/13 Perf "Specimen"	*Set of* 4	£350			

Figures of value take the place of both corner ornaments at the base of the 2d. and 3d.

1935 (6 May). *Silver Jubilee. As Nos.* 91/4 *of Antigua but ptd by B.W. P* 11 × 12.
114 2d. ultramarine and grey-black .. .. 2·00 2·50
a. Extra flagstaff £100
b. Short extra flagstaff .. .. .. 40·00
c. Lightning conductor .. .. .. 30·00
115 3d. brown and deep blue .. .. .. 4·50 5·00
a. Extra flagstaff £500
b. Short extra flagstaff £175
116 6d. green and indigo .. .. 7·50 7·50
a. Extra flagstaff £300
b. Short extra flagstaff £100
c. Lightning conductor .. .. .. 70·00
117 1s. slate and purple .. .. 14·00 18·00
a. Extra flagstaff £300
b. Short extra flagstaff £100
c. Lightning conductor .. .. .. 70·00
114/17 Perf "Specimen" .. .. *Set of* 4 85·00
For illustrations of plate varieties see Omnibus section following Zululand.

1937 (12 May). *Coronation. As Nos.* 13/15 *of Aden, but ptd by B.W. P* 11 × 11½.
118 ½d. green 50 45
119 2d. grey-black .. .. 1·75 1·40
120 3d. blue .. .. 3·00 2·25
118/20 Perf "Specimen" .. .. *Set of* 3 60·00

14 King George VI

15 Rock of Gibraltar

16 The Rock (North Side)

(Des Captain H. St. C. Garrod. Recess D.L.R.)

1938 (25 Feb)–**51.** *Designs as T* **14/16.** *Wmk Mult Script CA.*
121 ½d. deep green (*p* 13½ × 14) 15 20
122 1d. yellow-brown (*p* 14) .. .. .. 3·25 2·25
a. Perf 13½ .. .. 4·75 2·00
ab. Perf 13½. Wmk sideways .. .. 2·50 4·75
b. Perf 13. Wmk sideways. *Red-brn* (1942) 50 55
c. Perf 13. Wmk sideways. *Deep brn* (1944) 80 3·00
d. Perf 13, *Red-brown* (1949) 35 95
123 1½d. carmine (*p* 14) .. .. 11·00 2·25
a. Perf 13½ .. .. £130 30·00
123*b* 1½d. slate-violet (*p* 13) (1.1.43) 45 60
124 2d. grey (*p* 14) .. .. 5·50 90
a. Perf 13½ 70 45
ab. Perf 13½. Wmk sideways .. .. £375 28·00
b. Perf 13. Wmk sideways (1943) .. .. 70 1·10
124*c* 2d. carmine (*p* 13) (*wmk sideways*) (15.7.44) 80 50
125 3d. light blue (*p* 13½) .. .. .. 4·50 55
a. Perf 14 .. .. 42·00 10·00
b. Perf 13 (1942) 70 50
ba. Greenish blue (2.51) .. .. .. 2·00 2·50
125*c* 5d. red-orange (*p* 13) (15.9.47) .. .. 3·25 2·25
126 6d. carmine and grey-violet (*p* 13½) (16.3.38) 8·50 3·00
a. Perf 14 .. .. £100 1·00
b. Perf 13 (1942) .. .. .. 2·25 1·25
c. Perf 13. *Scarlet and grey-violet* (1945) .. 3·00 2·10
127 1s. black and green (*p* 14) (16.3.38) .. 13·00 14·00
a. Perf 13½ .. .. 24·00 8·00
b. Perf 13 (1942) .. .. .. 4·50 2·00
128 2s. black and brown (*p* 14) (16.3.38) .. 38·00 40·00
a. Perf 13½ .. .. 55·00 40·00
b. Perf 13 (1942) .. .. .. 9·00 6·00
129 5s. black and carmine (*p* 14) (16.3.38) .. 65·00 75·00
a. Perf 13½ .. .. 20·00 17·00
b. Perf 13 (1944) .. .. .. 17·00 14·00
130 10s. black and blue (*p* 14) (16.3.38) .. 50·00 55·00
a. Perf 13 (1943) .. .. .. 45·00 35·00
131 £1 orange (*p* 13½ × 14) (16.3.38) .. 48·00 48·00
121/31 .. .. *Set of* 14 £130 £110
121/31 Perf "Specimen" .. .. *Set of* 14 £400
Designs:—½d., £1, Type **14.** *Horiz as T* **15/16**—1d., 1½d. (*both*), Type **15**; 2d. (*both*), Type **16**; 3d., 5d. Europa Point; 6d. Moorish Castle; 1s. Southport Gate; 2s. Eliott Memorial; 5s. Government House; 10s. Catalan Bay.
The ½d., 1d. and both colours of the 2d. exist in coils constructed from normal sheets. These were originally joined vertically, but, because of technical problems, the 1d. and 2d. grey were subsequently issued in horizontal coils. The 2d. carmine only exists in the horizontal version.

1946 (12 Oct). *Victory. As Nos.* 28/9 *of Aden.*
132 ½d. green 25 30
133 3d. ultramarine 60 60
132/3 Perf "Specimen" .. .. *Set of* 2 60·00

1948 (1 Dec). *Royal Silver Wedding. As Nos.* 30/1 *of Aden.*
134 ½d. green 50 25
135 £1 brown-orange .. .. 85·00 75·00

1949 (10 Oct). *75th Anniv of Universal Postal Union. As Nos.* 114/17 *of Antigua.*
136 2d. carmine .. .. 1·75 1·25
137 3d. deep blue .. .. 3·25 2·50
138 6d. purple .. .. 4·00 3·75
139 1s. blue-green .. .. 7·00 7·50

NEW
CONSTITUTION
1950
(23)

1950 (1 Aug). *Inauguration of Legislative Council. Nos.* 124*c*, 125*b*, 126*b*, *and* 127*b optd as T* **23.**
140 16 2d. carmine .. .. 80 1·00
141 – 3d. light blue .. .. 85 1·00
142 – 6d. carmine and grey-violet .. .. 1·50 2·00
a. Opt double £300 £400
143 – 1s. black and green (R.) .. .. .. 2·00 3·75
On stamps from the lower part of the sheet of No. 142a the two impressions are almost coincident.

1953 (2 June). *Coronation. As No.* 47 *of Aden.*
144 ½d. black and bronze-green 20 15

24 Cargo and Passenger Wharves

25 Tower of Homage, Moorish Castle

26 Arms of Gibraltar

(Des N. Cummings. Recess (except £1, centre litho) De La Rue)

1953 (19 Oct). *T* **24/26** *and similar designs. Wmk Mult Script CA. P* 13.
145 ½d. indigo and grey-green 12 25
146 1d. bluish green (*shades*) 35 20
147 1½d. black .. .. 1·25 45
148 2d. deep olive-brown (*shades*) 90 15
149 2½d. carmine (*shades*) .. .. .. 1·25 25
150 3d. light blue (*shades*) .. .. .. 1·25 10
151 4d. ultramarine (*shades*) .. .. .. 1·50 75
152 5d. maroon (*shades*) 70 40
153 6d. black and pale blue (*shades*) 70 20
154 1s. pale blue and red-brown (*shades*) .. 1·00 55
155 2s. orange and reddish violet (*shades*) .. 18·00 3·50
156 5s. deep brown .. .. 23·00 12·00
157 10s. reddish brown and ultramarine .. .. 90·00 50·00
158 £1 scarlet and orange-yellow .. .. £100 55·00
145/58 .. .. *Set of* 14 £225 £110
Designs: *Horiz as T* **24**—1d. South View from Straits; 1½d. Tunney Fishing Industry; 2d. Southport Gate; 2½d. Sailing in the Bay; 3d. Ocean-going liner; 4d. Coaling wharf; 5d. Airport; 6d. Europa Point; 1s. Straits from Buena Vista; 2s. Rosia Bay and Straits; 5s. Main Entrance, Government House.
Nos. 145/6, 148 and 150 exist in coils, constructed from normal sheets.

1954 (10 May). *Royal Visit. As No.* 150 *but inscr* "ROYAL VISIT 1954" *at top.*
159 3d. greenish blue 25 30

38 Gibraltar Candytuft

40 Rock and Badge of Gibraltar Regiment

39 Moorish Castle

(Des J. Celecia (½d., 2d., 2½d., 2s., 10s.), N. A. Langdon (1d., 3d., 6d., 7d., 9d., 1s.), M. Bonilla (4d.), L. J. Gomez (5s.), Sgt. T. A. Griffiths (£1). Recess (£1) or photo (others) D.L.R.)

1960 (29 Oct). *Designs as T* **38/9**, *and T* **40.** *W* w **12** (*upright*). *P* 14 (£1) *or* 13 (*others*).
160 ½d. bright purple and emerald-green 15 30
161 1d. black and yellow-green 10 8
162 2d. indigo and orange-brown 15 10
163 2½d. black and blue (*shades*) 15 12
164 3d. deep blue and red-orange 25 8
165 4d. deep red-brown and turquoise .. .. 1·00 25
166 6d. sepia and emerald .. .. .. 1·00 20
167 7d. indigo and carmine-red .. .. .. 1·00 60
168 9d. grey-blue and greenish blue 70 55
169 1s. sepia and bluish green .. .. .. 1·25 45
170 2s. chocolate and ultramarine .. .. 7·50 2·50
171 5s. turquoise-blue and olive-brown .. .. 14·00 7·50
172 10s. yellow and blue .. .. 25·00 14·00
173 £1 black and brown-orange .. .. .. 35·00 24·00
160/73 .. .. *Set of* 14 75·00 45·00
Designs: *Horiz*—2d. St. George's Hall; 3d. The Rock by moonlight; 4d. Catalan Bay; 1s. Rock Ape; 2s. Barbary Partridge; 5s. Blue Rock Thrush. *Vert*—2½d. The Keys; 6d. Map of Gibraltar; 7d. Air terminal; 9d. American War Memorial; 10s. Rock Lily (*Narcissus niveus*).

Nos. 160/2, 164 and 166 exist in coils, constructed from normal sheets.
See also No. 199.

1963 (4 June). *Freedom from Hunger. As No.* 76 *of Aden.*
174 9d. sepia .. .. 17·00 11·00

1963 (2 Sept). *Red Cross Centenary. As Nos.* 147/8 *of Antigua.*
175 1d. red and black 50 15
176 9d. red and blue .. .. 18·00 11·00

1964 (23 Apr). 400*th Birth Anniv of William Shakespeare. As No.* 164 *of Antigua.*
177 7d. bistre-brown .. .. 1·40 35

NEW CONSTITUTION 1964.

(52)

53 Bream

1964 (16 Oct). *New Constitution. Nos.* 164 *and* 166 *optd with T* **52**.
178 3d. deep blue and red-orange 25 10
179 6d. sepia and emerald 30 20
a. No stop after "1964" (R.2/5) .. .. 9·00 8·00

1965 (17 May). *I.T.U. Centenary. As Nos.* 166/7 *of Antigua.*
180 4d. light emerald and yellow .. .. 3·50 50
181 2s. apple-green and deep blue .. .. 32·00 14·00

1965 (25 Oct). *International Co-operation Year. As Nos.* 168/9 *of Antigua.*
182 ½d. deep bluish green and lavender .. 55 30
183 4d. reddish purple and turquoise-green .. 2·00 80
The value of the ½d. stamp is shown as "1/2".

1966 (24 Jan). *Churchill Commemoration. As Nos.* 170/3 *of Antigua.*
184 ½d. new blue 20 15
185 1d. deep green 55 15
186 4d. brown .. .. 1·90 55
187 9d. bluish violet .. .. 2·00 2·00

1966 (1 July). *World Cup Football Championships. As Nos.* 176/7 *of Antigua.*
188 2½d. violet, yellow-green, lake & yellow-brn 1·50 35
189 6d. chocolate, blue-green, lake & yellow-brn 2·25 90

PRINTERS. All stamps from here to No. 239 were printed in photogravure by Harrison and Sons Ltd, London.

(Des A. Ryman)

1966 (27 Aug). *European Sea Angling Championships, Gibraltar. T* **53** *and similar designs. W* w **12**. *P* 13½ × 14 (1*s.*) *or* 14 × 13½ (*others*).
190 4d. rosine, bright blue and black 12 10
191 7d. rosine, deep olive-green and black 15 10
a. Black (value and inscr) omitted £450
192 1s. lake-brown, emerald and black 15 12
Designs: *Horiz*—7d. Scorpion Fish. *Vert*—1s. Stone Bass.

1966 (20 Sept). *Inauguration of W.H.O. Headquarters, Geneva. As Nos.* 178/9 *of Antigua.*
193 6d. black, yellow-green and light blue .. 3·00 1·50
194 9d. black, light purple and yellow-brown .. 3·00 1·75

56 "Our Lady of Europa"

57 H.M.S. *Victory*

(Des A. Ryman)

1966 (15 Nov). *Centenary of Re-enthronement of "Our Lady of Europa". W* w **12**. *P* 14 × 14½.
195 **56** 2s. bright blue and black .. .. 70 1·25

1966 (1 Dec). 20*th Anniv of U.N.E.S.C.O. As Nos.* 196/8 *of Antigua.*
196 2d. slate-violet, red, yellow and orange .. 30 10
197 7d. orange-yellow, violet and deep olive .. 90 15
198 5s. black, bright purple and orange .. 6·50 2·75

1966 (23 Dec). *As No.* 165 *but wmk* w **12** *sideways.*
199 4d. deep red-brown and turquoise 25 30

(Des A. Ryman)

1967 (3 Apr)–**69**. *Horiz designs as T* **57**. *Multicoloured. W* w **12**. *P* 14 × 14½.
200 ½d. Type **57** 5 12
201 1d. S.S. *Arab* 12 10
202 2d. H.M.S. *Carmania* 20 10
203 2½d. M.V. *Mons Calpe* 30 30
204 3d. S.S. *Canberra* 25 10
205 4d. H.M.S. *Hood* 35 10
205*a* 5d. Cable Ship *Mirror* (7.7.69) .. .. 1·50 45
206 6d. Xebec (sailing vessel) 75 20
207 7d. *Amerigo Vespucci* (training vessel) .. 80 40
208 9d. T.V. *Raffaello* .. .. 1·00 60
209 1s. H.M.S. *Royal Katherine* .. .. 1·00 45
210 2s. H.M.S. *Ark Royal* .. .. .. 5·00 1·75
211 5s. H.M.S. *Dreadnought* .. .. .. 8·00 5·50
212 10s. S.S. *Neuralia* .. .. 18·00 14·00
213 £1 *Mary Celeste* (sailing vessel) .. .. 27·00 23·00
200/13 .. .. *Set of* 15 55·00 42·00
The ½d., 1d., 2d., 3d., 6d., 2s., 5s. and £1 exist with PVA gum as well as gum arabic, but the 5d. exists with PVA gum only.
Nos. 201/2, 204/5 and 206 exist in coils constructed from normal sheets.

58 Aerial Ropeway

(Des A. Ryman)

1967 (15 June). *International Tourist Year. T* **58** *and similar designs but horiz. Multicoloured. W* w **12** (*sideways on* 7*d.*). *P* 14½ × 14 (7*d.*) *or* 14 × 14½ (*others*).
214 7d. Type **58** 15 10
215 9d. Shark fishing 15 10
216 1s. Skin-diving 15 10

59 Mary, Joseph and Child Jesus

60 Church Window

1967 (1 Nov). *Christmas. W* w **12** (*sideways on* 6*d.*). *P* 14.
217 **59** 2d. multicoloured 5 5
218 **60** 6d. multicoloured 10 10

61 Gen. Eliott and Route Map

62 Eliott directing Rescue Operations

(Des A. Ryman)

1967 (11 Dec). 250*th Birth Anniv of General Eliott. Multicoloured designs as T* **61** (4*d. to* 1*s.*) *or T* **62**. *W* w **12** (*sideways on horiz designs*). *P* 14 × 15 (1*s.*) *or* 15 × 14 (*others*).
219 4d. Type **61** 15 10
220 9d. Heathfield Tower and Monument, Sussex (38 × 22 *mm*) 20 15
221 1s. General Eliott (22 × 38 *mm*) 20 15
222 2s. Type **62** 80 65

65 Lord Baden-Powell

(Des A. Ryman)

1968 (27 Mar). 60*th Anniv of Gibraltar Scout Association. T* **65** *and similar horiz designs. W* w **12**. *P* 14 × 14½.
223 4d. buff and bluish violet 15 8
224 7d. ochre and blue-green 15 12
225 9d. bright blue, yellow-orange and black .. 15 15
226 1s. greenish yellow and emerald 15 15
Designs:—7d. Scout Flag over the Rock; 9d. Tent, scouts and salute; 1s. Scout badges.

66 Nurse and W.H.O. Emblem

68 King John signing Magna Carta

(Des A. Ryman)

1968 (1 July). 20*th Anniv of World Health Organization. T* **66** *and similar horiz design. W* w **12**. *P* 14 × 14½.
227 2d. ultramarine, black and yellow 8 8
228 4d. slate, black and pink 12 12
Design:—4d. Doctor and W.H.O. emblem.

(Des A. Ryman)

1968 (26 Aug). *Human Rights Year. T* **68** *and similar vert design. W* w **12** (*sideways*). *P* 13½ × 14.
229 1s. yellow-orange, brown and gold 15 15
230 2s. myrtle and gold 25 30
Design:—2s. "Freedom" and Rock of Gibraltar.

70 Shepherd, Lamb and Star

72 Parliament Houses

(Des A. Ryman)

1968 (1 Nov). *Christmas. T* **70** *and similar vert design. Multicoloured. W* w **12**. *P* 14½ × 13½.
231 4d. Type **70** 10 10
232 9d. Mary holding Holy Child 15 20

(Des A. Ryman)

1969 (26 May). *Commonwealth Parliamentary Association Conference. T* **72** *and similar designs. W* w **12** (*sideways on* 2*s.*). *P* 14 × 14½ (2*s.*) *or* 14½ × 14 (*others*).
233 4d. green and gold 15 8
234 9d. bluish violet and gold 25 15
235 2s. multicoloured 55 30
Designs: *Horiz*—9d. Parliamentary emblem and outline of "The Rock". *Vert*—2s. Clock Tower, Westminster (Big Ben) and arms of Gibraltar.

75 Silhouette of Rock, and Queen Elizabeth

77 Soldier and Cap Badge, Royal Anglian Regiment, 1969

(Des A. Ryman)

1969 (30 July). *New Constitution. W* w **12**. *P* 14 × 13½ (*in addition, the outline of the Rock is perforated*).
236 **75** ½d. gold and orange 5 5
237 5d. silver and bright green 25 12
a. Portrait and inscr in gold and silver*
238 7d. silver and bright purple 35 25
239 5s. gold and ultramarine .. .. 1·40 1·75
*No. 237a was first printed with the head and inscription in gold and then in silver but displaced slightly to lower left.

(Des A. Ryman. Photo D.L.R.)

1969 (6 Nov). *Military Uniforms* (1*st series*). *T* **77** *and similar vert designs. Multicoloured. W* w **12**. *P* 14.
240 1d. Royal Artillery officer, 1758 and modern cap badge 20 12
241 6d. Type **77** 65 65
242 9d. Royal Engineers' Artificer, 1786 and modern cap badge 90 90
243 2s. Private, Fox's Marines, 1704 and modern Royal Marines cap badge .. .. .. 6·00 4·50
Nos. 240/3 have a short history of the Regiment printed on the reverse side over the gum, therefore, once the gum is moistened the history disappears.
See also Nos. 248/51, 290/3, 300/3, 313/16, 331/4, 340/3 and 363/6.

80 "Madonna of the Chair" (detail, Raphael)

83 Europa Point

(Des A. Ryman. Photo Enschedé)

1969 (1 Dec). *Christmas. T* **80** *and similar vert designs. Multicoloured.* W w **12** (*sideways*). P 14 × *Roulette* 9.

244 5d. Type **80** 12 10
a. Strip of 3. Nos. 244/6 60
245 7d. "Virgin and Child" (detail, Morales) .. 15 12
246 1s. "The Virgin of the Rocks" (detail, Leonardo da Vinci) 20 20

Nos. 244/6 were issued together in *se-tenant* strips of three throughout the sheet.

(Des A. Ryman. Photo Enschedé)

1970 (8 June). *Europa Point.* W w **12**. P 13½.

247 **83** 2s. multicoloured 80 80

(Des A. Ryman. Photo D.L.R.)

1970 (28 Aug). *Military Uniforms (2nd series). Vert designs as T* **77**. *Multicoloured.* W w **12**. P 14.

248 2d. Royal Scots officer, 1839 and cap badge .. 40 25
249 5d. South Wales Borderers private, 1763 and cap badge.. .. .. 90 70
250 7d. Queen's Royal Regiment private, 1742 and cap badge .. .. 1·10 90
251 2s. Royal Irish Rangers piper, 1969 and cap badge .. .. 6·50 6·50

Nos. 248/51 have a short history of the Regiment printed on the reverse side under the gum.

88 No. 191a and Rock of Gibraltar

(Des A. Ryman. Litho D.L.R.)

1970 (18 Sept). *"Philympia 1970" Stamp Exhibition, London. T* **88** *and similar horiz design.* W w **12** (*sideways*). P 13.

252 1s. vermilion and bronze-green 25 25
253 2s. bright blue and magenta 45 35

Design:—2s. Victorian stamp (No. 23b) and Moorish Castle.

The stamps shown in the designs are well-known varieties with values omitted.

90 "The Virgin Mary" (stained-glass window by Gabriel Loire)

(Photo Enschedé)

1970 (1 Dec). *Christmas.* W w **12**. P 13 × 14.

254 **90** 2s. multicoloured 75 60

91 Saluting Battery, Rosia

92 Saluting Battery, Rosia, Modern View

(Des A. Ryman. Litho Questa)

1971 (15 Feb). *Decimal Currency. Designs as T* **91/2**. W w **12** (*sideways on horiz designs*). P 14.

255 ½p. multicoloured 10 10
a. Pair. Nos. 255/6 .. .. 20 20
256 ½p. multicoloured 10 10
257 1p. multicoloured 60 30
a. Pair. Nos. 257/8 .. .. 1·25 60
258 1p. multicoloured 60 30
259 1½p. multicoloured 20 15
a. Pair. Nos. 259/60 .. .. 40 30
260 1½p. multicoloured 20 15
261 2p. multicoloured .. .. 1·25 70
a. Pair. Nos. 261/2 .. .. 3·00 1·75
262 2p. multicoloured .. .. 1·25 70
263 2½p. multicoloured 20 15
a. Pair. Nos. 263/4 .. .. 40 30
264 2½p. multicoloured 20 15
265 3p. multicoloured 20 15
a. Pair. Nos. 265/6 .. .. 40 30
266 3p. multicoloured 20 15
267 4p. multicoloured .. .. 1·50 1·25
a. Pair. Nos. 267/8 .. .. 3·50 3·00
268 4p. multicoloured .. .. 1·50 1·25
269 5p. multicoloured 30 20
a. Pair. Nos. 269/70 .. .. 60 40
270 5p. multicoloured 30 20
271 7p. multicoloured 40 40
a. Pair. Nos. 271/2 .. .. 80 80
272 7p. multicoloured 40 40
273 8p. multicoloured 50 50
a. Pair. Nos. 273/4 .. .. 1·00 1·00
274 8p. multicoloured 50 50
275 9p. multicoloured 55 50
a. Pair. Nos. 275/6 .. .. 1·10 1·00
276 9p. multicoloured 55 50
277 10p. multicoloured 60 50
a. Pair. Nos. 277/8 .. .. 1·25 1·00
278 10p. multicoloured 60 50
279 12½p. multicoloured 70 75
a. Pair. Nos. 279/80 .. .. 1·40 1·50
280 12½p. multicoloured 70 75
281 25p. multicoloured .. .. 1·25 1·25
a. Pair. Nos. 281/2 .. .. 2·50 2·50
282 25p. multicoloured .. .. 1·25 1·25
283 50p. multicoloured .. .. 2·00 2·75
a. Pair. Nos. 283/4 .. .. 4·00 5·50
284 50p. multicoloured .. .. 2·00 2·75
285 £1 multicoloured .. .. 4·00 5·50
a. Pair. Nos. 285/6 .. .. 8·00 11·00
286 £1 multicoloured .. .. 4·00 5·50
255/86 .. .. *Set of* 32 27·00 28·00

Designs (the two versions of each value show the same Gibraltar view taken from an early 19th-century print (first design) or modern photograph (second design): *Horiz*—1p. Prince George of Cambridge Quarters and Trinity Church; 1½p. The Wellington Bust, Alameda Gardens; 2p. Gibraltar from the North Bastion; 2½p. Catalan Bay; 3p. Convent Garden; 4p. The Exchange and Spanish Chapel; 5p. Commercial Square and Library; 7p. South Barracks and Rosia Magazine; 8p. Moorish Mosque and Castle; 9p. Europa Pass Road; 10p. South Barracks from Rosia Bay; 12½p. Southport Gates; 25p. Trooping the Colour, The Alameda. *Vert*—50p. Europa Pass Gorge; £1 Prince Edward's Gate.

The two designs of each value were printed together, *se-tenant*, in horizontal and vertical pairs throughout.

See also Nos. 317/20 and 344/5.

93

94 Regimental Arms

(Des A. Ryman. Photo Harrison)

1971 (15 Feb). *Coil Stamps.* W w **12**. P 14½ × 14.

287 **93** ½p. red-orange 15 25
a. Coil strip (287 × 2, 288 × 2 and 289 *se-tenant*) .. .. 1·40 2·00
288 1p. blue 20 25
289 2p. bright green .. .. 75 1·10

(Des A. Ryman. Litho Questa)

1971 (6 Sept). *Military Uniforms (3rd series). Multicoloured designs as T* **77**, *showing uniform and cap-badge.* W w **12**. P 14.

290 1p. The Black Watch (1845).. .. .. 45 20
291 2p. Royal Regt of Fusiliers (1971) .. .. 1·10 50
292 4p. King's Own Royal Border Regt (1704) .. 1·90 1·25
293 10p. Devonshire and Dorset Regt (1801) .. 6·00 6·00

Nos. 290/3 have a short history of the Regiment printed on the reverse side under the gum.

(Des A. Ryman. Litho Harrison)

1971 (25 Sept). *Presentation of Colours to the Gibraltar Regiment.* W w **12** (*sideways*). P 12½ × 12.

294 **94** 3p. black, gold and red 30 30

95 Nativity Scene

96 Soldier Artificer, 1773

(Des A. Ryman. Photo Enschedé)

1971 (1 Dec). *Christmas. T* **95** *and similar horiz design. Multicoloured.* W w **12**. P 13 × 13½.

295 3p. Type **95** 70 50
296 5p. Mary and Joseph going to Bethlehem .. 90 80

(Des A. Ryman. Litho Questa)

1972 (6 Mar). *Bicentenary of Royal Engineers in Gibraltar. T* **96** *and similar multicoloured designs.* W w **12** (*sideways on* 1 *and* 3p.). P 13½ × 14 (5p.) *or* 14 × 13½ (*others*).

297 1p. Type **96** 65 25
298 3p. Modern tunneller .. .. 1·10 80
299 5p. Old and new uniforms and badge (*horiz*) 1·50 1·25

(Des A. Ryman. Litho Questa)

1972 (19 July). *Military Uniforms (4th series). Multicoloured designs as T* **77**. W w **12** (*sideways*). P 14.

300 1p. Duke of Cornwall's Light Infantry, 1704 35 20
301 3p. King's Royal Rifle Corps, 1830 .. .. 1·25 75
302 7p. Officer, 37th North Hampshire, 1825 .. 2·25 2·25
303 10p. Royal Navy, 1972 .. .. .. 2·75 2·75

Nos. 300/303 have a short history of the Regiment printed on the reverse side under the gum.

97 "Our Lady of Europa"

98 Keys of Gibraltar and *Narcissus niveus*

(Des A. Ryman. Litho Harrison)

1972 (4 Oct). *Christmas.* W w **12** (*sideways*). P 14½ × 14.

304 **97** 3p. multicoloured 15 20
305 5p. multicoloured 30 40

These stamps have an inscription printed on the reverse side.

(Des (from photograph by D. Groves) and photo Harrison)

1972 (20 Nov). *Royal Silver Wedding. Multicoloured; background colour given.* W w **12**. P 14 × 14½.

306 **98** 5p. carmine-red 35 35
307 7p. deep grey-green 35 35

99 Flags of Member Nations and E.E.C. Symbol

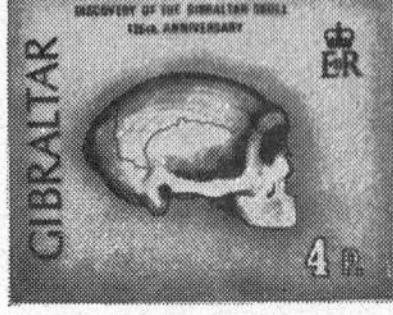

100 Skull

(Des A. Ryman. Litho Questa)

1973 (22 Feb). *Britain's Entry into E.E.C.* W w **12** (*sideways*). P 14½ × 14.

308 **99** 5p. multicoloured .. .. 1·00 75
309 10p. multicoloured .. .. 1·25 1·00

(Des A. Ryman. Litho B.W.)

1973 (22 May). *125th Anniv of Gibraltar Skull Discovery. T* **100** *and similar horiz designs. Multicoloured.* W w **12**. P 13 (10p.) *or* 13½ (*others*).

310 4p. Type **100** .. .. 1·00 65
311 6p. Prehistoric man .. .. 1·25 90
312 10p. Prehistoric family (40 × 26 *mm*) .. .. 1·90 1·75

(Des A. Ryman. Litho Questa)

1973 (22 Aug). *Military Uniforms (5th series). Multicoloured designs as T* **77**. W w **12** (*sideways*). P 14.

313 1p. King's Own Scottish Borderers, 1770 .. 45 20
314 4p. Royal Welch Fusiliers, 1800 .. .. 2·00 1·50
315 6p. Royal Northumberland Fusiliers, 1736 .. 2·75 2·75
316 10p. Grenadier Guards, 1898 .. .. .. 4·25 4·50

Nos. 313/16 have a short history of the Regiment printed on the reverse side under the gum.

1973 (12 Sept). *As Nos.* 261/2 *and* 267/8 *but* W w **12** *upright.*

317 2p. multicoloured 50 65
a. Pair. Nos. 317/18.. .. .. .. 1·00 1·25
318 2p. multicoloured 50 65
319 4p. multicoloured 75 90
a. Pair. Nos. 319/20.. .. .. .. 1·50 1·75
320 4p. multicoloured 75 90

101 "Nativity" (Danckerts)

102 Victorian Pillar-box

(Des and litho Enschedé)

1973 (17 Oct). *Christmas.* W w **12**. P 12½ × 12.

321 **101** 4p. violet and Venetian red 40 30
322 6p. magenta and turquoise-blue 60 50

1973 (14 Nov). *Royal Wedding. As Nos.* 165/6 *of Anguilla. Centre multicoloured.* W w **12** (*sideways*). P 13½.

323 6p. turquoise 20 20
324 14p. yellow-green 40 40

(Des A. Ryman. Litho Walsall)

1974 (2 May). *Centenary of Universal Postal Union.* *T* **102** *and similar vert designs. Multicoloured. (a)* W w **12** *(sideways). P* 14½.

325 2p. Type **102** 30 20
326 6p. Pillar-box of George VI 55 40
327 14p. Pillar-box of Elizabeth II 95 75

(b) No wmk. Imperf × roul 5. Self-adhesive (from booklets)*

328 2p. Type **102** 35 70
a. Booklet pane Nos. 328/30 *se-tenant* . . 5·00
b. Booklet pane Nos. 328 × 3 and 329 × 3 . . 2·75
329 6p. As No. 326 . . . . 60 1·00
330 14p. As No. 327 . . . . 3·75 6·00

*Nos. 328/30 were separated by various combinations of rotary-knife (giving a straight edge) and roulette.

(Des A. Ryman. Litho Questa)

1974 (21 Aug). *Military Uniforms (6th series). Multicoloured designs as T* **77.** W w **12** *(sideways). P* 14.

331 4p. East Lancashire Regt, 1742 . . . . 80 80
332 6p. Somerset Light Infantry, 1833 . . . . 1·00 1·00
333 10p. Royal Sussex Regt, 1790. . . . . . 1·75 1·75
334 16p. R.A.F. officer, 1974 . . . . . . 3·00 3·00

Nos. 331/4 have a short history of the regiment printed on the reverse side under the gum.

103 "Madonna with the Green Cushion" (Solario)

104 Churchill and Houses of Parliament

(Des A. Ryman and M. Infante. Litho Questa)

1974 (5 Nov). *Christmas. T* **103** *and similar vert design. Multi-coloured.* W w **14.** *P* 14.

335 4p. Type **103** 70 50
336 6p. "Madonna of the Meadow" (Bellini) . . 90 75

(Des L. Curtis. Litho Harrison)

1974 (30 Nov). *Birth Centenary of Sir Winston Churchill. T* **104** *and similar horiz design.* W w **12.** *P* 14 × 14½.

337 6p. black, reddish purple and light lavender 40 30
338 20p. brownish black, lake-brown and light orange-red . . . . 1·00 1·25
MS339 114 × 93 mm. Nos. 337/8. W w **12** (sideways). P 14. . . . . 2·75 3·00

Design:—20p. Churchill and battleship.

(Des A. Ryman. Litho Questa)

1975 (14 Mar). *Military Uniforms (7th series). Multicoloured designs as T* **77.** W w **14.** *P* 14.

340 4p. East Surrey Regt, 1846 . . . . . . 65 65
341 6p. Highland Light Infantry, 1777 . . . . 85 85
342 10p. Coldstream Guards, 1704 . . . . . . 1·25 1·25
343 20p. Gibraltar Regt, 1974 . . . . . . 2·25 2·25

Nos. 340/3 have a short history of each regiment printed on the reverse side under the gum.

1975 (9 July). *As Nos. 257/8 but* W w **14** *(sideways).*

344 1p. multicoloured 50 60
a. Pair. Nos. 344/5 . . . . 1·00 1·10
345 1p. multicoloured 50 60

105 Girl Guides' Badge

106 Child at Prayer

(Des A. Ryman. Litho Harrison)

1975 (10 Oct). *50th Anniv of Gibraltar Girl Guides.* W w **12.** *P* 13 × 13½.

346 **105** 5p. gold, light blue and dull violet . . 50 55
347 7p. gold, sepia and light lake-brown . . 60 70
348 – 15p. silver, brownish black & yellow-brn 85 95

No. 348 is a T **105** but shows a different badge.

(Des A. Ryman. Litho Walsall)

1975 (26 Nov). *Christmas. T* **106** *and similar vert designs. Multi-coloured.* W w **14** *(sideways). P* 14.

349 6p. Type **106** 55 55
a. Block of 6. Nos. 349/54 . . . . . . 3·00
350 6p. Angel with lute 55 55
351 6p. Child singing carols 55 55
352 6p. Three children 55 55
353 6p. Girl at prayer 55 55
354 6p. Boy and lamb 55 55
349/54 . . . . *Set of* 6 3·00 3·00

Nos. 349/54 were issued together *se-tenant* in small sheets of six (3 × 2) with the usual plate numbers and marginal inscriptions.

107 Bruges Madonna

108 Bicentennial Emblem and Arms of Gibraltar

(Des Jennifer Toombs. Litho Walsall)

1975 (17 Dec). *500th Birth Anniv of Michelangelo. T* **107** *and similar vert designs. Multicoloured. (a)* W w **14** *(sideways). P* 14.

355 6p. Type **107** 25 25
356 9p. Taddei Madonna 40 40
357 15p. Pietà 70 70

(b) No wmk. Imperf × roul 5. Self-adhesive (from booklets)*

358 6p. Type **107** 25 25
a. Booklet pane Nos. 358/60 *se-tenant* . . 1·25
b. Booklet pane Nos. 358 × 2, 359 × 2 and 360 × 2 . . . . 2·50
359 9p. As No. 356 . . . . 40 40
360 15p. As No. 357 . . . . 70 70

*Nos. 358/60 were separated by various combinations of rotary knife (giving a straight edge) and roulette.

(Des A. Ryman. Litho Walsall)

1976 (28 May). *Bicentenary of American Revolution.* W w **14** *(inverted). P* 14.

361 **108** 25p. multicoloured . . . . . . 1·25 1·40
MS362 85 × 133 mm. No. 361 × 4. . . . . . 5·00 5·50

The edges of **MS**362 are rouletted.

(Des A. Ryman. Litho Walsall)

1976 (21 July). *Military Uniforms (8th series). Multicoloured designs as T* **77.** W w **14** *(inverted). P* 14.

363 1p. Suffolk Regt, 1795 . . . . . . 20 20
364 6p. Northamptonshire Regt, 1779 . . . . 65 65
365 12p. Lancashire Fusiliers, 1793 . . . . 95 95
366 25p. Ordnance Corps, 1896 . . . . . . 1·75 1·75

Nos. 363/6 have a short history of each regiment printed on the reverse side under the gum.

109 The Holy Family

110 Queen Elizabeth II, Royal Arms and Gibraltar Arms

(Des A. Ryman. Litho Questa)

1976 (3 Nov). *Christmas. T* **109** *and similar vert designs showing stained-glass windows in St. Joseph's Church, Gibraltar. Multi-coloured.* W w **14.** *P* 14.

367 6p. Type **109** 40 25
368 9p. Madonna and Child 60 35
369 12p. St. Bernard 80 60
370 20p. Archangel Michael . . . . 1·50 1·50

(Des A. Ryman. Litho J.W.)

1977 (7 Feb). *Silver Jubilee.* W w **14.** *P* 13½.

371 **110** 6p. multicoloured 20 20
372 £1 multicoloured . . . . 2·25 2·75
MS373 124 × 115 mm. Nos. 371/2. P 13 . . . . 3·50 3·75

The outer edges of the miniature sheet are either guillotined or rouletted.

111 Toothed Orchid (*Orchis tridentata*)

(Des A. Ryman. Litho Questa)

1977 (1 Apr)–**82.** *Multicoloured designs as T* **111.** W w **14** *(sideways on horiz designs; inverted on £5). Chalk-surfaced paper (15p., £5). P* 14.

374 ½p. Type **111** 10 10
a. Chalk-surfaced paper (22.2.82) 15 20
375 1p. Red Mullet (*Mullus surmuletus*) (*horiz*) 10 10
376 2p. Large Blue butterfly (*Maculinea arion*) (*horiz*) 30 15
377 2½p. Sardinian Warbler (*Sylvia melanocephala*) 30 15
378 3p. Giant Squill (*Scilla peruviana*) 20 10
379 4p. Grey Wrasse (*Crenilabrus cinereus*) (*horiz*) 25 10
b. Chalk-surfaced paper (8.5.81) 25 10
380 5p. Red Admiral butterfly (*Vanessa atalanta*) (*horiz*) 45 20
381 6p. Black Kite (*Milvus migrans*) 45 20
382 9p. Shrubby Scorpion-vetch (*Coronilla valentina*) 75 60
383 10p. John Dory (fish) (*Zeus faber*) (*horiz*) . . 40 20
a. Chalk-surfaced paper (8.5.81) 40 30
384 12p. Clouded Yellow butterfly (*Colias crocea*) (*horiz*) . . . . 1·00 25
a. Chalk-surfaced paper (8.5.81) . . . . 1·00 30
384*b* 15p. Winged Asparagus Pea (*Tetragonolobus purpureus*) (12.11.80) 95 30
385 20p. Audouin's Gull (*Larus audouinii*) . . 1·00 50
386 25p. Barbary Nut (iris) (*Iris sisyrinchium*) . . 1·25 50
a. Chalk-surfaced paper (8.5.81) . . . . 1·25 60
387 50p. Swordfish (*Xiphias gladius*) (*horiz*) . . 2·00 95
a. Chalk-surfaced paper (8.5.81) . . . . 2·00 1·40
388 £1 Swallow-tail butterfly (*Papilio machaon*) (*horiz*) . . . . 4·75 2·25
389 £2 Hoopoe (*Upupa epops*) . . . . . . 7·50 5·50
389*a* £5 Arms of Gibraltar (16.5.79) . . . . 10·00 10·00
374/89*a* . . . . *Set of* 18 28·00 20·00

The ½p. to £2 values have a descriptive text printed on the reverse, beneath the gum.

The 9p. from the above issue exists with different dates in the imprint below the design.

112 "Our Lady of Europa" Stamp

(Des J. Cooter. Litho Questa)

1977 (27 May). *"Amphilex 77" Stamp Exhibition. Amsterdam. T* **112** *and similar vert designs. Multicoloured.* W w **14** *(sideways on 6p.; inverted on 12p.). P* 13½.

390 6p. Type **112** 20 30
391 12p. "Europa Point" stamp 35 55
392 25p. "E.E.C. Entry" stamp 45 80

113 "The Annunciation" (Rubens)

114 Aerial View of Gibraltar

(Des A. Ryman. Litho Enschedé)

1977 (2 Nov). *Christmas and Rubens' 400th Birth Anniv. T* **113** *and similar multicoloured designs.* W w **14** *(sideways on 12p.). P* 13½.

393 3p. Type **113** 20 10
394 9p. "The Adoration of the Magi" 45 30
395 12p. "The Adoration of the Magi" (*horiz*) . . 55 45
396 15p. "The Holy Family under the Apple Tree" 60 50
MS397 110 × 200 mm. Nos. 393/6 (wmk upright). . 1·75 1·90

(Des A. Ryman. Litho Enschedé)

1978 (3 May). *Gibraltar from Space. P* 13½.

398 **114** 12p. multicoloured 50 45
MS399 148 × 108 mm. 25 p. multicoloured . . 85 90

Design:—25p. Aerial view of Straits of Gibraltar.

115 Holyroodhouse

(Des and litho Walsall)

1978 (12 June). *25th Anniv of Coronation. T* **115** *and similar horiz designs. Multicoloured. (a) From sheets. P* 13½ × 14.

400 6p. Type **115** 25 20
401 9p. St. James's Palace 35 30
402 12p. Sandringham 40 45
403 18p. Balmoral 50 55

(b) From booklets. Imperf × roul 5. Self-adhesive*

404 12p. As No. 402 . . . . 35 50
a. Booklet pane. Nos. 404/5, each × 3 . . 2·00
405 18p. As No. 403 . . . . 40 60
406 25p. Windsor Castle 70 90
a. Booklet pane of 1. 70

*Nos. 404/5 were separated by various combinations of rotary-knife (giving a straight edge) and roulette. No. 406 exists only with straight edges.

116 "Sunderland", 1938–58 117 "Madonna with Animals"

(Des A. Theobald. Litho Harrison)

1978 (6 Sept). *60th Anniv of Royal Air Force. T* **116** *and similar horiz designs. Multicoloured. W* w **14** *(sideways). P* 14.

407 3p. Type **116** 15 8
408 9p. "Caudron", 1918 .. .. 45 35
409 12p. "Shackleton", 1953–66 .. .. 55 40
410 16p. "Hunter", 1954–77 .. .. 70 50
411 18p. "Nimrod", 1969–78 .. .. 80 60

(Des A. Ryman. Litho Questa)

1978 (1 Nov). *Christmas. Paintings by Dürer. T* **117** *and similar vert designs. Multicoloured. W* w **14.** *P* 14.

412 5p. Type **117** 25 12
413 9p. "The Nativity" 35 30
414 12p. "Madonna of the Goldfinch" 45 45
415 15p. "Adoration of the Magi" 55 55

118 Sir Rowland Hill and 1d. Stamp of 1886

(Des A. Ryman. Litho Format)

1979 (7 Feb). *Death Centenary of Sir Rowland Hill. T* **118** *and similar horiz designs. W* w **14** *(sideways). P* 13½ × 14.

416 3p. multicoloured 20 10
417 9p. multicoloured 40 40
418 12p. multicoloured 45 45
419 25p. black, dull claret and yellow 60 65

Designs:—9p. Sir Rowland Hill and 1p. coil stamp of 1971; 12p. Sir Rowland Hill and Post Office Regulations document, 1840; 25p. Sir Rowland Hill and "G" cancellation.

119 Posthorn, Dish Antenna and Early Telephone 120 African Child

(Des A. Ryman. Litho Format)

1979 (16 May). *Europa. Communications. W* w 14 *(sideways). P* 13½.

420 **119** 3p. green and pale green 45 10
421 9p. lake-brown and ochre .. .. 1·25 70
422 12p. ultramarine and dull violet-blue .. .. 1·60 85

(Des G. Hutchins. Litho Walsall)

1979 (14 Nov). *Christmas. International Year of the Child. T* **120** *and similar vert designs. Multicoloured. W* w **14** *(sideways). P* 14.

423 12p. Type **120** 45 35
a. Block of 6. Nos. 423/8 .. .. 2·40
424 12p. Asian child 45 35
425 12p. Polynesian child 45 35
426 12p. American Indian child 45 35
427 12p. Children of different races and Nativity scene 45 35
428 12p. European child 45 35
423/8 .. .. *Set of* 6 2·40 1·90

Nos. 423/8 were printed together, *se-tenant*, in blocks of 6, with margin separating the two blocks in each sheet.

121 Early Policemen 122 Peter Amigo (Archbishop)

(Des C. Abbott. Litho Questa)

1980 (5 Feb). *150th Anniv of Gibraltar Police Force. T* **121** *and similar horiz designs. Multicoloured. W* w **14** *(sideways). P* 14.

429 3p. Type **121** 15 5
430 6p. Policemen of 1895, early 1900s and 1980 25 15
431 12p. Policeman and police ambulance .. 45 30
432 37p. Policewoman and police motor-cyclist .. 1·10 95

(Des A. Ryman. Litho Questa)

1980 (6 May). *Europa. Personalities. T* **122** *and similar vert designs. Multicoloured. W* w **14** *(inverted on No.* 434). *P* 14½ × 14.

433 12p. Type **122** 35 35
434 12p. Gustavo Bacarisas (artist) 35 35
435 12p. John Mackintosh (philanthropist) 35 35

123 Queen Elizabeth the Queen Mother 124 "Horatio Nelson" (J. F. Rigaud)

(Des Harrison. Litho Questa)

1980 (4 Aug). *80th Birthday of Queen Elizabeth the Queen Mother. W* w 14 *(sideways). P* 14.

436 **123** 15p. multicoloured 50 45

(Des BG Studio. Litho Questa)

1980 (20 Aug). *175th Death Anniv of Nelson. Paintings. T* **124** *and similar multicoloured designs. W* w **14** *(sideways on* 9 *and* 40*p.). P* 14.

437 3p. Type **124** 15 5
438 9p. "H.M.S. *Victory*" (*horiz*) 40 25
439 15p. "Horatio Nelson" (Sir William Beechey) 45 35
440 40p. "H.M.S. *Victory* being towed into Gibraltar" (Clarkson Stanfield) (*horiz*) .. 1·25 1·00
MS441 159 × 99 mm. No. 439 .. .. 1·25 1·25

125 Three Kings 126 Hercules creating Mediterranean Sea

(Des A. Ryman. Litho Questa)

1980 (12 Nov). *Christmas. T* **125** *and similar horiz design, each in deep brown and orange-yellow. W* w **14** *(sideways). P* 14½.

442 15p. Type **125** 35 35
a. Horiz pair. Nos. 442/3 .. .. 70 70
443 15p. Nativity scene 35 35

Nos. 442/3 were printed together, *se-tenant*, in horizontal pairs throughout the sheet.

(Des G. Vasarhelyi. Litho Enschedé)

1981 (24 Feb). *Europa. Folklore. T* **126** *and similar vert design. Multicoloured. W* w 14. *P* 13½ × 13.

444 9p. Type **126** 25 25
445 15p. Hercules and Pillars of Hercules (Straits of Gibraltar) 40 35

127 Dining-room 128 Prince Charles and Lady Diana Spencer

(Des A. Ryman. Litho Harrison)

1981 (22 May). *450th Anniv of The Convent (Governor's Residence). T* **127** *and similar square designs. Multicoloured. W* w **14** *(sideways). P* 14½ × 14.

446 4p. Type **127** 15 10
447 14p. King's Chapel 40 40
448 15p. The Convent 40 40
449 55p. Cloister .. .. 1·40 1·40

(Des A. Ryman. Litho Questa)

1981 (27 July). *Royal Wedding. W* w **14** *(sideways). P* 14½.

450 **128** £1 multicoloured .. .. 3·00 3·00

129 130 Paper Aeroplane

(Des A. Ryman. Litho Questa)

1981 (2 Sept). *Booklet stamps. W* w 14 *(sideways). P* 13½ × 14.

451 **129** 1p. black 5 5
a. Booklet pane. Nos. 451/2 and 453 × 3 plus printed label 90
b. Booklet pane. Nos. 451/2 × 2 and 453 × 6 plus two printed labels .. .. 1·75
452 4p. Prussian blue 8 10
453 15p. light green 25 30

(Des A. Ryman. Litho Walsall)

1981 (29 Sept*). *50th Anniv of Gibraltar Airmail Service. T* **130** *and similar horiz designs. Multicoloured. W* w **14** *(sideways). P* 14½ × 14.

454 14p. Type **130** 45 30
455 15p. Airmail letters, post box and aircraft tail fin 45 30
456 55p. Aircraft circling globe .. .. 1·60 1·60

*This is the local release date. The Crown Agents released the stamps on 21 September.

131 Carol Singers 132 I.Y.D.P. Emblem and Stylised Faces

(Des Clive Torres (15p.); Peter Parody (55p.); adapted G. Vasarhelyi. Litho Questa)

1981 (19 Nov). *Christmas. Children's Drawings. T* **131** *and similar multicoloured design. W* w **14** *(sideways on* 15*p.). P* 14.

457 15p. Type **131** 50 30
458 55p. Postbox (*vert*) .. .. 1·40 1·40

(Des A. Ryman. Litho Questa)

1981 (19 Nov). *International Year For Disabled Persons. W* w **14** *(sideways). P* 14 × 14½.

459 **132** 14p. multicoloured 40 35

133 Douglas "DC 3" 134 Crest, H.M.S. *Opossum*

(Des A. Theobald. Litho J.W.)

1982 (10 Feb). *Aircraft. Horiz designs as T* 133. *Multicoloured. W* w **14.** *P* 14.

460 1p. Type **133** 5 5
461 2p. Vickers "Viking" 5 5
462 3p. Airspeed "Ambassador" 5 5
463 4p. Vickers "Viscount" 8 10
464 5p. Boeing "727" 8 10
465 10p. Vickers "Vanguard" 20 25
466 14p. Short "Solent" 25 30
467 15p. Fokker "F.27 (Friendship)" 25 30
468 17p. Boeing "737" 30 35
469 20p. BAC "One-eleven" 35 40
470 25p. Lockheed "Constellation" 45 50
471 50p. De Havilland "Comet 4B" 90 95
472 £1 Saro "Windhover" .. .. 1·75 1·90
473 £2 Hawker Siddeley "Trident 2" .. .. 3·50 3·75
474 £5 D.H. "89A (Dragon Rapide)" .. .. 9·00 9·25
460/74 .. .. *Set of* 15 16·00 17·00

(Des A. Ryman. Litho Questa)

1982 (14 Apr). *Naval Crests (1st series). T* **134** *and similar vert designs. Multicoloured. W* w **14.** *P* 14.

475 ½p. Type **134** 5 5
476 15½p. H.M.S. *Norfolk* 55 30
477 17p. H.M.S. *Fearless* 65 35
478 60p. H.M.S. *Rooke* .. .. 1·50 1·60

See also Nos. 493/6 and 510/13.

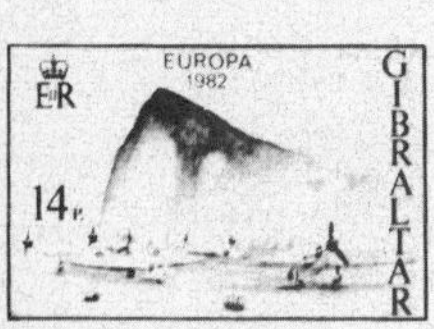

135 "Spitfires" at Gibraltar

136 Gibraltar Chamber of Commerce Centenary

(Des A. Ryman. Litho Questa)

1982 (11 June). *Europa. Operation Torch. T* **135** *and similar horiz design. Multicoloured. W* w **14** (*sideways*). *P* 14.

479	14p. Type **135** ..	40	35
480	17p. General Giraud, General Eisenhower and Gibraltar ..	45	40

(Des A. Ryman. Litho Questa)

1982 (22 Sept). *Anniversaries. T* **136** *and similar vert designs. Multicoloured. W* w 14 (*sideways*). *P* 14½.

481	½p. Type **136** ..	5	5
482	15½p. British Forces Postal Service centenary	40	35
483	60p. 75th anniv of Gibraltar Scout Association ..	1·40	1·40

137 Printed Circuit forming Map of World

(Des A. Ryman. Litho Harrison)

1982 (1 Oct). *International Direct Dialling. W* w **14** (*sideways*). *P* 14½.

484	**137**	17p. black, pale blue and bright orange	40	40

138 Gibraltar illuminated at Night and Holly

(Des A. Ryman. Litho Questa)

1982 (18 Nov). *Christmas. T* 138 *and similar horiz design. Multicoloured. W* w 14 (*sideways*). *P* 14 × 14½.

485	14p. Type **138** ..	30	30
486	17p. Gibraltar illuminated at night and Mistletoe ..	35	35

139 Yacht Marina

(Des Olympia Reyes. Litho Questa)

1983 (14 Mar). *Commonwealth Day. T* **139** *and similar multicoloured designs. W* w 14 (*sideways on* 4, 14*p*.). *P* 14.

487	4p. Type **139** ..	8	10
488	14p. Scouts and Guides Commonwealth Day Parade ..	30	35
489	17p. Flag of Gibraltar (*vert*) ..	35	40
490	60p. Queen Elizabeth II (from photo by Tim Graham) (*vert*) ..	1·25	1·40

140 St George's Hall Gallery

(Des A. Ryman. Litho Harrison)

1983 (21 May). *Europa. T* **140** *and similar horiz design. W* w **14** (*sideways*). *P* 13½ × 13.

491	16p. black and brown-ochre ..	30	35
492	19p. black and pale blue ..	40	45

Design:—19p. Water catchment slope.

(Des A. Ryman. Litho Questa)

1983 (1 July). *Naval Crests (2nd series). Vert designs as T* **134.** *Multicoloured. W* w **14.** *P* 14.

493	4p. H.M.S. *Faulknor* ..	8	10
494	14p. H.M.S. *Renown* ..	30	35
495	17p. H.M.S. *Ark Royal* ..	35	40
496	60p. H.M.S. *Sheffield* ..	1·25	1·40

141 Landport Gate, 1729

(Des Olympia Reyes. Litho Enschedé)

1983 (13 Sept). *Fortress Gibraltar in the 18th Century. T* **141** *and similar horiz designs. Multicoloured. W* w **14** (*sideways*). *P* 13 × 13½.

497	4p. Type **141** ..	8	10
498	17p. Koehler Gun, 1782 ..	35	40
499	77p. King's Bastion, 1779 ..	1·50	1·60
MS500	97 × 145 mm. Nos. 497/9 ..	1·90	

142 "Adoration of the Magi" (Raphael)

143 1932 2d. Stamp and Globe

(Des A. Ryman. Litho Questa)

1983 (17 Nov). *Christmas. 500th Birth Anniv of Raphael. T* **142** *and similar multicoloured designs. W* w **14** (*sideways on* 4*p*.). *P* 14.

501	4p. Type **142** ..	10	10
502	17p. "Madonna of Foligno" (*vert*) ..	35	35
503	60p. "Sistine Madonna" (*vert*) ..	1·25	1·40

(Des E. Field. Litho Walsall)

1984 (6 Mar). *Europa. Posts and Telecommunications. T* **143** *and similar vert design. Multicoloured. W* w **14.** *P* 14½ × 14.

504	17p. Type **143** ..	35	40
505	23p. Circuit board and globe ..	45	50

144 Hockey

145 Mississippi River Boat Float

(Des A. Ryman. Litho Walsall)

1984 (25 May). *Sports. T* **144** *and similar horiz designs. Multicoloured. W* w **14** (*sideways*). *P* 14 × 14½.

506	20p. Type **144** ..	40	45
507	21p. Basketball ..	40	45
508	26p. Rowing ..	55	60
509	29p. Football ..	60	65

(Des A. Ryman. Litho Walsall)

1984 (21 Sept). *Naval Crests (3rd series). Vert designs as T* **134.** *Multicoloured. W* w **14.** *P* 13½ × 13.

510	20p. H.M.S. *Active* ..	40	45
511	21p. H.M.S. *Foxhound* ..	40	45
512	26p. H.M.S. *Valiant* ..	55	60
513	29p. H.M.S. *Hood* ..	60	65

(Des A. Ryman. Litho Questa)

1984 (7 Nov). *Christmas. Epiphany Floats. T* **145** *and similar horiz design. Multicoloured. W* w **14** (*sideways*). *P* 14 × 14½.

514	20p. Type **145** ..	40	45
515	80p. Roman Temple float ..	1·60	1·75

POSTAGE DUE STAMPS

D 1

D 2

D 3 Gibraltar Coat of Arms

(Typo D.L.R.)

1956 (1 Dec). *Chalky paper. Wmk Mult Script CA. P* 14.

D1	D **1**	1d. green ..	3·75	3·50
D2		2d. sepia ..	5·50	5·50
D3		4d. blue ..	7·00	7·00

1971 (15 Feb). *As Nos.* D1/3 *but inscr in decimal currency. W* w **12.** *P* 17½ × 18.

D4	D **1**	½p. green ..	1·00	1·50
D5		1p. sepia ..	1·10	1·50
D6		2p. blue ..	1·50	1·75

(Des A. Ryman. Litho Questa)

1976 (13 Oct). *W* w **14.** *P* 14 × 13½.

D 7	D **2**	1p. light red-orange ..	8	10
D 8		3p. bright blue ..	12	20
D 9		5p. orange-vermilion ..	15	25
D10		7p. reddish violet ..	20	30
D11		10p. greenish slate ..	30	40
D12		20p. green ..	55	65
D7/12		.. *Set of* 6	1·25	1·75

(Des A. Ryman. Litho Irish Security Stamp Ptg Ltd)

1984 (2 July). *W* w **14** (*sideways*). *P* 15 × 14.

D13	D **3**	1p. black ..	5	5
D14		3p. vermilion ..	5	5
D15		5p. ultramarine ..	8	10
D16		10p. new blue ..	20	25
D17		25p. deep mauve ..	45	50
D18		50p. reddish orange ..	90	95
D19		£1 blue-green ..	1·75	1·90
D13/19		.. *Set of* 7	3·25	3·50

Gilbert and Ellice Islands

The stamps of NEW ZEALAND were used at the New Zealand Postal Agencies on Fanning Island (1902 to 1939) and Washington Island (1921 to 1934).

PRICES FOR STAMPS ON COVER TO 1945

Nos. 1/7	*from* × 5
Nos. 8/11	*from* × 8
Nos. 12/24	*from* × 4
Nos. 26/35	*from* × 5
Nos. 36/9	*from* × 3
Nos. 40/2	*from* × 8
Nos. 43/54	*from* × 4
Nos. D1/8	*from* × 4

BRITISH PROTECTORATE

GILBERT&ELLICE

PROTECTORATE

(1)

2 Pandanus Pine

1911 (1 Jan). *Stamps of Fiji optd with T* 1. *Wmk Mult Crown CA.*

1	23	½d. green, O	16·00	22·00
2		1d. red, O	45·00	48·00
3	24	2d. grey, O	11·00	16·00
4	23	2½d. ultramarine, O	15·00	38·00
5		5d. purple and olive-green, C	35·00	48·00
6	24	6d. dull and bright purple, C	35·00	48·00
7	23	1s. black/*green*, C (R.)	28·00	32·00
1/7		*Set of* 7	£170	£225
1/7 Optd "Specimen"		*Set of* 7	£500	

The 2d. to 6d. are on special printings which were not issued without overprint.

(Recess D.L.R.)

1911. *Wmk Mult Crown CA. P* 14.

8	2	½d. green	3·00	9·50
9		1d. carmine	2·25	8·00
10		2d. grey	2·00	7·50
11		2½d. blue	2·00	9·00
8/11 Optd "Specimen"		*Set of* 4	£140	

3

WAR TAX

(5)

(Typo D.L.R.)

1912–24. *Wmk Mult Crown CA. P* 14.

12	3	½d. green, O	70	1·50
		a. Yellow-green (1914)	2·25	3·00
13		1d. carmine, O	1·75	2·50
		a. Scarlet (1916)	2·75	5·50
14		2d. greyish slate, O (1916)	12·00	15·00
15		2½d. bright blue, O (1916)	3·00	8·50
16		3d. purple/*yellow*, C (1919)	1·25	3·50
17		4d. black and red/*yellow*, C	1·25	4·25
18		5d. dull purple and sage-green, C	4·50	13·00
19		6d. dull and bright purple, C	1·75	9·50
20		1s. black/*green*, C	5·00	13·00
21		2s. purple and blue/*blue*, C	20·00	25·00
22		2s. 6d. black and red/*blue*, C	22·00	28·00
23		5s. green and red/*yellow*, C	32·00	45·00
24		£1 purple and black/*red*, C (Die II) (1924) (S. £500)	£1000	£2000
12/24		*Set of* 13	£1000	£2000
12/23 Optd "Specimen"		*Set of* 12	£450	

CROWN COLONY

1918 (June). *Optd with T* 5.

26	3	1d. red (Optd S. £55)	45	3·00

1922–27. *Wmk Mult Script CA. P* 14.

27	3	½d. green, O (1923)	40	1·75
28		1d. violet, O (1927)	1·00	2·25
29		1½d. scarlet, O (1924)	1·90	2·50
30		2d. slate-grey, O	3·00	6·50
35		10s. green and red/*emerald*, C (1924)	£225	£250
27/35 Optd "Specimen"		*Set of* 5	£425	

1935 (6 May). *Silver Jubilee. As Nos.* 91/4 *of Antigua, but ptd by B.W. P* 11 × 12.

36	1d. ultramarine and grey-black	1·75	6·00
	d. Double flagstaff	20·00	
37	1½d. deep blue and scarlet	1·75	5·00
	d. Double flagstaff	20·00	
38	3d. brown and deep blue	7·00	9·50
	d. Double flagstaff	30·00	
39	1s. slate and purple	24·00	29·00
	d. Double flagstaff	60·00	
36/9 Perf "Specimen"	*Set of* 4	85·00	

For illustration of plate variety see Omnibus section following Zululand.

1937 (12 May). *Coronation. As Nos.* 13/15 *of Aden.*

40	1d. violet	45	35
41	1½d. scarlet	60	40
42	3d. bright blue	75	60
40/2 Perf "Specimen"	*Set of* 3	55·00	

6 Great Frigate Bird

7 Pandanus Pine

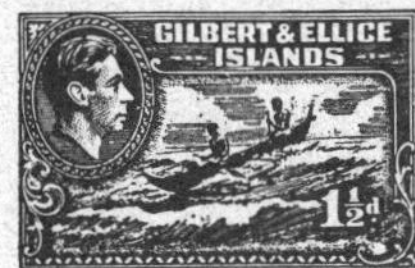

8 Canoe crossing Reef

(Recess B.W. (½d., 2d., 2s. 6d.), Waterlow (1d., 5d., 6d., 2s., 5s.), D.L.R. (1½d., 2½d., 3d., 1s.))

1939 (14 Jan)–**55.** *T* 6/8 *and similar horiz designs. Wmk Mult Script CA (sideways on ½d., 2d. and 2s. 6d.).*

43	½d. slate-blue & blue-green (*p* 11½ × 11)	25	60
44	1d. emerald-green and purple (*p* 12½)	25	60
45	1½d. black and carmine (*p* 13½)	55	85
46	2d. red-brown and black (*p* 11½ × 11)	40	90
47	2½d. black and olive-green (*p* 13½)	35	90
48	3d. black and ultramarine (*p* 13½)	45	70
	a. Perf 12. *Black and bright blue* (24.8.55)	2·00	2·25
49	5d. bright blue and sepia (*p* 12½)	2·00	1·50
50	6d. olive-green and violet (*p* 12½)	80	1·00
51	1s. black and turquoise-blue (*p* 13½)	2·25	1·25
	a. Perf 12 (8.5.51)	7·50	7·00
52	2s. bright blue and vermilion (*p* 12½)	8·00	9·00
53	2s. 6d. blue & emerald-green (*p* 11½ × 11)	11·00	12·00
54	5s. scarlet and bright blue (*p* 12½)	18·00	18·00
43/54	*Set of* 12	40·00	42·00
43/54 Perf "Specimen"	*Set of* 12	£110	

Designs: *As T* 6—2d. Canoe and boat-house; 2s. 6d. Gilbert Islands canoe. *As T* 7—5d. Ellice Islands canoe; 6d. Coconut palms; 2s. H.M.C.S. *Nimanoa*; 5s. Coat of arms. *As T* 8—2½d. Native house; 3d. Seascape; 1s. Cantilever jetty, Ocean Island.

1946 (16 Dec). *Victory. As Nos.* 28/9 *of Aden.*

55	1d. purple	35	30
56	3d. blue	35	30
55/6 Perf "Specimen"	*Set of* 2	35·00	

1949 (29 Aug). *Royal Silver Wedding. As Nos.* 30/1 *of Aden.*

57	1d. violet	40	50
58	£1 scarlet	38·00	55·00

1949 (10 Oct). *75th Anniv of U.P.U. As Nos.* 114/17 *of Antigua.*

59	1d. purple	65	65
60	2d. grey-black	1·60	1·25
61	3d. deep blue	2·25	1·90
62	1s. blue	3·50	3·75

1953 (2 June). *Coronation. As No.* 47 *of Aden.*

63	2d. black and grey-black	70	1·25

18 Great Frigate Bird

19 Loading Phosphate from Cantilever

(Recess B.W. (½d., 2d., 2s. 6d.), Waterlow (1d., 5d., 6d., 2s., 5s.), D.L.R. (2½d., 3d., 1s., 10s.) and after 1962, 1d., 5d.)

1956 (1 Aug). *Designs previously used for King George VI issue; but with portrait of Queen Elizabeth II as in T* 18. *Wmk Mult Script CA. P* 11½ × 11 *(½d., 2d., 2s. 6d.),* 12½ *(1d., 5d., 6d., 2s., 5s.) or* 12 *(2½d., 3d., 1s., 10s.).*

64	½d. black and deep bright blue	25	20
65	1d. brown-olive and deep violet	25	15
66	2d. bluish green and deep purple (*shades*)	1·00	45
67	2½d. black and myrtle-green	80	70
68	3d. black and carmine-red	80	60
69	5d. ultramarine and red-orange (*shades*)	2·50	1·75
70	6d. chestnut and black-brown	90	70
71	1s. black and bronze-green	1·00	60
72	2s. deep bright blue and sepia	10·00	4·00
73	2s. 6d. scarlet and deep blue	8·50	5·00
74	5s. greenish blue and bluish green	15·00	8·00
75	10s. black and turquoise	32·00	24·00
64/75	*Set of* 12	65·00	42·00

Designs: *Horiz* (30 × 22½ *mm*)—1d. Pandanus pine; 5d. Ellice Islands canoe; 6d. Coconut palms; 2s. H.M.C.S. *Nimanoa*; 5s. Coat of arms. (35½ × 22½ *mm*)—2d. Canoe and boat-house; 2½d. Native house; 3d. Seascape; 1s. Cantilever jetty, Ocean Island; 2s. 6d. Gilbert Islands canoe; 10s. Canoe crossing reef.

See also Nos. 85/6.

(Des R. Turrell (2d.), M. Thoma (2½d), M. A. W. Hook and A. Larkins (1s.). Photo D.L.R.)

1960 (1 May). *Diamond Jubilee of Phosphate Discovery at Ocean Island. T* 19 *and similar horiz designs.* W w 12. *P* 12.

76	2d. green and carmine-rose	70	35
77	2½d. black and olive-green	70	40
78	1s. black and deep turquoise	80	60

Designs:—2½d. Phosphate rock; 1s. Phosphate mining.

1963 (1 Aug). *Freedom from Hunger. As No.* 76 *of Aden.*

79	10d. ultramarine	6·00	2·00

1963 (5 Oct). *Red Cross Centenary. As Nos.* 147/8 *of Antigua.*

80	2d. red and black	2·00	80
81	10d. red and blue	7·00	3·75

22 D.H. "Heron" Aircraft and Route Map

24 D.H. "Heron" Aircraft over Tarawa Lagoon

23 Eastern Reef Heron in Flight

(Des Margaret Barwick. Litho Enschedé)

1964 (20 July). *First Air Service.* W w 12 *(sideways, 3d., 3s. 7d.). P* 11 × 11½ *(1s.) or* 11½ × 11 *(others).*

82	22	3d. blue, black and light blue	60	30
83	23	1s. light blue, black and deep blue	80	45
84	24	3s. 7d. deep green, black and light emerald	2·00	1·00

(Recess B.W. (2d.), D.L.R. (6d.))

1964 (30 Oct)–**65.** *As Nos.* 66 *and* 70 *but wmk* w 12.

85	2d. bluish green and purple	1·25	1·25
86	6d. chestnut and black-brown (26.4.65)*	2·75	3·25

*Earliest known postmark date.

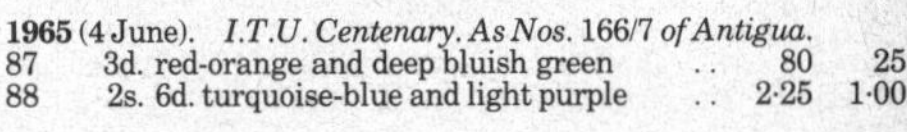

1965 (4 June). *I.T.U. Centenary. As Nos.* 166/7 *of Antigua.*

87	3d. red-orange and deep bluish green	80	25
88	2s. 6d. turquoise-blue and light purple	2·25	1·00

25 Maneaba and Gilbertese Man blowing Bu Shell

26 Gilbertese Women's Dance

(Des V. Whiteley from drawings by Margaret Barwick. Litho B.W.)

1965 (16 Aug). *Vert designs as T* 25 *(½d. to 2s.) or horiz designs as T* 26 *(3s. 7d. to £1). Centres multicoloured.* W w 12. *P* 12 × 11 *(½d. to 2s.) or* 11 × 12 *(3s. 7d. to £1).*

89	½d. turquoise-green	5	5
90	1d. deep violet-blue	8	5
91	2d. bistre	10	5
92	3d. rose-red	12	5
93	4d. purple	15	5
94	5d. cerise	25	5
95	6d. turquoise-blue	25	5
96	7d. bistre-brown	45	5
97	1s. bluish violet	50	5
98	1s. 6d. lemon	1·25	65
99	2s. yellow-olive	1·50	1·00
100	3s. 7d. new blue	2·50	1·25
101	5s. light yellow-olive	2·75	1·50
102	10s. dull green	6·00	3·00
103	£1 light turquoise-blue	12·00	10·00
89/103	*Set of* 15	25·00	16·00

Designs:—1d. Ellice Islanders reef fishing by flare; 2d. Gilbertese girl weaving head garland; 3d. Gilbertese woman performing Ruoia; 4d. Gilbertese man performing Kamei; 5d. Gilbertese girl drawing water; 6d. Ellice islander performing a Fatele; 7d. Ellice youths performing spear dance; 1s. Gilbertese girl tending Ikaroa Babai plant; 1s. 6d. Ellice islanders dancing a Fatele; 2s. Ellice islanders pounding Pulaka; 5s. Gilbertese boys playing stick game; 10s. Ellice youths beating the box for the Fatele; £1 Coat of arms.

1965 (25 Oct). *International Co-operation Year. As Nos.* 168/9 *of Antigua.*

104	½d. reddish purple and turquoise-green	5	5
105	3s. 7d. deep bluish green and lavender	2·00	70

1966 (24 Jan). *Churchill Commemoration. As Nos.* 170/3 *of Antigua.*

106	½d. new blue	5	5
107	3d. deep green	50	25
108	3s. brown	2·50	90
109	3s. 7d. bluish violet	2·50	90

(New Currency. 100 cents = $1 Australian)

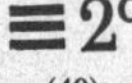

(40)

41 H.M.S. *Royalist*

1966 (14 Feb). *Decimal currency. Nos. 89/103 surch as T* **40**.

No.	Description	Unused	Used
110	1 c. on 1d. deep violet-blue	5	5
111	2 c. on 2d. bistre	8	5
112	3 c. on 3d. rose-red	10	5
113	4 c. on ½d. turquoise-green	12	5
114	5 c. on 6d. turquoise-blue	15	5
115	6 c. on 4d. purple	20	5
116	8 c. on 5d. cerise	25	5
117	10 c. on 1s. bluish violet	30	5
118	15 c. on 7d. bistre-brown	1·25	30
119	20 c. on 1s. 6d. lemon	1·00	70
120	25 c. on 2s. yellow-olive	1·25	80
121	35 c. on 3s. 7d. new blue	1·75	1·00
122	50 c. on 5s. light yellow-olive	2·00	1·00
123	$1 on 10s. dull green	3·00	1·75
124	$2 on £1 light turquoise-blue	5·50	5·00
110/24	*Set of* 15	15·00	9·75

1966 (1 July). *World Cup Football Championships. As Nos.* 176/7 *of Antigua.*

No.	Description	Unused	Used
125	3 c. violet, yellow-green, lake & yellow-brn	25	10
126	35 c. chocolate, blue-green, lake & yell-brn	1·25	70

1966 (20 Sept). *Inauguration of W.H.O. Headquarters, Geneva. As Nos.* 178/9 *of Antigua.*

No.	Description	Unused	Used
127	3 c. black, yellow-green and light blue	35	10
128	12 c. black, light purple and yellow-brown	90	55

1966 (1 Dec). *20th Anniv of U.N.E.S.C.O. As Nos.* 196/8 *of Antigua.*

No.	Description	Unused	Used
129	5 c. slate-violet, red, yellow and orange	70	25
130	10 c. orange-yellow, violet and deep olive	1·50	55
131	20 c. black, bright purple and orange	3·50	1·50

(Des V. Whiteley. Photo Harrison)

1967 (1 Sept). *75th Anniv of the Protectorate. T* **41** *and similar horiz designs. W* w **12**. *P* 14½.

No.	Description	Unused	Used
132	3 c. red, blue and myrtle-green	20	10
133	10 c. multicoloured	25	15
134	35 c. sepia, orange-yellow & dp bluish green	50	45

Designs:—10 c. Trading Post; 35 c. Island family.

44 Gilbertese Women's Dance

1968 (1 Jan). *Decimal Currency. Designs as Nos.* 89/103 *but with values inscr in decimal currency as T* **44**. *W* w **12** *(sideways on horiz designs). P* 12 × 11 *(vert) or* 11 × 12 *(horiz).*

No.	Description	Unused	Used
135	1 c. deep violet-blue (as 1d.)	5	5
136	2 c. bistre (as 2d.)	8	5
137	3 c. rose-red (as 3d.)	10	5
138	4 c. turquoise-green (as ½d.)	12	5
139	5 c. turquoise-blue (as 6d.)	15	5
140	6 c. purple (as 4d.)	20	5
141	8 c. cerise (as 5d.)	25	5
142	10 c. bluish violet (as 1s.)	30	5
143	15 c. bistre-brown (as 7d.)	85	45
144	20 c. lemon (as 1s. 6d.)	1·25	50
145	25 c. yellow-olive (as 2s.)	1·50	65
146	35 c. new blue	2·25	1·25
147	50 c. light yellow-olive (as 5s.)	3·00	1·50
148	$1 dull green (as 10s.)	4·00	2·50
149	$2 light turquoise-blue (as £1)	11·00	6·00
135/49	*Set of* 15	23·00	12·00

45 Map of Tarawa Atoll

(Des V. Whiteley. Photo D.L.R.)

1968 (21 Nov). *25th Anniv of the Battle of Tarawa. T* **45** *and similar designs. Multicoloured. W* w **12** *(sideways). P* 14.

No.	Description	Unused	Used
150	3 c. Type **45**	20	25
151	10 c. Marines landing	35	35
152	15 c. Beach-head assault	40	40
153	35 c. Raising U.S. and British flags	60	55

46 Young Pupil against outline of Abemama Island

47 "Virgin and Child" in Pacific Setting

(Des J.W. (from original designs by Mrs V. J. Anderson and Miss A. Loveridge). Litho D.L.R.)

1969 (2 June). *End of Inaugural Year of South Pacific University. T* **46** *and similar horiz designs. W* w **12** *(sideways). P* 12½.

No.	Description	Unused	Used
154	3 c. multicoloured	20	20
155	10 c. multicoloured	30	20
156	35 c. black, brown and grey-green	1·00	70

Designs:—10 c. Boy and girl students and Tarawa atoll; 35 c. University graduate and South Pacific islands.

(Des Jennifer Toombs. Litho B.W.)

1969 (20 Oct). *Christmas. W* w **12** *(sideways). P* 11½.

No.	Type	Description	Unused	Used
157	–	2 c. olive-grn & multicoloured *(shades)*	30	30
158	**47**	10 c. olive-grn & multicoloured *(shades)*	45	45

Design:—2 c. As T **47** but foreground has grass instead of sand.

48 "The Kiss of Life"

(Des Manate Tenang Manate. Litho J.W.)

1970 (9 Mar*). *Centenary of British Red Cross. W* w **12** *(sideways). P* 14.

No.	Type	Description	Unused	Used
159	**48**	10 c. multicoloured	35	25
160	–	15 c. multicoloured	65	50
161	–	35 c. multicoloured	1·25	75

Nos. 160/1 are as T 48, but arranged differently.

*The above were released by the Crown Agents on 2 March, but not sold locally until the 9 March.

49 Foetus and Patients

(Des Jennifer Toombs. Litho Enschedé)

1970 (26 June). *25th Anniv of United Nations. T* **49** *and similar horiz designs. W* w **12** *(sideways). P* 12½ × 13.

No.	Description	Unused	Used
162	5 c. multicoloured	30	35
163	10 c. black, grey and red	45	50
164	15 c. multicoloured	60	60
165	35 c. new blue, black and turquoise-green	90	65

Designs:—10 c. Nurse and surgical instruments; 15 c. X-ray plate and technician; 35 c. U.N. emblem and map.

53 Map of Gilbert Islands

57 "Child with Halo" (T. Collis)

(Des G. Vasarhelyi. Litho Harrison)

1970 (1 Sept). *Centenary of Landing in Gilbert Islands by London Missionary Society. T* **53** *and similar designs. W* w **12** *(sideways on vert designs). P* 14½ × 14 *(2 c., 35 c.) or* 14 × 14½ *(others).*

No.	Description	Unused	Used
166	2 c. multicoloured	20	20
167	10 c. black and pale green	60	45
168	25 c. chestnut and cobalt	70	70
169	35 c. turquoise-blue, black and red	90	80

Designs: *Vert*—10 c. Sailing-ship *John Williams III*; 25 c. Rev. S. J. Whitmee. *Horiz*—35 c. M.V. *John Williams VII*.

(Des L. Curtis. Litho Format)

1970 (3 Oct). *Christmas. Sketches. T* **57** *and similar vert designs. Multicoloured. W* w **12**. *P* 14½.

No.	Description	Unused	Used
170	2 c. Type **57**	15	10
171	10 c. "Sanctuary, Tarawa Cathedral" (Mrs. A. Burroughs)	45	35
172	35 c. "Three ships inside star" (Mrs. C. Barnett)	80	80

60 Casting Nets

(Des G. Drummond. Litho Walsall)

1971 (31 May). *Multicoloured designs as T* **60**. *W* w **12** *(sideways on* 2, 3, 4, 5, 20, 25 *and* 35 *c.). P* 14.

No.	Description	Unused	Used
173	1 c. Cutting toddy *(vert)*	8	8
174	2 c. Lagoon fishing	15	10
175	3 c. Cleaning pandanus leaves	15	12
176	4 c. Type **60**	20	15
177	5 c. Gilbertese canoe	35	25
178	6 c. De-husking coconuts *(vert)*	30	25
179	8 c. Weaving pandanus fronds *(vert)*	35	25
180	10 c. Weaving a basket *(vert)*	40	30
181	15 c. Tiger shark and fishermen *(vert)*	2·25	90
182	20 c. Beating a rolled pandanus leaf	2·00	1·50
183	25 c. Loading copra	2·00	90
184	35 c. Fishing at night	3·25	1·75
185	50 c. Local handicrafts *(vert)*	3·50	2·25
186	$1 Weaving coconut screens *(vert)*	8·00	5·00
187	$2 Coat of Arms *(vert)*	20·00	12·00
173/87	*Set of* 15	38·00	23·00

See also Nos. 203/7.

61 House of Representatives

62 Pacific Nativity Scene

(Des V. Whiteley. Litho J.W.)

1971 (1 Aug). *New Constitution. T* **61** *and similar horiz design. Multicoloured. W* w **12** *(sideways). P* 14.

No.	Description	Unused	Used
188	3 c. Type **61**	20	20
189	10 c. Maneaba Betio (Assembly hut)	50	50

(Des L. Curtis and T. Collis. Litho Questa)

1971 (1 Oct). *Christmas. T* **62** *and similar vert designs. W* w **12**. *P* 14 × 14½.

No.	Description	Unused	Used
190	3 c. black, yellow and ultramarine	20	20
191	10 c. black, gold and turquoise-blue	40	35
192	35 c. black, gold and magenta	1·00	80

Designs:—10 c. Star and palm leaves; 35 c. Outrigger canoe and star.

63 Emblem and Young Boys

(Des G. Vasarhelyi. Litho Questa)

1971 (11 Dec). *25th Anniv of UNICEF. T* **63** *and similar horiz designs, showing UNICEF emblem and young boys. W* w **12** *(sideways). P* 14.

No.	Description	Unused	Used
193	3 c. multicoloured	30	25
194	10 c. multicoloured	70	40
195	35 c. multicoloured	2·00	1·40

64 Flag and Map of South Pacific

(Des A. New. Litho Questa)

1972 (21 Feb). *25th Anniv of South Pacific Commission. T* **64** *and similar horiz designs. Multicoloured. W* w **12**. *P* 13½.

No.	Description	Unused	Used
196	3 c. Type **64**	15	20
197	10 c. Flag and native boats	25	35
198	35 c. Flags of member nations	70	1·00

MINIMUM PRICE

The minimum price quoted is 5p which represents a handling charge rather than a basis for valuing common stamps. For further notes about prices see introductory pages.

65 *Alveopora* **66** Star of Peace

(Des Sylvia Goaman after original designs by H. Wickison. Litho Questa)

1972 (26 May). *Coral. T* **65** *and similar horiz designs. Multicoloured. W* w **12** *(sideways). P* 14.

199	3 c. Type **65**	40	25
200	10 c. *Euphyllia*	80	55
201	15 c. *Melithea*	1·25	65
202	35 c. *Spongodes*	2·00	1·00

1972 (7 Sept)–**73**. *As Nos.* 174, 177/8 *and* 181/2 *but W* w **12** *upright on* 2, 5 *and* 20 *c.; sideways on* 6 *and* 15 *c.*

203	2 c. Lagoon fishing (13.6.73)	1·75	1·75
204	5 c. Gilbertese canoe	2·00	2·00
205	6 c. De-husking coconuts (13.6.73)	3·00	3·00
206	15 c. Tiger shark and fishermen	4·25	4·25
207	20 c. Beating a rolled pandanus leaf	4·50	4·50

(Des T. Matarena (35 c.), Father Bermond (others); adapted by Jennifer Toombs. Litho Questa)

1972 (15 Sept). *Christmas. T* **66** *and similar multicoloured designs. W* w **12** *(sideways on* 3 *and* 10 *c.). P* 13½.

208	3 c. Type **66**	15	15
209	10 c. "The Nativity"	35	25
210	35 c. Baby in "manger" *(horiz)*	60	70

67 Floral Head-dresses

(Des (from photograph by D. Groves) and photo Harrison)

1972 (20 Nov). *Royal Silver Wedding. Multicoloured; background colour given. W* w **12.** *P* 14 × 14½.

211	**67**	3 c. brown-olive	12	12
212		35 c. lake-brown	55	40

68 Funafuti ("The Land of Bananas") **69** Dancer

(Des H. Wickison; adapted J. Cooter. Litho Walsall)

1973 (5 Mar). *Legends of Island Names* (1*st series*). *T* **68** *and similar horiz designs. Multicoloured. W* w **12.** *P* 14½ × 14.

213	3 c. Type **68**	25	25
214	10 c. Butaritari ("The Smell of the Sea")	55	50
215	25 c. Tarawa ("The Centre of the World")	1·25	1·00
216	35 c. Abemama ("The Land of the Moon")	1·75	80

See also Nos. 252/5.

(Des Sister Juliette (3 c.), R. P. Turner (10 and 35 c.), C. Potts (50 c.); adapted Jennifer Toombs. Litho Questa)

1973 (24 Sept). *Christmas. T* **69** *and similar vert designs. Multicoloured. W* w **12** *(sideways). P* 14.

217	3 c. Type **69**	25	20
218	10 c. Canoe and lagoon	50	50
219	35 c. Lagoon at evening	1·10	80
220	50 c. Map of Christmas Island	1·40	1·10

1973 (14 Nov). *Royal Wedding. As Nos.* 165/6 *of Anguilla. Centre multicoloured. W* w **12** *(sideways). P* 13½.

221	3 c. pale green	10	10
222	35 c. Prussian blue	40	40

70 Meteorological Observation

(Des E. S. Cheek; adapted PAD Studio. Litho Questa)

1973 (26 Nov). *I.M.O./W.M.O. Centenary. T* **70** *and similar horiz designs. Multicoloured. W* w **12.** *P* 14.

223	3 c. Type **70**	1·60	1·50
224	10 c. Island observing-station	2·00	1·75
225	35 c. Wind-finding radar	3·50	2·50
226	50 c. World weather watch stations	4·50	4·00

71 Te Mataaua Crest

(Des J. Cooter. Litho Questa)

1974 (4 Mar). *Canoe Crests. T* **71** *and similar horiz designs showing sailing craft and the canoe crests given. Multicoloured. W* w **12.** *P* 13½.

227	3 c. Type **71**	25	20
228	10 c. Te Nimta-wawa	55	50
229	35 c. Tara-tara-venei-na	1·50	75
230	50 c. Te Bou-uoua	2·00	1·25
MS231	154 × 130 mm. Nos. 227/30	8·00	8·00

72 £1 Stamp of 1924 and Te Koroba (canoe)

(Des E. S. Cheek; adapted J. Cooter. Litho Questa)

1974 (10 June). *Centenary of Universal Postal Union. T* **72** *and similar horiz designs. W* w **12.** *P* 14.

232	4 c. multicoloured	30	20
233	10 c. multicoloured	50	40
234	25 c. multicoloured	80	70
235	35 c. light vermilion and black	90	80

Designs:—10 c. 5s. stamp of 1939 and sailing vessel *Kiakia*; 25 c. $2 stamp of 1971 and B.A.C. "1-11"; 35 c. U.P.U. emblem.

73 Toy Canoe **74** North Front Entrance, Blenheim Palace

(Des H. Wickison and G. J. Hayward; adapted J. Cooter. Litho Questa)

1974 (5 Sept). *Christmas. T* **73** *and similar horiz designs. Multicoloured. W* w **12** *(sideways). P* 14.

236	4 c. Type **73**	30	15
237	10 c. Toy windmill	40	40
238	25 c. Coconut "ball"	60	60
239	35 c. Canoes and constellation Pleiades	70	70

(Des J. Cooter. Litho Questa)

1974 (30 Nov). *Birth Centenary of Sir Winston Churchill. T* **74** *and similar vert designs. Multicoloured. W* w **14.** *P* 14.

240	4 c. Type **74**	20	15
241	10 c. Churchill painting	40	35
242	35 c. Churchill's statue, London	65	55

75 Barometer Crab

(Des J. Cooter. Litho Questa)

1975 (27 Jan). *Crabs. T* **75** *and similar horiz designs. Multicoloured. W* w **12** *(sideways). P* 14.

243	4 c. Type **75**	35	20
244	10 c. *Ranina ranina*	65	45
245	25 c. Pelagic Swimming Crab	1·40	95
246	35 c. Ghost Crab	1·60	1·40

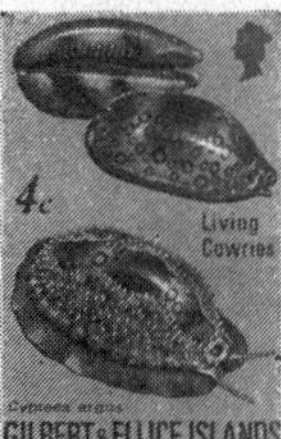

76 Eyed Cowrie **77** "Christ is Born"

(Des E. S. Cheek; adapted J. Cooter. Litho Questa)

1975 (26 May). *Cowrie Shells. T* **76** *and similar vert designs. Multicoloured. W* w **14.** *P* 14.

247	4 c. Type **76**	45	20
248	10 c. Sieve Cowrie	80	40
249	25 c. Mole Cowrie	1·75	1·25
250	35 c. Map Cowrie	2·50	1·50
MS251	146 × 137 mm. Nos. 247/50	8·00	9·50

(Des J. Cooter. Litho Questa)

1975 (1 Aug). *Legends of Island Names* (2*nd series*). *Horiz designs as T* **68.** *Multicoloured. W* w **12** *(sideways). P* 14.

252	4 c. Beru ("The Bud")	25	20
253	10 c. Onotoa ("Six Giants")	45	40
254	25 c. Abaiang ("Land to the North")	1·00	75
255	35 c. Marakei ("Fish-trap floating on eaves")	1·25	1·00

(Des C. J. Barnett (4 and 25 c.), Philatelic Advisory Committee (10 c.), P. T. Burangke (35 c.); adapted J. Cooter. Litho Questa)

1975 (22 Sept). *Christmas. T* **77** *and similar vert designs. Multicoloured. W* w **14.** *P* 14.

256	4 c. Type **77**	25	20
257	10 c. Protestant Chapel, Tarawa	45	40
258	25 c. Catholic Church, Ocean Island	90	1·00
259	35 c. Fishermen and star	1·00	1·10

POSTAGE DUE STAMPS

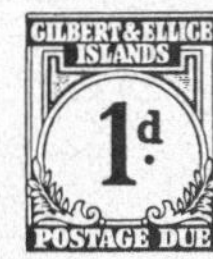

D 1

(Typo B.W.)

1940. *Wmk Mult Script CA. P* 12.

D1	D **1**	1d. emerald-green	3·00	5·50
D2		2d. scarlet	3·75	6·50
D3		3d. brown	5·50	10·00
D4		4d. blue	7·50	15·00
D5		5d. grey-green	8·50	17·00
D6		6d. purple	9·00	19·00
D7		1s. violet	15·00	35·00
D8		1s. 6d. turquoise-green	40·00	80·00
D1/8		*Set of* 8	85·00	£170
D1/8 Perf "Specimen"		*Set of* 8	£150	

Stamps for the Gilbert and Ellice Islands were withdrawn on 31 December 1975 when the separate colonies of the GILBERT ISLANDS and TUVALU were created.

Gilbert Islands

On 1 January 1976, the Gilbert Islands and Tuvalu (Ellice Islands) became separate Crown Colonies.

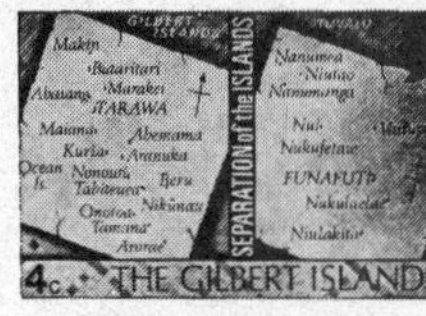

THE GILBERT ISLANDS

1 Charts of Gilbert Islands and Tuvalu (formerly Ellice) Islands (2)

(Des J. Cooter. Litho Questa)

1976 (2 Jan). *Separation of the Islands. T* **1** *and similar horiz design. Multicoloured. W* w **14** *(sideways). P* 14.

1	4 c. Type **1**	1·25	1·50
2	35 c. Maps of Tarawa and Funafuti	4·25	5·00

1976 (2 Jan). *Nos.* 173/86 *of Gilbert & Ellice Is optd as T* **2.**

(*a*) *W* w **12** *(sideways on Nos.* 5/7 *and* 9/10)

3	1 c. Cutting toddy (R.)	25	12
4	2 c. Lagoon fishing (R.)	50	40
5	2 c. Lagoon fishing *(wmk sideways)* (R.)	50	30
6	3 c. Cleaning pandanus leaves (R.)	20·00	17·00
7	4 c. Casting nets (R.)	35	35
8	20 c. Beating a pandanus leaf (R.)	†	85·00
9	20 c. Beating a pandanus leaf *(wmk sideways)* (R.)	4·50	3·25
10	25 c. Loading copra	50·00	55·00
	a. Opt double (Blk. + R.)	£250	
10*b*	50 c. Local handicrafts	£600	£700

(b) W w **14** (*sideways on* 3, 5, 20, 25 *and* 35 c.; *inverted on others*)
11 1 c. Cutting toddy (R.) 20 20
12 3 c. Cleaning pandanus leaves (R.) 40 30
13 5 c. Gilbertese canoe (R.) 60 45
14 6 c. De-husking coconuts 60 50
15 8 c. Weaving pandanus fronds (R.) 80 60
16 10 c. Weaving a basket 85 65
17 15 c. Tiger Shark .. .. 2·00 1·50
18 20 c. Beating a pandanus leaf (R.) .. .. 2·75 1·75
19 25 c. Loading copra .. .. 4·00 2·00
20 35 c. Fishing at night (Gold) .. .. .. 5·50 5·00
21 50 c. Local handicrafts .. .. .. 10·00 9·00
22 $1 Weaving coconut screens (R.) .. .. 18·00 18·00
a. Opt double £240
3, 4, 7 *and* 12/22 .. .. .. *Set of* 14 42·00 35·00

3 M.V. *Teraaka*

(Des J. Cooter. Litho Questa)

1976 (1 July). *Horiz designs as T* **3**. *Multicoloured. W* w **14** (*sideways*). *P* 14.
23 1 c. Type **3** 12 12
24 3 c. M.V. *Tautunu* 20 20
25 4 c. Moorish Idol 20 20
26 5 c. Hibiscus 20 20
27 6 c. Eastern Reef Heron 35 25
28 7 c. Tarawa Cathedral 25 25
29 8 c. Frangipani 25 25
30 10 c. Maneaba building 30 30
31 12 c. Betio Harbour 45 45
32 15 c. Evening scene 55 45
33 20 c. Marakei Atoll 55 55
34 35 c. Tanginteba Chapel 80 80
35 40 c. Flamboyant tree 85 85
36 50 c. *Hypolimnas bolina elliciana* (butterfly) .. 2·25 2·25
37 $1 Ferry *Tabakea* .. .. 3·75 5·00
38 $2 National flag .. .. 4·75 7·00
23/38 .. .. *Set of* 16 14·00 17·00

4 Church

5 Porcupine Fish Helmet

(Des P. Powell. Litho Questa)

1976 (15 Sept). *Christmas. Children's Drawings. T* **4** *and similar multicoloured designs. W* w **14** (*sideways on* 5 *and* 35 c.). *P* 14.
39 5 c. Type **4** 80 65
40 15 c. Feasting (*vert*) .. .. 1·50 1·00
41 20 c. Maneaba (*vert*) .. .. 1·75 1·40
42 35 c. Dancing .. .. 2·50 1·60

(Des J. Cooter. Litho J.W.)

1976 (6 Dec). *Artefacts. T* **5** *and similar vert designs. Multicoloured. W* w **14**. *P* 13.
43 5 c. Type **5** .. .. 1·00 60
44 15 c. Shark's Teeth Dagger .. .. .. 2·00 1·50
45 20 c. Fighting Gauntlet .. .. .. 2·25 1·75
46 35 c. Coconut Body Armour .. .. .. 2·50 2·25
MS47 140 × 130 mm. Nos. 43/6. P 14 .. .. 15·00 14·00

6 Queen in Coronation Robes

7 Commodore Byron and *Dolphin*

(Des J. Cooter. Litho Questa)

1977 (7 Feb). *Silver Jubilee. T* **6** *and similar vert designs. Multicoloured. W* w **14**. *P* 14.
48 8 c. Prince Charles' visit, 1970 .. .. 65 55
49 20 c. Prince Philip's visit, 1959 .. .. 80 90
50 40 c. Type **6** .. .. 1·00 1·50

(Des J. Cooter. Litho Questa)

1977 (1 June). *Explorers. T* **7** *and similar horiz designs. Multicoloured. W* w **14** (*sideways*). *P* 14.
51 5 c. Type **7** .. .. 1·50 1·50
52 15 c. Capt. Fanning and *Betsey* .. .. 2·50 2·50
53 20 c. Admiral Bellingshausen and *Vostok* .. 3·00 3·00
54 35 c. Capt. Wilkes and *Vincennes* .. .. 5·00 5·00

8 H.M.S. *Resolution* and H.M.S. *Discovery*

9 Emblem and Island Scene

(Des J. Cooter. Litho Questa)

1977 (12 Sept). *Christmas and Bicentenary of Capt. Cook's Discovery of Christmas Is. T* **8** *and similar multicoloured designs. W* w **14** (*sideways on* 15 *and* 40 c.). *P* 14.
55 8 c. Type **8** 90 75
56 15 c. Logbook entry (*horiz*) .. .. .. 1·40 1·10
57 20 c. Capt. Cook .. .. 1·75 1·40
58 40 c. Landing party (*horiz*) .. .. .. 3·75 3·00
MS59 140 × 140 mm. Nos. 55/8. Wmk sideways 11·00 12·00

(Des J. Cooter. Litho J.W.)

1977 (5 Dec). *50th Anniv of Scouting in the Gilbert Is. T* **9** *and similar multicoloured designs. W* w **14** (*sideways on* 15 *and* 20 c.). *P* 13.
60 8 c. Type **9** 65 60
61 15 c. Patrol meeting (*horiz*) .. .. .. 85 1·00
62 20 c. Mat making (*horiz*) .. .. .. 90 1·00
63 40 c. Canoeing .. .. 1·40 1·25

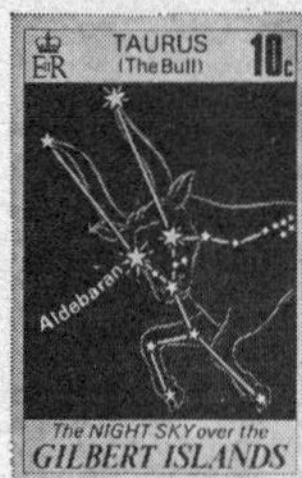

10 Taurus (The Bull)

11 Unicorn of Scotland

(Des J. Cooter. Litho Questa)

1978 (20 Feb). *Night Sky over the Gilbert Is. T* **10** *and similar vert designs. W* w **14**. *P* 14.
64 10 c. black and light new blue 65 50
65 20 c. black and light rose-red 90 90
66 25 c. black and sage-green 90 90
67 45 c. black and orange .. .. 1·50 1·50
Designs:—20 c. Canis Major (the Great Dog); 25 c. Scorpio (the Scorpion); 45 c. Orion (the Giant Warrior).

(Des C. Abbott. Litho Questa)

1978 (21 Apr). *25th Anniv of Coronation. T* **11** *and similar vert designs. P* 15.
68 45 c. green, bluish violet and silver 65 90
a. Sheetlet. Nos. 68/70 × 2 .. .. .. 3·50
69 45 c. multicoloured 65 90
70 45 c. green, bluish violet and silver 65 90
Designs:—No. 68, Type 11; No. 69, Queen Elizabeth II; No. 70, Great Frigate Bird.
Nos. 68/70 were printed together in small sheets of 6, containing two *se-tenant* strips of 3, with horizontal gutter margin between.

12 Birds in Flight to Tarawa

(Des local artists; adapted G. Hutchins. Litho Enschedé)

1978 (5 June). *25th Anniv of Return of King George V School to Tarawa. T* **12** *and similar horiz designs. Multicoloured. W* w **14** (*sideways*). *P* 14 × 13.
71 10 c. Type **12** 50 50
72 20 c. Tarawa, Abemama and school badge .. 90 90
73 25 c. Rejoicing islanders 90 90
74 45 c. King George V School on Tarawa and Abemama .. .. 1·25 1·00

13 "Te Kaue ni Maie"

14 *Endeavour*

(Des W. Walsh. Litho J.W.)

1978 (25 Sept). *Christmas. Kaue (traditional head decorations). T* **13** *and similar horiz designs. Multicoloured. W* w **14** (*sideways*). *P* 14.
75 10 c. Type **13** 40 40
76 20 c. "Te Itera" 55 55
77 25 c. "Te Bau" 60 60
78 45 c. "Te Tai" 75 90
MS79 149 × 99 mm. Nos. 75/8. P 13 × 13½ .. 4·50 6·00

(Des and litho (45 c. also embossed) Walsall)

1979 (22 Feb*). *Bicentenary of Captain Cook's Voyages, 1768–79. T* **14** *and similar vert designs. P* 11.
80 10 c. multicoloured 40 30
81 20 c. multicoloured 55 45
82 25 c. black, light green and pale lilac 65 55
83 45 c. multicoloured .. .. 1·00 95
Designs:—20 c. Green Turtle; 25 c. Quadrant; 45 c. Flaxman/Wedgwood medallion of Captain Cook.
*This was the local issue date; the stamps were released in London on 15 January.

The Gilbert Islands achieved independence on 12 July 1979 and were renamed KIRIBATI.

Gold Coast

CROWN COLONY

PRICES FOR STAMPS ON COVER TO 1945	
Nos. 1/3	*from* × 6
Nos. 4/8	*from* × 4
Nos. 9/10	*from* × 3
Nos. 11/19	*from* × 6
No. 20	*from* × 3
Nos. 22/5	—
Nos. 26/34	*from* × 4
Nos. 35/6	*from* × 8
Nos. 38/69	*from* × 4
Nos. 70/98	*from* × 3
Nos. 100/2	—
Nos. 103/12	*from* × 5
Nos. 113/16	*from* × 3
Nos. 117/19	*from* × 4
Nos. 120/32	*from* × 3
Nos. D1/4	*from* × 6

1

ONE PENNY.

(2)

(Typo D.L.R.)

1875 (July). *Wmk Crown CC. P* 12½.
1 **1** 1d. blue .. .. £400 65·00
2 4d. magenta .. .. £450 70·00
3 6d. orange .. .. £600 55·00

1876–79. *Wmk Crown CC. P* 14.
4 **1** ½d. olive-yellow (1879) .. .. .. 24·00 22·00
5 1d. blue .. .. 13·00 6·50
a. Bisected diag (½d.) (on cover) .. † £1200
6 2d. green (1879) .. .. 30·00 14·00
a. Bisected diag (1d.) (on cover) .. † £1300
7 4d. magenta .. .. £180 9·00
a. Quartered (1d.) (on cover) .. .. † £3250
8 6d. orange .. .. 90·00 18·00

1883 (May). *No. 7 surch locally.*
8*a* **1** "1d." on 4d. magenta .. .. ..

1883. *Wmk Crown CA. P* 14.
9 **1** ½d. olive-yellow (January) .. .. 95·00 27·00
10 1d. blue (May) .. .. £800 55·00

1884 (Aug)–**91.** *Wmk Crown CA. P* 14.
11 **1** ½d. green 65 55
a. Dull green 45 50
12 1d. rose-carmine 70 60
a. Carmine 60 40
b. Bisected diag (½d.) on cover .. .. † £2000

13 1 2d. grey 1·75 1·90
a. Value omitted
b. Slate 1·60 1·25
14 2½d. ultramarine and orange (13.3.91) 95 85
15 3d. olive-yellow (9.89) 5·00 4·00
a. Olive 3·50 4·00
16 4d. deep mauve (3.85) 1·75 1·75
a. Rosy mauve 2·50 2·50
17 6d. orange (1.89) 2·75 2·50
a. Orange-brown 4·50 2·50
18 1s. violet (1888) 17·00 12·00
a. Bright mauve 5·00 2·00
19 2s. yellow-brown (1888) 65·00 26·00
a. Deep brown 22·00 15·00
11/19a Set of 9 35·00 25·00
14/15, 18/19 Optd "Specimen" Set of 4 £150

1889 (Mar). *No. 17 surch with T* **2**.
20 1 1d. on 6d. orange £120 55·00

In some sheets examples may be found with the bar and "PENNY" spaced 8 mm, the normal spacing being 7 mm.

3

4

1889 (Sept)–**94**. *Wmk Crown CA. P* 14.
22 3 5s. dull mauve and blue 28·00 14·00
23 10s. dull mauve and red 70·00 20·00
a. Dull mauve and carmine £130 50·00
24 20s. green and red £3250
25 20s. dull mauve and black/red (1894) £150 32·00
22/5 Optd "Specimen" Set of 4 £650

1898–1902. *Wmk Crown CA. P* 14.
26 3 ½d. dull mauve and green 50 40
27 1d. dull mauve and rose 40 40
27a 4 2d. dull mauve and orange-red (1902) 13·00 20·00
28 3 2½d. dull mauve and ultramarine 3·50 5·00
29 4 3d. dull mauve and orange 4·50 2·50
30 6d. dull mauve and violet 4·50 2·75
31 3 1s. green and black 6·50 7·00
32 2s. green and carmine 18·00 17·00
33 5s. green and mauve (1900) 40·00 18·00
34 10s. green and brown (1900) 85·00 27·00
26/34 Set of 10 £160 90·00
26/34 Optd "Specimen" Set of 10 £300

1901 (6 Oct). *Nos. 28 and 30 surch with T* **2**.
35 1d. on 2½d. dull mauve and ultramarine 1·00 3·25
36 1d. on 6d. dull mauve and violet 1·25 3·25
a. "ONE" omitted £400 £425

6

7

8

1902. *Wmk Crown CA. P* 14.
38 6 ½d. dull purple and green 60 65
39 1d. dull purple and carmine 65 60
40 7 2d. dull purple and orange-red 2·75 2·75
41 6 2½d. dull purple and ultramarine 6·50 6·50
42 7 3d. dull purple and orange 2·50 1·25
43 6d. dull purple and violet 2·50 2·40
44 6 1s. green and black 3·50 4·50
45 2s. green and carmine 14·00 8·50
46 5s. green and mauve 18·00 18·00
47 10s. green and brown 35·00 38·00
48 20s. purple and black/red £100 80·00
38/48 Set of 11 £160 £150
38/48 Optd "Specimen" Set of 11 £300

1904–7. *Wmk Mult Crown CA. P* 14.
49 6 ½d. dull purple and green, **O** (3.07) 1·75 1·75
50 1d. dull purple and carmine, **OC** 1·00 50
51 7 2d. dull purple and orange-red, **OC** 3·00 1·25
52 6 2½d. dull purple & ultramarine, **O** (10.06) 25·00 16·00
53 7 3d. dull purple and orange, **OC** (10.05) 6·50 2·00
54 6d. dull purple and violet, **CO** (9.06) 16·00 6·00
57 2s. 6d. green and yellow, **C** (3.06) (Optd S. £80) 35·00 38·00
49/57 Set of 7 80·00 60·00

1907–13. *Wmk Mult Crown CA. P* 14.
59 6 ½d. dull green, **O** 80 60
a. Blue-green 1·50 90
60 1d. red, **O** 80 35
61 7 2d. greyish slate, **O** (1909) 2·00 70
62 6 2½d. blue, **O** 3·50 1·50
63 7 3d. purple/yellow, **C** (1909) 4·00 1·00
64 6d. dull and deep purple, **C** (1908) 8·00 2·25
a. Dull and bright purple, **C** (1911) 3·25 3·00
65 6 1s. black/green, **C** (1909) 7·00 1·50
66 2s. purple and blue/blue, **OC** (1910) 11·00 13·00
67 7 2s. 6d. blue and red/blue, **C** (1911) 18·00 22·00
68 6 5s. green and red/yellow, **C** (1913) 35·00 48·00
59/68 Set of 10 75·00 80·00
59/68 Optd "Specimen" Set of 10 £170

A 10s. green and red on green, and a 20s. purple and black on red, both Type **6**, were prepared for use but not issued. Both exist overprinted "Specimen" (*Price for 10s. in this condition £650*).

(Typo D.L.R.)

1908 (Nov). *Wmk Mult Crown CA. P* 14.
69 8 1d. red, **O** (Optd S. £45) 25 10

9

10

11

(Typo D.L.R.)

1913–21. *Ordinary paper (½d. to 2½d.) or chalk-surfaced paper (others). Wmk Mult Crown CA. P* 14.
70 9 ½d. green 65 45
a. Yellow-green (1916) 90 90
72 10 1d. red 25 12
a. Scarlet (1919) 65 40
74 11 2d. grey 4·00 1·75
a. Slate-grey 6·50 1·75
76 9 2½d. bright blue 1·10 90
77 11 3d. purple/yellow (8.15) 1·10 50
a. White back (9.13) (Optd S. £40) 55 65
b. On orange-buff (1919) 4·00 3·00
c. On pale yellow (Die II) (1919) 5·00 4·25
78 6d. dull and bright purple 3·00 2·00
79 9 1s. black/green 1·10 1·00
a. Wmk sideways
b. On blue green, olive back (1921) 1·10 1·25
c. On emerald back (Die I) (1921) 3·00 2·00
d. On emerald back (Die II) (1921) 3·50 1·50
80 2s. purple and blue/blue (Die I) 8·00 2·50
a. Die II (1921) £110 60·00
81 11 2s. 6d. black and red/blue (Die I) 13·00 7·00
a. Die II (1921) 28·00 28·00
82 9 5s. green and red/yellow (1916) 13·00 22·00
a. White back (10.13) (Optd S. £45) 11·00 16·00
b. On orange-buff 20·00 25·00
c. On pale yellow (Die I) (1921) 32·00 40·00
d. Die II (1921) 22·00 42·00
83 10s. green and red/green 30·00 45·00
a. On blue-green, olive back (1919) 20·00 30·00
b. On emerald back (1921) 30·00 42·00
84 20s. purple and black/red (1916) 85·00 70·00
70/84 Set of 12 £130 £120
70/84 Optd "Specimen" Set of 12 £300
79b/d Optd "Specimen" Set of 3 70·00

WAR TAX

ONE PENNY

(12)

13 King George V and Christiansborg Castle

1918 (May). *Surch with T* **12**.
85 10 1d. on 1d. red (Optd S. £60) 15 35

1921–24. *Ordinary paper (½d. to 3d.) or chalk-surfaced paper (others). Wmk Mult Script CA. P* 14.
86 9 ½d. green 25 30
87 10 1d. chocolate-brown (1922) 25 10
88 11 1½d. red (1922) 25 15
89 2d. grey 35 15
90 9 2½d. yellow-orange (1922) 35 4·00
91 11 3d. bright blue (1922) 35 50
94 6d. dull and bright purple 1·00 1·90
95 9 1s. black/emerald (1924) 1·40 2·75
96 2s. purple and blue/blue (1923) 4·75 5·50
97 11 2s. 6d. black and red/blue (1924) 6·50 9·00
98 9 5s. green and red/pale yellow (1924) 13·00 17·00
100 11 15s. dull purple and green (Die I) £140 £170
a. Die II (1924) (Optd S. £300) £130 £170
102 £2 green and orange (Die I) £450 £500
86/100a Set of 12 £140 £190
86/102 Optd "Specimen" Set of 13 £800

In Nos. 88, 100 and 102 the words "GOLD COAST" are in distinctly larger letters.

(Photo Harrison)

1928 (1 Aug). *Wmk Mult Script CA. P* 13½ × 15.
103 13 ½d. green 15 25
104 1d. red-brown 15 10
105 1½d. scarlet 75 1·75
106 2d. slate 30 15
107 2½d. orange-yellow 1·10 4·25
108 3d. blue 1·10 50
109 6d. black and purple 1·25 70
110 1s. black and vermilion 3·00 2·50
111 2s. black and violet 9·00 5·00
112 5s. carmine and olive-green 25·00 30·00
103/12 Set of 10 38·00 40·00
103/12 Optd "Specimen" Set of 10 £325

1935 (6 May). *Silver Jubilee. As Nos. 91/4 of Antigua, but printed by B.W. P* 11 × 12.
113 1d. ultramarine and grey-black 50 30
a. Extra flagstaff £110
b. Short extra flagstaff 40·00
c. Lightning conductor 40·00
114 3d. brown and deep blue 3·25 4·00
a. Extra flagstaff £100
c. Lightning conductor 40·00
115 6d. green and indigo 4·50 6·50
a. Extra flagstaff £100
b. Short extra flagstaff 40·00
c. Lightning conductor 40·00
116 1s. slate and purple 5·50 7·00
a. Extra flagstaff £100
b. Short extra flagstaff 40·00
c. Lightning conductor 40·00
113/16 Perf "Specimen" Set of 4 55·00

For illustrations of plate varieties see Omnibus Section following Zululand.

1937 (12 May). *Coronation. As Nos. 13/15 of Aden, but printed by B.W. P* 11 × 11½.
117 1d. buff 45 30
118 2d. slate 55 60
119 3d. blue 80 95
117/19 Perf "Specimen" Set of 3 45·00

14

15 King George VI and Christiansborg Castle, Accra

(Recess B.W.)

1938 (1 Apr)–**41**. *Wmk Mult Script CA. P* 11½ × 12.*
120 14 ½d. green 20 5
121 1d. red-brown 25 5
122 1½d. scarlet 35 10
123 2d. slate 35 5
124 3d. blue 35 5
125 4d. magenta 55 30
126 6d. purple 60 5
127 9d. orange 80 70
128 15 1s. black and olive-green 75 10
129 1s. 3d. brown & turquoise-bl (12.4.41) 55 20
130 2s. blue and violet 3·00 2·50
131 5s. olive-green and carmine 4·50 6·00
132 10s. black and violet (1940) 8·00 12·00
120/32 Set of 13 18·00 20·00
120/32 Perf "Specimen" Set of 13 £140

*Nos. 120 to 132, except 1s. 3d. and 10s., exist in two perforations: (*a*) Line-perf 12, from early printings; (*b*) Comb-perf 12 × 11.7 (vertical design) or 11.7 × 12 (horiz design), from later printings. The 1s. 3d. and 10s. exist only comb-perf 11.7 × 12.

1946 (14 Oct). *Victory. As Nos. 28/9 of Aden. P* 13½ × 14.
133 2d. slate-violet 3·25 2·00
a. Perf 13½ 35 25
134 4d. claret 4·75 2·25
a. Perf 13½ 45 55
133/4 Perf "Specimen" Set of 2 48·00

16 Northern Territories Mounted Constabulary

17 Christiansborg Castle

(Des B. A. Johnston (1½d.), M. Ziorkley and B. A. Abban (2d.), P.O. draughtsman (2½d.), C. Gomez (1s.), M. Ziorkley (10s.); others from photographs. Recess B.W.)

1948 (1 July). *T* **16/17** *and similar designs. Wmk Mult Script CA. P* 12 × 11½ *(vert) or* 11½ × 12 *(horiz).*
135 ½d. emerald-green 20 20
136 1d. blue 20 5
137 1½d. scarlet 45 60
138 2d. purple-brown 45 5
139 2½d. yellow-brown and scarlet 65 1·10
140 3d. light blue 65 10
141 4d. magenta 80 1·00
142 6d. black and orange 50 10
143 1s. black and vermilion 55 10
144 2s. sage-green and magenta 3·25 1·50
145 5s. purple and black 9·50 3·50
146 10s. black and sage-green 13·00 8·00
135/46 Set of 12 27·00 14·50
135/46 Perf "Specimen" Set of 12 £225

Designs: *Horiz*—1½d. Emblem of Joint Provincial Council; 2½d. Map showing position of Gold Coast; 3d. Manganese mine; 4d. Lake Bosumtwi; 1s. Breaking cocoa pods; 2s. Trooping the Colour; 5s. Surfboats. *Vert*—2d. Talking drums; 6d. Cocoa farmer; 10s. Forest.

1948 (20 Dec). *Royal Silver Wedding. As Nos. 30/1 of Aden.*
147 1½d. scarlet 25 15
148 10s. grey-olive 15·00 16·00

1949 (10 Oct). *75th Anniv of U.P.U. As Nos. 114/17 of Antigua.*
149 2d. red-brown 30 50
150 2½d. orange 1·75 2·50
151 3d. deep blue 1·75 2·25
152 1s. blue-green 2·25 2·25

PRICES OF SETS

Set prices are given for many issues, generally those containing five stamps or more. Definitive sets include one of each value or major colour change, but do not cover different perforations, die types or minor shades. Where a choice is possible the set prices are based on the cheapest versions of the stamps included in the listings.

28 Northern Territories Mounted Constabulary

(Recess B.W.)

1952 (19 Dec)–**54**. *Designs previously used for King George VI issue, but with portrait of Queen Elizabeth II, as in T* **28**. *Portrait faces left on ½d., 4d., 6d., 1s. and 5s. Wmk Mult Script CA. P* 12 × 11½ (*vert*) *or* 11½ × 12 (*horiz*).

153 ½d. yellow-brown and scarlet (*shades*) (1.4.53) 5 5
154 1d. deep blue (1.3.54) 15 5
155 1½d. emerald-green (1.4.53) 25 55
156 2d. chocolate (1.3.54) 30 5
157 2½d. scarlet 35 35
158 3d. magenta (1.4.53) 35 5
159 4d. blue (1.4.53) 30 10
160 6d. black and orange (1.3.54) 30 5
161 1s. black and orange-red (1.3.54) 30 5
162 2s. brown-olive and carmine (1.3.54) .. 2·50 15
163 5s. purple and black (1.3.54) .. .. 8·00 1·50
164 10s. black and olive-green (1.3.54) .. 9·50 3·00
153/64 .. .. *Set of* 12 20·00 5·50

Designs: *Horiz*—½d. Map showing position of Gold Coast; 1d. Christiansborg Castle; 1½d. Emblem of Joint Provincial Council; 3d. Manganese mine; 4d. Lake Bosumtwi; 1s. Breaking cocoa pods; 2s. Trooping the colour; 5s. Surfboats. *Vert*—2d. Talking drums; 6d. Cocoa farmer; 10s. Forest.

Nos. 153/4 exist in coils constructed from normal sheets.

1953 (2 June). *Coronation. As No. 47 of Aden, but ptd by B.W.*

165 2d. black and sepia 20 8

POSTAGE DUE STAMPS

D 1

(Typo D.L.R.)

1923. *Yellowish toned paper. Wmk Mult Script CA. P* 14.

D1 D 1 ½d. black .. .. 20·00 30·00
D2 1d. black 70 80
D3 2d. black .. .. 9·50 11·00
D4 3d. black .. .. 11·00 7·50
D1/4 Optd "Specimen" .. .. *Set of* 4 60·00

1951–52. *Chalk-surfaced paper. Wmk Mult Script CA. P* 14.

D5 D 1 2d. black (13.12.51) .. .. .. 1·50 2·00
a. Error. Crown missing, W 9*a* .. 55·00
b. Error. St. Edward's Crown, W 9*b* 35·00
D6 3d. black (13.12.51) .. .. .. 1·50 2·25
a. Error. Crown missing, W 9*a* .. 55·00
b. Error. St. Edward's Crown, W 9*b* 35·00
D7 6d. black (1.10.52) .. .. .. 2·50 5·50
a. Error. Crown missing, W 9*a* .. 65·00
b. Error. St. Edward's Crown, W 9*b* .. 45·00
D8 1s. black (1.10.52) .. .. .. 4·50 9·00
b. Error. St. Edward's Crown, W 9*b* .. 65·00

On 6 March 1957 Gold Coast became the Dominion of GHANA.

Grenada

The earliest recorded postmark of the British administration of Grenada dates from 1784, and, although details of the early period are somewhat sparse, it would appear that the island's postal service was operated as a branch of the British G.P.O. In addition to a Packet Agency at St. George's, the capital, it is known that a further agency existed at Carriacou, in the Grenadines, for a few years after 1842.

Stamps of Great Britain were supplied to the St. George's office from 1858 until the colony assumed responsibility for the postal service in September 1860. Following the take-over the crowned-circle handstamp, No. CC2, was again used until the Grenada adhesives were issued in 1861.

There was no internal postal service before 1861.

For illustrations of the handstamp and postmark types see BRITISH POST OFFICE ABROAD notes, following GREAT BRITAIN.

CARRIACOU

CROWNED-CIRCLE HANDSTAMPS

CC1 CC 1 CARRIACOU (13.11.1846) .. .. .. †

Although recorded in the G.P.O. proof book no example of No. CC1 has been reported used from Grenada.

ST. GEORGE'S

CROWNED-CIRCLE HANDSTAMPS

CC2 CC 1 GRENADA (R.) (24.10.1850) *Price on cover* £750

Stamps of GREAT BRITAIN *cancelled* "A 15" *as Type* **2**

1858 *to* **1860**.

Z1 1d. rose-red (1857), *perf* 14 .. .. £325
Z2 2d. blue (1858) (Plate No. 7) £400
Z3 4d. rose (1857) £275
Z4 6d. lilac (1856) £190
Z5 1s. green (1856) £800

PRICES FOR STAMPS ON COVER TO 1945	
Nos. 1/3	*from* × 10
Nos. 4/13	*from* × 5
Nos. 14/19	*from* × 6
Nos. 20/3	*from* × 8
Nos. 24/7	*from* × 10
No. 28	—
No. 29	*from* × 5
Nos. 30/6	*from* × 8
Nos. 37/9	*from* × 4
No. 40	*from* × 20
Nos. 41/7	*from* × 4
Nos. 48/101	*from* × 3
Nos. 109/11	*from* × 5
Nos. 112/48	*from* × 3
Nos. 149/51	*from* × 6
Nos. 152/63	*from* × 2
Nos. D1/3	*from* × 25
Nos. D4/7	*from* × 12
Nos. D8/14	*from* × 20

CROWN COLONY

PRINTERS. Types **1** and **5** recess-printed by Perkins, Bacon and Co.

1

2 Small Star

(Eng C. H. Jeens)

1861 (June)–**62**. *No wmk. Wove paper.* (*a*) *Rough perf* 14 *to* 16.

1 1 1d. bluish green £2750 £275
2 1d. green (5.62) .. .. 65·00 65·00
a. Imperf between (horiz pair) ..
3 6d. rose (*shades*) .. .. .. £750 90·00

(*b*) *Perf* 11 *to* 12½

3*a* 1 6d. lake-red (5.62) £850

No. 3*a* is only known unused, and has also been seen on laid paper. (*Price* £1100).

SIDEWAYS WATERMARK. W **2/3** when sideways show two points of star downwards.

1863–71 *W* **2** (*Small Star*). *Rough perf* 14 *to* 16.

4 1 1d. green (3.64) .. .. 60·00 26·00
5 1d. yellowish green .. .. .. 95·00 32·00
6 6d. rose (*shades*) (5.63) .. .. .. £550 30·00
7 6d. orange-red (*shades*) (5.66) .. £550 30·00
8 6d. dull rose-red (wmk sideways) .. £3000 £200
9 6d. vermilion (5.71) .. .. .. £550 30·00
a. Double impression .. .. .. — £1750

The sideways wmk is an identifying aid to the rare shade, No. 8. Normally in this issue the wmk is upright, but it also exists sideways.

1873 (Jan). *W* **2** (*Small Star sideways*). *Clean-cut perf* 15.

10 1 1d. deep green .. .. 65·00 28·00
a. Bisected diag (on cover) .. .. † £5000
b. Imperf between (pair) .. .. — £3000

3 Large Star

4 Broad-pointed Star

1873 (Sept)–**74**. *W* **3** (*Large Star*). *Intermediate perf* 15.

11 1 1d. blue-green (wmk sideways) (2.74) .. 55·00 26·00
a. Double impression .. .. ..
12 6d. orange-vermilion (upright wmk) .. £500 29·00

5

POSTAGE

ONE SHILLING

(6)

NOTE. The early ½d., 2½d., 4d. and 1s. postage stamps were made by surcharging the undenominated Type **5** design.

The surcharges were from two founts of type—one about 1½ mm high, the other 2 mm high—so there are short and tall letters on the same stamp; also the spacing varies considerably, so that the length of the words varies.

1875 (July). *Surch with T* **6**. *W* **3**. *P* 14.

13 5 1s. deep mauve (B.) .. .. .. £600 23·00
a. "SHLLIING" .. .. .. — £950
b. "NE SHILLING" .. .. .. — £2250
c. Inverted "S" in "POSTAGE" .. £3500 £650
d. "OSTAGE" .. ..

1875 (Dec.) *W* **3** (*Large Star, upright*).

14 1 1d. green *to* yellow-green (*p* 14) .. 32·00 24·00
a. Bisected diag (on cover) .. .. † £5000
15 1d. green (*p* 15) £7000 £2000

No. 14 was perforated at Somerset House. 40 sheets of No. 15 were perforated by Perkins, Bacon to replace spoilages and to complete the order.

1878 (Sept). *W* **2** (*Small Star, sideways*). *Intermediate perf* 15.

16 1 1d. green .. .. £225 35·00
17 6d. deep vermilion .. .. .. £600 35·00
a. Double impression .. .. .. — £1500

1879 (Dec). *W* **2** (*Small Star, upright*). *Rough perf* 15.

18 1 1d. pale green (*thin paper*) .. .. £300 18·00
a. Double impression .. .. ..

1881 (April). *W* **2** (*Small Star, sideways*). *Rough perf* 14½.

19 1 1d. green .. .. £110 18·00
a. Bisected diag (on cover) .. .. † £5000

POSTAGE POSTAGE POSTAGE

HALF-PENNY — TWO PENCE HALF-PENNY — FOUR PENCE

(7) (8) (9)

1881 (April). *Surch with T* **7/9**. *P* 14½. (*a*) *Wmk Large Star, T* **3**.

20 5 ½d. pale mauve .. .. 29·00 14·00
21 ½d. deep mauve .. .. 11·00 14·00
a. Imperf (pair) £275
ab. Ditto. "OSTAGE" (R.9/4.) £3000
b. Surch double £275
c. "OSTAGE" (R.9/4) £140 £130
d. No hyphen £130 £110
e. "ALF-PENNY" £2250
f. Wmk upright .. .. .. — £350
g. Ditto. "OSTAGE" (R.9/4) .. .. — £2000
22 2½d. rose-lake .. .. 32·00 15·00
a. Imperf (pair) £325
b. Imperf between (horiz pair) .. £1900
c. No stop .. .. £160 95·00
d. "PENCF" (R.8/12) £250 £180
23 4d. blue .. .. 90·00 19·00

The watermark is normally *sideways* on the ½d.

(*b*) *Wmk Broad-pointed Star, T* **4**

24 5 2½d. rose-lake .. .. £120 29·00
a. No stop £550 £200
b. "PENCF" (R.8/12) £600 £250
25 2½d. claret £375 £120
a. No stop £950 £475
b. "PENCF" (R.8/12) £1300 £600
25*c* 2½d. deep claret £600 £225
d. No stop £2250 £900
e. "PENCF" (R.8/12) £2750 £1100
26 4d. blue £200 £175

Examples of the "F" for "E" error on the 2½d. value should not be confused with a somewhat similar broken "E" variety. The latter is always without the stop and shows other damage to the "E". The authentic error always occurs with the full stop shown.

The "no stop" variety occurs on R.3/4, R.6/2, R.8/3 and R.9/7.

ONE PENNY POSTAGE. POSTAGE POSTAGE

(10) (11) (12)

1883 (Jan). *Revenue stamps* (*T* **5** *with green surcharge as in T* **10**) *optd for postage. W* **2** (*Small Star*). *P* 14½.

(*a*) *Optd horizontally with T* **11**.

27 5 1d. orange .. .. £170 38·00
a. "POSTAGE" inverted £1600 £1100
b. "POSTAGE" double £1200 £1100
c. Inverted "S" in "POSTAGE" .. £550 £500
d. Bisected diag (on cover) .. .. † £2750

(*b*) *Optd diagonally with T* **11** *twice on each stamp, the stamp being cut and each half used as* ½*d*.

28 5 Half of 1d. orange £500 £275
a. Unsevered pair £3500 £1300
b. "POSTAGE" inverted .. .. — £1100

(*c*) *Optd with T* **12**, *the stamps divided diagonally and each half used as* ½*d*.

29 5 Half of 1d. orange £160 £120
a. Unsevered pair £1200 £600

Nos. 27/9 exist with wmk either upright or sideways.

1d. Revenue stamps are known with "POSTAGE" written by hand, in red or black. These were apparently used, but not officially authorised.

13

d.
1
POSTAGE.

(14)

15

(Typo D.L.R.)

1883. *Wmk Crown CA. P* 14.

30 13 ½d. dull green (February) .. .. 1·90 1·90
a. *Tête-bêche* (pair) .. .. .. 5·50 13·00

31 13 1d. carmine (February) .. .. .. 25·00 5·50
a. *Tête-bêche* (pair) £225 £250
32 2½d. ultramarine (May) .. .. .. 9·00 2·75
a. *Tête-bêche* (pair) .. .. 28·00 38·00
33 4d. greyish slate (May).. .. .. .. 7·00 8·00
a. *Tête-bêche* (pair) .. .. 20·00 23·00
34 6d. mauve (May) .. .. 10·00 10·00
a. *Tête-bêche* (pair) .. .. 35·00 60·00
35 8d. grey-brown (February) .. .. .. 20·00 20·00
a. *Tête-bêche* (pair) .. .. 60·00 95·00
36 1s. pale violet (April) £120 £100
a. *Tête-bêche* (pair) £750
30/36 .. .. *Set of* 7 £170 £130

Types **13** and **15** were printed in rows *tête-bêche* in the sheets.

1886. *Revenue stamps* (*T* **5** *with green surch as T* **10**), *surch with T* **14**. *P* 14. (*a*) *Wmk Large Star, T* 3.
37 5 1d. on 1½d. orange (October) .. .. 28·00 28·00
a. Surch inverted £225 £225
b. Surch double £225 £225
c. "THRFE" £225 £225
d. "PFNCE" £225 £225
e. "HALH" £225 £225
f. Bisected diag (on cover) .. .. .. † £1400
38 1d. on 1s. orange (December) .. .. 28·00 28·00
a. "POSTAGE" (no stop) .. ..
b. "SHILLNG" £400 £350
c. Wide space (3½ mm) between "ONE" and "SHILLING" £400 £350
d. Bisected diag (on cover) .. .. † £1400

(*b*) *Wmk Small Star, T* 2
39 5 1d. on 4d. orange (November) .. .. £110 80·00

1887 (Jan). *Wmk Crown CA. P* 14.
40 15 1d. carmine (Optd S. £35) .. .. .. 1·00 70
a. *Tête-bêche* (pair) .. .. 2·75 15·00

4d.
POSTAGE
(16)

HALF
PENNY
POSTAGE
(17)

1888 (31 Mar)–**91**. *Revenue stamps* (*T* **5** *with green surch as T* **10**) *further surcharged. W* 2. *P* 14½, *and No.* 35.

I. *Surch with T* **16**.
(*a*) 4 *mm between value and* "POSTAGE"
41 5 4d. on 2s. orange .. .. 22·00 22·00
a. Upright "d" £275 £275
b. Wide space (2¼mm) between "TWO" and "SHILLINGS" £110 £110
c. First "S" in "SHILLINGS" inverted £300 £300
d. Imperf between (horiz pair) .. ..

(*b*) 5 *mm between value and* "POSTAGE"
42 5 4d. on 2s. orange .. .. 32·00 38·00
a. Wide spacing (as 41b) £190 £225
b. "S" inverted (as 41c) £550 £550

II. *Surch as T* **17** (December 1889)
43 5 ½d. on 2s. orange .. .. 22·00 28·00
a. Surch double £275 £300
b. Wide spacing (as 41b) £110 £120
c. "S" inverted (as 41c) £275 £275

POSTAGE
AND 1d.
REVENUE
(18)

POSTAGE
AND
REVENUE
1d.
(19)

2½d.
(20)

III. *Surch with T* **18** (December 1890)
44 5 1d. on 2s. orange .. .. 70·00 70·00
a. Surcharge inverted.. .. .. .. £275
b. Wide spacing (as 41b) £190 £190
c. "S" inverted (as 41c) £400

IV. *Surch with T* **19** (January 1891)
45 5 1d. on 2s. orange .. .. 25·00 25·00
a. No stop after "1d" £225
b. Wide spacing (as 41b) £190
c. "S" inverted (as 41c) £400
46 13 1d. on 8d. grey-brown .. .. .. 22·00 22·00
a. *Tête-bêche* (pair) .. .. .. 75·00
b. Surcharge inverted.. .. .. .. £275 £275
c. No stop after "1d" £225 £225

V. *Surch with T* **20** (December 1891)
47 13 2½d. on 8d. grey-brown (Optd S. £65) 26·00 22·00
a. *Tête-bêche* (pair) £110
b. Inverted surcharge .. .. ..
c. Double surcharge £550 £750
d. Double surcharge, one inverted .. £400 £400
e. Treble surcharge .. .. — £850

There are two types of fraction; in one the "1" has horizontal serif and the "2" commences in a ball; in the other the "1" has sloping serif and the "2" is without ball.

Each type occurs 30 times in the pane of 60.

See also Nos. D4/7.

GRENADA 1d
21

GRENADA 8d
22

GRENADA LA CONCEPCION
23 Flagship of Columbus. (Columbus named Grenada "La Concepcion")

(Type D.L.R.)

1895 (6 Sept)–**99**. *Wmk Crown CA. P* 14.
48 22 ½d. mauve and green (9.99) .. .. 90 1·40
49 21 1d. mauve and carmine (5.96) .. .. 1·40 50
50 2d. mauve and brown ((9.99) .. .. 25·00 32·00
51 2½d. mauve and ultramarine .. .. 8·50 2·00
52 22 3d. mauve and orange .. .. .. 11·00 14·00
53 21 6d. mauve and green .. .. .. 6·00 9·00
54 22 8d. mauve and black .. .. .. 18·00 23·00
55 1s. green and orange .. .. .. 22·00 27·00
48/55 .. .. *Set of* 8 85·00 £100
48/55 Optd "Specimen" .. .. *Set of* 8 £160

(Recess D.L.R.)

1898 (15 Aug). *400th Anniv of Discovery of Grenada by Columbus. Wmk Crown CC. P* 14
56 23 2½d. ultramarine (Optd S. £110) .. 15·00 15·00
a. Bluish paper .. .. 30·00 40·00

GRENADA POSTAGE & REVENUE ½d
24

GRENADA POSTAGE & REVENUE 1d
25

(Typo D.L.R.)

1902. *Wmk Crown CA. P* 14.
57 24 ½d. dull purple and green .. .. 80 1·10
58 25 1d. dull purple and carmine 90 55
59 2d. dull purple and brown .. .. 4·00 7·00
60 2½d. dull purple and ultramarine .. 5·00 6·00
61 24 3d. dull purple and orange .. .. 4·00 6·00
62 25 6d. dull purple and green .. .. 7·00 12·00
63 24 1s. green and orange .. .. .. 12·00 18·00
64 2s. green and ultramarine .. .. 18·00 30·00
65 25 5s. green and carmine .. .. .. 25·00 38·00
66 24 10s. green and purple .. .. .. 85·00 £120
57/66 .. .. *Set of* 10 £150 £225
57/66 Optd "Specimen" .. .. *Set of* 10 £275

1904–6. *Wmk Mult Crown CA. P* 14.
67 24 ½d. purple and green, O (1905).. .. 9·50 13·00
68 25 1d. purple and carmine, O .. .. 6·50 4·25
69 2d. purple and brown, O (1905) .. 18·00 24·00
70 2½d. purple and ultramarine, O (1905) .. 18·00 24·00
71 24 3d. purple and orange, OC (1905) .. 6·50 11·00
72 25 6d. purple and green, OC (1906) .. 8·00 11·00
73 24 1s. green and orange, O (1905) .. 12·00 20·00
74 2s. green and ultramarine, OC (1906) 20·00 32·00
75 25 5s. green and carmine, O (1906) .. 30·00 45·00
76 24 10s. green and purple, O (1906).. .. £110 £170
67/76 .. .. *Set of* 10 £225 £325

GRENADA HALF ½ PENNY
GRENADA THREE 3 PENCE
26 Badge of the Colony 27

(Recess D.L.R.)

1906. *Wmk Mult Crown CA. P*14.
77 26 ½d. green 65 70
78 1d. carmine 50 30
79 2d. orange .. .. 3·50 5·50
80 2½d. blue .. .. 5·50 5·50
a. Ultramarine .. .. 8·00 7·00

(Typo D.L.R.)

1908. *Wmk Crown CA. P* 14.
82 27 1s. black/*green*, C .. .. .. 15·00 26·00
83 10s. green and red/*green*, C .. .. 80·00 £140

1908–11. *Wmk Mult Crown CA. P* 14.
84 27 3d. dull purple/*yellow*, C .. .. 2·25 4·50
85 6d. dull purple and purple, C .. .. 12·00 20·00
86 1s. black/*green*, C (1911) .. .. 5·00 8·00
87 2s. blue and purple/*blue*, C .. .. 12·00 13·00
88 5s. green and red/*yellow*, C .. .. 32·00 40·00
77/88 .. .. *Set of* 11 £150 £225
77/80, 82/5, 87/8 Optd "Specimen" .. *Set of* 10 £300

½d GRENADA ½d
28

WAR TAX
(29)

WAR TAX
(30)

(Typo D.L.R.)

1913 (3 Jan)–**1922**. *Wmk Mult Crown CA. P* 14.
89 28 ½d. yellow-green, O 70 70
90 ½d. green, O 40 60
91 1d. red, O 45 40
92 1d. scarlet, O (1916) 60 40
93 2d. orange, O .. .. 60 1·10
94 2½d. bright blue, O .. .. .. 2·00 2·75
95 2½d. dull blue, O (1920) .. .. .. 3·50 6·00
96 3d. purple/*yellow*, C .. .. .. 80 2·25
a. White back (3.14) (Optd S. £30) .. 1·40 5·00
b. On lemon (1917) .. .. .. 2·75 5·00
c. On pale yellow (1921) .. .. .. 3·75 6·50
97 28 6d. dull and bright purple, C .. .. 2·25 5·00
98 1s. black *green*, C .. .. .. 3·50 5·50
a. White back (3.14) (Optd S. £30) .. 2·25 5·50
b. On blue-green, olive back (1917) .. 35·00 45·00
c. On emerald surface .. .. .. 2·25 6·00
d. On emerald back (6.22) (Optd S. £30) 2·25 6·00
99 2s. purple and blue/*blue*, C .. .. 4·75 8·00
100 5s. green and red/*yellow*, C .. .. 12·00 23·00
a. On pale yellow (1921) (Optd S. £45) 18·00 29·00
101 10s. green and red/*green*, C .. .. 38·00 55·00
a. On emerald back (6.22) (Optd S. £55) 38·00 55·00
89/101*a* .. .. *Set of* 10 55·00 90·00
89/101 Optd "Specimen" .. .. *Set of* 10 £200
98 Optd in red instead of black .. ..

1916 (1 June). *Optd by Govt Press, St. George's. With T* **29**.
109 28 1d. red (*shades*) (H/SS. £65) .. .. 3·25 5·50
a. Opt inverted £275
b. "T△X" .. .. 42·00 60·00

A small "A" in "WAR", 2 mm high is found on Nos. 29, 38 and 48 of the setting of 60 and a very small "A" in "TAX", 1½ mm high, on No. 11. Value about twice normal. The normal "A" is 2¼ mm high. No. 109b is on No. 56 of the setting.

1916 (1 Sept)–**18**. *Optd with T* **30** *in London*.
111 28 1d. scarlet 45 45
a. Carmine-red/bluish (5.18).. .. .. 3·50 3·25
111 Optd "Specimen" .. .. 45·00

1921–32. *T* **28**. *Wmk Mult Script CA. P* 14.
112 ½d. green, O 35 45
113 1d. carmine-red, O 35 50
114 1d. brown, O (1923).. .. .. .. 40 40
115 1½d. rose-red, O (6.22) 55 55
116 2d. orange, O 50 85
117 2d. grey, O (1926) .. .. 2·00 2·25
117*a* 2½d. dull blue.. .. .. 1·40 2·00
118 2½d. grey, O (6.22) .. .. 90 5·00
119 2½d. bright blue, O (1926) .. .. .. 80 2·25
120 2½d. ultramarine O (1931) .. .. .. 3·75 5·50
120*a* 2½d. chalky blue and blue, O (1932).. 18·00 25·00
121 3d. bright blue, O (6.22) .. .. .. 2·50 5·00
122 3d. purple/*yellow*, C (1926) .. .. 80 3·50
123 4d. black and red/*yellow*, C (1926) .. 80 5·00
124 5d. dull purple and sage-green, C (27.12.22) 1·60 5·50
125 6d. dull and bright purple, C .. .. 2·25 7·50
126 6d. black and carmine, C (1926) .. .. 3·50 6·00
127 9d. dull purple and black, C (27.12.22) 2·25 5·50
128 1s. black/*emerald*, C (1923).. .. .. 5·00 13·00
129 1s. chestnut, C (1926) .. .. .. 9·00 14·00
130 2s. purple and blue/*blue*, C (1922) .. 8·00 13·00
131 2s. 6d. black and carmine/*blue*, C (1929) .. 9·50 15·00
132 3s. green and violet, C (27.12.22) .. 10·00 20·00
133 5s. green and red/*pale yellow*, C (1923) 17·00 28·00
134 10s. green and red/*emerald*, C (1923) .. 45·00 70·00
112/19, 121/34 .. .. .. *Set of* 22 £110 £200
112/34 Optd/Perf "Specimen" .. *Set of* 23 £500

31 Grand Anse Beach

32 Badge of the Colony

33 Grand Etang

34 St. George's

(Recess Waterlow)

1934 (23 Oct)–**36**. *Wmk Mult Script CA* (*sideways on T* **32**). *P* 12½.
135 31 ½d. green 40 65
a. Perf 12½ × 13½ (1936) .. .. 5·00 10·00
136 32 1d. black and sepia .. .. .. 2·25 2·00
a. Perf 13½ × 12½ (1936) .. .. 2·50 5·00
137 33 1½d. black and scarlet .. .. .. 2·50 2·25
a. Perf 12½ × 13½ (1936) .. .. 4·50 5·50
138 32 2d. black and orange 80 90
139 34 2½d. blue 50 90
140 32 3d. black and olive-green .. .. 1·00 1·75
141 6d. black and purple .. .. .. 2·00 3·00
142 1s. black and brown .. .. .. 4·00 6·50
143 2s. 6d. black and ultramarine .. 15·00 22·00
144 5s. black and violet .. .. .. 32·00 40·00
135/144 .. .. *Set of* 10 55·00 70·00
135/44 Perf "Specimen" .. .. *Set of* 10 £160

1935 (6 May). *Silver Jubilee. As T* **13** *of Antigua but ptd by Waterlow. P* 11 × 12.
145 ½d. black and green.. .. .. .. 30 50
146 1d. ultramarine and grey 55 50
147 1½d. deep blue and scarlet .. .. .. 85 1·00
148 1s. slate and purple.. .. .. .. 7·00 9·50
145/8 Perf "Specimen" .. .. *Set of* 4 50·00

1937 (12 May). *Coronation. As T* **2** *of Aden but ptd by B.W. P* 11 × 11½.
149 1d. violet 20 40
150 1½d. carmine 20 40
151 2½d. blue 45 75
149/51 Perf "Specimen" .. .. *Set of* 3 30·00

35 King George VI

(Photo Harrison)

1937 (12 July)–**45**. *Wmk Mult Script CA. P* 15 × 14.
152 **35** ½d. brown, **CO** .. 10 10
a. Chocolate, **CO** (1.45) .. 15 15
The ordinary paper is thick, smooth and opaque.

35 Grand Anse Beach

40 Badge of the Colony

(Recess D.L.R. (10s.), Waterlow (others))

1938 (16 Mar)–**50**. *As T* **31/4** (*but portrait of King George VI as in T* **36**) *and T* **40**. *Wmk Mult Script CA* (*sideways on T* **32**). *P* 12½ *or* 12 × 13 (10s.).
153 **36** ½d. yellow-green .. 2·00 45
a. Perf 12½ × 13½ (1938) .. 1·50 1·10
b. Perf 12½. *Blue-green* .. 20 25
ba. Perf 12½ × 13½. *Blue-green* .. 1·75 2·75
154 **32** 1d. black and sepia .. 12 12
a. Perf 13½ × 12½ (1938) .. 25 12
155 **33** 1½d. black and scarlet .. 40 12
a. Perf 12½ × 13½ (1938) .. 1·75 50
156 **32** 2d. black and orange .. 15 12
a. Perf 12½ × 13½ (1938) .. 40 12
157 **34** 2½d. bright blue .. 20 15
a. Perf 12½ × 13½ (?March 1950) .. £2750 £170
158 **32** 3d. black and olive-green .. 2·75 1·25
a. Perf 13½ × 12½ (16.3.38) .. 3·00 1·40
ab. Perf 13½ × 12½. *Black and brown-olive* (1942) .. 80 90
b. Perf 12½. *Black & brown-olive* (16.8.50) .. 70 85
159 6d. black and purple .. 60 30
a. Perf 13½ × 12½ (1942) .. 60 30
160 1s. black and brown .. 60 50
a. Perf 13½ × 12½ (1941) .. 1·25 90
161 2s. black and ultramarine .. 4·25 1·90
a. Perf 13½ × 12½ (1941) .. 7·50 1·75
162 5s. black and violet .. 5·00 3·75
a. Perf 13½ × 12½ (1947) .. 3·75 6·00
163 **40** 10s. slate-blue and carmine (*narrow*) (*p* 12 × 13) .. 18·00 16·00
a. Perf 14. *Pale blue and carmine-rose* (*narrow*) .. 45·00 42·00
b. Perf 14. *Slate-blue and carmine* (*narrow*) (1943) .. 8·00 8·00
c. Perf 12. *Slate-blue and carmine* (*narrow*) (1943) .. £180 £180
d. Perf 14. *Slate-blue and claret* (*wide*) (1944) .. 40·00 20·00
e. Perf 14. *Blue-black and carmine* (*wide*) (1947) .. 22·00 25·00
152/163b .. *Set of* 12 17·00 14·50
152/63 Perf "Specimen" .. *Set of* 12 £130

In the earlier printings of the 10s. the paper was dampened before printing and the subsequent shrinkage produced narrow frames 23½ to 23¾ mm wide. Later printings were made on dry paper producing wide frames 24¼ mm wide.

No. 163a is one of the earlier printings line perf 13.8 × 14.1.

No. 163b is line-perf 14.1.

Nos. 163a and 163b may be found with gum more or less yellow due to local climatic conditions.

1946 (25 Sept). *Victory. As Nos.* 28/9 *of Aden.*
164 1½d. carmine .. 15 15
165 3½d. blue .. 25 20
164/5 Perf "Specimen" .. *Set of* 2 40·00

1948 (27 Oct). *Royal Silver Wedding. As Nos.* 30/1 *of Aden.*
166 1½d. scarlet .. 15 15
167 10s. slate-green .. 9·00 13·00

(New Currency. 100 cents = 1 West Indian dollar)

1949 (10 Oct). *75th Anniv of Universal Postal Union. As Nos.* 114/17 *of Antigua.*
168 5 c. ultramarine .. 25 20
169 6 c. olive .. 50 40
170 12 c. magenta .. 85 70
171 24 c. red-brown .. 90 90

41 King George VI

42 Badge of the Colony

43 Badge of the Colony

(Recess B.W. (T **41**), D.L.R. (others))

1951 (8 Jan). *Wmk Mult Script CA. P* 11½ (*T* **41**), 11½ × 12½ (*T* **42**), *and* 11½ × 13 (*T* **43**).
172 **41** ½ c. black and red-brown .. 25 70
173 1 c. black and emerald-green .. 30 25
174 2 c. black and brown .. 30 25
175 3 c. black and rose-carmine .. 40 20
176 4 c. black and orange .. 45 80
177 5 c. black and violet .. 45 30
178 6 c. black and olive .. 45 25
179 7 c. black and light blue .. 45 20
180 12 c. black and purple .. 2·00 1·50
181 **42** 25 c. black and sepia .. 3·25 1·75
182 50 c. black and blue .. 3·25 1·25
183 $1.50, black and yellow-orange .. 15·00 11·00
184 **43** $2.50, slate-blue and carmine .. 9·00 11·00
172/184 .. *Set of* 13 32·00 27·00

1951 (16 Feb). *Inauguration of B.W.I. University College. As Nos.* 118/19 *of Antigua.*
185 3 c. black and carmine .. 20 20
186 6 c. black and olive .. 20 30

NEW CONSTITUTION

1951

(44)

1951 (21 Sept). *New Constitution. Optd with T* **44** *by B.W.*
187 **41** 3 c. black and rose-carmine .. 15 30
188 4 c. black and orange .. 15 40
189 5 c. black and violet (R.) .. 15 30
190 12 c. black and purple .. 20 40

1953 (3 June). *Coronation. As No.* 47 *of Aden*
191 3 c. black and carmine-red .. 10 8

45 Queen Elizabeth II

46 Badge of the Colony

47 Badge of the Colony

(Recess B.W. (T **45**), D.L.R. (T **46/7**))

1953 (15 June)–**59**. *Wmk Mult Script CA. P* 11½ (*T* **45**), 11½ × 12½ (*T* **46**), *or* 11½ × 13 (*T* **47**).
192 **45** ½ c. black and brown (28.12.53) .. 5 5
193 1 c. black and deep emerald .. 5 5
194 2 c. black and sepia (15.9.53) .. 5 5
195 3 c. black and carmine-red (22.2.54) .. 8 5
196 4 c. black and brown-orange (22.2.54) .. 8 5
197 5 c. black and deep violet (22.2.54) .. 8 5
198 6 c. black and olive-green (28.12.53) .. 12 10
199 7 c. black and blue (6.6.55) .. 12 5
200 12 c. black and reddish purple .. 15 5
201 **46** 25 c. black and sepia (10.1.55) .. 70 20
202 50 c. black and deep blue (2.12.55) .. 90 40
203 $1.50, black & brown-orange (2.12.55) 6·50 6·50
204 **47** $2.50, slate-blue & carmine (16.11.59) 12·00 7·00
192/204 .. *Set of* 13 19·00 13·00

On 23 December 1965, No. 203 was issued surcharged "2" but this was intended for fiscal and revenue purposes and it was not authorised to be used postally, although some are known to have passed through the mail.

1958 (22 Apr). *Inauguration of British Caribbean Federation. As Nos.* 135/7 *of Antigua.*
205 3 c. deep green .. 10 5
206 6 c. blue .. 12 30
207 12 c. scarlet .. 15 10

48 Queen Victoria, Queen Elizabeth II, Mail Van and Post Office, St. George's

(Photo Harrison)

1961 (1 June). *Grenada Stamp Centenary. T* **48** *and similar horiz designs. W* w **12**. *P* 14½ × 14.
208 3 c. crimson and black .. 10 10
209 8 c. bright blue and orange .. 20 15
210 25 c. lake and blue .. 35 25

Designs:—8 c. Queen Victoria, Queen Elizabeth II and *La Concepcion*; 25 c. Queen Victoria, Queen Elizabeth II, R.M.S.P. *Solent* and "Dakota" aircraft.

1963 (4 June). *Freedom from Hunger. As No.* 76 *of Aden.*
211 8 c. bluish green .. 25 15

1963 (2 Sept). *Red Cross Centenary. As Nos.* 147/8 *of Antigua.*
212 3 c. red and black .. 10 10
213 25 c. red and blue .. 35 25

1964 (12 May)–**66**. *As Nos.* 194/8, 201/1, *but wmk* w **12**.
214 **45** 2 c. black and sepia .. 5 5
215 3 c. black and carmine-red .. 8 5
216 4 c. black and brown-orange .. 8 15
217 5 c. black and deep violet .. 10 5
218 6 c. black and olive-green (4.1.66) .. £200 65·00
219 12 c. black and reddish purple .. 15 5
220 **46** 25 c. black and sepia .. 60 30

1965 (17 May). *I.T.U. Centenary. As Nos.* 166/7 *of Antigua.*
221 2 c. red-orange and yellow-olive .. 5 5
222 50 c. lemon and light red .. 40 30

1965 (25 Oct). *International Co-operation Year. As Nos.* 168/9 *of Antigua*
223 1 c. reddish purple and turquoise-green .. 5 5
224 25 c. deep bluish green and lavender .. 20 15

1966 (24 Jan). *Churchill Commemoration. As Nos.* 170/3 *of Antigua.*
225 1 c. new blue .. 5 5
226 3 c. deep green .. 10 5
227 25 c. brown .. 20 20
228 35 c. bluish violet .. 30 30

1966 (4 Feb). *Royal Visit. As Nos.* 174/5 *of Antigua.*
229 3 c. black and ultramarine .. 10 10
230 35 c. black and magenta .. 30 20

52 Hillsborough, Carriacou

53 Badge of the Colony

54 Queen Elizabeth II

55 Map of Grenada

(Des V. Whiteley. Photo Harrison)

1966 (1 Apr). *Horiz designs as T* **52**, *and T* **53/5**. *Multicoloured. W* w **12**. *P* 14½ ($1, $2, $3) *or* 14½ × 13½ (*others*).
231 1 c. Type **52** .. 5 5
232 2 c. Bougainvillea .. 5 5
233 3 c. Flamboyant plant .. 5 5
234 5 c. Levera beach .. 8 5
235 6 c. Carenage, St. George's .. 8 5
236 8 c. Annandale Falls .. 8 5
237 10 c. Cocoa pods .. 8 5
238 12 c. Inner Harbour .. 12 10
239 15 c. Nutmeg .. 15 10
240 25 c. St. George's .. 25 15
241 35 c. Grand Anse beach .. 40 20
242 50 c. Bananas .. 80 60
243 $1 Type **53** .. 2·00 1·25
244 $2 Type **54** .. 3·75 3·50
245 $3 Type **55** .. 4·00 4·00
231/45 .. *Set of* 15 11·00 9·00

1966 (1 July). *World Cup Football Championships. As Nos.* 176/7 *of Antigua.*
246 5 c. violet, yellow-green, lake & yellow-brn 10 5
247 50 c. chocolate, blue-green, lake & yelllow-brn 30 25

1966 (20 Sept). *Inauguration of W.H.O. Headquarters, Geneva. As Nos.* 178/9 *of Antigua.*
248 8 c. black, yellow-green and light blue .. 10 10
249 25 c. black, light purple and yellow-brown .. 20 20

1966 (1 Dec). *20th Anniv of U.N.E.S.C.O. As Nos.* 196/8 *of Antigua.*
250 2 c. slate-violet, red, yellow and orange .. 5 5
251 15 c. orange-yellow, violet and deep olive .. 15 10
252 50 c. black, bright purple and orange .. 45 40

ASSOCIATED STATEHOOD

ASSOCIATED STATEHOOD 1967

(67)

(68)

1967 (3 Mar). *Statehood. Nos.* 232/3, 236 *and* 240 *optd with T* **67**, *in silver*
253 2 c. Bougainvillea .. 5 5
254 3 c. Flamboyant plant .. 5 5
255 8 c. Annandale Falls .. 5 5
256 25 c. St. George's .. 15 20

1967 (June). *World Fair, Montreal. Nos. 232, 237, 239 and 243/4 surch as T 68 or optd with "Expo" emblem only.*

257 1 c. on 15 c. Nutmeg 5 5
 a. Surch and opt albino .. .. .. 14·00
258 2 c. Bougainvillea 5 5
259 3 c. on 10 c. Cocoa pods 5 5
260 $1 Type **53** 30 35
261 $2 Type **54** 45 50

ASSOCIATED
STATEHOOD

(69) **70** Kennedy and Local Flower

1967 (Oct). *Statehood. Nos. 231/45 optd with T* **69**.

262 1 c. Type **52** 5 5
263 2 c. Bougainvillea 5 5
264 3 c. Flamboyant plant 5 5
265 5 c. Levera beach 8 8
266 6 c. Carenage, St. George's 8 8
267 8 c. Annandale Falls 8 8
268 10 c. Cocoa pods 10 10
269 12 c. Inner Harbour 10 12
270 15 c. Nutmeg 12 12
271 25 c. St. George's 20 20
272 35 c. Grand Anse beach 35 35
273 50 c. Bananas 60 60
274 $1 Type **53** .. .. 1·25 1·25
275 $2 Type **54** .. .. 2·50 2·50
276 $3 Type **55** .. .. 3·25 3·25
262/76 .. .. *Set of* 15 8·00 8·00

See also No. 295

(Des M. Shamir. Photo Harrison)

1968 (13 Jan). *50th Birth Anniv of President Kennedy. T* **70** *and similar horiz designs. Multicoloured. P* 14½ × 14.

277 1 c. Type **70** 5 5
278 15 c. Type **70** 10 10
279 25 c. Kennedy and strelitzia 15 15
280 35 c. Kennedy and roses 25 15
281 50 c. As 25 c. 35 20
282 $1 As 35 c. 50 40
277/82 .. .. *Set of* 6 1·25 95

73 Scout Bugler **76** "Near Antibes"

(Des K. Plowitz. Photo Govt Printer, Israel)

1968 (17 Feb). *World Scout Jamboree, Idaho. T* **73** *and similar vert designs. Multicoloured. P* 13 × 13½.

283 1 c. Type **73** 5 5
284 2 c. Scouts camping 5 5
285 3 c. Lord Baden-Powell 5 5
286 35 c. Type **73** 35 15
287 50 c. As 2 c. 40 20
288 $1 As 3 c. 75 40
283/8 .. .. *Set of* 6 1·50 80

(Des G. Vasarhelyi. Photo Harrison)

1968 (23 Mar). *Paintings by Sir Winston Churchill. T* **76** *and similar horiz designs. Multicoloured. P* 14 × 14½.

289 10 c. Type **76** 10 8
290 12 c. "The Mediterranean" 12 8
291 15 c. "St. Jean Cap Ferratt" 15 10
292 25 c. Type **76** 25 15
293 35 c. As 15 c. 35 20
294 50 c. Sir Winston painting 45 25
289/94 .. .. *Set of* 6 1·25 80

$5

(80)

CHILDREN
NEED
MILK

2cts. + 3cts.

(81)

CHILDREN
NEED
MILK

1c. + 3cts.

(82)

1968 (18 May). *No. 275 surch with T* **80**

295 **54** $5 on $2 multicoloured .. .. 2·75 4·00

1968 (22 July–19 Aug). *"Children Need Milk".*

(*a*) *Nos. 244/5 surch locally as T* **81** (22 July)

296 **54** 2 c. + 3 c. on $2 multicoloured 12 15
297 **55** 3 c. + 3 c. on $3 multicoloured 12 15
 a. Surch inverted .. .. .. 50·00 35·00
 b. Surch double .. .. .. 30·00

(*b*) *Nos. 243/4 surch locally as T* **82** (19 Aug)

298 **53** 1 c. + 3 c. on $1 multicoloured .. .. 50 1·25
 a. Surch on No. 274 .. .. .. 70·00
 b. Surch double .. .. .. 65·00
299 **54** 2 c. + 3 c. on $2 multicoloured .. .. 22·00 28·00
 a. Surch on No. 275 .. .. .. 80·00

83 Edith McGuire (U.S.A.)

86 Hibiscus

(Des M. Shamir. Photo Harrison)

1968 (24 Sept). *Olympic Games, Mexico. T* **83** *and similar square designs. P* 12½.

300 1 c. brown, black and blue 5 5
301 2 c. orange, brown, blue and lilac 5 5
 a. Orange (badge, etc.) omitted
302 3 c. scarlet, brown and dull green 5 5
 a. Scarlet (rings, "MEXICO" etc.) omitted
303 10 c. brown, black, blue and vermilion .. 5 5
304 50 c. orange, brown, blue and turquoise .. 25 30
305 60 c. scarlet, brown and red-orange 30 40
300/305 .. .. *Set of* 6 65 80

Designs:—2, 50 c. Arthur Wint (Jamaica); 3, 60 c. Ferreira da Silva (Brazil); 10 c. Type **83**.

Nos. 300/2 and 303/5 were issued in separate composite sheets containing three strips of three, with three *se-tenant* labels showing Greek athlete (Nos. 300/2) or Discobolos (Nos. 303/5). (*Price for two sheets £6 mint, £8 used.*)

(Des G. Vasarhelyi (No. 314*a*), V. Whiteley (75 c.), M. Shamir (others). Litho Format (Nos. 314*a* and 317*a*). Photo Harrison (others))

1968 (Oct)–**71**. *Multicoloured designs as T* **86**. *P* 13½ (*Nos. 314a and 317a*), 13½ × 14½ (*vert except No. 314a*) *or* 14½ × 13½ (*horiz except No. 317a*).

306 1 c. Type **86** 10 5
307 2 c. Strelitzia 10 5
308 3 c. Bougainvillea (1.7.69) 10 5
309 5 c. Rock Hind (*horiz*) (4.2.69) 12 5
310 6 c. Sailfish 12 5
311 8 c. Snapper (*horiz*) (1.7.69) 12 5
312 10 c. Giant Toad (*horiz*) (4.2.69) 12 5
313 12 c. Turtle 15 12
314 15 c. Tree Boa (*horiz*) 70 60
314*a* 15 c. Thunbergia (1970) .. .. .. 3·50 1·75
315 25 c. Opossum (4.2.69) 40 20
316 35 c. Armadillo (*horiz*) (1.7.69) 45 20
317 50 c. Mona Monkey 60 25
317*a* 75 c. Yacht in St. George's Harbour (*horiz*) (9.10.71) .. .. 8·00 4·00
318 $1 Bananaquit .. .. 1·50 1·50
319 $2 Brown Pelican (4.2.69) .. .. .. 3·00 4·25
320 $3 Magnificent Frigate Bird .. .. 3·75 5·50
321 $5 Bare-eyed Thrush (1.7.69) .. .. 5·00 9·00
306/21 .. .. *Set of* 18 25·00 25·00

Nos. 314*a*, 317*a* and the dollar values are larger—29 × 45½, 44 × 28½ and 25½ × 48 mm respectively.

102 Kidney Transplant

106 "The Adoration of the Kings" (Veronese)

(Des M. Shamir. Litho B.W.)

1968 (25 Nov). *20th Anniv of World Health Organization. T* **102** *and similar vert designs. Multicoloured. P* 13 × 13½.

322 5 c. Type **102** 5 5
323 25 c. Heart transplant 15 15
324 35 c. Lung transplant 20 15
325 50 c. Eye transplant 25 25

(Photo Harrison)

1968 (3 Dec). *Christmas. T* **106** *and similar square designs. P* 12½.

326 5 c. multicoloured 5 5
327 15 c. multicoloured 10 10
328 35 c. multicoloured 20 20
329 $1 multicoloured 45 60

Designs:—15 c. "Madonna and Child with Sts. John and Catherine" (Titian); 35 c. "Adoration of the Kings" (Botticelli); $1 "A Warrior Adoring" (Catena).

VISIT CARIFTA EXPO '69
April 5-30
5c

(110)

1969 (Feb). *Caribbean Free Trade Area Exhibition. Nos. 300/5 surch in red as T* **110**.

330 5 c. on 1 c. brown, black and blue 5 5
331 8 c. on 2 c. orange, brown, blue and lilac .. 5 5
332 25 c. on 3 c. scarlet, brown and dull green .. 10 10
333 35 c. on 10 c. brown, black, blue and vermilion 15 15
334 $1 on 50 c. orange, brown, blue & turquoise 25 35
335 $2 on 60 c. scarlet, brown and red-orange .. 55 70
 a. Scarlet (rings, "MEXICO" etc) omitted .. † –
330/5 .. .. *Set of* 6 1·00 1·40

The centre of the composite sheets is also overprinted with a commemorative inscription publicising CARIFTA EXPO 1969 (*Price for two sheets £11 mint or used*).

111 Dame Hylda Bynoe (Governor) and Island Scene

(Des and litho D.L.R.)

1969 (1 May). *Carifta Expo 1969. T* **111** *and similar horiz designs. Multicoloured. P* 13 × 13½.

336 5 c. Type **111** 5 5
337 15 c. Premier E. M. Gairy and Island scene .. 10 10
338 50 c. Type **111** 15 15
339 60 c. Emblems of 1958 and 1967 World's Fairs 15 15

114 Dame Hylda Bynoe

115 "Balshazzar's Feast" (Rembrandt)

(Photo Enschedé)

1969 (8 June). *Human Rights Year. T* **114/15** *and similar multi-coloured design. P* 12½ × 13 ($1) *or* 13 × 12½ (*others*).

340 5 c. Type **114** 5 5
341 25 c. Dr. Martin Luther King (*vert*) 10 10
342 35 c. Type **114** 10 10
343 $1 Type **115** 25 40

117 Batsman playing Off-drive

(Des M. Shamir and L. W. Denyer. Photo Harrison)

1969 (1 Aug). *Cricket. T* **117** *and similar horiz designs. P* 14 × 14½.

344 3 c. yellow, brown and ultramarine 30 15
345 10 c. multicoloured 40 25
346 25 c. brown, ochre and myrtle-green 85 90
347 35 c. multicoloured .. .. 1·25 1·25

Designs:—10 c. Batsman playing defensive stroke; 25 c. Batsman sweeping ball; 35 c. Batsman playing on-drive.

Nos. 344/7 were each issued in small sheets of 9 (3 × 3) with decorative borders.

129 Astronaut handling Moon Rock

(Des G. Vasarhelyi. Photo)

1969 (24 Sept). *First Man on the Moon. T* **129** *and similar multi-coloured designs. P* 13½ (½ c.) *or* 12½ (*others*).

348 ½ c. As Type **129** but larger (56 × 35 *mm*) .. 5 5
349 1 c. Moon rocket and moon 5 5
350 2 c. Module landing 5 5
351 3 c. Declaration left on moon 5 5
352 8 c. Module leaving rocket 8 8
353 25 c. Rocket lifting-off (*vert*) 20 20

354 35 c. Spacecraft in orbit (*vert*) 30 30
355 50 c. Capsule with parachutes (*vert*) 40 40
356 $1 Type **129** 65 65
348/56 .. .. *Set of* 9 1·50 1·50
MS357 115 × 90 mm. Nos. 351 and 356. Imperf 1·10 1·25

130 Gandhi

(Des A. Robledo. Litho B.W.)

1969 (8 Oct). *Birth Centenary of Mahatma Gandhi. T* **130** *and similar designs. P* 11½.
358 **130** 6 c. multicoloured 20 10
359 – 15 c. multicoloured 35 15
360 25 c. multicoloured 50 25
361 – $1 multicoloured .. .. 1·60 1·25
MS362 155 × 122 mm. Nos. 358/61. Imperf. 2·75 3·75
Designs: *Vert*—15 c. Gandhi standing; 25 c. Gandhi walking. *Horiz*—$1 Head of Gandhi.

1969

2c

(134)

135 "Blackbeard" (Edward Teach)

1969 (23 Dec). *Christmas. Nos. 326/9 surch with T* **134** *in black (2 c.) or optd with new date only in silver (others).*
363 2 c. on 15 c. multicoloured 5 5
a. Surch inverted .. .. 50·00
364 5 c. multicoloured 5 5
365 35 c. multicoloured 20 20
a. Opt inverted .. .. 50·00
366 $1 multicoloured 55 75
a. Opt inverted .. .. 50·00

(Des K. Plowitz. Recess B.W.)

1970 (2 Feb). *Pirates. T* **135** *and similar vert designs. P* 13½.
367 15 c. black 55 15
368 25 c. dull green 80 20
369 50 c. lilac .. .. 1·40 45
370 $1 carmine .. .. 2·50 1·75
Designs:—25 c. Anne Bonney; 50 c. Jean Lafitte; $1 Mary Read.

(139)

(140)

1970 (18 Mar). *No. 348 surch with T* **139**.
371 5 c. on ½ c. multicoloured 8 8
a. Surch double .. .. 55·00
b. Surch with T 140 .. .. 1·00 1·25

141 "The Last Supper" (detail, **142** Del Sarto)

(Des and litho B.W.)

1970 (13 Apr). *Easter. Paintings. T* **141/2** *and similar vert designs. Multicoloured. P* 11½.
372 5 c. } Type **141/2** 5 5
373 5 c. } .. 5 5
374 15 c. } "Christ crowned with Thorns" (detail, .. 10 12
375 15 c. } Van Dyck) 10 12
376 25 c. } "The Passion of Christ" (detail, .. 15 20
377 25 c. } Memling) 15 20
378 60 c. } "Christ in the Tomb" (detail, Rubens) .. 35 45
379 60 c. } .. 35 45
372/9 .. .. *Set of* 8 1·10 1·50
MS380 120 × 140 mm. Nos. 376/9 .. .. 1·10 1·50
Nos. 372/9 were issued with each design spread over two *se-tenant* stamps of the same denomination.

149 Girl with Kittens in Pram

(Des A. Robledo. Litho Questa)

1970 (27 May). *Birth Bicentenary of William Wordsworth (poet). "Children and Pets". T* **149** *and similar horiz designs. Multicoloured. P* 11.
381 5 c. Type **149** 15 10
382 15 c. Girl with puppy and kitten 25 15
383 30 c. Boy with fishing rod and cat 45 20
384 60 c. Boys and girls with cats and dogs .. 65 50
MS385 Two sheets each 114 × 126 mm. Nos. 381, 383 and Nos. 382, 384. Imperf .. .. .. 2·00 2·50

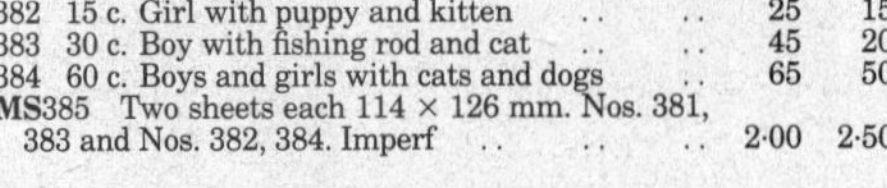

153 Parliament of India

(Des G. Vasarhelyi. Litho Questa)

1970 (15 June). *Seventh Regional Conference of Commonwealth Parliamentary Association. T* **153** *and similar horiz designs. Multicoloured. P* 14
386 5 c. Type **153** 5 5
387 25 c. Parliament of Great Britain, Westminster 10 10
388 50 c. Parliament of Canada 20 20
389 60 c. Parliament of Grenada 20 20
MS390 126 × 90 mm. Nos. 386/9 .. .. .. 80 1·25

157 Tower of the Sun

(Litho Kyodo Printing Co, Tokyo)

1970 (8 Aug). *World Fair, Osaka. T* **157** *and similar multi-coloured designs. P* 13.
391 1 c. Type **157** 5 5
392 2 c. Livelihood and Industry Pavilion (*horiz*) 5 5
393 3 c. Flower painting, 1634 .. .. .. 5 5
394 10 c. "Adam and Eve" (Tintoretto) (*horiz*) .. 10 10
395 25 c. O.E.C.D. (Organisation for Economic Co-operation and Development) Pavilion (*horiz*) 15 15
396 50 c. San Francisco Pavilion 30 40
391/6 .. .. *Set of* 6 60 70
MS397 121 × 91 mm. $1 Japanese Pavilion (56 × 34 *mm*) 75 85

164 Roosevelt and "Raising U.S. Flag on Iwo Jima"

(Litho Questa)

1970 (3 Sept). *25th Anniv of Ending of World War II. T* **164** *and similar horiz designs. Multicoloured. P* 11.
398 ½ c. Type **164** 5 5
399 5 c. Zhukov and "Fall of Berlin" 30 20
400 15 c. Churchill and "Evacuation at Dunkirk" 60 45
401 25 c. De Gaulle and "Liberation of Paris" .. 1·00 95
402 50 c. Eisenhower and "D-Day Landing" .. 2·00 2·00
403 60 c. Montgomery and "Battle of Alamein" .. 2·50 2·50
398/403 .. .. *Set of* 6 6·00 5·50
MS404 163 × 113 mm. Nos. 398, 400, 402/3 .. 6·00 7·00
a. Brown (panel) on 60 c. value omitted ..

(**169**)

170 U.P.U. Emblem, Building and Transport

1970 (18 Sept). *"Philympia 1970" Stamp Exhibition, London. Nos. 353/6 optd with T* **169**
405 25 c. Rocket lifting-off 10 10
a. Albino opt .. .. 10·00
b. Opt inverted .. ..
406 35 c. Spacecraft in orbit 15 15
a. Albino opt .. .. 40·00
407 50 c. Capsule with parachutes 25 30
a. Albino opt .. .. 6·50
408 $1 Type **129** (Sil.) (optd vert upwards) .. 35 60
a. Albino opt .. .. 15·00
The miniature sheet was also overprinted but we understand that only 300 of these were put on sale in Grenada.

(Litho Questa)

1970 (17 Oct). *New U.P.U. Headquarters Building. T* **170** *and similar multicoloured designs. P* 14.
409 15 c. Type **170** 10 10
410 25 c. As Type **170**, but modern transport .. 15 15
411 50 c. Sir Rowland Hill and U.P.U. Building .. 30 35
412 $1 Abraham Lincoln and U.P.U. Building .. 65 95
MS413 79 × 85 mm. Nos. 411/12 .. .. .. 2·00 2·50
The 50 c. and $1 are both vertical designs.

171 "The Madonna of the Goldfinch" (Tiepolo)

172 19th-Century Nursing

(Des G. Vasarhelyi. Litho Questa)

1970 (5 Dec). *Christmas. T* **171** *and similar vert designs. Multi-coloured. P* 13½.
414 ½ c. Type **171** 5 5
415 ½ c. "The Virgin and Child with St. Peter and St. Paul" (Bouts) 5 5
416 ½ c. "The Virgin and Child" (Bellini) .. 5 5
417 2 c. "The Madonna of the Basket" (Correggio) 5 5
418 3 c. Type **171** 5 5
419 35 c. As No. 415 .. .. 30 20
420 50 c. As 2 c. 45 40
421 $1 As No. 416 .. .. 90 60
414/21 .. .. *Set of* 8 1·75 1·25
MS422 102 × 87 mm. Nos. 420/1 .. .. .. 2·50 2·75

(Des G. Vasarhelyi. Litho Questa)

1970 (12 Dec). *Centenary of British Red Cross. T* **172** *and similar horiz designs. Multicoloured. P* 14½ × 14.
423 5 c. Type **172** 15 12
424 15 c. Military Ambulance, 1918 .. .. 20 20
425 25 c. First-Aid Post, 1941 .. .. .. 30 30
426 60 c. Red Cross Transport, 1970 .. .. 75 75
MS427 113 × 82 mm. Nos. 423/6 .. .. 1·50 1·60
a. Error. Imperf .. .. 20·00

173 John Dewey and Art Lesson

(Des G. Vasarhelyi. Litho Questa)

1971 (1 May). *International Education Year* (1970). *T* **173** *and similar horiz designs. Multicoloured. P* 13½.
428 5 c. Type **173** 12 10
429 10 c. Jean-Jacques Rousseau and "Alphabetisation" 20 10
430 50 c. Maimonides and laboratory 60 40
431 $1 Bertrand Russell and mathematics class 1·40 75
MS432 90 × 98 mm. Nos. 430/1 .. .. .. 2·00 2·25

ALTERED CATALOGUE NUMBERS

Any Catalogue numbers altered from the last edition are shown as a list in the introductory pages.

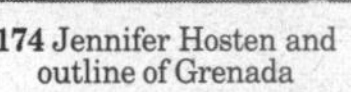

174 Jennifer Hosten and outline of Grenada

176 "Napolean reviewing the Guard" (E. Detaille)

175 French and Canadian Scouts

(Des local artist; adapted G. Drummond. Litho Format)

1971 (1 June). *Winner of "Miss World" Competition* (1970). *P* 13½.
433 **174** 5 c. multicoloured 10 10
434 10 c. multicoloured 20 15
435 15 c. multicoloured 30 25
436 25 c. multicoloured 50 35
437 35 c. multicoloured 80 60
438 50 c. multicoloured .. .. 1·50 1·25
433/8 .. .. *Set of* 6 3·00 2·40
MS439 92 × 89 mm. **174** 50 c. multicoloured. Printed on silk. Imperf .. .. 1·40 1·75

(Litho Format)

1971 (11 Sept). *13th World Scout Jamboree, Asagiri, Japan. T* **175** *and similar horiz designs. Multicoloured. P* 11.
440 5 c. Type **175** 10 8
441 35 c. German and American scouts 45 35
442 50 c. Australian and Japanese scouts.. .. 65 55
443 75 c. Grenada and British scouts 90 80
MS444 101 × 114 mm. Nos. 442/3 .. .. .. 1·90 2·25

(Des G. Vasarhelyi. Litho Questa)

1971 (9 Oct). *150th Death Anniversary of Napolean Bonaparte. T* **176** *and similar vert designs showing paintings. Multicoloured. P* 13½.
445 5 c. Type **176** 15 15
446 15 c. "Napoleon before Madrid" (Vernet) .. 30 30
447 35 c. "Napoleon crossing Mt St. Bernard" (David) 75 75
448 $2 "Napoleon in his Study" (David).. .. 3·00 3·00
MS449 101 × 76 mm. No. 447. Imperf .. .. 1·40 1·60

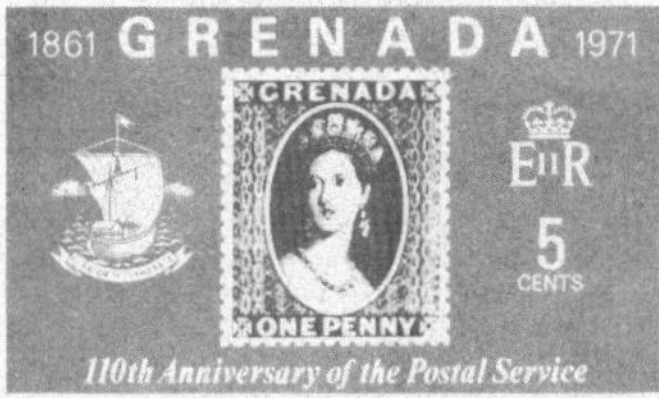

177 1d. Stamp of 1861 and Badge of Grenada

(Des R. Granger Barrett. Litho Questa)

1971 (6 Nov). *110th Anniv of the Postal Service. T* **177** *and similar horiz designs. Multicoloured. W w* **12** (*sideways**). *P* 11.
450 5 c. Type **177** 15 8
451 15 c. 6d. stamp of 1861 and Queen Elizabeth II 25 12
452 35 c. 1d. and 6d. stamps of 1861 and badge of Grenada 60 40
453 50 c. Scroll and 1d. stamp of 1861 .. .. 80 60
MS454 96 × 114 mm. Nos. 452/3 .. .. 1·25 1·60
* This issue is printed on thick paper and consequently the watermark is very faint.

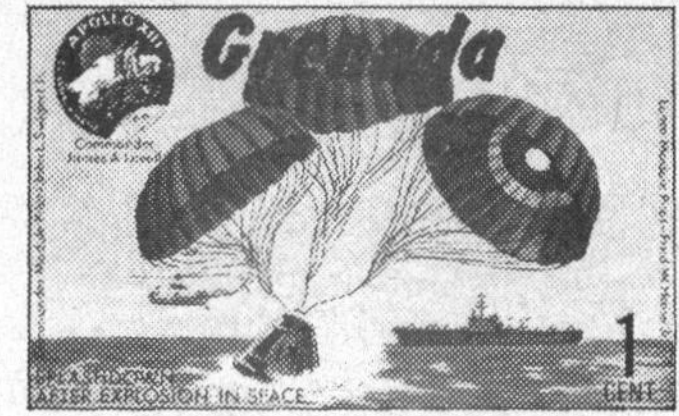

178 Apollo Splashdown

(Des R. Granger Barrett. Litho Questa)

1971 (13 Nov). *Apollo Moon Exploration Series. T* **178** *and similar multicoloured designs. P* 11.
455 1 c. Type **178** 5 5
456 2 c. Recovery of Apollo 13 .. .. .. 5 5
457 3 c. Separation of Lunar Module from Apollo 14.. .. .. 5 5
458 10 c. Shepard and Mitchell taking samples of moon rock 25 20
459 25 c. Moon Buggy 60 45
460 $1 Apollo 15 blast-off (*vert*) .. .. .. 2·00 2·00
455/60 .. .. *Set of* 6 2·75 2·50
MS461 77 × 108 mm. 50 c. as $1 .. .. .. 1·75 2·25

179 67th Regiment of Foot, 1787

180 "The Adoration of the Kings" (Memling)

(Des G. Vasarhelyi. Litho Format)

1971 (11 Dec). *Military Uniforms. T* **179** *and similar vert designs. Multicoloured. P* 13½.
462 ½ c. Type **179** 5 5
463 1 c. 45th Regiment of Foot, 1792 .. .. 5 5
464 2 c. 29th Regiment of Foot, 1794 .. .. 5 5
465 10 c. 9th Regiment of Foot, 1801 .. .. 45 45
466 25 c. 2nd Regiment of Foot, 1815 .. .. 85 85
467 $1 70th Regiment of Foot, 1764 .. .. 2·50 2·50
462/7 .. .. *Set of* 6 3·50 3·50
MS468 108 × 99 mm. Nos. 466/7. P 15 .. .. 4·50 4·50

(Des G. Vasarhelyi. Litho Questa)

1972 (15 Jan). *Christmas* (1971). *T* **180** *and similar vert designs. Multicoloured. P* 14 × 13½.
469 15 c. Type **180** 20 20
470 25 c. "Madonna and Child" (Michelangelo) .. 30 30
471 50 c. "Madonna and Child" (Murillo) 40 40
472 50 c. "The Virgin with the Apple" (Memling) 55 55
MS473 105 × 80 mm. $1 "The Adoration of the Kings" (Mostaert) .. .. 1·40 1·60

═ 35c (Olympic rings)

WINTER OLYMPICS FEB. 3-13, 1972 SAPPORO, JAPAN

(181)

VOTE FEB. 28 1972

(182)

1972 (3 Feb). *Winter Olympic Games, Sapporo, Japan. Nos.* 462/4 *and* **MS**468 *surch or optd only* (**MS**475).

(*a*) *Postage. As T* 181
474 $2 on 2 c. multicoloured .. .. .. 1·60 1·75
MS475 108 × 99 mm. Nos. 466/7 (R.) .. .. 2·50 2·75

(*b*) *Air. As T* 181, *but additionally surch* "AIR MAIL"
476 35 c. on ½ c. multicoloured 35 40
477 50 c. on 1 c. multicoloured 45 50

1972 (25 Feb). *General Election. Nos.* 307/8, 310 *and* 315 *optd with T* **182**.
478 2 c. multicoloured 10 10
479 3 c. multicoloured 10 10
a. Opt inverted .. ..
480 6 c. multicoloured 20 20
481 25 c. multicoloured 40 50

183 King Arthur

(Litho Questa)

1972 (4 Mar). *U.N.I.C.E.F. T* **183** *and similar multicoloured designs. P* 14.
482 ½ c. Type **183** 5 5
483 1 c. Robin Hood 5 5
484 2 c. Robinson Crusoe (*vert*) 5 5
485 25 c. Type **183** 20 20
486 50 c. As No. 483 .. .. 40 40
487 75 c. As No. 484 .. .. 60 60
488 $1 Mary and her little lamb (*vert*) 90 90
482/8 .. .. *Set of* 7 2·00 2·00
MS489 65 × 98 mm. No. 488 .. .. .. 1·25 1·40

INTERPEX 1972

(184)

═ 12¢

(185)

AIR MAIL

(186)

1972 (17 Mar). *"Interpex" Stamp Exhibition, New York. Nos.* 433/9 *optd with T* **184**.
490 **174** 5 c. multicoloured 8 8
491 10 c. multicoloured 10 10
492 15 c. multicoloured 20 15
493 25 c. multicoloured 30 20
494 35 c. multicoloured 40 30
495 50 c. multicoloured 60 45
a. Vert pair, top stamp with opt omitted £100
490/5 .. .. *Set of* 6 1·50 1·10
MS496 92 × 89 mm. **174** 50 c. multicoloured. Printed on silk. Imperf .. .. 11·00 13·00

1972 (20 Apr). *Nos.* 306/8 *surch with T* **185**, *and No.* 433 *surch similarly, but with obliterating bars under* "12c".
497 12 c. on 1 c. Type **88** 40 40
498 12 c. on 2 c. Strelitzia 40 40
499 12 c. on 3 c. Bougainvillea 40 40
500 12 c. on 5 c. Type **174** 40 40

1972. *Air.* (*a*) *Nos.* 306/12, 314*a*/17 *and* 318/21 *optd as T* **186** *or surch in addition* (2 May)
501 5 c. Rock Hind 5 5
a. Opt double .. ..
502 8 c. Snapper 8 8
a. Opt double .. ..
503 10 c. Giant Toad 10 8
a. Opt double .. .. 40·00
504 15 c. Thunbergia 15 10
505 25 c. Opossum 30 20
a. Horiz pair, one without opt .. ..
506 30 c. on 1 c. Type **86** 35 25
507 35 c. Armadillo 35 25
508 40 c. on 2 c. Strelitzia 40 25
509 45 c. on 3 c. Bougainvillea 45 35
510 50 c. Mona Monkey 45 35
a. Horiz pair, one without opt .. .. 70·00
511 60 c. on 5 c. Rock Hind 50 40
512 70 c. on 6 c. Sailfish 60 50
513 $1 Bananaquit 95 60
514 $1.35 on 8 c. Snapper .. .. .. 1·50 85
515 $2 Brown Pelican .. .. 2·25 1·50
516 $3 Magnificent Frigate Bird .. .. 3·25 2·25
517 $5 Bare-eyed Thrush .. .. .. 4·50 4·50

(*b*) *Nos.* 440/3 *optd as T* **186** (5 June)
518 **175** 5 c. multicoloured 8 8
519 – 35 c. multicoloured 35 30
520 – 50 c. multicoloured 45 45
521 – 75 c. multicoloured 70 70
501/21 .. .. *Set of* 21 16·00 12·00

187 Yachting

(Litho Format)

1972 (8 Sept) *Olympic Games, Munich. T* **187** *and similar multicoloured designs. P* 14. (*a*) *Postage.*
522 ½ c. Type **187** 5 5
523 1 c. Show-jumping 5 5
524 2 c. Running (*vert*) 5 5
525 35 c. As 2 c. 60 35
526 50 c. As 1 c. 90 55

(*b*) *Air*
527 25 c. Boxing 40 25
528 $1 As 25 c. .. .. 1·75 1·00
522/8 .. .. *Set of* 7 3·50 2·00
MS529 82 × 85 mm. 60 c. as 25 c. and 70 c. as 1 c. 1·60 2·00

188 Badge of Grenada and Nutmegs

(Des (from photographs by D. Groves) and photo Harrison)

1972 (20 Nov). *Royal Silver Wedding. Multicoloured; background colour given. W w* **12**. *P* 14 × 14½.
530 **188** 8 c. olive-brown 12 12
531 $1 ultramarine 55 65

MINIMUM PRICE

The minimum price quoted is 5p which represents a handling charge rather than a basis for valuing common stamps. For further notes about prices see introductory pages.

189 Boy Scout Saluting　　190 Madonna and Child

(Des R. Granger Barrett. Litho Questa)

1972 (2 Dec). *65th Anniv of Boy Scouts. T* **189** *and similar horiz designs. Multicoloured. P* 14. (*a*) *Postage.*

532 ½ c. Type **189** 5 5
533 1 c. Scouts knotting ropes .. 5 5
534 2 c. Scouts shaking hands .. 5 5
535 3 c. Lord Baden-Powell .. 5 5
536 75 c. As 2 c. .. 1·50 95
537 $1 As 3 c. .. 1·75 1·25

(*b*) *Air*

538 25 c. Type **189** .. 60 40
539 35 c. As 1 c. .. 80 50
532/9 .. *Set of* 8 4·25 3·00
MS540 87 × 88 mm. 60 c. as 3 c., and 70 c. as 2 c. 3·00 3·00

(Des V. Whiteley. Litho Format)

1972 (9 Dec). *Christmas. T* **190** *and similar vert designs. Multicoloured. P* 13½.

541 1 c. Type **190** .. 5 5
542 3 c. The Three Kings .. 5 5
543 5 c. The Nativity .. 5 5
544 25 c. Type **190** .. 20 20
545 35 c. As 3 c. .. 25 25
546 $1 As 5 c. .. 75 75
541/6 .. *Set of* 6 1·25 1·25
MS547 102 × 76 mm. 60 c. Type **190** and 70 c. as 3 c. P 15 .. 1·25 1·75

191 Greater Flamingoes

(Des M. and G. Shamir. Litho Questa)

1973 (26 Jan). *National Zoo. T* **191** *and similar horiz designs. Multicoloured. P* 14½.

548 25 c. Type **191** .. 70 50
549 35 c. Tapir .. 80 65
550 60 c. Blue and Yellow Macaw, and Scarlet Macaw .. 1·40 1·25
551 70 c. Leopard .. 1·50 1·50

192 Class II Racing Yacht

(Des V. Whiteley. Litho Format)

1973 (26 Feb). *Yachting. T* **192** *and similar horiz designs. Multicoloured. P* 13½.

552 25 c. Type **192** .. 45 30
553 35 c. Harbour, St George's .. 55 40
554 60 c. Yacht *Bloodhound* .. 85 75
555 70 c. St. George's .. 1·00 90

193 Helios (Greek god) and Earth orbiting the Sun

(Des G. Vasarhelyi. Litho Format)

1973 (6 July). *I.M.O./W.M.O. Centenary. T* **193** *and similar horiz designs showing Greek Gods. Multicoloured. P* 13½.

556 ½ c. Type **193** .. 5 5
557 1 c. Poseidon and "Normad" storm detector 5 5
558 2 c. Zeus and radarscope .. 5 5
559 3 c. Iris and weather balloon .. 5 5
560 35 c. Hermes and "ATS-3" satellite .. 40 30
561 50 c. Zephyrus and diagram of pressure zones 55 50
562 75 c. Demeter and space photo .. 80 75
563 $1 Selene and rainfall diagram .. 95 1·00
556/63 .. *Set of* 8 2·50 2·50
MS564 123 × 92 mm. $2 Computer weather map (42 × 31 *mm*). P 13½. .. 1·75 1·90

194 Racing Class Yachts　　195 Ignatius Semmelweis (obstetrician)

(Des G. Drummond. Litho Format)

1973 (3 Aug). *Carriacou Regatta. T* **194** *and similar horiz designs. Multicoloured. P* 13½.

565 ½ c. Type **194** .. 5 5
566 1 c. Cruising Class Yacht .. 5 5
567 2 c. Open-decked sloops .. 5 5
568 35 c. *The Mermaid* (sloop) .. 35 35
569 50 c. St. George's Harbour .. 50 50
570 75 c. Map of Carriacou .. 70 70
571 $1 Boat-building .. 90 90
565/71 .. *Set of* 7 2·40 2·40
MS572 109 × 88 mm. $2 End of Race .. 2·25 2·50

(Des G. Vasarhelyi. Litho Format)

1973 (17 Sept). *25th Anniv of W.H.O. T* **195** *and similar vert designs. Multicoloured. P* 14½.

573 ½ c. Type **195** .. 5 5
574 1 c. Louis Pasteur .. 5 5
575 2 c. Edward Jenner .. 5 5
576 3 c. Sigmund Freud .. 5 5
577 25 c. Emil Von Behring (bacteriologist) .. 45 20
578 35 c. Carl Jung .. 55 30
579 50 c. Charles Calmette (bacteriologist) .. 80 40
580 $1 William Harvey .. 1·25 75
573/80 .. *Set of* 8 2·75 1·60
MS581 105 × 80 mm. $2 Marie Curie .. 2·50 2·50

196 Princess Anne and Capt. Mark Phillips　　197 "Virgin and Child" (Maratti)

(Des G. Drummond. Litho Format)

1973 (14 Nov). *Royal Wedding. P* 13½.

582 **196** 25 c. multicoloured .. 15 15
583 $2 multicoloured .. 65 65
MS584 79 × 100 mm. 75 c. and $1 as Nos. 582/3 .. 75 80

(Litho Format)

1973 (10 Dec). *Christmas. T* **197** *and similar vert designs. Multicoloured. P* 14½.

585 ½ c. Type **197** .. 5 5
586 1 c. "Madonna and Child" (Crivelli) .. 5 5
587 2 c. "Virgin and Child with Two Angels" (Verrocchio) .. 5 5
588 3 c. "Adoration of the Shepherds" (Roberti) .. 5 5
589 25 c. "The Holy Family with the Infant Baptist" (Baroccio) .. 15 15
590 35 c. "The Holy Family" (Bronzino) .. 25 25
591 75 c. "Mystic Nativity" (Botticelli) .. 60 60
592 $1 "Adoration of the Kings" (Geertgen) .. 75 75
585/92 .. *Set of* 8 1·75 1·75
MS593 89 × 89 mm. $2 "Adoration of the Kings" (Mostaert) (30 × 45 *mm*). P 13½ .. 1·60 1·90

INDEPENDENT

INDEPENDENCE
7TH FEB. 1974

(198)

199 Creative Arts Theatre, Jamaica Campus

1974 (7 Feb). *Independence. Nos.* 306/9, 311/13, 315/16 *and* 317*a*/21 *optd as T* **198**

594 1 c. Hibiscus .. 5 5
595 2 c. Strelitzia .. 8 5
596 3 c. Bougainvillea .. 10 8
597 5 c. Rock Hind .. 10 8
598 8 c. Snapper .. 15 12
599 10 c. Giant Toad .. 20 15
600 12 c. Turtle .. 20 15
601 25 c. Opossum .. 45 35
602 35 c. Armadillo .. 75 50
603 75 c. Yacht in St. George's Harbour .. 2·00 1·25
604 $1 Bananaquit .. 5·00 1·50
605 $2 Brown Pelican .. 10·00 3·50
606 $3 Magnificent Frigate Bird .. 16·00 5·00
607 $5 Bare-eyed Thrush .. 25·00 9·50
594/607 .. *Set of* 14 55·00 20·00

(Des G. Drummond. Litho Format)

1974 (10 Apr). *25th Anniv of University of West Indies. T* **199** *and similar multicoloured designs. P* 13½ × 14.

608 10 c. Type **199** .. 10 8
609 25 c. Marryshow House .. 15 15
610 50 c. Chapel, Jamaica Campus (*vert*) .. 35 35
611 $1 University arms (*vert*) .. 55 60
MS612 69 × 86 mm. $2 as No. 611 .. 1·25 1·75

200 Nutmeg Pods and Scarlet Mace　　201 Footballers (West Germany v Chile)

(Des G. Drummond. Litho Format)

1974 (19 Aug). *Independence.* T **200** *and similar vert designs. Multicoloured. P* 13½.

613 3 c. Type **200** .. 5 5
614 8 c. Map of Grenada .. 8 8
615 25 c. Prime Minister Eric Gairy .. 25 25
616 35 c. Grand Anse Beach and flag .. 30 30
617 $1 Coat of arms .. 75 50
MS618 91 × 125 mm. $2 as $1 .. 1·50 2·00

(Des G. Vasarhelyi. Litho Format)

1974 (3 Sept). *World Cup Football Championships, West Germany. T* **201** *and similar multicoloured designs showing footballers of the countries given. P* 14½.

619 ½ c. Type **201** .. 5 5
620 1 c. East Germany v Australia .. 5 5
621 2 c. Yugoslavia v Brazil .. 5 5
622 10 c. Scotland v Zaire .. 10 5
623 25 c. Netherlands v Uruguay .. 25 15
624 50 c. Sweden v Bulgaria .. 40 25
625 75 c. Italy v Haiti .. 60 35
626 $1 Poland v Argentina .. 80 50
619/26 .. *Set of* 8 2·00 1·25
MS627 114 × 76 mm. $2 Country flags. P 13 .. 1·75 1·90

202 Early U.S. Mail-trains and "Concorde"

(Des G. Vasarhelyi. Litho Format)

1974 (8 Oct). *Centenary of Universal Postal Union. T* **202** *and similar horiz designs. Multicoloured. P* 14½.

628 ½ c. Type **202** .. 5 5
629 1 c. Mailboat *Caesar* (1839) and helicopter .. 5 5
630 2 c. Airmail transport .. 5 5
631 8 c. Pigeon post (1480) and telephone dial .. 15 10
632 15 c. 18th-century bellman and tracking antenna .. 20 15
633 25 c. Messenger (1450) and satellite .. 30 25
634 35 c. French pillar-box (1850) and mail-boat .. 50 40
635 $1 18th-century German postman and mail-train of the future .. 1·40 1·00
628/35 .. *Set of* 8 2·40 1·90
MS636 105 × 66 mm. $2 St. Gotthard mail-coach (1735). P 13 .. 1·75 2·00

203 Sir Winston Churchill　　204 "Madonna and Child of the Eucharist" (Botticelli)

(Des G. Vasarhelyi. Litho Format)

1974 (28 Oct). *Birth Centenary of Sir Winston Churchill. T* **203** *and similar portrait design. P* 13½.

637 **203** 35 c. multicoloured .. 35 35
638 – $2 multicoloured .. 1·25 1·25
MS639 129 × 96 mm. 75 c. as 35 c. and $1 as $2 1·10 1·50

(Des. M. Shamir. Litho Format)

1974 (18 Nov). *Christmas. T* **204** *and similar vert designs, showing "The Madonna and Child" by the artists given. Multicoloured. P* 14½.

640 ½ c. Type **204** . . 5 5
641 1 c. Niccolo di Pietro . . 5 5
642 2 c. Van der Weyden . . 5 5
643 3 c. Bastiani . . 5 5
644 10 c. Giovanni . . 8 8
645 25 c. Van der Weyden . . 30 20
646 50 c. Botticelli . . 45 35
647 $1 Mantegna . . 90 65
640/7 . . *Set of* 8 1·75 1·40
MS648 117 × 96 mm. $2 as 1 c. P 13 . . 1·75 1·90

205 Yachts, Port Saline

(Des G. Drummond. Litho Format)

1975 (13 Jan)–**78**. *Multicoloured designs as T* **205**. A. *P* 14½ (½ *to* 50 *c.*) *or* 13½ (75 *c. to* $10). B. *P* 13.

		A		B	
649	½ c. Type **205**	5	5	†	
650	1 c. Yacht club race	5	5	5	5
651	2 c. Carenage taxi	5	5	5	5
652	3 c. Large working boats	10	5	10	5
653	5 c. Deep-water dock	10	5	10	5
654	6 c. Cocoa beans in drying trays	10	5	10	5
655	8 c. Nutmegs	10	5	†	
656	10 c. Rum distillery, River Antoine Estate, *c* 1785	10	5	15	10
657	12 c. Cocoa tree	10	5	†	
658	15 c. Fishermen at Fontenoy	10	8	15	12
659	20 c. Parliament Building, St. George's	12	12	20	20
660	25 c. Fort George cannons	20	15	25	25
661	35 c. Pearls Airport	20	15	†	—
662	50 c. General Post Office	30	30	45	45
663	75 c. Carib's Leap, Sauteurs Bay (45 × 28 *mm*)	45	45	†	
664	$1 Carenage, St. George's (45 × 28 mm)	65	65	†	
665	$2 St. George's Harbour by night (45 × 28 mm)	1·25	1·50	†	
666	$3 Grand Anse Beach (45 × 28 *mm*)	1·75	2·50	†	
667	$5 Canoe Bay and Black Bay from Point Saline Lighthouse (45 × 28 *mm*)	2·50	3·25	†	
668	$10 Sugar-loaf Island from Levera Beach (45 × 28 *mm*)	6·00	6·00	†	
649/68	*Set of* 20	13·00	14·00	†	

Dates of issue: A. Perf 13½—13.1.75, ½ c. to 50 c.; 22.1.75, 75 c. to $5; 26.3.75, $10. B. Perf 13—1978

206 Sail-fish

(Des V. Whiteley. Litho Format)

1975 (3 Feb). *Big Game Fishing. T* **206** *and similar horiz designs. Multicoloured. P* 14½.

669 ½ c. Type **206** . . 5 5
670 1 c. Blue Marlin . . 5 5
671 2 c. White Marlin . . 5 5
672 10 c. Yellowfin Tuna . . 10 5
673 25 c. Wahoo . . 25 15
674 50 c. Dolphin . . 45 25
675 70 c. Grouper . . 70 45
676 $1 Great Barracuda . . 90 60
669/76 . . *Set of* 8 2·25 1·50
MS677 107 × 80 mm. $2 Blue Pointer or Mako Shark. P 13 . . 1·60 1·75

207 Granadilla Barbadine

208 Dove, Grenada Flag and U.N. Emblem

(Des G. Vasarhelyi. Litho Format)

1975 (26 Feb). *Flowers. T* **207** *and similar horiz designs. Multicoloured. P* 14½.

678 ½ c. Type **207** . . 5 5
679 1 c. Bleeding Heart (Easter Lily) . . 5 5
680 2 c. Poinsettia . . 5 5
681 3 c. Cocoa flower . . 5 5
682 10 c. Gladioli . . 15 5
683 25 c. Redhead/Yellowhead . . 35 15
684 50 c. Plumbago . . 60 25
685 $1 Orange flower . . 95 50
678/85 . . *Set of* 8 2·00 1·00
MS686 102 × 82 mm. $2 Barbados Gooseberry. P 13 . . 1·75 1·75

(Des G. Drummond. Litho Format)

1975 (19 Mar). *Grenada's Admission to the U.N.* (1974). *T* **208** *and similar vert designs. Multicoloured. P* 14½.

687 ½ c. Type **208** . . 5 5
688 1 c. Grenada and U.N. flags . . 5 5
689 2 c. Grenada coat of arms . . 5 5
690 35 c. U.N. emblem over map of Grenada . . 20 15
691 50 c. U.N. buildings and flags . . 30 25
692 $2 U.N. emblem and scroll . . 75 80
687/92 . . *Set of* 6 1·25 1·25
MS693 122 × 91 mm. 75 c. Type **208** and $1 as 2 c. P 13 . . 1·00 1·25

CANCELLED REMAINDERS*. Some of the following issues have been remaindered, cancelled-to-order, at a fraction of their face-value. For all practical purposes these are indistinguishable from genuine postally used copies. Our used quotations which are indicated by an asterisk are the same for cancelled-to-order or postally used copies.

209 Paul Revere's Midnight Ride

210 "Blood of the Redeemer" (G. Bellini)

(Des J. Cornel (½ to 10 c.), PAD Studio (40 c. to $1), J.W. (**MS**704). Litho Format)

1975 (6 May). *Bicentenary of American Revolution* (1*st issue*). *T* **209** *and similar multicoloured designs. P* 14½.

(*a*) *Postage. Horiz designs*

694 ½ c. Type **209** . . 5 5*
695 1 c. Crispus Attucks . . 5 5*
696 2 c. Patrick Henry . . 5 5*
697 3 c. Franklin visits Washington . . 5 5*
698 5 c. Rebel troops . . 8 5*
699 10 c. John Paul Jones . . 10 5*

(*b*) *Air. Vert designs*

700 40 c. "John Hancock" (Copley) . . 40 12*
701 50 c. "Benjamin Franklin" (Roslin) . . 55 15*
702 75 c. "John Adams" (Copley) . . 75 20*
703 $1 "Lafayette" (Casanova) . . 90 25*
694/703 . . *Set of* 10 2·50 70*
MS704 Two sheets 131 × 102 mm: $2 Grenada arms and U.S. seal; $2 Grenada and U.S. flags. P 13½ . . 3·50 60*

Stamps from **MS**704 are horiz and larger: 47½ × 35mm.

Nos. 694/703 also exist perf 13 (*Price for set of* 10 £2.50 *mint or used*) from additional sheetlets of 5 stamps and 1 label. Stamps perforated 14½ are from normal sheets of 40.

See also Nos. 785/92.

(Des M. Shamir. Litho Format)

1975 (21 May). *Easter. T* **210** *and similar vert designs. Multicoloured. P* 14½.

705 ½ c. Type **210** . . 5 5*
706 1 c. "Pietà" (Bellini) . . 5 5*
707 2 c. "The Entombment" (Van der Weyden) . . 5 5*
708 3 c. "Pietà" (Bellini) . . 5 5*
709 35 c. "Pietà" (Bellini) . . 25 8*
710 75 c. "The Dead Christ" (Bellini) . . 60 10*
711 $1 "The Dead Christ supported by Angels" (Procaccini) . . 85 12*
705/11 . . *Set of* 7 1·75 40*
MS712 117 × 100 mm. $2 "Pietà" (Botticelli). P 13 1·50 30*

211 Wildlife Study

212 Leafy Jewel Box

(Des J.W. Litho Format)

1975 (2 July). *14th World Scout Jamboree, Norway. T* **211** *and similar horiz designs. Multicoloured. P* 14.

713 ½ c. Type **211** . . 5 5*
714 1 c. Sailing . . 5 5*
715 2 c. Map-reading . . 5 5*
716 35 c. First-aid . . 40 5*
717 40 c. Physical training . . 45 8*
718 75 c. Mountaineering . . 75 12*
719 $2 Sing-song . . 1·90 30*
713/19 . . *Set of* 7 3·25 60*
MS720 106 × 80 mm. $1 Boat-building . . 1·25 20*

(Des J.W. Litho Questa)

1975 (1 Aug). *Seashells. T* **212** *and similar vert designs. Multicoloured. P* 14.

721 ½ c. Type **212** . . 5 5*
722 1 c. Emerald Nerite . . 5 5*
723 2 c. Yellow Cockle . . 5 5*
724 25 c. Purple Sea Snail . . 40 5*
725 50 c. Turkey Wing . . 70 8*
726 75 c. West Indian Fighting Conch . . 1·25 12*
727 $1 Noble Wentletrap . . 1·50 20*
721/7 . . *Set of* 7 3·50 50*
MS728 102 × 76 mm. $2 Music Volute . . 2·00 30*

213 Lady or Large Tiger

214 Rowing

(Des J.W. Litho Format)

1975 (22 Sept). *Butterflies. T* **213** *and similar vert designs. Multicoloured. P* 14.

729 ½ c. Type **213** . . 5 5*
730 1 c. Five Continent . . 5 5*
731 2 c. Large Striped Blue . . 5 5*
732 35 c. Gonatryx . . 40 5*
733 45 c. Spear-winged Cattleheart . . 45 10*
734 75 c. Rusty Nymula . . 85 15*
735 $2 Blue Night . . 2·00 30*
729/35 . . *Set of* 7 3·50 60*
MS736 108 × 83 mm. $1 *Papilio lycophron* . . 90 20*

(Des J.W. Litho Questa)

1975 (13 Oct). *Pan-American Games, Mexico City. T* **214** *and similar vert designs. Multicoloured. P* 14.

737 ½ c. Type **214** . . 5 5*
738 1 c. Swimming . . 5 5*
739 2 c. Show-jumping . . 5 5*
740 35 c. Gymnastics . . 15 5*
741 45 c. Football . . 20 10*
742 75 c. Boxing . . 40 15*
743 $2 Cycling . . 1·00 30*
737/43 . . *Set of* 7 1·75 60*
MS744 106 × 81 mm. $1 Yachting . . 80 20*

215 "The Boy David" (Michelangelo)

216 "Madonna and Child" (Filippino Lippi)

(Des M. and G. Shamir. Litho J.W.)

1975 (3 Nov). *500th Birth Anniv of Michelangelo. T* **215** *and similar vert designs. Multicoloured. P* 14.

745 ½ c. Type **215** . . 5 5*
746 1 c. "Young Man" (detail) . . 5 5*
747 2 c. "Moses" . . 5 5*
748 40 c. "Prophet Zachariah" . . 30 8*
749 50 c. "St John the Baptist" . . 35 10*
750 75 c. "Judith and Holofernes" . . 65 15*
751 $2 "Doni Madonna" (detail from "Holy Family") . . 1·60 35*
745/51 . . *Set of* 7 2·75 60*
MS752 104 × 89 mm. $1 "Madonna" (head from Pietà) . . 90 20*

The sculpture on No. 749 though ascribed to Michelangelo, shows a work by Francesco Sangallo.

(Des M. Shamir. Litho Questa)

1975 (8 Dec). *Christmas. T* **216** *and similar vert designs showing "Virgin and Child". Multicoloured. P* 14.

753 ½ c. Type **216** . . 5 5*
754 1 c. Mantegna . . 5 5*
755 2 c. Luis de Morales . . 5 5*
756 35 c. G. M. Morandi . . 20 8*
757 50 c. Antonello da Messina . . 25 10*
758 75 c. Dürer . . 45 15*
759 $1 Velasquez . . 60 15*
753/9 . . *Set of* 7 1·50 45*
MS760 125 × 98 mm. $2 Bellini . . 1·25 30*

217 Bananaquit **218** Carnival Time

(Des G. Drummond. Litho Questa)

1976 (20 Jan). *Flora and Fauna. T* **217** *and similar multicoloured designs. P* 14.
761 ½ c. Type **217** . . 5 5
762 1 c. Orange-rumped Agouti . . 5 5
763 2 c. Hawksbill Turtle (*horiz*) . . 5 5
764 5 c. Dwarf Poinciana . . 10 10
765 35 c. Albacore (*horiz*) . . 90 45
766 40 c. Cardinal's Guard . . 95 50
767 $2 Antillean Armadillo (*horiz*) . . 4·00 2·50
761/67 . . *Set of* 7 5·50 3·25
MS768 82 × 89 mm. $1 Belted Kingfisher . . 2·00 1·75

(Des G. Drummond. Litho Questa)

1976 (25 Feb). *Tourism. T* **218** *and similar horiz designs. Multicoloured. P* 14.
769 ½ c. Type **218** . . 5 5
770 1 c. Scuba diving . . 5 5
771 2 c. Cruise Ship *Southward* at St. George's . . 5 5
772 35 c. Game fishing . . 40 20
773 50 c. St. George's Golf Course . . 60 35
774 75 c. Tennis . . 85 55
775 $1 Ancient rock carvings at Mount Rich 1·10 75
769/75 . . *Set of* 7 2·75 1·75
MS776 100 × 73 mm. $2 Small boat sailing . . 2·00 1·50

219 "Pietà" (Master of Okolicsno) **220** Sharpshooters

(Des M. and G. Shamir. Litho Questa)

1976 (29 Mar). *Easter. T* **219** *and similar vert designs by the artists listed. Multicoloured. P* 14.
777 ½ c. Type **219** . . 5 5
778 1 c. Correggio . . 5 5
779 2 c. Van der Weyden . . 5 5
780 3 c. Dürer . . 5 5
781 35 c. Master of the Holy Spirit . . 25 15
782 75 c. Raphael . . 45 40
783 $1 Raphael . . 60 50
777/83 . . *Set of* 7 1·25 1·00
MS784 108 × 86 mm. $2 Crespi . . 1·25 1·25

(Des J.W. Litho Questa)

1976 (15 Apr). *Bicentenary of American Revolution (2nd issue). T* **220** *and similar vert designs. Multicoloured. P* 14.
785 ½ c. Type **220** . . 5 5
786 1 c. Defending the Liberty Pole . . 5 5
787 2 c. Loading muskets . . 5 5
788 35 c. The fight for Liberty . . 40 30
789 50 c. Peace Treaty, 1783 . . 60 40
790 $1 Drummers . . 1·25 80
791 $3 Gunboat . . 2·75 2·25
785/91 . . *Set of* 7 4·50 3·50
MS792 93 × 79 mm. 75 c. as 35 c. and $2 as 50 c. 3·00 3·00

221 Nature Study **222** Volleyball

(Des G. Vasarhelyi. Litho Questa)

1976 (1 June). *50th Anniv of Girl Guides in Grenada. T* **221** *and similar vert designs. Multicoloured. P* 14.
793 ½ c. Type **221** . . 5 5
794 1 c. Campfire cooking . . 5 5
795 2 c. First Aid . . 5 5
796 50 c. Camping . . 55 25
797 75 c. Home economics . . 85 40
798 $2 First Aid . . 3·00 1·50
793/8 . . *Set of* 6 4·25 2·00
MS799 111 × 85 mm. $1 Painting . . 1·25 1·25

(Des J.W. Litho Questa)

1976 (21 June). *Olympic Games, Montreal. T* **222** *and similar vert designs. Multicoloured. P* 14.
800 ½ c. Type **222** 5 5
801 1 c. Cycling . . 5 5
802 2 c. Rowing . . 5 5
803 35 c. Judo . . 20 20
804 45 c. Hockey . . 25 25
805 75 c. Gymnastics . . 55 50
806 $1 High jump . . 80 75
800/6 . . *Set of* 7 1·75 1·60
MS807 106 × 81 mm. $3 Equestrian event . . 2·25 2·25

223 "Cha-U-Kao at the Moulin Rouge" **224** Piper "Apache"

(Des M. Shamir. Litho Questa)

1976 (20 July). *75th Death Anniv of Toulouse Lautrec. T* **223** *and similar vert designs. Multicoloured. P* 14.
808 ½ c. Type **223** . . 5 5
809 1 c. "Quadrille at the Moulin Rouge" . . 5 5
810 2 c. "Profile of a Woman" . . 5 5
811 3 c. "Salon in the Rue des Moulins" . . 5 5
812 40 c. "The Laundryman" . . 40 25
813 50 c. "Marcelle Lender dancing the Bolero" . . 45 30
814 $2 "Signor Boileau at the Cafe" . . 1·75 1·25
808/14 . . *Set of* 7 2·50 1·75
MS815 152 × 125 mm. $1 "Woman with Boa" . . 75 75

1976 (26 July). *West Indian Victory in World Cricket Cup. As Nos.* 559/60 *of Barbados.*
816 35 c. Map of the Caribbean . . 75 35
817 $1 The Prudential Cup . . 2·25 1·50

(Des J.W. Litho Questa)

1976 (18 Aug). *Aeroplanes. T* **224** *and similar horiz designs. Multicoloured. P* 14.
818 ½ c. Type **224** . . 5 5
819 1 c. Beech "Twin Bonanza" . . 5 5
820 2 c. D.H. "Twin Otter" . . 5 5
821 40 c. Britten Norman "Islander" . . 55 35
822 50 c. D.H. "Heron" . . 65 45
823 $2 H.S. "748" . . 2·50 1·75
818/23 . . *Set of* 6 3·50 2·40
MS824 75 × 83 mm. $3 B.A.C. "1-11" . . 2·50 2·50

225 Satellite Assembly **226** S.S. *Geestland*

(Des PAD Studio. Litho Questa)

1976 (1 Sept). *Viking and Helios Space Missions. T* **225** *and similar multicoloured designs. P* 14.
825 ½ c. Type **225** . . 5 5
826 1 c. Helios satellite . . 5 5
827 2 c. Helios encapsulation . . 5 5
828 15 c. Systems test . . 15 8
829 45 c. Viking lander (*horiz*) . . 25 25
830 75 c. Lander on Mars . . 45 45
831 $2 Viking encapsulation . . 1·25 1·25
825/31 . . *Set of* 7 2·00 2·00
MS832 110 × 85 mm. $3 Orbiter and lander . . 1·50 1·90

(Des J.W. Litho Format)

1976 (3 Nov). *Ships. T* **226** *and similar horiz designs. Multicoloured. P* 14½.
833 ½ c. Type **226** . . 5 5
834 1 c. M. V. *Federal Palm* . . 5 5
835 2 c. H.M.S. *Blake* . . 5 5
836 25 c. M. V. *Vistafjord* . . 35 25
837 75 c. S.S. *Canberra* . . 90 70
838 $1 S.S. *Regina* . . 1·25 80
839 $5 S.S. *Arandora Star* . . 5·50 4·25
833/39 . . *Set of* 7 7·50 5·50
MS840 91 × 78 mm. $2 *Santa Maria* . . 2·00 2·25

227 "Altarpiece of San Barnaba" (Botticelli)

(Des PAD Studio. Litho Questa)

1976 (8 Dec). *Christmas. T* **227** *and similar horiz designs. Multicoloured. P* 14.
841 ½ c. Type **227** . . 5 5
842 1 c. "Annunciation" (Botticelli) . . 5 5
843 2 c. "Madonna of Chancellor Rolin" (Jan van Eyck) . . 5 5
844 35 c. "Annunciation" (Fra Filippo Lippi) 15 15
845 50 c. "Madonna of the Magnificat" (Botticelli) 30 30
846 75 c. "Madonna of the Pomegranate" (Botticelli) . . 40 40
847 $3 "Madonna with St. Cosmas and Other Saints" (Botticelli) . . 1·50 1·50
841/7 . . *Set of* 7 2·25 2·25
MS848 71 × 57 mm. $2 "Gypsy Madonna" (Titian) 1·10 1·25

228 Alexander Graham Bell and Telephones **229** Coronation Scene

(Des G. Vasarhelyi. Litho Questa)

1976 (17 Dec). *Telephone Centenary. T* **228** *and similar horiz designs. Multicoloured. P* 14.
849 ½ c. Type **228** . . 5 5
850 1 c. Telephone-users within globe . . 5 5
851 2 c. Telephone satellite . . 5 5
852 18 c. Telephone viewer and console . . 12 12
853 40 c. Satellite and tracking stations . . 35 35
854 $1 Satellite transmitting to ships . . 70 70
855 $2 Dish aerial and modern telephone 1·40 1·40
849/55 . . *Set of* 7 2·40 2·40
MS856 107 × 80 mm. $5 Globe encircled by flags 3·25 3·50

(Des J.W. Litho Questa (Nos. 857/62), Walsall (863/6))

1977 (8 Feb). *Silver Jubilee. T* **229** *and similar vert designs. Multicoloured. (a) Sheet stamps. P* 13½ × 14.
857 ½ c. Type **229** . . 5 5
858 1 c. Sceptre and orb . . 5 5
859 35 c. Queen on horseback . . 30 20
860 $2 Spoon and ampulla . . 85 65
861 $2.50 Queen and Prince Philip . . 95 70
MS862 103 × 79 mm. $5 Royal Visit to Grenada . . 1·90 2·00

Nos. 857/61 also exist perf 11½ × 12 (*Price for set of* 5 *£*2 *mint or used*) from additional sheetlets of 5 stamps and 1 label. They also have different frame colours to those perforated 13½ × 14, which come from normal sheets of 40.

(*b*) *Booklet stamps. Roul* 5 × *imperf**. *Self-adhesive*
863 35 c. As No. 861 . . 25 25
a. Booklet pane of 6 . . 1·50
864 50 c. As No. 860 . . 55 70
a. Booklet pane. Nos. 864/6 . . 4·00
865 $1 As No. 858 . . 1·00 1·50
866 $3 As No. 859 . . 2·75 3·75

*No. 863/6 are separated by various combinations of rotary knife (giving a straight edge) and roulette.

230 Water Skiing

(Des G. Drummond. Litho Questa)

1977 (Apr). *Easter Water Parade. T* **230** *and similar horiz designs. Multicoloured. P* 14.
867 ½ c. Type **230** . . 5 5
868 1 c. Speedboat race . . 5 5
869 2 c. Row boat race . . 5 5
870 22 c. Swimming . . 20 20
871 35 c. Work boat race . . 35 35
872 75 c. Water polo . . 65 65
873 $2 Game fishing . . 1·60 1·60
867/73 . . *Set of* 7 2·75 2·75
MS874 115 × 85 mm. $3 Yacht race . . 2·25 2·25

231 Meeting Place, Grand Anse Beach

(Litho Questa)

1977 (14 June). *Seventh Meeting of Organization of American States. P* 14.
875 **231** 35 c. multicoloured . . 20 20
876 $1 multicoloured . . 55 55
877 $2 multicoloured . . 80 90

232 Rafting

(Des G. Drummond. Litho Questa)

1977 (6 Sept). *Caribbean Scout Jamboree, Jamaica. T* **232** *and similar horiz designs. Multicoloured. P* 14.

878 ½ c. Type **232** 5 5
879 1 c. Tug-of-war 5 5
880 2 c. Sea Scouts regatta 5 5
881 18 c. Camp fire.. .. .. 20 12
882 40 c. Field kitchen 55 35
883 $1 Scouts and sea scouts .. .. .. 1·25 70
884 $2 Hiking and map reading.. .. .. 2·00 1·40
878/84 .. .. *Set of* 7 3·75 2·40
MS885 107 × 85 mm. $3 Semaphore .. .. 2·50 2·50

233 Angel and Shepherd

Royal Visit W. I. 1977
(234)

(Des G. Vasarhelyi. Litho Questa)

1977 (3 Nov). *Christmas. T* **233** *and similar horiz designs showing ceiling panels from the church of St. Martin in Zillis. Multicoloured. P* 14.

886 ½ c. Type **233** 5 5
887 1 c. St. Joseph 5 5
888 2 c. Virgin and Child Fleeing to Egypt .. 5 5
889 22 c. Angel 12 10
890 35 c. A Magus on horseback 20 15
891 75 c. Three horses 45 35
892 $2 Virgin and Child.. .. .. 1·25 95
886/92 .. .. *Set of* 7 1·90 1·50
MS893 85 × 112 mm. $3 Magus offering gifts .. 1·60 1·60

1977 (10 Nov). *Royal Visit. Nos.* 857/62 *optd with T* **234**. *P* 13½ × 14 (35 c. $2.50) *or* 11½ × 12 (*others*).

894 ½ c. Type **229** 5 5
895 1 c. Sceptre and orb 5 5
896 35 c. Queen on horseback 40 20
897 $2 Spoon and ampulla 85 65
898 $2.50, Queen and Prince Philip 90 70
MS899 103 × 79 mm. $5 Royal Visit to Grenada .. 1·90 2·25

Nos. 894/5 only exist perforated 11½ × 12, but the remaining three values come perforated 13½ × 14 or 11½ × 12 (*Nos.* 896/8 *perf* 11½ × 12. *Price for set of* 3 £1.90 *mint or used.*)

235 Christjaan Eijkman (Medicine)
236 Count von Zeppelin and First Zeppelin Airship

(Des J.W. Litho Questa)

1978 (25 Jan). *Nobel Prize Winners. T* **235** *and similar vert designs. Multicoloured. P* 14.

900 ½ c. Type **235** 5 5
901 1 c. Sir Winston Churchill (Literature) .. 5 5
902 2 c. Woodrow Wilson (Peace) 5 5
903 35 c. Frederic Passy (Peace) 30 20
904 $1 Albert Einstein (Physics) 85 50
905 $3 Carl Bosch (Chemistry) .. .. .. 2·25 1·50
900/5 .. .. *Set of* 6 3·25 2·10
MS906 114 × 99 mm. $2 Alfred Nobel .. .. 1·40 1·40

(Des G. Vasarhelyi. Litho Questa)

1978 (13 Feb). *75th Anniv of First Zeppelin Flight and 50th Anniv of Lindbergh's Transatlantic Flight. T* **236** *and similar horiz designs. Multicoloured. P* 14.

907 ½ c. Type **236** 5 5
908 1 c. Lindbergh with *Spirit of St. Louis* .. 5 5
909 2 c. Airship *Deutschland* 5 5
910 22 c. Lindbergh's arrival in France 10 10
911 75 c. Lindbergh and *Spirit of St. Louis* in flight 40 40
912 $1 Zeppelin over Alps 55 55
913 $3 Zeppelin over White House .. .. 1·60 1·60
907/13 .. .. *Set of* 7 2·50 2·50
MS914 103 × 85 mm. 35 c. Lindbergh in cockpit; $2 Count von Zeppelin and airship .. .. .. 1·75 1·90

NEW INFORMATION

The editor is always interested to correspond with people who have new information that will improve or correct the Catalogue.

237 Rocket Launching
238 Black-headed Gull

(Des J.W. Litho Questa)

1978 (28 Feb). *Space Shuttle. T* **237** *and similar vert designs. Multicoloured. P* 14.

915 ½ c. Type **237** 5 5
916 1 c. Booster jettison 5 5
917 2 c. External tank jettison 5 5
918 18 c. Space shuttle in orbit 15 15
919 75 c. Satellite placement 45 45
920 $2 Landing approach .. .. .. 1·25 1·25
915/20 .. .. *Set of* 6 1·75 1·75
MS921 103 × 85 mm. $3 Shuttle after landing .. 1·40 1·50

(Des G. Drummond. Litho Questa)

1978 (9 Mar). *Wild Birds of Grenada. T* **238** *and similar vert designs. Multicoloured. P* 14.

922 ½ c. Type **238** 5 5
923 1 c. Wilson's Petrel 5 5
924 2 c. Killdeer Plover 5 5
925 50 c. White-necked Jacobin 65 40
926 75 c. Blue-faced Booby 90 65
927 $1 Broad-winged Hawk .. .. .. 1·50 1·00
928 $2 Red-necked Pigeon .. .. .. 2·75 2·50
922/8 .. .. *Set of* 7 5·50 4·25
MS929 103 × 94 mm. $3 Scarlet Ibis .. .. 3·50 3·50

239 "The Landing of Marie de Medici at Marseilles"
240 Ludwig van Beethoven

(Des PAD Studio. Litho Questa)

1978 (30 Mar). *400th Birth Anniv of Rubens. T* **239** *and similar vert designs showing paintings. Multicoloured. P* 13½ × 14.

930 5 c. Type **239** 5 5
931 15 c. "Rubens and Isabella Brandt" 8 8
932 18 c. "Marchesa Brigida Spindola-Doria" .. 10 10
933 25 c. "Ludovicus Nonninus" 12 12
934 45 c. "Helene Fourment and her Children" .. 20 20
935 75 c. "Clara Serena Rubens" 35 35
936 $3 "Le Chapeau de Paille" .. .. .. 1·40 1·40
930/6 .. .. *Set of* 7 2·00 2·00
MS937 65 × 100 mm. $5 "Self Portrait" .. .. 2·00 2·10

(Des PAD Studio. Litho Questa)

1978 (24 Apr). *150th Death Anniv of Beethoven. T* **240** *and similar multicoloured designs. P* 14.

938 5 c. Type **240** 8 8
939 15 c. Woman violinist (*horiz*) 12 10
940 18 c. Musical instruments (*horiz*) 20 15
941 22 c. Piano (*horiz*) 20 15
942 50 c. Violins 50 45
943 75 c. Piano and sonata score 70 60
944 $3 Beethoven's portrait and home (*horiz*) 2·75 2·25
938/44 .. .. *Set of* 7 4·00 3·50
MS945 83 × 62 mm. $2 Beethoven and score .. 1·90 1·90

241 King Edward's Chair
242 Queen Elizabeth II taking Salute at Trooping the Colour

(Des J.W. Litho Questa. (Nos. 946/9). Manufactured by Walsall. (Nos. 950/2))

1978 (2 May–14 June). *25th Anniv of Coronation. Multicoloured.*

(*a*) *Sheet stamps. Vert designs as T* **241**. *P* 14 (14 June)

946 35 c. Type **241** 15 20
947 $2 Queen with regalia 85 70
948 $2.50, St. Edward's Crown .. .. .. 1·00 80
MS949 102 × 76 mm. $5 Queen and Prince Philip 2·00 1·75

(*b*) *Booklet stamps. Vert designs as T* **242**. *Roul* 5 × *imperf**. *Self-adhesive* (2 May)

950 25 c. Type **242** 12 15
a. Booklet pane. Nos. 950/1, each × 3 .. 80
951 35 c. Queen taking part in Maundy Thursday ceremony.. .. .. 15 25
952 $5 Queen and Prince Philip at Opening of Parliament .. .. 2·00 2·75
a. Booklet pane of 1 .. .. .. 2·00

Nos. 946/8 also exist perf 12 (*Price for set of* 3 £1·90 *mint or used*) from additional sheetlets of 3 stamps and 1 label, issued 2 June. These have different frame colours from the stamps perforated 14, which come from normal sheets of 50.

*Nos. 950/1 are separated by various combinations of rotary-knife (giving a straight edge) and roulette. No. 952 exists only with straight edges.

243 Goalkeeper reaching for Ball
244 Aerial Phenomena, Germany, 1561 and U.S.A., 1952

(Des M. Rubin. Litho Format)

1978 (1 Aug). *World Cup Football Championship, Argentina. T* **243** *and similar vert designs showing goalkeeper reaching for ball. P* 14½.

953 40 c. multicoloured 15 20
954 60 c. multicoloured 25 30
955 90 c. multicoloured 40 40
956 $2 multicoloured .. .. 90 1·00
MS957 130 × 97 mm. $2.50, multicoloured .. 1·00 1·10

(Des G. Vasarhelyi. Litho Format)

1978 (17 Aug). *U.F.O. Research. T* **244** *and similar horiz designs. Multicoloured. P* 14½.

958 5 c. Type **244** 5 5
959 35 c. Various aerial phenomena, 1950 .. 25 25
960 $3 U.F.O.'s, 1965 .. .. 1·75 1·75
MS961 112 × 89 mm. $2 Sir Eric Gairy and U.F.O. research laboratory .. .. 1·25 1·25

245 Wright Glider, 1902

(Des G. Vasarhelyi. Litho Questa)

1978 (28 Aug). *75th Anniv of Powered Flight. T* **245** *and similar horiz designs. Multicoloured. P* 14.

962 5 c. Type **245** 5 5
963 15 c. *Flyer* 1, 1903 .. .. 10 10
964 18 c. *Flyer* 3 .. .. 10 10
965 22 c. *Flyer* 3 from above 12 12
966 50 c. Orville Wright and *Flyer* 25 25
967 75 c. *Flyer* 3 in Pau, France, 1908 .. .. 35 35
968 $3 Wilbur Wright and glider .. .. 1·60 1·25
962/8 .. .. *Set of* 7 2·40 2·00
MS969 114 × 85 mm. $2 Wright glider 90 90

246 Cook and Hawaiian Feast
247 "Paumgartner Altarpiece" (detail)

(Des G. Vasarhelyi. Litho Questa)

1978 (5 Dec). *Bicentenary of Discovery of Hawaii and 250th Birth Anniv of Captain Cook. T* **246** *and similar horiz designs. Multicoloured. P* 14.

970 18 c. Type **246** 25 15
971 35 c. Cook and Hawaiian warriors 40 25
972 75 c. Cook and Honolulu Harbour 60 50
973 $3 Cook (statue) and H.M.S. *Resolution* .. 2·00 1·75
MS974 116 × 88 mm. $4 Cook and death scene .. 2·50 3·00

(Des M. Rubin. Litho Questa)

1978 (20 Dec). *Christmas. Paintings by Dürer. T* **247** *and similar vert designs. Multicoloured. P* 14.

975 40 c. Type **247** 25 25

976 60 c. "The Adoration of the Magi" 35 35
977 90 c. "The Virgin and Child" 45 45
978 $2 "Virgin and Child with St. Anne" (detail) 95 95
MS979 113 × 83 mm. $4 "Madonna and Child" .. 2·00 2·25

248 National Convention and Cultural Centre (interior) **249** *Acalypha hispida*

(Des BG Studio. Litho Questa)

1979 (8 Feb). *5th Anniv of Independence. T* **248** *and similar vert designs. Multicoloured. P* 14.

980 5 c. Type **248** 5 5
981 18 c. National Convention and Cultural Centre (exterior) 8 10
982 22 c. Easter Water Parade, 1978 .. .. 10 12
983 35 c. Sir Eric M. Gairy (Prime Minister) .. 15 20
984 $3 The Cross, Fort Frederick .. .. 1·25 1·40

(Des J.W. Litho Questa)

1979 (26 Feb). *Flowers. T* **249** *and similar vert designs. Multicoloured. P* 14.

985 18 c. Type **249** 10 10
986 50 c. *Hibiscus rosa sinensis* 30 25
987 $1 *Thunbergia grandiflora* 55 45
988 $3 *Nerium oleander* .. .. 1·60 1·75
MS989 115 × 90 mm. $2 *Lagerstroemia speciosa* 1·00 1·10

250 Birds in Flight **251** Children playing Cricket

(Des M. Rubin. Litho Questa)

1979 (15 Mar). *30th Anniv of Declaration of Human Rights. T* **250** *and similar vert design. Multicoloured. P* 14.

990 15 c. Type **250** 5 5
991 $2 Bird in flight 75 80

(Des J.W. Litho Questa)

1979 (23 April). *International Year of the Child. T* **251** *and similar vert designs. Multicoloured. P* 14.

992 18 c. Type **251** 15 15
993 22 c. Children playing baseball 20 20
994 $5 Children playing in tree .. .. .. 4·50 3·50
MS995 114 × 92 mm. $4 Children with model spaceship .. .. 2·75 2·75

252 "Around the World in 80 Days"

(Des G. Vasarhelyi. Litho Questa)

1979 (4 May). *150th Birth Anniv of Jules Verne (author). T* **252** *and similar horiz designs showing scenes from his books and modern technological developments. Multicoloured. P* 14.

996 18 c. Type **252** 15 15
997 35 c. "20,000 Leagues under the Sea" 25 25
998 75 c. "From the Earth to the Moon" 40 40
999 $3 "Master of the World" .. .. .. 1·40 1·40
MS1000 110 × 85 mm. $4 "Clipper of the Clouds" 1·75 1·90

253 Mail Runner, Africa (early 19th-century) **254** "The Pistol of Peace" (vaccination gun), Map of Grenada and Children

(Des J.W. Litho Questa)

1979 (23 July). *Death Centenary of Sir Rowland Hill. T* **253** *and similar horiz designs. Multicoloured. P* 14.

1001 20 c. Type **253** 10 10
1002 40 c. Pony Express, America (mid 19th-century) 20 20
1003 $1 Pigeon post 45 45
1004 $3 Mail coach, Europe (18th-19th-century) 1·25 1·50
MS1005 127 × 100 mm. $5 Sir Rowland Hill and 1891 1d. on 8d. *tête-bêche* block of 4 .. .. 1·90 2·00

Nos. 1001/4 also exist perf 12 (*Price for set of 4 £1.75 mint or used*) from additional sheetlets of 5 stamps and 1 label, issued 8 August. These have different background colours from the stamps perforated 14, which come from normal sheets of 40.

(Des G. Vasarhelyi. Litho Questa)

1979 (20 Aug). *International Year of the Child. "Grenada—First Nation 100% Immunized". P* 14.

1006 **254** 5 c. multicoloured 5 5
1007 $1 multicoloured 55 60

255 Reef Shark

(Des G. Drummond. Litho Questa)

1979 (22 Aug). *Marine Wildlife. T* **225** *and similar horiz designs. Mutlicoloured. P* 14.

1008 40 c. Type **255** 20 20
1009 45 c. Spotted Eagle Ray 20 20
1010 50 c. Manytooth Conger 25 25
1011 60 c. Golden Olive (shell) 30 30
1012 70 c. West Indian Murex (shell) 35 35
1013 75 c. Giant Tun (shell) 35 35
1014 90 c. Brown Booby 40 40
1015 $1 Magnificent Frigate Bird 45 45
1008/15 .. .. *Set of* 8 2·25 2·25
MS1016 109 × 78 mm. $2.50, Sooty Tern .. 1·00 1·00

256 The Flight into Egypt

(Des W. Grout. Litho Questa)

1979 (19 Oct). *Christmas. Religious Tapestries. T* **256** *and similar multicoloured designs. P* 14.

1017 6 c. Type **256** 5 5
1018 25 c. The Flight into Egypt (detail) 10 12
1019 30 c. Angel (*vert*) 12 15
1020 40 c. Doge Marino Grimani (detail) (*vert*) .. 15 20
1021 90 c. The Annunciation to the Shepherds (*vert*) 35 40
1022 $1 The Flight into Egypt (Rome) (*vert*) .. 40 45
1023 $2 The Virgin in Glory (*vert*) 75 80
1017/23 .. .. *Set of* 7 1·75 2·00
MS1024 111 × 148 mm. $4 Doge Marino Grimani (*vert*) .. .. 1·50 1·60

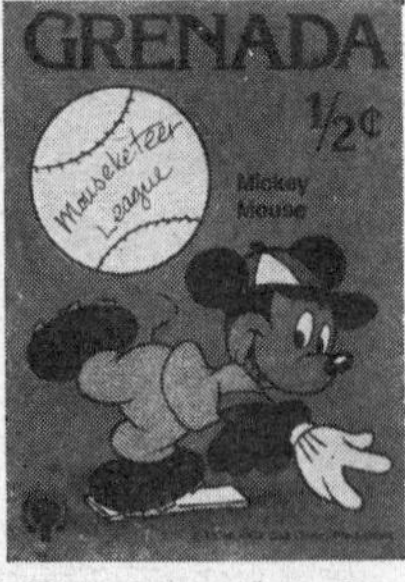

257 Mickey Mouse playing Baseball **258** Paul Harris (founder)

(Litho Format)

1979 (2 Nov). *International Year of the Child. Walt Disney Cartoon Characters. T* **257** *and similar vert designs showing characters playing sports. Multicoloured. P* 11.

1025 ½ c. Type **257** 5 5
1026 1 c. Donald Duck high-jumping 5 5
1027 2 c. Goofy playing basketball 5 5
1028 3 c. Goofy hurdling 5 5
1029 4 c. Donald Duck playing golf 5 5
1030 5 c. Mickey Mouse playing cricket 5 5
1031 10 c. Mickey Mouse playing football 5 5
1032 $2 Mickey Mouse playing tennis .. .. 1·00 1·00
1033 $2.50, Minnie Mouse riding horse .. .. 1·25 1·25
1025/33 .. .. *Set of* 9 2·40 2·40
MS1034 125 × 100 mm. $3 Goofy in riding gear. P 13½. .. .. 1·25 1·40

(Des J.W. Litho Questa)

1980 (25 Feb). *75th Anniv of Rotary International. T* **258** *and similar vert designs. Multicoloured. P* 14.

1035 6 c. Type **258** 5 5
1036 30 c. "Health" 15 15
1037 90 c. "Hunger" 40 40
1038 $2 "Humanity" 85 90
MS1039 104 × 89 mm. $4 Rotary International emblem .. .. 1·50 1·60

PEOPLE'S REVOLUTION
13 MARCH 1979
(259)

1980 (28 Feb–8 Apr). *1st Anniv of Revolution (1st issue). Nos.* 651A/2A, 654A/7A, 659A, 660B *and* 662A/8A *optd with T* **259**.

1040 2 c. Carenage taxi 5 5
a. Optd on No. 651B .. .. .. 8·50
1041 3 c. Large working boats 5 5
a. Optd on No. 652B .. .. .. 8·50
1042 6 c. Cocoa beans in drying trays 5 5
1043 8 c. Nutmegs 5 5
1044 10 c. River Antoine Estate Rum Distillery, *c.* 1785 .. .. 5 5
1045 12 c. Cocoa Tree 5 5
1046 20 c. Parliament Building, St. George's .. 5 5
1047 25 c. Fort George cannons (8.4.80) 10 12
1048 50 c. General Post Office 20 25
1049 75 c. Caribs Leap, Sauteurs Bay 25 30
1050 $1 Carenage, St. George's 35 40
1051 $2 St. George's Harbour by night 65 85
1052 $3 Grand Anse Beach .. .. .. 1·10 1·50
1053 $5 Canoe Bay and Black Bay from Point Saline Lighthouse .. .. 1·60 2·00
1054 $10 Sugar Loaf Island from Levera Beach .. 3·25 4·00
1040/54 .. .. *Set of* 15 7·00 8·50

See also Nos. 1069/73.

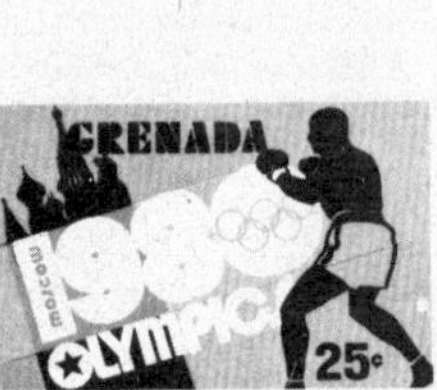

260 Boxing **261** Tropical Kingbird

(Des Design Images Inc. Litho Questa)

1980 (24 Mar). *Olympic Games, Moscow. T* **260** *and similar horiz designs. Multicoloured. P* 14.

1055 25 c. Type **260** 15 15
1056 40 c. Cycling 25 25
1057 90 c. Show-jumping 45 45
1058 $2 Running .. .. 1·00 1·00
MS1059 128 × 95 mm. $4 Sailing .. .. .. 1·75 1·90

(Des G. Drummond. Litho Questa)

1980 (8 Apr). *Wild Birds. T* **261** *and similar vert designs. Multicoloured. P* 14.

1060 20 c. Type **261** 25 10
1061 40 c. Rufous-breasted Hermit 35 20
1062 $1 Troupial 70 75
1063 $2 Ruddy Quail Dove .. .. .. 1·40 1·40
MS1064 85 × 114 mm. $3 Prairie Warbler .. 1·75 2·00

LONDON 1980
(262)

263 Free Hot Lunch at Schools

1980 (6 May). *"London 1980" International Stamp Exhibition. Nos.* 1001/4 *optd with T* **262**. *P* 12.

1065 20 c. Type **253** 20 20
1066 40 c. Pony Express, America (mid 19th-century) 30 30
1067 $1 Pigeon Post 60 60
1068 $3 Mail coach, Europe (18th-19th-century) 1·75 1·75

(Des M. Diamond. Litho Questa)

1980 (19 May). *1st Anniv of Revolution (2nd issue). T* **263** *and similar horiz designs. Multicoloured. P* 14.

1069 10 c. Type **263** 5 5
1070 40 c. "From tree to can" (agro-industry) .. 15 20
1071 $1 National Health care 40 45
1072 $2 New housing projects 75 90
MS1073 110 × 85 mm. $5 Prime Minister Maurice Bishop (*vert*) .. .. 1·90 2·00

264 Jamb Statues, West Portal, Chartres Cathedral

(Des J.W. Litho Questa)

1980 (15 July). *Famous Works of Art. T* **264** *and similar horiz designs. Multicoloured. P* 13½.

1074 8 c. Type **264** 5 5
1075 10 c. "Les Demoiselles D'Avignon" (painting by Picasso) 5 5
1076 40 c. Winged Victory of Samothrace (statue) 15 20
1077 50 c. "The Night Watch" (painting by Rembrandt) 20 25
1078 $1 "Portrait of Edward VI as a Child" (painting by Holbein the Younger) .. 40 45
1079 $3 Portrait head of Queen Nefertiti (carving).. .. .. 1·25 1·40
1074/9 .. .. *Set of* 6 1·90 2·10
MS1080 101 × 101 mm. $4 "Weier Haws" (detail of painting by Dürer) (*vert*) .. .. .. 1·50 1·60

265 Carib Canoes

(Des G. Drummond. Litho Questa)

1980 (9 Sept)–**84**. *Shipping. Horiz designs as T* **265**. *Multicoloured.* A. *P* 14. *No imprint.* B. *P* 12. *With imprint date at foot of designs.*

		A		B	
1081	½ c. Type **265**	5	5	5	5
1082	1 c. Boat building	5	5	†	
1083	2 c. Small working boat ..	5	5	†	
1084	4 c. Columbus' *Santa Maria*	5	5	†	
1085	5 c. West Indiaman barque, *circa* 1840..	5	5	5	5
1086	6 c. R.M.S.P. *Orinoco, circa* 1851	5	5	†	
1087	10 c. Working schooner ..	5	5	5	8
1088	12 c. Trimaran at Grand Anse anchorage	5	5	†	
1089	15 c. Spice Island cruising yacht *Petite Amie*	8	10	†	
1090	20 c. Fishing pirogue	10	12	10	12
1091	25 c. Harbour police launch ..	12	15	12	15
1092	30 c. Grand Anse speed-boat ..	15	20	15	20
1093	40 c. M.V. *Seimstrand*	20	25	20	25
1094	50 c. Three-masted schooner *Ariadne*	30	35	30	35
1095	90 c. M.V. *Geestide*	50	55	†	
1096	$1 M.V. *Cunard Countess* ..	55	60	†	
1097	$3 Rum-runner	1·75	2·00	1·75	2·00
1098	$5 S.S. *Statendam* off St. George's	3·25	3·50	3·75	3·50
1099	$10 Coast-guard patrol boat	5·75	6·00	5·75	6·00
1081/99	.. .. *Set of* 19	11·50	12·50	†	
1081/98	.. .. *Set of* 11	†		10·50	11·50

Dates of issue:—1982 (dated "1982") Nos. 1081B, 1085B, 1087B, 1090B/3B, 1097B/83; 1.84 (dated "1984") Nos. 1094B, 1099B.

(Litho Walsall)

1980 (25 Sept). *Christmas. Walt Disney Cartoon Scenes from "Snow White and the Seven Dwarfs". Horiz designs as T* **257**. *Multicoloured. P* 11.

1100 ½ c. Snow White at well 5 5
1101 1 c. The Wicked Queen 5 5
1102 2 c. Snow White singing to animals .. 5 5
1103 3 c. Snow White doing housework for Dwarfs 5 5
1104 4 c. The Seven Dwarfs 5 5
1105 5 c. Snow White with Dwarfs 5 5
1106 10 c. Witch offering Snow White apple .. 5 5
1107 $2.50, Snow White with Prince, and Dwarfs 1·40 1·40
1108 $3 Snow White and Prince.. .. .. 2·00 2·00
1100/8 .. .. *Set of* 9 3·50 3·50
MS1109 127 × 102 mm. $4 Snow White sleeping (*vert*) .. .. 1·75 1·90

(Litho Format)

1981 (19 Jan). *50th Anniv of Walt Disney's Cartoon Character, Pluto. Vert designs as T* **257**. *Multicoloured. P* 13½.

1110 $2 Pluto with birthday cake .. .. 1·25 1·25
MS1111 127 × 102 mm. $4 Pluto in scene from film *Pueblo Pluto* .. .. 2·10 2·25

No. 1110 was printed in small sheets of 8 stamps.

266 Revolution and Grenada Flags

1981 (13 Mar). *Festival of the Revolution. T* **266** *and similar triangular designs. Multicoloured. Litho. P* 12½.

1112 5 c. Type **266** 5 5
1113 10 c. Teacher, pupil, book and pencil ("education") 5 5
1114 15 c. Food processing plant ("industry") .. 5 5
1115 25 c. Selection of fruits and farm scene ("agriculture") 12 12
1116 40 c. Crawfish and boat ("fishing") 20 20
1117 90 c. Liner arriving at St. George's Harbour ("shipping") 50 50
1118 $1 Straw-work ("native handicrafts") .. 60 60
1119 $3 Map of Caribbean with expanded view of Grenada .. .. 1·75 1·75
1112/19 .. .. *Set of* 8 3·00 3·00

(Litho Format)

1981 (7 Apr). *Easter. Walt Disney Cartoon Characters. Vert designs as T* **257**. *Multicoloured. P* 11.

1120 35 c. Mickey Mouse and Goofy 25 25
1121 40 c. Donald Duck, Chip and Daisy Duck .. 25 25
1122 $2 Minnie Mouse .. .. 1·40 1·40
1123 $2.50, Pluto and Mickey Mouse .. .. 1·60 1·60
MS1124 127 × 101 mm. $4 Goofy. P 13½ .. 2·40 2·50

267 "Woman-Flower"

268 Prince Charles playing Polo

(Des J.W. Litho Questa)

1981 (28 Apr). *Birth Centenary of Picasso. T* **267** *and similar vert designs. Multicoloured. P* 13½ × 14.

1125 25 c. Type **267** 15 15
1126 30 c. "Portrait of Madame" 20 20
1127 90 c. "Cavalier with Pipe" 55 55
1128 $4 "Large Heads" .. .. 2·40 2·40
MS1129 128 × 103 mm. $5 "Woman on the Banks of the Seine" (after Courbet). Imperf .. .. 2·75 3·00

(Des J.W. Litho Format)

1981 (16 June). *Royal Wedding. T* **268** *and similar vert designs. Multicoloured.* (*a*) *P* 14½.

1130 50 c. Prince Charles and Lady Diana Spencer 30 30
1131 $2 Holyrood House.. .. .. .. 1·00 1·10
1132 $4 Type **268** .. .. 1·90 2·25
a. Imperf (pair) £400
MS1133 98 × 84 mm. $5 Glass Coach .. .. 2·40 2·50

(*b*) *P* 14½ × 14

1134 30 c. As 50 c. 20 20
1135 40 c. As $2 .. .. 30 30

The 30 and 40 c. values were each printed in small sheets of 6 including one *se-tenant* stamp-size label.

The $4 value, with changed background colour, also exists perforated 14½ × 14 (*price* £1.50 *mint or used*) from similar sheetlets in addition to the original version issued in sheets of 40.

269 Lady Diana Spencer

270 "The Bath" (Mary Cassatt)

(Manufactured by Walsall)

1981 (16 June). *Royal Wedding. Booklet stamps. T* **269** *and similar vert designs. Multicoloured. Roul* 5 × *imperf**. *Self-adhesive.*

1136 $1 Type **269** 60 70
a. Booklet pane. Nos. 1136/7 each × 3 .. 5·00
1137 $2 Prince Charles .. .. 1·10 1·25
1138 $5 Prince Charles and Lady Diana Spencer 3·00 3·00
a. Booklet pane of 1.. .. .. .. 3·00

*The $1 and $2 values were each separated by various combinations of rotary knife (giving a straight edge) and roulette. The $5 value exists only with straight edges.

(Des BG Studio. Litho Questa)

1981 (Oct). *"Decade for Women". Paintings. T* **270** *and similar multicoloured designs. P* 14.

1139 15 c. Type **270** 10 10
1140 40 c. "Mademoiselle Charlotte du Val d'Ognes" (Constance Marie Charpentier) 25 25
1141 60 c. "Self-portrait" (Mary Beale) 40 40
1142 $3 "Woman in White Stockings" (Suzanne Valadon) .. .. 1·75 1·75
MS1143 101 × 77 mm. $5 "The Artist hesitating between the Arts of Music and Painting" (Angelica Kauffman) (*horiz*) .. .. 2·75 2·75

(Litho Questa)

1981 (Nov). *Christmas. Horiz designs as T* **257** *showing scenes from Walt Disney's cartoon film "Cinderella". P* 13½.

1144 ½ c. multicoloured 5 5
1145 1 c. multicoloured 5 5
1146 2 c. multicoloured 5 5
1147 3 c. multicoloured 5 5
1148 4 c. multicoloured 5 5
1149 5 c. multicoloured 5 5
1150 10 c. multicoloured 5 5
1151 $2.50, multicoloured .. .. 1·50 1·50
1152 $3 multicoloured .. .. 1·75 1·75
1144/52 .. .. *Set of* 9 3·25 3·25
MS1153 127 × 103 mm. $5 multicoloured .. 2·50 2·75

271 Landing

272 West German Footballer and Flag

(Des M. Brodie. Litho Format)

1981 (12 Nov). *Space Shuttle Project. T* **271** *and similar vert designs. Multicoloured. P* 14½.

1154 30 c. Type **271** 20 20
1155 60 c. Working in space 40 40
1156 70 c. Lift off 45 45
1157 $3 Separation .. .. 1·75 1·75
MS1158 117 × 89 mm. $5 In orbit .. .. 2·50 2·50

(Des Clover Mill. Litho Format)

1981 (30 Nov.) *World Cup Football Championship, Spain* (1982). *T* **272** *and similar multicoloured designs. P* 14.

1159 25 c. + 10 c. Type **272** 25 30
1160 40 c. + 20 c. Argentinian footballer and flag 35 40
1161 50 c. + 25 c. Brazilian footballer and flag .. 45 50
1162 $1 + 50 c. English footballer and flag .. 85 95
MS1163 141 × 128 mm. $5 + 50 c. Spanish orange mascot and Jules Rimet Trophy (*vert*) .. 2·75 3·00

Nos. 1159/62 were each printed in sheetlets of 12 on an overall background design showing a football.

273 General Post Office, St. George's

274 Artist without Hands

(Des J.W. Litho Format)

1981 (10 Dec). *Centenary of U.P.U. Membership. T* **273** *and similar horiz designs. Multicoloured. P* 15.

1164 25 c. Type **273** 15 15
1165 30 c. 1861 1d. stamp 20 20
1166 90 c. 1970 New U.P.U. Headquarters Building 25 c. commemorative 50 50
1167 $4 1961 Stamp Centenary 25 c. commemorative .. .. 2·00 2·00
MS1168 113 × 87 mm. $5 1974 Centenary of U.P.U. ½ c. commemorative .. .. .. 2·40 2·50

(Litho Questa)

1982 (4 Feb). *International Year for the Disabled* (1981). *T* **274** *and similar vert designs. Multicoloured. P* 14.

1169 30 c. Type **274** 20 20
1170 40 c. Computer operator without hands .. 25 25
1171 70 c. Blind schoolteacher teaching braille .. 45 45
1172 $3 Midget playing drums .. .. .. 1·75 1·75
MS1173 101 × 72 mm. $4 Auto mechanic confined to wheelchair .. .. 2·00 2·25

275 Tending Vegetable Patch

276 Flambeau

1982 (19 Feb). *75th Anniv of Boy Scout Movement and 125th Birth Anniv of Lord Baden-Powell. T* **275** *and similar horiz designs. Multicoloured. P* 14½.

1174 70 c. Type **275** 45 45
1175 90 c. Map-reading 50 50
1176 $1 Bee-keeping 60 60
1177 $4 Hospital reading .. .. 2·00 2·00
MS1178 100 × 71 mm. $5 Presentation of trophies 2·40 2·50

(Des G. Drummond. Litho Questa)

1982 (24 Mar). *Butterflies. T* **276** *and similar vert designs. Multicoloured. P* 14.

1179 10 c. Type **276** 15 15
1180 60 c. Large Orange Sulphur 40 40
1181 $1 Red Anartia 70 70
1182 $3 Polydamas Swallowtail.. .. .. 2·00 2·00
MS1183 111 × 85 mm. $5 Caribbean Buckeye .. 2·75 3·00

277 "Saying Grace"

278 Kensington Palace

(Des M.B.I. Studio. Litho Questa)

1982 (14 Apr). *Norman Rockwell (painter) Commemoration. T* **277** *and similar vert designs. Multicoloured. P* 14 × 13½.

1184 15 c. Type **277** 10 10
1185 30 c. "Card Tricks" 20 20
1186 60 c. "Pharmacist" 35 35
1187 70 c. "Pals" 45 45

(Des PAD Studio. Litho Questa)

1982 (1 July). *21st Birthday of Princess of Wales. T* **278** *and similar vert designs. Multicoloured. P* 14½ × 14.

1188 50 c. Type **278** 25 30
1189 60 c. Type **278** 40 35
1190 $1 Prince and Princess of Wales 50 55
1191 $2 As $1 .. .. 1·00 1·00
1192 $3 Princess of Wales .. .. 1·60 1·75
1193 $4 As $3 .. .. 2·00 1·90
1188/93 .. .. *Set of* 6 5·50 5·50
MS1194 103 × 75 mm. $5 Princess Diana (*different*) .. .. 2·40 2·50

Nos. 1188, 1190 and 1192 come from sheetlets of 5 stamps and 1 label.

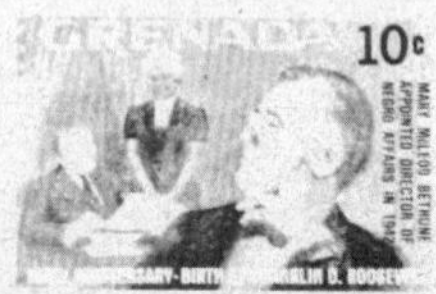

279 Mary McLeod Bethune appointed Director of Negro Affairs, 1942

(Des Design Images. Litho Questa)

1982 (27 July). *Birth Centenary of Franklin D. Roosevelt. T* **279** *and similar horiz designs. Multicoloured. P* 14.

1195 10 c. Type **279** 5 5
1196 60 c. Huddie Ledbetter ("Leadbelly") in concert (Works Progress administration) 35 35
1197 $1.10, Signing bill No. 8802, 1941 (Fair Employment committee) 65 65
1198 $3 Farm Security administration .. .. 1·75 1·75
MS1199 100 × 70 mm. $5 William Hastie, first Negro judicial appointee .. .. 2·40 2·50

1982 (30 Aug). *Birth of Prince William of Wales. Nos.* 1188/94 *optd with T* 171 *of Antigua.*

1200 50 c. Type **278** 25 30
1201 60 c. Type **278** 30 35
1202 $1 Prince and Princess of Wales 50 55
1203 $2 As $1 .. .. 95 1·00
1204 $3 Princess of Wales .. .. 1·60 1·75
1205 $4 As $3 .. .. 1·75 1·90
1200/5 .. .. *Set of* 6 4·75 5·50
MS1206 103 × 75 mm. $5 Princess Diana (*different*) .. .. 2·40 2·50

Nos. 1200, 1202 and 1204 come from sheetlets of 5 stamps and 1 label.

280 Apostle and Tormentor

(Des Clover Mill. Litho Format)

1982 (2 Sept). *Easter. Details from Painting "The Way to Calvary" by Raphael. T* **280** *and similar multicoloured designs. P* 14 × 14½ (40 c.) *or* 14½ × 14 (*others*).

1207 40 c. Type **280** 25 25
1208 70 c. Captain of the guards (*vert*) 45 45
1209 $1.10, Christ and apostle (*vert*) 65 65
1210 $4 Mourners (*vert*) .. .. 2·00 2·00
MS1211 102 × 126 mm. $5 Christ falls beneath the cross (*vert*) .. .. 2·40 2·50

281 "Orient Express"

(Des Artists International. Litho Format)

1982 (4 Oct). *Famous Trains of the World. T* **281** *and similar horiz designs. Multicoloured. P* 15 × 14½.

1212 30 c. Type **281** 20 20
1213 60 c. "Trans-Siberian Express" 35 35
1214 70 c. "Fleche D'Or" 45 45
1215 90 c. "Flying Scotsman" 50 50
1216 $1 German Federal Railways 65 65
1217 $3 German National Railways .. .. .. 1·75 1·75
1212/17 .. .. *Set of* 6 3·50 3·50
MS1218 109 × 81 mm. $5 "20th Century Limited" 2·50 3·00

282 Footballers

283 Killer Whale

(Des D. Miller. Litho Questa)

1982 (2 Dec). *World Cup Football Championship Winners. T* **282** *and similar horiz designs. P* 14 × 13½.

1219 60 c. multicoloured 35 35
1220 $4 multicoloured .. .. 2·50 2·75
MS1221 93 × 119 mm. $5 multicoloured .. .. 2·50 2·75

(Litho Questa)

1982 (14 Dec). *Christmas. Horiz designs as T* **257** *depicting scenes from Walt Disney's cartoon film "Robin Hood". P* 13½.

1222 ½ c. multicoloured 5 5
1223 1 c. multicoloured 5 5
1224 2 c. multicoloured 5 5
1225 3 c. multicoloured 5 5
1226 4 c. multicoloured 5 5
1227 5 c. multicoloured 5 5
1228 10 c. multicoloured 10 10
1229 $2.50, multicoloured .. .. 1·50 1·50
1230 $3 multicoloured .. .. 1·75 1·75
1222/30 .. .. *Set of* 9 3·25 3·25
MS1231 121 × 96 mm. $5 multicoloured .. .. 2·40 2·50

(Des Artists International. Litho Questa)

1983 (10 Jan). *Save the Whales. T* **283** *and similar vert designs. Multicoloured. P* 14.

1232 15 c. Type **283** 10 10
1233 40 c. Sperm Whale 25 25
1234 70 c. Blue Whale 45 45
1235 $3 Common Dolphin .. .. 1·75 1·75
MS1236 84 × 74 mm. $5 Humpback Whale .. 2·50 2·75

284 "Construction of Ark"

(Des Design Images. Litho Format)

1983 (15 Feb). *500th Birth Anniv of Raphael. T* **284** *and similar horiz designs showing painting details. Multicoloured. P* 13½.

1237 25 c. Type **284** 12 15
1238 30 c. "Jacob's Vision" 15 20
1239 90 c. "Joseph interprets the Dreams to his Brothers" 40 45
1240 $4 "Joseph interprets Pharaoh's Dreams" 1·90 2·00
MS1241 128 × 100 mm. $5 "Creation of the Animals" .. .. 2·50 2·75

285 Dentistry at Health Centre

(Des J.W. Litho Questa)

1983 (14 Mar). *Commonwealth Day. T* **285** *and similar horiz designs. Multicoloured. P* 14.

1242 10 c. Type **285** 5 8
1243 70 c. Airport runway construction 35 40
1244 $1.10, Tourism 55 60
1245 $3 Boat-building .. .. 1·40 1·50

286 Maritime Communications via Satellite

(Des G. Vasarhelyi. Litho Questa)

1983 (29 Mar). *World Communications Year. T* **286** *and similar horiz designs. Multicoloured. P* 14.

1246 30 c. Type **286** 15 20
1247 40 c. Rural telephone installation 20 25
1248 $2.50, Satellite weather map .. .. 1·25 1·40
1249 $3 Airport control room .. .. .. 1·40 1·50
MS1250 111 × 85 mm. $5 Communications satellite .. .. 2·50 2·75

287 Franklin Sport Sedan, 1928

(Des J. Mendola. Litho Format)

1983 (4 May). *75th Anniv of Model "T" Ford Car. T* **287** *and similar horiz designs showing cars of the 20th century. Multicoloured. P* 14½.

1251 6 c. Type **287** 5 5
1252 10 c. Delage "D8", 1933 .. .. 5 8
1253 40 c. Alvis, 1938 .. .. 20 25
1254 60 c. Invicta "S-type" tourer, 1931 .. .. 30 35
1255 70 c. Alfa-Romeo "1750 Gran Sport", 1930 .. 35 40
1256 90 c. Isotta Fraschini, 1930 .. .. .. 40 45
1257 $1 Bugatti "Royale Type 41" 45 50
1258 $2 BMW "328", 1938 .. .. 95 1·00
1259 $3 Marmon "V16", 1931 .. .. .. 1·40 1·50
1260 $4 Lincoln "K8" saloon, 1932 .. .. 1·90 2·00
1251/60 .. .. *Set of* 10 5·50 6·00
MS1261 114 × 90 mm. $5 Cougar "XR 7", 1972 .. 2·50 2·75

Nos. 1251/60 were each issued in sheets of eight stamps with a stamp-size label in the centre position.

288 *Norge* (airship)

(Des W. Wright. Litho Questa)

1983 (18 July). *Bicentenary of Manned Flight. T* **288** *and similar multicoloured designs. P* 14.

1262 30 c. Type **288** 15 20
1263 60 c. Gloster "VI" seaplane 30 35
1264 $1.10, Curtiss "NC-4" flying boat 50 55
1265 $4 Dornier "Do 18" flying boat .. .. 1·90 2·00
MS1266 114 × 85 mm. $5 Modern hot-air balloon (*vert*) .. .. 2·50 2·75

289 Morty

(Litho Format)

1983 (7 Nov). *Christmas. T* **289** *and similar vert designs showing Disney cartoon characters in scenes from "It's beginning to look a lot like Christmas" (song). Multicoloured. P* 11.

1267 ½ c. Type **289** 5 5
1268 1 c. Ludwig von Drake 5 5
1269 2 c. Gyro Gearloose 5 5
1270 3 c. Pluto and Figaro 5 5
1271 4 c. Morty and Ferdie 5 5
1272 5 c. Mickey Mouse and Goofy 5 5
1273 10 c. Chip'n Dale 5 5
1274 $2.50, Mickey and Minnie Mouse .. .. 1·40 1·50
1275 $3 Donald and Grandma Duck .. .. 1·75 1·90
1267/75 .. .. *Set of* 9 3·25 3·50
MS1276 127 × 102 mm. $5 Goofy with Christmas tree. P 13½ .. .. 2·75 3·00

290 Daisy Duck on Pommel Horse

291 William I

(Litho Questa)

1984 (17 Jan–May). *Olympic Games, Los Angeles. T* **290** *and similar horiz designs showing Disney cartoon characters in Olympic events. Multicoloured. A. Inscr.* "1984 LOS ANGELES". *P* 14 × 13½. B. *Inscr.* "1984 OLYMPICS LOS ANGELES" *and Olympic emblem. P* 12 (May).

		A		B	
1277	½ c. Type **290**	5	5	5	5
1278	1 c. Mickey Mouse boxing	5	5	5	5
1279	2 c. Daisy Duck in archery event	5	5	5	5
1280	3 c. Clarabelle Cow on uneven bars	5	5	5	5
1281	4 c. Mickey and Minnie Mouse in hurdles race	5	5	5	5
1282	5 c. Donald Duck with Chip and Dale weightlifting	5	5	5	5
1283	$1 Little Hiawatha in single kayak	55	60	55	60
1284	$2 The Tortoise and the Hare in marathon	1·10	1·25	1·10	1·25
1285	$3 Mickey Mouse pole-vaulting	1·75	1·90	1·75	1·90
1277/85	*Set of* 9	3·50	3·75	3·50	3·75
MS1286	127 × 101 mm. $5 Donald Duck in medley relay (*vert*). P 13½ × 14	2·75	3·00	2·75	3·00

1984 (25 Jan). *British Monarchs. T* **291** *and similar vert designs. Multicoloured. Litho. P* 14.

1287	$4 Type **291**	2·50	2·75
	a. Sheetlet. Nos. 1287/93	17·50	
1288	$4 William II	2·50	2·75
1289	$4 Henry I	2·50	2·75
1290	$4 Stephen	2·50	2·75
1291	$4 Henry II	2·50	2·75
1292	$4 Richard I	2·50	2·75
1293	$4 John	2·50	2·75
1294	$4 Henry III	2·50	2·75
	a. Sheetlet. Nos. 1294/1300	17·50	
1295	$4 Edward I	2·50	2·75
1296	$4 Edward II	2·50	2·75
1297	$4 Edward III	2·50	2·75
1298	$4 Richard II	2·50	2·75
1299	$4 Henry IV	2·50	2·75
1300	$4 Henry V	2·50	2·75
1301	$4 Henry VI	2·50	2·75
	a. Sheetlet. Nos. 1301/7	17·50	
1302	$4 Edward IV	2·50	2·75
1303	$4 Edward V	2·50	2·75
1304	$4 Richard III	2·50	2·75
1305	$4 Henry VII	2·50	2·75
1306	$4 Henry VIII	2·50	2·75
1307	$4 Edward VI	2·50	2·75
1308	$4 Lady Jane Grey	2·50	2·75
	a. Sheetlet. Nos. 1308/14	17·50	
1309	$4 Mary I	2·50	2·75
1310	$4 Elizabeth I	2·50	2·75
1311	$4 James I	2·50	2·75
1312	$4 Charles I	2·50	2·75
1313	$4 Charles II	2·50	2·75
1314	$4 James II	2·50	2·75
1315	$4 William III	2·50	2·75
	a. Sheetlet. Nos. 1315/21	17·50	
1316	$4 Mary II	2·50	2·75
1317	$4 Anne	2·50	2·75
1318	$4 George I	2·50	2·75
1319	$4 George II	2·50	2·75
1320	$4 George III	2·50	2·75
1321	$4 George IV	2·50	2·75
1322	$4 William IV	2·50	2·75
	a. Sheetlet. Nos. 1322/8	17·50	
1323	$4 Victoria	2·50	2·75
1324	$4 Edward VII	2·50	2·75
1325	$4 George V	2·50	2·75
1326	$4 Edward VIII	2·50	2·75
1327	$4 George VI	2·50	2·75
1328	$4 Elizabeth II	2·50	2·75
1287/1328	*Set of* 42	95·00	£100

Nos. 1287/93, 1294/1300, 1301/7, 1308/14, 1315/21 and 1322/8 were printed together, in small sheets of 8 including one *se-tenant* stamp-size label.

Although announced as all being issued on 25 January 1984 the different sheetlets were distributed at monthly intervals.

292 Lantana

(Des P.U.B. Graphics. Litho Format)

1984 (9 Apr). *Flowers. T* **292** *and similar horiz designs. Multicoloured. P* 15.

1329	25 c. Type **292**	15	20
1330	30 c. Plumbago	20	25
1331	90 c. Spider Lily	60	65
1332	$4 Giant Alocasia	2·50	2·75
MS1333	108 × 90 mm. $5 Orange Trumpet Vine	3·25	3·50

293 Blue Parrot Fish

19TH U.P.U CONGRESS - HAMBURG

(294)

(Litho Questa)

1984 (21 May). *Coral Reef Fishes. T* **293** *and similar horiz designs. Multicoloured. P* 14.

1334	10 c. Type **293**	8	10
1335	30 c. Flame-back Cherub Fish	20	25
1336	70 c. Painted Wrasse	45	50
1337	90 c. Straight-tailed Razor Fish	60	65
MS1338	81 × 85 mm. $5 Spanish Hogfish	3·25	3·50

1984 (19 June). *Universal Postal Union Congress, Hamburg. Nos.* 1331/3 *optd with T* **294**.

1339	90 c. Spider Lily	60	65
1340	$4 Giant Alocasia	2·50	2·75
MS1341	108 × 90 mm. $5 Orange Trumpet Vine	3·25	3·50

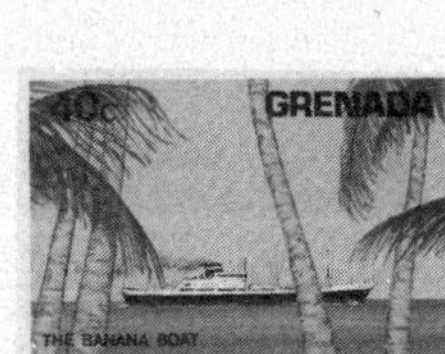

295 Cargo Ship

296 "The Night" (detail) (Correggio)

(Des Artists International. Litho Format)

1984 (16 July). *Ships. T* **295** *and similar horiz designs. Multicoloured. P* 15.

1342	40 c. Type **295**	25	30
1343	70 c. *Queen Elizabeth II*	45	50
1344	90 c. Sailing boats	60	65
1345	$4 *Amerikanis*	2·50	2·75
MS1346	107 × 80 mm. $5 Spanish Galleon	3·25	3·50

(Litho Questa)

1984 (22 Aug). *450th Death Anniv of Correggio (painter). T* **296** *and similar vert designs showing paintings. Multicoloured. P* 14.

1347	10 c. Type **296**	8	10
1348	30 c. "The Virgin adoring the Child"	20	25
1349	90 c. "The Mystical Marriage of St. Catherine with St. Sebastian"	60	65
1350	$4 "The Madonna and the Fruit Basket"	2·50	2·75
MS1351	54 × 73 mm. $5 "The Madonna at the Spring"	3·25	3·50

297 "L'Absinthe" (Degas)

GRENADA $1.10 Puffing Billy Salute to Australia

298 Train on "Puffing Billy" Line, Victoria

(Litho Questa)

1984 (22 Aug). *150th Birth Anniv of Edgar Degas (painter). T* **297** *and similar multicoloured designs showing paintings. P* 14.

1352	25 c. Type **297**	15	20
1353	70 c. "Pouting" (*horiz*)	45	50
1354	$1.10, "The Millinery Shop"	70	75
1355	$3 "The Bellelli Family" (*horiz*)	2·00	2·10
MS1356	84 × 54 mm. $5 "The Cotton Market"	3·25	3·50

(Des Bonny Redecker. Litho Questa)

1984 (21 Sept). *"Ausipex" International Stamp Exhibition, Melbourne. T* **298** *and similar vert designs. Multicoloured. P* 14.

1357	$1.10, Type **298**	70	75
1358	$4 Yacht *Australia II* (winner of America's Cup)	2·50	2·75
MS1359	107 × 76 mm. $5 Melbourne tram	3·25	3·50

299 *Locomotion* (1825)

OPENING OF POINT SALINE INT'L AIRPORT

(300)

(Des J.W. Litho Format)

1984 (3 Oct). *Railway Locomotives. T* **299** *and similar horiz designs. Multicoloured. P* 15.

1360	30 c. Type **299**	20	25
1361	40 c. *Novelty* (1829)	25	30
1362	60 c. *Washington Farmer* (1836)	40	45
1363	70 c. French Crampton type (1859)	45	50
1364	90 c. Dutch State Railways (1873)	60	65
1365	$1.10, *Champion* (1882)	70	75
1366	$2 Webb Compound type (1893)	1·25	1·40
1367	$4 Berlin "No. 74" (1900)	2·50	2·75
1360/7	*Set of* 8	5·75	6·25
MS1368	Two sheets, each 100 × 70 mm. (a) $5 Crampton *Phoenix* (1863); (b) $5 Mikado type (1897)	6·50	7·00

1984 (28 Oct). *Opening of Point Saline International Airport. Nos.* 1247 *and* 1249/50 *optd as T* **300**.

1369	40 c. Rural telephone installation	25	30
1370	$3 Airport control room	1·75	1·90
MS1371	111 × 85 mm. $5 Communications satellite	3·00	3·25

On No. **MS**1371 the overprint, 54 × 8 mm., appears in two lines on the sheet margin only.

301 Donald Duck as Father Christmas looking into Mirror

302 Clapper Rail

(Litho Questa)

1984 (26 Nov). *Christmas. Walt Disney Cartoon Characters. T* **301** *and similar vert designs. Multicoloured. P* 12 ($2) *or* 13½ × 14 (*others*).

1372	45 c. Type **301**	30	35
1373	60 c. Donald Duck filling stocking with presents	35	40
1374	90 c. As Father Christmas pulling a sleigh	55	60
1375	$2 As Father Christmas decorating Christmas tree	1·25	1·40
1376	$4 Donald Duck and nephews singing carols	2·40	2·50
MS1377	127 × 102 mm. $5 As Father Christmas in sleigh	3·00	3·25

No. 1375 was printed in sheetlets of 8 stamps.

(Litho Questa)

1985 (11 Feb.) *Birth Bicentenary of John J. Audubon (ornithologist). T* **302** *and similar multicoloured designs showing illustrations from "Birds of America". P* 14.

1378	50 c. Type **302**	30	35
1379	70 c. Hooded Warbler	40	45
1380	90 c. Flicker	55	60
1381	$4 Bohemian Waxwing	2·40	2·50
MS1382	82 × 112 mm. $5 Pigeon Hawk (*horiz*)	3·00	3·25

POSTAGE DUE STAMPS

D 1

1d. SURCHARGE POSTAGE

(D 2)

(Typo D.L.R.)

1892 (18 Apr–Oct). (*a*) *Type* D 1. *Wmk Crown CA. P* 14.

D1	D 1	1d. blue-black	8·00	4·00
D2		2d. blue-black	23·00	4·00
D3		3d. blue-black	27·00	6·50
		(*b*) *Nos.* 34 *and* 35 *surch locally as Type* D 2		
D4	13	1d. on 6d. mauve (10.92)	18·00	3·50
		a. *Tête-bêche* (pair)	75·00	
		b. Surch double	—	65·00
D5		1d. on 8d. grey-brown (8.92)	£100	8·00
		a. *Tête-bêche* (pair)	£550	
D6		2d. on 6d. mauve (10.92)	38·00	5·00
		a. *Tête-bêche* (pair)	£150	
D7		2d. on 8d. grey-brown (8.92)	£225	15·00
		a. *Tête-bêche* (pair)	£1000	

It seems unlikely that Nos. D4/7 were required or used for postage due purposes as supplies of Nos. D1/3 were received in April or May and the earliest used copy is dated 12 July.

The provisionals were used in the period of August to November but their usage was mainly philatelic. It is known that there was a shortage of 1d. postage stamps from late July to early August, but this was met by the use of Nos. 44/45 which were still available then.

It is therefore believed that the provisionals were intended for use as postage stamps (as indicated by the word "POSTAGE" in the surcharge) but we are left with the fact that their use was purely philatelic.

1906 (July)–11. *Wmk Mult Crown CA. P* 14.

D 8	D 1	1d. blue-black (1911)	1·25	1·75
D 9		2d. blue-black	2·00	1·75
D10		3d. blue-black (9.06)	4·00	4·50

1921 (Dec)–**22**. *As Type* D **1**, *but inscr* "POSTAGE DUE". *Wmk Mult Script CA. P* 14.

D11	1d. black	90	1·00
D12	1½d. black (15.12.22)	1·75	2·75
D13	2d. black	1·75	1·75
D14	3d. black	1·75	2·75
D11/14	Optd "Specimen" *Set of* 4	80·00	

1952 (1 Mar). *As Type* D **1**, *but inscr* "POSTAGE DUE". *Value in cents. Chalk-surfaced paper. Wmk Mult Script CA. P* 14.

D15	2 c. black	40	1·50
	a. Error. Crown missing. W **9***a*	32·00	
	b. Error. St. Edward Crown. W **9***b*	20·00	
D16	4 c. black	50	1·75
	a. Error. Crown missing. W **9***a*	32·00	
	b. Error. St. Edward Crown. W **9***b*	20·00	
D17	6 c. black	75	3·50
	a. Error. Crown missing. W **9***a*	35·00	
	b. Error. St. Edward Crown. W **9***b*	32·00	
D18	8 c. black	1·40	4·75
	a. Error. Crown missing. W **9***a*	48·00	
	b. Error. St. Edward Crown. W **9***b*	38·00	

OFFICIAL STAMPS

P.R.G.

(O 1)

(= People's Revolutionary Government)

1982 (June). *Various stamps optd with Type* O **1**.

(*a*) *Nos.* 1085A/97A *and* 1099A

O 1	5 c. West Indiaman barque, *circa* 1840	5	5
O 2	6 c. R.M.S.P. *Orinoco*, *circa* 1851	5	5
O 3	10 c. Working Schooner	5	5
O 4	12 c. Trimaran at Grand Anse anchorage	5	5
O 5	15 c. Spice Island cruising yacht *Petite Amie*	5	8
O 6	20 c. Fishing pirogue	8	10
O 7	25 c. Harbour police launch	10	10
O 8	30 c. Grand Anse speedboat	12	12
O 9	40 c. M.V. *Seimstrand*	15	20
O10	50 c. Three-masted schooner *Ariadne*	20	25
O11	90 c. M.V. *Geestide*	40	35
O12	$1 M.V. *Cunard Countess*	40	40
O13	$3 Rum-runner	1·25	1·25
O14	$10 Coast-guard patrol boat	4·25	3·75

(*b*) *Nos.* 1130/2 *and* 1134/5

O15	30 c. Prince Charles and Lady Diana Spencer	1·50	1·75
O16	40 c. Holyrood House	2·00	2·25
O17	50 c. Prince Charles and Lady Diana Spencer	1·00	1·25
O18	$2 Holyrood House	2·50	2·75
O19	$4 Type **268**	6·50	7·00
O1/19	*Set of* 19	18·00	19·00

The $4 from sheetlets, perforated 14½ × 14 and with changed background colour, also exists with this overprint (*Price* £8.50 *mint*, £9 *used*).

GRENADINES OF GRENADA

Part of a group of islands north of Grenada, the most important of which is Carriacou. The Grenadine islands further north are administered by St. Vincent, and their stamps are listed after that country.

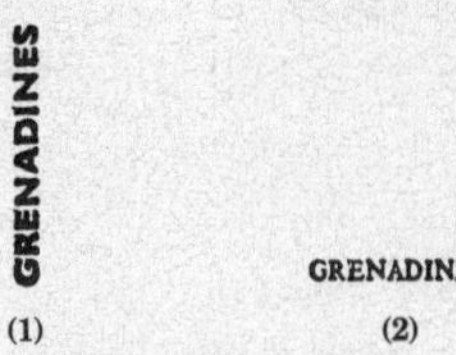

(1) (2)

1973 (29 Dec). *Royal Wedding. Nos.* 582/4 *of Grenada optd with T* **1**.

1	**196** 25 c. multicoloured	20	20
2	$2 multicoloured	90	70
	a. Albino opt		
MS3	79 × 100 mm. 75 c. and $1 as Nos. 1/2	1·00	80

1974 (29 May). *Nos.* 306 *etc of Grenada optd with T* **2**.

4	1 c. multicoloured	5	5
5	2 c. multicoloured	5	5
6	3 c. multicoloured	5	5
7	5 c. multicoloured	5	5
8	8 c. multicoloured	8	8
9	10 c. multicoloured	8	8
10	12 c. multicoloured	10	8
11	25 c. multicoloured	20	15
12	$1 multicoloured	1·75	80
13	$2 multicoloured	2·75	1·50
14	$3 multicoloured	3·25	2·25
15	$5 multicoloured	5·00	3·50
4/15	*Set of* 12	12·00	8·00

1974 (17 Sept). *World Cup Football Championships. As Nos.* 619/27 *of Grenada but additionally inscr* "GRENADINES".

16	½ c. Type **201**	5	5
17	1 c. East Germany v Australia	5	5
18	2 c. Yugoslavia v Brazil	5	5
19	10 c. Scotland v Zaire	8	5
20	25 c. Netherlands v Uruguay	20	15
21	50 c. Sweden v Bulgaria	35	25
22	75 c. Italy v Haiti	45	30
23	$1 Poland v Argentina	55	40
16/23	*Set of* 8	1·50	1·10
MS24	114 × 76 mm. $2 Country flags	1·25	1·40

1974 (8 Oct). *Centenary of Universal Postal Union. Designs as Nos.* 628 *etc of Grenada, but additionally inscr* "GRENADINES".

25	8 c. Mailboat *Caesar* (1839) and helicopter	10	8
26	25 c. Messenger (1450) and satellite	25	20
27	35 c. Airmail transport	25	25
28	$1 Type **202**	60	70
MS29	172 × 109 mm. $1 Bellman and antenna; $2 18th-century postman and mail-train of the future. P 13	1·50	1·90

1974 (11 Nov). *Birth Centenary of Sir Winston Churchill. As Nos.* 637/9 *of Grenada but additionally inscr* "GRENADINES".

30	**203** 35 c. multicoloured	25	25
31	– $2 multicoloured	85	75
MS32	129 × 96 mm. 75 c. as 35 c. and $1 as $2	75	80

1974 (27 Nov). *Christmas. As Nos.* 640/8 *of Grenada but additionally inscr* "GRENADINES".

33	½ c. Type **204**	5	5
34	1 c. Niccolo di Pietro	5	5
35	2 c. Van der Weyden	5	5
36	3 c. Bastiani	5	5
37	10 c. Giovanni	8	8
38	25 c. Van der Weyden	15	15
39	50 c. Botticelli	25	25
40	$1 Mantegna	40	40
33/40	*Set of* 8	90	90
MS41	117 × 96 mm. $2 as 1 c.	85	1·00

CANCELLED REMAINDERS*. Some of the following issues have been remaindered, cancelled-to-order, at a fraction of their face value. For all practical purposes these are indistinguishable from genuine postally used copies. Our used quotations, which are indicated by an asterisk, are the same for cancelled-to-order or postally used copies.

1975 (17 Feb). *Big Game Fishing. As Nos.* 669 *etc of Grenada, but additionally inscr* "GRENADINES" *and background colours changed.*

42	½ c. Type **206**	5	5
43	1 c. Blue Marlin	5	5
44	2 c. White Marlin	5	5
45	10 c. Yellow Tuna	8	8
46	25 c. Wahoo	20	15
47	50 c. Dolphin	35	25
48	70 c. Grouper	50	30
49	$1 Great Barracuda	65	45
42/9	*Set of* 8	1·75	1·25
MS50	107 × 80 mm. $2 Blue Pointer or Mako Shark	1·40	1·50

1975 (11 Mar). *Flowers. As Nos.* 678 *etc of Grenada, but additionally inscr.* "GRENADINES".

51	½ c. Type **207**	5	5
52	1 c. Bleeding Heart (Easter Lily)	5	5
53	2 c. Poinsettia	5	5
54	3 c. Cocoa flower	5	5
55	10 c. Gladioli	8	8
56	25 c. Redhead/Yellowhead	20	15
57	50 c. Plumbago	35	25
58	$1 Orange flower	55	35
51/8	*Set of* 8	1·25	90
MS59	102 × 82 mm. $2 Barbados Gooseberry	1·25	1·40

3 "Christ Crowned with Thorns" (Titian)

4 "Dawn" (detail from Medici Tomb)

(Des M. Shamir. Litho Format)

1975 (24 June). *Easter. T* **3** *and similar vert designs showing Crucifixion and Deposition scenes by the artists listed. Multicoloured. P* 14½.

60	½ c. Type **3**	5	5*
61	1 c. Giotto	5	5*
62	2 c. Tintoretto	5	5*
63	3 c. Cranach	5	5*
64	35 c. Caravaggio	15	5*
65	75 c. Tiepolo	35	10*
66	$2 Velasquez	80	30*
60/6	*Set of* 7	1·25	60*
MS67	105 × 90 mm. $1 Titian. P 13	50	30

(Des M. Shamir. Litho Format)

1975 (16 July). 500*th Birth Anniv of Michelangelo. T* **4** *and similar vert designs. Multicoloured. P* 14½.

68	½ c. Type **4**	5	5*
69	1 c. "Delphic Sibyl"	5	5*
70	2 c. "Giuliano de Medici"	5	5*
71	40 c. "The Creation" (detail)	20	5*
72	50 c. "Lorenzo de Medici"	25	5*
73	75 c. "Persian Sibyl"	40	10*
74	$2 "Head of Christ"	80	20*
68/74	*Set of* 7	1·60	50*
MS75	118 × 96 mm. $1 "The Prophet Jeremiah". P 13	60	30

1975 (12 Aug). *Butterflies. Designs as Nos.* 729 *etc of Grenada, but additionally inscr* "GRENADINES". *P* 14½.

76	½ c. Emperor	5	5
77	1 c. Queen	5	5
78	2 c. Tiger Pierid	5	5
79	35 c. Cracker	35	20
80	45 c. Scarce Bamboo Page	45	25
81	75 c. Apricot	70	40
82	$2 Purple King Shoemaker	1·40	1·00
76/82	*Set of* 7	2·75	1·75
MS83	104 × 77 mm. $1 Bamboo Page P. 13	85	85

5 Progress "Standard" Badge

(Des J.W. Litho Format)

1975 (22 Aug). 14*th World Scout Jamboree, Norway. T* **5** *and similar horiz designs. Multicoloured. P* 14½.

84	½ c. Type **5**	5	5*
85	1 c. Boatman's badge	5	5*
86	2 c. Coxswain's badge	5	5*
87	35 c. Interpreter's badge	25	5*
88	45 c. Ambulance badge	30	5*
89	75 c. Chief Scout's award	50	10*
90	$2 Queen's Scout award	1·10	20*
84/90	*Set of* 7	2·00	50*
MS91	106 × 80 mm. $1 Venture award. P 13	80	15*

6 The Surrender of Lord Cornwallis

(Des J.W. Litho Questa)

1975 (30 Sept)–**76**. *Bicentenary of American Revolution* (1*st issue*). *Multicoloured.* (*a*) *Horiz designs as T* **6**. *P* 14.

92	½ c. Type **6**	5	5*
93	1 c. Minute-men	5	5*
94	2 c. Paul Revere's ride	5	5*
95	3 c. Battle of Bunker Hill	5	5*
96	5 c. Fifer and drummers	5	5*
97	45 c. Backwoodsman	50	8*
98	75 c. Boston Tea Party	65	8*
99	$2 Naval engagement	1·75	8*

(*b*) *Larger designs. P* 11 (16.1.76)

100	$2 George Washington (35 × 60 *mm*)	2·00	1·50
101	$2 White House and flags (60 × 35 *mm*)	2·00	1·50
92/101	*Set of* 10	6·50	3·25
MS102	Two sheets 113 × 128 mm containing No. 100, and 128 × 113 mm containing No. 101. Imperf	4·00	3·00

See also Nos. 176/**MS**183

7 Fencing

8 "Madonna and Child" (Dürer)

(Des J.W. Ltd. Litho Format)

1975 (27 Oct). *Pan-American Games, Mexico City. T* **7** *and similar horiz designs. Multicoloured. P* 14½.

103 ½ c. Type **7** 5 5*
104 1 c. Hurdling 5 5*
105 2 c. Pole-vaulting 5 5*
106 35 c. Weightlifting 15 5*
107 45 c. Throwing the javelin 15 5*
108 75 c. Throwing the discus 30 10*
109 $2 Diving 75 20*
103/109 . . *Set of* 7 1·25 50*
MS110 78 × 104 mm. $1 Sprinter. P 13 . . 50 15*

1975 (5 Nov)–**76**. *As Nos.* 649A/68A *of Grenada but additionally inscribed* "GRENADINES". *Multicoloured.*

111 ½ c. Yachts, Port Saline . . 5 5
112 1 c. Yacht Club race, St. George's . . 5 5
113 2 c. Carenage taxi . . 5 5
114 3 c. Large working boats . . 5 5
115 5 c. Deep-water dock, St. George's . . 5 5
116 6 c. Cocoa beans in drying trays . . 5 5
117 8 c. Nutmegs . . 5 5
118 10 c. Rum distillery, River Antoine Estate, *circa* 1785 . . 5 5
119 12 c. Cocoa tree . . 5 5
120 15 c. Fishermen landing catch at Fontenoy . . 5 5
121 20 c. Parliament Building, St. George's . . 8 8
122 25 c. Fort George cannons . . 10 10
123 35 c. Pearls Airport . . 15 15
124 50 c. General Post Office . . 20 20
125 75 c. Caribs Leap, Sauteurs Bay . . 40 40
126 $1 Carenage, St. George's . . 60 60
127 $2 St. George's Harbour by night . . 1·25 1·25
128 $3 Grand Anse beach . . 1·75 1·75
129 $5 Canoe Bay and Black Bay from Point Saline Lighthouse . . 3·00 3·00
130 $10 Sugar-loaf Island from Levera Beach (1.76) . . 5·00 5·00
111/30 . . *Set of* 20 12·00 12·00

(Des M. Shamir. Litho Questa)

1975 (17 Dec). *Christmas. T* **8** *and similar vert designs showing "Virgin and Child". Multicoloured. P* 14.

131 ½ c. Type **8** . . 5 5*
132 1 c. Dürer . . 5 5*
133 2 c. Correggio . . 5 5*
134 40 c. Botticelli . . 20 5*
135 50 c. Niccolo da Cremona . . 25 5*
136 75 c. Correggio . . 30 10*
137 $2 Correggio . . 70 20*
131/7 . . *Set of* 7 1·40 50*
MS138 114 × 102 mm. $1 Bellini . . 50 15*

9 Bleeding Tooth

(Des J.W. Litho Questa)

1976 (13 Jan). *Shells. T* **9** *and similar horiz designs. Multicoloured. P* 14.

139 ½ c. Type **9** . . 5 5*
140 1 c. Wedge Clam . . 5 5*
141 2 c. Hawk Wing Conch . . 5 5*
142 3 c. *Distorsio clathrata* . . 5 5*
143 25 c. Scotch Bonnet . . 20 5*
144 50 c. King Helmet . . 40 12*
145 75 c. Queen Conch . . 65 15*
139/45 . . *Set of* 7 1·25 30*
MS146 79 × 105 mm. $2 Atlantic Triton . . 1·25 30*

10 Cocoa Thrush

(Des J.W. Litho Questa)

1976 (4 Feb). *Flora and Fauna. T* **10** *and similar horiz designs. Multicoloured. P* 14.

147 ½ c. *Lignum vitae* . . 5 5
148 1 c. Type **10** . . 5 5
149 2 c. Tarantula . . 5 5
150 35 c. Hooded Tanager . . 65 45
151 50 c. *Nyctaginaceae* . . 80 50
152 75 c. Grenada Dove . . 1·50 1·25
153 $1 Marine Toad . . 2·00 1·50
147/53 . . *Set of* 7 4·50 3·50
MS154 108 × 84 mm. $2 Blue-hooded Euphonia 3·50 3·50

11 Hooked Sailfish

(Des G. Drummond. Litho Questa)

1976 (17 Feb). *Tourism. T* **11** *and similar horiz designs. Multicoloured. P* 14.

155 ½ c. Type **11** . . 5 5
156 1 c. Careened schooner, Carriacou . . 5 5
157 2 c. Carriacou Annual Regatta . . 5 5
158 18 c. Boat building on Carriacou . . 15 12
159 22 c. Workboat race, Carriacou Regatta . . 20 15
160 75 c. Cruising off Petit Martinique . . 50 40
161 $1 Water skiing . . 65 55
155/61 . . *Set of* 7 1·50 1·25
MS162 105 × 87 mm. $2 Yacht racing at Carriacou 1·25 1·40

12 Making a Camp Fire

13 "Christ Mocked" (Bosch)

(Des G. Vasarhelyi. Litho Questa)

1976 (17 Mar). *50th Anniv of Girl Guides in Grenada. T* **12** *and similar horiz designs. Multicoloured. P* 14.

163 ½ c. Type **12** . . 5 5
164 1 c. First aid . . 5 5
165 2 c. Nature study . . 5 5
166 50 c. Cookery . . 40 40
167 $1 Sketching . . 80 80
MS168 85 × 110 mm. $2 Guide playing guitar . . 1·60 1·75

(Des PAD Studio. Litho Questa)

1976 (28 Apr). *Easter. T* **13** *and similar vert designs. Multicoloured. P* 14.

169 ½ c. Type **13** . . 5 5
170 1 c. "Christ Crucified" (Antonello da Messina) 5 5
171 2 c. "Adoration of the Trinity" (Dürer) . . 5 5
172 3 c. "Lamentation of Christ" (Dürer) . . 5 5
173 35 c. "The Entombment" (Van der Weyden) . . 25 25
174 $3 "The Entombment" (Raphael) . . 1·50 2·00
169/74 . . *Set of* 6 1·75 2·25
MS175 57 × 72 mm. $2 "Blood of the Redeemer" (G. Bellini) . . 1·25 1·60

14 Frigate *South Carolina*

(Des J.W. Litho Questa)

1976 (18 May). *Bicentenary of American Revolution* (2nd issue). *T* **14** *and similar horiz designs. Multicoloured. P* 14.

176 ½ c. Type **14** . . 5 5
177 1 c. Schooner *Lee* . . 5 5
178 2 c. H.M.S. *Roebuck* . . 5 5
179 35 c. *Andrea Doria* . . 85 55
180 50 c. Sloop *The Providence* . . 1·00 70
181 $1 American flagship *Alfred* . . 2·50 1·75
182 $2 Frigate *Confederacy* . . 3·50 3·00
176/82 . . *Set of* 7 7·00 5·50
MS183 72 × 85 mm. $3 Cutter *Revenge* . . 5·00 5·00

15 Piper "Apache"

(Des J.W. Litho Format)

1976 (10 June). *Aeroplanes. T* **15** *and similar horiz designs. Multicoloured. P* 14.

184 ½ c. Type **15** . . 5 5
185 1 c. Beech "Twin Bonanza" . . 5 5
186 2 c. D.H. "Twin Otter" . . 5 5
187 40 c. Britten Norman "Islander" . . 35 35
188 50 c. D.H. "Heron" . . 40 40
189 $2 H.S. "748" . . 2·25 1·75
184/9 . . *Set of* 6 2·75 2·40
MS190 71 × 85 mm. $3 B.A.C. "1-11" . . 2·75 2·75

16 Cycling

17 "Virgin and Child" (Cima)

(Des J.W. Litho Format)

1976 (1 July). *Olympic Games, Montreal. T* **16** *and similar horiz designs. Multicoloured. P* 14.

191 ½ c. Type **16** . . 5 5
192 1 c. Pommel horse . . 5 5
193 2 c. Hurdling . . 5 5
194 35 c. Shot putting . . 15 15
195 45 c. Diving . . 20 20
196 75 c. Sprinting . . 35 35
197 $2 Rowing . . 80 80
191/7 . . *Set of* 7 1·50 1·50
MS198 101 × 76 mm. $3 Sailing . . 1·75 1·90

(Litho Format)

1976 (19 Oct). *Christmas. T* **17** *and similar multicoloured designs. P* 13½.

199 ½ c. Type **17** . . 5 5
200 1 c. "The Nativity" (Romanino) . . 5 5
201 2 c. "The Nativity" (Romanino) (*different*) . . 5 5
202 35 c. "Adoration of the Kings" (Bruegel) . . 25 25
203 50 c. "Madonna and Child" (Girolamo) . . 30 30
204 75 c. "Adoration of the Magi" (Giorgione) (*horiz*) . . 40 40
205 $2 "Adoration of the Kings" (School of Fra Angelico) (*horiz*) . . 75 85
199/205 . . *Set of* 7 1·60 1·75
MS206 120 × 100 mm. $3 "The Holy Family" (Garofalo) . . 1·25 1·60

18 Alexander Graham Bell and First Telephone

(Des G. Vasarhelyi. Litho Questa)

1977 (28 Jan). *Telephone Centenary* (1976). *T* **18** *and similar horiz designs showing Alexander Graham Bell and telephone. Multicoloured. P* 14.

207 ½ c. Type **18** . . 5 5
208 1 c. Telephone, 1895 . . 5 5
209 2 c. Telephone, 1900 . . 5 5
210 35 c. Telephone, 1915 . . 35 35
211 75 c. Telephone, 1920 . . 65 65
212 $1 Telephone, 1929 . . 90 90
213 $2 Telephone, 1963 . . 1·75 1·75
207/13 . . *Set of* 7 3·50 3·50
MS214 107 × 78 mm. $3 Telephone, 1976 . . 2·00 2·25

19 Coronation Coach

20 Royal Visit

(Des Jennifer Toombs. Litho and embossed Walsall. (Nos. 215/18). Des and litho Walsall (Nos. 219/22))

1977 (7 Feb). *Silver Jubilee. Multicoloured.*

(*a*) *Sheet stamps. Horiz designs as T* **19**. *P* 13½

215 35 c. Type **19** . . 25 15
216 $2 Queen entering Abbey . . 1·00 60
217 $4 Queen crowned . . 1·50 85
MS218 100 × 70 mm. $5 The Mall on Coronation Night . . 1·90 1·60

Nos. 215/17 also exist perf 11 (*Price for set of* 3 £2.50 *mint or used*) from additional sheetlets of 3 stamps and 1 label. These have different background colours from the stamps perforated 13½, which come from normal sheets of 25.

(*b*) *Booklet stamps. Vert designs as T* **20**. *Roul* 5 × *imperf.** *Self-adhesive*

219 35 c. Type **20** . . 15 15
a. Booklet pane of 6 . . 1·00
220 50 c. Crown of St. Edward . . 40 60
a. Booklet pane. Nos. 220/2 . . 3·00

221 $2 The Queen and Prince Charles 1·50 1·40
222 $5 Royal Standard 1·60 1·50

*Nos. 219/22 are separated by various combinations of rotary knife (giving a straight edge) and roulette.

21 "Disrobing of Christ" (Fra Angelico)

22 "The Virgin adoring the Child" (Correggio)

(Des J.W. Litho Questa)

1977 (5 July). *Easter. Vert designs as T* **21** *showing paintings by the artists given. Multicoloured. P* 14.

223 ½ c. Type **21** 5 5
224 1 c. Fra Angelico 5 5
225 2 c. El Greco 5 5
226 18 c. El Greco 12 12
227 35 c. Fra Angelico 25 25
228 50 c. Giottino 30 30
229 $2 Antonello da Messina 1·10 1·10
223/9 *Set of* 7 1·60 1·60
MS230 121 × 94 mm. $3 Fra Angelico 1·50 1·50

(Des J.W. Litho Questa)

1977 (17 Nov). *Christmas. T* **22** *and similar vert designs. Multicoloured. P* 14.

231 ½ c. Type **22** 5 5
232 1 c. "Virgin and Child" (Giorgione) 5 5
233 2 c. "Virgin and Child" (Morales) 5 5
234 18 c. "Madonna della Tenda" (Raphael) 8 10
235 35 c. "Rest on the Flight into Egypt" (Van Dyck) 15 15
236 50 c. "Madonna and Child" (Lippi) 25 25
237 $2 "Virgin and Child" (Lippi) (*different*) 90 90
231/7 *Set of* 7 1·25 1·25
MS238 114 × 99 mm. $3 "Virgin and Child with Angels and Saints" (Ghirlandaio) 1·50 1·60

ROYAL VISIT W.I. 1977

(23)

1977 (23 Nov). *Royal Visit. Nos.* 215/18 *optd with T* **23**. *P* 13½.

239 35 c. Type **19** 35 20
240 $2 Queen entering Abbey 1·25 75
241 $4 Queen crowned 1·50 95
MS242 100 × 70 mm. $5 The Mall on Coronation Night 2·25 1·50

This overprint also exists on the stamps perforated 11, mentioned below No. **MS**218 (*Price for set of* 3 £2 *mint or used*).

24 Life-saving

(Des G. Drummond. Litho Questa)

1977 (7 Dec). *Caribbean Scout Jamboree, Jamaica. T* **24** *and similar horiz designs. Multicoloured. P* 14.

243 ½ c. Type **24** 5 5
244 1 c. Overnight hike 5 5
245 2 c. Cubs tying knots 5 5
246 22 c. Erecting a tent 15 10
247 35 c. Gang show limbo dance 25 15
248 75 c. Campfire cooking 60 35
249 $3 Sea Scouts' yacht race 2·25 2·00
243/9 *Set of* 7 3·00 2·50
MS250 109 × 85 mm. $2 Pioneering project—Spring bridge 1·60 1·60

25 Blast-off

(Des J.W. Litho Questa)

1978 (3 Feb). *Space Shuttle. T* **25** *and similar horiz designs. Multicoloured. P* 14.

251 ½ c. Type **25** 5 5
252 1 c. Booster jettison 5 5
253 2 c. External tank jettison 5 5
254 22 c. Working in orbit 10 10
255 50 c. Shuttle re-entry 25 25
256 $3 Shuttle landing 1·50 1·50
251/6 *Set of* 6 1·75 1·75
MS257 85 × 103 mm. $2 Shuttle being towed 1·10 1·25

26 Alfred Nobel and Physiology/Medicine Medal

(Des J.W. Litho Questa)

1978 (22 Feb). *Nobel Prize Awards. T* **26** *and similar horiz designs. Multicoloured. P* 14.

258 ½ c. Type **26** 5 5
259 1 c. Physics and Chemistry medal 5 5
260 2 c. Peace medal 5 5
261 22 c. Nobel Institute, Oslo 10 10
262 75 c. Peace Prize committee 35 35
263 $3 Literature medal 1·50 1·50
258/63 *Set of* 6 1·90 1·90
MS264 127 × 103 mm. $2 Peace medal and Nobel's will 1·10 1·25

27 German Zeppelin Stamp of 1930

(Des J.W. Litho Questa)

1978 (15 Mar). *75th Anniv of First Zeppelin Flight and 50th Anniv of Lindbergh's Trans-atlantic Flight. T* **27** *and similar horiz designs. Multicoloured. P* 14 × 13½.

265 5 c. Type **27** 5 5
266 15 c. French "Concorde" stamp, 1970 8 8
267 25 c. Liechtenstein Zeppelin stamp, 1931 12 12
268 35 c. Panama Lindbergh stamp, 1928 20 20
269 50 c. Russian airship stamp, 1931 25 25
270 $3 Spanish Lindbergh stamp, 1930 1·50 1·50
265/70 *Set of* 6 2·00 2·00
MS271 140 × 79 mm. 75 c. U.S.A. Lindbergh stamp, 1927; $2 German *Hindenburg* stamp, 1936 1·40 1·60

28 Coronation Ring

29 Drummer, Royal Regiment of Fusiliers.

(Des J.W. Litho Questa (Nos. 272/5). Manufactured by Walsall (Nos. 276/8))

1978 (12 Apr). *25th Anniv of Coronation. Multicoloured.*

(*a*) *Sheet stamps. Horiz designs as T* **28**. *P* 14

272 50 c. Type **28** 45 30
273 $2 Queen's Orb 80 70
274 $2.50, Imperial State Crown 90 80
MS275 97 × 67 mm. $5 Queen Elizabeth II 2·00 1·60

Nos. 272/4 also exist perf 12 (*Price for set of* 3 £2 *mint or used*) from additional sheetlets of 3 stamps and 1 label, issued 2 June. These have different background colours from the stamps perforated 14, which come from normal sheets of 50.

(*b*) *Booklet stamps. Vert designs as T* **29**. *Roul* 5 × *imperf.* * *Self-adhesive*

276 18 c. Type **29** 15 30
a. Booklet pane. Nos. 276/7 × 3 1·10
277 50 c. Drummer, Royal Anglian Regiment 25 45
278 $5 Drum Major, Queen's Regiment 2·00 2·50
a. Booklet pane of 1 2·00

*Nos. 276/7 are separated by various combinations of rotary-knife (giving a straight edge) and roulette. No. 278 exists only with straight edges.

30 "Le Chapeau de Paille"

31 Wright *Flyer*

(Litho Questa)

1978 (18 May). *400th Birth Anniv of Rubens. T* **30** *and similar vert designs. Multicoloured. P* 14.

279 5 c. Type **30** 5 5
280 15 c. "Achilles slaying Hector" 8 8
281 18 c. "Helene Fourment and her Children" 10 10
282 22 c. "Rubens and Isabella Brandt" 12 12
283 35 c. "The Ildefonso Altarpiece" 20 20
284 $3 "Heads of Negroes" (detail) 1·25 1·40
279/84 *Set of* 6 1·60 1·60
MS285 85 × 127 mm. $2 "Self-portrait" 1·00 1·10

(Des BG Studio. Litho Questa)

1978 (10 Aug). *75th Anniv of Powered Flight. T* **31** *and similar designs. P* 14.

286 5 c. black, chestnut and pale blue 5 5
287 15 c. black, vermilion and yellow-ochre 5 5
288 18 c. black, vermilion and yellow-ochre 5 5
289 25 c. multicoloured 10 15
290 35 c. black, purple and magenta 15 20
291 75 c. multicoloured 30 35
292 $3 black, magenta and new blue 1·25 1·40
286/92 *Set of* 7 1·75 2·00
MS293 126 × 83 mm. $2 black, blue and bright blue-green 80 90

Designs: *Vert*—15 c. Orville Wright; 18 c. Wilbur Wright. *Horiz*—25, 75 c., $3, Wright *Flyer* (*all different*); 35 c. Wright glider; $2, Various Wright aircraft.

32 Audubon's Shearwater

33 Players with Ball

(Des Jennifer Toombs. Litho Questa)

1978 (28 Sept). *Birds. T* **32** *and similar multicoloured designs. P* 14.

294 5 c. Type **32** 10 10
295 10 c. Semi-palmated Plover 15 15
296 18 c. Purple-throated Carib (*horiz*) 20 20
297 22 c. Red-billed Whistling Duck (*horiz*) 25 25
298 40 c. Purple Martin (*horiz*) 45 45
299 $1 White-tailed Tropic Bird 1·40 1·40
300 $2 Long-billed Curlew 2·50 2·50
294/300 *Set of* 7 4·50 4·50
MS301 78 × 78 mm. $5 Snowy Egret 4·25 4·25

(Des G. Vasarhelyi. Litho Questa)

1978 (2 Nov). *World Cup Football Championship, Argentina. T* **33** *and similar vert designs showing football scenes. P* 14.

302 15 c. multicoloured 5 5
303 35 c. multicoloured 20 20
304 50 c. multicoloured 25 25
305 $3 multicoloured 1·60 1·60
MS306 114 × 85 mm. $2 multicoloured 1·00 1·10

34 Captain Cook and Kalaniopu (king of Hawaii), 1778

35 "Virgin at Prayer"

(Des BG Studio. Litho Questa)

1978 (13 Dec). *250th Birth Anniv of Captain Cook and Bicentenary of Discovery of Hawaii. T* **34** *and similar horiz designs. Multicoloured. P* 14.

307 18 c. Type **34** 25 10
308 22 c. Captain Cook and native of Hawaii 30 12
309 50 c. Captain Cook and death scene, 14 February 1779 65 30
310 $3 Captain Cook and offering ceremony 2·75 2·25
MS311 171 × 113 mm. $4 *Resolution* (*vert*) 3·00 3·50

(Des M. Rubin. Litho Questa)

1978 (20 Dec). *Christmas. Paintings by Dürer. T* **35** *and similar vert designs. Multicoloured. P* 14.

312 40 c. Type **35** 20 20
313 60 c. "The Dresden Altarpiece" 30 35
314 90 c. "Madonna and Child with St. Anne" 40 45
315 $2 "Madonna and Child with Pear" 80 90
MS316 114 × 84 mm. $4 "Salvator Mundi" 1·75 1·90

36 *Strelitzia reginae*

37 Children with Pig

(Des J.W. Litho Questa)

1979 (15 Feb). *Flowers. T* **36** *and similar vert designs. Multicoloured. P* 14.
317 22 c. Type **36** 20 15
318 40 c. *Euphorbia pulcherrima* 30 25
319 $1 *Heliconia humilis* 70 60
320 $3 *Thunbergia alata* .. .. .. 1·75 1·40
MS321 114 × 90 mm. $2 *Bougainvillea glabra* .. 1·00 1·00

(Des G. Drummond. Litho Questa)

1979 (22 Mar). *International Year of the Child. T* **37** *and similar horiz designs. Multicoloured. P* 14.
322 18 c. Type **37** 10 10
323 50 c. Children with donkey 25 25
324 $1 Children with goats 30 35
325 $3 Children fishing .. .. 1·25 1·50
MS326 104 × 86 mm. $4 Child with coconuts .. 1·50 1·60

38 20,000 *Leagues Under the Sea*

(Des G. Vasarhelyi. Litho Questa)

1979 (20 Apr). *150th Birth Anniv of Jules Verne (author). T* **38** *and similar horiz designs showing scenes from his books and modern technological developments. Multicoloured. P* 14.
327 18 c. Type **38** 10 10
328 38 c. *From the Earth to the Moon* 20 20
329 75 c. *From the Earth to the Moon (different)* .. 35 35
330 $3 *Five Weeks in a Balloon* .. .. .. 1·25 1·50
MS331 111 × 86 mm. $4 *Around the World in 80 days* .. .. 1·50 1·60

39 Sir Rowland Hill and Mail Van

(Des BG Studio. Litho Questa)

1979 (30 July). *Death Centenary of Sir Rowland Hill. T* **39** *and similar horiz designs showing Sir Rowland Hill and mail transport. Multicoloured. P* 14.
332 15 c. Type **39** 10 10
333 $1 Ship 55 55
334 $2 Train 95 95
335 $3 "Concorde" .. .. 1·50 1·50
MS336 85 × 67 mm. $4 Sir Rowland Hill .. 1·50 1·60

Nos. 332/5 also exist perf 12 (*Price for set of* 4 £3 *mint or used*) from additional sheetlets of 5 stamps and 1 label issued 6 September. These have different background colours to the stamps perforated 14, which come from normal sheets of 40.

40 "Virgin and Child Enthroned" (11th-century Byzantine)

41 Great Hammerhead Shark

(Des G. Vasarhelyi. Litho Questa)

1979 (23 Oct). *Christmas. Sculptures. T* **40** *and similar vert designs. Multicoloured. P* 14.
337 6 c. Type **40** 5 5
338 25 c. "Presentation in the Temple" (Andre Beauneveu) 10 12
339 30 c. "Flight to Egypt", Utrecht, *circa* 1510 .. 12 15
340 40 c. "Madonna and Child" (Jacopo della Quercia) 15 20
341 90 c. "Madonna della Mela" (Luca della Robbia) 35 40
342 $1 "Madonna and Child" (Antonio Rossellino) 40 45
343 $2 "Madonna", Antwerp, 1700 .. .. 75 80
337/43 .. .. *Set of* 7 1·75 2·00
MS344 125 × 95 mm. $4 "Virgin", Krumau .. 1·50 1·60

(Des J.W. Litho Questa)

1979 (9 Nov). *Marine Life. T* **41** *and similar horiz designs. Multicoloured. P* 14 × 13½.
345 40 c. Type **41** 25 25
346 45 c. Banded Butterflyfish 25 25
347 50 c. Permit (fish) 30 30
348 60 c. Threaded Turban (shell) 35 35
349 70 c. Milk Conch (shell) 40 40
350 75 c. Great Blue Heron 40 40
351 90 c. Coloured Atlantic Natica (shell) 50 50
352 $1 Red-footed Booby 55 55
345/52 .. .. *Set of* 8 2·75 2·75
MS353 99 × 86 mm. $2.50 Collared Plover .. 1·25 1·25

42 Goofy as Doctor

43 Classroom

(Litho Format)

1979 (12 Dec). *International Year of the Child. Walt Disney Cartoon Characters. T* **42** *and similar multicoloured designs showing characters at various occupations. P* 11.
354 ½ c. Type **42** 5 5
355 1 c. Mickey Mouse as admiral 5 5
356 2 c. Goofy as fireman 5 5
357 3 c. Minnie Mouse as nurse 5 5
358 4 c. Mickey Mouse as drum major 5 5
359 5 c. Donald Duck as policeman 5 5
360 10 c. Donald Duck as pilot 5 5
361 $2 Goofy as postman (*horiz*) .. .. 1·25 1·25
362 $2.50, Donald Duck as train driver (*horiz*) .. 1·40 1·40
354/62 .. .. *Set of* 9 2·75 2·75
MS363 128 × 102 mm. $3 Mickey Mouse as fireman. P 13½ .. .. 1·75 1·90

1980 (10 Mar). *1st Anniv of Revolution. Nos.* 116 *and* 119/30 *optd with T* **258** *of Grenada.*
364 6 c. Cocoa beans in drying trays 5 5
365 12 c. Cocoa Tree 5 5
366 15 c. Fishermen landing catch at Fontenoy .. 5 5
367 20 c. Parliament Building, St. George's .. 5 5
368 25 c. Fort George cannons 10 10
369 35 c. Pearls Airport 15 15
370 50 c. General Post Office 25 25
371 75 c. Caribs Leap, Sauteurs Bay 30 30
372 $1 Carenage, St. George's 40 40
373 $2 St. George's Harbour by night 70 70
374 $3 Grand Anse Beach .. .. .. 1·40 1·40
375 $5 Canoe Bay and Black Bay from Point Saline Lighthouse .. .. 1·90 1·90
376 $10 Sugar Loaf Island from Levera Beach .. 3·50 3·50
364/76 .. .. *Set of* 13 8·00 8·00

(Des BG Studio. Litho Questa)

1980 (12 Mar). *75th Anniv of Rotary International. T* **43** *and similar horiz designs. Multicoloured. P* 14.
377 6 c. Type **43** 5 5
378 30 c. Rotary International emblem encircled by people of different races 15 15
379 60 c. Rotary International executive presenting doctor with cheque 30 35
380 $3 Nurses with young patients .. .. 1·25 1·50
MS381 85 × 72 mm. $4 Paul P. Harris (founder) 1·50 1·60

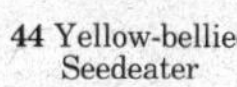

44 Yellow-bellied Seedeater

45 Running

(Des G. Drummond. Litho Questa)

1980 (14 Apr). *Wild Birds. T* **44** *and similar vert designs. Multicoloured. P* 14.
382 25 c. Type **44** 35 15
383 40 c. Blue-hooded Euphonia 45 25
384 90 c. Yellow Warbler 90 80
385 $2 Tropical Mockingbird .. .. .. 1·60 1·60
MS386 83 × 110 mm. $3 Barn Owl .. .. 2·25 2·25

(Des G. Vasarhelyi. Litho Questa)

1980 (21 Apr). *Olympic Games, Moscow. T* **45** *and similar horiz designs. Multicoloured. P* 14.
387 30 c. Type **45** 12 15
388 40 c. Football 15 20
389 90 c. Boxing 35 40
390 $2 Wrestling 75 90
MS391 104 × 75 mm. $4 Athletes in silhouette .. 1·50 1·60

LONDON 1980

(**46**)

47 Longspine Squirrelfish

1980 (6 May). *"London 1980" International Stamp Exhibition. Nos.* 332/5 *optd with T* **46**. *P* 12.
392 15 c. Type **39** 15 15
393 $1 Ship 50 50
394 $2 Train 85 85
395 $3 "Concorde" .. .. 1·40 1·50

(Des G. Drummond. Litho Questa)

1980 (6 Aug). *Fishes. Horiz designs as T* **47**. *Multicoloured. P* 14.
396 ½ c. Type **47** 5 5
397 1 c. Blue Chromis 5 5
398 2 c. Foureye Butterfly Fish 5 5
399 4 c. Sergeant Major 5 5
400 5 c. Yellowtail Snapper 5 5
401 6 c. Mutton Snapper 5 5
402 10 c. Cocoa Damselfish 5 8
403 12 c. Royal Gramma 5 8
404 15 c. Cherubfish 8 10
405 20 c. Blackbar Soldierfish 10 12
406 25 c. Comb Grouper 12 15
407 30 c. Longsnout Butterflyfish 15 20
408 40 c. Pudding Wife 20 25
409 50 c. Midnight Parrotfish 30 35
410 90 c. Redspotted Hawkfish 50 55
411 $1 Hogfish 55 60
412 $3 Beau Gregory .. .. 1·75 2·00
413 $5 Rock Beauty .. .. 2·75 3·00
414 $10 Barred Hamlet .. .. 5·75 6·00
396/414 .. .. *Set of* 19 11·25 12·25

(Litho Walsall)

1980 (7 Oct). *Christmas. Walt Disney Cartoon Scenes from "Bambi". Horiz designs as T* **42**. *Multicoloured. P* 11.
415 ½ c. Bambi with Mother 5 5
416 1 c. Bambi with quails 5 5
417 2 c. Bambi meets Thumper the rabbit 5 5
418 3 c. Bambi meets Flower the skunk 5 5
419 4 c. Bambi and Faline 5 5
420 5 c. Bambi with his father 5 5
421 10 c. Bambi on ice 5 5
422 $2.50, Faline with foals .. .. .. 1·25 1·25
423 $3 Bambi and Faline .. .. .. 1·50 1·50
415/23 .. .. *Set of* 9 2·75 2·75
MS424 127 × 102 mm. $4 Bambi as Prince of the Forest (*vert*) .. .. 1·75 1·90

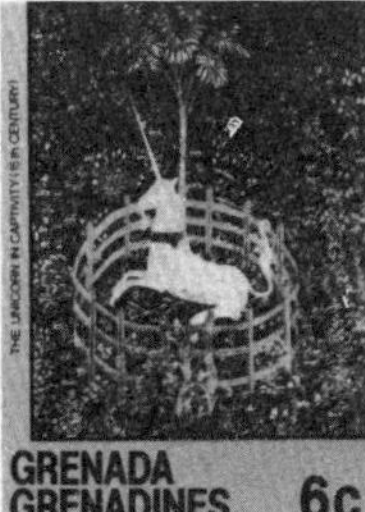

48 "The Unicorn in Captivity" (15th-century unknown artist)

49 "Bust of a Woman"

(Litho Format)

1981 (25 Jan). *Paintings. T* **48** *and similar multicoloured designs. P* 13½.
425 6 c. Type **48** 5 5
426 10 c. "The Fighting *Temeraire*" (Turner) (*horiz*) 8 8
427 25 c. "Sunday Afternoon on the Ile de la Grande-Jatte" (Georges-Pierre Seurat) (*horiz*) 15 15
428 90 c. "Max Schmitt in a Single Scull" (Thomas Eakins) (*horiz*) 55 55
429 $2 "The Burial of the Count of Orgaz" (El Greco) .. .. 1·10 1·10
430 $3 "George Washington" (Gilbert Stuart) .. 1·50 1·50
425/30 .. .. *Set of* 6 3·00 3·00
MS431 66 × 101 mm. $5 "Kaiser Karl de Grosse" (detail, Dürer) .. .. 2·50 2·50

(Litho Format)

1981 (26 Jan). *50th Anniv of Walt Disney's Cartoon Character, Pluto. Vert designs as T* **42**. *Multicoloured. P* 13½.
432 $2 Mickey Mouse serving birthday cake to Pluto .. .. 1·25 1·25
MS433 127 × 101 mm. $4 Pluto in scene from film *Pluto's Dream House* .. .. 2·25 2·40

No. 432 was printed in small sheets of 8 stamps.

(Litho Format)

1981 (14 Apr). *Easter. Walt Disney Cartoon Characters. Vert designs as T* **42**. *Multicoloured. P* 11.
434 35 c. Chip 25 25
435 40 c. Dewey 25 25
436 $2 Huey .. .. 1·10 1·10
437 $2.50, Mickey Mouse .. .. 1·40 1·40
MS438 126 × 102 mm. $4 Jiminy Cricket. P 13½ 2·10 2·25

(Des J.W. Litho Questa)

1981 (5 May). *Birth Centenary of Picasso. T* **49** *and similar vert designs. Multicoloured. P* 14.
439 6 c. Type **49** 5 5
440 40 c. Woman (study for "Les Demoiselles d'Avignon") 25 25
441 90 c. "Nude with raised Arms (The Dancer of Avignon)" 55 55
442 $4 "The Dryad" .. .. 2·10 2·10
MS443 103 × 128 mm. $5 "Les Demoiselles d'Avignon". Imperf .. .. 2·50 2·50

50 Balmoral Castle

51 Lady Diana Spencer

(Des J.W. Litho Format)

1981 (16 June). *Royal Wedding. T* **50** *and similar vert designs. Multicoloured.* (a) *P* 14½.

444 40 c. Prince Charles and Lady Diana Spencer .. 25 25
445 $2 Type **50** .. .. 1·00 1·00
446 $4 Prince Charles as parachutist .. .. 1·90 1·90
MS447 97 × 84 mm. $5 Royal Coach .. .. 2·25 2·25

(*b*) *P* 14½ × 14

448 30 c. As No. 444 .. .. 25 25
449 40 c. Type **50** 30 30

The 30 and 40 c. values were each printed in small sheets of 6 including one *se-tenant* stamp-size label.

The $4 value, with changed background colour, also exists perforated 14½ × 14 (*price* £1·50 *mint or used*) from similar sheetlets in addition to the original version from sheets of 40.

(Manufactured by Walsall)

1981 (16 June). *Royal Wedding. Booklet stamps. T* **51** *and similar multicoloured designs. Roul* 5 × *imperf**. *Self-adhesive.*

450 $1 Type **51** 55 55
a. Booklet pane. Nos. 450/1 each × 3 .. 4·50
451 $2 Prince Charles .. .. 1·00 1·00
452 $5 Prince Charles and Lady Diana Spencer (*horiz*) .. .. 3·25 3·25
a. Booklet pane of 1 .. .. 3·25

*The $1 and $2 values were each separated by various combinations of rotary knife (giving a straight edge) and roulette. The $5 value exists only with straight edges.

52 Amy Johnson (1st solo flight, Britain to Australia by Woman, May 1930)

53 "747" Carrier

(Des BG Studio. Litho Questa)

1981 (13 Oct). *"Decade for Women". Famous Female Aviators. T* **52** *and similar vert designs. Multicoloured. P* 14.

453 30 c. Type **52** 20 20
454 70 c. Mme la Baronne de Laroche (1st qualified woman pilot, March 1910) 45 45
455 $1.10, Ruth Nichols (solo Atlantic flight attempt, June 1931) 60 60
456 $3 Amelia Earhart (1st North Atlantic solo flight by woman, May 1932) .. .. 1·75 1·75
MS457 90 × 85 mm. $5 Valentina Nikolayeva-Tereshkova (1st woman in space, June 1963) .. 2·25 2·25

(Litho Questa)

1981 (2 Nov). *Christmas. Horiz designs as T* **42** *showing scenes from Walt Disney's cartoon film "Lady and the Tramp". P* 13½.

458 ½ c. multicoloured 5 5
459 1 c. multicoloured 5 5
460 2 c. multicoloured 5 5
461 3 c. multicoloured 5 5
462 4 c. multicoloured 5 5
463 5 c. multicoloured 5 5
464 10 c. multicoloured 5 5
465 $2.50, multicoloured .. .. 1·25 1·25
466 $3 multicoloured .. .. 1·50 1·50
458/66 .. .. *Set of* 9 2·75 2·75
MS467 128 × 103 mm. $5 multicoloured .. .. 2·25 2·40

(Des M. Brodie. Litho Format)

1981 (2 Nov). *Space Shuttle Project. T* **53** *and similar horiz designs. Multicoloured. P* 14½.

468 10 c. Type **53** 8 8
469 40 c. Re-entry 20 20
470 $1.10, External tank separation 60 60
471 $3 Touchdown .. .. 1·60 1·60
MS472 117 × 89 mm. $5 Launch .. .. .. 2·25 2·40

OMNIBUS ISSUES

Details, together with prices for complete sets, of the various Omnibus issues from the 1935 Silver Jubilee series to date are included in a special section following Zululand at the end of the catalogue.

54 Footballer

55 Mail Van and Stage-Coach

(Des Clover Mill. Litho Questa)

1981 (30 Nov). *World Cup Football Championship, Spain* (1982). *T* **54** *and similar vert designs showing footballers. P* 14.

473 20 c. multicoloured 10 10
474 40 c. multicoloured 20 20
475 $1 multicoloured 55 55
476 $2 multicoloured .. .. 1·10 1·10
MS477 106 × 128 mm. $4 multicoloured .. .. 2·10 2·25

Nos. 473/6 were each printed in small sheets of 6 including one *se-tenant* stamp-size label.

(Des G. Vasarhelyi. Litho Format)

1982 (13 Jan). *Centenary of U.P.U. Membership. T* **55** *and similar horiz designs. Multicoloured. P* 14½.

478 30 c. Type **55** 15 15
479 40 c. U.P.U. emblem 20 20
480 $2.50, Liner and sailing ship .. .. .. 1·25 1·25
481 $4 Airliner and biplane .. .. 2·10 2·10
MS482 117 × 78 mm. $5 Streamlined diesel-electric, and steam trains .. .. 2·40 2·50

56 National Sports Meeting

(Des M. Diamond. Litho Format)

1982 (19 Feb). *75th Anniv of Boy Scout Movement and* 125*th Birth Anniv of Lord Baden-Powell. T* **56** *and similar horiz designs. Multicoloured. P* 14½.

483 6 c. Type **56** 5 5
484 90 c. Sea scouts sailing 45 45
485 $1.10, Handicraft 65 65
486 $3 Animal tending .. .. 1·60 1·60
MS487 100 × 71 mm. $5 Music around campfire .. 2·25 2·50

57 White Peacock

58 Prince and Princess of Wales

(Des J.W. Litho Questa)

1982 (24 Mar). *Butterflies. T* **57** *and similar horiz designs. Multicoloured. P* 14.

488 30 c. Type **57** 20 20
489 40 c. St. Vincent Long-tail Skipper 25 25
490 $1.10, Painted Lady 65 65
491 $3 Orion .. .. 1·60 1·60
MS492 103 × 77 mm. $5 Silver Spot .. .. 2·25 2·50

(Des PAD Studio. Litho Questa)

1982 (1 July). *21st Birthday of Princess of Wales. T* **58** *and similar vert designs. Multicoloured. P* 14½ × 14.

493 50 c. Blenheim Palace 30 30
494 60 c. As 50 c. 40 35
495 $1 Type **58** 50 50
496 $2 Type **58** .. .. 1·00 1·00
497 $3 Princess of Wales .. .. 1·60 1·40
498 $4 As $3 .. .. 2·00 1·75
493/8 .. .. *Set of* 6 5·50 4·75
MS499 103 × 75 mm. $5 Princess Diana (*different*) 2·40 2·25

Nos. 493, 495 and 497 come from sheetlets of 5 stamps and 1 label.

59 "New Deal"—Soil Conservation

60 "Presentation of Christ in the Temple"

(Des M. Diamond. Litho Questa)

1982 (27 July). *Birth Centenary of Franklin D. Roosevelt. T* **59** *and similar horiz designs. Multicoloured. P* 14.

500 30 c. Type **59** 15 15
501 40 c. Roosevelt and George Washington Carver (scientist) 20 20
502 70 c. Civilian conservation corps and reafforestation 45 45
503 $3 Roosevelt with Pres. Barclay of Liberia, Casablanca Conference, 1943 .. .. 1·60 1·60
MS504 100 × 72 mm. $5 Roosevelt delivering address at Howard University .. .. 2·25 2·40

1982 (30 Aug). *Birth of Prince William of Wales. Nos.* 493/9 *optd with T* **171** *of Antigua.*

505 50 c. Blenheim Palace 30 30
506 60 c. As 50 c. 35 35
507 $1 Type **58** 50 50
508 $2 Type **58** .. .. 1·00 1·00
509 $3 Princess of Wales .. .. 1·40 1·40
510 $4 As $3 .. .. 1·75 1·75
505/10 .. .. *Set of* 6 4·75 4·75
MS511 103 × 75 mm. $5 Princess Diana (*different*) 2·10 2·25

Nos. 505, 507 and 509 come from sheetlets of 5 stamps and 1 label.

(Des Clover Mill. Litho Format)

1982 (2 Sept). *Easter. T* **60** *and similar vert designs depicting Easter paintings by Rembrandt. Multicoloured. P* 14½.

512 30 c. Type **60** 15 15
513 60 c. "Descent from the Cross" 30 30
514 $2 "Raising of the Cross" .. .. .. 1·10 1·10
515 $4 "Resurrection of Christ" .. .. .. 2·10 2·25
MS516 101 × 126 mm. $5 "The Risen Christ" .. 2·25 2·40

61 "Santa Fe"

(Des Artists International. Litho Format)

1982 (4 Oct). *Famous Trains of the World. T* **61** *and similar vert designs. Multicoloured. P* 15.

517 10 c. Type **61** 12 12
518 40 c. "Mistral" 30 30
519 70 c. "Rheingold" 45 45
520 $1 "ET 403" 55 55
521 $1.10, "Mallard" 65 65
522 $2 "Tokaido" .. .. 1·25 1·25
517/22 .. .. *Set of* 6 3·00 3·00
MS523 121 × 95 mm. $5 "Settebello" .. .. 2·50 2·75

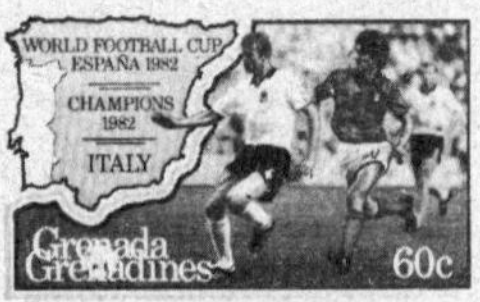

62 Footballers

(Des D. Miller. Litho Questa)

1982 (2 Dec). *World Cup Football Championship Winners. T* **62** *and similar horiz designs. P* 14 × 13½.

524 60 c. multicoloured 35 35
525 $4 multicoloured .. .. 2·10 2·10
MS526 92 × 134 mm. $5 multicoloured .. .. 2·40 2·50

(Litho Questa)

1982 (14 Dec). *Christmas. Horiz designs as T* **42** *showing scenes from Walt Disney's cartoon film "The Rescuers". P* 13½.

527 ½ c. multicoloured 5 5
528 1 c. multicoloured 5 5
529 2 c. multicoloured 5 5
530 3 c. multicoloured 5 5
531 4 c. multicoloured 5 5
532 5 c. multicoloured 5 5
533 10 c. multicoloured 8 8
534 $2.50, multicoloured .. .. 1·25 1·25
535 $3 multicoloured .. .. 1·50 1·50
527/35 .. .. *Set of* 9 2·75 2·75
MS536 120 × 96 mm. $5 multicoloured .. .. 2·25 2·25

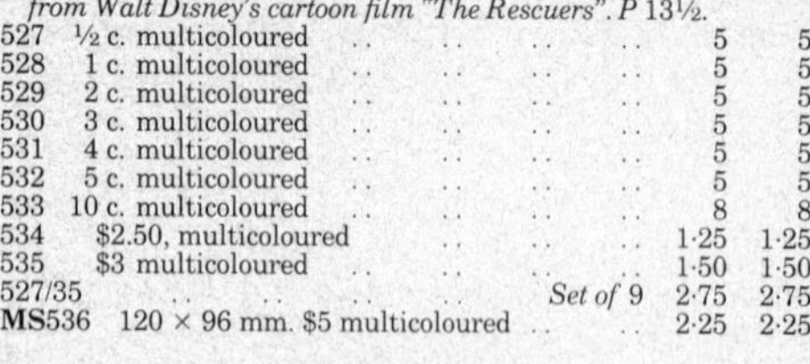

63 Pilot Whale

(Des Artists International. Litho Questa)

1983 (10 Jan). *Save the Whales. T* **63** *and similar horiz designs. Multicoloured. P* 14.

537 10 c. Type **63** 15 15
538 60 c. Dall Porpoise 45 45
539 $1.10, Humpback Whale 70 70
540 $3 Bowfin Whale .. .. 1·90 1·90
MS541 113 × 84 mm. $5 Spotted Dolphin .. .. 2·50 2·75

64 "David and Goliath"

(Des Design Images. Litho Format)

1983 (15 Feb). *500th Birth Anniv of Raphael. T* **64** *and similar horiz designs showing painting details. Multicoloured. P* 13½.
542 25 c. Type **64** .. 12 15
543 30 c. "David sees Bathsheba" .. 15 20
544 90 c. "Triumph of David" .. 40 45
545 $4 "Anointing of Solomon" .. 1·90 2·00
MS546 126 × 101 mm. $5 "Anointing of David" .. 2·50 2·75

65 Voice and Visual Communication

(Des Artists International. Litho Questa)

1983 (7 Apr). *World Communications Year. T* **65** *and similar horiz designs. Multicoloured. P* 14.
547 30 c. Type **65** .. 15 20
548 60 c. Ambulance .. 30 35
549 $1.10, Helicopters .. 50 55
550 $3 Satellite .. 1·40 1·50
MS551 127 × 85 mm. $5 Diver and dolphin .. 2·75 3·00

66 Chrysler "Imperial Roadster", 1931

(Des R. Sauber. Litho Format)

1983 (4 May). *75th Anniv of Model "T" Ford Car. T* **66** *and similar horiz designs showing cars of the 20th century. Multicoloured. P* 14½.
552 10 c. Type **66** .. 5 8
553 30 c. Doble steam car, 1925 .. 15 20
554 40 c. Ford "Mustang", 1965 .. 20 25
555 60 c. Packard tourer, 1930 .. 30 35
556 70 c. Mercer "Raceabout" 1913 .. 35 40
557 90 c. Corvette "Stingray", 1963 .. 40 45
558 $1.10, Auburn "851 Supercharger Speedster", 1935 .. 50 55
559 $2.50, Pierce-Arrow "Silver Arrow", 1933 .. 1·10 1·25
560 $3 Duesenberg dual cowl phaeton, 1929 .. 1·40 1·50
561 $4 Mercedes-Benz "SSK", 1928 .. 1·90 2·00
552/61 .. *Set of* 10 5·50 6·50
MS562 119 × 90 mm. $5 McFarlan "Knickerbocker" cabriolet, 1923 .. 2·50 2·75

Nos. 552/61 were each issued in sheets of eight stamps with a stamp-size label in the centre position.

67 Short "Solent" Flying Boat

(Des W. Wright. Litho Questa)

1983 (18 July). *Bicentenary of Manned Flight. T* **67** *and similar horiz designs. Multicoloured. P* 14.
563 40 c. Type **67** .. 20 25
564 70 c. Curtiss "R3C-2" seaplane .. 35 40
565 90 c. Hawker "Nimrod" biplane .. 40 45
566 $4 Montgolfier balloon .. 1·90 2·00
MS567 112 × 85 mm. $5 *Viktoria Luise* (airship) .. 2·50 2·75

68 Goofy

69 Weightlifting

(Litho Walsall)

1983 (7 Nov). *Christmas. T* **68** *and similar vert designs showing Disney cartoon characters in scenes from "Jingle Bells" (Christmas carol). Multicoloured. P* 11.
568 ½ c. Type **68** .. 5 5
569 1 c. Clarabelle Cow .. 5 5
570 2 c. Donald Duck .. 5 5
571 3 c. Pluto .. 5 5
572 4 c. Morty and Ferdie .. 5 5
573 5 c. Huey, Dewey and Louie .. 5 5
574 10 c. Daisy and Chip 'n Dale .. 5 8
575 $2.50, Big Bad Wolf .. 1·40 1·50
576 $3 Mickey Mouse .. 1·75 1·90
568/76 .. *Set of* 9 3·25 3·50
MS577 102 × 124 mm. $5 Donald Duck in sleigh. P 13½ .. 2·75 3·00

(Des N. Waldman. Litho Questa)

1984 (9 Jan). *Olympic Games, Los Angeles. T* **69** *and similar vert designs. Multicoloured. P* 14.
578 30 c. Type **69** .. 15 20
579 60 c. Gymnastics .. 35 40
580 70 c. Archery .. 40 45
581 $4 Sailing .. 2·25 2·40
MS582 70 × 102 mm. $5 Basketball .. 2·75 3·00

70 Frangipani

71 Goofy

(Des J. Cooter. Litho Questa)

1984 (9 Apr). *Flowers. T* **70** *and similar vert designs. Multicoloured. P* 15.
583 15 c. Type **70** .. 10 12
584 40 c. Dwarf Poinciana .. 25 30
585 70 c. Walking Iris .. 45 50
586 $4 Lady's Slipper .. 2·50 2·75
MS587 66 × 57 mm. $5 Brazilian Glory Vine .. 3·25 3·50

(Litho Format)

1984 (1 May). *Easter. T* **71** *and similar vert designs showing Disney cartoon characters with Easter hats. Multicoloured. P* 11.
588 ½ c. Type **71** .. 5 5
589 1 c. Chip and Dale .. 5 5
590 2 c. Daisy Duck and Huey .. 5 5
591 3 c. Daisy Duck .. 5 5
592 4 c. Donald Duck .. 5 5
593 5 c. Merlin and Madam Mim .. 5 5
594 10 c. Flower .. 8 10
595 $2 Minnie and Mickey Mouse .. 1·25 1·40
596 $4 Minnie Mouse .. 2·50 2·75
588/96 .. *Set of* 9 3·50 4·00
MS597 126 × 100 mm. $5 Minnie Mouse (*different*). P 13½ × 14 .. 3·25 3·50

72 Bobolink

19TH U.P.U CONGRESS
HAMBURG

(**73**)

(Litho Questa)

1984 (21 May). *Songbirds. T* **72** *and similar horiz designs. Multicoloured. P* 14.
598 40 c. Type **72** .. 25 30
599 50 c. Eastern Kingbird .. 35 40
600 60 c. Barn Swallow .. 40 45
601 70 c. Yellow Warbler .. 45 50
602 $1 Rose-breasted Grosbeak .. 65 70
603 $1.10, Yellowthroat .. 70 75
604 $2 Catbird .. 1·25 1·40
598/604 .. *Set of* 7 3·50 3·75
MS605 71 × 65 mm. $5 Fork-tailed Flycatcher .. 3·25 3·50

1984 (19 June). *Universal Postal Union Congress, Hamburg. Nos.* 585/7 *optd with T* 73.
606 70 c. Walking Iris .. 45 50
607 $4 Lady's Slipper .. 2·50 2·75
MS608 66 × 57 mm. $5 Brazilian Glory Vine .. 3·25 3·50

74 *Geeststar*

(Litho Format)

1984 (16 July). *Ships. T* **74** *and similar horiz designs. Multicoloured. P* 15.
609 30 c. Type **74** .. 20 25
610 60 c. *Daphne* .. 40 45
611 $1.10, *Southwind* .. 70 75
612 $4 *Oceanic* .. 2·50 2·75
MS613 108 × 80 mm. $5 Pirate ship .. 3·25 3·50

(Litho Questa)

1984 (22 Aug). *450th Death Anniv of Correggio (painter). Multicoloured designs as T* **296** *of Grenada showing paintings. P* 14.
614 10 c. "The Hunt—Blowing the Horn" .. 8 10
615 30 c. "St. John the Evangelist" (*horiz*) .. 20 25
616 90 c. "The Hunt—The Deer's Head" .. 60 65
617 $4 "The Virgin crowned by Christ" (*horiz*) .. 2·50 2·75
MS618 73 × 63 mm. $5 "Martyrdom of the Four Saints" .. 3·25 3·50

(Litho Questa)

1984 (22 Aug). *150th Birth Anniv of Edgar Degas (painter). Vert designs as T* **297** *of Grenada showing paintings. Multicoloured. P* 14.
619 25 c. "The Song of the Dog" .. 15 20
620 70 c. "Cafe-concert" .. 45 50
621 $1.10, "The Orchestra of the Opera" .. 70 75
622 $3 "The Dance Lesson" .. 2·00 2·10
MS623 53 × 73 mm. $5 "Madame Camus at the Piano" .. 3·25 3·50

(Des Bonny Redecker. Litho Questa)

1984 (21 Sept). *"Ausipex" International Stamp Exhibition, Melbourne. Horiz designs as T* **298** *of Grenada. Multicoloured. P* 14.
624 $1.10, Queen Victoria Gardens, Melbourne 70 75
625 $4 Ayers Rock .. 2·50 2·75
MS626 107 × 76 mm. $5 River Yarra, Melbourne 3·25 3·50

75 Col. Steven's Model (1825)

(Des Bonny Redecker. Litho Format)

1984 (3 Oct). *Railway Locomotives. T* **75** *and similar horiz designs. Multicoloured. P* 15.
627 20 c. Type **75** .. 12 15
628 50 c. *Royal George* (1827) .. 35 40
629 60 c. *Stourbridge Lion* (1829) .. 40 45
630 70 c. *Liverpool* (1830) .. 45 50
631 90 c. *South Carolina* (1832) .. 60 65
632 $1.10, *Monster* (1836) .. 70 75
633 $2 *Lafayette* (1837) .. 1·25 1·40
634 $4 *Lion* (1838) .. 2·50 2·75
627/34 .. *Set of* 8 5·75 6·25
MS635 Two sheets, each 100 × 70 mm. (a) $5 Sequin's engine (1829); (b) $5 *Der Adler* (1835) .. *Set of* 2 *sheets* 6·50 7·00

1984 (28 Oct). *Opening of Point Saline International Airport. Nos.* 547, 549 *and* **MS**551 *optd as T* **300** *of Grenada.*
636 30 c. Type **65** .. 20 25
637 $1.10, Helicopters .. 70 75
MS638 127 × 85 mm. $5 Diver and dolphin .. 3·25 3·50

The overprint on No. **MS**638 appears on the sheet margin as for No. **MS**1371 of Grenada.

OFFICIAL STAMPS

1982 (June). *Various stamps optd with Type* O **1** *of Grenada.*

(*a*) *Nos.* 400/12 *and* 414
O 1 5 c. Yellowtail Snapper .. 5 5
O 2 6 c. Mutton Snapper .. 5 5
O 3 10 c. Cocoa Damselfish .. 5 5
O 4 12 c. Royal Gramma .. 5 5
O 5 15 c. Cherubfish .. 5 8
O 6 20 c. Blackbar Soldierfish .. 8 10
O 7 25 c. Comb Grouper .. 10 10
O 8 30 c. Longsnout Butterflyfish .. 12 12
O 9 40 c. Pudding Wife .. 15 20
O10 50 c. Midnight Parrotfish .. 20 25
O11 90 c. Redspotted Hawkfish .. 40 35
O12 $1 Hogfish .. 40 40
O13 $3 Beau Gregory .. 1·25 1·25
O14 $10 Barred Hamlet .. 4·25 3·75

(*b*) *Nos.* 444/6 *and* 448/9
O15 30 c. Prince Charles and Lady Diana Spencer 1·50 1·75
O16 40 c. Prince Charles and Lady Diana Spencer 1·00 1·25
O17 40 c. Type **50** .. 2·00 2·25
O18 $2 Type **50** .. 2·50 2·75
O19 $4 Prince Charles as parachutist .. 6·50 7·00

The Royal Wedding $4 from sheetlets, perforated 14½ × 14 and with changed background colour, also exists with this overprint (*Price* £8.50 *mint*, £9 *used*).

(c) *Nos.* 473/6

O20	**54**	20 c. multicoloured	8	10
O21	–	40 c. multicoloured	15	20
O22	–	$1 multicoloured	35	40
O23	–	$2 multicoloured	70	75
O1/23		.. .. *Set of* 23	19·00	20·00

Griqualand West

Griqualand West was situated to the North of Cape Colony, bounded on the north by what became British Bechuanaland and on the east by the Orange Free State.

The area was settled in the early nineteenth century by the Griqua tribal group, although many members of the tribe, including the paramount chief, migrated to Griqualand East (between Basutoland and the east coast of South Africa) in 1861–63. There was little European involvement in Griqualand West before 1866, but in that year the diamond fields along the Vaal River were discovered. Sovereignty was subsequently claimed by the Griqua Chief, the Orange Free State and the South African Republic (Transvaal). In 1871 the British authorities arbitrated in favour of the Griqua Chief who promptly ceded his territory to Great Britain. Griqualand West became a separate Crown Colony in 1873.

During the initial stages of the prospecting boom mail was passed via the Orange Free State, but a post office connected to the Cape Colony postal system was opened at Klip Drift (subsequently Barkly) in late 1870. Further offices at De Beer's New Rush (subsequently Kimberley), Douglas and Du Toit's Pan (subsequently Beaconsfield) were open by September 1873.

Cape of Good Hope stamps were in use from October 1871, but those originating in Griqualand West can only be identified after the introduction of Barred Oval Diamond Numeral cancellations in 1873. Numbers known to have been issued in the territory are:

1 De Beers N.R. (New Rush) (subsequently Kimberley)
3 Junction R. & M. (Riet and Modder Rivers)
4 Barkly
6 or 9 Du Toit's Pan (subsequently Beaconsfield)
8 Langford (transferred to Douglas)
10 Thornhall

PRICES FOR STAMPS ON COVER

The stamps of Griqualand West are worth from × 8 the price quoted for used stamps, when on cover from the territory.

Stamps of the Cape of Good Hope, Crown CC, perf 14, overprinted.

1874 (Sept). *T* **4** *with manuscript surcharge.*

1		1d. in red on 4d. blue	£550	£800

G. W.

1877 (Mar). *T* **6** *optd.* "G.W." *as above.* (a) *In black.*

2		1d. carmine-red	£350	60·00
		a. Overprint double	†	£750
		(b) *In red*		
3		4d. blue	£250	50·00

G (1) G (2) G (3) G (4) G (5) G (6)

G (7) G (8) G (9) G (10) G (11)

G (12) *G* (13) *G* (14)

1877 (Apr)–**78.** *T* **4** (4*d.* (*Nos.* 17/23), 6*d. and* 1*s.*) *and T* **6** (*others*) *optd with large capital letter.* (a) *First printing. Optd in black on* 1*d. or red* (*others*). *Seven principal varieties of opt* (*T* **1, 2, 3, 4, 5, 6,** *and* **8**).

4	**1**	½d. grey-black	9·00	9·00
5	**2**	½d. grey-black	13·00	15·00
6	**3**	½d. grey-black	6·00	7·50
7	**4**	½d. grey-black	13·00	13·00
8	**5**	½d. grey-black	15·00	14·00
9	**6**	½d. grey-black	9·00	8·00
10	**8**	½d. grey-black		
11	**1**	1d. carmine-red	5·50	5·50
12	**2**	1d. carmine-red	16·00	14·00
13	**3**	1d. carmine-red	7·50	7·50
14	**4**	1d. carmine-red	11·00	11·00
15	**5**	1d. carmine-red	30·00	16·00
16	**6**	1d. carmine-red	7·50	7·00
17	**1**	4d. blue (T **4**)	60·00	9·00
18	**2**	4d. blue (T **4**)	£180	50·00
19	**3**	4d. blue (T **4**)	£140	20·00
20	**4**	4d. blue (T **4**)	£150	80·00
21	**5**	4d. blue (T **4**)	£150	90·00
22	**6**	4d. blue (T **4**)	90·00	22·00
23	**8**	4d. blue (T **4**)		
24	**1**	4d. blue (T **6**)	55·00	7·50
25	**2**	4d. blue (T **6**)	—	45·00
26	**3**	4d. blue (T **6**)	70·00	13·00
27	**4**	4d. blue (T **6**)	70·00	13·00
28	**5**	4d. blue (T **6**)	£120	50·00
29	**6**	4d. blue (T **6**)	48·00	12·00
30	**8**	4d. blue (T **6**)	£700	
31	**1**	6d. dull violet	35·00	14·00
32	**2**	6d. dull violet	90·00	32·00
33	**3**	6d. dull violet	50·00	11·00
34	**4**	6d. dull violet	95·00	45·00
35	**5**	6d. dull violet	90·00	45·00
36	**6**	6d. dull violet	50·00	11·00
37	**8**	6d. dull violet		
38	**1**	1s. green	48·00	10·00
		a. Opt inverted	—	£200
39	**2**	1s. green	85·00	23·00
		a. Opt inverted		
40	**3**	1s. green	24·00	7·50
41	**4**	1s. green	85·00	11·00
		a. Opt inverted		
42	**5**	1s. green	85·00	14·00
43	**6**	1s. green	45·00	10·00
		a. Opt inverted		
44	**8**	1s. green		
45	**1**	5s. orange	£200	9·00
46	**2**	5s. orange	—	25·00
47	**3**	5s. orange	£225	9·00
48	**4**	5s. orange	—	18·00
49	**5**	5s. orange	£350	15·00
50	**6**	5s. orange	£225	9·00
51	**8**	5s. orange	£1100	

The setting of the above was in two panes of 60. Sub-types of Types **1** and **2** are found. The 1d., Type **8**, of this setting can only be distinguished when *se-tenant* with Type **3**.

(b) *Second printing, in black for all values. Nine principal varieties of opt* (*T* **6** *to* **14**) (1878)

52	**7**	1d. carmine-red	7·00	7·00
53	**8**	1d. carmine-red	7·50	7·50
54	**9**	1d. carmine-red	13·00	22·00
55	**10**	1d. carmine-red	55·00	
56	**11**	1d. carmine-red	13·00	13·00
57	**12**	1d. carmine-red	55·00	55·00
58	**13**	1d. carmine-red	50·00	45·00
59	**14**	1d. carmine-red	£275	£275
60	**6**	4d. blue (T **6**)	£130	40·00
61	**7**	4d. blue (T **6**)	45·00	11·00
62	**8**	4d. blue (T **6**)	£130	28·00
63	**9**	4d. blue (T **6**)	55·00	13·00
64	**10**	4d. blue (T **6**)	£325	£100
65	**11**	4d. blue (T **6**)	£130	28·00
66	**12**	4d. blue (T **6**)	£170	50·00
67	**13**	4d. blue (T **6**)	£200	£130
68	**14**	4d. blue (T **6**)	—	£100
69	**6**	6d. dull violet	£200	55·00
70	**7**	6d. dull violet	90·00	45·00
		a. Opt double		
71	**8**	6d. dull violet	£200	50·00
72	**9**	6d. dull violet	£120	55·00
		a. Opt double		
73	**10**	6d. dull violet	£200	
74	**11**	6d. dull violet	£550	£200
75	**12**	6d. dull violet	£200	90·00
76	**13**	6d. dull violet	£325	£140
77	**14**	6d. dull violet	£700	£250

The 1d., T **6**, of this printing can only be distinguished from the same variety of the first printing when it is *se-tenant* with another type.

The type without horizontal or vertical serifs, previously illustrated as T **10**, is a broken "G" of the type now shown under that number.

Minor varieties may be found of T **7** and **12**.

Red overprints on the 4d., 1s. and 5s. Type **7** and 1s. and 5s. Type **8** exist but there is no evidence as to their status.

G (15) *G* (16) G (17)

1878 (July)–**79.** *T* **4** (4*d.* (*Nos.* 86/7), 6*d. and* 1*s.*) *and T* **6** (*others*) *optd with small capital letter.* (a) *First printing, in red or in black.*

(i) *Red overprint*

78	**15**	½d. grey-black	4·25	5·50
		a. Opt inverted	5·50	5·50
		b. Opt double	30·00	
		c. Opt double, both inverted	50·00	
79	**16**	½d. grey-black	5·50	5·50
		a. Opt inverted	5·50	7·00
		b. Opt double	50·00	50·00
		c. Opt double, both inverted		
80	**15**	4d. blue (T **6**)	£160	70·00
		a. Opt inverted	£550	50·00
81	**16**	4d. blue (T **6**)	—	55·00
		a. Opt inverted	£180	55·00
		(ii) *Black overprint*		
82	**15**	½d. grey-black	£130	70·00
		a. Opt inverted	£130	
		b. Black opt normal with additional red opt T **15** inverted	£200	
		c. Ditto, but red opt is T **16**	70·00	
83	**16**	½d. grey-black	23·00	23·00
		a. Opt inverted	23·00	23·00
		b. Black opt normal, with additional red opt T **15** inverted	90·00	
84	**15**	1d. carmine-red	5·50	4·00
		a. Opt inverted	5·50	5·50
		b. Ditto, with additional red opt T **15** inverted	19·00	20·00
		c. Ditto, with additional red opt T **16** inverted		
		d. Opt double	£120	30·00
		e. Opt double, both inverted	£120	45·00
85	**16**	1d. carmine-red	5·50	5·50
		a. Opt inverted	45·00	19·00
		b. Ditto with additional red opt T **16** inverted	45·00	45·00
		c. Opt double	—	55·00
		d. Opt double, both inverted	—	70·00
86	**15**	4d. blue (T **4**)	—	85·00
87	**16**	4d. blue (T **4**)	—	90·00
88	**15**	4d. blue (T **6**)	45·00	13·00
		a. Opt inverted	£130	55·00
		b. Opt double	—	£130
		c. Opt double, both inverted		
89	**16**	4d. blue (T **6**)	90·00	7·00
		a. Opt inverted	£140	19·00
		b. Opt double	—	£140
		c. Opt double, both inverted		
90	**15**	6d. dull violet	50·00	15·00
91	**16**	6d. dull violet	—	15·00
		(b) *Second printing, in black only* (1879)		
92	**17**	½d. grey-black	5·50	4·50
		a. Opt double	£200	£200
93		1d. carmine-red	5·50	3·25
		a. Opt inverted	—	70·00
		b. Opt double	—	£110
		c. Opt treble		

94 **17** 4d. blue (T **6**) 5·50 3·25
b. Opt double — 90·00
95 6d. mauve 50·00 5·50
a. Opt inverted — 22·00
b. Opt double £350 £130
96 1s. green 30·00 3·25
a. Opt double £170 75·00
97 5s. orange £170 5·50
a. Opt double £200 55·00
b. Opt treble — £200

Besides the type shown above, which is the normal, there are in this printing three or four minor varieties differing in the shape and size of the body of the letter. In this setting are also found at least two varieties very like the upright "antique" of the first printing in small capitals.

Beware of forged overprints.

Griqualand West was merged with Cape Colony in 1880 and the overprinted stamps became obsolete in October, 1880. The remaining stock was returned from Kimberley to Cape Town and redistributed among various post offices in Cape Colony, where they were used as ordinary Cape stamps.

Guyana

(*formerly* British Guiana)

GUYANA INDEPENDENCE 1966

(73)

1966 (26 May)–**67.** *Various stamps as Nos.* 331/45 *of British Guiana, optd with T* **73,** *by De La Rue.* (i) *Wmk Mult Script CA.*

379 2 c. myrtle-green 5 5
380 3 c. brown-olive and red-brown 2·25 1·50
381 4 c. violet 5 5
383 6 c. yellow-green 5 5
384 8 c. ultramarine 5 5
385 12 c. black and reddish brown 5 8
392 $5 ultramarine and black 42·00 30·00
379/92 *Set of* 7 42·00 30·00

(ii) *Wmk w* **12**. A. *Upright*. B. *Sideways*

No.	Value	A		B	
393	1 c.	5	5	5	5
	a. Opt omitted	70·00	—	†	
395	3 c.	5	5	†	
396	4 c.	5	5	5	5
397	5 c.	5	5	†	
398	6 c.	5	8	†	
399	8 c.	8	15	5	5
400	12 c.	10	15	10	12
401	24 c.	25	15	25	20
402	36 c.	25	25	20	20
403	48 c.	5·00	4·50	25	25
404	72 c.	35	60	55	80
405	$1	50	50	80	80
406	$2	75	1·25	1·00	1·25
407	$5	2·50	3·75	3·00	4·00
393A/407A	*Set of* 14	9·00	10·50		
393B/407B	*Set of* 11			5·75	7·00

Dates of issue: Of the above, the 1 c., 4 c., 6 c. (W w **12** upright) and the 12 c., 36 c., 72 c., $2 and $5 (W w **12** sideways) were issued on 28.2.67; the 8 c. upright wmk and the $1 sideways wmk, on 14.3.67; the rest on 26.5.66.

No. 393a is listed here as an error as there is no evidence of the 1 c. basic stamp having been issued as a printing with Block CA watermark.

See also Nos. 420/40.

74 Flag and Map

75 Arms of Guyana

(Des V. Whiteley. Photo Harrison)

1966 (26 May). *Independence. P* 14½.
408 **74** 5 c. multicoloured 5 5
409 15 c. multicoloured 5 5
410 **75** 25 c. multicoloured 10 5
411 $1 multicoloured 35 40

76 Bank Building

(Des R. Granger Barrett. Photo Enschedé)

1966 (11 Oct). *Opening of Bank of Guyana. P* 13½ × 14.
412 **76** 5 c. multicoloured 5 5
413 25 c. multicoloured 10 5

CANCELLED REMAINDERS.* In 1969 remainders of some issues were put on the market cancelled-to-order in such a way as to be indistinguishable from genuine postally used copies for all practical purposes. Our used quotations which are indicated by an asterisk are the same for cancelled-to-order or postally used copies.

77 British Guiana One Cent Stamp of 1856

(Des V. Whiteley. Litho D.L.R.)

1967 (23 Feb). *World's Rarest Stamp Commemoration. P* 12½.
414 **77** 5 c. black, magenta, silver & light ochre 5 5*
415 25 c. black, magenta, gold and light green 10 5*

78 Château Margot

GUYANA INDEPENDENCE 1966

(82)

(Des R. Granger Barrett. Photo Harrison)

1967 (26 May). *First Anniv of Independence. T* **78** *and similar multicoloured designs. P* 14 (6 c.), 14½ × 14 (15 c.) *or* 14 × 14½ (*others*).
416 6 c. Type **78** 5 5*
417 15 c. Independence Arch 5 5*
418 25 c. Fort Island (*horiz*) 10 5*
419 $1 National Assembly (*horiz*) 30 25

1967–68. *Stamps as Nos.* 331/45 *of British Guiana optd with T* **82** *locally.*

(i) *Wmk Mult Script CA*
420 1 c. black (3.10.67) 5 5
a. Opt inverted 28·00
421 2 c. myrtle-green (3.10.67) 5 5
a. "1966" for "GUYANA" 17·00
422 3 c. brown-olive and red-brown (3.10.67) 10 5
a. "1966" for "GUYANA" 12·00
b. Vert pair, one without opt £300
423 4 c. violet (*shades*) (10.67) 5 5
b. Opt inverted 35·00
424 6 c. yellow-green (11.67) 5 5
a. "1966" for "GUYANA" 18·00
b. Opt inverted 32·00
425 8 c. ultramarine (12.67) 5 5
426 12 c. black and brown (12.67) 5 5
426*a* 24 c. black and orange (date?) £120 65·00
427 $2 reddish mauve (12.67) 1·25 1·75
428 $5 ultramarine and black (12.67) 2·25 2·50

(ii) *Wmk* w **12** (*upright*)
429 1 c. black (2.68) 5 5
430 2 c. myrtle-green (2.68) 5 5
431 3 c. brown-olive and red-brown (*shades*) (3.10.67) 5 5
a. "1966" for "GUYANA" 75·00
b. Opt inverted 18·00
432 4 c. violet (2.68) 10 10
433 5 c. scarlet and black (*shades*) (3.10.67) 20 25
434 6 c. yellow-green (2.68) 10 12
435 24 c. black and bright orange (11.12.67) 12 12
a. Opt double, one diagonal (horiz pair)
436 36 c. rose-carmine and black (12.67) 12 15
437 48 c. bright ultramarine and Venetian red (12.67) 30 40
a. Opt inverted 35·00
438 72 c. carmine and emerald (12.67) 50 50
439 $1 pink, yellow, green and black (12.67) 75 70
440 $2 reddish mauve (12.67) 1·75 2·00
420/40 (*excl.* 426*a*) *Set of* 21 7·00 8·00

The "1966" errors occurred on R. 7/10 and were later corrected. Nos. 425/8 and 436/40 were issued in mid-December, but some were cancelled-to-order with a November date in error.

83 "Millie" (Blue and Yellow Macaw)

84 Wicket-keeping

(Des V. Whiteley. Photo Harrison)

1967–68. *Christmas. P* 14½ × 14. (*a*) *First issue* (6 Nov 1967).
441 **83** 5 c. yellow, new blue, blk & bronze-grn 5 5*
442 25 c. yellow, new blue, black and violet 15 5*
(*b*) *Second issue. Colours changed* (22 Jan 1968)
443 **83** 5 c. yellow, new blue, black and red 5 5*
444 25 c. yellow, new blue, blk & apple-grn 15 5*

(Des V. Whiteley. Photo Harrison)

1968 (8 Jan). *M.C.C.'s West Indies Tour. T* **84** *and similar vert designs. P* 14.
445 5 c. Type **84** 10 5*
a. Strip of 3. Nos. 445/7 70
446 6 c. Batting 10 5*
447 25 c. Bowling 30 8*

Nos. 445/7 were issued in small sheets of 9 containing three *se-tenant* strips.

87 Sunfish

102 "Christ of St John of the Cross" (Salvador Dali)

(Des R. Granger Barrett. Photo Harrison)

1968 (4 Mar). *Multicoloured designs as T* **87**, *showing fish* (1 *to* 6 c.), *birds* (10 *to* 40 c.) *or animals* (*others*). *No wmk. P* 14 × 14½.
448 1 c. Type **87** 5 5
449 2 c. Pirai 5 5
450 3 c. Lukunani 5 5
451 5 c. Hassar 5 5
452 6 c. Patua 10 5
453 10 c. Spix's Guan (*vert*) 30 5
454 15 c. Harpy Eagle (*vert*) 40 5
455 20 c. Hoatzin (*vert*) 40 5
456 25 c. Guianan Cock of the Rock (*vert*) 45 5
457 40 c. Great Kiskadee (*vert*) 45 20
458 50 c. Accouri 70 40
459 60 c. Peccary 80 45
460 $1 Labba 1·25 75
461 $2 Armadillo 3·50 2·50
462 $5 Ocelot 5·00 4·50
448/62 *Set of* 15 12·00 8·00

For Nos. 448/62 with W **106** see Nos. 485/99.

(Des and photo Harrison)

1968 (25 Mar). *Easter. P* 14.
463 **102** 5 c. multicoloured 5 5*
464 25 c. multicoloured 12 5*

103 "Efficiency Year"

104 "Savings Bonds"

(Des W. Starzmann. Litho B.W.)

1968 (22 July). *"Savings Bonds and Efficiency". P* 14.
465 **103** 6 c. multicoloured 5 5*
466 25 c. multicoloured 8 5*
467 **104** 30 c. multicoloured 12 5*
468 40 c. multicoloured 15 5*

105 Open Book, Star and Crescent

(Des R. Gates. Photo D.L.R.)

1968 (9 Oct). *1400th Anniv of the Holy Quran. P* 14.
469 **105** 6 c. black, gold and flesh 5 5*
470 25 c. black, gold and lilac 8 5*
471 30 c. black, gold and light apple-green 12 5*
472 40 c. black, gold and cobalt 15 5*

106 Lotus Blossoms

107 Broadcasting Greetings

(Des L. Pritchard; adapted G. Vasarhelyi. Litho D.L.R.)

1968 (11 Nov). *Christmas. T* **107** *and similar vert design. W* **106.** *P* 14.
473 6 c. brown, blue and green 5 5*
474 25 c. brown, reddish violet and green 10 5*
475 30 c. blue-green and turquoise-green 12 5*
476 40 c. red and turquoise-green 12 5*
Designs:—25 c. Type **107**; 30, 40 c. Map showing radio link, Guyana–Trinidad.

109 Festival Ceremony

(Des J. Cooter. Litho P.B.)

1969 (26 Feb). *Hindu Festival of Phagwah. T* **109** *and similar horiz design. Multicoloured. W* **106** *(sideways). P* 13½.
477 6 c. Type **109** 5 5
478 25 c. Ladies spraying scent 8 5
479 30 c. Type **109** 12 8
480 40 c. As 25 c. 15 12

111 "Sacrament of the Last Supper" (Dali)

112 Map showing "CARIFTA" Countries

(Photo D.L.R.)

1969 (10 Mar). *Easter. W* **106** *(sideways). P* 13½ × 13.
481 **111** 6 c. multicoloured 5 5
482 25 c. multicoloured 8 5
483 30 c. multicoloured 12 12
484 40 c. multicoloured 15 12

1969–71. *As Nos.* 448/62, *but Wmk* **106** *(sideways on* 1 *to* 6 *c. and* 50 *c. to* $5*). Chalk-surfaced paper.*
485 1 c. Type **87** 5 5
486 2 c. Pirai 5 5
487 3 c. Lukunani 5 5
488 5 c. Hassar 5 5
489 6 c. Patua 5 5
490 10 c. Spix's Guan 15 8
a. Glazed paper (21.12.71) 30 30
491 15 c. Harpy Eagle 20 12
a. Glazed paper (21.12.71) 45 60
492 20 c. Hoatzin 20 15
493 25 c. Guianan Cock of the Rock 20 10
a. Glazed paper (21.12.71) 55 60
494 40 c. Great Kiskadee 70 40
495 50 c. Accouri 50 40
496 60 c. Peccary 55 55
497 $1 Labba 85 95
a. Glazed paper (21.12.71) 2·00 2·50
498 $2 Armadillo 3·50 4·50
499 $5 Ocelot 7·50 9·50
485/99 *Set of* 15 13·00 15·00

These were put on sale by the Crown Agents on 25 March 1969 but although supplies were sent to Guyana in time they were not released there until needed as ample supplies remained of the stamps without watermark. It is understood that the 3 c. and 5 c. were put on sale in early May 1969 followed by the 25 c. but there are no records of when the remainder were released.

(Des J. Cooter. Litho P.B.)

1969 (30 Apr). *First Anniv of CARIFTA (Caribbean Free Trade Area). T* **112** *and similar design. W* **106** *(sideways on* 25 *c.). P* 13½.
500 6 c. rose-red, ultramarine and turquoise-blue 5 5
501 25 c. lemon, brown and rose-red 10 10
Design: *Horiz*—25 c. "Strength in Unity".

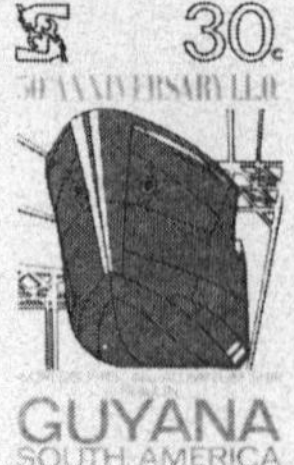

114 First all-Aluminium Ship

116 Scouts raising Flag

(Des R. Gates. Litho B.W.)

1969 (30 Apr). *50th Anniv of International Labour Organization. T* **114** *and similar design. W* **106** *(sideways on* 40 *c.). P* 12 × 11 (30 *c.*) *or* 11 × 12 (40 *c.*).
502 30 c. turquoise-blue, black and silver 15 10
503 40 c. multicoloured 20 12
Design: *Horiz*—40 c. Bauxite processing plant.

(Des Jennifer Toombs. Litho B.W.)

1969 (13 Aug). *Third Caribbean Scout Jamboree and Diamond Jubilee of Scouting in Guyana. T* **116** *and similar horiz design. Multicoloured. W* **106** *(sideways). P* 13.
504 6 c. Type **116** 5 5
505 8 c. Camp-fire cooking 5 5
506 25 c. Type **116** 10 5
507 30 c. As 8 c. 12 10
508 50 c. Type **116** 30 30

118 Gandhi and Spinning-wheel

119 "Mother Sally Dance Troupe"

(Des G. Drummond. Litho Format)

1969 (1 Oct). *Birth Centenary of Mahatma Gandhi. W* **106** *(sideways). P* 14½.
509 **118** 6 c. black, brown and yellowish olive 20 10
510 15 c. black, brown and lilac 30 20

(Des V. Whiteley (5, 25 c.), J.W. (others). Litho B.W. (5, 25 c.), D.L.R. (others))

1969 (17 Nov). *Christmas. T* **119** *and similar vert design. Multicoloured. No wmk* (5, 25 *c.*) *or W* **106.** *P* 13½ (5, 25 *c.*) *or* 13 × 13½ *(others).*
511 5 c. Type **119** 5 5
a. Opt omitted 28·00
b. Opt double 25·00
512 6 c. City Hall, Georgetown *(horiz)* 5 5
a. Opt omitted 28·00
b. Opt inverted 30·00
513 25 c. Type **119** 15 5
a. Opt omitted 28·00
514 60 c. As 6 c. 25 30
Nos. 511/14 are previously unissued stamps optd as in T **119** by Guyana Lithographic Co, Ltd.

121 Forbes Burnham and Map

125 "The Descent from the Cross"

(Des L. Curtis. Litho D.L.R.)

1970 (23 Feb). *Republic Day. T* **121** *and similar designs. W* **106** *(sideways on* 15 *and* 25 *c.). P* 14.
515 5 c. sepia, ochre and pale blue 5 5
516 6 c. multicoloured 5 5
517 15 c. multicoloured 8 8
518 25 c. multicoloured 12 12

Designs: *Vert*—6 c. "Rural Self-help". *Horiz*—15 c. University of Guyana; 25 c. Guyana House.

(Des J. Cooter. Litho Questa)

1970 (24 Mar). *Easter. Paintings by Rubens. T* **125** *and similar vert design. Multicoloured. W* **106** *(inverted). P* 14 × 14½.
519 5 c. Type **125** 5 5
520 6 c. "Christ on the Cross" 5 5
521 15 c. Type **125** 10 12
522 25 c. As 6 c. 12 10

127 "Peace" and U.N. Emblem

128 "Mother and Child" (Philip Moore)

(Des and litho Harrison)

1970 (26 Oct). *25th Anniv of United Nations. T* **127** *and similar horiz design. Multicoloured. W* **106.** *P* 14.
523 5 c. Type **127** 5 5
524 6 c. U.N. Emblem, Gold-panning and Drilling 5 5
525 15 c. Type **127** 8 8
526 25 c. As 6 c. 12 12

(Des Harrison. Litho J.W.)

1970 (8 Dec). *Christmas. W* **106.** *P* 13½.
527 **128** 5 c. multicoloured 5 5
528 6 c. multicoloured 5 5
529 15 c. multicoloured 10 12
530 25 c. multicoloured 12 10

129 National Co-operative Bank

130 Racial Equality Symbol

(Des E. Samuels. Litho J.W.)

1971 (23 Feb). *Republic Day. W* **106** *(sideways). P* 14.
531 **129** 6 c. multicoloured 5 5
532 15 c. multicoloured 10 12
533 25 c. multicoloured 12 12

(Des E. Samuels. Litho Harrison)

1971 (22 Mar). *Racial Equality Year. W* **106.** *P* 14.
534 **130** 5 c. multicoloured 5 5
535 6 c. multicoloured 5 5
536 15 c. multicoloured 8 10
537 25 c. multicoloured 10 12

131 Young Volunteer felling Tree (from painting by J. Criswick).

132 Yellow Allamanda

(Des and litho Harrison)

1971 (19 July). *First Anniv of Self-help Road Project. W* **106.** *P* 14.
538 **131** 5 c. multicoloured 5 5
539 20 c. multicoloured 12 10
540 25 c. multicoloured 12 10
541 50 c. multicoloured 20 25

Two types of 25 c.:

I Flowers facing up. Value in centre.

II Flowers facing down. Value to right. Colours changed.

(Des V. Whiteley (1 to 40 c.), PAD Studio (others). Litho D.L.R. (1 to 6 c.), J.W. (10 c. to 40 c.), Format (50 c. to $5))

1971 (17 Sept)–**76.** *Flowering Plants. Vert designs as T* **132.** *Multicoloured. W* **106.** *P* 13 × 13½ (1 *to* 6 *c.*) *or* 13½ (10 *c. to* $5).
542 1 c. Pitcher Plant of Mt Roraima (15.1.72) 5 5
543 2 c. Type **132** *(shades)* 5 5
544 3 c. Hanging Heliconia 5 5
545 5 c. Annatto tree 5 5
546 6 c. Cannon-ball tree 8 5

547 10 c. Cattleya (18.9.72) 35 10
a. Perf 13 (28.1.76) 40 12
548 15 c. Christmas Orchid (18.9.72) 45 8
a. Perf 13 (3.9.76) 40 15
549 20 c. *Paphinia cristata* (18.9.72) 45 20
a. Perf 13 (28.1.76) 50 20
550 25 c. Marabunta (I) (18.9.72) .. .. 90 1·00
550*a* 25 c. Marabunta (II) (20.8.73) 30 15
ab. Perf 13 (3.9.76) 45 30
551 40 c. Tiger Beard (18.9.72) 40 30
552 50 c. *Guzmania ligulata* (3.9.73) 40 30
553 60 c. Soldier's Cap (3.9.73) 40 30
554 $1 *Chelonanthus uliginoides* (3.9.73) 50 45
555 $2 *Norantea guianensis* (3.9.73) .. 90 1·50
556 $5 *Odontadenia grandiflora* (3.9.73) .. 1·75 3·25
542/56 .. .. *Set of* 16 6·25 7·00

The watermark is often indistinct, particularly on the early printings.

133 Child praying at Bedside

134 Obverse and Reverse of Guyana $1 Coin

(Des V. Bassoo (T 133), M. Austin (25, 50 c.). Litho J.W.)

1971 (29 Nov). *Christmas. T* **133** *and similar vert design. Multicoloured. W* **106** *(sideways on* 5 c. *and* 20 c.*). P* 13½.
557 5 c. Type **133** 5 5
558 20 c. Type **133** 12 10
559 25 c. Carnival Masquerader 12 10
560 50 c. As 25 c. 25 30

(Des G. Drummond. Litho Questa)

1972 (23 Feb). *Republic Day. T* **134** *and similar vert design. W* **106** *(sideways). P* 14½ × 14.
561 **134** 5 c. silver, black and orange-red .. 5 5
562 – 20 c. silver, black and magenta .. 15 10
563 **134** 25 c. silver, black and ultramarine .. 20 15
564 – 50 c. silver, black and yellow-green .. 30 30
Design:—20, 50 c. Reverse and obverse of Guyana $1 coin.

135 Hands and Irrigation Canal

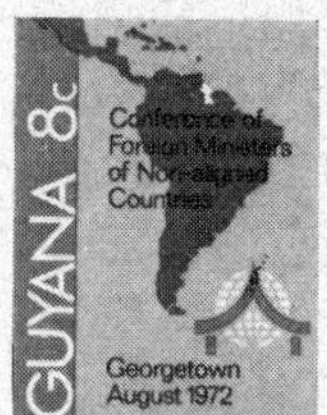

136 Map and Emblem

(Des J. Criswick. Litho J.W.)

1972 (3 Apr). *Youman Nabi (Mohammed's Birthday). W* **106**. *P* 14.
565 **135** 5 c. multicoloured 5 5
566 25 c. multicoloured 12 10
567 30 c. multicoloured 12 10
568 60 c. multicoloured 25 30

(Des J. Criswick. Litho J.W.)

1972 (20 July). *Conference of Foreign Ministers of Non-aligned Countries. W* **106**. *P* 13½.
569 **136** 8 c. multicoloured 5 5
570 25 c. multicoloured 12 12
571 40 c. multicoloured 20 20
572 50 c. multicoloured 25 25

137 Hand reaching for Sun

138 Joseph, Mary, and the Infant Jesus

(Des G. Bowen. Litho J.W.)

1972 (25 Aug). *First Caribbean Festival of Arts. W* **106**. *P* 13½.
573 **137** 8 c. multicoloured 5 5
574 25 c. multicoloured 12 12
575 40 c. multicoloured 20 20
576 50 c. multicoloured 25 25

(Des Megan Anderson. Litho B.W.)

1972 (18 Oct). *Christmas. W* **106**. *P* 13 × 13½.
577 **138** 8 c. multicoloured 5 5
578 25 c. multicoloured 12 12
579 **138** 40 c. multicoloured 25 25
580 50 c. multicoloured 25 25

139 Umana Yana (Meeting-house)

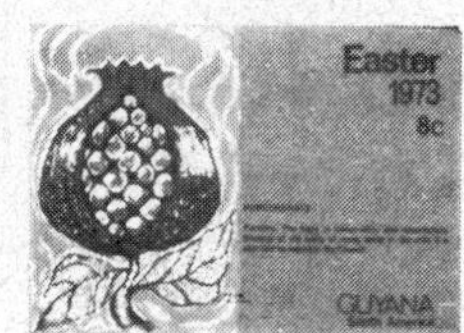

140 Pomegranate

(Des J. Cooter. Litho Questa)

1973 (23 Feb). *Republic Day. T* **139** *and similar vert design. Multicoloured. W* **106**. *P* 14.
581 8 c. Type **139** 5 5
582 25 c. Bethel Chapel 10 10
583 40 c. As 25 c. 15 20
584 50 c. Type **139** 20 20

(Des E. Samuels. Litho Format)

1973 (19 Apr). *Easter. T* **140** *and similar multicoloured design. W* **106** *(sideways on* 25 *and* 40 c.*). P* 14½ *(*8, 50 c.*) or* 13½ *(others).*
585 8 c. Type **140** 5 5
586 25 c. Cross and map (34 × 47 *mm*) .. 10 10
587 40 c. As 25 c. 15 20
588 50 c. Type **140** 20 20

141 Stylized Blood Cell

142 Steel-Band Players

(Des S. Greaves. Litho Harrison)

1973 (1 Oct). *25th Anniv of Guyana Red Cross. W* **106**. *P* 14.
589 **141** 8 c. vermilion and black 5 5
590 25 c. vermilion and bright purple .. 20 15
591 40 c. vermilion and ultramarine .. 25 30
592 50 c. vermilion and blackish olive .. 35 35

(Des E. Samuels; adapted J. Cooter. Litho Questa)

1973 (20 Nov). *Christmas. T* **142** *and similar vert design. Multicoloured. W* **106**. *P* 14 *(*8, 25 c.*) or* 13½ *(others).*
593 8 c. Type **142** 5 5
594 25 c. Type **142** 10 10
595 40 c. "Virgin and Child" (stained-glass window) (34 × 47 *mm*) 20 25
596 50 c. As 40 c. 20 25

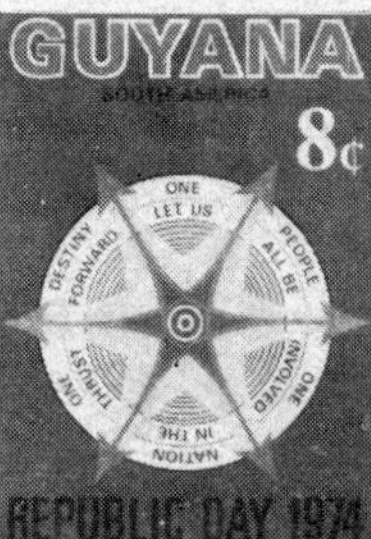

143 Symbol of Progress

(144)

(Des PAD Studio. Litho Questa)

1974 (23 Feb). *Republic Day. T* **143** *and similar vert design. Multicoloured. W* **106**. *P* 13½.
597 8 c. Type **143** 5 5
598 25 c. Wai-Wai Indian 10 10
599 40 c. Type **143** 15 20
600 50 c. As 25 c. 20 25

1974 (18 Mar). *No. 546 surch with T* **144**.
601 8 c. on 6 c. Cannon-ball tree 12 12
See also No. 620.

OMNIBUS ISSUES

Details, together with prices for complete sets, of the various Omnibus issues from the 1935 Silver Jubilee series to date are included in a special section following Zululand at the end of the catalogue.

145 Kite with Crucifixion Motif

146 British Guiana 24 c. Stamp of 1874

(Des R. Savory; adapted J. Cooter. Litho Questa)

1974 (8 Apr). *Easter. T* **145** *and similar vert design. W* **106**. *P* 13½.
602 **145** 8 c. multicoloured 5 5
603 – 25 c. black and dull green 10 10
604 – 40 c. black and magenta 15 20
605 **145** 50 c. multicoloured 20 25
Design:—Nos. 603/4, "Crucifixion" in pre-Columbian style.

(Des R. Savory. Litho Harrison)

1974 (18 June). *Centenary of Universal Postal Union. T* **146** *and similar horiz design. W* **106** *(sideways on* 8 *and* 40 c.*). P* 13½ × 14 *(*8, 40 c.*) or* 14 *(others).*
606 **146** 8 c. multicoloured 5 5
607 – 25 c. bright yellow-green, deep slate-violet and black 20 10
608 **146** 40 c. multicoloured 25 20
609 – 50 c. bright yellow-green, reddish chestnut and black 30 25
Design (42 × 25 *mm*):—25 c., 50 c. U.P.U. emblem and Guyana postman.

147 Guides with Banner

148 Buck Toyeau

(Des M. Broodhagen; adapted J. Cooter. Litho Questa)

1974 (1 Aug). *Girl Guides' Golden Jubilee. T* **147** *and similar horiz design. Multicoloured. W* **106** *(sideways). P* 14½.
610 8 c. Type **147** 10 8
611 25 c. Guides in camp 25 15
612 40 c. As 25 c. 35 35
613 50 c. Type **147** 35 35
MS614 170 × 137 mm. Nos. 610/13 .. 1·40 1·40

(Des S. Greaves and R. Granger Barrett. Litho Enschedé)

1974 (18 Nov). *Christmas. T* **148** *and similar vert designs. Multicoloured. W* **106**. *P* 13½ × 13.
615 8 c. Type **148** 5 5
616 35 c. Five-fingers and awaras 25 20
617 50 c. Pawpaw and tangerine 40 30
618 $1 Pineapple and sapodilla 70 70
MS619 127 × 94 mm. Nos. 615/18 .. 1·75 1·90

1975 (20 Jan). *No. 544 surch as T* **144**.
620 8 c. on 3 c. Hanging Heliconia 12 15

149 Golden Arrow of Courage

150 Old Sluice Gate

(Des L. Curtis. Litho D.L.R.)

1975 (23 Feb). *Republic Day. Guyana Orders and Decorations. T* **149** *and similar vert designs. W* **106**. *P* 13½.
621 10 c. Type **149** 5 5
622 35 c. Cacique's Crown of Honour .. 20 15
623 50 c. Cacique's Crown of Valour .. 25 20
624 $1 Order of Excellence 45 60

(Des E. Samuels; adapted PAD Studio. Litho Questa)

1975 (2 May). *Silver Jubilee of International Commission on Irrigation and Drainage. T* **150** *and similar horiz design. Multicoloured. W* **106** *(sideways on* 35 c. *and* $1*). P* 14.
625 10 c. Type **150** 5 5
626 35 c. Modern sluice gate 20 20
627 50 c. Type **150** 30 30
628 $1 As 35 c. 60 60
MS629 162 × 121 mm. Nos. 625/8. Wmk sideways 1·40 1·60

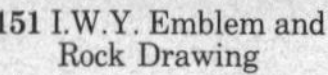

151 I.W.Y. Emblem and Rock Drawing

152 Freedom Monument

(Des C. Henriques; adapted PAD Studio. Litho Questa)

1975 (1 July). *International Women's Year. T* **151** *and similar horiz designs showing different rock drawings. W* **106** *(sideways). P* 14.

630 **151** 10 c. grey-green and yellow 5 5
631 – 35 c. reddish violet and greenish blue 25 15
632 – 50 c. royal blue and orange 35 20
633 – $1 brown and bright blue 60 50
MS634 178 × 89 mm. Nos. 630/3 1·60 1·75

(Des PAD Studio. Litho Questa)

1975 (26 Aug). *Namibia Day. T* **152** *and similar vert design. Multicoloured. W* **106.** *P* 14.

635 10 c. Type **152** 5 5
636 35 c. Unveiling of Monument 25 15
637 50 c. Type **152** 35 20
638 $1 As 35 c. 55 45

153 G.N.S. Emblem

154 Court Building, 1875 and Forester's Badge

(Des C. Henriques; adapted PAD Studio. Litho Questa)

1975 (1 Oct*). *First Anniv of National Service. W* **106.** *P* 14.

639 **153** 10 c. greenish yellow, light green and light reddish violet 5 5
640 – 35 c. orange, lt green & reddish violet 20 15
641 – 50 c. light violet-blue, light green and light yellow-brown 30 20
642 – $1 light mauve, dull green & lt emerald 65 50
MS643 196 × 133 mm. Nos. 639/42. W **106** (inverted) 1·40 1·50

*This is the local date of issue; the Crown Agents released the stamps a day later.

Nos. 640/2 are as T **153** but have different symbols within the circle.

(Des R. Savory; adapted PAD Studio. Litho Questa)

1975 (14 Nov). *Centenary of Guyanese Ancient Order of Foresters. T* **154** *and similar horiz designs. Multicoloured. W* **106** *(sideways). P* 14.

644 10 c. Type **154** 5 5
645 35 c. Rock drawing of hunter and quarry 15 10
646 50 c. Crossed axes and bugle-horn 25 15
647 $1 Bow and arrow 60 50
MS648 129 × 97 mm. Nos. 644/7 1·25 1·50

35c

(155)

156 Shoulder Flash

1976 (10 Feb). *No. 553 surch with T* **155.**

649 35 c. on 60 c. Soldier's Cap 25 30

(Des C. Henriques; adapted J.W. Litho Questa)

1976 (29 Mar). *50th Anniv of the St. John's Ambulance in Guyana. T* **156** *and similar vert designs. W* **106.** *P* 14.

650 **156** 8 c. silver, black and magenta 8 5
651 – 15 c. silver, black and orange 15 10
652 – 35 c. silver, black and green 30 25
653 – 40 c. silver, black and new blue 35 30

Nos. 651/3 are as T **156** but show different shoulder flashes.

157 Triumphal Arch

158 Flame in Archway

(Des C. Henriques. Litho J.W.)

1976 (25 May). *Tenth Anniv of Independence. T* **157** *and similar vert designs. Multicoloured. W* **106.** *P* 13½.

654 8 c. Type **157** 5 5
655 15 c. Stylised Victoria Regia lily 10 8
656 35 c. "Onward to Socialism" 20 15
657 40 c. Worker pointing the way 25 25
MS658 120 × 100 mm. Nos. 654/7. P 14½ 70 85

1976 (3 Aug). *West Indian Victory in World Cricket Cup. As Nos. 559/60 of Barbados.*

659 15 c. Map of the Caribbean 85 45
660 15 c. Prudential Cup 85 45

(Des G. Vasarhelyi. Litho J.W.)

1976 (21 Oct). *Deepavali Festival. T* **158** *and similar vert designs. Multicoloured. W* **106.** *P* 14.

661 8 c. Type **158** 8 5
662 15 c. Flame in hand 12 8
663 35 c. Flame in bowl 25 25
664 40 c. Goddess Latchmi 25 30
MS665 94 × 109 mm. Nos. 661/4 70 75

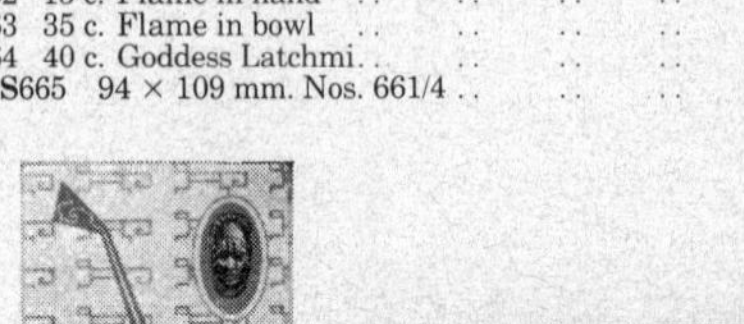

159 Festival Emblem and "Musical Instrument"

160 1 c. and 5 c. Coins

(Des C. Henriques. Litho Questa)

1977 (1 Feb). *Second World Black and African Festival of Arts and Culture, Nigeria. W* **106.** *P* 14.

666 **159** 10 c. dull red, black and gold 12 10
667 35 c. deep violet, black and gold 35 25
668 50 c. ultramarine, black and gold 45 35
669 $1 blue-green, black and gold 85 85
MS670 90 × 157 mm. Nos. 666/9 1·75 2·25

The above were scheduled for release in 1975, and when finally issued had the original inscription obliterated and a new one applied by overprinting.

(Des J.W. Litho Questa)

1977 (26 May). *New Coinage. T* **160** *and similar horiz designs. W* **106.** *P* 14.

671 8 c. multicoloured 8 8
672 15 c. yellow-brown, grey and black 12 12
673 35 c. bright yellow-green, grey and black 30 30
674 40 c. carmine-red, grey and black 35 35
675 $1 multicoloured 70 80
676 $2 multicoloured 1·40 1·60
671/6 *Set of* 6 2·75 3·00

Designs:—15 c. 10 and 25 c. coins; 35 c. 50 c. and $1 coins; 40 c. $5 and $10 coins; $1 $50 and $100 coins; $2 Reverse of $1 coin.

161 Hand Pump, *circa* 1850

162 Cuffy Monument

(Des J. Porteous Wood. Litho Harrison)

1977 (15 Nov). *National Fire Prevention Week. T* **161** *and similar horiz designs. Multicoloured. W* **106.** *P* 14 × 14½.

677 8 c. Type **161** 8 5
678 15 c. Steam engine, *circa* 1860 15 10
679 35 c. Fire engine, *circa* 1930 30 30
680 40 c. Fire engine, 1977 35 35

(Des BG Studio. Litho Questa)

1977 (7 Dec). *Cuffy Monument (commemorating 1763 Slave Revolt). W* **106.** *P* 14.

681 **162** 8 c. multicoloured 5 5
682 – 15 c. multicoloured 10 8
683 **162** 35 c. multicoloured 25 25
684 – 40 c. multicoloured 30 30

Nos. 682 and 684 show a different view of the monument.

163 Manatee

(Des BG Studio. Litho Questa)

1978 (15 Feb). *Wildlife Conservation. T* **163** *and similar multicoloured designs. W* **106** *(sideways on 8 and 15 c.). P* 14.

685 8 c. Type **163** 15 5
686 15 c. Giant sea turtle 25 15
687 35 c. Harpy Eagle (*vert*) 60 35
688 40 c. Iguana (*vert*) 65 40

164 L. F. S. Burnham (Prime Minister) and Parliament Buildings, Georgetown

165 Dr. George Giglioli (scientist and physician)

1978 (27 Apr). *25th Anniv of Prime Minister's Entry into Parliament. T* **164** *and similar horiz designs. W* **106** *(sideways). P* 13½ × 14.

689 8 c. black, violet and bluish grey 5 5
690 15 c. black, light violet-blue and bluish grey 10 8
691 35 c. black, red and bluish grey 15 20
692 40 c. black, red-orange and bluish grey 20 25
MS693 176 × 118 mm. Nos. 689/92 70 75

Designs:—15 c. Burnham, graduate and children ("Free Education"); 35 c. Burnham and industrial works (Nationalization of Bauxite industry); 40 c. Burnham and village scene ("The Co-operative Village").

(Des J.W. Litho Harrison)

1978 (4 Sept). *National Science Research Council. T* **165** *and similar multicoloured designs. W* **106** *(sideways on 10 and 50 c.). P* 13½ × 14 *(10, 50 c.) or* 14 × 13½ *(others).*

694 10 c. Type **165** 8 5
695 30 c. Institute of Applied Science and Technology (*horiz*) 25 25
696 50 c. Emblem of National Science Research Council 35 35
697 60 c. Emblem of Commonwealth Science Council (commemorating the 10th Meeting) (*horiz*) 35 35

166 *Prepona pheridamas*

167 *Agrias claudina*

(Des J. Cooter. Litho J.W.)

1978 (1 Oct)–**80.** *Butterflies. Horiz designs as T* **166** *(5 to 60 c.) or vert as T* **167** *($1 to $10). Multicoloured. W* **106.** *P* 14 × 13½ *(5 to 60 c.) or* 13 *($1 to $10).*

698 5 c. Type **166** 5 5
699 10 c. *Archonias bellona* 10 5
700 15 c. *Eryphanis polyxena* 15 5
701 20 c. *Helicopis cupido* 15 5
702 25 c. *Nessaea batesii* 15 8
702*a* 30 c. *Nymphidium mantus* (25.1.80) 20 15
703 35 c. *Siderone galanthis* 25 10
704 40 c. *Morpho rhetenor* (male) 25 12
705 50 c. *Hamadryas amphinome* 30 15
705*a* 60 c. *Papilio androgeus* (25.1.80) 30 30
706 $1 Type **167** 55 35
707 $2 *Morpho rhetenor* (female) 1·00 70
708 $5 *Morpho deidamia* 2·25 1·90
708*a* $10 *Elbella patrobas* (25.1.80) 3·75 3·50
698/708*a* *Set of* 14 8·50 6·75

168 Amerindian Stone-chip Grater in Preparation

169 Dish Aerial by Night

(Des L. Curtis. Litho Questa)

1978 (18 Dec). *National/International Heritage Year. T* **168** *and similar vert designs. Multicoloured. W* **106.** *P* 14.

709	10 c. Type **168** ..	5	5
710	30 c. Cassiri and decorated Amerindian jars ..	20	15
711	50 c. Fort Kyk-over-al ..	30	30
712	60 c. Fort Island ..	30	35

(Des L. Curtis. Litho Questa)

1979 (7 Feb). *Satellite Earth Station. T* **169** *and similar horiz designs. Multicoloured. W* **106** *(sideways). P* 14 × 14½.

713	10 c. Type **169** ..	5	5
714	30 c. Dish aerial by day ..	20	15
715	50 c. Satellite with solar veins ..	30	25
716	$3 Cylinder satellite ..	1·75	1·40

170 Sir Rowland Hill and British Guiana 1850 12 c. "Cottonreel" Stamp

171 "Me and my Sister"

(Des and litho J.W.)

1979 (11 June). *Death Centenary of Sir Rowland Hill. T* **170** *and similar multicoloured designs. W* **106** *(sideways on* 10 *and* 50 *c.). P* 14.

717	10 c. Type **170** ..	10	5
718	30 c. British Guiana 1856 1 c. black on magenta stamp *(vert)* ..	20	15
719	50 c. British Guiana 1898 1 c. stamp ..	30	25
720	$3 Printing press used for early British Guiana stamps *(vert)* ..	1·40	1·75

(Des J.W. Litho Questa)

1979 (20 Aug). *International Year of the Child. Paintings by local children. T* **171** *and similar multicoloured designs. W* **106** *(sideways on* 30, 50 *c. and* $3). *P* 13½.

721	10 c. Type **171** ..	8	5
722	30 c. "Fun with the Fowls" *(horiz)* ..	15	20
723	50 c. "Two Boys catching Ducks" *(horiz)* ..	20	25
724	$3 "Mango Season" *(horiz)* ..	1·25	1·60

172 "An 8 Hour Day"

173 Guyana Flag

(Des C. Rodriguez. Litho Walsall)

1979 (27 Sept). *60th Anniv of Guyana Labour Union. T* **172** *and similar multicoloured designs. W* **106** *(sideways on* 30 *c.). P* 14 × 14½ (30 *c.) or* 14½ × 14 *(others).*

725	10 c. Type **172** ..	5	5
726	30 c. "Abolition of Night Baking" *(horiz)* ..	12	12
727	50 c. "Introduction of the Workmen's Compensation Ordinance" ..	25	25
728	$3 H. N. Critchlow (founder) ..	1·10	1·10

(Des BG Studio. Litho Questa)

1980 (23 Feb). *10th Anniv of Republic. T* **173** *and similar horiz designs. W* **106** *(sideways). P* 14.

729	10 c. multicoloured ..	5	5
730	35 c. black and red-orange ..	15	15
731	60 c. multicoloured ..	25	25
732	$3 multicoloured ..	1·25	1·25

Designs:—35 c. View of Demerara River Bridge; 60 c. Kaieteur Falls; $3 "Makanaima the Great Ancestral Spirit of the Amerindians".

174 Snoek

GUYANA 10c

175 Children's Convalescent Home (Community Service)

(Des J.W. Litho Questa)

1980 (6 May). *"London 1980" International Stamp Exhibition. Fishes. T* **174** *and similar horiz designs. Multicoloured. W* **106** *(sideways). P* 14½.

733	35 c. Type **174** ..	20	20
	a. Block of 12. Nos. 733/44 ..	2·10	
734	35 c. Haimara ..	20	20
735	35 c. Electric Eel ..	20	20
736	35 c. Golden Rivulus ..	20	20
737	35 c. Pencil Fish ..	20	20
738	35 c. Four-eyed Fish ..	20	20
739	35 c. Pirai or Carib Fish ..	20	20
740	35 c. Smoking Hassar ..	20	20
741	35 c. Devil Ray ..	20	20
742	35 c. Flying Patwa ..	20	20
743	35 c. Arapaima Pirariucii ..	20	20
744	35 c. Lukanani ..	20	20
733/44	.. *Set of* 12	2·10	2·10

Nos. 733/44 were printed together, *se-tenant*, in a block of 12 within the sheetlet containing one of each design.

(Des local artist; adapted J.W. Litho Walsall)

1980 (23 June). *75th Anniv of Rotary International. T* **175** *and similar multicoloured designs. W* **106** *(sideways on* 10 *and* 30 *c.). P* 14.

745	10 c. Type **175** ..	8	5
746	30 c. Rotary Club of Georgetown and Rotary emblems ..	15	15
747	50 c. District 404 emblem *(vert)* ..	30	30
748	$3 Rotary anniversary emblem *(vert)* ..	1·50	1·25

176 "C" encircling Globe, Caduceus Emblem and Sea

177 *Virola surinamensis*

(Des L. Curtis. Litho Enschedé)

1980 (23 Sept). *25th Anniv of Commonwealth Caribbean Medical Research Council. T* **176** *and similar horiz designs. Multicoloured. W* **106** *(sideways). P* 13.

749	10 c. Type **176** ..	5	5
750	60 c. Researcher with microscope, Caduceus emblem, stethoscope and beach scene ..	30	30
751	$3 Caduceus emblem, "C" encircling researcher and island silhouettes ..	1·10	1·25

(Des L. Curtis. Litho Format)

1980 (1 Dec). *Christmas. Trees and Foliage. T* **177** *and similar horiz designs. Multicoloured. W* **106** *(sideways). P* 13½.

752	10 c. Type **177** ..	5	5
753	30 c. *Hymenaea courbaril* ..	12	12
754	50 c. *Mora excelsa* ..	20	20
755	$3 *Peltogyne venosa* ..	1·25	1·25

178 Tree Porcupine (179)

(Des G. Drummond. Litho Questa)

1981 (2 Mar). *Wildlife. T* **178** *and similar horiz designs. Multicoloured. W* **106** *(sideways). P* 14.

756	30 c. Type **178** ..	20	20
	a. Sheetlet of 12. Nos. 756/67 ..	2·10	
757	30 c. Howler Monkey ..	20	20
758	30 c. Squirrel Monkey ..	20	20
759	30 c. Two-toed Sloth ..	20	20
760	30 c. Tapir ..	20	20
761	30 c. Collared Peccary ..	20	20
762	30 c. Six-banded Armadillo ..	20	20
763	30 c. Ant Eater ..	20	20
764	30 c. Great Ant Eater ..	20	20
765	30 c. Mouse Opossum ..	20	20
766	30 c. Four-eyed Opossum ..	20	20
767	30 c. Orange-rumped Agouti ..	20	20
756/67	.. *Set of* 12	2·10	2·10

Nos. 756/67 were printed together, *se-tenant*, within the sheet of 12.

See also No. 852.

1981 (4 May). *Liberation of Southern Africa Conference. No.* 635 *surch with T* **179**.

768	$1.05 on 10 c. Type **152** ..	40	50

ROYAL WEDDING 1981 $3·60 X

(180)

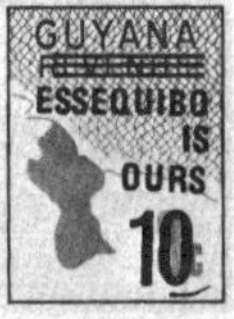

181 Map of Guyana

7.20 (182)

1981 (6 May). *Royal Wedding* (1*st issue*). *Nos.* 554 *and* 556 *surch as T* **180.** A. *In blue.* B. *In black.*

		A		B	
769	$3.60 on $5 *Odontadenia grandiflora* ..	6·00	6·00	2·00	2·00
	a. Surch inverted ..	£195	—	†	
	b. Surch double ..	75·00	—	†	
770	$7.20 on $1 *Chelonanthus uliginoides* ..	4·00	4·00	7·00	7·00
	a. Surch on No. 556 ..	†		£200	—
	b. Surch double ..	£100	—	†	

See also Nos. 841/3 and 930/6.

1981 (11 May). *W* **106.** *P* 13.

771	**181**	10 c. on 3 c. black, ind & Venetian red ..	25	5
772		30 c. on 2 c. black, ind & greenish grey ..	30	12
773		50 c. on 2 c. black, ind & greenish grey ..	40	20
774		60 c. on 2 c. black, ind & greenish grey ..	50	25
775		75 c. on 3 c. black, ind & Venetian red ..	50	35
		a. Surch double ..	50·00	

Nos. 771/5 are fiscal stamps surcharged for postal use.
See also Nos. 940/76, 988/9 and 1029.

1981 (11 May). *No.* 544 *surch with T* **182**.

775*b*	720 on 3 c. Hanging Heliconia ..	60·00	15·00

1981

(183)

1981 (8 June). *Optd with T* **183**.

776	**105**	25 c. black, gold and lilac (R.) ..	10	12
777		30 c. black, gold & lt apple-green (R.) ..	15	15
778	–	35 c. multicoloured (No. 645) (R.) ..	15	15
779	–	$1 multicoloured (No. 554) ..	1·00	50

210

7 (184) X (185) ESSEQUIBO IS OURS 15 (186) ESSEQUIBO IS OURS 15 (186*a*)

1981 (8 June–1 July). *Nos.* 545 *and* 556 *surch with T* **184** *(No.* 780) *or as T* **185**.

780	75 c. on 5 c. Annatto tree ..	60	30
781	210 c. on $5 *Odontadenia grandiflora* ..	1·00	70
781*a*	220 c. on 5 c. Annatto tree ..	35·00	8·00

1981 (8 June). *Nos.* D8/11 *surch in black* (15 *c.) or red (others).* A. *As T* **186**. B. *As T* **186***a*.

			A		B	
782	**D 2**	10 c. on 2 c. black ..	25	5	40	10
783		15 c. on 12 c. bright scarlet	25	15	45	25
784		20 c. on 1 c. olive ..	20	20	25	25
785		45 c. on 2 c. black ..	75	25	1·00	50
786		55 c. on 4 c. dull ultram ..	30	30	2·50	2·50
787		60 c. on 4 c. dull ultram ..	†		40	25
		a. "ESSEOUIBO" ..	†		—	—
788		65 c. on 2 c. black ..	40	40	60	60
789		70 c. on 4 c. dull ultram ..	1·00	1·00	1·25	1·25
790		80 c. on 4 c. dull ultram ..	35	40	50	60
782A/90A		.. *Set of* 8	3·25	2·50		
782B/90B		.. *Set of* 9			6·25	5·50

No. 787Ba occurs on at least two positions of the sheet.

1981 (187) 1981 (188) 1981 (189)

1981 (8 June–1 July). *Nos.* 491, 494 *and* 555 *optd with T* **187, 188** *or* **189**.

791	15 c. Harpy Eagle (R.) ..	10	5
	a. Opt omitted (in vert pair with normal) ..	†	—
	b. Opt in black ..	35·00	5·00
792	40 c. Great Kiskadee (1.7.81) ..	40	30
	a. Opt double ..	28·00	
793	$2 *Norantea guianensis* (1.7.81) ..	1·50	90

MINIMUM PRICE

The minimum price quoted is 5p which represents a handling charge rather than a basis for valuing common stamps. For further notes about prices see introductory pages.

X 120

50c ■ ■

(190) (191)

150

X

(192)

1981 (1 July). *(a) Postage. (i) No.* 545 *surch with T* **190**.
794 50 c. on 5 c. Annatto tree 25 20
a. Surch inverted .. .. 6·00

(ii) *No.* 554 *surch as T* **191**
795 120 c. on $1 *Chelonanthus uliginoides* .. 65 50
796 140 c. on $1 *Chelonanthus uliginoides* .. 60 50

(iii) *Nos.* F7 *and* F9 *surch as T* **192**
797 150 c. on $2 *Norantea guianensis* 50 50
798 360 c. on $2 *Norantea guianensis* .. .. 3·00 1·50
799 720 c. on 60 c. Soldier's Cap .. .. .. 2·50 2·75

(iv) *Nos.* 556 *and* 716 *surch as T* **185**
800 220 c. on $3 Cylinder satellite .. .. 1·00 75
801 250 c. on $5 *Odontadenia grandiflora* .. 1·00 80
802 280 c. on $5 *Odontadenia grandiflora* .. 1·25 1·25
803 375 c. on $5 *Odontadenia grandiflora* .. 1·40 1·40

(b) *Air. No.* 843 *with commemorative opt cancelled by three bars*
804 $1.10 on $2 *Norantea guianensis* .. .. 30·00 15·00

100

15 AIR

(193) (194)

1981 (1 July). *No.* 485 *surch. (a) Postage. With T* **193**.
805 15 c. on 1 c. Type **87** 10 5
a. Strip of 3. Nos. 805/7 85

(b) *Air. As T* **194**
806 100 c. on 1 c. Type **87** 35 35
807 110 c. on 1 c. Type **87** 40 40

Nos. 805/7 were printed together, in horizontal and vertical strips of 3 throughout sheets containing thirty-six 15 c. stamps and thirty-two of each of the other values.

ESSEQUIBO IS OURS (195) ESSEQUIBO IS OURS (195*a*) 1981 (196)

1981 (1 July). *No.* 700 *optd.* A. *With T* **195**. B. *With T* **195a**.

		A		B	
808	15 c. *Eryphanis polyxena*	5	5	10	10

1981 (7 July–15 Sept). *Various stamps optd with T* **196**.
809 – 15 c. multicoloured (No. 548) 60 5
810 – 15 c. multicoloured (No. 659) 75 20
811 – 15 c. multicoloured (No. 660) 75 20
811*a* – 40 c. multicoloured (No. F5) .. .. — £180
812 – 50 c. multicoloured (No. 623) 80 20
813 **150** 50 c. multicoloured 70 25
814 – 50 c. royal blue and orange (No. 632) .. 7·00 1·00
815 – 50 c. multicoloured (No. 646) 80 25
816 **159** 50 c. ultramarine, black and gold .. 3·00 1·00
817 – 50 c. multicoloured (No. F6) 75 30
818 – 60 c. multicoloured (No. 731) (15.9.81) .. 60 25
819 – 60 c. multicoloured (No. 750) (15.9.81) .. 60 25
820 – $1 multicoloured (No. 624) .. .. 4·50 1·00
821 **159** $1 blue-green, black and gold .. .. 1·40 50
822 – $2 multicoloured (No. 555) .. .. 1·75 1·00
823 – $3 multicoloured (No. 732) .. .. 2·00 95
824 – $5 multicoloured (No. 556) .. .. 1·75 1·75

PRICES OF SETS

Set prices are given for many issues, generally those containing five stamps or more. Definitive sets include one of each value or major colour change, but do not cover different perforations, die types or minor shades. Where a choice is possible the set prices are based on the cheapest versions of the stamps included in the listings.

55 (197) 55 (198)

110 (199)

440 (200) 440 (201)

550 (202) 550 (203)

240 (204)

1981 (7 July–15 Sept). *(a) Various stamps surch as T* **197/203**.
825 **116** 55 c. on 6 c. multicoloured (surch T **197**) (15.9.81) 60 70
a. Surch with T **198** .. .. .. 6·00 3·00
b. Vert pair. Nos. 825/a .. .. 6·50 4·00
826 **111** 70 c. on 6 c. multicoloured (15.9.81) .. 25 30
827 100 c. on 6 c. multicoloured 30 35
a. Surch inverted .. .. .. 3·00 1·00
828 – 100 c. on 8 c. multicoloured (No. 505) .. 40 40
829 **152** 100 c. on $1.05 on 10 c. mult (No. 768) .. 12·00 3·00
830 **116** 110 c. on 6 c. multicoloured 90 40
831 **149** 110 c. on 10 c. multicoloured 90 40
832 **151** 110 c. on 10 c. grey-green and yellow .. 1·75 70
833 **154** 110 c. on 10 c. multicoloured .. .. 1·50 70
834 – 125 c. on $2 multicoloured (No. 555) .. 4·00 1·00
835 **116** 180 c. on 6 c. multicoloured (15.9.81) .. 1·50 65
836 400 c. on 6 c. multicoloured .. .. 1·75 1·40
837 440 c. on 6 c. multicoloured (surch T **200**) 6·00 4·00
a. Surch with T **201** .. .. .. 1·75 1·50
b. Vert pair. Nos. 837/a .. .. 7·00 6·00
838 – 550 c. on $10 multicoloured (No. O9) (surch T **202**) (15.9.81) .. .. 2·25 1·75
a. Surch with T **203** .. .. .. 5·00 5·00
b. Vert pair. Nos. 838/a .. .. 7·50 7·00
839 – 625 c. on 40 c. multicoloured (No. F5) .. 3·00 2·75

(b) *No.* 728 *surch with T* **204**
840 – 240 c. on $3 multicoloured (15.9.81) .. 4·00 1·25

Nos. 825/a, 837/a and 838/a were each printed together, *se-tenant*, in vertical pairs throughout sheets containing five of these pairs plus an additional fifteen examples of Nos. 825, 837a and 838.

Royal Wedding 1981 X (205) Royal Wedding 1981 75 60 X (206)

Air Mail X 1.10 Royal Wedding 1981 (207)

1981 (22 July). *Royal Wedding (2nd issue). (a) Postage. Nos.* 544 *and* 556 *surch with T* **205/6**.
841 60 c. on 3 c. Hanging Heliconia .. .. 1·00 1·00
a. Surch inverted £110
b. "Royal Wedding" diagonal (as T **206**) .. £100
c. Surch double (T **205** + T **206**) £100
d. Surch T **205** double £120
842 75 c. on $5 *Odontadenia grandiflora* .. 1·25 1·25

(b) *Air. No.* 555 *surch with T* **207**
843 $1.10 on $2 *Norantea guianensis* .. .. 1·60 1·60
a. Surch double £110
b. Surch inverted £150

It is believed No. 841b comes from trial sheets which were accidentally included in supplies of the normal No. 841.

Espana 82 220 X (208) 1831-1981 Von Stephan 330 (209)

1981 (22 July). *World Cup Football Championship, Spain* (1982) *(1st issue). No.* 545 *surch with T* **208**.
844 220 c. on 5 c. Annatto tree .. .. .. 1·10 90
See also Nos. 937/9.

1981 (22 July). 150*th Birth Anniv of Heinrich von Stephan (founder of U.P.U.). No.* 720 *surch with T* **209**.
845 330 c. on $3 Printing press used for early British Guiana stamps .. .. .. 1·50 1·25

12 

(211)

1981 (24 Aug). *No.* 452 *surch as T* **211**.
847 12 c. on 12 c. on 6 c. Patua 30 25
a. Large surch omitted .. .. .. 15·00
848 15 c. on 10 c. on 6 c. Patua 15 10
a. Horiz pair. Nos. 848/9 .. .. .. 30 30
849 15 c. on 30 c. on 6 c. Patua 15 10
850 15 c. on 50 c. on 6 c. Patua 15 10
a. Horiz pair. Nos. 850/1 .. .. .. 30 30
851 15 c. on 60 c. on 6 c. Patua 15 10

Nos. 847/51 are further surcharges on previously unissued stamps.

Nos. 848/9 and 850/1 were each printed together, *se-tenant*, in horizontal pairs throughout the sheet.

1981 (1 Sept). *As No.* 762 *but perf* 12.
852 30 c. Six-banded Armadillo 15 15
No. 852 was printed in sheets of 50.

214 Coromantyn Free Negro Armed Ranger, *circa* 1772 and Cuffy Monument

215 Louis Braille

(Des G. Drummond. Litho Rosenbaum Bros, Vienna)

1981 (1 Oct). 16*th Anniv of Guyana Defence Force. T* **214** *and similar vert designs. Multicoloured. W* **106**. *P* 13½.
853 15 c. on 10 c. Type **214** 15 10
854 50 c. Private, 27th Foot Regiment, *circa* 1825 25 30
855 $1 on 30 c. Private, Col. Fourgeoud's Marines, *circa* 1775 .. .. .. 50 50
856 $1.10 on $3 W.O. and N.C.O., Guyana Defence Force, 1966 .. .. 70 50

The 15 c., $1 and $1.10 values are surcharged on previously unissued stamps.

(Des G. Vasarhelyi. Litho Questa)

1981 (2 Nov). *International Year for Disabled Persons. Famous Disabled People. T* **215** *and similar horiz designs. Multicoloured. W* **106** *(sideways). P* 13½ × 14.
857 15 c. on 10 c. Type **215** 15 10
858 50 c. Helen Keller and Rajkumari Singh .. 55 45
859 $1 on 60 c. Beethoven and Sonny Thomas .. 50 50
860 $1.10 on $3 Renoir 75 55

The 15 c., $1 and $1.10 values are surcharged on previously unissued stamps.

12 (216) X 50 AIR (217)

1981 (10 Nov). *Nos.* 452 *and* 489 *surch. (a) Postage. With T* **216**.

		A. On No. 452		*B. On No.* 489	
861	12 c. on 6 c. Patua	15	10	15	10
	(b) Air. As T **217**				
862	50 c. on 6 c. Patua	35	25	25	25
	a. Horiz pair. Nos. 862/3	1·00	75	90	75
863	$1 on 6 c. Patua	65	45	65	45

Nos. 862/3 were printed together, *se-tenant*, in horizontal pairs throughout the sheet.

All sheets of Nos. 861B/3B and about half of Nos. 861A/3A contained 36 examples of the 12 c., 35 of the 50 c. and 29 of the $1. On the remainder of the unwatermarked sheets there were the same number of the 12 c., but 34 of the 50 c. and 30 of the $1.

1981

(218)

1981 (14 Nov). *Nos. 548 and 554/5 optd with T* **218** *in red.*

864 15 c. Christmas Orchid 75 5
 a. Optd on No. 548a 3·50
865 $1 *Chelonanthus uliginoides* 35 35
866 $2 *Norantea guianensis* 90 95

110 (219) — Nov 81 / 110 (220) — 50c (221)

1981 (14 Nov). *(a) Nos. 601, 620, 644, and O1 surch with T* **219/20** *in blue.*

867 100 c. on 10 c. Type **154** (surch T **219**) 1·00 45
868 110 c. on 110 c. on 8 c. on 3 c. Hanging Heliconia (surch T **219** + **220**) 1·50 60
 a. Type **220** albino 25·00
869 110 c. on 110 c. on 8 c. on 6 c. Cannon-ball tree (surch T **219**+ **220**) 1·75 75
869*a* 110 c. on 10 c. on 25 c. Marabunta (surch T **219** vert) 1·75 75

(b) Nos. 717, 720, 728, 749, 751 and 755 surch with T **220**

870 110 c. on 10 c. Type **170** (R.) 70 40
 a. Surch albino 15·00
871 110 c. on 10 c. Type **176** (B.) 2·50 90
872 110 c. on $3 Printing press used for early British Guiana stamps (R.) (surch vert) 70 45
873 110 c. on $3 H.N. Critchlow (B.) (surch vert) 3·00 70
874 110 c. on $3 Caduceus emblem, "C" encircling researcher, and island silhouettes (B.) 75 45
 a. Surch in red 2·25 1·25
875 110 c. on 43 *Peltogyne venosa* (B.) 2·00 80
 a. Surch in red 35·00 6·00

(c) No. 698 surch with T **221**

876 50 c. on 5 c. Type **166** 20 20

X X / Human Rights / Day / 1981 / 110 AIR

222 Yellow Allamanda (*Allamanda cathartica*)

(223)

1981 (14 Nov)–**82.** *Flowers. Coil stamps. Vert designs as T* **222.** *W* **106.** *P* 15 × 14.

877 15 c. on 2 c. grey-lilac, blue & turquoise-green 15 15
 a. Vert pair. Nos. 877/8 50 45
 b. New blue surch (12.82) 10 10
 ba. Vert pair. Nos. 877b/8b 65 50
878 15 c. on 8 c. grey-lilac, blue and mauve 15 15
 b. New blue surch (12.82) 10 10

Design:—15 c. on 8 c. Mazaruni Pride (*Sipanea prolensis*).

Nos. 877/8 are surcharges on previously unissued stamps and were printed together, *se-tenant*, in vertical pairs throughout the coil.

1981 (14 Nov). *Air. Human Rights Day. No. 748 surch with T* **223** *in blue.*

879 110 c. on $3 Rotary anniversary emblem 2·00 1·50

U.N.I.C.E.F. / 1946 - 1981 / 125 XX

(224)

1981 (14 Nov). *35th Anniv of U.N.I.C.E.F. No. 724 surch with T* **224.**

880 125 c. on $3 "Mango Season" 1·00 60

Cancun 81 / 50c

(224*a*)

1981 (14 Nov). *"Cancun 81" International Conference. No. 698 surch with T* **224***a*.

880*a* 50 c. on 5 c. Type **166** 1·50 60

GUYANA

225 Tape Measure and Guyana Metrication Board Van

1982

(226)

(Des local artist; adapted A. Theobald. Litho Questa)

1982 (18 Jan). *Metrication. T* **225** *and similar vert designs. Multicoloured. W* **106.** *P* 14½ × 14.

881 15 c. Type **225** 10 8
 a. Sheetlet of 6. Nos. 881/6 55
882 15 c. "Metric man" 10 8
883 15 c. "Postal service goes metric" 10 8
884 15 c. Weighing child on metric scales 10 8
885 15 c. Canje Bridge 10 8
886 15 c. Tap filling litre bucket 10 8
881/6 *Set of* 6 55 45

Nos. 881/6 were printed together, *se-tenant*, in a sheetlet of 6.

1982 (8 Feb). *Various stamps optd with T* **226** *in blue.*

887 – 20 c. multicoloured (No. 549) 90 20
 a. Optd on No. 549a 3·50 1·50
888 **105** 25 c. black, gold and lilac 50 25
889 – 25 c. multicoloured (No. 550*a*) 70 35
 a. Optd on No. 550 10·00 3·00
 b. Optd on No. 550ab 6·00 2·00

See also Nos. 914/17, 919/21, 923/4, 977, 992/8, 1001, 1004, 1006/8, 1015, 1017, 1059 and 1117.

20c (227)

20 (228)

POSTAGE (229)

1982 (8 Feb). *Nos. 506, 546 and 601 surch or optd as T* **227/9**.

890 20 c. on 6 c. Cannon-ball tree (surch T **227**) (G.) 45 30
891 20 c. on 6 c. Cannon-ball tree (surch T **228**) (B.) 45 30
892 25 c. Type **116** (optd T **229**) (B.) 40 12
893 125 c. on 8 c. on 6 c. Cannon-ball tree (surch T **228**) (B.) 50 50

ESSEQUIBO / $1 IS OURS / IN DEFENCE OF GUYANA

230 Guyana Soldier and Flag

1982 (8 Feb). *Savings Campaign. W* **106.** *P* 14 × 14½.

894 **230** $1 multicoloured 40 40

No. 894 is a fiscal stamp overprinted for postal use.

110 X / BADEN POWELL / 1857 - 1982

(231)

1982 (15–22 Feb). *125th Birth Anniv of Lord Baden-Powell and 75th Anniv of Boy Scout Movement. Nos. 543, 545 and 601 surch as T* **231.**

895 15 c. on 2 c. Type **132** (surch T **231**) (22 Feb) 5 5
 a. Sheetlet of 25. Nos. 895/6, each × 8, Nos. 897/8, each × 4 and No. 899 6·00
896 15 c. on 2 c. Type **132** (surch "Scout Movement 1907–1982") (22 Feb) 5 5
897 15 c. on 2 c. Type **132** (surch "1907–1982") (22 Feb) 15 15
898 15 c. on 2 c. Type **132** (surch "1857–1982") (22 Feb) 15 15
899 15 c. on 2 c. Type **132** (surch "1982") (22 Feb) 5 5
900 110 c. on 5 c. Annatto tree (surch T **231**) 40 40
 a. Sheetlet of 25. Nos. 900/1, each × 8, Nos. 902/3, each × 4, and No. 904 (22 Feb) 12·00
901 110 c. on 5 c. Annatto tree (surch "Scout Movement 1907–1982") 40 40
902 110 c. on 5 c. Annatto tree (surch "1907–1982") (22 Feb) 80 80
903 110 c. on 5 c. Annatto tree (surch "1857–1982") (22 Feb) 80 80
904 110 c. on 5 c. Annatto tree (surch "1982") (22 Feb) 60 40
905 125 c. on 8 c. on 6 c. Cannon-ball tree (surch T **231**) (G.) 50 50
 a. Sheetlet of 25. Nos. 905/6, each × 8, Nos. 907/8, each × 4, and No. 909 (22 Feb) 12·50
906 125 c. on 8 c. on 6 c. Cannon-ball tree (surch "Scout Movement 1907–1982") (G.) 50 50
907 125 c. on 8 c. on 6 c. Cannon-ball tree (surch "1907–1982") (G.) (22 Feb) 1·00 90
908 125 c. on 8 c. on 6 c. Cannon-ball tree (surch "1857–1982") (G.) (22 Feb) 1·00 90
909 125 c. on 8 c. on 6 c. Cannon-ball tree (surch "1982") (G.) (22 Feb) 75 50
895/909 *Set of* 15 6·00 6·00

In addition to the sheetlets of 25, Nos. 895a, 900a and 905a, Nos. 899/901, 904/6 and 909 also come from sheets containing one type of surcharge only.

100 / Geo Washington / 1732 .. 1982 (232)

GEORGE WASHINGTON 1732 — 1982 (233)

1982 (15 Feb). *250th Birth Anniv of George Washington. Nos. 708, 718 and 720 surch as T* **232** *or optd only with T* **233.**

910 100 c. on $3 Printing press used for early British Guiana stamps 45 50
911 400 c. on 30 c. British Guiana 1856 1 c. black on magenta stamp 1·75 1·90
 a. Surch inverted 20·00
912 $5 *Morpho deidamia* (B.) 5·00 2·25

1982 (3 Mar). *Savings Campaign. Horiz design as T* **230.** *Multicoloured. W* **106.** *P* 14 × 14½.

913 110 c. on $5 Guyana male and female soldiers with flag 60 40

No. 913 is a fiscal stamp surcharged for postal use.

See also No. 990.

45 (234) — 20 (235) — 210 (236)

1982 (15 Mar). *Easter. Nos. 481/4 optd with T* **226**, *in blue, or surch as T* **234.**

914 **111** 25 c. multicoloured 35 20
915 30 c. multicoloured 30 15
916 45 c. on 6 c. multicoloured (B.) 45 35
917 75 c. on 40 c. multicoloured (R.) 75 35

1982 (15 Mar). *No. 703 surch with T* **235.**

918 20 c. on 35 c. *Siderone galanthis* 10 10

1982 (8 Apr). *No. F5 optd with T* **226** *and surch as T* **228** *in blue.*

919 180 c. on 40 c. Tiger Beard 4·00 70

1982 (23 Apr). *Nos. 555/6 optd with T* **226** *in blue.*

920 $2 *Norantea guianensis* 1·10 70
921 $5 *Odontadenia grandiflora* 1·90 1·60

1982 (23 Apr). *No. 542 surch as T* **228** *in blue.*

922 220 c. on 1 c. Pitcher Plant of Mt Roraima 2·00 75

1982 (27 Apr). *Nos. 472 and 684 optd with T* **226** *in blue.*

923 **105** 40 c. black, gold and cobalt 45 20
924 – 40 c. multicoloured 75 40

1982 (27 Apr). *Nos. 469, 751, 842 and 843 surch as T* **228,** *vertically, (Nos. 925/7), or as T* **236** *(others), all in blue.*

925 **105** 80 c. on 6 c. black, gold and flesh 30 35
926 85 c. on 6 c. black, gold and flesh 45 35
927 – 160 c. on $1.10 on $2 multicoloured (No. 843) 3·00 1·00
928 – 210 c. on $3 multicoloured (No. 751) (surch reading up) 1·40 90
 a. Surch reading down 15·00
929 – 235 c. on 75 c. on $5 multicoloured (No. 842) 15·00 3·00

The surcharge on No. 929 is as Type **236**, but horizontal.

85 (237) — 130 (238)

170 (239)

1982 (27 Apr–May). *Royal Wedding (3rd issue). Coil stamps. Nos. 841/3 surch as T* **237** *(No. 930),* **238** *(Nos. 931/2, 934/5) or* **239** *(others).*

930 85 c. on 60 c. on 3 c. Hanging Heliconia 30 35
931 130 c. on 60 c. on 3 c. Hanging Heliconia 95 55
 a. Surch (as T **238**) inverted £140
932 160 c. on $1.10 on $2 *Norantea guianensis* (vert surch) 3·00 2·00
 a. Surch (as T **238**) double £110
933 170 c. on $1.10 on $2 *Norantea guianensis* 8·00 4·00

934 210 c. on 75 c. on $5 *Odontadenia grandiflora* (B.) .. .. 1·25 90
a. Surch (as T **238**) inverted £100
935 235 c. on 75 c. on $5 *Odontadenia grandiflora* 2·00 1·50
936 330 c. on $1.10 on $2 *Norantea guianensis* .. 10·00 2·00
930/6 .. .. *Set of* 7 23·00 11·00

ESPANA
1982
(240)

220 AIR
Princess
of Wales
1961 - 1982
(241)

1982 (15 May). *World Cup Football Championship, Spain (2nd issue). Nos.* 544, 546 *and* 554 *optd with T* **240** *or surch also as T* **228**.
937 $1 *Chelonanthus uliginoides* 75 80
938 110 c. on 3 c. Hanging Heliconia (B.).. .. 75 55
939 250 c. on 6 c. Cannon-ball tree (B.) .. .. 1·75 1·25

1982 (17 May). *W* **106**. *P* 13.
940 **181** 15 c. on 2 c. black, ind & greenish grey 50 20
a. Opt ("ESSEQUIBO etc") omitted 25·00
941 20 c. on 2 c. black, ind & greenish grey 75 40
942 25 c. on 2 c. black, ind & greenish grey 1·00 30
943 30 c. on 2 c. black, ind & greenish grey 40 15
944 40 c. on 2 c. black, ind & greenish grey 75 40
a. Surch inverted .. .. .. 28·00
945 45 c. on 2 c. black, ind & greenish grey 1·50 50
946 50 c. on 2 c. black, ind & greenish grey 40 40
a. Opt ("ESSEQUIBO etc") omitted 28·00
947 60 c. on 2 c. black, ind & greenish grey 1·00 25
948 75 c. on 2 c. black, ind & greenish grey 90 30
949 80 c. on 2 c. black, ind & greenish grey 50 30
950 85 c. on 2 c. black, ind & greenish grey 75 35
951 100 c. on 3 c. black, ind and Venetian red 60 35
952 110 c. on 3 c. black, ind and Venetian red 80 40
953 120 c. on 3 c. black, ind and Venetian red 1·50 45
954 125 c. on 3 c. black, ind and Venetian red 1·25 45
955 130 c. on 3 c. black, ind and Venetian red 90 50
a. Surch inverted .. .. .. 28·00
956 150 c. on 3 c. black, ind and Venetian red 1·00 55
957 160 c. on 3 c. black, ind and Venetian red 1·50 60
958 170 c. on 3 c. black, ind and Venetian red 1·25 65
959 175 c. on 3 c. black, ind and Venetian red 1·75 65
960 180 c. on 3 c. black, ind and Venetian red 2·25 70
961 200 c. on 3 c. black, ind and Venetian red 2·00 70
962 210 c. on 3 c. black, ind and Venetian red 2·25 75
963 220 c. on 3 c. black, ind and Venetian red 2·50 75
964 235 c. on 3 c. black, ind and Venetian red 2·75 80
965 240 c. on 3 c. black, ind and Venetian red 1·75 85
966 250 c. on 3 c. black, ind and Venetian red 2·00 80
967 300 c. on 3 c. black, ind and Venetian red 3·00 1·10
968 330 c. on 3 c. black, ind and Venetian red 2·50 1·25
969 375 c. on 3 c. black, ind and Venetian red 2·00 1·40
970 400 c. on 3 c. black, ind and Venetian red 3·00 1·40
971 440 c. on 3 c. black, ind and Venetian red 4·00 1·60
972 500 c. on 3 c. black, ind and Venetian red 2·00 1·75
973 550 c. on 3 c. black, ind and Venetian red 2·25 1·75
974 625 c. on 3 c. black, ind and Venetian red 3·00 2·25
975 1500 c. on 2 c. black, ind & greenish grey 9·00 5·50
976 2000 c. on 2 c. black, ind & greenish grey 10·00 7·00
940/76 .. .. *Set of* 37 55·00 32·00

Nos. 940/76 are fiscal stamps, surcharged for postal use, as Type **181**, but with the overprinted inscription and face value redrawn. On the 15 to 85 c., the surcharged face value is in blue, on the 100 to 625 c. in black, and on the 1500 and 2000 c. in red.

For 25 c. and 40 c. surcharges in black see Nos. 988/9 and for the 25 c. in red, No. 1029.

1982 (7 June). *No.* 548 *optd with T* **226** *in blue.*
977 15 c. Christmas Orchid 80 5
a. Optd on No. 548a.. .. .. .. 45·00 12·00

1982 (15 June). *No.* O14 *optd with T* **229** *in blue.*
978 110 c. on 6 c. Type **116** 80 35

1982 (25 June). *Air. 21st Birthday of Princess of Wales. Nos.* 542, 545 *and* 555 *surch as T* **241**.
979 110 c. on 5 c. Annatto tree (R.) .. .. 1·25 60
a. Surch in black .. .. 95·00
980 220 c. on 1 c. Pitcher Plant of Mt Roraima .. 2·25 1·00
981 330 c. on $2 *Norantea guianensis* (B.) .. 3·00 1·75

GUYANA
H.R.H.
Prince William
21st June 1982
000
000000000 $1.10
(242)

H.R.H.
Prince William
21st June 1982
$2.20
(243)

1982 (12 July). *Birth of Prince William of Wales. Surch as T* **242** *(50 c. and $1.10) or with T* **243** *(others), all in blue.*

(a) On stamps of British Guiana
982 50 c. on 2 c. myrtle-green (No. 332) 40 45
983 $1.10 on 3 c. brown-olive and red-brown (No. 354) .. .. 1·00 80
a. Surch inverted .. .. 75·00
b. Surch double .. ..
c. Surch on No. 333.. .. .. .. 1·50 75
ca. Surch inverted .. .. 75·00
cb. Surch double .. .. 90·00
cc. Surch as T **243** (lines at foot) ..

(b) On stamps of Guyana previously optd "GUYANA INDEPENDENCE 1966"
984 50 c. on 2 c. myrtle-green (No. 430) .. .. 4·50 3·00
985 $1.10 on 3 c. brown-olive and red-brown (No. 431) .. .. 7·00 3·00
a. Surch on No. 422.. .. .. .. 90·00 10·00
986 $1.25 on 6 c. yellow-green (No. 398A) .. 85 90
a. Surch inverted .. .. 85·00
b. Surch double .. .. 90·00
c. Surch on No. 434.. .. .. .. 6·00 4·00
987 $2.20 on 24 c. black and brownish orange (No. 401B) .. .. 1·75 1·75
a. Surch inverted .. .. 95·00
b. Surch on No. 401A .. .. .. 80·00 15·00
c. Surch on No. 435.. .. .. .. 55·00 25·00
982/7 .. .. *Set of* 6 14·00 4·00

Nos. 982, 983c and 985a have Mult Script CA watermark and the remainder watermark w **12** (sideways on No. 987).

1982 (13 July). *As Nos.* 942 *and* 944 *but with surcharged face values in black.*
988 **181** 25 c. on 2 c. black, ind & greenish grey .. 40 30
989 40 c. on 2 c. black, ind & greenish grey .. 15 15

1982 (13 July). *Savings Campaign. Coil stamp. As No.* 913 *but showing inverted comma before* "OURS" *in overprint.*
990 110 c. on $5 Guyana male and female soldiers with flag .. .. 4·00 50

ITALY
$2.35
(244)

50
C.A. & CARIB
GAMES
1982
(245)

1982 (15 July). *Italy's Victory in World Cup Football Championships. No.* F7 *optd as T* **240** *and surch with T* **244**, *both in blue.*
991 $2.35 on 180 c. on 60 c. Soldier's Cap .. 1·75 95

1982 (16 Aug). *Wildlife Protection. Nos.* 687 *and* 733/8 *optd with T* **226** *in blue.*
992 35 c. Harpy Eagle 50 40
993 35 c. Type **174** .. .. 1·75 40
a. Block of 6. Nos. 993/8 .. .. 10·00
994 35 c. Haimara .. .. 1·75 40
995 35 c. Electric Eel .. .. 1·75 40
996 35 c. Golden Rivulus .. .. 1·75 40
997 35 c. Pencil Fish .. .. 1·75 40
998 35 c. Four-eyed Fish .. .. 1·75 40
992/8 .. .. *Set of* 7 10·00 2·50

1982 (16 Aug). *Central American and Caribbean Games, Havana. Nos.* 542/3 *surch as T* **245**.
999 50 c. on 2 c. Type **132** .. .. .. 1·25 45
1000 60 c. on 1 c. Pitcher Plant of Mt Roraima .. 1·50 30

1982 (15 Sept). *No.* 730 *optd with T* **226** *in blue.*
1001 35 c. black and red-orange 30 20

1982 (15 Sept). *Nos.* 841 *and* 979 *further surch as T* **228** *(No.* 1003 *has solid bar) in blue.*
1002 130 c. on 60 c. on 3 c. Hanging Heliconia .. 3·00 1·00
a. Surch as T **228** inverted £150
1003 170 c. on 110 c. on 5 c. Annatto tree .. .. 4·50 1·00

1982 (15 Sept). *No.* 841 *optd with T* **226** *and surch as T* **228**, *both in blue.*
1004 440 c. on 60 c. on 3 c. Hanging Heliconia .. 20·00 2·00
a. T **226** and T **228** both inverted .. £150
b. Surch and optd on No. 841b .. .. 20·00
c. Without opt T **226** .. .. .. 10·00 2·50

No. 1004c also differs from No. 1004 by showing a "c" after the surcharge "60" on Type **205**.

Commonwealth
GAMES
AUSTRALIA
1982
1.25
(246)

INT.
FOOD DAY
1982
(247)

1982 (27 Sept). *Commonwealth Games, Brisbane, Australia. No.* 546 *surch with T* **246** *in blue.*
1005 $1.25 on 6 c. Cannon-ball tree .. .. .. 1·25 50

1982 (1 Oct). *Nos.* 552, 641 *and* 719 *optd with T* **226** *(vertically on Nos.* 1007/8) *in blue.*
1006 50 c. multicoloured (No. 552) .. .. .. 1·00 25
1007 50 c. light violet-blue, light green and light yellow-brown (No. 641) 75 25
1008 50 c. multicoloured (No. 719) 35 25

1982 (1 Oct). *Various. Official stamps additionally optd for postal purposes as T* **229**, *but smaller (29 mm in length), all in blue.*
1009 15 c. Christmas Orchid (No. O11) (vert opt).. 1·50 8
1010 50 c. *Guzmania ligulata* (No. O2) (vert opt) .. 75 25
1011 100 c. on $3 Cylinder satellite (No. O7) .. 1·00 50

1982 (15 Oct). *International Food Day. No.* 617 *optd with T* **247** *in blue.*
1012 50 c. Pawpaw and tangerine .. .. .. 15·00 1·50

INT. YEAR
OF THE
ELDERLY
(248)

Dr. R. KOCH
CENTENARY
TBC BACILLUS
DISCOVERY
(249)

F. D. ROOSEVELT
1882-1982
(250)

1982 (15 Oct). *International Year of the Elderly. No.* 747 *optd with T* **248** *in blue.*
1013 50 c. District 404 emblem .. .. .. 3·50 50

1982 (15 Oct). *Centenary of Robert Koch's Discovery of Tubercle Bacillus. No.* 750 *optd with T* **249** *in blue.*
1014 60 c. Researcher with microscope, Caduceus emblem, stethoscope and beach scene .. 1·00 30

1982 (15 Oct). *International Decade for Women. No.* 633 *optd with T* **226** *in blue.*
1015 $1 brown and bright blue .. .. .. 3·00 80
a. Opt inverted .. .. 20·00

1982 (15 Oct). *Birth Centenary of F. D. Roosevelt (American statesman). No.* 706 *optd with T* **250** *in blue.*
1016 $1 Type **167** 60 45

GAC Inaug. Flight
Georgetown—
Boa Vista, Brasil
200
(251)

50
CARICOM
Heads of Gov't
Conference
July 1982
(252)

1982 (15 Oct). *1st Anniv of G.A.C. Inaugural Flight Georgetown to Boa Vista, Brazil. No.* 842 *optd with T* **226** *and surch with T* **251**, *both in blue.*
1017 200 c. on 75 c. on $5 *Odontadenia grandiflora* 15·00 3·00

1982 (18 Nov). *CARICOM Heads of Government Conference, Kingston, Jamaica. Nos.* 881/6 *surch with T* **252**.
1018 50 c. on 15 c. Type **225**.. .. .. .. 1·00 30
a. Sheetlet of 6. Nos. 1018/23 .. .. 5·25
1019 50 c. on 15 c. "Metric man" .. .. .. 1·00 30
1020 50 c. on 15 c. "Postal service goes metric" .. 1·00 30
1021 50 c. on 15 c. Weighing child on metric scales .. 1·00 30
1022 50 c. on 15 c. Canje Bridge .. .. .. 1·00 30
1023 50 c. on 15 c. Tap filling litre bucket .. .. 1·00 30
1018/23 .. .. *Set of* 6 5·25 1·75

CHRISTMAS
1982
(253)

15
(254)

50
(255)

1982 (1 Dec). *Christmas. Nos.* 895/9 *optd with T* **253** *in red.*
1024 15 c. on 2 c. Type **132** (surch T **231**) 20 15
a. Sheetlet of 25. Nos. 1024/5, each × 8, Nos. 1026/7, each × 4 and No. 1028 .. .. 8·00
1025 15 c. on 2 c. Type **132** (surch "Scout Movement 1907–1982") 20 15
1026 15 c. on 2 c. Type **132** (surch "1907–1982") .. 30 25
1027 15 c. on 2 c. Type **132** (surch "1857–1982") .. 30 25
1028 15 c. on 2 c. Type **132** (surch "1982") .. .. 2·50 2·50

Nos. 1024/8 were only issued in the *se-tenant* sheetlets of 25.

1982 (15 Dec). *As No.* 942 *but with surcharged face value in red.*
1029 **181** 25 c. on 2 c. black, indigo and greenish grey 50 12

1982 (15 Dec). *Nos.* 543 *and* 546 *surch as T* **254**.
1030 15 c. on 2 c. Type **132** (B.) 10 8
1031 20 c. on 6 c. Cannon-ball tree (Blk.) 25 10

For similar surcharges in different colours see Nos. 1034/5 and 1063; and for surcharges incorporating "c" Nos. 1085/7 and 1098/9.

1982 (15 Dec). *No. 489 surch as T* **255**.
1032 50 c. on 6 c. Patua 20 25
1033 100 c. on 6 c. Patua 40 45

1983 (5 Jan). *As Nos.* 1030/1, *but with colours of surcharge changed.*
1034 15 c. on 2 c. Type **132** (Blk.) 5 8
1035 20 c. on 6 c. Cannon-ball tree (G.) 8 10

1983
(256)

POSTAGE
(257)

60th BIRTHDAY ANNIVERSARY OF OUR PRESIDENT
25c
ALL
GUYANA
OUR HERITAGE
258 Guyana Flag (inscr "60th BIRTHDAY ANNIVERSARY")

1983 (1 Feb). *Optd with T* **256**.
1036 – 15 c. multicoloured (No. 655) (opt vert) 5·00 2·00
1037 – 15 c. yellow-brown, grey and black (No. 672) 50 8
1038 – 15 c. multicoloured (No. 682) (opt vert) .. 40 8
1039 **214** 15 c. on 10 c. multicoloured (opt vert) .. 35 8
1040 **215** 15 c. on 10 c. multicoloured 15 8
1041 – 50 c. multicoloured (No. 646) .. .. 2·00 25
1042 – 50 c. multicoloured (No. 696) (opt vert) .. 2·50 25
1043 – 50 c. multicoloured (No. 719) .. .. 1·50 25
1036/43 .. .. *Set of* 8 11·00 3·00
See also Nos. 1060/1, 1069/70, 1072/9, 1096, 1101 and 1110/16.

1983 (1 Feb). *No.* O5 *optd for postal purposes with T* **257** *in red.*
1044 15 c. Harpy Eagle 5 8

1983 (8 Feb). *National Heritage. Nos.* 710/12 *and No.* 778 *surch as T* **234** *in black (No.* 1045) *or blue (others).*
1045 90 c. on 30 c. Cassiri and decorated Amerindian jars .. .. 2·10 1·60
1046 90 c. on 35 c. Rock drawing of hunter and quarry 35 50
1047 90 c. on 50 c. Fork Kyk-over-al .. .. .. 2·10 1·60
1048 90 c. on 60 c. Fort Island .. .. 1·40 50

(Litho Format)

1983 (19 Feb). *President Burnham's 60th Birthday and 30 Years in Parliament. T* **258** *and similar multicoloured designs. W* **106** *(sideways)* (25 c., $1.30). *P* 13 ($1.30) *or* 14 *(others).*
1049 25 c. Type **258** 15 20
a. Horiz pair. Nos. 1049/50.. .. .. .. 30 40
1050 25 c. As T **258**, but position of flag reversed and inscr "30th ANNIVERSARY IN PARLIAMENT" 15 20
1051 $1.30, Youth display (41 × 25 *mm*).. .. .. 75 65
1052 $6 Presidential standard (43½ × 25 *mm*) .. 2·50 2·75
Nos. 1049/50 were printed together, *se-tenant*, in horizontal pairs throughout the sheet.
For stamps as Nos. 1049/50, but without commemorative inscriptions, see Nos. 1108/9.

FIFTY CENTS
(259)

20 X
(260)

1983 (7 Mar). *Surch as T* **259**.
1053 **170** 50 c. on 10 c. mult (No. 717) (R.) .. 35 25
1054 – 50 c. on 400 c. on 30 c. multicoloured (No. 911) (surch vert) 55 25
1055 **152** $1 on 10 c. multicoloured (No. 635) (surch vert).. .. .. .. 4·00 45
1056 $1 on $1.05 on 10 c. multicoloured (No. 768) (surch vert) .. .. .. 2·00 45
1056*a* – $1 on $1.10 on $2 multicoloured (No. 843).. .. .. 6·00 2·00
1057 – $1 on 220 c. on 5 c. mult (No. 844) (B.) 5·50 1·00
1058 – $1 on 330 c. on $2 mult (No. 981) (B.) 40 45
1059 – $1 on $12 on $1.10 on $2 mult (similar to No. P3) (B.) .. .. .. 15·00 5·00
1053/9.. .. .. *Set of* 8 30·00 9·50
Nos. 1057/9 have thin bars cancelling previous surcharges, and, in addition, No. 1059 is optd with T **226** in blue.
See also Nos. 1062 and 1080/4.

1983 (7 Mar). *No.* 859 *optd with T* **256**.
1060 $1 on 60 c. Beethoven and Sonny Thomas .. 75 45

1983 (11 Mar). *Conference of Foreign Ministers of Non-aligned Countries, New Delhi. No.* 569 *surch with T* **259** *and No.* 570 *optd with T* **256**.
1061 **136** 25 c. multicoloured (opt vert) .. .. 4·00 25
1062 50 c. on 8 c. mult (surch vert) (R.) .. 2·50 25

1983 (14 Mar). *As No.* 1030, *but colour of surcharge changed.*
1063 15 c. on 2 c. Type **132** (R.) 5 8

1983 (14 Mar). *No.* 771 *further surch with T* **260** *in blue.*
1064 **181** 20 c. on 10 c. on 3 c. black, indigo and Venetian red 25 10

Commonwealth Day 14 March 1983

$1.30
(261)

262

1983 (14 Mar). *Commonwealth Day. Nos.* 398A *and* 401B *surch as T* **261** *in black* (25 c., $1.30) *or blue (others).*
1065 25 c.on 6 c. yellow-green .. .. .. 2·50 20
1066 $1.20 on 6 c. yellow-green 75 50
1067 $1.30 on 24 c. black and bright orange 55 55
1068 $2.40 on 24 c. black and bright orange 1·00 1·25

1983 (17 Mar). *Easter. Nos.* 482/3 *optd with T* **256**.
1069 **111** 25 c. multicoloured 10 12
1070 30 c. multicoloured 30 15

1983 (17 Mar). *25th Anniv of International Maritime Organization. British Guiana fiscal stamp optd in red as T* **262**. *Wmk Mult Crown CA. P* 14.
1071 $4.80, bright blue and deep dull green .. 22·00 12·00

1983 (1 Apr). *Optd with T* **256**.
1072 **152** 50 c. multicoloured (No. 637) (opt vert) .. 1·00 25
1073 **159** 50 c. ultramarine, black and gold (No. 668) (opt vert) .. .. .. 4·00 25
1074 – 50 c. multicoloured (No. 854) (opt vert) .. 50 25
1075 – 50 c. multicoloured (No. 858) 30 25
1076 – $1 multicoloured (No. 628) .. .. 6·00 45
1077 – $1 multicoloured (No. 638) (vert opt) .. 3·50 45
1078 – $1 multicoloured (No. 675) .. .. 3·00 45
1079 – $1 on 30 c. mult (No. 855) (vert opt) .. 1·00 45
1072/9 .. .. *Set of* 8 17·00 2·60

1983 (1 Apr). *Surch with T* **259**, *vertically, in black (No.* 1082) *or blue (others).*
1080 **148** 50 c. on 8 c. multicoloured (No. 615) .. 1·00 25
1081 **162** 50 c. on 8 c. multicoloured (No. 681) .. 4·00 25
1082 **171** 50 c. on 10 c. multicoloured (No. 721) .. 1·25 25
1083 – 50 c. on 10 c. on 25 c. mult (No. O1) .. 1·25 25
1084 – 50 c. on 330 c. on $3 mult (No. 845) .. 75 25

1983 (2 May). *Surch as T* **254**, *but with* "c" *after new face value.*
1085 **105** 15 c. on 6 c. black, gold and flesh (No. 469) (B.) 8 10
1086 – 20 c. on 6 c. multicoloured (No. 546) .. 10 12
1087 **111** 50 c. on 6 c. multicoloured (No. 481) .. 25 30
For No. 1085 with black overprint, see No. 1098.

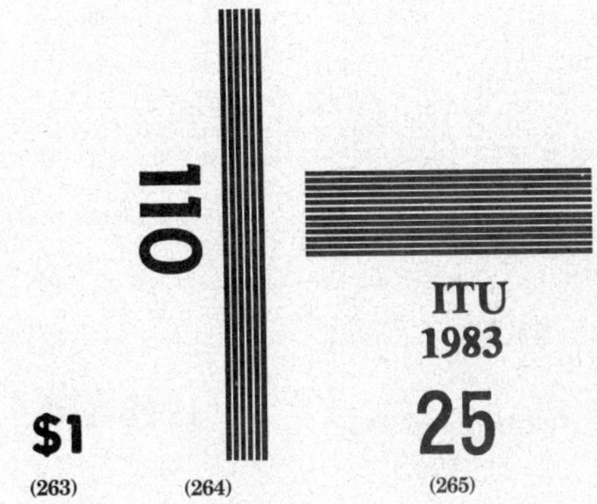

$1
(263) (264) (265)

1983 (2 May). *No.* 489 *surch with T* **263**.
1088 $1 on 6 c. Patua 45 50

1983 (2 May). *No.* 639 *surch with T* **264** *in blue.*
1089 **153** 110 c. on 10 c. greenish yellow, light green and light reddish violet .. 1·25 50

1983 (2 May). *Nos.* 551 *and* 556 *surch as T* **228** *in blue.*
1090 250 c. on 40 c. Tiger Beard .. .. .. 2·00 1·25
1091 400 c. on $5 *Odontadenia grandiflora* .. 2·00 1·90

1983 (17 May). *World Telecommunications and Health Day. Nos.* 842 *and* 980 *further surch as T* **265**.
1092 25 c. on 220 c. on 1 c. Pitcher Plant of Mt Roraima (surch T **265**) (R.) 25 20
a. Sheetlet of 25. Nos. 1092/3 each × 8 and No. 1094 × 9 .. .. 6·50
1093 25 c. on 220 c. on 1 c. Pitcher Plant of Mt Roraima (surch "WHO 1983 25") (R.) .. 25 20
1094 25 c. on 220 c. on 1 c. Pitcher Plant of Mt Roraima (surch "17 MAY '83 ITU/WHO 25") (R.).. .. .. 25 20
1095 $4.50 on 75 c. on $5 *Odontadenia grandiflora* (surch "ITU/WHO 17 MAY 1983") (B.) .. .. 10·00 3·00
a. Surch on 235 c. on 75 c. on $5 (No. 929).. 13·00 4·00

1983 (18 May). *30th Anniv of President's Entry into Parliament. Nos.* 690 *and* 692 *surch as T* **259**, *the former additionally optd with T* **256**.
1096 $1 on 15 c. black, light violet-blue and bluish grey .. .. 5·00 50
1097 $1 on 40 c. black, red-orange and bluish grey 6·00 50
No. **MS**693 was also reissued with examples of Nos. 1096/7 affixed over the 8 c. and 35 c. values, and an example of No. 1050 added to the righthand sheet margin. These miniature sheets, revalued to $6, numbered on the reverse and cancelled with First Day of Issue postmarks, were for presentation purposes and were not available for postage.

1983 (23 May). *Surch as T* **254**, *but with* "c" *after new face value.*
1098 **105** 15 c. on 6 c. black, gold and flesh (No. 469) (Blk.) 8 10
1099 – 50 c. on 6 c. multicoloured (No. 489) (Blk.) 25 30

1983 (23 May). *No.* 546 *surch as T* **228**, *but with* "c" *after new face value.*
1100 20 c. on 6 c. Cannon-ball tree 10 12

1983 (23 May). *No.* 611 *optd with T* **256**.
1101 25 c. Guides in camp .. .. 12·00 1·00

$1
(266)

(267)

XXX
(268)

1983 (23 May). *No.* 489 *surch with T* **266** *in red.*
1102 $1 on 6 c. Patua 45 50

1983 (15 June). *15th World Scout Jamboree, Alberta. Nos.* 835/6 *and* O13 *additionally surch or optd as T* **267**.
1103 – $1.30 on 100 c. on 8 c. multicoloured .. 1·25 65
1104 **116** 180 c. on 6 c. multicoloured .. .. 1·25 1·00
1105 $3.90 on 400 c. on 6 c. multicoloured .. 2·00 1·90

1983 (22 June). *Nos.* 659/60 *surch as T* **254**.
1106 60 c. on 15 c. Map of the Caribbean .. .. 3·00 35
1107 $1.50 on 15 c. Prudential Cup .. .. 3·50 80

1983 (1 July). *As Nos.* 1049/50, *but without commemorative inscr above flag. W* **106** *(sideways). P* 14.
1108 25 c. As Type **258** 12 15
a. Horiz pair. Nos. 1108/9 25
1109 25 c. As No. 1050 .. .. 12 15
Nos. 1108/9 were printed together, *se-tenant* in horizontal pairs throughout the sheet.

1983 (1 July). *Optd with T* **256**.
1110 **105** 30 c. black, gold and light apple-green (No. 471) 15 20
1111 – 30 c. multicoloured (No. 695) .. .. 1·50 20
1112 – 30 c. multicoloured (No. 718) (opt vert) .. 75 20
1113 – 30 c. multicoloured (No. 722) .. .. 1·00 20
1114 – 30 c. multicoloured (No. 746) .. .. 1·00 20
1115 – 60 c. multicoloured (No. 697) .. .. 2·00 20
1116 – 60 c. multicoloured (No. 731) .. .. 3·50 20
1110/16 .. .. *Set of* 7 9·00 1·25

1983 (1 July). *No.* 553 *optd with T* **226** *in blue.*
1117 60 c. Soldier's Cap .. .. 1·25 35

1983 (1 July). *Surch as T* **264** *in blue.*
1118 **157** 120 c. on 8 c. multicoloured (No. 654) .. 1·00 60
1119 **159** 120 c. on 10 c. dull red, black and gold (No. 666) 90 60
1120 – 120 c. on 35 c. multicoloured (No. 622) .. 1·25 60
1121 – 120 c. on 35 c. orange, light green and reddish violet (No. 640) .. 1·25 60

1983 (1 July). *Nos.* 716 *and* 729 *surch as T* **268**.
1122 120 c. on 10 c. Type **173** (R.) .. .. .. 1·25 60
1123 120 c. on 375 c. on $3 Cylinder satellite .. 1·00 60
No. 1123 also carries an otherwise unissued surcharge in red, reading "INTERNATIONAL SCIENCE YEAR 1982 375". As issued much of this is obliterated by two heavy bars.

CARICOM DAY 1983
120
GUYANA
(269)

60
XXX
(270)

1983 (1 July). *British Guiana No.* D1a *and Guyana No.* D8 *surch with T* **269** *in blue.*
1124 D **1** 120 c. on 1 c. deep green.. .. .. 1·50 60
1125 D **2** 120 c. on 1 c. olive .. .. .. 1·00 60

1983 (1 July). *CARICOM Day. No.* 823 *additionally surch with T* **270** *in red.*
1126 60 c. on $3 "Makanaima the Great Ancestral Spirit of the Amerindians" .. .. 1·25 35

271 *Kurupukari*

1983 (11 July*). *Riverboats. T* **271** *and similar horiz designs. Litho. W* **106**. *P* 14.
1127 30 c. black and vermilion 15 20
a. *Tête-bêche* (vert pair) 30
1128 60 c. black and bright reddish violet .. 30 35
a. *Tête-bêche* (vert pair) 60
1129 120 c. black and greenish yellow 55 60
a. *Tête-bêche* (vert pair) .. .. .. 1·10
1130 130 c. black 60 65
a. *Tête-bêche* (vert pair) .. .. .. 1·25
1131 150 c. black and bright emerald 75 80
a. *Tête-bêche* (vert pair) .. .. .. 1·50
Designs:—60 c. *Makouria*; 120 c. *Powis*; 130 c. *Pomeroon*; 150 c. *Lukanani*.
*Although not finally issued until 11 July First Day Covers of Nos. 1127/31 are postmarked with the intended release date of 1 July.
Nos. 1127/31 were each issued in sheets of 80 (10 × 8) with the bottom three rows inverted forming *tête-bêche* vertical pairs from Rows 5 and 6.

2.30

(272)

1983 (22 July). *Unissued Royal Wedding surcharge, similar to No.* 843, *surch as T* **272** *in blue.*
1132 $2.30 on $1.10 on $2 *Norantea guianensis* .. 10·00 4·00
1133 $3.20 on $1.10 on $2 *Norantea guianensis* .. 12·00 4·00

BW (273)

Mont Golfier 1783-1983 (274)

1983 (5 Sept). *Bicentenary of Manned Flight and 20th Anniv of Guyana Airways. Nos.* 701/2*a optd as T* **273/4**, *in red (Nos.* 1134/47) *or blue (Nos.* 1148/68).
1134 20 c. multicoloured (optd T 273) 8 10
a. Sheetlet of 25. Nos. 1134/8 each × 4 and 1139 × 5 .. .. 2·50
1135 20 c. multicoloured (optd "LM") 8 10
1136 20 c. multicoloured (optd "GY 1963 1983") .. 8 10
1137 20 c. multicoloured (optd "JW") 8 10
1138 20 c. multicoloured (optd "CU") 8 10
1139 20 c. multicoloured (optd T 274) 8 10
1140 25 c. multicoloured (optd "BGI") 50 25
a. Sheetlet of 25. Nos. 1140 × 2, 1141 × 8, 1142/44 each × 2, 1145 × 5 and 1146/7 each × 2 .. .. 9·00
1141 25 c. multicoloured (optd "GEO") 15 12
1142 25 c. multicoloured (optd "MIA") 50 25
1143 25 c. multicoloured (optd "BVB") 50 25
1144 25 c. multicoloured (optd "PBM") 50 25
1145 25 c. multicoloured (optd T 274) 20 12
1146 25 c. multicoloured (optd "POS") 50 25
1147 25 c. multicoloured (optd "JFK") 50 25
1148 30 c. multicoloured (optd "AHL") 25 15
a. Sheetlet of 25. Nos. 1148/54, 1155 × 5 and 1156/68 .. .. 7·00
1149 30 c. multicoloured (optd "BCG") 25 15
1150 30 c. multicoloured (optd "BMJ") 25 15
1151 30 c. multicoloured (optd "EKE") 25 15
1152 30 c. multicoloured (optd "GEO") 25 15
1153 30 c. multicoloured (optd "GFO") 25 15
1154 30 c. multicoloured (optd "IBM") 25 15
1155 30 c. multicoloured (optd T 274) 25 15
1156 30 c. multicoloured (optd "KAI") 25 15
1157 30 c. multicoloured (optd "KAR") 25 15
1158 30 c. multicoloured (optd "KPG") 25 15
1159 30 c. multicoloured (optd "KRG") 25 15
1160 30 c. multicoloured (optd "KTO") 25 15
1161 30 c. multicoloured (optd "LTM") 25 15
1162 30 c. multicoloured (optd "MHA") 25 15
1163 30 c. multicoloured (optd "MWJ") 25 15
1164 30 c. multicoloured (optd "MYM") 25 15
1165 30 c. multicoloured (optd "NAI") 25 15
1166 30 c. multicoloured (optd "ORJ") 25 15
1167 30 c. multicoloured (optd "USI") 25 15
1168 30 c. multicoloured (optd "VEG") 25 15
1134/68 .. .. *Set of* 35 8·00 4·50

The overprints on the 20 c. value represent airlines, on the 25 c. international airports and on the 30 c. internal airports. Those on Nos. 1150 and 1154 were incorrect and examples of the former exist with the manuscript correction "PMT".

240 (275) **240** (275*a*)

1983 (14 Sept). *No.* 649 *surch with T* **275** *in blue.*
1169 240 c. on 35 c. on 60 c. Soldier's Cap .. .. 95 1·00
a. Surch with T 275*a* .. .. 95 1·00
b. Pair. Nos. 1169/a .. .. .. 1·90

Types **275** and **275***a* occur *se-tenant* within the sheet.

FAO 1983

30

(276)

277 G.B. 1857 1d. with Georgetown "AO3" Postmark

1983 (15 Sept). *F.A.O. Fisheries Project. Nos.* 485 *and* 487 *surch as T* **276** *in red.*
1170 30 c. on 1 c. Type 87 .. .. 12 15
1171 $2.60 on 3 c. Lukunani .. .. 1·10 1·25

1983 (1 Oct). *125th Anniv of Use of Great Britain Stamps in Guyana. T* **277** *and similar square designs. Litho. W* **106**. *P* 14½.

(*a*) *Inscriptions in black*

1172 **277** 25 c. lake-brown and black 10 12
a. *Tête-bêche* (pair) 20
1173 – 30 c. rose-red and black 12 15
a. *Tête-bêche* (pair) 25
1174 – 60 c. bright violet and black 25 30
a. *Tête-bêche* (pair) 50
1175 – 120 c. dull green and black 50 55
a. *Tête-bêche* (pair) .. .. .. 1·00

(*b*) *Inscriptions in bright blue*

1176 **277** 25 c. lake-brown and black 10 12
a. Block of 4. Nos. 1176/9 40
1177 – 25 c. rose-red and black 10 12
1178 – 25 c. bright violet and black 10 12
1179 – 25 c. dull green and black 10 12
1180 **277** 30 c. lake-brown and black 12 15
a. Block of 4. Nos. 1180/3 50
1181 – 30 c. rose-red and black 12 15
1182 – 30 c. bright violet and black 12 15
1183 – 30 c. dull green and black 12 15
1184 **277** 45 c. lake-brown and black 20 25
a. Block of 4. Nos. 1184/7 80
1185 – 45 c. rose-red and black 20 25
1186 – 45 c. bright violet and black 20 25
1187 – 45 c. dull green and black 20 25
1188 **277** 120 c. lake-brown and black 50 55
a. Block of 4. Nos. 1188/91 .. .. 2·50
1189 – 130 c. rose-red and black 55 60
1190 – 150 c. bright violet and black 65 70
1191 – 200 c. dull green and black 90 95
1172/91 .. .. *Set of* 20 4·50 5·00

Designs:—Nos. 1173, 1177, 1181, 1185, 1189, G.B. 1857 4d. rose; Nos. 1174, 1178, 1182, 1186, 1190, G.B. 1856 6d. lilac; Nos. 1175, 1179, 1183, 1187, 1191, G.B. 1856 1s. green.

Each design incorporates the "A03" postmark except Nos. 1189/91 which show mythical postmarks of the Crowned-circle type inscribed "DEMERARA", "BERBICE" or "ESSEQUIBO".

Nos. 1172/5 were each printed in sheets with the bottom row inverted, forming vertical *tête-bêche* pairs. Nos. 1176/87 were issued in sheets of 60, one for each value, with the four designs *se-tenant*. Nos. 1188/91 were issued in sheets of 20, containing five *se-tenant* blocks.

INT. COMMUNICATIONS YEAR 50

(278)

75

(279)

1983 (15 Oct). *International Communications Year. No.* 716 *surch with T* **278**.
1192 50 c. on 375 c. on $3 Cylinder satellite .. 2·50 25

No. 1192 also carries an otherwise unissued "375" surcharge. As issued much of this surcharge is obliterated by two groups of six thin horizontal lines.

1983 (15 Oct). *St. John's Ambulance Commemoration. Nos.* 650 *and* 653 *surch as T* **279**, *vertically on No.* 1194.
1193 **156** 75 c. on 8 c. silver, black and magenta .. 1·00 30
1194 – $1.20 on 40 c. silver, black and new blue 2·00 50

$1.20

Int. Food Day 1983

(280)

1918-1983

I.L.O.

(281)

1983 (15 Oct). *International Food Day. No.* 616 *surch with T* **280**.
1195 $1.20 on 35 c. Five-fingers and awaras .. 45 50

1983 (15 Oct). *65th Anniv of I.L.O. and 25th Death Anniv. of H. N. Critchlow (founder of Guyana Labour Union). No.* 840 *further optd with T* **281**.
1196 240 c. on $3 H. N. Critchlow 90 95

25c.

(282)

1983 Human Rights Day

(283)

1983 (1 Nov). *Deepavali Festival. Nos.* 661 *and* 663/4 *surch as T* **282**.
1197 25 c. on 8 c. Type **158** 10 12
1198 $1.50 on 35 c. Flame in bowl 55 60
1199 $1.50 on 40 c. Goddess Latchmi 55 60

On Nos. 1198/9 the original face values are obliterated by "XX" and the surcharges are horizontal.

1983 (3 Nov). *No.* 732 *optd with T* **226** *and No.* 798 *further optd with T* **256**, *both vertically reading upwards.*
1200 $3 "Makanaima the Great Ancestral Spirit of the Amerindians" (B.) .. .. 95 1·00
a. Opt reading downwards .. .. 12·00
1201 360 c. on $2 *Norantea guianensis* .. .. 1·25 1·40

1983 (15 Nov). *Wildlife Protection. Nos.* 686 *and* 688 *surch as T* **234**, *and No.* 852 *optd with T* **256**.
1202 30 c. Six-banded Armadillo 12 15
1203 60 c. on 15 c. Giant sea turtle 25 30
1204 $1.20 on 40 c. Iguana 45 50

1983 (1 Dec). *Human Rights Day. No.* 748 *optd with T* **283**.
1205 $3 Rotary anniversary emblem .. .. 1·10 1·25

LOS ANGELES 1984

●●● **55** ●●●

(284)

1983 (6 Dec). *Olympic Games, Los Angeles* (1984). *Nos.* 733/44 *surch with T* **284**.
1206 55 c. on 125 c. on 35 c. Type **174** 20 25
a. Block of 12. Nos. 1206/17 .. .. 2·25
1207 55 c. on 125 c. on 35 c. Haimara 20 25
1208 55 c. on 125 c. on 35 c. Electric Eel 20 25
1209 55 c. on 125 c. on 35 c. Golden Rivulus .. 20 25
1210 55 c. on 125 c. on 35 c. Pencil Fish 20 25
1211 55 c. on 125 c. on 35 c. Four-eyed Fish .. 20 25
1212 55 c. on 125 c. on 35 c. Pirai or Carib Fish .. 20 25
1213 55 c. on 125 c. on 35 c. Smoking Hassar .. 20 25
1214 55 c. on 125 c. on 35 c. Devil Ray 20 25
1215 55 c. on 125 c. on 35 c. Flying Patwa 20 25
1216 55 c. on 125 c. on 35 c. Arapaima Pirariucii .. 20 25
1217 55 c. on 125 c. on 35 c. Lukanani 20 25
1206/17 .. .. *Set of* 12 2·25 2·75

In addition to Type **284** Nos. 1206/17 show an additional "125" surcharge beneath the lefthand row of dots.

1983 (14 Dec). *No.* F7 *with unissued* "ESPANA 1982" *surch, as Nos.* 938/9, *in blue further optd with T* **256** *vertically.*
1218 180 c. on 60 c. Soldier's Cap 60 65

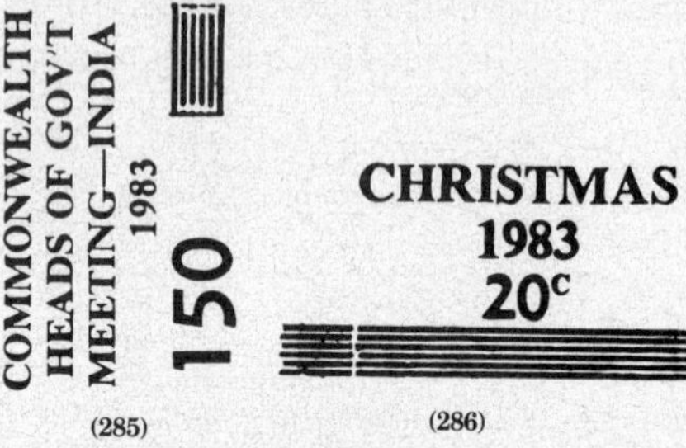

(285) (286)

1983 (14 Dec). *Commonwealth Heads of Government Meeting, New Delhi. No.* 542 *surch with T* **285**.
1219 150 c. on 1 c. Pitcher Plant of Mt Roraima .. 55 60

1983 (14 Dec). *Christmas. Nos.* 861A/B *further surch with T* **286**.
A. *No wmk* B. *Wmk* **106**
1220 20 c. on 12 c. on 6 c. Patua .. 8 10 8 10

1984 (8 Jan). *No.* F9 *optd as T* **229**, *but smaller* 29 × 6 *mm, vertically in blue.*
1221 $2 *Norantea guianensis* 65 70

17¢

(287)

1984 (Jan). *Flowers. Unissued coil stamps as T* **222** *handstamped with T* **287** *in blue.*
1222 17 c. on 2 c. grey-lilac, blue & turquoise-green 8 10
a. Vert pair. Nos. 1222/3 15
1223 17 c. on 8 c. grey-lilac, blue and mauve .. 8 10

Nos. 1222/3 were intended for use on 8 c. postal stationery envelopes to uprate them to the new price of 25 c.

ALL OUR HERITAGE 1984

● **25** (288) ● **25** (289)

1984

● **25** (290) ● **25** (291)

1984 (24 Feb). *Republic Day. No.* 703 *surch as T* **288/91** *in black and No.* 705*a optd as T* **288/9** *in blue.*
1224 25 c. on 35 c. multicoloured (surch T 288) .. 10 12
a. Sheetlet of 25. No. 1224 × 6, Nos. 1225/7 each × 4, Nos. 1228/30 each × 2 and No. 1231 .. .. 2·50
1225 25 c. on 35 c. multicoloured (surch T 289) .. 10 12
1226 25 c. on 35 c. multi (surch "REPUBLIC DAY") 10 12
1227 25 c. on 35 c. multicoloured (surch T 290) .. 10 12
1228 25 c. on 35 c. multi (surch "BERBICE") .. 20 15
1229 25 c. on 35 c. multi (surch "DEMERARA") .. 20 15
1230 25 c. on 35 c. multi (surch "ESSEQUIBO") .. 20 15
1231 25 c. on 35 c. multicoloured (surch T 291) .. 40 35
1232 60 c. multicoloured (opt T 288) 25 30
a. Sheetlet of 25. Nos. 1232/3 each × 8 and No. 1234 × 9 .. .. 5·75
1233 60 c. multicoloured (opt "REPUBLIC DAY") .. 25 30
1234 60 c. multicoloured (opt T 289) 25 30
1224/34 .. .. *Set of* 11 1·90 1·75

OLYMPIC GAMES 84

POSTAGE 25 ¢ (+ 2.25 SURTAX)

(292)

1984 (1 Mar). *Guyana Olympic Committee Appeal. Nos.* 841/3 *handstamped with T* **292** *in blue.*

1235 25 c. +2.25 c. on 60 c. on 3 c. Hanging Heliconia .. 4·00 4·00
1236 25 c. +2.25 c. on 75 c. on $5 *Odontadenia grandiflora* .. .. 4·00 1·50
1237 25 c. +2.25 c. on $1.10 on $2 *Norantea guianensis* .. .. 4·00 1·50

Nos. 1235/7 come from stamp booklets, the $2.25 charity premium on each stamp being donated to the local Olympic Committee Appeal Fund. All examples of these handstamps are inverted.

Protecting Our Heritage (293)

XXXX 90 (294)

1984 (5 Mar). *Nature Protection. Various stamps optd with T* **293** *in black (except for No.* 1239 *in blue) with some additionally surch as T* **272** *(Nos.* 1238/40, 1250/1 *and* 1254/5*) or as T* **294** *(Nos.* 1242, 1247 *and* 1252/3*) all in blue.*

1238 20 c. on 15 c. multicoloured (No. 491) (opt + surch vert) 8 10
a. Opt T **293** in blue .. .. 9·00 50
1239 20 c. on 15 c. multicoloured (No. 791) (opt + surch vert) 8 10
1240 20 c. on 15 c. multicoloured (No. 1044) (opt + surch vert) 8 10
a. Opt T **293** in blue .. .. .. 12·00 1·00
1241 25 c. multicoloured (No. 550*a*) .. .. 2·00 12
a. On No. 550ab .. .. 22·00 3·00
1242 30 c. on 15 c. multicoloured (No. 548) .. 3·00 15
1243 40 c. multicoloured (No. 494) (opt vert) .. 15 20
1244 50 c. multicoloured (No. 552) 20 25
1245 50 c. multicoloured (No. F6) 20 25
a. Opt Type F **1** double .. .. .. 35·00
1246 60 c. multicoloured (No. 459) 25 30
a. On No. 496 .. .. 22·00 4·00
1247 90 c. on 40 c. multicoloured (No. 551) .. 35 40
a. On No. F5 .. .. 32·00 6·00
1248 180 c. on 40 c. multicoloured (No. 919) .. 65 70
1249 $2 multicoloured (No. 461) .. .. 2·00 1·25
1250 225 c. on 10 c. multicoloured (No. 491a) (opt + surch vert) 85 90
1251 260 c. on $1 multicoloured (No. 497*a*) .. 95 1·00
1252 320 c. on 40 c. multicoloured (No. 551) .. 1·10 1·25
1253 350 c. on 40 c. multicoloured (No. 551) .. 1·25 1·50
1254 390 c. on 50 c. multicoloured (No. 495) .. 1·50 1·75
a. On No. 458 .. .. 70·00 20·00
1255 450 c. on $5 multicoloured (No. 499) .. 1·60 1·90
1238/55 .. .. *Set of* 18 14·00 10·00

(295) (296)

1984 (17 Mar). *Easter. Nos.* 483 *and* 916/17 *optd with T* **295**, *and No.* 481 *surch as T* **272**, *but without decimal point, all in blue.*

1256 **111** 30 c. multicoloured 15 20
1257 45 c. on 6 c. multicoloured 20 25
1258 75 c. on 40 c. multicoloured 30 35
1259 130 c. on 6 c. multicoloured 55 60

No. 1258 exists with the previous surcharge either at the right or in the centre of the design.

1984 (2 Apr). *Nos.* 937/9 *and* 991 *surch as T* **294**.

1260 75 c. on $1 *Chelonanthus uliginoides* .. 30 35
1261 75 c. on 110 c. on 3 c. Hanging Heliconia .. 30 35
1262 225 c. on 250 c. on 6 c. Cannon-ball tree .. 95 1·00
1263 230 c. on $2.35 on 180 c. on 60 c. Soldier's Cap 95 1·00

1984 (2 May). *Nos.* 899/901, 904/6 *and* 909 *surch as T* **294**.

1264 20 c. on 15 c. on 2 c. Type **132** (No. 899) .. 8 10
1265 75 c. on 110 c. on 5 c. Annatto tree (No. 904) 30 35
1266 90 c. on 110 c. on 5 c. Annatto tree (No. 900) (B.) 40 45
1267 90 c. on 110 c. on 5 c. Annatto tree (No. 901) (B.) 40 45
1268 120 c. on 125 c. on 8 c. on 6 c. Cannon-ball tree (No. 905) 50 55
1269 120 c. on 125 c. on 8 c. on 6 c. Cannon-ball tree (No. 906) 50 55
1270 120 c. on 125 c. on 8 c. on 6 c. Cannon-ball tree (No. 909) 50 55
1264/70 .. .. *Set of* 7 2·40 2·50

Nos. 1264/70 were surcharged on the sheets which contained one type of the previous surcharge only.

1984 (17 May). *World Telecommunications and Health Day. Nos.* 802 *and* 980 *surch as T* **296** *in blue.*

1271 25 c. on 220 c. on 1 c. Pitcher Plant of Mt Roraima (surch T **296**) 20 20
a. Sheetlet of 25. Nos. 1271/2 each × 8 and No. 1273 × 9 .. .. 4·50
1272 25 c. on 220 c. on 1 c. Pitcher Plant of Mt Roraima (surch "WHO DAY 1984") .. 20 20
1273 25 c. on 220 c. on 1 c. Pitcher Plant of Mt Roraima (surch "ITU/WHO DAY 1984") 20 20
1274 $4.50 on 280 c. on $5 *Odontadenis grandiflora* (surch "ITU/WHO DAY 1984") .. 1·75 1·75

The surcharge is horizontal on No. 1274 and vertical on the others.

1984 (11 June). *No.* 1005 *surch vertically as T* **272**, *but without decimal point.*

1275 120 c. on $1.25 on 6 c. Cannon-ball tree .. 50 55

1984 (15 June). *World Forestry Conference. Nos.* 752/5 *surch as T* **272**, *but without decimal point, or optd with T* **295** *($3), and No.* 875 *surch as T* **294**.

1276 55 c. on 30 c. *Hymenaea courbaril* .. 25 30
1277 75 c. on 110 c. on $3 *Peltogyne venosa* (B.) .. 30 35
1278 160 c. on 50 c. *Mora excelsa* (B.) 65 70
1279 260 c. on 10 c. Type **177** (B.) .. .. 1·10 1·25
1280 $3 *Peltogyne venosa* (B.) .. .. 1·25 1·40

1984 (18 June). *No.* 625 *surch vertically as T* **294**.

1281 55 c. on 110 c. on 10 c. Type **150** 25 30
1282 90 c. on 110 c. on 10 c. Type **150** (B.) 40 45

Nos. 1281/2 also carry an otherwise unissued 110 c. surcharge in blue as Type **264**.

UPU Congress 1984 Hamburg (297)

60 (298)

1984 (19 June). *U.P.U. Congress, Hamburg. Nos.* 1188/91 *optd with T* **297**.

1283 120 c. lake-brown and black 50 55
a. Block of 4. Nos. 1283/6 .. .. .. 2·25
1284 130 c. rose-red and black 55 60
1285 150 c. bright violet and black 60 65
1286 200 c. dull green and black 80 85

1984 (21 June). *Nos.* 982/3 *and* 986/7 *surch with T* **298** *(60 c.) or as T* **272**, *but without the decimal point (others).*

1287 45 c. on 2 c. myrtle-green 20 25
1288 60 c. on $1.10 on 3 c. brown-olive and red-brown (B.) 25 30
a. Surch on No. 983c 25 30
1289 120 c. on $1.25 on 6 c. yellow-green 50 55
1290 200 c. on $2.20 on 24 c. black and brownish orange (B.) 80 85

1984 (30 June). *Nos.* 979/80 *and* 1003 *surch as T* **294**, *and No.* 981 *optd vertically with T* **295**.

1291 75 c. on 110 c. on 5 c. Annatto tree 30 35
1292 120 c. on 170 c. on 110 c. on 5 c. Annatto tree 50 55
1293 200 c. on 220 c. on 1 c. Pitcher Plant of Mt Roraima (B.) 80 85
1294 330 c. on $2 *Norantea guianensis* (B.) .. 1·40 1·50

CARICOM DAY 1984

60 XX

(299)

1984 (30 June). *CARICOM Day. No.* 1200 *additionally surch with T* **299**.

1295 60 c. on $3 "Makanaima the Great Ancestral Spirit of the Amerindians" 25 30

1984 (30 June). *No.* 544 *surch as T* **275** *in blue.*

1296 150 c. on 3 c. Hanging Heliconia 60 65

60
CARICOM
HEADS OF GOV'T
CONFERENCE
JULY 1984

(300)

301 Children and Thatched School

1984 (2 July). *CARICOM Heads of Government Conference. No.* 544 *surch with T* **300** *in blue.*

1297 60 c. on 3 c. Hanging Heliconia 25 30

1984 (16 July). *Centenary of Guyana Teachers' Association. T* **301** *and similar horiz designs. Multicoloured. Litho. W* **106** *(sideways). P* 14.

1298 25 c. Type **301** 10 12
a. Block of 4. Nos. 1298/301 35
1299 25 c. Torch and graduates 10 12
1300 25 c. Torch and target emblem 10 12
1301 25 c. Teachers of 1884 and 1984 in front of school 10 12

Nos. 1298/301 were printed together, *se-tenant*, in blocks of 4 throughout the sheet.

INT. CHESS FED. 1924-1984
25 XX
(302)

25 TRACK AND FIELD
(303)

1984 (20 July). *50th Anniv of International Chess Federation. No.* 1048 *optd or surch as T* **302** *or optd with T* **295**, *all in blue.*

1302 25 c. on 90 c. on 60 c. Fort Island (surch T **302**) 10 12
a. Sheetlet of 25. No. 1302 × 16 and No. 1303 × 9 .. .. 2·50
1303 25 c. on 90 c. on 60 c. Fort Island (opt T **295**) .. 10 12
1304 75 c. on 90 c. on 60 c. Fort Island (surch T **302**) 30 35
a. Sheetlet of 25. No. 1304 × 16 and No. 1305 × 9 .. .. 7·50
1305 75 c. on 90 c. on 60 c. Fort Island (opt T **295**) .. 30 35
1306 90 c. on 60 c. Fort Island (opt T **302**) 40 45
a. Sheetlet of 25. No. 1306 × 16 and No. 1307 × 9 .. .. 10·00
1307 90 c. on 60 c. Fort Island (opt T **295**) 40 45
1302/7 .. .. *Set of* 6 1·40 1·60

Overprints as Type **295** occur in the central horizontal and vertical rows of each sheet.

1984 (28 July). *Olympic Games, Los Angeles. No.* 1051 *surch as T* **303** *in blue.*

1308 25 c. on $1.30, multicoloured (surch T **303**) .. 20 25
a. Booklet pane of 10. No. 1308 × 4 and Nos. 1309/10, each × 3 .. .. 2·00
b. Coil strip of 5. Nos. 1308 × 2, 1311 × 2 and 1312 .. .. 1·00
1309 25 c. on $1.30, mult (surch "BOXING") .. 20 25
1310 25 c. on $1.30, mult (surch "OLYMPIC GAMES 1984 LOS ANGELES") .. 20 25
1311 25 c. on $1.30, mult (surch "CYCLING") .. 20 25
1312 25 c. on $1.30, mult (surch "OLYMPIC GAMES 1984") 20 25
1313 $1.20 on $1.30, multicoloured (surch T **303**) 1·00 1·10
a. Booklet pane of 10. No. 1313 × 4 and Nos. 1314/15 each × 3 .. .. 10·00
b. Coil strip of 5. Nos. 1313 × 2, 1316 × 2 and 1317 .. .. 5·00
1314 $1.20 on $1.30, mult (surch "BOXING") .. 1·00 1·10
1315 $1.20 on $1.30, mult (surch "OLYMPIC GAMES 1984 LOS ANGELES") .. 1·00 1·10
1316 $1.20 on $1.30, mult (surch "CYCLING") .. 1·00 1·10
1317 $1.20 on $1.30, multicoloured (surch "OLYMPIC GAMES 1984") .. .. 1·00 1·10
1308/17 .. .. *Set of* 10 5·25 6·00

Nos. 1308 and 1313 come from booklets and coils, Nos. 1309/10 and 1314/15 from booklets only, and Nos. 1311/12 and 1316/17 from coils only.

The coils were constructed from normal sheets with coil joins on every fifth stamp.

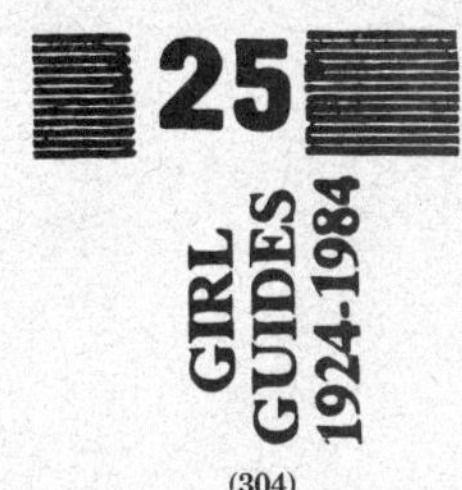

(304)

1984 (15 Aug). *60th Anniv of Girl Guide Movement in Guyana. Nos.* 900/9 *surch with T* **304** *in blue.*

1318 25 c. on 110 c. on 5 c. Annatto tree (No. 900) 10 12
a. Sheetlet of 25. Nos. 1318/19, each × 8, Nos. 1320/1, each × 4 and No. 1322 .. 2·50
1319 25 c. on 110 c. on 5 c. Annatto tree (No. 901) .. 10 12
1320 25 c. on 110 c. on 5 c. Annatto tree (No. 902) .. 10 12
1321 25 c. on 110 c. on 5 c. Annatto tree (No. 903) .. 10 12
1322 25 c. on 110 c. on 5 c. Annatto tree (No. 904) .. 50 40
1323 25 c. on 125 c. on 8 c. on 6 c. Cannon-ball tree (No. 905) 10 12
a. Sheetlet of 25. Nos. 1323/4, each × 8, Nos. 1325/6, each × 4 and No. 1327 .. 2·50
1324 25 c. on 125 c. on 8 c. on 6 c. Cannon-ball tree (No. 906) 10 12
1325 25 c. on 125 c. on 8 c. on 6 c. Cannon-ball tree (No. 907) 10 12
1326 25 c. on 125 c. on 8 c. on 6 c. Cannon-ball tree (No. 908) 10 12
1327 25 c. on 125 c. on 8 c. on 6 c. Cannon-ball tree (No. 909) 50 40
1318/27 .. .. *Set of* 10 1·50 1·40

PARCEL POST STAMPS

PARCEL POST

X $15.00 X $15.00

(P 1)

PARCEL POST $12.00

(P 2)

1981 (8 June). *No. 554 surch as Type* P **1**.
P1 $15 on $1 *Chelonanthus uliginoides* . . . . 5·00 4·50
P2 $20 on $1 *Chelonanthus uliginoides* . . . . 6·50 6·50

1983 (15 Jan). *No. 843 surch with Type* P **2** *in blue.*
P3 $12 on $1.10 on $2 *Norantea guianensis* . . 15·00 5·50

Parcel Post
$12.00

(P 3)

1983 (14 Sept). *Unissued Royal Wedding surch, similar to No.* 843, *further surch with Type* P **3** *in blue.*
P4 $12 on $1.10 on $2 *Norantea guianensis* . . 12·00 5·00

POSTAGE DUE STAMPS

POSTAGE DUE 4c GUYANA

D 2

(Typo D.L.R.)

1967–68. *Chalky paper.* W w **12**. *P* 14.
D5 D **2** 2 c. black (11.12.68) . . . . 70 1·40
D6 4 c. deep ultramarine 30 85
D7 12 c. reddish scarlet . . . . 50 1·40

1973 (24 May). *Glazed, ordinary paper.* W **106**. *P* 14.
D 8 D **2** 1 c. olive 12 25
D 9 2 c. black 12 25
D10 4 c. dull ultramarine 15 30
D11 12 c. bright scarlet 30 40

10 OPS

(O 1)

OPS

(O 2)

OPS

(O 3)

1981 (8 June). *Nos.* 556, F4a *and* F6/7 *surch or optd with Types* O **1/3**.
O1 10 c. on 25 c. Marabunta (Blk+R.) . . . . 2·50 1·50
O2 50 c. *Guzmania ligulata* (R.) . . . . . . 1·25 50
O3 60 c. Soldier's Cap (R.) . . . . 1·00 30
O4 $5 *Odontadenia grandiflora* (opt Type O 3) (R.) . . . . 4·25 2·25

OPS

(O 4)

OPS 100

(O 5)

1981 (1 July). (*a*) *Postage. Nos.* 491, 708*a*, 716, 834 *and* F9 *optd or surch as Types* P **3/5** *or additionally surch as T* **227**.
O 5 15 c. Harpy Eagle (opt Type O 4) 40 10
O 6 30 c. on $2 *Norantea guianensis* (No. F9) (opt Type O 3) (Blk+R.) 50 15
O 7 100 c. on $3 Cylinder satellite (surch Type O 5) (Blk+R.) . . . . 2·25 40
O 8 125 c. on $2 *Norantea guianensis* (opt Type O 3) (R.) . . . . 3·00 45
O 9 $10 *Elbella patrobas* (opt Type O 3) . . 4·00 3·25

(*b*) *Air. No.* 804 *optd with Type* O **3** *in red*
O10 $1.10 on $2 *Norantea guianensis* . . . . 18·00 15·00
a. Opt Type O 3 double £110

1981 (7 July). *Nos.* 548, 719, 828 *and* 830 *optd with Type* O **3**.
O11 15 c. Christmas Orchid . . . . . . 3·00 75
O12 50 c. British Guiana 1898 1 c. stamp . . 1·25 25
O13 100 c. on 8 c. Camp-fire cooking . . . . 3·75 35
O14 110 c. on 6 c. Type **116** . . . . . . 4·50 60

OPS

(O 6)

OPS 250

(O 7)

1982 (17 May). (*a*) *Postage.* (i) *Various stamps optd with Type* O **6** *in blue.*
O16 – 20 c. multicoloured (No. 701) 10 12
O17 **136** 40 c. multicoloured 75 25
O18 – 40 c. carm-red, grey & black (No. 674) 1·00 25
O19 – $2 multicoloured (No. 676) . . . . 6·00 1·00

(ii) *No.* 911 *additionally surch with Type* O **7** *in blue*
O20 – 250 c. on 400 c. on 30 c. multicoloured 80 80

(*b*) *Air. No.* 980 *additionally optd with Type* O **6** *in blue*
O21 – 220 c. on 1 c. multicoloured . . . . 5·00 1·00

1982 (12 July). *No.* F9 *optd with Type* O **3** *in red.*
O22 $2 *Norantea guianensis* . . . . . . 10·00 2·00

1982 (15 Sept). *Air. No.* 979 *optd with Type* O **6**.
O23 110 c. on 5 c. Annatto tree . . . . . . 4·50 1·00

1984 (2 Apr). *No.* 912 *surch as Type* O **7** *vertically, in blue (except for No.* O26 *which has "OPS" in blue and "225" in black).*
O24 150 c. on $5 multicoloured 55 60
O25 200 c. on $5 multicoloured 70 75
O26 225 c. on $5 multicoloured 80 85
O27 230 c. on $5 multicoloured 80 85
O28 260 c. on $5 multicoloured . . . . . . 95 1·00
O29 320 c. on $5 multicoloured . . . . . . 1·10 1·25
O30 350 c. on $5 multicoloured . . . . . . 1·25 1·40
O31 600 c. on $5 multicoloured . . . . . . 2·10 2·25
O24/31 . . . . *Set of* 8 7·50 8·00

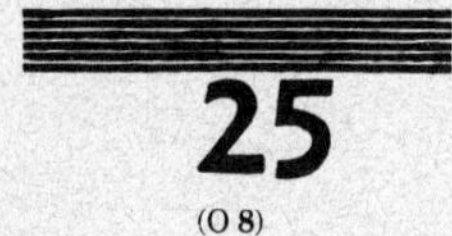

(O 8)

1984 (25 June). *Nos.* O21 *and* O23 *surch as Type* O **8** (25 c., 60 c.) *or as T* **294** *(others), and No.* 981 *optd vertically with Type* O **6**.
O32 25 c. on 110 c. on 5 c. Annatto tree 10 12
O33 30 c. on 110 c. on 5 c. Annatto tree (B.) . . 12 15
O34 45 c. on 220 c. on 1 c. Pitcher Plant of Mt Roraima 15 20
O35 55 c. on 110 c. on 5 c. Annatto tree 20 25
O36 60 c. on 220 c. on 1 c. Pitcher Plant of Mt Roraima 20 25
O37 75 c. on 220 c. on 1 c. Pitcher Plant of Mt Roraima 25 30
O38 90 c. on 220 c. on 1 c. Pitcher Plant of Mt Roraima (B.) 35 40
O39 120 c. on 220 c. on 1 c. Pitcher Plant of Mt Roraima 45 50
O40 130 c. on 220 c. on 1 c. Pitcher Plant of Mt Roraima (B.) 50 55
O41 330 c. on $2 *Norantea guianensis* (B.) . . 1·10 1·25
O32/41 . . . . *Set of* 10 3·00 3·50

OFFICIAL PARCEL POST STAMPS

1981 (8 June). *Nos.* P1/2 *optd with Type* O **3** *in red.*
OP1 $15 on $1 *Chelonanthus uliginoides* . . . . 5·00 4·50
a. Opt in black . . . . 45·00 8·00
OP2 $20 on $1 *Chelonanthus uliginoides* . . . . 6·50 6·50

OPS

Parcel Post
$12.00

(OP 1)

1983 (15 Jan). *No.* 843 *surch with Type* OP **1**, *and optd with T* **226**, *both in blue.*
OP3 $12 on $1.10 on $2 *Norantea guianensis* . . 35·00 10·00

1983 (22 Aug). *As No.* OP3, *but additionally optd with Type* O **6**.
OP4 $12 on $1.10 on $2 *Norantea guianensis* . . 15·00 7·50

1983 (3 Nov). *No.* P4 *additionally optd with Type* O **6** *in blue.*
OP5 $12 on $1.10 on $2 *Norantea guianensis* . . 8·00 5·00

POSTAL FISCAL STAMPS

REVENUE ONLY

*

(F 1)

1975 (1 Nov). *Nos.* 543/5 *and* 550*a*/56 *optd with Type* F **1**.
F 1 2 c. Type **132** 25 20
F 2 3 c. Hanging Heliconia 25 20
F 3 5 c. Annatto tree 40 20
F 4 25 c. Marabunta (Type II) 50 20
a. Optd on No. 550 (Type I) . . . . . . 15·00 13·00
F 5 40 c. Tiger Beard 25 30
F 6 50 c. *Guzmania ligulata* 30 40
F 7 60 c. Soldier's Cap 40 50
F 8 $1 *Chelonanthus uliginoides* 75 80
F 9 $2 *Norantea guianensis* . . . . . . 1·50 1·75
F10 $5 *Odontadenia grandiflora* . . . . 5·00 4·00
F1/F10 . . . . *Set of* 10 8·50 7·50

Although intended for fiscal use Nos. F1/10 were allowed, by the postal authorities, as "an act of grace" to do duty as postage stamps until 30 June 1976.

Heligoland

Stamps of HAMBURG (see Part 7 (*Germany*) of this catalogue) were used in Heligoland until 16 April 1867. The Free City of Hamburg ran the Heligoland postal service between 1796 and 1 June 1866. Its stamps continued in use on the island until replaced by Heligoland issues.

PRICES FOR STAMPS ON COVER

Nos. 1/31	*from* × 3
Nos. 32/3	—

Collectors should be on their guard against reprints of Heligoland stamps, which are very numerous and of little value. Beware also of forgeries and forged cancellations on both originals and reprints.

PRINTERS. All the stamps of Heligoland were typographed at the Imperial Printing Works, Berlin.

1

2

3

(Des Wedding. Die eng E. Schilling)

1867. *Head embossed in colourless relief. Roul.*
1 1 ½ sch. green and rose (Die I) £275 £550
2 ½ sch. green and rose (Die II) £700 £1000
3 1 sch. rose and blue-green £150 £150
4 2 sch. rose and grass-green . . . . 7·00 50·00
5 6 sch. green and rose . . . . . . 9·00 £250

In Nos. 1 to 9, the second colour is that of the spandrels in the ½ and 1 sch., and of the central background also in the 2 and 6 sch. In Die I the small curl below the chignon is solid and projects downwards, while in Die II it is in the shape of a hook opening to the left.

1869–72. *P* 13½ × 14½.
6 1 ½ sch. yellow-green and rose £150 £160
7 ½ sch. blue-green and rose £125 £140
8 1 sch. rose and pale blue-green £100 £125
9 1 sch. rose and yellow-green £100 £125

1873. *New values. P* 13½ × 14½.
10 1 ¼ sch. rose and green . . . . . . 21·00 £1400
a. Error. Green and rose . . . . 80·00 £2000
11 ¼ sch. deep rose and pale green . . . . 80·00 £1400
12 ¾ sch. green and rose . . . . . . 21·00 £1100
13 1½ sch. green and rose . . . . . . 50·00 £250

In Nos. 10, 10a, 11 and 13 the second colour is that of the central background.

In No. 12 the second colour is also that of the side labels and side marginal lines.

No. 10a results from a printing of the ¼ sch. in the colours of the 1½ sch.

(Des H. Gätke. Die eng E. Schilling)

1875. *Head embossed in colourless relief. P* 13½ × 14½.
15 2 1 pf. (¼d.) deep green and rose . . 6·00 £500
16 2 pf. (½d.) deep rose and green . . 6·00 £575
17 5 pf. (¾d.) deep yellow-green and rose 6·00 16·00
18 5 pf. (¾d.) deep green and rose . . 8·50 35·00
19 10 pf. (1½d.) deep rose and deep green . . 20·00 18·00
20 10 pf. (1½d.) scarlet and pale blue-green 6·00 18·00
21 10 pf. (1½d.) rose aniline & pale yellow-green . . . . 55·00 22·00
22 25 pf. (3d.) deep green and rose . . 8·00 24·00
23 50 pf. (6d.) rose and green . . . . 13·00 24·00

The first colour given above is that of the central background, the second that of the frame.

(Des H. Gätke. Die eng A. Schiffner)

1876. *P* 13½ × 14½.
24 3 3 pf. (⅝d.) green, red and yellow-orange £125 £750
24*a* 3 pf. (⅝d.) pale green, red and yellow . . £125 £750
25 20 pf. (2½d.) rose, green and yellow . . 90·00 55·00
26 20 pf. (2½d.) rose-carmine, deep green and orange . . . . . . £100 50·00
27 20 pf. (2½d.) dull red, pale green and lemon . . . . 11·00 20·00
28 20 pf. (2½d.) vermilion aniline, bright green and lemon . . . . 11·00 20·00

Colours. 3 pf. (1) Frame and top band of shield. (2) Centre band of shield. (3) Border of shield.

20 pf. (1) Frame and centre band. (2) Upper band. (3) Border of shield.

4

5

(Des H. Gätke. Die eng A. Schiffner)

1879. (*a*) *P* 13½ × 14½.
29 4 1 m. (1s.) deep green, scarlet and black . . 80·00 £200
30 1 m. (1s.) deep green, rose aniline & blk. . 90·00 £200
31 5 5 m. (5s.) deep green, rose aniline & blk. . £100 £950

(*b*) *P* 11½
32 4 1 m. (1s.) deep green, scarlet and black £400
33 5 5 m. (5s.) deep green, scarlet and black £400
a. Imperf between (pair) £2000

The stamps perf 11½ are given above on the ground that specimens exist on the original envelopes and are known to have been genuinely postally used.

Numerous reprints of the ¼ sch. (including the *error*), ½ sch. (Die II), ¾ sch., 1 sch., 1½ sch., 2 sch., 6 sch., 1 pf., 2 pf. and 3 pf. were made between 1875 and 1895. It is impossible to describe them all here. Collectors should exercise caution in purchasing stamps of which reprints exist.

Heligoland was ceded to Germany on 9 Aug 1890.

Hong Kong

CROWN COLONY

The Hong Kong Post Office was established in February 1841, when much of the business previously transacted through the Macao postal agency was transferred to the island. The first cancellation is known from April 1842, but local control of the posts was shortlived as the Hong Kong Post Office became a branch of the British G.P.O. following the ratification of the Treaty of Nanking on 26 June 1843.

The colonial authorities resumed control of the postal service on 1 May 1860, although the previously established postal agencies in the Chinese Treaty Ports remained part of the British G.P.O. system until 1868.

For illustrations of the handstamp types see BRITISH POST OFFICES ABROAD notes, following GREAT BRITAIN.

CROWNED-CIRCLE HANDSTAMPS

CC1 CC1 HONG KONG (R.) (17.10.1843) *Price on cover* £550
CC2 CC1b HONG KONG (R.) (21.8.1844) *Price on cover* £375
CC3 CC3 HONG KONG (R.) (16.6.1852) *Price on cover* £250

We no longer list the Great Britain stamps with obliteration "B 62" within oval. The Government notificaiion dated 29 November 1862 stated that only the Hong Kong stamps to be issued on 8 December would be available for postage and the stamps formerly listed were all issued in Great Britain later than the date of the notice.

PRICES FOR STAMPS ON COVER TO 1945

Nos. 1/7	*from* × 4
Nos. 8/27	*from* × 5
Nos. 28/36	*from* × 4
Nos. 37/9	*from* × 5
Nos. 40/4	*from* × 4
Nos. 45/8	*from* × 10
Nos. 49/50	*from* × 4
No. 51	*from* × 15
Nos. 52/61	*from* × 5
Nos. 62/99	*from* × 4
Nos. 100/32	*from* × 3
Nos. 133/6	*from* × 2
Nos. 137/9	*from* × 4
Nos. 140/68	*from* × 2
Nos. D1/12	*from* × 8
Nos. F1/11	*from* × 4
No. F12	*from* × 3
Nos. P1/3	*from* × 2

PRINTERS. All definitive stamps up to 1960 were typographed by De La Rue & Co.

CONDITION. Mint or fine used specimens of the earlier Hong Kong stamps are rarely met with and are worth considerably more than our prices which are for stamps in average condition. Inferior specimens can be supplied at much lower prices.

1

2

3

1862 (8 Dec). *No wmk. P* 14.
1 1 2 c. brown . . . . £170 45·00
a. Deep brown . . . . . . £275 50·00
2 8 c. yellow-buff . . . . . . £300 30·00
3 12 c. pale greenish blue . . . . . . £200 28·00
4 3 18 c. lilac . . . . £225 25·00
5 24 c. green . . . . £500 55·00
6 48 c. rose £1400 £170
7 96 c. brownish grey £1800 £180

1863–70. *Wmk Crown CC. P* 14.
8 1 2 c. deep brown (1865) . . . . . . £100 14·00
a. Brown . . . . 50·00 3·75
b. Pale yellowish brown . . . . . . 60·00 5·50
9 2 4 c. grey (1863) . . . . . . 35·00 6·00
a. Slate . . . . 27·00 3·00
b. Deep slate . . . . 55·00 4·75
c. Greenish grey . . . . . . £120 20·00
d. Bluish slate . . . . . . £190 10·00
e. Perf 12½ (1870) £3000 £250
10 6 c. lilac (1863) . . . . . . £180 5·50
a. Mauve . . . . £180 6·50
11 1 8 c. pale dull orange (1865) . . . . £200 5·00
a. Brownish orange . . . . . . £170 6·00
b. Bright orange . . . . . . £190 4·50
12 12 c. pale greenish blue (1864?) . . . . £350 17·00
a. Pale blue . . . . 12·00 4·00
b. Deep blue . . . . 90·00 6·50
13 3 18 c. lilac (1866) £1500 £200
14 24 c. green (1865) . . . . . . £190 7·00
a. Pale green . . . . £300 10·00
b. Deep green . . . . £375 15·00
15 2 30 c. vermilion (1863) . . . . . . £350 8·50
a. Orange-vermilion . . . . . . £275 10·00
16 30 c. mauve (1871) . . . . . . 85·00 4·75
17 48 c. pale rose (1865) . . . . . . £400 25·00
a. Rose-carmine . . . . . . £425 17·00
b. Bright claret . . . . . . † —
18 96 c. olive-bistre (1865) £10000 £425
19 96 c. brownish grey (1866) . . . . £425 20·00
a. Brownish black . . . . . . £550 17·00

There is a wide range of shades in this issue, of which we can only indicate the main groups.

No. 12 is the same shade as No. 3 without wmk, the impression having a waxy appearance.

Only one used copy of No. 17*b* is known.

See also Nos. 22 and 28/31.

16 cents.	*28* *cents.*	5 cents.	10 cents.
(4)	(5)	(6)	(7)

No. 20b

1876. *Nos.* 13 *and* 16 *surch with T* 4 *or* 5.
20 3 16 c. on 18 c. lilac (June?) £850 £110
a. Space between "n" and "t" £2250 £350
b. Space between "s" and stop
21 2 28 c. on 30 c. mauve (July?) . . . . £500 40·00

1877 (Aug). *New value. Wmk Crown CC. P* 14.
22 3 16 c. yellow . . . . £400 38·00

1880 (Mar). *Surch with T* 6 *or* 7.
23 1 5 c. on 8 c. bright orange (No. 11*b*) . . £250 45·00
a. Surch inverted . . . . . . — £6500
b. Surch double . . . . . . — £7500
24 3 5 c. on 18 c. lilac (No. 13) . . . . £160 25·00
25 1 10 c. on 12 c. pale blue (No. 12*a*) . . £200 30·00
a. Blue . . . . £325 35·00
26 3 10 c. on 16 c. yellow (No. 22) . . . . £900 70·00
a. Surch inverted . . . . . . — £11000
27 10 c. on 24 c. green (No. 14) . . . . £375 50·00

1880. *Colours changed and new values. Wmk Crown CC. P* 14.
28 1 2 c. dull rose (July) . . . . . . 26·00 7·00
a. Rose . . . . 35·00 8·00
29 2 5 c. blue (Nov) . . . . . . £100 9·50
30 10 c. mauve (Nov) . . . . . . £120 6·50
31 3 48 c. brown . . . . £300 45·00

1882–83. *Wmk Crown CA. P* 14.
32 1 2 c. rose-lake . . . . . . 35·00 12·00
a. Rose-pink . . . . . . 60·00 18·00
b. Perf 12 . . . . . . £10000
33 2 c. carmine (1883) . . . . . . 3·50 25
a. Aniline carmine . . . . . . 4·00 25
34 2 5 c. pale blue . . . . . . 3·75 35
a. Blue . . . . 3·75 35
35 10 c. dull mauve . . . . . . £250 4·50
36 10 c. green (1883) . . . . . . 28·00 1·40
a. Deep blue-green . . . . . . £750 25·00

20 CENTS	50 CENTS	1 DOLLAR
(8)	(9)	(10)

1885 (June). *Surch with T* 8 *to* 10. *Wmk Crown CA. P* 14.
37 2 20 c. on 30 c. orange-red . . . . 27·00 3·50
a. Surch double £3000
38 3 50 c. on 48 c. yellowish brown . . . . £120 8·00
39 $1 on 96 c. grey-olive . . . . £200 19·00
37/9 Optd "Specimen" . . . . *Set of* 3 £500

1891–92. *Wmk Crown CA. P* 14. (*a*) *Colours changed* (1.1.91).
40 2 10 c. purple/*red* . . . . . . 3·50 25
41 30 c. yellowish green . . . . . . 60·00 20·00
a. Grey-green . . . . . . 17·00 6·00
40, 41*a* Optd "Specimen" . . . . *Set of* 2 £350

(*b*) *Colours changed and surch with T* 8 *to* 10.
42 2 20 c. on 30 c. yellowish green (No. 41) . . £100 60·00
a. Grey-green (No. 41*a*) . . . . 75·00 42·00
43 3 50 c. on 48 c. dull purple (1892) £180 £120
44 $1 on 96 c. purple/*red* £300 £120
42*a*/44 Optd "Specimen" . . . . *Set of* 3 £500

Nos. 41/2 should not be confused with faded or washed copies of the grey-green, which turns to a very yellow-green shade when dampened.

贰	五十	壹員
(11) (20 c.)	(12) (50 c.)	(13) ($1)

1891. *Surch with T* **8/10** *as Nos. 42/4 but handstamped Chinese characters added at top of label at left (T* **11/13***).*
45 **2** 20 c. on 30 c. yellowish green .. .. 23·00 3·00
a. Grey-green .. .. .. 9·00 1·90
b. "20 CENTS" double .. ..
46 **3** 50 c. on 48 c. dull purple.. .. .. 22·00 3·50
47 $1 on 96 c. purple/*red* .. .. .. £140 10·00

Type **11** consists of a single character for "2" intended to over-stamp the "3" to convert the 30 c. to 20 c. Six different chops were made and three of the 50 c. Type **12**.

The errors of the Chinese surcharges previously listed on the above issue and also on Nos. 52 and 55 are now omitted as being outside the scope of the catalogue. While some without doubt possess philatelic merit, it is impossible to distinguish between the genuine errors and the clandestine copies made to order with the original chops. No. 55c is retained as this represents a distinctly different chop which was used for the last part of the printing.

1841
Hong Kong
JUBILEE
1891
(14)

7
cents.
(15)

14
cents.
(16)

1891 (22 Jan). *50th Anniv of Colony. Optd with T* **14**.
48 **1** 2 c. carmine (No. 33) .. .. .. £200 75·00
a. Short "J" in "JUBILEE" £325 £110
b. Short "U" in "JUBILEE" £325 £110
c. Broken "1" in "1891" £450 £170
d. Tall narrow "K" in "KONG" £650 £350
e. Opt double £7000 £5500
f. Space between "O" and "N" of "HONG" £1400 £600

This overprint was applied in a setting of 12, and other less marked varieties therefore exist.

1891. *Surch with T* **15** *or* **16**.
49 **2** 7 c. on 10 c. green (No. 36) (Jan) .. 28·00 12·00
a. Antique "t" in "cents" £425 £140
b. Surch double £3500 £1000
50 14 c. on 30 c. mauve (No. 16) (Apr) .. 70·00 38·00
a. Antique "t" in "cents" £1700 £850

The true antique "t" must not be confused with a small "t" with short foot, which is sometimes mistaken for it. In the antique "t" the cross-bar is accurately bisected by the vertical stroke, the latter being thick at the top. The lower curve bends towards the right and does not turn upwards so far as in the normal.

Dangerous forgeries of these two surcharges exist.

1896. *Wmk Crown CA. P* 14.
51 **2** 4 c. slate-grey .. .. 3·25 30

1898 (1 Apr). *Wmk Crown CA. P* 14.

(a) Surch with T **10**, *and handstamped Chinese characters as T* **13**.
52 **3** $1 on 96 c. black .. .. .. 42·00 15·00
a. Grey-black .. .. 42·00 15·00

(b) Surch with T **10** *only*
53 **3** $1 on 96 c. black £400 £450
a. Grey-black (Optd S. £350) £400 £400

10
CENTS
(17)

拾
(18)

拾
(19)

1898 (April). *(a) Surch with T* **17**.
54 **2** 10 c. on 30 c. grey-green (No. 41*a*) .. £200 £300
a. Figures "10" widely spaced (1½ mm)

(b) As No. 54, but with Chinese character, T **18**, *in addition*
55 **2** 10 c. on 30 c. grey-green (No. 41*a*) (H/S S. £140) .. .. 16·00 18·00
a. Yellowish green (Optd S. £140) .. 60·00
b. Figures "10" widely spaced (1½ mm) £225 £150
c. Chinese character large (Type **19**) .. £400 £225

1900 (Aug)–**02**. *Wmk Crown CA. P* 14.
56 **1** 2 c. dull green .. .. 2·00 30
57 **2** 4 c. carmine .. .. 1·00 30
58 5 c. yellow .. .. 4·50 3·25
59 10 c. ultramarine .. .. .. 7·50 1·60
60 **1** 12 c. blue (2.02) .. .. .. 12·00 18·00
61 **2** 30 c. brown (12.01) .. .. .. 9·50 11·00
56/61 .. .. *Set of* 6 32·00 32·00
56/9, 61 Optd "Specimen" .. .. *Set of* 5 £325

HONG KONG TWO CENTS
20

HONG KONG FIVE CENTS
21

HONG KONG 6 CENTS
22

HONG KONG 12 CENTS
23

1903. *Wmk Crown CA. P* 14.
62 **20** 1 c. dull purple and brown 35 25
63 2 c. dull green 75 60
64 **21** 4 c. purple/*red* 75 25
65 5 c. dull green and brown-orange .. 2·25 1·90
66 8 c. slate and violet .. .. .. 2·75 90
67 **20** 10 c. purple and blue/*blue* .. .. 3·25 50
68 **23** 12 c. green and purple/*yellow* .. .. 3·50 1·75
69 20 c. slate and chestnut .. .. .. 4·25 1·25
70 **22** 30 c. dull green and black .. .. 6·00 3·25
71 **23** 50 c. dull green and magenta .. .. 11·00 9·00
72 **20** $1 purple and sage-green .. .. 22·00 9·50
73 **23** $2 slate and scarlet .. .. .. 45·00 45·00
74 **22** $3 slate and dull blue .. .. .. 48·00 42·00
75 **23** $5 purple and blue-green .. .. £130 80·00
76 **22** $10 slate and orange/*blue* £450 £275
62/76 .. .. *Set of* 15 £650 £425
62/76 Optd "Specimen" .. .. *Set of* 15 £750

1904–7. *Wmk Mult Crown CA. P* 14.
77 **20** 2 c. dull green, **CO** 50 35
78 **21** 4 c. purple/*red*, **CO** 50 25
79 5 c. dull green and brown-orange, **CO** .. 1·90 95
80 8 c. slate and violet, **C** (1907) .. .. 3·25 2·50
81 **20** 10 c. purple and blue/*blue*, **O** .. .. 3·25 80
82 **23** 12 c. green and purple/*yellow*, **C** (1907) .. 3·25 3·50
83 20 c. slate and chestnut, **CO** .. .. 3·25 1·50
84 **22** 30 c. dull green and black, **CO** .. .. 4·50 3·25
85 **23** 50 c. green and magenta, **CO** .. .. 9·50 3·50
86 **20** $1 purple and sage-green, **CO** .. .. 20·00 7·00
87 **23** $2 slate and scarlet, **CO** .. .. 45·00 27·00
88 **22** $3 slate and dull blue, **C** .. .. 50·00 38·00
89 **23** $5 purple and blue-green, **C** .. .. £110 60·00
90 **22** $10 slate and orange/*blue*, **CO** £425 £275
77/90 .. .. *Set of* 14 £600 £375

1907–11. *Colours changed and new value. Wmk Mult Crown CA. P* 14.
91 **20** 1 c. brown, **O** (1910) 95 75
92 2 c. deep green, **O** .. .. .. 3·25 50
a. Green .. .. 2·75 35
93 **21** 4 c. carmine-red, **O** 95 30
94 **22** 6 c. orange-vermilion and purple, **C** .. 5·00 1·75
95 **20** 10 c. bright ultramarine, **O** .. .. 2·75 40
96 **23** 20 c. purple and sage-green, **C** (1911) .. 20·00 8·50
97 **22** 30 c. purple and orange-yellow, **C** (1911) 16·00 7·00
98 **23** 50 c. black/*green*, **C** (1911) .. .. 15·00 4·00
99 $2 carmine-red and black, **C** (1910) .. 85·00 50·00
91/9 .. .. *Set of* 9 £130 65·00
91, 93/9 Optd "Specimen" .. .. *Set of* 8 £400

HONG KONG 1c ONE CENT 1c
24

HONG KONG 4c FOUR CENTS 4c
25

HONG KONG 6 CENTS
26

HONG KONG 20 CENTS
27

HONG KONG 25 CENTS 25
28

(A)

(B)

In Type A of the 25 c. the upper Chinese character in the left-hand label has a short vertical stroke crossing it at the foot. In Type B this stroke is absent.

1912–21. *Wmk Mult Crown CA. P* 14.
100 **24** 1 c. brown, **O** 75 30
a. Black-brown .. .. .. 2·00 45
b. Crown broken at right (R.9/4) .. £150 £110
101 2 c. deep green, **O** .. .. .. 1·25 25
a. Green .. .. 1·60 25
102 **25** 4 c. carmine-red, **O** .. .. .. 1·40 20
a. Scarlet .. .. 3·25 30
103 **26** 6 c. yellow-orange, **O** .. .. .. 2·75 1·00
a. Brown-orange .. .. .. 2·50 90
104 **25** 8 c. grey, **O** .. .. 8·00 2·40
a. Slate .. .. 10·00 2·25
105 **24** 10 c. ultramarine, **O** .. .. .. 11·00 35
a. Deep bright ultramarine .. .. 9·50 25
106 **27** 12 c. purple/*yellow*, **C** .. .. .. 2·50 1·75
a. White back (Optd S. £50) .. .. 4·00 3·75
107 20 c. purple and sage-green, **C** .. .. 1·75 90
108 **28** 25 c. purple and magenta, **C** (Type A) (1914) .. .. 5·00 3·50
109 25 c. purple and magenta, **C** (Type B) (1920) .. .. 26·00 18·00
110 **26** 30 c. purple and orange-yellow, **C** .. 10·00 3·75
a. Purple and orange .. .. .. 7·00 2·00
111 **27** 50 c. black/*blue-green*, **C** .. .. .. 3·75 80
a. White back (Optd S. £70) .. .. 3·75 1·25
b. On blue-green, olive back .. .. £110 9·00
c. On emerald surface .. .. .. 15·00 5·50
d. On emerald back (Optd S. £70) .. 7·50 4·75
112 **24** $1 purple and blue/*blue*, **C** .. .. 10·00 3·00
113 **27** $2 carmine-red and grey-black, **C** .. 26·00 12·00
114 **26** $3 green and purple, **C** .. .. .. 42·00 25·00
115 **27** $5 green and red/*green*, **C** .. .. £120 60·00
a. White back (Optd S. £80) .. .. £120 50·00
b. On blue-green, olive back (Optd S. £90) .. .. £400 48·00
116 **26** $10 purple and black/*red*, **C** .. .. £140 50·00
100/16 .. .. *Set of* 17 £300 £140
100/16 Optd "Specimen" .. .. *Set of* 17 £900

1921–37. *Wmk Mult Script CA. P* 14.
117 **24** 1 c. brown, **O** 40 35
b. Crown broken at right (R.9/4)
118 2 c. blue-green, **O** 55 20
a. Yellow-green 90 30
118*b* **24** 2 c. grey, **O** (4.37) .. .. .. 1·90 2·50
119 **25** 3 c. grey, **O** (1931) 75 60
120 4 c. carmine-rose, **O** 55 30
a. Carmine-red 55 20
b. Top of lower Chinese characters at right broken off .. .. .. 80·00 60·00
121 5 c. violet, **O** (1931) 80 15
122 8 c. grey, **O** .. .. 4·25 10·00
123 8 c. orange, **O** (1924) 90 95
124 **24** 10 c. bright ultramarine, **O** 55 15
124*a* **27** 12 c. purple/*yellow*, **C** (1933) .. .. 2·75 75
125 20 c. purple and sage-green, **C** .. .. 1·75 25
126 **28** 25 c. purple and magenta, **C** (B) .. .. 1·00 60
127 **26** 30 c. purple and chrome-yellow, **C** .. 3·25 1·25
a. Purple and orange-yellow .. .. 7·00 1·75
128 **27** 50 c. black/*emerald*, **C** (1924) .. .. 5·50 60
129 **24** $1 purple and blue/*blue*, **C** .. .. 10·00 1·75
130 **27** $2 carmine-red and grey-black, **C** .. 32·00 6·00
131 **26** $3 green and dull purple, **C** (1926) .. 75·00 14·00
132 **27** $5 green and red/*emerald*, **C** (1925) .. £110 20·00
117/132 .. .. *Set of* 18 £200 55·00
117/32 Optd/Perf "Specimen" .. .. *Set of* 18 £800

1935 (6 May). *Silver Jubilee. As Nos. 91/4 of Antigua, but ptd by B.W. P* 11 × 12.
133 3 c. ultramarine and grey-black .. .. 3·00 3·25
c. Lightning conductor .. .. .. 60·00
134 5 c. green and indigo .. .. .. 4·50 2·75
a. Extra flagstaff £225 £250
b. Short extra flagstaff .. .. .. 90·00
c. Lightning conductor .. .. .. 70·00
135 10 c. brown and deep blue .. .. .. 7·00 2·00
136 20 c. slate and purple .. .. .. 23·00 12·00
b. Short extra flagstaff £120
133/6 Perf "Specimen" .. .. *Set of* 4 £150

For illustrations of plate varieties see Omnibus section following Zululand.

1937 (12 May). *Coronation. As Nos. 13/15 of Aden, but ptd by B.W. P* 11 × 11½.
137 4 c. green 90 65
138 15 c. carmine .. .. 3·00 1·75
139 25 c. blue .. .. 4·00 2·00
137/9 Perf "Specimen" .. .. *Set of* 3 £100

HONGKONG FOUR CENTS
29 King George VI

1938–52. *Wmk Mult Script CA. P* 14.
140 **29** 1 c. brown (24.5.38) 20 50
a. Pale brown (27.2.52) .. .. .. 30 1·00
141 2 c. grey (5.4.38) 25 20
a. Perf 14½ × 14 (1942) .. .. .. 80 2·50
142 4 c. orange (5.4.38) 60 20
a. Perf 14½ × 14 (28.9.45) .. .. 85 1·50
143 5 c. green (24.5.38) 60 12
a. Perf 14½ × 14 (12.41) .. .. .. 45 1·50
144 8 c. red-brown (1.11.41) .. .. .. 40 1·75
a. Imperf .. ..
145 10 c. bright violet (13.4.38) .. .. 6·50 75
a. Dull reddish violet (9.4.46) .. .. 1·00 15
b. Reddish lilac (9.4.47) .. .. .. 1·40 35
c. Perf 14½ × 14. *Dull violet* (12.41) .. 1·25 20
146 15 c. scarlet (13.4.38) 30 20
147 20 c. black (1.2.46) 30 30
148 20 c. scarlet-vermilion (1.4.48) 90 35
a. Rose-red (25.4.51) .. .. .. 1·50 90
149 25 c. bright blue (5.4.38) .. .. .. 2·00 45
150 25 c. pale sage-green (9.4.46) .. .. 80 1·75
151 30 c. yellow-olive (13.4.38) .. .. 55·00 3·50
a. Perf 14½ × 14. *Sage-green* (12.41) 6·50 6·50
152 30 c. blue (9.4.46) .. .. 1·00 15
153 50 c. reddish purple, **O** (13.4.38) .. .. 3·50 25
a. Bright purple, **C** (9.4.47) .. .. 1·25 10
b. Perf 14½ × 14. *Deep magenta* (12.41) .. .. 2·75 50
154 80 c. carmine, **C** (2.2.48) .. .. .. 2·00 60
155 $1 dull lilac and blue, **C** .. .. 2·50 1·50
a. Pale reddish lilac and blue, **O** (11.41) 8·50 1·60
156 $1 red-orange and green, **OC** (9.4.46) .. 2·50 20
a. Yellow-orange and green, **C** (6.11.52) 7·00 3·00
157 $2 red-orange and green, **C** (25.5.38) .. 70·00 9·00
158 $2 reddish violet and scarlet, **OC** (9.4.46) .. .. 3·75 50
159 $5 dull lilac and scarlet, **C** (2.6.38) .. 26·00 22·00
160 $5 green and violet, **O** (9.4.46) .. .. 28·00 2·75
a. Yellowish green and violet, **OC** (9.4.46) .. .. 40·00 2·75
161 $10 green and violet, **C** (2.6.38) .. .. £190 38·00
162 $10 bright lilac and blue, **O** (9.4.46) .. 50·00 12·00
a. Reddish violet and blue, **C** (9.4.47) .. 75·00 18·00
140/62 .. .. *Set of* 23 £350 85·00
140/62 Perf "Specimen" .. .. *Set of* 23 £1200

The varieties perf 14½ × 14 with the exception of the 4 c. were printed and perforated by Bradbury, Wilkinson & Co, Ltd, from De La Rue plates and are on rough-surfaced paper. The dates quoted for these are London release dates and it is not known if supplies reached Hong Kong before the Japanese occupation.

The 4 c. is on smoother paper and was printed by Harrison & Sons in 1941 and issued in sheets of 120 (12 × 10) instead of two panes of 60 (6 × 10); it was not released until 1945. It is believed that Harrison also printed some of the 8 c. on smooth paper at the same time.

Also in 1941 Williams, Lea & Co printed the 1 c. and $1 to $10 in perf 14 from De La Rue plates.

Nos. 160/*a* were separate printings released in Hong Kong on the same day.

No. 144a. One imperforate sheet was found and most of the stamps were sold singly to the public at a branch P.O. and used for postage.

30 Street Scene **31** Liner and Junk

(Des W. E. Jones. Recess B.W.)

1941 (26 Feb). *Centenary of British Occupation. T* **30/1** *and similar designs. Wmk Mult Script CA (sideways on horiz designs). P* 13½ × 13 (2 *c. and* 25 *c.) or* 13 × 13½ *(others).*
163 2 c. orange and chocolate .. .. .. 80 1·40
164 4 c. bright purple and carmine .. .. 1·75 1·75
165 5 c. black and green 60 25
166 15 c. black and scarlet .. .. 3·25 70
167 25 c. chocolate and blue .. .. .. 4·50 2·25
168 $1 blue and orange .. .. 15·00 6·00
163/168 .. .. *Set of* 6 23·00 11·00
163/8 Perf "Specimen" .. .. *Set of* 6 £275
Designs: *Horiz*—5 c. The University; 15 c. The Harbour; $1 China Clipper and Seaplane. *Vert*—25 c. The Hong Kong Bank.

36 King George VI and Phoenix **37** Queen Elizabeth II

(Des W. E. Jones. Recess D.L.R.)

1946 (29 Aug). *Victory. Wmk Mult Script CA. P* 13.
169 **36** 30 c. blue and red .. .. .. 1·00 80
170 $1 brown and red .. .. 1·75 1·00
169/70 Perf "Specimen" .. .. *Set of* 2 £160

1948 (22 Dec). *Royal Silver Wedding. As Nos.* 30/1 *of Aden.*
171 10 c. violet 80 40
172 $10 carmine .. .. 80·00 60·00

1949 (10 Oct). *75th Anniv of Universal Postal Union. As Nos.* 114/17 *of Antigua.*
173 10 c. violet 85 30
174 20 c. carmine-red .. .. 4·25 1·75
175 30 c. deep blue .. .. 4·00 1·75
176 80 c. bright reddish purple .. .. .. 11·00 6·00

1953 (2 June). *Coronation. As No.* 47 *of Aden.*
177 10 c. black and slate-lilac 60 5

1954 (5 Jan)–**60.** *Ordinary paper* (5, 10, 15 *c.) or chalk-surfaced paper (others). Wmk Mult Script CA. P* 14.
178 **37** 5 c. orange 20 5
a. Imperf (pair) £650
179 10 c. lilac (*shades*) 25 5
180 15 c. green (*shades*) 50 15
181 20 c. brown, C 50 15
182 25 c. scarlet (*shades*), C 50 15
183 30 c. grey (*shades*), C 50 5
184 40 c. bright blue (*shades*), C 60 10
185 50 c. reddish purple, C 60 5
186 65 c. grey, C (20.6.60) .. .. .. 14·00 4·75
187 $1 orange and green, C .. .. .. 1·50 5
188 $1.30, blue and red (*shades*), C (20.6.60) 16·00 1·00
189 $2 reddish violet and scarlet (*shades*), C 7·00 30
190 $5 green and purple (*shades*), C .. 35·00 1·00
191 $10 reddish violet & brt blue (*shades*), C 40·00 2·50
178/191 .. .. *Set of* 14 £110 9·50
No. 178a. One sheet was found: 90 stamps imperf, 10 perf three sides only.

38 University Arms **39** Statue of Queen Victoria

(Des and photo Harrison)

1961 (11 Sept). *Golden Jubilee of Hong Kong University. W* w **12.** *P* 11½ × 12.
192 **38** $1 multicoloured .. .. .. 2·25 80
a. Gold ptg omitted £500

(Des Cheung Yat-man. Photo Harrison)

1962 (4 May). *Stamp Centenary. W* w **12.** *P* 14½.
193 **39** 10 c. black and magenta 15 10
194 20 c. black and light blue 50 30
195 50 c. black and bistre 50 15

40 Queen Elizabeth II (after Annigoni) **41**

(Photo Harrison)

1962 (4 Oct)–**73.** *W* w **12** *(upright). Chalk-surfaced paper. P* 15 × 14 (5 *c. to* $1) *or* 14 × 14½ *(others).*
196 **40** 5 c. red-orange 5 5
197 10 c. bright reddish violet (*shades*) .. 12 5
b. Glazed paper. *Reddish violet* (14.4.72) 15 5
198 15 c. emerald 20 8
199 20 c. red-brown (*shades*) 25 8
b. Glazed paper. *Brown* (27.9.72) .. 30 12
200 25 c. cerise 40 30
201 30 c. deep grey-blue (*shades*) 25 8
b. Glazed paper. *Chalky blue* (27.9.72) 35 8
202 40 c. deep bluish green 35 15
203 50 c. scarlet (*shades*) 30 5
b. Glazed paper. *Vermilion* (27.9.72) .. 1·50 15
204 65 c. ultramarine .. .. 3·50 1·25
205 $1 sepia .. .. 5·50 10
206 **41** $1.30, multicoloured .. .. .. 1·50 5
c. Glazed paper (3.2.71) .. .. 2·00 30
207 $2 multicoloured .. .. 3·75 15
c. Glazed paper (1973)* .. .. 50·00 2·50
208 $5 multicoloured .. .. 8·50 50
b. Glazed paper (3.2.71) .. .. 12·00 3·00
209 $10 multicoloured .. .. 20·00 1·50
a. Glazed paper (1973)* .. .. £150 22·00
210 $20 multicoloured .. .. 27·00 5·50
196/210 .. .. *Set of* 15 65·00 8·75
*These are from printings which were sent to Hong Kong in March 1973 but not released in London.
The $1.30 to $20 exist with PVA gum as well as gum arabic. The glazed paper printings are with PVA gum only.
See also Nos. 222, etc.

1963 (4 June). *Freedom from Hunger. As No.* 76 *of Aden, but additionally inscr in Chinese characters.*
211 $1.30, bluish green .. .. 28·00 7·00

1963 (2 Sept). *Red Cross Centenary. As Nos.* 147/8 *of Antigua, but additionally inscr in Chinese characters at right.*
212 10 c. red and black .. .. 1·25 15
213 $1.30, red and blue .. .. 14·00 3·25

1965 (17 May). *I.T.U. Centenary. As Nos.* 166/7 *of Antigua.*
214 10 c. light purple and orange-yellow .. .. 1·00 15
215 $1.30, olive-yellow and deep bluish green .. 15·00 2·50

1965 (25 Oct). *International Co-operation Year. As Nos.* 168/9 *of Antigua.*
216 10 c. reddish purple and turquoise-green .. 1·00 12
217 $1.30, dp bluish green & lavender (*shades*) 14·00 2·50

1966 (24 Jan). *Churchill Commemoration. As Nos.* 170/3 *of Antigua but additionally inscr in Chinese characters.*
218 10 c. new blue .. .. 1·50 10
219 50 c. deep green .. .. 3·50 50
220 $1.30, brown .. .. 7·50 4·75
221 $2 bluish violet .. .. 9·50 6·00

1966 (6 Sept)–**72.** *As Nos.* 196/208 *and* 210 *but wmk W* w **12** *(sideways). Chalk-surfaced paper* (5 *c. to* $1) *or glazed, ordinary paper* ($1.30 *to* $20).
222 **40** 5 c. red-orange (20.3.67)* 15 5
223 10 c. reddish violet (31.3.67)* 20 5
224 15 c. emerald (31.3.67)* 30 10
225 20 c. red-brown 35 10
a. Glazed, ordinary paper (14.4.72) .. 30 15
226 25 c. cerise (31.3.67)* 45 35
a. Glazed, ordinary paper (14.4.72) .. 45 40
227 30 c. deep grey-blue (31.3.70) 45 10
a. Glazed, ordinary paper (14.4.72) .. 50 15
228 40 c. deep bluish green (1967) 50 12
a. Glazed, ordinary paper (14.4.72) .. 60 35
229 50 c. scarlet (31.3.67)* 60 10
230 65 c. ultramarine (*shades*) (29.3.67)* .. 2·50 2·25
231 $1 sepia (29.3.67)* .. .. .. 5·50 35
232 **41** $1.30, multicoloured (14.4.72) .. .. 2·50 60
233 $2 multicoloured (13.12.71) .. .. 5·50 90
234 $5 multicoloured (13.12.71) .. .. 20·00 3·00
236 $20 multicoloured (14.4.72) .. .. 75·00 32·00
222/36 .. .. *Set of* 14 £100 38·00
*Earliest known postmark dates.
The 5 c. to 25 c., 40 c. and 50 c. exist with PVA gum as well as gum arabic, but the 30 c., and all stamps on glazed paper exist with PVA gum only.

1966 (20 Sept). *Inauguration of W.H.O. Headquarters, Geneva. As Nos.* 178/9 *of Antigua, but additionally inscr in Chinese characters.*
237 10 c. black, yellow-green and light blue .. 1·25 10
238 50 c. black, light purple and yellow-brown .. 2·75 75

1966 (1 Dec). *20th Anniv of U.N.E.S.C.O. As Nos.* 196/8 *of Antigua, but additionally inscr in Chinese characters.*
239 10 c. slate-violet, red, yellow and orange .. 1·50 12
240 50 c. orange-yellow, violet and deep olive .. 4·75 90
241 $2 black, light purple and orange .. .. 25·00 10·00

42 Rams' Heads on Chinese Lanterns

(Des V. Whiteley. Photo Harrison)

1967 (17 Jan). *Chinese New Year ("Year of the Ram"). T* **42** *and similar horiz design. W* w **12** *(sideways). P* 14½.
242 10 c. rosine, olive-green and light yellow-olive 75 12
243 $1.30, emerald, rosine and light yellow-olive 9·50 4·25
Design:—$1.30, Three rams.

44 Cable Route Map

(Des V. Whiteley. Photo Harrison)

1967 (30 Mar). *Completion of Malaysia–Hong Kong Link of SEACOM Telephone Cable. W* w **12.** *P* 12½.
244 **44** $1.30, new blue and red .. .. 7·50 1·75

45 Monkeys in Tree ("Year of the Monkey")

(Des R. Granger Barrett. Photo Harrison)

1968 (23 Jan). *Chinese New Year ("Year of the Monkey"). T* **45** *and similar horiz design. W* w **12** *(sideways). P* 14.
245 10 c. gold, black and scarlet .. .. .. 1·10 12
246 $1.30, gold, black and scarlet .. .. 8·50 3·75
Design:—$1.30, Family of monkeys.

47 Liner at Ocean Terminal

(Des and litho D.L.R.)

1968 (24 Apr). *Sea Craft. T* **47** *and similar horiz designs. P* 13.
247 10 c. multicoloured 60 10
248 20 c. cobalt-blue, black and brown .. .. 1·00 35
249 40 c. orange, black and mauve .. .. 3·50 3·25
250 50 c. orange-red, black and green .. .. 3·75 50
a. Green omitted £300
251 $1 greenish yellow, black and red .. .. 8·00 2·00
252 $1.30, Prussian blue, black and pink .. 10·00 3·00
247/52 .. .. *Set of* 6 24·00 8·50
Designs:—20 c. Pleasure launch; 40 c. Car ferry; 50 c. Passenger ferry; $1, Sampan; $1.30, Junk.

53 *Bauhinia blakeana* **54** Arms of Hong Kong

(Des V. Whiteley. Photo Harrison)

1968 (25 Sept)–**73.** *W* w **12.** *P* 14 × 14½.

(a) Upright wmk. Chalk-surfaced paper
253 **53** 65 c. multicoloured 70 20
a. Glazed ordinary paper (3.73) .. 7·00 2·00
254 **54** $1 multicoloured 90 30

(b) Sideways wmk. Glazed, ordinary paper
254*a* **53** 65 c. multicoloured (27.9.72) .. .. 3·50 1·50
254*b* **54** $1 multicoloured (13.12.71) .. .. 2·50 80
Nos. 253/4 exist with PVA gum as well as gum arabic; Nos. 254*a/b* with PVA gum only.

55 "Aladdin's Lamp" and Human Rights Emblem

(Des R. Granger Barrett. Litho B.W.)

1968 (20 Nov). *Human Rights Year. W* w **12** *(sideways). P* 13½.
255 **55** 10 c. orange, black and myrtle-green .. 45 8
256 50 c. yellow, black & dp reddish purple .. 1·50 80

56 Cockerel

(Des R. Granger Barrett. Photo Enschedé)

1969 (11 Feb). *Chinese New Year ("Year of the Cock"). T* **56** *and similar multicoloured design. P* 13 × 13½ (10 *c.*) *or* 13½ × 13 ($1.30).
257 10 c. Type **56** .. .. 1·00 12
258 $1.30, Cockerel (*vert*) .. .. .. 12·00 5·00

58 Arms of Chinese University

59 Earth Station and Satellite

(Des V. Whiteley. Photo Govt Ptg Bureau, Tokyo)

1969 (26 Aug). *Establishment of Chinese University of Hong Kong. P* 13½.
259 **58** 40 c. violet, gold and pale turquoise-blue 90 75

(Des V. Whiteley. Photo Harrison)

1969 (24 Sept). *Opening of Communications Satellite Tracking Station. W* w **12**. *P* 14 × 14½.
260 **59** $1 multicoloured .. .. .. 3·75 1·50

60 Chow's Head

62 "Expo 70" Emblem

(Des R. Granger Barrett. Photo D.L.R.)

1970 (28 Jan). *Chinese New Year ("Year of the Dog"). T* **60** *and similar design. W* w **12** (*sideways on* $1.30). *P* 14.
261 10 c. lemon-yellow, orange-brown and black .. 1·60 20
262 $1.30, multicoloured .. .. .. 14·00 4·50
Design: *Horiz*—$1.30, Chow standing.

(Des and litho B.W.)

1970 (14 Mar). *World Fair, Osaka. T* **62** *and similar multicoloured design. W* w **12** (*sideways on* 25 *c.*). *P* 13½ × 13 (15 *c.*) *or* 13 × 13½ (25 *c.*).
263 15 c. Type **62** 25 20
264 25 c. Expo '70 Emblem and Junks (*horiz*) .. 60 40

64 Plaque in Tung Wah Hospital

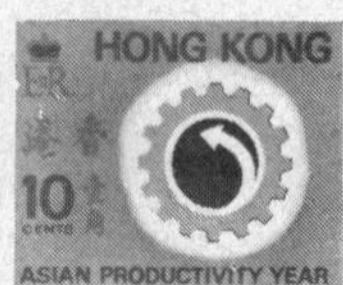

65 Symbol

(Des M. F. Griffith. Photo Harrison)

1970 (9 Apr). *Centenary of Tung Wah Hospital. W* w **12** (*sideways*). *P* 14.
265 **64** 10 c. multicoloured 20 8
266 50 c. multicoloured .. .. .. 1·00 50

(Des J. Cooter. Litho B.W.)

1970 (5 Aug). *Asian Productivity Year. W* w **12**. *P* 14 × 13½.
267 **65** 10 c. multicoloured 20 10

66 Pig

(Des Kan Tai-Keung. Photo Govt Ptg Bureau, Tokyo)

1971 (20 Jan). *Chinese New Year ("Year of the Pig"). P* 13½.
268 **66** 10 c. multicoloured .. .. .. 1·50 15
269 $1.30, multicoloured .. .. .. 8·00 3·75

67 "60" and Scout Badge

68 Festival Emblem

(Des Kan Tai-Keung. Litho Harrison)

1971 (23 July). *Diamond Jubilee of Scouting in Hong Kong. W* w **12** (*sideways*). *P* 14 × 14½.
270 **67** 10 c. black, scarlet and yellow 15 5
271 50 c. black, green and blue 80 45
272 $2 black, magenta and bluish violet .. 4·00 6·25

(Des Kan Tai-Keung. Litho J.W.)

1971 (2 Nov). *Hong Kong Festival. T* **68** *and similar designs. W* w **12** (*sideways on* 10 *c. and* 50 *c.*). *P* 13½ × 14 (10 *c.*) *or* 14 (*others*).
273 **68** 10 c. orange and purple 30 5
274 – 50 c. multicoloured 60 35
275 – $1 multicoloured .. .. .. 1·75 1·75
Designs: *Horiz* (39 × 23 *mm*)—50 c. Coloured streamers. *Vert* (23 × 39 *mm*)—$1 "Orchid".

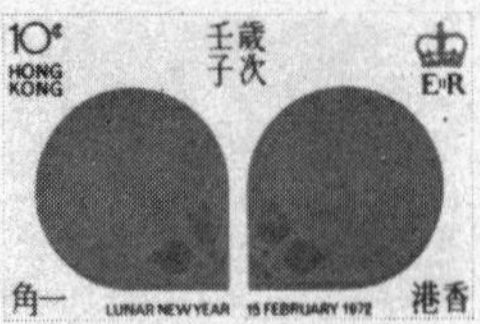

69 Stylised Rats

(Des Kan Tai-Keung. Photo D.L.R.)

1972 (8 Feb). *Chinese New Year ("Year of the Rat"). W* w **12**. *P* 13½ × 13.
276 **69** 10 c. red, gold and black 30 5
277 $1.30, gold, red and black .. .. 4·00 3·25

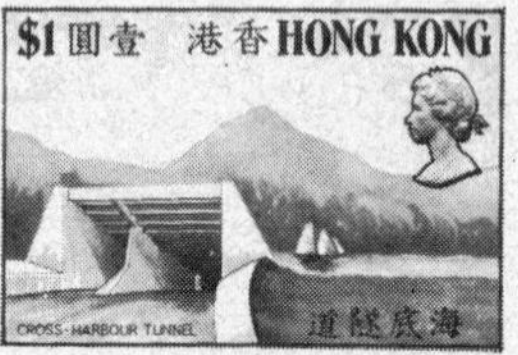

70 Tunnel Entrance

(Des G. Drummond from painting by G. Baxter. Litho Harrison)

1972 (20 Oct). *Opening of Cross-Harbour Tunnel. W* w **12**. *P* 14 × 14½.
278 **70** $1 multicoloured .. .. .. 2·25 1·75

71 Phoenix and Dragon

72 Ox

(Des (from photograph by D. Groves) and photo Harrison)

1972 (20 Nov). *Royal Silver Wedding. W* w **12**. *P* 14 × 14½.
279 **71** 10 c. multicoloured 10 5
280 50 c. multicoloured 45 40

(Des R. Granger Barrett. Photo Harrison)

1973 (25 Jan). *Chinese New Year ("Year of the Ox"). W* w **12** (*sideways on* 10 *c.*). *P* 14.
281 **72** 10 c. reddish orange, brown and black .. 50 8
282 – $1.30, lt yellow, yellow-orange & black 5·50 5·00
Design:—$1.30, similar to 10 c., but horiz.

73 Queen Elizabeth II **74**

(Des from coinage. Photo ($10 and $20 also embossed) Harrison)

1973 (12 June). *W* w **12** (*sideways on* 15, 30, 40 *c.*, $1.30, 2, 5, 10, $20). *P* 14½ × 14 (*Nos.* 283/91) *or* 14 × 14½ (292/6).
283 **73** 10 c. bright orange 30 5
a. Wmk sideways (from coils) 45 40
284 15 c. yellow-green .. .. .. 1·40 25
285 20 c. reddish violet 35 8
286 25 c. lake-brown .. .. 2·00 60
287 30 c. ultramarine 70 10
288 40 c. turquoise-blue 85 20
289 50 c. light orange-vermilion 75 15
290 65 c. greenish bistre .. .. .. 3·00 2·25
291 $1 bottle-green .. .. .. 1·75 20
292 **74** $1.30, pale yellow and reddish violet .. 1·50 35
293 $2 pale green and reddish brown .. 2·25 50
294 **74** $5 pink and royal blue .. .. .. 4·25 1·75
295 $10 pink and deep blackish olive .. 9·00 4·00
296 $20 pink and brownish black .. 20·00 13·00
283/96 .. .. .. *Set of* 14 42·00 21·00
Nos. 295/6 are known with embossing omitted, but it has been reported that such errors can be faked.
See also Nos. 311/24*c* and 340/53.

1973 (14 Nov). *Royal Wedding. As Nos.* 165/6 *of Anguilla, but additionally inscr in Chinese characters.*
297 50 c. ochre 25 15
298 $2 bright mauve 55 70

75 Festival Symbols forming Chinese Character

(Des Kan Tai-Keung. Litho B.W.)

1973 (23 Nov). *Hong Kong Festival. T* **75** *and similar horiz designs. W* w **12**. *P* 14.
299 **75** 10 c. brownish red and bright green .. 15 5
300 – 50 c. deep magenta and reddish orange .. 50 30
301 – $1 bright green and deep mauve .. 1·00 1·40
Each value has the festival symbols arranged to form a Chinese character. "Hong" on the 10 c.; "Kong" on the 50 c.; "Festival" on the $1.

76 Tiger

77 Chinese Mask

(Des R. Granger Barrett. Litho Harrison)

1974 (8 Jan). *Chinese New Year ("Year of the Tiger"). W* w **12** (*sideways on* $1.30). *P* 14.
302 **76** 10 c. multicoloured 50 5
303 – $1.30, multicoloured .. .. .. 6·00 4·25
Design:—$1.30, Similar to T **76**, but vert.

(Des R. Hookham. Litho Enschedé)

1974 (1 Feb). *Arts Festival. Vert designs as T* **77** *showing Chinese opera masks. W* w **12** (*sideways*). *P* 12 × 12½.
304 **77** 10 c. multicoloured 40 5
305 – $1 multicoloured .. .. .. 3·00 2·75
306 – $2 multicoloured .. .. .. 3·75 3·00
MS307 159 × 94 mm. Nos. 304/6. Wmk upright. P 14 × 13 .. .. 15·00 20·00

78 Pigeons with Letters

(Des Kan Tai-Keung. Litho Harrison)

1974 (9 Oct). *Centenary of Universal Postal Union. T* **78** *and similar horiz designs. W* w **12** (*sideways on* 10 *and* 50 *c.*). *P* 14.
308 10 c. light greenish blue, light yellow-green and slate-black 25 5
a. No wmk .. .. 35·00
309 50 c. deep mauve, orange and slate-black .. 80 30
310 $2 multicoloured .. .. 1·60 2·50
Designs:—50 c. Globe within letter; $2 Hands holding letters.

1975 (21 Jan)–**81**. *New values* (60, 70, 80 *and* 90 *c.*) *or as Nos.* 283/96 *but W* w **14** (*sideways on* 10, 20, 25, 50, 65 *c. and* $1).
311 **73** 10 c. bright orange (21.2.75) 25 5
a. Wmk upright (from coils) (10.78) .. 30 40
312 15 c. yellow-green (21.1.75) .. .. 3·00 80
313 20 c. reddish violet (*shades*) (19.3.75) .. 15 5
314 25 c. lake-brown (19.3.75) .. .. 3·50 1·25
315 30 c. ultramarine (*shades*) (9.4.75) .. 40 10
316 40 c. turquoise-blue (19.3.75) 50 15
317 50 c. light orange-vermilion (19.3.75) .. 50 12
318 60 c. lavender (4.5.77) 65 15
319 65 c. greenish bistre (19.3.75) .. .. 3·75 2·75
320 70 c. yellow (*shades*) (4.5.77) 70 15
321 80 c. bright magenta (*shades*) (4.5.77) .. 70 20
321*b* 90 c. sepia (1.10.81) 80 80
322 $1 bottle-green (*shades*) (19.3.75) .. 1·25 30
323 **74** $1.30, pale yell & reddish vio (19.3.75) 1·40 30
324 $2 pale green and reddish brown (*shades*) (19.3.75) .. .. .. 1·50 60
324*a* $5 pink & royal blue (*shades*) (20.4.78) 2·00 70
324*b* $10 pink & dp blackish olive (20.4.78) .. 2·50 1·75
324*c* $20 pink and brownish black (20.4.78) .. 5·00 5·00
311/24*c* .. .. *Set of* 18 27·00 13·50
Nos. 324*b*/*c* are known with the embossing omitted. See note after No. 296.

79 Stylized Rabbit

(Des Kan Tai-Keung. Litho Harrison)

1975 (5 Feb). *Chinese New Year ("Year of the Rabbit"). T* **79** *and similar horiz design. P* 14. *(a) No wmk.*
325 **79** 10 c. silver and light red 30 8
326 – $1.30, gold and light green .. .. 4·25 3·25

(b) W w **12**

327 **79** 10 c. silver and light red 40 8
328 – $1.30, gold and light green .. .. 5·00 4·50
Design:—$1.30, Pair of rabbits.

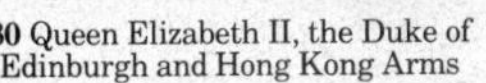

80 Queen Elizabeth II, the Duke of Edinburgh and Hong Kong Arms

81 Mid-Autumn Festival

1975 (30 Apr). *Royal Visit. W w* **14** *(sideways). P* 13½.
329 **80** $1.30, multicoloured .. .. 2·25 2·25
330 $2 multicoloured .. .. 2·75 2·75

(Des Tao Ho. Litho De La Rue, Bogotá)

1975 (31 July). *Hong Kong Festivals of* 1975. *T* **81** *and similar vert designs. Multicoloured. No wmk. P* 13½ × 14.
331 50 c. Type **81** 45 20
332 $1 Dragon-boat Festival .. .. .. 1·50 1·75
333 $2 Tin Hau Festival .. .. 1·75 2·00
MS334 102 × 83 mm. Nos. 331/3 .. .. .. 7·00 8·00

82 Melodious Laughing Thrush

83 Dragon

(Des C. Kuan. Litho Harrison)

1975 (29 Oct). *Birds. T* **82** *and similar vert designs. Multicoloured. W w* **14.** *P* 14.
335 50 c. Type **82** 90 20
336 $1.30, Chinese Bulbul .. .. .. 3·25 3·00
337 $2 Black-capped Kingfisher .. .. .. 3·50 3·50

(Des Kan Tai-Keung. Litho Questa)

1976 (21 Jan). *Chinese New Year ("Year of the Dragon"). T* **83** *and similar horiz design. W w* **14** *(sideways). P* 14½.
338 **83** 20 c. mauve, dull lake and gold 35 8
339 – $1.30, light yellow-green, lt red & gold 2·75 2·75
No. 339 is as T **83** but has the design reversed.

1976 (20 Feb–19 Mar). *As Nos.* 283, 285, 287 *and* 293/6 *but without wmk.*
340 **73** 10 c. bright orange (coil stamp) (19.3.76) 4·50 4·50
342 20 c. reddish violet .. .. .. 1·00 40
a. Imperf (pair) £275
344 30 c. ultramarine .. .. 1·25 60
350 **74** $2 pale green and reddish brown .. 6·00 2·75
351 $5 pink and royal blue .. .. .. 9·00 9·00
352 $10 pink and deep blackish olive (19.3.76) .. .. 23·00 18·00
353 $20 pink and brownish black (19.3.76) 48·00 32·00
340/53 .. .. *Set of* 7 85·00 60·00
No. 353 is known with the embossing omitted. See note after No. 296.

84 "60" and Girl Guides Badge

85 "Postal Services" in Chinese Characters

(Des P. Ma. Photo Harrison)

1976 (23 Apr). *Girl Guides Diamond Jubilee. T* **84** *and similar horiz design. Multicoloured. W w* **12.** *P* 14.
354 20 c. Type **84** 25 5
355 $1.30, Badge, stylised diamond and "60" .. 1·25 1·75

(Des Tao Ho. Litho Harrison)

1976 (11 Aug). *Opening of new G.P.O. T* **85** *and similar vert designs. W w* **14.** *P* 14.
356 20 c. yellow-green, lt greenish grey & black .. 20 5
357 $1.30, reddish orge, lt greenish grey & blk .. 1·00 90
358 $2 yellow, light greenish grey and black .. 1·25 1·50
Designs:—$1.30, Old G.P.O.; $2 New G.P.O.

86 Snake on Branch

(Des Jennie Wong. Litho J.W.)

1977 (6 Jan). *Chinese New Year ("Year of the Snake"). T* **86** *and similar horiz design. W w* **14** *(sideways). P* 13½.
359 **86** 20 c. multicoloured 35 8
360 – $1.30, multicoloured .. .. .. 2·50 3·25
The $1.30 shows a snake facing left.

87 Presentation of the Orb

88 Tramcars

(Des Hong Kong Govt Services Dept; adapted J.W. Litho Harrison)

1977 (7 Feb). *Silver Jubilee. T* **87** *and similar multicoloured designs. W w* **14** *(sideways on $2). P* 14½ × 14 *($2) or* 14 × 14½ *(others).*
361 20 c. Type **78** 20 5
362 $1.30, Queen's visit, 1975 .. .. .. 75 1·10
363 $2 The Orb *(vert)* .. .. 85 1·10

(Des Tao Ho. Litho J.W.)

1977 (30 June). *Tourism. T* **88** *and similar vert designs. Multicoloured. W w* **14.** *P* 13½.
364 20 c. Type **88** 20 5
365 60 c. Star Ferryboat 90 80
366 $1.30, The Peak tram .. .. .. 1·25 70
367 $2 Junk and sampan .. .. 2·00 90

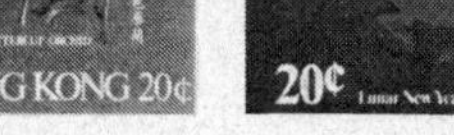

89 Buttercup Orchid

90 Horse

(Des Beryl Walden. Litho Questa)

1977 (12 Oct). *Orchids. T* **89** *and similar vert designs. Multicoloured. W w* **14.** *P* 14.
368 20 c. Type **89** 45 5
369 $1.30, Lady's Slipper Orchid .. .. 1·60 1·60
370 $2 Susan Orchid .. .. 2·00 2·00

(Des Graphic Atelier Ltd, Hong Kong. Litho Harrison)

1978 (26 Jan). *Chinese New Year ("Year of the Horse"). W w* 14 *(sideways). P* 14½ × 14.
371 **90** 20 c. magenta, yellow-olive & brn-olive .. 20 10
372 $1.30, orange, yellow-brn & reddish brn 1·75 1·90

91 Queen Elizabeth II

92 Girl and Boy holding Hands

(Des G. Vasarhelyi. Litho Harrison)

1978 (2 June). *25th Anniv of Coronation. W w* **14.** *P* 14 × 14½.
373 **91** 20 c. magenta and ultramarine 15 10
374 $1.30, ultramarine and magenta .. 75 75

(Des Annette Walker. Litho Harrison)

1978 (8 Nov). *Centenary of Po Leung Kuk (child care organisation). T* **92** *and similar horiz design. Multicoloured. W w* **14** *(sideways). P* 14 × 14½.
375 20 c. Type **92** 10 5
376 $1.30, Ring of children 75 90

93 Electronics Industry

94 *Precis orithya orithya*

(Litho Harrison)

1979 (9 Jan). *Industries. T* **93** *and similar horiz designs. W w* **14** *(sideways). P* 14½.
377 20 c. orange-yellow, olive-yellow & yell-olive 10 5
378 $1.30, multicoloured 65 75
379 $2 multicoloured 80 75
Designs:—$1.30, Toy industry; $2, Garment industry.

(Des Jane Thatcher. Photo Harrison)

1979 (20 June). *Butterflies. T* **94** *and similar vert designs. Multicoloured. No wmk. P* 14.
380 20 c. Type **94** 15 5
381 $1 *Graphium sarpedon sarpedon* 45 45
382 $1.30, *Heliophorus epicles phoenicoparyphus* 60 60
383 $2 *Danus genutia genutia* .. .. .. 90 1·25

95 Diagrammatic view of Railway Station

96 Tsui Shing Lau Pagoda

(Des Tao Ho. Litho J.W.)

1979 (1 Oct). *Mass Transit Railway. T* **95** *and similar horiz designs. Multicoloured. W w* **14** *(sideways). P* 13½.
384 20 c. Type **95** 15 5
385 $1.30, Diagrammatic view of car 55 50
386 $2 Plan showing route of railway 70 85

(Des D. Leonard. Litho J.W.)

1980 (14 May). *Rural Architecture. T* **96** *and similar designs. W w* **14** *(sideways on $1.30 and $2). P* 13 × 13½ *(20 c.) or* 13½ × 13 *(others).*
387 20 c. black, magenta and yellow 10 5
388 $1.30, multicoloured 60 75
389 $2 multicoloured .. .. 75 1·00
Designs: *Horiz*—$1.30, Village House, Sai O; $2, Ching Chung Koon Temple.

97 Queen Elizabeth the Queen Mother

98 Botanical Gardens

(Des Harrison. Litho Questa)

1980 (4 Aug). *80th Birthday of Queen Elizabeth the Queen Mother.* W w **14** (*sideways*). *P* 14.
390 **97** $1.30, multicoloured 55 65

(Des D. Chan. Litho J.W.)

1980 (12 Nov). *Parks. T* **98** *and similar vert designs. Multicoloured.* W w **14**. *P* 13½.
391 20 c. Type **98** 10 10
392 $1 Ocean Park 35 40
393 $1.30, Kowloon Park 50 55
394 $2 Country Parks 70 85

99 *Epinephelus akaara* **100** Wedding Bouquet from Hong Kong

(Des Jane Thatcher. Litho J.W.)

1981 (28 Jan). *Fishes. T* **99** *and similar horiz designs. Multicoloured.* W w **14** (*sideways*). *P* 13½.
395 20 c. Type **99** 5 5
396 $1 *Nemipterus virgatus* 30 30
397 $1.30, *Choerodon azurio* 35 35
398 $2 *Scarus ghobban* 50 50

(Des J.W. Photo Harrison)

1981 (29 July). *Royal Wedding. T* **100** *and similar vert designs. Multicoloured.* W w **14** (*sideways*). *P* 14.
399 20 c. Type **100** 10 10
400 $1.30, Prince Charles in Hong Kong .. 35 35
401 $5 Prince Charles and Lady Diana Spencer 1·25 1·25

101 Suburban Development **102** "Victoria from the Harbour, c 1855"

(Des Tao Ho. Litho J.W.)

1981 (14 Oct). *Public Housing. T* **101** *and similar vert designs showing suburban development.* W w **14** (*inverted on No.* **MS**406). *P* 13½.
402 20 c. multicoloured 10 10
403 $1 multicoloured 30 30
404 $1.30, multicoloured 40 40
405 $2 multicoloured 60 60
MS406 148 × 105 mm. Nos. 402/5 .. .. .. 1·90 2·25

(Des R. Solley. Litho Questa)

1982 (5 Jan). *Port of Hong Kong, Past and Present. T* **102** *and similar horiz designs. Multicoloured.* W w **14**. *P* 14½.
407 20 c. Type **102** 12 10
408 $1 "West Point, Hong Kong, 1847" 35 35
409 $1.30, Fleet of Junks 45 50
410 $2 Liner *Queen Elizabeth 2* at Hong Kong .. 70 70

103 Five-banded Civet

(Des Karen Phillipps. Litho Harrison)

1982 (4 May). *Wild Animals. T* **103** *and similar horiz designs.* W w **14** (*sideways*). *P* 14½.
411 20 c. black, salmon-pink and olive-bistre .. 12 10
412 $1 multicoloured 40 40
413 $1.30, black, emerald and yellow-orange .. 45 45
414 $5 black, orange-brown and greenish yellow 1·25 1·25
Designs:—$1 Pangolin; $1.30, Chinese Porcupine; $5 Barking Deer.

104 Queen Elizabeth II **105**

(Des and photo ($5 to $50 also embossed) Harrison)

1982 (30 Aug). W w **14** (*sideways on Nos.* 427/30). *P* 14½ × 14 (*Nos.* 415/26) *or* 14 × 14½ (*others*).
415 **104** 10 c. bright carmine, carmine and lemon 5 5
416 20 c. bluish violet, violet and lavender .. 5 5
417 30 c. bluish violet, violet and salmon .. 5 5
418 40 c. vermilion and pale blue 8 10
419 50 c. chestnut, orange-brn & sage-green 10 12
420 60 c. bright purple and brownish grey .. 12 15
421 70 c. dp grey-grn, myrtle-grn & orge-yell 15 20
422 80 c. bistre-brown, lt brown & sage-grn 15 20
423 90 c. bottle-green, deep grey-green and pale turquoise-green 20 25
424 $1 reddish orge, red-orge & pale rose .. 20 25
425 $1.30, turquoise-blue and mauve .. 25 30
426 $2 ultramarine and flesh 40 50
427 **105** $5 dp magenta, brt purple & olive-yell 1·00 1·10
428 $10 sepia and grey-brown .. .. 2·00 2·25
429 $20 deep claret and pale blue .. .. 4·00 4·50
430 $50 deep claret and brownish grey .. 10·00 10·50
415/30 .. .. *Set of* 16 17·00 18·00
Nos. 415/30 come with a fluorescent security marking, "Hong Kong" in Chinese characters encircled by the same in English, printed over the central oval of the design.
Nos. 415 and 424 also exist from coils.
No. 428 is known with the embossing omitted. See note after No. 296.

106 Table Tennis **107** Dancing

(Des A. Wong. Litho J.W.)

1982 (20 Oct). *Sport for the Disabled. T* **106** *and similar horiz designs. Multicoloured.* W w **14**. *P* 14 × 14½.
431 30 c. Type **106** 12 5
432 $1 Racing 25 25
433 $1.30, Basketball 30 30
434 $5 Archery .. .. 1·10 1·10

(Des Tao Ho. Litho J.W.)

1983 (26 Jan). *Performing Arts. T* **107** *and similar vert designs.* W w **14** (*sideways*). *P* 14.
435 30 c. cobalt and deep grey-blue 10 10
436 $1.30, rose and brown-purple 25 30
437 $5 bright green and deep green .. .. 1·00 1·25
Designs:—$1.30, "Theatre"; $5 "Music".

108 Aerial View of Hong Kong

(Des local artist. Litho Enschedé)

1983 (14 Mar). *Commonwealth Day. T* **108** *and similar horiz designs. Multicoloured.* W w **14** (*sideways*). *P* 14 × 13.
438 30 c. Type **108** 10 10
439 $1 *Liverpool Bay* (container ship) 20 25
440 $1.30, Hong Kong flag 25 30
441 $5 Queen Elizabeth II and Hong Kong .. 95 1·00

109 Victoria Harbour

(Des Tao Ho. Litho Harrison)

1983 (17 Aug). *Hong Kong by Night. T* **109** *and similar horiz designs. Multicoloured.* W w **14** (*sideways*). *P* 14.
442 30 c. Type **109** 10 10
443 $1 Space Museum, Tsim Sha Tsui Cultural Centre 20 25
444 $1.30, Fireworks display 25 30
445 $5 *Jumbo*, floating restaurant .. .. 95 1·00

110 Old and New Observatory Buildings

(Des C. Shun Wah. Litho Harrison)

1983 (23 Nov). *Centenary of Hong Kong Observatory. T* **110** *and similar horiz designs.* W w **14** (*sideways*). *P* 14½ × 14.
446 40 c. yellow-orange, bistre-brown and black .. 10 10
447 $1 reddish mauve, deep mauve and black .. 20 25
448 $1.30, new blue, steel-blue and black .. 25 30
449 $5 olive-yellow, brown-olive and black .. 95 1·00
Designs:—$1 Wind-measuring equipment; $1.30, Thermometer; $5 Ancient and modern seismometers.

111 "DH 86" *Dorado* (Hong Kong-Penang Service, 1936)

(Des M. Harris. Litho J.W.)

1984 (7 Mar). *Aviation in Hong Kong. T* **111** *and similar multicoloured designs.* W w **14** (*sideways on* 40 c. *to* $1.30, *inverted on* $5). *P* 13½.
450 40 c. Type **111** 8 10
451 $1 Sikorsky "S-42B" (San Francisco-Hong Kong Service, 1937) 20 25
452 $1.30, Cathay-Pacific "Jumbo" jet leaving Kai Tak Airport 25 30
453 $5 Baldwin brothers' balloon, 1891 (*vert*) .. 90 95

112 Map by Capt E. Belcher, 1836

(Des R. Solley. Litho B.D.T.)

1984 (21 June). *Maps of Hong Kong. T* **112** *and similar horiz designs. Multicoloured.* W w **14** (*sideways*). *P* 14.
454 40 c. Type **112** 10 12
455 $1 Bartholomew map of 1929 .. .. 25 30
456 $1.30, Early map of Hong Kong waters .. 30 35
457 $5 Chinese-style map of 1819 .. .. 1·25 1·40

113 Cockerel

(Des J. Yim. Litho Cartor, France)

1984 (6 Sept). *Chinese Lanterns. T* **113** *and similar horiz designs showing stylised animals as lanterns. Multicoloured.* W w **14** (*sideways*). *P* 13½ × 13.
458 40 c. Type **113** 10 12
459 $1 Dog 25 30
460 $1.30, Butterfly 30 35
461 $5 Fish .. .. 1·25 1·40

114 Jockey on Horse and Nurse with Baby ("Health Care")

(Des M. Harris. Litho Walsall)

1984 (21 Nov). *Centenary of Royal Hong Kong Jockey Club. T* **114** *and similar horiz designs showing aspects of Club's charity work. Multicoloured.* W w **14** (*sideways*). *P* 14½.
462 40 c. Type **114** 10 12
463 $1 Disabled man playing handball ("Support for Disabled") 25 30
464 $1.30, Ballerina ("The Arts") 30 35
465 $5 Penguins ("Ocean Park") .. .. .. 1·25 1·40
MS466 178 × 98 mm. Nos. 462/5 .. .. .. 1·90 2·00

POSTAGE DUE STAMPS

PRINTERS. Nos. D1/23 were typographed by De La Rue & Co.

D 1 Post-office Scales

1923 (Dec)–**56.** *Wmk Mult Script CA. P* 14.

No.	Type	Description	Unused	Used
D1	D 1	1 c. brown, **O**	90	80
		a. Wmk sideways (1931)	90	1·00
		b. Chalk-surfaced paper, wmk sideways (21.3.56)	20	70
D2		2 c. green	3·50	3·50
		a. Wmk sideways (1928)	4·00	4·00
D3		4 c. scarlet	6·50	3·75
		a. Wmk sideways (1928)	7·50	5·50
D4		6 c. yellow	8·00	9·50
		a. Wmk sideways (1931)	9·50	12·00
D5		10 c. bright ultramarine	14·00	6·50
		a. Wmk sideways (1934)	19·00	10·00
D1/5		Optd "Specimen" *Set of* 5	£200	

1938 (Feb)–**63.** *Wmk Mult Script CA* (*sideways*). *P* 14.

No.	Type	Description	Unused	Used
D 6	D 1	2 c. grey, **O**	4·25	3·50
		a. Chalky paper (21.3.56)	85	1·25
D 7		4 c. orange, **O**	5·50	3·25
		a. Chalky paper. *Orange-yellow* (23.5.61)	2·75	4·00
D 8		6 c. scarlet	7·00	5·00
D 9		8 c. chestnut (26.2.46)	6·50	7·50
D10		10 c. violet, **O**	8·00	1·00
		a. Chalky paper (17.9.63)	3·50	90
D11		20 c. black (26.2.46)	7·00	6·50
D12		50 c. blue (7.47)	18·00	13·00
D6a/12		*Set of* 7	42·00	35·00
D6/12		Perf "Specimen" *Set of* 7	£350	

1965 (15 Apr)–**72.** *Chalk-surfaced paper. P* 14.

No.	Type	Description	Unused	Used
		(*a*) *Wmk* w **12** (*sideways*)		
D13	D 1	4 c. yellow-orange	2·75	4·50
D14		5 c. red (13.5.69)	1·50	2·50
		a. Glazed paper (17.11.72)	3·75	6·00
D15		10 c. violet (27.6.67)	1·50	1·25
D16		20 c. black (1965)	3·25	4·50
D17		50 c. deep blue (*shades*) (1965)	7·00	9·00
		(*b*) *Wmk* w **12** (*upright*)		
D18	D 1	5 c. red (20.7.67)	1·00	2·00
D19		50 c. deep blue (26.8.70)	7·00	8·00

The 5 c. is smaller, 21 × 18 mm.

1972 (17 Nov)–**74.** *Glazed, ordinary paper.* W w **12** (*sideways*).

No.	Type	Description	Unused	Used
		(*a*) *P* 14 × 14½		
D20	D 1	10 c. bright reddish violet	1·25	2·00
D21		20 c. grey-black	3·00	4·50
D22		50 c. deep dull blue	5·50	8·00
		(*b*) *P* 13½ × 14		
D23	D 1	5 c. brown-red (1.5.74)	75	1·25

(Typo Walsall)

1976 (19 Mar*)–**78.** *Smaller design* (21 × 17 *mm*) *with redrawn value-tablet. Glazed, ordinary paper.* W w **14**. *P* 14.

No.	Type	Description	Unused	Used
D25	D 1	10 c. bright reddish violet	20	35
		a. Chalk-surfaced paper (15.12.78)	5	5
D26		20 c. grey-black	35	55
		a. Chalk-surfaced paper (15.12.78)	5	5
D27		50 c. deep dull blue	50	95
		a. Chalk-surfaced paper (15.12.78)	10	12
D28		$1 yellow (1.4.76)	95	1·50
		a. Chalk-surfaced paper (15.12.78)	20	25

*This is the London release date. It is believed that the stamps were not released locally until 14 April.

POSTCARD STAMPS

Stamps specially surcharged for use on Postcards

3 CENTS (P 1) **THREE** (P 2)

1879 (1 April). *Nos.* 22 *and* 13 *surch as Type* P **1**.

No.	Type	Description	Unused	Used
P1	3	3 c. on 16 c. yellow (No. 22)	£150	£200
P2		5 c. on 18 c. lilac (No. 13)	£120	£200

1879 (Nov). *No.* P2 *surch with Type* P **2**.

No.	Type	Description	Unused	Used
P3	3	3 c. on 5 c. on 18 c. lilac	£1700	£2250

POSTAL FISCAL STAMPS

I. Stamps inscribed "STAMP DUTY"

NOTE. The dated circular "Hong Kong" cancellation with "PAID ALL" in lower segment normally indicates fiscal, not postal, use, but a few instances are known where it was applied *in red*, for postal purposes.

F 1

F 2

F 3

1874–1902. *Wmk Crown CC.* (*a*) *P* 15½ × 15.

No.	Type	Description	Unused	Used
F1	F 1	$2 olive-green	£130	27·00
		a. Thin paper	£180	35·00
F2	F 2	$3 dull violet	95·00	20·00
		a. Thin paper	£180	26·00
		b. Bluish paper		
F3	F 3	$10 rose-carmine	£2500	£300
		(*b*) *P* 14		
F4	F 1	$2 dull bluish green (1890)	£130	70·00
F5	F 2	$3 dull mauve (1902)	£130	70·00
		a. Bluish paper		
F6	F 3	$10 grey-green (? 1884)	£1500	
F4/5		Optd "Specimen" *Set of* 2	£350	

12 CENTS. (F 4) **5 DOLLARS** (F 5)

1882. *No.* F3 *surch with Type* F 4.

No.	Type	Description	Unused	Used
F7	F 3	12 c. on $10 rose-carmine	£250	£100

1891 (Jan). *Surch with Type* F **5**. *Wmk Crown CA. P* 14.

No.	Type	Description	Unused	Used
F8	F 3	$5 on $10 purple/*red* (Optd S. £130)	£120	60·00

F 6

(F 7)

F 8

1890. *Wmk Crown CA. P* 14.

No.	Type	Description	Unused	Used
F9	F 6	2 c. dull purple	13·00	4·50

1897 (Sept). *Surch with Type* F 7.

No.	Type	Description	Unused	Used
F10	F 1	$1 on $2 olive-green (No. F1)	55·00	20·00
		a. Chinese surch wholly omitted	£700	£500
F11		$1 on $2 dull bluish green (No. F4) (H/S S. £100)	£110	60·00
		a. Chinese surch wholly omitted	£400	£250
		b. Diagonal portion of Chinese surch omitted		

1938 (11 Jan). *Wmk Mult Script CA. P* 14.

No.	Type	Description	Unused	Used
F12	F 8	5 c. green	32·00	4·50

Authorised for postal use from 11 to 20 January 1938 (both dates inclusive).

II. Stamps overprinted "S.O." (Stamp Office), or "S.D." (Stamp Duty)

S. O. **S. D.**

(S 1)

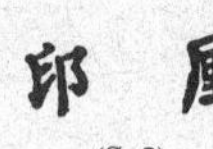

(S 2)

1891. *Optd with Types* S **1** *or* S **2**.

No.	Type	Description	Unused	Used
S1	S 1	2 c. carmine (No. 33)	£300	£110
S2	S 2	2 c. carmine (No. 33)	£200	65·00
S3	S 1	10 c. purple/*red* (No. 40)	£400	£175

Other fiscal stamps are found apparently postally used, but there is no evidence that this use was authorised.

JAPANESE OCCUPATION OF HONG KONG

PRICES FOR STAMPS ON COVER
Nos. J1/3 *from* × 7

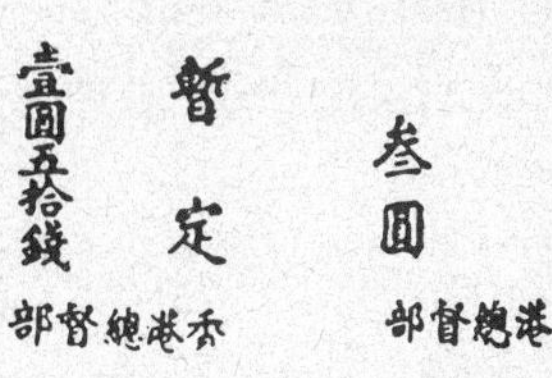

(1) (2)

1945 (Apr). *Stamps of Japan surch with T* **1** (*No.* J1) *or as T* **2**.

No.	Description	Unused	Used
J1	1.50 yen on 1 s. brown	5·50	4·25
J2	3 yen on 2 s. scarlet	2·25	3·25
J3	5 yen on 5 s. claret	£300	45·00

Designs (18½ × 22 *mm*):—1 s. Girl Worker; 2 s. Gen. Nogi; 5 s. Admiral Togo.

No. J3 has four characters of value similarly arranged but differing from T **2**.

BRITISH POST OFFICES IN CHINA

PRICES FOR STAMPS ON COVER

Nos. 1/14	*from* × 6
Nos. 15/17	—
Nos. 18/28	*from* × 8

CHINA

(1)

1917 (1 Jan)–**21.** *Stamps of Hong Kong,* 1912–21 (*wmk Mult Crown CA*), *optd with T* **1**, *at Somerset House.*

No.	Description	Unused	Used
1	1 c. brown, **O**	35	50
	a. Crown broken at side	£120	
	b. Black-brown, **O**	40	60
2	2 c. green, **O**	25	30
3	4 c. carmine-red, **O**	30	15
4	6 c. orange, **O**	70	60
5	8 c. slate, **O**	90	75
6	10 c. ultramarine, **O**	75	20
7	12 c. purple/*yellow,* **C**	1·40	1·75
8	20 c. purple and sage-green, **C**	2·25	45
9	25 c. purple and magenta, **C** (A)	3·25	4·50
11	30 c. purple and orange-yellow, **C**	5·50	3·50
12	50 c. black/*blue-green* (*olive back*), **C**	8·50	1·50
	a. On emerald surface (1917?)	7·00	2·25
	b. On emerald back (1919)	5·50	1·75
	c. On white back (1920)	16·00	4·00
13	$1 reddish purple and bright blue/*blue,* **C**	16·00	4·00
	a. Grey-purple and blue/blue, **C** (1921)	13·00	4·25
14	$2 carmine-red and grey-black, **C**	45·00	32·00
15	$3 green and purple, **C**	60·00	50·00
16	$5 green and red/*blue-green* (*olive back*), **C**	80·00	50·00
17	$10 purple and black/*red,* **C**	£275	£100
1/17	*Set of* 16	£450	£225
12/17	H/S "Specimen" *Set of* 6	£1200	

1922 (Mar)–**27.** *As last, but wmk Mult Script CA.*

No.	Description	Unused	Used
18	1 c. brown, **O**	25	65
19	2 c. green, **O**	55	80
20	4 c. carmine-rose, **O**	55	55
	a. Lower Chinese character at right broken at top	70·00	55·00
21	6 c. orange-yellow, **O**	75	1·75
22	8 c. grey, **O**	90	1·75
23	10 c. bright ultramarine, **O**	65	75
24	20 c. purple and sage-green, **C**	1·50	1·60
25	25 c. purple and magenta, **C** (B)	3·25	5·50
26	50 c. black/*emerald,* **C** (1927) (H/S S. £200)	10·00	17·00
27	$1 purple and blue/*blue,* **C**	10·00	12·00
28	$2 carmine-red and grey-black, **C**	£110	55·00
18/28	*Set of* 11	£120	85·00

Great Britain held Treaty privileges at various Chinese ports, where agencies of the Hong Kong Post Office were in operation using Hong Kong stamps. The overprinted stamps Nos. 1/17 were introduced on 1 January 1917 for use in the then-existing agencies of Amoy, Canton, Chefoo, Foochow, Hankow, Hoihow, Ningpo, Shanghai, Swatow and Tientsin. They were also supplied to the British naval base of Wei Hai Wei leased from China in 1898 and which had two Post Offices (Port Edward and Liu Kung Tau).

The British P.O.s in the Treaty Ports closed by agreement with the Chinese on 30 November 1922, but the above overprinted issues continued in use at the Wei Hai Wei offices until they in turn closed on 30 September 1930.

India

PRICES FOR STAMPS ON COVER TO 1945

Nos. S1/3	*from* × 2
No. 1	†
Nos. 2/26	*from* × 3
Nos. 27/30	—
Nos. 31/4	*from* × 8
Nos. 35/49	*from* × 3
Nos. 50	†
Nos. 51/3	*from* × 4
Nos. 54/65	*from* × 2
Nos. 66/8	*from* × 5
Nos. 69/74	*from* × 3
Nos. 73/277	*from* × 2
Nos. O1/14	*from* × 4
Nos. O15/18	—
No. O19	*from* × 5
Nos. O20/30*a*	*from* × 8
No. O30*b*	†
Nos. O31/133	*from* × 6
Nos. O135/150	*from* × 2

ISSUE FOR SIND PROVINCE

1

1852 (1 July). "Scinde Dawk." *Embossed.*

S1	1	½ a. white	£4000	£1200
S2		½ a. blue	£9500	£3250
S3		½ a. scarlet	—	£6500

These stamps were issued under the authority of Sir Bartle Frere, Commissioner in Sind. They were suppressed in October 1854.

No. S3 is on sealing wax (usually cracked). Perfect copies are very rare.

EAST INDIA COMPANY ADMINISTRATION

2 (*Much reduced*)

3

The ½ a., 1 a. and 4 a. were lithographed in Calcutta at the office of the Surveyor-General. The die was engraved by Mr Maniruddin (spelling uncertain). *Ungummed* paper watermarked as T **2** (the "No. 4" paper) with the Arms of the East India Co in the sheet. The watermark is sideways on the ½ a. and 1 a., and upright on the 4 a. where the paper was trimmed so that only the central portion showing the oval and the arms was used. Imperforate.

1854 (April).

1	3	½ a. vermilion	£650

This stamp, with 9½ arches in the side border, was prepared for use and a supply was sent to Bombay, but was not officially issued.

ILLUSTRATIONS. Types 4/8 are shown twice actual size.

4

1854 (1 Oct). *Die I.*

2	4	½ a. blue	27·00	11·00
		a. Printed on both sides	—	£3250
3		½ a. pale blue	45·00	11·00
4		½ a. deep blue	35·00	14·00
5		½ a. indigo	70·00	25·00

We give the official date of issue, but copies are known which were put on sale as much as a fortnight earlier.

These stamps were printed between 5 May and 29 July 1854 (Printing 30 millions).

4*a*

Die II

6	4*a*	½ a. blue	40·00	70·00
7		½ a. indigo	40·00	70·00

The bulk were printed beteen 1 and 12 August 1854, with some extra sheets on or before 2 November (Printing about 2 millions).

5

Die III

8	5	½ a. pale blue	£600	30·00
8*a*		½ a. blue	£600	30·00
9		½ a. greenish blue	£900	£150
10		½ a. deep blue	£650	50·00

These stamps were printed between 3 July and 25 August 1855 (Printing about 4¾ millions).

THE THREE DIES OF THE ½ ANNA

DIE I. *Chignon shading* mostly solid blobs of colour. *Corner ornaments,* solid blue stars with long points, always conspicuous. *Band below diadem* always heavily shaded. *Diadem and jewels.* The middle and right-hand jewels usually show a clearly defined cross. *Outer frame lines.* Stamps with white or faintly shaded chignons and weak frame lines are usually Die I (worn state).

DIE II. *Chignon* normally shows much less shading. A strong line of colour separates hair and chignon. *Corner ornaments.* The right blue star is characteristic (see illustration) but tends to disappear. It never obliterates the white cross. *Band below diadem.* As Die I but heavier, sometimes solid. *Diadem and jewels.* As Die I but usually fainter. *Outer frame lines.* Always strong and conspicuous.

DIE III. *Chignon shading* shows numerous fine lines, often blurred. *Corner ornaments* have a small hollow blue star with short points, which tends to disappear as in Die II. *Band below diadem,* shows light shading or hardly any shading. *Diadem and jewels.* Jewels usually marked with a solid squat star. The ornaments between the stars appear in the shape of a characteristic white "w". *Frame lines* variable.

The above notes give the general characteristics of the three Dies, but there are a few exceptions due to retouching, etc.

6 (*See note below No.* 14)

Die I

11	6	1 a. deep red	£160	35·00
12		1 a. red	£130	32·00

Printing of these stamps commenced on 26 July 1854, and continued into August (Printing, see note below No. 14).

7

*Die II: With more lines in the chignon than in Die I, and with white curved line where chignon joins head**

13	7	1 a. deep red	60·00	28·00
14		1 a. dull red	30·00	30·00

*Very worn printings of Die II may be found with chignon nearly as white as in Die I.

In stamps of Die I, however, the small blob of red projecting from the hair into the chignon is always visible.

These stamps were printed in August and September 1854 (Total printing, Dies I and II together, about 7¾ millions).

8

Die III. With pointed bust

15	8	1 a. red	£900	£150
16		1 a. dull red	£900	£150

These stamps were printed between 7 July and 25 August 1855 (Printing, about 1½ millions).

9

NOTE. Our catalogue prices for Four Annas stamps are for cut-square specimens, with clear margins and in good condition. Cut-to-shape copies are worth from 3% to 20% of these prices according to condition.

Four Dies of the Head:—

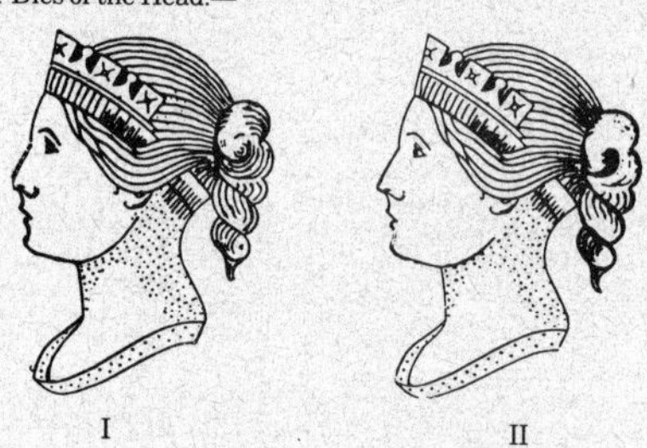

I II

DIE I. Band of diadem and chignon strongly shaded.

DIE II. Lines in band of diadem worn. Few lines in the upper part of the chignon, which, however, shows a strong drawn comma-like mark.

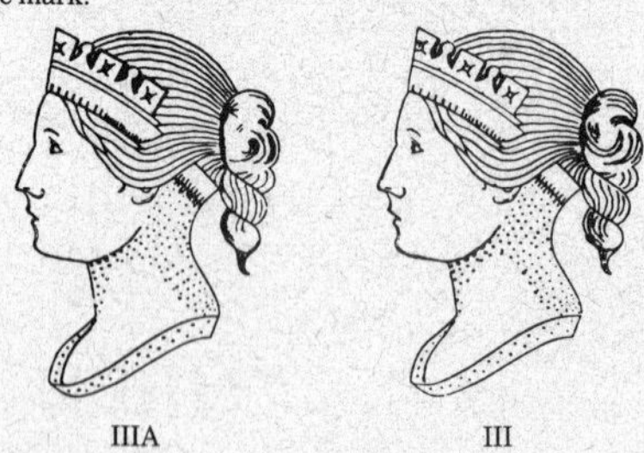

IIIA III

DIE IIIA. Upper part of chignon partly redrawn, showing two short, curved vertical lines in the NE corner. "Comma" has disappeared.

DIE III. Upper part of chignon completely redrawn, but band of diadem shows only a few short lines.

Two Dies of the Frame:—

Die I. Outer frame lines weak. Very small dots of colour, or none at all, in the "R" and "A's". The white lines to the right of "INDIA" are separated, by a line of colour, from the inner white circle.

Die II. Outer frame lines strengthened. Dots in the "R" and "A's" strong. White lines to right of "INDIA" break into inner white circle.

1854 (15 Oct). *W* **2** *upright, central portion only. Imperf.*

1st Printing. Head Die I. Frame Die I. Stamps widely spaced and separated by blue wavy line.

No.	Type	Description	Un	Used	Us pr
17	**9**	4 a. indigo and red	£2200	£400	£1300
18		4 a. blue and pale red	£2200	£400	£1300
		a. Head inverted (*cut to shape*)	—	£10000/ £35000	—

This printing was made between 13 and 28 Oct 1854 (Printing, 206,040).

2nd Printing. Head Die II. Frame Die I. Stamps widely spaced and separated by blue wavy line.

No.	Type	Description	Un	Used	Us pr
19	**9**	4 a. blue and red	£2000	£275	£800
20		4 a. indigo and deep red	£2000	£300	£900

This printing was made between 1 and 13 Dec 1854 (Printing, 393,960).

This is known with head double.

3rd Printing. Head Dies II, IIIA and III. Frame Dies I and II. Stamps widely spaced and separated by wavy line.

No.	Type	Description	Un	Used	Us pr
21	**9**	4 a. bright blue and bright red (Head III, Frame I)	£5000	£800	£2500
		a. Head II, Frame I	—	£1200	—
		b. Head IIIA, Frame I	—	£1100	£3500
		c. Head III, Frame II	—	—	£5000

This printing was made between 10 March and 2 April 1855 (Printing, 138,960).

4th Printing. Head Die III. Frame Die II. Stamps closely spaced 2 to 2½ mm without separating line.

No.	Type	Description	Un	Used	Us pr
22	**9**	4 a. deep blue and red	£1600	£250	£700
23		4 a. blue and red	£1500	£225	£650
24		4 a. pale blue and pale red	£1600	£250	£700

This printing was made between 3 April and 9 May 1855 (Printing, 540,960).

This is known with head double.

5th Printing. Head Die III. Frame Die II. Stamps spaced 4 to 6 mm without separating line.

No.	Type	Description	Un	Used	Us pr
25	**9**	4 a. blue and rose-red	£2000	£350	£1200
26		4 a. deep blue and red	£2100	£300	£1100

This printing was made between 4 Oct and 3 Nov 1855 (Printing, 380,064).

Serrated perf about 18, or pin-perf

No.	Description	Un	Used	Us pr
27	½ a. blue (Die I)			
28	1 a. red (Die I)			
29	1 a. red (Die II)	—	£500	—
30	4 a. blue and red (Die II)	—	£1100	—

This is believed to be an unofficial perforation. Most of the known specimens bear Madras circle postmarks (C122 to C126), but some are known with Bombay postmarks. Beware of fakes.

10

11

(Plate made at Mint, Calcutta. Typo Stamp Office)

1854 (6 Oct). *Sheet wmk sideways, as W* **2** *but with* "No. 3" *at top left.* Imperf.*

No.	Type	Description	Un	Used
31	**10**	2 a. green (*shades*)	48·00	22·00
34		2 a. emerald-green	£600	

*The 2 a. was also printed on paper with sheet wmk incorporating the words "STAMP OFFICE. One Anna", etc. (*Price* £110 *un or us*).

Apart from the rare emerald-green shade, there is a range of shades of No. 31 varying from bluish to yellowish green.

Many stamps show traces of lines external to the design shown in our illustration. Stamps with this frame on all four sides are scarce.

Many reprints of the ½, 1, 2, and 4 a. exist.

PRINTERS. All Indian stamps from No. 35 to 200 were typographed by De La Rue & Co.

1855 (Oct). *Blue glazed paper. No wmk. P* 14.

No.	Type	Description	Un	Used
35	**11**	4 a. black	£100	10·00
		a. Imperf (pair)	£500	£500
		b. Bisected (on cover)	†	£2750
36		8 a. carmine (Die I)	£100	12·00
		a. Imperf (pair)	£500	£500
		b. Bisected (on cover)	†	£4000

The first supply of the 4 a. was on white paper, but it is difficult to distinguish it from No. 45.

In the 8 a. the paper varies from deep blue to almost white.

For difference between Die I and Die II in the 8 a., see illustrations above No. 73.

1856–64. *No wmk. Paper yellowish to white. P* 14.

No.	Type	Description	Un	Used
37	**11**	½ a. blue (Die I)	5·00	50
		a. Imperf (pair)	£275	£375
38		½ a. pale blue (Die I)	5·00	50
39		1 a. brown	7·00	80
		a. Imperf between (vert pair)		
		b. Imperf (pair)	£600	
		c. Bisected (on cover)	†	£5500
40		1 a. deep brown	7·00	1·00
41		2 a. dull pink	42·00	12·00
		a. Imperf (pair)	£650	£650
42		2 a. yellow-buff	17·00	7·50
		a. Imperf (pair)	£650	£700
43		2 a. yellow	20·00	8·00
44		2 a. orange	28·00	8·50
		a. Imperf (pair)	£600	£650
45		4 a. black	26·00	5·50
		a. Bisected diagonally (2 a.) (on cover)	†	£2750
		b. Imperf (pair)	£650	£650
46		4 a. grey-black	23·00	4·75
47		4 a. green (1864)	75·00	18·00
48		8 a. carmine (Die I)	18·00	7·50
49		8 a. pale carmine (Die I)	18·00	7·50
		a. Bisected (4 a.) (on cover)	†	£6000

Prepared for use, but not officially issued

No.	Type	Description	Un	Used
50	**11**	2 a. yellow-green	£300	£350
		a. Imperf (pair)	£650	

This stamp is known with trial obliterations, and a few are known postally used. It also exists *imperf*, but is not known used thus.

For difference between Die I and Die II in the ½ a., see illustrations above No. 73.

CROWN COLONY

On the 1 November 1858, Her Majesty Queen Victoria assumed the government of the territories in India "heretofore administered in trust by the Honourable East India Company".

12

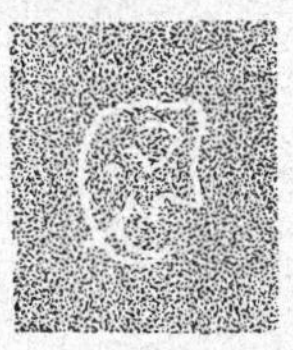

13

1860 (9 May). *No wmk. P* 14.

No.	Type	Description	Un	Used
51	**12**	8 p. purple/*bluish*	85·00	42·00
52		8 p. purple/*white*	8·00	5·50
		a. Bisected diagonally (4 p.) (on cover)	†	£7000
		b. Imperf (pair)	£550	£600
53		8 p. mauve	8·00	6·00

The bisected stamps of the issues of 1855–60 listed above were used exclusively in the Straits Settlements during shortage of stocks of certain values. Prices are for Singapore cancellations on original. Penang marks are considerably rarer.

1865. *Paper yellowish to white. W* **13**. *P* 14.

No.	Type	Description	Un	Used
54	**11**	½ a. blue (Die I)	1·75	20
		a. Imperf	—	£425
55		½ a. pale blue (Die I)	1·25	20
56	**12**	8 p. purple	5·50	4·50
57		8 p. mauve	5·50	4·50
58	**11**	1 a. pale brown	2·00	20
59		1 a. deep brown	1·90	20
60		1 a. chocolate	3·25	20
61		2 a. yellow	13·00	4·00
62		2 a. orange	14·00	1·10
		a. Imperf	—	£750
63		2 a. brown-orange	9·50	2·75
64		4 a. green	60·00	18·00
65		8 a. carmine (Die I)	£275	70·00

The 8 p. mauve, No. 57, is found variously surcharged "NINE" or "NINE PIE" by local postmasters, to indicate that it was being sold for 9 pies, as was the case during 1874. Such surcharges were made without Government sanction.

The stamps of India, wmk Elephant's Head, surcharged with a crown and value in "cents", were used in the Straits Settlements.

14

POSTAGE (15)

POSTACE (16)

1866 (28 June). *T* **14** *optd. P* 14 (*at sides only*). (*a*) *As T* **15**.

No.	Description	Un	Used
66	6 a. purple (G.)	£275	£110
	a. Overprint inverted	—	£6500

There are 20 different types of this overprint.

(*b*) *With T* **16**

No.	Description	Un	Used
68	6 a. purple (G.)	£400	£130

MINIMUM PRICE

The minimum price quoted is 5p which represents a handling charge rather than a basis for valuing common stamps. For further notes about prices see introductory pages.

17

18

Die I

Die II

Two Dies of 4 a:—

Die I.—Mouth closed, line from corner of mouth downwards only. Pointed chin.

Die II.—Mouth slightly open; lips, chin, and throat defined by line of colour. Rounded chin.

1866 (Sept)–**1878.** *W* **13**. *P* 14.

No.	Type	Description	Un	Used
69	**17**	4 a. green (Die I)	9·50	45
70		4 a. deep green (Die I)	9·50	45
71		4 a. blue-green (Die II) (1878)	9·00	40
72	**18**	6 a. 8 p. slate (5.67)	18·00	20·00
		a. Imperf (pair)	£850	

Die I (8 a.)

(Die I (½ a.)

Die II (8 a.)

Die II (½ a.)

1868 (1 Jan). *Die II. Profile redrawn and different diadem. W* **13**. *P* 14.

No.	Type	Description	Un	Used
73	**11**	8 a. rose (Die II)	9·00	4·25
74		8 a. pale rose (Die II)	9·50	4·25

1873. *Die II. Features, especially the mouth, more firmly drawn. W* **13**. *P* 14.

No.	Type	Description	Un	Used
75	**11**	½ a. deep blue (Die II)	1·00	15
76		½ a. blue (Die II)	1·00	15

19

20

1874 (18 July–1 Sept). *W* **13**. *P* 14.

No.	Type	Description	Un	Used
77	**19**	9 p. bright mauve (18.7.74)	6·00	6·00
78		9 p. pale mauve	6·00	6·00
79	**20**	1 r. slate (1.9.74)	14·00	12·00

21

22

1876 (19 Aug). *W* **13**. *P* 14.

No.	Type	Description	Un	Used
80	**21**	6 a. olive-bistre	4·75	2·40
81		6 a. pale brown	4·50	2·40
82	**22**	12 a. Venetian red	6·00	8·00

EMPIRE

Queen Victoria assumed the title of Empress of India in 1877, and the inscription on the stamps was altered from "EAST INDIA" to "INDIA".

23

24

25

26

27

28

29 30 31

32 33 34

1882 (1 Jan)–**88.** *W* **34**. *P* 14.

84	**23**	½ a. deep blue-green (1883)	40	10
85		½ a. blue-green	40	10
		a. Double impression	£130	
86	**24**	9 p. rose (1883)	70	1·40
87		9 p. aniline carmine	70	1·25
88	**25**	1 a. brown-purple (1883)	75	12
89		1 a. plum	75	10
90	**26**	1 a. 6 p. sepia	95	60
91	**27**	2 a. pale blue (1883)	1·50	12
92		2 a. blue	1·60	12
		a. Double impression	£200	£200
93	**28**	3 a. orange	8·50	3·25
94		3 a. brown-orange	2·75	10
95	**29**	4 a. olive-green (6.85)	6·00	12
96		4 a. slate-green	6·00	12
97	**30**	4 a. 6 p. yellow-green (1.5.86)	6·00	5·50
98	**31**	8 a. dull mauve (1883)	8·00	2·00
99		8 a. magenta	7·50	2·00
100	**32**	12 a. purple/*red* (1.4.88)	4·25	2·00
101	**33**	1 r. slate (1883)	6·50	3·00

No. 92a is from a sheet of 2 a. stamps with a very marked double impression issued in Karachi in 1896–97. Most of the stamps were used on telegrams.

2½ As.

(35)

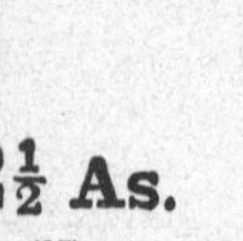

36 37

1891 (1 Jan). *No.* 97 *surch with T* **35** *by Govt Press, Calcutta.*

102	**30**	2½ a. on 4½ a. yellow-green	2·00	2·50

There are several varieties in this surcharge due to variations in the relative positions of the letters and figures.

1892 (Jan)–**97.** *W* **34**. *P* 14.

103	**36**	2½ a. yellow-green	80	60
104		2½ a. pale blue-green (1897)	1·50	60
105	**37**	1 r. green and rose	8·00	4·00
106		1 r. green and aniline carmine ..	5·00	3·00

1/4

38 (39) 40

USED HIGH VALUES. It is necessary to emphasise that used prices quoted for the following and all later high value stamps are for postally used copies.

(Head of Queen from portrait by von Angeli)

1895 (1 Sept). *W* **34**. *P* 14.

107	**38**	2 r. carmine and yellow-brown.. ..	28·00	12·00
107*a*		2 r. carmine and brown..	30·00	12·00
108		3 r. brown and green	30·00	14·00
109		5 r. ultramarine and violet	30·00	22·00

1898 (1 Oct). *No.* 85 *surch with T* **39** *by Govt Press, Calcutta.*

110	**23**	¼ on ½ a. blue-green	10	10
		a. Surch double	48·00	
		b. Double impression of stamp ..	£120	

1899. *W* **34**. *P* 14.

111	**40**	3 p. aniline carmine	12	10

1900 (1 Oct)–**02.** *W* **34**. *P* 14.

112	**40**	3 p. grey	12	20
113	**23**	½ a. pale yellow-green..	30	10
114		½ a. yellow-green	30	10
115	**25**	1 a. carmine	30	10
116	**27**	2 a. pale violet..	2·25	45
117		2 a. mauve (1902)	2·75	80
118	**36**	2½ a. ultramarine	3·50	3·75

41 42 43

44 45 46

47 48 49

50 51 52

1902 (9 Aug)–**11.** *W* **34**. *P* 14.

119	**41**	3 p. grey	25	20
120		3 p. slate-grey (1904)	15	12
121	**42**	½ a. yellow-green	35	20
122		½ a. green	35	20
123	**43**	1 a. carmine	45	10
124	**44**	2 a. violet (13.5.03)	1·50	35
125		2 a. mauve	1·50	30
126	**45**	2½ a. ultramarine (1902)	2·75	25
127	**46**	3 a. orange-brown (1902)	3·00	25
128	**47**	4 a. olive (20.4.03)	3·00	25
129		4 a. pale olive	3·00	25
130		4 a. olive-brown	6·50	2·50
131	**48**	6 a. olive-bistre (6.8.03)	9·00	4·25
132		6 a. maize	9·00	4·25
133	**49**	8 a. mauve (8.5.03)	7·50	1·60
134		8 a. magenta (1910)	9·00	1·60
135	**50**	12 a. purple/*red* (1903)	7·50	3·00
136	**51**	1 r. green and carmine (1903) ..	6·00	90
137		1 r. green and scarlet (1911) ..	17·00	1·75
138	**52**	2 r. rose-red and yellow-brown (1903) .	15·00	3·50
139		2 r. carmine and yellow-brown ..	15·00	3·25
140		3 r. brown and green (1904)	20·00	19·00
141		3 r. red-brown and green (1911) ..	22·00	19·00
142		5 r. ultramarine and violet (1904) ..	48·00	35·00
143		5 r. ultramarine and deep lilac (1911) .	55·00	35·00
144		10 r. green and carmine (1909) ..	70·00	20·00
146		15 r. blue and olive-brown (1909) ..	£125	42·00
147		25 r. brownish orange and blue (1909)..	£750	£800
119/147		.. .. *Set of* 17	£900	£800

No. 147 can often be found with telegraph cancellation; these can be supplied at one third of the price given above.

1905 (2 Feb). *No.* 122 *surch with T* **39**.

148	**42**	¼ on ½ a. green	15	15
		a. Surch inverted	—	£250

It is doubtful if No. 148a exists unused with genuine surcharge.

53 54

1906 (Dec)–**07.** *W* **34**. *P* 14.

149	**53**	½ a. green (12.06)	20	5
150	**54**	1 a. carmine (1.07)	20	5

55 56 57

58* 59 60

61 62 63

64 65 66

67

*T **58**. Two types of the 1½ a.; (A) As illustrated. (B) Inscribed "1½ As". "ONE AND A HALF ANNAS".

1911 (Dec)–**22.** *W* **34**. *P* 14.

151	**55**	3 p. pale grey	20	10
152		3 p. grey	15	5
153		3 p. slate-grey	15	10
154		3 p. blue-slate (1922)	60	20
155	**56**	½ a. yellow-green	30	5
		a. Double print	75·00	
156		½ a. pale blue-green	30	10
159	**57**	1 a. rose-carmine	80	10
160		1 a. carmine	80	10
161		1 a. aniline carmine	1·00	10
162		1 a. pale rose-carmine, **C** (1918) ..	1·40	10
163	**58**	1½ a. chocolate (Type A) (1919) ..	1·50	15
164		1½ a. grey-brown (Type A)	3·00	90
165		1½ a. chocolate (Type B) (1921).. ..	1·75	1·75
166	**59**	2 a. dull purple	1·00	5
167		2 a. mauve	1·00	15
168		2 a. violet	3·00	20
169		2 a. bright purple (Jan 1919)	3·00	20
170	**60**	2½ a. ultramarine	2·25	2·75
171	**61**	2½ a. ultramarine (1913)	1·25	8
172	**62**	3 a. dull orange	2·50	15
173		3 a. orange-brown	2·50	12
174	**63**	4 a. deep olive	3·25	12
175		4 a. olive-green	3·00	10
176	**64**	6 a. bistre	3·75	90
177		6 a. yellow-bistre	3·75	1·00
178		6 a. deep bistre-brown	7·00	1·25
179	**65**	8 a. purple	8·00	50
180		8 a. mauve	9·50	50
181		8 a. deep lilac	9·50	60
182		8 a. bright aniline mauve	11·00	80
183	**66**	12 a. dull claret..	9·50	60
184		12 a. claret	9·50	80
185	**67**	1 r. brown and green	14·00	1·25
186		1 r. red-brown and blue-green ..	9·50	70
187		2 r. carmine and brown	13·00	80
188		5 r. ultramarine and violet	28·00	2·50
189		10 r. green and scarlet	55·00	5·50
190		15 r. blue and olive	£110	10·00
191		25 r. orange and blue	£200	24·00
151/191		.. .. *Set of* 17	£400	45·00

A variety of the 3 pies exists with line joining "P" and "S" of the value at right, sometimes described as "3 Rs".

FORGERIES.—Collectors are warned against forgeries of all the later surcharges of India, and particularly the errors.

NINE

PIES

(68)

1921. *T* **57** *surch with T* **68**.

192		9 p. on 1 a. rose-carmine	15	8
		a. Error. "NINE-NINE"	25·00	
		b. Error "PIES—PIES"	25·00	
		c. Surch double	50·00	55·00
193		9 p. on 1 a. carmine-pink	25	12
194		9 p. on 1 a. aniline carmine	15	12

1922. *T* **56** *surch with T* **39**.

195		¼ on ½ a. yellow-green	12	12
		a. Surch inverted	8·00	
		b. Surch omitted (in pair with normal) ..	£120	
196		¼ on ½ a. blue-green	12	12

1922–26. *W* **34**. *P* 14.

197	**57**	1 a. chocolate	30	5
198	**58**	1½ a. rose-carmine (Type B)	70	30
199	**61**	2½ a. orange	4·25	4·25
200	**62**	3 a. ultramarine	14·00	90

69 70 71

PRINTERS. The following issues of postage and contemporary official stamps were all printed by the Security Printing Press, Nasik, *unless otherwise stated.*

1926–31. *Typo. W* **69**. *P* 14.
201 **55** 3 p. slate 20 5
202 **56** ½ a. green 40 5
203 **57** 1 a. chocolate 40 5
a. *Tête-bêche* (pair) .. .. .. 1·50 3·50
204 **58** 1½ a. rose-carmine (Type B) .. .. 1·25 5
205 **59** 2 a. bright purple .. .. .. 2·75 3·00
206 **70** 2 a. purple 90 5
a. *Tête-bêche* (pair) .. .. .. 7·00 16·00
207 **61** 2½ a. orange 75 5
208 **62** 3 a. ultramarine .. .. .. 3·50 80
209 3 a. blue (1931) .. .. .. 3·75 10
210 **63** 4 a. pale sage-green .. .. .. 1·50 5
211 **71** 4 a. sage-green .. .. .. 4·25 5
212 **65** 8 a. reddish purple .. .. .. 5·50 5
213 **66** 12 a. claret .. .. 6·50 15
214 **67** 1 r. chocolate and green .. .. 6·00 10
215 2 r. carmine and orange .. .. 7·50 65
216 5 r. ultramarine and purple .. .. 15·00 1·75
217 10 r. green and scarlet .. .. .. 45·00 3·00
218 15 r. blue and olive (1928) .. .. 18·00 20·00
219 25 r. orange and blue .. .. .. 95·00 24·00
201/219 .. .. *Set of* 16 £180 42·00

72 D.H. "Hercules"

(Des R. Grant. Litho)

1929 (22 Oct). *Air. W* **69** *(sideways). P* 14.
220 **72** 2 a. deep blue-green .. .. .. 1·10 70
221 3 a. blue .. .. 1·25 2·00
222 4 a. olive-green .. .. 3·00 1·75
223 6 a. bistre .. .. 3·50 3·00
224 8 a. purple .. .. 4·50 4·50
225 12 a. rose-red .. .. 15·00 15·00
220/225 .. .. *Set of* 6 25·00 24·00

73 Purana Qila

(Des H. W. Barr. Litho)

1931 (9 Feb). *Inauguration of New Delhi. T* **73** *and similar horiz designs. W* **69** *(sideways). P* 13½ × 14.
226 ¼ a. olive-green and orange-brown .. .. 30 1·00
227 ½ a. violet and green 35 40
228 1 a. mauve and chocolate 60 20
229 2 a. green and blue .. .. .. 1·25 90
230 3 a. chocolate and carmine .. .. 2·25 3·25
231 1 r. violet and green .. .. .. 14·00 16·00
226/231 .. .. *Set of* 6 17·00 19·00

Designs:—No. 227, War Memorial Arch; No. 228, Council House; No. 229, The Viceroy's House; No. 230, Government of India Secretariat; No. 231, Dominion Columns and the Secretariat.

79 80 81 82 83

(T **82/3** des T. I. Archer. 9 p. litho and typo; 1¼ a., 3½ a. litho; others typo)

1932–36. *W* **69**. *P* 14.
232 **79** ½ a. green (1934) 25 5
233 **80** 9 p. deep green (22.4.32) 25 5
234 **81** 1 a. chocolate (1934) 30 5
235 **82** 1¼ a. mauve (22.4.32) 25 5
236 **70** 2 a. vermilion .. .. 14·00 7·50
236*a* **59** 2 a. vermilion (1934) .. .. .. 9·00 95
236*b* 2 a. vermilion *(small die)* (1936) .. 3·75 40
237 **62** 3 a. carmine 70 5
238 **83** 3½ a. ultramarine (22.4.32) .. .. 1·50 5
239 **64** 6 a. bistre (1935) .. .. .. 12·00 4·25
232/239 .. .. *Set of* 9 30·00 11·00

No. 236*a* measures 19 × 22.6 mm and No. 236*b* 18.4 × 21.8 mm.

84 Gateway of India, Bombay

1935 (6 May). *Silver Jubilee, T* **84** *and similar horiz designs. Litho W* **69** *(sideways). P* 13½ × 14.
240 ½ a. black and yellow-green 40 5
241 9 p. black and grey-green 40 5
242 1 a. black and brown 45 5
243 1¼ a. black and bright violet 45 5
244 2½ a. black and orange 50 45
245 3½ a. black and dull ultramarine .. .. 1·00 1·75
246 8 a. black and purple .. .. .. 4·00 2·50
240/246 .. .. *Set of* 7 6·50 4·25

Designs:—9 p. Victoria Memorial, Calcutta; 1 a. Rameswaram Temple, Madras; 1¼ a. Jain Temple, Calcutta; 2½ a. Taj Mahal, Agra; 3½ a. Golden Temple, Amritsar; 8 a. Pagoda in Mandalay.

91 King George VI

92 Dak Runner

93 King George VI

1937 (23 Aug–15 Dec). *Typo. W* **69**. *P* 13½ × 14 *or* 14 × 13½ *(T* **93**).
247 **91** 3 p. slate 25 5
248 ½ a. red-brown 20 5
249 9 p. green (23.8.37) 70 12
250 1 a. carmine (23.8.37) 15 5
a. *Tête-bêche* (vert pair) 30 85
251 **92** 2 a. vermilion 80 5
252 – 2½ a. bright violet 40 5
253 – 3 a. yellow-green .. .. .. 1·00 5
254 – 3½ a. bright blue 75 80
255 – 4 a. brown .. .. 3·50 5
256 – 6 a. turquoise-green .. .. .. 3·50 15
257 – 8 a. slate-violet .. .. .. 2·25 10
258 – 12 a. lake .. .. 7·00 40
259 **93** 1 r. grey and red-brown .. .. 1·00 5
260 2 r. purple and brown .. .. .. 4·25 8
261 5 r. green and blue .. .. .. 11·00 15
262 10 r. purple and claret .. .. .. 15·00 35
263 15 r. brown and green .. .. .. 55·00 55·00
264 25 r. slate-violet and purple .. .. 45·00 10·00
247/264 .. .. *Set of* 18 £140 60·00

Designs: *Horiz as T* **92**—2½ a. Dak bullock cart; 3 a. Dak tonga; 3½ a. Dak camel; 4 a. Mail train; 6 a. Mail steamer; 8 a. Mail lorry; 12 a. Mail plane (small head).

100*a* King George VI **101** King George VI **102**

103 Mail Plane (large head)

(*T* **100*a*/102** des T. I. Archer. Typo)

1940–43. *W* **69**. *P* 13½ × 14.
265 **100*a*** 3 p. slate 20 5
266 ½ a. purple (1.10.42) 20 5
267 9 p. green 20 5
268 1 a. carmine (1.4.43) 25 5
269 **101** 1 a. 3 p. bistre 50 5
269*a* 1½ a. dull violet (9.42) 40 5
270 2 a. vermilion 25 5
271 3 a. bright violet (1942) 25 5
272 3½ a. bright blue 40 5
273 **102** 4 a. brown 40 5
274 6 a. turquoise-green 65 10
275 8 a. slate-violet 65 5
276 12 a. lake .. .. 1·60 20
277 **103** 14 a. purple (15.10.40) .. .. .. 2·25 20
265/277 .. .. *Set of* 14 7·50 90

The 1½ a. and 3 a. were at first printed by lithography and were of finer execution and without Jubilee lines in the sheet margins.

105 "Victory" and King George VI

3 PIES

(106)

1946 (2 Jan). *Victory. Litho. W* **69**. *P* 13.
278 **105** 9 p. yellow-green (8.2.46) 15 5
279 1½ a. dull violet 15 5
280 3½ a. bright blue 25 25
281 12 a. claret (8.2.46) 30 30

1946 (8 Aug). *Surch with T* **106**.
282 **101** 3 p. on 1 a. 3 p. bistre 5 5

DOMINION

301 Asokan Capital (Inscr reads "Long Live India")

302 Indian National Flag

303 Douglas DC4

(Des T. I. Archer. Litho)

1947 (21 Nov–15 Dec). *Independence. W* **69**. *P* 14 × 13½ (1½ *a.*) *or* 13½ × 14 *(others)*.
301 **301** 1½ a. grey-green (15 Dec) 20 5
302 **302** 3½ a. orange-red, blue and green .. 40 30
303 **303** 12 a. ultramarine (15 Dec) .. .. 1·75 85

304 Lockheed "Constellation"

(Des T. I. Archer. Litho)

1948 (29 May). *Air. Inauguration of India-U.K. Air Service. W* **69**. *P* 13½ × 14.
304 **304** 12 a. black and ultramarine .. .. 1·50 80

305 Mahatma Gandhi **306**

(Photo Courvoisier)

1948 (15 Aug). *First Anniv of Independence. P* 11½.
305 **305** 1½ a. brown 60 12
306 3½ a. violet .. .. 1·50 85
307 12 a. grey-green .. .. .. 2·50 75
308 **306** 10 r. purple-brown and lake .. .. 80·00 70·00

307 Ajanta Panel

308 Konarak Horse

309 Trimurti

310 Bodhisattva

311 Nataraja

312 Sanchi Stupa, East Gate

313 Bodh Gaya Temple

314 Bhuvanesvara

315 Gol Gumbad, Bijapur

316 Kandarya Mahadeva Temple

317 Golden Temple, Amritsar

318 Victory Tower, Chittorgarh

319 Red Fort, Delhi

320 Taj Mahal, Agra

321 Qutb Minar, Delhi

322 Satrunjaya Temple, Palitana

(Des T. I. Archer and I. M. Das. Typo (low values), litho (rupee values))

1949 (15 Aug). *W* **69** (*sideways on Nos.* 310, 320 *and* 323*a*). *P* 14 (3 *p. to* 2 *a.*), 13½ (3 *a. to* 12 *a.*), 14 × 13½ (1 *r. and* 10 *r.*), 13½ × 14 (2 *r. and* 5 *r.*), 13 (15 *r.*).

309	**307**	3 p. slate-violet	15	5
310	**308**	6 p. purple-brown	25	5
311	**309**	9 p. yellow-green	40	5
312	**310**	1 a. turquoise	60	5
313	**311**	2 a. carmine	80	5
314	**312**	3 a. brown-orange	1·50	5
315	**313**	3½ a. bright blue	4·00	2·50
316	**314**	4 a. lake	7·50	5
317	**315**	6 a. violet	2·50	5
318	**316**	8 a. turquoise-green	2·25	5
319	**317**	12 a. dull blue	1·75	15
320	**318**	1 r. dull violet and green	11·00	5
321	**319**	2 r. claret and violet	5·00	15
322	**320**	5 r. blue-green and red-brown	17·00	45
323	**321**	10 r. purple-brown and deep blue	20·00	2·75
		a. Purple-brown and blue	28·00	2·75
324	**322**	15 r. brown and claret	15·00	8·50
309/324		*Set of* 16	80·00	13·00

For T **310** with statue reversed, see No. 333.

ALTERED CATALOGUE NUMBERS

Any Catalogue numbers altered from the last edition are shown as a list in the introductory pages.

323 Globe and Asokan Capital

1949 (10 Oct). *75th Anniv of U.P.U. Litho. W* **69**. *P* 13.

325	**323**	9 p. green	75	85
326		2 a. rose	1·50	1·00
327		3½ a. bright blue	2·50	2·75
328		12 a. brown-purple	4·75	3·25

REPUBLIC

324 Rejoicing Crowds

328 As T **310**, but statue reversed

(Des D. J. Keymer & Co. Litho)

1950 (26 Jan). *Inauguration of Republic. T* **324** *and similar designs. W* **69** (*sideways on* 3½ *a.*). *P* 13.

329	2 a. scarlet	80	15
330	3½ a. ultramarine	2·25	2·75
331	4 a. violet	2·25	40
332	12 a. maroon	4·25	2·00

Designs: *Vert*—3½ a. Quill, ink-well and verse. *Horiz*—4 a. Ear of corn and plough; 12 a. Spinning-wheel and cloth.

1950 (15 July)–**51**. *Typo. W* **69**. *P* 14 (1 *a.*), 13½ (*others*).

333	**328**	1 a. turquoise	1·60	5
333*a*	**313**	2½ a. lake (30.4.51)	90	45
333*b*	**314**	4 a. bright blue (30.4.51)	3·25	5

329 *Stegodon ganesa*

330 Torch

1951 (13 Jan). *Centenary of Geological Survey of India. Litho. W* **69**. *P* 13.

334	**329**	2 a. black and claret	70	35

1951 (4 Mar). *First Asian Games, New Delhi. Litho. W* **69** (*sideways*). *P* 14.

335	**330**	2 a. reddish purple and brown-orange	85	20
336		12 a. chocolate and light blue	4·50	90

PROCESS. All the following issues were printed in photogravure, *except where otherwise stated.*

331 Kabir

332 Locomotives in 1853 and 1953

1952 (1 Oct). *Indian Saints and Poets. T* **331** *and similar vert designs. W* **69**. *P* 14.

337	9 p. bright emerald-green	30	10
338	1 a. carmine	35	5
339	2 a. orange-red	70	5
340	4 a. bright blue	2·25	10
341	4½ a. bright mauve	40	10
342	12 a. brown	3·50	50
337/42	*Set of* 6	6·50	80

Designs:—1 a. Tulsidas; 2 a. Meera; 4 a. Surdas; 4½ a. Ghalib; 12 a. Tagore.

1953 (16 Apr). *Railway Centenary. W* **69**. *P* 14½ × 14.

343	**332**	2 a. black	30	5

333 Mount Everest

1953 (2 Oct). *Conquest of Mount Everest. W* **69**. *P* 14½ × 14.

344	**333**	2 a. bright violet	40	10
345		14 a. brown	4·75	50

334 Telegraph Poles of 1851 and 1951

1953 (1 Nov). *Centenary of Indian Telegraphs. W* **69**. *P* 14½ × 14.

346	**334**	2 a. blue-green	35	10
347		12 a. blue	4·75	50

335 Postal Transport, 1854

1954 (1 Oct). *Stamp Centenary. T* **335** *and similar horiz designs. W* **69**. *P* 14½ × 14.

348	1 a. reddish purple	25	5
349	2 a. cerise	40	5
350	4 a. orange-brown	2·40	15
351	14 a. blue	2·50	50

Designs:—2, 14 a. "Airmail"; 4 a. Postal transport, 1954.

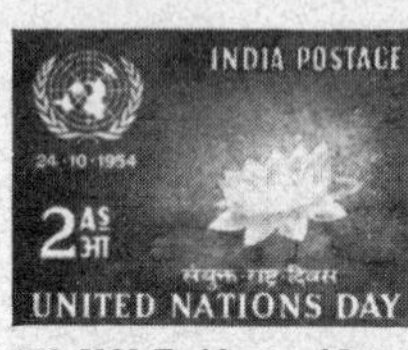

338 U.N. Emblem and Lotus

1954 (24 Oct). *United Nations Day. W* **69** (*sideways*). *P* 13.

352	**338**	2 a. turquoise-green	15	5

339 Forest Research Institute

1954 (11 Dec). *Fourth World Forestry Congress, Dehra Dun. W* **69**. *P* 14½ × 14.

353	**339**	2 a. ultramarine	12	5

340 Tractor

344 Woman Spinning

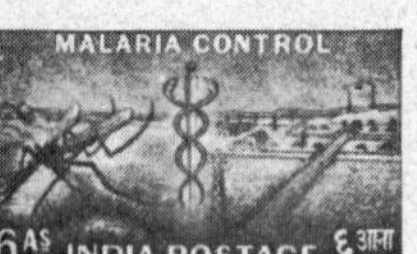

347 "Malaria Control" (Mosquito and Staff of Aesculapius)

1955 (26 Jan). *Five Year Plan. T* **340**, **344**, **347** *and similar designs. W* **69** (*sideways on small horiz designs*). *P* 14 × 14½ (*small horiz*) *or* 14½ × 14 (*others*).

354	3 p. bright purple	5	5
355	6 p. violet	8	5
356	9 p. orange-brown	10	5
357	1 a. blue-green	20	5
358	2 a. light blue	20	5
359	3 a. pale blue-green	25	5
360	4 a. rose-carmine	25	5
361	6 a. yellow-brown	25	5
362	8 a. blue	1·75	5
363	10 a. turquoise-green	45	45
364	12 a. bright blue	60	5
365	14 a. bright green	90	25
366	1 r. deep dull green	4·50	5
367	1 r. 2 a. grey	2·25	2·50
368	1 r. 8 a. reddish purple	4·00	2·75
369	2 r. cerise	3·75	10
370	5 r. brown	11·00	30
371	10 r. orange	14·00	1·00
354/71	*Set of* 18	40·00	7·00

Designs: *Horiz* (*as T* **340**)—6 p. Power loom; 9 p. Bullock-driven well; 1 a. Damodar Valley Dam; 4 a. Bullocks; 8 a. Chittaranjan Locomotive Works; 12 a. Hindustan Aircraft Factory, Bangalore; 1 r. Telephone engineer; 2 r. Rare Earth Factory, Alwaye; 5 r. Sindri Fertiliser Factory; 10 r. Steel plant. (*As T* **347**)—10 a. Marine Drive, Bombay; 14 a. Kashmir landscape; 1 r. 2 a. Cape Comorin; 1 r. 8 a. Mt Kangchenjunga. *Vert* (*as T* **344**)—3 a. Woman weaving with hand loom.

For stamps as Nos. 366, 369/71 but W **374** see Nos. 413/16.

358 Bodhi Tree

359 Round Parasol and Bodhi Tree

(Des C. Pakrashi (2 a.), R. D'Silva (14 a.))

1956 (24 May). *Buddha Jayanti.* W **69** (*sideways on* 14 *a.*). *P* 13 × 13½ (2 *a.*) *or* 13½ × 13 (14 *a.*).
372 **358** 2 a. sepia 12 10
373 **359** 14 a. vermilion .. .. 2·00 1·50

360 Lokmanya Bal Gangadhar Tilak

361 Map of India

1956 (23 July). *Birth Centenary of Tilak (journalist).* W **69**. *P* 13 × 13½.
374 **360** 2 a. chestnut 10 5

(New Currency 100 n(aye) p(aise) = 1 rupee.)

1957 (1 Apr)–**58**. W **69** (*sideways*). *P* 14 × 14½.

375	**361**	1 n.p. blue-green	5	5
376		2 n.p. light brown	5	5
377		3 n.p. deep brown	5	5
378		5 n.p. bright green	3·00	5
379		6 n.p. grey	8	5
379*a*		8 n.p. light blue-green (7.5.58)	40	45
380		10 n.p. deep dull green	3·25	5
381		13 n.p. bright carmine-red	20	5
381*a*		15 n.p. violet (16.1.58)	25	5
382		20 n.p. blue	25	5
383		25 n.p. ultramarine	25	5
384		50 n.p. orange	2·25	5
385		75 n.p. reddish purple	1·25	5
385*a*		90 n.p. bright purple (16.1.58)	70	30
375/85*a*		*Set of* 14	11·00	85

The 8, 15 and 90 n.p. have their value expressed as "nP".
For similar stamps but W **374** see Nos. 399/412.

362 The Rani of Jhansi

363 Shrine

1957 (15 Aug). *Indian Mutiny Centenary.* W **69**. *P* 14½ × 14 (15 *n.p.*) *or* 13 × 13½ (90 *n.p.*).
386 **362** 15 n.p. brown 15 5
387 **363** 90 n.p. reddish purple .. .. 1·50 40

364 Henri Dunant and Conference Emblem

365 "Nutrition"

1957 (28 Oct). *19th International Red Cross Conference, New Delhi.* W **69** (*sideways*). *P* 13½ × 13.
388 **364** 15 n.p. deep grey and carmine 5 5

1957 (14 Nov). *National Children's Day. T* **365** *and similar designs.* W **69** (*sideways on* 90 *n.p.*). *P* 14 × 13½ (90 *n.p.*) *or* 13½ × 14 (*others*).
389 8 n.p. reddish purple 8 10
390 15 n.p. turquoise-green 10 5
391 90 n.p. orange-brown 30 15
Designs: *Horiz*—15 n.p. "Education". *Vert*—90 n.p. "Recreation".

OMNIBUS ISSUES

Details, together with prices for complete sets, of the various Omnibus issues from the 1935 Silver Jubilee series to date are included in a special section following Zululand at the end of the catalogue.

368 Bombay University

369 Calcutta University

1957 (31 Dec). *Centenary of Indian Universities. T* **368/9** *and similar design.* W **69** (*sideways on T* **368**). *P* 14 × 14½ (*No.* 392) *or* 13½ × 14 (*others*).
392 10 n.p. violet 8 5
393 10 n.p. grey 8 5
394 10 n.p. light brown 8 5
Design: *Horiz as T* **369**—No. 394, Madras University.

371 J. N. Tata (founder) and Steel Plant

372 Dr. D. K. Karve

1958 (1 Mar). *50th Anniv of Steel Industry.* W **69**. *P* 14½ × 14.
395 **371** 15 n.p. orange-red 5 5

1958 (18 Apr). *Birth Centenary of Karve (educationalist).* W **69** (*sideways*). *P* 14.
396 **372** 15 n.p. orange-brown 5 5

373 "Wapiti" and "Hunter" Aircraft

374 Asokan Capital

1958 (30 Apr). *Silver Jubilee of Indian Air Force.* W **69**. *P* 14½ × 14.
397 **373** 15 n.p. blue 15 5
398 90 n.p. ultramarine .. .. 1·25 70

1958–63. *As Nos.* 366, 369/71 *and* 375/85*a but* W **374**.

399	**361**	1 n.p. blue-green (1960)	5	5
		a. Imperf (pair)	90·00	
400		2 n.p. light brown (27.10.58)	5	5
401		3 n.p. deep brown (1958)	5	5
402		5 n.p. bright green (27.10.58)	8	5
403		6 n.p. grey (1963)	15	30
404		8 n.p. light blue-green (1958)	10	5
405		10 n.p. deep dull green (27.10.58)	15	5
406		13 n.p. bright carmine-red (1963)	12	30
407		15 n.p. violet (10.60)	15	5
408		20 n.p. blue (27.10.58)	25	5
409		25 n.p. ultramarine (27.10.58)	25	5
410		50 n.p. orange (1959)	30	5
411		75 n.p. reddish purple (1959)	40	5
412		90 n.p. bright purple (1960)	75	10
413	–	1 r. deep dull green (1959)	1·00	5
414	–	2 r. cerise (1959)	2·75	5
415	–	5 r. brown (1959)	8·00	45
416	–	10 r. orange (1959)	16·00	2·25
399/416		*Set of* 18	28·00	3·75

The 5, 10, 15, 20, 25 and 50 n.p. with serial numbers on the back are coil stamps prepared from sheets for experimenting with coil machines. In the event the machines were not purchased and the stamps were sold over the counter.

375 Bipin Chandra Pal

376 Nurse with Child Patient

1958 (7 Nov). *Birth Centenary of Pal (patriot).* W **374**. *P* 14 × 13½.
418 **375** 15 n.p. deep dull green 5 5

1958 (14 Nov). *National Children's Day.* W **374**. *P* 14 × 13½.
419 **376** 15 n.p. violet 5 5

377 Jagadis Chandra Bose

378 Exhibition Gate

1958 (30 Nov). *Birth Centenary of Bose (botanist).* W **374**. *P* 14 × 13½.
420 **377** 15 n.p. deep turquoise-green 5 5

1958 (30 Dec). *India* 1958 *Exhibition, New Delhi.* W **374** (*sideways*). *P* 14½ × 14.
421 **378** 15 n.p. reddish purple 5 5

379 Sir Jamsetjee Jejeebhoy

380 "The Triumph of Labour" (after Chowdhury)

1959 (15 Apr). *Death Centenary of Jejeebhoy (philanthropist).* W **374**. *P* 14 × 13½.
422 **379** 15 n.p. brown 5 5

1959 (15 June). *40th Anniv of International Labour Organization.* W **374** (*sideways*). *P* 14½ × 14.
423 **380** 15 n.p. dull green 5 5

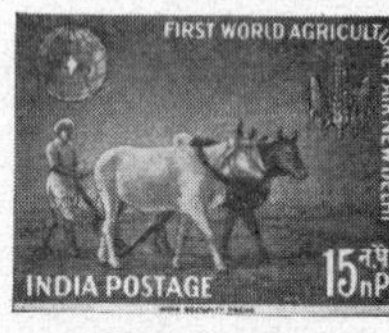

381 Boys awaiting admission to Children's Home

382 "Agriculture"

1959 (14 Nov). *National Children's Day.* W **374**. *P* 14 × 14½.
424 **381** 15 n.p. deep dull green 5 5
a. Imperf (pair) £130

1959 (30 Dec). *First World Agricultural Fair, New Delhi.* W **374**. *P* 13½ × 13.
425 **382** 15 n.p. grey 5 5

383 Thiruvalluvar (poet)

1960 (15 Feb). *Thiruvalluvar Commemoration.* W **374**. *P* 14 × 13½.
426 **383** 15 n.p. reddish purple 5 5

384 Yaksha pleading with the Cloud (from the "Meghaduta")

385 Shakuntala writing a letter to Dushyanta (from the "Shakuntala")

1960 (22 June). *Kalidasa (poet) Commemoration.* W **374**. *P* 13.
427 **384** 15 n.p. grey 5 5
428 **385** 1 r. 3 n.p. pale yellow and brown .. 40 10

386 S. Bharati (poet)

387 Dr. M. Visvesvaraya

1960 (11 Sept). *Subramania Bharati Commemoration.* W **374**. *P* 14 × 13½.
429 **386** 15 n.p. blue 5 5

1960 (15 Sept). *Birth Centenary of Dr. M. Visvesvaraya (engineer).* W **374**. *P* 13 × 13½.
430 **387** 15 n.p. brown and bright carmine .. 5 5

388 "Children's Health"

1960 (14 Nov). *Children's Day. W* **374**. *P* 13½ × 13.
431 **388** 15 n.p. deep dull green 5 5

389 Children greeting U.N. Emblem

390 Tyagaraja (Indian Saint)

1960 (11 Dec). *U.N.I.C.E.F. Day. W* **374**. *P* 13½ × 13.
432 **389** 15 n.p. orange-brown and olive-brown 5 5

1961 (6 Jan). *Tyagaraja Commemoration. W* **374**. *P* 14 × 13½.
433 **390** 15 n.p. greenish blue 5 5

391 "First Aerial Post" cancellation

392 "Air India" Boeing 707 jetliner and Humber-Sommer plane

1961 (18 Feb). *50th Anniv of First Official Airmail Flight, Allahabad-Naini. T* **391/2** *and similar design. W* **374**. *P* 14 *(5 n.p.) or* 13 × 13½ *(others).*
434 5 n.p. olive-drab 25 10
435 15 n.p. deep green and grey 90 30
436 1 r. purple and grey .. .. 3·75 1·25
Design: *Horiz as T* **392**—1 r. H. Pecquet flying Humber-Sommer plane and "Aerial Post" cancellation.

394 Shivaji on horseback

395 Motilal Nehru (politician)

1961 (17 Apr). *Shivaji Commemoration. W* **374**. *P* 13 × 13½.
437 **394** 15 n.p. brown and green.. .. .. .. 10 5

1961 (6 May). *Birth Centenary of Pandit Motilal Nehru. W* **374**. *P* 14.
438 **395** 15 n.p. olive-brown and brown-orange .. 5 5

396 Tagore (poet)

397 All India Radio Emblem and Transmitting Aerials

1961 (7 May). *Birth Centenary of Rabindranath Tagore. W* **374**. *P* 13 × 13½.
439 **396** 15 n.p. yellow-orange and blue-green .. 10 5

1961 (8 June). *Silver Jubilee of All India Radio. W* **374**. *P* 13½ × 13.
440 **397** 15 n.p. ultramarine 10 5

398 P. Chandra Ray

399 V. N. Bhatkande

1961 (2 Aug). *Birth Centenary of Ray (scientist). W* **374**. *P* 14 × 13½.
441 **398** 15 n.p. grey 5 5

1961 (1 Sept). *Birth Centenary of Bhatkande (musician). W* **374**. *P* 13 × 13½.
442 **399** 15 n.p. olive-brown 10 5

400 Child at Lathe

401 Fair Emblem and Main Gate

1961 (14 Nov). *Children's Day. W* **374**. *P* 14 × 13½.
443 **400** 15 n.p. brown 10 5

1961 (14 Nov). *Indian Industries Fair, New Delhi. W* **374**. *P* 14 × 14½.
444 **401** 15 n.p. blue and carmine 10 5

402 Indian Forest

1961 (21 Nov). *Centenary of Scientific Forestry. W* **374**. *P* 13 × 13½.
445 **402** 15 n.p. green and brown.. .. .. 10 5

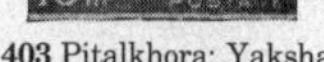

403 Pitalkhora: Yaksha

404 Kalibangan Seal

1961 (14 Dec). *Centenary of Indian Archaeological Survey. W* **374**. *P* 14 × 13½ *(15 n.p.) or* 13½ × 14 *(90 n.p.).*
446 **403** 15 n.p. orange-brown 10 8
447 **404** 90 n.p. yellow-olive and light brown .. 35 20

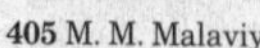

405 M. M. Malaviya

406 Gauhati Refinery

1961 (7 May). *Birth Centenary of Rabindranath Tagore. W* **374**. *P* 13 × 13½.
439 **396** 15 n.p. yellow-orange and blue-green .. 10 5

1961 (8 June). *Silver Jubilee of All India Radio. W* **374**. *P* 13½ × 13.
440 **397** 15 n.p. ultramarine 10 5

ALTERED CATALOGUE NUMBERS

Any Catalogue numbers altered from the last edition are shown as a list in the introductory pages.

407 Bhikaiji Cama

408 Panchayati at work and Parliament Building

1962 (26 Jan). *Birth Centenary of Bhikaiji Cama (revolutionary). W* **374**. *P* 14.
450 **407** 15 n.p. reddish purple 10 5

1962 (26 Jan). *Panchayati Raj Commemoration. W* **374**. *P* 13 × 13½.
451 **408** 15 n.p. bright purple 10 5

409 D. Saraswati (religious educator)

410 G. S. Vidhyarthi (patriot)

1962 (4 Mar). *Saraswati Commemoration. W* **374**. *P* 14.
452 **409** 15 n.p. orange-brown 10 5

1962 (25 Mar). *Vidhyarthi Commemoration. W* **374**. *P* 14 × 13½.
453 **410** 15 n.p. red-brown 10 5

411 Malaria Eradication Emblem

412 Dr. R. Prasad (former President of India)

1962 (7 Apr). *Malaria Eradication. W* **374**. *P* 13 × 13½.
454 **411** 15 n.p. yellow and claret 10 5

1962 (13 May). *Dr. Rajendra Prasad Commemoration. W* **374**. *P* 13.
455 **412** 15 n.p. bright purple *(shades)* 10 5

413 Calcutta High Court

416 Ramabai Ranade

1962. *Centenary of Indian High Courts. T* **413** *and similar horiz designs. W* **374**. *P* 14.
456 15 n.p. dull green (1 July) 10 5
457 15 n.p. red-brown (6 August).. .. .. 10 5
458 15 n.p. slate (14 August) 10 5
Designs:—No. 457, Madras High Court; No. 458, Bombay High Court.

1962 (15 Aug). *Birth Centenary of Ramabai Ranade (social reformer). W* **374**. *P* 14 × 13½
459 **416** 15 n.p. orange-brown 10 5

417 Indian One-horned Rhinoceros

418 "Passing the Flag to Youth"

1962 (1 Oct). *Wild Life Week. W* **374**. *P* 13½ × 14.
460 **417** 15 n.p. red-brown and deep turquoise .. 12 8

INSCRIPTIONS. From No. 461 onwards all designs are inscribed "BHARAT" in Devanagri, in addition to "INDIA" in English.

1962 (14 Nov). *Children's Day. W* **374**. *P* 13½ × 13.
461 **418** 15 n.p. orange-red and turquoise-green 10 5

419 Human Eye within Lotus Blossom **420** S. Ramanujan

1962 (3 Dec). *19th International Ophthalmology Congress, New Delhi.* W **374**. *P* 13½ × 13.
462 **419** 15 n.p. deep olive-brown 10 5

1962 (22 Dec). *75th Birth Anniv of Ramanujan (mathematician).* W **374**. *P* 13½ × 14.
463 **420** 15 n.p. deep olive-brown 10 5

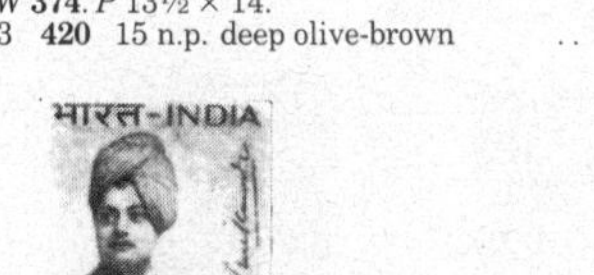

Re.1

421 S. Vivekananda **(422)**

1963 (17 Jan). *Birth Centenary of Vivekananda (philosopher).* W **374**. *P* 14 × 14½.
464 **421** 15 n.p. orange-brown and yellow-olive .. 10 5

1963 (2 Feb). *No.* 428 *surch with T* **422**.
465 **385** 1 r. on 1 r. 3 n.p. pale yellow & brn .. 50 10

423 Hands reaching for F.A.O. Emblem **424** Henri Dunant (founder) and Centenary Emblem

1963 (21 Mar). *Freedom from Hunger.* W **374**. *P* 13.
466 **423** 15 n.p. grey-blue 35 5

1963 (8 May). *Red Cross Centenary.* W **374**. *P* 13.
467 **424** 15 n.p. red and grey 20 5
a. Red (cross) omitted £1800

425 Artillery and Helicopter

1963 (15 Aug). *Defence Campaign. T* **425** *and similar horiz design.* W **374**. *P* 14.
468 15 n.p. grey-green 25 8
469 1 r. red-brown 90 30
Design:—1 r. Sentry and parachutists.

427 D. Naoroji (patriot) **428** Mrs. Annie Besant (patriot and theosophist, born 1847). (Stamp wrongly dated "1837")

1963 (4 Sept). *Dadabhoy Naoroji Commemoration.* W **374**. *P* 13.
470 **427** 15 n.p. grey 5 5

1963 (1 Oct). *Mrs. Annie Besant Commemoration.* W **374**. *P* 13½ × 14.
471 **428** 15 n.p. turquoise-green 5 5

OMNIBUS ISSUES

Details, together with prices for complete sets, of the various Omnibus issues from the 1935 Silver Jubilee series to date are included in a special section following Zululand at the end of the catalogue.

429 Gaur **430** Himalayan Panda

1963 (7 Oct). *Wild Life Preservation. T* **429/30** *and similar designs.* W **374**. *P* 13½ × 14 (10 *n.p.*) *or* 13 (*others*).
472 10 n.p. black and yellow-orange 50 40
473 15 n.p. orange-brown and green 60 15
474 30 n.p. slate and yellow-ochre .. .. 1·25 25
475 50 n.p. orange and deep grey-green .. .. 2·00 45
476 1 r. light brown and blue .. .. .. 2·00 45
Designs: *Vert*—30 n.p. Indian elephant. *Horiz* (*as T* **430**)—50 n.p. Tiger; 1 r. Indian lion.

434 "School Meals" **435** Eleanor Roosevelt at Spinning-wheel

1963 (14 Nov). *Children's Day.* W **374**. *P* 14 × 13½.
477 **434** 15 n.p. bistre-brown 5 5

1963 (10 Dec). *15th Anniv of Declaration of Human Rights.* W **374**. *P* 13½ × 13.
478 **435** 15 n.p. reddish purple 5 5

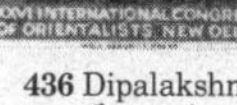

436 Dipalakshmi (bronze) **437** Gopabandhu Das (patriot and social reformer)

1964 (4 Jan). *26th International Orientalists Congress, New Delhi.* W **374**. *P* 13 × 13½.
479 **436** 15 n.p. deep ultramarine 5 5

1964 (4 Jan). *Gopabandhu Das Commemoration.* W **374**. *P* 13 × 13½.
480 **437** 15 n.p. deep dull purple 5 5

438 Purandaradasa

1964 (14 Jan). *400th Death Anniv of Purandaradasa (musician).* W **374**. *P* 13 × 13½.
481 **438** 15 n.p. light brown 5 5

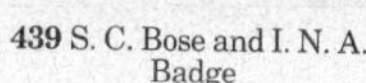

439 S. C. Bose and I. N. A. Badge **440** Bose and Indian National Army

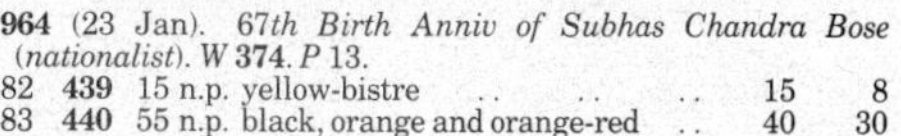

1964 (23 Jan). *67th Birth Anniv of Subhas Chandra Bose (nationalist).* W **374**. *P* 13.
482 **439** 15 n.p. yellow-bistre 15 8
483 **440** 55 n.p. black, orange and orange-red .. 40 30

441 Sarojini Naidu **442** Kasturba Gandhi

1964 (13 Feb). *85th Birth Anniv of Mrs. Sarojini Naidu (patriot).* W **374**. *P* 14.
484 **441** 15 n.p. deep grey-green and purple .. 5 5

1964 (22 Feb). *20th Death Anniv of Kasturba Gandhi.* W **374**. *P* 14 × 13½.
485 **442** 15 n.p. orange-brown 5 5

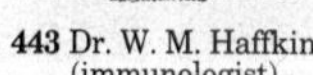

443 Dr. W. M. Haffkine (immunologist) **444** Jawaharlal Nehru (statesman)

1964 (16 Mar). *Haffkine Commemoration.* W **374**. *P* 13.
486 **443** 15 n.p. deep purple-brown/*buff* 10 5

(Value expressed as paisa instead of naye paise.)

1964 (12 June). *Nehru Mourning Issue. No wmk. P* 13½ × 13.
487 **444** 15 p. deep slate 5 5

445 Sir A. Mookerjee **446** Sri Aurobindo

1964 (29 June). *Birth Centenary of Sir Asutosh Mookerjee (education reformer).* W **374**. *P* 13½ × 13.
488 **445** 15 p. bistre-brown and yellow-olive .. 5 5

1964 (15 Aug). *92nd Birth Anniv of Sri Aurobindo (religious leader).* W **374**. *P* 13 × 13½.
489 **446** 15 p. dull purple 5 5

447 Raja R. Roy (social reformer) **448** I.S.O. Emblem and Globe

1964 (27 Sept). *Raja Rammohun Roy Commemoration.* W **374**. *P* 13 × 13½.
490 **447** 15 n.p. brown 5 5

1964 (9 Nov). *Sixth International Organization for Standardization General Assembly, Bombay. No wmk. P* 13 × 13½.
491 **448** 15 p. carmine 5 5

449 Jawaharlal Nehru (medallion) **450** St. Thomas (after statue, Ortona Cathedral, Italy)

1964 (14 Nov). *Children's Day. No wmk. P* 14 × 13½.
492 **449** 15 p. slate 5 5

1964 (2 Dec). *St. Thomas Commemoration. No wmk. P* 14 × 13½.
493 **450** 15 p. reddish purple 5 5
No. 493 was issued on the occasion of Pope Paul's visit to India.

451 Globe

452 J. Tata (industrialist)

1964 (14 Dec). *22nd International Geological Congress.* W **374**. *P* 14 × 13½.
494 **451** 15 p. blue-green 5 5

1965 (7 Jan). *Jamsetji Tata Commemoration. No wmk. P* 13½ × 13.
495 **452** 15 p. dull purple and orange 5 5

453 Lala Lajpat Rai

454 Globe and Congress Emblem

1965 (28 Jan). *Birth Centenary of Lala Lajpat Rai (patriot). No wmk. P* 13 × 13½.
496 **453** 15 p. light brown 5 5

1965 (8 Feb). *20th International Chamber of Commerce Congress, New Delhi. No wmk. P* 13½ × 13.
497 **454** 15 p. grey-green and carmine 5 5

455 Freighter *Jalausha* and Visakhapatnam

456 Abraham Lincoln

1965 (5 Apr). *National Maritime Day.* W **374** *(sideways). P* 14½ × 14.
498 **455** 15 p. blue 15 5

1965 (15 Apr). *Death Centenary of Abraham Lincoln.* W **374**. *P* 13.
499 **456** 15 p. brown and yellow-ochre 5 5

457 I.T.U. Emblem and Symbols

458 "Everlasting Flame"

1965 (17 May). *I.T.U. Centenary.* W **374** *(sideways). P* 14½ × 14.
500 **457** 15 p. reddish purple 30 10

1965 (27 May). *First Anniv of Nehru's Death.* W **374**. *P* 13.
501 **458** 15 p. carmine and blue 5 5

459 I.C.Y. Emblem

460 Climbers on Summit

1965 (26 June). *International Co-operation Year. No wmk. P* 13½ × 13.
502 **459** 15 p. deep olive and yellow-brown .. 30 15

1965 (15 Aug). *Indian Mount Everest Expedition. No wmk. P* 13.
503 **460** 15 p. deep reddish purple 10 5

461 Bidri Vase

462 Brass Lamp

466 Electric Locomotive

474 Medieval Sculpture

475 Dal Lake, Kashmir

1965–75. *T* **461/2, 466, 474/5** *and similar designs.*

(*a*) W **374** (*sideways on* 2, 3, 5, 6, 8, 30, 50, 60 *p.*, 2, 5, 10 *r.*). *P* 14 × 14½ (4, 10, 15, 20, 40, 70 *p.*, 1 *r.*) *or* 14½ × 14 (*others*)
504 2 p. red-brown (16.10.67) 5 10
505 3 p. brown-olive (16.10.67) 5 10
505*a* 4 p. lake-brown (*shades*) (15.5.68) 5 10
506 5 p. cerise (16.10.67) 5 5
a. Imperf (pair) £130
507 6 p. grey-black (1.7.66) 5 10
508 8 p. red-brown (15.3.67) 25 30
509 10 p. new blue (1.7.66) 25 5
510 15 p. bronze-green (15.8.65) 10 5
511 20 p. purple (16.10.67) 12 5
512 30 p. sepia (15.3.67) 12 5
513 40 p. maroon (2.10.68) 12 5
514 50 p. blue-green (15.3.67) 20 5
515 60 p. deep grey (16.10.67) 35 10
516 70 p. chalky blue (15.3.67) 60 8
517 1 r. red-brown and plum (1.7.66) 60 5
518 2 r. new blue and deep slate-violet (15.3.67) 2·50 5
519 5 r. deep slate-violet and brown (15.3.67) .. 2·75 25
520 10 r. black and bronze-green (14.11.65) .. 6·50 80
504/20 .. .. *Set of* 18 13·00 2·00

(*b*) *No wmk. P* 14½ × 14
520*a* 5 p. cerise (12.5.74*) 5 5

(*c*) *Wmk Large Star and* "INDIA GOVT"† *in sheet. P* 14½ × 14
521 2 p. red-brown (1.3.75) 5 5
521*a* 5 p. cerise (1.3.75) 5 5

Designs: *Horiz* (*as T* **466**)—4 p. Coffee berries; 15 p. Plucking tea; 20 p. Folland "Gnat" fighter aircraft; 40 p. Calcutta G.P.O.; 70 p. Hampi Chariot (sculpture). (*As T* **475**)—5 r. Bhakra Dam, Punjab; 10 r. Atomic Reactor, Trombay. *Vert* (*as T* **461/2**)—5 p. "Family Planning"; 6 p. Konarak Elephant; 8 p. Chital (spotted deer); 30 p. Indian dolls; 50 p. Mangoes; 60 p. Somnath Temple.

*Earliest known date of issue.

†The arrangement of this watermark in the sheet results in the words and the star appearing upright, inverted or sideways.

Crude postal forgeries exist of No. 511, without watermark and rough perf 15.

See also Nos. 721/38.

479 G. B. Pant (statesman)

481 C. Das

482 Vidyapati (poet)

480 V. Patel

1965 (10 Sept). *Govind Ballabh Pant Commemoration.* W **374**. *P* 13.
522 **479** 15 p. brown and deep green 5 5

1965 (31 Oct). *90th Birth Anniv of Vallabhbhai Patel (statesman).* W **374**. *P* 14 × 13½.
523 **480** 15 p. blackish brown 5 5

1965 (5 Nov). *95th Birth Anniv of Chittaranjan Das (lawyer and patriot).* W **374**. *P* 13.
524 **481** 15 p. yellow-brown 5 5

1965 (17 Nov). *Vidyapati Commemoration.* W **374**. *P* 14 × 14½.
525 **482** 15 p. yellow-brown 5 5

483 Sikandra, Agra

484 Soldier, Fighters and Warship

1966 (24 Jan). *Pacific Area Travel Association Conference. New Delhi. No wmk. P* 13½ × 14.
526 **483** 15 p. slate 5 5

1966 (26 Jan). *Indian Armed Forces. No wmk. P* 14.
527 **484** 15 p. violet 5 8

485 Lal Bahadur Shastri (statesman)

486 Kambar (poet)

1966 (26 Jan). *Shastri Mourning Issue. No wmk. P* 13 × 13½.
528 **485** 15 p. black 5 5

1966 (5 Apr). *Kambar Commemoration. P* 14 × 14½.
529 **486** 15 p. grey-green 5 5

487 B. R. Ambedkar

488 Kunwar Singh (patriot)

1966 (14 Apr). *75th Birth Anniv of Dr. B. R. Ambedkar (lawyer and reformer). P* 14 × 13½.
530 **487** 15 p. purple-brown 5 5

1966 (23 Apr). *Kunwar Singh Commemoration. P* 14 × 13½.
531 **488** 15 p. chestnut 5 5

489 G. K. Gokhale

490 Acharya Dvivedi (writer)

1966 (9 May). *Birth Centenary of G. K. Gokhale (patriot). P* 13 ½ × 13.
532 **489** 15 p. brown-purple and pale yellow .. 5 5

1966 (15 May). *Dvivedi Commemoration. P* 13½ × 14.
533 **490** 15 p. drab 5 5

491 Maharaja Ranjit Singh (warrior)

492 Homi Bhabha (scientist) and Nuclear Reactor

1966 (28 June). *Maharaja Ranjit Singh Commemoration. P* 14 × 13½.
534 **491** 15 p. purple 10 8

1966 (4 Aug). *Homi Bhabha Commemoration. P* 14½ × 14.
535 **492** 15 p. dull purple 10 8

493 A. K. Azad (scholar)

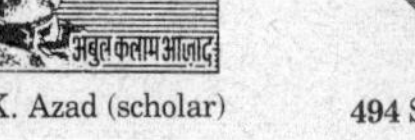
494 Swami Tirtha

1966 (11 Nov). *Abul Kalam Azad Commemoration. P* 13½ × 14.
536 **493** 15 p. chalky blue 5 5

1966 (11 Nov). *60th Death Anniv of Swami Rama Tirtha (social reformer). P* 13 × 13½.
537 **494** 15 p. turquoise-blue 10 8

495 Infant and Dove Emblem

496 Allahabad High Court

(Des C. Pakrashi)

1966 (14 Nov). *Children's Day. P* 13 × 13½.
538 **495** 15 p. bright purple 8 5

1966 (25 Nov). *Centenary of Allahabad High Court. P* 14½ × 14.
539 **496** 15 p. dull purple 8 10

497 Indian Family

498 Hockey Game

1966 (12 Dec). *Family Planning. P* 13.
540 **497** 15 p. brown 5 8

1966 (31 Dec). *India's Hockey Victory in Fifth Asian Games. P* 13.
541 **498** 15 p. new blue 10 8

499 "Jai Kisan"

500 Voter and Polling Booth

1967 (11 Jan). *First Anniv of Shastri's Death. P* 13½ × 14.
542 **499** 15 p. yellow-green 5 5

1967 (13 Jan). *Indian General Election. P* 13½ × 14.
543 **500** 15 p. red-brown 5 5

501 Guru Dwara Shrine, Patna

502 Taj Mahal

1967 (17 Jan). *300th Birth Anniv (in 1966) of Guru Gobind Singh (National leader). P* 14 × 13½.
544 **501** 15 p. bluish violet 5 5

1967 (19 Mar). *International Tourist Year. P* 14½ × 14.
545 **502** 15 p. bistre-brown and orange 10 5

503 Nandalal Bose and "Garuda"

504 Survey Emblem and Activities

1967 (16 Apr). *First Death Anniv of Nandalal Bose (painter). P* 14 × 13½.
546 **503** 15 p. bistre-brown 5 5

1967 (1 May). *Survey of India Bicentenary. P* 13½ × 13.
547 **504** 15 p. reddish lilac 10 8

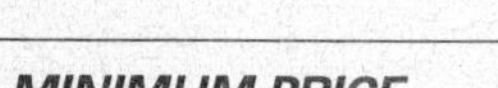

MINIMUM PRICE

The minimum price quoted is 5p which represents a handling charge rather than a basis for valuing common stamps. For further notes about prices see introductory pages.

505 Basaveswara

506 Narsinha Mehta (poet)

1967 (11 May). *800th Death Anniv of Basaveswara (reformer and statesman). P* 13½ × 14.
548 **505** 15 p. orange-red 5 5

1967 (30 May). *Narsinha Mehta Commemoration. P* 14 × 13½.
549 **506** 15 p. blackish brown 5 5

507 Maharana Pratap (warrior)

508 Narayana Guru (reformer)

1967 (11 June). *Maharana Pratap Commemoration. P* 14 × 14½.
550 **507** 15 p. red-brown 5 5

1967 (21 Aug). *Narayana Guru Commemoration. P* 14.
551 **508** 15 p. brown 5 8

509 President Radhakrishnan

510 Martyrs' Memorial, Patna

1967 (5 Sept). *Radhakrishnan Commemoration. P* 13.
552 **509** 15 p. claret 5 8

1967 (1 Oct). *25th Anniv of "Quit India" Movement. P* 14½ × 14.
553 **510** 15 p. lake 5 5

511 Route Map

512 Wrestling

1967 (9 Nov). *Centenary of Indo-European Telegraph Service. P* 13½ × 14.
554 **511** 15 p. black and light blue 5 8

1967 (12 Nov). *World Wrestling Championships. P* 13½ × 14.
555 **512** 15 p. purple and light orange-brown .. 5 8

513 Nehru leading Naga Tribesmen

514 Rashbehari Basu (nationalist)

1967 (1 Dec). *"Nehru and Nagaland". P* 13 × 13½.
556 **513** 15 p. ultramarine 5 8

1967 (26 Dec). *Rashbehari Basu Commemoration. P* 14.
557 **514** 15 p. maroon 5 5

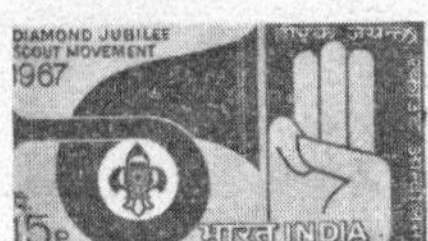

515 Bugle, Badge and Scout Salute

1967 (27 Dec). *Diamond Jubilee of Scout Movement. P* 14½ × 14.
558 **515** 15 p. chestnut 10 5

516 Men embracing Universe

517 Globe and Book of Tamil

1968 (1 Jan). *Human Rights Year. P* 13.
559 **516** 15 p. bronze-green 8 5

1968 (3 Jan). *International Conference-Seminar of Tamil Studies, Madras. P* 13.
560 **517** 15 p. reddish lilac 8 5

518 U.N. Emblem and Transport

519 Quill and Bow Symbol

1968 (1 Feb). *United Nations Conference on Trade and Development. P* 14½ × 14.
561 **518** 15 p. turquoise-blue 10 5

1968 (20 Feb). *Amrita Bazar Patrika (Newspaper) Centenary. P* 13½ × 14.
562 **519** 15 p. sepia and orange-yellow 10 8

520 Maxim Gorky

521 Emblem and Medal

1968 (28 Mar). *Birth Centenary of Maxim Gorky. P* 13½.
563 **520** 15 p. plum 10 8

1968 (31 Mar). *First Triennale, New Delhi. P* 13.
564 **521** 15 p. orange, royal blue and light blue .. 5 5
a. Orange omitted £450

522 Letter-box and "100,000"

523 Stalks of Wheat, Agricultural Institute and Production Graph

(Des C. Pakrashi)

1968 (1 July). *Opening of 100,000th Indian Post Office. P* 13.
565 **522** 20 p. red, blue and black 5 5

1968 (17 July). *Wheat Revolution. P* 13.
566 **523** 20 p. bluish green and orange-brown .. 5 5

524 "Self-portrait"

525 Lakshminath Bezbaruah

(Des from self-portrait)

1968 (17 Sept). *30th Death Anniv of Gaganendranath Tagore (painter). P* 13.
567 **524** 20 p. brown-purple and ochre 5 8

1968 (5 Oct). *Birth Centenary of Lakshminath Bezbaruah (writer). P* 13½ × 14.
568 **525** 20 p. blackish brown 10 5

526 Athlete's Legs and Olympic Rings

1968 (12 Oct). *Olympic Games, Mexico. P* 14½ × 14.

569	526	20 p. brown and grey	15	5
570		1 r. sepia and brown-olive	40	25

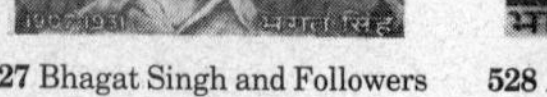

527 Bhagat Singh and Followers

528 Azad Hind Flag, Swords and Chandra Bose (founder)

1968 (19 Oct). *61st Birth Anniv of Bhagat Singh (revolutionary). P* 13.

571	527	20 p. yellow-brown	5	5

1968 (21 Oct). *25th Anniv of Azad Hind Government. P* 14 × 14½.

572	528	20 p. deep blue	5	5

529 Sister Nivedita

530 Marie Curie and Radium Treatment

1968 (27 Oct). *Birth Centenary of Sister Nivedita. P* 14 × 14½.

573	529	20 p. deep bluish green	5	8

1968 (6 Nov). *Birth Centenary of Marie Curie. P* 14½ × 14.

574	530	20 p. slate-lilac	30	10

531 Map of the World

532 Cochin Synagogue

1968 (1 Dec). *21st International Geographical Congress. P* 13.

575	531	20 p. new blue	8	5

1968 (15 Dec). *400th Anniv of Cochin Synagogue. P* 13.

576	532	20 p. blue and carmine	15	8

533 I.N.S. *Nilgiri*

534 Red-billed Blue Magpie

1968 (15 Dec). *Navy Day. P* 13.

577	533	20 p. grey-blue	25	10

1968 (31 Dec). *Birds. T* **534** *and similar designs. P* 14 × 14½ (1 *r.*) *or* 14½ × 14 (*others*).

578	20 p. multicoloured	40	10
579	50 p. scarlet, black and turquoise-green	95	25
580	1 r. deep blue, yellow-brown and pale blue	1·50	80
581	2 r. multicoloured	1·60	1·40

Designs: *Horiz*—50 p. Brown-fronted Pied Woodpecker; 2 r. Yellow-backed Slaty-headed Sunbird. *Vert*—1 r. Scimitar Babbler.

538 Bankim Chandra Chatterjee

539 Dr. Bhagavan Das

1969 (1 Jan). *130th Birth Anniv of Bankim Chandra Chatterjee (writer). P* 13½.

582	538	20 p. ultramarine	5	5

1969 (12 Jan). *Death Centenary of Dr. Bhagavan Das (philosopher). P* 13½.

583	539	20 p. pale chocolate	5	5

540 Dr. Martin Luther King

541 Mirza Ghalib and Letter Seal

1969 (25 Jan). *Martin Luther King Commemoration. P* 13½.

584	540	20 p. deep olive-brown	5	5

1969 (17 Feb). *Death Centenary of Mirza Ghalib (poet). P* 14½ × 14.

585	541	20 p. sepia, brown-red and flesh	5	5

542 Osmania University

1969 (15 Mar). *50th Anniv of Osmania University. P* 14½ × 14.

586	542	20 p. olive-green	5	5

543 Rafi Ahmed Kidwai

1969 (1 Apr). *20th Anniv of "ALL-UP" Air Mail Scheme. P* 13.

587	543	20 p. deep blue	5	5

544 I.L.O. Badge and Emblem

545 Memorial, and Hands dropping Flowers

1969 (11 Apr). *50th Anniv of International Labour Organisation. P* 14½ × 14.

588	544	20 p. chestnut	5	5

1969 (13 Apr). *50th Anniv of Jallianwala Bagh Massacre. P* 14 × 13½.

589	545	20 p. rose-carmine	5	5

546 Shri Nageswara Rao (patriot)

547 Ardaseer Cursetjee Wadia, and Ships

1969 (1 May). *Kasinadhuni Nageswara Rao Pantulu Commemoration. P* 13½ × 14.

590	546	20 p. brown	5	5

1969 (27 May). *Ardaseer Cursetjee Wadia (ship building engineer). P* 14½ × 14.

591	547	20 p. turquoise-green	10	5

548 Serampore College

549 Dr. Zakir Husain

1969 (7 June). *150th Anniv of Serampore College. P* 13½.

592	548	20 p. plum	5	5

1969 (11 June). *President Dr. Zakir Husain (patriot) Commemoration. P* 13.

593	549	20 p. sepia	5	5

550 Laxmanrao Kirloskar

1969 (20 June). *Birth Centenary of Laxmanrao Kirloskar (agriculturalist). P* 13.

594	550	20 p. grey-black	5	5

551 Gandhi and his Wife

552 Gandhi's Head and Shoulders

553 Gandhi walking (woodcut)

554 Gandhi with Charkha

(Des Suraj Sadan (20 p.), P. Chitnis (75 p.), Indian Security Press (1 r.) and C. Pakrashi (5 r.))

1969 (2 Oct). *Birth Centenary of Mahatma Gandhi. P* 13½ × 14 (20 *p.*), 14 × 14½ (1 *r.*) *or* 13 (*others*).

595	551	20 p. blackish brown	20	5
596	552	75 p. cinnamon and drab	85	30
597	553	1 r. blue	1·00	60
598	554	5 r. greyish brown and red-orange	4·00	3·75

555 Oil Tanker and I.M.C.O. Emblem

1969 (14 Oct). *10th Anniv of Inter-Governmental Maritime Consultative Organization. P* 13.

599	555	20 p. violet-blue	20	10

556 Outline of Parliament Building and Globe

557 Astronaut walking beside Space Module on Moon

1969 (30 Oct). *57th Inter-Parliamentary Conference, New Delhi. P* 14½ × 14.

600	556	20 p. new blue	5	5

1969 (19 Nov). *First Man on the Moon. P* 14 × 14½.

601	557	20 p. olive-brown	5	5

558 "Shri Nankana Sahib Gurudwara"

559 Tiger's Head and Hands holding Globe

1969 (23 Nov). *500th Birth Anniv of Guru Nanak. P* 13½.

602	558	20 p. slate-violet	8	5

1969 (24 Nov). *International Union for the Conservation of Nature and Natural Resources Conference, New Delhi. P* 14½ × 14.

603	559	20 p. orange-brown and bronze-green	15	8

560 Sadhu Vaswani

561 Thakkar Bapa

1969 (25 Nov). *90th Birth Anniv of Sadhu Vaswani (educationist). P* 14 × 14½.
604 **560** 20 p. grey 5 5

1969 (29 Nov). *Birth Centenary of Thakkar Bapa (humanitarian). P* 13½.
605 **561** 20 p. chocolate 5 5

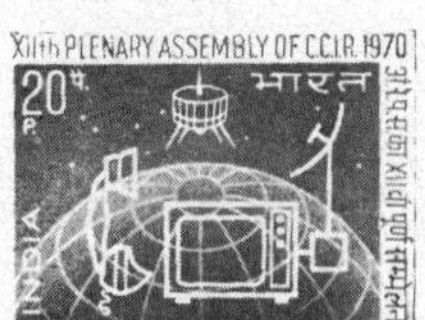

562 Satellite, Television, Telephone and Globe

563 Thiru Annadurai

1970 (21 Jan). *12th Plenary Assembly of International Radio Consultative Committee. P* 13.
606 **562** 20 p. Prussian blue 5 5

1970 (3 Feb). *First Death Anniv of Thiru Annadurai (statesman). P* 13.
607 **563** 20 p. reddish purple and royal blue . . 5 5

564 M. N. Kishore and Printing Press

565 Nalanda College

1970 (19 Feb). *Munshi Newal Kishore (publisher) Commemoration. P* 13.
608 **564** 20 p. lake 5 8

1970 (27 Mar). *Centenary of Nalanda College. P* 14½ × 14.
609 **565** 20 p. brown 10 8

566 Swami Shraddhanand (social reformer)

567 Lenin

1970 (30 Mar). *Swami Shraddhanand Commemoration. P* 14 × 13½.
610 **566** 20 p. yellow-brown 10 5

1970 (22 Apr). *Birth Centenary of Lenin. P* 13.
611 **567** 20 p. orange-brown and sepia 10 5

568 New U.P.U. H.Q. Building

569 Sher Shah Suri (15th-century ruler)

1970 (20 May). *New U.P.U. Headquarters Building. P* 13.
612 **568** 20 p. emerald, grey and black 8 8

1970 (22 May). *Sher Shah Suri Commemoration. P* 13.
613 **569** 20 p. deep bluish green 8 8

570 V. D. Savarkar (patriot) and Cellular Jail

571 "UN" and Globe

1970 (28 May). *V. D. Savarkar Commemoration. P* 13.
614 **570** 20 p. orange-brown 5 8

1970 (26 June). *25th Anniv of United Nations. P* 13.
615 **571** 20 p. light new blue 5 5

572 Symbol and Workers

1970 (18 Aug). *Asian Productivity Year. P* 14½ × 14.
616 **572** 20 p. violet 5 8

573 Dr. Montessori and I.E.Y. Emblem

1970 (31 Aug). *Birth Centenary of Dr. Maria Montessori (educationist). P* 13.
617 **573** 20 p. dull purple 5 5

574 J. N. Mukherjee (revolutionary) and Horse

575 V. S. Srinivasa Sastri

1970 (9 Sept). *Jatindra Nath Mukherjee Commemoration. P* 14½ × 14.
618 **574** 20 p. chocolate 5 8

1970 (22 Sept). *Srinivasa Sastri (educationist). P* 13 × 13½.
619 **575** 20 p. yellow and brown-purple 5 5

576 I. C. Vidyasagar

577 Maharishi Valmiki

1970 (26 Sept). *50th Birth Anniv of I. C. Vidyasagar (educationist). P* 13.
620 **576** 20 p. brown and purple 5 5

1970 (14 Oct). *Maharishi Valmiki (holy poet). P* 13.
621 **577** 20 p. purple 5 8

578 Calcutta Port

1970 (17 Oct). *Centenary of Calcutta Port Trust. P* 13½ × 13.
622 **578** 20 p. greenish blue 5 5

579 University Building

1970 (29 Oct). *50th Anniv of Jamia Millia Islamia University. P* 14½ × 14.
623 **579** 20 p. yellow-green 5 5

580 Jamnalal Bajaj

581 Nurse and Patient

1970 (4 Nov). *Jamnalal Bajaj (patriot). W* **374**. *P* 13½ × 13.
624 **580** 20 p. olive-grey 5 5

1970 (5 Nov). *50th Anniv of Indian Red Cross. W* **374** *(sideways). P* 13 × 13½.
625 **581** 20 p. red and greenish blue 10 5

582 Sant Namdeo

583 Beethoven

1970 (9 Nov). *700th Anniv of Sant (Saint) Namdeo. W* **374**. *P* 13.
626 **582** 20 p. orange 10 5

1970 (16 Dec). *Birth Bicentenary of Beethoven. P* 13.
627 **583** 20 p. orange and greyish black 12 5

584 Children examining Stamps

585 Girl Guide

1970 (23 Dec). *Indian National Philatelic Exhibition. T* **584** *and similar horiz design. P* 13.
628 20 p. orange and myrtle-green 10 8
629 1 r. orange-brown and pale yellow-brown . . 45 35
Design:—1 r. Gandhi commemorative through magnifier.

1970 (27 Dec). *Diamond Jubilee of Girl Guide Movement. P* 13.
630 **585** 20 p. maroon 10 5

586 Hands and Lamp (Emblem)

587 Vidyapith Building

1971 (11 Jan). *Indian Life Insurance. P* 13.
631 **586** 20 p. sepia and crimson 5 5

1971 (10 Feb). *Golden Jubilee of Kashi Vidyapith. P* 14½ × 14.
632 **587** 20 p. blackish brown 5 5

588 Saint Ravidas

589 C. F. Andrews

1971 (10 Feb). *Guru Ravidas (15th-cent Saint). P* 13.
633 **588** 20 p. lake 5 5

1971 (12 Feb). *Birth Centenary of Deenabandhu C. F. Andrews (philosopher). P* 13 × 13½.
634 **589** 20 p. chestnut 5 5

590 Acharya Narendra Deo (reformer)

591 Crowd and "100"

1971 (19 Feb). *15th Death Anniv of Acharya Narendra Deo. P* 13.
635 **590** 20 p. dull green 5 5

1971 (10 Mar). *Census Centenary. P* 13.
636 **591** 20 p. brown and blue 5 5

592 Sri Ramana Maharishi (mystic)

593 Raja Ravi Varma and "Damayanti and the Swan"

1971 (14 Apr). *21st Death Anniv of Ramana Maharishi. P* 13½.
637 **592** 20 p. orange and sepia 5 5

1971 (29 Apr). *65th Death Anniv of Ravi Varma (artist). P* 13.
638 **593** 20 p. green 5 5

594 Dadasaheb Phalke (cinematographer) and Camera

595 "Abhisarika" (Abanindranath Tagore)

1971 (30 Apr). *Birth Centenary of Dadasaheb Phalke. P* 13½ × 13.
639 **594** 20 p. deep maroon 10 5

1971 (7 Aug). *Abanindranath Tagore Commemoration. P* 14 × 14½.
640 **595** 20 p. grey, buff-yellow & blackish brown 5 5

596 Swami Virjanand (Vedic scholar)

597 Cyrus the Great and Procession

1971 (14 Sept). *Swami Virjanand Commemoration. P* 13½.
641 **596** 20 p. chestnut 5 5

1971 (12 Oct). *2500th Anniv of Charter of Cyrus the Great. P* 13.
642 **597** 20 p. blackish brown 10 5

598 Globe and Money Box

1971 (31 Oct). *World Thrift Day. P* 14½ × 14.
643 **598** 20 p. blue-grey 5 5

599 Ajanta Caves Painting

600 Women at Work

1971 (4 Nov). *25th Anniv of U.N.E.S.C.O. P* 13.
644 **599** 20 p. red-brown 15 5

(Des from painting by Geeta Gupta)

1971 (14 Nov). *Children's Day. P* 14 × 14½.
645 **600** 20 p. scarlet 5 5

शरणार्थी सहायता REFUGEE RELIEF
(601)

Refugee Relief
(602)

शरणार्थी सहायता REFUGEE RELIEF
(603)

REFUGEE RELIEF
(604)

REFUGEE RELIEF
(605)

Refugee Relief
(606)

Refugee relief
(606*a*)

शरणार्थी सहायता Refugee Relief
(606*b*)

607 Refugees

1971. *Obligatory Tax. Refugee Relief.*

(*a*) *Provisional issues. No.* 506 *variously optd*

(i) *For all India, optd at Nasik*
646 **601** 5 p. cerise (15 Nov) 5 5
a. Opt double . . . . 7·00

(ii) *For various areas*
647 **602** 5 p. Bangalore 40 15
a. Opt double, one inverted . . . .
648 **603** 5 p. Jaipur 90 20
649 **604** 5 p. Rajasthan 90 20
a. Error. "RELIEF REFUGEE" . . 12·00
b. Opt inverted . . . .
650 **605** 5 p. New Delhi 80 20
a. Opt inverted . . . . 4·00
650*b* **606** 5 p. Goa . . . . 2·25 50
650*c* **606*a*** 5 p. Jabalpur . . . .
650*d* **606*b*** 5 p. Alwar . . . .

(*b*) *Definitive issue. W* **374**. *P* 14 × 14½
651 **607** 5 p. carmine (1 Dec) 5 5

From 15 November 1971 and 31 March 1973, the Indian Government levied a 5 p. surcharge on all mail, except postcards and newspapers, for the relief of refugees from the former East Pakistan.

As supplies of the provisional overprint could not be sent to all Indian post offices in time, local postmasters were authorised to make their own overprints. Most of these were applied by rubber stamps and so we do not list them. Those listed have typographed overprints and No. 649 also has a rubber handstamp in native language. Some of the above overprints were also used in areas other than those where they were produced.

608 C. V. Raman (scientist) and Jewel

1971 (21 Nov). *Dr. C. V. Raman Commemoration. P* 13.
652 **608** 20 p. orange and deep brown 5 5

609 Visva Bharati Building and Rabindranath Tagore (pioneer)

1971 (24 Dec). *Golden Jubilee of Visva Bharati. P* 14½ × 14.
653 **609** 20 p. sepia and yellow-brown 5 5

610 Cricketers

611 Map and Satellite

1971 (30 Dec). *Indian Cricket Victories. P* 14½ × 14.
654 **610** 20 p. green, myrtle-green and sage-green 75 30

1972 (26 Feb). *Arvi Satellite Earth Station. P* 13½.
655 **611** 20 p. plum 10 5

OMNIBUS ISSUES

Details, together with prices for complete sets, of the various Omnibus issues from the 1935 Silver Jubilee series to date are included in a special section following Zululand at the end of the catalogue.

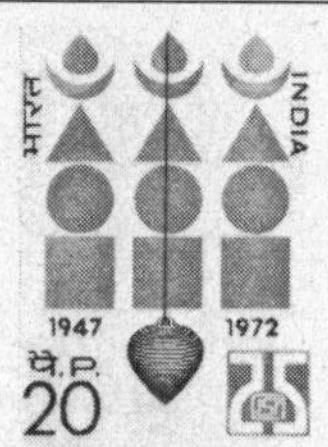

612 Elemental Symbols and Plumb-line

613 Signal-box Panel

1972 (29 May). *Silver Jubilee of Indian Standards Institution. P* 13.
656 **612** 20 p. turquoise-grey and black 5 5

1972 (30 June). *50th Anniv of International Railways Union. P* 13.
657 **613** 20 p. multicoloured 30 20

614 Hockey-player

615 Symbol of Sri Aurobindo

1972 (10 Aug). *Olympic Games, Munich. T* **614** *and similar horiz design. P* 13.
658 20 p. deep bluish violet 15 5
659 1 r. 45, light turquoise-green & brown-lake 90 1·25
Design:—1 r. 45, Various sports.

1972 (15 Aug). *Birth Centenary of Sri Aurobindo. P* 13½.
660 **615** 20 p. yellow and new blue 5 5

616 Celebrating Independence Day in front of Parliament

617 Inter-Services Crest

1972 (15 Aug). *25th Anniversary of Independence (1st issue). P* 13.
661 **616** 20 p. multicoloured 10 5
See also Nos. 673/4.

1972 (15 Aug). *Defence Services Commemoration. P* 13.
662 **617** 20 p. multicoloured 20 10

618 V. O. Chidambaram Pillai (lawyer and politician) and Ship

619 Bhai Vir Singh

1972 (5 Sept). *Birth Centenary of V. O. Chidambaram Pillai. P* 13.
663 **618** 20 p. new blue and purple-brown 20 10

1972 (16 Oct). *Birth Centenary of Bhai Vir Singh (poet and saint). P* 13.
664 **619** 20 p. plum 5 5

620 T. Prakasam

621 Vemana

1972 (16 Oct). *Birth Centenary of T. Prakasam (lawyer). P* 13.
665 **620** 20 p. brown 5 5

1972 (16 Oct). *300th Birth Anniv of Vemana (poet). W* **374**. *P* 13½ × 14.
666 **621** 20 p. black 5 5

622 Bertrand Russell **623** Symbol of "Asia 72"

1972 (16 Oct). *Birth Centenary of Bertrand Russell (philosopher). P* 13½ × 14.
667 **622** 1 r. 45, black . . . . 85 1·00

1972 (3 Nov). *"Asia '72" (Third Asian International Trade Fair). T* **623** *and similar vert design. W* **374**. *P* 13.
668 20 p. black and orange. 12 10
669 1 r. 45, orange and slate-black 55 80
Design:—1 r. 45, Hand of Buddha.

624 V. A. Sarabhai and Rocket **625** Flag of U.S.S.R. and Kremlin Tower

1972 (30 Dec). *First Death Anniv of Vikram A. Sarabhai (scientist). P* 13.
670 **624** 20 p. brown and myrtle-green 5 5

1972 (30 Dec). *50th Anniv of U.S.S.R. P* 13.
671 **625** 20 p. light yellow and red 5 5

626 Exhibition Symbol **627** "Democracy"

1973 (8 Jan). *"Indipex '73" Stamp Exhibition (1st issue). P* 13.
672 **626** 1 r. 45, light mauve, gold and black . . 45 60
See also Nos. 701/**MS**704.

1973 (26 Jan). *25th Anniv of Independence (2nd issue). T* **627** *and similar multicoloured design. P* 13 (20 *p.*) *or* 14½ × 14 (1 *r.* 45).
673 20 p. Type **627** 12 10
674 1 r. 45, "Gnat" fighters over India Gate (38 × 20 *mm*) 75 90

628 Sri Ramakrishna Paramahamsa (religious leader) **629** Postal Corps Emblem

1973 (18 Feb). *Sri Ramakrishna Paramahamsa Commemoration. P* 13.
675 **628** 20 p. light brown 10 10

1973 (1 Mar). *First Anniv of Army Postal Service Corps. P* 13.
676 **629** 20 p. deep ultramarine and vermilion . . 25 15

630 Flag and Map of Bangladesh **631** Kumaran Asan

(Des C. Pakrashi)

1973 (10 Apr). *"Jai Bangla" (Inauguration of First Bangladesh Parliament). P* 13.
677 **630** 20 p. multicoloured 10 10

1973 (12 Apr). *Birth Centenary of Kumaran Asan (writer and poet). P* 13.
678 **631** 20 p. sepia 15 20

632 Flag and Flames **633** Dr. B. R. Ambedkar (social thinker and agitator)

(Des C. Pakrashi)

1973 (13 Apr). *Homage to Martyrs for Independence. P* 13.
679 **632** 20 p. multicoloured 10 10

(Des Charanjit Lal)

1973 (14 Apr). *Ambedkar Commemoration. P* 13.
680 **633** 20 p. bronze-green and deep purple . . 10 15

634 "Radha-Kishangarh" (Nihal Chand) **635** The Himalayas

1973 (5 May). *Indian Miniature Paintings. T* **634** *and similar vert designs. Multicoloured. P* 13.
681 20 p. Type **634** 20 15
682 50 p. "Dance Duet" (Aurangzeb's period) . . 50 45
683 1 r. "Lovers on a Camel" (Nasir-ud-din) . . 1·25 1·50
684 2 r. "Chained Elephant" (Zain-al-Abidin) . . 1·75 2·00

1973 (15 May). *15th Anniv of Indian Mountaineering Foundation. P* 13.
685 **635** 20 p. blue 20 20

636 Tail of Boeing "747" **637** Cross, Church of St. Thomas' Mount, Madras

(Des Air-India Art Studies from photograph by Jehangir Gazdar)

1973 (8 June). *25th Anniv of Air-India's International Services. P* 13.
686 **636** 1 r. 45, indigo and carmine-red . . 1·00 1·25

1973 (3 July). *19th Death Centenary of St. Thomas. P* 13.
687 **637** 20 p. blue-grey and agate 8 12

638 Michael Madhusudan Dutt (poet—Death Centenary) **639** A. O. Hume

1973 (21 July). *Centenaries. T* **638** *and similar horiz designs. P* 13.
688 20 p. sage-green and orange-brown 10 15
a. Orange-brown omitted £300
689 30 p. red-brown 12 20
690 50 p. deep brown 25 35
691 1 r. dull violet and orange-vermilion . . . 50 65
Designs:—30 p. V. D. Paluskar (musician—Birth Centenary); 50 p. Dr. Hansen (Centenary of discovery of leprosy bacillus); 1 r. Nicolaus Copernicus (astronomer—Fifth Birth Centenary).

1973 (31 July). *A. O. Hume Commemoration. P* 13.
692 **639** 20 p. grey 10 15

640 Gandhi and Nehru **641** R. C. Dutt

(Des C. Pakrashi from photograph)

1973 (15 Aug). *Gandhi and Nehru Commemoration. P* 13.
693 **640** 20 p. multicoloured 10 5

1973 (27 Sept). *R. C. Dutt Commemoration. P* 13.
694 **641** 20 p. brown 10 15

642 K. S. Ranjitsinhji **643** Vithalbhai Patel (nationalist)

1973 (27 Sept). *K. S. Ranjitsinhji Commemoration. P* 13.
695 **642** 30 p. myrtle-green 80 60

1973 (27 Sept). *Vithalbhai Patel Commemoration. P* 13.
696 **643** 50 p. light red-brown 10 15

644 President's Bodyguard **645** Interpol Emblem

1973 (30 Sept). *Bicentenary of President's Bodyguard. P* 13.
697 **644** 20 p. multicoloured 30 20

1973 (9 Oct). *50th Anniv of Interpol. P* 13.
698 **645** 20 p. brown 25 10

646 Syed Ahmad Khan (social reformer) **647** "Children at Play" (detail, Bela Raval)

1973 (17 Oct). *Syed Ahmad Khan Commemoration. P* 13.
699 **646** 20 p. sepia 10 15

1973 (14 Nov). *Children's Day. P* 13.
700 **647** 20 p. multicoloured 15 10

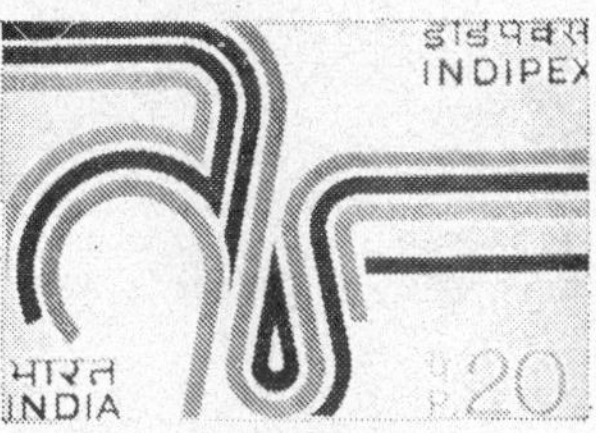

648 Indipex Emblem

1973 (14 Nov). *"Indipex '73" Philatelic Exhibition, New Delhi (2nd issue). T* **648** *and similar multicoloured designs. P* 13½ × 13 (2 *r.*) *or* 13 × 13½ *(others).*
701 20 p. Type **648** 15 25
702 1 r. Ceremonial elephant and 1½ a. stamp of 1947 (*vert*) . . . . . . 90 1·00
703 2 r. Common Peafowl (*vert*) . . . . 1·40 1·50
MS704 127 × 127 mm. Nos. 672 and 701/3. Imperf 4·75 5·50

NEW INFORMATION

The editor is always interested to correspond with people who have new information that will improve or correct the Catalogue.

649 Emblem of National Cadet Corps

650 Chakravarti Rajagopalachari (statesman)

1973 (25 Nov). *Silver Jubilee of National Cadet Corps. P* 13.
705 **649** 20 p. multicoloured 20 10

1973 (25 Dec). *C. Rajagopalachari Commemoration. P* 13.
706 **650** 20 p. olive-brown 10 10

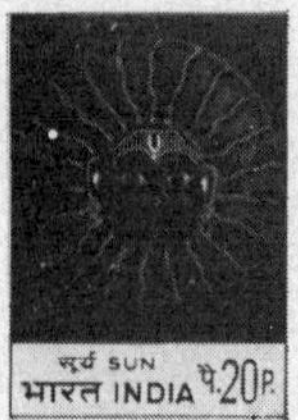

651 "Sun" Mask

652 Chhatrapati

1974 (15 Apr). *Indian Masks. T* **651** *and similar multicoloured designs. P* 13.
707 20 p. Type **651** 10 5
708 50 p. "Moon" mask 25 20
709 1 r. "Narasimha" 70 70
710 2 r. "Ravana" (*horiz*) .. .. 1·25 1·50
MS711 109 × 135 mm. Nos. 707/10 .. .. 3·75 4·00

1974 (2 June). *300th Anniv of Coronation of Chhatrapati Shri Shivaji Maharaj (patriot and ruler). P* 13.
712 **652** 25 p. multicoloured 15 5

653 Maithili Sharan Gupta (poet)

654 Kandukuri Veeresalingam (reformer)

1974 (3 July). *Indian Personalities* (1*st series*). *T* **653** *and similar vert designs. P* 13.
713 25 p. chestnut 15 20
714 25 p. deep brown 15 20
715 25 p. sepia 15 20
Portraits:—No. 714, Jainarain Vyas (politician and journalist); No. 715, Utkal Gourab Madhusudan Das (social reformer).

1974 (15 July). *Indian Personalities* (2*nd series*). *T* **654** *and similar vert designs. P* 13.
716 25 p. lake-brown 15 15
717 50 p. dull purple 30 40
718 1 r. chestnut-brown 45 50
Portraits:—50 p. Tipu Sultan (patriot); 1 r. Max Mueller (Sanskrit scholar).

655 Kamala Nehru

(Des Charanjit Lal)

1974 (1 Aug). *Kamala Nehru Commemoration. P* 14½ × 14.
719 **655** 25 p. multicoloured 10 15

656 W. P. Y. Emblem

1974 (14 Aug). *World Population Year. P* 13½.
720 **656** 25 p. maroon and buff 5 5

LARGE STAR AND INDIA GOVT WATERMARK. Two types exist of this sheet watermark. The initial arrangement resulted in the stars appearing upright, inverted and sideways, in either direction, within the same sheet.

Printings issued from the beginning of 1980 shows a second type on which the stars in each sheet all point in the same direction. All commemoratives with this watermark used the second type.

657 Chital

657b Bidri Vase

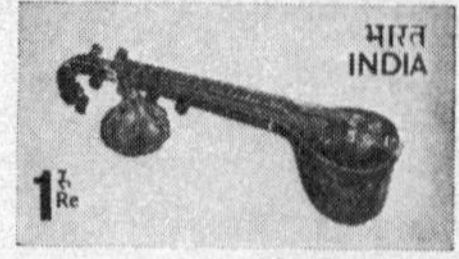

657a Vina

Two types of No. 732:

25 गांधीजी GANDHIJI　　25 गांधीजी GANDHIJI

I　　II

Type I. Left shoulder cut square. Top of Hindi inscription aligns with edge of shoulder.

Type II. Shoulder ends in point. Top of English inscription aligns with edge of shoulder. Portrait redrawn slightly smaller.

Two types of No. 736:

I　　II

Type I. "INDIA" inscription falls below foot of main design. Distance between foot of "2" in face value and top of Hindi inscription 11 mm.

Type II. "INDIA" above foot of design. Distance between "2" and inscription 10½ mm. Inscription redrawn slightly smaller.

1974 (20 Aug)–**83**. *P* 14 × 14½ (10, 20, 50 *p.*) *or* 14½ × 14 (*others*).

(*a*) *Various designs with values expressed with* "p" *or* "Re" *as T* **657***a*. *W* **374** (*sideways*)
721 – 15 p. blackish brown (deep background) (1.10.74) 30 5
722 **657** 25 p. sepia (20.8.74) 45 5
　a. Imperf (pair)
723 **657a** 1 r. red-brown and black (1.10.74) .. 1·50 30
　a. Black (face value and inscr) omitted

(*b*) *Various designs with values expressed in numerals only as in T* **657***b*

(i) *Wmk Large Star and* "INDIA GOVT" *in sheet**
724 **657b** 2 p. red-brown (*photo*) (1.11.76) .. 5 5
724*a* 2 p. pale reddish brown (*litho*) (15.3.79) 5 5
725 – 5 p. cerise (as No. 506) (1.11.76) .. 5 5
727 **466** 10 p. new blue (5.7.79) 5 5

(ii) *W* **374** (*sideways on* 15, 25, 30, 60 *p.*, 1, 2, 5, 10 *r.*)
729 **466** 10 p. new blue (1.11.76) 5 5
730 – 15 p. blackish brown (light background) (15.7.75) 10 5
731 – 20 p. deep dull green (15.7.75) 5 5
　a. Imperf (horiz pair) .. .. ..
732 – 25 p. reddish brown (I) (1978) 10 5
　a. Type II (5.79) .. .. ..
732*b* – 30 p. sepia (as No. 512) (1.5.79) 10 5
733 – 50 p. deep violet (15.7.75) 10 5
734 – 60 p. deep grey (as No. 515) (1.11.76) .. 15 8
735 **657a** 1 r. red-brown and grey-black (15.7.75) 30 12
736 – 2 r. violet and blackish brown (I) (15.7.75) 80 25
　a. Type II (1977) 80 25
737 – 5 r. deep slate-violet and brown (as No. 519) (1.11.76) 85 55
738 – 10 r. slate and bronze-green (as No. 520) (1.11.76) .. .. 1·10 1·10
　b. Perf 12½ × 13 (22.10.83) .. .. 1·10 1·10
721/38 .. .. *Set of* 18 5·50 2·75

Designs: *Vert as T* **657**, **657***b*:—15 p. Tiger; 25 p. Gandhi. *Horiz* (20 × 17 *mm*)—20 p. Handicrafts toy; 50 p. Demoiselle Crane in flight. *Horiz as T* **657***a*:—2 r. Himalayas.

*See note below No. 720. Nos. 724*a* and 727 exist on both types of watermark, Nos. 724 and 725 on the first type only.

No. 724*a* can be easily identified by the background of horizontal lines.

For stamps as No. 732, but with face value changed to 30 p., 35 p. or 50 p. see Nos. 968, 979 and 1073.

The 2 r. value with the blackish brown omitted is a chemically produced fake.

658 President Giri

659 U.P.U. Emblem

(Des Charanjit Lal)

1974 (24 Aug). *Giri Commemoration. P* 13.
739 **658** 25 p. multicoloured 10 10

(Des C. Pakrashi (25 p.), A. Ramachandran (1 r.), Jyoti Bhatt (2 r.))

1974 (3 Oct). *Centenary of Universal Postal Union. T* **659** *and similar designs. P* 13.
740 25 p. violet-blue, royal blue and black .. 15 5
741 1 r. multicoloured .. .. 1·40 1·50
742 2 r. multicoloured .. .. 1·90 2·00
　a. Red (inscr etc) omitted .. ..
MS743 108 × 108 mm. Nos. 740/2 .. .. 4·75 6·00
Designs: *Horiz*—1 r. Birds and nest, "Madhubani" style. *Vert*—2 r. Arrows around globe.

660 Woman Flute-player (sculpture)

661 Nicholas Roerich (medallion by H. Dropsy)

(Des Benoy Sarkar)

1974 (9 Oct). *Mathura Museum. T* **660** *and similar vert design. P* 13½.
744 25 p. chestnut and blackish brown 20 10
　a. Horiz pair. Nos. 744/5 .. .. .. 40 50
745 25 p. chestnut and blackish brown 20 10
Design:—No. 745, Vidyadhara with garland.
Nos. 744/5 were printed together within the sheet, horizontally *se-tenant*.

1974 (9 Oct). *Birth Centenary of Professor Roerich. P* 13.
746 **661** 1 r. deep blue-green & greenish yellow 40 55

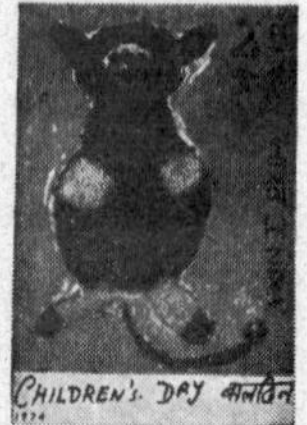

662 Pavapuri Temple

663 "Cat" (Rajesh Bhatia)

(Des Benoy Sarkar)

1974 (13 Nov). 2,500*th Anniv of Bhagwan Mahavira's attainment of Nirvana. P* 13.
747 **662** 25 p. indigo 15 10

1974 (14 Nov). *Children's Day. P* 13.
748 **663** 25 p. multicoloured 20 10

MINIMUM PRICE

The minimum price quoted is 5p which represents a handling charge rather than a basis for valuing common stamps. For further notes about prices see introductory pages.

664 Indian Dancers **665** Territorial Army Badge

(Des from painting by Amita Shah)

1974 (14 Nov). *25th Anniv of UNICEF in India. P* 14½ × 14.
749 **664** 25 p. multicoloured 20 10
a. Black (name, value and background) omitted £200

(Des Benoy Sarkar)

1974 (16 Nov). *25th Anniv of Indian Territorial Army. P* 13.
750 **665** 25 p. black, bright yellow and emerald .. 30 10

666 Krishna as Gopal Bal with Cows (Rajasthan painting on cloth) **667** Symbols and Child's Face

1974 (2 Dec). *19th International Dairy Congress, New Delhi. P* 13½.
751 **666** 25 p. brown-purple and brown-ochre .. 15 10

(Des Benoy Sarkar)

1974 (8 Dec). *Help for Retarded Children. P* 13.
752 **667** 25 p. red-orange and black 10 10

668 Marconi **669** St. Francis Xavier's Shrine

1974 (12 Dec). *Birth Centenary of Guglielmo Marconi (radio pioneer). P* 13.
753 **668** 2 r. deep slate .. .. 90 1·25

1974 (24 Dec). *St Francis Xavier Celebration. P* 13.
754 **669** 25 p. multicoloured 10 10

670 Saraswati (Deity of Language and Learning) **671** Parliament House, New Delhi

1975 (10 Jan). *World Hindi Convention, Nagpur. P* 14 × 14½.
755 **670** 25 p. slate and carmine-red 15 10
For similar stamp see No. 761.

1975 (26 Jan). *25th Anniv of Republic. P* 13.
756 **671** 25 p. grey-black, silver and azure .. 15 10

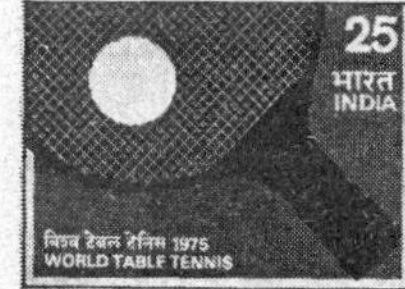

672 Table-tennis Bat

1975 (6 Feb). *World Table-tennis Championships, Calcutta. P* 13.
757 **672** 25 p. black, vermilion and yellow-olive 20 10

673 "Equality, Development and Peace" **674** Stylised Cannon

(Des Shyama Sarabhai)

1975 (16 Feb). *International Women's Year. P* 13.
758 **673** 25 p. multicoloured 15 10

(Des Benoy Sarkar)

1975 (8 Apr). *Bicentenary of Indian Army Ordnance Corps. P* 13.
759 **674** 25 p. multicoloured 25 15

675 Arya Samaj Emblem **676** Saraswati

1975 (11 Apr). *Centenary of Arya Samaj Movement. P* 13.
760 **675** 25 p. light red-orange & brownish black 15 10

1975 (12 Apr). *World Telugu Language Conference, Hyderabad. P* 14 × 14½.
761 **676** 25 p. black and deep bluish green .. 15 10

677 Satellite "Aryabhata"

1975 (20 Apr). *Launch of First Indian Satellite. P* 13.
762 **677** 25 p. lt blue, deep indigo & dull purple .. 20 10

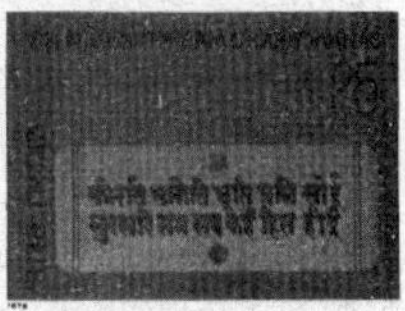

678 Blue-winged Pitta **679** "Ramcharitmanas" (poem by Goswami Tulsidas)

(Des J. P. Irani)

1975 (28 Apr). *Indian Birds. T* **678** *and similar multicoloured designs. P* 13.
763 25 p. Type **678** 25 10
764 50 p. Asian Black-headed Oriole 50 35
765 1 r. Western Tragopan (*vert*) .. .. .. 1·25 1·50
766 2 r. Himalayan Monal Pheasant (*vert*) .. 1·75 2·00

(Des R. K. Joshi)

1975 (24 May). *Ramcharitmanas Commemoration. P* 13.
767 **679** 25 p. black, orange-yellow & vermilion .. 15 10

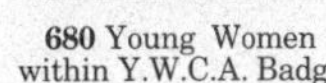

680 Young Women within Y.W.C.A. Badge **681** "The Creation"

(Des Benoy Sarkar)

1975 (20 June). *Centenary of Indian Y.W.C.A. P* 13.
768 **680** 25 p. multicoloured 15 10

1975 (28 June). *500th Birth Anniv of Michelangelo. T* **681** *and similar designs showing "Creation" frescoes from Sistine Chapel. P* 14 × 13½.
769 50 p. multicoloured 35 40
a. Block of 4. Nos 769/72 .. .. .. 1·40
ab. Black (inscr & face value) omitted ..
770 50 p. multicoloured 35 40
771 50 p. multicoloured 35 40
772 50 p. multicoloured 35 40

T **681** illustrates No. 769. Nos. 770 and 772 are horizontal designs, size 49 × 34 mm.

Nos. 769/72 were printed in *se-tenant* blocks of four within the sheet, forming two composite designs in horizontal pairs.

682 Commission Emblem **683** Stylised Ground Antenna

1975 (28 July). *25th Anniv of International Commission on Irrigation and Drainage. P* 13½.
773 **682** 25 p. multicoloured 15 10

(Des Benoy Sarkar)

1975 (1 Aug). *Satellite Instructional Television Experiment. P* 13.
774 **683** 25 p. multicoloured 15 10

684 St. Arunagirinathar **685** Commemorative Text

1975 (14 Aug). *600th Birth Anniv of St. Arunagirinathar. P* 13½.
775 **684** 50 p. dull purple and slate-black .. 45 45

1975 (26 Aug). *Namibia Day. P* 13½.
776 **685** 25 p. grey-black and rose-red 15 10

686 Mir Anees (poet) **687** Memorial Temple to Ahilyabai Holkar (ruler)

1975 (4 Sept). *Indian Celebrities. P* 13½ (*No.* 777) *or* 13 (*No.* 778).
777 **686** 25 p. blackish green 15 15
778 **687** 25 p. chestnut 15 15

688 Bharata Natyam **689** Ameer Khusrau

1975 (20 Oct). *Indian Dances. T* **688** *and similar vert designs. Multicoloured. P* 13.
779 25 p. Type **688** 20 5
780 50 p. Orissi 40 20
781 75 p. Kathak 50 20
782 1 r. Kathakali 75 75
783 1 r. 50, Kuchipudi .. .. 1·25 1·50
784 2 r. Manipuri .. .. 1·50 2·00
779/84 .. .. *Set of* 6 4·25 4·25

1975 (24 Oct). *650th Death of Anniv of Ameer Khusrau (poet). P* 13.
785 **689** 50 p. reddish brown and buff 15 10

690 V. K. Krishna Menon **691** Text of Poem

1975 (24 Oct). *First Death Anniv of V. K. Krishna Menon (statesman). P* 13 × 13½.
786 **690** 25 p. olive 15 10

(Des R. K. Joshi)

1975 (24 Oct). *Birth Bicentenary of Bahadur Shah Zafar. P* 13½ × 13.
787 **691** 1 r. black, stone and yellow-brown .. 55 70

692 Sansadiya Soudha, New Delhi

693 V. Patel

1975 (28 Oct). *21st Commonwealth Parliamentary Conference, New Delhi. P* 14½ × 14.
788 **692** 2 r. olive .. .. 95 1·25

1975 (31 Oct). *Birth Centenary of Vallabhbhai Patel (statesman). P* 13 × 13½.
789 **693** 25 p. slate-green 15 10

694 N. C. Bardoloi

695 "Cow" (drawing by Sanjay Nathubhai Patel)

1975 (3 Nov). *Birth Centenary of Nabin Chandra Bardoloi (politician). P* 13 × 13½.
790 **694** 25 p. reddish brown 15 10

1975 (14 Nov). *Children's Day. P* 13½ × 13.
791 **695** 25 p. multicoloured 15 10

696 Printing Works, Nasik Road

697 Gurdwara Sisganj (site of martyrdom)

1975 (13 Dec). *50th Anniv of India Security Press. P* 13.
792 **696** 25 p. multicoloured 15 10

1975 (16 Dec). *Tercentenary of the Martyrdom of Guru Tegh Bahadur. P* 13.
793 **697** 25 p. multicoloured 15 10

698 Theosophical Society Emblem

699 Weather Cock

1975 (20 Dec). *Centenary of the Theosophical Society. P* 13.
794 **698** 25 p. multicoloured 15 10

(Des Benoy Sarkar)

1975 (24 Dec). *Centenary of the Indian Meteorological Department. P* 13 × 13½.
795 **699** 25 p. multicoloured 20 10

700 Early Mail Cart

701 L. N. Mishra (politician)

(Des Benoy Sarkar)

1975 (25 Dec). *"Inpex 75" National Philatelic Exhibition, Calcutta. T* **700** *and similar vert design. P* 13.
796 **700** 25 p. black and lake-brown 20 10
797 – 2 r. grey-brown, brown-purple & black 1·00 1·25
Design:—2 r. Indian Bishop Mark, 1775.

1976 (3 Jan). *1st Anniv of Mishra's Death. P* 13.
798 **701** 25 p. olive-sepia 15 10

702 Tiger

703 Painted Storks

1976 (24 Jan). *Birth Centenary of Jim Corbett (naturalist). P* 13.
799 **702** 25 p. multicoloured 25 10

(Des Charanjit Lal)

1976 (10 Feb). *Keoladeo Ghana Bird Sanctuary, Bharatpur. P* 13.
800 **703** 25 p. multicoloured 30 15

704 Vijayanta Tank

705 Alexander Graham Bell

1976 (4 Mar). *Bicentenary of 16th Light Cavalry Regt. P* 13.
801 **704** 25 p. multicoloured 30 15

1976 (10 Mar). *Alexander Graham Bell Commemoration. P* 13.
802 **705** 25 p. grey-black and yellow-ochre .. 20 10

706 Muthuswami Dikshitar

707 Eye and Red Cross

1976 (18 Mar). *Birth Bicentenary of Dikshitar (composer). P* 13½.
803 **706** 25 p. purple 15 10

(Des Benoy Sarkar)

1976 (7 Apr). *World Health Day. Prevention of Blindness. P* 13.
804 **707** 25 p. reddish brown and dull vermilion .. 20 10

708 "Industries"

709 Diesel Locomotive, 1963

(Des Benoy Sarkar)

1976 (30 Apr). *Industrial Development. P* 13.
805 **708** 25 p. multicoloured 10 10

1976 (15 May). *Locomotives. T* **709** *and similar horiz designs. Multicoloured. P* 14½ × 14.
806 25 p. Type **709** 25 5
807 50 p. Steam locomotive, 1895 .. .. .. 65 30
808 1 r. Steam locomotive, 1963 .. .. .. 1·40 1·00
809 2 r. Steam locomotive, 1853 .. .. .. 1·90 1·75

710 Nehru

711

712

Three types of Nehru portrait *(illustrated actual size)*
Type 710. Portrait measures 24 mm at base. First character above "NEHRU" has two prongs.
Type 711. Whole portrait is larger, measuring 25½ mm at base. Character above "NEHRU" has three prongs.
Type 712. Small portrait, 23 mm at base, with smaller inscription. Character above "NEHRU" has three prongs.

1976. *T* **710/12** *and similar vert design. W* **374**. *P* 13½.
810 **710** 25 p. dull violet (27.5.76) 25 25
810*a* **711** 25 p. dull violet (9.76) 25 25
810*b* **712** 25 p. dull violet (14.11.76) 25 25
811 – 25 p. red-brown (2.10.76) 25 25
a. Imperf (pair) .. .. ..
Design:—No. 811, Gandhi.
For these designs in a smaller size see Nos. 732, 968/9, 979/80 and 1073/4.

713 "Spirit of 76" (Willard)

714 K. Kamaraj (politician)

1976 (29 May). *Bicentenary of American Revolution. P* 13.
812 **713** 2 r. 80, multicoloured .. .. .. 1·10 1·10

1976 (15 July). *Kamaraj Commemoration. P* 13.
813 **714** 25 p. sepia 5 5

715 "Shooting"

716 Subhadra Kumari Chauhan (poetess)

(Des Gopi Gajwani (25 p., 1 r.), Sukumar Shankar (1 r. 50), India Security Press (2 r. 80))

1976 (17 July). *Olympic Games, Montreal. T* **715** *and similar vert designs. P* 13.
814 25 p. deep violet and vermilion 20 5
815 1 r. multicoloured 75 65
816 1 r. 50, deep mauve and grey-black .. 1·00 1·00
817 2 r. 80, multicoloured .. .. .. 1·40 1·60
Designs:—1 r. Shot-put; 1 r. 50, Hockey; 2 r. 80, Sprinting.

1976 (6 Aug). *S. K. Chauhan Commemoration. P* 13.
818 **716** 25 p. grey-blue 5 5

717 Param Vir Chakra Medal

718 University Building, Bombay

(Des Benoy Sarkar)

1976 (15 Aug). *Param Vir Chakra Commemoration. P* 13.
819 **717** 25 p. multicoloured 5 5

1976 (3 Sept). *50th Anniv of Shreemati Nathibai Damodar Thackersey Women's University. P* 13½.
820 **718** 25 p. bluish violet 5 5

719 Bharatendu Harischandra (poet) **720** S. C. Chatterji (writer)

1976 (9 Sept). *Harischandra Commemoration. P* 13.
821 **719** 25 p. agate 5 5

1976 (15 Sept). *Birth Centenary of S. C. Chatterji. P* 13.
822 **720** 25 p. grey-black 5 5

721 Planned Family **722** Maharaja Agrasen and Coins

(Des A. K. Nagar)

1976 (22 Sept). *Family Planning. P* 14 × 14½.
823 **721** 25 p. multicoloured 5 5

1976 (24 Sept). *Maharaja Agrasen. P* 13.
824 **722** 25 p. red-brown 5 5

723 Swamp Deer **724** Hands holding Hearts

(Des from photos by Rajesh Bedi)

1976 (1 Oct). *Wildlife. T* **723** *and similar multicoloured designs. P* 14 × 14½ (25, 50 *p.*) *or* 14½ × 14 (*others*).
825 25 p. Type **723** 20 15
826 50 p. Lion 60 50
827 1 r. Leopard (*horiz*) 75 90
828 2 r. Caracal (*horiz*) .. .. 1·25 1·60

(Des B. G. Varma)

1976 (1 Oct). *Voluntary Blood Donation. P* 13.
829 **724** 25 p. yellow-ochre, scarlet and black .. 5 5

725 Suryakant Tripathi ("Nirala") **726** Painting of Folk-tale (H. D. Bhatia)

1976 (15 Oct). *80th Birth Anniv of "Nirala" (poet and novelist). P* 13.
830 **725** 25 p. deep blue 5 5

1976 (14 Nov). *Children's Day. P* 13½ × 14.
831 **726** 25 p. multicoloured 5 5

OMNIBUS ISSUES

Details, together with prices for complete sets, of the various Omnibus issues from the 1935 Silver Jubilee series to date are included in a special section following Zululand at the end of the catalogue.

727 Hiralal Shastri (politician) **728** Dr. Hari Singh Gour (lawyer)

1976 (24 Nov). *Shastri Commemoration. P* 13.
832 **727** 25 p. sepia 5 5

1976 (26 Nov). *Dr. Gour Commemoration. P* 13.
833 **728** 25 p. deep reddish purple 5 5

729 A 300 B2 Airbus **730** Hybrid Coconut Palm

1976 (1 Dec). *Inauguration of Indian Airlines' Airbus. P* 14½ × 14.
834 **729** 2 r. multicoloured .. .. 95 1·25

1976 (27 Dec). *Diamond Jubilee of Coconut Research. P* 13.
835 **730** 25 p. multicoloured 5 5

731 First Stanza of *Vande Mataram* (patriotic song by B. C. Chatterjee)

1976 (30 Dec). *"Vande Mataram" Commemoration. P* 13.
836 **731** 25 p. multicoloured 5 5

732 Globe and Film Strip **733** Seismograph and Crack in Earth's Crust

1977 (3 Jan). *Sixth International Film Festival of India, New Delhi. P* 13.
837 **732** 2 r. multicoloured 70 85

1977 (10 Jan). *Sixth World Conference on Earthquake Engineering, New Delhi. P* 13.
838 **733** 2 r. deep plum .. .. 80 1·00

734 Tarun Ram Phookun **735** Paramahansa Yogananda (religious leader)

1977 (22 Jan). *Birth Centenary of Tarun Ram Phookun (politician). P* 13.
839 **734** 25 p. blackish brown 5 5

1977 (7 Mar). *Yogananda Commemoration. P* 13.
840 **735** 25 p. reddish orange 5 5

736 Asian Regional Red Cross Emblem **737** Fahkruddin Ali Ahmed

1977 (9 Mar). *First Asian Regional Red Cross Conference, New Delhi. P* 13.
841 **736** 2 r. pink, deep blue and scarlet.. .. 1·00 1·25

1977 (22 Mar). *Death of President Ahmed. P* 13.
842 **737** 25 p. multicoloured 5 5

738 Emblem of Asian-Oceanic Postal Union

1977 (1 Apr). *15th Anniv of Asian-Oceanic Postal Union. P* 13.
843 **738** 2 r. multicoloured .. .. 90 1·00

739 Narottam Morarjee and Ship **740** Makhanlal Chaturvedi (writer and poet)

1977 (2 Apr). *Birth Centenary of Morarjee (industrialist). P* 13.
844 **739** 25 p. greenish blue 10 5

1977 (4 Apr). *Chaturvedi Commemoration. P* 13.
845 **740** 25 p. lake-brown 5 5

741 Mahaprabhu Vallabhacharya (philosopher) **742** Federation Emblem

1977 (14 Apr). *Vallabhacharya Commemoration. P* 13.
846 **741** 1 r. sepia 35 40

1977 (23 Apr). *50th Anniv of Federation of Indian Chambers of Commerce and Industry. P* 13.
847 **742** 25 p. dull purple, brown-ochre and buff .. 5 5

744 "Environment Protection" **745** Rajya Sabha Chamber

1977 (5 July). *World Environment Day. P* 13.
848 **744** 2 r. multicoloured 60 75

1977 (21 June). *25th Anniv of Rajya Sabha (Upper House of Parliament). P* 13.
849 **745** 25 p. multicoloured 5 5

746 Lotus

(Des from paintings by J. P. Irani)

1977 (1 July). *Indian Flowers. T* **746** *and similar multicoloured designs. P* 14½ × 14 *(25 p., 2 r.) or* 14 × 14½ *(others).*

850 25 p. Type **746** 15 5
a. Black (inscription) omitted .. ..
851 50 p. Rhododendron (*vert*) 30 30
852 1 r. Kadamba (*vert*) 65 65
853 2 r. Gloriosa Lily .. .. 1·00 1·25

747 Berliner Gramophone

748 Coomaraswamy and Siva

(Des Benoy Sarkar)

1977 (20 July). *Centenary of Sound Recording. P* 13.
854 **747** 2 r. yellow-brown and black .. .. 80 1·00

1977 (22 Aug). *Birth Centenary of A. K. Coomaraswamy (art historian). P* 13.
855 **748** 25 p. multicoloured 5 5

749 Ganga Ram and Hospital

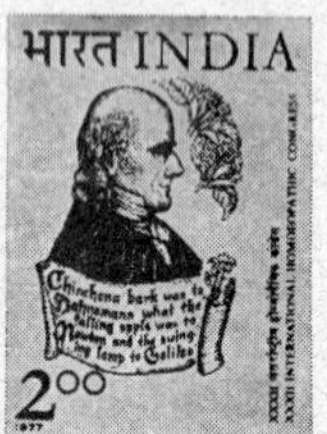

750 Dr. Samuel Hahnemann (founder of homeopathy)

1977 (4 Sept). *50th Death Anniv of Ganga Ram (social reformer). P* 14½ × 14.
856 **749** 25 p. maroon 5 5

1977 (6 Oct). *32nd International Homeopathic Congress, New Delhi. P* 13.
857 **750** 2 r. black and green .. .. .. 75 1·00

751 Ram Manohar Lohia (politician)

752 Early Punjabi Postman

1977 (12 Oct). *R. M. Lohia Commemoration. P* 13.
858 **751** 25 p. red-brown 5 5

1977 (12 Oct). *"Inpex-77" Philatelic Exhibition. Bangalore. T* **752** *and similar horiz design. P* 13 *(25 p.) or* 13½ × 14 *(2 r.).*
859 25 p. multicoloured 15 15
860 2 r. olive-grey/*flesh* .. .. 80 1·25
Design:—2 r. "Lion and Palm" essay, 1853.

753 Scarlet "Scinde Dawks" of 1852

754 "Mother and Child" (Khajuraho sculpture)

1977 (19 Oct). *"Asiana 77" Philatelic Exhibition, Bangalore. T* **753** *and similar horiz design. P* 13.
861 1 r. orange, black and yellow 50 70
862 3 r. orange, black and light blue .. .. 1·00 1·40
Design:—3 r. Foreign mail arriving at Ballard Pier, Bombay, 1927.

1977 (23 Oct). *15th International Congress of Pediatrics, New Delhi. P* 13.
863 **754** 2 r. reddish brown and grey .. .. 80 1·00

755 Kittur Rani Channamma (warrior queen)

756 Symbolic Sun

1977 (23 Oct). *Kittur Rani Channamma Commemoration. P* 13.
864 **755** 25 p. grey-green 10 5

1977 (8 Nov). *Union Public Service Commission Commemoration. P* 13.
865 **756** 25 p. multicoloured 15 10

757 Ear of Corn

758 "Cats" (Nikur Dilipbhai)

(Des Benoy Sarkar)

1977 (13 Nov). *"Agriexpo 77" Agricultural Exhibition, Pragati Maidan. W* **374** *(sideways). P* 13.
866 **757** 25 p. blue-green 15 10

1977 (14 Nov). *Children's Day. T* **758** *and similar horiz design. Multicoloured. P* 13.
867 25 p. Type **758** 20 15
868 1 r. "Friends" (Bhavsar Ashish Ramanlal) .. 75 80

759 Jotirao Phooley (social reformer)

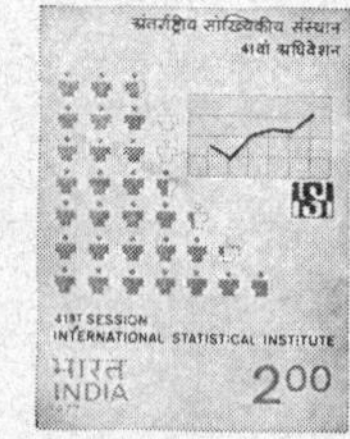

760 Diagram of Population Growth

1977 (28 Nov). *Indian Personalities. T* **759** *and similar vert design. W* **374** *(sideways). P* 13.
869 25 p. brown-olive 15 15
870 25 p. chestnut 15 15
Portrait:—No. 870, Senapti Bapat (revolutionary).

1977 (13 Dec). *41st Session of International Statistical Institute, New Delhi. P* 13.
871 **760** 2 r. blue-green and red .. .. .. 80 1·00

761 Kamta Prasad Guru and Vyakarna (Hindi Grammar)

762 Kremlin Tower and Soviet Flag

1977 (25 Dec). *Kamta Prasad Guru Commemoration. W* **374** *(sideways). P* 13½ × 14.
872 **761** 25 p. deep brown 10 5

1977 (30 Dec). *60th Anniv of October Revolution. P* 13.
873 **762** 1 r. multicoloured 45 60

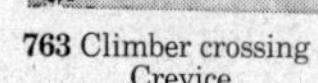

763 Climber crossing a Crevice

764 "Shikara" on Lake Dal

1978 (15 Jan). *Conquest of Kanchenjunga (1977). T* **763** *and similar horiz design. Multicoloured. P* 13
874 25 p. Type **763** 10 10
875 1 r. Indian flag near summit 45 60

1978 (23 Jan). *27th Pacific Area Travel Association Conference, New Delhi. P* 13.
876 **764** 1 r. multicoloured 60 60

765 Children in Library

766 The Mother-Pondicherry (philosopher)

1978 (11 Feb). *Third World Book Fair, New Delhi. P* 13.
877 **765** 1 r. chestnut and slate 45 60

1978 (21 Feb). *Birth Centenary of the Mother-Pondicherry. P* 13.
878 **766** 25 p. brown and light grey 10 10

767 Wheat and Globe

768 Nanalal Dalpatram Kavi (poet)

1978 (23 Feb). *Fifth International Wheat Genetics Symposium, New Delhi. P* 13.
879 **767** 25 p. yellow and blue-green 10 10

1978 (16 Mar). *Nanalal Kavi Commemoration. W* **374** *(sideways). P* 13.
880 **768** 25 p. red-brown 10 10

769 Surjya Sen (revolutionary)

770 "Two Vaishnavas" (Jamini Roy)

1978 (22 Mar). *Surjya Sen Commemoration. W* **374** *(sideways). P* 13.
881 **769** 25 p. sepia and orange-red 10 10

1978 (23 Mar). *Modern Indian Paintings. T* **770** *and similar vert designs. Multicoloured. P* 14.
882 25 p. Type **770** 15 10
a. Black (face value and inscr) omitted ..
883 50 p. "The Mosque" (Sailoz Mookherjea) .. 35 25
884 1 r. "Head" (Rabindranath Tagore) 60 70
885 2 r. "Hill Women" (Amrita Sher Gil) .. 85 1·10

771 "Self-portrait" (Rubens)

772 Charlie Chaplin

1978 (4 Apr). *400th Birth Anniv of Rubens. P* 13.
886 **771** 2 r. multicoloured .. .. 1·10 1·60

1978 (16 Apr). *Charlie Chaplin Commemoration. P* 13.
887 **772** 25 p. Prussian blue and gold 20 15

773 Deendayal Upadhyaya (statesman)

774 Syama Prasad Mookerjee

1978 (5 May). *Deendayal Upadhyaya Commemoration. P* 13.
888 **773** 25 p. olive-brown and pale orange .. 5 5

1978 (6 July). *Syama Prasad Mookerjee (statesman) Commemoration. P* 13 × 13½.
889 **774** 25 p. brown-olive 5 5

775 Airavat (mythological) elephant), Jain Temple, Gujerat (Kachchh Museum)

776 Krishna and Arjuna in Battle Chariot

1978 (27 July). *Treasures from Indian Museums. T* **775** *and similar multicoloured designs. P* 13 × 13½ (25, 50 *p.*) *or* 13½ × 13 (*others*).
890 25 p. Type **775** 15 10
891 50 p. Kalpadruma (magical tree), Besnagar (Indian Museum) 40 30
892 1 r. Obverse and reverse of Kushan gold coin (National Museum) (*horiz*) 65 70
893 2 r. Dagger and knife of Emperor Jehangir, Mughal (Salar Jung Museum) (*horiz*) .. 90 1·25

1978 (25 Aug). *Bhagawadgeeta (Divine Song of India). P* 13.
894 **776** 25 p. gold and vermilion 5 5

777 Bethune College

778 E. V. Ramasami

1978 (4 Sept). *Centenary of Bethune College, Calcutta. P* 13.
895 **777** 25 p. deep brown and deep green .. 5 5

1978 (17 Sept). *E. V. Ramasami (reformer) Commemoration. P* 13.
896 **778** 25 p. black 5 5

779 Uday Shankar

780 Leo Tolstoy

1978 (26 Sept). *Uday Shankar (dancer) Commemoration. P* 13.
897 **779** 25 p. reddish brown and stone 5 5

1978 (2 Oct). *150th Birth Anniv of Leo Tolstoy (writer). P* 13.
898 **780** 1 r. multicoloured 25 25

781 Vallathol Narayana Menon

782 "Two Friends" (Dinesh Sharma)

1978 (15 Oct). *Birth Centenary of Vallathol Narayana Menon (poet). P* 13.
899 **781** 25 p. bright purple and brown 5 5

1978 (14 Nov). *Children's Day. P* 13.
900 **782** 25 p. multicoloured 5 5

783 Machine Operator

784 Sowars (cavalrymen)

1978 (17 Nov). *National Small Industries Fair. P* 13½.
901 **783** 25 p. bronze-green 5 5

1978 (25 Nov). *175th Anniv of Skinner's Horse (cavalry regiment). P* 13.
902 **784** 25 p. multicoloured 15 15

785 Mohammad Ali Jauhar

786 Chakravarti Rajagopalachari

1978 (10 Dec). *Birth Centenary of Mohammad Ali Jauhar (patriot). P* 13.
903 **785** 25 p. olive-green 5 5

1978 (10 Dec). *Birth Centenary of Chakravarti Rajagopalachari (first post-independence Governor-General). P* 13.
904 **786** 25 p. lake-brown 5 5

787 Wright Brothers and *Flyer*

788 Ravenshaw College

1978 (23 Dec). *75th Anniv of Powered Flight. W* **374** (*sideways*). *P* 13 × 13½.
905 **787** 1 r. purple and yellow-ochre 20 20

1978 (24 Dec). *Centenary of Ravenshaw College. P* 14.
906 **788** 25 p. lake and deep green 5 5

789 Schubert

790 Uniforms of 1799, 1901 and 1979 with Badge

1978 (25 Dec). *150th Death Anniv of Franz Schubert (composer). P* 13.
907 **789** 1 r. multicoloured 25 30

(Des Charanjit Lal)

1979 (20 Feb). *Punjab Regiment. P* 13.
908 **790** 25 p. multicoloured 15 10

791 Bhai Parmanand

792 Gandhi with Young Boy

1979 (24 Feb). *Bhai Parmanand (historian) Commemoration. P* 13.
909 **791** 25 p. deep violet-blue 5 5

1979 (5 Mar). *International Year of the Child. T* **792** *and similar vert design. P* 13.
910 25 p. reddish brown and scarlet-vermilion .. 5 5
911 1 r. reddish brown and yellow-orange .. 15 25
Design:—1 r. Indian I.Y.C. emblem.

During October 1979 two stamps inscribed "HAPPY CHILD NATION'S PRIDE" with face values of 50 p. and 1 r. were issued to post offices. These were intended for sale as charity labels, without postal validity, the proceeds going to a Child Welfare fund. It would seem that the instructions issued were unclear, however, as some post offices sold these labels as postage stamps and accepted mail franked with them.

793 Albert Einstein

794 Rajarshi Shahu Chhatrapati

1979 (14 Mar). *Birth Centenary of Albert Einstein (physicist). P* 13.
912 **793** 1 r. blue-black 20 25

1979 (1 May). *Rajarshi Shahu Chhatrapati (ruler of Kolhapur State, 1874–1922, and precursor of social reform in India) Commemoration. P* 13.
913 **794** 25 p. deep dull purple 5 5

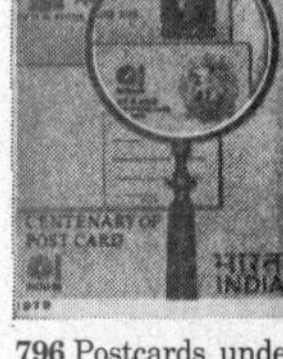

795 Exhibition Logo

796 Postcards under Magnifying Glass

1979 (2 July). *"India 80" International Stamp Exhibition (1st issue). P* 13.
914 **795** 30 p. deep green and orange 5 5
See also Nos. 942/5 and 955/8.

1979 (2 July). *Centenary of Indian Postcards. P* 13.
915 **796** 50 p. multicoloured 12 20

797 Raja Mahendra Pratap

798 Flounder, Herring and Prawn

799 Rubber Tapping

1979 (15 Aug). *Raja Mahendra Pratap (revolutionary and patriot) Commemoration. P* 13.
916 **797** 30 p. brown-olive 5 5

1979 (3 Sept)–**84**. *Designs on T* **798/9**. *P* 14½ × 14 (15, 20, 35 *p.*, 1, 2 *r.*), 13 (5*p.* (*No.* 938, 3 *r.* 25, 10 *r.*) *or* 14 × 14½ (*others*).

(*a*) *Photo. Wmk Large Star and* "INDIA GOVT" *in sheet**
917 2 p. slate-violet (31.3.80) 5 5
918 5 p. new blue (26.11.79) 5 5
919 15 p. deep bluish green (10.3.80) 5 5

(*b*) *Photo. W* **374** (*sideways on* 15, 20, 35 *p.*, 1, 2 *r.*, 2 *r.* 25, 2 *r.* 80, 3 *r.* 25, *and* 10 *r.*)
920 2 p. slate-violet (25.3.81) 5 5
921 5 p. new blue (25.3.81) 5 5
a. Perf 13 (5.7.82) 5 5
922 10 p. deep green (25.1.82) 5 5
a. Perf 13 (5.7.82) 5 5
923 15 p. deep bluish-green (25.3.81) 5 5
a. Perf 13 (5.7.82) 5 5
924 20 p. Indian red (25.3.81) 5 5
a. Perf 13 (5.7.82) 5 5
925 25 p. red-brown (26.11.79) 5 5
a. Perf 13 (5.7.82) 5 5
926 30 p. yellowish green 5 5
a. Perf 13 (6.4.82) 5 5
927 35 p. cerise (15.9.80) 5 5
a. Perf 13 (5.7.82) 5 5
928 50 p. deep violet (25.1.82) 5 5
a. Perf 13 (5.7.82) 5 5
929 1 r. bistre-brown (17.6.80) 12 5
a. Perf 13 (10.11.83) 12 15
932 2 r. deep rose-lilac (7.12.80) 25 25
a. Perf 13 (10.11.83) 25 30
933 2 r. 25, red and blue-green (25.3.81) .. 25 25
a. Wmk upright .. ..
934 2 r. 80, red and blue-green (25.3.81) .. 35 40
a. Wmk upright .. ..
934*b* 3 r. 25, reddish orange & blue-grn (28.12.82) 35 40
ba. Wmk upright .. ..

935 5 r. red and emerald (23.11.80) 60 65
a. Wmk sideways .. ..
b. Perf 13 × 12½ (*wmk upright*) (11.8.83) 60 65
936 10 r. maroon and bright green (24.2.84) .. 1·25 1·40
920/36 .. .. *Set of* 16 3·50 3·75

(c) *Litho. Wmk Large Star and "INDIA GOVT" in sheet** (2 *p.*) *or* W 374 (*sideways*) (5*p.*)
937 2 p. slate-violet (2.2.81) 5 5
938 5 p. new blue (29.11.82) 5 8

Designs: *Horiz as T* 798—2 p. Adult education class; 10 p. Irrigation canal; 25 p. Chick hatching from egg; 30 p. Harvesting maize; 50 p. Woman dairy farmer, cows and milk bottles. (36 × 19 *mm*)—10 r. Forest and hillside. *Vert as T* 798—15 p. Farmer and agriculture symbols; 20 p. Mother feeding child; 35 p. "Family". (17 × 28 *mm*)—1 r. Cotton plant; 2 r. Weaving. *Vert as T* 799—2 r. 25, Cashew; 2 r. 80, Apples; 3 r. 25, Oranges.

Nos. 920/1 and 923/4 were originally intended for issue on 9 March 1981 and First Day Covers showing this date are known from at least one post office.

No. 937 can be easily identified by the background of horizontal lines.

*See note concerning this watermark below No. 720. The 2 p. and 5 p. exist on both types of this watermark, the others on the second type only.

800 Jatindra Nath Das

801 De Havilland "Puss Moth" Aeroplane

1979 (13 Sept). 50*th Death Anniv of Jatindra Nath Das* (*revolutionary*). *P* 13.
941 **800** 30 p. blackish brown 5 5

1979 (15 Oct). *Air. "India 80" International Stamp Exhibition* (2*nd issue*). *Mail-carrying Aircraft. T* **801** *and similar horiz designs. Multicoloured. P* 14½ × 14.
942 30 p. Type **801** 10 10
943 50 p. Indian Air Force "Chetak" helicopter .. 15 20
944 1 r. Indian Airlines Boeing "737" airliner .. 25 30
945 2 r. Air India Boeing "747" airliner 45 60

802 Early and Modern Lightbulbs

803 Gilgit Record

1979 (21 Oct). *Centenary of Electric Lightbulb. P* 13.
946 **802** 1 r. brown-purple 12 20

1979 (23 Oct). *National Archives. P* 14½ × 14.
947 **803** 30 p. yellow-ochre and sepia 5 5

804 Hirakud Dam

805 Fair Emblem

1979 (29 Oct). 50*th Anniv, and* 13*th Congress, of International Commission on Large Dams. P* 13.
948 **804** 30 p. lake-brown and deep blue-green .. 5 5

1979 (10 Nov). *India International Trade Fair. P* 13.
949 **805** 1 r. grey-black and salmon 12 15

806 Child learning to Read

1979 (10 Nov). *International Children's Book Fair, New Delhi. P* 14½ × 14.
950 **806** 30 p. multicoloured 5 5

807 Dove with Olive Branch and I.A.E.A. Emblem

1979 (4 Dec). 23*rd I.A.E.A.* (*International Atomic Energy Agency*) *Conference, New Delhi. P* 13.
951 **807** 1 r. multicoloured 12 15

808 "Hindustan Pushpak" Aeroplane and "Rohini-1" Glider

809 Gurdwara Baoli Sahib Temple, Goindwal, Amritsar District

(Des R. N. Pasricha)

1979 (10 Dec). *Flying and Gliding. P* 13.
952 **808** 30 p. black, orange-brown and blue .. 5 5

1979 (21 Dec). 500*th Birth Anniv of Guru Amar Das. P* 13.
953 **809** 30 p. multicoloured 5 5

810 Ring of People encircling U.N. Emblem and Cog-wheel

811 Army Post Office and Postmarks

1980 (21 Jan). 3*rd U.N.I.D.O.* (*United Nations Industrial Development Organisation*) *General Conference, New Delhi. P* 13.
954 **810** 1 r. multicoloured 12 15

(Des Benoy Sarkar (30, 50 p.), India Security Press (others))

1980 (25 Jan). *"India 80" International Stamp Exhibition* (3*rd issue*). *T* **811** *and similar vert designs. No wmk* (1 *r.*) *or Large Star and "INDIA GOVT" in sheet** (*others*). *P* 13.
955 30 p. grey-olive 5 5
956 50 p. bistre-brown and dull olive-bistre .. 10 15
957 1 r. Venetian red 15 25
958 2 r. olive-brown 25 40

Designs:—50 p. Money order; 1 r. Copper ticket; 2 r. Sir Rowland Hill and birthplace at Kidderminster.

*See note below No. 720.

812 Energy Symbols

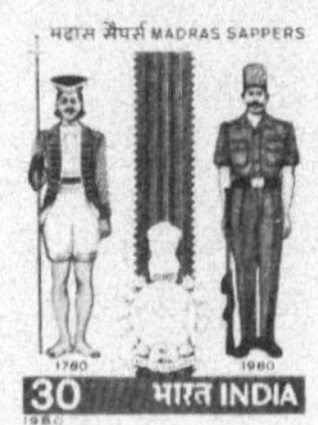
813 Uniforms of 1780 and 1980, Crest and Ribbon

(Des C. Pakrashi)

1980 (17 Feb). *Institution of Engineers* (*India*) *Commemoration. Wmk Large Star and "INDIA GOVT" in sheet. P* 13.
959 **812** 30 p. gold and blue 5 5

1980 (26 Feb). *Bicentenary of Madras Sappers. P* 13.
960 **813** 30 p. multicoloured 5 5

814 Books

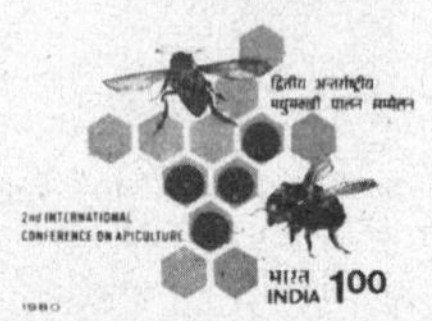
815 Bees and Honey-comb

(Des J. Gupta)

1980 (29 Feb). 4*th World Book Fair, New Delhi. Wmk Large Star and "INDIA GOVT" in sheet. P* 13.
961 **814** 30 p. new blue 5 5

(Des M. Bardhan)

1980 (29 Feb). 2*nd International Apiculture Conference, New Delhi. P* 13.
962 **815** 1 r. deep brown and olive-bistre .. 12 20

816 Welthy Fisher and Saksharta Nicketan (Literacy House), Lucknow

817 Darul-Uloom, Deoband

(Des M. Choudhury)

1980 (18 Mar). *Welthy Fisher* (*teacher*) *Commemoration. Wmk Large Star and "INDIA GOVT" in sheet. P* 13.
963 **816** 30 p. chalky blue 5 5

(Des S. Charanjit Lal)

1980 (21 Mar). *Darul-Uloom* (*college*), *Deoband Commemoration. Wmk Large Star and "INDIA GOVT" in sheet. P* 13.
964 **817** 30 p. deep grey-green 5 5

818 Keshub Chunder Sen

819 Chhatrapati Shivaji Maharaj

1980 (15 Apr). *Keshub Chunder Sen* (*religious and social reformer*) *Commemoration. Wmk. Large Star and "INDIA GOVT" in sheet. P* 13.
965 **818** 30 p. bistre-brown 5 5

1980 (21 Apr). 300*th Death Anniv of Chhatrapati Shivaji Maharaj* (*warrior*). *P* 13.
966 **819** 30 p. multicoloured 5 5

820 Table Tennis

821 N. M. Joshi

1980 (9 May). *Asian Table Tennis Championships, Calcutta. Wmk Large Star and "INDIA GOVT" in sheet. P* 13.
967 **820** 30 p. deep reddish purple 5 5

1980 (27 May). *Designs as Nos.* 732 *and* 810*b. Size* 17 × 20 *mm.* W **374** (*sideways*). *P* 14½ × 14.
968 30 p. red-brown (Gandhi) 10 10
969 30 p. dull violet (Nehru) 10 10

1980 (5 June). *N. M. Joshi* (*trade-unionist*) *Commemoration. Wmk Large Star and "INDIA GOVT" in sheet. P* 13.
970 **821** 30 p. magenta 5 5

822 Mahakavi Ulloor

823 S. M. Zamin Ali

1980 (6 June). *Mahakavi Ulloor* (*poet*) *Commemoration. Wmk Large Star and "INDIA GOVT" in sheet. P* 13.
971 **822** 30 p. maroon 10 10

1980 (25 June). *S. M. Zamin Ali (educationalist and poet) Commemoration. Wmk Large Star and* "INDIA GOVT" *in sheet. P* 13.
972 **823** 30 p. bronze-green 5 5

824 Helen Keller **825** High-jumping

1980 (27 June). *Birth Centenary of Helen Keller (campaigner for the handicapped). P* 13.
973 **824** 30 p. black and dull orange 5 5

1980 (19 July). *Olympic Games, Moscow. T* **825** *and similar vert design. Multicoloured. P* 13½ × 14.
974 1 r. Type **825** 12 15
975 2 r. 80, Horse-riding 35 40

826 Prem Chand **827** Mother Teresa and Nobel Peace Prize Medallion

1980 (31 July). *Birth Centenary of Prem Chand (writer). Wmk Large Star and* "INDIA GOVT" *in sheet. P* 13.
976 **826** 30 p. red-brown 5 5

1980 (27 Aug). *Mother Teresa (Nobel Peace Prizewinner,* 1979) *Commemoration. Wmk Large Star and* "INDIA GOVT" *in sheet. P* 13.
977 **827** 30 p. bluish violet 10 5

828 Lord Mountbatten **829** Scottish Church College, Calcutta

1980 (28 Aug). *Lord Mountbatten Commemoration. P* 13.
978 **828** 2 r. 80, multicoloured 50 70

1980 (1 Sept)–**82**. *As Nos.* 968/9, *but new face value.*
979 35 p. red-brown (Gandhi) (16.9.80) 5 5
a. Perf 13 (5.7.82) 5 5
980 35 p. dull violet (Nehru) 5 5
a. Perf 13 (5.7.82) 5 5

(Des C. Pakrashi)

1980 (27 Sept). 150*th Anniv of Scottish Church College, Calcutta. Wmk Large Star and* "INDIA GOVT" *in sheet. P* 13.
981 **829** 35 p. deep rose-lilac 5 5

830 Rajah Annamalai Chettiar

831 Gandhi marching to Dandi

1980 (30 Sept). *Rajah Annamalai Chettiar (statesman and educationalist) Commemoration. P* 14 × 14½.
982 **830** 35 p. deep lilac 5 5

(Des S. Ramachandran)

1980 (2 Oct). *"Dandi March" (Gandhi's defiance of Salt Tax Law) Commemoration. T* **831** *and similar vert design. P* 14½ × 14.
983 35 p. black, turquoise-blue and gold 5 5
a. Horiz pair. Nos. 983/4 .. .. 10 10
984 35 p. black, deep mauve and gold 5 5
Design:—No. 983, Type **831**; No. 984, Gandhi picking up handful of salt at Dandi.

No. 984 with the deep mauve omitted is a chemically produced fake.

Nos. 983/4 were printed together, *se-tenant*, in horizontal pairs throughout the sheet.

832 Jayaprakash Narayan

833 Great Indian Bustard

(Des Directorate of Advertising and Visual Publicity, New Delhi)

1980 (8 Oct). *Jayaprakash Narayan (politician and freedom fighter) Commemoration. Wmk Large Star and* "INDIA GOVT" *in sheet. P* 14 × 14½.
985 **832** 35 p. chocolate 5 5

(Des J. Irani)

1980 (1 Nov). *International Symposium on Bustards, Jaipur. P* 13.
986 **833** 2 r. 30, multicoloured 30 35

834 Arabic Commemorative Inscription

(Des B. Makhmoor)

1980 (3 Nov). *Moslem Year* 1400 *A.H. Commemoration. P* 13.
987 **834** 35 p. multicoloured 5 5

835 Girls Dancing

836 Dhyan Chand

(Des P. Paul)

1980 (14 Nov). *Children's Day. P* 13½ × 13.
988 **835** 35 p. multicoloured 5 5

1980 (3 Dec). *Dhyan Chand (hockey player) Commemoration. P* 14 × 14½.
989 **836** 35 p. red-brown 5 5

837 Gold Mining

838 M. A. Ansari

1980 (20 Dec). *Centenary of Kolar Gold Fields, Karnataka. P* 13.
990 **837** 1 r. multicoloured 12 15

1980 (25 Dec). *M. A. Ansari (medical practitioner and politician) Commemoration. Wmk Large Star and* "INDIA GOVT" *in sheet. P* 14 × 14½.
991 **838** 35 p. dull olive 5 5

839 India Government Mint, Bombay

840 Bride from Tamil Nadu

1980 (27 Dec). 150*th Anniv of India Government Mint. Bombay. P* 13.
992 **839** 35 p. black, silver and dull blue 5 5

1980 (30 Dec). *Brides in Traditional Costume. T* **840** *and similar vert designs. Multicoloured. P* 13.
993 1 r. Type **840** 20 20
994 1 r. Bride from Rajasthan 20 20
995 1 r. Bride from Kashmir 20 20
996 1 r. Bride from Bengal 20 20

841 Mazharul Haque

842 St. Stephen's College

1981 (2 Jan). *Mazharul Haque (politician) Commemoration. Wmk Large Star and* "INDIA GOVT" *in sheet. P* 14 × 14½.
997 **841** 35 p. chalky blue 5 5

1981 (1 Feb). *Centenary of St. Stephen's College, Delhi. Wmk Large Star and* "INDIA GOVT" *in sheet. P* 14 × 14½.
998 **842** 35 p. dull scarlet 5 5

843 Gommateshwara

844 G. V. Mavalankar

1981 (9 Feb). *Millenium of Gommateshwara (statue at Shravanabelgola. P* 14 × 14½.
999 **843** 1 r. multicoloured 12 15

1981 (27 Feb). 25*th Death Anniv of G. V. Mavalankar (parliamentarian). P* 14 × 14½.
1000 **844** 35 p. Venetian red 5 5

845 Flame of Martyrdom

846 Heinrich von Stephan and U.P.U. Emblem

(Des D. Dey)

1981 (23 Mar). *"Homage to Martyrs". P* 14 × 14½.
1001 **845** 35 p. multicoloured 5 5

1981 (8 Apr). 150*th Birth Anniv of Heinrich von Stephan (founder of U.P.U.). P* 14½ × 14.
1002 **846** 1 r. red-brown and new blue 15 15

847 Disabled Child being helped by Able-bodied Child

848 Bhil

(Des K. Raha)

1981 (20 Apr). *International Year for Disabled Persons. P* 14½ × 14.
1003 **847** 1 r. black and blue 12 15

(Des from photographs by A. Pareek (No. 1004), S. Dutta (No. 1005). S. Theodore Baskaran (No. 1006), Kikrumielie Angami (No. 1007))

1981 (30 May). *Native Tribes. T* **848** *and similar vert designs. Multicoloured. P* 14.
1004 1 r. Type **848** 20 20
1005 1 r. Dandami Maria 20 20
1006 1 r. Toda 20 20
1007 1 r. Khlamngam Naga 20 20

849 Stylised Trees

850 Nilmoni Phukan

(Des M. Bardhan)

1981 (15 June). *Conservation of Forests. P* 14 × 14½.
1008 **849** 1 r. multicoloured 12 15

1981 (22 June). *Nilmoni Phukan (poet) Commemoration. P* 14 × 14½.
1009 **850** 35 p. red-brown 5 5

851 Sanjay Gandhi

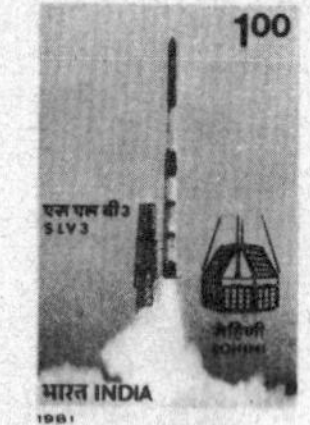

852 Launch of "SLV 3" and Diagram of "Rohini"

(Des C. Pakrashi)

1981 (23 June). *First Death Anniv of Sanjay Gandhi (politician). P* 13.
1010 **851** 35 p. multicoloured 5 5

1981 (18 July). *Launch of "SLV 3" Rocket with "Rohini" Satellite. P* 14 × 14½.
1011 **852** 1 r. black, pink and pale blue 10 12

853 Games Logo

854 Flame of the Forest

(Des M. Chaudhury (No. 1013))

1981 (28 July). *Asian Games, New Delhi (1st issue). T* **853** *and similar horiz design. Multicoloured. P* 13½ × 13.
1012 1 r. Type **853** 10 12
1013 1 r. Games emblem and stylised hockey players 10 12
See also Nos. 1026, 1033, 1057, 1059 and 1061/6.

(Des from photographs by K. Vaid (35 p., 2 r.), R. Bedi (others))

1981 (1 Sept). *Flowering Trees. T* **854** *and similar vert designs. Multicoloured. P* 13 × 13½.
1014 35 p. Type **854** 5 5
1015 50 p. Crateva 10 5
1016 1 r. Golden Shower 15 15
1017 2 r. Bauhinia 35 40

855 W.F.D. Emblem and Wheat

856 *Stichophthalma camadeva*

(Des M. Bardhan)

1981 (16 Oct). *World Food Day. P* 14 × 14½.
1018 **855** 1 r. greenish yellow and Prussian blue 10 12

(Des from paintings by M. Mandal)

1981 (20 Oct). *Butterflies. T* **856** *and similar multicoloured designs. P* 13.
1019 35 p. Type **856** 5 5
1020 50 p. *Cethosia biblis* 10 5
1021 1 r. *Cyrestis achates (vert)* 15 15
1022 2 r. *Teinopalpus imperialis (vert)* 35 40

857 Bellary Raghava

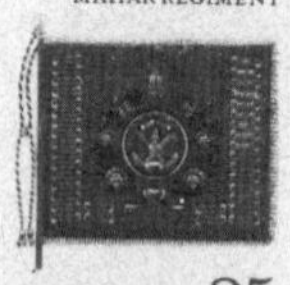

858 Regimental Colour

1981 (31 Oct). *Bellary Raghava (actor) Commemoration. P* 14½ × 14.
1023 **857** 35 p. brown-olive 5 5

1981 (9 Nov). *40th Anniv of Mahar Regiment. P* 13 × 13½.
1024 **858** 35 p. multicoloured 5 5

859 "Toyseller" (Kumari Ruchita Sharma)

860 Rajghat Stadium

1981 (14 Nov). *Children's Day. Child's Painting. P* 14 × 14½.
1025 **859** 35 p. multicoloured 5 5

1981 (19 Nov). *Asian Games, New Delhi (2nd issue). P* 13½ × 13.
1026 **860** 1 r. multicoloured 10 12

861 Kashi Prasad Jayasawal and Yaudheya Coin

862 India and P.L.O. Flags, and People

1981 (27 Nov). *Birth Centenary of Kashi Prasad Jayasawal (lawyer and historian). P* 14 × 14½.
1027 **861** 35 p. chalky blue 5 5

(Des B. Makhmoor)

1981 (29 Nov). *Palestinian Solidarity. P* 14½ × 14.
1028 **862** 1 r. multicoloured 10 12

863 I.N.S. *Taragiri*

864 Henry Heras and Indus Valley Seal

1981 (4 Dec). *Indian Navy Day. P* 14½ × 14.
1029 **863** 35 p. multicoloured 5 5

1981 (14 Dec). *Henry Heras (historian) Commemoration. P* 14½ × 14.
1030 **864** 35 p. deep rose-lilac 5 5

865 Map of South-East Asia showing Cable Route

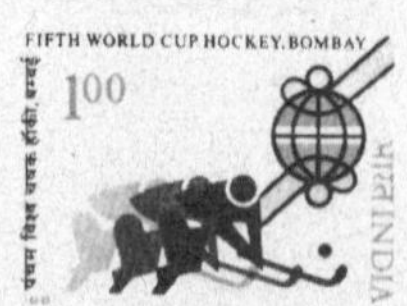

866 Stylised Hockey-players and Championship Emblem

1981 (24 Dec). *I.O.C.O.M. (Indian Ocean Commonwealth Cable) Submarine Telephone Cable. P* 13½ × 13.
1031 **865** 1 r. multicoloured 10 12

(Des C. Lal)

1981 (29 Dec). *World Cup Hockey Championship, Bombay. P* 13½ × 13.
1032 **866** 1 r. multicoloured 10 12

NEW INFORMATION

The editor is always interested to correspond with people who have new information that will improve or correct the Catalogue.

867 Jawaharlal Nehru Stadium

868 Early and Modern Telephones

1981 (30 Dec). *Asian Games, New Delhi (3rd issue). P* 13½ × 13.
1033 **867** 1 r. multicoloured 10 12

(Des C. Pakrashi)

1982 (28 Jan). *Centenary of Telephone Services. P* 13.
1034 **868** 2 r. black, new blue and olive-grey .. 20 25

869 Map of World

870 Sir J. J. School of Art

1982 (8 Feb). *International Soil Science Congress, New Delhi. P* 13.
1035 **869** 1 r. multicoloured 10 12

(Des M. Patel)

1982 (2 Mar). *125th Anniv of Sir J. J. School of Art, Bombay. P* 14 × 14½.
1036 **870** 35 p. multicoloured 5 5

871 "Three Musicians"

872 Deer (stone carving), 5th-century A.D.

1982 (15 Mar). *Birth Centenary of Picasso* (1981). *P* 14.
1037 **871** 2 r. 85, multicoloured 25 30

1982 (23 Mar). *Festival of India. Ancient Sculpture. T* **872** *and similar vert design. Multicoloured. P* 14 × 14½.
1038 2 r. Type **872** 20 25
1039 3 r. 05, Kaliya Mardana (bronze statue), 9th-century A.D. 30 35

873 Radio Telescope, Ooty

874 Robert Koch and Symbol of Disease

1982 (23 Mar). *Festival of India. Science and Technology. P* 13½ × 13.
1040 **873** 3 r. 05, multicoloured 30 35

(Des A. Ramachandran)

1982 (24 Mar). *Centenary of Robert Koch's Discovery of Tubercle Bacillus. P* 13½ × 13.
1041 **874** 35 p. deep rose-lilac 5 5

875 Durgabai Deshmukh

876 *Meconopsis aculeata*

1982 (9 May). *First Death Anniv of Durgabai Deshmukh (social reformer). P* 14½ × 14.
1042 **875** 35 p. blue 5 5

1982 (29 May). *Himalayan Flowers. T* **876** *and similar vert designs. Multicoloured. P* 14.
1043 35 p. Type **876** 5 5
1044 1 r. *Indula grandiflora* 10 12
1045 2 r. *Arisaema wallachianum* 20 25
1046 2 r. 85, *Saussurea obvallata* 30 35

877 "Apple" Satellite

878 Bidhan Chandra Roy

1982 (19 June). *1st Anniv of "Apple" Satellite Launch. P* 13½ × 13.
1047 **877** 2 r. multicoloured 20 25

1982 (1 July). *Birth Centenary of Bidhan Chandra Roy (doctor and politician). P* 15 × 14.
1048 **878** 50 p. chestnut 5 8

879 "Sagar Samrat" Oil Rig

880 "Bindu" (painting by Raza)

1982 (14 Aug). *25th Anniv of Oil and Natural Gas Commission. P* 13½ × 13.
1049 **879** 1 r. multicoloured 10 12

1982 (17 Sept). *Festival of India. Contemporary Art. T* **880** *and similar vert design. Multicoloured. P* 14 × 14½.
1050 2 r. Type **880** 20 25
1051 3 r. 05, "Between the Spider and the Lamp" (painting by M. F. Hussain) 30 35

881 Kashmir Stag

882 "Wapiti" and "Mig-25" Aircraft

1982 (1 Oct). *Wildlife Conservation. P* 13 × 13½.
1052 **881** 2 r. 85, multicoloured 30 35

1982 (8 Oct). *50th Anniv of Indian Air Force. P* 13½ × 13.
1053 **882** 1 r. multicoloured 10 12

883 J. Tata with "Puss Moth"

884 Police Patrol

1982 (15 Oct). *50th Anniv of Civil Aviation in India. P* 13½ × 13.
1054 **883** 3 r. 25, multicoloured 35 40

(Des B. Prakash)

1982 (21 Oct). *Police Commemoration Day. P* 13.
1055 **884** 50 p. bronze-green 5 8

885 Coins and Economic Symbols

886 Wrestling Bout

(Des S. Jha)

1982 (23 Oct). *Centenary of Post Office Savings Bank. P* 13.
1056 **885** 50 p. brown and cinnamon 5 8

(Des A. Ramachandran)

1982 (30 Oct). *Asian Games, New Delhi (4th issue). P* 13½ × 14.
1057 **886** 1 r. multicoloured 10 12

887 Troposcatter Communication Link

888 Krishna shooting Arrow at Fish

1982 (2 Nov). *1st Anniv of Troposcatter Communication Link between India and U.S.S.R. P* 13.
1058 **887** 3 r. 05, multicoloured 30 35

(Des A. Ramachandran)

1982 (6 Nov). *Asian Games, New Delhi (5th issue). P* 13½ × 14.
1059 **888** 1 r. multicoloured 10 12

889 "Mother and Child"

890 Stylised Cyclists

(Des D. Sharma)

1982 (14 Nov). *Children's Day. P* 14 × 14½.
1060 **889** 50 p. multicoloured 5 8

(Des C. Pakrashi (50 p.), B. Prakash (3 r. 25))

1982 (19 Nov). *Asian Games, New Delhi (6th issue). T* **890** *and similar horiz designs. Multicoloured. P* 13.
1061 50 p. Type **890** 5 8
1062 2 r. Javelin-throwing 25 25
1063 2 r. 85, Discus-throwing 30 35
1064 3 r. 25, Football 40 45

891 Yachting

892 Chetwode Building

(Des C. Pakrashi)

1982 (25 Nov). *Asian Games, New Delhi (7th issue). T* **891** *and similar horiz design. Multicoloured. P* 13.
1065 2 r. Type **891** 20 25
1066 2 r. 85, Rowing 30 35

1982 (10 Dec). *50th Anniv of Indian Military Academy. P* 13.
1067 **892** 50 p. multicoloured 5 8

893 Purushottamdas Tandon

894 Darjeeling Himalayan Railway

1982 (15 Dec). *Birth Centenary of Purushottamdas Tandon. P* 12½ × 13.
1068 **893** 50 p. yellow-brown 5 8

1982 (18 Dec). *Centenary of Darjeeling Himalayan Railway. P* 13.
1069 **894** 2 r. 85, multicoloured 30 35

895 Vintage Rail Coach and Silhouette of Steam Engine

896 Antarctic Camp

(Des C. Pakrashi)

1982 (30 Dec). *"Inpex 82" Stamp Exhibition. T* **895** *and similar multicoloured design. P* 13 *(50 p.) or* 13½ × 14 *(2 r.).*
1070 50 p. Type **895** 5 8
1071 2 r. 1854 ½ a. stamp and 1947 3½ a. Independence commemorative (33 × 44 *mm*) 25 30

1983 (9 Jan). *First Indian Antarctic Expedition. P* 13.
1072 **896** 1 r. multicoloured 12 15

1983 (25 Jan). *As Nos.* 968/9, *but new face value. W* **374** *(sideways). P* 12½ × 13.
1073 50 p. red-brown (Gandhi) 5 8
1074 50 p. deep ultramarine (Nehru) 5 8

897 Roosevelt with Stamp Collection

898 "Siberian (Great White) Cranes at Bharatpur" (Diane Pierce)

1983 (30 Jan). *Birth Centenary of Franklin D. Roosevelt (American statesman)* (1982). *P* 12½ × 13.
1075 **897** 3 r. 25, bistre-brown 40 45

1983 (7 Feb). *International Crane Workshop, Bharatpur. P* 13.
1076 **898** 2 r. 85, multicoloured 35 40

899 Jat Regiment Uniforms Past and Present

900 Non-aligned Summit Logo

(Des C. Lal)

1983 (16 Feb). *Presentation of Colours to Battalions of the Jat Regiment. P* 13.
1077 **899** 50 p. multicoloured 5 8

(Des N. Srivastava)

1983 (7 Mar). *7th Non-aligned Summit Conference, New Delhi. T* **900** *and similar horiz design. P* 13.
1078 1 r. bistre, orange-brown and black 12 15
1079 2 r. multicoloured 25 30
Design:—2 r. Nehru.

901 Shore Temple, Mahabalipuram

902 Acropolis and Olympic Emblems

(Des R. Pasricha)

1983 (14 Mar). *Commonwealth Day. T* **901** *and similar horiz design. Multicoloured. P* 13.
1080 1 r. Type **901** 12 15
1081 2 r. Gomukh, Gangotri Glacier 25 30

(Des B. Makhmoor)

1983 (25 Mar). *International Olympic Committee Session, New Delhi. P* 13.
1082 **902** 1 r. multicoloured 12 15

903 "St. Francis and Brother Falcon" (statue by Giovanni Collina)

904 Karl Marx and *Das Kapital*

1983 (4 Apr). *800th Birth Anniv of St. Francis of Assisi. P* 13.
1083 **903** 1 r. bistre-brown 12 15

1983 (5 May). *Death Centenary of Karl Marx. P* 13.
1084 **904** 1 r. brown 12 15

905 Darwin and Map of Voyage

(Des M. Mandal)

1983 (18 May). *Death Centenary* (1982) *of Charles Darwin* (*naturalist*). *P* 13.
1085 **905** 2 r. multicoloured 25 30

906 Central Indian Barasinga (deer) **907** Globe and Satellite

1983 (30 May). *50th Anniv of Kanha National Park*. *P* 13.
1086 **906** 1 r. multicoloured 12 15

(Des M. Mandal)

1983 (18 July). *World Communications Year*. *P* 13 × 12½.
1087 **907** 1 r. multicoloured 12 15

908 Simon Bolivar

1983 (24 July). *Birth Bicentenary of Simon Bolivar* (*South American statesman*). *P* 12½ × 13.
1088 **908** 2 r. multicoloured 25 30

909 Meera Behn **910** Ram Nath Chopra

(Des C. Pakrashi (No. 1091))

1983 (9 Aug). *India's Struggle for Freedom* (*1st series*) *T* **909** *and similar designs*. *P* 14 × 13½ (*No.* 1091) *or* 13 × 12½ (*others*).
1089 50 p. dull vermilion and dull green .. 5 8
a. Horiz pair. Nos. 1089/90 .. .. 10 15
1090 50 p. lt brown, dull green & dull vermilion .. 5 8
1091 50 p. multicoloured 5 8
Designs: *Vert*—No. 1089, Type **909**; No. 1090, Mahadev Desai, *Horiz* (43 × 31 *mm*)—No. 1091, Quit India Resolution.
Nos. 1089/90 were printed together, *se-tenant*, in horizontal pairs throughout the sheet.
See also Nos. 1122/5.

1983 (17 Aug). *Ram Nath Chopra* (*pharmacologist*) *Commemoration*. *P* 12½ × 13.
1092 **910** 50 p. Venetian red 5 8

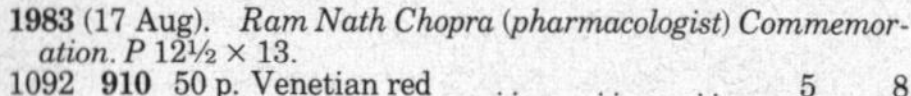

911 Nanda Devi Mountain **912** Great Indian Hornbill

1983 (27 Aug). *25th Anniv of Indian Mountaineering Federation*. *P* 13.
1093 **911** 2 r. multicoloured 25 30

(Des J. Irani)

1983 (15 Sept). *Centenary of Natural History Museum, Bombay*. *P* 13.
1094 **912** 1 r. multicoloured 12 15

913 View of Garden **914** Golden Langur

1983 (23 Sept). *Rock Garden, Chandigarh*. *P* 13.
1095 **913** 1 r. multicoloured 12 15

1983 (1 Oct). *Indian Wildlife. Monkeys*. *T* **914** *and similar horiz design. Multicoloured*. *P* 13.
1096 1 r. Type **914** 12 15
1097 2 r. Long-tailed Macaque 25 30

915 Ghats of Varanasi **916** Krishna Kanta Handique

1983 (3 Oct). *Fifth General Assembly of World Tourism Organization*. *P* 14 × 13½.
1098 **915** 2 r. multicoloured 25 30

1983 (7 Oct). *Krishna Kanta Handique* (*scholar*) *Commemoration*. *P* 13 × 12½.
1099 **916** 50 p. deep blue 5 8

917 Hemu Kalani **918** Woman and Child (from "Festival" by Kashyap Premsawala)

1983 (18 Oct). *Hemu Kalani* (*revolutionary*) *Commemoration*. *P* 13 × 12½.
1100 **917** 50 p. reddish brown, yellow-green and red-orange 5 8

1983 (14 Nov). *Children's Day*. *P* 13 × 13½.
1101 **918** 50 p. multicoloured 5 8

919 Acharya Vinoba Bhave **920** *Udan Khatola*, First Indian Hot Air Balloon

1983 (15 Nov). *1st Death Anniv of Acharya Vinoba Bhave* (*social reformer*). *P* 13 × 12½.
1102 **919** 50 p. olive-sepia, green and orange .. 8 10

1983 (21 Nov). *Bicentenary of Manned Flight*. *T* **920** *and similar vert design. Multicoloured*. *P* 13.
1103 1 r. Type **920** 12 15
1104 2 r. Montgolfier balloon 25 30

921 Tiger **922** Commonwealth Logo

1983 (22 Nov). *Ten Years of "Project Tiger"*. *P* 13 × 13½.
1105 **921** 2 r. multicoloured 25 30

(Des K. Raha (1 r.))

1983 (23 Nov). *Commonwealth Heads of Government Meeting, New Delhi*. *T* **922** *and similar vert design. Multicoloured*. *P* 13 × 12½.
1106 1 r. Type **922** 12 15
1107 2 r. Early 19th-century Goanese couple .. 25 30

923 "Pratiksha" **924** Surendranath Banerjee

1983 (5 Dec). *Birth Cent of Nanda Lal Bose* (*artist*). *P* 13 × 12½.
1108 **923** 1 r. multicoloured 12 15

1983 (28 Dec). *Surendranath Banerjee* (*politicial reformer*) *Commemoration*. *P* 13 × 12½.
1109 **924** 50 p. olive-green, yellow-green & orge .. 8 10

925 Lancer in Ceremonial Uniform **926** Troopers in Ceremonial Uniform, and Tank

1984 (7 Jan). *Bicentenary of 7th Light Cavalry Regiment*. *P* 13 × 12½.
1110 **925** 1 r. multicoloured 12 15

1984 (9 Jan). *Presentation of Regimental Guidon to the Deccan Horse*. *P* 13 × 13½.
1111 **926** 1 r. multicoloured 12 15

927 Society Building and William Jones (founder) **928** Insurance Logo

1984 (15 Jan). *Bicentenary of Asiatic Society*. *P* 13.
1112 **927** 1 r. emerald and bright purple 12 15

(Des S. Jha)

1984 (1 Feb). *Centenary of Postal Life Insurance*. *P* 13 × 13½.
1113 **928** 1 r. multicoloured 12 15

929 "Sea Harrier" Aircraft

(Des Capt. A. Dhir and S. Dheer)

1984 (12 Feb). *President's Review of the Fleet*. *T* **929** *and similar horiz designs. Multicoloured*. *P* 13½ × 13.
1114 1 r. Type **929** 12 15
a. Block of 4. Nos. 1114/17 45
1115 1 r. Aircraft carrier 12 15
1116 1 r. Submarine 12 15
1117 1 r. Missile destroyer 12 15
Nos. 1114/7 were printed in *se-tenant* blocks of four within the sheet, forming a composite design.

MINIMUM PRICE

The minimum price quoted is 5p which represents a handling charge rather than a basis for valuing common stamps. For further notes about prices see introductory pages.

930 I.L.A. Logo and Hemispheres

931 Vasudeo Balvant Phadke

(Des J. Irani)

1984 (20 Feb). *12th International Leprosy Congress. P* 13.
1118 **930** 1 r. multicoloured 12 15

(Des C. Pakrashi)

1984 (21 Feb). *Vasudeo Balvant Phadke (revolutionary) Commemoration. P* 13.
1119 **931** 50 p. deep brownish olive, yellow-green and bright orange 8 10

932 "Salyut 7"

933 Baba Kanshi Ram

(Des R. Pasricha)

1984 (3 Apr). *Indo-Soviet Manned Space Flight. P* 14.
1120 **932** 3 r. multicoloured 40 45

1984 (23 Apr). *Baba Kanshi Ram (revolutionary) Commemoration. P* 13.
1121 **933** 50 p. bistre-brown, emerald & brt orge 8 10

934 Tatya Tope

935 G. D. Birla

(Des C. Pakrashi)

1984 (10 May). *India's Struggle for Freedom (2nd series). T* **934** *and similar vert designs. Multicoloured. P* 13½.
1122 50 p. Type **934** 8 10
1123 50 p. Nana Sahib 8 10
1124 50 p. Begum Hazrat Mahal 8 10
1125 50 p. Mangal Pandey 8 10

1984 (11 June). *90th Birth Anniv of G. D. Birla (industrialist). P* 13.
1126 **935** 50 p. chocolate 8 10

936 Basketball

937 Gwalior

(Des K. Reha and S. Jha)

1984 (28 July). *Olympic Games, Los Angeles. T* **936** *and similar multicoloured designs. P* 13.
1127 50 p. Type **936** 8 10
1128 1 r. High jumping 12 15
1129 2 r. Gymnastics (*horiz*) 30 35
1130 2 r. 50, Weightlifting (*horiz*) 35 40

1984 (3 Aug). *Forts. T* **937** *and similar multicoloured designs. P* 13½ × 13 (*50 p., 2 r.*) *or* 13 × 13½ (*others*).
1131 50 p. Type **937** 8 10
1132 1 r. Vellore (*vert*) 12 15
1133 1 r. 50, Simhagad (*vert*) 20 25
1134 2 r. Jodhpur 30 35

MINIMUM PRICE

The minimum price quoted is 5p which represents a handling charge rather than a basis for valuing common stamps. For further notes about prices see introductory pages.

938 B.V. Paradkar and Newspaper

939 Dr. D. N. Wadia and Institute of Himalayan Geology, Dehradun

1984 (14 Sept). *B. V. Paradkar (journalist) Commemoration. P* 13 × 13½.
1135 **938** 50 p. reddish brown 8 10

1984 (23 Oct). *Birth Centenary (1983) of Dr. D. N. Wadia (geologist). P* 13.
1136 **939** 1 r. multicoloured 12 15

OFFICIAL STAMPS

Stamps overprinted "POSTAL SERVICE" or "I.P.N." were not used as postage stamps, and are therefore omitted.

Service.
(O 1)

(Optd by the Military Orphanage Press, Calcutta)

1866 (1 Aug)–72. *Optd with Type* O 1. *P* 14. (*a*) *No wmk.*
O 1 11 ½ a. blue .. .. — 40·00
O 2 ½ a. pale blue .. .. — 40·00
a. Optd inverted .. ..
O 3 1 a. brown .. .. — 45·00
O 4 1 a. deep brown .. .. — 45·00
O 5 8 a. carmine .. .. 4·50 11·00

(*b*) *Wmk Elephant's Head, T* 13
O 6 11 ½ a. blue .. .. 55·00 11·00
O 7 ½ a. pale blue .. .. 55·00 11·00
a. Opt inverted .. .. ..
b. No dot on "i" (No. 50 on pane) ..
c. No stop (No. 77 on pane) .. .. — £130
O 8 12 8 p. purple (1.72) .. .. .. 14·00 17·00
a. No dot on "i" .. .. .. 90·00
b. No stop .. .. 90·00 90·00
O 9 11 1 a. brown .. .. 50·00 14·00
O10 1 a. deep brown .. .. 50·00 14·00
a. No dot on "i" .. .. ..
b. No stop .. ..
O11 2 a. orange .. .. 40·00 18·00
O12 2 a. yellow .. .. 42·00 18·00
a. Opt inverted .. .. ..
b. Imperf .. ..
O13 4 a. green .. .. 38·00 35·00
a. Opt inverted £400 £325
O14 17 4 a. green (Die I) £225 £100

A variety with wide and more open capital "S" occurs six times in sheets of all values except No. O8. Price four times the normal.

Reprints exist of Nos. O6, O9 and O14; the latter is Die II instead of Die I.

Reprints of the overprint have also been made, in different setting, on the 8 pies, purple, no watermark.

O 2

O 6

O 3

O 4

(No. O15 surch at Calcutta, others optd at Madras)

1866 (Oct). *Fiscal stamps surch or optd.*

(*a*) *Surch as in Type* O 2. *Thick blue glazed paper. Imperf × perf* 14
O15 O 2 2 a. purple £475 £150

(*b*) *Optd "SERVICE POSTAGE" in two lines as in Types* O 3/4 *and similar type. Imperf × perf* 14
O16 – 2 a. purple (G.) £550 £275
O17 O 3 4 a. purple (G.) £950 £475
O18 O 4 8 a. purple (G.) £3250 £1600

(*c*) *Optd "SERVICE POSTAGE" in semi-circle. Wmk Large Crown. P* 15½ × 15
O19 O 6 ½ a. mauve/*lilac* (G.) .. .. .. £175 75·00
a. Opt double £1400

So-called reprints of Nos. O15 to O18 are known, but in these the surcharge differs entirely in the spacing, etc., of the words; they are more properly described as Government imitations. The imitations of No. O15 have surcharge in *black* or in *green*. No. O19 exists with reprinted overprint which has a full stop after "POSTAGE".

PRINTERS. The following stamps up to No. O108 were overprinted by De La Rue and thereafter Official stamps were printed or overprinted by the Security Printing Press at Nasik.

Service. (O 7)

On H. S. M. (O 8)

On H. S. M. (O 9)

1867–73. *Optd with Type* O **7**. *Wmk Elephant's Head. T* **13**. *P* 14.
O20 **11** ½ a. blue (Die I) 3·50 40
O21 ½ a. pale blue (Die I) 3·50 45
O22 ½ a. blue (Die II) (1873) 65·00 25·00
O23 1 a. brown 4·25 45
O24 1 a. deep brown 4·25 50
O25 1 a. chocolate 4·25 65
O26 2 a. yellow 4·00 2·50
O27 2 a. orange 3·75 2·25
O28 **17** 4 a. pale green (Die I) 3·25 2·00
O29 4 a. green (Die I) 3·00 2·00
O30 **11** 8 a. rose (Die II) (1868) 3·25 2·00
O30*a* 8 a. pale rose (Die II) 3·25 2·00

Prepared for use, but not issued
O30*b* **18** 6 a. 8 p. slate 95·00

1874–82. *Optd with Type* O **8**. (*a*) *In black.*
O31 **11** ½ a. blue (Die II) 1·25 20
O32 1 a. brown 1·25 20
O33 2 a. yellow 7·50 3·50
O33*a* 2 a. orange 7·50 3·25
O34 **17** 4 a. green (Die I) 3·50 2·50
O35 **11** 8 a. rose (Die II) 3·50 2·00

(*b*) *Optd in blue-black*
O36 **11** ½ a. blue (Die II) (1882) 95·00 16·00
O37 1 a. brown (1882) £150 45·00

1883–99. *Wmk Star, T* **34**. *P* 14. *Optd with Type* O **9**.
O37*a* **40** 3 p. aniline carmine (1899) 20 5
O38 **23** ½ a. deep blue-green 20 5
a. Opt double — 75·00
O39 ½ a. blue-green 20 5
O40 **25** 1 a. brown-purple 25 5
a. Opt inverted 60·00 75·00
b. Opt double — £110
O41 1 a. plum 25 5
O42 **27** 2 a. pale blue 1·00 8
O43 2 a. blue 80 10
O44 **29** 4 a. olive-green 1·10 10
O44*a* 4 a. slate-green 1·10 10
O45 **31** 8 a. dull mauve 2·00 40
O46 8 a. magenta 1·40 12
O47 **37** 1 r. green and rose (1892) 4·00 40
O48 1 r. green and carmine (1892) 3·50 40
O37*a*/48 *Set of* 7 6·50 75

1900 *Colours changed. Optd with Type* O **9**.
O49 **23** ½ a. pale yellow-green 35 10
O49*a* ½ a. yellow-green 35 10
O50 **25** 1 a. carmine 35 5
a. Opt inverted — 85·00
b. Opt double — £125
O51 **27** 2 a. pale violet 4·50 25
O52 2 a. mauve 5·50 35

1902–9. *Stamps of King Edward VII optd with Type* O **9**.
O54 **41** 3 p. grey (1903) 70 20
O55 3 p. slate-grey (1905) 55 20
O56 **42** ½ a. green 90 8
O57 **43** 1 a. carmine 70 5
O58 **44** 2 a. violet 2·25 10
O59 2 a. mauve 1·75 10
O60 **47** 4 a. olive 2·00 10
O61 4 a. pale olive 2·00 10
O62 **48** 6 a. olive-bistre (1909) 2·25 12
O63 **49** 8 a. mauve 4·00 15
O64 8 a. magenta 4·00 15
O65 **51** 1 r. green and carmine (1905) 4·00 12
O54/65 *Set of* 8 14·50 85

1906. *New types. Optd with Type* O **9**.
O66 **53** ½ a. green 25 5
O67 **54** 1 a. carmine 60 5

On

H. S.

M.
(O 9*a*)

1909. *Optd with Type* O **9*a***.
O68 **52** 2 r. carmine and yellow-brown 7·00 60
O68*a* 2 r. rose-red and yellow-brown 7·00 80
O69 5 r. ultramarine and violet 14·00 1·50
O70 10 r. green and carmine 15·00 5·50
O70*a* 10 r. green and scarlet 22·00 8·50
O71 15 r. blue and olive-brown 50·00 28·00
O72 25 r. brownish orange and blue £160 55·00

NINE

SERVICE (O 10)(14 mm)

SERVICE (O 11) (21½) mm)

PIES (O 12)

1912. *Stamps of King George V (wmk Single Star, T* **34**) *optd with Type* O **10** *or* O **11** *(rupee values).*
O73 **55** 3 p. grey 15 5
O74 3 p. slate-grey 15 5
O75 3 p. blue-slate 30 10
O76 **56** ½ a. yellow-green 15 5
a. Overprint double 60·00
O77 ½ a. pale blue-green 15 10
O80 **57** 1 a. rose-carmine 40 10
O81 **57** 1 a. carmine 40 10
O82 1 a. aniline carmine 40 10
a. Overprint double — 65·00
O83 **59** 2 a. mauve 45 10
O84 2 a. purple 45 10
O85 **63** 4 a. deep olive 1·00 10
O86 4 a. olive-green 1·00 10
O87 **64** 6 a. yellow-bistre 1·50 1·25
O88 6 a. deep bistre-brown 3·25 1·90
O89 **65** 8 a. purple 2·25 25
O89*a* 8 a. mauve 2·25 20
O90 8 a. bright aniline mauve 7·00 90
O91 **67** 1 r. red-brown and blue-green 2·25 15
O92 2 r. rose-carmine and brown 3·00 1·00
O93 5 r. ultramarine and violet 11·00 3·50
O94 10 r. green and scarlet 27·00 11·00
O95 15 r. blue and olive 55·00 45·00
O96 25 r. orange and blue £140 50·00
O73/96 *Set of* 13 £225 £100

1921. *No.* O80 *surch with Type* O **12**.
O97 **57** 9 p. on 1 a. rose-carmine 12 12

1922. *No.* 197 *optd with Type* O **10**.
O98 **57** 1 a. chocolate 35 5

ONE RUPEE (O 13)

ONE RUPEE (O 14)

1925. *Official stamps surcharged.*

(*a*) *Issue of* 1909, *as Type* O 13
O 99 **52** 1 r. on 15 r. blue and olive 3·75 2·25
O100 1 r. on 25 r chestnut and blue 17·00 20·00
O101 2 r. on 10 r green and scarlet 3·50 2·25
O101*a* 2 r. on 10 r. green and carmine £100 45·00

(*b*) Issue of 1912, *with Type* O 14
O102 **67** 1 r. on 15 r. blue and olive 17·00 20·00
O103 1 r. on 25 r. orange and blue 4·00 3·25
a. Surch inverted £275

(*c*) Issue of 1912, *as Type* O 13
O104 **67** 2 r. on 10 r. green and scarlet £500

Examples of the above showing other surcharge errors are believed to be of clandestine origin.

ONE ANNA (O 15)

SERVICE ONE ANNA (O 16)

1926. *No.* O62 *surch with Type* O **15**.
O105 **48** 1 a. on 6 a. olive-bistre 40 25

1926. *Postage stamps of* 1911–22 *(wmk Single Star), surch as Type* O **16**.
O106 **58** 1 a. on 1½ a. chocolate (A) 20 5
O107 1 a. on 1½ a. chocolate (B) 45 12
a. Error. On 1 a. chocolate (197) £130
O108 **61** 1 a. on 2½ a. ultramarine 60 1·10

The surcharge on No. O108 has no bars at top.

SERVICE (O 17)(13½ mm)

SERVICE (O 18) (19½ mm)

1926–31. *Stamps of King George V (wmk Multiple Star, T* **69**) *optd with Types* O **17** *or* O **18** *(rupee values).*
O109 **55** 3 p. slate (1.10.29) 12 5
O110 **56** ½ a. green (1931) 45 5
O111 **57** 1 a. chocolate 12 5
O112 **70** 2 a. purple 12 5
O113 **71** 4 a. sage-green 15 8
O115 **65** 8 a. reddish purple 40 10
O116 **66** 12 a. claret 40 25
O117 **67** 1 r. chocolate and green (1930) 1·25 15
O118 2 r. carmine and orange (1930) 5·00 2·50
O120 10 r. green and scarlet (1931) 55·00 35·00
O109/20 *Set of* 10 55·00 35·00

1930. *As No.* O111, *but optd as Type* O **10** *(14 mm).*
O125 **57** 1 a. chocolate 22·00 2·00

1932–36. *Stamps of King George V (wmk Mult Star, T* **69**) *optd with Type* O **17**.
O126 **79** ½ a. green (1935) 35 5
O127 **80** 9 p. deep green 12 5
O127*a* **81** 1 a. chocolate (1936) 12 5
O128 **82** 1¼ a. mauve 15 5
O129 **70** 2 a. vermilion 50 10
O130 **59** 2 a. vermilion (1935) 95 1·10
O130*a* 2 a. vermilion (*small die*) (1936) 60 10
O131 **61** 2½ a. orange (22.4.32) 12 15
O132 **63** 4 a. sage-green (1935) 60 15
O133 **64** 6 a. bistre (1936) 4·00 2·75
O126/33 *Set of* 9 6·00 3·00

1937–39. *Stamps of King George VI optd as Types* O **17** *or* O **18** *(rupee values).*
O135 **91** ½ a. red-brown (1938) 2·25 15
O136 9 p. green (1937) 4·00 5
O137 1 a. carmine (1937) 90 5
O138 **93** 1 r. grey and red-brown (5.38) 50 12
O139 2 r. purple and brown (5.38) 3·50 70
O140 5 r. green and blue (10.38) 3·50 2·00
O141 10 r. purple and claret (1939) 13·00 3·50
O135/41 *Set of* 7 25·00 6·00

SERVICE 1A (O 19)

INDIA POSTAGE 3 PS 3 PS SERVICE (O 20)

1939 (May). *Stamp of King George V, surch with Type* O **19**.
O142 **82** 1 a. on 1½ a. mauve 2·25 25

(Des T. I. Archer)

1939 (1 June)–**42.** *Typo. W* **69**. *P* 14.
O143 O **20** 3 p. slate 20 5
O144 ½ a. red-brown 20 5
O144*a* ½ a. purple (1942) 20 5
O145 9 p. green 25 5
O146 1 a. carmine 25 5
O146*a* 1 a. 3 p. bistre (1941) 2·50 40
O146*b* 1½ a. dull violet (1942) 75 5
O147 2 a. vermilion 70 5
O148 2½ a. bright violet 70 15
O149 4 a. brown 75 5
O150 8 a. slate-violet 2·25 20
O143/50 *Set of* 11 8·00 1·10

1948 (Aug). *First Anniv Indian Independence. Mahatma Gandhi postage stamps optd* "SERVICE", *as Type* O **17**.
O150*a* **305** 1½ a. brown 42·00 30·00
O150*b* 3½ a. violet £375 £325
O150*c* 12 a. grey-green £1350 £1350
O150*d* **306** 10 r. purple-brown and lake £5000

SERVICE POSTAGE 3 PS INDIA (O 21)

SERVICE POSTAGE 1 Re INDIA (O 22)

O 21 Asokan Capital O 22

(Des T. I. Archer)

1950 (2 Jan)–**51.** *Typo* (O **21**) *or litho* (O **22**). *W* **69**. *P* 14.
O151 O **21** 3 p. slate-violet (1.7.50) 5 5
O152 6 p. purple-brown (1.7.50) 10 5
O153 9 p. green (1.7.50) 20 5
O154 1 a. turquoise (1.7.50) 25 5
O155 2 a. carmine (1.7.50) 35 5
O156 3 a. red-orange (1.7.50) 80 30
O157 4 a. lake (1.7.50) 3·25 10
O158 4 a. ultramarine (1.10.51) 50 5
O159 6 a. bright violet (1.7.50) 80 30
O160 8 a. red-brown (1.7.50) 90 5
O161 O **22** 1 r. violet 1·40 5
O162 2 r. rose-carmine 1·50 25
O163 5 r. bluish green 3·50 1·50
O164 10 r. reddish brown 6·50 3·75
O151/64 *Set of* 14 18·00 5·50

1957 (1 Apr)–**58.** *Value in naye paise. Typo* (*t*) *or litho* (*l*). *W* **69**. *P* 14.
O165 O **21** 1 n.p. slate (*l*) 5 5
a. Slate-black (*l*) 10 10
b. Greenish slate (*t*) 5 5
O166 2 n.p. blackish violet (*t*) 5 5
O167 3 n.p. chocolate (*t*) 5 5
O168 5 n.p. green (*l*) 5 5
a. Deep emerald (*t*) 5 5
O169 6 n.p. turquoise-blue (*t*) 5 5
O170 13 n.p. scarlet (*t*) 5 5
O171 15 n.p. reddish violet (*l*) (6.58) 8 12
a. Reddish violet (*t*) 35 40
O172 20 n.p. red (*l*) 10 5
a. Vermilion (*t*) 10 5
O173 25 n.p. violet-blue (*l*) 15 5
a. Ultramarine (*t*) 15 5
O174 50 n.p. red-brown (*l*) 25 15
a. Reddish brown (*t*) 25 25
O165/74 *Set of* 10 80 55

1958–71. *As Nos.* O165/74*a and* O161/4 *but W* **374** *(upright). Litho* (*l*) *or typo* (*t*). *P* 14.
O175 O **21** 1 n.p. slate-black (*t*) (1.59) 5 5
O176 2 n.p. blackish violet (*t*) (1.59) 5 5
O177 3 n.p. chocolate (*t*) (11.58) 5 5
O178 5 n.p. deep emerald (*t*) (11.58) 5 5
O179 6 n.p. turquoise-blue (*t*) (5.59) 5 5
O180 10 n.p. deep grey-green (*l*) (1963) 15 15
a. Deep grey-green (*t*) (1966?) 10 12
O181 13 n.p. scarlet (*t*) (1963) 12 10
O182 15 n.p. deep violet (*t*) (11.58) 8 5
a. Light reddish violet (*t*) (1961) 8 5
O183 20 n.p. vermilion (*t*) (5.59) 8 5
a. Red (*t*) (1966?) 8 12
O184 25 n.p. ultramarine (*t*) (7.59) 8 5
O185 50 n.p. reddish brown (*t*) (6.59) 12 5
a. Chestnut (*l*) (1966?) 12 12
O186 O **22** 1 r. reddish violet (*t*) (2.59) 15 5
O187 2 r. rose-carmine (*l*) (1960) 35 10
a. Wmk sideways. *Pale rose-carmine* (*l*) (1969?) 35 15

O188 O **22** 5 r. slate-green (*l*) (7.59) 90 40
a. Wmk sideways. *Deep grey-green* (*l*) (1969?) 60 40
O189 10 r. brown-lake (*l*) (7.59) 2·00 80
a. Wmk sideways (*l*) (1971) 2·00 1·25
O175/89 *Set of* 15 3·75 1·75

O **23** (*see also* Type O **26**)

(O **24**)

O **25**

1967 (20 Mar)–**74**? *Photo. W* **374** (*sideways*). *P* 15 × 14.
O190 O **23** 2 p. violet (1974?) 5 5
O191 5 p. green (1974?) 5 5
O192 10 p. myrtle-green (1974?) 10 5
O193 15 p. plum (2.7.73) 10 10
O194 20 p. red (1974?) 60 60
O195 30 p. ultramarine (1973) 15 15
O196 50 p. chestnut (2.7.73) 35 35
O197 1 r. dull purple (*shades*) (20.3.67) 15 5
O190/7 *Set of* 8 1·25 1·25

1967 (15 Nov)–**74**(?). *Wmk Large Star and* "INDIA GOVT" *in sheet*. Photo. P* 15 × 14. *No gum.*
O200 O **23** 2 p. violet 5 5
O201 3 p. chocolate 5 5
O202 5 p. green (*shades*) 5 5
O203 6 p. turquoise-blue 5 5
O204 10 p. myrtle-green (*shades*) 5 5
O205 15 p. plum 5 5
O206 20 p. red 5 5
O207 25 p. carmine-red (1974?) 5 5
O208 30 p. ultramarine 5 5
O209 50 p. chestnut 8 8
O200/9 *Set of* 10 30 25

*The arrangement of this watermark in the sheet results in the words and the star appearing upright, inverted or sideways.

1971. *Obligatory Tax. Refugee Relief.*

(*a*) *Provisional issue. No.* 0202 *optd with Type* O **24**
O210 O **23** 5 p. yellowish green (*shades*) 10 5

(*b*) *Issue for Bangalore. No.* O202 *optd with T* **602**
O211 O **23** 5 p. yellowish green 30 15
a. Opt inverted 3·00

(*c*) *Issue for Goa. No.* O202 *optd with T* **606**
O212 O **23** 5 p. yellowish green

(*d*) *Definitive issue. Wmk Large Star and* "INDIA GOVT" *in sheet*. Litho. P* 15 × 14. *No gum.*
O213 O **25** 5 p. yellowish-green 5 5
a. *Yellow-green*

*See note below No. O209.

The surcharge on mail for the relief of refugees from the former East Pakistan referred to in the note after No. 651 also applied to official mail. The cost of the stamps used by each Government Department was charged against its budget and the additional charge for refugee stamps meant that each Department had to spend less to keep within its budget.

O **26**

O **27**

1976 (1 Apr)–**80**. *Redrawn, showing face-value in figures only and smaller Capital with Hindi motto beneath. P* 15 × 14. (*a*) *Wmk Large Star and* "INDIA GOVT" *in sheet.* No gum.*
O214 O **26** 2 p. deep violet-blue 5 5
O215 5 p. yellowish green 5 5
O216 10 p. myrtle-green (*shades*) 5 5
O217 15 p. deep purple 5 5
O218 20 p. Indian red 5 5
O219 25 p. rose-carmine (*shades*) 5 5
O220 30 p. chalky blue (1.5.79) 5 5
O221 35 p. violet (6.12.80) 5 5
O222 50 p. chestnut 5 5
O223 1 r. deep brownish purple (13.8.80) 12 12

(*b*) *W* **374** (*sideways*)
O224 O **26** 1 r. deep brownish purple 12 12
O225 – 2 r. rose-red (date?) 30 30
a. Wmk upright 25 25
O226 – 5 r. deep green (date?) 65 65
a. Wmk upright (1978) 60 60
O227 – 10 r. brown-lake (date?) 1·25 1·25
a. Wmk upright 1·10 1·10
O214/27a *Set of* 13 1·90 1·90

The 2, 5 and 10 r. are larger, size as Type O **22**.

*See note below No. 720. The 2 p. value is only known on the first type of watermark, the 35, 50 p. and 1 r. values on the second and the remaining values on both.

1981 (Feb). *Redrawn showing revised border design and inscriptions, with face value figures now in bottom corners. Wmk Large Star and* "INDIA GOVT" *in sheet. P* 15 × 14.
O228 O **27** 2 r. rose-red 20 25
O229 5 r. deep green 50 55
O230 10 r. brown-lake 1·00 1·10

1981 (10 Dec). *As Nos.* O215/19, O221/3 *and* O228/30 *but printed on cream paper. Unwatermarked. Imperf.*
O231 O **26** 5 p. dull yellowish green 5 5
O232 10 p. deep green 5 5
O233 15 p. deep reddish violet 5 5
O234 20 p. dull vermilion 5 5
O235 25 p. bright rose 5 5
O236 35 p. violet 5 5
O237 50 p. orange-brown 5 8
O238 1 r. deep dull purple 10 12
O239 O **27** 2 r. orange-vermilion 20 25
O240 5 r. deep dull green 50 55
O241 10 r. lake-brown 1·00 1·10
O231/41 *Set of* 11 2·00 2·10

Some values have been seen unofficially pin-perforated.

1982 (22 Nov). *As Nos.* 215/23 *and* 228/30. *Wmk Large Star and* "INDIA GOVT" *in sheet. P* 12½ × 13.
O242 O **26** 5 p. light green 5 5
O243 10 p. deep dull green 5 5
O244 15 p. blackish purple 5 5
O245 20 p. Indian red 5 5
O246 25 p. cerise 5 5
O247 30 p. deep ultramarine 5 5
O248 35 p. bluish violet 5 5
O249 50 p. reddish brown 8 10
O250 1 r. deep purple-brown 12 15
O251 O **27** 2 r. rose-red 25 30
O252 5 r. grey-green 55 60
O253 10 r. chocolate 1·10 1·25
O242/53 *Set of* 12 2·25 2·50

1984 (16 Apr). *As Nos.* O215/18, O220/3 *and* O228/30, *but W* **374** (*sideways*). *P* 12½ × 13.
O254 O **26** 5 p. yellowish green 5 5
O255 10 p. deep dull green 5 5
O256 15 p. blackish purple 5 5
O257 20 p. Indian red 5 5
O258 30 p. deep ultramarine 5 5
O259 35 p. bluish violet 5 5
O260 50 p. reddish brown 8 10
O261 1 r. deep purple-brown 12 15
O262 O **27** 2 r. rose-red 25 30
O263 5 r. grey-green 60 65
O264 10 r. chocolate 1·25 1·40
O254/64 *Set of* 11 2·40 2·75

CHINA EXPEDITIONARY FORCE

PRICES FOR STAMPS ON COVER
Nos. C1/10 *from* × 15
No. C10*a* †
Nos. C11/22 *from* × 8
Nos. C23/34 *from* × 20

C. E. F.
(C 1)

Stamps of India overprinted with Type* C 1, *in black

1900. *Stamps of Queen Victoria.*
C 1 **40** 3 p. carmine 30 30
C 2 **23** ½ a. green 30 30
C 3 **25** 1 a. brown-purple 50 50
C 4 **27** 2 a. ultramarine 2·00 3·00
C 5 **36** 2½ a. green 2·25 3·25
C 6 **28** 3 a. orange 3·50 7·50
C 7 **29** 4 a. olive-green 2·50 3·50
a. Opt double, one albino
C 8 **31** 8 a. magenta 2·75 4·75
C 9 **32** 12 a. purple/*red* 3·75 10·00
C10 **37** 1 r. green and carmine 5·50 7·00
C1/10 *Set of* 10 21·00 35·00

Prepared, but not issued
C10*a* **26** 1 a. 6 p. sepia £100

1904 (27 Feb).
C11 **25** 1 a. carmine 15·00 11·00

1904. *Stamps of King Edward VII.*
C12 **41** 3 p. grey 60 95
aa. Opt double, one albino £140
a. *Slate-grey* 90 1·40
C13 **43** 1 a. carmine 1·25 1·00
C14 **44** 2 a. pale violet 3·50 1·50
C15 **45** 2½ a. ultramarine 3·00 4·50
C16 **46** 3 a. orange-brown 3·50 4·75
C17 **47** 4 a. olive-green 7·00 9·50
C18 **49** 8 a. magenta 7·00 8·50
a. *Mauve*
C19 **50** 12 a. purple/*red* 9·00 18·00
C20 **51** 1 r. green and carmine 12·00 22·00
C12/20 *Set of* 9 42·00 65·00

1909. "POSTAGE & REVENUE."
C21 **53** ½ a. green (No. 149) 60 70
C22 **54** 1 a. carmine (No. 150) 60 35

1913–21. *Stamps of King George V. Wmk Star.*
C23 **55** 3 p. slate-grey (1913) 60 2·00
C24 **56** ½ a. green 70 2·00
C25 **57** 1 a. aniline carmine 90 1·40
C26 **58** 1½ a. chocolate (Type A) 4·00 15·00
C27 **59** 2 a. mauve 3·25 11·00
C28 **61** 2½ a. bright blue 5·00 8·50
C29 **62** 3 a. orange-brown 7·00 15·00
C30 **63** 4 a. olive-green 12·00 35·00
C32 **65** 8 a. mauve 12·00 45·00
C33 **66** 12 a. claret 12·00 50·00
C34 **67** 1 r. red-brown and blue-green 35·00 90·00
C23/34 *Set of* 11 85·00 £250

INDIAN EXPEDITIONARY FORCES 1914–22

PRICES FOR STAMPS ON COVER
Nos. E1/13 *from* × 10

I. E. F.
(E 1)

1914. *Stamps of India (King George V) optd with Type* E **1**.
E 1 **55** 3 p. slate-grey 25 30
a. No stop after "F" 15·00 15·00
b. No stop after "E" 20·00 20·00
c. Opt double 25·00 25·00
E 2 **56** ½ a. yellow-green 25 30
a. No stop after "F" 22·00 22·00
b. Opt double
E 3 **57** 1 a. aniline carmine 25 25
a. No stop after "F" 25·00 25·00
E 4 1 a. carmine 80 60
E 5 **59** 2 a. mauve 45 40
a. No stop after "F" 50·00 50·00
b. No stop after "E" 55·00 55·00
E 6 **61** 2½ a. ultramarine 65 1·00
a. No stop after "F" 55·00 60·00
E 7 **62** 3 a. orange-brown 60 60
a. No stop after "F" 55·00 60·00
E 8 **63** 4 a. olive-green 60 80
a. No stop after "F" 60·00 65·00
E 9 **65** 8 a. purple 1·25 1·00
a. No stop after "F" 75·00 75·00
E10 8 a. mauve 6·00 7·00
E11 **66** 12 a. dull claret 6·00 8·50
a. No stop after "F" £100 £110
E12 12 a. claret 3·75 10·00
E13 **67** 1 r. red-brown and blue-green 5·50 10·00
a. Opt double, one albino £100
E1/13 *Set of* 10 13·00 21·00

INDIAN CUSTODIAN FORCES IN KOREA

भारतीय
संरक्षा कटक
कोरिया
(K 1)

1953 (17 Oct). *Stamps of India optd with Type* K **1**.
K 1 **307** 3 p. slate-violet 20 55
K 2 **308** 6 p. purple-brown 25 65
K 3 **309** 9 p. yellow-green 30 90
K 4 **328** 1 a. turquoise 45 95
K 5 **311** 2 a. carmine 90 1·40
K 6 **313** 2½ a. lake 1·50 3·25
K 7 **312** 3 a. brown-orange 1·75 3·25
K 8 **314** 4 a. bright blue 2·25 3·75
K 9 **315** 6 a. violet 6·00 9·50
K10 **316** 8 a. turquoise-green 5·50 9·50
K11 **317** 12 a. dull blue 9·00 16·00
K12 **318** 1 r. dull violet and green 12·00 22·00
K1/12 *Set of* 12 35·00 65·00

PRICES OF SETS

Set prices are given for many issues, generally those containing five stamps or more. Definitive sets include one of each value or major colour change, but do not cover different perforations, die types or minor shades. Where a choice is possible the set prices are based on the cheapest versions of the stamps included in the listings.

INDIAN U.N. FORCE IN CONGO

U.N. FORCE
(INDIA)
CONGO

(U 1)

1962 (15 Jan). *Stamps of India optd with Type* U **1**. *W* **69** *(sideways)* (13 *n.p.*) *or W* **374** *(others)*.

U1	**361**	1 n.p. blue-green	8	25
U2		2 n.p. light brown	8	25
U3		5 n.p. bright green	10	20
U4		8 n.p. light blue-green	12	25
U5		13 n.p. bright carmine-red	20	70
U6		50 n.p. orange	40	1·50
U1/6		*Set of* 6	90	2·75

INDIAN U.N. FORCE IN GAZA (PALESTINE) UNEF

UNEF

(G 1)

1965 (15 Jan). *No.* 492 *of India optd with Type* G **1**.

G1	**449**	15 p. slate (C.)	15	40

INTERNATIONAL COMMISSION IN INDO-CHINA

अन्तर्राष्ट्रीय आयोग कम्बोज (N 1) अन्तर्राष्ट्रीय आयोग लाओस (N 2) अन्तर्राष्ट्रीय आयोग वियत नाम (N 3)

1954 (1 Dec). *Stamps of India. W* **69**.

		(*a*) *Optd as Type* N **1**, *for use in Cambodia*		
N 1	**307**	3 p. slate-violet	12	45
N 2	**328**	1 a. turquoise	40	50
N 3	**311**	2 a. carmine	60	80
N 4	**316**	8 a. turquoise-green	2·75	5·00
N 5	**317**	12 a. dull blue	3·25	6·00
		(*b*) *Optd as Type* N **2**, *for use in Laos*		
N 6	**307**	3 p. slate-violet	12	45
N 7	**328**	1 a. turquoise	40	50
N 8	**311**	2 a. carmine	60	80
N 9	**316**	8 a. turquoise-green	2·75	5·00
N10	**317**	12 a. dull blue	3·25	6·00
		(*c*) *Optd as Type* N **3**, *for use in Vietnam*		
N11	**307**	3 p. slate-violet	12	45
N12	**328**	1 a. turquoise	40	50
N13	**311**	2 a. carmine	60	80
N14	**316**	8 a. turquoise-green	2·75	5·00
N15	**317**	12 a. dull blue	3·25	6·00
N1/15		*Set of* 15	19·00	35·00

1957 (1 Apr). *Stamps of India. W* **69** *(sideways)*.

		(*a*) *Optd as Type* N **1**, *for use in Cambodia*		
N16	**361**	2 n.p. light brown	15	20
N17		6 n.p. grey	25	30
N18		13 n.p. bright carmine-red	40	40
N19		50 n.p. orange	1·25	2·25
N20		75 n.p. reddish purple	1·50	2·75
		(*b*) *Optd as Type* N **2**, *for use in Laos*		
N21	**361**	2 n.p. light brown	15	20
N22		6 n.p. grey	25	30
N23		13 n.p. bright carmine-red	40	40
N24		50 n.p. orange	1·25	2·25
N25		75 n.p. reddish purple	1·50	2·75
		(*c*) *Optd as Type* N **3**, *for use in Vietnam*		
N26	**361**	2 n.p. light brown	15	20
N27		6 n.p. grey	25	30
N28		13 n.p. bright carmine-red	40	40
N29		50 n.p. orange	1·25	2·25
N30		75 n.p. reddish purple	1·50	2·75
N16/30		*Set of* 15	9·50	16·00

1962–65. *Stamps of India. W* **374**.

		(*a*) *Optd as Type* N **1**, *for use in Cambodia*		
N32	**361**	2 n.p. light brown	75	2·25
		(*b*) *Optd as Type* N **2**, *for use in Laos*		
N38	**361**	2 n.p. light brown	75	2·25
N39		3 n.p. deep brown (1.8.63)	30	50
N40		5 n.p. bright green (1.8.63)	20	35
N41		50 n.p. orange (1965)	80	2·00
N42		75 n.p. reddish purple (1965)	1·25	2·50
		(*c*) *Optd as Type* N **3**, *for use in Vietnam*		
N43	**361**	1 n.p. blue-green	40	70
N44		2 n.p. light brown	75	2·25
N45		3 n.p. deep brown (1963?)	25	40
N46		5 n.p. bright green (1963)	15	30
N47		50 n.p. orange (1965)	80	2·00
N48		75 n.p. reddish-purple (1965)	1·25	2·50
N32/48		*Set of* 12	7·00	16·00

ICC (N 4) ICC (N 5)

1965 (15 Jan). *No.* 492 *of India optd with Type* N **4**, *for use in Laos and Vietnam.*

N49	**449**	15 p. slate (C.)	30	70

1968 (2 Oct). *Nos.* 504/5, 506, 509/10, 515 *and* 517/18 *etc of India optd as Type* N **5**, *in red, for use in Laos and Vietnam.*

N50		2 p. red-brown	10	30
N51		3 p. brown-olive	10	30
N52		5 p. cerise	10	15
N53		10 p. new blue	30	30
N54		15 p. bronze-green	30	30
N55		60 p. deep grey	35	90
N56		1 r. red-brown and plum	50	1·00
N57		2 r. new blue and deep slate-violet	1·25	3·00
N50/7		*Set of* 8	2·75	5·75

INDIAN NATIONAL ARMY

The following are stated to have been used in the Japanese-occupied areas of India during the drive on Imphal. Issued by the Indian National Army.

Typo. No gum. Perf 11½ or imperf. 1 p. violet, 1 p. maroon, 1 a. green.

JAPANESE OCCUPATION OF THE ANDAMAN AND NICOBAR ISLANDS

The Andaman Islands in the Bay of Bengal were occupied on the 23 March 1942 and the Nicobar Islands in July 1942. Civil administration was resumed in October 1945.

The following Indian stamps were surcharged with large figures preceded by a decimal point:—

Postage stamps—.3 on ½ a. (No. 248), .5 on 1 a. (No. 250), .10 on 2 a. (No. 236*b*), .30 on 6 a. (No. 274).

Official stamps—.10 on 1 a. 3 p. (No. O146*b*), .20 on 3 p. (No. O143) from booklet panes, .20 in red on 3 p. (No. O143).

INDIAN CONVENTION STATES

The following issues resulted from a series of postal conventions agreed between the Imperial Government and the state administrations of Patiala (1 October 1884), Gwalior, Jind and Nabha (1 July 1885), and Chamba and Faridkot (1 January 1887).

Under the terms of these conventions the British Indian Post Office supplied overprinted British India issues to the state administrations which, in turn, had to conform to a number of conditions covering the issue of stamps, rates of postage and the exchange of mail.

Such overprinted issues were valid for postage within the state of issue, to other "Convention States" and to destinations in British India.

Stamps of Chamba, Gwalior, Jind, Nabha and Patiala ceased to be valid for postage on 1 January 1951, when they were replaced by those of the Republic of India, valid from 1 April 1950.

Stamps of India overprinted

In the Queen Victoria issues we omit varities due to broken type, including the numerous small "A" varieties which may have come about through damaged type. We do, however, list the small "G" in "GWALIOR" as this was definitely the result of the use of type of the wrong size.

Variations in the length of the words due to unequal spacing when setting are also omitted.

CHAMBA

PRICES FOR STAMPS ON COVER	
Nos. 1/27	*from* × 7
Nos. 28/120	*from* × 4
Nos. O1/86	*from* × 8

CHAMBA STATE (1) CHAMBA (2)

1886–95. *Queen Victoria. Optd with T* **1**.

1	**23**	½ a. blue-green	10	10
		a. "CHMABA"	65·00	
		b. "8TATE"	90·00	
2	**25**	1 a. brown-purple	10	10
		a. "CHMABA"	£125	
		b. "8TATE"	£125	
3		1 a. plum	15	20
4	**26**	1½ a. sepia (1895)	80	1·40
5	**27**	2 a. dull blue	30	35
		a. "CHAMBA" double		
		b. "CHMABA"	£325	
		c. "8TATE"	£275	
6	**27**	2 a. ultramarine	45	55
7	**36**	2½ a. green (1895)	10·00	18·00
8	**28**	3 a. orange (1887)	3·00	4·50
		a. "CHMABA"	£950	
9		3 a. brown-orange	40	45
10	**29**	4 a. olive-green	40	50
		a. "CHMABA"	£475	
		b. "8TATE"	£550	
11		4 a. slate-green	60	75
12	**21**	6 a. olive-bistre (1890)	80	1·50
13		6 a. bistre-brown	1·25	2·00
14	**31**	8 a. dull mauve (1887)	1·50	2·00
		a. "CHMABA"	£850	
15		8 a. magenta	1·00	1·50
16	**32**	12 a. purple/*red* (1890)	1·25	1·75
		a. "CHMABA"	£1100	
		b. "8TATE"	£1400	
17	**33**	1 r. slate (1887)	17·00	35·00
		a. "CHMABA"	£1800	
18	**37**	1 r. green and carmine (1895)	1·25	2·00
19	**38**	2 r. carmine and yellow-brown (1895)	29·00	40·00
20		3 r. brown and green (1895)	32·00	45·00
21		5 r. ultramarine and violet (1895)	35·00	50·00
		a. Opt double, one albino		
1/21		*Set of* 15	£120	£180

1900–4. *Colours changed.*

22	**40**	3 p. carmine	10	12
23		3 p. grey (1904)	15	25
		a. Opt inverted	40·00	
24	**23**	½ a. pale yellow-green (1902)	12	20
25		½ a. yellow-green	12	15
26	**25**	1 a. carmine (1902)	12	15
27	**27**	2 a. pale violet (1903)	5·00	8·00

1903–5. *King Edward VII. Optd with T* **1**.

28	**41**	3 p. pale grey	8	8
29		3 p. slate-grey (1905)	8	8
30	**42**	½ a. green	8	8
31	**43**	1 a. carmine	8	8
32	**44**	2 a. pale violet (1904)	25	25
33		2 a. mauve	25	30
34	**46**	3 a. orange-brown (1905)	60	80
35	**47**	4 a. olive (1904)	80	1·00
36	**48**	6 a. olive-bistre (1905)	1·25	2·00
37	**49**	8 a. dull mauve (1904)	1·25	1·50
38		8 a. magenta	1·60	2·25
39	**50**	12 a. purple/*red* (1905)	1·60	2·50
40	**51**	1 r. green and carmine (1904)	1·75	3·00
28/40		*Set of* 10	7·00	10·00

1907. *Nos.* 149/50 *of India optd with T* **1**.

41	**53**	½ a. green	15	25
42	**54**	1 a. carmine	20	25

1913. *King George V optd with T* **1**.

43	**55**	3 p. slate-grey	8	10
44	**56**	½ a. green	8	10
45	**57**	1 a. rose-carmine	20	20
46		1 a. aniline carmine	8	10
47	**59**	2 a. mauve	20	30
48	**62**	3 a. orange-brown	45	70
49	**63**	4 a. olive	60	75
50	**64**	6 a. olive-bistre	60	90
51	**65**	8 a. purple	80	1·00
52	**66**	12 a. dull claret	1·25	2·00
53	**67**	1 r. brown and green	2·25	3·50
43/53		*Set of* 10	5·50	8·50

1921. *No.* 192 *of India optd with T* **2**.

54	**57**	9 p. on 1 a. rose-carmine	80	1·50

1922–27. *Optd with T* **1**. *New values, etc.*

55	**57**	1 a. chocolate	10	10
56	**58**	1½ a. chocolate (Type A)	12·00	20·00
57		1½ a. chocolate (Type B)	25	40
58		1½ a. rose-carmine (Type B) (1927)	70	1·25
59	**61**	2½ a. ultramarine	70	1·25
60		2½ a. orange (1927)	70	1·25
61	**62**	3 a. ultramarine	1·10	1·75

CHAMBA STATE (3) CHAMBA STATE (4)

1927–37. *King George V (Nasik printing, wmk Mult Star). Optd at Nasik with T* **3** *or* **4** (1 *r.*).

62	**55**	3 p. slate (1928)	8	10
63	**56**	½ a. green (1928)	8	10
64	**80**	9 p. deep green (1932)	15	30
65	**57**	1 a. chocolate	8	10
66	**82**	1¼ a. mauve	12	20
67	**58**	1½ a. rose-carmine (B) (1932)	30	50
68	**70**	2 a. purple (1928)	25	30
69	**61**	2½ a. orange (1932)	40	60
70	**62**	3 a. bright blue (1928)	60	1·00
71	**71**	4 a. sage-green (1928)	40	45
72	**64**	6 a. bistre (1937)	24·00	38·00
73	**65**	8 a. reddish purple (1928)	60	1·25
74	**66**	12 a. claret (1928)	1·10	2·25
75	**67**	1 r. chocolate and green (1928)	2·00	2·75
62/75		*Set of* 14	27·00	42·00

The 9 p. exists printed by lithography or typography.

1935–36. *New types and colours. Optd with T* **3**.

76	**79**	½ a. green	10	30
77	**81**	1 a. chocolate	10	15
78	**59**	2 a. vermilion (No. 236*a*)	15	50
79		2 a. vermilion (*small die*, No. 236*b*)	30·00	40·00
80	**62**	3 a. carmine	75	1·25
81	**63**	4 a. sage-green (1936)	75	1·10

CHAMBA STATE (5) CHAMBA (6) CHAMBA (7)

1938. *King George VI. Nos.* 247/64 *optd with T* **3** (3 *p. to* 1 *a.*), *T* **5** (2 *a. to* 12 *a.*) *or T* **4** *(rupee values)*.

82	**91**	3 p. slate	60	90
83		½ a. red-brown	40	75
84		9 p. green	80	1·25
85		1 a. carmine	40	50
86	**92**	2 a. vermilion	65	1·50

87 – 2½ a. bright violet 75 1·60
88 – 3 a. yellow-green 3·00 5·00
89 – 3½ a. bright blue 1·00 2·25
90 – 4 a. brown 1·00 2·25
91 – 6 a. turquoise-green 6·00 11·00
92 – 8 a. slate-violet 1·75 3·75
93 – 12 a. lake 3·00 7·00
94 **93** 1 r. grey and red-brown 7·00 11·00
95 2 r. purple and brown 17·00 22·00
96 5 r. green and blue 35·00 40·00
97 10 r. purple and claret 90·00 £100
98 15 r. brown and green £160 £180
99 25 r. slate-violet and purple £250 £275
82/99 *Set of* 18 £525 £600

1942–47. *Optd with T* **6** *(to 12 a.),* "CHAMBA" *only, as in T* **5** *(14 a.) or T* **7** *(rupee values). (a) Stamps of* 1937.
100 **91** ½ a. red-brown 2·50 3·00
101 1 a. carmine 2·75 3·25
102 **93** 1 r. grey and red-brown 16·00 16·00
103 2 r. purple and brown 17·00 22·00
104 5 r. green and blue 45·00 50·00
105 10 r. purple and claret 80·00 90·00
106 15 r. brown and green £170 £180
107 25 r. slate-violet and purple £275 £300
100/107 *Set of* 8 £550 £600

(b) Stamps of 1940–43
108 **100a** 3 p. slate 25 50
109 ½ a. purple (1943) 35 50
110 9 p. green 25 60
111 1 a. carmine (1943) 40 50
112 **101** 1½ a. dull violet (1943) 35 80
113 2 a. vermilion (1943) 50 80
114 3 a. bright violet 60 1·00
115 3½ a. bright blue 1·00 2·50
116 **102** 4 a. brown 75 1·25
117 6 a. turquoise-green 1·50 5·00
118 8 a. slate-violet 2·00 6·00
119 12 a. lake 3·25 10·00
120 **103** 14 a. purple (1947) 9·00 12·00
108/120 *Set of* 13 18·00 38·00

The 3 a. exists printed by lithography or typography.

OFFICIAL STAMPS

SERVICE

CHAMBA STATE
(O 1)

1886–98. *Queen Victoria. Optd with Type* O **1**.
O 1 **23** ½ a. blue-green 8 8
a. "CHMABA" 45·00 50·00
b. "SERV CE" £120
c. "8TATE" 85·00
O 2 **25** 1 a. brown-purple 8 8
a. "CHMABA" 85·00 90·00
b. "SERV CE" £180
c. "8TATE" £110
O 3 1 a. plum 8 8
a. "SERVICE" double 85·00 85·00
O 4 **27** 2 a. dull blue 25 30
a. "CHMABA" £300
O 5 2 a. ultramarine (1887) 15 20
O 6 **28** 3 a. orange (1890) 10·00 15·00
a. "CHMABA" £550
O 7 3 a. brown-orange 1·00 1·50
O 8 **29** 4 a. olive-green 25 30
a. "CHMABA" £300
b. "SERV CE" £650
c. "8TATE" £350
O 9 4 a. slate-green 60 75
O10 **21** 6 a. olive-bistre (1890) 80 1·00
O11 6 a. bistre-brown 15·00 20·00
O12 **31** 8 a. dull mauve (1887) 65 90
a. "CHMABA" £900
O13 8 a. magenta 70 1·00
O14 32 12 a. purple/*red* (1890) 7·00 11·00
a. "C[illegible]MABA" £1100
b. "[illegible]TE"
O15 **33** 1 r. slate (1890) 11·00 16·00
a. "CHMABA" £900
O16 **37** 1 r. green and carmine (1898) 4·50 7·00
O1/16 *Set of* 10 23·00 35·00

Printings up to and including that of December 1895 had the "SERVICE" overprint applied to sheets of stamps already overprinted with Type 1. From the printing of September 1898 onwards both "SERVICE" and "CHAMBA STATE" were overprinted at the same time. Nos. O6, O8 and O12 only exist using the first method, and No. O16 was only printed using the second.

1902–4. *Colours changed. Optd as Type* O **1**.
O17 **40** 3 p. grey (1904) 12 20
O18 **23** ½ a. pale yellow-green 10 15
O19 ½ a. yellow-green 25 15
O20 **25** 1 a. carmine 30 35
O21 **27** 2 a. pale violet (1903) 3·25 5·00

1903–5. *King Edward VII. Stamps of India optd as Type* O **1**.
O22 **41** 3 p. pale grey 12 8
O23 3 p. slate-grey (1905) 8 10
O24 **42** ½ a. yellow-green 8 8
O25 **43** 1 a. carmine 8 8
O26 **44** 2 a. pale violet (1904) 60 40
O27 2 a. mauve 30 35
O28 **47** 4 a. olive (1905) 1·00 1·25
O29 **49** 8 a. dull mauve (1905) 1·10 1·50
O30 8 a. magenta 1·75 2·25
O31 **51** 1 r. green and carmine (1905) 1·25 1·60
O22/31 *Set of* 7 3·50 4·25

The 2 a. mauve King Edward VII, overprinted "On H.M.S.", was discovered in Calcutta, but was not sent to Chamba, and is an unissued variety. (*Price un.* £12).

1907. *Nos.* 149/50 *of India, optd with Type* O **1**.
O32 **53** ½ a. green 15 15
a. Opt inverted £750
O33 **54** 1 a. carmine 50 50

The error, No. O32a was due to an inverted cliché which was corrected after a few sheets had been printed.

1913–14. *King George V Official stamps (wmk Single Star) optd with T* **1**.
O34 **55** 3 p. slate-grey 8 10
O35 3 p. grey 8 10
O36 **56** ½ a. yellow-green 8 10
O37 ½ a. pale blue-green 20 15
O38 **57** 1 a. aniline carmine 8 8
O39 1 a. rose-carmine 25 15
O40 **59** 2 a. mauve (1914) 45 75
O41 **63** 4 a. olive 65 1·00
O42 **65** 8 a. purple 1·10 1·50
O43 **67** 1 r. brown and green (1914) 2·00 3·00
O34/43 *Set of* 7 4·00 6·00

1914. *King George V. Optd with Type* O **1**.
O44 **59** 2 a. mauve 5·00
O45 **63** 4 a. olive 10·00

1921. *No.* O97 *of India optd with T* **2** *at top*.
O46 **57** 9 p. on 1 a. rose-carmine 20 60

1925. *As* 1913–14. *New colour*.
O47 **57** 1 a. chocolate 25 25

CHAMBA STATE SERVICE
(O 2)

CHAMBA STATE SERVICE
(O 3)

1927–39. *King George V (Nasik printing, wmk Mult Star), optd at Nasik with Type* O **2** *or* O **3** *(rupee values)*.
O48 **55** 3 p. slate 10 12
O49 **56** ½ a. green 10 12
O50 **80** 9 p. deep green 15 45
O51 **57** 1 a. chocolate 10 8
O52 **82** 1¼ a. mauve 15 20
O53 **70** 2 a. purple 15 20
O54 **71** 4 a. sage-green 25 30
O55 **65** 8 a. reddish purple 50 1·00
O56 **66** 12 a. claret 1·00 1·75
O57 **67** 1 r. chocolate and green 2·00 2·75
O58 2 r. carmine and orange (1939) 10·00
O59 5 r. ultramarine and purple (1939) 20·00
O60 10 r. green and scarlet (1939) 27·00
O48/60 *Set of* 13 55·00

1935–39. *New types and colours. Optd with Type* O **2**.
O61 **79** ½ a. green 10 12
O62 **81** 1 a. chocolate 12 12
O63 **59** 2 a. vermilion 30 40
O64 2 a. vermilion (*small die*) (1939) 30 60
O65 **63** 4 a. sage-green (1936) 30 50

1939–40. *King George VI. Optd with Type* O **2** *or* O **3** *(rupee values)*.
O66 **91** 9 p. green 1·50 2·00
O67 1 a. carmine 1·00 1·00
O68 **93** 1 r. grey and red-brown (1940?) £400 £450
O69 2 r. purple and brown (1939) 17·00 24·00
O70 5 r. green and blue (1939) 30·00 40·00
O71 10 r. purple and claret (1939) 60·00 75·00
O66/71 *Set of* 6 £450 £525

CHAMBA SERVICE
(O 4)

1940–43. *(a) Official stamps optd with T* **6**.
O72 **O 20** 3 p. slate 30 30
O73 ½ a. red-brown 1·50 1·00
O74 ½ a. purple (1943) 70 70
O75 9 p. green 40 70
O76 1 a. carmine (1941) 30 30
O77 1 a. 3 p. bistre (1941) 14·00 8·50
O78 1½ a. dull violet (1943) 1·00 1·00
O79 2 a. vermilion 90 1·00
O80 2½ a. bright violet (1941) 1·10 2·50
O81 4 a. brown 1·50 2·25
O82 8 a. slate-violet 3·25 4·50

(b) Postage stamps optd with Type O **4**.
O83 **93** 1 r. grey and red-brown (1942) 10·00 14·00
O84 2 r. purple and brown (1942) 14·00 18·00
O85 5 r. green and blue (1942) 30·00 35·00
O86 10 r. purple and claret (1942) 50·00 60·00
O72/86 *Set of* 14 £110 £130

FARIDKOT

For earlier issues, see under INDIAN FEUDATORY STATES

PRICES FOR STAMPS ON COVER	
Nos. 1/17	*from* × 12
Nos. O1/15	*from* × 12

FARIDKOT STATE
(1)

1887 (1 Jan)–**1900.** *Queen Victoria. Optd with T* **1**.
1 **23** ½ a. deep green 15 20
a. "ARIDKOT"
2 **25** 1 a. brown-purple 30 55
3 1 a. plum 50 55
4 **27** 2 a. blue 85 1·00
5 2 a. deep blue 80 1·00
6 **28** 3 a. orange 1·25 1·50
7 3 a. brown-orange 1·00 1·50
8 **29** 4 a. olive-green 1·10 1·50
a. "ARIDKOT" £175
9 **29** 4 a. slate-green 1·25 1·75
10 **21** 6 a. olive-bistre 2·50 3·50
a. "ARIDKOT" £200
11 6 a. bistre-brown 1·75 3·00
12 **31** 8 a. dull mauve 2·25 3·50
a. "ARIDKOT" £300
13 8 a. magenta 2·50 4·50
14 **32** 12 a. purple/*red* (1900) 21·00 35·00
15 **33** 1 r. slate 19·00 32·00
a. "ARIDKOT" £950
16 **37** 1 r. green and carmine (1893) 8·00 10·00
1/16 *Set of* 10 50·00 80·00

The ½ a., 1 a., 2 a., 3 a., 4 a., 8 a. and 1 r. are known with broken "O" (looking like a "C") in "FARIDKOT".

1900. *Optd with T* **1**.
17 **40** 3 p. carmine 50 1·50

OFFICIAL STAMPS

SERVICE

FARIDKOT STATE
(O 1)

1886–98. *Queen Victoria. Optd with Type* O **1**.
O 1 **23** ½ a. deep green 15 20
a. "SERV CE" £120
O 2 **25** 1 a. brown-purple 40 45
O 3 1 a. plum 45 45
a. "SERV CE" £150
O 4 **27** 2 a. dull blue 80 1·00
a. "SERV CE" £225
O 5 2 a. deep blue 70 1·00
O 6 **28** 3 a. orange 2·75 3·00
O 7 3 a. brown-orange (12.98) 1·50 3·00
O 8 **29** 4 a. olive-green 1·25 1·50
a. "SERV CE" £325
b. "ARIDKOT"
O 9 4 a. slate-green 1·50 2·00
O10 **21** 6 a. olive-bistre 12·00 18·00
a. "ARIDKOT" £180
b. "SERVIC" £275
O11 6 a. bistre-brown 6·50 9·50
O12 **31** 8 a. dull mauve 1·75 2·50
a. "SERV CE" £375
O13 8 a. magenta 3·00 4·50
O14 **33** 1 r. slate 19·00 25·00
O15 **37** 1 r. green and carmine (12.98) 26·00 45·00
O1/15 *Set of* 9 50·00 80·00

The ½ a., 1 a., 2 a., 3 a., 4 a. and 8 a. are known with the broken "O".

Printings up to and including that of November 1895 had the "SERVICE" overprint applied to sheets already overprinted with Type 1. From December 1898 onwards "SERVICE" and "FARIDKOT STATE" were overprinted at one operation to provide fresh supplies of Nos. O1/3, O7 and O13.

This State ceased to use overprinted stamps after 31 March 1901.

GWALIOR

PRICES FOR STAMPS ON COVER	
Nos. 1/3	*from* × 8
Nos. 4/11	—
Nos. 12/66	*from* × 4
Nos. 67/128	*from* × 3
Nos. 129/37	*from* × 5
Nos. O1/94	*from* × 6

OVERPRINTS. From 1885 to 1926 these were applied by the Government of India Central Printing Press, Calcutta, and from 1927 at the Security Press, Nasik, *unless otherwise stated.*

गवालियर

GWALIOR
(1)

GWALIOR गवालियर
(2)

1885–96. *Queen Victoria. I. Optd with T* **1**.

(a) Space between two lines of overprint 13 *mm. Hindi inscription* 13 *to* 14 *mm long* (1 May 1885)
1 **23** ½ a. blue-green 15·00 8·50
2 **25** 1 a. brown-purple 25·00 13·00
3 **27** 2 a. dull blue 16·00 8·50

A variety exists of the ½ a. in which the space between the two lines of overprint is only 9½ mm but this is probably from a proof sheet.

(b) Space between two lines of overprint 15 *mm on* 4 *a. and* 6 *a. and* 16 *to* 17 *mm on other values* (1 June 1885)

A. *Hindi inscription* 13 *to* 14 *mm long*
B. *Hindi inscription* 15 *to* 15½ *mm long*

			A		B	
4	**23**	½ a. blue-green	9·00	—	12·00	—
5	**25**	1 a. brown-purple	10·00	—	14·00	—
6	**26**	1½ a. sepia	14·00	—	22·00	—
7	**27**	2 a. dull blue	12·00	—	20·00	—
8	**17**	4 a. green	18·00	—	28·00	—
9	**21**	6 a. olive-bistre	18·00	—	30·00	—
10	**31**	8 a. dull mauve	18·00	—	30·00	—
11	**33**	1 r. slate	20·00	—	32·00	—
4/11		*Set of* 8	£110			

The two types of overprint on these stamps occur in the same settings, with about a quarter of the stamps in each sheet showing the long inscription (B). Nos. 4/7 and 10/11 were overprinted in sheets of 240 and Nos. 8/9 in sheets of 320. *Se-tenant* pairs exist and are rare.

II. *Optd with T* **2**

A. *Hindi inscription 13 to 14 mm long*
B. *Hindi inscription 15 to 15½ mm long*

(*a*) *In red* (Sept–Oct 1885)

A B
12 **23** ½ a. blue-green 20 20 35 50
13 **27** 2 a. dull blue .. .. 4·00 4·50 11·00 13·00
14 **17** 4 a. green (Oct) .. .. 8·50 7·50 22·00 24·00
15 **33** 1 r. slate .. .. 6·50 6·50 15·00 18·00

No. 14 was overprinted in sheets of 320, about 80 stamps being Type B. The remaining three values were from a setting of 240 containing 166 as Type A and 74 as Type B.
Reprints have been made of Nos. 12 to 15, but the majority of the specimens have the word "REPRINT" overprinted upon them.

(*b*) *In black* (1885–96)
16 **23** ½ a. blue-green (1889) 25 15 12 8
a. Opt double .. — — 80·00 —
b. "GWALICR" .. † 38·00 40·00
c. Small "G" .. † 28·00 28·00
17 **24** 9 p. carmine (1891) .. 22·00 30·00 30·00 38·00
18 **25** 1 a. brown-purple .. 15 12 12 8
19 1 a. plum .. † 10 8
a. Small "G" .. † 30·00 30·00
20 **26** 1½ a. sepia .. 15 15 15 15
21 **27** 2 a. dull blue .. 1·00 70 30 8
22 2 a. deep blue .. 1·25 85 45 15
a. Small "G" .. † 45·00 45·00
23 **36** 2½ a. yellow-green (1896) .. † 2·50 3·50
a. "GWALICR" .. † £200
24 **28** 3 a. orange .. 1·50 1·25 6·00 5·00
25 3 a. brown-orange .. 1·25 90 20 15
a. Small "G" .. † 55·00 55·00
26 **29** 4 a. olive-green (1889) .. 1·00 75 75 65
27 4 a. slate-green .. 1·25 75 55 30
a. Small "G" .. † 60·00 60·00
28 **21** 6 a. olive-bistre .. 90 1·00 80 70
29 6 a. bistre-brown .. 45 50 55 65
30 **31** 8 a. dull mauve w8 .. 4·00 5·00 55 50
31 8 a. magenta .. † 1·60 1·60
32 **32** 12 a. purple/*red* (1891) .. 3·50 4·50 65 55
a. Pair, with and without opt .. † — —
33 **33** 1 r. slate (1889) .. 30·00 — 65 65
34 **37** 1 r. green and carmine (1896) .. † 1·60 2·00
a. "GWALICR" .. † £250 —
35 **38** 2 r. carmine and yellow-brown (1896) .. † 8·50 6·50
a. Small "G" .. † 70·00 70·00
36 3 r. brown and green (1896) .. † 15·00 8·00
a. Small "G" .. † 80·00 —
37 5 r. ultramarine and violet (1896) .. † 18·00 11·00
a. Small "G" .. † 90·00 —
16/37 .. *Set of* 16 65·00 55·00

Printings to 1891 continued to use the setting showing both types, but subsequently a new setting containing Type B overprints only was used.
The ½ a., 1 a., 2 a. and 3 a. exist with space between "I" and "O" of "GWALIOR".

1899–1908. (*a*) *Optd with T* **2** (B).
38 **40** 3 p. carmine .. 8 8
a. Opt inverted .. £125 85·00
b. Small "G" .. 32·00 32·00
39 3 p. grey (1904) .. 4·00 16·00
a. Small "G" .. 75·00
40 **23** ½ a. pale yellow-green (1901) .. 10 12
40*a* ½ a. yellow-green (1903) .. 55 65
41 **25** 1 a. carmine (1901) .. 10 8
42 **27** 2 a. pale violet (1901) .. 35 50
43 **36** 2½ a. ultramarine (1903) .. 65 85
38/43 .. *Set of* 6 4·75 16·00

(*b*) *Optd as T* **2**, *but* "GWALIOR" *13 mm long. Optd spaced 2¾ mm* (1908)
44 **38** 3 r. brown and green .. 42·00 45·00
45 5 r. ultramarine and violet .. 42·00 42·00

1903–08. *King Edward VII. Optd as T* **2**.
A. "GWALIOR" *14 mm long. Overprint spaced 1¾ mm*
B. "GWALIOR" *13 mm long. Overprint spaced 2¾ mm* (1908)
A B
46 **41** 3 p. pale grey .. 8 8 10 8
a. Slate-grey (1905) .. 8 8 10 8
48 **42** ½ a. green .. 8 8 †
49 **43** 1 a. carmine .. 8 8 50 50
50 **44** 2 a. pale violet (1904) .. 25 12 †
a. Mauve .. 20 8 15 8
52 **45** 2½ a. ultramarine (1904) .. 6·50 10·00 35 70
53 **46** 3 a. orange-brown (1904) 30 15 30 12
54 **47** 4 a. olive .. 55 40 †
a. Pale olive .. 65 45 55 25
56 **48** 6 a. olive-bistre (1906) .. 80 65 80 60
57 **49** 8 a. dull mauve (1905) .. 75 55 2·50 1·25
a. Magenta .. † 1·25 90
59 **50** 12 a. purple/*red* (1905) .. 1·00 1·10 1·00 1·10
60 **51** 1 r. green and carmine (1905) .. 1·10 1·00 1·75 1·00
61 **52** 2 r. carmine & yellow-brn 32·00 35·00 7·50 8·50
62 3 r. brown and green (1908) .. † 16·00 18·00
a. Red-brown and green † 22·00 24·00
63 5 r. ultramarine and violet (1908) .. † 14·00 16·00
46/63 .. *Set of* 14 38·00 42·00

1907. *Nos. 149 and 150 of India optd as T* **2**.
(*a*) "GWALIOR" *14 mm long. Overprint spaced 1¾ mm*
64 **53** ½ a. green .. 8 8
(*b*) "GWALIOR" *13 mm long. Overprint spaced 2¾ mm*
65 **53** ½ a. green .. 8 8
66 **54** 1 a. carmine .. 10 8

1912–14. *King George V. Optd as T* **2**.
67 **55** 3 p. slate-grey .. 8 8
a. Opt double .. † —
68 **56** ½ a. green .. 10 8
a. Opt inverted ..
69 **57** 1 a. aniline carmine .. 10 8
a. Opt double .. 27·00
70 **59** 2 a. mauve .. 20 8
71 **62** 3 a. orange-brown .. 30 12
72 **63** 4 a. olive (1913) .. 25 12
73 **64** 6 a. olive-bistre .. 55 35
74 **65** 8 a. purple (1913) .. 40 15
75 **66** 12 a. dull claret (1914) .. 60 60
76 **67** 1 r. brown and green .. 1·10 55
a. Opt double, one albino .. 50·00
b. Opt double .. £100
77 2 r. carmine-rose and brown .. 4·50 1·10
a. Opt double one albino .. 60·00
78 5 r. ultramarine and violet .. 15·00 6·00
a. Opt double, one albino .. 60·00
67/78 .. *Set of* 12 21·00 8·00

GWALIOR
(3)

1922. *No. 192 of India optd with T* **3**.
79 **57** 9 p. on 1 a. rose-carmine .. 8 12

1923–7. *Optd as T* **2**. *New colours and values.*
80 **57** 1 a. chocolate (1925) .. 10 8
81 **58** 1½ a. chocolate (B) (1925) .. 30 35
82 1½ a. rose-carmine (B) (1927) .. 15 12
83 **61** 2½ a. ultramarine (1925) .. 55 65
84 2½ a. orange (1927) .. 20 12
85 **62** 3 a. ultramarine (1924) .. 30 15

GWALIOR
गवालियर
(4)

GWALIOR
गवालियर
(5)

1928–36. *King George V (Nasik printing, wmk Mult Star), optd at Nasik with T* **4** *or* **5** (*rupee values*).
86 **55** 3 p. slate (1932) .. 8 8
87 **56** ½ a. green (1930) .. 10 8
88 **80** 9 p. deep green (1933) .. 15 12
89 **57** 1 a. chocolate .. 8 8
90 **82** 1¼ a. mauve (1936) .. 12 8
91 **70** 2 a. purple .. 15 8
92 **62** 3 a. bright blue .. 35 20
93 **71** 4 a. sage-green .. 55 15
94 **65** 8 a. reddish purple .. 75 30
95 **66** 12 a. claret .. 80 70
96 **67** 1 r. chocolate and green .. 1·40 1·25
97 2 r. carmine and orange .. 3·00 2·75
98 5 r. ultramarine and purple (1929) .. 12·00 12·00
99 10 r. green and scarlet (1930) .. 24·00 24·00
100 15 r. blue and olive (1930) .. 38·00 42·00
101 25 r. orange and blue (1930) .. 70·00 75·00
86/101 .. *Set of* 16 £130 £140

1936. *New types and colours. Optd with T* **4**.
102 **79** ½ a. green .. 10 10
103 **81** 1 a. chocolate .. 8 8
104 **59** 2 a. vermilion .. 15 20

1938–48. *King George VI. Nos. 247/50, 253, 255/6, and 259/64 optd with T* **4** *or* **5** (*rupee values*).
105 **91** 3 p. slate .. 1·00 20
106 ½ a. red-brown .. 1·00 15
107 9 p. green (1939) .. 20·00 6·00
108 1 a. carmine .. 1·00 20
109 – 3 a. yellow-green (1939) .. 1·25 1·10
110 – 4 a. brown .. 9·00 3·50
111 – 6 a. turquoise-green (1939) .. 2·00 1·75
112 **93** 1 r. grey and red-brown (1942) .. 2·00 1·50
113 2 r. purple and brown (1948) .. 9·00 7·00
114 5 r. green and blue (1948) .. 26·00 25·00
115 10 r. purple and claret (1948) .. 40·00 40·00
116 15 r. brown and green (1948) .. 90·00 80·00
117 25 r. slate-violet and purple (1948) .. £120 90·00
105/117 .. *Set of* 13 £275 £225

1942–5. *King George VI. Optd with T* **4**.
118 **100*a*** 3 p. slate .. 15 10
119 ½ a. purple (1943) .. 15 10
120 9 p. green .. 15 10
121 1 a. carmine (1943) .. 15 10
a. Opt double .. 32·00 32·00
122 **101** 1½ a. dull violet .. 45 20
123 2 a. vermilion .. 30 20
124 3 a. bright violet .. 65 40
125 **102** 4 a. brown .. 60 40
126 6 a. turquoise-green (1945) .. 7·00 7·00
127 8 a. slate-violet (1944) .. 3·50 3·50
128 12 a. lake (1943) .. 6·50 6·50
118/128 .. *Set of* 11 17·00 17·00

The 1½ a. and 3 a. exist printed by lithography or typography.

GWALIOR
गवालियर
(6)

1949. *King George VI. Optd with T* **6** *at the Alizah Printing Press, Gwalior.*
129 **100*a*** 3 p. slate .. 60 50
130 ½ a. purple .. 60 50
131 1 a. carmine .. 75 60
132 **101** 2 a. vermilion .. 2·50 1·50
133 3 a. bright violet .. 8·00 7·00
134 **102** 4 a. brown .. 3·25 3·00
135 6 a. turquoise-green .. 18·00 20·00
136 8 a. slate-violet .. 38·00 25·00
137 12 a. lake .. £125 65·00
129/137 .. *Set of* 9 £180 £110

OFFICIAL STAMPS

गवालियर
सरविस
(O 1)

गवालियर
सरविस
(O 2)

1895–96. *Queen Victoria. Optd with Type* O **1**.
O 1 **23** ½ a. blue-green .. 8 8
a. Hindi characters transposed .. 14·00 14·00
b. 4th Hindi character omitted .. 60·00 16·00
c. Opt double .. — £110
O 2 **25** 1 a. brown-purple .. 60 15
O 3 1 a. plum .. 20 8
a. Hindi characters transposed .. 16·00 16·00
b. 4th Hindi character omitted .. — 21·00
O 4 **27** 2 a. dull blue .. 40 10
O 5 2 a. deep blue .. 30 12
a. Hindi characters transposed .. 30·00
b. 4th Hindi character omitted .. 40·00 45·00
O 6 **29** 4 a. olive-green .. 60 60
a. Hindi characters transposed .. 85·00 90·00
b. 4th Hindi character omitted .. — £125
O 7 4 a. slate-green .. 60 40
O 8 **31** 8 a. dull mauve .. 1·10 1·10
O 9 8 a. magenta .. 80 70
a. Hindi characters transposed .. £450 £475
b. 4th Hindi character omitted ..
O10 **37** 1 r. green and carmine (1896) .. 2·50 3·00
a. Hindi characters transposed .. £700
O1/10 .. *Set of* 6 4·00 4·00

In the errors listed above it is the last two Hindi characters that are transposed, so that the word reads "Sersiv". The error occurs on R.19/1 in the sheet from the early printings up to May 1896.

1901–4. *Colours changed.*
O23 **40** 3 p. carmine (1902) .. 20 30
O24 3 p. grey (1904) .. 80 1·10
O25 **23** ½ a. pale yellow-green .. 30 8
O26 ½ a. yellow-green .. 12 10
O27 **25** 1 a. carmine .. 45 10
O28 **27** 2 a. pale violet (1903) .. 75 90

1903–5. *King Edward VII. Optd as Type* O **1**.
(*a*) *Overprint spaced 10 mm*
O29 **41** 3 p. pale grey .. 25 8
a. Slate-grey (1905) .. 20 8
O31 **42** ½ a. green .. 40 8
O32 **43** 1 a. carmine .. 30 8
O33 **44** 2 a. pale violet (1905) .. 60 30
a. Mauve .. 45 10
O35 **47** 4 a. olive (1905) .. 1·40 70
O36 **49** 8 a. dull mauve (1905) .. 1·25 70
a. Magenta .. 1·75 90
O38 **51** 1 r. green and carmine (1905) .. 1·60 1·10
O29/38 .. *Set of* 7 5·00 2·50
(*b*) *Overprint spaced 8 mm*
O39 **41** 3 p. pale grey .. 60 12
a. Slate-grey .. 60 12
O41 **42** ½ a. green .. 35 8
O42 **43** 1 a. carmine .. 35 10
O43 **44** 2 a. mauve .. 1·25 20
O44 **47** 4 a. olive .. 1·75 70
O45 **49** 8 a. dull mauve .. 2·75 1·40
O46 **51** 1 r. green and carmine .. 3·25 3·25
O39/46 .. *Set of* 7 9·00 5·00

1907. *Nos. 149 and 150 of India optd as Type* O **1**.
(*a*) *Overprint spaced 10 mm*
O47 **53** ½ a. green .. 40 8
O48 **54** 1 a. carmine .. 40 8
(*b*) *Overprint spaced 8 mm*
O49 **53** ½ a. green .. 35 10
O50 **54** 1 a. carmine .. 13·00 4·00

1913–23. *King George V. Optd with Type* O **1**.
O51 **55** 3 p. slate-grey .. 12 8
O52 **56** ½ a. green .. 12 8
O53 **57** 1 a. rose-carmine .. 25 8
a. Aniline carmine .. 12 8
ab. Opt double .. 50·00
O54 1 a. chocolate (1923) .. 25 8
O55 **59** 2 a. mauve .. 25 8
O56 **63** 4 a. olive .. 40 15
O57 **65** 8 a. purple .. 50 30
O58 **67** 1 r. brown and green .. 2·50 2·00
O51/58 .. *Set of* 8 3·75 2·50

1922. *No. O97 of India optd with T* **3**.
O59 **57** 9 p. on 1 a. rose-carmine .. 12 12

1927–35. *King George V (Nasik printing, wmk Mult Star), optd at Nasik as Type* O **1** (*but top line measures 13 mm instead of 14 mm*) *or with Type* O **2** (*rupee values*).
O61 **55** 3 p. slate .. 8 8
O62 **56** ½ a. green .. 8 8
O63 **80** 9 p. deep green (1935) .. 8 10
O64 **57** 1 a. chocolate .. 8 8
O65 **82** 1¼ a. mauve (1933) .. 20 8
O66 **70** 2 a. purple .. 12 8
O67 **71** 4 a. sage-green .. 25 15
O68 **65** 8 a. reddish purple (1928) .. 40 25
O69 **67** 1 r. chocolate and green .. 60 50
O70 2 r. carmine and orange (1935) .. 1·50 2·25
O71 5 r. ultramarine and purple (1932) .. 10·00 16·00
O72 10 r. green and scarlet (1932) .. 20·00 28·00
O61/72 .. *Set of* 12 30·00 45·00

1936–37. *New types. Optd as Type* O **1** (*13 mm*).
O73 **79** ½ a. green .. 8 8
O74 **81** 1 a. chocolate .. 8 8
O75 **59** 2 a. vermilion .. 12 10
O76 2 a. vermilion (*small die*) .. 30 15
O77 **63** 4 a. sage-green (1937) .. 25 15

1938. *King George VI. Optd as Type* O **1** *(13 mm).*
O78 **91** ½ a. red-brown 1·50 20
O79 1 a. carmine 1·10 20

ग्वालियर (O 3)   1A—1A (O 4)

1940–42. *Official stamps optd with Type* O **3**.
O80 **O 20** 3 p. slate 70 25
O81 ½ a. red-brown 2·50 1·25
O82 ½ a. purple (1942) 70 35
O83 9 p. green (1942) 70 45
O84 1 a. carmine 70 35
O85 1 a. 3 p. bistre (1942) 2·25 1·40
O86 1½ a. dull violet (1942) 80 70
O87 2 a. vermilion 80 70
O88 4 a. brown (1942) 90 90
O89 8 a. slate-violet (1942) 2·25 2·25
O80/9 *Set of* 10 11·00 8·00

1942. *Stamp of* 1932 *(King George V) optd with Type* O **1** *and surch with Type* O **4**.
O90 **82** 1 a. on 1¼ a. mauve 5·00 2·25

1942–47. *King George VI. Optd with Type* O **2**.
O91 **93** 1 r. grey and red-brown 1·75 2·25
O92 2 r. purple and brown 9·00 11·00
O93 5 r. green and blue (1943) 28·00 38·00
O94 10 r. purple and claret (1947) 50·00 70·00

JIND

For earlier issues, see under INDIAN FEUDATORY STATES

PRICES FOR STAMPS ON COVER

Nos. 1/6	*from* x 12
Nos. 7/16	—
Nos. 17/40	*from* × 5
Nos. 41/149	*from* × 4
Nos. O1/86	*from* × 6

JHIND STATE (1)   JEEND STATE (2)   JHIND STATE (3)

1885. *Queen Victoria. Optd with T* **1**.
1 **23** ½ a. blue-green 45 50
a. Opt inverted 38·00 38·00
2 **25** 1 a. brown-purple 5·00 6·00
a. Opt inverted £175
3 **27** 2 a. dull blue 3·50 4·00
a. Opt inverted £100
4 **17** 4 a. green 13·00 15·00
5 **31** 8 a. dull mauve 70·00
a. Opt inverted £1000
6 **33** 1 r. slate 70·00
a. Opt inverted £1000

All six values exist with reprinted overprint. In these, words "JHIND" and "STATE" are 8 and 9 mm in length respectively, whereas in the originals the words are 9 and 9½ mm.

1885. *Optd with T* **2**.
7 **23** ½ a. blue-green (R.) 17·00
8 **25** 1 a. brown-purple 17·00
9 **27** 2 a. dull blue (R.) 20·00
10 **17** 4 a. green (R.) 24·00
11 **31** 8 a. dull mauve 28·00
12 **33** 1 r. slate (R.) 28·00
7/12 *Set of* 6 £120

1886. *Optd with T* **3**, *in red.*
13 **23** ½ a. blue-green 6·00
a. "JEIND" for "JHIND" £120
14 **27** 2 a. dull blue 8·00
a. "JEIND" for "JHIND" £180
15 **17** 4 a. green 10·00
a. Opt double, one albino
16 **33** 1 r. slate 18·00
a. "JEIND" for "JHIND" £700

1886–98. *Optd with T* **3**.
17 **23** ½ a. blue-green (1888) 8 10
a. Opt inverted £130
18 **25** 1 a. brown-purple 10 10
a. "JEIND" for "JHIND" £160
19 1 a. plum 25 15
20 **26** 1½ a. sepia (1897) 50 60
21 **27** 2 a. dull blue (1891) 20 25
22 2 a. ultramarine 25 25
23 **28** 3 a. brown-orange 25 30
24 **29** 4 a. olive-green (1891) 40 45
25 4 a. slate-green 60 70
26 **21** 6 a. olive-bistre (1891) 80 1·25
27 6 a. bistre-brown 50 1·00
28 **31** 8 a. dull mauve 80 1·00
a. "JEIND" for "JHIND" £600
29 8 a. magenta 80 1·00
30 **32** 12 a. purple/*red* (1897) 90 1·10
31 **33** 1 r. slate (1891) 6·00 7·50
32 **37** 1 r. green and carmine (1898) 4·50 6·00
33 **38** 2 r. carmine and yellow-brown (1897) 65·00 90·00
34 3 r. brown and green 90·00 £120
35 5 r. ultramarine and violet (1897) £100 £130
17/35 *Set of* 14 £240 £325

Varieties exist in which the word "JHIND" measures 10½ mm and 9¾ mm instead of 10 mm. Such varieties are to be found on Nos. 17, 18, 21, 24, 28 and 31.

1900–4. *Colours changed.*
36 **40** 3 p. carmine 10 20
37 3 p. grey (1904) 10 25
38 **23** ½ a. pale yellow-green (1902) 20 45
39 ½ a. yellow-green 90 1·10
40 **25** 1 a. carmine (1902) 15 35

1903–9. *King Edward VII. Optd with T* **3**.
41 **41** 3 p. pale grey 8 8
42 3 p. slate-grey (1905) 8 10
43 **42** ½ a. green 8 8
44 **43** 1 a. carmine 10 10
45 **44** 2 a. pale violet 25 25
46 2 a. mauve (1906) 25 25
47 **45** 2½ a. ultramarine (1909) 20 50
48 **46** 3 a. orange-brown 20 20
a. Opt double 75·00
49 **47** 4 a. olive 40 50
50 4 a. pale olive 40 50
51 **48** 6 a. bistre (1905) 60 90
52 **49** 8 a. dull mauve 60 85
53 8 a. magenta 85 1·25
54 **50** 12 a. purple/*red* (1905) 1·40 1·75
55 **51** 1 r. green and carmine (1905) 1·50 1·75
41/55 *Set of* 11 4·50 6·00

1907–9. *Nos.* 149/50 *of India optd with T* **3**.
56 **53** ½ a. green 8 8
57 **54** 1 a. carmine (1909) 8 8

1913. *King George V. Optd with T* **3**.
58 **55** 3 p. slate-grey 8 15
59 **56** ½ a. green 8 12
60 **57** 1 a. aniline carmine 8 12
61 **59** 2 a. mauve 12 35
62 **62** 3 a. orange-brown 1·50 2·75
63 **64** 6 a. olive-bistre 3·25 5·00
58/63 *Set of* 6 4·75 7·50

JIND STATE (4)   JIND STATE (5)   JIND STATE (6)

1914–27. *King George V. Optd with T* **4**.
64 **55** 3 p. slate-grey 8 8
65 **56** ½ a. green 8 8
66 **57** 1 a. aniline carmine 8 8
67 **58** 1½ a. chocolate (Type A) (1922) 30 55
68 1½ a. chocolate (Type B) (1924) 30 50
69 **59** 2 a. mauve 15 20
70 **61** 2½ a. ultramarine (1922) 30 60
71 **62** 3 a. orange-brown 25 50
72 **63** 4 a. olive 25 50
73 **64** 6 a. olive-bistre 40 80
74 **65** 8 a. purple 40 60
75 **66** 12 a. dull claret 45 80
76 **67** 1 r. brown and green 1·10 1·40
a. Opt double, one albino
77 2 r. carmine and yellow-brown 5·00 7·50
78 5 r. ultramarine and violet 22·00 32·00
64/78 *Set of* 15 28·00 42·00

1922. *No.* 192 *of India optd "JIND" in block capitals.*
79 **57** 9 p. on 1 a. rose-carmine 2·50 3·25

1924–27. *Optd with T* **4**. *New colours.*
80 **57** 1 a. chocolate 12 15
81 **58** 1½ a. rose-carmine (Type B) 15 45
82 **61** 2½ a. orange 30 70
83 **62** 3 a. bright blue 50 1·25

1927–37. *King George V (Nasik printing, wmk Mult Star), optd at Nasik with T* **5** *or* **6** *(rupee values).*
84 **55** 3 p. slate 8 8
85 **56** ½ a. green 8 10
86 **80** 9 p. deep green 12 20
87 **57** 1 a. chocolate 8 8
88 **82** 1¼ a. mauve 12 15
89 **58** 1½ a. rose-carmine (Type B) 15 30
90 **70** 2 a. purple 15 15
91 **61** 2½ a. orange 20 60
92 **62** 3 a. bright blue 25 50
93 **83** 3½ a. ultramarine (1937) 35 1·00
94 **71** 4 a. sage-green 25 30
95 **64** 6 a. bistre (1937) 40 1·25
96 **65** 8 a. reddish purple 40 60
97 **66** 12 a. claret 65 1·00
98 **67** 1 r. chocolate and green 80 1·25
99 2 r. carmine and orange 8·00 12·00
100 5 r. ultramarine and purple 10·00 11·00
101 10 r. green and carmine 20·00 20·00
102 15 r. blue and olive 40·00 70·00
103 25 r. orange and blue 55·00 90·00
84/103 *Set of* 20 £120 £180

1934. *New types and colours. Optd with T* **5**.
104 **79** ½ a. green 8 10
105 **81** 1 a. chocolate 10 10
106 **59** 2 a. vermilion 15 20
107 **62** 3 a. carmine 35 35
108 **63** 4 a. sage-green 30 35

1937–38. *King George VI. Nos.* 247/64 *optd with T* **5** *or T* **6** *(rupee values).*
109 **91** 3 p. slate 60 60
110 ½ a. red-brown 30 50
111 9 p. green (1937) 50 80
112 1 a. carmine (1937) 30 40
113 **92** 2 a. vermilion 40 1·50
114 – 2½ a. bright violet 40 1·50
115 – 3 a. yellow-green 60 1·50
116 – 3½ a. bright blue 50 1·75
117 – 4 a. brown 50 1·75
118 – 6 a. turquoise-green 80 2·75
119 – 8 a. slate-violet 1·00 2·75
120 – 12 a. lake 1·50 4·00
121 **93** 1 r. grey and red-brown 4·00 5·00
122 2 r. purple and brown 8·00 9·00
123 5 r. green and blue 26·00 24·00
124 10 r. purple and claret 48·00 45·00
125 15 r. brown and green £140 £160
126 25 r. slate-violet and purple £170 £200
109/126 *Set of* 18 £350 £400

JIND
(7)

1941–43. *King George VI. Optd with T* **7**. *(a) Stamps of* 1937.
127 **91** 3 p. slate 3·50 3·50
128 ½ a. red-brown 2·00 2·00
129 9 p. green 3·75 4·00
130 1 a. carmine 2·25 2·25
131 **93** 1 r. grey and red-brown 4·00 5·00
132 2 r. purple and brown 8·00 9·00
133 5 r. green and blue 24·00 25·00
134 10 r. purple and claret 45·00 48·00
135 15 r. brown and green 85·00 90·00
136 25 r. slate-violet and purple £130 £150
127/136 *Set of* 10 £275 £300

(b) Stamps of 1940–43
137 **100***a* 3 p. slate (1942) 40 45
138 ½ a. purple (1943) 40 45
139 9 p. green (1942) 40 45
140 1 a. carmine (1942) 40 40
141 **101** 1 a. 3p. bistre 60 1·00
142 1½ a. dull violet (1942) 1·50 1·50
143 2 a. vermilion 60 60
144 3 a. bright violet (1942) 80 90
145 3½ a. bright blue 80 1·10
146 **102** 4 a. brown 70 90
147 6 a. turquoise-green 1·25 1·75
148 8 a. slate-violet 1·75 2·50
149 12 a. lake 4·00 5·00
137/149 *Set of* 13 12·00 15·00

The 1½ a. and 3 a. exist printed by lithography or typography.

OFFICIAL STAMPS

SERVICE

SERVICE (O 14)   SERVICE (O 15)   JHIND STATE (O 16)

1885. *Queen Victoria. Nos.* 1/3 *of Jind optd with Type* O **14**.
O1 **23** ½ a. blue-green 25 25
a. Opt Type 1 inverted 40·00 24·00
O2 **25** 1 a. brown-purple 15 10
a. Opt Type 1 inverted 7·00 7·00
O3 **27** 2 a. dull blue 16·00 16·00
a. Opt Type 1 inverted £200

The three values have had the overprint reprinted in the same way as the ordinary stamps of 1885. See note after No. 6.

1885. *Nos.* 7/9 *of Jind optd with Type* O **15**.
O7 **23** ½ a. blue-green (R.) 18·00
O8 **25** 1 a. brown-purple 18·00
O9 **27** 2 a. dull blue (R.) 22·00

1886. *Optd with Type* O **16**, *in red.*
O10 **23** ½ a. blue-green 7·00
a. "ERVICE"
b. "JEIND" £140
O11 **27** 2 a. dull blue 12·00
a. "ERVICE"
b. "JEIND" £225

1886–97. *Optd with Type* O **16**.
O12 **23** ½ a. blue-green (1888) 25 8
O13 **25** 1 a. brown-purple 7·00
a. "ERVICE"
b. "JEIND" £140
O14 1 a. plum 75 10
O15 **27** 2 a. dull blue (1893) 45 30
O16 2 a. ultramarine 30 25
O17 **29** 4 a. olive-green (1892) 40 30
O18 4 a. slate-green 90 60
O19 **31** 8 a. dull mauve (1892) 1·25 1·60
O20 8 a. magenta 2·50 4·50
O21 **37** 1 r. green and carmine (1897) 6·00 9·00
O12/21 *Set of* 6 8·00 10·00

Varieties mentioned in note after No. 35 exist on Nos. O12, O15, O17 and O20.

Printings up to and including that of October 1897 had the "SERVICE" overprint. Type O **15**, applied to sheets already overprinted with Type **3**. From the printing of December 1899 onwards "SERVICE" and "JHIND STATE" were overprinted at one operation, as Type O **16**, to provide fresh supplies of Nos. O12, O14 and O21.

1902. *Colour changed. Optd with Type* O **16**.
O22 **23** ½ a. yellow-green 20 10

1903–6. *King Edward VII stamps of India optd with Type* O **16**.
O23 **41** 3 p. pale grey 12 8
O24 3 p. slate-grey (1906) 8 8
O25 **42** ½ a. green 40 8
a. "HIND" — £110
O26 **43** 1 a. carmine 40 8
a. "HIND" — £110
O27 **44** 2 a. pale violet 30 20
O28 2 a. mauve 15 10
O29 **47** 4 a. olive 45 40
O30 **49** 8 a. dull mauve 3·00 1·75
O31 8 a. magenta 2·50 1·75
O32 **51** 1 r. green and carmine (1906) 3·00 2·50
O23/32 *Set of* 7 6·50 4·50

1907. *Nos.* 149/50 *of India optd with Type* O **16**.
O33 **53** ½ a. green 15 8
O34 **54** 1 a. carmine 15 8

1914–27. *King George V. Official stamps of India optd with T* **4**.
O35 **55** 3 p. slate-grey 8 8
O36 **56** ½ a. green 8 8
O37 **57** 1 a. aniline carmine 8 8
O38 1 a. pale rose-carmine 15 8
O39 **59** 2 a. mauve 12 8
O40 **63** 4 a. olive 15 10
O41 **64** 6 a. yellow-bistre 40 75
O42 **65** 8 a. purple 20 25
O43 **67** 1 r. brown and green 90 70

O44 **67** 2 r. carmine and yellow-brown .. .. 6·50 8·00
O45 5 r. ultramarine and violet .. .. 15·00 20·00
O35/45 .. .. *Set of* 10 21·00 27·00

1924. *As* 1914-27. *New colour.*
O46 **57** 1 a. chocolate 8 8

JIND STATE SERVICE (O 17) — JIND STATE SERVICE (O 18) — JIND SERVICE (O 19)

1927–37. *King George V (Nasik printing, wmk Mult Star), optd with Types* O 17 *or* O 18 *(rupee values).*
O47 **55** 3 p. slate 8 8
O48 **56** ½ a. green 12 12
O49 **80** 9 p. deep green 15 15
O50 **57** 1 a. chocolate 8 8
O51 **82** 1¼ a. mauve 10 10
O52 **70** 2 a. purple 12 12
O53 **61** 2½ a. orange (1937) 20 35
O54 **71** 4 a. sage-green 15 15
O55 **64** 6 a. bistre (1937) .. .. .. 35 1·00
O56 **65** 8 a. reddish purple 35 50
O57 **66** 12 a. claret .. .. 50 1·00
O58 **67** 1 r. chocolate and green .. .. 80 1·10
O59 2 r. carmine and orange .. .. 5·00 6·00
O60 5 r. ultramarine and purple .. .. 10·00 18·00
O61 10 r. green and carmine .. .. 18·00 22·00
O47/61 .. .. *Set of* 15 32·00 45·00
The 9 p. exists printed by lithography or typography.

1934. *Optd with Type* O **17**.
O62 **79** ½ a. green 8 8
O63 **81** 1 a. chocolate 8 8
O64 **59** 2 a. vermilion 12 12
O65 **63** 4 a. sage-green 20 20

1937–40. *King George VI. Optd with Types* O **17** *or* O **18** *(rupee values).*
O66 **91** ½ a. red-brown (1938) .. .. .. 6·00 30
O67 9 p. green 60 70
O68 1 a. carmine 40 30
O69 **93** 1 r. grey and red-brown (1940) .. .. 8·00 8·00
O70 2 r. purple and brown (1940) .. .. 17·00 18·00
O71 5 r. green and blue (1940) .. .. 35·00 40·00
O72 10 r. purple and claret (1940) .. .. 55·00 70·00
O66/72 .. .. *Set of* 7 £110 £120

1939–43. (a) *Official stamps optd with T* **7**.
O73 O **20** 3 p. slate 15 15
O74 ½ a. red-brown .. .. .. 3·00 1·50
O75 ½ a. purple (1943) 20 20
O76 9 p. green 50 40
O77 1 a. carmine 40 15
O78 1½ a. dull violet (1942) 80 60
O79 2 a. vermilion 30 25
O80 2½ a. bright violet 40 70
O81 4 a. brown 70 70
O82 8 a. slate-violet .. .. .. 1·00 1·25

(b) *Postage stamps optd with Type* O **19**
O83 **93** 1 r. grey and red-brown (1942) .. .. 8·00 8·00
O84 2 r. purple and brown (1942) .. .. 11·00 14·00
O85 5 r. green and blue (1942) .. .. 30·00 38·00
O86 10 r. purple and claret (1942) .. .. 65·00 75·00
O73/86 .. .. *Set of* 14 £110 £130

NABHA

PRICES FOR STAMPS ON COVER	
Nos. 1/3	*from* × 12
Nos. 4/6	—
Nos. 10/36	*from* × 6
Nos. 37/117	*from* × 4
Nos. O1/68	*from* × 8

NABHA STATE (1) — NABHA STATE (2)

1885 (May). *Queen Victoria. Optd with T* **1**.
1 **23** ½ a. blue-green 75 50
2 **25** 1 a. brown-purple .. .. .. 13·00 18·00
3 **27** 2 a. dull blue .. .. 7·50 8·50
4 **17** 4 a. green .. .. 22·00 32·00
5 **31** 8 a. dull mauve .. .. 90·00
6 **33** 1 r. slate .. .. 90·00
1/6 .. .. *Set of* 6 £200
All six values have had the overprint reprinted. On the reprints the words "NABHA" and "STATE" both measure 9¼ mm in length, whereas on the originals these words measure 11 and 10 mm respectively. The varieties with overprint double come from the reprints.

1885–1900. *Optd with T* **2**. (a) *In red* (Nov 1885).
10 **23** ½ a. blue-green 15 20
11 **27** 2 a. dull blue 40 50
12 **17** 4 a. green .. .. 13·00 22·00
13 **33** 1 r. slate .. .. 32·00 42·00

(b) *In black* (1887–97)
14 **23** ½ a. blue-green 8 8
15 **24** 9 p. carmine (1892) 35 50
16 **25** 1 a. brown-purple 20 10
17 1 a. plum 10 8
18 **26** 1½ a. sepia (1891) 25 40
a. "ABHA" for "NABHA" £100
19 **27** 2 a. dull blue 25 15
20 2 a. ultramarine 25 20
21 **28** 3 a. orange (1889) .. .. .. 1·25 2·00
22 3 a. brown-orange 30 25
23 **29** 4 a. olive-green 25 25
24 4 a. slate-green 35 35
25 **21** 6 a. olive-bistre (1889) .. .. .. 80 1·00
26 6 a. bistre-brown .. .. 80 1·00
27 **31** 8 a. dull mauve 65 80
28 **32** 12 a. purple/*red* (1889) 65 90
29 **33** 1 r. slate .. .. 5·50 8·00
30 **37** 1 r. green and carmine (1893) .. .. 1·40 1·75
a. "N BHA" for "NABHA" .. ..
31 **38** 2 r. carmine and yellow-brown (1897) 50·00 65·00
32 3 r. brown and green (1897) .. .. 50·00 65·00
33 5 r. ultramarine and violet (1897) .. 55·00 70·00
14/33 .. .. *Set of* 15 £140 £190

(c) *New value. In black* (Nov 1900)
36 **40** 3 p. carmine 8 8

1903–09. *King Edward VII. Optd with T* **2**.
37 **41** 3 p. pale grey 8 8
37*a* 3 p. slate-grey (1906) 8 8
38 **42** ½ a. green 8 8
a. "NABH" £100
39 **43** 1 a. carmine 12 12
40 **44** 2 a. pale violet 30 30
40*a* 2 a. mauve 25 20
40*b* **45** 2½ a. ultramarine (1909) .. .. 25·00 35·00
41 **46** 3 a. orange-brown 30 30
42 **47** 4 a. olive 40 45
43 **48** 6 a. olive-bistre 50 75
44 **49** 8 a. dull mauve 60 75
44*a* 8 a. magenta .. .. 85 1·10
45 **50** 12 a. purple/*red* .. .. .. 90 1·40
46 **51** 1 r. green and carmine .. .. 1·10 1·40
37/46 .. .. *Set of* 11 27·00 38·00

1907. *Nos.* 149/50 *of India optd with T* **2**.
47 **53** ½ a. green 10 10
48 **54** 1 a. carmine 20 25

1913. *King George V. Optd with T* **2**.
49 **55** 3 p. slate 8 8
50 **56** ½ a. green 8 8
51 **57** 1 a. aniline carmine 8 8
52 **59** 2 a. mauve 15 20
53 **62** 3 a. orange-brown 20 25
54 **63** 4 a. olive 25 30
55 **64** 6 a. olive-bistre 30 45
56 **65** 8 a. purple 30 40
57 **66** 12 a. dull claret 50 75
58 **67** 1 r. brown and green .. .. .. 80 1·00
a. Opt double, one albino ..
49/58 .. .. *Set of* 10 2·25 3·00

1924. *As* 1913. *New colour.*
59 **57** 1 a. chocolate 60 60

NABHA STATE (3) — NABHA STATE (4)

1928–37. *King George V (Nasik printing, wmk Mult Star), optd as T* **3** *or* **4** *(rupee values).*
60 **55** 3 p. slate (1932) 8 10
61 **56** ½ a. green 8 10
61*a* **80** 9 p. deep green (1934) 15 20
62 **57** 1 a. chocolate 8 10
63 **82** 1¼ a. mauve (1937) 15 25
64 **70** 2 a. purple (1932) 25 20
65 **61** 2½ a. orange (1932) 25 40
66 **62** 3 a. bright blue (1930) 35 50
67 **71** 4 a. sage-green (1932) 40 45
71 **67** 2 r. carmine and orange (1932) .. 6·00 10·00
72 5 r. ultramarine and purple (1932) .. 18·00 28·00
60/72 .. .. *Set of* 11 23·00 38·00
The 9 p. exists printed by lithography or typography.

1936–37. *New types and colours. Optd as T* **3**.
73 **79** ½ a. green 10 12
74 **81** 1 a. chocolate 10 12
75 **62** 3 a. carmine (1937) 60 75
76 **63** 4 a. slate-green (1937) 55 60

NABHA STATE (5) — NABHA (6)

1938. *King George VI. Nos.* 247/64 *optd as T* **3** *(3 p. to 1 a.), T* **5** *(2 a. to 12 a.) or T* **4** *(rupee values).*
77 **91** 3 p. slate .. .. 3·50 70
78 ½ a. red-brown 60 50
79 9 p. green .. .. 11·00 7·00
80 1 a. carmine 40 30
81 **92** 2 a. vermilion .. .. 60 1·25
82 – 2½ a. bright violet .. .. .. 70 1·60
83 – 3 a. yellow-green .. .. .. 80 1·60
84 – 3½ a. bright blue .. .. .. 90 2·00
85 – 4 a. brown .. .. 1·10 1·75
86 – 6 a. turquoise-green .. .. .. 1·40 3·00
87 – 8 a. slate-violet .. .. .. 2·25 3·50
88 – 12 a. lake .. .. 3·00 5·00
89 **93** 1 r. grey and red-brown .. .. .. 4·50 5·50
90 2 r. purple and brown .. .. .. 10·00 13·00
91 5 r. green and blue .. .. .. 35·00 42·00
92 10 r. purple and claret .. .. .. 70·00 85·00
93 15 r. brown and green £130 £175
94 25 r. slate-violet and purple £170 £225
77/94 .. .. *Set of* 18 £400 £525

1941–45. *King George VI. Optd with T* **6**. (a) *Stamps of* 1937.
95 **91** 3 p. slate (1942) .. .. .. 18·00 2·50
96 ½ a. red-brown (1942) .. .. .. 42·00 11·00
97 9 p. green (1942) .. .. .. 16·00 4·50
98 1 a. carmine (1942) .. .. .. 11·00 3·25

(b) *Stamps of* 1940-43
105 **100*a*** 3 p. slate (1942) 40 40
106 ½ a. purple (1943) 50 40
107 9 p. green (1942) 40 45
108 1 a. carmine (1945) 40 40
109 **101** 1 a. 3 p. bistre 60 70
110 1½ a. dull violet (1942) 60 60
111 2 a. vermilion (1943) 60 65
112 3 a. bright violet (1943) .. .. 1·25 1·60
113 3½ a. bright blue (1944) .. .. 2·00 2·50
114 **102** 4 a. brown .. .. 1·40 1·40
115 6 a. turquoise-green (1943) .. .. 2·00 4·50
116 8 a. slate-violet (1943) .. .. 1·75 3·50
117 12 a. lake (1943) .. .. .. 4·00 5·50
105/117 .. .. *Set of* 13 13·00 20·00
The 1½ a. exists printed by lithography or typography.

OFFICIAL STAMPS

SERVICE

SERVICE (O 8) — NABHA STATE (O 9)

1885 (May). *Nos.* 1/3 *of Nabha optd with Type* O **8**.
O1 **23** ½ a. blue-green 40 30
O2 **25** 1 a. brown-purple 20 12
a. Opt Type O 8 double .. .. † £250
O3 **27** 2 a. dull blue .. .. 24·00 28·00
The three values have had the overprint reprinted in the same way as the ordinary stamps of 1885.

1885–97. *Optd with Type* O **9**. (a) *In red* (Nov 1885).
O 4 **23** ½ a. blue-green 70 80
O 5 **27** 2 a. deep blue 40 50

(b) *In black* (1888–97)
O 6 **23** ½ a. blue-green 8 8
a. "SERVICE." with stop .. .. 25·00 2·25
b. "S ATE" for "STATE" .. ..
O 7 **25** 1 a. brown-purple (1892) 15 10
O 8 1 a. plum 20 10
a. "SERVICE." with stop .. .. 4·50 1·25
b. "NABHA STATE" double .. .. — £110
O 9 **27** 2 a. dull blue 25 25
O10 2 a. ultramarine 35 35
O11 **28** 3 a. orange (1891) .. .. .. 4·50 6·00
O12 3 a. brown-orange .. .. .. 4·00 6·00
O13 **29** 4 a. olive-green 35 30
O14 4 a. slate-green 40 35
O15 **21** 6 a. olive-bistre (1889) .. .. .. 1·25 1·60
O16 6 a. bistre-brown .. .. .. 60·00
O17 **31** 8 a. dull mauve (1889) 55 65
O18 **32** 12 a. purple/*red* (1889) .. .. .. 4·50 5·50
O19 **33** 1 r. slate (1889) .. .. .. 13·00 25·00
O20 **37** 1 r. green and carmine (1.97) .. .. 10·00 15·00
O6/20 .. .. *Set of* 10 30·00 40·00
Printings up to and including that of August 1895 had the "SERVICE" overprint applied to sheets of stamps already overprinted with Type **2**. From the printing of January 1897 onwards the two parts of the overprint were applied at one operation. This method was only used for printings of the ½ a., 1 a. and 1 r. (O20).

1903–06. *King Edward VII stamps of India optd with Type* O **9**.
O24 **41** 3 p. pale grey (1906) 60 70
O25 3 p. slate-grey (1906) 55 65
O26 **42** ½ a. green 20 10
O27 **43** 1 a. carmine 10 10
O28 **44** 2 a. pale violet 35 40
O29 2 a. mauve 35 40
O30 **47** 4 a. olive 50 45
O32 **49** 8 a. dull mauve 70 70
O33 8 a. magenta .. .. 1·10 1·25
O34 **51** 1 r. green and carmine .. .. .. 1·25 1·60
O24/34 .. .. *Set of* 7 3·25 3·50

1907. *Nos.* 149/50 *of India optd with Type* O **9**.
O35 **53** ½ a. green 10 10
O36 **54** 1 a. carmine 15 20

1913. *King George V. Optd with Type* O 9.
O37 **63** 4 a. olive .. .. 10·00
O38 **67** 1 r. brown and green .. .. .. 50·00

1913. *Official stamps of India optd with T* **2**.
O39 **55** 3 p. slate-grey 20 40
O39*a* 3 p. bluish slate 20 40
O40 **56** ½ a. green 12 10
O41 **57** 1 a. aniline carmine 12 10
O42 **59** 2 a. mauve 15 15
O43 **63** 4 a. olive 25 25
O44 **65** 8 a. dull mauve 60 60
O46 **67** 1 r. brown and green .. .. .. 1·25 1·25
O39/46 .. .. Set of 7 2·25 2·50

NABHA STATE SERVICE (O 10) — NABHA SERVICE (O 11)

1932–42?. *King George V (Nasik printing, wmk Mult Star), optd at Nasik with Type* O **10**.
O47 **55** 3 p. slate 8 8
O50 **81** 1 a. chocolate (1935) 10 10
O50*a* **63** 4 a. sage-green (1942?) .. .. .. 3·00 1·50
O51 **65** 8 a. reddish purple (1937) .. .. 1·10 1·40

1938. *King George VI. Optd as Type* O **10**.
O54 **91** 9 p. green .. .. 1·50 1·50
O55 1 a. carmine .. .. 1·25 70

1940–43. (a) *Official stamps optd with T* **6**.
O56 O **20** 3 p. slate (1942) 40 30
O57 ½ a. red-brown (1942) 50 40
O57*a* ½ a. purple (1943) 40 30
O58 9 p. green 40 40
O59 1 a. carmine (1942) 30 30
O61 1½ a. dull violet (1942) 40 50
O62 2 a. vermilion (1942) 40 45
O64 4 a. brown (1942) .. .. .. 1·25 1·40
O65 8 a. slate-violet (1942) .. .. .. 2·00 2·75

(b) *Postage stamps optd with Type* O **11**.
O66 **93** 1 r. grey and red-brown (1942) .. .. 6·00 7·50
O67 2 r. purple and brown (1942) .. .. 16·00 18·00
O68 5 r. green and blue (1942) .. .. 40·00 45·00
O56/68 .. .. *Set of* 11 60·00 70·00

PATIALA

PRICES FOR STAMPS ON COVER

Nos. 1/6	from × 7
Nos. 7/34	from × 4
Nos. 35/45	from × 5
Nos. 46/115	from × 3
Nos. O1/84	from × 8

PUTTIALLA STATE (1) — PUTTIALLA STATE (2) — PATIALA STATE (3)

1884. *Queen Victoria. Optd with T* **1**, *in red.*

1 **23** ½ a. blue-green 45 45
 a. Opt double, one sideways £140 £100
2 **25** 1 a. brown-purple, 11·00 12·00
 a. Opt double
 b. Optd in red and in black £125
3 **27** 2 a. dull blue 4·50 4·50
4 **17** 4 a. green 9·00 11·00
5 **31** 8 a. dull mauve 80·00 £100
 a. Opt inverted
 b. Optd in red and in black 21·00
6 **33** 1 r. slate 48·00 60·00
1/6 *Set of* 6 £140 £170

1885. *Optd with T* **2**. (*a*) *In red.*

7 **23** ½ a. blue-green 20 20
 a. "AUTTIALLA" 7·00
 b. "STATE" only
8 **27** 2 a. dull blue 45 30
 a. "AUTTIALLA" 10·00
9 **17** 4 a. green 85 85
 a. Optd in red and in black 70·00
10 **33** 1 r. slate 4·00 8·00
 a. "AUTTIALLA" 95·00

(*b*) *In black*

11 **25** 1 a. brown-purple 12 10
 a. Optd in red and in black 2·50
 b. "AUTTIALLA" 18·00
 ba. Ditto. Optd in red and in black £150 £160
 c. Opt double
12 **31** 8 a. dull mauve 3·00 4·50
 a. "AUTTIALLA" 85·00
 b. Opt double, one albino 45·00
7/12 *Set of* 6 7·50 12·00

The ½, 2 and 4 a. (T **29**), and 1 r. (all overprinted in black), are proofs.

All six values exist with reprinted overprints, and the error "AUTTIALLA STATE" has been reprinted in complete sheets on all values and in addition in black on the ½, 2, 4 a., and 1 r. Nearly all these however, are found with the word "REPRINT" overprinted upon them.

The error "PUTTILLA" formerly catalogued is considered doubtful.

1891–96. *Optd with T* **3**.

13 **23** ½ a. blue-green 8 8
14 **24** 9 p. carmine 25 35
15 **25** 1 a. brown-purple 12 10
16 1 a. plum 20 10
 a. "PATIALA" omitted 70·00 70·00
17 **26** 1½ a. sepia 25 30
18 **27** 2 a. dull blue (1896) 30 15
19 2 a. ultramarine 30 15
20 **28** 3 a. brown-orange 25 30
21 **29** 4 a. olive-green (1896) 30 35
 a. "PATIALA" omitted £110 85·00
22 4 a. slate-green 30 35
23 **21** 6 a. bistre-brown 40 45
24 6 a. olive-bistre 1·00
25 **31** 8 a. dull mauve
26 8 a. magenta (1896) 50 60
27 **32** 12 a. purple/*red* 60 75
28 **37** 1 r. green and carmine (1896) 3·25 4·00
29 **38** 2 r. carmine and yellow-brown (1895) 42·00
30 3 r. brown and green (1895) 55·00
31 5 r. ultramarine and violet (1895) 65·00
13/31 *Set of* 14 £150

1899–1902. *Colours changed and new value. Optd with T* **3**.

32 **40** 3 p. carmine (1899) 8 8
33 **23** ½ a. pale yellow-green 8 10
34 **25** 1 a. carmine 10 12

1903–06. *King Edward VII. Optd with T* **3**.

35 **41** 3 p. pale grey 8 8
36 3 p. slate-grey (1906) 8 8
37 **42** ½ a. green 8 8
38 **43** 1 a. carmine 8 8
 a. Opt omitted (horiz pair with normal)
39 **44** 2 a. pale violet 12 12
 a. Mauve 50 40
40 **46** 3 a. orange-brown 15 15
41 **47** 4 a. olive (1905) 45 40
42 **48** 6 a. olive-bistre (1905) 55 65
43 **49** 8 a. dull mauve (1906) 70 80
44 **50** 12 a. purple/*red* (1906) 90 1·10
45 **51** 1 r. green and carmine (1905) 1·10 1·25
35/45 *Set of* 10 3·75 4·25

1912. *Nos.* 149/50 *of India optd with T* **3**.

46 **53** ½ a. green 8 8
47 **54** 1 a. carmine 10 8

1912–26. *King George V. Optd with T* **3**.

48 **55** 3 p. slate-grey 8 8
49 **56** ½ a. green 8 8
50 **57** 1 a. aniline carmine 8 8
51 **58** 1½ a. chocolate (Type A) (1922) 35 45
52 **59** 2 a. mauve 12 15
53 **62** 3 a. orange-brown 30 30
54 **63** 4 a. olive 30 30
55 **64** 6 a. yellow-brown 75 85
 a. Yellow-bistre 55 65
56 **65** 8 a. purple 45 45
57 **66** 12 a. dull claret 65 85
58 **67** 1 r. brown and green 2·50 2·00
59 2 r. carmine and yellow-brown (1926) 6·00 12·00
60 5 r. ultramarine and violet (1926) 14·00 18·00

1923–6. *As* 1912–26. *New colours.*

61 **57** 1 a. chocolate 8 8
62 **62** 3 a. ultramarine (1926) 35 55
48/62 *Set of* 15 23·00 32·00

PATIALA STATE (4) — PATIALA STATE (5)

1928–34. *King George V (Nasik printing, wmk Mult Star) optd at Nasik with T* **4** *or* **5** (*rupee values*).

63 **55** 3 p. slate (1932) 10 8
64 **56** ½ a. green 8 8
65 **80** 9 p. deep green (1934) 12 15
66 **57** 1 a. chocolate 12 10
67 **82** 1¼ a. mauve (1933) 15 15
68 **70** 2 a. purple 15 15
69 **61** 2½ a. orange (1934) 25 30
70 **62** 3 a. bright blue (1929) 30 35
71 **71** 4 a. sage-green 40 45
72 **65** 8 a. reddish purple (1933) 70 60
73 **67** 1 r. chocolate and green (1933) 1·60 1·25
74 2 r. carmine and orange 3·25 7·00
63/74 *Set of* 12 6·50 9·50

The 9 p. exists printed by lithography or typography.

1935–7. *Optd with T* **4**.

75 **79** ½ a. blue-green (1937) 8 8
76 **81** 1 a. chocolate (1936) 8 8
77 **59** 2 a. vermilion (No. 236*a*) (1936) 12 15
78 **62** 3 a. carmine 50 60
79 **63** 4 a. sage-green 25 35

PATIALA STATE (6) — PATIALA (7) — PATIALA (8)

1937–8. *King George VI. Nos.* 247/64 *optd with T* **4** (3 *p. to* 1 *a.*), *T* **6** (2 *a. to* 12 *a.*), *or T* **5** (*rupee values*).

80 **91** 3 p. slate 16·00 4·50
81 ½ a. red-brown 1·75 50
82 9 p. green (1937) 1·40 1·00
83 1 a. carmine (1937) 40 30
84 **92** 2 a. vermilion 80 1·50
85 – 2½ a. bright violet 90 2·00
86 – 3 a. yellow-green 90 1·75
87 – 3½ a. bright blue 1·50 3·00
88 – 4 a. brown 2·00 2·25
89 – 6 a. turquoise-green 2·50 4·00
90 – 8 a. slate-violet 3·00 5·00
91 – 12 a. lake 4·50 7·00
92 **93** 1 r. grey and red-brown 15·00 13·00
93 2 r. purple and brown 18·00 20·00
94 5 r. green and blue 26·00 28·00
95 10 r. purple and claret 55·00 65·00
96 15 r. brown and green £100 £120
97 25 r. slate-violet and purple £150 £170
80/97 *Set of* 18 £350 £400

1941–6. *King George VI. Optd with T* **7** *or* **8** (*rupee value*).

(*a*) *Stamps of* 1937

98 **91** 3 p. slate 7·50 1·50
99 ½ a. red-brown 5·00 1·50
100 9 p. green 27·00 3·50
101 1 a. carmine 8·00 2·00
102 **93** 1 r. grey and red-brown (1946) 7·50 7·50

(*b*) *Stamps of* 1940-43

103 **100*a*** 3 p. slate (1942) 40 20
104 ½ a. purple (1943) 40 20
105 9 p. green (1942) 40 20
 a. Opt omitted (vert pair with normal) £1500
106 1 a. carmine (1944) 35 20
107 **101** 1 a. 3 p. bistre 1·10 1·25
108 1½ a. violet (1942) 40 45
109 2 a. vermilion (1944) 60 35
110 3 a. bright violet (1944) 75 90
111 3½ a. bright blue (1944) 1·60 2·00
112 **102** 4 a. brown (1944) 1·00 1·40
113 6 a. turquoise-green (1944) 1·25 2·25
114 8 a. slate-violet (1844) 1·60 2·50
115 12 a. lake (1945) 4·50 7·00
103/115 *Set of* 13 13·00 17·00

The 1½ a. exists printed by lithography or typography.

OFFICIAL STAMPS

SERVICE (O 2) — SERVICE (O 3)

1884. *Nos.* 1/3 *of Patiala optd with Type O* **2**, *in black.*

O1 **23** ½ a. blue-green 1·00 15
O2 **25** 1 a. brown-purple 20 8
 a. Opt Type **1** inverted £140 70·00
 b. Opt Type **1** double — 45·00
 c. "SERVICE" double £140 75·00
 d. "SERVICE" inverted — £225
O3 **27** 2 a. dull blue £350 20·00

1885–90. (*a*) *No.* 7 *of Patiala optd with Type O* **2**, *in black.*

O4 **23** ½ a. blue-green 15 8
 a. "SERVICE" double — 70·00
 b. "AUTTIALLA" 24·00 8·50

(*b*) *No.* 11 *of Patiala optd with Type O* **2**, *in black*

O5 **25** 1 a. brown-purple 20 8
 a. "SERVICE" double £110 £110
 b. "SERVICE" double, one inverted — £160
 c. "AUTTIALLA" 75·00 22·00

(*c*) *As No.* 7 *of Patiala, but optd in black, and No.* 8, *optd with Type O* **3**

O6 **23** ½ a. blue-green (Bk.) (1890) 12 8
O7 **27** 2 a. dull blue (R.) 12 8
 a. "SERVICE" double, one inverted 35·00

There are reprints of Nos. O4, O5 and O7. The first has the word "SERVICE" in the large type in *red* instead of the small type in *black*, and the second has the word in the large type in *black* in place of the small type. The 2 a. with Type O **3**, in *black*, is a proof. The ½ a. "AUTTIALLA" has also been reprinted, but nearly all the above have been overprinted "REPRINT".

SERVICE

PATIALA STATE (O 4) — PATIALA STATE SERVICE (O 5) — PATIALA STATE SERVICE (O 6)

1891 (Nov)–**1900**. *Optd with Type* O **4**, *in black.*

O 8 **23** ½ a. blue-green (9.95) 8 8
 a. "SERVICE" inverted 40·00
 b. "I" of "SERVICE" omitted £100
O 9 **25** 1 a. plum (10.1900) 30 8
 a. "SERVICE" inverted 40·00
O10 **27** 2 a. dull blue (12.98) 50 50
 a. Deep blue 50 50
 b. "SERVICE" inverted 45·00
O12 **28** 3 a. brown-orange 15 15
 a. "I" of "SERVICE" omitted
O13 **29** 4 a. olive-green 20 15
 a. Slate-green (9.95) 15 10
 b. "I" of SERVICE" omitted
O15 **21** 6 a. bistre-brown 35 30
O16 **31** 8 a. dull mauve 35 35
 a. Magenta (12.98) 40 50
 b. "I" of "SERVICE" omitted
O18 **32** 12 a. purple/*red* 45 50
 a. "I" of "SERVICE" omitted
O19 **33** 1 r. slate 55 55
 a. "I" of "SERVICE" omitted
O8/19 *Set of* 9 2·50 2·25

Stamps from the first printing of November 1891 (Nos. O12/13, O15/16, O18/19) had the "SERVICE" overprint, as Type O **3**, applied to sheets already overprinted with Type **3**. Subsequent printings of Nos. O8/10*a*, O13*a* and O16*a* had both overprints applied at one operation as shown on Type O **4**.

The errors with "SERVICE" inverted occur from a trial printing, in two operations, during 1894, which was probably not issued. Some of the "I" omitted varieties may also come from the same trial printing.

1902 (Jan)–**03**. *Optd with Type* O **4**.

O20 **25** 1 a. carmine 8 8
O21 **37** 1 r. green and carmine (5.03) 7·00 9·00

1903–10. *King Edward VII stamps of India optd with Type* O **4**.

O22 **41** 3 p. pale grey 8 8
 a. Slate-grey (1909) 8 8
O24 **42** ½ a. green 8 8
O25 **43** 1 a. carmine 8 8
O26 **44** 2 a. pale violet (1905) 15 10
 a. Mauve 15 10
O28 **46** 3 a. orange-brown 1·25 1·50
O29 **47** 4 a. olive (1905) 25 20
O30 **49** 8 a. dull mauve 45 35
 a. Magenta (1910) 60 50
O32 **51** 1 r. green and carmine (1906) 80 80
O22/32 *Set of* 8 2·75 2·75

1907. *Nos.* 149/50 *of India optd with Type* O **4**.

O33 **53** ½ a. green 8 8
O34 **54** 1 a. carmine 8 8

1913–26. *King George V. Official stamps of India optd with T* **3**.

O35 **55** 3 p. slate-grey 12 8
 a. Bluish slate (1926) 15 12
O36 **56** ½ a. green 8 8
O37 **57** 1 a. carmine 8 8
O38 1 a. brown (1925) 25 10
O39 **59** 2 a. mauve 15 8
O40 **63** 4 a. olive 20 20
O41 **64** 6 a. yellow-bistre (1926) 40 60
O42 **65** 8 a. purple 35 35
O43 **67** 1 r. brown and green 1·25 1·25
O44 2 r. carmine and yellow-brown (1926) 4·00 5·50
O45 5 r. ultramarine and violet (1926) 10·00 12·00
O35/45 *Set of* 11 15·00 18·00

1927–36. *King George V (Nasik printing, wmk Mult Star), optd at Nasik with* Type O **5** *or Type* O **6** (*rupee values*).

O47 **55** 3 p. slate 8 8
 a. Blue opt 10 10
O48 **56** ½ a. green (1932) 8 8
O49 **57** 1 a. chocolate 8 8
O50 **82** 1¼ a. mauve (1932) 10 8
O51 **70** 2 a. purple 12 15
O52 2 a. vermilion (1933) 20 25
O53 **61** 2½ a. orange (1933) 20 20
O54 **71** 4 a. sage-green (1935) 20 20
O55 **65** 8 a. reddish purple (1929) 50 50
O56 **67** 1 r. chocolate and green (1929) 1·50 80
O57 2 r. carmine and orange (1936) 3·00 4·00
O47/57 *Set of* 11 5·50 5·75

1935–9. *New types. Optd with Type* O **5**.

O58 **79** ½ a. green (1936) 8 8
O59 **81** 1 a. chocolate (1936) 8 8
O60 **59** 2 a. vermilion 12 12
O61 2 a. vermilion (*small die*) (1939) 25 30
O62 **63** 4 a. sage-green (1936) 20 20

1937–39. *King George VI. Optd with Types* O **5** *or* O **6** (*rupee values*).

O63 **91** ½ a. red-brown (1938) 1·10 50
O64 9 p. green (1938) 15·00 22·00
O65 1 a. carmine 1·50 50
O66 **93** 1 r. grey and red-brown (1939) 3·00 3·00
O67 2 r. purple and brown (1939) 15·00 12·00
O68 5 r. green and blue (1939) 30·00 30·00
O63/8 *Set of* 6 60·00 60·00

1A ——— 1A (O 7)   1A SERVICE 1A (O 8)   PATIALA SERVICE (O 9)

1939–40. *Stamp of 1932 (King George V).*

(a) Optd with Types O 5 and O 7
O69 82 1 a. on 1¼ a. mauve .. .. .. 1·40 1·25

(b) Optd with T 4 and O 8
O70 82 1 a. on 1¼ a. mauve (1940) .. .. 1·00 1·25

"SERVICE" measures 9¼ mm on No. O69 but only 8¾ mm on O70.

1939–44. *(a) Official stamps optd with T 7.*
O71 O 20 3 p. slate (1940) 15 15
O72 ½ a. red-brown 15 15
O73 ½ a. purple (1942) 15 15
O74 9 p. green 15 15
O75 1 a. carmine 15 15
O76 1 a. 3 p. bistre (1941) 50 30
O77 1½ a. dull violet (1944) 25 20
O78 2 a. vermilion (1940) 50 30
O79 2½ a. bright violet (1940) 35 60
O80 4 a. brown (1943) 50 50
O81 8 a. slate-violet (1944) .. .. 1·00 1·25

(b) Postage stamps optd with Type O 9
O82 93 1 r. grey and red-brown (1943) .. .. 3·50 3·00
O83 2 r. purple and brown (1944) .. .. 8·50 8·50
O84 5 r. green and blue (1944) .. .. 18·00 19·00
O71/84 .. .. *Set of* 14 30·00 30·00

INDIAN FEUDATORY STATES

These stamps were only valid for use within their respective states, *unless otherwise indicated.*

Postage stamps of the Indian States, current at that date, were replaced by those of the Republic of India on 1 April 1950.

Unless otherwise stated, all became obsolete on 1 May 1950 (with the exception of the "Anchal" stamps of Travancore-Cochin, which remained current until 1 July 1951 or Sept 1951 for the Official issues).

ALWAR

PRICES FOR STAMPS ON COVER
Nos. 1/5 *from* × 15

1 (1 a.).

1877. *Litho. Rouletted.*
1 1 ¼ a. grey-blue 85 35
a. Ultramarine 90 30
b. Imperf between (pair) .. .. — 27·00
c. Bright greenish blue .. .. 20·00 7·00
2 1 a. brown .. .. 1·00 60
a. Imperf between (pair) .. .. 45·00 45·00
b. Red-brown 85 70
c. Chocolate .. .. 12·00 8·00

1899–1901. *Redrawn. P 12. (a) Wide margins between stamps.*
3 1 ¼ a. slate-blue .. .. 4·00 1·75
a. Imperf between (horiz pair) .. £225
b. Imperf between (vert pair) £250
4 ¼ a. emerald-green £550

(b) Narrower margins (1901)
5 1 ¼ a. emerald-green .. .. .. 2·50 1·10
a. Imperf between (horiz pair) .. £130
b. Imperf between (vert pair) £130 £140
c. Imperf horiz (vert pair) £140
d. Imperf (pair) £140
e. Pale yellow-green .. .. .. 5·00 1·75
ea. Imperf (pair) £175

In the redrawn type only the bottom outer frameline is thick, whereas in the original 1877 issue the left-hand frameline is also thick, as shown in Type 1.

The stamps of Alwar became obsolete on 1 July 1902.

BAHAWALPUR

See after PAKISTAN

BAMRA

PRICES FOR STAMPS ON COVER
Nos. 1/6 —
Nos. 8/40 *from* × 20

Raja Sir Sudhal Deo, 1869–1903

GUM. The stamps of Bamra were issued without gum.

BAMRA postage — 1 (¼ a.)   BAMRA postage — 1*a*   BAMRA postage — 2 (½ a.)

BAMRA postage — 3 (1 a.)   BAMRA postage — 4 (2 a.)   BAMRA postage — 5 (4 a.)

BAMRA postage — 6 (8 a.)

(illustrations actual size)

(Typo Jagannata Ballabh Press, Deogarh)

1888. *Imperf.*
1 1 ¼ a. black/*yellow* .. .. .. 65·00
a. "g" inverted (R.5/1) £1400
b. Last native character inverted .. £1600
c. Last native character as Type 1*a* .. £1600
2 2 ½ a. black/*rose* .. .. .. 50·00
a. "g" inverted (R.5/1) £1350
3 3 1 a. black/*blue* .. .. .. 40·00
a. "g" inverted (R.5/1) £1300
b. Scroll inverted (R.8/4) £1100
4 4 2 a. black/*green* .. .. .. 50·00
a. "a" omitted (R.8/3) £1350
b. Scroll inverted (R.8/4) £1100
5 5 4 a. black/*yellow* .. .. .. 40·00
a. "a" omitted (R.8/3) £1300
b. Scroll inverted (R.8/4) £1100
6 6 8 a. black/*rose* .. .. .. 35·00
a. "a" omitted (R.8/3) £1250
b. Horiz pair, one printed on back .. £275
c. Scroll inverted (R.8/4) £1000

These stamps were all printed from the same plate of 96 stamps, 12 × 8, but for some values only part of the plate was used. There are 96 varieties of the ½, 4 and 8 a., 72 of the 1 a., 80 of the 2 a. and not less than 88 of the ¼ a.

The scroll ornament can be found pointing to either the right or the left.

There are two forms of the third native character. In the first five horizontal rows it is as in T 1 and in the last three rows as in T 4.

These stamps have been reprinted: the ¼ a. and ½ a. in blocks of 8 varieties (all showing scroll pointing to right), and all the values in blocks of 20 varieties (all showing scroll pointing to left). On the reprints the fourth character is of a quite different shape.

8

1890 (July)–93. *Black on coloured paper. Nos. 24/5 and 39/40 show face value as* "One Rupee". *(a)* "Postage" *with capital* "P".
8 8 ¼ a. on *rose-lilac* 40 50
a. "Eeudatory" .. .. .. 10·00 12·00
b. "Quatrer" .. .. .. 10·00 12·00
c. Inverted "e" in "Postage" .. .. 10·00 12·00
9 ¼ a. on *bright rose* 45 50
10 ¼ a. on *reddish purple* 30 35
a. First "a" in "anna" inverted .. 22·00 22·00
b. "AMRA" inverted .. .. .. 35·00 35·00
c. "M" and second "A" in "BAMRA" inverted .. .. .. 42·00 42·00
11 ½ a. on *dull green* 50 60
a. "Eeudatory" .. .. .. 20·00 22·00
12 ½ a. on *blue-green* 60 60
13 1 a. on *bistre-yellow* .. .. .. 90 1·25
a. "Eeudatory" .. .. .. 40·00 45·00
14 1 a. on *orange-yellow* .. .. .. 30·00 30·00
a. "annas" for "anna" .. .. .. 80·00 80·00
15 2 a. on *rose-lilac* .. .. .. 6·00 7·00
a. "Eeudatory" .. .. .. 70·00 75·00
16 2 a. on *bright rose* .. .. .. 1·40 1·40
17 2 a. on *dull rose* .. .. .. 1·60 1·25
18 4 a. on *rose-lilac* £250 £275
a. "Eeudatory" £800 £800
19 4 a. on *dull rose* .. .. .. 2·50 2·50
a. "Eeudatory" £125 £125
b. "BAMBA" £140 £140
20 4 a. on *bright rose* .. .. .. 1·75 2·00
20*a* 4 a. on *deep pink* .. .. .. 8·00 6·00
21 8 a. on *rose-lilac* .. .. .. 18·00 20·00
a. "Foudatory" and "Postagc" .. .. 95·00 95·00
b. "BAMBA" .. .. .. 95·00 95·00
22 8 a. on *bright rose* .. .. .. 4·25 4·25
23 8 a. on *dull rose* .. .. .. 4·50 5·00
24 1 r. on *rose-lilac* .. .. .. 28·00 32·00
a. "Eeudatory" £140 £140
b. "BAMBA" £120 £120
c. "Postagc" £120 £120
25 1 r. on *bright rose* .. .. .. 20·00 20·00
a. Small "r" in "rupee" £150 £150

(b) "postage" *with small* "p" (1891–93)
26 8 ¼ a. on *bright rose* 60 60
27 ¼ a. on *reddish purple* 35 40
28 ½ a. on *dull green* 60 65
a. First "a" in "anna" inverted .. 11·00 12·00
29 ½ a. on *blue-green* 60 65
a. First "a" in "anna" inverted .. 10·00 11·00
30 1 a. on *bistre-yellow* .. .. .. 1·25 1·40
31 1 a. on *orange-yellow* .. .. .. 30·00 30·00
32 2 a. on *bright rose* .. .. .. 1·60 1·75
33 2 a. on *dull rose* .. .. .. 1·75 1·50
34 4 a. on *dull rose* .. .. .. 3·00 2·75
35 4 a. on *bright rose* .. .. .. 2·25 2·50
35*a* 4 a. on *deep pink* .. .. .. 10·00 7·00
36 8 a. on *rose-lilac* .. .. .. 24·00 26·00
37 8 a. on *bright rose* .. .. .. 5·00 5·50
38 8 8 a. on *dull rose* .. .. .. 5·50 6·00
39 1 r. on *rose-lilac* .. .. .. 35·00 38·00
40 1 r. on *bright rose* .. .. .. 28·00 28·00
a. Small "r" in "rupee" £170 £170
b. Small "r" in "rupee" and native characters in the order 2, 3, 1, 4, 5 £1400 £1400

There are 10 settings of Type 8. The first setting (of 20 varieties) has capital "P" throughout. The remaining settings (of 16 varieties) have capital "P" and small "p" mixed.

For the first setting the 8 a. and 1 r. values were printed within the same block, the ten lefthand stamps being 8 a. values and the ten righthand stamps 1 r.

The various stamps were distributed between the settings as follows:
Setting I—Nos. 8/c, 11/a, 13/a, 15/a, 18/19a, 21, 24/a.
Setting II—Nos. 19, 19b, 21/b, 24, 24b/c, 34, 36, 39
Setting III—Nos. 9, 11, 13, 16, 26, 28, 30, 32
Setting IV—Nos. 20, 22, 25, 35, 37, 40
Setting V—Nos. 10, 10b/c, 20*a*, 27, 35*a*
Setting VI—Nos. 11, 12, 28, 28a, 29/a
Setting VII—Nos. 10/a, 12, 17, 19, 23, 25a, 27, 29, 33/4, 38, 40a/b
Setting VIII—Nos. 17, 33
Setting IX—Nos. 10/a, 12, 14/a, 17, 19, 23, 27, 29, 31, 33/4, 38
Setting X—Nos. 19, 34

There are 4 sizes of the central ornament, which represents an elephant's trunk holding a stick:—*(a)* 4 mm long; *(b)* 5 mm; *(c)* 6½ mm; *(d)* 11 mm. These ornaments are found pointing to right or left, either upright or inverted.

Ornaments *(a)* are found in all settings; *(b)* in all settings from Settings III to X; *(c)* in Settings I and II; and *(d)* only in Setting I.

The stamps of Bamra have been obsolete since 1 January 1895.

BARWANI

PRICES FOR STAMPS ON COVER
Nos. 1/31 *from* × 10
Nos. 32/43 *from* × 8

PROCESS. All Barwani stamps are typographed from clichés, and are in sheets of 4, *unless otherwise indicated.*

Issues to about 1930 were printed by the Barwani State Printing Press, and subsequently by the Rising Star Printing Press of Mhow, Indore State (possibly printing in Barwani).

GUM. Nos. 1/31 were issued without gum.

BOOKLET PANES. Those stamps which were printed in sheets of 4 were issued in stamp booklets, binding holes appearing in the side margin.

1 Rana Ranjitsingh   2   Rana Ranjitsingh 3

1921 (Mar?). *Clear impression. Medium wove paper. P 7 all round.*
1 1 ¼ a. blue-green (dull *to* deep) .. .. 60·00 80·00
2 ½ a. dull blue .. .. .. 90·00 £120

1921 (June?). *Blurred impression. Soft wove paper. P 7 on two or three sides.*
3 1 ¼ a. green (*shades*) .. .. .. 9·00 18·00
4 ½ a. ultramarine (dull *to* pale) .. .. 15·00 25·00

NOTE. As the small sheets of Barwani stamps were often not perforated all round, many of the earlier stamps are perforated on two or three sides only. Owing to the elementary method of printing, the colours vary greatly in depth, even within a single sheet.

1921. *Clear impression. Vertically laid bâtonné paper. Imperf.*
5 1 ¼ a. green (*shades*) .. .. .. 7·00
a. On toned paper .. .. ..
6 ½ a. green (*shades*) .. .. .. 4·00
a. Perf 11 at top or bottom only .. 4·00
b. On toned paper .. .. .. 4·00
ba. Perf 11 at top or bottom only .. 4·00

It is suggested that No. 5 may be an error due to printing from the wrong plate.

1922 (?). *Clear impression. Thickish glazed wove paper. P 7 on two or three sides.*
7 1 ¼ a. dull blue .. .. .. 42·00

1922. *Smooth, soft medium wove paper. P 7 on two or three sides.*

(a) Clear impression
8 1 ¼ a. deep grey-blue .. .. .. 11·00

(b) Poor impression
9 1 ¼ a. steel blue .. .. .. 4·50

Examples of No. 9 exist with perforations on all four sides.

1922. *P 11 on two or three sides.*

(a) Thick, glazed white wove paper
10 2 1 a. vermilion (*shades*) .. .. 1·25 5·00
a. Imperf between (vert pair) .. .. 85·00
11 2 a. purple (*to* violet) .. .. 1·50 5·00
a. Doubly printed .. .. .. 80·00
b. Imperf between (pair) .. .. 80·00 80·00

(b) Thick, toned wove paper
12 2 2 a. purple .. .. .. 9·00 15·00

1922. *Poor impression. Thin, poor wove paper. Pin-perf 8½ on two or three sides.*
13 1 ¼ a. grey (*to* grey-blue) .. .. 1·00
a. Imperf (pair) .. .. .. 50·00
b. Imperf between (vert pair) .. .. 50·00

1923. *Thin, smooth, unglazed wove paper. P 11 on two or three sides.*

14 1 ½ a. green (pale *to* deep) .. .. .. 1·10 3·00
a. Imperf between (pair) .. .. 60·00
15 2 1 a. vermilion £900

1923. *Poor impression. Thick, soft wove paper. P 7 on two or three sides.*

16 1 ½ a. green (pale *to* deep) .. .. .. 15·00

No. 16 also exists perforated on all four sides.

1923 (Mar?). *Poor quality wove paper. P 7 on two or three sides.*

17 1 ¼ a. black .. .. 25·00 35·00
a. Imperf between (horiz pair) .. £300

1923 (May?). *Horizontally laid bâtonné paper. P 12.*

18 1 ¼ a. rose (*shades*) .. .. .. 80 1·40
a. Imperf between (vert pair) .. .. 60·00
b. Pin perf 6 .. .. 30·00 22·00
c. Perf compound of 12 and 6 .. .. 22·00
d. Pin perf 7 .. ..

No. 18 was issued in sheets of 12 (3 panes of 4) and was printed on paper showing a sheet watermark of Britannia and a double-lined inscription.

1925 (?). *Vertically laid bâtonné paper. P 11.*

19 1 ¼ a. blue (pale *to* deep) .. .. .. 80 1·50

No. 19 was issued in sheets of 8 and was printed on paper with a sheet watermark of a shell and an inscription "SHELL" in double-lined capitals.

1927. *Very poor impression. Thin, brittle wove paper. P 7.*

20 1 ¼ a. milky blue (*shades*) .. .. .. 9·00 12·00
21 ½ a. yellow-green (*shades*) .. .. 10·00
a. Imperf between (horiz pair) .. £140
22 3 4 a. orange-brown .. .. .. 28·00
a. Imperf between (horiz pair) .. £180

On Nos. 20/1 the portrait is nearly invisible.

1927. *Thick wove paper. Sewing maching perf 6–10.*

23 3 4 a. yellow-brown .. .. .. 38·00
a. Perf 7 .. .. 22·00
b. Orange-brown .. .. .. 45·00

1928–32 (?). *Thick glazed paper.* (a) *P 7.*

24 1 ¼ a. deep bright blue .. .. .. 5·50
25 ½ a. bright yellow-green .. .. .. 6·50

(b) *P 10½ (rough)* (Nov 1928)

26 1 ¼ a. ultramarine .. .. .. 1·75
a. *Tête-bêche* (horiz pair) .. .. 10·00
27 ½ a. apple-green .. .. 2·25
a. *Tête-bêche* (vert pair) .. .. 10·00

(c) *P 11 (clean-cut)* (1929-32?)

28 1 ¼ a. bright blue .. .. 70 1·25
a. Indigo .. .. 1·50 2·25
ab. Imperf between (horiz pair) .. 35·00
b. Deep dull blue .. .. .. 70 1·25
ba. Imperf between (vert pair) .. .. 50·00
c. Ultramarine .. .. .. 2·00 2·75
29 ½ a. myrtle-green .. .. .. 70 1·25
a. Imperf between (horiz pair) .. 45·00
b. Turquoise-green .. .. .. 2·25 2·75
ba. Imperf between (vert pair) .. .. 55·00
30 2 1 a. rose-carmine (1931) .. .. 5·00 9·00
a. Imperf between (vert pair) .. .. — £120
31 3 4 a. salmon (*to* orange) (1931) .. .. 26·00 38·00
a. Imperf between (horiz pair) .. £225

No. 26 was printed in sheets of 8 (4 × 2) with the two centre pairs *tête-bêche* while No. 27 in similar sheets, had the two horizontal rows *tête-bêche*. Both sheets are always found with one long side imperforate.

Nos. 28/31 were printed in sheets of 8 the two lower values existing either 4 × 2 or 2 × 4 and the two higher values 4 × 2 only. No *tête-bêche* pairs were included in these printings. It is believed that a small printing of No. 31 was produced in sheets of 4, but details are uncertain.

4 Rana Devi Singh 5

1932–47. *Medium to thick wove paper.*

A. *Close setting* (2½–4½ *mm*). *P 11, 12 or compound* (1932–8?)
B. *Wide setting* (6–7 *mm*). *P 11* (1938–48)

			A		B	
32	4	¼ a. slate	80	3·00	1·40	3·00
33		½ a. blue-green	1·25	3·00	1·75	3·50
34		1 a. brown	1·75	3·50	2·50	4·50
		a. Chocolate. Perf 8½ (1947)		†	6·00	9·00
35		2 a. purple (*shades*) ..	3·00	6·00		†
		a. Rose-carmine ..		†	30·00	—
36		4 a. olive-green	7·00	11·00	10·00	16·00

The measurements given in the heading indicate the vertical spacing between impressions. There are eight settings of this interesting issue: four "Close" where the over-all stamp dimensions from centre to centre of perfs vary in width from 21½ to 23 mm and in height from 25 to 27½ mm; three "Wide", width 23–23½ mm and height 29–30 mm and one "Medium" (26½ × 31 mm) (No. 34*a* only).

1935–48. *P 11.*

A. *Close setting* (3–4½ *mm*). *Thick, cream-surfaced wove paper*
B. *Wide setting* (7–10 *mm*). *Medium to thick wove paper* (1938–48)

			A		B	
37	1	¼ a. black	1·40	—	2·00	3·50
38		½ a. blue-green	6·50	—		†
		a. Yellowish green ..	4·00	—	3·00	4·50
39	2	1 a. brown (*shades*) ..	3·00	5·00	3·50	—
		a. Perf 8½ (5 mm) (1948)		†	4·50	—
40		2 a. bright purple ..		†	32·00	48·00
41		2 a. rose-carmine (1945?)		†	12·00	—
42	3	4 a. sage-green	13·00	20·00	8·50	—
		a. Pale sage-green (1945?)		†	6·00	9·00

There were two "Close" settings (over-all stamp size 25 × 29 mm) and six "Wide" settings with over-all sizes 26½–31½ × 31–36½ mm. There was also one "Medium" setting (26½ × 31 mm) but this was confined to the 1 a. perf 8½, No. 39a.

1938. *P 11.*

43 5 1 a. brown .. .. 8·00 16·00

Stamps printed in red with designs similar to Types **3** and **5** were intended for fiscal use.

The stamps of Barwani became obsolete on 1 July 1948.

BHOPAL

PRICES FOR STAMPS ON COVER	
Nos. 1/100	*from* × 10
Nos. O301/57	*from* × 15

The correct English inscription on these stamps is "H.H. NAWAB SHAH JAHAN BEGAM". In the case of Nos. 22 and 23 the normal stamps are spelt "BEGAN" and specimens with "BEGAM" are "errors".

As the stamps were printed from lithographic stones on which each unit was drawn separately by hand, numerous errors of spelling occurred. These are constant on all sheets and are listed. Some of our illustrations inadvertently include errors of spelling.

ILLUSTRATIONS. Types **1**/**3***a* and **6**/**12***a* are shown actual size.

EMBOSSING. Nos. 1/99 were only valid for postage when embossed with the device, in Urdu, of the ruling Begam. On T **1**/**3** and **6** to **12***a*. this was intended to fill the central part of the design. Almost all varieties can be found with the embossing inverted or sideways, as well as upright.

Shah Jahan Sultan Jahan

(*actual size*)

The various basic types were often in concurrent use but for greater convenience the following list is arranged according to types instead of being in strict chronological order.

GUM. Nos. 1/99 were issued without gum.

Nawab Shah Jahan Begam, 16 November 1868–15 June 1901

1 (¼ a.)

1872. *Litho.* (a) *Double frame. Sheets of 20* (5 × 4)

1 1 ¼ a. black £200 £200
a. "BFGAM" (R.3/1) £1200 £1200
b. "BEGAN" (R.2/2, R.4/4) £800 £800
c. "EGAM" (R.4/5) £1200 £1200
2 ½ a. red .. .. 10·00 12·00
a. "BFGAM" (R.3/1) .. .. .. 60·00 65·00
b. "BEGAN" (R.2/2, R.4/4) .. .. 40·00 45·00
c. "EGAM" (R.4/5) .. .. .. 60·00 65·00

2 (½ a.)

(*b*) *Single frame. Sheets of 20* (4 × 5)

3 2 ¼ a. black .. .. — £2000
4 ½ a. red .. .. 3·50 4·50
a. "NWAB" (R.2/2) .. .. .. 20·00 25·00

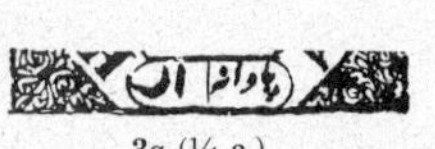

3 (¼ a.) 3*a* (¼ a.)

1878 (Jan). *All lettered "EEGAM" for "BEGAM". Sheets of 20* (4 × 5).

(*a*) *Plate* 1. *Frame lines extend horiz and vert between stamps throughout sheet*

5 3 ¼ a. black 60 90

(*b*) *Plate* 2. *Frame lines normal*

5*a* 3*a* ¼ a. black 60 90

Apart from the frame line difference between Types **3** and **3***a* the stamps can also be distinguished by the differences in the value tablets, notably the thin vertical line in the centre in Type **3***a* compared with the slightly diagonal and heavier line in Type **3**.

4 (¼ a.) 5 (½ a.)

1878 (June?)–**79**. *Value in parenthesis* (*Nos.* 6/7). *Sheets of 32* (4 × 8). *Imperf.*

6 4 ¼ a. green (1879) .. .. .. 7·00 8·00
7 ¼ a. green (*perf*) (1879) .. .. .. 8·00 9·00
8 5 ½ a. red .. .. 2·50 3·00
a. "JAHN" (R.5/2) .. .. .. 20·00
b. "NWAB" (R.3/2, R.4/2) .. .. 14·00
c. "EEGAM" (R.1/3) .. .. .. 20·00
9 ½ a. brown .. .. 18·00 20·00
a. "JAHN" (R.5/2) £110
b. "NWAB" (R.3/2, R.4/2) .. .. 70·00
c. "EEGAM" (R.1/3) £110

The ¼ a. shows the "N" of "NAWAB" reversed on R.6/4 and the "N" of "JAHAN" reversed on R.1/2–4 and R.2/2–4.

1880. *T* **5** *redrawn; value not in parenthesis. Sheets of* 32 (4 × 8)

(*a*) *Imperf*

10 ¼ a. blue-green .. .. 3·50
a. "NAWA" (R.2/2–4) .. .. .. 16·00
b. "CHAH" (R.8/3) .. .. .. 27·00
11 ½ a. brown-red .. .. 5·00 6·00

(*b*) *Perf*

12 ¼ a. blue-green .. .. 4·00
a. "NAWA" (R.2/2–4) .. .. .. 20·00
b. "CHAH" (R.8/3) .. .. .. 35·00
13 ½ a. brown-red .. .. 2·50

The ¼ a. shows the "N" of "NAWAB" reversed on R.8/4.

1884. *T* **5** *again redrawn. Sheets of* 32 (4 × 8), *some with value in parenthesis, others not. Perf.*

14 ¼ a. greenish blue .. .. .. 2·50
a. "ANAWAB" (R.4/1–4) .. .. 22·00

In this plate there is a slanting dash under and to left of the letters "JA" of "JAHAN," instead of a character like a large comma, as on all previous varieties of this design. With the exception of R.1/1 all stamps in the sheet show "N" of "JAHAN" reversed.

1895. *T* **5** *again redrawn. Sheets of* 8 (2 × 4). *Laid paper.*

15 ¼ a. red (*imperf*) .. .. 85 1·00
16 ¼ a. red (*perf*) .. .. — 50·00

In these cases where the same design has been redrawn several times, and each time in a number of varieties of type, it is not easy to distinguish the various issues. Nos. 6 and 7 may be distinguished from Nos. 10 and 12 by the presence or absence of the parenthesis marks (); 8, 9 and 11 differ principally in colour; 8 and 15 are very much alike, but differ in the value as well as in paper.

6 (1 a.)

1881. *Sheets of* 24 (4 × 6). *Imperf.*

17 6 ¼ a. black .. .. 70 1·40
a. "NWAB" (R.6/2–4) .. .. .. 3·00
18 ½ a. red .. .. 1·00 2·00
a. "NWAB" (R.6/2–4) .. .. .. 4·50
19 1 a. brown .. .. 1·00 2·00
a. "NWAB" (R.6/2–4) .. .. .. 4·50
20 2 a. blue .. .. 1·00 2·00
a. "NWAB" (R.6/2–4) .. .. .. 4·50
21 4 a. buff .. .. 5·50 9·00
a. "NWAB" (R.6/2–4) .. .. .. 18·00

In this issue all values were produced from the same drawing, and therefore show exactly the same varieties of type. The value at foot in this and all the following issues is given in only one form.

7 (½ a.)

1886. *Similar to T* **6** *but normally lettered (incorrectly)* "BEGAN"; *larger lettering. Sheets of* 32 (4 × 8). (a) *Imperf.*

22 **7** ½ a. pale red 70 90
a. "BEGAM" (R.2/1) .. .. 7·00
b. "NWAB" (R.3/4) .. .. 7·00

(b) *Perf*

23 **7** ½ a. pale red .. .. 35·00
a. "BEGAM" (R.2/1) £250
b. "NWAB" (R.3/4) £250

8 (4 a.)

1886. *T* **8**. *T* **6** *redrawn. Sheets of* 24 (4 × 6). *The* "M" *of* "BEGAM" *is an inverted* "W". *The width of the stamps is rather greater than the height.* (a) *Wove paper. Imperf.*

24 **8** 4 a. yellow .. .. 75·00
a. "EEGAM" (R.2/3–4, R.3/3–4, R.4/2, R.4/4, R.6/1) .. .. ..

(b) *Laid paper*

25 **8** 4 a. yellow (*imperf*) .. .. 5·00
a. "EEGAM" (R.2/3–4, R.3/3–4, R.4/2, R.4/4, R.6/1) .. .. 10·00
26 4 a. yellow (*perf*) .. .. 3·00 4·00
a. "EEGAM" (R.2/3–4, R.3/3–4, R.4/2, R.4/4, R.6/1) .. .. 6·00 7·00

1889. *T* **6** *again redrawn. Sheets of* 32 (4 × 8) *lettered* "BEGAN."

27 ¼ a. black (*perf*) 70 80
a. "EEGAN" (R.7/3) .. .. 7·00 8·00
28 ¼ a. black (*imperf*) .. .. 1·10 1·10
a. "EEGAN" (R.7/3) .. .. 12·00 13·00

9 (¼ a.)

1889–90. *T* **9**. *T* **6** *again redrawn. Sheets of* 24 (4 × 6), *all with* "M" *like an inverted* "W". *Wove paper.* (a) *Imperf.*

29 **9** ¼ a. black 45 70
30 1 a. brown .. .. 85 1·00
a. "EEGAM" (R.2/3) .. .. 7·50 8·50
b. "BBGAM" (R.3/1) .. .. 7·50 8·50
31 2 a. blue 75 85
a. "BBEGAM" (R.1/2) .. .. 6·50 7·00
b. "NAWAH" (R.4/2) .. .. 6·50 7·00
32 4 a. orange-yellow .. .. 1·25 1·75

(b) *Perf*

33 **9** ¼ a. black 70 75
34 1 a. brown 75 85
a. "EEGAM" (R.2/3) .. .. 6·50 7·00
b. "BBGAM" (R.3/1) .. .. 6·50 7·00
35 2 a. blue 75 85
a. "BBEGAM" (R.1/2) .. .. 6·50 7·50
b. "NAWAH" (R.4/2) .. .. 6·50 7·50
36 4 a. orange-yellow .. .. 1·50 2·00

Nos. 32 and 36 are nearly square, in many cases rather larger in height than in width.

1891. *As last, but sheets of* 32 (4 × 8).

37 **9** ½ a. red (*imperf*) 75 80
38 ½ a. red (*perf*) 75 80

1894–98. *T* **6** *again redrawn;* (a) *Sheets of* 24 (4 × 6), *almost all showing a character inside the octagon below, as in T* **9**. *Wove paper.*

39 1 a. deep brown (*imperf*) .. .. 1·25 1·25
a. Red-brown .. .. 17·00
b. Printed both sides .. .. — £350
41 1 a. deep brown (*perf*) .. .. 1·75 1·75

10 (1 a.)

(b) *As Nos.* 39/41, *but printed from a fresh transfer* (?), *showing the lines blurred and shaky. Wove paper. Imperf* (1898)

42 **10** 1 a. purple-brown .. .. 2·00 2·50
a. "NAWAH" (R.4/1) .. .. 13·00 14·00
43 1 a. purple-brown/*buff* .. .. 2·00 2·50
a. "NAWAH" (R.4/1) .. .. 13·00 14·00
b. Printed on both sides .. .. ..

The above are known without embossing.

11 (¼ a.)

1895. *Sheets of* 8 (2 × 4), *lettered* "EEGAM". *White laid paper.*

44 **11** ¼ a. black (*imperf*) .. .. 1·10 1·10
a. "A" inserted (R.4/2) .. .. 5·00 5·00
45 ¼ a. black (*perf*) .. .. 10·00 7·00
a. "NAW B" (R.4/2) £200 £200

On the perf stamp the second "A" in "NAWAB" was missing on R.4/2 in the setting. This letter was later inserted for the imperf printing varying progressively from small to large.

12 (½ a.)

1895. *Narrow label at bottom. Sheets of* 8 (2 × 4), *lettered* "W W" *for* "H H". *Laid paper.*

46 **12** ½ a. black (*imperf*) 80 90

12*a*

1895. *Sheets of* 8 (2 × 4). *Laid paper.*

47 **12*a*** ½ a. red (*imperf*) 85 90

No. 47 is a combination of Types **1** and **6**, having the double outer frame to the octagon and the value in one form only.

13 (¼ a.) (**14** (¼ a.))

1884. *Sheets of* 32 (4 × 8). *Perf.*

48 **13** ¼ a. blue-green £125 £150
a. "JAN" (R.2/1–2, R.3/1, R3/3–4, R.4/1–3, R.5/1–3) £125
b. "BEGM" (R.2/3–4) £350
c. "NWAB" and "JAN" (R.3/2) £600
ca. "NWAB" and "JN" (R.5/4) £600
d. "SHAHAN" (R.4/4) £600
e. "JAHA" (R.6/2–4) £250

1895. *T* **14**, *double-lined frame round each stamp. Sheets of* 6 (2 × 3), *lettered* "JAN". *Laid paper.*

49 **14** ¼ a. bright green (*imperf*) .. .. .. 1·50 2·00

15 (½ a.) **16** (¼ a.)

1884. *Sheets of* 32 (4 × 8). *Laid paper.*

50 **15** ¼ a. blue-green (*imperf*) .. .. 24·00 26·00
b. "NWAB" (R.1/1) £175
b. "SAH" (R.1/4) £175
c. "NAWA" and "JANAN" (R.3/2) £175
51 ¼ a. blue-green (*perf*) 30 60
a. "NWAB" (R.1/1) .. .. 3·00
b. "SAH" (R.1/4) .. .. 3·00
c. "NAWA" and "JANAN" (R.3/2) .. .. 3·00
d. Imperf between (vert pair) .. .. .. 50·00
52 ½ a. black (*imperf*) 50 60
a. "NWAB" (R.1/1) .. .. 5·00
b. "SAH" (R.1/4) .. .. 5·00
c. "NAWA" and "JANAN" (R.3/2) .. .. 5·00
53 ½ a. black (*perf*) 30 60
a. "NWAB" (R.1/1) .. .. 3·00
b. "SAH" (R.1/4) .. .. 3·00
c. "NAWA" and "JANAN" (R.3/2) .. .. 3·00

The ¼ a. of this issue is in *blue-green*, or *greenish blue*. Both values were printed from the same stone, the value alone being altered. There are therefore the same varieties of each. These are the only stamps of this design on laid paper.

Both values show the "N" of "NAWAB" reversed on R.1/1–4, R.2/1–4, R.3/1–4 and the "N" of "JAHAN" reversed on R.1/1–4, R.2/1–4, R.3/4.

1886. *T* **15** *redrawn. Sheets of* 32 (4 × 8). *Wove paper.*

54 ¼ a. green (*imperf*) 25 30
a. "NAWA" (R.6/3–4) .. .. 1·50
b. "NWAB" (R.1/1) .. .. 2·50
c. "NWABA" (R.7/4) .. .. 2·50
d. "NAWAA" (R.6/2) .. .. 2·50
e. "BEGAAM" and "NWABA" (R.7/3) .. 2·50
55 ¼ a. green (*perf*) 25 30
a. "NAWA" (R.6/3–4) .. .. 1·50
b. "NWAB" (R.1/1) .. .. 2·50
c. "NWABA" (R.7/4) .. .. 2·50
d. "NAWAA" (R.6/2) .. .. 2·50
e. "BEGAAM" and "NWABA" (R.7/3) .. 2·50
56 ½ a. red (*imperf*) 40 45
a. "SAH" (R.1/4) .. .. 3·00
b. "NAWABA" (R.6/3–4) .. .. .. 2·50

The ¼ a. varies from *yellow-green* to *deep green*.

All examples of the ¼ a. value show the "N" of "NAWAB" reversed. On the same value the "N" of "JAHAN" is reversed on all positions except R.3/2, R.4/1, R.4/3. On the ½ a. both "N"s are always reversed.

1888. *T* **15** *again redrawn. Sheets of* 32 (4 × 8), *letters in upper angles smaller.* "N" *of* "NAWAB" *correct. Wove paper.*

57 ¼ a. deep green (*imperf*) 35 45
a. "SAH" (R.6/2) .. .. 3·00
b. "NAWA" (R.4/4) .. .. 3·00
58 ¼ a. deep green (*perf*) 45 50
a. "SAH" (R.6/2) .. .. 4·00
b. "NAWA" (R.4/4) .. .. 4·00

Nos. 50 to 58 have the dash under the letter "JA" as in No. 14.

1891. *T* **15** *again redrawn. Sheets of* 32 (4 × 8), *lettered* "NWAB." *Wove paper.* (a) *Imperf.*

59 ½ a. red 40 50
a. "SAH" (R.2/4) .. .. 3·00

(b) *P 3 to 4½, or about 7*

60 ½ a. red 60 70
a. "SAH" (R.2/4) .. .. 4·50

Nos. 59 and 60 have the comma under "JA". The "N" of "JAHAN" is reversed on R.1/1–3, R.2/1–2.

1894. *T* **15** *again redrawn; letters in corners larger than in* 1888, *value in very small characters. Sheets of* 32 (4 × 8), *all with* "G" *in left-hand lower corner. Wove paper.*

61 ¼ a. green (*imperf*) 55 60
a. "NAWAH" (R.4/4) .. .. 5·50
b. Value in brackets (R.1/1) .. .. .. 5·50
62 ¼ a. green (*perf*) 65 70
a. "NAWAH" (R.4/4) .. .. 6·50
b. Value in brackets (R.1/1) .. .. .. 6·50

Nos. 61 and 62 have neither the dash nor the comma under "JA".

1896. *T* **16**; *oval narrower, stops after* "H.H.", *space after* "NAWAB". *The line down the centre is under the first* "H" *of* "SHAH" *or between* "HA" *instead of being under the second* "H" *or between* "AH". *Sheets of* 32 (4 × 8). *Wove paper. Imperf.*

63 **16** ¼ a. bright green 25 25
a. "SHAN" (R.1/1) .. .. 2·50
64 ¼ a. pale green 30 30
a. "SHAN" (R.1/1) .. .. 3·00
65 ¼ a. black 30 30
a. "SHAN" (R.1/1) .. .. 3·00

1899. *T* **15** *redrawn. Sheets of* 32 (4 × 8), *the first* "A" *of* "NAWAB" *always absent. Numerous defective and malformed letters. Wove paper. Imperf.*

66 ½ a. black .. .. 1·00 1·50
a. "NWASBAHJANNI" (R.2/4) .. .. .. 9·00 12·00
b. "SBAH" (R.3/3, R.4/3–4, R.5/1–2, R.6/4) 4·50 6·00
c. "SBAN" (R.8/2) .. .. 9·00 12·00
d. "NWIB" (R.3/2) .. .. 9·00 12·00
e. "BEIAM" (R.4/4) .. .. 9·00 12·00
f. "SHH" (R.6/3) .. .. 9·00 12·00
g. "SBAH" and "BBGAM" (R.3/4) .. .. 9·00 12·00
h. "BBGAM" (R.1/3) .. .. 9·00 12·00

17 (8 a.) (**18** (¼ a.))

1890. *T* **17**. *Sheets of* 10 (2 × 5). *Single-line frame to each stamp.*

(a) *Wove paper*

67 **17** 8 a. slate-green (*imperf*) .. .. .. 18·00 20·00
a. "HAH" (R.3/1, R.4/1, R.5/1) .. .. 42·00
b. "JABAN" (R.2/2) .. .. 42·00
68 8 a. slate-green (*perf*) .. .. .. 18·00 20·00
a. "HAH" (R.3/1, R.4/1, R.5/1) .. .. 42·00
b. "JABAN" (R.2/2) .. .. 42·00

(b) *Thin laid paper*

69 **17** 8 a. green-black (*imperf*) .. .. .. 22·00 24·00
a. "HAH" (R.3/1, R.4/1, R.5/1) .. .. 50·00
b. "JABAN" (R.2/2) .. .. 50·00
70 8 a. green-black (*perf*) .. .. .. 22·00 24·00
a. "HAH" (R.3/1, R.4/1, R.5/1) .. .. 50·00
b. "JABAN" (R.2/2) .. .. 50·00

The "N" of "NAWAB" is reversed on R.5/2 and the "N" of "JAHAN" on R.1/1–2, R.2/2, R.3/2, R.4/2 and R.5/2.

1893. *T* **17** *redrawn. No frame to each stamp, but a frame to the sheet. Sheets of* 10 (2 × 5). (a) *Wove paper.*

71 8 a. green-black (*imperf*) .. .. .. 15·00 15·00
72 8 a. green-black (*perf*) .. .. .. 17·00 17·00

(b) *Thin laid paper. Imperf*

73 8 a. green-black .. .. 35·00 38·00

1898. *Defective transfer from the stone of 1893. Lettering irregular. Sheets of 10 (2 × 5). Wove paper. Imperf.*
74 8 a. green-black 18·00 18·00
a. Reversed "E" in "BEGAM" (R.1/2, R.3/2) 50·00
75 8 a. black 18·00 18·00
a. Reversed "E" in "BEGAM" (R.1/2, R.3/2) 50·00

1896–1901. *Sheets of 32 (4 × 8). (a) Wove paper. Imperf.*
76 **18** ¼ a. black 50 50
(b) Printed from a fresh transfer (?), lines shaky (1899)
77 **18** ¼ a. black 1·25 1·25
(c) The same, on thick wove paper (1901)
78 **18** ¼ a. black 60·00 60·00

Nawab Sultan Jahan Begam, 16 June 1901–17 May 1926

19 (¼ a.)

20

1902. *T* **19**. *With the octagonal embossed device of the previous issues. Sheets of 16 (4 × 4) ¼ a. or 8 (2 × 4) others. Thin, yellowish wove paper. Imperf.*
79 **19** ¼ a. rose 1·50 1·75
80 ¼ a. rose-red 1·50 1·75
81 ½ a. black 2·00 2·25
a. Printed both sides £325
82 1 a. brown 2·50 3·00
83 1 a. red-brown 2·50 3·00
84 2 a. blue 6·50 7·50
85 4 a. orange 28·00 32·00
86 4 a. yellow 25·00 28·00
87 8 a. lilac 35·00 40·00
88 1 r. rose 48·00 55·00

1903. *With a circular embossed device. Sheets of 16 (4 × 4) ¼ a. (two plates) or 8 (2 × 4) (others).*

			A. *Wove paper.* A		B. *Laid paper* B	
89	**19**	¼ a. rose-red	40	45	50	—
90		¼ a. red	50	60	30	—
91		½ a. black	35	50	60	90
92		1 a. brown	90	1·10	10·00	—
93		1 a. red-brown	1·40	—	—	—
94		2 a. blue	2·25	2·75	22·00	—
95		4 a. orange	†		40·00	40·00
96		4 a. yellow	18·00	22·00	35·00	35·00
97		8 a. lilac	28·00	32·00	—	—
98		1 r. rose	35·00	40·00	75·00	—

1903. *No. 71 optd with initial of the new Begam in red.*
99 8 a. green-black 32·00 35·00
a. Opt inverted 70·00 70·00

Some of the previous stamps remained on sale (and probably in use) after the issue of the series of 1902, and some of these were afterwards put on sale with the new form of embossing; fresh plates were made of some of the old designs, in imitation of the earlier issues, and impressions from these were also sold with the new embossed device. We no longer list these doubtful items.

(Recess Perkins, Bacon & Co)

1908. *P* 13½.
100 **20** 1 a. green 1·25 60
a. Printed both sides £100
b. Imperf (pair)

The ordinary postage stamps of Bhopal became obsolete on 1 July 1908.

OFFICIAL STAMPS

SERVICE (O 1) **SERVICE** (O 2)

(Recess and optd Perkins, Bacon)

1908–11. *As T* **20**, *but inscribed* "H.H. BEGUM'S SERVICE" *at left. No wmk.* P 13 *to* 14. *Overprinted. (a) With Type* O **1**.
O301 ½ a. yellow-green 1·10 10
a. Pair, one without overprint £110
b. Opt double, one inverted 75·00
ba. Ditto. Imperf (pair) 85·00
c. Opt inverted 75·00
d. Imperf between (horiz pair) £160
O302 1 a. carmine-red 1·10 12
a. Opt inverted 45·00 45·00
b. Imperf (pair) 65·00
c. *Red* 1·10 10
O303 2 a. ultramarine 10·00 12
a. Imperf (pair) 50·00
O304 4 a. brown (1911) 8·00 15
(b) With Type O **2**
O305 ½ a. yellow-green 1·25 15
O306 1 a. carmine-red 3·50 90
O307 2 a. ultramarine 3·50 25
a. Opt inverted 30·00
O308 4 a. brown (1911) 40·00 25
a. Opt inverted 30·00
b. Opt double 65·00
c. Imperf (pair) 75·00
d. Imperf (pair) and opt inverted 75·00

The two overprints differ in the shape of the letters, noticeably in the "R".

Nawab Mohammad Hamidullah. Khan
17 May 1926 to transfer of administration to India, 1 June 1949

SERVICE
(O 3)

(O 4)

(Des T. I. Archer. Litho Indian Govt Ptg Wks, Nasik)

1930 (1 July)–**31**. *Type* O **4** (25½ × 30½ *mm*) *optd with Type* O **3**. *P* 14.
O309 O **4** ½ a. sage-green (1931) 1·00 15
O310 1 a. carmine-red 1·40 10
O311 2 a. ultramarine 1·75 10
O312 4 a. chocolate 2·00 20

The ½ a., 2 a. and 4 a. are inscribed "POSTAGE" at left.

(Litho Perkins, Bacon)

1932–34. *As Type* O **4** (21 × 25 *mm*), *but inscr* "POSTAGE" *at left. Optd with Type* O **1**. *(a)* "BHOPAL STATE" *at right. P* 13.
O313 ¼ a. orange 1·25 25
a. Perf 11½ (1933) 2·25 15
b. Perf 14 (1934) 6·50 25
c. Perf 13½ (1934) 5·50 1·00
ca. Pair, one without opt 55·00
(b) "BHOPAL GOVT" *at right. P* 13½
O314 ½ a. yellow-green 80 10
O315 1 a. carmine-red 1·10 10
O316 2 a. ultramarine 1·75 45
O317 4 a. chocolate 2·25 60
a. Perf 14 (1934) 7·00 40

No. O317 is comb-perforated and No. O317a line-perforated.

¼A (O 5) THREE PIES (O 6) ONE ANNA (O 7)

1935–36. *Nos.* O314, O316 *and* O317 *surch as Types* O **5** *to* O **7**.
O318 O **5** ¼ a. on ½ a. yellow-green (R.) 4·50 2·50
a. Surch inverted 60·00 50·00
O319 O **6** 3 p. on ½ a. yellow-green (R.) 45 45
a. "THEEE PIES" 25·00 25·00
b. THRFE" for "THREE" 25·00 25·00
c. Surch inverted 40·00 35·00
O320 O **5** ¼ a. on 2 a. ultramarine (R.) 4·50 2·00
a. Surch inverted 60·00 50·00
O321 O **6** 3 p. on 2 a. ultramarine (R.) 45 45
a. Surch inverted 40·00 35·00
b. "THEEE PIES" 25·00 25·00
ba. Ditto. Surch inverted £200 £200
c. "THRFE" for "THREE" 25·00 25·00
ca. Ditto. Surch inverted £200 £200
O322 O **5** ¼ a. on 4 a. chocolate (R.) £110 38·00
O323 ¼ a. on 4 a. chocolate (No. O317a) (Blk.) (23.5.36) 13·00 9·00
O324 O **6** 3 p. on 4 a. chocolate (R.) 35·00 16·00
a. "THEEE PIES" £130 £110
c. "THRFE" for "THREE" £130 £110
O325 3 p. on 4 a. chocolate (No. O317a) (Blk.) (25.5.36) 2·00 1·25
a. "THRER" for "THREE" 55·00 48·00
b. "FHREE" for "THREE" 55·00 48·00
c. "PISE" for "PIES" 80·00 80·00
d. "PIFS" for "PIES" 55·00 48·00
O326 O **7** 1 a. on ½ a. yellow-green (V.) 45 45
a. Surch inverted 35·00 35·00
b. First "N" in "ANNA" inverted 25·00 25·00
ba. Ditto. Surch inverted £125 £125
O327 1 a. on 2 a. ultramarine (R.) 45 35
a. Surch inverted 35·00 35·00
b. First "N" in "ANNA" inverted 25·00 25·00
ba. Ditto. Surch inverted £125 £125
c. "ANNO" £500 £500
O327*d* 1 a. on 2 a. ultramarine (V.) 35·00 35·00
da. Surch inverted 85·00 85·00
db. First "N" in "ANNA" inverted £125 £125
dc. Ditto. Surch inverted £300 £300
O328 1 a. on 2 a. ultram (Blk.) (25.5.36) 60 40
O329 1 a. on 4 a. chocolate (B.) 50 40
a. First "N" in "ANNA" inverted 25·00 25·00
b. Perf 14 1·75 1·50

Nos. O318 to O325 are arranged in composite sheets of 100 (10 × 10). The two upper horizontal rows of each value are surcharged as Type O **5** and the next five rows as Type O **6**. The remaining three rows are also surcharged as Type O **6** but in a slightly narrower setting.

The surcharge on No. O323 differs from Type O **5** in the shape of the figures and letter.

O 8

(Des T. I. Archer. Litho Indian Govt Ptg Wks, Nasik (No. O330). Typo Bhopal Govt Ptg Wks (others))

1935–39. *As Type* O **8**.
(a) Litho. Inscr "BHOPAL GOVT POSTAGE". *Optd* "SERVICE" (13½ *mm*). *P* 13½
O330 1 a. 3 p. blue and claret 20 15

(b) Typo. Inscr "BHOPAL STATE POSTAGE". *Optd* "SERVICE" (11 *mm*). *P* 12
O331 1 a. 6 p. blue and claret (1937) 20 20
a. Imperf between (pair) 55·00 55·00
b. Opt omitted 55·00 55·00
c. Opt double, one inverted 75·00 75·00
d. Imperf (pair) — 55·00
e. Blue printing double 40·00 40·00
O332 1 a. 6 p. claret (1939) 20 20
a. Imperf between (pair) 50·00 50·00
b. Opt omitted 65·00 65·00
c. Opt double, one inverted 65·00 65·00
d. Opt double 60·00 60·00

PRINTERS. From No. O333 all issues were printed by the Bhopal Govt Ptg Wks in typography.

O **9**

O **10** The Moti Mahal

1936 (July)–**38**. *Optd* "SERVICE". *P* 12.
O333 O **9** ¼ a. orange (Br.) 15 12
a. Imperf between (vert pair) 55·00 55·00
b. Opt inverted 55·00 55·00
c. Black opt 10·00 6·00
ca. Ditto. Opt inverted 80·00 80·00
O334 ¼ a. yellow (Br.) (1938) 15 10
O335 1 a. scarlet 15 10
a. Imperf between (horiz pair) 32·00 32·00
b. Imperf between (vert pair) 50·00 50·00
c. Imperf between (block of four) £100 £100

1936–49. *As Type* O **10** *(various palaces). P* 12.
(a) Optd "SERVICE" (13½ *mm*)
O336 ½ a. purple-brown and yellow-green 15 10
a. Imperf between (vert pair) — 35·00
ab. Imperf between (horiz pair) — 35·00
b. Opt double 45·00 35·00
c. Frame double 20·00 9·00
d. *Purple-brown and green* (1938) 20 12
(b) Optd "SERVICE" (11 *mm*)
O337 2 a. brown and blue (1937) 15 15
a. Imperf between (pair) 38·00 38·00
b. Opt inverted 45·00 45·00
c. Pair, one without opt 80·00
d. As c. but opt inverted £140
O338 2 a. green and violet (1938) 50 15
a. Imperf between (vert pair) 38·00 38·00
b. Imperf between (vert strip of 3) 40·00 40·00
c. Frame double 48·00 40·00
d. Centre double — 40·00
O339 4 a. blue and brown (1937) 60 50
a. Imperf between (pair) 55·00 55·00
b. Opt omitted 55·00 55·00
c. Opt double 55·00 55·00
d. *Blue and reddish brown* (1938) 70 50
da. Opt omitted — 50·00
O340 8 a. bright purple and blue (1938) 80 65
a. Imperf between (pair) 70·00 70·00
b. Opt omitted 55·00 55·00
c. Opt double 55·00 55·00
d. Imperf between (horiz pair) and opt omitted — 80·00
O341 1 r. blue and reddish purple (Br.) (1938) 1·50 1·00
a. Opt in black (1942) 11·00 9·00
ab. *Light blue and bright purple* 25·00 25·00
(c) Optd "SERVICE" (11½ *mm*) *with serifs*
O342 1 r. dull blue and bright purple (Blk.) (1949) 28·00 28·00
a. "SREVICE" for "SERVICE" 70·00 70·00
b. "SERVICE" omitted
(b) Optd "SERVICE" (13½ *mm*) *with serifs*
O343 8 a. bright purple and blue (1949) 38·00 40·00
a. "SERAICE" for "SERVICE" £120 £130
b. Fig "1" for "I" in "SERVICE" £110 £120

The ½ a. is inscr "BHOPAL GOVT" below the arms, other values have "BHOPAL STATE".

Designs:—(37½ × 22½ *mm*) 2 a. The Moti Masjid; 4 a. Taj Mahal and Be-Nazir Palaces. (39 × 24 *mm*)–8 a. Ahmadabad Palace. (45½ × 27½ *mm*)—1 r. Rait Ghat.

O **11** Tiger

O **13** The Moti Mahal

1940. *As Type* O **11** *(animals). P* 12.
O344 ¼ a. bright blue 75 20
O345 1 a. bright purple (Chital) 3·00 40

1941. *As Type* O **8** *but coloured centre inscr* "SERVICE"; *bottom frame inscr* "BHOPAL STATE POSTAGE". *P* 12.
O346 1 a. 3 p. emerald-green 20 12
a. Imperf between (pair) £110 £110

1944–47. *As Type* O **13** *(various palaces). P* 12.
O347 ½ a. green 30 30
a. Imperf (pair) — 27·00
b. Imperf between (vert pair) 38·00 38·00
c. Doubly printed 35·00 35·00
O348 2 a. violet 1·00 60
a. Imperf (pair) — 27·00
b. Imperf between (pair) *(shades)* 60·00 60·00
c. *Bright purple* (1946) 60 60
ca. Doubly printed 35·00 35·00
d. *Mauve* (1947) 2·50 2·00
e. Error. Chocolate — 50·00

O349		4 a. chocolate	75	50
		a. Imperf (pair)	—	35·00
		b. Imperf between (horiz pair)	45·00	45·00
		c. Doubly printed	—	45·00

Design inscr "BHOPAL STATE":—2 a. The Moti Masjid; 4 a. Be-Nazir Palaces.

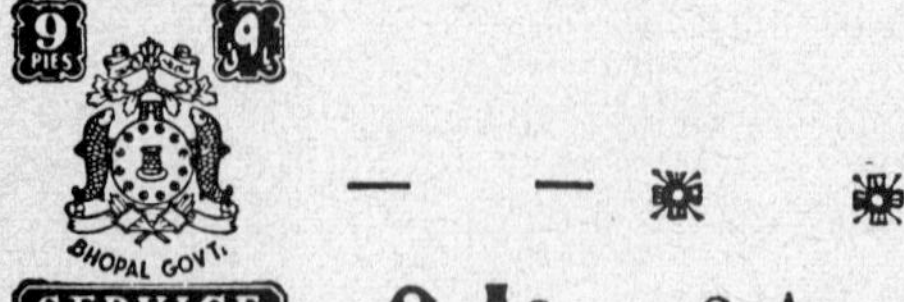

O 14 Arms of Bhopal (O 15) (O 16)

1945–49. *P* 12.

O350	O 14	3 p. bright blue	15	10
		a. Imperf between (pair)	30·00	30·00
		b. Stamp doubly printed	25·00	
O351		9 p. chestnut (*shades*)	2·00	75
		a. Imperf (pair)	—	35·00
		b. Orange-brown	3·00	3·00
O352		1 a. purple	35	12
		a. Imperf horiz (vert pair)		
		b. Violet (1946)	2·00	70
O353		1½ a. claret	60	40
		a. Imperf between (pair)	—	35·00
O354		3 a. yellow	1·00	1·25
		a. Imperf (pair)	—	35·00
		b. Imperf horiz (vert pair)	45·00	50·00
		c. Imperf vert (horiz pair)		
		d. Orange-brown (1949)	18·00	20·00
O355		6 a. carmine	6·00	8·00
		a. Imperf (pair)	—	40·00
		b. Imperf horiz (vert pair)	—	50·00
		c. Imperf vert (horiz pair)	—	50·00

1949 (July). *Surch with Type* O 15. *P* 12.

O356	O 14	2 a. on 1½ a. claret	60	80
		a. Stop omitted	8·00	9·00
		b. Imperf (pair)	75·00	75·00
		ba. Stop omitted (pair)	£225	£225

The "stop omitted" variety occurs twice in the sheet of 81.

1949. *Surch with Type* O 16. *Imperf or p* 12.

O357	O 14	2 a. on 1½ a. claret	£225	£180

There are three types of the figure "2" in the surcharge.

BHOR

PRICES FOR STAMPS ON COVER

The stamps of Bhor are very rare used on cover.

GUM. The stamps of Bhor were issued without gum.

1

2

1879. *Very thick to thin native paper. Imperf.*

1	1	½ a. carmine (*shades*)	2·00	2·50
		a. *Tête-bêche* (pair)	£160	
2	2	1 a. carmine (*shades*)	2·25	2·75

3 Pant Sachiv Shankarro Chimnaji

1901. *Typo. Wove paper. Imperf.*

3	3	½ a. red	6·00	28·00

BIJAWAR

PRICES FOR STAMPS ON COVER

The stamps of Bijawar are very rare used on cover.

1 Maharaja Sir Sarwant Singh Bahadur 2

(Typo Lakshmi Art Ptg Works, Bombay)

1935 (1 July)–**36.** (*a*) *P* 11.

1	1	3 p. brown	45	60
		a. Imperf (pair)	5·50	
		b. Imperf between (vert pair)	35·00	
2		6 p. carmine	45	60
		a. Imperf (pair)	35·00	
		b. Imperf between (vert or horiz pair)	35·00	
3		9 p. violet	50	65
		a. Imperf (pair)	65·00	
		b. Imperf between (vert or horiz pair)	35·00	
4		1 a. blue	65	90
		a. Imperf (pair)	35·00	
		b. Imperf between (vert or horiz pair)	35·00	
		c. Imperf vert (horiz strip of 3)	65·00	
5		2 a. deep green	85	1·25
		a. Imperf (pair)	65·00	
		b. Imperf between (vert or horiz pair)	11·00	

(*b*) *Roul* 7 (1936)

6	1	3 p. brown	50	85
		a. Printed on gummed side	60·00	
7		6 p. carmine	70	1·40
8		9 p. violet	1·10	2·00
9		1 a. blue	1·75	3·50
10		2 a. deep green	2·25	4·50

1937 (May). *Typo. P* 9.

11	2	4 a. orange	1·75	4·00
		a. Imperf between (vert pair)	£100	
		b. Imperf (pair)	£200	
12		6 a. lemon	2·25	4·50
		a. Imperf between (vert pair)	£100	
		b. Imperf (pair)	£200	
13		8 a. emerald-green	3·00	6·00
		a. Imperf (pair)	£200	
14		12 a. greenish blue	4·00	8·00
		a. Imperf (pair)	£200	
15		1 r. bright violet	10·00	20·00
		a. "1 Rs" for "1 R"	30·00	50·00
		b. Imperf (pair)	£200	
		ba. "1 Rs" for "1 R"	£600	

The stamps of Bijawar were withdrawn in 1941.

BUNDI

PRICES FOR STAMPS ON COVER

No. 1	*from* × 2
No. 2	*from* × 5
Nos. 3/53	*from* × 10
Nos. 54/63	*from* × 5
Nos. 64/78	*from* × 2
Nos. 79/92	*from* × 10
Nos. O1/52	*from* × 15
Nos. O53/9	*from* × 20

GUM. Nos. 1/17 were issued without gum.

ILLUSTRATIONS. Types **1/10** and **12/19** are shown actual size.

In Nos. 1 to 17 characters denoting the value are below the dagger, except in Nos. 2a, 11 and 17.

All Bundi stamps until 1914, are imperf.

1

1894 (May). *Each stamp with a distinct frame and the stamps not connected by the framing lines. Laid or wove paper.*

1	1	½ a. slate-grey	£2500	£1500
		a. Last two letters of value below the rest	—	£2750

2 (Block of four stamps)

1894 (Dec). *Stamps joined together, with no space between them. Thin wove paper.*

2	2	½ a. slate-grey	9·00	9·00
		a. Value at top, name below	£130	£130
		b. Right upper ornament omitted	£325	£325
		c. Last two letters of value below the rest	£450	£450
		d. Left lower ornament omitted	£325	£325

3

1896 (Nov). *Dagger shorter, lines thicker. Stamps separate. Laid paper.*

3	3	½ a. slate-grey	1·25	1·60
		a. Last two letters of value below the rest	£170	£170

4 (1 anna)

5 (2 annas)

6 (2 annas)

1897–98. *No shading in centre of blade of dagger. The stamps have spaces between them, but are connected by the framing lines, both vertically and horizontally. Laid paper.*

I. *Blade of dagger comparatively narrow, and either triangular, as in T* **4** *and* **6**, *or with the left-hand corner not touching the bar behind it, as in T* **5** (1897-98)

4	4	1 a. brick-red	7·50	8·50
5	5	1 a. brick-red	7·50	8·50
6		2 a. yellowish green	9·00	10·00
7	6	2 a. emerald-green	9·00	10·00
8	5	4 a. green	18·00	20·00
9		8 a. brick-red	32·00	35·00
10		1 r. yellow/*blue*	50·00	55·00

7

II. *Blade varying in shape, but as a rule not touching the bar; value above and name below the dagger, instead of the reverse* (Jan 1898)

11	7	4 a. emerald-green	9·00	
		a. Yellow-green	10·00	

8 (½ anna)

9 (8 annas)

III. *Blade wider and (except on the ½ a.) almost diamond shaped; it nearly always touches the bar* (1898–1900)

12	8	½ a. slate-grey (5.2.98)	70	70
13	9	1 a. brick-red (7.98)	90	75
14		2 a. pale green (9.11.98)	2·75	2·75
		a. First two characters of value (= two) omitted	£250	£250
15		8 a. brick-red (7.98)	4·50	5·00
16		1 r. yellow/*blue* (7.98)	7·50	8·00
		a. On wove paper	9·00	10·00

10

IV. *Inscriptions as on No.* 11; *point of dagger to left* (9.11.98)

17 **10** 4 a. green .. .. 7·00 7·50
a. Yellow-green .. .. 7·00 7·50

All the above stamps are lithographed in larger sheets, containing as many varieties of type as there are stamps in the sheets.

11 Raja protecting Sacred Cows

12 **13**

Top tablet. 1st character of 2nd group differs.

14 **16**

Top tablet. 1st character of 2nd group changed again. Loop at bottom of character in T **14** is sometimes attached.
Bottom tablet. In T **16** first character of 2nd group changed.

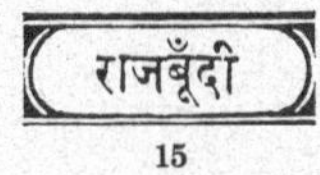

15

Top tablet. As T **14** but run together as one group.

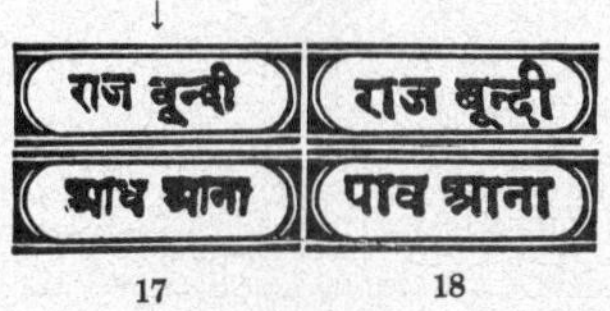

17 **18**

Top tablet. T **17** is as T **16** but 2nd group has four characters. T **18** is as T **17** but both tablets have larger characters.

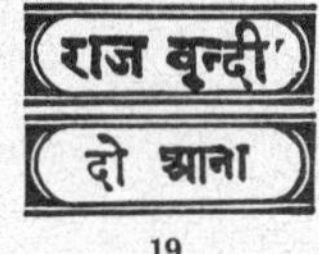

19

As T **18** but bottom tablet has smaller characters.

The denominations may be identified from the following illustrations. The ½ a., 3 a. and rupee values can be easily distinguished by their colours.

Bottom tablets:—

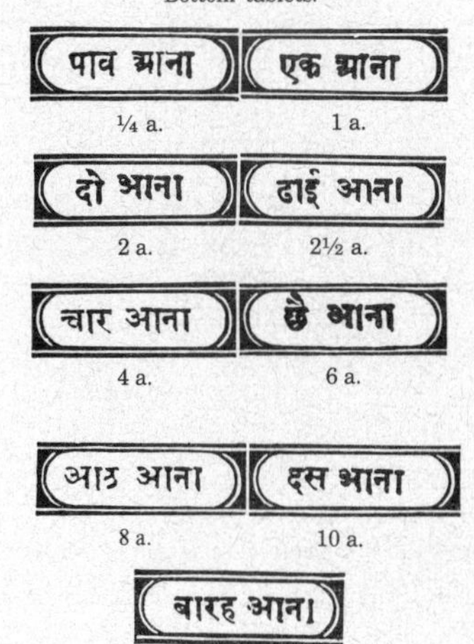

¼ a. 1 a.
2 a. 2½ a.
4 a. 6 a.
8 a. 10 a.
12 a.

1914–41. *T* **11**. *Typo. Ungummed paper except Nos.* 73/78.

I. *Rouletted in colour*

A. *Top tablet as T* **12**. *Thin to medium wove paper*

18 ½ a. black .. .. 1·50 3·00
19 1 a. deep red .. .. 90 1·75
20 2 a. emerald 90
a. Deep green (coarse ptg) .. .. .. 1·25 2·00
21 2½ a. olive-yellow (*shades*) .. .. .. 2·50 4·00
22 3 a. brown .. .. 3·50
23 4 a. yellow-green .. .. 17·00
24 6 a. ultramarine .. .. 10·00
25 1 r. violet .. .. 17·00

B. *Top tablet as T* **13**. *Thin wove or pelure paper*

26 ¼ a. indigo (*shades*) 60 90
a. Ultramarine .. .. 1·00
27 ½ a. black 70 80
28 1 a. vermilion 75
a. Carmine .. .. 1·10 1·50
b. Brown-red .. .. 1·25
29 2 a. emerald-green (*shades*) .. .. .. 1·25
30 2½ a. olive-yellow (*shades*) .. .. .. 1·75 2·75
31 3 a. brown .. .. 1·25
32 4 a. yellow-green .. .. 3·50 5·00
32*a* 4 a. pale olive-yellow .. .. .. 38·00
33 6 a. ultramarine .. .. 7·50
a. Indigo .. .. 7·50
34 8 a. orange-brown .. .. 7·50
35 10 a. deep olive .. .. 80·00
36 12 a. blue-green £140
36*a* 1 r. violet .. .. 16·00

The pelure papers often appear similar to laid paper.
Stamps in Type **13** can be found *se-tenant*, with those as Type **14**.

C. *Tablets as T* **14**. *Thin to medium wove paper*

37 ¼ a. indigo .. .. 70 1·00
a. Deep blue 65
b. Ultramarine .. .. 3·00 3·00
38 ½ a. black 60 80
39 1 a. red-brown .. .. 2·00 2·75
a. Deep red .. .. 1·50 2·00
b. Carmine .. .. 2·00 2·75
40 2 a. emerald .. .. 1·75 2·50
a. Sage-green .. .. 2·50
41 4 a. yellow-green .. .. 9·00 12·00
a. Pale green .. .. 10·00 13·00
b. Bright apple-green .. .. .. 20·00 20·00
41*c* 4 a. pale olive-yellow .. .. .. 28·00
42 8 a. orange .. .. 6·00 9·00
43 10 a. deep to pale olive .. .. .. 6·00 9·00
43*a* 10 a. yellow-brown .. .. 11·00
44 12 a. blue-green .. .. 6·00 9·00
45 1 r. lilac .. .. 18·00 24·00
46 2 r. red-brown and black .. .. .. 35·00
a. Brown and black .. .. .. 40·00 45·00
47 3 r. blue and brown .. .. 65·00 75·00
a. Brown (inscriptions) inverted £1200
48 4 r. green and red £170
49 5 r. red and green £180

Stamps in Type **14** can be found *se-tenant* with those as Type **13** (¼ a. to 12 a.) or as Type **16** (¼ a. only).

D. *Top tablet as T* **15**. *Thin to medium wove paper*

50 2½ a. buff .. .. 7·00 9·00
a. Chestnut .. .. 9·00 11·00
51 3 a. brown (*shades*) .. .. 11·00 11·00
a. Semi-circle and dot omitted from 4th character .. .. 26·00 26·00
52 10 a. olive .. .. 20·00
a. 4th character turned to left instead of downwards .. .. 32·00
53 12 a. grey-green .. .. 28·00
a. 4th character turned to left instead of downwards .. .. 45·00

E. *Tablets as T* **16**. (*a*) *Medium wove paper*

54 ¼ a. deep blue .. .. 4·00 4·00
a. Ultramarine .. .. 9·00 7·00
54*b* ¼ a. deep slate .. .. 13·00 10·00
55 ½ a. black .. .. 4·50 6·00
56 1 a. dull red .. .. 10·00 10·00
a. Deep red .. .. 10·00
57 3 a. brown (*shades*) .. .. 11·00 11·00
58 4 a. olive-green .. .. 65·00 55·00
a. Bright apple-green .. .. .. 75·00
58*b* 4 a. pale olive-yellow .. .. ..

(*b*) *Very thick wove paper*

59 ¼ a. indigo .. .. 5·00 5·00
60 ½ a. black .. .. 11·00
61 1 a. scarlet .. .. 5·50 5·50

(*c*) *Medium horizontally laid paper*

62 ¼ a. indigo (*shades*) .. .. 5·50 5·00
63 1 a. red .. .. 6·50 6·50

Stamps in Type **16** can be found *se-tenant* with those as Type **14** (Nos. 54/*a* only).

F. *Tablets as T* **17**. *Medium wove paper* (*except* 1 *a.*)

64 ½ a. black .. .. 4·00 5·50
a. Vert laid paper .. .. 70·00 55·00
b. Horiz laid paper .. .. 75·00 75·00
65 1 a. red (*horiz laid paper*) .. .. .. 70·00 50·00
66 4 a. green £160 £160
a. Horiz laid paper .. .. 24·00 20·00

G. *Tablets as T* **18**

67 ¼ a. ultramarine .. .. 1·40 3·00
68 ½ a. black .. .. £100 60·00
69 1 a. scarlet (*shades*) .. .. 4·00 6·00
70 4 a. green .. .. 16·00 16·00
71 4 r. green and red £160
72 5 r. red and green £180

II. *P* 11. *Tablets as T* **18**

73 ¼ a. ultramarine .. .. 25·00 27·00
a. Turquoise-blue .. .. 1·40 5·00
74 ½ a. black .. .. 20·00 20·00
75 1 a. scarlet .. .. £120 75·00
a. Carmine .. .. 9·00 16·00
76 2 a. green .. .. 20·00

H. *Tablets as T* **19**

77 ½ a. black .. .. £100 90·00
78 2 a. green .. .. 40·00 40·00

20

1941–45. *Typo. P* 11.

79 **20** 3 p. bright blue .. .. 50 1·00
80 6 p. deep blue .. .. 75 1·25
81 1 a. orange-red .. .. 1·00 1·50
82 2 a. chestnut .. .. 4·00 5·00
a. Deep brown (no gum) (1945) .. 6·00 6·50
83 4 a. bright green .. .. 6·00 9·00
84 8 a. dull green .. .. 10·00 15·00
85 1 r. deep blue .. .. 15·00 22·00

The first printing only of Nos. 79/85 is usual with gum; all further printings, including No. 82*a*, are without gum.

21 Maharao Rajah Bahadur Singh **22** Bundi

(Typo *Times of India* Press, Bombay)

1947. *P* 11.

86 **21** ¼ a. blue-green .. .. 30 2·50
87 ½ a. violet .. .. 30 3·50
88 1 a. yellow-green .. .. 40 4·50
89 – 2 a. vermilion 80
90 – 4 a. orange .. .. 1·00
91 **22** 8 a. ultramarine .. .. 2·25
92 1 r. chocolate .. .. 5·00

On the 2 and 4 a. the Rajah is in Indian dress.

OFFICIAL STAMPS

बूंदी BUNDI

सरविस SERVICE

(O 1) (O 2)

BUNDI

SERVICE

(O 3)

1918–41. *T* **11** *handstamped as Types* O **1/3**. *Ungummed paper except Nos.* O47/52.

A. *Optd with Type* O **1**. B. *Optd with Type* O **2**. C. *Optd with Type* O **3**.

I. *Rouletted in colour*

		A		B		C	
A. *Top tablet as T* **12**.							
O 1	2 a. emerald	2·25	—	—	—	†	
	a. Deep green (coarse ptg) ..	6·00	—	9·00	—	28·00	—
	b. Red opt ..	6·50	—	7·50	—	†	
O 2	2½ a. olive-yellow (*shades*) ..	2·25	4·00	5·00	7·00	30·00	—
	a. Red opt ..	5·50	—	14·00	—	†	
O 3	3 a. brown ..	3·25	5·00	7·00	—	†	
	a. Green opt ..	8·00	—	†		†	
O 4	6 a. ultramarine	10·00	—	14·00	—	30·00	—
	a. Red opt ..	23·00	—	27·00	—	32·00	—
O 5	1 r. violet ..	19·00	—	23·00	—	†	
B. *Top tablet as T* **13**.							
O 6	¼ a. indigo ..	65	85	1·00	—	—	—
	a. Red opt ..	65	85	1·25	—	7·00	9·00
O 7	½ a. black ..	2·25	—	1·50	—	5·50	—
	a. Red opt ..	2·25	—	5·50	—	16·00	—
O 8	1 a. vermilion ..	1·25	—	1·75	—	8·00	—
	a. Carmine ..	1·75	—	3·00	—	†	
	b. Brown-red ..	†		4·50	—	†	
O 9	2 a. emerald-green (*shades*)	4·00	—	8·50	—	†	
O10	4 a. yellow-green	8·00	—	14·00	—	†	
O10*a*	4 a. pl olive-yellow	45·00	—	—	—	†	
O11	6 a. ultramarine	9·00	—	†		†	
	a. Indigo ..	10·00	—	12·00	—	†	
	b. Red opt ..	11·00	—	13·00	—	†	
O12	8 a. orange-brown	15·00	—	28·00	—	45·00	—
O13	10 a. deep olive ..	65·00	—	85·00	—	95·00	—
	a. Red opt ..	85·00	—	95·00	—	£110	—
O14	12 a. blue-green ..	£100	£100	£100	—	†	
	a. Red opt ..	†		†		£110	—
O14*b*	1 r. violet ..	65·00	—	†		†	
C. *Tablets as T* **14**.							
O15	¼ a. deep blue ..	1·25	—	1·50	—	6·00	—
	a. Red opt ..	1·00	—	3·00	—	†	
	b. Green opt ..	1·50	—	4·50	—	†	
	c. Ultramarine	16·00	—	16·00	—	45·00	—
	d. Ditto. Red opt	25·00	—	25·00	—	60·00	—
O16	½ a. black ..	2·25	—	2·50	—	7·50	—
	a. Red opt ..	65	—	5·50	—	15·00	15·00
	b. Green opt ..	1·50	—	†		†	
O17	1 a. red-brown ..	2·00	—	†		†	
	a. Deep red ..	1·75	—	2·25	—	8·00	—
O18	2 a. emerald ..	4·00	—	5·00	—	†	
	a. Red opt ..	†		17·00	—	†	
	b. Sage-green ..	7·00	—	9·00	—	18·00	24·00
O19	4 a. yellow-green .	8·00	—	16·00	—	†	
	a. Pale green ..	10·00	—	18·00	—	†	
O19*b*	4 a. pl olive-yellow	35·00	—	—	—	†	
O20	8 a. orange ..	14·00	—	22·00	—	35·00	—

No.	Description	A		B		C	
O21	10 a. deep to pl olive	14·00	—	22·00	—	35·00	—
	a. Red opt ..	20·00	—	35·00	—	48·00	—
O22	12 a. blue-green ..	17·00	17·00	20·00	—	†	
	a. Red opt ..	†		†		65·00	—
O23	1 r. lilac ..	42·00	—	†		†	
O24	2 r. brown and blk	90·00	—	90·00	—	†	
	a. Red-brown & black ..	90·00	90·00	90·00	—	†	
	b. Red opt ..	†		£110	—	†	
O25	3 r. blue and brn	£110	—	£110	—	†	
	a. Red opt ..	£125	—	†		†	
O26	4 r. green and red	£275	—	£300	—	†	
O27	5 r. red and green	£275	—	£300	—	†	
	D. *Top tablet as T* **15**.						
O28	2½ a. buff	12·00	—	14·00	—	†	
	a. Chestnut ..	14·00	—	†		†	
	b. Red opt ..	28·00	—	†		†	
O29	3 a. brn (*shades*) ..	12·00	—	18·00	—	†	
	a. Variety as No. 51a	28·00	—	—	—	†	
	b. Red opt ..	†		40·00	—	†	
O30	10 a. olive ..	22·00	—	28·00	—	42·00	—
	a. Variety as No. 52a	40·00	—	55·00	—	†	
	b. Red opt ..	30·00	—	†		†	
O31	12 a. grey-green ..	24·00	—	35·00	—	45·00	—
	a. Variety as No. 53a	45·00	—	60·00	—	†	
	b. Red opt ..	45·00	—	45·00	—	†	
	E. *Tablets as T* **16**. (*a*) *Medium wove paper*.						
O32	¼ a. deep blue ..	†		5·00	—	†	
	a. Red opt ..	8·50	—	4·50	—	†	
	b. Ultram. Red opt	32·00	—	32·00	—	†	
O32*c*	¼ a. deep slate ..	15·00	—	15·00	—	†	
	ca. Red opt ..	15·00	—	15·00	—	†	
O33	½ a. black ..	13·00	—	13·00	—	†	
	a. Red opt ..	13·00	—	13·00	—	†	
O34	1 a. deep red ..	17·00	—	17·00	—	35·00	—
O35	3 a. brn (*shades*) ..	29·00	—	35·00	—	60·00	—
	a. Red opt ..	48·00	—	60·00	—	†	
	(*b*) *Very thick wove paper*						
O36	¼ a. indigo ..	9·00	—	12·00	—	†	
	a. Red opt ..	9·00	—	12·00	—	†	
	b. Green opt ..	8·00	—	†		†	
O37	½ a. black ..	16·00	—	16·00	—	†	
O38	1 a. scarlet ..	9·00	—	10·00	—	†	
	(*c*) *Medium horizontally laid paper*						
O39	¼ a. indigo (*shades*) ..	6·50	—	8·00	—	†	
	a. Red opt ..	5·50	—	5·50	—	16·00	—
O40	1 a. red	13·00	—	13·00	—	†	
	a. Red opt ..	32·00	—	32·00	—	†	
	F. *Tablets as T* **17**. *Medium wove paper* (*except 4a.*).						
O41	½ a. black ..	42·00	—	55·00	—	†	
	a. Vert laid paper ..	70·00	—	80·00	—	†	
	b. Ditto. Red opt	70·00	—	80·00	—	†	
	c. Horiz laid paper (R.) ..	80·00	—	80·00	—	†	
O42	4 a. green (*horiz laid paper*) ..	55·00	—	†		†	
	a. Red opt ..	65·00	—	†		†	
	G. *Tablets as T* **18**.						
O43	¼ a. ultramarine	55·00	—	95·00	—	†	
	a. Red opt ..	60·00	—	60·00	—	†	
O44	½ a. black ..	£130	—	£130	—	†	
	a. Red opt ..	£130	—	†		£150	—
O45	1 a. scarlet ..	70·00	—	70·00	—	£130	—
O46	4 a. green ..	80·00	—	80·00	—	£140	—
	a. Red opt ..	£120	—	†		£150	—
	II. *P* 11. *Tablets as T* **18**						
O47	¼ a. ultramarine	40·00	50·00	45·00	—	55·00	—
	a. Red opt ..	50·00	—	55·00	—	†	
	b. Turquoise-blue	38·00	—	55·00	—	55·00	—
	c. Ditto. Red opt	60·00	—	†		†	
O48	½ a. black ..	40·00	—	50·00	50·00	70·00	—
	a. Red opt ..	50·00	—	75·00	—	50·00	—
O49	1 a. scarlet ..	£125	£125	£140	£140	£140	—
	a. Carmine ..	60·00	—	50·00	—	55·00	—
O50	2 a. green ..	42·00	—	55·00	—	45·00	—
	H. *Tablets as T* **19**.						
O51	½ a. black ..	80·00	—	85·00	—	95·00	—
O52	2 a. green ..	60·00	—	85·00	—	†	

Until 1941 it was the general practice to carry official mail free but some of the above undoubtedly exist postally used.

1941. *Nos.* 79 *to* 85 *optd* "SERVICE".

No.	Type	Description	Unused	Used
O53	**20**	3 p. bright blue (R.)	1·00	1·50
O54		6 p. deep blue (R.)	1·75	2·50
O55		1 a. orange-red	3·00	4·00
O56		2 a. brown	5·50	7·50
O57		4 a. bright green	18·00	25·00
O58		8 a. dull green	25·00	35·00
O59		1 r. deep blue (R.)	35·00	50·00

On 25 March 1948 Bundi became part of the Rajasthan Union.

BUSSAHIR (BASHAHR)

PRICES FOR STAMPS ON COVER	
Nos. 1/21	*from* × 8
Nos. 22/23	*from* × 2
Nos. 24/43	*from* × 8

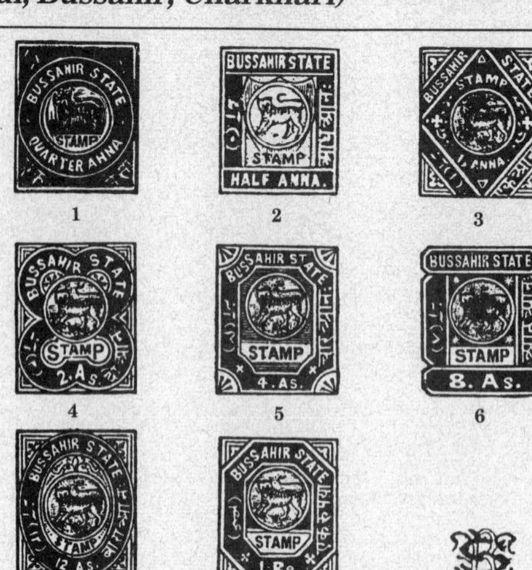

1 2 3 4 5 6 7 8 (9)

The initials are those of the Tika Raghunath Singh, son of the then Raja, who was the organiser and former director of the State Post Office.

1895 (20 June). *Laid paper. Optd with T* **9** *in pale greenish blue* (B.), *rose* (R.), *mauve* (M.) *or lake* (L.). *With or without gum.*

(*a*) *Imperf.*

No.	Type	Description	Unused	Used
1	**1**	¼ a. pink (M.) (1.9.95)	55·00	
2	**2**	½ a. grey (R.M.)	85·00	
3	**3**	1 a. vermilion (M.)	32·00	
4	**4**	2 a. orange-yellow (R.M.L.)	11·00	45·00
5	**5**	4 a. slate-violet (R.M.L.)	18·00	
		a. Without monogram	55·00	
6	**6**	8 a. red-brown (B.M.)	17·00	30·00
		a. Without monogram	50·00	
		b. Thick paper	50·00	
7	**7**	12 a. green (L.)	35·00	
8	**8**	1 r. ultramarine (R.M.L.)	18·00	
		a. Without monogram	50·00	

(*b*) *Perf with a sewing machine; gauge and size of holes varying between 7 and 11½*

No.	Type	Description	Unused	Used
9	**1**	¼ a. pink (B.M.)	18·00	32·00
		a. Without monogram	45·00	50·00
10	**2**	½ a. grey (R.)	14·00	32·00
		a. Without monogram	45·00	
11	**3**	1 a. vermilion (M.)	14·00	35·00
12	**4**	2 a. orange-yellow (B.M.)	15·00	45·00
13	**5**	4 a. slate-violet (B.R.M.)	16·00	50·00
		a. Without monogram	38·00	
14	**6**	8 a. red-brown (B.R.M.)	14·00	50·00
		a. Without monogram	40·00	
15	**7**	12 a. green (R.M.L.)	18·00	
		a. Without monogram	40·00	
16	**8**	1 r. ultramarine (R.M.)	15·00	35·00
		a. Without monogram	45·00	

1899. *As* 1895, *but pin-perf or rouletted.*

No.	Type	Description	Unused	Used
17	**3**	1 a. vermilion (M.)	40·00	60·00
18	**4**	2 a. orange-yellow (M.L.)	20·00	45·00
		a. Without monogram	40·00	
19	**5**	4 a. slate-violet (B.R.M.L.)	30·00	
20	**7**	12 a. green (R.)	45·00	
21	**8**	1 r. ultramarine (R.)	45·00	

Nos. 1 to 21 were in sheets of 24. They seem to have been overprinted and perforated as required. Those first issued for use were perforated, but they were subsequently supplied imperf, both to collectors and for use. Nos. 17 to 21 were some of the last supplies. No rule seems to have been observed as to the colour of the overprinted monogram; pale blue, rose and mauve were used from the first. The pale blue varies to greenish blue or blue-green, and appears quite green on the yellow stamps. The lake is possibly a mixture of the mauve and the rose—it is a quite distinct colour and apparently later than the others. Specimens without overprint are either remainders left in the Treasury or copies that have escaped accidentally; they have been found sticking to the backs of others that bore the overprint.

Varieties may also be found doubly overprinted, in two different colours.

10

11

12

T 11. Lines of shading above and at bottom left and right of shield.
T 12. White dots above shield and ornaments in bottom corners.

13 14 15 16

(Printed at the Bussahir Press by Maulavi Karam Bakhsh)

1896–98. *Wove paper. Optd with monogram* "R.S.", *T* **9**, *in colours as* 1895 *issue. Printed singly from line-engraved dies. With or without gum. Imperf, pin perf or rouletted.*

No.	Type	Description	Unused	Used
22	**10**	¼ a. deep violet (R.)	—	95·00
23	**11**	½ a. grey-blue (*shades*) (R.)	£160	70·00

1900–01. *As Nos.* 22/3, *but lithographed in sheets of various sizes. No gum.*

(*a*) *Imperf*

No.	Type	Description	Unused	Used
24	**10**	¼ a. slate-violet (B.R.M.L.)	2·50	
25	**11**	½ a. blue (*shades*) (R.M.)	2·50	14·00
		a. Without monogram		
26	**13**	1 a. olive (*shades*) (R.M.L.)	9·00	14·00

(*b*) *Pin-perf or rouletted*

No.	Type	Description	Unused	Used
27	**10**	¼ a. slate-violet (R.M.L.)	3·25	8·00
28	**11**	½ a. blue (*shades*) (R.M.L.)	8·00	12·00
29	**13**	1 a. olive (*shades*) (R.M.L.)	9·00	15·00
30	**14**	2 a. orange-yellow (B.)	£100	£110

The ¼ a. and ½ a. are in sheets of 24, the 1 a. and 2a. in blocks of 4.

1900–01. ¼ a., 1 *a, colours changed;* ½ *a. redrawn type;* 2 *a. with dash before* "STATE" *and characters in lower left label;* 4 *a. new value. No gum.*

(*a*) *Imperf*

No.	Type	Description	Unused	Used
31	**10**	¼ a. vermilion (B.M.)	1·10	2·50
		a. Without monogram		
31*b*	**12**	½ a. blue (M.)	2·50	
32	**13**	1 a. vermilion (B.M.)	2·00	4·00
33	**15**	2 a. ochre (M.) (9.00)	9·00	
34		2 a. yellow (M.) (11.00)	9·00	
35		2 a. orange (B.M.) (1901)	8·00	
36	**16**	4 a. claret (B.R.M.)	13·00	37·00
		a. Without monogram	16·00	

(*b*) *Pin-perf or rouletted*

No.	Type	Description	Unused	Used
37	**10**	¼ a. vermilion (B.M.)	1·25	
37*a*	**12**	½ a. blue (M.)	3·00	
38	**13**	1 a. vermilion (B.M.)	1·25	3·00
39		1 a. brown-red (3.01)	—	45·00
40	**15**	2 a. ochre (B.M.) (9.00)	9·00	
41		2 a. yellow (B.R.M.) (11.00)	10·00	13·00
42		2 a. orange (B.M.) (1901)	10·00	13·00
43	**16**	4 a. claret (B.R.M.)	17·00	

The ¼ a., ½ a. and 1 a. are in sheets of 24; the 2 a. in sheets of 50 differing throughout in the dash and the characters added at lower left; the 4 a. in sheets of 28.

(17)

The stamps formerly catalogued with large overprint "R.N.S." (T **17**) are now believed never to have been issued for use.

Remainders are also found with overprint "P.S.", the initials of Padam Singh who succeeded Raghunath Singh in the direction of the Post Office, and with the original monogram "R.S." in a damaged state, giving it the appearance of a double-lined "R."

The stamps of Bussahir have been obsolete since 1 April 1901. Numerous remainders were sold after this date, and all values were later reprinted in the colours of the originals, or in fancy colours, from the original stones, or from new ones. Printings were also made from new types, similar to those of the second issue of the 8 a., 12 a., and 1 r. values, in sheets of 8.

Reprints are frequently found on laid paper.

Collectors are warned against obliterated copies bearing the Rampur postmark with date "19 MA 1900." Many thousand remainders and reprints were thus obliterated for export after the closing of the State Post Office.

CHARKHARI

PRICES FOR STAMPS ON COVER	
Nos. 1/4	*from* × 2
Nos. 5/26	*from* × 20
Nos. 27/44	*from* × 5
Nos. 45/53	*from* × 50
Nos. 54/6	*from* × 8

1

The top row shows the figures of value used in the stamps of 1894-97, and the bottom row those for the 1904 issue. In the 4 a. the figure slopes slightly to the right in the first issue, and to the left in the second.

1894. *No gum. Imperf.*

No.	Type	Description	Unused	Used
1	**1**	¼ anna, rose	£1200	£1200
2		1 annas, dull green	£1600	£2250
3		2 annas, dull green	£1200	
4		4 annas, dull green	£1000	

1897. *Inscr* "ANNA". *No gum. Imperf.*

No.	Type	Description	Unused	Used
5	**1**	¼ a. magenta	4·00	5·00
		a. Purple	1·75	2·25
		b. Violet	1·75	2·25
6		½ a. purple	2·25	3·50
		a. Violet	3·50	4·00

7 1 1 a. blue-green .. .. 4·00 4·50
a. Turquoise-blue .. .. 4·00 4·50
b. Indigo .. .. 6·00 7·00
8 2 a. blue-green .. .. 7·00 8·00
a. Turquoise-blue .. .. 7·00 8·00
b. Indigo .. .. 9·00 10·00
9 4 a. blue-green .. .. 6·00 9·00
a. Turquoise-blue .. .. 6·00 9·00
b. Indigo .. .. 15·00 18·00

Minor varieties may be found with the first "A" in "ANNA" not printed.

All values are known on various coloured papers, but these are proofs or trial impressions.

1904. *Numerals changed as illustrated above. No gum.*
10 1 ¼ a. violet .. .. 4·00 5·00
11 ½ a. violet .. .. 4·50 5·00
12 1 a. green .. .. 11·00 13·00
13 2 a. green .. .. 14·00 16·00
14 4 a. green .. .. 18·00 20·00

Stamps of this issue can be found showing part of the paper-marker's watermark. "Mercantile Script Extra Strong John Haddon & Co.".

2 (Right-hand sword over left)

Type I

Type II

Type I. "P" of "POSTAGE" in same size as other letters. "E" small with long upper and lower arms. White dot often appears on one or both of the sword hilts.
Type II. "P" larger than the other letters. "E" large with short upper and lower arms. No dots occur on the hilts.

1909–19. *Litho in Calcutta. Wove paper. P* 11. (*a*) *Type* I.
15 2 1 p. chestnut .. .. 28·00 35·00
a. Pale chestnut .. .. .. 1·75 7·50
b. Orange-brown .. .. .. 5·00 20·00
16 1 p. turquoise-blue 30 40
a. Imperf between (horiz pair) .. £140
b. Greenish blue (1911) 35 40
17 ½ a. rose-red (*shades*) 65 90
18 1 a. yellow-olive (*shades*) .. .. 75 1·00
19 2 a. blue (*shades*) .. .. .. 2·00 2·75
20 4 a. deep green .. .. 2·75 4·00
21 8 a. brick-red .. .. 3·50 5·50
22 1 r. pale chestnut .. .. .. 6·50 9·00

(*b*) *Type* II
24 2 1 p. turquoise-blue 70 70
25 ½ a. vermilion 70
a. Imperf (pair) £240
26 1 a. yellow-olive (1919) .. .. .. 1·00
a. Sage-green .. .. 1·25 1·50

No. 15, from the original printing, shows an upstroke to the "1", not present on other brown printings of this value.
See also Nos. 31/44.

3 — "ᒧI" below Swords. Right sword overlaps left. Double frame lines.

4 — "JI" below Swords. Left sword overlaps right. Single frame line.

1912–17. *Handstamped. No gum. Imperf.*
27 3 1 p. violet .. .. 85·00 50·00
a. Dull purple .. .. 85·00 50·00
28 4 1 p. violet (1917) .. .. .. 12·00 8·00
a. Dull purple .. .. 12·00 8·00
b. *Tête-bêche* (pair) .. .. .. 60·00 60·00

5 (*actual size* 63 × 25 *mm*)

6 (Left-hand sword over right)

1922. *Handstamped. No gum.* (*a*) *Wove paper. Imperf.*
29 5 1 a. violet .. .. 35·00 40·00
a. Dull purple .. .. 40·00 45·00

(*b*) *Laid paper. P* 11
30 5 1 a. violet .. .. 45·00 55·00

(Typo State Ptg Press, Charkhari)

1930–45. *No gum. Imperf.*
31 6 1 p. deep blue .. .. 20 4·00
a. Vert pair, top ptd inverted on back, bottom normal upright .. .. 27·00
b. *Tête-bêche* (pair) .. .. .. 38·00
32 1 p. dull *to* light green (*pelure*) (1943) .. 25·00 35·00
33 1 p. violet (1943) .. .. 9·00 16·00
a. *Tête-bêche* (pair) .. .. .. 30·00
34 ½ a. deep olive .. .. 25 4·00
35 ½ a. red-brown (1940) .. .. .. 50 6·00
a. *Tête-bêche* (pair) .. .. .. 38·00
36 ½ a. black (*pelure*) (1943) .. .. 32·00 40·00
37 ½ a. red (1943) .. .. 13·00 18·00
a. *Tête-bêche* (pair) .. .. .. 35·00
38 ½ a. grey-brown .. .. 55·00 £110
39 1 a. green .. .. 45 4·00
40 1 a. chocolate (1940) .. .. .. 50 5·00
a. *Tête-bêche* (pair) .. .. .. 30·00
41 1 a. red (1940) .. .. 42·00 50·00
42 2 a. light blue .. .. 1·25 7·00
a. *Tête-bêche* (pair) .. .. .. 8·50
43 2 a. greenish grey (1941?) .. .. 20·00 32·00
a. *Tête-bêche* (pair) .. .. .. 48·00
b. Yellow-green (1945) .. .. ..
44 4 a. carmine .. .. 6·00 12·00
a. *Tête-bêche* (pair) .. .. .. 18·00 35·00

7 Imlia Palace

½ As.
(8)

(Typo Lakshmi Art Ptg Works, Bombay)

1931 (25 June). *T* 7 *and similar designs. P* 11 *or* 12.
45 ½ a. blue-green 8 8
a. Imperf between (horiz pair) .. .. 11·00 10·00
46 1 a. blackish brown 8 8
a. Imperf between (horiz or vert pair) .. 9·00 8·00
47 2 a. violet 8 8
a. Imperf between (horiz pair) .. .. 16·00
48 4 a. olive-green 10 8
a. Imperf between (vert pair) .. .. 18·00
49 8 a. magenta 12 8
a. Imperf between (horiz or vert pair) .. 14·00 11·00
50 1 r. green and rose 20 12
a. Imperf between (vert pair) .. .. 22·00 22·00
51 2 r. red and brown 60 20
a. Imperf horiz (vert pair) .. .. 16·00 13·00
52 3 r. chocolate and blue-green 90 25
a. Imperf between (horiz pair) .. .. 30·00 30·00
53 5 r. turquoise and purple .. .. 1·25 45
a. Imperf between (horiz pair) .. .. 30·00 30·00

Designs:—½ a. The Lake; 2 a. Industrial School; 4 a. Bird's-eye view of City; 8 a. The Fort; 1 r. Guest House. 2 r. Palace Gate; 3 r. Temples at Rainpur; 5 r. Goverdhan Temple.

This issue was the subject of speculative manipulation, large stocks being thrown on the market cancelled-to-order at very low prices and unused at less than face value. Numerous errors, probably produced clandestinely, exist. The issue was an authorized one but was eventually withdrawn by the State authorities.

1940. *Nos.* 21/2 *surch as T* 8.
54 2 ½ a. on 8 a. brick-red .. .. .. 16·00 30·00
a. No space between "½" and "As." .. 17·00 32·00
b. Surch inverted £200
c. "1" of "½" inverted £170
55 1 a. on 1 r. chestnut .. .. .. 30·00 45·00
a. Surch inverted £200
56 "1 ANNA" on 1 r. chestnut £250

COCHIN

(6 puttans = 5 annas. 12 pies = 1 anna; 16 annas = 1 rupee)

Stamps of Cochin were also valid for postage in Travancore.

PRICES FOR STAMPS ON COVER	
Nos. 1/3	*from* × 30
Nos. 4/5	*from* × 10
Nos. 6/6*b*	*from* × 3
Nos. 7/9	*from* × 20
Nos. 11/22	*from* × 15
Nos. 26/128	*from* × 8
Nos. O1/105	*from* × 15

1

2

(Dies eng P. Orr & Sons, Madras; typo Cochin Govt, Ernakulam)

1892 (1 April). *No wmk, or wmk large Umbrella in the sheet. P* 12.
1 1 ½ put. buff .. .. 2·00 1·00
a. Orange-buff .. .. .. 2·00 1·00
b. Yellow .. .. 2·50 1·25
c. Imperf (pair) £250 £250
2 1 put. purple .. .. 2·50 1·25
a. Error. Deep violet (colour of 2 p.) 70·00 70·00
3 2 2 put. deep violet .. .. .. 1·00 1·00

1896 (End). *Similar to T* 1, *but* 28 × 33 *mm. P* 12.
(*a*) *Wmk Arms and inscription in sheet*
4 1 put. violet .. .. 22·00 30·00
(*b*) *Wmk Conch Shell to each stamp*
5 1 put. deep violet .. .. .. 15·00 20·00

This stamp was originally printed for provisional use as a fiscal; afterwards it was authorized for postal use.

(*c*) *On laid paper*
6 1 ½ put. orange-buff £325 £110
a. Orange .. .. — £110
b. Yellow .. .. — £110

WATERMARKS. Prior to the 1911–23 issue, printed by Perkins, Bacon & Co, little attention was paid to the position of the watermark. Inverted and sideways watermarks are frequently found in the 1898 and 1903 issues.

1897. *Wmk a small Umbrella on each stamp. P* 12.
7 1 ½ put. buff .. .. 2·00 1·25
a. Orange .. .. 1·50 1·00
ab. *Orange*. Imperf (pair) .. ..
b. yellow .. .. 1·75 1·00
8 1 put. purple .. .. 1·75 1·25
a. Error. Deep violet (colour of 2 p.) 30·00 30·00
9 2 2 put. deep violet .. .. .. 3·00 2·50
a. Imperf (pair) £200 £200

The paper watermarked with a small umbrella is more transparent than that of the previous issue. The wmk is not easy to distinguish.

3

4

5

6

1898. *Thin yellowish paper. Wmk small Umbrella on each stamp. With or without gum. P* 12.
11 3 3 pies, blue .. .. 1·00 50
a. Imperf between (horiz pair) .. £175
12 4 ½ put. green .. .. 2·00 40
a. Imperf between (horiz pair) ..
13 5 1 put. pink .. .. 1·75 55
a. *Tête-bêche* (pair) £1700 £1700
b. Laid paper .. .. .. — £1600
ba. Laid paper. *Tête-bêche* (pair) .. — £5500
c. Red .. .. 1·75 40
d. Carmine-red .. .. .. 2·25 40
14 6 2 put. deep violet .. .. .. 3·00 1·75
a. Imperf between (vert pair) .. £150

1903. *Thick white paper. Wmk small Umbrella on each stamp. With or without gum. P* 12.
16 3 3 pies, blue 25 8
17 4 ½ put. green 50 8
a. Stamp sideways (in pair) £600 £600
18 5 1 put. pink .. .. 1·10 12
a. *Tête-bêche* (pair) £2000 £2000
19 6 2 put. deep violet .. .. .. 1·40 20
a. Double impression .. .. — £125

(7)

(7*a*)

1909. *T* 3 (*paper and perf of* 1903), *surch with T* 7. *Wmk is always sideways. No gum.*
22 3 2 on 3 pies, rosy mauve 20 25
a. Surch T 7 inverted .. .. 70·00 70·00
b. Surch T 7*a* £180 £160
c. Stamps *tête-bêche* £100 £100
d. Stamps and surchs *tête-bêche* .. £120 £120

Varieties a, c and d were caused by the inversion of one stamp (No. 7) in the plate and the consequent inversion of the corresponding surcharge to correct the error.

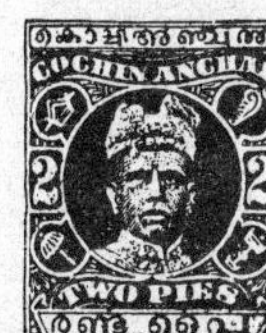

8 Raja Sir Sri Rama Varma I

8*a*

(Recess Perkins, Bacon & Co)

1911–23. *Currency in pies and annas. W* 8*a*. *P* 14.
26 8 2 p. brown 20 8
a. Imperf (pair) .. .. .. — £175
27 3 p. blue 15 8
a. Perf 14 × 12½ .. .. .. 20·00 12·00
28 4 p. green 70 8
28*a* 4 p. apple-green .. .. .. 2·50 40
29 9 p. carmine .. .. 1·10 8
a. Wmk sideways .. .. ..
30 1 a. brown-orange .. .. .. 1·10 8
31 1½ a. purple .. .. 3·75 40
32 2 a. grey .. .. 7·50 40
33 3 a. vermilion .. .. 40·00 40·00

9 Maharaja Sir Sri Rama Varma II 10

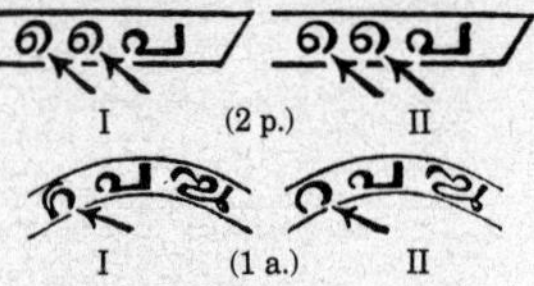

I (2 p.) II

I (1 a.) II

(Recess Perkins, Bacon & Co)

1918–22. W **8a**. *P* 13½ *or* 14.

35	**10**	2 p. brown (Die I)	3·75	10
		a. Imperf (pair)		
		b. Die II	90	8
36		4 p. green (1919)	95	8
37		6 p. red-brown (1922)	70	8
38		8 p. sepia (1922)	1·40	8
39		9 p. carmine	6·50	12
40		10 p. blue (1922)	1·00	8
41	**9**	1 a. orange (Die I)	5·00	20
		a. Die II	3·00	20
42	**10**	1½ a. purple (1921)	2·25	8
43		2 a. grey	4·25	12
44		2¼ a. yellow-green (1922)	4·25	40
45		3 a. vermilion	11·00	40

2 2 2

Two pies **Two pies** **Two pies**
(11) (12) (13)

2 2

Two Pies **Two Pies**
(14) (15)

1922–29. *T* **8** (*P* 14), *surch with T* **11/15**.

46	**11**	2 p. on 3 p. blue	40	30
		a. Surch double	75·00	
47	**12**	2 p. on 3 p. blue	1·50	60
		a. Surch double	90·00	
		b. Capital "P" in "Pies"	20·00	16·00
		ba. Surch double		
48	**13**	2 p. on 3 p. blue (6.24)	60	30
		a. Capital "P" in "Pies"	15·00	12·00
		b. Perf 14 × 12½	18·00	15·00
		ba. Ditto. Capital "P" in "Pies".. ..	85·00	65·00
49	**14**	2 p. on 3 p. blue (1929)	75	75
		a. Surch double	£150	£150
		b. Surch with Type **15**..	60·00	60·00
		ba. Ditto. Surch double..	£350	£350

There are four settings of these overprints. The first (July 1922) consisted of 39 stamps with Type **11**, and 9 with Type **12**, and in Type **11** the centre of the "2" is above the "o" of "Two". In the second setting (May 1924) there were 36 of Type **11** and 12 of Type **12**, and the centre of the figure is above the space between "Two" and "Pies". The third setting (June 1924) consists of stamps with Type **13** only.

The fourth setting (1929) was also in sheets of 48, No. 49b being the first stamp in the fourth row.

ONE ANNA
ഒരു അണ
(16)
ANCHAL & REVENUE

Three Pies
൩ 3
മൂന്നു പൈ
(17)

1928. *Surch with T* **16**.

50	**10**	1 a. on 2¼ a. yellow-green	6·00	12·00
		a. "REVENUF" for "REVENUE" ..	40·00	50·00

1932–33. *Surch as T* **17**. *W* **8a**. *P* 14.

51	**10**	3 p. on 4 p. green	95	55
52	**10**	3 p. on 8 p. sepia..	95	75
53		9 p. on 10 p. blue	1·50	75

18 Maharaja Sir Sri Rama Varma III

(Recess Perkins, Bacon & Co)

1933–38. *T* **18** (*but frame and inscription of* 1 *a. as T* **9**). *W* **8a**. *P* 13 × 13½.

54	**18**	2 p. brown (1936)	60	8
55		4 p. green	70	8
56		6 p. red-brown..	80	8
57	–	1 a. brown-orange	80	8
58	**18**	1 a. 8 p. carmine	3·50	1·25
59		2 a. grey (1938)	1·75	8
60		2¼ a. yellow-green	1·75	8
61		3 a. vermilion (1938)	3·50	12
62		3 a. 4 p. violet	1·75	70
63		6 a. 8 p. sepia	2·00	1·25
64		10 a. blue	3·50	1·75

For stamps in this design, but lithographed, see Nos. 67/71.

1934. *Surcharged as T* **14**. *W* **8a**. *P* 14.

65	**10**	6 p. on 8 p. sepia (R.)	1·00	45
66		6 p. on 10 p. blue (R.)	3·25	60

"DOUBLE PRINTS". The errors previously listed under this description are now identified as blanket offsets, a type of variety outside the scope of this catalogue. Examples occur on issues from 1938 onwards.

SPACING OF OVERPRINTS AND SURCHARGES. The typeset overprints and surcharges issued from 1939 onwards show considerable differences in spacing. Except for specialists, however, these differences have little significance as they occur within the same settings and do not represent separate printings.

(Litho The Associated Printers, Madras)

1938. *W* **8a** (A) *P* 11 *or* (B) *P* 13 × 13½.

			A		B	
67	**18**	2 p. brown	85	8	5·00	25
68		4 p. green	85	8	6·00	75
69		6 p. red-brown	2·25	8	—	—
70		1 a. brown-orange ..	16·00	18·00	32·00	38·00
71		2¼ a. sage-green	7·50	12	10·00	60

ANCHAL
(19)

THREE PIES
(20)

SURCHARGED

ANCHAL

ONE ANNA
THREE PIES
(21)

NINE PIES
(22)

ANCHAL **ANCHAL**

NINE PIES
(23)

SURCHARGED
NINE PIES
(24)

ANCHAL
(25)

1939–44. *T* **18** *variously optd or surch.*

I. *Recess-printed stamps. Nos.* 57/8

72	3 p. on 1 a. 8 p. carmine (T **20**)	30·00	28·00
73	3 p. on 1 a. 8 p. carmine (T **21**)	3·50	1·00
74	6 p. on 1 a. 8 p. carmine (T **20**)	1·75	1·00
75	1 a. brown-orange (T **19**)	1·50	8
76	1 a. 3 p. on 1 a. 8 p. carmine (T **21**)	1·25	15

II. *Lithographed stamps. Nos.* 68 *and* 70. A. *P* 11. B. *P*. 13 × 13½

		A		B	
77	3 p. on 4 p. (T **21**)	6·00	40	11·00	70
78	6 p. on 1 a. (T **22**)	60·00	30·00	†	
79	6 p. on 1 a. (T **23**)	60·00	50·00	18·00	9·00
80	9 p. on 1 a. (T **22**)	18·00	20·00	†	
81	9 p. on 1 a. (T **23**)	†		48·00	16·00
82	9 p. on 1 a. (T **24**)	†		11·00	50
83	1 a. (T **19**)	16·00	8	50·00	30·00
84	1 a. (T **25**)	4·00	1·50	7·00	50

26 Maharaja Sri Kerala Varma I

27 (*The actual measurement of this wmk is* 6¼ × 3⅝ *in.*)

(Litho The Associated Printers, Madras)

1943. *Frame of* 1 *a. inscr* "ANCHAL & REVENUE". A. *P* 11. B. *P* 13 × 13½. (*a*) *W* **8a**.

			A		B	
85	**26**	2 p. grey-brown.. ..	—	—	50	10
85*a*		4 p. green	†		90·00	65·00
85*b*		1 a. brown-orange ..	†		55·00	40·00
		(*b*) *W* **27**				
86	**26**	2 p. grey-brown.. ..	—	£150	22·00	12
87		4 p. green	3·50	55	12·00	4·50
88		6 p. red-brown	10·00	1·00	1·00	8
89		9 p. ultramarine ..	4·50	1·00	†	
		a. Imperf between (horiz pair)	£500	—	†	
90		1 a. brown-orange ..	28·00	24·00	75·00	45·00
91		2¼ a. yellow-green ..	17·00	5·00	3·00	12

Part of W **27** appears on many stamps in each sheet, while others are entirely without wmk.

1944. *T* **26** *variously opt or surch.* A. *P* 11. B. *P* 13 × 13½

(*a*) *W* **8a**.

		A		B	
92	3 p. on 4 p. (T **21**)	†		35·00	4·00
92*a*	9 p. on 1 a. (T **23**)	†		5·00	65
92*b*	9 p. on 1 a. (T **24**)	†		35	8
92*c*	1 a. on 3 p. on 1 a. (T **21**) ..	†		£750	£600
	(*b*) *W* **27**				
93	2 p. on 6 p. (T **20**)	60	12	50	12
94	3 p. on 4 p. (T **20**)	70	8	†	
95	3 p. on 4 p. (T **21**)	†		60	8
96	3 p. on 6 p. (T **20**)	70	15	30	10
97	4 p. on 6 p. (T **20**)	†		1·50	40

28 Maharaja Sri Ravi Varma 29

I

II

(Litho The Associated Printers, Madras)

1944–48. *W* **27**. *No gum*. (*a*) *Type* I. *P* 11.

98	**28**	9 p. ultramarine (1944)..	5·00	1·25
		(*b*) *Type* II. *P* 13		
98*a*	**28**	9 p. ultramarine (1946)..	3·00	50
		ab. Perf 13 × 13½	5·00	70
99		1 a. 3 p. magenta (1948)	7·00	60
		a. Perf 13 × 13½	11·00	1·10
100		1 a. 9 p. ultramarine (*shades*) (1948) ..	11·00	1·00

Nos. 98*a*/100 are line-perforated, Nos. 98ab and 99a comb-perforated.

(Litho The Associated Printers, Madras)

1946–48. *Frame of* 1 *a. inscr* "ANCHAL & REVENUE". *W* **27**. *No gum* (*except for stamps perf* 11). *P* 13.

101	**29**	2 p. chocolate	1·00	10
		a. Imperf horiz (vert pair)	£375	£375
		c. Perf 11	14·00	60
		d. Perf 11 × 13	£125	55·00
102		3 p. carmine	2·00	10
103		4 p. grey-green	£1000	7·00
104		6 p. red-brown (1947)	7·00	25
		a. Perf 11	60·00	35
105		9 p. ultramarine	2·25	10
		a. Imperf between (horiz pair) ..	£600	
106		1 a. orange (1948)	6·00	6·00
		a. Perf 11	£250	
107		2 a. black	12·00	40
		a. Perf 11	55·00	50
108		3 a. vermilion	15·00	40

30 Maharaja Sri Kerala Varma II

(Litho The Associated Printers, Madras)

1948–50. W **27**. P 11.
109 **30** 2 p. grey-brown .. .. 2·75 12
a. Imperf between (horiz pair) .. £325 £325
110 3 p. carmine .. .. 1·00 10
a. Imperf between (vert pair).. .. £325 £325
111 4 p. green .. .. 2·75 12
a. Imperf between (horiz pair) .. £250 £250
112 6 p. chestnut .. .. 2·75 12
a. Imperf between (horiz pair) .. £550 £550
113 9 p. ultramarine .. .. 1·10 12
114 2 a. black .. .. 14·00 25
115 3 a. orange-red .. .. 15·00 35
a. Imperf between (horiz pair) .. £800 £800
116 3 a. 4 p. violet (1950) .. .. .. 45·00 70·00

31 Chinese Nets

32 Dutch Palace

(Litho The Associated Printers, Madras)

1949. W **27**. P 11.
117 **31** 2 a. black .. .. 60 1·00
a. Imperf vert (horiz pair) £325
118 **32** 2¼ a. green .. .. 60 1·00
a. Imperf vert (horiz pair) £325

SIX PIES

ആറു പൈ
(33)

പൈ Normal

പൈ Error

Due to similarities between two Malayalam characters some values of the 1948 provisional issue exist with an error in the second word of the Malayalam surcharge. On Nos. 119, 122 and O103 this occurs twice in the setting of 48. No. 125 shows four examples and No. O104b one. Most instances are as illustrated above, but in two instances on the setting for No. 125 the error occurs on the second character.

1949. *Surch as T* **33**. (i) *On* 1944–48 *issue*. P 13.
119 **28** 6 p. on 1 a. 3 p. magenta .. .. .. 1·00 30
a. Incorrect character .. .. .. 10·00 5·00
120 1 a. on 1 a. 9 p. ultramarine (R.) .. 2·00 20
(ii) *On* 1946–48 *issue*
121 **29** 3 p. on 9 p. ultramarine.. .. .. 6·00 2·75
122 6 p. on 1 a. 3 p. magenta .. .. 1·25 40
b. Incorrect character .. .. .. 11·00 5·50
123 1 a. on 1 a. 9 p. ultramarine (R.) .. 3·75 20
a. Surch in black .. .. ..
b. Black surch with smaller native characters 7½ mm instead of 10 mm long .. ..
(iii) *On* 1948–50 *issue*
124 **30** 3 p. on 9 p. ultramarine.. .. .. 5·00 5·00
a. Larger native characters 20 mm instead of 16½ mm long .. 1·25 30
b. Surch double £120
125 3 p. on 9 p. ultramarine (R.) .. .. 1·60 40
a. Incorrect character .. .. .. 9·00 4·50
126 6 p. on 9 p. ultramarine (R.) .. .. 2·40 80
Nos. 122/3 were not issued without surcharge.

1949. *Surch as T* **20**. W **27**. P 13.
127 **29** 6 p. on 1 a. orange .. .. .. 28·00 35·00
128 9 p. on 1 a. orange .. .. .. 22·00 27·00

From 1 July 1949 Cochin became part of the combined state of Travancore-Cochin.

OFFICIAL STAMPS

On C G S (O 1)
ON C G S (O 2 Small "ON")
ON C G S (O 3 "G" without serif)

1913. *Optd with Type* O 1 (3 *p.*) *or* O 2 (*others*).
O1 **8** 3 p. blue (R.) .. .. 30·00 8
a. Black opt .. ..
O2 4 p. green (*wmk sideways*) .. .. 7·00 8
a. Opt inverted .. .. .. — £190
O3 **8** 9 p. carmine .. .. 27·00 8
a. Wmk sideways .. .. 13·00 8
O4 1½ a. purple .. .. 17·00 12
a. Opt double.. .. .. .. £200
O5 2 a. grey .. .. 15·00 10
O6 3 a. vermilion .. .. 18·00 15
O7 6 a. violet .. .. 15·00 2·00
O8 12 a. ultramarine .. .. 22·00 5·00
O9 1½ r. deep green.. .. .. .. 22·00 25·00

1919–33. *Optd as Type* O 3.
O10 **10** 4 p. green .. .. 3·50 8
a. Opt double.. .. .. .. £175
O11 6 p. red-brown (1922) .. .. .. 3·75 8
a. Opt double.. .. .. .. £175
O12 8 p. sepia .. .. 6·00 8
O13 9 p. carmine .. .. 12·00 12
O14 10 p. blue .. .. 6·00 8
O15 1½ a. purple (1921) .. .. .. 5·50 8
O16 2 a. grey .. .. 12·00 8
O17 2¼ a. yellow-green .. .. .. 5·50 8
a. Opt double.. .. .. .. — £300
O18 3 a. vermilion .. .. 12·00 25
a. Opt inverted .. .. .. — £300
O19 6 a. violet (1924) .. .. .. 15·00 50
O19*a* 12 a. ultramarine (1929) .. .. 17·00 2·75
O19*b* 1½ r. deep green (1933).. .. .. 25·00 38·00

8 Eight pies (O 4 27½ mm high)
ON C G S (O 5 Straight back to "C")
ON C G S (O 6 Circular "O"; "N" without serifs)

1923 (Jan)–**24.** *T* **8** *and* **10** *surch with Type* O 4.
O20 8 p. on 9 p. carmine (No. O3).. .. .. £125 15
a. "Pies" for "pies" (R.4/8) .. .. — 30·00
b. Wmk sideways £100 10
ba. "Pies" for "pies" (R.4/8) .. .. — 16·00
c. Surch double .. .. .. — £200
O21 8 p. on 9 p. carmine (No. O13) (11.24) .. 70·00 8
a. "Pies" for "pies" (R.4/8) .. .. — 11·00
b. Surch double .. .. ..
Varieties with smaller "i" or "t" in "Eight" and small "i" in "Pies" are also known from a number of positions in the setting.

1925 (Apr). *T* **10** *surch as Type* O 4.
O22 10 p. on 9 p. carmine (No. O13) .. .. 65·00 12
a. Surch inverted .. .. ..
b. Surch double .. .. ..
c. Surch 25 mm high .. .. — 75

1929. *T* **8** *surch as Type* O 4.
O23 10 p. on 9 p. carmine (No. O3).. .. .. £150 7·00

1931. *Optd with Type* O 5.
O24 **10** 4 p. green .. .. 22·00 1·10
a. Inverted "S" .. .. .. 70·00 9·00
O25 6 p. red-brown .. .. 7·00 8
a. Inverted "S" .. .. .. 38·00 3·50
O26 8 p. sepia .. .. 6·00 8
a. Inverted "S" .. .. .. 35·00 3·50
O27 10 p. blue.. .. .. 6·00 8
a. Inverted "S" .. .. .. 35·00 3·50
O28 2 a. grey.. .. .. 7·00 8
a. Inverted "S" .. .. .. 42·00 4·00
O29 3 a. vermilion .. .. 8·00 15
a. Inverted "S" .. .. .. 48·00 6·00
O30 6 a. violet .. .. 50·00 5·00
a. Inverted "S" .. .. .. £175 42·00

Pie3
No. O32b

1933. *Nos.* O26/7 *surch as T* **14**, *in red*.
O32 **10** 6 p. on 8 p. sepia.. .. .. .. 1·75 12
a. Inverted "S" .. .. .. 12·00 3·50
b. "3" for "S" in "Pies".. .. ..
O33 6 p. on 10 p. blue .. .. 5·00 10
a. Inverted "S" .. .. .. 30·00 3·50
The inverted "S" varieties occur on R.2/1 of one setting of this overprint only.

1933–44. *Recess-printed stamps of* 1933-38 *optd*.
(*a*) *With Type* O 5
O34 **18** 4 p. green 65 8
O35 6 p. red-brown 85 8
O36 1 a. brown-orange .. .. .. 6·00 8
O37 1 a. 8 p. carmine .. .. .. 3·50 8
O38 2 a. grey .. .. 6·00 8
O39 2¼ a. yellow-green .. .. .. 3·50 8
O40 3 a. vermilion .. .. 11·00 8
O41 3 a. 4 p. violet .. .. 3·50 12
O42 6 a. 8 p. sepia .. .. 3·50 15
O43 10 a. blue .. .. 3·50 20
(*b*) *With Type* O 6 (*typo*)
O44 **18** 1 a. brown-orange .. .. .. 35·00 10
O45 2 a. grey-black .. .. 24·00 15
O46 3 a. vermilion .. .. 10·00 25

ON C G S (O 7 Curved back to "c")
ON C G S (O 8)
ON C G S (O 9 Circular "O"; N with serifs)
ON C G S (O 10 Oval "O")
ON C G S (O 11)

1938–44. *Lithographed stamps of* 1938. W **8a**, *optd*.
(*a*) *With Type* O 7 *or* O 8 (1 *a*). I. P 11. II. P 13 × 13½.

			I		II	
O47	**18**	4 p. green	4·50	50	7·00	1·25
		a. Inverted "S" ..	5·50	70	†	
O48		6 p. red-brown ..	3·00	8	†	
		a. Inverted "S" ..	3·50	12	†	
O49		1 a. brown-orange ..	£110	2·50	†	
O50		2 a. grey-black ..	3·00	8	†	
		a. Inverted "S" ..	3·50	12	†	
		(*b*) *With Type* O 9 (*litho*) *or* O 10 (6 *p*.)				
O51	**18**	6 p. red-brown ..	†		1·50	30
O52		1 a. brown-orange ..	1·75	8	†	
O53		3 a. vermilion ..	3·50	15	†	
		(*c*) *With Type* O **11**				
O53*a*	**18**	6 p. red-brown ..	£425	£250	†	

The inverted "S" varieties, Nos. O47a, O48a and O50a, occur 21 times in the setting of 48.

1943. *Unissued stamps optd with Type* O **10**. *Litho*. W **27**. I. P 11. II. P 13 × 13½.

			I		II	
O54	**18**	4 p. green ..	50·00	12·00	40	20
O55		6 p. red-brown ..	70·00	12·00	22·00	1·00
O56		1 a. brown-orange ..	20·00	3·00	1·25	1·25
O56*a*		2 a. grey-black ..	40·00	50	†	
		ab. Opt omitted ..	—	£130	†	
O56*b*		2¼ a. sage-green ..	£150	7·00	†	
O56*c*		3 a. vermilion ..	15·00	4·00	†	

1943. *Official stamps variously surch with T* **20** *or* **21**.
(i) *On* 1½ *a. purple, of* 1919–33
O57 **10** 9 p. on 1½ a. (T **20**) .. .. .. 95·00 2·50
(ii) *On recess-printed* 1 *a.* 8 *p. carmine of* 1933–44 (*Type* O **5** *opt*)
O58 3 p. on 1 a. 8 p. (T **21**).. .. .. .. 25 15
O59 9 p. on 1 a. 8 p. (T **20**).. .. .. .. 45·00 9·00
O60 1 a. 9 p. on 1 a. 8 p. (T **20**) 90 15
O61 1 a. 9 p. on 1 a. 8 p. (T **21**) 80 15
(iii) *On lithographed stamps of* 1938–44. *T* **18**. I. P 11. II. P 13 × 13½
(*a*) W **8a**

		I		II	
O62	3 p. on 4 p. (Types O 7 and **20**)	†		3·50	30
	a. Surch double			—	£110
O63	3 p. on 4 p. (Types O 7 and **21**)	†		50·00	20·00
O64	3 p. on 1 a. (Types O 9 and **20**)	1·50	20	†	
O65	9 p. on 1 a. (Types O 9 and **20**)	45·00	3·00	†	
O66	1 a. 3 p. on 1 a. (Types O 9 and **21**)	55·00	32·00	†	
	(*b*) W **27**				
O67	3 p. on 4 p. (Types O 10 and **20**)	†		45·00	35·00
O67*a*	3 p. on 1 a. (Types O 10 and **20**)	45·00	25·00	55·00	25·00

1944. *Optd with Type* O **10**. W **27**. P 13 × 13½.
O68 **26** 4 p. green .. .. 4·00 15
a. Perf 11 .. .. 27·00 1·50
b. Perf 13 .. .. — 10·00
O69 6 p. red-brown 25 8
a. Opt double.. .. .. .. 45·00 45·00
b. Perf 11 .. .. 25 8
c. Perf 13 .. .. 10·00 2·00
O70 1 a. brown-orange .. .. .. £750 35·00
O71 2 a. black 45 15
O72 2¼ a. yellow-green .. .. .. 1·50 20
a. Optd both sides .. .. ..
O73 3 a. vermilion .. .. 2·00 40
a. Perf 11 .. .. 2·00 40
Stamps perforated 13 × 13½ are from a comb machine; those perforated 13 from a line perforator.

1944. *Optd with Type* O **10** *and variously surch as Types* **20** *and* **21**. W **27**.

			I		II	
O74	**26**	3 p. on 4 p. (T **20**).. ..	5·00	40	1·00	8
		b. Optd Type O **10** on both sides ..	—	—	†	
O75		3 p. on 4 p. (T **21**) ..	£120	60·00	3·50	25
O76		3 p. on 1 a. (T **20**).. ..	†		3·50	40
O77		9 p. on 6 p. (T **20**).. ..	†		2·50	10
O78		9 p. on 6 p. (T **21**).. ..	†		1·00	10
O79		1 a. 3 p. on 1 a. (T **20**) ..	†		2·25	10
O80		1 a. 3 p. on 1 a. (T **21**) ..	†		2·25	10

1946–47. *Stamps of* 1944-48 *optd with Type* O **10**. *Type* II. P 13.
O81 **28** 9 p. ultramarine .. .. .. 1·25 20
a. Stamp printed both sides £100 £100
b. Perf 13 × 13½ 40 8
O82 1 a. 3 p. magenta (1947) 40 12
a. Opt double .. .. .. 15·00 12·00
b. Optd both sides, opt double on reverse .. .. 25·00
O83 1 a. 9 p. ultramarine (1947) 35 15
a. Opt double .. .. ..

1948. *Stamps of 1946–48 and unissued values optd with Type* O **2**. *P* 13.
O84 **29** 3 p. carmine 20 12
O85 4 p. grey-green .. .. 15·00 5·00
O86 6 p. red-brown 90 12
O87 9 p. ultramarine .. .. 1·25 12
O88 1 a. 3 p. magenta .. .. 1·40 20
O89 1 a. 9 p. ultramarine .. .. 1·50 60
O90 2 a. black .. .. 1·50 35
O91 2¼ a. yellow-green .. .. 2·50 75

1949. *Stamps of 1948–50 and unissued values optd with Type* O **7**.
O92 **30** 3 p. carmine 30 12
O93 4 p. green 30 12
a. Imperf between (pair) £425 £425
b. Optd on reverse .. .. .. 35·00 35·00
O94 6 p. chestnut 30 12
a. Imperf between (vert pair) ..
O95 9 p. ultramarine 35 12
O96 2 a. black 60 15
O97 2¼ a. yellow-green .. .. 1·25 35
O98 3 a. orange-red .. .. 1·10 25
O99 3 a. 4 p. violet .. .. 6·00 6·50

Nos. O92/9 exist with "C" for "G" in the overprint which occurs once on the sheet. Also Nos. O92/8, O103/4 and O104b exist with a flat back to "G" which occurs twice on the sheet.

1949. *Official stamps surch as T* **33**. (i) *On* 1944 *issue*.
O100 **28** 1 a. on 1 a. 9 p. ultramarine (R.) .. 60 12

(ii) *On* 1948 *issue*
O101 **29** 1 a. on 1 a. 9 p. ultramarine (R.) .. 3·00 1·25

(iii) *On* 1949 *issue*
O103 **30** 6 p. on 3 p. carmine 30 15
a. Imperf between (vert pair) .. £425 £425
b. Surch double £225 £225
c. "C" for "G" in opt .. .. .. 4·00 4·00
d. Incorrect character .. .. 5·00 5·00
O104 9 p. on 4 p. green (*18 mm long*) .. 50 25
a. Imperf between (horiz pair) .. £325
b. Larger native characters, 22 mm long 50 40
ba. Ditto. Imperf between (horiz pair) £375 £375
bb. Incorrect character .. .. 7·00 7·00
c. "C" for "G" in opt .. .. .. 6·00 6·00
ca. Ditto. Larger native characters, 22 mm long .. .. .. 6·00 6·00

1949. *No.* 124*a*, *but with lines of surch* 17½ *mm apart, optd* "SERVICE".
O105 **30** 3 p. on 9 p. ultramarine 60 35

For later issues see TRAVANCORE-COCHIN

DHAR

PRICES FOR STAMPS ON COVER
The stamps of Dhar are very rare used on cover.

1

2

अर्धा बलड. No. 1c
अर्धा लबड. No. 1d
आर्धा डबल. No. 2

1897–1900. *Type-set. Colour-fugitive paper. With oval handstamp in black. No gum. Imperf.*
1 **1** ½ p. black/*red* (three characters at bottom left) 30 35
a. Handstamp omitted .. .. 70·00
b. Line below upper inscription (R.2/2) 75·00 75·00
c. Character transposed (R.2/3) .. 10·00
d. Character transposed (R.2/5) .. 50·00
2 ½ p. black/*red* (four characters at bottom left) 35 45
a. Handstamp omitted .. .. 75·00
3 ¼ a. black/*orange* 50 70
a. Handstamp omitted .. .. 70·00
4 ½ a. black/*magenta* 50 70
a. Handstamp omitted .. .. 75·00 75·00
b. Line below upper inscription (R.2/2) 80·00 80·00
5 1 a. black/*green* .. .. .. 1·50 2·00
a. Handstamp omitted .. .. 90·00
b. Printed both sides .. ..
c. Line below upper inscription (R.2/2) 95·00 95·00
6 2 a. black/*yellow* .. .. .. 12·00 18·00
e. Top right corner ornament transposed with one from top of frame (R.2/5) £100 £125

Nos. 1/6 were each issued in sheets of 10 (5 × 2), but may, on the evidence of a single sheet of the ½ pice value, have been printed in sheets of 20 containing two of the issued sheets *tête-bêche*.

Research has identified individual characteristics for stamps printed from each position in the sheet.

The same research suggests that the type remained assembled during the entire period of production, being amended as necessary to provide the different values. Seven main settings have been identified with changes sometimes occurring during their use which form sub-settings.

The distribution of stamps between the main settings was as follows:
Setting I—½ p.
Setting II—½ a., 1 a.
Setting III—1 a.
Setting IV—½ p., ½ a., 1 a.
Setting V—½ p.
Setting VI—½ p. (No. 2), ¼ a.
Setting VII—2 a.

The listed constant errors all occurred during Setting IV.

In No. 1c the three characters forming the second word in the lower inscription are transposed to the order (2) (3) (1) and in No. 1d to the order (3) (2) (1).

On Nos. 1b, 4b and 5c the line which normally appears above the upper inscription is transposed so that it appears below the characters.

All values show many other constant varieties including mistakes in the corner and border ornaments, and also both constant and non-constant missing lines, dots and characters.

Examples of complete forgeries and faked varieties on genuine stamps exist.

(Typo at Bombay)

1898–1900. *P* 11 *to* 12.
7 **2** ½ a. carmine .. .. 85 1·00
a. Imperf (pair) .. .. .. 30·00
b. Deep rose 75 90
8 1 a. claret 75 90
9 1 a. reddish violet .. .. .. 2·25 2·75
a. Imperf between (pair) £120
b. Imperf (pair) .. .. .. 50·00
10 2 a. deep green .. .. 3·25

The stamps of Dhar have been obsolete since 31 March 1901.

DUTTIA (DATIA)

PRICES FOR STAMPS ON COVER
Nos. 1/15 —
Nos. 16/40 *from* × 30

GUM. The stamps of Duttia (*except No.* 28b) were issued without gum.

1 (4 a.) Ganesh.

2 (½ a.)

2*a* (2 a.)

1893. *Imperf.*
1 **1** ¼ a. black/*orange* £1300
2 ½ a. black/*blue-green* £1300
3 **2** 1 a. red £1500
4 **1** 2 a. black/*yellow* £1500
5 4 a. black/*rose* £1250

Stamps of Type **1** come with or without the handstamp as shown in Type **2** (same value in either state).

1896? *Rosettes in lower corners. Imperf.*
5*a* **2a** ½ a. black/*green* £2500
5*b* 2 a. grey-blue/*yellow* £1750

1897? *Imperf.*
6 **2½** a. black/*green* .. .. 12·00
a. Value in one group .. .. .. 20·00
b. Ditto. *Tête-bêche* (horiz pair) .. £175
7 1 a. black/*white* .. .. .. 26·00 45·00
a. *Tête-bêche* (pair) £300
b. Laid paper .. .. 10·00
8 2 a. black/*yellow* .. .. 15·00
9 2 a. black/*lemon* .. .. 22·00
10 4 a. black/*rose* .. .. 15·00
a. *Tête-bêche* (pair) £150

3 (½ a.)

4 (¼ a.)

1897. *Name spelt* "DATIA." *Imperf.*
12 **3** ½ a. black/*green* .. .. 42·00
13 1 a. black/*white* .. .. 42·00
14 2 a. black/*yellow* .. .. 50·00
a. *Tête-bêche* (vert pair) £250
15 4 a. black/*rose* .. .. 48·00
a. *Tête-bêche* (vert pair) £250

1899–1906.

(*a*) *Rouletted in colour or in black, horizontally and at end of rows*
16 **4** ¼ a. vermilion 60
a. Rose-red 70
b. Pale rose 75
c. Lake .. .. 75 1·50
d. Carmine .. .. 1·50
e. Brownish red .. .. .. 1·50
ea. *Tête-bêche* (pair) £2250
17 ½ a. black/*blue-green* .. .. .. 65 1·50
a. On deep green .. .. .. 1·00
b. On yellow-green (pelure) 80
c. On dull green (1906) .. .. 1·00
18 1 a. black/*white* .. .. 70 1·75
19 2 a. black/*lemon-yellow* .. .. .. 1·40
a. On orange-yellow .. .. .. 1·60
b. On buff-yellow .. .. .. 1·40 3·00
c. On pale yellow (1906) .. .. 1·60 3·00
20 4 a. black/*deep rose* .. .. .. 1·25 3·00
a. *Tête-bêche* (pair) .. .. ..

(*b*) *Rouletted in colour between horizontal rows, but imperf at top and bottom and at ends of rows*
20*b* **4** ¼ a. brownish red .. .. 6·50
21 1 a. black/*white* .. .. 4·50

1904–5. *Without rouletting.*
22 **4** ¼ a. red .. .. 1·75
23 ½ a. black/*green* .. .. 6·00
24 1 a. black (1905) .. .. 3·00 6·00

1911. *P* 13½. *Stamps very wide apart.*
25 **4** ¼ a. carmine .. .. 2·00
a. Imperf horiz (vert pair) .. .. 90·00
b. Stamps closer together (with gum) 3·75 6·50
c. As b. Imperf vert (horiz pair) .. 75·00
25*d* 1 a. black .. .. 45·00

1912? *Printed close together.* (*a*) *Coloured roulette* × *imperf.*
26 **4** ½ a. black/*green* .. .. 4·00

(*b*) *Printed wide apart. P* 13½ × *coloured roulette.* (¼ *a.*) *or* 13½ × *imperf* (½ *a.*)
27 **4** ¼ a. carmine .. .. 1·60
28 ½ a. black/*dull green* .. .. .. 3·75 6·50

1916. *Colours changed. Imperf.*
29 **4** ¼ a. deep blue .. .. 1·25 3·00
30 ½ a. green .. .. 2·75 5·00
31 1 a. purple .. .. 3·50 6·00
a. *Tête-bêche* (pair) .. .. .. 18·00
32 2 a. brown .. .. 7·00 12·00
33 2 a. lilac .. .. 6·00 12·00
34 4 a. Venetian red (date?) .. .. .. 30·00

1918. *Colours changed.* (*a*) *Imperf.*
35 **4** ½ a. blue .. .. 70 1·75
36 1 a. pink .. .. 1·25

(*b*) *P* 11½
37 **4** ¼ a. black .. .. 3·50

1920. *Rouletted.*
38 **4** ¼ a. blue .. .. 1·00 1·50
a. Roul × perf 7 .. .. .. 16·00 16·00
39 ½ a. pink .. .. 1·25 2·00
a. Roul × perf 7 .. .. .. 27·00

1920? *Rough perf about* 7.
40 **4** ½ a. dull red .. .. 4·00 6·00

All the stamps of Duttia were impressed with a circular handstamp (as a rule in *blue*) before issue.

This handstamp shows the figure of Ganesh in the centre, surrounded by an inscription in Devanagari reading "DATIYA STET POSTAJ 1893". Stamps could not be used for postage without this control mark.

FARIDKOT

PRICES FOR STAMPS ON COVER
Nos. N1/4 *from* × 10
Nos. N5/8 *from* × 30

GUM. The stamps of Faridkot (Nos. N1/8) were issued without gum.

N 1 (1 folus)

N 2 (1 paisa)

N 3

1879–86. *Rough, handstamped impression. Imperf.*

(*a*) *Native thick laid paper*
N1 **N 1** 1 f. ultramarine .. .. .. 27·00 30·00
N2 **N 2** 1 p. ultramarine .. .. .. 38·00 42·00

(*b*) *Ordinary laid paper*
N3 **N 1** 1 f. ultramarine .. .. .. 14·00 16·00
N4 **N 2** 1 p. ultramarine .. .. .. 30·00 40·00

(*c*) *Wove paper, thick to thinnish*
N5 **N 1** 1 f. ultramarine .. .. .. 1·00 1·10
a. *Tête-bêche* (pair) .. .. .. 38·00
N6 **N 2** 1 p. ultramarine .. .. .. 1·00 1·50

(*d*) *Thin wove whity brown paper*
N7 **N 2** 1 p. ultramarine .. .. .. 9·00 12·00

(*e*) *Wove paper*
N8 **N 3** 1 p. ultramarine .. .. .. 1·25
a. *Tête-bêche* (pair) .. .. .. 38·00

It is doubtful whether stamps of Type N 3 were ever used for postage.

Impressions of these types in various colours, the ½ a. labels, and the later printings from re-engraved dies, were never in circulation at all.

Faridkot became a convention state and from 1887 used the Indian stamps overprinted which are listed under the Convention States.

HYDERABAD

PRICES FOR STAMPS ON COVER
Nos. 1/3 *from* × 10
Nos. 4/12 —
Nos. 13/60 *from* × 5
Nos. O1/53 *from* × 10

The official title of the State in English was The Dominions of the Nizam and in Urdu "Sarkar-i-Asafia" (State of the successors of Asaf). This Urdu inscription appears in many of the designs.

1

2

(Eng Mr. Rapkin. Plates by Nissen & Parker, London. Recess Mint, Hyderabad)

1869 (8 Sept). *P* 11½.

1	**1**	1 a. olive-green	8·50	8·00
		a. Imperf between (pair)	£100	90·00
		b. Imperf (pair)	85·00	85·00

Reprints in the colour of the issue, and also in fancy colours, were made in 1880 on white wove paper, perforated 12½.

1870 (16 May). *Locally engraved; 240 varieties of each value; wove paper. Recess. P* 11½.

2	**2**	½ a. brown	5·00	5·00
3		2 a. sage-green	28·00	25·00

Stamps exist showing traces of lines in the paper, but they do not appear to be printed on true laid paper.

Reprints of both values were made in 1880 on white wove paper, perforated 12½: the ½ a. in grey-brown, yellow-brown, sea-green and dull blue, and the 2 a. in bright green and in blue-green.

3

A
Normal

2 a.

B
Variety

In A the coloured lines surrounding each of the four labels join a coloured circle round their inner edge, in B this circle is missing.

C 3 a. D

C. Normal
D. Character ∧ omitted

(Plates by Bradbury, Wilkinson & Co. Recess Mint, Hyderabad)

1871–1909. (*a*) *No wmk*. (i) *Rough perf* 11½.

4	**3**	½ a. red-brown	15·00	15·00
5		1 a. purple-brown	45·00	50·00
6		2 a. green (A)	£100	
7		3 a. ochre-brown	25·00	28·00
8		4 a. slate	50·00	55·00
9		8 a. deep brown		
10		12 a. dull blue	90·00	90·00
		(ii) *Pin-perf* 8–9		
11	**3**	½ a. red-brown	80·00	70·00
12		1 a. drab	£110	60·00
		(iii) *P* 12½		
13	**3**	½ a. orange-brown	20	8
		a. Imperf vert (horiz pair)	55·00	55·00
		b. Brick-red	20	8
		ba. Imperf vert (horiz pair)	55·00	55·00
		bb. Doubly printed	50·00	50·00
		c. Rose-red	25	8
		d. Error. Magenta	32·00	10·00
14		1 a. purple-brown	80	1·00
		a. Doubly printed	60·00	60·00
		b. Drab	15	8
		ba. Imperf (pair)	—	65·00
		bb. Doubly printed	60·00	60·00
		c. Grey-black	30	8
		d. Black (1909)	30	8
		da. Doubly printed	60·00	60·00
		db. Imperf vert (horiz pair)	75·00	75·00
		dc. Imperf horiz (vert pair)	75·00	75·00
15		2 a. green (A)	30	10
		a. Deep green (A)	40	10
		b. Blue-green (A)	40	10
		ba. Blue-green (B)	45·00	35·00
		c. Pale green (A)	35	12
		ca. Pale green (B)	45·00	35·00
		d. Sage-green (A) (1909)	35	12
		da. Sage-green (B)	—	35·00
16		3 a. ochre-brown (C)	45	25
		a. Chestnut (C)	40	25
		aa. Character omitted (D)	65·00	55·00
17		4 a. slate	70	50
		a. Imperf vert (horiz pair)	£200	£200
		b. Greenish grey	60	45
		c. Olive-green	2·00	1·60
18		8 a. deep brown	1·50	1·25
		a. Imperf vert (horiz pair)	£250	
19		12 a. pale ultramarine	2·25	2·50
		a. Grey-green	2·00	2·25
		(*b*) *W* **7**. *P* 12½		
19*b*	**3**	1 a. black (1909)	—	4·00
19*c*		2 a. sage-green (A) (1909)	—	12·00
		ca. Sage-green (B)		

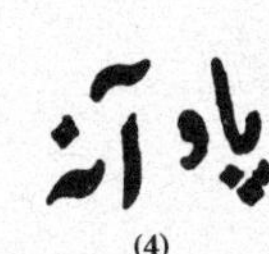

(4)

5

1898. *Surch with T* **4**. *P* 12½.

20	**3**	¼ a. on ½ a. orange-brown	75	75
		a. Surch inverted	25·00	20·00

(Des Khusrat Ullah. Recess Mint, Hyderabad)

1900 (20 Sept). *P* 12½.

21	**5**	¼ a. deep blue	3·00	1·50
		a. Pale blue	3·00	1·50

6

7

(Plates by Allan G. Wyon, London. Recess Mint, Hyderabad.)

1905 (7 Aug). *Wmk T* **7**. *P* 12½.

22	**6**	¼ a. dull blue	1·25	12
		a. Imperf (pair)	26·00	26·00
		b. Dull ultramarine	3·00	30
		ba. Perf 11 × 12½	15·00	15·00
		c. Pale blue-green	4·50	60
23		½ a. orange	2·50	25
		a. Perf 11		
		b. Vermilion	2·00	25
		ba. Imperf (pair)	24·00	24·00
		c. Yellow	30·00	25·00

1908–11. *W* **7**. *Various perfs, also compound.*

A. *Perf* 12½. B. *Perf* 11½, 12

			A		B	
24	**6**	¼ a. grey	45	8	80	10
		a. Imperf between (horiz pair)	50·00	50·00	†	
25		½ a. green	50	8	1·00	8
		a. Pale green	50	8	1·00	8
		b. Blue-green	5·00	90	†	
26		1 a. carmine	1·50	8	1·00	12
		a. Double impression, Perf 12½ × 11	—	—	†	
27		2 a. lilac	50	8	1·00	15
28		3 a. brown-orange (1909)	60	12	3·00	40
29		4 a. olive-green (1909)	60	10	5·00	50
30		8 a. purple (1911)	3·00	60	—	—
31		12 a. blue-green (1911)	7·00	3·50	2·75	3·00

C. *Perf* 11. D. *Perf* 13½

			C		D	
24	**6**	¼ a. grcy	6·00	4·00	†	
25		½ a. green	†		—	—
26		1 a. carmine	9·00	5·00	†	
27		2 a. lilac	1·75	15	80	8
		a. Imperf between (pair)	†		50·00	50·00
		b. Rose-lilac	†		1·10	8
28		3 a. brown-orange (1909)	60	15	60	8
29		4 a. olive-green (1909)	8·00	2·00	50	8
		a. Imperf between (pair)	60·00	60·00	†	
30		8 a. purple (1911)	1·25	50	75	20
31		12 a. blue-green (1911)	—	—	1·50	60

1912. *New plates eng by Bradbury, Wilkinson & Co. Perfs as before, or compound.*

			A		B	
32	**6**	¼ a. grey-black	30	8	40	8
		a. Imperf between (pair)	55·00	55·00	†	
34		½ a. deep green	40	8	75	8
		b. Imperf (pair)	30·00	30·00	†	

			C		D	
32	**6**	¼ a. grey-black	60	8	15	8
33		¼ a. lilac (*shades*)	†		15	8
		a. Imperf horiz (vert pair)	†		—	—
34		½ a. deep green	2·50	8	8·00	8·00
		a. Imperf between (pair)	—	—	50·00	50·00

In Wyon's ¼ a. stamp the fraction of value is closer to the end of the label than in the B.W. issue. In the Wyon ¼ a. and ½ a. the value in English and the label below are further apart than in the B.W.

Wyon's ¼ a. measures 19½ × 20 mm and the ½ a. 19½ × 20½ mm; both stamps from the Bradbury plates measure 19¾ × 21½ mm.

8 Symbols

9

1915. *Inscr* "Post & Receipt". *Various perfs as above, and compound.*

			A		C		D	
35	**8**	½ a. green	3·00	30	60	8	45	8
		a. Imperf between (pair)	50·00	50·00	50·00	50·00	40·00	40·00
		b. Imperf (pair)	45·00	40·00	†		†	
		c. Emerald-green	†		†		3·00	1·00
36		1 a. carmine	2·50	25	75	12	60	8
		a. Imperf between (pair)	50·00	50·00	†		†	
		b. Imperf (pair)	45·00	40·00	†		†	
		c. Perf 12½ × 11	5·50	3·50	†		†	
		d. Scarlet	18·00	18·00	5·50	4·50	1·00	8
		da. Imperf between (pair)	†		†		50·00	50·00

For ½ a. claret, see No. 58.

1927 (1 Feb). *As W* **7** *but larger. P* 13½.

37	**9**	1 r. yellow	7·00	11·00

10 (4 pies) **11** (8 pies)

1930 (6 May). *Surch as T* **10** *and* **11**. *W* **7**. *P* 13½.

38	**6**	4 p. on ¼ a. grey-black (R.)	30·00	7·00
		a. Perf 11	—	£110
		b. Perf 12½	70·00	30·00
39		4 p. on ¼ a. purple (R.)	8	8
		a. Imperf between (pair)	£275	£275
		b. Surch double	†	—
		c. Perf 11	£300	£300
		d. Black surch	£300	£300
40	**8**	8 p. on ½ a. green (R.)	8	8
		a. Imperf between (horiz pair)	90·00	75·00
		b. Perf 11	90·00	75·00
		c. Perf 12½		

12 Symbols

13 The Char Minar

14 Bidar College

(Plates by De La Rue. Recess Stamps Office, Hyderabad)

1931 (12 Nov)–**47**. *T* **12** *to* **14** (*and similar types*). *W* **7**. *Wove paper. P* 13½.

41	**12**	4 p. black	12	8
		a. Laid paper (1947)	4·00	3·50
		b. Imperf (pair)	45·00	
42		8 p. green	12	8
		a. Imperf between (vert pair)	£550	£550
		b. Imperf (pair)	45·00	
		c. Laid paper (1947)	4·00	3·50
43	**13**	1 a. brown (*shades*)	15	8
44	–	2 a. violet (*shades*)	35	10
		a. Imperf (pair)	90·00	
45	–	4 a. ultramarine	70	12
		a. Imperf (pair)	£120	
46	–	8 a. orange	1·60	40
		a. Yellow-orange (1944)	38·00	25·00
47	**14**	12 a. scarlet	3·00	3·50
48	–	1 r. yellow	3·00	2·50

Designs (*as T* **14**): *Horiz*—2 a. High Court of Justice; 4 a. Osman Sagar Reservoir. *Vert*—8 a. Entrance to Ajanta Caves; 1 r. Victory Tower, Daulatabad.

Nos. 41a and 42c have a large sheet watermark "NIZAM's GOVERNMENT" and arms, but this does not appear on all stamps.

15 Unani General Hospital

16 Family Reunion

(Litho Indian Security Printing Press, Nasik)

1937 (13 Feb). *Various horiz designs as T* **15**, *inscr* "H.E.H. THE NIZAM'S SILVER JUBILEE". *P* 14.

49	4 p. slate and violet	15	15
50	8 p. slate and brown	15	15
51	1 a. slate and orange-yellow	20	20
52	2 a. slate and green	50	50

Designs:—8 p. Osmania General Hospital; 1 a. Osmania University; 2 a. Osmania Jubilee Hall.

(Des T. I. Archer. Typo)

1945 (6 Dec). *Victory. W* **7** *(very faint). Wove paper. P* 13½.

No.	Type	Description	Unused	Used
53	**16**	1 a. blue ..	10	10
		a. Imperf between (vert pair) ..	£475	
		b. Laid paper ..	25	30

No. 53b has a large sheet wmk reading "HYDERABAD GOVERNMENT", in circular frame, but parts of this do not appear on all stamps.

17 Town Hall

18 Power House, Hyderabad

(Des. T. I. Archer. Litho Government Press)

1947 (17 Feb). *Reformed Legislature. P* 13½.

No.	Type	Description	Unused	Used
54	**17**	1 a. black ..	15	15
		a. Imperf between (pair) ..	£650	£650

(Des T. I. Archer. Typo)

1947–49. *As T* **18** *(inscr* "H. E. H. THE NIZAM'S GOVT. POSTAGE"*). W* **7**. *P* 13½.

No.	Description	Unused	Used
55	1 a. 4 p. green ..	40	30
56	3 a. greenish blue ..	40	30
	a. Bluish green ..	50	40
57	6 a. sepia ..	3·00	2·75
	a. Red-brown (1949) ..	20·00	18·00
	ab. Imperf (pair) ..	50·00	

Designs:—3 a. Kaktyai Arch, Warangal Fort; 6 a. Golkunda Fort.

1947. *As* 1915 *issue but colour changed. P* 13½.

No.	Type	Description	Unused	Used
58	**8**	½ a. claret ..	50	50
		a. Imperf between (horizontal pair) ..	£275	£275

An Independence commemorative set of four, 4 p., 8 p., 1 a. and 2 a., was prepared in 1947, but not issued.

1948. *As T* **12** ("POSTAGE" *at foot). Recess. W* **7**. *P* 13½.

No.	Description	Unused	Used
59	6 p. claret ..	70	70

Following intervention by the forces of the Dominion of India during September 1948 the Hyderabad postal system was taken over by the Dominion authorities, operating as an agency of the India Post Office.

1949. *T* **12** ("POSTAGE" *at top). Litho. W* **7**. *P* 13½.

No.	Type	Description	Unused	Used
60	**12**	2 p. bistre-brown ..	1·00	70
		a. Imperf between (horizontal pair) ..	£475	£475
		b. Imperf (pair) ..	£475	£475

No. 60 was prepared by altering a plate of No. 41, each impression being amended individually.

OFFICIAL STAMPS

Official stamps became valid for postage within India from 1910.

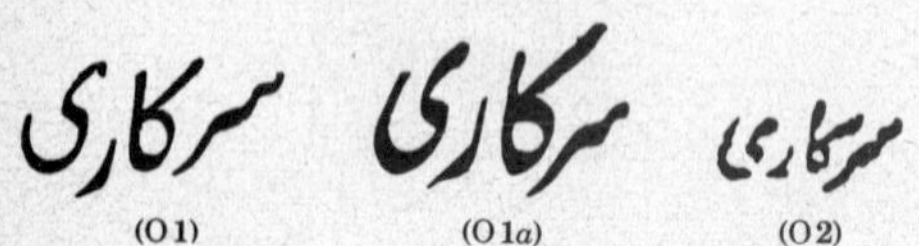

(O 1) (O 1*a*) (O 2)

1873. I. *Handstamped as Type* O 1. A. *In red.* B. *In black.*

No.	Type	Description	A		B	
O1	**1**	1 a. olive-green ..	—	12·00	—	—
O2	**2**	½ a. brown ..	—	26·00	—	22·00
O3		2 a. sage-green ..	—	45·00	—	35·00

Varieties of Type O 1 occur.

Imitations of these overprints on genuine stamps and on reprints are found horizontally or vertically in various shades of red, in magenta and in black.

II. *T* **3** *optd as Type* O **1**. A. *In red.* B. *In black.*
(*a*) *Rough perf* 11½.

No.	Description	A		B	
O 4	½ a. red-brown ..	—	—	—	—
O 5	1 a. purple-brown ..	—	—	£100	—
O 6	2 a. green ..	—	—	—	—
O 7	4 a. slate ..	—	—	—	—
O 8	8 a. deep brown ..	—	—	—	—
	(*b*) *Pin perf* 8–9				
O 8*a*	1 a. drab ..	†		5·50	—
	(*c*) *P* 12½				
O 9	½ a. red-brown ..	2·50	2·50	1·25	75
	a. Opt inverted ..	†		—	—
O11	1 a. purple-brown ..	4·00	3·00	—	1·50
O12	1 a. drab ..	2·50	—	75	75
	a. Opt inverted ..	†		—	—
O13	2 a. green (*to* deep) ..	3·50	3·50	1·25	1·25
	a. Opt inverted ..	†		—	—
O14	3 a. ochre-brown ..	—	—	3·50	—
O15	4 a. slate ..	8·00	5·00	2·50	2·50
O16	8 a. deep brown ..	12·00	—	8·00	6·50
	a. Imperf between (pair) ..	£250	—	†	
O17	12 a. blue ..	10·00	—	8·50	—

The use of Official Stamps (Sarkari) was discontinued in 1878, but was resumed in 1909, when the current stamps were overprinted from a new die.

1909–11. *Optd with Type* O **1***a*. (*a*) *On Type* **3**. *P* 12½.

No.	Description	Unused	Used
O18	½ a. orange-brown ..	—	2·50
	a. Opt inverted ..		
O19	1 a. black ..	5·00	8
O20	2 a. sage-green (No. 15*d*) ..	6·00	12
	a. Optd on No. 15*da* ..	—	10·00
O20*b*	3 a. ochre-brown ..	1·25	70
O20*c*	4 a. greenish grey ..	—	3·25
O20*d*	8 a. deep brown ..		
O20*e*	12 a. grey-green ..		

(*b*) *On Type* **6**. A. *Perf* 12½. B. *Perf* 11½, 12. C. *Perf* 11

No.	Description	A		B		C	
O21	½ a. orange ..	15·00	1·00	†		†	
	a. Vermilion ..	10·00	10	†		†	
	b. Opt inverted	55·00	55·00	†		†	
O22	½ a. green (W.) ..	3·00	8	3·50	12	—	—
	a. Pale green (W.) ..	3·00	8	3·50	12	—	—
	b. Opt inverted	†		40·00	28·00	†	
	c. Imperf between (pair)	50·00	50·00	†		†	
O23	1 a. carmine ..	8·00	10	10·00	25	—	4·00
	a. Opt double ..	45·00	—	†		†	
	b. Perf 12½ × 11	—	3·00	†		†	
O24	2 a. lilac ..	9·00	10	10·00	35	—	—
O25	3 a. brown-orange	20·00	7·50	25·00	10·00	—	10·00
	a. Opt inverted	—	55·00	†		†	
O26	4 a. olive-green (1911) ..	6·00	20	10·00	1·00	—	5·00
O27	8 a. purple (1911)	5·00	30	8·00	60	†	
O28	12 a. blue-green (1911) ..	5·00	30	6·00	40	—	—
	a. Perf 12 × 12½	†		—	—	†	
	b. Imperf between (horiz pair) ..	†		—	—	†	

The Wyon and Bradbury, Wilkinson stamps are distinguished above and below by the use of the letters (W.) and (B.W.) respectively.

1911–12. *T* **6** *optd with Type* O **2**. *Various perfs, also compound.*

A. *Perf* 12½. B. *Perf* 11½, 12

No.	Description	A		B	
O29	¼ a. grey (W.) ..	6·00	20	14·00	10
O30	¼ a. grey-black (B.W.) ..	40	8	1·00	8
	a. Opt inverted ..	—	—	—	—
	b. Pair, one without opt ..	—	—	—	—
O32	½ a. pale green (W.) ..	4·50	10	—	10
O33	½ a. deep green (B.W.) ..	40	8	—	12
	a. Opt inverted ..	25·00	14·00	†	
	c. Perf 11 × 12½ ..	25·00	25·00	†	
O34	1 a. carmine ..	50	10	1·50	12
	a. Opt inverted ..	—	12·00	†	
	b. Perf 11 × 12½ ..	25·00	25·00	†	
O35	2 a. lilac ..	75	10	2·50	20
O36	3 a. brown-orange ..	2·00	20	5·50	40
	a. Opt inverted ..	—	40·00	†	
O37	4 a. olive-green ..	2·00	20	1·50	20
	a. Opt inverted ..	50·00	40·00	—	—
O38	8 a. purple ..	—	—	—	—
O39	12 a. blue-green ..	—	—	—	—

C. *Perf* 11. D. *Perf* 13½

No.	Description	C		D	
O29	¼ a. grey (W.) ..	15·00	10·00	—	—
O30	¼ a. grey-black (B.W.) ..	30	8	30	8
O31	¼ a. lilac (*shades*) (B.W.) ..	—	—	20	8
	a. Imperf horiz (vert pair) ..	†		50·00	40·00
O32	½ a. pale green (W.) ..	†		—	—
O33	½ a. deep green (B.W.) ..	35	8	40	8
	a. Opt inverted ..	25·00	15·00	†	
	b. Imperf between (pair) ..	38·00	38·00	38·00	35·00
O34	1 a. carmine ..	50	12	—	—
O35	2 a. lilac ..	55	12	1·50	10
	a. Imperf between (horiz pair)	†		50·00	50·00
	b. Rose-lilac ..	†		2·00	12
O36	3 a. brown-orange ..	3·00	20	6·50	15
	a. Opt inverted ..	45·00	45·00	45·00	45·00
O37	4 a. olive-green ..	1·50	12	1·00	10
	a. Opt inverted ..	†		45·00	40·00
O38	8 a. purple ..	15·00	5·00	1·75	20
O39	12 a. blue-green ..	—	—	2·50	30

1917–20. *T* **8** *optd with Type* O **2**. *Various perfs as above, also compound.*

No.	Description	A		C		D	
O40	½ a. green ..	—	2·00	1·25	15	45	8
	a. Opt inverted	†		—	13·00	—	12·00
	b. Pair, one without opt ..	†		—	—	†	
	c. Imperf between (pair) ..	†		†		45·00	38·00
	d. Perf 11 × 13½ or 13½ × 11 ..	†		†		25·00	25·00
	e. Emerald-green	†		†		—	40
O41	1 a. carmine ..	—	1·50	1·75	12	55	8
	a. Opt inverted ..	†		—	9·00	†	
	b. Opt double ..	†		†		40·00	40·00
	c. Imperf between (vert pair) ..	†		†		48·00	48·00
	d. Scarlet (1920)	†		†		70	8
	da. Stamp doubly printed ..	†		†		42·00	42·00
	db. Imperf between (pair) ..	†		†		45·00	45·00

1930–34. *T* **6** *and* **8** *optd as Type* O **2** *and surch at top of stamp, in red, as T* **10** *or* **11**.

No.	Description	Unused	Used
O42	4 p. on ¼ a. grey-black (O30) (1934) ..	48·00	15·00
	a. Red surch superimposed on Type O **2** ..		
	b. Type O **2** superimposed on red surch ..		
O43	4 p. on ¼ a. lilac (O31) ..	40	10
	a. Red surch superimposed on Type O **2** ..	13·00	2·00
	ab. Type O **2** superimposed on red surch ..	15·00	4·00
	b. Imperf between (horiz pair) ..	70·00	55·00
	c. Imperf horiz (vert pair) ..	70·00	55·00
	d. Imperf horiz (vert strip of 3) ..		
	e. Red surch double ..	—	35·00
	f. Black opt double ..		
O44	8 p. on ½ a. green (O40) ..	35	10
	a. Red surch superimposed on Type O **2** ..	11·00	25
	b. Type O **2** superimposed on red surch ..	15·00	1·25
	c. Imperf between (pair) ..	70·00	55·00
	d. Red surch double ..	40·00	35·00
	e. Stamp doubly printed ..		
O45	8 p. on ½ a. green (O33) ..	£110	55·00

Normal copies of Nos. O42/4 have the red surcharge above the official overprint, Type O **2**, but on No. O45 the red surcharge is always superimposed on the black overprint.

1934–44. *Nos.* 41/8 *optd with Type* O **2**.

No.	Description	Unused	Used
O46	4 p. black ..	20	8
	a. Imperf (pair) ..	48·00	
	b. Imperf between (pair) ..	£500	£500
O47	8 p. green ..	15	8
	a. Opt inverted ..	£150	£150
	b. Imperf between (pair) ..	£500	£500
	c. Opt double ..	£150	£120
O48	1 a. brown ..	20	8
	a. Imperf between (pair) ..	£400	£400
O49	2 a. violet ..	40	8
	a. Imperf between (pair) ..	£550	£550
O50	4 a. ultramarine ..	90	12
O51	8 a. orange (1935) ..	3·00	50
	a. Yellow-orange (1944) ..	—	35·00
O52	12 a. scarlet (1935) ..	3·50	1·25
O53	1 r. yellow (1935) ..	4·00	2·00

1947. *No.* 58 *optd with Type* O **2**.

No.	Type	Description	Unused	Used
O54	**8**	½ a. claret ..	1·60	1·25
		a. Pair, one without opt ..		

1949. *No.* 60 *optd with Type* O **2**.

No.	Type	Description	Unused	Used
O55	**12**	2 p. bistre-brown ..	1·50	1·25

1950. *No.* 59 *optd with Type* O **2**.

No.	Description	Unused	Used
O56	6 p. claret ..	2·00	1·75

IDAR

PRICES FOR STAMPS ON COVER
Nos. 1/6 *from* × 3

The Idar postal service carried Official mail only.

1 Maharaja Shri Himatsinhji 2

The Idar postal service carried Official mail only.

1 Maharaja Shri Himatsinhji 2

(Typo M. N. Kothari & Sons, Bombay)

1939 (21 Feb). *P* 11. (*a*) *White panels.*

No.	Type	Description	Unused	Used
1	1	½ a. emerald ..	3·25	12·00
		aa. Imperf between (pair) ..	£140	
		a. Yellow-green ..	3·75	12·00
		b. As a. Thick paper ..	6·00	
		(*b*) *Coloured panels*		
2	1	½ a. green (*shades*) ..	4·00	14·00

In No. 2 the whole design is composed of half-tone dots. In No. 1 the dots are confined to the oval portrait.

(Typo P. G. Mehta & Co., Himmatnagar)

1944 (21 Oct). *P* 12.

No.	Type	Description	Unused	Used
3	2	½ a. blue-green ..	40	10·00
		a. Imperf between (vert pair) ..	60·00	
		b. Yellow-green ..	75	12·00
		ba. Imperf between (vert pair) ..	12·00	
4		1 a. violet ..	30	10·00
		a. Imperf (pair) ..	£140	
		b. Imperf vert (horiz pair) ..	£150	
5		2 a. blue ..	50	12·00
		a. Imperf between (vert or horiz pair)	45·00	
6		4 a. vermilion ..	2·40	15·00
		a. Doubly printed ..	£110	

Nos. 1 to 6 are from booklet panes of 4 stamps, producing single stamps with one or two adjacent sides imperf.

The 4 a. violet is believed to be a colour trial.

INDORE

(HOLKAR STATE)

PRICES FOR STAMPS ON COVER
Nos. 1/15 *from* × 20
Nos. 16/43 *from* × 6
Nos. S1/7 *from* × 40

1 Maharaja Tukoji Rao II Holkar XI

(Litho Waterlow & Sons)

1886. *P* 15. (*a*) *Thick white paper.*

No.	Type	Description	Unused	Used
1	1	½ a. bright mauve ..	3·50	3·50
		(*b*) *Thin white or yellowish paper*		
2	1	½ a. pale mauve ..	1·10	1·25
		a. Dull mauve ..	1·25	1·50

2 Type I

2*a* Type II

TYPES 2 AND 2a. In addition to the difference in the topline character (marked by arrow), the two Types can be distinguished by the difference in the angles of the 6-pointed stars and the appearance of the lettering. In Type I the top characters are smaller and more cramped than the bottom; in Type II both are in the same style and similarly spaced.

1889. *No gum. Imperf.*
3 2 ½ a. black/*pink* 3·50 3·50
4 2*a* ½ a. black/*pink* 1·40 1·40
a. *Tête-bêche* (pair) 50·00

3 Maharaja Shivaji Rao Holkar XII — 4 Maharaja Tukoji Rao III Holkar XIII — 5

(Recess Waterlow)

1889–92. *Medium wove paper. P 14 to 15.*
5 3 ¼ a. orange (9.2.92) 15 12
a. Imperf between (pair) £125 £125
b. Very thick wove paper 50 40
c. *Yellow* 15 12
6 ½ a. dull violet 85 60
a. *Brown-purple* 15 12
b. Imperf between (pair) £110 £110
7 1 a. green (7.2.92) 65 50
a. Imperf between (pair) £125 £125
b. Very thick wove paper
8 2 a. vermilion (7.2.92) 1·25 1·25
a. Very thick wove paper 3·50 3·50

(Recess Perkins, Bacon & Co)

1904–20. *P 13½, 14.*
9 4 ¼ a. orange 15 10
10 5 ½ a. lake (1909) 1·50 10
a. *Brown-lake (shades)* 3·25 35
b. Imperf (pair) 16·00
11 1 a. green 2·40 12
a. Imperf (pair) £125
b. Perf 12½ (1920) † 27·00
12 2 a. brown 4·25 35
a. Imperf (pair) 75·00
13 3 a. violet 5·00 80
14 4 a. ultramarine 6·00 70
a. *Dull blue* 6·50 60

पाव आना.

(6)

7 Maharaja Yeshwant Rao II Holkar XIV

1905. *No. 6a surch* "QUARTER ANNA" *in Devanagari, as T* **6**.
15 3 ¼ a. on ½ a. brown-purple 1·50 3·00

NOTE. From 1 March 1908 the use of Indore stamps was restricted to official mail. Nos. S1/7 were withdrawn and replaced by Nos. 9/14.

(Recess Perkins, Bacon & Co)

1927–37. *P 13 to 14.*
16 7 ¼ a. orange (*a*) (*d*) (*e*) 25 8
17 ½ a. claret (*a*) (*d*) (*e*) 25 8
18 1 a. green (*a*) (*d*) (*e*) 35 8
19 1¼ a. green (*c*) (*d*) (1933) 40 15
20 2 a. sepia (*a*) 2·40 80
21 2 a. bluish green (*d*) (1936) 1·00 60
a. Imperf (pair) 25·00 40·00
22 3 a. deep violet (*a*) 2·25 3·25
23 3 a. Prussian blue (*d*) (1935?) 18·00
a. Imperf (pair) 30·00 50·00
24 3½ a. violet (*d*) (1934) 3·50 6·00
a. Imperf (pair) 40·00 50·00
25 4 a. ultramarine (*a*) 3·25 2·00
26 4 a. yellow-brown (*d*) (1937) 4·50 1·50
a. Imperf (pair) 30·00 50·00
27 8 a. slate-grey (*a*) 5·50 6·00
28 8 a. red-orange (*d*) (1937) 6·50 6·50
29 12 a. carmine (*d*) (1934) 11·00 12·00
30 – 1 r. black and light blue (*b*) 13·00 14·00
31 – 2 r. black and carmine (*b*) 23·00 25·00
32 – 5 r. black & brown-orange (*b*) 26·00 29·00

Nos. 30/32 are as Type **7**, but larger, size 23 × 28 mm.

Perforations. Five different perforating heads were used for this issue: (*a*) comb 13·6; (*b*) comb 13·9; (*c*) line 13·2; (*d*) line 13·8; (*e*) line 14·2. Values on which each perforation occur are indicated above.

QUARTER ANNA

(8)

9

1940 (1 Aug). *Surch in words as T* **8**.
33 7 ¼ a. on 5 r. black and brown-orange (*b*) 75 25
a. Surch double (Blk. + G.) — £125
34 ½ a. on 2 r. black and carmine (*b*) 1·25 25
35 1 a. on 1¼ a. green (*c*) (*d*) (*e*) 1·25 35
b. Surch inverted (*d*) 80·00

(Typo "*Times of India*" Press, Bombay)

1941–46. *P* 11.
36 9 ¼ a. red-orange 50 8
37 ½ a. claret 75 8
38 1 a. green 60 10
39 1¼ a. yellow-green 1·50 30
a. Imperf (pair) £140
40 2 a. turquoise-blue 7·50 1·50
41 4 a. yellow-brown (1946) 11·00 9·00

Larger size (23 × 28 mm)
42 2 r. black and carmine (1943) 13·00 25·00
43 5 r. black and yellow-orange (1943) 16·00 30·00

OFFICIAL STAMPS

SERVICE (S 1) — **SERVICE** (S 2)

1904–6. (*a*) *Optd with Type* S 1.
S1 4 ¼ a. orange (1906) 10 10
S2 5 ½ a. lake 8 8
a. Opt inverted 14·00
b. Opt double 14·00
c. Imperf (pair) 25·00
d. *Brown-lake* 8 8
da. Opt inverted 14·00
S3 1 a. green 10 10
S4 2 a. brown (1905) 30 20
a. Pair, one without opt £400
S5 3 a. violet (1906) 1·75 1·10
a. Imperf (pair) £100
S6 4 a. ultramarine (1905) 2·00 1·40

(*b*) *Optd with Type* S 2
S7 5 ½ a. lake 8 30
a. Opt double 55·00

Types S 1 and S 2 differ chiefly in the shape of the letter "R".

JAIPUR

PRICES FOR STAMPS ON COVER	
Nos. 1, 3/5	*from* × 10
No. 2	*from* × 2
Nos. 6/70	*from* × 4
Nos. 71/80	*from* × 6
Nos. O1/34	*from* × 8

1 Chariot of the Sun God, Surya 2

½ a. 36 varieties (2 plates). Plate I stamps 2½ mm apart horizontally; Plate II stamps 4½ mm apart.
1 a. and 2 a. 12 varieties.

1904.
(*a*) *Value at sides in small letters and characters. Roughly perf* 14
1 1 ½ a. pale blue (Plate I) 25·00 35·00
a. *Ultramarine* 25·00 35·00
b. Imperf, *ultramarine*
2 ½ a. grey-blue (Plate II) — £200
a. Imperf £300 £350
3 1 a. dull red 2·00 3·00
a. *Scarlet* 2·50
4 2 a. pale green 2·50 4·50
a. *Emerald-green* 3·50

(*b*) *Value in larger letters and characters. 24 varieties on one plate. Roughly perf* 14
5 2 ½ a. pale blue 2·75 3·00
a. *Deep blue* 3·00 3·25
b. *Ultramarine* 3·00 3·25
c. Imperf £300

3 Chariot of the Sun God, Surya

(Recess Perkins, Bacon & Co)

1904. *P* 12.
6 3 ½ a. blue 3·00 2·50
a. Perf 12½ 6·50 4·50
b. Perf comp of 12 and 12½ 14·00 14·00
7 1 a. brown-red 27·00 27·00
a. Perf 12½ 48·00 48·00
b. Perf comp of 12 and 12½ £120 £120
c. *Carmine* 2·25 1·75
ca. Imperf between (vert pair) £160 £190
cb. Perf comp of 12 and 12½ 10·00 10·00
8 2 a. deep green 6·50 6·50
a. Perf 12½ 30·00 25·00
b. Perf comp of 12 and 12½ 25·00 25·00

1905–8. *P* 13½.
9 3 ¼ a. olive-yellow (1906) 15 15
10 ½ a. blue 30 30
a. *Indigo* 40 40
11 1 a. brown-red (1906) 4·25 4·25
a. *Bright red* (1908) 45 40
12 2 a. deep green 1·25 1·00
13 4 a. chestnut 2·50 2·50
14 8 a. bright violet 3·50 3·50
15 1 r. yellow 6·50 7·00
a. *Orange-yellow* 8·00 8·50
b. *Yellow-ochre* 9·00 10·00

4 Chariot of the Sun God, Surya

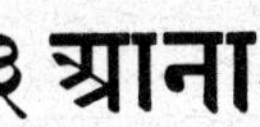

(5)

(Typo Jail Press, Jaipur)

1911. *Thin wove paper. No gum. Imperf. Six varieties of each value.*
16 4 ¼ a. green 1·25 1·60
a. Printed double
ab. Ditto, one inverted
b. "¼" inverted at right upper corner 5·00
c. No stop after "STATE" 5·00
17 ¼ a. greenish yellow 30 40
a. "¼" inverted in right upper corner 1·50
b. No stop after "STATE" 1·50
18 ½ a. ultramarine 30 40
a. Printed double 2·00
b. No stop after "STATE" 75
c. Large "J" in "JAIPUR" 75
d. "½" for "½" at lower left 1·50
19 ½ a. grey-blue 50 60
a. No stop after "STATE" 1·25
b. Large "J" in "JAIPUR" 1·25
c. "½" for "½" at lower left 2·25
20 1 a. rose-red 30 40
a. Printed double 50·00
21 2 a. greyish green 4·25 5·50
a. *Deep green* 4·25 5·50
ab. Printed double 50·00

One sheet of the ¼ a. is known in blue.

(Typo Jail Press, Jaipur)

1913–18. *Paper-maker's wmk* "DORLING & CO. LONDON" *in sheet. P* 11.
22 3 ¼ a. pale olive-yellow 12 15
a. Imperf between (horiz pair) 85·00 85·00
23 ¼ a. olive 12 15
a. Imperf between (vert or horiz pair) 85·00 85·00
b. Doubly printed
24 ¼ a. bistre 12 20
25 ½ a. pale ultramarine 12 15
a. Imperf between (pair) 90·00 90·00
b. *Blue* 12 15
26 1 a. carmine (1918) 30 35
a. Imperf between (vert pair) 90·00 90·00
27 1 a. rose-red 1·60 2·25
28 1 a. scarlet 25 30
a. Imperf between (vert pair) 90·00 90·00
29 2 a. green (1918) 75 90
30 4 a. chocolate 90 1·10
31 4 a. pale brown 1·00 1·25
a. Imperf between (horiz pair) £125

1926. *Surch with T* **5**.
32 3 3 a. on 8 a. bright violet (R.) 90 1·10
a. Surch inverted £140 £120
33 3 a. on 1 r. yellow (R.) 90 1·25
a. Surch inverted £140 £120
b. *Orange-yellow*
c. *Yellow-ochre* 4·50

1928. *As* 1913–18 *issue. Wmk* "DORLING & CO. LONDON" (½ *a.*, 1 *a.*, 2 *a.*) *or* "OVERLAND BANK" (*all values*) *in sheet. No gum. P* 12.
34 3 ½ a. ultramarine 6·00 4·50
a. Perf comp of 12 and 11 8·00 5·50
35 1 a. rose-red 12·00 9·00
36 1 a. scarlet 12·00 9·00
a. Perf comp of 12 and 11 15·00 11·00
37 2 a. green 35·00 20·00
38 8 a. bright violet £160
39 1 r. orange-vermilion £100

The "OVERLAND BANK" paper has a coarser texture. The ½ a. and 2 a. values also exist on this paper perforated 11, but such stamps are difficult to distinguish from examples of Nos. 25 and 29.

6 Chariot of the Sun God, Surya

7 Maharaja Sir Man Singh Bahadur

8 Sowar in Armour

(Des T. I. Archer. Litho Indian Security Printing Press, Nasik)

1931 (14 Mar). *Investiture of Maharaja. T* **6/8** *and similar designs. No wmk. P* 14.

No.	Type	Description	Unused	Used
40		¼ a. black and deep lake	20	20
41		½ a. black and violet	20	12
42		1 a. black and blue	2·25	1·50
43		2 a. black and buff	2·25	1·75
44		2½ a. black and carmine	12·00	15·00
45		3 a. black and myrtle	12·00	15·00
46		4 a. black and olive-green	9·00	12·00
47		6 a. black and deep blue	9·00	12·00
48		8 a. black and chocolate	11·00	15·00
49		1 r. black and pale olive	12·00	18·00
50		2 r. black and yellow-green	15·00	24·00
51		5 r. black and purple	20·00	30·00

Designs: *Vert*—1 a. Elephant and state banner; 2½ a. Common Peafowl; 8 a. Sireh-Deorhi Gate. *Horiz*—3 a. Bullock carriage; 4 a. Elephant carriage; 6 a. Albert Museum; 1 r. Chandra Mahal; 2 r. Amber Palace; 5 r. Maharajas Jai Singh and Sir Man Singh.

Eighteen of these sets were issued for presentation purposes with a special overprint "INVESTITURE—MARCH 14, 1931" in red.

10 Maharaja Sir Man Singh Bahadur

One
Rupee

(11)

(Des T. I. Archer. Litho Indian Security Printing Press, Nasik)

1932–46. *P* 14. (*a*) *Inscr* "POSTAGE & REVENUE".

No.	Type	Description	Unused	Used
52	**10**	1 a. black and blue	25	12
53		2 a. black and buff	30	20
54		4 a. black and grey-green	60	60
55		8 a. black and chocolate	1·00	1·25
56		1 r. black and yellow-bistre	10·00	14·00
57		2 r. black and yellow-green	35·00	50·00
		(*b*) *Inscr* "POSTAGE"		
58	**7**	¼ a. black and brown-lake	15	8
59		¾ a. black and brown-red (1943?)	25	12
60		1 a. black and blue (1943?)	25	12
61		2 a. black and buff (1943?)	30	20
62		2½ a. black and carmine	35	30
63		3 a. black and green	40	25
64		4 a. black and grey-green (1943?)	70	1·00
65		6 a. black and deep blue	1·40	2·25
		a. Black and pale blue (1946)	2·50	3·75
66		8 a. black and chocolate (1946)	2·00	3·00
67		1 r. black and yellow-bistre (1946)	8·00	12·00

1936. *Nos.* 57 *and* 51 *surch with T* **11**.

No.	Type	Description	Unused	Used
68	**10**	1 r. on 2 r. black and yellow-green (R.)	2·50	3·75
69	–	1 r. on 5 r. black and purple	2·25	3·50

पाव आना

(12)

13 Maharaja and Amber Palace

1938 (Dec). *No.* 41 *surch* "QUARTER ANNA" *in Devanagari, T* **12**.

No.	Type	Description	Unused	Used
70	**7**	¼ a. on ½ a. black and violet (R.)	2·00	2·25

(Recess D.L.R.)

1947 (Dec)–**48**. *Silver Jubilee of Maharaja's Accession to Throne. Various designs as T* **13**. *P* 13½ × 14.

No.	Type	Description	Unused	Used
71		¼ a. red-brown and green (5.48)	12	20
72		½ a. green and violet	12	20
73		¾ a. black and lake (5.48)	12	20
74		1 a. red-brown and ultramarine	30	40
75		2 a. violet and scarlet	20	35
76		3 a. green and black (5.48)	30	50
77		4 a. ultramarine and brown	45	75
78		8 a. vermilion and brown	75	1·25
79		1 r. purple and green (5.48)	1·50	2·25

Designs:—¼ a. Palace Gate; ¾ a. Map of Jaipur; 1 a. Observatory; 2 a. Wind Palace; 3 a. Coat of Arms; 4 a. Amber Fort Gate; 8 a. Chariot of the Sun; 1 r. Maharaja's portrait between State flags.

3 PIES

(14)

1947 (Dec). *No.* 41 *surch with T* **14**.

No.	Type	Description	Unused	Used
80	**7**	3 p. on ½ a. black and violet (R.)	5·00	5·50
		a. "PIE" for "PIES"	28·00	28·00
		b. Bars at left vertical	32·00	32·00
		c. Surch inverted	30·00	28·00
		d. Surch inverted and "PIE" for "PIES"	£100	85·00
		e. Surch double, one inverted	42·00	40·00
		f. As variety e, but inverted surch showing "PIE" for "PIES"	£110	£100

OFFICIAL STAMPS

SERVICE (O 1) SERVICE (O 2)

1928 (13 Nov)–**31**. *T* **3** *typographed. No gum (except for Nos.* O6/*a*). *P* 11, 12, *or compound. Wmk* "DORLING & CO. LONDON" (4 *a.*) *or* "OVERLAND BANK" (*others*). (*a*) *Optd with Type* O **1**.

No.	Type	Description	Unused	Used
O 1		¼ a. olive	25	35
		a. Bistre	15	20
O 2		½ a. pale ultramarine (Blk.)	15	10
		a. Imperf between (horiz pair)	60·00	60·00
		b. Opt inverted	—	85·00
		c. Opt double (R. and Blk.)	—	85·00
O 3		½ a. pale ultramarine (R.) (13.10.30)	15	15
		a. Imperf between (horiz pair)		
O 3c		1 a. rose-red	25	20
		d. Imperf between (horiz pair)	70·00	70·00
O 4		1 a. scarlet	75	50
		a. Opt inverted	70·00	70·00
O 5		2 a. green	40	40
		a. Imperf between (vert pair)	70·00	70·00
		b. Imperf between (horiz pair)	80·00	80·00
O 6		4 a. pale brown (with gum)	2·00	2·25
		a. Chocolate (with gum)	2·00	2·25
O 7		8 a. bright violet (R.) (13.10.30)	20·00	25·00
O 8		1 r. orange-vermilion	38·00	48·00
		(*b*) *Optd with Type* O **2**		
O 9		½ a. ultramarine (Blk.) (11.2.31)	60·00	15
		a. Imperf between (horiz pair)	£225	£125
O10		½ a. ultramarine (R.) (15.10.30)	85·00	15
		a. Imperf between (vert pair)	£275	£125
O11		8 a. bright violet (11.2.31)	£150	£140
O12		1 r. orange-vermilion (11.2.31)	£180	£170

SERVICE (O 3) आध आना (O 4)

1931–7. *Nos.* 41/3 *and* 46 *optd at Nasik with Type* O **3**, *in red.*

No.	Type	Description	Unused	Used
O13	**7**	½ a. black and violet	20	8
O14	**8**	1 a. black and blue	£150	1·50
O15		2 a. black and buff (1936)	1·75	1·25
O16	**6**	4 a. black and olive-green (1937)	2·25	1·50

1932. *No.* O5 *surch with Type* O **4**.

No.	Type	Description	Unused	Used
O17	**3**	½ a. on 2 a. green	90·00	30

1932–7. *Nos.* 52/6 *optd at Nasik with Type* O **3**, *in red.*

No.	Type	Description	Unused	Used
O18	**10**	1 a. black and blue	30	10
O19		2 a. black and buff	50	12
O20		4 a. black and grey-green (1937)	4·50	2·75
O21		8 a. black and chocolate	1·25	1·00
O22		1 r. black and yellow-bistre	5·50	4·25

1932–46. *Stamps of* 1932–46, *inscr* "POSTAGE".

No.	Type	Description	Unused	Used
		(*a*) *Optd at Nasik with Type* O **3**, *in red*		
O23	**7**	¼ a. black and brown-lake (1936)	25	8
O24		¾ a. black and brown-red (1944)	35	10
O25		1 a. black and blue (1941?)	75	30
O26		2 a. black and buff	65	40
O27		2½ a. black and carmine (1946)	1·10	3·00
O28		4 a. black and grey-green (1946)	1·10	60
O29		8 a. black and chocolate (1946)	1·75	1·40
O30		1 r. black and yellow-bistre (date?)	£250	
		(*b*) *Optd locally as Type* O **2** (16 *mm long*), *in black*		
O31	**7**	¼ a. black and red-brown (1936)	45·00	40·00

9 PIES

(O 5)

1947. *No.* O25 *surch with Type* O **5**, *in red.*

No.	Type	Description	Unused	Used
O32	**7**	9 p. on 1 a. black and blue	20	15

1947 (Dec). *No.* O14 *surch as T* **14**, *but* "3 PIES" *placed higher.*

No.	Type	Description	Unused	Used
O33	**7**	3 p. on ½ a. black and violet (R.)	3·25	3·25
		a. Surch double, one inverted	38·00	38·00
		b. "PIE" for "PIES"	£140	£140
		c. Surch inverted	£600	£600

1949. *No.* O14 *surch* "THREE-QUARTER ANNA" *in Devanagari, as T* **12**, *but with two bars on each side.*

No.	Type	Description	Unused	Used
O34	**7**	¾ a. on ½ a. black and violet (R.)	3·50	3·25
		a. Surch double	£550	£550

There are three different types of surcharge in the setting of 30, which vary in one or other of the Devanagari characters.

On 30 March 1949 Jaipur became part of the Rajasthan Union.

JAMMU AND KASHMIR

PRICES FOR STAMPS ON COVER	
Nos. 1/49	*from* × 4
No. 50	*from* × 2
Nos. 52/88	*from* × 3
Nos. 90/101	*from* × 10
Nos. 101*b*/23	*from* × 5
Nos. 124/36	*from* × 10
Nos. 138/9	*from* × 100
Nos. 140/61*a*	*from* × 15
Nos. 162/8	*from* × 5
Nos. O1/18	*from* × 30

ILLUSTRATIONS. Designs of Jammu and Kashmir are illustrated actual size.

1 (½ a.)

2 (1 a.)

3 (4 a.)

Characters denoting the value (on the circular stamps only) are approximately as shown in the central circles of the stamps illustrated above.

These characters were taken from Punjabi merchants' notation and were not familiar to most of the inhabitants of the state. Type **1** was certainly the ½ anna value, but there has long been controversy over the correct face values of Types **2** and **3**.

The study of surviving material suggests that, to some extent, this confusion involved contemporary post office officials. Although covers posted at Jammu, where the stamps were in use for twelve years, show Type **2** used as the 1 a. value and Type **3** as the 4 a., those originating from Srinagar (Kashmir) during 1866–68 show both Types **2** and **3** used as 1 a. stamps.

In the following listing we have followed contemporary usage at Jammu and this reflects the prevailing opinion amongst modern authorities.

GUM. The stamps of Jammu and Kashmir were issued without gum.

A. *Handstamped in watercolours*

1866 (23 Mar)–**67**. *Native paper, thick to thin, usually having the appearance of laid paper and tinted grey or brown. For Jammu and Kashmir.*

No.	Type	Description	Cut □ Unused	Cut □ Used	Cut O Unused	Cut O Used
1	**1**	½ a. grey-black	65·00	38·00	12·00	4·00
2	**2**	1 a. grey-black	£170	—	20·00	—
3	**3**	4 a. grey-black	£120	—	16·00	20·00
4	**2**	1 a. royal blue	£350	£200	—	15·00
4*a*	**1**	½ a. ultramarine	—	—		†
5	**2**	1 a. ultramarine	£120	38·00	—	7·00
6	**3**	4 a. ultramarine	£275	£110	42·00	20·00
7		4 a. indigo (1867)	£1200	£350	—	£120

1869–72. *Reissued for use in Jammu only.*

No.	Type	Description	Cut □ Unused	Cut □ Used	Cut O Unused	Cut O Used
8	**1**	½ a. red	25·00	—	4·50	—
9	**2**	1 a. red	42·00	—	7·50	—
10	**3**	4 a. red	12·00	20·00	2·50	—
11	**1**	½ a. orange-red	55·00	—	10·00	—
12	**2**	1 a. orange-red	55·00	—	10·00	—
13	**3**	4 a. orange-red	17·00	—	5·50	—
13*a*		4 a. carmine-red				
13*b*		4 a. orange (1872)				

1869–76. *Special Printings.*

No.	Type	Description	Cut □ Unused	Cut □ Used	Cut O Unused	Cut O Used
14	**1**	½ a. deep black	6·50	—	1·00	—
15	**2**	1 a. deep black	70·00	—	9·00	—
16	**3**	4 a. deep black	55·00	—	8·00	—
17	**1**	½ a. bright blue	35·00	—	3·00	—
18	**2**	1 a. bright blue	30·00	—	2·50	—
19	**3**	4 a. bright blue	35·00	—	3·00	—
20	**1**	½ a. emerald-green	45·00	—	2·50	—
21	**2**	1 a. emerald-green	50·00	—	4·00	—
22	**3**	4 a. emerald-green	50·00	—	4·00	—
23*a*	**1**	½ a. yellow	£200	—	12·00	—
24	**2**	1 a. yellow	£250	—	12·00	—
25	**3**	4 a. yellow	£250	—	12·00	—
25*a*		4 a. deep blue-black (1876)	£300	£130	—	—

These special printings were available for use, but little used.

B. *Handstamped in oil colours. Heavy blurred prints*

1877–78. (*a*). *Native paper.*

No.	Type	Description	Cut □ Unused	Cut □ Used	Cut O Unused	Cut O Used
26	**1**	½ a. red	8·00	11·00	2·25	3·00
27	**2**	1 a. red	8·50	—	2·25	—
28	**3**	4 a. red	£100	£325	15·00	—
29	**1**	½ a. black	7·50	16·00	2·10	3·00
32		½ a. slate-blue	35·00	—	5·25	—
34	**2**	1 a. slate-blue	7·50	—	1·25	—
35	**1**	½ a. sage-green	£100	—	10·00	—
36	**2**	1 a. sage-green	£110	—	10·00	—
37	**3**	4 a. sage-green	£110	—	10·00	—
		(*b*) *European laid paper, medium to thick*				
38	**1**	½ a. red	—	£150	—	40·00
39	**3**	4 a. red	£200	—	8·00	—

41	**1**	½ a. black	7·00	15·00	1·00	3·00
44		½ a. slate-blue	7·00	—	1·00	—
45	**2**	1 a. slate-blue	16·00	—	2·25	—
46	**3**	4 a. slate-blue	£200	—	—	—
47		4 a. sage-green	£700	—	£325	—
48	**1**	½ a. yellow	70·00	—	10·00	—

(c) *Thick yellowish wove paper*

49	**1**	½ a. red (1878)	—	£300	—	£130

Forgeries exist of the ½ a. and 1 a. in types which were at one time supposed to be authentic.

Reprints and imitations (of which some of each were found in the official remainder stock) exist in a great variety of fancy colours, both on native paper, usually thinner and smoother than that of the originals, and on various thin European *wove* papers, on which the originals were never printed.

The imitations, which do not agree in type with the above illustrations, are also to be found on *laid* paper.

All the reprints, etc. are in oil colours or printer's ink. The originals in oil colour are usually blurred, particularly when on native paper. The reprints, etc. are usually clear.

(3*a*)

1877. *Provisional. Seal obliterator of Jammu handstamped in red watercolour on pieces of native paper, and used as a ½ anna stamp.*

50	**3*a***	(½ a.) rose-red	—	£250

FOR USE IN JAMMU

½ a. ½ a.

1 a. **4** ½ a.

T **4** to **11** have a star at the top of the oval band; the characters denoting the value are in the upper part of the inner oval. All are dated 1923, corresponding with A.D. 1866.

T **4**. *Printed in blocks of four, three varieties of ½ anna and one of 1 anna.*

1867. *In watercolour on native paper.*

52	½ a. grey-black	£100	45·00
53	1 a. grey-black	£650	£250
54	½ a. indigo	45·00	35·00
55	1 a. indigo	60·00	45·00
56	½ a. deep ultramarine	45·00	40·00
57	1 a. deep ultramarine	75·00	50·00
58	½ a. deep violet-blue	45·00	35·00
59	1 a. deep violet-blue	£110	70·00

1868–77. *In watercolour on native paper.*

60	½ a. red (*shades*)	3·00	3·00
61	1 a. red (*shades*)	5·00	5·00
62	½ a. orange-red	75·00	15·00
63	1 a. orange-red	65·00	15·00
64	½ a. orange	65·00	60·00
65	1 a. orange	£200	£150

1874–6. *Special printings; in watercolour on native paper.*

66	½ a. bright blue	£120	60·00
67	1 a. bright blue	60·00	65·00
68	½ a. emerald-green	£450	£350
69	1 a. emerald-green	£600	£400
69*a*	½ a. jet-black	65·00	85·00
69*b*	1 a. jet-black	£400	£350

1877. *In oil colour.* (*a*) *Native paper.*

70	½ a. red	8·00	5·00
71	1 a. red	17·00	13·00
72	½ a. brown-red	—	28·00
73	1 a. brown-red	—	80·00
74	½ a. black	—	£175
75	1 a. black	—	£300
76	½ a. deep blue-black	—	£450
77	1 a. deep blue-black	—	£2500

(*b*) *Laid paper (medium or thick)*

78	½ a. red	—	£200

(*c*) *Thick wove paper*

79	½ a. red	—	£175
80	1 a. red		

(*d*) *Thin laid, bâtonné paper*

84	½ a. red	—	£700
85	1 a. red	—	£2750

The circular and rectangular stamps listed under the heading "Special Printings" did not supersede those in *red*, which was the normal colour for Jammu down to 1878. It is not known for what reason other colours were used during that period, but these stamps were printed in 1874 or 1875 and were certainly put into use. The rectangular stamps were again printed in *black* (jet-black, as against the greyish black of the 1867 printings) at that time, and impressions of the two periods can also be distinguished by the obliterations, which until 1868 were in *magenta* and after that in *black*.

There are reprints of these, in *oil* colour, *brown-red* and *bright blue*, on native paper; they are very clearly printed, which is not the case with the originals in *oil* colour.

FOR USE IN KASHMIR

5

1866 (Sept(?)). *Printed from a single die. Native laid paper.*

86	**5**	½ a. black	£850	£275

Forgeries of this stamp are commonly found, copied from an illustration in *Le Timbre-Poste*.

6 (½ a.)

7 (1 a.)

1867. *Native laid paper.*

87	**6**	½ a. black	£650	75·00
88	**7**	1 a. black	£1100	£160

Printed in sheets of 25 (5 × 5), the four top rows being ½ a. and the bottom row 1 a.

8 (¼ a.)

9 (2 a.)

10 (4 a.)

11 (8 a.)

1867. *Native laid paper.*

90	**8**	¼ a. black	45	45
91	**6**	½ a. ultramarine	70	40
92		½ a. violet-blue	90	60
93	**7**	1 a. ultramarine	£2250	£850
94		1 a. orange	5·00	3·00
95		1 a. brown-orange	4·00	3·00
96		1 a. orange-vermilion	4·50	3·50
97	**9**	2 a. yellow	4·50	3·50
98		2 a. buff	5·00	3·50
99	**10**	4 a. green	10·00	8·00
		a. *Tête-bêche* (pair)	£100	
100		4 a. sage-green	50·00	20·00
100*a*		4 a. myrtle-green	£400	£400
101	**11**	8 a. red	11·00	10·00
		a. *Tête-bêche* (pair)	£100	

Of the above, the ½ a. and 1 a. were printed from the same plate of 25 as Nos. 87/8, the ¼ a. and 2 a. from a new plate of 10 (5 × 2), the top row being ¼ a. and the lower 2 a., and the 4 a. and 8 a. from single dies. Varieties at one time catalogued upon European papers were apparently never put into circulation, though some of them were printed while these stamps were still in use.

Nos. 86 to 101 are in watercolour.

PRICES OF SETS

Set prices are given for many issues, generally those containing five stamps or more. Definitive sets include one of each value or major colour change, but do not cover different perforations, die types or minor shades. Where a choice is possible the set prices are based on the cheapest versions of the stamps included in the listings.

FOR USE IN JAMMU AND KASHMIR

In the following issues there are 15 varieties on the sheets of the ⅛ a., ¼ a. and ½ a.; 20 varieties of the 1 a. and 2 a. and 8 varieties of the 4 a. and 8 a. The value is in the lower part of the central oval.

12 (¼ a.)

13 (½ a.)

14 (1 a.)

15 (2 a.)

16 (4 a.)

17 (8 a.)

1878–79. *Provisional printings.*

I. *Ordinary white laid paper, of varying thickness*

(*a*) *Rough perf* 10 *to* 12 (i) *or* 13 *to* 16 (ii)

101*b*	**12**	¼ a. red (i)		
102	**13**	½ a. red (i)	11·00	7·00
103	**14**	1 a. red (ii)	£500	
104	**13**	½ a. slate-violet (i)	42·00	42·00
104*a*	**14**	1 a. violet (ii)		

(*b*) *Imperf*

105	**13**	½ a. slate-violet (*shades*)	15·00	15·00
106	**14**	1 a. slate-purple	17·00	17·00
107		1 a. mauve	18·00	18·00
108	**15**	2 a. violet	19·00	19·00
109		2 a. bright mauve	19·00	19·00
110		2 a. slate-blue	20·00	20·00
111		2 a. dull blue	32·00	32·00
112	**12**	¼ a. red	11·00	11·00
113	**13**	½ a. red	5·00	5·00
114	**14**	1 a. red	5·00	5·00
115	**15**	2 a. red	30·00	27·00
116	**16**	4 a. red	35·00	32·00

II. *Medium wove paper.* (*a*) *Rough perf* 10 *to* 12

117	**13**	½ a. red	—	25·00

(*b*) *Imperf*

117*b*	**12**	¼ a. red		
118	**13**	½ a. red	4·50	4·50
119	**14**	1 a. red	4·50	4·50
120	**15**	2 a. red	16·00	4·50

III. *Thick wove paper. Imperf*

121	**13**	½ a. red	10·00	
122	**14**	1 a. red	15·00	5·00
123	**15**	2 a. red	5·50	5·50

1879. *Definitive issue. Thin wove paper, fine to coarse.*

(*d*) *Rough perf* 10 *to* 12

124	**13**	½ a. red	35·00	25·00

(*b*) *Imperf*

125	**12**	¼ a. red	75	75
126	**13**	½ a. red	45	45
127	**14**	1 a. red	75	75
		a. Bisected (½ a.) (on cover)		† £2250
128	**15**	2 a. red	1·10	1·10
129	**16**	4 a. red	1·75	2·25
130	**17**	8 a. red	2·00	2·50

1880 (Mar). *Provisional printing in watercolour on thin bâtonné paper. Imperf.*

130*a*	**12**	¼ a. ultramarine	£325	£225

1881–83. *As Nos.* 124 *to* 130. *Colour changed.*

(*a*) *Rough perf* 10 *to* 12

130*b*	**13**	½ a. orange		

(*b*) *Imperf*

131	**12**	¼ a. orange	6·00	4·00
132	**13**	½ a. orange	18·00	11·00
133	**14**	1 a. orange	12·00	6·00
		a. Bisected (½ a.) (on cover)		† £2250
134	**15**	2 a. orange	13·00	7·00
135	**16**	4 a. orange	20·00	
136	**17**	8 a. orange	32·00	

No. 127a was used at Leh in April 1883 and No. 133a was used there later.

Nos. 125/30 and 132/6 were re-issued between 1890 and 1894 and used concurrently with the stamps which follow. Such re-issues can be identified by the "three-circle" cancellations, introduced in December 1890.

18 (⅛ a.)

1883–94. *New colours. Thin wove papers, toned, coarse to fine, or fine white* (1889). *Imperf.*

No.	Type	Description	Unused	Used
138	18	⅛ a. yellow-brown	12	20
139		⅛ a. yellow	12	20
140	12	¼ a. sepia	30	12
141		¼ a. brown	20	12
		a. Double impression	£1100	
142		¼ a. pale brown	20	12
		a. Error. Green	35·00	
143	13	½ a. dull blue	4·00	
144		½ a. bright blue	40·00	
145		½ a. vermillion	50	25
146		½ a. rose	50	40
147		½ a. orange-red	45	20
148	14	1 a. greenish grey	30	30
149		1 a. bright green	40	45
		a. Double impression		
150		1 a. dull green	25	25
151		1 a. blue-green	50	
152	15	2 a. red/*yellow*	50	50
153		2 a. red/*yellow-green*	70	80
154		2 a. red/*deep green*	1·50	1·50
155	16	4 a. deep green	1·75	1·75
156		4 a. green	1·75	1·75
157		4 a. pale green	2·00	2·00
158		4 a. sage-green	1·75	
159	17	8 a. pale blue	4·00	4·00
159*a*		8 a. deep blue	6·00	5·50
160		8 a. bright blue	5·50	5·50
161		8 a. indigo-blue	7·50	7·50
161*a*		8 a. slate-lilac	10·00	10·00

Well-executed forgeries of the ¼ a. to 8 a. have come from India, mostly postmarked; they may be detected by the type, which does not agree with any variety on the genuine sheets, and also, in the low values, by the margins being filled in with colour, all but a thin white frame round the stamp. The forgeries of the 8 a. are in sheets of eight like the originals.

Other forgeries of nearly all values also exist, showing all varieties of type. All values are on thin, coarse wove paper.

In February 1890, a forgery, in watercolour, of the ½ a. orange, appeared, and many have been found genuinely used (*Price* £1.25).

Nos. 143 and 144 were never issued.

Examples of the ¼ a. brown, ½ a. orange-red and 1 a. green on wove paper exist with clean-cut perf 12.

There is a reference in the Jammu and Kashmir State Administration Report covering 1890–91 to the re-introduction of perforating and the machine-gumming of paper at the Jammu printing works.

The few known examples, the ¼ a. being only recorded used, the others unused or used, would appear to date from this period, but there is, as yet, no direct confirmation as to their status.

1887–94. *Thin creamy laid paper. Imperf.*

No.	Type	Description	Unused	Used
162	18	⅛ a. yellow	13·00	14·00
163	12	¼ a. brown	9·00	6·00
164	13	½ a. brown-red (March 1887)	—	35·00
165		½ a. orange-red	6·00	4·75
166	14	1 a. grey-green	£120	£110
168	17	8 a. blue (*Printed in watercolour*)	£200	£200
		a. On wove paper	£140	£140

19

T **19** represents a ¼ a. stamp, which exists in sheets of twelve varieties, in *red* and *black*, on thin wove and laid papers, also in *red* on native paper, but which does not appear ever to have been issued for use. It was first seen in 1886.

The ¼ a. *brown*, and the 4 a. *green*, exist on ordinary white laid paper; the ½ a. *red* on native paper; the ¼ a. in *bright green*, on thin white wove (this may be an error in the colour of the 4 a.); and the 8 a. in *lilac* on thin white wove. None of these are known to have been in use.

OFFICIAL STAMPS

1878. I. *White laid paper.* (*a*) *Rough perf* 10 *to* 12.

No.	Type	Description	Unused	Used
O1	13	½ a. black		
		(*b*) *Imperf*		
O2	13	½ a. black	4·00	4·00
O3	14	1 a. black	5·00	5·00
O4	15	2 a. black	6·00	7·00
		II. *Medium wove paper. Imperf*		
O5	14	1 a. black		

1880–94. *Thin wove papers, toned, coarse to fine, or fine white* (1889). *Imperf.*

No.	Type	Description	Unused	Used
O 6	12	¼ a. black	15	15
		a. Double print	£110	
O 7	13	½ a. black	12	12
O 8	14	1 a. black	20	12
O 9	15	2 a. black	25	20
O10	16	4 a. black	35	35
O11	17	8 a. black	40	40

1887–94. *Thin creamy laid paper. Imperf.*

No.	Type	Description	Unused	Used
O12	12	¼ a. black	2·00	2·50
O13	13	½ a. black	1·50	2·00
O14	14	1 a. black	1·50	2·00
O15	15	2 a. black	30·00	
O16	16	4 a. black	22·00	25·00
O17	17	8 a. black	25·00	28·00

1889. *Stout white wove paper. Imperf.*

No.	Type	Description	Unused	Used
O18	12	¼ a. black	80·00	

The stamps of Jammu and Kashmir have been obsolete since 1 November 1894.

JASDAN

PRICES FOR STAMPS ON COVER
The stamps of Jasdan are rare used on cover.

1 Sun

(Typo L. V. Indap & Co, Bombay)

1942 (15 Mar)–**47**(?). *Stamps from booklet panes. Various perfs.*

No.	Type	Description	Unused	Used
1	1	1 a. myrtle-green (*p* 10½ × *imperf*)	35·00	
2		1 a. light green (*p* 10½ × *imperf*)	12·00	
3		1 a. pale yellow-green (*p* 8½ × *imperf*)	2·00	
4		1 a. dull yellow-green (*p* 10)	2·50	
5		1 a. bluish green (*p* 9)	2·50	

Nos. 1/3 were issued in panes of four with the stamps imperforate on one or two sides; Nos. 4/5 were in panes of eight perforated all round.

A 1 a. rose with the arms of Jasdan in the centre is a fiscal stamp.

Jasdan was merged with the United State of Kathiawar on 15 February 1948 and renamed the United State of Saurashtra.

JHALAWAR

PRICES FOR STAMPS ON COVER
Nos. 1/2 *from* × 25

(Figure of an Apsara, "RHEMBA", a dancing nymph of the Hindu Paradise)

1 (1 paisa) **2** (¼ anna)

1887–90. *Laid paper. No gum.*

No.	Type	Description	Unused	Used
1	1	1 p. yellow-green	1·25	1·75
		a. Blue-green	5·00	3·50
2	2	¼ a. green (*shades*)	60	90

The stamps formerly listed as on wove paper are from sheets on laid paper, with the laid lines almost invisible.

The stamps of Jhalawar have been obsolete since 1 November 1900.

JIND

PRICES FOR STAMPS ON COVER
Nos. J1/34 *from* × 50

ILLUSTRATIONS. Designs of Jind are illustrated actual size.

J **1** (½ a.)

J **2** (1 a.)

J **3** (2 a.)

J **4** (4 a.)

J **5** (8 a.)

(The letter "R" on stamp is the initial of Raghbir Singh, at one time Rajah)

(Litho Jind State Rajah's Press, Sungroor)

1874. *Thin yellowish paper. Imperf.*

No.	Type	Description	Unused	Used
J1	J 1	½ a. blue	4·00	2·00
		a. No frame to value. (Retouched all over)	£140	£120
J2	J 2	1 a. rosy mauve	7·00	6·00
J3	J 3	2 a. yellow	1·00	2·50
J4		2 a. brown-buff	12·00	7·00
J5	J 4	4 a. green	18·00	5·00
J6	J 5	8 a. dull purple	£100	48·00
J6*a*		8 a. bluish violet	£100	48·00
J7		8 a. slate-blue	£100	48·00

1876. *Bluish laid card-paper. No gum. Imperf.*

No.	Type	Description	Unused	Used
J 8	J 1	½ a. blue	25	1·00
J 9	J 2	1 a. purple	50	1·50
J10	J 3	2 a. brown	60	2·25
J11	J 4	4 a. green	1·00	2·50
J11*a*	J 5	8 a. bluish violet	7·00	10·00
J12		8 a. slate-blue	7·00	10·00
J13		8 a. steel-blue	12·00	15·00

Stocks of the ½ a. (No. J8) and 2 a. (No. J4) were perforated 12 in 1885 for use as fiscal stamps.

J **6** (¼ a.)

J **7** (½ a.)

J **8** (1 a.)

J **9** (2 a.)

J **10** (4 a.)

J **11** (8 a.)

(Litho Jind State Rajah's Press, Sungroor)

1882–85. *Types* J **6** *to* J **11**. 25 *varieties of each value. No gum.* A. *Imperf* (1882–4). B. *P* 12 (1885). (*a*) *Thin yellowish wove paper.*

No.	Description	A		B	
J15	¼ a. buff (*shades*)	25	35	25	40
J16	¼ a. red-brown	25	35	60	—
	a. Doubly printed	28·00	—	†	
J17	½ a. lemon	50	50	15·00	15·00
J18	½ a. buff	70	70	40	50
J19	½ a. brown-buff	70	60	70	80
J20	1 a. brown (*shades*)	70	60	60	70
J21	2 a. blue	90	1·25	1·00	1·40
J22	2 a. deep blue	90	1·00	1·10	1·40
J23	4 a. sage-green	80	90	1·25	1·60
J24	4 a. blue-green	1·10	1·40	2·00	—
	a. Imperf between (pair)	†		£150	—
J25	8 a. red	3·00	2·50	5·00	—
	(*b*) *Various thick laid papers*				
J26	¼ a. brown-buff	2·50	—	8·00	—
J27	½ a. lemon	2·50	—	18·00	15·00
J27*a*	½ a. brown-buff	—	—	†	
J28	1 a. brown	2·25	—	3·00	—
J29	2 a. blue	14·00	—	14·00	—
J30	8 a. red	3·00	5·00	3·00	4·00
	(*c*) *Thick white wove paper*				
J31	¼ a. brown-buff	7·00	—	†	
J32	½ a. brown-buff	12·00	—	†	
J33	1 a. brown	3·50	—	—	—
J34	8 a. red	4·50	5·00	6·00	—

The perforated stamps ceased to be used for postal purposes in July 1885, but are said to have been used later as fiscals. Other varieties exist, but they must either be fiscals or reprints, and it is not quite certain that all of those listed above were issued as early as 1885.

Jind became a convention state and from 1885 used the Indian stamps overprinted which are listed under the Convention States.

KISHANGARH

PRICES FOR STAMPS ON COVER

Nos. 1/3	—
Nos. 4/91	*from* × 8
Nos. O1/32	*from* × 30

GUM. The stamps of Kishangarh were issued without gum, *except for* Nos. 42/50 and O 17/24.

1

1899. *Wove paper.*

1	**1**	1 a. green (*imperf*)	18·00	27·00
2		1 a. green (*pin-perf*)	32·00	

1900. *Thin white wove paper. Imperf.*

3	**1**	1 a. blue	£275	

ILLUSTRATIONS. Types 2 to 10*a* are shown actual size.

2 (¼ a.)

3 (½ a.)

4 (1 a.)

5 (2 a.)
Maharaja Sardul Singh

6 (4 a.)

7 (1 r.)

8 (2 r.)

9 (5 r.)

1899–1901. *Thin white wove paper.* (*a*) *Imperf.*

4	**2**	¼ a. green	75·00	
5		¼ a. carmine	75	
		a. Rose-pink	30	
6		¼ a. magenta	5·00	5·00
		a. Doubly printed	75·00	75·00
7	**3**	½ a. lilac	27·00	30·00
8		½ a. red	£150	£100
9		½ a. green	18·00	16·00
10		½ a. pale yellow-olive	20·00	18·00
		a. Bistre-brown	20·00	18·00
11		½ a. slate-blue	85	1·00
		a. Pair, one stamp sideways	£1000	
		b. Deep blue	85	1·00
		c. Light blue	55	70
12	**4**	1 a. slate	2·50	1·75
		a. Laid paper	27·00	
12*b*		1 a. pink	50·00	60·00
13		1 a. mauve	1·25	1·00
		a. Laid paper	27·00	
14		1 a. brown-lilac	1·10	90
		a. Laid paper	27·00	
15	**5**	2 a. dull orange	5·00	5·00
		a. Laid paper	75·00	75·00
16	**6**	4 a. chocolate	2·00	
		a. Lake-brown	2·50	2·50
		b. Chestnut	2·50	2·50
		c. Laid paper (*shades*)	40·00	40·00
17	**7**	1 r. brown-lilac	25·00	
18		1 r. dull green	17·00	
19	**8**	2 r. brown-red	65·00	
		a. Laid paper	55·00	
20	**9**	5 r. mauve	48·00	
		a. Laid paper	60·00	

(*b*) *Pin-perf* 12½ *or* 14

21	**2**	¼ a. green	45·00	60·00
		a. Imperf between (pair)	£150	£150
22		¼ a. carmine	50	70
		a. Rose-pink	25	40
		b. Rose		
23		¼ a. magenta	18·00	18·00
		a. Bright purple		
		ab. Doubly printed		
24	**3**	½ a. green	13·00	13·00
		a. Imperf between (pair)	60·00	60·00
25		½ a. pale yellow-olive	15·00	15·00
		a. Imperf vert (horiz pair)	70·00	70·00
		b. Bistre-brown	15·00	15·00
26		½ a. deep blue	75	60
		a. Light blue	40	40
		ab. Doubly printed	40·00	40·00
27	**4**	1 a. slate	2·00	1·40
		a. Laid paper	30·00	16·00
27*b*		1 a. pink	40·00	
28		1 a. mauve	75	60
		a. Laid paper	30·00	13·00
29		1 a. brown-lilac	75	60
		a. Laid paper	30·00	13·00
30	**5**	2 a. dull orange	5·00	4·00
31	**6**	4 a. chocolate	2·00	2·00
		a. Lake-brown	2·50	2·50
		b. Chestnut	3·25	3·25
		c. Laid paper (*shades*)	32·00	32·00
32	**7**	1 r. dull green	14·00	17·00
		a. Laid paper	70·00	
33		1 r. pale olive-yellow	£120	£120
34	**8**	2 r. brown-red	38·00	
		a. Laid paper	55·00	
35	**9**	5 r. mauve	32·00	
		a. Laid paper	60·00	

All the above, both imperf and pin-perf, exist in vertical *tête-bêche* pairs imperf between from the centre of the sheet.

10 (¼ a.)

10*a* (1 r.)

1901. *Toned wove paper. Pin-perf.*

36	**10**	¼ a. dull pink	14·00	13·00
37	**4**	1 a. violet	27·00	24·00
38	**10*a***	1 r. dull green	16·00	16·00

These were printed from plates: Nos. 36 and 37 in sheets of 24, No. 38 in sheets of 16. All the others, except Nos. 1, 2 and 3, were printed singly on paper with spaces ruled in pencil.

The 1 a. (No. 37) differs from T 4 in having an inscription in native characters below the words "ONE ANNA".

11 (½ a.)

12 Maharaja Sardul Singh

1903. *Thick white wove glazed paper. Imperf.*

39	**11**	½ a. pink	5·00	4·50
		a. Printed both sides	£700	£700
40	**12**	2 a. dull yellow	4·00	4·00

12*a* (8 a.)

1904. *Thin paper. Pin-perf.*

41	**12*a***	8 a. grey	5·00	
		a. *Tête-bêche* (pair)	20·00	
		b. Doubly printed	55·00	55·00

13 Maharaja Madan Singh **14**

(Recess Perkins Bacon & Co)

1904–5. *With gum. P* 12½.

42	**13**	¼ a. carmine	35	35
		a. Perf 13½	30	30
43		½ a. chestnut	45	55
		a. Perf 13½	30	30
44		1 a. blue	1·10	1·10
		a. Perf 13½	35	35
45		2 a. orange-yellow	6·00	6·50
		a. Perf 13½	12·00	9·00
46		4 a. brown	6·50	6·50
		a. Perf 13½	6·50	6·50
47		8 a. violet (1905)	6·00	7·00
48		1 r. green	7·50	8·50
49		2 r. olive-yellow	11·00	15·00
50		5 r. purple-brown	17·00	24·00

Stamps in other colours, all perforated 13½, are colour trials.

1912. *Printed from half-tone blocks. No ornaments to left and right of value in English; large ornaments on either side of value in Hindi. Small stop after* "STATE". (*a*) *Thin wove paper. Rouletted.*

51	**14**	2 a. deep violet ("TWO ANNA")	3·00	6·00
		a. *Tête-bêche* (pair)	8·00	
		b. Imperf (pair)	75·00	

No. 51 is printed in four rows, each inverted in respect to that above and below it.

(*b*) *Thick white chalk-surfaced paper. Rouletted*

52	**14**	2 a. lilac ("TWO ANNA")	£100	85·00

(*c*) *Thick white chalk-surfaced paper. Rouletted in colour* (*Medallion only in half-tone*)

53	**14**	¼ a. ultramarine	10·00	12·00

1913. *No ornaments on either side of value in English. Small ornaments in bottom label. With stop after* "STATE". *Thick white chalk-surfaced paper. Rouletted.*

54	**14**	2 a. purple ("TWO ANNAS")	3·00	6·00

15

पाव अना

No. 59e. This occurs on R. 3/3 on one setting only

2 TWO ANNAS 2 — No. 60. Small figures

2 TWO ANNAS 2 — No. 60b. Large figures

(Typo Diamond Soap Works, Kishangarh)

1913 (Aug). *Thick surfaced paper. Half-tone centre. Type-set inscriptions. Rouletted. Inscr* "KISHANGARH".

59	**15**	¼ a. pale blue	20	25
		a. Imperf (pair)	7·00	
		b. Roul × imperf (horiz pair)	18·00	
		c. "OUARTER"	5·00	
		ca. As last, imperf (pair)	28·00	
		cb. As last, roul × imperf	45·00	
		d. "KISHANGAHR"	5·00	
		da. As last, imperf (pair)	28·00	
		db. As last, roul × imperf	45·00	
		e. Character omitted	7·00	7·00
		ea. As last, imperf (pair)	32·00	
60		2 a. purple	10·00	13·00
		a. "KISHANGAHR"	85·00	85·00
		b. Large figures "2"	60·00	60·00

1913–16. *Stamps printed far apart, horizontally and vertically, otherwise as No.* 54, *except as noted below.*

63	**14**	¼ a. blue	20	25
64		½ a. green (1915)	20	25
		a. Printed both sides	85·00	
		b. Imperf (pair)	£125	
		c. Emerald-green (1916)	1·75	1·75
65		1 a. red	1·00	1·10
		a. Without stop*	1·25	1·40
66		2 a. purple ("TWO ANNAS") (1915)	5·00	6·00
67		4 a. bright blue	6·50	7·50
68		8 a. brown	7·00	10·00
69		1 r. mauve	12·00	18·00
70		2 r. deep green	22·00	30·00
71		5 r. brown	35·00	45·00

*For this issue, ornaments were added on either side of the English value (except in the ¼ a.) and the inscription in the right label was without stop, except in the case of No. 65.

In Nos. 70 and 71 the value is expressed as "RUPIES" instead of "RUPEES".

Initial printings of the ¼ a., 1 a. and 4 a. values were in sheets of 20 containing two pairs of 10 separated by a central gutter margin. Stamps from these sheets measure 20 × 25½ mm and have heavier screening dots on the perforation margins than on the designs. Subsequent printings of these stamps, and of the other values in the set, were from single pane sheets of 20 on which the designs measured 19½ × 24¾ mm and with the screening dots uniform across the sheet.

FISCAL STAMPS. Most of Nos. 63/71 exist in other colours but they are fiscal stamps.

16 Maharaja Yagyanarain Singhji **17**

1928–36. *Thick surfaced paper. Typo. Pin-perf.*

72 16 ¼ a. light blue 35 50
73 ½ a. yellow-green 45 55
a. *Deep green* 50 65
ab. Imperf (pair) .. .. 35·00 35·00
ac. Imperf between (vert or horiz pair) 35·00 35·00
74 17 1 a. carmine 60 75
a. Imperf (pair) .. .. 40·00 40·00
75 2 a. purple .. .. 3·00 4·00
75*a* 2 a. magenta (1936) .. .. .. 4·00 5·00
76 16 4 a. chestnut .. .. 1·25 1·75
a. Imperf (pair) .. ..
77 8 a. violet .. .. 4·00 5·50
78 1 r. light green .. .. 8·50 12·00
79 2 r. lemon-yellow (1929) .. .. .. 18·00 24·00
80 5 r. claret (1929) .. .. 25·00 32·00
a. Imperf (pair) .. .. 90·00

The 4 a. to 5 r. are slightly larger than, but otherwise similar to, the ¼ a. and ½ a. The 8 a. has a dotted background covering the whole design.

1944–48. *As last, but thick, soft, unsurfaced paper. Poor impression. Typo. Pin-perf.*

81 16 ¼ a. pale dull blue (1945) .. .. 90 1·10
a. Imperf (pair) .. .. 28·00
82 ¼ a. greenish blue (1947) .. .. 1·00 1·25
a. Imperf (pair) .. .. 28·00
83 ½ a. deep green .. .. 80 1·10
a. Imperf (pair) .. .. 28·00
b. Imperf between (vert or horiz pair) 32·00 32·00
84 ½ a. yellow-green (1947) .. .. 1·25 1·25
a. Imperf (pair) .. .. 28·00 28·00
b. Imperf between (vert or horiz pair) 32·00 32·00
85 17 1 a. carmine-red .. .. 2·00 1·50
a. Imperf (pair) .. .. 30·00 30·00
b. Imperf between (vert or horiz pair) 35·00 35·00
c. *Red-orange* (1948) .. .. .. 15·00 10·00
86 2 a. bright magenta (1945) .. .. 5·00 6·00
a. Imperf (pair) .. .. 32·00
87 2 a. maroon (1945) .. .. .. 20·00 15·00
a. Imperf (pair) .. .. 35·00 35·00
b. Imperf between (vert or horiz pair) 40·00 40·00
88 16 4 a. brown (1945) .. .. 20·00 15·00
89 8 a. violet (1945) .. .. 27·00 30·00
90 1 r. green (1945) .. .. 40·00 45·00
91 5 r. claret (1945) £100 £100

OFFICIAL STAMPS

ON
K S
D

(O 1)

1918. *Handstamped with Type* O 1.

(*a*) *Stamps of* 1899–1901. (i) *Imperf*

O 1 2 ¼ a. rose-pink .. .. — 5·00
O 2 4 1 a. mauve .. .. — 8·00
O 3 1 a. brown-lilac .. .. — 2·25
O 4 6 4 a. chocolate .. .. — 20·00

(ii) *Pin-perf*

O 5 2 ¼ a. green .. .. — 30·00
O 6 ¼ a. rose-pink 40 30
O 7 3 ½ a. light blue .. .. — 13·00
O 8 4 1 a. mauve .. .. 2·00 1·50
O 9 1 a. brown-lilac .. .. 2·00 1·50
O10 5 2 a. dull orange .. .. — 38·00
O11 6 4 a. chocolate .. .. 13·00 13·00
O12 7 1 r. dull green .. .. 38·00 38·00
O13 8 2 r. brown-red £100 £100
O14 9 5 r. mauve £150 £150

(*b*) *Stamps of* 1903 *and* 1904

O15 12 2 a. dull yellow .. .. 16·00 12·00
a. Stamp printed both sides .. .. — £200
b. Red opt .. .. — 32·00
O16 12*a* 8 a. grey .. .. 17·00 17·00
a. Red opt .. .. — 32·00

(*c*) *Stamps of* 1904–5. *P* 13½ (¼ *a. to* 4 *a.*) *or* 12½ (*others*)

O17 13 ¼ a. carmine .. .. 16·00 16·00
O18 ½ a. chestnut 55 35
O19 1 a. blue .. .. 6·00 5·00
a. Red opt .. .. 7·00 7·00
O20 2 a. orange-yellow .. ..
O21 4 a. brown .. .. 12·00 12·00
a. Red opt .. .. 14·00 14·00
O22 8 a. violet .. .. 45·00 45·00
a. Red opt .. .. — 42·00
O23 1 r. green £120 £120
a. Red opt .. .. — £110
O24 5 r. purple-brown .. ..

(*d*) *Stamps of* 1913

O25 15 ¼ a. pale blue .. .. 6·00
a. "OUARTER" .. .. 22·00
b. "KISHANGAHR" .. .. 22·00
c. Character omitted .. .. 22·00
O26 14 2 a. purple (No. 54) .. .. .. — 25·00
a. Red opt .. .. — 20·00
O27 15 2 a. purple .. .. 25·00
a. "KISHANGAHR" £110
b. Large figures "2" £110

(*e*) *Stamps of* 1913–16

O28 14 ¼ a. blue 50 50
a. Red opt .. .. 1·50 1·50
O29 ½ a. green 75 75
a. Red opt .. .. 1·50 1·50
O30 1 a. red .. .. 1·25 1·25
a. Without stop .. .. 1·00 1·00
ab. Red opt .. ..
O31 2 a. purple .. .. 4·50 3·50
a. Red opt .. .. — 15·00
O32 4 a. bright blue .. .. 17·00 15·00
a. Red opt .. .. — 20·00
O33 14 8 a. brown .. .. 28·00 28·00
a. Red opt .. .. — 32·00
O34 1 r. lilac .. .. 50·00 50·00
O35 2 r. deep green .. ..
O36 5 r. brown .. ..

This overprint is found inverted as often as it is upright; and many other "errors" exist.

On 25 March 1948 Kishangarh became part of the Rajasthan Union.

LAS BELA

PRICES FOR STAMPS ON COVER
Nos. 1/12 *from* × 8

1

2

(Litho Thacker & Co, Bombay)

1897–98. *Thick paper. Pin-perf.*

1 1 ½ a. black on *white* .. .. 6·50 5·50

1898–1900. *Pin-perf.*

2 1 ½ a. black on *greyish blue* (1898) .. 5·00 4·00
3 ½ a. black on *greenish grey* (1899) .. 5·00 4·00
a. "BFLA" for "BELA" .. .. .. 32·00
4 ½ a. black on *thin white surfaced paper* (1899) .. .. 11·00
5 ½ a. black on *slate* (1900) .. .. 14·00
a. Imperf between (pair) £100

1901–2. *Pin-perf.*

6 1 ½ a. black on *pale grey* .. .. .. 6·00 6·00
a. "BFLA" for "BELA" .. .. .. 32·00
7 ½ a. black on *pale green* (1902) .. 8·00 9·00
8 2 1 a. black on *orange* .. .. .. 8·00 9·00

There are at least 14 settings of the above ½ a. stamps, the sheets varying from 16 to 30 stamps.

1904. *Stamps printed wider apart. Pin-perf.*

11 1 ½ a. black on *pale blue* .. .. .. 6·00 6·00
a. Imperf between (pair) £125
12 ½ a. black on *pale green* .. .. .. 6·00 6·00

There are three plates of the above two stamps, each consisting of 18 varieties.

All the coloured papers of the ½ a. show coloured fibres, similar to those in granite paper.

The stamps of Las Bela have been obsolete since 1 April 1907.

MORVI

PRICES FOR STAMPS ON COVER
Nos. 1/19 *from* × 8

1

2

3

Maharaja Sir Lakhdirji Waghji

1931 (1 April). *Typo. P* 12.

(*a*) *Printed in blocks of four. Stamps* 10 *mm apart* (*Nos.* 1/2) *or* 6½ *mm apart* (*No.* 3). *Perf on two or three sides*

1 1 3 p. deep red .. .. 5·00 8·00
2 ½ a. blue .. .. 11·00 16·00
3 2 a. yellow-brown .. .. 50·00 70·00

(*b*) *Printed in two blocks of four. Stamps* 5½ *mm apart. Perf on four sides*

4 1 3 p. bright scarlet .. .. 1·25 1·75
a. Error. Dull blue .. .. 3·75 7·50
b. Ditto. Double print .. .. .. 90·00
5 ½ a. dull blue .. .. 1·75 2·50
6 1 a. brown-red .. .. 2·75 4·50
7 2 a. yellow-brown .. .. 4·00 6·50

1932–33. *Horizontal background lines wider apart and portrait smaller than in T* 1. *Typo. P* 11.

8 2 3 p. carmine-rose (*shades*) .. .. 50 1·00
9 6 p. green .. .. 70 1·40
a. *Emerald-green* .. .. 60 1·25
10 1 a. ultramarine (*to deep*) .. .. 1·25 2·50
a. Imperf between (vert pair) .. £250
11 2 a. bright violet (1933) .. .. 10·00 12·00
a. Imperf between (vert pair) .. £275

1934. *Typo. London ptg. P* 14.

12 3 3 p. carmine .. .. 60 1·00
13 6 p. emerald-green .. .. .. 60 1·25
14 1 a. purple-brown .. .. .. 1·00 2·00
a. Imperf between (horiz pair) .. † £225
15 2 a. bright violet .. .. 1·25 2·50

1935–48. *Typo. Morvi Press ptg. Rough perf* 11.

16 3 3 p. scarlet (*shades*) 40 75
a. Imperf between (horiz pair) .. £225
17 6 p. grey-green .. .. 50 1·00
a. *Emerald-green* .. .. 3·50 6·00
18 3 1 a. brown .. .. 6·00 8·00
a. *Pale yellow-brown* .. .. .. 10·00 13·00
b. *Chocolate* .. .. 8·00 10·00
19 2 a. dull violet (*to deep*) .. .. .. 3·50 7·50

Nos. 17*a*, 18*a* and 18*b* were issued between 1944 and 1948.

Morvi was incorporated in the Union of Saurashtra on 15 February 1948.

NANDGAON

PRICES FOR STAMPS ON COVER
The stamps of Nandgaon are very rare used on cover.

GUM. The stamps of Nandgaon were issued without gum.

1

1892 (Feb).

1 1 ½ a. blue .. .. 1·25 30·00
a. *Dull blue* .. .. 2·50
2 2 a. rose .. .. 10·00 55·00

Collectors are warned against copies of T 1 with faked postmarks. Genuinely used they are very rare.

(2)

3 (2 a.)

("M.B.D." = Rajah Machant Balram Das)

1893–94.

(i) *Printed wide apart on the sheet, no wavy lines between stamps*

(*a*) *Optd with T* 2 *in purple or grey*

3 3 2 a. red .. .. 12·00

(*b*) *Without overprint*

4 3 ½ a. green .. .. 10·00
5 2 a. red .. .. 5·00

(ii) *Printed closer together, wavy lines between stamps*

(*a*) *Optd with T* 2 *in purple or grey*

6 3 ½ a. green .. .. 85 1·10
a. *Sage-green* .. .. 1·10
7 1 a. rose (*laid paper*) .. .. .. 10·00 17·00
8 1 a. rose (*wove paper*) .. .. .. 3·50 4·50
9 2 a. dull carmine .. .. 3·00 4·00

(*b*) *Without overprint*

10 3 ½ a. green .. .. 10·00 12·00
11 1 a. rose (*laid paper*) .. .. .. 90·00
12 1 a. rose (*wove paper*) .. .. .. 18·00 22·00

It has been stated that no stamps were regularly issued for postal use without the "control" mark, T 2, but it is very doubtful if this is correct. The overprint probably indicates official use.

The 1 a. exists in *ultramarine* and in *brown*, but these appear to be reprints.

The stamps of Nandgaon have been obsolete since 1 January 1895.

NAWANAGAR

PRICES FOR STAMPS ON COVER
The stamps of Nawanagar are very rare used on cover.

GUM. The stamps of Nawanagar were issued without gum.

1 (1 docra)

2 (2 docra)

3 (3 docra)

1877. *Laid paper.* (*a*) *Imperf.*

1 1 1 doc. blue (*shades*) .. .. 40 10·00
a. *Tête-bêche* (pair) £850

(*b*) *Perf* 12½ (*line*) *or* 11 (*harrow*)

2 1 1 doc. slate-blue .. .. 38·00 50·00
a. *Tête-bêche* (pair) (*p* 11) £1200

1877. *T* 2 *and* 3. *Black impression. Wove paper. Thick horizontal and vertical frame lines.*

A. *Stamp* 14½–15 *mm wide.* B. *Stamp* 16 *mm wide.* C. *Stamp* 19 *mm wide.*

		A	B	C
2*b*	1 doc. *deep mauve*	80·00	80·00	70·00
2*c*	2 doc. *green*	†	†	£500
2*d*	3 doc. *yellow*	†	†	£650

Prices are for used. These stamps are not known unused.

1880. *As last, but thin frame lines, as illustrated.*
D. *Stamp 15 to 18 mm wide.* E. *Stamp 14 mm wide.*

No.	Description	D		E	
3	1 doc. *deep mauve*	70	2·50	†	
	a. On rose	50	—	60	1·10
4	1 doc. *magenta*	†		40	—
5	2 doc. *yellow-green*	1·10	4·50	1·10	3·00
	a. On blue-green	2·00	—	3·00	—
	b. Error. Yellow	£250	—	†	
6	3 doc. *orange-yellow*	3·00	—	†	
	a. On yellow	4·50	8·00	2·50	4·00
	ab. On yellow. Laid paper	55·00	—	40·00	—

There are several different settings of each value of this series.

No. 5b occurs in the sheet of the 3 doc. value from one setting only, but is also known as a complete sheet of 2 doc. stamps on yellow paper.

4 (1 docra)

1893. P 12. (*a*) *Thick paper.*

No.	Type	Description	Unused	Used
8	4	1 doc. black	90	
		a. Imperf (pair)	£100	
9		3 doc. orange	2·50	
		(*b*) *Thick laid paper*		
10	4	1 doc. black	55·00	
		(*c*) *Thin wove paper*		
11	4	1 doc. black *to* grey	25	50
		a. Imperf between (pair)	£130	
		b. Imperf (pair)	£100	
12		2 doc. green	40	75
		a. Imperf (pair)	£100	
13		3 doc. orange-yellow	70	1·25
		a. Imperf between (pair)	£130	
		b. Orange	60	1·25
		ba. Imperf (pair)	£100	
		(*d*) *Thin, soft wove paper*		
14	4	1 doc. black		
15		2 doc. deep green	4·00	
16		3 doc. brown-orange	5·00	

Cancellations for postal purposes were large oval seals, applied in black. Other forms of cancellation were only used on remainders.

The stamps of Nawanagar became obsolete on 1 January 1895.

NEPAL

Nepal being an independent state, its stamps will be found listed in Part 21 (*South-East Asia*) of this catalogue.

ORCHHA

PRICES FOR STAMPS ON COVER

Nos. 1/2	—
Nos. 3/7	*from* × 10
Nos. 8/30	*from* × 50
Nos. 31/45	*from* × 4

A set of four stamps, ½ a. red, 1 a. violet, 2 a. yellow and 4 a. deep blue-green, in a design similar to T 2, was prepared in 1897 with State authority but not put into use. These exist both imperforate and pin-perforated.

1

2

(T 1/2 litho Shri Pratap Prabhakar)

1913. *Background to arms unshaded. Very blurred impression. Wove paper. No gum. Imperf.*

No.	Type	Description	Unused	Used
1	1	½ a. green	16·00	24·00
2		1 a. red	16·00	

1914–17. *Background shaded with short horizontal lines. Clearer impression. Wove paper. No gum. Imperf.*

No.	Type	Description	Unused	Used
3	2	¼ a. bright ultramarine	70	1·50
		a. Grey-blue	35	60
		b. Deep blue	90	1·50
		ba. Laid paper	75·00	
4		½ a. green (*shades*)	40	60
		a. Dull green	1·25	1·75
		b. Apple-green	1·40	1·75
5		1 a. scarlet	1·25	1·75
		a. Indian red	2·50	4·00
		b. Carmine	2·50	4·00
		ba. Laid paper	65·00	
6		2 a. red-brown (1916)	4·50	6·50
		a. Light brown	6·00	8·00
		b. Chestnut	6·50	8·50
7		4 a. ochre (1917)	10·00	12·00
		a. Yellow-orange	8·00	10·00
		b. Yellow	10·00	12·00

There are two sizes of T 2 in the setting of 8 (4 × 2). In each value stamps from the upper row are slightly taller than those from the lower.

3 Maharaja Vir Singh Deo Bahadur 4

(Typo Lakshmi Art Ptg Wks, Bombay)

1935 (1 Apr). *Thick, chalk-surfaced wove paper.* P 9½, 10, 10 × 9½, 11, 11 × 9½, 11½, 11½ × 11, 11½ × 12, 12 *or* 12 × 11.

No.	Type	Description	Unused	Used
8	3	¼ a. purple and slate	15	20
		a. Ordinary paper	15	20
		ab. Imperf between (vert pair)	10·00	
		ac. Imperf vert (horiz pair)	15·00	
9		½ a. olive-grey and emerald	15	20
		a. Imperf (pair)		
10		¾ a. magenta and deep myrtle-green	15	20
11		1 a. myrtle-green and purple-brown	15	20
		a. Imperf (pair)	—	32·00
12		1¼ a. slate and mauve	20	25
		a. Imperf (pair)	—	45·00
13		1½ a. brown and scarlet	20	25
		a. Imperf between (vert pair)		
14		2 a. blue and red-orange	20	25
		a. Imperf (pair)	9·00	
15		2½ a. olive-brown and dull orange	20	30
		a. Imperf (pair)	9·00	
16		3 a. bright blue and magenta	20	30
17		4 a. deep reddish purple and sage-green	25	35
		a. Imperf (pair)	7·50	
18		6 a. black and pale ochre	30	40
		a. Imperf (pair)	7·50	
19		8 a. brown and purple	35	45
		a. Imperf (pair)	7·50	
20		12 a. bright emerald and bright purple	40	50
		a. Imperf (pair)	7·50	
21		12 a. pale greenish blue and bright purple	8·00	10·00
22		1 r. chocolate and myrtle-green	50	60
		a. Imperf (pair)	8·00	
		b. Imperf between (horiz pair)		
23	4	1 r. chocolate and myrtle-green	1·00	1·25
24	3	2 r. purple-brown and bistre-yellow	60	80
		a. Imperf (pair)	9·00	
25		3 r. black and greenish blue	70	90
		a. Imperf (pair)	9·00	
26		4 r. black and brown	85	1·10
		a. Imperf (pair)	9·00	
27		5 r. bright blue and plum	1·25	1·60
		a. Imperf (pair)	9·00	
28		10 r. bronze-green and cerise	2·50	3·00
		a. Imperf (pair)	10·00	
29		15 r. black and bronze-green	5·00	6·00
		a. Imperf (pair)	11·00	
30		25 r. red-orange and blue	7·50	8·50
		a. Imperf (pair)	14·00	

Values to 5 r. except the 1 a., are inscribed "POSTAGE", and the remaining values "POSTAGE & REVENUE".

The central portrait of Type 3 is taken from a half-tone block and consists of large square dots. The portrait of Type 4 has a background of lines.

Owing to a lack of proper State control considerable quantities of these stamps circulated at below face value and the issue was subsequently withdrawn, supplies being exchanged for the 1939–42 issue. We are, however, now satisfied that the lower values at least did genuine postal duty until 1939.

Used prices are for stamps cancelled-to-order, postally used examples being worth considerably more.

5 H.H. The Maharaja of Orchha 6

(Litho Indian Security Printing Press, Nasik)

1939–42? P 13½ × 14 (T 5) *or* 14 × 13½ (T 6).

No.	Type	Description	Unused	Used
31	5	¼ a. chocolate	30	8·00
32		½ a. yellow-green	30	7·00
33		¾ a. bright blue	35	12·00
34		1 a. scarlet	45	7·00
35		1¼ a. blue	60	12·00
36		1½ a. mauve	75	
37		2 a. vermilion	75	10·00
38		2½ a. turquoise-green	95	
39		3 a. slate-violet	1·25	
40		4 a. slate	1·60	11·00
41		8 a. magenta	3·25	
42	6	1 r. grey-green	5·50	
43		2 r. bright violet	16·00	
44		5 r. yellow-orange	50·00	
45		10 r. turquoise-green (1942)	£110	

POONCH

PRICES FOR STAMPS ON COVER

Nos. 1/2	*from* × 3
Nos. 3/62	*from* × 10
Nos. O1/10	*from* × 30

GUM. The stamps of Poonch were issued without gum, except for some examples of Nos. 7/10.

The stamps of Poonch are all imperforate, and printed in water-colours.

ILLUSTRATIONS. Designs of Poonch are illustrated actual size.

1

2

1876. T 1 (22 × 21 *mm*). *Yellowish white, wove paper.*

No.	Type	Description	Unused	Used
1		6 p. red	—	70·00

1877. *As* T 1 (19 × 17 *mm*). *Same paper.*

No.	Type	Description	Unused	Used
1*a*		½ a. red	£3500	£1000

1879. T 2 (21 × 19 *mm*). *Same paper.*

No.	Type	Description	Unused	Used
2		½ a. red	—	£500

3 (½ a.)

4 (1 a.)

5 (2 a.)

6 (4 a.)

1880. *Yellowish white, wove paper.*

No.	Type	Description	Unused	Used
3	3	½ a. red	18·00	9·00
4	4	1 a. red	18·00	10·00
5	5	2 a. red	20·00	18·00
6	6	4 a. red	25·00	20·00

1884. *Toned wove bâtonné paper.*

No.	Type	Description	Unused	Used
7	3	½ a. red	2·75	2·75
8	4	1 a. red	3·50	
9	5	2 a. red	5·50	5·50
10	6	4 a. red	7·00	

These are sometimes found gummed.

7 (1 pice)

1884–87. *Various papers.* (*a*) *White laid bâtonné or ribbed bâtonné.*

No.	Type	Description	Unused	Used
11	7	1 p. red	5·00	5·00
12	3	½ a. red	50	55
13	4	1 a. red	55	
14	5	2 a. red	90	1·00
15	6	4 a. red	2·50	
		(*b*) *Thick white laid paper*		
22	7	1 p. red	2·50	
23	3	½ a. red	6·00	
24	4	1 a. red	9·00	
25	5	2 a. red	14·00	
26	6	4 a. red	20·00	
		(*c*) *Yellow wove bâtonné*		
27	7	1 p. red	2·00	2·00
		a. Pair, one stamp sideways		
28	3	½ a. red	2·00	2·00
29	4	1 a. red	4·50	
30	5	2 a. red	2·00	2·75
31	6	4 a. red	2·00	2·00
		(*d*) *Orange-buff wove bâtonné*		
32	7	1 p. red	40	40
		a. Pair, one stamp sideways	10·00	
33	3	½ a. red	5·50	
34	5	2 a. red	9·00	
35	6	4 a. red	5·50	
		(*e*) *Yellow laid paper*		
36	7	1 p. red	65	65
37	3	½ a. red	2·00	
38	4	1 a. red	3·50	
39	5	2 a. red	4·50	4·50
40	6	4 a. red	7·50	
		(*f*) *Yellow laid bâtonné*		
41	7	1 p. red	5·00	2·75
		(*g*) *Buff laid or ribbed bâtonné paper thicker than* (*d*)		
42	4	1 a. red	12·00	
43	6	4 a. red	16·00	

(h) Blue-green laid paper (1887)

No.	Type	Description	Unused	Used
44	**3**	½ a. red	4·00	
45	**4**	1 a. red	2·00	2·75
46	**5**	2 a. red	4·00	
47	**6**	4 a. red	5·00	

(i) Yellow-green laid paper

No.	Type	Description	Unused	Used
48	**3**	½ a. red		

(j) Blue-green wove bâtonné

No.	Type	Description	Unused	Used
49	**7**	1 p. red	11·00	15·00
50	**4**	1 a. red	30	45

(k) Lavender wove bâtonné

No.	Type	Description	Unused	Used
51	**4**	1 a. red	17·00	
52	**5**	2 a. red	30	50

(l) Various coloured papers

No.	Type	Description	Unused	Used
53	**7**	1 p. red/*grey-blue laid*	3·00	3·00
54		1 p. red/*lilac laid*	38·00	40·00
55		1 p. red/*blue wove bâtonné*	40	45
		a. Pair, one stamp sideways		

1888. *Printed in aniline rose on various papers.*

No.	Type	Description	Unused	Used
56	**7**	1 p. on *blue wove bâtonné*	1·50	
57		1 p. on *buff laid*	3·00	
58	**3**	½ a. on *white laid*	5·00	
59	**4**	1 a. on *green laid*	8·00	7·00
60		1 a. on *green wove bâtonné*	2·50	2·00
61	**5**	2 a. on *lavender wove bâtonné*	2·50	2·00
62	**6**	4 a. on *yellow laid*	6·00	6·00

OFFICIAL STAMPS

1888. *(a) White laid bâtonné paper.*

No.	Type	Description	Unused	Used
O 1	**7**	1 p. black	35	45
		a. Pair, one stamp sideways	8·00	
O 2	**3**	½ a. black	45	60
O 3	**4**	1 a. black	55	
O 4	**5**	2 a. black	60	65
O 5	**6**	4 a. black	1·00	1·00

(b) White toned wove bâtonné paper

No.	Type	Description	Unused	Used
O 6	**7**	1 p. black	80	
O 7	**3**	½ a. black	1·75	1·75
O 8	**4**	1 a. black	4·00	4·00
O 9	**5**	2 a. black	3·00	2·75
O10	**6**	4 a. black	4·50	

The stamps of Poonch have been obsolete since 1894.

RAJASTHAN

Rajasthan was formed in 1948–49 from a number of States in Rajputana; these included Bundi, Jaipur and Kishangarh, whose posts continued to function more or less separately until ordered by the Indian Government to close on 1 April 1950.

PRICES FOR STAMPS ON COVER

Nos. 1/65 *from* × 10

BUNDI

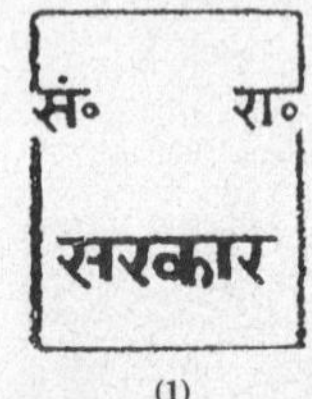

(1)

1949. *Nos.* 86/92 *of Bundi. (a) Handstamped with T* **1**.

A. *In black.* B. *In violet.* C. *In blue*

No.	Description	A	B	C
1	¼ a. blue-green	60	90	12·00
	a. Pair, one without opt	38·00	†	†
2	½ a. violet	65	65	5·50
	a. Pair, one without opt	†	50·00	†
3	1 a. yellow-green	65	5·50	7·00
	a. Pair, one without opt	†	50·00	†
4	2 a. vermilion	4·50	12·00	—
5	4 a. orange	7·50	3·50	14·00
6	8 a. ultramarine	1·50	1·50	9·00
7	1 r. chocolate	—	50·00	22·00

The above prices are for unused, used stamps being worth about three times the unused prices. Most of these handstamps are known, sideways, inverted or double.

(b) Machine-printed as T **1** *in black*

No.	Description	Unused	Used
8	¼ a. blue-green		
9	½ a. violet		
10	1 a. yellow-green		
11	2 a. vermilion	1·25	7·00
	a. Opt inverted	40·00	
12	4 a. orange	1·00	7·00
	a. Opt double	40·00	
13	8 a. ultramarine	27·00	
	a. Opt inverted	75·00	
14	1 r. chocolate	5·50	

JAIPUR

राजस्थान

RAJASTHAN

(2)

1949. *T* **7** *of Jaipur optd with T* **2**.

No.	Description	Unused	Used
15	¼ a. black and brown-lake (No. 58) (B.)	1·00	2·75
16	½ a. black and violet (No. 41) (R.)	1·10	2·75
17	¾ a. black and brown-red (No. 59) (Blue-blk.)	1·10	3·00
	a. Opt in pale blue	7·00	9·00
18	1 a. black and blue (No. 60) (R.)	2·00	3·50
19	2 a. black and buff (No. 61) (R.)	2·00	4·50
20	2½ a. black and carmine (No. 62) (B.)	2·00	7·00
21	3 a. black and green (No. 63) (R.)	2·40	7·00
22	4 a. black and grey-green (No. 64) (R.)	3·00	10·00
23	6 a. black and pale blue (No. 65*a*) (R.)	3·00	10·00
24	8 a. black and chocolate (No. 66) (R.)	7·00	14·00
25	1 r. black and yellow-bistre (No. 67) (R.)	10·00	35·00

KISHANGARH

1948–49. *Various stamps of Kishangarh handstamped with T* **1** *in red.*

(a) On stamps of 1899–1901

No.	Type	Description	Unused	Used
26		¼ a. pink (No. 5*a*) (B.)	38·00	
27		½ a. deep blue (No. 26)	38·00	
28		1 a. lilac (No. 29)	15·00	
29		1 a. brown-lilac (No. 29*b*)	14·00	
		b. Imperf (pair)	35·00	
30		4 a. chocolate (No. 31)	25·00	
31		1 r. dull green (No. 32)	50·00	
31*a*		2 r. brown-red (No. 34)	60·00	
32		5 r. mauve (No. 35)	70·00	

(b) On stamps of 1904–05

No.	Type	Description	Unused	Used
33	**13**	½ a. chestnut	15·00	
33*a*		1 a. blue		
34		4 a. brown	12·00	
		a. Blue handstamp	75·00	
35	**12*a***	8 a. grey	32·00	
36	**13**	8 a. violet	11·00	
37		1 r. green	14·00	
38		2 r. olive-yellow	14·00	
39		5 r. purple-brown	14·00	
		a. Blue handstamp	80·00	

(c) On stamps of 1912–16

No.	Type	Description	Unused	Used
40	**14**	½ a. green (No. 64)	15·00	12·00
41		1 a. red	15·00	17·00
42		2 a. deep violet (No. 51)	20·00	
43		2 a. purple (No. 66)	1·25	4·00
44		4 a. bright blue	30·00	
45		8 a. brown	4·00	
46		1 r. mauve	10·00	
47		2 r. deep green	10·00	
48		5 r. brown	45·00	

(d) On stamps of 1928–36

No.	Type	Description	Unused	Used
49	**16**	½ a. yellow-green	13·00	
50		4 a. chestnut	18·00	
51		8 a. violet	8·00	
52		1 r. light green	15·00	
53		2 r. lemon-yellow	15·00	
54		5 r. claret	£15·00	

(e) On stamps of 1944–47

No.	Type	Description	Unused	Used
55	**16**	¼ a. pale dull blue	16·00	16·00
56		¼ a. greenish blue	18·00	18·00
57		½ a. deep green	7·00	7·00
58	**17**	1 a. carmine-red	10·00	10·00
59		2 a. bright magenta	14·00	
60		2 a. maroon (*imperf*)	20·00	20·00
61	**16**	4 a. brown	1·00	2·50
62		8 a. violet	9·00	
63		1 r. green	7·00	
64		2 r. yellow	50·00	
65		5 r. red-brown	40·00	

Nos. 64/5 were not issued without the Rajasthan overprint.

RAJPIPLA

PRICES FOR STAMPS ON COVER

The stamps of Rajpipla are very rare used on cover.

1 (1 pice)

2 (2 a.)

3 (4 a.)

1880. *With or without gum* (1 *p.*) *or no gum* (*others*). *P* 11 (1 *p.*) *or* 12½.

No.	Type	Description	Unused	Used
1	**1**	1 p. blue	60	2·50
2	**2**	2 a. green	8·00	11·00
		a. Imperf between (pair)	£325	£325
3	**3**	4 a. red	4·00	6·00

These stamps became obsolete in 1886.

SIRMOOR

PRICES FOR STAMPS ON COVER

The stamps of Sirmoor are very rare used on cover.

1 (1 pice)

2

3 Raja Sir Shamsher Parkash

1876 (June)–**80.** *P* 11½.

No.	Type	Description	Unused	Used
1	**1**	1 p. pale green	5·00	
2		1 p. blue (on *laid* paper) (1880)	4·00	40·00
		a. Imperf between (pair)	£120	
		b. Imperf (pair)	£120	

(Printed at Calcutta)

1892. *Thick wove paper. P* 11½.

No.	Type	Description	Unused	Used
3	**2**	1 p. yellow-green	45	50
		a. Imperf between (pair)	45·00	
		b. Deep green	35	40
		ba. Imperf between (pair)	45·00	45·00
4		1 p. blue	45	45
		a. Imperf between (pair)	38·00	38·00
		b. Imperf (pair)	60·00	

These were originally made as reprints, about 1891, to supply collectors, but there being very little demand for them they were put into use. The design was copied (including the perforations) from an illustration in a dealer's catalogue.

A B

C D

There were seven printings of the 3 and 6 pies, six of the 1 anna, and four of the 2 annas, the last being used overprinted for official use (Nos. 99/102), all in sheets of seventy, made up of groups of transfers showing two or more minor varieties. There are two distinct varieties of the 3 p. and 6 p., as shown in Types A and B, C and D. Of these B and D are the types of the sixth printing of those values, and A and C those of all the other printings.

A and C have large white dots evenly placed between the ends of the upper and lower inscriptions; B has small white dots, and less space between the ends of the inscriptions; D has large spaces, and large white dots *not* in the centres of the spaces, especially at the left side.

The last printing of each value is only known with the Waterlow overprint, T **18**.

Roman figures denote printings.

(Litho Waterlow & Sons)

1885–96. *P* 14 *to* 15.

No.	Type	Description	Unused	Used
5	**3**	3 p. chocolate (A), I, IV	35	25
6		3 p. brown (B), VI	15	15
7		3 p. orange (A), II, III, IV, V	40	15
8		3 p. orange (B), VI	15	10
		a. Imperf (pair)	£400	
9		6 p. blue-green (C), I	1·10	85
10		6 p. bright green (C), III	16·00	16·00
11		6 p. green (C), II, IV	70	45
12		6 p. deep green (C), V	25	20
13		6 p. yellowish green (D), VI	40	40
14		1 a. bright blue, I	65	65
15		1 a. dull blue, III	4·50	4·50
16		1 a. steel-blue, IV	22·00	22·00
17		1 a. grey-blue, V	70	60
18		1 a. slate-blue, VI	85	1·00
19		2 a. pink, I	5·00	6·00
20		2 a. carmine, V	4·00	3·75
21		2 a. rose-red, VI	4·00	4·25

3 p. orange Printings III and IV are rare, being worth at least six times the value of other printings.

4

5 Raja Sir Shamsher Parkash

(Recess Waterlow & Sons)

1895–99. *P* 12 *to* 15 *and compounds.*

No.	Type	Description	Unused	Used
22	**4**	3 p. orange-brown	50	30
23		6 p. green	50	30
24		1 a. blue	50	30
25		2 a. rose	1·25	1·25
26		3 a. yellow-green	4·00	6·50
27		4 a. deep green	4·50	6·50
28		8 a. deep blue	5·00	8·00
29		1 r. vermilion	7·00	12·00

(Recess Waterlow & Sons)

1899. *P* 13 *to* 15.

No.	Type	Description	Unused	Used
30	**5**	3 a. yellow-green	1·75	4·50
31		4 a. deep green	2·75	7·00
32		8 a. deep blue	3·50	8·00
33		1 r. vermilion	6·50	10·00

OFFICIAL STAMPS

NOTE. The varieties occurring in the machine-printed "On S.S.S." overprints may, of course, also be found in the inverted and double overprints, and many of them are known thus.

I. MACHINE-PRINTED

On

S. S.

S.

(11)

1890. *Optd with T* **11**. (*a*) *In black.*

50	3	6 p. green	£140	£140
		a. Stop before first "S"		
51		2 a. rose-red	32·00	40·00
		a. Stop before first "S"	£110	

(*b*) *In red*

52	3	6 p. green	3·50	1·50
		a. Stop before first "S"	40·00	25·00
53		1 a. blue	13·00	8·00
		a. Stop before first "S"	80·00	

(*c*) *Doubly optd in red and in black*

53*b*	3	6 p. green	£900	
		c. Stop before first "S" (R.)		

On On

S. S. S. S.

S. S.

(12) (13)

1891. *Optd with T* **12**. (*a*) *In black.*

54	3	3 p. orange	1·10	5·00
		a. Opt inverted	70·00	
55		6 p. green	1·50	1·50
		a. Opt double	65·00	
		b. No stop after lower "S"	20·00	20·00
		c. Raised stop before lower "S"	38·00	38·00
56		1 a. blue	60·00	60·00
57		2 a. rose-red	11·00	

(*b*) *In red*

58	3	6 p. green	9·00	5·00
		a. Opt inverted	—	70·00
		b. Opt double	—	60·00
59		1 a. blue	12·00	22·00
		a. Opt inverted	£130	£120
		b. Opt double	£130	£120
		c. No stop after lower "S"	55·00	65·00

1892–97. *Optd with T* **13**. (*a*) *In black.*

60	3	3 p. orange	40	40
		a. Opt inverted	65·00	65·00
		b. First "S" inverted and stop raised	5·00	5·00
		c. No stop after lower "S"	5·00	5·00
		d. Raised stop after second "S"	12·00	12·00
61		6 p. green	1·00	50
		a. First "S" inverted and stop raised	10·00	8·00
		b. Raised stop after second "S"	10·00	8·00
62		1 a. blue	5·50	2·50
		a. Opt double	90·00	80·00
		b. First "S" inverted and stop raised	16·00	12·00
		c. No stop after lower "S"	22·00	22·00
		d. Raised stop after second "S"	18·00	18·00
63		2 a. rose-red	9·50	9·50
		a. Opt inverted	£110	90·00
		b. First "S" inverted and stop raised	35·00	35·00
		c. No stop after lower "S"	35·00	35·00
		d. Raised stop after second "S"	45·00	45·00

(*b*) *In red*

64	3	6 p. green	1·00	60
		a. Opt inverted	55·00	55·00
		b. First "S" inverted and stop raised	9·00	7·00
65		1 a. blue	6·00	1·25
		a. Opt inverted	65·00	55·00
		b. Opt double	90·00	70·00
		c. First "S" inverted and stop raised	15·00	10·00
		d. No stop after lower "S"	15·00	10·00

(*c*) *Doubly overprinted in black and red*

65*e*	3	6 p. green		

There are six settings of this overprint. The inverted "S" occurs in the 2nd and 5th settings, and the missing stop in the 2nd setting of all values except the 6 p. In the 5th setting occurs the raised stop after second "S".

On On

S. S. S. S.

S. S.

(14) (15)

1896. *Optd as T* **14**.

66	3	3 p. orange	5·00	2·25
		a. Comma after first "S"	32·00	30·00
		b. Opt inverted		
		c. Opt double	†	£125
67		6 p. green	5·00	85
		a. Comma after first "S"	35·00	25·00
		b. Comma after lower "S"	35·00	25·00
		c. "S" at right inverted	40·00	30·00
68	3	1 a. blue	5·00	1·75
		a. Comma after first "S"	45·00	28·00
		b. Comma after lower "S"	45·00	28·00
69		2 a. carmine	13·00	13·00
		a. Comma after first "S"	£100	£100

There are four settings of this overprint. (1) 23 mm high, includes the comma after lower "S"; (2) 25 mm high, with variety, comma after first "S"; (3) and (4) 25 mm high, with no important varieties.

1898 (Nov). *Optd with T* **15**.

70	3	6 p. green	45·00	3·50
		a. Small "S" at right	—	25·00
		b. Comma after lower "S"	—	35·00
		c. Lower "S" inverted and stop raised	—	35·00
71		1 a. blue	55·00	5·00
		a. Small "S" at right	—	35·00
		b. Small "S" without stop	—	45·00

There are two settings of this overprint. Nos. 70a and 71a/b occur in the first setting, and Nos. 70b/c in the second setting.

On On

S. S. S. S.

S. S.

(16) (17)

1899. *Optd with T* **16**.

72	3	3 p. orange	—	4·50
73		6 p. green	—	5·50

1900. *Optd as T* **17**.

74	3	3 p. orange	—	4·00
		a. Raised stop after lower "S"	—	32·00
75		6 p. green	—	4·00
		a. Raised stop after lower "S"	—	32·00
		b. Comma after first "S"	—	38·00
76		1 a. blue	—	5·00
		a. Raised stop after lower "S"	—	40·00
77		2 a. carmine	—	35·00
		a. Raised stop after lower "S"	—	£110

There are two settings of this overprint: (1) 22 mm high, with raised stop variety; (2) 23 mm high, with "comma" variety on the 6 pies.

On On

S. S. S S

S. S

(18) (19)

(Optd by Waterlow & Sons)

1900. *Optd with T* **18**.

78	3	3 p. orange	80	1·00
79		6 p. green	40	45
80		1 a. blue	35	35
81		2 a. carmine	3·25	5·50

II. HANDSTAMPED. The words "On" and each letter "S" struck separately

1894. *Handstamped with T* **19**. (*a*) *In black.*

82	3	3 p. orange	2·75	2·75
		a. "On" sideways	60·00	
83		6 p. green	5·00	5·00
		a. "On" only	60·00	60·00
84		1 a. blue	6·00	6·00
85		2 a. rose-red	10·00	10·00
		a. "On" only	60·00	
		b. "On" sideways	70·00	

(*b*) *In red*

86	3	6 p. green	22·00	
86*a*		1 a. blue	65·00	

1896. *Handstamped with letters similar to those of T* **13**, *with stops, but irregular.*

87	3	3 p. orange	55·00	45·00
88		6 p. green	55·00	45·00
		a. "On" omitted	90·00	
88*b*		1 a. blue	65·00	65·00
89		2 a. rose-red	75·00	

1896. *Handstamped with letters similar to those of T* **14**, *with stops, but irregular.*

90	3	3 p. orange	8·00	8·00
		a. "On" double	65·00	
91		6 p. green	14·00	14·00
92		1 a. blue	22·00	22·00
93		2 a. rose-red	22·00	22·00

In No. 90a the second "On" is over the lower "S".

ON On

S S S S

S S

(20) (21)

1896. (*a*) *Handstamped with T* **20**.

94	3	3 p. orange	40·00	40·00
95		2 a. rose-red	45·00	45·00

(*b*) *Handstamped with T* **21**

96	3	3 p. orange	60·00	60·00
97		6 p. green		
98		1 a. blue	60·00	
98*a*		2 a. carmine	70·00	

On On

S S S S

S S

(22) (23)

(*c*) *Handstamped with T* **22**

99	3	3 p. orange	65·00	
100		6 p. green	85·00	
101		1 a. blue	£110	

(*d*) *Handstamped with T* **23**

102	3	3 p. orange	10·00	10·00
103		6 p. green	14·00	14·00
		a. "On" only	—	60·00
104		1 a. blue	17·00	17·00
		a. "On" only	—	60·00
105		2 a. rose-red	20·00	20·00

On

S S

S

(24)

(*e*) *Handstamped with T* **24**

105*a*	3	6 p. green	—	75·00

(*f*) *Mixed overprints*

(i) *Handstamped "On" as in T* **19**, *and machine-printed opt T* **13** *complete*

106	3	6 p. green		

(ii) *Handstamped opt as T* **14**, *and machine-printed opt T* **13**, *complete*

107	3	6 p. green		

Various other types of these handstamps are known to exist, but in the absence of evidence of their authenticity we do not list them. It is stated that stamps of T 4 were never officially overprinted.

The stamps of Sirmoor have been obsolete since 1 April 1902.

SORUTH

PRICES FOR STAMPS ON COVER

Nos. 1/15	*from* × 5
Nos. 16/57	*from* × 10
Nos. O1/13	*from* × 20
Nos. 58/61	*from* × 10
Nos. O14/22	*from* × 10

The name "Saurashtra" corrupted to "Sorath" or "Soruth", was originally used for all the territory later known as Kathiawar. Strictly speaking the name should have been applied only to a portion of Kathiawar including the state of Junagadh. As collectors have known these issues under the heading of "Soruth" for so long, we retain the name.

The currency was 40 docras = 1 koree but early stamps are inscribed in "annas of a koree", one "anna" being a sixteenth of a koree.

GUM. Nos. 1/47 of Soruth were issued without gum.

A. JUNAGADH

1

(="Saurashtra Post 1864–65")

1864 (Nov). *Handstamped in water-colour. Imperf.*

1	1	(1 a.) black/*azure* (laid)	£225	17·00
2		(1 a.) black/*grey* (laid)	£225	17·00
3		(1 a.) black/*azure* (wove)	—	55·00
4		(1 a.) black/*cream* (wove)	—	65·00

ILLUSTRATIONS. Types **2** to **11** are shown actual size.

2 (1 a.) **3** (1 a.)

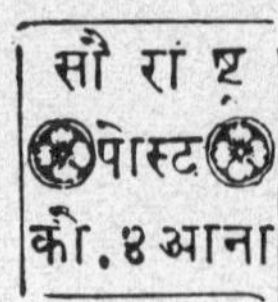
4 (4 a.)

5 (4 a.)

(Type-set at Junagadh Sarkari Saurashtra Nitiprakash Ptg Press)

1867–68. *T* **2** *to* **5** *(two characters, Devanagri and Gujerati respectively for "1" and "4" as shown in the illustrations). Imperf.*

A. *Inscriptions in Gujerati characters*

5 1 a. black/*yellowish* (wove) .. .. ..

B. *Inscriptions in Devanagri characters (as in the illustrations)*

I. *Accents over first letters in top and bottom lines. Wove paper*

6 1 a. red/*green* .. — £800
7 1 a. red/*blue* .. — £800
8 1 a. black/*pink* .. 75·00 30·00
9 2 a. black/*yellow* (1868) .. — £800

II. *Accents over second letters in top and bottom lines*

(*a*) *Wove paper*

10 **2** 1 a. black/*pink* .. 70·00 30·00

(*b*) *Laid paper*

11 **2** 1 a. black/*azure* .. 30·00 8·00
12 **3** 1 a. black/*azure* .. 48·00 16·00
13 1 a. red/*white* .. 12·00 12·00
14 **4** 4 a. black/*white* .. 70·00 80·00
15 **5** 4 a. black/*white* .. 90·00 90·00

Official imitations, consisting of 1 a. carmine-red on white wove and white laid, 1 a. black on blue wove, 4 a. black on white wove, 4 a. black on blue wove, 4 a. red on white laid—all imperforate; 1 a. carmine-red on white laid, 1 a. black on blue wove, 4 a. black on white laid and blue wove—all perforated 12, were made in 1890. Entire sheets of originals have 20 stamps, the imitations only 4 or 16.

6

7

(Dies eng John Dickinson & Sons, London. Typo Junagadh Sarkari Saurashtra Nitiprakash Ptg Press)

1877. *Imperf.*

(*a*) *Medium laid paper, lines wide apart*
(*b*) *Thick laid paper, lines wide apart*
(*c*) *Thick laid paper, lines close together*

16 **6** 1 a. green (*a*) .. 30 30
17 1 a. green (*b*) .. 30 30
18 1 a. green (*c*) .. 30 30
a. Printed both sides .. £180
19 **7** 4 a. vermilion (*a*) .. 80 1·00
20 4 a. vermilion/*toned* (*b*) .. 80 1·00
a. Printed both sides .. £180
21 4 a. scarlet/*bluish* (*b*) .. 80 1·00

1890. *P* 12. (*a*) *Wove paper.*

22 **6** 1 a. green .. 65 65
a. Imperf (pair) .. 15·00 15·00
b. Error. Blue .. £500 £500
c. Imperf horiz (vert pair) .. 35·00
23 **7** 4 a. red .. 1·10 1·25
a. Imperf (pair) .. 25·00 25·00

(*b*) *Toned laid paper*

24 **6** 1 a. green .. 15 20
25 1 a. emerald-green .. 45 55
a. Error. Blue .. £500 £500
26 **7** 4 a. red .. 60 60
27 4 a. carmine .. 70 70

(*c*) *Bluish white laid paper*

28 **6** 1 a. green .. 70 85
a. Imperf between (pair) .. 45·00 45·00
29 4 a. scarlet .. 1·75 2·75

There is a very wide range of colours in both values. The laid paper is found both vertical and horizontal.

The 1 a. was issued in sheets of 20 varieties, with marginal inscriptions; the 4 a. is in horizontal strips of 5 varieties.

(Indian currency)

Three pies.
ત્રણ પાઇ.
(8)

One anna.
એક આનો.
(9)

1913. *Surch in Indian currency with T* **8** *or* **9**. *P* 12.

(*a*) *On yellowish wove paper*

34 **6** 3 p. on 1 a. emerald .. 12 15
a. Imperf (pair) ..

(*b*) *On white wove paper*

35 **6** 3 p. on 1 a. emerald .. 12 15
a. Imperf between (pair) .. 50·00 50·00
b. Surch inverted .. 20·00 20·00
c. Surch double .. † —
36 **7** 1 a. on 4 a. carmine .. 1·50 2·00
a. Imperf (pair) ..
b. Surch both sides .. £300
c. Capital "A" in "Anna" .. 8·00

(*c*) *On white laid paper*

37 **6** 3 p. on 1 a. emerald .. — 24·00
a. Imperf (pair) .. — 55·00
38 **7** 1 a. on 4 a. red .. 5·00 6·00
a. Capital "A" in "Anna" .. 30·00 35·00
b. Surch inverted .. £250
c. Surch double .. £250
d. Surch double, one inverted .. £250

(*d*) *On toned wove paper*

39 **7** 1 a. on 4 a. red .. 90 1·25
a. Imperf (pair) ..
b. Capital "A" in "Anna" .. 6·00
c. Surch inverted .. £200
d. Imperf between (horiz pair) ..

10

11

(Dies eng Thaker & Co, Bombay. Typo Junagadh State Press)

1914 (1 Sept). *New plates. T* **6/7** *redrawn as T* **10/11**. *Wove paper. P* 12.

40 **10** 3 p. bright green .. 35 35
a. Imperf (pair) .. 1·00 1·25
b. Imperf vert (horiz pair) .. 24·00
c. Laid paper .. 50 55
ca. Imperf (pair) .. 1·25 1·60
41 **11** 1 a. red .. 50 60
a. Imperf (pair) .. 5·00 6·00
b. Imperf between (pair) .. £175
c. Laid paper .. 12·00 7·00

12 Nawab Sir Mahabatkhanji III 13

(Dies eng Popatlal Bhimji Pandya. Typo Junagadh State Press)

1923 (1 Sept). *Blurred impression. Laid paper. Pin-perf* 12.

42 **12** 1 a. red .. 3·00 3·50
Sheets of 16 stamps (8 × 2).

ત્રણ પાઇ
(14)

ત્રણ પાઈ
(14*a*)

1923 (1 Sept). *Surch with T* **14**.

43 **12** 3 p. on 1 a. red .. 1·75 2·00
a. Surch with T **14*a*** .. 2·75 3·00

Four stamps in the setting have surch. T **14*a***, i.e. with top of last character curved to right.

1923 (Oct). *Blurred impression. Wove paper. Pin-perf* 12, *small holes.*

44 **13** 3 p. mauve .. 35 40

1924–29. *Clear impression. P* 12, *large holes.* (*a*) *Wove paper.*

45 **13** 3 p. mauve (1.24) .. 50 35
46 **12** 1 a. red (4.24) .. 2·00 2·50
a. Imperf (pair) .. 24·00 28·00

(*b*) *Laid paper*

47 **13** 3 p. mauve (1929) .. 50 50
a. Imperf (pair) .. 2·50 3·50
b. Imperf between (horiz pair) .. 3·00 4·50

The first plate of the 3 p., which printed No. 44, produced unsatisfactory impressions, so it was replaced by a second plate, from which No. 45 comes. Sheets printed from the first plate had very large margins.

The 1 a. is also from a new plate, giving a clearer impression. Sheets of 16 stamps (4 × 4). The laid paper shows a sheet watermark of the State Arms within a circular inscription.

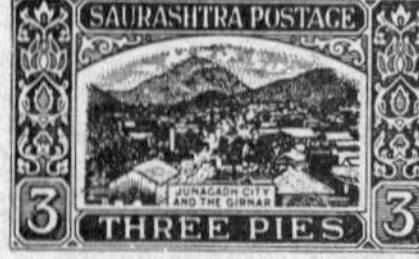

15 Junagadh City

16 Gir Lion

17 Nawab Sir Mahabatkhanji III

18 Kathi Horse

(Litho Indian Security Printing Press, Nasik)

1929 (1 Oct). *P* 14. *Inscr* "POSTAGE".

49 **15** 3 p. black and blackish green .. 45 12
50 **16** ½ a. black and deep blue .. 3·25 8
51 **17** 1 a. black and carmine .. 2·00 85
52 **18** 2 a. black and dull orange .. 6·00 1·25
a. Grey and dull yellow .. 32·00 1·00
53 **15** 3 a. black and carmine .. 1·50 1·25
54 **16** 4 a. black and purple .. 9·00 6·50
55 **18** 8 a. black and yellow-green .. 10·00 8·50
56 **17** 1 r. black and pale blue .. 4·50 8·00

1936. *As T* **17**, *but inscr* "POSTAGE AND REVENUE". *P* 14.

57 **17** 1 a. black and carmine .. 1·00 90

OFFICIAL STAMPS

SARKARI
(O 1)

1929 (1 Oct). *Optd with Type* O **1**, *in vermilion, at Nasik.*

O1 **15** 3 p. black and blackish green .. 15 8
a. Red opt .. 25 15
O2 **16** ½ a. black and deep blue .. 30 8
a. Red opt .. 50 15
O3 **17** 1 a. black and carmine (No. 51) .. 25 10
a. Red opt .. 50 20
O4 **18** 2 a. black and dull orange .. 2·00 25
a. Grey and dull yellow .. 6·50 60
b. Red opt .. 6·50 1·25
O5 **15** 3 a. black and carmine .. 40 20
a. Red opt .. 3·50 1·50
O6 **16** 4 a. black and purple .. 1·00 40
a. Red opt .. 7·00 1·75
O7 **18** 8 a. black and yellow-green .. 1·75 80
O8 **17** 1 r. black and pale blue .. 2·25 3·00

SARKARI
(O 2)

SARKARI
(O 3)

1932. *Optd with Types* O **2** (3 *a.*, 1 *r.*) *or* O **3** (others), *all in red, at Junagadh State Press.*

O 9 **15** 3 a. black and carmine .. 22·00 7·00
a. Optd with Type O **3** .. 12·00 12·00
O10 **16** 4 a. black and purple .. 20·00 15·00
O11 **18** 8 a. black and yellow-green .. 25·00 16·00
O12 **17** 1 r. black and pale blue .. 40·00 40·00
a. Optd with Type O **3** .. 25·00 28·00

1938. *No.* 57 *optd with Type* O **1**, *in vermilion.*

O13 **17** 1 a. black and carmine .. 1·75 35
a. Brown-red opt .. 1·75 55

The state was occupied by Indian troops on 9 November 1947.

B. UNITED STATE OF SAURASHTRA

Under the new Constitution of India the United State of Saurashtra was formed on 15 February 1948, comprising 31 former states and 191 estates of Kathiawar, including Jasdan, Morvi, Nawanagar and Wadhwan. A referendum was held in Junagadh which then joined the United State on 20 January 1949. However, it is believed that the following issues were in use only in Junagadh.

The following issues were surcharged at the Junagadh State Press.

POSTAGE & REVENUE

ONE ANNA
(19)

Postage & Revenue

ONE ANNA
(20)

1949. *Stamps of* 1929 *surch.* (*a*) *With T* **19** *in red.*

58 **16** 1 a. on ½ a. black and deep blue .. 4·25 1·50
a. Surch double .. £130 £120
b. "AFNA" for "ANNA" and inverted "N" in "REVENUE" .. £375
c. Larger first "A" in "ANNA" .. £100 75·00

(*b*) *With T* **20** *in green*

59 **18** 1 a. on 2 a. grey and dull yellow .. 3·50 1·50

No. 58*c* occurs on position 10.

A number of other varieties occur on No. 58, including: small "V" in "REVENUE" (No. 8); small "N" in "REVENUE" (Nos. 9, 13 and 14); small "E" in "POSTAGE" (No. 12); thick "A" in "POSTAGE" (No. 19); inverted "N" in "REVENUE" and small second "A" in "ANNA" (No. 25); small "O" in "ONE" (No. 26); small "V" and "U" in "REVENUE" (No. 28); small "N" in "ONE" (No. 37).

In No. 59 no stop after "ANNA" is known on Nos. 4, 17, 25, 34 and 38 and small "N" in "ONE" on Nos. 9, 11, 26 and 31.

21

1949 (Sept). *Court Fee stamps of Bhavnagar state optd* "SAURASHTRA" *and further optd* "U.S.S. REVENUE & POSTAGE" *as in T* **21**, *in black. Typo. P* 11.

60 21 1 a. purple .. .. .. 2·25 2·00
a. "POSTAGE" omitted £130 £130
b. Opt double £130 £130

Minor varieties include small "S" in "POSTAGE" (Nos. 9 and 49); small "N" in "REVENUE" (Nos. 15 and 55); small "U" in "REVENUE" (Nos. 18 and 58); small "V" in "REVENUE" (Nos. 24, 37, 64 and 77); and small "O" in "POSTAGE" (Nos. 31 and 71).
Various missing stop varieties also occur.

POSTAGE & REVENUE
ONE ANNA
(22)

1950 (Mar). *Stamp of* 1929 *surch with T* **22**.

61 15 1 a. on 3 p. black and blackish green .. 11·00 11·00
a. "P" of "POSTAGE" omitted .. £130 £130
b. "O" of "ONE" omitted £130 £130

Other minor varieties include small "S" in "POSTAGE" with small "V" in "REVENUE" (Nos. 14 and 26) and small "V" in "REVENUE" (No. 11).

OFFICIAL STAMPS

1948–49. *Nos.* O4/O7 *surch* "ONE ANNA" ($2\frac{1}{4}$ *mm high*).

O14 18 1 a. on 2 a. grey & dull yell (B.) (8.48) .. £400 20·00
O15 15 1 a. on 3 a. black and carmine (10.48) .. £400 21·00
a. Surch double .. .. .. † £600
O16 16 1 a. on 4 a. black and purple (1.49) .. £140 17·00
a. "ANNE" for "ANNA" £1600 £250
b. "ANNN" for "ANNA" £1600 £250
O17 18 1 a. on 8 a. black and yellow-green (1.49) £140 17·00
a. "ANNE" for "ANNA" £1600 £250
b. "ANNN" for "ANNA" £1600 £250

Numerous minor varieties of fount occur in this surcharge.

1948 (Nov). *Handstamped* "ONE ANNA" (4 *mm high*).

O18 17 1 a. on 1 r. (No. O8) .. .. £140 16·00
O19 1 a. on 1 r. (No. O12a) .. .. 80·00 18·00
a. Optd on No. O12 .. .. .. — 35·00

A used copy of No. O12 is known overprinted as on Nos. O14/17 in black which may have come from a proof sheet.

1949 (Jan). *Postage stamps optd with Type* O **3**, *in red*.

O20 15 3 p. black and blackish green .. £140 6·00
O21 16 ½ a. black and deep blue .. .. £150 6·00
O22 18 1 a. on 2 a. grey and dull yellow (No. 59) 25·00 11·00

Various wrong fount letters occur in the above surcharges.
Various stamps exist with "Sarkari" in manuscript.

The United State of Saurashtra posts were integrated with the Indian Postal Service on 1 April 1950.

TRAVANCORE

PRICES FOR STAMPS ON COVER

Nos. 1/77	*from* × 10
Nos. O1/108	*from* × 15

(16 cash = 1 chuckram; 28 chuckrams = 1 rupee)

"Anchel" or "Anchal" = Post Office Department.

The stamps of Travancore were valid on mail posted to Cochin.

PRINTERS. All stamps of Travancore were printed by the Stamp Manufactory, Trivandrum, *unless otherwise stated*.

PRINTING METHODS. The dies were engraved on brass from which electrotypes were made and locked together in a forme for printing the stamps. As individual electrotypes became worn they were replaced by new ones and their positions in the forme were sometimes changed. This makes it difficult to plate the early issues. From 1901 plates were made which are characterised by a frame (or "Jubilee" line) round the margins of the sheets.

Up to the 6 cash of 1910 the dies were engraved by Dharmalingham Asari.

SHADES. We list only the main groups of shades but there are many others in view of the large number of printings and the use of fugitive inks. Sometimes shade variation is noticeable within the same sheet.

1 Conch or Chank Shell

1888 (16 Oct). *As T* 1, *but each value differs slightly. Laid paper. P* 12.

1 1 1 ch. ultramarine (*shades*) .. .. 2·50 2·50
2 1 2 ch. red .. .. 4·50 5·00
3 4 ch. green .. .. 14·00 14·00

The paper bears a large sheet watermark showing a large conch shell surmounted by "GOVERNMENT" in large outline letters, in an arch with "OF TRAVANCORE" at foot in a straight line. Many stamps in the sheet are without watermark.
These stamps on laid paper in abnormal colours are proofs.

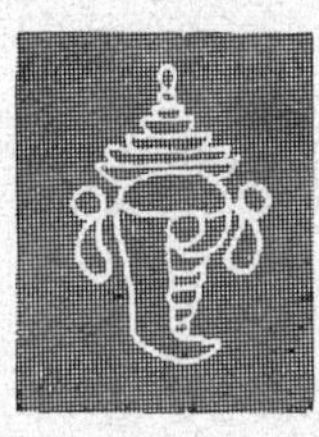

2

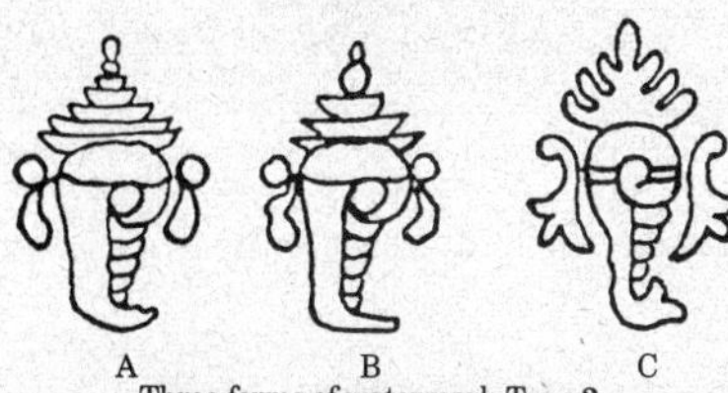

A B C
Three forms of watermark Type **2**.
(*as seen from the front of the stamp*)

WATERMARKS AND PAPERS.

Type A appeared upright on early printings of the 1, 2 and 4 ch. values on odd-sized sheets which did not fit the number of shells. Later it was always sideways with 15 mm between the shells on standard-sized sheets of 84 (14 × 6) containing 60 shells (10 × 6). It therefore never appears centred on the stamps and it occurs on hand-made papers only.

Type B is similar in shape but can easily be distinguished as it is invariably upright, with 11 mm between the shells, and is well centred on the stamps. It also occurs only on handmade papers. It was introduced in 1904 and from 1915, when Type A was brought back into use, it was employed concurrently until 1925.

Type C is quite different in shape and always occurs upright on machine-made papers. There are two versions. The first, in use from 1925 to 1939, has 84 shells 11 mm apart and is always well centred. The second, introduced in 1929 and believed not to have been used after 1930, has 60 shells (12 × 5) 15 mm apart and is invariably badly centred and some stamps in the sheet have no watermark. We do not distinguish between these two in the lists, but stamps known to exist in the second version are indicated in footnotes. The machine-made paper is generally smoother and of more even texture.

NO WATERMARK VARIETIES. Some of these were formerly listed but we have now decided to omit them as they do not occur in full sheets. They arise in the following circumstances: (*a*) on sheets with wmk A; (*b*) on sheets with the wide-spaced form of wmk C; and (*c*) on late printings of the pictorial issues of 1939–46. They are best collected in pairs, with and without watermark.

DATES OF ISSUE. In the absence of more definite information the dates quoted usually refer to the first reported date of new printings on different watermarks but many were not noted at the time and the dates of these are indicated by a query. Dated postmarks on single stamps are difficult to find.

3

4

5

6

7

8

1889–1904. *Wove paper. Wmk A (upright or sideways). P* 12 (*sometimes rough*).

4 1 ½ ch. slate-lilac (1894) 45 12
a. Doubly printed .. .. .. — 75·00
b. Reddish lilac 35 8
ba. Imperf between (vert pair) .. 75·00 75·00
bb. Doubly printed .. .. .. — 75·00
c. Purple (1899) 30 8
ca. Doubly printed .. .. .. — 75·00
d. Dull purple (1904) 30 8
5 5 ¾ ch. black (14.3.01) 25 8
6 1 1 ch. ultramarine 60 12
a. *Tête-bêche* (pair) £2000 £1250
b. Doubly printed .. .. .. — £130
c. Imperf vert (horiz pair) .. ..
d. Pale ultramarine (1892) .. .. 1·50 12
e. Violet-blue (1901) .. .. 1·75 30
7 2 ch. salmon (1890) .. .. 1·50 25
a. Rose (1891) .. .. .. 1·50 12
ab. Imperf (pair) £130
b. Pale pink (1899) .. .. 1·50 25
ba. Imperf between (vert pair) .. 75·00 75·00
bb. Doubly printed £120 £120
c. Red (1904) .. .. .. 1·10 12
ca. Imperf between (horiz pair) .. 70·00 70·00
8 1 4 ch. green .. .. 1·10 40
a. Yellow-green (1901) .. .. 1·50 40
b. Dull green (1904) .. .. 2·50 45
ba. Doubly printed .. .. .. — £130

Nos. 6, 6*d*, 7 and 8 occur with the watermark upright and sideways. No. 7*a* is known only with the watermark upright. The remainder exist only with the watermark sideways.

The sheet sizes were as follows:
½ ch. 56 (14 × 4) except for No. 4*d* which was 84 (14 × 6) with border.
¾ ch. 84 (14 × 6) with border.
1 ch. No. 6, 80 (10 × 8) and later 84 (14 × 6) with border; No. 6*d*, 96 (16 × 6); No. 6*e*, 84 (14 × 6) with border.
2 ch. No. 7, 80 (10 × 8); No. 7*a*, 70 (10 × 7); Nos. 7*b*, 7*c*, 60 (10 × 6).
4 ch. No. 8, 60 (10 × 6); Nos. 8*a*/*b*, 84 (14 × 6) with border.

After 1904 all stamps in Types **3** to **8** were in standard-sized sheets of 84 (14 × 6) with border.

For later printings watermarked Type A, see Nos. 23/30.

1904–21? *Wmk B, upright (centred). P* 12, *sometimes rough*.

9 3 4 ca. pink (11.08) 10 5
a. Imperf between (vert pair) .. 75·00 75·00
10 1 6 ca. chestnut (2.10) 25 5
a. Imperf between (horiz pair) .. — 70·00
11 ½ ch. reddish lilac 10 5
a. Reddish violet 10 5
b. Lilac 10 5
c. "CHUCRRAM" .. .. .. 3·50 3·00
12 4 10 ca. pink (1921?) .. .. .. 8·00 3·00
13 5 ¾ ch. black 25 5
14 1 1 ch. indigo 35 8
a. Deep blue (1911) 85 25
b. Grey-blue (1912) 35 8
15 1¼ ch. claret (*shades*) (12.19) 25 10
a. Imperf between (horiz pair) .. 75·00 75·00
16 2 ch. salmon .. .. 7·50 2·00
a. Red 40 8
17 6 3 ch. violet (11.3.11) 55 8
a. Imperf between (vert pair) .. 70·00 70·00
b. Imperf between (vert strip of 3) .. £120 £100
18 1 4 ch. dull green .. .. 1·75 80
a. Slate-green .. .. 1·10 35
19 7 7 ch. claret (1916) .. .. .. 1·60 40
a. Error. Carmine-red .. .. .. — 50·00
20 8 14 ch. orange-yellow (1916) .. .. 2·40 70
a. Imperf vert (horiz strip of 3) .. £120 £120

1/4 (9) 1 C (10)

1906. *Surch as T* **9**. *Wmk* B.

21 1 ¼ on ½ ch. reddish lilac 8 5
a. Reddish violet 8 5
b. Lilac 8 5
c. "CHUCRRAM" .. .. .. 3·00 3·00
d. Surch inverted .. .. .. 20·00 16·00
22 ⅜ on ½ ch. reddish lilac 20 5
a. Reddish violet 8 5
b. Lilac 8 5
c. "CHUCRRAM" .. .. .. 3·00 3·00
d. Surch inverted .. .. .. 30·00 30·00
e. Surch double .. .. ..
f. "8" omitted .. .. .. — 40·00

1915–21. *Reversion to wmk* A (*sideways*). *P* 12 (*sometimes rough*).

23 3 4 ca. pink (1915) .. .. .. 1·75 15
24 4 5 ca. olive-bistre (30.10.21) 25 10
a. Imperf between (horiz pair) .. 40·00 40·00
b. Imperf between (horiz strip of 3) .. 85·00 85·00
c. "TRAVANCOPE" .. .. .. — 8·00
25 1 6 ca. orange-brown (date?) 75 12
26 ½ ch. reddish violet (date?) 30 12
a. "CHUCRRAM" .. .. .. 4·50 3·25
b. Imperf between (horiz pair) .. 70·00 70·00
27 4 10 ca. pink (30.10.21) 25 8
28 1 1 ch. grey-blue (date?) .. .. .. 1·40 15
a. Deep blue .. .. 1·40 15
29 1¼ ch. claret (12.19) .. .. .. 1·75 12
30 6 3 ch. reddish lilac (date?) .. .. 1·75 35

1921 (Mar). *Surch as T* **10**. *Wmk* A.

31 3 1 c. on 4 ca. pink 10 12
a. Surch inverted .. .. .. 11·00 8·00
32 11 5 c. on 1 ch. grey-blue (R.) 12 12
a. Deep blue 12 12
b. Stamp printed both sides .. ..
c. Imperf between (vert pair) .. .. — 65·00
d. Surch inverted .. .. .. 11·00 7·00
e. Surch double .. .. .. 18·00 12·00
f. On wmk B. *Deep blue* .. .. 6·50 6·50

1925–39. *Wmk* C. *Machine-made paper. P* 12.

33 4 5 ca. olive-bistre (1926) .. .. .. 1·75 75
a. Imperf between (horiz pair) .. 30·00 30·00
b. "TRAVANCOPE" .. .. .. — 7·00
34 5 ca. chocolate (1930) 70 30
a. Imperf between (horiz pair) .. 30·00 30·00
b. Imperf between (vert pair) .. 35·00 35·00
35 1 6 ca. brown-red (date?) .. .. .. 1·10 8
a. Imperf between (horiz pair) .. 18·00 18·00
b. Imperf between (vert pair) .. 30·00 30·00
c. Printed both sides .. .. .. 55·00 55·00
d. Perf 12½ .. .. 3·50 70
e. Perf comp of 12 and 12½ .. .. 10·00 5·00
f. Perf 12½ × 11 .. .. .. — 25·00
36 ½ ch. reddish violet (date?) .. .. 3·50 3·50
a. "CHUCRRAM" .. .. .. 28·00
37 4 10 ca. pink (1926) 70 8
a. Imperf between (horiz pair) .. 30·00 30·00
b. Imperf between (vert pair) .. 16·00 16·00
38 5 ¾ ch. black (1932) .. .. .. 1·75 30
39 ¾ ch. mauve (16.11.32) 25 8
a. Perf 12½ .. .. 3·00 70
ab. Imperf between (horiz pair) .. 42·00
b. Perf comp of 12 and 12½ .. .. 8·00 4·25

40 5 ¾ ch. reddish violet (1939) 35 10
a. Perf 12½ 3·00 70
b. Perf comp of 12 and 12½ 6·00 2·00
c. Perf 11 — 20·00
d. Perf comp of 12 and 11 — 20·00
41 1 1 ch. slate-blue (date?) 35 10
a. Indigo 75 12
b. Imperf between (horiz pair) 70·00 70·00
c. Imperf between (vert pair) 70·00 70·00
d. Perf 12½ 3·75 90
42 1½ ch. rose (1932) 35 10
a. Imperf between (horiz strip of 3) 70·00 70·00
b. Perf 12½ 7·50 2·75
c. Perf comp of 12 and 12½
43 2 ch. carmine-red (date?) 3·25 30
44 6 3 ch. violet (1926) 80 12
a. Imperf between (vert pair) 65·00 65·00
b. Perf 12½ 14·00 8·00
c. Perf comp of 12 and 12½ 14·00 8·00
45 1 4 ch. grey-green (date?) 2·25 35
46 7 7 ch. claret (1925) 2·25 80
a. Carmine-red (date?) 60·00 55·00
b. Brown-purple (1932) 4·25 1·25
ba. Perf. 12½ 8·00 8·00
bb. Perf comp of 12 and 12½ 8·00 8·00
46*c* 8 14 ch. orange-yellow (*p* 12½) (date?) 50·00

It is believed that the 12½ perforation and the perf 12 and 12½ compound were introduced in 1937 and that the 11 perforation came later, probably in 1939.

The 5 ca. chocolate, 6 ca., 10 ca. and 3 ch. also exist on the wide-spaced watermark (60 shells to the sheet of 84).

11 Sri Padmanabha Shrine

12 State Chariot

13 Maharaja Sir Bala Rama Varma

(Des M. R. Madhawan Unnithan. Plates by Calcutta Chromotype Co. Typo Stamp Manufactory, Trivandrum)

1931 (6 Nov). *Coronation. Cream or white paper. Wmk C. P* 11½, 12.
47 **11** 6 ca. black and green 25 25
a. Imperf between (horiz pair) £200
48 **12** 10 ca. black and ultramarine 25 25
49 **13** 3 ch. black and purple 30 30

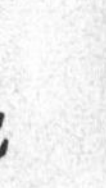

1 C (14) 1 C (15)

16 Maharaja Sir Bala Rama Varma and Subramania Shrine

1932 (14 Jan). (i) *Surch as T* **14**. (*a*) *Wmk* A (*sideways*).
50 1 1 c. on 1¼ ch. claret 10 12
a. Imperf between (horiz pair) 60·00 60·00
b. Surch inverted 4·25 6·00
c. Surch double 18·00 18·00
d. Pair, one without surch 65·00 65·00
e. "c" omitted 40·00 40·00
51 2 c. on 1¼ ch. claret 10 10
a. Surch inverted 4·25 6·00
b. Surch double 18·00 18·00
c. Surch double, one inverted 50·00
d. Surch treble 45·00
e. Surch treble, one inverted 70·00 70·00
f. Pair, one without surch 70·00 70·00
g. "2" omitted 40·00 40·00
h. "c" omitted 35·00 35·00

(*b*) *Wmk* B (*upright*)
52 1 1 c. on 1¼ ch. claret 75 75
a. Surch inverted 14·00 14·00
b. Surch double 20·00 20·00
53 2 c. on 1¼ ch claret 1·40 1·50
a. Imperf between (horiz pair) 60·00 60·00

(*c*) *Wmk* C
54 1 1 c. on 1¼ ch. claret 4·00 3·50
a. Surch inverted 20·00 20·00
55 2 c. on 1¼ ch. claret 4·50 3·00

(ii) *Surch as T* **10**. *Wmk* B
56 1 2 c. on 1¼ ch. claret 4·25 5·00
a. Surch double, one albino

1932 (Mar?). *Surch as T* **15**. *Wmk* C.
57 4 1 c. on 5 ca. chocolate 12 12
a. Imperf between (horiz pair) 85·00 85·00
b. Surch inverted 8·50 10·00
c. Surch inverted on back only 26·00 26·00
d. Pair, one without surch 48·00 48·00
e. "1" omitted 26·00 26·00
f. "C" omitted — 26·00
g. "TRAVANCOPE" 8·50
58 1 c. on 5 ca. slate-purple 15 15
a. Surch inverted — 65·00
b. "1" inverted 40·00 40·00
59 4 2 c. on 10 ca. pink 12 12
a. Imperf between (horiz pair) 65·00 65·00
b. Surch inverted 6·00 7·00
c. Surch double 14·00 17·00
d. Surch double, one inverted 35·00 35·00
e. Surch double, both inverted 22·00 22·00

No. 58 was not issued without the surcharge.

(Plates by Indian Security Printing Press, Nasik. Typo Stamp Manufactory, Trivandrum)

1937 (29 Mar). *Temple Entry Proclamation. T* **16** *and similar horiz designs. Wmk* C. *P* 12.
60 6 ca. carmine 15 12
a. Imperf between (horiz strip of 3) £250
b. Perf 12½ 35 30
c. Compound perf 9·00 9·00
61 12 ca. bright blue 20 15
a. Perf 12½ 35 30
ab. Imperf between (vert pair) £225
b. Compound perf 12·00
62 1½ ch. yellow-green 35 30
a. Imperf between (vert pair) £175
b. Perf 12½ 2·50 1·50
63 3 ch. violet 45 30
a. Perf 12½ 0 75 50

Designs:—Maharaja's portrait and temples—12 ca. Sri Padmanabha; 1½ ch. Mahadeva; 3 ch. Kanyakumari.

COMPOUND PERFS. This term covers stamps perf compound of 12½ and 11, 12 and 11 or 12 and 12½, and where two or more combinations exist the prices are for the commonest. Such compounds can occur on values which do not exist perf 12 all round.

17 Lake Ashtamudi

18 Maharaja Sir Bala Rama Varma

(Des Nilakantha Pellai. Plates by Indian Security Printing Press, Nasik. Typo Stamp Manufactory, Trivandrum)

1939 (9 May). *Maharaja's 27th Birthday. T* **17/18** *and similar designs. Wmk* C. *P* 12½.
64 1 ch. yellow-green 15 10
a. Imperf between (horiz pair) 6·50 6·50
b. Perf 11 60 12
ba. Imperf between (vert pair) 6·50 6·50
bb. Imperf between (vert strip of 3) 10·00 10·00
c. Perf 12 90 35
ca. Imperf between (horiz pair) 7·00 7·00
cb. Imperf between (vert pair) 7·00 7·00
d. Compound perf 2·25 1·50
da. Imperf between (vert pair) 14·00 14·00
65 1½ ch. scarlet 35 30
a. Doubly printed 25·00 25·00
b. Imperf between (horiz pair) 11·00 11·00
c. Imperf between (vert pair) 8·00 8·00
d. Perf 11 3·00 4·00
da. Imperf horiz (vert pair) 11·00
e. Perf 12 3·50 2·40
f. Perf 13½ 11·00 11·00
g. Compound perf 5·00 3·00
66 2 ch. orange 25 20
a. Perf 11 2·00 30
b. Perf 12 5·00 2·40
c. Compound perf 5·00 2·40
67 3 ch. brown 25 10
a. Doubly printed 18·00 18·00
b. Imperf between (horiz pair) 10·00 10·00
c. Perf 11 1·60 35
ca. Doubly printed 16·00 16·00
d. Perf 12 2·25 70
da. Imperf between (vert pair) 15·00 15·00
e. Compound perf 3·00 1·50
68 4 ch. red 50 40
a. Perf 11 2·25 50
b. Perf 12 3·00 70
c. Compound perf 14·00 14·00
69 7 ch. pale blue 75 90
a. Perf 11 7·00 4·00
ab. Blue 8·00 4·50
b. Compound perf 12·00 7·50
70 14 ch. turquoise-green 1·50 2·50
a. Perf 11 3·00 4·50

Designs: *Vert as T* **18**—1½ ch., 3 ch. Portraits of Maharaja in different frames. *Horiz as T* **17**—4 ch. Sri Padmanabha Shrine; 7 ch. Cape Comorin; 14 ch. Pachipari Reservoir.

19 Maharaja and Aruvikara Falls

2 CASH (**20**)

(Des Nilakantha Pellai. Plates by Indian Security Printing Press, Nasik. Typo Stamp Manufactory, Trivandrum)

1941 (20 Oct). *Maharaja's 29th Birthday. T* **19** *and similar horiz design. Wmk* C. *P* 12½.
71 6 ca. blackish violet 20 8
a. Perf 11 60 10
ab. Imperf between (vert pair) 8·50 8·50
ac. Imperf horiz (vert pair) 10·00 10·00
b. Perf 12 2·00 80
ba. Imperf between (horiz pair) 7·50 7·50
bb. Imperf between (vert pair) 10·00 10·00
bc. Imperf between (vert strip of 3) 8·50 8·50
c. Compound perf 90 60
72 ¾ ch. brown 20 8
a. Perf 11 60 10
ab. Imperf between (horiz pair) 13·00 13·00
ac. Imperf between (vert pair) 8·50 8·50
ad. Imperf between (vert strip of 3) 8·50 8·50
b. Perf 12 4·00 2·75
c. Compound perf 2·00 1·10

Design:—¾ ch. Maharaja and Marchanda Varma Bridge, Alwaye.

1943 (17 Sept). *Nos.* 65, 71 (*colour changed*) *and* 72 *surch as T* **20**. *P* 12½.
73 2 ca. on 1½ ch. scarlet 10 10
a. Imperf between (vert pair) 16·00 16·00
b. "2" omitted 40·00 40·00
c. "CA" omitted 75·00 75·00
d. "ASH" omitted 75·00 75·00
e. Perf 11 10 10
ea. "CA" omitted 75·00 75·00
f. Compound perf 55 55
fa. Imperf between (vert pair) 25·00 25·00
fb. "2" omitted 40·00 40·00
74 4 ca. on ¾ ch. brown 30 10
a. Perf 11 30 10
b. Perf 12 — 15·00
c. Compound perf 1·60 1·00
75 8 ca. on 6 ca. scarlet 40 10
a. Perf 11 40 10
ab. Imperf between (horiz pair) 18·00 18·00
b. Perf 12 — 15·00
c. Compound perf 3·50 3·00

21 Maharaja Sir Bala Rama Varma

SPECIAL (**22**)

(Des Nilakantha Pellai. Plates by Indian Security Printing Press, Nasik. Typo Stamp Manufactory, Trivandrum)

1946 (24 Oct). *Maharaja's 34th Birthday. Wmk* C. *P* 12½.
76 **21** 8 ca. carmine 3·00 1·50
a. Perf 11 70 70
b. Perf 12 6·00 3·00
ba. Imperf between (horiz pair) 18·00 18·00
bb. Imperf between (horiz strip of 3) 30·00 30·00

1946. *No.* O103 *revalidated for ordinary postage with opt T* **22**, *in orange. P* 12½.
77 **19** 6 ca. blackish violet 4·25 1·50
a. Perf 11 9·50 4·25
b. Compound perf 5·00 2·00

OFFICIAL STAMPS

GUM. Soon after 1911 the Official stamps were issued without gum. Thus only the initial printings of the 1, 2, 3 and 4 ch. values were gummed. As Nos. O38/9, O41/2 and O95 were overprinted on stamps intended for normal postage these, also, have gum.

PRINTINGS. Sometimes special printings of postage stamps were made specifically for overprinting for Official use, thus accounting for Official stamps appearing with watermarks or in shades not listed in the postage issues.

SETTINGS. These are based on the study of complete sheets of 84, and the measurements given are those of the majority of stamps on the sheet. Examples are known showing different measurements as each overprint was set individually in loose type, but these are not included in the listings.

On S S (O 1) On S S (O 2)

Rounded "O"

1911 (16 Aug)–**26**. *Contemporary stamps optd with Type* O 1 (13 *mm wide*). *P* 12, *sometimes rough*. (*a*) *Wmk* B (*upright*) (16.8.11–21).
O 1 3 4 ca. pink (1916) 10 8
a. Opt inverted 18·00 16·00
b. Opt double 28·00 18·00
c. "S S" inverted 4·50 3·50
d. Imperf (pair) 50·00 50·00
O 2 1 6 ca. chestnut (date ?) 9·00 9·00
O 3 ½ ch. reddish lilac (R.) (1919) 70 35
a. "CHUCRRAM" 6·00 4·25
O 4 4 10 ca. pink (1921) 5·00 1·60
a. "O" inverted 15·00 7·00
b. Left "S" inverted 15·00 7·00
c. Right "S" inverted 15·00 7·00
O 5 1 1 ch. grey-blue (R.) 30 8
a. Imperf between (vert pair) 60·00 60·00
b. Opt inverted 7·00 4·25
c. Opt double 48·00 42·00
d. "nO" for "On" 65·00 65·00
e. "O" inverted 3·50 1·10
f. Left "S" inverted 3·50 1·10
g. Right "S" inverted 3·50 1·10
h. "S S" inverted — 6·50
O 6 2 ch. red 30 8
a. Opt inverted 8·00 8·00
b. "O" inverted 4·00 1·10
c. Left "S" inverted 4·00 1·10
d. Right "S" inverted 4·00 1·10
O 7 2 ch. red (B.) (date ?) — 24·00

O 8 6 3 ch. violet 30 8
a. Imperf between (vert pair) 55·00 55·00
b. Imperf vert (horiz strip of 4) 80·00
c. Opt inverted 10·00 10·00
d. Opt double 45·00 45·00
e. Right "S" inverted 4·00 1·00
f. Right "S" omitted 38·00 38·00
g. Left "S" omitted 38·00 38·00
O 9 3 ch. violet (B.) (date ?) 28·00 16·00
O10 1 4 ch. slate-green 55 8
a. Imperf between (pair) 45·00 45·00
b. Opt inverted 14·00 11·00
c. Opt double 45·00 45·00
d. "O" inverted 6·00 2·40
e. Left "S" inverted 6·00 2·40
f. Right "S" inverted 6·00 2·40
g. Left "S" omitted 35·00 35·00
O11 4 ch. slate-green (B.) (1921) 28·00 13·00
a. "O" inverted 80·00 38·00
b. Left "S" inverted 80·00 38·00
c. Right "S" inverted 80·00 38·00

(b) *Wmk A (sideways)* (1919–25)

O12 3 4 ca. pink 80 12
a. Imperf (pair) 70·00 70·00
b. Opt inverted 16·00 11·00
c. "O" inverted 5·00 1·75
d. Left "S" inverted 5·00 1·75
e. Right "S" inverted 5·00 1·75
O13 4 ca. pink (B.) (1921) 10·00 1·00
a. "O" inverted — 10·00
O14 4 5 ca. olive-bistre (1921) 25 10
a. Opt inverted 9·00 7·00
b. "O" inverted 2·25 1·25
c. Left "S" inverted 2·25 1·25
d. Right "S" inverted 2·25 1·25
O15 1 6 ca. orange-brown (1921) 12 8
a. Imperf between (vert pair) 55·00 55·00
b. Opt inverted 9·00 8·00
c. Opt double 18·00 18·00
d. "O" inverted 2·00 80
e. Left "S" inverted 2·00 80
f. Right "S" inverted 2·00 80
O16 6 ca. orange-brown (B.) (1921) 7·00 1·75
a. Opt inverted 55·00 55·00
b. "O" inverted 30·00 12·00
c. Left "S" inverted 30·00 12·00
d. Right "S" inverted 30·00 12·00
O17 ½ ch. reddish violet (R.) (date?) 15 8
a. *Reddish lilac* (date?) 15 8
b. Imperf between (horiz pair) 50·00 50·00
c. Imperf between (vert pair) 40·00 40·00
d. Stamp doubly printed 45·00 45·00
e. Opt inverted 7·50 3·00
f. Opt double, both inverted 50·00 50·00
g. "CHUCRRAM" 4·00 2·75
h. "On" omitted — 50·00
i. Right "S" inverted — 5·50
j. Right "S" omitted — 50·00
O18 4 10 ca. pink (3.21) 25 10
a. *Scarlet* (1925?) — 4·00
b. Opt inverted 15·00 10·00
c. Opt double 28·00 20·00
d. "O" inverted 2·25 1·25
e. Left "S" inverted 2·25 1·25
f. Right "S" inverted 2·25 1·25
O19 10 ca. pink (B.) (date ?) 16·00 6·00
a. Opt inverted — 40·00
b. "O" inverted — 24·00
O20 1 1 ch. grey-blue (R.) (date ?) 1·75 70
a. *Deep blue* 1·75 70
b. "O" inverted 11·00 6·00
c. Left "S" inverted 11·00 6·00
O21 1¼ ch. claret (12.19) 35 12
a. Stamp doubly printed — 50·00
b. Opt inverted 9·00 8·00
c. Opt double 35·00 35·00
d. "O" inverted 4·00 1·60
e. Left "S" inverted 4·00 1·60
f. Right "S" inverted 4·00 1·60
g. Error. Carmine 50·00
O22 1¼ ch. claret (B.) (1921) 25·00 15·00
a. "O" inverted 70·00 45·00
b. Left "S" inverted 70·00 45·00
c. Right "S" inverted 70·00 45·00

(c) *Wmk C* (1925–30)

O23 4 5 ca. olive-bistre (1926) 25 12
a. Imperf between (horiz pair) 50·00 50·00
b. Opt inverted 11·00 10·00
c. "O" inverted 2·25 1·25
d. Left "S" inverted 2·25 1·25
e. Right "S" inverted 2·25 1·25
O23*f* 5 ca. chocolate (1930) 8·50
fa. Opt inverted — 32·00
O24 10 ca. pink (1926) 50 12
a. Imperf between (vert pair) 55·00 55·00
b. Opt inverted 24·00 24·00
c. "O" inverted 4·00 1·60
d. Left "S" inverted 4·00 1·60
e. Right "S" inverted 4·00 1·60
O25 1 1¼ ch. claret (1926) 1·60 40
a. "O" inverted 9·00 3·00
b. Left "S" inverted 9·00 3·00
c. Right "S" inverted 9·00 3·00
O26 7 7 ch. claret 1·50 30
a. "O" inverted 9·00 2·50
b. Left "S" inverted 9·00 2·50
c. Right "S" inverted 9·00 2·50
d. Error. Carmine-red 60·00
O27 8 14 ch. orange-yellow 1·75 40
a. "O" inverted 10·00 3·00
b. Left "S" inverted 10·00 3·00
c. Right "S" inverted 10·00 3·00

1926–30. *Contemporary stamps optd with Type* O **2** *(16½ mm wide). Wmk C. P 12.*

O28 4 5 ca. olive-bistre 1·25 40
a. Right "S" inverted 7·00 3·00
O29 5 ca. chocolate (1930) 12 12
a. Imperf between (vert pair) — 80·00
b. Opt inverted 15·00 15·00
c. "O" inverted 1·75 1·75
d. Left "S" inverted 1·75 1·75
O30 1 6 ca. brown-red (date?) 1·40 80
a. "O" inverted 7·50 4·50
b. Left "S" inverted 7·50 4·50
O31 4 10 ca. pink 25 10
a. Imperf between (horiz pair) 28·00 28·00
b. Imperf between (vert pair) 25·00 25·00
c. Imperf vert (horiz strip of 3) 38·00 38·00
d. Opt inverted 9·00 9·00
e. "Ou" for "On" 28·00 28·00
f. "O" inverted 2·50 1·25
g. Left "S" inverted 2·50 1·25
h. Right "S" inverted 2·50 1·25
i. Left "S" omitted 22·00 22·00
O32 1 1¼ ch. claret (*shades*) 1·50 30
a. Imperf between (horiz pair) 45·00
b. Imperf between (vert pair) 45·00
c. Opt inverted 16·00 16·00
d. "O" inverted 9·00 2·50
e. Left "S" inverted 9·00 2·50
f. Right "S" inverted 9·00 2·50
g. Left "S" omitted 45·00 45·00
h. Right "S" omitted 45·00 45·00
O33 6 3 ch. violet 7·00 70
a. Opt inverted 70·00 50·00
b. "O" inverted 25·00 14·00
c. "O" omitted 50·00 50·00
d. "Ou" for "On" 75·00 75·00
e. Left "S" inverted — 15·00
O34 7 7 ch. claret (date?) 22·00 1·75
O35 8 14 ch. orange-yellow 10·00 85
a. Imperf between (vert pair) 60·00
b. "O" inverted 30·00 7·00

The 5 ca. olive-bistre, 3 ch. and 7 ch. exist only with the normal watermark spaced 11 mm; the 5 ca. chocolate and 14 ch. exist only with the wide 15 mm spacing; the 6 ca., 10 ca. and 1¼ ch. exist in both forms.

On S S (O 3) — On S S (O 4) Italic "S S" — On S S (O 5)

1930. *Wmk C. P 12. (a) Optd with Type* O 3.

O36 4 10 ca. pink 25·00 15·00
O37 1 1¼ ch. carmine-rose 2·00 1·50

(b) *Optd with Type* O 4

O38 5 ¾ ch. black (R.) 30 8
a. Left "S" omitted 28·00
b. Right "S" omitted 28·00
c. Large roman "S" at left — 24·00

(c) *Optd with Type* O 5

O39 5 ¾ ch. black (R.) 25 8
a. Opt inverted 50·00 50·00
b. "n" omitted 30·00 30·00
O40 1 4 ch. slate-green (R.) 12·00 6·00

On S S (O 6) — On S S (O 7) Oval "O" — On S S (O 8)

1930–39 (?). *Contemporary stamps overprinted. P 12.*

(a) *With Type* O **6** *(16 mm high)* (i) *Wmk A*

O41 3 4 ca. pink 6·00 8·00
a. Large right "S" as Type O **2** 38·00 42·00

(ii) *Wmk B*

O42 3 4 ca. pink 7·50 10·00
a. Large right "S" as Type O **2** 45·00 50·00

(iii) *Wmk C*

O43 1 6 ca. brown-red (1932) 25 10
a. Opt inverted 15·00 15·00
b. Opt double 26·00 26·00
c. "O" inverted 8·00 5·00
O44 4 10 ca. pink 1·60 90
O45 5 ¾ ch. mauve (1933) 35 8
a. Imperf between (horiz pair) 28·00 28·00
b. Imperf between (horiz strip of 3) 45·00 45·00
c. Imperf between (vert pair) 28·00 28·00
d. Stamp doubly printed — 50·00
e. Perf 12½ 2·00 40
f. Perf comp of 12 and 12½ 4·00 75
g. Right "S" inverted — 8·50
O46 1 1¼ ch. carmine-rose 8·00 2·75
a. Opt double 55·00 35·00
b. Large right "S" as Type O **2** 48·00 28·00
O47 4 ch. grey-green 1·50 90
O48 4 ch. grey-green (R.) (27.10.30) 70 12
a. Imperf between (horiz pair) 40·00 40·00
b. Opt double 21·00 21·00
c. "O" inverted 12·00 8·00
d. Large right "S" as Type O **2** 18·00 14·00
O49 8 14 ch. orange-yellow (1931) 3·25 70
a. Imperf between (vert pair) 30·00 30·00

For the 1½ ch. and 3 ch., and for Nos. O43 and O48/9 but perf 12½, see Nos. O66/70 (new setting combining Types O **6** and O **8**).

(b) *With Type* O **7** *(14 mm high). Wmk C*

O50 3 4 ca. pink 5·00 6·00
a. "O" inverted 30·00 30·00
O51 4 5 ca. chocolate (1932) 14·00 14·00
a. Opt inverted 65·00 65·00
O52 1 6 ca. brown-red 12 8
a. Imperf between (vert pair) 45·00 45·00
b. Opt inverted 30·00 30·00
c. Opt double 28·00 28·00
d. "nO" for "On" 45·00 45·00
e. Right "S" inverted 6·50 4·50
f. Left "S" omitted 32·00 32·00
g. Large "n" as Type O **5** 16·00 10·00
h. Large italic left "S" as Type O **5** 16·00 10·00
i. Perf 12½ — 3·75
j. Perf compound of 12 and 12½
O53 ½ ch. reddish violet (1932) 25 12
a. "CHUCRRAM" 5·50 4·50
b. "Ou" for "On" 22·00 22·00
c. Left "S" omitted 32·00 32·00
d. "O" of "On" omitted 60·00
O54 ½ ch. reddish violet (R.) (1935) 12 10
a. Imperf between (vert pair) — 38·00
b. "CHUCRRAM" 3·00 3·00
c. Left "S" inverted — 7·00
O55 4 10 ca. pink (date?) 1·25 55
a. Imperf between (horiz pair) 10·00 10·00
b. Imperf between (vert pair) 10·00 10·00
c. "O" inverted 8·00 6·00
d. Right "S" inverted 8·00 6·00
O56 5 ¾ ch. mauve (1933?) 25 8
a. Imperf between (vert pair) — 38·00
b. "Ou" for "On" 30·00 30·00
c. "O" inverted 5·50 5·50
d. Right "S" inverted — 6·50
e. Perf comp of 12 and 12½ 7·50 5·00
O57 1 1 ch. deep blue (R.) (1935) 70 12
a. *Slate-blue* 70 12
b. Imperf between (horiz pair) 30·00 30·00
c. Imperf between (vert pair) 22·00 22·00
d. Perf 12½ 5·00 1·50
e. Perf comp of 12 and 12½ 7·00 2·50
O58 1¼ ch. claret 1·10 50
O59 1½ ch. rose (1933) 35 12
a. Imperf between (vert pair) 32·00 32·00
b. Opt double 28·00 28·00
c. "O" inverted 3·50 2·40
d. "O" and "n" inverted 24·00 20·00
e. Large "n" as Type O **5** 18·00 14·00
f. Large italic left "S" as Type O **5** 18·00 14·00
g. Left "S" inverted — 7·50
h. Perf 12½ — 4·00
i. Perf comp of 12 and 12½ — 5·50
O60 6 3 ch. reddish violet (1933) 1·10 40
a. "O" inverted 8·00 6·00
O61 3 ch. violet (R.) (1934) 60 12
a. Imperf between (horiz pair) 32·00 25·00
b. Imperf between (vert pair) 32·00 25·00
c. Opt inverted 28·00 24·00
d. "O" inverted 5·50 3·50
e. Perf 12½ — 1·50
f. Perf comp of 12 and 12½ — 3·50
O62 1 4 ch. grey-green (1934) — 50·00
O63 4 ch. grey-green (R.) (1935?) 80 12
a. "Ou" for "On" 28·00 28·00
O64 7 7 ch. claret (*shades*) 1·10 25
a. Imperf between (vert pair) 22·00 22·00
b. Left "S" inverted 16·00 8·00
c. Perf 12½ — 3·00
d. Perf comp of 12 and 12½ — 5·00
da. Imperf between (vert pair) 35·00 35·00
db. Imperf between (vert strip of 3) 45·00 45·00
O65 8 14 ch. orange (1933) 1·50 40
a. Imperf between (horiz pair) 22·00 22·00
b. Imperf between (vert pair) 28·00 28·00
c. Opt inverted 30·00 30·00

(c) *New setting combining Type* O **8** *(18 mm high) in top row with Type* O **6** *(16 mm high) for remainder. Wmk C* (dates?)

A. *Type* O **8**. B. *Type* O **6**

			A		B	
O66	1	6 ca. brown-red	4·00	2·00	†	
		a. Perf 12½	4·00	2·00	85	40
		ab. Imperf between (vert pair)	†		32·00	32·00
		ac. "O" inverted	†		10·00	7·00
		g. Perf comp of 12 and 12½			—	6·00
O67		1½ ch. rose	7·00	3·50	1·75	35
		a. Perf 12½	8·00	4·00	2·25	45
		ab. "O" inverted	†		7·50	3·50
O68	6	3 ch. violet (R.)	11·00	4·50	2·50	65
		a. Perf 12½	13·00	5·50	3·50	75
		b. Perf comp of 12 and 12½	18·00	7·00	5·50	2·25
O69	1	4 ch. grey-green (R.)	18·00	9·00	†	
		a. Perf 12½	16·00	8·00	4·50	2·00
		ab. Imperf between (horiz pair)	†		55·00	55·00
O70	8	14 ch. orange-yellow	12·00	6·00	†	
		a. Perf 12½	10·00	5·00	3·00	75

Nos. O66B and O69/70B naturally exist but are not distinguishable from Nos. O43 and O48/9.

Nos. O66/70A/B in vertical *se-tenant* pairs are very scarce.

As with the postage issues it is believed that the 12½ and compound perforations were issued between 1937 and 1939.

1 ch 8 c (O 9) — 1 ch Wrong fount "1 c"

1932. *Official stamps surch as T* **14** *or with Type* O **9**. *P* 12.

(a) *With opt Type* O 1 (i) *Wmk A*

O71 4 6 c. on 5 ca. olive-bistre 6·00 3·00
a. "O" inverted 22·00 11·00
b. Left "S" inverted 22·00 11·00
c. Right "S" inverted 22·00 11·00

(ii) *Wmk* C

O72 4 6 c. on 5 ca. olive-bistre . . 3·50 1·50
a. "O" inverted . . 15·00 7·00
b. Left "S" inverted . . 15·00 7·00
c. Right "S" inverted . . 15·00 7·00
O73 12 c. on 10 ca. pink . . 15·00 15·00

(*b*) *With opt Type* O **2**. *Wmk* C

O74 4 6 c. on 5 ca. olive-bistre . . 1·25 40
a. Opt and surch inverted . . 22·00 22·00
b. Surch inverted . . 16·00
c. Left "S" inverted . . 7·50 3·25
d. Right "S" inverted . . 7·50 3·25
e. "6" omitted . . — 30·00
O75 6 c. on 5 ca. chocolate . . 12 12
a. Surch inverted . . 9·00 9·00
b. Surch double . . 48·00 48·00
c. Surch double, one inverted . . 48·00 48·00
d. "O" inverted . . 1·75 1·75
e. Left "S" inverted . . 1·75 1·75
O76 12 c. on 10 ca. pink . . 12 12
a. Opt inverted . . 6·50 6·50
b. Surch inverted . . 6·50 6·50
c. Opt and surch inverted . . 13·00 13·00
d. Pair, one without surch . . £150
e. "O" inverted . . 1·75 1·75
f. Left "S" inverted . . 1·75 1·75
g. "Ou" for "On" . . 28·00 28·00
i. "c" omitted . . 24·00 24·00
j. Wide "S" at right . . — 20·00
O77 1 1 ch. 8 c. on 1¼ ch. claret . . 35 20
a. Surch inverted . . 30·00 30·00
b. "O" inverted . . 3·00 1·75
c. Left "S" inverted . . 3·00 1·75
d. Right "S" inverted . . 3·00 1·75
e. Wrong fount "1 c" . . 10·00 8·50

(*c*) *With opt Type* O **3**. *Wmk* C

O78 4 12 c. on 10 ca. pink . . — 75·00
O79 1 1 ch. 8 c. on 1¼ ch. carmine-rose . . 16·00 12·00
a. "n" omitted . . 95·00
b. Wrong fount "1 c" . . 70·00 50·00

(*d*) *With opt Type* O **6**. *Wmk* C

O80 4 12 c. on 10 ca. pink . . 10·00 4·50
O81 1 1 ch. 8 c. on 1¼ ch. carmine-rose . . 18·00 8·00
a. Wrong fount "1 c" . . 70·00 40·00
b. Brown-red . . — 10·00

(*e*) *With opt Type* O **7**. *Wmk* C

O82 4 6 c. on 5 ca. chocolate . . 12 12
a. Opt inverted . . 24·00 24·00
b. Surch inverted . . 11·00 11·00
c. Right "S" omitted . . 28·00 28·00
d. Two quads for right "S" . . £450
e. Right "S" inverted . . 10·00
O83 12 c. on 10 ca. pink . . 12 12
a. Opt inverted . . 7·00 7·00
b. Surch inverted . . 6·00 6·00
c. Opt and surch inverted . . 22·00 22·00
d. Opt double . . 24·00 24·00
da. Opt double, one albino, and surch inverted . . 35·00
e. "O" inverted . . 4·50 4·50
f. Right "S" inverted . . 4·50 4·50
g. "On" omitted . . 25·00 25·00
h. "n" omitted . . 25·00 25·00
i. "c." omitted . . 18·00 18·00
O84 1 1 ch. 8 c. on 1¼ ch. claret . . 35 25
a. Imperf between (vert pair) . . 48·00 48·00
b. Opt omitted . . 55·00 55·00
c. Surch inverted . . 14·00 14·00
d. Surch double . . 25·00 25·00
e. "O" inverted . . 4·00 2·50
f. Wrong fount "1 c" . . 10·00 8·00

SERVICE (O 10) 13 mm — **SERVICE** (O 11) 13½ mm — **SERVICE 8 CASH** (O 12)

1939–41. *Nos. 35 and 40 with type-set opt, Type* O **10**. *P* 12½.

O85 1 6 ca. brown-red (1941) . . 70 10
a. Perf 11 . . 1·00 35
b. Perf 12 . . 70 20
c. Compound perf . . 70 70
O86 5 ¾ ch. reddish violet . . 12·00 5·00
a. Perf 12 . . 3·00 35
b. Compound perf . . 15·00 10·00

1939 (9 Nov). *Maharaja's 27th Birthday. Nos. 64/70 with type-set opt, Type* O **10**. *P* 12½.

O87 1 ch. yellow-green . . 25 12
O88 1½ ch. scarlet . . 40 20
a. "SESVICE" . . 18·00 16·00
b. Perf 12 . . 2·25 1·50
ba. "SESVICE" . . — 28·00
bb. Imperf between (horiz pair) . . — 45·00
c. Compound perf . . 2·00 70
O89 2 ch. orange . . 35 35
a. "SESVICE" . . 22·00 22·00
b. Compound perf . . 7·00 7·00
O90 3 ch. brown . . 25 10
a. "SESVICE" . . 16·00 13·00
b. Perf 12 . . 75 40
ba. "SESVICE" . . — 20·00
c. Compound perf . . 2·50 1·25
O91 4 ch. red . . 60 40
O92 7 ch. pale blue . . 1·00 70
O93 14 ch. turquoise-green . . 1·75 1·25

1940 (?)–**45.** *Nos. 40a and 42b optd with Type* O **11**. *P* 12½.

O94 5 ¾ ch. reddish violet . . 2·40 12
a. Imperf between (horiz pair) . . 40·00 40·00
b. Perf 11 . . 4·00 35
c. Perf 12 . . 2·40 10
d. Compound perf . . 4·50 75
O95 1 1½ ch. rose (1945) . . 4·00 4·00
a. Perf 12 . . 1·00 80
b. Compound perf . . 8·00 8·00

1942 (?). *Nos. 64/70 optd with Type* O **11**. *P* 12½.

O 96 1 ch. yellow-green . . 20 8
a. Imperf between (vert pair) . . 14·00 14·00
b. Opt inverted . . 16·00 14·00
c. Opt double . . 18·00 18·00
d. Perf 11 . . 30 8
da. Imperf between (vert pair) . . 12·00 12·00
db. Opt double . . 15·00 15·00
e. Perf 12 . . 75 25
ea. Imperf between (vert pair) . . 17·00 17·00
eb. Stamp doubly printed . . 30·00 30·00
ec. Opt inverted . . 18·00 18·00
ed. Opt double . . 16·00 16·00
f. Compound perf . . 1·25 80
g. "S" inverted . . — 25·00
O 97 1½ ch. scarlet . . 35 12
a. Imperf between (horiz pair) . . 25·00 25·00
b. Perf 11 . . 50 25
ba. Imperf between (vert pair) . . 25·00 25·00
bb. Imperf between (vert strip of 3) . . 25·00 25·00
bc. Imperf between (horiz pair) . . — 25·00
c. Perf 12 . . 90 35
ca. Imperf between (vert strip of 3) . . 35·00 35·00
d. Compound perf . . 85 35
e. Imperf (pair) . . 24·00
O 98 2 ch. orange . . 60 30
a. Perf 11 . . 1·75 40
b. Perf 12 . . 6·00 6·00
ba. Imperf between (vert pair) . . 38·00 38·00
c. Compound perf . . 8·00 8·00
O 99 3 ch. brown . . 35 10
a. Perf 11 . . 65 15
b. Perf 12 . . 1·00 35
ba. Imperf between (vert pair) . . 38·00 38·00
c. Compound perf . . 3·00 1·50
O100 4 ch. red . . 60 35
a. Perf 11 . . 1·00 35
b. Perf 12 . . 2·25 90
c. Compound perf . . 8·00 8·00
O101 7 ch. pale blue . . 1·00 35
a. Perf 11 . . 1·75 75
b. Perf 12 . . 4·50 3·00
c. Compound perf . . 7·50 3·00
d. Blue (p 11) . . 2·00 85
da. Perf 12 . . 3·50 1·60
db. Compound perf . . 7·50 3·50
O102 14 ch. turquoise-green . . 1·75 70
a. Perf 11 . . 3·25 1·50
b. Perf 12 . . 4·50 2·40
c. Compound perf . . 8·00 3·00

1942. *Maharaja's 29th Birthday. Nos 71/2 optd with Type* O **11**. *P* 12½.

O103 6 ca. blackish violet . . 25 10
a. Perf 11 . . 70 25
b. Perf 12 . . 3·50 1·50
c. Compound perf . . 1·50 70
O104 ¾ ch. brown . . 25 10
a. Imperf between (vert pair) . . — 38·00
b. Perf 11 . . 90 15
c. Perf 12 . . 2·50 1·10
d. Compound perf . . 2·00 85

1943. *Surch with Type* O **12**. *P* 12½.

O105 19 8 ca. on 6 ca. scarlet . . 25 10
a. Perf 11 . . 40 10
ab. Surch inverted . . — £100
b. Compound perf . . 1·50 1·25

1945. *Nos. 73/4 optd with Type* O **11**. *P* 12½.

O106 2 ca. on 1½ ch. scarlet . . 10 10
a. Perf 11 . . 10 10
ab. Pair, one without surch . . 60·00 60·00
b. Compound perf . . 70 70
ba. "2" omitted . . 30·00 30·00
O107 4 ca. on ¾ ch. brown . . 40 10
a. Perf 11 . . 40 10
b. Compound perf . . 1·10 70

1947. *Maharaja's 34th Birthday. Optd with Type* O **11**. *P* 11.

O108 21 8 ca. carmine . . 1·10 70
a. Imperf between (horiz pair) . . 30·00 30·00
b. Opt double . . — 55·00
c. Perf 12½ . . 3·00 1·10
ca. Stamp doubly printed . . 35·00 35·00
d. Perf 12 . . 3·50 1·10
da. Stamp doubly printed . . 28·00 28·00

From 1 July 1949 Travancore formed part of the new State of Travancore-Cochin and stamps of Travancore surcharged in Indian currency were used.

TRAVANCORE-COCHIN

On 1 July 1949 the United State of Travancore and Cochin was formed ("U.S.T.C.") and the name was changed to State of Travancore-Cochin ("T.C.") by the new constitution of India on 26 January 1950.

PRICES FOR STAMPS ON COVER	
Nos. 1/13	*from* × 8
Nos. O1/17	*from* × 15

NO WATERMARK VARIETIES. These were formerly listed but we have now decided to omit them as they do not occur in full sheets. They are best collected in pairs, with and without watermarks.

COMPOUND PERFS. The notes above Type **17** of Travancore also apply here.

VALIDITY OF STAMPS. From 6 June 1950 the stamps of Travancore-Cochin were valid on mail from both Indian and state post offices to destinations in India and abroad.

ONE ANNA
ഒരണ
(1)

2 p. on 6 ca.

രണ്ടു പൈസ — Normal
രണ്ടു രൈസ — Variety: 1st character of 2nd group as 1st character of 1st group

1949 (1 July). *Stamps of Travancore surch in* "PIES" *or* "ANNAS" *as T* **1**. *P* 12½.

1 19 2 p. on 6 ca. blackish violet (R.) . . 25 10
a. Surch inverted . . 12·00 12·00
b. Character error . . 25·00 25·00
c. "O" inverted . . 10·00 10·00
d. Perf 11 . . 30 15
da. Imperf between (vert pair) . . 13·00 13·00
db. Pair, one without surch . . 24·00 24·00
dc. Character error . . 20·00 20·00
e. Perf 12 . . 8 8
ea. Imperf between (horiz pair) . . 6·00 6·00
eb. Imperf between (vert pair) . . 4·25 4·25
ec. Surch inverted . . 11·00 11·00
ed. Character error . . 32·00 32·00
f. Perf 14 . . — £150
g. Imperf (pair) . . 8·50 8·50
h. Compound perf . . — 10·00
2 21 4 p. on 8 ca. carmine . . 15 8
a. Surch inverted . . 12·00 12·00
b. "S" inverted . . 20·00 20·00
c. Perf 11 . . 25 10
ca. Imperf between (vert pair) . . 17·00 17·00
cb. Surch inverted . . 17·00 17·00
cc. Pair, one without surch . . 27·00 27·00
cd. "FOUP" for "FOUR" . . 30·00 30·00
ce. "S" inverted . . 20·00 20·00
d. Perf 12 . . 30 30
da. Imperf between (vert pair) . . 9·00 9·00
db. Pair, one without surch . . 25·00 25·00
dc. "FOUP" for "FOUR" . . 30·00 30·00
dd. "S" inverted . . 22·00 22·00
e. Imperf (pair) . . 35·00 35·00
f. Compound perf . . — 10·00
3 17 ½ a. on 1 ch. yellow-green . . 30 25
a. "NANA" for "ANNA" . . 29·00 29·00
b. Inverted "H" in "HALF" . . 35·00 35·00
c. Perf 11 . . 25 12
ca. Imperf between (vert pair) . . 9·00 9·00
cb. Surch inverted . . 12·00 12·00
cc. "NANA" for "ANNA" . . 35·00 35·00
cd. Inverted "H" in "HALF" . . 35·00 35·00
d. Perf 12 . . 10 8
da. Imperf between (horiz pair) . . 6·00 6·00
db. Imperf between (vert pair) . . 4·25 4·25
dc. Surch inverted . . 5·00 5·00
dd. "NANA" for "ANNA" . . 26·00 26·00
e. Perf 14 . . — £150
f. Imperf (pair) . . 8·50 8·50
g. Compound perf . . — 10·00
4 18 1 a. on 2 ch. orange . . 30 25
a. Perf 11 . . 15 15
ab. Surch double . . 32·00
b. Perf 12 . . 40 25
ba. Imperf between (horiz pair) . . 3·50 3·50
bb. Imperf between (vert pair) . . 3·50 3·50
c. Perf 13½ . . 18·00 2·00
d. Imperf (pair) . . 8·50 8·50
e. Compound perf . . 11·00
5 – 2 a. on 4 ch. red (68) . . 35 25
a. Surch inverted . . 45·00 45·00
b. "O" inverted . . 10·00 9·00
c. Perf 11 . . 30 25
ca. "O" inverted . . — 9·00
d. Perf 12 . . 55 55
e. Compound perf . . 7·50 7·50
f. Imperf (pair) . . 45·00 45·00
6 18 3 a. on 7 ch. pale blue (69) . . 3·25 1·75
a. Perf 11 . . 3·00 1·50
ab. Blue . . 10·00 4·00
b. Perf 12 . . 3·50 2·40
c. Compound perf . . 8·50 7·50
ca. Blue . . 15·00 15·00
7 – 6 a. on 14 ch. turquoise-green (70) . . 2·25 1·50
a. Accent omitted from native surch . . 35·00 35·00
b. Perf 11 . . 3·00 2·40
ba. Accent omitted from native surch . . 40·00 40·00
c. Perf 12 . . 3·50 3·50
ca. Accent omitted from native surch . . 40·00 40·00
d. Compound perf . . 10·00 10·00
e. Imperf (pair) . . 45·00 45·00

There are two settings of the ½ a. surcharge. In one the first native character is under the second downstroke of the "H" and in the other it is under the first downstroke of the "A" of "HALF". They occur on stamps perf 12½, 11 and 12 equally commonly and also on the Official stamps.

U. S. T. C. (2) — **T.-C.** (3) — **SIX PIES** (4)

1949. *No. 106 of Cochin optd with T* **2**.

8 29 1 a. orange . . 4·50 9·00
a. No stop after "S" . . 45·00
b. Raised stop after "T" . . 45·00

1950 (1 Apr). *No. 106 of Cochin optd with T* **3**.

9 29 1 a. orange . . 3·50 7·00
a. No stop after "T" . . 45·00
b. Opt inverted . . £150
ba. No stop after "T" . . £1500

The no stop variety occurs on No. 5 in the sheet and again on No. 8 in conjunction with a short hyphen.

1950 (1 Apr). *No. 9 surch as T* **4**.

10 29 6 p. on 1 a. orange . . 1·00 2·00
a. No stop after "T" . . 17·00
b. Error. Surch on No. 8 . . 40·00
ba. No stop after "S" . . £375
bb. Raised stop after "T" . . £375

11 **29** 9 p. on 1 a. orange 1·00 2·00
a. No stop after "T" 17·00
b. Error. Surch on No. 8 90·00
ba. No stop after "S" £550
bb. Raised stop after "T" £550

5 Conch or Chank Shell

6 Palm Trees

(Litho Indian Security Printing Press, Nasik)

1950. *W* **69** *of India. P* 14.
12 **5** 2 p. rose-carmine 40 1·10
13 **6** 4 p. ultramarine 65 1·60

The ordinary issues of Travancore-Cochin became obsolete on 1 July 1951.

OFFICIAL STAMPS

VALIDITY. Travancore-Cochin official stamps were valid for use throughout India from 30 September 1950.

SERVICE (O 1) **SERVICE** (O 2)

1949–51. *Stamps of Travancore surch with value as T* **1** *and optd* "SERVICE". *No gum. P* 12½. *(a) With Type* O **1**.

(i) *Wmk* C *of Travancore*
O 1 **19** 2 p. on 6 ca. blackish violet (R.) 10 8
a. Imperf between (vert pair) 18·00 18·00
b. Character error 14·00 14·00
c. "O" inverted 9·00 9·00
d. Perf 11 10 8
da. Imperf between (vert pair) 22·00 22·00
db. Character error 14·00 14·00
dc. "O" inverted 9·00 9·00
e. Perf 12 25 25
ea. Imperf between (horiz pair) 6·00 6·00
eb. Imperf between (vert pair) 6·00 6·00
ec. Character error 18·00 18·00
ed. "O" inverted 11·00
ee. Block of four imperf between (horiz and vert) 14·00
f. Imperf (pair) 8·00 8·00
O 2 **21** 4 p. on 8 ca. carmine 30 12
a. "FOUB" for "FOUR" 24·00 22·00
b. Perf 11 25 12
ba. "FOUB" for "FOUR" 24·00 22·00
c. Perf 12 25 15
ca. "FOUB" for "FOUR" 28·00 24·00
d. Compound perf 14·00 14·00
O 3 **17** ½ a. on 1 ch. yellow-green 15 12
a. Pair, one without surch 22·00 22·00
b. Surch inverted 11·00 11·00
c. "NANA" for "ANNA" 27·00 22·00
d. Perf 11 25 15
da. Pair, one without surch 27·00 27·00
db. Surch inverted 17·00 17·00
dc. "NANA" for "ANNA" 30·00 22·00
e. Perf 12 2·25 1·00
ea. "NANA" for "ANNA" 48·00 42·00
eb. Pair, one without surch 27·00
O 4 **18** 1 a. on 2 ch. orange 6·00 4·50
a. Surch inverted £100
b. Pair, one without surch £300
c. Perf 11 5·50 5·00
O 5 – 2 a. on 4 ch. red (68) 65 35
a. Pair, one without surch 45·00
b. Perf 11 1·00 45
ba. Imperf between (vert pair) 45·00 45·00
c. Perf 12 90 45
d. Compound perf — 13·00
e. Imperf (pair) 12·00 12·00
O 6 – 3 a. on 7 ch. pale blue (69) 75 60
a. Imperf between (vert pair) 9·00 9·00
b. Blue 4·00 2·50
c. Perf 11 1·25 60
ca. Blue 4·00 2·50
d. Perf 12 1·50 1·25
da. Imperf between (horiz pair) 8·00 8·00
db. Imperf between (vert pair) 6·00 6·00
dc. Block of four imperf between (horiz and vert) 12·00 12·00
dd. Blue 3·50 2·00
e. Imperf (pair) 11·00 11·00
O 7 – 6 a. on 14 ch. turquoise-green (70) 1·75 1·25
a. Imperf between (vert pair) 16·00 16·00
b. Perf 11 2·25 1·25
c. Perf 12 6·00 3·00
ca. Imperf between (horiz pair) 14·00 14·00
cb. Imperf between (vert pair) 17·00 17·00
cc. Block of four imperf between (horiz and vert) 25·00
d. Imperf (pair) 14·00 14·00

(ii) *W* **27** *of Cochin*
O 8 **19** 2 p. on 6 ca. blackish violet (R.) 8 8
a. Type O 1 double 14·00
b. Perf 11 15 15
c. Perf 12 30 30
O 9 – 2 a. on 4 ch. red (68) 40 30
a. Perf 11 40 30
b. Compound perf 15·00 15·00

(b) With Type O **2**

(i) *Wmk* C *of Travancore*
O10 **21** 4 p. on 8 ca. carmine 8 8
a. "FOUB" for "FOUR" 27·00 20·00
b. 2nd "E" of "SERVICE" in wrong fount — 30·00
c. "S" in "PIES" inverted — 20·00
d. Perf 11 12 8
da. Imperf between (horiz pair) 3·50 3·50
db. Imperf between (vert pair) 5·50 5·50
dc. "FOUB" for "FOUR" 27·00 20·00
dd. 2nd "E" of "SERVICE" in wrong fount — 30·00
de. "S" in "PIES" inverted — 20·00
df. Block of four imperf between (horiz and vert) 10·00
e. Perf 12 15 12
ea. Imperf between (horiz pair) 1·75 1·75
eb. Imperf between (vert pair) 1·75 1·75
ec. Block of four imperf between (horiz and vert) 4·00 4·00
ed. "FOUB" for "FOUR" 27·00 20·00
ef. 2nd "E" of "SERVICE" in wrong fount 28·00 28·00
f. Perf 13½ 2·50 1·75
g. Compound perf 8·00 8·00
h. Imperf (pair) 8·50 8·50
O11 **17** ½ a. on 1 ch. yellow-green 10 8
a. "AANA" for "ANNA" 24·00 18·00
b. Perf 11 8 8
ba. Imperf between (horiz pair) 7·50 7·50
bb. Imperf between (vert pair) 5·00 5·00
bc. Block of four imperf between (horiz and vert) 12·00 12·00
bd. "AANA" for "ANNA" 24·00 18·00
c. Perf 12 10 8
ca. Imperf between (horiz pair) 3·50 3·50
cb. Imperf between (vert pair) 3·50 3·50
cc. "AANA" for "ANNA" 24·00 18·00
cd. Block of four imperf between (horiz and vert) 15·00
d. Compound perf 5·50 4·50
da. "AANA" for "ANNA" — 40·00
e. Imperf (pair) 6·00 6·00
O12 **18** 1 a. on 2 ch. orange 20 20
a. Imperf between (vert pair) 11·00 11·00
b. Perf 11 50 50
ba. Imperf between (horiz pair) 4·50 4·50
bb. Imperf between (vert pair) 6·50 6·50
c. Perf 12 20 20
ca. Imperf between (horiz pair) 3·50 3·50
cb. Imperf between (vert pair) 3·00 3·00
cc. Block of four imperf between (horiz and vert) 7·50 7·50
d. Compound perf 5·50 5·50
e. Imperf (pair) 14·00 14·00
O13 – 2 a. on 4 ch. red (68) 1·10 80
a. "O" inverted — 11·00
b. Perf 11 1·10 1·10
ba. "O" inverted — 11·00
c. Perf 12 2·00 1·10
ca. Imperf between (vert pair) 45·00 45·00
cb. "O" inverted — 11·00
d. Compound perf 8·00 6·50
O14 – 3 a. on 7 ch. pale blue (69) 1·10 75
a. "S" inverted in "SERVICE" 30·00 30·00
b. First "E" inverted 42·00 42·00
c. "C" inverted 42·00 42·00
d. Second "E" inverted 42·00 42·00
e. Perf 11 1·10 75
ea. "S" inverted in "SERVICE" 30·00 30·00
f. Perf 12 1·25 85
fa. "S" inverted in "SERVICE" 35·00 35·00
g. Compound perf 22·00 22·00
h. Imperf (pair) 32·00 32·00
O15 – 6 a. on 14 ch. turquoise-green (70) 1·10 1·00
a. Accent omitted from native surch 14·00 11·00
b. "S" inverted in "SERVICE" 40·00 35·00
c. Perf 11 3·50 1·75
ca. Accent omitted from native surch 27·00 18·00
cb. "S" inverted in "SERVICE" 50·00 40·00
d. Perf 12 7·00 2·00
da. Accent omitted from native surch 45·00 20·00
db. "S" inverted in "SERVICE" 55·00 40·00
e. Compound perf 22·00 22·00

(ii) *W* **27** *of Cochin*
O16 **17** ½ a. on 1 ch. yellow-green 10 10
a. Perf 11 8 8
b. Perf 12 8·50 6·00
c. Compound perf 5·50 3·50
O17 **18** 1 a. on 2 ch. orange 30 25
a. Perf 11 50 40
b. Perf 12 — 5·00
c. Perf 13½ 2·50 1·75
d. Compound perf 3·50 3·50

Nos. O2, O10, O12 and O17 have the value at top in English and at bottom in native characters with "SERVICE" in between. All others have "SERVICE" below the surcharge.

Type O **2** was overprinted at one operation with the surcharges.

The Official stamps became obsolete in September 1951.

WADHWAN

PRICES FOR STAMPS ON COVER

No. 1	—
Nos. 2/6	*from* × 50

1

1888. *(a) Thin toned wove paper.*

(i) *Irregular perf* 12½ *(small holes)*
1 **1** ½ pice, black (II) 12·00
a. Imperf between (pair)

(ii) *P* 12½ *(large holes)*
2 **1** ½ pice, black (I, III) 6·00 24·00

(b) Medium toned wove paper
3 **1** ½ pice, black (III) (*p* 12½) 5·00 17·00
4 ½ pice, black (V) (*p* 12) 3·00 4·00

1892 (?). *Thick wove paper. P* 12.
5 **1** ½ pice, black/*toned* (VI, VII) 3·00 3·50
6 ½ pice, black/*white* (IV) 3·00 3·50
a. Perf compound of 12 and 11 6·00

The stamps were lithographed from seven stones (as indicated by Roman figures), in sheets of from 20 to 42 units, distinguishable by flaws.

The stamps of Wadhwan became obsolete on 1 January 1895.

Ionian Islands

The British occupation of the Ionian Islands was completed in 1814 and the archipelago was placed under the protection of Great Britain by the Treaty of Paris in 1815. The United States of Ionia were given local self-government, which included responsibility for the postal services. Crowned-circle handstamps were, however, supplied in 1844, although it is believed these were intended for use on prepaid mail to foreign destinations.

Examples of the Great Britain 1855 1d. red-brown stamp are known used at Corfu, but there is little information available concerning such usage.

For illustrations of the handstamp types see BRITISH POST OFFICES ABROAD notes, following GREAT BRITAIN.

CEPHALONIA

CROWNED-CIRCLE HANDSTAMPS

CC1 **CC 1** CEPHALONIA (19.4.1844) .. *Price on cover* £800

CORFU

CROWNED-CIRCLE HANDSTAMPS

CC2 **CC 1** CORFU (19.4.1844) .. .. *Price on cover* £500
CC3 **CC 1** CORFU (G. or B.) (1844) .. .. *Price on cover* —

Stamps of GREAT BRITAIN *cancelled with No.* CC2.
Z1 1d. red-brown (1855) Die II, *wmk* Large Crown, *perf* 14 .. .. £700

ZANTE

CROWNED-CIRCLE HANDSTAMPS

CC4 **CC 1** ZANTE (G. or B.) (19.4.1844) .. *Price on cover* £800

Nos. CC1/2 were later, *circa* 1860/1, struck in green (Cephalonia) or red (Corfu).

It is believed that examples of No. CC4 in black are from an unauthorised use of this handstamp. A similar handstamp, but without "PAID AT" was introduced in 1861.

PRICES FOR STAMPS ON COVER
Nos. 1/3 *from* × 10

1

(Recess Perkins, Bacon & Co)

1859 (15 May). *Imperf.*
1 **1** (½d.) orange (no wmk) .. .. .. 70·00 £500
2 (1d.) blue (wmk "2") .. .. .. 18·00 £175
3 (2d.) carmine (wmk "1") .. .. .. 13·00 £175

On 30 May 1864, the islands were ceded to Greece, and these stamps became obsolete.

Great care should be exercised in buying used stamps, on or off cover, as forged postmarks are plentiful.

Iraq

(Currency. 16 annas = 1 rupee)

I. ISSUES FOR BAGHDAD

PRICES FOR STAMPS ON COVER
Nos 1/25 *from* × 6

BRITISH OCCUPATION

British and Indian troops occupied the port of Basra on 22 November 1914 to protect the oil pipeline. They then advanced up the rivers, and after a hard campaign took Baghdad from the Turks on 11 March 1917.

IN BRITISH BAGHDAD OCCUPATION 2 Ans

(1)

1917 (Sept). *Stamps of Turkey, surch as T* 1.
(*a*) *Pictorial designs of* 1914. *T* **32**, *etc., and* **31** (*Mosque of Selim*)
1 **32** ¼ a. on 2 pa. claret .. .. .. 90·00 90·00
a. "IN BRITISH" omitted £3250
2 **34** ¼ a. on 5 pa. dull purple .. .. .. 55·00 55·00
a. Value omitted £2750
3 **36** ½ a. on 10 pa. green £550 £500
4 **31** ½ a. on 10 pa. green £1200 £1400
5 **37** 1 a. on 20 pa. red £500 £450
a. "BAGHDAD" double £1300
6 **38** 2 a. on 1 pi. bright blue £100 £100

(*b*) *As* (*a*), *but overprinted with small five-pointed Star*
7 **37** 1 a. on 20 pa. red (B.) £250 £250
a. "OCCUPATION" omitted £2000
8 **38** 2 a. on 1 pi. bright blue (R.) £3000 £5000

(*c*) *Postal Jubilee stamps*
9 **60** ½ a. on 10 pa. carmine £450 £450
10 1 a. on 20 pa. blue £900 £900
a. Value omitted £3500
11 2 a. on 1 pi. black and violet .. .. 60·00 60·00
a. "BAGHDAD" omitted £1500

(*d*) *T* **30** *with opt T* **26**
12 **30** 2 a. on 1 pi. ultramarine £300 £300

(*e*) *Stamps optd with Star and Arabic date* "1331" *within Crescent. T* **53** (*except No.* 16, *T* **57**, *five-pointed Star*)
13 **30** ½ a. on 10 pa. green (R.) .. .. .. 60·00 60·00
14 1 a. on 20 pa. rose £550 £550
a. Value omitted £3000 £3250
b. Optd with T **26** also £3250 £3500
c. First "D" of "BAGHDAD" omitted £2250
15 **23** 1 a. on 20 pa. rose (No. 554a) £600 £600
a. Value omitted £3500
16 **21** 1 a. on 20 pa. carmine (No. 732) .. £3500 £3750
17 **30** 2 a. on 1 pi. ultramarine (R.) .. .. 70·00 70·00
a. "BAGHDAD" omitted .. .. .. † —
18 **21** 2 a. on 1 pi. dull blue (No. 543) (R.) .. £140 £140
a. "OCCUPATION" omitted ..

(*f*) *Stamps with similar opt, but date between Star and Crescent* (*Nos.* 19 *and* 22, *T* **54**; *others T* **55**, *five-pointed Star*)
19 **23** ½ a. on 10 pa. grey-green (No. 609a) (R.) 70·00 70·00
a. "OCCUPATION" omitted £2250
20 **60** ½ a. on 10 pa. carmine (B.) £130 £130
21 **30** 1 a. on 20 pa. rose .. .. .. 70·00 70·00
22 **28** 1 a. on 20 pa. rose (Plate II) (No. 617) .. £550 £550
23 **15** 1 a. on 10 pa. on 20 pa. claret (No. 630) £140 £140
a. "OCCUPATION" omitted £1600 £1500
24 **30** 2 a. on 1 pi. ultramarine (R.) £160 £160
a. "OCCUPATION" omitted £2750
b. "BAGHDAD" omitted £2750
25 **28** 2 a. on 1 pi. ultramarine (Pl. II) (No. 649) £1300 £1300

The last group (*f*) have the Crescent obliterated in violet-black ink, as this included the inscription, "Tax for the relief of children of martyrs."

II. ISSUES FOR MOSUL

PRICES FOR STAMPS ON COVER
Nos. 1/8 *from* × 6

BRITISH OCCUPATION

A British and Indian force, designated Indian Expeditionary Force "D", occupied Mosul on 10 November 1918.

POSTAGE
I.E.F. 'D'
1 Anna

(1)

4 4
I (*normal*) II (*small*)

(*a*) Central design shows large "tougra" or sign-manual of El Ghazi 7 mm high.
(*b*) Smaller "tougra" of Sultan Rechad 5½ mm high.

1919 (Feb). *Turkish Fiscal stamps surch as T* **1**. *P* 11½ (½ *a.*), 12 (1 *a.*), *or* 12½ (*others*).
1 ½ a. on 1 pi. green and red .. .. .. 1·40 1·40
2 1 a. on 20 pa. black/*red* (*a*) .. .. .. 1·40 1·40
a. Imperf between (pair) £500
3 1 a. on 20 pa. black/*red* (*b*) .. .. .. 4·00 3·00
b. Surch double .. .. ..
4 2½ a. on 1 pi. mauve and yellow (*b*) .. .. 1·50 1·50
a. No bar to fraction .. .. .. 25·00 35·00
b. Surch double .. .. ..
5 3 a. on 20 pa. green (*a*) .. .. .. 1·60 1·60
6 3 a. on 20 pa. green and orange (*b*) .. .. 20·00 30·00
7 4 a. on 1 pi. deep violet (*a*) (I) .. .. 3·00 3·50
a. "4" omitted £1400
b. Small "4" (II) .. .. .. 4·00 4·50
c. Surch double .. .. ..
ca. Surch double, one with "4" omitted ..
8 8 a. on 10 pa. lake (*a*) .. .. .. 4·00 4·50
a. Surch inverted £350 £350
b. Surch double £350 £350
c. No comma after "D" .. .. .. 22·00 30·00
d. Inverted. No comma after "D" .. ..
e. Error. 8 a. on 1 pi. deep violet £1700

In December 1925 the League of Nations awarded the vilayet of Mosul to Iraq.

III. ISSUES FOR IRAQ

PRICES FOR STAMPS ON COVER
Nos. 1/18 *from* × 4
Nos. 41/154 *from* × 2
Nos. O19/171 *from* × 2

BRITISH OCCUPATION

IN BRITISH IRAQ OCCUPATION 1An.

(1)

A

B

1918 (1 Sept)–**21**. *Turkish pictorial issue of* 1914, *surch as T* **1**. *P* 12.

(*a*) *No wmk. Tougra as* A (1 Sept 1918–20)
1 **34** ¼ a. on 5 pa. dull purple 25 25
2 **36** ½ a. on 10 pa. green 25 25
3 **37** 1 a. on 20 pa. red 25 25
4 **34** 1½ a. on 5 pa. dull purple (1920) 60 50
5 **38** 2½ a. on 1 pi. bright blue 70 60
a. Surch inverted £2500
6 **39** 3 a. on 1½ pi. grey and rose 40 35
a. Surch double (Bk. + R.) £1700 £2250
7 **40** 4 a. on 1¾ pi. red-brown and grey .. 45 35
a. Centre inverted .. .. .. — £9000
8 **41** 6 a. on 2 pi. black and green .. .. 90 1·25
9 **42** 8 a. on 2½ pi. green and orange 90 60
a. Surch inverted .. .. .. † —
10 **43** 12 a. on 5 pi. deep lilac .. .. .. 1·50 1·25
11 **44** 1 r. on 10 pi. red-brown .. .. .. 2·00 1·40
12 **45** 2 r. on 25 pi. yellow-green .. .. 5·00 2·50
13 **46** 5 r. on 50 pi. rose .. .. .. 16·00 10·00
14 **47** 10 r. on 100 pi. indigo .. .. .. 25·00 15·00
1/14 .. .. *Set of* 14 45·00 30·00
1/3, 5/14 Perf "Specimen" .. .. *Set of* 13 £250

(*b*) *No wmk. Tougra as* B (*one device instead of two*) (1921)
15 **44** 1 r. on 10 pi. red-brown .. .. .. 90·00 19·00

(*c*) *Wmk Mult Script CA* (1921)
16 **36** ½ a. on 10 pa. green 40 50
17 **34** 1½ a. on 5 pa. dull purple 50 50
18 **45** 2 r. on 25 pi. yellow-green .. .. 8·00 6·00
16/18 Optd "Specimen" .. .. *Set of* 3 50·00

LEAGUE OF NATIONS MANDATE

On 25 April 1920 the Supreme Council of the Allies assigned to the United Kingdom a mandate under the League of Nations to administer Iraq.

The Emir Faisal, King of Syria in 1920, was proclaimed King of Iraq on 23 August 1921.

King Faisal I
23 August 1921–8 September 1933

2 Sunni Mosque, Muadhdham

3 Winged Cherub

4 Allegory of Date Palm

(Des Miss Edith Cheesman (½ a., 1 a., 4 a., 6 a., 8 a., 2 r., 5 r., 10 r.) and Mrs. C. C. Garbett (Miss M. J. Maynard) (remainder). Recess Bradbury, Wilkinson)

1923 (May)–**25**. *T* **2/4** *and similar designs. Wmk Mult Script CA* (*sideways on* 1½ *a.*, 4 *a.*, 8 *a.*, 5 *r.*). *P* 12.
41 **2** ½ a. olive-green 10 10
42 – 1 a. brown 15 10
43 **3** 1½ a. lake 20 10
44 – 2 a. orange-buff 30 15
45 – 3 a. grey-blue 30 15
46 – 4 a. violet 50 25
47 – 6 a. greenish blue 80 30
48 – 8 a. olive-bistre 90 40
49 **4** 1 r. brown and blue-green .. .. 1·50 90
50 **2** 2 r. black .. .. 7·00 5·00
51 2 r. olive-bistre (1925) .. .. .. 6·00 3·00
52 – 5 r. orange .. .. 15·00 8·00
53 – 10 r. lake .. .. 20·00 10·00
41/53 .. .. *Set of* 13 45·00 25·00
41/53 Optd "Specimen" .. .. *Set of* 13 £225

Designs: *Horiz* (*as T* **2**)—1 a. Gufas on the Tigris; 2 a. Bull from Babylonian wall-sculpture; 3 a. Arch of Ctesiphon; 6 a., 10 r. Shiar Mosque, Kadhimain. *Vert* (*as T* **3**)—4 a., 8 a., 5 r. Tribal Standard, Dulaim Camel Corps.

With the exception of Nos. 49 and 50, later printings of these stamps and of No. 78 are on a thinner paper.

10 11 12
King Faisal I

(Recess Bradbury, Wilkinson)

1927. *Wmk Mult Script CA. P* 12.
78 **10** 1 r. red-brown (Optd S. £30) .. .. 3·00 50
See note below No. 53.

(Recess Bradbury, Wilkinson)

1931. *Wmk Mult Script CA. P* 12.
80 **11** ½ a. green 10 10
81 1 a. red-brown 15 8
82 1½ a. scarlet 40 30
83 2 a. orange 20 10
84 3 a. blue 40 10
85 4 a. slate-purple 80 70
86 6 a. greenish blue 80 60
87 8 a. deep green .. .. 1·00 70
88 **12** 1 r. chocolate .. .. 2·50 90
89 2 r. yellow-brown .. .. 3·50 2·00
90 5 r. orange .. .. 10·00 10·00
91 10 r. scarlet .. .. 26·00 26·00
92 **10** 25 r. violet £550 £550
80/91 .. .. *Set of* 12 40·00 38·00
80/91 Perf "Specimen" .. .. *Set of* 12 £175

(New Currency. 1000 fils = 1 dinar)

فلس ١٠ 10 Fils (13)

١ دينار ٢ ½ Dinar (14)

(Surcharged at Govt Ptg Wks, Baghdad)

1932 (1 Apr). *Nos.* 80/92 *and* 46 *surch in* "Fils" *or* "Dinar" *as T* 13 *or* 14.
106 **11** 2 f. on ½ a. green (R.) 10 5
107 3 f. on ½ a. green 10 5
a. Surch double .. .. 85·00
b. Surch inverted .. .. 85·00
108 4 f. on 1 a. red-brown (G.) 15 15
109 5 f. on 1 a. red-brown 12 5
a. Inverted Arabic "5" .. .. .. 25·00 30·00
110 8 f. on 1½ a. scarlet 25 20
a. Surch inverted £100
111 10 f. on 2 a. orange 20 5
a. Inverted Arabic "1" .. .. .. 15·00 15·00
112 15 f. on 3 a. blue 25 60
113 20 f. on 4 a. slate-purple 60 65
114 – 25 f. on 4 a. violet (No. 46) 60 55
a. "Flis" for "Fils" £150 £200
b. Inverted Arabic "5" £175 £250
c. Vars a and b in *se-tenant* pair .. £500
115 **11** 30 f. on 6 a. greenish blue 60 40
116 40 f. on 8 a. deep green .. .. .. 1·00 1·25
117 **12** 75 f. on 1 r. chocolate .. .. .. 1·25 1·25
a. Inverted Arabic "5" .. .. .. 20·00 28·00
118 100 f. on 2 r. yellow-brown .. .. .. 3·00 3·00
119 200 f. on 5 r. orange .. .. .. 7·00 5·50
120 ½ d. on 10 r. scarlet .. .. .. 20·00 20·00
a. No bar in English "½" £250 £300
121 **10** 1 d. on 25 r. violet .. .. .. 50·00 50·00
106/121 .. .. *Set of* 16 75·00 75·00
106/121 Perf "Specimen" .. .. *Set of* 16 £175

3 FILS فلس ٣ (15)

1932 (9 May). *T* 10 *to* 12, *but with values altered to* "FILS" *or* "DINAR" *as in T* 15. *Wmk Mult Script CA. P* 12.
138 **11** 2 f. ultramarine 5 5
139 3 f. green 8 5
140 4 f. brown-purple 5 5
141 5 f. grey-green 5 5
142 8 f. scarlet 8 8
143 10 f. yellow 8 5
144 15 f. blue 15 5
145 20 f. orange 15 15
146 25 f. mauve 25 15
147 30 f. bronze-green 25 15
148 40 f. violet 40 40
149 **12** 50 f. brown 40 20
150 75 f. dull ultramarine .. .. .. 1·00 60
151 100 f. deep green .. .. 1·50 50
152 200 f. scarlet .. .. 5·00 2·00
153 **10** ½ d. deep blue .. .. 10·00 7·50
154 1 d. claret .. .. 30·00 20·00
138/154 .. .. *Set of* 17 45·00 28·00
138/54 Perf "Specimen" .. .. *Set of* 17 £175

OFFICIAL STAMPS

ON STATE SERVICE (O 1)

1920–23. *As Nos.* 1/18, *but surch includes additional wording* "ON STATE SERVICE" *as Type* O 1 *in black.*

(*a*) *No wmk. Tougra as* A (1920)
O19 **36** ½ a. on 10 pa. blue-green 30 15
O20 **37** 1 a. on 20 pa. red 30 15
O21 **34** 1½ a. on 5 pa. purple-brown 60 30
O22 **38** 2½ a. on 1 pi. blue 80 80
O23 **39** 3 a. on 1½ pi. black and rose 80 50
O24 **40** 4 a. on 1¾ pi. red-brown and grey-blue 1·40 60
O25 **41** 6 a. on 2 pi. black and green .. .. 1·25 80
O26 **42** 8 a. on 2½ pi. yellow-green & orge-brn 1·40 1·00
O27 **43** 12 a. on 5 pi. purple .. .. 1·50 1·50
O28 **44** 1 r. on 10 pi. red-brown .. .. .. 3·00 2·50
O29 **45** 2 r. on 25 pi. olive-green .. .. .. 7·50 5·00
O30 **46** 5 r. on 50 pi. rose-carmine .. .. .. 18·00 10·00
O31 **47** 10 r. on 100 pi. slate-blue .. .. .. 35·00 25·00
O19/31 .. .. *Set of* 13 65·00 42·00

(*b*) *No wmk. Tougra as* B (*No.* 15) (1922)
O32 **44** 1 r. on 10 pi. red-brown .. .. .. 10·00 7·00

(*c*) *Wmk Mult Script CA* (1921–23)
O33 **36** ½ a. on 10 pa. green 12 12
O34 **37** 1 a. on 20 pa. red 15 15
O35 **34** 1½ a. on 5 pa. purple-brown 30 30
O36 **40** 4 a. on 1¾ pi. red-brown and grey-blue 50 50
O37 **41** 6 a. on 2 pi. black and green (1923) .. 4·00 6·00
O38 **42** 8 a. on 2½ pi. yellow-green & orge-brn 1·25 1·25
O39 **43** 12 a. on 5 pi. purple (1923) .. .. 4·00 6·00
O40 **45** 2 r. on 25 pi. olive-green (1923) .. 11·00 15·00
O33/40 .. .. *Set of* 8 20·00 26·00
O33/40 Perf/Optd "Specimen" .. *Set of* 8 £120

ON STATE SERVICE (O 2)

ON STATE SERVICE (O 3)

1923. *Optd with Types* O 2 (*horiz designs*) *or* O 3 (*vert designs*).
O54 **2** ½ a. olive-green 10 10
O55 – 1 a. brown 15 10
O56 **3** 1½ a. lake 40 30
O57 – 2 a. orange-buff 15 20
O58 – 3 a. grey-blue 50 30
O59 – 4 a. violet 80 40
O60 – 6 a. greenish blue .. .. 1·00 50
O61 – 8 a. olive-bistre .. .. 1·00 60
O62 **4** 1 r. brown and blue-green .. .. .. 1·90 1·00
O63 **2** 2 r. black (R.) .. .. 8·00 3·00
O64 – 5 r. orange .. .. 20·00 8·00
O65 – 10 r. lake .. .. 35·00 22·00
O54/65 .. .. *Set of* 12 60·00 32·00
O54/65 Optd "Specimen" .. .. *Set of* 12 £200

ON STATE SERVICE رسمي (O 4)

ON STATE SERVICE رسمي (O 5)

1924–25. *Optd with Types* O 4 (*horiz designs*) *or* O 5 (*vert designs*).
O66 **2** ½ a. olive-green 10 8
O67 – 1 a. brown 10 8
O68 **3** 1½ a. lake 10 8
O69 – 2 a. orange-buff 20 8
O70 – 3 a. grey-blue 20 10
O71 – 4 a. violet 40 12
O72 – 6 a. greenish blue 60 25
O73 – 8 a. olive-bistre 80 40
O74 **4** 1 r. brown and blue-green .. .. .. 3·50 80
O75 **2** 2 r. olive-bistre (1925) .. .. .. 6·00 2·50
O76 – 5 r. orange .. .. 15·00 10·00
O77 – 10 r. lake .. .. 30·00 15·00
O66/77 .. .. *Set of* 12 50·00 26·00
O66/77 Optd "Specimen" .. .. *Set of* 12 £200

1927. *Optd with Type* O 5.
O79 **10** 1 r. red-brown (Optd S. £30) .. .. 2·50 60

ON STATE SERVICE

ON STATE SERVICE رسمي (O 6)

رسمي (O 7)

1931. *Optd.* (*a*) *As Type* O 6.
O 93 **11** ½ a. green 10 30
O 94 1 a. red-brown 12 10
O 95 1½ a. scarlet .. .. 3·00 3·00
O 96 2 a. orange 30 10
O 97 3 a. blue 50 40
O 98 4 a. slate-purple 60 30
O 99 6 a. greenish blue .. .. 1·00 1·50
O100 8 a. deep green .. .. 1·25 1·50

(*b*) *As Type* O 7, *horizontally*
O101 **12** 1 r. chocolate .. .. 3·00 3·00
O102 2 r. yellow-brown .. .. 5·00 5·00
O103 5 r. orange .. .. 15·00 15·00
O104 10 r. scarlet .. .. 25·00 30·00

(*c*) *As Type* O 7, *vertically upwards*
O105 **10** 25 r. violet £600 £625
O93/104 .. .. *Set of* 12 50·00 55·00
O93/105 Perf "Specimen" .. .. *Set of* 13 £200

1932 (1 Apr). *Official issues of* 1924–25 *and* 1931 *surch in* "FILS" *or* "DINAR", *as T* 13 *or* 14.
O122 **11** 3 f. on ½ a. green 20 35
a. Pair, one without surch £175
O123 4 f. on 1 a. red-brown (G.) 10 8
O124 5 f. on 1 a. red-brown 10 8
a. Inverted Arabic "5" .. .. .. 25·00 20·00
O125 **3** 8 f. on 1½ a. lake (No. O68) 25 15
O126 **11** 10 f. on 2 a. orange 25 8
a. Inverted Arabic "1" .. .. .. 15·00 15·00
O127 **11** 15 f. on 3 a. blue 45 25
O128 20 f. on 4 a. slate-purple 45 20
O129 25 f. on 4 a. slate-purple 55 25
O130 – 30 f. on 6 a. greenish blue (No. O72) .. 60 40
O131 **11** 40 f. on 8 a. deep green 90 45
a. "Flis" for "Fils" £175 £250
O132 **12** 50 f. on 1 r. chocolate .. .. .. 1·25 1·10
a. Inverted Arabic "5" .. .. .. 35·00 35·00
O133 75 f. on 1 r. chocolate .. .. .. 2·25 2·25
a. Inverted Arabic "5" .. .. .. 30·00 28·00
O134 **2** 100 f. on 2 r. olive-bistre .. .. .. 2·00 2·00
O135 – 200 f. on 5 r. orange (No. O76) .. .. 4·00 4·00
O136 – ½ d. on 10 r. lake (No. O77) .. .. 15·00 15·00
a. No bar in English "½" £250
O137 **10** 1 d. on 25 r. violet .. .. .. 50·00 50·00
O122/37 .. .. *Set of* 16 70·00 70·00

1932 (9 May). *Optd.* (*a*) *As Type* O 6.
O155 **11** 2 f. ultramarine 15 5
O156 3 f. green 15 5
O157 4 f. brown-purple 20 5
O158 5 f. grey-green 20 5
O159 8 f. scarlet 20 5
O160 10 f. yellow 25 8
O161 15 f. blue 25 8
O162 20 f. orange 25 10
O163 25 f. mauve 55 20
O164 30 f. bronze-green 70 20
O165 40 f. violet 70 20

(*b*) *As Type* O 7, *horizontally*
O166 **12** 50 f. brown 60 20
O167 75 f. dull ultramarine 90 35
O168 100 f. deep green .. .. 1·50 35
O169 200 f. scarlet .. .. 5·00 2·00

(*c*) *As Type* O 7, *vertically upwards*
O170 **10** ½ d. deep blue .. .. 6·00 4·00
O171 1 d. claret .. .. 20·00 20·00
O155/71 .. .. *Set of* 17 35·00 25·00
O155/71 Perf "Specimen" .. .. *Set of* 17 £300

The British Mandate was given up on 3 October 1932 and Iraq became an independent kingdom. Later issues will be found listed in Part 19 (*Middle East*) of this catalogue.

Ireland (Republic)

All the issues of Ireland are listed together here, in this section of the Gibbons Catalogue, purely as a matter of convenience to collectors.

PRICES FOR STAMPS ON COVER TO 1945

Nos. 1/15	*from* × 5
Nos. 17/21	*from* × 3
Nos. 22/5*a*	*from* × 4
Nos. 26/9*a*	*from* × 5
Nos. 30/43	*from* × 4
Nos. 44/6	—
Nos. 47/63	*from* × 5
Nos. 64/6	*from* × 3
Nos. 67/70	*from* × 6
Nos. 71/82	*from* × 2
Nos. 83/8	*from* × 3
Nos. 89/98	*from* × 2
Nos. 99/104	*from* × 3
Nos. 105/37	*from* × 2
Nos. D1/4	*from* × 7
Nos. D5/14	*from* × 6

PROVISIONAL GOVERNMENT

16 January—6 December 1922

***Stamps of Great Britain overprinted. T* 104/8, *W* 100; *T* 109, *W* 110**

Rialtaṡ Sealadaċ na hÉireann 1922 (1)

Rialtaṡ Sealadaċ na hÉireann 1922. (2)

Rialtaṡ Sealadaċ na hÉireann 1922 (3)

("Provisional Government of Ireland, 1922")

1922 (17 Feb). *T* 104 *to* 108 (*W* 100) *and* 109 *of Great Britain overprinted in black.*

(*a*) *With T* 1, *by Dollard Printing House, Ltd. Optd in black**
1 **105** ½d. green 25 25
a. Opt inverted £550 £650
2 **104** 1d. scarlet 40 25
a. Opt inverted £275 £375
b. Opt double, both inverted, one albino £350 £400
3 1d. carmine-red 75 40
4 2½d. bright blue .. .. 1·25 2·50
5 **106** 3d. bluish violet .. .. 2·50 3·25
6 4d. grey-green .. .. 2·75 5·50

7 **107** 5d. yellow-brown . . . . 5·50 10·00
8 **108** 9d. agate . . . . 15·00 14·00
9 10d. turquoise-blue . . . . 9·00 14·00
1/9 . . . . *Set of* 8 32·00 45·00

*All values except 2½d. and 4d. are known with greyish black overprint, but these are difficult to distinguish.

The ½d. with red overprint is a trial or proof printing (*Price* £150).

Bogus inverted T **1** overprints exist on the 2d., 4d., 9d. and 1s. values.

(*b*) *With T* **2**, *by Alex Thom & Co, Ltd*

10 **105** 1½d. red-brown . . . . 1·25 75
a. Error. "PENCF" £500 £475
12 **106** 2d. orange (Die I) . . . . . . 1·50 50
a. Opt inverted £250 £325
13 2d. orange (Die II) . . . . . . 1·75 60
a. Opt inverted £450 £550
14 **107** 6d. reddish purple, **C** . . . . . . 9·00 4·00
15 **108** 1s. bistre-brown . . . . . . 15·00 8·00

Varieties occur throughout the T **2** overprint in the relative positions of the lines of the overprint, the "R" of "Rialtas" being over either the "Se" or "S" of "Sealadac" or intermediately.

(*c*) *With T* **3**

17 **109** 2s. 6d. chocolate-brown . . . . 35·00 55·00
18 2s. 6d. sepia-brown . . . . 40·00 60·00
19 5s. rose-red . . . . 70·00 £110
21 10s. dull grey-blue £160 £240

1922 (1 April–July). *Optd by Dollard with T* **1**, *in red or carmine.*

22 **104** 2½d. bright blue (R.) . . . . 1·50 2·50
23 **106** 4d. grey-green (R.) . . . . 9·00 12·00
24 4d. grey-green (C.) (July) . . . . 40·00 55·00
25 **108** 9d. agate (R.) . . . . 14·00 14·00
25*a* 9d. agate (C.) (July) . . . . 85·00 80·00

1922 (19 June–Aug). *Optd as T* **2**, *in black, by Harrison & Sons, for use in horiz and vert coils.*

26 **105** ½d. green . . . . 3·00 6·00
27 **104** 1d. scarlet . . . . 2·00 4·50
28 **105** 1½d. red-brown (21.6) . . . . 5·00 15·00
29 **106** 2d. bright orange (Die I) . . . . 11·00 16·00
29*a* 2d. bright orange (Die II) (August) . . 15·00 18·00

The Harrison overprint measures 15 × 17 mm (maximum) against the 14½ × 16 mm of T **2** (Thom printing) and is a much bolder black than the latter, while the individual letters are taller, the "i" of "Rialtas" being specially outstanding.

The "R" of "Rialtas" is always over the "Se" of "Sealadac".

1922. *Optd by Thom.*

(*a*) *As T* **2** *but bolder, in dull to shiny blue-black or red* (June–Nov)

30 **105** ½d. green . . . . 1·25 95
31 **104** 1d. scarlet 50 30
a. "Q" for "O" (No. 357ab) . . £1800 £1800
b. Reversed "Q" for "O" (No. 357ac) . . £475 £325
32 **105** 1½d. red-brown . . . . 5·00 3·75
33 **106** 2d. orange (Die I) . . . . 19·00 2·25
34 2d. orange (Die II) . . . . 2·50 70
35 **104** 2½d. blue (R.) . . . . 7·00 13·00
36 **106** 3d. violet . . . . 1·75 2·75
37 4d. grey-green (R.) . . . . 2·50 4·00
38 **107** 5d. yellow-brown . . . . 3·50 6·50
39 6d. reddish purple, **C** . . . . 5·00 3·50
40 **108** 9d. agate (R.) . . . . 11·00 13·00
41 9d. olive-green (R.) . . . . 7·50 15·00
42 10d. turquoise-blue . . . . 25·00 32·00
43 1s. bistre-brown . . . . 11·00 10·00
30/43 . . . . *Set of* 14 90·00 95·00

Both 2d. stamps exist with the overprint inverted but there remains some doubt as to whether they were issued.

These Thom printings are distinguishable from the Harrison printings by the size of the overprint, and from the previous Thom printings by the intensity and colour of the overprint, the latter being best seen when the stamp is looked through with a strong light behind it.

(*b*) *As with T* **3**, *but bolder, in shiny blue-black* (Oct–Dec)

44 **109** 2s. 6d. chocolate-brown £190 £225
45 5s. rose-red £185 £240
46 10s. dull grey-blue £950 £1000

The above differ from Nos. 17/21 not only in the bolder impression and colour of the ink but also in the "h" and "é" of "héireann" which are closer together.

Rialtas Sealadac na hÉireann 1922.

(4)

Saorstát Éireann 1922

(5 Wide date)
("Irish Free State 1922")

1922 (21 Nov–Dec). *Optd by Thom with T* **4** (*wider setting*) *in shiny blue-black.*

47 **105** ½d. green . . . . 1·00 1·50
a. Opt in jet-black . . . . 95·00 85·00
48 **104** 1d. scarlet . . . . 1·50 2·00
49 **105** 1½d. red-brown (4 December) . . 2·00 6·00
50 **106** 2d. orange (Die II) . . . . 10·00 6·00
51 **108** 1s. olive-bistre (4 December) . . 25·00 32·00

The overprint T 4 measures 15¾ × 16 mm (maximum).

IRISH FREE STATE

6 December 1922—29 December 1937

1922 (Dec)–**23.**

(*a*) *Optd by Thom with T* **5**, *in dull to shiny blue-black or red*

52 **105** ½d. green 15 25
a. No accent in "Saorstat" . . £1300 £1300
b. Accent inserted by hand . . £110 £120
53 **104** 1d. scarlet 15 25
aa. No accent in "Saorstat" . . £7000 £7000
a. No accent and final "t" missing . . £7000 £6000
b. Accent inserted by hand . . £150 £180
c. Accent and "t" inserted . . £250 £300
d. Reversed "Q" for "O" (No. 357ac) . . £500 £425
54 **105** 1½d. red-brown . . . . 2·00 5·50
55 **106** 2d. orange (Die II) . . . . 1·25 1·75
56 **104** 2½d. bright blue (R.) (6.1.23) . . 1·40 3·50
a. No accent . . £180 £225
57 **106** 3d. bluish violet (6.1.23) . . 3·25 6·50
a. No accent . . £350 £375
58 4d. grey-green (R.) (16.1.23) . . 2·00 3·25
a. No accent . . £225 £250
59 **107** 5d. yellow-brown . . 2·50 4·50
60 6d. reddish purple, **C** . . 2·00 2·25
a. Accent inserted by hand . . £1100 £950
61 **108** 9d. olive-green (R.) . . 2·50 5·00
a. No accent . . £350 £375
62 10d. turquoise-blue . . 17·00 30·00
63 1s. bistre-brown . . 12·00 10·00
a. No accent . . £7000 £8000
b. Accent inserted by hand . . £950 £750
64 **109** 2s. 6d. chocolate-brown . . 35·00 45·00
a. Major Re-entry . . £1200 £1400
b. No accent . . £500 £550
c. Accent reversed . . £550 £650
65 5s. rose-red . . 75·00 £100
a. No accent . . £600 £700
b. Accent reversed . . £700 £500
66 10s. dull grey-blue . . £140 £210
a. No accent . . £2750 £3200
b. Accent reversed . . £3250 £4000
52/66 . . . . *Set of* 15 £275 £350

The accents inserted by hand are in dull black. The reversed accents are grave (thus "à") instead of acute ("á"). A variety with "S" of "Saorstat" directly over "é" of "éireann", instead of to left, may be found in all values except the 2½d. and 4d. In the 2s. 6d., 5s. and 10s. it is very slightly to the left in the "S" over "é" variety, bringing the "á" of "Saorstat" directly above the last "n" of "éireann".

(*b*) *Optd with T* **5**, *in dull or shiny blue-black, by Harrison, for use in horiz or vert coils* (7.3.23)

67 ½d. green . . . . 1·50 3·50
a. Long "1" in "1922" . . 15·00 22·00
68 1d. scarlet . . . . 2·50 7·00
a. Long "1" in "1922" . . 60·00 £100
69 1½d. red-brown . . . . 8·00 20·00
a. Long "1" in "1922" . . 90·00 £150
70 2d. orange (Die II) . . . . 2·00 5·50
a. Long "1" in "1922" . . 16·00 28·00

In the Harrison overprint the characters are rather bolder than those of the Thom overprint, and the foot of the "1" of "1922" is usually rounded instead of square. The long "1" in "1922" has a serif at foot. The second "e" of "éireann" appears to be slightly raised.

PRINTERS. The following and all subsequent issues to No. 148 were printed at the Government Printing Works, Dublin, *unless otherwise stated.*

6 "Sword of Light"

7 Map of Ireland

8 Arms of Ireland

9 Celtic Cross

10

(Des J. J. O'Reilly, T **6**; J. Ingram, T **7**; Miss M. Girling, T **8**; and Miss L. Williams, T **9**. Typo. Plates made by Royal Mint, London)

1922 (6 Dec)–**34.** *W* **10**. *P* 15 × 14.

71 **6** ½d. bright green (20.4.23) . . 40 30
a. Imperf × perf 14, wmk sideways (11.34) . . 30·00 35·00
72 **7** 1d. carmine (23.2.23) . . 30 10
a. Perf 15 × imperf (single perf) (1933) 80·00 £130
c. Perf 15 × imperf (7.34) . . 20·00 25·00
d. Booklet pane. Three stamps plus three printed labels . . £250
73 1½d. claret (2.2.23) . . 1·50 1·50
74 2d. grey-green (6.12.22) . . 30 10
a. Imperf × perf 14, wmk sideways (11.34) . . 45·00 60·00
b. Perf 15 × imperf (1934) . . £9500 £1500
75 **8** 2½d. red-brown (7.9.23) . . 2·50 2·50
76 **9** 3d. ultramarine (16.3.23) . . 1·75 1·50
77 **8** 4d. slate-blue (28.9.23) . . 2·50 2·00
78 **6** 5d. deep violet (11.5.23) . . 12·00 8·00
79 6d. claret (21.12.23) . . 3·00 3·50
80 **8** 9d. deep violet (26.10.23) . . 15·00 14·00
81 **9** 10d. brown (11.5.23) . . 12·00 15·00
82 **6** 1s. light blue (15.6.23) . . 40·00 9·00
71/82 . . . . *Set of* 12 80·00 50·00

No. 72a is imperf vertically except for a single perf at each top corner. It was issued for use in automatic machines.

See also Nos. 111/22 and 227/8.

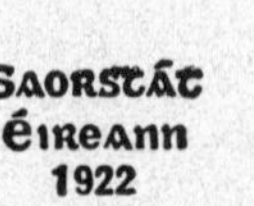

(11 Narrow Date)

12 Daniel O'Connell

1925 (Aug)–**28.** *T* **109** *of Great Britain* (*Bradbury, Wilkinson printing*) *optd at the Government Printing Works, Dublin or by Harrison and Sons.* (*a*) *With T* **11** *in black or grey-black* (25.8.25).

83 2s. 6d. chocolate-brown . . 45·00 65·00
a. Wide and narrow date (pair) (1927) . . £300
84 5s. rose-red . . 60·00 80·00
a. Wide and narrow date (pair) (1927) . . £500
85 10s. dull grey-blue . . £140 £225
a. Wide and narrow date (pair) (1927) . . £1400

The varieties with wide and narrow date *se-tenant* are from what is known as the "composite setting," in which some stamps showed the wide date, as T **5**, while in others the figures were close together, as in T **11**.

Single specimens of this printing with wide date may be distinguished from Nos. 64 to 66 by the colour of the ink, which is black or grey-black in the composite setting and blue-black in the Thom printing.

The type of the "composite" overprint usually shows distinct signs of wear.

(*b*) *As T* **5** (*wide date*) *in black* (1927–28)

86 2s. 6d. chocolate-brown (9.12.27) . . 35·00 38·00
a. Circumflex accent over "a" . . £300 £325
b. No accent over "a" . . £450 £450
c. Flat accent on "a" . . £350 £375
87 5s. rose-red (2.28) . . 80·00 80·00
a. Circumflex accent over "a" . . £525 £525
c. Flat accent on "a" . . £550 £550
88 10s. dull grey-blue (15.2.28) . . £180 £190
a. Circumflex accent over "a" . . £1200 £1200
c. Flat accent on "a" . . £1300 £1400

This printing can be distinguished from the Thom overprints in dull black, by the clear, heavy impression (in deep black) which often shows in relief on the back of the stamp.

The variety showing a circumflex accent over the "a" occurred on R.9/2. The overprint in this position finally deteriorated to such an extent that some examples of the 2s. 6d. were without accent (No. 86b). A new cliché was then introduced with the accent virtually flat and which also showed damage to the "a" and the crossbar of the "t".

(Des L. Whelan. Typo)

1929 (22 June). *Catholic Emancipation Centenary. W* **10**. *P* 15 × 14.

89 **12** 2d. grey-green 50 30
90 3d. blue . . . . 5·00 9·00
91 9d. bright violet . . . . 6·00 8·00

13 Shannon Barrage

14 Reaper

(Des E. L. Lawrenson. Typo)

1930 (15 Oct). *Completion of Shannon Hydro-Electric Scheme. W* **10**. *P* 15 × 14.

92 **13** 2d. agate 65 20

(T **14** and **15** des G. Atkinson. Typo)

1931 (12 June). *Bicentenary of the Royal Dublin Society. W* **10**. *P* 15 × 14.

93 **14** 2d. blue 75 20

15 The Cross of Cong

16 Adoration of the Cross

17 Hurler

1932 (12 May). *International Eucharistic Congress. W* **10**. *P* 15 × 14.

94 **15** 2d. grey-green . . . . 1·25 25
95 3d. blue . . . . 3·00 4·50

(T **16** to **19** des R. J. King. Typo)

1933 (18 Sept). *"Holy Year". W* **10**. *P* 15 × 14.

96 **16** 2d. grey-green 50 30
97 3d. blue . . . . 3·50 3·50

1934 (27 July). *Golden Jubilee of the Gaelic Athletic Association. W* **10**. *P* 15 × 14.

98 **17** 2d. green 70 20

1935 (Mar–July). *T* **109** *of Great Britain* (*Waterlow printings*) *optd as T* **5** (*wide date*), *at the Government Printing Works, Dublin.*

99 **109** 2s. 6d. chocolate (No. 450) . . 40·00 50·00
a. Flat accent on "a" (R. 9/2) . . £300 £250
100 5s. bright rose-red (No. 451) . . £125 £120
a. Flat accent on "a" (R. 9/2) . . £400 £350
101 10s. indigo (No. 452) . . £550 £550
a. Flat accent on "a" (R. 9/2) . . £1300 £1000

18 St. Patrick

19 Ireland and New Constitution

1937 (8 Sept). *W* **10**. *P* 14 × 15.
102 **18** 2s. 6d. emerald-green £110 85·00
103 5s. maroon £140 £100
104 10s. deep blue £110 75·00
See also Nos. 123/5.

EIRE

29 December 1937—17 April 1949

1937 (29 Dec). *Constitution Day. W* **10**. *P* 15 × 14.
105 **19** 2d. claret 1·00 30
106 3d. blue 6·00 3·00
For similar stamps see Nos. 176/7.

20 Father Mathew

(Des S. Keating. Typo)

1938 (1 July). *Centenary of Temperance Crusade. W* **10**. *P* 15 × 14.
107 **20** 2d. black 1·00 50
108 3d. blue 10·00 6·50

21 George Washington, American Eagle and Irish Harp

22

(Des G. Atkinson. Typo)

1939 (1 Mar). *150th Anniv of U.S. Constitution and Installation of First U.S. President. W* **10**. *P* 15 × 14.
109 **21** 2d. scarlet 1·00 70
110 3d. blue 11·00 8·50

SIZE OF WATERMARK. T **22** can be found in various sizes from about 8 to 10 mm high. This is due to the use of two different dandy rolls supplied by different firms and to the effects of paper shrinkage and other factors such as pressure and machine speed.

1940–68. *Typo. W* **22**. *P* 15 × 14 *or* 14 × 15 (2*s*. 6*d*. *to* 10*s*.).
111 **6** ½d. bright green (24.11.40) 1·00 40
112 **7** 1d. carmine (26.10.40) 30 5
a. From coils. Perf 14 × imperf (9.40) 45·00 55·00
b. From coils. Perf 15 × imperf (20.3.46) 25·00 15·00
c. Booklet pane. Three stamps plus three printed labels £650
113 1½d. claret (1.40) 12·00 70
114 2d. grey-green (1.40) 30 5
115 **8** 2½d. red-brown (3.41) 9·00 10
116 **9** 3d. blue (12.40) 40 5
117 **8** 4d. slate-blue (12.40) 45 5
118 **6** 5d. deep violet (7.40) 40 5
119 6d. claret (3.42) 1·50 40
aa. Chalky paper (1967) 85 90
119*a* 8d. scarlet (12.9.49) 1·00 1·00
120 **8** 9d. deep violet (7.40) 90 75
121 **9** 10d. brown (7.40) 1·00 40
121*a* 11d. rose (12.9.49) 1·50 1·50
122 **6** 1s. light blue (6.40) £125 10·00
123 **18** 2s. 6d. emerald-green (10.2.43) 35·00 1·75
a. Chalky paper (1968?) 3·25 2·75
124 5s. maroon (15.12.42) 22·00 2·00
b. Chalky paper (1968?) 5·50 3·50
125 10s. deep blue (7.45) 85·00 4·50
a. Chalky paper (1968) 8·50 7·50
111/25a *Set of* 17 £150 21·00
There is a wide range of shades and also variation in paper used in this issue.
See also Nos. 227/8.

(**23** *Trans* "In memory of the rising of 1916")

24 Volunteer and G.P.O., Dublin

1941 (12 Apr). *25th Anniv of Easter Rising* (1916). *Provisional issue. T* **7** *and* **9** (2*d. in new colour*), *optd with T* **23**.
126 **7** 2d. orange (G.) 3·00 75
127 **9** 3d. blue (V.) 48·00 16·00

(Des V. Brown. Typo)

1941 (27 Oct). *25th Anniv of Easter Rising* (1916). *Definitive issue. W* **22**. *P* 15 × 14.
128 **24** 2½d. blue-black 1·10 15

25 Dr. Douglas Hyde

26 Sir William Rowan Hamilton

27 Bro. Michael O'Clery

(Des S. O'Sullivan. Typo)

1943 (31 July). *50th Anniv of Founding of Gaelic League. W* **22**. *P* 15 × 14.
129 **25** ½d. green 75 25
130 2½d. claret 1·25 30

(Des S. O'Sullivan from a bust by Hogan. Typo)

1943 (13 Nov). *Centenary of Announcement of Discovery of Quaternions. W* **22**. *P* 15 × 14.
131 **26** ½d. green 1·00 50
132 2½d. brown 1·00 50

(Des R. J. King. Typo)

1944 (30 June). *Tercentenary of Death of Michael O'Clery. (Commemorating the "Annals of the Four Masters"). W* **22** (*sideways*). *P* 14 × 15.
133 **27** ½d. emerald-green 25 5
134 1s. red-brown 75 5
Although issued as commemoratives these two stamps were kept in use as part of the current issue, replacing Nos. 111 and 122.

28 Edmund Ignatius Rice

29 "Youth Sowing Seeds of Freedom"

(Des S. O'Sullivan. Typo)

1944 (29 Aug). *Death Centenary of Edmund Rice (founder of Irish Christian Brothers). W* **22**. *P* 15 × 14.
135 **28** 2½d. slate 90 40

(Des R. J. King. Typo)

1945 (15 Sept). *Centenary of Death of Thomas Davis (founder of Young Ireland Movement). W* **22**. *P* 15 × 14.
136 **29** 2½d. blue 75 20
137 6d. claret 7·00 4·50

30 "Country and Homestead"

(Des R. J. King. Typo)

1946 (16 Sept). *Birth Centenaries of Davitt and Parnell (land reformers). W* **22**. *P* 15 × 14.
138 **30** 2½d. scarlet 75 30
139 3d. blue 5·00 3·75

31 Angel Victor over Rock of Cashel

(Des R. J. King. Recess Waterlow until 1961, then De La Rue)

1948 (7 Apr)–**65**. *Air. T* **31** *and similar horiz designs. W* **22**. *P* 15 (1*s*. 5*d*.) *or* 15 × 14 (*others*).
140 **31** 1d. chocolate (4.4.49) 6·00 5·00
141 – 3d. blue 9·50 7·00
142 – 6d. magenta 1·00 50
142*a* – 8d. lake-brown (13.12.54) 3·00 1·25
143 – 1s. green (4.4.49) 1·50 60
143*a* **31** 1s. 3d. red-orange (13.12.54) 3·50 1·00
143*b* 1s. 5d. deep ultramarine (1.4.65) 3·50 1·00
140/143*b* *Set of* 7 25·00 15·00
Designs:—3d., 8d. Lough Derg; 6d. Croagh Patrick; 1s. Glendalough.

35 Theobald Wolfe Tone

(Des K. Uhlemann. Typo)

1948 (19 Nov). *150th Anniv of Insurrection. W* **22**. *P* 15 × 14.
144 **35** 2½d. reddish purple 1·00 15
145 3d. violet 8·00 5·50

REPUBLIC OF IRELAND

18 April 1949

36 Leinster House and Arms of Provinces

37 J. C. Mangan

(Des Muriel Brandt. Typo)

1949 (21 Nov). *International Recognition of Republic. W* **22**. *P* 15 × 14.
146 **36** 2½d. reddish brown 50 30
147 3d. bright blue 4·75 3·50

(Des R. J. King. Typo)

1949 (5 Dec). *Death Centenary of James Clarence Mangan (poet). W* **22**. *P* 15 × 14.
148 **37** 1d. green 3·25 50

38 Statue of St. Peter

39 Thomas Moore

40 Irish Harp

(Recess Waterlow & Sons)

1950 (11 Sept). *Holy Year. W* **22**. *P* 12½.
149 **38** 2½d. violet 60 45
150 3d. blue 12·00 10·00
151 9d. brown 14·00 9·00

PRINTERS. Nos. 152 to 200 were recess-printed by De La Rue & Co, Dublin, *unless otherwise stated.*

1952 (10 Nov). *Death Centenary of Thomas Moore (poet). W* **22**. *P* 13.
152 **39** 2½d. reddish purple 50 5
153 3½d. deep olive-green 4·00 3·25

(Des F. O'Ryan. Typo Government Printing Works, Dublin)

1953 (9 Feb). *"An Tostal" (Ireland at Home) Festival. W* **22** (*sideways*). *P* 14 × 15.
154 **40** 2½d. emerald-green 80 50
155 1s. 4d. blue 22·00 22·00

41 Robert Emmet

42 Madonna and Child (Della Robbia)

43 Cardinal Newman (first Rector)

(Eng L. Downey)

1953 (21 Sept). *150th Death Anniv of Emmet (patriot). W* **22**. *P* 13.
156 **41** 3d. deep bluish green 1·50 30
157 1s. 3d. carmine 40·00 15·00

(Eng A. R. Lane)

1954 (24 May). *Marian Year. W* **22**. *P* 15.
158 **42** 3d. blue 2·00 15
159 5d. myrtle-green 8·00 7·00

(Des L. Whelan. Typo Govt Printing Works, Dublin)

1954 (19 July). *Centenary of Founding of Catholic University of Ireland. W* **22**. *P* 15 × 14.
160 **43** 2d. bright purple 1·75 15
161 1s. 3d. blue 16·00 9·00

44 Statue of Commodore Barry

45 John Redmond

46 Thomas O'Crohan

(Des and eng H. Woyty-Wimmer)

1956 (16 Sept). *Barry Commemoration. W* **22**. *P* 15.
162 **44** 3d. slate-lilac 1·00 10
163 1s. 3d. deep blue 12·00 9·00

1957 (11 June). *Birth Centenary of John Redmond (politician). W* **22**. *P* 14 × 15.
164 **45** 3d. deep blue 1·25 10
165 1s. 3d. brown-purple 15·00 9·00

1957 (1 July). *Birth Centenary of Thomas O'Crohan (author). W* **22**. *P* 14 × 15.
166 **46** 2d. maroon 3·00 30
a. Wmk sideways
167 5d. violet 5·50 5·50

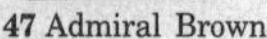

47 Admiral Brown 48 "Father Wadding" (Ribera) 49 Tom Clarke

(Des S. O'Sullivan. Typo Govt Printing Works, Dublin)

1957 (23 Sept). *Death Centenary of Admiral William Brown. W* **22.** *P* 15 × 14.
168 **47** 3d. blue . . . . 2·00 35
169 1s. 3d. carmine . . . . 45·00 19·00

1957 (25 Nov). *300th Death Anniv of Father Luke Wadding (theologian). W* **22.** *P* 15.
170 **48** 3d. deep blue 70 10
171 1s. 3d. lake . . . . 18·00 8·50

1958 (28 July). *Birth Centenary of Thomas J. ("Tom") Clarke (patriot). W* **22.** *P* 15.
172 **49** 3d. deep green 75 10
173 1s. 3d. red-brown . . . . 13·00 8·50

50 Mother Mary Aikenhead 51 Arthur Guinness

(Recess Imprimerie Belge de Securité, Brussels, subsidiary of Waterlow & Sons)

1958 (20 Oct). *Death Centenary of Mother Mary Aikenhead (foundress of Irish Sisters of Charity). W* **22.** *P* 15 × 14.
174 **50** 3d. Prussian blue 75 10
175 1s. 3d. rose-carmine . . . . 17·00 8·00

(Typo Govt Printing Works, Dublin)

1958 (29 Dec). *21st Anniv of the Irish Constitution. W* **22.** *P* 15 × 14.
176 **19** 3d. brown 75 10
177 5d. emerald-green . . . . 5·50 5·00

1959 (20 July). *Bicentenary of Guinness Brewery. W* **22.** *P* 15.
178 **51** 3d. brown-purple 80 10
179 1s. 3d. blue . . . . 13·00 8·50

52 "The Flight of the Holy Family"

(Des K. Uhlemann)

1960 (20 June). *World Refugee Year. W* **22.** *P* 15.
180 **52** 3d. purple 40 5
181 1s. 3d. sepia . . . . 1·25 2·50

53 Conference Emblem

(Des P. Rahikainen)

1960 (19 Sept). *Europa. W* **22.** *P* 15.
182 **53** 6d. light brown . . . . 2·50 2·50
183 1s. 3d. violet . . . . 13·00 15·00

The ink of No. 183 is fugitive.

54 Dublin Airport, De Havilland "Dragon" and Boeing "720" jet aircraft 55 St. Patrick

(Des J. Flanagan and D. R. Lowther)

1961 (26 June). *25th Anniv of Aer Lingus. W* **22.** *P* 15.
184 **54** 6d. blue . . . . 1·50 2·00
185 1s. 3d. green . . . . 3·75 4·00

(Recess B.W.)

1961 (25 Sept). *Fifteenth Death Centenary of St. Patrick. W* **22.** *P* 14½.
186 **55** 3d. blue 75 10
187 **55** 8d. purple . . . . 1·90 3·00
188 1s. 3d. green . . . . 1·90 2·50

56 J. O'Donovan and E. O'Curry

(Recess B.W.)

1962 (26 Mar). *Death Centenaries of O'Donovan and O'Curry (scholars). W* **22.** *P* 15.
189 **56** 3d. carmine 50 5
190 1s. 3d. purple . . . . 4·75 3·00

57 Europa "Tree"

(Des L. Weyer)

1962 (17 Sept). *Europa. W* **22.** *P* 15.
191 **57** 6d. carmine-red 60 65
192 1s. 3d. turquoise . . . . 1·25 1·75

58 Campaign Emblem

(Des K. Uhlemann)

1963 (21 Mar). *Freedom from Hunger. W* **22.** *P* 15.
193 **58** 4d. deep violet 50 5
194 1s. 3d. scarlet . . . . 2·00 1·75

59 "Co-operation"

(Des A. Holm)

1963 (16 Sept). *Europa. W* **22.** *P* 15.
195 **59** 6d. carmine . . . . 1·00 75
196 1s. 3d. blue . . . . 4·00 4·00

60 Centenary Emblem

(Des P. Wildbur. Photo Harrison & Sons)

1963 (2 Dec). *Centenary of Red Cross. W* **22.** *P* 14½ × 14.
197 **60** 4d. red and grey 30 5
198 1s. 3d. red, grey and light emerald . . . 1·25 1·75

61 Wolfe Tone

(Des P. Wildbur)

1964 (13 Apr). *Birth Bicentenary of Wolfe Tone (revolutionary). W* **22.** *P* 15.
199 **61** 4d. black . . . . 1·00 5
200 1s. 3d. ultramarine . . . . 4·25 3·75

62 Irish Pavilion at Fair

(Des A. Devane. Photo Harrison & Sons)

1964 (20 July). *New York World's Fair. W* **22.** *P* 14½ × 14.
201 **62** 5d. blue-grey, brown, violet & yellow-ol 95 5
a. Brown omitted* . . . . . .
202 1s. 5d. blue-grey, brown, turquoise-blue and light yellow-green . . . . . . 4·00 4·50

*No. 201a comes from the top row of a sheet and shows part of the brown cross which would appear in the sheet margin. As the second horizontal row was normal it would appear that the brown cylinder was incorrectly registered.

63 Europa "Flower" 64 "Waves of Communication"

(Des G. Bétemps. Photo Harrison)

1964 (14 Sept). *Europa. W* **22** *(sideways). P* 14 × 14½.
203 **63** 8d. olive-green and blue . . . . . 1·50 1·50
204 1s. 5d. red-brown and orange . . . . 4·50 2·50

(Des P. Wildbur. Photo Harrison)

1965 (17 May). *I.T.U. Centenary. W* **22.** *P* 14½ × 14.
205 **64** 3d. blue and green 60 10
206 8d. black and green . . . . 2·00 2·00

PRINTERS. Nos. 207 onwards were photogravure-printed by the Stamping Branch of the Revenue Commissioners, Dublin *unless otherwise stated.*

65 W. B. Yeats (poet) 66 I.C.Y. Emblem

(Des R. Kyne, from drawing by S. O'Sullivan)

1965 (14 June). *Yeats' Birth Centenary. W* **22** *(sideways). P* 15.
207 **65** 5d. black, orange-brown and deep green 1·00 5
208 1s. 5d. black, grey-green and brown . . 4·00 3·50

1965 (16 Aug). *International Co-operation Year. W* **22.** *P* 15.
209 **66** 3d. ultramarine and new blue . . . . 1·00 10
210 10d. deep brown and brown . . . . . 4·50 6·50

67 Europa "Sprig"

(Des H. Karlsson)

1965 (27 Sept). *Europa. W* **22.** *P* 15.
211 **67** 8d. black and brown-red . . . . . 1·00 1·50
212 1s. 5d. purple and light turquoise-blue 3·00 2·75

68 James Connolly

69 "Marching to Freedom"

(Des E. Delaney (No. 216), R. Kyne, after portraits by S. O'Sullivan (others))

1966 (12 Apr). *50th Anniv of Easter Rising. T* **68/9** *and similar horiz portraits. W* **22.** *P* 15.
213 3d. black and greenish blue 30 10
a. Horiz pair. Nos. 213/14 . . . . . . 2·00 1·75
214 3d. black and bronze-green 30 10
215 5d. black and yellow-olive 30 5
a. Horiz pair. Nos. 215/16 . . . . . . 2·00 1·75
216 5d. black, orange and blue-green 30 5
217 7d. black and light orange-brown . . . . 1·25 2·00
a. Horiz pair. Nos. 217/18 . . . . . . 4·75 12·00
218 7d. black and blue-green . . . . 1·25 2·00
219 1s. 5d. black and turquoise . . . . . . 1·25 1·50
a. Horiz pair. Nos. 219/20 . . . . . . 5·00 12·00
220 1s. 5d. black and bright green . . . . . 1·25 1·50
213/20 . . . . *Set of* 8 12·50 6·50

Designs:—No. 213, Type **68**; No. 214, Thomas J. Clarke; No. 215, P. H. Pearse; No. 216, Type **69**; No. 217, Eamonn Ceannt; No. 218, Sean MacDiarmada; No. 219, Thomas MacDonagh; No. 220, Joseph Plunkett.

Nos. 213/14, 215/16, 217/18 and 219/20 were each printed together, *se-tenant*, in horizontal pairs throughout the sheet.

76 R. Casement

77 Europa "Ship"

(Des R. Kyne)

1966 (3 Aug). *50th Death Anniv of Roger Casement (patriot). W* **22** *(sideways). P* 15.

221	**76**	5d. black	15	5
222		1s. red-brown	65	80

(Des R. Kyne, after G. and J. Bender)

1966 (26 Sept). *Europa. W* **22** *(sideways). P* 15.

223	**77**	7d. emerald and orange	50	65
224		1s. 5d. emerald and light grey	1·25	1·25

78 Interior of Abbey (from lithograph)

79 Cogwheels

1966 (8 Nov). *750th Anniv of Ballintubber Abbey. W* **22**. *P* 15.

225	**78**	5d. red-brown	15	5
226		1s. black	40	70

1966–67. *As Nos.* 116, 118 *but photo. Smaller design* (17 × 21 *mm). Chalk-surfaced paper. W* **22**. *P* 15.

227	**9**	3d. blue (1.8.67)	70	45
228	**6**	5d. bright violet (1.12.66)	1·00	50

No. 228 was only issued in booklets at first but was released in sheets on 1.4.68 in a slightly brighter shade. In the sheet stamps the lines of shading are more regular.

(Des O. Bonnevalle)

1967 (2 May). *Europa. W* **22** *(sideways). P* 15.

229	**79**	7d. light emerald, gold and pale cream	50	60
230		1s. 5d. carmine-red, gold and pale cream	1·25	1·25

80 Maple Leaves

(Des P. Hickey)

1967 (28 Aug). *Canadian Centennial. W* **22**. *P* 15.

231	**80**	5d. multicoloured	15	15
232		1s. 5d. multicoloured	30	90

81 Rock of Cashel (from photo by Edwin Smith)

1967 (25 Sept). *International Tourist Year. W* **22** *(inverted). P* 15.

233	**81**	7d. sepia	20	30
234		10d. slate-blue	40	60

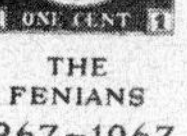

82 1 c. Fenian Stamp Essay

83 24 c. Fenian Stamp Essay

1967 (23 Oct). *Centenary of Fenian Rising. W* **22** *(sideways). P* 15.

235	**82**	5d. black and light green	10	5
236	**83**	1s. black and light pink	25	55

84 Jonathan Swift

85 Gulliver and Lilliputians

(Des M. Byrne)

1967 (30 Nov). *300th Birth Anniv of Jonathan Swift. W* **22** *(sideways). P* 15.

237	**84**	3d. black and olive-grey	15	5
238	**85**	1s. 5d. blackish brown and pale blue	25	60

86 Europa "Key"

(Des H. Schwarzenbach and M. Biggs)

1968 (29 Apr). *Europa. W* **22**. *P* 15.

239	**86**	7d. brown-red, gold and brown	60	70
240		1s. 5d. new blue, gold and brown	1·00	1·25

87 St Mary's Cathedral, Limerick

(Des from photo by J. J. Bambury. Recess B.W.)

1968 (26 Aug). *800th Anniv of St. Mary's Cathedral, Limerick. W* **22**. *P* 15.

241	**87**	5d. Prussian blue	12	5
242		10d. yellow-green	45	1·25

88 Countess Markievicz

89 James Connolly

1968 (23 Sept). *Birth Centenary of Countess Markievicz (patriot). W* **22**. *P* 15.

243	**88**	3d. black	12	5
244		1s. 5d. deep blue and blue	30	70

1968 (23 Sept). *Birth Centenary of James Connolly (patriot). W* **22** *(sideways). P* 15.

245	**89**	6d. deep brown and chocolate	25	50
246		1s. blksh grn, apple-grn & myrtle-grn	30	40

90 Stylised Dog (brooch)

91 Stag

92 Winged Ox (Symbol of St. Luke)

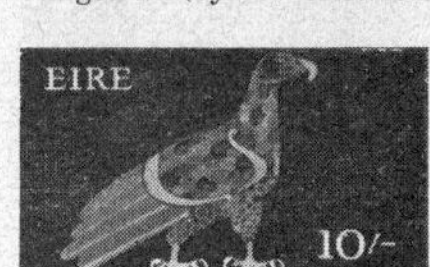

93 Eagle (Symbol of St. John The Evangelist)

(Des H. Gerl)

1968–70. *Pence values expressed with* "p". *W* **22** *(sideways on* ½*d. to* 1*s.* 9*d.). P* 15.

247	**90**	½d. red-orange (7.6.69)	5	20
248		1d. pale yellow-green (7.6.69)	15	5
		a. Coil stamp. Perf 14 × 15 (8.70?)	1·00	3·00
249	**90**	2d. light ochre (14.10.68)	20	5
		a. Coil stamp. Perf 14 × 15 (8.70?)	1·00	3·00
250		3d. blue (7.6.69)	35	5
		a. Coil stamp. Perf 14 × 15 (8.70?)	1·00	2·50
251		4d. deep brown-red (31.3.69)	25	10
252		5d. myrtle-green (31.3.69)	40	70
253		6d. bistre-brown (24.2.69)	30	12
254	**91**	7d. brown and yellow (7.6.69)	75	2·25
255		8d. chocolate & orange-brown (14.10.68)	75	1·25
256		9d. slate-blue and olive-green (24.2.69)	1·25	60
257		10d. chocolate and bluish violet (31.3.69)	1·50	2·00
258		1s. chocolate and red-brown (31.3.69)	60	35
259		1s. 9d. black & lt turquoise-bl (24.2.69)	3·00	2·50
260	**92**	2s. 6d. multicoloured (14.10.68)	4·00	70
261		5s. multicoloured (24.2.69)	8·00	1·25
262	**93**	10s. multicoloured (14.10.68)	18·00	2·75
247/62		*Set of* 16	35·00	13·00

The 1d., 2d., 3d., 5d., 6d., 9d., 1s. and 2s. 6d. exist with PVA gum as well as gum arabic. The coil stamps exist on PVA only, and the rest on gum arabic only.

See also Nos. 287/301, 339/59 and 478/83.

94 Human Rights Emblem

95 Dail Eireann Assembly

1968 (4 Nov). *Human Rights Year. W* **22** *(sideways). P* 15.

263	**94**	5d. yellow, gold and black	15	5
264		7d. yellow, gold and red	30	60

(Des M. Byrne)

1969 (21 Jan). *50th Anniv of Dail Eireann (First National Parliament). W* **22** *(sideways). P* 15 × 14½.

265	**95**	6d. myrtle-green	10	5
266		9d. Prussian blue	30	80

96 Colonnade

97 Quadruple I.L.O. Emblems

(Des L. Gasbarra and G. Belli; adapted Myra Maguire)

1969 (28 Apr). *Europa. W* **22**. *P* 15.

267	**96**	9d. grey, ochre and ultramarine	65	1·00
268		1s. 9d. grey, gold and scarlet	1·25	1·25

(Des K. C. Dābczewski)

1969 (14 July). *50th Anniv of International Labour Organization. W* **22** *(sideways). P* 15.

269	**97**	6d. black and grey	15	5
270		9d. black and yellow	30	60

98 "The Last Supper and Crucifixion" (Evie Hone Window, Eton Chapel)

(Des R. Kyne)

1969 (1 Sept). *Contemporary Irish Art* (*1st issue*). *W* **22** *(sideways). P* 15 × 14½.

271	**98**	1s. multicoloured	45	1·50

See also Nos. 280, 306, 317, 329, 362, 375, 398, 408, 452, 470 and 498.

99 Mahatma Gandhi

1969 (2 Oct). *Birth Centenary of Mahatma Gandhi*. W **22**. *P* 15.
272 **99** 6d. black and green 25 5
273 1s. 9d. black and yellow 60 90

100 Symbolic Bird in Tree

(Des D. Harrington)

1970 (23 Feb). *European Conservation Year*. W **22**. *P* 15.
274 **100** 6d. bistre and black 25 10
275 9d. slate-violet and black 70 70

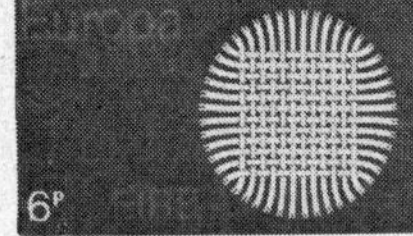

101 "Flaming Sun"

(Des L. le Brocquy)

1970 (4 May). *Europa*. W **22**. *P* 15.
276 **101** 6d. bright violet and silver 30 15
277 9d. brown and silver 90 90
278 1s. 9d. deep olive-grey and silver .. 1·50 1·25

102 "Sailing Boats" (Peter Monamy)

103 "Madonna of Eire" (Mainie Jellett)

(Des P. Wildbur and P. Scott)

1970 (13 July). *250th Anniv of Royal Cork Yacht Club*. W **22**. *P* 15.
279 **102** 4d. multicoloured 20 10

1970 (1 Sept). *Contemporary Irish Art* (2nd issue). W **22** (*sideways*). *P* 15.
280 **103** 1s. multicoloured 30 45

104 Thomas MacCurtain

106 Kevin Barry

(Des P. Wildbur)

1970 (26 Oct). *50th Death Anniversaries of Irish Patriots*. T **104** *and similar vert design*. W **22** (*sideways*). *P* 15.
281 9d. black, bluish violet and greyish black .. 90 95
a. Pair. Nos. 281/2 .. .. 3·50 4·50
282 9d. black, bluish violet and greyish black .. 90 95
283 2s. 9d. black, new blue and greyish black .. 2·00 2·25
a. Pair. Nos. 283/4 .. .. 8·00 15·00
284 2s. 9d. black, new blue and greyish black .. 2·00 2·25

Designs:—Nos. 281 and 283, Type **104**; others, Terence MacSwiney.

Nos. 281/2 and 283/4 were each printed together, *se-tenant*, in horizontal and vertical pairs throughout the sheet.

(Des P. Wildbur)

1970 (2 Nov). *50th Death Anniv of Kevin Barry* (*patriot*). W **22** (*inverted*). *P* 15.
285 **106** 6d. olive-green 20 10
286 1s. 2d. royal blue 60 80

106a Stylized Dog (Brooch)

107 "Europa Chain"

Two types of 10 p.:
I. Outline and markings of the ox in lilac.
II. Outline and markings in brown.

1971 (15 Feb)–**75**. *Decimal Currency. Designs as Nos.* 247/62 *but with* "p" *omitted as in T* **106a**. W **22** (*sideways on* 10, 12, 20 *and* 50 *p.*). *P* 15.
287 **106a** ½p. bright green 10 5
a. Wmk sideways .. .. .. 10·00 12·00
288 1p. blue .. .. 1·25 12
a. Coil stamp. Perf 14 × 14½ (20.2.71) 75 50
b. Coil strip. 288a *se-tenant* with 289a and 291a (20.2.71) .. .. 2·00
c. Wmk sideways 20 25
d. Booklet pane. No. 288c × 5 plus one *se-tenant* label (11.3.74) .. .. 1·00
289 1½p. lake-brown 40 30
a. Coil stamp. Perf 14 × 14½ (20.2.71) 50 50
b. Coil strip. 289a *se-tenant* with 291a, 294a and 290a (24.2.72) .. 3·00
c. Coil strip. 289a × 2 *se-tenant* with 290a and 295b (29.1.74) .. .. 3·00
290 2p. myrtle-green 40 10
a. Coil stamp. Perf 14 × 14½ (24.2.72) 50 50
b. Wmk sideways (27.1.75) 50 50
c. Booklet pane. No. 290b × 5 plus one *se-tenant* label (27.1.75) .. .. 2·00
291 2½p. sepia 75 20
a. Coil stamp. Perf 14 × 14½ (20.2.71) 50 50
b. Wmk sideways .. .. .. 2·50 3·00
292 3p. cinnamon 40 20
293 3½p. orange-brown 50 45
294 4p. pale bluish violet 50 5
a. Coil stamp. Perf 14 × 14½ (24.2.72) .. .. .. 1·50 1·00
295 **91** 5p. brown and yellow-olive .. .. 1·75 50
295a **106a** 5p. bright yellow-green (29.1.74) .. 2·75 65
b. Coil stamp. Perf 14 × 14½ (29.1.74) .. .. .. 1·50 1·25
c. Wmk sideways (11.3.74) .. .. 1·00 1·00
d. Booklet pane. No. 295c × 5 plus one *se-tenant* label (11.3.74) .. .. 4·50
296 **91** 6p. blackish brown and slate .. .. 3·50 60
296a 7p. indigo and olive-green (29.1.74) .. 6·00 3·00
297 7½p. chocolate and reddish lilac .. 1·00 50
298 9p. black and turquoise-green .. 3·25 70
299 **92** 10p. multicoloured (I) .. .. 17·00 6·00
299a 10p. multicoloured (II) .. .. 11·00 1·00
299b 12p. multicoloured (29.1.74) .. .. 1·00 75
300 20p. multicoloured .. .. .. 5·00 60
301 **93** 50p. multicoloured .. .. .. 18·00 2·00
287/301 .. .. .. *Set of* 18 50·00 10·00

The ½, 1, 2, 2½p. and 5 p. (No. 295a) with watermark sideways all come from stamp booklets and exist with one or two sides imperforate.

See also Nos. 339/59 and 478/83.

(Des H. Haflidason; adapted P. Wildbur)

1971 (3 May). *Europa*. W **22** (*sideways*). *P* 15.
302 **107** 4p. sepia and olive-yellow 40 30
303 6p. black and new blue .. .. .. 2·50 2·00

108 J. M. Synge

109 "An Island Man" (Jack B. Yeats)

(Des R. Kyne from a portrait by Jack B. Yeats)

1971 (19 July). *Birth Centenary of J. M. Synge* (*playwright*). W **22**. *P* 15.
304 **108** 4p. multicoloured 30 10
305 10p. multicoloured .. .. .. 1·25 1·25

(Des P. Wildbur)

1971 (30 Aug). *Contemporary Irish Art* (3*rd issue*). *Birth Centenary of J. B. Yeats* (*artist*). W **22**. *P* 15.
306 **109** 6p. multicoloured .. .. .. 1·00 75

110 Racial Harmony Symbol

111 "Madonna and Child" (statue by J. Hughes)

(Des P. Wildbur. Litho Harrison)

1971 (18 Oct). *Racial Equality Year*. *No wmk*. *P* 14 × 14½.
307 **110** 4p. red 30 5
308 10p. black .. .. 1·00 1·25

(Des R. Kyne)

1971 (15 Nov). *Christmas*. W **22**. *P* 15.
309 **111** 2½p. black, gold and deep bluish green 30 5
310 6p. black, gold and ultramarine .. 1·00 1·25

112 Heart

(Des L. le Brocquy)

1972 (7 Apr). *World Health Day*. W **22** (*sideways*). *P* 15.
311 **112** 2½p. gold and brown 75 50
312 12p. silver and grey .. .. .. 2·50 2·50

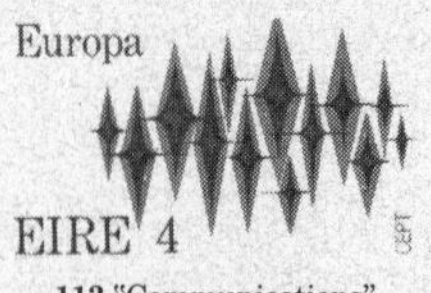

113 "Communications"

(Des P. Huovinen and P. Wildbur)

1972 (1 May). *Europa*. W **22** (*sideways*). *P* 15.
313 **113** 4p. orange, black and silver .. .. 2·50 50
314 6p. blue, black and silver .. .. 5·00 3·75

114 Dove and Moon

115 "Black Lake" (Gerard Dillon)

(Des P. Scott)

1972 (1 June). *The Patriot Dead*, 1922–23. W **22**. *P* 15.
315 **114** 4p. grey-blue, light orange & deep blue 25 5
316 6p. dp yellow-grn, lemon & dp dull grn 1·00 75

(Des P. Wildbur)

1972 (10 July). *Contemporary Irish Art* (4*th issue*). W **22** (*sideways*). *P* 15.
317 **115** 3p. multicoloured 50 50

116 "Horseman" (Carved Slab)

117 Madonna and Child (from Book of Kells)

(Des P. Scott)

1972 (28 Aug). *50th Anniv of Olympic Council of Ireland*. W **22**. *P* 15.
318 **116** 3p. bright yellow, black and gold .. 25 20
319 6p. salmon, black and gold .. .. 1·00 80

WATERMARK. All issues from here onwards are on unwatermarked paper.

(Des P. Scott)

1972 (16 Oct). *Christmas*. *P* 15.
320 **117** 2½p. multicoloured (*shades*) 30 5
321 4p. multicoloured .. .. .. 1·00 70
322 12p. multicoloured .. .. .. 1·25 1·00

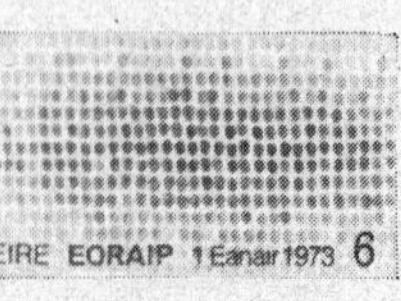

118 2d. Stamp of 1922

119 Celtic Head Motif

(Des Stamping Branch of the Revenue Commissioners, Dublin)

1972 (6 Dec). *50th Anniv of the First Irish Postage Stamp*. *P* 15.
323 **118** 6p. light grey and grey-green 50 50
MS324 72 × 104 mm. No. 323 × 4 .. .. 12·00 17·00

(Des L. le Brocquy)

1973 (1 Jan). *Entry into European Communities*. *P* 15.
325 **119** 6p. multicoloured .. .. .. 75 1·25
326 12p. multicoloured .. .. .. 1·75 1·75

120 Europa "Posthorn"

(Des L. Anisdahl; adapted R. Kyne)

1973 (30 Apr). *Europa. P* 15.
327 **120** 4p. bright blue 50 10
328 6p. black .. .. 1·90 1·50

121 "Berlin Blues II" (W. Scott) **122** Weather Map

(Adapted by R. Scott)

1973 (9 Aug). *Contemporary Irish Art (5th issue). P* 15 × 14½.
329 **121** 5p. ultramarine and grey-black .. 50 20

(Des R. Ballagh)

1973 (4 Sept). *I.M.O./W.M.O. Centenary. P* 14½ × 15.
330 **122** 3½p. multicoloured 25 10
331 12p. multicoloured .. .. 1·50 1·25

123 Tractor ploughing **124** "Flight into Egypt" (Jan de Cock)

(Des P. Scott)

1973 (5 Oct). *World Ploughing Championships, Wellington Bridge. P* 15 × 14½.
332 **123** 5p. multicoloured 20 10
333 7p. multicoloured .. .. 1·25 80

(Des D. Kiely)

1973 (1 Nov). *Christmas. P* 15.
334 **124** 3½p. multicoloured 20 5
335 12p. multicoloured .. .. 1·50 1·00

125 Daunt Island Lightship and Ballycotton Lifeboat, 1936 **126** "Edmund Burke" (statue by J. H. Foley)

(Des M. Byrne from painting by B. Gribble)

1974 (28 Mar). *150th Anniv of Royal National Lifeboat Institution. P* 15 × 14½.
336 **125** 5p. multicoloured 30 20

(Des P. Wildbur)

1974 (29 Apr). *Europa. P* 14½ × 15.
337 **126** 5p. black and pale violet-blue 50 10
338 7p. black and light emerald .. .. 3·00 2·25

1974–83. *Designs as Nos.* 287 *etc. No wmk. P* 15.
339 **106*a*** ½p. bright green (5.6.78) 5 5
340 1p. blue (14.2.75) 5 5
a. Coil stamp. Perf 14 × 14½. (21.3.77) 20 20
b. Coil strip. 340a *se-tenant* with 341a × 2 and 344a (21.3.77) 90
341 2p. myrtle-green (7.4.76) 5 5
a. Coil stamp. Perf 14 × 14½. (21.3.77) 15 15
342 3p. cinnamon (14.2.75) 5 5
343 3½p. orange-brown (9.10.74) .. .. 3·50 2·50
344 5p. bright yellow-green (16.8.74) .. 8 5
a. Coil stamp. Perf 14 × 14½ (21.3.77) 40 40
345 **91** 6p. blackish brown & slate (16.10.74) 1·75 1·50
346 **106*a*** 6p. slate (17.6.75) 20 5
347 **91** 7p. indigo and olive-green (27.9.74) .. 2·00 60
348 **106*a*** 7p. deep yellow-green (17.6.75) .. 35 5
a. Booklet pane. No. 348 × 5 plus *se-tenant* label (21.3.77) .. .. 7·50
349 **91** 8p. deep brown and deep orange-brown (17.6.75) .. .. 1·25 1·25
350 **106*a*** 8p. chestnut (14.7.76) 12 5
351 **91** 9p. black and turquoise-green (12.74) 1·25 45
352 **106*a*** 9p. greenish slate (14.7.76) 15 5
352*a* 9½p. vermilion (3.12.79) 15 15
353 **92** 10p. multicoloured (II) (12.74) .. .. 2·25 60
354 **91** 10p. black and violet-blue (14.7.76) .. 1·00 30
354*a* **106*a*** 10p. deep mauve (8.6.77) 20 5
355 **91** 11p. black and rose-carmine (14.7.76) .. 45 10
355*a* 12p. black and bright green (8.6.77) .. 50 20
355*b* **106*a*** 12p. yellowish green (26.3.80) 20 5
355*c* **91** 13p. reddish brown and red-brown (26.3.80) 25 20
356 **92** 15p. multicoloured (17.6.74) .. .. 1·00 30
356*a* **106*a*** 15p. ultramarine (10.7.80) 25 10
356*b* **91** 16p. black & dull yellow-grn (10.7.80) 30 25
356*c* **92** 17p. multicoloured (8.6.77) 40 10
357 20p. multicoloured (13.6.74) 45 20
358 **93** 50p. multicoloured (12.74) .. .. 1·25 75
359 £1 multicoloured (17.6.75) .. .. 2·75 1·75
339/59 .. .. *Set of* 29 19·00 10·50

For 18p., 19p., 22p., 24p., 26p. and 29p. values printed by lithography, see Nos. 478/83.

Stamps with one or two sides imperf come from the booklet pane.

127 "Oliver Goldsmith" (statue by J. H. Foley) **128** "Kitchen Table" (Norah McGuiness)

(Des P. Wildbur)

1974 (24 June). *Death Bicentenary of Oliver Goldsmith (writer). P* 14½ × 15.
360 **127** 3½p. black and olive-yellow 40 10
361 12p. black and bright yellowish green .. 1·75 1·50

(Design adapted by Norah McGuiness. Photo Harrison)

1974 (19 Aug). *Contemporary Irish Art (6th issue). P* 14 × 14½.
362 **128** 5p. multicoloured 45 20

129 Rugby Players **130** U.P.U. "Postmark"

(Design adapted from Irish Press photograph. Eng C. Slania. Recess (3½p.) or recess and photo (12p.) Harrison)

1974 (9 Sept). *Centenary of Irish Rugby Football Union. P* 14½ × 14.
363 **129** 3½p. greenish black (*shades*) 25 5
364 12p. multicoloured .. .. .. 2·00 1·50

(Des R. Ballagh)

1974 (9 Oct). *Centenary of Universal Postal Union. P* 14½ × 15.
365 **130** 5p. light yellowish green and black .. 20 5
366 7p. light ultramarine and black .. 60 75

131 "Madonna and Child" (Bellini) **132** "Peace"

(Des P. Wildbur)

1974 (14 Nov). *Christmas. P* 14½ × 15.
367 **131** 5p. multicoloured 20 5
368 15p. multicoloured .. .. 1·60 90

(Des Alexandra Wejchert)

1975 (24 Mar). *International Women's Year. P* 14½ × 15.
369 **132** 8p. brt reddish purple & ultramarine .. 60 75
370 15p. ultramarine and bright green .. 1·00 1·25

133 "Castletown Hunt" (R. Healy)

(Des R. Kyne)

1975 (28 Apr). *Europa. P* 15 × 14½.
371 **133** 7p. grey-black 50 15
372 9p. dull blue-green .. .. .. 1·25 1·25

134 Putting

(Des from photographs by J. McManus)

1975 (26 June). *Ninth European Amateur Golf Team Championship, Killarney. P* 15 × 14½.
373 **134** 6p. multicoloured (*shades*) 50 40
374 – 9p. multicoloured (*shades*) .. .. 1·25 1·00

The 9p. is similar to T **134** but shows a different view of the putting green.

135 "Bird of Prey" (sculpture by Oisin Kelly) **136** Nano Nagle (founder) and Waifs

(Design adapted by the artist)

1975 (28 June). *Contemporary Irish Art (7th issue). P* 15 × 14½.
375 **135** 15p. yellow-brown 90 70

(Des Kilkenny Design Workshops)

1975 (1 Sept). *Bicentenary of Presentation Order of Nuns. P* 14½ × 15.
376 **136** 5p. black and pale blue.. .. .. 25 15
377 7p. black and light stone 45 40

137 Tower of St. Anne's Church, Shandon **138** St. Oliver Plunkett (commemorative medal by Imogen Stuart)

(Des P. Scott)

1975 (6 Oct). *European Architectural Heritage Year. T* **137** *and similar vert design. P* 12½.
378 **137** 5p. blackish brown 25 5
379 6p. multicoloured 65 85
380 – 7p. steel-blue 65 15
381 – 9p. multicoloured 90 90

Design:—Nos. 380/1, Interior of Holycross Abbey, Co. Tipperary.

(Design adapted by the artist. Recess Harrison)

1975 (13 Oct). *Canonisation of Oliver Plunkett. P* 14 × 14½.
382 **138** 7p. black 25 10
383 15p. chestnut .. .. 85 1·40

139 "Madonna and Child" (Fra Filippo Lippi) **140** James Larkin (from a drawing by Sean O'Sullivan)

(Des P. Wildbur)

1975 (13 Nov). *Christmas. P* 15.
384 **139** 5p. multicoloured 20 5
385 7p. multicoloured 30 5
386 10p. multicoloured .. .. 75 1·00

(Des P. Wildbur)

1976 (21 Jan). *Birth Centenary of James Larkin (Trade Union leader). P* 14½ × 15.
387 **140** 7p. deep bluish green and pale grey .. 25 10
388 11p. sepia and yellow-ochre .. .. 1·25 1·25

141 Alexander Graham Bell   142 1847 Benjamin Franklin Essay

(Des R. Ballagh)

1976 (10 Mar). *Telephone Centenary. P* 14½ × 15.
389 **141** 9p. multicoloured 25 10
390 15p. multicoloured .. .. 1·25 1·25

(Des L. le Brocquy; graphics by P. Wildbur. Litho Irish Security Stamp Printing Ltd)

1976 (17 May). *Bicentenary of American Revolution. T* **142** *and similar horiz designs. P* 14½ × 14.
391 7p. ultramarine, light red and silver .. 25 10
a. Silver (inscr) omitted .. .. .. † £200
392 8p. ultramarine, light red and silver .. 60 1·00
393 9p. violet-blue, orange and silver .. 60 15
394 15p. light rose-red, grey-blue and silver .. 80 70
a. Silver (face-value and inscr) omitted .. £500 £600
MS395 95 × 75 mm. Nos. 391/4 .. .. .. 10·00 11·00
a. Silver omitted £1200
Designs:—7p. Thirteen stars; 8p. Fifty stars; 9, 15p. Type **142**.
No. **MS**395 exists with the sheet margins overprinted in blue to commemorate "Stampa 76", the Irish National Stamp Exhibition.

143 Spirit Barrel

(Des P. Hickey)

1976 (1 July). *Europa. Irish Delft. T* **143** *and similar horiz design. Multicoloured. P* 15 × 14.
396 9p. Type **143** 35 20
397 11p. Dish 75 80

144 "The Lobster Pots, West of Ireland" (Paul Henry)

(Des R. McGrath)

1976 (30 Aug). *Contemporary Irish Art (8th issue). P* 15.
398 **144** 15p. multicoloured .. .. .. 1·25 85

145 Radio Waves

(Des G. Shepherd and A. O'Donnell. Litho De La Rue Smurfit Ltd, Dublin)

1976 (5 Oct). *50th Anniv of Irish Broadcasting Service. T* **145** *and similar vert design. P* 14½ × 14 (9*p.*) *or* 14 × 14½ (11*p.*).
399 9p. light new blue and bottle-green 35 40
400 11p. agate, orange-red and light new blue .. 1·75 1·50
Design:—11p. Transmitter, radio waves and globe.

146 "The Nativity" (Lorenzo Monaco)

(Des R. McGrath)

1976 (11 Nov). *Christmas. P* 15 × 14½.
401 **146** 7p. multicoloured 20 25
402 9p. multicoloured 50 50
403 15p. multicoloured .. .. .. 1·00 1·00

MINIMUM PRICE

The minimum price quoted is 5p which represents a handling charge rather than a basis for valuing common stamps. For further notes about prices see introductory pages.

147 16th Century Manuscript   148 Ballynahinch, Galway

(Des P. Hickey)

1977 (9 May). *Centenaries of National Library* (8*p.*) *and National Museum* (10*p.*). *T* **147** *and similar horiz design. Multicoloured. P* 15 × 14½.
404 8p. Type **147** 40 40
405 10p. Prehistoric stone 80 60

(Des E. van der Grijn. Litho Irish Security Stamp Printing Ltd)

1977 (27 June). *Europa. T* **148** *and similar vert design. Multicoloured. P* 14 × 15.
406 10p. Type **148** 50 30
407 12p. Lough Tay, Wicklow .. .. .. 1·75 1·75

149 "Head" (Louis le Brocquy)   150 Guide and Tents

(Design adapted by the artist. Litho Irish Security Stamp Ptg Ltd)

1977 (8 Aug). *Contemporary Irish Art (9th issue). P* 14 × 14½.
408 **149** 17p. multicoloured 80 90

(Des R. Ballagh)

1977 (22 Aug). *Scouting and Guiding. T* **150** *and similar horiz design. Multicoloured. P* 15 × 14½.
409 8p. Type **150** 40 15
410 17p. Tent and Scout saluting .. .. .. 1·25 1·00

151 "The Shanachie" (drawing by Jack B. Yeats)   152 "Electricity" (Golden Jubilee of Electricity Supply Board)

(Des L. Miller (10p.), R. Ballagh (12p.). Litho Irish Security Stamp Printing Ltd)

1977 (12 Sept). *Anniversaries. T* **151** *and similar horiz design. P* 14 × 14½ (10*p.*) *or* 14½ × 14 (12*p.*).
411 10p. black 40 15
412 12p. black .. .. 85 1·10
Designs and events:—10p. Type **151** (Golden Jubilee of Irish Folklore Society); 12p. The philosopher Eriugena (1100th Death Anniv).

(Des R. Ballagh (10p.), P. Hickey (12p.), B. Blackshaw (17p.). Photo Stamping Branch of the Revenue Commissioners (12p.); Litho Irish Security Stamp Ptg Ltd (others))

1977 (10 Oct). *Golden Jubilees. T* **152** *and similar horiz designs. P* 15 × 14½ (12*p.*) *or* 15 × 14 (*others*).
413 10p. multicoloured 25 10
414 12p. multicoloured 55 85
415 17p. grey-black and grey-brown 65 70
Designs:—12p. Bulls (from contemporary coinage) (Jubilee of Agricultural Credit Corporation); 17p. Greyhound (Jubilee of Greyhound Track Racing).

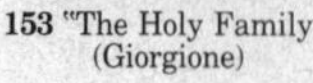

153 "The Holy Family" (Giorgione)   154 *Bremen* in Flight

(Des R. McGrath)

1977 (3 Nov). *Christmas. P* 14½ × 15.
416 **153** 8p. multicoloured 25 5
417 10p. multicoloured 40 5
418 17p. multicoloured .. .. .. 85 1·00

(Des R. Ballagh. Litho Irish Security Stamp Ptg Ltd)

1978 (13 Apr). *50th Anniv of First East–West Transatlantic Flight. P* 14 × 14½.
419 **154** 10p. bright blue and black 30 15
420 – 17p. olive-brown and black 65 80
The 17p. is as T **154**, but shows a different sky and sea.

155 Spring Gentian   156 Catherine McAuley

(Des Wendy Walsh. Litho Irish Security Stamp Ptg Ltd)

1978 (12 June). *Wild Flowers. T* **155** *and similar vert designs. Multicoloured. P* 14 × 15.
421 8p. Type **155** 30 10
422 10p. Strawberry tree 35 5
423 11p. Large-flowered Butterwort 50 30
424 17p. St. Dabeoc's Heath .. .. .. 1·25 1·10

(Des R. Ballagh (10p.), R. Kyne (11p.), E. van der Grijn (17p.). Litho Irish Security Stamp Ptg Ltd)

1978 (18 Sept). *Anniversaries and Events. T* **156** *and similar multicoloured designs. P* 14½ × 14 (11*p.*) *or* 14 × 14½ (*others*).
425 10p. Type **156** 25 15
426 11p. Doctor performing vaccination (*horiz*) .. 30 30
427 17p. "Self Portrait" 65 65
Events:—10p. Birth bicentenary of Catherine McAuley (founder of Sisters of Mercy); 11p. Global Eradication of Smallpox; 17p. Birth centenary of Sir William Orpen (painter).

157 Diagram of Drilling Rig   158 Farthing

(Des R. Ballagh. Litho Irish Security Stamp Ptg Ltd)

1978 (18 Oct). *Arrival Onshore of Natural Gas. P* 14 × 14½.
428 **157** 10p. maroon, turquoise-green and bistre 30 20

(Des P. Wildbur and R. Mercer)

1978 (26 Oct). *50th Anniv of Irish Currency. T* **158** *and similar horiz designs. P* 15 × 14½.
429 8p. black, copper and deep bluish green .. 20 15
430 10p. black, silver and blue-green 25 5
431 11p. black, copper and chocolate 35 40
432 17p. black, silver and deep blue 75 90
Designs:—10p. Florin; 11p. Penny; 17p. Half-crown.

159 "The Virgin and Child" (Guercino)   160 Conolly Folly, Castletown

(Des P. Wildbur)

1978 (16 Nov). *Christmas. P* 14½ × 15.
433 **159** 8p. purple-brown, gold and pale turquoise-green 20 5
434 10p. purple-brown, chocolate and pale turquoise-green 25 5
435 17p. purple-brown, deep blue-green and pale turquoise-green .. .. 75 1·10

(Des R. McGrath)

1978 (6 Dec). *Europa. Architecture. T* **160** *and similar horiz design. P* 15 × 14½.
436 10p. lake-brown and red-brown 30 15
437 11p. green and deep green 45 60
Design:—11p. Dromoland Belvedere.

161 Athletes in Cross-country Race

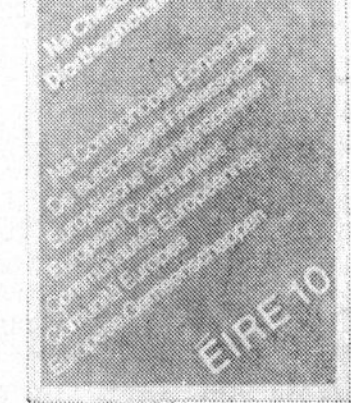

162 "European Communities" (in languages of member nations)

(Des R. Mercer. Litho Irish Security Stamp Ptg Ltd)

1979 (20 Aug). *7th World Cross-country Championships, Limerick. P* 14½ × 14.
438 **161** 8p. multicoloured 20 20

(Des P. Wildbur)

1979 (20 Aug). *First Direct Elections to European Assembly. P* 14½ × 15.
439 **162** 10p. dull turquoise-green 20 15
440 11p. reddish violet 30 40

163 Sir Rowland Hill 164 Wren (*Troglodytes troglodytes*)

(Des C. Harrison. Litho Irish Security Stamp Ptg Ltd)

1979 (20 Aug). *Death Centenary of Sir Rowland Hill. P* 14 × 14½.
441 **163** 17p. black, brownish grey and red .. 45 45

(Des Wendy Walsh. Litho Irish Security Stamp Ptg Ltd)

1979 (30 Aug). *Birds. T* **164** *and similar horiz designs. Multicoloured. P* 14½ × 14.
442 8p. Type **164** 20 20
443 10p. Great Crested Grebe (*Podiceps cristatus*) 30 5
444 11p. White-fronted Goose (*Anser albifrons flavirostris*) 30 30
445 17p. Peregrine Falcon (*Falco peregrinus*) .. 75 80

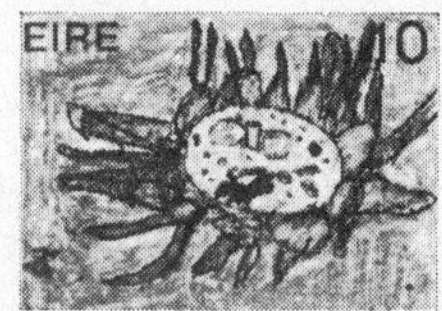

165 "A Happy Flower" (David Gallagher)

(Des P. Wildbur. Litho Irish Security Stamp Ptg Ltd)

1979 (13 Sept). *International Year of the Child. Paintings by Children. T* **165** *and similar multicoloured designs. P* 14 × 14½ (11p.) *or* 14½ × 14 (*others*).
446 10p. Type **165** 25 25
447 11p. "Myself and My Skipping Rope" (Lucy Norman) (*vert*) 30 35
448 17p. "Swans on a Lake" (Nicola O'Dwyer) .. 50 60

166 Pope John Paul II

(Des P. Byrne. Litho Irish Security Stamp Ptg Ltd)

1979 (29 Sept). *Visit of Pope John Paul II. P* 14½ × 14.
449 **166** 12p. multicoloured 30 20

167 Brother and Child

(Des R. Kyne (9½p.), P. Scott (11p.), R. Mercer (20p.). Photo Stamping Branch of the Revenue Commissioners, Dublin (11p.), Litho Irish Security Stamp Ptg Ltd (others))

1979 (4 Oct). *Commemorations. T* **167** *and similar designs. P* 14½ × 14 (9½p.), 14½ × 15 (11p.) *or* 14 × 14½ (*others*).
450 9½p. black and pale claret 20 15
451 11p. black, reddish orange and bright blue .. 30 35
452 20p. multicoloured 60 65

Designs and commemorations: *Horiz*—9½p. Type **167** (centenary of Hospitaller Order of St. John of God in Ireland); 20p. "Seated Figure" (sculpture by F. E. McWilliam) (Contemporary Irish Art (10th issue)). *Vert*—11p. Windmill and Sun (International Energy Conservation Month).

168 Patrick Pearse, "Liberty" and General Post Office, Dublin

169 Madonna and Child (panel painting from Domnach Airgid Shrine)

(Des R. Ballagh)

1979 (10 Nov). *Birth Centenary of Patrick Pearse (patriot). P* 15 × 14½.
453 **168** 12p. multicoloured 30 15

(Des Ewa Gargulinska)

1979 (15 Nov). *Christmas. P* 14½ × 15.
454 **169** 9½p. multicoloured 15 5
455 20p. multicoloured 45 55

170 Bianconi Long Car, 1836

171 John Baptist de la Salle (founder)

(Des P. Wildbur. Litho Irish Security Stamp Ptg Ltd)

1979 (6 Dec). *Europa. Communications. T* **170** *and similar horiz design. Multicoloured. P* 14½ × 14.
456 12p. Type **170** 25 20
457 13p. Transatlantic cable, Valentia, 1866 .. 30 40

(Des P. Wildbur. Litho Irish Security Stamp Ptg Ltd)

1980 (19 Mar). *Centenary of arrival of De La Salle Order. P* 14 × 14½.
458 **171** 12p. multicoloured 30 25

172 George Bernard Shaw

173 Stoat (*Mustela erminea hibernica*)

(Des P. Byrne. Litho Irish Security Stamp Ptg Ltd)

1980 (7 May). *Europa. Personalities. T* **172** *and similar multicoloured design. P* 14 × 14½.
459 12p. Type **172** 30 20
460 13p. Oscar Wilde (28 × 38 *mm*) 30 35

(Des Wendy Walsh. Litho Irish Security Stamp Ptg Ltd)

1980 (30 July). *Wildlife. T* **173** *and similar vert designs. Multicoloured. P* 14 × 14½.
461 12p. Type **173** 30 15
462 15p. Irish Hare (*Lepus timidus hibernicus*) .. 35 15
463 16p. Fox (*Vulpes vulpes*) 35 25
464 25p. Red Deer (*Cervus elaphus*) 65 85
MS465 73 × 97 mm. Nos. 461/4 .. .. .. 3·00 3·75

No. **MS**465 exists with the sheet margins overprinted to commemorate "STAMPA 80", the Irish National Stamp Exhibition, in black or red.

MINIMUM PRICE

The minimum price quoted is 5p which represents a handling charge rather than a basis for valuing common stamps. For further notes about prices see introductory pages.

174 Playing Bodhran and Whistle

175 Sean O'Casey

(Des J. Dixon and P. Wildbur. Litho Irish Security Stamp Ptg Ltd)

1980 (25 Sept). *Traditional Music and Dance. T* **174** *and similar vert designs. Multicoloured. P* 14 × 14½.
466 12p. Type **174** 25 5
467 15p. Playing Uilleann pipes 30 15
468 25p. Dancing 55 75

(Des P. Wildbur (12p.), P. Scott (25p.). Litho Irish Security Stamp Ptg Ltd)

1980 (23 Oct). *Commemorations. T* **175** *and similar vert design. P* 14 × 14½.
469 12p. multicoloured 25 20
470 25p. black, buff and drab 50 45

Designs and commemorations:—12p. Type **175** (Birth centenary of Sean O'Casey (playwright)); 25p. "Gold Painting No. 57" (Patrick Scott) (Contemporary Irish Art (11th issue)).

176 Nativity Scene (painting by Geraldine McNulty)

177 Boyle Air-pump, 1659

(Des P. Wildbur)

1980 (13 Nov). *Christmas. P* 14½ × 15.
471 **176** 12p. multicoloured 25 5
472 15p. multicoloured 30 5
473 25p. multicoloured 65 85

(Des P. Wildbur. Litho Irish Security Stamp Ptg Ltd)

1981 (12 Mar). *Irish Science and Technology. T* **177** *and similar vert designs. Multicoloured. P* 14 × 14½.
474 12p. Type **177** 25 15
475 15p. Ferguson tractor, 1936 .. .. .. 30 15
476 16p. Parsons turbine, 1884 .. .. .. 35 40
477 25p. Holland submarine, 1878 .. .. 60 70

(Litho Irish Security Stamp Ptg Ltd)

1981 (27 Apr)–**82.** *No wmk. P* 14 × 14½.
478 **106a** 18p. dull claret 25 25
479 19p. light blue 30 30
480 22p. dull turquoise-blue (1.9.81) .. 45 35
481 24p. drab (29.10.81) 35 35
482 26p. blue-green (1.4.82) 55 45
483 29p. purple (1.4.82) 60 50
478/83 .. .. *Set of* 6 2·25 2·00

178 "The Legend of the Cock and the Pot"

179 Cycling

(Des P. Byrne. Litho Irish Security Stamp Ptg Ltd)

1981 (4 May). *Europa. Folklore. Paintings by Maria Simonds-Gooding. T* **178** *and similar vert design. P* 14 × 14½.
491 18p. black, orange-yellow and carmine .. 35 15
492 19p. black, yellow-orange and yellow .. 40 45

Design:—19p. "The Angel with the Scales of Judgement".

(Des R. Ballagh. Litho Irish Security Stamp Ptg Ltd)

1981 (24 June). *50th Anniv of "An Óige" (Irish Youth Hostel Association). T* **179** *and similar multicoloured designs. P* 14 × 14½ (15, 30p.) *or* 14½ × 14 (*others*).
493 15p. Type **179** 30 35
494 18p. Hill-walking (*horiz*) 40 15
495 19p. Mountaineering (*horiz*) 40 50
496 30p. Rock-climbing 65 50

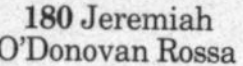

180 Jeremiah O'Donovan Rossa

181 "Railway Embankment" (W. J. Leech)

(Des C. Harrison. Litho Irish Security Stamp Ptg Ltd)

1981 (31 Aug). *150th Birth Anniv of Jeremiah O'Donovan Rossa (politician). P* 14 × 14½.

497 **180** 15p. multicoloured 30 30

(Des P. Wildbur. Litho Irish Security Stamp Ptg Ltd)

1981 (31 Aug). *Contemporary Irish Art (12th issue). P* 14½ × 14.

498 **181** 30p. multicoloured 60 60

182 James Hoban and White House

183 "Arkle" (steeplechaser)

(Des B. Thompson. Litho Irish Security Stamp Ptg Ltd)

1981 (29 Sept). *150th Death Anniv of James Hoban (White House architect). P* 14½ × 14.

499 **182** 18p. multicoloured 35 30

(Des Wendy Walsh and P. Wildbur. Litho Irish Security Stamp Ptg Ltd)

1981 (23 Oct). *Famous Irish Horses. T* **183** *and similar horiz designs. Multicoloured. P* 14½ × 14.

500	18p. Type **183**	30	40
	a. Pair. Nos. 500/1	60	80
501	18p. "Boomerang" (showjumper)	30	40
502	22p. "King of Diamonds" (Draught horse) ..	45	45
503	24p. "Ballymoss" (flatracer)	45	45
504	36p. "Coosheen Finn" (Connemara pony) ..	70	70

The 18p values were printed together, *se-tenant*, in horizontal and vertical pairs throughout the sheet.

184 "Nativity" (F. Barocci)

185 Eviction Scene

(Des P. Wildbur. Litho Irish Security Stamp Ptg Ltd)

1981 (19 Nov). *Christmas. P* 14 × 14½.

505	**184**	18p. multicoloured	35	10
506		22p. multicoloured	45	10
507		36p. multicoloured	75	90

(Des R. Mercer (18p.), P. Wildbur (22p.). Litho Irish Security Stamp Ptg Ltd)

1981 (10 Dec). *Anniversaries. T* **185** *and similar multicoloured design. P* 14 × 14½ *(18p.) or* 14½ × 14 *(22p.).*

508 18p. Type **185** 30 30

509 22p. Royal Dublin Society emblem (*horiz*) .. 40 40

Anniversaries—18p. Centenary of Land Law (Ireland) Act; 22p. 250th of Royal Dublin Society (organization for the advancement of agriculture, industry, art and science).

186 Upper Lake, Killarney National Park

187 "The Stigmatization of St Francis" (Sassetta)

(Des P. Wildbur. Litho Irish Security Stamp Ptg Ltd)

1982 (26 Feb). *50th Anniv of Killarney National Park. T* **186** *and similar horiz design. Multicoloured. P* 14½ × 14.

510 18p. Type **186** 30 30

511 36p. Eagle's Nest 75 75

(Des P. Wildbur (22p.), M. Craig (24p.). Litho Irish Security Stamp Ptg Ltd)

1982 (2 Apr). *Religious Anniversaries. T* **187** *and similar horiz design. P* 14 × 14½ *(22p.) or* 14½ × 14 *(24p.).*

512 22p. multicoloured 40 40

513 24p. olive-brown 45 45

Designs and anniversaries:—22p. Type **187** (800th birth anniv of St Francis of Assissi (founder of Franciscan Order)); 24p. Francis Makemie (founder of American Presbyterianism) and old Presbyterian Church, Ramelton, Co Donegal (300th anniv of ordination).

188 The Great Famine, 1845–50

189 Pádraic Ó Conaire (writer) (Birth Centenary)

(Des P. Wildbur. Litho Irish Security Stamp Ptg Ltd)

1982 (4 May). *Europa. Historic Events. T* **188** *and similar design. P* 14 × 14½ *(26p.) or* 14½ × 14 *(29p.).*

514 26p. black and stone 50 45

515 29p. multicoloured 55 50

Design: *Horiz*—29p. The coming of Christianity to Ireland.

(Des P. Wildbur. Litho Irish Security Stamp Ptg Ltd)

1982 (16 June). *Anniversaries of Cultural Figures. T* **189** *and similar vert designs. P* 14 × 14½.

516	22p. black and light blue	45	40
517	26p. black and sepia	55	45
518	29p. black and blue	60	55
519	44p. black and greenish grey	85	90

Designs and anniversaries:—26p. James Joyce (writer) (birth centenary); 29p. John Field (musician) (birth bicentenary); 44p. Charles Kickham (writer) (death centenary).

190 Porbeagle Shark (*Lamna nasus*)

191 Galway Hooker

(Des Wendy Walsh and P. Wildbur. Litho Irish Security Stamp Ptg Ltd)

1982 (29 July). *Marine Life. T* **190** *and similar horiz designs. Multicoloured. P* 14½ × 14.

520	22p. Type **190**	45	40
521	22p. Oyster (*Ostrea edulis*)	45	40
522	26p. Salmon (*Salmo salár*)	55	50
523	29p. Dublin Bay prawn (*Nephrops norvegicus*)	60	60

(Des P. Wildbur. Litho Irish Security Stamp Ptg Ltd)

1982 (21 Sept). *Irish Boats. T* **191** *and similar multicoloured designs. P* 14 × 14½ *(Nos. 524 and 526) or* 14½ × 14 *(others).*

524	22p. Type **191**	45	40
525	22p. Currach (*horiz*)	45	40
526	26p. *Asgard II*	55	50
527	29p. Howth 17-Footer (*horiz*)	60	60

192 "Irish House of Commons" (painting by Francis Wheatley)

193 "Madonna and Child" (sculpture)

(Des P. Wildbur (22p.) or R. Ballagh (26p.). Litho Irish Security Stamp Ptg Ltd)

1982 (14 Oct). *Bicentenary of Grattan's Parliament (22p.) and Birth Centenary of Eamon de Valera (26p.). T* **192** *and similar multicoloured design. P* 14½ × 14 *(22p.) or* 14 × 14½ *(26p.).*

528 22p. Type **192** 35 30

529 26p. Eamon de Valera (*vert*) 40 35

(Des P. Wildbur. Litho Irish Security Stamp Ptg Ltd)

1982 (11 Nov). *Christmas. P* 14 × 14½.

530	**193**	22p. multicoloured	35	30
531		26p. multicoloured	40	35

194 Aughnanure Castle

195 Ouzel Galley Goblet

(Des M. Craig and P. Wildbur. Litho Irish Security Stamp Ptg Ltd)

1982 (15 Dec)–**84.** *Irish Architecture. T* **194** *and similar designs. P* 15 × 14 *(15, 20, 22, 23, 26, 50p., £1, £5) or* 14 × 15 *(others).*

532	–	1p. dull violet-blue (6.7.83)	5	5
533	–	2p. deep yellow-green (6.7.83)	5	5
534	–	3p. black (6.7.83)	5	5
535	–	4p. maroon (16.3.83)	5	8
		a. Booklet pane. Nos. 535 × 3, 543 × 4 and 1 label (15.8.83)	1·50	
		b. Booklet pane. Nos. 535 × 3, 543 × 5 and 545 × 4 (9.7.84)	3·25	
536	–	5p. olive-sepia (6.7.83)	8	10
537	–	6p. deep grey-blue (16.3.83)	10	12
538	–	7p. dull yellow-green (16.3.83)	10	12
539	–	10p. black (6.7.83)	15	20
540	–	12p. purple-brown (6.7.83)	20	25
541	**194**	15p. deep yellow-green (6.7.83)	25	30
542		20p. deep brown-purple (16.3.83) ..	30	35
543		22p. chalky blue	35	40
544	–	23p. yellow-green (16.3.83)	35	40
545	–	26p. blackish brown	40	45
546	–	29p. deep yellow-green	45	50
547	–	30p. black (16.3.83)	45	50
548	–	44p. black and grey	65	70
549	–	50p. dull ultramarine and grey (16.3.83)	75	80
550	–	£1 bistre-brown and grey	1·50	1·60
551	–	£5 crimson and grey	7·50	8·00
532/51		.. .. *Set of* 20	12·50	13·50

Designs: *Horiz* (*As T* **194**)—1p. to 5p. Central Pavilion, Dublin Botanic Gardens; 6p. to 12p. Dr. Steevens' Hospital, Dublin; 29, 30p. St. Mac Dara's Church. (37 × 21 *mm*)—50p. Casino, Marino; £1 Cahir Castle; £5 Central Bus Station, Dublin. *Vert* (*As T* **194**)—23, 26p. Cormac's Chapel. (21 × 37 *mm*)—44p. Killarney Cathedral.

Stamps from booklet panes Nos. 535a/b come with one side imperforate. No. 535b comes from £2 Discount booklet and shows "Booklet Stamp" printed over the gum on the reverse of each stamp.

(Des P. Wildbur (22p.), C. Harrison (26p.). Litho Irish Security Stamp Ptg Ltd)

1983 (23 Feb). *Bicentenaries of Dublin Chamber of Commerce (22p.) and Bank of Ireland (26p.). T* **195** *and similar multicoloured design. P* 14 × 14½ *(22p.) or* 14½ × 14 *(26p.).*

552 22p. Type **195** 30 35

553 26p. Bank of Ireland building (*horiz*) 40 45

196 Pádraig O Siochfhradha (writer and teacher) (Birth cent)

197 Neolithic Carved Pattern, Newgrange Tomb

(Des C. Harrison (26p.), R. Ballagh (29p.). Litho Irish Security Stamp Ptg Ltd)

1983 (7 Apr). *Anniversaries. T* **196** *and similar vert design. Multicoloured. P* 14 × 14½.

554 26p. Type **196** 40 45

555 29p. Young Boys' Brigade member (Centenary) 45 50

(Des L. le Brocquy (26p.), P. Wildbur (29p.). Litho Irish Security Stamp Ptg Ltd)

1983 (4 May). *Europa. T* **197** *and similar horiz design. P* 14½ × 14.

556 26p. grey-black and gold 40 45

557 29p. black, blackish brown and gold 45 50

Design:—29p. Sir William Rowan Hamilton's formulae for the multiplication of quaternions.

198 Kerry Blue Terrier

(Des Wendy Walsh and L. Miller. Litho Irish Security Stamp Ptg Ltd)

1983 (23 June). *Irish Dogs. T* **198** *and similar horiz designs. Multicoloured. P* 14½ × 14.

558	22p. Type **198**	30	35
559	26p. Irish Wolfhound	40	45
560	26p. Irish Water Spaniel	40	45
561	29p. Irish Terrier	45	50
562	44p. Irish Setters	65	70
MS563	142 × 80 mm. Nos. 558/62	2·00	2·25

No. **MS**563 exists with the sheet margins overprinted in blue to ommemorate "STAMPA 83", the Irish National Stamp xhibition.

99 Animals (Irish Society for the revention of Cruelty to Animals)

200 Postman with Bicycle

Des Wendy Walsh (No. 564), B. Murphy (No. 566), K. Uhlemann No. 567), R. Ballagh (others). Litho Irish Security Stamp Ptg Ltd)

983 (11 Aug). *Anniversaries and Commemorations. T* **199** *and similar designs. P* 14½ × 14 *(Nos.* 564, 566) *or* 14 × 14½ *(others).*
64 **199** 22p. multicoloured 30 35
65 – 22p. multicoloured 30 35
66 – 26p. multicoloured 40 45
67 – 26p. multicoloured 40 45
68 – 44p. grey-blue and black 60 70

Designs: *Vert*—No. 565, Sean Mac Diarmada (patriot) (birth ent); No. 567, "St. Vincent de Paul in the Streets of Paris" (150th anniv of Society of St. Vincent de Paul); No. 568, "Andrew Jackson" Frank McKelvey) (President of the United States). *Horiz*—No. 66, "100" (Centenary of Industrial Credit Company).

(Des R. Ballagh. Litho Irish Security Stamp Ptg Ltd)

983 (15 Sept). *World Communications Year. T* **200** *and similar vert design. Multicoloured. P* 14 × 14½.
69 22p. Type **200** 30 35
70 29p. Dish antenna 45 50

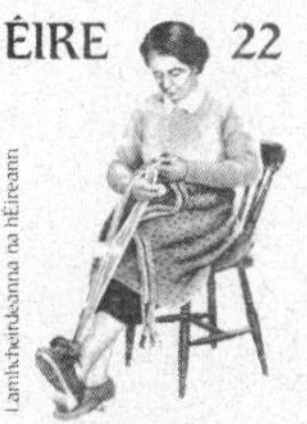

201 Weaving

202 "La Natividad" (R. van der Weyden)

(Des R. Mercer. Litho Irish Security Stamp Ptg Ltd)

983 (13 Oct). *Irish Handicrafts. T* **201** *and similar vert designs. Multicoloured. P* 14 × 14½.
71 22p. Type **201** 30 35
72 26p. Basketmaking 40 45
73 29p. Irish crochet 45 50
74 44p. Harpmaking 65 70

(Des and litho Irish Security Stamp Ptg Ltd)

983 (30 Nov). *Christmas. P* 14 × 14½.
75 **202** 22p. multicoloured 35 40
76 26p. multicoloured 40 45

203 *Princess* (Dublin and Kingstown Railway)

(Des C. Rycroft. Litho Irish Security Stamp Ptg Ltd)

984 (30 Jan). *150th Anniv of Irish Railways. T* **203** *and similar horiz designs. Multicoloured. P* 15 × 14.
77 23p. Type **203** 40 45
78 26p. *Macha* (Great Southern Railway) .. 40 45
79 29p. *Kestrel* (Great Northern Railway) .. 50 55
80 44p. Two-car electric unit (Coras Iompair Eireann) 70 75
MS581 129 × 77 mm. Nos. 577/80 .. .. .. 1·90 2·00

No. **MS**581 exists with the sheet margins overprinted in black to commemorate "STAMPA 84", the Irish National Stamp Exhibition.

204 *Sorbus hibernica*

(Des Wendy Walsh and P. Wildbur. Litho Irish Security Stamp Ptg Ltd)

1984 (1 Mar). *Irish Trees. T* **204** *and similar horiz designs. Multicoloured. P* 15 × 14.
82 22p. Type **204** 35 40
83 26p. *Taxus baccata fastigiata* 45 50
84 29p. *Salix hibernica* 50 55
85 44p. *Betula pubescens* 75 80

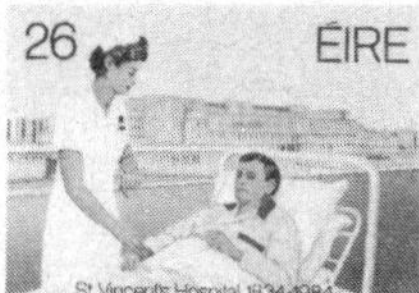

205 St. Vincent's Hospital, Dublin

(Des B. Donegan, adapted by C. Vis (26p.), B. Murphy (44p.). Litho Irish Security Stamp Ptg Ltd)

1984 (12 Apr). *150th Anniv of St. Vincent's Hospital and Bicentenary of Royal College of Surgeons. T* **205** *and similar horiz design. Multicoloured. P* 15 × 14.
586 26p. Type **205** 45 50
587 44p. Royal College and logo 75 80

206 C.E.P.T. 25th Anniversary Logo

(Des J. Larrivière. Litho Irish Security Stamp Ptg Ltd)

1984 (10 May). *Europa. P* 15 × 14.
588 **206** 26p. blue, deep dull blue and black .. 45 50
589 29p. light green, blue-green and black .. 50 55

207 Flags on Ballot Box

208 John McCormack

(Des R. Ballagh. Litho Irish Security Stamp Ptg Ltd)

1984 (10 May). *Second Direct Elections to European Assembly. P* 15 × 14.
590 **207** 26p. multicoloured 45 50

(Des R. Mercer and J. Sharpe. Litho Irish Security Stamp Ptg Ltd)

1984 (6 June). *Birth Centenary of John McCormack (tenor). P* 14 × 15.
591 **208** 22p. multicoloured 35 40

209 Hammer-throwing

(Des L. le Brocquy and P. Wildbur. Litho Irish Security Stamp Ptg Ltd)

1984 (21 June). *Olympic Games, Los Angeles. T* **209** *and similar horiz designs. P* 15 × 14.
592 22p. deep mauve, black and gold 35 40
593 26p. violet, black and gold 45 50
594 29p. bright blue, black and gold 50 55

Designs:—26p. Hurdling; 29p. Running.

210 Hurling

211 Galway Mayoral Chain (500th Anniv of Mayoral Charter)

(Des C. Harrison. Litho Irish Security Stamp Ptg Ltd)

1984 (23 Aug). *Centenary of Gaelic Athletic Association. T* **210** *and similar multicoloured design. P* 15 × 14 *(22p.) or* 14 × 15 *(26p.).*
595 22p. Type **210** 35 40
596 26p. Irish football *(vert)* 45 50

(Des P. Wildbur. Litho Irish Security Stamp Ptg Ltd)

1984 (18 Sept). *Anniversaries. T* **211** *and similar multicoloured design. P* 14 × 15 *(26p.) or* 15 × 14 *(44p.).*
597 26p. Type **211** 45 50
598 44p. St. Brendan (from 15th-cent Bodleian manuscript) (1500th birth anniv) *(horiz)* 75 80

212 Hands passing Letter

213 "Virgin and Child" (Sassoferrato)

(Litho Irish Security Stamp Ptg Ltd)

1984 (19 Oct). *Bicentenary of the Irish Post Office. P* 15 × 14.
599 **212** 26p. multicoloured 45 50

(Des O'Connor O'Sullivan Advertising (17p.), P. Wildbur (others). Litho Irish Security Stamp Ptg Ltd)

1984 (26 Nov). *Christmas. T* **213** *and similar multicoloured design. P* 15 × 14 *(17p.) or* 14 × 15 *(others).*
600 17p. Christmas star *(horiz)* 25 30
601 22p. Type **213** 35 40
602 26p. Type **213** 45 50

No. 600 represented a special concession rate for Christmas card postings to addresses within Ireland and Great Britain between 26 November and 8 December 1984.

POSTAGE DUE STAMPS

From 1922 to 1925 Great Britain postage due stamps in both script and block watermarks were used without overprint.

D 1

D 2

(Des Ruby McConnell. Typo Govt Printing Works, Dublin)

1925 (20 Feb). *W* **10.** *P* 14 × 15.
D1 D 1 ½d. emerald-green .. .. 20·00 22·00
D2 1d. carmine .. .. 16·00 4·50
a. Wmk sideways .. .. 85·00 35·00
D3 2d. deep green .. .. 28·00 6·50
a. Wmk sideways .. .. 50·00 14·00
D4 6d. plum .. .. 6·00 7·00

1940–70. *W* **22.** *P* 14 × 15.
D 5 D 1 ½d. emerald-green (1942) .. .. 20·00 18·00
D 6 1d. carmine (1941) 85 50
D 7 1½d. vermilion (1953) .. .. .. 2·50 5·00
D 8 2d. deep green (1940) .. .. .. 1·25 60
D 9 3d. blue (10.11.52) .. .. .. 1·25 90
D10 5d. blue-violet (3.3.43) .. .. .. 2·75 5·00
D11 6d. plum (21.3.60) .. .. .. 1·75 1·25
a. Wmk sideways (1968) .. .. 1·75 2·25
D12 8d. orange (30.10.62) .. .. .. 7·50 7·00
D13 10d. bright purple (27.1.65) .. .. 8·00 8·00
D14 1s. apple-green (10.2.69) .. .. 20·00 7·00
a. Wmk sideways (1970) .. .. 32·00 11·00
D5/14 .. .. *Set of* 10 60·00 50·00

1971 (15 Feb). *As Nos. D5/14, but with values in decimal currency and colours changed. W* **22.** *P* 14 × 15.
D15 D 1 1p. sepia 40 40
a. Wmk sideways .. .. 1·00 1·50
D16 1½p. light emerald 30 60
D17 3p. stone .. .. 1·25 85
D18 4p. orange .. .. 1·25 1·25
D19 5p. greenish blue .. .. 1·50 1·50
D20 7p. bright yellow 40 65
D21 8p. scarlet 45 70
D15/21 .. .. *Set of* 7 5·00 5·50

1978 (20 Mar). *As Nos. D17/19, but no wmk. P* 14 × 15.
D22 D 1 3p. stone .. .. 2·50 4·00
D23 4p. orange .. .. 3·50 5·00
D24 5p. greenish blue .. .. 2·75 4·00

The above are on whiter paper and the colours are brighter.

1980 (11 June). *Photo. P* 15.
D25 D 2 1p. apple green 5 5
D26 2p. dull blue 5 5
D27 4p. myrtle-green 5 5
D28 6p. flesh 10 10
D29 8p. chalky blue 12 12
D30 18p. green 25 25
D31 24p. bright yellowish green 40 40
D25/31 .. .. *Set of* 7 80 90

THOMOND AND LONG ISLAND

Labels inscribed "Principality of Thomond" appeared on the philatelic market in the early 1960s. Thomond is the name of a district in western Ireland. The area does not have its own administration or postal service and the labels were not recognised by the Department of Posts & Telegraphs, Dublin.

Local carriage labels were issued for Long Island, County Cork in April 1973; they were intended to cover the cost of taking mail from the island to the nearest mainland post office. A local service operated for a few weeks before it was suppressed by the Irish Post Office. As the stamps were not accepted for national or international mail they are not listed here.

Jamaica

Records show that the first local Postmaster for Jamaica on a regular basis was appointed as early as 1671, although a reasonably organised service did not evolve until 1687–8. In the early years of the 18th century overseas mail was carried by the British packets, but between 1704 and 1711 this service was run on a commercial basis by Edmund Dummer. Following the collapse of the Dummer scheme Jamaica was virtually without a Post Office until 1720 and it was not until 1755 that overseas mail was again carried by British packets.

The stamps of Great Britain were used on the island from 8 May 1858 to August 1860. Although there had been much friction between the local inhabitants and the British G.P.O. it was not until 1 August 1860 that the Jamaica authorities assumed responsibility for the postal service.

For illustrations of postmark types see BRITISH POST OFFICES ABROAD notes, following GREAT BRITAIN.

KINGSTON

Stamps of GREAT BRITAIN *cancelled* "A 01" *as Type* **2**

1858 *to* **1860.**

Z1	1d. rose-red (1857), *perf* 16	£170
Z2	1d. rose-red (1857), *perf* 14	25·00
Z4	4d. rose (1857)	35·00
Z5	6d. lilac (1856)	35·00
Z6	1s. green (1856)	70·00

Stamps of GREAT BRITAIN *cancelled* "A 01" *as Type* **7** *(Duplex)*

1859 *to* **1860.**

Z 7	1d. rose-red (1857), *perf* 14	£160
Z 9	4d. rose (1857)	35·00
Z10	6d. lilac (1856)	35·00
Z11	1s. green (1856)	£225

Stamps of GREAT BRITAIN *cancelled* "A 01" *as Type* **3**

1859 *to* **1860.**

Z12	1d. rose-red (1857), *perf* 14	£200
Z14	4d. rose (1857)	£120
	a. Thick glazed paper	£400
Z15	6d. lilac (1856)	£120
Z16	1s. green (1856)	

Cancellation "A 01" was later used by the London, Foreign Branch Office.

OTHER JAMAICA POST OFFICES

British stamps were issued to several District post offices between 8 May 1858 and 1 March 1859 (i.e. before the Obliterators A 27–A 78 were issued). These can only be distinguished (off the cover) when they have the Town's date-stamp on them. They are worth about three times the price of those with an obliteration number.

Stamps of GREAT BRITAIN *cancelled* "A 27" *to* "A 78" *as Type* **2**

1859 *to* **1860.**

"A 27". ALEXANDRIA

Z17	1d. rose-red (1857), *perf* 14	£425
Z17*a*	2d. blue (1855) Large Crown, *perf* 14 (Plate 6)	£475
Z18	4d. rose (1857)	£160
Z19	6d. lilac (1856)	£375

"A 28". ANNOTTO BAY

Z20	1d. rose-red (1857), *perf* 14	£300
Z21	4d. rose (1857)	70·00
Z22	6d. lilac (1856)	£225

"A 29". BATH

Z23	1d. rose-red (1857), *perf* 14	£120
Z24	4d. rose (1857)	85·00
Z25	6d. lilac (1856)	£400

"A 30". BLACK RIVER

Z26	1d. rose-red (1857), *perf* 14	£120
Z27	4d. rose (1857)	50·00
Z28	6d. lilac (1856)	£120

"A 31". BROWN'S TOWN

Z29	1d. rose-red (1857), *perf* 14	£160
Z30	4d. rose (1857)	£160
Z31	6d. lilac (1856)	£160

"A 32". BUFF BAY

Z32	1d. rose-red (1857), *perf* 14	£120
Z33	4d. rose (1857)	
Z34	6d. lilac (1856)	£120

"A 33". CHAPLETON

Z35	1d. rose-red (1857), *perf* 14	£160
Z36	4d. rose (1857)	95·00
Z37	6d. lilac (1856)	£160

"A 34". CLAREMONT

Z38	1d. rose-red (1857), *perf* 14	£300
Z39	4d. rose (1857)	£150
Z40	6d. lilac (1856)	£300

"A 35". CLARENDON
(Near Four Paths)

Z41	1d. rose-red (1857), *perf* 14	£250
Z42	4d. rose (1857)	£100
Z43	6d. lilac (1856)	£160

"A 36". DRY HARBOUR

Z44	1d. rose-red (1857), *perf* 14	£375
Z45	4d. rose (1857)	£300
Z46	6d. lilac (1856)	£250

"A 37". DUNCANS

Z47	1d. rose-red (1857), *perf* 14	
Z48	4d. rose (1857)	£375
Z49	6d. lilac (1856)	£250

"A 38". EWARTON

A 38 was sent out to EWARTON but it is believed that this office was closed towards the end of 1858 before it arrived as no genuine used specimens have been found on British stamps.

"A 39". FALMOUTH

Z53	1d. rose-red (1857), *perf* 14	75·00
Z54	4d. rose (1857)	35·00
Z55	6d. lilac (1856)	55·00
Z56	1s. green (1856)	£425

"A 40". FLINT RIVER
(Near Hopewell)

Z57	1d. rose-red (1857), *perf* 14	£150
Z58	4d. rose (1857)	£100
Z59	6d. lilac (1856)	£150
Z60	1s. green (1856)	£425

"A 41". GAYLE

Z61	1d. rose-red (1857), *perf* 14	£450
Z62	4d. rose (1857)	£120
Z63	6d. lilac (1856)	£130
Z64	1s. green (1856)	£170

"A 42". GOLDEN SPRING
(Near Stony Hill)

Z65	1d. rose-red (1857), *perf* 14	£170
Z66	4d. rose (1857)	£150
Z67	6d. lilac (1856)	£400
Z68	1s. green (1856)	£425

"A 43". GORDON TOWN

Z69	1d. rose-red (1857), *perf* 14	
Z70	4d. rose (1857)	
Z71	6d. lilac (1856)	£450

"A 44". GOSHEN
(Near Santa Cruz)

Z72	1d. rose-red (1857), *perf* 14	£120
Z73	4d. rose (1857)	£110
Z74	6d. lilac (1856)	50·00

"A 45". GRANGE HILL

Z75	1d. rose-red (1857), *perf* 14	£150
Z76	4d. rose (1857)	38·00
Z77	6d. lilac (1856)	55·00
Z77*a*	1s. green (1856)	£375

"A 46". GREEN ISLAND

Z78	1d. rose-red (1857), *perf* 14	£300
Z79	4d. rose (1857)	£150
Z80	6d. lilac (1856)	£250
Z81	1s. green (1856)	£425

"A 47". HIGHGATE

Z82	1d. rose-red (1857), *perf* 14	£170
Z83	4d. rose (1857)	£110
Z84	6d. lilac (1856)	£170

"A 48". HOPE BAY

Z85	1d. rose-red (1857), *perf* 14	£400
Z86	4d. rose (1857)	£150
Z87	6d. lilac (1856)	£400

"A 49". LILLIPUT
(Near Balaclava)

Z88	1d. rose-red (1857), *perf* 14	£150
Z89	4d. rose (1857)	£150
Z90	6d. lilac (1856)	75·00

"A 50". LITTLE RIVER

A 50 was sent out for use at LITTLE RIVER, but it is believed that this office closed late in 1858, before the obliterator could be issued. No specimen has yet been found used on British stamps.

"A 51". LUCEA

Z91	1d. rose-red (1857), *perf* 14	£225
Z92	4d. rose (1857)	48·00
Z93	6d. lilac (1856)	£150

"A 52". MANCHIONEAL

Z94	1d. rose-red (1857), *perf* 14	£300
Z95	4d. rose (1857)	£160
Z96	6d. lilac (1856)	

"A 53". MANDEVILLE

Z97	1d. rose-red (1857), *perf* 14	£160
Z98	4d. rose (1857)	50·00
Z99	6d. lilac (1856)	£140

"A 54". MAY HILL
(Near Spur Tree)

Z100	1d. rose-red (1857), *perf* 14	75·00
Z101	4d. rose (1857)	75·00
Z102	6d. lilac (1856)	50·00

"A 55". MILE GULLY

Z103	1d. rose-red (1857), *perf* 14	£250
Z104	4d. rose (1857)	£150
Z105	6d. lilac (1856)	£150

"A 56". MONEAGUE

Z106	1d. rose-red (1857), *perf* 14	£150
Z107	4d. rose (1857)	£190
Z108	6d. lilac (1856)	£400

"A 57". MONTEGO BAY

Z109	1d. rose-red (1857), *perf* 14	£160
Z110	4d. rose (1857)	40·00
Z111	6d. lilac (1856)	50·00
Z112	1s. green (1856)	£425

"A 58". MONTPELIER

Z113	1d. rose-red (1857), *perf* 14	
Z114	4d. rose (1857)	
Z115	6d. lilac (1856)	£650

"A 59". MORANT BAY

Z116	1d. rose-red (1857), *perf* 14	£300
Z117	4d. rose (1857)	50·00
Z118	6d. lilac (1856)	50·00

"A 60". OCHO RIOS

Z119	1d. rose-red (1857), *perf* 14	
Z120	4d. rose (1857)	75·0
Z121	6d. lilac (1856)	£14

"A 61". OLD HARBOUR

Z122	1d. rose-red (1857), *perf* 14	£15
Z123	4d. rose (1857)	£11
Z124	6d. lilac (1856)	£11

"A 62". PLANTAIN GARDEN RIVER
(Near Golden Grove)

Z125	1d. rose-red (1857), *perf* 14	£11
Z126	4d. rose (1857)	80·0
Z127	6d. lilac (1856)	£11

"A 63". PEAR TREE GROVE

No genuine specimen of A 63 has been found on a British stamp

"A 64". PORT ANTONIO

Z131	1d. rose-red (1857), *perf* 14	£37
Z132	4d. rose (1857)	£22
Z133	6d. lilac (1856)	£22

"A 65". PORT MORANT

Z134	1d. rose-red (1857), *perf* 14	£22
Z135	4d. rose (1857)	85·0
Z136	6d. lilac (1856)	£22

"A 66". PORT MARIA

Z137	1d. rose-red (1857), *perf* 14	£15
Z138	4d. rose (1857)	55·0
Z139	6d. lilac (1856)	£22

"A 67". PORT ROYAL

Z140	1d. rose-red (1857), *perf* 14	£30
Z140*a*	2d. blue (1858) (plate 9)	
Z141	4d. rose (1857)	£30
Z142	6d. lilac (1856)	£30

"A 68". PORUS

Z143	1d. rose-red (1857), *perf* 14	£15
Z144	4d. rose (1857)	70·0
Z145	6d. lilac (1856)	£30

"A 69". RAMBLE

Z146	1d. rose-red (1857), *perf* 14	£15
Z147	4d. rose (1857)	£15
	a. Thick glazed paper	£40
Z149	6d. lilac (1856)	£22

"A 70". RIO BUENO

Z150	1d. rose-red (1857), *perf* 14	
Z151	4d. rose (1857)	£13
Z152	6d. lilac (1856)	85·0

"A 71". RODNEY HALL
(Now called Linstead)

Z153	1d. rose-red (1857), *perf* 14	£12
Z154	4d. rose (1857)	80·0
Z155	6d. lilac (1856)	£11

"A 72". SAINT DAVID
(Now called Yallahs)

Z156	1d. rose-red (1857), *perf* 14	£15
Z157	4d. rose (1857)	£30
Z158	6d. lilac (1856)	

"A 73". ST. ANN'S BAY

Z159	1d. rose-red (1857), *perf* 14	£15
Z160	4d. rose (1857)	75·0
Z161	6d. lilac (1856)	£15

"A 74". SALT GUT
(Near Oracabessa)

Z162	1d. rose-red (1857), *perf* 14	£14
Z163	4d. rose (1857)	
Z164	6d. lilac (1856)	£15

"A 75". SAVANNA-LA-MAR

Z165	1d. rose-red (1857), *perf* 14	50·0
Z166	4d. rose (1857)	40·0
Z167	6d. lilac (1856)	£15
Z168	1s. green (1856)	£37

"A 76". SPANISH TOWN

Z169	1d. rose-red (1857), *perf* 14	85·0
Z170	4d. rose (1857)	40·0
Z171	6d. lilac (1856)	85·0
Z172	1s. green (1856)	£25

"A 77". STEWART TOWN

Z173	1d. rose-red (1857), *perf* 14	£40
Z174	4d. rose (1857)	£25
Z175	6d. lilac (1856)	£15

"A 78". VERE
(Now called Alley)

Z176	1d. rose-red (1857), *perf* 14	£22
Z177	4d. rose (1857)	75·0
Z178	6d. lilac (1856)	50·0
Z179	1s. green (1856)	£42

The use of British stamps in Jamaica after August 1860 fo civilian mail, was unauthorised by the P.M.G. of Great Britain.

PRICES OF SETS

Set prices are given for many issues, generally thos containing five stamps or more. Definitive set include one of each value or major colour change but do not cover different perforations, die types o minor shades. Where a choice is possible the se prices are based on the cheapest versions of th stamps included in the listings.

PRICES FOR STAMPS ON COVER

Nos. 1/6	*from* × 3
Nos. 7/15	*from* × 6
Nos. 16/26	*from* × 8
Nos. 27/9	*from* × 6
No. 30	*from* × 4
Nos. 31/2	*from* × 10
Nos. 33/6	*from* × 5
Nos. 37/45	*from* × 3
Nos. 46/56	*from* × 2
No. 57	*from* × 4
Nos. 58/67	*from* × 3
Nos. 68/77	*from* × 5
Nos. 78/89	*from* × 3
Nos. 90/103	*from* × 4
Nos. 104/7	*from* × 5
Nos. 108/17	*from* × 3
Nos. 118/20	*from* × 5
Nos. 121/33*a*	*from* × 4
Nos. 134/40	*from* × 8
Nos. F1/9	*from* × 3
Nos. O1/5	*from* × 30

CROWN COLONY

PRINTERS. Until 1923, all the stamps of Jamaica were typographed by De La Rue & Co, Ltd, London, *unless otherwise stated.*

The official dates of issue are given, where known, but where definite information is not available the dates are those of earliest known use, etc.

CONDITION. Mint or fine used specimens of stamps with the pineapple watermark are rarely met with and are worth considerably more than our prices which are for stamps in average condition. Inferior specimens can be supplied at much lower prices.

1 2 3 4 5 6 7 A

1860 (23 Nov)–**63.** *W* **7.** *P* 14.

1	1	1d. pale blue	60·00	14·00
		a. Pale greenish blue	65·00	18·00
		b. Blue	50·00	10·00
		c. Deep blue	85·00	25·00
		d. Bisected (½d.) (11.61) (on cover)	†	£650
2	2	2d. rose	£175	35·00
		a. Deep rose	£110	35·00
3	3	3d. green (10.9.63)	£130	28·00
4	4	4d. brown-orange	£200	28·00
		a. Red-orange	£200	18·00
5	5	6d. dull lilac	£180	18·00
		a. Grey-purple	£275	32·00
		b. Deep purple	£800	40·00
6	6	1s. yellow-brown	£450	27·00
		a. Purple-brown	£500	27·00
		b. Dull brown	£180	32·00
		c. "$" for "S" in "SHILLING" (A)	£1600	£800

The diagonal bisection of the 1d. was authorized by a P.O. notice dated 20 November 1861. Specimens are only of value when on original envelope or wrapper. The authority was withdrawn as from 1 December 1872. Fakes are frequently met with. Other bisections were unauthorized.

The so-called "dollar variety" of the 1s. occurs once in each sheet of stamps in all shades and in later colours, etc, on the second stamp in the second row of the left upper pane. The prices quoted above are for the dull brown shade, the prices for the other shades being proportionate to their normal value.

All values except the 3d. are known imperf, mint only.

There are two types of watermark in the 3d. and 1s., one being short and squat and the other elongated.

8

9

10

1870–83. *Wmk Crown CC.* (*a*) *P* 14.

7	8	½d. claret (29.10.72)	10·00	3·00
		a. Deep claret (1883)	11·00	3·00
8	1	1d. blue (20.8.73)	23·00	1·50
		a. Deep blue	27·00	1·50
9	2	2d. rose (4.70)	32·00	55
		a. Deep rose	70·00	75
10	3	3d. green (1.3.70)	80·00	4·00
11	4	4d. brown-orange (1872)	£150	5·50
		a. Red-orange	£350	3·25
12	5	6d. mauve (10.3.71)	40·00	5·50
13	6	1s. dull-brown (*to* deep) (23.2.73)	25·00	8·50
		a. "$" for "S" in "SHILLING" (A)	£1200	£800
		(*b*) *P* 12½		
14	9	2s. Venetian red (27.8.75)	40·00	15·00
15	10	5s. lilac (27.8.75)	90·00	£120
7/15		*Set of* 9	£400	£120

The ½d., 1d., 4d., 2s. and 5s. are known imperforate.

1883–97. *Wmk Crown CA. P* 14.

16	8	½d. yellow-green (1885)	2·00	35
		a. Green	65	25
17	1	1d. blue (1884)	£400	8·50
18		1d. rose (*to* deep) (3.3.85)	25·00	1·25
		a. Carmine	9·00	1·10
19	2	2d. rose (*to* deep) (17.3.84)	£100	4·25
20		2d. grey (1885)	40·00	80
		a. Slate	25·00	55
21	3	3d. sage-green (1886)	4·50	85
		a. Pale olive-green	2·75	1·00
22	4	4d. red-orange* (9.3.83)	£350	13·00
		a. Red-brown (*shades*)	2·50	35
23	5	6d. deep yellow (4.10.90)	14·00	8·00
		a. Orange-yellow	8·50	4·50
24	6	1s. brown (*to* deep) (3.97)	9·00	5·50
		a. "$" for "S" in "SHILLING" (A)	£950	£500
		b. Chocolate	15·00	11·00
25	9	2s. Venetian red (1897)	42·00	20·00
26	10	5s. lilac (1897)	65·00	65·00
16/26		*Set of* 11	£550	95·00
16, 18, 20, 21, 22 and 23 Optd "Specimen"		*Set of* 6	£400	

*No. 22 is the same colour as No. 11*a*.

The 1d. carmine, 2d. slate, and 2s. are known imperf. All values to the 6d. inclusive are known perf 12. These are proofs.

11

TWO PENCE
HALF-PENNY

(12)

1889–91. *Value tablet in second colour. Wmk Crown CA. P* 14.

27	11	1d. purple and mauve (8.3.89)	1·75	20
28		2d. green (8.3.89)	12·00	3·50
		a. Deep green (*brown gum*)	4·00	3·75
29		2½d. dull purple and blue (25.2.91)	4·50	85
27/9 Optd "Specimen"		*Set of* 3	£120	

A very wide range of shades may be found in the 1d. The headplate was printed in many shades of purple, and the duty-plate in various shades of mauve and purple and also in carmine, etc. The variations in the other values are not so numerous nor so pronounced.

1890 (4(?) June). *No. 22a surch with T* **12** *by C. Vendyres, Kingston.*

30	4	2½d. on 4d. red-brown	27·00	8·50
		a. Spacing between lines of surch 1½ mm	32·00	17·00
		b. Surch double	£325	£225
		c. "PFNNY" for "PENNY"	75·00	65·00
		ca. Ditto and broken "K" for "Y"	£130	£110

This provisional was issued pending receipt of No. 29 which is listed above for convenience of reference.

Three settings exist. (1) Ten varieties arranged in a single vertical row and repeated six times in the pane. (2) Twelve varieties, in two horizontal rows of six, repeated five times, alternate rows show 1 and 1½ mm spacing between lines of surcharge. (3) Three varieties, arranged horizontally and repeated twenty times. All these settings can be reconstructed by examination of the spacing and relative position of the words of the surcharge and of the broken letters, etc, which are numerous.

A variety reading "PFNNK", with the "K" unbroken, is a forgery.

Varieties c. and ca. may be found in the double surcharge.

Surcharges misplaced either horizontally or vertically are met with, the normal position being central at the foot of the stamp with "HALF-PENNY" covering the old value.

13 Llandovery Falls, Jamaica (photo by Dr. J. Johnston)

14 Arms of Jamaica

(Recess D.L.R.)

1900–1. *Wmk Crown CC* (*sideways*). *P* 14.

31	13	1d. red (1.5.00)	90	25
32		1d. slate-black and red (25.9.01)	2·25	25
		a. Blued paper	£110	£100
		b. Imperf between (pair)	£3500	
31/32 Optd "Specimen"		*Set of* 2	£160	

Many shades exist of both centre and frame of the bi-coloured 1d. which was, of course, printed from two plates and the design shows minor differences from that of the 1d. red which was printed from a single plate.

(Typo D.L.R.)

1903–4. *Wmk Crown CA. P* 14.

33	14	½d. grey and dull green (16.11.03)	1·75	55
		a. "SER.ET" for "SERVIET"	40·00	45·00
34		1d. grey and carmine (24.2.04)	1·75	40
		a. "SER.ET" for "SERVIET"	32·00	35·00
35		2½d. grey and ultramarine (16.11.03)	2·50	1·00
		a. "SER.ET" for "SERVIET"	60·00	70·00
36		5d. grey and yellow (1.3.04)	18·00	26·00
		a. "SER.ET" for "SERVIET"	£900	£950
33/6 Optd "Specimen"		*Set of* 4	£110	

The "SER.ET" variety occurs once in each sheet of stamps on the second stamp in the fourth row of the left upper pane.

The centres of the above and later bi-coloured stamps in the Arms type vary in colour from grey to grey-black.

15 Arms type redrawn 16

1905–11. *Wmk Mult Crown CA. P* 14. (*a*) *Arms types.*

37	14	½d. grey and dull green, **C** (24.11.05)	1·25	45
		a. "SER.ET" for "SERVIET"	32·00	32·00
38	15	½d. yellow-green, **O** (8.11.06)	2·25	45
		a. Dull green	1·00	30
		b. Deep green	1·10	30
39	14	1d. grey and carmine, **C** (20.11.05)	10·00	40
40	16	1d. carmine, **O** (1.10.06)	1·25	15
41	14	2½d. grey and ultramarine, **C** (12.11.07)	2·75	1·50
42		2½d. pale ultramarine, **O** (21.9.10)	3·00	1·75
		a. Deep ultramarine, **O**	3·50	1·75
43		5d. grey and orange-yellow, **C** (24.4.07)	21·00	26·00
		a. "SER.ET" for "SERVIET"	£1000	£1100
44		6d. dull and bright purple, **C** (18.8.11)	10·00	15·00
45		5s. grey and violet, **C** (11.05)	55·00	50·00
37/45		*Set of* 9	95·00	85·00
38, 40, 42, 44, 45 Optd "Specimen"		*Set of* 5	£150	

See note below No. 36 concerning grey centres.

		(*b*) *Queen Victoria types*		
46	3	3d. olive-green, **O** (15.5.05)	5·00	1·00
		a. Sage-green, **O** (1907)	4·00	90
47		3d. purple/*yellow,* **O** (10.3.10)	4·00	2·50
		a. Pale purple/yellow, **C** (11.7.10)	2·25	1·40
48	4	4d. red-brown, **O** (6.6.08)	45·00	30·00
49		4d. black/*yellow,* **C** (21.9.10)	12·00	25·00
50		4d. red/*yellow,* **O** (3.10.11)	2·25	6·50
51	5	6d. dull orange, **O** (27.6.06)	17·00	21·00
		a. Golden yellow, **O** (9.09)	22·00	25·00
52		6d. lilac, **O** (19.11.09)	18·00	18·00
		a. Purple, **C** (7.10)	8·50	11·00
53	6	1s. brown, **O** (11.06)	16·00	11·00
		a. Deep brown, **O**	27·00	13·00
		b. "$" for "S" in "SHILLING" (A)	£1200	£1200
54		1s. black/*green,* **C** (21.9.10)	6·00	11·00
		a. "$" for "S" in "SHILLING" (A)	£1300	£1300
55	9	2s. Venetian red, **O** (11.08)	90·00	£110
56		2s. purple/*blue,* **C** (21.9.10)	15·00	12·00
46/56		*Set of* 11	£190	£200
47, 49, 50, 52, 54, 56 Optd "Specimen"		*Set of* 6	£170	

17

18

(T **17/18** typo D.L.R.)

1911 (3 Feb). *Wmk Mult Crown CA. P* 14.

57	17	2d. grey, **O** (Optd S. £32)	3·50	12·00

1912–20. *Wmk Mult Crown CA. P* 14.

58	18	1d. carmine-red, **O** (5.12.12)	25	10
		a. Scarlet, **O** (1916)	35	12
59		1½d. brown-orange, **O** (13.7.16)	1·40	25
		a. Yellow-orange, **O**	5·50	1·00
		b. Wmk sideways	†	—
60		2d. grey, **O** (2.8.12)	1·25	2·75
		a. Slate-grey, **O**	1·25	2·50
61		2½d. blue, **O** (13.2.13)	95	30
		a. Deep bright blue, **O**	1·40	45
62		3d. purple/*yellow,* **C** (6.3.12)	95	80
		a. White back, **C** (2.4.13)	95	80
		b. On lemon, **C** (25.9.16) (Optd S. £28)	3·50	1·25
63		4d. black and red/*yellow,* **C** (4.4.13)	2·00	1·50
		a. White back, **C** (7.5.14)	1·40	3·00
		b. On lemon, **C** (1916) (Optd S. £32)	15·00	12·00
		c. On pale yellow, **C** (1919)	22·00	12·00
64		6d. dull and bright purple, **C** (14.11.12)	5·00	6·00
		a. Dull purple and bright mauve, **C** (1915)	1·75	2·00
		b. Dull purple & brt magenta, **C** (1920)	2·25	2·25
65		1s. black/*green,* **C** (2.8.12)	3·25	3·00
		a. White back, **C** (4.1.15)	2·25	4·50
		b. On blue-green, olive back, **C** (1920)	7·00	5·00
66		2s. purple & brt blue/*blue,* **C** (10.1.19)	9·00	14·00
67		5s. green and red/*yellow,* **C** (5.9.19)	35·00	50·00
		a. On pale yellow, **C**	40·00	55·00
		b. On orange-buff, **C**	£100	£110
58/67		*Set of* 10	48·00	65·00
58/67 Optd "Specimen"		*Set of* 10	£170	

For the ½d. in this design and the 6d. with Script wmk see Nos. 107 and 90.

The paper of No. 67 is a bright yellow and the gum rough and dull. No. 67*a* is on practically the normal creamy "pale yellow" paper, and the gum is smooth and shiny. The paper of No. 67*b* approaches the "coffee" colour of the true "orange-buff", and the colours of both head and frame are paler, the latter being of a carmine tone.

RED CROSS LABELS. A voluntary organization, the Jamaica War Stamp League later the Jamaica Patriotic Stamp League, was founded in November 1915 by Mr. Lewis Ashenheim, a Kingston solicitor. The aims of the League were to support the British Red Cross, collect funds for the purchase of aircraft for the Royal Flying Corps and the relief of Polish Jews.

One fund-raising method used was the sale, from 1 December 1915, of ½d. charity labels. These labels, which were available from post offices, depicted a bi-plane above a cross and were printed in red by Dennison Manufacturing Company, Framingham, U.S.A., the sheets being perforated 12.

From 22 December 1915 supplies of the labels were overprinted "JAMAICA" in red, the colour of this overprint being changed to black from 15 January 1916. Copies sold from 11 March 1916 carried an additional "Half-Penny" surcharge, also in black.

Such labels had no postal validity when used by the general public, but, by special order of the Governor, were accepted for the payment of postage on the League's official mail. To obtain this concession the envelopes were to be inscribed "Red Cross Business" or "Jamaica Patriotic Stamp League" and the labels used endorsed with Mr. Ashenheim's signature. Such covers are rare.

WAR STAMP. (19)

WAR STAMP. (20)

WAR STAMP. (21)

(T **19/21** optd locally)

1916 (1 April–Sept). *Optd with T* **19**.
68 **15** ½d. yellow-green 25 55
a. No stop after "STAMP" .. .. 7·50 11·00
b. Opt double .. .. 55·00 55·00
c. Opt inverted .. .. .. 45·00 55·00
d. Blue-green 35 60
da. No stop after "STAMP" .. .. 6·00 7·00
69 **18** 3d. purple/*yellow* (white back) .. .. 2·75 4·50
a. On lemon (6.16) .. .. .. 2·00 4·50
aa. No stop after "STAMP" .. .. 15·00 20·00
b. On pale yellow (9.16) .. .. 2·00 4·50

Minor varieties: ½d. (i) Small "P"; (ii) Space between "W" and "A"; (iii) "WARISTAMP" (raised quad between words); (iv) Two stops after "STAMP". 3d. "WARISTAMP".

NOTE. The above and succeeding stamps with "WAR STAMP" overprint were issued for payment of a special war tax on letters and postcards or on parcels. Ordinary unoverprinted stamps could also be used for this purpose.

1916 (Sept–Dec). *Optd with T* **20**.
70 **15** ½d. blue-green (*shades*) (2.10.16) .. 25 45
a. No stop after "STAMP" .. .. 9·00 12·00
b. Opt omitted (in pair with normal) .. £275 £200
c. "R" inserted by hand £250 £180
71 **18** 1½d. orange (1.9.16) 30 30
aa. Wmk sideways .. .. .. — £1100
a. No stop after "STAMP" .. .. 5·00 4·75
b. "S" in "STAMP" omitted .. .. 38·00 35·00
c. "S" inserted by hand £200
d. "R" in "WAR" omitted £275 £200
e. "R" inserted by hand £225 £180
f. Inverted "d" for "P" £150 £120
72 3d. purple/*lemon* (2.10.16) .. .. 50 1·25
aa. Opt inverted £375
a. No stop after "STAMP" .. .. 15·00 15·00
b. "S" in "STAMP" omitted £180 £130
c. "S" inserted by hand £150 £140
d. "S" inserted inverted £250 £175
e. On yellow (12.16) .. .. 6·00 8·50
ea. "S" in "STAMP" omitted £250 £160
eb. "S" inserted by hand £250 £160
ec. "S" inserted inverted £300 £170

Minor varieties, such as raised quads, small stop, double stop, spaced letters and letters of different sizes, also exist in this overprint.

1917 (March). *Optd with T* **21**.
73 **15** ½d. blue-green (*shades*) (25.3.17) .. 25 40
a. No stop after "STAMP" .. .. 6·50 7·50
b. Stop inserted and "P" impressed a second time £140
c. Optd on back only .. .. .. 45·00
d. Opt inverted .. .. .. 7·50 10·00
74 **18** 1½d. orange (3.3.17) 12 15
aa. Wmk sideways .. .. .. — £1200
a. No stop after "STAMP" .. .. 8·50 9·00
b. Stop inserted and "P" impressed a second time £190
c. Opt double .. .. 60·00 65·00
d. Opt inverted .. .. .. 65·00 60·00
75 3d. purple/*yellow* (3.3.17) 35 45
a. No stop after "STAMP" .. .. 10·00 10·00
b. Stop inserted and "P" impressed a second time £170
c. Opt inverted £140
d. Opt sideways (reading up) £190
da. Opt omitted (in horiz pair with No. 75d) £850

No. 75da shows the left-hand stamp as No. 75d and the right-hand stamp without overprint.

There are numerous minor varieties in this overprint.

WAR STAMP (22)

1919 (4 Oct). *Optd with T* **22** *by D.L.R.*
76 **15** ½d. green (R.) 10 15
77 **18** 3d. purple/*yellow* (R.) .. .. 1·50 2·75
a. Pale purple/buff (R.) .. .. 45 1·25
b. Deep purple/buff (R.) .. .. 3·50 4·50
76/7 Optd "Specimen" .. .. *Set of* 2 90·00

We list the most distinct variations in the 3d. The buff tone of the paper varies considerably in depth.

23 Jamaica Exhibition 1891

24 Arawak Woman preparing Cassava

25 War Contingent embarking

26 King's House, Spanish Town

Re-entry. Nos. 80a, 93a

The greater part of the design is re-entered, the hull showing in very solid colour and the people appear very blurred. There are also minor re-entries on stamps above (R. 7/4 and 6/4).

27 Return of War Contingent

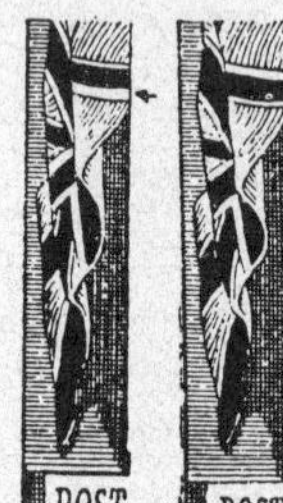
A B

28 Landing of Columbus

29 Cathedral, Spanish Town

34

(Typo (½d., 1d.), recess (others) D.L.R.)

1919–21. *T* **23/29, 34** *and similar vert designs. Wmk Mult Crown CA (sideways on* 1*d.,* 1½*d. and* 10*s.). P* 14.
78 **23** ½d. green and olive-green, **C** (12.11.20) 45 30
79 **24** 1d. carmine and orange, **C** (3.10.21) .. 2·50 80
80 **25** 1½d. green (*shades*) (4.7.19) 30 35
a. Major re-entry (R. 8/4) .. .. 20·00
81 **26** 2d. indigo and green (18.2.21) .. .. 1·00 2·00
82 **27** 2½d. deep blue and blue (A) (18.2.21) .. 11·00 4·50
a. Blue-black and deep blue (A) .. 1·60 1·75
83 **28** 3d. myrtle-green and blue (8.4.21) .. 1·40 65
84 **29** 4d. brown and deep green (21.2.21) .. 3·00 6·00
85 – 1s. orange-yellow & red-orge (10.12.20) 6·50 6·50
a. Frame inverted £15000 £9000
86 – 2s. light blue and brown (10.12.20) .. 18·00 22·00
87 – 3s. violet-blue and orange (10.12.20) .. 29·00 40·00
88 – 5s. blue and yellow-orange (15.4.21) .. 65·00 60·00
a. Blue and pale dull orange .. .. 60·00 55·00
89 **34** 10s. myrtle-green (6.5.20) £120 £250
78/89 .. .. *Set of* 12 £225 £350
78/89 Optd "Specimen" .. .. *Set of* 12 £300

Designs: *Vert*—1s. Statue of Queen Victoria, Kingston; 2s. Admiral Rodney Memorial; 3s. Sir Charles Metcalfe Monument; 5s. Jamaican scenery.

The 2½d. of the above series showed the Union Jack at left, incorrectly, as indicated in illustration A. In the issue on paper with Script wmk the design was corrected (Illustration B).

A 6d. stamp illustrating the abolition of slavery was prepared and sent out in April 1921, but for political reasons was not issued and the stock was destroyed. Copies overprinted "Specimen" are known on both the Mult CA and Script CA papers, and are worth £750 each. Price without "Specimen" on Script CA £12000.

1921 (21 Oct). *Wmk Mult Script CA. P* 14.
90 **18** 6d. dull purple and bright magenta, **C** (Optd S. £32) .. .. .. 13·00 7·5

For ½d. value, see No. 107.

35 "POSTAGE & REVENUE" added

36 Port Royal in 1853

(Printing as before; the 6d. recess-printed)

1921–29. *As Nos.* 78/89. *Wmk Mult Script CA (sideways on* 1*d. and* 1½*d.). P* 14.
91 **23** ½d. green and olive-green, **C** (5.2.22) .. 55 3
a. Green and deep olive-green, **C** .. 45 2
92 **35** 1d. carmine and orange, **C** (5.12.22) .. 1·75 2
93 **25** 1½d. green (*shades*) (2.2.21) 40 2
a. Major re-entry (R. 8/4) .. .. 25·00
94 **26** 2d. indigo and green (4.11.21) .. .. 3·00 3
a. Indigo and grey-green (1925) .. 3·50 5
95 **27** 2½d. deep blue and blue (B) (4.11.21) .. 5·50 7
a. Dull blue and blue (B) .. .. 6·00 5
96 **28** 3d. myrtle-green and blue (6.3.22) .. 1·75 3
a. Green and pale blue 50 2
97 **29** 4d. brown and deep green (5.12.21) .. 65 2
a. Chocolate and dull green 50 2
98 **36** 6d. black and blue (5.12.22) .. .. 17·00 3·5
a. Grey and dull blue .. .. .. 16·00 2·5
99 – 1s. orange and red-orange (4.11.21) .. 3·25 6
a. Orange-yellow and brown-orange .. 2·25 3
100 – 2s. light blue and brown (5.2.22) .. 3·25 1·2
101 – 3s. violet-blue and orange (23.8.21) .. 16·00 22·0
102 – 5s. blue and yellow-brown (8.11.23) .. 25·00 26·0
a. Blue and pale dull orange .. .. 45·00 45·0
b. Blue and yellow-orange (1927) .. 28·00 26·0
c. Blue and pale bistre-brown (1929) .. 28·00 26·0
103 **34** 10s. myrtle-green (March (?) 1922) .. 60·00 65·0
91/103 .. .. *Set of* 13 £120 £10
91/103 Optd "Specimen" .. .. *Set of* 13 £300

The frame of No. 102*a* is the same colour as that of No. 88*a*.

The designs of all values of the pictorial series, with the exception of the 5s. and 10s. (which originated with the Governor, Sir Leslie Probyn), were selected by Mr. F. C. Cundall, F.S.A. The 1d. and 5s. were drawn by Miss Cundall, the 3d. by Mrs. Cundall, and the 10s. by De La Rue & Co. The 6d. is from a lithograph. The other designs are from photographs, the frames of all being the work of Miss Cundall and Miss Wood.

37

38

39

(Centres from photos by Miss V. F. Taylor. Frames des F. C. Cundall, F.S.A., and drawn by Miss Cundall. Recess B.W.)

1923 (1 Nov). *Child Welfare. Wmk Mult Script CA. P* 12.
104 **37** ½d. +½d. black and green .. .. 1·75 3·5
105 **38** 1d. +½d. black and scarlet .. .. 8·00 12·0
106 **39** 2½d. +½d. black and blue .. .. 18·00 27·0
104/6 Optd "Specimen" .. .. *Set of* 3 £200

Sold at a premium of ½d. for the Child Welfare League, these stamps were on sale annually from 1 November to 31 January until 31 January 1927, when their sale ceased, the remainders being destroyed on 21 February 1927.

"Bow" flaw (R.18/12)

1927 (3 Nov). *Wmk Mult Script CA. P* 14.
107 **18** ½d. green, **O** (Optd S. £45) 15 1
a. Bow flaw .. .. 20·00

40

41

42

Die I

Die II

(Recess D.L.R.)

1929–32. *Wmk Mult Script CA. P* 14.
108 **40** 1d. scarlet (Die I) 40 15
a. Die II (1932) 20 15
109 **41** 1½d. chocolate 30 40
110 **42** 9d. maroon .. .. 6·50 5·00
108/10 Perf "Specimen" .. .. *Set of* 3 75·00

In Die I the shading below JAMAICA is formed of thickened parallel lines, and in Die II of diagonal cross-hatching.

43 Coco Palms at Columbus Cove

44 Wag Water River, St. Andrew

45 Priestman's River, Portland

(Dies eng and recess Waterlow)

1932. *Wmk Mult Script CA (sideways on 2d. and 2½d.). P* 12½.
111 **43** 2d. black and green (late 1932) .. 4·00 2·25
a. Imperf between (vert pair) £1900
112 **44** 2½d. turquoise-blue & ultram (5.3.32) .. 2·50 2·75
a. Imperf between (vert pair) £2250 £2250
113 **45** 6d. grey-black and purple (2.32) .. 6·00 5·00
111/13 Perf "Specimen" .. .. *Set of* 3 75·00

1935 (6 May). *Silver Jubilee. As Nos.* 91/4 *of Antigua, but ptd by B.W. P* 11 × 12.
114 1d. deep blue and scarlet 20 20
115 1½d. ultramarine and grey-black 25 35
a. Extra flagstaff .. .. 70·00 £100
b. Short extra flagstaff .. .. .. 20·00
c. Lightning conductor .. .. .. 20·00
116 6d. green and indigo .. .. 3·75 5·50
a. Extra flagstaff £120 £160
c. Lightning conductor .. .. .. 35·00
117 1s. slate and purple .. .. 3·75 5·50
a. Extra flagstaff £225 £300
b. Short extra flagstaff .. .. .. 65·00
c. Lightning conductor .. .. .. 65·00
114/17 Perf "Specimen" .. .. *Set of* 4 75·00

For illustrations of plate varieties see Omnibus section following Zululand.

1937 (12 May). *Coronation. As Nos.* 13/15 *of Aden.*
118 1d. scarlet 30 20
119 1½d. grey-black 50 40
120 2½d. bright blue .. .. 1·00 80
118/20 Perf "Specimen" .. .. *Set of* 3 45·00

46 King George VI

47 Coco Palms at Columbus Cove

48 Bananas

49 Citrus Grove

50 Kingston Harbour

51 Sugar Industry

52 Bamboo Walk

53 King George VI

53a Tobacco Growing and Cigar Making

(Recess D.L.R. (T **46**, 5s. and 10s.), Waterlow (others))

1938–52. *T* **46** *to* **53***a and as Nos.* 88, 112/113, *but with inset portrait of King George VI, as in T* **47**. *Wmk Mult Script CA. P* 13½ × 14 (½*d.*, 1*d.*, 1½*d.*), 14 (5*s.*, 10*s.*) *or* 12½ (*others*).
121 **46** ½d. blue-green (10.10.38) 10 10
a. Wmk sideways .. .. .. † £1700
121*b* ½d. orange (25.10.51) 30 20
122 1d. scarlet (10.10.38) 15 10
122*a* 1d. blue-green (25.10.51) 75 40
123 1½d. brown (10.10.38) 15 10
124 **47** 2d. grey and green 30 12
a. Perf 13 × 13½ 35 25
b. Perf 12½ × 13 (1951) 50 35
125 **44** 2½d. greenish blue and ultramarine .. 2·50 2·75
126 **48** 3d. ultramarine and green 40 30
126*a* 3d. greenish blue & ultram (15.8.49) .. 90 55
126*b* 3d. green and scarlet (1.7.52) 70 30
127 **49** 4d. brown and green 40 25
128 **45** 6d. grey and purple 40 20
a. Perf 13½ × 13 (10.10.50) 40 20
129 **50** 9d. lake 60 35
130 **51** 1s. green and purple-brown 65 25
131 **52** 2s. blue and chocolate .. .. 3·50 70
132 – 5s. slate-blue and yellow-orange .. 6·50 2·75
a. Perf 13 (24.10.49) .. .. .. 8·00 6·50
ab. Blue and orange (10.10.50) .. .. 6·50 3·25
133 **53** 10s. myrtle-green .. .. .. 13·00 8·00
aa. Perf 13 (10.10.50) .. .. .. 11·00 10·00
133*a* **53***a* £1 chocolate and violet (15.8.49) .. 48·00 40·00
121/33*a* .. .. *Set of* 18 70·00 55·00
121/33 Perf "Specimen" .. .. *Set of* 13 £160

The 5s. is known line perf exactly 14 all round instead of the normal comb perf which measures 13.8 × 13.7.

SELF-GOVERNMENT

54 Courthouse, Falmouth

55 King Charles II and King George VI

56 Institute of Jamaica

(Recess Waterlow)

1945 (20 Aug)–**46.** *New Constitution. T* **54/6** *and similar designs. Wmk Mult Script CA. P* 12½.
134 **54** 1½d. sepia 15 15
a. Perf 12½ × 13 (1946) 85 25
135 **55** 2d. green .. .. 1·50 70
a. Perf 12½ × 13 (1945) 15 30
136 **56** 3d. ultramarine 15 20
a. Perf 13 (1946) .. .. .. 1·25 80
137 – 4½d. slate 20 30
a. Perf 13 (1946) .. .. .. 1·25 80
138 – 2s. red-brown 70 80
139 – 5s. indigo .. .. 1·00 1·75
140 **56** 10s. green .. .. 1·75 3·75
134/140 .. .. *Set of* 7 3·75 6·50
134/40 Perf "Specimen" .. .. *Set of* 7 £200

Designs: *Vert* (*as T* **54**)—2s. "Labour and Learning". *Horiz* (*as T* **56**)—4½d. House of Assembly; 5s. Scroll, flag and King George VI.

1946 (14 Oct). *Victory. As Nos.* 28/9 *of Aden. P* 13½ × 14.
141 1½d. purple-brown 25 12
a. Perf 13½ 25 20
142 3d. blue 40 45
a. Perf 13½ 75 75
141/2 Perf "Specimen" .. .. *Set of* 2 48·00

1948 (1 Dec). *Royal Silver Wedding. As Nos.* 30/1 *of Aden.*
143 1½d. red-brown 25 30
144 £1 scarlet .. .. 35·00 48·00

1949 (10 Oct). *75th Anniv of Universal Postal Union. As Nos.* 114/17 *of Antigua.*
145 1½d. red-brown 30 25
146 2d. deep blue-green 65 55
147 3d. deep blue 90 90
148 6d. purple .. .. 1·25 1·00

1951 (16 Feb). *Inauguration of B.W.I. University College. As Nos.* 118/19 *of Antigua.*
149 2d. black and red-brown 25 15
150 6d. grey-black and purple 55 45

60 Scout Badge and Map of Caribbean

61 Scout Badge and Map of Jamaica

(Litho B.W.)

1952 (5 Mar). *First Caribbean Scout Jamboree. Wmk Mult Script CA. P* 13½ × 13 (2*d.*) *or* 13 × 13½ (6*d.*).
151 **60** 2d. blue, apple-green and black .. 20 25
152 **61** 6d. yellow-green, carmine-red and black 40 60

1953 (2 June). *Coronation. As No.* 47 *of Aden.*
153 2d. black and deep yellow-green 10 5

62 Coco Palms at Columbus Cove

(Recess Waterlow)

1953 (25 Nov). *Royal Visit. Wmk Mult Script CA. P* 12½ × 13.
154 **62** 2d. grey-black and green 10 12

63 Man-o'-War at Port Royal

(Recess D.L.R.)

1955 (10 May). *Tercentenary Issue. T* **63** *and similar horiz designs. Wmk Mult Script CA. P* 12½.
155 2d. black and olive-green 20 8
156 2½d. black and deep bright blue 15 50
157 3d. black and claret 15 45
158 6d. black and carmine-red 20 35

Designs:—2½d. Old Montego Bay; 3d. Old Kingston; 6d. Proclamation of Abolition of Slavery, 1838.

67 Palms

71 Mahoe

75 Blue Mountain Peak

79 Arms of Jamaica

80 Arms of Jamaica

(Recess B.W. (T **79/80**), D.L.R. (others))

1956. *T* **67, 71, 75, 79/80** *and similar designs. Wmk Mult Script CA. P* 13 (*½d. to* 6*d.*), 13½ (8*d. to* 2*s.*) *or* 11½ (3*s. to* £1).

No.	Type	Description	Unused	Used
159	**67**	½d. black and deep orange-red (1.5)	8	5
160	–	1d. black and emerald (1.5)	10	5
161	–	2d. black and carmine-red (2.8)	12	5
162	–	2½d. black and deep bright blue (2.8)	25	40
163	**71**	3d. emerald and red-brown (17.12)	25	5
164	–	4d. bronze-green and blue (17.12)	30	12
165	–	5d. scarlet and bronze-green (17.12)	45	1·00
166	–	6d. black and deep rose-red (3.9)	1·25	10
167	**75**	8d. ultramarine and red-orange (15.11)	25	12
168	–	1s. yellow-green and blue (15.11)	40	12
169	–	1s. 6d. ultram & reddish pur (15.11)	55	12
170	–	2s. blue & bronze-green (*shades*) (15.11)	2·25	65
171	**79**	3s. black and blue (2.8)	95	60
172		5s. black and carmine-red (15.8)	2·25	75
173	**80**	10s. black and blue-green (15.8)	8·50	5·00
174		£1 black and purple (15.8)	16·00	6·00
159/174		*Set of* 16	30·00	14·00

Designs:—*Vert* (*as T* **67, 71**)—1d. Sugar Cane; 2d. Pineapples; 2½d. Bananas; 4d. Breadfruit; 5d. Ackee; 6d. Streamertail. *Horiz.* (*as T* **75**)—1s. Royal Botanic Gardens, Hope; 1s. 6d. Rafting on the Rio Grande; 2s. Fort Charles.

1958 (22 Apr). *Inauguration of British Caribbean Federation. As Nos.* 135/7 *of Antigua.*

No.	Description	Unused	Used
175	2d. deep green	15	5
176	5d. blue	25	70
177	6d. scarlet	25	20

81 "Britannia" flying over 1860 Packet-Steamer

83 1s. Stamps of 1860 and 1956

(Recess Waterlow)

1960 (4 Jan). *Stamp Centenary. T* **81, 83** *and similar design. W* w **12.** *P* 13 × 13½ (1*s.*) *or* 13½ × 14 (*others*).

No.	Description	Unused	Used
178	2d. blue and reddish purple	15	5
179	6d. carmine and olive-green	20	10
180	1s. red-brown, yellow-green and blue	25	30

Design: *As T* 81—6d. Postal mule-cart and motor-van.

INDEPENDENT

1 1
9 9
6 6
2 2

INDEPENDENCE
(84)

INDEPENDENCE 1962
(85)

86 Military Bugler and Map

(Des V. Whiteley. Photo D.L.R. (2, 4d., 1s. 6d., 5s.))

1962 (8 Aug)–**63.** *Independence.*

(*a*) *Nos.* 159/60, 162, 171, 173/4 *optd as T* **84** *and Nos.* 163, 165/8, 170 *optd with T* **85**

No.	Type	Description	Unused	Used
181	**67**	½d. black and deep orange-red	5	10
182	–	1d. black and emerald	5	5
183	–	2½d. black and deep bright blue	10	40
184	**71**	3d. emerald and red-brown	10	10
185	–	5d. scarlet and bronze-green	20	70
186	–	6d. black and deep rose-red	75	10
187	**75**	8d. ultramarine and red-orange (*opt at upper left*)	20	25
		a. Opt at lower left (17.9.63?)	25	25
188	–	1s. yellow-green and blue	30	15
189	–	2s. blue and bronze-green (*shades*)	1·00	60
190	**79**	3s. black and blue	2·00	2·00
191	**80**	10s. black and blue-green	5·00	7·50
192		£1 black and purple	8·50	11·00

(*b*) *Horiz designs as T* **86.** *W* w **12.** *P* 13

No.	Description	Unused	Used
193	2d. multicoloured	10	5
194	4d. multicoloured	15	10
195	1s. 6d. black and red	55	70
196	5s. multicoloured	1·25	2·00
181/96	*Set of* 16	18·00	23·00

Designs:—2, 4d. Type **86**; 1s. 6d. Gordon House and banner; 5s. Map, factories and fruit.

89 Kingston Seal, Weightlifting, Boxing, Football and Cycling

(Photo Harrison)

1962 (11 Aug). *Ninth Central American and Caribbean Games, Kingston. T* **89** *and similar horiz designs. W* w **12.** *P* 14½ × 14.

No.	Description	Unused	Used
197	1d. sepia and carmine-red	5	5
198	6d. sepia and greenish blue	10	10
199	8d. sepia and bistre	15	15
200	2s. multicoloured	35	60

Designs:—6d. Kingston seal, diving, sailing, swimming and water polo; 8d. Kingston seal, pole-vaulting, javelin throwing, discus throwing, relay-racing and hurdling; 2s. Kingston coat of arms and athlete.

An imperf miniature sheet exists, but this was never available at face value or at any post office.

93 Farmer and Crops

94 Carole Joan Crawford ("Miss World 1963")

(Des M. Goaman. Litho D.L.R.)

1963 (4 June). *Freedom from Hunger. P* 12½.

No.	Type	Description	Unused	Used
201	**93**	1d. multicoloured	15	5
202		8d. multicoloured	50	25

1963 (4 Sept). *Red Cross Centenary. As Nos.* 147/8 *of Antigua.*

No.	Description	Unused	Used
203	2d. red and black	15	10
204	1s. 6d. red and blue	40	65

1963–64. *As Nos.* 181/90, *but wmk* w **12**.

No.	Type	Description	Unused	Used
205	**67**	½d. black and deep orange-red (3.12.63*)	5	12
206	–	1d. black and emerald (3.4.64)	10	15
207	–	2½d. black and deep bright blue (3.4.64)	45	70
208	**71**	3d. emerald and red-brown (17.12.63*)	20	15
209	–	5d. scarlet and bronze-green (3.4.64)	65	1·25
210	**75**	8d. ultramarine and red-orange (3.4.64)	50	85
211	–	1s. yellow-green and blue (21.12.63*)	1·50	1·75
212	–	2s. deep blue and deep bronze-green (3.4.64)	2·25	3·75
213	**79**	3s. black and blue (5.2.64)	7·50	13·00
205/13		*Set of* 9	12·00	21·00

The overprint on the 8d., 1s. and 2s. is at lower left, the others are as before.

*These are the earliest known dates recorded in Jamaica.

(Des and photo D.L.R.)

1964 (14 Feb–25 May). *"Miss World* 1963*" Commemoration. P* 13.

No.	Type	Description	Unused	Used
214	**94**	3d. multicoloured	8	5
215		1s. multicoloured	15	15
216		1s. 6d. multicoloured	20	30
MS216*a*		153 × 101 mm. Nos. 214/16. Imperf (25.5.64)	80	1·00

95 *Lignum Vitae*

97 Blue Mahoe

103 Gypsum Industry

109 Arms of Jamaica

111 Multiple "J" and Pineapple

(Des V. Whiteley. Photo Harrison)

1964 (4 May). *T* **95, 97, 103, 109** *and similar designs. W* **111** *P* 14½ (1*d.*, 2*d.*, 2½*d.*, 6*d.*, 8*d.*), 14 × 14½ (1½*d.*, 3*d.*, 4*d.*, 10*s.*) 14½ × 14 (9*d.*, 1*s.*, 3*s.*, 5*s.*, £1) *or* 13½ × 14½ (1*s.* 6*d.*, 2*s.*).

No.	Description	Unused	Used
217	1d. violet-blue, dp green & lt brown (*shades*)	12	5
218	1½d. multicoloured	15	5
219	2d. red, yellow and grey-green	15	5
220	2½d. multicoloured	45	60
221	3d. yellow, black and emerald	15	5
222	4d. ochre and violet	35	5
223	6d. multicoloured	85	8
224	8d. multicoloured (*shades*)	1·25	60
225	9d. blue and yellow-bistre	60	15
226	1s. black and light brown	30	12
	a. Light brown omitted	£150	
	b. Black omitted	£350	
227	1s. 6d. black, light blue and buff	75	20
228	2s. red-brown, black and light blue	1·75	25
229	3s. blue and dull green	1·50	80
	a. Perf 13½ × 14½	1·50	1·25
230	5s. black, ochre and blue	1·75	75
231	10s. multicoloured	1·90	2·00
	a. Blue ("JAMAICA", etc) omitted	£170	
232	£1 multicoloured	3·25	3·75
217/32	*Set of* 16	14·00	8·50

Designs:—*Horiz.* (*As T* **95**)—1½d. Ackee; 2½d. Land shells; 3d. National flag over Jamaica; 4d. *Murex antillarum*; 6d. *Papilio homerus*; 8d. Streamertail. *As T* **103**—1s. National Stadium; 1s. 6d. Palisadoes International Airport; 2s. Bauxite mining; 3s. Blue Marlin (sport fishing); 5s. Exploration of sunken city, Port Royal; £1 Queen Elizabeth II and national flag.

112 Scout Belt

113 Globe, Scout Hat and Scarf

114 Scout Badge and Alligator

(Photo Harrison)

1964 (27 Aug). *Sixth Inter-American Scout Conference, Kingston. W* **111.** *P* 14 (1*s.*) *or* 14½ × 14 (*others*).

No.	Type	Description	Unused	Used
233	**112**	3d. red, black and pink	5	5
234	**113**	8d. bright blue, olive and black	12	20
235	**114**	1s. gold, deep blue and light blue	15	25

115 Gordon House, Kingston

118 Eleanor Roosevelt

(Des V. Whiteley. Photo Harrison)

1964 (16 Nov). *Tenth Commonwealth Parliamentary Conference, Kingston. T* **115** *and similar horiz designs. W* **111.** *P* 14½ × 14.

No.	Description	Unused	Used
236	3d. black and yellow-green	5	5
237	6d. black and carmine-red	10	10
238	1s. 6d. black and bright blue	20	25

Designs:—6d. Headquarters House, Kingston; 1s. 6d. House of Assembly, Spanish Town.

(Des V. Whiteley. Photo Harrison)

1964 (10 Dec). 16*th Anniv of Declaration of Human Rights. W* **111.** *P* 14½ × 14.

No.	Type	Description	Unused	Used
239	**118**	1s. black, red and light green	12	15

119 Guides' Emblem on Map

120 Guide Emblems

(Photo Harrison)

965 (17 May). *Golden Jubilee of Jamaica Girl Guides Association.* W **111** *(sideways on 3d.).* P 14 × 14½ *(3d.) or* 14 (1s.).
40 **119** 3d. yellow, green and light blue .. 8 8
41 **120** 1s. yellow, black and apple-green .. 15 25

121 Uniform Cap

122 Flag-bearer and Drummer

(Photo Harrison)

1965 (23 Aug). *Salvation Army Centenary.* W **111.** P 14 × 14½ *(3d.) or* 14½ × 14 *(1s. 6d.).*
242 **121** 3d. multicoloured 5 5
243 **122** 1s. 6d. multicoloured 25 25

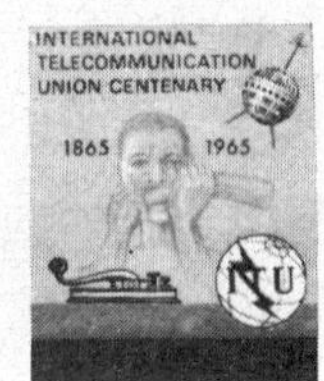

123 Paul Bogle, William Gordon and Morant Bay Court House

124 Abeng-blower, "Telstar", Morse Key and I.T.U. Emblem

(Photo Enschedé)

1965 (29 Dec). *Centenary of Morant Bay Rebellion. No wmk.* P 14 × 13.
244 **123** 3d. light brown, ultramarine and black 5 5
245 1s. 6d. lt brown, yellow-green & black 15 15
246 3s. light brown, rose and black .. 30 35

(Photo Harrison)

1965 (29 Dec). *I.T.U. Centenary.* W **111.** P 14 × 14½.
247 **124** 1s. black, grey-blue and red 50 15

ROYAL VISIT
MARCH 1966

(**125**)

126 Sir Winston Churchill

1966 (3 Mar). *Royal Visit. Nos.* 221, 223, 226/7 *optd with T* **125.**
248 3d. yellow, black and emerald 15 8
249 6d. multicoloured 40 10
250 1s. black and light brown 45 20
251 1s. 6d. black, light blue and buff .. 55 60

(Des Jennifer Toombs. Photo Harrison)

1966 (18 April). *Churchill Commemoration.* W **111.** P 14.
252 **126** 6d. black and olive-green 30 30
253 1s. bistre-brown and deep violet-blue .. 65 80

127 Statue of Athlete and Flags

131 Bolivar's Statue and Flags of Jamaica and Venezuela

(Des V. Whiteley. Photo Harrison)

1966 (4 Aug). *Eighth British Empire and Commonwealth Games. T* **127** *and similar horiz designs.* W **111.** P 14½ × 14.
254 3d. multicoloured 5 5
255 6d. multicoloured 12 10
256 1s. multicoloured 20 20
257 3s. bright gold and deep blue *(shades)* .. 35 65
MS258 128 × 103 mm. Nos. 254/7. Imperf 2·75 3·50
Designs:—6d. Racing cyclists; 1s. Stadium, Kingston; 3s. Games emblem.
No. **MS**258 has been seen with the whole printing inverted except for the brown background.

(Des and photo Harrison)

1966 (5 Dec). *150th Anniv of "Jamaica Letter".* W **111.** P 14 × 15.
259 **131** 8d. multicoloured 20 12

NEW INFORMATION

The editor is always interested to correspond with people who have new information that will improve or correct the Catalogue.

132 Jamaican Pavilion

133 Sir Donald Sangster (Prime Minister)

(Des V. Whiteley. Photo Harrison)

1967 (28 Apr). *World Fair, Montreal.* W **111.** P 14½.
260 **132** 6d. multicoloured 8 8
261 1s. multicoloured 12 12

(Des and photo Enschedé)

1967 (28 Aug). *Sangster Memorial Issue.* P 13½.
262 **133** 3d. multicoloured 5 5
263 1s. 6d. multicoloured 15 20

134 Traffic Duty

135 Personnel of the Force

(Des V. Whiteley. Photo Enschedé)

1967 (28 Nov). *Centenary of the Constabulary Force. T* **134/5** *and similar horiz design. Multicoloured.* W **111.** P 13½ × 14.
264 3d. Type **134** 10 10
a. Wmk sideways 10 10
265 1s. Type **135** 20 20
266 1s. 6d. Badge and Constables of 1867 and 1967 *(as T* **134**) 30 30

1968 (8 Feb). *M.C.C.'s West Indies Tour. As Nos.* 445/7 *of Guyana, but inscr.* "JAMAICA". *Multicoloured.* W **111** *(sideways).* P 14.
267 6d. Wicket-keeping 15 25
a. Horiz strip of 3. Nos. 267/9 .. .. 1·50
268 6d. Batting 15 25
269 6d. Bowling 15 25
Nos. 267/9 were issued in small sheets of 9 comprising three *se-tenant* strips as No. 267a.
Nos. 267/9 exist on PVA gum as well as on gum arabic.

137 Sir Alexander and Lady Bustamante

(Des and photo Harrison)

1968 (23 May). *Labour Day.* W **111.** P 14.
270 **137** 3d. rose and black 5 5
271 1s. olive and black 12 20

138 Human Rights Emblem over Map of Jamaica

(Photo Harrison)

1968 (3 Dec). *Human Rights Year. T* **138** *and similar multicoloured designs.* W **111.** P 14.
272 3d. Type **138** 5 5
a. Gold (flame) omitted .. .. .. 95·00
273 1s. Hands cupping Human Rights emblem *(vert)* 12 15
274 3s. Jamaican holding "Human Rights" .. 35 55
a. Gold (flame) omitted .. .. .. 95·00
Three designs, showing 3d. Bowls of Grain, 1s. Abacus, 3s. Hands in Prayer, were prepared but not issued.

141 ILO Emblem

142 Nurse, and Children being weighed and measured

(Des V. Whiteley. Litho Format)

1969 (23 May). *50th Anniv of International Labour Organization.* P 14.
275 **141** 6d. orange-yellow and blackish brown 10 10
276 3s. bright emerald and blackish brown 30 50

(Des and photo Harrison)

1969 (30 May). *20th Anniv of W.H.O. T* **142** *and similar designs.* W **111.** P 14.
277 6d. grey, brown and orange 10 10
278 1s. black, sepia and blue-green 15 20
279 3s. grey-black, brown and pale bright blue 35 70
Designs: *Horiz*—1s. Malaria eradication. *Vert*—3s. Trainee nurse.

(New Currency. 100 cents = 1 dollar)

C-DAY
8th September
1969
1c

(**145**)

146 "The Adoration of the Kings" (detail, Foppa)

1969 (8 Sept). *Decimal currency. Nos.* 217, 219, 221/3 *and* 225/32 *surch as T* **145.** *Sterling values unobliterated except* 1 c. *to* 4 c. *and* 8 c.
280 1 c. on 1d. violet-blue, dp green & lt brown .. 5 5
281 2 c. on 2d. red, yellow and grey-green .. 5 5
282 3 c. on 3d. yellow, black and emerald .. 8 5
283 4 c. on 4d. ochre and violet 25 10
284 5 c. on 6d. multicoloured 35 10
285 8 c. on 9d. blue and yellow-bistre 15 20
286 10 c. on 1s. black and light brown 20 15
287 15 c. on 1s. 6d. black, light blue and buff .. 30 45
288 20 c. on 2s. red-brown, black & lt blue .. 50 55
289 30 c. on 3s. blue and dull green .. .. 1·75 2·50
290 50 c. on 5s. black, ochre and blue .. .. 1·75 2·50
291 $1 on 10s. multicoloured .. .. 2·25 4·50
292 $2 on £1 multicoloured .. .. 3·75 7·50
280/92 .. .. *Set of* 13 10·00 17·00
No. 281 exists with PVA gum as well as gum arabic.

(Des J. Cooter. Litho D.L.R.)

1969 (25 Oct). *Christmas. Paintings. T* **146** *and similar vert designs. Multicoloured.* W **111.** P 13.
293 2 c. Type **146** 5 5
294 5 c. "Madonna, Child and St. John" (Raphael) 10 12
295 8 c. "The Adoration of the Kings" (detail, Dosso Dossi) 12 15

149 Half Penny, 1869

151 George William Gordon

(Des G. Drummond. Litho P.B.)

1969 (27 Oct). *Centenary of First Jamaican Coins. T* **149** *and similar horiz design.* W **111.** P 12½.
296 3 c. silver, black and mauve 35 60
b. Wmk sideways 10 10
297 15 c. silver, black and light emerald 15 15
Design:—15 c. One penny, 1869.

(Des G. Vasarhelyi. Litho Enschedé)

1970 (11 Mar). *National Heroes. T* **151** *and similar vert designs. Multicoloured.* P 12 × 12½.
298 1 c. Type **151** 5 5
299 3 c. Sir Alexander Bustamante 5 5
300 5 c. Norman Manley 8 5
301 10 c. Marcus Garvey 12 10
302 15 c. Paul Bogle 15 25

156 "Christ appearing to St. Peter" (Carracci)

2c

(159)

(Des G. Drummond. Photo Enschedé)

1970 (23 Mar). *Easter. T* **156** *and similar vert designs. Multi-coloured. W* **111.** *P* 12 × 12½.
303 3 c. Type **156** 5 5
304 10 c. "Christ Crucified" (Antonello da Messina) 15 10
305 20 c. Easter Lily 30 35

1970 (16 July). *No.* 219 *surch with T* **159.**
306 2 c. on 2d. red, yellow and grey-green .. 12 20

160 *Lignum Vitae* 161 Cable Ship *Dacia*

1970 (7 Sept–2 Nov). *Decimal Currency. Designs as Nos.* 217/32 *but inscr as T* **160** *in new currency. W* **111** (*sideways on* 2, 4, 15, 20 *c. and* $1). *P* 14½ (1, 5 *c.*), 14 × 14½ (4 *c.*, $1), 13½ × 14½ (15, 20 *c.*) *or* 14½ × 14 (*others*).
307 1 c. violet-blue, deep green & lt brown .. 20 5
308 2 c. red, yellow and grey-green (as 2d.) .. 25 5
309 3 c. yellow, black and emerald (as 3d.) .. 25 5
310 4 c. ochre and violet (as 4d.) 55 5
311 5 c. multicoloured (as 6d.) .. .. .. 1·40 10
312 8 c. blue and yellow-bistre (as 9d.) 65 15
a. Wmk sideways 70 80
313 10 c. black and light brown (as 1s.) 35 15
314 15 c. black, light blue and buff (as 1s. 6d.) (2.11) 1·25 60
315 20 c. red-brown, black & lt blue (as 2s.) (2.11) 1·25 75
316 30 c. blue and dull green (as 3s.) (2.11) .. 1·75 80
317 50 c. black, ochre and blue (as 5s.) (2.11) .. 3·00 2·75
318 $1 multicoloured (as 10s.) (2.11) .. .. 3·25 3·00
319 $2 multicoloured (as £1) (2.11) .. .. 5·00 5·50
307/19 .. .. *Set of* 13 17·00 13·00

(Des G. Drummond. Litho J.W.)

1970 (12 Oct). *Centenary of Telegraph Service. T* **161** *and similar horiz designs. W* **111** (*sideways*). *P* 14½ × 14.
320 3 c. yellow, red and black 20 10
321 10 c. black and turquoise 40 35
322 50 c. multicoloured .. .. 1·90 1·90
Designs:—10 c. Bright's cable gear aboard *Dacia*; 50 c. Morse key and chart.

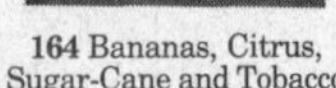

164 Bananas, Citrus, Sugar-Cane and Tobacco 165 "The Projector" (1845)

(Des G. Drummond. Litho Questa)

1970 (2 Nov). *75th Anniv of Jamaican Agricultural Society. W* **111.** *P* 14.
323 **164** 2 c. multicoloured 10 10
324 10 c. multicoloured 25 40

(Des V. Whiteley. Litho Format)

1970 (21 Nov). *125th Anniv of Jamaican Railways. T* **165** *and similar horiz designs. Multicoloured. W* **111** (*sideways*). *P* 13½.
325 3 c. Type **165** 25 12
326 15 c. Engine "54" (1944) 90 80
327 50 c. Engine "102" (1967) .. .. .. 2·50 3·00

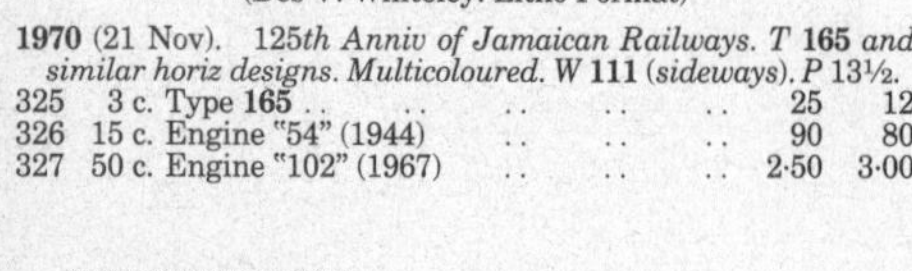

168 Church of St. Jago de la Vega 169 Henry Morgan and Ships

(Des R. Granger Barrett. Litho J.W.)

1971 (22 Feb). *Centenary of Disestablishment of the Church of England in Jamaica. T* **168** *and similar vert design. Multi-coloured. W* **111.** *P* 14½.
328 3 c. Type **168** 5 5
329 10 c. Type **168** 10 10
330 20 c. Type **168** 25 40
331 30 c. Emblem of Church of England in Jamaica 35 65

(Des J.W. Litho Questa)

1971 (10 May). *Pirates and Buccaneers. T* **169** *and similar horiz designs. Multicoloured. W* **111** (*sideways*). *P* 14.
332 3 c. Type **169** 30 12
333 15 c. Mary Read, Anne Bonny and trial pamphlet .. .. 1·00 80
334 30 c. Pirate schooner attacking merchantman 1·90 2·50

170 1s. Stamp of 1919 with Frame Inverted 171 Satellite and Dish Aerial

(Des Jennifer Toombs. Litho J.W.)

1971 (30 Oct). *Tercentenary of Post Office Establishment. T* **170** *and similar designs. W* **111** (*sideways, except* 50 *c.*). *P* 13½.
335 3 c. black and lake 20 10
336 5 c. grey-black and bright green 25 15
337 8 c. black and violet 35 35
338 10 c. brown, black and indigo 40 40
339 20 c. multicoloured .. .. 75 1·25
340 50 c. ochre, black and slate .. .. .. 1·75 2·75
335/40 .. .. *Set of* 6 3·25 4·50
Designs: *Horiz*—3 c. Dummer packet letter, 1705; 5 c. Pre-stamp inland letter, 1793; 8 c. Harbour St. P.O., Kingston, 1820; 10 c. Modern stamp and cancellation; 20 c. British stamps used in Jamaica, 1859.

(Des Cable & Wireless Ltd. Litho J.W.)

1972 (17 Feb). *Opening of Jamaican Earth Satellite Station. W* **111.** *P* 14 × 13½.
341 **171** 3 c. multicoloured 15 10
342 15 c. multicoloured 70 70
343 50 c. multicoloured .. .. .. 2·10 2·75

172 Causeway, Kingston Harbour 173 Air Jamaica Hostess and Aircraft

(Des J.W. Litho Format)

1972 (17 Apr–2 Oct). *Multicoloured designs as T* **172** (1 *to* 6 *c.*) *or* **173** (8 *c. to* $2). *W* **111** (*sideways on horiz designs*). *P* 14½ × 14 (1, 2 *c.*), 14 × 14½ (3, 4, 5, 6 *c.*) *or* 13½ (*others*).
344 1 c. Pimento (*vert*) (5.6) 5 5
345 2 c. Red Ginger (*vert*) (5.6) 5 5
346 3 c. Bauxite Industry (5.6) 5 5
347 4 c. Type **172** 5 5
348 5 c. Oil Refinery (5.6) 5 5
349 6 c. Senate Building, University of the West Indies (5.6) 5 5
350 8 c. National Stadium (5.6) 10 5
351 9 c. Devon House (5.6) 10 5
352 10 c. Type **173** 15 5
353 15 c. Old Iron Bridge, Spanish Town (*vert*) (2.10) 25 10
354 20 c. College of Arts, Science and Technology (2.10) 25 15
355 30 c. Dunn's River Falls (*vert*) (2.10) 35 25
356 50 c. River rafting (5.6) 70 40
357 $1 Jamaica House (2.10) 90 65
358 $2 Kings House (2.10) .. .. .. 1·75 1·50
344/58 .. .. *Set of* 15 4·25 3·25

TENTH
ANNIVERSARY
INDEPENDENCE
1962-1972

(174)

175 Arms of Kingston

1972 (8 Aug). *Tenth Anniv of Independence. Nos.* 346, 352 *and* 356 *optd as T* **174.**
359 3 c. Bauxite Industry 10 8
360 10 c. Type **173** 25 25
361 50 c. River rafting .. .. 1·25 2·25

(Des R. Granger Barrett. Litho J.W.)

1972 (4 Dec). *Centenary of Kingston as Capital. W* **111** (*sideways on* 50 *c.*). *P* 13½ × 14 (5 *and* 30 *c.*) *or* 14 × 13½ (50 *c.*).
362 **175** 5 c. multicoloured 12 10
363 30 c. multicoloured 70 90
364 – 50 c. multicoloured .. .. .. 1·25 1·75
The 50 c. is as T **175**, but horiz.

176 Mongoose on Map

(Des R. Granger Barrett. Litho Questa)

1973 (9 Apr). *Centenary of Introduction of the Mongoose. T* **176** *and similar horiz designs. W* **111** (*sideways*). *P* 14 × 14½.
365 8 c. light apple-green, yellow-green and black 12 20
366 40 c. light cobalt, light blue and black .. 65 1·25
367 60 c. salmon-pink, brownish salmon & black 1·00 2·00
MS368 165 × 95 mm. Nos. 365/7 .. .. 1·75 3·00
Designs:—40 c. Mongoose and rat; 60 c. Mongoose and chicken.

177 *Euphorbia punicea*

(Des Sylvia Goaman. Litho Questa)

1973 (9 July). *Flora. T* **177** *and similar diamond-shaped designs. Multicoloured. W* **111.** *P* 14.
369 1 c. Type **177** 5 5
370 6 c. *Hylocereus triangularis* 15 15
371 9 c. *Columnea argentea* 20 20
372 15 c. *Portlandia grandiflora* 35 35
373 30 c. *Samyda pubescens* .. .. .. 75 1·00
374 50 c. *Cordia sebestena* .. .. 1·50 1·90
369/74 .. .. *Set of* 6 2·75 3·25

178 *Broughtonia sanguinea*

(Des Sylvia Goaman. Litho B.W.)

1973 (8 Oct). *Orchids. T* **178** *and similar multicoloured designs. W* **111** (*sideways on* 5 *c.*, $1, **MS**379). *P* 14 × 13½ (5 *c.*, $1) *or* 13½ × 14 (*others*).
375 5 c. Type **178** 20 10
376 10 c. *Arpophyllum jamaicense* (*vert*) 45 25
377 20 c. *Oncidium pulchellum* (*vert*) .. .. 1·00 80
378 $1 *Brassia maculata* .. .. .. 4·00 4·50
MS379 161 × 95 mm. Nos. 375/8. P 12 .. 5·00 5·50

179 *Mary*, 1808–15 180 "Journeys"

(Des J. Cooter. Litho J.W.)

1974 (8 Apr). *Mail Packet Boats. T* **179** *and similar horiz designs. Multicoloured. W* **111** (*sideways on Nos.* 380/3, *upright on* **MS**384). *P* 13½ (5 *c.*, 50 *c.*) *or* 14 (*others*).
380 5 c. Type **179** 20 10
a. Perf 14 .. .. 6·50 1·75
381 10 c. *Queensbury*, 1814–27 .. .. .. 35 25
382 15 c. *Sheldrake*, 1829–34 .. .. .. 65 80
383 50 c. *Thames*, 1842 .. .. 2·50 3·00
MS384 133 × 159 mm. Nos. 380/4. P 13½ (*sold at* 90 *c.*) .. .. 4·00 4·75

(Des R. Granger Barrett. Litho Questa)

1974 (1 Aug). *National Dance Theatre Company. T* **180** *and similar vert designs showing dance-works. Multicoloured.* **W 111.** *P* 13½.
385 5 c. Type **180** 10 8
386 10 c. "Jamaican Promenade" 20 20
387 30 c. "Jamaican Promenade" 60 85
388 50 c. "Misa Criolla" .. .. 1·10 1·75
MS389 161 × 102 mm. Nos. 385/8 (*sold at* $1) .. 2·50 3·00

181 U.P.U. Emblem and Globe

(Des V. Whiteley. Litho J.W.)

1974 (9 Oct). *Centenary of Universal Postal Union.* **W 111** (*sideways*). *P* 14.
390 **181** 5 c. multicoloured 15 8
391 9 c. multicoloured 20 30
392 50 c. multicoloured .. .. .. 1·00 1·90

182 Senate Building and Sir Hugh Wooding

183 Commonwealth Symbol

(Des R. Granger Barrett. Litho Questa)

1975 (13 Jan). *25th Anniv of University of West Indies. T* **182** *and similar horiz design. Multicoloured.* **W 111** (*sideways*). *P* 14.
393 5 c. Type **182** 5 8
394 10 c. University Chapel and H.R.H. Princess Alice 15 20
395 30 c. Type **182** 45 70
396 50 c. As 10 c. .. .. 75 1·40

(Des C. Abbott. Litho Questa)

1975 (29 Apr). *Heads of Commonwealth Conference. T* **183** *and similar square designs. Multicoloured.* **W 111.** *P* 13½.
397 5 c. Type **183** 15 8
398 10 c. Jamaican coat of arms 30 20
399 30 c. Dove of Peace .. .. 80 1·10
400 50 c. Jamaican flag .. .. 1·50 1·90

184 *Graphium marcellinus*

185 Koo Koo or Actor Boy

(Des J. Cooter. Litho Questa)

1975 (25 Aug). *Butterflies (1st series). T* **184** *and similar vert designs showing the family Papilionidae. Multicoloured.* **W 111.** *P* 14.
401 10 c. Type **184** 55 30
402 20 c. *Papilo thoas melonius* .. .. .. 1·10 80
403 25 c. *Papilo thersites* .. .. 1·25 1·00
404 30 c. *Papilo homerus* .. .. 1·50 1·75
MS405 134 × 179 mm. Nos. 401/4 (*sold at* 95 c.) 5·00 6·50
See also Nos. 429/**MS**433 and 443/**MS**447.

(Des C. Abbott. Litho J.W.)

1975 (3 Nov). *Christmas. T* **185** *and similar vert designs showing Belisario prints of "John Canoe" (Christmas) Festival (1st series). Multicoloured.* **W 111.** *P* 14.
406 8 c. Type **185** 15 15
407 10 c. Red Set-girls 15 20
408 20 c. French Set-girls 35 60
409 50 c. Jaw-bone or House John Canoe .. .. 1·00 1·90
MS410 138 × 141 mm. Nos. 406/9. P 13½ (*sold at* $1) .. .. 2·75 3·25
See also Nos. 421/**MS**424.

186 Bordone Map, 1528

(Des L. Curtis. Litho Questa)

1976 (12 Mar). *16th Century Maps of Jamaica. T* **186** *and similar horiz designs.* **W 111** (*sideways*). *P* 13½.
411 10 c. brown, light stone and light vermilion 20 20
412 20 c. multicoloured 40 50
413 30 c. multicoloured .. .. 70 1·10
414 50 c. multicoloured .. .. 1·00 1·75
Designs—20 c. Porcacchi map, 1576; 30 c. DeBry map, 1594; 50 c. Langenes map, 1598.
See also Nos. 425/8.

187 Olympic Rings

(Des Sir H. McDonald: adapted V. Whiteley Studio. Litho Walsall)

1976 (14 June). *Olympic Games, Montreal.* **W 111** (*sideways*). *P* 13½.
415 **187** 10 c. multicoloured 20 20
416 20 c. multicoloured 45 50
417 25 c. multicoloured 50 75
418 50 c. multicoloured .. .. .. 80 1·60

1976 (9 Aug). *West Indian Victory in World Cricket Cup. As Nos.* 559/60 *of Barbados. P* 14.
419 10 c. Map of the Caribbean 40 40
420 25 c. Prudential Cup .. .. 85 1·00

(Des C. Abbott. Litho J.W.)

1976 (8 Nov). *Christmas. Belisario Prints (2nd series). Multicoloured designs as T* **185.** **W 111.** *P* 13½.
421 10 c. Queen of the set-girls 20 20
422 20 c. Band of the Jaw-bone John Canoe .. 45 45
423 50 c. Koo Koo (actor-boy) .. .. .. 1·10 1·10
MS424 110 × 140 mm. Nos. 421/3. P 14 × 14½ (*sold at* 90 c.) .. .. 2·25 2·75

(Des L. Curtis. Litho J.W.)

1977 (28 Feb). *17th Century Maps of Jamaica. Designs as T* **186.** **W 111** (*sideways*). *P* 13.
425 9 c. multicoloured 25 20
426 10 c. multicoloured 25 20
427 25 c. grey-black, pale blue and bright blue .. 75 1·25
428 40 c. grey-black, light turquoise and grey-blue 1·10 1·50
Designs:—9 c. Hickeringill map, 1661; 10 c. Ogilby map, 1671; 25 c. Visscher map, 1680; 40 c. Thornton map, 1689.

(Des J. Cooter. Litho J.W.)

1977 (9 May). *Butterflies (2nd series). Multicoloured designs as T* **184** *showing the families Nymphalidae and Pieridae.* **W 111.** *P* 13½.
429 10 c. *Eurema elathea* 40 20
430 20 c. *Dynamine egaea egaea* 95 65
431 25 c. *Atlantea pantoni* .. .. 1·25 1·50
432 40 c. *Hypolinnas misippus* .. .. .. 1·75 2·25
MS433 139 × 122 mm. Nos. 429/32. P 14½ (*sold at* $1.05) .. .. 4·50 6·00

188 Map, Scout Emblem and Streamertail

189 Trumpeter

(Des Daphne Padden. Litho Questa)

1977 (5 Aug). *Sixth Caribbean Jamboree, Jamaica. Multicoloured; background colours given.* **W 111** (*sideways*). *P* 13½.
434 **188** 10 c. new blue 25 20
435 20 c. light yellow-green 55 55
436 25 c. orange 60 60
437 50 c. light magenta .. .. .. 1·25 1·60

(Des C. Abbott. Litho Questa)

1977 (19 Dec). *50th Anniv of Jamaica Military Band. T* **189** *and similar multicoloured designs.* **W 111** (*sideways on horiz designs*). *P* 14.
438 9 c. Type **189** 20 15
439 10 c. Clarinet players 20 15
440 20 c. Two kettle drummers (*vert*) 60 70
441 25 c. Cellist and trumpeter (*vert*) .. .. 80 1·00
MS442 120 × 137 mm. Nos. 438/41. Wmk sideways (*sold at* 75 c.) .. .. 3·75 4·25

(Des J. Cooter. Litho Walsall)

1978 (17 Apr). *Butterflies (3rd series). Multicoloured designs as T* **184.** **W 111.** *P* 14.
443 10 c. *Callophrys crethona* 25 10
444 20 c. *Siproeta stelenes stelenes* 50 30
445 25 c. *Urbanus proteus* 65 55
446 50 c. *Anaea troglodyta portia* .. .. .. 1·40 1·60
MS447 100 × 125 mm. Nos. 443/6 (*sold at* $1.15) 2·50 2·75
a. Error. Imperf £175

OMNIBUS ISSUES

Details, together with prices for complete sets, of the various Omnibus issues from the 1935 Silver Jubilee series to date are included in a special section following Zululand at the end of the catalogue.

190 Half-figure with Canopy

191 Norman Manley (statue)

(Des J. Cooter. Litho J.W.)

1978 (10 July). *Arawak Artefacts (1st series). T* **190** *and similar vert designs.* **W 111.** *P* 13½ × 13.
448 10 c. deep brown, yellow and black 10 10
449 20 c. deep brown, mauve and black 20 20
450 50 c. deep brown, apple-green and black .. 45 45
MS451 135 × 90 mm. Nos. 448/50. P 14 (*sold at* 90 c.) .. .. 80 1·25
Designs:—20 c. Standing figure; 50 c. Birdman.
See also Nos. 479/83.

(Des and litho J.W.)

1978 (25 Sept). *24th Commonwealth Parliamentary Conference. T* **191** *and similar vert designs. Multicoloured.* **W 111.** *P* 13.
452 10 c. Type **191** 10 10
453 20 c. Sir Alexander Bustamante (statue) .. 20 20
454 25 c. City of Kingston Crest 25 30
455 40 c. Gordon House Chamber, House of Representatives 45 60

192 Band and Banner

193 "Negro Aroused" (sculpture by Edna Manley)

(Des V. Whiteley. Litho J.W.)

1978 (4 Dec). *Christmas. Centenary of Salvation Army. T* **192** *and similar horiz designs. Multicoloured.* **W 111** (*sideways*). *P* 14.
456 10 c. Type **192** 12 10
457 20 c. Trumpeter 25 20
458 25 c. Banner 30 30
459 50 c. William Booth (founder) 55 65

(Des G. Hutchins. Litho J.W.)

1978 (11 Dec). *International Anti-Apartheid Year.* **W 111.** *P* 13.
460 **193** 10 c. multicoloured 10 10

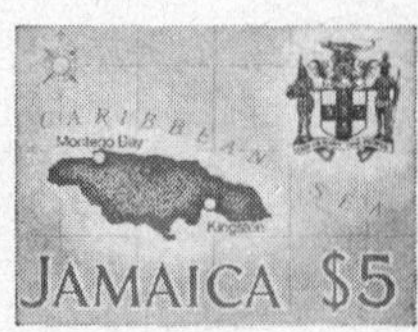

194 Tennis, Montego Bay

195 Arms and Map of Jamaica

(Des and litho Harrison ($5). Des Walsall. Litho J.W. (others))

1979 (15 Jan)–**84.** *Vert designs as T* **194,** *and T* **195.** *Multicoloured. White ordinary paper (15, 65, 75 c., $5) or cream chalk-surfaced paper (others).* **W 111** (*sideways on* $5). *P* 14½ × 14 ($5) *or* 13½ (*others*).
461 1 c. Type **194** (26.11.79) 5 5
462 2 c. Golf, Tryall, Hanover (26.11.79) 5 5
a. White ordinary paper (8.84) 5 5
463 4 c. Horse riding, Negril Beach (26.11.79) .. 5 5
a. White ordinary paper (8.84) 5 5
464 5 c. Old waterwheel, Tryall, Hanover (26.11.79) 5 5
a. White ordinary paper (27.8.82) 5 5
465 6 c. Fern Gully, Ocho Rios (26.11.79) .. 5 5
466 7 c. Dunn's River Falls, Ocho Rios (26.11.79) 5 5
467 8 c. Jamaican Tody (bird) (28.4.80) 5 5
468 10 c. Jamaican Mango (bird) (28.4.80) .. 5 5
a. White ordinary paper (27.8.82) 5 5
469 12 c. Yellow-billed Amazon (28.4.80) 5 5
470 15 c. Streamertail (bird) (28.4.80) 5 8
471 35 c. White-chinned Thrush (28.4.80) .. 12 15
472 50 c. Jamaican Woodpecker (28.4.80) 15 20
473 65 c. Rafting, Martha Brae Trelawny (28.4.80) 20 25
474 75 c. Blue Marlin Fleet, Port Antonio (28.4.80) 25 30
475 $1 Scuba Diving, Ocho Rios (28.4.80) .. 30 35
a. White ordinary paper (27.8.82) 30 35
476 $2 Sailing boats, Montego Bay (28.4.80) .. 60 65
a. White ordinary paper (27.8.82) 60 65
477 $5 Type **195** .. .. 1·50 1·75
461/77 .. .. *Set of* 17 3·25 3·75

TENTH ANNIVERSARY AIR JAMAICA 1st APRIL 1979

(196)

197 Grinding Stone, *circa* 400 BC.

1979 (2 Apr). *10th Anniv of Air Jamaica. No. 352 optd with T* **196.**

478 10 c. Type **173** 10 15

(Des D. Bowen. Litho Questa)

1979 (23 Apr). *Arawak Artefacts (2nd series). T* **197** *and similar multicoloured designs. W* **111** *(sideways on 10, 20 and 25 c.). P* 14.

479 5 c. Type **197** 5 5
480 10 c. Stone implements, *c*. 500 AD *(horiz)* .. 10 15
481 20 c. Cooking pot, *c*. 300 AD *(horiz)* 20 30
482 25 c. Serving boat, *c*. 300 AD *(horiz)* 20 35
483 50 c. Storage jar fragment, *c*. 300 AD.. .. 40 55

198 1962 1s. 6d. Independence Commemorative Stamp

(Des J.W. from a local design by J. Mahfood. Litho Walsall)

1979 (13 Aug). *Death Centenary of Sir Rowland Hill. T* **198** *and similar horiz designs showing stamps and Sir Rowland Hill. W* **111** *(sideways). P* 14.

484 10 c. black, scarlet-vermilion & brt scarlet .. 8 5
485 20 c. orange-yellow and yellowish brown .. 15 20
486 25 c. mauve and blue 20 25
487 50 c. multicoloured 30 45
MS488 146 × 94 mm. No. 485 *(sold at 30 c.)* .. 30 40

Designs:—20 c. 1920 1s. with frame inverted; 25 c. 1860 6d.; 50 c. 1968 3d. Human Rights Year commemorative.

199 Group of Children

(Des J.W. Litho Harrison)

1979 (1 Oct). *Christmas. International Year of the Child. T* **199** *and similar multicoloured designs. W* **111** *(sideways on 10, 25 and 50 c.). P* 14.

489 10 c. Type **199** 5 5
490 20 c. Doll *(vert)*.. .. .. 15 20
491 25 c. "The Family" (painting by child) .. 15 25
492 50 c. "House on the Hill" (painting by child) .. 30 45

200 Date Tree Hall, 1886 (original home of Institute)

(Des G. Drummond. Litho Walsall)

1980 (25 Feb). *Centenary of Institute of Jamaica. T* **200** *and similar multicoloured designs. W* **111** *(sideways on 5, 15 and 50 c.). P* 13½.

493 5 c. Type **200** 5 5
494 15 c. Institute building, 1980 .. .. .. 10 15
495 35 c. Microfilm reader *(vert)* 25 35
496 50 c. Hawksbill Turtle and Green Turtle .. 30 40
497 75 c. Jamaican Owl *(vert)* 50 75

201 Don Quarrie (200 Metres, 1976)

(Des BG Studio. Litho Walsall)

1980 (21 July). *Olympic Games, Moscow. Jamaican Olympic Athletics Gold Medal Winners. T* **201** *and similar horiz designs. Multicoloured. W* **111** *(sideways). P* 13.

498 15 c. Type **201** 30 45
499 35 c. Arthur Wint (4 × 400 Metres Relay, 1952) 70 90
a. Horiz strip of 4. Nos. 499/502 .. .. 2·75
500 35 c. Leslie Laing (4 × 400 Metres Relay, 1952) 70 90
501 35 c. Herbert McKenley (4 × 400 Metres Relay, 1952) 70 90
502 35 c. George Rhoden (4 × 400 Metres Relay, 1952) 70 90

Nos. 499/502 were printed together, *se-tenant*, in horizontal strips of 4 throughout the sheet.

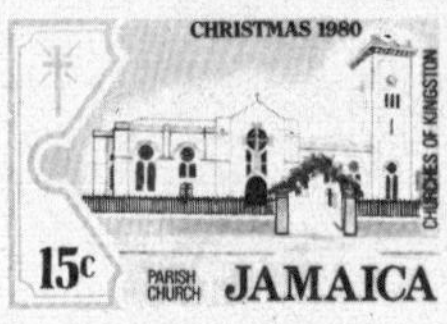

202 Parish Church

203 Blood Cup Sponge

(Des J.W. Litho Harrison)

1980 (24 Nov). *Christmas. Churches (1st series). T* **202** *and similar horiz designs. Multicoloured. W* **111** *(sideways). P* 14.

503 15 c. Type **202** 10 10
504 20 c. Coke Memorial Church 12 12
505 25 c. Church of the Redeemer.. .. .. 15 15
506 $5 Holy Trinity Cathedral .. .. .. 2·75 3·00
MS507 120 × 139 mm. Nos. 503/6. P 14½ *(sold at $5.70)* .. .. 3·25 3·75

See also Nos. 537/40 and 570/2.

(Des J. Mahfood. Litho Walsall)

1981 (27 Feb). *Marine Life (1st series). T* **203** *and similar multicoloured designs. W* **111** *(sideways on 45 and 75 c.). P* 14.

508 20 c. Type **203** 15 20
509 45 c. Tube Sponge *(horiz)* 35 40
510 60 c. Black Coral 45 50
511 75 c. Tyre Reef *(horiz)* 55 60

See also Nos. 541/5.

204 Jamaican Hutia (or Indian Coney)

205 White Orchid

(Des D. Bowen. Litho Questa)

1981 (25 May). *Jamaican Hutia (or Indian Coney). T* **204** *and similar horiz designs. Multicoloured. W* **111.** *P* 14.

512 20 c. Hutia facing right 20 20
a. Horiz strip of 4. Nos. 512/15 70
513 20 c. Type **204** 20 20
514 20 c. Hutia facing left and eating 20 20
515 20 c. Hutia family 20 20

Nos. 512/15 were printed together, *se-tenant*, in horizontal strips of 4 throughout the sheet.

(Des J.W. Litho Format)

1981 (29 July). *Royal Wedding. T* **205** *and similar vert designs. Multicoloured. W w* **14** *(sideways). P* 13½ *($5) or* 15 *(others).*

516 20 c. Type **205** 20 20
a. Perf 15 × 14 .. .. 25 25
ab. Booklet pane. Nos. 516a/19a .. .. 7·00
517 45 c. Royal Coach 35 35
a. Perf 15 × 14 .. .. 50 50
518 60 c. Prince Charles and Lady Diana Spencer 50 50
a. Perf 15 × 14 .. .. 60 60
519 $5 St. James' Palace .. .. 3·50 3·50
a. Perf 15 × 14 .. .. 6·00 6·00
MS520 98 × 85 mm. No. 519. Wmk upright. P 13½ 3·50 3·50

Nos. 516/19 also exist perforated 14½ ($5) or 13½ (others) *(price for set of 4 £4 mint or used)* from additional sheetlets of 5 stamps and one label.

Nos. 516a/19a are from $6.25 stamp booklets.

206 Blind Man at Work

207 W.F.D. Emblem on 1964 1½d. Definitive

(Des G. Vasarhelyi. Litho J.W.)

1981 (14 Sept). *International Year for Disabled Persons. T* **206** *and similar horiz designs. Multicoloured. W* **111** *(sideways). P* 13.

521 20 c. Type **206** 20 20
522 45 c. Painting with the mouth 50 50
523 60 c. Deaf student communicating with sign language 60 60
524 $1.50, Basketball players .. .. .. 1·40 1·40

(Des J. Mahfood. Litho J.W.)

1981 (16 Oct). *World Food Day. Stamps on Stamps. T* **207** *and similar designs showing W.F.D. emblems on various definitives. W* **111** *(sideways on 20 c., $2 and $4). P* 13.

525 20 c. multicoloured 20 20
526 45 c. black, rose and orange 50 50
527 $2 black, violet-blue and green .. .. 1·75 1·75
528 $4 black, green and light brown .. .. 3·25 3·25

Designs: *Vert as T* **207**—45 c. 1922 1d. (40 × 26 *mm.*)—$2 As 1938 3d. but with W.F.D. emblem replacing King's head; $4 As 1938 1s. but with W.F.D. emblem replacing King's head.

Nos. 525/8 were so designed that the face values obliterated those on the stamps depicted.

208 "Survival" (song title)

209 Webb Memorial Baptist Church

(Litho Format)

1981 (20 Oct). *Bob Marley (musician) Commemoration. T* **208** *and similar vert designs inscribed with song titles. In black and vermilion ($5.25) or multicoloured (others). W w* **14** *(sideways). P* 15.

529 1 c. Type **208** 5 5
530 2 c. "Exodus" 5 5
531 3 c. "Is this Love" 5 5
532 15 c. "Coming in from the Cold"* 20 20
533 20 c. "Positive Vibration"† 30 25
534 60 c. "War" 95 75
535 $3 "Could you be Loved" .. .. .. 7·00 5·00
529/35 .. .. *Set of* 7 8·00 5·50
MS536 134 × 110 mm. $5.25, Bob Marley (wmk upright) .. .. 7·00 7·50

*Part of initial "C" of song title inscription does not show on the design.

†Incorrectly inscribed "OSITIVE VIBRATION".

(Des J.W. Litho Questa)

1981 (11 Dec). *Christmas. Churches (2nd series). T* **209** *and similar horiz designs. Multicoloured. W* **111** *(sideways). P* 14.

537 10 c. Type **209** 10 5
538 45 c. Church of God in Jamaica 45 45
539 $5 Bryce United Church .. .. .. 3·50 3·75
MS540 120 × 168 mm. Nos. 537/9 (wmk upright). P 12 .. .. 4·00 4·50

210 Gorgonian Coral

211 Cub Scout

(Des J. Mahfood; adapted PAD Studio. Litho Questa)

1982 (22 Feb). *Marine Life (2nd series). T* **210** *and similar multicoloured designs. W* **111** *(sideways on 45, 60, 75 c. and $3). P* 14.

541 20 c. Type **210** 20 20
542 45 c. Hard Sponge and diver *(horiz)* 45 45
543 60 c. Sea Cow *(horiz)* 55 55
544 75 c. Plume Worm *(horiz)* 70 70
545 $3 Coral Banded Shrimp *(horiz)* .. .. 2·40 2·40

(Des L. Curtis. Litho J.W.)

1982 (12 July). *75th Anniv of Boy Scout Movement. T* **211** *and similar vert designs. Multicoloured. W* **111.** *P* 13½ × 13.

546 20 c. Type **211** 20 20
547 45 c. Scout camp 45 45
548 60 c. "Out of Many, One People" 55 55
549 $2 Lord Baden-Powell .. .. .. 1·75 1·75
MS550 80 × 130 mm. Nos. 546/9 .. .. .. 3·00 3·50

212 *Lignum vitae* (national flower)

213 Prey Captured

(Des R. Sauer. Litho Questa)

1982 (30 Aug). *21st Birthday of Princess of Wales. T* **212** *and similar vert designs. W* **111.** *P* 14½ × 14.

551 20 c. Type **212** 20 20
a. Booklet pane. Nos. 551/3. .. .. 1·00

552 45 c. Carriage ride 35 35
553 60 c. Wedding 50 50
554 75 c. *Saxifraga longifolia* 70 70
a. Booklet pane. Nos. 554/6 .. .. .. 4·00
555 $2 Princess of Wales .. .. .. 1·50 1·50
556 $3 *Viola gracilis major* .. .. .. 2·00 2·00
551/6 .. .. *Set of* 6 4·75 4·75
MS557 106 × 75 mm. $5 Honeymoon photograph 3·50 3·50

Nos. 554 and 556 were printed in small sheets of 6 including one *se-tenant*, stamp-size, label. The other values were printed in sheets of 40.

1982 (13 Sept). *Birth of Prince William of Wales. Nos.* 551/7 *optd with T* 171 *of Antigua.*
558 20 c. Type **212** 20 20
a. Booklet pane. Nos. 558/60 .. .. 1·00
559 45 c. Carriage ride 35 35
560 60 c. Wedding 50 50
561 75 c. *Saxifraga longifolia* 70 70
a. Booklet pane. Nos. 561/3 .. .. .. 4·00
562 $2 Princess of Wales .. .. .. 1·50 1·50
563 $3 *Viola gracilis major* .. .. .. 2·00 2·00
558/63 .. .. *Set of* 6 4·75 4·75
MS564 106 × 75 mm. $5 Honeymoon photograph 3·50 3·50

(Des N. Arlott. Litho Questa)

1982 (25 Oct). *Jamaican Lizard Cuckoo. T* **213** *and similar vert designs. Multicoloured. W* **111**. *P* 14½.
565 $1 Type **213** 80 80
a. Horiz strip of 5. Nos. 565/9 .. .. 3·50
566 $1 Searching for prey 80 80
567 $1 Calling prior to prey search 80 80
568 $1 Adult landing 80 80
569 $1 Adult flying in 80 80

Nos. 565/9 were printed in horizontal *se-tenant* strips of 5 throughout the sheet.

(Des and litho J.W.)

1982 (8 Dec). *Christmas. Churches (3rd series). Horiz designs as T* **209**. *Multicoloured. W* 111 (*sideways*). *P* 13.
570 20 c. United Pentecostal Church 20 20
571 45 c. Disciples of Christ Church 40 40
572 75 c. Open Bible Church 70 70

214 Queen Elizabeth II

215 Folk Dancing

(Des D. Miller. Litho Walsall)

1983 (14 Feb). *Royal Visit. T* **214** *and similar vert design. Multicoloured. W* **111**. *P* 14.
573 $2 Type **214** .. .. 1·50 1·60
574 $3 Coat of Arms .. .. 2·25 2·40

(Des Walsall. Litho Format)

1983 (14 Mar). *Commonwealth Day. T* **215** *and similar horiz designs. Multicoloured. W* 111 (*sideways*). *P* 14.
575 20 c. Type **215** 15 20
576 45 c. Bauxite mining 35 40
577 75 c. World map showing position of Jamaica 55 60
578 $2 Coat of arms and family .. .. .. 1·50 1·60

216 General Cargo Ship at Wharf

217 Norman Manley and Sir Alexander Bustamante

(Des A. Theobald. Litho Format)

1983 (17 Mar). *25th Anniv of International Maritime Organization. T* **216** *and similar horiz designs. Multicoloured. P* 14.
579 15 c. Type **216** 12 15
580 20 c. Cruise liner at Kingston 15 20
581 45 c. Container ship entering port 35 40
582 $1 Tanker passing International Seabed Headquarters Building 75 80

(Des D. Miller. Litho Harrison)

1983 (25 July). *21st Anniv of Independence. W* **111**. *P* 14.
583 **217** 15 c. multicoloured 12 15
584 20 c. multicoloured 15 20
585 45 c. multicoloured 35 40

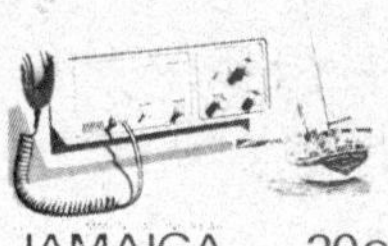

218 Ship-to-Shore Radio

219 "Racing at Caymanas" (Sidney Mclaren)

1983 (18 Oct). *World Communications Year. T* **218** *and similar horiz designs. Multicoloured. W* **111** (*sideways*). *P* 14.
586 20 c. Type **218** 15 20
587 45 c. Postal services 35 40
588 75 c. Telephone communications 55 60
589 $1 T.V. via satellite 75 80

(Des D. Miller. Litho J.W.)

1983 (12 Dec). *Christmas. Paintings. T* **219** *and similar multicoloured designs. W* **111** (*sideways on* 15 *c.*, 20 *c.*). *P* 13 × 13½ (15 *c.*, 20 *c.*) *or* 13½ × 13 (*others*).
590 15 c. Type **219** 5 5
591 20 c. "Seated Figures" (Karl Parboosingh) .. 8 10
592 75 c. "The Petitioner" (Henry Daley) (*vert*) .. 30 35
593 $2 "Banana Plantation" (John Dunkley) (*vert*) 85 90

220 Sir Alexander Bustamante

221 "D.H. 60G Gipsy Moth" Seaplane

(Des D. Miller. Litho Questa)

1984 (24 Feb). *Birth Centenary of Sir Alexander Bustamante. T* **220** *and similar vert design. Multicoloured. W* **111**. *P* 14.
594 20 c. Type **220** 8 10
a. Horiz pair. Nos. 594/5 .. .. .. 15 20
595 20 c. Birthplace, Blenheim 8 10

Nos. 594/5 were printed together, *se-tenant*, in horizontal pairs throughout the sheet.

(Des A. Theobald. Litho Questa)

1984 (11 June). *Seaplanes and Flying Boats. T* **221** *and similar horiz designs. Multicoloured. W* **111** (*sideways*). *P* 14.
596 25 c. Type **221** 10 12
597 55 c. Consolidated "Commodore" flying boat .. 20 25
598 $1.50, Sikorsky "S-38" flying boat 55 60
599 $3 Sikorsky "S-40" flying boat .. .. 1·00 1·10

222 Cycling

223

(Des G. Vasarhelyi. Litho J.W.)

1984 (11 July). *Olympic Games, Los Angeles. T* **222** *and similar horiz designs. Multicoloured. W* **111** (*sideways*). *P* 14.
600 25 c. Type **222** 10 12
601 55 c. Relay running 20 25
602 $1.50, Start of race 55 60
603 $3 Finish of race .. .. 1·00 1·10
MS604 135 × 105 mm. Nos. 600/3 (*sold at* $5.40). P 13 × 13½ .. .. 1·90 2·00

1984 (7 Aug). *Nos.* 465 *and* 469 *surch as T* **223**.
605 5 c. on 6 c. Fern Gully, Ocho Rios 5 5
606 10 c. on 12 c. Yellow-billed Amazon 5 5

224 Head of Jamaican Boa Snake

(Des I. Loe. Litho Questa)

1984 (22 Oct). *Jamaican Boa Snake. T* **224** *and similar horiz designs. Multicoloured. W* **111** (*sideways*). *P* 14½.
607 25 c. Type **224** 10 12
608 55 c. Boa snake on branch over stream .. 20 25
609 70 c. Snake with young 25 30
610 $1 Snake on log 35 40
MS611 133 × 97 mm. As Nos. 607/10 but without W.W.F. emblem (*sold at* $2.60) 90 95

225 *Enterprise* (1845)

(Des D. Hartley-Marjoram. Litho Enschedé)

1984 (16 Nov). *Early Railway Locomotives. T* **225** *and similar horiz designs. Multicoloured. W* **111** (*sideways*). *P* 13½ × 13.
612 25 c. Type **225** 10 12
613 55 c. Tank locomotive (1880) 20 25
614 $1.50, Kitson-Meyer tank locomotive (1904) 55 60
615 $3 Superheated locomotive (1916) .. .. 1·00 1·10

POSTAL FISCALS

Revenue stamps were authorised for postal use by Post Office notice of 12 October 1887.

CONDITION. The note at the beginning also applies to Nos. F1/6.

F 1

(Typo D.L.R.)

1865–71 (Issued). *P* 14. (*a*) *Wmk Pineapple* (*T* 7).
F1 F 1 1d. rose (1865) .. .. 60·00 75·00
a. Imperf £250
(*b*) *Wmk Crown CC*
F2 F 1 1d. rose (1868) .. .. 35·00 40·00
(*c*) *Wmk CA over Crown* (*Type* w **7** *sideways, covering two stamps*)
F3 F 1 1d. rose (1870 or 1871) .. .. .. 7·00 6·00
a. Imperf .. ..

F 2

F 3

(Typo D.L.R.)

1855–74 (Issued). *Glazed paper. P* 14. (*a*) *No wmk.*
F4 F 2 1½d. blue/*blue* (1857) .. .. .. 30·00 32·00
a. Imperf (1855) .. .. ..
b. *Blue on white* .. .. .. 40·00 45·00
F5 3d. purple/*blue* (1857) .. .. .. 30·00 38·00
a. Imperf (1855) .. .. ..
b. *Purple on lilac* (1857) .. .. 32·00 38·00
ba. Imperf (1855) .. .. ..
c. *Purple on white* (1857) .. .. 32·00 35·00
(*b*) *Wmk Crown CC*
F6 F 2 3d. purple/*lilac* (1874) .. .. .. 2·75 3·50

All the above stamps *imperf* are exceedingly rare postally used.

1858 (1 Jan). (Issued). *No wmk. P* 15½ × 15.
F7 F 3 1s. rose/*bluish* .. .. 50·00 55·00
F8 5s. lilac/*bluish* £250 £325
F9 10s. green/*bluish* £275 £325

Telegraph stamps were also used postally, but no authority was given for such use.

OFFICIAL STAMPS

OFFICIAL (O 1) **OFFICIAL** (O 2)

1890 (1 April). *No.* 16 *optd with Type* O 1 *by C. Vendryes, Kingston.*

(*a*) "OFFICIAL" 17 *to* 17½ *mm long*
O1 8 ½d. green .. .. 1·25 80
a. "O" omitted £400
b. One "I" omitted .. .. ..
c. Both "I"s omitted £500 £500
d. "L" omitted .. .. — £500
e. Opt inverted .. .. 45·00 50·00
f. Opt double .. .. 45·00 50·00
g. Opt. double, one inverted £300 £300
h. Opt double, one vertical £550
j. Pair, overprints *tête-bêche* .. ..
(*b*) "OFFICIAL" 15 *to* 16 *mm long*
O2 8 ½d. green .. .. 9·50 9·50
a. Opt double £450

There were four (or possibly five) settings of this overprint, all but one being of the longer type. There are numerous minor varieties, due to broken type, etc. (*e.g.* a broken "E" used for "F").

Stamps with the 17–17½ mm opt were reissued in 1894 during a temporary shortage of No. O3.

1890–1. *Optd with Type* O **2** *by D.L.R. Wmk Crown CA. P* 14.
O3 8 ½d. green (1891) 75 20
O4 11 1d. rose (1.4.90) .. .. 1·25 30
O5 2d. grey (1.4.90) .. .. 2·00 50
O3/5 Optd "Specimen" .. .. *Set of* 3 £100

PRICES OF SETS

Set prices are given for many issues, generally those containing five stamps or more. Definitive sets include one of each value or major colour change, but do not cover different perforations, die types or minor shades. Where a choice is possible the set prices are based on the cheapest versions of the stamps included in the listings.

Jordan
see Transjordan

Kenya

INDEPENDENT

1 Cattle Ranching

2 Wood-carving

3 National Assembly

(Des V. Whiteley. Photo Harrison)

1963 (12 Dec). *Independence. T* **1/3** *and similar designs. P* 14 × 15 (*small designs*) *or* 14½ (*others*).

1 5 c. brown, deep blue, green and bistre .. 10 5
2 10 c. brown 10 5
3 15 c. magenta 10 5
4 20 c. black and yellow-green 12 5
5 30 c. black and yellow 12 5
6 40 c. brown and light blue 15 20
7 50 c. crimson, black and green 15 5
8 65 c. deep turquoise-green and yellow .. 55 65
9 1s. multicoloured 25 5
10 1s. 30, brown, black and yellow-green .. 80 5
11 2s. multicoloured 65 20
12 5s. brown, ultramarine and yellow-green .. 1·75 40
13 10s. brown and deep blue .. .. .. 6·50 1·25
14 20s. black and rose .. .. 9·00 4·00
1/14 .. .. *Set of* 14 18·00 6·00

Designs: As *T* **1/2**—15 c. Heavy industry; 20 c. Timber industry; 30 c. Jomo Kenyatta and Mt Kenya; 40 c. Fishing industry; 50 c. Kenya flag; 65 c. Pyrethrum industry. *As T* **3**—1s. 30, Tourism (Treetops Hotel); 2s. Coffee industry; 5s. Tea industry; 10s. Mombasa Port; 20s. Royal College, Nairobi.

The 10 c. was produced in coils of 1000 in addition to normal sheets.

REPUBLIC

4 Cockerel

(Des M. Goaman. Photo J. Enschedé)

1964 (12 Dec). *Inauguration of Republic T* **4** *and similar vert designs. Multicoloured. P* 13 × 12½.

15 15 c. Type **4** 15 5
16 30 c. President Kenyatta 30 10
17 50 c. Lion 45 20
18 1s. 30, Hartlaub's Turaco .. .. .. 2·25 75
19 2s. 50, Nandi flame .. .. 4·75 6·00

5 Thomson's Gazelle

6 Sable Antelope

7 Greater Kudu

(Des Rena Fennessy. Photo Harrison)

1966 (12 Dec)–**71.** *Various designs as T* **5/7.** *Chalk-surfaced paper. P* 14 × 14½ (5 *c. to* 70 *c.*) *or* 14½ (*others*).

20 5 c. orange, black and sepia 5 5
21 10 c. black and apple-green 5 5
a. Glazed, ordinary paper (13.7.71) .. 25 20
22 15 c. black and orange 5 5
a. Glazed, ordinary paper (13.7.71) .. 25 20
23 20 c. ochre, black and blue 8 5
a. Glazed, ordinary paper (22.1.71) .. 40 20
24 30 c. Prussian blue, blue and black 10 5
25 40 c. black and yellow-brown 15 8
a. Glazed, ordinary paper (19.2.71) .. 55 30
26 50 c. black and red-orange 15 5
a. Glazed, ordinary paper (19.2.71) .. 60 20
27 65 c. black and light green .. .. .. 1·75 1·50
28 70 c. black and claret (15.9.69) .. .. 1·75 90
a. Glazed, ordinary paper (19.2.71) .. 2·25 2·25
29 1s. olive-brown, black and slate-blue .. 30 5
a. Glazed, ordinary paper (22.1.71) .. 95 30
30 1s. 30, indigo, light olive-green and black .. 1·50 12
31 1s. 50, black, orange-brown and dull sage-green (15.9.69) .. .. 2·00 1·75
a. Glazed, ordinary paper (22.1.71) .. 3·50 3·50
32 2s. 50, yellow, black and olive-brown .. 2·25 90
a. Glazed, ordinary paper (22.1.71) .. 4·00 4·50
33 5s. yellow, black and emerald .. .. 1·50 60
a. Glazed, ordinary paper (22.1.71) .. 4·50 4·50
34 10s. yellow-ochre, black and red-brown .. 5·00 2·25
35 20s. yellow-ochre, yellow-orange, blk & gold 12·00 6·50
20/35 .. .. *Set of* 16 26·00 13·50
21a/33a .. .. *Set of* 10 15·00 15·00

Designs: *As T* **5/6**—15 c. Ant bear; 20 c. Bush-baby; 30 c. Warthog; 40 c. Zebra; 50 c. Buffalo; 65 c. Rhinoceros; 70 c. Ostrich. *As T* **7**—1s. 30, Elephant; 1s. 50, Bat-eared fox; 2s. 50, Cheetah; 5s. Vervet monkey; 10s. Pangolin; 20s. Lion.

On chalk-surfaced paper, all values except 30 c., 50 c. and 2s. 50 exist with PVA gum as well as gum arabic but the 70 c. and 1s. 50 exist with PVA gum only. The stamps on glazed, ordinary paper exist with PVA gum only.

Nos. 21 and 26 exist in coils constructed from normal sheets.

8 Rose Dawn

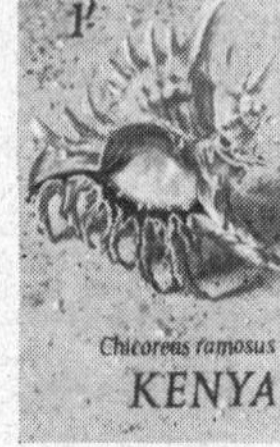

9 Rock Shell

(10)

50 c. A. Inscr "*Janthina globosa*".
B. Inscr "*Janthina janthina*".

70 c. C. Inscr "*Nautilus pompileus*".
D. Inscr "*Nautilus pompilius*".

(Des Rena Fennessy. Photo Harrison)

1971 (15 Dec)–**74.** *T* **8/9** *and similar vert designs showing sea-shells. Multicoloured.* (*a*) *Size as T* **8.** *P* 14½ × 14.

36 5 c. Type **8** 5 5
37 10 c. Bishop's Cap (*shades*) 10 5
38 15 c. Strawberry Shell 15 5
39 20 c. Black Prince 15 5
40 30 c. Mermaid's Ear 20 5
41 40 c. Top Shell 25 5
42 50 c. Violet Shell (A) 45 8
43 50 c. Violet Shell (B) (21.1.74) .. .. .. 3·50 25
44 60 c. Cameo 45 12
45 70 c. Pearly Nautilus (C) 70 80
46 70 c. Pearly Nautilus (D) (21.1.74) .. .. 3·50 1·25

(*b*) *Size as T* **9.** *P* 14

47 1s. Type **9** (*shades*) 30 10
48 1s. 50, Triton 80 10
49 2s. 50, Neptune's Trumpet .. .. .. 1·50 10
50 5s. Turban Shell (*shades*) .. .. .. 2·00 40
51 10s. Cloth of Gold .. .. 4·00 30
52 20s. Spider Shell (*shades*) .. .. .. 9·00 1·25
36/52 .. .. *Set of* 17 24·00 3·50

1975 (17 Nov). *Nos.* 48/9 *and* 52 *surch as T* **10.**

53 2s. on 1s. 50, Triton .. .. 1·50 1·00
54 3s. on 2s. 50, Neptune's Trumpet .. .. 14·00 13·00
55 40s. on 20s. Spider Shell .. .. .. 10·00 10·00

The surcharge on No. 55 does not have a dot beneath the stroke following the face value.

For commemorative stamps, issued between 1964 and 1976, inscribed "UGANDA KENYA TANGANYIKA AND ZANZIBAR" (or "TANZANIA UGANDA KENYA") see under KENYA, UGANDA AND TANGANYIKA.

11 Microwave Tower

12 Akii Bua, Ugandan Hurdler

(Des H. Nickelsen. Litho Format)

1976 (15 Apr). *Telecommunications Development. T* **11** *and similar multicoloured designs. P* 14.

56 50 c. Type **11** 12 5
57 1s. Cordless switchboard (*horiz*) 25 10
58 2s. Telephones 60 60
59 3s. Message Switching Centre (*horiz*) .. 75 75
MS60 120 × 120 mm. Nos. 56/9. Imperf .. .. 1·60 1·60

(Des Beryl Moore. Litho Format)

1976 (7 July*). *Olympic Games, Montreal. T* **12** *and similar horiz designs. Multicoloured. P* 14½.

61 50 c. Type **12** 15 5
62 1s. Filbert Bayi, Tanzanian runner 30 10
63 2s. Steve Muchoki, Kenyan boxer 75 45
64 3s. Olympic flame and East African flags .. 85 65
MS65 129 × 154 mm. Nos. 61/4. P 13 .. .. 6·50 6·50

*This is the local date of issue; the Crown Agents released the stamps two days earlier.

13 Tanzania–Zambia Railway

14 Nile Perch

(Des H. Moghul. Litho Format)

1976 (4 Oct). *Railway Transport. T* **13** *and similar horiz designs. Multicoloured. P* 14½.

66 50 c. Type **13** 25 5
67 1s. Nile Bridge, Uganda 50 15
68 2s. Nakuru Station, Kenya .. .. .. 2·00 1·00
69 3s. Class A locomotive, 1896 .. .. 2·25 1·40
MS70 154 × 103 mm. Nos. 66/9. P 13 .. .. 6·50 6·00

(Des Adrienne Kennaway. Litho Format)

1977 (10 Jan). *Game Fish of East Africa. T* **14** *and similar vert designs. Multicoloured. P* 14.

71 50 c. Type **14** 20 5
72 1s. Tilapia 40 10
73 3s. Sailfish .. .. 2·00 75
74 5s. Black Marlin .. .. 2·25 1·00
MS75 153 × 129 mm. Nos. 71/4 .. .. .. 5·50 2·75

15 Maasai Manyatta (village), Kenya

(Des Rena Fennessy. Litho Questa)

1977 (15 Jan). *Second World Black and African Festival of Arts and Culture, Nigeria. T* **15** *and similar horiz designs. Multicoloured. P* 13½.

76 50 c. Type **15** 20 5
77 1s. "Heartbeat of Africa" (Ugandan dancers) 40 10
78 2s. Makonde sculpture, Tanzania .. .. 1·00 75
79 3s. "Early Man and Technology" (skinning animal) .. .. 1·40 1·40
MS80 132 × 109 mm. Nos. 76/9 .. .. .. 2·75 2·75

16 Rally-car and Villagers

(Litho Questa)

1977 (5 Apr). *25th Anniv of Safari Rally. T* **16** *and similar horiz designs. Multicoloured. P* 14.

81 50 c. Type **16** 20 5
82 1s. President Kenyatta starting rally 40 15
83 2s. Car fording river .. .. 1·00 80
84 5s. Car and elephants .. .. .. 1·90 1·60
MS85 126 × 93 mm. Nos. 81/4 .. .. .. 3·75 3·75

17 Canon Kivebulaya

(Des Beryl Moore. Litho Questa)

1977 (30 June). *Centenary of Ugandan Church. T* **17** *and similar horiz designs. Multicoloured. P* 14 × 13½.

86	50 c. Type **17**	15	5
87	1s. Modern Namirembe Cathedral	25	15
88	2s. The first Cathedral	75	75
89	5s. Early congregation, Kigezi	1·60	1·60
MS90	126 × 94 mm. Nos. 86/9	2·75	2·75

18 Sagana Royal Lodge, Nyeri, 1952

(Des G. Vasarhelyi (50s.), J. Cooter (others). Litho Questa)

1977 (20 July). *Silver Jubilee. T* **18** *and similar multicoloured designs. P* 13½.

91	2s. Type **18**	45	45
92	5s. Treetops Hotel (*vert*)	75	75
93	10s. Queen Elizabeth and President Kenyatta	1·10	1·50
94	15s. Royal visit, 1972	1·50	2·25
MS95	Two sheets: (a) 140 × 60 mm, No. 94; (b) 152 × 127 mm, 50s. Queen and Prince Philip in Treetops Hotel .. *Set of* 2	7·00	12·00

19 Pancake Tortoise

(Des Rena Fennessy. Litho Questa)

1977 (26 Sept). *Endangered Species. T* **19** *and similar horiz designs. Multicoloured. P* 14.

96	50 c. Type **19**	20	8
97	1s. Nile Crocodile	35	15
98	2s. Hunter's Hartebeest	1·25	95
99	3s. Red Colobus monkey	1·75	1·50
100	5s. Dugong	2·50	2·25
MS101	127 × 101 mm. Nos. 97/100	6·00	6·00

20 Kenya–Ethiopia Border Point

(Litho Questa)

1977 (10 Nov). *Nairobi–Addis Ababa Highway. T* **20** *and similar horiz designs. Multicoloured. P* 14.

102	50 c. Type **20**	20	8
103	1s. Archer's Post	35	12
104	2s. Thika Flyover	1·25	80
105	5s. Marsabit Game Lodge	2·75	2·00
MS106	144 × 91 mm. Nos. 102/5	4·25	3·50

21 Gypsum

22 Amethyst

(Des Rena Fennessy. Photo Harrison)

1977 (10 Dec*). *Minerals. Multicoloured designs.*

(*a*) *Vert as T* **21**. *P* 14½ × 14

107	10 c. Type **21**	10	5
108	20 c. Trona	10	5
109	30 c. Kyanite	15	5
110	40 c. Amazonite	15	5
111	50 c. Galena	15	5
112	70 c. Silicified wood	20	5
113	80 c. Fluorite	20	5

(*b*) *Horiz as T* **22**. *P* 14

114	1s. Type **22**	20	5
	a. Gold (face value and inscr) omitted		
115	1s. 50, Agate	30	10
116	2s. Tourmaline	30	20
117	3s. Aquamarine	45	30
118	5s. Rhodolite Garnet	70	60
119	10s. Sapphire	1·25	1·00
120	20s. Ruby	2·50	1·75
121	40s. Green Grossular Garnet	5·00	4·50
107/21	*Set of* 15	11·00	8·00

*This is the local issue date. The stamps were released in London on 9 December.

23 Joe Kadenge (Kenya) and Forwards

(Des H. Moghul. Litho Questa)

1978 (10 Apr). *World Cup Football Championship, Argentina. T* **23** *and similar horiz designs showing footballers. Multicoloured. P* 14 × 13½.

122	50 c. Type **23**	15	8
123	1s. Mohamed Chuma (Tanzania) and Cup presentation	30	15
124	2s. Omari Kidevu (Zanzibar) and goalmouth scene	70	60
125	3s. Polly Ouma (Uganda) and three forwards	1·00	95
MS126	136 × 81 mm. Nos. 122/5	2·00	2·00

24 Boxing

(Des H. Moghul. Photo Heraclio Fournier)

1978 (17 July). *Commonwealth Games, Edmonton. T* **24** *and similar horiz designs. Multicoloured. P* 13 × 14.

127	50 c. Type **24**	12	10
128	1s. Welcoming Olympic Games Team, 1968	25	20
129	3s. Javelin throwing	75	75
130	5s. President Kenyatta admiring boxer's trophy	1·00	1·00

25 "Overloading is Dangerous"

(Litho Walsall)

1978 (18 Sept). *Road Safety. T* **25** *and similar horiz designs. Multicoloured. P* 13½.

131	50 c. Type **25**	12	10
132	1s. "Speed does not pay"	25	20
133	1s. 50, "Ignoring Traffic Signs may cause death"	35	25
134	2s. "Slow down at School Crossing"	70	60
135	3s. "Never cross a continuous line"	80	70
136	5s. "Approach Railway Level Crossing with extreme caution"	1·50	1·50
131/6	*Set of* 6	2·75	2·75

26 President Kenyatta at Mass Rally, 1963

27 Freedom Fighters, Namibia

(Des Beryl Moore. Litho J.W.)

1978 (16 Oct). *Kenyatta Day. T* **26** *and similar horiz designs. Multicoloured. P* 14.

137	50 c. "Harambee Water Project"	12	10
138	1s. Handing over of Independence Instruments, 1963	25	20
139	2s. Type **26**	45	45
140	3s. "Harambee, 15 Great Years"	70	70
141	5s. "Struggle for Independence, 1952"	1·00	1·00

(Des L. Curtis. Litho Questa)

1978 (11 Dec*). *International Anti-Apartheid Year. T* **27** *and similar horiz designs. P* 14 × 14½.

142	50 c. multicoloured	12	10
143	1s. black and cobalt	25	20
144	2s. multicoloured	45	45
145	3s. multicoloured	65	65
146	5s. multicoloured	95	95

Designs:—1s. International seminar on apartheid, racial discrimination and colonialism in South Africa; 2s. Steve Biko's tombstone; 3s. Nelson Mandela; 5s. Bishop Lamont.

*This is the local date of issue; the Crown Agents released the stamps the previous day.

28 Children Playing

(Des Beryl Moore. Litho Walsall)

1979 (5 Feb). *International Year of the Child. T* **28** *and similar horiz designs. Multicoloured. P* 13½ × 14.

147	50 c. Type **28**	12	10
148	2s. Child fishing	50	50
149	3s. Children singing and dancing	75	75
150	5s. Children working with camels	95	95

29 "The Lion and the Jewel"

30 Blind Telephone Operator

(Des Beryl Moore. Litho Enschedé)

1979 (6 Apr). *Kenya National Theatre. T* **29** *and similar horiz designs. Multicoloured. P* 13 × 13½.

151	50 c. Type **29**	12	10
152	1s. Scene from "Utisi"	25	20
153	2s. "Entertainment past and present" (programmes from past productions)	40	40
154	3s. Kenya National Theatre	60	60
155	5s. Nairobi City Players production of "Genesis"	90	90

(Litho Harrison)

1979 (29 June*). *50th Anniv of Salvation Army Social Services. T* **30** *and similar multicoloured designs. P* 13½ × 13 (50 c., 1s.) *or* 13 × 13½ (*others*).

156	50 c. Type **30**	15	10
157	1s. Care for the Aged	30	20
158	3s. Village polytechnic (*horiz*)	85	70
159	5s. Vocational training (*horiz*)	1·40	1·40

*This is the local date of issue; the Crown Agents released the stamps on 4 June.

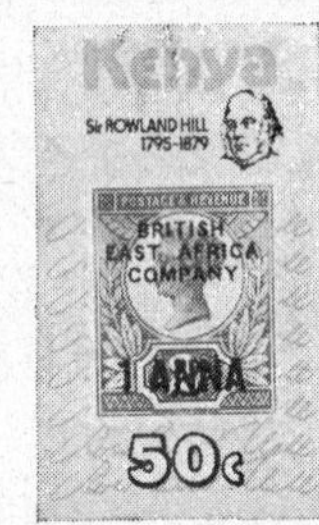

31 "Father of the Nation" (Kenyatta's funeral procession)

32 British East Africa Company 1890 1 a. Stamp

(Des H. Moghul. Litho Questa)

1979 (21 Aug*). *1st Death Anniv of President Kenyatta. T* **31** *and similar vert designs. Multicoloured. P* 13½ × 14.

160	50 c. Type **31**	10	10
161	1s. "First President of Kenya" (Kenyatta receiving independence)	20	20
162	3s. "Kenyatta the politician" (speaking at rally)	60	60
163	5s. "A true son of Kenya" (Kenyatta as a boy carpenter)	80	90

*This is the local date of issue; the Crown Agents did not release the stamps until 29 August.

(Des J.W. Litho Harrison)

1979 (27 Nov). *Death Centenary of Sir Rowland Hill. T* **32** *and similar vert designs showing stamps. P* 14 × 14½.

164	50 c. multicoloured	10	10
165	1s. multicoloured	20	20
166	2s. black, magenta and yellow-ochre	30	35
167	5s. multicoloured	75	90

Designs:—1s. Kenya, Uganda and Tanganyika 1935 1s.; 2s.; Penny Black; 5s. 1964 Inauguration of Republic 2s.50, commemorative.

33 Roads, Globe and Conference Emblem

(Des H. Moghul. Litho Questa)

1980 (10 Jan). *I.R.F. (International Road Federation) African Highway Conference, Nairobi. T* **33** *and similar horiz designs. Multicoloured. P* 14 × 13½.

168 50 c. Type **33** 10 10
169 1s. New weighbridge, Athi River 20 20
170 3s. New Nyali Bridge, Mombasa 55 55
171 5s. Highway to Jomo Kenyatta International Airport 85 85

34 Mobile Unit in action, Masailand

35 Statue of Sir Rowland Hill

(Des Beryl Moore. Litho Questa)

1980 (20 Mar). *Flying Doctor Service. T* **34** *and similar multicoloured designs. P* 14½.

172 50 c. Type **34** 10 10
173 1s. Donkey transport to Turkana airstrip (*vert*) 20 20
174 3s. Surgical team in action at outstation (*vert*) 50 50
175 5s. Emergency airlift from North Eastern Province 75 75
MS176 146 × 133 mm. Nos. 172/5 1·50 1·60

(Des J.W. Litho Questa)

1980 (6 May). *"London 1980" International Stamp Exhibition. P* 14.

177 **35** 25s. multicoloured 3·00 3·50
MS178 114 × 101 mm. No. 177 3·25 3·75

36 Pope John Paul II

37 *Taeniura lymma*

(Des Sister Frances Randal. Litho Italian Govt Ptg Works, Rome)

1980 (8 May). *Papal Visit. T* **36** *and similar multicoloured designs. P* 13.

179 50 c. Type **36** 15 10
180 1s. Pope John Paul II, cathedral and coat of arms (*vert*) 25 20
181 5s. Pope John Paul II, Papal and Kenyan flags on dove symbol (*vert*) 80 70
182 10s. President Moi, Pope John Paul II and map of Africa 1·60 1·50

(Des Adrienne Kennaway. Litho Harrison)

1980 (27 June). *Marine Life. T* **37** *and similar vert designs. Multicoloured. P* 14.

183 50 c. Type **37** 10 10
184 2s. *Amphiprion allardi* 40 30
185 3s. *Chromodoris quadricolor* 60 50
186 5s. *Eretmochelys imbricata* 85 75

38 National Archives

(Des A. Odhuno; adapted L. Curtis. Litho Questa)

1980 (9 Oct). *Historic Buildings. T* **38** *and similar horiz designs. Multicoloured. P* 14.

187 50 c. Type **38** 15 10
188 1s. Provincial Commissioner's Office, Nairobi 20 12
189 1s. 50, Nairobi House 25 20
190 2s. Norfolk Hotel 35 35
191 3s. McMillan Library 45 50
192 5s. Kipande House 70 80
187/92 *Set of* 6 1·90 1·90

39 "Disabled Enjoys Affection"

(Des H. Moghul. Litho Enschedé)

1981 (10 Feb). *International Year for Disabled Persons. T* **39** *and similar horiz designs. Multicoloured. P* 14 × 13.

193 50 c. Type **39** 15 10
194 1s. President Moi presenting Kenyan flag to Disabled Olympic Games team captain 20 12
195 3s. Blind people climbing Mount Kenya, 1975 45 45
196 5s. Disabled artist at work 75 75

40 Longonot Complex

(Des H. Moghul. Litho Harrison)

1981 (15 Apr). *Satellite Communications. T* **40** *and similar horiz designs. Multicoloured. P* 14 × 14½.

197 50 c. Type **40** 15 10
198 2s. "Intelsat V" 40 40
199 3s. "Longonot I" 50 50
200 5s. "Longonot II" 75 80

41 Kenyatta Conference Centre

42 St. Paul's Cathedral

(Des L. Curtis. Litho Questa (**MS**206) or J.W. (others))

1981 (17 June*). *O.A.U. (Organisation of African Unity) Summit Conference, Nairobi. T* **41** *and similar horiz designs in black, bistre-yellow and new blue* (1s.) *or multicoloured (others). P* 13½.

201 50 c. Type **41** 15 10
202 1s. "Panaftel" earth stations 20 12
203 3s. Parliament Building 40 40
204 5s. Jomo Kenyatta International Airport 70 70
205 10s. O.A.U. flag 1·25 1·25
MS206 110 × 110 mm. No. 205. P 14½ × 14 1·25 1·50

*This is the local date of issue; the Crown Agents did not release the stamps until 24 June.

(Des A. Theobald. Litho Questa)

1981 (29 July). *Royal Wedding. T* **42** *and similar vert designs. Multicoloured. P* 14.

207 50 c. Prince Charles and President Daniel Arap Moi 20 10
208 3s. Type **42** 55 45
209 5s. H.M.Y. *Britannia* 85 65
210 10s. Prince Charles on safari in Kenya 1·25 1·10
MS211 85 × 102 mm. 25s. Prince Charles and Lady Diana Spencer 3·25 3·25

Nos. 207/10 also exist perforated 12 (*price for set of* 4 *£*2·50 *mint or used*) from additional sheetlets of five stamps and one label.

Insufficient supplies of No. **MS**211 were received by 29 July for a full distribution, but subsequently the miniature sheet was freely available.

43 Reticulated Giraffe

44 "Technical Development"

(Des Rena Fennessy. Litho Questa)

1981 (31 Aug). *Rare Animals. T* **43** *and similar vert designs. Multicoloured. P* 14½.

212 50 c. Type **43** 15 5
213 2s. Bongo 45 30
214 5s. Roan Antelope 85 75
215 10s. Mangabey 1·40 1·50

(Des H. Moghul, adapted L. Curtis. Litho Questa)

1981 (16 Oct). *World Food Day. T* **44** *and similar vert designs. Multicoloured. P* 14.

216 50 c. Type **44** 10 5
217 1s. "Mwea rice projects" 15 10
218 2s. "Irrigation schemes" 30 30
219 5s. "Breeding livestock" 65 65

45 Kamba

46 *Australopithecus boisei*

(Des Adrienne Kennaway. Litho Harrison)

1981 (18 Dec). *Ceremonial Costumes* (*1st series*). *T* **45** *and similar vert designs. Multicoloured. P* 14½ × 13½.

220 50 c. Type **45** 10 5
221 1s. Turkana 15 10
222 2s. Giriama 30 30
223 3s. Masai 40 40
224 5s. Luo 65 65

See also Nos. 329/33.

(Des Adrienne Kennaway. Litho Format)

1982 (19 Jan). *"Origins of Mankind". Skulls. T* **46** *and similar horiz designs. Multicoloured. P* 13½ × 14.

225 50 c. Type **46** 10 5
226 2s. *Homo erectus* 35 30
227 3s. *Homo habilis* 55 45
228 5s. *Proconsul africanus* 85 70

47 Tree-planting

(Des L. Curtis. Litho Harrison)

1982 (9 June). *75th Anniv of Boy Scout Movement (Nos. 229, 231, 233 and 235) and 60th Anniv of Girl Guide Movement (Nos. 230, 232, 234 and 236). T* **47** *and similar horiz designs. Multicoloured. P* 14½.

229 70 c. Type **47** 15 10
a. Horiz pair. Nos. 229/30 30 30
230 70 c. Paying homage 15 10
231 3s. 50, "Be Prepared" 50 35
a. Horiz pair. Nos. 231/2 1·00 1·00
232 3s. 50, "International Friendship" 50 35
233 5s. Helping disabled 70 50
a. Horiz pair. Nos. 233/4 1·40 1·40
234 5s. Community service 70 50
235 6s. 50, Paxtu Cottage (Lord Baden-Powell's home) 90 65
a. Horiz pair. Nos. 235/6 1·75 1·75
236 6s. 50, Lady Baden-Powell 90 65
229/36 *Set of* 8 4·00 4·00
MS237 112 × 112 mm. Nos. 229, 231, 233 and 235 2·25 2·50

The two designs of each value were printed together, *se-tenant*, in horizontal pairs throughout the sheet.

48 Footballer displaying Shooting Skill

(Des local artist. Litho Harrison)

1982 (5 July). *World Cup Football Championships, Spain. T* **48** *and similar triangular designs showing footballers silhouetted against world map. Multicoloured. P* 12½.

238 70 c. Type **48** 10 8
239 3s. 50, Heading 40 40
240 5s. Goalkeeping 60 60
241 10s. Dribbling 1·10 1·10
MS242 101 × 76 mm. 20s. Tackling. P 13 × 14 2·50 2·75

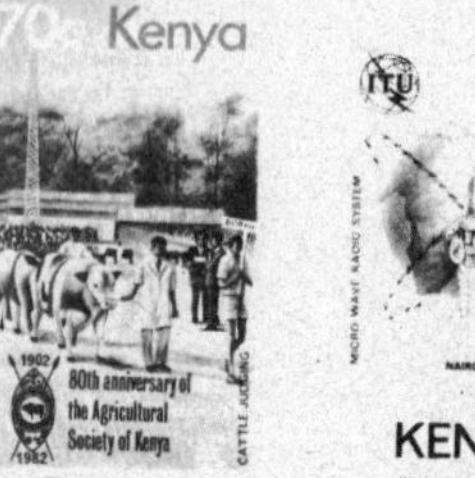

49 Cattle Judging

50 Micro-wave Radio System

(**51**)

(Des H. Moghul. Litho Harrison)

1982 (28 Sept). *80th Anniv of Agricultural Society of Kenya. T* **49** *and similar vert designs. Multicoloured. P* 14½.

243 70 c. Type **49** 12 10
244 2s. 50, Farm machinery 30 30

245 3s. 50, Musical ride 45 45
246 6s. 50, Agricultural Society emblem .. 70 70

(Des H. Moghul. Photo Courvoisier)

1982 (21 Oct). *I.T.U. Plenipotentiary Conference, Nairobi. T* **50** *and similar vert designs. Multicoloured. P* 11½.
247 70 c. Type **50** 12 10
248 3s. 50, Sea-to-shore service link 45 45
249 5s. Rural telecommunications system .. 60 60
250 6s. 50, I.T.U. emblem 70 70

1982 (22 Nov). *No.* 113 *surch with T* **51**, *in white on a black panel.*
251 70 c. on 80 c. Fluorite 5 10

52 Container Cranes

(Des R. Vigurs. Litho Questa)

1983 (20 Jan). *5th Anniv of Kenya Ports Authority. T* **52** *and similar horiz designs. P* 14.
252 70 c. Type **52** 10 8
253 2s. Port by night 25 25
254 3s. 50, Container cranes (*different*) 45 45
255 5s. Map of Mombasa Port 70 70
MS256 125 × 85 mm. Nos. 252/5 .. .. .. 1·40 1·50

53 Shada Zambarau **54** Waridi Kikuba

(Des Rena Fennessy. Photo Harrison)

1983 (15 Feb). *Flowers. Multicoloured. P* 14 × 14½.

(*a*) *Vert designs as T* **53**
257 10 c. Type **53** 5 5
258 20 c. Kilua Kingulima 5 5
259 30 c. Mwalika Mwiya 5 5
260 40 c. Ziyungi Buluu 5 5
261 50 c. Kilua Habashia 5 5
262 70 c. Chanuo Kato 5 5

(*b*) *Vert designs as T* **54**
263 1s. Type **54** 10 12
264 1s. 50, Mshomoro Mtambazi 15 20
265 2s. Papatuo Boti 20 25
266 2s. 50, Tumba Mboni 25 30
267 3s. 50, Mtongo Mbeja 35 40
268 5s. Nyungu Chepuo 50 55
269 10s. Muafunili .. .. 95 1·00
270 20s. Mbake Nyanza .. .. .. 1·90 2·00
271 40s. Njuga Pagwa .. .. .. 3·75 4·00
257/71 .. .. *Set of* 15 7·50 8·00

55 Coffee Plucking **56** Examining Parcels

(Des C. Fernandes. Litho Harrison)

1983 (14 Mar). *Commonwealth Day. T* **55** *and similar multi-coloured designs. P* 14½ × 14 (10s.) *or* 14 × 14½ (*others*).
272 70 c. Type **55** 8 10
273 2s. President Daniel Arap Moi 20 25
274 5s. Satellite view of Earth 50 55
275 10s. Masai dance (*horiz*) .. .. .. 1·00 1·10

(Des H. Moghul. Litho Harrison)

1983 (11 May). *30th Anniv of Customs Co-operation Council. T* **56** *and similar vert designs. Multicoloured. P* 14.
276 70 c. Type **56** 8 10
277 2s. 50, Customs Headquarters, Mombasa .. 25 30
278 3s. 50, Customs Council Headquarters, Brussels 35 40
279 10s. Customs patrol boat .. .. .. 1·00 1·10

ALTERED CATALOGUE NUMBERS

Any Catalogue numbers altered from the last edition are shown as a list in the introductory pages.

57 Communications via Satellite **58** Ships in Kilindini Harbour

(Litho Harrison)

1983 (4 July). *World Communications Year. T* **57** *and similar multicoloured designs. P* 14 × 14½ (70 c., 2s. 50) *or* 14½ × 14 (*others*).
280 70 c. Type **57** 8 10
281 2s. 50, "Telephone and Postal Services" .. 25 30
282 3s. 50, Communications by sea and air (*horiz*) 35 40
283 5s. Road and rail communications (*horiz*) .. 50 55

(Litho Harrison)

1983 (22 Sept). *25th Anniv of Intergovernmental Maritime Organization. T* **58** *and similar horiz designs. Multicoloured. P* 14.
284 70 c. Type **58** 8 10
285 2s. 50, Life-saving devices 25 30
286 3s. 50, Mombasa container terminal .. 35 40
287 10s. Marine park .. .. 1·00 1·10

59 President Moi signing Visitors' Book

(Litho Harrison)

1983 (31 Oct). *29th Commonwealth Parliamentary Conference. T* **59** *and similar multicoloured designs. P* 14.
288 70 c. Type **59** 8 10
289 2s. 50, Parliament building, Nairobi (*vert*) .. 25 30
290 5s. State opening of Parliament (*vert*) .. 50 55
MS291 122 × 141 mm. Nos. 288/90 .. .. 85 90

60 Kenyan and British Flags

1983 (10 Nov). *Royal Visit. T* **60** *and similar horiz designs. Multi-coloured. P* 14.
292 70 c. Type **60** 8 10
293 3s. 50, Sagana State Lodge 35 40
294 5s. Treetops Hotel 50 55
295 10s. Queen Elizabeth II and President Moi .. 1·00 1·10
MS296 126 × 100 mm. 25s. Designs as Nos. 292/5, but without face values. Imperf .. .. .. 1·90 2·00

61 President Moi **62** White-backed Night Heron

(Des and litho Harrison)

1983 (9 Dec). *20th Anniv of Independence. T* **61** *and similar horiz designs. Multicoloured. P* 14½.
297 70 c. Type **61** 8 10
298 2s. President Moi planting tree 20 25
299 3s. 50, Kenyan flag and emblem 35 40
300 5s. School milk scheme 50 55
301 10s. People of Kenya .. .. 1·00 1·10
MS302 126 × 93 mm. 25s. Designs as Nos. 297 and 299/301, but without face values. Imperf. .. .. 2·10 2·25

(Des Agnes Odero. Litho Harrison)

1984 (6 Feb). *Rare Birds of Kenya. T* **62** *and similar vert designs. Multicoloured. P* 14½ × 13½.
303 70 c. Type **62** 8 10
304 2s. 50, Quail Plover 25 30
305 3s. 50, Heller's Ground Thrush 40 45
306 5s. Yellow Gonolek 55 60
307 10s. White-winged Apalis .. .. .. 1·10 1·25

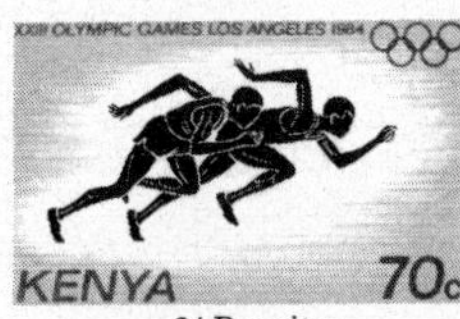

63 Radar Tower **64** Running

(Des C. Fernandes. Litho Harrison)

1984 (2 Apr). *40th Anniv of International Civil Aviation Organization. T* **63** *and similar multicoloured designs. P* 14.
308 70 c. Type **63** 8 10
309 2s. 50, Kenya School of Aviation (*horiz*) .. 25 30
310 3s. 50, Aircraft taking off from Moi airport (*horiz*) 40 45
311 5s. Air traffic control centre 55 60

(Des and litho Harrison)

1984 (21 May). *Olympic Games, Los Angeles. T* **64** *and similar horiz designs. P* 14½.
312 70 c. black, bright yellow-green and bronze-green 8 10
313 2s. 50, black, bright magenta and reddish violet 25 30
314 5s. black, pale turquoise-blue and steel blue 55 60
315 10s. black, bistre-yellow and brown .. .. 1·10 1·25
MS316 130 × 121 mm. 25s. Designs as Nos. 312/15 but without face values. Imperf .. .. 2·50 2·75
Designs:—2s. 50, Hurdling; 5s. Boxing; 10s. Hockey.

65 Conference and Kenya Library Association Logos **66** Doves and Cross

(Des and litho Harrison)

1984 (28 June). *50th Conference of the International Federation of Library Associations. T* **65** *and similar horiz designs. Multi-coloured. P* 14½.
317 70 c. Type **65** 8 10
318 3s. 50, Mobile library 40 45
319 5s. Adult library 55 60
320 10s. Children's library .. .. .. 1·10 1·25

(Des K. Bisley. Litho Harrison)

1984 (23 Aug). *4th World Conference on Religion and Peace. T* **66** *and similar vert designs, each showing a different central symbol. Multicoloured. P* 14½.
321 70 c. Type **66** 8 10
322 2s. 50, Arabic inscription 25 30
323 3s. 50, Peace emblem 40 45
324 6s. 50, Star and Crescent 70 75

67 Export Year Logo **68** Knight and Nyayo National Stadium

(Litho Harrison)

1984 (1 Oct). *Kenya Export Year. T* **67** *and similar multicoloured designs. P* 14½.
325 70 c. Type **67** 8 10
326 3s. 50, Forklift truck with air cargo (*horiz*) 40 45
327 5s. Loading ship's cargo 55 60
328 10s. Kenyan products (*horiz*) .. .. 1·10 1·25

(Litho Harrison)

1984 (5 Nov). *Ceremonial Costumes* (2nd series). *Vert designs as T* **45**. *Multicoloured. P* 14½ × 13½.
329 70 c. Luhya 5 8
330 2s. Kikuyu 20 25
331 3s. 50, Pokomo 40 45
332 5s. Nandi 55 60
333 10s. Rendile .. .. 1·10 1·25

(Litho Harrison)

1984 (21 Dec). *60th Anniv of World Chess Federation. T* **68** *and similar horiz designs. Multicoloured. P* 14½.
334 70 c. Type **68** 5 10
335 2s. 50, Rook and Fort Jesus 25 30
336 3s. 50, Bishop and National Monument .. 35 40
337 5s. Queen and Parliament Building 50 55
338 10s. King and Nyayo Fountain .. .. 1·00 1·10

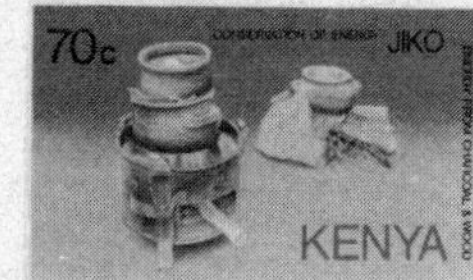

69 Cooking with Wood-burning Stove and Charcoal Fire

(Des H. Moghul. Litho J.W.)

1985 (22 Jan). *Energy Conservation. T* **69** *and similar horiz designs. Multicoloured. P* 13½.
339 70 c. Type **69** 5 5
340 2s. Solar energy panel on roof 15 20
341 3s. 50, Production of gas from cow dung .. 30 35
342 10s. Ploughing with oxen .. .. .. 95 1·00
MS343 110 × 85 mm. 20s. Designs as Nos. 339/42, but without face values .. .. 1·90 2·00

POSTAGE DUE STAMPS

The Postage Due stamps of Kenya, Uganda and Tanganyika were used in Kenya until 2 January 1967.

D 3

(Litho D.L.R.)

1967 (3 Jan)–**70**. *Chalk-surfaced paper. P* 14 × 13½.
D13 D 3 5 c. scarlet 15 40
a. Perf 14. *Dull scarlet*, **O** (16.12.69) .. 10 35
D14 10 c. green 20 40
a. Perf 14, **O** (16.12.69) 15 40
D15 20 c. blue 40 70
a. Perf 14. *Deep blue*, **O** (16.12.69) .. 25 70
D16 30 c. brown 55 90
a. Perf 14. *Light red-brown*, **O** (16.12.69) 35 90
D17 40 c. bright purple .. .. .. 65 1·75
a. Perf 14. *Pale bright purple*, **O** (16.12.69) .. .. .. 45 1·75
D18 1s. bright orange .. .. .. 1·50 3·50
a. Perf 14. *Dull bright orange*, **O** (18.2.70) .. .. .. 1·00 3·50
D13/18 .. .. *Set of* 6 3·00 7·00
D13a/18a .. .. *Set of* 6 2·10 7·00

1971 (13 July)–**73**. *P* 14 × 15. (a) *Chalk-surfaced paper* (13.7.71).
D19 D 3 10 c. green 40 85
D20 20 c. deep dull blue .. .. .. 55 1·40
D21 30 c. red-brown .. .. .. 70 1·60
D22 1s. dull bright orange .. .. .. 1·90 4·75

(b) *Glazed, ordinary paper* (20.2.73)
D23 D 3 5 c. bright scarlet 12 40
D24 10 c. dull yellow-green 20 50
D25 20 c. deep blue 30 80
D27 40 c. bright purple .. .. .. 50 1·60
D28 1s. bright orange .. .. .. 1·25 4·25

1973 (12 Dec). *Glazed, ordinary paper. P* 15.
D29 D 3 5 c. red 5 5
D30 10 c. emerald 15 40
D31 20 c. deep blue 25 65
D32 30 c. red-brown 30 90
D33 40 c. bright purple .. .. .. 1·25 1·75
D34 1s. bright orange .. .. .. 1·50 3·75
D29/34 .. .. .. *Set of* 6 3·25 6·75

1979 (27 Mar). *Chalk-surfaced paper. P* 14.
D35 D 3 10 c. bright emerald 10 15
D36 20 c. deep dull blue 12 20
D37 30 c. dull red-brown 5 5
D38 40 c. bright reddish purple 20 30
D39 80 c. dull red 8 10
D40 1s. bright reddish orange 10 12
D35/40 .. .. .. *Set of* 6 55 80

1983 (Dec). *W* w **14**. *P* 14.
D41 D 3 10 c. yellowish green 5 5
D42 20 c. deep blue 5 5
D43 40 c. bright purple 5 5

OFFICIAL STAMPS

Intended for use on official correspondence of the Kenya Government only but there is no evidence that they were so used.

OFFICIAL

(O 4)

(15 c. 30 c. opt typo; others in photogravure)

1964 (1 Oct). *Nos.* 1/5 *and* 7 *optd with Type* O 4.
O21 5 c. brown, deep blue, green and bistre .. 8
O22 10 c. brown 10
O23 15 c. magenta 12
O24 20 c. black and yellow-green 20
O25 30 c. black and yellow 30
O26 50 c. crimson, black and green 85
O21/26 .. .. .. *Set of* 6 1·50

ALTERED CATALOGUE NUMBERS

Any Catalogue numbers altered from the last edition are shown as a list in the introductory pages.

Kenya, Uganda and Tanganyika (Tanzania)

For earlier issues see BRITISH EAST AFRICA and UGANDA.
For the issues of the Mandated Territory of Tanganyika and the war-time issues that preceded them, see TANGANYIKA.

PRICES FOR STAMPS ON COVER TO 1945	
Nos. 1/43	*from* × 3
Nos. 44/75	*from* × 2
Nos. 76/95	*from* × 3
Nos. 96/105	—
Nos. 110/23	*from* × 2
Nos. 124/7	*from* × 3
Nos. 128/30	*from* × 5
Nos. 131/54	*from* × 3
Nos. D1/12	*from* × 8

PRINTERS. All the stamps issued between 1903 and 1927 were typographed by De La Rue & Co. Ltd, London.

USED HIGH VALUES. Beware of cleaned fiscally cancelled copies with faked postmarks.

EAST AFRICA AND UGANDA

1

2

1903–4. *P* 14. (a) *Wmk Crown CA*.
1 1 ½ a. green .. .. 1·50 2·00
2 1 a. grey and red .. .. .. 1·60 75
3 2 a. dull and bright purple .. .. 5·50 6·00
4 2½ a. blue .. .. 13·00 17·00
5 3 a. brown-purple and green .. .. 11·00 13·00
6 4 a. grey-green and black .. .. 11·00 13·00
7 5 a. grey and orange-brown .. .. 22·00 26·00
8 8 a. grey and pale blue .. .. 22·00 24·00

(b) *Wmk Crown CC*
9 2 1 r. green, **OC** .. .. .. 14·00 17·00
10 2 r. dull and bright purple, **O** .. .. 26·00 30·00
11 3 r. grey-green and black, **O** .. .. 28·00 40·00
12 4 r. grey and emerald-green, **O** .. .. 45·00 50·00
13 5 r. grey and red, **O** .. .. .. 45·00 50·00
14 10 r. grey and ultramarine, **OC** .. .. 90·00 90·00
15 20 r. grey and stone, **O** (Optd S. £140) .. £550 £450
16 50 r. grey and red-brown, **O** (Optd S. £300) £1100 £1000
1/13 .. .. *Set of* 13 £250 £225
1/14 Optd "Specimen" .. .. *Set of* 14 £300

1904–07. *Wmk Mult Crown CA. P* 14.
17 1 ½ a. grey-green, **OC** .. .. .. 1·25 50
18 1 a. grey and red, **OC** 90 50
19 2 a. dull and bright purple, **OC** .. 3·50 3·75
20 2½ a. blue, **O** .. .. .. 12·00 16·00
21 2½ a. ultramarine and blue, **O** .. .. 8·00 12·00
22 3 a. brown-purple and green, **OC** .. 4·50 8·00
23 4 a. grey-green and black, **OC** .. .. 8·00 10·00
24 5 a. grey and orange-brown, **OC** .. 8·00 10·00
25 8 a. grey and pale blue, **OC** .. .. 9·50 10·00
26 2 1 r. green, **C** (1907) .. .. .. 17·00 17·00
27 2 r. dull and bright purple, **C** (1906) .. 26·00 26·00
28 3 r. grey-green and black, **C** (1907) .. 35·00 42·00
29 4 r. grey and emerald-green, **C** (1907) 35·00 48·00
30 5 r. grey and red, **C** (1907) .. .. 38·00 48·00
31 10 r. grey and ultramarine, **C** (1907) .. £110 90·00
32 20 r. grey and stone, **C** (1907) £300 £300
33 50 r. grey and red-brown, **C** (1907) .. £1250 £1000
17/30 .. .. *Set of* 13 £170 £200

(New Currency. 100 cents = 1 rupee)

1907–08. *Wmk Mult Crown CA. P* 14.
34 1 1 c. brown, **O** (1908) 30 30
35 3 c. grey-green, **O** 70 60
a. *Blue-green*, **O** 60 90
36 6 c. red, **O** .. .. 1·50 20
37 10 c. lilac and pale olive, **C** .. .. 7·50 7·00
38 12 c. dull and bright purple, **C** .. .. 4·50 4·00
39 15 c. bright blue, **O** .. .. .. 7·50 7·50
40 25 c. grey-green and black, **C** .. .. 5·50 7·50
41 50 c. grey-green and orange-brown, **C** .. 7·50 10·00
42 75 c. grey and pale blue, **C** (1908) .. 9·00 15·00
34/42 .. .. *Set of* 9 40·00 48·00
34/42 Optd "Specimen" .. .. *Set of* 9 £180

Original

Redrawn

1910. *T* 1 *redrawn. Printed from a single plate. Wmk Mult Crown CA. P* 14.
43 6 c. red, **O** .. .. 3·75 40

In the redrawn type a fine white line has been cut around the value tablets and above the name tablet separating the latter from the leaves above, EAST AFRICA AND UGANDA is in shorter and thicker letters and PROTECTORATES in taller letters than in No. 36.

3

4

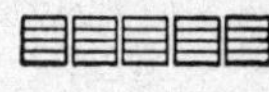

4
cents

(5)

1912–21. *Wmk Mult Crown CA. P* 14.
44 3 1 c. black, **O** 35 55
45 3 c. green, **O** .. .. 1·75 45
a. *Deep blue-green*, **O** (1917) .. .. 1·75 35
46 6 c. red, **O** 50 40
a. *Scarlet*, **O** (1917) .. .. .. 3·50 50
47 10 c. yellow-orange, **O** .. .. .. 3·50 40
a. *Orange*, **O** (1921) .. .. .. 4·00 50
48 12 c. slate-grey, **O** .. .. .. 2·75 1·75
49 15 c. bright blue, **O** .. .. .. 2·75 1·25
50 25 c. black and red/*yellow*, **C** .. .. 1·25 90
a. *White back* (5.14) (Optd S. £20) .. 1·25 1·75
b. *On lemon* (1916) (Optd S. £20) .. 7·50 7·00
c. *On orange-buff* (1921) .. .. 15·00 3·25
d. *On pale yellow* (1921) .. .. 7·50 3·00
51 50 c. black and lilac, **C** .. .. .. 3·25 2·25
52 75 c. black/*green* **C** .. .. .. 4·25 6·50
a. *White back* (5.14) (Optd S. £20) .. 3·00 7·00
b. *On blue-grn, ol back* (Optd S. £20) 8·50 6·00
c. *On emerald, olive back* (1919) .. 48·00 55·00
d. *On emerald back* (1921) .. .. 12·00 14·00
53 4 1 r. black/*green*, **C** .. .. .. 6·00 5·50
a. *On emerald back* (1919) .. .. 10·00 12·00
54 2 r. red and black/*blue*, **C** .. .. 20·00 26·00
55 3 r. violet and green, **C** .. .. 20·00 27·00
56 4 r. red and green/*yellow*, **C** .. .. 40·00 50·00
a. *On pale yellow* .. .. .. 45·00 55·00
57 5 r. blue and dull purple, **C** .. .. 40·00 55·00
58 10 r. red and green/*green*, **C** .. .. 60·00 75·00
59 20 r. black and purple/*red*, **C** £190 £170
60 20 r. purple and blue/*blue*, **C** (1918) .. £225 £190
61 50 r. carmine & grn, **CO** (Optd S. £160) £550 £550
a. *Dull rose-red and dull greyish green*, **O** £550 £550
62 100 r. purple & blk/*red*, **C** (Optd S. £400) £1750 £1000
63 500 r. grn & red/*green*, **C** (Optd S. £950) £7000
44/58 .. .. *Set of* 15 £180 £225
44/60 Optd "Specimen" .. .. *Set of* 17 £500

For values in this series overprinted "G.E.A." (German East Africa) see Tanzania Nos. 45/62.

1919 (7 Apr). *T* 3 *surch with T* 5 *by the Swift Press, Nairobi*.
64 4 c. on 6 c. scarlet (*shades*) 20 30
a. Bars omitted .. .. 20·00 32·00
b. Surch double .. .. 65·00 80·00
c. Surch inverted £100 £130
d. Pair, one without surch £200 £250
64 H/S "Specimen" .. .. 55·00

1921–22. *Wmk Mult Script CA. P* 14.
65 3 1 c. black, **O** 60 45
66 3 c. green, **O** .. .. 85 1·40
a. *Blue-green*, **O** .. .. .. 4·00 4·25
67 6 c. carmine-red, **O** .. .. .. 1·75 1·75
68 10 c. orange, **O** (12.21) .. .. .. 3·25 60
69 12 c. slate-grey, **O** .. .. .. 6·00 14·00
70 15 c. bright blue, **O** .. .. .. 4·25 8·50
71 50 c. black and dull purple, **C** .. .. 12·00 18·00
72 4 2 r. red and black/*blue*, **C** .. .. 35·00 50·00
73 3 r. violet and green, **C** .. .. 45·00 60·00
74 5 r. blue and dull purple, **C** .. .. 65·00 85·00
75 50 r. carmine and green, **C** (Optd S. £150) £1000 £1000
65/74 .. .. *Set of* 10 £150 £225
65/74 Optd "Specimen" .. .. *Set of* 10 £225

For values in this series overprinted "G.E.A." see Tanzania Nos. 63/73.

KENYA AND UGANDA

(New Currency. 100 cents = 1 shilling)

6

7

1922 (1 Nov)–**27**. *Wmk Script CA. P* 14.
(a) *Wmk upright. Ordinary paper*
76 6 1 c. pale brown 50 50
a. *Deep brown* (1923) 90 90
77 5 c. dull violet .. .. 1·50 25
a. *Bright violet* .. .. 1·50 90
78 5 c. green (1927) .. .. 1·50 10
79 10 c. green .. .. 1·25 15
80 10 c. black (5.27) .. .. 1·25 12
81 12 c. jet-black .. .. 6·00 11·00
a. *Grey-black* .. .. 2·25 6·00
82 15 c. rose-carmine 80 20
83 20 c. dull orange-yellow .. .. .. 3·00 10
a. *Bright orange* .. .. 2·75 5
84 30 c. ultramarine .. .. 1·10 40
85 50 c. grey .. .. 2·25 30
86 75 c. olive .. .. 3·50 6·50

(b) Wmk sideways. Chalky paper

87 7 1s. green . . . . 4·50 1·75
88 2s. dull purple . . . . 7·50 5·50
89 2s. 50 c. brown (1.10.25) . . 26·00 60·00
90 3s. brownish grey . . . . 17·00 13·00
a. Jet-black . . . . 25·00 23·00
91 4s. grey (1.10.25) . . . . 32·00 60·00
92 5s. carmine-red . . . . 27·00 27·00
93 7s. 50 c. orange-yellow (1.10.25) . . 65·00 £130
94 10s. bright blue . . . . 60·00 60·00
95 £1 black and orange . . £140 £190
96 £2 green and purple (1.10.25) (S. £150) £750
97 £3 purple & yellow (1.10.25) (S. £175) £1000
98 £4 black & mag (1.10.25) (S. £275) . . £1600
99 £5 black and blue (S. £325) . . £2000
100 £10 black and green (S. £350) . . £5500
101 £20 red and green (1.10.25) (S. £550) . . £7500
102 £25 black and red (S. £600) . . £9000
103 £50 black and brown (S. £800) . . £11000
104 £75 purple and grey (1.10.25) (S. £850) £17000
105 £100 red and black (1.10.25) (S. £900) . . £19000
76/95 . . *Set of* 20 £350 £500
76/95 Optd "Specimen" . . *Set of* 20 £550

Specimen copies of Nos. 96/105 are all overprinted.

KENYA, UGANDA AND TANGANYIKA

The postal administrations of Kenya, Tanganyika and Uganda were amalgamated on 1 January 1933. On the independence of the three territories the combined administration became the East African Posts and Telecommunications Corporation.

8 Crowned Cranes

9 Dhow on Lake Victoria

10 East African Lion

11 Kilimanjaro

12 Jinja Bridge by Ripon Falls

13 Mt. Kenya

14 Lake Naivasha

I II

(Des 1 c., 20 c., 10s., R. C. Luck, 10 c., £1, A. Ross. 15 c., 2s., G. Gill Holmes, 30 c., 5s., R. N. Ambasana. 65 c., L. R. Cutts. T **10** typo, remainder recess D.L.R.).

1935 (1 May)–**36**. *Wmk Mult Script CA. P* 12 × 13 (**10**), 14 (**9** *and* **14**) *and* 13 (*remainder*).

110 8 1 c. black and red-brown . . 12 25
111 9 5 c. black and green (I) . . 20 10
a. Perf 13 × 12 (I) . . £175 60·00
b. Rope joined to sail (II) (perf 14) . . 3·00 80
c. Rope joined to sail (II) (perf 13 × 12) £200 50·00
112 10 10 c. black and yellow, C . . 1·75 20
113 11 15 c. black and scarlet . . 75 15
114 8 20 c. black and orange . . 50 15
115 12 30 c. black and blue . . 55 75
116 9 50 c. bright purple and black (I) . . 1·25 35
117 13 65 c. black and brown . . 1·25 2·75
118 14 1s. black and green . . 1·25 1·10
a. Perf 13 × 12 (1936) . . £550 48·00
119 11 2s. lake and purple . . 7·50 8·50
120 14 3s. blue and black . . 9·50 14·00
a. Perf 13 × 12 . . £850
121 12 5s. black and carmine . . 24·00 25·00
122 8 10s. purple and blue . . 48·00 48·00
123 10 £1 black and red, C . . £130 £120
110/23 . . *Set of* 14 £200 £190
110/23 Perf "Specimen" . . *Set of* 14 £200

Line through "0" of 1910 (R.4/2)

1935 (6 May). *Silver Jubilee. As T* **13** *of Antigua.*

124 20 c. light blue and olive-green . . 30 12
125 30 c. brown and deep blue . . 1·75 1·50
e. Horiz line from turret . . 10·00
126 65 c. green and indigo . . 3·75 4·25
e. Horiz line from turret . . 20·00
127 1s. slate and purple . . 4·50 4·50
e. Horiz line from turret . . 25·00
g. Line through "0" of 1910 . . 45·00
124/7 Perf "Specimen" . . *Set of* 4 55·00

For illustration of the other plate variety see Omnibus section following Zululand.

1937 (12 May). *Coronation As T* **2** *of Aden.*

128 5 c. green . . 25 10
129 20 c. orange . . 35 10
130 30 c. bright blue . . 65 55
128/30 Perf "Specimen" . . *Set of* 3 38·00

15 Dhow on Lake Victoria

Retouch on 1 c. (Pl 2, R. 9/6)

Retouch on 10 c. and 1s. (Pl 7B, R. 5/10 and 6/7)

With dot

Dot removed

In the 50 c., on Frame-plate 3, the dot was removed by retouching on all but five stamps (R.5/2, 6/1, 7/2, 7/4, and 9/1). In addition, other stamps show traces of the dot where the retouching was not completely effective.

PERFORATIONS. In this issue, to aid identification, the perforations are indicated to the nearest quarter.

(T **10** typo, others recess D.L.R.)

1938 (11 Apr)–**54**. *As T* **8** *to* **14** (*but with portrait of King George VI in place of King George V, as in T* **15**). *Wmk Mult Script CA.*

131 8 1 c. black and red-brown (*p* 13¼) (2.5.38) 35 35
a. Perf 13¼ × 13¾. *Black & chocolate-brown* (1942) . . 20 30
ab. Retouched value tablet . . 16·00 12·00
ac. Black & dp chocolate-brown (1946) 55 30
ad. Ditto. Retouched tablet . . 16·00 12·00
ae. Black and red-brown (26.9.51) . . 20 30
132 15 5 c. black and green (II) (*p* 13 × 11¾) . . 20 15
133 5 c. reddish brown & orange (*p* 13 × 11¾) (1.6.49) . . 25 65
a. Perf 13 × 12½ (14.6.50) . . 25 60
134 14 10 c. red-brn & orge (*p* 13 × 11¾) (2.5.38) 20 15
a. Perf 14 (1941) . . 35·00 5·00
135 10 c. black and green (*p* 13 × 11¾) (1.6.49) . . 15 30
a. Mountain retouch . . 15·00 13·00
b. Perf 13 × 12½ (14.6.50) . . 20 20
136 10 c. brown and grey (*p* 13 × 12½) (1.4.52) . . 20 20
137 11 15 c. black and rose-red (*p* 13¼) (2.5.38) 50 15
a. Perf 13¾ × 13¼ (2.43) . . 35 50
138 15 c. black & green (*p* 13¾ × 13¼) (1.4.52) . . 45 1·25
139 8 20 c. black and orange (*p* 13¼) (2.5.38) . . 2·25 40
a. Perf 14 (1941) . . 15·00 2·00
b. Perf 13¼ × 13¾ (1.6.42) . . 40 5
ba. Deep black and deep orange (8.51) 65 30
140 15 25 c. blk & carm-red (*p* 13 × 12½) (1.4.52) 1·40 1·60
141 12 30 c. black & dull vio-bl (*p* 13¼) (2.5.38) 5·50 70
a. Perf 14 (1941) . . 65·00 9·00
b. Perf 13¼ × 13¾ (9.42) . . 30 15
142 30 c. dull pur & brn (*p* 13¼ × 13¾) (1.4.52) . . 35 15
143 8 40 c. black and blue (*p* 13¼ × 13¾) (1.4.52) . . 65 65
144 15 50 c. pur & blk (II) (*p* 13 × 11¾) (2.5.38) 55 15
a. Rope not joined to sail (I) . . £180 90·00
b. Dull claret and black (29.7.47) . . 55 25
c. Brown-purple and black (4.48) . . 70 25
d. Reddish purple and black (28.4.49) 70 25
e. Ditto. Perf 13 × 12½ (10.49) . . 45 5
ea. Dot removed (14.6.50) . . 6·00 3·50
eb. Ditto. In pair with normal . . £130 60·00
145 14 1s. black & yellowish brn (*p* 13 × 11¾) (2.5.38) . . 45 10
a. Black and brown (9.42) . . 90 30
ab. Mountain retouch (7.49) . . 32·00 15·00
b. Perf 13 × 12½ (10.49) . . 70 10
ba. Deep black and brown (clearer impression) (14.6.50) . . 75 30
146 11 2s. lake-brn & brn-pur (*p* 13¼) (2.5.38) 20·00 2·25
a. Perf 14 (1941) . . 25·00 7·50
b. Perf 13¾ × 13¼ (24.2.44) . . 4·00 20
147 14 3s. dull ultramarine & blk (*p* 13 × 11¾) (2.5.38) . . 5·00 1·25
a. Deep violet-blue and black (29.7.47) 6·50 2·00
b. Ditto. Perf 13 × 12½ (14.6.50) . . 5·00 1·75
148 12 5s. black and carmine (*p* 13¼) (2.5.38) 32·00 7·00
a. Perf 14 (1941) . . 15·00 3·75
b. Perf 13¼ × 13¾ (24.2.44) . . 5·50 45
149 8 10s. purple and blue (*p* 13¼) (2.5.38) . . 55·00 12·00
a. Perf 14. *Reddish purple & blue* (1941) . . 42·00 20·00
b. Perf 13¼ × 13¾ (24.2.44) . . 9·50 3·50
150 10 £1 blk & red (*p* 11¾ × 13), **C** (12.10.38) £160 55·00
a. Perf 14, **C** (1941) . . 12·00 8·50
ab. Ordinary paper (24.2.44) . . 11·00 8·00
b. Perf 12½. **C** (21.1.54) . . 18·00 20·00
131/150ab (*cheapest*) . . *Set of* 20 35·00 17·00
131/150 Perf "Specimen" . . *Set of* 13 £130

Stamps perf 14, together with Nos. 131a, 137a, 139b, 141b, 146b, 148b and 149b, are known as "Blitz perfs", the differences in perforation being the result of air raid damage to the De La Rue works in which the perforators normally used were destroyed.

10c
KENYA
TANGANYIKA
UGANDA
(**16**)

17 Lake Naivasha

1941 (1 July)–**42**. *Pictorial Stamps of South Africa variously surch as T* **16** *by Government Printer, Pretoria. Inscr alternately in English and Afrikaans.*

		Unused pair	*Used pair*
151	5 c. on 1d. grey and carmine (No. 56)	80	1·75
152	10 c. on 3d. ultramarine (No. 59)	1·25	1·75
153	20 c. on 6d. green and vermilion (No. 61*a*)	80	1·75
154	70 c. on 1s. brown and chalky blue (No. 62) (20.4.42)	1·25	2·00
151/4	Handstamped "Specimen" *Set of 4 pairs*	£170	

1946 (11 Nov). *Victory. As Nos.* 28/9 *of Aden.*

		Unused	*Used*
155	20 c. red-orange	12	10
156	30 c. blue	12	10
155/6	Perf "Specimen" *Set of* 2	45·00	

1948 (1 Dec). *Royal Silver Wedding. As Nos.* 30/1 *of Aden.*

157 20 c. orange . . 25 5
158 £1 scarlet . . 35·00 38·00

1949 (10 Oct). *75th Anniv of Universal Postal Union. As Nos.* 114/17 *of Antigua.*

159 20 c. red-orange . . 25 5
160 30 c. deep blue . . 60 40
161 50 c. grey . . 60 25
162 1s. red-brown . . 1·50 1·00

(Recess D.L.R.)

1952 (1 Feb). *Visit of Princess Elizabeth and Duke of Edinburgh. Wmk Mult Script CA. P* 13 × 12½.

163 **17** 10 c. black and green . . 10 30
164 1s. black and brown . . 45 2·25

1953 (2 June). *Coronation. As No.* 47 *of Aden.*

165 20 c. black and red-orange . . 15 5

1954 (28 Apr). *Royal Visit. As No.* 171 *but inscr* "ROYAL VISIT 1954" *below portrait.*

166 30 c. black and deep ultramarine . . 10 15

18 Owen Falls Dam

19 Giraffe

20 Royal Lodge, Sagana

21 Queen Elizabeth II

(Des G. Gill Holmes (10, 50 c.), H. Grieme (15 c., 1s. 30, 5s.), R. McLellan Sim (10s.), De La Rue (65 c., 2s., £1), O.C. Meronti (others). Recess D.L.R.)

1954 (1 June)–**59**. *Designs as T* **18/21**. *Wmk Mult Script CA. P* 13 (£1); *others,* 12½ × 13 (*vert*) *or* 13 × 12½ (*horiz*).

167 5 c. black and deep brown . . 8 8
a. Vignette inverted . . – £10000
168 10 c. carmine-red . . 10 5
169 15 c. black and light blue (28.3.58) . . 35 12
a. Redrawn. Stop below "c" of "15 c" (29.4.59) 35 10
170 20 c. black and orange . . 15 5
a. Imperf (pair) . . £400
171 30 c. black and deep ultramarine . . 12 5
172 40 c. bistre-brown (28.3.58) . . 85 20
173 50 c. reddish purple (*shades*) . . 20 5
174 65 c. bluish green and brown-purple (1.12.55) 1·50 60
175 1s. black and claret . . 30 5
176 1s. 30, orange and deep lilac (1.12.55) . . 1·50 5
177 2s. black and green (*shades*) . . 1·75 12

178 5s. black and orange 5·50 40
179 10s. black and deep ultramarine 7·50 1·00
180 £1 brown-red and black (*shades*) 22·00 5·00
167/180 *Set of* 14 38·00 7·00

Designs: *Vert as T* **18/19**—5, 30 c. Type **18**; 10, 50 c. Type **19**; 20, 40 c., 1s. Lion. *Horiz. as T* **20**—15 c., 1s. 30, 5s. Elephants; 65 c., 2s. Kilimanjaro.

Only one used copy of No. 167a is known.

25 Map of E. Africa showing Lakes

(Recess Waterlow)

1958 (30 July). *Centenary of Discovery of Lakes Tanganyika and Victoria by Burton and Speke. W* w **12**. *P* 12½.

181 **25** 40 c. blue and deep green 30 20
182 1s. 30 c. green and violet 50 50

26 Sisal **27** Cotton

28 Mt Kenya and Giant Plants **29** Queen Elizabeth II

(Des M. Goaman. Photo (5 c. to 65 c.), recess (others) D.L.R.)

1960 (1 Oct). *Designs as T* **26/9**. *W* w **12**. *P* 15 × 14 (5 *c. to* 65 *c.*), 13 (20*s.*) *or* 14 (*others*).

183 5 c. Prussian blue 5 5
184 10 c. yellow-green 5 5
185 15 c. dull purple 10 5
186 20 c. magenta 10 5
187 25 c. bronze-green 40 40
188 30 c. vermilion 12 5
189 40 c. greenish blue 15 5
190 50 c. slate-violet 15 5
191 65 c. yellow-olive 40 60
192 1s. deep reddish violet and reddish purple 25 5
193 1s. 30, chocolate and brown-red 30 5
194 2s. deep grey-blue and greenish blue 45 15
195 2s. 50, olive-green and deep bluish green 70 70
196 5s. rose-red and purple 2·25 45
197 10s. blackish green and olive-green 4·25 1·75
198 20s. violet-blue and lake 11·00 6·50
183/198 *Set of* 16 18·00 9·50

Designs: *Vert as T* **26/7**—15 c. Coffee; 20 c. Gnu; 25 c. Ostrich; 30 c. Thomson's Gazelle; 40 c. Manta Ray; 50 c. Zebra; 65 c. Cheetah. *Horiz as T* **28**—1s. 30, Murchison Falls and Hippopotamus; 2s. Mt Kilimanjaro and Giraffe; 2s. 50, Candelabra Tree and Rhinoceros; 5s. Crater Lake and Mountains of the Moon; 10s. Ngorongoro Crater and Buffalo.

The 10 c. and 50 c. exist in coils with the designs slightly shorter in height, a wider horizontal gutter every eleven stamps and, in the case of the 10 c. only, printed with a coarser 200 screen instead of the normal 250. (*Price* 10 *c.* 5*p. unused.*) Plate 2 of 30 c. shows coarser 200 screen. (*Price* 25*p. unused.*)

30 Land Tillage

(Des V. Whiteley. Photo Harrison)

1963 (21 Mar). *Freedom from Hunger. T* **30** *and similar horiz design. P* 14½.

199 **30** 15 c. blue and yellow-olive 12 5
200 – 30 c. red-brown and yellow 20 5
201 **30** 50 c. blue and orange-brown 30 12
202 – 1s. 30, red-brown and light blue 70 45

Design:—30 c., 1s. 30, African with Corncob.

31 Scholars and Open Book

(Photo Harrison)

1963 (28 June). *Founding of East African University. P* 14½.

203 **31** 30 c. lake, violet, black and greenish blue 8 5
204 1s. 30, lake, blue, red & lt yellow-brown 25 25

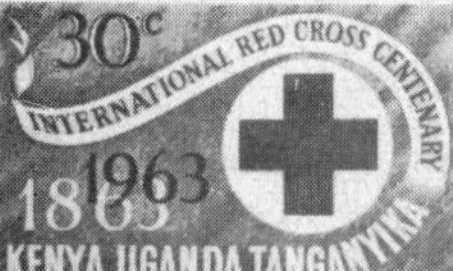

32 Red Cross Emblem

(Des V. Whiteley. Photo Harrison)

1963 (2 Sept). *Centenary of Red Cross. P* 14½.

205 **32** 30 c. red and blue 30 5
206 50 c. red and yellow-brown 40 20

PRINTERS. All the following stamps were printed in photogravure by Harrison, *unless otherwise stated.*

33 Chrysanthemum Emblems **34**

35 East African "Flags"

(Des V. Whiteley)

1964 (21 Oct). *Olympic Games. Tokyo. P* 14½.

207 **33** 30 c. yellow and reddish violet 8 5
208 **34** 50 c. deep reddish violet and yellow 10 5
209 **35** 1 s. 30, orange-yellow, dp green & lt blue 25 20
210 2 s. 50, magenta, deep violet-blue & lt bl 30 70

KENYA, UGANDA AND TANZANIA

The following stamps were issued by the East African Postal Administration for use in Uganda, Kenya and Tanzania, excluding Zanzibar.

36 Rally Badge **37** Cars *en route*

1965 (15 Apr*). 13*th East African Safari Rally. P* 14.

211 **36** 30 c. black, yellow and turquoise 8 5
212 50 c. black, yellow and brown 10 5
a. Imperf (pair)
213 **37** 1 s. 30, dp bluish green, yell-ochre & blue 25 25
214 2 s. 50, dp bluish green, brn-red & lt blue 45 1·00

*This is the local release date. The Crown Agents in London issued the stamps the previous day.

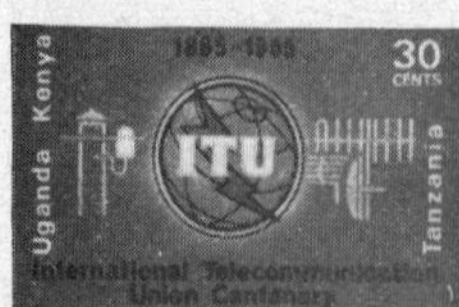

38 I.T.U. Emblem and Symbols

1965 (17 May). *I.T.U. Centenary. P* 14½.

215 **38** 30 c. gold, chocolate and magenta 12 5
216 50 c. gold, chocolate and grey 15 5
217 1 s. 30, gold, chocolate and blue 45 15
218 2 s. 50, gold, chocolate & turquoise-grn 95 75

39 I.C.Y. Emblem

1965 (4 Aug). *International Co-operation Year. P* 14½ × 14.

219 **39** 30 c. deep bluish green and gold 12 5
220 50 c. black and gold 20 5
221 1 s. 30, ultramarine and gold 45 30
222 2 s. 50, carmine-red and gold 1·00 1·25

40 Game Park Lodge, Tanzania

(Des Rena Fennessy)

1966 (4 Apr). *Tourism. T* **40** *and similar horiz designs. Multicoloured. P* 14½.

223 30 c. Type **40** 10 5
224 50 c. Murchison Falls, Uganda 15 5
a. Blue omitted
225 1 s. 30, Lesser Flamingoes, Lake Nakuru, Kenya 40 15
226 2 s. 50, Deep Sea Fishing, Tanzania 75 70

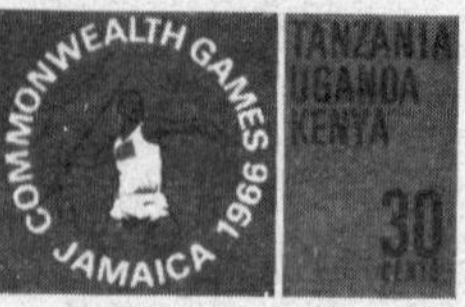

41 Games Emblem

(Des Harrison)

1966 (2 Aug). *Eighth British Empire and Commonwealth Games Jamaica. P* 14½.

227 **41** 30 c. black, gold, turq-green & grey 8 5
228 50 c. black, gold, cobalt and cerise 10 5
229 1 s. 30, blk, gold, rosine & dp bluish grn 20 15
230 2 s. 50, black, gold, lake and ultramarine 35 60

42 U.N.E.S.C.O. Emblem

(Des Harrison)

1966 (3 Oct). 20*th Anniv of U.N.E.S.C.O. P* 14½ × 14.

231 **42** 30 c. black, emerald and red 15 5
232 50 c. black, emerald and light brown 20 5
233 1 s. 30, black, emerald and grey 60 30
234 2 s. 50, black, emerald and yellow 1·50 1·40

43 D.H. "Dragon Rapide"

(Des R. Granger Barrett)

1967 (23 Jan). 21*st Anniv of East African Airways. T* **43** *and similar horiz designs. P* 14½.

235 30 c. slate-violet, greenish blue & myrtle-grn 15 5
236 50 c. multicoloured 25 5
a. Red omitted
237 1 s. 30, multicoloured 70 30
238 2 s. 50, multicoloured 1·40 1·90

Designs:—50 c. "Super VC-10"; 1 s. 30, "Comet 4"; 2 s. 50, "F-27 Friendship".

44 Pillar Tomb **45** Rock Painting

(Des Rena Fennessy)

1967 (2 May). *Archaeological Relics. T* **44/5** *and similar designs. P* 14½.

239 30 c. ochre, black and deep reddish purple 10 5
240 50 c. orange-red, black and greyish brown 15 5
241 1 s. 30, black, greenish, yellow and deep yellow-green 30 15
242 2 s. 50, black, ochre and brown-red 70 1·00

Designs:—1 s. 30, Clay head; 2 s. 50, Proconsul skull.

48 Unified Symbols of Kenya, Tanzania, and Uganda

(Des Rena Fennessy)

1967 (1 Dec). *Foundation of East African Community. P* 14½ × 14.

243	**48**	5 s. gold, black and grey	95	1·50

49 Mountaineering

(Des Rena Fennessy)

1968 (4 Mar). *Mountains of East Africa. T* **49** *and similar horiz designs. Multicoloured. P* 14.

244	30 c. Type **49**	10	5
245	50 c. Mount Kenya	15	5
246	1 s. 30, Mount Kilimanjaro	40	25
247	2 s. 50, Ruwenzori Mountains	75	1·50

50 Family and Rural Hospital

(Des Rena Fennessy. Litho D.L.R.)

1968 (13 May). *20th Anniv of World Health Organization. T* **50** *and similar horiz designs. P* 13½.

248	30 c. deep yellow-green, lilac and chocolate ..	8	5
249	50 c. slate-lilac, lilac and black	10	5
250	1 s. 30, yellow-brown, lilac and chocolate ..	20	25
251	2 s. 50, grey, black and reddish lilac.. ..	50	1·25

Designs:—50 c. Family and nurse; 1 s. 30, Family and microscope; 2 s. 50, Family and hypodermic syringe.

51 Olympic Stadium, Mexico City

(Des V. Whiteley)

1968 (14 Oct). *Olympic Games, Mexico. T* **51** *and similar designs. P* 14.

252	30 c. light green and black	8	5
253	50 c. black and blue-green	10	5
254	1 s. 30, carmine-red, black and grey.. ..	20	15
255	2 s. 50, blackish brown and yellow-brown ..	50	95

Designs: *Horiz*—50 c. High-diving boards; 1 s. 30, Running tracks. *Vert*—2 s. 50, Boxing ring.

52 M.V. *Umoja*

(Des A. Grosart)

1969 (20 Jan). *Water Transport. T* **52** *and similar horiz designs. P* 14.

256	30 c. deep blue, light blue and slate-grey ..	15	5
257	50 c. multicoloured	25	5
258	1 s. 30, bronze-green, greenish blue and blue	60	25
259	2 s. 50, red-orange, deep blue and pale blue..	1·40	1·00

Designs:—50 c. S.S. *Harambee*; 1 s. 30, M.V. *Victoria*; 2 s. 50, *St. Michael*.

53 I.L.O. Emblem and Agriculture

54 Pope Paul VI and Ruwenzori Mountains

(Des Rena Fennessy)

1969 (14 Apr). *50th Anniv of International Labour Organization. T* **53** *and similar horiz designs. P* 14.

260	30 c. black, green and greenish yellow ..	8	5
261	50 c. black, plum, cerise and rose	10	5
262	1 s. 30, black, orange-brown & yellow-orange	20	15
263	2 s. 50, black, ultramarine & turquoise-blue	35	60

Designs:—50 c. I.L.O. emblem and building work; 1 s. 30, I.L.O. emblem and factory workers; 2 s. 50, I.L.O. emblem and shipping.

(Des Harrison)

1969 (31 July). *Visit of Pope Paul VI to Uganda. P* 14.

264	**54**	30 c. black, gold and royal blue	5	5
265		70 c. black, gold and claret	12	10
266		1 s. 50, black, gold and deep blue ..	25	35
267		2 s. 50, black, gold and violet	40	85

55 Euphorbia Tree shaped as Africa and Emblem

56 Marimba

(Des Rena Fennessy. Litho B.W.)

1969 (8 Dec). *Fifth Anniv of African Development Bank. P* 13½.

268	**55**	30 c. dp bluish green, gold & blue-green	5	5
269		70 c. dp bluish green, gold & reddish pur	12	5
270		1 s. 50, dp bluish grn, gold & lt turq-bl	20	25
271		2 s. 50, dp bluish grn, gold & orge-brn	35	85

(Des Rena Fennessy. Litho B.W.)

1970 (16 Feb). *Musical Instruments. T* **56** *and similar horiz designs. P* 11 × 12.

272	30 c. buff, yellow-brown and bistre-brown ..	10	5
273	70 c. olive-green, yellow-brown and yellow ..	20	5
274	1 s. 50, chocolate and yellow..	35	25
275	2 s. 50, salmon, yellow and chocolate ..	70	1·40

Designs:—70 c. Amadinda; 1 s. 50, Nzomari; 2 s. 50, Adeudeu.

57 Satellite Earth Station

58 Athlete

(Des V. Whiteley. Litho J.W.)

1970 (18 May). *Inauguration of East African Satellite Earth Station. T* **57** *and similar horiz designs. P* 14½ × 14.

276	30 c. multicoloured	8	5
277	70 c. multicoloured	15	5
278	1 s. 50, black, slate-violet and pale orange ..	30	30
279	2 s. 50, multicoloured	70	1·10

Designs:—70 c. Transmitter in daytime; 1 s. 50, Transmitter at night; 2 s. 50, Earth and satellite.

(Des Rena Fennessy. Litho Walsall)

1970 (13 July). *Ninth Commonwealth Games. P* 14 × 14½.

280	**58**	30 c. orange-brown and black	5	5
281		70 c. olive-green and black	10	5
282		1 s. 50, slate-lilac and black	20	25
283		2 s. 50, turquoise-blue and black ..	35	90

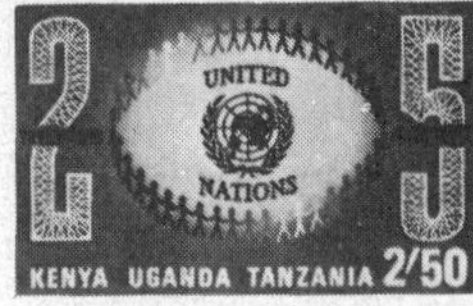

59 "25" and U.N. Emblem

(Des Rena Fennessy)

1970 (19 Oct). *25th Anniv of United Nations. P* 14½.

284	**59**	30 c. multicoloured	10	5
285		70 c. multicoloured	20	5
286		1 s. 50, multicoloured	40	30
287		2 s. 50, multicoloured	85	1·50

60 Balance and Weight Equivalents

(Des and litho J.W.)

1971 (4 Jan). *Conversion to Metric System. T* **60** *and similar horiz designs. Multicoloured. P* 14½ × 14.

288	30 c. Type **60**	10	5
289	70 c. Fahrenheit and Centigrade Thermometers	20	5
290	1 s. 50, Petrol Pump and Liquid Capacities ..	40	35
291	2 s. 50, Surveyors and Land Measures ..	85	1·60

61 11 Class Locomotive

(Des Rena Fennessy)

1971 (5 Apr). *Railway Transport. T* **61** *and similar horiz designs. Multicoloured. P* 14.

292	30 c. Type **61**	25	5
293	70 c. 90 Class Locomotive	50	5
294	1 s. 50, 59 Class Locomotive..	1·50	1·25
295	2 s. 50, 30 Class Locomotive..	3·00	4·00
MS296	120 × 88 mm. Nos. 292/5	9·00	9·00

62 Syringe and Cow

(Des Rena Fennessy. Litho)

1971 (5 July). *O.A.U. Rinderpest Campaign. T* **62** *and similar horiz design. P* 14.

297	**62**	30 c. black, pale yell-brn & pale yell-grn	8	5
298	–	70 c. black, pale slate-blue & pale yell-brn	15	5
299	**62**	1 s. 50, black, plum & pale yell-brn	35	30
300	–	2 s. 50, black, brown-red & pale yell-brn	65	1·40

Design:—70 c., 2 s. 50, As T **62**, but with bull facing right.

63 Livingstone meets Stanley

(Des and litho J.W.)

1971 (28 Oct). *Centenary of Livingstone and Stanley meeting at Ujiji. P* 13½ × 14.

301	**63**	5 s. multicoloured	85	2·00

64 President Nyerere and Supporters

(Des G. Drummond. Litho J.W.)

1971 (9 Dec). *Tenth Anniv of Tanzanian Independence. T* **64** *and similar horiz designs. Multicoloured. P* 13½.

302	30 c. Type **64**	10	5
303	70 c. Ujamaa village	20	12
304	1 s. 50, Dar es Salaam University	55	65
305	2 s. 50, Kilimanjaro airport	1·40	2·50

65 Flags and Trade Fair Emblem

(Des Trade Fair Publicity Agents. Litho Questa)

1972 (23 Feb). *All-Africa Trade Fair. P* 13½ × 14.

306	**65**	30 c. multicoloured	10	5
307		70 c. multicoloured	20	5
308		1 s. 50, multicoloured	45	45
309		2 s. 50, multicoloured	90	1·60

66 Child with Cup

(Des Rena Fennessy. Litho Questa)

1972 (24 Apr). *25th Anniv of UNICEF. T* **66** *and similar horiz designs. Multicoloured. P* 14 × 14½.
310 30 c. Type **66** 8 5
311 70 c. Children with ball 15 5
312 1 s. 50, Child at blackboard 35 35
313 2 s. 50, Child and tractor .. .. .. 70 1·40

67 Hurdling

(Des G. Vasarhelyi. Litho J.W.)

1972 (28 Aug). *Olympic Games, Munich. T* **67** *and similar horiz designs. Multicoloured. P* 14.
314 40 c. Type **67** 20 5
315 70 c. Running 25 5
316 1 s. 50, Boxing 50 30
317 2 s. 50, Hockey .. .. 1·00 1·50
MS318 131 × 98 mm. Nos. 314/17 .. .. .. 5·50 7·00

68 Ugandan Kobs

(Des G. Drummond. Litho D.L.R.)

1972 (9 Oct). *Tenth Anniv of Ugandan Independence. T* **68** *and similar horiz designs. Multicoloured. P* 14.
319 40 c. Type **68** 15 5
320 70 c. Conference Centre 25 5
321 1 s. 50, Makerere University 60 60
322 2 s. 50, Coat of Arms .. .. 1·60 2·75
MS323 132 × 120 mm. Nos. 319/22. P 13 × 14 .. 5·00 6·50

69 Community Flag

(Des Rena Fennessy. Litho)

1972 (1 Dec). *Fifth Anniv of East African Community. P* 14½ × 14.
324 **69** 5 s. multicoloured .. .. .. 1·75 2·50

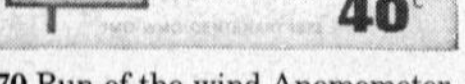

70 Run-of-the-wind Anemometer

71 "Learning by Serving"

(Des P. Powell. Litho)

1973 (1 Mar*). *I.M.O./W.M.O. Centenary. T* **70** *and similar multicoloured designs. P* 14½.
325 40 c. Type **70** 12 5
326 70 c. Weather balloon (*vert*) 20 5
327 1 s. 50, Meteorological rocket 50 35
328 2 s. 50, Satellite receiving aerial .. .. 1·00 1·75

No. 325 exists with country name at foot instead of at top, and also with country name omitted (or with imprint or plate numbers in lieu). These are because of faulty registration of the perforation comb.

*This is the local release date. The Crown Agents in London did not place the stamps on sale until 5 March.

(Des Rena Fennessy. Litho)

1973 (16 July). *24th World Scout Conference, Nairobi. T* **71** *and similar vert designs. P* 14.
329 40 c. multicoloured 20 5
330 70 c. Venetian red, reddish violet and black .. 30 5
331 1 s. 50, cobalt, reddish violet and black .. 70 50
332 2 s. 50, multicoloured .. .. .. 1·60 2·25

Designs:—70 c. Baden-Powell's grave, Nyeri; 1 s. 50, World Scout emblem; 2 s. 50, Lord Baden-Powell.

72 Kenyatta Conference Centre

(Des Marketing Communications Ltd, Nairobi; adapted J. Cooter. Litho D.L.R.)

1973 (29 Sept*). *I.M.F./World Bank Conference. T* **72** *and similar designs. P* 13½ × 14 (1 s. 50) *or* 14 × 13½ (*others*).
333 40 c. sage-green, light greenish grey & black 12 5
334 70 c. orange-brown, greenish grey and black 20 5
335 1 s. 50, multicoloured .. .. .. 70 1·25
336 2 s. 50, orange, greenish grey and black .. 1·25 1·75
MS337 166 × 141 mm. Nos. 333/6. Imperf .. 2·75 3·75

Designs:—Nos. 334/6 show different arrangements of Bank emblems and the Conference Centre, the 1 s. 50 being vertical.

*This is the local release date. The Crown Agents in London issued the stamps on 24 September.

73 Police Dog-handler

74 Tea Factory

(Des C. Abbott. Litho Questa)

1973 (24 Oct)–**74**. *50th Anniv of Interpol. T* **73** *and similar vert designs. P* 14.
338 40 c. yellow, blue and black 12 5
339 70 c. turquoise-green, orange-yellow & black 20 5
340 1 s. 50, light violet, yellow and black .. 45 60
341 2 s. 50, light yellow-green, red-orange and black (I) .. .. 1·75 2·75
342 2 s. 50, light yellow-green, red-orange, and black (II) (25.2.74) .. .. .. 1·75 2·75

Designs:—70 c. East African Policeman; 1 s. 50, Interpol emblem; 2 s. 50, Interpol H.Q.

Nos. 341/2. Type I inscribed "St. Clans"; Type II corrected to "St. Cloud".

(Des G. Drummond. Litho Enschedé)

1973 (12 Dec). *10th Anniv of Kenya's Independence. T* **74** *and similar horiz designs. Multicoloured. P* 13 × 13½.
343 40 c. Type **74** 15 5
344 70 c. Kenyatta Hospital 20 5
345 1 s. 50, Nairobi Airport 50 45
346 2 s. 50, Kindaruma hydro-electric scheme .. 95 2·10

75 Party H.Q.

(Des PAD Studio. Litho D.L.R.)

1974 (12 Jan). *Tenth Anniv of Zanzibar's Revolution. T* **75** *and similar horiz designs. Multicoloured. P* 13½.
347 40 c. Type **75** 12 5
348 70 c. Housing scheme 20 5
349 1 s. 50, Colour T.V. 45 50
350 2 s. 50, Amaan Stadium .. .. .. 95 2·25

76 "Symbol of Union"

(Des Jennifer Toombs. Litho Questa)

1974 (26 Apr). *Tenth Anniv of Tanganyika–Zanzibar Union. T* **76** *and similar horiz designs. Multicoloured. P* 14½.
351 40 c. Type **76** 15 5
352 70 c. Handclasp and map 20 12
353 1 s. 50, "Communications" 50 60
354 2 s. 50, Flags of Tanu, Tanzania and Afro-Shirazi Party .. .. 1·60 2·75

77 East African Family ("Stability of the Home")

(Des locally; adapted PAD Studio. Litho)

1974 (15 July). *17th Social Welfare Conference, Nairobi. T* **77** *and similar horiz designs. P* 14½.
355 40 c. greenish yellow, lake-brown and black .. 12 5
356 70 c. multicoloured 20 5
357 1 s. 50, olive-green, yellow-green and black 50 50
358 2 s. 50, light rose, reddish violet and black .. 90 1·75

Designs:—70 c. Dawn and drummer (U.N. Second Development Plan); 1 s. 50, Agricultural scene (Rural Development Plan); 2 s. 50, Transport and telephone ("Communications").

78 New Postal H.Q., Kampala

(Des Rena Fennessy. Litho)

1974 (9 Oct). *Centenary of Universal Postal Union. T* **78** *and similar horiz designs. Multicoloured. P* 14½.
359 40 c. Type **78** 12 5
360 70 c. Mail-train and post-van 25 5
361 1 s. 50, U.P.U. Building, Berne 40 45
362 2 s. 50, Loading mail into "VC-10" .. .. 1·00 1·75

79 Family-planning Clinic

(Des C. Abbott. Litho)

1974 (16 Dec). *World Population Year. T* **79** *and similar horiz designs. P* 14.
363 40 c. multicoloured 15 5
364 70 c. deep reddish violet and scarlet 20 5
365 1 s. 50, multicoloured 50 50
366 2 s. 50, apple-green, blue-green & bluish blk 90 1·90

Designs:—70 c. "Tug of war"; 1 s. 50, Population "scales"; 2 s. 50, W.P.Y. emblem.

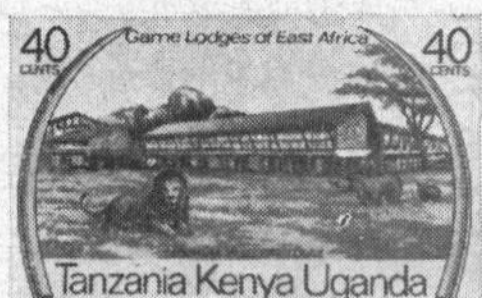

80 Seronera Wild-Life Lodge, Tanzania

(Des R. Granger Barrett. Litho)

1975 (26 Feb*). *East Africa Game Lodges. T* **80** *and similar horiz designs. Multicoloured. P* 14.
367 40 c. Type **80** 15 5
368 70 c. Mweya Safari Lodge, Uganda 25 10
369 1 s. 50, "Ark"—Aberdare Forest Lodge, Kenya 60 60
370 2 s. 50, Paraa Safari Lodge, Uganda .. 1·60 2·50

*This is the local release date. The Crown Agents in London issued the stamps on 24 February.

81 Kitana (wooden comb), Bajun of Kenya

82 International Airport, Entebbe

(Des Mrs. Gombe of the E.A.P.T.; adapted C. Abbott. Litho Questa)

1975 (5 May). *African Arts. T* **81** *and similar vert designs. Multicoloured. P* 13½.
371 50 c. Type **81** 15 5
372 1 s. Earring, Chaga of Tanzania 30 15
373 2 s. Okoco (armlet), Acholi of Uganda .. 65 70
374 3 s. Kitete (Kamba gourd), Kenya .. .. 1·00 1·50

(Des PAD Studio. Litho State Ptg Wks, Warsaw)

1975 (28 July). *O.A.U. Summit Conference, Kampala. T* **82** *and similar multicoloured designs. P* 11.
375 50 c. Type **82** 15 5
376 1 s. Map of Africa and flag (*vert*) 30 15
377 2 s. Nile Hotel, Kampala .. .. .. 80 1·10
378 3 s. Martyrs' Shrine, Namugongo (*vert*) .. 1·40 2·00

83 Ahmed ("Presidential" Elephant) **84** Maasai Manyatta (village), Kenya

(Des locally. Litho State Ptg Wks, Warsaw)

1975 (11 Sept). *Rare Animals. T* **83** *and similar vert designs. Multicoloured. P* 11.

379	50 c. Type **83**	20	5
380	1 s. Albino buffalo	40	20
381	2 s. Ahmed in grounds of National Museum	1·40	1·50
382	3 s. Abbott's Duiker	1·90	2·50

(Des Rena Fennessy. Litho Questa)

1975 (3 Nov). *Second World Black and African Festival of Arts and Culture, Nigeria* (1977). *T* **84** *and similar horiz designs. Multicoloured. P* 13½ × 14.

383	50 c. Type **84**	15	5
384	1 s. "Heartbeat of Africa" (Ugandan dancers)	30	10
385	2 s. Makonde sculpture, Tanzania	90	90
386	3 s. "Early Man and Technology" (skinning animal)	1·40	1·75

For similar stamps see Nos. 76/80 of Kenya and the corresponding issues of Tanzania and Uganda.

85 Fokker "Friendship" at Nairobi Airport

(Des local artist. Litho State Security Ptg Wks, Warsaw)

1976 (2 Jan). *30th Anniv of East African Airways. T* **85** *and similar triangular designs. Multicoloured. P* 11½.

387	50 c. Type **85**	15	5
	a. Black (aircraft) and blue omitted	†	£450
388	1 s. "DC 9" at Kilimanjaro Airport	30	30
389	2 s. Super "VC 10" at Entebbe Airport	1·40	1·50
390	3 s. East African Airways Crest	1·75	2·00

Two black plates were used for each of Nos. 387/9: one for the frame and the other for the centre. No. 387a, three used copies of which are known, has the printing from the blue and centre black plates omitted.

Further commemorative issues were released during 1976–78, using common designs, but inscribed for one republic only. These are listed under KENYA, TANZANIA, or UGANDA.

Co-operation between the postal services of the three member countries virtually ceased after 30 June 1977, the postal services of Kenya, Tanzania and Uganda then operating independently.

OFFICIAL STAMPS

For use on official correspondence of the Tanganyika Government.

OFFICIAL

(O 1)

1959 (1 July). *Nos.* 167/71, 173 *and* 175/80 *optd as Type* O **1**.

O 1	5 c. black and deep brown	5	5
O 2	10 c. carmine-red	5	5
O 3	15 c. black and light blue (No. 169a)	5	5
O 4	20 c. black and orange	5	5
	a. Opt double	—	£350
O 5	30 c. black and deep ultramarine	8	5
O 6	50 c. reddish purple	12	5
O 7	1s. black and claret	20	5
O 8	1s. 30, orange and deep lilac	45	20
O 9	2s. black and bronze-green	70	40
O10	5s. black and orange	1·75	1·25
O11	10s. black and deep ultramarine	3·50	3·50
O12	£1 brown-red and black	9·50	11·00
O1/12	*Set of* 12	15·00	15·00

The 30 c., 50 c. and 1s. exist with overprint double, but with the two impressions almost coincident.

OFFICIAL (O 2) **OFFICIAL** (O 3)

1960 (18 Oct). *Nos.* 183/6, 188, 190, 192 *and* 196 *optd with Type* O **2** (*cents values*) *or* O **3**.

O13	5 c. Prussian blue	5	5
O14	10 c. yellow-green	5	5
O15	15 c. dull purple	5	5
O16	20 c. magenta	5	5
O17	30 c. vermilion	8	8
O18	50 c. slate-violet	12	10
O19	1s. deep reddish violet and reddish purple	35	10
O20	5s. rose-red and purple	2·75	2·00
O13/20	*Set of* 8	3·25	2·25

POSTAGE DUE STAMPS

D 1

D 2

(Typo Waterlow)

1928–33. *Wmk Mult Script CA. P* 15 × 14.

D1	D **1** 5 c. violet	55	80
D2	10 c. vermilion	65	70
D3	20 c. yellow-green	90	2·50
D4	30 c. brown (1931)	3·25	5·00
D5	40 c. dull blue	3·50	8·00
D6	1s. grey-green (1933)	23·00	30·00
D1/6	*Set of* 6	29·00	42·00
D1/6 Optd/Perf "Specimen"	*Set of* 6	80·00	

(Typo D.L.R.)

1935 (1 May)–**60**. *Wmk Mult Script CA. P* 14.

D 7	D **2** 5 c. violet	40	60
D 8	10 c. scarlet	30	15
D 9	20 c. green	40	35
D10	30 c. brown	60	75
	a. Bistre-brown (19.7.60)	60	75
D11	40 c. ultramarine	2·00	3·75
D12	1s. grey	4·50	7·00
D7/12	*Set of* 6	7·50	11·50
D7/12 Perf "Specimen"	*Set of* 6	60·00	

Kiribati

(*formerly* Gilbert Islands)

INDEPENDENT

15 Kiribati Flag

(Des G. Drummond. Litho Questa)

1979 (12 July). *Independence. T* **15** *and similar horiz design. Multicoloured. W* w **14** (*sideways*). *P* 14.

84	10 c. Type **15**	25	25
85	45 c. Houses of Parliament and Maneaba ni Maungatabu (House of Assembly)	75	1·00

16 M.V. *Teraaka* (training ship) **17** Gilbert and Ellice Islands 1911 ½d. Stamp

(Des J. Cooter. Litho Questa)

1979 (12 July)–**80**. *Horiz designs as T* **16**. *Multicoloured. W* w **14** (*sideways*). *P* 14.

86	1 c. Type **16**	10	5
87	3 c. M.V. *Tautunu* (T class inter-island touring vessel)	10	8
88	5 c. Hibiscus	10	10
89	7 c. Catholic Cathedral, Tarawa	10	10
90	10 c. Maneaba, Bikenibeu	10	10
91	12 c. Betio Harbour	15	15
92	15 c. Eastern Reef Heron	35	20
93	20 c. Flamboyant Tree	25	25
94	25 c. Moorish Idol (fish)	30	30
95	30 c. Frangipani	30	30
96	35 c. G.I.P.C. Chapel, Tangintebu	35	35
97	50 c. *Hypolimnas bolina elliciana* (butterfly)	75	55
98	$1 *Tabakea* (Tarawa Lagoon ferry)	1·10	1·10
99	$2 Evening scene	2·00	2·00
99*a*	$5 National flag (27.8.80)	9·50	10·00
86/99*a*	*Set of* 15	14·00	14·00

See also Nos. 121/35.

(Des J.W. Litho Questa)

1979 (27 Sept). *Death Centenary of Sir Rowland Hill. T* **17** *and similar vert designs showing stamps. Multicoloured. W* w **14**. *P* 14.

100	10 c. Type **17**	20	20
101	20 c. Gilbert and Ellice Islands 1956 2s. 6d. definitive	30	35
102	25 c. Great Britain 1902 2s. 6d.	35	40
103	45 c. Gilbert and Ellice Islands 1924 10s.	50	60
MS104	113 × 110 mm. Nos. 100/3	1·75	1·75

OMNIBUS ISSUES

Details, together with prices for complete sets, of the various Omnibus issues from the 1935 Silver Jubilee series to date are included in a special section following Zululand at the end of the catalogue.

18 Boy with Clam Shell

(Des D. Bowen. Litho Enschedé)

1979 (28 Nov). *International Year of the Child. T* **18** *and similar multicoloured designs. W* w **14** (*sideways on* 20 *c.*). *P* 13 × 13½ (20 *c.*) *or* 13½ × 13 (*others*).

105	10 c. Type **18**	15	15
106	20 c. Child climbing coconut tree (*horiz*)	25	30
107	45 c. Girl reading	50	60
108	$1 Child in costume	95	1·40

19 Downrange Station, Christmas Island

(Des J. Cooter. Litho Format)

1980 (20 Feb). *Satellite Tracking. T* **19** *and similar multicoloured designs. P* 14½.

109	25 c. Type **19**	30	30
110	45 c. Map of South Pacific showing trajectory of Experimental Communications Satellite	50	50
111	$1 Rocket launch, Tanegashima, Japan (*vert*)	1·40	1·40

20 T.S. *Teraaka*

(Litho Format)

1980 (30 Apr). *"London 1980" International Stamp Exhibition. T* **20** *and similar horiz designs. Multicoloured. P* 14½.

112	12 c. Type **20**	12	15
113	25 c. Loading Air Tungaru aeroplane, Bonriki Airport	25	30
114	30 c. Radio Operator	30	35
115	$1 Bairiki Post Office	1·10	1·25
MS116	139 × 116 mm. Nos. 112/15. P 14 × 14½	1·75	2·00

Nos. 112/15 were each printed in sheets of 12 containing *se-tenant* stamp-size labels in positions 4 and 6.

21 *Achaea janata*

(Des J. Cooter. Litho Questa)

1980 (27 Aug). *Moths. T* **21** *and similar horiz designs. Multicoloured. P* 14.

117	12 c. Type **21**	20	15
118	25 c. *Ethmia nigroapicella*	35	35
119	30 c. *Utetheisa pulchelloides*	40	40
120	50 c. *Anua coronata*	55	55

1980 (27 Aug)–**81**. *As Nos.* 86/99*a but no wmk.*

121	1 c. Type **16** (4.81)	10	15
122	3 c. M.V. *Tautunu* (T class inter-island touring vessel) (6.1.81)	10	15
123	5 c. Hibiscus	10	15
124	7 c. Catholic Cathedral, Tarawa	10	15
125	10 c. Maneaba, Bikenibeu (19.11.80)	12	15
126	12 c. Betio Harbour (11.12.80)	15	15
127	15 c. Eastern Reef Heron (11.12.80)	35	20
128	20 c. Flamboyant Tree (6.1.81)	25	30
129	25 c. Moorish Idol (19.11.80)	35	35
130	30 c. Frangipani (4.81)	35	35
131	35 c. G.I.P.C. Chapel, Tangintebu (4.81)	35	40
132	50 c. *Hypolimnas bolina elliciana* (butterfly) (4.81)	75	70
133	$1 *Tabakea* (Tarawa Lagoon ferry) (11.12.80)	1·40	1·75
134	$2 Evening scene (11.12.80)	2·25	2·75
135	$5 National flag (11.12.80)	4·75	5·00
121/35	*Set of* 15	10·00	12·00

22 Captain Cook Hotel, Christmas Island

(Des J. Cooter. Litho Format)

1980 (19 Nov). *Development. T* **22** *and similar horiz designs. Multicoloured. P* 13½ × 14.

136	10 c. Type **22**	10	12
137	20 c. Sports Stadium	20	25
138	25 c. International Airport, Bonriki	25	30
139	35 c. National Library and Archives	35	40
140	$1 Otintai Hotel	1·00	1·10

23 *Acalypha godseffiana*

(Des J. Cooter. Litho Format)

1981 (18 Feb). *Flowers. T* **23** *and similar vert designs. Multicoloured. W* w **15**. *P* 14 × 13½.

141	12 c. Type **23**	20	15
142	30 c. *Hibiscus schizopetalus*	40	35
143	35 c. *Calotropis gigantea*	45	45
144	50 c. *Euphorbia pulcherrima*	60	60

25 Maps of Abaiang and Marakei, and String Figures

(Des J. Cooter. Litho Format)

1981 (6 May). *Island Maps (1st series). T* **25** *and similar horiz designs. Multicoloured. W* w **15** *(sideways). P* 13½ × 14.

145	12 c. Type **25**	20	20
146	30 c. Maps of Little Makin and Butaritari, and village house	40	40
147	35 c. Map of Maiana, and coral road	45	45
148	$1 Map of Christmas Island, and Captain Cook's *Resolution*	1·60	1·60

See also Nos. 201/4 and 215/18.

26 *Katherine*

27 Prince Charles and Lady Diana Spencer

(Des D. Shults. Litho Questa)

1981 (29 July–26 Nov). *Royal Wedding. Horiz designs as T* **26**, *showing Royal Yachts, and T* **27**. *Multicoloured. (a) W* w **15**. *P* 14.

149	12 c. Type **26**	15	15
	a. Sheetlet. No. 149 × 6 and No. 150	1·25	
150	12 c. Type **27**	40	40
151	50 c. *Osborne*	60	60
	a. Sheetlet No. 151 × 6 and No. 152	4·50	
152	50 c. Type **27**	1·25	1·25
153	$2 *Britannia*	2·25	2·25
	a. Sheetlet. No. 153 × 6 and No. 154	18·00	
154	$2 Type **27**	6·50	6·50
149/154	*Set of* 6	9·50	9·50
MS155	120 × 109 mm. $1.20, Type **27**. Wmk sideways. P 12 (26 Nov)	3·50	3·50

(b) Booklet stamps. No wmk. P 12 (26 Nov)

156	12 c. Type **26**	15	15
	a. Booklet pane. No. 156 × 4	60	
157	50 c. Type **27**	75	80
	a. Booklet pane. No. 157 × 2	1·50	

Nos. 49/54 were printed in sheetlets of seven stamps of the same face value, each containing six of the "Royal Yacht" design and one as Type **27**.

Nos. 156/7 come from $1.96 stamp booklets.

28 Tuna Bait Breeding Centre, Bonriki Fish Farm

(Des G. Drummond. Litho Questa)

1981 (19 Nov). *Tuna Fishing Industry. T* **28** *and similar horiz designs. Multicoloured. W* w **15**. *P* 14.

158	12 c. Type **28**	12	12
159	30 c. Tuna fishing	30	30
160	35 c. Cold storage, Betio	35	35
161	50 c. Government Tuna Fishing Vessel *Nei Manganibuka*	60	60
MS162	134 × 99 mm. Nos. 158/61. Wmk sideways	1·25	1·40

29 Pomarine Skua

(Des G. Drummond. Litho Questa)

1982 (18 Feb)–**83**. *Birds. Multicoloured designs as T* **29**. *P* 14.

163	1 c. Type **29**	5	5
164	2 c. Mallard	5	5
165	4 c. White-winged Petrel	5	5
166	5 c. Blue-faced Booby	5	5
167	7 c. Friendly Quail Dove	8	10
168	8 c. Shoveler	10	12
169	12 c. Polynesian Reed Warbler	15	20
170	15 c. American Golden Plover	20	25
171	20 c. Eastern Reef Heron	25	30
171*a*	25 c. Common Noddy (31.1.83)	30	35
172	30 c. Brown Booby	35	40
173	35 c. Audubon's Shearwater	40	45
174	40 c. White-throated Storm Petrel (*vert*)	45	50
175	50 c. Bristle-thighed Curlew (*vert*)	60	65
176	$1 Kuhl's Lory (*vert*)	1·10	1·25
177	$2 Long-tailed Koel (*vert*)	2·25	2·50
178	$5 Great Frigate Bird (*vert*)	5·75	6·00
163/78	*Set of* 17	11·00	12·00

30 De Havilland "DH114 (Heron)"

31 Mary of Teck, Princess of Wales, 1893

(Des G. Drummond. Litho Format)

1982 (18 Feb). *Inauguration of Air Tungaru Airline. T* **30** *and similar horiz designs. Multicoloured. W* w **15** *(sideways). P* 14.

179	12 c. Type **30**	15	15
180	30 c. Britten-Norman "Trislander"	40	40
181	35 c. Casa "212 (Aviocar)"	45	45
182	50 c. Boeing "727"	60	60

(Des D. Shults and J. Cooter. Litho Format)

1982 (19 May). *21st Birthday of Princess of Wales. T* **31** *and similar vert designs. Multicoloured. W* w **15**. *P* 13½ × 14.

183	12 c. Type **31**	15	15
184	50 c. Coat of Arms of Mary of Teck	60	60
185	$1 Diana, Princess of Wales	1·25	1·25

The 12 c. design is incorrectly dated; Mary of Teck became Princess of Wales in 1901.

1982 (14 July). *Birth of Prince William of Wales. Nos.* 183/5 *optd with T* **19** *of St. Kitts.*

186	12 c. Type **31**	15	15
187	50 c. Coat of arms of Mary of Teck	60	60
	a. Opt inverted	55·00	
188	$1 Diana, Princess of Wales	1·25	1·25

32 First Aid Practice

(Des J. Cooter. Litho Format)

1982 (12 Aug). *75th Anniv of Boy Scout Movement. T* **32** *and similar horiz designs. Multicoloured. W* w **15** *(sideways). P* 13½ × 14.

189	12 c. Type **32**	15	15
190	25 c. Boat repairs	30	30
191	30 c. On parade	35	35
192	50 c. Gilbert Islands 1977 8 c. Scouting stamp and "75"	60	60

33 Queen and Duke of Edinburgh with Local Dancer

(Des PAD Studio. Litho Walsall)

1982 (23 Oct). *Royal Visit. T* **33** *and similar horiz designs. Multicoloured. W* w **15** *(sideways). P* 14.

193	12 c. Type **33**	15	15
194	25 c. Queen, Duke of Edinburgh and outrigger canoe	30	30
195	35 c. New Philatelic Bureau building	40	40
MS196	88 × 76 mm. 50 c. Queen Elizabeth II	60	60

On No. **MS**/196 the captions on the map for the islands of Teraina and Tabuaeren have been transposed.

34 "Obaia, The Feathered" (Kiribati legend)

(Des J.W. Litho Format)

1983 (14 Mar). *Commonwealth Day. T* **34** *and similar horiz designs. Multicoloured. W* w **15** *(sideways). P* 14.

197	12 c. Type **34**	15	20
198	30 c. Robert Louis Stevenson Hotel, Abemama	35	40
199	50 c. Cargo ship off Betio	60	65
200	$1 Map of Kiribati	1·25	1·40

(Des J. Cooter. Litho Format)

1983 (19 May). *Island Maps (2nd series). Multicoloured designs as T* **25**. *W* w **15** *(sideways on 12 and 25 c.). P* 13½ × 14 *(horiz) or* 14 × 13½ *(vert).*

201	12 c. Beru, Nikunau and canoe	15	20
202	25 c. Abemama, Aranuka, Kuria and fish	30	35
203	35 c. Nonouti and reef fishing (*vert*)	40	45
204	50 c. Tarawa and House of Assembly (*vert*)	60	65

35 Collecting Coconuts

(Des G. Drummond. Litho Questa)

1983 (8 Aug). *Copra Industry. T* **35** *and similar horiz designs. Multicoloured. W* w **15**. *P* 14.

205	12 c. Type **35**	15	20
206	25 c. Selecting coconuts for copra	30	35
207	30 c. Removing husks	35	40
208	35 c. Drying copra	40	45
209	50 c. Loading copra at Betio	60	65

36 War Memorials

(Des J. Cooter. Litho Format)

1983 (17 Nov). *40th Anniv of Battle of Tarawa. T* **36** *and similar horiz designs. Multicoloured. W* w **15** *(sideways). P* 14.

210	12 c. Type **36**	15	20
211	30 c. Maps of Tarawa and Pacific Ocean	35	40
212	35 c. Gun emplacement	40	45
213	50 c. Modern and war-time landscapes	60	65
214	$1 Aircraft carrier U.S.S. *Tarawa*	1·25	1·40

(Des J. Cooter. Litho Format)

1984 (14 Feb). *Island Maps (3rd series). Multicoloured designs as T* **25**. *W* w **15** *(sideways). P* 13½ × 14.

215	12 c. Teraina and Captain Fanning's ship *Betsey*, 1798	15	20
216	30 c. Nikumaroro and Hawksbill Turtle	40	45
217	35 c. Kanton and local postmark	50	55
218	50 c. Banaba and Flying Fish	70	75

37 Tug *Riki*

(Des J. Cooter. Litho J.W.)

1984 (9 May). *Kiribati Shipping Corporation. T* **37** *and similar horiz designs. Multicoloured. W w* **15** *(sideways). P* 14.

219	12 c. Type **37**	..	20	25
220	35 c. Ferry *Nei Nimanoa*	..	45	50
221	50 c. Ferry *Nei Tebaa*	..	70	75
222	$1 Cargo ship *Nei Momi*	..	1·40	1·50
MS223	115 × 98 mm. Nos. 219/222. P 13 × 13½		2·75	3·00

38 Water and Sewage Schemes

(Des J. Cooter. Litho Format)

1984 (21 Aug). *"Ausipex" International Stamp Exhibition, Melbourne. T* **38** *and similar horiz designs. Multicoloured. W w* **15** *(sideways). P* 13½ × 14.

224	12 c. Type **38**	..	20	25
225	30 c. *Nouamake*, fishing boat	..	40	45
226	35 c. Overseas training schemes	..	45	50
227	50 c. International communications link	..	70	75

39 "Tabakea supporting Banaba"

(Des Jennifer Toombs. Litho Format)

1984 (21 Nov). *Kiribati Legends. T* **39** *and similar horiz designs. Multicoloured. W w* **15** *(sideways). P* 14.

228	12 c. Type **39**	..	20	25
229	30 c. "Nakaa, Judge of the Dead"	..	40	45
230	35 c. "Naareau and Dragonfly"	..	45	50
231	50 c. "Whistling Ghosts"	..	70	75

POSTAGE DUE STAMPS

D 1 Kiribati Coat of Arms

(Litho Format)

1981 (27 Aug). *P* 14.

D1	D 1	1 c. black and magenta	5	5
D2		2 c. black and greenish blue	5	5
D3		5 c. black and bright green	5	5
D4		10 c. black and chestnut	12	12
D5		20 c. black and bright blue	25	25
D6		30 c. black and brown-ochre	35	35
D7		40 c. black and purple	45	45
D8		50 c. black and deep blue-green	60	60
D9		$1 black and orange-red	1·10	1·10
D1/9		*Set of* 9	2·75	2·75

OFFICIAL STAMPS

O.K.G.S. (O 1)

O.K.G.S. (O 2)

1981 (May). *Optd with Type* O **1**. A. *On Nos.* 86, 90/3, 95 *and* 97/9*a*, *W* w **14**. B. *On Nos.* 121/35. *No wmk.*

		A		B	
O 1	1 c. Type **16**	4·00	4·00	5	5
O 2	3 c. M.V. *Tautunu* (T class inter-island touring vessel)	†		5	5
O 3	5 c. Hibiscus	†		5	5
O 4	7 c. Catholic Cathedral, Tarawa	†		8	10
O 5	10 c. Maneaba, Bikenibeu	40·00	40·00	10	12
	a. Opt double	†		90·00	—
O 6	12 c. Betio Harbour	9·50	9·50	12	15
O 7	15 c. Reef Egret	40·00	40·00	15	20
O 8	20 c. Flamboyant Tree	20·00	20·00	20	25
O 9	25 c. Moorish Idol	†		25	30
O10	30 c. Frangipani	14·00	14·00	30	35
	a. Opt double	†		60·00	—
O11	35 c. G.I.P.C. Chapel, Tangintebu	†		35	40
O12	50 c. *Hypolimnas bolina eliciana* (butterfly)	14·00	14·00	50	55
	a. Opt double	†		75·00	—
	b. Opt inverted	†		85·00	—
O13	$1 *Tabakea* (Tarawa Lagoon ferry)	30·00	30·00	1·00	1·00
O14	$2 Evening scene	35·00	35·00	2·00	2·25
	a. Opt double	†		£150	—
O15	$5 National flag	10·00	10·00	5·00	5·00
	a. Opt inverted	£200	—	†	
O1A/15A	*Set of* 10	£190	£190		
O1B/15B	*Set of* 15			9·00	9·50

1983. *Nos.* 86, 90/3, 95 *and* 97/9 *optd with Type* O **2**.

O16	1 c. Type **16**	5·00	5·00
O17	10 c. Maneaba, Bikenibeu	25·00	15·00
O18	12 c. Betio Harbour	10·00	8·00
O19	15 c. Eastern Reef Heron	25·00	25·00
O20	20 c. Flamboyant Tree	15·00	12·00
O21	30 c. Frangipani	12·00	10·00
O22	50 c. *Hypolimnas bolina elliciana* (butterfly)	15·00	12·00
O23	$1 *Tabakea* (Tarawa Lagoon ferry)	20·00	15·00
O24	$2 Evening scene	25·00	20·00
O16/24	*Set of* 9	£140	£110

1983 (28 June). *Nos.* 169, 172/3, 175 *and* 177 *optd with Type* O **2**.

O25	12 c. Polynesian Reed Warbler	15	20
O26	30 c. Brown Booby	35	40
O27	35 c. Audubon's Shearwater	40	45
O28	50 c. Bristle-thighed Curlew	60	65
O29	$2 Long-tailed Koel	2·25	2·50

Kuwait

Kuwait, an independent Arab shaikhdom since 1756, placed itself under British protection in 1899 to counter the spread of Ottoman influence in the Arabian Gulf.

The first, somewhat limited, postal service, via Bushire, commenced with the appointment of a Political Agent to Kuwait in August 1904. Because of diplomatic problems this system continued until 21 January 1915 when a regular Indian post office was established.

Limited supplies of Indian stamps were used by the Political Agency postal service, but these became available to the general public from 21 January 1915. Stamps seen postally used from Kuwait before 1923 are usually ½ a., 1 a., 1 r. or 5 r. values, with the occasional Official issue. Much more common are values to 15 r., both postage and Official, used telegraphically.

Before 1910 the name of the shaikhdom was spelt "KOWEIT" and this spelling appears on various circular postmarks used between 1915 and 1923. The more modern version of the name was first used for a postal cancellation in 1923.

1915 "KOWEIT"

1923 "KUWAIT"

In 1921 responsibility for the Kuwait postal service passed to the Iraq Post Office, but later it reverted to Indian administration some time before 1929.

PRICES FOR STAMPS ON COVER TO 1945	
Nos. 1/15	*from* × 5
Nos. 16/29	*from* × 3
Nos. 31/51	*from* × 2
Nos. 52/63	*from* × 4
Nos. O1/27	*from* × 10

USED HIGH VALUES. It is necessary to emphasize that used prices quoted for high value stamps are for postally used examples.

KUWAIT (1)

KUWAIT (2)

1923 (1 Apr)–**24**. *Stamps of India (King George V), optd with T* **1** *or* **2** *(rupee values, 15½ mm). Star wmk. P* 14.

1	**56**	½ a. green	60	1·50
		a. Opt double		
		b. Vert pair, one without opt		
2	**57**	1 a. chocolate	80	1·25
		a. Opt double		
		b. Opt omitted (lower stamp of vert pair)		
3	**58**	1½ a. chocolate (A)	75	1·75
4	**59**	2 a. violet	75	65
		a. Bright purple		
5	**61**	2 a. 6 p. ultramarine	1·50	5·50
6	**62**	3 a. orange-brown	3·50	13·00
7		3 a. ultramarine (1924)	7·00	95
8	**63**	4 a. deep olive	6·00	10·00
		a. Olive-green		
9	**64**	6 a. yellow-bistre	8·00	12·00
10	**65**	8 a. purple	8·00	12·00
		a. Mauve		
11	**66**	12 a. claret	12·00	16·00
12	**67**	1 r. brown and green	12·00	6·00
		a. Red-brown and blue-green	15·00	10·00
13		2 r. carmine and yellow-brown	45·00	90·00
14		5 r. ultramarine and violet	85·00	£200
15		10 r. green and scarlet	£130	£450
1/15		*Set of* 15	£300	£750

Essays of the overprint using the obsolete spelling "KOWEIT" were prepared in 1923 and can be found on the original 14 values of the postage stamps and on the 13 stamps of the Official series. (*Price for set of* 27 *unused* £19000).

Nos. 1/4 and 6/7 are all known with inverted overprint. It is doubtful if such errors were actually sold at the Kuwait Post Office, although some are known on registered or ordinary covers.

From 22 April 1929 the post office in Kuwait was again placed under the control of the Iraq Mandate postal administration.

KUWAIT (3) KUWAIT (4)

1929–37. *Stamps of India (King George V, Nasik printing), optd with T* **3** *or* **4** *(rupee values). Mult Star wmk. P* 14.

No.	Type	Description	Unused	Used
16	**56**	½ a. green	65	1·00
16*a*	**79**	½ a. green (1934)	4·00	60
17	**57**	1 a. chocolate	9·00	95
17*a*	**81**	1 a. chocolate (1934)	3·25	60
18	**70**	2 a. purple	1·40	50
19		2 a. vermilion	35·00	42·00
19*a*	**59**	2 a. vermilion (1934)	10·00	7·00
19*b*		2 a. vermilion (*small die*) (1937)	1·75	1·40
20	**62**	3 a. bright blue	6·50	1·60
21		3 a. carmine	8·50	8·50
22	**71**	4 a. sage-green	30·00	42·00
22*a*	**63**	4 a. sage-green (1934)	5·00	6·00
22*b*	**64**	6 a. bistre (1937)	8·00	10·00
23	**65**	8 a. reddish purple	10·00	11·00
24	**66**	12 a. claret (1933)	17·00	18·00
25	**67**	1 r. chocolate and green	13·00	11·00
26		2 r. carmine and orange	35·00	42·00
27		5 r. ultramarine and purple (1937)	£100	£160
28		10 r. green and scarlet (1934)	£180	£325
29		15 r. blue and olive (1937)	£375	£650
16/29		*Set of* 20	£800	£1200

1933 (Feb)–**34.** *Air. Stamps of India optd as T* **2** *(16½ mm).*

No.	Type	Description	Unused	Used
31	**72**	2 a. deep blue-green	13·00	20·00
32		3 a. blue	3·00	3·50
		a. Stamp doubly printed	£850	£650
33		4 a. drab	£160	£275
34		6 a. bistre (2.34)	5·00	6·50

1939. *Nos.* 247/8, 251, 253, 255/63 *of India optd with T* **3** *or* **4** *(rupee values).*

No.	Type	Description	Unused	Used
36	**91**	½ a. red-brown	85	60
38		1 a. carmine	1·00	60
39	**92**	2 a. vermilion	1·50	1·00
41	–	3 a. yellow-green	1·75	1·25
43	–	4 a. brown	3·75	4·50
44	–	6 a. turquoise-green	4·00	4·50
45	–	8 a. slate-violet	8·50	9·00
46	–	12 a. lake	11·00	11·00
47	**93**	1 r. grey and red-brown	2·50	1·90
48		2 r. purple and brown	5·00	5·00
49		5 r. green and blue	12·00	13·00
50		10 r. purple and claret	70·00	55·00
		a. Opt double	£300	£300
51		15 r. brown and green	90·00	£120
36/51		*Set of* 13	£190	£200

Following the rebellion in Iraq control of the Kuwait postal service was assumed by the Indian authorities.

Unoverprinted stamps of INDIA were used in Kuwait between 1942 and 1945.

1945. *Stamps of India (King George VI, on white background) optd with T* **3**.

No.	Type	Description	Unused	Used
52	**100*a***	3 p. slate	70	75
53		½ a. purple	70	50
54		9 p. green	70	1·00
55		1 a. carmine	70	70
56	**101**	1½ a. dull violet	70	1·00
57		2 a. vermilion	70	1·00
58		3 a. bright violet	70	1·00
59		3½ a. bright blue	80	1·25
60	**102**	4 a. brown	70	1·25
60*a*		6 a. turquoise-green	9·50	11·00
61		8 a. slate-violet	90	90
62		12 a. lake	1·25	2·25
63	**103**	14 a. purple	8·00	12·00
52/63		*Set of* 13	23·00	32·00

Following a short period of Pakistani control, from August 1947 the Kuwait postal service passed to British administration on 1 April 1948.

KUWAIT 1 ANNA (5)

KUWAIT 5 RUPEES (6)

NOTE. From 1948 onwards, for stamps with similar surcharges, but without name of country, see British Postal Agencies in Eastern Arabia.

1948 (1 Apr)–**49.** *Stamps of Great Britain (K.G. VI), surch as T* **5** *or* **6** *(rupee values).*

No.	Type	Description	Unused	Used
64	**128**	½ a. on ½d. pale green	12	25
65		1 a. on 1d. pale scarlet	12	25
66		1½ a. on 1½d. pale red-brown	12	25
67		2 a. on 2d. pale orange	12	25
68		2½ a. on 2½d. light ultramarine	12	40
69		3 a. on 3d. pale violet	12	15
		a. Pair, one surch albino	£1200	£750
70	**129**	6 a. on 6d. purple	20	15
71	**130**	1 r. on 1s. bistre-brown	50	50
72	**131**	2 r. on 2s. 6d. yellow-green	1·50	3·25
73		5 r. on 5s. red	4·25	6·50
73*a*	**132**	10 r. on 10s. ultramarine (4.7.49)	45·00	23·00
64/73*a*		*Set of* 11	48·00	32·00

KUWAIT 2½ ANNAS (7)

KUWAIT 15 RUPEES (8)

1948 (26 Apr). *Royal Silver Wedding. Nos.* 493/4 *of Great Britain surch with T* **7** *or* **8**.

No.	Type	Description	Unused	Used
74	**137**	2½ a. on 2½d. ultramarine	30	15
75	**138**	15 r. on £1 blue	38·00	55·00
		a. Short bars (R.3/4)		

No. 75a has the bars cancelling the original face value 3 mm long instead of the 3½ mm of the normal surcharge.

1948 (29 July). *Olympic Games. Nos.* 495/8 *of Great Britain surch as T* **7**, *but in one line (6 a.) or two lines (others).*

No.	Type	Description	Unused	Used
76	**139**	2½ a. on 2½d. ultramarine	35	50
77	**140**	3 a. on 3d. violet	40	70
78	**141**	6 a. on 6d. bright purple	70	85
79	**142**	1 r. on 1s. brown	1·10	1·25

1949 (10 Oct). *75th Anniv of U.P.U. Nos.* 499/502 *of Great Britain surch* "KUWAIT" *and new values.*

No.	Type	Description	Unused	Used
80	**143**	2½ a. on 2½d. ultramarine	35	60
81	**144**	3 a. on 3d. violet	75	85
82	**145**	6 a. on 6d. bright purple	90	1·00
83	**146**	1 r. on 1s. brown	1·75	1·25

KUWAIT KUWAIT

2 RUPEES Type I — 2 RUPEES Type II (8*a*)

KUWAIT 10 RUPEES Type I

KUWAIT 10 RUPEES Type II (8*b*)

2 r. Type I Type-set surcharge. "2" level with "RUPEES". Surcharge sharp.

Type II. Plate-printed surcharge. "2" raised. Surcharge worn.

10 r. Type I. Type-set surcharge. "1" and "O" spaced. Surcharge sharp and clean.

Type II. Plate-printed surcharge. "1" and "O" closer together. Surcharge appears heavy and worn, see especially "A", "R" and "P".

1950 (2 Oct)–**55.** *Nos.* 503/11 *of Great Britain surch as T* **5** *or* **8*a/b*** *(rupee values).*

No.	Type	Description	Unused	Used
84	**128**	½ a. on ½d. pale orange (3.5.51)	20	35
85		1 a. on 1d. light ultramarine (3.5.51)	20	30
86		1½ a. on 1½d. pale green (3.5.51)	20	50
87		2 a. on 2d. pale red-brown (3.5.51)	20	35
88		2½ a. on 2½d. pale scarlet (3.5.51)	35	35
89	**129**	4 a. on 4d. light ultramarine	25	25
90	**147**	2 r. on 2s. 6d. yellow-green (I) (3.5.51)	10·00	4·75
		a. Type II surch (1955)	£130	38·00
91	**148**	5 r. on 5s. red (3.5.51)	20·00	7·50
92	**149**	10 r. on 10s. ultramarine (I) (3.5.51)	32·00	9·00
		a. Type II surch (1953)	£140	45·00
84/92		*Set of* 9	60·00	22·00

No. 92a is known with surch spaced 10 mm apart instead of 9 mm.

1952 (10 Dec)–**54.** *Stamps of Great Britain (Queen Elizabeth II). Wmk Tudor Crown, surch as T* **5**.

No.	Type	Description	Unused	Used
93	**154**	½ a. on ½d. orange-red (31.8.53)	15	5
94		1 a. on 1d. ultramarine (31.8.53)	15	5
95		1½ a. on 1½d. green	15	5
96		2 a. on 2d. red-brown (31.8.53)	25	5
97	**155**	2½ a. on 2½d. carmine-red	15	5
98		3 a. on 3d. deep lilac (B.) (18.1.54)	40	5
99	**156**	4 a. on 4d. ultramarine (2.11.53)	1·25	35
100	**157**	6 a. on 6d. reddish purple (18.1.54)	85	5
101	**160**	12 a. on 1s. 3d. green (2.11.53)	4·50	1·75
102	**159**	1 r. on 1s. 6d. grey-blue (2.11.53)	4·50	60
93/102		*Set of* 10	11·00	2·40

1953 (3 June). *Coronation. Stamps of Great Britain surch* "KUWAIT" *and new values.*

No.	Type	Description	Unused	Used
103	**161**	2½ a. on 2½d. carmine-red	1·25	75
104	**162**	4 a. on 4d. ultramarine	2·25	1·25
105	**163**	12 a. on 1s. 3d. deep yellow-green	3·00	2·75
106	**164**	1 r. on 1s. 6d. deep grey-blue	3·00	2·00

PRICES OF SETS

Set prices are given for many issues, generally those containing five stamps or more. Definitive sets include one of each value or major colour change, but do not cover different perforations, die types or minor shades. Where a choice is possible the set prices are based on the cheapest versions of the stamps included in the listings.

KUWAIT 2 RUPEES I — KUWAIT 2 RUPEES II (9)

KUWAIT 5 RUPEES I — KUWAIT 5 RUPEES II (10)

KUWAIT 10 RUPEES I — KUWAIT 10 RUPEES II (11)

Type I (9/11). Type-set overprints. Bold (generally thicker) letters with sharp corners and straight edges. Bars close together and usually slightly longer than in Type II.

Type II (9/11). Plate-printed overprints. Thinner letters, rounder corners and rough edges. Bars wider apart.

1955–57. *Nos.* 536/8 *of Great Britain surch.*

No.	Type	Description	I (23.9.55) Unused	I Used	II (10.10.57) Unused	II Used
107	**166**	2 r. on 2s. 6d. black-brown	7·50	1·50	32·00	8·00
108	**167**	5 r. on 5s. rose-red	16·00	4·75	50·00	15·00
109	**168**	10 r. on 10s. ultramarine	19·00	9·00	£120	70·00

1956. *Stamps of Great Britain (Queen Elizabeth II). Wmk St. Edward's Crown, surch* "KUWAIT" *and new value.*

No.	Type	Description	Unused	Used
110	**154**	½ a. on ½d. orange-red	8	5
111		1 a. on 1d. ultramarine	12	10
112		1½ a. on 1½d. green	15	8
113		2 a. on 2d. red-brown	15	8
114	**155**	2½ a. on 2½d. carmine-red	30	15
116	**156**	4 a. on 4d. ultramarine	4·50	1·00
117	**157**	6 a. on 6d. reddish purple	80	15
118	**160**	12 a. on 1s. 3d. green	9·50	3·75
119	**159**	1 r. on 1s. 6d. grey-blue	1·50	25
110/19		*Set of* 9	15·00	5·00

(New Currency. 100 naye paise = 1 rupee)

KUWAIT NP 1 NP (12) — KUWAIT 3 NP NP (13) — KUWAIT 75 NP (14)

1957 (1 June)–**58.** *Stamps of Great Britain (Queen Elizabeth II). W* **165**, *St. Edward's Crown, surch as T* **12** *(1, 15, 25, 40, 50 n.p.),* **14** *(75 n.p.) or* **13** *(others).*

No.	Type	Description	Unused	Used
120	**157**	1 n.p. on 5d. brown	5	20
121	**154**	3 n.p. on ½d. orange-red	20	25
122		6 n.p. on 1d. ultramarine	20	20
123		9 n.p. on 1½d. green	25	12
124		12 n.p. on 2d. light red-brown	30	20
125	**155**	15 n.p. on 2½d. carmine-red (Type I)	30	15
		a. Type II (11.58)	28·00	28·00
126		20 n.p. on 3d. deep lilac (B.)	30	5
127	**156**	25 n.p. on 4d. ultramarine	1·50	1·75
128	**157**	40 n.p. on 6d. reddish purple	65	5
129	**158**	50 n.p. on 9d. bronze-green	4·25	2·50
130	**160**	75 n.p. on 1s. 3d. green	4·25	2·25
120/30		*Set of* 11	11·00	7·00

15 Shaikh Abdullah as-Salim as-Sabah

(Recess D.L.R.)

1958 (1 Feb). *P* 12½.

No.	Type	Description	Unused	Used
131	**35**	5 n.p. bluish green	12	5
132		10 n.p. rose-red (*shades*)	12	5
136		40 n.p. maroon	75	25

Nos. 131/6 were only valid for internal use in Kuwait prior to 1 February 1959. Further values were added to this series following the closure of the British Agency Post Offices on 31 January 1959. Responsibility of the postal service then passed to the Kuwait Government and later issues are listed in Part 19 (*Middle East*) of this catalogue.

OFFICIAL STAMPS

KUWAIT SERVICE (O 1)   KUWAIT SERVICE (O 2)

1923–24. *Stamps of India (King George V), optd with Type* O **1** *or* O **2** *(rupee values, 15½–16 mm). Star Wmk. P* 14.
O 1 **56** ½ a. green .. 35 2·00
a. Opt double ..
O 2 **57** 1 a. chocolate .. 40 1·75
a. Opt double ..
O 3 **58** 1½ a. chocolate (A) .. 1·25 5·00
O 4 **59** 2 a. violet .. 2·00 5·50
a. Bright purple
O 5 **61** 2 a. 6p. ultramarine .. 2·75 9·00
O 6 **62** 3 a. orange-brown .. 5·00 17·00
O 7 3 a. ultramarine (1924) .. 1·75 7·50
O 8 **63** 4 a. olive-green .. 3·00 15·00
O 9 **65** 8 a. purple .. 4·25 16·00
a. Mauve
O10 **67** 1 r. brown and green .. 9·00 35·00
a. Opt double, one albino
O11 2 r. carmine and yellow-brown .. 16·00 55·00
O12 5 r. ultramarine and violet .. 48·00 £170
a. Opt double, one albino
O13 10 r. green and scarlet .. 90·00 £300
O14 15 r. blue and olive .. £120 £425
O1/14 .. *Set of* 14 £275 £1000

1929–33. *Stamps of India (Nasik printing) optd as Types* O **1** *(spaced 10 mm) or* O **2** *(14½ mm × 19–20 mm wide). Mult Star wmk. P* 14.
O16 **57** 1 a. chocolate .. 45 2·50
O17 **70** 2 a. purple .. 20·00 30·00
O19 **62** 3 a. blue .. 1·25 4·25
O20 **71** 4 a. sage-green .. 4·25 13·00
O21 **65** 8 a. reddish purple .. 2·75 15·00
O22 **66** 12 a. claret .. 9·50 28·00
O23 **67** 1 r. chocolate and green .. 7·00 45·00
O24 2 r. carmine and orange .. 11·00 90·00
O25 5 r. ultramarine and purple .. 27·00 £225
O26 10 r. green and scarlet .. 65·00 £350
O27 15 r. blue and olive .. £110 £600
O16/27 .. *Set of* 11 £225 £1200

Labuan

CROWN COLONY

Stamps of the STRAITS SETTLEMENTS were used in Labuan prior to 1879. Covers of 1864 are also known franked with stamps of INDIA or HONG KONG.

PRICES FOR STAMPS ON COVER	
Nos. 1/4	—
Nos. 5/10	*from* × 15
Nos. 11/13	—
Nos. 14/21	*from* × 10
Nos. 22/5	—
Nos. 26/38	*from* × 10
Nos. 39/47	*from* × 100
Nos. 49/50	*from* × 10
Nos. 51/7	*from* × 60
Nos. 62/74	*from* × 15
Nos. 75/9	*from* × 30
Nos. 80/8	*from* × 20
Nos. 89/97	*from* × 15
Nos. 98/110	*from* × 10
Nos. 111/35	*from* × 30
Nos. 136/40	—
Nos. D1/9	*from* × 15

1

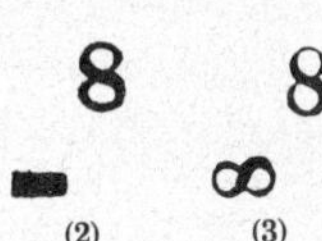
(2) (3)

(Recess D.L.R.)

1879 (May). *Wmk CA over Crown, sideways. P* 14.
1 **1** 2 c. blue-green .. £450 £450
2 6 c. orange-brown .. £100 90·00
3 12 c. carmine .. £600 £350
4 16 c. blue .. 27·00 30·00

This watermark is always found sideways, and extends over two stamps, a single specimen showing only a portion of the Crown or the letters CA, these being tall and far apart. This paper was chiefly used for long fiscal stamps.

1880 (Jan)–**82.** *Wmk Crown CC. P* 14.
5 **1** 2 c. yellow-green .. 5·00 6·00
6 6 c. orange-brown .. 30·00 30·00
7 8 c. carmine (4.82) .. 30·00 30·00
8 10 c. brown .. 27·00 30·00
9 12 c. carmine .. 70·00 70·00
10 16 c. blue (1881) .. 27·00 35·00
5/10 .. *Set of* 6 £175 £175

1880 (Aug). (*a*) *No. 9 surch, with numerals in centre, in black, and the original value obliterated, as T* **2**, *in red or black.*
11 8 c. on 12 c. carmine .. £450 £400
a. "8" inverted .. £450 £400
b. "12" not obliterated .. £550 £500
c. As b. with "8" inverted ..

(*b*) *No. 4 surch with two upright figures and No. 9 surch with numeral in centre, and another across the original value as T* **3**.
12 6 c. on 16 c. blue (R.) .. £800 £475
a. With one "6" only
13 8 c. on 12 c. carmine .. £500 £450
a. Both "8's" upright
b. Upright "8" inverted .. £600 £500

EIGHT CENTS (4)   Eight Cents (5)   One Dollar A.S.H. (6)

1881 (Mar). *No. 9 surch as T* **4**.
14 8 c. on 12 c. carmine .. £100 £110

1881 (June). *No. 9 surch as T* **5**.
15 8 c. on 12 c. carmine .. 30·00 35·00
a. Surch double .. £275 £275
b. Surch inverted .. £900
c. "Eighr" .. £3000

The error "Eighr" was No. 6 in the first printing, but this was soon corrected.

1883. *Wmk Crown CA. P* 14.
17 **1** 2 c. green .. 4·00 4·50
a. Imperf between (horiz pair) .. £1000
18 8 c. carmine .. 50·00 35·00
19 10 c. yellow-brown .. 13·00 14·00
20 16 c. blue .. 24·00 26·00
21 40 c. amber .. 7·00 9·00

1883 (May). *No. 10 surch "One Dollar A.S.H." by hand, as T* **6**.
22 **1** $1 on 16 c. blue (R.) .. £1900

The initials are those of the postmaster, Mr. A. S. Hamilton.

2 CENTS (7)   2 Cents (8)

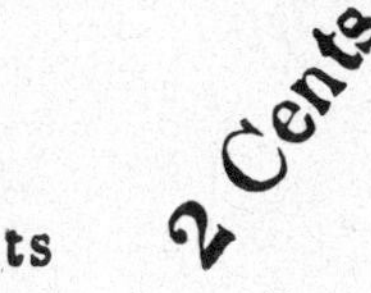

(9)

1885 (June). *Nos. 18 and 10 handstamped as T* **7**.
23 **1** 2 c. on 8 c. carmine .. 28·00
24 2 c. on 16 c. blue .. £500 £450

1885 (June). *No. 20 surch as T* **8**.
25 **1** 2 c. on 16 c. blue .. 38·00 42·00
a. Surch double .. — £1100

1885 (Sept). *No. 18 handstamped diag as T* **9**.
26 **1** 2 c. on 8 c. carmine .. 15·00 20·00

1885–86. *Wmk Crown CA. P* 14.
30 **1** 2 c. rose-red (9.85) .. 1·00 1·75
a. Pale rose-red (5.86) .. 1·00 1·75
31 8 c. deep violet (9.85) .. 7·00 6·00
a. Mauve (5.86) .. 6·00 6·00
32 10 c. sepia (5.86) .. 2·75 5·50
33 16 c. grey (5.86) .. 25·00 18·00
30/33 Optd "Specimen" .. *Set of* 4 £160

ISSUES OF BRITISH NORTH BORNEO COMPANY

From 1 January 1890 while remaining a Crown Colony, the administration of Labuan was transferred to the British North Borneo Co, which issued the following stamps.

6 Cents (10)   Two Cents (11)   Six Cents (12)

1891 (Aug). *T* **1** *surch as T* **10**. *P* 14.
34 6 c. on 8 c. deep violet (No. 31) .. 14·00 14·00
a. Surch inverted .. 24·00 24·00
b. Surch double .. £110
c. Surch double, one inverted .. £180
d. "Cents" omitted .. £180 £180
e. Imperf between (horiz pair)
35 6 c. on 8 c. mauve (No. 31*a*) .. 2·00 2·25
a. Surch inverted .. 14·00 14·00
b. Surch double, one inverted
c. Surch double, both inverted .. £200
d. "6" omitted .. £180
e. Pair, one without surcharge .. £275 £275
f. Inverted. "Cents" omitted .. £180
g. Pair, one without surch, one surch inverted .. £300
36 6 c. on 8 c. mauve (R.) (No. 31*a*) .. £225 £110
a. Surch inverted .. £225 £110
37 6 c. on 16 c. blue (No. 4) .. £1200 £1100
a. Surch inverted .. £1800 £1500
38 6 c. on 40 c. amber (No. 21) .. £1400 £1500
a. Surch inverted .. £1900 £1700

There are two different versions of Type **10** with the lines of the surcharge either 1 mm or 2 mm apart.

(Recess D.L.R.)

1892–93. *No. wmk. P* 14.
39 **1** 2 c. rose-lake .. 80 1·25
40 6 c. bright green .. 1·50 1·50
41 8 c. violet .. 1·25 1·75
a. Pale violet (1893) .. 1·50 1·75
43 10 c. brown .. 1·25 1·50
a. Sepia-brown (1893) .. 1·10 1·75
45 12 c. bright blue .. 1·25 1·60
46 16 c. grey .. 1·90 1·75
47 40 c. ochre .. 6·00 7·50
a. Brown-buff (1893) .. 10·00 12·00
39/47 .. *Set of* 7 13·00 15·00

The 6 c., 12 c., 16 c. and 40 c. are in sheets of 10, as are all the earlier issues. The other values are in sheets of 30.

1892 (Dec). *Nos. 47 and 46 surch locally as T* **11** *or* **12**.
49 **1** 2 c. on 40 c. ochre (13 December) .. 48·00 42·00
a. Surch inverted .. £110 £140
50 6 c. on 16 c. grey (20 December) .. 80·00 70·00
a. Surch inverted .. £150 £130

There are 10 types of each of these surcharges.

(Litho D.L.R.)

1894 (April). *No wmk. P* 14.
51 **1** 2 c. carmine-pink .. 1·10 1·40
52 6 c. bright green .. 3·00 2·50
a. Imperf between (horiz pair) .. £900
53 8 c. bright mauve .. 5·00 3·00
54 10 c. brown .. 5·50 3·00
55 12 c. pale blue .. 6·00 5·50
56 16 c. grey .. 7·00 4·00
57 40 c. orange-buff .. 10·00 7·50
51/57 .. *Set of* 7 32·00 24·00
51/57 H/S "Specimen" .. *Set of* 7 £120

Collectors are warned against forgeries of this issue.

CANCELLED-TO-ORDER. The used prices quoted are for stamps postally used. However, Nos. 51/79, 83/101, 116c/26 and D1/9 exist cancelled-to-order and are worth from 30p. each, except for errors and those quoted.

PERFORATION. There are a number of small variations in the perforation of the Waterlow issues of 1894 to 1905 which we believe to be due to irregularity of the pins rather than different perforators.

In the following lists, stamps perf 12, 12½, 13 or compound are described as perf 12–13, stamps perf 13½, 14 or compound are described as perf 13½–14 and those perf 14½, 15 or compound are listed as perf 14½–15. In addition the 13½–14 perforation exists compound with 14½–15 and with 12–13, whilst perf 16 comes from a separate perforator.

13

LABUAN 40 CENTS (14)

1894 (May)–**96.** *T* **24/32** *of North Borneo (colours changed), with "LABUAN" engraved on vignette plate as in T* **13**. *P* 14½–15.

(*a*) *Name and central part of design in black*
62 **24** 1 c. grey-mauve .. 90 1·25
a. Imperf between (vert pair) .. £250 £175
b. Perf 13½–14 .. 1·10
c. Perf 13½–14, comp 14½–15
d. Perf 13½–14, comp 12–13 ..
e. Perf 12–13 ..
63 **25** 2 c. blue .. 1·10 1·10
a. Imperf (pair) .. £250
b. Perf 13½–14 .. 90 1·10
c. Perf 13½–14, comp 14½–15
d. Perf 13½–14, comp 12–13 ..
e. Perf 12–13 ..
64 **26** 3 c. ochre .. 1·10
a. Perf 13½–14 .. 1·10 1·25
b. Perf 13½–14, comp 14½–15
c. Perf 13½–14, comp 12–13 ..
d. Perf 12–13 ..
65 **27** 5 c. green .. 2·25 3·50
a. Perf 13½–14 .. 2·25 1·60
ab. Imperf between (horiz pair)
b. Perf 13½–14, comp 12–13 .. 2·25
67 **28** 6 c. brown-lake .. 1·75 1·50
a. Imperf (pair) (*canc*) .. † £200
b. Perf 13½–14 (*canc* £1·25) ..
c. Perf 13½–14, comp 14½–15 (*canc* 70p.)
d. Perf 13½–14, comp 12–13 ..
e. Perf 12–13 ..
68 **29** 8 c. rose-red .. 4·75 5·50
a. Perf 13½–14 .. 4·75 5·50
69 8 c. pink (1896) .. 1·25 4·00
a. Perf 13½–14 .. 3·75
70 **30** 12 c. orange-vermilion .. 5·50 7·50
a. Perf 13½–14 (*canc* £2)
b. Perf 12–13 ..
c. Perf 13½–14, comp 12–13 ..
71 **31** 18 c. olive-brown .. 5·50 7·50
a. Perf 13½–14 .. 7·00
72 18 c. olive-bistre (1896) .. 7·00 6·50
a. Perf 13½–14 .. 7·00 7·50
b. Perf 13½–14, comp 12–13 ..

(*b*) *Name and central part in blue*
73 **32** 24 c. pale mauve .. 4·75 7·00
a. Perf 13½–14 .. 4·75 7·00
74 24 c. dull lilac (1896) .. 4·75
a. Perf 13½–14 .. 4·75
62/74 Optd "Specimen" .. *Set of* 9 £140

1895 (June). *No. 83 of North Borneo* ($1 *inscr* "STATE OF NORTH BORNEO") *surch as T* **14**.
75 **32c** 4 c. on $1 scarlet .. 90 1·10
76 10 c. on $1 scarlet .. 1·10 1·40

77 20 c. on $1 scarlet .. .. .. 3·25 2·40
78 30 c. on $1 scarlet .. .. .. 2·50 2·75
79 40 c. on $1 scarlet .. .. .. 3·75 2·75
75/79 Optd "Specimen" .. .. *Set of* 5 £110

No. 76 exists with the figures of the surcharge 2½ mm away from "CENTS". The normal setting has a space of 4 mm. Examples of the narrow setting have, so far, only been seen on cancelled-to-order stamps.

LABUAN (15) — 1846 JUBILEE 1896 (16) — 4 CENTS (17)

1895. *T* **32***a to* **32***c of North Borneo (as Nos.* 81 *to* 83, *but colours changed) optd with T* **15**.
80 25 c. green .. .. 10·00 10·00
a. Opt omitted (*canc* £1·25) .. .. .. 4·00
b. Imperf. Opt omitted .. .. .. 16·00
c. Imperf (pair). Stamps ptd double, one inverted .. ..
81 50 c. maroon .. .. 13·00 13·00
a. Opt omitted (*canc* £1·25) .. .. .. 4·50
b. Imperf. Opt omitted .. .. .. 16·00
c. Imperf (pair). Stamps ptd both sides ..
82 $1 blue .. .. 16·00 10·00
a. Opt omitted (*canc* £1·25) .. .. .. 6·00
b. Imperf. Opt omitted .. .. .. 16·00
80/82 Optd "Specimen" .. .. *Set of* 3 60·00

1896 (24 Sept). *Jubilee of Cession of Labuan to Gt Britain. Nos.* 62 *to* 68 *optd with T* **16**. *P* 14½–15.
83 1 c. black and grey-mauve .. .. .. 3·75 8·00
a. Opt double .. .. 70·00 70·00
b. Opt in orange .. .. 90·00 90·00
c. "JEBILEE" .. .. — £160
d. "JUBILE" (R. 3/10) .. .. ..
e. Perf 13½–14 .. .. 3·75
f. Perf 13½–14, comp 12–13 .. .. 3·75 3·75
g. Perf 12–13 .. ..
84 2 c. black and blue .. .. .. 4·00 5·00
a. Imperf horiz (vert pair) £140
b. "JEBILEE" £325
c. "JUBILE" (R.3/10) .. .. ..
d. Perf 13½–14 .. .. 4·00 5·00
e. Perf 13½–14, comp 14½–15 .. ..
f. Perf 13½–14, comp 12–13 .. ..
85 3 c. black and ochre .. .. .. 5·00 6·50
a. Opt double .. .. 65·00 35·00
b. Opt treble £650
c. "JEBILEE" .. .. — £700
d. Perf 13½–14 .. .. 9·00 9·00
e. Perf 13½–14, comp 14½–15 .. ..
86 5 c. black and green .. .. .. 6·50 6·50
a. Opt double .. .. 75·00 75·00
b. Perf 13½–14 .. .. 6·50 6·50
c. Perf 13½–14, comp 12–13 .. ..
87 6 c. black and brown-lake .. .. .. 6·50 6·50
a. Opt double .. .. 90·00 90·00
b. "JUBILE" (R. 3/10) .. .. ..
c. Perf 13½–14, comp 14½–15 .. ..
88 8 c. black and pink .. .. .. 6·50 6·50
a. Perf 13½–14 .. .. 6·50 6·50
b. Perf 13½–14, comp 14½–15 .. ..
83/88 .. .. *Set of* 6 28·00 32·00
83/88 Optd "Specimen" .. .. *Set of* 6 £170

No. 84b is known in a vertical strip of 3 imperf horizonally except at the base of the bottom stamp.

1897 (Apr)–**1901**. *T* **34/45** *of North Borneo (colours changed), optd* "LABUAN" *as in T* **13**. *Name and central part in black* (24 *c. in blue*). *P* 13½–14.
89 **34** 1 c. greyish purple (*p* 14½–15) .. .. 2·00 2·00
a. Perf 13½–14, comp 14½–15 .. ..
b. Brown (1901) .. .. .. 2·00 2·00
ba. Perf 14½–15 .. .. ..
bb. Perf 16 .. .. 2·00 2·00
90 **35** 2 c. blue .. .. 3·00 1·60
a. Imperf between (vert pair) .. .. † £150
b. Perf 14½–15 .. ..
c. Perf 13½–14. comp 12–13 .. .. 5·00
d. Perf 16 .. ..
91 **36** 3 c. ochre .. .. 2·50 3·00
a. Imperf between (vert pair) .. .. † —
b. Perf 14½–15 .. .. .. 2·50 3·00
c. Perf 13½–14, comp 12–13 .. ..
92 **38** 5 c. green .. .. 4·00 5·00
a. Perf 14½–15 .. .. ..
b. Perf 13½–14, comp 12–13 .. ..
93 **39** 6 c. brown-lake .. .. .. 2·75 5·50
a. Imperf between (vert pair) .. .. † £150
b. Perf 14½–15 .. .. .. 1·90 5·50
c. Perf 13½–14, comp 12–13 (*canc* £3)
94 **40** 8 c. rose-red .. ..
a. Perf 14½–15 .. .. .. 3·00 2·25
b. Perf 13½–14, comp 12–13 (*canc* £2·75) .. .. ..
c. Vermilion .. .. 2·00
ca. Perf 16 (*canc* £3) .. ..
95 **42** 12 c. vermilion .. .. .. 7·50 10·00
a. Perf 14½–15 .. .. .. 4·50
96 **44** 18 c. olive-bistre .. .. .. 3·75 5·50
a. Imperf between (vert pair) .. .. † —
b. Perf 16 .. ..
97 **45** 24 c. grey-lilac .. .. .. 4·75 6·50
a. Perf 14½–15 .. .. ..
89/97 Optd "Specimen" .. .. *Set of* 9 £150

The 12, 18 and 24 c. above were errors; in the 12 c., "LABUAN" is over the value at the top; the 18 c. has "POSTAL REVENUE" instead of "POSTAGE AND REVENUE", and the 24 c. is without "POSTAGE AND REVENUE".

1897 (Nov)–**98**. (*a*) *Types of North Borneo (colours changed), optd.* "LABUAN" *as in T* **13**. *P* 13½–14.
98 **42** 12 c. black and vermilion (3.98) (*canc* £1·50) .. .. ..
a. Perf 14½–15 .. .. .. 8·00 9·00
b. Perf 13½–14, comp 14½–15 ..
c. Perf 16 .. ..
99 **46** 18 c. black and olive-bistre .. ..
a. Perf 14½–15 .. .. .. 18·00 20·00
b. Perf 16 (*canc* £6·50) .. ..
100 **47** 24 c. blue and lilac-brown .. .. 6·00 9·00
a. Perf 14½–15 .. .. .. 6·00 9·00
b. Perf 13½–14, comp 12–13 .. ..
c. Perf 16 .. ..
d. Blue and ochre (*p* 14½–15) ..
98, 100 Optd "Specimen" .. .. *Set of* 2 38·00

In the 12 c. "LABUAN" is now correctly placed at foot of stamp. The 18 c. and 24 c. have the inscriptions on the stamps corrected, but the 18 c. still has "LABUAN" *over* the value at foot, and was further corrected as follows.

(*b*) *As No.* 99, *but* "LABUAN" *at top*
101 **46** 18 c. black and olive-bistre (Optd S. £25) 7·50 8·00
a. Perf 14½–15 .. .. .. 7·50 8·00
b. Perf 13½–14, comp 12–13 .. .. 4·00 4·50
c. Perf 12–13 .. ..

1899. *Surch with T* **17**. (*a*) *P* 14½–15.
102 **38** 4 c. on 5 c. (No. 92a) .. .. .. 6·50 9·50
103 **39** 4 c. on 6 c. (No. 93b) .. .. .. 6·50 9·50
a. Perf 13½–14 .. .. .. 12·00
b. Perf 13½–14, comp 12–13 .. ..
104 **40** 4 c. on 8 c. (No. 94a) .. .. ..
a. Perf 13½–14 .. .. .. 6·50 9·50
b. Perf 13½–14, comp 12–13 .. .. 12·00
c. Perf 12–13 .. ..
105 **42** 4 c. on 12 c. (No. 98a) .. .. 6·50 9·50
a. Perf 13½–14 .. .. .. 12·00
b. Perf 16 .. ..
c. Perf 13½–14, comp 12–13 .. ..
106 **46** 4 c. on 18 c (No. 101a) .. .. 6·50 9·50
a. Surch double £225 £275
107 **47** 4 c. on 24 c. (No. 100a) .. .. 6·50 9·50
a. Perf 13½–14 .. .. .. 6·50
b. Perf 13½–14, comp 12–13 .. .. — 4·00
c. Perf 16 .. .. 11·00

(*b*) *P* 14
108 **32***a* 4 c. on 25 c. (No. 80) .. .. 5·50 7·50
109 **32***b* 4 c. on 50 c. (No. 81) .. .. 5·50 7·50
110 **32***c* 4 c. on $1 (No. 82) .. .. 5·50 7·50
102/110 Optd "Specimen" .. *Set of* 9 £150

The 1 c., 2 c. and 3 c. values of this set were also surcharged "4 CENTS" but were not issued. They exist overprinted "Specimen" (*price* £150 *the set of three*).

1900–02. *Types of North Borneo, optd* "LABUAN" *as in T* **13**, *in green on* 16 *c. P* 13½–14.
111 **35** 2 c. black and green .. .. .. 1·75 3·00
a. Perf 13½–14, comp 12–13 .. ..
112 **37** 4 c. black and yellow-brown .. .. 2·75 6·00
a. Imperf between (vert pair) £140
b. Perf 13½–14, comp 12–13 .. ..
113 4 c. black and carmine (8.1900) .. 2·40 1·50
a. Perf 14½–15 .. .. .. 2·40 1·50
b. Perf 13½–14, comp 12–13 .. .. 4·00 2·00
c. Perf 16 .. ..
114 **38** 5 c. black and pale blue .. .. .. 5·00 6·00
a. Perf 13½–14, comp 12–13 .. ..
115 **41** 10 c. brn & slate-lilac (*p* 14½–15) (1902) 5·50
116 **43** 16 c. green and chestnut (1902) .. .. 8·00
a. Perf 13½–14, comp 12–13 .. .. 8·00 9·00
b. Perf 12–13 .. ..
c. Perf 14½–15 .. ..
111/116 Optd "Specimen" .. .. *Set of* 6 £120

18 — 4 cents (19)

(Recess Waterlow)

1902 (Sept)–**03**. *P* 13½–14.
116*d* **18** 1 c. black and purple (10.03) 85 95
da. Perf 14½–15 .. .. ..
117 2 c. black and green 85 50
a. Perf 14½–15 .. .. ..
117*b* 3 c. black and sepia (10.03) .. .. 1·00 85
118 4 c. black and carmine 80 50
a. Perf 14½–15 .. .. ..
119 8 c. black and vermilion 40 90
a. Perf 14½–15 .. .. ..
120 10 c. brown and slate-blue 70 90
a. Imperf between (vert pair) (*canc*) .. † £160
b. Perf 14½–15 .. .. ..
121 12 c. black and yellow .. .. .. 1·10 1·40
a. Perf 16 .. .. 1·10
122 16 c. green and brown .. .. .. 70 1·25
a. Imperf between (vert pair) .. .. † —
123 18 c. black and pale brown .. .. 70 2·25
124 25 c. green and greenish blue .. .. 70 2·25
a. Perf 14½–15 .. .. ..
b. Error. Blk & greenish bl (*canc*) .. † 70·00
125 50 c. dull purple and lilac .. .. 2·50 4·50
a. Perf 13½–14, comp 12–13 .. ..
126 $1 claret and orange .. .. .. 1·40 7·50
a. Perf 14½–15 .. .. ..
116*d*/126 .. .. .. *Set of* 12 8·50 21·00
116*d*/26 Optd "Specimen" .. .. *Set of* 12 £200

1904 (Dec). *Issues of* 1895 *and* 1897–8 *surch with T* **19**.

(*a*) *P* 14½–15.
127 **38** 4 c. on 5 c. (No. 92a) .. .. .. 5·50 8·50
128 **39** 4 c. on 6 c. (No. 93b) .. .. .. 5·50 8·50
129 **40** 4 c. on 8 c. (No. 94a) .. .. .. 5·50 8·50
130 **42** 4 c. on 12 c. (No. 98a) .. .. 5·50 8·50
a. Perf 16 .. .. 8·00
131 **46** 4 c. on 18 c. (No. 101) (*p* 13½–14) .. 5·50 8·50
a. Perf 13½–14, comp 12–13 .. .. 8·50
b. Perf 12–13 .. ..
132 **47** 4 c. on 24 c. (No. 100a) .. .. 5·50 8·50
a. Perf 13½–14 .. .. .. 5·50
b. Perf 13½–14, comp 12–13 .. .. 8·50
c. Perf 16 .. ..

(*b*) *P* 14
133 **32***a* 4 c. on 25 c. (No. 80) .. .. 5·50 8·50
134 **32***b* 4 c. on 50 c. (No. 81) .. .. 5·50 8·50
a. Surch double £200
b. Surch triple .. .. ..
135 **32***c* 4 c. on $1 (No. 82) .. .. .. 5·50 8·50

LABUAN (20) — LABUAN (21)

1905 (Feb-Nov). *Nos.* 81, 83 (*in Labuan colour*), *and* 84/6 *of North Borneo optd locally with T* **20** (25 *c.*, $2) *or* **21** *others*).
136 **32***a* 25 c. indigo £500 £300
137 **32***c* $1 blue .. .. † £300
138 **32***d* $2 dull green £2250 £900
139 **14** $5 bright purple £2750 £950
140 **15** $10 brown (11.05) .. .. .. † £2000

Dangerous forgeries exist.
The overprint on No. 138 is 12 mm long.
No. 137 is said to have been issued in 1896.

POSTAGE DUE STAMPS

POSTAGE DUE (D 1)

1901. *Optd with Type* D 1, *reading vertically upwards. P* 13½–14.
D1 **35** 2 c. black and green (111) .. .. 5·00 2·00
a. Opt double £110
b. Perf 13½–14, comp 12–13 .. ..
D2 **36** 3 c. black and ochre (91) .. .. 5·00
a. Perf 13½–14, comp 12–13 .. ..
D3 **37** 4 c. black and carmine (113) .. .. 5·50
a. Opt double (*canc*) .. .. .. — 75·00
b. Perf 14½–15 .. .. .. 5·50
D4 **38** 5 c. blk & pale bl (114) (*canc* £2·40) .. 5·00
a. Perf 14½–15 .. .. .. 5·00
b. Perf 13½–14, comp 12–13 .. ..
D5 **39** 6 c. black and brown-lake (93) .. .. 6·00
a. Perf 14½–15 .. .. ..
b. Perf 16 .. .. 8·50
D6 **40** 8 c. black and vermilion (94c) .. .. 8·00
a. Frame inverted (*p* 14½–15) (*canc*) — £1500
b. Perf 14½–15 .. .. .. 5·50
c. Perf 16 .. .. 9·50
d. Black and rose-red (94) .. .. 11·00
da. Perf 14½–15 (*canc* £6·50) .. ..
db. Perf 13½–14, comp 12–13 .. ..
D7 **42** 12 c. black and vermilion (98) (*canc* £8) 13·00 22·00
a. Opt reading downwards (*canc*) .. — £110
b. Perf 14½–15 .. .. .. 16·00
D8 **46** 18 c. black & olive-bistre (101) (*p*14½–15) 4·25
D9 **47** 24 c. blue and lilac-brown (100) .. .. 6·50
a. Perf 13½–14, comp 12–13 .. ..
b. Perf 14½–15 .. .. .. 7·50
ba. Blue and ochre .. .. .. 11·00
c. Perf 16 .. .. 7·50
D1/9b .. .. *Set of* 9 50·00

By Letters Patent dated 30 October 1906, Labuan was incorporated with Straits Settlements and ceased issuing its own stamps. In 1946 it became part of the Colony of North Borneo.

Lagos

A British Consul was established at Lagos during 1851 as part of the anti-slavery policy, but the territory was not placed under British administration until the treaty of August 1861.

Although a postal service had been established by the British G.P.O. in 1851 no postal markings were supplied to Lagos until 1859. The British G.P.O. retained control of the postal service until 1874, when it became the responsibility of the colonial authorities.

For illustrations of handstamp types see BRITISH POST OFFICES ABROAD notes, following GREAT BRITAIN.

CROWNED-CIRCLE HANDSTAMPS

CC1 CC 4 LAGOS (19.2.1859) .. .. *Price on cover* £1000

PRICES FOR STAMPS ON COVER	
Nos. 1/9	*from* × 6
Nos. 10/41	*from* × 5
No. 42	*from* × 15
Nos. 44/53	*from* × 5
Nos. 54/63	*from* × 4

PRINTERS. All the stamps of Lagos were typographed by D.L.R.

1

1874 (10 June)–**75**. *Wmk Crown CC. P* 12½.
1 1 1d. lilac-mauve .. .. 48·00 28·00
2 2d. blue .. .. 45·00 26·00
3 3d. red-brown (3.75) .. .. .. 85·00 40·00
4 3d. red-brown and chestnut .. .. 70·00 40·00
5 4d. carmine .. .. 60·00 40·00
6 6d. blue-green .. .. 65·00 15·00
8 1s. orange (value 15½ mm) (3.75) .. £250 £120
9 1s. orange (value 16½ mm) .. .. £200 55·00
1/9 .. .. *Set of* 6 £650 £275

1876. *Wmk Crown CC. P* 14.
10 1 1d. lilac-mauve .. .. 32·00 10·00
11 2d. blue .. .. 35·00 11·00
12 3d. red-brown .. .. 85·00 18·00
13 3d. chestnut .. .. 85·00 30·00
14 4d. carmine .. .. £120 10·00
a. Wmk sideways £800 £120
15 6d. green .. .. 50·00 11·00
16 1s. orange (value 16½ mm long) .. £400 60·00
10/16 .. .. *Set of* 6 £650 £130

1882 (June). *Wmk Crown CA. P* 14.
17 1 1d. lilac-mauve .. .. 15·00 10·00
18 2d. blue .. .. 85·00 8·00
19 3d. chestnut .. .. 11·00 8·00
20 4d. carmine .. .. 70·00 10·00

1884 (Dec)–**86**. *New values and colours. Wmk Crown CA. P* 14.
21 1 ½d. dull green (2.86) 50 40
22 1d. rose-carmine .. .. 1·00 50
23 2d. grey .. .. 26·00 9·00
24 4d. pale violet .. .. 35·00 10·00
25 6d. olive-green .. .. 9·00 11·00
26 1s. orange (3.85) .. .. .. 9·00 13·00
27 2s. 6d. olive-black (10.86) £350 £300
28 5s. blue (10.86) £700 £350
29 10s. purple-brown (10.86) £1500 £900
21/9 .. .. *Set of* 9 £2250 £1400
27/9 Optd "Specimen" .. .. *Set of* 3 £800

We would warn collectors against clever forgeries of Nos. 27 to 29 on genuinely watermarked paper.

2½ PENNY A

2½ PENNY B

1887 (Mar)–**1902**. *Wmk Crown CA. P* 14.
30 1 2d. dull mauve and blue .. .. 1·75 1·50
31 2½d. ultramarine (A) (12.90) .. .. 1·50 2·00
a. Larger letters of value (B) .. .. 18·00 17·00
b. Blue .. .. 80·00 50·00
32 3d. dull mauve and chestnut (4.91) .. 4·00 4·75
33 4d. dull mauve and black .. .. 4·00 4·50
34 5d. dull mauve and green (2.94) .. 4·00 13·00
35 6d. dull mauve and mauve .. .. 9·00 10·00
a. Dull mauve and carmine (10.02) .. 8·50 13·00
36 7½d. dull mauve and carmine (2.94) .. 5·00 14·00
37 10d. dull mauve and yellow (2.94) .. 6·50 13·00
38 1s. yellow-green and black .. .. 7·00 13·00
a. Blue-green and black .. .. 9·50 15·00
39 2s. 6d. green and carmine .. .. 22·00 35·00
40 5s. green and blue .. .. .. 32·00 60·00
41 10s. green and brown .. .. .. 60·00 95·00
30/41 .. .. *Set of* 12 £140 £250
30/41 Optd "Specimen" .. .. *Set of* 12 £350

HALF PENNY

(2)

3

1893 (Aug). *No. 33 surch with T* 2.
42 1 ½d. on 4d. dull mauve and black .. 3·50 4·00
a. Surch double .. .. .. 55·00 55·00
b. Surch treble .. .. .. 60·00
c. Error. ½d. on 2d. (No. 30) .. £11000 £11000

There were four settings of this surcharge, a scarce setting in which "HALF PENNY" is 16½ mm and three others in which the length is 16 mm. Of No. 42c, one copy is known unused and one used.

1904 (22 Jan–Nov). *Wmk Crown CA. P* 14.
44 3 ½d. dull green and green .. .. 4·00 6·50
45 1d. purple and black/*red* .. .. 1·25 75
46 2d. dull purple and blue .. .. 9·00 17·00
47 2½d. dull purple and blue/*blue* (B) .. 3·00 5·00
a. Smaller letters of value as A .. 7·50 9·00
48 3d. dull purple and brown .. .. 4·00 7·50
49 6d. dull purple and mauve .. .. 26·00 12·00
50 1s. green and black .. .. 28·00 24·00
51 2s. 6d. green and carmine .. .. 70·00 90·00
52 5s. green and blue £150 £225
53 10s. green and brown (Nov) .. £300 £450
44/53 .. .. *Set of* 10 £550 £700
44/53 Optd "Specimen" .. .. *Set of* 10 £500

1904–05. *Wmk Mult Crown CA. P* 14
54 3 ½d. dull green and green, **OC** (30.10.04) 1·25 1·25
55 1d. purple and black/*red* **OC** (22.10.04) 30 20
56 2d. dull purple and blue, **OC** (2.05) .. 2·00 2·50
57 2½d. dull purple and blue/*blue* (B), **C** (13.10.05) .. .. 4·00 8·00
a. Smaller letters of value as A .. 55·00 70·00
58 3d. dull purple and brown, **OC** (27.4.05) 2·75 3·00
59 6d. dull purple and mauve, **OC** (31.10.05) .. .. 4·50 5·00
60 1s. green and black, **OC** (15.10.04) .. 6·00 5·50
61 2s. 6d. green and carmine, **OC** (3.12.04) 14·00 18·00
62 5s. green and blue, **OC** (1.05) .. .. 15·00 26·00
63 10s. green and brown, **OC** (3.12.04) .. 50·00 75·00
54/63 .. .. *Set of* 10 90·00 £130

Lagos was incorporated into the Colony and Protectorate of Southern Nigeria, previously formed from Niger Coast Protectorate and part of the Niger Company territories, on 16 February 1906. Stamps of Lagos were then authorised for use throughout Southern Nigeria.

Leeward Islands

Issues superseding the earlier issues, or in concurrent use with the later issues (from 1903), of Antigua, Dominica (to 31 December 1939), Montserrat, Nevis, St. Christopher, St. Kitta-Nevis, and Virgin Islands.

PRICES FOR STAMPS ON COVER TO 1945

Nos. 1/8	*from* × 8
Nos. 9/16	*from* × 10
Nos. 17/19	*from* × 8
Nos. 20/8	*from* × 5
Nos. 29/35	*from* × 4
Nos. 36/45	*from* × 5
Nos. 46/57	*from* × 4
Nos. 58/87	*from* × 5
Nos. 88/91	*from* × 6
Nos. 92/4	*from* × 10
Nos. 95/114	*from* × 5

PRINTERS. All the stamps of Leeward Islands were typographed by De La Rue & Co, Ltd, London, *except where otherwise stated.*

1

2

1890. *Name and value in second colour. Wmk Crown CA. P* 14.
1 1 ½d. dull mauve and green 70 50
2 1d. dull mauve and rose .. .. 1·25 35
3 2½d. dull mauve and blue .. .. 3·50 60
4 4d. dull mauve and orange .. .. 5·00 8·00
5 6d. dull mauve and brown .. .. 6·00 8·00
6 7d. dull mauve and slate .. .. 4·00 8·00
7 2 1s. green and carmine .. .. .. 25·00 32·00
8 5s. green and blue £180 £225
1/8 .. .. *Set of* 8 £200 £250
1/8 Optd "Specimen" .. .. *Set of* 8 £250

The colours of this issue are fugitive.

SEXAGENARY 1887 VR

(3)

One Penny

(4)

One Penny

(5)

1897 (22 July). *Queen Victoria's Diamond Jubilee. Handstamped with T* 3.
9 1 ½d. dull mauve and green .. .. 6·00 8·00
a. Opt double £1200
10 1d. dull mauve and rose .. .. 6·00 8·50
a. Opt double £1000
b. Opt triple £3000
11 2½d. dull mauve and blue .. .. 8·00 8·50
a. Opt double £1200
12 4d. dull mauve and orange .. .. 22·00 26·00
a. Opt double £1200
13 6d. dull mauve and brown .. .. 38·00 40·00
a. Opt double £1400
14 7d. dull mauve and slate .. .. 40·00 50·00
a. Opt double £1400
15 2 1s. green and carmine £180 £225
a. Opt double £1800
16 5s. green and blue £900 £900
a. Opt double £5000
9/16 .. .. *Set of* 8 £1100 £1200

Beware of forgeries.

1902. *Nos. 4/6 surch.*
17 4 1d. on 4d. dull mauve and orange .. 1·60 4·25
a. Pair, one with tall narrow "O" in "One" .. .. 22·00 24·00
b. Surch double .. .. ..
18 1d. on 6d. dull mauve and brown .. 1·00 4·00
a. Pair, one with tall narrow "O" in "One" .. .. 28·00 28·00
19 5 1d. on 7d. dull mauve and slate .. 1·60 4·00

6

7

8

1902. *Wmk Crown CA. P* 14.
20 6 ½d. dull purple and green .. .. 60 1·00
21 1d. dull purple and carmine .. .. 1·25 30
22 7 2d. dull purple and ochre .. .. 2·75 4·00
23 6 2½d. dull purple and ultramarine .. 3·00 3·00
a. Wide "A" in "LEEWARD" .. .. 40·00 40·00
24 7 3d. dull purple and black .. .. 2·50 6·00
25 6 6d. dull purple and brown .. .. 3·00 8·50
26 8 1s. green and carmine .. .. .. 8·50 11·00
27 7 2s. 6d. green and black .. .. .. 23·00 35·00
28 8 5s. green and blue .. .. .. 30·00 50·00
20/8 .. .. *Set of* 9 65·00 £110
20/8 Optd "Specimen" .. .. *Set of* 9 £190

1905–8. *Wmk Mult Crown CA. P* 14.
29 6 ½d. dull purple and green, **OC** (1906) .. 65 1·40
30 1d. dull purple and carmine, **C** (1906) .. 1·75 70
31 7 2d. dull purple and ochre, **C** (1908) .. 3·25 8·50
32 6 2½d. dull purple & ultram, **C** (1906) .. 15·00 15·00
a. Wide "A" in "LEEWARD" .. .. 90·00 £100
33 7 3d. dull purple and black, **OC** .. .. 7·50 11·00
34 6 6d. dull purple and brown, **C** (1908) .. 16·00 25·00
35 8 1s. green and carmine, **C** (1908) .. 25·00 32·00
29/35 .. .. *Set of* 7 65·00 85·00

1907–11. *Wmk Mult Crown CA. P* 14.
36 7 ¼d. brown, **O** (4.7.09) 20 75
37 6 ½d. dull green, **O** 50 50
38 1d. bright red, **O** 90 35
a. Rose-carmine .. .. .. 8·00 45
39 7 2d. grey, **O** (1911) .. .. .. 1·00 6·00
40 6 2½d. bright blue, **O** .. .. .. 1·40 3·25
a. Wide "A" in "LEEWARD" .. .. 60·00 60·00
41 7 3d. purple/*yellow*, **C** (1910) .. .. 2·00 5·50
42 6 6d. dull and bright purple, **C** (1911) .. 3·00 5·50
43 8 1s. black/*green*, **C** (1911) .. .. 7·00 13·00
44 7 2s. 6d. black and red/*blue*, **C** (1911) .. 26·00 38·00
45 8 5s. green and red/*yellow*, **C** (1911) .. 38·00 55·00
36/45 .. .. *Set of* 10 70·00 £120
36/45 Optd "Specimen" .. .. *Set of* 10 £190

10

11

12

13

1912–22. *Wmk Mult Crown CA. P* 14.
46 10 ¼d. brown, **O** 30 20
a. Pale brown 30 35
47 11 ½d. yellow-green, **O** (2.13) 75 40
a. Deep green 85 50
48 1d. carmine-red, **O** 75 25
a. Bright scarlet (1915) 90 30
49 10 2d. slate-grey, **O** (2.13) .. .. 60 1·40
50 11 2½d. bright blue, **O** .. .. .. 5·50 7·00
a. Deep bright blue .. .. .. 4·50 3·25
51 10 3d. purple/*yellow*, **C** (2.13) .. .. 60 3·50
a. White back (Optd S. £35) (11.13) .. 22·00 30·00
b. On lemon (1916) .. .. .. 2·00 6·00
c. On orange-buff .. .. .. 1·25 4·00
d. On pale yellow (Optd S. £30) (1919) 15·00 23·00
52 4d. blk & red/*pale yell*, **C** (Die II) (1922) 1·00 5·50
53 11 6d. dull and bright purple, **C** (2.13) .. 1·50 5·00
54 12 1s. black/*green*, **C** (2.13) .. .. 5·00 6·00
a. White back (Optd S.£35) (11.13) .. 20·00 30·00
b. On blue-green, olive back (Optd S. £35) (1914) .. .. 1·75 5·50
55 10 2s. pur & blue/*blue*, **C** (Die II) (1922) .. 5·50 11·00
56 2s. 6d. black and red/*blue*, **C** (2.13) .. 20·00 23·00
57 12 5s. green and red/*yellow*, **C** (1915) .. 24·00 35·00
a. White back (Optd S. £40) (11.13) .. 30·00 40·00
b. On lemon (1916) .. .. .. 12·00 23·00
c. On orange-buff (1920?) .. ..
46/57 .. .. *Set of* 12 45·00 75·00
46/57 Optd "Specimen" .. .. *Set of* 12 £225

1921–32. *Wmk Mult Script CA, except* £1 (*Mult Crown CA*). *P* 14.

(*a*) *Die* II (1921–29)
58 10 ¼d. brown, **O** (1.4.22) 25 85
59 11 ½d. blue-green, **O** (1921) 20 30
60 1d. carmine-red, **O** (1921) 25 20
61 1d. bright violet, **O** (8.22) 25 25
62 1d. bright scarlet, **O** (1929) 25 15
63 10 1½d. carmine-red, **O** (1926) 40 60
64 1½d. red-brown, **O** (1929) 20 15
65 2d. slate-grey, **O** (6.22) 60 60
66 11 2½d. orange-yellow, **O** (7.23) .. .. 8·00 22·00
67 2½d. bright blue, **O** (1927) 75 60
68 10 3d. light ultramarine, **O** (7.23) .. 7·00 15·00
a. Deep ultramarine .. .. .. 14·00 25·00
69 3d. purple/*yellow*, **C** (1927) .. .. 65 3·00
70 4d. black and red/*pale yellow*, **C** (1924) 1·25 6·50
71 5d. dull purple and olive-green, **C** (1.4.22) .. .. 60 2·75
72 11 6d. dull and bright purple, **C** (1923) .. 6·50 13·00
73 12 1s. black/*emerald*, **C** (1923) .. .. 2·00 5·50
74 10 2s. purple and blue/*blue*, **C** (1.4.22) .. 20·00 30·00
a. Red-purple and blue/blue, **C** (1926) 8·00 15·00
75 2s. 6d. black and red/*blue*, **C** (1923) .. 10·00 24·00
76 3s. bright green and violet, **C** (1.4.22) 14·00 24·00
77 4s. black and red, **C** (1.4.22) .. .. 15·00 30·00
78 12 5s. green and red/*pale yellow*, **C** (1923) 35·00 45·00
79 13 10s. green and red/*green*, **C** (1928) .. 60·00 70·00
80 £1 purple and black/*red*, **C** (1928) .. £225 £275
58/80 .. .. *Set of* 22 £350 £500
58/80 Optd/Perf "Specimen" .. .. *Set of* 23 £600

(b) *Reversion to Die* I (*Plate* 23) (1931–32)

No.	Type	Description		Unused	Used
81	10	¼d. brown, **O**		65	1·00
82	11	½d. blue-green, **O** (1931)		75	2·50
83		1d. bright scarlet, **O**		75	25
84	10	1½d. red-brown, **O**		80	1·40
85	11	2½d. bright blue, **O**		3·00	3·00
86		6d. dull and bright purple, **C**		8·00	14·00
87	12	1s. black/*emerald*, **C**		18·00	25·00
81/7			*Set of* 7	29·00	42·00

1935 (6 May). *Silver Jubilee. As Nos.* 91/4 *of Antigua but printed by Waterlow. P* 11 × 12.

No.	Description		Unused	Used
88	1d. deep blue and scarlet		35	45
89	1½d. ultramarine and grey		40	65
90	2½d. brown and deep blue		1·75	3·00
91	1s. slate and purple		7·00	10·00
88/91 Perf "Specimen"		*Set of* 4	55·00	

1937 (12 May). *Coronation. As Nos.* 13/15 *of Aden.*

No.	Description		Unused	Used
92	1d. scarlet		30	25
93	1½d. buff		30	30
94	2½d. bright blue		45	45
92/4 Perf "Specimen"		*Set of* 3	45·00	

14 15

(Die A) (Die B)

In Die B the figure "1" has a broader top and more projecting serif.

1938 (25 Nov)–**51**. *T* **14** (*and similar type, but with shaded value tablet,* ½d., 1d., 2½d., 6d.) *and* **15** (10s., £1). *P* 14.

(a) *Wmk Mult Script CA*

No.	Description	Unused	Used
95	¼d. brown, **O**	20	10
	a. *Deep brown*, **C** (13.6.49)	25	25
96	½d. emerald	25	25
97	½d. slate-grey, **C** (1.7.49)	30	20
98	1d. scarlet (Die A)	2·75	1·25
99	1d. scarlet (*shades*) (Die B) (1940)	40	25
	a. *Carmine* (9.42)	70	2·75
	b. *Red* (13.9.48)	90	90
100	1d. blue-green, **C** (1.7.49)	45	10
101	1½d. chestnut	25	10
102	1½d. yellow-orange and black, **C** (1.7.49)	50	15
103	2d. olive-grey	25	15
	a. *Slate-grey* (11.42)	2·50	2·50
104	2d. scarlet, **C** (1.7.49)	1·40	45
	a. *Vermilion* (24.10.51)	4·00	3·75
105	2½d. bright blue	75	35
	a. *Light bright blue* (11.42)	25	20
106	2½d. black and purple, **C** (1.7.49)	55	25
107	3d. orange, **C**	14·00	1·60
	a. *Pale orange*, **O** (11.42)	30	30
108	3d. bright blue, **C** (1.7.49)	65	20
109	6d. deep dull and bright purple, **C**	4·00	2·00
	a. *Purple and deep magenta*, **CO** (9.42)	60	35
110	1s. black/*emerald*, **CO**	1·25	80
	a. *Grey and black/emerald*, **O** (8.42)	10·00	6·00
	b. *Black and grey/emerald*, **O** (11.42)	50·00	10·00
111	2s. reddish purple and blue/*blue*, **CO**	4·25	1·25
	a. *Deep purple and blue/blue*, **O** (11.47)	2·50	1·40
112	5s. green and red/*yellow*, **CO**	11·00	11·00
	a. *Bright green and red/yellow*, **C** (24.10.51)	14·00	12·00
113	10s. bluish green and deep red/*green*, **C**	55·00	35·00
	a. *Pale green and dull red/green*, **O** (3.42)	40·00	27·00
	b. *Dp green & dp vermilion/green*, **O** (6.44)	45·00	35·00

(b) *Wmk Mult Crown CA*

No.	Description		Unused	Used
114	£1 brown-purple and black/*red*, **C**		£160	£120
	a. *Purple and black/carmine*, **C** (3.42)		38·00	30·00
	b. *Brown-purple & blk/salmon*, **C** (3.12.43)		25·00	28·00
	c. Perf 13, *Violet & black/scar*, **C** (13.12.51)		25·00	30·00
	ac. Wmk sideways (*p* 13)		£1250	
95/114*b*		*Set of* 19	75·00	60·00
95/114 Perf "Specimen"		*Set of* 13	£225	

1946 (1 Nov). *Victory. As Nos.* 28/9 *of Aden.*

No.	Description		Unused	Used
115	1½d. brown		15	12
116	3d. red-orange		15	12
115/16 Perf "Specimen"		*Set of* 2	40·00	

1949 (2 Jan). *Royal Silver Wedding. As Nos.* 30/1 *of Aden.*

No.	Description	Unused	Used
117	2½d. ultramarine	12	12
118	5s. green	6·50	8·00

1949 (10 Oct). *75th Anniv of Universal Postal Union. As Nos.* 114/17 *of Antigua.*

No.	Description	Unused	Used
119	2½d. blue-black	25	20
120	3d. deep blue	1·10	90
121	6d. magenta	1·25	95
122	1s. blue-green	1·40	1·00

1951 (16 Feb). *Inauguration of B.W.I. University College. As Nos.* 118/19 *of Antigua.*

No.	Description	Unused	Used
123	3 c. orange and black	20	15
124	12 c. rose-carmine and reddish violet	40	35

1953 (2 June). *Coronation. As No.* 47 *of Aden.*

No.	Description	Unused	Used
125	3 c. black and green	10	30

NEW INFORMATION

The editor is always interested to correspond with people who have new information that will improve or correct the Catalogue.

16 Queen Elizabeth II 17

1954. (22 Feb). *Chalk-surfaced paper. Wmk Mult Script CA. P* 14 (*T* **16**) *or* 13 (*T* **17**)

No.	Type	Description		Unused	Used
126	16	½ c. brown		5	5
127		1 c. grey		5	5
128		2 c. green		5	5
129		3 c. yellow-orange and black		5	5
130		4 c. rose-red		5	5
131		5 c. black and brown-purple		5	5
132		6 c. yellow-orange		8	5
133		8 c. ultramarine		25	5
134		12 c. dull and reddish purple		20	5
135		24 c. black and green		30	5
136		48 c. dull purple and ultramarine		3·00	2·75
137		60 c. brown and green		3·50	1·75
138		$1.20, yellow-green and rose-red		3·50	3·50
139	17	$2.40, bluish green and red		3·75	7·50
140		$4.80, brown-purple and black		5·50	9·00
126/40			*Set of* 15	18·00	22·00

The 3 c., 4 c., 6 c., 8 c., 24 c., 48 c., 60 c. and $1.20 have their value tablets unshaded.

The stamps of Leeward Islands were withdrawn and invalidated on 1 July 1956.

Lesotho

(*formerly* Basutoland)

INDEPENDENT KINGDOM

31 Moshoeshoe I and Moshoeshoe II

(Des and photo Harrison)

1966 (4 Oct). *Independence. P* 12½ × 13.

No.	Type	Description	Unused	Used
106	31	2½ c. light brown, black and red	8	5
107		5 c. light brown, black and new blue	10	5
108		10 c. light brown, black and emerald	10	10
109		20 c. light brown, black and bright purple	20	20

LESOTHO

(32)

33 "Education, Culture and Science"

1966 (1 Nov). *Stamps of Basutoland optd as T* **32**. A., *Nos.* 69/71 *and* 73/9 (*Script CA wmk*), B, *Nos.* 84/96 *and unissued* 1 *r.* (*wmk* w **12**).

No.	Description		A Unused	A Used	B Unused	B Used
110	½ c. grey-black and sepia		5	5	†	
111	1 c. grey-blk and bluish grn		5	5	5	5
112	2 c. deep bright blue & orange		20	10	†	
113	2½ c. pale yell-grn & rose-red		†		20	5
114	3½ c. ind & dp ultram		20	20	†	
115	5 c. chestnut & dp grey-grn		25	10	20	10
116	10 c. bronze-green and purple		25	10	†	
117	12½ c. brown & turq-green		1·50	70	65	65
118	25 c. deep ultram & crimson		75	75	†	
119	50 c. black and carmine-red		2·00	1·60	1·50	1·25
120	1 r. black and maroon		3·00	3·00	3·00	2·25
	a. "LSEOTHO"		60·00	—	35·00	—
	b. Opt double		80·00	—	†	
110A/120A		*Set of* 10	7·50	6·00		
111B/120B		*Set of* 6			5·00	4·00

(Des V. Whiteley. Litho D.L.R.)

1966 (1 Dec). *20th Anniv of U.N.E.S.C.O. P* 14½ × 14.

No.	Type	Description	Unused	Used
121	33	2½ c. orange-yellow and emerald-green	15	5
122		5 c. light green and olive	25	5
123		12½ c. light blue and red	55	15
124		25 c. red-orange and deep greenish blue	85	40

34 Maize 35 Moshoeshoe II

(Des and photo Harrison)

1967 (1 Apr). *Designs as T* **34/5**. *No Wmk. P* 14½ × 13½ (2 *r.*) *or* 13½ × 14½ (*others*).

No.	Description		Unused	Used
125	½ c. bluish green and light bluish violet		5	5
126	1 c. sepia and rose-red		5	5
127	2 c. orange-yellow and light green		5	5
128	2½ c. black and ochre		8	5
129	3½ c. chalky blue and yellow		8	8
130	5 c. bistre and new blue		10	10
131	10 c. yellow-brown and bluish grey		15	10
132	12½ c. black and red-orange		25	30
133	25 c. black and bright blue		75	55
134	50 c. black, new blue and turquoise		2·25	1·00
135	1 r. multicoloured		2·75	1·75
136	2 r. black, gold and magenta		5·00	4·50
125/36		*Set of* 12	10·50	7·50

Designs: *Horiz as T* **34**—1 c. Cattle; 2 c. Agaves (wrongly inscr "Aloes"); 2½ c. Basotho Hat; 3½ c. Merino Sheep ("Wool"); 5 c. Basotho Pony; 10 c. Wheat; 12½ c. Angora Goat ("Mohair"); 25 c. Maletsunyane Falls; 50 c. Diamonds; 1 r. Arms of Lesotho.

See also Nos. 147/59 and 191/203.

46 Students and University

(Des V. Whiteley. Photo Harrison)

1967 (7 Apr). *First Conferment of University Degrees. P* 14 × 14½.

No.	Type	Description	Unused	Used
137	46	1 c. sepia, ultram & light yellow-orange	5	5
138		2½ c. sepia, ultram & light greenish blue	8	5
139		12½ c. sepia, ultramarine and rose	15	12
140		25 c. sepia, ultramarine and light violet	20	15

47 Statue of Moshoeshoe I

(Des and photo Harrison)

1967 (4 Oct). *First Anniv of Independence. T* **47** *and similar triangular designs. P* 14½ × 14.

No.	Description	Unused	Used
141	2½ c. black and light yellow-green	5	5
142	12½ c. multicoloured	25	20
143	25 c. black, green and light ochre	40	30

Designs:—12½ c. Lesotho flag; 25 c. Crocodile (national emblem).

50 Lord Baden-Powell and Scout Saluting

(Des V. Whiteley. Photo Harrison)

1967 (1 Nov). *60th Anniv of Scout Movement. P* 14 × 14½.

No.	Type	Description	Unused	Used
144	50	15 c. multicoloured	25	15

51 W.H.O. Emblem and World Map

(Des G. Vasarhelyi. Photo Harrison)

1968 (7 Apr). *20th Anniv of World Health Organization. T* **51** *and similar horiz design. P* 14 × 14½.

No.	Description	Unused	Used
145	2½ c. blue, gold and carmine-red	8	5
	a. Gold (emblem) omitted		
146	25 c. multicoloured	25	25

Design:—25 c. Nurse and child.

53 Basotho Hat

54 Sorghum

1968–69. *As Nos.* 125/36 *and T* **54**, *but wmk* **53** (*sideways on* 2 *r.*).

No.	Description	Unused	Used
147	½ c. bluish green and light bluish violet (*shades*)(26.11.68)	5	5
148	1 c. sepia and rose-red (26.11.68)	8	5
149	2 c. orange-yellow and light green (*shades*) (26.11.68)	12	5
150	2½ c. black and ochre (*shades*) (21.10.68)	15	10
151	3 c. chocolate, green & yell-brown (1.8.68)	20	20
152	3½ c. chalky blue and yellow (26.11.68)	20	15
153	5 c. bistre and new blue (22.7.68)	25	15
154	10 c. yellow-brown and pale bluish grey (26.11.68)	40	25
155	12½ c. black and red-orange (30.9.69)	70	45
156	25 c. black and bright blue (30.9.69)	1·25	1·00
157	50 c. black, new blue and turquoise (30.9.69)	3·50	2·50
158	1 r. multicoloured (26.11.68)	5·00	5·00
159	2 r. black, gold and magenta (30.9.69)	18·00	15·00
147/59	*Set of* 13	27·00	23·00

55 Running Hunters

(Des Jennifer Toombs. Photo Harrison)

1968 (1 Nov). *Rock Paintings. T* **55** *and similar designs. W* **53** (*sideways on* 5 *c.*, 15 *c.*). *P* 14 × 14½ (5 *c.*, 15 *c.*) *or* 14½ × 14 (*others*).

No.	Description	Unused	Used
160	3 c. yellow-brown. lt blue-green & blackish green	15	12
161	3½ c. greenish yellow, yellow-olive and sepia	20	15
162	5 c. Venetian red, yell-ochre & blackish brn	30	20
163	10 c. yellow, rose and deep maroon	50	35
164	15 c. light buff, pale olive-yell & blackish brn	75	55
165	20 c. yellow-grn, greenish yellow & blackish brown	85	70
166	25 c. yellow, orange-brown and black	1·00	85
160/6	*Set of* 7	3·25	2·75

Designs: *Horiz*—3½ c. Baboons; 10 c. Archers; 20 c. Eland; 25 c. Hunting scene. *Vert*—5 c. Javelin throwing; 15 c. Blue Cranes.

62 Queen Elizabeth II Hospital

(Des C. R. Househam and G. Drummond. Litho P.B.)

1969 (11 Mar). *Centenary of Maseru (capital). T* **62** *and similar horiz designs. Multicoloured. W* **53** (*sideways*). *P* 14 × 13½.

No.	Description	Unused	Used
167	2½ c. Type **62**	5	5
168	10 c. Lesotho Radio Station	15	10
169	12½ c. Leabua Jonathan Airport	20	15
170	25 c. Royal Palace	25	25

66 Rally Car passing Mosotho Horseman

(Des P. Wheeler. Photo Harrison)

1969 (26 Sept). *Roof of Africa Car Rally. T* **66** *and similar horiz designs. W* **53**. *P* 14.

No.	Description	Unused	Used
171	2½ c. yellow, mauve and plum	8	5
172	12½ c. cobalt, greenish yellow and olive-grey	20	10
173	15 c. blue, black and mauve	25	20
174	20 c. black, red and yellow	25	20

Designs:—12½ c. Rally car on mountain road; 15 c. Chequered flags and mountain scenery; 20 c. Map of rally route and Rally Trophy.

71 Gryponyx and Footprints

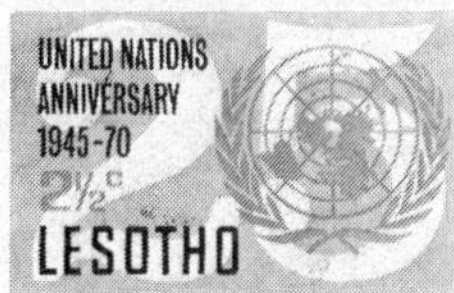

75 Moshoeshoe I, when a Young Man

(Des Jennifer Toombs. Photo Harrison)

1970 (5 Jan). *Prehistoric Footprints (1st series.) T* **71** *and similar designs. W* **53** (*sideways*). *P* 14 × 14½ (3 *c.*) *or* 14½ × 14 (*others*).

No.	Description	Unused	Used
175	3 c. pale brown, yellow-brown and sepia	25	25
176	5 c. dull purple, pink and sepia	40	40
177	10 c. pale yellow, black, and sepia	75	75
178	15 c. olive-yellow, black and sepia	1·25	1·50
179	25 c. cobalt and black	2·75	3·00

Designs: (60 × 23 *mm*)—3 c. Dinosaur footprints at Moyeni. (40 × 24 *mm*)—10 c. Plateosauravus and footprints; 15 c. Tritylodon and footprints; 25 c. Massospondylus and footprints.

See also Nos. 596/8.

(Des G. Vasarhelyi. Litho D.L.R.)

1970 (11 Mar). *Death Centenary of King Moshoeshoe I. T* **75** *and similar vert design. W* **53**. *P* 13½.

No.	Description	Unused	Used
180	2½ c. pale green and magenta	8	5
181	25 c. pale blue and chesnut	20	25

Design:—25 c. Moshoeshoe I as an old man.

77 U.N. Emblem and "25"

1970 (26 June). *25th Anniv of United Nations. T* **77** *and similar horiz designs. W* **53** (*sideways*). *P* 14½ × 14.

No.	Description	Unused	Used
182	2½ c. light pink, light blue and maroon	5	5
183	10 c. multicoloured	10	10
184	12½ c. brown-red, cobalt and drab	15	15
185	25 c. multicoloured	20	30

Designs:— 10 c. U.N. Building; 12½ c. "People of the World"; 25 c. Symbolic dove.

78 Basotho Hat Gift Shop, Maseru

(Des G. Drummond. Litho Questa)

1970 (27 Oct). *Tourism. T* **78** *and similar horiz designs. Multicoloured. W* **53** (*sideways*). *P* 14.

No.	Description	Unused	Used
186	2½ c. Type **78**	10	5
187	5 c. Trout fishing	30	5
188	10 c. Pony trekking	35	15
189	12½ c. Skiing	45	25
190	20 c. Holiday Inn, Maseru	65	60

79 Maize 80 Lammergeier

(Des Harrison. Litho Questa)

1971 (4 Jan–1 Apr). *As Nos.* 147/58 *but in new format omitting portrait of Moshoeshoe II, as in T* **79**. 4 *c. and* 2 *r. in new designs. W* **53** (*sideways except* 2 *r.*). *P* 14.

No.	Description	Unused	Used
191	½ c. blue-green and light bluish violet	5	5
192	1 c. brown and orange-red	8	5
193	2 c. yellow and green	10	5
194	2½ c. black, olive-green and yellow-ochre	10	5
195	3 c. brown, green and yellow-ochre	12	5
196	3½ c. indigo and yellow	12	10
196*a*	4 c. multicoloured (1.4.71)	20	5
197	5 c. yellow-brown and pale blue	15	5
198	10 c. orange-brown and grey-blue	25	5
199	12½ c. chocolate and yellow-orange	30	30
200	25 c. slate and pale bright blue	60	65
201	50 c. black, pale blue and turquoise-green	2·00	1·40
202	1 r. multicoloured	2·25	2·75
203	2 r. yellow-brown and ultramarine	4·00	3·75
191/203	*Set of* 14	9·00	8·50

Designs: *Horiz*—4 c. National flag. *Vert*—2 r. Statue of Moshoeshoe I.

For 2 r. value without watermark see No. 401.

(Des R. Granger Barrett. Litho J.W.)

1971 (1 Mar). *Birds. T* **80** *and similar vert designs. Multicoloured. W* **53**. *P* 14.

No.	Description	Unused	Used
204	2½ c. Type **80**	60	10
205	5 c. Bald Ibis	1·25	1·25
206	10 c. Rufous Rockjumper	1·75	1·75
207	12½ c. Blue Bustard	2·00	2·00
208	15 c. Painted Snipe	2·75	2·75
209	20 c. Golden-breasted Bunting	2·75	2·75
210	25 c. Ground Woodpecker	3·00	3·00
204/10	*Set of* 7	13·00	13·00

81 Lionel Collett Dam

(Des G. Drummond. Litho J.W.)

1971 (15 July). *Soil Conservation. T* **81** *and similar horiz designs. Multicoloured. W* **53** (*sideways*). *P* 14.

No.	Description	Unused	Used
211	4 c. Type **81**	10	5
212	10 c. Contour ridges	25	15
213	15 c. Earth dams	45	35
214	25 c. Beaver dams	55	70

82 Diamond Mining

(Des J.W. Litho Questa)

1971 (4 Oct). *Development. T* **82** *and similar horiz designs. Multicoloured. W* **53** (*sideways*). *P* 14.

No.	Description	Unused	Used
215	4 c. Type **82**	20	5
216	10 c. Pottery	25	15
217	15 c. Weaving	40	35
218	20 c. Construction	45	70

83 Mail Cart 84 Sprinting

(Des D. B. Picton-Phillips. Litho Questa)

1972 (3 Jan). *Post Office Centenary. T* **83** *and similar designs. W* **53** (*sideways on* 5, 10 *and* 20 *c.*). *P* 14 × 13½ (15 *c.*) *or* 13½ × 14 (*others*).

No.	Description	Unused	Used
219	5 c. pale pink and black	20	15
220	10 c. multicoloured	25	15
221	15 c. pale drab, light blue and black	55	45
222	20 c. multicoloured	75	1·00

Designs: *Horiz*—10 c. Postal bus; 20 c. Maseru P.O. *Vert*—15 c. Cape of Good Hope 4d. stamp of 1876.

(Des J. W. Litho Questa)

1972 (1 Sept). *Olympic Games. Munich. T* **84** *and similar vert designs. Multicoloured. W* **53**. *P* 14.

No.	Description	Unused	Used
223	4 c. Type **84**	12	5
224	10 c. Shot putting	20	15
225	15 c. Hurdling	30	30
226	25 c. Long-jumping	40	50

85 "Adoration of the Shepherds" (Matthias Stomer)

(Des and litho J.W.)

1972 (1 Dec). *Christmas. W* **53** (*sideways*). *P* 14.

No.	Type	Description	Unused	Used
227	**85**	4 c. multicoloured	12	5
228		10 c. multicoloured	20	15
229		25 c. multicoloured	45	70

O.A.U.
10th Anniversary
Freedom in Unity

86 W.H.O. Emblem (87)

(Des. J. Cooter. Litho Questa)

1973 (7 Apr). *25th Anniv of W.H.O. W* **53**. *P* 13½.
230 **86** 20 c. greenish blue and yellow 30 35

1973 (25 May). *Tenth Anniv of O.A.U. Nos.* 194 *and* 196*a*/8 *optd with T* **87** *by Govt Printer, Maseru.*
231 2½ c. black, olive-green and yellow-ochre .. 20 20
232 4 c. multicoloured 25 25
a. Horiz pair, one without opt £150
233 5 c. yellow-brown and pale blue 30 30
234 10 c. orange-brown and grey-blue 35 35

88 Basotho Hat and W.F.P. Emblem

(Des locally; adapted J. Cooter. Litho Format)

1973 (1 June). *Tenth Anniv of World Food Programme. T* **88** *and similar horiz designs. Multicoloured. W* **53** (*sideways*). *P* 13½.
235 4 c. Type **88** 12 5
236 15 c. School feeding 45 45
237 20 c. Infant feeding 50 45
a. Imperf (pair) .. ..
238 25 c. "Food for Work" 55 55

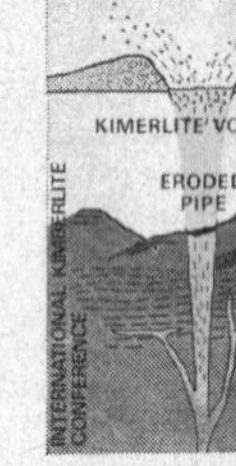

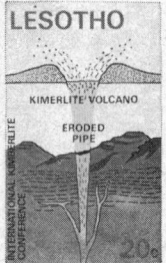

89 Mountain Beauty **90** Kimberlite Volcano

(Des A. McLeod; artwork G. Drummond. Litho Questa)

1973 (3 Sept). *Butterflies. T* **89** *and similar horiz designs. Multicoloured. W* **53** (*sideways*). *P* 14.
239 4 c. Type **89** 25 10
240 5 c. Christmas Butterfly 35 25
241 10 c. Painted Lady 70 50
242 15 c. Yellow Pansy .. .. 1·00 1·00
243 20 c. Blue Pansy .. .. 1·00 1·00
244 25 c. African Monarch .. .. 1·50 1·75
245 30 c. Orange Tip .. .. 1·75 2·00
239/45 .. .. *Set of* 7 6·00 6·00

(Des PAD Studio. Litho Questa)

1973 (1 Oct). *International Kimberlite Conference. T* **90** *and similar multicoloured designs. W* **53** (*sideways on* 10 *and* 15 *c.*). *P* 13½.
246 10 c. Map of diamond mines (*horiz*) 75 65
247 15 c. Kimberlite-diamond rock (*horiz*) .. 1·00 1·00
248 20 c. Type **90** .. .. 1·10 1·10
249 30 c. Diamond prospecting .. .. .. 2·00 2·75
Type **90** is incorrectly inscribed "KIMERLITE VOLCANO".

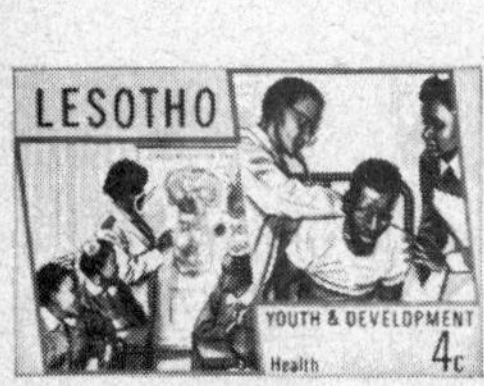

91 "Health" **92** Open Book and Wreath

(Des R. Granger Barrett. Litho Questa)

1974 (18 Feb). *Youth and Development. T* **91** *and similar horiz designs. Multicoloured. W* **53** (*sideways*). *P* 13½.
250 4 c. Type **91** 10 5
251 10 c. "Education" 20 15
252 20 c. "Agriculture" 30 30
253 25 c. "Industry" 40 50
254 30 c. "Service" 45 60

(Des PAD Studio. Litho Questa)

1974 (7 Apr). *Tenth Anniv of U.B.L.S. T* **92** *and similar vert designs. Multicoloured. W* **53**. *P* 14.
255 10 c. Type **92** 15 10
256 15 c. Flags, mortar-board and scroll 25 20
257 20 c. Map of Africa 30 30
258 25 c. King Moshoeshoe II capping a graduate 30 40

NEW INFORMATION

The editor is always interested to correspond with people who have new information that will improve or correct the Catalogue.

93 Senqunyane River Bridge, Marakabei

(Des J. Cooter. Litho Questa)

1974 (26 June). *Rivers and Bridges. T* **93** *and similar horiz designs. Multicoloured. W* **53** (*sideways*). *P* 14½.
259 4 c. Type **93** 10 10
260 5 c. Tsoelike River and bridge 12 12
261 10 c. Makhaleng River Bridge 25 25
262 15 c. Seaka Bridge, Orange/Senqu River .. 55 55
263 20 c. Masianokeng Bridge, Phuthiatsana River 60 60
264 25 c. Mahobong Bridge, Hlotse River 70 70
259/64 .. .. *Set of* 6 2·10 2·10

94 U.P.U. Emblem

(Des R. Granger Barrett. Litho Enschedé)

1974 (6 Sept). *Centenary of Universal Postal Union. T* **94** *and similar horiz designs. W* **53** (*sideways*). *P* 13½ × 13.
265 4 c. light emerald and black 10 5
266 10 c. orange, greenish yellow and black .. 20 20
267 15 c. multicoloured 35 35
268 20 c. multicoloured 45 45
Designs:—10 c. Map of air-mail routes; 15 c. Post Office H.Q., Maseru; 20 c. Horseman taking rural mail.
On No. 266 the inscriptions for the airstrips at Makhotlong and Mohlanapeng were transposed in error.

95 Siege of Thaba-Bosiu

(Des Jennifer Toombs. Litho Enschedé)

1974 (25 Nov). *150th Anniv of Establishment of Thaba-Bosiu as Capital. T* **95** *and similar multicoloured designs. W* **53** (*sideways on* 4 *and* 5 *c.*). *P* 12½ × 12 (4 *and* 5 *c.*) *or* 12 × 12½ (*others*).
269 4 c. Type **95** 15 5
270 5 c. The wreath-laying 20 10
271 10 c. Moshoeshoe I (*vert*) 40 15
272 20 c. Makoanyane, the warrior (*vert*) 90 70

96 Mamokhorong

(Des PAD Studio. Litho Questa)

1975 (25 Jan). *Basotho Musical Instruments. T* **96** *and similar horiz designs. Multicoloured. W* **53** (*sideways*). *P* 14.
273 4 c. Type **96** 10 5
274 10 c. Lesiba 20 25
275 15 c. Setolotolo 30 40
276 20 c. Meropa 30 50
MS277 108 × 92 mm. Nos. 273/6 .. .. .. 1·75 2·00

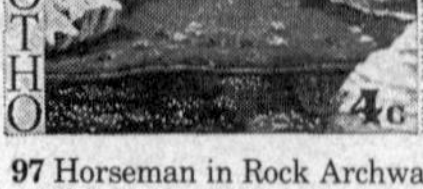

97 Horseman in Rock Archway **98** Morena Moshoeshoe I

(Des J. Cooter. Litho Questa)

1975 (15 Apr). *Sehlabathebe National Park. T* **97** *and similar horiz designs. Multicoloured. W* **53** (*sideways*). *P* 14.
278 4 c. Type **97** 15 10
279 5 c. Mountain view through arch 15 12
280 15 c. Antelope by stream 50 40
281 20 c. Mountains and lake 60 50
282 25 c. Tourists by frozen waterfall 65 60

(Des G. Vasarhelyi. Litho Questa)

1975 (10 Sept). *Leaders of Lesotho. T* **98** *and similar vert designs. W* **53**. *P* 14.
283 3 c. black and light blue 8 8
284 4 c. black and light mauve 8 8
285 5 c. black and pink 10 10
286 6 c. black and light grey-brown 12 12
287 10 c. black and light claret 20 20
288 15 c. black and light orange-red 35 35
289 20 c. black and dull green 45 45
290 25 c. black and azure 55 55
283/90 .. .. *Set of* 8 1·75 1·75
Designs:—4 c. King Moshoeshoe II; 5 c. Morena Letsie I; 6 c. Morena Lerotholi; 10 c. Morena Letsie II; 15 c. Morena Griffith; 20 c. Morena Seeiso Griffith Lerotholi; 25 c. Mofumahali Mantsebo Seeiso, O.B.E.
The 25 c. also commemorates International Women's Year.

99 Mokhibo Dance

(Des PAD Studio. Litho Questa)

1975 (17 Dec). *Traditional Dances. T* **99** *and similar horiz designs. Multicoloured. W* **53** (*sideways*). *P* 14 × 14½.
291 4 c. Type **99** 10 5
292 10 c. Ndlamo 20 15
293 15 c. Baleseli 35 45
294 20 c. Mohobelo 45 55
MS295 111 × 100 mm. Nos. 291/94 .. .. 2·25 2·50

100 Enrolment

(Des L. Curtis. Litho Questa)

1976 (20 Feb). *25th Anniv of the Lesotho Red Cross. T* **100** *and similar horiz designs. Multicoloured. W* **53** (*sideways*). *P* 14.
296 4 c. Type **100** 15 5
297 10 c. Medical aid 30 15
298 15 c. Rural service 55 55
299 25 c. Relief supplies 65 65

101 Tapestry **102** Football

(Des V. Whiteley Studio. Litho Format)

1976 (2 June)–**78**. *Multicoloured designs as T* **101**. *W* **53** (*sideways on* 2 *to* 50 *c.*). *P* 14.
300 2 c. Type **101** 5 5
301 3 c. Mosotho horseman 10 5
302 4 c. Map of Lesotho 20 5
303 5 c. Lesotho Brown diamond 25 5
304 10 c. Lesotho Bank 20 5
305 15 c. Lesotho and O.A.U. flags 45 20
306 25 c. Sehlabathebe National Park 60 35
307 40 c. Pottery 70 50
308 50 c. Prehistoric rock art .. .. .. 1·50 1·00
309 1 r. King Moshoeshoe II (*vert*) .. .. 1·75 2·00
300/309 .. .. *Set of* 10 5·25 3·75
For 25 c., 40 c. and 50 c. values on unwatermarked paper, see Nos. 398/400.

(Des P. Powell. Litho Questa)

1976 (9 Aug). *Olympic Games, Montreal. T* **102** *and similar vert designs. Multicoloured. W* **53**. *P* 14.
310 4 c. Type **102** 10 5
311 10 c. Weightlifting 25 20
312 15 c. Boxing 55 30
313 25 c. Throwing the discus 75 55

103 "Rising Sun" **104** Telephones, 1876 and 1976

(Des L. Curtis. Litho Questa)

1976 (4 Oct). *Tenth Anniv of Independence. T* **103** *and similar vert designs. Multicoloured. W* **53**. *P* 14.

314 4 c. Type **103** 8 5
315 10 c. Open gates 20 20
316 15 c. Broken chains 35 35
317 25 c. Aeroplane over hotel 50 50

(Des and litho J.W.)

1976 (6 Dec). *Telephone Centenary. T* **104** *and similar horiz designs. Multicoloured. W* **53** *(sideways). P* 13.

318 4 c. Type **104** 10 5
319 10 c. Early handset and telephone-user, 1976 20 20
320 15 c. Wall telephone and telephone exchange 30 35
321 25 c. Stick telephone and Alexander Graham Bell 50 65

105 *Aloe striatula*

106 Rock Rabbit

(Des D. Findlay. Litho Walsall)

1977 (14 Feb). *Aloes and Succulents. T* **105** *and similar vert designs. Multicoloured. W* **53** *(inverted). P* 14.

322 3 c. Type **105** 25 8
323 4 c. *Aloe aristata* 30 10
324 5 c. *Kniphofia caulescens* 35 12
325 10 c. *Euphorbia pulvinata* 55 40
326 15 c. *Aloe saponaria* .. .. 1·00 1·00
327 20 c. *Caralluma lutea* .. .. 1·40 1·40
328 25 c. *Aloe polyphylla* .. .. 1·75 1·75
322/8 .. .. *Set of* 7 5·00 4·50

(Des D. Findlay. Litho Questa)

1977 (25 Apr). *Animals. T* **106** *and similar horiz designs. Multicoloured. W* **53** *(sideways). P* 14.

329 4 c. Type **106** 25 10
330 5 c. Porcupine 30 12
331 10 c. Polecat 55 40
332 15 c. Klipspringer .. .. 1·00 1·00
333 25 c. Baboon .. .. 1·60 1·60

107 "Rheumatic Man"

108 *Barbus holubi*

(Des C. Abbott. Litho Questa)

1977 (4 July). *World Rheumatism Year. T* **107** *and similar vert designs showing the "Rheumatic Man". W* **53**. *P* 14.

334 4 c. yellow and red 10 5
335 10 c. new blue and deep blue 25 25
336 15 c. yellow and blue-green 45 45
337 25 c. orange-red and black 70 70

Designs:—10 c. Man surrounded by "pain"; 15 c. Man surrounded by "chain"; 25 c. Man supporting globe.

(Des D. Findlay. Litho Questa)

1977 (28 Sept). *Fish. T* **108** *and similar horiz designs. Multicoloured. W* **53** *(sideways). P* 14.

338 4 c. Type **108** 15 5
339 10 c. *Labeo capensis* 30 25
340 15 c. *Salmo gairdneri* 50 50
341 25 c. *Oreodaimon quathlambae* 80 80

(**109**)

110 Black and White Heads

1977 (7 Dec*). *No.* 198 *surch with T* **109** *by Govt Printer, Maseru.*

342 3 c. on 10 c. yellow-brown and pale bluish grey 1·25 1·00

*Earliest known date of use.

(Des Jennifer Toombs. Litho Walsall)

1977 (12 Dec). *Decade for Action to Combat Racism. T* **110** *and similar vert designs. W* **53**. *P* 14.

343 4 c. chocolate and mauve 10 5
344 10 c. chocolate and light new blue 20 20
345 15 c. chocolate and light orange 30 30
346 25 c. chocolate and light turquoise-green .. 50 50

Designs:—10 c. Jigsaw pieces; 15 c. Cogwheels; 25 c. Handshake.

(Des D. Findlay. Litho Questa)

1978 (13 Feb). *Flowers. Vert designs similar to T* **105**. *Multicoloured. W* **53**. *P* 14.

347 2 c. *Papaver aculeatum* 5 5
348 3 c. *Diascia integerrima* 8 8
349 4 c. *Helichrysum trilineatum* 10 10
350 5 c. *Zaluzianskya maritima* 12 12
351 10 c. *Gladiolus natalensis* 20 20
352 15 c. *Chironia krebsii* 30 30
353 25 c. *Wahlenbergia undulata* 50 50
354 40 c. *Brunsvigia radulosa* 85 85
347/54 .. .. *Set of* 8 2·00 2·00

111 Edward Jenner performing Vaccination

112 Tsoloane Falls

(Des G. Hutchins. Litho J.W.)

1978 (8 May). *Global Eradication of Smallpox. T* **111** *and similar vert design. Multicoloured. W* **53**. *P* 13.

355 5 c. Type **111** 12 5
356 25 c. Head of child and W.H.O. emblem .. 55 55

(Des Kobus De Beer Art Studio. Litho Questa)

1978 (28 July). *Waterfalls. T* **112** *and similar vert designs. Multicoloured. W* **53**. *P* 14.

357 4 c. Type **112** 15 5
358 10 c. Qiloane Falls 40 30
359 15 c. Tsoelikana Falls 65 55
360 25 c. Maletsunyane Falls 90 90

113 Wright *Flyer*, 1903

114 *Orthetrum farinosum*

(Des L. Curtis. Litho Harrison)

1978 (9 Oct). *75th Anniv of Powered Flight. T* **113** *and similar horiz design. W* **53** *(sideways). P* 14½ × 14.

361 5 c. black, brown-ochre and new blue .. 15 5
362 25 c. multicoloured 50 45

Design:—25 c. Wilbur and Orville Wright.

(Des D. Findlay. Litho Questa)

1978 (18 Dec). *Insects. T* **114** *and similar vert designs. Multicoloured. W* **53**. *P* 14.

363 4 c. Type **114** 10 5
364 10 c. *Phymateus viridipes* 20 20
365 15 c. *Belonogaster lateritius* 30 30
366 25 c. *Sphodromantis gastrica* 50 55

115 Oudehout Branch in flower

116 Mampharoane

(Des D. Findlay. Litho Questa)

1979 (26 Mar). *Trees. T* **115** *and similar vert designs showing branches in flower. Multicoloured. W* **53**. *P* 14.

367 4 c. Type **115** 15 5
368 10 c. Wild Olive 25 20
369 15 c. Blinkblaar 45 50
370 25 c. Cape Holly 80 90

(New Curency. 100 lisente = 1 (ma)loti)

(Des D. Findlay. Litho Questa)

1979 (1 June). *Reptiles. T* **116** *and similar horiz designs. Multicoloured. P* 14. *A. No wmk. B. W* **53** *(sideways).*

		A		B	
371	4 s. Type **116** ..	10	8	10	8
372	10 s. Qoaane ..	25	20	25	20
373	15 s. Leupa ..	40	50	40	50
374	25 s. Masumu ..	80	90	80	90

117 Basutoland 1933 1d. Stamp

118 Detail of Painting "Children's Games" by Brueghel

(Des J.W. Litho Format)

1979 (22 Oct). *Death Centenary of Sir Rowland Hill. T* **117** *and similar vert designs showing stamps. P* 14.

375 4 s. multicoloured 10 5
376 15 s. multicoloured 25 25
377 25 s. black, yellow-orange and olive-bistre .. 35 40
MS378 118 × 95 mm. 50 s. multicoloured .. 70 80

Designs:—15 s. Basutoland 1962 ½ c. definitive; 25 s. Penny Black; 50 s. 1972 15 c. Post Office Centenary commemorative.

(Des C. Abbott. Litho Questa)

1979 (10 Dec). *International Year of the Child. T* **118** *and similar vert designs showing details of the painting "Children's Games" by Brueghel. W* **53**. *P* 14.

379 4 s. multicoloured 5 5
380 10 s. multicoloured 15 15
381 15 s. multicoloured 30 30
MS382 113 × 88 mm. 25 s. multicoloured *(horiz)* (wmk sideways) 40 45

119 Beer Strainer, Broom and Mat

(Des Kobus de Beer Art Studio. Litho Walsall)

1980 (18 Feb). *Grasswork. T* **119** *and similar horiz designs. Multicoloured. W* **53** *(sideways). P* 14.

383 4 s. Type **119** 5 5
384 10 s. Winnowing Basket 12 15
385 15 s. Basotho Hat 20 30
386 25 s. Grain storage 35 40

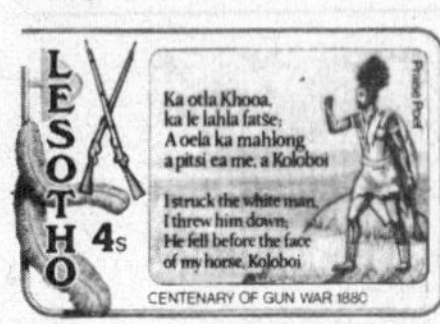

120 Praise Poet

(Des BG Studio. Litho Walsall)

1980 (6 May). *Centenary of Gun War. T* **120** *and similar horiz designs. Multicoloured. P* 14.

387 4 s. Type **120** 10 5
388 5 s. Lerotholi (commander of Basotho Army) 10 5
389 10 s. Ambush at Qalabane 20 15
390 15 s. Snider and Martini-Henry rifles .. 35 25
391 25 s. Map showing main areas of action .. 45 35

121 Olympic Flame, Flags and Kremlin

S
=
(**122**)

(Des G. Vasarhelyi. Litho Format)

1980 (20 Sept). *Olympic Games, Moscow. T* **121** *and similar horiz designs. Multicoloured. P* 14½.

392 25 s. Type **121** 30 30
a. Horiz strip of 5. Nos. 392/6 .. 1·40
393 25 s. Doves, flame and flags 30 30
394 25 s. Football 30 30
395 25 s. Running 30 30
396 25 s. Opening ceremony 30 30
MS397 110 × 85 mm. 1 m. 40, Ancient and modern athletes carrying Olympic torch .. .. 1·60 1·60

Nos. 392/6 were printed together, *se-tenant*, in horizontal strips of 5 throughout the sheet.

1980. *As Nos.* 203 *and* 306/8, *but without wmk.*

398 25 c. Sehlabathebe National Park .. .. 2·50
399 40 c. Pottery .. .. 9·00
400 50 c. Prehistoric rock art .. .. 10·00
401 2 r. Statue of Moshoeshoe I (yellow-brown and ultramarine) .. .. 4·00 4·50

1980 (20 Oct)–**81**. *As Nos.* 300/5, 309 *and* 398/401 *surch as T* **122** *or with new figures of value* (5 *s.* (*No.* 410A), 6, 75 *s.*, 1 *and* 2 *m.*). A. *By typo (locally)*. B. *By litho (London)*.

(*a*) *W* **53** (*sideways on* 2, 3, 6, 10, 40, 50 *and* 75 *s.*)

No.	Description	A		B	
402	2 s. on 2 c. Type **101**	5	5	5	5
403	3 s. on 3 c. Mosotho horseman	5	5	5	5
404	6 s. on 4 c. Map of Lesotho	5	5	5	5
	a. Surch double	†	—	†	
	b. Albino surch	†	—	—	—
405	10 s. on 10 c. Lesotho Bank	8	10	5·00	5·50
405*a*	25 s. on 25 c. Sehlabathebe National Park	5·00	5·00	†	
406	40 s. on 40 c. Pottery	45	50	45	50
407	50 s. on 50 c. Prehistoric rock art	1·25	—	50	55
408	75 s. on 15 c. Lesotho and O.A.U. flags	70	75	†	
409	1 m. on 1 r. King Moshoeshoe II (Sil.)	95	1·00	†	
	a. Surch double, one inverted	55·00	—	†	
	(*b*) *No wmk*				
410	5 s. on 5 c. Lesotho Brown diamond	5	5	5	5
	a. Third surch (Basotho hat and "5 s.") double	—	—	†	
	b. Basotho hat and "5 s." surch albino	—	—	†	
	c. Basotho hat and "5 s." omitted	25·00	—	†	
	d. Second surch ("6 s." and bars) albino	28·00	—	†	
411	10 s. on 10 c. Lesotho Bank	†		8	10
412	25 s. on 25 c. Sehlabathebe National Park	25	30	25	30
	a. Surch double	28·00	—	†	
413	40 s. on 40 c. Pottery	5·00	5·00	†	
414	50 s. on 50 c. Prehistoric rock art	50	55	†	
415	75 s. on 15 c. Lesotho and O.A.U. flags	†		70	75
416	1 m. on 1 r. King Moshoeshoe II (Blk. and Sil.)	†		95	1·00
417	2 m. on 2 r. Statue of Moshoeshoe I (yell-brn & ultramarine)	1·90	2·00	1·90	2·00
402/17	*Set of* 12			4·50	4·75

No. 410A is a further surcharge on No. 410B. Initially sheets of No. 410B were locally surcharged "6 s.", but this was later obliterated by a Basotho hat emblem and a further "5 s." surcharge added, both in typography.

The surcharge on No. 416 is similar to that on No. 409 but has the cancelling bars printed in black and the new face value in silver.

On each value except the 5 s. and 1 m. stamps, the design of the surcharge on the local printing is identical to that on the London printing. Stamps from the local printing can easily be identified from those of the London printing as indentations are clearly visible on the reverse of stamps with the typographed surcharge.

It is believed that the local surcharges were not placed on general sale before 1 December 1980. No. 410A did not appear until 20 January 1981.

123 Beer Mug

124 Queen Elizabeth the Queen Mother and Prince Charles

(Des G. Vasarhelyi (No. **MS**422), Kobus de Beer Art Studio (others). Litho Format (No. **MS**422), Questa (others)).

1980 (20 Nov). *Pottery. T* **123** *and similar horiz designs. Multicoloured. W* **53** (*sideways*). *P* 14.

No.	Description		
418	4 s. Type **123**	10	5
419	10 s. Beer brewing pot	15	12
420	15 s. Water pot	20	20
421	25 s. Pot shapes	30	35
MS422	150 × 110 mm. 40 s. × 4 Wedgwood plaques of Prince Philip; Queen Elizabeth II; Prince Charles; Princess Anne (*each* 22 × 35 *mm*). P 14 × 14½	1·75	1·90

No. **MS**422 was issued to commemorate the 250th birth anniversary of Josiah Wedgwood.

(Des G. Vasarhelyi. Litho Format)

1980 (1 Dec). *80th Birthday of Queen Elizabeth the Queen Mother. T* **124** *and similar multicoloured designs. P* 14½.

No.	Description		
423	5 s. Type **124**	25	25
	a. Horiz strip of 3. Nos. 423/5	1·60	
424	10 s. Queen Elizabeth the Queen Mother	30	30
425	1 m. Basutoland 1947 Royal Visit 2d. commemorative and flags (54 × 44 *mm*)	1·25	1·25

Nos. 423/5 were printed together, *se-tenant*, in horizontal strips of 3 throughout small sheets of nine stamps.

125 Lesotho Evangelical Church, Morija

(Des G. Vasarhelyi. Litho Format (75 s., 1 m. 50), Harrison (others))

1980 (8 Dec). *Christmas. T* **125** *and similar horiz designs. Multicoloured. No wmk* (75 *s.*) *or W* **53** (*others*). *P* 14 × 14½.

No.	Description		
426	4 s. Type **125**	10	5
427	15 s. St. Agnes' Anglican Church, Teyateyaneng	20	20
428	25 s. Cathedral of Our Lady of Victories, Maseru	35	35
429	75 s. University Chapel, Roma	1·00	1·00
MS430	110 × 85 mm. 1 m. 50, Nativity scene (43 × 29 *mm*). No wmk. P 14½	1·60	1·75

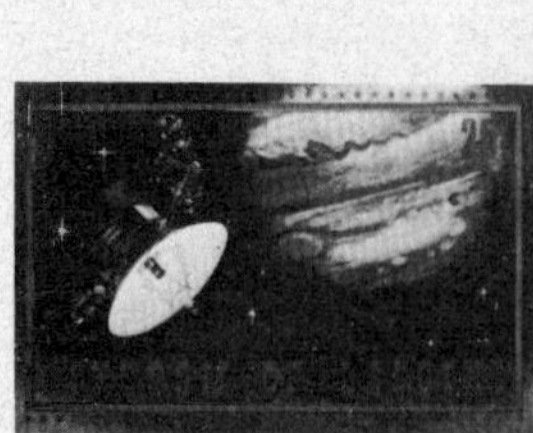

126 "Voyager" Satellite and Jpiter

127 Greater Kestrel

(Des G. Vasarhelyi. Litho Format)

1981 (15 Mar). *Space Exploration. T* **126** *and similar horiz designs. Multicoloured. P* 13½ × 14.

No.	Description		
431	25 s. Type **126**	40	40
	a. Horiz strip of 5. Nos. 431/5	1·75	
432	25 s. "Voyager" and Saturn	40	40
433	25 s. "Voyager" passing Saturn	40	40
434	25 s. "Space Shuttle" releasing satellite	40	40
435	25 s. "Space Shuttle" launch	40	40
MS436	111 × 85 mm. 1 m. 40, Saturn	2·00	2·00

Nos. 431/5 were printed together, *se-tenant*, in horizontal strips of 5 throughout the sheet.

(Des G. Vasarhelyi. Litho Format)

1981 (20 Apr–Dec). *Birds. Multicoloured designs as T* **127**. *P* 14½.

No.	Description		
437	1 s. Type **127**	5	5
	a. Perf 13 (12.81)	5	5
438	2 s. Speckled Pigeon (*horiz*)	5	5
	a. Perf 13 (12.81)	5	5
439	3 s. South African Crowned Crane	5	5
440	5 s. Bokmakierie Shrike	5	5
	a. Perf 13 (12.81)	5	5
441	6 s. Cape Robin Chat	5	5
442	7 s. Yellow Canary	8	10
443	10 s. Red-billed Pintail (*horiz*)	10	12
	a. Perf 13 (12.81)	10	12
444	25 s. Malachite Kingfisher	25	30
445	40 s. Yellow-tufted Malachite Sunbird (*horiz*)	40	40
446	60 s. Cape Longclaw (*horiz*)	60	60
447	75 s. Hoopoe (*horiz*)	80	70
448	1 m. Red Bishop (*horiz*)	1·10	1·25
449	2 m. Egyptian Goose (*horiz*)	2·10	2·25
450	5 m. Lilac-breasted Roller (*horiz*)	5·00	5·50
437/50	*Set of* 14	10·00	10·00

See also Nos. 500/13.

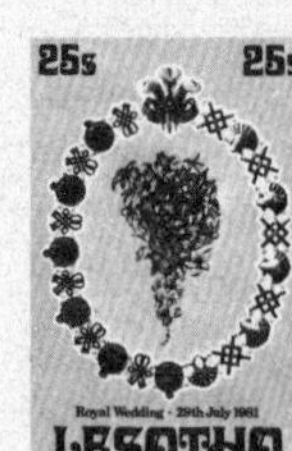

128 Wedding Bouquet from Lesotho

(Des J.W. Litho Format)

1981 (22 July). *Royal Wedding. T* **128** *and similar vert designs. Multicoloured. P* 14.

No.	Description		
451	25 s. Type **128**	40	40
	a. Booklet pane. No. 451 × 3 plus printed label	1·10	
	b. Booklet pane. Nos. 451/3 plus printed label	2·10	
452	50 s. Prince Charles riding	75	75
	a. Booklet pane. No. 452 × 3 plus printed label	2·25	
453	75 s. Prince Charles and Lady Diana Spencer	1·00	1·00
	a. Booklet pane. No. 453 × 3 plus printed label	3·00	

Nos. 451/3 also exist imperforate from a restricted printing (*price for set of* 3 £30 *mint*).

129 Prince Charles and Lady Diana Spencer

(Des G. Vasarhelyi. Litho Format)

1981 (5 Sept). *Royal Wedding (2nd issue). Sheet* 115 × 90 *mm. P* 14½.

No.	Description		
MS454	**129** 1 m. 50, multicoloured	2·40	2·40

No. **MS**454 also exists imperforate from a restricted printing (*price* £12 *mint*).

130 "Santa planning his Annual Visit"

131 Duke of Edinburgh, Award Scheme Emblem and Flags

1981 (5 Oct). *Christmas. Paintings by Norman Rockwell* (6 *to* 60 *s.*) *or Botticelli* (1 *m.* 25). *T* **130** *and similar multicoloured designs. P* 13½.

No.	Description		
455	6 s. Type **130**	10	5
456	10 s. "Santa reading his Mail"	15	12
457	15 s. "The Little Spooners"	20	20
458	20 s. "Raleigh Rockwell Travels"	30	30
459	25 s. "Ride 'em Cowboy"	35	35
460	60 s. "The Discovery"	80	80
455/60	*Set of* 6		
MS461	111 × 85 mm. 1 m. 25, "Mystic Nativity" (48 × 31 *mm*). P 13½ × 14	1·75	1·60

(Des G. Vasarhelyi. Litho Format)

1981 (5 Nov). *25th Anniv of Duke of Edinburgh Award Scheme. T* **131** *and similar multicoloured designs. P* 14½.

No.	Description		
462	6 s. Type **131**	12	12
463	7 s. Tree planting	12	12
464	25 s. Gardening	40	40
465	40 s. Mountain climbing	60	60
466	75 s. Award Scheme emblem	1·00	1·00
MS467	111 × 85 mm. 1 m. 40, Duke of Edinburgh (45 × 30 *mm*)	1·90	1·90

132 African Wild Cat

(Des G. Vasarhelyi. Litho Format)

1981 (16 Nov). *Wildlife. T* **132** *and similar multicoloured designs. P* 13½ (6, 25 *s.*) *or* 14½ (*others*).

No.	Description		
468	6 s. Type **132**	12	5
469	20 s. Chacma Baboon (44 × 31 *mm*)	40	40
470	25 s. Cape Eland	50	50
471	40 s. Porcupine (44 × 31 *mm*)	75	75
472	50 s. Oribi	85	85
MS473	111 × 85 mm. 1 m. 50, Black-backed Jackal (47 × 31 *mm*). P 13½ × 14	2·40	2·75

133 Scout Bugler

(Des G. Vasarhelyi. Litho Format)

1982 (5 Mar). *75th Anniv of Boy Scout Movement. T* **133** *and similar horiz designs. Multicoloured. P* 13½.

No.	Description		
474	6 s. Type **133**	15	15
	a. Booklet pane. Nos. 474/8 × 2 and **MS**479	6·50	
475	30 s. Scouts hiking	45	45
476	40 s. Scout sketching	60	60
477	50 s. Scout with flag	70	70
478	75 s. Scouts saluting	1·00	1·00
MS479	117 × 92 mm. 1 m. 50, Lord Baden-Powell	2·40	2·75

134 Jules Rimet Trophy with Footballers and Flags of 1930 Finalists (Argentina and Uruguay)

(Des G. Vasarhelyi. Litho Format)

1982 (14 Apr). *World Cup Football Championship, Spain. T* **134** *and similar horiz designs showing World Football Cup with players and flags of countries in past finals* (Nos. 480/90). *Multicoloured. P* 14½.

480 15 s. Type **134** 20 20
a. Sheetlet. Nos. 480/91 .. .. .. 2·10
481 15 s. Jules Rimet Trophy with Czechoslovakia and Italy, 1934 .. .. 20 20
482 15 s. Jules Rimet Trophy with Hungary and Italy, 1938 .. .. 20 20
483 15 s. Jules Rimet Trophy with Brazil and Uruguay, 1950 .. .. 20 20
484 15 s. Jules Rimet Trophy with Hungary and West Germany, 1954 .. .. .. 20 20
485 15 s. Jules Rimet Trophy with Sweden and Brazil, 1958 .. .. 20 20
486 15 s. Jules Rimet Trophy with Czechoslovakia and Brazil, 1962 .. .. 20 20
487 15 s. Jules Rimet Trophy with West Germany and England, 1966 .. .. .. 20 20
488 15 s. Jules Rimet Trophy with Italy and Brazil, 1970 .. .. 20 20
489 15 s. World Cup with Holland and West Germany, 1974 .. .. 20 20
490 15 s. World Cup with Holland and Argentina, 1978 .. .. 20 20
491 15 s. World Cup and map of World on footballs 20 20
480/91 .. .. *Set of* 12 2·10 2·10
MS492 118 × 93 mm. 1 m. 25, Bernabeu Stadium, Madrid (47 × 35 *mm*). P 13½ .. .. .. 2·00 2·25

Nos. 480/91 were printed together, *se-tenant*, in a sheetlet of 12.

135 Portrait of George Washington

136 Lady Diana Spencer in Tetbury, May 1981

(Des G. Vasarhelyi. Litho Format)

1982 (7 June). *250th Birth Anniv of George Washington. T* **135** *and similar horiz designs. Multicoloured. P* 14 × 13½.

493 6 s. Type **135** 10 8
494 7 s. Washington with step-children and dog 10 10
495 10 s. Washington with Indian chief 15 10
496 25 s. Washington with troops 35 35
497 40 s. Washington arriving in New York .. 50 50
498 1 m. Washington on parade .. .. .. 1·25 1·25
493/8 .. .. *Set of* 6 2·25 2·25
MS499 117 × 92 mm. 1 m. 25, Washington crossing the Delaware .. .. 1·50 1·50

1982 (14 June). *As Nos.* 437/50 *but W w* **14** (*sideways on Nos.* 500, 502/5 *and* 507).

500 1 s. Type **127** 5 5
501 2 s. Speckled Pigeon (*horiz*) 5 5
502 3 s. South African Crowned Crane 5 5
503 5 s. Bokmakierie Shrike 5 5
504 6 s. Cape Robin Chat 5 8
505 7 s. Yellow Canary 8 10
506 10 s. Red-billed Pintail (*horiz*) 10 10
507 25 s. Malachite Kingfisher 25 25
508 40 s. Yellow-tufted Malachite Sunbird (*horiz*) 40 35
509 60 s. Cape Longclaw (*horiz*) 60 50
510 75 s. Hoopoe (*horiz*) 80 60
511 1 m. Red Bishop (*horiz*) .. .. .. 1·10 90
512 2 m. Egyptian Goose (*horiz*) .. .. .. 2·10 1·90
513 5 m. Lilac-breasted Roller (*horiz*) .. .. 5·00 5·00
500/13 .. .. *Set of* 14 9·50 9·00

(Des Jennifer Toombs. Litho Format)

1982 (1 July). *21st Birthday of Princess of Wales. T* **136** *and similar vert designs. Multicoloured. W w* **14**. A. *P* 13½. B. *P* 13½ × 14.

		A		B	
514	30 s. Lesotho coat of arms ..	50	50	30	30
515	50 s. Type **136**	45	50	75	80
516	75 s. Wedding picture at Buckingham Palace	75	80	70	70
517	1 m. Formal portrait	1·00	1·25	1·00	1·25

137 Mosotho reading Sesotho Bible

138 Birthday Greetings

(Des G. Vasarhelyi. Litho Format)

1982 (20 Aug). *Centenary of Sesotho Bible, T* **137** *and similar multicoloured designs. P* 14½.

518 6 s. Type **137** 10 10
a. Horiz strip of 3. Nos. 518/20 .. .. 1·25
519 15 s. Sesotho Bible and Virgin Mary holding infant Jesus 20 20
520 1 m. Sesotho Bible and Cathedral (62 × 42 *mm*) .. .. 1·00 1·25

Nos. 518/20 were printed together, *se-tenant*, in horizontal strips of 3 throughout the sheet.

(Des G. Vasarhelyi. Litho Questa)

1982 (30 Sept). *Birth of Prince William of Wales. T* **138** *and similar vert design. Multicoloured. P* 14 × 13½.

521 6 s. Type **138** 12 12
a. Sheetlet. No. 521 and 522 × 5 .. .. 4·00
522 60 s. Princess Diana and Prince William of Wales 80 80

Nos. 521/2 come from sheetlets of 6 containing one 6 s. and five 60 s. stamps.

139 "A Partridge in a Pear Tree"

(Litho Format)

1982 (1 Dec). *Christmas. "The Twelve Days of Christmas". T* **139** *and similar horiz designs depicting Walt Disney cartoon characters. Multicoloured. P* 11.

523 2 s. Type **139** 5 5
a. Horiz pair. Nos. 523/4 .. .. .. 10 10
524 2 s. "Two turtle doves" 5 5
525 3 s. "Three French hens" 5 5
a. Horiz pair. Nos. 525/6 .. .. .. 10 10
526 3 s. "Four calling birds" 5 5
527 4 s. "Five golden rings" 5 8
a. Horiz pair. Nos. 527/8 .. .. .. 10 15
528 4 s. "Six geese a-laying" 5 8
529 75 s. "Seven swans a-swimming" 90 95
a. Horiz pair. Nos. 529/30 .. .. .. 1·75 1·90
530 75 s. "Eight maids a-milking" 90 95
523/30 .. .. *Set of* 8 1·90 2·10
MS531 126 × 101 mm. 1 m. 50, "Nine ladies dancing, ten lords a-leaping, eleven pipers piping, twelve drummers drumming". P 13½ .. .. 1·75 2·00

Nos. 523/4, 525/6, 527/8 and 529/30 were each printed in horizontal *se-tenant* pairs throughout the sheet.

140 *Lepista cafforum*

(Des G. Vasarhelyi. Litho Format)

1983 (11 Jan). *Fungi. T* **140** *and similar horiz designs. Multicoloured. P* 14½.

532 10 s. Type **140** 8 10
a. *Tête-bêche* (vert pair) 15 20
b. Booklet pane. Nos. 532/5 .. .. 1·75
c. Booklet pane. Nos. 532/3 40
533 30 s. *Broomeia congregata* 25 30
a. *Tête-bêche* (vert pair) 50 60
534 50 s. *Afroboletus luteolus* 45 50
a. *Tête-bêche* (vert pair) .. .. .. 90 1·00
535 75 s. *Lentinus tuber-regium* 60 75
a. *Tête-bêche* (vert pair) .. .. .. 1·25 1·50

Nos. 532/5 were each printed in sheets of 36 stamps plus 4 labels as the fourth horizontal row. The stamps in horizontal rows two, six, eight and ten were inverted, forming vertical *tête-bêche* pairs.

141 Ba-Leseli Dance

(Des J.W. Litho Format)

1983 (14 Mar). *Commonwealth Day. T* **141** *and similar multicoloured designs. P* 14½.

536 5 s. Type **141** 5 8
537 30 s. Tapestry weaving 35 40
538 60 s. Queen Elizabeth II (*vert*) 70 75
539 75 s. King Moshoeshoe II (*vert*) 90 95

142 "Dancers in a Trance" (rock painting from Ntloana Tsoana)

(Des G. Drummond. Litho Format)

1983 (20 May). *Rock Paintings. T* **142** *and similar multicoloured designs. P* 14½.

540 6 s. Type **142** 5 8
541 25 s. "Baboons", Sehonghong 30 35
542 60 s. "Hunters attacking Mountain Reedbuck", Makhetha 70 75
543 75 s. "Eland", Lehaha la Likhomo 90 95
MS544 166 × 84 mm. Nos. 540/3 and 10 s. "Cattle herding", Sehonghong (52 × 52 *mm*) .. .. 1·90 2·10

143 Montgolfier Balloon, 1783

(Des J.W. Litho Format)

1983 (11 July). *Bicentenary of Manned Flight. T* **143** *and similar multicoloured designs. P* 14½.

545 7 s. Type **143** 10 8
a. Booklet pane. Nos. 545/8 .. .. 2·25
546 30 s. Wright brothers and *Flyer* 35 40
547 60 s. First airmail flight 70 75
548 1 m. "Concorde" .. .. 1·25 1·50
MS549 180 × 92 mm. Nos. 545/8 and 6 s. Dornier "228" of Lesotho Airways (60 × 60 *mm*) .. .. 2·40 2·75

144 Rev. Eugene Casalis

(Des G. Vasarhelyi. Litho Questa)

1983 (5 Sept). *150th Anniv of Arrival of the French Missionaries. T* **144** *and similar horiz designs. Multicoloured. P* 13½ × 14.

550 6 s. Type **144** 5 8
a. *Tête-bêche* (vert pair) 10 15
551 25 s. The founding of Morija 30 35
a. *Tête-bêche* (vert pair) 60 70
552 40 s. Baptism of Libe 50 55
a. *Tête-bêche* (vert pair) .. .. .. 1·00 1·10
553 75 s. Map of Lesotho 90 95
a. *Tête-bêche* (vert pair) .. .. .. 1·75 1·90

Nos. 550/3 were each issued in sheets of 20 containing two panes (2 × 5) separated by a vertical gutter. Within these sheets horizontal rows two and four are inverted forming *tête-bêche* vertical pairs.

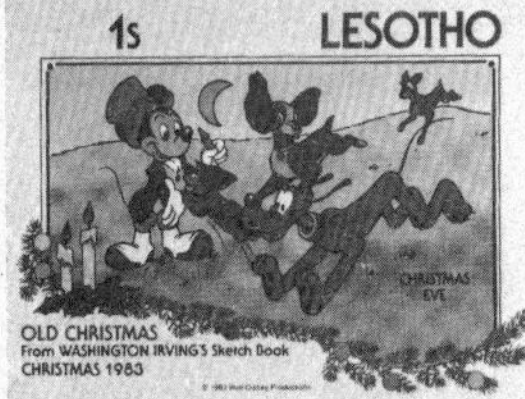

145 Mickey Mouse and Pluto Greeted by Friends

(Litho Questa)

1983 (18 Oct). *Christmas. T* **145** *and similar horiz designs showing Disney cartoon characters in scenes from "Old Christmas" (Washington Irving's sketchbook). Multicoloured. P* 13½.

554 1 s. Type **145** 5 5
555 2 s. Donald Duck and Pluto 5 5
556 3 s. Donald Duck with Huey, Dewey and Louie 5 5
557 4 s. Goofy, Donald Duck and Mickey Mouse 5 5
558 5 s. Goofy holding turkey, Donald Duck and Mickey Mouse 8 10
559 6 s. Goofy and Mickey Mouse 8 10
560 7 s. Donald and Daisy Duck 8 10
561 1 m. Goofy and Clarabell .. .. .. 95 1·00
554/61 .. .. *Set of* 8 1·25 1·40
MS562 132 × 113 mm. 1 m. 75, Scrooge McDuck, Pluto and Donald Duck .. .. 1·60 1·75

146 African Monarch

(Des and litho Format)

1984 (20 Jan). *Butterflies. T* **146** *and similar horiz designs. Multicoloured. P* 14.

563 1 s. Type **146** 5 5
564 2 s. Mountain Beauty 5 5
565 3 s. Orange Tip 5 5
566 4 s. Blue Pansy 5 5

567 5 s. Yellow Pansy 5 5
568 6 s. African Migrant 5 8
569 7 s. African Leopard 8 10
570 10 s. Suffused Acraea 10 12
571 15 s. Painted Lady 12 15
572 20 s. Lemon Traveller 15 20
573 30 s. Foxy Charaxes 25 30
574 50 s. Broad-bordered Grass Yellow .. 40 45
575 60 s. Meadow White 50 55
576 75 s. Queen Purple Tip 65 70
577 1 m. Diadem 85 90
578 5 m. Christmas Butterfly .. .. .. 4·25 4·50
563/78 .. .. *Set of* 16 6·75 7·25

147 "Thou Shalt not have Strange Gods before Me"

(Des G. Vasarhelyi. Litho Format)

1984 (30 Mar). *Easter. The Ten Commandments. T* **147** *and similar vert designs. Multicoloured. P* 13½ × 14.
579 20 s. Type **147** 20 25
a. Sheetlet. Nos. 579/88 .. .. .. 1·75
580 20 s. "Thou shalt not take the name of the Lord thy God in vain" 20 25
581 20 s. "Remember thou keep holy the Lord's Day" 20 25
582 20 s. "Honour thy father and mother" .. 20 25
583 20 s. "Thou shalt not kill" 20 25
584 20 s. "Thou shalt not commit adultery" .. 20 25
585 20 s. "Thou shalt not steal" 20 25
586 20 s. "Thou shalt not bear false witness against thy neighbour" 20 25
587 20 s. "Thou shalt not covet thy neighbour's wife" 20 25
588 20 s. "Thou shalt not covet thy neighbour's goods" 20 25
579/88 .. .. *Set of* 10 1·75 2·25
MS589 102 × 73 mm. 1 m. 50, Moses with Tablets (45 × 28 *mm*). P 14. .. .. 1·50 1·60

Nos. 579/88 were printed together in small sheets of 12 including 2 *se-tenant* stamp-size labels.

148 Torch Bearer

(Des G. Vasarhelyi. Litho Format)

1984 (3 May). *Olympic Games, Los Angeles. T* **148** *and similar horiz designs. Multicoloured. P* 13½ × 14.
590 10 s. Type **148** 10 12
591 30 s. Horse-riding 30 35
592 50 s. Swimming 50 55
593 75 s. Basketball 70 75
594 1 m. Running .. .. 95 1·00
MS595 101 × 72 mm. 1 m. 50, Olympic Flame and flags .. .. 1·50 1·60

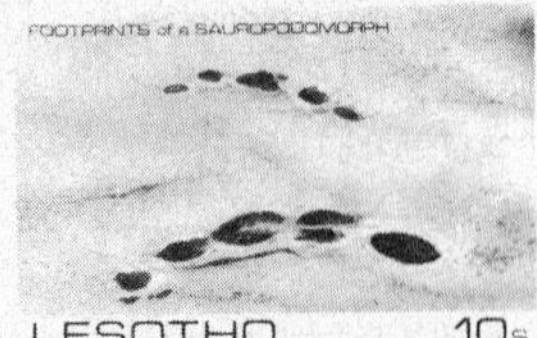

149 Sauropodomorph Footprints

(Des G. Drummond. Litho Format)

1984 (2 July). *Prehistoric Footprints (2nd series). T* **149** *and similar horiz designs. Multicoloured. P* 13½ × 14.
596 10 s. Type **149** 10 12
597 30 s. Lesothosaurus footprints 30 35
598 50 s. Footprint of carnivorous dinosaur .. 50 55

150 Wells Fargo Coach, 1852

(Des G. Vasarhelyi. Litho Format)

1984 (5 Sept). *"Ausipex" International Stamp Exhibition, Melbourne, and Bicentenary of First Mail Coach Run. T* **150** *and similar horiz designs. Multicoloured. P* 14.
599 6 s. Type **150** 5 8
a. Sheetlet. Nos. 599 × 4 and No. 603 .. 70
600 7 s. Basotho mail cart, *circa* 1900 .. .. 8 10
a. Sheetlet. No. 600 × 4 and No. 603 .. 80
601 10 s. Bath mail coach, 1784 .. .. .. 10 12
a. Sheetlet. No. 601 × 4 and No. 603 .. 90
602 30 s. Cobb coach, 1853 .. .. 30 35
a. Sheetlet. No. 602 × 4 and No. 603 .. 1·60
603 50 s. Exhibition logo and Royal Exhibition Buildings, Melbourne (82 × 25 *mm*) 50 55
MS604. 147 × 98 mm. 1 m. 75, G.B. Penny Black, Basutoland 1934 "OFFICIAL" optd 6d. and Western Australia 1854 4d. with frame inverted (82 × 25 *mm*) .. .. 1·60 1·75

In addition to the listed sheetlets, Nos. 599/602 also exist in separate sheets of 50. No. 603 only comes from the sheetlets.

151 "The Orient Express" (1900)

(Des Walsall. Litho Format)

1984 (5 Nov). *Railways of the World. T* **151** *and similar horiz designs. Multicoloured. P* 14 × 13½.
605 6 s. Type **151** 5 8
606 15 s. German State Railways Class "05" No. 05001 (1935) 15 20
607 30 s. Caledonian Railway *Cardean* (1906) .. 30 35
608 60 s. Santa Fe "Super Chief" (1940) 60 65
609 1 m. L.N.E.R. "Flying Scotsman" (1934) .. 95 1·00
MS610 108 × 82 mm. 2 m. South African Railways "The Blue Train" (1972) .. .. 2·00 2·10

152 Cape Eland Calf

(Des G. Drummond. Litho Format)

1984 (20 Dec). *Baby Animals. T* **152** *and similar horiz designs. Multicoloured. P* 14 × 13½ (1 *m.*) *or* 15 (*others*).
611 15 s. Type **152** 15 20
612 20 s. Young Chacma Baboons 20 25
613 30 s. Oribi calf 25 30
614 75 s. Young Red Rock Hares 65 70
615 1 m. Black-backed Jackal pups (46 × 27 *mm*) 85 90

POSTAGE DUE STAMPS

1966 (1 Nov). *Nos. D9/10 of Basutoland optd as T* **32** *but smaller.*
D11 D **2** 1 c. carmine 25 60
a. "LSEOTHO" (R.4/7) .. .. 25·00
D12 5 c. deep reddish violet .. .. 50 1·25
a. "LSEOTHO" (R.4/7) .. .. 45·00

No. D11 exists with the overprint centred near the foot of the stamp (just above "POSTAGE DUE") (*price* £50 *mint*). It is believed that this comes from a proof sheet which was issued in the normal way. It contains the "LSEOTHO" error, which only occurred in the first printing.

D 1

(Litho B.W.)

1967 (18 Apr). *No wmk. P* 13½.
D13 D **1** 1 c. blue 20 40
D14 2 c. brown-rose 20 50
D15 5 c. emerald 40 95

1976 (30 Nov). *W* **53** (*sideways*). *P* 13½.
D17 D **1** 2 c. rose-red 5 5
D18 5 c. emerald 5 8

Appendix

The following stamps have either been issued in excess of postal needs, or have not been made available to the public in reasonable quantities at face value. Miniature sheets, imperforate stamps etc., are excluded from this section.

1981–83

15*th Anniv of Independence. Classic Stamps of the World.* 10 m. × 40, each embossed on gold foil.

Long Island

PRICES FOR STAMPS ON COVER

Most covers from Long Island are philatelic and these are worth from × 2 the prices quoted for used stamps.

The Turkish island of Chustan (or Keustan) in the Gulf of Smyrna was occupied by the Royal Navy during April 1916 and renamed Long Island.

The following stamps were provided by the Civil Administrator, Lieut-Cmdr H. Pirie-Gordon, for the postal service inaugurated on 7 May 1916.

(1)

2

1916 (7 May). *Turkish fiscal stamps surch by typewriter as in T* **1**. *No wmk. P* 12.
1 ½d. on 20 pa. green and buff (new value in red, remainder of surch in black) .. £2000 £4000
2 1d. on 10 pa. carmine and buff £2500
3 2½d. on 1 pi. violet and buff (R.) £2250

Quantities issued: ½d. 25; 1d. 20; 2½d. 25.

1916 (7 May). *Typewritten as T* **2** *in various colours of ribbon and carbon. Each stamp initialled by the Civil Administrator. No gum. Imperf.*

(*a*) *On pale green paper with horizontal grey lines. No wmk. Sheets of* 16 *or* 12 *with stamps initialled in red ink.*
4 ½d. black £425
a. "G.R.I." double £1300
b. "7" for "&" .. ..
5 ½d. blue £425
b. "7" for "&" .. ..
6 ½d. mauve £450
a. "G.R.I." double £950

Quantity issued: 140 in all.

(*b*) *On thin horiz laid paper with sheet wmk of* "SILVER LINEN" *in double-lined capitals. Sheets of* 20 *with stamps initialled in red ink.*
7 ½d. black £200
a. "postage" for "Postage" £475
8 ½d. blue £200
9 ½d. mauve £125
a. "postage" for "Postage" £425
b. "7" for "&" £425
10 1d. black £110
a. "7" for "&" £425
b. "Rvevue" for "Revenue" .. .. ..
11 1d. blue £100
c. "postage" for "Postage" £375
e. "G.R?I?" for "G.R.I." £750
f. "ONR" for "ONE" £375
12 1d. mauve £170 £170
a. "7" for "&" £425
f. "ONR" for "ONE" £500
g. "Postegg" for "Postage" £425
13 1d. red £100 £110
a. "7" for "&" £425
f. "ONR for "ONE" £425
14 2½d. black £300
15 2½d. blue £300 £350
16 2½d. mauve £300
17 6d. black (*inscr* "SIX PENCE") £425
19 6d. mauve (*inscr* "SIX PENCE") £160 £180
a. "SIXPENCE" (one word) £500
20 1s. black £100
a. "ISLANA" for "ISLAND" £375
b. "Postge" for "Postage" £500
c. "Rebenue for "Revenue" .. .. ..
21 1s. blue £175
22 1s. mauve .. .. 90·00
b. "ISLANA" for "ISLAND" £425
c. "Rebenue" for "Revenue" £550

Quantities issued (all colours); ½d. 280; 1d. 1068; 2½d. 80; 6d. 100; 1s. 532.

(*c*) *On thin wove paper. No wmk. Sheets of* 24 *with stamps initialled in indelible pencil.*
23 ½d. black £150
25 ½d. mauve £300
26 1d. black £150 £175
27 1d. red £400 £350
30 2d. black £140
a. "ISTAD" for "ISLAND" £1200
b. Error. 1d. and 2d. *se-tenant* £1300
c. Initialled in red ink .. .. ..
31 2d. mauve £140
a. Error. 1d. and 2d. *se-tenant* £1500
32 2½d. black £130 £120
33 2½d. blue £400
34 2½d. mauve £350 £350
35 6d. black £140 £140
a. "Rvenne" for "Revenue" £425
b. Error. 2d. and 6d. *se-tenant*, also "ISLND" for "ISLAND" £1700
36 6d. blue £250
b. Error. 2d. and 6d. *se-tenant*, also "ISLND" for "ISLAND" .. .. ..

Quantities issued (all colours); ½d. 144; 1d. 144; 2d. 288; 2½d. 144; 6d. 240.

TOP COPIES AND CARBONS. It is believed that the production sequence of the typewritten stamps was as follows:

Nos. 4/6 Three sheets of black top copies, two of 12 and one of 16
Three sheets of blue carbons, two of 12 and one of 16
Five sheets of mauve carbons, all of 12

Nos. 7/9 *Sheets of* 20
Three sheets of black top copies
Three sheets of blue carbons
Eight sheets of mauve carbons

Nos. 10/13 *Sheets of* 20
Eleven sheets of red top copies
Fifteen sheets of black carbons
Six sheets of blue carbons
Twenty-two sheets of mauve carbons

Nos. 14/16 *Sheets of* 20
One sheet of black top copies
One sheet of blue carbons
Two sheets of mauve carbons

Nos. 17/19 *Sheets of* 20
One sheet of black top copies
One sheet of blue carbons*
Three sheets of mauve carbons

Nos. 20/22 *Sheets of* 20
Five sheets of black top copies
Nine sheets of black carbons
Two sheets of blue carbons
Twelve sheets of mauve carbons

Nos. 23/5 *Sheets of* 24
One sheet of black top copies
Three sheets of black carbons
One sheet of blue carbons*
One sheet of mauve carbons

Nos. 26/9 *Sheets of* 24
One sheet of red top copies
Three sheets of black carbons
One sheet of blue carbons*
One sheet of mauve carbons*

Nos. 30/1 *Sheets of* 24
Two sheets of black top copies
Six sheets of black carbons (inc one as No. 30c)
Four sheets of mauve carbons

Nos. 32/4 *Sheets of* 24
One sheet of black top copies
Three sheets of black carbons
One sheet of blue carbons
One sheet of mauve carbons

Nos. 35/6 *Sheets of* 24
Two sheets of black top copies
Six sheets of black carbons
Two sheets of blue carbons

*These carbons are described in written records, but their existence has yet to be confirmed by actual examples.

The stamps of Long Island were withdrawn on 26 May 1916, after which the remaining unsold examples of Nos. 7/36 were destroyed.

Madagascar

PRICES FOR STAMPS ON COVER

Nos. 1/49	*from* × 5
Nos. 50/6	*from* × 20
Nos. 57/62	—

BRITISH CONSULAR MAIL

CONDITION. Due to the type of paper used, stamps of the British Consular Mail are usually found with slight faults, especially thins. Our prices are for average examples, really fine stamps being worth a premium.

USED STAMPS. Postmarks are not usually found on these issues. Cancellations usually take the form of a manuscript line or cross in crayon, ink or pencil or as five parallel horizontal bars in black or red, approximately 15 mm long.

1

2

1884 (Mar). *Rouletted vertically in colour. With circular handstamp,* "BRITISH VICE CONSULTATE ANTANANARIVO" *in black.*

(a) Inscribed "LETTER"

1 1 6d. magenta .. £225 £250
a. Handstamp in violet .. £525 £600
2 1 1s. magenta .. £130 £140
3 1s. 6d. magenta .. £130 £140
4 2s. magenta .. £500 £525

(b) Inscribed "POSTAL PACKET"

5 1 1d. magenta (1 oz) .. £130 £140
a. Without handstamp .. £900 £1000
6 2d. magenta (2 oz) .. £150 £140
7 3d. magenta (3 oz) .. £130 £140
8 4d. magenta (1 oz) ..
a. Handstamp in violet .. £500 £550
b. Without handstamp .. £1200 £1200
c. Altered by pen to "4 oz" .. £550 £600

Several of the values are known with the handstamp inverted and also double printed.

1886. *No. 2 with* "SHILLING" *erased and* "PENNY" *written above in red ink, and the same stamp with* "1 oz." *altered in red to* "4½d." *and the Vice-Consul's initials,* "W.C.P.", *added.*

9 1 1d. on 1s. magenta ..
10 4½d. on 1s. magenta ..

1886. *Colour changed.*

11 1 6d. rose-red .. £180 £170

1886. *As T* 1, *but handstamp reading* "British Consular Mail—ANTANANARIVO."

12 4d. magenta (Blk.) .. £1100 £1100
13 4d. magenta (V.) .. £1200 £1200

Nos. 1 to 13 were printed in horizontal strips of four, two with the full stops normal and two with one of the full stops appearing as a small circle. This "hollow stop" appears after the "B" in the 1d., 4d., 6d. and 2s. and after the "M" in the 2d., 3d., 1s. and 1s. 6d.

1886. *Rouletted vertically in colour.*

(a) With period after "POSTAGE" *and value*

A. *Handstamp in black.* B. *In violet.*

			A		B	
14	2	1d. rose	45·00	45·00	90·00	90·00
15		1½d. rose	£140	£140	£225	£250
16		2d. rose	45·00	45·00	90·00	90·00
17		3d. rose	£140	£140	90·00	90·00
18		4½d. rose	£130	£130	£110	£110
19		8d. rose	£200	£200	£250	£250
20		9d. rose	—	—	£525	£525

(b) Without period after "POSTAGE" *and value. Handstamp in violet.*

21 2 1d. rose .. £500 £500
22 1½d. rose .. £550 £550
23 3d. rose .. £800 £800
24 4½d. rose .. £450 £475
25 6d. rose .. £450 £475

(c) Period after value. "POSTAGE" *measures 24½ mm in place of 29½ mm. Handstamp in violet*

26 2 4d. rose .. £140 £160
27 8d. rose .. £450 £450
28 1s. 6d. rose .. £900 £1000
29 2s. rose .. £800 £800
a. Handstamp in black ..

1886. *As T* 2, *but handstamp reading* "BRITISH CONSULAR MAIL, ANTANANARIVO". *Rouletted vertically in colour.*

(a) With period after "POSTAGE" *and the value*

A. *Handstamp in black.* B. *In violet.*

		A		B
30	1d. rose	30·00	32·00	†
31	1½d. rose	30·00	32·00	†
32	2d. rose	32·00	32·00	†
33	3d. rose	32·00	32·00	†
34	4½d. rose	32·00	32·00	†
35	8d. rose	32·00	38·00	£700 £700
36	9d. rose	32·00	38·00	85·00 85·00
	a. Without handstamp	£700	£700	

C. *Handstamp in red*

37 3d. rose .. — £1300
38 4½d. rose .. — £1200

(b) Without period after "POSTAGE" *and the value*

A. *Handstamp in black.* B. *In violet*

		A		B	
39	1d. rose	30·00	30·00	32·00	32·00
	a. Without handstamp	£300	£300		
40	1½d. rose	30·00	30·00	35·00	35·00
	a. Without handstamp	£300	£300		
41	2d. rose	30·00	30·00	32·00	32·00
42	3d. rose	30·00	30·00	32·00	32·00
	a. Without handstamp	£700	£700		
43	4½d. rose	32·00	32·00	38·00	38·00
	a. Without handstamp	£800	£800		
44	6d. rose	32·00	32·00	90·00	90·00
	a. Without handstamp	£900	£900		

(c) Period after value. "POSTAGE" *24½ mm long in place of 29½ mm.*

A. *Handstamp in black.* B. *In violet.*

		A		B	
45	4d. rose	32·00	32·00	90·00	90·00
	a. Without handstamp	£525	£525		
46	8d. rose	£120	£120	£140	£140
	a. Without handstamp	£700	£700		
47	1s. rose	70·00	70·00	£350	£350
	a. Without handstamp	£700	£700		
48	1s. 6d. rose	£160	£160	£525	£525
	a. Without handstamp	£1000	£1000		
49	2s. rose	£250	£250	£525	£525
	a. Without handstamp	£1000	£1000		

These stamps were suppressed in 1887.

BRITISH INLAND MAIL

USED STAMPS. Postmarks are found on the following issues.

4

5 Malagasy Runners

1895 (Jan). *Type-set at Antananarivo. Rouletted in black.*

(a) Thick laid paper

50 4 4d. black .. 15·00 14·00
a. "FUOR" for "FOUR" .. — £475

(b) Wove paper

51 4 1d. blue-grey .. 14·00 12·00
52 6d. pale yellow .. 14·00 14·00
53 8d. salmon .. 14·00 14·00
54 1s. fawn .. 25·00 14·00
55 2s. bright rose .. 25·00 16·00
a. Italic "2" at left .. £110 90·00
56 4s. grey .. 40·00 14·00

There are six types of each value, printed in groups repeated four times on each sheet; the upper and lower groups are *tête-bêche*.

(Litho John Haddon & Co London)

1895 (Mar). *The inscription in the lower label varies for each value. P* 12.

57 5 2d. blue .. 5·00
a. Imperf between (pair) .. £500
58 4d. rose .. 5·00
a. Imperf between (pair) .. £450
59 6d. green .. 5·00
a. Imperf between (pair) .. £500
60 1s. slate-blue .. 6·50
a. Imperf between (pair) .. £500
61 2s. chocolate .. 7·00
a. Imperf between (pair) .. £500
62 4s. bright purple .. 10·00
a. Imperf between (pair)

This post was suppressed when the French entered Antananarivo at the end of September 1895.

Malawi

(*formerly* Nyasaland)

INDEPENDENT

44 Dr. H. Banda (Prime Minister) and Independence Monument

(Des M. Goaman. Photo Harrison)

1964 (6 July). *Independence. T* **44** *and similar horiz designs. P* 14½.

211 3d. yellow-olive and deep sepia .. 5 5
212 6d. red, gold, blue, carmine and lake .. 10 5
213 1s. 3d. red, green, black and bluish violet .. 10 5
214 2s. 6d. multicoloured .. 20 30

Designs:—6d. Banda and rising sun. 1s. 3d. Banda and Malawi flag; 2s. 6d. Banda and Malawi coat of arms.

48 Tung Tree

49 Christmas Star and Globe

(Des V. Whiteley. Photo Harrison)

1964 (6 July)–**65**. *As Nos.* 199/210 *of Nyasaland but inscr* "MALAWI" *and T* **48** *(9d.). No wmk. P* 14½.

215 ½d. reddish violet .. 8 10
216 1d. black and green .. 12 5
217 2d. light red-brown .. 12 5
218 3d. red-brown, yellow-green & bistre-brown 15 5
219 4d. black and orange-yellow .. 25 15
220 6d. bluish violet, yellow-green and light blue 25 5
221 9d. bistre-brown, green and yellow .. 35 15
222 1s. brown, turquoise-blue and pale yellow .. 30 5
223 1s. 3d. bronze-green and chestnut .. 75 40

224 2s. 6d. brown and blue . . . . . . 1·75 1·40
225 5s. blue, green, yellow and sepia . . . . 1·75 2·75
225*a* 5s. blue, green, yellow and sepia (1.6.65) . . 3·00 1·50
226 10s. green, orange-brown and black . . . . 3·50 2·50
227 £1 deep reddish purple and yellow . . . . 9·50 7·00
215/27 . . . . *Set of* 14 20·00 14·00

No. 225*a* is inscribed "LAKE MALAWI" instead of "LAKE NYASA".

See also Nos. 252/62.

(Des V. Whiteley. Photo Harrison)

1964 (1 Dec). *Christmas. P* 14½.
228 **49** 3d. blue-green and gold 5 5
229 6d. magenta and gold 12 5
230 1s. 3d. reddish violet and gold 20 10
231 2s. 6d. blue and gold 40 40
MS231*a* 83 × 126 mm. Nos. 228/31. Imperf . . 2·50 2·25

1/6

50 Coins (**51**)

(Des V. Whiteley. Photo Enschedé)

1965 (1 Mar). *Malawi's First Coinage. Coins in black and silver. P* 13½.
232 **50** 3d. green 8 5
233 9d. magenta 15 5
234 1s. 6d. purple 20 10
235 3s. blue 40 30
MS235*a* 126 × 104 mm. Nos. 232/5. Imperf . . 1·25 1·40

1965 (14 June). *Nos.* 223/4 *surch as T* **51**.
236 1s. 6d. on 1s. 3d. bronze-green and chestnut 40 20
237 3s. on 2s. 6d. brown and blue 50 45

On No. 237 "3/–" occurs below the bars.

52 Chilembwe leading Rebels

(Des M. Goaman. Photo Harrison)

1965 (20 Aug). *50th Anniv of* 1915 *Rising. P* 14 × 14½.
238 **52** 3d. violet and light olive-green . . 5 5
239 9d. olive-brown and red-orange . . 8 5
240 1s. 6d. red-brown and grey-blue . . 12 10
241 3s. turquoise-green and slate-blue . . 30 30
MS241*a* 127 × 83 mm. Nos. 238/41 . . . . 6·50 7·50

53 "Learning and Scholarship"

(Des H. E. Baxter. Photo Harrison)

1965 (6 Oct). *Opening of Malawi University. P* 14½.
242 **53** 3d. black and emerald 5 5
243 9d. black and magenta 8 5
244 1s. 6d. black and reddish violet . . 12 10
245 3s. black and blue 25 30
MS246 127 × 84 mm. Nos. 242/5 . . . . 6·50 4·75

54 *Papilio ophidicephalus mkuwadzi*

(Des V. Whiteley. Photo Enschedé)

1966 (15 Feb). *Malawi Butterflies. T* **54** *and similar horiz designs. Multicoloured. P* 13½.
247 4d. Type **54** 50 5
248 9d. *Papilio magdae* 95 10
249 1s. 6d. *Epamera handmani* . . . . . . 1·10 75
250 3s. *Amauris crawshayi* . . . . . . 2·50 2·75
MS251 130 × 100 mm. Nos. 247/50 . . . . 9·50 11·00

55 Cockerels

56 Burley Tobacco

57 *Cyrestis camillus sublineatus* (butterfly)

(New values des V. Whiteley (1s. 6d.), M. Goaman (£2). Photo Harrison)

1966–67. *As Nos.* 215 *etc. but W* **55** *(sideways on* ½*d.,* 2*d.), and new values and designs* (1*s.* 6*d.,* £2). *P* 14½.
252 – ½d. reddish violet (1.4.66) 10 5
253 – 1d. black and green (1.4.66) 15 5
254 – 2d. light red-brown (16.5.67) 15 5
255 – 3d. red-brn, yell-grn & bis-brn (27.6.67) 20 5
256 – 6d. bluish vio, yell-grn & lt bl (16.5.67) 25 5
257 **48** 9d. bistre-brown, green & yell (16.5.67) 35 5
258 – 1s. brown, turq-blue & pale yell (1.4.66) 25 5
259 **56** 1s. 6d. chocolate & yell-grn (15.11.66) 55 25
260 – 5s. blue, green, yellow & sepia (16.5.67) 8·50 2·00
261 – 10s. green, orange-brown & blk (16.5.67) 17·00 5·50
262 **57** £2 black, orange-yellow, pale yellow and slate-violet (7.9.66) . . . . 25·00 26·00
252/62 . . . . . . *Set of* 11 45·00 30·00

No. 260 is inscribed "LAKE MALAWI".

The 2d. exists with both PVA gum and gum arabic.

58 British Central Africa 6d. Stamp of 1891 **59** President Banda

(Des V. Whiteley. Photo Harrison)

1966 (4 May–10 June). *75th Anniv of Postal Services. W* **55**. *P* 14½.
263 **58** 4d. grey-blue and yellow-green . . 12 5
264 9d. grey-blue and claret 20 5
265 1s. 6d. grey-blue and reddish lilac . . 35 10
266 3s. grey-blue and new blue . . 75 75
MS267 83 × 127 mm. Nos. 263/6 (10 June) . . 4·00 3·25

REPUBLIC

(Des M. Goaman. Photo Harrison)

1966 (6 July). *Republic Day. W* **55**. *P* 14 × 14½.
268 **59** 4d. brown, silver and emerald 5 5
269 9d. brown, silver and magenta . . 8 5
270 1s. 6d. brown, silver and violet . . 12 10
271 3s. brown, silver and blue 25 30
MS272 83 × 127 mm. Nos. 268/71 . . . . 2·50 2·50

60 Bethlehem

(Des and photo Harrison)

1966 (12 Oct). *Christmas. W* **55**. *P* 14½.
273 **60** 4d. myrtle-green and gold 12 5
274 9d. brown-purple and gold 30 5
275 1s. 6d. orange-red and gold 45 10
276 3s. blue and gold . . . . 1·00 1·00

61 *Ilala I*

(Des Mrs. H. Breggar. Photo Harrison)

1967 (4 Jan). *Lake Malawi Steamers. T* **61** *and similar horiz designs. W* **55**. *P* 14½.
277 4d. black, yellow and bright green 20 5
278 9d. black, yellow and magenta 30 10
279 1s. 6d., black, red and violet 50 35
280 3s. black, red and bright blue . . . . 1·75 1·50

Designs:—9d. *Dove*; 1s. 6d. *Chauncy Maples* (wrongly inscr "Chauncey"); 3s. *Gwendolen*.

62 Turquoise-gold Chichlid

(Des R. Granger Barrett. Photo Enschedé)

1967 (3 May). *Lake Malawi Chichlids. T* **62** *and similar horiz designs. Multicoloured. W* **55** *(sideways). P* 12½ × 12.
281 4d. Type **62** 15 10
282 9d. Red Finned chichlid 25 15
283 1s. 6d. Zebra chichlid 45 40
284 3s. Golden chichlid . . . . . . 2·00 1·50
a. Imperf (pair) £120

63 Rising Sun and Gearwheel

(Des Jennifer Toombs. Litho D.L.R.)

1967 (5 July). *Industrial Development. P* 13½ × 13.
285 **63** 4d. black and emerald 5 5
286 9d. black and carmine 8 5
287 1s. 6d. black and reddish violet . . 12 10
288 3s. black and bright blue 25 30
MS289 134 × 108 mm. Nos. 285/8 . . . . 1·50 1·60

64 Mary and Joseph beside Crib

(Des Jennifer Toombs. Photo Harrison)

1967 (21 Nov–1 Dec). *Christmas. W* **55**. *P* 14 × 14½.
290 **64** 4d. royal blue and turquoise-green . . 8 5
291 9d. royal blue and light red 10 5
292 1s. 6d. royal blue and yellow 15 10
293 3s. royal blue and new blue 35 40
MS294 114 × 100 mm. Nos. 290/3. Wmk sideways. P 14 × 13½ (1 Dec) . . . . . . 3·00 4·00

65 *Calotropis procera*

(Des G. Drummond. Litho D.L.R.)

1968 (24 Apr). *Wild Flowers. T* **65** *and similar horiz designs. Multicoloured. W* **55** *(sideways). P* 13½ × 13.
295 4d. Type **65** 15 5
296 9d. *Borreria dibrachiata* 30 10
297 1s. 6d. *Hibiscus rhodanthus* 35 20
298 3s. *Bidens pinnatipartita* 70 60
MS299 135 × 91 mm. Nos. 295/8 . . . . 3·00 3·00

66 Saddleback Steam Engine, "Thistle No. 1"

(Des R. Granger Barrett. Photo Harrison)

1968 (24 July). *Malawi Locomotives. T* **66** *and similar horiz designs. W* **55**. *P* 14 × 14½.
300 4d. grey-green, slate-blue and red 30 12
301 9d. red, slate-blue and myrtle-green . . 50 30
302 1s. 6d. multicoloured . . . . . . 1·25 65
303 3s. multicoloured . . . . . . 2·00 1·75
MS304 120 × 88 mm. Nos. 300/3. P 14½ . . 4·75 5·50

Designs:—9d. "G" class steam engine; 1s. 6d. Diesel electric locomotive, "Zambesi"; 3s. Diesel rail car.

67 "The Nativity" (Piero della Francesca)

(Des and photo Harrison)

1968 (6 Nov). *Christmas. Paintings. T* **67** *and similar horiz designs. Multicoloured.* W **55** (*sideways on* 4d.). *P* 14 × 14½.

305 4d. Type **67** 10 5
306 9d. "The Adoration of the Shepherds" (Murillo) 12 5
307 1s. 6d. "The Adoration of the Shepherds" (Reni) 15 15
308 3s. "Nativity with God the Father and Holy Ghost" (Pittoni) 30 40
MS309 115 × 101 mm. Nos. 305/8. P 14 × 13½ 1·75 2·50

68 Scarlet-chested Sunbird

69 Nyasa Lovebird

70 Carmine Bee Eater

(Des V. Whiteley. Photo Harrison)

1968 (13 Nov). *Birds. T* **68/70** *and similar designs. Multicoloured.* W **55** (*sideways on* 1d. *to* 4d. *and* 3s. *to* £1). *P* 14½.

310 1d. Type **68** 10 5
311 2d. Violet Starling 15 8
312 3d. White-browed Robin Chat 20 8
313 4d. Red-billed Fire Finch 30 20
a. Red omitted .. ..
314 6d. Type **69** 35 12
315 9d. Yellow-rumped Bishop 50 50
316 1s. Type **70** 60 25
317 1s. 6d. Grey-headed Bush Shrike .. .. 4·50 4·50
318 2s. Paradise Whydah .. .. 5·00 5·00
319 3s. African Paradise Flycatcher .. .. 4·50 3·50
320 5s. Bateleur .. .. 4·50 3·50
321 10s. Saddle-bill Stork .. .. 6·00 7·50
322 £1 Purple Heron .. .. 13·00 16·00
323 £2 Knysna Turaco .. .. 35·00 42·00
310/323 .. .. *Set of* 14 65·00 75·00

Sizes:—2d. to 4d. as T **68**; 9d. as T **69**; 1s. 6d., 2s., £2 as T **70**; 3s. to £1 as T **70** but vertical.

No. 310 exists in coils, constructed from normal sheets.

71 I.L.O. Emblem

(Des G. Drummond. Photo, emblem die-stamped Harrison)

1969 (5 Feb). *50th Anniv of the International Labour Organization.* W **55** (*sideways on No.* **MS**328). *P* 14.

324 **71** 4d. gold and myrtle-green 8 5
325 9d. gold and chocolate 10 5
326 1s. 6d. gold and blackish brown 15 10
327 3s. gold and indigo 30 25
MS328 127 × 89 mm. Nos. 324/7 .. .. .. 11·00 11·00

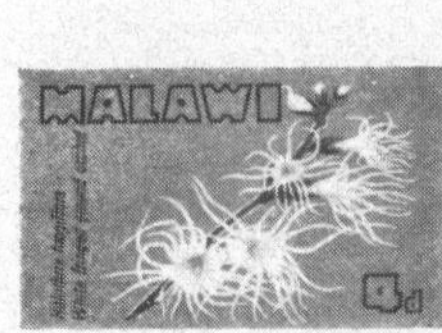

72 White-fringed Ground Orchid

73 African Development Bank Emblem

(Des J.W. Litho B.W.)

1969 (9 July). *Orchids of Malawi. T* **72** *and similar horiz designs. Multicoloured.* W **55**. *P* 13½ × 13.

329 4d. Type **72** 30 5
330 9d. Red Ground orchid 40 20
331 1s. 6d. Leopard Tree orchid 75 40
332 3s. Blue Ground orchid .. .. .. 2·25 2·75
MS333 118 × 86 mm. Nos. 329/32 .. .. 3·25 4·00

(Des G. Vasarhelyi. Litho D.L.R.)

1969 (10 Sept). *Fifth Anniv of African Development Bank.* W **55**. *P* 14.

334 **73** 4d. yellow, yellow-ochre and chocolate 8 5
335 9d. yellow, yellow-ochre & myrtle-green 10 8
336 1s. 6d. yellow, yell-ochre & blackish brn 12 12
337 3s. yellow, yellow-ochre and indigo .. 20 30
MS338 102 × 137 mm. Nos. 334/7 .. .. 1·00 1·50

74 Dove over Bethlehem

75 Elegant Grasshopper

(Des Jennifer Toombs. Photo Harrison)

1969 (5 Nov). *Christmas.* W **55**. *P* 14½ × 14.

339 **74** 2d. black and olive-yellow 5 5
340 4d. black and deep turquoise 8 5
341 9d. black and scarlet 12 8
342 1s. 6d. black & deep bluish violet .. 15 12
343 3s. black and ultramarine 40 40
MS344 130 × 71 mm. Nos. 339/43 .. .. 2·50 3·00

(Des V. Whiteley. Litho Format)

1970 (4 Feb). *Insects of Malawi. T* **75** *and similar vert designs. Multicoloured.* W **55**. *P* 14.

345 4d. Type **75** 15 5
346 9d. Beam Blister beetle 25 10
347 1s. 6d. Pumpkin ladybird 45 20
348 3s. Praying mantis .. .. 1·00 85
MS349 86 × 137 mm. Nos. 345/8 .. .. 1·90 2·50

Rand Easter Show
1970

(**76**)

1970 (18 Mar). *Rand Easter Show. No.* 317 *optd with T* **76**.

350 1s. 6d. multicoloured 35 60

77 Runner

(Des J. Cooter. Litho B.W.)

1970 (3 June). *Ninth British Commonwealth Games, Edinburgh.* W **55**. *P* 13.

351 **77** 4d. royal blue and blue-green 8 5
352 9d. royal blue and carmine 10 8
353 1s. 6d. royal blue and dull yellow .. 12 12
354 3s. royal blue and new blue 30 30
MS355 146 × 96 mm. Nos. 351/4 .. .. 1·25 1·50

(New Currency, 100 tambalas = 1 kwacha)

10t

(**78**)

79 *Aegocera trimenii*

1970 (2 Sept). *Decimal Currency. Nos.* 316 *and* 318 *surch as T* **78**.

356 10 t. on 1s. multicoloured 30 25
a. Surch double .. .. .. † —
357 20 t. on 2s. multicoloured 70 70

(Des R. Granger Barrett. Litho B.W.)

1970 (30 Sept). *Moths. T* **79** *and similar horiz designs. Multicoloured.* W **55**. *P* 11 × 11½.

358 4d. Type **79** 30 5
359 9d. *Epiphora bauhiniae* 40 10
360 1s. 6d. *Parasa karschi* 65 30
361 3s. *Teracotona euprepia* .. .. .. 1·50 2·25
MS362 112 × 92 mm. Nos. 358/61 .. .. 3·00 4·00

80 Mother and Child

30t
Special
United
Kingdom
Delivery
Service

(**81**)

(Des Brother W. Meyer. Litho J.W.)

1970 (4 Nov). *Christmas.* W **55** (*sideways*). *P* 14.

363 **80** 2d. black and light yellow 10 5
364 **80** 4d. black and emerald 12 5
365 9d. black and orange-red 20 10
366 1s. 6d. black and light purple 25 15
367 3s. black and blue 55 50
MS368 166 × 100 mm. Nos. 363/7 .. .. 1·60 2·25

1971 (8 Feb). *No.* 319 *surch with T* **81**.

369 30 t. on 3s. multicoloured .. .. .. 35 2·50

No. 369 was issued for use on letters carried by an emergency airmail service from Malawi to Great Britain during the British postal strike. The fee of 30 t. was to cover the charge for delivery by a private service, and ordinary stamps to pay the normal airmail fee had to be affixed as well.

The strike ended on 8 March, when private delivery services were withdrawn.

82 Decimal Coinage and Cockerel

(Des V. Whiteley. Litho Format)

1971 (15 Feb). *Decimal Coinage.* W **55** (*sideways*). *P* 14.

370 **82** 3 t. multicoloured 8 5
371 8 t. multicoloured 15 15
372 15 t. multicoloured 35 35
373 30 t. multicoloured 75 75
MS374 140 × 101 mm. Nos. 370/73 .. .. 1·50 1·75

83 Greater Kudu

84 Eland

(Des and litho J.W.)

1971 (15 Feb)–**74**. *Decimal Currency. Antelopes. Vert designs as T* **83** (1 *t. to* 8 *t.*), *or T* **84** (*others*). *Multicoloured.* W **55** (*sideways on* 1 *t. to* 8 *t.*). *P* 13½ × 14 (1 *t to* 8 *t.*) *or* 14½ (*others*).

375 1 t. Type **83** 10 5
a. Coil stamp. P 14½ × 14 .. .. 15 30
b. Perf 14† (12.11.74) 35 35
376 2 t. Nyala 15 5
377 3 t. Reed Buck 20 5
a. Perf 14† (12.11.74) 35 40
378 5 t. Puku 40 5
a. Perf 14† (12.11.74) 40 45
379 8 t. Impala 45 5
380 10 t. Type **84** (*shades*) 60 20
381 15 t. Klipspringer 75 40
382 20 t. Livingstone's Suni .. .. .. 1·25 50
383 30 t. Roan Antelope .. .. .. 1·60 70
384 50 t. Waterbuck .. .. 1·50 75
385 1 k. Bushbuck .. .. 3·50 2·50
386 2 k. Red Duiker .. .. 5·50 4·50
387 4 k. Grey Duiker .. .. 16·00 17·00
375/87 .. .. *Set of* 13 28·00 24·00

No. 387 is incorrectly inscr "Gray Duiker".

† These actually gauge 14·2 × 14 instead of 13·7 × 14 and are line-perforated; in blocks they can easily be distinguished as in alternate rows across the sheet the horizontal perfs have two holes where they cross the vertical perfs; the watermark is also sideways inverted.

85 Christ on the Cross

87 *Holarrhena febrifuga*

(Des G. Drummond. Litho Questa)

1971 (7 Apr). *Easter. Details from Painting "The Small Passion" by Dürer. T* **85** *and similar vert design.* W **55**. *P* 13½.

388 3 t. black and green 5 5
a. Pair. Nos. 388/9 .. .. .. 10 10
389 3 t. black and green 5 5
390 8 t. black and orange-red 15 15
a. Pair. Nos. 390/1 .. .. .. 30 30
391 8 t. black and orange-red 15 15
392 15 t. black and violet 30 30
a. Pair. Nos. 392/3 .. .. .. 60 60
393 15 t. black and violet 30 30
394 30 t. black and bright blue 50 50
a. Pair. Nos. 394/5 .. .. .. 1·00 1·00
395 30 t. black and bright blue 50 50
388/95 .. .. *Set of* 8 1·75 1·75
MS396 Two sheets each 95 × 145 mm (a) Nos. 388, 390, 392 and 394; (b) Nos. 389, 391, 393 and 395 2·50 2·75

Designs:—Nos. 388, 390, 392 and 394, Type **85**; Nos. 389, 391, 393 and 395, The Resurrection.

Nos. 388/9, 390/1, 392/3 and 394/5 were each printed together, *se-tenant*, in pairs throughout the sheet.

(Des G. Drummond. Litho J.W.)

1971 (14 July). *Flowering Shrubs and Trees. T* **87** *and similar vert designs. Multicoloured.* W **55**. *P* 14.

397		3 t. Type **87**	12	5
398		8 t. *Brachystegia spiciformis*	20	12
399		15 t. *Securidaca longepedunculata*	35	30
400		30 t. *Pterocarpus rotundifolius*	55	60
MS401		102 × 135 mm. Nos. 397/400	2·00	2·25

88 Drum Major

89 "Madonna and Child" (William Dyce)

(Des J.W. Litho Questa)

1971 (5 Oct). *50th Anniv of Malawi Police Force.* W **55**. *P* 14 × 14½.

402	**88**	30 t. multicoloured	85	1·25

(Des J. Cooter. Litho Format)

1971 (10 Nov). *Christmas. T* **89** *and similar vert designs. Multicoloured.* W **55**. *P* 14½.

403		3 t. Type **89**	12	5
404		8 t. "The Holy Family" (M. Schöngauer)	20	15
405		15 t. "The Holy Family with St. John" (Raphael)	45	50
406		30 t. "The Holy Family" (Bronzino)	80	1·10
MS407		101 × 139 mm. Nos. 403/6	2·75	3·00

90 Vickers "Viscount"

(Des R. Granger Barrett. Litho Questa)

1972 (9 Feb). *Air. Malawi Aircraft. T* **90** *and similar horiz designs. Multicoloured.* W **55** (*sideways*). *P* 13½.

408		3 t. Type **90**	10	5
409		8 t. Hawker Siddeley "748"	25	20
410		15 t. Britten-Norman "Islander"	60	55
411		30 t. B.A.C. "One-Eleven"	1·00	1·00
MS412		143 × 94 mm. Nos. 408/11	3·25	3·50

91 Figures (Chencherere Hill)

92 Boxing

(Des R. Granger Barrett. Litho Format)

1972 (10 May). *Rock Paintings. T* **91** *and similar horiz designs.* W **55** (*sideways*). *P* 13½.

413		3 t. apple-green, grey-green and black	12	5
414		8 t. red, grey and black	30	15
415		15 t. multicoloured	50	45
416		30 t. multicoloured	90	1·00
MS417		121 × 97 mm. Nos. 413/16. P 15	2·00	2·25

Designs:—8 t. Lizard and cat (Chencherere Hill); 15 t. Schematics (Diwa Hill); 30 t. Sun through rain (Mikolongwe Hill).

(Des local artist. Litho Harrison)

1972 (9 Aug). *Olympic Games, Munich.* W **55** (*sideways*). *P* 14 × 14½.

418	**92**	3 t. multicoloured	5	5
419		8 t. multicoloured	15	15
420		15 t. multicoloured	25	30
421		30 t. multicoloured	65	75
MS422		110 × 92 mm. Nos. 418/21. P 14 × 13½	1·50	1·60

PRICES OF SETS

Set prices are given for many issues, generally those containing five stamps or more. Definitive sets include one of each value or major colour change, but do not cover different perforations, die types or minor shades. Where a choice is possible the set prices are based on the cheapest versions of the stamps included in the listings.

93 Arms of Malawi

94 "Adoration of the Kings" (Orcagna)

(Des G. Drummond. Litho Questa)

1972 (20 Oct). *Commonwealth Parliamentary Conference.* W **55**. *P* 13½.

423	**93**	15 t. multicoloured	35	45

(Des V. Whiteley. Litho Questa)

1972 (8 Nov). *Christmas. T* **94** *and similar vert designs. Multicoloured.* W **55**. *P* 14½ × 14.

424		3 t. Type **94**	10	5
425		8 t. "Madonna and Child Enthroned" (Florentine School)	20	10
426		15 t. "Virgin and Child" (Crivelli)	40	30
427		30 t. "Virgin and Child with St. Anne" (Flemish School)	70	1·00
MS428		95 × 121 mm. Nos. 424/7	1·90	2·50

"MALAŴI". All issues from No. 429 onwards have a circumflex accent over the "W", to give the correct pronunciation of "Malavi".

95 *Charaxes bohemani*

(Des PAD Studio. Litho Questa)

1973 (7 Feb–5 Apr). *Butterflies. T* **95** *and similar horiz designs. Multicoloured.* W **55** (*sideways*). *P* 13½ × 14.

429		3 t. Type **95**	20	5
430		8 t. *Uranothauma crawshayi*	45	20
431		15 t. *Charaxes acuminatus*	65	40
432		30 t. Inscr "EUPHAEDRA ZADDACHI"	3·00	4·00
433		30 t. Corrected to "AMAURIS ANSORGEI" (5 Apr)	3·00	4·00
MS434		145 × 95 mm. Nos. 429/32	7·00	8·00

96 Livingstone and Map

(Des J.W. Litho Format)

1973 (1 May). *Death Centenary of David Livingstone* (1*st issue*). W **55** (*sideways*). *P* 13½ × 14.

435	**96**	3 t. multicoloured	10	5
436		8 t. multicoloured	20	10
437		15 t. multicoloured	40	35
438		30 t. multicoloured	85	95
MS439		144 × 95 mm. Nos. 435/8	1·60	1·75

See also Nos. 450/**MS**451.

97 Thumb Dulcitone

(Des Jennifer Toombs. Litho Questa)

1973 (8 Aug). *Musical Instruments. T* **97** *and similar multicoloured designs.* W **55** (*sideways on* 8, 15 *t. and* **MS**444). *P* 14.

440		3 t. Type **97**	8	5
441		8 t. Hand zither (*vert*)	15	10
442		15 t. Hand drum (*vert*)	30	30
443		30 t. One-stringed fiddle	70	1·10
MS444		120 × 103 mm. Nos. 440/3	1·75	1·90

98 The Magi

(Des J.W. Litho Format)

1973 (7 Nov). *Christmas.* W **55** (*sideways*). *P* 13½.

445	**98**	3 t. greenish blue, dp lilac & dull ultram	8	5
446		8 t. salmon-red, bluish lilac & red-brn	20	20
447		15 t. reddish mve, greenish bl & dp mve	40	40
448		30 t. orange-yell, bluish lilac & lt lake-brn	85	85
MS449		165 × 114 mm. Nos. 445/8	1·75	2·00

99 Stained-glass Window, Livingstonia Mission

(Des PAD Studio. Litho Questa)

1973 (12 Dec). *Death Centenary of David Livingstone* (2*nd issue*). W **55** (*sideways*). *P* 13½.

450	**99**	50 t. multicoloured	80	1·25
MS451		71 × 77 mm. No. 450	1·60	1·75

100 Largemouth Black Bass

(Des Sylvia Goaman. Litho Questa)

1974 (20 Feb). *35th Anniv of Malawi Angling Society. T* **100** *and similar horiz designs. Multicoloured.* W **55** (*sideways*). *P* 14.

452		3 t. Type **100**	15	5
453		8 t. Rainbow Trout	30	20
454		15 t. Lake Salmon	50	40
455		30 t. Tiger Fish	95	95
MS456		169 × 93 mm. Nos. 452/5	1·75	1·90

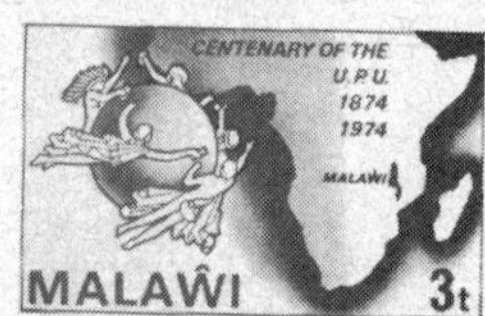

101 U.P.U. Monument and Map of Africa

(Des J. Cooter. Litho J.W.)

1974 (24 Apr). *Centenary of Universal Postal Union.* W **55** (*sideways*). *P* 13½ (*Nos.* 460/**MS**461) *or* 14½ × 14 (*others*).

457	**101**	3 t. green and ochre	10	5
		a. Perf 13½ (pair)		
458		8 t. red and ochre	20	15
459		15 t. violet and ochre	35	35
460		30 t. indigo and ochre	75	90
MS461		115 × 146 mm. Nos. 457/60	1·90	2·25
		a. Perf 14½ × 14	†	—

No. 457a comes from normal sheets and not No. **MS**461. It can also be identified as a marginal single.

102 Capital Hill, Lilongwe

(Des PAD Studio. Litho Questa)

1974 (3 July). *Tenth Anniv of Independence.* W **55** (*sideways*). *P* 14.

462	**102**	3 t. multicoloured	8	5
463		8 t. multicoloured	20	15
464		15 t. multicoloured	30	30
465		30 t. multicoloured	55	60
MS466		120 × 86 mm. Nos. 462/5	1·25	1·40

103 "Madonna of the Meadow" (Bellini)

104 Arms of Malawi

(Des Jennifer Toombs. Litho Enschedé)

1974 (4 Dec). *Christmas. T* **103** *and similar horiz designs. Multicoloured.* W **55** (*sideways*). *P* 13 × 13½.

467		3 t. Type **103**	8	5
468		8 t. "The Holy Family with Sts. John and Elizabeth" (Jordaens)	20	15
469		15 t. "The Nativity" (Pieter de Grebber)	45	45
470		30 t. "Adoration of the Shepherds" (Lorenzo di Credi)	85	85
MS471		163 × 107 mm. Nos. 467/70	1·60	1·75

(Des and litho Harrison)

1975 (1 Feb)–**84**. *Coil stamp. W* **55** *(sideways). P* 14½ × 14.
472 **104** 1 t. deep blue 10 15
472*a* 5 t. bright carmine (20.9.84) 5 8

105 African Snipe

106 Spur-winged Goose

(Des J.W. Litho Questa)

1975 (19 Feb). *Birds. T* **105/6** *and similar multicoloured designs. W* **55** *(sideways on* 2, 3, 8, 50 *t.*, 1 *k.*, 4 *k.*). *White, ordinary paper.*

(*a*) *Size as T* **105**. *P* 13½ × 14 (1, 5 *t.*) *or* 14 × 13½ (*others*)
473 1 t. Type **105** 20 12
474 2 t. Double-banded Sandgrouse 35 15
475 3 t. Blue Quail 70 40
476 5 t. Bare-throated Francolin 50 10
477 8 t. Harlequin Quail 65 15

(*b*) *Size as T* **106**. *P* 14
478 10 t. Type **106** .. .. 1·00 50
479 15 t. Barrow's Bustard .. .. .. 1·40 1·00
480 20 t. Comb Duck 70 55
481 30 t. Helmet Guineafowl (*shades*) 70 70
482 50 t. African Pigmy Goose .. .. .. 1·75 1·60
483 1 k. Garganey .. .. 3·00 3·25
484 2 k. White-faced Whistling Duck .. .. 10·00 9·50
485 4 k. African Green Pigeon .. .. .. 13·00 15·00
473/85 .. .. *Set of* 13 30·00 30·00
See also Nos. 501/4

107 M.V. *Mpasa*

108 *Habenaria splendens*

(Des R. Granger Barrett. Litho J.W.)

1975 (12 Mar). *Ships of Lake Malawi. T* **107** *and similar horiz designs. Multicoloured. W* **55** *(sideways). P* 13½.
486 3 t. Type **107** 15 5
487 8 t. M.V. *Ilala II* 30 12
488 15 t. M.V. *Chauncy Maples* 50 30
489 30 t. M.V. *Nkwazi* .. .. 1·00 80
MS490 105 × 142 mm. Nos. 486/9. P 14 .. .. 2·00 2·50

(Des Sylvia Goaman. Litho Questa)

1975 (6 June). *Malawi Orchids. T* **108** *and similar vert designs. Multicoloured. W* **55**. *P* 14.
491 3 t. Type **108** 15 5
492 10 t. *Eulophia cucullata* 35 25
493 20 t. *Disa welwitschii* 55 40
494 40 t. *Angraecum conchiferum* 90 85
MS495 127 × 111 mm. Nos. 491/4 .. .. 2·00 2·50

109 Bush Baby

10th ACP
Ministerial
Conference
1975

(**110**)

(Des R. Granger Barrett. Litho Walsall)

1975 (3 Sept). *Malawi Animals. T* **109** *and similar vert designs. Multicoloured. W* **55** *(inverted). P* 14.
496 3 t. Type **109** 8 5
497 10 t. Leopard 25 20
498 20 t. Roan Antelope 45 35
499 40 t. Burchell's Zebra .. .. 90 1·25
MS500 88 × 130 mm. Nos. 496/9. W **55** (sideways) 1·75 2·00

1975 (1 Oct). *As Nos.* 473 *etc, but no wmk. Toned, chalk-surfaced paper.*
501 3 t. Blue Quail 50 35
502 10 t. Type **106** 90 50
503 15 t. Barrow's Bustard .. .. .. 1·10 1·10
504 2 k. White-faced Whistling Duck .. .. 9·50 9·50
Nos. 505/13 vacant.

1975 (9 Dec). *Tenth Africa, Caribbean and Pacific Ministerial Conference. No.* 482 *optd with T* **110**.
514 50 t. African Pigmy Goose .. .. .. 95 1·10

111 "A Castle with the Adoration of the Magi"

112 Alexander Graham Bell

(Des PAD Studio. Litho J.W.)

1975 (12 Dec). *Christmas. T* **111** *and similar horiz designs showing religious medallions. Multicoloured. W* **55** (*sideways*). *P* 13 × 13½.
515 3 t. Type **111** 8 5
516 10 t. "The Nativity" 20 15
517 20 t. "The Adoration of the Magi" 40 35
518 40 t. "The Angel appearing to the Shepherds" 90 90
MS519 98 × 168 mm. Nos. 515/18. P 14 .. .. 1·75 1·90

(Des C. Abbott. Litho Questa)

1976 (24 Mar). *Centenary of the Telephone.* W **55**. *P* 14.
520 **112** 3 t. black and dull green 8 5
521 10 t. black and magenta 20 15
522 20 t. black and light reddish violet .. 40 40
523 40 t. black and bright blue 90 95
MS524 137 × 114 mm. Nos. 520/3 .. .. 1·50 1·60

113 President Banda

114 Bagnall Shunter

(Des PAD Studio. Litho J.W.)

1976 (2 July). *Tenth Anniv of the Republic. Multicoloured; frame colour given.* W **55**. *P* 13.
525 **113** 3 t. green 8 5
526 10 t. magenta 20 15
527 20 t. new blue 35 35
528 40 t. dull ultramarine 75 85
MS529 102 × 112 mm. Nos. 524/8. P 13½ .. 1·40 1·50

(Des G. Drummond. Litho Questa)

1976 (1 Oct). *Malawi Locomotives. T* **114** *and similar horiz designs. Multicoloured. W* **55** *(sideways). P* 14½ × 14.
530 3 t. Type **114** 15 5
531 10 t. Shire Class loco 40 20
532 20 t. Nippon Sharyo loco 80 80
533 40 t. Hunslet shunter .. .. .. 1·75 1·75
MS534 130 × 118 mm. Nos. 530/3 .. .. 2·75 2·75

Blantyre
Mission
Centenary
1876-1976

(**115**)

116 Child on Bed of Straw

1976 (22 Oct). *Centenary of Blantyre Mission. Nos.* 503 *and* 481 *optd with T* **115**.
535 15 t. Barrow's Bustard 45 55
536 30 t. Helmet Guineafowl .. .. .. 80 1·00

(Des Jennifer Toombs. Litho Walsall)

1976 (6 Dec). *Christmas.* W **55**. *P* 14.
537 **116** 3 t. multicoloured 8 5
538 10 t. multicoloured 20 15
539 20 t. multicoloured 40 35
540 40 t. multicoloured 90 90
MS541 135 × 95 mm. Nos. 537/40 .. .. 1·50 1·60

117 Man and Woman

118 Chileka Airport

(Des G. Hutchins. Litho Questa)

1977 (1 Apr). *Handicrafts. T* **117** *and similar multicoloured designs showing wood-carvings. W* **55** *(sideways on* 10 *and* 20 *t.). P* 14.
542 4 t. Type **117** 8 5
543 10 t. Elephant (*horiz*) 20 15
544 20 t. Rhino (*horiz*) 40 35
545 40 t. Deer 90 90
MS546 153 × 112 mm. Nos. 542/5. Wmk sideways 1·75 1·90

(Des Harrison. Litho Walsall)

1977 (12 July). *Transport. T* **118** *and similar horiz designs. Multicoloured. W* **55** *(sideways). P* 14½ × 14.
547 4 t. Type **118** 12 5
548 10 t. Blantyre-Lilongwe Road 25 15
549 20 t. M.V. *Ilala II* 60 55
550 40 t. Blantyre-Nacala rail line .. .. 1·25 1·40
MS551 127 × 83 mm. Nos. 547/50 .. .. 2·25 2·50

119 *Pseudotropheus johanni*

120 "Madonna and Child with St. Catherine and the Blessed Stefano Maconi" (Borgognone)

(Des R. Granger Barrett. Litho J.W.)

1977 (4 Oct). *Fish of Lake Malawi. T* **119** *and similar horiz designs. Multicoloured. P* 13½. A. *No wmk.* B. *W* **55** *(sideways).*

		A		B	
552	4 t. Type **119**	10	5	10	5
553	10 t. *Pseudotropheus livingstoni*	20	20	20	20
554	20 t. *Pseudotropheus zebra* ..	40	40	—	1·50
555	40 t. *Genyochromis mento* ..	95	95	95	95
MS556	147 × 99 mm. Nos. 552/5. P 13	1·60	1·75	1·60	1·75

(Des G. Hutchins. Litho Enschedé)

1977 (21 Nov). *Christmas. T* **120** *and similar vert designs. Multicoloured; frame colours given. No wmk. P* 14 × 13½.
557 4 t. deep blue-green 10 5
558 10 t. light vermilion 25 20
559 20 t. dull violet 55 40
560 40 t. blue .. .. 1·00 90
MS561 150 × 116 mm. Nos. 557/60 .. .. 1·75 1·90
Designs:—10 t. "Madonna and Child with the Eternal Father and Angels" (Borgognone); 20 t. Bottigella altarpiece (detail, Foppa); 40 t. "Madonna of the Fountain" (van Eyck).

121 "Entry of Christ into Jerusalem" (Giotto)

122 Nyala

(Des G. Hutchins. Litho Cartor S.A., France)

1978 (1 Mar). *Easter T* **121** *and similar vert designs showing paintings by Giotto. Multicoloured. P* 12 × 12½.
562 4 t. Type **121** 5 5
563 10 t. "The Crucifixion" 15 15
564 20 t. "Descent from the Cross" 35 30
565 40 t. "Jesus appears before Mary" 85 75
MS566 150 × 99 mm. Nos. 562/5 .. .. .. 1·50 1·60

(Des G. Hutchins. Litho Enschedé)

1978 (1 June). *Wildlife. T* **122** *and similar multicoloured designs. P* 13½ × 13 (4, 40 *t.*) *or* 13 × 13½ (*others*).
567 4 t. Type **122** 15 5
568 10 t. Lion (*horiz*) 30 15
569 20 t. Burchell's Zebra (*horiz*) 50 35
570 40 t. Reedbuck .. .. 1·00 85
MS571 173 × 113 mm. Nos. 567/70 .. .. 1·90 2·00

123 Malamulo Seventh Day Adventist Church

124 *Vanilla polylepis*

(Des and litho Walsall)

1978 (15 Nov). *Christmas. Churches. T* **123** *and similar horiz designs. Multicoloured. W* **55** *(sideways). P* 13½.
572 4 t. Type **123** 10 5

573 10 t. Likoma Cathedral 20 15
574 20 t. St. Michael's and All Angels', Blantyre .. 35 35
575 40 t. Zomba Catholic Cathedral 75 75
MS576 190 × 105 mm. Nos. 572/5 .. .. 1·40 1·50

(Des G. Drummond. Litho J.W.)

1979 (2 Jan)–**82**. *Orchids. Vert designs as T* **124**. *Multicoloured. W* **55**. *P* 13½.
577 1 t. Type **124** 10 5
578 2 t. *Cirrhopetalum umbellatum* 10 5
579 5 t. *Calanthe natalensis* 15 5
580 7 t. *Ansellia gigantea* 15 10
581 8 t. *Tridactyle bicaudata* 15 10
582 10 t. *Acampe pachyglossa* 20 12
583 15 t. *Eulophia quartiniana* 25 15
584 20 t. *Cyrtorchis arcuata (variabilis)* 30 25
585 30 t. *Eulophia tricristata* 45 30
586 50 t. *Disa hamatopetala* 60 50
587 75 t. *Cynorchis glandulosa* .. .. .. 1·00 75
588 1 k. *Aerangis kotschyana* .. .. .. 1·25 90
589 1 k. 50, *Polystachya dendrobiiflora* .. .. 1·75 1·40
590 2 k. *Disa ornithantha* .. .. 2·00 1·90
591 4 k. *Cyrtorchis praetermissa* .. .. .. 4·00 4·00
577/91 .. .. *Set of* 15 11·50 9·50

125 Tsamba

126 Train crossing Viaduct

(Des L. Curtis. Litho Questa)

1979 (21 Jan). *National Tree Planting Day. T* **125** *and similar vert designs. Multicoloured. W* **55**. *P* 13½.
592 5 t. Type **125** 10 5
593 10 t. Mulanje Cedar 20 15
594 20 t. Mlombwa 35 35
595 40 t. Mbawa 75 75
MS596 118 × 153 mm. Nos. 592/5 .. .. 1·40 1·60

(Des J.W. Litho Questa)

1979 (17 Feb). *Opening of Salima-Lilongwe Railway. T* **126** *and similar horiz designs. Multicoloured. W* **55** *(sideways) (5 t.) or no wmk (others). P* 14½.
597 5 t. Type **126** 25 5
598 10 t. Train at station 40 15
599 20 t. Train rounding bend 65 50
600 40 t. Train passing through cutting .. .. 1·00 1·10
MS601 153 × 103 mm. Nos. 597/600 W **55** (sideways) .. .. 2·00 1·90
Examples of an unissued 4 t. value as Type **126** exist from supplies sent to Malawi before it was decided to increase the internal postage rate to 5 t. (*Price £175 mint*).

127 Young Child

(Des BG Studio. Litho Questa)

1979 (10 July). *International Year of the Child. T* **127** *and similar horiz designs showing young children. Multicoloured; background colours given. W* **55** *(sideways). P* 13½.
602 5 t. green 10 5
603 10 t. red 20 15
604 20 t. mauve 35 35
605 40 t. blue 70 70

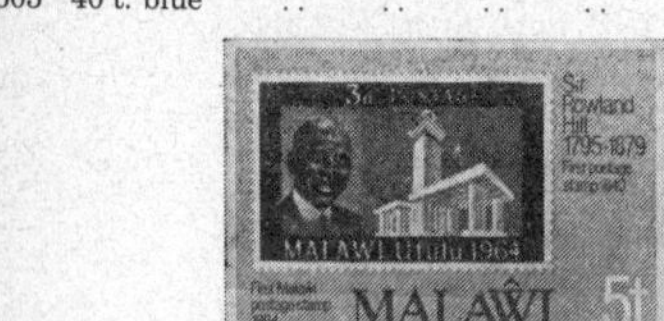

128 1964 3d. Independence Commemorative Stamp

(Des J.W. Litho Enschedé)

1979 (17 Sept). *Death Centenary of Sir Rowland Hill. T* **128** *and similar horiz designs showing 1964 Independence commemorative stamps. Multicoloured. W* **55** *(sideways). P* 13 × 13½.
606 5 t. Type **128** 10 5
607 10 t. 6d. value 15 15
608 20 t. 1s. 3d. value 30 35
609 40 t. 2s. 6d. value 55 70
MS610 163 × 108 mm. Nos. 606/9 .. .. 1·25 1·40

ALTERED CATALOGUE NUMBERS

Any Catalogue numbers altered from the last edition are shown as a list in the introductory pages.

129 River Landscape

130 Limbe Rotary Club Emblem

(Des BG Studio. Litho Format)

1979 (15 Nov). *Christmas. T* **129** *and similar horiz designs showing landscapes. Multicoloured. W* **55** *(sideways). P* 13½ × 14.
611 5 t. Type **129** 5 5
612 10 t. Sunset 15 15
613 20 t. Forest and hill 35 30
614 40 t. Plain and mountain 70 65

(Des L. Curtis. Litho J.W.)

1980 (23 Feb). *75th Anniv of Rotary International. T* **130** *and similar vert designs. W* **55**. *P* 13½.
615 5 t. multicoloured 8 5
616 10 t. multicoloured 15 15
617 20 t. multicoloured 30 30
618 40 t. ultramarine and gold 75 75
MS619 105 × 144 mm. Nos. 615/18. P 14 × 14½. 1·25 1·25
Designs:—10 t. Blantyre Rotary Club pennant; 20 t. Lilongwe Rotary Club pennant; 40 t. Rotary International emblem.

131 Mangochi District Post Office

132 Agate Nodule

(Des C. Abbott. Litho Walsall)

1980 (6 May). *"London 1980" International Stamp Exhibition. T* **131** *and similar horiz designs. W* **55** *(sideways). P* 14½ × 14.
620 5 t. black and blue-green 5 5
621 10 t. black and vermilion 12 15
622 20 t. black and violet 25 30
623 1 k. black and deep blue .. .. .. 1·40 1·60
MS624 114 × 89 mm. Nos. 620/3 .. .. .. 1·75 1·90
Designs:–10 t. New Blantyre Sorting Office; 20 t. Mail Transfer Hut, Walala; 1 k. First Nyasaland Post Office, Chiromo.

(Des G. Drummond. Litho J.W.)

1980 (20 Aug). *Gemstones. T* **132** *and similar vert designs. Multicoloured. W* **55**. *P* 13.
625 5 t. Type **132** 15 5
626 10 t. Sunstone 20 12
627 20 t. Smoky Quartz 40 30
628 1 k. Kyanite crystal .. .. 2·25 2·25

133 Elephants

134 Livingstone's Suni

(Des C. Abbott. Litho J.W.)

1980 (10 Nov). *Christmas. Children's Paintings. T* **133** *and similar horiz designs. Multicoloured. W* **55** *(sideways). P* 13.
629 5 t. Type **133** 5 5
630 10 t. Flowers 12 12
631 20 t. Train 25 25
632 1 k. Malachite Kingfisher .. .. .. 1·40 1·40

(Des G. Drummond. Litho Questa)

1981 (4 Feb). *Wildlife. T* **134** *and similar horiz designs. Multicoloured. W* **55** *(sideways). P* 14.
633 7 t. Type **134** 10 5
634 10 t. Blue Duiker 15 12
635 20 t. African Buffalo 25 25
636 1 k. Lichtenstein's Hartebeest .. .. .. 1·50 1·50

135 "Kanjedza II" Standard "A" Earth Station

(Des L. Curtis. Litho Harrison)

1981 (2 May). *International Communications. T* **135** *and similar horiz designs. Multicoloured. W* **55** *(sideways). P* 14½.
637 7 t. Type **135** 10 5
638 10 t. Blantyre International Gateway Exchange 15 12
639 20 t. "Kanjedza I" standard "B" earth station 25 25
640 1 k. "Satellite communications" .. .. 1·50 1·50
MS641 101 × 151 mm. Nos. 637/40 .. .. 2·00 2·25

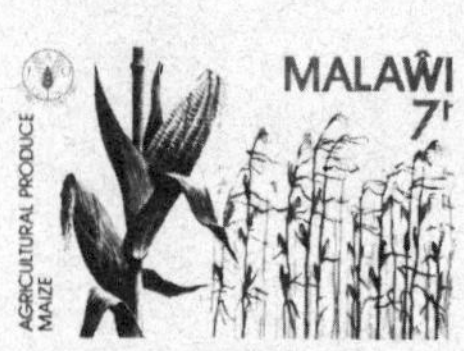

136 Maize

137 "The Adoration of the Shepherds" (Murillo)

(Des Jennifer Toombs. Litho Harrison)

1981 (11 Sept). *World Food Day. Agricultural Produce. T* **136** *and similar horiz designs. Multicoloured. W* **55** *(sideways). P* 14.
642 7 t. Type **136** 10 10
643 10 t. Rice 15 12
644 20 t. Finger-millet 25 25
645 1 k. Wheat .. .. 1·25 1·25

(Des BG Studio. Litho J.W.)

1981 (26 Nov). *Christmas. Paintings. T* **137** *and similar multicoloured designs. W* **55** *(sideways on* 10 *and* 20 *t.). P* 13½ × 13 *(*7 *t.,* 1 *k.) or* 13 × 13½ *(others).*
646 7 t. Type **137** 15 10
647 10 t. "The Holy Family" (Lippi) (*horiz*) .. 20 12
648 20 t. "The Adoration of the Shepherds" (Louis le Nain) (*horiz*) 35 25
649 1 k. "The Virgin and Child, St. John the Baptist and an Angel" (Paolo Morando) 1·25 1·25

138 Impala Herd

(Des A. Theobald. Litho Harrison)

1982 (15 Mar). *National Parks. Wildlife. T* **138** *and similar horiz designs. Multicoloured. W* **55** *(sideways). P* 14½ × 14.
650 7 t. Type **138** 15 10
651 10 t. Lions 20 12
652 20 t. Kudu 35 25
653 1 k. Greater Flamingoes .. .. .. 1·50 1·50

139 Kamuzu Academy

140 Attacker challenging Goalkeeper

(Des PAD Studio. Litho Questa)

1982 (1 July). *Kamuzu Academy. T* **139** *and similar horiz designs showing buildings. W* **55** *(sideways). P* 14½.
654 7 t. multicoloured 12 10
655 20 t. multicoloured 25 25
656 30 t. multicoloured 35 40
657 1 k. multicoloured .. .. 1·10 1·25

(Des and litho Harrison)

1982 (8 Sept). *World Cup Football Championship, Spain. T* **140** *and similar vert designs. Multicoloured. W* **55**. *P* 14 × 15.
658 7 t. Type **140** 10 8
659 20 t. FIFA World Cup trophy 25 25
660 30 t. Football stadium 40 40
MS661 80 × 59 mm. 1 k. Football .. .. 1·25 1·40

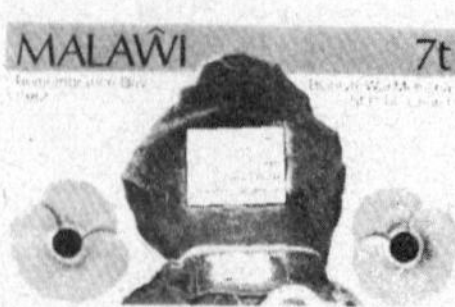

141 Blantyre War Memorial, St. Paul's Church

(Des W. Fenton. Litho Format)

1982 (5 Nov). *Remembrance Day. T* **141** *and similar horiz designs. Multicoloured. W* **55** *(sideways). P* 14½ × 14.
662 7 t. Type **141** 10 8
663 20 t. Zomba war memorial 20 25

664 30 t. Chichiri war memorial 35 40
665 1 k. Lilongwe war memorial .. .. .. 1·10 1·50

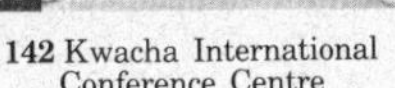

142 Kwacha International Conference Centre **143** "Christ and St. Peter"

(Des Walsall. Litho Format)

1983 (14 Mar). *Commonwealth Day. T* **142** *and similar horiz designs. Multicoloured. W* **55** *(sideways). P* 14.
666 7 t. Type **142** 8 10
667 20 t. Tea-picking, Mulanje 20 25
668 30 t. World map showing position of Malawi 35 40
669 1 k. President Dr. H. Kamuzu Banda .. 1·10 1·25

(Des C. Abbott. Litho Format)

1983 (4 Apr). *500th Birth Anniv of Raphael. Details from the cartoon for "The Miraculous Draught of Fishes" Tapestry. T* **143** *and similar multicoloured designs. W* **55** *(sideways on 30 t.). P* 14.
670 7 t. Type **143** 8 10
671 20 t. "Hauling in the Catch" 20 25
672 30 t. "Fishing Village" (*horiz*) 35 40
MS673 110 × 90 mm. 1 k. "Apostle" .. .. 1·10 1·25

144 Pair by Lake **145** Kamuzu International Airport

(Des N. Arlott. Litho Questa)

1983 (11 July). *African Fish Eagle. T* **144** *and similar vert designs. Multicoloured. W* **55**. *P* 14.
674 30 t. Type **144** .. .. 22.. 40 45
a. Horiz strip of 5. Nos. 674/8 .. .. 1·75
675 30 t. Making gull-like call 40 45
676 30 t. Diving on prey 40 45
677 30 t. Carrying fish 40 45
678 30 t. Feeding on catch 40 45

Nos. 674/8 were printed together, *se-tenant*, in horizontal strips of 5 throughout the sheet, the backgrounds of each design forming a composite picture of Lake Malawi.

(Des A. Theobald. Litho Questa)

1983 (31 Aug). *Bicentenary of Manned Flight. T* **145** *and similar horiz designs. Multicoloured. W* **55** *(sideways). P* 14.
679 7 t. Type **145** 8 10
680 20 t. Kamuzu International Airport (*different*) 20 25
681 30 t. BAC "One Eleven" 35 40
682 1 k. Flying boat at Cape Maclear .. .. 1·10 1·25
MS683 100 × 121 mm. Nos. 679/82 .. .. 1·60 1·75

146 *Clerodendrum myricoides* **147** *Melanochromis auratus*

(Des R. Reader. Litho J.W.)

1983 (16 Oct). *Christmas. Flowers. T* **146** *and similar vert designs. Multicoloured. P* 13 *(20 t.) or* 14 *(others)*.
684 7 t. Type **146** 8 10
a. Perf 13 .. .. 15·00
685 20 t. *Gloriosa superba* 20 25
686 30 t. *Gladiolus laxiflorus* 35 40
687 1 k. *Aframomum angustifolium* .. .. 1·10 1·25

(Des L. Curtis. Litho Harrison)

1984 (2 Jan). *Fishes. T* **147** *and similar horiz designs. Multicoloured. W* **55** *(sideways). P* 14½ × 14.
688 1 t. Type **147** 5 5
689 2 t. *Haplochromis compressiceps* 5 5
690 5 t. *Labeotropheus fuelleborni* 5 8
691 7 t. *Pseudotropheus lombardoi* 8 10
692 8 t. Gold *Pseudotropheus zebra* 8 10
693 10 t. *Trematocranus jacobfreibergi* 10 12
694 15 t. *Melanochromis crabro* 15 20
695 20 t. Marbled *Pseudotropheus zebra* 20 25
696 30 t. *Labidochromis caeruleus* 30 35
697 40 t. *Haplochromis venustus* 40 45
698 50 t. *Aulonacara of* Thumbi 50 55
699 75 t. *Melanochromis vermivorus* 75 80
700 1 k. *Pseudotropheus zebra* .. .. .. 1·00 1·10
701 2 k. *Trematocranus spp.* .. .. .. 2·00 2·25
702 4 k. *Aulonacara of* Mbenje .. .. .. 4·00 4·25
688/702 .. .. *Set of* 15 8·75 9·50

148 Nyika Red Hare **149** Running

(Des Garden Studios. Litho Format)

1984 (2 Feb). *Small Mammals. T* **148** *and similar horiz designs. Multicoloured. W* **55** *(sideways). P* 14.
703 7 t. Type **148** 8 10
704 20 t. Sun Squirrel 20 25
705 30 t. Hedgehog 30 35
706 1 k. *Genetta tigrina* .. .. 1·10 1·25

(Des C. Collins. Litho Harrison)

1984 (1 June). *Olympic Games, Los Angeles. T* **149** *and similar vert designs. Multicoloured. W* **55** *(sideways). P* 14.
707 7 t. Type **149** 8 10
708 20 t. Boxing 25 30
709 30 t. Cycling 35 40
710 1 k. Long jumping .. .. 1·10 1·25
MS711 90 × 128 mm. Nos. 707/10. Wmk upright 1·75 1·90

150 *Euphaedra neophron* **151** "The Virgin and Child" (Duccio)

(Des and photo Courvoisier)

1984 (1 Aug). *Butterflies. T* **150** *and similar vert designs. Granite paper. P* 11½.
712 7 t. multicoloured 8 10
713 20 t. lemon, blackish brown and red 25 30
714 30 t. multicoloured 35 40
715 1 k. multicoloured .. .. 1·10 1·25

Designs:—20 t. *Papilio dardanus*; 30 t. *Antanartia schaeneia*; 1 k. *Spindasis*.

(Des C. Abbott. Litho Harrison)

1984 (22 Oct). *Christmas. Religious Paintings. T* **151** *and similar vert designs. Multicoloured. W* **55**. *P* 14½.
716 7 t. Type **151** 8 10
717 20 t. "Madonna and Child" (Raphael) .. 25 30
718 30 t. "The Virgin and Child" (ascr to Lippi) .. 35 40
719 1 k. "The Wilton Diptych" .. .. .. 1·10 1·25

152 *Leucopaxillus gracillimus*

(Des A. Jardine. Litho Harrison)

1985 (23 Jan). *Fungi. T* **152** *and similar horiz designs. Multicoloured. W* **55** *(sideways). P* 14½ × 14.
720 7 t. Type **152** 8 10
721 20 t. *Limacella guttata* 20 25
722 30 t. *Termitomyces eurrhizus* 30 35
723 1 k. *Xerulina asprata* 90 95

POSTAGE DUE STAMPS

D 1

(Litho Bradbury, Wilkinson)

1967 (1 Sept). *W* **55**. *P* 11½.
D 6 D 1 1d. carmine 15 30
D 7 2d. sepia 20 35
D 8 4d. reddish violet 25 50
D 9 6d. blue 30 60
D10 8d. emerald 45 75
D11 1s. black .. .. 60 1·10
D6/11 .. .. *Set of* 6 1·75 3·25

1971 (15 Feb). *As Nos.* D6/11 *but values in tambalas. W* **55**. *P* 11½.
D12 D 1 2 t. greenish drab 20 40
D13 4 t. bright mauve 25 40
D14 6 t. royal blue 15 35
D15 8 t. dull green 30 45
D16 10 t. blackish brown 35 70

(Litho Walsall)

1975–84. *Design redrawn, with circumflex accent over "W" of "MALAWI". P* 14. (*a*) *W* **55** *(sideways)*.
D17 D 1 2 t. chestnut (15.9.75) 45 80
D18 2 t. brown (14.6.82) 5 5
D19 4 t. deep mauve (14.6.82) 5 5
D20 6 t. royal blue (9.84) 5 5
D21 8 t. green (9.84) 8 10
D22 10 t. black (14.6.82) 10 12

(*b*) *No wmk*
D23 D 1 2 t. brown (19.10.77) 25 35
D24 4 t. mauve (19.10.77) 25 40
D25 8 t. green (15.12.78) 25 40
D26 10 t. brownish grey (19.10.77) 30 45

Malaysia

The Federation of Malaysia was set up on 16 September 1963, and consisted of the former Malayan Federation, the State of Singapore and the two former Crown Colonies in Borneo, Sabah (North Borneo) and Sarawak. Singapore left the federation to become an independent republic on 9 August 1965.

Malaysia now consists of thirteen States (11 in Peninsular Malaysia and two in Borneo), together with the Federal Territories of Kuala Lumpur and Labuan.

The philatelic history of the component parts of the federation is most complex. Under this heading are now listed previous issues made by the States of the Federation with the exception of LABUAN, SABAH (NORTH BORNEO) and SARAWAK. These, together with SINGAPORE, continue to appear in the normal alphabetical sequence.

The method adopted is to show the general issues for the area first, before dealing with the issues for the individual States. The section is divided as follows:

I. STRAITS SETTLEMENTS
II. FEDERATED MALAY STATES
III. MALAYAN POSTAL UNION
IV. MALAYA (BRITISH MILITARY ADMINISTRATION)
V. MALAYAN FEDERATION
VI. MALAYSIA
VII. MALAYSIAN STATES—Johore, Kedah, Kelantan, Malacca, Negri Sembilan (with Sungei Ujong), Pahang, Penang, Perak, Perlis, Selangor, Trengganu
VIII. JAPANESE OCCUPATION
IX. THAI OCCUPATION

I. STRAITS SETTLEMENTS

The three original Settlements, Malacca, Penang (with Province Wellesley) and Singapore (including Christmas Island and Cocos (Keeling) Islands) were formed into a Crown Colony during 1867. Labuan was attached to the colony in 1896, becoming the fourth Settlement in 1906.

The stamps of India were used in the three Straits Settlements of Malacca, Penang and Singapore from late in 1854 until 31 August 1867. During this period the Settlements were administered by the Government of Bengal and formed part of the Bengal Postal Circle. On 1 September 1867 they became a separate Crown Colony and the stamps of India were demonetised.

In the 1856 series of Indian octagonal numbered postmarks Malacca was assigned B 109, Penang B 147 and Singapore B 172.

1856 Series Postmarks

These were replaced in the mid-1860's by duplex type cancellations for Penang (1863) and Singapore (1865). Postmarks from this series are identifiable when on cover or where sufficient of the left-hand duplex is legible.

Duplex Cancellations

Not all issues of India during this period were available in the Straits Settlements and some, particularly the 1865 issue with Elephant Head watermark, are very scarce used there.

PRICES FOR STAMPS ON COVER

Nos. 1/9	*from* × 10
Nos. 11/19	*from* × 8
Nos. 20/47	*from* × 5
Nos. 48/9	*from* × 10
Nos. 50/71	*from* × 5
No. 72	—
Nos. 73/8	*from* × 6
No. 79	—
No. 80	*from* × 10
No. 81	—
Nos. 82/5	*from* × 5
Nos. 86/7	*from* × 10
Nos. 88/94	*from* × 5
Nos. 95/105	*from* × 6
Nos. 106/9	*from* × 10
Nos. 110/21	*from* × 5
No. 122	—
Nos. 123/6	*from* × 4
Nos. 127/38	*from* × 3
Nos. 139/40	—
Nos. 141/51	*from* × 12
Nos. 152/67	*from* × 3
Nos. 168/9	—
Nos. 193/212	*from* × 3
Nos. 213/15	—
Nos. 216/17	*from* × 10
Nos. 218/40*a*	*from* × 3
Nos. 240*b*/*d*	—
Nos. 241/55	*from* × 15
Nos. 256/9	*from* × 4
Nos. 260/98	*from* × 3
Nos. D1/6	*from* × 20

PRINTERS. All Straits Settlements issues were printed in typography by De La Rue & Co, Ltd, London, *unless otherwise stated.*

THREE HALF CENTS (1)   32 CENTS (2)

1867 (1 Sept). *Stamps of India surch as T* **1** *or* **2** (24 *c.*, 32 *c.*). *Wmk Elephant's Head. P* 14.

No.	Type	Description	Unused	Used
1	**11**	1½ c. on ½ a. blue (Die I) (R.)	50·00	£120
2		2 c. on 1 a. brown (R.)	50·00	50·00
3		3 c. on 1 a. brown (B.)	55·00	55·00
4		4 c. on 1 a. brown (Bk.)	£100	£150
5		6 c. on 2 a. yellow (P.)	£180	£150
6		8 c. on 2 a. yellow (G.)	70·00	40·00
7	**17**	12 c. on 4 a. green (R.)	£200	£200
		a. Surch double	£600	
8	**11**	24 c. on 8 a. rose (Die II) (B.)	£140	60·00
9		32 c. on 2 a. yellow (Bk.)	£130	60·00

The 32 c. was re-issued for postal use in 1884.

No. 7a is only known unused.

Used examples of these stamps are very rarely seen without disfiguring firm's "chops". Stamps without "chop" are worth a premium over the prices quoted.

1869 (?). *No.* 1 *with* "THREE HALF" *deleted and* "2" *written above, in black manuscript.*

No.	Description	Unused	Used
10	2 on 1½ c. on ½ a. blue	£2750	£2250

This stamp has been known from very early days and was apparently used in the Straits Settlements, but nothing is known of its history.

5

6

7

8

9

1867 (Dec)–**72**. *Wmk Crown CC. P* 14. *Ornaments in corners differ for each value.*

No.	Type	Description	Unused	Used
11	**5**	2 c. brown (6.68)	3·00	1·40
		a. Yellow-brown	4·25	1·60
		b. Deep brown	18·00	7·00
12		4 c. rose (7.68)	4·25	2·75
		a. Deep rose	8·00	3·50
13		6 c. dull lilac (1.68)	15·00	9·50
		a. Bright lilac	15·00	9·50
14	**6**	8 c. orange-yellow	22·00	5·50
		a. Orange	22·00	7·00
15		12 c. blue	20·00	4·50
		a. Ultramarine	20·00	7·50
16	**7**	24 c. blue-green	22·00	4·50
		a. Yellow-green	30·00	13·00
17	**8**	30 c. claret (12.72)	30·00	8·00
18	**9**	32 c. pale red	£100	27·00
19		96 c. grey	70·00	20·00
		a. Perf 12½ (6.71)	£850	£225

Five Cents. (10)   Seven Cents. (11)

1879 (May). *Nos.* 14*a and* 18 *surch with T* **10** *and* **11**.

No.	Type	Description	Unused	Used
20	**6**	5 c. on 8 c. orange	38·00	38·00
		a. No stop after "Cents"	£250	£300
		b. "F i" spaced	£275	£325
21	**9**	7 c. on 32 c. pale red	35·00	35·00
		a. No stop after "Cents"	£225	£275

10 cents. (12)

10 (*a*) 10 (*b*) 10 (*c*) 10 (*d*)
10 (*e*) 10 (*f*) 10 (*g*) 10 (*h*)
10 (*i*) 10 (*j*) 10 (*jj*) 10 (*k*) 10 (*l*)

(*a*) "1" thin curved serif and thin foot, "0" narrow.
(*b*) "1" thick curved serif and thick foot; "0" broad. Both numerals heavy.
(*c*) "1" as (*a*); "0" as (*b*)
(*d*) "1" as (*a*) but thicker; "0" as (*a*)
(*e*) As (*a*) but sides of "0" thicker.
(*f*) "1" as (*d*); "0" as (*e*)
(*g*) As (*a*) but "0" narrower.
(*h*) "1" thin, curved serif and thick foot; "0" as (*g*)
(*i*) "1" as (*b*); "0" as (*a*)
(*j*) "1" as (*d*); "0" as (*g*) but raised.
(*jj*) "1" as (*a*) but shorter, and with shorter serif and thicker foot; "0" as (*g*) but level with "1".
(*k*) "1" as (*jj*); "0" as (*d*)
(*l*) "1" straight serif; "0" as (*d*).

1880 (Mar). *No.* 17 *surch with T* **12** (*ten varieties of figures* "10").

No.	Description	Unused	Used
22	10 c. on 30 c. claret (*a*)	70·00	30·00
23	10 c. on 30 c. claret (*b*)	70·00	30·00
24	10 c. on 30 c. claret (*c*)	£650	£200
25	10 c. on 30 c. claret (*d*)	£325	90·00
26	10 c. on 30 c. claret (*e*)	£800	£300
27	10 c. on 30 c. claret (*f*)	£800	£300
28	10 c. on 30 c. claret (*g*)	£400	£225
29	10 c. on 30 c. claret (*h*)	£800	£300
30	10 c. on 30 c. claret (*i*	£800	£300
31	10 c. on 30 c. claret (*j*)	£800	£300
32	10 c. on 30 c. claret (*jj*)	£850	£300

No. 23 is known with large stop after "cents" and also with stop low.

1880 (April). *No.* 17 *surch as T* **12** *but without* "*cents.*" (*eight varieties of figures* "10").

No.	Description	Unused	Used
33	10 on 30 c. claret (*a*)	48·00	45·00
34	10 on 30 c. claret (*b*)	55·00	35·00
35	10 on 30 c. claret (*c*)	£200	£100
36	10 on 30 c. claret (*g*)	£500	£275
37	10 on 30 c. claret (*i*)	£600	£275
38	10 on 30 c. claret (*k*)	£800	£500
39	10 on 30 c. claret (*l*)	£800	£500
40	10 on 30 c. claret (*m*)		

Variety (*m*) has the "1" as (*b*) and the "0" as (*g*).

5 cents. (13)   5 cents. (14)   5 cents. (15)

1880 (Aug). *No.* 14*a surch with T* **13** *to* **15**.

No.	Type	Description	Unused	Used
41	**13**	5 c. on 8 c. orange	40·00	45·00
42	**14**	5 c. on 8 c. orange	38·00	45·00
43	**15**	5 c. on 8 c. orange	£130	£140

In this setting, the first four rows of the pane have surcharge T **13**; the next five, T **14**; and the last, T **15**.

10 cents. (16)   5 cents. (17)

1880–81. *Nos.* 13, 15/*a and* 17 *surch with T* **16**.

No.	Description	Unused	Used
44	10 c. on 6 c. lilac (11.81)	17·00	11·00
45	10 c. on 12 c. ultramarine (1.81)	24·00	16·00
	a. Blue	16·00	11·00
46	10 c. on 30 c. claret (12.80)	80·00	35·00

A second printing of the 10 c. on 6 c. has the surcharge heavier and the "10" usually more to the left or right of "cents".

1882 (Jan). *No.* 12 *surch with T* **17**.

No.	Description	Unused	Used
47	5 c. on 4 c. rose	£190	£275

18

19

TWO CENTS (20)

1882 (Jan). *Wmk Crown CC. P* 14.
48 **18** 5 c. purple-brown .. .. .. 38·00 25·00
49 **19** 10 c. slate (Optd S. £65) .. .. .. 95·00 32·00

1882. *Wmk Crown CA. P* 14.
50 **5** 2 c. brown (Aug) .. .. .. 95·00 22·00
51 4 c. rose (April) .. .. .. 50·00 7·00
52 **6** 8 c. orange (Sept) .. .. .. 2·50 45
53 **19** 10 c. slate (Oct) .. .. .. 1·75 45

1883 (Apr). *Nos.* 52 *and* 18 *surch with T* **20**.
(*a*) "CENTS" in narrow letters.
(*b*) Wide "E".
(*c*) Wide "EN" and "S".
(*d*) Wide "N".
(*e*) Wide "S".
(*f*) Wide "E" and "S".
54 **6** 2 c. on 8 c. orange (*a*) .. .. .. 30·00 30·00
a. Surch double £1200 £750
55 2 c. on 8 c. orange (*c*) .. .. .. 70·00 60·00
56 2 c. on 8 c. orange (*d*) .. .. .. 26·00 42·00
57 2 c. on 8 c. orange (*e*) .. .. .. 30·00 27·00
58 2 c. on 8 c. orange (*f*) .. .. .. 30·00 27·00
59 **9** 2 c. on 32 c. pale red (*b*) .. .. .. £190 70·00
a. Surch double
60 2 c. on 32 c. pale red (*e*) .. .. .. £190 70·00
Nos. 54/60 were surcharged in triplets as follows:—
2 *c. on* 8 *c.* (*e*) + (*f*) + (*d*) with (*a*) as a single unit for the top row only. Also (*a*) + (*a*) + (*a*) with (*c*) as the single unit.
2 *c. on* 32 *c.* (*e*) + (*b*) + (*e*) with (*b*) as the single unit.

2 Cents. (21)　4 Cents (22)　8 Cents (23)

1883 (July). *Nos.* 51 *and* 15 *surch with T* **21**.
61 2 c. on 4 c. rose .. .. .. 15·00 18·00
a. "s" of "Cents" inverted £850 £1000
62 2 c. on 12 c. blue .. .. .. 75·00 55·00
a. "s" of "Cents" inverted £1400 £1100

1883 (July)–**91.** *Wmk Crown CA. P* 14.
63 **5** 2 c. pale rose .. .. .. 4·00 1·00
a. Bright rose 35 20
64 4 c. pale brown .. .. .. 2·50 90
a. Deep brown .. .. .. 7·00 2·50
b. Olive-bistre £175
65 **18** 5 c. blue (8.83) 80 30
66 **5** 6 c. lilac (11.84) .. .. .. 11·00 6·50
a. Violet .. .. .. 1·60 1·25
67 **6** 12 c. brown-purple .. .. .. 7·00 4·00
68 **7** 24 c. yellow-green (2.84) .. .. .. 25·00 2·25
a. Blue-green .. .. .. 3·00 1·75
69 **8** 30 c. claret (9.91) .. .. .. 6·00 3·25
70 **9** 32 c. orange-vermilion (1.87) .. .. 6·50 2·25
71 96 c. olive-grey (8.88) .. .. .. 40·00 24·00
63*a*/71 .. .. .. *Set of* 9 60·00 35·00
63/65, 67 Optd "Specimen" .. .. *Set of* 4 £130

1884 (Feb–Aug). *Surch with T* **22** *or* **23**.
72 **18** 4 c. on 5 c. blue (Aug) £1700 £2250
73 4 c. on 5 c. blue (R.) (Aug) .. .. .. 42·00 42·00
74 **6** 8 c. on 12 c. blue (*CC*) (Feb) .. .. 80·00 65·00
75 8 c. on 12 c. brown-purple (Aug) .. .. £100 80·00
No. 75 is known with "s" of "Cents" low.

1884 (Aug). *Surch with T* **20**.
76 **18** 2 c. on 5 c. blue (*a*) .. .. .. 30·00 48·00
77 2 c. on 5 c. blue (*b*) .. .. .. 30·00 48·00
78 2 c. on 5 c. blue (*c*) .. .. .. 30·00 48·00
a. Pair, with and without surch
b. Surch double
Nos. 76/8 were surcharged in a triplet composed of (*c*) + (*a*) + (*b*). In Type (*a*) the letters "TS" are below the line of the word.

8 (24)　3 CENTS (25)　THREE CENTS (26)

1884 (Sept). *Nos.* 73 *and* 75 *surch with large numeral, as T* **24**, *in addition, in red.*
79 **18** "4" on 4 c. in *red* on 5 c. blue .. .. — £6000
80 **6** "8" on 8 c. in *black* on 12 c. dull purple 80·00 90·00
a. T **24** double £1200
81 "8" on 8 c. in *blue* on 12 c. dull purple £3000
No. 80 is known with "s" of "Cents" low.

1885. *No.* 65 *and T* **9** *in new colour, wmk Crown CA, surch with T* **25** *and* **26**.
82 **25** 3 c. on 5 c. blue (Sept) .. .. .. 45·00 £175
a. Surch double £1200
83 **26** 3 c. on 32 c. pl mag (Dec) (Optd S. £40) .. 1·40 2·25
a. Deep magenta .. .. .. 1·25 1·25

3 cents (27)　2 Cents (28)

1886 (Apr). *No.* 48 *surch with T* **27**.
84 **18** 3 c. on 5 c. purple-brown .. .. .. 85·00 £100

1887 (July). *No.* 65 *surch with T* **28**.
85 **18** 2 c. on 5 c. blue .. .. .. 10·00 14·00
a. "C" of "Cents" omitted .. .. .. — £1100
b. Surch double £375 £325
Nos. 82, 84 and 85 were surcharged in triplet settings.

10 CENTS (29)　THIRTY CENTS (30)

1891 (Nov). *Nos.* 68 *and* 70 *surch with T* **29** *and* **30**.
86 **7** 10 c. on 24 c. yellow-green .. .. .. 1·25 1·40
a. Narrow "0" in "10" .. .. .. 17·00 22·00
87 **9** 30 c. on 32 c. orange-vermilion .. .. 4·50 5·00
The "R" of "THIRTY" and "N" of "CENTS" are found wide or narrow and in all possible combinations.

ONE CENT (31)　ONE CENT (32)

1892. *Stamps of* 1882–91 (*wmk Crown CA*) *surch with T* **31**.
88 1 c. on 2 c. rose (March) 60 65
89 1 c. on 4 c. brown (April) .. .. .. 2·00 1·75
a. Surch double £500
90 1 c. on 6 c. lilac (Feb) .. .. .. 90 1·25
a. Surch double, one inverted £500 £400
91 1 c. on 8 c. orange (Jan) 60 75
92 1 c. on 12 c. brown-purple (Mar) .. .. 3·50 7·00
The following varieties may be found in T **31**:—(1) narrow "N" in "ONE" and "CENT"; (2) wide "N" in "ONE" and "CENT"; (3) narrow "N" in "ONE", wide "N" in "CENT"; (4) wide "N" in "ONE", narrow "N" in "CENT"; (5) narrow "O" in "ONE"; (6) antique "E" in "CENT".

1892–94. *Colours changed. Wmk Crown CA. P* 14. *Surch with T* **32** *and* **26**.
93 **6** 1 c. on 8 c. green (3.92) 35 60
94 **9** 3 c. on 32 c. carmine-rose (6.94) 60 80
a. Surch omitted £2750
93/94 Optd "Specimen" .. .. *Set of* 2 85·00

33

34

4 cents. (35)

1892–99. *Wmk Crown CA. P* 14.
95 **33** 1 c. green (9.92) 40 30
96 3 c. carmine-rose (2.95) .. .. .. 2·00 50
97 3 c. brown (3.99) .. .. .. 1·40 35
a. Yellow-brown .. .. .. 1·60 50
98 **5** 4 c. deep carmine (7.99) .. .. .. 1·40 50
99 **18** 5 c. brown (6.94) .. .. .. 1·60 70
100 5 c. magenta (7.99) .. .. .. 1·60 1·00
101 **6** 8 c. ultramarine (6.94) .. .. .. 1·60 40
a. Bright blue .. .. .. 2·25 50
102 12 c. claret (3.94) .. .. .. 5·00 5·00
103 **33** 25 c. purple-brown and green (3.92) .. 7·50 2·75
a. Dull purple and green .. .. 7·50 2·50
104 50 c. olive-green and carmine (3.92) .. 15·00 3·25
105 **34** $5 orange and carmine (10.98) .. £350 £350
99/105 .. .. .. *Set of* 11 £350 £350
99/101, 103/5 Optd "Specimen" .. *Set of* 10 £325

1898 (26 Dec). *T* **18** *and* **6** *surch with T* **35**.
106 4 c. on 5 c. brown (No. 99) .. .. .. 80 2·00
107 4 c. on 5 c. blue (No. 65) .. .. .. 1·25 2·25
a. Surch double
108 4 c. on 8 c. ultramarine (No. 101) .. .. 80 2·25
a. Surch double £475 £450
b. Bright blue (No. 101*a*) .. .. .. 1·00 80
Nos. 107 and 108*b* exist with stop spaced 1½ mm from the "S".

FOUR CENTS (36)

37

38

1899 (Mar). *T* **18** (*wmk Crown CA. P* 14), *surch with T* **36**.
109 4 c. on 5 c. carmine (Optd S. £22) 35 15
a. Surch omitted £4250
No. 109a is only known unused.

1902. *Wmk Crown CA. P* 14.
110 **37** 1 c. grey-green 20 45
a. Pale green .. .. .. 1·40 50
111 3 c. dull purple and orange 30 35
112 4 c. purple/*red* .. .. .. 1·75 35
113 **38** 5 c. dull purple .. .. .. 1·75 40
114 8 c. purple/*blue* .. .. .. 3·00 35
115 10 c. purple and black/*yellow* .. .. 5·50 1·00
116 **37** 25 c. dull purple and green .. .. 6·00 3·50
117 **38** 30 c. grey and carmine .. .. 10·00 8·00
118 **37** 50 c. deep green and carmine .. .. 10·00 8·00
a. Dull green and carmine .. .. 14·00 12·00
119 **38** $1 dull green and black .. .. 20·00 20·00
120 **37** $2 dull purple and black .. .. 40·00 40·00
121 **38** $5 dull green and brown-orange .. £100 55·00
122 **37** $100 purple & grn/*yellow* (Optd S. £400) £3250
110/21 .. .. .. *Set of* 12 £180 £120
110/21 Optd "Specimen" .. .. *Set of* 12 £275

39

40

41

42

1903–4. *Wmk Crown CA. P* 14.
123 **39** 1 c. grey-green 30 95
124 **40** 3 c. dull purple .. .. .. 3·00 1·75
125 **41** 4 c. purple/*red* 75 45
126 **42** 8 c. purple/*blue* .. .. .. 6·00 1·75
123/6 Optd "Specimen" .. .. *Set of* 4 £120

1904–6. *Wmk Multiple Crown CA. P* 14.
127 **39** 1 c. deep green, **OC** 45 15
128 **40** 3 c. dull purple, **OC** 25 35
a. Plum, **O** .. .. .. 2·00 55
129 **41** 4 c. purple/*red*, **OC** 65 20
130 **38** 5 c. dull purple, **OC** (1906) .. .. 2·25 2·25
131 **42** 8 c. purple/*blue*, **OC** .. .. .. 4·50 50
132 **38** 10 c. purple and black/*yellow* **OC** .. 1·60 45
133 **37** 25 c. dull purple and green, **OC** .. .. 6·50 5·00
134 **38** 30 c. grey and carmine, **OC** .. .. 9·00 4·50
135 **37** 50 c. dull green and carmine, **OC** .. 9·00 6·00
136 **38** $1 dull green and black, **OC** .. .. 15·00 7·50
137 **37** $2 dull purple and black, **C** .. .. 48·00 45·00
138 **38** $5 dull green and brown-orange, **OC** 60·00 55·00
139 **37** $25 grey-green & blk, **C** (Optd S. £150) £750 £475
140 $100 purple and green/*yellow*, **C** £4000
127/38 .. .. .. *Set of* 12 £140 £110

STRAITS SETTLEMENTS. (43)　Straits Settlements. (44)

STRAITS SETTLEMENTS. FOUR CENTS. (45)

1907. *T* **18** *of Labuan* (*Nos.* 116c, *etc.*) *optd with T* **43** *or* **44** (10 c.), *or surch with T* **45**, *in brownish red or black. P* 13½–14.
141 1 c. black and purple (*p* 14½–15) .. .. 24·00 32·00
142 2 c. black and green .. .. .. 75·00 85·00
a. Perf 14½–15
143 3 c. black and sepia .. .. .. 16·00 22·00
144 4 c. on 12 c. black and yellow .. .. 1·25 3·50
a. No stop after "CENTS" .. .. 75·00
145 4 c. on 16 c. green and brown (Blk.) .. 1·25 3·25
a. "STRAITS SETTLEMENTS" double (Br.-R.+Blk.) £450 £400
b. Ditto. In vert pair with normal
146 4 c. on 18 c. black and pale brown .. .. 1·00 3·00
a. No stop after "CENTS" .. .. 80·00
b. "FOUR CENTS" and bar double .. £3000
c. "FOUR CENTS" and bar 1½ mm below normal position (pair with normal) .. £175
147 8 c. black and vermilion .. .. .. 1·25 4·25
148 10 c. brown and slate .. .. .. 2·50 3·75
a. No stop after "SETTLEMENTS" .. 70·00
149 25 c. green and greenish blue .. .. .. 2·75 8·50
a. Perf 14½–15
b. Perf 13½–14 comp 14½–15
150 50 c. dull purple and lilac .. .. .. 8·50 18·00
151 $1 claret and orange .. .. .. 35·00 38·00
a. Perf 14½–15
141/51 .. .. .. *Set of* 11 £150 £200
No. 146c only occurred in a few sheets of the first printing.
The 2 c. also exists perf 14 all round and is rare.

46

47

1906–11. *Wmk Mult Crown CA. P* 14.
152 **39** 1 c. blue-green, **O** (1910) .. .. 1·25 90
153 **40** 3 c. red, **O** (1908) 35 20
154 **41** 4 c. red, **O** (1907) .. .. .. 1·25 75
155 4 c. dull purple, **OC** (1908) 30 20
156 4 c. claret, **O** (1911) .. .. .. 75 1·25
157 **38** 5 c. orange, **O** (1909) .. .. .. 2·75 50
158 **42** 8 c. blue, **O** (1906) 65 40
159 **38** 10 c. purple/*yellow*, **OC** (1908) 75 20
160 **47** 21 c. dull purple and claret, **C** (11.10) .. 3·75 12·00
161 **37** 25 c. dull and bright purple, **C** (1909) .. 4·75 3·75
162 **38** 30 c. purple and orange-yellow, **C** (1909) 5·00 1·25
163 **47** 45 c. black/*green*, **C** (11.10) .. .. 3·00 4·00
164 **37** 50 c. black/*green*, **C** (1910) .. .. 3·50 1·40
165 **38** $1 black and red/*blue*, **C** (1911) .. 9·50 6·50
166 **37** $2 green and red/*yellow*, **C** (1909) .. 15·00 14·00
167 **38** $5 green and red/*green*, **C** (1910) .. 48·00 42·00
168 **46** $25 purple and blue/*blue*, **C** (1911) (Optd S. £150) £550 £200
169 $500 purple and orange, **C** (1910) (Optd S. £850) £25000
152/67 .. .. .. *Set of* 16 90·00 80·00
153/67 Optd "Specimen" .. .. *Set of* 15 £250
Beware of dangerous forgeries of No. 169.

48

49

50

51

52

53

54

1912–23. $25, $100 *and* $500 *as T* **46**, *but with head of King George V. Wmk Mult Crown CA. P* 14.

193	48	1 c. green, O (9.12)	45	40
		a. Pale green (1.14)	45	40
		b. Blue-green (1917)	45	40
194		1 c. black, O (2.19)	20	40
195	52	2 c. green, O (10.19)	25	40
196	49	3 c. red, O (2.13)	75	30
		a. Scarlet (2.17)	20	20
197	50	4 c. dull purple, C (3.13)	90	50
		a. Wmk sideways	30·00	30·00
198		4 c. rose-scarlet, O (2.19)	90	40
		a. Carmine	90	40
199	51	5 c. orange, O (8.12)	85	45
		a. Yellow-orange	1·25	45
200	52	6 c. dull claret, O (3.20)	1·75	95
		a. Deep claret	4·25	2·50
201		8 c. ultramarine, O (3.13)	50	45
202	51	10 c. purple/*yellow*, C (8.12)	70	40
		a. White back (9.13) (Optd S. £27)	50	50
		b. On lemon (1916) (Optd S. £42)	8·00	1·25
203		10 c. deep bright blue, O (2.19)	4·50	55
		a. Bright blue	3·75	55
204	53	21 c. dull and bright purple, C (11.13)	3·75	5·50
205	54	25 c. dull purple and mauve, C (7.14)	3·75	2·75
206		25 c. dull purple and violet, C (1919)	9·00	2·75
207	51	30 c. dull purple and orange, C (12.14)	2·75	2·00
208	53	45 c. black/*green*, C (*white back*) (12.14)	3·50	7·50
		a. On blue-green, olive back (7.18) (Optd S. £27)	2·75	4·50
		b. On emerald back (6.22)	2·75	7·50
209	54	50 c. black/*green*, C (7.14)	5·50	2·25
		a. On blue-green, olive back (1918)	7·00	2·75
		b. On emerald back (10.21)	7·00	2·75
		c. On emerald back (Die II) (3.23) (Optd S. £27)	3·25	2·50
210	51	$1 black and red/*blue*, C (10.14)	8·00	5·00
211	54	$2 green and red/*yellow*, C (7.15)	11·00	9·50
		a. White back (7.14) (Optd S. £28)	7·50	8·00
		b. On orange-buff (1920)	22·00	26·00
		c. On pale yellow (1921)	26·00	28·00
212	51	$5 green and red/*green*, C (4.15)	45·00	19·00
		a. White back, OC (11.13) (Optd S. £28)	45·00	20·00
		b. On blue-green, olive back (1918)	45·00	18·00
		c. On emerald back (6.21)	60·00	45·00
		d. Die II (1923) (Optd S. £55)	35·00	25·00
213	–	$25 purple & blue/*blue*, C (Optd S. £100)	£550	£150
214	–	$100 carm & blk/*blue*, C (Optd S. £225)	£2500	
215	–	$500 purple and orange-brown, C (8.12) (Optd S. £500)	£14000	
193/212		*Set of* 20	80·00	48·00
193/212 Optd "Specimen"		*Set of* 19	£475	

The 6 c. is similar to T **52**, but the head is in a beaded oval as in T **53**. The 2 c., 6 c. (and 12 c. below) have figures of value on a circular ground while in the 8 c. this is of oval shape.

RED CROSS

2c.

(55)

MALAYA-
BORNEO
EXHIBITION.

(56)

1917 (May). *Surch with T* **55**.

216	49	2 c. on 3 c. scarlet	1·25	6·50
		a. No stop	60·00	85·00
217	50	2 c. on 4 c. dull purple	1·25	6·50
		a. No stop	60·00	85·00

Type I

Type II

Two types of duty plate in the 25 c. In Type II the solid shading forming the back of the figure 2 extends to the top of the curve; the upturned end of the foot of the 2 is short; two background lines above figure 5; c close to 5; STRAITS SETTLEMENTS in taller letters.

1921–33. *Wmk Mult Script CA. P* 14.

218	48	1 c. black, O (3.22)	15	10
219	52	2 c. green, O (5.21)	12	10
220		2 c. brown, O (12.25)	2·50	2·50
221	49	3 c. green, O (9.23)	90	60
222	50	4 c. carmine-red, O (10.21)	2·00	1·50
223		4 c. bright violet, O (8.24)	20	10
224		4 c. orange, O (8.29)	50	10
225	51	5 c. orange, O (Die II) (5.21)	45	25
		a. Die I (12.22)	55	25
226		5 c. brown, O (Die II) (2.32)	70	10
		a. Die I (1933)	70	10
227	52	6 c. dull claret, O (10.22)	55	35
228		6 c. rose-pink, O (2.25)	8·00	3·75
229		6 c. scarlet, O (1.27)	1·75	15
230	51	10 c. bright blue, O (Die I) (3.21)	1·75	30
231		10 c. purple/*yellow*, C (Die I) (6.25)	2·75	3·25
		a. Die II. *On pale yellow* (11.26)	1·25	10
		b. Die I. *On pale yellow* (1933)	90	25
232	52	12 c. bright blue, O (1.22)	85	10
233	53	21 c. dull and bright purple, C (2.23)	6·50	12·00
234	54	25 c. dull purple and mauve, C (Die I, Type I) (2.23)	17·00	16·00
		a. Die II. Type I (9.23)	12·00	3·75
		b. Die II. Type II (1927)	3·25	1·75
235	51	30 c. dull purple & orge, C (Die I) (5.21)	13·00	17·00
		a. Die II (1923)	2·50	50
236	53	35 c. dull purple & orge-yellow, C (8.22)	7·50	5·00
		a. Dull purple and orange	4·25	5·50
237		35 c. scarlet and purple, C (4.31)	7·00	7·00
238	54	50 c. black/*emerald*, C (9.25)	1·50	50
239	51	$1 black and red/*blue*, C (6.22)	5·50	80
240	54	$2 green and red/*pale yellow*, C (5.25)	10·00	8·50
240*a*	51	$5 green and red/*green*, C (8.26)	40·00	24·00
240*b*	–	$25 pur & bl/*bl*, C (5.23) (Optd S. £100)	£300	75·00
240*c*	–	$100 carmine and black/*blue*, C (5.23) (Optd S. £175)	£1200	
240*d*	–	$500 purple and orange-brown, C (4.23) (Optd S. £325)	£8500	
218/40*a*		*Set of* 24	90·00	65·00
218/40*a* (*excl.* 229) Optd/Perf "Specimen"		*Set of* 23	£400	

Nos. 240*b/d* are as Type **46**, but with portrait of George V.

An 8 c. in carmine was prepared but not issued (Optd "Specimen" £150).

The paper of No. 231b is the normal *pale yellow* at the back, but with a bright yellow surface. No. 231 is on paper of a *pale lemon* tint and the impression is smudgy.

1922 (31 Mar). *T* **48** *and* **50** *to* **54**, *overprinted with T* **56**.

(a) Wmk Mult Crown CA

241	2 c. green	11·00	20·00
242	4 c. scarlet	2·75	7·00
243	5 c. orange	4·25	8·00
244	8 c. ultramarine	1·75	4·00
245	25 c. dull purple and mauve (No. 202)	4·00	11·00
246	45 c. black/*blue-green* (*olive back*)	3·50	12·00
	a. On green (*white back*)	6·00	15·00
247	$1 black and red/*blue*	95·00	£200
248	$2 green and red/*orange-buff*	28·00	55·00
	a. On pale yellow	45·00	90·00
249	$5 green and red/*blue-green* (*olive back*)	£190	£275

(b) Wmk Mult Script CA

250	1 c. black	50	2·00
251	2 c. green	2·00	5·50
252	4 c. carmine-red	2·25	6·50
253	5 c. orange (Die II)	3·25	8·00
254	10 c. bright blue (Die I)	3·00	10·00
255	$1 black and red/*blue* (Die II)	20·00	55·00
241/55	*Set of* 11	£225	£400

The following varieties may be found in most values and occur five times in each pane of 60: (a) Small second "A" in "MALAYA." (b) No stop. (c) No hyphen. (d) Oval last "O" in "BORNEO," (e) "EXH.BITION."

1935 (6 May). *Silver Jubilee. As Nos. 91/4 of Antigua but ptd by Waterlow & Sons. P* 11 × 12.

256	5 c. ultramarine and grey	40	20
257	8 c. green and indigo	1·00	1·00
258	12 c. brown and deep blue	1·75	1·25
259	25 c. slate and purple	2·75	2·25
256/9 Perf "Specimen"	*Set of* 4	50·00	

57

58

1936 (1 Jan)–**37.** *Chalk-surfaced paper. Wmk Mult Script CA. P* 14.

260	57	1 c. black (1.1.37)	12	15
261		2 c. green (1.2.36)	15	15
262		4 c. orange (15.6.36)	20	15
263		5 c. brown (1.8.36)	20	10
264		6 c. scarlet (1.2.36)	90	12
265		8 c. grey	40	35
266		10 c. dull purple (1.7.36)	90	35
267		12 c. bright ultramarine (1.9.36)	3·25	1·75
268		25 c. dull purple and scarlet (1.2.36)	1·25	25
269		30 c. dull purple and orange	1·60	1·25
270		40 c. scarlet and dull purple	2·00	2·00
271		50 c. black/*emerald* (1.9.36)	2·50	1·50
272		$1 black and red/*blue* (1.7.36)	6·00	2·25
273		$2 green and scarlet (1.4.36)	18·00	11·00
274		$5 green and red/*emerald* (1.1.37)	35·00	22·00
260/74		*Set of* 15	65·00	38·00
260/74 Perf "Specimen"		*Set of* 15	£180	

1937 (12 May). *Coronation. As Nos. 13/15 of Aden.*

275	4 c. orange	30	10
276	8 c. grey-black	55	10
277	12 c. bright blue	65	60
275/7 Perf "Specimen"	*Set of* 3	45·00	

1937–41. *Chalk-surfaced or ordinary paper* (**O**). *Wmk Mult Script CA. P* 14 *or* 15 × 14 (15 c.). *(a) Die I (printed at two operations).*

278	58	1 c. black (1.1.38)	30	5
279		2 c. green (6.12.37)	50	20
280		4 c. orange (1.1.38)	1·50	25
281	58	5 c. brown (19.11.37)	1·50	15
282		6 c. scarlet (10.1.38)	1·25	5
283		8 c. grey (26.1.38)	5·50	15
284		10 c. dull purple (8.11.37)	1·50	10
285		12 c. ultramarine (10.1.38)	1·75	10
286		25 c. dull purple and scarlet (11.12.37)	9·50	90
287		30 c. dull purple and orange (1.12.37)	9·00	95
288		40 c. scarlet and dull purple (20.12.37)	6·50	1·75
289		50 c. black/*emerald* (26.1.38)	3·00	15
290		$1 black and red/*blue* (26.1.38)	3·25	30
291		$2 green and scarlet (26.1.38)	17·00	3·50
292		$5 green and red/*emerald* (26.1.38)	22·00	4·25

(b) Die II (printed at one operation)

293	58	2 c. green (28.12.38)	2·50	30
294		2 c. orange (6.10.41)	35	1·75
295		3 c. green, O (5.9.41)	90	1·75
296		4 c. orange (29.10.38)	8·50	25
297		5 c. brown (18.2.39)	2·25	5
298		15 c. ultramarine, O (6.10.41)	2·00	5·50
278/98		*Set of* 18	80·00	20·00
278/92, 294/5, 298 Perf "Specimen"		*Set of* 18	£275	

Die I. Lines of background outside central oval touch the oval and the foliage of the palm tree is usually joined to the oval frame. The downward-pointing palm frond, opposite the King's eye, has two points.

Die II. Lines of background are separated from the oval by a white line and the foliage of the palm trees does not touch the outer frame. The palm frond has only one point.

The 6 c. grey, 8c. scarlet and $5 purple and orange were issued only with the BMA overprint, but the 8 c. without opt is known although in this state it was never issued.

POSTAGE DUE STAMPS

D 1

1924–26. *Wmk Mult Script CA. P* 14.

D1	D 1	1 c. violet	2·50	2·00
D2		2 c. black	2·50	70
D3		4 c. green (1926)	2·00	5·50
D4		8 c. scarlet	4·50	75
D5		10 c. orange	4·50	1·25
D6		12 c. bright blue	7·00	80
D1/6		*Set of* 6	21·00	10·00
D1/6 Optd "Specimen"		*Set of* 6	£225	

For later issues of Postage Due stamps, see MALAYAN POSTAL UNION.

The Straits Settlements were occupied by the Japanese in 1942. After the Second World War the stamps of MALAYA (BRITISH MILITARY ADMINISTRATION) were used. In 1946 Singapore became a separate Crown Colony and Labuan was transferred to North Borneo. Separate stamps were issued for Malacca and Penang, which both joined the Malayan Federation on 1 February 1948.

II. FEDERATED MALAY STATES

On 1 July 1896, the States of Negri Sembilan, Pahang, Perak and Selangor were organised on a federal basis to be known as the Federated Malay States. For the time being each State continued with individual issues, but stamps for the use of the Federation replaced these in 1900.

Due to problems of stamp supply issues of the STRAITS SETTLEMENTS were validated for use in the Federated Malay States between 16 July 1900, and 1 January 1902.

PRICES FOR STAMPS ON COVER

Nos. 1/13	*from* × 8
No. 14	—
Nos. 15/22	*from* × 10
Nos. 23/5	*from* × 3
No. 26	—
Nos. 27/50	*from* × 6
No. 51	—
Nos. 52/81	*from* × 5
No. 82	—
Nos. D1/6	*from* × 10

PRINTERS. All issues of the Federated Malay States were printed in typography by De La Rue & Co, Ltd, London, *unless otherwise stated.*

FEDERATED
MALAY STATES

(1)

FEDERATED
MALAY STATES

(2)

1900. *Optd with T* **1** (*cent values*) *or* **2** (*dollar values*).

(a) Stamps of Negri Sembilan (T 3)

1	1 c. dull purple and green	1·60	2·75
2	2 c. dull purple and brown	17·00	23·00
3	3 c. dull purple and black	2·25	3·00
4	5 c. dull purple and olive-yellow	24·00	28·00
5	10 c. dull purple and orange	1·60	6·50
6	20 c. green and olive	25·00	40·00
7	25 c. green and carmine	60·00	70·00
8	50 c. green and black	32·00	48·00
1/8	*Set of* 8	£150	£200
1/8 Optd "Specimen"	*Set of* 8	£150	

(*b*) *Stamps of Perak* (*T* **31** *and* **32**)
9 5 c. dull purple and olive-yellow .. .. 14·00 25·00
10 10 c. dull purple and orange .. .. .. 24·00 30·00
a. Bar omitted £425
11 $1 green and pale green .. .. .. 65·00 70·00
12 $2 green and carmine .. .. .. 60·00 70·00
13 $5 green and ultramarine £120 £130
14 $25 green and orange (Optd S. £250) .. £2000
11/13 Optd "Specimen" .. .. *Set of* 3 £100

3

4

1900–1. *P* 14. (*a*) *T* **3**. *Wmk Crown CA, sideways* (1901).
15 1 c. black and green 25 40
a. Grey and green 35 40
b. Grey-brown and green .. .. .. 1·75 25
16 3 c. black and brown .. .. .. 1·75 60
a. Grey and brown .. .. .. 1·25 50
b. Grey-brown and brown 40 25
17 4 c. black and carmine .. .. .. 3·50 90
a. Grey and carmine .. .. .. 3·50 90
b. Grey-brown and carmine .. .. 3·75 40
18 5 c. green and carmine/*yellow* .. .. 2·00 2·75
19 8 c. black and ultramarine .. .. .. 17·00 3·75
a. Grey and ultramarine .. .. .. 17·00 3·75
b. Grey-brown and ultramarine .. .. 17·00 3·75
20 10 c. black and claret .. .. .. 16·00 2·25
a. Grey and claret .. .. .. 14·00 1·25
b. Black and purple .. .. .. 23·00 1·40
c. Grey and purple .. .. .. 13·00 1·25
d. Grey-brown and purple .. .. .. 17·00 1·25
21 20 c. mauve and black .. .. .. 16·00 3·00
22 50 c. black and orange-brown .. .. .. 42·00 22·00
a. Grey and orange-brown .. .. .. 42·00 17·00
b. Grey-brown and orange-brown .. .. 42·00 17·00
15/22 .. .. *Set of* 8 85·00 26·00
15/22 Optd "Specimen" .. .. *Set of* 8 £200

Later printings in 1903–4 show the two upper lines of shading in the background at the corner nearest to the "S" of "STATE" blurred and running into one another, whereas in earlier printings these lines are distinct. Two plates were used for printing the central design of T 3. In Plate 1 the lines of background are regular throughout, but in Plate 2 they are lighter around the head and back of the tiger. The 5 c. was the only value with single wmk to be printed from Plate 2. Stamps with multiple wmk were printed for a short time from Plate 1, and show the two blurred lines of background near "S" of "STATE," but the majority of these stamps were printed from Plate 2 and later plates.

(*b*) *T* **4**. *Wmk Crown CC* (1900)
23 $1 green and pale green .. .. .. 38·00 35·00
24 $2 green and carmine .. .. .. 45·00 50·00
25 $5 green and bright ultramarine .. .. 70·00 65·00
a. Green and pale ultramarine .. .. 70·00 65·00
26 $25 green and orange (Optd S. £225) .. £700 £375
23/5 Optd "Specimen" .. .. *Set of* 3 £140

Two dies for 1 c. green and 4 c. scarlet

Die I. "Head" and duty plates. Thick frame line below "MALAY" and in the 1 c. the "c" is thin whilst in the 4 c. it is thick.

Die II. Single working plate. Thin frame line below "MALAY" and in the 1 c. the "c" is thicker whilst in the 4 c. it is thinner.

1904–22. *T* **3** *and* **4** *(dollar values). Wmk Mult Crown CA (sideways in T* **3**). *Ordinary paper except where otherwise indicated. P* 14.
27 1 c. grey and green (10.10.04) .. .. 18·00 3·25
a. Grey-brown and green .. .. 5·00 1·25
28 1 c. green (Die I) (8.7.06) 60 45
29 1 c. green (Die II) 60 45
a. Yellow-green .. .. .. 4·00 40
b. Blue-green .. .. .. 5·50 45
30 1 c. deep brown (21.1.19) .. .. 3·00 1·75
31 2 c. green (18.2.19) 45 50
32 3 c. grey and brown, **O** .. .. 7·50 1·00
a. Grey-brown and brown, **OC** .. .. 4·00 45
33 3 c. brown (11.7.06) .. .. .. 2·00 25
34 3 c. carmine (2.2.09) .. .. .. 1·75 10
a. Scarlet (1.17) .. .. .. 3·50 25
35 3 c. grey (29.10.18) .. .. .. 1·50 45
36 4 c. grey and scarlet, **O** (10.10.04) .. 7·00 95
a. Grey and rose, **C** .. .. .. 3·00 65
b. Grey-brown and scarlet, **O** .. .. 4·00 45
c. Black and scarlet, **O** .. .. 7·50 55
d. Black and rose, **O** .. .. .. 2·75 40
e. Black and deep rose (aniline), **O** (1909) .. 17·00 1·75
f. Jet-black and rose, **O** (1914) .. .. 4·50 55
37 4 c. scarlet (Die I) (11.2.19) .. .. 1·75 90
38 4 c. scarlet (Die II) (15.4.19) 80 25
a. Wmk upright (2.22) .. .. ..
39 5 c. green and carmine/*yellow*, **CO** (5.06) .. 3·75 1·40
a. Deep green and carmine/yellow, **O** .. 1·60 1·50
b. On orange-buff, **O** (1921) .. .. 3·50 1·50
c. On pale yellow (4.22) .. .. 2·25 1·50
40 6 c. orange (11.2.19) .. .. .. 3·00 1·50
41 8 c. grey and ultramarine, **O** (3.05) .. 11·00 7·50
a. Grey-brown and ultramarine, **OC** (12.05) 6·00 2·75
b. Wmk upright, **O** (3.07) .. .. 5·00 2·75
42 8 c. ultramarine (8.3.10) .. .. .. 11·00 1·25
a. Deep blue (1918) .. .. 12·00 1·75
43 10 c. grey-brown and claret, **OC** (10.10.04) .. 5·00 55
a. Black and claret, **O** .. .. .. 3·25 25
b. Grey-brown and purple, **O** (1905) .. 8·50 50
c. Black and purple, **O** .. .. .. 6·00 75
d. Jet-black and bright purple, **O** (1914) .. 8·00 55
44 10 c. deep blue (3.6.19) .. .. .. 6·00 1·25
a. Bright blue .. .. 6·50 1·40
b. Wmk upright (inverted) .. .. ..
45 20 c. mauve and black, **OC** (3.05) .. .. 2·00 45
46 35 c. scarlet/*pale yellow* (25.8.22) .. .. 13·00 13·00
47 50 c. grey and orange, **O** (3.05) .. .. 15·00 2·00
a. Grey-brown & orange-brn, **OC** (1906) .. 14·00 2·50
b. Grey and orange-brown, **C** .. .. 14·00 2·50
c. Black and orange-brown, **C** .. .. 23·00 2·50
d. Jet-black and orange-brown, **C** (1914) .. 23·00 2·25
e. Wmk upright (inverted) .. .. .. † —
48 $1 grey-green and green, **C** (11.07) .. .. 25·00 20·00
a. Green and pale green .. .. .. 25·00 20·00
49 $2 green and carmine, **C** (12.07) .. .. 45·00 45·00
50 $5 green and blue, **C** (1.08) .. .. .. 65·00 75·00
51 $25 green and orange, **C** (8.10) £600 £300
27/50 .. .. *Set of* 22 £190 £150
28, 30/1, 33/5, 37, 40, 42, 44, 46 Optd "Specimen" .. .. *Set of* 11 £350

Nos. 29/*b*, 30, 31, 33, 34/*a* and 35 were printed from single working plates and all the rest from double plates.

Most examples of No. 47e have fiscal cancellations, but at least one is known postally used.

1922–34. *Wmk Mult Script CA (sideways in T* **3**). *P* 14.
52 **3** 1 c. deep brown, **O** (1.8.22) .. .. 2·50 2·25
53 1 c. black, **O** (12.6.23) 60 25
54 2 c. brown, **O** (5.8.25) .. .. .. 3·75 2·50
55 2 c. green, **O** (15.6.26) 45 15
56 3 c. grey, **O** (27.12.22) .. .. .. 4·00 4·25
57 3 c. green, **O** (22.1.24) .. .. .. 5·50 2·50
58 3 c. brown, **O** (31.5.27) 50 40
59 4 c. carmine-red, **O** (Die II) (27.11.23) .. 2·25 45
60 4 c. orange, **O** (9.11.26) 40 15
a. No watermark .. .. .. £200 85·00
61 5 c. mauve/*pale yellow*, **O** (17.3.22) .. 75 35
62 5 c. brown, **O** (1.3.32) .. .. .. 1·00 15
63 6 c. orange, **O** (2.5.22) 55 45
64 6 c. scarlet, **O** (9.11.26) 65 15
65 10 c. bright blue, **O** (23.10.23) .. .. 1·50 2·75
66 10 c. black and blue, **O** (18.1.24*) .. .. 2·00 1·25
67 10 c. purple/*pale yellow*, **C** (14.7.31) .. 6·50 80
68 12 c. ultramarine, **O** (12.9.22) .. .. 1·75 30
69 20 c. dull purple and black, **OC** (3.4.23) .. 4·00 40
70 25 c. purple & brt magenta, **C** (3.9.29) .. 3·00 1·25
71 30 c. purple and orange-yellow, **C** (3.9.29) 4·50 95
72 35 c. scarlet/*pale yellow*, **O** (6.11.28) .. 7·00 9·00
73 35 c. scarlet and purple, **C** (29.9.31) .. 15·00 15·00
74 50 c. black and orange, **C** (24.4.24) .. 12·00 4·50
a. Black and orange-brown .. .. 12·00 4·50
75 50 c. black/*green*, **C** (16.6.31) .. .. 5·50 2·75
76 **4** $1 pale green and green, **C** (2.2.26) .. 22·00 20·00
a. Grey-green and emerald, **C** (5.10.26) 14·00 13·00
77 **3** $1 black and red/*blue*, **C** (10.3.31) .. 15·00 3·00
78 **4** $2 green and carmine, **C** (17.8.26) .. 16·00 23·00
79 **3** $2 green and red/*yellow*, **C** (6.2.34) .. 32·00 28·00
80 **4** $5 green and blue, **C** (24.2.25) .. .. 60·00 70·00
81 **3** $5 green and red/*green*, **C** (7.34) .. £110 £120
82 **4** $25 grn & orge, **C** (14.2.28) (Optd S. £80) £500 £225
52/81 .. .. *Set of* 30 £300 £275
52/81 Optd/Perf "Specimen" .. .. *Set of* 30 £550

Nos. 52, 56 and 59 were printed from single working plates and the rest from double plates.

*No. 66 was released in London by the Crown Agents some months earlier but this is the official date of issue in the States.

The 5 c. in mauve on white Script paper is the result of soaking early printings of No. 61 in water.

POSTAGE DUE STAMPS

D 1

(Typo Waterlow)

1924 (1 Dec)–**26.** *Wmk Mult Script CA (sideways). P* 15 × 14.
D1 D **1** 1 c. violet .. .. 2·50 1·25
D2 2 c. black .. .. 1·50 1·50
D3 4 c. green (4.26) .. .. 3·25 4·50
D4 8 c. red .. .. 4·25 11·00
D5 10 c. orange .. .. 5·50 11·00
D6 12 c. blue .. .. 8·50 15·00
D1/6 .. .. *Set of* 6 23·00 40·00
D1/6 Optd "Specimen" .. .. *Set of* 6 £160

The issues of the Federated Malay States were replaced by stamps for the individual States from 1935 onwards.

III. MALAYAN POSTAL UNION

The Malayan Postal Union was organised in 1935 and, initially, covered the Straits Settlements and the Federated Malay States. Stamps of the Straits Settlements together with issues for the individual States continued to be used, but Malayan Postal Union postage due stamps were introduced in 1936.

Following the end of the Second World War the use of these postage dues spread throughout Malaya and to Singapore.

PRICES FOR STAMPS ON COVER TO 1945
Nos. D1/6 *from* × 10
Nos. D7/13 *from* × 4

POSTAGE DUE STAMPS

D 1

10

cents

(D 2)

(Typo Waterlow until 1961, then D.L.R.)

1936–38. *Wmk Mult Script CA. P* 15 × 14.
D1 D **1** 1 c. slate-purple (1938) .. .. .. 1·60 1·00
D2 4 c. green .. .. 2·50 1·50
D3 8 c. scarlet .. .. 3·25 5·00
D4 10 c. yellow-orange .. .. .. 2·25 30
D5 12 c. pale ultramarine .. .. .. 3·25 6·00
D6 50 c. black (1.38) .. .. .. 7·50 11·00
D1/6 .. .. *Set of* 6 19·00 22·00
D1/6 Perf "Specimen" .. .. *Set of* 6 95·00

For use in Negri Sembilan, Pahang, Perak, Selangor and Straits Settlements including Singapore.

1945–49. *New values and colours. Wmk Mult Script CA. P* 15 × 14.
D 7 D **1** 1 c. purple .. .. 1·50 2·50
D 8 3 c. green .. .. 8·50 11·00
D 9 5 c. scarlet .. .. 12·00 14·00
D10 8 c. yell-orange (1949) (Perf S. £100) .. 24·00 18·00
D11 9 c. yellow-orange .. .. .. 55·00 40·00
D12 15 c. pale ultramarine .. .. .. 60·00 48·00
D13 20 c. blue (1948) (Perf S. £75) .. .. 12·00 14·00
D7/13 .. .. *Set of* 7 £150 £130

1951 (8 Aug)–**62.** *Wmk Mult Script CA. P* 14.
D14 D **1** 1 c. violet (21.8.52) 25 45
D15 2 c. deep slate-blue (16.11.53) 25 55
a. Perf 12½ (15.11.60) .. .. .. 55 2·50
b. Perf 12½. Chalky paper (10.7.62) .. 35 3·00
ba. Ditto. Imperf between (vert pair) ..
D16 3 c. deep green (21.8.52) .. .. .. 6·50 5·50
D17 4 c. sepia (16.11.53) 45 90
a. Perf 12½ (15.11.60) .. .. .. 80 4·00
b. Perf 12½. *Bistre-brown.* Chalky paper (10.7.62) .. .. .. 70 3·50
D18 5 c. vermilion .. .. 8·00 7·00
D19 8 c. yellow-orange .. .. .. 1·75 1·75
D20 12 c. bright purple (1.2.54) .. .. 1·00 1·75
a. Perf 12½. Chalky paper (10.7.62) .. 1·50 5·50
D21 20 c. blue .. .. 4·00 4·50
a. Perf 12½. *Deep blue* (10.12.57) .. 4·00 15·00
b. Perf 12½. *Deep blue.* Chalky paper (15.10.63) .. .. .. 4·00 14·00
D14/21 .. .. *Set of* 8 20·00 20·00

Nos. D7 to D21b were for use in the Federation and Singapore, and from 1963 throughout Malaysia.

1964 (14 Apr)–**65.** *Chalk-surfaced paper. Wmk w* **12** *(sideways on* 1 c.). *P* 12½.
D22 D **1** 1 c. maroon .. .. 30 1·10
a. Perf 12. Wmk upright (4.5.65) .. 25 1·10
D23 2 c. deep slate-blue .. .. .. 45 3·00
a. Perf 12 (9.3.65) .. .. .. 35 3·75
D24 4 c. bistre-brown .. .. .. 75 3·00
a. Perf 12 (9.3.65) .. .. .. 50 3·75
D25 8 c. yellow-orange (*p* 12) (4.5.65) .. 2·75 4·25
D27 12 c. bright purple .. .. .. 1·50 7·00
a. Perf 12 (4.5.65) .. .. .. 1·50 8·00
D28 20 c. deep blue .. .. 3·50 15·00
a. Perf 12 (4.5.65) .. .. .. 2·75 18·00
D22/8 .. .. *Set of* 6 7·25 30·00

1965 (Jan). *As No.* D19 *surch locally with Type* D **2**.
D29 D **1** 10 c. on 8 c. yellow-orange .. .. 25 1·25

First supplies of this stamp differed from No. D19 in that they had been climatically affected but later a fresh printing of No. D19 was surcharged.

1967? *Unsurfaced paper. Wmk w* **12**. *P* 15 × 14.
D30 D **1** 50 c. black £300 £130

Nos. D22/9 were for use throughout Malaysia and Singapore. They were superseded on 15 August 1966 by the postage dues inscribed "MALAYSIA", but continued in use, together with No. D30, for Singapore until 31 January 1968 when they were replaced by Singapore Postage Dues.

IV. MALAYA (BRITISH MILITARY ADMINISTRATION)

For use throughout all Malay States and in Singapore. From 1948 this general issue was gradually replaced by individual issues for each state.

B M A
MALAYA
(1)

1945–48. *T* **58** *of Straits Settlements optd with T* **1**. *Values* 1 c. *to* 15 c. *from Die I (double-plate printing) or Die II (single-plate printing). Wmk Mult Script CA. P* 14 *or* 15 × 14 *(No.* 11).
1 1 c. black, **CO** (I) (R.) 5 5
2 2 c. orange, **OC** (II) 5 5
3 2 c. orange, **O** (I) (1946) .. .. .. 1·40 2·50
4 3 c. yellow-green, **O** (II) 15 5
a. Blue-green, **OC** (II) (1947) 20 10
5 5 c. brown, **C** (II) 5 5
6 6 c. grey, **OC** (II) 5 5
7 8 c. scarlet, **O** (II) 5 5
8 10 c. slate-purple, **C** (I) 5 5
a. Purple, **OC** (I) (1945) 12 5
b. Magenta, **C** (I) (1948) 25 5
9 10 c. purple, **C** (II) (1948) .. .. 2·50 10
10 12 c. bright ultramarine, **C** (I) .. .. 1·40 1·75
11 15 c. bright ultramarine, **O** (II) .. .. 1·75 3·00
12 15 c. bright ultramarine, **OC** (II) (R.) .. 15 5
a. Blue, **OC** (II) (R.) (1947) .. .. 6·00 75
13 25 c. dull purple and scarlet, **OC** 40 5

14	50 c. black/*emerald*, **CO** (I) (R.) (1946)	..	40	5
15	$1 black and red, **O** ..	..	1·00	5
16	$2 green and scarlet, **O**	..	1·50	40
17	$5 green and red/*emerald*, **C**	..	42·00	48·00
18	$5 purple and orange, **O**	..	4·00	1·50
1/18		*Set of* 15	45·00	48·00
1/11, 13/16, 18 Perf "Specimen"		*Set of* 14	£300	

The 8 c. grey with "B M A" opt was prepared but not officially issued.

Nos. 3 and 9 do not exist without the overprint.

Nos. 1, 2, 6, 7, 8*a* and 13 exist also on thin, rough ordinary paper.

No. 8*a* with reddish purple medallion and dull purple frame is from a printing with the head in fugitive ink which discolours with moisture.

Stamps in the Crown Colony Victory design were prepared for the Malayan Union in 1946, but not issued. Examples of the 8 c. carmine from this issue were stolen from stock awaiting destruction.

V. MALAYAN FEDERATION

The Malayan Federation, formed in 1948 by Malacca, Penang, the four Federated Malay States and the five Unfederated States, became an independent member of the British Commonwealth on 31 August 1957.

Commemoratives and a limited series of definitives were issued by the Federation and were used concurrently with the stamps from the individual States.

1 Tapping Rubber

4 Map of the Federation

(Centre recess, frame litho (6 c., 25 c.); centre litho, frame recess (12 c.); recess (30 c.), D.L.R.)

1957 (5 May)–**61**. *T* **1, 4** *and similar designs.* W w **12.** *P* 13 × 12½ (*No.* 4) *or* 13 (*others*).

1	6 c. dp blue, red, yell & grey-bl (*shades*)	10	5
2	12 c. red, yellow, blue, black and scarlet	25	5
3	25 c. mar, red, yell & dull greenish blue ..	40	5
4	30 c. orange-red and lake ..	40	15
	a. Perf 13. *Orange-red and deep lake* (*shades*) (20.6.61)	40	10

Designs: *Horiz*—12 c. Federation coat of arms; 25 c. Tin dredge.

5 Chief Minister Tengku Abdul Rahman and Populace greeting Independence

(Des A. B. Saman. Recess Waterlow)

1957 (31 Aug). *Independence Day. Wmk Mult Script CA. P* 12½.

5	**5**	10 c. bistre-brown ..	8	5

6 United Nations Emblem

7 United Nations Emblem

(Recess D.L.R.)

1958 (5 Mar). *U.N. Economic Commission for Asia and Far East Conference, Kuala Lumpur.* W w **12.** *P* 13½ (12 *c.*) *or* 12½ (30 *c.*).

6	**6**	12 c. carmine-red ..	35	40
7	**7**	30 c. maroon ..	50	20

8 Merdeka Stadium, Kuala Lumpur

9 The Yang di-Pertuan Agong (Abdul Rahman)

(Photo Harrison)

1958 (31 Aug). *First Anniv of Independence.* W w **12.** *P* 13½ × 14½ (10 *c.*) *or* 14½ × 13½ (30 *c.*).

8	**8**	10 c. green, yellow, red and blue ..	15	5
9	**9**	30 c. red, yellow, violet-blue and green ..	40	12

10 "Human Rights"

11 Malayan with Torch of Freedom

(Des J. P. Hendroff. Litho (10 c.), photo (30 c.) D.L.R.)

1958 (10 Dec). *Tenth Anniv of Declaration of Human Rights.*

(*a*) *W* w **12.** *P* 12½ × 13

10	**10**	10 c. blue, black, carmine and orange ..	15	5

(*b*) *Wmk Mult Script CA. P* 13 × 12½

11	**11**	30 c. deep green ..	40	15

12 Mace and Malayan Peoples

(Photo Enschedé)

1959 (12 Sept). *Inauguration of Parliament. No wmk. P* 13 × 14.

12	**12**	4 c. rose-red ..	10	5
13		10 c. violet ..	10	5
14		25 c. yellow-green ..	50	20

13

14

(Recess D.L.R.)

1960 (7 Apr). *World Refugee Year.* W w **12.** *P* 13½ (12 *c.*) *or* 12½ × 13 (30 *c.*).

15	**13**	12 c. purple ..	35	40
16	**14**	30 c. deep green ..	45	10

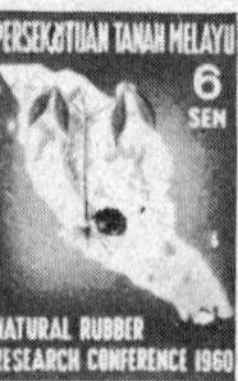

15 Seedling Rubber Tree and Map

16 The Yang di-Pertuan Agong (Syed Putra)

(Photo Japanese Govt Ptg Wks)

1960 (19 Sept). *Natural Rubber Research Conference and 15th International Rubber Study Group Meeting, Kuala Lumpur. T* **15** *and similar vert design. No wmk. P* 13.

17	6 c. yellow-green, black, orange & red-brown	20	10
18	30 c. yellow-green, black, orange & bright blue	50	12

No. 18 is inscribed "INTERNATIONAL RUBBER STUDY GROUP 15th MEETING KUALA LUMPUR" at foot.

(Photo Harrison)

1961 (4 Jan). *Installation of Yang di-Pertuan Agong, Tuanku Syed Putra.* W w **12.** *P* 14 × 14½.

19	**16**	10 c. black and blue ..	10	5

17 Colombo Plan Emblem

18 Malaria Eradication Emblem

(Photo Japanese Govt Ptg Works)

1961 (30 Oct). *Colombo Plan Conference, Kuala Lumpur. P* 13.

20	**17**	12 c. black and magenta ..	35	70
21		25 c. black and apple-green ..	80	45
22		30 c. black and turquoise-blue ..	70	15

(Photo Harrison)

1962 (7 Apr). *Malaria Eradication.* W w **13.** *P* 14 × 14½.

23	**18**	25 c. orange-brown ..	30	25
24		30 c. deep lilac ..	40	12
25		50 c. ultramarine ..	60	15

19 Palmyra Palm Leaf

20 "Shadows of the Future"

(Photo Harrison)

1962 (21 July). *National Language Month.* W w **13** (*upright or inverted*). *P* 13½.

26	**19**	10 c. light brown and deep reddish violet	15	5
27		20 c. light brown and deep bluish green	30	25
28		50 c. light brown and magenta ..	60	60

(Photo Enschedé)

1962 (1 Oct). *Introduction of Free Primary Education.* W w **13.** *P* 13½.

29	**20**	10 c. bright purple ..	10	5
30		25 c. ochre ..	30	30
31		30 c. emerald ..	60	10

21 Harvester and Fisherman

22 Dam and Pylon

(Photo Courvoisier)

1963 (21 Mar). *Freedom from Hunger. P* 11½.

32	**21**	25 c. carmine and apple-green ..	60	45
33		30 c. carmine and crimson ..	75	30
34		50 c. carmine and bright blue ..	90	30

(Photo Harrison)

1963 (26 June). *Cameron Highlands Hydro-Electric Scheme.* W w **13.** *P* 14.

35	**22**	20 c. green and reddish violet ..	35	10
36		30 c. blue-green and ultramarine ..	45	20

The definitive general issue for Malaysia and the low value sets for the individual states superseded the stamps of the Malayan Federation by 15 November 1965.

VI. MALAYSIA

On 16 September 1963, the Malayan Federation, Sabah (North Borneo), Sarawak and Singapore formed the Federation of Malaysia. Singapore left the Federation on 9 August 1965, and became an independent republic.

Individual issues for the component States continued, but were restricted to low value definitives and the occasional "State" commemorative. The higher value definitives and the vast majority of commemoratives were issued on a "National" basis.

A. NATIONAL ISSUES

General issues for use throughout the Malaysian Federation.

1 Federation Map

2 Bouquet of Orchids

(Photo Harrison)

1963 (16 Sept). *Inauguration of Federation.* W w **13.** *P* 14½.

1	**1**	10 c. yellow and bluish violet ..	15	5
		a. Yellow omitted ..	75·00	
2		12 c. yellow and deep green ..	60	60
3		50 c. yellow and chocolate ..	75	5

(Photo Enschedé)

1963 (3 Oct). *Fourth World Orchid Conference, Singapore. No wmk. P* 13 × 14.

4	**2**	6 c. multicoloured ..	70	25
5		25 c. multicoloured ..	1·25	45

4 Parliament House, Kuala Lumpur

(Des V. Whiteley. Photo Harrison)

1963 (4 Nov). *Ninth Commonwealth Parliamentary Conference, Kuala Lumpur. W* w **13** (*inverted*). *P* 13½.

7	**4**	20 c. deep magenta and gold	35	20
8		30 c. deep green and gold	40	20

5 "Flame of Freedom" and Emblems of Goodwill, Health and Charity

6 Microwave Tower and I.T.U. Emblem

(Photo Harrison)

1964 (10 Oct). *Eleanor Roosevelt Commemoration. W* w **13**. *P* 14½ × 13½.

9	**5**	25 c. black, red and greenish blue ..	20	12
10		30 c. black, red and deep lilac	25	10
11		50 c. black, red and ochre-yellow ..	40	10

(Photo Courvoisier)

1965 (17 May). *I.T.U. Centenary. P* 11½.

12	**6**	2 c. multicoloured	15	30
13		25 c. multicoloured	60	45
14		50 c. multicoloured	1·25	30

7 National Mosque

8 Air Terminal

(Photo Harrison)

1965 (27 Aug). *Opening of National Mosque, Kuala Lumpur. W* w **13**. *P* 14 × 14½.

15	**7**	6 c. carmine	10	8
16		15 c. red-brown	20	8
17		20 c. deep bluish green	25	12

(Photo Harrison)

1965 (30 Aug). *Opening of International Airport, Kuala Lumpur. W* w **13**. *P* 14½ × 14.

18	**8**	15 c. black, yellow-green and new blue ..	25	8
19		30 c. black, yellow-green and magenta ..	45	20

9 Crested Wood Partridge

17 Sepak Raga (ball game) and Football

(Des A. Fraser-Brunner. Photo Harrison)

1965 (9 Sept). *T* **9** *and similar vert designs. Multicoloured. W* w **13**. *P* 14½.

20	25 c. Type **9**	50	5
21	30 c. Blue-backed Fairy Bluebird	60	5
	a. Blue omitted	75·00	
22	50 c. Black-eyed Oriole	70	5
	a. Yellow omitted	55·00	
	b. Imperf (pair)	£160	
23	75 c. Rhinoceros Hornbill	1·25	5
24	$1 Zebra Dove	1·75	5
25	$2 Great Argus Pheasant	4·00	30
	a. Imperf (pair)	£150	
26	$5 Asiatic Paradise Flycatcher	12·00	1·10
27	$10 Blue-tailed Pitta	27·00	4·50
	a. Imperf (pair)	£200	
20/7	.. .. *Set of* 8	42·00	5·50

All values except the 75 c. and $10 exist with PVA gum as well as gum arabic.

(Des E. A. F. Anthony. Litho Japanese Govt Ptg Wks)

1965 (14 Dec). *Third South East Asian Peninsular Games. T* **17** *and similar vert designs. P* 13 × 13½.

28	25 c. black and olive-green	50	60
29	30 c. black and bright purple	50	20
30	50 c. black and light blue	90	35

Designs:—30 c. Running; 50 c. Diving.

20 National Monument

21 The Yang di-Pertuan Agong (Ismail Nasiruddin Shah)

(Photo Harrison)

1966 (8 Feb). *National Monument, Kuala Lumpur. W* w **13**. *P* 13½.

31	**20**	10 c. multicoloured	20	5
32		20 c. multicoloured	40	15

(Photo Japanese Govt Ptg Wks)

1966 (11 Apr). *Installation of Yang di-Pertuan Agong, Tuanku Ismail Nasiruddin Shah. P* 13½.

33	**21**	15 c. black and light yellow	15	5
34		50 c. black and greenish blue	50	25

22 School Building

23 "Agriculture"

(Photo D.L.R.)

1966 (21 Oct). *150th Anniv of Penang Free School. W* w **13** (*sideways*). *P* 13.

35	**22**	20 c. multicoloured	35	8
36		50 c. multicoloured	70	25

The 50 c. is also inscr "ULANG TAHUN KE-150" at foot and bears a shield at bottom left corner.

(Des Enche Ng Peng Nam. Photo Japanese Govt Ptg Wks)

1966 (1 Dec). *First Malaysia Plan. T* **23** *and similar horiz designs. Multicoloured. P* 13½.

37	15 c. Type **23**	30	10
38	15 c. "Rural Health"	30	10
39	15 c. "Communications"	50	15
40	15 c. "Education"	30	10
41	15 c. "Irrigation"	30	10

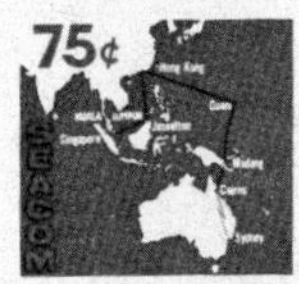

28 Cable Route Maps

(Des Enche Ng Peng Nam. Photo Japanese Govt Ptg Wks)

1967 (30 Mar). *Completion of Malaysia–Hong Kong Link of SEACOM Telephone Cable. P* 13½.

42	**28**	30 c. multicoloured	80	25
43		75 c. multicoloured	2·50	2·50

29 Hibiscus and Rulers

(Photo Harrison)

1967 (31 Aug). *Tenth Anniv of Independence. W* w **13**. *P* 14½.

44	**29**	15 c. multicoloured	30	5
45		50 c. multicoloured	75	30

30 Mace and Shield

31 Straits Settlements 1867 8 c. and Malaysia 1965 25 c. Definitive

(Des Enche Ng Peng Nam. Photo Harrison)

1967 (8 Sept). *Centenary of Sarawak Council. W* w **13**. *P* 14½.

46	**30**	15 c. multicoloured	12	5
47		50 c. multicoloured	40	25

(Des Enche Ng Peng Nam. Photo Japanese Govt Ptg Works)

1967 (2 Dec). *Stamp Centenary. T* **31** *and similar shaped designs. Multicoloured. P* 11½.

48	25 c. Type **31**	70	75
49	30 c. Straits Settlements 1867 24 c. and Malaysia 1965 30 c. definitive ..	70	40
50	50 c. Straits Settlements 1867 32 c. and Malaysia 1965 50 c. definitive	90	60

Nos. 48/50 were each printed in sheets with the stamps arranged *tête-bêche*.

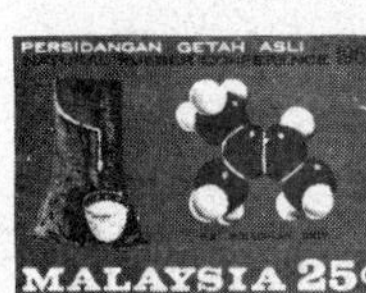

34 Tapping Rubber, and Molecular Unit

37 Mexican Sombrero and Blanket with Olympic Rings

(Litho B.W.)

1968 (29 Aug). *Natural Rubber Conference, Kuala Lumpur. T* **34** *and similar horiz designs. Multicoloured. W* w **13**. *P* 12.

51	25 c. Type **34**	40	12
52	30 c. Tapping rubber, and export consignment	50	20
53	50 c. Tapping rubber, and aircraft tyres ..	70	30

(Litho B.W.)

1968 (12 Oct). *Olympic Games, Mexico. T* **37** *and similar vert design. Multicoloured. W* w **13**. *P* 12 × 11½.

54	30 c. Type **37**	40	15
55	75 c. Olympic rings and Mexican embroidery	75	40

39 Tunku Abdul Rahman against background of Pandanus Weave

40

(Photo Japanese Govt Ptg Wks)

1969 (8 Feb). *Solidarity Week. T* **39/40** *and similar multicoloured design. P* 13½.

56	15 c. Type **39**	20	5
57	20 c. Type **40**	30	20
58	50 c. Tunku Abdul Rahman with pandanus pattern (*horiz*)	45	20

42 Peasant Girl with Sheaves of Paddy

(Des Enche Hoessein Anas. Photo Harrison)

1969 (8 Dec). *National Rice Year. W* w **13**. *P* 13½.

59	**42**	15 c. multicoloured	30	5
60		75 c. multicoloured	90	55

43 Satellite tracking Aerial

44 "Intelsat III" in Orbit

(Photo Enschedé)

1970 (6 Apr). *Satellite Earth Station. W* w **13**. *P* 14 × 13 (15 *c.*) *or* 13½ × 13 (30 *c.*).

61	**43**	15 c. multicoloured	60	15
62	**44**	30 c. multicoloured*	75	60
63		30 c. multicoloured*	75	60

No. 61 was issued horizontally *tête-bêche* in the sheets.

*Nos. 62/3 are of the same design, differing only in the lettering colours (No. 62 white; No. 63 gold).

MINIMUM PRICE

The minimum price quoted is 5p which represents a handling charge rather than a basis for valuing common stamps. For further notes about prices see introductory pages.

45 Blue-banded King Crow Butterfly

46 Emblem

(Des V. Whiteley. Litho B.W. (to 1976) or Harrison)

1970 (31 Aug–16 Nov). *Butterflies. T* **45** *and similar vert designs. Multicoloured. P* 13 × 13½.

64 25 c. Type **45** 50 5
65 30 c. Saturn 55 5
66 50 c. Common Nawab 80 5
67 75 c. Great Mormon 90 5
68 $1 Orange Albatross (16.11) .. .. 1·25 5
69 $2 Raja Brooke's Birdwing (16.11) .. .. 3·00 30
70 $5 Centaur Oak Bird (16.11) .. .. 5·50 1·00
71 $10 Royal Assyrian (16.11) .. .. .. 12·00 3·75
64/71 .. .. *Set of* 8 22·00 4·75

See also Nos. 144/5.

(Litho Harrison)

1970 (7 Sept). *50th Anniv of International Labour Organization. P* 14 × 13½.

72 **46** 30 c. grey and new blue 40 20
73 75 c. pink and new blue 70 60

47 U.N. Emblem encircled by Doves

50 The Yang di-Pertuan Agong (Tuanku Abdul)

(Des Enche Ng Peng Nam. Litho D.L.R.)

1970 (24 Oct). *25th Anniv of United Nations. T* **47** *and similar horiz designs. P* 13 × 12½.

74 25 c. gold, black and brown 35 30
75 30 c. multicoloured 45 35
76 50 c. black and pale yellow-olive 75 75

Designs:—30 c. Line of doves and U.N. emblem; 50 c. Doves looping U.N. emblem.

(Des Union Art Corp. Photo Harrison)

1971 (20 Feb). *Installation of Yang di-Pertuan Agong (Paramount Ruler of Malaysia). P* 14½ × 14.

77 **50** 10 c. black, gold and lemon 25 5
a. Gold (value and inscr) omitted .. £160
78 15 c. black, gold and bright mauve .. 30 5
79 50 c. black, gold and new blue .. .. 85 1·25

51 Bank Negara Complex

(Photo Harrison)

1971 (15 May). *Opening of Bank Negara Building. P* 13½ *(and around design).*

80 **51** 25 c. black and silver 70 60
81 50 c. black and gold 90 65

52 Aerial view of Parliament Buildings

(Des Union Art Corp. Litho Harrison)

1971 (13 Sept). *17th Commonwealth Parliamentary Association Conference, Kuala Lumpur. T* **52** *and similar multicoloured design. P* 13½ (25 *c.*) *or* 12½ × 13 (75*c.*).

82 25 c. Type **52** 65 35
83 75 c. Ground view of Parliament Buildings (73 × 23½ *mm*) .. .. 1·25 1·40

53 54 55

Malaysian Carnival

(Des locally. Litho Harrison)

1971 (18 Sept). *Visit A.S.E.A.N.* Year. P* 14½.

84 **53** 30 c. multicoloured 70 25
a. Horiz strip of 3. Nos. 84/6 .. .. 1·90
85 **54** 30 c. multicoloured 70 25
86 **55** 30 c. multicoloured 70 25

*A.S.E.A.N. = Association of South East Asian Nations.

Nos. 84/6 were printed together, *se-tenant*, in horizontal strips of 3 throughout the sheet, forming a composite design.

56 Trees, Elephant and Tiger

57 Athletics

(Des from children's drawings. Litho Harrison)

1971 (2 Oct). *25th Anniv of U.N.I.C.E.F. T* **56** *and similar multicoloured designs. P* 12½.

87 15 c. Type **56** 40 10
a. Horiz strip of 5. Nos. 87/91 .. .. 1·75
88 15 c. Cat and kittens 40 10
89 15 c. Sun, flower and bird (22 × 29 *mm*) .. 40 10
90 15 c. Monkey, elephant and lion in jungle .. 40 10
91 15 c. Spider and butterflies 40 10

Nos. 87/91 were issued in horizontal *se-tenant* strips of 5 throughout the sheet.

(Des Union Art Corp. Litho B.W.)

1971 (11 Dec). *Sixth S.E.A.P.* Games, Kuala Lumpur. T* **57** *and similar horiz designs. Multicoloured. P* 14½ × 14.

92 25 c. Type **57** 35 25
93 30 c. Sepak Raga players 50 35
94 50 c. Hockey 80 75

*S.E.A.P. = South East Asian Peninsula.

58 59 60

Map and Tourist Attractions

(Des locally. Litho Harrison)

1972 (31 Jan). *Pacific Area Tourist Association Conference. P* 14 × 14½.

95 **58** 30 c. multicoloured 70 20
a. Horiz strip of 3. Nos. 95/7 .. .. 1·90
96 **59** 30 c. multicoloured 70 20
97 **60** 30 c. multicoloured 70 20

Nos. 95/7 were printed together, *se-tenant*, in horizontal strips of 3 throughout the sheet forming a composite design.

61 Kuala Lumpur City Hall

(Des from colour transparencies. Litho Harrison)

1972 (1 Feb). *City Status for Kuala Lumpur. T* **61** *and similar horiz design. Multicoloured. P* 14½ × 14.

98 25 c. Type **61** 50 75
99 50 c. City Hall in floodlights 75 75

ALTERED CATALOGUE NUMBERS

Any Catalogue numbers altered from the last edition are shown as a list in the introductory pages.

62 SOCSO Emblem

63 W.H.O. Emblem

(Des B.W. Litho Harrison)

1973 (2 July). *Social Security Organisation. P* 13½.

100 **62** 10 c. multicoloured 15 12
101 15 c. multicoloured 30 8
102 50 c. multicoloured .. .. .. 85 1·25

(Des Union Advertising. Litho B.W.)

1973 (1 Aug). *25th Anniv of W.H.O. T* **63** *and similar vert design. P* 13.

103 30 c. multicoloured 45 20
104 75 c. multicoloured .. .. 1·25 1·40

64 Fireworks, National Flag and Flower

65 Emblems of Interpol and Royal Malaysian Police

(Des Clover Associates. Litho Harrison)

1973 (31 Aug). *Tenth Anniv of Malaysia. P* 13½.

105 **64** 10 c. multicoloured 20 10
106 15 c. multicoloured 25 10
107 50 c. multicoloured .. .. .. 95 1·25

(Des Union Advertising. Litho Harrison)

1973 (15 Sept). *50th Anniv of Interpol. T* **65** *and similar vert design. Multicoloured. P* 13½.

108 25 c. Type **65** 60 40
109 75 c. Emblems within "50" .. .. .. 1·50 1·60

66 Aeroplane and M.A.S. Emblem

(Des Art Dept, Malaysia Airline System. Litho Harrison)

1973 (1 Oct). *Foundation of Malaysia Airline System. P* 14½.

110 **66** 15 c. multicoloured 25 10
111 30 c. multicoloured 45 50
112 50 c. multicoloured .. .. .. 75 1·25

67 Kuala Lumpur

(Des Malaysian Advertising Services. Litho B.W.)

1974 (1 Feb). *Establishment of Kuala Lumpur as Federal Territory. P* 12½ × 13.

113 **67** 25 c. multicoloured 40 40
114 50 c. multicoloured .. .. .. 85 1·10

68 Development Projects

69 Scout Badge and Map

(Des Malaysian Advertising Services. Litho Rosenbaum Bros, Vienna)

1974 (25 Apr). *Seventh Annual Meeting of Asian Development Bank's Board of Governors, Kuala Lumpur. P* 13½.

115 **68** 30 c. multicoloured 35 40
116 75 c. multicoloured .. .. .. 1·00 1·10

(Des Malaysian Advertising Services. Litho Harrison)

1974 (1 Aug). *Malaysian Scout Jamboree. T* **69** *and similar multicoloured designs. P* 13 × 13½ (15 *c.*) *or* 14 × 13½ (*others*).

117 10 c. Type **69** 25 8
118 15 c. Scouts saluting and flags (46 × 24 *mm*) 40 20
119 50 c. Scout badge .. .. 1·50 1·60

70 Coat of Arms and Power Installations

(Des Malaysian Advertising Services. Litho Harrison)

1974 (1 Sept). *25th Anniv of National Electricity Board. T* **70** *and similar multicoloured design. P* 14 (30 c.) *or* 14 × 14½ (75 c.).
120 30 c. Type **70** . . 40 35
121 75 c. National Electricity Board Building (37 × 27 *mm*) . . 1·25 1·40

71 U.P.U. and Post Office Emblems within "100"

(Des Clover Associates. Litho Harrison)

1974 (9 Oct). *Centenary of Universal Postal Union. P* 14½ × 14.
122 **71** 25 c. dull yell-grn, brt yell & lt rose-carm 30 25
123 30 c. lt new blue, brt yell & lt rose-carm 35 30
124 75 c. brownish orange, bright yellow and light rose-carmine . . 85 1·40

72 Gravel Pump in Tin Mine **73** Hockey-players, World Cup and Federation Emblem

(Des Malaysian Advertising Service. Litho D.L.R.)

1974 (31 Oct). *Fourth World Tin Conference, Kuala Lumpur. T* **72** *and similar horiz designs. Multicoloured. P* 13½.
125 15 c. Type **72** . . 30 8
126 20 c. Open-cast mine . . 40 20
127 50 c. Dredge within "ingot" . . 1·25 1·50

(Des Malaysian Advertising Services. Litho Harrison)

1975 (1 Mar). *Third World Cup Hockey Championships. P* 13½ × 13.
128 **73** 30 c. multicoloured . . 70 50
129 75 c. multicoloured . . 2·00 1·75

74 Congress Emblem **75** Emblem of M.K.P.W. (Malayan Women's Organisation)

(Des Malaysian Advertising Services. Litho Harrison)

1975 (1 May). *25th Anniv of Malaysian Trade Union Congress. P* 14 × 14½.
130 **74** 20 c. multicoloured . . 30 35
131 25 c. multicoloured . . 45 40
132 30 c. multicoloured . . 60 75

(Des Malaysian Advertising Services. Litho Harrison)

1975 (25 Aug). *International Women's Year. P* 14.
133 **75** 10 c. multicoloured . . 20 10
134 15 c. multicoloured . . 35 15
135 50 c. multicoloured . . 1·00 1·60

76 Ubudiah Mosque, Kuala Kangsar **77** Plantation and Emblem

(Des Malaysian Advertising Services. Litho Harrison)

1975 (22 Sept). *Koran Reading Competition. T* **76** *and similar horiz designs. Multicoloured. P* 14.
136 15 c. Type **76** . . 40 12
a. Horiz strip of 5. Nos. 136/40 . . 1·75
137 15 c. Zahir Mosque, Alor Star . . 40 12
138 15 c. National Mosque, Kuala Lumpur . . 40 12
139 15 c. Sultan Abu Bakar Mosque, Johore Bahru 40 12
140 15 c. Kuching State Mosque, Sarawak . . 40 12
The above were printed together, horizontally *se-tenant* throughout the sheet.

(Des E. Sulaiman bin Haji Hassan and E. Hoh Lian Yong. Litho Harrison)

1975 (22 Oct). *50th Anniv of Malaysian Rubber Research Institute. T* **77** *and similar horiz designs. Multicoloured. P* 14 × 14½.
141 10 c. Type **77** . . 20 8
142 30 c. Latex cup and emblem . . 60 60
143 75 c. Natural rubber in test-tubes . . 1·25 1·60

77a *Hebomoia glaucippe aturia* **78** Scrub Typhus

(Photo Harrison)

1976 (19 Jan). *Coil Stamps. T* **77a** *and similar horiz design. Multicoloured. P* 13½.
144 10 c. Type **77a** . . 30 80
145 15 c. *Precis orithya wallacei* . . 35 1·25

(Des Lap Loy Fong (25 c.), Lee Eng Kee (others). Litho Harrison)

1976 (6 Feb). *75th Anniv of the Institute of Medical Research. T* **78** *and similar vert designs. Multicoloured. P* 14.
146 20 c. Type **78** . . 25 15
147 25 c. Malaria diagnosis . . 40 20
148 $1 Beri-beri . . 1·60 2·25

79 The Yang di-Pertuan Agong (Sultan Yahya Petra) **80** State Council Complex

(Des Union Advertising. Photo Harrison)

1976 (28 Feb). *Installation of Yang di-Pertuan Agong. P* 14½ × 13½.
149 **79** 10 c. black, bistre and yellow . . 20 8
150 15 c. black, bistre and bright mauve . . 30 10
151 50 c. black, bistre and ultramarine . . 2·00 2·25

(Des Aini bin Abdul Rahman. Litho Harrison)

1976 (17 Aug). *Opening of the State Council Complex and Administrative Building, Sarawak. P* 12½.
152 **80** 15 c. grey-green and light yellow . . 25 8
153 20 c. grey-green and light bright mauve 35 30
154 50 c. grey-green and pale blue . . 80 1·25

81 E.P.F. Building **82** Blind People at Work

(Litho Harrison)

1976 (18 Oct). *25th Anniv of Employees' Provident Fund. T* **81** *and similar multicoloured designs. P* 14½ (25 c.) *or* 13½ × 14½ *(others)*.
155 10 c. Type **81** . . 15 8
156 25 c. E.P.F. emblems (27 × 27 *mm*) . . 25 25
157 50 c. E.P.F. Building at night . . 60 90

(Des Malayan Association for the Blind, Messrs Advertising Sales Promotion and Hexxon Grafic. Litho Harrison)

1976 (20 Nov). *25th Anniv of Malayan Association for the Blind. T* **82** *and similar horiz design. Multicoloured. P* 13½ × 14½.
158 10 c. Type **82** . . 15 8
159 75 c. Blind man and shadow . . 1·25 1·25

83 Independence Celebrations, 1957 **84** F.E.L.D.A. Village Scheme

(Des Hexxon Grafic. Photo Harrison)

1977 (14 Jan). *First Death Anniversary of Tun Abdul Razak (Prime Minister). T* **83** *and similar horiz designs, each sepia and gold. P* 14.
160 15 c. Type **83** . . 30 10
a. Horiz strip of 5. Nos. 160/4 . . 1·40
161 15 c. "Education" . . 30 10
162 15 c. Tun Razak and map ("Development") . . 30 10
163 15 c. "Rukunegara" (National Philosophy) . . 30 10
164 15 c. A.S.E.A.N. meeting . . 30 10
The above were printed together, horizontally *se-tenant* throughout the sheet.

(Des Halim Teh and Basyuni Sumrah. Litho Harrison)

1977 (7 July). *21st Anniv of Federal Land Development Authority (F.E.L.D.A.). T* **84** *and similar horiz design. Multicoloured. P* 13½ × 14.
165 15 c. Type **84** . . 25 10
166 30 c. Oil Palm settlement . . 60 70

85 Figure "10" **86** Games Logos

(Des Hexxon Grafic. Litho Harrison)

1977 (8 Aug). *Tenth Anniv of A.S.E.A.N. (Association of South East Asian Nations). T* **85** *and similar horiz design. Multicoloured. P* 13½ × 14½.
167 10 c. Type **85** . . 15 5
168 75 c. Flags of members . . 90 95

(Des PTM Communications & Co. Litho Harrison)

1977 (19 Nov). *9th South East Asia Games, Kuala Lumpur. T* **86** *and similar horiz designs. Multicoloured. P* 13½ × 14½.
169 10 c. Type **86** . . 10 5
170 20 c. "Ball" . . 30 15
171 75 c. Symbolic athletes . . 1·10 1·40

87 Islamic Development Bank Emblem **88** Mobile Post Office

(Des Queen's Advertising. Litho J.W.)

1978 (15 Mar). *Islamic Development Bank Board of Governors Meeting, Kuala Lumpur. P* 14.
172 **87** 30 c. multicoloured . . 25 15
173 75 c. multicoloured . . 80 75

(Des Hexxon Grafic. Litho J.W.)

1978 (10 July). *4th Commonwealth Postal Administrations Conference, Kuala Lumpur. T* **88** *and similar horiz designs. Multicoloured. P* 13½ × 13.
174 10 c. Type **88** . . 10 5
175 25 c. G.P.O., Kuala Lumpur . . 35 20
176 50 c. Postal delivery by motor-cycle . . 65 45

89 Boy Scout Emblem **90** Dome of the Rock, Jerusalem

(Des Aini bin Abdul Rahman. Litho J.W.)

1978 (26 July). *4th Malaysian Boy Scout Jamboree, Sarawak. T* **89** *and similar horiz design. Multicoloured. P* 13½ × 13.
177 15 c. Type **89** . . 15 5
178 $1 Bees and honeycomb . . 1·00 1·00

(Des Union Advertising. Litho Harrison)

1978 (21 Aug). *"Freedom of Palestine". P* 12½.
179 **90** 15 c. multicoloured . . 25 5
180 30 c. multicoloured . . 60 55

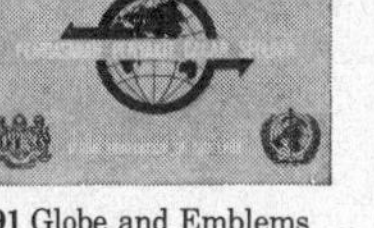

91 Globe and Emblems **92** "Seratus Tahun Getah Asli" and Tapping Knives Symbol

(Litho Harrison)

1978 (30 Sept). *Global Eradication of Smallpox. P* 13½ × 14½.
181 **91** 15 c. black, rosine and new blue . . 20 25
182 30 c. black, rosine and yellowish green . . 35 15
183 50 c. black, rosine and rose-pink . . 60 60

(Des Azmi bin Anuar. Litho J.W.)

1978 (28 Nov). *Centenary of Rubber Industry. T* **92** *and similar horiz designs. P* 13½ × 13.
184 10 c. gold and blue-green . . 10 5
185 20 c. ultramarine, brown & brt yellow-green 20 10
186 75 c. gold and blue-green . . 80 90
Designs:—20 c. Rubber tree seedling and part of "maxi stump"; 75 c. Graphic design of rubber tree, latex cup and globe arranged to form "100".

93 Sultan of Selangor's New Palace

(Des Queen's Advertising. Litho Harrison)

1978 (7 Dec). *Inauguration of Shah Alam New Town as State Capital of Selangor. T* **93** *and similar horiz designs. Multicoloured. P* 13½ × 14½.

187 10 c. Type **93** 10 5
188 30 c. Shah Alam (aerial view) 25 20
189 75 c. Shah Alam 75 85

94 Tiger (*Panthera tigris*)

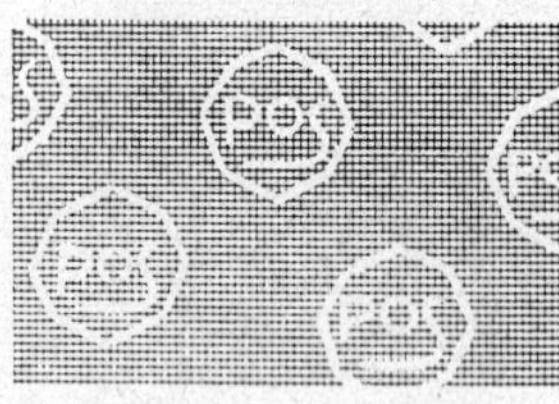

95 Multiple "POS" in Octagon

(Des Ong Soo Keat; adapted Malaysian Advertising Services. Litho Asher and Co, Melbourne)

1979 (4 Jan). *Wildlife. Multicoloured designs as T* **94**. *W* **95** *(inverted on $10 or sideways on others). P* 14½.

190 30 c. Type **94** 20 5
191 40 c. Flying Lemur (*Cynocephalus variegatus*) 25 5
192 50 c. Chevrotain (*Tragulus javanicus*) .. 30 5
193 75 c. Pangolin (*Manis javanicus*) 45 5
194 $1 Turtle (*Dermochelys coriacae*) 60 5
195 $2 Tapir (*Tapirus indicus*) .. .. .. 1·25 10
196 $5 Gaur (*Bos gaurus*) .. .. .. 3·00 60
197 $10 Orang-utan (*Pongo pygmaeus*) (*vert*) .. 6·00 3·00
190/7 .. .. *Set of* 8 10·50 3·50

96 View of Central Bank of Malaysia

97 I.Y.C. Emblem

(Des Union Advertising. Litho J.W.)

1979 (26 Jan). *20th Anniv of Central Bank of Malaysia. T* **96** *and similar vert design showing view of bank building. P* 13.

198 10 c. multicoloured 10 5
199 75 c. multicoloured 75 65

(Des Queen's Advertising. Litho Harrison)

1979 (24 Feb). *International Year of the Child. T* **97** *and similar vert designs. P* 14½ × 14.

200 10 c. gold, blue and salmon 15 10
201 15 c. multicoloured 25 10
202 $1 multicoloured .. .. 1·40 1·25

Designs:—15 c. Children of different races holding hands in front of globe; $1 Children taking part in various activities.

98 Dam and Power Station

99 Exhibition Emblem

(Des National Electricity Board. Litho Harrison)

1979 (19 Sept). *Opening of Hydro-Electric Power Station, Temengor. T* **98** *and similar horiz designs showing views of power station and dam. P* 13½ × 14½.

203 15 c. multicoloured 15 10
204 25 c. multicoloured 35 35
205 50 c. multicoloured 60 50

(Des Malaysian Advertising Services. Litho J.W.)

1979 (20 Sept). *World Telecommunications Exhibition, Geneva. T* **99** *and similar designs. P* 14 (50 c.) *or* 13 (*others*).

206 10 c. orange, ultramarine and silver 5 5
207 15 c. multicoloured 20 10
208 50 c. multicoloured 60 50

Designs: (34 × 24 *mm*)—15 c. Telephone receiver joining one half of World to the other. (39 × 28 *mm*)—50 c. Communications equipment.

100 Sultan Haji Ahmad Shah

101 Pahang and Sarawak Maps within Telephone Dials

(Des Malaysian Advertising Services. Litho Harrison)

1980 (10 July). *Installation of Yang di-Pertuan Agong (Sultan Haji Ahmad Shah). P* 14.

209 **100** 10 c. black, gold and yellow 5 5
210 15 c. black, gold and bright purple .. 20 10
211 50 c. black, gold and new blue 60 50

(Des Malaysian Advertising Services. Litho J.W.)

1980 (31 Aug). *Kuantan-Kuching Submarine Cable Project. T* **101** *and similar horiz designs. Multicoloured. P* 13.

212 10 c. Type **101** 5 5
213 15 c. Kuantan and Kuching views within telephone dials 20 10
214 50 c. Pahang and Sarawak Maps within telephone receiver 60 50

102 Bangi Campus

103 Mecca

(Des Malaysian Advertising Services. Litho J.W.)

1980 (2 Sept). *10th Anniv of National University of Malaysia. T* **102** *and similar horiz designs. Multicoloured. P* 13.

215 10 c. Type **102** 5 5
216 15 c. Jalan Pantai Baru campus 20 10
217 75 c. Great Hall 65 70

(Des Malaysian Advertising Services. Litho J.W.)

1980 (9 Nov). *Moslem Year* 1400 *A.H. Commemoration. P* 13.

218 **103** 15 c. multicoloured 20 10
219 50 c. multicoloured 50 45

The 50 c. value is as T **103** but the inscriptions are in Roman lettering and the country name is to the left of the design.

104 Disabled Child learning to Walk

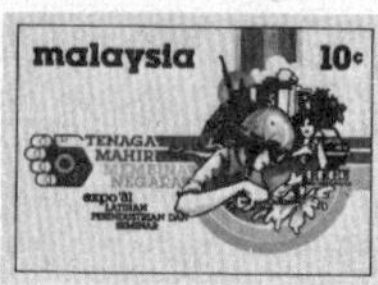

105 Industrial Scene

(Des Malaysian Advertising Services. Litho J.W.)

1981 (14 Feb). *International Year for Disabled Persons. T* **104** *and similar vert designs. Multicoloured. P* 13½ × 13.

220 10 c. Type **104** 5 5
221 15 c. Disabled woman sewing 20 10
222 75 c. Disabled athlete throwing javelin .. 80 80

(Des Malaysian Advertising Services. Litho J.W.)

1981 (2 May). *"Expo '81" Industrial Training Exposition, Kuala Lumpur and Seminar, Genting Highlands. T* **105** *and similar horiz designs. Multicoloured. P* 13½ × 13.

223 10 c. Type **105** 5 5
224 15 c. Worker and bulldozer 15 10
225 30 c. Workers at ship-building yard 25 25
226 75 c. Agriculture and fishing produce, workers and machinery 65 70

106 "25"

(Des A. Yusof and Malaysian Advertising Services. Litho J.W.)

1981 (17 June). *25th Anniv of Malaysian National Committee for World Energy Conferences. T* **106** *and similar horiz designs. Multicoloured. P* 13½ × 13.

227 10 c. Type **106** 5 5
228 15 c. Drawings showing importance of energy sources in industry 15 10
229 75 c. Symbols of various energy sources .. 70 70

107 Drawing showing development of Sabah from Village to Urbanised Area

(Des Creative Concepts. Litho J.W.)

1981 (31 Aug). *Centenary of Sabah. T* **107** *and similar horiz design. Multicoloured. P* 12.

230 15 c. Type **107** 15 5
231 80 c. Drawing showing traditional and modern methods of agriculture 60 70

108 *Samanea saman*

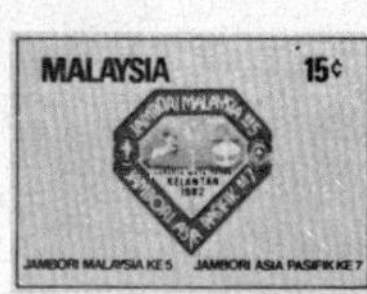

109 Jamboree Emblem

(Des Yusof bin Hadji Saman. Litho J.W.)

1981 (16 Dec). *Trees. T* **108** *and similar multicoloured designs P* 14.

232 15 c. Type **108** 15 5
233 50 c. *Dyera costulata* (*vert*) 45 35
234 80 c. *Dryobalanops aromatica* (*vert*) 65 80

(Des P. Lim (15 c.), Datuk Syed Hashim bin Abdullah (others) Litho J.W.)

1982 (10 Apr). *5th Malaysian/7th Asia–Pacific Boy Scout Jamboree. T* **109** *and similar horiz designs. Multicoloured P* 13½ × 13.

235 15 c. Type **109** 15 10
236 50 c. Malaysian flag and scout emblem .. 40 30
237 80 c. Malaysian and Asia–Pacific scout emblems 70 85

110 A.S.E.A.N. Building and Emblem

111 Dome of the Rock, Jerusalem

(Litho J.W.)

1982 (8 Aug). *15th Anniv Ministerial Meeting of A.S.E.A.N. (Association of South East Asian Nations). T* **110** *and similar horiz design. Multicoloured. P* 14.

238 15 c. Type **110** 15 8
239 $1 Flags of member nations 60 55

(Litho J.W.)

1982 (21 Aug). *"Freedom of Palestine". P* 13½.

240 **111** 15 c. gold, blue-green and black 20 10
241 $1 silver, pale turquoise-green & blk .. 90 80

112 Views of Kuala Lumpur in 1957 and 1982

(Des Ministry of Information. Litho Rosenbaum Bros, Vienna)

1982 (31 Aug). *25th Anniv of Independence. T* **112** *and similar horiz designs. Multicoloured. P* 14 × 13½.

242 10 c. Type **112** 10 8
243 15 c. Malaysian industries 15 10
244 50 c. Soldiers on parade 35 35
245 80 c. Independence ceremony 65 70
MS246 120 × 190 mm. Nos. 242/5 .. .. 1·25 1·50

113 Shadow Play

(Des N. Ajib. Litho J.W.)

1982 (30 Oct). *Traditional Games. T* **113** *and similar horiz designs. Multicoloured. P* 13.

247 10 c. Type **113** 10 8
248 15 c. Cross Top 12 8
249 75 c. Kite flying 55 60

114 Sabah Hats

(Litho Harrison)

982 (26 Nov). *Malaysian Handicrafts. T* **114** *and similar horiz designs. Multicoloured. P* 13 × 13½.
50 10 c. Type **114** 5 8
51 15 c. Gold-threaded cloth 10 10
52 75 c. Sarawak pottery 55 60

115 Gas Exploitation Logo **116** Flag of Malaysia

(Litho Security Printers (M), Malaysia)

983 (22 Jan). *Export of Liquefied Natural Gas from Bintulu Field, Sarawak. T* **115** *and similar horiz designs. Multicoloured. P* 12.
53 15 c. Type **115** 10 10
54 20 c. *Tenaga Satu* (liquid gas tanker) 15 15
55 $1 Gas drilling equipment 60 60

(Litho J.W.)

983 (14 Mar). *Commonwealth Day. T* **116** *and similar horiz designs. Multicoloured. P* 13½ × 14.
56 15 c. Type **116** 10 10
57 20 c. The King of Malaysia 15 15
58 40 c. Oil palm tree and refinery 25 25
59 $1 Satellite view of Earth 60 70

117 *Tilapia nilotica*

(Des and litho Security Printers (M), Malaysia)

983 (15 June). *Freshwater Fishes. T* **117** *and similar horiz designs. Multicoloured. P* 12.
60 20 c. Type **117** 15 15
a. Horiz pair. Nos. 260/1 .. .. 30 30
61 20 c. *Cyprinus carpie* 15 15
62 40 c. *Puntius gonionotus* 25 25
a. Horiz pair. Nos. 262/3 .. .. 50 50
b. Perf 13½ × 14 .. .. 3·00 2·50
ba. Horiz pair. Nos. 262b/3b .. .. .. 6·00 5·00
63 40 c. *Ctenopharyngodon idellus* 25 25
b. Perf 13½ × 14 .. .. 3·00 2·50

Nos. 260/1 and 262/3 were each printed together, *se-tenant*, in orizontal pairs throughout the sheet.

118 Lower Pergau River Bridge

Des Malaysian Public Works Dept. Litho Security Printers (M), Malaysia)

983 (11 July). *Opening of East–West Highway. T* **118** *and similar horiz designs. Multicoloured. P* 13½ × 13.
64 15 c. Type **118** 10 10
65 20 c. Perak river reservoir bridge 15 15
66 $1 Map showing East–West highway .. 65 65

119 Northrop "RF-5E" Fighter **120** Helmeted Hornbill

(Des and litho J.W.)

983 (16 Sept). *50th Anniv of Malaysian Armed Forces. T* **119** *and similar horiz designs. Multicoloured. P* 13.
67 15 c. Type **119** 10 10
68 20 c. Ship launching missile 15 15
69 40 c. Battle of Pasir Panjang 30 30
70 80 c. Trooping the Colour 50 50
MS271 130 × 85 mm. Nos. 267/70. P 13½ .. 90 1·10

(Des P. Ket. Litho Security Printers (M), Malaysia)

1983 (26 Oct). *Hornbills of Malaysia. T* **120** *and similar vert designs. Multicoloured. P* 13½.
272 15 c. Type **120** 10 10
273 20 c. Wrinkled Hornbill 15 15
274 50 c. Long-crested Hornbill 35 35
275 $1 Rhinoceros Hornbill 65 65

121 Bank Building, Ipoh **122** Sky-scraper and Mosque, Kuala Lumpur

(Des P. Hoong. Litho Security Printers (M), Malaysia)

1984 (26 Jan). *25th Anniv of Bank Negara. T* **121** *and similar horiz design. Multicoloured. P* 13½ × 14.
276 20 c. Type **121** 12 15
277 $1 Bank building, Alor Setar 60 65

(Des Mara Institute of Technology. Litho Security Printers (M), Malaysia)

1984 (1 Feb). *10th Anniv of Federal Territory of Kuala Lumpur. T* **122** *and similar multicoloured designs. P* 13½ × 14 (80 c.) *or* 14 × 13½ (*others*).
278 20 c. Type **122** 12 15
279 40 c. Aerial view 25 30
280 80 c. Gardens and clock-tower (*horiz*) 50 55

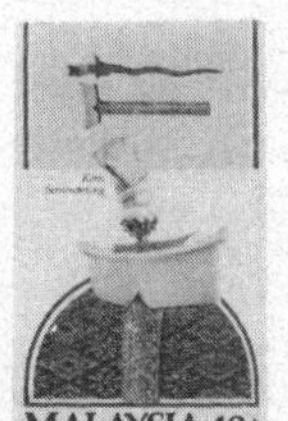

123 Map showing Industries **124** Semenanjung Keris

(Litho Security Printers (M), Malaysia)

1984 (16 Apr). *Formation of Labuan Federal Territory. T* **123** *and similar vert design. Multicoloured. P* 13½ × 14½.
281 20 c. Type **123** 15 20
282 $1 Flag and map of Labuan 70 75

(Des P. Khang Kowe Ket. Litho Harrison)

1984 (30 May). *Traditional Malay Weapons. T* **124** *and similar vert designs. Multicoloured. P* 13½ × 14.
283 40 c. Type **124** 30 35
a. Block of 4. Nos. 283/6 .. .. 1·10
284 40 c. Pekakak keris 30 35
285 40 c. Jawa keris 30 35
286 40 c. Lada tumbuk 30 35

Nos. 283/6 were printed in *se-tenant* blocks of four throughout the sheet.

125 Map of World and Transmitter **126** Facsimile Service

(Des Dept of Broadcasting. Litho Harrison)

1984 (23 June). *20th Anniv of Asia–Pacific Broadcasting Union. T* **125** *and similar horiz design. Multicoloured. P* 13½ × 14½.
287 20 c. Type **125** 15 20
288 $1 Clasped hands within "20" 70 75

(Des Mark Johan and Associates. Litho Security Printers (M), Malaysia)

1984 (29 Oct). *Opening of New General Post Office, Kuala Lumpur. T* **126** *and similar horiz designs. Multicoloured. P* 12.
289 15 c. Type **126** 10 12
290 20 c. New G.P.O. building 15 20
291 $1 Mailbag conveyor 70 75

127 Yang di Pertuan Agong **128** White Hibiscus

(Des P. Ket. Litho Security Printers (M), Malaysia)

1984 (15 Nov). *Installation of Yang di Pertuan Agong. T* **127** *and similar design. P* 12.
292 **127** 15 c. multicoloured 10 12
293 20 c. multicoloured 12 15
294 – 40 c. multicoloured 25 30
295 – 80 c. multicoloured 50 55

Design: *Horiz* — 40 c., 80 c. Yang di Pertuan Agong and Federal Crest.

(Litho Security Printers (M), Malaysia)

1984 (12 Dec). *Hibiscus. T* **128** *and similar vert designs. Multicoloured. P* 13½.
296 10 c. Type **128** 8 10
297 20 c. Red Hibiscus 12 15
298 40 c. Pink Hibiscus 25 30
299 $1 Orange Hibiscus 65 70

B. FEDERAL TERRITORY ISSUES

Kuala Lumpur, previously part of Selangor state, was established as a Federal Territory on 1 February 1974.

The following stamps were produced for use there, corresponding to the low value definitives provided for the states of the federation.

The island of Labuan, formerly part of Sabah, became the second Federal Territory on 16 April 1984, when Nos. K1/13 replaced the low value definitives of Sabah previously used there.

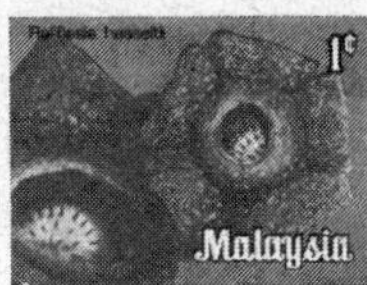

K 1 *Rafflesia hasseltii*

(Des M. Yusof bin Mohammed; adapted Malaysian Advertising Services. Litho Asher and Co., Melbourne)

1979 (30 Apr). *Flowers. Horiz designs as Type* **K 1**. *Multicoloured. W* **95** (*sideways*). *P* 15 × 14½.
K1 1 c. Type K 1 .. .. 5 5
K2 2 c. *Pterocarpus indicus* 5 5
K3 5 c. *Lagerstroemia speciosa* 5 5
K4 10 c. *Durio zibethinus* 8 5
K5 15 c. *Hibiscus rosa-sinensis* 10 5
K6 20 c. *Rhododendron scortechinii* 15 5
K7 25 c. *Phaeomeria speciosa* 15 5
K1/7 .. .. *Set of* 7 55 20

For higher values used in conjunction with this series see Nos. 190/7.

1984 (Mar–Sept). *As Nos.* K4/6 *but without wmk.*
K11 10 c. *Durio zibethinus* (9.84) 8 10
K12 15 c. *Hibiscus rosa-sinensis* 10 12
K13 20 c. *Rhododendron scortechinii* 15 20

For shade differences between 1979 and 1984 printings, see below Johore No. 200.

POSTAGE DUE STAMPS

Until 15 August 1966 the postage due stamps of MALAYAN POSTAL UNION were in use throughout MALAYSIA.

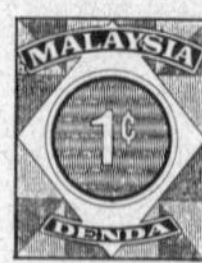

D 1

(Litho Harrison)

1966 (15 Aug)–**71.** *Ordinary paper.* W w **13** (*upright*). *P* 14½ × 14.

No.	Type	Description	Unused	Used
D1	D 1	1 c. rose	5	5
D2		2 c. indigo	20	30
D3		4 c. apple-green	5	5
D4		8 c. blue-green	35	65
		a. Bright blue-green, **C** (1.6.71)	35	70
D5		10 c. bright blue	35	65
		a. Chalky paper (1.6.71)	35	70
D6		12 c. reddish violet	8	5
D7		20 c. red-brown	40	1·00
		a. Brown-purple (shades), **C** (22.4.69)	65	1·40
D8		50 c. brownish bistre	1·25	2·75
		a. Olive-bistre, **C** (1.6.71)	1·50	3·00
D1/8		*Set of* 8	2·40	5·00

1972 (23 May). *Glazed paper.* W w **13** (*sideways*). *P* 14½ × 14.

No.	Type	Description	Unused	Used
D12	D 1	8 c. turquoise-green	40	70
D13		10 c. dull ultramarine	40	70
D15		20 c. pale chocolate	60	1·00
D16		50 c. pale olive-bistre	95	1·50

1980. *No wmk. P* 14½ × 14.

No.	Type	Description	Unused	Used
D17	D 1	2 c. indigo	5	5
D18		8 c. blue-green	5	5
D19		10 c. dull ultramarine	8	5
D20		20 c. pale chocolate	15	10
D21		50 c. pale olive-bistre	30	25

VII. MALAYSIAN STATES

PRINTERS. All Malaysian States stamps were printed in typography by De La Rue and Co, Ltd, London, *unless otherwise stated.*

JOHORE

One of the Unfederated States.

PRICES FOR STAMPS ON COVER TO 1945	
Nos. 1/2	—
No. 3	*from* × 6
No. 4	—
Nos. 5/6	*from* × 6
No. 7	—
Nos. 8/15	*from* × 10
No. 16	—
Nos. 17/20	*from* × 5
Nos. 21/31	*from* × 6
Nos. 32/8	*from* × 10
Nos. 39/53	*from* × 4
Nos. 54/60	*from* × 3
Nos. 61/74	*from* × 5
Nos. 75/7	—
Nos. 78/87	*from* × 8
No. 88	*from* × 10
Nos. 89/102	*from* × 6
Nos. 103/25	*from* × 5
Nos. 126/8	—
Nos. 129/30	*from* × 6
Nos. D1/5	*from* × 10

1876 (July). *T* **5** *of Straits optd with Crescent and Star. Wmk Crown CC.*

No.	Type	Description	Unused	Used
1		2 c. brown	£5000	£3000
		a. Opt double		

From Sept 1878 to Aug 1884 no overprinted stamps were supplied by Singapore to Johore.

1884–91. *T* **5** *of Straits Settlements optd. Wmk Crown CA. P* 14.

JOHORE (1) — JOHORE. (2) — JOHORE (3)

(i) *Believed optd locally* (1884–85)

No.	Type	Description	Unused	Used
2	1	2 c. rose (6.84)	£700	
3	2	2 c. rose (3.85)	45·00	50·00
		a. Short lower bar to "E"		
4	3	2 c. rose (1885)		

JOHORE (4) Variety (*a*) — JOHORE (5)

Type **4**: (*a*) "H" and "E" wide; (*b*) "H" wide, "E" narrow.

(ii) *Optd at Singapore*

(*a*) *Spelt* "JOHORE" (1884–86)

No.	Type	Description	Unused	Used
5	4	2 c. rose (*a*) (Opt 16 mm long) (8.84)	£250	£120
		a. Opt double	£750	
		b. Opt 16¾ mm long	£225	£120
		ba. Opt double	—	£500
6		2 c. rose (*b*) (Opt 16 mm long) (8.84)	£250	£120
		a. Opt double		
7	5	2 c. rose (4.86)	20·00	22·00

Nos. 5, 6, and 5b make up a triplet setting.

JOHOR (6) Variety (*c*) — JOHOR (7) — JOHOR (8)

JOHOR (9) — JOHOR (10) — JOHOR (11)

Type **6**: (*c*) All letters narrow; (*d*) "H" wide.

(*b*) *Spelt* "JOHOR" (1884–91)

No.	Type	Description	Unused	Used
8	6	2 c. rose (*c*) (8.84)	5·50	6·50
9	7	2 c. rose (10.84)	4·25	4·25
		a. Thin narrow "J"	30·00	35·00
10	8	2 c. rose (1.85)	15·00	15·00
11	6	2 c. rose (*d*) (2.85)	15·00	15·00
12	9	2 c. rose (4.86)	12·00	14·00
13	7	2 c. rose (with stop) (1888)	15·00	16·00
		a. Thin narrow "J"	90·00	£100
		b. Opt double	£400	
14		2 c. bright rose (1890)	12·00	12·00
		a. Thin narrow "J" (R.6/6)	60·00	60·00
15	10	2 c. bright rose (9.90)	3·75	4·25
		a. Large wide "J"		
16	11	2 c. deep rose (1891)	£4250	

There are several triplet settings of No. 8, the word varying from 12 to 15 mm. No. 11 (wide "H") occurs in the first unit of one setting with two units of No. 8.

Two CENTS (12) — *Two* CENTS (13)

Two CENTS (14) — Two CENTS (15)

1891 (May). *T* **7** *of Straits Settlements optd with name as T* **7** *and surch as T* **12** *to* **15**.

No.	Type	Description	Unused	Used
17	12	2 c. on 24 c. green	16·00	22·00
		a. "CENST" (R.5/4)	£275	£200
18	13	2 c. on 24 c. green	22·00	26·0
		a. Thin, narrow "J" (R.6/6)	60·00	75·0
19	14	2 c. on 24 c. green	11·00	15·0
20	15	2 c. on 24 c. green	16·00	20·0

Nos. 17/20 come from the same setting of 60. Type **12** occurs o horizontal rows 1 to 5, Type **13** on row 6, Type **14** on rows 7, 8 an 9 and Type **15** on row 10.

16 Sultan Aboubakar

3 cents. (17)

KEMAHKOTAA (18)

1891 (16 Nov)–**94.** *No wmk. P* 14.

No.	Type	Description	Unused	Used
21	16	1 c. dull purple and mauve (7.94)	45	6
22		2 c. dull purple and yellow	50	1·7
23		3 c. dull purple and carmine (7.94)	85	5
24		4 c. dull purple and black	4·50	1·7
25		5 c. dull purple and green	12·00	15·0
26		6 c. dull purple and blue	12·00	17·0
27		$1 green and carmine	24·00	42·0
21/7		*Set of* 7	48·00	70·0

1894 (March). *Surch with T* **17**.

No.	Type	Description	Unused	Used
28	16	3 c. on 4 c. dull purple and black	90	6
		a. No stop (R.5/12)	22·00	22·0
29		3 c. on 5 c. dull purple and green	1·25	2·0
		a. No stop (R.5/12)	22·00	24·0
30		3 c. on 6 c. dull purple and blue	1·25	2·0
		a. No stop (R.5/12)	22·00	24·0
31		3 c. on $1 green and carmine	9·50	15·0
		a. No stop (R.5/12)	48·00	55·0

1896 (March). *Coronation of Sultan. Optd with T* **18**.

No.	Type	Description	Unused	Used
32	16	1 c. dull purple and mauve	60	1·2
		a. "KETAHKOTAAN"	3·50	6·0
33		2 c. dull purple and yellow	45	1·2
		a. "KETAHKOTAAN"	3·75	5·0
34		3 c. dull purple and carmine	85	1·7
		a. "KETAHKOTAAN"	3·75	8·5
35		4 c. dull purple and black	1·25	2·7
		a. "KETAHKOTAAN"	2·75	5·5
36		5 c. dull purple and green	6·00	7·5
		a. "KETAHKOTAAN"	5·50	8·0
37		6 c. dull purple and blue	2·50	5·0
		a. "KETAHKOTAAN"	3·50	6·5
38		$1 green and carmine	32·00	40·0
		a. "KETAHKOTAAN"	35·00	55·0
32/8		*Set of* 7	38·00	55·0

19 Sultan Ibrahim **20**

21

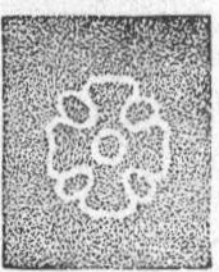

22

1896 (26 Aug)–**1899.** *W* **22.** *P* 14.

No.	Type	Description	Unused	Used
39	19	1 c. green	85	4
40		2 c. green and blue	40	2
41		3 c. green and purple	1·00	4
42		4 c. green and carmine	50	3
43		4 c. yellow and red (1899)	75	6
44		5 c. green and brown	90	1·5
45		6 c. green and yellow	1·00	1·9
46	20	10 c. green and black (1898)	8·50	16·0
47		25 c. green and mauve (1898)	9·00	17·0
48		50 c. green and carmine (1898)	12·00	22·0
49	19	$1 dull purple and green (1898)	17·00	26·0
50	21	$2 dull purple and carmine (1898)	18·00	30·0
51		$3 dull purple and blue (1898)	26·00	40·0
52		$4 dull purple and brown (1898)	28·00	48·0
53		$5 dull purple and yellow (1898)	60·00	85·0
39/53		*Set of* 15	£170	£25

3 cents. (23) — 10 cents. (24)

1903 (April). *Surch with T* **23** *or* **24**.

No.	Type	Description	Unused	Used
54	19	3 c. on 4 c. yellow and red	65	1·1
		a. Original value uncancelled	2·75	5·0
55		10 c. on 4 c. green and carmine	2·50	4·5
		a. Tall "1" in "10"	40·00	50·0
		b. Original value uncancelled	24·00	35·0
		ba. As b. with tall "1" in "10"	£425	£55

The bars on these stamps were ruled by hand with pen and ink.

50 Cents. (25) — One Dollar (26)

1903 (Oct). *Surch with T* **25** *or* **26**.

No.	Type	Description	Unused	Used
56	21	50 c. on $3 dull purple and blue	18·00	30·0
57		$1 on $2 dull purple and carmine	48·00	60·0
		a. "e" of "One" inverted	£900	

10 CENTS.

(27)

)04. *Surch as T* **27**.
3 **19** 10 c. on 4 c. yellow and red (Apr) .. 32·00 40·00
a. Surcharge double £4500
) 10 c. on 4 c. green and carmine (Aug) .. 11·00 15·00
) **21** 50 c. on $5 dull purple and yellow (May) 45·00 48·00

28 **29** **30** Sultan Sir Ibrahim

)04 (Sept). *W* **22.** *P* 14.
1 **28** 1 c. dull purple and green, **OC** 25 30
2 2 c. dull purple and orange, **OC** .. 75 1·00
3 3 c. dull purple and olive-black, **O** .. 60 55
4 4 c. dull purple and carmine, **O** .. 3·25 1·25
5 5 c. dull purple and sage-green, **O** .. 80 2·75
5 **30** 8 c. dull purple and blue, **O** .. .. 2·50 3·25
7 **29** 10 c. dull purple and black, **OC** .. .. 5·50 6·50
3 25 c. dull purple and green, **O** .. .. 3·50 6·50
9 50 c. dull purple and red, **O** .. .. 8·00 9·00
) **28** $1 green and mauve, **O** .. .. 15·00 20·00
1 **30** $2 green and carmine, **O** .. .. 22·00 30·00
2 $3 green and blue, **O** .. .. .. 24·00 35·00
3 $4 green and brown, **O** .. .. 27·00 40·00
4 $5 green and orange, **O** .. .. 40·00 45·00
5 **29** $10 green and black, **O** .. .. .. 55·00 75·00
6 $50 green and ultramarine, **O** £170 £180
7 $100 green and scarlet, **O** £325 £375
1/75 .. .. *Set of* 15 £190 £250

)10 (Dec)–**19.** *Wmk Mult Rosettes* (*vertical*). *P* 14.
3 **28** 1 c. dull purple and green, **C** (1912) .. 15 15
9 2 c. dull purple and orange, **C** (1912) 80 65
) 3 c. dull purple and olive-black, **C** (1912) 2·50 80
a. Wmk horizontal (1910) .. .. 3·50 1·75
1 4 c. dull purple and carmine, **C** (1912) .. 1·50 55
a. Wmk horizontal (1910) .. .. 4·00 2·50
2 5 c. dull purple and sage-green, **C** (1912) 1·25 45
3 **30** 8 c. dull purple and blue, **C** (1912) .. 3·25 4·00
4 **29** 10 c. dull purple and black, **C** (1912) .. 5·00 2·50
a. Wmk horizontal (1911) .. .. 13·00 9·50
5 25 c. dull purple and green, **C** (1912) .. 3·25 7·00
6 50 c. dull purple and red, **C** (1919) .. 24·00 30·00
7 **28** $1 green and mauve, **C** (1918). . .. 40·00 48·00
3/87 .. .. *Set of* 10 70·00 85·00

3 CENTS.

(31)

32 Sultan Sir Ibrahim and Sultana

)12 (March). *No.* 66 *surch with T* **31**.
8 3 c. on 8 c. dull purple and blue, **O** .. .. 1·75 2·00
a. "T" of "CENTS" omitted £375

)18–21. *Chalk-surfaced paper. Wmk Mult Crown CA. P* 14.
89 **28** 2 c. dull purple and green (1919) .. 40 80
90 2 c. purple and orange (1921) 40 80
91 4 c. dull purple and red 55 20
92 5 c. dull purple and sage-green (1920) .. 1·40 2·00
93 **29** 10 c. dull purple and blue .. .. 1·50 1·75
94 21 c. dull purple and orange (1919) .. 3·00 4·50
95 25 c. dull purple and green (1920) .. 6·50 10·00
96 50 c. dull purple and red (1920) .. .. 6·00 10·00
97 **28** $1 green and mauve .. .. .. 11·00 16·00
98 **30** $2 green and carmine .. .. .. 18·00 27·00
99 $3 green and blue .. .. .. 28·00 40·00
00 $4 green and brown .. .. .. 28·00 40·00
01 $5 green and orange .. .. .. 38·00 48·00
02 **29** $10 green and black .. .. .. 75·00 90·00
9/102 .. .. *Set of* 14 £200 £250
9/102 Optd "Specimen" .. .. *Set of* 14 £350

)22–40. *Chalk-surfaced paper. Wmk Mult Script CA. P* 14.
03 **28** 1 c. dull purple and black 30 20
04 2 c. purple and sepia (1924) .. .. 1·00 1·60
05 2 c. green (1928) 30 40
06 3 c. green (1925) .. .. .. 1·75 2·75
07 3 c. purple and sepia (1928) .. .. 85 1·50
08 4 c. purple and carmine (1924) .. .. 1·75 20
09 5 c. dull purple and sage-green 30 30
10 6 c. dull purple and claret 45 40
11 **29** 10 c. dull purple and blue .. .. 7·50 10·00
12 10 c. dull purple and yellow (1922) .. 30 35
13 **28** 12 c. dull purple and blue .. .. 2·00 1·50
14 12 c. ultramarine (1940) .. .. .. 16·00 13·00
15 **29** 21 c. dull purple and orange (1928) .. 4·00 3·50
16 25 c. dull purple and myrtle .. .. 1·40 1·40
17 **30** 30 c. dull purple and orange (1936) .. 2·00 2·75
18 40 c. dull purple and brown (1936) .. 2·75 4·25
19 **29** 50 c. dull purple and red .. .. .. 2·00 1·75
20 **28** $1 green and mauve .. .. .. 3·00 1·75
21 **30** $2 green and carmine (1923) .. .. 8·00 4·50
22 $3 green and blue (1925) .. .. 22·00 30·00
23 $4 green and brown (1926) .. .. 27·00 35·00
24 $5 green and orange .. .. .. 27·00 35·00
25 **29** $10 green and black (1924) .. .. 90·00 £110
26 $50 green and ultram (Optd S. £150) .. £400
27 $100 green and scarlet (Optd S. £275) .. £1000
28 **30** $500 blue and red (1926) (Optd S. £750) £13000
03/25 .. .. *Set of* 23 £200 £225
03/25 Optd/Perf "Specimen" .. *Set of* 23 £475

(Recess Waterlow)

1935 (15 May). *Wmk Mult Script CA* (*sideways*). *P* 12½.
129 **32** 8 c. bright violet and slate 85 80
129 Perf "Specimen" .. .. 50·00

33 Sultan Sir Ibrahim **34**

(Recess D.L.R.)

1940 (Feb). *Wmk Mult Script CA. P* 13½.
130 **33** 8 c. black and pale blue .. .. .. 1·75 30
130 Perf "Specimen" .. .. 48·00

1948 (1 Dec). *Royal Silver Wedding. As Nos.* 30/1 *of Aden.*
131 10 c. violet 15 15
132 $5 green .. .. 25·00 30·00

1949 (2 May)–**55.** *Wmk Mult Script CA. Chalk-surfaced paper. P* 17½ × 18.
133 **34** 1 c. black 5 10
134 2 c. orange 8 10
a. Orange-yellow (22.1.52) 8 20
135 3 c. green (*shades*) 45 30
136 4 c. brown 12 5
136*a* 5 c. bright purple (1.9.52) 25 20
137 6 c. grey 20 5
a. Pale grey (22.1.52) 25 20
ac. Error. St. Edward's Crown W **9***b* .. £275
138 8 c. scarlet .. .. 45 1·25
138*a* 8 c. green (1.9.52) .. .. .. 75 1·50
139 10 c. magenta 20 5
aa. Imperf (pair) £650
139*a* 12 c. scarlet (1.9.52) .. .. .. 1·25 1·75
140 15 c. ultramarine 50 10
141 20 c. black and green .. .. .. 70 1·00
141*a* 20 c. bright blue (1.9.52) 80 5
142 25 c. purple and orange 35 5
142*a* 30 c. scarlet and purple (5.9.55) .. .. 2·75 1·50
142*b* 35 c. scarlet and purple (1.9.52) .. .. 1·25 1·75
143 40 c. red and purple .. .. .. 1·75 3·50
144 50 c. black and blue 60 5
145 $1 blue and purple .. .. .. 2·00 75
146 $2 green and scarlet .. .. .. 8·50 3·50
147 $5 green and brown .. .. .. 22·00 8·50
133/47 .. .. *Set of* 21 42·00 23·00

1949 (10 Oct). *75th Anniv of U.P.U. As Nos.* 114/17 *of Antigua.*
148 10 c. purple 25 15
149 15 c. deep blue .. .. 65 1·25
150 25 c. orange .. .. 75 1·50
151 50 c. blue-black .. .. 1·50 1·75

1953 (2 June). *Coronation. As No.* 47 *of Aden.*
152 10 c. black and reddish purple 25 5

35 Sultan Sir Ibrahim **36** Sultan Sir Ismail and Johore Coat of Arms

(Recess D.L.R.)

1955 (1 Nov). *Diamond Jubilee of Sultan. Wmk Mult Script CA. P* 14.
153 **35** 10 c. carmine-red 15 8

(Photo Courvoisier)

1960 (10 Feb). *Coronation of Sultan. No wmk. P* 11½.
154 **36** 10 c. multicoloured 10 8

1960. *As T* **10/19** *of Kedah, but with portrait of Sultan Ismail. P* 13½ ($1); *others* 12½ × 13 (*vert*) *or* 13 × 12½ (*horiz*).
155 1 c. black (7.10.60) 10 20
156 2 c. orange-red (7.10.60) 10 12
157 4 c. sepia (19.8.60) 10 5
158 5 c. carmine-lake (7.10.60) 10 5
159 8 c. myrtle-green (9.12.60) .. .. .. 1·25 45
160 10 c. deep maroon (10.6.60) 15 5
161 20 c. blue (9.12.60) 20 5
162 50 c. black and bright blue (19.8.60) 30 5
163 $1 ultramarine and reddish purple (9.12.60) 1·25 90
164 $2 bronze-green and scarlet (9.12.60) .. 3·50 4·00
165 $5 brown and bronze-green (7.10.60) .. 12·00 12·00
155/65 .. .. *Set of* 11 17·00 16·00

In No. 161 there are only two figures in the boat, the steersman being missing. In the 20 c. value for all the other States there are three figures.

The 6, 12, 25 and 30 c. values used with this issue were Nos. 1/4 of Malayan Federation.

37 *Vanda hookeriana* (Inset portrait of Sultan Ismail)

(Des A. Fraser-Brunner. Photo Harrison)

1965 (15 Nov). *T* **37** *and similar horiz designs. W* w **13** (*upright*). *P* 14½.
166 1 c. Type **37** 8 25
a. Black omitted (orchid's name and part of flower) .. .. 45·00
167 2 c. *Arundina graminifolia* 8 20
168 5 c. *Paphiopedilum niveum* 10 5
169 6 c. *Spathoglottis plicata* 12 5
170 10 c. *Arachnis flos-aeris* 20 5
171 15 c. *Rhyncostylis retusa* 55 8
a. Green (face value and leaves) omitted ..
172 20 c. *Phalaenopsis violacea* 80 25
a. Bright purple (blooms) omitted .. .. 30·00
166/72 .. .. *Set of* 7 1·75 80

The 2 c. to 15 c. exist with both PVA gum and gum arabic.

The 2 c. with black (name of state, arms and head) omitted is listed under Sarawak No. 213a as there is some evidence that a sheet was issued there; if it also exists from any of the other states it would, of course, be identical.

The higher values used with this issue were Nos. 20/27 of Malaysia.

1970. *As No.* 166 *and* 170 *but W* w **13** (*sideways*).
173 1 c. multicoloured (20.11) 15 45
174 10 c. multicoloured (27.5) 40 70

44 Malayan Jezebel (Inset portrait of Sultan Ismail) **45** *Rafflesia hasseltii* (Inset portrait of Sultan Ismail)

(Des V. Whiteley)

1971 (1 Feb)–**78.** *Butterflies. T* **44** *and similar horiz designs. Multicoloured. No wmk. P* 13½ × 13.

(*a*) *Litho by Bradbury, Wilkinson*
175 1 c. Type **44** 5 10
176 2 c. Black-veined Tiger 5 10
177 5 c. Clipper Butterfly 15 5
178 6 c. Lime Butterfly 15 10
179 10 c. Great Orange Tip 15 5
180 15 c. Blue Pansy Butterfly 30 5
181 20 c. Wanderer 35 10
175/81 .. .. *Set of* 7 1·10 50

(*b*) *Photo by Harrison* (1977–78)
182 1 c. Type **44** 25 25
183 2 c. Black-veined Tiger 15 15
184 5 c. Clipper Butterfly 20 12
185 10 c. Great Orange Tip 25 10
186 15 c. Blue Pansy 50 25
187 20 c. Wanderer 70 40
182/7 .. .. *Set of* 6 1·90 1·10

The higher values used with this issue were Nos. 64/71 of Malaysia.

DIFFERENCES BETWEEN LITHO AND PHOTO PRINTINGS. Stamps from the photogravure printings can be easily identified by the appearance of certain features. The differences are most easily observed on the face values and inscriptions. Stamps printed by lithography show straight edges to letters and figures, but when those produced by photogravure are examined under a magnifying glass it will be seen that these edges are broken by the photogravure screen.

In addition the backgrounds and portraits of those stamps of this series printed by lithography show a regular screen of dots, a feature not visible on those printed by the photogravure process.

(Des M. Yusof bin Mohammed; adapted Malaysian Advertising Services. Litho Asher and Co., Melbourne)

1979 (30 Apr). *Flowers. Horiz designs as T* **45.** *Multicoloured. W* **95** *of Malaysia* (*sideways*). *P* 15 × 14½.
188 1 c. Type **45** 5 5
189 2 c. *Pterocarpus indicus* 5 5
190 5 c. *Lagerstroemia speciosa* 5 5
191 10 c. *Durio zibethinus* 8 5
192 15 c. *Hibiscus rosa-sinensis* 10 5
193 20 c. *Rhododendron scortechinii* 15 5
194 25 c. *Phaeomeria speciosa* 15 5
188/94 .. .. *Set of* 7 55 25

For higher values used in conjunction with this series see Nos. 190/7 of Malaysia.

1984 (Mar–Sept). *As Nos.* 190/3 *but without wmk.*
197 5 c. *Lagerstroemia speciosa* 5 5
198 10 c. *Durio zibethinus* (9.84) 8 10
199 15 c. *Hibiscus rosa-sinensis* 10 12
200 20 c. *Rhododendron scortechinii* 15 20

On the 5 c. No. 197 the name colour is turquoise-blue instead of the dull blue of No. 190. The 20 c. No. 200 has a bronze-green background instead of blackish brown. The "Johor" inscriptions are also redrawn.

POSTAGE DUE STAMPS

D 1

(Typo Waterlow)

1938 (1 Jan). *Wmk Mult Script CA. P* 12½.

D1	D 1	1 c. carmine	3·50	8·00
D2		4 c. green	8·00	18·00
D3		8 c. orange	13·00	27·00
D4		10 c. brown	13·00	22·00
D5		12 c. purple	18·00	38·00
D1/5 Perf "Specimen"		*Set of* 5	£100	

KEDAH

One of the Unfederated States.

Stamps of THAILAND were used in Kedah at Hlor Star (from 1883), Kuala Muda (from 1907), Kulin (from 1907) and Langkaui (from 1908) until the state was transferred to the protection of Great Britain in 1909. Issues of the FEDERATED MALAY STATES were used in Kedah from 1909 until 1912.

PRICES FOR STAMPS ON COVER TO 1945	
Nos. 1/14	*from* × 7
Nos. 15/23	*from* × 5
Nos. 24/40	*from* × 3
Nos. 41/8	*from* × 10
Nos. 49/51	—
Nos. 52/9	*from* × 4
Nos. 60/8	*from* × 3
Nos. 68*a*/9*a*	*from* × 4

1 Sheaf of Rice　　2 Malay ploughing

3 Council Chamber

1912 (July). *Wmk Mult Crown CA (sideways on* 10 *c. to* $5). *P* 14.

1	1	1 c. black and green	25	35
2		3 c. black and red	1·50	65
3		4 c. rose and grey	5·50	35
4		5 c. green and chestnut	2·00	3·00
5		8 c. black and ultramarine	85	2·50
6	2	10 c. blue and sepia	1·75	1·25
7		20 c. black and green	2·75	5·00
8		30 c. black and rose	2·75	7·00
9		40 c. black and purple	5·00	10·50
10		50 c. brown and blue	7·00	11·00
11	3	$1 black and red/*yellow*	13·00	20·00
12		$2 green and brown	13·00	24·00
13		$3 black and blue/*blue*	38·00	60·00
14		$5 black and red	48·00	75·00
1/14		*Set of* 14	£130	£200
1/14 Optd "Specimen"		*Set of* 14	£325	

(i)

(ii)

DOUBLE AND SINGLE PLATES. (i) Printed from separate plates for frame and centre, with dotted shading extending close to the central sheaf. Soft impression of centre with little clear detail.

(ii) Printed from single plate, with white space around sheaf. Centre more deeply etched with sharp image.

1919–21. *New colours and values. Wmk Mult Crown CA (sideways on* 21 *c.,* 25 *c.). P* 14.

15	1	1 c. brown (i)	45	60
18		2 c. green (ii)	40	40
19		3 c. deep purple (i)	65	1·25
20		4 c. rose (i)	1·25	25
21		4 c. red (ii)	65	30
22	2	21 c. purple	6·50	16·00
23		25 c. blue and purple (1921)	2·50	9·00
15/23 Optd "Specimen"		*Set of* 6	£150	

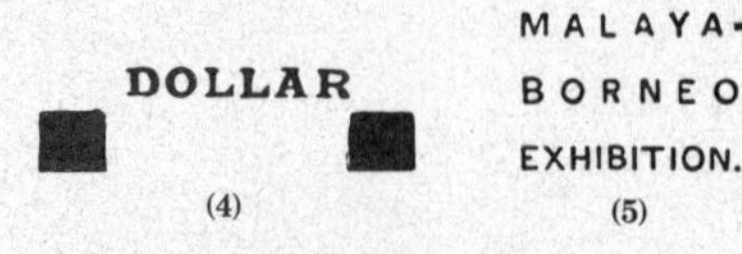

(4)　　(5)

(Surch by Ribeiro & Co, Penang)

1919. *Surch as T* 4.

24	3	50 c. on $2 green and brown	38·00	48·00
		a. "C" of "CENTS" inserted by hand	£900	£725
25		$1 on $3 black and blue/*blue*	26·00	40·00

In 1919 1 c., 3 c. and 4 c. (both purple and scarlet) stamps of Straits Settlements were authorized for use in Kedah during temporary shortage of Kedah stamps. Stamps so used can be identified by the postmark.

1921–24. *Wmk Mult Script CA (sideways on* 10 *c. to* $5). *P* 14.

26	1	1 c. brown (ii)	40	2
27		2 c. dull green (ii) (Die I)*	25	4
28		3 c. deep purple (ii)	1·10	1·5
29		4 c. deep carmine (ii)	3·50	2
30	2	10 c. blue and sepia	1·00	1·2
31		20 c. black and yellow-green	1·75	3·2
32		21 c. mauve and purple	3·25	10·0
33		25 c. blue and purple	2·50	3·5
34		30 c. black and rose	3·25	3·0
35		40 c. black and purple	3·75	10·0
36		50 c. brown and grey-blue	1·75	3·0
37	3	$1 black and red/*yellow*	8·00	8·0
38		$2 myrtle and brown	17·00	38·0
39		$3 black and blue/*blue*	28·00	45·0
40		$5 black and deep carmine	48·00	75·0
26/40		*Set of* 15	£110	£18
26/40 Optd "Specimen"		*Set of* 15	£300	

*For 2 c., Die II, see No. 69.

1922 (31 Mar). *Optd as T* **5** *at Singapore.*

I. "BORNEO" 14 *mm. long.*

(*a*) *Wmk Mult Crown CA*

41	1	2 c. green (ii)	3·50	13·0
42	2	21 c. mauve and purple	14·00	55·0
43		25 c. blue and purple	18·00	55·0
		a. Overprint inverted	£850	
44		50 c. brown and grey-blue	17·00	75·0

(*b*) *Wmk Mult Script CA*

45	1	1 c. brown (ii)	2·25	10·0
46		3 c. purple (ii)	2·75	14·0
47		4 c. deep carmine (ii)	3·25	20·0
48	2	10 c. blue and sepia	6·00	28·0
41/8		*Set of* 8	60·00	£25

There are setting variations in the size and shape of the letters, stop raised, stop omitted, etc., etc.

II. "BORNEO" 15–15½ *mm long. Wmk Mult Crown CA*

49	2	21 c. mauve and purple	16·00	55·0
50		25 c. blue and purple	25·00	65·0
51		50 c. brown and grey-blue	42·00	80·0

1922–36. *New colours, etc. Wmk Mult Script CA (sideways on* 12, 35 *c.). P* 14.

52	1	1 c. black (ii) (Die I)*	15	1
53		3 c. green (ii)	1·50	8
54		4 c. violet (ii) (1926)	1·40	2
55		5 c. yellow (ii)	1·00	1
56		6 c. carmine (ii) (Die I) (1926)*	70	8
57		8 c. grey-black (10.36)	7·00	1
58	2	12 c. black and indigo (1926)	3·25	8·0
59		35 c. purple (1926)	8·50	20·0
52/9		*Set of* 8	21·00	28·0
52/9 Optd/Perf "Specimen"		*Set of* 8	£130	

*For 1 c. and 6 c. Die II, see Nos. 68*a* and 69*a*.

6 Sultan Abdul Hamid Halimshah

(Recess Waterlow)

1937 (30 June). *Wmk Mult Script CA. P* 12½.

60	6	10 c. ultramarine and sepia	1·00	1
61		12 c. black and violet	8·00	14·0
62		25 c. ultramarine and purple	3·00	5·5
63		30 c. green and scarlet	6·00	7·5
64		40 c. black and purple	80	8·5
65		50 c. brown and blue	2·50	4·5
66		$1 black and green	2·50	7·0
67		$2 green and brown	60·00	65·0
68		$5 black and scarlet	22·00	45·0
60/8		*Set of* 9	95·00	£14
60/8 Perf "Specimen"		*Set of* 9	£170	

I　　II　　I　　II

1938–40. *As Nos.* 52, 27 *and* 56, *but redrawn as Dies* II.

68*a*	1	1 c. black	25·00	5·5
69		2 c. bright green (1940)	65·00	12·0
69*a*		6 c. carmine-red (1940)	40·00	32·0

1 c. Die II. Figures "1" have square-cut corners instead of rounded, and larger top serif. Larger "C". Line perf.

2 c. Die II. Figures "2" have circular instead of oval drops and the letters "c" are thin and tall instead of thick and rounded. Size of design: 19½ × 23 mm instead of about 18½ × 22½ mm. Line perf.

6 c. Die II. Design measures 19¼ × 22¼ mm instead of 18¾ × 22½ mm (No. 56). Note also shade of Die II. Line perf.

1948 (1 Dec). *Royal Silver Wedding. As Nos.* 30/1 *of Aden.*

70	10 c. violet	25	3
71	$5 carmine	25·00	35·0

1949 (10 Oct). *75th Anniv of U.P.U. As Nos.* 114/17 *of Antigua.*

72	10 c. purple	25	3
73	15 c. deep blue	55	1·5
74	25 c. orange	80	1·5
75	50 c. blue-black	1·60	2·7

7 Sheaf of Rice

8 Sultan Tunku Badlishah

950 (1 June)–**55.** *Wmk Mult Script CA. Chalk-surfaced paper. P* 17½ × 18.

'6	**7**	1 c. black	5	30
'7		2 c. orange	8	30
'8		3 c. green	20	85
'9		4 c. brown	10	10
'9*a*		5 c. bright purple (*shades*) (1.9.52)	25	30
0		6 c. grey	10	15
1		8 c. scarlet	35	1·50
1*a*		8 c. green (*shades*) (1.9.52)	75	1·75
2		10 c. magenta	15	5
2*a*		12 c. scarlet (1.9.52)	85	2·25
3		15 c. ultramarine	40	45
4		20 c. black and green	50	2·50
4*a*		20 c. bright blue (1.9.52)	85	10
5	**8**	25 c. purple and orange	35	25
5*a*		30 c. scarlet and purple (5.9.55)	2·75	1·75
5*b*		35 c. scarlet and purple (1.9.52)	85	2·00
6		40 c. red and purple	1·25	5·50
7		50 c. black and blue	60	15
8		$1 blue and purple	2·25	1·50
9		$2 green and scarlet	16·00	20·00
0		$5 green and brown	22·00	25·00
'6/90		*Set of* 21	45·00	60·00

953 (2 June). *Coronation. As No.* 47 *of Aden.*

1 10 c. black and reddish purple . . 25 5

9 Copra

10 Pineapples

11 Ricefield

12 Masjid Alwi Mosque, Kangar

13 East Coast Railway

14 Tiger

15 Fishing Craft

16 Aborigines with Blowpipes

17 Government Offices

18 Bersilat

19 Weaving

(Recess D.L.R.)

957. *Inset portrait of Sultan Tunku Badlishah. W* w **12.** *P* 13 × 12½ (1 *c. to* 8 *c.*), 12½ × 13 (10*c.*, 20 *c.*), 12½ (50 *c.*, $2, $5) *or* 13½ ($1).

92	**9**	1 c. black (21.8)	5	35
93	**10**	2 c. orange-red (25.7)	5	40
94	**11**	4 c. sepia (21.8)	5	8
95	**12**	5 c. carmine-lake (21.8)	5	12
96	**13**	8 c. myrtle-green (21.8)	2·50	2·75
97	**14**	10 c. deep brown (4.8)	15	5
98	**15**	20 c. blue (26.6)	30	45
99	**16**	50 c. black and blue (25.7)	50	85
100	**17**	$1 ultramarine & reddish purple (25.7)	3·75	5·50
101	**18**	$2 bronze-green and scarlet (21.8)	8·00	14·00
102	**19**	$5 brown and bronze-green (26.6)	14·00	20·00
92/102		*Set of* 11	26·00	40·00

The 6, 12, 25 and 30 c. values used with this issue were Nos. 1/4 of Malayan Federation.

20 Sultan Abdul Halim Mu'Adzam Shah

21 Sultan Abdul Halim Mu'Adzam Shah

(Photo Harrison)

1959 (20 Feb). *Installation of the Sultan. W* w **12.** *P* 14 × 14½.

103 **20** 10 c. multicoloured . . 10 8

1959 (1 July)–**62.** *As Nos.* 92/102 *but with inset portrait of Sultan Abdul as in T* **21.**

104	**21**	1 c. black	5	20
105	**10**	2 c. orange-red	5	30
106	**11**	4 c. sepia	5	5
107	**12**	5 c. carmine-lake	5	5
108	**13**	8 c. myrtle-green	95	1·25
109	**14**	10 c. deep brown	15	5
109*a*		10 c. deep maroon (19.12.61)	25	5
110	**15**	20 c. blue	25	10
111	**16**	50 c. black and blue (*p* 12½)	30	35
		a. Perf 12½ × 13 (14.6.60)	30	10
112	**17**	$1 ultramarine and reddish purple	1·25	2·25
113	**18**	$2 bronze-green and scarlet	4·50	8·00
114	**19**	$5 brown and bronze-green (*p* 12½)	11·00	15·00
		a. Perf 13 × 12½ (26.11.62)	9·50	12·00
104/14		*Set of* 12	15·00	22·00

22 *Vanda hookeriana*

23 Black-veined Tiger

1965 (15 Nov). *As Nos.* 166/72 *of Johore but with inset portrait of Sultan Abdul as in T* **22.** *W* w **13** (*upright*).

115	1 c. multicoloured	8	25
	a. Black omitted (orchid's name and part of flower)	40·00	
116	2 c. multicoloured	8	20
117	5 c. multicoloured	10	5
	a. Black (country name and head) omitted	55·00	
118	6 c. multicoloured	12	5
119	10 c. multicoloured	20	5
120	15 c. multicoloured	55	15
121	20 c. multicoloured	80	40
115/21	*Set of* 7	1·75	1·00

The 1 c. to 15 c. exist with PVA gum as well as gum arabic.

The 6 c. value exists with black (country name, arms and head) omitted and is listed under Sarawak where it was issued.

The higher values used with this issue were Nos. 20/27 of Malaysia.

1970 (27 May). *As Nos.* 115 *and* 119 *but W* w **13** (*sideways*).

122	**22**	1 c. multicoloured	20	50
123	–	10 c. multicoloured	65	1·00

1971 (1 Feb)–**78.** *As Nos.* 175/87 *of Johore but with portrait of Sultan Abdul as in T* **23.** (*a*) *Litho by Bradbury, Wilkinson.*

124	1 c. multicoloured	5	15
125	2 c. multicoloured	5	15
126	5 c. multicoloured	15	5
127	6 c. multicoloured	15	10
128	10 c. multicoloured	15	5
129	15 c. multicoloured	30	8
130	20 c. multicoloured	35	15
124/30	*Set of* 7	1·10	55

(*b*) *Photo by Harrison* (1977–78)

130*a*	2 c. multicoloured		
131	5 c. multicoloured	20	12
132	10 c. multicoloured	25	10
133	15 c. multicoloured	50	30
134	20 c. multicoloured	70	55

The higher values used with this issue were Nos. 64/71 of Malaysia.

For differences between litho and photo printings, see after Johore No. 187.

24 *Pterocarpus indicus*

25 Sultan Abdul Halim Mu'Adzam Shah

1979 (30 Apr). *As Nos.* 188/94 *of Johore but with portrait of Sultan Abdul as in T* **24.**

135	1 c. *Rafflesia hasseltii*	5	5
136	2 c. Type **24**	5	5
137	5 c. *Lagerstroemia speciosa*	5	5
138	10 c. *Durio zibethinus*	8	5
139	15 c. *Hibiscus rosa-sinensis*	10	5
140	20 c. *Rhododendron scortechinii*	15	5
141	25 c. *Phaeomeria speciosa*	15	5
135/41	*Set of* 7	55	25

For higher values used in conjunction with this series see Nos. 190/7 of Malaysia.

(Des and litho Security Printers (M), Malaysia)

1983 (15 July). *Silver Jubilee of Sultan's Installation. T* **25** *and similar multicoloured designs. P* 13 × 13½ (20 *c.*) *or* 13½ × 13 (*others*).

142	20 c. Type **25**	12	20
143	40 c. Paddy fields (*horiz*)	20	25
144	60 c. Paddy fields and Mount Jerai (*horiz*)	35	40

1984 (Mar). *As No.* 140 *but without wmk.*

150 20 c. *Rhododendron scortechinii* . . 15 20

For shade difference between 1979 and 1984 printings, see below Johore No. 200.

KELANTAN

One of the Unfederated States.

Until 1909 the stamps of THAILAND were used by the post offices at Kota Bharu and Batu Menkebang. From 1909 until the introduction of Kelantan stamps in 1911 the issues of the FEDERATED MALAY STATES were in use.

PRICES FOR STAMPS ON COVER TO 1945

Nos. 1/11	*from* × 4
No. 12	—
Nos. 13/23	*from* × 7
Nos. 30/8	*from* × 10
Nos. 39/*a*	*from* × 4
Nos. 40/54	*from* × 8

1

MALAYA
BORNEO
EXHIBITION
(2)

1911 (Jan). *Wmk Mult Crown CA. P* 14.
1 1 1 c. yellow-green, **O** 75 50
a. Blue-green, **O** 40 40
2 3 c. red, **O** 55 15
3 4 c. black and red, **O** 70 15
4 5 c. green and red/*yellow,* **O** .. .. .. 1·00 20
5 8 c. ultramarine, **O** .. .. 2·75 1·50
6 10 c. black and mauve, **O** .. .. .. 4·75 25
7 30 c. dull purple and red, **O** .. .. .. 6·50 2·50
a. Purple and carmine, **C** .. .. .. 14·00 8·50
8 50 c. black and orange, **C** .. .. .. 4·75 3·50
9 $1 green and emerald, **C** .. .. .. 28·00 38·00
10 $2 green and carmine, **C** .. .. .. 1·75 7·50
11 $5 green and blue, **C** .. .. .. 12·00 16·00
12 $25 green and orange, **C** .. .. .. 48·00 70·00
1/12 .. .. *Set of* 12 £100 £130
1/12 Optd "Specimen" .. .. *Set of* 12 £275

1915. *Colours changed. Wmk Mult Crown CA. P* 14.
13 1 $1 green and brown, **C** (Optd S. £45) 23·00 4·50

1921–28. *Wmk Mult Script CA. P* 14.
14 1 1 c. dull green, **C** .. .. .. 2·25 80
15 1 c. black, **O** (1923) 50 60
16 2 c. brown, **O** (1922) .. .. .. 2·75 3·50
16*a* 2 c. green, **O** (1926) 70 60
16*b* 3 c. brown, **O** (1927) .. .. .. 1·40 2·25
17 4 c. black and red, **O** (1922) 25 30
18 5 c. green and red/*pale yellow,* **O** (1922) 50 10
19 6 c. claret, **O** (1922) .. .. .. 2·50 3·50
19*a* 6 c. scarlet, **O** (1928) .. .. .. 4·00 5·50
20 10 c. black and mauve, **O** .. .. .. 1·75 20
21 30 c. purple and carmine, **C** (1926) .. 3·00 5·50
22 50 c. black and orange, **C** (1925) .. 4·25 10·00
23 $1 green and brown, **C** (1924) .. .. 19·00 30·00
14/23 .. .. *Set of* 13 38·00 55·00
14/23 Optd "Specimen" .. .. *Set of* 13 £275

For the 4 c., 5 c. and 6 c. surcharged, see issues under "Japanese Occupation".

1922 (31 Mar). *Optd with T* **2** *by Govt Survey Office, Khota Bharu.*

(*a*) *Wmk Mult Crown CA*
30 1 4 c. black and red .. .. .. 2·75 12·00
31 5 c. green and red/*pale yellow* .. .. 3·50 13·00
32 30 c. dull purple and red .. .. .. 4·00 23·00
33 50 c. black and orange .. .. .. 6·50 26·00
34 $1 green and brown .. .. .. 20·00 55·00
35 $2 green and carmine .. .. .. 45·00 £110
36 $5 green and blue £130 £200

(*b*) *Wmk Mult Script CA*
37 1 1 c. green .. .. 2·25 10·00
38 10 c. black and mauve .. .. .. 4·75 20·00
30/8 .. .. *Set of* 9 £200 £425

3 Sultan Ismail 4

(Recess D.L.R.)

1928–33. *Wmk Mult Script CA. P* 12.
39 3 $1 blue (Perf S. £32) .. .. .. 14·00 35·00
a. Perf 14 (1933) .. .. .. 35·00 40·00

(Recess B.W.)

1937 (July)–**40.** *Wmk Mult Script CA. P* 12.
40 4 1 c. grey-olive and yellow 25 65
41 2 c. green 35 20
42 4 c. scarlet .. .. 1·10 90
43 5 c. red-brown .. .. 1·50 15
44 6 c. lake (10.37) .. .. 2·75 80
45 8 c. grey-olive .. .. 1·75 25
46 10 c. purple (10.37) .. .. .. 4·00 2·00
47 12 c. blue .. .. 1·25 3·75
48 25 c. vermilion and violet .. .. 3·25 4·50
49 30 c. violet and scarlet (10.37) .. .. 12·00 16·00
50 40 c. orange and blue-green .. .. 5·50 12·00
51 50 c. grey-olive and orange (10.37) .. 15·00 16·00
52 $1 violet and blue-green (10.37) .. 6·00 9·50
53 $2 red-brown and scarlet (3.40) .. £140 £325
54 $5 vermilion and lake (3.40) £225 £375
40/54 .. .. *Set of* 15 £375 £700
40/54 Perf "Specimen" .. .. *Set of* 15 £375

For above issue surcharged see issues under "Japanese Occupation".

1948 (1 Dec). *Royal Silver Wedding. As Nos.* 30/1 *of Aden.*
55 10 c. violet 25 50
56 $5 carmine .. .. 24·00 48·00

1949 (10 Oct). *75th Anniv of Universal Postal Union. As Nos.* 114/17 *of Antigua.*
57 10 c. purple 30 45
58 15 c. deep blue .. .. 85 1·75
59 25 c. orange .. .. 95 2·75
60 50 c. blue-black .. .. 2·00 2·50

5 Sultan Tengku Ibrahim

6 Sultan Yahya Petra and Crest of Kelantan

1951 (11 July)–**55.** *Chalk-surfaced paper. Wmk Mult Script CA. P* 17½ × 18.
61 5 1 c. black 5 30
62 2 c. orange (*shades*) 8 30
63 3 c. green 30 90
64 4 c. brown 10 15
65 5 c. bright purple (*shades*) (1.9.52) .. 25 40
66 6 c. grey 10 20
67 8 c. scarlet .. .. 40 1·50
68 8 c. green (1.9.52) .. .. .. 75 2·25
69 10 c. magenta 15 5
70 12 c. scarlet (1.9.52) .. .. .. 75 2·50
71 15 c. ultramarine 40 70
72 20 c. black and green .. .. .. 60 2·50
73 20 c. bright blue (1.9.52) 80 70
74 25 c. purple and orange 50 65
75 30 c. scarlet and purple (5.9.55) .. 3·00 2·50
76 35 c. scarlet and purple (1.9.52) .. 90 2·50
77 40 c. red and purple .. .. .. 1·25 6·50
78 50 c. black and blue 60 70
79 $1 blue and purple .. .. .. 2·00 1·50
80 $2 green and scarlet .. .. .. 11·00 22·00
81 $5 green and brown (*shades*) .. .. 28·00 40·00
61/81 .. .. *Set of* 21 48·00 80·00

1953 (2 June). *Coronation. As No.* 47 *of Aden.*
82 10 c. black and reddish purple 25 20

1957 (26 June)–**63.** *As Nos.* 92/102 *of Kedah but with inset portrait of Sultan Tengku Ibrahim.*
83 9 1 c. black (21.8.57) 5 20
84 10 2 c. orange-red (25.7.57) 10 30
a. Red-orange (17.11.59) .. .. 1·25 1·75
85 11 4 c. sepia (21.8.57) 10 5
86 12 5 c. carmine-lake (21.8.57) 10 5
87 13 8 c. myrtle-green (21.8.57) 80 80
88 14 10 c. deep brown (4.8.57) 15 5
89 10 c. deep maroon (19.4.61) .. .. 1·00 1·25
90 15 20 c. blue 25 25
91 16 50 c. black and blue (*p* 12½) (25.7.57) .. 30 35
a. Perf 12½ × 13 (28.6.60) 30 25
92 17 $1 ultramarine & reddish pur (25.7.57) 1·50 1·00
93 18 $2 bronze-grn & scar (*p* 12½) (21.8.57) 3·75 7·00
a. Perf 13 × 12½ (9.4.63) .. .. 4·00 7·00
94 19 $5 brown and bronze-green (*p* 12½) .. 11·00 13·00
a. Perf 13 × 12½ (13.8.63) .. .. 11·00 13·00
83/94 .. .. *Set of* 12 17·00 22·00

The 6, 12, 25 and 30 c. values used with this issue were Nos. 1/4 of Malayan Federation.

(Photo Harrison)

1961 (17 July). *Installation of the Sultan.* W w **12**. *P* 15 × 14.
95 6 10 c. multicoloured 12 8

7 Sultan Yahya Petra

8 *Vanda hookeriana*

(Recess D.L.R.)

1961–62. *As Nos.* 92/8 *of Kedah but with inset portrait of Sultan Yahya Petra as in T* **7**. W w **13**. *P* 12½ × 13 (*vert*) *or* 13 × 12½ (*horiz*).
96 1 c. black (1.3.62) 5 20
97 2 c. orange-red (1.3.62) 5 30
98 4 c. sepia (1.3.62) 8 5
99 5 c. carmine-lake (1.3.62) 8 5
100 8 c. myrtle-green (*shades*) (1.3.62) .. 75 1·00
101 10 c. deep maroon (2.12.61) 15 5
102 20 c. blue (1.3.62) 30 30
96/102 .. .. *Set of* 7 1·25 1·75

1965 (15 Nov). *As Nos.* 166/72 *of Johore but with inset portrait of Sultan Yahya Petra as in T* **8**. W w **13** (*upright*).
103 1 c. multicoloured 10 20
a. Magenta omitted .. .. 25·00
104 2 c. multicoloured 10 20
105 5 c. multicoloured 15
106 6 c. multicoloured 15 1
107 10 c. multicoloured 20
108 15 c. multicoloured 55 2
109 20 c. multicoloured 80 5
a. Bright purple (blooms) omitted .. .. 32·00
103/9 .. .. *Set of* 7 1·90 1·2

The 5 c. and 10 c. exist with PVA gum as well as gum arabic.

The higher values used with this issue were Nos. 20/27 of Malaysia.

1970 (20 Nov). *As Nos.* 103 *and* 107 *but W* w **13** (*sideways*).
110 8 1 c. multicoloured 20 5
111 – 10 c. multicoloured .. .. .. 75 1·1

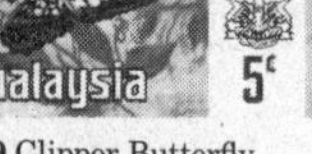

9 Clipper Butterfly **10** *Lagerstroemia speciosa*

1971 (1 Feb)–**78.** *As Nos.* 175/87 *of Johore but with portrait of Sultan Yahya Petra and arms, as in T* **9**. (*a*) *Litho by Bradbury Wilkinson.*
112 1 c. multicoloured 8 2
113 2 c. multicoloured 8 2
114 5 c. multicoloured 15
115 6 c. multicoloured 15
116 10 c. multicoloured 15
117 15 c. multicoloured 30 1
a. Black (state inscription, portrait and arms) omitted .. .. 65·00
118 20 c. multicoloured 35 2
112/18 .. .. *Set of* 7 1·10 8

(*b*) *Photo by Harrison* (1977–78)
119 1 c. multicoloured 10 1
120 5 c. multicoloured 20 1
121 10 c. multicoloured 25 1
122 15 c. multicoloured 50 5

The higher values used with this issue were Nos. 64/71 of Malaysia.

For differences between litho and photo printings, see after Johore No. 187.

On No. 117a only the country inscription, portrait and arms are omitted, the remainder of the black printing being as normal. The design was produced using two black plates, one for the main design, value and inscription and the other to apply the state name head and arms. It is this plate which is omitted from No. 117a.

1979 (30 Apr). *As Nos.* 188/94 *of Johore but with portrait of Sultan Yahya Petra as in T* **10**.
123 1 c. *Rafflesia hasseltii* 5
124 2 c. *Pterocarpus indicus* 5
125 5 c. Type **10** 5
126 10 c. *Durio zibethinus* 8
127 15 c. *Hibiscus rosa-sinensis* 10
128 20 c. *Rhododendron scortechinii* 15 1
129 25 c. *Phaeomeria speciosa* 15 1
123/9 .. .. *Set of* 7 55 4

For higher values used in conjunction with this series see Nos 190/7 of Malaysia.

11 Sultan Tengku Ismail Petra

(Des M. A. B. bin Saman. Litho Harrison)

1980 (30 Mar). *Coronation of Sultan Tengku Ismail Petra. P* 14.
130 11 10 c. multicoloured 5 5
131 15 c. multicoloured 10 10
132 50 c. multicoloured 30 45

1984 (Mar–Sept). *As Nos.* 126 *and* 128 *but without wmk.*
136 10 c. *Durio zibethinus* (9.84) 8 1
138 20 c. *Rhododendron scortechinii* 15 2

For shade difference between 1979 and 1984 printings, see below Johore No. 200. On No. 138 the portrait and state arms have been redrawn smaller.

MALACCA

One of the Straits Settlements.
Issues from 1965 are inscribed "MELAKA".

1948 (1 Dec). *Royal Silver Wedding. As Nos. 30/1 of Aden.*
1 10 c. violet .. 25 40
2 $5 brown .. 30·00 45·00

1949 (1 Mar)–**52.** *As T* **58** *of Straits Settlements, but inscr "MALACCA" at foot. Wmk Mult Script CA. Chalk-surfaced paper. P* 17½ × 18.
3 1 c. black .. 12 40
4 2 c. orange .. 12 45
5 3 c. green .. 15 90
6 4 c. brown .. 12 10
6a 5 c. bright purple (1.9.52) .. 45 70
7 6 c. grey .. 12 25
8 8 c. scarlet .. 35 1·75
8a 8 c. green (1.9.52) .. 85 1·60
9 10 c. purple .. 15 10
9a 12 c. scarlet (1.9.52) .. 95 1·75
10 15 c. ultramarine .. 40 60
11 20 c. black and green .. 35 2·25
11a 20 c. bright blue (1.9.52) .. 1·25 90
12 25 c. purple and orange .. 25 50
12a 35 c. scarlet and purple (1.9.52) .. 1·00 1·50
13 40 c. red and purple .. 1·25 6·50
14 50 c. black and blue .. 60 45
15 $1 blue and purple .. 4·00 5·50
16 $2 green and scarlet .. 8·00 17·00
17 $5 green and brown .. 22·00 32·00
3/17 .. *Set of* 20 38·00 65·00

1949 (10 Oct). *75th Anniv of U.P.U. As Nos. 114/17 of Antigua.*
18 10 c. purple .. 20 45
19 15 c. deep blue .. 70 2·25
20 25 c. orange .. 80 3·00
21 50 c. blue-black .. 1·50 4·50

1953 (2 June). *Coronation. As No. 47 of Aden.*
22 10 c. black and reddish purple .. 20 10

1 Queen Elizabeth II

2 Copra

1954 (9 June)–**55.** *Chalk-surfaced paper. Wmk Mult Script CA. P* 17½ × 18.
23 1 1 c. black (27.4.55) .. 5 20
24 2 c. yellow-orange (27.4.55) .. 10 30
25 4 c. brown (*shades*) .. 20 15
26 5 c. bright purple (12.7.54) .. 20 50
27 6 c. grey .. 10 15
28 8 c. green (5.1.55) .. 30 75
29 10 c. brown-purple (*shades*) (1.7.54) .. 15 5
30 12 c. rose-red (5.1.55) .. 30 75
31 20 c. bright blue (5.1.55) .. 30 40
32 25 c. brown-purple & yell-orge (27.4.55) 35 25
33 30 c. rose-red and brown-purple (5.9.55) 40 20
34 35 c. rose-red and brown-purple (8.9.54) 50 85
35 50 c. black and bright blue (5.1.55) .. 60 25
36 $1 bright blue and brown-purple (8.9.54) .. 2·25 2·75
37 $2 emerald and scarlet (27.4.55) .. 11·00 16·00
38 $5 emerald and brown (27.4.55) .. 15·00 22·00
23/8 .. *Set of* 16 28·00 40·00

1957. *As Nos. 92/102 of Kedah but with inset portrait of Queen Elizabeth II.*
39 **9** 1 c. black (21.8) .. 5 40
40 **10** 2 c. orange-red (25.7) .. 5 40
41 **11** 4 c. sepia (21.8) .. 8 10
42 **12** 5 c. carmine-lake (21.8) .. 8 10
43 **13** 8 c. myrtle-green (21.8) .. 1·50 2·00
44 **14** 10 c. deep brown (4.8) .. 15 5
45 **15** 20 c. blue (26.6) .. 30 50
46 **16** 50 c. black and blue (25.7) .. 40 50
47 **17** $1 ultramarine and reddish purple (25.7) .. 2·25 3·00
48 **18** $2 bronze-green and scarlet (21.8) .. 4·25 11·00
49 **19** $5 brown and bronze-green (26.6) .. 10·00 15·00
39/49 .. *Set of* 11 17·00 30·00

The 6, 12, 25 and 30 c. values used with this issue were Nos. 1/4 of Malayan Federation.

(Recess D.L.R.)

1960 (15 Mar)–**62.** *As Nos. 39/49, but with inset picture of Melaka tree and Pelandok (mouse deer) as in T* **2**. *W w* **12**. *P* 13 × 12½ (1 c. *to* 8 c., $2, $5), 12½ × 13 (10 c. *to* 50 c.) *or* 13½ ($1).
50 1 c. black .. 5 30
51 2 c. orange-red .. 5 30
52 4 c. sepia .. 5 5
53 5 c. carmine-lake .. 5 5
54 8 c. myrtle-green .. 95 60
55 10 c. deep maroon .. 15 5
56 20 c. blue .. 20 5
57 50 c. black and blue .. 40 25
 a. Black and ultramarine (9.1.62) .. 35 5
58 $1 ultramarine and reddish purple .. 1·50 1·50
59 $2 bronze-green and scarlet .. 3·50 3·50
60 $5 brown and bronze-green .. 9·00 4·50
50/60 .. *Set of* 11 14·50 10·00

3 *Vanda hookeriana*

4 Lime Butterfly

1965 (15 Nov). *As Nos. 166/72 of Johore but with Arms of Malacca inset and inscr "MELAKA" as in T* **3**. *W w* **13** (*upright*).
61 1 c. multicoloured .. 8 15
62 2 c. multicoloured .. 8 15
63 5 c. multicoloured .. 12 5
64 6 c. multicoloured .. 15 5
65 10 c. multicoloured .. 15 5
66 15 c. multicoloured .. 55 15
67 20 c. multicoloured (*shades*) .. 80 25
61/7 .. *Set of* 7 1·75 75

The 5 c., 6 c., 10 c. and 20 c. exist with PVA gum as well as gum arabic.

The higher values used with this issue were Nos. 20/27 of Malaysia.

1970. *As Nos. 61 and 65 but W w* **13** (*sideways*).
68 **3** 1 c. multicoloured (27.5.70) .. 20 55
69 – 10 c. multicoloured (20.11.70) .. 80 1·25

1971 (1 Feb)–**78.** *As Nos. 175/87 of Johore but with arms of Malacca and inscr "melaka", as in T* **4**. (a) *Litho by Bradbury, Wilkinson.*
70 1 c. multicoloured .. 5 15
71 2 c. multicoloured .. 5 15
72 5 c. multicoloured .. 15 5
73 6 c. multicoloured .. 15 10
74 10 c. multicoloured .. 15 5
75 15 c. multicoloured .. 30 10
76 20 c. multicoloured .. 35 15
70/6 .. *Set of* 7 1·10 70

(b) *Photo by Harrison* (1977–78)
77 1 c. multicoloured .. 20 35
78 5 c. multicoloured .. 20 12
79 10 c. multicoloured .. 25 15
80 15 c. multicoloured .. 50 45
81 20 c. multicoloured .. 70 80

The higher values used with this issue were Nos. 64/71 of Malaysia.

For differences between litho and photo printings, see after Johore No. 187.

5 *Durio zibethinus*

1979 (30 Apr). *As Nos. 188/94 of Johore but with Arms of Malacca and inscr. "melaka" as in T* **5**.
82 1 c. *Rafflesia hasseltii* .. 5 5
83 2 c. *Pterocarpus indicus* .. 5 5
84 5 c. *Lagerstroemia speciosa* .. 5 5
85 10 c. Type **5** .. 8 5
86 15 c. *Hibiscus rosa-sinensis* .. 10 5
87 20 c. *Rhododendron scortechinii* .. 15 10
88 25 c. *Phaeomeria speciosa* .. 15 12
82/8 .. *Set of* 7 55 40

For higher values used in conjunction with this series see Nos. 190/7 of Malaysia.

NEGRI SEMBILAN

One of the Federated Malay States, being a federation of smaller states, reconstituted in 1887. Sungei Ujong, taken under British protection in 1873, was absorbed into Negri Sembilan in 1895.

A. SUNGEI UJONG

PRICES FOR STAMPS ON COVER

Nos. 1/16	—
Nos. 17/28	*from* × 25
Nos. 29/39	*from* × 8
Nos. 40/50	*from* × 10
Nos. 51/6	*from* × 25

(1) (2) (3)

T* 5 *of Straits Settlements, wmk Crown CC, optd

1878. *Optd with T* **1**.
1 **1** 2 c. brown .. £1500 £1400

The 2 c. brown, Wmk Crown CC, optd with letters "S.U." is a trial, not an issued stamp.

1881–82. *Optd as T* **2**.
Varieties. (*a*) *"S" wide.* (*b*) *All letters narrow.* (*c*) *Letters "N" wide.* (*d*) *"N," "E" of "SUNGEI," and "U," "NG" of "UJONG" wide.* (*e*) *"G," "J" and "O" narrow.* (*f*) *"GE" and "JO" narrow.* (*h*) *"S" and "E" wide.* (*i*) *"N" of "UJONG" wide.*
2 **2** 2 c. brown (*a*) .. 42·00
 a. "S" inverted .. £600
3 2 c. brown (*b*) .. 42·00
4 2 c. brown (*d*) .. 42·00
5 2 c. brown (*e*) .. 42·00
6 2 c. brown (*f*) .. 42·00
7 4 c. rose (*a*) .. £550
8 4 c. rose (*b*) .. £425
9 4 c. rose (*h*) ..

On the 2 c. brown, the word "SUNGEI" was printed as a triplet and "UJONG" as a single unit. Triplets are known of: 1881 (*a*)+(*b*)+(*b*); 1881 (*d*)+(*e*)+(*f*).

On the 4 c. rose, "SUNGEI" and "UJONG" were printed as separate triplets. 1882 (*b*)+(*a*)+(*b*) for "SUNGEI" *and* (*b*)+(*b*)+(*b*) for "UJONG". The setting of (*h*) is not known.

1881. *Optd as T* **3**.
10 **3** 2 c. brown (*a*) .. £175
11 2 c. brown (*b*) .. £350
12 2 c. brown (*c*) .. £350 £350
13 2 c. brown (*i*) .. £500

In the above settings, "SUNGEI" was printed as a triplet and "UJONG" as a single unit. A known triplet consists of: 1881 (*b*)+(*b*)+(*a*). Varieties (*i*) and (*c*) form the first and third units of another setting. A third setting appears to consist of three units of (*b*).

T* 5 *of Straits Settlements, wmk Crown CA, optd or surch

1882. *Optd with letters "S.U." (with stops).*
14 2 c. brown .. 55·00
15 4 c. rose .. £1100 £1200

1882. *"SU" without stops.*
16 2 c. brown .. 50·00 65·00

1882–84. (*a*). *Optd with T* **2**. *Variety* (*k*) *"E" wide.*
17 **2** 2 c. brown (*a*) .. £130 90·00
18 2 c. brown (*b*) .. £120 85·00
19 2 c. rose (*a*) .. 32·00 35·00
20 2 c. rose (*b*) .. 32·00 35·00
21 2 c. rose (*h*) .. 32·00 35·00
22 2 c. rose (*i*) .. 32·00 35·00
 a. "UJONG" double ..
23 2 c. rose (*k*) .. 25·00 28·00
24 8 c. orange (*a*) .. £550 £350
25 8 c. orange (*b*) .. £550 £350
26 10 c. slate (*a*) .. £170 £150
27 10 c. slate (*b*) .. £150 £150

On all the above "SUNGEI" and "UJONG" were printed as separate triplets. The 2 c. brown and the 8 c. and 10 c. were overprinted with the same triplets as were used for the 4 c. rose, CC. The "SUNGEI" triplet of this was: 1882 (*b*)+(*a*)+(*b*).

The 2 c. rose was overprinted in two settings of: 1884 (*b*)+(*a*)+(*h*) and (*h*)+(*k*)+(*i*).

(*b*) *Optd with T* **3**
28 **3** 10 c. slate (*b*) .. — £160

SUNGEI UJONG (4) SUNGEI UJONG (5) Sungei Ujong (6)

1883. *Optd with T* **4**, *with stop after "UJONG".*
29 **4** 2 c. brown (*b*) .. 23·00 26·00
30 2 c. brown (*h*) .. 22·00 25·00
31 2 c. brown (*i*) .. 22·00 25·00
31*a* 8 c. orange (*b*) ..

1884. *Optd with T* **4**, *without stop.*
32 **4** 2 c. rose (*b*) .. 19·00 22·00
33 2 c. rose (*h*) .. 19·00 22·00
34 2 c. rose (*k*) .. 19·00 22·00
35 4 c. brown (*b*) .. 65·00 75·00
36 4 c. brown (*h*) .. 65·00 75·00
37 4 c. brown (*k*) .. 65·00 75·00

"SUNGEI" and "UJONG" were printed as separate triplets on Nos. 29 to 37. The triplets on the 2 c. brown were: (*b*)+(*h*)+(*i*) and on the 2 c. rose and 4 c. brown (*h*)+(*k*)+(*b*).

1885–90. *Overprinted with name in various types.*
38 **5** 2 c. rose (without stop) .. .. .. 11·00 14·00
39 **6** 2 c. rose .. .. 12·00 14·00
a. Opt double £250 £250

SUNGEI UJONG (7) SUNGEI UJONG (8)

SUNGEI UJONG (9) SUNGEI UJONG (10)

40 **7** 2 c. rose (1886) .. .. 24·00 27·00
41 **8** 2 c. rose (1886) .. .. 23·00 24·00
a. Opt double .. .. ..
42 **9** 2 c. rose (*long* "J") (1886) .. .. 24·00 27·00
a. Opt double .. ..
43 **10** 2 c. rose (1887) .. .. 7·50 12·00
44 **5** 2 c. rose (with stop) (1889) .. .. 21·00 24·00
a. "UNJOG." £1200 £1400

SUNGEI UJONG (11) SUNGEI UJONG (12)

45 **11** 2 c. rose (1889) .. .. 4·50 6·50
46 **12** 2 c. rose (1890) .. .. 11·00 12·00
No. 45 exists with narrow "E" (only 2 mm wide) which occurs in two positions on two of the three settings.
No. 46 has two varieties in the setting—antique "G" in "SUNGEI" and antique "G" in "UJONG".

SUNGEI UJONG Two CENTS (13) SUNGEI UJONG *Two* CENTS (14)

SUNGEI UJONG *Two* CENTS (15)

1891. *T* **7** *of Straits Settlements surch.*
47 **13** 2 c. on 24 c. green .. .. .. 65·00 75·00
48 **14** 2 c. on 24 c. green .. .. .. 95·00 £120
49 **15** 2 c. on 24 c. green .. .. .. 48·00 55·00
50 – 2 c. on 24 c. green* £190 £190
No. 49 has the antique "G" varieties as on No. 46.
*On No. 50 the word "TWO" is as in T 13 and the word "CENTS" smaller (9 instead of 10 mm).

16 17 3 CENTS (18)

1891–94. *Wmk Crown CA. P* 14.
51 **16** 2 c. rose .. .. 4·50 8·00
52 2 c. orange (1894) .. .. .. 1·40 4·00
53 5 c. blue (1893) .. .. 1·75 5·50
51/3 Optd "Specimen" .. .. *Set of* 3 85·00

1894. *Surch as T* **18**.
54 **16** 1 c. on 5 c. green 65 70
55 3 c. on 5 c. rose .. .. 65 1·75

1895. *Wmk Crown CA. P* 14.
56 **17** 3 c. dull purple and carmine .. .. 1·25 75
54/6 Optd "Specimen" .. .. *Set of* 3 60·00

B. NEGRI SEMBILAN

Stamps of the STRAITS SETTLEMENTS were used in Negri Sembilan during 1891, until replaced by the stamps listed below.

PRICES FOR STAMPS ON COVER TO 1945

No. 1	*from* × 50
Nos. 2/4	*from* × 8
Nos. 5/14	*from* × 5
Nos. 15/20	*from* × 6
Nos. 21/49	*from* × 4

Negri Sembilan (1) 2 3

1891 (Aug?). *T* **5** *of Straits Settlements (wmk Crown CA) optd with T* 1.
1 2 c. rose .. .. 2·25 4·00

1891–94. *Wmk Crown CA. P* 14.
2 **2** 1 c. green (1893) .. .. 2·50 1·25
3 2 c. rose .. .. 3·75 4·00
4 5 c. blue (1894) .. .. 14·00 17·00
2/4 Optd "Specimen" .. .. .. *Set of* 3 90·00

1896–99. *Wmk Crown CA. P* 14.
5 **3** 1 c. dull purple and green (1899) .. 2·50 2·75
6 2 c. dull purple and brown .. .. 15·00 24·00
7 3 c. dull purple and carmine .. .. 2·50 75
8 5 c. dull purple and orange-yellow .. 4·25 4·75
9 8 c. dull purple and ultramarine .. 10·00 11·00
10 10 c. dull purple and orange .. .. 15·00 13·00
11 15 c. green and violet .. .. .. 20·00 22·00
12 20 c. green and olive .. .. .. 26·00 30·00
13 25 c. green and carmine .. .. .. 32·00 42·00
14 50 c. green and black .. .. .. 45·00 48·00
5/14 .. .. *Set of* 10 £150 £180
5/14 Optd "Specimen" .. .. *Set of* 10 £190

Four cents. (4) Four cents. (5)

1898 (Dec)–**1899.** (*a*) *Surch as T* 4.
15 **3** 1 c. on 15 c. green and violet .. .. 65·00 80·00
a. Raised stop £180 £200
16 **2** 4 c. on 1 c. green .. .. 1·25 4·00
17 **3** 4 c. on 3 c. dull purple and carmine .. 3·00 6·00
a. Pair, one without surch £600 £650
b. Surcharge double £350 £300
ba. Ditto. "Four cents" albino .. ..
c. Surcharge inverted.. .. .. £130 £130
d. "cents" repeated at left £110 £120
e. "Four" repeated at right £110 £120
f. Without bar £350 £300
g. Bar double .. .. † £475
18 **2** 4 c. on 5 c. blue .. .. 1·25 4·25
On Nos. 15 and 17 the bar is at the top of the stamp.

(*b*) *Surch as T* **5**
19 **3** 4 c. on 8 c. dull pur & ultram (G.) (12.98) 2·75 3·75
a. Pair, one without surch £725 £650
b. Surch double £525
c. Surch double (G.+R.) £650 £650
20 4 c. on 8 c. dull purple & ultramarine (Bk.) £250 £275

The general issues for FEDERATED MALAY STATES were used in Negri Sembilan from 1900 until 1935.

6 Arms of Negri Sembilan 7

1935 (2 Dec)–**41.** *Chalk-surfaced or ordinary paper* (**O**). *Wmk Mult Script CA. P* 14.
21 **6** 1 c. black (1.1.36) 25 35
22 2 c. green (1.1.36) 90 60
23 2 c. orange (11.12.41) .. .. .. 50 4·75
24 3 c. green (21.8.41) .. .. .. 50 3·25
25 4 c. orange 30 15
26 5 c. brown (5.12.35) 45 10
27 6 c. scarlet (1.1.37) .. .. .. 3·00 3·50
a. Stop omitted at right (R.10/9) .. 38·00 38·00
28 6 c. grey, **O** (18.12.41) .. .. 1·75 14·00
a. Stop omitted at right (R.10/9) .. 30·00 55·00
29 8 c. grey .. .. 1·25 10
30 10 c. dull purple (1.1.36) 40 30
31 12 c. bright ultramarine (1.1.36) .. 1·40 65
32 15 c. ultramarine, **O** (1.10.41) .. 2·25 14·00
33 25 c. dull purple and scarlet (1.4.36) .. 85 1·50
34 30 c. dull purple and orange (1.1.36) .. 3·25 4·50
35 40 c. scarlet and dull purple .. .. 1·10 5·50
36 50 c. black/*emerald* (1.2.36) .. .. 4·25 1·50
37 $1 black and red/*blue* (1.4.36) .. .. 2·25 2·75
38 $2 green and scarlet (16.5.36) .. .. 26·00 26·00
39 $5 green and red/*emerald* (16.5.36) .. 20·00 35·00
21/39 .. .. *Set of* 19 60·00 £110
21/39 Perf "Specimen" .. .. *Set of* 19 £275
An 8 c. scarlet was issued but only with opt during Japanese Occupation of Malaya. Unoverprinted specimens result from leakages.

1948 (1 Dec). *Royal Silver Wedding. As Nos.* 30/1 *of Aden.*
40 10 c. violet 20 15
41 $5 green .. .. 25·00 30·00

1949 (1 Apr)–**55.** *Chalk-surfaced paper. Wmk Mult Script CA. P* 17½ × 18.
42 **7** 1 c. black 5 12
43 2 c. orange 8 10
44 3 c. green 12 30
45 4 c. brown 12 5
46 5 c. bright purple (*shades*) (1.9.52) .. 25 2
47 6 c. grey (*shades*) 12
48 8 c. scarlet 30 7
49 8 c. green (1.9.52) .. .. .. 1·50 1·5
50 10 c. purple 15 5
51 12 c. scarlet (1.9.52) .. .. .. 1·50 1·5
52 15 c. ultramarine 30 1
53 20 c. black and green 35 7
54 20 c. bright blue (1.9.52) 80 5
55 25 c. purple and orange 30 5
56 30 c. scarlet and purple (5.9.55) .. .. 2·50 1·2
57 35 c. scarlet and purple (1.9.52) .. .. 80 1·2
58 40 c. red and purple .. .. .. 75 3·0
59 50 c. black and blue 60 1
60 $1 blue and purple .. .. .. 2·00 5
61 $2 green and scarlet .. .. .. 7·00 5·0
62 $5 green and brown .. .. .. 35·00 20·0
42/62 .. .. *Set of* 21 48·00 32·0

1949 (10 Oct). *75th Anniv of U.P.U. As Nos.* 114/17 *of Antigua.*
63 10 c. purple 25 1
64 15 c. deep blue 70 8
65 25 c. orange .. .. 75 1·5
66 50 c. blue-black .. .. 1·40 3·25

1953 (2 June). *Coronation. As No.* 47 *of Aden.*
67 10 c. black and reddish purple 25 5

1957 (26 June)–**63.** *As Nos.* 92/102 *of Kedah but with inset Arms of Negri Sembilan.*
68 **9** 1 c. black (21.8.57) 5 5
69 **10** 2 c. orange-red (25.7.57) 5 5
70 **11** 4 c. sepia (21.8.57) 5 5
71 **12** 5 c. carmine-lake (21.8.57) 5 5
72 **13** 8 c. myrtle-green (21.8.57) 85 30
73 **14** 10 c. deep brown (4.8.57) 15 5
74 10 c. deep maroon (10.1.61) 25 5
75 **15** 20 c. blue 25 5
76 **16** 50 c. black and blue (*p* 12½) (25.7.57) .. 35 20
a. Perf 12½ × 13 (19.7.60) 30 5
77 **17** $1 ultramarine & reddish pur (25.7.57) 1·25 45
78 **18** $2 bronze-green & scarlet (*p* 12½) (21.8.57) .. .. 3·00 5·5
a. Perf 13 × 12½ (15.1.63) .. .. 3·50 5·5
79 **19** $5 brown and bronze-green (*p* 12½) .. 10·00 12·0
a. Perf 13 × 12½ (6.3.62) .. .. 10·00 8·0
ab. Perf 13 × 12½. *Brown and yellow-olive* (13.11.62) .. .. .. 50·00 35·0
68/79 .. .. *Set of* 12 14·50 12·0
The 6, 12, 25 and 30 c. values used with this issue were Nos. 1/4 of Malayan Federation.

8 Tuanku Munawir 9 *Vanda hookeriana*

(Photo Enschedé)

1961 (17 Apr). *Installation of Tuanku Munawir as Yang di-Pertuan Besar of Negri Sembilan. No wmk. P* 14 × 13.
80 **8** 10 c. multicoloured 10 8

1965 (15 Nov). *As Nos.* 166/72 *of Johore but with Arms of Negri Sembilan inset and inscr.* "NEGERI SEMBILAN" *as in T* **9**. *W w* **13** (*upright*).
81 1 c. multicoloured 8 12
82 2 c. multicoloured 8 12
83 5 c. multicoloured 10 5
84 6 c. multicoloured 12 5
85 10 c. multicoloured 15 5
86 15 c. multicoloured 55 8
87 20 c. multicoloured (*shades*) 80 12
81/7 .. .. *Set of* 7 1·75 55
The 2 c., 6 c., 15 c. and 20 c. exist with PVA gum as well as gum arabic.
The higher values used with this issue were Nos. 20/27 of Malaysia.
See also No. 90.

10 Negri Sembilan Crest and Tuanku Ja'afar 11 Great Orange Tip

(Des Z. Noor. Photo Japanese Govt Ptg Wks)

1968 (8 Apr). *Installation of Tuanku Ja'afar as Yang di-Pertuan Besar of Negri Sembilan. P* 13.
88 **10** 15 c. multicoloured 15 10
89 50 c. multicoloured 40 70

1970 (27 May). *As No.* 81 *but with W w* **13** (*sideways*).
90 **9** 1 c. multicoloured 35 90

1971 (1 Feb)–**78.** *As Nos.* 175/87 *of Johore but with Arms of Negri Sembilan and inscr* "negeri sembilan", *as in T* **11**.

(*a*) *Litho by Bradbury, Wilkinson*
91 1 c. multicoloured 5 12
92 2 c. multicoloured 5 12
93 5 c. multicoloured 15 5
94 6 c. multicoloured 15 10
95 10 c. multicoloured 15 5
96 15 c. multicoloured 30 8
97 20 c. multicoloured 35 8
91/7 .. .. *Set of* 7 1·10 55

(*b*) *Photo by Harrison* (1977–78)
98 2 c. multicoloured 20 35
99 5 c. multicoloured 20 12
100 10 c. multicoloured 30 10

101 15 c. multicoloured 50 30
102 20 c. multicoloured 70 50

The higher values used with this issue were Nos. 64/71 of Malaysia.

For differences between litho and photo printings, see after Johore No. 187.

12 *Hibiscus rosa-sinensis*

1979 (30 Apr). *As Nos. 188/94 of Johore but with Arms of Negri Sembilan and inscr* "negeri sembilan" *as in T* **12**.

103 1 c. *Rafflesia hasseltii* 5 5
104 2 c. *Pterocarpus indicus* 5 5
105 5 c. *Lagerstroemia speciosa* 5 5
106 10 c. *Durio zibethinus* 8 5
107 15 c. Type **12** 10 5
108 20 c. *Rhododendron scortechinii* 15 5
109 25 c. *Phaeomeria speciosa* 15 5
103/9 .. .. *Set of* 7 55 20

For higher values used in conjunction with this series see Nos. 190/7 of Malaysia.

1984 (Mar–Sept). *As Nos.* 106 *and* 108, *but without wmk.*

113 10 c. *Durio zibethinus* (9.84) 8 10
115 20 c. *Rhododendron scortechinii* 15 20

For shade differences between 1979 and 1984 printings see below Johore No. 200.

PAHANG

One of the Federated Malay States

PRICES FOR STAMPS ON COVER TO 1945	
Nos. 1/3	*from* × 9
Nos. 4/6	*from* × 15
No. 7	—
Nos. 8/10	*from* × 5
Nos. 11/13	*from* × 12
Nos. 14/16	*from* × 6
Nos. 17/18	*from* × 4
Nos. 19/24	*from* × 3
No. 25	*from* × 8
Nos. 26/7	—
No. 28	*from* × 8
Nos. 29/46	*from* × 4

T 5, 6, 19 and 7 of Straits Settlements (wmk Crown CA) optd or surch

PAHANG (A) PAHANG (B)

1889 (Jan).

1 A 2 c. rose .. .. 28·00 27·00
2 8 c. orange £1400 £1300
3 10 c. slate £250 £250

The 8 c. and 10 c. were overprinted in triplet form.

1889.

4 B 2 c. rose .. .. 5·00 6·00
a. Antique letters £375

The letters of the overprint on No. 4a are thinner and appear broader than those on No. 4.

PAHANG (C) PAHANG (D)

1890.

5 C 2 c. rose £850 £650
6 D 2 c. rose .. .. 35·00 16·00

1891. *Optd as No. 6 and surch with new value with bar through old value.*

7 Two CENTS on 24 c. green £175

No. 7 has the word "Two" as in No. 8 and "CENTS" as in No. 10, but in roman capitals.

PAHANG Two CENTS (E) PAHANG *Two* CENTS (F) PAHANG *Two* CENTS (G)

1891.

8 E 2 c. on 24 c. green .. .. .. 30·00 32·00
9 F 2 c. on 24 c. green .. .. .. 60·00 60·00
10 G 2 c. on 24 c. green .. .. .. 30·00 32·00

1

2

1891–95. *Wmk Crown CA. P* 14.

11 1 1 c. green (1895) .. .. .. 3·25 2·50
12 2 c. rose 90 90
13 5 c. blue (1893) .. .. .. 3·50 7·00
11/13 Optd "Specimen" .. .. *Set of* 3 75·00

1895–99. *Wmk Crown CA. P* 14.

14 2 3 c. dull purple and carmine .. .. 1·75 90
15 4 c. dull purple and carmine (1899) .. 2·75 3·50
16 5 c. dull purple and olive-yellow .. 9·50 11·00
14/16 Optd "Specimen" .. .. *Set of* 3 75·00

1897 (Aug). *No. 13 divided diagonally, top half surch* "3 c." *in MS., bottom half surch* "2 c." *and* "5" *struck out in MS., both halves being initialled* "J.F.O." *in MS.*

17 2 c. on half of 5 c. blue (R.) £500 £250
a. Surch in black .. .. — £1100
b. Divided horiz. Surch in red .. .. — £225
18 3 c. on half 5 c. blue (R.) £500 £250
a. Surch in black £1750 £1100
b. Divided horiz. Surch in red .. .. — £225

The initials stand for John Fortescue Owen, District Treasurer at Kuala Lipis, where the provisionals were made.

Pahang. (3) Pahang. (4)

1898. (*a*) *T 31 of Perak optd with T* 3.

19 10 c. dull purple and orange .. .. .. 12·00 18·00
20 25 c. green and carmine .. .. .. 26·00 32·00
21 50 c. green and black .. .. .. 50·00 50·00
22 50 c. dull purple and greenish black .. .. 75·00 75·00

(*b*) *Nos. 72 and 75 of Perak, optd with T* 4

23 $1 green and pale green .. .. .. 70·00 70·00
24 $5 green and ultramarine £225 £225

ALTERED CATALOGUE NUMBERS

Any Catalogue numbers altered from the last edition are shown as a list in the introductory pages.

Pahang Four cents (5) Four cents. (6)

1898. (*a*) *T 31 of Perak surch with T* 5.

25 4 c. on 8 c. dull purple and ultramarine .. 3·00 4·75
a. Surch inverted £900 £600
b. Surch double £350

(*b*) *T 5 on plain paper (no stamp), but issued for postage*

26 4 c. black .. .. — £400
27 5 c. black £250

1899. *No. 16 surch with T* 6.

28 4 c. on 5 c. dull purple and olive-yellow 8·00 13·00

The general issues for the FEDERATED MALAY STATES were used in Pahang from 1900 until 1935.

7 Sultan Sir Abu Bakar

8 Sultan Sir Abu Bakar

1935–41. *Chalk-surfaced or ordinary paper* (**O**). *Wmk Mult Script CA. P* 14.

29 7 1 c. black 12 40
30 2 c. green 50 40
31 3 c. green, **OC** .. .. 45 2·75
32 4 c. orange 25 40
33 5 c. brown 65 10
34 6 c. scarlet .. .. 4·50 4·75
35 8 c. grey 80 10
36 8 c. scarlet (11.12.41) .. .. .. 60 8·50
37 10 c. dull purple 40 25
38 12 c. bright ultramarine .. .. .. 1·50 2·25
39 15 c. ultramarine, **O** .. .. .. 1·50 13·00
40 25 c. dull purple and scarlet .. .. 1·25 1·50
41 30 c. dull purple and orange .. .. 90 1·40
42 40 c. scarlet and dull purple .. .. 1·25 3·00
43 50 c. black/*emerald* .. .. .. 5·00 1·60
44 $1 black and red/*blue* .. .. .. 3·50 6·50
45 $2 green and scarlet .. .. .. 30·00 48·00
46 $5 green and red/*emerald* .. .. 13·00 48·00
29/46 .. .. *Set of* 18 60·00 £130
29/46 Perf "Specimen" .. .. *Set of* 18 £170

A 2 c. orange and a 6 c. grey were prepared but not officially issued.

Dates of issue as for Negri Sembilan.

1948 (1 Dec). *Royal Silver Wedding. As Nos.* 30/1 *of Aden.*

47 10 c. violet 20 40
48 $5 green .. .. 26·00 45·00

1949 (10 Oct). *75th Anniv of Universal Postal Union. As Nos.* 114/17 *of Antigua.*

49 10 c. purple 20 25
50 15 c. deep blue 55 85
51 25 c. orange .. .. 60 1·50
52 50 c. blue-black .. .. 1·25 2·25

1950 (1 June)–**55.** *Wmk Mult Script CA. Chalk-surfaced paper. P* 17½ × 18.

53 8 1 c. black 5 20
54 2 c. orange 8 20
55 3 c. green 25 65
56 4 c. brown (*shades*) 12 5
57 5 c. bright purple (*shades*) (1.9.52) .. 25 20
58 6 c. grey 12 10
59 8 c. scarlet .. .. 30 1·50
60 8 c. green (1.9.52) .. .. 85 1·25
61 10 c. magenta 15 5
62 12 c. scarlet (1.9.52) .. .. .. 85 2·00
63 15 c. ultramarine 30 30
64 20 c. black and green .. .. .. 45 2·25
65 20 c. bright blue (*shades*) (1.9.52) .. 75 10
66 25 c. purple and orange 35 15
67 30 c. scarlet and brown-purple (*shades*) (5.9.55) .. .. .. 3·25 1·00
68 35 c. scarlet and purple (1.9.52) .. .. 75 1·00
69 40 c. red and purple .. .. .. 1·50 5·50
70 50 c. black and blue 60 15
71 $1 blue and purple .. .. .. 2·00 90
72 $2 green and scarlet .. .. .. 9·50 15·00
73 $5 green and brown (*shades*) .. .. 22·00 32·00
53/73 .. .. *Set of* 21 40·00 60·00

1953 (2 June). *Coronation. As No.* 47 *of Aden.*

74 10 c. black and reddish purple 25 5

1957 (26 June)–**62.** *As Nos.* 92/102 *of Kedah but with inset portrait of Sultan Sir Abu Bakar.*

75 9 1 c. black (21.8.57) 5 10
76 10 2 c. orange-red (25.7.57) 5 10
77 11 4 c. sepia (21.8.57) 5 5
78 12 5 c. carmine-lake (21.8.57) 5 5
79 13 8 c. myrtle-green (21.8.57) 80 60
80 14 10 c. deep brown (4.8.57) 15 5
81 10 c. deep maroon (21.2.61) 25 5
82 15 20 c. blue 25 5
83 16 50 c. black and blue (*p* 12½) (25.7.57) .. 35 25
a. Perf 12½ × 13 (17.5.60) 30 12
84 17 $1 ultramarine & reddish pur (25.7.57) 1·25 75
85 18 $2 bronze-grn & scar (*p* 12½) (21.8.57) 3·50 4·75
a. Perf 13 × 12½ (13.11.62) .. .. 3·50 5·00

86 **19** $5 brown and bronze-green (*p* 12½) 7·50 8·50
a. Perf 13 × 12½ (17.5.60) .. .. 8·50 8·50
b. Perf 13 × 12½. *Brown and yellow-olive* (23.10.62) .. .. .. 15·00 20·00
75/86 .. .. *Set of* 12 13·00 13·50

The 6, 12, 25 and 30 c. values used with this issue were Nos. 1/4 of Malayan Federation.

9 *Vanda hookeriana*

10 Blue Pansy Butterfly

1965 (15 Nov). *As Nos. 166/72 of Johore but with inset portrait of Sultan Sir Abu Bakar as in T* **9**. *W w* **13** (*upright*).

87 1 c. multicoloured 8 20
88 2 c. multicoloured 8 5
89 5 c. multicoloured 10 5
90 6 c. multicoloured 12 5
91 10 c. multicoloured 15 5
92 15 c. multicoloured 55 10
93 20 c. multicoloured 80 25
87/93 .. .. *Set of* 7 1·75 70

The 2 c., 5 c. and 6 c. exist with PVA gum as well as gum arabic.
The higher values used with this issue were Nos. 20/27 of Malaysia.

1970 (27 May). *As Nos.* 87 *and* 91 *but W w* **13** (*sideways*).

94 **9** 1 c. multicoloured 15 70
95 – 10 c. multicoloured .. .. 55 1·75

(Litho B.W.)

1971 (1 Feb). *As Nos. 175/81 of Johore but with portrait of Sultan Sir Abu Bakar and arms, as in T* **10**.

96 1 c. multicoloured 8 15
97 2 c. multicoloured 8 15
98 5 c. multicoloured 15 5
99 6 c. multicoloured 15 5
100 10 c. multicoloured 15 5
101 15 c. multicoloured 30 12
102 20 c. multicoloured 35 12
96/102 .. .. *Set of* 7 1·10 60

The higher values used with this issue were Nos. 64/71 of Malaysia.

11 Sultan Haji Ahmad Shah

12 *Rhododendron scortechinii*

(Des Union Advertising. Litho Harrison)

1975 (8 May). *Installation of the Sultan. P* 14 × 14½.

103 **11** 10 c. slate-green, light lilac and gold .. 10 5
104 15 c. greenish black, yellow & dp green .. 12 10
105 50 c. black, light violet-bl & greenish blk 70 1·40

(Photo Harrison)

1977 (5 Sept)–**78**. *As Nos. 97/8, 100/2 but with portraits of Sultan Haji Ahmad Shah.*

106 2 c. multicoloured (1978) .. .. .. 25·00
107 5 c. multicoloured 30 20
108 10 c. multicoloured (10.2.78) 40 25
109 15 c. multicoloured (13.1.78) 50 40
a. Black (face value, etc.)* omitted .. ..
110 20 c. multicoloured (1978) 70 75

*There were two black cylinders used for No. 109, one to apply the portrait and state details, the other the face value and parts of the main design.
The higher values used with this issue were Nos. 64/71 of Malaysia.

1979 (30 Apr). *As Nos. 188/94 of Johore but with portrait of Sultan Haji Ahmad Shah as in T* **12**.

111 1 c. *Rafflesia hasseltii* 5 5
112 2 c. *Pterocarpus indicus* 5 5
113 5 c. *Lagerstroemia speciosa* 5 5
114 10 c. *Durio zibethinus* 8 5
115 15 c. *Hibiscus rosa-sinensis* 10 5
116 20 c. Type **12** 15 5
117 25 c. *Phaeomeria speciosa* 15 5
111/17 .. .. *Set of* 7 55 20

For higher values used in conjunction with this series see Nos. 190/7 of Malaysia.

1984 (Mar). *As No. 113 but without wmk.*

120 5 c. *Lagerstroemia speciosa* 5 5

For shade differences between 1979 and 1984 printings see below Johore No. 200.

PENANG

One of the Straits Settlements.
Issues from 1965 are inscribed "PULAU PINANG".

1948 (1 Dec). *Royal Silver Wedding. As Nos. 30/1 of Aden.*

1 10 c. violet 25 10
2 $5 brown .. .. 30·00 35·00

1949 (21 Feb)–**52**. *As T* **58** *of Straits Settlements, but inscr* "PENANG" *at foot. Wmk Mult Script CA. Chalk-surfaced paper. P* 17½ × 18.

3 1 c. black 8 8
4 2 c. orange 8 8
5 3 c. green 12 12
6 4 c. brown 8 5
7 5 c. bright purple (1.9.52) 40 40
8 6 c. grey 12 8
9 8 c. scarlet .. .. 25 1·60
10 8 c. green (1.9.52) .. .. 55 1·00
11 10 c. purple 15 5
12 12 c. scarlet (1.9.52) .. .. 55 1·50
13 15 c. ultramarine 20 30
14 20 c. black and green .. .. 30 1·00
15 20 c. bright blue (1.9.52) 45 15
16 25 c. purple and orange 25 12
17 35 c. scarlet and purple (1.9.52) 60 85
18 40 c. red and purple .. .. 65 4·75
19 50 c. black and blue 60 15
20 $1 blue and purple .. .. 3·00 25
21 $2 green and scarlet .. .. 6·00 75
22 $5 green and brown .. .. 22·00 1·75
3/22 .. .. *Set of* 20 32·00 13·50

1949 (10 Oct). *75th Anniv of U.P.U. As Nos. 114/17 of Antigua.*

23 10 c. purple 15 10
24 15 c. deep blue 55 40
25 25 c. orange 65 70
26 50 c. blue-black .. .. 1·75 2·00

1953 (2 June). *Coronation. As No. 47 of Aden.*

27 10 c. black and reddish purple 25 5

1954 (9 June)–**55**. *As T* **1** *of Malacca* (*Queen Elizabeth II*) *but inscr* "PENANG" *at foot. Chalk-surfaced paper. Wmk Mult Script CA. P* 17½ × 18.

28 1 c. black (5.1.55) 5 30
29 2 c. yellow-orange (8.9.54) 10 20
30 4 c. brown (*shades*) (1.9.54) 15 10
31 5 c. bright purple (*shades*) (1.10.54) 30 20
32 6 c. grey 20 15
33 8 c. green (5.1.55) 30 90
34 10 c. brown-purple (1.9.54) 15 5
35 12 c. rose-red (5.1.55) .. .. 30 1·25
36 20 c. bright blue (1.9.54) 30 15
37 25 c. brown-purple and yellow-orange (1.12.54) 35 10
38 30 c. rose-red and brown-purple (5.9.55) .. 40 15
39 35 c. rose-red and brown-purple (8.9.54) .. 50 25
40 50 c. black and bright blue (1.12.54) 50 10
41 $1 bright blue and brown-purple (1.10.54) .. 2·00 20
42 $2 emerald and scarlet (1.10.54) .. .. 4·00 2·50
43 $5 emerald and brown (5.1.55) .. .. 17·00 4·50
28/43 .. .. *Set of* 16 24·00 10·00

1957. *As Nos. 92/102 of Kedah, but with inset portrait of Queen Elizabeth II.*

44 **9** 1 c. black (21.8) 5 25
45 **10** 2 c. orange-red (25.7) 5 25
46 **11** 4 c. sepia (21.8) 5 5
47 **12** 5 c. carmine-lake (21.8) 5 5
48 **13** 8 c. myrtle-green (21.8) 95 40
49 **14** 10 c. deep brown (4.8) 15 5
50 **15** 20 c. blue (26.6) 20 20
51 **16** 50 c. black and blue (25.7) 30 12
52 **17** $1 ultramarine and reddish purple (25.7) .. .. 2·25 35
53 **18** $2 bronze-green and scarlet (21.8) .. 5·00 5·00
54 **19** $5 brown and bronze-green (26.6) .. 9·00 3·50
44/54 .. .. *Set of* 11 16·00 9·00

The note after No. 86 of Pahang also applies here.

1 Copra

2 *Vanda hookeriana*

(Recess D.L.R.)

1960 (15 Mar). *As Nos. 44/54, but with inset Arms of Penang as in T* **1**. *W w* **12**. *P* 13 × 12½ (1 c. *to* 8 c., $2, $5), 12½ × 13 (10 c. *to* 50 c.) *or* 13½ ($1).

55 1 c. black 5 10
56 2 c. orange-red 5 10
57 4 c. sepia 5 5
58 5 c. carmine-lake 5 5
59 8 c. myrtle-green 95 45
60 10 c. deep maroon 15 5
61 20 c. blue 20 5
62 50 c. black and blue 20 5
a. Imperf (pair) £180
63 $1 ultramarine and reddish purple .. .. 1·00 12
64 $2 bronze-green and scarlet .. .. .. 2·50 1·25
65 $5 brown and bronze-green .. .. .. 7·00 2·25
55/65 .. .. *Set of* 11 11·00 4·00

No. 62a comes from a sheet purchased at the Penang Post Office which had the upper five horizontal rows imperforate.

1965 (15 Nov). *As Nos. 166/72 of Johore but with Arms of Penang inset and inscr* "PULAU PINANG" *as in T* **2**. *W w* **13** (*upright*).

66 1 c. multicoloured 8 10
67 2 c. multicoloured 8 5
68 5 c. multicoloured 10 5
a. Blue (background and inscr) omitted .. 22·00
ab. Blue and yellow omitted .. .. .. 35·00
69 6 c. multicoloured 12 5
70 10 c. multicoloured (*shades*) 15 5
71 15 c. multicoloured 55 5
a. Green (value and leaves) omitted .. 50·00
72 20 c. multicoloured 80 8
a. Bright purple (blooms) omitted .. .. 70·00
66/72 .. .. *Set of* 7 1·75 35

The 2 c., 5 c., 6 c., 10 c. and 20 c. exist with PVA gum as well as gum arabic.
The higher values used with this issue were Nos. 20/27 of Malaysia.

1970. *As Nos. 66 and 70 but W w* **13** (*sideways*).

73 **2** 1 c. multicoloured (27.5.70) 15 80
74 – 10 c. multicoloured (20.11.70) .. .. 1·00 1·50

3 Wanderer

4 *Phaeomeria speciosa*

1971 (1 Feb)–**78**. *As Nos. 175/87 of Johore, but with Arms of Penang and inscr* "pulau pinang", *as in T* **3**.

(*a*) *Litho by Bradbury Wilkinson*

75 1 c. multicoloured 5 15
76 2 c. multicoloured 5 15
77 5 c. multicoloured 15 5
78 6 c. multicoloured 15 5
79 10 c. multicoloured 15 5
80 15 c. multicoloured 30 8
81 20 c. multicoloured 35 8
75/81 .. .. *Set of* 7 1·10 55

(*b*) *Photo by Harrison* (1977–78)

81*a* 1 c. multicoloured .. ..
82 5 c. multicoloured 25 12
83 10 c. multicoloured 25 10
84 15 c. multicoloured 50 30
85 20 c. multicoloured 75 45

The higher values used with this issue were Nos. 64/71 of Malaysia.
For differences between litho and photo printings, see after Johore No. 187.

1979 (30 Apr). *As Nos. 188/94 of Johore but with Arms of Penang and inscr* "pulau pinang" *as in T* **4**.

86 1 c. *Rafflesia hasseltii* 5 5
87 2 c. *Pterocarpus indicus* 5 5
88 5 c. *Lagerstroemia speciosa* 5 5
89 10 c. *Durio zibethinus* 8 5
90 15 c. *Hibiscus rosa-sinensis* 10 5
91 20 c. *Rhododendron scortechinii* 15 5
92 25 c. Type **4** 15 5
86/92 .. .. *Set of* 7 55 20

For higher values used in conjunction with this series see Nos. 190/7 of Malaysia.

PERAK

One of the Federated Malay States.

The stamps of the STRAITS SETTLEMENTS were used in Perak from 1874 until 1878.

PRICES FOR STAMPS ON COVER TO 1945

No. 1	—
Nos. 2/8	*from* × 10
Nos. 9/13	*from* × 20
Nos. 14/15	*from* × 5
Nos. 16/17	*from* × 10
Nos. 18/20	*from* × 15
No. 21	—
No. 22/4	*from* × 10
No. 25	*from* × 50
No. 26	*from* × 15
Nos. 27/9	—
No. 30	*from* × 60
Nos. 31/2	—
Nos. 33/4	*from* × 10
Nos. 35/40	*from* × 12
No. 41	—
Nos. 42/55	*from* × 6
Nos. 57/61	*from* × 12
Nos. 62/75	*from* × 10
No. 76	—
Nos. 77/83	*from* × 5
Nos. 84/98	*from* × 4
Nos. 99/117	*from* × 3

The Official stamps of Perak are rare used on cover.

1878. *T 5 of Straits Settlements optd with Crescent Star and "P" in an oval. Wmk Crown CC.*
1 2 c. brown £950 £750

PERAK (1) Variety (*f*)   PERAK (2)

1880–81. *T 5 of Straits Settlements. Wmk Crown CC, optd as T* **1**.

Varieties. (a) All letters wide. (b) All letters wide, but close together. (c) "R" narrow. (d) "R" and "A" narrow. (e) "P" and "K" wide. (f) All letters narrow. (g) All letters narrow, but close together.

2 1 2 c. brown (*a*) .. .. — £100
3 2 c. brown (*b*) .. .. — 90·00
4 2 c. brown (*c*) .. .. 35·00 38·00
5 2 c. brown (*d*) .. .. 35·00 38·00
6 2 c. brown (*e*) .. .. 90·00 80·00
7 2 c. brown (*f*) .. .. 32·00 38·00
8 2 c. brown (*g*) £110 £100

Variety (*a*) is a single unit setting (1880). Triplet settings are as follows:—1880 (*b*)+(*b*)+(*b*); 1881 (*d*)+(*c*)+(*c*); 1881 (*c*)+(*c*)+(*e*). Variety (*g*) (1880) may be either a single unit or a triplet setting. Variety (*f*) (1881) is probably a triplet setting.

1881. *Same type and wmk, optd with T* **2**.
9 2 2 c. brown .. .. 11·00 11·00

1882–83. *Same type optd as T* **1**. *Wmk Crown CA.*

Varieties. (h) "E" wide. (k) "A" wide

10 1 2 c. brown (*f*) .. .. 8·00 9·50
a. Opt double .. ..
11 2 c. rose (*f*) .. .. 7·00 8·00
12 2 c. rose (*h*) .. .. 7·50 8·50
a. Opt double £450
13 2 c. rose (*k*) .. .. 8·00 8·50

Triplet settings are as follows:—1882, 2 c. brown (*f*)+(*f*)+(*f*). 1883, 2 c. rose (*f*)+(*k*)+(*h*); (*h*)+(*f*)+(*f*); (*h*)+(*f*)+(*k*).

2 CENTS PERAK (3)   2 CENTS PERAK (3*a*)   PERAK (4)

T 5 of Straits Settlements surch or optd. Wmk Crown CA

1883 (July). *Surch vertically upwards.*

(a) "E" of "PERAK" wide (1¾ mm)
14 3 2 c. on 4 c. rose £300 £200

(b) All letters narrow ("E" 1½ mm wide)
15 3 2 c. on 4 c. rose £250 £200

Setting composed of two separate triplets, one for "2 CENTS" and one for "PERAK", the latter composed of two units of No. 15 and one of No. 14. This setting was employed on the lower nine rows of the sheet.

(c) Unified surch ("2 CENTS" spaced 19¾ × 3¼ mm and "PERAK" set closer)
15*a* 3*a* 2 c. on 4 c. rose £500
ab. On Straits No. 12 (wmk Crown CC)

It is believed that T 3*a* occurs only in the top row of the sheet.

1884–90.
16 4 2 c. rose ("E" wide) .. .. .. 85 1·00
a. "PERAK" double .. .. .. — £375
b. "PERAK" inverted £200
17 2 c. rose ("E" narrow) .. .. .. 8·00 9·00
a. "PERAK" inverted £200 £170

Triplet settings occur of:—1884. Nos. 17+16+16; Nos. 16+16+16. There is a setting of 30 (3 × 10) (1888) which contained two units of No. 17, also several settings of 60 (6 × 10) (1888–90) one of which contained three units of No. 17.

The variety "PERAK" inverted occurs in a triple setting and also in one setting of 60.

PERAK (5)   PERAK (6)   PERAK (7)

1886.
18 5 2 c. rose .. .. 60 1·25
a. "FERAK" £100 £100
19 6 2 c. rose .. .. 1·00 3·00
a. Opt double £850
20 7 2 c. rose .. .. 25·00 30·00

No. 18a is usually found with the "F" altered in ink to "P". Nos. 19 and 20 are each triplet settings.

1 CENT (7*a*)   ONE CENT PERAK (8)   1 CENT PERAK (9)

1886? *No. 16 surch with T* 7*a*.
20*a* 5 1 c. on 2 c. rose £1200

1886. *Surch vertically. (a) No stop.*
21 8 1 c. on 2 c. rose £225

(b) Stop after "PERAK"
22 8 1 c. on 2 c. rose .. .. 15·00 16·00
a. Surch double .. ..
23 1 c. on 2 c. (letters "N" wide) .. .. 16·00 16·00

A triplet setting composed of Nos. 22+23+22.

1886.
24 9 1 c. on 2 c. rose .. .. 19·00 20·00
a. Surch double £1300

A triplet setting.

One CENT PERAK (10)   ONE CENT PERAK (11)

1886.
25 10 1 c. on 2 c. rose .. .. 85 1·75
a. "One" inverted £600
b. Surch double £600

A triplet setting. The error occurred in the third unit on part of the printing only.

1887. *Surch vertically.*
26 11 1 c. on 2 c. rose (B.) .. .. .. 7·50 9·50
27 1 c. on 2 c. rose (Blk.) £900 £750

I CENT PERAK (12)   1 CENT PERAK (13)

1886.
28 12 1 c. on 2 c. rose £130 £130

The figure "1" in T **12** is a small roman character. A triplet setting.

1887.
29 13 1 c. on 2 c. rose £500

One CENT PERAK (14)   PERAK ONE CENT. (15)   One CENT PERAK (16)

1887–90.
30 14 1 c. on 2 c. rose 45 90
a. Surch double .. ..

The first printings were in triplet form. Another printing was in a setting of 30 (3 × 10). In later printings it formed the upper five rows of settings of 60.

1889. *As No. 30 but with serifed italic "K".*
31 1 c. on 2 c. rose .. .. 35·00 50·00

1889. *Surch as T* **14**, *but "CENT" in roman (upright) letters as in T* **17**.
32 1 c. on 2 c. rose £225 £225

1889.
33 15 1 c. on 2 c. rose .. .. 35·00 32·00
34 16 1 c. on 2 c. rose .. .. 25·00 32·00

One CENT PERAK (17)   One CENT PERAK (18)   One CENT PERAK. (19)

1889–90.
35 17 1 c. on 2 c. rose .. .. 6·00 7·00
a. "PREAK" £180 £180
36 18 1 c. on 2 c. rose .. .. 3·50 3·75
37 19 1 c. on 2 c. rose .. .. 3·50 3·75

PERAK ONE CENT (20)   One CENT PERAK (21)   PERAK (22)

1890.
38 20 1 c. on 2 c. rose .. .. — 90·00
39 21 1 c. on 2 c. rose .. .. 7·00 6·00

1891.
40 22 2 c. rose .. .. 6·50 12·00

1891. *Optd "PERAK" only, in bold roman letters 2¾ mm high and 13 mm long.*
41 2 c. rose .. ..

PERAK One CENT (23)   PERAK One CENT (24)   PERAK One CENT (25)

PERAK One CENT (26)   PERAK One CENT (27)   PERAK One CENT (28)   PERAK Two CENTS (29)

1891. *Stamps of Straits Settlements surch in settings of 60.*

(a) Without bar through original value
42 23 1 c. on 2 c. rose £120
a. Narrow "O" in "One" .. ..
42*b* 24 1 c. on 2 c. rose £600
42*c* 25 1 c. on 2 c. rose £180
42*d* 26 1 c. on 2 c. rose £400

(b) With bar through original value
43 23 1 c. on 2 c. rose 65 85
a. Narrow "O" in "One" .. .. 6·50 9·00
44 24 1 c. on 2 c. rose .. .. 2·25 3·00
45 25 1 c. on 2 c. rose 45 85
46 26 1 c. on 2 c. rose .. .. 2·25 3·00
47 23 1 c. on 6 c. lilac .. .. 12·00 12·00
48 27 1 c. on 6 c. lilac .. .. 18·00 22·00
49 28 1 c. on 6 c. lilac .. .. 32·00 35·00
50 25 1 c. on 6 c. lilac .. .. 18·00 22·00
51 26 1 c. on 6 c. lilac .. .. 18·00 22·00
52 29 2 c. on 24 c. green .. .. .. 4·00 4·00
53 27 2 c. on 24 c. green .. .. .. 22·00 22·00
54 28 2 c. on 24 c. green .. .. .. 18·00 18·00
55 25 2 c. on 24 c. green .. .. .. 12·00 12·00
56 26 2 c. on 24 c. green .. .. .. 16·00 16·00

The settings for these three surcharges were all based on that used for the 1 c. on 6 c. For this value Type **23** occurs on rows 1 to 5, Type **27** on row 6, Type **28** on row 7, Type **25** on rows 8 and 9, and Type **26** on row 10.

It would appear that this setting was later reset for the other two surcharges with, in each instance, much of the original type reused.

For the 1 c. on 2 c. Type **23** again appears on rows 1 to 5, Type **24** on row 6, Type **25** on rows 7 to 9, and Type **26** on row 10.

For the 2 c. on 24 c. Type **29** occurs on rows 1 to 5, Type **27** on row 6, Type **28** on row 7, Type **25** on rows 8 and 9, and Type **26** on row 10.

The 1 c. on 2 c. without bar come from a small first printing. The variety, "narrow 'O' " (Nos. 42a, 43a), is on row 3, stamp 3.

30

3 CENTS (30*a*)

1892 (1 Jan)–**95.** *Wmk Crown CA. P* 14.
57 30 1 c. green 85 20
58 2 c. rose .. .. 1·00 45
59 2 c. orange (9.9.95) .. .. .. 35 2·75
60 5 c. blue .. .. 1·25 2·50
57/60 Optd "Specimen" .. .. *Set of* 4 £100

1895 (18 Apr). *Surch with T* **30***a*.
61 30 3 c. on 5 c. rose (Optd S. £25) .. .. 55 1·00

31

32

1895–99. *P* 14. *(a) T* **31**. *Wmk Crown CA.*
62 1 c. dull purple and green 55 70
63 2 c. dull purple and brown 75 65
64 3 c. dull purple and carmine .. .. .. 1·50 30
65 4 c. dull purple and carmine (1899) .. .. 2·50 3·75
66 5 c. dull purple and olive-yellow .. .. 2·25 90
67 8 c. dull purple and ultramarine .. .. 10·00 1·00
68 10 c. dull purple and orange .. .. .. 5·50 1·00
69 25 c. green and carmine .. .. .. 38·00 10·00
70 50 c. dull purple and greenish black .. .. 19·00 14·00
71 50 c. green and black (1899) .. .. .. 45·00 45·00

(b) T **32**. *Wmk Crown CC*
72 $1 green and pale green .. .. .. 48·00 35·00
73 $2 green and carmine .. .. .. 70·00 60·00
74 $3 green and ochre .. .. 60·00 60·00
75 $5 green and ultramarine £200 £170
76 $25 green and orange (S. £120) £1200 £350
62/72 .. .. *Set of* 11 £150 £100
62/75 Optd "Specimen" .. .. .. *Set of* 14 £275

One Cent. (33)   ONE CENT. (34)

Three Cent. (35)   Three Cent. (36)

1900. *Stamps of 1895–99 surch.*
77 33 1 c. on 2 c. dull purple and brown .. 35 65
a. Antique "e" in "One" .. .. 28·00 28·00
b. Antique "e" in "Cent" .. .. 26·00 26·00
78 34 1 c. on 4 c. dull purple and carmine .. 35 90
79 33 1 c. on 5 c. dull purple and olive-yellow 40 2·00
a. Antique "e" in "One" .. .. 28·00 28·00
b. Antique "e" in "Cent" .. .. 26·00 26·00
80 35 3 c. on 8 c. dull purple and ultramarine 2·00 2·75
a. Antique "e" in "Cent" .. .. 42·00 42·00
b. No stop after "Cent" .. .. 45·00 45·00
c. Surch double £110 £110
81 3 c. on 50 c. green and black .. 80 2·00
a. Antique "e" in "Cent" .. .. 48·00 48·00
b. No stop after "Cent" .. .. 45·00 45·00
82 36 3 c. on $1 green and pale green .. 30·00 38·00
a. Small "t" in "Cent" £110 £120
b. Surch double .. ..
83 3 c. on $2 green and carmine .. .. 15·00 24·00
77/83 .. .. *Set of* 7 45·00 65·00

The general issues for the FEDERATED MALAY STATES were used in Perak from 1900 until 1935.

37 Sultan Iskandar 38

1935–37. *Chalk-surfaced paper. Wmk Mult Script CA. P* 14.
84 37 1 c. black .. 15 10
85 2 c. green .. 20 10
86 4 c. orange .. 30 15
87 5 c. brown .. 20 10
88 6 c. scarlet .. 2·00 1·75
89 8 c. grey .. 60 10
90 10 c. dull purple .. 20 15
91 12 c. bright ultramarine .. 80 1·25
92 25 c. dull purple and scarlet .. 65 85
93 30 c. dull purple and orange .. 1·00 1·75
94 40 c. scarlet and dull purple .. 2·75 4·25
95 50 c. black/*emerald* .. 2·75 2·00
96 $1 black and red/*blue* .. 4·00 2·25
97 $2 green and scarlet .. 10·00 14·00
98 $5 green and red/*emerald* .. 28·00 25·00
84/98 .. *Set of* 15 48·00 48·00
84/98 Perf "Specimen" *Set of* 15 £180
Dates of issue as for Negri Sembilan.

1938 (2 May)–**41.** *Chalk-surfaced or ordinary paper* (**O**). *Wmk Mult Script CA. P* 14.
99 38 1 c. black (4.39) .. 60 15
100 2 c. green (13.1.39) .. 1·50 12
101 2 c. orange, **OC** (30.10.41) .. 35 2·40
102 3 c. green, **OC** (1941) .. 50 50
103 4 c. orange (5.39) .. 2·50 15
104 5 c. brown (1.2.39) .. 40 5
105 6 c. scarlet (1939) .. 10·00 15
106 8 c. grey (1.12.38) .. 3·75 5
107 8 c. scarlet (1941) .. 1·00 8·50
108 10 c. dull purple (17.10.38) .. 2·75 10
109 12 c. bright ultramarine (17.10.38) .. 5·50 4·00
110 15 c. bright ultramarine, **O** (1941) .. 1·75 12·00
111 25 c. dull purple and scarlet (1939) .. 14·00 4·25
112 30 c. dull purple and orange (17.10.38) .. 1·75 4·25
113 40 c. scarlet and dull purple .. 8·50 3·75
114 50 c. black/*emerald* (17.10.38) .. 3·25 1·25
115 $1 black and red/*blue* (1940) .. 27·00 17·00
116 $2 green and scarlet (9.40) .. 60·00 45·00
117 $5 green and red/*emerald* (1.41) .. £170 £190
99/117 .. *Set of* 19 £275 £275
99/117 Perf "Specimen" *Set of* 19 £350

1948 (1 Dec). *Royal Silver Wedding. As Nos.* 30/1 *of Aden.*
118 10 c. violet .. 20 15
119 $5 green .. 24·00 23·00

1949 (10 Oct). *75th Anniv of Universal Postal Union. As Nos.* 114/17 *of Antigua.*
120 10 c. purple .. 15 5
121 15 c. deep blue .. 70 45
122 25 c. orange .. 80 85
123 50 c. blue-black .. 2·25 2·25

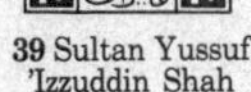

39 Sultan Yussuf 'Izzuddin Shah   40 Sultan Idris Shah

1950 (17 Aug)–**55.** *Chalk-surfaced paper. Wmk Mult Script CA. P* 17½ × 18.
124 39 1 c. black .. 5 5
125 2 c. orange .. 10 5
126 3 c. green (*shades*) .. 50 20
127 4 c. brown (*shades*) .. 10 5
128 5 c. bright purple (*shades*) (1.9.52) .. 30 12
129 6 c. grey .. 12 5
130 8 c. scarlet .. 25 75
131 8 c. green (1.9.52) .. 1·00 60
132 10 c. purple (*shades*) .. 12 5
133 12 c. scarlet (1.9.52) .. 1·00 80
134 15 c. ultramarine .. 25 15
135 20 c. black and green .. 30 30
136 20 c. bright blue (1.9.52) .. 75 5
137 25 c. purple and orange .. 30 5
138 30 c. scarlet and purple (5.9.55) .. 2·75 50
139 35 c. scarlet and purple (1.9.52) .. 80 60
140 40 c. red and purple .. 85 3·00
141 50 c. black and blue .. 50 5
142 $1 blue and purple .. 3·00 20
143 $2 green and scarlet .. 5·50 70
144 $5 green and brown .. 25·00 6·00
124/44 .. *Set of* 21 40·00 13·00

1953 (2 June). *Coronation. As No.* 47 *of Aden.*
145 10 c. black and reddish purple .. 25 5

1957 (26 June)–**61.** *As Nos.* 92/102 *of Kedah but with inset portrait of Sultan Yussuf 'Izzuddin Shah.*
146 1 c. black (21.8.57) .. 5 10
147 2 c. orange-red (25.7.57) .. 5 5
a. Red-orange (15.12.59) .. 10 15
148 4 c. sepia (21.8.57) .. 5 5
149 5 c. carmine-lake (21.8.57) .. 5 5
150 8 c. myrtle-green (21.8.57) .. 1·40 30
151 10 c. deep brown (4.8.57) .. 15 5
152 10 c. deep maroon (21.2.61) .. 25 5
153 20 c. blue .. 20 5
154 50 c. black and blue (*p* 12½) (25.7.57) .. 25 10
a. Perf 12½ × 13 (24.5.60) .. 25 5
155 $1 ultramarine and reddish purple (25.7.57) 2·00 10
156 $2 bronze-green & scar (*p* 12½) (21.8.57) .. 2·75 1·75
a. Perf 13 × 12½ (21.2.61) .. 2·75 1·00
157 $5 brown and bronze-green (*p* 12½) .. 8·00 3·50
a. Perf 13 × 12½ (24.5.60) .. 8·00 2·25
146/57 .. *Set of* 12 14·00 3·50
The 6, 12, 25 and 30 c. values used with this issue were Nos. 1/4 of Malayan Federation.

(Photo Harrison)

1963 (26 Oct). *Installation of the Sultan of Perak. W w* **13**. *P* 14½.
158 40 10 c. red, black, blue and yellow .. 10 8

41 *Vanda hookeriana*   **42** Malayan Jezebel

1965 (15 Nov). *As Nos.* 166/72 *of Johore but with inset portrait of Sultan Idris as in T* **41**. *W w* **13** (*upright*).
159 1 c. multicoloured .. 8 20
160 2 c. multicoloured .. 8 12
161 5 c. multicoloured (*shades*) .. 10 5
162 6 c. multicoloured .. 12 5
163 10 c. multicoloured .. 15 5
164 15 c. multicoloured .. 55 5
a. Magenta (background) omitted .. 60·00
b. Black (country name and head) omitted 80·00
165 20 c. multicoloured .. 80 12
a. Bright purple (blooms) omitted .. 22·00
159/65 .. *Set of* 7 1·75 55
No. 164b comes from a horizontal strip of three, the centre stamp having the black completely omitted. The two outer stamps show the colour partly omitted.
The 2 c. to 15 c. exist with PVA gum as well as gum arabic.
The higher values used with this issue were Nos. 20/27 of Malaysia.

1970. *As Nos.* 159 *and* 163, *but W w* **13** (*sideways*).
166 41 1 c. multicoloured (27.5.70) .. 15 35
167 – 10 c. multicoloured (20.11.70) .. 75 90

1971 (1 Feb)–**78.** *As Nos.* 175/87 *of Johore, but with portrait of Sultan Idris and arms, as in T* **42**.

(*a*) *Litho by Bradbury, Wilkinson*
168 1 c. multicoloured .. 5 12
169 2 c. multicoloured .. 5 12
170 5 c. multicoloured .. 15 5
171 6 c. multicoloured .. 15 5
172 10 c. multicoloured .. 15 5
173 15 c. multicoloured .. 30 8
174 20 c. multicoloured .. 35 8
168/74 .. *Set of* 7 1·10 50

(*b*) *Photo by Harrison* (1977–78)
175 1 c. multicoloured .. 10 20
176 5 c. multicoloured .. 20 12
177 10 c. multicoloured .. 25 10
178 15 c. multicoloured .. 50 25
179 20 c. multicoloured .. 75 35
The higher values used with this issue were Nos. 64/71 of Malaysia.
For differences between litho and photo printings, see after Johore, No. 187.

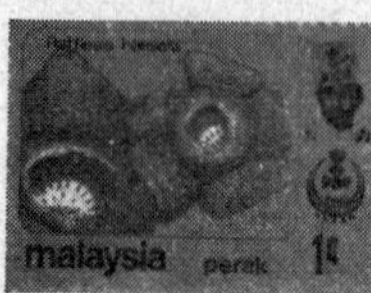

43 *Rafflesia hasseltii*

1979 (30 Apr). *As Nos.* 188/94 *of Johore but with portrait of Sultan Idris as in T* **43**.
180 1 c. Type **43** .. 5 5
181 2 c. *Pterocarpus indicus* .. 5 5
182 5 c. *Lagerstroemia speciosa* .. 5 5
183 10 c. *Durio zibethinus* .. 8 5
184 15 c. *Hibiscus rosa-sinensis* .. 10 5
185 20 c. *Rhododendron scortechinii* .. 15 5
186 25 c. *Phaeomeria speciosa* .. 15 5
180/6 .. *Set of* 7 55 20
For higher values used in conjunction with this series see Nos. 190/7 of Malaysia.

1984 (Mar–Sept). *As No.* 182/3 *but without wmk.*
189 5 c. *Lagerstroemia speciosa* .. 5 5
190 10 c. *Durio zibethinus* (9.84) .. 8 10
For shade differences between 1979 and 1984 printings see below Johore No. 200.
On No. 189 the portrait and arms are redrawn smaller.

OFFICIAL STAMPS

P.G.S. (O 1)   Service. (O 2)

1889 (1 Nov). *Stamps of Straits Settlements optd with Type* O **1**. *Wmk Crown CC* (*Nos.* O6 *and* O8) *or Crown CA* (*others*).
O1 2 c. rose .. 2·50 2·50
a. Overprint double .. £850 £850
b. No stop after "S" .. 27·00 28·00
c. Wide space between "G" and "S" .. 30·00 32·00
O2 4 c. brown .. 6·50 9·00
a. No stop after "S" .. 60·00 75·00
b. Wide space between "G" and "S" .. 50·00 60·00
O3 6 c. lilac .. 18·00 25·00
a. Wide space between "G" and "S" .. 60·00 75·00
O4 8 c. orange .. 22·00 25·00
a. Wide space between "G" and "S" .. 60·00 75·00
O5 10 c. slate .. 35·00 35·00
a. Wide space between "G" and "S" .. 95·00 95·00
O6 12 c. blue (CC) .. 70·00 80·00
a. Wide space between "G" and "S" .. £225
O7 12 c. brown-purple (CA) .. £110 £130
a. Wide space between "G" and "S" .. £225
O8 24 c. green (CC) .. £250 £275
a. Wide space between "G" and "S" .. £650
O9 24 c. green (CA) .. 70·00 80·00
a. Wide space between "G" and "S" .. £225

1894 (1 June). *No.* 60 *optd with Type* O **2**.
O10 5 c. blue .. 11·00 90
a. Overprint inverted .. 95·00 95·00

1897. *No.* 66 *optd with Type* O **2**.
O11 5 c. dull purple and olive-yellow .. 1·40 45
a. Overprint double .. 90·00 90·00

PERLIS

One of the Unfederated States.

The stamps of THAILAND were used in Perlis at Kangar (Muang Perlis) until the State was transferred to the protection of Great Britain in 1909. Issues of the FEDERATED MALAY STATES were in use from 1909 until 1912 and these were replaced by the stamps of KEDAH between 1912 and 1942.

1948 (1 Dec). *Royal Silver Wedding. As Nos. 30/1 of Aden.*

No.	Type	Description	Unused	Used
1		10 c. violet	25	70
2		$5 brown	27·00	48·00

1949 (10 Oct). *75th Anniv of U.P.U. As Nos. 114/17 of Antigua.*

No.	Type	Description	Unused	Used
3		10 c. purple	25	60
4		15 c. deep blue	75	2·00
5		25 c. orange	90	2·25
6		50 c. blue-black	2·25	4·75

1 Raja Syed Putra

2 *Vanda hookeriana*

1951 (26 Mar)–**55.** *Chalk-surfaced paper. Wmk Mult Script CA. P* 17½ × 18.

No.	Type	Description	Unused	Used
7	1	1 c. black	5	40
8		2 c. orange	10	40
9		3 c. green	40	1·50
10		4 c. brown	12	25
11		5 c. bright purple (1.9.52)	30	65
12		6 c. grey	15	25
13		8 c. scarlet	35	1·50
14		8 c. green (1.9.52)	75	1·75
15		10 c. purple	15	20
16		12 c. scarlet (1.9.52)	75	1·75
17		15 c. ultramarine	60	1·50
18		20 c. black and green	80	2·50
19		20 c. bright blue (1.9.52)	85	75
20		25 c. purple and orange	50	90
21		30 c. scarlet and purple (5.9.55)	3·00	3·75
22		35 c. scarlet and purple (1.9.52)	1·00	2·75
23		40 c. red and purple	1·50	6·00
24		50 c. black and blue	60	90
25		$1 blue and purple	3·00	6·00
26		$2 green and scarlet	8·50	22·00
27		$5 green and brown	27·00	42·00
7/27		*Set of* 21	45·00	85·00

1953 (2 June). *Coronation. As No. 47 of Aden.*

No.	Type	Description	Unused	Used
28		10 c. black and reddish purple	25	60

1957 (26 June)–**62.** *As Nos. 92/102 of Kedah but with inset portrait of Raja Syed Putra.*

No.	Type	Description	Unused	Used
29	**9**	1 c. black (21.8.57)	5	10
30	**10**	2 c. orange-red (25.7.57)	8	12
31	**11**	4 c. sepia (21.8.57)	8	5
32	**12**	5 c. carmine-lake (21.8.57)	10	10
33	**13**	8 c. myrtle-green (21.8.57)	1·40	80
34	**14**	10 c. deep brown (4.8.57)	15	15
35		10 c. deep maroon (14.3.61)	30	12
36	**15**	20 c. blue	25	35
37	**16**	50 c. black and blue (*p* 12½) (25.7.57)	30	60
		a. Perf 12½ × 13 (8.5.62)	30	50
38	**17**	$1 ultram & reddish purple (25.7.57)	2·00	4·00
39	**18**	$2 bronze-green and scarlet (25.7.57)	3·50	6·00
40	**19**	$5 brown and bronze-green (21.8.57)	9·50	12·00
29/40		*Set of* 12	16·00	22·00

The 6, 12, 25 and 30 c. values used with this issue were Nos. 1/4 of Malayan Federation.

1965 (15 Nov). *As Nos. 166/72 of Johore but with inset portrait of Tunku Bendahara Abu Bakar as in T* **2**.

No.	Type	Description	Unused	Used
41		1 c. multicoloured	8	25
42		2 c. multicoloured	8	30
43		5 c. multicoloured	15	5
44		6 c. multicoloured	20	10
45		10 c. multicoloured	20	10
46		15 c. multicoloured	55	35
47		20 c. multicoloured	80	45
41/7		*Set of* 7	1·90	1·40

The 6 c. exists with PVA gum as well as gum arabic.

The higher values used with this issue were Nos. 20/27 of Malaysia.

3 Black-veined Tiger

4 Raja Syed Putra

1971 (1 Feb)–**78.** *As Nos. 175/87 of Johore but with portrait of Raja Syed Putra and Arms, as in T* **3**.

(*a*) *Litho by Bradbury, Wilkinson*

No.	Type	Description	Unused	Used
48		1 c. multicoloured	5	15
49		2 c. multicoloured	5	15
50		5 c. multicoloured	15	5
51		6 c. multicoloured	15	12
52		10 c. multicoloured	15	5
53		15 c. multicoloured	30	25
54		20 c. multicoloured	35	25
48/54		*Set of* 7	1·10	90

(*b*) *Photo by Harrison* (1977–78)

No.	Type	Description	Unused	Used
54*a*		10 c. multicoloured		
55		15 c. multicoloured	40	60
55*a*		20 c. multicoloured	4·00	4·00

The higher values used with this issue were Nos. 64/71 of Malaysia.

For differences between litho and photo printings, see after Johore No. 187.

(Des Citizen Studio and Engravers. Litho Enschedé)

1971 (28 Mar). *25th Anniv of Installation of Raja Syed Putra. P* 13½ × 13.

No.	Type	Description	Unused	Used
56	**4**	10 c. multicoloured	12	8
57		15 c. multicoloured	15	15
58		50 c. multicoloured	70	1·00

5 *Pterocarpus indicus*

1979 (30 Apr). *As Nos. 188/94 of Johore but with portrait of Raja Syed Putra as in T* **5**.

No.	Type	Description	Unused	Used
59		1 c. *Rafflesia hasseltii*	5	5
60		2 c. Type **5**	5	5
61		5 c. *Lagerstroemia speciosa*	5	5
62		10 c. *Durio zibethinus*	8	5
63		15 c. *Hibiscus rosa-sinensis*	10	5
64		20 c. *Rhododendron scortechinii*	15	10
65		25 c. *Phaeomeria speciosa*	15	12
59/65		*Set of* 7	55	40

For higher values used in conjunction with this series see Nos. 190/7 of Malaysia.

SELANGOR

One of the Federated Malay States.

The stamps of the STRAITS SETTLEMENTS were used in Selangor from 1874 until 1881.

PRICES FOR STAMPS ON COVER TO 1945

Nos. 1/2	*from* × 20
Nos. 3/7	—
Nos. 8/18	*from* × 6
Nos. 19/29	*from* × 8
Nos. 30/2	*from* × 20
Nos. 33/5	*from* × 15
Nos. 36/8	*from* × 10
Nos. 39/41	—
Nos. 42/3	*from* × 4
Nos. 44/8	*from* × 5
Nos. 49/53	*from* × 20
Nos. 54/66	*from* × 6
Nos. 66*a*/7	*from* × 4
Nos. 68/85	*from* × 3
Nos. 86/7	*from* × 4

The Straits Settlements 1867 2 c. brown with Crown CC watermark (No. 11) has been known since 1881 overprinted in black with a crescent and star over a capital S, all within an oval, similar in style to the overprints listed for Perak and Sungei Ujong.

The status of this item remains unclear, but it may well represent the first issue of distinctive stamps for Selangor. This overprint should not be confused with a somewhat similar cancellation used on Selangor stamps of the same period. This cancellation differs in having a circular frame with the capital S shown above the crescent and star. It is usually struck in red.

A similar overprint in red on the Straits Settlements 2 c. brown with Crown CA watermark is known to be bogus.

SELANGOR

(1)

1881–82. *T* **5** *of Straits Settlements, wmk Crown CC, optd as T* **1**.

Varieties. (*a*) *All letters narrow.* (*b*) "S" wide. (*c*) "S", "E", "A", *and* "N" *wide.* (*d*) "SELAN" *wide.* (*e*) "SEL" *and* "N" *wide.* (*f*) "EL" *wide.* (*g*) "E" *wide.* (*s*) "N" *wide.*

No.	Type	Description	Unused	Used
1	1	2 c. brown (*a*)	15·00	16·00
		a. "S" inverted	75·00	85·00
2		2 c. brown (*b*)	17·00	23·00
3		2 c. brown (*c*)	42·00	50·00
4		2 c. brown (*d*)	42·00	50·00
5		2 c. brown (*e*)	45·00	55·00
6		2 c. brown (*s*)	—	£1000

Overprinted in triplets composed of: 1881 (*a*) + (*b*) + (*a*); 1881 (*b*) + (*a*) + (*a*); 1882 (*c*) + (*e*) + (*d*). The setting containing (*s*) (1881) is not known.

1882. *Same type, wmk Crown CA, optd with capital* "S".

No.	Type	Description	Unused	Used
7		2 c. brown	—	£1000

1882–83. *T* **5** *of Straits Settlements, wmk Crown CA optd as T* **1**.

Varieties. (*i*) "SEL", "N", *and* "G" *wide.* (*j*) "E" *and* "ANG" *wide.* (*k*) "ELANG" *wide.* (*l*) "SE" *and* "N" *wide.* (*m*) "S" *and* "N" *wide.* (*n*) "S" *and* "A" *wide.* (*o*) "S" *and* "L" *wide.*

No.	Type	Description	Unused	Used
8	1	2 c. brown (*a*)	27·00	27·00
9		2 c. brown (*b*)	30·00	30·00
10		2 c. brown (*f*)	42·00	42·00
11		2 c. brown (*g*)	40·00	40·00
12		2 c. brown (*i*)	40·00	40·00
13		2 c. brown (*j*)	40·00	40·00
14		2 c. brown (*k*)	40·00	40·00
15		2 c. brown (*l*)	24·00	24·00
16		2 c. brown (*m*)	24·00	24·00
17		2 c. brown (*n*)	75·00	75·00
18		2 c. brown (*o*)	—	£500

Triplets are known of: 1882 (*i*) + (*j*) + (*k*); 1883 (*n*) + (*g*) + (*f*); 1883 (*l*) + (*b*) + (*m*); 1882 (*b*) + (*a*) + (*a*) are known in a pair; 1883 (*o*) is the first unit of a triplet but the second and third units are not yet known.

1883–85. *Wmk Crown CA.*

Varieties. (*p*) "E" *and* "A" *wide.* (*q*) "A" *wide.* (*r*) "L" *wide.* (*s*) "N" *wide.* (*t*) *all letters wide.* (*u*) "A" *narrow.* (*v*) "L" *narrow.*

No.	Type	Description	Unused	Used
19	1	2 c. rose (*b*)	20·00	23·00
20		2 c. rose (*f*)	16·00	16·00
21		2 c. rose (*g*)	16·00	18·00
22		2 c. rose (*o*)	23·00	23·00
23		2 c. rose (*p*)	20·00	22·00
24		2 c. rose (*q*)	28·00	24·00
25		2 c. rose (*r*)	35·00	25·00
26		2 c. rose (*s*)	22·00	20·00
27		2 c. rose (*t*)	28·00	24·00
28		2 c. rose (*u*)	16·00	22·00
29		2 c. rose (*v*)	16·00	17·00

Triplets are known of: 1883 (*o*) + (*g*) + (*g*); 1884 (*s*) + (*s*) + (*f*); 1884 (*b*) + (*p*) + (*f*); 1885 (*v*) + (*u*) + (*v*). The settings containing (1884) (*q*) and (*r*) and (1885) (*t*) are not known.

The 2 c. with all letters narrow, formerly listed, does not exist. Specimens with the wide "A" or wide "L" may be mistaken for this variety where these letters are defective, but may be detected by the spacing.

T* 5 *of Straits Settlements, wmk Crown CA, optd "SELANGOR" in various types

SELANGOR	SELANGOR	*Selangor*
(2)	(3)	(4)

1885.

No.	Type	Description	Unused	Used
30	2	2 c. rose	2·25	2·75
		a. Opt double	—	£600
31	3	2 c. rose (Oct)	3·50	4·00
32	4	2 c. rose	£300	£350

SELANGOR (5) SELANGOR. (6)

1886 (May)–**87.**

33	**5**	2 c. rose	8·00	8·00
34	**6**	2 c. rose (with stop) (8.87)	4·50	4·75
35		2 c. rose (without stop) (1887)	2·75	2·75

SELANGOR (7) SELANGOR (8)

SELANGOR (9)

1889. (a) *Optd vertically.*

36	**7**	2 c. rose	£110	20·00
37	**8**	2 c. rose (Feb)	40·00	32·00
38	**9**	2 c. rose (Feb)	8·00	5·00
		(b) *Opt similar to T 8, but diagonal*		
39		2 c. rose	£450	
		(c) *Opt as T 9 horizontally*		
40		2 c. rose	£1500	

1890. *Optd with T 6 vertically. No stop.*

41	2 c. deep rose	7·50	8·50

SELANGOR (10) SELANGOR (11)

1890–91.

42	**10**	2 c. rose	28·00	2·25
43	**11**	2 c. deep rose (1891)	£180	£130

SELANGOR Two CENTS (12) SELANGOR Two CENTS (13) SELANGOR Two CENTS (14)

SELANGOR Two CENTS (15) SELANGOR Two CENTS (16)

1891. *T* **7** *of Straits Settlements, surch horizontally, with bar obliterating old value.*

44	**12**	2 c. on 24 c. green	6·00	8·50
45	**13**	2 c. on 24 c. green	40·00	50·00
46	**14**	2 c. on 24 c. green	40·00	50·00
47	**15**	2 c. on 24 c. green	28·00	35·00
		a. "SELANGCR"		
48	**16**	2 c. on 24 c. green	40·00	50·00

Nos. 44/8 come from the one setting used to surcharge the panes of sixty. No. 44 occurs in rows 1 to 5, No. 45 on row 6, No. 46 on row 7, No. 47 on rows 8 and 9, and No. 48 on row 10.

The error, No. 47a, occurs in the first printing only and is No. 45 (R.8/3) on the pane.

17

3 CENTS (17*a*)

1891–95. *Wmk Crown CA. P* 14.

49	**17**	1 c. green	80	40
50		2 c. rose	1·50	45
51		2 c. orange (1895)	65	45
52		5 c. blue	3·75	2·00
49/52 Optd "Specimen"		*Set of* 4	90·00	

1894. *Surch with T* **17***a*.

53	**17**	3 c. on 5 c. rose (Optd S. £30)	55	40

18 19

1895–98. *Wmk Crown CA or Crown CC (dollar values). P* 14.

54	**18**	3 c. dull purple and carmine	2·75	25
55		5 c. dull purple and olive-yellow	50	30
56		8 c. dull purple and ultramarine	27·00	7·00
57		10 c. dull purple and orange	4·50	30
58		25 c. green and carmine	28·00	20·00
59		50 c. green and black	90·00	35·00
60		50 c. dull purple and greenish black	15·00	9·00
61	**19**	$1 green and yellow-green	24·00	20·00
62		$2 green and carmine	50·00	42·00
63		$3 green and ochre	£100	60·00
64		$5 green and blue	50·00	60·00
65		$10 green and purple (S. £90)	£200	£100
66		$25 green and orange (S. £175)	£525	
54/62		*Set of* 9	£225	£120
54/64 Optd "Specimen"		*Set of* 11	£190	

One cent. (20) Three cents. (21)

1900. *Nos. 55 and 59 surch with T* **20** *or* **21**.

66*a*	**18**	1 c. on 5 c. dull purple and olive-yellow	18·00	24·00
66*b*		1 c. on 50 c. green and black	1·00	3·75
		c. "cent" repeated at left	£650	
67		3 c. on 50 c. green and black	6·00	7·00
		a. Antique "t" in "cents"	65·00	65·00

The general issues for the FEDERATED MALAY STATES were used in Selangor from 1900 until 1935.

22 Mosque at Palace, Klang

23 Sultan Suleiman

(Des E. J. McNaughton)

1935–41. *Chalk-surfaced or ordinary paper* (**O**). *Wmk Mult Script CA. P* 14 *or* 14 × 14½ (*No.* 70).

68	**22**	1 c. black	25	5
69		2 c. green	20	5
70		2 c. orange, **OC** (21.8.41)	15	2·00
		a. Perf 14, **O** (9.41)	7·00	2·25
71		3 c. green, **OC**	35	2·00
72		4 c. orange	20	5
73		5 c. brown	20	5
74		6 c. scarlet	2·75	15
75		8 c. grey	40	15
76		10 c. dull purple	40	5
77		12 c. bright ultramarine	2·25	20
78		15 c. bright ultramarine, **O**	1·90	13·00
79		25 c. dull purple and scarlet	1·50	1·75
80		30 c. dull purple and orange	2·25	2·75
81		40 c. scarlet and dull purple	2·50	4·00
82		50 c. black/*emerald*	1·90	50
83	**23**	$1 black and rose/*blue*	5·00	70
84		$2 green and scarlet	18·00	10·00
85		$5 green and red/*emerald*	45·00	32·00
68/85		*Set of* 18	75·00	65·00
68/85 Perf "Specimen"		*Set of* 18	£250	

Dates of issue as for Negri Sembilan, except Nos. 70/a.

Supplies of an unissued 8 c. scarlet were diverted to Australia in 1941. Examples circulating result from leakages of this supply.

24 Sultan Hisamud-din Alam Shah 25

1941. *Wmk Mult Script CA. P* 14.

86	**24**	$1 black and red/*blue*, **C** (15.4.41)	5·50	8·00
87		$2 grn & scar, **C** (7.7.41) (Perf S. £70)	25·00	30·00

A $5 green and red on emerald, T **24**, was issued overprinted during the Japanese occupation of Malaya. Unoverprinted examples are known, but were not issued thus.

1948 (1 Dec). *Royal Silver Wedding. As Nos.* 30/1 *of Aden.*

88	10 c. violet	20	8
89	$5 green	26·00	30·00

1949 (12 Sept)–**55.** *Chalk-surfaced paper. Wmk Mult Script CA. P* 17½ × 18.

90	**25**	1 c. black	5	12
91		2 c. orange	8	12
92		3 c. green	20	65
93		4 c. brown	10	5
94		5 c. bright purple (*shades*) (1.9.52)	20	10
95		6 c. grey	12	5
96		8 c. scarlet	25	1·00
97		8 c. green (1.9.52)	65	70
98		10 c. purple	12	5
99		12 c. scarlet (1.9.52)	80	90
100		15 c. ultramarine	25	10
101		20 c. black and green	40	35
102		20 c. bright blue (1.9.52)	80	5
103		25 c. purple and orange	35	5
104		30 c. scarlet and purple (5.9.55)	2·75	50
105		35 c. scarlet and purple (1.9.52)	80	80
106		40 c. scarlet and purple	90	2·00
107		50 c. black and blue	50	5
108		$1 blue and purple	2·25	10
109		$2 green and scarlet	6·00	25
110		$5 green and brown	26·00	1·25
90/110		*Set of* 21	40·00	8·00

1949 (10 Oct). *75th Anniv of Universal Postal Union. As Nos.* 114/17 *of Antigua.*

111	10 c. purple	15	5
112	15 c. deep blue	45	45
113	25 c. orange	50	60
114	50 c. blue-black	1·10	90

1953 (2 June). *Coronation. As No.* 47 *of Aden.*

115	10 c. black and reddish purple	25	5

1957 (26 June)–**61.** *As Nos.* 92/102 *of Kedah but with inset portrait of Sultan Hisamud-din Alam Shah.*

116	1 c. black (21.8.57)	5	20
117	2 c. orange-red (*shades*) (25.7.57)	5	15
118	4 c. sepia (21.8.57)	5	5
119	5 c. carmine-lake (21.8.57)	5	5
120	8 c. myrtle-green (21.8.57)	1·10	20
121	10 c. deep brown (4.8.57)	15	5
122	10 c. deep maroon (9.5.61)	25	5
123	20 c. blue	25	5
124	50 c. black and blue (*p* 12½) (25.7.57)	25	5
	a. Perf 12½ × 13 (10.5.60)	25	5
125	$1 ultramarine and reddish purple (25.7.57)	1·25	10
126	$2 bronze-green & scarlet (*p* 12½) (21.8.57)	2·25	1·00
	a. Perf 13 × 12½ (6.12.60)	2·00	1·00
127	$5 brown and bronze-green (*p* 12½)	6·50	1·50
	a. Perf 13 × 12½ (10.5.60)	4·75	1·00
116/27a	*Set of* 12	9·00	2·50

The 6, 12 and 30 c. values used with this issue were Nos. 1/4 of Malayan Federation.

26 Sultan Salahuddin Abdul Aziz Shah

27 Sultan Salahuddin Abdul Aziz Shah

(Photo Harrison)

1961 (28 June). *Installation of the Sultan.* W w **12.** *P* 15 × 14.

128	**26**	10 c. multicoloured	10	5
		a. Black ptg misplaced	£110	

No. 128a is "The Double-headed Sultan" error, from one sheet where the majority of the stamps showed considerable black printing misplacement.

1961–62. *As Nos.* 92/8 *of Kedah but with inset portrait of Sultan Salahuddin Abdul Aziz as in T* **27.** W w **13.** *P* 12½ × 13 (*vert*) *or* 13 × 12½ (*horiz*).

129	1 c. black (1.3.62)	5	30
130	2 c. orange-red (1.3.62)	5	20
131	4 c. sepia (1.3.62)	5	5
132	5 c. carmine-lake (1.3.62)	5	5
133	8 c. myrtle-green (1.3.62)	60	35
134	10 c. deep maroon (1.11.61)	10	5
135	20 c. blue (1.3.62)	20	5
129/35	*Set of* 7	1·00	85

28 *Vanda hookeriana*

29 Clipper Butterfly

1965 (15 Nov). *As Nos.* 166/72 *of Johore but with inset portrait of Sultan Salahuddin Abdul Aziz Shah as in T* **28**.

136	1 c. multicoloured	8	5
	a. Magenta omitted	24·00	
137	2 c. multicoloured	8	12
138	5 c. multicoloured	10	5
139	6 c. multicoloured	12	5
140	10 c. multicoloured	15	5
141	15 c. multicoloured	55	5
	a. Green (value and leaves) omitted	90·00	
142	20 c. multicoloured	80	8
	a. Bright purple (blooms) omitted	23·00	
136/42	*Set of* 7	1·75	40

The 2 c. to 20 c. values exist with PVA gum as well as gum arabic.

The higher values used with this issue were Nos. 20/27 of Malaysia.

1970 (20 Nov). *As Nos.* 136 *etc. but* W w **13** (*sideways*).

143	**28**	1 c. multicoloured	15	30
144	–	10 c. multicoloured	40	15
145	–	20 c. multicoloured	90	75

1971 (1 Feb)–**78.** *As Nos.* 175/87 *of Johore but with portrait of Sultan Salahuddin Abdul Aziz Shah and Arms, as in T* **29**.

	(a) *Litho by Bradbury, Wilkinson*		
146	1 c. multicoloured	5	15
147	2 c. multicoloured	5	20
148	5 c. multicoloured	15	5
149	6 c. multicoloured	15	5
150	10 c. multicoloured	20	5
	a. Black (state inscr, portrait and arms) omitted		
151	15 c. multicoloured	30	5
152	20 c. multicoloured	35	5
146/52	*Set of* 7	1·10	50
	(b) *Photo by Harrison* (1977–78)		
153	1 c. multicoloured	10	20
154	5 c. multicoloured	20	10
155	10 c. multicoloured	30	10
156	15 c. multicoloured	50	25
157	20 c. multicoloured	60	35

The higher values used with this issue were Nos. 64/71 of Malaysia.

For differences between litho and photo printings see after Johore No. 187.

A used example of No. 150 has been seen with the magenta apparently missing.

For explanation of No. 150a, see note below No. 122 of Kelantan.

NEW INFORMATION

The editor is always interested to correspond with people who have new information that will improve or correct the Catalogue.

30 *Lagerstroemia speciosa*

1979 (30 Apr). *As Nos.* 188/94 *of Johore but with portrait of Sultan Salahuddin Abdul Aziz Shah as in T* **30**.

No.	Description	Unused	Used
158	1 c. *Rafflesia hasseltii*	5	5
159	2 c. *Pterocarpus indicus*	5	5
160	5 c. Type **30**	5	5
161	10 c. *Durio zibethinus*	8	5
162	15 c. *Hibiscus rosa-sinensis*	10	5
163	20 c. *Rhododendron scortechinii*	15	5
164	25 c. *Phaeomeria speciosa*	15	5
158/64	*Set of* 7	55	20

For higher values used in conjunction with this series see Nos. 190/7 of Malaysia.

1984 (Mar). *As Nos.* 160 *and* 163 *but without wmk.*

No.	Description	Unused	Used
166	5 c. Type **30**	5	5
169	20 c. *Rhododendron scortechinii*	15	20

For shade differences between 1979 and 1984 printings, see below Johore No. 200.

TRENGGANU

One of the Unfederated States.

The stamps of the STRAITS SETTLEMENTS were used in Trengganu during 1910, pending arrival of the stamps listed below.

PRICES FOR STAMPS ON COVER TO 1945

Nos. 1/17	*from* × 8
No. 18	—
Nos. 19/22	*from* × 6
Nos. 23/33	*from* × 8
Nos. 34/6	—
Nos. 37/47	*from* × 15
Nos. 48/60	*from* × 6
Nos. D1/4	*from* × 10

RED CROSS

2c.

1 Sultan Zain ul ab din 2 (3)

1910–19. *T* **1** *and* **2** *($5 and $25). Wmk Mult Crown CA. P* 14.

No.	Type	Description	Unused	Used
1	1	1 c. blue-green, **O**	70	90
		a. Green, **O**	75	75
2		2 c. brown and purple, **C** (1915)	80	90
3		3 c. carmine-red, **O**	1·75	1·75
4		4 c. orange, **O**	2·25	4·00
5		4 c. red-brown and green, **C** (1915)	2·00	3·75
5*a*		4 c. carmine-red, **O** (1919)	70	1·50
6		5 c. grey, **O**	1·25	2·25
7		5 c. grey and brown, **C** (1915)	2·75	2·00
8		8 c. ultramarine, **O**	1·25	4·50
9		10 c. purple/*yellow*	4·00	6·00
		a. On pale yellow	3·00	2·50
10		10 c. green and red/*yellow*, **O** (1915)	1·50	3·25
11		20 c. dull and bright purple, **C**	3·25	4·50
12		25 c. green and dull purple, **C** (1915)	4·00	8·50
13		30 c. dull purple and black, **C** (1915)	4·00	8·50
14		50 c. black/*green*, **C**	5·00	6·50
15		$1 black and carmine/*blue*, **C**	9·00	17·00
16		$3 green and red/*green*, **C** (1915)	45·00	60·00
17	2	$5 green and dull purple, **C**	85·00	£130
18		$25 rose-carm & grn, **C** (Optd S. £150)	£650	
1/17		*Set of* 18	£150	£225
1/17 Optd "Specimen"		*Set of* 18	£375	

1917 (Oct). *Surch with T* **3**.

No.	Type	Description	Unused	Used
19	1	2 c. on 3 c. carmine-red	40	2·00
		a. Comma after "2 c."	2·75	6·00
		b. "SS" in "CROSS" inverted	£180	£180
		c. "CSOSS" for "CROSS"	35·00	45·00
		d. "2" in thick block type	8·50	15·00
		e. Surch inverted	£375	£375
		f. Pair, one without surch	£650	£600
20		2 c. on 4 c. orange	80	3·75
		a. Comma after "2 c."	9·00	20·00
		b. "SS" in "CROSS" inverted	£550	£300
		c. "CSOSS" for "CROSS"	£110	£140
		d. Surch double	£300	
21		2 c. on 8 c. ultramarine	85	6·50
		a. Comma after "2 c."	9·00	23·00
		b. "SS" in "CROSS" inverted	£550	
		c. "CSOSS" for "CROSS"	90·00	£100
		d. "RED CROSS" double	£250	

1918. *Colour changed.*

No.	Type	Description	Unused	Used
22	1	2 c. on 4 c. red-brown and green	1·40	7·50
		a. Pair, one without surch	£450	

During a temporary shortage in 1921, 2 c., 4 c. and 6 c. stamps of the STRAITS SETTLEMENTS were authorised for use in Trengganu.

2 CENTS

4 Sultan Suleiman 5 (6)

1921. *Chalk-surfaced paper. P* 14. (*a*) *Wmk Mult Crown CA.*

No.	Type	Description	Unused	Used
23	4	$1 purple and blue/*blue*	11·00	14·00
24		$3 green and red/*emerald*	35·00	48·00
25	5	$5 green and red/*pale yellow*	55·00	75·00

(*b*) *Wmk Mult Script CA*

No.	Type	Description	Unused	Used
26	4	2 c. green	70	15
27		4 c. carmine-red	50	12
28		5 c. grey and deep brown	2·50	2·50
29		10 c. bright blue	2·75	15
30		20 c. dull purple and orange	2·50	2·50
31		25 c. green and deep purple	2·75	2·50
32		30 c. dull purple and black	3·25	1·25
33		50 c. green and bright carmine	3·25	1·25
34	5	$25 purple and blue (S. £70)	£400	£450
35		$50 green and yellow (S. £150)	£950	£1300
36		$100 green and scarlet (S. £300)	£3000	
23/33		*Set of* 11	£110	£130
23/33 Optd "Specimen"		*Set of* 11	£250	

1922 (31 Mar). *Optd* "MALAYA–BORNEO EXHIBITION" *as T* **56** *of Straits Settlements at Singapore.*

No.	Type	Description	Unused	Used
37	4	2 c. green	75	6·00
38		4 c. carmine-red	3·00	7·50
39	1	5 c. grey and brown	3·00	8·50
40		10 c. green and red/*yellow*	3·00	9·50
41		20 c. dull and bright purple	2·00	10·00
42		25 c. green and dull purple	2·00	11·00
43		30 c. dull purple and black	2·25	11·00
44		50 c. black/*green*	2·50	12·00
45		$1 black and carmine/*blue*	13·00	30·00
46		$3 green and red/*green*	£110	£250
47	2	$5 green and dull purple	£190	£375
37/47		*Set of* 11	£300	£650

Minor varieties of this overprint exist as in Straits Settlements.

1924–38. *New values, etc. Chalk-surfaced paper. Wmk Mult Script CA. P* 14.

No.	Type	Description	Unused	Used
48	4	1 c. black (1926)	40	20
49		3 c. green (1926)	50	85
50		3 c. brown (1938)	4·25	4·25
51		5 c. purple/*yellow* (1926)	1·25	80
52		6 c. orange (1924)	3·25	40
53		8 c. grey (1938)	6·00	80
54		12 c. bright ultramarine (1926)	3·75	4·25
55		35 c. carmine/*yellow* (1926)	3·75	8·00
56		$1 purple and blue/*blue* (1929)	10·00	5·50
57		$3 green and red/*green* (1926)	28·00	42·00
58	5	$5 green and red/*yellow* (1938)	£225	£550
48/58		*Set of* 11	£250	£550
48/58 Optd/Perf "Specimen"		*Set of* 11	£325	

The 2 c. yellow, 6 c. grey, 8 c. red and 15 c. blue were issued, but only with opt during the Japanese occupation of Malaya. Unoverprinted specimens are due to leakages.

1941 (1 May). *Nos.* 51 *and* 29 *surch as T* **6**.

No.	Type	Description	Unused	Used
59	4	2 c. on 5 c. purple/*yellow*	6·50	4·50
60		8 c. on 10 c. bright blue	9·00	7·50

1948 (1 Dec). *Royal Silver Wedding. As Nos.* 30/1 *of Aden.*

No.	Description	Unused	Used
61	10 c. violet	20	25
62	$5 carmine	28·00	40·00

1949 (10 Oct). *75th Anniv of Universal Postal Union. As Nos.* 114/17 *of Antigua.*

No.	Description	Unused	Used
63	10 c. purple	20	35
64	15 c. deep blue	80	1·60
65	25 c. orange	85	2·25
66	50 c. blue-black	1·90	2·40

7 Sultan Ismail **8** *Vanda hookeriana*

1949 (27 Dec)–**55.** *Chalk-surfaced paper. Wmk Mult Script CA. P* 17½ × 18.

No.	Type	Description	Unused	Used
67	7	1 c. black	5	30
68		2 c. orange	10	30
69		3 c. green	25	80
70		4 c. brown	10	15
71		5 c. bright purple (1.9.52)	25	50
72		6 c. grey	15	15
73		8 c. scarlet	35	80
74		8 c. green (*shades*) (1.9.52)	65	1·25
75		10 c. purple	15	10
76		12 c. scarlet (1.9.52)	65	1·50
77		15 c. ultramarine	25	50
78		20 c. black and green	50	1·25
79		20 c. bright blue (1.9.52)	80	50
80		25 c. purple and orange	40	65
81		30 c. scarlet and purple (5.9.55)	2·25	1·75
82		35 c. scarlet and purple (1.9.52)	1·00	1·75
83		40 c. red and purple	1·25	6·00
84		50 c. black and blue	50	45
85		$1 blue and purple	2·00	2·00
86		$2 green and scarlet	8·00	17·00
87		$5 green and brown	35·00	38·00
67/87		*Set of* 21	48·00	65·00

1953 (2 June). *Coronation. As No.* 47 *of Aden.*

No.	Description	Unused	Used
88	10 c. black and reddish purple	25	30

1957 (26 June)–**63.** *As Nos.* 92/102 *of Kedah, but with inset portrait of Sultan Ismail.*

No.	Description	Unused	Used
89	1 c. black (21.8.57)	5	20
90	2 c. orange-red (25.7.57)	5	30
	a. Red-orange (21.2.61)	1·75	2·25
91	4 c. sepia (21.8.57)	5	5
92	5 c. carmine-lake (21.8.57)	5	5
93	8 c. myrtle-green (21.8.57)	1·50	60
94	10 c. deep brown (4.8.57)	15	5
94*a*	10 c. deep maroon (21.2.61)	25	5
95	20 c. blue	25	15
96	50 c. black and blue (*p* 12½) (25.7.57)	30	45
	a. Perf 12½ × 13 (17.5.60)	50	75
	ab. Black and ultramarine (20.3.62)	25	35
97	$1 ultramarine and reddish purple (25.7.57)	1·50	2·25
98	$2 bronze-green and scarlet (21.8.57)	5·50	7·00
99	$5 brown and bronze-green	8·00	8·50
	a. Perf 13 × 12½ (13.8.63)	8·00	8·00
89/99a	*Set of* 12	16·00	17·00

The 6, 12, 25 and 30 c. values used with this issue were Nos. 1/4 of Malayan Federation.

1965 (15 Nov). *As Nos.* 166/72 *of Johore but with inset portrait of Sultan Ismail Nasiruddin Shah as in T* **8**.

No.	Description	Unused	Used
100	1 c. multicoloured	8	15
101	2 c. multicoloured	8	20
102	5 c. multicoloured	10	5
103	6 c. multicoloured	15	5
104	10 c. multicoloured	20	5
105	15 c. multicoloured	55	10
106	20 c. multicoloured	80	15
	a. Bright purple (blooms) omitted	27·00	
100/6	*Set of* 7	1·75	65

The 5 c. value exists with PVA gum as well as gum arabic.

No. 101a, formerly listed here, is now listed as Sarawak No. 213a.

The higher values used with this issue were Nos. 20/27 of Malaysia.

9 Sultan of Trengganu

10 Lime Butterfly

(Des Enche Nik Zainal Abidin. Photo Harrison)

1970 (16 Dec). *25th Anniv of Installation of H.R.H. Tuanku Ismail Nasiruddin Shah as Sultan of Trengganu. P* 14½ × 13½.

107 **9** 10 c. multicoloured 10 10
108 15 c. multicoloured 20 15
109 50 c. multicoloured .. .. 65 1·25

1971 (1 Feb)–**78**. *As Nos.* 175/87 *of Johore but with portrait of Sultan Ismail Nasiruddin Shah and Arms, as in T* **10**.

(*a*) *Litho by Bradbury, Wilkinson*

110 1 c. multicoloured 5 20
111 2 c. multicoloured 5 20
112 5 c. multicoloured 15 5
113 6 c. multicoloured 15 8
114 10 c. multicoloured 20 5
115 15 c. multicoloured 30 10
116 20 c. multicoloured 30 20
110/16 .. .. *Set of* 7 1·10 80

(*b*) *Photo by Harrison* (1977–78)

116*a* 5 c. multicoloured .. ..
117 10 c. multicoloured 40 50
117*a* 15 c. multicoloured 50 50

The higher values used with this issue were Nos. 64/71 of Malaysia.

For differences between litho and photo printings, see after Johore No. 187.

11 *Durio zibethinus*

12 Sultan Mahmud

1979 (30 Apr). *As Nos.* 188/94 *of Johore but with portrait of Sultan Ismail Nasiruddin Shah as in T* **11**.

118 1 c. *Rafflesia hasseltii* 5 5
119 2 c. *Pterocarpus indicus* 5 5
120 5 c. *Lagerstroemia speciosa* 5 5
121 10 c. Type **11** 8 5
122 15 c. *Hibiscus rosa-sinensis* 10 5
123 20 c. *Rhododendron scortechinii* 15 5
124 25 c. *Phaeomeria speciosa* 15 5
118/24 .. .. *Set of* 7 55 30

For higher values used in conjunction with this series see Nos. 190/7 of Malaysia.

(Des Malaysian Advertising Services. Litho Harrison)

1981 (21 Mar). *Installation of Sultan Mahmud. P* 14.

125 **12** 10 c. black, gold and new blue 5 5
126 15 c. black, gold and yellow 10 10
127 50 c. black, gold and bright purple .. 30 50

1984 (Mar). *As No.* 124 *but without wmk.*

134 25 c. *Phaeomeria speciosa* 15 20

On No. 134 the portrait and state arms have been redrawn smaller.

POSTAGE DUE STAMPS

D 1

1937 (10 Aug). *Wmk Mult Script CA. P* 14.

D1 D **1** 1 c. scarlet .. .. 6·50 25·00
D2 4 c. green .. .. 6·50 25·00
D3 8 c. yellow .. .. 45·00 £140
D4 10 c. brown .. .. 48·00 85·00
D1/4 Perf "Specimen" .. .. *Set of* 4 £150

VIII. JAPANESE OCCUPATION

PRICES FOR STAMPS ON COVER

Nos. J1/110	*from* × 6
Nos. J111/13	—
Nos. J114/25	*from* × 10
Nos. J128/70	*from* × 8
Nos. J172/85	*from* × 12
Nos. J186/8	*from* × 15
Nos. J189/203	*from* × 10
Nos. J203*b/v*	*from* × 12
Nos. J204/16	*from* × 20
Nos. J217/57	*from* × 12
Nos. J258/70	*from* × 10
Nos. J270*a/g*	—
Nos. J271/84	*from* × 20
Nos. JD1/7	*from* × 20
Nos. JD8/16	*from* × 30
Nos. JD17/28	*from* × 12
Nos. JD29/41	*from* × 30
Nos. JK1/29	*from* × 10

A. MALAYA

For convenience we have included in one list the stamps of various States which could be used throughout Malaya and those which were issued and used in one State or district only, the latter being indicated by footnotes.

Collectors are warned against forgeries of the various overprints, particularly on the scarcer stamps.

The stamps listed below were all valid for postal use. A number of others overprinted with Types **2** or **4** were subsequently made available by favour and are known as "request stamps". Although they had postal validity they were not on sale to the public.

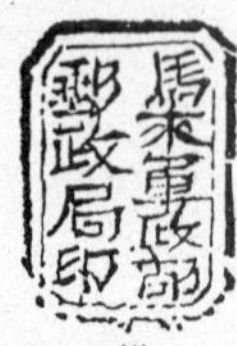

(**1**)
"Seal of Post Office of Malayan Military Dept"

(**2**) (Upright)

(Handstamped at Singapore)

1942 (16 Mar). *Stamps of Straits Settlements optd with T* **1**, *in red.*

J1 **58** 1 c. black .. .. 6·50 7·50
J2 2 c. orange .. .. 7·50 8·50
J3 3 c. green .. .. 26·00 32·00
J4 8 c. grey .. .. 10·00 10·00
J5 15 c. ultramarine .. .. 10·00 9·00

The overprint Type **1** has a double-lined frame, although the two lines are not always apparent, as in the illustration. Three chops were used, differing slightly in the shape of the characters, but forgeries also exist. It is distinguishable from Type **2** by its extra width, measuring approximately 14 mm against 12½ mm.

(Handstamped at Singapore and Kuala Lumpur)

1942 (3 Apr). *Stamps optd with T* **2**. (*a*) *On Straits Settlements.*

J 6 **58** 1 c. black (R.) .. .. 2·00 2·00
a. Black opt .. .. 55·00 55·00
b. Violet opt .. .. 60·00 60·00
J 7 2 c. green (V.) £550 £550
J 8 2 c. orange (R.) .. .. 2·25 2·25
a. Black opt .. .. 22·00 26·00
b. Violet opt .. .. 22·00 26·00
c. Brown opt .. .. 75·00 85·00
J 9 3 c. green (R.) .. .. 2·25 2·25
a. Black opt .. .. 60·00 60·00
b. Violet opt .. .. 60·00 60·00
J10 5 c. brown (R.) .. .. 10·00 10·00
a. Black opt .. .. 75·00 75·00
J12 8 c. grey (R.) .. .. 2·50 2·25
a. Black opt .. .. 55·00 55·00
J13 10 c. dull purple (R.) .. .. .. 12·00 14·00
a. Brown opt £200 £200
J14 12 c. ultramarine (R.) .. .. .. 32·00 38·00
J15 15 c. ultramarine (R.) .. .. .. 3·25 2·75
a. Violet opt .. .. 75·00 75·00
J17 30 c. dull purple and orange (R.) £425 £450
J18 40 c. scarlet and dull purple (R.) .. .. 32·00 38·00
a. Brown opt .. .. 75·00 60·00
J19 50 c. black/*emerald* (R.) .. .. .. 22·00 22·00
J20 $1 black and red/*blue* (R.) .. .. 30·00 32·00
J21 $2 green and scarlet (R.) .. .. 60·00 60·00
J22 $5 green and red/*emerald* (R.) .. .. 85·00 85·00

(*b*) *On Negri Sembilan*

J23 **6** 1 c. black (R.) .. .. 11·00 12·00
a. Violet opt .. .. 11·00 11·00
b. Brown opt .. .. 10·00 11·00
c. Black opt .. .. 11·00 22·00
J24 2 c. orange (R.) .. .. 6·50 7·50
a. Violet opt .. .. 18·00 14·00
b. Black opt .. .. 12·00 14·00
c. Brown opt .. .. 13·00 14·00
J25 3 c. green (R.) .. .. 10·00 11·00
a. Violet opt .. .. 18·00 21·00
b. Violet opt (sideways) £100 £100
c. Brown opt .. .. 18·00 21·00
J27 5 c. brown .. .. 10·00 11·00
a. Brown opt .. .. 9·00 10·00
b. Red opt .. .. 6·50 7·50
c. Violet opt .. .. 18·00 18·00
J29 6 c. grey .. .. 55·00 55·00
a. Brown opt £180 £180
J31 8 c. scarlet .. .. 12·00 24·00
J32 10 c. dull purple .. .. 27·00 30·00
a. Red opt .. .. 22·00 22·00
b. Brown opt .. .. 55·00 55·00
J32*c* 12 c. bright ultramarine (Br.) £250 £250
J33 15 c. ultramarine (R.) .. .. .. 7·50 7·50
a. Violet opt .. .. 16·00 16·00
J34 25 c. dull purple and scarlet .. .. 16·00 16·00
a. Red opt .. .. 40·00 50·00
b. Brown opt .. .. 75·00 95·00
J35 **6** 30 c. dull purple and orange .. .. 50·00 60·00
a. Brown opt £200 £225
J36 40 c. scarlet and dull purple £170 £180
a. Brown opt £375 £400
J37 50 c. black/*emerald* .. .. .. 55·00 65·00
J38 $1 black and red/*blue* .. .. .. 38·00 40·00
a. Red opt .. .. 60·00 65·00
b. Brown opt £140 £140
J39 $5 green and red/*emerald* £140 £170
a. Red opt £140 £170

(*c*) *On Pahang*

J40 **7** 1 c. black .. .. 16·00 18·00
a. Red opt .. .. 16·00 18·00
b. Violet opt .. .. 65·00 75·00
c. Brown opt .. .. 55·00 55·00
J41 3 c. green .. .. 30·00 38·00
a. Red opt £160 £200
b. Violet opt £225 £225
J42 5 c. brown .. .. 5·00 4·50
a. Red opt .. .. 40·00 42·00
b. Brown opt .. .. 60·00 60·00
c. Violet opt £110 £110
J44 8 c. grey .. .. 55·00 55·00
J45 8 c. scarlet .. .. 10·00 7·00
a. Red opt .. .. 28·00 32·00
b. Violet opt .. .. 28·00 32·00
c. Brown opt .. .. 38·00 40·00
J46 10 c. dull purple .. .. 18·00 20·00
a. Red opt .. .. 28·00 32·00
b. Brown opt .. .. 90·00 95·00
J47 12 c. bright ultramarine £525 £500
a. Red opt £800 £800
J48 15 c. ultramarine .. .. 28·00 28·00
a. Red opt .. .. 42·00 42·00
b. Violet opt £180 £180
c. Brown opt .. .. 90·00 90·00
J49 25 c. dull purple and scarlet .. .. 15·00 19·00
J50 30 c. dull purple and orange .. .. 11·00 15·00
a. Red opt .. .. 90·00 £110
J51 40 c. scarlet and dull purple .. .. 8·50 12·00
a. Brown opt .. .. 70·00 75·00
b. Red opt .. .. 18·00 18·00
J52 50 c. black/*emerald* .. .. .. 85·00 £100
a. Red opt £170 £180
J53 $1 black and red/*blue* (R.) .. .. 40·00 42·00
a. Black opt .. .. 75·00 75·00
b. Brown opt £180 £180
J54 $5 green and red/*emerald* £250 £275
a. Red opt £275 £275

(*d*) *On Perak*

J55 **38** 1 c. black .. .. 12·00 12·00
a. Violet opt .. .. 30·00 32·00
b. Brown opt .. .. 38·00 38·00
J57 2 c. orange .. .. 7·50 8·50
a. Violet opt .. .. 30·00 32·00
b. Red opt .. .. 12·00 11·00
c. Brown opt .. .. 28·00 28·00
J58 3 c. green .. .. 16·00 16·00
a. Violet opt .. .. 75·00 85·00
b. Brown opt .. .. 65·00 70·00
c. Red opt .. .. 65·00 70·00
J59 5 c. brown .. .. 3·75 4·00
a. Brown opt .. .. 12·00 12·00
b. Violet opt .. .. 40·00 50·00
c. Red opt .. .. 40·00 50·00
J61 8 c. grey .. .. 16·00 16·00
a. Red opt .. .. 85·00 95·00
b. Brown opt .. .. 85·00 95·00
J62 8 c. scarlet .. .. 8·00 25·00
a. Violet opt .. .. 85·00
J63 10 c. dull purple .. .. 8·50 16·00
a. Red opt .. .. 40·00 42·00
J64 12 c. bright ultramarine .. .. .. 42·00 50·00
J65 15 c. ultramarine .. .. 12·00 18·00
a. Red opt .. .. 28·00 28·00
b. Violet opt .. .. 60·00 60·00
c. Brown opt .. .. 55·00 55·00
J66 25 c. dull purple and scarlet .. .. 8·50 11·00
J67 30 c. dull purple and orange .. .. 16·00 24·00
a. Brown opt .. .. 55·00 60·00
b. Red opt .. .. 28·00 28·00
J68 40 c. scarlet and dull purple .. .. 85·00 95·00
a. Brown opt £180 £180
J69 50 c. black/*emerald* .. .. .. 20·00 24·00
a. Red opt .. .. 28·00 28·00
b. Brown opt .. .. 55·00 55·00
J70 $1 black and red/*blue* £100 £125
a. Brown opt £225
J71 $2 green and scarlet £425 £425
J72 $5 green and red/*emerald* £300
a. Brown opt £500

(*e*) *On Selangor*

J73 **22** 1 c. black, S .. .. 4·50 4·50
a. Red opt, SU .. .. 7·50 8·00
b. Violet opt, SU .. .. 16·00 21·00
J74 2 c. green, U £225 £225
a. Violet opt, U £350 £350
J75 2 c. orange (*p* 14 × 15), S .. .. 18·00 21·00
a. Red opt, U .. .. 42·00 48·00
b. Violet opt, U .. .. 75·00 55·00
c. Brown opt, S .. .. 18·00 21·00
J76 2 c. orange (*p* 14), S .. .. .. 23·00 27·00
a. Red opt, U .. .. 50·00 50·00
b. Violet opt, U £120 £120
J77 3 c. green, SU .. .. 7·50 8·50
a. Red opt, SU .. .. 7·50 8·50
b. Violet opt, S .. .. 27·00 30·00
c. Brown opt, SU .. .. 7·50 7·50
J78 5 c. brown, S .. .. 3·25 2·75
a. Red opt, S .. .. 7·50 7·50
b. Violet opt, SU .. .. 12·00 13·00
c. Brown opt, SU .. .. 23·00 23·00
J79 6 c. scarlet, S .. .. 85·00 85·00
a. Red opt, S £100 £100
b. Brown opt, S £160
J80 8 c. grey, S .. .. 7·50 8·50
a. Red opt, SU .. .. 12·00 14·00
b. Violet opt, U .. .. 16·00 18·00
c. Brown opt, S .. .. 26·00 16·00

J81 22 10 c. dull purple, S .. .. .. 7·50 10·00
a. Red opt, S .. .. 21·00 21·00
b. Brown opt, S .. .. 16·00 12·00
J82 12 c. bright ultramarine, S .. .. 18·00 16·00
a. Red opt, S .. .. 38·00 38·00
b. Brown opt, S .. .. 38·00 38·00
J83 15 c. ultramarine, S .. .. .. 7·50 8·50
a. Red opt, SU .. .. 16·00 18·00
b. Violet opt, U .. .. 65·00 60·00
c. Brown opt, S .. .. 16·00 18·00
J84 25 c. dull purple and scarlet, S .. .. 42·00 50·00
a. Red opt, S .. .. 40·00 42·00
J85 30 c. dull purple and orange, S .. .. 10·00 13·00
a. Brown opt, S .. .. 50·00 50·00
J86 40 c. scarlet and dull purple, S .. .. 28·00 30·00
a. Brown opt, S .. .. 65·00 55·00
J87 50 c. black/*emerald*, S .. .. .. 20·00 22·00
a. Red opt, S .. .. 32·00 35·00
b. Brown opt, S .. .. 35·00 38·00
J88 24 $1 black and red/*blue* .. .. .. 24·00 24·00
a. Red opt .. .. 50·00 55·00
J89 $2 green and scarlet .. .. .. 30·00 32·00
a. Red opt .. .. 75·00 80·00
J91 $5 green and red/*emerald* .. .. 40·00 40·00

On T **22** the overprint is normally sideways (with "top" to either right or left), but on T **24** it is always upright.
S=Sideways
U=Upright
SU=Sideways or upright (our prices being for the cheaper).

(f) On Trengganu (all Script wmk)

J 92 4 1 c. black .. .. 55·00 55·00
a. Red opt .. .. 65·00 75·00
b. Brown opt £120 £120
J 93 2 c. green .. .. 75·00 85·00
a. Red opt .. .. 85·00 95·00
b. Brown opt £120 £120
J 94 2 c. on 5 c. purple/*yellow* (No. 59) .. 55·00 55·00
a. Red opt .. .. 32·00 32·00
J 95 3 c. brown .. .. 55·00 55·00
a. Brown opt £160 £160
J 96 4 c. carmine-red .. .. .. 80·00 65·00
J 97 5 c. purple/*yellow* .. .. .. 6·50 7·50
a. Red opt .. .. 9·50
J 98 6 c. orange .. .. 6·50 9·50
a. Red opt .. .. 11·00
b. Brown opt .. .. 55·00 55·00
J 99 8 c. grey .. .. 7·50 7·50
a. Brown to red opt .. .. .. 18·00
J100 8 c. on 10 c. bright blue (No. 60) .. 9·00 12·00
a. Red opt .. .. 18·00
J101 10 c. bright blue .. .. .. 7·50 10·00
a. Red opt .. .. 18·00
b. Brown opt .. .. 65·00 65·00
J102 12 c. bright ultramarine .. .. .. 6·50 8·50
a. Red opt .. .. 18·00
J103 20 c. dull purple and orange .. .. 7·50 9·50
a. Red opt .. .. 12·00
J104 25 c. green and deep purple .. .. 6·50 9·00
a. Red opt .. .. 12·00
b. Brown opt .. .. 42·00 42·00
J105 30 c. dull purple and black .. .. 6·50 9·00
a. Red opt .. .. 12·00
J106 35 c. carmine/*yellow* .. .. .. 6·50 9·00
a. Red opt .. .. 12·00
J107 50 c. green and bright carmine .. .. 32·00 38·00
J108 $1 purple and blue/*blue* £625 £625
J109 $3 green and red/*green* .. .. 32·00 35·00
a. Red opt .. .. 35·00
J110 5 $5 green and red/*yellow* .. .. 65·00 75·00
J111 $25 purple and blue £300
a. Red opt £600
J112 $50 green and yellow £950
J113 $100 green and scarlet £425

Nos. J92/113 were issued in Trengganu only.

Specialists recognise nine slightly different chops as Type **2**. Of these nine two are believed to have been used in Singapore and the remainder at Kuala Lumpur.

軍政部
マラッカ州
政廳之印

(3 "Seal of the Government Office of the Malacca Military Dept." (approx size))

1942 (23 Apr). *Stamps of Straits Settlements handstamped as T* **3**, *in red, each impression covering four stamps.*

			Single Un.	Used
J114	58	1 c. black	38·00	38·00
J115		2 c. orange	24·00	30·00
J116		3 c. green	38·00	38·00
J117		5 c. brown	55·00	60·00
J118		8 c. grey	65·00	60·00
J119		10 c. dull purple	38·00	38·00
J120		12 c. ultramarine	42·00	42·00
J121		15 c. ultramarine	38·00	38·00
J123		40 c. scarlet and dull purple ..	£100	£100
J124		50 c. black/*emerald*	£300	£300
J125		$1 black and red/*blue*	£350	£350

Nos. J114 to J125 were issued in Malacca only. Blocks of 4 showing the complete handstamp are worth from six times the price of a single stamp.

DAI NIPPON
2602
MALAYA
(4)

DAI NIPPON
2602
MALAYA
2 Cents
(5)

SELANGOR
EXHIBITION
DAI NIPPON
2602
MALAYA
(6)

1942. *Optd with T* **4**. *(a) On Straits Settlements.*

J128 58 2 c. orange 50 50
a. Opt inverted .. .. .. 7·00 8·00
b. Opt double, one inverted .. .. 32·00 38·00
J129 3 c. green .. .. 30·00 35·00
J130 8 c. grey .. .. 1·75 1·75
a. Opt inverted .. .. .. 13·00 18·00
J131 15 c. blue .. .. 5·00 4·00

(b) On Negri Sembilan

J132 6 1 c. black 70 70
a. Opt inverted .. .. .. 8·00 12·00
b. Opt double, one inverted .. .. 24·00 30·00
J133 2 c. orange 85 65
J134 3 c. green 65 55
J135 5 c. brown 45 65
J136 6 c. grey .. .. 90 1·00
a. Opt inverted .. .. .. — £425
J137 8 c. scarlet .. .. 1·60 1·40
J138 10 c. dull purple .. .. .. 3·50 3·00
J139 15 c. ultramarine .. .. .. 3·00 3·50
J140 25 c. dull purple and scarlet .. .. 1·50 3·50
J141 30 c. dull purple and orange .. .. 2·50 3·00
J142 $1 black and red/*blue* .. .. 80·00 90·00

(c) On Pahang

J143 7 1 c. black 35 40
J144 5 c. brown 55 70
J145 8 c. scarlet .. .. 14·00 1·90
J146 10 c. dull purple .. .. .. 8·50 4·50
J147 12 c. bright ultramarine .. .. 1·10 1·40
J148 25 c. dull purple and scarlet .. .. 3·25 4·25
J149 30 c. dull purple and orange .. .. 80 1·90

(d) On Perak

J151 38 2 c. orange 55 65
a. Opt inverted .. .. .. 12·00 14·00
J152 3 c. green 50 60
a. Opt inverted .. .. .. 10·00 12·00
J154 8 c. scarlet 60 40
a. Opt inverted .. .. .. 4·50 4·75
b. Opt double, one inverted £100 £120
c. Opt omitted (in pair with normal) £180
J155 10 c. dull purple .. .. .. 3·50 5·00
J156 15 c. ultramarine .. .. .. 2·25 1·75
J158 50 c. black/*emerald* .. .. .. 1·75 2·25
J159 $1 black and red/*blue* £130 £170
J160 $5 green and red/*emerald* .. .. 24·00 28·00
a. Opt inverted £180 £200

(e) On Selangor

J162 22 3 c. green 40 50
J165 12 c. bright ultramarine .. .. 1·10 1·75
J166 15 c. ultramarine .. .. .. 2·75 2·00
J168 40 c. scarlet and dull purple .. .. 2·00 2·25
J170 $2 green and scarlet .. .. 10·00 12·00

On T **22** the overprint is sideways, with "top" to left or right.

(f) On Trengganu (all Script wmk)

J172 4 1 c. black .. .. 4·00 4·25
J173 2 c. green .. .. 85·00 £100
J174 2 c. on 5 c. purple/*yellow* (No. 59) .. 4·00 4·25
J175 3 c. brown .. .. 6·00 7·50
J176 4 c. carmine-red .. .. .. 4·00 5·50
J177 5 c. purple/*yellow* .. .. .. 4·00 4·25
J178 6 c. orange .. .. 4·00 5·50
J179 8 c. grey .. .. 38·00 14·00
J180 8 c. on 10 c. bright blue (No. 60) .. 3·25 4·00
J181 12 c. bright ultramarine .. .. 3·25 5·00
J182 20 c. dull purple and orange .. .. 4·50 6·50
J183 25 c. green and deep purple .. .. 5·00 8·00
J184 30 c. dull purple and black .. .. 5·00 8·00
J185 $3 green and red/*green* .. .. 30·00 40·00

Nos. J172/85 were issued in Trengganu only.

1942. *No. 104 of Perak surch with T* **5**.

J186 38 2 c. on 5 c. brown .. .. .. 1·25 70

1942 (3 Nov). *Agri-horticultural Exhibition. Nos. 294 and 283 of Straits Settlements optd with T* **6**.

J187 58 2 c. orange .. .. 6·00 7·00
a. "C" for "G" in "SELANGOR" .. 80·00 95·00
b. Opt inverted £275 £275
J188 8 c. grey .. .. 5·00 6·00
a. "C" for "G" in "SELANGOR" .. 80·00 95·00
b. Opt inverted £275 £275

Nos. J187/8 were only issued in Selangor.

DAI NIPPON
2602
(7)

DAI NIPPON
2602
(8)

1942 (13 May). *Stamps of Kedah (Script wmk) optd. (a) With T* **7**.

J189 1 1 c. black (R.) .. .. .. 1·10 1·25
J190 2 c. bright green (R.) .. .. 15·00 16·00
J191 4 c. violet (R.) .. .. .. 1·10 1·25
J192 5 c. yellow (R.) 85 85
a. Black opt £110 £110
J193 6 c. carmine-red .. .. .. 85 1·40
J194 8 c. grey-black (R.) .. .. .. 1·40 1·10

(b) With T **8**

J195 6 10 c. ultramarine and sepia (R.) .. 2·00 2·25
J196 12 c. black and violet (R.) .. .. 5·50 8·00
J197 25 c. ultramarine and purple (R.) .. 2·75 3·00
a. Black opt .. .. .. 90·00 £100
J198 30 c. green and scarlet (R.) .. .. 28·00 32·00
J199 40 c. black and purple (R.) .. .. 7·00 11·00
J200 50 c. brown and blue (R.) .. .. 8·00 13·00
J201 $1 black and green (R.) .. .. 80·00 80·00
a. Opt inverted £200 £200
J202 6 $2 green and brown (R.) .. .. 80·00 80·00
J203 $5 black and scarlet (R.) .. .. 24·00 24·00
a. Black opt £190 £200

Nos. J189 to J203a were issued in Kedah only.

(8*a*)
Okugawa Seal

(8*b*)
Ochiburi Seal

(8*c*)
Okugawa-Ryo Seal

1942 (30 Mar). *Straits Settlements stamps optd.*

(a) As T **8***a* *(three forms of this seal)*

J203*b* 58 1 c. black .. .. 3·50 3·50
J203*c* 2 c. orange .. .. 10·00 10·00
J203*d* 3 c. green .. .. 8·00 8·50
J203*e* 5 c. brown .. .. 8·00 8·50
J203*f* 8 c. grey .. .. 10·00 10·00
J203*g* 10 c. dull purple .. .. .. 10·00 10·00
J203*h* 12 c. ultramarine .. .. .. 10·00 10·00
J203*i* 15 c. ultramarine .. .. .. 10·00 10·00
J203*j* 40 c. scarlet and dull purple .. .. 38·00 38·00
J203*k* 50 c. black/*emerald* .. .. .. 38·00 38·00
J203*l* $1 black and red/*blue* .. .. 50·00 50·00
J203*m* $2 green and scarlet £100 £100
J203*n* $5 green and red/*emerald* £325 £375

(b) With T **8***b*

J203*o* 58 1 c. black .. .. 16·00 24·00
J203*p* 2 c. orange .. .. 16·00 24·00
J203*q* 3 c. green .. .. 16·00 24·00
J203*r* 5 c. brown £225 £225
J203*s* 8 c. grey .. .. 13·00 16·00
J203*t* 10 c. dull purple .. .. .. 13·00 16·00
J203*u* 12 c. ultramarine .. .. .. 13·00 16·00
J203*v* 15 c. ultramarine .. .. .. 13·00 16·00

Nos. J203*b*/*v* were issued only in Penang.

We have seen the 2 c. orange and 3 c. green overprinted with T **8***c* supported by Expert Committee certificates and the 1 c. is also reported to exist. These are believed to be revenue stamps that have done postal duty without authorisation.

DAI NIPPON
2602
PENANG
(9)

DAI NIPPON
YUBIN
2 Cents
(10)
("Japanese Postal Service")

1942 (15 Apr). *Straits Settlements stamps optd with T* **9**.

J204 58 1 c. black (R.) 65 70
a. Opt inverted .. .. .. 50·00 50·00
J205 2 c. orange .. .. 2·75 2·25
a. "PE" for "PENANG" .. .. 28·00 32·00
b. Opt inverted .. .. .. 65·00
c. Opt double .. ..
J206 3 c. green (R.) .. .. .. 85 1·00
J207 5 c. brown (R.) 65 75
a. "N PPON" .. .. 48·00
b. Opt double .. ..
J208 8 c. grey (R.) .. .. 2·00 1·40
a. "N PPON" .. .. 20·00 24·00
b. Opt. double, one inverted .. .. 60·00
J209 10 c. dull purple (R.) .. .. .. 1·50 1·75
a. Opt double £100
J210 12 c. ultramarine (R.) .. .. .. 1·75 2·25
a. "N PPON" £120
b. Opt double £100
J211 15 c. ultramarine (R.) .. .. .. 1·75 2·00
a. "N PPON" .. .. 50·00
b. Opt inverted £150
c. Opt double £150
J212 40 c. scarlet and dull purple .. .. 2·25 2·75
J213 50 c. black/*emerald* (R.) .. .. 3·00 5·00
J214 $1 black and red/*blue* .. .. 5·00 7·50
J215 $2 green and scarlet .. .. .. 16·00 22·00
J216 $5 green and red/*emerald* £180 £200

Nos. J204/16 were issued in Penang and Wellesley Province only.

1942 (Dec). *Perak stamps surch or optd only, as in T* **10**.

J217 38 1 c. black .. .. 2·00 2·50
a. Opt inverted .. .. .. 19·00 22·00
J218 2 c. on 5 c. brown .. .. .. 2·75 2·75
a. "DAI NIPPON YUBIN" inverted .. 17·00 18·00
b. Ditto and "2 Cents" omitted .. 30·00 40·00
J219 8 c. scarlet .. .. 2·25 1·00
a. Opt inverted .. .. .. 10·00 14·00

In December 1942 contemporary Japanese 3, 5, 8 and 25 s. stamps were issued without overprint in Singapore and the 1, 2, 4, 6, 7, 10, 30 and 50 s. and 1 y. values were issued in February 1943.

大日本郵便
(11)

大日本郵便
(11*a*) Error. Second Character Sideways

大日本郵便
("Japanese Postal Service")
(12)

6cts.
(14)

6 cts.
(15)

2 Cents
(16)

6 cts.
(17)

$1.00
(18)

1943–45. *Stamps of the various Malayan territories optd with T* **11** *or* **12** *(so-called "Kanji" characters), in black or red, some stamps surch in addition as T* **14** *to* **18**. *(a) On Straits Settlements (opt T* **11**).

J221 **58** 8 c. grey (Blk.) 60 50
a. Opt inverted .. .. .. 25·00 25·00
b. Red opt 60 60
J222 12 c. ultramarine .. .. .. 55 1·25
J223 40 c. scarlet and dull purple .. .. 65 1·00

(b) On Negri Sembilan (opt T **11**)
J224 **6** 1 c. black 25 40
a. Opt inverted .. .. .. 7·00 10·00
b. Error. T **11*a*** .. .. .. 11·00 11·00
ba. T **11*a*** inverted £300
J225 2 c. on 5 c. brown (T **14**) 25 30
J226 6 c. on 5 c. brown (T **15**) 35 45
J227 25 c. dull purple and scarlet .. .. 1·10 1·25

(c) On Pahang (opt T **11**)
J228 **7** 6 c. on 5 c. brown (T **14**) 60 75
J229 6 c. on 5 c. brown (T **15**) .. .. 1·00 1·25

(d) On Perak (opt T **11**)
J230 **38** 1 c. black 35 50
a. Error. T **11*a*** .. .. .. 80·00 85·00
J232 2 c. on 5 c. brown (T **14**) 50 50
a. Opt and surch inverted .. .. 18·00 25·00
b. Opt only inverted .. .. 18·00 25·00
c. Error. T **11*a*** .. .. .. 28·00 30·00
J233 2 c. on 5 c. brown (T **16**) 45 45
a. Opt and surch inverted .. .. 18·00 27·00
b. Surch only inverted .. .. 18·00 27·00
c. Error. T **11*a*** .. .. .. 20·00 22·00
ca. Opt and surch inverted £500
cb. Surch only inverted £475
J235 5 c. brown 45 40
a. Opt inverted .. .. .. 25·00 28·00
b. Error. T **11*a*** £160 £300
J237 8 c. scarlet 55 50
a. Opt inverted .. .. .. 19·00 22·00
b. Error. T **11*a*** .. .. .. 45·00 50·00
ba. T **11*a*** inverted £475
J238 10 c. dull purple 60 50
J239 30 c. dull purple and orange .. .. 1·25 2·00
J240 50 c. black/*emerald* .. .. .. 3·00 3·25
J241 $5 green and red/*emerald* .. .. 35·00 38·00

(e) On Selangor
(i) *Opt T* **11** *placed horizontally either way on T* **22** *and vertically on T* **24**
J242 **22** 1 c. black 65 65
J243 3 c. green 40 45
a. Error. T **11*a*** .. .. .. 12·00 16·00
J244 12 c. bright ultramarine 45 80
a. Error. T **11*a*** .. .. .. 12·00 16·00
J245 15 c. ultramarine .. .. .. 2·75 2·75
a. Error. T **11*a*** .. .. .. 20·00 25·00
J246 **24** $1 black and red/*blue* .. .. .. 3·00 4·00
a. Error. T **11*a*** £180 £200
b. Opt inverted £200 £200
J247 $2 green and scarlet .. .. .. 10·00 12·00
J248 $5 green and red/*emerald* .. .. 24·00 27·00
a. Opt inverted £200 £200

(ii) *Opt T* **12**
J249 **22** 1 c. black (R.) 35 50
J250 2 c. on 5 c. brown (T **15**) (R.) .. 20 50
J251 3 c. on 5 c. brown (T **15**) 20 50
a. "s" in "cts" inverted .. .. 25·00 38·00
b. Comma after "cts" .. .. 25·00 38·00
J252 5 c. brown (R.) 30 50
J253 6 c. on 5 c. brown (T **15**) 12 55
J254 6 c. on 5 c. brown (T **17**) 15 40
a. "6" inverted £375
J255 15 c. ultramarine .. .. .. 5·00 5·00
J256 $1.00 on 10 c. dull purple (T **18**) .. 25 1·00
J257 $1.50 on 30 c. dull purple and orange (T **18**) .. .. 25 1·00

(f) On Trengganu (opt T **11**)
J258 **4** 1 c. black .. .. 3·50 8·50
J259 2 c. green .. .. 3·50 11·00
J260 2 c. on 5 c. purple/*yellow* (No. 59) .. 3·00 10·00
J261 5 c. purple/*yellow* .. .. .. 3·00 10·00
J262 6 c. orange .. .. 5·00 12·00
J263 8 c. grey .. .. 26·00 32·00
J264 8 c. on 10 c. bright blue (No. 60) .. 11·00 22·00
J265 10 c. bright blue .. .. .. 45·00 85·00
J266 12 c. bright ultramarine .. .. .. 6·00 16·00
J267 20 c. dull purple and orange .. .. 6·00 16·00
J268 25 c. green and deep purple .. .. 6·00 18·00
J269 30 c. dull purple and black .. .. 6·00 18·00
J270 35 c. carmine/*yellow* .. .. .. 6·00 18·00

Nos. J258/70 were issued in Trengganu only.

大日本
マライ郵便
50 セント
(18*a*)

大日本
マライ郵便
1 ドル
(18*b*)

大日本
マライ郵便
1½ドル
(18*c*)

1944 (16 Dec). *Stamps intended for use on Red Cross letters. Surch with T* **18*a/c***. *(a) On Straits Settlements.*
J270*a* **58** 50 c. on 50 c. black/*emerald* .. .. 5·00 10·00
J270*b* $1 on $1 black and red/*blue* .. .. 7·00 15·00
J270*c* $1.50 on $2 green and scarlet .. 15·00 35·00

(b) On Johore
J270*d* **29** 50 c. on 50 c. dull purple and red .. 5·00 10·00
J270*e* $1.50 on $2 green and carmine .. 4·00 8·00

(c) On Selangor
J270*f* **24** $1 on $1 black and red/*blue* .. .. 4·00 9·00
J270*g* $1.50 on $2 green and scarlet .. 5·00 10·00

No. J270*a/g* were issued in Singapore but were withdrawn after one day, probably because supplies of Nos. J256/7 were received and issued on the 18 December.

19 Tapping Rubber

20 Fruit

24 Japanese Shrine, Singapore

(Litho in Batavia)

1943. *T* **19/20, 24** *and similar designs. P* 12½.
J271 **19** 1 c. grey-green (1 Oct) 15 15
J272 **20** 2 c. pale emerald (1 June) 12 12
J273 **19** 3 c. drab (1 Oct) 12 12
J274 – 4 c. carmine-rose (29 Apr) 12 12
J275 – 8 c. dull blue (29 Apr) 15 15
J276 – 10 c. brown-purple (1 Oct) 15 15
J277 **24** 15 c. violet (1 Oct) 35 35
J278 – 30 c. olive-green (1 Oct) 35 35
J279 – 50 c. blue (1 Oct) 75 65
J280 – 70 c. blue (1 Oct) .. .. .. 7·50 7·00
J271/80 .. .. *Set of* 10 8·50 8·00

Designs: *Vert*—4 c. Tin-dredger; 8 c. War memorial; 10 c. Huts; 30 c. Sago palms; 50 c. Straits of Johore. *Horiz*—70 c. Malay Mosque, Kuala Lumpur.

28 Ploughman

29 Rice-planting

1943 (1 Sept). *Savings Campaign. Litho. P* 12½.
J281 **28** 8 c. violet .. .. 5·00 2·25
J282 15 c. scarlet .. .. 4·50 2·25

(Des Hon Chin. Litho)

1944 (15 Feb). *"Re-birth" of Malaya. P* 12½.
J283 **29** 8 c. rose-red .. .. 4·00 2·25
J284 15 c. magenta .. .. 4·00 2·50

POSTAGE DUE STAMPS

Postage Due stamps of the various Malayan territories overprinted.

1942 (3 Apr). *Handstamped with T* **2** *in black.*

(a) On Malayan Postal Union
JD 1 **D 1** 1 c. slate-purple .. .. .. 5·00 6·00
a. Red opt .. .. .. 10·00 11·00
b. Brown opt .. .. .. 22·00 27·00
JD 2 3 c. green .. .. 5·00 6·50
a. Red opt .. .. .. 17·00 30·00
JD 3 4 c. green .. .. 5·00 4·00
a. Red opt .. .. .. 12·00 16·00
b. Brown opt .. .. .. 30·00 35·00
JD 4 8 c. scarlet .. .. 7·50 8·50
a. Red opt .. .. .. 22·00 22·00
b. Brown opt .. .. .. 30·00 30·00
JD 5 10 c. yellow-orange .. .. .. 7·50 9·00
a. Red opt .. .. .. 7·50 9·00
b. Brown opt .. .. .. 14·00 16·00
JD 6 12 c. ultramarine .. .. .. 9·00 11·00
a. Red opt .. .. .. 16·00 20·00
JD 7 50 c. black .. .. 16·00 20·00
a. Red opt .. .. .. 38·00 42·00

(b) On Johore
JD 8 **D 1** 1 c. carmine (R.) .. .. .. 28·00
a. Black opt .. .. .. 26·00
JD 9 4 c. green (R.) .. .. .. 28·00
a. Black opt .. .. .. 35·00
JD10 8 c. orange (R.) .. .. .. 40·00
a. Black opt .. .. .. 28·00
JD11 10 c. brown (R.) .. .. .. 11·00
a. Black opt .. .. .. 10·00
JD12 12 c. purple (R.) .. .. .. 15·00
a. Black opt .. .. .. 14·00

The above were issued only in Johore.

(c) On Trengganu
JD13 **D 1** 1 c. scarlet .. .. 24·00 28·00
JD14 4 c. green .. .. 28·00 25·00
a. Red opt .. .. .. 24·00 28·00
JD15 8 c. yellow .. .. 10·00 22·00
JD16 10 c. brown .. .. 10·00 22·00

Nos. JD13/16 were issued in Trengganu only.

1942 (23 Apr). *Handstamped on Malayan Postal Union with T* **3**, *in red, each impression covering four stamps.*
JD17 **D 1** 1 c. slate-purple .. .. .. 32·00 32·00
JD18 4 c. green .. .. 50·00 50·00
JD19 8 c. scarlet £450 £450
JD20 10 c. yellow-orange .. .. .. 65·00 65·00
JD21 12 c. ultramarine .. .. .. 85·00 95·00
JD22 50 c. black £450 £600

Nos. JD17/22 were issued in Malacca only. Prices quoted are for single stamps. Blocks of four showing the complete handstamp are worth from six times the price of a single stamp.

1942. *Optd on Malayan Postal Union with T* **4**, *in black.*
JD23 **D 1** 1 c. slate-purple .. .. .. 70 1·00
JD24 3 c. green .. .. 1·60 2·25
JD25 4 c. green .. .. 2·00 2·50
JD26 8 c. scarlet .. .. 2·50 3·50
JD27 10 c. yellow-orange .. .. .. 1·60 2·25
JD28 12 c. ultramarine .. .. .. 1·60 2·25

1943–45. *Optd with T* **11**. *(a) On Malayan Postal Union.*
JD29 **D 1** 1 c. slate-purple 30 75
JD30 3 c. green 30 85
JD31 4 c. green .. .. 16·00 22·00
JD32 5 c. scarlet .. .. 50 1·25
JD33 9 c. yellow-orange .. .. .. 60 1·50
a. Opt inverted .. .. .. 24·00 25·00
JD34 10 c. yellow-orange .. .. .. 60 1·75
a. Opt inverted .. .. .. 38·00 38·00
JD35 12 c. ultramarine .. .. .. 60 2·00
JD36 15 c. ultramarine .. .. .. 60 2·00

(b) On Johore
JD37 **D 1** 1 c. carmine .. .. 75 2·50
a. Error. Optd with T **11*a*** .. .. 22·00 35·00
JD38 4 c. green .. .. 75 2·50
a. Error. Optd with T **11*a*** .. .. 22·00 35·00
JD39 8 c. orange .. .. 2·25 5·00
a. Error. Optd with T **11*a*** .. .. 32·00 42·00
JD40 10 c. brown .. .. 1·75 6·00
a. Error. Optd with T **11*a*** .. .. 32·00 42·00
JD41 12 c. purple .. .. 1·75 6·00
a. Error. Optd with T **11*a*** .. .. 32·00 42·00

Nos. JD37/41 were used only in Johore. Postage stamps of Johore optd with Type **4** were authorised for use for revenue purposes only.

B. KELANTAN

40 CENTS
(JK 1)

$1.00
(JK 2)

Sunagawa Seal

Handa Seal

1942 (June). *Kelantan stamps surch as Type* **JK 1** *or* **JK 2** *(dollar values). (a) With Sunagawa Seal in red.*
JK 1 **4** 1 c. on 50 c. grey-olive and orange .. 65·00 75·00
JK 2 2 c. on 40 c. orange and blue-green .. 55·00 65·00
JK 3 4 c. on 30 c. violet and scarlet £200 £225
JK 4 5 c. on 12 c. blue (R.) .. .. .. 42·00 45·00
JK 5 6 c. on 25 c. vermilion and violet .. 55·00 70·00
JK 6 8 c. on 5 c. red-brown (R.) .. .. 65·00 70·00
JK 7 10 c. on 6 c. lake .. .. .. 42·00 50·00
JK 8 12 c. on 8 c. grey-olive (R.) .. .. 30·00 38·00
JK 9 25 c. on 10 c. purple (R.) £350 £375
JK10 30 c. on 4 c. scarlet £375 £425
JK11 40 c. on 2 c. green (R.) .. .. .. 35·00 42·00
JK12 50 c. on 1 c. grey-olive and yellow .. £200 £225
JK13 **1** $1 on 4 c. black & red (R., bars Blk.) .. 32·00 38·00
JK14 $2 on 5 c. green and red/*yellow* (R.) .. 32·00 38·00
JK15 $5 on 6 c. scarlet .. .. .. 32·00 38·00

(b) With Handa Seal in red
JK16 **4** 12 c. on 8 c. grey-olive (R.) .. .. 55·00 65·00

1 Cents
(JK 3)

1942. *Kelantan stamps surcharged as Type* **JK 3**.

(a) With Sunagawa Seal in red
JK17 **4** 1 c. on 50 c. grey-olive and orange .. 42·00 42·00
JK18 2 c. on 40 c. orange and blue-green .. 42·00 42·00
JK19 5 c. on 12 c. blue (R.) .. .. .. 30·00 32·00
JK20 8 c. on 5 c. red-brown (R.) .. .. 30·00 30·00
JK21 10 c. on 6 c. lake .. .. .. 30·00 32·00
JK22 12 c. on 8 c. grey-olive (R.) .. .. 32·00 35·00
JK23 30 c. on 4 c. scarlet £425 £450
JK24 40 c. on 2 c. green (R.) .. .. .. 38·00 42·00
JK25 50 c. on 1 c. grey-olive and yellow .. £140 £160

(b) With Handa Seal in red
JK26 **4** 1 c. on 50 c. grey-olive and orange .. 45·00 55·00
JK27 2 c. on 40 c. orange and blue-green .. 45·00 55·00
JK28 8 c. on 5 c. red-brown .. .. .. 45·00 55·00
JK29 10 c. on 6 c. lake .. .. .. 45·00 55·00

The above stamps all exist with error "Cente" for "Cents" (No. 41 on sheet). They are worth about five times the prices for the normal stamps.

All the above were overprinted with the personal Seals of Sunagawa, the Governor, or of Handa, the Assistant Governor, to indicate that these were Japanese stamps. Some of these also exist without the seals and come from remainder stocks sent to Singapore and Kuala Lumpur after Kelantan was ceded to Thailand.

IX. THAI OCCUPATION

Stamps issued for use in the four Malay States of Kedah, Kelantan, Perlis and Trengganu, ceded by Japan to Thailand on 19 October 1943 and restored to British rule on the defeat of the Japanese.

PRICES FOR STAMPS ON COVER	
Nos. TK1/5	*from* × 25
Nos. TM1/6	*from* × 20
Nos. TT1/29	*from* × 10

A. KELANTAN

TK 1

(Ptd at Khota Baru)

1943 (15 Nov). *Surch with value and inscr in black. No gum. P* 11.

TK1	TK 1	1 c. violet	30·00	35·00
TK2		2 c. violet	30·00	35·00
		a. Violet omitted	£180	
TK3		4 c. violet	30·00	35·00
		a. Violet omitted		
TK4		8 c. violet	30·00	35·00
		a. Violet omitted	£125	
TK5		10 c. violet	30·00	50·00

The above bear sheet watermarks in the form of "STANDARD" in block capitals with curved "CROWN" above and "AGENTS" below in double-lined capitals. This watermark occurs four times in the sheet.

These stamps but with centres printed in red were for fiscal use.

B. MALAYA

TM 1 War Memorial

(Litho Survey Dept)

1943 (Dec). *Thick opaque, or thin semi-transparent paper. Gummed or ungummed. P* 12½ *or* 11½ × 11.

TM1	TM 1	1 c. yellow	3·00	4·00
TM2		2 c. red-brown	2·00	2·75
		a. Imperf (pair)	£150	
TM3		3 c. green	4·00	5·00
TM4		4 c. purple	2·00	3·50
TM5		8 c. carmine	1·50	3·50
TM6		15 c. blue	4·00	5·50

C. TRENGGANU

TRENGGANU

(TT 1)

(Overprinted at Trengganu Survey Office)

1944 (1 Oct). *Various stamps optd with Type* TT 1.

(i) *On Trengganu stamp optd with T* **2**

TT 1	**4**	8 c. grey (J99)	40·00	20·00

(ii) *On stamps optd with T* **4**. (*a*) *Pahang*

TT 2	**7**	12 c. bright ultramarine (J147)	40·00	20·00

(*b*) *Trengganu*

TT 3	**4**	2 c. on 5 c. purple/*yellow* (J174)*	40·00	40·00
TT 4		8 c. on 10 c. bright bl (J180) (inverted)	20·00	20·00
TT 5		12 c. brt ultramarine (J181) (inverted)	20·00	20·00

*This is spelt "TRENGANU" with one "G".

(iii) *On stamps optd with T* **11**. (*a*) *Straits Settlements*

TT 6	**58**	12 c. ultramarine (J222)	40·00	40·00
TT 7		40 c. scarlet and dull purple (J223)	40·00	40·00

(*b*) *On Perak*

TT 8	**38**	30 c. dull purple and orange (J239)	75·00	40·00

(*c*) *On Selangor*

TT 9	**22**	3 c. green (J243)	20·00	20·00
TT10		12 c. bright ultramarine (J244) (L. to R.)	15·00	15·00
TT11		12 c. bright ultramarine (J244) (R. to L.)	12·00	12·00
		a. Error. T **11***a*	£350	£350

(iv) *On Selangor stamps optd with T* **12**

TT12	**22**	2 c. on 5 c. brown (J250)	40·00	40·00
TT13		3 c. on 5 c. brown (J251)	40·00	40·00

(v) *On pictorials of* 1943 (*Nos.* J271 *etc.*)

TT14	**19**	1 c. grey-green	40·00	50·00
TT15	**20**	2 c. pale emerald	40·00	25·00
TT16	**19**	3 c. drab	45·00	45·00
TT17	**21**	4 c. carmine-rose	45·00	45·00
TT18	**22**	8 c. dull blue	80·00	80·00
TT19	**23**	10 c. brown-purple		
TT20	**24**	15 c. violet	50·00	40·00
TT21	**25**	30 c. olive-green	50·00	30·00
TT22	**26**	50 c. blue	80·00	80·00
TT23	**27**	70 c. blue	£140	£140

(vi) *On Savings Campaign stamps* (*Nos.* J281/2)

TT24	**28**	8 c. violet	95·00	95·00
TT25		15 c. scarlet	95·00	95·00

(vii) *On stamps of Japan*

TT26	–	5 s. claret (No. 396)	55·00	70·00
TT27	–	25 s. brown and chocolate (No. 329)	25·00	15·00
TT28	–	30 s. blue-green (No. 330)	55·00	40·00

(viii) *On Trengganu Postage Due stamp optd with T* **2**

TT29	D 1	1 c. scarlet (JD13)	£300	£300

PRICES OF SETS

Set prices are given for many issues, generally those containing five stamps or more. Definitive sets include one of each value or major colour change, but do not cover different perforations, die types or minor shades. Where a choice is possible the set prices are based on the cheapest versions of the stamps included in the listings.

Maldive Islands

PRICES FOR STAMPS ON COVER TO 1945

Nos. 1/6	*from* × 10
Nos. 7/10	*from* × 50
Nos. 11/20	*from* × 20

BRITISH PROTECTORATE

MALDIVES

(1)

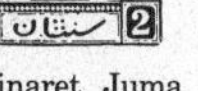

2 Minaret, Juma Mosque, Malé

3

1906. *Stamps of Ceylon optd with T* **1**. *Wmk Mult Crown CA. P* 14.

1	**44**	2 c. orange-brown, O	10·00	12·00
2	**45**	3 c. green, O	15·00	17·00
3		4 c. orange and ultramarine, O	35·00	50·00
4	**46**	5 c. dull purple, C	7·00	7·00
5	**48**	15 c. blue, O	60·00	80·00
6		25 c. bistre, O	75·00	80·00
1/6		*Set of* 6	£175	£225

(Recess D.L.R.)

1909 (May). *T* **2** (18½ × 22½ *mm*). *W* **3**. *P* 14.

7	**2**	2 c. orange-brown	1·75	60
8		3 c. deep myrtle	40	60
9		5 c. purple	40	50
10		10 c. carmine	1·00	1·00

4

(Photo Harrison)

1933. *T* **2** *redrawn* (*reduced to* 18 × 21½ *mm*). *W* **4**. *P* 15 × 14.

11	**2**	2 c. grey	75	80
12		3 c. red-brown	70	90
13		5 c. claret (*vert wmk*)	6·50	7·00
14		5 c. mauve (*horiz wmk*)	3·00	5·50
15		6 c. scarlet	1·10	1·10
16		10 c. green	55	55
17		15 c. black	1·25	1·75
18		25 c. brown	2·00	2·00
19		50 c. purple	2·00	1·75
20		1 r. deep blue	3·25	2·75
11/20		*Set of* 10	19·00	22·00

All values exist with both vert and horiz wmks.

(New Currency. 100 larees=1 rupee)

5 Palm Tree and Boat

(Recess B.W.)

1950 (24 Dec). *P* 13.

21	**5**	2 l. olive-green	80	80
22		3 l. blue	2·25	1·25
23		5 l. emerald-green	2·25	1·50
24		6 l. red-brown	80	50
25		10 l. scarlet	1·00	50
26		15 l. orange	1·00	60
27		25 l. purple	1·50	70
28		50 l. violet	2·00	1·25
29		1 r. chocolate	11·00	13·00
21/9		*Set of* 9	20·00	18·00

7 Fish

8 Native Products

(Recess B.W.)

1952. *P* 13.

30	**7**	3 l. blue	35	20
31	**8**	5 l. emerald	12	10

The Maldive Islands became a republic on 1 January 1953, but reverted to a sultanate in 1954.

9 Malé Harbour

10 Fort and Building

(Recess B.W.)

1956 (Feb). *P* 13½ (*T* **9**) *or* 11½ × 11 (*T* **10**).

32	**9**	2 l. purple	5	5
33		3 l. slate	5	5
34		5 l. red-brown	5	5
35		6 l. blackish violet	5	5
36		10 l. emerald	5	5
37		15 l. chocolate	5	5
38		25 l. rose-red	8	5
39		50 l. orange	12	5
40	**10**	1 r. bluish green	15	5
41		5 r. blue	90	90
42		10 r. magenta	2·00	2·00
32/42		*Set of* 11	3·00	3·00

11 Cycling

12 Basketball

(Des C. Bottiau. Recess and typo B.W.)

1960 (20 Aug). *Olympic Games. P* 11½ × 11 (*T* **11**) *or* 11 × 11½ (*T* **12**).

43	**11**	2 l. purple and green	5	5
44		3 l. greenish slate and purple	5	5
45		5 l. red-brown and ultramarine	5	5
46		10 l. emerald-green and brown	5	5
47		15 l. sepia and blue	5	5
48	**12**	25 l. rose-red and olive	10	5
49		50 l. orange and violet	15	10
50		1 r. emerald and purple	25	35
43/50		*Set of* 8	70	65

13 Tomb of Sultan

14 Custom House

(Recess B.W.)

1960 (15 Oct). *T* **13**, **14** *and similar horiz designs. P* 11½ × 11.

51	2 l. purple	5	5
52	3 l. emerald-green	5	5
53	5 l. orange-brown	5	5
54	6 l. bright blue	5	5
55	10 l. carmine	5	5
56	15 l. sepia	5	5
57	25 l. deep violet	5	5
58	50 l. slate-grey	10	5
59	1 r. orange	15	5
60	5 r. deep ultramarine	1·75	1·25
61	10 r. grey-green	4·00	2·50
51/61	*Set of* 11	5·75	3·75

Designs:—5 l. Cowrie shells; 6 l. Old Royal Palace; 10 l. Road to Juma Mosque, Malé; 15 l. Council house; 25 l. New Government Secretariat; 50 l. Prime Minister's office; 1 r. Old Ruler's tomb; 5 r. Old Ruler's tomb (distant view); 10 r. Maldivian Port.

Higher values were also issued, intended mainly for fiscal use.

24 "Care of Refugees"

(Recess B.W.)

1960 (15 Oct). *World Refugee Year. P* 11½ × 11.

62	**24**	2 l. deep violet, orange and green	5	5
63		3 l. brown, green and red	5	5
64		5 l. deep green, sepia and red	5	5
65		10 l. bluish green, reddish violet and red	5	5
66		15 l. reddish violet, grey-green and red	5	5
67		25 l. blue, red-brown and bronze-green	5	5
68		50 l. yellow-olive, rose-red and blue	10	5
69		1 r. carmine, slate and violet	25	45
62/9		*Set of* 8	45	50

MINIMUM PRICE

The minimum price quoted is 5p which represents a handling charge rather than a basis for valuing common stamps. For further notes about prices see introductory pages.

25 Coconuts

26 Map of Malé

(Photo Harrison)

1961 (20 Apr). *P 14 × 14½ (Nos. 70/74) or 14½ × 14 (others).*

70 **25** 2 l. yellow-brown and deep green .. 5 5
71 3 l. yellow-brown and bright blue .. 5 5
72 5 l. yellow-brown and magenta .. 5 5
73 10 l. yellow-brown and red-orange .. 5 5
74 15 l. yellow-brown and black 5 5
75 **26** 25 l. multicoloured 5 5
76 50 l. multicoloured 10 5
77 1 r. multicoloured 20 25
70/7 .. .. *Set of* 8 45 50

27 5 c. Stamp of 1906

30 Malaria Eradication Emblem

(Des M. Shamir. Photo Harrison)

1961 (9 Sept). *55th Anniv of First Maldivian Stamp. T* **27** *and similar horiz designs. P 14½ × 14.*

78 2 l. brown-purple, ultramarine & lt green .. 5 5
79 3 l. brown-purple, ultramarine & lt green .. 5 5
80 5 l. brown-purple, ultramarine & lt green .. 5 5
81 6 l. brown-purple, ultramarine & lt green .. 5 5
82 10 l. green, claret and maroon 5 5
83 15 l. green, claret and maroon 5 5
84 20 l. green, claret and maroon 10 10
85 25 l. claret, green and black 10 10
86 50 l. claret, green and black 35 35
87 1 r. claret, green and black 65 65
78/87 .. .. *Set of* 10 1·25 1·25
MS87*a* 114 × 88 mm. No. 87 (block of four). Imperf 1·75 2·00

Designs:—2 to 6 l. Type **27**; 10 to 20 l. 1906 3 c. and posthorn; 25 l. to 1 r. 1906 2 c. and olive sprig.

(Recess B.W.)

1962 (7 Apr). *Malaria Eradication. P 13½ × 13.*

88 **30** 2 l. chestnut 5 5
89 3 l. emerald 5 5
90 5 l. turquoise-blue 5 5
91 10 l. red 5 5
92 – 15 l. deep purple-brown 5 5
93 – 25 l. deep blue 5 5
94 – 50 l. deep green 10 10
95 – 1 r. purple 25 30
88/95 .. .. *Set of* 8 50 55

Nos. 92/5 are as T **30**, but have English inscriptions at the side.

31 Children of Europe and America

33 Sultan Mohamed Farid Didi

(Des C. Bottiau. Photo Harrison)

1962 (9 Sept). *15th Anniv of U.N.I.C.E.F. T* **31** *and similar horiz design. Multicoloured. P 14½ × 14.*

96 2 l. Type **31** 5 5
97 6 l. Type **31** 5 5
98 10 l. Type **31** 5 5
99 15 l. Type **31** 5 5
100 25 l. Children of Middle East and Far East 5 5
101 50 l. As 25 l. 8 8
102 1 r. As 25 l. 12 20
103 5 r. As 25 l. .. .. 55 1·25
96/103 .. .. *Set of* 8 80 1·50

(Photo Harrison)

1962 (29 Nov). *Ninth Anniv of Enthronement of Sultan. P 14 × 14½.*

104 **33** 3 l. orange-brown and bluish green 5 5
105 5 l. orange-brown and indigo .. 5 5
106 10 l. orange-brown and blue 5 5
107 20 l. orange-brown and olive-green .. 5 5
108 50 l. orange-brown and deep magenta .. 10 15
109 1 r. orange-brown and slate-lilac .. 15 30
104/9 .. .. *Set of* 6 40 60

34 Angel Fish

(Des R. Hegeman. Photo Enschedé)

1963 (2 Feb). *Tropical Fish. T* **34** *and similar triangular designs. Multicoloured. P 13½.*

110 2 l. Type **34** 5 5
111 3 l. Type **34** 5 5
112 5 l. Type **34** 5 5
113 10 l. Moorish Idol 5 5
114 25 l. As 10 l. 10 10
115 50 l. Soldier Fish 12 12
116 1 r. Surgeon Fish 30 30
117 5 r. Butterfly Fish .. .. 2·50 3·25
110/17 .. .. *Set of* 8 2·75 3·50

39 Fishes in Net

40 Handful of Grain

(Photo State Ptg Wks, Vienna)

1963 (21 Mar). *Freedom from Hunger. P 12.*

118 **39** 2 l. brown and deep bluish green .. 10 5
119 **40** 5 l. brown and orange-red 20 8
120 **39** 7 l. brown and turquoise 25 8
121 **40** 10 l. brown and blue 35 15
122 **39** 25 l. brown and brown-red .. .. 1·40 80
123 **40** 50 l. brown and violet .. .. 2·75 2·50
124 **39** 1 r. brown and deep magenta .. 4·25 4·75
118/24 .. .. *Set of* 7 8·50 7·50

41 Centenary Emblem

42 Maldivian Scout Badge

(Photo Harrison)

1963 (Oct). *Centenary of Red Cross. P 14 × 14½.*

125 **41** 2 l. red and deep purple 10 5
126 15 l. red and deep bluish green 20 10
127 50 l. red and deep brown.. .. .. 60 25
128 1 r. red and indigo .. .. .. 1·25 50
129 4 r. red and deep brown-olive .. .. 6·50 7·00

(Photo Enschedé)

1964. *World Scout Jamboree, Marathon (1963). P 13½.*

130 **42** 2 l. green and violet 5 5
131 3 l. green and bistre-brown 5 5
132 25 l. green and blue 10 10
133 1 r. green and crimson 45 65

43 Mosque, Malé

44 Putting the Shot

(Recess B.W.)

1964 (10 Aug). *"Maldives Embrace Islam". W w* **12**. *P 11½.*

134 **43** 2 l. purple 5 5
135 3 l. emerald-green 5 5
136 10 l. carmine 5 5
137 40 l. deep dull purple 10 8
138 60 l. blue 15 12
139 85 l. orange-brown 20 15
134/9 .. .. *Set of* 6 50 40

(Litho Enschedé)

1964 (Oct). *Olympic Games, Tokyo. T* **44** *and similar horiz design. W w* **12**. *P 14 × 13½.*

140 2 l. deep maroon and turquoise-blue .. 5 5
141 3 l. crimson and chestnut 5 5
142 5 l. bronze-green and deep green .. 5 5
143 10 l. slate-violet and reddish purple .. 5 5
144 15 l. sepia and yellow-brown 10 5
145 25 l. indigo and deep blue 20 10
146 50 l. deep olive-green and yellow-olive .. 40 20
147 1 r. deep maroon and olive-grey .. 70 40
140/7 .. .. *Set of* 8 1·40 70
MS147*a* 126 × 140 mm. Nos. 145/7. Imperf .. 1·75 2·25

Designs:—2 to 10 l. Type **44**; 15 l. to 1 r. Running.

46 Telecommunications Satellite

(Des M. Shamir. Photo Harrison)

1965 (1 July). *International Quiet Sun Years. P 14½.*

148 **46** 5 l. blue 5 5
149 10 l. brown 5 5
150 25 l. green 15 10
151 1 r. deep magenta 45 35

On 26 July 1965, Maldive Islands became independent and left the British Commonwealth.

INDEPENDENT SULTANATE

Sultan Mohamed Farid Didi
29 November 1953–10 November 1968

47 Isis (wall carving, Abu Simbel)

48 President Kennedy and Doves

1965 (1 Sept). *Nubian Monuments Preservation. T* **47** *and similar vert design. W w* **12**. *P 14½.*

152 **47** 2 l. bluish green and brown-purple .. 5 5
153 – 3 l. lake and deep green 5 5
154 **47** 5 l. dull green and brown-purple .. 5 5
155 – 10 l. steel-blue and orange 5 5
156 **47** 15 l. red-brown and deep violet 10 5
157 – 25 l. reddish purple and deep blue .. 15 8
158 **47** 50 l. yellow-green and sepia 25 15
159 – 1 r. ochre and myrtle-green 50 30
152/9 .. .. *Set of* 8 1·00 70

Design:—3, 10, 25 l., 1 r. Rameses II on throne (wall carving, Abu Simbel).

(Photo State Ptg Wks, Vienna)

1965 (10 Oct). *Second Death Anniv of President Kennedy. T* **48** *and similar horiz design. P 12.*

160 **48** 2 l. black and mauve 5 5
161 5 l. bistre-brown and mauve 5 5
162 25 l. indigo and mauve 8 8
163 – 1 r. brt reddish purple, yellow & bl-grn 30 30
164 – 2 r. bronze-green, yellow & blue-green 55 55
MS164*a* 150 × 130 mm. No. 164 in block of four. Imperf .. .. 2·50 2·50

Design:—1 r., 2 r. Pres. Kennedy and hands holding olive-branch.

49 "XX" and U.N. Flag

50 I.C.Y. Emblem

(Des O. Adler. Photo State Ptg Wks, Vienna)

1965 (24 Nov). *20th Anniv of U.N. P 12.*

165 **49** 3 l. turquoise-blue and red-brown .. 5 5
166 10 l. turquoise-blue and violet 5 5
167 1 r. turquoise-blue and bronze-green .. 35 35

(Des M. and G. Shamir. Photo State Ptg Wks, Vienna)

1965 (20 Dec). *International Co-operation Year. P 12.*

168 **50** 5 l. brown and yellow-bistre 5 5
169 15 l. brown and slate-lilac 10 5
170 50 l. brown and yellow-olive 25 15
171 1 r. brown and orange-red 70 60
172 2 r. brown and new blue .. .. 1·25 1·00
MS173 101 × 126 mm. Nos. 170/2. Imperf .. 2·10 2·10

51 Seashells

(Des M. and G. Shamir. Photo State Ptg Wks, Vienna)

1966 (1 June). *T* **51** *and similar multicoloured designs. P* 12.

174 2 l. Type **51** 5 5
175 3 l. Yellow flowers 5 5
176 5 l. Seashells (*different*) 5 5
177 7 l. Camellias 5 5
178 10 l. Type **51** 5 5
179 15 l. Crab Plover and Seagull 15 5
180 20 l. Yellow flowers 15 8
181 30 l. Type **51** 20 8
182 50 l. Crab Plover and Seagull 45 15
183 1 r. Type **51** 55 25
184 1 r. Camellias 55 25
185 1 r. 50, Yellow flowers 75 35
186 2 r. Camellias 1·00 55
187 5 r. Crab Plover and Seagull 3·25 2·25
188 10 r. Seashells (*different*) 5·50 4·75
174/88 *Set of* 15 11·50 8·00

The 3 l., 7 l., 20 l., 1 r. (No. 184), 1 r. 50 and 2 r. are diamond-shaped (43½ × 43½ mm); the others are horizontal designs as T **51**.

52 Maldivian Flag

(Des M. and G. Shamir. Litho Harrison)

1966 (26 July). *First Anniv of Independence. P* 14 × 14½.

189 **52** 10 l. green, red and turquoise 8 8
190 1 r. green, red, brown & orange-yellow 30 30

53 "Luna 9" on Moon

(Des M. and G. Shamir. Litho Harrison)

1966 (1 Nov). *Space Rendezvous and Moon Landing. T* **53** *and similar horiz designs. W w* **12**. *P* 15 × 14.

191 10 l. light brown, grey-blue and bright blue 8 8
192 25 l. green and carmine 8 8
193 50 l. orange-brown and green 12 12
194 1 r. turquoise-blue and chestnut 35 35
195 2 r. green and violet 65 65
196 5 r. rose-pink and deep turquoise-blue 1·60 1·60
191/6 *Set of* 6 2·50 2·50
MS197 108 × 126 mm. Nos. 194/6. Imperf 2·75 2·75

Designs:—25 l., 1 r., 5 r. "Gemini 6" and "7" rendezvous in space; 2 r. "Gemini" spaceship as seen from the other spaceship; 50 l. Type **53**.

54 U.N.E.S.C.O. Emblem, and Owl on Book

55 Sir Winston Churchill and Cortège

(Litho Harrison)

1966 (15 Nov). *20th Anniv of U.N.E.S.C.O. T* **54** *and similar vert designs. W w* **12**. *Multicoloured. P* 15 × 14.

198 1 l. Type **54** 5 5
199 3 l. U.N.E.S.C.O. emblem, and globe and microscope 5 5
200 5 l. U.N.E.S.C.O. emblem, and mask, violin and palette 5 5
201 50 l. Type **54** 20 20
202 1 r. Design as 3 l. 50 40
203 5 r. Design as 5 l. 3·25 3·25
198/203 *Set of* 6 3·50 3·50

(Des M. and G. Shamir. Litho Harrison)

1967 (1 Jan). *Churchill Commemoration. T* **55** *and similar horiz design. Flag in red and blue. P* 14½ × 13½.

204 **55** 2 l. olive-brown 5 5
205 – 10 l. turquoise-blue 8 8
206 **55** 15 l. green 15 8
207 – 25 l. violet 20 8
208 – 1 r. brown 80 45
209 **55** 2 r. 50, crimson 2·00 1·25
204/9 *Set of* 6 2·75 1·75

Design:—10 l., 25 l., 1 r. Churchill and catafalque.

IMPERFORATE STAMPS. From Nos. 210/**MS**217 onwards some sets and perforated miniature sheets exist imperforate from limited printings.

56 Footballers and Jules Rimet Cup

(Des M. and G. Shamir. Photo Govt Printer, Israel)

1967 (22 Mar). *England's Victory in World Cup Football Championships. T* **56** *and similar horiz designs. P* 14 × 13½.

210 2 l. greenish blue, black and red 5 5
211 3 l. red, black and yellow-olive 5 5
212 5 l. greenish yellow, black & reddish violet 5 5
213 25 l. orange, black and emerald 10 8
214 50 l. green, black and orange 30 15
215 1 r. orange, black and greenish blue 75 35
216 2 r. brown, red, royal blue and black 1·50 1·25
210/16 *Set of* 7 2·50 1·75
MS217 100 × 121 mm. Nos. 214/16. Imperf 2·50 2·50

Designs:—3 l. to 50 l. Various football scenes; 1 r. Type **56**; 2 r. Emblem on Union Jack, and Clock Tower, Westminster.

57 Clown Butterfly Fish

(Des M. and G. Shamir. Photo Govt Printer, Israel)

1967 (1 May). *Tropical Fishes. T* **57** *and similar horiz designs. Multicoloured. P* 14.

218 2 l. Type **57** 5 5
219 3 l. Striped Puffer 5 5
220 5 l. Blue Spotted Boxfish 5 5
221 6 l. Picasso Fish 5 5
222 50 l. Blue Angelfish 45 15
223 1 r. Blue Spotted Boxfish 90 35
224 2 r. Blue Angelfish 1·75 1·25
218/24 *Set of* 7 2·75 1·75

58 Hawker Siddeley "HS748" over Airport Building

(Des M. and G. Shamir. Photo Govt Printer, Israel)

1967 (26 July). *Inauguration of Hulule Airport. T* **58** *and similar horiz design. P* 14 × 13½.

225 2 l. reddish violet and yellow-olive 5 5
226 5 l. deep green and lavender 5 5
227 10 l. reddish violet and light turquoise-green 8 8
228 15 l. deep green and yellow-ochre 8 8
229 30 l. deep ultramarine and light blue 12 8
230 50 l. deep brown and magenta 25 15
231 5 r. deep ultramarine and yellow-orange 1·75 1·75
232 10 r. deep brown and blue 3·25 3·25
225/32 *Set of* 8 5·00 4·75

Designs:—2 l., 10 l., 30 l., 5 r. T **58**; 5 l., 15 l., 50 l., 10 r. Airport building and aircraft. Higher values were also issued, intended mainly for fiscal use.

59 "Man and Music" Pavilion

International Tourist Year 1967

(60)

(Des M. and G. Shamir. Photo Govt Printer, Israel)

1967 (Sept). *World Fair, Montreal. T* **59** *and similar horiz design. Multicoloured. P* 14 × 13½.

233 2 l. Type **59** 5 5
234 5 l. "Man and His Community" Pavilion 5 5
235 10 l. Type **59** 5 5
236 50 l. As 5 l. 15 15
237 1 r. Type **59** 30 30
238 2 r. As 5 l. 55 55
233/8 *Set of* 6 1·10 1·10
MS239 102 × 137 mm. Nos. 237/8. Imperf 1·10 1·10

1967 (1 Dec). *International Tourist Year. Nos. 225/32 optd as T* **60** *(in one or three lines), in gold.*

240 2 l. reddish violet and yellow-olive 5 5
241 5 l. deep green and lavender 5 5
242 10 l. reddish violet and light turquoise-green 5 5
243 15 l. deep green and yellow-ochre 8 8
244 30 l. deep ultramarine and light blue 8 8
245 50 l. deep brown and magenta 8 8
246 5 r. deep ultramarine and yellow-orange 1·50 1·50
247 10 r. deep brown and blue 3·00 3·00
240/7 *Set of* 8 4·50 4·50

61 Cub signalling and Lord Baden-Powell

62 French Satellite "A 1"

(Litho Harrison)

1968 (1 Jan). *Maldivian Scouts and Cubs. T* **61** *and similar vert design. P* 14 × 14½.

248 **61** 1 l. brown, green and yellow 5 5
249 – 3 l. carmine, bright blue and light blue 5 5
250 **61** 25 l. bluish violet, lake and orange-red 15 10
251 – 1 r. blackish green, chest & apple-green 65 50

Design:—3 l., 1 r. Scouts and Lord Baden-Powell.

(Des M. and G. Shamir. Photo Govt Printer, Israel)

1968 (27 Jan). *Space Martyrs. Triangular designs as T* **62**. *P* 14.

252 2 l. magenta and ultramarine 5 5
253 3 l. violet and yellow-brown 5 5
254 7 l. olive-brown and lake 5 5
255 10 l. deep blue, pale drab and black 5 5
256 25 l. bright emerald and reddish violet 8 8
257 50 l. blue and orange-brown 20 20
258 1 r. purple-brown and deep bluish green 40 40
259 2 r. deep brown, pale blue and black 70 70
260 5 r. magenta, light drab and black 1·75 1·75
252/60 *Set of* 9 3·00 3·00
MS261 110 × 155 mm. Nos. 258/9. Imperf 1·50 1·50

Designs:—2 l., 50 l. Type **62**; 3 l., 25 l. "Luna 10"; 7 l., 1 r. "Orbiter" and "Mariner"; 10 l., 2 r. Astronauts White, Grissom and Chaffee; 5 r. Cosmonaut V. M. Komarov.

63 Putting the Shot

64 "Adriatic Seascape" (Bonington)

(Des M. Shamir. Litho Harrison)

1968 (Feb). *Olympic Games, Mexico* (1967) (*1st issue*). *T* **63** *and similar vert design. Multicoloured. P* 14½.

262 2 l. Type **63** 5 5
263 6 l. Throwing the discus 5 5
264 10 l. Type **63** 5 5
265 15 l. As 6 l. 5 5
266 1 r. Type **63** 35 35
267 2 r. 50, As 6 l. 65 65
262/7 *Set of* 6 1·10 1·10

See also Nos. 294/7.

(Des M. Shamir. Litho Govt Printer, Israel)

1968 (1 Apr). *Paintings. T* **64** *and similar horiz designs. Multicoloured. P* 14.

268 50 l. Type **64** 15 12
269 1 r. "Ulysses deriding Polyphemus" (Turner) 35 35
270 2 r. "Sailing Boat at Argenteuil" (Monet) 75 75
271 5 r. "Fishing Boats at Les Saintes-Maries" (Van Gogh) 2·25 2·25

65 *Graf Zeppelin* and Montgolfier's Balloon

(Des M. Shamir. Photo Govt Printer, Israel)

1968 (1 June). *Development of Civil Aviation. T* **65** *and similar horiz designs. P* 14 × 13½.

272 2 l. orange-brown, yellow-green & ultram 5 5
273 3 l. turquoise-blue, violet & orange-brown 5 5
274 5 l. slate-green, crimson and turquoise-blue 5 5
275 7 l. bright blue, purple and red-orange 15 5
276 10 l. brown, turquoise-blue and bright purple 15 5
277 50 l. crimson, slate-green and yellow-olive 35 15
278 1 r. emerald, blue and vermilion 65 25
279 2 r. maroon, bistre and bright blue 2·50 2·50
272/9 *Set of* 8 3·50 2·75

Designs:—3 l., 1 r. Boeing "707" and Douglas "DC-3"; 5 l., 50 l. Wright Brothers aircraft and Lilienthal's glider; 7 l., 2 r. Projected Boeing Supersonic "733" and "Concorde"; 10 l. Type **65**.

66 W.H.O. Building, Geneva

International Boy Scout Jamboree, Farragut Park, Idaho, U.S.A. August 1-9, 1967

(67)

(Litho Harrison)

1968 (15 July). *20th Anniv of World Health Organisation. P* 14½ × 13½.
280 **66** 10 l. violet, turquoise-bl & lt greenish bl .. 5 5
281 25 l. bronze-green, yell-brn & orge-yell .. 10 5
282 1 r. deep brown, emerald & brt green .. 45 30
283 2 r. bluish violet, magenta and mauve .. 95 85

1968 (1 Aug). *First Anniv of Scout Jamboree, Idaho. Nos.* 248/51 *optd with T* **67**.
284 2 l. brown, green and yellow.. .. .. 5 5
285 3 l. carmine, bright blue and light blue .. 5 5
286 25 l. bluish violet, lake and orange-red .. 15 15
287 1 r. blackish green, chestnut & apple-green 55 45

68 Curlew and Redshank

1968 (24 Sept). *T* **68** *and similar horiz designs. Photo. Multicoloured. P* 14 × 13½.
288 2 l. Type **68** 5 5
289 10 l. Conches 5 5
290 25 l. Shells 15 10
291 50 l. Type **68** 50 15
292 1 r. Conches 75 40
293 2 r. Shells .. .. 1·60 1·50
288/93 .. .. *Set of* 6 2·75 2·00

69 Throwing the Discus

(Des M. Shamir. Photo Govt Printer, Israel)

1968 (12 Oct). *Olympic Games, Mexico (2nd issue). T* **69** *and similar multicoloured designs. P* 14.
294 10 l. Type **69** 5 5
295 50 l. Running 10 5
296 1 r. Cycling 35 35
297 2 r. Basketball 75 75

INDEPENDENT REPUBLIC
11 November 1968

70 Fishing Boat **71** "The Thinker" (Rodin)

(Photo Harrison)

1968 (11 Nov). *Republic Day. T* **70** *and similar horiz design. P* 14 × 14½.
298 10 l. brown, ultramarine and lt yellow-green 15 5
299 1 r. green, red and bright blue 80 40
Design:—1 r. National flag, crest and map.

(Des M. Shamir. Litho Rosenbaum Brothers, Vienna)

1969 (10 Apr). *U.N.E.S.C.O. "Human Rights". T* **71** *and similar vert designs, showing sculptures by Rodin. Multicoloured. P* 13½.
300 6 l. Type **71** 5 5
301 10 l. "Hands" 5 5
302 1 r. 50, "Eve" 75 60
303 2 r. 50, "Adam" .. .. 1·25 95
MS304 112 × 130 mm. Nos. 302/3. Imperf .. 2·00 2·00

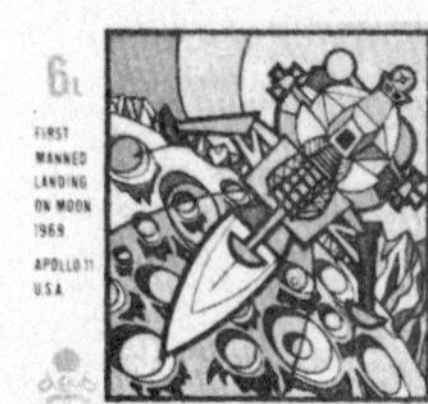

72 Module nearing Moon's Surface

(Des M. Shamir. Litho Govt Printer, Israel)

1969 (25 Sept). *First Man on the Moon. T* **72** *and similar square designs. Multicoloured. P* 14.
305 6 l. Type **72** 5 5
306 10 l. Astronaut with hatchet 5 5
307 1 r. 50, Astronaut and module 60 60
308 2 r. 50, Astronaut using camera .. .. 1·00 75
MS309 101 × 130 mm. Nos. 305/8. Imperf .. 1·60 1·60

Gold Medal Winner
Mohamed Gammoudi
5000 m. run
Tunisia
REPUBLIC OF MALDIVES

(73)

1969 (1 Dec). *Gold-medal Winners, Olympic Games, Mexico* (1968). *Nos.* 295/6 *optd with T* **73**, *or similar inscr honouring P. Trentin (cycling) of France.*
310 50 l. multicoloured 40 40
311 1 r. multicoloured 60 60

74 Red-striped Butterfly Fish

(Des M. Shamir. Litho)

1970 (Jan). *Tropical Fish. T* **74** *and similar diamond-shaped designs. Multicoloured. P* 10½.
312 2 l. Type **74** 5 5
313 5 l. Spotted Triggerfish 5 5
314 25 l. Scorpion Fish 15 10
315 50 l. Forceps Fish 35 30
316 1 r. Imperial Angelfish 70 55
317 2 r. Regal Angelfish .. .. 1·75 1·40
312/17 .. .. *Set of* 6 2·75 2·25

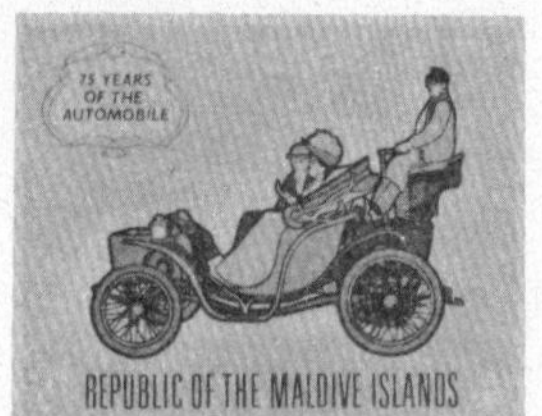

75 Columbia Dauman Victoria, 1899

(Des M. Shamir. Litho)

1970 (1 Feb). *"75 Years of the Automobile". T* **75** *and similar horiz designs. Multicoloured. P* 12.
318 2 l. Type **75** 5 5
319 5 l. Duryea phaeton, 1902 .. .. 5 5
320 7 l. Packard S-24, 1906 .. .. 5 5
321 10 l. Autocar Runabout, 1907.. .. .. .. 5 5
322 25 l. Type **75** 15 8
323 50 l. As 5 l. 35 15
324 1 r. As 7 l. 75 35
325 2 r. As 10 l. .. .. 1·60 1·50
318/25 .. .. *Set of* 8 2·75 2·00
MS326 95 × 143 mm. Nos. 324/5. P 11½ .. 2·50 2·50

76 U.N. Headquarters, New York **77** Ship and Light Buoy

(Des M. Shamir. Litho Rosenbaum Brothers, Vienna)

1970 (26 June). *25th Anniv of United Nations. T* **76** *and similar horiz designs. Multicoloured. P* 13½.
327 2 l. Type **76** 5 5
328 10 l. Surgical operation (W.H.O.) 8 8
329 25 l. Student, actress and musician (U.N.E.S.C.O.) 15 10
330 50 l. Children at work and play (U.N.I.C.E.F.) 25 15
331 1 r. Fish, corn and farm animals (F.A.O.) .. 55 35
332 2 r. Miner hewing coal (I.L.O.) .. .. 1·25 1·25
327/32 .. .. *Set of* 6 2·10 1·75

(Des M. Shamir. Litho)

1970 (26 July). *10th Anniv of Inter-governmental Maritime Consultative Organization. T* **77** *and similar vert design. Multicoloured. P* 13½.
333 50 l. Type **77** 45 40
334 1 r. Ship and lighthouse .. .. 1·00 85

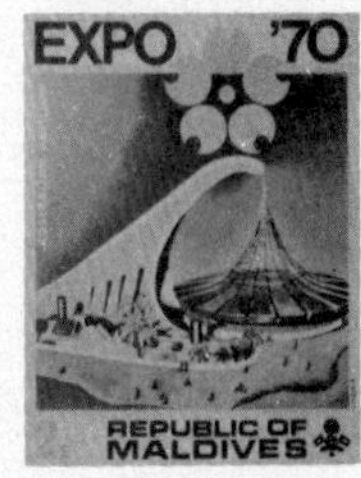

78 "Guitar-player and Masqueraders" (A. Watteau) **79** Australian Pavilion

(Des M. Shamir. Litho Govt Printer, Israel)

1970 (1 Aug). *Famous Paintings showing the Guitar. T* **78** *and similar vert designs. Multicoloured. P* 14.
335 3 l. Type **78** 5 5
336 7 l. "Spanish Guitarist" (E. Manet) 5 5
337 50 l. "Costumed Player" (Watteau) 15 15
338 1 r. "Mandoline-player" (Roberti) 35 35
339 2 r. 50, "Guitar-player and Lady" (Watteau) 1·25 1·25
340 5 r. "Mandoline-player" (Frans Hals) .. 2·25 2·25
335/40 .. .. *Set of* 6 3·75 3·75
MS341 132 × 80 mm. Nos. 339/40. Roul .. .. 3·50 4·25

(Des M. Shamir. Litho Rosenbaum Brothers, Vienna)

1970 (1 Aug). *"EXPO 70" World Fair, Osaka, Japan. T* **79** *and similar vert designs. Multicoloured. P* 13½.
342 2 l. Type **79** 5 5
343 3 l. West German Pavilion 5 5
344 10 l. U.S.A. Pavilion 8 8
345 25 l. British Pavilion 10 10
346 50 l. Soviet Pavilion 20 20
347 1 r. Japanese Pavilion 40 40
342/7 .. .. *Set of* 6 80 80

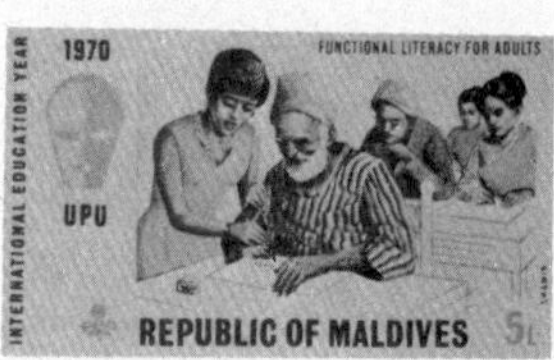

80 Learning the Alphabet

(Des M. Shamir. Litho Govt Printer, Israel)

1970 (7 Sept). *International Education Year. T* **80** *and similar horiz designs. Multicoloured. P* 14.
348 5 l. Type **80** 5 5
349 10 l. Training teachers 5 5
350 25 l. Geography lesson 12 12
351 50 l. School inspector 20 20
352 1 r. Education by television 35 35

Philympia
London 1970

(81)

82 Footballers

1970 (18 Sept). *"Philympia 1970" Stamp Exhibition, London. Nos.* 306/**MS**309 *optd with T* **81**, *in silver.*
353 10 l. multicoloured 5 5
354 1 r. 50, multicoloured 65 65
355 2 r. 50, multicoloured 90 90
MS356 101 × 130 mm. Nos. 305/8 optd. Imperf .. 2·75 2·75

(Des M. Shamir. Litho Rosenbaum Brothers, Vienna)

1970 (Dec). *World Cup Football Championships, Mexico. T* **82** *and similar vert designs, each showing football scenes and outline of the Jules Rimet Trophy. P* 13½.
357 3 l. multicoloured 5 5
358 6 l. multicoloured 5 5
359 7 l. multicoloured 5 5
360 25 l. multicoloured 15 10
361 1 r. multicoloured 55 60

ALTERED CATALOGUE NUMBERS

Any Catalogue numbers altered from the last edition are shown as a list in the introductory pages.

83 Little Boy and U.N.I.C.E.F. Flag

84 Astronauts Lovell, Haise and Swigert

(Des M. Shamir. Litho State Printing Works, Budapest)

1971 (1 Apr). *25th Anniv of U.N.I.C.E.F. T* **83** *and similar vert design. Multicoloured. P* 12.

362	5 l. Type **83**	5	5
363	10 l. Little girl with U.N.I.C.E.F. balloon	5	5
364	1 r. Type **83**	45	45
365	2 r. As 10 l.	1·00	1·00

(Des M. Shamir. Litho Govt Printer, Israel)

1971 (27 Apr). *Safe Return of "Apollo 13". T* **84** *and similar vert designs. Multicoloured. P* 14.

366	5 l. Type **84**	5	5
367	20 l. Explosion in Space	5	5
368	1 r. Splashdown	40	40

85 "Multiracial Flower"

86 "Mme. Charpentier and her Children" (Renoir)

(Des M. Shamir. Litho)

1971 (3 May). *Racial Equality Year. P* 14.

369	**85**	10 l. multicoloured	5	5
370		25 l. multicoloured	12	12

1971 (Aug). *Famous Paintings showing "Mother and Child". T* **86** *and similar vert designs. Multicoloured. Litho. P* 12.

371	5 l. Type **86**	5	5
372	7 l. "Susanna van Collen and her Daughter" (Rembrandt)	5	5
373	10 l. "Madonna nursing the Child" (Titian)	5	5
374	20 l. "Baroness Belleli and her Children" (Degas)	10	10
375	25 l. "The Cradle" (Morisot)	10	10
376	1 r. "Helena Fourment and her Children" (Rubens)	50	50
377	3 r. "On the Terrace" (Renoir)	1·60	1·60
371/7	*Set of* 7	2·25	2·25

87 Alan Shepard

88 "Ballerina" (Degas)

(Photo State Ptg Works, Vienna)

1971 (11 Nov). *Moon Flight of "Apollo 14".* T **87** *and similar vert designs. Multicoloured. P* 12½.

378	6 l. Type **87**	5	5
379	10 l. Stuart Roosa	5	5
380	1 r. 50, Edgar Mitchell	90	90
381	5 r. Mission insignia	3·25	3·25

(Litho Rosenbaum Brothers, Vienna)

1971 (19 Nov). *Famous Paintings showing "Dancers". T* **88** *and similar vert designs. Multicoloured. P* 14.

382	5 l. Type **88**	5	5
383	10 l. "Dancing Couple" (Renoir)	8	8
384	2 r. "Spanish Dancer" (Manet)	1·00	1·00
385	5 r. "Ballerinas" (Degas)	2·25	2·25
386	10 r. "La Goulue at the Moulin Rouge" (Toulouse-Lautrec)	3·75	3·75

ROYAL VISIT 1972

(89)

90 Book Year Emblem

1972 (13 Mar). *Visit of Queen Elizabeth II and Prince Philip. Nos.* 382/6 *optd with T* **89**.

387	5 l. multicoloured	5	5
388	10 l. multicoloured	8	8
389	2 r. multicoloured	1·75	1·75
390	5 r. multicoloured	3·25	3·25
391	10 r. multicoloured	6·00	6·00

(Des M. Shamir. Litho Bradbury, Wilkinson)

1972 (1 May). *International Book Year. P* 13 × 13½.

392	**90**	25 l. multicoloured	12	12
393		5 r. multicoloured	1·60	1·60

91 Scottish Costume

93 Cross-country Skiing

92 Stegosaurus

(Des M. Shamir. Litho State Printing Works, Budapest)

1972 (15 May). *National Costumes of the World. T* **91** *and similar vert designs. Multicoloured. P* 12.

394	10 l. Type **91**	5	5
395	15 l. Netherlands	5	5
396	25 l. Norway	15	15
397	50 l. Hungary	30	30
398	1 r. Austria	60	60
399	2 r. Spain	1·50	1·50
394/9	*Set of* 6	2·40	2·40

(Des M. Shamir. Litho Rosenbaum Brothers, Vienna)

1972 (31 May). *Prehistoric Animals. T* **92** *and similar horiz designs. Multicoloured. P* 14.

400	2 l. Type **92**	5	5
401	7 l. Edaphosaurus	10	10
402	25 l. Diplodocus	25	25
403	50 l. Triceratops	40	40
404	2 r. Pteranodon	1·75	1·75
405	5 r. Tyrannosaurus	3·50	3·50
400/5	*Set of* 6	5·50	5·50

An imperforate miniature sheet containing Nos. 404/5 also exists, but was never freely available.

(Des M. Shamir. Litho Rosenbaum Brothers, Vienna)

1972 (June). *Winter Olympic Games, Sapporo, Japan. T* **93** *and similar vert designs. Multicoloured. P* 14.

406	3 l. Type **93**	5	5
407	6 l. Bob-sleighing	5	5
408	15 l. Speed-skating	5	5
409	50 l. Ski-jumping	25	25
410	1 r. Figure-skating (pair)	50	50
411	2 r. 50, Ice-hockey	1·40	1·40
406/11	*Set of* 6	2·00	2·00

94 Scout Saluting

95 Cycling

(Des M. Shamir. Litho Govt Printer, Israel)

1972 (1 Aug). *13th World Scout Jamboree, Asagiri, Japan* (1971). *T* **94** *and similar vert designs. Multicoloured. P* 14.

412	10 l. Type **92**	5	5
413	15 l. Scout signalling	5	5
414	50 l. Scout blowing bugle	45	35
415	1 r. Scout beating drum	95	75

PRINTERS AND PROCESS. *Unless otherwise stated,* all the following issues were lithographed by Format International Security Printers Ltd, London.

1972 (30 Oct). *Olympic Games, Munich. T* **95** *and similar vert designs. Multicoloured. P* 14½ × 14.

416	5 l. Type **95**	5	5
417	10 l. Running	5	5
418	25 l. Wrestling	10	10
419	50 l. Hurdling	25	25
420	2 r. Boxing	85	85
421	5 r. Volleyball	1·90	1·90
416/21	*Set of* 6	3·00	3·00
MS422	92 × 120 mm. 3 r. As 50 l.; 4 r. As 10 l. P 15	3·00	3·50

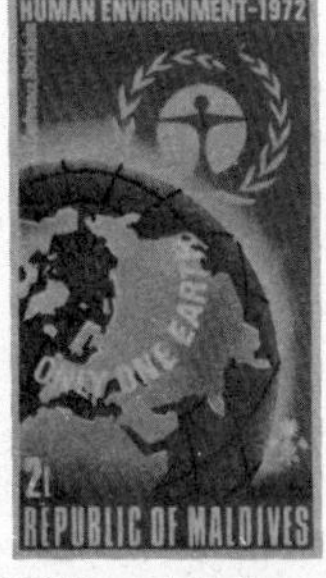

96 Globe and Conference Emblem

97 "Flowers" (Van Gogh)

(Litho Harrison)

1972 (15 Nov). *U.N. Environmental Conservation Conference, Stockholm. P* 14½.

423	**96**	2 l. multicoloured	5	5
424		3 l. multicoloured	5	5
425		15 l. multicoloured	5	5
426		50 l. multicoloured	20	20
427		2 r. 50, multicoloured	1·25	1·25

(Des M. Shamir)

1973 (Mar). *Floral Paintings. T* **97** *and similar vert designs. Multicoloured. P* 13½.

428	1 l. Type **97**	5	5
429	2 l. "Flowers in Jug" (Renoir)	5	5
430	3 l. "Chrysanthemums" (Renoir)	5	5
431	50 l. "Mixed Bouquet" (Bosschaert)	12	12
432	1 r. As 3 l.	35	35
433	5 r. As 2 l.	1·60	1·60
428/33	*Set of* 6	2·00	2·00
MS434	120 × 94 mm. 2 r. as 50 l.; 3 r. Type **97**. P 15	1·60	1·60

LEMECHEV
MIDDLE-WEIGHT
GOLD MEDALLIST

(98)

99 Animal Care

1973 (Apr). *Gold-medal Winners, Munich Olympic Games. Nos.* 420/**MS**422 *optd with T* **98** *or similar commemorative inscr, in blue.*

435	2 r. multicoloured	1·00	1·00
436	5 r. multicoloured	1·90	1·90
MS437	92 × 120 mm. 3 r. multicoloured; 4 r. multicoloured	2·75	2·75

Overprints:—2 r. Type **98**; 5 r. "JAPAN GOLD MEDAL WINNERS" (volleyball). Miniature sheet:—3 r. "EHRHARDT 100 METER HURDLES GOLD MEDALLIST"; 4 r. "SHORTER MARATHON GOLD MEDALLIST".

(Des M. Shamir)

1973 (Aug). *International Scouting Congress, Nairobi and Addis Ababa. T* **99** *and similar horiz designs. Multicoloured. P* 14½.

438	1 l. Type **99**	5	5
439	2 l. Lifesaving	5	5
440	3 l. Agricultural training	5	5
441	4 l. Carpentry	5	5
442	5 l. Playing leapfrog	5	5
443	1 r. As 2 l.	55	55
444	2 r. As 4 l.	95	95
445	3 r. Type **99**	1·40	1·40
438/45	*Set of* 8	2·75	2·75
MS446	101 × 79 mm. 5 r. As 3 l.	2·25	2·75

100 *Makaira herscheli*

1973 (Aug). *Fishes. T* **100** *and similar horiz designs. Multicoloured. P* 14½.

447	1 l. Type **100**	5	5
448	2 l. *Katsuwonus pelamys*	5	5
449	3 l. *Thunnus thynnus*	5	5

450	5 l. *Coryphaena hippurus*	5	5
451	60 l. *Lutjanus gibbus*	25	25
452	75 l. As 60 l.	30	30
453	1 r. 50, *Variola louti*	65	65
454	2 r. 50, As 5 l.	75	75
455	3 r. *Plectropoma maculatum*	1·25	1·25
456	10 r. *Scomberomorus commerson*	4·25	4·25
447/56	*Set of* 10	7·00	7·00
MS457	119 × 123 mm. 4 r. As 2 l.; 5 r. Type **100**	4·25	4·50

Nos. 451/2 are smaller, size 29 × 22 mm.

101 Golden-fronted Leafbird

102 *Lantana camara*

(Des M. Shamir)

1973 (Oct). *Fauna. T* **101** *and similar diamond-shaped designs. Multicoloured. P* 14½.

458	1 l. Type **101**	5	5
459	2 l. Fruit bat	5	5
460	3 l. Land tortoise	5	5
461	4 l. *Kallima inachus* (butterfly)	5	5
462	50 l. As 3 l.	30	25
463	2 r. Type **101**	2·25	2·75
464	3 r. As 2 l.	2·75	2·75
458/64	*Set of* 7	5·00	5·00
MS465	66 × 74 mm. 5 r. As 4 l.	4·50	4·75

(Litho Questa)

1973 (19 Dec). *Flowers of the Maldive Islands. T* **102** *and similar vert designs. Multicoloured. P* 14.

466	1 l. Type **102**	5	5
467	2 l. *Nerium oleander*	5	5
468	3 l. *Rosa polyantha*	5	5
469	4 l. *Hibiscus manihot*	5	5
470	5 l. *Bougainvillea glabra*	5	5
471	10 l. *Plumera alba*	5	5
472	50 l. *Poinsettia pulcherrima*	15	15
473	5 r. *Ononis natrix*	2·00	2·00
466/73	*Set of* 8	2·25	2·25
MS474	110 × 100 mm. 2 r. As 3 l.; 3 r. As 10 l.	2·25	2·40

103 "Tiros" Weather Satellite

(Des M. Shamir)

1974 (10 Jan). *Centenary of World Meteorological Organization. T* **103** *and similar horiz designs. Multicoloured. P* 14½.

475	1 l. Type **103**	5	5
476	2 l. "Nimbus" satellite	5	5
477	3 l. "Nomad" maritime weather station	5	5
478	4 l. Scanner, A.P.T. Instant Weather Picture equipment	5	5
479	5 l. Richard's wind-speed recorder	5	5
480	2 r. Type **103**	1·25	1·25
481	3 r. As 3 l.	1·50	1·50
475/81	*Set of* 7	2·75	2·75
MS482	110 × 79 mm. 10 r. As 2 l.	4·25	5·50

104 "Apollo" Spacecraft and Pres. Kennedy

(Des M. Shamir)

1974 (1 Feb). *American and Russian Space Exploration Projects. T* **104** *and similar horiz designs. Multicoloured. P* 14½.

483	1 l. Type **104**	5	5
484	2 l. "Mercury" capsule and John Glenn	5	5
485	3 l. "Vostok 1" and Yuri Gagarin	5	5
486	4 l. "Vostok 6" and Valentina Tereshkova	5	5
487	5 l. "Soyuz 11" and "Salyut" space-station	5	5
488	2 r. "Skylab" space laboratory	1·25	1·25
489	3 r. As 2 l.	1·50	1·50
483/9	*Set of* 7	2·75	2·75
MS490	103 × 80 mm. 10 r. Type **104**	4·25	5·50

105 Copernicus and "Skylab" Space Laboratory

106 "Maternity" (Picasso)

(Des G. Vasarhelyi)

1974 (10 Apr). *500th Birth Anniv of Nicholas Copernicus (astronomer). T* **105** *and similar horiz designs. Multicoloured. P* 14½.

491	1 l. Type **105**	5	5
492	2 l. Orbital space-station of the future	5	5
493	3 l. Proposed "Space-shuttle" craft	5	5
494	4 l. "Mariner 2" Venus probe	5	5
495	5 l. "Mariner 4" Mars probe	5	5
496	25 l. Type **105**	10	10
497	1 r. 50, As 2 l.	75	75
498	5 r. As 3 l.	2·50	2·50
491/8	*Set of* 8	3·25	3·25
MS499	106 × 80 mm. 10 r. "Copernicus" orbital observatory	5·50	7·00

(Des M. Shamir. Litho Questa)

1974 (May). *Paintings by Picasso. T* **106** *and similar vert designs. Multicoloured. P* 14.

500	1 l. Type **106**	5	5
501	2 l. "Harlequin and Friend"	5	5
502	3 l. "Pierrot Sitting"	5	5
503	20 l. "Three Musicians"	8	8
504	75 l. "L'Aficionado"	20	20
505	5 r. "Still Life"	1·75	1·75
500/5	*Set of* 6	2·00	2·00
MS506	100 × 101 mm. 2 r. As 20 l.; 3 r. As 5 r.	1·90	1·90

107 U.P.U. Emblem, Steam and Diesel Locomotives

108 Footballers

(Des M. Shamir)

1974 (May). *Centenary of Universal Postal Union. T* **107** *and similar horiz designs. Multicoloured. P* 14½.

507	1 l. Type **107**	5	5
508	2 l. Paddle-steamer and modern mailboat	5	5
509	3 l. Airship and Boeing "747" airliner	5	5
510	1 r. 50, Mailcoach and motor van	85	85
511	2 r. 50, As 2 l.	1·60	1·60
512	5 r. Type **107**	4·00	4·00
507/12	*Set of* 6	6·00	6·00
MS513	126 × 105 mm. 4 r. Type **107**	3·50	3·50

Nos. 507/12 were first issued in sheets of 50, but were later released in small sheets of five stamps and one label. These small sheets were perforated 13½.

(Des M. Shamir)

1974 (June). *World Cup Football Championships, West Germany. T* **108** *and similar vert designs, showing football scenes. P* 14½.

514	1 l. multicoloured	5	5
515	2 l. multicoloured	5	5
516	3 l. multicoloured	5	5
517	4 l. multicoloured	5	5
518	75 l. multicoloured	30	30
519	4 r. multicoloured	1·00	1·00
520	5 r. multicoloured	1·75	1·75
514/20	*Set of* 7	3·00	3·00
MS521	88 × 95 mm. 10 r. multicoloured	3·25	3·25

109 "Capricorn"

110 Churchill and Bomber Aircraft

(Des G. Vasarhelyi)

1974 (3 July). *Signs of the Zodiac. T* **109** *and similar horiz designs. Multicoloured. P* 14½.

522	1 l. Type **109**	5	5
523	2 l. "Aquarius"	5	5
524	3 l. "Pisces"	5	5
525	4 l. "Aries"	5	5
526	5 l. "Taurus"	5	5
527	6 l. "Gemini"	5	5
528	7 l. "Cancer"	5	5
529	10 l. "Leo"	5	5
530	15 l. "Virgo"	5	5
531	20 l. "Libra"	5	5
532	25 l. "Scorpio"	8	8
533	5 r. "Sagittarius"	3·50	3·50
522/33	*Set of* 12	3·75	3·75
MS534	119 × 99 mm. 10 r. "The Sun" (49 × 37 *mm*). P 13½	6·50	7·50

(Des M. Shamir)

1974 (30 Nov). *Birth Centenary of Sir Winston Churchill. T* **110** *and similar horiz designs. Multicoloured. P* 14½.

535	1 l. Type **110**	5	5
536	2 l. Churchill as pilot	5	5
537	3 l. Churchill as First Lord of the Admiralty	5	5
538	4 l. Churchill and aircraft carrier	5	5
539	5 l. Churchill and fighter aircraft	5	5
540	60 l. Churchill and anti-aircraft battery	45	45
541	75 l. Churchill and tank in desert	55	55
542	5 r. Churchill and flying-boat	4·00	4·00
535/42	*Set of* 8	5·00	5·00
MS543	113 × 83 mm. 10 r. As 4 l.	6·50	7·00

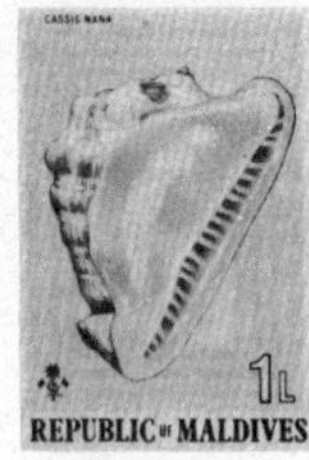

111 *Cassia nana*

112 Royal Throne

(Des M. Shamir)

1975 (25 Jan). *Seashells and Cowries. T* **111** *and similar multicoloured designs. P* 14 × 13½ (60 *l.*, 75 *l.*) *or* 14½ (*others*).

544	1 l. Type **111**	5	5
545	2 l. *Murex triremus*	5	5
546	3 l. *Harpa major*	5	5
547	4 l. *Lambis chiragra*	5	5
548	5 l. *Conus pennaceus*	5	5
549	60 l. *Cypraea diliculum* (22 × 30 *mm*)	40	40
550	75 l. *Clanculus pharaonis* (22 × 30 *mm*)	50	50
551	5 r. *Chicoreus ramosus*	3·50	3·50
544/51	*Set of* 8	4·25	4·25
MS552	152 × 126 mm. 2 r. As 3 l.; 3 r. as 2 l.	3·50	4·00

(Des M. Shamir. Litho Questa)

1975 (22 Feb). *Historical Relics and Monuments. T* **112** *and similar multicoloured designs. P* 14.

553	1 l. Type **112**	5	5
554	10 l. Candlesticks	5	5
555	25 l. Lamp-tree	10	10
556	60 l. Royal umbrellas	20	20
557	75 l. Eid-Miskith Mosque (*horiz*)	25	25
558	3 r. Tomb of Al-Hafiz Abu-al Barakath-al Barubari (*horiz*)	1·10	1·10
553/8	*Set of* 6	1·60	1·60

113 Guavas

114 *Phyllangia*

(Des M. Shamir)

1975 (Mar). *Fruits. T* **113** *and similar vert designs. Multicoloured. P* 14½.

559	2 l. Type **113**	5	5
560	4 l. Maldive mulberry	5	5
561	5 l. Mountain apples	5	5
562	10 l. Bananas	5	5
563	20 l. Mangoes	5	5
564	50 l. Papaya	15	10
565	1 r. Pomegranates	30	25
566	5 r. Coconut	1·75	1·90
559/66	*Set of* 8	2·25	2·25
MS567	136 × 102 mm. 2 r. As 10 l.; 3 r. As 2 l.	2·00	2·25

(Des M. Shamir)

1975 (6 June). *Marine Life. T* **114** *and similar triangular designs. Multicoloured. P* 14½.

568	1 l. Type **114**	5	5
569	2 l. *Madrepora oculata*	5	5
570	3 l. *Acropora gravida*	5	5
571	4 l. *Stylotella*	5	5
572	5 l. *Acrophora cervicornis*	5	5
573	60 l. *Strongylocentrotus purpuratus*	45	45
574	75 l. *Pisaster ochraceus*	55	55
575	5 r. *Marthasterias glacialis*	3·50	3·50
568/75	*Set of* 8	4·50	4·50
MS576	155 × 98 mm. 4 r. As 1 l. Imperf	3·00	4·00

115 Clock Tower and Customs Building within "10"

14th Boy Scout Jamboree
July 29 – August 7, 1975

(**116**)

(Des M. Shamir)

1975 (26 July). *10th Anniv of Independence. T* **115** *and similar horiz designs. Multicoloured. P* 14½.

577 4 l. Type **115** 5 5
578 5 l. Government Offices 5 5
579 7 l. Waterfront 5 5
580 15 l. Mosque and minaret 5 5
581 10 r. Sultan Park and museum .. .. 3·75 4·50

1975 (26 July). *"Nordjamb 75" World Scout Jamboree, Norway. Nos.* 443/5 *and* **MS**446 *optd with T* **116**.

582 1 r. multicoloured 30 30
583 2 r. multicoloured 50 50
584 3 r. multicoloured .. .. 1·00 1·00
MS585 101 × 79 mm. 5 r. multicoloured .. .. 1·75 1·75

117 Madura—Prau Bedang

118 *Brahmaea wallichii*

(Des M. Shamir)

1975 (Aug). *Ships. T* **117** *and similar multicoloured designs. P* 14½.

586 1 l. Type **117** 5 5
587 2 l. Ganges patile 5 5
588 3 l. Indian palla (*vert*) 5 5
589 4 l. "Odhi" (*vert*) 5 5
590 5 l. Maldivian schooner 5 5
591 25 l. *Cutty Sark* 20 20
592 1 r. Maldivian baggala (*vert*).. .. .. 70 70
593 5 r. Freighter *Maldive Courage* .. .. 3·25 3·25
586/93 .. .. *Set of* 8 4·00 4·00
MS594 99 × 85 mm. 10 r. As 1 l. .. .. 5·00 5·50

(Des M. Shamir)

1975 (7 Sept). *Butterflies. T* **118** *and similar horiz designs. Multicoloured. P* 14½.

595 1 l. Type **118** 5 5
596 2 l. *Teinopalpus imperialis* 5 5
597 3 l. *Cethosia biblis* 5 5
598 4 l. *Hestia jasonia* 5 5
599 5 l. *Apatura ilia* 5 5
600 25 l. *Kallima horsfieldi* 35 35
601 1 r. 50, *Hebomoia leucippe* .. .. .. 1·50 1·50
602 5 r. *Papilio memnon* .. .. 5·50 5·50
595/602 .. .. .. *Set of* 8 7·00 7·00
MS603 134 × 97 mm. 10 r. As 25 l. .. .. 8·00 8·50

119 "The Dying Captive"

120 Beaker and Vase

1975 (9 Oct). *500th Birth Anniv of Michelangelo. T* **119** *and similar vert designs. Multicoloured. P* 14½.

604 1 l. Type **119** 5 5
605 2 l. Detail of "The Last Judgement".. .. .. 5 5
606 3 l. "Apollo" 5 5
607 4 l. Detail of Sistine Chapel ceiling 5 5
608 5 l. "Bacchus" 5 5
609 1 r. Detail of "The Last Judgement" (*different*) 25 15
610 2 r. "David" 75 60
611 5 r. "Cumaean Sibyl" .. .. 2·00 1·90
604/11 .. .. *Set of* 8 2·75 2·50
MS612 123 × 113 mm. 10 r. As 2 r. .. .. 3·75 4·75

The 1, 3, 5 l. and 2, 10 r. are sculptures; the other values show details of the frescoes in the Sistine Chapel.

(Des M. Shamir. Litho Questa)

1975 (Dec). *Maldivian Lacquerware. T* **120** *and similar vert designs. Multicoloured. P* 14.

613 2 l. Type **120** 5 5
614 4 l. Boxes 5 5
615 50 l. Jar with lid 20 20
616 75 l. Bowls with covers 30 30
617 1 r. Craftsman at work 40 40

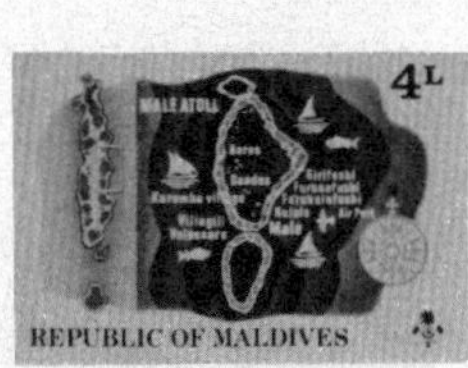

121 Map of Maldives

122 Cross-country Skiing

(Des M. Shamir. Litho Questa)

1975 (25 Dec). *Tourism. T* **121** *and similar horiz designs. Multicoloured. P* 14.

618 4 l. Type **121** 5 5
619 5 l. Motor launch and small craft 5 5
620 7 l. Sailing boats 5 5
621 15 l. Underwater fishing 5 5
622 3 r. Hulule Airport .. .. 1·40 1·40
623 10 r. Motor cruisers .. .. 4·00 4·00
618/23 .. .. *Set of* 6 5·00 5·00

(Des M. Shamir)

1976 (10 Jan). *Winter Olympic Games, Innsbruck, Austria. T* **122** *and similar vert designs. Multicoloured. P* 15.

624 1 l. Type **122** 5 5
625 2 l. Speed ice-skating 5 5
626 3 l. Pairs figure-skating 5 5
627 4 l. Four-man bobsleigh 5 5
628 5 l. Ski-jumping 5 5
629 25 l. Women's figure-skating 15 10
630 1 r. 15, Slalom skiing 55 55
631 4 r. Ice-hockey .. .. 1·75 1·90
624/31 .. .. *Set of* 8 2·40 2·50
MS632 93 × 117 mm. 10 r. Downhill skiing .. 3·75 4·75

123 "General Burgoyne" (Reynolds)

124 Thomas Edison

1976 (15 Feb). *Bicentenary of American Revolution. T* **123** *and similar multicoloured designs. P* 15.

633 1 l. Type **123** 5 5
634 2 l. "John Hancock" (Copley) 5 5
635 3 l. "Death of General Montgomery" (Trumbull) (*horiz*) 5 5
636 4 l. "Paul Revere" (Copley) 5 5
637 5 l. "Battle of Bunker Hill" (Trumbull) (*horiz*) 5 5
638 2 r. "The Crossing of the Delaware" (Sully) (*horiz*) .. .. 1·25 1·25
639 3 r. "Samuel Adams" (Copley) .. .. 1·75 1·75
640 5 r. "Surrender of Cornwallis" (Trumbull) (*horiz*) .. .. 2·25 2·25
633/40 .. .. *Set of* 8 4·75 4·75
MS641 147 × 95 mm. 10 r. "Washington at Dorchester Heights" (Stuart) .. .. 5·00 6·00

1976 (10 Mar). *Telephone Centenary. T* **124** *and similar horiz designs. Multicoloured. P* 15.

642 1 l. Type **124** 5 5
643 2 l. Alexander Graham Bell 5 5
644 3 l. Telephones of 1919, 1937 and 1972 .. 5 5
645 10 l. Cable entrance into station 5 5
646 20 l. Equaliser circuit assembly 10 10
647 1 r. Ship laying cable.. .. .. .. 55 55
648 10 r. "Intelsat IV-A" and Earth Station .. 4·00 4·00
642/8 .. .. *Set of* 7 4·25 4·25
MS649 156 × 105 mm. 4 r. Early telephones .. 2·50 3·00

MAY 29TH–JUNE 6TH
"INTERPHIL" 1976

(**125**)

126 Wrestling

1976 (29 May). *"Interphil 76" International Stamp Exhibition, Philadelphia. Nos.* 638/**MS**641 *optd with T* **125**, *in blue* (5 r.) *or silver* (*others*).

650 2 r. multicoloured 80 80
651 3 r. multicoloured .. .. 1·25 1·25
652 5 r. multicoloured .. .. 1·75 1·75
MS653 147 × 95 mm. 10 r. multicoloured .. 3·75 4·75

(Des M. Shamir)

1976 (June). *Olympic Games, Montreal. T* **126** *and similar vert designs. Multicoloured. P* 15.

654 1 l. Type **126** 5 5
655 2 l. Putting the shot 5 5
656 3 l. Hurdling 5 5
657 4 l. Hockey 5 5
658 5 l. Running 5 5
659 6 l. Javelin-throwing 5 5
660 1 r. 50, Discus-throwing 80 80
661 5 r. Volleyball .. .. 2·25 2·25
654/61 .. .. *Set of* 8 3·00 3·00
MS662 135 × 106 mm. 10 r. Throwing the hammer 3·75 4·00

127 *Dolichos lablab*

128 "Viking" approaching Mars

(Des M. Shamir. Litho Questa)

1976 (26 July)–**77**. *Vegetables. T* **127** *and similar vert designs. Multicoloured. P* 14.

663 2 l. Type **127** 5 5
664 4 l. *Moringa pterygosperma* 5 5
665 10 l. *Solanum melongena* 5 5
666 20 l. *Moringa pterygosperma* (1977) 35 35
667 50 l. *Cucumis sativus* 40 40
668 75 l. *Trichosanthes anguina* 55 55
669 1 r. *Momordica charantia* 65 65
670 2 r. *Trichosanthes anguina* (1977) .. .. 1·75 1·75
663/70 .. .. *Set of* 8 3·50 3·50

1976 (2 Dec). *"Viking" Space Mission. T* **128** *and similar horiz design. Multicoloured. P* 14.

671 5 r. Type **128** .. .. 2·50 2·50
MS672 121 × 89 mm. 20 r. Landing module on Mars .. .. 8·00 8·50

129 Coronation Ceremony

1977 (6 Feb). *Silver Jubilee of Queen Elizabeth II. T* **129** *and similar horiz designs. Multicoloured. P* 14 × 13½.

673 1 l. Type **129** 5 5
674 2 l. Queen and Prince Philip.. .. .. 5 5
675 3 l. Royal couple with Princes Andrew and Edward 5 5
676 1 r. 15, Queen with Archbishops 45 35
677 3 r. State coach in procession .. .. 1·00 75
678 4 r. Royal couple with Prince Charles and Princess Anne .. .. 1·60 1·25
673/8 .. .. *Set of* 6 2·75 2·10
MS679 120 × 77 mm. 10 r. Queen and Prince Charles .. .. 3·00 3·00

Nos. 673/8 also exist perf 12 (*Price per set of* 6 £2.75) from additional sheetlets of five stamps and one label in changed colours.

130 Beethoven and Organ

(Des M. Shamir)

1977 (26 Mar). *150th Death Anniv of Ludwig van Beethoven (composer). T* **130** *and similar horiz designs. Multicoloured. P* 14.

680 1 l. Type **130** 5 5
681 2 l. Portrait and manuscript of *Moonlight Sonata* 5 5
682 3 l. With Goethe at Teplitz 5 5
683 4 l. Portrait and string instruments.. .. 5 5
684 5 l. Beethoven's home, Heiligenstadt .. 5 5
685 25 l. Hands and gold medals 15 15
686 2 r. Portrait and part of *Missa solemnis* .. 1·00 65
687 5 r. Portrait and hearing-aids .. .. 2·25 1·75
680/7 .. .. *Set of* 8 3·25 2·40
MS688 121 × 92 mm. 4 r. Death mask and room where composer died .. .. 2·00 2·50

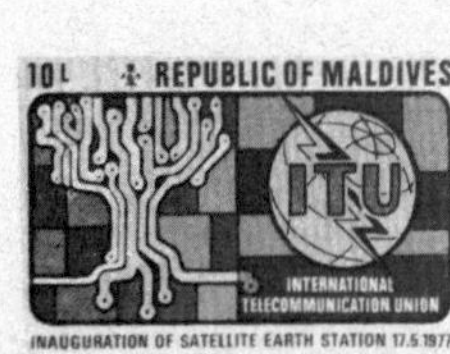

131 Printed Circuit and I.T.U. Emblem

T.GAINSBOROUGH
250th ANNIVERSARY OF BIRTH
1L
REPUBLIC OF MALDIVES

132 "Miss Anne Ford" (Gainsborough)

(Des M. Shamir. Litho Questa)

1977 (17 May). *Inauguration of Satellite Earth Station. T* **131** *and similar horiz designs. Multicoloured. P* 14.

689 10 l. Type **131** 5 5
690 90 l. Central telegraph office 45 45
691 10 r. Satellite Earth station .. .. .. 5·00 5·00
MS692 100 × 85 mm. 5 r. "Intelsat IV-A" satellite over Maldives .. .. 2·75 3·25

(Des M. Shamir. Litho Questa)

1977 (20 May). *Artists' Birth Anniversaries. T* **132** *and similar vert designs. Multicoloured. P* 14.

693 1 l. Type **132** (250th anniv) 5 5
694 2 l. Group painting by Rubens (400th anniv) 5 5
695 3 l. "Girl with Dog" (Titian) (500th anniv) .. 5 5
696 4 l. "Mrs. Thomas Graham" (Gainsborough) 5 5
697 5 l. "Artist with Isabella Brant" (Rubens) .. 5 5
698 95 l. Portrait by Titian 40 40
699 1 r. Portrait by Gainsborough 40 40
700 10 r. "Isabella Brant" (Rubens) .. .. 3·50 3·00
693/700 .. .. *Set of* 8 4·00 3·75
MS701 152 × 116 mm. 5 r. "Self-portrait" (Titian) 1·75 2·00

133 Lesser Frigate Birds

134 Charles Lindbergh

(Des M. Shamir)

1977 (26 July). *Birds. T* **133** *and similar vert designs. Multicoloured. P* 14½.

702 1 l. Type **133** .. 5 5
703 2 l. Crab Plover .. 5 5
704 3 l. White-tailed Tropic Bird .. 5 5
705 4 l. Wedge-tailed Shearwater .. 5 5
706 5 l. Grey Heron .. 5 5
707 20 l. White Tern .. 20 20
708 95 l. Cattle Egret .. 95 95
709 1 r. 25, Black-naped Tern .. 1·40 1·40
710 5 r. Pheasant Coucal .. 5·50 5·50
702/10 .. *Set of* 9 7·50 7·50
MS711 124 × 117 mm. 10 r. Striated Heron .. 9·50 11·00

(Des M. Shamir)

1977 (31 Oct). *50th Anniv of Lindbergh's Transatlantic Flight and 75th Anniv of First Navigable Airships. T* **134** *and similar multicoloured designs. P* 14½.

712 1 l. Type **134** .. 5 5
713 2 l. Lindbergh and *Spirit of St. Louis* .. 5 5
714 3 l. "Mohawk" aircraft (*horiz*) .. 5 5
715 4 l. Julliot's airship *Lebaudy I* (*horiz*) .. 5 5
716 5 l. Airship *Graf Zeppelin* and portrait of Zeppelin .. 5 5
717 1 r. Airship *Los Angeles* (*horiz*) .. 40 30
718 3 r. Lindbergh and Henry Ford .. 1·10 80
719 10 r. Vickers rigid airship .. 3·25 2·40
712/19 .. *Set of* 8 4·50 3·25
MS720 148 × 114 mm. 5 r. *Spirit of St. Louis*, Statue of Liberty and Eiffel Tower; 7 r. 50, Airship *L 31* over battleship .. 4·25 5·50

135 Boat Building

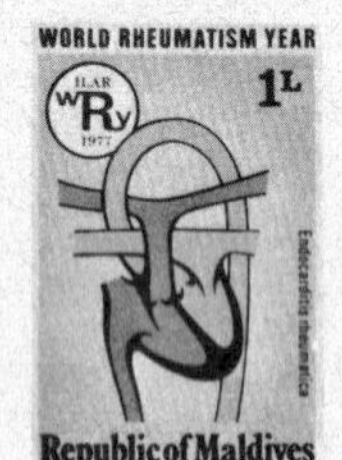

136 Rheumatic Heart

(Des M. Shamir. Litho J. Waddington)

1977 (11 Nov). *Occupations. T* **135** *and similar multicoloured designs. P* 13½ × 13 (2 *r.*) *or* 13 × 13½ (*others*).

721 6 l. Type **135** .. 5 5
722 15 l. Fishing .. 10 5
723 20 l. Cadjan weaving .. 10 5
724 90 l. Mat weaving .. 30 30
725 2 r. Lace making (*vert*) .. 65 65

(Des M. Shamir. Litho Questa)

1977 (Dec). *World Rheumatism Year. T* **136** *and similar vert designs. Multicoloured. P* 14.

726 1 l. Type **136** .. 5 5
727 50 l. Rheumatic shoulder .. 15 10
728 2 r. Rheumatic fingers .. 75 65
729 3 r. Rheumatic knee .. 1·10 1·00

137 Lilienthal's Glider

138 Newgate Prison

(Des M. Shamir. Litho Questa)

1978 (27 Feb). *75th Anniv of First Powered Aircraft. T* **137** *and similar horiz designs. Multicoloured. P* 13 × 13½.

730 1 l. Type **137** .. 5 5
731 2 l. Chanute's glider .. 5 5
732 3 l. Wright testing glider, 1900 .. 5 5
733 4 l. Roe's aircraft .. 5 5
734 5 l. Wright demonstrating aircraft to King Alfonso of Spain .. 5 5
735 10 l. Roe's second biplane .. 5 5
736 20 l. Wright Brothers and A. G. Bell .. 10 10
737 95 l. Hadley's triplane .. 45 45
738 5 r. "BE 2"s at Upavon, 1914 .. 2·25 2·25
730/8 .. *Set of* 9 2·75 2·75
MS739 98 × 82 mm. 10 r. Wright Brothers' *Flyer* .. 3·75 4·00

1978 (15 Mar). *World Eradication of Smallpox. T* **138** *and similar multicoloured designs. P* 14.

740 15 l. Foundling Hospital, London (*horiz*) .. 10 10
741 50 l. Type **138** .. 30 30
742 2 r. Edward Jenner .. 1·25 1·25

139 Television Set

140 Mas Odi

(Des M. Shamir. Litho J. Waddington)

1978 (29 Mar). *Inauguration of Television in Maldives. T* **139** *and similar multicoloured designs. P* 13 × 13½ (1 *r.* 50) *or* 13½ × 13 (*others*).

743 15 l. Type **139** .. 5 5
744 25 l. Television aerials .. 10 10
745 1 r. 50, Control desk (*horiz*) .. 70 70

(Des M. Shamir)

1978 (27 Apr). *Ships. T* **140** *and similar multicoloured designs. P* 14½.

746 1 l. Type **140** .. 5 5
747 2 l. Baththeli .. 5 5
748 3 l. Bandu odi (*vert*) .. 5 5
749 5 l. Maldive trader .. 5 5
750 1 r. Fath-hul baaree (*vert*) .. 35 20
751 1 r. 25, Mas dhoni .. 55 40
752 3 r. Bangala (*vert*) .. 1·25 70
753 4 r. As No. 751 .. 1·60 90
746/53 .. *Set of* 8 3·50 2·10
MS754 152 × 138 mm. 1 r. As No. 747; 4 r. As No. 751 .. 1·90 2·00

141 Ampulla

142 Capt. Cook

(Des M. Shamir. Litho Questa)

1978 (15 May). *25th Anniv of Coronation of Queen Elizabeth II. T* **141** *and similar vert designs. Multicoloured. P* 14.

755 1 l. Type **141** .. 5 5
756 2 l. Sceptre with dove .. 5 5
757 3 l. Golden orb .. 5 5
758 1 r. 15, St. Edward's Crown .. 25 20
759 2 r. Sceptre with cross .. 60 45
760 5 r. Queen Elizabeth II .. 1·40 1·00
755/60 .. *Set of* 6 2·10 1·50
MS761 108 × 106 mm. 10 r. Anointing spoon 2·75 2·75

Nos. 755/60 were also each issued in small sheets of three stamps and one label, perf 12, in changed colours.

(Des M. Shamir)

1978 (15 July). *250th Birth Anniv of Capt. James Cook and Bicentenary of Discovery of Hawaii. T* **142** *and similar multicoloured designs. P* 14½.

762 1 l. Type **142** .. 5 5
763 2 l. Statue of Kamehameha I of Hawaii .. 5 5
764 3 l. H.M.S. *Endeavour* .. 5 5
765 25 l. Route of Cook's third voyage .. 35 35
766 75 l. *Resolution, Discovery* and map of Hawaiian Islands (*horiz*) .. 85 85
767 1 r. 50, Cook meeting Hawaiian islanders on ship (*horiz*) .. 1·60 1·60
768 10 r. Death of Cook (*horiz*) .. 7·00 7·00
762/8 .. *Set of* 7 9·00 9·00
MS769 100 × 92 mm. 5 r. H.M.S. *Endeavour* (*different*) .. 4·00 4·50

143 *Schizophrys aspera*

144 "Four Apostles"

1978 (30 Aug). *Crustaceans. T* **143** *and similar multicoloured designs. P* 14.

770 1 l. Type **143** .. 5 5
771 2 l. *Atergatis floridus* .. 5 5
772 3 l. *Perenon planissimum* .. 5 5
773 90 l. *Portunus granulatus* .. 40 40
774 1 r. *Carpilius maculatus* .. 40 40
775 2 r. *Huenia proteus* .. 75 75
776 25 r. *Etisus laevimanus* .. 7·50 8·50
770/6 .. *Set of* 7 8·50 9·00
MS777 147 × 146 mm. 2 r. *Panulirus longipes* (*vert*) 80 80

(Des BG Studio. Litho Questa)

1978 (28 Oct). *450th Death Anniv of Albrecht Dürer (artist). T* **144** *and similar designs. P* 14.

778 10 l. multicoloured .. 5 5
779 20 l. multicoloured .. 10 10
780 55 l. multicoloured .. 20 20
781 1 r. black, cinnamon and brown .. 30 30
782 1 r. 80, multicoloured .. 50 50
783 3 r. multicoloured .. 1·00 1·00
778/83 .. *Set of* 6 1·90 1·90
MS784 141 × 122 mm. 10 r. multicoloured .. 3·00 3·00

Designs: *Vert*—20 l. "Self-portrait at 27", 55 l. "Madonna and Child with a Pear"; 1 r. 80, "Hare"; 3 r. "Great Piece of Turf"; 10 r. "Columbine". *Horiz*—1 r. "Rhinoceros".

145 T.V. Tower and Building

146 Human Rights Emblem

(Des M. Shamir)

1978 (11 Nov). *Tenth Anniv of Republic. T* **145** *and similar horiz designs. Multicoloured. P* 14½.

785 1 l. Fishing vessel .. 5 5
786 5 l. Montessori School .. 5 5
787 10 l. Type **145** .. 5 5
788 25 l. Islet .. 8 5
789 50 l. Boeing "737" .. 12 10
790 95 l. Beach scene .. 25 20
791 1 r. 25, Fishing boat at night .. 30 25
792 2 r. President's official residence .. 50 40
793 5 r. Masjidh Afeefuddin (mosque) .. 1·50 1·25
785/93 .. *Set of* 9 2·50 2·10
MS794 119 × 88 mm. 3 r. Fisherman casting net 85 85

1978 (10 Dec). *30th Anniv of Declaration of Human Rights. P* 14.

795 **146** 30 l. pale magenta, dp mauve and green 15 15
796 90 l. yellow-ochre, red-brown and green 40 40
797 1 r. 80, lt greenish blue, dp blue & grn .. 70 70

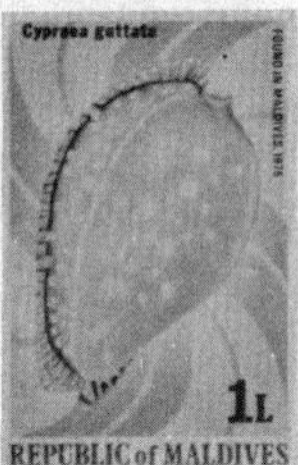

147 *Cypraea guttata*

148 Delivery by Bellman

(Des M. Shamir. Litho Questa)

1979 (Jan). *Shells. T* **147** *and similar vert designs. Multicoloured. P* 14.

798 1 l. Type **147** .. 5 5
799 2 l. *Conus imperialis* .. 5 5
800 3 l. *Turbo marmoratus* .. 5 5
801 10 l. *Lambis truncata* .. 5 5
802 1 r. *Cypraea leucodon* .. 40 40
803 1 r. 80, *Conus figulinus* .. 75 75
804 3 r. *Conus gloria-maris* .. 1·10 1·10
798/804 .. *Set of* 7 2·25 2·25
MS805 141 × 110 mm. 5 r. *Vasum turbinellus* 1·60 1·75

(Des M. Shamir. Litho Questa)

1979 (28 Feb). *Death Centenary of Sir Rowland Hill. T* **148** *and similar multicoloured designs. P* 14.

806 1 l. Type **148** .. 5 5
807 2 l. Mail coach, 1840 (*horiz*) .. 5 5
808 3 l. First London letter box, 1855 .. 5 5
809 1 r. 55, Penny Black stamps and posthorn .. 50 50
810 5 r. Maldives 15 c. stamp, 1906, and carrier pigeon .. 1·40 1·40
MS811 132 × 107 mm. 10 r. Sir Rowland Hill .. 3·00 3·00

Nos. 806/10 were also each issued in small sheets of five stamps and one label, perf 12, in changed colours.

149 Girl with Teddy Bear

150 "White Feathers"

(Des M. Sharmir. Litho Questa)

1979 (10 May). *International Year of the Child (1st issue). T* **149** *and similar vert designs. Multicoloured. P* 14.
812 5 l. Type **149** 5 5
813 1 r. 25, Boy with model sailing boat 45 40
814 2 r. Boy with toy rocket 55 40
815 3 r. Boy with toy airship 75 60
MS816 108 × 109 mm. 5 r. Boy with toy train 1·40 1·40
See also Nos. 838/**MS**847.

(Des M. Shamir)

1979 (25 June). *25th Death Anniv of Henri Matisse (artist). T* **150** *and similar horiz designs. Multicoloured. P* 14.
817 20 l. Type **150** 8 5
818 25 l. "Joy of Life" 10 8
819 30 l. "Eggplants" 10 8
820 1 r. 50, "Harmony in Red" 40 35
821 5 r. "Still-life" 1·10 85
MS822 135 × 95 mm. 4 r. "Water Pitcher" 1·00 1·00

151 Sari with Overdress

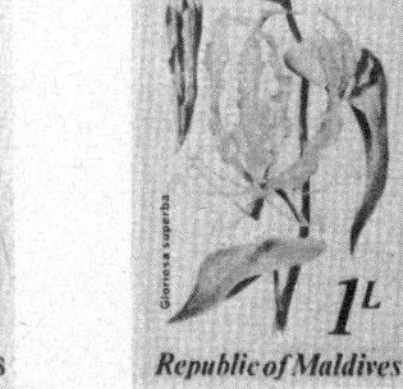

152 *Gloriosa superba*

(Des M. Shamir. Litho Questa)

1979 (22 Aug). *National Costumes. T* **151** *and similar vert designs. Multicoloured. P* 14.
823 50 l. Type **151** 20 20
824 75 l. Sashed apron dress 35 35
825 90 l. Serape 40 40
826 95 l. Ankle-length printed dress 45 45

(Des M. Shamir. Litho Questa)

1979 (29 Oct). *Flowers. T* **152** *and similar vert designs. Multicoloured. P* 14.
827 1 l. Type **152** 5 5
828 3 l. *Hibiscus tiliaceus* 5 5
829 50 l. *Barringtonia asiatica* 20 20
830 1 r. *Abutilon indicum* 40 40
831 5 r. *Guettarda speciosa* 1·75 1·75
MS832 94 × 85 mm. 4 r. *Pandanus odoratissimus* 1·60 1·75

153 Weaving

(Litho Questa)

1979 (11 Nov). *Handicraft Exhibition. T* **153** *and similar horiz designs. Multicoloured. P* 14.
833 5 l. Type **153** 5 5
834 10 l. Lacquerwork 5 5
835 1 r. 30, Tortoiseshell jewellery 45 40
836 2 r. Carved woodwork 70 60
MS837 125 × 85 mm. 5 r. Gold and silver jewellery 1·50 1·60

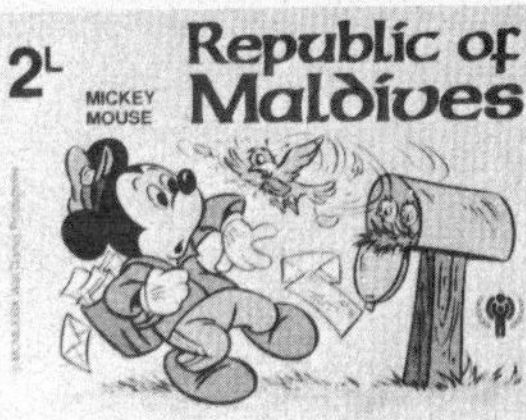

154 Mickey Mouse attacked by Bird

(Des Walt Disney Productions)

1979 (10 Dec). *International Year of the Child (2nd issue). T* **154** *and similar multicoloured designs. P* 11.
838 1 l. Goofy delivering parcel on motor-scooter (*vert*) 5 5
839 2 l. Type **154** 5 5
840 3 l. Goofy half-covered with letters 5 5
841 4 l. Pluto licking Minnie Mouse's envelopes 5 5
842 5 l. Mickey Mouse delivering letters on roller-skates (*vert*) 5 5
843 10 l. Donald Duck placing letter in mail-box 5 5
844 15 l. Chip and Dale carrying letter 8 5
845 1 r. 50, Donald Duck on monocycle (*vert*) 75 75
846 5 r. Donald Duck with ostrich in crate (*vert*) 2·25 2·25
838/46 *Set of* 9 3·00 3·00
MS847 127 × 102 mm. 4 r. Pluto putting parcel in mail-box. P 13½ 1·75 2·00

NEW INFORMATION

The editor is always interested to correspond with people who have new information that will improve or correct the Catalogue.

155 Post-Ramadan Dancing

(Litho Questa)

1980 (19 Jan). *National Day. T* **155** *and similar horiz designs. Multicoloured. P* 14.
848 5 l. Type **155** 5 5
849 15 l. Musicians and dancer, Eeduu Festival 8 5
850 95 l. Sultan's ceremonial band 30 25
851 2 r. Dancer and drummers, Circumcision Festival 55 35
MS852 131 × 99 mm. 5 r. Swordsmen 1·40 1·40

156 Leatherback Turtle (*Dermochelys coriacea*)

157 Paul Harris (*founder*)

(Des M. Shamir. Litho Questa)

1980 (17 Feb). *Turtle Conservation Campaign. T* **156** *and similar horiz designs. Multicoloured. P* 14.
853 1 l. Type **156** 5 5
854 2 l. Flatback turtle (*Chelonia depressa*) 5 5
855 5 l. Hawksbill turtle (*Eretmochelys imbricata*) 5 5
856 10 l. Loggerhead turtle (*Caretta caretta*) 5 5
857 75 l. Olive Ridley turtle (*Lepidochelys olivacea*) 30 20
858 10 r. Atlantic Ridley turtle (*Lepidochelys kempii*) 3·25 2·75
853/8 *Set of* 6 3·25 2·75
MS859 85 × 107 mm. 4 r. Green turtle (*Chelonia mydas*) 1·50 1·50

(Des J. Waddington Studio. Litho Questa)

1980 (7 Apr). *75th Anniv of Rotary International. T* **157** *and similar vert designs. Multicoloured. P* 14.
860 75 l. Type **157** 25 10
861 90 l. Family (Humanity) 30 20
862 1 r. Wheat (Hunger) 30 25
863 10 r. Caduceus of Hermes (Health) 3·00 2·75
MS864 109 × 85 mm. 5 r. Globe 1·50 1·60

LONDON 1980
(158)

159 Swimming

1980 (6 May). *"London 1980" International Stamp Exhibition. Nos.* 809/**MS**811 *optd with T* **158**.
865 1 r. 55, multicoloured 40 35
866 5 r. multicoloured 1·10 75
MS867 132 × 107 mm. 10 r. multicoloured 2·50 2·50
On No. **MS**867 the overprint is horizontal.

(Des J. Waddington Studio. Litho Questa)

1980 (4 June). *Olympic Games, Moscow. T* **159** *and similar horiz designs. Multicoloured. P* 14.
868 10 l. Type **159** 5 5
869 50 l. Running 25 15
870 3 r. Putting the shot 1·10 1·00
871 4 r. High jump 1·40 1·25
MS872 105 × 85 mm. 5 r. Weightlifting 1·60 1·75

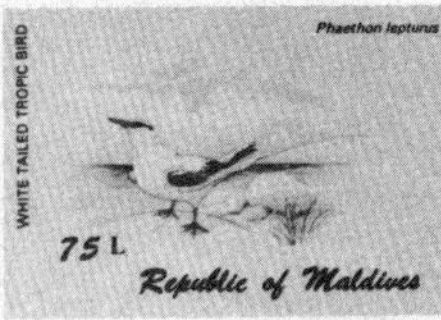

160 White-tailed Tropic Bird

(Des A. Abbas. Litho Questa)

1980 (10 July). *Birds. T* **160** *and similar horiz designs. Multicoloured. P* 14.
873 75 l. Type **160** 25 15
874 95 l. Sooty Tern 35 30
875 1 r. Common Noddy 35 30
876 1 r. 55, Curlew 50 40
877 2 r. Wilson's Petrel 60 40
878 4 r. Caspian Tern 1·10 75
873/8 *Set of* 6 2·75 2·10
MS879 124 × 85 mm. 5 r. Red-footed Booby and Brown Booby 1·40 1·50

161 Seal of Ibrahim II

(Litho Questa)

1980 (26 July). *Seals of the Sultans. T* **161** *and similar horiz designs. Each purple-brown and black. P* 14.
880 1 l. Type **161** 5 5
881 2 l. Mohammed Imadudeen II 5 5
882 5 l. Bin Haji Ali 5 5
883 1 r. Kuda Mohammed Rasgefaanu 30 25
884 2 r. Ibrahim Iskander I 50 30
MS885 131 × 95 mm. 3 r. Ibrahim Iskander I (*different*) 85 85

162 Queen Elizabeth the Queen Mother

(Des and litho Questa)

1980 (29 Sept). *Queen Mother's 80th Birthday. P* 14.
886 **162** 4 r. multicoloured 1·10 95
MS887 85 × 110 mm. **162** 5 r. multicoloured 1·25 1·25

163 Munnaru

(Des A. Abbas and M. Hassan)

1980 (9 Nov). *1400th Anniv of Hegira. T* **163** *and similar horiz designs. Multicoloured. P* 15.
888 5 l. Type **163** 5 5
889 10 l. Hukuru Miskiiy mosque 5 5
890 30 l. Medhuziyaaraiy (shrine of saint) 10 8
891 55 l. Writing tablets with verses of Koran 12 8
892 90 l. Mother teaching child Koran 25 20
MS893 124 × 101 mm. 2 r. Map of Maldives and coat of arms 60 60

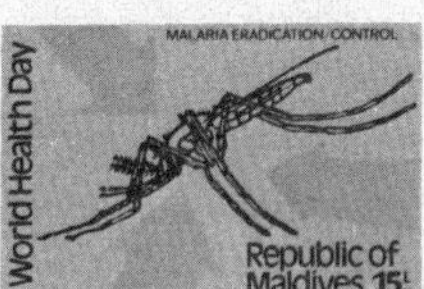

164 Malaria Eradication

(Des J. Waddington Studio. Litho Questa)

1980 (30 Nov). *World Health Day. T* **164** *and similar horiz designs. P* 14.
894 15 l. black, yellow and vermilion 10 5
895 25 l. multicoloured 10 5
896 1 r. 50, orange-brown, yellow-ochre & black 60 45
897 5 r. multicoloured 1·50 1·40
MS898 68 × 85 mm. 4 r. black, greenish blue and azure 1·25 1·50
Designs:—25 l. Food (Nutrition); 1 r. 50, Molar and toothbrush (Dental health); 4, 5 r. People and medical equipment (Clinics).

165 White Rabbit

(Des Walt Disney Productions)

1980 (22 Dec). *Scenes from Film "Alice in Wonderland". T* **165** *and similar horiz designs. Multicoloured. P* 11.
899 1 l. Type **165** 5 5
900 2 l. Alice falling into Wonderland 5 5
901 3 l. Alice too big to go through door 5 5
902 4 l. Alice and Tweedledum and Tweedledee 5 5
903 5 l. Alice and the caterpillar 5 5
904 10 l. Cheshire cat 5 5
905 15 l. Alice painting the roses 8 5
906 2 r. 50, Alice and the Queen of Hearts 90 75
907 4 r. Alice on trial 1·40 1·10
899/907 *Set of* 9 2·25 1·90
MS908 126 × 101 mm. 5 r. Alice at the Mad Hatter's tea-party. P 13½ 1·60 1·75

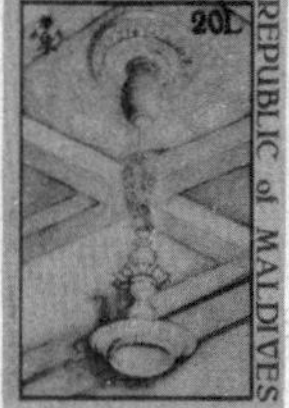

166 Indian Ocean Ridley Turtle   167 Pendant Lamp

(Des A. Abbas and Maniku. Litho Questa)

1980 (29 Dec). *Marine Life. T* **166** *and similar horiz designs. Multicoloured. P* 14.
909 90 l. Type **166** .. 40 35
910 1 r. 25, Angel fishes .. 55 50
911 2 r. Spiny lobster .. 75 75
MS912 140 × 94 mm. 4 r. Fishes .. 1·50 1·60

1981 (7 Jan). *National Day. T* **167** *and similar multicoloured designs. P* 14½.
913 10 l. Tomb of Ghaazee Muhammad Thakurufaan (*horiz*) .. 5 5
914 20 l. Type **167** .. 8 8
915 30 l. Chair used by Muhammad Thakurufaan 10 8
916 95 l. Muhammad Thakurufaan's palace (*horiz*) 25 20
917 10 r. Cushioned divan .. 2·75 2·50

168 Prince Charles and Lady Diana Spencer   169 First Majlis Chamber

(Des and litho J.W.)

1981 (22 June). *Royal Wedding. T* **168** *and similar vert designs. Multicoloured. P* 14.
918 1 r. Type **168** .. 30 30
919 2 r. Buckingham Palace .. 50 50
920 5 r. Prince Charles, polo player .. 1·25 1·25
MS921 95 × 83 mm. 10 r. State coach .. 2·75 2·75
Nos. 918/20 also exist perforated 12 (*Price for set of* 3 £2 *mint or used*) from additional sheets of five stamps and one label. These stamps have changed background colours.

(Des I. Azeez)

1981 (27 June). *50th Anniv of Citizens' Majlis (grievance rights). T* **169** *and similar multicoloured designs. P* 14½.
922 95 l. Type **169** .. 20 20
923 1 r. Sultan Muhammed Shamsuddin III .. 25 25
MS924 137 × 94 mm. 4 r. First written constitution (*horiz*) .. 90 1·00

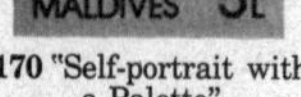

170 "Self-portrait with a Palette"   171 Airmail Envelope

(Des J.W. Litho Questa)

1981 (July). *Birth Centenary of Pablo Picasso. T* **170** *and similar vert designs. Multicoloured. P* 13½ × 14.
925 5 l. Type **170** .. 5 5
926 10 l. "Woman in Blue" .. 5 5
927 25 l. "Boy with Pipe" .. 10 10
928 30 l. "Card Player" .. 10 10
929 90 l. "Sailor" .. 25 25
930 3 r. "Self-portrait" .. 60 60
931 5 r. "Harlequin" .. 90 90
925/31 .. *Set of* 7 1·90 1·90
MS932 106 × 130 mm. 10 r. "Child holding a Dove". Imperf .. 1·60 1·75

(Des and litho Questa)

1981 (9 Sept). *75th Anniv of Postal Service. P* 14.
933 **171** 25 l. multicoloured .. 10 10
934 75 l. multicoloured .. 25 25
935 5 r. multicoloured .. 1·10 1·10

ALTERED CATALOGUE NUMBERS

Any Catalogue numbers altered from the last edition are shown as a list in the introductory pages.

172 Aircraft taking off   173 Homer

(Des A. Abbas. Litho Questa)

1981 (11 Nov). *Male International Airport. T* **172** *and similar horiz designs. Multicoloured. P* 14.
936 5 l. Type **172** .. 5 5
937 20 l. Passengers leaving aircraft .. 10 10
938 1 r. 80, Refuelling .. 55 55
939 4 r. Plan of airport .. 1·10 1·10
MS940 106 × 79 mm. 5 r. Aerial view of airport .. 1·25 1·50

(Des J.W.)

1981 (18 Nov). *International Year of Disabled People. T* **173** *and similar vert designs. Multicoloured. P* 14½.
941 2 l. Type **174** .. 5 5
942 5 l. Miguel Cervantes .. 5 5
943 1 r. Beethoven .. 45 45
944 5 r. Van Gogh .. 1·40 1·40
MS945 116 × 91 mm. 4 r. Helen Keller and Anne Sullivan .. 1·25 1·50

174 Preparation of Maldive Fish   175 Collecting Bait

(Des Central Art Palace. Litho Questa)

1981 (25 Nov). *Decade for Women. T* **174** *and similar vert designs. Multicoloured. P* 14.
946 20 l. Type **174** .. 5 5
947 90 l. 16th century Maldive women .. 20 20
948 1 r. Farming .. 25 25
949 2 r. Coir rope making .. 45 45

(Des I. Azeez. Litho Questa)

1981 (10 Dec). *Fishermen's Day. T* **175** *and similar horiz designs. Multicoloured. P* 14.
950 5 l. Type **175** .. 5 5
951 15 l. Fishing boats .. 10 10
952 90 l. Fisherman with catch .. 30 30
953 1 r. 30, Sorting fish .. 45 45
MS954 147 × 101 mm. 3 r. Loading fish for export 80 90

176 Bread Fruit

(Des Design Images. Litho Questa)

1981 (30 Dec). *World Food Day. T* **176** *and similar horiz designs. Multicoloured. P* 14.
955 10 l. Type **176** .. 5 5
956 25 l. Hen with chicks .. 10 10
957 30 l. Maize .. 10 10
958 75 l. Skipjack Tuna .. 20 20
959 1 r. Pumpkin .. 25 25
960 2 r. Coconuts .. 45 45
955/60 .. *Set of* 6 1·10 1·10
MS961 110 × 85 mm. 5 r. Eggplant .. 1·00 1·25

177 Pluto and Cat   178 Balmoral

(Des Walt Disney Productions. Litho Format)

1982 (29 Mar). *50th Anniv of Pluto (Walt Disney cartoon character). T* **177** *and similar multicoloured design. P* 13½.
962 4 r. Type **177** .. 95 95
MS963 127 × 101 mm. 6 r. Pluto (scene from *The Pointer*) .. 1·50 1·50

(Des PAD Studio. Litho Questa)

1982 (1 July). *21st Birthday of Princess of Wales. T* **178** *and similar vert designs. Multicoloured. P* 14½ × 14.
964 95 l. Type **178** .. 20 20
965 3 r. Prince and Princess of Wales .. 55 55
966 5 r. Princess on aircraft steps .. 85 85
MS967 103 × 75 mm. 8 r. Princess of Wales .. 1·50 1·60

COMMONWEALTH MEMBER
9 July 1982

179 Scout saluting and Camp-site   180 Footballer

(Des D. Miller. Litho Questa)

1982 (9 Aug). *75th Anniv of Boy Scout Movement. T* **179** *and similar horiz designs. Multicoloured. P* 14.
968 1 r. 30, Type **179** .. 25 30
969 1 r. 80, Lighting a fire .. 35 40
970 4 r. Life-saving .. 75 80
971 5 r. Map-reading .. 95 1·00
MS972 128 × 66 mm. 10 r. Scout emblem and flag of the Maldives .. 1·75 2·00

(Des M. and S. Gerber Studio. Litho Questa)

1982 (4 Oct). *World Cup Football Championship, Spain. T* **180** *and similar square designs. P* 13½.
973 90 l. multicoloured .. 20 20
974 1 r. 50, multicoloured .. 30 30
975 3 r. multicoloured .. 55 55
976 5 r. multicoloured .. 85 85
MS977 94 × 63 mm. 10 r. multicoloured .. 1·75 1·90

1982 (18 Oct). *Birth of Prince William of Wales. Nos.* 964/7 *optd with T* **171** *of Antigua.*
978 95 l. Type **178** .. 20 20
979 3 r. Prince and Princess of Wales .. 55 55
980 5 r. Princess on aircraft steps .. 85 85
MS981 103 × 75 mm. 8 r. Princess of Wales .. 1·50 1·60

181 Basic Education Scheme   182 Koch isolates the Bacillus

(Des and litho Harrison)

1982 (15 Nov). *National Education. T* **181** *and similar horiz designs. Multicoloured. P* 14.
982 90 l. Type **181** .. 15 20
983 95 l. Primary education .. 15 20
984 1 r. 30, Teacher training .. 20 25
985 2 r. 50, Printing educational material .. 40 45
MS986 100 × 70 mm. 6 r. Thaana typewriter keyboard .. 1·00 1·10

(Des Artists International. Litho Format)

1982 (22 Nov). *Centenary of Robert Koch's Discovery of Tubercle Bacillus. T* **182** *and similar multicoloured designs. P* 14.
987 5 l. Type **182** .. 5 5
988 15 l. Micro-organism and microscope .. 5 8
989 95 l. Dr. Robert Koch in 1905 .. 20 25
990 3 r. Dr. Koch and plates from publication .. 60 60
MS991 77 × 61 mm. 5 r. Koch in his laboratory (*horiz*) .. 80 90

183 Blohm and Voss "Ha 139" Seaplane

(Des W. Wright. Litho Questa)

1983 (28 July). *Bicentenary of Manned Flight. T* **183** *and similar horiz designs. Multicoloured. P* 14.
992 90 l. Type **183** .. 15 20
993 1 r. 45, Macchi-Castoldi "MC.72" .. 20 25
994 4 r. Boeing "F4B-3" .. 65 70
995 5 r. *La France* airship .. 80 85
MS996 110 × 85 mm. 10 r. Nadar's *Le Geant* .. 1·75 1·90

184 "Curved Dash" Oldsmobile, 1902

(Des Publishers Graphics Inc. Litho Format)

1983 (Aug). *Classic Motor Cars. T* **184** *and similar horiz designs. Multicoloured. P* 14½.

997 5 l. Type **184** 5 5
998 30 l. Aston Martin "Tourer", 1932 .. .. 5 5
999 40 l. Lamborghini "Muira", 1966 .. .. 8 10
1000 1 r. Mercedes-Benz "300SL", 1945 .. .. 20 25
1001 1 r. 45, Stutz "Bearcat", 1913 .. .. 30 35
1002 5 r. Lotus "Elite", 1958 .. .. .. 95 1·00
997/1002 .. .. *Set of* 6 1·50 1·60
MS1003 132 × 103 mm. 10 r. Grand Prix "Sunbeam", 1924. P 14½ .. .. 1·90 2·00

Nos. 997/1002 were each issued in sheets of 9, including one *se-tenant* label.

185 Roughtooth Dolphin

(Des D. Miller. Litho Questa)

1983 (6 Sept). *Marine Mammals. T* **185** *and similar horiz designs. Multicoloured. P* 14.

1004 30 l. Type **185** 5 5
1005 40 l. Indo-pacific Humpback Dolphin 8 10
1006 4 r. Finless Porpoise 75 80
1007 6 r. Pygmy Sperm Whale .. .. .. 1·10 1·25
MS1008 82 × 90 mm. 5 r. Striped Dolphin .. 95 1·10

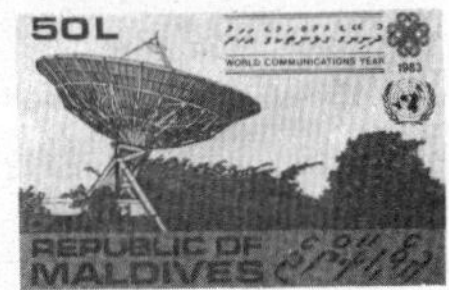

186 Dish Aerial

(Des PAD Studio. Litho Questa)

1983 (9 Oct). *World Communications Year. T* **186** *and similar horiz designs. Multicoloured. P* 14.

1009 50 l. Type **186** 10 12
1010 1 r. Land, sea and air communications .. 20 25
1011 2 r. Ship-to-shore communication 40 45
1012 10 r. Air traffic controller .. .. .. 1·90 2·00
MS1013 91 × 76 mm. 20 r. Telecommunications 3·75 4·00

187 "La Donna Gravida"

(Des M. Diamond. Litho Questa)

1983 (25 Oct). *500th Birth Anniv of Raphael. T* **187** *and similar vert designs showing paintings. Multicoloured. P* 13½.

1014 90 l. Type **187** 20 25
1015 3 r. "Giovanna d'Aragona" (detail) 60 65
1016 4 r. "Woman with Unicorn" 80 85
1017 6 r. "La Muta" .. .. 1·25 1·40
MS1018 121 × 97 mm. 10 r. "The Knight's Dream" (detail) .. .. 1·90 2·00

188 Refugee Camp

(Litho Questa)

1983 (29 Nov). *Solidarity with the Palestinians. T* **188** *and similar horiz designs each showing the Dome of the Rock, Jerusalem. Multicoloured. P* 13½ × 14.

1019 4 r. Type **188** 80 85
1020 5 r. Refugee holding dead child .. .. 95 1·00
1021 6 r. Child carrying food .. .. .. 1·25 1·40

189 Education Facilities

190 Baseball

(Des I. Azeez. Litho Questa)

1983 (10 Dec). *National Development Programme. T* **189** *and similar horiz designs. Multicoloured. P* 13½.

1022 7 l. Type **189** 5 5
1023 10 l. Health service and education 5 5
1024 5 r. Growing more food .. .. .. 95 1·00
1025 6 r. Fisheries development .. .. .. 1·10 1·25
MS1026 134 × 93 mm. 10 r. Air transport .. 1·90 2·00

(Des PAD Studio. Litho Questa)

1984 (10 Mar). *Olympic Games, Los Angeles. T* **190** *and similar vert designs. Multicoloured. P* 14.

1027 50 l. Type **190** 12 15
1028 1 r. 55, Backstroke swimming 35 40
1029 3 r. Judo 75 80
1030 4 r. Shot-putting .. .. 1·00 1·10
MS1031 85 × 105 mm. 10 r. Team Handball .. 2·40 2·50

Rf1.45

19th UPU
CONGRESS HAMBURG

(**191**) (**192**)

1984 (19 June). *Universal Postal Union Congress, Hamburg. Nos.* 994/6 *optd as T* **191**.

1032 4 r. Boeing "F4B-3" .. .. 1·00 1·10
1033 5 r. *La France* airship .. .. .. 1·25 1·40
MS1034 110 × 85 mm. 10 r. Nadar's *Le Geant* .. 2·40 2·50

1984 (20 Aug). *Surch as T* **192**. (a) *On Nos.* 964/7.

1035 1 r. 45 on 95 l. Type **178** .. .. .. 5·00 3·00
1036 1 r. 45 on 3 r. Prince and Princess of Wales 5·00 3·00
1037 1 r. 45 on 5 r. Princess on aircraft steps .. 5·00 3·00
MS1038 103 × 75 mm. 1 r. 45 on 8 r. Princess of Wales .. .. 16·00 12·00

(b) *On Nos.* 978/81

1039 1 r. 45 on 95 l. Type **178** .. .. .. 5·00 3·00
1040 1 r. 45 on 3 r. Prince and Princess of Wales 5·00 3·00
1041 1 r. 45 on 5 r. Princess on aircraft steps .. 5·00 3·00
MS1042 103 × 75 mm. 1 r. 45 on 8 r. Princess of Wales .. .. 16·00 12·00

193 Hands breaking Manacles

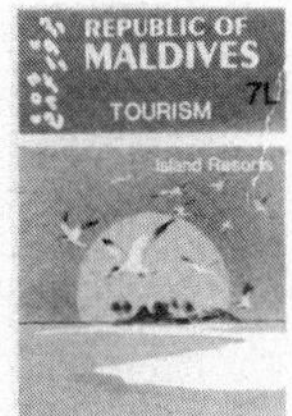

194 Island Resort and Sea Birds

(Litho Format)

1984 (26 Aug). *Namibia Day. T* **193** *and similar horiz designs. Multicoloured. P* 15.

1043 6 r. Type **193** .. .. 1·50 1·60
1044 8 r. Namibia family .. .. 2·00 2·10
MS1045 129 × 104 mm. 10 r. Map of Namibia .. 2·40 2·50

(Litho Questa)

1984 (12 Sept). *Tourism. T* **194** *and similar vert designs. Multicoloured. P* 14.

1046 7 l. Type **194** 5 5
1047 15 l. Dhow 5 5
1048 20 l. Snorkelling 5 8
1049 2 r. Wind-surfing 45 50
1050 4 r. Aqualung diving 90 95
1051 6 r. Night fishing .. .. 1·40 1·50
1052 8 r. Big Game fishing .. .. 1·75 1·90
1053 10 r. Turtle on beach .. .. 2·10 2·25
1046/53 .. .. *Set of* 8 6·00 6·50

195 Frangipani

(Litho Format)

1984 (21 Sept). *"Ausipex" International Stamp Exhibition, Melbourne. T* **195** *and similar horiz designs showing flowers. Multicoloured. P* 15.

1054 5 r. Type **195** .. .. 1·25 1·40
1055 10 r. Cooktown Orchid .. .. 2·40 2·50
MS1056 105 × 77 mm. 15 r. Sun Orchid .. .. 3·75 4·00

Malta

Early records of the postal services under the British Occupation are fragmentary, but it is known that an Island Postmaster was appointed in 1804. A British Packet Agency was established in 1806 and it later became customary for the same individual to hold the two appointments together. The inland posts continued to be the responsibility of the local administration, but the overseas mails formed part of the British G.P.O. system.

The stamps of Great Britain were used on overseas mails from August 1857. During the period of the Crimean War letters franked with Great Britain stamps from the Crimea were cancelled at Malta with a wavy line obliterator. Such postmarks are known between April 1855 and September 1856.

The British G.P.O. relinquished control of the overseas posts on 31 December 1884 when Great Britain stamps were replaced by those of Malta.

For illustrations of the postmark types see BRITISH POST OFFICES ABROAD notes, following GREAT BRITAIN.

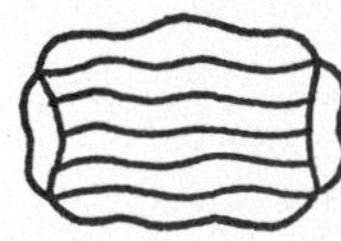

Wavy Lines

1855–56. *Stamps of* GREAT BRITAIN *cancelled with wavy lines obliteration as shown above.*

Z1 1d. red-brown (1854), Die I, *wmk*, Small Crown, *perf* 16 .. .. £800
Z2 1d. red-brown (1855), Die II, *wmk* Small Crown, *perf* 14 .. .. £800
a. Very blued paper
Z3 1d. red-brown (1855), Die II, *wmk* Large Crown, *perf* 16 .. .. £800
Z4 2d. blue (1855), *wmk* Large Crown, *perf* 14 .. Plate No. 5.
Z5 6d. (1854) embossed .. ..
Z6 1s. (1847) embossed .. ..

It is now established that this obliterator was sent to Malta and used on mail in transit emanating from the Crimea.

1857–85.

Stamps of GREAT BRITAIN *cancelled "M" as Type* 1.

Z 7 1d. red-brown (1841) £700
Z 8 1d. red-brown, Die I, *wmk* Small Crown, *perf* 16 .. 55·00
Z 9 1d. red-brown, Die II, *wmk* Small Crown, *perf* 16 £700
Z10 1d. red-brown, Die II (1855), *wmk* Small Crown, *perf* 14 .. .. £120
Z11 1d. red-brown, Die II (1855), *wmk* Large Crown, *perf* 14 .. .. 45·00
Z12 1d. rose-red (1857), *wmk* Large Crown, *perf* 14 .. 17·00
Z13 2d. blue (1841), *imperf* £1700
Z14 2d. blue (1854) *wmk* Small Crown, *perf* 16 .. £550 Plate No. 4.
Z15 2d. blue (1855), *wmk* Large Crown, *perf* 14 *From* 55·00 Plate Nos. 5, 6.
Z16 2d. blue (1858), *wmk* Large Crown, *perf* 16 .. £200 Plate No. 6.
Z17 2d. blue (1858) (Plate Nos. 7, 8, 9) . .. *From* 25·00
Z18 4d. rose (1857) .. .. 35·00
a. Thick glazed paper £170
Z19 6d. violet (1854), embossed £1400
Z20 6d. lilac (1856) .. .. 40·00
a. Thick paper £190
Z21 6d. lilac (1856) (blued *paper*) £850
Z22 1s. green (1856) £150
a. Thick paper .. ..

Stamps of GREAT BRITAIN *cancelled "A 25" as in Types* **2**, **5**, **6**, **8** *or* **11**.

Z23 ½d. rose-red (1870–79) .. .. .. *From* 15·00 Plate Nos. 4, 5, 6, 8, 9, 10, 11, 12, 13, 14, 15, 19, 20.
Z24 1d. red-brown (1841), *imperf* £900
Z25 1d. red-brown (1854), *wmk* Small Crown, *perf* 16 £190
Z26 1d. red-brown (1855), *wmk* Large Crown, *perf* 14 46·00
Z27 1d. rose-red (1857), *wmk* Large Crown, *perf* 14 .. 7·50
Z28 1d. rose-red (1861), Alphabet IV .. .. ..
Z29 1d. rose-red (1862), Alphabet II (Res Plate No. 16) 60·00
Z30 1d. rose-red (1864–79) .. .. .. *From* 11·00 Plate Nos, 71, 72, 73, 74, 76, 78, 79, 80, 81, 82, 83, 84, 85, 86, 87, 88, 89, 90, 91, 92, 93, 94, 95, 96, 97, 98, 99, 100, 101, 102, 103, 104, 105, 106, 107, 108, 109, 110, 111, 112, 113, 114, 115, 116, 117, 118, 119, 120, 121, 122, 123, 124, 125, 127, 129, 130, 131, 132, 133, 134, 135, 136, 137, 138, 139, 140, 141, 142, 143, 144, 145, 146, 147, 148, 149, 150, 151, 152, 153, 154, 155, 156, 157, 158, 159, 160, 161, 162, 163, 164, 165, 166, 167, 168, 169, 170, 171, 172, 173, 174, 175, 176, 177, 178, 179, 180, 181, 182, 183, 184, 185, 186, 187, 188, 189, 190, 191, 192, 193, 194, 195, 196, 197, 198, 199, 200, 201, 202, 203, 204, 205, 206, 207, 208, 209, 210, 211, 212, 213, 214, 215, 216, 217, 218, 219, 220, 221, 222, 223, 224.
Z31 1½d. lake-red (1870–79) (Plate Nos. 1, 3) .. *From* £200
Z32 2d. blue (1841), *imperf* £1800
Z33 2d. blue (1855) *wmk* Large Crown *perf* 14 .. 35·00
Z34 2d. blue (1858–69) .. .. *From* 15·00 Plate Nos. 7, 8, 9, 12, 13, 14, 15.
Z35 2½d. rosy mauve (1875) (blued *paper*) .. *From* 50·00 Plate Nos. 1, 2.
Z36 2½d. rosy mauve (1875–76) (Plate Nos. 1, 2, 3) *From* 27·00
Z37 2½d. rosy mauve (*Error of Lettering*) £2250
Z38 2½d. rosy mauve (1876–79) .. .. *From* 18·00 Plate Nos. 3, 4, 5, 6, 7, 8, 9, 10, 11, 12, 13, 14, 15, 16, 17.
Z39 2½d. blue (1880–81) (Plate Nos. 17, 18, 19, 20) *From* 9·00
Z40 2½d. blue (1881) (Plate Nos. 21, 22, 23) .. *From* 6·00
Z41 3d. carmine-rose (1862) £100
Z42 3d. rose (1865) (Plate No. 4) .. .. .. 50·00

No.	Description		Price
Z43	3d. rose (1867–73)	From	18·00
	Plate Nos. 4, 5, 6, 7, 8, 9, 10.		
Z44	3d. rose (1873–76)	From	17·00
	Plate Nos. 11, 12, 14, 15, 16, 17, 18, 19, 20.		
Z45	3d. rose (1881) (Plate Nos. 20, 21)	From	50·00
Z46	3d. on 3d. lilac (1883)		£350
Z47	4d. rose (or rose-carmine) (1857)		27·00
	a. Thick glazed paper		£110
Z48	4d. red (1862) (Plate Nos. 3, 4)	From	35·00
Z49	4d. vermilion (1865–73)	From	18·00
	Plate Nos. 7, 8, 9, 10, 11, 12, 13, 14.		
Z50	4d. vermilion (1876) (Plate No. 15)		£190
Z51	4d. sage-green (1877) (Plate Nos. 15, 16)	From	75·00
Z52	4d. grey-brown (1880) *wmk* Large Garter		90·00
	Plate No. 17.		
Z53	4d. grey-brown (1880) *wmk* Crown	From	15·00
	Plate Nos. 17, 18.		
Z54	6d. violet (1854), embossed		£1200
Z55	6d. lilac (1856)		40·00
	a. Thick paper		
Z56	6d. lilac (1862) (Plate Nos. 3, 4)	From	35·00
Z57	6d. lilac (1865–67) (Plate Nos. 5, 6)	From	32·00
Z58	6d. lilac (1865–67) (*Wmk error*)		
Z59	6d. lilac (1867) (Plate No. 6)		40·00
Z60	6d. violet (1867–70) (Plate Nos. 6, 8, 9)	From	32·00
Z61	6d. buff (1872–73) (Plate Nos. 11, 12)	From	£160
Z62	6d. chestnut (1872) (Plate No. 11)		32·00
Z63	6d. grey (1873) (Plate No. 12)		42·00
Z64	6d. grey (1873–80)	From	24·00
	Plate Nos. 13, 14, 15, 16, 17.		
Z65	6d. grey (1881–82) (Plate Nos. 17, 18)	From	15·00
Z66	6d. on 6d. lilac (1883)		£140
Z67	8d. orange (1876)		£250
Z68	9d. straw (1862)		£475
Z69	9d. bistre (1862)		£475
Z70	9d. straw (1865)		£475
Z71	9d. straw (1867)		£600
Z72	10d. red-brown (1867)		£250
Z73	1s. (1847), embossed		£1200
Z74	1s. green (1856)		70·00
Z75	1s. green (1856) (thick *paper*)		£250
Z76	1s. green (1862)		55·00
Z77	1s. green ("K" *variety*)		£2250
Z78	1s. green (1865) (Plate No. 4)		35·00
Z79	1s. green (1867–73) (Plate Nos. 4, 5, 6, 7)	From	8·50
Z80	1s. green (1873–77)	From	28·00
	Plate Nos. 8, 9, 10, 11, 12, 13.		
Z81	1s. orange-brown (1880) (Plate No. 13)		£225
Z82	1s. orange-brown (1881) (Plate Nos. 13, 14)	From	30·00
Z83	2s. blue (*shades*) (1867)	From	85·00
Z84	2s. brown (1880)		£1700
Z85	5s. rose (1867–74) (Plate Nos. 1, 2)	From	£300
Z86	5s. rose (1882) (Plate No. 4), blue *paper*		£900
Z87	5s. rose (1882) (Plate No. 4), white *paper*		£900
Z88	10s. grey-green (1878)		£1600

1880.

No.	Description	Price
Z89	½d. deep green	8·50
Z90	½d. pale green	8·50
Z91	1d. Venetian red	7·50
Z92	1½d. Venetian red	25·00
Z93	2d. pale rose	25·00
Z94	2d. deep rose	25·00
Z95	5d. indigo	50·00

1881.

No.	Description	Price
Z96	1d. lilac (14 *dots*)	13·00
Z97	1d. lilac (16 *dots*)	5·00

1883–4.

No.	Description		Price
Z 98–Z102	½d. slate-blue; 1½d., 2d, 2½d., 3d.	From	8·50
Z103–Z107	4d. 5d., 6d., 9d., 1s.	From	60·00
Z108	5s. rose (blued *paper*)		£900
Z109	5s. rose (white *paper*)		£700

POSTAL FISCALS

No.	Description	Price
Z110	1d. purple (1871) *wmk* Anchor	£700
Z111	1d. purple (1881) *wmk* Orb	£550

PRICES FOR STAMPS ON COVER TO 1945

Nos. 1/3	*from* × 3
Nos. 4/19	*from* × 5
Nos. 20/9	*from* × 6
No. 30	—
Nos. 31/3	*from* × 4
Nos. 34/7	*from* × 10
Nos. 38/88	*from* × 4
Nos. 92/3	*from* × 5
Nos. 97/103	*from* × 3
Nos. 104/5	—
Nos. 106/20	*from* × 3
No. 121	—
Nos. 122/38	*from* × 3
Nos. 139/40	—
Nos. 141/72	*from* × 4
Nos. 173/209	*from* × 3
Nos. 210/31	*from* × 2
Nos. D1/10	*from* × 30
Nos. D11/20	*from* × 15

CROWN COLONY

PRINTERS. Nos. 1/156. Printed by De La Rue; typographed *except where otherwise stated.*

1

Type 1

The first Government local post was established on 10 June 1853 and, as an experiment, mail was carried free of charge. During 1859 the Council of Government decided that a rate of ½d. per ½ ounce should be charged for this service and stamps in Type 1 were ordered for this purpose. Both the new rate and the stamps were introduced on 1 December 1860. Until 1885 the ½d. stamps were intended for the local service only; mail for abroad being handled by the British Post Office on Malta, using G.B. stamps.

Specialists now recognise 29 printings in shades of yellow and one in green during the period to 1884. These printings can be linked to the changes in watermark and perforation as follows:

Ptg 1—Blued paper without wmk. P 14.
Ptgs 2 and 3—White paper without wmk. P 14.
Ptgs 4 to 9, 11, 13 to 19, 22 to 24—Crown CC wmk. P 14.
Ptg 10—Crown CC wmk. P 12½ (rough).
Ptg 12—Crown CC wmk. P 12½ (clean-cut).
Ptgs 20 and 21—Crown CC wmk. P 14 × 12½.
Ptgs 25 to 28, 30—Crown CA wmk. P 14.
Ptg 29—In green (No. 20).

PRICES. The unused prices for Nos. 1/17 are for stamps without full gum. Well centred copies with full original gum are worth 50% more.

1860 (1 Dec)–**63.** *No wmk. P* 14. (*a*) *Blued paper.*

No.	Description	Unused	Used
1	½d. buff (1.2.60)	£1000	£650
	a. Imperf	£8500	
	(*b*) *White paper*		
2	½d. brown-orange (11.61)	£850	£375
3	½d. buff (1.63)	£750	£375
	a. Pale buff	£800	£400

No. 1 is printed in fugitive ink.

The printing on No. 2 gives a very blurred and muddy impression; on Nos. 3/3*a* the impression is clear.

Specks of carmine can often be detected with a magnifying glass on Nos. 2/3*a*, and also on No. 4. Examples also exist on which parts of the design are in pure rose, due to defective mixing of the ink.

(Des E. Fuchs)

1863–81. *Wmk Crown CC.* (*a*) *P* 14.

No.	Description	Unused	Used
4	½d. buff (6.63)	75·00	42·00
5	½d. bright orange (11.64)	£110	65·00
6	½d. brown-red (4.67)	£300	65·00
7	½d. dull orange (4.70)	£110	45·00
8	½d. orange-buff (5.72)	£110	45·00
9	½d. golden yellow (aniline) (10.74)	£275	£275
10	½d. yellow-buff (9.75)	85·00	60·00
11	½d. pale buff (3.77)	85·00	45·00
12	½d. bright orange-yellow (4.80)	50·00	42·00
13	½d. yellow (4.81)	50·00	38·00
	(*b*) *P* 12½ *rough* (*No.* 14) *or clean-cut* (*No.* 15)		
14	½d. buff-brown (11.68)	65·00	50·00
	a. Imperf between (vert pair)		
15	½d. yellow-orange (5.71)	£150	£140
	(*c*) *P* 14 × 12½		
16	½d. yellow-buff (7.78)	£125	85·00
	a. Perf 12½ × 14		
17	½d. yellow (2.79)	£125	85·00

Examples of No. 4 from the 1863 printing are on thin, surfaced paper; later printings in the same shade were on unsurfaced paper.

The ink used for No. 5 is mineral and, unlike that on No. 9, does not stain the paper.

Some variations of shade on No. 6 may be described as chestnut. The ink of No. 6 is clear and never muddy, although some examples are over-inked. Deeper shades of No. 4, with which examples of No. 6 might be confused, have muddy ink.

1882 (Mar)–**84.** *Wmk Crown CA. P* 14.

No.	Description	Unused	Used
18	½d. orange-yellow	17·00	32·00
19	½d. red-orange (9.84)	17·00	32·00

2

3

4

5

1885 (1 Jan)–**90.** *Wmk Crown CA. P* 14.

No.	Type	Description		Unused	Used
20	1	½d. green		1·40	65
21	2	1d. rose		35·00	25·00
22		1d. carmine (1890)		2·50	1·50
23	3	2d. grey		2·50	1·75
24	4	2½d. dull blue		20·00	1·75
25		2½d. bright blue		20·00	1·75
26		2½d. ultramarine		20·00	1·75
27	3	4d. brown		7·00	7·00
		a. Imperf (pair)		£3250	£3000
28		1s. violet		35·00	28·00
29		1s. pale violet (1890)		50·00	28·00
20/29			*Set of* 6	60·00	38·00
20/28 Optd "Specimen"			*Set of* 6	£1500	

Although not valid for postage until 1 January 1885 these stamps were available at the G.P.O., Valletta from 27 December 1884.

Three unused examples of the ½d. green, No. 20, are known line perforated 12. It is believed that these originated from proof books, the stamp not being issued for use with this perforation.

1886 (1 Jan). *Wmk Crown CC. P* 14.

No.	Type	Description	Unused	Used
30	5	5s. rose (Optd S. £400)	£160	£130

6 Harbour of Valletta

7 Gozo Fishing Boat

8 Ancient Maltese Galley

9 Emblematic figure of Malta

10 Shipwreck of St. Paul

(T **6/10** recess)

1899 (4 Feb)–**1901.** *P* 14. (*a*) *Wmk Crown CA* (*sideways on* ¼*d*).

No.	Type	Description	Unused	Used
31	6	¼d. brown (1.1.01)	1·40	1·00
		a. Red-brown	1·25	75
32	7	4½d. sepia	12·00	10·00
33	8	5d. vermilion	22·00	18·00
		(*b*) *Wmk Crown CC*		
34	9	2s. 6d. olive-grey	30·00	26·00
35	10	10s. blue-black	£100	75·00

One Penny

(11)

12

1902 (4 July). *Nos.* 24 *and* 25 *surch locally at Govt Ptg Office with T* **11**.

No.	Description	Unused	Used
36	1d. on 2½d. dull blue (Optd S. £100)	65	75
	a. Surch double	£2500	£2250
	b. "One Pnney" (R. 9/2)	32·00	35·00
	ba. Surch double, with "One Pnney"		
37	1d. on 2½d. bright blue	65	75
	a. "One Pnney" (R. 9/2)	32·00	35·00

(Des E. Fuchs)

1903 (Mar)–**4.** *Wmk Crown CA. P* 14.

No.	Type	Description		Unused	Used
38	12	½d. green		2·00	15
39		1d. black and red (5.03)		5·50	15
40		2d. purple and grey		11·00	7·00
41		2½d. maroon and blue (9.03)		12·00	2·50
42		3d. grey and purple		2·00	1·25
43		4d. black and brown (5.04)		26·00	22·00
44		1s. grey and violet (4.03)		16·00	10·00
38/44			*Set of* 7	65·00	38·00
38/44 Optd "Specimen"			*Set of* 7	£225	

1904–14. *Wmk Mult Crown CA* (*sideways on* ¼*d.*). *P* 14.

No.	Type	Description		Unused	Used
45	6	¼d. red-brown (10.10.05)		1·00	25
		a. Deep brown (1910)		1·00	15
47	12	½d. green (11.04)		2·75	45
		a. Deep green (1909)		1·75	15
48		1d. black and red (4.05)		4·00	20
49		1d. red (4.07)		1·10	15
50		2d. purple and grey (2.05)		4·00	90
51		2d. grey (10.11)		1·60	1·75
52		2½d. maroon and blue (10.04)		4·00	85
53		2½d. bright blue (1.11)		4·75	1·90
54		4d. black and brown (4.06)		12·00	8·50
55		4d. black and red/*yellow* (11.11)		4·00	3·25
57	7	4½d. brown (27.2.05)		16·00	9·00
58		4½d. orange (8.12)		6·00	5·00
59	8	5d. vermilion (20.2.05)		13·00	5·50
60		5d. pale sage-green (1909)		6·00	7·00
		a. Deep sage-green (1914)		12·00	12·00
61	12	1s. grey and violet (12.04)		28·00	5·50
62		1s. black/*green* (3.11)		8·00	8·00
63		5s. green and red/*yellow*, **C** (12.10)		75·00	75·00
45/63			*Set of* 17	£170	£120
45/63 (1907/11 *colours*) Optd "Specimen"			*Set of* 10	£475	

13

14

15

1914–21. *Wmk Mult Crown CA. P* 14.

No.	Type	Description	Unused	Used
69	13	¼d. brown, **O** (2.1.14)	25	15
		a. Deep brown (1919)	50	45
71		½d. green, **O** (20.1.14)	1·00	25
		aa. Wmk sideways	—	£850
		a. Deep green (1919)	70	40
73		1d. carmine-red, **O** (15.4.14)	1·00	20
		a. Scarlet (1915)	1·60	50
75		2d. grey, **O** (12.8.14)	6·50	5·50
		a. Deep slate (1919)	9·00	8·00
77		2½d. bright blue, **O** (11.3.14)	70	40

78 14 3d. purple/*yellow*, C (1.5.20) .. .. .. 7·00 7·00
a. On orange-buff .. .. 9·50 12·00
79 6 4d. black, C (21.8.15) .. .. .. 12·00 5·00
a. Grey-black (1916) .. .. .. 17·00 8·50
80 13 6d. dull and bright purple, C (10.3.14) .. 8·50 9·00
a. Dull purple and magenta (1918) .. 8·50 9·00
81 14 1s. black/*green* (*white back*), C (2.1.14) .. 12·00 13·00
a. On green, green back (Optd S. £45) (1915) .. .. 14·00 11·00
ab. Wmk sideways £800 £500
b. On blue-green, olive back (1918) .. 14·00 11·00
c. On emerald surface (1920) .. .. 12·00 11·00
d. On emerald back (1921) .. .. 16·00 15·00
86 15 2s. purple & brt blue/*blue*, C (15.4.14) .. 45·00 28·00
a. Dull purple and blue/blue (1921) .. 45·00 32·00
87 9 2s. 6d. olive-green, O (1919) .. .. 38·00 45·00
a. Olive-grey (1920) .. .. .. 38·00 45·00
88 15 5s. green and red/*yellow*, C (21.3.17) .. 70·00 80·00
69/88 .. .. *Set of* 12 £180 £170
69/88 (*excl.* 87) Optd "Specimen" .. *Set of* 11 £600

The design of Nos. 79/*a* differs in various details from that of Type **6**.

We have only seen one copy of No. 71aa; it is in used condition.

A 3d. purple on yellow on white back, T **14**, was prepared for use but not issued. It exists overprinted "Specimen", *price* £150.

WAR TAX

(16) (17) (18)

1917–18. *Optd with T* **16**, *by De La Rue.*
92 13 ½d. deep green (14.12.17*) 35 35
93 12 3d. grey and purple (3.3.18*) .. .. 3·50 6·50
92/3 Optd. "Specimen" .. .. *Set of* 2 £200
*These are the earliest known dates of use.

(T **17** recess)

1919. *Wmk Mult Crown CA. P* 14.
96 17 10s. black (Optd S. £1200) £4500 £5500

1921 (16 Feb)–**22.** *Wmk Mult Script CA. P* 14.
97 13 ¼d. brown, O (12.1.22) .. .. .. 50 4·00
98 ½d. green, O (19.1.22) .. .. .. 1·25 4·75
99 1d. scarlet, O (12.21) 55 55
100 18 2d. grey, O .. .. 4·50 1·25
101 13 2½d. bright blue, O (15.1.22) .. .. 3·25 6·00
102 6d. dull and bright purple, C (19.1.22) 17·00 23·00
103 15 2s. purple and blue/*blue*, C (19.1.22) .. 90·00 £150
104 17 10s. black, O (19.1.22) £450 £550
97/104 .. .. *Set of* 8 £500 £650
97/104 Optd "Specimen" .. .. *Set of* 8 £750

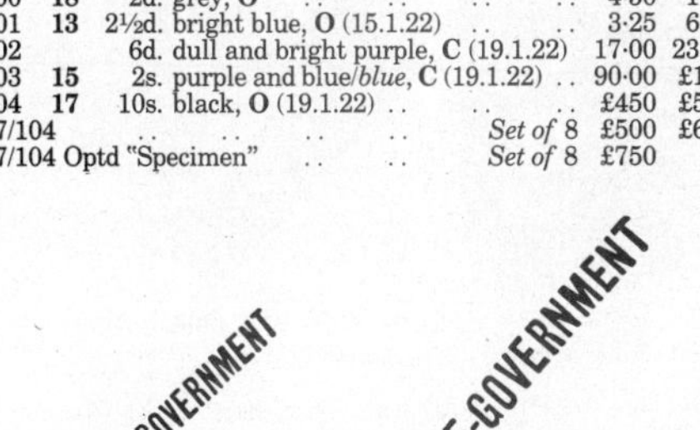

(19) (20)

1922 (12 Jan–Apr). *Optd with T* **19** *or* **20** *(large stamps), at Govt Printing Office, Valletta. (a) Wmk Crown CC.*
105 10 10s. blue-black, O (R.) £225 £250

(b) Wmk Mult Crown CA
106 13 ½d. green, O 30 40
107 2½d. bright blue, O .. .. .. 2·50 4·50
108 14 3d. purple/*orange-buff*, C .. .. 1·60 5·50
109 13 6d. dull and bright purple, C .. .. 1·60 5·50
110 14 1s. black/*emerald*, C .. .. .. 3·25 4·75
111 15 2s. dull purple and blue/*blue*, C (R.) .. £325 £400
112 9 2s. 6d. olive-grey, O .. .. .. 22·00 30·00
113 15 5s. green and red/*yellow*, C .. .. 45·00 55·00
106/13 .. .. *Set of* 8 £350 £450

(c) Wmk Mult Script CA
114 13 ¼d. brown, O 20 30
115 ½d. green, O (29.4) 55 75
116 1d. scarlet, O 30 30
117 18 2d. grey, O .. .. 1·40 1·40
118 13 2½d. bright blue, O (15.1) .. .. 60 1·00
119 6d. dull and bright purple, C (19.4) .. 4·00 5·50
120 15 2s. dull purple & blue/*bl*, C (R.) (25.1) 35·00 50·00
121 17 10s. black, O (R.) (9.3) £140 £150
114/21 .. .. *Set of* 8 £160 £190

One Farthing

(21)

22

23

1922 (15 Apr). *No. 100 surch with T* **21**, *at Govt Printing Office, Valletta.*
122 18 ¼d. on 2d. grey 15 30

(Des C. Dingli (T **22**) and G. Vella (**23**))

1922 (1 Aug)–**26.** *Wmk Mult Script CA (sideways on T* **22**, *except No. 140). P* 14. *(a) Typo. Chalk-surfaced paper.*
123 22 ¼d. brown (22.8.22) 30 40
a. Chocolate-brown 35 25
124 ½d. green 35 15
125 1d. orange and purple 70 50
126 1d. bright violet (28.4.24) 80 35
127 1½d. brown-red (1.10.23) 85 25
128 2d. bistre-brown and turquoise (28.8.22) 30 25
129 2½d. ultramarine (16.2.26) .. .. 1·00 3·25
130 3d. cobalt (28.8.22) .. .. .. 1·75 1·75
a. Bright ultramarine .. .. 1·75 1·75
131 3d. black/*yellow* (16.2.26) .. .. 1·75 3·25
132 4d. yellow and bright blue (28.8.22) .. 1·50 1·40
133 6d. olive-green and violet .. .. 1·75 1·75
134 23 1s. indigo and sepia .. .. .. 3·75 3·50
135 2s. brown and blue .. .. .. 6·50 8·50
136 2s. 6d. brt magenta & black (28.8.22) 9·50 9·50
137 5s. orange-yellow and bright ultramarine (28.8.22) .. .. .. 15·00 20·00
138 10s. slate-grey and brown (28.8.22) .. 35·00 48·00

(b) Recess
139 22 £1 black and carmine-red (28.8.22) £130 £170
140 £1 black and bright carmine (14.5.25) £130 £170
123/39 .. .. *Set of* 17 £180 £250
123/39 Optd "Specimen" .. *Set of* 17 £800

No. 139 has the watermark sideways and No. 140 has it upright.

Two pence halfpenny

(24)

POSTAGE

(25)

1925. *Surch with T* **24**, *at Govt Printing Office, Valletta.*
141 22 2½d. on 3d. cobalt (3 Dec) .. .. 90 1·00
142 2½d. on 3d. bright ultramarine (9 Dec) 1·10 1·00

1926 (1 April). *Optd with T* **25**, *at Govt Printing Office, Valletta.*
143 22 ¼d. brown 20 60
144 ½d. green 20 25
145 1d. bright violet 35 45
146 1½d. brown-red 40 40
147 2d. bistre-brown and turquoise .. 40 45
148 2½d. ultramarine 70 70
149 3d. black/*yellow* 55 85
a. Opt inverted £225 £375
150 4d. yellow and bright blue .. .. 3·00 4·00
151 6d. olive-green and violet .. .. 2·00 1·60
152 23 1s. indigo and sepia .. .. .. 4·25 5·00
153 2s. brown and blue .. .. .. 40·00 50·00
154 2s. 6d. bright magenta and black .. 13·00 20·00
155 5s. orange-yellow & brt ultramarine 12·00 20·00
156 10s. slate-grey and brown .. .. 12·00 18·00
143/156 .. .. *Set of* 14 80·00 £110

26

27 Valletta Harbour

28 St. Publius **33** St. Paul

(T **26** typo, others recess Waterlow)

1926 (6 Apr)–**27.** *T* **26/8**, **33** *and similar designs. Inscr "POSTAGE". Wmk Mult Script CA. P* 15 × 14 *(T* **26**) *or* 12½ *(others).*
157 26 ¼d. brown 25 20
158 ½d. yellow-green (5.8.26) 35 20
159 1d. rose-red (1.4.27) 30 25
160 1½d. chestnut (7.10.26) 60 20
161 2d. greenish grey (1.4.27) .. .. 3·25 4·50
162 2½d. blue (1.4.27) .. .. .. 2·25 70
162*a* 3d. violet (1.4.27) .. .. .. 2·25 2·75
163 4d. black and red .. .. .. 4·50 5·50
164 4½d. lavender and ochre .. .. 4·50 5·50
165 6d. violet and scarlet (5.5.26) .. 4·50 5·00
166 27 1s. black .. .. 4·50 4·50
167 28 1s. 6d. black and green .. .. 9·00 9·00
168 – 2s. black and purple .. .. .. 12·00 15·00
169 – 2s. 6d. black and vermilion .. .. 16·00 20·00
170 – 3s. black and blue .. .. .. 16·00 24·00
171 – 5s. black and green (5.5.26) .. .. 24·00 35·00
172 33 10s. black and carmine (9.2.27) .. 75·00 90·00
157/72 .. .. *Set of* 17 £160 £200
157/72 Optd "Specimen" .. *Set of* 17 £650

Designs: *Vert*—2s. 6d. Gozo boat; 3s. Neptune; *Horiz*—2s. Mdina (Notabile); 5s. Ruins at Mnajdra.

AIR MAIL

(34)

POSTAGE AND REVENUE

(35)

POSTAGE AND REVENUE.

(36)

1928 (1 Apr). *Air. Optd with T* **34**.
173 26 6d. violet and scarlet .. .. .. 6·00 7·00

1928 (1 Oct–Dec). *As Nos.* 157/72, *optd.*
174 35 ¼d. brown 25 15
175 ½d. yellow-green 25 15
176 1d. rose-red 45 80
177 1d. chestnut (5.12.28) .. .. .. 1·40 20
178 1½d. chestnut 55 70
179 1½d. rose-red (5.12.28) .. .. .. 1·75 30
180 2d. greenish grey .. .. .. 4·00 5·50
181 2½d. blue .. .. 1·60 30
182 3d. violet .. .. 2·00 70
183 4d. black and red .. .. .. 1·60 2·50
184 4½d. lavender and ochre .. .. 4·00 3·00
185 6d. violet and scarlet .. .. .. 3·50 3·50
186 36 1s. black (R.) .. .. 3·50 3·50
187 1s. 6d. black and green (R.) .. .. 9·00 13·00
188 2s. black and purple (R.) .. .. 15·00 22·00
189 2s. 6d. black and vermilion (R.) .. 22·00 27·00
190 3s. black and blue (R.) .. .. 22·00 30·00
191 5s. black and green (R.) .. .. 35·00 45·00
192 10s. black and carmine (R.) .. .. 75·00 95·00
174/92 .. .. *Set of* 19 £180 £225
174/92 Optd "Specimen" .. *Set of* 19 £700

1930 (20 Oct). *As Nos.* 157/172, *but inscr* "POSTAGE (&) REVENUE".
193 ¼d. brown 20 15
194 ½d. yellow-green 30 10
195 1d. chestnut 30 10
196 1½d. rose-red 50 20
197 2d. greenish grey .. .. .. 1·00 80
198 2½d. blue .. .. 1·25 25
199 3d. violet .. .. 1·75 70
200 4d. black and red .. .. .. 2·25 3·50
201 4½d. lavender and ochre .. .. 2·75 3·75
202 6d. violet and scarlet .. .. .. 2·75 2·75
203 1s. black .. .. 7·00 8·50
204 1s. 6d. black and green .. .. 9·00 13·00
205 2s. black and purple .. .. .. 11·00 18·00
206 2s. 6d. black and vermilion .. .. 24·00 32·00
207 3s. black and blue .. .. .. 27·00 35·00
208 5s. black and green .. .. .. 35·00 42·00
209 10s. black and carmine .. .. 80·00 90·00
193/209 .. .. *Set of* 17 £180 £225
193/209 Perf "Specimen" .. *Set of* 17 £650

1935 (6 May). *Silver Jubilee. As Nos.* 91/4 *of Antigua, but printed by B.W. P* 11 × 12.
210 ½d. black and green 25 25
a. Extra flagstaff .. .. .. 38·00
b. Short extra flagstaff .. .. 20·00
c. Lightning conductor .. .. 15·00
211 2½d. brown and deep blue .. .. 2·50 2·50
a. Extra flagstaff £130
b. Short extra flagstaff .. .. 70·00
c. Lightning conductor .. .. 50·00
212 6d. light blue and olive-green .. .. 7·00 7·00
a. Extra flagstaff £150
b. Short extra flagstaff .. .. 80·00
c. Lightning conductor .. .. 60·00
213 1s. slate and purple .. .. .. 14·00 18·00
a. Extra flagstaff £350
b. Short extra flagstaff £160
c. Lightning conductor £120
210/13 Perf "Specimen" .. *Set of* 4 75·00

For illustration of plate varieties see Omnibus section following Zululand.

Examples of the ½d., 6d. and 1s. values are known with the extra flagstaff erased from the stamp with a sharp point.

1937 (12 May). *Coronation. As Nos.* 13/15 *of Aden.*
214 ½d. green 10 10
215 1½d. scarlet 25 15
a. Brown-lake £375 £400
216 2½d. bright blue 60 70
214/16 Perf "Specimen" .. *Set of* 3 48·00

37 Grand Harbour, Valletta

38 H.M.S. *St. Angelo*

39 Verdala Palace

40 Hypogeum, Hal Saflieni

(Recess Waterlow)

1938 (17 Feb*)–**43.** *T* **37/40** *and similar designs. Wmk Mult Script CA (sideways on No.* 217). *P* 12½.
217 37 ¼d. brown 10 5
218 38 ½d. green 20 5
218*a* ½d. red-brown (8.3.43) 15 10
219 39 1d. red-brown 75 15
219*a* 1d. green (8.3.43) 15 5
220 40 1½d. scarlet 20 12
220*a* 1½d. slate-black (8.3.43) 15 12
221 – 2d. slate-black 55 55
221*a* – 2d. scarlet (8.3.43) 15 10
222 – 2½d. greyish blue 35 35
222*a* – 2½d. dull violet (8.3.43) 50 10
223 – 3d. dull violet 35 50
223*a* – 3d. blue (8.3.43) 25 15
224 – 4½d. olive-green and yellow-brown .. 75 20
225 – 6d. olive-green and scarlet 45 30
226 – 1s. black 90 70

227 – 1s. 6d. black and olive-green . . . . 3·25 4·00
228 – 2s. green and deep blue . . . . 3·25 3·25
229 – 2s. 6d. black and scarlet . . . . 4·50 4·75
230 – 5s. black and green . . . . . . 7·50 8·00
231 – 10s. black and carmine . . . . 19·00 20·00
217/231 . . . . *Set of* 21 38·00 40·00
217/31 Perf "Specimen" . . . . *Set of* 21 £375

Designs: *Horiz* (*as T* **39**)—2d. Victoria and citadel, Gozo; 2½d. De l'Isle entering Mdina; 4½d. Ruins at Mnajdra; 1s. 6d. St. Publius; 2s. Mdina Cathedral; 2s. 6d. Statue of Neptune. *Vert* (*as T* **40**)—3d. St. John's Co-Cathedral; 6d. Statue of Manoel de Vilhena; 1s. Maltese girl wearing faldetta; 5s. Palace Square, Valletta; 10s. St. Paul.

*This is the local date of issue but the stamps were released in London on 15 February.

1946 (3 Dec). *Victory. As Nos.* 28/9 *of Aden, but inscr* "MALTA" *between Maltese Cross and George Cross.*
232 1d. green 10 10
233 3d. blue 30 30
232/3 Perf "Specimen" . . . . *Set of* 2 50·00

SELF-GOVERNMENT

(52)

(Optd by Waterlow)

1948 (25 Nov)–**53.** *New Constitution. As Nos.* 217/231 *but optd as T* **52**; *reading up on ½d. and 5s., down on other values, and smaller on ¼d. value.*
234 **37** ¼d. brown 10 10
235 **38** ½d. red-brown 12 5
236 **39** 1d. green 25 5
236*a* 1d. grey (R.) (8.1.53) 15 10
237 **40** 1½d. blue-black (R.) 30 12
237*a* 1½d. green (8.1.53) 15 10
b. Opt omitted . . . . . . — £4500
238 – 2d. scarlet 25 12
238*a* – 2d. yellow-ochre (8.1.53) 20 10
239 – 2½d. dull violet (R.) 15 10
239*a* – 2½d. scarlet-vermilion (8.1.53) . . 75 75
240 – 3d. blue (R.) 20 20
240*a* – 3d. dull violet (R.) (8.1.53) 35 20
241 – 4½d. olive-green and yellow-brown . . 90 1·40
241*a* – 4½d. olive-green & dp ultram (R.) (8.1.53) 90 80
242 – 6d. olive-green and scarlet 30 25
243 – 1s. black . . . . 1·25 1·00
244 – 1s. 6d. black and olive-green . . 2·50 2·50
245 – 2s. green and deep blue (R.) . . . . 3·25 2·75
246 – 2s. 6d. black and scarlet . . . . 8·00 5·50
247 – 5s. black and green (R.) . . . . 11·00 8·50
248 – 10s. black and carmine . . . . 28·00 30·00
234/248 . . . . *Set of* 21 50·00 48·00

1949 (4 Jan). *Royal Silver Wedding. As Nos.* 30/1 *of Aden, but inscr* "MALTA" *between Maltese Cross and George Cross* (*recess* £1).
249 1d. green 20 10
250 £1 indigo . . . . 55·00 60·00

1949 (10 Oct). *75th Anniv of Universal Postal Union. As Nos.* 114/17 *of Antigua, but inscr* "MALTA" (*recess*).
251 2½d. violet 25 30
252 3d. deep blue 75 60
253 6d. carmine-red . . . . 1·75 1·10
254 1s. blue-black . . . . 2·50 3·00

53 Queen Elizabeth II when Princess

54 "Our Lady of Mount Carmel" (attrib Palladino)

(T **53/4**. Recess B.W.)

1950 (1 Dec). *Visit of Princess Elizabeth to Malta. Wmk Mult Script CA. P* 12 × 11½.
255 **53** 1d. green 10 10
256 3d. blue 40 30
257 1s. black 75 85

1951 (12 July). *Seventh Centenary of the Scapular. Wmk Mult Script CA. P* 12 × 11½.
258 **54** 1d. green 10 10
259 3d. violet 15 15
260 1s. black 60 80

1953 (3 June). *Coronation. As No.* 47 *of Aden.*
261 1½d. black and deep yellow-green 10 5

55 St. John's Co-Cathedral

56 "Immaculate Conception" (Caruana) (altar-piece, Cospicua)

(Recess Waterlow)

1954 (3 May). *Royal Visit. Wmk Mult Script CA. P* 12½.
262 **55** 3d. violet 20 12

(Photo Harrison)

1954 (8 Sept). *Centenary of Dogma of the Immaculate Conception. Wmk Mult Script CA. Chalk-surfaced paper. P* 14½ × 14.
263 **56** 1½d. emerald 15 5
264 3d. bright blue 15 5
265 1s. grey-black 50 65

57 Monument of the Great Siege, 1565

62 Auberge de Castile

(Recess Waterlow (2s. 6d. to £1). B.W. (others))

1956 (23 Jan)–**57.** *T* **57**, **62** *and similar designs. Wmk Mult Script CA. P* 14 × 13½ (*2s. 6d. to* £1), 11½ (*others*).
266 ¼d. violet 5 5
267 ½d. orange 8 5
268 1d. black (9.2.56) 12 5
269 1½d. bluish green (9.2.56) 12 5
270 2d. brown (*shades*) (9.2.56) 12 5
271 2½d. orange-brown 20 30
272 3d. rose-red (22.3.56) 20 5
273 4½d. deep blue 25 20
274 6d. indigo (9.2.56) 30 10
275 8d. bistre-brown . . . . 70 1·00
276 1s. deep reddish violet 60 12
277 1s. 6d. deep turquoise-green . . . . 2·25 30
278 2s. olive-green . . . . 2·75 1·25
279 2s. 6d. chestnut (22.3.56) . . . . . . 4·75 2·50
280 5s. green (11.10.56) . . . . . . 11·00 5·00
281 10s. carmine-red (19.11.56) . . . . . . 45·00 16·00
282 £1 yellow-brown (5.1.57) . . . . . . 45·00 27·00
266/282 . . . . *Set of* 17 £100 48·00

Designs:—*Vert*—½d. Wignacourt aqueduct horsetrough; 1d. Victory church; 1½d. War memorial; 2d. Mosta dome; 3d. The King's scroll; 4½d. Roosevelt's scroll; 8d. Vedette; 1s. Mdina gate; 1s. 6d. "Les Gavroches" (statue); 2s. Monument of Christ the King; 2s. 6d. Grand Master Cottoner's monument; 5s. Grand Master Perellos's monument; 10s. St. Paul; £1 Baptism of Christ. *Horiz*—6d. Neolithic Temples at Tarxien.

74 "Defence of Malta"

75 Searchlights over Malta

(Des E. Cremona. Photo Harrison)

1957 (15 Apr). *George Cross Commemoration. Cross in silver. T* **74/5** *and similar design. Wmk Mult Script CA. P* 14½ × 14 (*3d.*) *or* 14 × 14½ (*others*).
283 1½d. deep dull green 10 5
284 3d. vermilion 15 5
285 1s. reddish brown 25 30

Design: *Vert*—1s. Bombed buildings.

77 "Design"

(Des E. Cremona. Photo Harrison)

1958 (15 Feb). *Technical Education in Malta. T* **77** *and similar designs. W* w **12**. *P* 14 × 14½ (*3d.*) *or* 14½ × 14 (*others*).
286 1½d. black and deep green 10 10
287 3d. black, scarlet and grey 15 5
288 1s. grey, bright purple and black 35 60

Designs: *Vert*—3d. "Construction". *Horiz*—1s. Technical School, Paola.

80 Bombed-out Family

81 Sea Raid on Grand Harbour, Valletta

(Des E. Cremona. Photo Harrison)

1958 (15 Apr). *George Cross Commemoration. Cross in first colour, outlined in silver. T* **80/1** *and similar design. W* w **12**. *P* 14 × 14½ (*3d.*) *or* 14½ × 14 (*others*).
289 1½d. blue-green and black 12 5
290 3d. red and black 15 5
291 1s. reddish violet and black 35 60

Design: *Horiz*—1s. Searchlight crew.

83 Air Raid Casualties

84 "For Gallantry"

(Des E. Cremona. Photo Harrison)

1959 (15 Apr). *George Cross Commemoration. T* **83/4** *and similar design. W* w **12**. *P* 14½ × 14 (*3d.*) *or* 14 × 14½ (*others*).
292 1½d. grey-green, black and gold 10 10
293 3d. reddish violet, black and gold 15 5
294 1s. blue-grey, black and gold 40 70

Design: *Vert*—1s. Maltese under bombardment.

86 Shipwreck of St. Paul (after Palombi)

87 Statue of St. Paul, Rabat, Malta

(Des E. Cremona. Photo Harrison)

1960 (9 Feb). *19th Centenary of the Shipwreck of St. Paul. T* **86/7** *and similar designs. W* w **12**. *P* 13 (*1½d., 3d., 6d.*) *or* 14 × 14½ (*others*).
295 1½d. blue, gold and yellow-brown 20 5
a. Gold (dates and crosses) omitted . . 55·00
296 3d. bright purple, gold and blue 25 5
297 6d. carmine, gold and pale grey 40 10
298 8d. black and gold 60 70
299 1s. maroon and gold 60 25
300 2s. 6d. blue, deep bluish green and gold . . 3·75 4·00
a. Gold omitted £140
295/300 . . . . *Set of* 6 5·00 4·75

Designs: *Vert as T* **86**—3d. Consecration of St. Publius (first Bishop of Malta) (after Palombi); 6d. Departure of St. Paul (after Palombi). *Diamond shaped as T* **87**—1s. Angel with *Acts of the Apostles*; 2s. 6d. St. Paul with *Second Epistle to the Corinthians.*

92 Stamp of 1860

(Centre litho; frame recess. Waterlow)

1960 (1 Dec). *Stamp Centenary. W* w **12**. *P* 13½.
301 **92** 1½d. buff, pale blue and green (*shades*) 10 5
302 3d. buff, pale blue and deep carmine 15 5
303 6d. buff, pale blue and ultramarine . . 35 65

93 George Cross

(Photo Harrison)

1961 (15 Apr). *George Cross Commemoration. T* **93** *and similar designs showing medal. W* w **12**. *P* 15 × 14.

304		1½d. black, cream and bistre	15	10
305		3d. olive-brown and greenish blue.. ..	25	5
306		1s. olive-green, lilac & dp reddish violet ..	60	1·25

96 "Madonna Damascena"

(Photo Harrison)

1962 (7 Sept). *Great Siege Commemoration. T* **96** *and similar vert designs. W* w **12**. *P* 13 × 12.

307		2d. bright blue	8	5
308		3d. red	8	5
309		6d. bronze-green	20	15
310		1s. brown-purple	40	40

Designs:—3d. Great Siege Monument; 6d. Grand Master La Valette; 1s. Assault on Fort St. Elmo.

1963 (4 June). *Freedom from Hunger. As No.* 76 *of Aden.*

311		1s. 6d. sepia	5·00	2·75

1963 (2 Sept). *Red Cross Centenary. As No.* 147/8 *of Antigua.*

312		2d. red and black	25	12
313		1s. 6d. red and blue	3·75	3·75

1963 (15 Oct)–**64**. *As Nos.* 268 *and* 270, *but wmk* w **12**.

314	**59**	1d. black	40	30
315	**61**	2d. deep brown (11.7.64*)	1·00	1·00

*This is the earliest known date recorded in Malta.

100 Bruce, Zammit and Microscope

101 Goat and Laboratory Equipment

(Des E. Cremona. Photo Harrison)

1964 (14 April). *Anti-Brucellosis Congress. W* w **12**. *P* 14.

316	**100**	2d. light brown, black and bluish green	12	5
		a. Black omitted	£180	
317	**101**	1s. 6d. black and maroon	80	55

102 "Nicola Cotoner tending Sick Man" (M. Preti)

105 Maltese Cross (*Upright*)

In this illustration the points of the crosses meet in a vertical line. When the watermark is sideways they meet in a horizontal line.

(Des E. Cremona. Photo Harrison)

1964 (5 Sept). *First European Catholic Doctors' Congress, Vienna. T* **102** *and similar horiz designs. W* **105** *(sideways). P* 13½ × 11½.

318		2d. red, black, gold and grey-blue	20	10
319		6d. red, black, gold and bistre	60	40
320		1s. 6d. red, black, gold and reddish violet ..	1·50	1·25

Designs:—6d. St. Luke and Hospital; 1s. 6d. Sacra Infermeria, Valletta.

INDEPENDENT

106 Dove and British Crown

109 "The Nativity"

(Des E. Cremona. Photo Harrison)

1964 (21 Sept). *Independence. T* **106** *and similar vert designs. W* **105**. *P* 14½ × 13½.

321		2d. olive-brown, red and gold	30	5
322		3d. brown-purple, red and gold	30	5
323		6d. slate, red and gold	70	20
324		1s. blue, red and gold	1·00	35
325		1s. 6d. indigo, red and gold	5·00	3·50
326		2s. 6d. deep violet-blue, red and gold ..	5·50	6·00
321/6		.. .. *Set of* 6	12·00	9·00

Designs:—2d., 1s. Type **106**; 3d., 1s. 6d. Dove and Pope's Tiara; 6d., 2s. 6d. Dove and U.N. emblem.

(Des E. Cremona. Photo D.L.R.)

1964 (3 Nov). *Christmas. W* **105** *(sideways). P* 13 × 13½.

327	**109**	2d. bright purple and gold	20	5
328		4d. bright blue and gold	40	20
329		8d. deep bluish green and gold ..	80	1·10

110 Neolithic Era

117 Maltese Navy

119 British Rule

(Des E. Cremona. Photo Harrison)

1965 (7 Jan)–**70**. *Chalk-surfaced paper. T* **110**, **117**, **119** *and similar designs. W* **105**. *P* 14 × 14½ *(vert) or* 14½ *(horiz).*

330		½d. multicoloured	5	5
		a. "½d" (white) printed twice†		
331		1d. multicoloured	5	5
		a. Gold (ancient lettering) omitted ..	35·00	
332		1½d. multicoloured	8	8
333		2d. multicoloured	8	5
334		2½d. multicoloured	12	5
		a. Orange omitted*	35·00	
335		3d. multicoloured	10	5
		a. Gold (windows) omitted..	25·00	
		b. "MALTA" (silver) omitted	30·00	
		c. Imperf (pair)	£275	
336		4d. multicoloured	12	5
		a. "KNIGHTS OF MALTA" (silver) omitted	30·00	
337		4½d. multicoloured	25	20
337*a*		5d. multicoloured (1.8.70)	35	20
		b. "FORTIFICATIONS" (gold) omitted ..	42·00	
338		6d. multicoloured	20	5
		a. "MALTA" (silver) omitted	38·00	
339		8d. multicoloured	20	5
		a. Gold (centre) omitted	25·00	
		b. Gold (frame) omitted	28·00	
339*c*		10d. multicoloured (1.8.70)	60	50
340		1s. multicoloured	30	5
		a. Gold (centre) omitted	30·00	
		b. Gold (framework) omitted	35·00	
341		1s. 3d. multicoloured	75	1·00
		a. Gold (centre) omitted	38·00	
		b. Gold (framework) omitted	38·00	
		c. Imperf (pair)	£300	
342		1s. 6d. multicoloured	50	12
		a. Head (black) omitted	£180	
		b. Gold (centre) omitted	32·00	
		c. Gold (frame) omitted	32·00	
343		2s. multicoloured	75	15
		a. Gold (centre) omitted	38·00	
		b. Gold (framework) omitted	38·00	
344		2s. 6d. multicoloured	85	80
345		3s. multicoloured	1·00	1·25
		a. Gold (framework) omitted	27·00	
346		5s. multicoloured	3·00	1·75
		a. Gold (framework) omitted	40·00	
347		10s. multicoloured	4·00	3·25
		a. Gold (centre) omitted	50·00	
348		£1 multicoloured	4·75	7·00
330/48		.. .. *Set of* 21	16·00	15·00

Designs: *Vert*—1d. Punic era; 1½d. Roman era; 2d. Proto Christian era; 2½d. Saracenic era; 3d. Siculo Norman era; 4d. Knights of Malta; 5d. Fortifications; 6d. French occupation. *Horiz*—10d. Naval arsenal; 1s. Maltese corps of the British army; 1s. 3d. International Eucharistic congress, 1913; 1s. 6d. Self-government, 1921; 2s. Gozo civic council; 2s. 6d. State of Malta; 3s. Independence, 1964; 5s. HAFMED (Allied forces, Mediterranean); 10s. The Maltese Islands (map); £1 Patron saints.

*The effect of this is to leave the Saracenic pattern as a pink colour.

†Second impression is 6½ mm lower or 3 mm to the left, stamps with almost coincidental double impression are common.

The ½d. and 1d. had white printing plates. Two silver plates were used on the 4d., one for "KNIGHTS OF MALTA" and the other for "MALTA". Two gold plates were used for the 8d. to 10s., one for the framework and the other for the gold in the central part of the designs.

The ½d. to 4d., 1s. and 1s. 6d. to 5s. values exist with PVA gum as well as gum arabic and the 5d. and 10d. have PVA gum only.

129 "Dante" (Raphael)

(Des E. Cremona. Photo Govt Ptg Works, Rome)

1965 (7 July). *700th Birth Anniv of Dante. P* 14.

349	**129**	2d. indigo	10	5
350		6d. bronze-green	20	10
351		2s. chocolate	80	1·00

130 Turkish Camp

131 Turkish Armada

(Des E. Cremona. Photo Harrison)

1965 (1 Sept). *400th Anniv of Great Siege. T* **130/1** *and similar designs. W* **105** *(sideways). P* 13 *(6d., 1s.) or* 14½ × 14 *(others).*

352		2d. olive-green, red and black	25	5
353		3d. olive-green, red, black and light drab ..	25	5
354		6d. multicoloured	50	15
		a. Gold (framework and dates) omitted ..	£140	
355		8d. red, gold, indigo and blue	1·00	1·25
356		1s. red, gold and deep grey-blue	1·00	30
357		1s. 6d. ochre, red and black	2·25	1·00
358		2s. 6d. sepia, black, red and yellow-olive ..	4·25	4·75
352/8		.. .. *Set of* 7	8·50	7·00

Designs: *Square (as T* **130**)—3d. Battle scene; 8d. Arrival of relief force; 1s. 6d. "Allegory of Victory" (from mural by M. Preti); 2s. 6d. Victory medal. *Vert (as T* **131**)—1s. Grand Master J. de La Valette's arms.

137 "The Three Kings"

138 Sir Winston Churchill

(Des E. Cremona. Photo Enschedé)

1965 (7 Oct). *Christmas. W* **105** *(sideways). P* 11 × 11½.

359	**137**	1d. slate-purple and red	5	5
360		4d. slate-purple and blue	90	70
361		1s. 3d. slate-purple and bright purple	90	90

(Des E. Cremona. Photo Harrison)

1966 (24 Jan). *Churchill Commemoration. T* **138** *and similar square design. W* **105** *(sideways). P* 14½ × 14.

362	**138**	2d. black, red and gold..	15	5
363	–	3d. bronze-green, yellow-olive and gold	20	5
364	**138**	1s. maroon, red and gold	25	15
365	–	1s. 6d. chalky blue, violet-blue and gold	50	45

Design:—3d., 1s. 6d. Sir Winston Churchill and George Cross.

140 Grand Master La Valette

145 President Kennedy and Memorial

(Des E. Cremona. Photo State Ptg Works, Vienna)

1966 (28 Mar). *400th Anniv of Valletta. T* **140** *and similar square designs. Multicoloured. W* **105** *(sideways). P* 12.

366		2d. Type **140**	5	5
367		3d. Pope Pius V	5	5
		a. Gold omitted		
368		6d. Map of Valletta	15	10
369		1s. Francesco Laparelli (architect)	15	15
370		2s. 6d. Girolamo Cassar (architect)	40	70

(Des E. Cremona. Photo Harrison)

1966 (28 May). *President Kennedy Commemoration. W* **105** *(sideways). P* 15 × 14.

No.	Type	Description	Unused	Used
371	**145**	3d. olive, gold and black	10	5
		a. Gold inscr omitted	50·00	
372		1s. 6d. Prussian blue, gold and black	20	35

146 "Trade"

(Des E. Cremona. Photo D.L.R.)

1966 (16 June). *Tenth Malta Trade Fair. W* **105** *(sideways). P* 13½.

No.	Type	Description	Unused	Used
373	**146**	2d. multicoloured	8	5
374		8d. multicoloured	35	35
375		2s. 6d. multicoloured	45	60

147 "The Child in the Manger" **148** George Cross

(Des E. Cremona. Photo D.L.R.)

1966 (7 Oct). *Christmas. W* **105**. *P* 13½.

No.	Type	Description	Unused	Used
376	**147**	1d. black, gold, turquoise-bl & slate-pur	5	5
377		4d. black, gold, ultramarine & slate-pur	8	5
378		1s. 3d. black, gold, brt pur & slate-pur	12	15
		a. Gold omitted	28·00	

(Des E. Cremona. Photo Harrison)

1967 (1 Mar). *25th Anniv of George Cross Award to Malta. W* **105** *(sideways). P* 14½ × 14.

No.	Type	Description	Unused	Used
379	**148**	2d. multicoloured	5	5
380		4d. multicoloured	5	5
381		3s. multicoloured	20	30

149 Crucifixion of St. Peter

150 Open Bible and Episcopal Emblems

(Des E. Cremona. Photo Harrison)

1967 (28 June). *1900th Anniv of Martyrdom of Saints Peter and Paul. T* **149/50** *and similar design. W* **105** *(sideways). P* 13½ × 14½ *(8d.) or* 14½ *(others).*

No.	Type	Description	Unused	Used
382		2d. chestnut, orange and black	5	5
383		8d. yellow-olive, gold and black	15	15
384		3s. blue, light blue and black	15	20

Design:—*Square as T* **149**—3s. Beheading of St. Paul.

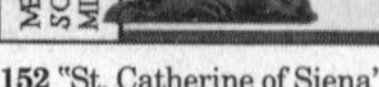

152 "St. Catherine of Siena" **156** Temple Ruins, Tarxien

(Des E. Cremona. Photo Enschedé)

1967 (1 Aug). *300th Death Anniv of Melchior Gafa (sculptor). T* **152** *and similar horiz designs. Multicoloured. W* **105** *(sideways). P* 13½ × 13.

No.	Type	Description	Unused	Used
385		2d. Type **152**	5	5
386		4d. "St. Thomas of Villanova"	8	5
387		1s. 6d. "Baptism of Christ" (detail) ..	12	15
388		2s. 6d. "St. John the Baptist" (from "Baptism of Christ")	15	20

(Des E. Cremona. Photo Harrison)

1967 (12 Sept). *15th International Historical Architecture Congress, Valletta. T* **156** *and similar square designs. Multicoloured. W* **105**. *P* 15 × 14½.

No.	Type	Description	Unused	Used
389		2d. Type **156**	5	5
390		6d. Facade of Palazzo Falzon, Notabile	10	10
391		1s. Parish Church, Birkirkara	10	10
392		3s. Portal, Auberge de Castille	25	25

160 "Angels" **161** "Crib" **162** "Angels"

(Des E. Cremona. Photo D.L.R.)

1967 (20 Oct). *Christmas. W* **105** *(sideways). P* 14.

No.	Type	Description	Unused	Used
393	**160**	1d. multicoloured	5	5
		a. In triptych with Nos. 394/5 ..	20	20
		b. White stars (red omitted)	55·00	
394	**161**	8d. multicoloured	8	8
395	**162**	1s. 4d. multicoloured	10	10

Nos. 393/5 were issued in sheets of 60 of each value (arranged *tête-bêche*), and also in sheets containing the three values *se-tenant*, thus forming a triptych of the Nativity.

163 Queen Elizabeth II and Arms of Malta

(Des E. Cremona. Photo Harrison)

1967 (13 Nov). *Royal Visit. T* **163** *and similar designs. W* **105** *(sideways on 2d., 3s.). P* 14 × 15 *(4d.) or* 15 × 14 *(others).*

No.	Type	Description	Unused	Used
396		2d. multicoloured	5	5
397		4d. black, brown-purple and gold ..	10	5
398		3s. multicoloured	20	30

Designs: *Vert*—4d. Queen in Robes of Order of St. Michael and St. George. *Horiz*—3s. Queen and outline of Malta.

166 Human Rights Emblem and People **167**

(Des E. Cremona. Photo Harrison)

1968 (2 May). *Human Rights Year. W* **105**. *P* 12½ *(6d.) or* 14½ *(others).*

No.	Type	Description	Unused	Used
399	**166**	2d. multicoloured	5	5
400	**167**	6d. multicoloured	5	5
401	–	2s. multicoloured	15	15

The design of the 2s. value is a reverse of Type **166**.

169 Fair "Products"

(Des E. Cremona. Photo Harrison)

1968 (1 June). *Malta International Trade Fair. W* **105** *(sideways). P* 14½ × 14.

No.	Type	Description	Unused	Used
402	**169**	4d. multicoloured	8	5
403		8d. multicoloured	15	15
404		3s. multicoloured	20	30

170 Arms of the Order of St. John and La Valette **171** "La Valette" (A. de Favray)

172 La Valette's Tomb **173** Angels and Scroll bearing Date of Death

(Des E. Cremona. Photo Govt Printer, Israel)

1968 (1 Aug). *Fourth Death Centenary of Grand Master La Valette. W* **105** *(upright, 1s. 6d.; sideways, others). P* 13 × 14 *(1d., 1s. 6d.) or* 14 × 13 *(others).*

No.	Type	Description	Unused	Used
405	**170**	1d. multicoloured	5	5
406	**171**	8d. multicoloured	15	15
407	**172**	1s. 6d. multicoloured	15	15
408	**173**	2s. 6d. multicoloured	15	25

174 Star of Bethlehem and Angel waking Shepherds **177** "Agriculture"

(Des E. Cremona. Photo Harrison)

1968 (3 Oct). *Christmas. T* **174** *and similar shaped designs. Multicoloured. W* **105** *(sideways). P* 14½ × 14.

No.	Type	Description	Unused	Used
409		1d. Type **174**	5	5
410		8d. Mary and Joseph with shepherd watching over cradle	10	10
411		1s. 4d. Three Wise Men and Star of Bethlehem	15	20

The shortest side at top and the long side at the bottom both gauge 14½, the other three sides are 14. Nos. 409/11 were issued in sheets of 60 arranged in ten strips of six, alternately upright and inverted.

(Des E. Cremona. Photo Enschedé)

1968 (21 Oct). *Sixth Food and Agricultural Organization Regional Conference for Europe. T* **177** *and similar vert designs. Multicoloured. W* **105** *(sideways). P* 12½ × 12.

No.	Type	Description	Unused	Used
412		4d. Type **177**	8	5
413		1s. F.A.O. emblem and coin	12	15
414		2s. 6d. "Agriculture" sowing seeds	20	35

180 Mahatma Gandhi **181** I.L.O. Emblem

(Des E. Cremona. Photo Enschedé)

1969 (24 Mar). *Birth Centenary of Mahatma Gandhi. W* **105**. *P* 12 × 12½.

No.	Type	Description	Unused	Used
415	**180**	1s. 6d. blackish brown, black and gold	25	10

(Des E. Cremona. Photo Harrison)

1969 (26 May). *50th Anniv of International Labour Organization. W* **105** *(sideways). P* 13½ × 14½.

No.	Type	Description	Unused	Used
416	**181**	2d. indigo, gold and turquoise	5	5
417		6d. sepia, gold and chestnut	5	5

182 Robert Samut

(Des E. Cremona. Photo D.L.R.)

1969 (26 July). *Birth Centenary of Robert Samut (composer of Maltese National Anthem). W* **105** *(sideways). P* 13.

No.	Type	Description	Unused	Used
418	**182**	2d. multicoloured	12	5

NEW INFORMATION

The editor is always interested to correspond with people who have new information that will improve or correct the Catalogue.

183 Dove of Peace, U.N. Emblem and Sea-Bed

(Des E. Cremona. Photo D.L.R.)

1969 (26 July). *United Nations Resolution on Oceanic Resources. W* **105** *(sideways). P* 13.
419 **183** 5d. multicoloured .. 12 5

184 "Swallows" returning to Malta

(Des E. Cremona. Photo D.L.R.)

1969 (26 July). *Maltese Migrants' Convention. W* **105** *(sideways). P* 13.
420 **184** 10d. black, gold and yellow-olive .. 12 5

185 University Arms and Grand Master de Fonseca (founder)

(Des E. Cremona. Photo D.L.R.)

1969 (26 July). *Bicentenary of University of Malta. W* **105** *(sideways). P* 13.
421 **185** 2s. multicoloured .. 15 30

186 1919 Monument

187 Flag of Malta and Birds

(Des E. Cremona. Photo Enschedé)

1969 (20 Sept). *Fifth Anniv of Independence. T* **186/7** *and similar designs. W* **105** *(upright on 5d., sideways others). P* 13½ × 12½ *(2d.),* 12 × 12½ *(5d.), or* 12½ × 12 *(others).*
422 2d. multicoloured .. 8 5
423 5d. black, red and gold .. 8 5
424 10d. black, turquoise-blue and gold .. 15 15
425 1s. 6d. multicoloured .. 15 30
426 2s. 6d. black, olive-brown and gold .. 25 50
Designs:—*Vert as T* **187**—10d. "Tourism"; 1s. 6d. U.N. and Council of Europe emblems; 2s. 6d. "Trade and Industry".

191 Peasants playing Tambourine and Bagpipes

(Des E. Cremona. Litho D.L.R.)

1969 (8 Nov). *Christmas. Children's Welfare Fund. T* **191** *and similar horiz designs. Multicoloured. W* **105** *(sideways). P* 12½.
427 1d. + 1d. Type **191** .. 5 5
a. In triptych with Nos. 428/9 .. 25 30
428 5d. + 1d. Angels playing trumpet and harp .. 8 10
429 1s. 6d. + 3d. Choir boys singing .. 12 15
Nos. 427/9 were issued in sheets of 60 of each value, and also in sheets containing the three values *se-tenant*, thus forming the triptych No. 427a.

194 "The Beheading of St. John" (Caravaggio)

(Des E. Cremona. Photo Enschedé)

1970 (21 Mar). *13th Council of Europe Art Exhibition. T* **194** *and similar multicoloured designs. W* **105** *(upright, 10d., 2s.; sideways, others). P* 14 × 13 *(1d., 8d.),* 12 *(10d., 2s.) or* 13 × 13½ *(others).*
430 1d. Type **194** .. 5 5
431 2d. "St. John the Baptist" (M. Preti) (45 × 32 *mm*) .. 5 5
432 5d. Interior of St. John's Co-Cathedral, Valletta (39 × 39 *mm*) .. 8 5
433 6d. "Allegory of the Order" (Neapolitan School) (45 × 32 *mm*) .. 10 8
434 8d. "St. Jerome" (Caravaggio) .. 15 30
435 10d. Articles from the Order of St. John in Malta (63 × 21 *mm*) .. 15 15
436 1s. 6d. "The Blessed Gerard receiving Godfrey de Bouillon" (A. de Favray) (45 × 35 *mm*) .. 25 50
437 2s. Cape and Stolone (16th-century) (63 × 21 *mm*) .. 30 65
430/37 .. *Set of* 8 1·00 1·60

202 Artist's Impression of Fujiyama

(Des E. Cremona. Photo D.L.R.)

1970 (29 May). *World Fair, Osaka. W* **105** *(sideways). P* 15.
438 **202** 2d. multicoloured .. 5 5
439 5d. multicoloured .. 8 5
440 3s. multicoloured .. 30 50

203 "Peace and Justice"

204 Carol-Singers, Church and Star

(Des J. Casha. Litho Harrison)

1970 (30 Sept). *25th Anniv of United Nations. W* **105**. *P* 14 × 14½.
441 **203** 2d. multicoloured .. 5 5
442 5d. multicoloured .. 10 5
443 2s. 6d. multicoloured .. 25 50

(Des E. Cremona. Photo Govt Printer, Israel)

1970 (7 Nov). *Christmas. T* **204** *and similar vert designs. Multicoloured. W* **105** *(sideways). P* 14 × 13.
444 1d. + ½d. Type **204** .. 5 5
445 10d. + 2d. Church, star and angels with Infant 25 40
446 1s. 6d. + 3d. Church, star and nativity scene 25 45

207 Books and Quill

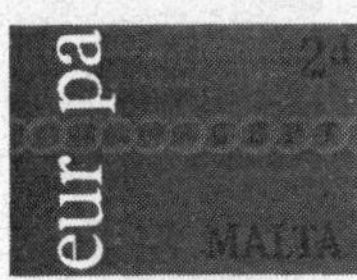

208 Dun Karm, Books, Pens and Lamp

(Des H. Alden (1s. 6d.), A. Agius (2s.). Litho D.L.R.)

1971 (20 Mar). *Literary Anniversaries. Death Bicentenary* (1970) *of De Soldanis (historian)* (1s. 6d.) *and Birth Centenary of Dun Karm (poet)* (2s.). *W* **105** *(sideways). P* 13 × 13½.
447 **207** 1s. 6d. multicoloured .. 20 30
448 **208** 2s. multicoloured .. 25 45

209 Europa "Chain"

(Des H. Haflidason; adapted E. Cremona. Litho Harrison)

1971 (3 May). *Europa. W* **105** *(sideways). P* 13½ × 14½.
449 **209** 2d. orange, black and yellow-olive .. 12 5
450 5d. orange, black and vermilion .. 15 5
451 1s. 6d. orange, black and slate .. 45 65

210 "St. Joseph, Patron of the Universal Church" (G. Cali)

211 *Centaurea spathulata*

(Des E. Cremona. Litho D.L.R.)

1971 (24 July). *Centenary of Proclamation of St. Joseph as Patron Saint of Catholic Church, and 50th Anniv of the Coronation of the Statue of "Our Lady of Victories". T* **210** *and similar horiz design. Multicoloured. W* **105** *(sideways). P* 13 × 13½.
452 2d. Type **210** .. 5 5
453 5d. Statue of "Our Lady of Victories" and galley .. 5 5
454 10d. Type **210** .. 20 20
455 1s. 6d. As 5d. .. 45 70

(Des Reno Psaila. Litho Harrison)

1971 (18 Sept). *National Plant and Bird of Malta. T* **211** *and similar horiz design. Multicoloured. W* **105** *(sideways on 5d. and 10d.). P* 14½ × 14.
456 2d. Type **211** .. 5 5
457 5d. Blue Rock Thrush .. 10 5
458 10d. As 5d. .. 25 10
459 1s. 6d. Type **211** .. 35 75

212 Angel

(Des E. Cremona. Litho Format)

1971 (8 Nov). *Christmas. T* **212** *and similar horiz designs. Multicoloured. W* **105** *(sideways). P* 13½ × 14.
460 1d. + ½d. Type **212** .. 5 5
461 10d. + 2d. Mary and the Child Jesus .. 30 45
462 1s. 6d. + 3d. Joseph lying awake .. 50 75
MS463 131 × 113 mm. Nos. 460/2. P 15 .. 1·00 1·50

213 Heart and W.H.O. Emblem

214 Maltese Cross

(Des A. Agius. Litho Format)

1972 (20 Mar). *World Health Day. W* **105**. *P* 13½ × 14.
464 **213** 2d. multicoloured .. 5 5
465 10d. multicoloured .. 15 20
466 2s. 6d. multicoloured .. 70 1·25

(New Currency. 10 mils = 1 cent; 100 cents = 1 Maltese pound)

(Des G. Pace. Litho Format)

1972 (16 May). *Decimal Currency. T* **214** *and similar vert designs showing decimal coins. Multicoloured. W* **105**. *P* 14 *(2 m., 3 m., 2 c.),* 14½ × 14 *(5 m., 1 c., 5 c.) or* 13½ *(10 c., 50 c.).*
467 2 m. Type **214** .. 5 5
468 3 m. Bee on honeycomb .. 5 5
469 5 m. Earthen lampstand .. 5 5
470 1 c. George Cross .. 8 5
471 2 c. Classical head .. 10 5
472 5 c. Ritual altar .. 20 5
473 10 c. Grandmaster's galley .. 40 10
474 50 c. Great Siege Monument .. 1·40 2·50
467/74 .. *Set of* 8 2·00 2·75
Sizes:—2 m., 3 m. and 2 c. as T **214**; 5 m., 1 c. and 5 c. 22 × 27 mm; 10 c. and 50 c. 27 × 35 mm.

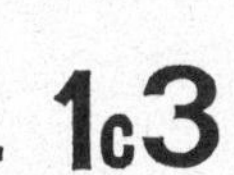

(**215**)

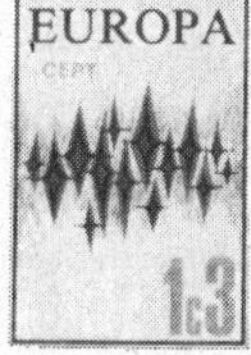

216 "Communications"

1972 (30 Sept). *Nos.* 337*a*, 339 *and* 341 *surch as T* **215**, *by Govt. Printing Works, Valletta.*
475 1 c. 3 on 5d. multicoloured .. 10 8
476 3 c. on 8d. multicoloured .. 10 10
a. Surch inverted .. 45·00
b. Gold (frame) omitted .. 55·00
477 5 c. on 1s. 3d. multicoloured .. 12 20
a. Surch double .. 50·00
b. Surch inverted .. 25·00
c. Gold (centre) omitted .. 35·00

PRINTERS. All stamps from No. 478 onwards were printed in lithography by Printex Ltd, Malta.

(Des P. Huovinen; adapted G. Pace)

1972 (11 Nov). *Europa. W* **105** *(sideways). P* 13.
478 **216** 1 c. 3, multicoloured .. 8 5
479 3 c. multicoloured .. 12 5
480 5 c. multicoloured .. 25 25
481 7 c. 5, multicoloured .. 30 65

217 Angel

(Des E. Cremona)

1972 (9 Dec). *Christmas. T* **217** *and similar horiz designs. W* **105** *(sideways). P* 13½.

482 8 m. + 2 m. dull sepia, brownish grey and gold .. 5 5
483 3 c. + 1 c. plum, lavender and gold 30 45
484 7 c. 5 + 1 c. 5, indigo, azure and gold .. 40 60
MS485 137 × 113 mm. Nos. 482/4 . .. .. 1·75 2·50

Designs:—No. 483, Angel with tambourine; No. 484, Singing angel.

See also Nos. 507/10.

218 Archaeology

219 Europa "Posthorn"

(Des E. Cremona)

1973 (31 Mar)–**76.** *T* **218** *and similar designs. Multicoloured. W* **105** *(sideways). P* 13½ × 14 *(Nos.* 500/*a) or* 13½ *(others).*

486 2 m. Type **218** 5 5
487 4 m. History 5 5
a. Gold (inscr and decoration) omitted .. 75·00
b. Imperf (pair) £325
488 5 m. Folklore 5 5
489 8 m. Industry 5 5
490 1 c. Fishing industry 10 5
491 1 c. 3, Pottery.. .. .. 10 5
492 2 c. Agriculture 10 5
493 3 c. Sport 12 5
494 4 c. Yacht Marina 15 10
495 5 c. Fiesta 15 5
496 7 c. 5, Regatta 30 10
497 10 c. Voluntary service 30 10
498 50 c. Education .. .. 1·25 1·40
499 £1 Religion .. .. 2·40 2·50
500 £2 Coat of arms *(horiz)* .. .. 15·00 15·00
a. Gold omitted .. ..
500*b* £2 National Emblem *(horiz)* (28.1.76) .. 9·00 9·00
486/500*b* .. .. *Set of* 16 26·00 26·00

Nos. 500/*b* are larger, 32 × 27 mm.

(Des L. Anisdahl; adapted G. Pace)

1973 (2 June). *Europa. W* **105**. *P* 14.

501 **219** 3 c. multicoloured 20 12
502 5 c. multicoloured 30 35
503 7 c. 5, multicoloured 35 65

220 Emblem, and Woman holding Corn

221 Girolamo Cassar (architect)

(Des H. Alden)

1973 (6 Oct). *Anniversaries. T* **220** *and similar vert designs showing emblem and allegorical figures. W* **105** *(sideways). P* 13½.

504 1 c. 3, multicoloured 5 5
505 7 c. 5, multicoloured 40 65
506 10 c. multicoloured 50 70

Anniversaries:—1 c. 3, Tenth Anniv of World Food Programme; 7 c. 5, 25th Anniv of W.H.O.; 10 c. 25th Anniv of Universal Declaration of Human Rights.

(Des E. Cremona)

1973 (10 Nov). *Christmas. Horiz designs as T* **217**. *Multicoloured. W* **105** *(sideways). P* 13½.

507 8 m. + 2 m. Angels and organ pipes 15 10
508 3 c. + 1 c. Madonna and Child 50 65
509 7 c. 5 + 1 c. 5, Buildings and Star .. .. 70 1·10
MS510 137 × 112 mm. Nos. 507/9 .. .. 3·00 3·50

(Des E. Cremona)

1974 (12 Jan). *Prominent Maltese. T* **221** *and similar vert designs. W* **105**. *P* 14.

511 1 c. 3, dull myrtle-grn, dull grey-grn & gold .. 10 5
512 3 c. deep turquoise, grey-blue and gold .. 15 5
513 5 c. dull sepia, deep slate-green and gold .. 25 25
514 7 c. 5, slate-blue, light slate-blue and gold .. 30 65
515 10 c. purple, dull purple and gold 50 75

Designs:—3 c. Giuseppe Barth (ophthalmologist); 5 c. Nicolo' Isouard (composer); 7 c. 5, John Borg (botanist); 10 c. Antonio Sciortino (sculptor).

222 "Air Malta" Emblem

(Des E. Cremona)

1974 (30 Mar). *Air. T* **222** *and similar horiz design. Multicoloured. W* **105** *(sideways). P* 13½.

516 3 c. Type **222** 12 5
517 4 c. Boeing "707" 15 5
518 5 c. Type **222** 20 5
519 7 c. 5, As 4 c. 30 5
520 20 c. Type **222** 80 90
521 25 c. As 4 c. 80 90
522 35 c. Type **222** .. .. 1·50 2·00
516/22 .. .. *Set of* 7 3·50 3·50

223 Prehistoric Sculpture

(Des E. Cremona)

1974 (13 July). *Europa. T* **223** *and similar designs. W* **105** *(sideways on Nos.* 523 *and* 525). *P* 13½.

523 1 c. 3, slate-blue, grey-black and gold .. 10 10
524 3 c. light bistre-brown, grey-black and gold 20 20
525 5 c. purple, grey-black and gold .. 35 40
526 7 c. 5, dull green, grey-black and gold .. 55 80

Designs: *Vert*—3 c. Old Cathedral Door, Mdina; 7 c. 5, "Vetlina" (sculpture by A. Sciortino). *Horiz*—5 c. Silver Monstrance.

224 Heinrich von Stephan (founder) and Land Transport

225 Decorative Star and Nativity Scene

(Des S. and G. Sullivan)

1974 (20 Sept). *Centenary of Universal Postal Union. T* **224** *and similar horiz designs. W* **105**. *P* 13½ × 14.

527 1 c. 3, blue-green, lt violet-blue & yell-orge .. 10 5
528 5 c. brown, dull vermilion and yellow-green 25 10
529 7 c. 5, dp dull blue, lt violet-blue & yell-grn .. 35 30
530 50 c. purple, dull vermilion and yellow-orange 1·50 2·50
MS531 126 × 91 mm. Nos. 527/30 .. .. 2·50 3·75

Designs (each containing portrait as T **224**):—5 c. S. S. *Washington* and modern liner; 7 c. 5, Balloon and Boeing "747"; 50 c. U.P.U. Buildings, 1874 and 1974.

(Des E. Cremona)

1974 (22 Nov). *Christmas. T* **225** *and similar vert designs, each with decorative star. Multicoloured. W* **105** *(sideways). P* 14.

532 8 m. + 2 m. Type **225** 15 12
533 3 c. + 1 c. "Shepherds" 25 30
534 5 c. + 1 c. "Shepherds with gifts" 35 65
535 7 c. 5 + 1 c. 5, "The Magi" 45 70

REPUBLIC

226 Swearing-in of Prime Minister

(Des E. Cremona)

1975 (31 Mar). *Inauguration of Republic. T* **226** *and similar horiz designs. W* **105** *(sideways). P* 14.

536 1 c. 3, multicoloured 12 5
537 5 c. rose-red and grey-black 35 20
538 25 c. multicoloured .. .. 1·60 2·50

Designs:—5 c. National flag; 25 c. Minister of Justice, President and Prime Minister.

227 Mother and Child ("Family Life")

(Des D. Friggieri)

1975 (30 May). *International Women's Year. T* **227** *and similar horiz design. W* **105**. *P* 13½ × 14.

539 **227** 1 c. 3, light violet and gold 35 5
540 – 3 c. light blue and gold 60 15
541 **227** 5 c. dull olive-sepia and gold .. .. 1·25 30
542 – 20 c. chestnut and gold .. .. .. 5·50 6·50

Design:—3 c., 20 c. Office secretary ("Public Life").

228 "Allegory of Malta" (Francesco de Mura)

(Des E. Cremona)

1975 (15 July). *Europa. T* **228** *and similar horiz design. Multicoloured. W* **105**. *P* 14 × 13½.

543 5 c. Type **228** 30 30
544 15 c. "Judith and Holofernes" (Valentin de Boulogne) .. .. 80 1·10

The 15 c. is a smaller design than the 5 c. (47 × 23 mm), though the perforated area is the same.

229 Plan of Ggantija Temple

(Des R. England)

1975 (16 Sept). *European Architectural Heritage Year. T* **229** *and similar horiz designs. W* **105** *(sideways). P* 13½.

545 1 c. 3, brownish black and light orange-red .. 10 5
546 3 c. dull purple, lt orange-red & blackish brn 30 20
547 5 c. blackish brown and light orange-red 60 60
548 25 c. dull grey-olive, light orange-red and brownish black .. .. 3·00 4·75

Designs:—3 c. Mdina skyline; 5 c. View of Victoria, Gozo; 25 c. Silhouette of Fort St. Angelo.

230 Farm Animals

231 "The Right to Work"

(Des E. Cremona)

1975 (4 Nov). *Christmas. T* **230** *and similar multicoloured designs. W* **105** *(sideways). P* 13½.

549 8 m. + 2 m. Type **230** 35 25
a. In triptych with Nos. 550/1 .. .. 5·50 6·50
550 3 c. + 1 c. Nativity scene (50 × 23 *mm*) .. 1·25 1·25
551 7 c. 5 + 1 c. 5, Approach of the Magi .. 1·50 1·75

Nos. 549/51 were issued in sheets of 50 of each value, and also in sheets containing the three values horizontally *se-tenant*, thus forming the triptych No. 549a which is a composite design of "The Nativity" by Master Alberto.

(Des A. de Giovanni)

1975 (12 Dec). *First Anniv of Republic. T* **231** *and similar vert designs. W* **105**. *P* 14.

552 1 c. 3, multicoloured 10 5
553 5 c. multicoloured 50 40
554 25 c. deep rose, light steel-blue and black .. 2·25 2·50

Designs:—5 c. "Safeguarding the Environment"; 25 c. National Flag.

232 "Festa Tar-Rahal"

233 Waterpolo

(Des M. Camilleri)

1976 (26 Feb). *Maltese Folklore. T* **232** *and similar multicoloured designs. W* **105** *(sideways on* 5 c. *and* 7 c. 5). *P* 14.

555 1 c. 3, Type **232** 15 8
556 5 c. "L-Imnarja" *(horiz)* 25 10
557 7 c. 5, "Il-Karnival" *(horiz)* .. .. .. 95 1·40
558 10 c. "Il-Gimgha L-Kbira" .. .. 1·40 1·75

(Des H. Alden)

1976 (28 Apr). *Olympic Games, Montreal. T* **233** *and similar horiz designs. Multicoloured. W* **105**. *P* 13½ × 14.

559 1 c. 7, Type **233** 10 5
560 5 c. Sailing 50 30
561 30 c. Athletics .. .. 2·25 3·00

234 Lace-making

(Des F. Portelli)

1976 (8 July). *Europa. T* **234** *and similar horiz design. Multicoloured. W* **105** *(sideways). P* 13½ × 14.

562 7 c. Type **234** 40 50
563 15 c. Stone carving 50 80

235 Nicola Cotoner

(Des E. Cremona)

1976 (14 Sept). 300*th Anniv of School of Anatomy and Surgery. T* **235** *and similar horiz designs. Multicoloured. W* **105** *(sideways). P* 13½.

564 2 c. Type **235** 5 5
565 5 c. Arm 12 5
566 7 c. Giuseppe Zammit 25 10
567 11 c. Sacra Infermeria.. .. .. 1·00 1·60

236 St. John the Baptist and St. Michael

237 Jean de la Valette's Armour

(**238**)

(Des E. Cremona)

1976 (23 Nov). *Christmas. Designs showing portions of "Madonna and Saints" by Domenico di Michelino. Multicoloured. W* **105** *(sideways on No.* 571). *P* 13½ × 14 *(No.* 571) *or* 13½ *(others).*

568 1 c. + 5 m. Type **236** .. 35 20
569 5 c. + 1 c. Madonna and Child .. 1·00 70
570 7 c. + 1 c. 5, St. Christopher and St. Nicholas 1·25 1·40
571 10 c. + 2 c. Complete painting (32 × 27 *mm*) .. 1·40 1·75

(Des J. Briffa)

1977 (20 Jan). *Suits of Armour. T* **237** *and similar vert designs. Multicoloured. W* **105.** *P* 13½.

572 2 c. Type **237** .. 15 5
573 7 c. Aloph de Wignacourt's armour .. 40 10
574 11 c. Jean Jacques de Verdelin's armour .. 55 90

1977 (24 Mar). *No.* 336 *surch with T* **238** *by Govt Printing Press, Malta.*

575 **116** 1 c. 7 on 4d. multicoloured .. 25 25
a. "KNIGHTS OF MALTA" (silver) omitted .. 65·00

239 "Annunciation"

240 Map and Radio Aerial

(Des E. Cremona)

1977 (30 Mar). *400th Birth Anniversary of Rubens. Flemish tapestries (1st series) showing his paintings as T* **239**. *Multicoloured. W* **105** *(sideways). P* 14.

576 2 c. Type **239** .. 10 5
577 7 c. "Four Evangelists" .. 30 5
578 11 c. "Nativity" .. 65 65
579 20 c. "Adoration of the Magi" .. 1·00 1·60

See also Nos. 592/5, 615/18 and 638/40.

(Des H. Borg)

1977 (17 May). *World Telecommunication Day. T* **240** *and similar design. W* **105** *(sideways on* 1 *and* 6 *c.). P* 14 × 13½ *(1 and 6 c.) or* 13½ × 14 *(others).*

580 **240** 1 c. black, green and vermilion .. 5 5
581 6 c. black, grey-blue and vermilion .. 20 15
582 – 8 c. black, chestnut and vermilion .. 30 30
583 – 17 c. black, dull mauve and vermilion .. 65 75

Design: *Horiz*—8 and 17 c. Map, aerial and aeroplane tail-fin.

241 Ta' L-Isperanza

242 "Aid to Handi-capped Workers" (detail from Workers' Monument)

(Des G. French)

1977 (5 July). *Europa. T* **241** *and similar horiz design. Multicoloured. W* **105** *(sideways). P* 13½.

584 7 c. Type **241** .. 40 15
585 20 c. Is-Salini .. 45 65

(Des A. Agius)

1977 (12 Oct). *Maltese Worker Commemoration. T* **242** *and similar designs. W* **105** *(sideways on* 20 *c.). P* 13½.

586 2 c. orange-brown and light brown .. 10 5
587 7 c. chestnut and brown .. 25 5
588 20 c. multicoloured .. 75 1·10

Designs: *Vert*—7 c. "Stoneworker, modern industry and ship-building" (monument detail). *Horiz*—20 c. "Mother with Dead Son" and Service Medal.

243 The Shepherds

244 "Young Lady on Horseback and Trooper"

(Des E. Cremona)

1977 (16 Nov). *Christmas. T* **243** *and similar horiz designs. Multicoloured. W* **105** *(sideways). P* 13½ × 14.

589 1 c. + 5 m. Type **243** .. 25 15
a. In triptych with Nos. 590/1 .. 1·25
590 7 c. + 1 c. The Nativity .. 35 40
591 11 c. + 1 c. 5, Flight into Egypt .. 50 55

Nos. 589/91 were issued in sheets of 50 of each value, and also in sheets containing the three values *se-tenant*, thus forming the triptych No. 589a.

(Des E. Cremona)

1978 (26 Jan). *Flemish Tapestries (2nd series). Horiz designs similar to T* **239**. *Multicoloured. W* **105** *(sideways). P* 14.

592 2 c. "The Entry into Jerusalem" (artist unknown) .. 10 5
593 7 c. "The Last Supper" (after Poussin) .. 25 12
594 11 c. "The Raising of the Cross" (after Rubens) 35 40
595 25 c. "The Resurrection" (after Rubens) .. 85 1·00

(Des A. Camilleri)

1978 (7 Mar). *450th Death Anniv of Albrecht Dürer. T* **244** *and similar vert designs. W* **105.** *P* 14.

596 1 c. 7, black, vermilion and deep blue .. 5 5
597 8 c. black, vermilion and slate .. 40 40
598 17 c. black, vermilion and deep slate .. 65 80

Designs:—8 c. "The Bag-piper"; 17 c. "The Virgin and Child with a Monkey".

245 Monument to Grand Master Nicola Cotoner (Foggini)

246 Goalkeeper

(Des E. Cremona)

1978 (26 Apr). *Europa. Monuments. T* **245** *and similar vert design. Multicoloured. W* **105.** *P* 14 × 13½.

599 7 c. Type **245** .. 20 5
600 25 c. Monument to Grand Master Ramon Perellos (Mazzuoli) .. 70 80

Nos. 599/600 were each printed in sheets including two *se-tenant* stamp-size labels.

(Des A. de Giovanni)

1978 (6 June). *World Cup Football Championship, Argentina. T* **246** *and similar vert designs. Multicoloured. W* **105** *(sideways). P* 14 × 13½.

601 2 c. Type **246** .. 10 5
602 11 c. Players heading ball .. 45 30
603 15 c. Tackling .. 65 75
MS604 125 × 90 mm. Nos. 601/3 .. 1·50 1·75

247 Airliner over Megalithic Temple

(Des R. Caruana)

1978 (3 Oct). *Air. Horiz designs as T* **247**. *Multicoloured. W* **105** *(sideways). P* 13½.

605 5 c. Type **247** .. 20 5
606 7 c. Air Malta Boeing "720B" .. 25 5
607 11 c. Boeing "747" taking off from Luqa Airport 35 5
608 17 c. Type **247** .. 55 45
609 20 c. As 7 c. .. 70 60
610 75 c. As 11 c. .. 2·50 2·25
605/10 .. *Set of* 6 4·00 3·00

248 Folk Musicians and Village Church

249 Fishing Boat and Aircraft Carrier

(Des E. Cremona)

1978 (9 Nov). *Christmas. T* **248** *and similar multicoloured designs. W* **105** *(sideways). P* 13½ *(11 c.) or* 14 *(others).*

611 1 c. + 5 m. Type **248** .. 10 10
612 5 c. + 1 c. Choir of Angels .. 25 30
613 7 c. + 1 c. 5, Carol singers .. 35 40
614 11 c. + 3 c. Folk musicians, church, angels and carol singers (58 × 23 *mm*) .. 40 60

The 1, 5 and 7 c. values depict details of the complete design shown on the 11 c. value.

(Des E. Cremona)

1979 (24 Jan). *Flemish Tapestries (3rd series). Horiz designs as T* **239** *showing paintings by Rubens. Multicoloured. W* **105** *(sideways). P* 14.

615 2 c. "The Triumph of the Catholic Church" .. 5 5
616 7 c. "The Triumph of Charity" .. 20 10
617 11 c. "The Triumph of Faith" .. 45 35
618 25 c. "The Triumph of Truth" .. 85 1·00

(Des E. Cremona)

1979 (31 Mar). *End of Military Facilities Agreement. T* **249** *and similar vert designs. Multicoloured. W* **105** *(sideways). P* 13½.

619 2 c. Type **249** .. 5 5
620 5 c. Raising the flag ceremony .. 12 5
621 7 c. Departing soldier and olive sprig .. 15 10
622 8 c. Type **249** .. 50 60
623 17 c. As 5 c. .. 70 80
624 20 c. As 7 c. .. 70 80
619/24 .. *Set of* 6 2·00 2·10

250 Speronara (small sailing vessel) and Tail of Air Malta Airliner

251 Children on Globe

(Des E. Cremona)

1979 (9 May). *Europa. Communications. T* **250** *and similar vert design. Multicoloured. W* **105** *(sideways). P* 14.

625 7 c. Type **250** .. 25 15
626 25 c. Coastal watch tower and radio link towers 75 75

(Des A. Bonnici (2 c.), A. Pisani (7 c.), M. French (11 c.))

1979 (13 June). *International Year of the Child. T* **251** *and similar multicoloured designs. W* **105** *(sideways). P* 14 × 13½ *(2 c.) or* 14 *(others).*

627 2 c. Type **251** .. 5 5
628 7 c. Children flying kites (27 × 33 *mm*) .. 25 5
629 11 c. Children in circle (27 × 33 *mm*). .. 40 55

252 Shells (*Gibbula nivosa*)

(Des R. Pitré)

1979 (10 Oct). *Marine Life. T* **252** *and similar horiz designs. Multicoloured. W* **105.** *P* 13½.

630 2 c. Type **252** .. 10 5
631 5 c. Loggerhead Turtle (*Garetta garetta*) .. 20 5
632 7 c. Dolphin Fish (*Coryphaena hippurus*) .. 30 5
633 25 c. Noble Pen Shell (*Pinna nobilis*) .. 1·00 1·25

253 "The Nativity" (detail)

(Des E. Cremona)

1979 (14 Nov). *Christmas. Paintings by G. Cali. T* **253** *and similar horiz designs. Multicoloured. W* **105.** *P* 14 × 13½.

634 1 c. + 5 m. Type **253** .. 5 5
635 5 c. + 1 c. "The Flight into Egypt" (detail) .. 20 20
636 7 c. + 1 c. 5, "The Nativity" .. 30 30
637 11 c. + 3 c. "The Flight into Egypt" .. 80 80

(Des E. Cremona)

1980 (30 Jan). *Flemish Tapestries (4th series). Horiz designs as T* **239** *taken from paintings. Multicoloured. W* **105** *(sideways). P* 14.

638 2 c. "The Institution of Corpus Domini" (Rubens) .. 15 10
639 8 c. "The Destruction of Idolatry" (Rubens) .. 35 40
MS640 114 × 86 mm. 50 c. "Grand Master Perellos with St. Jude and St. Simon" (unknown Maltese artist) (*vert*) .. 1·60 1·75

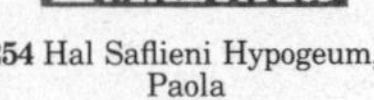

254 Hal Saflieni Hypogeum, Paola　　**255** Dun Gorg Preca

1980 (15 Feb). *International Restoration of Maltese Monuments Campaign. T* **254** *and similar multicoloured designs. W* **105** *(sideways on* 8 *and* 12 *c.). P* 14.

641　2 c. 5, Type **254** .. .. 10　8
642　6 c. Vilhena Palace, Mdina .. .. .. 25　15
643　8 c. Victoria Citadel, Gozo *(horiz)* .. .. 30　30
644　12 c. Fort St. Elmo, Valletta *(horiz)* .. .. 40　40

(Des R. Pitré)

1980 (12 Apr). *Birth Centenary of Dun Gorg Preca (founder of Society of Christian Doctrine). W* **105** *(sideways). P* 14 × 13½.

645　**255**　2 c. 5, black and grey .. .. .. 12　10

256 Ruzar Briffa (poet)　　**257** "Annunciation"

(Des V. Apap)

1980 (29 Apr). *Europa. Personalities. T* **256** *and similar horiz design. W* **105** *(sideways). P* 13½ × 14.

646　8 c. black, brown-ochre and bronze-green .. 40　30
647　30 c. brown, brown-olive and brown-lake .. 1·00　80

Designs:—30 c. Nikiol Anton Vassalli (scholar and patriot).

(Des R. Pitré)

1980 (7 Oct). *Christmas. Paintings by A. Inglott. T* **257** *and similar multicoloured designs. W* **105** *(sideways on* 12 *c.). P* 14 *(*12 *c.) or* 13½ *(others).*

648　2 c. + 5 m. Type **257** .. .. 10　5
649　6 c. + 1 c. "Conception" .. .. .. 25　20
650　8 c. + 1 c. 5, "Nativity" .. .. .. 30　35
651　12 c. + 3 c. "Annunciation", "Conception" and "Nativity" (47 × 38 *mm*) .. .. 45　50

The paintings from the 2, 6 and 8 c. values are united to form the triptych on the 12 c. value.

258 Chess Pieces　　**259** Barn Owl (*Tyto alba*)

(Des H. Borg)

1980 (20 Nov). *Chess Olympiad and F.I.D.E. (International Chess Federation) Congress. T* **258** *and similar multicoloured designs. W* **105** *(sideways on* 30 *c.). P* 14 × 13½ *(*30 *c.) or* 13½ × 14 *(others).*

652　2 c. 5, Type **258** .. .. 15　5
653　8 c. Chess pieces *(different)* .. .. .. 40　25
654　30 c. Chess pieces *(vert)* .. .. .. 1·00　1·10

(Des M. Burlò)

1981 (20 Jan). *Birds. T* **259** *and similar vert designs. Multicoloured. W* **105** *(sideways). P* 13½.

655　3 c. Type **259** .. .. 15　12
656　8 c. Sardinian Warbler (*Sylvia melanocephala*) .. .. 35　25
657　12 c. Woodchat Shrike (*Lanius senator*) .. 45　45
658　23 c. British Storm Petrel (*Hydrobates pelagicus*) .. .. 1·00　1·10

260 Traditional Horse Race　　**261** Stylised "25"

(Des H. Borg)

1981 (28 Apr). *Europa. Folklore. T* **260** *and similar vert design. Multicoloured. W* **105** *(sideways). P* 14.

659　8 c. Type **260** .. .. 40　30
660　30 c. Attempting to retrieve flag from end of "gostra" (greasy pole) .. .. .. 1·10　1·10

The two values were each printed in sheets including two *se-tenant* stamp-size labels.

(Des A. de Giovanni)

1981 (12 June). *25th Maltese International Trade Fair. W* **105** *(sideways). P* 13½.

661　**261**　4 c. multicoloured .. .. 15　12
662　　25 c. multicoloured .. .. 95　95

262 Disabled Artist at Work　　**263** Wheat Ear in Conical Flask

(Des A. Camilleri)

1981 (17 July). *International Year for Disabled Persons. T* **262** *and similar vert design. Multicoloured. W* **105** *(sideways). P* 13½.

663　3 c. Type **262** .. .. 15　10
664　35 c. Disabled child playing football .. .. 1·25　1·25

(Des R. Caruana)

1981 (16 Oct). *World Food Day. W* **105** *(sideways). P* 14.

665　**263**　8 c. multicoloured .. .. 25　20
666　　23 c. multicoloured .. .. 95　95

264 Megalithic Building　　**265** Children and Nativity Scene

(Des F. Portelli)

1981 (31 Oct). *History of Maltese Industry. Horiz designs as T* **264**. *Multicoloured. W* **105**. *P* 14.

667　5 m. Type **264** .. .. 5　5
668　1 c. Cotton production .. .. 5　5
669　2 c. Early ship-building .. .. 5　5
670　3 c. Currency minting .. .. 8　10
671　5 c. "Art" .. .. 15　12
672　6 c. Fishing .. .. 15　12
673　7 c. Agriculture .. .. 25　30
674　8 c. Stone quarrying .. .. 25　30
675　10 c. Grape pressing .. .. 30　35
676　12 c. Modern ship-building .. .. .. 35　40
677　15 c. Energy .. .. 50　55
678　20 c. Telecommunications .. .. .. 65　70
679　25 c. "Industry" .. .. 80　85
680　50 c. Drilling for water .. .. .. 1·75　1·90
681　£1 Sea transport .. .. 3·25　3·50
682　£3 Air transport .. .. 9·75　10·00
667/82 .. .. *Set of* 16　16·50　17·00

(Des A. Bugeja)

1981 (18 Nov). *Christmas. T* **265** *and similar multicoloured designs. W* **105** *(sideways). P* 14.

683　2 c. + 1 c. Type **265** .. .. 15　10
684　8 c. + 2 c. Christmas Eve procession *(horiz)* .. 40　40
685　20 c. + 3 c. Preaching midnight sermon .. 85　85

266 Shipbuilding　　**267** Elderly Man and Has-Serh (home for elderly)

(Des N. Attard)

1982 (29 Jan). *Shipbuilding Industry. T* **266** *and similar vert designs showing different scenes. W* **105** *(sideways). P* 13½.

686　3 c. multicoloured .. .. 12　10
687　8 c. multicoloured .. .. 25　25
688　13 c. multicoloured .. .. 45　45
689　27 c. multicoloured .. .. 1·10　1·10

(Des R. Pitré)

1982 (16 Mar). *Care of Elderly. T* **267** *and similar horiz design. Multicoloured. W* **105**. *P* 14 × 13½.

690　8 c. Type **267** .. .. 30　20
691　30 c. Elderly woman and Has-Zmien (hospital for elderly) .. .. 1·10　1·10

268 Redemption of Islands by Maltese, 1428

(Des F. Portelli)

1982 (29 Apr). *Europa. Historical Events. T* **268** *and similar horiz design. Multicoloured. W* **105**. *P* 14 × 13½.

692　8 c. Type **268** .. .. 30　20
693　30 c. Declaration of rights by Maltese, 1802 .. 95　1·10

Nos. 692/3 were each printed in sheets containing 2 *se-tenant* stamp-size labels.

269 Stylised Footballer

(Des R. Caruana)

1982 (11 June). *World Cup Football Championship, Spain. T* **269** *and similar horiz designs showing stylised footballers. W* **105**. *P* 14.

694　3 c. multicoloured .. .. 10　10
695　12 c. multicoloured .. .. 50　50
696　15 c. multicoloured .. .. 60　60
MS697　125 × 90 mm. Nos. 694/6 .. .. .. 1·10　1·10

270 Angel appearing to Shepherds

(Des J. Mallia)

1982 (8 Oct). *Christmas. T* **270** *and similar multicoloured designs. W* **105** *(sideways). P* 14 *(No.* 700*) or* 13½ *(others).*

698　2 c. + 1 c. Type **270** .. .. 10　8
699　8 c. + 2 c. Nativity and Three Wise Men bearing gifts .. .. 35　35
700　20 c. + 3 c. Nativity scene *(larger* 45 × 37 *mm)* 80　80

The designs from the 2 and 8 c. values are united to form the design of the 20 c. stamp.

271 Brigantin

(Des N. Attard)

1982 (13 Nov). *Maltese Ships (1st series). T* **271** *and similar horiz designs. Multicoloured. W.* **105**. *P* 14 × 13½.

701　3 c. Type **271** .. .. 10　8
702　8 c. Tartana .. .. 30　25
703　12 c. Xambekk .. .. 45　45
704　20 c. Xprunara .. .. 75　75

See also Nos. 725/8.

272 *Manning Wardle*, 1883

(Des R. Caruana)

1983 (21 Jan). *Centenary of Malta Railway. T* **272** *and similar horiz designs. Multicoloured. W* **105**. *P* 14 × 13½.

705　3 c. Type **272** .. .. 10　12
706　13 c. *Black Hawthorn*, 1884 .. .. .. 40　45
707　27 c. *Beyer Peacock*, 1895 .. .. .. 90　95

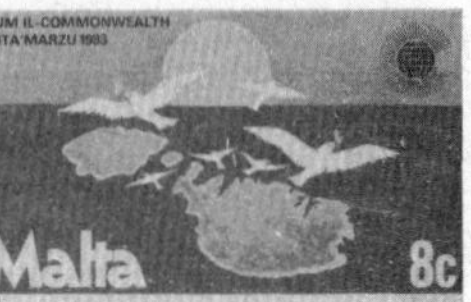

273 Peace Doves leaving Malta

(Des C. Cassar)

1983 (14 Mar). *Commonwealth Day. T* **273** *and similar multi-coloured designs. W* **105** *(sideways on vert designs). P* 14 × 13½ (8, 12 *c.*) *or* 13½ × 14 (*others*).
708 8 c. Type **273** 25 30
709 12 c. Tourist landmarks 35 40
710 15 c. Holiday beach (*vert*) 45 50
711 23 c. Ship-building (*vert*) 70 75

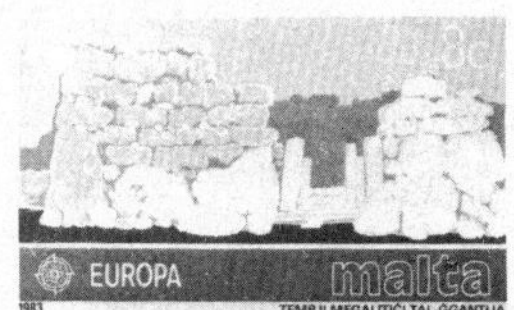

274 Ggantija Megalithic Temples, Gozo

(Des T. Bugeja (8 c.), R. Caruana (30 c.))

1983 (5 May). *Europa. T* **274** *and similar horiz design. Multi-coloured. W* **105**. *P* 14 × 13½.
712 8 c. Type **274** 25 30
713 30 c. Fort St. Angelo 90 95
Nos. 712/13 were each printed in sheets including two *se-tenant* stamp-size labels.

275 Dish Aerials (World Communications Year)

(Des D. Friggieri)

1983 (14 July). *Anniversaries and Events. T* **275** *and similar horiz designs. Multicoloured. W* **105** *(sideways). P* 13½ × 14.
714 3 c. Type **275** 10 12
715 7 c. Ships' prows and badge (25th anniv of I.M.O. Convention) 20 25
716 13 c. Container lorries and badge (30th anniv of Customs Co-operation Council) .. 40 45
717 20 c. Stadium and emblem (9th Mediterranean Games) 60 65

276 Monsignor Giuseppe de Piro

277 Annunciation

(Des E. Barthet)

1983 (1 Sept). *50th Death Anniv of Monsignor Giuseppe de Piro. W* **105** *(sideways). P* 14.
718 **276** 3 c. multicoloured 10 12

(Des N. Attard)

1983 (6 Sept). *Christmas. T* **277** *and similar vert designs. Multi-coloured. W* **105** *(sideways). P* 13½ × 14.
719 2 c. + 1 c. Type **277** 10 12
720 8 c. + 2 c. The Nativity 30 35
721 20 c. + 3 c. Adoration of the Magi 70 75

278 Workers at Meeting

(Des F. Portelli)

1983 (5 Oct). *40th Anniv of General Workers' Union. T* **278** *and similar horiz designs. Multicoloured. W* **105**. *P* 14 × 13½.
722 3 c. Type **278** 10 12
723 8 c. Worker with family 20 25
724 27 c. Union H.Q. Building 80 85

(Des N. Attard)

1983 (17 Nov). *Maltese Ships (2nd series). Horiz designs as T* **271**. *Multicoloured. W* **105**. *P* 14 × 13½.
725 2 c. *Strangier* 5 8
726 12 c. *Tigre* 35 40
727 13 c. *La Speranza* 40 45
728 20 c. *Wignacourt* 60 65

279 Boeing "737"

(Des R. Caruana)

1984 (26 Jan). *Air. T* **279** *and similar horiz designs. Multi-coloured. W* **105**. *P* 14 × 13½.
729 7 c. Type **279** 25 30
730 8 c. Boeing "720B" 25 30
731 16 c. Vickers "Vanguard" 50 55
732 23 c. Vickers "Viscount" 75 80
733 27 c. Douglas "DC.3 Dakota" 85 90
734 38 c. A.W. "Atlanta" .. .. 1·25 1·40
735 75 c. Dornier "Wal" .. .. 2·40 2·50
729/35 .. .. *Set of* 7 5·50 6·00

280 C.E.P.T. 25th Anniversary Logo

281 Early Policeman

(Des J. Larrivière and L. Borg)

1984 (27 Apr). *Europa. W* **105**. *P* 13½.
736 **280** 8 c. green, black and gold 30 35
737 30 c. carmine-lake, black and gold .. 1·10 1·25
Nos. 736/7 were each printed in sheets including two *se-tenant* stamp-size labels.

(Des T. Bugeja)

1984 (14 June). *170th Anniv of Malta Police Force. T* **281** *and similar vert designs. Multicoloured. W* **105**. *P* 14 × 13½.
738 3 c. Type **281** 12 15
739 8 c. Mounted police 30 35
740 11 c. Motorcycle policeman 40 45
741 25 c. Policeman and firemen 90 95

282 Running

283 "The Visitation" (Pietro Caruana)

(Des L. Micallef)

1984 (26 July). *Olympic Games, Los Angeles. T* **282** *and similar vert designs. Multicoloured. W* **105** *(sideways). P* 14.
742 7 c. Type **282** 25 30
743 12 c. Gymnastics 50 55
744 23 c. Swimming 85 90

(Des L. Micallef)

1984 (5 Oct). *Christmas. Paintings from Church of Our Lady of Porto Salvo, Valletta. T* **283** *and similar multicoloured designs. W* **105** *(sideways on horiz designs). P* 14.
745 2 c. + 1 c. Type **283** 12 15
746 8 c. + 2 c. "The Epiphany" (Rafel Caruana) (*horiz*) 35 40
747 20 c. + 3 c. "Jesus among the Doctors" (Rafel Caruana) (*horiz*) 85 90

284 Dove on Map

285 1885 ½d. Green Stamp

(Des L. Micallef)

1984 (12 Dec). *10th Anniv of Republic. T* **284** *and similar vert designs. Multicoloured. W* **105** *(sideways). P* 14.
748 3 c. Type **284** 12 15
749 8 c. Fort St. Angelo 30 35
750 30 c. Hands .. .. 1·10 1·25

(Des N. Attard)

1985 (2 Jan). *Centenary of Malta Post Office. T* **285** *and similar vert designs showing stamps of* 1885. *Multicoloured. W* **105**. *P* 14.
751 3 c. Type **285** 10 12
752 8 c. 1885 1d. rose 25 30
753 12 c. 1885 2½d. dull blue 40 45
754 20 c. 1885 4d. brown 70 75
MS755 165 × 90 mm. Nos. 751/4. Wmk sideways 1·10 1·25

POSTAGE DUE STAMPS

POSTAGE DUE
½d.
MALTA.

D 1

D 2

D 3 Maltese Lace

1925 (16 Apr). *Type-set by Govt. Printing Office, Valletta. Imperf.*
D 1 D 1 ½d. black .. .. 1·25 2·25
D 2 1d. black .. .. 1·25 1·75
D 3 1½d. black .. .. 1·75 2·50
D 4 2d. black .. .. 3·00 3·50
D 5 2½d. black .. .. 3·00 3·50
a. "2" of "½" omitted £550 £700
D 6 3d. black/*grey* .. .. 5·00 7·00
D 7 4d. black/*buff* .. .. 5·00 6·00
D 8 6d. black/*buff* .. .. 5·50 7·00
D 9 1s. black/*buff* .. .. 11·00 14·00
D10 1s. 6d. black/*buff* .. .. .. 17·00 26·00
D1/10 .. .. *Set of* 10 48·00 65·00
All the above may be had in *tête-bêche* pairs from the junction of the panes, price about four times that of a single stamp. Dangerous forgeries of No. D5a are in circulation.

(Typo B.W.)

1925 (21 July). *Wmk Mult Script CA (sideways). P* 12.
D11 D 2 ½d. green .. .. 1·25 1·25
D12 1d. violet .. .. 1·25 90
D13 1½d. brown .. .. 1·25 1·25
D14 2d. grey .. .. 12·00 12·00
D15 2½d. orange .. .. 1·75 2·00
D16 3d. blue .. .. 1·75 1·75
D17 4d. olive-green .. .. 18·00 18·00
D18 6d. purple .. .. 1·75 2·00
D19 1s. black .. .. 5·00 6·00
D20 1s. 6d. carmine .. .. 6·50 10·00
D11/20 .. .. *Set of* 10 45·00 50·00
D11/20 Optd "Specimen" .. .. *Set of* 10 £200

1953 (5 Nov)–**57**. *Chalk-surfaced paper. Wmk Mult Script CA (sideways). P* 12.
D21 D 2 ½d. emerald 60 60
D22 1d. purple (*shades*) 60 60
D23 1½d. yellow-brown .. .. 4·00 4·00
D24 2d. grey-brown (*shades*) (20.3.57) .. 14·00 12·00
D25 3d. deep slate-blue .. .. 2·00 2·00
D26 4d. yellow-olive .. .. 9·00 9·00
D21/6 .. .. *Set of* 6 27·00 25·00

1966 (Oct). *As No.* D24, *but wmk* w **12** *(sideways).*
D27 D 2 2d. grey-brown .. .. 30·00 30·00

1967–70. *Ordinary paper. W* **105** *(sideways).*

(*a*) *P* 12, *line* (9.11.67)
D28 D 2 ½d. emerald .. .. 7·50 10·50
D29 1d. purple .. .. 7·50 10·50
D30 2d. blackish brown .. .. 7·50 10·50
D31 4d. yellow-olive £120 £140

(*b*) *P* 12½, *comb* (30.5.68–70)
D32 D 2 ½d. emerald 20 30
D33 1d. purple 20 20
D34 1½d. yellow-brown 35 50
a. Orange-brown (23.10.70) .. .. 90 1·50
D35 2d. blackish brown .. .. 1·00 80
a. Brownish black (23.10.70) .. .. 1·00 1·50
D36 2½d. yellow-orange 80 80
D37 3d. deep slate-blue 80 60
D38 4d. yellow-olive .. .. 1·75 1·00
D39 6d. purple .. .. 1·40 1·25
D40 1s. black .. .. 2·00 2·00
D41 1s. 6d. carmine .. .. 3·50 4·00
D32/41 .. .. *Set of* 10 11·00 10·00
The above are the local release dates. In the 12½ perforation the London release dates were 21 May for the ½d. to 4d. and 4 June for the 6d. to 1s. 6d.
Nos. D34*a* and D35*a* are on glazed paper.

(Des G. Pace Litho Printex Ltd, Malta)

1973 (28 Apr). *W* **105**. *P* 13 × 13½.
D42 D 3 2 m. grey-brown and reddish brown .. 5 5
D43 3 m. dull orange and Indian red .. 5 5
D44 5 m. rose and bright scarlet 5 5
D45 1 c. turquoise and bottle green .. 5 5
D46 2 c. slate and black 5 5
D47 3 c. light yellow-brown and red-brown 8 8
D48 5 c. dull blue and royal blue 15 12
D49 10 c. reddish lilac and plum 30 30
D42/9 .. .. *Set of* 8 60 60

OMNIBUS ISSUES

Details, together with prices for complete sets, of the various Omnibus issues from the 1935 Silver Jubilee series to date are included in a special section following Zululand at the end of the catalogue.

Mauritius

GREAT BRITAIN STAMPS USED IN MAURITIUS. We no longer list the Great Britain stamps with obliteration "B 53" as there is no evidence that British stamps were available from the Mauritius Post Office.

PRICES FOR STAMPS ON COVER TO 1945

The classic issues, Nos. 1/34, are rare used on cover

Nos. 35/41	*from* × 2
Nos. 42/72	*from* × 3
Nos. 74/5	†
Nos. 76/82	*from* × 5
Nos. 83/91	*from* × 6
Nos. 92/103	*from* × 4
Nos. 104/8	*from* × 3
Nos. 110/14	*from* × 10
Nos. 115/24	*from* × 8
Nos. 125/32	*from* × 7
No. 133	*from* × 4
Nos. 134/5	*from* × 10
No. 136	*from* × 8
Nos. 137/42	*from* × 6
Nos. 143/9	*from* × 5
Nos. 150/223	*from* × 3
No. 224	—
Nos. 225/7	*from* × 10
Nos. 228/44	*from* × 6
Nos. 245/8	*from* × 3
Nos. 249/63	*from* × 2
Nos. E1/6	*from* × 10
Nos. D1/7	*from* × 40
Nos. R1/4	*from* × 15

CROWN COLONY

Nos. 1/34b were printed in Mauritius.

1 ("POST OFFICE")

2 ("POST PAID")

3

(Engraved on copper by J. O. Barnard)

1847 (21 Sept). *Head of Queen on groundwork of diagonal and perpendicular lines. Imperf.*

1	**1**	1d. orange-red	£375000	£140000
2		2d. deep blue	£240000	£140000

A single plate contained one example of each value.

It is generally agreed that fifteen examples of No. 1 have survived (including two unused) and twelve of No. 2 (including four unused).

NOTE. Our prices for early Mauritius are for stamps in very fine condition. Exceptional copies are worth more, poorer copies considerably less.

(Engraved on copper by J. O. Barnard)

1848 (June). *T* **2**. 12 *varieties on the sheet. Imperf.*

A. *Earliest impressions. Design deep, sharp and clear. Diagonal lines predominate. Thick paper (Period of use:* 1*d.* 1853–54, 2*d.* 1848–49)

3	1d. orange-vermilion/*yellowish*	£19000	£13000
4	2d. indigo-blue/*grey to bluish*	£23000	£13000
	a. "PENOE" for "PENCE	£34000	£23000
5	2d. deep blue/*grey to bluish*	£25000	£13000
	a. "PENOE" for "PENCE"	—	£26000

B. *Early impressions. Design sharp and clear but some lines slightly weakened. Paper not so thick, grey to yellowish white or bluish (Period of use:* 1*d.* 1853–55, 2*d.* 1849–54).

6	1d. vermilion	£11000	£5000
7	1d. orange-vermilion	£12000	£5000
8	2d. blue	£15000	£5500
	a. "PENOE" for "PENCE"	£18000	£9000
9	2d. deep blue	£19000	£6000

C. *Intermediate impressions. White patches appear where design has worn. Paper yellowish white, grey or bluish, of poorish quality (Period of use:* 1*d and* 2*d.* 1854–57)

10	1d. bright vermilion	£7500	£2000
11	1d. dull vermilion	£7500	£2000
12	1d. red	£7500	£1900
13	2d. deep blue	£7000	£2000
14	2d. blue	£5000	£2000
	a. "PENOE" for "PENCE" (*shades*) *from*	£10000	£4000
15	2d. light blue	£5000	£2000

D. *Worn impressions. Much of design worn away but some diagonal lines distinct. Paper yellowish, grey or bluish, of poorish quality (Period of use:* 1*d.* 1857–59, 2*d.* 1855–58)

16	1d. red/*yellowish or grey*	£1300	£275
17	1d. red-brown/*yellowish or grey*	£1300	£275
18	1d. red/*bluish*	£800	£275
19	1d. red-brown/*bluish*	£750	£275
20	2d. blue (*shades*)/*yellowish or grey*	£1300	£550
	a. "PENOE" for "PENCE" .. .. *from*	—	£800
21	2d. grey-blue/*yellowish or grey*	£1500	£550
22	2d. blue (*shades*)/*bluish*	£1300	£500
	a. Doubly printed		

E. *Latest impressions. Almost none of design showing except part of Queen's head and frame. Paper yellowish, grey or bluish, of poorish quality (Period of use:* 1*d.* 1859, 2*d.* 1856–58)

23	1d. red	£700	£275
24	1d. red-brown	£750	£275
25	2d. grey-blue/*bluish*	£750	£300
	a. "PENOE" for "PENCE"	£1300	£700

F. *Retouched impression. Retouching to Queen's head and frame. Paper bluish of poor quality (Period of use* 2*d.* 1857–58)

25*b*	2d. greyish blue/*bluish*		

The "PENOE" stamp is No. 7 on the sheet.

Earliest known use of the 2d. value is on 19 June 1848, but the 1d. value is not known used before 27 September 1853.

(Engraved on copper by J. Lapirot)

1859 (March). 12 *varieties on the sheet. Imperf. Early impressions.*

26	**3**	2d. deep blue	£3500	£1700
27		2d. blue	£2500	£1500

1859 (July). *Intermediate prints. Lines of background, etc, partly worn away.*

28	**3**	2d. blue	£1800	£600

1859 (Oct). *Worn impressions; bluish-paper.*

29	**3**	2d. blue	£750	£375

4

5

(T **4**. The 1848 plate re-engraved by R. Sherwin)

1859 (Oct). *Bluish paper. Imperf.*

30	**4**	2d. deep blue	£22000	£3000

The 1d. plate was also re-engraved, but was not put into use. Reprints in black were made in 1877 from both 1d. and 2d. re-engraved plates. Coloured autotype illustrations were prepared from these reprints and 600 were included in the R.P.S.L. handbook on *British Africa* in 1900. Further reprints in black were made in 1911 after the plates had been presented to the R.P.S.L. and defaced.

(Lithographed by L. A. Dardenne)

1859 (Dec). *White laid paper. Imperf.*

31	**5**	1d. deep red	£2000	£900
31*a*		1d. red	£1500	£600
32		1d. dull vermilion	£1000	£550
33		2d. slate-blue	£2000	£600
33*a*		2d. blue	£900	£400
34		2d. pale blue	£800	£300
		a. Heavy retouch on neck	—	£1000
		b. Slight retouches (several varieties)	—	£550

6

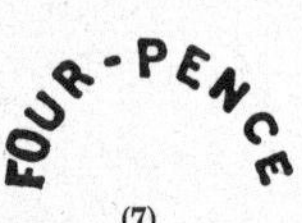

(7)

8

(Recess P.B.)

1854 (8 Apr)*. *Surch with T* **7**. *Imperf.*

35	**6**	4d. green	£725	£425

*Although originally gazetted for use from the above date, research into the archives suggests that No. 35 was not actually issued until sometime in 1858, being mentioned in a further ordinance dated 30 April. The earliest dated postmark known is 27 March 1858.

1858–62. *No value expressed. Imperf.*

36	**6**	(4d.) green	£450	£250
37		(6d.) vermilion	17·00	25·00
38		(9d.) dull magenta	£450	£250
		a. Reissued as (1d.) value (11.62) ..	†	£160

Examples of the design in dull magenta used as a 1d. value (No. 38a) can be identified by the use of the "B 53" cancellation.

Prepared for use, but not issued

39	**6**	(No value), red-brown (1859)	3·00	
40		(No value), blue (1858)	2·75	

Remainders of these were overprinted "L.P.E. 1890" in *red*, perforated at the London Philatelic Exhibition and sold as souvenirs.

(Recess P.B.)

1859. *Imperf.*

42	**8**	6d. blue	£475	32·00
43		1s. vermilion	£1800	45·00

1861. *Colours corrected. Imperf.*

44	**8**	6d. dull purple-slate	20·00	20·00
45		1s. yellow-green	£180	70·00

1862. *Intermediate perf* 14 *to* 16.

46	**8**	6d. slate	17·00	20·00
		a. Imperf between (pair)	£900	
47		1s. deep green	£1200	£300

9

10

(Typo D.L.R.)

1860–3. *No wmk. P* 14.

48	**9**	1d. purple-brown	50·00	12·00
49		2d. blue	65·00	18·00
50		4d. rose	65·00	12·00
51		6d. green (1862)	£300	75·00
52		6d. slate (1863)	70·00	48·00
53		9d. dull purple	50·00	29·00
54		1s. buff (1862)	£120	45·00
55		1s. green (1863)	£325	£110

1863–72. *Wmk Crown CC. P* 14.

56	**9**	1d. purple-brown (1870)	15·00	5·00
57		1d. brown	20·00	6·50
58		1d. bistre	26·00	6·50
59		2d. pale blue	26·00	5·50
60		2d. bright blue	23·00	5·50
		a. Imperf (pair)	£900	£900
61		3d. deep red	42·00	19·00
61*a*		3d. dull red	26·00	10·00
62		4d. rose	28·00	5·00
63		6d. dull violet (1864)	40·00	22·00
64		6d. yellow-green (1865)	45·00	12·00
65		6d. blue-green	42·00	5·50
66		9d. yellow-green (1872)	95·00	65·00
67	**10**	10d. maroon (1872)	55·00	15·00
68	**9**	1s. yellow	60·00	14·00
69		1s. orange	60·00	14·00
70		1s. blue (1870)	65·00	15·00
71		5s. rosy mauve	70·00	25·00
72		5s. bright mauve (1865)	95·00	22·00

½ *d* HALF PENNY

(11)

HALF PENNY

(12)

Prepared for use, but not issued. No. 53 *surch with T* **11**

74	**9**	½d. on 9d. dull purple (R.) (Optd S. £90)	£450	
		a. "PRNNY"		
75		½d. on 9d. dull purple (Bk.)	£550	

1876. *Nos.* 53 *and* 67 *surch with T* **12**.

76	**9**	½d. on 9d. dull purple	4·00	6·50
		a. Surch inverted	£225	
		b. Surch double		
77	**10**	½d. on 10d. maroon	2·50	9·00

HALF PENNY

(13)

One Penny

(14)

One Shilling

(15)

1877. *T* **9** *and* **10**, *wmk Crown CC, surch with T* **13**/**15**. *P* 14.

79	½d. on 10d. rose (Apr)	6·50	12·00
80	1d. on 4d. rose-carmine (6 Dec) ..	9·00	12·00
81	1s. on 5s. rosy mauve (6 Dec) ..	£130	65·00
82	1s. on 5s. bright mauve (6 Dec) ..	£175	90·00

"CANCELLED" OVERPRINTS. Following the change of currency in 1878 various issues with face values in sterling were overprinted "CANCELLED" in serifed type and sold as remainders. The stamps involved were Nos. 53, 56/62, 64, 67/8, 71/2, 74/6, 79 and 81/2.

Examples of such overprints on stamps between Nos. 53 and 72 are worth about the same as the prices quoted for used, on Nos. 74/6 they are worth 12% of the unused price, on No. 79 65% and on Nos. 81/2 20%.

2 CENTS

(16)

2 Rs. 50 C.

(17)

1878 (3 Jan). *T* **10** *(with lower label blank) surch with T* **16**. *Wmk Crown CC. P* 14.

83	2 c. dull rose	4·25	4·50

1878. *Surch as T* **16** *or* **17**. *Wmk Crown CC. P* 14.

84	**9**	4 c. on 1d. bistre	6·00	5·00
85		8 c. on 2d. blue	12·00	1·90
86		13 c. on 3d. orange-red	6·50	8·00
87		17 c. on 4d. rose	35·00	2·50
88		25 c. on 6d. slate-blue	42·00	4·75
89		38 c. on 9d. pale violet	16·00	14·00
90		50 c. on 1s. green	18·00	3·50
91		2 r. 50 c. on 5s. bright mauve	15·00	9·00
84/91		.. .. *Set of* 8	£130	42·00

18

19

20

21

22

23

24

25

26

(Type D.L.R.)

1879–80. *Wmk Crown CC. P* 14.
92 **18** 2 c. Venetian red .. .. .. 17·00 11·00
93 **19** 4 c. orange (1879) .. .. .. 18·00 4·00
94 **20** 8 c. blue .. .. 11·00 2·00
95 **21** 13 c. slate .. .. 80·00 40·00
96 **22** 17 c. rose .. .. 17·00 4·50
97 **23** 25 c. olive-yellow (1879) .. .. 50·00 9·50
98 **24** 38 c. bright purple .. .. .. 85·00 60·00
99 **25** 50 c. green .. .. 3·00 2·50
100 **26** 2 r. 50 c. brown-purple .. .. .. 22·00 18·00
92/100 .. .. *Set of* 9 £275 £140

1882–83. *Wmk Crown CA. P* 14.
101 **18** 2 c. Venetian red .. .. .. 4·75 4·75
102 **19** 4 c. orange .. .. 20·00 3·75
103 **23** 25 c. olive-yellow (1883) .. .. .. 3·50 1·90

16 CENTS (27)

SIXTEEN CENTS (28)

(*a*) Surcharge 14 mm long and 3½ high.
(*b*) Surcharge 15 mm long and 3½ high.
(*c*) Surcharge 15 mm long and 2½ high.

1883 (26 Feb). *No. 96 surch as T* **27**.
104 **22** 16 c. on 17 c. rose (*a*) .. .. .. 22·00 17·00
a. Surch double .. .. ..
105 16 c. on 17 c. rose (*b*) .. .. .. 24·00 17·00
106 16 c. on 17 c. rose (*c*) .. .. .. 45·00 35·00

1883 (14 July). *Wmk Crown CA. Surch with T* **28**. *P* 14.
107 **22** 16 c. on 17 c. rose.. .. .. .. 10·00 2·25

2 CENTS (29)

30

2 CENTS (31)

1885 (11 May). *No. 98 surch with T* **29**.
108 **24** 2 c. on 38 c. bright purple .. .. 32·00 26·00
a. Without bar .. .. .. — 48·00
b. Surch inverted £170 £170
c. Surch double £240

(Typo D.L.R.)

1885–91. *Wmk Crown CA. P* 14.
110 **18** 2 c. green 90 50
111 **19** 4 c. carmine 80 25
112 **20** 8 c. blue (1891) .. .. .. 1·25 1·25
113 **30** 16 c. chestnut .. .. 1·50 60
114 **25** 50 c. orange (1887) .. .. .. 18·00 10·00
110/14 *excl* 112 optd "Specimen" .. *Set of* 4 75·00

1887 (6 July). *No. 95 surch with T* **31**.
115 **21** 2 c. on 13 c. slate (R.) .. .. .. 13·00 16·00
a. Surch inverted .. .. .. 50·00 60·00
b. Surch double .. .. .. — £190
c. Surch double, one on back of stamp £225

TWO CENTS (32)

TWO CENTS (33)

1891 (Sept). *Various stamps surcharged.*
117 **32** 2 c. on 4 c. (No. 111) 50 40
a. Surch inverted .. .. .. 48·00
b. Surch double .. .. .. 55·00 48·00
c. Surch double, one inverted.. .. 55·00 50·00
118 2 c. on 17 c. (No. 96) .. .. .. 20·00 24·00
a. Surch inverted £110
b. Surch double £170 £170
119 **33** 2 c. on 38 c. (No. 89) .. .. .. 1·50 4·25
a. Surch inverted .. .. .. 90·00
b. Surch double £180 £180
c. Surch double, one inverted.. .. 38·00
120 **32** 2 c. on 38 c. (No. 98) .. .. .. 4·00 5·00
a. Surch inverted £160
b. Surch double .. .. .. 48·00
c. Surch double, one inverted.. .. 48·00

Minor varieties are also known with portions of the surcharge missing, due to defective printing.

ONE CENT (34)

ONE CENT (35)

1893 (1 Jan). *Surch with T* **34/5**. *Wmk Crown CA. P* 14.
123 **18** 1 c. on 2 c. pale violet (Optd S. £27) .. 40 60
124 **30** 1 c. on 16 c. chestnut 45 90

1893–4. *Wmk Crown CA. P* 14.
125 **18** 1 c. pale violet 40 70
126 **30** 15 c. chestnut 70 60
127 15 c. blue .. .. 2·50 60
125/27 Optd "Specimen" .. .. *Set of* 3 35·00

36

37

(Typo D.L.R.)

1895–9. *Wmk Crown CA. P* 14.
128 **36** 1 c. dull purple and ultramarine (8.7.97) 25 25
129 2 c. dull purple and orange (8.7.97) .. 1·60 25
130 3 c. dull purple and deep purple .. 85 85
131 4 c. dull purple and emerald .. .. 2·00 55
131*a* 6 c. green and rose-red (1899) .. .. 2·25 90
132 18 c. green and ultramarine (8.7.97) .. 6·00 5·00
128/32 .. .. *Set of* 6 11·50 7·00
128/32 Optd "Specimen" .. .. *Set of* 6 £110

(Des R. S. du Verge. Typo D.L.R.)

1898 (21 Apr*). *Jubilee issue. Wmk CA over Crown, sideways. P* 14.
133 **37** 36 c. orange & ultramarine (Optd S. £55) 13·00 13·00
*Earliest known postmark.

6 CENTS (38)

15 CENTS (39)

1899. *Nos. 132/33 surcharged.*
134 **38** 6 c. on 18 c. green and ultramarine (R.) 25 30
a. Surch inverted .. .. .. £120 90·00
135 **39** 15 c. on 36 c. orange and ultramarine (B.) 2·50 2·00
a. Bar of surch omitted £110

The space between "6" and "CENTS" varies from 2½ to 4 mm.

40 Admiral Mahé de Labourdonnais, Governor of Mauritius, 1735–46

(Recess D.L.R.)

1899 (15 Dec). *Birth Bicentenary of Labourdonnais. Wmk Crown CC. P* 14.
136 **40** 15 c. ultramarine (Optd S. £75) .. .. 9·00 3·00

4 Cents (41)

12 CENTS (42)

1900. *No. 113 surch with T* **41**.
137 **30** 4 c. on 16 c. chestnut 70 80

1900. *Wmk Crown CA. P* 14.
138 **36** 1 c. grey and black 80 20
139 2 c. dull and bright purple 30 20
140 4 c. purple and carmine/*yellow* 90 50
141 15 c. green and orange .. .. 4·75 7·50
138/41 Optd "Specimen" .. .. *Set of* 4 55·00

1902. *No. 132 surch with T* **42**.
142 **36** 12 c. on 18 c. green and ultramarine 2·00 7·50

The bar cancelling the original value seems in some cases to be one thick bar and in others two thin ones.

Postage & Revenue. (43)

44

1902. *Various stamps optd with T* **43**.
143 4 c. purple and carmine/*yellow* (No. 140) .. 40 25
144 6 c. green and red (No. 131*a*) .. .. 90 1·75
145 15 c. green and orange (No. 141) 60 75
146 25 c. olive-yellow (No. 103) .. .. 1·10 2·50
147 50 c. green (No. 99) .. .. .. 4·00 1·25
148 2 r. 50 c. brown-purple (No. 100) .. 21·00 27·00
143/48 .. .. *Set of* 6 25·00 30·00

1902. *No. 133 surch as T* **42**, *but with longer bar.*
149 **37** 12 c. on 36 c. orange and ultramarine 1·90 2·25
a. Surch inverted £200 £190

The note below No. 142 also applies to No. 149.

(Typo D.L.R.)

1902–5. *T* **36** *and* **44** *(rupee values). Wmk Crown CC (1 r.) or Crown CA (others), sideways on 2 r. 50 and 5 r. P* 14.
150 3 c. green and carmine/*yellow* 90 60
151 4 c. grey-green and violet .. .. 80 1·10
152 4 c. black and carmine/*blue* .. .. .. 1·50 12
153 5 c. dull and bright purple/*buff* .. .. 3·00 15·00
154 5 c. dull purple and black/*buff* .. .. 1·60 1·75
155 6 c. purple and carmine/*red* 60 25
156 8 c. green and black/*buff* .. .. .. 1·10 3·00
157 12 c. grey-black and carmine .. .. 1·50 1·40
158 15 c. black and blue/*blue* (1905) .. .. 10·00 3·50
159 25 c. green and carmine/*green*, **OC** .. 3·00 6·50
160 50 c. dull green and deep green/*yellow* .. 6·00 12·00
161 1 r. grey-black and carmine .. .. 15·00 11·00
162 2 r. 50, green and black/*blue*.. .. 15·00 20·00
163 5 r. purple and carmine/*red* .. .. 42·00 48·00
150/63 .. .. *Set of* 14 90·00 £110
150/63 Optd "Specimen" .. .. *Set of* 14 £200

1904–7. *T* **36** *and* **44** *(1 r.). Wmk Mult Crown CA. P* 14.
164 1 c. grey and black, **C** (1907).. .. 2·25 1·25
165 2 c. dull and bright purple, **OC** (1905) .. 1·50 20
166 3 c. green and carmine/*yellow*, **C** .. 9·00 2·75
167 4 c. black and carmine/*blue*, **OC** .. 1·00 10
168 6 c. purple and carmine/*red*, **OC** .. 50 10
171 15 c. black and blue/*blue*, **C** (1907) .. 3·75 1·00
174 50 c. green and deep green/*yellow*, **C** .. 1·25 3·00
175 1 r. grey-black and carmine, **C** (1907) .. 17·00 16·00
164/75 .. .. *Set of* 8 32·00 22·00

46

(47)

(Typo D.L.R.)

1910. *Wmk Mult Crown CA. P* 14.
181 **46** 1 c. black, **O** 10 10
182 2 c. brown, **O** 80 10
183 3 c. green, **O** 45 55
184 4 c. pale yellow-green and carmine, **O** .. 70 10
185 **47** 5 c. grey and carmine, **O** .. .. 70 1·60
186 **46** 6 c. carmine-red, **O** 40 30
a. Pale red .. .. .. 2·00 25
187 8 c. orange, **O** .. .. .. 95 1·90
188 **47** 12 c. greyish slate, **O** 40 85
189 **46** 15 c. blue, **O** .. .. 2·00 25
190 **47** 25 c. black and red/*yellow*, **C** .. .. 3·50 8·50
191 50 c. dull purple and black, **C** .. .. 3·00 8·50
192 1 r. black/*green*, **C** .. .. .. 5·50 6·50
193 2 r. 50, black and red/*blue*, **C** .. .. 8·50 15·00
194 5 r. green and red/*yellow*, **C** .. .. 17·00 26·00
195 10 r. green and red/*green*, **C** .. .. 70·00 90·00
181/95 .. .. .. *Set of* 15 £100 £140
181/95 Optd "Specimen" .. .. *Set of* 15 £225

In Nos. 188, 190 and 195, the value labels are as in T **49**.

48

49

(Typo D.L.R.)

1913–23. *T* **48** *and* **49** *(12 c., 25 c. and 10 r.). Wmk Mult Crown CA. P* 14.
196 5 c. grey and carmine, **O** (1915) .. .. 1·25 1·25
197 5 c. slate-grey and carmine, **O** .. .. 4·00 4·00
198 12 c. greyish slate, **O** (1915) 75 75
199 25 c. black and red/*yellow*, **C** (1913) .. 1·00 1·40
a. White back (1916) .. .. 2·50 4·00
b. On orange-buff .. .. 20·00 23·00
c. On pale yellow (Die I) .. .. 16·00 20·00
d. On pale yellow (Die II) (Optd S. £28) 1·25 6·00
200 50 c. dull purple and black, **C** (Die I) .. 12·00 16·00
201 1 r. black/*blue-green (olive back)*, **C** (1917) .. 2·25 4·50
a. On emerald surface .. .. 5·50 16·00
b. On emerald back (Die II) (Optd £35) 3·00 6·00
202 2 r. 50, black and red/*blue*, **C**.. .. 8·50 15·00
203 5 r. green and red/*orange-buff*, **C** .. 13·00 20·00
a. On pale yellow (Die I) .. .. 13·00 20·00
b. On pale yellow (Die II) .. .. 25·00 38·00
204 10 r. green and red/*green*, **C** .. .. 18·00 26·00
a. On blue-green, olive back £600
b. On emerald surface .. .. 18·00 26·00
c. On emerald back (Die I) .. .. 18·00 26·00
d. On emerald back (Die II) (Opt S. £28) 16·00 27·00
196/204 .. .. .. *Set of* 8 48·00 75·00
196/204 Optd "Specimen" (Die I) .. *Set of* 8 £150

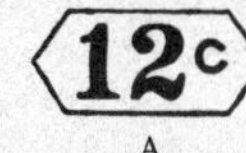

A

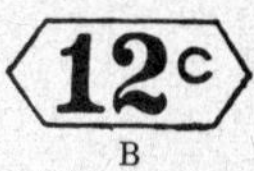

B

Two types of duty plate in the 12 c. In Type B the letters of "MAURITIUS" are larger; the extremities of the downstroke and the tail of the "2" are pointed, instead of square, and the "c" is larger.

1921–34. *Wmk Mult Script CA. P* 14. (*a*) *T* **46**.
205 1 c. black, **O** 25 45
206 2 c. brown, **O** 30 10
207 4 c. pale olive-green and carmine, **O** .. 1·50 2·25
208 4 c. green, **O** 70 10
209 6 c. carmine, **O** .. .. 7·00 6·00
210 6 c. bright mauve, **O** 65 40
210*a* 8 c. orange, **O**.. .. .. .. 2·50 4·00
211 10 c. grey, **O** .. .. 3·00 4·50
212 12 c. carmine-red, **O** .. .. .. 80 1·10
213 15 c. blue, **O** .. .. 5·00 1·50
214 20 c. blue, **O** .. .. 2·75 1·40
205/214 .. .. .. *Set of* 11 22·00 20·00
205/12, 214 Optd "Specimen" .. *Set of* 10 £160

(b) T 48 and 49
215 5 c. grey and carmine, O (Die II) 10 10
215a 5 c. grey and carmine, O (Die I) (1932) .. 60 15
216 12 c. grey, O (1921) (A) .. .. 50 3·25
216a 12 c. pale grey, O (1928) (A) (Optd S. £24) .. 25 30
216b 12 c. grey, O (1934) (B) (Optd S. £24) 30 30
217 12 c. carmine-red, O (1922) .. .. 45 2·50
218 25 c. black and red/pale yellow, C (Die II) .. 25 35
218a 25 c. black & red/pale yellow, C (Die I) (1932) 75 5·00
219 50 c. dull purple and black, C (Die II) .. .. 4·00 3·50
220 1 r. black/emerald, C (Die II) 80 80
220a 1 r. black/emerald, C (Die I) (1932) .. .. 6·00 10·00
221 2 r. 50 c. black and red/blue, C .. .. 6·00 5·50
222 5 r. green and red/yellow, C .. .. .. 13·00 24·00
223 10 r. green and red/emerald, C (1928) .. 20·00 32·00
215/223 .. .. Set of 9 40·00 60·00
215/23 Optd "Specimen" .. .. Set of 9 £140

1924. As T 44, but Arms similar to T 46. Wmk Mult Script CA. P 14.
224 50 r. dull purple and green, C £850 £1100
224 Optd "Specimen" £225

3
Cents
(50)

51

1925. T 46 surch as T 50.
225 3 c. on 4 c. green .. .. 1·50 1·50
226 10 c. on 12 c. carmine-red 30 25
227 15 c. on 20 c. blue 45 70
225/7 Optd "Specimen" .. .. Set of 3 95·00

1926. Wmk Mult Script CA. P 14.
228 48 2 c. purple/yellow, O 15 25
229 3 c. green, O 65 75
230 4 c. brown, O 30 75
231 10 c. carmine-red, O 75 80
232 12 c. grey, O .. .. 60 1·40
233 15 c. cobalt, O .. .. 1·40 45
234 20 c. purple, O .. .. 3·75 6·50
228/234 .. .. .. Set of 7 7·00 10·00
228/32, 234 Optd "Specimen" .. Set of 6 £120

1926–34. As T 49 (King). Wmk Mult Script CA. P 14.
235 1 c. black, O 10 35
236 2 c. brown, O 10 10
237 3 c. green, O 30 70
238 4 c. sage-green and carmine, O (Die II) (1927) 60 60
238a 4 c. sage-green and carmine, O (Die I) (1932) 3·25 7·50
238b 4 c. green, O (Die I)(1933) .. .. 40 1·25
239 6 c. sepia, O (1928) .. .. .. 30 1·40
240 8 c. orange, O .. .. 40 2·00
241 10 c. carmine-red, O (Die II) 30 10
241a 10 c. carmine-red, O (Die I) (1932) .. 30 1·25
242 15 c. Prussian blue, O (1928) .. .. 1·00 1·00
243 20 c. purple, O (1927) .. .. .. 55 1·40
244 20 c. Prussian blue, O (Die I) (1933) .. 4·00 3·00
244a 20 c. Prussian blue, O (Die II) (1934) .. 4·00 1·75
235/244 .. .. .. Set of 11 7·25 9·50
235/244 (excl 238a, 241a). Optd/Perf "Specimen"
.. .. Set of 11 £150

1935 (6 May). Silver Jubilee. As Nos. 91/4 of Antigua.
245 5 c. ultramarine and grey 15 10
246 12 c. green and indigo 85 40
247 20 c. brown and deep blue .. .. 2·50 1·60
248 1 r. slate and purple .. .. .. 22·00 24·00
245/8 Perf "Specimen" .. .. Set of 4 60·00

1937 (12 May). Coronation. As Nos. 13/15 of Aden.
249 5 c. violet 25 12
250 12 c. scarlet 25 20
251 20 c. bright blue 30 12
249/251 Perf "Specimen" .. .. Set of 3 40·00

(Typo D.L.R.)

1938–49. T 51 and similar types. Wmk Mult Script CA. P 14.
252 2 c. olive-grey (9.3.38) 15 5
a. Perf 15 × 14 (1942) 20 20
253 3 c. reddish purple and scarlet (27.10.38) .. 25 15
a. Reddish lilac and red (4.43) 25 15
254 4 c. dull green (26.2.38) 25 25
a. Deep dull green (4.43) 25 25
255 5 c. slate-lilac (23.2.38) 25 10
a. Pale lilac (shades) (4.43) 25 12
b. Perf 15 × 14 (1942) .. .. .. 7·00 45
256 10 c. rose-red (9.3.38) 30 15
a. Deep reddish rose (shades) (4.43) .. 30 10
b. Perf 15 × 14. Pale reddish rose (1942) .. 6·50 2·00
257 12 c. salmon (shades) (26.2.38) 25 10
a. Perf 15 × 14 (1942) .. .. .. 20·00 4·00
258 20 c. blue (26.2.38) 35 10
259 25 c. brown-purple, CO (2.3.38) 35 10
260 1 r. grey-brown, CO (2.3.38) 90 50
a. Drab, C (4.49) .. .. .. 1·25 70
261 2 r. 50, pale violet, CO (2.3.38) .. .. 7·00 5·00
a. Slate-violet, C (4.48) .. .. .. 20·00 13·00
262 5 r. olive-green, CO (2.3.38) .. .. 16·00 15·00
a. Sage-green, O (4.43) .. .. .. 16·00 15·00
263 10 r. reddish purple (shades), CO (2.3.38) .. 11·00 13·00
252/263 .. .. .. Set of 12 35·00 30·00
252/263 Perf "Specimen" .. .. Set of 12 £120

The stamps perf 15 × 14 were printed by Bradbury, Wilkinson from De La Rue plates and issued only in the colony in 1942. De La Rue printings of the 2 c. to 20 c. in 1943–45 were on thin, whiter paper. 1943–45 printings of the 25 c. to 10 r. were on unsurfaced paper.

1946 (20 Nov). Victory. As Nos. 28/9 of Aden.
264 5 c. lilac 15 10
265 20 c. blue 20 10
264/5 Perf "Specimen" .. .. Set of 2 45·00

52 1d. "Post Office" Mauritius and King George VI

(Recess B.W.)

1948 (22 Mar). Centenary of First British Colonial Postage Stamp. P 11½ × 11.
266 52 5 c. orange and magenta 10 10
267 12 c. orange and green 10 10
268 – 20 c. blue and light blue 10 10
269 – 1 r. blue and red-brown 20 20
266/9 Perf "Specimen" .. .. Set of 4 £130

Design:–20 c., 1 r. As T 52 but showing 2d. "Post Office" Mauritius.

1948 (25 Oct). Royal Silver Wedding. As Nos. 30/1 of Aden.
270 5 c. violet 12 5
271 10 r. magenta .. .. 11·00 15·00

1949 (10 Oct). 75th Anniv of U.P.U. As Nos. 114/17 of Antigua.
272 12 c. carmine 60 60
273 20 c. deep blue 80 60
274 35 c. purple 90 65
275 1 r. sepia .. .. 1·10 65

53 Sugar Factory

55 Aloe Plant

(Photo Harrison)

1950 (1 July). T 53, 55 and similar designs. Wmk Mult Script CA. Chalk surfaced paper. P 13½ × 14½ (horiz), 14½ × 13½ (vert).
276 1 c. bright purple 12 45
277 2 c. rose-carmine 25 10
278 3 c. yellow-green .. .. .. 1·00 75
279 4 c. green 25 15
280 5 c. blue 20 10
281 10 c. scarlet 75 80
282 12 c. olive-green .. .. .. 1·25 55
283 20 c. ultramarine 30 40
284 25 c. brown-purple 40 60
285 35 c. violet 35 40
286 50 c. emerald-green 60 60
287 1 r. sepia .. .. 1·00 70
288 2 r. 50, orange .. .. .. 6·50 6·50
289 5 r. red-brown .. .. .. 7·00 10·00
290 10 r. dull blue .. .. .. 17·00 14·00
276/290 .. .. .. Set of 15 32·00 32·00

Designs: Horiz—2 c. Grand Port; 5 c. Rempart Mountain; 10 c. Transporting cane; 12 c. Dodo and map; 35 c. Government House; 1 r. Mauritius deer; 2 r. 50, Port Louis; 5 r. Beach scene; 10 r. Arms of Mauritius. Vert—4 c. Tamarind Falls; 20 c. Legend of Paul and Virginie (inscr "VIRGINIA"); 25 c. Labourdonnais statue; 50 c. Pieter Both Mountain.

The latitude is incorrectly shown on No. 282. This was corrected before the same design was used for No. 302a.

1953 (2 June). Coronation. As No. 47 of Aden.
291 10 c. black and emerald 25 10

68 Tamarind Falls

69 Historical Museum, Mahebourg

(Photo Harrison)

1953 (3 Nov)–**54.** Designs previously used for King George VI issue, but with portrait of Queen Elizabeth II as in T 68/9. Wmk Mult Script CA. Chalk-surfaced paper. P 13½ × 14½ (horiz) or 14½ × 13½ (vert).
293 2 c. bright carmine (1.6.54) 5 5
294 3 c. yellow-green (1.6.54) 30 40
295 4 c. bright purple 8 15
296 5 c. Prussian blue (1.6.54) 10 5
297 10 c. bluish green (shades) 15 5
298 15 c. scarlet 15 5
299 20 c. brown-purple 20 5
300 25 c. bright ultramarine (shades) .. 30 5
301 35 c. reddish violet (1.6.54) 35 5
302 50 c. bright green 50 30
302a 60 c. deep green (shades) (2.8.54) .. 1·40 5
303 1 r. sepia (shades) 50 10
304 2 r. 50, orange (1.6.54) .. .. 6·50 3·75
305 5 r. red-brown (shades) (1.6.54) .. .. 8·00 4·00
306 10 r. deep grey-blue (1.6.54) .. .. 12·00 1·75
293/306 .. .. .. Set of 15 27·00 9·00

Designs: Horiz—2 c. Grand Port; 4 c. Sugar factory; 5 c. Rempart Mountain; 35 c. Government House; 60 c. Dodo and map; 1 r Mauritius deer; 2 r. 50, Port Louis; 5 r. Beach scene; 10 r. Arms of Mauritius. Vert—3 c. Aloe plant; 20 c. Labourdonnais statue; 25 c. Legend of Paul and Virginie; 50 c. Pieter Both Mountain.

Nos. 296 and 300 exist in coils, constructed from normal sheets. See also Nos. 314/16.

70 Queen Elizabeth II and King George III (after Lawrence)

(Litho Enschedé)

1961 (11 Jan). 150th Anniv of British Post Office in Mauritius. W w 12. P 13½ × 14.
307 70 10 c. black and brown-red 15 5
308 20 c. ultramarine and light blue 25 20
309 35 c. black and yellow 30 20
310 1 r. deep maroon and green 50 65

1963 (4 June). Freedom from Hunger. As No. 76 of Aden.
311 60 c. reddish violet 60 25

1963 (2 Sept). Red Cross Centenary. As Nos. 147/8 of Antigua.
312 10 c. red and black 20 10
313 60 c. red and blue 70 35

1963 (12 Nov)–**64.** As Nos. 297, 302a and 304 but wmk w 12.
314 68 10 c. bluish green (shades) (1964) .. 25 12
315 59 60 c. bronze-green (28.5.64) .. .. 1·25 40
316 65 2 r. 50, orange .. .. .. 4·75 7·50

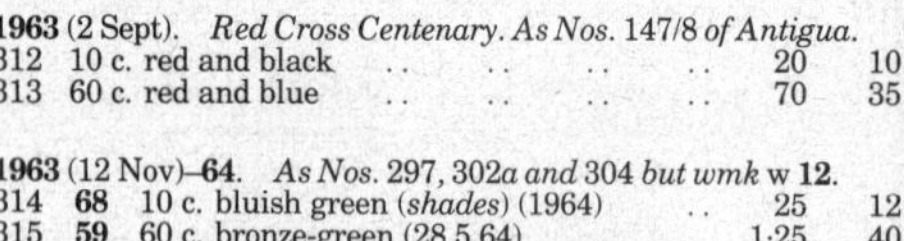

71 Bourbon White Eye

(Des D. M. Reid-Henry. Photo Harrison)

1965 (16 Mar). Horiz designs as T 71. W w 12 (upright). Multicoloured; background colours given. P 14½ × 14.
317 2 c. lemon 5 20
318 3 c. brown 5 20
319 4 c. light reddish purple 8 15
a. Mauve-pink omitted* .. .. .. 24·00
320 5 c. grey-brown 20 5
321 10 c. light grey-green 20 5
322 15 c. pale grey 25 8
323 20 c. light yellow-bistre 30 10
324 25 c. bluish grey 30 12
325 35 c. greyish blue 40 10
326 50 c. light yellow-buff 35 12
327 60 c. light greenish yellow 40 15
328 1 r. light yellow-olive 60 15
329 2 r. 50, pale stone .. .. .. 4·25 2·25
330 5 r. pale grey-blue .. .. .. 10·00 4·25
331 10 r. pale bluish green .. .. .. 14·00 5·00
317/31 .. .. .. Set of 15 28·00 12·00

Designs:—3 c. Rodriguez Fody; 4 c. Olive White-eye; 5 c. Mascarene Paradise Flycatcher; 10 c. Mauritius Fody; 15 c. Mauritius Parakeet; 20 c. Mauritius Greybird; 25 c. Mauritius Kestrel; 35 c. Pink Pigeon; 50 c. Reunion Bulbul; 60 c. Dutch Pigeon (extinct); 1 r. Mauritius Dodo (extinct); 2 r. 50, Rodriguez Solitaire (extinct); 5 r. Red Rail (extinct); 10 r. Broad-billed Parrot (extinct).

The 50 c. and 2 r. 50 exist with PVA gum as well as gum arabic.
No. 320 exists in coils, constructed from normal sheets.
See also Nos. 340/1 and 370/5.

1965 (17 May). I.T.U. Centenary. As Nos. 166/7 of Antigua.
332 10 c. red-orange and apple-green 20 5
333 60 c. yellow and bluish violet 65 25

1965 (25 Oct). International Co-operation Year. As Nos. 168/9 of Antigua.
334 10 c. reddish purple and turquoise-green .. 15 5
335 60 c. deep bluish green and lavender 50 15

1966 (24 Jan). Churchill Commemoration. As Nos. 170/3 of Antigua.
336 2 c. new blue 5 20
337 10 c. deep green 25 5
338 60 c. brown .. .. 1·40 30
339 1 r. bluish violet .. .. 1·60 55

1966–67. As Nos. 320, 325 but wmk w 12 sideways.
340 5 c. grey-brown (1966) 10 5
341 35 c. greyish blue (27.6.67) 20 15

1966 (1 Dec). 20th Anniv of U.N.E.S.C.O. As Nos. 196/8 of Antigua.
342 5 c. slate-violet, red, yellow and orange .. 15 15
343 10 c. orange-yellow, violet and deep olive .. 40 5
344 60 c. black, bright purple and orange .. .. 1·25 40

SELF-GOVERNMENT

86 Red-tailed Tropic Bird

(Des D. M. Reid-Henry. Photo Harrison)

1967 (1 Sept). *Self-Government. T* **86** *and similar horiz designs. Multicoloured.* W w **12**. *P* 14½.

345	2 c. Type **86**	12	15
346	10 c. Rodriguez Brush Warbler	12	5
347	60 c. Rodriguez Parakeet (extinct)	25	15
348	1 r. Grey-rumped Swiftlet	60	25

SELF GOVERNMENT 1967

(90)

1967 (1 Dec). *Self-Government. As Nos.* 317/31 *but wmk sideways on Nos.* 352/3 *and* 357. *Optd with T* **90**. *P* 14 × 14½.

349	2 c. lemon	10	20
350	3 c. brown	10	20
351	4 c. light reddish purple	10	20
352	5 c. grey-brown	10	5
353	10 c. light grey-green	10	5
354	15 c. pale grey	10	8
355	20 c. light yellow-bistre	15	10
356	25 c. bluish grey	15	12
357	35 c. greyish blue	20	12
358	50 c. light yellow-buff	25	20
359	60 c. light greenish yellow	30	15
360	1 r. light yellow-olive	50	20
361	2 r. 50, pale stone	1·50	2·25
362	5 r. pale grey-blue	2·50	4·25
363	10 r. pale bluish green	5·00	7·50
349/63	*Set of* 15	10·00	14·00

INDEPENDENT

91 Flag of Mauritius

(Litho D.L.R.)

1968 (12 Mar). *Independence. T* **91** *and similar horiz design. P* 13½ × 13.

364	**91**	2 c. multicoloured	5	20
365	–	3 c. multicoloured	10	20
366	**91**	15 c. multicoloured	12	10
367	–	20 c. multicoloured	15	10
368	**91**	60 c. multicoloured	25	15
369	–	1 r. multicoloured	40	20
364/9		*Set of* 6	95	85

Design:—3 c., 20 c. and 1 r. Arms and Dodo emblem.

1968 (12 July). *As Nos.* 317/18, 322/3 *and* 327/8 *but background colours changed as below.*

370	2 c. olive-yellow	15	40
371	3 c. cobalt	35	60
372	15 c. cinnamon	55	20
373	20 c. buff	90	30
374	60 c. rose	90	40
375	1 r. reddish purple	1·75	1·00
370/5	*Set of* 6	4·00	2·50

93 Dominique rescues Paul and Virginie

(Des V. Whiteley, from prints. Litho Format)

1968 (2 Dec). *Bicentenary of Bernardin de St. Pierre's Visit to Mauritius. Multicoloured designs as T* **93**. *P* 13½.

376	2 c. Type **93**	5	20
377	15 c. Paul and Virginie crossing the river	10	5
378	50 c. Visit of Labourdonnais to Madame de la Tour (*horiz*)	20	10
379	60 c. Meeting of Paul and Virginie in Confidence (*vert*)	20	10
380	1 r. Departure of Virginie for Europe (*horiz*)	35	25
381	2 r. 50, Bernardin de St. Pierre (*vert*)	1·00	1·90
376/81	*Set of* 6	1·75	2·40

99 Batardé

(Des J. Vinson (3 c., 20 c., 1 r.), R. Granger Barrett (others). Photo Harrison)

1969 (12 Mar)–**73**. W w **12** (*sideways on* 2, 3, 4, 5, 10, 15, 60 *and* 75 c.). *Chalk-surfaced paper. P* 14.

382	2 c. multicoloured	10	10
383	3 c. multicoloured	10	10
384	4 c. multicoloured	20	15
385	5 c. multicoloured	20	5
386	10 c. scarlet, black and flesh	25	5
387	15 c. ochre, black and cobalt	25	5
388	20 c. multicoloured	25	5
	a. Glazed ordinary paper (20.2.73)	20	30
389	25 c. red, black and pale apple-green	25	20
	a. Glazed ordinary paper (22.1.71)	65	40
390	30 c. multicoloured	35	15
	a. Glazed, ordinary paper (20.2.73)	40	45
391	35 c. multicoloured	45	15
	a. Glazed ordinary paper (3.2.71)	90	20
392	40 c. multicoloured	35	40
	a. Glazed ordinary paper (20.2.73)	30	40
393	50 c. multicoloured	50	15
	a. Glazed ordinary paper (22.1.71)	55	20
394	60 c. black, rose and ultramarine	60	5
395	75 c. multicoloured	60	55
396	1 r. multicoloured	50	30
	a. Glazed ordinary paper (22.1.71)	75	30
397	2 r. 50, multicoloured	3·25	4·25
	a. Glazed ordinary paper (20.2.73)	2·50	3·25
398	5 r. multicoloured	6·00	7·00
	a. Glazed ordinary paper (22.1.71)	4·50	5·00
399	10 r. multicoloured	6·00	8·00
382/99	*Set of* 18	18·00	19·00
388a/98a	*Set of* 9	9·75	9·50

Designs:—3 c. Red Reef Crab; 4 c. Episcopal Mitre; 5 c. Bourse; 10 c. Starfish; 15 c. Sea Urchin; 20 c. Fiddler Crab; 25 c. Spiny Shrimp; 30 c. Single Harp Shells, and Double Harp Shell; 35 c. Argonaute; 40 c. Nudibranch; 50 c. Violet and Orange Spider Shells; 60 c. Blue Marlin; 75 c. *Conus clytospira*; 1 r. Dolphin; 2 r. Spiny Lobster; 5 r. Sacré Chien Rouge; 10 r. Croissant Queue Jaune.

Nos. 385/6 exist in coils constructed from normal sheets.

See also Nos. 437/54 and 475/91.

117 Gandhi as Law Student **124** Frangourinier Cane-crusher (18th cent)

(Des J. W. Litho Format)

1969 (1 July). *Birth Centenary of Mahatma Gandhi. T* **117** *and similar vert designs. Multicoloured.* W w **12**. *P* 13½.

400	2 c. Type **117**	10	5
401	15 c. Gandhi as stretcher-bearer during Zulu Revolt	20	5
402	50 c. Gandhi as Satyagrahi in South Africa	30	20
403	60 c. Gandhi at No. 10 Downing Street, London	45	15
404	1 r. Gandhi in Mauritius, 1901	50	25
405	2 r. 50, Gandhi, the "Apostle of Truth and Non-Violence"	1·25	1·75
400/5	*Set of* 6	2·50	2·25
MS406	153 × 153 mm. Nos. 400/5	4·50	5·00

(Des V. Whiteley. Photo Enschedé)

1969 (22 Dec).* *150th Anniv of Telfair's Improvements to the Sugar Industry. T* **124** *and similar multicoloured designs.* W w **12** (*sideways on* 2 c. *to* 1 r.), *P* 11½ × 11 (2 r. 50) *or* 11 × 11½ (*others*).

407	2 c. Three-roller Vertical Mill	5	20
408	15 c. Type **124**	10	10
409	60 c. Beau Rivage Factory, 1867	35	10
410	1 r. Mon Désert-Alma Factory, 1969	40	15
411	2 r. 50, Dr. Charles Telfair (*vert*)	1·00	1·50
MS412	159 × 88 mm. Nos. 407/11†. Wmk sideways. P 11 × 11½	2·50	3·00

*This was the local release date but the Crown Agents issued the stamps on 15 December.

† In the miniature sheet the 2 r. 50 is perf 11 at the top and imperf on the other three sides.

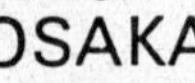

(128)

129 Morne Plage, Mountain and Lufthansa Airliner

1970 (7 Apr). *World Fair, Osaka. Nos.* 394 *and* 396 *optd with T* **128** *by Harrison & Sons.*

413	60 c. black, rose and ultramarine	15	20
414	1 r. multicoloured	15	20

(Des H. Rose. Litho G. Gehringer, Kaiserslautern, Germany)

1970 (2 May). *Inauguration of Lufthansa Flight, Mauritius-Frankfurt. T* **129** *and similar multicoloured design. P* 14.

415	25 c. Type **129**	10	10
416	50 c. Airliner and Map (*vert*)	15	15

131 Lenin as a Student **133** 2d. "Post Office" Mauritius and original Post Office

(Photo State Ptg Works, Moscow)

1970 (15 May). *Birth Centenary of Lenin. T* **131** *and similar vert design. P* 12 × 11½.

417	15 c. blackish green and silver	15	8
418	75 c. blackish brown and gold	55	60

Design:—75 c. Lenin as Founder of U.S.S.R.

(Des and litho D.L.R.)

1970 (15 Oct). *Port Louis, Old and New. T* **133** *and similar horiz designs. Multicoloured.* W w **12** (*sideways*). *P* 14.

419	5 c. Type **133**	5	5
420	15 c. G.P.O. Building (built 1870)	10	5
421	50 c. Mail Coach (*c.* 1870)	20	10
422	75 c. Port Louis Harbour (1970)	35	20
423	2 r. 50, Arrival of Pierre A. de Suffren (1783)	1·50	1·75
MS424	165 × 95 mm. Nos. 419/23	3·50	5·00

138 U.N. Emblem and Symbols

(Des Jennifer Toombs. Litho Format)

1970 (24 Oct). *25th Anniv of United Nations.* W w **12** (*sideways*). *P* 14½.

425	**138**	10 c. multicoloured	8	5
426		60 c. multicoloured	30	30

139 Rainbow over Waterfall

(Des R. Granger Barrett from local ideas (60 c.), R. Granger Barrett from local ideas and adapted by N. Mossae (others). Litho Format)

1971 (12 Apr). *Tourism. T* **139** *and similar horiz designs. Multicoloured.* W w **12** (*sideways*). *P* 14.

427	10 c. Type **139**	12	5
428	15 c. Trois Mamelles Mountains	15	5
429	60 c. Beach scene	30	10
430	2 r. 50, Marine life	1·75	2·10

Nos. 427/30 are inscribed on the reverse with details of tourist attractions in Mauritius.

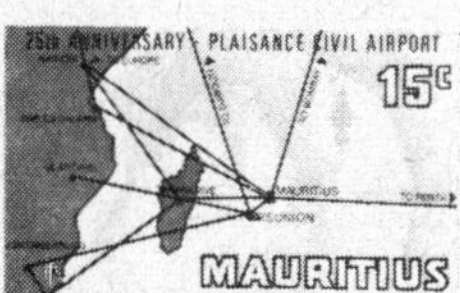

140 "Crossroads" of Indian Ocean

(Des R. Granger Barrett (60 c.) or V. Whiteley (others). Litho Harrison)

1971 (23 Oct). *25th Anniv of Plaisance Airport. T* **140** *and similar horiz designs. Multicoloured.* W w **12** (*sideways on* 15 c.). *P* 14.

431	15 c. Type **140**	10	5
432	60 c. "Boeing 707" and Terminal Buildings	25	20
433	1 r. Air Hostesses on gangway	40	30
434	2 r. 50, *Roland Garros* (aeroplane), Choisy Airfield, 1937	2·00	3·25

141 Princess Margaret Orthopaedic Centre

(Des and litho Harrison)

1971 (2 Nov). *Third Commonwealth Medical Conference. T* **141** *and similar horiz design. Multicoloured.* W w **12**. *P* 14 × 13½.

435	10 c. Type **141**	5	5
436	75 c. Operation Theatre in National Hospital	20	25

1972–74. *As Nos.* 382/99 *but* W w **12** *upright* (2, 3, 4, 5, 10, 15, 60, 75 c.) *or sideways* (*others*).

A. *Glazed, ordinary paper.* B. *Chalk-surfaced paper*

		A		B	
437	2 c. multicoloured	10	20	15	30
438	3 c. multicoloured	15	30	15	40
439	4 c. multicoloured	†		35	50
440	5 c. multicoloured	35	20	30	10
441	10 c. scarlet, black and flesh	40	20	45	10
442	15 c. ochre, black and cobalt . .	40	25	35	10
443	20 c. multicoloured	†		35	30
444	25 c. red, black & apple-green . .	†		35	30
445	30 c. multicoloured	†		35	30
446	35 c. multicoloured	†		50	30
447	40 c. multicoloured	†		50	40
448	50 c. multicoloured	†		35	10
449	60 c. black, rose & ultramarine	50	60	35	5
450	75 c. multicoloured	1·40	2·00	50	40
451	1 r. multicoloured	†		50	20
452	2 r. 50, multicoloured	†		2·25	4·00
453	5 r. multicoloured	†		3·50	2·50
454	10 r. multicoloured	†		8·00	10·00
437/450A	. . . . *Set of* 7	3·00	3·25		
437/454B	. . . . *Set of* 18			17·00	18·00

Nos. 440B and 444B exist in coils, constructed from normal sheets.

Dates of issue:

Glazed paper—10.1.72, 5 c., 10 c.; 20.2.73, 2 c., 3 c., 15 c., 60 c., 75 c.

Chalk-surfaced paper—8.11.73, 10 c., 20 c., 30 c., 35 c., 40 c., 75 c., 1 r., 10 r.; 12.12.73, 25 c., 50 c., 2 r. 50, 5 r.; 25.2.74, 5 c., 15 c., 60 c.; 13.6.74, 2 c., 3 c., 4 c.

142 Queen Elizabeth and Prince Philip

(Des and photo Harrison)

1972 (24 Mar). *Royal Visit. T* **142** *and similar multicoloured design.* W w **12**. *P* 14.

455	15 c. Type **142**	15	5
456	2 r. 50, Queen Elizabeth II (*vert*)	2·50	2·50

143 Theatre Façade

(Des and litho Harrison)

1972 (26 June). *150th Anniversary of Port Louis Theatre. T* **143** *and similar horiz design. Multicoloured.* W w **12**. *P* 14.

457	10 c. Type **143**	5	5
458	1 r. Theatre Auditorium	20	25

144 Pirate Dhow

(Des and litho Harrison)

1972 (17 Nov). *Pirates and Privateers. T* **144** *and similar multicoloured designs.* W w **12** (*sideways on* 60 c. *and* 1 r.). *P* 14½ × 14 (60 c., 1 r.) *or* 14 × 14½ (*others*).

459	15 c. Type **144**	15	5
460	60 c. Treasure chest (*vert*)	45	20
461	1 r. Lemene and *L'Hirondelle* (*vert*) . .	50	40
462	2 r. 50, Robert Surcouf	2·75	4·50

145 Mauritius University **146** Map and Hands

(Des and litho Harrison)

1973 (10 Apr). *Fifth Anniv of Independence. T* **145** *and similar horiz designs. Multicoloured.* W w **12** (*sideways*). *P* 14.

463	15 c. Type **145**	5	5
464	60 c. Tea Development	12	12
465	1 r. Bank of Mauritius	20	25

(Des and litho Harrison)

1973 (25 Apr). *O.C.A.M.* Conference. T* **146** *and similar multicoloured design.* W w **12** (*sideways on* 10 c.). *P* 14½ × 14 (10 c.) *or* 14 × 14½ (2 r. 50).

466	10 c. O.C.A.M. emblem (*horiz*)	5	5
467	2 r. 50, Type **146**	90	1·25

*O.C.A.M. = Organisation Commune Africaine Malgache et Mauricienne.

147 W.H.O. Emblem

(Des and litho Harrison)

1973 (20 Nov). *25th Anniv of W.H.O.* W w **12**. *P* 14.

468	**147**	1 r. multicoloured	25	25
		a. Wmk sideways	25	25

148 Meteorological Station, Vacoas.

(Des and litho Harrison)

1973 (27 Nov). *I.M.O./W.M.O. Centenary.* W w **12** (*sideways*). *P* 14.

469	**148**	75 c. multicoloured	30	35

149 Capture of the *Kent* **150** P. Commerson (naturalist)

(Des and litho Harrison)

1974 (21 Mar). *Birth Bicent of Robert Surcouf (privateer).* W w **12** (*sideways*). *P* 14.

470	**149**	60 c. multicoloured	50	35

(Des and litho Harrison)

1974 (18 Apr). *Death Bicent of Philibert Commerson* (1973). W w **12**. *P* 14½.

471	**150**	2 r. 50, multicoloured	60	75

151 Cow being Milked

(Des and litho Harrison)

1974 (23 Oct). *Eighth F.A.O. Regional Conference for Africa, Mauritius.* W w **12** (*sideways*). *P* 14.

472	**151**	60 c. multicoloured	25	20

152 Mail Train

(Des and litho Harrison)

1974 (4 Dec). *Centenary of Universal Postal Union. T* **152** *and similar horiz design. Multicoloured.* W w **12**. *P* 14.

473	15 c. Type **152**	10	8
474	1 r. New G.P.O., Port Louis	70	65

1975–77. *As Nos.* 382/99 *but* W w **14** (*sideways on* 2 *to* 15 c., 60 c. *and* 75 c.). *Chalk-surfaced paper.*

475	2 c. multicoloured (16.8.77)	40	30
476	3 c. multicoloured (16.8.77)	40	30
477	4 c. multicoloured (16.8.77)	40	30
478	5 c. multicoloured (19.3.75)	40	25
479	15 c. ochre, black and cobalt (21.1.75) . .	30	25
480	20 c. multicoloured (19.3.76)	30	20
	a. Grey (background) omitted . .	£110	
481	25 c. red, black and apple-green (19.3.75) . .	35	30
482	30 c. multicoloured (21.1.75)	35	30
483	35 c. multicoloured (19.3.76)	50	20
484	40 c. multicoloured (19.3.76)	50	20
485	50 c. multicoloured (19.3.76)	50	15
486	60 c. black, rose and ultramarine (16.8.77) . .	1·25	40
487	75 c. multicoloured (19.4.77)	1·25	40
488	1 r. multicoloured (19.3.76)	65	25
489	2 r. 50, multicoloured (16.8.77)	6·00	4·00
490	5 r. multicoloured (21.1.75)	5·00	7·50
491	10 r. multicoloured (21.1.75)	9·00	11·00
475/91	. . . . *Set of* 17	25·00	25·00

No. 492 vacant.

153 "Cottage Life" (F. Leroy)

(Des and litho Harrison)

1975 (6 Mar). *Aspects of Mauritian Life. T* **153** *and similar multicoloured designs showing paintings.* W w **14** (*sideways on* 15 c., 60 c. *and* 2 r. 50). *P* 14.

493	15 c. Type **153**	10	5
494	60 c. "Milk Seller" (A. Richard) (*vert*) . .	20	15
	a. Brown and stone (ornaments and frame) double		
495	1 r. "Entrance of Port Louis Market" (Thuillier)	30	30
496	2 r. 50, "Washerwoman" (Max Boulleé) (*vert*)	90	1·25

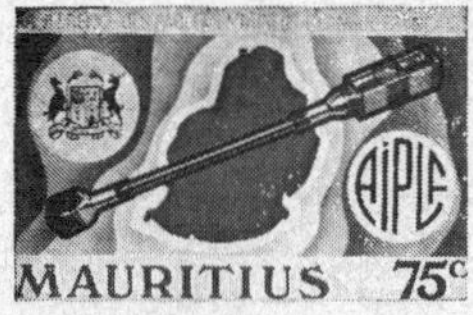

154 Mace across Map

(Des Harrison. Litho Questa)

1975 (21 Nov). *French-speaking Parliamentary Assemblies Conference. Port Louis.* W w **14** (*sideways*). *P* 14.

497	**154**	75 c. multicoloured	25	35

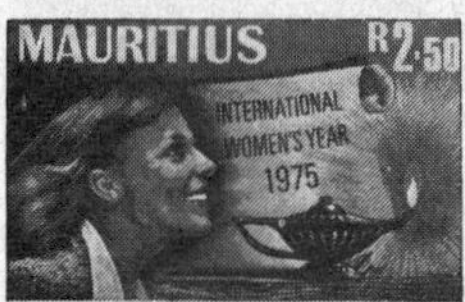

155 Woman with Lamp ("The Light of the World")

(Des A. H. Abdoolah; adapted Harrison. Litho Questa)

1975 (5 Dec). *International Women's Year.* W w **14** (*sideways*). *P* 14½.

498	**155**	2 r. 50, multicoloured	1·00	1·50

156 Parched Landscape

(Des Harrison (50 c.), J.W. Ltd (60 c.) Litho Questa)

1976 (26 Feb). *Drought in Africa. T* **156** *and similar design. Multicoloured.* W w **14** (*sideways on* 50 c.). *P* 14.

499	50 c. Type **156**	25	30
500	60 c. Map of Africa and carcass (*vert*) . .	30	30

157 *Pierre Loti*, 1953–70

(Des J. W. Litho Questa)

1976 (2 July). *Mail Carriers to Mauritius. T* **157** *and similar horiz designs. Multicoloured.* W w **14** (*sideways*). *P* 14½ × 14.

501	10 c. Type **157**	10	5
502	15 c. *Secunder*, 1907	15	5
503	50 c. *Hindoostan*, 1842	35	20
504	60 c. *St Geran*, 1740	40	20
505	2 r. 50, *Maën*, 1638	2·25	3·25
MS506	115 × 138 mm. Nos. 501/5	3·00	3·75

158 "The Flame of Hindi carried across the Seas" **159** Conference Logo and Map of Mauritius

(Des N. Nagalingum (Type **158**), C. R. Prakashi and R. B. Kailash (1 r. 20); adapted J. W. Litho Questa)

1976 (28 Aug). *Second World Hindi Convention. T* **158** *and similar horiz design. Multicoloured. W w* **14** *(sideways). P* 14.
507 10 c. Type **158** 5 5
508 75 c. Type **158** 20 30
509 1 r. 20, Hindi script 40 50

(Des J. W. Litho Questa)

1976 (22 Sept). *22nd Commonwealth Parliamentary Association Conference. T* **159** *and similar vert design. Multicoloured. W w* **14**. *P* 14.
510 1 r. Type **159** 25 25
511 2 r. 50, Conference logo .. .. 80 1·00

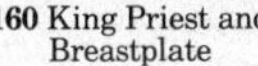

160 King Priest and Breastplate

161 Sega Scene

(Des J. W. Litho Walsall)

1976 (15 Dec). *Moenjodaro Excavations, Pakistan. T* **160** *and similar vert designs. Multicoloured. W w* **14**. *P* 14.
512 60 c. Type **160** 15 10
513 1 r. House with well and goblet 40 25
514 2 r. 50, Terracotta figurine and necklace .. 1·10 1·10

(Des BG Studio. Litho J.W.)

1977 (20 Jan). *Second World Black and African Festival of Arts and Culture, Nigeria. W w* **14** *(sideways). P* 13.
515 **161** 1 r. multicoloured 40 25

162 The Queen with Sceptre and Rod

163 *Hugonia tomentosa*

(Des L. Curtis. Litho Harrison)

1977 (7 Feb). *Silver Jubilee. T* **162** *and similar vert designs. Multicoloured. W w* **14** *(sideways). P* 14½ × 14.
516 50 c. The Queen at Mauritius Legislative Assembly, 1972 .. .. 15 10
517 75 c. Type **162** 25 20
518 5 r. Presentation of Sceptre and Rod .. .. 70 1·25

(Des Jennifer Toombs. Litho Questa)

1977 (22 Sept). *Indigenous Flowers. T* **163** *and similar multi-coloured designs. W w* **14** *(sideways on* 20 c. *and* 1 *r.* 50). *P* 14.
519 20 c. Type **163** 10 10
520 1 r. *Ochna mauritiana (vert)* 30 25
521 1 r. 50, *Dombeya acutangula* 45 35
522 5 r. *Trochetia blackburniana (vert)* .. .. 1·75 2·00
MS523 130 × 130 mm. Nos. 519/22. Wmk sideways 2·50 2·75

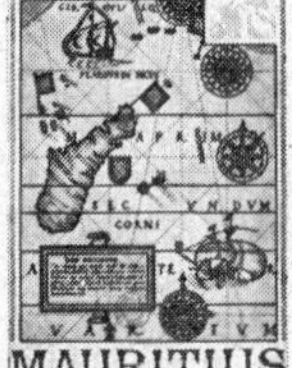

164 "Twin Otter"

165 Portuguese Map of Mauritius, 1519

(Des A. Theobald. Litho Questa)

1977 (31 Oct). *Inaugural International Flight of Air Mauritius. T* **164** *and similar horiz designs. Multicoloured. W w* 14 *(sideways). P* 14½ × 14.
524 25 c. Type **164** 8 5
525 50 c. "Twin Otter" and Air Mauritius emblem 12 10
526 75 c. Piper "Navajo" and Boeing "747" .. 25 25
527 5 r. Boeing "707" .. .. 2·00 2·25
MS528 110 × 152 mm. Nos. 524/7 .. .. .. 2·25 2·50

(Des Harrison. Litho J.W.)

1978 (12 Mar)–**84**. *Designs as T* **165** *in light brown, chestnut and black (25 r.) or multicoloured (others). W w* **14** *(sideways on horiz designs). P* 13½. A. *Without imprint.* B. *With imprint date at foot.*

		A		B	
529	10 c. Type **165**	5	5	5	5
530	15 c. Dutch Occupation, 1638–1710 *(horiz)*	5	5	†	
531	20 c. Van Keulen's map, *c.* 1700 *(horiz)*	5	5	†	
532	25 c. Settlement on Rodriguez, 1691	5	5	5	†
533	35 c. French charter, 1715	5	5	5	5
534	50 c. Construction of Port Louis, *c.* 1736 *(horiz)*	5	5	5	5
535	60 c. Pierre Poivre, *c.* 1767	5	5	†	
536	70 c. Bellin's map, 1763 *(horiz)*	5	8	†	
537	75 c. First coinage, 1794	8	10	8	10
538	90 c. Battle of Grand Port, 1810 *(horiz)*	8	10	†	
539	1 r. British landing, 1810 *(horiz)*	10	12	†	
540	1 r. 20, Government House, *c.* 1840 *(horiz)*	12	15	†	
541	1 r. 25, Lady Gomm's ball, 1847	15	20	15	20
542	1 r. 50, Indian immigration, 1835 *(horiz)*	15	20	†	
543	2 r. Race course, *c.* 1870 *(horiz)*	20	25	20	25
544	3 r. Place d'Armes, *c.* 1880 *(horiz)*	30	35	†	
545	5 r. Royal Visit postcard, 1901 *(horiz)*	55	60	†	
546	10 r. Royal College, 1914 *(horiz)*	1·00	1·10	†	
547	15 r. Unfurling Mauritian flag, 1968	1·50	1·60	†	
548	25 r. First Mauritian Governor-General and Prime Minister *(horiz)*	2·50	2·75	†	
529/48	*Set of* 20	6·25	6·75		

Dates of issue: 12.3.78, Nos. 529A/48A; 15.6.83, Nos. 537B, 541B, 543B; 1.84, No. 533B; 11.84, Nos. 529B, 532B, 534B.

166 Dodo

167 Problem of Infection, World War I

(Des Jennifer Toombs. Litho Questa)

1978 (21 Apr). *25th Anniv of Coronation. T* **166** *and similar vert designs. P* 15.
549 3 r. grey-blue, black and new blue 55 65
a. Sheetlet, Nos. 549/51, each × 2 .. .. 3·00
550 3 r. multicoloured 55 65
551 3 r. grey-blue, black and new blue 55 65

Designs:—No. 549, Antelope of Bohun; 550, Queen Elizabeth II.

Nos. 549/51 were printed together in small sheets of 6, containing two *se-tenant* strips of 3 with horizontal gutter margin between.

(Des Jennifer Toombs. Litho Enschedé)

1978 (3 Aug). *50th Anniv of Discovery of Penicillin. T* **167** *and similar horiz designs. W w* **14** *(sideways). P* 13½ × 14.
552 20 c. multicoloured 5 5
553 1 r. multicoloured 20 20
554 1 r. 50, black, olive-bistre & dp bluish grn .. 30 30
555 5 r. multicoloured .. .. 1·50 1·75
MS556 150 × 90 mm. Nos. 552/5 .. .. .. 2·00 2·50

Designs:—1 r. First mould-growth, 1928; 1 r. 50, *Penicillium notatum*; 5 r. Sir Alexander Fleming.

168 Citrus Butterfly

169 Ornate Table

(Des G. Drummond. Litho Walsall)

1978 (21 Sept). *World Wildlife. T* **168** *and similar horiz designs. Multicoloured. W w* **14** *(sideways). P* 13½ × 14.
557 20 c. Type **168** 15 5
558 1 r. Geckos 30 20
559 1 r. 50, Flying Fox 50 35
560 5 r. Mauritius Kestrel .. .. 2·00 2·75
MS561 154 × 148 mm. Nos. 557/60 .. .. .. 2·75 3·25

(Des C. Abbott. Litho Questa)

1978 (21 Dec). *Bicentenary of Reconstruction of Chateau Le Réduit. T* **169** *and similar vert designs. Multicoloured. W w* **14**. *P* 14½ × 14.
562 15 c. Type **169** 5 5
563 75 c. Chateau Le Réduit 20 15
564 3 r. Le Réduit gardens 80 80

OMNIBUS ISSUES

Details, together with prices for complete sets, of the various Omnibus issues from the 1935 Silver Jubilee series to date are included in a special section following Zululand at the end of the catalogue.

170 Whitcomb Locomotive "65H.P.", 1949

171 Father Laval and Crucifix

(Des G. Hutchins. Litho Questa)

1979 (1 Feb). *Railway Locomotives. T* **170** *and similar horiz designs. Multicoloured. W w* **14** *(sideways). P* 14½.
565 20 c. Type **170** 10 5
566 1 r. "Sir William", 1922 .. .. 35 20
567 1 r. 50, Kitson type, 1930 .. .. 45 45
568 2 r. Garratt type, 1927 .. .. 65 85
MS569 128 × 128 mm. Nos. 565/8 .. .. .. 1·75 2·00

(Des J. W. Litho Questa)

1979 (30 Apr). *Beatification of Father Laval (missionary). T* **171** *and similar multicoloured designs. W w* **14** *(sideways on* 5 *r). P* 14.
570 20 c. Type **171** 5 5
571 1 r. 50, Father Laval 30 30
572 5 r. Father Laval's tomb *(horiz)* .. .. 1·00 1·25
MS573 150 × 96 mm. Nos. 570/2 (wmk upright) .. 1·50 1·60

172 Astronaut descending from Lunar Module

173 Great Britain 1855 4d. Stamp and Sir Rowland Hill

(Manufactured by Walsall)

1979 (20 July). *10th Anniv of Moon Landing. T* **172** *and similar vert designs. Multicoloured. Imperf × roul* 5*. *Self-adhesive (from booklets).*
574 20 c. Type **172** 15 15
a. Booklet pane. Nos. 574/6 .. .. .. 2·25
b. Booklet pane. Nos. 574/5, each × 3 .. 2·25
575 3 r. Astronaut performing experiment on Moon 70 80
576 5 r. Astronaut on Moon .. .. 1·50 2·00

*Nos. 574/6 are separated by various combinations of rotary-knife (giving a straight edge) and roulette.

(Des J. W. Litho Questa)

1979 (27 Aug). *Death Centenary of Sir Rowland Hill. T* **173** *and similar vert designs showing stamps and Sir Rowland Hill. Multicoloured. W w* **14**. *P* 14.
577 25 c. Type **173** 10 5
578 2 r. 1954 60 c. definitive 50 55
579 5 r. 1847 1d. "POST OFFICE" .. .. .. 95 1·10
MS580 120 × 89 mm. 3 r. 1847 2d. "POST OFFICE" 60 75

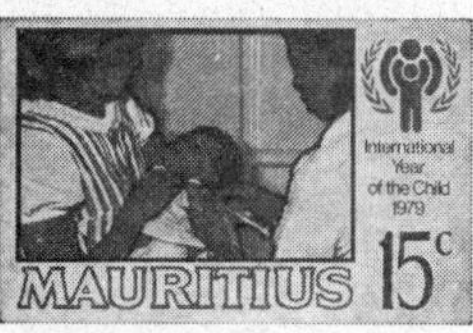

174 Young Child being Vaccinated

(Des V. Whiteley Studio. Litho Questa)

1979 (11 Oct). *International Year of the Child. T* **174** *and similar designs in black, ultramarine and bright blue (*1 *r.) or multi-coloured (others). W w* 14 *(sideways on* 15, 25 *c.,* 1 *r.* 50, *and* 3 *r.). P* 14½ × 14.
581 15 c. Type **174** 5 5
582 25 c. Children playing 8 5
583 1 r. I.Y.C. emblem *(vert)* 20 20
584 1 r. 50, Girls in chemistry laboratory 30 30
585 3 r. Boy operating lathe 60 70

175 The Liénard Obelisk

176 *Emirne*

(Des L. Curtis. Litho Questa)

1980 (24 Jan). *Pamplemousses Botanical Gardens. T* **175** *and similar horiz designs. Multicoloured. W w* 14 *(sideways). P* 14 × 14½.
586 20 c. Type **175** 8 5
587 25 c. Poivre Avenue 8 5

588 1 r. Varieties of Vacoas 20 20
589 2 r. Giant Water Lilies 35 35
590 5 r. Mon Plaisir (mansion) 85 90
MS591 152 × 105 mm. Nos. 586/90 .. .. 1·50 1·60

(Des J. W. Litho Walsall)

1980 (6 May). *"London 1980" International Stamp Exhibition. Mail-carrying Ships. T* **176** *and similar horiz designs. Multicoloured. W* w **14** *(sideways). P* 14½ × 14.
592 25 c. Type **176** 5 5
593 1 r. *Boissevain* 25 20
594 2 r. *La Boudeuse* 55 45
595 5 r. *Sea Breeze* .. .. 1·10 1·25

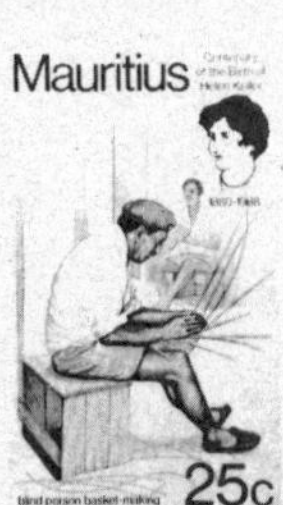

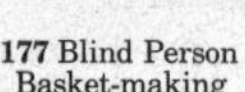

177 Blind Person Basket-making

178 Prime Minister Sir Seewoosagur Ramgoolam

(Des J. W. Litho Harrison)

1980 (27 June). *Birth Centenary of Helen Keller (campaigner for the handicapped). T* **177** *and similar vert designs. Multicoloured.* W w **14**. *P* 14.
596 25 c. Type **177** 5 5
597 1 r. Deaf child under instruction 20 20
598 2 r. 50, Helen reading braille 45 55
599 5 r. Helen at graduation, 1904 .. .. 85 95

(Des Walsall. Litho and gold foil embossed Questa)

1980 (18 Sept). *80th Birthday and 40th Year in Parliament of Prime Minister Sir Seewoosagur Ramgoolam. W* w **14**. *P* 13½.
600 **178** 15 r. multicoloured .. .. .. 1·90 2·00
No. 600 was printed in sheets of 4 stamps.

179 Headquarters, Mauritius Institute

(Des BG Studio. Litho J.W.)

1980 (1 Oct). *Centenary of Mauritius Institute. T* **179** *and similar horiz designs. Multicoloured. W* w **14** *(sideways). P* 13.
601 25 c. Type **179** 5 5
602 2 r. Rare copy of Veda 50 35
603 2 r. 50, Rare cone 60 55
604 5 r. "Le Torrent" (painting by Harpignies) .. 90 1·00

180 *Hibiscus liliiflorus*

181 Beau-Bassin/Rose Hill

(Des Jennifer Toombs. Litho Questa)

1981 (15 Jan). *Flowers. T* **180** *and similar vert designs. Multicoloured. W* w **14**. *P* 14.
605 25 c. Type **180** 5 5
606 2 r. *Erythrospermum monticolum* 40 40
607 2 r. 50, *Chasalia boryana* 50 50
608 5 r. *Hibiscus columnaris* 80 95

(Des. L. Curtis. Litho J.W.)

1981 (10 Apr). *Coats of Arms of Mauritius Towns. T* **181** *and similar vert designs. Multicoloured.* W w **14**. *P* 13½ × 13.
609 25 c. Type **181** 5 5
610 1 r. 50, Curepipe 30 30
611 2 r. Quatre-Bornes 35 35
612 2 r. 50, Vacoas/Phoenix 45 45
613 5 r. Port Louis 75 75
MS614 130 × 130 mm. Nos. 609/13. *P* 14 .. 1·90 2·00

182 Prince Charles as Colonel-in-Chief, Royal Regiment of Wales

183 Emmanuel Anquetil and Guy Rozemont

(Des J. W. Litho Questa)

1981 (22 July). *Royal Wedding. T* **182** *and similar vert designs. Multicoloured. W* w **14**. *P* 14.
615 25 c. Wedding bouquet from Mauritius .. 5 5
616 2 r. 50, Type **182** 40 45
617 10 r. Prince Charles and Lady Diana Spencer 1·25 1·40

(Des G. Vasarhelyi. Litho Questa)

1981 (27 Aug). *Famous Politicians and Physician* (5 *r*). *T* **183** *and similar horiz designs. W* w **14** *(sideways). P* 14½.
618 20 c. black and carmine 5 5
619 25 c. black and lemon 5 5
620 1 r. 25, black and emerald 25 20
621 1 r. 50, black and rose-red 30 25
622 2 r. black and ultramarine 35 35
623 2 r. 50, black and orange-brown 40 40
624 5 r. black and turquoise-blue 75 75
618/24 .. .. *Set of* 7 1·90 1·90
Designs:—25 c. Remy Ollier and Sookdeo Bissoondoyal; 1 r. 25, Maurice Curé and Barthélemy Ohsan; 1 r. 50, Sir Guy Forget and Renganaden Seeneevassen; 2 r. Sir Abdul Razak Mohamed and Jules Koenig; 2 r. 50, Abdoollatiff Mahomed Osman and Dazzi Rama (Pandit Sahadeo); 5 r. Sir Thomas Lewis and electrocardiogram.

184 Drummer and Piper

185 "Skills"

(Des Jennifer Toombs. Litho Format)

1981 (16 Sept). *Religion and Culture. T* **184** *and similar multicoloured designs. W* w **14** *(sideways on* 20 *c. and* 5 *r.). P* 14 × 13½ (20 c.), 13½ × 14 (2 r.) *or* 13½ (5 *r.*).
625 20 c. Type **184** 5 5
626 2 r. Swami Sivananda (*vert*) 35 35
627 2 r. Chinese Pagoda 80 80
The 20 c. value commemorates the World Tamil Culture Conference (1980).

(Des BG Studio. Litho Questa)

1981 (15 Oct). *25th Anniv of Duke of Edinburgh Award Scheme. T* **185** *and similar vert designs. Multicoloured. W* w **14**. *P* 14.
628 25 c. Type **185** 5 5
629 1 r. 25, "Service" 20 20
630 5 r. "Expeditions" 80 80
631 10 r. Duke of Edinburgh .. .. .. 1·40 1·40

186 Ka'aba (sacred shrine, Great Mosque of Mecca)

187 Scout Emblem

(Des Jennifer Toombs. Litho Questa)

1981 (26 Nov). *Moslem Year 1400A.H. Commemoration. T* **186** *and similar vert designs. Multicoloured. W* w 14. *P* 14½ × 14.
632 25 c. Type **186** 5 5
633 2 r. Mecca 30 30
634 5 r. Mecca and Ka'aba 70 70

(Des C. Abbott. Litho Walsall)

1982 (22 Feb). *75th Anniv of Boy Scout Movement and 70th Anniv of Scouting in Mauritius. T* **187** *and similar horiz designs. W* w **14** *(sideways). P* 14 × 14½.
635 25 c. deep lilac and light green 5 5
636 2 r. deep brown and brown-ochre 25 25
637 5 r. deep green and yellow-olive 70 70
638 10 r. deep green and new blue .. .. 1·40 1·40
Designs:—2 r. Lord Baden-Powell and Baden-Powell House; 5 r. Grand Howl; 10 r. Ascent of Pieter Both.

188 Charles Darwin

189 Bride and Groom at Buckingham Palace

(Des L. Curtis. Litho Questa)

1982 (19 Apr). *150th Anniv of Charles Darwin's Voyage. T* **188** *and similar horiz designs. Multicoloured. W* w **14** *(sideways). P* 14.
639 25 c. Type **188** 5 5
a. Yellow (background to side panels) omitted .. ..
640 2 r. Darwin's telescope 30 30
641 2 r. 50, Darwin's elephant ride 35 35
642 10 r. *Beagle* beached for repairs .. .. 1·40 1·40

(Des Jennifer Toombs. Litho J. W.)

1982 (1 July). *21st Birthday of Princess of Wales. T* **189** *and similar vert designs. Multicoloured. W* w **14**. *P* 13.
643 25 c. Mauritius coat of arms 5 5
644 2 r. 50, Princess Diana in Chesterfield, November 1981 .. .. 30 30
645 5 r. Type **189** 55 55
646 10 r. Formal portrait .. .. 1·10 1·25

190 Prince and Princess of Wales with Prince William

191 Bois Fandamane Plant

(Des Harrison. Litho Walsall)

1982 (22 Sept). *Birth of Prince William of Wales. W* w **14** *(sideways). P* 14 × 14½.
647 **190** 2 r. 50, multicoloured 30 25

(Des Harrison. Litho Format)

1982 (15 Dec). *Centenary of Robert Koch's Discovery of Tubercle Bacillus. T* **191** *and similar vert designs. Multicoloured. W* w **14**. *P* 14.
648 25 c. Type **191** 5 5
649 1 r. 25, Central market, Port Louis 15 15
650 2 r. Bois Banane plant 25 25
651 5 r. Platte de Lézard plant 55 55
652 10 r. Dr. Robert Koch .. .. 1·00 1·00

192 Arms and Flag of Mauritius

193 Early Wall-mounted Telephone

(Des and litho J.W.)

1983 (14 Mar). *Commonwealth Day. T* **192** *and similar horiz designs. Multicoloured. W* w **14** *(sideways). P* 13.
653 25 c. Type **192** 5 5
654 2 r. 50, Satellite view of Mauritius 25 30
655 5 r. Harvesting sugar cane 50 55
656 10 r. Port Louis harbour .. .. .. 1·00 1·10

(Des G. Vasarhelyi. Litho Format)

1983 (24 June). *World Communications Year. T* **193** *and similar multicoloured designs. W* w **14** *(sideways on* 1 *r.* 25 *and* 10 *r.).*
657 25 c. Type **193** 5 5
658 1 r. 25, Early telegraph apparatus (*horiz*) .. 12 15
659 2 r. Earth satellite station 20 25
660 10 r. First hot air balloon in Mauritius, 1784 (*horiz*) .. .. 1·00 1·10

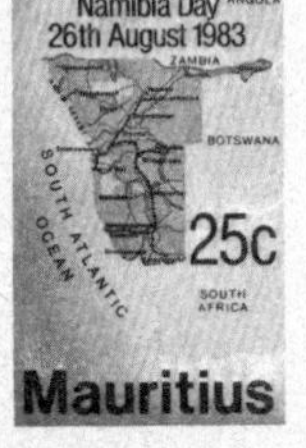

194 Map of Namibia

195 Fish Trap

(Des J. W. Litho Questa)

1983 (26 Aug). *Namibia Day. T* **194** *and similar vert designs. Multicoloured.* W w **14**. *P* 14.

661	25 c. Type **194**	5	5
662	2 r. 50, Hands breaking chains	25	30
663	5 r. Family and settlement	50	55
664	10 r. Diamond mining	1·00	1·10

(Des Walsall. Litho Format)

1983 (25 Sept). *Fishery Resources. T* **195** *and similar multi-coloured designs.* W w**14** (*sideways on* 1 r. *and* 10 r.). *P* 14.

665	25 c. Type **195**	5	5
666	1 r. Fishing boat (*horiz*)	10	12
667	5 r. Game fishing	50	55
668	10 r. Octopus drying (*horiz*)	1·00	1·10

196 Swami Dayananda

197 Adolf von Plevitz

(Des A. Theobald. Litho Questa)

1983 (3 Nov). *Death Centenary of Swami Dayananda. T* **196** *and similar vert designs. Multicoloured.* W w **14**. *P* 14.

669	25 c. Type **196**	5	5
670	35 c. Last meeting with father	5	8
671	2 r. Receiving religious instruction	20	25
672	5 r. Swami demonstrating strength	50	55
673	10 r. At a religious gathering	1·00	1·10

(Des L. Curtis. Litho Harrison)

1983 (8 Dec). *125th Anniv of the Arrival in Mauritius of Adolf von Plevitz (social reformer). T* **197** *and similar horiz designs. Multi-coloured.* W w **14** (*sideways*). *P* 14 × 14½.

674	25 c. Type **197**	5	8
675	1 r. 25, La Laura Government school	12	15
676	5 r. Von Plevitz addressing 1872 Commission of Enquiry	50	55
677	10 r. Von Plevitz with Indian farm workers	1·00	1·10

Mauritius 25c

198 Courtship Chase

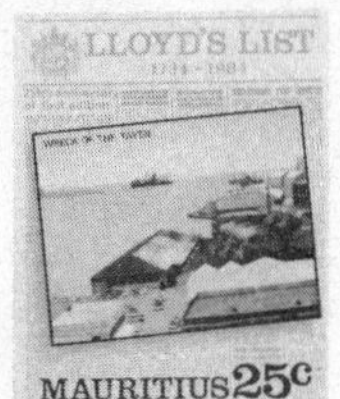

199 Wreck of S.S. *Tayeb*

(Des N. Arlott. Litho Format)

1984 (26 Mar). *The Kestrel. T* **198** *and similar multicoloured designs.* W w **14** (*sideways on* 25 c. *and* 2 r. 50). *P* 14.

678	25 c. Type **198**	5	5
679	2 r. Kestrel in tree (*vert*)	25	30
680	2 r. 50, Young Kestrel	30	35
681	10 r. Head (*vert*)	1·10	1·25

(Des M. Joyce. Litho Questa)

1984 (23 May). *250th Anniv of "Lloyd's List" (newspaper). T* **199** *and similar vert designs. Multicoloured.* W w **14**. *P* 14½ × 14.

682	25 c. Type **199**	5	5
683	1 r. S.S. *Taher*	12	15
684	5 r. East Indiaman *Triton*	60	65
685	10 r. M.S. *Astor*	1·10	1·25

200 Blue Latan Palm

201 Slave Girl

(Des Jennifer Toombs. Litho Format)

1984 (23 July). *Palm Trees. T* **200** *and similar vert designs. Multi-coloured.* W w **14**. *P* 14½.

686	25 c. Type **200**	5	5
687	50 c. *Hyophorbe vaughanii*	8	10
688	2 r. 50, *Tectiphiala ferox*	30	35
689	5 r. Round Island Bottle-palm	60	65
690	10 r. *Hyophorbe amaricaulis*	1·10	1·25

(Des C. Abbott. Litho Walsall)

1984 (20 Aug). *150th Anniv of the Abolition of Slavery and of the Introduction of Indian Immigrants. T* **201** *and similar designs.* W w **14** (*sideways on* 2 r., 10 r.). *P* 14½.

691	25 c. deep rose-lilac, rose-lilac and bistre	5	5
692	1 r. deep rose-lilac, rose-lilac and bistre	12	15
693	2 r. deep rose-lilac and rose-lilac	25	30
694	10 r. deep rose-lilac and rose-lilac	1·10	1·25

Designs: *Vert*—1 r. Slave market. *Horiz*—2 r. Indian immigrant family; 10 r. Arrival of Indian immigrants.

202 75th Anniversary Production of *Faust* and Leoville L'Homme

(Des Walsall. Litho Questa)

1984 (10 Sept). *Centenary of Alliance Francaise (cultural organization). T* **202** *and similar horiz designs. Multicoloured.* W w **14** (*sideways*). *P* 14½ × 14.

695	25 c. Type **202**	5	5
696	1 r. 25, Prize-giving ceremony and Aunauth Beejadbur	15	20
697	5 r. First headquarters and Hector Clarenc	60	65
698	10 r. Lion Mountain and Labourdonnais	1·10	1·25

EXPRESS DELIVERY STAMPS

EXPRESS DELIVERY 15c. (E 1)

EXPRESS DELIVERY (INLAND) 15c. (E 2)

EXPRESS DELIVERY (INLAND) 15 c. (E 3)

EXPRESS DELIVERY (INLAND) 15 c (E 4)

Type E **2**. "(INLAND)" was inserted at a second printing on stamps already surcharged with Type E **1** (No. E1).
Type E **3**. New setting made at one printing. More space above and below "(INLAND)".
Type E **4**. New setting with smaller "15 c" and no stop.

1903–04. *No.* 136 *surch in red.*

E1	E **1**	15 c. on 15 c. ultramarine	5·50	8·50
E2	E **2**	15 c. on 15 c. ultramarine	7·50	11·00
		a. "A" inverted	£150	£180
E3	E **3**	15 c. on 15 c. ultramarine	3·50	1·50
		a. Surch inverted	—	£110
		b. Surch double, both inverted		
		c. Imperf between (vert pair)		
E4	E **4**	15 c. on 15 c. ultramarine (1904)	£100	£100
		a. Surch inverted		
		b. Surch double		
		c. Surch double, both inverted		
		d. "c" omitted	—	£900

(FOREIGN) EXPRESS DELIVERY 18 CENTS (E 5)

1904. *T* **44** (*without value in label*), *wmk Crown CC, surch with Type* E **5**. *P* 14.

E5	18 c. green	3·25	4·50
	a. Exclamation mark for "I" in "FOREIGN"	£180	

1904. *T* **44** *surch with Type* E **3**.

E6	15 c. grey-green (R.)	1·40	1·60
	a. Surch inverted	£110	£110
	b. Surch double		
	c. Surch double, one "LNIAND"	£110	£110

POSTAGE DUE STAMPS

D 1

POSTAGE DUE 10c (D 2)

(Typo Waterlow)

1933–54. *Wmk Mult Script CA. P* 15 × 14.

D1	D **1**	2 c. black	30	60
D2		4 c. violet	30	80
D3		6 c. scarlet	40	1·25
D4		10 c. green	40	70
D5		20 c. bright blue	50	1·50
D6		50 c. deep magenta (1.3.54)	50	2·75
D7	D **1**	1 r. orange (1.3.54)	80	3·50
D1/7		*Set of* 7	2·75	10·00
D1/5 Perf "Specimen"		*Set of* 5	60·00	

(Typo D.L.R.)

1966–69. *Chalk-surfaced paper. Wmk* w **12**. *P* 15 × 14.

D 8	D **1**	2 c. black (11.7.67)	25	70
D 9		4 c. slate-lilac (7.1.69)	25	60
D10		6 c. red-orange (7.1.69)	25	80
		a. Perf 13½ × 14	18·00	
D11		10 c. yellow-green (16.2.67)	25	40
D12		20 c. blue (*shades*) (3.1.66)	45	1·40
D13		50 c. deep magenta (*shades*) (7.1.69)	65	2·00
D8/13		*Set of* 6	1·75	4·50

1982 (25 Oct). *Nos.* 530A/1A, 535A, 540A, 542A *and* 547A *optd as Type* D **2**, *by J. W. Dunn Printers Ltd.*

D14	10 c. on 15 c. Dutch Occupation, 1638–1710	5	5
D15	20 c. on 20 c. Van Keulen's map, *circa* 1700	5	5
D16	50 c. on 60 c. Pierre Poivre, *circa* 1767	5	8
D17	1 r. on 1 r. 20, Government House, *circa* 1840	10	12
D18	1 r. 50 on 1 r. 50, Indian immigration, 1835	15	20
D19	5 r. on 15 r. Unfurling Mauritian flag, 1968	55	60
D14/19	*Set of* 6	85	95

FISCALS USED FOR POSTAGE

INLAND REVENUE (F 1)

INLAND (F 2) REVENUE

MAURITIUS REVENUE INLAND 4 (F 3)

1889. *T* **19**, *wmk Crown CA, optd. P* 14.

R1	F **1**	4 c. carmine	3·00	6·00
R2	F **2**	4 c. lilac	4·00	9·50

(Typo D.L.R.)

1896–98. *Wmk Crown CA. P* 14.

R3	F **3**	4 c. dull purple	12·00
R4		4 c. green (1898)	12·00

Montserrat

A local post office operated on Montserrat from some time in the 18th century, although the first recorded postal marking does not occur until 1807. A branch of the British G.P.O. was established at Plymouth, the island capital, in 1852.

The stamps of Great Britain were used from 1858 until the overseas postal service reverted to local control on 1 April 1860.

In the interim period between 1860 and the introduction of Montserrat stamps in 1876 No. CC1 and a similar "uncrowned" handstamp were again used.

For illustrations of the handstamp and postmark types see BRITISH POST OFFICES ABROAD notes, following GREAT BRITAIN.

PLYMOUTH

CROWNED-CIRCLE HANDSTAMPS

CC1 CC 5 MONTSERRAT (R.) (15.7.1852) *Price on cover* £2500

Stamps of GREAT BRITAIN *cancelled* "A 08" *as Type* **2**.

1858 *to* **1860**.
Z1 1d. rose-red (1857), *perf* 14 .. £1100
Z2 4d. rose (1857)
Z3 6d. lilac (1856) .. £450
Z4 1s. green (1856)

PRICES FOR STAMPS ON COVER TO 1945

Nos. 1/2	*from* × 15
No. 3	†
Nos. 4/5	*from* × 4
Nos. 6/13	*from* × 5
Nos. 14/22	*from* × 4
No. 23	—
Nos. 24/33	*from* × 4
Nos. 35/47	*from* × 3
No. 48	—
Nos. 49/59	*from* × 3
Nos. 60/2	*from* × 15
Nos. 63/83	*from* × 3
Nos. 84/93	*from* × 4
Nos. 94/7	*from* × 3
Nos. 98/100	*from* × 8
Nos. 101/12	*from* × 5

1

MONTSERRAT
(2)

3 (Die I)

(T 1 recess D.L.R.)

1876 (Sept). *Stamps of Antigua optd with T* **2**. *Wmk Crown CC. P* 14.
1 1 1d. red .. 22·00 25·00
a. Bisected (½d.) (on cover) .. † £1700
b. Inverted "S" .. £1600 £1600
2 6d. green .. 45·00 35·00
a. Bisect (used as 2½d.) (on cover)
b. Inverted "S" .. £2500 £2500
3 6d. blue-green .. £1300
a. Inverted "S" .. £5000

No. 1 was bisected and used for a ½d. in 1883. This bisected stamp is found surcharged with a small "½" in *black* and also in *red*; both were unofficial and they did not emanate from the Montserrat P.O. The 6d. in blue-green is only known unused.

(T 3 typo D.L.R.)

1880 (Jan). *Wmk Crown CC. P* 14.
4 3 2½d. red-brown .. £325 £225
5 4d. blue .. £140 80·00

1884–85. *Wmk Crown CA. P* 14.
6 3 ½d. dull green .. 2·75 5·00
7 1 1d. red .. 9·00 20·00
a. Inverted "S" .. £1300 £1300
b. Rose-red .. 13·00 14·00
ba. Bisected vert (½d.) (on cover) .. † £1500
9 3 2½d. red-brown .. £225 £100
10 2½d. ultramarine .. 14·00 16·00
11 4d. blue .. £3250 £350
12 4d. mauve .. 8·00 10·00
10, 12 Optd "Specimen" *Set of* 2 40·00

1884 (May). *Wmk Crown CA. P* 12.
13 1 1d. red .. 55·00 45·00
a. Inverted "S" .. £3000 £2000
b. Bisected (½d.) (on cover) .. † £1700

The stamps for Montserrat were temporarily superseded by the general issue for Leeward Islands in 1890, but the following issues were in concurrent use with the stamps inscribed "LEEWARD ISLANDS" until 1 July 1956, when Leeward Islands stamps were withdrawn and invalidated.

MINIMUM PRICE

The minimum price quoted is 5p which represents a handling charge rather than a basis for valuing common stamps. For further notes about prices see introductory pages.

4 Device of the Colony

5

(Typo D.L.R.)

1903. (*a*) *Wmk Crown CA. P* 14.
14 4 ½d. grey-green and green .. 1·40 4·50
15 1d. grey-black and red .. 1·10 1·10
16 2d. grey and brown .. 5·50 8·50
17 2½d. grey and blue .. 4·00 5·50
18 3d. dull orange and deep purple .. 7·00 11·00
19 6d. dull purple and olive .. 7·00 14·00
20 1s. green and bright purple .. 12·00 18·00
21 2s. green and brown-orange .. 13·00 20·00
22 2s. 6d. green and black .. 24·00 32·00

(*b*) *Wmk Crown CC. P* 14
23 5 5s. black and scarlet .. £140 £180
14/23 .. *Set of* 10 £190 £250
14/23 Optd "Specimen" *Set of* 10 £300

1903–8. *Wmk Mult Crown CA. P* 14.
24 4 ½d. grey-green and green, **OC** .. 60 90
25 1d. grey-black and red, **C** (1908) .. 12·00 12·00
26 2d. grey and brown, **OC** .. 1·50 2·75
27 2½d. grey and blue, **C** (1905) .. 5·00 7·00
28 3d. dull orange and deep purple, **OC** .. 3·75 4·50
29 6d. dull purple and olive, **OC** .. 4·75 9·00
30 1s. green and bright purple, **C** (1908) .. 7·00 6·50
31 2s. green and orange, **C** (1908) .. 18·00 30·00
32 2s. 6d. green and black, **C** (1908) .. 30·00 32·00
33 5 5s. black and red, **C** (1907) .. 95·00 £110
24/33 .. *Set of* 10 £150 £190

1908–13. *Wmk Mult Crown CA. P* 14.
35 4 ½d. deep green, **O** .. 1·25 1·00
36 1d. rose-red, **O** .. 1·60 55
38 2d. greyish-slate, **O** .. 2·75 7·00
39 2½d. blue, **O** .. 4·00 7·00
40 3d. purple/*yellow*, **C** .. 2·75 7·50
a. White back (1913) (Optd. S. £16) .. 4·50 8·00
43 6d. dull and deep purple, **C** .. 8·50 16·00
a. Dull and bright purple .. 8·50 15·00
44 1s. black/*green*, **C** .. 7·00 12·00
45 2s. purple and bright blue/*blue*, **C** .. 24·00 30·00
46 2s. 6d. black and red/*blue*, **C** .. 30·00 38·00
47 5 5s. red and green/*yellow*, **C** .. 60·00 70·00
35/47 .. *Set of* 10 £120 £160
35/47 Optd "Specimen" *Set of* 10 £250

7

8

WAR STAMP
(9)

(T 7/8 typo D.L.R.)

1914. *Wmk Mult Crown CA. P* 14.
48 7 5s. red and green/*yellow*, **C** .. 90·00 95·00
48 Optd "Specimen" .. £140

1916–23. *Wmk Mult Crown CA. P* 14.
49 8 ½d. green, **O** .. 30 55
50 1d. scarlet, **O** .. 50 75
a. Carmine-red .. 3·75 4·00
51 2d. grey, **O** .. 1·75 5·00
52 2½d. bright blue, **O** .. 3·50 6·50
53 3d. purple/*yellow*, **C** .. 2·25 5·00
a. On pale yellow (Optd S. £19) .. 3·00 5·50
54 4d. grey-black & red/*pl yellow*, **C** (1923) 5·00 12·00
55 6d. dull and deep purple, **C** .. 4·00 11·00
56 1s. black/*blue-green* (*olive back*), **C** .. 4·50 11·00
57 2s. purple and blue/*blue*, **C** .. 7·50 15·00
58 2s. 6d. black and red/*blue*, **C** .. 15·00 24·00
59 5s. green and red/*yellow*, **C** .. 27·00 45·00
49/59 .. *Set of* 11 65·00 £120
49/59 Optd "Specimen" *Set of* 11 £180

1917 (Oct)–**18**. *No.* 49 *optd with T* **9**.
60 8 ½d. green (R.) .. 20 50
61 ½d. green (Blk.) (1918) .. 25 50
a. Deep green .. 35 50

1919. *T* **8**. *Special printing in orange. Value and* "WAR STAMP" *as T* **9** *inserted in black at one printing.*
62 1½d. black and orange .. 15 45
60/2 Optd "Specimen" *Set of* 3 80·00

1922–9. *Wmk Mult Script CA. P* 14.
63 8 ¼d. brown, **O** .. 40 85
64 ½d. green, **O** .. 30 40
65 1d. bright violet, **O** .. 40 55
66 1d. carmine, **O** (1929) .. 1·40 1·40
67 1½d. orange-yellow, **O** .. 4·25 8·50
68 1½d. carmine, **O** .. 40 1·25
69 1½d. red-brown, **O** (1929) .. 60 1·10
70 2d. grey, **O** .. 1·25 1·90
71 2½d. deep bright blue, **O** .. 4·00 6·50
a. Pale bright blue (1926) (Optd S. £28) 1·50 1·60
72 2½d. orange-yellow, **O** (1923) .. 3·50 9·00
73 3d. dull blue, **O** (1923) .. 1·10 5·00
74 3d. purple/*yellow*, **C** (1927) .. 1·60 4·75
75 4d. black and red/*pale yellow*, **C** .. 1·10 3·00
76 5d. dull purple and olive, **C** .. 5·00 10·00
77 6d. pale and bright purple, **C** .. 1·60 6·00

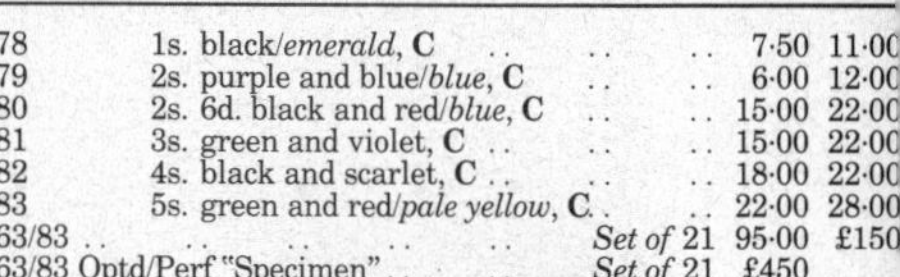
78 1s. black/*emerald*, **C** .. 7·50 11·00
79 2s. purple and blue/*blue*, **C** .. 6·00 12·00
80 2s. 6d. black and red/*blue*, **C** .. 15·00 22·00
81 3s. green and violet, **C** .. 15·00 22·00
82 4s. black and scarlet, **C** .. 18·00 22·00
83 5s. green and red/*pale yellow*, **C** .. 22·00 28·00
63/83 .. *Set of* 21 95·00 £150
63/83 Optd/Perf "Specimen" .. *Set of* 21 £450

10 Plymouth

(Recess D.L.R.)

1932 (18 April). *Tercentenary. Wmk Mult Script CA. P* 14.
84 10 ½d. green .. 1·25 2·50
85 1d. scarlet .. 1·25 2·00
86 1½d. red-brown .. 2·75 4·50
87 2d. grey .. 3·50 7·00
88 2½d. ultramarine .. 3·50 8·50
89 3d. orange .. 6·00 9·50
90 6d. violet .. 8·50 14·00
91 1s. olive-brown .. 15·00 22·00
92 2s. 6d. purple .. 85·00 £110
93 5s. chocolate .. £180 £200
84/93 .. *Set of* 10 £275 £350
84/93 Perf "Specimen" *Set of* 10 £450

1935 (6 May). *Silver Jubilee. As Nos.* 91/4 *of Antigua, but printed by Waterlow & Sons. P* 11 × 12.
94 1d. deep blue and scarlet .. 1·00 75
95 1½d. ultramarine and grey .. 85 1·60
96 2½d. brown and deep blue .. 3·25 5·50
97 1s. slate and purple .. 14·00 18·00
94/7 Perf "Specimen" *Set of* 4 75·00

1937 (12 May). *Coronation. As Nos.* 13/15 *of Aden.*
98 1d. scarlet .. 20 35
99 1½d. yellow-brown .. 30 35
100 2½d. bright blue .. 30 50
98/100 Perf "Specimen" *Set of* 3 50·00

11 Carr's Bay

12 Sea Island Cotton

13 Botanic Station

(Recess D.L.R.)

1938 (2 Aug)–**48**. *Wmk Mult Script CA.*
101 11 ½d. blue-green (*p* 13) .. 30 45
a. Perf 14 (1942) .. 12 30
102 12 1d. carmine (*p* 13) .. 45 40
a. Perf 14 (1943) .. 20 15
103 1½d. purple (*p* 13) .. 6·50 1·50
a. Perf 14 (1942) .. 12 12
104 13 2d. orange (*p* 13) .. 4·25 1·75
a. Perf 14 (1942) .. 20 15
105 12 2½d. ultramarine (*p* 13) .. 45 45
a. Perf 14 (1943) .. 20 12
106 11 3d. brown (*p* 13) .. 80 55
a. Perf 14, *Red-brown* (1942) .. 20 35
ab. Deep brown (1943) .. 3·00 3·75
107 13 6d. violet (*p* 13) .. 1·75 1·10
a. Perf 14 (1943) .. 70 35
108 11 1s. lake (*p* 13) .. 4·00 2·50
a. Perf 14 (1942) .. 90 50
109 13 2s. 6d. slate-blue (*p* 13) .. 5·50 2·50
a. Perf 14 (1943) .. 6·50 5·50
110 11 5s. rose-carmine (*p* 13) .. 16·00 12·00
a. Perf 14 (1942) .. 4·25 3·75
111 13 10s. pale blue (*p* 12) (1948) .. 16·00 22·00
112 11 £1 black (*p* 12) (1948) .. 28·00 30·00
101a/112 .. *Set of* 12 50·00 55·00
101/12 Perf "Specimen" *Set of* 12 £300

1946 (1 Nov). *Victory. As Nos.* 28/9 *of Aden.*
113 1½d. purple .. 15 15
114 3d. chocolate .. 20 15
113/14 Perf "Specimen" *Set of* 2 55·00

1949 (3 Jan). *Royal Silver Wedding. As Nos.* 30/1 *of Aden.*
115 2½d. ultramarine .. 12 12
116 5s. carmine .. 6·50 9·00

1949 (10 Oct). *75th Anniv of Universal Postal Union. As Nos.* 114/17 *of Antigua.*
117 2½d. ultramarine .. 30 40
118 3d. brown .. 40 65
119 6d. purple .. 1·00 1·10
120 1s. purple .. 1·40 1·75

(New Currency. 100 cents = 1 dollar)

1951 (16 Feb). *Inauguration of B.W.I. University College. As Nos.* 118/19 *of Antigua.*
121 3 c. black and purple .. 45 45
122 12 c. black and violet .. 80 80

14 Government House 18 Badge of Presidency

(Recess B.W.)

1951 (17 Sept). *T* **14, 18** *and similar horiz designs. Wmk Mult Script CA. P* 11½ × 11.

123	**14**	1 c. black	20	40
124	–	2 c. green	20	35
125	–	3 c. orange-brown	30	30
126	–	4 c. carmine	30	30
127	–	5 c. reddish violet	30	30
128	**18**	6 c. olive-brown	30	55
129	–	8 c. deep blue	35	35
130	–	12 c. blue and chocolate	45	50
131	–	24 c. carmine and yellow-green	75	75
132	–	60 c. black and carmine	3·00	3·25
133	–	$1.20, yellow-green and blue	8·00	8·00
134	–	$2.40, black and green	8·00	11·00
135	**18**	$4.80, black and purple	21·00	27·00
123/135		*Set of* 13	38·00	48·00

Designs:—2 c., $1.20, Sea Island cotton: cultivation; 3 c. Map of colony; 4, 24 c. Picking tomatoes; 5, 12 c. St. Anthony's Church; 8, 60 c. Sea Island cotton: ginning; $2.40, Government House.

1953 (2 June). *Coronation. As No.* 47 *of Aden.*

136	2 c. black and deep green	20	15

22 Government House

Types **16** and **18**: I. inscr "PRESIDENCY". II. inscr "COLONY".

(Recess B.W.)

1953 (15 Oct)–**58**. *As King George VI issue, but with portrait of Queen Elizabeth II as in T* **22**. *Wmk Mult Script CA. P* 11½ × 11.

136*a*	–	½ c. deep violet (I) (3.7.56)	5	5
136*b*	–	½ c. deep violet (II) (1.9.58)	5	12
137	**22**	1 c. black	5	5
138	–	2 c. green	10	5
139	–	3 c. orange-brown (I)	8	10
139*a*	–	3 c. orange-brown (II) (1.9.58)	25	15
140	–	4 c. carmine-red (1.6.55)	25	8
141	–	5 c. reddish lilac (1.6.55)	25	8
142	**18**	6 c. deep bistre-brown (I) (1.6.55)	15	10
142*a*		6 c. dp bistre-brn (II) (*shades*) (1.9.58)	40	20
143	–	8 c. deep bright blue (1.6.55)	20	10
144	–	12 c. blue and red-brown (1.6.55)	55	8
145	–	24 c. carmine-red and green (1.6.55)	70	12
145*a*	–	48 c. yellow-olive and purple (15.10.57)	5·50	2·00
146	–	60 c. black and carmine (1.6.55)	2·00	80
147	–	$1.20, green and greenish blue (1.6.55)	3·75	4·00
148	–	$2.40, black and bluish green (1.6.55)	4·25	6·50
149	**18**	$4.80, black & deep purple (I) (1.6.55)	10·00	15·00
149*a*		$4.80, black & dp purple (II) (1.9.58)	11·00	14·00
136*a*/149*a*		*Set of* 15	25·00	25·00

Extra designs:—½, 3 c. Map of colony; 48 c. Sea Island cotton: cultivation.

See also No. 157.

1958 (22 Apr). *Inauguration of British Caribbean Federation. As Nos.* 135/7 *of Antigua.*

150	3 c. deep green	15	20
151	6 c. blue	15	25
152	12 c. scarlet	20	15

1963 (8 July). *Freedom from Hunger. As No.* 76 *of Aden.*

153	12 c. reddish violet	50	20

1963 (2 Sept). *Red Cross Centenary. As Nos.* 147/8 *of Antigua.*

154	4 c. red and black	10	10
155	12 c. red and blue	55	40

1964 (23 April). *400th Birth Anniv of William Shakespeare. As No.* 164 *of Antigua.*

156	12 c. indigo	15	12

1964 (29 Oct). *As No.* 138 *but wmk* w **12**.

157	2 c. green	20	20

1965 (17 May). *I.T.U. Centenary. As Nos.* 166/7 *of Antigua.*

158	4 c. vermilion and violet	15	10
159	48 c. light emerald and carmine	55	45

23 Pineapple 24 Avocado

(Des Sylvia Goaman. Photo Harrison)

1965 (16 Aug). *T* **23/4** *and similar vert designs showing vegetables, fruit or plants. Multicoloured.* W w **12** (*upright*). *P* 15 × 14.

160	1 c. Type **23**	5	5
161	2 c. Type **24**	5	5
162	3 c. Soursop	5	5
163	4 c. Pepper	5	5
164	5 c. Mango	5	5
165	6 c. Tomato	5	5
166	8 c. Guava	8	5
167	10 c. Ochro	10	5
168	12 c. Lime	12	5
169	20 c. Orange	20	15
170	24 c. Banana	20	10
171	42 c. Onion	75	1·00
172	48 c. Cabbage	75	1·10
173	60 c. Pawpaw	1·25	1·25
174	$1.20, Pumpkin	3·50	2·25
175	$2.40, Sweet potato	8·50	4·00
176	$4.80, Egg plant	9·50	11·00
160/76	*Set of* 17	22·00	19·00

See also Nos. 213/22.

1965 (25 Oct). *International Co-operation Year. As Nos.* 168/9 *of Antigua.*

177	2 c. reddish purple and turquoise-green	10	10
178	12 c. deep bluish green and lavender	25	15

1966 (26 Jan). *Churchill Commemoration. As Nos.* 170/3 *of Antigua.*

179	1 c. new blue	5	5
180	2 c. deep green	8	5
181	24 c. brown	35	15
182	42 c. bluish violet	50	50

1966 (4 Feb). *Royal Visit. As Nos.* 174/5 *of Antigua.*

183	14 c. black and ultramarine	30	15
184	24 c. black and magenta	50	40

1966 (20 Sept). *Inauguration of W.H.O. Headquarters, Geneva. As Nos.* 178/9 *of Antigua.*

185	12 c. black, yellow-green and light blue	20	10
186	60 c. black, light purple and yellow-brown	45	25

1966 (1 Dec). *20th Anniv of U.N.E.S.C.O. As Nos.* 196/8 *of Antigua.*

187	4 c. slate-violet, red, yellow and orange	10	10
188	60 c. orange-yellow, violet and deep olive	25	25
189	$1.80, black, bright purple and orange	1·75	2·10

25 Yachting (26)

(Des and photo Harrison)

1967 (29 Dec). *International Tourist Year. T* **25** *and similar multicoloured designs.* W w **12** (*sideways on* 15 *c.*). *P* 14.

190	5 c. Type **25**	5	5
191	15 c. Waterfall near Chance Mountain (*vert*)	12	12
192	16 c. Fishing, skin-diving and swimming	12	12
193	24 c. Playing golf	20	15

1968 (6 May). *Nos.* 168, 170, 172 *and* 174/6 *surch as T* **26**. W w **12** (*upright*).

194	15 c. on 12 c. Lime	20	15
195	25 c. on 24 c. Banana	35	20
196	50 c. on 48 c. Cabbage	65	35
197	$1 on $1.20, Pumpkin	1·75	1·50
198	$2.50 on $2.40, Sweet potato	4·50	4·50
199	$5 on $4.80, Egg plant	6·00	6·00
194/9	*Set of* 6	12·00	12·00

See also Nos. 219 etc.

27 Sprinting 28 Sprinting, and Aztec Pillars

(Des G. Vasarhelyi. Photo Harrison)

1968 (31 July). *Olympic Games, Mexico. T* **27/8** *and similar designs.* W w **12** (*sideways on* $1). *P* 14.

200	15 c. deep claret, emerald and gold	5	5
201	25 c. blue, orange and gold	10	10
202	50 c. green, red and gold	25	15
203	$1 multicoloured	40	60

Designs: *Horiz as T* **27**—25 c. Weightlifting; 50 c. Gymnastics.

31 Alexander Hamilton

(Des and photo Harrison)

1968 (6 Dec*). *Human Rights Year. T* **31** *and similar horiz designs. Multicoloured.* W w **12**. *P* 14 × 14½.

204	5 c. Type **31**	5	5
205	15 c. Albert T. Marryshow	8	10
206	25 c. William Wilberforce	10	12
207	50 c. Dag Hammarskjöld	25	25
208	$1 Dr. Martin Luther King	50	60

*Although first day covers were postmarked 2 December, these stamps were not put on sale in Montserrat until 6 December.

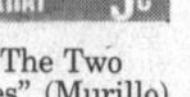

32 "The Two Trinities" (Murillo) 33 "The Adoration of the Kings" (detail, Botticelli)

(Des and photo Harrison)

1968 (16 Dec). *Christmas.* W w **12** (*sideways*). *P* 14½ × 14.

209	**32**	5 c. multicoloured	5	5
210	**33**	15 c. multicoloured	8	8
211	**32**	25 c. multicoloured	12	12
212	**33**	50 c. multicoloured	25	30

1969–70. *As Nos.* 160/4, 167, 169 *and* 194/6 *but wmk* w **12** *sideways*.

213	1 c. Type **23** (24.6.69)	8	8
214	2 c. Type **24** (23.4.70)	75	60
215	3 c. Soursop (24.6.69)	20	20
216	4 c. Pepper (24.6.69)	25	25
217	5 c. Mango (23.4.70)	1·00	75
218	10 c. Ochro (24.6.69)	65	50
219	15 c. on 12 c. Lime (24.6.69)	75	75
220	20 c. Orange (17.3.69)	85	90
221	25 c. on 24 c. Banana (24.6.69)	1·40	1·50
222	50 c. on 48 c. Cabbage (24.6.69)	2·75	4·00
213/22	*Set of* 10	7·50	8·50

The 1 c., 3 c., 4 c., 10 c., 15 c. and 20 c. exist with PVA gum as well as gum arabic, but the 2 c. and 5 c. exist with PVA gum only.

34 Map showing "CARIFTA" Countries 35 "Strength in Unity"

(Des J. Cooter. Photo Harrison)

1969 (27 May). *First Anniv of CARIFTA (Caribbean Free Trade Area).* W w **12** (*sideways on T* **34**). *P* 14.

223	**34**	15 c. multicoloured	8	8
224		20 c. multicoloured	8	8
225	**35**	35 c. multicoloured	12	12
226		50 c. multicoloured	20	30

36 Telephone Receiver and Map of Montserrat 40 Dolphin

(Des R. Reid, adapted by V. Whiteley. Litho P.B.)

1969 (29 July). *Development Projects. T* **36** *and similar vert designs. Multicoloured.* W w **12**. *P* 13½.

227	15 c. Type **36**	10	8
228	25 c. School symbols and map	15	12
229	50 c. "HS 748" aircraft and map	20	25
230	$1 Electricity pylon and map	40	60

(Des Harrison. Photo Enschedé)

1969 (1 Nov). *Game Fish. T* **40** *and similar horiz designs. Multicoloured. P* 13 × 13½.

231	5 c. Type **40**	10	5
232	15 c. Atlantic sailfish	25	10
233	25 c. Blackfin tuna	35	20
234	40 c. Spanish mackerel	55	45

PRICES OF SETS

Set prices are given for many issues, generally those containing five stamps or more. Definitive sets include one of each value or major colour change, but do not cover different perforations, die types or minor shades. Where a choice is possible the set prices are based on the cheapest versions of the stamps included in the listings.

41 King Caspar before the Virgin and Child (detail) (Norman 16th-cent stained glass window) 42 "Nativity" (Leonard Limosin)

(Des J. Cooter. Litho D.L.R.)

1969 (10 Dec). *Christmas. Paintings multicoloured; frame colours given.* W w **12** (*sideways on* 50 c.). *P* 13.

235	**41**	15 c. black, gold and violet	8	8
236		25 c. black and vermilion	12	12
237	**42**	50 c. black, ultramarine & yellow-orange	20	30

43 "Red Cross Sale"

(Des and litho J.W.)

1970 (13 Apr). *Centenary of British Red Cross. T* **43** *and similar horiz designs. Multicoloured.* W w **12** (*sideways*). *P* 14½ × 14.

238	3 c. Type **43**	5	5
239	4 c. School for deaf children	5	5
240	15 c. Transport services for disabled	12	15
241	20 c. Workshop	12	15

44 Red-footed Booby 45 "Madonna and Child with Animals" (Brueghel the Elder, after Dürer)

(Des V. Whiteley. Photo Harrison)

1970 (2 July)–**74**. *Birds. T* **44** *and similar multicoloured designs.* W w **12** (*sideways on vert designs and upright on horiz designs*). *P* 14 × 14½ (*horiz*) *or* 14½ × 14 (*vert*).

A. *Chalk-surfaced paper* (2.7.70).
B. *Glazed, ordinary paper* (30.10.74, $10; 22.1.71, *others*).

		A		B	
242	1 c. Type **44**	8	8	†	
243	2 c. American Kestrel	12	12	25	40
244	3 c. Magnificent Frigate Bird	12	12	†	
245	4 c. Great Egret	15	12	†	
246	5 c. Brown Pelican	15	12	30	35
247	10 c. Bananaquit	25	20	55	40
248	15 c. Smooth-billed Ani	30	30	90	90
249	20 c. Red-billed Tropic Bird	35	35	75	65
250	25 c. Montserrat Oriole	50	50	1·25	1·25
251	50 c. Green-throated Carib	1·50	85	2·00	2·25
252	$1 Antillean Crested Humming-bird	2·50	1·75	3·75	4·00
253	$2.50, Little Blue Heron	3·00	3·50	6·50	7·50
254	$5 Purple-throated Carib	7·00	9·00	14·00	15·00
254*a*	$10 Forest Thrush	†		13·00	13·00
242A/54A	*Set of* 13	14·50	15·00		
243B/54*a*B	*Set of* 11			38·00	40·00

The 1 c. 15 c., 20 c., 25 c., $1, $5 and $10 are horizontal, and the remainder are vertical designs.

See also Nos. 295/302.

(Des G. Drummond. Litho D.L.R.)

1970 (1 Oct).* *Christmas. T* **45** *and similar multicoloured design.* W w **12**. *P* 13½ × 14.

255	5 c. Type **45**	10	5
256	15 c. "The Adoration of the Shepherds" (Domenichino)	15	12
257	20 c. Type **45**	15	15
258	$1 As 15 c.	70	80

*This was the local date of issue but the stamps were released by the Crown Agents on 21 September.

46 War Memorial 47 Girl Guide and Badge

(Des V. Whiteley. Litho J.W.)

1970 (30 Nov). *Tourism. T* **46** *and similar horiz designs. Multicoloured.* W w **12** (*sideways*). *P* 14½ × 14.

259	5 c. Type **46**	10	8
260	15 c. Plymouth from Fort St. George	20	12
261	25 c. Carr's Bay	25	20
262	50 c. Golf Fairway	65	50
MS263	135 × 109 mm. Nos. 259/62	2·00	2·50

(Des V. Whiteley. Litho Questa)

1970 (31 Dec). *Diamond Jubilee of Montserrat Girl Guides. T* **47** *and similar vert design. Multicoloured.* W w **12**. *P* 14.

264	10 c. Type **47**	12	10
265	15 c. Brownie and Badge	15	15
266	25 c. As 15 c.	25	25
267	40 c. Type **47**	50	40

48 "Descent from the Cross" (Van Hemessen) 49 D.F.C. and D.F.M. in Searchlights

(Des J.W. Photo Enschedé)

1971 (22 Mar). *Easter. T* **48** *and similar vert design. Multicoloured.* W w **12**. *P* 13½.

268	5 c. Type **48**	8	5
269	15 c. "Noli me tangere" (Orcagna)	12	20
270	20 c. Type **48**	15	15
271	40 c. As 15 c.	20	30

(Des Col. A. Maynard. Litho Questa)

1971 (8 July). *Golden Jubilee of Commonwealth Ex-Services League. T* **49** *and similar vert designs. Multicoloured.* W w **12**. *P* 14.

272	10 c. Type **49**	10	10
273	20 c. M.C., M.M. and jungle patrol	20	20
274	40 c. D.S.C., D.S.M. and submarine action	35	40
275	$1 V.C. and soldier attacking bunker	1·00	1·25

50 "The Nativity with Saints" (Romanino) 51 Piper "Apache"

(Des G. Drummond. Litho Questa)

1971 (16 Sept). *Christmas. T* **50** *and similar vert design. Multicoloured.* W w **12**. *P* 14 × 13½.

276	5 c. Type **50**	10	5
277	15 c. "Choir of Angels" (Simon Marmion)	15	15
278	20 c. Type **50**	15	15
279	$1 As 15 c.	80	90

(Des and litho J.W.)

1971 (16 Dec). *14th Anniv of Inauguration of L.I.A.T. (Leeward Islands Air Transport). T* **51** *and similar horiz designs. Multicoloured.* W w **12** (*sideways*). *P* 13½.

280	5 c. Type **51**	8	8
281	10 c. Beech "Twin Bonanza"	12	12
282	15 c. De Havilland "Heron"	35	35
283	20 c. Britten Norman "Islander"	40	40
284	40 c. De Havilland "Twin Otter"	1·00	75
285	75 c. Hawker Siddeley "748"	2·75	2·50
280/5	*Set of* 6	4·00	3·75
MS286	203 × 102 mm. Nos. 280/5	10·00	11·00

52 "Chapel of Christ in Gethsemane", Coventry Cathedral 53 Lizard

(Des G. Drummond. Litho A. & M.)

1972 (9 Mar). *Easter. T* **52** *and similar horiz design. Multicoloured.* W w **12**. *P* 13.

287	5 c. Type **52**	8	8
288	10 c. "The Agony in the Garden" (Bellini)	12	12
289	20 c. Type **52**	20	20
290	75 c. As 10 c.	70	1·00

(Des G. Drummond. Litho Questa)

1972 (20 July). *Reptiles. T* **53** *and similar multicoloured designs.* W w **12** (*sideways on* 40 c. *and* $1). *P* 14½.

291	15 c. Type **53**	15	15
292	20 c. Mountain Chicken (frog)	20	20
293	40 c. Iguana (*horiz*)	40	45
294	$1 Tortoise (*horiz*)	2·50	2·50

1972 (21 July)–**74**. *As No.* 242 *etc., but* W w **12**, *sideways on horiz designs* (1, 15, 20, 25 c.) *and upright on vert designs* (*others*). *Glazed, ordinary paper.*

295	1 c. Type **44**	20	30
	a. Chalk-surfaced paper (4.2.74)	40	30
296	2 c. American Kestrel	40	25
	a. Chalk-surfaced paper (4.2.74)	40	30
297	3 c. Magnificent Frigate Bird	40	30
298	4 c. Great Egret (*chalk-surfaced paper*) (4.2.74)	30	45
299	5 c. Brown Pelican (8.3.73)	40	15
	a. Chalk-surfaced paper (4.2.74)	40	55
300	15 c. Smooth-billed Ani (8.3.73)	35	40
	a. Chalk-surfaced paper (2.10.73)	70	1·00
301	20 c. Red-billed Tropic Bird (*chalk-surfaced paper*) (2.10.73)	90	1·25
302	25 c. Montserrat Oriole (*chalk-surfaced paper*) (17.5.74)	2·50	2·75
295/302	*Set of* 8	5·00	5·25

54 "Madonna of the Chair" (Raphael)

(Des J. Cooter. Litho Format)

1972 (18 Oct). *Christmas. T* **54** *and similar horiz designs. Multicoloured.* W w **12**. *P* 13½.

303	10 c. Type **54**	12	12
304	35 c. "Virgin and Child with Cherub" (Fungai)	30	15
305	50 c. "Madonna of the Magnificat" (Botticelli)	90	1·00
306	$1 "Virgin and Child with St. John and an Angel" (Botticelli)	1·25	1·50

55 Lime, Tomatoes and Pawpaw 56 *Passiflora herbertiana*

(Des (from photographs by D. Groves) and photo Harrison)

1972 (20 Nov). *Royal Silver Wedding. Multicoloured; background colour given.* W w **12**. *P* 14 × 14½.

307	**55**	35 c. rose	25	25
308		$1 bright blue	30	40

(Des J. Cooter. Litho Walsall)

1973 (9 Apr). *Easter. T* **56** *and similar vert designs showing passion-flowers. Multicoloured.* W w **12**. *P* 13½.

309	20 c. Type **56**	30	25
310	35 c. *P. vitifolia*	45	40
311	75 c. *P. amabilis*	2·75	2·25
312	$1 *P. alata-caerulea*	3·00	2·50

Nos. 309/12 are inscribed on the reverse with information about the passion-flower.

ALTERED CATALOGUE NUMBERS

Any Catalogue numbers altered from the last edition are shown as a list in the introductory pages.

57 Montserrat Monastery, Spain **58** "Virgin and Child" (School of Gerard David)

(Des J. Cooter. Litho Format)

1973 (9 July). *480th Anniv of Columbus's Discovery of Montserrat. T* **57** *and similar horiz designs. Multicoloured.* W w **12**. *P* 13½.

313	10 c. Type **57**	15	15
314	35 c. Columbus sighting Montserrat	45	45
315	60 c. Columbus's ship off Montserrat	2·25	2·50
316	$1 Colony badge and map of voyage ..	2·75	3·00
MS317	126 × 134 mm. Nos. 313/16	18·00	19·00

(Des J. Cooter. Litho Questa)

1973 (22 Oct). *Christmas. T* **58** *and similar vert designs. Multicoloured.* W w **12** (*sideways*). *P* 13½.

318	20 c. Type **58**	20	15
319	35 c. "The Holy Family with St. John" (Jordaens)	30	20
320	50 c. "Virgin and Child" (Bellini)	1·25	1·40
321	90 c. "Virgin and Child with Flowers" (Dolci)	2·25	2·25

1973 (14 Nov). *Royal Wedding. As Nos.* 165/6 *of Anguilla. Centre multicoloured.* W w **12** (*sideways*). *P* 13½.

322	35 c. sage-green	20	10
323	$1 violet-blue	30	30

59 Steel Band

(Des J. W. Litho Questa)

1974 (8 Apr). *25th Anniv of University of West Indies. T* **59** *and similar designs. Multicoloured.* W w **12** (*sideways on* 20 c., $1 *and* **MS**328).

324	20 c. Type **59**	25	25
325	35 c. Masqueraders (*vert*)	45	45
326	60 c. Student weaving (*vert*)	1·90	1·90
327	$1 University Centre, Montserrat	2·10	2·10
MS328	130 × 89 mm. Nos. 324/7	9·00	9·00

60 Hands with Letters

02¢
═══
(61)

(Des P. Powell. Litho Walsall)

1974 (3 July). *Centenary of Universal Postal Union. T* **60** *and similar horiz design.* W w **12**. *P* 14½ × 14.

329	**60**	1 c. multicoloured	5	5
330	–	2 c. lt rose-red, orange-verm & blk ..	5	5
331	**60**	3 c. multicoloured	8	8
332	–	5 c. lt yellow-orange, reddish orge & blk	12	12
333	**60**	50 c. multicoloured	50	50
334	–	$1 pale blue, turquoise-blue and black	1·10	1·10
329/34		.. .. *Set of* 6	1·75	1·75

Designs:—2 c., 5 c., $1 Figures from U.P.U. Monument.

1974 (2 Oct). *Various stamps surch as T* **61**.

335	2 c. on $1 (No. 252B)	75	75
336	5 c. on 50 c. (No. 333)	1·00	1·25
337	10 c. on 60 c. (No. 326)	4·00	4·50
338	20 c. on $1 (No. 252B)	1·50	1·75
339	35 c. on $1 (No. 334)	3·00	3·00

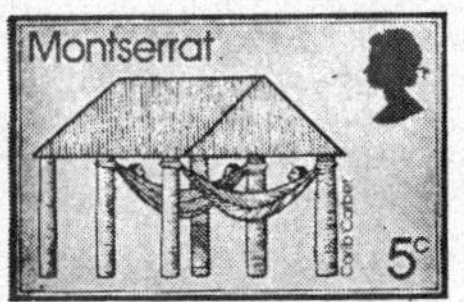

62 Churchill and Houses of Parliament **63** Carib "Carbet"

(Des R. Granger Barrett. Litho D.L.R.)

1974 (30 Nov). *Birth Centenary of Sir Winston Churchill. T* **62** *and similar vert design. Multicoloured. No wmk. P* 13 × 13½.

340	35 c. Type **62**	20	25
341	70 c. Churchill and Blenheim Palace	40	45
MS342	81 × 85 mm. Nos. 340/1	80	95

(Des C. Abbott. Litho Walsall)

1975 (3 Mar). *Carib Artefacts. T* **63** *and similar horiz designs.*

(*a*) W w **12** (*sideways*). *From sheets. P* 14

343	5 c. lake-brown, yellow and black	10	8
344	20 c. black, lake-brown and yellow	15	15
345	35 c. black, yellow and lake-brown	25	25
346	70 c. yellow, lake-brown and black	50	65

(*b*) *No wmk. Self-adhesive with advertisements on the reverse. From booklets. Rouletted*

347	5 c. lake-brown, yellow and black	12	25
	a. Booklet pane. Nos. 347/50 *se-tenant* ..	90	
348	20 c. black, lake-brown and yellow	15	25
	a. Booklet pane. Nos. 348 × 3 and No. 349 × 3	90	
349	35 c. black, yellow and lake-brown	15	25
350	20 c. yellow, lake-brown and black	55	70

Designs:—20 c. "Caracoli"; 35 c. Club or mace; 70 c. Canoe.

64 One-Bitt Coin

(Des J. Cooter. Litho Questa)

1975 (1 Sept). *Local Coinage,* 1785–1801. *T* **64** *and similar diamond-shaped designs.* W w **14** (*sideways*). *P* 13½.

351	5 c. black, light violet-blue and silver ..	8	8
352	10 c. black, salmon and silver	15	15
353	35 c. black, light blue-green and silver ..	35	35
354	$2 black, bright rose and silver	2·50	2·75
MS355	142 × 142 mm. Nos. 351/4	3·00	3·75

Designs:—10 c. Eighth dollar; 35 c. Quarter dollar; $2 One dollar.

No. **MS**355 has details of the coins depicted printed on the reverse side, beneath the gum.

65 1d. and 6d. Stamps of 1876 **66** "The Trinity"

(Des J. Cooter. Litho J. W.)

1976 (5 Jan). *Centenary of First Montserrat Postage Stamp. T* **65** *and similar horiz designs.* W w **12** (*sideways*). *P* 13.

356	5 c. deep carmine, yellowish green and black	10	10
357	10 c. light yellow-ochre, scarlet and black ..	15	15
358	40 c. multicoloured	50	50
359	55 c. deep mauve, yellowish green and black	60	60
360	70 c. multicoloured	80	80
361	$1.10, yellowish green, brt blue & grey-blk ..	1·25	1·25
356/61	.. .. *Set of* 6	3·00	3·00
MS362	170 × 159 mm. Nos. 356/61. P 13½ ..	4·00	4·50

Designs:—10 c. G.P.O. and bisected 1d. stamp; 40 c. Bisects on cover; 55 c. G.B. 6d. used in Montserrat and local 6d. of 1876; 70 c. Stamps for 2½d. rate, 1876; $1.10, Packet boat *Antelope* and 6d. stamp.

(Des J. Cooter. Litho Questa)

1976 (5 Apr). *Easter. Unissued stamps prepared for Easter* 1975 *with values and date obliterated by black bars. T* **66** *and similar vert designs showing paintings by Orcagna. Multicoloured.* W w **14**. *P* 13½.

363	15 c. on 5 c. Type **66**	12	12
364	40 c. on 35 c. "The Resurrection"	20	25
365	55 c. on 70 c. "The Ascension"	30	35
366	$1.10 on $1 "Pentecost"	50	70
MS367	160 × 142 mm. Nos. 363/6	1·50	2·25
	a. Surch omitted	£200	

For No. 363 the "1" was added to the original 5 c. to make 15 c.

2¢
═══
(67)

68 White Frangipani

1976 (12 Apr). *Nos.* 244A, 246A *and* 247A *surch as T* **67**.

368	2 c. on 5 c. Brown Pelican	8	12
369	30 c. on 10 c. Bananaquit	15	25
370	45 c. on 3 c. Magnificent Frigate Bird ..	30	35
	a. Surch triple		
	b. Surch double	40·00	

(Des J. Cooter. Litho Questa)

1976 (5 July)–**80**. *Various horiz designs showing Flowering Trees as T* **68**. *Multicoloured. Ordinary paper.* W w **14** (*sideways*). *P* 13½.

371	1 c. Type **68**	5	5
372	2 c. Cannon-ball Tree	10	5
373	3 c. Lignum vitae	10	5
374	5 c. Malay apple	12	5
375	10 c. Jacaranda	20	5
376	15 c. Orchid Tree	25	8
	a. Chalk-surfaced paper (8.80)	45	45
377	20 c. Manjak	25	8
	a. Chalk-surfaced paper (8.80)	45	45
378	25 c. Tamarind	25	10
379	40 c. Flame of the Forest	35	20
380	55 c. Pink Cassia	40	25
381	70 c. Long John	50	30
382	$1 Saman	65	40
383	$2.50, Immortelle	1·75	1·75
384	$5 Yellow Poui	3·25	3·25
385	$10 Flamboyant	6·00	6·50
371/85	.. .. *Set of* 15	13·00	12·00

69 Mary and Joseph **70** Hudson River Review, 1976

(Des L. Curtis. Litho Format)

1976 (4 Oct). *Christmas. T* **69** *and similar vert designs. Multicoloured.* W w **14**. *P* 14.

386	15 c. Type **69**	12	10
387	20 c. The Shepherds	20	10
388	55 c. Mary and Jesus	35	30
389	$1.10, The Magi	75	70
MS390	95 × 135 mm. Nos. 386/9	1·50	2·00

(Des and litho J.W.)

1976 (13 Dec). *Bicentenary of American Revolution. T* **70** *and similar vert designs. Multicoloured.* W w **14**. *P* 13.

391	15 c. Type **70**	30	20
392	40 c. } The *Raleigh* attacking	60	40
393	75 c. } H.M.S. *Druid*, 1777*	70	45
394	$1.25, Hudson River Review	1·50	75
MS395	95 × 145 mm. Nos. 391/4. P 13½ ..	3·75	3·75

*The date is wrongly given on the stamps as "1776".

Nos. 392/3 and 391 and 394 were printed in horizontal *se-tenant* pairs throughout the sheet, each pair forming a composite design.

71 The Crowning **72** *Ipomoea alba*

(Des G. Vasarhelyi. Litho J.W.)

1977 (7 Feb). *Silver Jubilee. T* **71** *and similar horiz designs. Multicoloured.* W w **14** (*sideways*). *P* 13.

396	30 c. Royal Visit, 1966	35	45
397	45 c. Cannons firing salute	40	50
398	$1 Type **71**	60	85

(Des J. Cooter. Litho Questa)

1977 (1 June). *Flowers of the Night. T* **72** *and similar multi-coloured designs.* W w **14** (*sideways on* 40 *and* 55 c.). *P* 14.

399	15 c. Type **72**	15	10
400	40 c. *Epiphyllum hookeri* (*horiz*)	40	30
401	55 c. *Cereus hexagonus* (*horiz*)	50	45
402	$1.50, *Cestrum nocturnum*	1·75	1·25
MS403	126 × 130 mm. Nos. 399/402. Wmk sideways	2·75	3·00

73 Princess Anne laying Foundation Stone of Glendon Hospital

(Des BG Studio. Litho Questa)

1977 (3 Oct). *Development. T* **73** *and similar horiz designs. Multi-coloured.* W w **14** (*sideways*). *P* 14½ × 14.

404	20 c. Type **73**	15	10
405	40 c. Ship in Plymouth Port	30	25

406 55 c. Glendon Hospital 40 30
407 $1.50, Jetty at Plymouth Port .. .. 1·10 1·00
MS408 146 × 105 mm. Nos. 404/7 .. .. 2·50 2·25

$1.00

SILVER JUBILEE 1977
ROYAL VISIT
TO THE CARIBBEAN

(74)

1977 (28 Oct). *Royal Visit. Nos.* 380/1 *and* 383 *surch locally with* T **74**.
409 $1 on 55 c. Pink Cassia 55 55
410 $1 on 70 c. Long John 55 55
411 $1 on $2.50, Immortelle 55 55

75 The Stable at Bethlehem **76** Four-eye Butterflyfish

(Des L. Curtis. Litho Walsall)

1977 (14 Nov). *Christmas.* T **75** *and similar vert designs. Multi-coloured.* W w **14**. *P* 14 × 14½.
412 5 c. Type **75** 5 5
413 40 c. The Three Kings 20 20
414 55 c. Three Ships 30 30
415 $2 Three Angels .. .. .. 95 1·25
MS416 119 × 115 mm. Nos. 412/15 .. .. 1·60 1·90

(Des J.W. Litho Walsall)

1978 (15 Mar). *Fish.* T **76** *and similar horiz designs. Multi-coloured.* W w **14** (*sideways*). *P* 14.
417 30 c. Type **76** 25 20
418 40 c. French Angelfish 30 25
419 55 c. Blue Tang 45 35
420 $1.50, Queen Triggerfish .. .. 1·50 1·40
MS421 152 × 102 mm. Nos. 417/20 .. .. 3·00 2·50

77 St. Paul's Cathedral **78** *Alpinia speciosa*

(Des G. Drummond. Litho J.W.)

1978 (2 June). *25th Anniv of Coronation.* T **77** *and similar horiz designs. Multicoloured.* W w **14** (*sideways*). *P* 13.
422 40 c. Type **77** 15 20
423 55 c. Chichester Cathedral 30 25
424 $1 Lincoln Cathedral 65 45
425 $2.50, Llandaff Cathedral .. .. .. 1·00 90
MS426 130 × 102 mm. Nos. 422/5. P 13½ × 14 .. 1·90 1·75
Nos. 422/5 were each printed in sheets including two *se-tenant* stamp-size labels.

(Des J. Cooter. Litho J.W.)

1978 (18 Sept). *Flowers.* T **78** *and similar vert designs. Multi-coloured.* W w **14**. *P* 13½ × 13.
427 40 c. Type **78** 25 15
428 55 c. *Allamanda cathartica* 35 25
429 $1 *Petrea volubilis* 60 55
430 $2 *Hippeastrum puniceum* .. .. .. 1·25 1·00

79 Private, 21st (Royal North British Fusiliers), 1796 **80** Cub Scouts

(Des J.W. Litho Questa)

1978 (20 Nov). *Military Uniforms (1st series).* T **79** *and similar vert designs showing soldiers from British infantry regiments. Multicoloured.* W w **14**. *P* 14 × 14½.
431 30 c. Type **79** 20 20
432 40 c. Corporal, 86th (Royal County Down), 1831 .. .. 25 25
433 55 c. Sergeant, 14th (Buckinghamshire) 1837 40 40
434 $1.50, Officer, 55th (Westmorland), 1784 .. 95 95
MS435 140 × 89 mm. Nos. 431/4 .. .. .. 1·75 1·90
See also Nos. 441/5.

(Des J. W. Litho Walsall)

1979 (2 Apr). *50th Anniv of Boy Scout Movement on Montserrat.* T **80** *and similar multicoloured designs.* W w **14** (*sideways on* 40 *and* 55 c). *P* 14.
436 40 c. Type **80** 20 10
437 55 c. Scouts with signalling equipment .. 30 20
438 $1.25, Camp fire (*vert*) 60 55
439 $2 Oath ceremony (*vert*) .. .. 1·00 1·00
MS440 120 × 110 mm. Nos. 436/9 .. .. 2·25 2·25

(Des J.W. Litho Questa)

1979 (4 June). *Military Uniforms (2nd series). Vert designs as* T **79** *showing soldiers from infantry regiments. Multicoloured.* W w **14**. *P* 14 × 14½.
441 30 c. Private, 60th (Royal American), 1783 .. 20 20
442 40 c. Private, 1st West India, 1819 .. .. 25 25
443 55 c. Officer, 5th (Northumberland), 1819 .. 40 40
444 $2.50, Officer, 93rd (Sutherland Highlanders), 1830 .. .. 1·40 1·40
MS445 139 × 89 mm. Nos. 441/4 .. .. 2·25 2·50

81 Child reaching out to Adult

(Des G. Vasarhelyi. Litho Questa)

1979 (17 Sept). *International Year of the Child.* W w **14** (*sideways*). *P* 13½ × 14.
446 **81** $2 black, orange-brown and flesh .. 85 90
MS447 85 × 99 mm. No. 446 .. .. .. 3·50 4·00

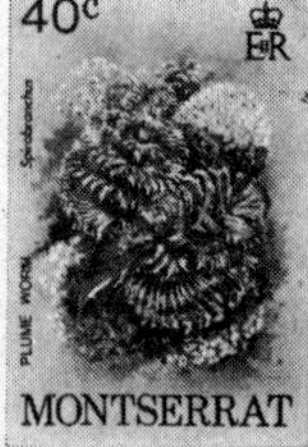

82 Sir Rowland Hill with Penny Black and Montserrat 1876 1d. Stamp **83** Plume Worm

(Des G. Vasarhelyi. Litho Questa)

1979 (1 Oct). *Death Centenary of Sir Rowland Hill and Centenary of U.P.U. Membership.* T **82** *and similar horiz designs. Multi-coloured.* W w **14** (*sideways*). *P* 14.
448 40 c. Type **82** 25 10
449 55 c. U.P.U. emblem and notice announcing Leeward Islands entry into Union .. 35 30
450 $1 1883 Letter following U.P.U. membership 55 60
451 $2 Great Britain Post Office Regulations notice and Sir Rowland Hill 80 95
MS452 135 × 154 mm. Nos. 448/51 .. .. 4·00 5·00

(Des G. Drummond. Litho Walsall)

1979 (26 Nov). *Marine Life.* T **83** *and similar vert designs. Multi-coloured.* W w **14**. *P* 14.
453 40 c. Type **83** 20 20
454 55 c. Sea Fans 30 30
455 $2 Coral and Sponge .. .. .. 1·00 1·00

84 Tree Frog

(Des J. Cooter. Litho Rosenbaum Bros, Vienna)

1980 (4 Feb). *Reptiles and Amphibians.* T **84** *and similar horiz designs. Multicoloured.* W w **14** (*sideways*). *P* 13½.
456 40 c. Type **84** 20 20
457 55 c. Tree Lizard 30 30
458 $1 Crapaud 55 55
459 $2 Wood Slave 90 90

85 *The Marquess of Salisbury* and 1838 Handstamps

75th Anniversary of
Rotary International

(86)

(Des BG Studio. Litho Questa)

1980 (14 Apr). *"London 1980" International Stamp Exhibition.* T **85** *and similar horiz designs. Multicoloured.* W w **14** (*sideways*). *P* 14.
460 40 c. Type **85** 20 25
461 55 c. "H.S. 748" aircraft and 1976 55 c. definitive 30 35
462 $1.20, *La Plata* (steam ship) and 1903 5s. stamp 50 60
463 $1.20, *Lady Hawkins* (steam ship) and 1932 Tercentenary 5s. commemorative .. 50 60
464 $1.20, *Avon* (paddle steamer) and Penny Red stamp with "A 08" postmark .. 50 60
465 $1.20, "Aeronca" aeroplane and 1953 $1.20 definitive 50 60
460/5 .. .. *Set of* 6 2·25 2·75
MS466 115 × 110 mm. Nos. 460/5. P 12 .. 2·50 3·00
Nos. 460/5 were each printed in sheets of 4 stamps and two *se-tenant* stamp-size labels.
Some sheets of No. 462 showed the red colour omitted from the map in the right-hand label.

1980 (7 July). *75th Anniv of Rotary International. No.* 383 *optd with* T **86**.
467 $2.50, Immortelle .. .. 1·10 1·25

87 Greek, French and U.S.A. Flags

(Des A. Theobald. Litho Questa)

1980 (7 July). *Olympic Games, Moscow.* T **87** *and similar horiz designs. Multicoloured.* W w **14** (*sideways*). *P* 13½ × 14.
468 40 c. Type **87** 15 20
469 55 c. Union, Swedish and Belgian flags .. 25 30
470 70 c. French, Dutch and U.S.A. flags .. 30 35
471 $1 German, Union and Finnish flags .. 45 50
472 $1.50, Australian, Italian and Japanese flags 65 70
473 $2 Mexican, West German and Canadian flags 90 95
474 $2.50, "The Discus Thrower" (sculpture by Miron) .. .. 1·10 1·25
468/74 .. .. .. *Set of* 7 3·50 3·75
MS475 150 × 100 mm. Nos. 468/74 .. .. 3·50 3·75
a. Bottom row of stamps in miniature sheet imperf on 3 sides £475
Nos. 468/74 were each printed in small sheets of 4 including one *se-tenant* stamp-size label.
No. **MS**475a shows the three stamps in the bottom row of the miniature sheet imperforate vertically and with no perforations between the stamps and the bottom margin.

XX 5¢

(88)

89 S.S. *Lady Nelson*, 1928

1980 (30 Sept). *Nos.* 371, 373, 376 *and* 379 *surch as* T **88**.
476 5 c. on 3 c. Lignum vitae 5 5
a. Surch double, one inverted .. .. 55·00
477 35 c. on 1 c. Type **68** 20 20
478 35 c. on 3 c. Lignum vitae 20 20
479 35 c. on 15 c. Orchid Tree 20 20
480 55 c. on 40 c. Flame of the Forest .. 30 30
a. Surch inverted .. .. .. 80·00
481 $5 on 40 c. Flame of the Forest .. .. 2·50 2·75
476/81 .. .. .. *Set of* 6 3·25 3·25

(Des J.W. Litho Walsall)

1980 (3 Nov). *Mail Packet Boats (1st series).* T **89** *and similar horiz designs. Multicoloured.* W w **14** (*sideways*). *P* 14.
482 40 c. Type **89** 20 20
483 55 c. R.M.S.P. *Chignecto*, 1913 .. .. 30 30
484 $1 R.M.S.P. *Solent*, 1878 .. .. 55 55
485 $2 R.M.S.P. *Dee*, 1841 .. .. .. 95 95
See also Nos. 615/19.

90 *Heliconius charitonius* **91** Spadefish

(Des J.W. Litho Questa)

1981 (2 Feb). *Butterflies.* T **90** *and similar square designs. Multi-coloured.* W w **14** (*inverted*). *P* 14.
486 50 c. Type **90** 60 50
487 65 c. *Pyrgus oileus* 70 60
488 $1.50, *Phoebis agarithe* 90 95
489 $2.50, *Danaus plexippus* .. .. .. 1·25 1·40
Nos. 486/9 were each printed in sheets including two *se-tenant* stamp-size labels.

(Des G. Drummond. Litho J.W.)

1981 (20 Mar). *Fishes. Vert designs as T* **91**. *Multicoloured. W* w **14**. *P* 13½ × 13.

490 5 c. Type **91** 10 5
491 10 c. Hogfish 10 5
492 15 c. Creole Wrasse 15 5
493 20 c. Yellow Damselfish 15 10
494 25 c. Sergeant Major 20 12
495 35 c. Clown Wrasse 25 20
496 45 c. Schoolmaster 30 25
497 55 c. Striped Parrotfish 40 30
498 65 c. Bigeye 40 30
499 75 c. French Grunt 50 35
500 $1 Rock Beauty 60 45
501 $2 Blue Chromis .. .. 1·00 90
502 $3 Fairy Basslet and Blueheads .. .. 1·60 1·60
503 $5 Cherubfish .. .. 2·75 2·75
504 $7.50, Longspine Squirrelfish .. .. .. 4·00 4·50
505 $10 Longsnout Butterflyfish .. .. .. 5·50 5·50
490/505 .. .. *Set of* 16 16·00 15·00

For stamps watermarked with W w **15** see Nos. 555/70.

92 Fort St. George

(Des J. Cooter. Litho Format)

1981 (18 May). *Montserrat National Trust. T* **92** *and similar horiz designs. Multicoloured. W* w **14** (*sideways*). *P* 13½ × 14.

506 50 c. Type **92** 30 30
507 65 c. Bird sanctuary, Fox's Bay 45 45
508 $1.50, Museum 85 85
509 $2.50, Bransby Point Battery, *circa* 1780 .. 1·40 1·40

(Des D. Shults. Litho Questa)

1981 (17 July–19 Nov). *Royal Wedding. Horiz designs as T* **26**/**27** *of Kiribati. Multicoloured.* (a) *W* w **15**. *P* 14.

510 90 c. *Charlotte* 30 35
a. Sheetlet. No. 510 × 6 and No. 511 .. 3·00
511 90 c. Prince Charles and Lady Diana Spencer 1·50 1·50
512 $3 *Portsmouth* .. .. 1·25 1·25
a. Sheetlet. No. 512 × 6 and No. 513 .. 9·00
513 $3 As No. 511 .. .. 3·50 3·50
514 $4 *Britannia* .. .. 1·60 1·60
a. Sheetlet No. 514 × 6 and No. 515 .. 12·00
515 $4 As No. 511 .. .. 4·50 4·50
MS516 120 × 109 mm. $5 As No. 511. Wmk sideways. P 12 (19 Nov) .. .. 2·50 2·50

(b) *Booklet stamps. No wmk. P* 12 (19 Nov)

517 90 c. As No. 510 .. .. 45 45
a. Booklet pane. No. 517 × 4 .. .. 1·75
518 $3 As No. 513 .. .. 1·60 1·75
a. Booklet pane No. 518 × 2 .. .. 3·25

Nos. 510/15 were printed in sheetlets of seven stamps of the same face value, each containing six of the "Royal Yacht" design and one of the larger design showing Prince Charles and Lady Diana.

Nos. 517/18 come from $13.20 stamp booklets.

93 H.M.S. *Dorsetshire* and Seaplane

94 Methodist Church, Bethel

(Des Court House Advertising Ltd. Litho Questa)

1981 (31 Aug). *50th Anniv of Montserrat Airmail Service. T* **93** *and similar horiz designs. Multicoloured. W* w **14** (*sideways*). *P* 14.

519 50 c. Type **93** 30 30
520 65 c. Beechcraft "Twin Bonanza" aeroplane .. 45 45
521 $1.50, De Havilland "Dragon Rapide" R.M. *Lord Shaftesbury* aeroplane 85 85
522 $2.50, Hawker Siddeley Avro "748" aeroplane and maps of Montserrat and Antigua .. .. 1·25 1·25

(Des J. Cooter. Litho Walsall)

1981 (16 Nov). *Christmas. Churches. T* **94** *and similar vert designs. Multicoloured. W* w **14**. *P* 14 × 13½.

523 50 c. Type **94** 30 30
524 65 c. St George's Anglican Church, Harris .. 45 45
525 $1.50, St Peter's Anglican Church, St Peters 85 85
526 $2.50, St Patrick's R.C. Church, Plymouth 1·25 1·25
MS527 176 × 120 mm. Nos. 523/6 .. .. 2·75 2·75

95 Rubiaceae (*Rondeletia buxifolia*)

96 Plymouth

(Des local artist. Litho Questa)

1982 (18 Jan). *Plant Life. T* **95** *and similar multicoloured designs. W* w **14** (*sideways on* 65 c. *and* $2.50). *P* 14½.

528 50 c. Type **95** 30 30
529 65 c. Boraginaceae (*Heliotropium ternatum*) (*horiz*) 40 40
530 $1.50, Simarubaceae (*Picramnia pentandra*) 85 85
531 $2.50, Ebenaceae (*Diospyrus revoluta*) (*horiz*) 1·25 1·25

(Litho Format)

1982 (17 Apr). *350th Anniv of Settlement of Montserrat by Sir Thomas Warner. W* w **14** (*sideways*). *P* 14½.

532 **96** 40 c. green 25 25
533 55 c. red 30 30
534 65 c. chestnut 35 35
535 75 c. olive-grey 40 40
536 85 c. bright blue 45 45
537 95 c. bright orange 50 50
538 $1 bright reddish violet 55 55
539 $1.50, brown-olive 70 70
540 $2 deep claret 90 90
541 $2.50, bistre-brown .. .. 1·25 1·25
532/41 .. .. *Set of* 10 5·00 5·00

Nos. 532/41 are based on the 1932 Tercentenary set.

97 Catherine of Aragon, Princess of Wales, 1501

98 Local Scout

(Des D. Shults and J. Cooter. Litho Format)

1982 (16 June). *21st Birthday of Princess of Wales. T* **97** *and similar vert designs. Multicoloured. W* w **15**. *P* 13½ × 14.

542 75 c. Type **97** 45 35
543 $1 Coat of Arms of Catherine of Aragon 60 50
544 $5 Diana, Princess of Wales .. .. 2·75 2·75

(Des D. Shults. Litho Format)

1982 (13 Sept). *75th Anniv of Boy Scout Movement. T* **98** *and similar vert design. Multicoloured. W* w **15**. *P* 14.

545 $1.50, Type **98** 70 70
546 $2.50, Lord Baden-Powell .. .. .. 1·10 1·10

99 Annunciation

(Des Jennifer Toombs. Litho Walsall)

1982 (18 Nov). *Christmas. T* **99** *and similar horiz designs. Multicoloured. W* w **14** (*sideways*). *P* 14.

547 35 c. Type **99** 20 20
548 75 c. Shepherd's Vision 40 40
549 $1.50, The Stable 85 85
550 $2.50, Flight into Egypt .. .. .. 1·10 1·10

100 *Lepthemis vesiculosa*

101 Blue-headed Hummingbird

(Des J. Cooter. Litho Walsall)

1983 (19 Jan). *Dragonflies. T* **100** *and similar horiz designs. Multicoloured. W* w **14** (*sideways*). *P* 13½ × 14.

551 50 c. Type **100** 25 30
552 65 c. *Orthemis ferruginea* 30 35
553 $1.50, *Triacanthagyna trifida* 70 75
554 $2.50, *Erythrodiplax umbrata* .. .. 1·25 1·25

1983 (12 Apr). *As Nos.* 490/505, *but W* w **15** *and imprint date* "1983" *added. P* 13½ × 13.

555 5 c. Type **91** 10 10
556 10 c. Hogfish 10 10
559 25 c. Sergeant Major 20 20
560 35 c. Clown Wrasse 30 30
564 75 c. French Grunt 50 55
565 $1 Rock Beauty 60 65
568 $5 Cherubfish .. .. 2·75 3·00
570 $10 Longsnout Butterflyfish .. .. .. 5·50 6·00
555/70 .. .. *Set of* 8 9·00 10·00

(Des G. Drummond. Litho Format)

1983 (24 May). *Hummingbirds. T* **101** *and similar vert designs. Multicoloured. W* w **14**. *P* 14.

571 35 c. Type **101** 35 35
572 75 c. Green-throated Carib 55 55
573 $2 Antillean Crested Hummingbird .. 1·40 1·40
574 $3 Purple-throated Carib .. .. .. 1·75 1·75

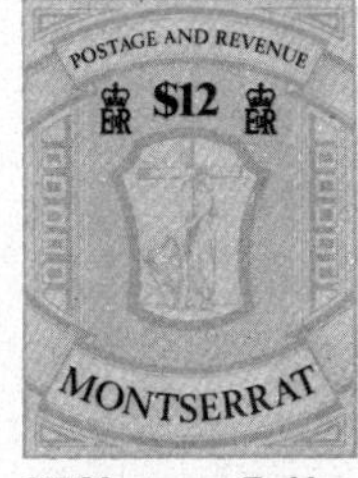

102 Montserrat Emblem

40¢

(**103**)

(Litho Harrison)

1983 (25 July). *W* w **14**. *P* 14½.

575 **102** $12 royal blue and rose .. .. .. 6·00 6·50
576 $30 rose and royal blue .. .. .. 15·00 15·50

1983 (15 Aug). *Various stamps surch as T* **103**. (a) *Nos.* 491, 498, 501 (*all W* w **14**), 559, 564 (*both W* w **15**).

577 40 c. on 25 c. Sergeant Major (No. 559) .. 20 20
a. Surch inverted .. .. 65·00
b. Surch on No. 494 .. .. 18·00 18·00
c. Error. Surch on 10 c. (No. 491) .. .. 45·00
578 70 c. on 10 c. Hogfish (No. 491) 35 35
a. Surch inverted .. .. 65·00
b. Surch on No. 556 .. .. 30·00 30·00
c. Surch omitted (in pair with normal) .. £160
d. Surch double .. .. 75·00
579 90 c. on 65 c. Bigeye (No. 498) 50 55
a. Error. Surch on 10 c. (No. 491) .. ..
b. Error. Surch on 75 c. (No. 499) .. .. 90·00
c. Surch double .. .. 75·00
580 $1.15 on 75 c. French Grunt (No. 564) .. 60 65
a. Surch on No. 499 .. .. 20·00 20·00
b. Error. Surch on 25 c. (No. 559) .. .. 45·00
c. Surch inverted .. .. 90·00
581 $1.50 on $2 Blue Chromis (No. 501) .. 80 85
a. Surch inverted .. .. 85·00
b. Error. Surch on 75 c. (No. 499) .. .. 90·00

(b) *Nos.* 512/15

582 70 c. on $3 *Portsmouth* 60 70
a. Sheetlet. No. 582 × 6 and No. 583 .. 4·00
b. Surch double .. .. 25·00
c. Surch inverted .. .. 35·00
d. Surch inverted (horiz pair) .. .. 70·00
583 70 c. on $3 Prince Charles and Lady Diana Spencer 60 70
b. Surch double .. .. 95·00
c. Surch inverted £125
584 $1.15 on $4 *Britannia* .. .. 1·00 1·10
a. Sheetlet. No. 584 × 6 and No. 585 .. 7·00
b. Surch double .. .. 28·00
c. Surch inverted .. .. 35·00
d. Surch inverted (horiz pair) .. .. 70·00
e. Error. Surch on $3 (No. 512) .. .. 35·00
585 $1.15 on $4 As No. 583 .. .. .. 1·00 1·10
b. Surch double .. .. 90·00
c. Surch inverted £125
e. Error. Surch on $3 (No. 513) .. .. 85·00
577/85 .. .. *Set of* 9 4·75 5·25

Nos. 582d and 584d show the long surcharge intended for Nos. 583 or 585 inverted across horizontal pairs of the smaller design. Nos. 583c and 585c show two examples of the smaller surcharge inverted.

104 Montgolfier Balloon, 1783

105 Boys dressed as Clowns

(Des A. Theobald. Litho Format)

1983 (19 Sept). *Bicentenary of Manned Flight. T* **104** *and similar multicoloured designs. W* w **14** (*sideways on* 75 c. *to* $2). *P* 14.

586 35 c. Type **104** 15 20
587 75 c. De Havilland "Twin Otter" (*horiz*) .. 35 40
588 $1.50, Lockheed "Vega" (*horiz*) 70 75
589 $2 *R 34* airship (*horiz*) .. .. .. 1·10 1·25
MS590 109 × 145 mm. Nos. 586/9. Wmk sideways 2·10 2·25

Nos. 586/9 were re-issued on 15 December 1983 overprinted "INAUGURAL FLIGHT Montserrat-Nevis-St. Kitts". It is understood nearly all of these overprints were used on Flown First Flight/Day Covers (*Price for set of* 4 *on First Flight Cover* £40).

(Des Jennifer Toombs. Litho Format)

1983 (18 Nov). *Christmas. Carnival. T* **105** *and similar horiz designs. Multicoloured. W w* **15** (*sideways*). *P* 14.
591 55 c. Type **105** 30 30
592 90 c. Girls dressed as silver star bursts 50 50
593 $1.15, Flower girls 60 65
594 $2 Masqueraders 1·10 1·25

106 Statue of Discus-thrower

107 Cattle Egret

(Des Court House Studio. Litho Questa)

1984 (26 Mar). *Olympic Games, Los Angeles. T* **106** *and similar vert designs. Multicoloured. W w* **15** (*sideways*). *P* 14.
595 90 c. Type **106** 50 55
596 $1 Olympic torch 55 60
597 $1.15, Olympic stadium, Los Angeles 65 70
598 $2.50, Olympic and American flags 1·25 1·40
MS599 110 × 110 mm. Nos. 595/8. Wmk upright 2·50 2·75

(Des G. Drummond. Litho Walsall)

1984 (11 May). *Birds of Montserrat. T* **107** *and similar multi-coloured designs. W w* **15** (*sideways on* 5 c. *to* 90 c.). *P* 14.
600 5 c. Type **107** 5 5
601 10 c. Carib Grackle 5 8
602 15 c. Common Gallinule 10 12
603 20 c. Brown Booby 12 15
604 25 c. Black-Whiskered Vireo 15 20
605 40 c. Scaly-breasted Thrasher 25 30
606 55 c. Laughing Gull 35 40
607 70 c. Glossy Ibis 40 45
608 90 c. Green Heron 55 60
609 $1 Belted Kingfisher (*vert*) 60 65
610 $1.15, Bananaquit (*vert*) 70 75
611 $3 Sparrow Hawk (*vert*) 1·75 1·90
612 $5 Forest Thrush (*vert*) 3·00 3·25
613 $7.50, Black-crowned Night Heron (*vert*) 4·50 4·75
614 $10 Bridled Quail Dove (*vert*) 6·00 6·25
600/14 *Set of* 15 16·75 17·75

(Des J.W. Litho Format)

1984 (9 July). *Mail Packet Boats* (2*nd series*). *Multicoloured designs as T* **89**. *W w* **15** (*sideways*). *P* 14.
615 55 c. R.M.S.P. *Tagus*, 1907 35 40
616 90 c. R.M.S.P. *Cobequid*, 1913 60 65
617 $1.15, Canadian National S.S. *Lady Drake*, 1942 80 85
618 $2 Harrison Line M.V. *Factor*, 1948 1·40 1·50
MS619 152 × 100 mm. Nos. 615/18. 3·25 3·50
No. **MS**619 also commemorates the 250th anniversary of *Lloyd's List* (newspaper).

108 Hermit Crab and Top Shell

(Des G. Drummond. Litho Questa)

1984 (24 Sept). *Marine Life. T* **108** *and similar horiz designs. Multicoloured. W w* **15** (*sideways*). *P* 14.
620 90 c. Type **108** 60 65
621 $1.15, Rough File Shell 80 85
622 $1.50, True Tulip Snail 1·00 1·10
623 $2.50, West Indian Fighting Conch 1·75 1·90

109 "Bull Man"

110 Mango

(Des Jennifer Toombs. Litho Questa)

1984 (12 Nov). *Christmas. Carnival Costumes. T* **109** *and similar horiz designs. Multicoloured. W w* **15** (*sideways*). *P* 14.
624 55 c. Type **109** 35 40
625 $1.15, Masquerader Captain 80 85
626 $1.50, "Fantasy" Carnival Queen 1·00 1·10
627 $2.30, "Ebony and Ivory" Carnival Queen 1·60 1·75

(Des G. Drummond. Litho Format)

1985 (8 Feb). *National Emblems. T* **110** *and similar vert designs. Multicoloured. W w* **15**. *P* 14.
628 $1.15, Type **110** 70 75
629 $1.50, Lobster Claw 90 95
630 $3 Montserrat Oriole 1·75 1·90

OFFICIAL STAMPS

O.H.M.S. (O 1)   **O.H.M.S.** (O 2)

1976 (12 Apr). *Various stamps, some already surcharged, optd locally with Type* O **1**.
O1 5 c. multicoloured (No. 246A) † 1·25
O2 10 c. multicoloured (No. 247A) † 2·00
a. Opt double † 60·00
b. Horiz pair, one stamp without opt † £250
O3 30 c. on 10 c. multicoloured (No. 369) † 4·00
a. Opt double † 60·00
O4 45 c. on 3 c. multicoloured (No. 370) † 5·00
O5 $5 multicoloured (No. 254A) † £200
O6 $10 multicoloured (No. 254*a*B) † £550
O1/6 *Set of* 6 † £700
These stamps were issued for use on mail from the Montserrat Philatelic Bureau. They were not available for sale in either unused or used condition.

1976 (1 Oct)–**80**. *Nos.* 374/8, 380/2 *and* 384/5 *optd with Type* O **2** locally.
O 7 5 c. Malay Apple † 15
a. Opt inverted † —
O 8 10 c. Jacaranda † 20
O 9 15 c. Orchid Tree † 25
a. Opt inverted † 95·00
O10 20 c. Manjak † 30
a. Opt inverted † 95·00
O11 25 c. Tamarind † 35
O12 55 c. Pink Cassia † 55
a. Opt inverted † —
O13 70 c. Long John † 60
O14 $1 Saman † 85
O15 $5 Yellow Poui † 3·00
O16 $10 Flamboyant (14.4.80) † 5·50
O7/16 *Set of* 10 † 10·50
Nos. O7/16 were not available in an unused condition, but were sold to the public cancelled-to-order.

O.H.M.S. (O 3)   O.H.M.S. (O 4)   O.H.M.S. 45¢ (O 5)

1980 (7 July). *Nos.* 374/8, 380/2 *and* 384/5 *optd with Type* O **3** *in Great Britain*.
O17 5 c. Malay Apple † 5
O18 10 c. Jacaranda † 5
O19 15 c. Orchid Tree † 10
O20 20 c. Manjak † 10
a. Opt double † 90·00
O21 25 c. Tamarind † 15
O22 55 c. Pink Cassia † 35
O23 70 c. Long John † 45
O24 $1 Saman † 60
O25 $5 Yellow Poui † 2·75
O26 $10 Flamboyant † 5·50
O17/26 *Set of* 10 † 9·00
Nos. O17/26 were not available in an unused condition, but were sold to the public cancelled-to-order.
These stamps were originally intended for issue on 3 November 1980, but certain values were placed on sale from 7 July onwards to meet shortages. Bulk supplies did not arrive on the island until early December 1980.

1980 (30 Sept). *Nos.* 374/82, 384/5 *and* 476, *together with surcharges on Nos.* 372, 376 *and* 379, *optd as Type* O **4** *locally*.
O27 5 c. Malay Apple † 5
O28 5 c. on 3 c. Lignum vitae † 5
O29 10 c. Jacaranda † 10
O30 15 c. Orchid Tree † 10
a. Opt double † 45·00
O31 20 c. Manjak † 15
a. Opt double † 40·00
O32 25 c. Tamarind † 15
O33 30 c. on 15 c. Orchid Tree † 20
O34 35 c. on 2 c. Cannon-ball Tree † 20
O35 40 c. Flame of the Forest † 25
O36 55 c. Pink Cassia † 35
O37 70 c. Long John † 50
O38 $1 Saman † 60
O39 $2.50 on 40 c. Flame of the Forest † 1·40
a. "O.H.M.S." opt omitted £160
O40 $5 Yellow Poui † 2·50
O41 $10 Flamboyant † 5·00
a. Opt double † 95·00
O27/41 *Set of* 15 † 10·50
Nos. O27/41 were not available in an unused condition, but were sold to the public cancelled-to-order. No. O39a was, however, found amongst supplies of the postage series.

1981 (20 Mar). *Nos.* 490/4, 496, 498, 500, 502/3 *and* 505 *optd with Type* O **4**.
O42 5 c. Type **91** 5 5
a. Opt inverted 65·00
O43 10 c. Hogfish 5 5
O44 15 c. Creole Wrasse 5 5
O45 20 c. Yellow Damselfish 8 10
O46 25 c. Sergeant Major 10 12
O47 45 c. Schoolmaster 20 15
a. Opt double 85·00
ab. Opt double, one on reverse † —
b. Opt inverted 85·00
O48 65 c. Bigeye 25 30
a. Opt inverted 80·00
O49 $1 Rock Beauty 50 55
O50 $3 Fairy Basslet and Blueheads 1·50 1·60
O51 $5 Cherubfish 2·50 2·75
O52 $10 Longsnout Butterflyfish 4·75 5·00
O42/52 *Set of* 11 9·00 9·50

1982 (17 Nov). *Nos.* 510/15 *surch as Type* O **5** (*in one line on Nos.* O54, O56 *and* O58).
O53 45 c. on 90 c. *Charlotte* 25 30
a. Sheetlet. No. O53 × 6 and No. O54 1·75
b. Surch double 50·00
c. Surch inverted 35·00
d. Surch inverted (horiz pair) 65·00
e. Horiz pair, one without surch 80·00
O54 45 c. on 90 c. Prince Charles and Lady Diana Spencer 30 30
b. Surch double 90·00
c. Surch inverted 70·00
O55 75 c. on $3 *Portsmouth* 35 35
a. Sheetlet. No. O55 × 6 and No. O56 2·25
b. Surch double 40·00
c. Surch inverted 28·00
d. Surch inverted (horiz pair) 55·00
e. Horiz pair, one without surch 80·00
f. Error. Surch on $4 (No. 514) 30·00
fa. Sheetlet. No. O55f × 6 and No. O56f £250
O56 75 c. on $3 Prince Charles and Lady Diana Spencer 45 45
b. Surch double 95·00
c. Surch inverted 50·00
f. Error. Surch on $4 (No. 515) 80·00
O57 $1 on $4 *Britannia* 50 50
a. Sheetlet. No. O57 × 6 and No. O58 3·50
b. Surch double 45·00
c. Surch inverted 25·00
d. Surch inverted (horiz pair) 55·00
e. Horiz pair, one without surch
O58 $1 on $4 Prince Charles and Lady Diana Spencer 60 60
b. Surch double £100
c. Surch inverted 60·00
O53/8 *Set of* 6 2·00 2·10
Nos. O53d, O55d and O57d show the long surcharge, intended for Nos. O54, O56 or O58, inverted across horizontal pairs of the smaller design. Nos. O54c, O56c and O58c show two examples as Type O 5 inverted on the same stamp.

70¢

O.H.M.S. (O 6)

1983 (19 Oct). *Nos.* 542/4 *surch as Type* O **6** *or optd only* ($1).
O59 70 c. on 75 c. Type **97** 50 40
O60 $1 Coat of Arms of Catherine of Aragon 60 50
O61 $1.50 on $5 Diana, Princess of Wales 85 80

Morocco Agencies

(British Post Offices)

Stamps of GREAT BRITAIN were used by the British Post Offices in Morocco from 1857 until 31 December 1885. The mail was forwarded via Gibraltar where the stamps were cancelled with the "A26" postmark used there. Mail originating from the Morocco Agencies can only be identified by markings on the covers involved, including a Tangier postmark, supplied in 1872, always struck alongside the stamps.

The British Post Offices in Morocco were under the control of the Gibraltar Post Office until 31 December 1906 and used the stamps of GIBRALTAR until 31 May 1898. By 1892 Agencies were open at Casablanca, Fez, Laroche, Mazagan, Mogador, Rabat, Saffi, Tangier and Tetuan.

PRICES FOR STAMPS ON COVER TO 1945

Nos. 1/16	*from* × 7
Nos. 17/30	*from* × 3
Nos. 31/74	*from* × 3
Nos. 75/6	*from* × 4
Nos. 112/24	*from* × 4
No. 125	—
Nos. 126/35	*from* × 5
Nos. 136/42	*from* × 2
Nos. 143/59	*from* × 3
Nos. 160/75	*from* × 8
Nos. 191/9	*from* × 5
Nos. 200/1	*from* × 3
Nos. 202/11	*from* × 4
Nos. 212/15	*from* × 5
Nos. 216/24	*from* × 8
Nos. 225/6	*from* × 2
Nos. 227/30	*from* × 8
Nos. 231/52	*from* × 6

The above prices apply to stamps used on cover from Morocco. Examples used on cover in Great Britain have little additional value.

I. "GIBRALTAR" PERIOD

For use at all British Post Offices in Morocco.

Morocco Agencies (1) Morocco Agencies (2) Morocco (3)

1898–99. *T 7 of Gibraltar optd.*

I *Locally (at "Gibraltar Chronicle" office). Type* **1** *(wide "M" and ear of "g" projecting upwards), in black.*

1 5 c. green .. 30 30
2 10 c. carmine .. 30 25
a. Opt double .. £500
b. Bisected (5 c.) (on cover) .. † £1100
3 20 c. olive-green .. 2·50 2·50
a. Opt double .. £450
b. *Olive-green and brown* .. 2·00 1·25
4 25 c. ultramarine .. 80 70
5 40 c. orange-brown .. 2·50 3·00
a. Blue opt .. 26·00 26·00
6 50 c. bright lilac .. 14·00 20·00
a. Blue opt .. 8·00 9·00
7 1 p. bistre and ultramarine .. 8·00 14·00
a. Blue opt .. £120 £110
8 2 p. black and carmine .. 5·00 14·00
1/8 .. *Set of* 8 30·00 48·00

The *blue* overprint can be easily distinguished by looking through the stamp in front of a strong light.

Overprint variety: "A" for "A". Prices for un; used 20% higher. 5 c. £20; 10 c. £300; 20 c. (No. 3 or 3*b*), £24; 25 c. £100; 40 c. £150; 50 c. £250; 1 p. £180; 2 p. £225.

This variety occurred in the first setting, No. 36 of right-hand pane. Numerous other minor varieties exist.

II (*London opt, in black. T* **2** *(narrow "M" and ear of "g" horizontal)* (1899).

9 5 c. green .. 20 20
10 10 c. carmine .. 25 15
11 20 c. olive-green .. 1·00 70
12 25 c. ultramarine .. 3·00 90
13 40 c. orange-brown .. 10·00 11·00
14 50 c. bright lilac .. 6·00 3·50
15 1 p. bistre and ultramarine .. 13·00 17·00
16 2 p. black and carmine .. 18·00 22·00
9/16 .. *Set of* 8 45·00 50·00
9/16 Optd "Specimen" .. *Set of* 8 £300

Overprint varieties: Prices for un; used 10% higher.

(A). Broad top to "M" (T **3**). No. 39 of left-hand pane. 5 c. £5; 10 c. £5; 20 c. £13; 25 c. £13; 40 c. £75; 50 c. £90; 1 p. £100; 2 p. £325.

(B). Hyphen between "n" and "c" of "Agencies". No. 17 of right-hand pane.

5 c. £5; 10 c. £5; 20 c. £13; 25 c. £13; 40 c. £75; 50 c. £80; 1 p. £100; 2 p. £325.

1903–5. *As T 8 of Gibraltar, but with value in Spanish currency, optd with T* **2**. *Wmk Crown CA. P* 14.

17 5 c. grey-green and green (1.03) .. 2·50 50
18 10 c. dull purple/*red* (8.03) .. 2·50 55
19 20 c. grey-green and carmine (9.04) .. 7·00 20·00
20 25 c. purple and black/*blue* (1.7.03) .. 1·25 55
21 50 c. purple and violet (3.7.05) .. 65·00 85·00
22 1 p. black and carmine (19.11.05) .. 65·00 80·00
23 2 p. black and blue (19.11.05) .. 70·00 80·00
17/23 .. *Set of* 7 £190 250
17/23 Optd "Specimen" .. *Set of* 7 £400

Overprint varieties: Prices for un; used 10% higher.

(A). As T **3**.

5 c. £20; 10 c. £20; 20 c. £35; 25 c. £32; 50 c. £325; 1 p. £275; 2 p. £325.

(B). Hyphen between "n" and "c".

5 c. £20; 10 c. £20; 20 c. £35; 25 c. £32; 50 c. £325; 1 p. £275; 2 p. £325.

1905 (Jan)–**06.** *As Nos. 17/23 but wmk Mult Crown CA.*

24 5 c. grey-green and green, **OC** (4.05) .. 45 60
25 10 c. dull purple/*red*, **OC** .. 65 25
26 20 c. grey-green and carmine, **O** (1.06) .. 2·00 8·50
27 25 c. purple and black/*blue*, **C** (6.06) .. 24·00 9·50
28 50 c. purple and violet, **C** (7.06) .. 9·50 14·00
29 1 p. black and carmine, **C** (11.05) .. 38·00 55·00
30 2 p. black and blue, **C** (11.05) .. 25·00 32·00
24/30 .. *Set of* 7 90·00 £110

Overprint varieties: Prices for un; used 10% higher.

(A). As T **3**.

5 c. £18; 10 c. £20; 20 c. £11; 25 c. £75; 50 c. £200; 1 p. £250; 2 p. £325.

(B). Hyphen between "n" and "c".

5 c. £850.

In 1907 control of the post offices was assumed by the Postmaster-General of Great Britain.

All the following issues are overprinted on Great Britain

II. BRITISH CURRENCY

Stamps overprinted "MOROCCO AGENCIES" only were primarily intended for use on parcels (and later, air-mail correspondence), and were on sale at British P.Os throughout Morocco including Tangier, until 1937.

PRICES. Our prices for used stamps with these overprints are for specimens used in Morocco. These stamps could be used in the United Kingdom, with official sanction, from the summer of 1950 onwards and with U.K. postmarks are worth about 25 per cent less.

MOROCCO AGENCIES (4) MOROCCO AGENCIES (5) MOROCCO AGENCIES (6)

1907–13. *King Edward VII optd as T* **4** *or* **5** *(2s. 6d.)*

(*a*) *De La Rue printings*

31 ½d. pale yellowish green, **O** .. 65 2·25
32 1d. scarlet, **O** .. 2·25 2·50
33 2d. grey-green and carmine, **C** .. 2·50 5·25
34 4d. green and chocolate-brown, **C** .. 18·00 4·25
35 4d. orange, **O** (1912) .. 3·50 4·00
36 6d. dull purple, **C** .. 6·50 4·75
37 1s. dull green and carmine, **C** .. 14·00 12·00
38 2s. 6d. pale dull purple, **C** .. 50·00 55·00
39 2s. 6d. dull purple, **C** .. 50·00 55·00
31/39 .. *Set of* 8 85·00 80·00
37/8 H/S "Specimen" .. *Set of* 2 £225

(*b*) *Later printings* (1913)

40 4d. bright orange, **O** (No. 286) .. 11·00 15·00
41 2s. 6d. dull purple, **O** (No. 315) .. 50·00 60·00

1914–31. *King George V. (a) Optd with T* **4**. **W 100.**

42 **105** ½d. green .. 25 65
43 **104** 1d. scarlet .. 25 25
44 **105** 1½d. red-brown (1921) .. 2·00 3·50
45 **106** 2d. orange (Die I) .. 1·50 70
46 3d. bluish violet (1921) .. 2·25 90
47 4d. grey-green (1921) .. 2·50 1·25
48 **107** 6d. reddish purple, **C** (1921) .. 8·50 12·00
49 **108** 1s. bistre-brown (1917) .. 15·00 2·40
a. Opt triple, two albino .. £120

(*b*) *Optd with T* **6**. (i) *Waterlow printing*

50 **109** 2s. 6d. sepia-brown (1914) .. 32·00 32·00
a. Re-entry .. £450 £400
b. Opt double, one albino .. £200

(ii) *De La Rue printings*

51 **109** 2s. 6d. yellow-brown (1917) .. 32·00 25·00
a. Opt double (1917) .. £1400 £1000
52 2s. 6d. grey-brown .. 27·00 28·00

(iii) *Bradbury Wilkinson printings*

53 **109** 2s. 6d. chocolate-brown .. 32·00 22·00
a. Opt double, one albino* .. £250
54 5s. rose-red (1931) .. 45·00 45·00
a. Opt triple, two albino
42/54 .. *Set of* 10 95·00 80·00
49/50, 54 H/S "Specimen" .. *Set of* 3 £350

*The albino overprint is quite clear, with the "MOROCCO" appearing just below "AGENCIES" of the normal overprint and a little to the right as seen from the back; however, this occurs with a second faint albino impression just below the normal overprint.

MOROCCO AGENCIES (7) S (A) MOROCCO AGENCIES (8) S (B)

(A) Opt 14 mm long; ends of "s" cut off diagonally.

(B) Opt 15½ mm long; ends of "s" cut off horizontally

1925–36. *King George V, optd with T* **7** (A) *or T* **8** (B). **W 111.**

			A		B	
55	**105**	½d. green ..	1·25	65	1·25	13·00
56		1½d. chestnut (1931)	12·00	14·00	†	
57	**106**	2d. orange	3·00	2·25	†	
58	**104**	2½d. blue ..	3·25	10·00	£110	30·00
59	**106**	4d. grey-green (1.36)	†		8·00	24·00
60	**107**	6d. purple, **O** (1931)	3·75	6·50	1·25	1·60
61	**108**	1s. bistre-brown ..	15·00	9·00	60·00	48·00
55/61 (*cheapest*) *Set of* 7			42·00	55·00		
61A H/S "Specimen" ..			80·00			

1935 (8 May). *Silver Jubilee stamps. Optd "MOROCCO AGENCIES" only, as in T* **17**.

62 **123** ½d. green (B.) .. 1·00 2·00
63 1d. scarlet (B.) .. 1·10 3·00
64 1½d. red-brown (B.) .. 3·00 6·50
65 2½d. blue (R.) .. 3·75 5·00

1935–37. *King George V. (a) Harrison photo ptgs optd with T* **8**.

66 **119** 1d. scarlet (1935) .. 80 65
67 **118** 1½d. red-brown (1936) .. 2·25 7·50
68 **120** 2d. orange (11.5.36) .. 40 40
69 **119** 2½d. ultramarine (11.2.36) .. 3·00 4·00
70 **120** 3d. violet (2.3.36) .. 40 30
71 4d. deep grey-green (19.5.36) .. 60 35
72 **122** 1s. bistre-brown (1936) .. 1·60 1·25

(*b*) *Waterlow re-engraved ptg optd with T* **6**

73 **109** 2s. 6d. chocolate-brown (No. 450) .. 27·00 24·00
74 5s. bright rose-red (No. 451) (2.3.37) .. 32·00 35·00
66/74 .. *Set of* 9 60·00 65·00
72/3 H/S "Specimen" .. *Set of* 2 £225

1936 (26 Oct)–**37.** *King Edward VIII, optd "MOROCCO AGENCIES" only, as in T* **18**.

A. MOROCCO 14½ mm long.

B. MOROCCO 15¼ mm long (5.1.37)

			A		B	
75	**124**	1d. scarlet ..	20	25	1·10	1·75
76		2½d. bright blue ..	20	25	1·10	1·60

The first two printings of both values showed all the stamps with the short overprint, Nos. 75A/6A.

On 5 January 1937 a further printing of both values was placed on sale in London which had all stamps, 24 in all, from the bottom two horizontal rows (Rows 19 and 20) with the long overprint, Nos. 75B/6B. Subsequent printings increased the number of long overprints in the sheet to 25 by the addition of R. 8/9, and, finally, to 31 (R. 1/7, R. 7/1, R. 8/1, R. 13/3, 4 and 10, R. 14/6, but without R. 8/9).

For the 1d. value all sheets from cylinder 2 show the first setting. Sheets from cylinder 6 were also used for the first, and for all subsequent settings. The 2½d. value was overprinted on sheets from cylinder 2 throughout.

In 1937 unoverprinted Great Britain stamps replaced overprinted "MOROCCO AGENCIES" issues as stocks became exhausted. In 1949 overprinted issues reappeared and were in use at Tetuan (Spanish Zone), the only remaining British P.O. apart from that at Tangier.

MOROCCO AGENCIES (9) MOROCCO AGENCIES (10)

1949 (16 Aug). *King George VI, optd with T* **9** *or* **10** *(2s. 6d., 5s.).*

77 **128** ½d. pale green .. 25 75
78 1d. pale scarlet .. 25 90
79 1½d. pale red-brown .. 30 75
80 2d. pale orange .. 30 90
81 2½d. light ultramarine .. 45 90
82 3d. pale violet .. 30 45
83 **129** 4d. grey-green .. 25 60
84 5d. brown .. 75 2·00
85 6d. purple .. 30 70
86 **130** 7d. emerald-green .. 50 2·00
87 8d. bright carmine .. 60 2·25
88 9d. deep olive-green .. 45 1·90
89 10d. turquoise-blue .. 50 2·00
90 11d. plum .. 1·40 1·75
91 1s. bistre-brown .. 1·50 1·50
92 **131** 2s. 6d. yellow-green .. 12·00 14·00
93 5s. red .. 32·00 30·00
77/93 .. *Set of* 17 48·00 60·00

1951 (3 May). *King George VI (Nos. 503/7, 509/10), optd with T* **9** *or* **10** *(2s. 6d., 5s.).*

94 **128** ½d. pale orange .. 20 25
95 1d. light ultramarine .. 20 25
96 1½d. pale green .. 25 40
97 2d. pale red-brown .. 25 45
98 2½d. pale scarlet .. 25 50
99 **147** 2s. 6d. yellow-green .. 11·00 12·00
100 **148** 5s. red .. 14·00 22·00
94/100 .. *Set of* 7 24·00 32·00

1952–55. *Queen Elizabeth II (Tudor Crown wmk), optd with T* **9**.

101 **154** ½d. orange-red (31.8.53) .. 10 10
102 1d. ultramarine (31.8.53) .. 15 20
103 1½d. green (5.12.52) .. 15 10
104 2d. red-brown (31.8.53) .. 25 30
105 **155** 2½d. carmine-red (5.12.52) .. 25 12
106 **156** 4d. ultramarine (1.3.55) .. 80 1·00
107 **157** 5d. brown (6.7.53) .. 1·00 1·00
108 6d. reddish purple (1.3.55) .. 1·00 1·00
109 **158** 8d. magenta (6.7.53) .. 2·50 3·25
110 **159** 1s. bistre-brown (6.7.53) .. 1·50 1·00
101/110 .. *Set of* 10 7·00 7·50

1956 (10 Sept). *Queen Elizabeth II (St. Edward's Crown wmk), optd with T* **9**.

111 **155** 2½d. carmine-red (No. 544) .. 1·50 2·75

Stamps overprinted "MOROCCO AGENCIES" were withdrawn from sale on 31 December 1956.

III. SPANISH CURRENCY

Stamps surcharged in Spanish currency were sold at British P.Os. throughout Morocco until the establishment of the French Zone and the Tangier International Zone, when their use was confined to the Spanish Zone.

MOROCCO AGENCIES 5 CENTIMOS (11) MOROCCO AGENCIES 6 PESETAS (12)

1907–13. *King Edward VII, surch as T* **11** *(5 c. to 1 p.) or* **12** *(3p. to 12 p.). (a) De La Rue printings.*

112 5 c. on ½d. pale yellowish green, **O** .. 25 20
113 10 c. on 1d. scarlet, **O** .. 25 25

114 15 c. on 1½d. purple and green, C 45 30
a. "1" of "15" omitted £2750
115 20 c. on 2d. grey-green and carmine, C .. 55 25
116 25 c. on 2½d. ultramarine, O .. .. .. 1·00 25
117 40 c. on 4d. green and chocolate-brown, C .. 1·60 4·25
118 40 c. on 4d. orange, O (1910) 55 95
119 50 c. on 5d. purple and ultramarine, C .. 2·50 75
120 1 p. on 10d. purple and carmine, C .. .. 5·50 7·50
a. No cross on crown .. .. ..
121 3 p. on 2s. 6d. pale dull purple, C .. .. 22·00 16·00
122 6 p. on 5s. carmine, O .. .. .. 55·00 48·00
123 12 p. on 10s. ultramarine, O .. .. .. 85·00 75·00
112/123 .. .. Set of 12 £150 £140
123 H/S "Specimen" £160

(b) Harrison printing
124 25 c. on 2½d. bright blue (No. 283) (1912) .. 13·00 14·00

(c) Somerset House printing
125 12 p. on 10s. bright blue (No. 319) (1913) .. £130 £130

1912. *King George V, surch as T* **11**.
126 5 c. on ½d. green (No. 339) .. .. .. 1·00 20
127 10 c. on 1d. scarlet (No. 342) .. .. .. 1·40 20
a. No cross on crown .. .. .. £130 80·00

MOROCCO AGENCIES 3 CENTIMOS (13)
MOROCCO AGENCIES 10 CENTIMOS (14)
MOROCCO AGENCIES 15 CENTIMOS (15)
MOROCCO AGENCIES 6 PESETAS (16)

1914–26. *King George V. (a) Surch as T* **11** *(5 c.),* **13** *(3 c. and 40 c)**, **15** *(15 c.) and* **14** *(remainder).* W **100**.
128 105 3 c. on ½d. green (1917) .. .. 25 1·90
129 5 c. on ½d. green 60 20
130 104 10 c. on 1d. scarlet 30 15
131 105 15 c. on 1½d. red-brown (1915) 30 15
a. Surch double, one albino ..
132 106 20 c. on 2d. orange (Die I) .. .. 55 1·00
a. Surch double, one albino ..
133 104 25 c. on 2½d. blue (*shades*) 55 40
134 106 40 c. on 4d. grey-green (1917) .. .. 4·50 5·50
a. Surch double, one albino ..
135 108 1p. on 10d. turquoise-blue .. .. 1·75 3·25
*The surcharge on Nos. 134, 148 and 158 is as T 13 for the value and T 15 for "MOROCCO AGENCIES".

(b) Surch as T **16**. *(i) Waterlow printings*
136 109 6 p. on 5s. rose-carmine .. .. .. 32·00 40·00
a. Surch double, one albino £140
b. Surch triple, two albino ..
137 6 p. on 5s. pale rose-carmine £130
a. Surch double, one albino ..
138 12 p. on 10s. indigo-blue (R.) £120 £100
a. Surch double, one albino £450
b. Surch triple, two albino ..
136, 138 H/S "Specimen" .. .. Set of 2 £275

(ii) De La Rue printings
139 109 3 p. on 2s. 6d. grey-brown (1918) .. 28·00 40·00
140 3 p. on 2s. 6d. yellow-brown .. .. 28·00 55·00
a. Surch double, one albino ..
141 12 p. on 10s. blue (R.) £140 £130
a. Surch double, one albino .. ..

(iii) Bradbury Wilkinson printings
142 109 3 p. on 2s. 6d. chocolate-brown (1926) 23·00 35·00
128/142 .. .. Set of 11 £170 £170

1925–31. *King George V, surch as T* **11**, **13**, **14** *or* **15**. W **111**.
143 105 5 c. on ½d. green (1931) .. .. 40 2·75
144 104 10 c. on 1d. scarlet (1929) .. .. 5·50 9·00
145 105 15 c. on 1½d. red-brown .. .. 14·00 13·00
146 106 20 c. on 2d. orange (1931) .. .. 3·00 4·75
a. Surch double, one albino ..
147 104 25 c. on 2½d. blue 65 95
148 106 40 c. on 4d. grey-green (1930) 75 50
a. Surch double, one albino ..
143/148 .. .. Set of 6 22·00 28·00

MOROCCO AGENCIES 10 CENTIMOS (17)
MOROCCO AGENCIES 10 CENTIMOS (18)

1935 (8 May). *Silver Jubilee, surch as T* **17**.
149 123 5 c. on ½d. green (B.) 50 45
150 10 c. on 1d. scarlet (B) .. .. .. 3·00 3·75
a. Pair, one with "CENTIMES" .. £1000
151 15 c. on 1½d. red-brown (B.) .. .. 90 5·00
152 25 c. on 2½d. blue (R.) .. .. .. 6·00 4·50
Beware of forgeries of the error, No. 150a.

1935–37. *King George V, surch as T* **11**, **13**, **14** *or* **15**.
153 118 5 c. on ½d. green (17.6.36) .. .. 45 1·25
154 119 10 c. on 1d. scarlet .. .. .. 80 1·75
155 118 15 c. on 1½d. red-brown .. .. 6·50 5·50
156 120 20 c. on 2d. orange (1936) 45 60
157 119 25 c. on 2½d. ultramarine (1936) .. 2·50 3·75
158 120 40 c. on 4d. deep grey-green (18.5.37) .. 35 2·25
159 122 1 p. on 10d. turquoise-blue (21.4.37) .. 45 45
153/159 .. .. Set of 7 10·50 14·00

1936 (26 Oct)–**37**. *King Edward VIII, surch as T* **18**.
A. "MOROCCO" 14¼ mm long.
B. "MOROCCO" 15¼ mm long (5.1.37)

				A		B	
160	124	5 c. on ½d. green	.. ..	15	15	†	
161		10 c. on 1d scarlet..	.. ..	15	25	40	60
162		15 c. on 1½d. red-brown	..	15	20	†	
163		25 c. on 2½d. bright blue	..	20	20	†	

The first three printings of the 10 c. on 1d. (from cyls 4, 5 and 6) showed all stamps with the short surcharge (No. 161A).

On 5 January 1937 a further printing was placed on sale in London which had 49 stamps in the sheet (R. 1/2 to 11, R. 2/1, 5 and 6, 8 and 9, R. 3/5, R. 4/5, R. 5/4 and 5, 10, R. 6/6 and 7, R. 7/8, R. 8/8, R. 9/8, R. 11/7, 9, R.13/2 to 5, 7 and 8, R. 14/1, 7, R. 15/7, 11, R. 16/5, 10, R. 17/4, 10 and 11, R. 18/1, R. 19/2, R. 20/1 and 2, 3, 7, 9) with the long surcharge (No. 161B). The next printing increased the number of long surcharges in the sheet to 50 (R. 10/2), but the final version, although retaining 50 long surcharges, showed them on R. 1/2 to 11, R. 17/5 to 8 and the entire rows 18, 19 and 20. The first two printings with long surcharges were from cylinder 6 and the last from cylinder 13.

MOROCCO 15 CENTIMOS AGENCIES (19)

1937 (13 May). *Coronation, surch as T* **19**.
164 126 15 c. on 1½d. maroon (B.) 35 25

MOROCCO AGENCIES 10 CENTIMOS (20)
MOROCCO AGENCIES 10 CENTIMOS (21)

1937 (June)–**52**. *King George VI, surch as T* **20**.
165 128 5 c. on ½d. green (B.) 30 35
166 10 c. on 1d. scarlet 30 40
167 15 c. on 1½d. red-brown (B.) (4.8.37) .. 30 50
168 25 c. on 2½d. ultramarine 30 45
169 129 40 c. on 4d. grey-green (9.40) .. .. 1·25 3·00
170 130 70 c. on 7d. emerald-green (9.40) .. 80 2·50
171 1 p. on 10d. turquoise-blue (16.6.52) .. 70 2·50
165/171 .. .. Set of 7 3·50 8·75

1940 (6 May). *Centenary of First Adhesive Postage Stamps, surch as T* **21**.
172 134 5 c. on ½d. green (B.) 25 60
173 10 c. on 1d. scarlet 25 60
174 15 c. on 1½d. red-brown (B.) 30 90
175 25 c. on 2½d. ultramarine 35 70

25 CENTIMOS MOROCCO AGENCIES (22)
45 PESETAS MOROCCO AGENCIES (23)

1948 (26 Apr). *Silver Wedding, surch with T* **22** *or* **23**.
176 137 25 c. on 2½d. ultramarine 30 30
177 138 45 p. on £1 blue .. .. 32·00 55·00

1948 (29 July). *Olympic Games, variously surch as T* **22**.
178 139 25 c. on 2½d. ultramarine 30 55
179 140 30 c. on 3d. violet.. .. .. .. 35 65
180 141 60 c. on 6d. bright purple 35 65
181 142 1 p. 20 c. on 1s. brown .. .. .. 70 1·25
a. Surch double £550

1951 (3 May)–**52**. *King George VI, surch as T* **20**.
182 128 5 c. on ½d. pale orange.. .. .. 1·25 1·25
183 10 c. on 1d. light ultramarine .. 1·50 1·25
184 15 c. on 1½d. pale green.. .. .. 1·50 1·25
185 25 c. on 2½d. pale scarlet .. .. 2·25 1·75
186 129 40 c. on 4d. light ultramarine (26.5.52) .. 1·40 3·50

1954–55. *Queen Elizabeth II (Tudor Crown wmk), surch as T* **20**.
187 154 5 c. on ½d. orange-red (1.9.54) 12 20
188 10 c. on 1d. ultramarine (1.3.55).. .. 30 25

1956. *Queen Elizabeth II (St. Edward's Crown wmk), surch as T* **20**.
189 154 5 c. on ½d. orange-red (June) 15 20
190 156 40 c. on 4d. ultramarine (15 Aug) .. 2·50 2·75

Stamps surcharged in Spanish currency were withdrawn from sale on 31 December 1956.

NEW INFORMATION

The editor is always interested to correspond with people who have new information that will improve or correct the Catalogue.

IV. FRENCH CURRENCY

Stamps surcharged in French currency were sold at British P.Os. in the French Zone.

MOROCCO AGENCIES 25 CENTIMES (24)
MOROCCO AGENCIES 1 FRANC (25)

1917–24. *King George V, surch as T* **24** *or* **25** *(1 f.).* W **100**.
191 105 3 c. on ½d. green (R.) .. .. .. 10 1·75
192 5 c. on ½d. green 10 10
193 104 10 c. on 1d. scarlet 45 30
194 105 15 c. on 1½d. red-brown .. .. .. 1·75 25
195 104 25 c. on 2½d. blue 30 20
196 106 40 c. on 4d. slate-green .. .. .. 1·40 45
197 107 50 c. on 5d. yellow-brown (1923).. .. 1·90 3·00
198 108 75 c. on 9d. olive-green (1924) .. .. 75 1·00
199 1 f. on 10d. turquoise-blue .. .. 1·40 1·40
a. Opt double, one albino £110
191/9 .. .. Set of 9 7·25 7·50

1924–32. *King George V, surch as T* **25**, *but closer vertical spacing.*
200 109 3 f. on 2s 6d. chocolate brown .. .. 22·00 11·00
a. Major re-entry £250 £275
b. *Reddish brown* .. .. .. 38·00 14·00
201 6 f. on 5s. rose-red (1932) .. .. 65·00 38·00
200/1 H/S "Specimen" .. .. Set of 2 £200

1925–34. *King George V, surch as T* **24** *or* **25** *(1 f.).* W **111**.
202 105 5 c. on ½d. green .. .. .. 25 1·75
203 104 10 c. on 1d. scarlet 20 25
204 105 15 c. on 1½d. red-brown .. .. .. 2·00 2·00
205 104 25 c. on 2½d. blue 25 25
206 106 40 c. on 4d. grey-green 85 70
207 107 50 c. on 5d. yellow-brown 85 25
208 108 75 c. on 9d. olive-green .. .. .. 2·00 25
209 90 c. on 9d. olive-green .. .. .. 1·60 3·00
210 1 f. on 10d. turquoise-blue 70 25
211 1 f. 50 on 1s. bistre-brown (H/S S. £45) 2·25 3·50
202/211 .. .. Set of 10 10·00 11·00

1935 (8 May). *Silver Jubilee, surch as T* **17**, *but in French currency.*
212 123 5 c. on ½d. green (B.) 15 20
213 10 c. on 1d. scarlet (B.) .. .. .. 1·00 2·25
214 15 c. on 1½d. red-brown (B.) 35 80
215 25 c. on 2½d. blue (R.) 50 60

1935–37. *King George V, surch as T* **24** *or* **25** *(1 f.).*
216 118 5 c. on ½d. green 35 40
217 119 10 c. on 1d. scarlet (2.3.36) 35 30
218 118 15 c. on 1½d. red brown 40 40
219 119 25 c. on 2½d. ultramarine (1936) .. 30 25
220 120 40 c. on 4d. deep grey-green (2.12.36) .. 30 25
221 121 50 c. on 5d. yellow-brown (1936).. .. 30 25
222 122 90 c. on 9d. deep olive-green (17.2.37) .. 60 50
223 1 f. on 10d. turquoise-blue (17.2.37) .. 35 30
224 1 f. 50 on 1s. bistre-brown (20.7.37) (Optd S. £26) 60 50

1935–36. *King George V (Waterlow re-engraved ptgs), surch as T* **25**, *but closer vertical spacing.*
225 109 3 f. on 2s. 6d. chocolate-brown (No. 450) 16·00 11·00
226 6 f. on 5s. bright rose-red (No. 451) (17.6.36) .. .. .. 22·00 26·00
216/226 .. .. .. Set of 11 38·00 35·00
225/6 H/S "Specimen" .. .. Set of 2 £175

1936 (26 Oct). *King Edward VIII, surch as T* **18**, *but in French currency.*
227 124 5 c. on ½d. green 15 20
a. Bar through "POSTAGE" £350
228 15 c. on 1½d. red-brown 20 25
No. 227a was probably caused by a piece of printer's rule. It can be found on various stamps from Row 18, righthand pane.

1937 (13 May). *Coronation, surch as T* **19**, *but in French currency.*
229 126 15 c. on 1½d. maroon (B.) 35 20

1937 (June). *King George VI, surch as T* **20**, *but in French currency.*
230 128 5 c. on ½d. green (B.) 30 50

Stamps surcharged in French currency were withdrawn from sale on 8 January 1938.

V. TANGIER INTERNATIONAL ZONE

This Zone was estalished in 1914, and the first specially overprinted stamps issued in 1927.

PRICES. Our note *re* U.K. usage (at beginning of Section II) also applies to "TANGIER" optd stamps.

TANGIER (26)
TANGIER TANGIER (27)

1927. *King George V, optd with T* **26**. W **111**.
231 105 ½d. green .. .. 1·00 25
a. Opt double, one albino ..
232 104 1d. scarlet 80 30
a. Inverted "Q" for "O" (R. 20/3) .. £800
233 105 1½d. chestnut .. .. 5·00 2·50
234 106 2d. orange .. .. 2·75 25
a. Opt double, one albino ..

1934–35. *King George V, optd with T* **26**.
235 **118** ½d. green 80 75
236 **119** 1d. scarlet 1·75 70
237 **118** 1½d. red-brown 30 20

1935 (8 May). *Silver Jubilee, optd with T* **27**.
238 **123** ½d. green (B.) 55 90
239 1d. scarlet 1·60 2·50
240 1½d. red-brown (B.) 50 60

1936 (26 Oct). *King Edward VIII, optd with T* **26**.
241 **124** ½d. green 15 15
242 1d. scarlet 15 15
243 1½d. red-brown 15 15

TANGIER TANGIER TANGIER
(28) (29)

1937 (13 May). *Coronation, optd with T* **28**.
244 **126** 1½d. maroon (B.) 50 20

1937. *King George VI, optd with T* **29**.
245 **128** ½d. green (B.) (June) 65 40
246 1d. scarlet (June) 65 40
247 1½d. red-brown (B.) (4 Aug) 65 45

TANGIER TANGIER
(30) (31)

1940 (6 May). *Centenary of First Adhesive Postage Stamps, optd with T* **30**.
248 **134** ½d. green (B.) 15 30
249 1d. scarlet 25 30
250 1½d. red-brown (B.) 50 55

1944. *King George VI, optd with T* **29**.
251 **128** ½d. pale green (B.) 40 40
252 1d. pale scarlet 1·00 90

1946 (11 June). *Victory, optd as T* **31**.
253 **135** 2½d. ultramarine 30 30
254 **136** 3d. violet 30 30
The opt on No. 254 is smaller (23 × 2½ mm).

1948 (26 Apr). *Royal Silver Wedding, optd with T* **30**.
255 **137** 2½d. ultramarine 30 15
a. Opt omitted (in vert pair with stamp optd at top) £1100
256 **138** £1 blue 40·00 50·00
No. 255a comes from a sheet in which the overprint is misplaced downwards resulting in the complete absence of the opt from the six stamps of the top row. On the rest of the sheet the opt falls at the top of each stamp instead of at the foot.

1948 (29 July). *Olympic Games, optd with T* **30**.
257 **139** 2½d. ultramarine 45 30
258 **140** 3d. violet 50 30
259 **141** 6d. bright purple 50 30
260 **142** 1s. brown 60 40

1949 (1 Jan). *King George VI, optd with T* **29**.
261 **128** 2d. pale orange 45 90
262 2½d. light ultramarine 30 35
263 3d. pale violet 30 30
264 **129** 4d. grey-green 60 1·75
265 5d. brown 60 1·50
266 6d. purple 35 45
267 **130** 7d. emerald-green 55 1·25
268 8d. bright carmine 85 2·50
269 9d. deep olive-green 50 1·60
270 10d. turquoise-blue 50 2·00
271 11d. plum 60 2·50
272 1s. bistre-brown 60 90
273 **131** 2s. 6d. yellow-green 6·00 7·50
274 5s. red 16·00 24·00
275 **132** 10s. ultramarine 40·00 45·00
261/275 *Set of* 15 60·00 85·00

1949 (10 Oct). *75th Anniv of U.P.U., optd with T* **30**.
276 **143** 2½d. ultramarine 45 45
277 **144** 3d. violet 45 60
278 **145** 6d. bright purple 50 55
279 **146** 1s. brown 60 85

1950 (2 Oct)–**51**. *King George VI, optd with T* **29** *or* **30** *(shilling values).*
280 **128** ½d. pale orange (3.5.51) 30 30
281 1d. light ultramarine (3.5.51) 55 30
282 1½d. pale green (3.5.51) 65 75
283 2d. pale red-brown (3.5.51) 70 90
284 2½d. pale scarlet (3.5.51) 85 65
285 **129** 4d. light ultramarine 1·10 2·25
286 **147** 2s. 6d. yellow-green (3.5.51) 3·50 2·50
287 **148** 5s. red (3.5.51) 8·50 10·00
288 **149** 10s. ultramarine (3.5.51) 18·00 20·00
280/288 *Set of* 9 30·00 35·00

1952–54. *Queen Elizabeth II (Tudor Crown wmk), optd with T* **29**.
289 **154** ½d. orange-red (31.8.53) 5 5
290 1d. ultramarine (31.8.53) 15 10
291 1½d. green (5.12.52) 15 8
292 2d. red-brown (31.8.53) 25 12
293 **155** 2½d. carmine-red (5.12.52) 25 8
294 3d. deep lilac (B.) (18.1.54) 25 8
295 **156** 4d. ultramarine (2.11.53) 45 60
296 **157** 5d. brown (6.7.53) 1·25 1·60
297 6d. reddish purple (18.1.54) 45 10
298 7d. bright green (18.1.54) 1·40 1·60
299 **158** 8d. magenta (6.7.53) 1·75 2·00
300 9d. bronze-green (8.2.54) 1·25 90
301 10d. Prussian blue (8.2.54) 2·75 3·00
302 11d. brown-purple (8.2.54) 2·75 3·00
303 **159** 1s. bistre-brown (6.7.53) 65 25
304 **160** 1s. 3d. green (2.11.53) 1·25 45
305 **159** 1s. 6d. grey-blue (2.11.53) 1·75 1·50
289/305 *Set of* 17 15·00 14·00

1953 (3 June). *Coronation, optd with T* **30**.
306 **161** 2½d. carmine-red 70 30
307 **162** 4d. ultramarine 1·25 1·25
308 **163** 1s. 3d. deep yellow-green 2·75 2·75
309 **164** 1s. 6d. deep grey-blue 3·00 2·75

1955 (23 Sept). *Queen Elizabeth II, optd with T* **30**.
310 **166** 2s. 6d. black-brown 5·50 4·25
311 **167** 5s. rose-red 16·00 16·00
312 **168** 10s. ultramarine 32·00 35·00

1956. *Queen Elizabeth II (St. Edward's Crown wmk), optd with T* **29**.
313 **154** ½d. orange-red (21 March) 5 5
314 1d. ultramarine (13 April) 25 20
315 1½d. green (22 Oct) 70 90
316 2d. red-brown (25 July) 1·50 1·50
317 2d. light red-brown (10 Dec) 60 50
318 **155** 2½d. carmine-red (19 Dec) 75 50
319 3d. deep lilac (B.) (22 Oct) 75 40
320 **156** 4d. ultramarine (25 June) 2·00 3·25
321 **157** 6d. reddish purple (22 Oct) 90 45
322 **160** 1s. 3d. green (26 Nov) 6·00 13·00
313/22 *Set of* 10 12·00 19·00

1857-1957 1857-1957 TANGIER

TANGIER
(32) (33)

1957 (1 Apr). *Centenary of British Post Office in Tangier.*
(a) Nos. 540/2 and 543b/56 optd as T **32** *or* **33** *(7d)*
323 **154** ½d. orange-red 5 5
324 1d. ultramarine 10 5
325 1½d. green 12 8
326 2d. light red-brown 12 8
327 **155** 2½d. carmine-red 15 8
328 3d. deep lilac (B.) 20 8
329 **156** 4d. ultramarine 30 20
330 **157** 5d. brown 35 35
331 6d. reddish purple 35 15
332 7d. bright green 40 30
333 **158** 8d. magenta 50 35
334 9d. bronze-green 50 35
a. "TANGIER" omitted £2750
335 10d. Prussian blue 55 35
336 11d. brown-purple 60 45
337 **159** 1s. bistre-brown 60 25
338 **160** 1s. 3d. green 1·00 50
339 **159** 1s. 6d. grey-blue 1·25 65
(b) Nos. 536/8 optd as T **32**
340 **166** 2s. 6d. black-brown 3·75 3·75
a. Hyphen omitted 60·00
b. Hyphen inserted 22·00
341 **167** 5s. rose-red 6·50 4·00
a. Hyphen omitted 60·00
b. Hyphen inserted 14·00
342 **168** 10s. ultramarine 10·00 6·50
a. Hyphen omitted 65·00
b. Hyphen inserted 17·00
323/42 *Set of* 20 25·00 17·00
Nos. 340a/b, 341a/b and 342a/b occur on stamp No. 34 in the sheet of 40 (4 × 10). They are best collected in marginal blocks of four from the bottom left corner of the sheet. Specialists recognise two forms of No. 340b; one where the hyphen on stamp No. 34 was inserted separately to correct the error, No. 340a; the other from a later printing where a new and corrected overprinting plate was used. *(Price £12 un.)*

All stamps overprinted "TANGIER" were withdrawn from sale on 30 April 1957.

Mosul

see Iraq

Muscat

An independent Arab Sultanate in Eastern Arabia with an Indian postal administration.

The Indian post office at Muscat town is officially recorded as having opened on 1 May 1864. Stamps of India were provided for its use, most surviving examples being of the ½ a. value, although others to the 8 a. are known.

The office was initially included in the Bombay Postal Circle and the first postmark, so far only recorded on stampless covers, was a single circle, 21½ mm in diameter, broken at the top by "MUSCAT" and with the date in two lines across the centre. This was followed by a cancellation showing the post office number, "309", within a diamond of 13, later 16, bars. It is believed that this was used in conjunction with a single ring date stamp inscribed "MUSCAT".

1864 Diamond

In 1869 the office was transferred to the Sind Circle, assigned a new number, "23", and issued with a duplex cancellation. Major reorganisation of the postal service in 1873 resulted in Muscat becoming office "K-4". For ten years from 1873 the cancellations do not, very confusingly, carry any indication of the year of use.

1869 Duplex

1873 Duplex

Muscat rejoined the Bombay Circle in 1879 and was issued with a cancellation showing a "B" within a square of horizontal bars. The date stamp used at this time was unique in that it carried the inscription "MASKAT", although the spelling reverted to the more usual form by 1882. The square cancellation had been replaced by a similar circular mark by 1884.

Subsequent postmarks were of various circular types, all inscribed "MUSCAT".

There was only one Indian post office in Muscat, but a further office did exist, from 12 April 1868, at the Muscat dependency of Guadur, a port on the Mekran coast of Baluchistan.

No cancellations have been reported from Guadur before its transfer to the Sind Circle in 1869. Cancellations are all similar in style to those for Muscat, Guadur being initially assigned number "24", although an office in Southern India is also known to have used this numeral. The 1869 duplex is interesting in that it is inscribed "GWADUR". Under the 1873 reorganisation the office became "4/K-1", this postmark using the "GUADUR" spelling.

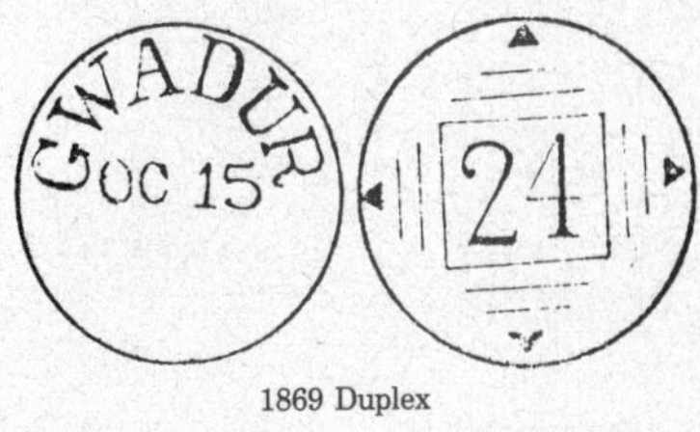

1869 Duplex

PRICES FOR STAMPS ON COVER	
Nos. 1/15	*from* × 30
Nos. O1/10	*from* × 50

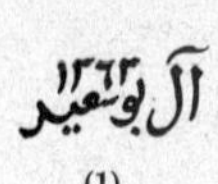

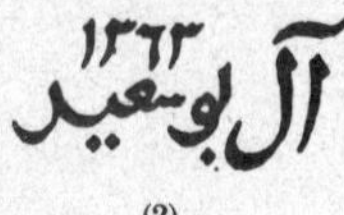

(1) (2)

1944 (20 Nov). *Bicentenary of Al-Busaid Dynasty. Stamps of India optd ("AL BUSAID 1363" in Arabic script) as T* **1** *or* **2** *(rupee values).*
1 **100a** 3 p. slate 12 70
2 ½ a. purple 12 70
3 9 p. green 12 70
4 1 a. carmine 12 70
5 **101** 1½ a. dull violet 12 70
6 2 a. vermilion 12 70
7 3 a. bright violet 12 80
8 3½ a. bright blue 12 80
9 **102** 4 a. brown 20 80
10 6 a. turquoise-green 30 95
11 8 a. slate-violet 30 2·00
12 12 a. lake 45 2·25
13 **103** 14 a. purple 45 2·75
14 **93** 1 r. grey and red-brown 35 3·75
15 2 r. purple and brown 1·00 8·00
1/15 *Set of* 15 3·50 24·00

OFFICIAL STAMPS

1944 (20 Nov). *Bicentenary of Al-Busaid Dynasty. Official stamps of India optd as T 1 or 2 (1 r).*

No.	Type	Description	Unused	Used
O 1	O 20	3 p. slate	12	1·75
O 2		½ a. purple	12	1·75
O 3		9 p. green	12	1·75
O 4		1 a. carmine	12	1·75
O 5		1½ a. dull violet	12	1·75
O 6		2 a. vermilion	12	1·75
O 7		2½ a. bright violet	12	1·75
O 8		4 a. brown	20	2·50
O 9		8 a. slate-violet	25	3·50
O10	93	1 r. grey and red-brown (No. O138)	70	8·00
O1/O10		*Set of* 10	1·75	24·00

From December 1947 there was a Pakistani postal administration and stamps of Pakistan were used until 31 March 1948. The subsequent British administration operated from 1 April 1948 to 29 April 1966 when the stamps of the BRITISH POSTAL AGENCIES IN EASTERN ARABIA were used.

Later issues for this area will be found listed under OMAN in Part 19 (*Middle East*) of this catalogue.

Nagaland

Labels inscribed "NAGALAND" with currency in cents and chaplees are considered to be propaganda labels.

Natal

PRICES FOR STAMPS ON COVER	
Nos. 1/7	*from* × 2
Nos. 9/25	*from* × 3
Nos. 26/56	*from* × 4
Nos. 57/8	—
Nos. 59/65	*from* × 4
Nos. 66/73	*from* × 5
Nos. 76/84	*from* × 4
Nos. 85/93	*from* × 3
Nos. 96/103	*from* × 6
Nos. 104/5	*from* × 5
Nos. 106/25	*from* × 6
Nos. 127/42	*from* × 4
Nos. 143/5a	—
Nos. 146/57	*from* × 4
No. 162	—
Nos. 165/71	*from* × 3
No. F1	—
Nos. O1/6	*from* × 10

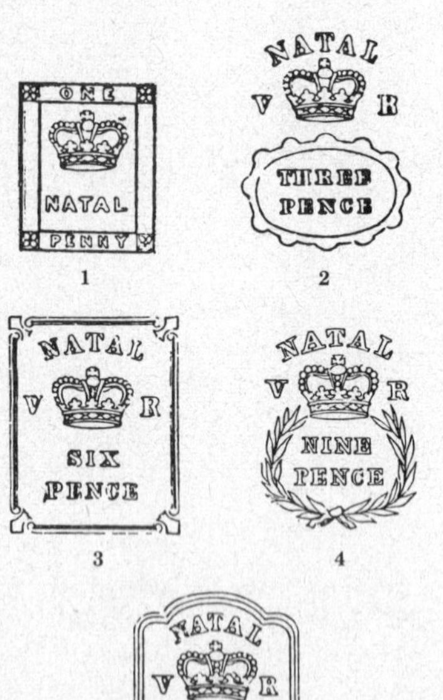

1 2 3 4 5

(Embossed in plain relief on coloured wove paper)

1857 (26 May, *the* 1d. *in* 1858). *Imperf.*

No.	Type	Description	Unused	Used
1	1	1d. rose	—	£1700
2		1d. buff	—	£950
3		1d. blue	—	£1100
4	2	3d. rose	—	£400
		a. *Tête-bêche* (pair)		
5	3	6d. green	—	£1100
6	4	9d. blue	—	£7000
7	5	1s. buff	—	£5500

All the above have been reprinted more than once, and the early reprints of some values cannot always be distinguished with certainty from originals.

Stamps on surface-coloured paper, perforated 12½, are fiscals.

NOTE. The value of the above stamps depends on their dimensions, and the clearness of the embossing, but our prices are for fine used.

6

7

(Recess P.B.)

1859–60. *No wmk. P* 14.

No.	Type	Description	Unused	Used
9	6	1d. rose-red	£110	70·00
10		3d. blue	85·00	42·00

1861. *No wmk. Intermediate perf* 14 *to* 16.

No.	Type	Description	Unused	Used
11	6	3d. blue	£170	65·00

1862. *No wmk. Rough perf* 14 *to* 16.

No.	Type	Description	Unused	Used
12	6	3d. blue	80·00	32·00
		a. Imperf between (pair)	£1400	
		b. Imperf (pair)	—	£1100
13		6d. grey	£120	45·00

1862. *Wmk Small Star. Rough perf* 14 *to* 16.

No.	Type	Description	Unused	Used
15	6	1d. rose-red	80·00	55·00

The 1d. and 3d. wmk. Star, imperf, are proofs, and are therefore not included. The 3d. wmk Star, perforated, is believed to exist only with forged watermark.

(Recess D.L.R.)

1863. *Thick paper. No wmk. P* 13.

No.	Type	Description	Unused	Used
18	6	1d. lake	65·00	25·00
19		1d. carmine-red	65·00	17·00

1864. *Wmk Crown CC. P* 12½.

No.	Type	Description	Unused	Used
20	6	1d. brown-red	£110	32·00
21		1d. rose	80·00	25·00
22		1d. bright-red	80·00	25·00
23		6d. lilac	50·00	15·00
24		6d. violet	38·00	25·00

(Typo D.L.R.)

1867 (April). *Wmk Crown CC. P* 14.

No.	Type	Description	Unused	Used
25	7	1s. green	£110	26·00

1869 (23 Aug). *Optd horiz in Natal. No wmk (3d.), wmk Crown CC (others). P 14 or 14–16 (3d.), 12½ (1d., 6d) or 14 (1s.).*

POSTAGE

Tall capitals

No.	Type	Description	Unused	Used
26	6	1d. rose	£200	48·00
27		1d. bright red	£200	48·00
28		3d. blue (No. 10)		
28*a*		3d. blue (No. 11)	£325	£190
28*b*		3d. blue (No. 12)	£200	55·00
29		6d. lilac	—	45·00
30		6d. violet	£300	45·00
31	7	1s. green	—	£950

Postage.

12¾ mm long

No.	Type	Description	Unused	Used
32	6	1d. rose	£200	50·00
33		1d. bright red	£200	50·00
		a. Opt double	—	£475
34		3d. blue (No. 10)	—	£200
34*a*		3d. blue (No. 11)	£325	£160
34*b*		3d. blue (No. 12)	£300	55·00
35		6d. lilac	£275	48·00
36		6d. violet	£200	48·00
37	7	1s. green	—	£350

Postage.

13¾ mm long

No.	Type	Description	Unused	Used
38	6	1d. rose	£325	95·00
39		1d. bright red	—	95·00
40		3d. blue (No. 10)		
40*a*		3d. blue (No. 11)		
40*b*		3d. blue (No. 12)	£800	£250
41		6d. lilac	—	£120
42		6d. violet	£700	£120
43	7	1s. green	—	£1400

Postage.

14½ to 15½ mm long

No.	Type	Description	Unused	Used
44	6	1d. rose	£325	£190
45		1d. bright red	£400	£170
46		3d. blue (No. 10)		
46*a*		3d. blue (No. 11)		£190
46*b*		3d. blue (No. 12)	—	£190
47		6d. lilac	—	60·00
48		6d. violet	£800	65·00
49	7	1s. green	—	£1400

POSTAGE.

With a stop

No.	Type	Description	Unused	Used
50	6	1d. rose	50·00	25·00
51		1d. bright red	£110	25·00
52		3d. blue (No. 10)	£160	38·00
53		3d. blue (No. 11)	80·00	35·00
54		3d. blue (No. 12)	£120	29·00
		a. Opt double	—	£600
54*b*		6d. lilac	80·00	35·00
55	6	6d. violet	70·00	35·00
56	7	1s. green	80·00	35·00

All values exist with this overprint at top or bottom of stamp.

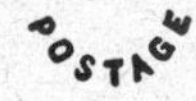

(8)

1870. *No. 25 optd with T 8.*

No.	Type	Description	Unused	Used
57	7	1s. green (C.)	£3000	
58		1s. green (Blk.)	£1500	£950
		a. Opt double	£2750	£1000
59		1s. green (G.)	35·00	10·00

For 1s. orange, see No. 108.

POSTAGE POSTAGE (9) POSTAGE (10) POSTAGE POSTAGE (11)

1870–73. *Optd with T 9. Wmk Crown CC. P* 12½.

No.	Type	Description	Unused	Used
60	6	1d. bright red	48·00	17·00
61		3d. bright blue (R.)	50·00	17·00
62		6d. mauve	95·00	32·00

1873 (July). *Optd up centre of stamp with T 10. Wmk Crown CC. P* 14.

No.	Type	Description	Unused	Used
63	7	1s. purple-brown	50·00	11·00

1874 (July). *No. 21 optd with T 11.*

No.	Type	Description	Unused	Used
65	7	1d. rose	£100	25·00
		a. Opt double		

12

13

14

15

16

(Typo D.L.R.)

1874–78. *Wmk Crown CC. P* 14.

No.	Type	Description	Unused	Used
66	12	1d. dull rose	11·00	1·25
67		1d. bright rose	11·00	1·25
68	13	3d. blue	22·00	13·00
		a. Perf 14 × 12½	£1000	£850
69	14	4d. brown (1878)	35·00	10·00
		a. Perf 12½	£200	60·00
70	15	6d. lilac	20·00	6·00
71	16	5s. maroon	85·00	20·00
		a. Perf 15½ × 15	90·00	60·00
72		5s. rose	60·00	18·00
73		5s. carmine (H/S S. £160)	55·00	20·00

The 5s. stamps normally have wmk sideways.

POSTAGE (17) POSTAGE (18) ½ HALF (19)

1875. *Wmk Crown CC. P 14 (1s.) or 12½ (others). (a) Optd with T 17.*

No.	Type	Description	Unused	Used
76	6	1d. rose	60·00	28·00
		a. Opt double	£475	£425
77		1d. bright red	55·00	48·00
		(b) Optd with T 18 (14½ mm long, without stop)		
81	6	1d. rose	35·00	30·00
		a. Opt inverted	£700	£400
82		1d. yellow	35·00	38·00
83		6d. violet	32·00	5·00
		a. Opt double	—	£550
		b. Opt inverted	£650	£300
84	7	1s. green	35·00	5·50
		a. Opt double	—	£325

TYPE 19. There are several varieties of this surcharge, of which T 19 is an example. They may be divided as follows:

(*a*) "½" 4½ mm high, "2" has straight foot.
(*b*) As last but "½" is 4 mm high.
(*c*) As last but "2" has curled foot.
(*d*) "½" 3½ mm. high, "2" has straight foot.
(*e*) As last but "2" has curled foot.
(*f*) As last but "2" smaller.

As the "½" and "HALF" were overprinted separately, they vary in relative position, and are frequently overlapping.

1877 (13 Feb). *No. 66 surch as T 19.*

No.	Type	Description	Unused	Used
85	12	½d. on 1d. rose (*a*)	15·00	55·00
		a. "½" double		
86		½d. on 1d. rose (*b*)	60·00	
87		½d. on 1d. rose (*c*)	48·00	
88		½d. on 1d. rose (*d*)	28·00	
89		½d. on 1d. rose (*e*)	29·00	
90		½d. on 1d. rose (*f*)	29·00	

POSTAGE

Half-penny

ONE HALF-
PENNY.

(21) 23 (24)

1877–79. *T* **6** *(wmk Crown CC, P 12½) surch as T* **21**.
91 ½d. on 1d. yellow .. .. 8·00 10·00
a. Surch inverted £200 £200
b. Surch double £200 £200
c. Surch omitted (lower stamp, vertical pair) £950 £850
d. "POSTAGE" omitted (in pair with normal) £1000
e. "S" of "POSTAGE" omitted £180 £170
f. "T" of "POSTAGE" omitted £180
92 1d. on 6d. violet .. .. 14·00 4·75
a. "S" of "POSTAGE" omitted £250
93 1d. on 6d. rose .. .. 32·00 17·00
a. Surch inverted .. .. — £160
b. Surch double .. .. — £190
c. Surch double, one inverted £250 £250
d. Surch four times £325 £160
e. "S" of "POSTAGE" omitted £250

No. 93c. is known with one surcharge showing variety "S" of "POSTAGE" omitted.

Other minor varieties exist in these surcharges.

(Typo D.L.R.)

1880 (13 Oct). *Wmk Crown CC. P* 14.
96 **23** ½d. blue-green .. .. 3·00 3·75
a. Imperf between (vert pair) .. ..

1882–89. *Wmk Crown CA. P* 14.
97 **23** ½d. blue-green .. .. 30·00 12·00
a. Dull green 40 30
99 **12** 1d. rose *(shades)* 40 30
a. Carmine .. .. 1·90 40
100 **13** 3d. blue .. .. 35·00 15·00
101 3d. grey (1889) 50 45
102 **14** 4d. brown .. .. 1·60 85
103 **15** 6d. mauve .. .. 1·75 90
97*a*, 99*a*, 101/3 H/S "Specimen" .. *Set of* 5 £375

1885 (26 Jan). *No. 99 surch with T* **24**.
104 **12** ½d. on 1d. rose .. .. 12·00 10·00

TWO PENCE

NATAL POSTAGE / TWO PENCE

TWOPENCE HALFPENNY

(25) 26 (27)

1886. *Surch locally with T* **25**.
105 **13** 2d. on 3d. grey .. .. 14·00 8·00

(Typo D.L.R.)

1887–89. *Wmk Crown CA. P* 14.
106 **26** 2d. olive-green Die I* (Optd S. £70) .. 13·00 65
107 2d. olive-green, Die II 90 65

*The differences between Dies I and II are shown in the Introduction.

1888. *Optd with T* **8**, *by D.L.R.*
108 **7** 1s. orange (C.) (H/S S. £90) .. .. 1·75 70
a. Opt double .. ..

1890. *Surch locally with T* **27**.
109 **14** 2½d. on 4d. brown (H/S S. £75) .. .. 8·00 6·50
a. "TWOPENGE" .. .. .. 60·00 60·00
b. "HALFPENN" .. .. .. — £160
c. Surch double £225 £160
d. Surch inverted £275 £225

POSTAGE.

Half-Penny

POSTAGE.

28 (29) Varieties of long-tailed letters

(Typo D.L.R.)

1891 (June). *Wmk Crown CA. P* 14.
113 **28** 2½d. bright blue (H/S S. £75) .. .. 1·25 90

1895 (12 Mar). *No. 24 surch with T* **29** *in carmine.*
114 ½d. on 6d. violet (H/S S. £65) .. .. .. 90 1·50
a. "Ealf-Penny" .. .. 18·00
b. "Half-Penny" .. .. 14·00
c. No stop after "POSTAGE" .. .. 15·00
d. Long "P" .. .. 2·00
e. Long "T" .. .. 2·00
f. Long "A" .. .. 2·00
g. Long "P" and "T" .. .. 2·50
h. Long "P" and "A" .. .. 2·00 3·50
i. Long "T" and "A" .. .. 2·00 3·50
k. Long "P", "T" and "A" .. .. .. 2·50
l. Surcharge double, one vertical £250
la. Surcharge double, "Ealf-Penny" .. ..
lb. Surcharge double, "Half-Penny" .. ..

No. 114 is known with surcharge double and widely spaced, but the second surcharge is extremely faint.

No. 114k is known without stop and also with comma instead of a stop after "POSTAGE".

HALF

(30) 31 32

1895 (18 Mar). *No. 99 surch with T* **30**.
125 HALF on 1d. rose *(shades)* (H/S S. £75) 80 85
a. Surch double £325 £325
b. "H" with longer left limb .. .. 20·00

No. 125b occurs on the second, fourth, sixth etc., stamps of the first vertical row of the righthand pane. It was very soon corrected.

In some printings what appears to be a broken "E" (with the top limb removed) was used instead of "L" in "HALF" on the last stamp in the sheet (*Price* £30)

(Typo D.L.R.)

1902–3. *Inscr* "POSTAGE REVENUE". *Wmk Crown CA. P* 14.
127 **31** ½d. blue-green 25 15
128 1d. carmine 30 20
129 1½d. green and black 35 60
130 2d. red and olive-green .. .. .. 1·10 50
131 2½d. bright blue .. .. 1·25 2·75
132 3d. purple and grey .. .. .. 1·10 35
133 4d. carmine and cinnamon .. .. 1·60 4·50
134 5d. black and orange .. .. .. 2·25 2·00
135 6d. green and brown-purple .. .. 2·50 1·25
136 1s. carmine and pale blue .. .. 4·25 1·40
137 2s. green and bright violet .. .. 20·00 14·00
138 2s. 6d. purple .. .. 22·00 18·00
139 4s. deep rose and maize .. .. 45·00 28·00
a. Imperf between (horiz pair) ..
127/139 .. .. *Set of* 13 90·00 65·00
127/39 Optd "Specimen" .. .. *Set of* 13 £300

No. 139a is also imperforate between stamp and left-hand margin.

(Typo D.L.R.)

1902–3. *Wmk Crown CC. P* 14.
140 **32** 5s. dull blue and rose .. .. .. 14·00 7·00
141 10s. deep rose and chocolate .. .. 45·00 14·00
142 £1 black and bright blue .. .. £110 42·00
143 £1 10s. green & violet (Optd S. £120) .. £200 65·00
144 £5 mauve and black (Optd S. £150) .. £1200 £180
145 £10 green and orange (Optd S. £450) .. £5500
145*a* £20 red and green (Optd S. £650) .. £9000
140/2 Optd "Specimen" .. .. *Set of* 3 £250

USED HIGH VALUES. Collectors are warned against fiscally used high value Natal stamps with penmarks cleaned off and forged postmarks added.

1904–8. *Wmk Mult Crown CA. P* 14.
146 **31** ½d. blue-green 30 15
147 1d. rose-carmine 30 15
148 1d. deep carmine 75 20
149 2d. red and olive-green .. .. .. 65 3·25
152 4d. carmine and cinnamon .. .. 2·00 1·50
153 5d. black and orange (1908) .. .. 4·00 4·00
155 1s. carmine and pale blue .. .. 24·00 7·50
156 2s. dull green and bright violet .. .. 27·00 20·00
157 2s. 6d. purple .. .. 28·00 18·00
162 **32** £1 10s. brown-orange and deep purple, **C** (1908) (Optd S. £300) £1000
146/157 .. .. *Set of* 9 80·00 50·00

1908–9. *Inscr* "POSTAGE POSTAGE". *Wmk Mult Crown CA. P* 14.
165 **31** 6d. dull and bright purple .. .. 4·25 2·50
166 1s. black/*green* .. .. 7·00 2·50
167 2s. purple and bright blue/*blue* .. .. 15·00 7·00
168 2s. 6d. black and red/*blue* .. .. 20·00 7·50
169 **32** 5s. green and red/*yellow* .. .. 25·00 13·00
170 10s. green and red/*green* .. .. 70·00 45·00
171 £1 purple and black/*red* £275 £120
165/170 .. .. *Set of* 6 £130 70·00
165/71 Optd "Specimen" .. .. *Set of* 7 £500

FISCALS USED FOR POSTAGE

1869. *Embossed on coloured wove, surfaced paper. P* 12½.
F1 **1** 1d. yellow .. .. 45·00 80·00

Examples of 1d. yellow and 6d. rose values as Type **6**, 1s. purple-brown as Type **7** and various values between 5s. and £10 in the design illustrated above are believed to exist postally used, but, as such use was not authorised, they are not now listed.

OFFICIAL STAMPS

OFFICIAL

(O 1)

1904. *T* **31**, *wmk Mult Crown CA, optd with Type* O **1**. *P* 14.
O1 ½d. blue-green .. .. 3·00 35
O2 1d. carmine .. .. 1·00 55
O3 2d. red and olive-green .. .. .. 8·50 7·50
O4 3d. purple and grey .. .. 3·50 5·00
O5 6d. green and brown-purple .. .. 17·00 14·00
O6 1s. carmine and pale blue .. .. 32·00 60·00

The use of stamps overprinted as above was discontinued after 30 May 1907. Stamps perforated with the letters "N.G.R." were for use on Government Railways.

Natal now uses the stamps of South Africa.

Nauru

Stamps of MARSHALL ISLANDS were used in Nauru from the opening of the German Colonial Post Office on 14 July 1905 until 8 September 1914.

Following the occupation by Australian forces the "N.W. PACIFIC ISLANDS" overprints on Australia (see NEW GUINEA) were used during the early months of 1916.

PRICES FOR STAMPS ON COVER TO 1945

Nos. 1/12	*from* × 10
Nos. 13/16	*from* × 3
Nos. 17/25	—
Nos. 26/39	*from* × 6
Nos. 40/3	*from* × 10
Nos. 44/7	*from* × 15

BRITISH MANDATE

NAURU NAURU NAURU

(1) (2) (3)

1916 (Oct)–**23.** *Stamps of Great Britain (1912–22) overprinted.*

(a) With T **1** *(12½ mm long) at foot*
1 **105** ½d. green .. .. 30 1·25
a. "NAUP.U" £275
b. Double opt, one albino £120
2 **104** 1d. bright scarlet .. .. 40 1·50
a. "NAUP.U" £275
2*b* 1d. carmine-red .. ..
ba. "NAUP.U" .. ..
bb. Double opt, one albino £170
3 **105** 1½d. red-brown (1923) .. .. .. 60·00 75·00
4 **106** 2d. orange (Die I) .. .. 1·75 4·00
a. "NAUP.U" £300
b. Double opt, one albino £120
5 2d. orange (Die II) (1923) .. .. 60·00 75·00
6 **104** 2½d. blue .. .. 3·25 5·00
a. "NAUP.U" £375
b. Double opt, one albino £170
7 **106** 3d. bluish violet .. .. 3·25 4·25
a. "NAUP.U" £375
b. Double opt, one albino £170
8 4d. slate-green .. .. 3·75 7·50
a. "NAUP.U" £400
b. Double opt, one albino £170
9 **107** 5d. yellow-brown .. .. 5·00 8·50
a. "NAUP.U" £400
b. Double opt, one albino £140
10 6d. purple, **C** .. .. 7·00 11·00
a. "NAUP.U" £400
b. Double opt, one albino £170
11 **108** 9d. agate .. .. 9·00 15·00
a. Double opt, one albino £170
12 1s. bistre-brown (H/S S. £100) .. .. 11·00 15·00
a. Double opt, one albino £170
1/12 .. .. *Set of* 11 90·00 £130

(b) With T **2** *(13½ mm long) at centre* (1923)
13 **105** ½d. green .. .. 11·00 38·00
14 **104** 1d. scarlet .. .. 17·00 38·00
15 **105** 1½d. red-brown .. .. 20·00 50·00
a. Double opt, one albino .. ..
16 **106** 2d. orange (Die II) .. .. 45·00 80·00

There is a constant variety consisting of short left stroke to "N" which occurs on Nos. 1, 2 2*b*, 4 (£30 *each*); 3 (£175); 5 (£180); 6, 7 (£38 *each*); 8, 9, 10 (£55 *each*); 11, 12 (£65 *each*). All unused prices.

(c) T **109** *optd with T* **3**. *(i) Waterlow printing*
17 5s. rose-carmine £2500 £2500
18 10s. indigo-blue (R.) (H/S S. £1400) £5500 £5250
a. Double opt, one albino £8000 £8000

(ii) De La Rue printing
19 2s. 6d. deep brown £500 £550
a. Double opt, one albino £1100
b. Treble opt, two albino £1200
20 2s. 6d. yellow-brown .. .. 70·00 80·00
a. Re-entry .. ..
21 2s. 6d. brown .. .. 75·00 80·00
22 5s. bright carmine *(shades)* £140 £140
a. Treble opt, two albino £550
23 10s. pale blue (R.) £400 £450
a. Treble opt. two albino .. .. ..
23*b* 10s. deep bright blue (R.) £750 £800
19, 21, 22 H/S "Specimen" .. .. *Set of* 3 £600

(iii) Bradbury, Wilkinson printing (1919)
24 2s. 6d. chocolate-brown .. .. .. 80·00 85·00
a. Major re-entry .. ..
b. Double opt, one albino £225
25 2s. 6d. pale brown .. .. 65·00 75·00
a. Double opt, one albino £175

AUSTRALIAN MANDATE

PRINTERS. See note at beginning of Australia.

4

(Des R. A. Harrison. Eng T. S. Harrison. Recess Note Printing Branch of the Treasury, Melbourne and from 1926 by the Commonwealth Bank of Australia)

1924–48. *T* 4. *No wmk. P* 11.
I. Rough surfaced, greyish paper (1924–34).
II. Shiny surfaced, white paper (1937–47).

No.	Description	I		II	
26	½d. chestnut	1·75	4·50	8·00	9·50
	a. Perf 14 (1947)	†		1·90	3·25
27	1d. green	1·75	4·50	3·75	4·50
28	1½d. scarlet	2·25	4·25	1·10	2·25
29	2d. orange	2·25	6·00	1·50	2·75
30	2½d. slate-blue	6·50	11·00	†	
30*a*	2½d. greenish blue (1934)	6·50	11·00	†	
30*b*	2½d. dull blue (1948)	†		1·50	3·25
	ba. Imperf between (pair)	†		£3500	£3500
31	3d. pale blue	3·00	6·50	†	
31*a*	3d. greenish grey	†		2·00	3·50
32	4d. olive-green	4·25	8·50	3·50	4·75
33	5d. brown	4·50	7·50	3·25	3·75
34	6d. dull violet	7·50	12·00	3·00	3·75
35	9d. olive-brown	8·50	16·00	8·50	12·00
36	1s. brown-lake	11·00	15·00	7·00	7·50
37	2s. 6d. grey-green	30·00	38·00	24·00	27·00
38	5s. claret	65·00	80·00	50·00	65·00
39	10s. yellow	£120	£130	70·00	80·00
26I/39I	*Set of* 14	£250	£325	†	
26II/39II	*Set of* 15	†		£160	£200

HIS MAJESTY'S JUBILEE.

1910 - 1935

(5)

6

1935 (12 July). *Silver Jubilee. T* 4 (*shiny surfaced, white paper*) *optd with T* **5**.

40	1½d. scarlet	1·00	1·50
41	2d. orange	1·50	4·25
42	2½d. dull blue	3·00	3·25
43	1s. brown-lake	8·50	10·00

(Recess John Ash, Melbourne)

1937 (10 May). *Coronation. P* 11.

44	**6**	1½d. scarlet	45	45
45		2d. orange	45	50
46		2½d. blue	45	45
47		1s. purple	60	70

7 Nauruan Netting Fish

8 Anibare Bay

15 Map of Nauru

(Recess Note Printing Branch, Commonwealth Bank, Melbourne, and from 1960 by Note Ptg Branch, Reserve Bank of Australia, Melbourne)

1954 (6 Feb.)–**61**. *T* **7/8, 15** *and similar designs. Toned paper. P* 13½ × 14½ (*horiz*) *or* 14½ × 13½ (*vert*).

48	½d. deep violet	15	5
	a. Violet (8.5.61)	15	5
49	1d. bluish green	15	5
	a. Emerald-green (*shades*) (8.5.61)	15	12
50	3½d. scarlet	1·50	40
	a. Vermilion (1958)		
51	4d. grey-blue	1·50	45
	a. Deep blue (1958)		
52	6d. orange	80	30
53	9d. claret	1·00	50
54	1s. deep purple	90	35
55	2s. 6d. deep green	9·00	3·50
56	5s. magenta	24·00	6·00
48/56	*Set of* 9	35·00	10·00

Designs: *Horiz*—3½d. Loading phosphate from cantilever; 4d. Great Frigate Bird; 6d. Nauruan canoe; 9d. Domaneab (Meeting-house); 2s. 6d. Buada lagoon. *Vert*—1s. Palm trees.

Nos. 48*a*, 49*a*, 50*a* and 51*a* are on white paper.

16 Micronesian Pigeon

17 Poison Nut

20 Capparis

21 White Tern

(Recess (10d., 2s. 3d.) or photo (others) Note Ptg Branch, Reserve Bank of Australia, Melbourne)

1963–65. *T* **16/17, 20/1** *and similar designs. P* 13½ × 13 (5*d.*), 13 × 13½ (8*d.*), 14 × 13½ (10*d.*), 15 × 14½ (1*s.* 3*d.*) *or* 13½ (*others*).

57	2d. black, blue, red-brn & orge-yell (3.5.65)	1·75	1·25
58	3d. multicoloured (16.4.64)	1·25	70
59	5d. multicoloured (22.4.63)	1·25	1·00
60	8d. black and green (1.7.63)	2·50	1·75
61	10d. black (16.4.64)	1·00	80
62	1s. 3d. blue, black & yellow-green (3.5.65)	7·00	4·50
63	2s. 3d. ultramarine (16.4.64)	6·50	3·00
64	3s. 3d. multicoloured (3.5.65)	12·00	10·00
57/64	*Set of* 8	30·00	21·00

Designs: *Vert*—5d. "Iyo" (*calophyllum*). *Horiz*—8d. Black Lizard; 2s. 3d. Coral pinnacles; 3s. 3d. Nightingale Reed Warbler.

1965 (14 Apr). 50*th Anniv of Gallipoli Landing. As T* **184** *of Australia, but slightly larger* (22 × 34½ *mm*). *Photo.*

65	5d. sepia, black and emerald	40	25

(New Currency. 100 cents = $1 Australian)

24 Anibare Bay

25 "Iyo" (*calophyllum*)

(Recess (1, 2, 3, 5, 8, 19, 25 c. and $1) or photo (others))

1966 (14 Feb–25 May). *Decimal Currency. Various stamps with values in cents and dollars as T* **24/5** *and some colours changed. Recess printed stamps on helecon paper.*

66	**24**	1 c. deep blue	20	10
67	**7**	2 c. brown-purple (25 May)	15	10
68	–	3 c. bluish green (as 3½d.) (25 May)	30	12
69	**25**	4 c. multicoloured	25	12
70	–	5 c. deep ultramarine (as 1s.) (25 May)	25	12
71	–	7 c. black and chestnut (as 8d.)	25	15
72	**20**	8 c. olive-green	30	15
73	–	10 c. red (as 4d.)	40	15
74	**21**	15 c. blue, black & yellow-green (25 May)	1·25	90
75	–	25 c. deep brown (as 2s. 3d.) (25 May)	75	60
76	**17**	30 c. multicoloured	2·50	1·50
77	–	35 c. multicoloured (as 3s. 3d.) (25 May)	4·00	2·50
78	**16**	50 c. multicoloured	6·00	3·25
79	–	$1 magenta (as 5s.)	6·50	5·50
66/79		*Set of* 14	20·00	14·00

The 25 c. is as No. 63, but larger, 27½ × 24½ mm.

REPUBLIC

Nauru became independent on 31 January 1968 and was later admitted into special membership of the Commonwealth.

REPUBLIC
OF
NAURU

(26)

1968 (31 Jan–15 May). *Nos.* 66/79 *optd with T* **26**.

80	**24**	1 c. deep blue (R.)	8	8
81	**7**	2 c. brown-purple	10	8
82	–	3 c. bluish green	12	10
83	**25**	4 c. multicoloured (15.5.68)	20	12
84	–	5 c. deep ultramarine (R.)	20	15
85	–	7 c. black and chestnut (R.) (15.5.68)	30	20
86	**20**	8 c. olive-green (R.)	40	20
87	–	10 c. red	45	20
88	**21**	15 c. blue, black and yellow-green	8·00	6·00
89	–	25 c. deep brown (R.)	70	45
90	**17**	30 c. multicoloured (15.5.68)	1·00	70
91	–	35 c. multicoloured (15.5.68)	3·50	1·75
92	**16**	50 c. multicoloured	5·00	2·25
93		$1 magenta	5·00	4·50
80/93		*Set of* 14	22·00	15·00

27 "Towards the Sunrise"

28 Planting Seedling, and Map

(Des H. Fallu (5 c.), Note Ptg Branch (10 c.). Photo Note Ptg Branch, Reserve Bank of Australia, Melbourne)

1968 (11 Sept). *Independence. P* 13½.

94	**27**	5 c. black, slate-lilac, orange-yellow and yellow-green	15	15
95	**28**	10 c. black, yellow-green and new blue	20	15

29 Flag of Independent Nauru

30 Island, "C" and Stars

(Des J. Mason. Photo Note Ptg Branch, Reserve Bank of Australia, Melbourne)

1969 (31 Jan). *P* 13 × 13½.

96	**29**	15 c. yellow, orange and royal blue	50	40

This is a definitive issue which was put on sale on the first anniversary of Independence.

(Des R. Brooks, Litho Format)

1972 (7 Feb). 25*th Anniv of South Pacific Commission. P* 14½ × 14.

97	**30**	25 c. multicoloured	1·00	1·25

Independence 1968-1973

(31)

1973 (31 Jan). *Fifth Anniv of Independence. No.* 96 *optd with T* **31** *in gold.*

98	**29**	15 c. yellow, orange and royal blue	1·00	1·75

32 Denea

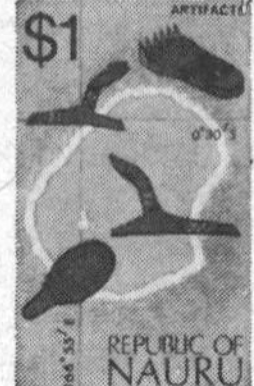

33 Artefacts and Map

(Des locally; adapted G. Vasarhelyi. Litho Format)

1973 (28 Mar*–25 July). *Various multicoloured designs as T* **32** (1 *to* 5 *c.*) *or T* **33** (*others*). *P* 14 (1 *to* 5 *c.*), 14½ × 14 (7, 8, 10, 30, 50 *c.*) *or* 14 × 14½ (*others*).

99	1 c. Ekwenababae	25	10
100	2 c. Kauwe Iud	40	12
101	3 c. Rimone	40	15
102	4 c. Type **32**	50	25
103	5 c. Erekogo	50	25
104	7 c. Ikimago (fish) (25.7)	40	25
105	8 c. Catching flying-fish (23.5)	40	25
106	10 c. Itsibweb (ball game) (23.5)	40	25
107	15 c. Nauruan wrestling (23.5)	45	35
108	20 c. Snaring Frigate Birds (23.5)	75	50
109	25 c. Nauruan girl (25.7)	75	60
110	30 c. Catching Noddy Birds (25.7)	1·50	1·00
111	50 c. Great Frigate Birds (25.7)	2·25	1·75
112	$1 Type **33**	3·75	3·25
99/112	*Set of* 14	12·00	8·00

The 1 to 5 c. show flowers, and the 7, 8, 10, 30, 50 c. are horiz designs.

*This is the local release date but the Crown Agents issued the stamps on 21 March.

34 Co-op Store

35 Phosphate Mining

(Des G. Vasarhelyi. Litho Format)

1973 (20 Dec). 50*th Anniv of Nauru Co-operative Society. T* **34** *and similar multicoloured designs. P* 14 × 14½ (50 *c.*) *or* 14½ × 14 (*others*).

113	5 c. Type **34**	1·00	1·25
114	25 c. Timothy Detudamo (founder)	1·00	70
115	50 c. N.C.S. trademark (*vert*)	3·00	2·25

(Des G. Vasarhelyi (7 c. from original by J. Mason; 10 c. from original by K. Depaune). Litho Format)

1974 (21 May). 175*th Anniv of First Contact with the Outside World. T* **35** *and similar horiz designs. Multicoloured. P* 13 × 13½ (7, 35, 50 *c.*) *or* 13½ × 13 (*others*).

116	7 c. M. V. *Eigamoiya*	1·75	1·75
117	10 c. Type **29**	1·50	75
118	15 c. Fokker Friendship *Nauru Chief*	1·75	80
119	25 c. Nauruan chief in early times	2·75	1·50
120	35 c. Capt. Fearn and the *Hunter*	14·00	11·00
121	50 c. The *Hunter* off Nauru	6·50	3·00
116/121	*Set of* 6	25·00	17·00

The 7, 35 and 50 c. are larger, 70 × 22 mm.

PRICES OF SETS

Set prices are given for many issues, generally those containing five stamps or more. Definitive sets include one of each value or major colour change, but do not cover different perforations, die types or minor shades. Where a choice is possible the set prices are based on the cheapest versions of the stamps included in the listings.

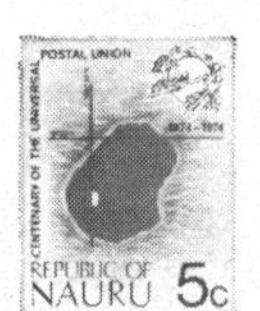

36 Map of Nauru

37 Rev. P. A. Delaporte

(Des G. Vasarhelyi. Litho Format)

1974 (23 July). *Centenary of Universal Postal Union. T* **36** *and similar multicoloured designs. P* 13½ × 14 (5 c.), 13 × 13½ ($1) *or* 13½ × 13 (*others*).
122 5 c. Type **36** .. .. 1·50 2·00
123 8 c. Nauru Post Office .. .. 1·50 1·50
124 20 c. Nauruan postman .. .. 1·50 90
125 $1 U.P.U. Building and Nauruan flag .. 3·00 2·25
MS126 157 × 105 mm. Nos. 122/5. Imperf .. 9·00 10·00
The 8 and 20 c. are horiz (33 × 21 mm), and the $1 is vert (21 × 33 mm).

(Des J.W. Litho Format)

1974 (10 Dec). *Christmas and 75th Anniv of Rev. Delaporte's Arrival. P* 14½.
127 **37** 15 c. multicoloured .. .. .. 1·00 80
128 20 c. multicoloured .. .. .. 1·50 1·25

38 Map of Nauru, Lump of Phosphate Rock and Albert Ellis

39 Micronesian Outrigger

(Des M. and Sylvia Goaman. Litho Format)

1975 (23 July). *Phosphate Mining Anniversaries. T* **38** *and similar horiz designs. Multicoloured. P* 14½ × 14.
129 5 c. Type **38** 30 20
130 7 c. Coolies and mine.. .. .. 45 30
131 15 c. Electric railway, barges and ship .. 1·50 80
132 25 c. Modern ore extraction .. .. .. 1·75 1·00
Anniversaries:—5 c. 75th Anniv of discovery; 7 c. 70th Anniv of Mining Agreement; 15 c. 55th Anniv of British Phosphate Commissioners; 25 c. 5th Anniv of Nauru Phosphate Corporation.

(Des M. and Sylvia Goaman. Litho Format)

1975 (1 Sept). *South Pacific Commission Conference, Nauru (1st issue). T* **39** *and similar horiz designs. Multicoloured. P* 13½ × 14.
133 20 c. Type **39** .. .. 1·50 1·25
a. Block of 4. Nos. 133/6 .. .. .. 6·00
134 20 c. Polynesian double-hull .. .. .. 1·50 1·25
135 20 c. Melanesian outrigger .. .. .. 1·50 1·25
136 20 c. Polynesian outrigger .. .. .. 1·50 1·25
Nos. 133/6 were printed in *se-tenant* blocks of four throughout the sheet.

40 New Civic Centre

41 "Our Lady" (Yaren Church)

(Des M. and Sylvia Goaman. Litho Format)

1975 (29 Sept). *South Pacific Commission Conference, Nauru (2nd issue). T* **40** *and similar horiz design. Multicoloured. P* 14.
137 30 c. Type **40** .. .. 1·00 95
138 50 c. Domaneab (meeting-house) .. .. 1·50 1·10

(Des M. and Sylvia Goaman. Litho Format)

1975 (7 Nov). *Christmas. T* **41** *and similar vert design showing stained-glass window. Multicoloured. P* 14½ × 14.
139 5 c. Type **41** 30 30
140 7 c. "Suffer little children. . ." (Orro Church) 35 40
141 15 c. As 7 c. 55 50
142 25 c. Type **41** 75 65

42 Flowers floating towards Nauru

(Des M. and Sylvia Goaman. Litho Format)

1976 (31 Jan*). *30th Anniv of the Return from Truk. T* **42** *and similar horiz designs. Multicoloured. P* 14½.
143 10 c. Type **42** 30 30
144 14 c. Nauru encircled by garland 35 40
145 25 c. Nightingale Reed Warbler and maps .. 80 80
146 40 c. Return of the islanders 90 90
*This is the local date of issue; the Crown Agents released the stamps one day earlier.

43 3d. and 9d. Stamps of 1916

(Des M. and Sylvia Goaman. Litho Format)

1976 (6 May). *60th Anniv of Nauruan Stamps. T* **43** *and similar horiz designs. Multicoloured. P* 13½.
147 10 c. Type **43** 30 30
148 15 c. 6d. and 1s. stamps 35 40
149 25 c. 2s. 6d. stamp 90 75
150 50 c. 5s. "Specimen" stamp .. .. .. 1·10 1·00
Nos. 147/8 show stamps with errors: the 3d. "Short N" and the 6d. "P" for "R".

44 *Pandanus mei* and Nauruan Ship

(Des M. and Sylvia Goaman. Litho Format)

1976 (26 July). *South Pacific Forum, Nauru. T* **44** *and similar horiz designs. Multicoloured. P* 13½.
151 10 c. Type **44** 85 45
152 20 c. *Tournefortia argentea* and Nauruan aircraft .. .. 1·10 70
153 30 c. *Thespesia populnea* and Nauru Tracking Station .. .. 1·60 90
154 40 c. *Cordia subcordata* and produce .. .. 1·90 1·00

45 Nauruan Choir

46 Nauru House and Coral Pinnacles

(Des G. Vasarhelyi. Litho Format)

1976 (17 Nov). *Christmas. T* **45** *and similar vert designs. Multicoloured. P* 13½.
155 15 c. Type **45** 50 50
a. Horiz pair. Nos. 155/6 .. .. .. 1·00 1·00
156 15 c. Nauruan choir 50 50
157 20 c. Angel in white dress 50 50
a. Horiz pair. Nos. 157/8 .. .. .. 1·00 1·00
158 20 c. Angel in red dress 50 50
Nos. 155/6 and 157/8 were printed horizontally *se-tenant* throughout the sheet, both forming composite designs.

(Des D. Gentleman. Photo Harrison)

1977 (14 Apr). *Opening of Nauru House, Melbourne. T* **46** *and similar vert design. Multicoloured. P* 14.
159 15 c. Type **46** 75 60
160 30 c. Nauru House and Melbourne skyline .. 1·00 90

47 Cable Laying Ship *Anglia*

48 Father Kayser and First Catholic Church

(Des D. Gentleman. Photo Harrison)

1977 (7 Sept). *75th Anniv of First Trans-Pacific Cable and 20th Anniv of First Artificial Earth Satellite. T* **47** *and similar vert designs. P* 14 × 14½.
161 7 c. multicoloured 30 25
162 15 c. light blue, grey and black 40 40
163 20 c. light blue, grey and black 50 45
164 25 c. multicoloured 50 50
Designs:—15 c. Tracking station, Nauru; 20 c. Stern of *Anglia*; 25 c. Dish aerial.

(Des D. Gentleman. Photo Harrison)

1977 (28 Nov). *Christmas. T* **48** *and similar vert designs. Multicoloured. P* 14½.
165 15 c. Type **48** 30 30
166 25 c. Congregational Church, Orro 40 40
167 30 c. Catholic Church, Arubo 40 40
No. 165 also commemorates the 75th anniversary of the Catholic Church on Nauru.

49 Arms of Nauru

4c

(**50**)

(Des G. Vasarhelyi. Litho Format)

1978 (31 Jan). *Tenth Anniv of Independence. P* 14½.
168 **49** 15 c. multicoloured 30 30
169 60 c. multicoloured 55 70

1978 (29 Mar). *Nos.* 159/60 *surch as T* **50** *by Format.*
170 4 c. on 15 c. Type **46** .. .. 6·50 8·00
171 5 c. on 15 c. Type **46** .. .. 6·50 8·00
172 8 c. on 30 c. No. 160 .. .. 6·50 8·00
173 10 c. on 30 c. No. 160 .. .. 6·50 8·00

51 Collecting Shellfish

52 A.P.U. Emblem

(Des D. Gentleman. Photo Harrison)

1978 (17 May)–**79.** *Horiz designs as T* **51** *in brown, blue and black* (4 c.), *grey, black and light blue* (20 c., $5) *or multicoloured* (*others*). *P* 14½.
174 1 c. Type **51** 5 5
175 2 c. Coral outcrop (6.6.79) 5 5
176 3 c. Reef scene (6.6.79) 5 5
177 4 c. Girl with fish (6.6.79) 5 5
178 5 c. Eastern Reef Heron (6.6.79) 5 5
179 7 c. Catching fish, Buada Lagoon 8 10
180 10 c. Ijuw Lagoon 12 12
181 15 c. Girl framed by coral 15 20
182 20 c. Pinnacles, Anibare Bay reef 25 25
183 25 c. Pinnacle at Meneng 30 30
184 30 c. Head of Great Frigate Bird 30 35
185 32 c. White-capped Noddy in coconut palm .. 35 35
186 40 c. Wandering Tattler 45 45
187 50 c. Great Frigate Birds on perch 55 55
188 $1 Old coral pinnacles at Topside .. .. 1·10 1·10
189 $2 New pinnacles at Topside .. .. 2·25 2·25
190 $5 Blackened pinnacles at Topside.. .. 6·00 5·50
174/90 .. .. *Set of* 17 11·00 10·00

(Litho Toppan Ptg Co, Ltd)

1978 (28 Aug). *14th General Assembly of Asian Parliamentarians' Union. T* **52** *and similar vert design. P* 13.
191 15 c. multicoloured .. .. 1·25 1·40
192 20 c. black, deep ultramarine and gold .. 1·25 1·40
Design:—20 c. As T **52** but different background.

53 Virgin and Child

54 Baden-Powell and Cub Scout

(Des R. Vigurs. Litho Format)

1978 (1 Nov). *Christmas. T* **53** *and similar multicoloured design. P* 14.
193 7 c. Type **53** 15 15
194 15 c. Angel in sun-rise scene (*horiz*) 25 25
195 20 c. As 15 c. 30 30
196 30 c. Type **53** 40 40

(Des J. Charles. Litho Format)

1978 (1 Dec). *70th Anniv of Boy Scout Movement. T* **54** *and similar horiz designs. Multicoloured. P* 13½.
197 20 c. Type **54** 35 45
198 30 c. Baden-Powell and Boy Scout 45 55
199 50 c. Baden-Powell and Rover Scout 55 65

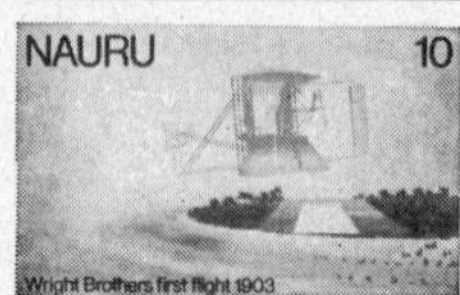

55 Wright *Flyer* over Nauru

(Des D. Gentleman. Litho Format)

1979 (24 Jan). *Flight Anniversaries. T* **55** *and similar horiz designs. Multicoloured. P* 14.
200 10 c. Type **55** 20 15
201 15 c. *Southern Cross* superimposed on nose of Boeing "727" 30 30
a. Pair. Nos. 201/2 .. .. 60 60
202 15 c. *Southern Cross* and Boeing "727" (front view) 30 30
203 30 c. Wright *Flyer* over Nauru airfield .. 40 40
Commemorations:—10, 30 c. 75th anniversary of powered flight; 15 c. 50th anniversary of Kingsford-Smith's Pacific flight.
Nos. 201/2 were printed together, *se-tenant*, in horizontal and vertical pairs throughout the sheet.

56 Sir Rowland Hill and Marshall Islands 10 pf. Stamp of 1901

(Des R. Granger Barrett. Litho Format)

1979 (27 Feb). *Death Centenary of Sir Rowland Hill. T* **56** *and similar horiz designs showing stamps and Sir Rowland Hill. Multicoloured. P* 14½.
204 5 c. Type **56** 15 15
a. Imperf (pair) £450
205 15 c. "NAURU" opt on Great Britain 10s. "Seahorse" of 1916–23 .. .. 30 30
a. Imperf (pair) £450
206 60 c. 1978 10th Anniversary of Independence 60 c. commemorative 55 70
a. Imperf (pair) .. ..
MS207 159 × 101 mm. Nos. 204/6 .. .. .. 1·00 1·40
a. Error. Imperf £550

57 Dish Antenna, Transmitting Station and Radio Mast **58** Smiling Child

(Des G. Vasarhelyi. Litho Format)

1979 (22 Aug). *50th Anniv of International Consultative Radio Committee. T* **57** *and similar horiz designs. Multicoloured. P* 14½.
208 7 c. Type **57** 15 15
209 32 c. Telex operator 35 40
210 40 c. Radio operator 45 50

(Des G. Vasarhelyi. Litho Format)

1979 (3 Oct). *International Year of the Child. T* **58** *and similar vert designs showing smiling children. P* 14½.
211 8 c. multicoloured 10 10
a. Horiz strip of 5. Nos. 211/15 .. .. 1·40
212 15 c. multicoloured 20 20
213 25 c. multicoloured 30 35
214 32 c. multicoloured 40 45
215 50 c. multicoloured 55 60
Nos. 211/15 were printed together, *se-tenant*, in horizontal strips of 5 throughout the sheet, forming a composite design.

59 Ekwenababae (flower), Scroll inscribed "Peace on Earth" and Star

(Des G. Vasarhelyi. Litho Format)

1979 (14 Nov). *Christmas. T* **59** *and similar horiz designs. Multicoloured. P* 14½.
216 7 c. Type **59** 15 15
217 15 c. *Thespia populnea* (flower), scroll inscribed "Goodwill toward Men" and star .. 20 20
218 20 c. Denea (flower), scroll inscribed "Peace on Earth" and star 20 20
219 30 c. Erekogo (flower), scroll inscribed "Goodwill toward Men" and star 30 30

60 Dassult "Falcon" over Melbourne

(Des G. Vasarhelyi. Litho Format)

1980 (28 Feb). *10th Anniv of Air Nauru. T* **60** *and similar horiz designs. Multicoloured. P* 14½.
220 15 c. Type **60** 20 25
221 20 c. Fokker "F28 (Fellowship)" over Tarawa 25 30
222 25 c. Boeing "727" over Hong Kong 25 30
223 30 c. Boeing "737" over Auckland 30 35

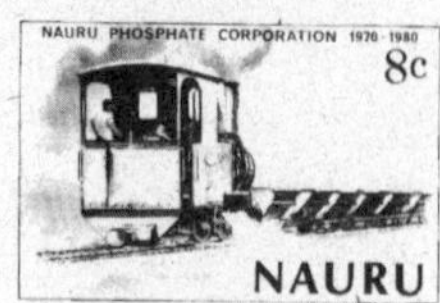

61 Steam Locomotive

(Des G. Vasarhelyi. Litho Format)

1980 (6 May). *10th Anniv of Nauru Phosphate Corporation. Railway Locomotives. T* **61** *and similar horiz designs. Multicoloured. P* 14½.
224 8 c. Type **61** 15 15
225 32 c. Electric locomotives 40 45
226 60 c. Diesel-electric locomotive 55 65
MS227 168 × 118 mm. Nos. 224/6. P 13 .. .. 1·10 1·40
No. **MS**227 also commemorates the "London 1980" International Stamp Exhibition.

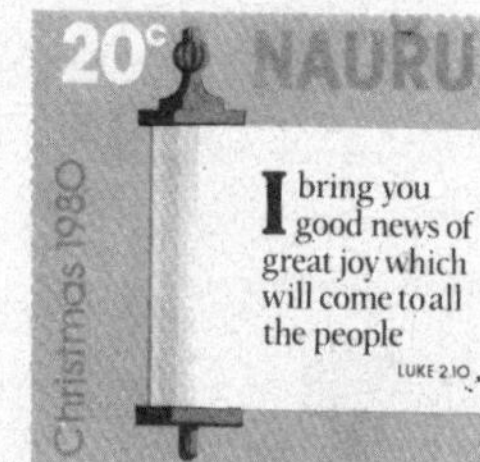

62 Verse 10 from Luke, Chapter 2 in English

(Des C. Abbott. Litho Format)

1980 (24 Sept). *Christmas. T* **62** *and similar square designs showing verses from Luke, chapter* 2. *Multicoloured. P* 14½.
228 20 c. Type **62** 20 25
a. Horiz pair. Nos. 228/9 40
229 20 c. Verse 10 in Nauruan 20 25
230 30 c. Verse 14 in English 30 35
a. Horiz pair. Nos. 230/1 60
231 30 c. Verse 14 in Nauruan 30 35
Nos. 228/9 and 230/1 were each printed together, *se-tenant*, in horizontal pairs throughout the sheet.
See also Nos. 248/51.

63 Nauruan, Australian, Union and New Zealand Flags on Aerial View of Nauru

(Des H. Woods. Litho Format)

1980 (3 Dec)–**81.** *20th Anniv of U.N. Declaration on the Granting of Independence to Colonial Countries and Peoples. T* **63** *and similar multicoloured designs. P* 14½ (25 *c.*) *or* 13½ (*others*).
232 25 c. Type **63** 30 35
233 30 c. U.N. Trusteeship Council (72 × 23 *mm*) (11.2.81) 35 40
234 50 c. Nauru independence ceremony, 1968 (72 × 23 *mm*) 60 65
The 25 c. value was printed in sheets including 5 *se-tenant* stamp-size labels; the other two values were each printed in sheets including 5 *se-tenant* half stamp-size labels.

64 Timothy Detudamo

(Des R. Granger Barrett. Litho Format)

1981 (11 Feb). *30th Anniv of Nauru Local Government Council. Head Chiefs. T* **64** *and similar horiz designs. Multicoloured. P* 14½.
235 20 c. Type **64** 30 30
236 30 c. Raymond Gadabu 40 40
237 50 c. Hammer DeRoburt 65 70

65 Casting Net by Hand

(Litho Questa)

1981 (22 May). *Fishing. T* **65** *and similar horiz designs. Multicoloured. P* 12 × 11½.
238 8 c. Type **65** 15 15
239 20 c. Ancient canoe 30 30
240 32 c. Powered boat 45 45
241 40 c. Fishing vessel 50 50
MS242 167 × 116 mm. No. 241 × 4. P 14 .. 1·90 2·00
No. **MS**242 was issued to commemorate the "WIPA 1981" International Stamp Exhibition, Vienna.

66 Bank of Nauru Emblem and Building **67** Inaugural Speech

(Des H. Woods. Litho Harrison)

1981 (21 July). *Fifth Anniv of Bank of Nauru. P* 14 × 14½.
243 **66** $1 multicoloured .. .. 1·25 1·25

(Des G. Vasarhelyi. Litho Questa)

1981 (24 Oct). *U.N. Day. E.S.C.A.P. (United Nations Economic and Social Commission for Asia and the Pacific) Events. T* **67** *and similar square designs. Multicoloured. P* 14 × 14½.
244 15 c. Type **67** 20 20
245 20 c. Presenting credentials 25 30
246 25 c. Unveiling plaque 35 35
247 30 c. Raising U.N. flag 35 40

(Des C. Abbott. Litho Format)

1981 (14 Nov). *Christmas. Bible Verses. Square designs as T* **62.** *Multicoloured. P* 14½.
248 20 c. Matthew 1, 23 in English 25 25
a. Horiz pair. Nos. 248/9 .. .. .. 50 50
249 20 c. Matthew 1, 23 in Nauruan 25 25
250 30 c. Luke 2, 11 in English 30 30
a. Horiz pair. Nos. 250/1 .. .. .. 60 60
251 30 c. Luke 2, 11 in Nauruan 30 30
Nos. 248/9 and 250/1 were each printed together, *se-tenant*, in horizontal pairs throughout the sheet.

68 Earth Satellite Station

(Des M. Rickards. Litho Format)

1981 (9 Dec). *Tenth Anniv of South Pacific Forum. T* **68** *and similar horiz designs. Multicoloured. P* 13½ × 14.
252 10 c. Type **68** 25 25
253 20 c. Ocean liner 35 35
254 30 c. Airliner 45 45
255 40 c. Local produce 65 65

69 Nauru Scouts leaving for 1935 Frankston Scout Jamboree

(Des C. Abbott. Litho Format)

1982 (23 Feb). *75th Anniv of Boy Scout Movement. T* **69** *and similar multicoloured designs. P* 14.
256 7 c. Type **69** 15 15
257 8 c. Two Nauru scouts on *Nauru Chief*, 1935 (*vert*) 15 15
258 15 c. Nauru scouts making pottery, 1935 (*vert*) 20 20
259 20 c. Lord Huntingfield addressing Nauru scouts, Frankston Jamboree, 1935 .. 25 25
260 25 c. Nauru cub and scout, 1982 .. .. .. 30 30
261 40 c. Nauru cubs, scouts and scouters, 1982 .. 45 45
256/61 .. .. *Set of* 6 1·40 1·40
MS262 152 × 114 mm. Nos. 256/61. Imperf .. 1·40 1·50
No. **MS**262 also commemorates Nauru's participation in the "Stampex" National Stamp Exhibition, London.
Nos. 256/61 were each printed in sheets including four *se-tenant* stamp-size labels.

ALTERED CATALOGUE NUMBERS

Any Catalogue numbers altered from the last edition are shown as a list in the introductory pages.

70 100kw Electricity Generating Plant under Construction (left side)

(Litho Irish Security Stamp Printing Ltd)

1982 (10 June). *Ocean Thermal Energy Conversion. T* **70** *and similar horiz designs. Multicoloured. P* 13½.

263 25 c. Type **70** 30 30
a. Horiz pair. Nos. 263/4 .. .. .. 60 60
264 25 c. 100kw Electricity Generating Plant under construction (right side) 30 30
265 40 c. Completed plant (left) 40 40
a. Horiz pair. Nos. 265/6 .. .. .. 80 80
266 40 c. Completed plant (right) 40 40

Nos. 263/4 and 265/6 were printed together, *se-tenant*, in horizontal pairs forming composite designs throughout sheets which also included two stamp-size and twelve half stamp-size labels.

71 S.S. *Fido* **72** Queen Elizabeth II on Horseback

(Des R. Littleford (5 c.), Debbie Ryder (10, 30 c.), Cecilia Eales (60 c.), Jane Evans ($1). Litho Format)

1982 (11 Oct). *75th Anniv of Phosphate Shipments. T* **71** *and similar horiz designs. Multicoloured. P* 14.

267 5 c. Type **71** 8 8
268 10 c. Locomotive "Nellie" 15 15
269 30 c. Modern Clyde diesel-electric loco .. 40 40
270 60 c. M.V. *Eigamoiya* 75 75
MS271 165 × 107 mm. $1 Phosphate-carrying ships of Nauru Pacific line (67 × 27 *mm*) .. .. 1·25 1·40

No. **MS**271 was issued to commemorate "ANPEX 82" National Stamp Exhibition, Brisbane.

(Des G. Vasarhelyi. Litho Format)

1982 (21 Oct). *Royal Visit. T* **72** *and similar multicoloured designs. P* 14½.

272 20 c. Type **72** 30 30
273 50 c. Prince Philip, Duke of Edinburgh .. 60 60
274 $1 Queen Elizabeth II and Prince Philip (*horiz*) .. .. 1·25 1·25

73 Father Bernard Lahn **74** Speaker of the Nauruan Parliament

(Des G. Vasarhelyi. Litho Format)

1982 (17 Nov). *Christmas. T* **73** *and similar horiz designs. Multicoloured. P* 14½.

275 20 c. Type **73** 30 30
276 30 c. Reverend Itubwa Amram 40 40
277 40 c. Pastor James Aingimen 45 50
278 50 c. Bishop Paul Mea 55 60

Nos. 275/8 were printed in sheets of 25 including 5 *se-tenant*, stamp-size, labels.

(Des G. Vasarhelyi. Litho Walsall)

1983 (23 Mar). *15th Anniv of Independence. T* **74** *and similar multicoloured designs. W* w 14 (*sideways on* 30, 50 *c.*). *P* 14.

279 15 c. Type **74** 20 25
280 20 c. Family Court in session 25 30
281 30 c. Law Courts building (*horiz*) 35 40
282 50 c. Parliamentary chamber (*horiz*) 60 65

75 Nauru Satellite Earth Station

(Des C. Abbott. Litho Questa)

1983 (11 May). *World Communications Year. T* **75** *and similar horiz designs. Multicoloured. W* w 14 (*sideways*). *P* 14.

283 5 c. Type **75** 5 8
284 10 c. Omni-directional range installation .. 12 15
285 20 c. Emergency short-wave radio 20 25
286 25 c. Radio Nauru control room 30 35
287 40 c. Unloading air mail 45 50

76 Return of Exiles from Truk on M.V. *Trienza*, 1946 **77** "The Holy Virgin, the Holy Child and St. John" (School of Raphael)

(Des D. Slater. Litho Format)

1983 (14 Sept). *Angam Day. T* **76** *and similar multicoloured designs. W* w **14** (*sideways on* 15 *c.*). *P* 13½ (15 *c.*) *or* 14 (*others*).

288 15 c. Type **76** 20 25
289 20 c. Mrs. Elsie Agio (exile community leader) 20 25
290 30 c. Child on scales 35 40
291 40 c. Nauruan children 45 50

Nos. 289/91 are vertical designs, each 25 × 41 mm.

(Des L. Curtis. Litho Questa)

1983 (16 Nov). *Christmas. T* **77** *and similar multicoloured designs. W* w **14** (*sideways on* 50 *c.*). *P* 14 × 14½ (50 *c.*) *or* 14½ × 14 (*others*).

292 5 c. Type **77** 8 8
293 15 c. "The Mystical Betrothal of St. Catherine with Jesus" (School of Veronese) .. 20 25
294 50 c. "Madonna on the Throne, surrounded by Angels" (School of Seville) (*horiz*) .. 60 65

78 S.S. *Ocean Queen* **79** 1974 U.P.U. $1 Stamp

(Des Beverley Barnard and L. Curtis. Litho Questa)

1984 (23 May). *250th Anniv of "Lloyd's List" (newspaper). T* **78** *and similar vert designs. Multicoloured. W* w **14**. *P* 14½ × 14.

295 20 c. Type **78** 30 35
296 25 c. M.V. *Enna G* 35 40
297 30 c. M.V. *Baron Minto* 40 45
298 40 c. Sinking of M.V. *Triadic* 55 60

(Des L. Curtis. Litho Format)

1984 (4 June). *Universal Postal Union Congress, Hamburg. W* w **14**. *P* 14.

299 **79** $1 multicoloured .. .. .. 1·40 1·50

80 Female Common Eggfly

(Des I. Loe. Litho B.D.T.)

1984 (24 July). *Butterflies. T* **80** *and similar horiz designs. Multicoloured. W* w 14 (*sideways*). *P* 14.

300 25 c. Type **80** 35 40
301 30 c. Male Common Eggfly 40 45
302 50 c. Wanderer 70 75

81 Coastal Scene **82** Buada Chapel

(Des A. Theobald. Litho Enschedé)

1984 (21 Sept). *Life in Nauru. T* **81** *and similar multicoloured designs. W* w **14** (*sideways on horiz designs*). *P* 13½ × 14 (1, 5, 10, 25, 40 *c.*, $2) *or* 14 × 13½ (*others*).

303 1 c. Type **81** 5 5
304 3 c. Nauruan woman (*vert*) 5 5
305 5 c. Modern fishing vessel 5 8
306 10 c. Golfer on the links 12 15
307 15 c. Excavating phosphate (*vert*) 20 25
308 20 c. Surveyor (*vert*) 25 30
309 25 c. Air Nauru airliner 30 35
310 30 c. Elderly Nauruan (*vert*) 35 40
311 40 c. Loading hospital patient on to aircraft .. 45 50
312 50 c. Skin-diver with fish (*vert*) 60 65
313 $1 Tennis player (*vert*) .. .. .. 1·10 1·25
314 $2 Anabar Lagoon .. .. 2·25 2·40
303/14 .. .. *Set of* 12 5·25 5·75

Nos. 303/14 were each issued in sheets of 9 with decorative margins.

(Des L. Curtis. Litho Format)

1984 (14 Nov). *Christmas. T* **82** *and similar multicoloured designs. W* w **14** (*sideways on* 50 *c.*). *P* 14.

315 30 c. Type **82** 40 45
316 40 c. Detudamo Memorial Church 55 60
317 50 c. Candle-light service, Kayser College (*horiz*) 70 75

83 Air Nauru Jet on Tarmac

(Des L. Curtis. Litho Walsall)

1985 (26 Feb). *15th Anniv of Air Nauru. T* **83** *and similar multicoloured designs. W* w **14** (*sideways on* 20 *c.*, 40 *c.*). *P* 14.

318 20 c. Type **83** 25 30
319 30 c. Stewardess on aircraft steps (*vert*) .. 35 40
320 40 c. Fokker "F28" over Nauru 45 50
321 50 c. Freight being loaded onto Boeing "727" (*vert*) 55 60

Nevis
see St. Kitts-Nevis

New Brunswick

PRICES FOR STAMPS ON COVER	
Nos. 1/6	*from* × 2
Nos. 7/19	*from* × 3

1 Royal Crown and Heraldic Flowers of the United Kingdom

(Recess P.B.)

1851 (5 Sept). *Blue paper. Imperf.*

1	**1**	3d. bright red	£1800	£400
2		3d. dull red	£2500	£400
		a. Bisected (1½d.) (on cover)	†	£2500
2*b*		6d. mustard-yellow	†	£2500
3		6d. yellow	£5000	£1000
4		6d. olive-yellow	£4500	£900
		a. Bisected (3d.) (on cover)	†	£3000
		b. Quartered (1½d.) (on cover) ..	†	£15000
5		1s. reddish mauve	£16000	£5500
6		1s. dull mauve	£14000	£4500
		a. Bisected (6d.) (on cover)	†	£25000
		b. Quartered (3d.) (on cover)	†	£20000

Reprints of all three values were made in 1890 on thin, hard, white paper. The 3d. is bright orange, the 6d. and 1s. violet-black.

Nos. 2a and 4b were to make up the 7½d. rate.

2 Locomotive

3

3a Charles Connell

4

5

6 Paddle-steamer *Washington*

7 King Edward VII when Prince of Wales

(Recess A.B.N. Co)

1860 (15 May)–**1863.** *No wmk. P* 12.

7	**2**	1 c. brown-purple	30·00	27·00
8		1 c. purple	13·00	15·00
9		1 c. dull claret	13·00	15·00
		a. Imperf between (horiz pair) ..	£500	
10	**3**	2 c. orange (1863)	11·00	14·00
11		2 c. orange-yellow	12·00	14·00
12		2 c. deep orange	11·00	14·00
		a. Imperf between (vert pair) ..	£450	
13	**3*a***	5 c. brown	£2750	
14	**4**	5 c. yellow-green	12·00	11·00
15		5 c. deep green	12·00	11·00
16		5 c. sap-green (deep yellowish green) ..	£300	40·00
17	**5**	10 c. red	28·00	22·00
		a. Bisected (5 c.) (on cover) (1860) ..	—	£850
18	**6**	12½ c. indigo	50·00	40·00
19	**7**	17 c. black	30·00	27·00

Beware of forged cancellations.

In March, 1868, issues of the Dominion of Canada replaced those of New Brunswick.

Newfoundland

The first local postmaster, at St. John's, was appointed in 1805, the overseas mails being routed via Halifax, Nova Scotia. A regular packet service was established between these two ports in 1840, the British G.P.O. assuming control of the overseas mails at the same time.

The responsibility for the overseas postal service reverted to the colonial administration on 1 July 1851.

For illustrations of the handstamp types see BRITISH POST OFFICES ABROAD notes, following GREAT BRITAIN.

ST. JOHN'S

CROWNED-CIRCLE HANDSTAMPS

CC1 CC **1a** ST. JOHNS NEWFOUNDLAND (R.) (27.6.1846) .. .. *Price on cover* £750

PRICES FOR STAMPS ON COVER TO 1945	
Nos. 1/24*e*	*from* × 2
Nos. 25/43	*from* × 3
Nos. 44/54	*from* × 4
Nos. 55/61	*from* × 5
Nos. 62/5*a*	*from* × 2
Nos. 66/79	*from* × 3
Nos. 80/1	*from* × 2
No. 82	—
Nos. 83/94	*from* × 5
Nos. 95/127	*from* × 2
Nos. 130/41	*from* × 3
Nos. 142/3	—
Nos. 144/8*f*	*from* × 2
Nos. 149/62	*from* × 3
No. 163	—
Nos. 164/78	*from* × 2
Nos. 179/90	*from* × 3
No. 191	—
Nos. 192/220	*from* × 2
No. 221	—
Nos. 222/9	*from* × 3
Nos. 230/4	*from* × 2
No. 235	—
Nos. 236/91	*from* × 2
Nos. D1/6	*from* × 10

1

2

4

3

5

Royal Crown and Heraldic flowers of the United Kingdom

(Recess P.B.)

1857 (1 Jan). *No wmk. Thick paper. Imperf.*

1	**1**	1d. brown-purple	75·00	£120
		a. Bisected (½d.) on cover	†	£6500
2	**2**	2d. scarlet-vermilion	£11000	£5500
3	**3**	3d. yellowish green	£275	£375
4	**4**	4d. scarlet-vermilion	£5000	£3750
		a. Bisected (2d.) (on cover)		
5	**1**	5d. brown-purple	£180	£300
6	**4**	6d. scarlet-vermilion	£10000	£2750
7	**5**	6½d. scarlet-vermilion	£2250	£2750
8	**4**	8d. scarlet-vermilion	£225	£300
		a. Bisected (4d.) (on cover)	†	£2500
9	**2**	1s. scarlet-vermilion	£13000	£3750
		a. Bisected (6d.) (on cover)	†	£9500

The 6d. and 8d. differ from the 4d. in many details, as does also the 1s. from the 2d.

1860. *Medium paper. Imperf.*

10	**2**	2d. orange-vermilion	£250	£300
11	**3**	3d. green *to* deep green*	45·00	£120
12	**4**	4d. orange-vermilion	£1900	£850
		a. Bisected (2d.) (on cover)	†	£7500
13	**1**	5d. Venetian red	45·00	£190
14	**4**	6d. orange-vermilion	£2500	£900
15	**2**	1s. orange-vermilion	£25000	£9000
		a. Bisected (6d.) (on cover)		

*No. 11 includes stamps from the November 1861 printing which are very difficult to distinguish.

The 1s. on horizontally or vertically *laid* paper is now considered to be a proof.

BISECTS. Collectors are warned against buying bisected stamps of these issues without a reliable guarantee.

1861. *New colours. Imperf.* (*a*) 1*st printing. Soft paper* (July).

16	**2**	2d. deep rose-lake	£150	£475
17	**4**	4d. deep rose-lake	45·00	£170
		a. Bisected (2d.) (on cover)		
18		6d. deep rose-lake	48·00	£180
		a. Bisected (3d.) (on cover)		
19	**5**	6½d. deep rose-lake	£250	£600
20	**2**	1s. deep rose-lake	£275	£600
		a. Bisected (6d.) (on cover)	†	£13000
		(*b*) 2*nd printing. Hard paper* (Nov)		
21	**1**	1d. chocolate-brown	£100	£175
		a. Red-brown	£3500	
22	**2**	2d. pale rose-lake	£110	£350
23	**4**	4d. pale rose-lake	16·00	80·00
24	**1**	5d. chocolate-brown	30·00	£250
		a. Red-brown	25·00	£150
24*b*	**4**	6d. pale rose-lake	14·00	£100
24*c*	**5**	6½d. pale rose-lake	40·00	£325
24*d*	**4**	8d. pale rose-lake	45·00	£350
24*e*	**2**	1s. pale rose-lake	18·00	£170

Stamps of the second printing of the pale rose-lake shades have a more transparent look due to the paper being generally thinner, but paper thickness alone is not a sure test for distinguishing the printings.

Stamps of this issue may be found with part of the paper-maker's watermark "STACEY WISE 1858".

Beware of buying used specimens of the stamps which are worth much less in unused condition, as many unused stamps have been provided with faked postmarks. A guarantee should be obtained.

6 Codfish

7 Seal on Ice-floe

8 Prince Consort

9 Queen Victoria

10 Schooner

11 Queen Victoria

(Recess A.B.N. Co)

1865 (Nov)–**70.** *P* 12. (*a*) *Thin yellowish paper.*

25	**6**	2 c. yellowish green	£120	22·00
		a. Bisected (1 c.) (on cover)	†	£3750
26	**7**	5 c. brown	£500	£190
		a. Bisected (2½ c.) (on cover)		
27	**8**	10 c. black	£225	55·00
		a. Bisected (5 c.) (on cover)	†	£2750
28	**9**	12 c. red-brown	£325	£150
		a. Bisected (6 c.) (on cover)		
29	**10**	13 c. orange-yellow	75·00	60·00
30	**11**	24 c. blue	32·00	30·00
		(*b*) *Medium white paper*		
31	**6**	2 c. bluish green (*to* deep)	60·00	22·00
32	**8**	10 c. black	£150	32·00
33	**9**	12 c. chestnut	28·00	28·00
33*a*	**11**	24 c. blue	£400	£140

12 King Edward VII when Prince of Wales

14 Queen Victoria

I

II

In Type II the white oval frame line is unbroken by the scroll containing the words "ONE CENT", the letters "N.F." are smaller and closer to the scroll, and there are other minor differences.

(Recess National Bank Note Co, New York)

1868. *P* 12.

34	**12**	1 c. dull purple (I)	38·00	40·00

(Recess A.B.N. Co)

1868–73. *P* 12.

35	**12**	1 c. brown-purple (II) (1871)	45·00	40·00
36	**14**	3 c. vermilion (1870)	£300	£100
37		3 c. blue (1873)	£350	16·00
38	**7**	5 c. black	£190	£100
39	**14**	6 c. rose (1870)	12·00	16·00

1876–79. *Rouletted.*

40	**12**	1 c. lake-purple (II) (1877)	50·00	30·00
41	**6**	2 c. bluish green (1879)	£120	70·00
42	**14**	3 c. blue (1877)	£250	10·00
43	**7**	5 c. blue (1876)	£170	11·00
		a. Imperf (pair)		

15 King Edward VII when Prince of Wales

16 Codfish

17

18 Seal on Ice-floe

(Recess British American Bank Note Co, Montreal)

1880. *P* 12.

44	**15**	1 c. dull grey-brown	13·00	10·00
		a. Dull brown	10·00	9·50
		b. Red-brown	15·00	11·00
46	**16**	2 c. yellow-green	22·00	16·00
47	**17**	3 c. pale dull blue	22·00	6·00
		a. Bright blue	48·00	4·50
48	**18**	5 c. pale dull blue	£190	8·00

19 Newfoundland Dog

20 Atlantic Brigantine

21 Queen Victoria

(Recess British American Bank Note Co, Montreal)

1887. *New colours and values. P* 12.

49	**19**	½ c. rose-red	6·00	7·50
50	**15**	1 c. blue-green	6·00	4·50
		a. Green	5·00	4·00
		b. Yellow-green	6·50	5·00
51	**16**	2 c. orange-vermilion	8·50	6·00
52	**17**	3 c. deep brown	12·00	4·00
53	**18**	5 c. deep blue	60·00	5·00
54	**20**	10 c. black	48·00	38·00
49/54		.. .. .. *Set of* 6	£130	60·00

For reissues of 1880/87 stamps in similar colours, see Nos. 62/65*a*.

(Recess B.A.B.N.)

1890. *P* 12.

55	**21**	3 c. deep slate	10·00	70
		a. Imperf (pair)		
56		3 c. slate-grey (*to* grey)	14·00	70
		a. Imperf between (pair)	£600	
57		3 c. slate-violet	11·00	2·00
58		3 c. grey-lilac	10·00	65
58*a*		3 c. brown-grey	10·00	4·50
58*b*		3 c. purple-grey	12·00	3·75

There is a very wide range of shades in this stamp, and those given only cover the main groups.

Stamps on pink paper are from a consignment recovered from the sea and which were affected by the salt water.

(Recess British American Bank Note Co, Montreal)

1894. *Changes of colour. P* 12.

59	**19**	½ c. black	5·00	5·50
59*a*	**18**	5 c. bright blue	23·00	6·00
60	**14**	6 c. crimson-lake	11·00	14·00
61	**9**	12 c. deep brown	23·00	30·00

The 6 c. is printed from the old American Bank Note Company's plates.

1896–97. *Reissues. P* 12.

62	**19**	½ c. orange-vermilion	30·00	35·00
63	**15**	1 c. deep green	5·00	4·50
63*a*		1 c. deep brown	22·00	19·00
64	**16**	2 c. green	18·00	16·00
65	**17**	3 c. deep blue	17·00	7·00
65*a*		3 c. chocolate-brown	32·00	25·00
62/65*a*		.. .. .. *Set of* 6	£110	95·00

The above were *reissued* for postal purposes. The colours were generally brighter than those of the original stamps.

22 Queen Victoria

23 Jean Cabot

24 Cape Bonavista

25 Caribou-hunting

26 Mining

27 Logging

28 Fishing

29 Cabot's Ship

30 Willow Grouse

31 Group of Seals

32 Salmon-fishing

33 Seal of the Colony

34 Iceberg off St. John's

35 Henry VII

(Recess A.B.N. Co)

1897 (24 June). *400th Anniv of Discovery of Newfoundland and 60th year of Queen Victoria's reign. P* 12.

66	**22**	1 c. green	2·00	2·00
67	**23**	2 c. bright rose	2·00	2·00
		a. Bisected (1 c.) on cover	†	£375
68	**24**	3 c. bright blue	3·25	1·50
		a. Bisected (1½ c.) on cover	†	£300
69	**25**	4 c. olive-green	4·00	3·50
70	**26**	5 c. violet	5·00	3·50
71	**27**	6 c. red-brown	4·50	4·50
		a. Bisected (3 c.) on cover	†	£300
72	**28**	8 c. orange	12·00	5·50
73	**29**	10 c. sepia	14·00	4·50
74	**30**	12 c. deep blue	20·00	5·50
75	**31**	15 c. bright scarlet	12·00	7·00
76	**32**	24 c. dull violet-blue	16·00	11·00
77	**33**	30 c. slate-blue	26·00	26·00
78	**34**	35 c. red	45·00	40·00
79	**35**	60 c. black	11·00	10·00
66/79		.. .. .. *Set of* 14	£160	£110

The 60 c. surcharged "TWO—2—CENTS" in three lines is an essay made in December 1918.

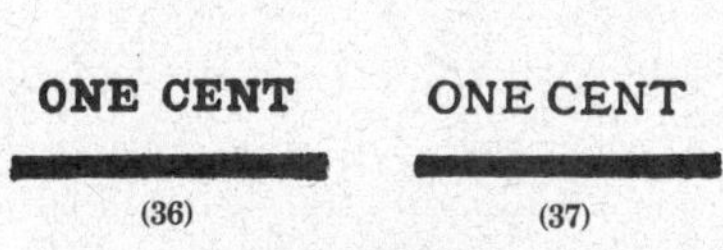

(36) (37) (38)

1897 (Oct). *T* **21** *surch with T* **36** *to* **38**.

80	**36**	1 c. on 3 c. grey-purple	14·00	14·00
		a. Double surch, one diagonal ..	£1100	
		b. Surch in red	£1100	
		c. Surch in red and black	£1100	
		d. Vert pair, one without lower bar and "ONE CENT"	£3500	
81	**37**	1 c. on 3 c. grey-purple	70·00	70·00
		a. Surch in red	£2750	
		b. Surch in red and black	£3000	
82	**38**	1 c. on 3 c. grey-purple	£450	£325
		a. Surch in red	£5000	
		b. Surch double in red	£6000	
		c. Surch in red and black	£6000	

This surcharge is known on stamps of various shades.

Dangerous forgeries exist of the errors.

39 Prince Edward later Duke of Windsor

40 Queen Victoria

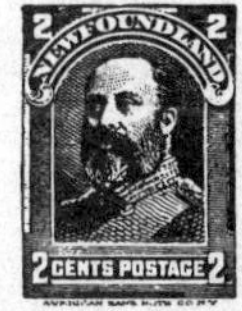

41 King Edward VII when Prince of Wales

42 Queen Alexandra when Princess of Wales

43 Queen Mary when Duchess of York

44 King George V when Duke of York

(Recess A.B.N. Co)

1897–1918. *P* 12.

83	**39**	½ c. olive (8.97)	3·00	3·00
		a. Imperf (pair)	£225	
84	**40**	1 c. carmine (12.97)	3·00	3·00
85		1 c. blue-green (6.98)	2·75	15
		a. Yellow-green	4·25	20
		b. Imperf between (pair)	£170	
86	**41**	2 c. orange (12.97)	2·25	2·50
		a. Imperf (pair)		
87		2 c. scarlet (6.98)	5·50	50
		a. Imperf (pair)	£225	
		b. Imperf between (pair)		
88	**42**	3 c. orange (6.98)	7·50	80
		a. Imperf between (pair)	£250	
		b. Imperf (pair)	£225	
		c. Red-orange/bluish (6.18) ..	14·00	5·50
89	**43**	4 c. violet (10.01)	15·00	4·00
		a. Imperf (pair)	£200	
90	**44**	5 c. blue (6.99)	15·00	3·50
83/90		.. .. .. *Set of* 8	48·00	16·00

No. 88c was an emergency war-time printing made by the American Bank Note Co from the old plate, pending receipt of the then current 3 c. from England.

The imperforate errors of this issue are found used, but only as philatelic "by favour" items. It is possible that No. 86a only exists in this condition.

45 Map of Newfoundland

(Recess A.B.N. Co)

1908 (Sept). *P* 12.

94	**45**	2 c. lake	11·00	1·00

46 King James I

47 Arms of Colonisation Co

48 John Guy

49 Guy's Ship

50 Cupids

51 Sir Francis Bacon

52 View of Mosquito

53 Logging Camp

54 Paper Mills

55 King Edward VII

56 King George V

(Litho Whitehead, Morris & Co, Ltd)

1910 (15 Aug). (*a*) *P* 12.

No.	Type	Description	Unused	Used
95	**46**	1 c. green	1·75	1·50
		a. "NFWFOUNDLAND"	55·00	85·00
		b. Imperf between (horiz pair)	£275	£300
96	**47**	2 c. rose-carmine	2·50	85
97	**48**	3 c. olive	7·00	11·00
98	**49**	4 c. violet	8·00	11·00
99	**50**	5 c. bright blue	6·00	4·75
100	**51**	6 c. claret (A)	42·00	60·00
100*a*		6 c. claret (B)	20·00	25·00
101	**52**	8 c. bistre-brown	30·00	40·00
102	**53**	9 c. olive-green	30·00	40·00
103	**54**	10 c. purple-slate	35·00	40·00
104	**55**	12 c. pale red-brown	35·00	40·00
		a. Imperf (pair)	£400	
105	**56**	15 c. black	32·00	40·00
95/105		*Set of* 11	£180	£225

6 c. (A) "Z" in "COLONIZATION" reversed. (B) "Z" correct.

(*b*) *P* 12 × 14

No.	Type	Description	Unused	Used
106	**46**	1 c. green	2·00	2·00
		a. "NFWFOUNDLAND"	50·00	
		b. Imperf between (pair)	£450	£500
		c. As a. in pair imperf between		
107	**47**	2 c. rose-carmine	3·00	80
		a. Imperf between (pair)	£400	
108	**50**	5 c. bright blue (*p* 14 × 12)	7·50	3·50

(*c*) *P* 12 × 11

No.	Type	Description	Unused	Used
109	**46**	1 c. green	1·50	1·25
		a. Imperf between (horiz pair)	£250	
		b. Imperf between (vert pair)	£300	
		c. "NFWFOUNDLAND"	65·00	65·00
		d. As c. in pair imperf vert		

(*d*) *P* 12 × 11½

No.	Type	Description	Unused	Used
110	**47**	2 c. rose-carmine	75·00	75·00

(Dies eng Macdonald & Sons. Recess A. Alexander & Sons, Ltd)

1911 (Feb). *Types as* **51** *to* **56**, *but recess printed. P* 14.

No.	Description	Unused	Used
111	6 c. claret (B)	16·00	24·00
112	8 c. yellow-brown	32·00	45·00
	a. Imperf between (horiz pair)	£400	
	b. Imperf (pair)	£300	
113	9 c. sage-green	28·00	45·00
	a. Imperf between (horiz pair)	£225	
114	10 c. purple-black	48·00	70·00
	a. Imperf between (horiz pair)	£300	
	b. Imperf (pair)	£250	
115	12 c. red-brown	40·00	55·00
116	15 c. slate-green	40·00	60·00
111/16	*Set of* 6	£180	£275

The 9 c. exists with paper-maker's wmk.

57 Queen Mary

58 King George V

59 Duke of Windsor when Prince of Wales

60 King George VI when Prince Albert

61 Princess Mary, the Princess Royal

62 Prince Henry Duke of Gloucester

63 Prince George, Duke of Kent

64 Prince John

65 Queen Alexandra

66 Duke of Connaught

67 Seal of Newfoundland

(1 c. to 5 c., 10 c. eng and recess D.L.R.; others eng Macdonald & Co, recess A. Alexander & Sons)

1911 (19 June)–**16.** *Coronation. P* 13½ × 14 (*comb*) (1 *c. to* 5 *c.,* 10 *c.*) *or* 14 (*line*) (*others*).

No.	Type	Description	Unused	Used
117	**57**	1 c. yellow-green	1·75	15
		a. Blue-green (1915)	1·60	15
118	**58**	2 c. carmine	1·60	12
		a. Rose-red (*blurred impression*). Perf 14 (1916)	4·00	55
119	**59**	3 c. red-brown	14·00	18·00
120	**60**	4 c. purple	14·00	17·00
121	**61**	5 c. ultramarine	7·00	1·75
122	**62**	6 c. slate-grey	16·00	22·00
123	**63**	8 c. aniline blue	45·00	70·00
		a. Greenish blue	45·00	75·00
124	**64**	9 c. violet-blue	15·00	24·00
125	**65**	10 c. deep green	18·00	25·00
126	**66**	12 c. plum	20·00	27·00
127	**67**	15 c. lake	17·00	25·00
117/27		*Set of* 11	£150	£200

The 2 c. rose-red, No. 118*a* is a poor war-time printing by Alexander & Sons.

Although No. 123 has a typical aniline appearance it is believed that the shade results from the thinning of non-aniline ink.

68 Caribou

FIRST
TRANS-
ATLANTIC
AIR POST
April, 1919.

(69)

(Des J. H. Noonan. Recess D.L.R.)

1919 (2 Jan). *Newfoundland Contingent,* 1914–1918. *P* 14.

No.	Type	Description	Unused	Used
130	**68**	1 c. green (*a*) (*b*)	60	30
131		2 c. scarlet (*a*) (*b*)	90	40
		a. Carmine-red (*b*)	1·50	45
132		3 c. brown (*a*) (*b*)	1·00	20
		a. Red-brown (*b*)	1·25	20
133		4 c. mauve (*a*)	1·75	75
		a. Purple (*b*)	1·75	75
134		5 c. ultramarine (*a*) (*b*)	1·50	70
135		6 c. slate-grey (*a*)	10·00	17·00
136		8 c. bright magenta (*a*)	8·00	15·00
137		10 c. deep grey-green (*a*)	3·75	3·50
138		12 c. orange (*a*)	18·00	28·00
139		15 c. indigo (*a*)	10·00	20·00
		a. Prussian blue (*a*)	80·00	£130
140		24 c. bistre-brown (*a*)	18·00	28·00
141		36 c. sage-green (*a*)	12·00	18·00
130/41		*Set of* 12	75·00	£120

Each value bears with "Trail of the Caribou" the name of a different action: 1 c. Suvla Bay; 3 c. Gueudecourt; 4 c. Beaumont Hamel; 6 c. Monchy; 10 c. Steenbeck; 15 c. Langemarck; 24 c. Cambrai; 36 c. Combles; 2 c., 5 c., 8 c., and 12 c. inscribed "Royal Naval Reserve-Ubique".

Perforations. Two perforating heads were used: (*a*) comb 14 × 13.9; (*b*) line 14.1 × 14.1.

1919 (12 Apr). *Air. Optd with T* **69,** *by Robinson & Co Ltd, at the offices of the "Daily News".*

No.	Type	Description	Unused	Used
142	**68**	3 c. brown	£12000	£8000

These stamps franked correspondence carried by Mr. Hawker on his Atlantic flight. 18 were damaged and destroyed, 95 used on letters, 11 given as presentation copies, and the remaining 76 were sold in aid of the Marine Disasters Fund.

1919 (April). *Optd in MS.* "Aerial Atlantic Mail. J.A.R."

No.	Type	Description	Unused	Used
142*a*	**68**	3 c. brown	—	£20000

This provisional was made by the Postmaster Mr. J. A. Robinson, for use on correspondence intended to be carried on the abortive Morgan-Raynham Trans-Atlantic flight. The mail was eventually delivered by sea.

In addition to the 25 to 30 used examples, one unused, no gum, copy of No. 142*a* is known.

Trans-Atlantic
AIR POST,
1919.
ONE DOLLAR.

(70)

THREE
CENTS

(71)

1919 (9 June). *Air. Surch with T* **70** *by J. W. Withers at the offices of the "Royal Gazette".*

No.	Type	Description	Unused	Used
143	**31**	$1 on 15 c. bright scarlet	90·00	48·00
		a. No comma after "AIR POST"	£200	£225
		b. As Var a and no stop after "1919"	£425	£425
		c. As Var a and "A" of "AIR" under "a" of "Trans"	£425	£425

These stamps were issued for use on the mail carried on the first successful flight across the Atlantic by Alcock and Brown, and on other projected Trans-Atlantic flights (Alcock flown cover, *Price* £2500).

The surcharge was applied in a setting of 25 of which 16 were normal, 7 as No. 143a, 1 as No. 143b and 1 as No. 143c.

1920 (Sept). *Surch as T* **71**, *by J. W. Withers.* (2 *c. with only one bar, at top of stamp.*)

A. Bars of surch 10½ mm apart. B. Bars 13½ mm apart.

No.	Type	Description	Unused	Used
144	**33**	2 c. on 30 c. slate-blue	6·00	7·50
		a. Surch inverted	£500	
145	**31**	3 c. on 15 c. bright scarlet (A)	70·00	70·00
		a. Surch inverted	£700	
146		3 c. on 15 c. bright scarlet (B)	7·00	7·50
147	**34**	3 c. on 35 c. red	6·50	7·50
		a. Surch inverted		
		b. Lower bar omitted	£110	£120
		c. "THREE" omitted	£1100	

Our prices for Nos. 147b and 147c are for stamps with lower bar or "THREE" entirely missing. The bar may be found in all stages of incompleteness and stamps showing broken bar are not of much value.

On the other hand, stamps showing either only the top or bottom of the letters "THREE" are scarce, though not as rare as No. 147c.

The 6 c. T **27**, surcharged "THREE CENTS," in red or black, is an essay. (*Price* £275). The 2 c. on 30 c. with red surcharge is a colour trial (*Price* £275).

AIR MAIL
to Halifax, N.S.
1921.

(72)

1921 (16 Nov). *Air. T* **34** *optd with T* **72.**

I. 2¾ *mm between* "AIR" *and* "MAIL"

No.	Description	Unused	Used
148	35 c. red	85·00	80·00
	a. No stop after "1921"	85·00	80·00
	b. No stop and first "1" of "1921" below "f" of "Halifax"	£200	£200
	c. As No. 148, inverted	£3000	
	d. As No. 148a, inverted	£3000	
	e. As No. 148b, inverted	£6000	

II. 1½ *mm between* "AIR" *and* "MAIL"

No.	Description	Unused	Used
148*f*	35 c. red	80·00	75·00
	g. No stop after "1921"	£100	95·00
	h. No stop and first "1" of "1921" below "f" of "Halifax"	£160	£160
	i. As No. 148f, inverted	£3750	
	k. As No. 148g, inverted	£4500	
	l. As No. 148h, inverted	£6000	

73 Twin Hills, Tor's Cove

74 South-West Arm, Trinity

75 Statue of the Fighting Newfoundlander, St. John's

(Recess D.L.R.)

1923 (9 July)–**26.** *T* **73/5** *and similar designs. P* 14 (*comb or line*).

No.	Description	Unused	Used
149	1 c. green	1·25	25
	a. Booklet pane of 8 (1926)	£250	
150	2 c. carmine	1·25	15
	a. Imperf (pair)	£225	
	b. Booklet pane of 8 (1926)	£140	
151	3 c. brown	1·10	12
152	4 c. deep purple	1·50	1·50
153	5 c. ultramarine	2·00	1·50
154	6 c. slate	2·50	4·50
155	8 c. purple	2·50	4·75
156	9 c. slate-green	12·00	22·00
157	10 c. violet	2·25	1·75
	a. Purple	2·25	2·25
158	11 c. sage-green	2·75	5·50
159	12 c. lake	3·50	6·50
160	15 c. Prussian blue	5·50	11·00
161	20 c. chestnut (28.4.24)	5·00	10·00
162	24 c. sepia (22.4.24)	27·00	48·00
149/62	*Set of* 14	60·00	£110

Designs: *Horiz* (*as T* **73**)—6 c. Upper Steadies, Humber River; 11 c. Shell Bird Island; 20 c. Placentia. (*As T* **74**)—8 c. Quidi Vidi, near St. John's; 9 c. Caribou crossing lake; 12 c. Mount Moriah, Bay of Islands. *Vert* (*as T* **75**)—4 c. Humber River; 5 c. Coast at Trinity; 10 c. Humber River Cañon; 15 c. Humber River near Little Rapids; 24 c. Topsail Falls.

Perforations. Three perforating heads were used: comb 13.8 × 14 (all values); line 13.7 and 14, and combinations of these two (for all except 6, 8, 9 and 11 c.).

Air Mail
DE PINEDO
1927

(87)

1927 (18 May). *Air. T* **35** *optd with T* **87**, *by Robinson & Co, Ltd.*

No.	Description	Unused	Used
163	60 c. black (R.)	£16000	£4750

For the mail carried by De Pinedo to Europe 300 stamps were overprinted, 230 used on correspondence, 66 presented to De Pinedo, Government Officials, etc., and 4 damaged and destroyed. Stamps without overprint were also used.

88 Newfoundland and Labrador

89 S.S. *Caribou*

90 King George V and Queen Mary

91 Duke of Windsor when Prince of Wales

92 Express Train

93 Hotel, St. John's

94 Heart's Content

95 Cabot Tower, St. John's

96 War Memorial, St. John's

97 G.P.O., St. John's

98 Trans-Atlantic flight

99 Colonial Building, St. John's

100 Grand Falls, Labrador

(Recess D.L.R.)

1928 (3 Jan)–**29**. *"Publicity" issue. P 13 to 14.*

No.	Type	Description	Unused	Used
164	**88**	1 c. deep green (*a*)	70	60
165	**89**	2 c. carmine (*b*)	90	50
166	**90**	3 c. brown (*b*) (*c*)	1·25	40
167	**91**	4 c. mauve (*b*)	1·75	2·00
		a. Rose-purple (1929)	5·50	7·50
168	**92**	5 c. slate-grey (*b*) (*c*)	3·00	2·75
169	**93**	6 c. ultramarine (*b*) (*c*)	2·25	5·00
170	**94**	8 c. red-brown (*c*)	3·50	7·50
171	**95**	9 c. deep green (*c*)	3·75	7·50
172	**96**	10 c. deep violet (*b*) (*c*)	4·00	3·75
173	**97**	12 c. carmine-lake (*c*)	3·00	7·50
174	**95**	14 c. brown-purple (*b*) (*c*)	4·00	7·00
175	**98**	15 c. deep blue (*c*)	3·75	8·50
176	**99**	20 c. grey-black (*b*) (*c*)	2·75	6·00
177	**97**	28 c. deep green (*c*)	12·00	20·00
178	**100**	30 c. sepia (*c*)	4·50	8·50
164/78		*Set of* 15	45·00	80·00

See also Nos. 179/87 and 198/208.

Perforations. Three perforating heads were used: (*a*) comb 14 × 13.9; (*b*) comb 13.5 × 12.75; (*c*) line 13.7 to 14 or compound.

MINIMUM PRICE

The minimum price quoted is 5p which represents a handling charge rather than a basis for valuing common stamps. For further notes about prices see introductory pages.

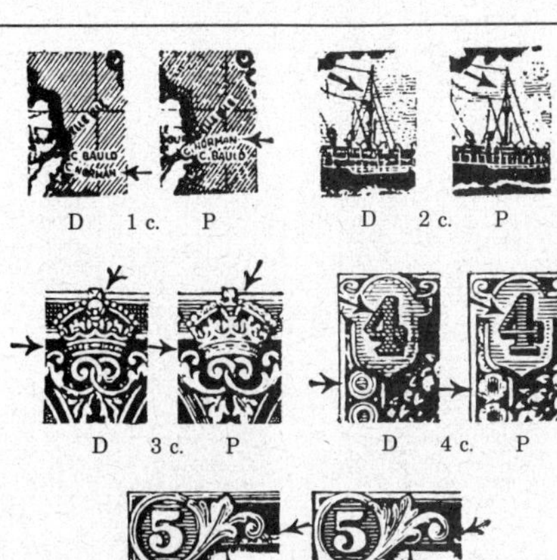

D 1 c. P D 2 c. P

D 3 c. P D 4 c. P

D 5 c. P

D 6 c. P D 10 c. P

D 15 c. P

D 20 c. P

D. "De La Rue" printing

P. "Perkins, Bacon" printing

1929–31. *"Perkins, Bacon" printing. Former types re-engraved. No wmk. P 13½ × 14.*

No.	Type	Description	Unused	Used
179	**88**	1 c. green (*a*) (*d*) (26.9.29)	1·50	50
		a. Imperf between (pair)	£120	
		b. Imperf (pair)	£110	
180	**89**	2 c. scarlet (*b*) (*d*) (10.8.29)	1·25	20
		a. Imperf (pair)	80·00	
181	**90**	3 c. red-brown (*c*) (10.8.29)	1·50	15
		a. Imperf (pair)	90·00	
182	**91**	4 c. reddish purple (*c*) (26.8.29)	2·00	65
		a. Imperf (pair)	95·00	
183	**92**	5 c. deep grey-green (*c*) (14.9.29)	2·00	1·75
184	**93**	6 c. ultramarine (*b*) (*d*) (8.11.29)	5·50	10·00
185	**96**	10 c. violet (*c*) (5.10.29)	2·50	2·50
186	**98**	15 c. blue (*c*) (1.30)	17·00	45·00
187	**99**	20 c. black (*d*) (1.1.31)	27·00	38·00
179/87		*Set of* 9	55·00	90·00

Perforations. Four perforating heads were used: (*a*) comb 14 × 13.9; (*b*) comb 13.6 × 13.5; (*c*) comb 13.6 × 13.8; (*d*) line 13.7 to 14 or compound.

THREE
CENTS

(101)

Trans-Atlantic
AIR MAIL
By B. M.
"Columbia"
September
1930
Fifty Cents

(102)

(Surch by Messrs D. R. Thistle, St. John's)

1929 (23 Aug). *Surch with T* **101**.

No.	Description	Unused	Used
188	3 c. on 6 c. slate (R.)	2·10	2·40
	a. Surch inverted	£600	£900
	b. Surch in black	£850	

1930 (25 Sept). *Air. T* **68** *surch with T* **102** *by Messrs D. R. Thistle.*

No.	Description	Unused	Used
191	50 c. on 36 c. sage-green	£4000	£3500

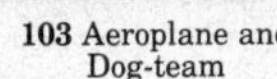

103 Aeroplane and Dog-team

104 Vickers-Vimy Biplane and early Sailing Packet

105 Routes of historic Transatlantic Flights

106

(Des A. B. Perlin. Recess P.B.)

1931. *Air. T* **103** *to* **105.** *P* 14. (*a*) *Without wmk* (2.1.31).

No.	Description	Unused	Used
192	15 c. chocolate	6·00	7·50
	a. Imperf between (horiz or vert pair)	£400	
	b. Imperf (pair)	£350	
193	50 c. green	14·00	17·00
	a. Imperf between (horiz or vert pair)	£400	£300
	b. Imperf (pair)	£375	
194	$1 deep blue	35·00	45·00
	a. Imperf between (horiz or vert pair)	£400	
	b. Imperf (pair)	£350	
	(*b*) *Wmk W* **106**, *sideways* (13.3.31)		
195	15 c. chocolate	5·00	7·00
	a. Pair, with and without wmk	29·00	
	b. Imperf between (horiz or vert pair)	£375	
	ba. Ditto, one without wmk (vert pair)		
	c. Imperf (pair)	£225	
	d. Wmk Cross (pair)	70·00	
196	50 c. green	22·00	30·00
	a. Imperf between (horiz or vert pair)	£375	
	b. Imperf (pair)	£250	
	c. Pair, with and without wmk		
197	$1 deep blue	50·00	70·00
	a. Imperf between (horiz or vert pair)	£500	
	b. Imperf horiz (vert pair)	£350	
	c. Pair, with and without wmk		
	d. Imperf (pair)	£300	

"WITH AND WITHOUT WMK" PAIRS listed in the issues from No. 195a onwards must have one stamp *completely* without any trace of watermark.

1931. *"Perkins, Bacon" printing (re-engraved types). W* **106.** *P 13½ to 14.*

No.	Type	Description	Unused	Used
198	**88**	1 c. green	1·50	1·00
		a. Imperf between (horiz pair)	£750	
199	**89**	2 c. scarlet	1·75	1·00
200	**90**	3 c. red-brown	1·75	80
201	**91**	4 c. reddish purple	2·50	2·25
202	**92**	5 c. deep grey-green	4·00	6·50
203	**93**	6 c. ultramarine (25.3.31)	9·00	16·00
204	**94**	8 c. chestnut (1.4.31)	9·00	16·00
205	**96**	10 c. violet	4·00	6·50
206	**98**	15 c. blue	17·00	35·00
207	**99**	20 c. black	19·00	10·00
208	**100**	30 c. sepia	13·00	24·00
198/208		*Set of* 11	70·00	£110

Perforations. Two perforating heads were used: comb 13.4 × 13.4 for 1 c.; comb 13.6 × 13.8 for other values.

107 Codfish

108 King George V

109 Queen Mary

110 Duke of Windsor when Prince of Wales

111 Caribou

112 Queen Elizabeth II when Princess

113 Salmon

114 Newfoundland Dog

115 Seal

116 Cape Race

117 Sealing Fleet

118 Fishing Fleet

(Recess P.B.)

1932 (1 Jan). *W* **106**. *P* 13½ *(comb).*

209 **107** 1 c. green .. .. 1·50 40
a. Imperf (pair) .. .. .. 90·00
b. Perf 13 (line) .. .. .. 22·00 25·00
ba. Imperf between (vert pair) £110
c. Booklet pane of 4 (*p* 13) £100
210 **108** 2 c. carmine .. .. 1·25 20
a. Imperf (pair) .. .. .. 90·00
b. Perf 13 (line) .. .. .. 15·00 17·00
c. Perf 14 (line). Small holes .. ..
d. Booklet pane of 4 (*p* 13½) .. .. 27·00
e. Booklet pane of 4 (*p* 13) .. .. 75·00
211 **109** 3 c. orange-brown 70 20
a. Imperf (pair) .. .. .. 90·00
b. Perf 13 (line) .. .. .. 24·00
c. Perf 14 (line). Small holes .. .. 18·00
ca. Imperf between (vert pair) £100
d. Booklet pane of 4 (*p* 13½) .. .. 80·00
e. Booklet pane of 4 (*p* 13) £110
f. Booklet pane of 4 (*p* 14) .. .. 80·00
212 **110** 4 c. bright violet .. .. .. 3·75 95
213 **111** 5 c. maroon .. .. 3·50 1·00
a. Imperf (pair) £180
214 **112** 6 c. light blue .. .. 7·00 11·00
215 **113** 10 c. black-brown .. .. .. 1·00 55
a. Imperf (pair) .. .. .. 90·00
216 **114** 14 c. black .. .. 2·50 3·25
a. Imperf (pair) £120
217 **115** 15 c. claret .. .. 2·50 2·50
a. Imperf (pair) £130
b. Perf 14 (line) .. .. .. 10·00 12·00
218 **116** 20 c. green .. .. 2·25 80
a. Imperf (pair) £130
b. Perf 14 (line) .. .. .. 28·00
219 **117** 25 c. slate .. .. 2·25 2·00
a. Imperf (pair) £130
b. Perf 14 (line) .. .. .. 10·00 12·00
ba. Imperf between (vert pair) £250
220 **118** 30 c. ultramarine .. .. .. 15·00 20·00
a. Imperf (pair) £325
b. Imperf between (vert pair) £450
c. Perf 14 (line) £160
209/20 .. .. *Set of* 12 40·00 38·00

For similar stamps perf 12½ see Nos. 276/289.

TRANS-ATLANTIC
WEST TO EAST
Per Dornier DO-X
May, 1932.
One Dollar and Fifty Cents

(119)

1932 (19 May). *Air. Surch as T* **119**, *by Messrs. D. R. Thistle. W* **106**. *P* 14.

221 **105** $1.50 on $1 deep blue (R.) £180 £225
a. Surch inverted £7500

120 Queen Mother, when Duchess of York

121 Paper Mills

122 Bell Island

(Recess P.B.)

1932–38. *Wmk W* **106** *(sideways on vert designs). P* 13½ *(comb).*

222 **107** 1 c. grey 20 10
a. Imperf (pair) .. .. .. 75·00
b. Perf 14 (line) .. .. .. 8·00
c. Perf 14 (line). Small holes .. .. 18·00
d. Pair, with and without wmk
e. Booklet pane of 4 (*p* 13½) .. .. 80·00
f. Booklet pane of 4 (*p* 14) .. .. 80·00
223 **108** 2 c. green 65 10
a. Imperf (pair) .. .. .. 90·00
b. Perf 14 (line) .. .. .. 8·00
ba. Imperf between (horiz pair) .. £250
c. Perf 14 (line). Small holes .. .. 13·00
d. Pair, with and without wmk .. 24·00
e. Booklet pane of 4 (*p* 13½) .. .. 26·00
f. Booklet pane of 4 (*p* 14) .. .. 35·00
224 **110** 4 c. carmine 40 10
a. Imperf (pair) .. .. .. 70·00
b. Perf 14 (line) .. .. .. 3·75
ba. Imperf between (horiz or vert pair) £120
225 **111** 5 c. violet (Die I) .. .. .. 4·50 40
a. Imperf (pair) .. .. .. 85·00
b. Perf 14 (line). Small holes .. .. 23·00
c. Die II 70 10
ca. Imperf (pair) £120
cb. Perf 14 (line) .. .. .. 18·00
cc. Imperf between (horiz pair) .. £180
cd. Pair, with and without wmk ..
226 **120** 7 c. red-brown .. .. 85 2·50
b. Perf 14 (line) .. .. ..
ba. Imperf between (horiz pair) .. £425
c. Imperf (pair) £120
227 **121** 8 c. brownish red .. .. .. 1·50 1·50
a. Imperf (pair) .. .. .. 70·00
228 **122** 24 c. bright blue .. .. .. 2·25 2·75
aa. Imperf (pair) £160
ab. Doubly printed £900
228*a* **118** 48 c. red-brown (1.1.38) .. .. 6·00 4·50
b. Imperf (pair) .. .. .. 70·00
222/8*a* .. .. *Set of* 8 11·00 10·50

No. 223. Two dies exist of the 2 c. Die I was used for No. 210 and both dies for No. 223. The differences, though numerous, are very slight.

No. 225. There are also two dies of the 5 c., Die I only being used for No. 213 and both dies for the violet stamp. In Die II the antler pointing to the "T" of "POSTAGE" is taller than the one pointing to the "S" and the individual hairs on the underside of the caribou's tail are distinct.

For similar stamps in a slightly larger size and perforated 12½ see Nos. 276/89.

(123) "L.&S."—Land and Sea

1933 (9 Feb). *Optd with T* **123** *for ordinary postal use, by Messrs D. R. Thistle. W* **106** *(sideways). P* 14.

229 **103** 15 c. chocolate .. .. 5·50 8·00
a. Pair, one without wmk .. .. 20·00
b. Opt reading up £1200
c. Vertical pair, one without surch .. £1700

124 Put to Flight

125 Land of Hearts Delight

(Des J. Scott. Recess P.B.)

1933 (31 May). *Air. T* **124/5** *and similar horiz designs. W* **106**. *P* 14 *(a) or* 11½ *(b).*

230 5 c. red-brown (*a*) .. .. .. 7·50 13·00
a. Imperf (pair) £130
b. Imperf between (horiz or vert pair) .. £2250
231 10 c. orange-yellow (*b*) .. .. .. 10·00 15·00
a. Imperf (pair) £110
232 30 c. light blue (*a*) .. .. .. 18·00 30·00
a. Imperf (pair) £250
233 60 c. green (*b*) .. .. 32·00 50·00
a. Imperf (pair) £250
234 75 c. yellow-brown (*a*) .. .. .. 32·00 50·00
a. Imperf (pair) £140
b. Imperf between (horiz or vert pair) .. £2250

Designs:—30 c. Spotting the herd; 60 c. News from home; 75 c. Labrador.

1933
GEN. BALBO
FLIGHT.
$4.50

(129)

(Surch by Robinson & Co, St. John's)

1933 (24 July). *Air. Balbo Transatlantic Mass Formation Flight. No. 234 surch with T* **129**. *W* **106**. *P* 14.

235 $4.50 on 75 c. yellow-brown £300 £350
a. Surch inverted £20000
b. Surch on 10 c. (No. 231) £20000

No. 235a. When this error was discovered the stamps were ordered to be officially destroyed but four copies which had been torn were recovered and skilfully repaired. In addition four undamaged examples exist and the price quoted is for one of these.

130 Sir Humphrey Gilbert

131 Compton Castle, Devon

132 Gilbert Coat of Arms

(Recess P.B.)

1933 (3 Aug). *350th Anniv of the Annexation by Sir Humphrey Gilbert. T* **130/2** *and similar designs. W* **106**. *P* 13½ *(comb).**

236 1 c. slate 70 80
a. Imperf (pair) .. .. .. 45·00
237 2 c. green 70 60
a. Imperf (pair) .. .. .. 60·00
b. Doubly printed £400
238 3 c. chestnut .. .. 70 1·25
239 4 c. carmine 70 50
a. Imperf (pair) .. .. .. 45·00
240 5 c. violet 85 95
241 7 c. greenish blue .. .. .. 6·50 11·00
a. Perf 14 .. .. 15·00 24·00
242 8 c. vermilion .. .. 6·50 9·50
a. Brownish red £250
b. Bisected (4 c.) (on cover) .. .. † £350
243 9 c. ultramarine .. .. 4·75 8·00
a. Imperf (pair) £150
b. Perf 14 .. .. 13·00 18·00
244 10 c. brown-lake .. .. 4·75 4·50
a. Imperf (pair) £300
b. Perf 14 .. .. 17·00 26·00
245 14 c. grey-black .. .. 10·00 18·00
a. Perf 14 .. .. 16·00 27·00
246 15 c. claret .. .. 14·00 20·00
247 20 c. grey-green .. .. 6·50 11·00
a. Perf 14 .. .. 13·00 18·00
248 24 c. maroon .. .. 14·00 24·00
a. Imperf (pair) £120
b. Perf 14 .. .. 20·00 30·00
249 32 c. olive-black .. .. 16·00 30·00
a. Perf 14 .. .. 22·00 40·00
236/49 .. .. *Set of* 14 80·00 £130

Designs: *Horiz*—4 c. Eton College; 7 c. Gilbert commissioned by Elizabeth; 8 c. Fleet leaving Plymouth, 1583; 9 c. Arrival at St. John's; 10 c. Annexation, 5 August 1583; 20 c. Map of Newfoundland. *Vert*—5 c. Anchor token; 14 c. Royal Arms; 15 c. Gilbert in the *Squirrel*; 24 c. Queen Elizabeth I. 32 c. Gilbert's statue at Truro.

**Perforations.* Two perforating heads were used: comb 13.4 × 13.4 for all values; line 13.8 (listed above as 14) for a second printing of some values.

1935 (6 May). *Silver Jubilee. As Nos.* 91/4 *of Antigua, but ptd by B.W. P* 11 × 12.

250 4 c. rosine 80 55
251 5 c. bright violet .. .. 1·40 80
252 7 c. blue .. .. 2·00 3·25
253 24 c. olive-green .. .. 4·50 4·50
250/3 Perf "Specimen" .. .. *Set of* 4 £120

1937 (12 May). *Coronation Issue. As Nos.* 13/15 *of Aden but name and value uncoloured on coloured background and ptd by B.W. P* 11 × 11½.

254 2 c. green 75 80
255 4 c. carmine 85 40
256 5 c. purple .. .. 1·40 1·40
254/6 Perf "Specimen" .. .. *Set of* 3 70·00

144 Codfish

Die I

Die II

No. 258. In Die II the shading of the King's face is heavier and dots have been added down the ridge of the nose. The top frame line is thicker and more uniform.

(Recess P.B.)

1937 (12 May). *Additional Coronation Issue. T* **144** *and similar horiz designs. W* **106**. A. *P* 14 *or* 13½ *(line).* B. *P* 13 *(comb.)*

		A		B	
257	1 c. grey	35	20	12·00	15·00
	a. Pair, with and without wmk	15·00		—	—
258	3 c. orange-brown (I)	1·25	55	1·10	50
	a. Pair, with and without wmk	42·00		†	
	b. Die I. Imperf between (horiz or vert pair)	£350		†	
	c. Die II	90	60	90	60
	d. Die II. Imperf between (horiz or vert pair) ..	£450		†	
	e. Die II. Pair, with and without wmk ..	—	—	80·00	—
259	7 c. bright ultramarine ..	1·25	1·00	70·00	—
	a. Pair, with and without wmk	—	—	†	
260	8 c. scarlet	1·25	1·00	2·50	2·75
	a. Pair, with and without wmk	30·00		†	
	b. Imperf between (horiz or vert pair)	£500		†	
	c. Imperf (pair)	£200			
261	10 c. deep olive	2·75	2·50	5·00	4·25
	a. Pair, with and without wmk	45·00		†	
262	14 c. black	2·50	2·25	£2000	£1000
	a. Pair, with and without wmk	30·00		†	
263	15 c. claret	4·50	4·00	5·50	5·50
	a. Pair, with and without wmk	32·00		48·00	—
	b. Imperf between (vert pair)	£275		†	
264	20 c. green	2·25	2·75	2·75	3·75
	a. Pair, with and without wmk	85·00		†	
	b. Imperf between (vert pair)	£475		†	
265	24 c. light blue	3·00	3·00	5·00	5·50
	a. Pair, with and without wmk	85·00		†	
	b. Imperf between (vert pair)	£500		†	
266	25 c. slate	3·25	3·00	12·00	12·00
	a. Pair, with and without wmk	55·00		†	
267	48 c. slate-purple	3·50	4·00	15·00	18·00
	a. Pair, with and without wmk	90·00		†	
	b. Imperf between (vert pair)	£500		†	
257/67	.. .. *Set of* 11	23·00	22·00		

Designs:—3 c. Map of Newfoundland; 7 c. Caribou; 8 c. Corner Brook paper mills; 10 c. Salmon; 14 c. Newfoundland dog; 15 c. Northern Seal; 20 c. Cape Race; 24 c. Bell Island; 25 c. Sealing fleet; 48 c. The Banks fishing fleet.

The line perforation "A" was produced by two machines measuring respectively 13.7 and 14.1. The comb perforation "B" measures 13.3 × 13.2.

Two used examples of No. 259B have now been identified on separate covers.

155 King George VI　**156** Queen Mother

(Recess P.B.)

1938 (12 May). *T* **155/6** *and similar vert designs. W* **106** *(sideways). P* 13½ *(comb).*
268　2 c. green . . . . 2·00　25
　a. Pair, with and without wmk £130
　b. Imperf (pair) . . . . 65·00
269　3 c. carmine . . . . 2·00　25
　a. Perf 14 (line) . . . . £225　£110
　b. Pair, with and without wmk £180
　c. Imperf (pair) . . . . 55·00
270　4 c. light blue . . . . 2·50　25
　a. Pair, with and without wmk . . . . 80·00
　b. Imperf (pair) . . . . 65·00
271　7 c. deep ultramarine . . . . 1·60　1·75
　a. Imperf (pair) . . . . 65·00

Designs:— 4 c. Queen Elizabeth II as princess; 7 c. Queen Mary.
For similar designs, perf 12½, see Nos. 277/281.

159 King George VI and Queen Elizabeth

(Recess B.W.)

1939 (17 June). *Royal Visit. No wmk. P* 13½.
272　**159**　5 c. deep ultramarine . . . . . . 1·25　90

2

▲　**CENTS**　

(160)

1939 (20 Nov). *No.* 272 *surch as T* **160**, *at St. John's.*
273　**159**　2 c. on 5 c. deep ultramarine (Br.) . . 1·40　1·25
274　　4 c. on 5 c. deep ultramarine (C.) . . 95　85

161 Grenfell on the *Strathcona* (after painting by Gribble)　**162** Memorial University College

(Recess C.B.N.)

1941 (1 Dec). *Sir Wilfred Grenfell's Labrador Mission. P* 12.
275　**161**　5 c. blue . . . . 25　25

(Recess Waterlow)

1941–44. *W* **106** *(sideways on vert designs). P* 12½ *(line).*
276　**107**　1 c. grey . . . . 35　15
277　**155**　2 c. green . . . . 35　10
278　**156**　3 c. carmine . . . . 45　5
　a. Pair, with and without wmk . . 55·00
279　–　4 c. blue (As No. 270) . . . . . . 80　12
　a. Pair, with and without wmk . . £100
280　**111**　5 c. violet (Die I) (*p* 13½ *comb*) . . . .
　a. Perf 12½ (line) (6.42) . . . . 85　30
　ab. Pair, with and without wmk . . 95·00
　ac. Printed double . . . .
　ad. Imperf vert (horiz pair) . . . .
　b. Imperf (pair) . . . .
281　–　7 c. deep ultramarine (As No. 271) . . 2·00　2·75
　a. Pair, with and without wmk . . £100
282　**121**　8 c. rose-red . . . . 1·50　2·00
　a. Pair, with and without wmk . . £100
283　**113**　10 c. black-brown . . . . 1·75　90
284　**114**　14 c. black . . . . 2·25　3·00
285　**115**　15 c. claret . . . . 3·25　4·00
286　**116**　20 c. green . . . . 3·50　3·50
287　**122**　24 c. blue . . . . 3·75　4·50
288　**117**　25 c. slate . . . . 4·00　4·75
289　**118**　48 c. red-brown (1944) . . . . . . 6·00　9·00
276/89 . . . . *Set of* 14　28·00　32·00

Nos. 276/89 are redrawn versions of previous designs with slightly larger dimensions; the 5 c., for example, measures 21 mm in width as opposed to the 20.4 mm of the Perkins Bacon printings.

No. 280. For Die I see note relating to No. 225.

(Recess C.B.N.)

1943 (2 Jan). *P* 12.
290　**162**　30 c. carmine . . . . 2·25　1·25

163 St. John's

TWO

CENTS

(164)

(Recess C.B.N.)

1943 (1 June). *Air. P* 12.
291　**163**　7 c. ultramarine . . . . 25　25

1946 (23 Mar). *Surch locally with T* **164**.
292　**162**　2 c. on 30 c. carmine . . . . . . 20　25

165 Queen Elizabeth II when Princess　**166** Cabot off Cape Bonavista

(Recess Waterlow)

1947 (21 Apr). *Princess Elizabeth's* 21*st Birthday. W* **106** *(sideways). P* 12½.
293　**165**　4 c. light blue . . . . 20　12

(Recess Waterlow)

1947 (23 June). 450*th Anniv of Cabot's Discovery of Newfoundland. W* **106** *(sideways). P* 12½.
294　**166**　5 c. mauve . . . . 25　25
　a. Imperf between (horiz pair) . . £750

POSTAGE DUE STAMPS

D 1

(Litho John Dickinson & Co, Ltd)

1939 (1 May)–**49.** *P* 10.
D1　D 1　1 c. green . . . . 2·00　3·75
　a. Perf 11 (1949) . . . . . . 3·00　7·00
D2　　2 c. vermilion . . . . 4·50　3·75
　a. Perf 11 × 9 (1946) . . . . 4·75　7·50
D3　　3 c. ultramarine . . . . 5·50　7·00
　a. Perf 11 × 9 (1949) . . . . 7·50　9·00
　b. Perf 9 . . . . £140
D4　　4 c. orange . . . . 6·00　8·50
　a. Perf 11 × 9 (May 1948) . . . . 9·50　15·00
D5　　5 c. brown . . . . 6·00　8·00
D6　　10 c. violet . . . . 6·00　8·00
　a. Perf 11 (W **106**) (1949) . . . . 7·00　22·00
　ab. Ditto. Imperf between (vert pair) . . £425

On 1 April 1949, Newfoundland joined the Confederation of Canada whose stamps it now uses.

New Guinea
(formerly New Britain)

Stamps of Germany and later of GERMAN NEW GUINEA were used in New Guinea from 1888 until 1914.

During the interim period between the "G.R.I." surcharges and the "N.W. PACIFIC ISLANDS" overprints, unoverprinted stamps of AUSTRALIA were utilised.

PRICES FOR STAMPS ON COVER

Nos. 1/30	*from* × 3
Nos. 31/2	—
Nos. 33/49	*from* × 3
Nos. 50/9	*from* × 2
Nos. 60/2	—
Nos. 63/4	*from* × 2
Nos. 65/81	*from* × 5
Nos. 83/5	—
Nos. 86/97	*from* × 5
No. 99	—
Nos. 100/16	*from* × 4
Nos. 117/18	—
Nos. 119/24	*from* × 4
Nos. 125/203	*from* × 2
Nos. 204/5	—
Nos. 206/11	*from* × 8
Nos. 212/25	*from* × 2
Nos. O1/33	*from* × 8

AUSTRALIAN OCCUPATION

Stamps of German New Guinea surcharged

G.R.I.
2d.
(1)

G.R.I.
1s.
(2)

G.R.I.
1d.
(3)

Measurements are taken from the bottom of the "R" to the top of the "d" in the low values, or to the top of the figure of value in the large stamps.

1914 (17 Oct). *Stamps of* 1901 *surch.*

(*a*) *As T* **1.** "G.R.I." *and value* 6 *mm apart*
1　1d. on 3 pf. brown . . . . 45·00　45·00
2　1d. on 5 pf. green . . . . 15·00　15·00
3　2d. on 10 pf. carmine . . . . . . 22·00　22·00
4　2d. on 20 pf. ultramarine . . . . . . 24·00　24·00
　a. "2d." doubly printed without the "G.R.I." £600
5　2½d. on 10 pf. carmine . . . . . . 55·00　50·00
6　2½d. on 20 pf. ultramarine . . . . . . 60·00　60·00
7　3d. on 25 pf. black and red/*yellow* . . . . £130　£120
8　3d. on 30 pf. black and orange/*buff* . . . . £120　£120
9　4d. on 40 pf. black and carmine . . . . £180　£170
　a. Surch double . . . . £800　£750
　b. Surch inverted £800
10　5d. on 50 pf. black and purple/*buff* . . . . £400　£300
11　8d. on 80 pf. black and carmine/*rose* . . £550　£650
　a. No stop . . . .

(*b*) *As T* **2.** "G.R.I." *and value* 3½ *to* 4 *mm apart*
12　1s. on 1 m. carmine . . . . £1200　£950
13　2s. on 2 m. blue . . . . £1400　£950
14　3s. on 3 m. violet-black . . . . . . £1600　£1000
15　5s. on 5 m. carmine and black . . . . £3750　£3000
　a. No stop after "I" . . . .
　b. No stops after "R" and "I" £5000

1914 (16 Dec). *Stamps of* 1901 *surch.*

(*a*) *As T* **1.** "G.R.I." *and value* 5 *mm apart*
16　1d. on 3 pf. brown . . . . 28·00　28·00
　a. Figure "1" omitted . . . . . . —　£225
　b. Surch double £200
　c. Surch inverted £180
17　1d. on 5 pf. green . . . . 8·00　8·00
　a. "d" inverted . . . . £500　£400
　b. No stops after "G R I" . . . . . . £100　90·00
　c. Surch double £300
　d. Small "I" . . . . 16·00　15·00
　e. "1d." double £160
　f. "G.I.R." for "G.R.I." £1400
18　2d. on 10 pf. carmine . . . . . . 15·00　14·00
　a. Surch double £400
　b. Surch double, one inverted . . . . £800　£750
　c. Error. Surcharged "G.I.R. 3d." £4500
　d. Stop before instead of after "G" £1400
　e. Error. "1d." for "2d." and stop before "G" £1100　£1000
19　2d. on 20 pf. ultramarine . . . . . . 20·00　18·00
　a. "R" inverted . . . . £1100　£1000
　b. Surch double £700
　c. Surch double, one inverted . . . . £1100　£1000
　d. Error. Surch "G.R.I. 1d." . . . . £3500　£3250
20　2½d. on 10 pf. carmine . . . . . . 55·00　45·00
21　2½d. on 20 pf. ultramarine . . . . . . £900　£850
　a. Surch double, one inverted . . . .
22　3d. on 25 pf. black and red/*yellow* . . . . 75·00　70·00
　a. "G.I.R." for "G.R.I." £1100
23　3d. on 30 pf. black and orange/*buff* . . . . 80·00　80·00
　a. "d" inverted . . . . —　£550
　b. Surch double £700
　c. Surch double, one inverted £1000
　d. Error. "1d" for "3d" £2500
24　4d. on 40 pf. black and carmine . . . . 65·00　70·00
　a. Surch double, one inverted £900
25　5d. on 50 pf. black and purple/*buff* . . . . £120　£120
　a. Figure "5" omitted £550
　b. Surch double £500
　c. Surch double, one inverted £550
　d. "G.I.R." for "G.R.I." . . . . . .
26　8d. on 80 pf. black and carmine/*rose* . . £500　£425
　a. Surch double, one inverted . . . . £1200　£1100
　b. Surch double . . . . £1200　£1100
　c. Surch triple . . . . £1200　£1100

(*b*) *As T* **2.** "G.R.I." *and value* 5½ *mm apart*
27　1s. on 1 m. carmine . . . . £1200　£900
28　2s. on 2 m. blue . . . . £1400　£900
　a. Surch double . . . .
29　3s. on 3 m. violet-black . . . . . . £1600　£1200
30　5s. on 5 m. carmine and black . . . . £4000　£3250

There appears to be also a third printing of most of the low values with 7½ mm between "G.R.I." and top of the "d".

1915. *Nos.* 18 *and* 19 *further surch as in T* **3**.
31　"1" on 2d. on 10 pf. £7000
32　"1" on 2d. on 20 pf. . . . . —　£4000

4　4*a*

1915. *Registration Labels surch* "G.R.I. 3d." *and used for postage. Each black and red on buff. Inscr* "(Deutsch Neuguinea)" *spelt in various ways as indicated.*

I. *With name of town in sans-serif letters as T* **4**
33　Rabaul "(Deutsch Neuguinea)" . . . . 90·00　65·00
　a. "G.R.I. 3d." double . . . . . . £650　£500
　b. No bracket before "Deutsch" . . . . £275　£275
　ba. No bracket and surch double . . . . £800　£750
　c. No stop after "I" . . . . . .
　d. "(Deutsch-Neuguinea)" . . . . . . £150　£110
　da. "G.R.I. 3d." double . . . . . .
34　Deulon "(Deutsch Neuguinea)" £3750
35　Friedrich-Wilhelmshafen "(Deutsch Neuguinea)" . . . . £100　£130
　a. No stop after "d" £250
　b. "(Deutsch-Neuguinea)" . . . . . . £100　£130
　ba. No stop after "d" £250
36　Herbertshöhe "(Deutsch Neuguinea)" . . £150　£180
　a. No stop after "d" £350
　b. "(Deutsch Neu-Guinea)" . . . . . . £225　£250
37　Käwieng "(Deutsch-Neuguinea)" . . . . £100　£150
　a. "Deutsch Neu-Guinea" . . . . . . £130　£150
　ab. No stop after "d" £250
　ac. "G.R.I." double . . . . . .
　ad. "3d." double . . . . . .

38 Kieta "(Deutsch-Neuguinea)" £300 £350
a. No bracket before "Deutsch" £500 £500
b. No stop after "d" £600
c. Surch omitted (righthand stamp of horiz pair)
39 Manus "(Deutsch Neuguinea)" £160 £200
a. "G.R.I. 3d." double £750
b. No bracket before "Deutsch" £250 £250
40 Stephansort "(Deutsch Neu-Guinea)" — £1200
a. No stop after "d" — £1500

II. *With name of town in letters with serifs as T* 4*a*

41 Friedrich-Wilhelmshafen "(Deutsch-Neuguinea)" £100 £130
b. No stop after "d" £250 £300
c. No stop after "I" £350 £400
d. No bracket before "Deutsch" £350 £400
e. No bracket after "Neuguinea" £350 £400
42 Käwieng "(Deutsch Neuguinea)" 90·00 £120
a. No stop after "d" £200
43 Manus "(Deutsch-Neuguinea)" £600 £800
a. No stop after "I" £1200 £800

OFFICIAL STAMPS

O. S.

G.R.I.

1d.

(O 5)

1914 (Oct). *Stamps of* 1901 *surch as Type* O 5. "G.R.I." *and value* 3½ *mm apart.*

O48 1d. on 3 pf. brown 12·00 16·00
O49 1d. on 5 pf. green 50·00 60·00

Stamps of Marshall Islands surcharged

1914 (16 Dec). *Stamps of* 1901.

(*a*) *As T* 1. "G.R.I." *and value* 5 *mm apart*

50 1d. on 3 pf. brown 28·00 27·00
a. "1" with straight serif 65·00 60·00
b. Surch inverted £700
51 1d. on 5 pf. green 40·00 42·00
a. No stop after "d"
b. "1" and "d" wider apart £300
52 2d. on 10 pf. carmine 11·00 12·00
a. No stop after "G" £350
b. Surch double £600
c. Surch double, one inverted £600
53 2d. on 20 pf. ultramarine 13·00 15·00
a. No stop after "d" 32·00
b. Surch double £400
c. Surch double, one inverted £850
54 3d. on 25 pf. black and red/*yellow* £250 £275
a. No stop after "d" £500 £500
b. Surch double £900 £850
c. Surch double, one inverted £1000
55 3d. on 30 pf. black and orange/*buff* £275 £275
a. No stop after "d" £500
56 4d. on 40 pf. black and carmine 80·00 90·00
a. No stop after "d" £150 £140
b. Surch inverted £850
57 5d. on 50 pf. black and purple/*buff* £100 £120
a. "5" only for "5d." £400
58 8d. on 80 pf. black and carmine/*rose* £450 £500

(*b*) *As T* 2. "G.R.I." *and value* 5½ *mm apart*

59 1s. on 1 m. carmine £1300 £850
a. No stop after "I" £1900
b. Surch double
60 2s. on 2 m. blue £900 £750
a. Surch double, one inverted — £1800
b. Large "S" after "2"
61 3s. on 3 m. violet-black £1900 £2000
a. Surch double
b. No stop after "I" £2500
62 5s. on 5 m. carmine and black £4500 £3750
a. Surch double, one inverted £7000 £5000

1915. *Nos.* 52 *and* 53 *further surch as in T* 3.

63 "1" on 2d. on 10 pf. carmine £140 £160
64 "1" on 2d. on 20 pf. ultramarine £2250 £1400

Stamps of Australia overprinted

N. W. PACIFIC ISLANDS.	N. W. PACIFIC ISLANDS.	N. W. PACIFIC ISLANDS.
(*a*)	(*b*)	(*c*)

(6)

7 (5)

8 (2)

9 (6)

The Type numbers shown in brackets are the equivalent Type numbers of Australia.

1915–16. *Stamps of Australia optd in black as T* 6 (*a*), (*b*) *or* (*c*).

(i) *W* 7. *P* 14 (4 Jan–15 March 1915)

65 5*a* ½d. green 1·00 2·00
66 ½d. bright green 1·00 2·00
67 1d. pale rose (Die I) (4.1) 1·00 2·00
68 1d. dull red (Die I) 2·00 3·00
69 1d. carmine-red (Die I) 2·00 3·00
a. Substituted cliché — £700
69*b* 1d. carmine-red (Die II) £250
c. Substituted cliché £1100
70 4d. yellow-orange 3·50 5·50
a. Line through "FOUR PENCE" £400 £450
71 4d. yellow £300 £325
72 5d. brown 5·00 9·00

(ii) *W* 8. *P* 12 (4 Jan 1915–March 1916)

73 1 2d. grey (Die I) 4·50 8·00
74 2½d. indigo (4.1.15) 2·75 7·00
76 3d. yellow-olive (Die I) 8·00 16·00
a. Die II £300 £350
ab. In pair with Die I £500 £550
77 3d. greenish olive (Die I) £190 £250
a. Die II £1300
ab. In pair with Die I £2250
78 6d. ultramarine 15·00 23·00
a. Retouched "E" £5000
79 9d. violet 20·00 35·00
81 1s. green 26·00 38·00
83 5s. grey and yellow (3.16) £750 £700
84 10s. grey and pink (12.15) £130 £160
85 £1 brown and ultramarine (12.15) £800 £950

(iii) *W* 7. *P* 12 (Oct 1915–July 1916)

86 1 2d. grey (Die I) 3·25 6·50
87 2½d. indigo (7.16) £7500 £7000
88 6d. ultramarine 7·50 12·00
89 9d. violet (12.15) 7·50 12·00
90 1s. emerald (12.15) 8·00 14·00
91 2s. brown (12.15) 90·00 £100
92 5s. grey and yellow (12.15) 90·00 £100

(iv) *W* 9. *P* 12 (Dec 1915–Aug 1916)

94 1 2d. grey (Die I) 4·00 6·50
a. Die II 8·50 13·00
ab. In pair with Die I £150
96 3d. yellow-olive (Die I) 4·50 11·00
a. Die II 65·00 50·00
ab. In pair with Die I £110
97 2s. brown (8.16) 25·00 45·00
99 £1 brown and ultramarine (8.16) £500 £600

Dates for Nos. 67 and 74 are issue dates. All other dates are those of despatch. Nos. 65/6, 68/73, 76/81 were despatched on 15 March 1915.

SETTINGS. Type 6 exists in three slightly different versions, illustrated above as (*a*), (*b*), *and* (*c*). These differ in the letters "S" of "ISLANDS" as follows:

(*a*) Both "SS" normal.
(*b*) First "S" with small head and large tail and second "S" normal.
(*c*) Both "SS" with small head and large tail.

It has been established, by the study of minor variations, that there are actually six settings of the overprint, including that represented by T 11, but the following are the different arrangements of Type 6 (*a*), (*b*) and (*c*) which occur.

A. Horizontal rows 1 and 2 all Type (*a*). Row 3 all Type (*b*). Rows 4 and 5 all Type (*c*).

B. (½d. green only). As A, except that the types in the bottom row run (*c*) (*c*) (*c*) (*b*) (*c*).

C. As A, but bottom row now shows types (*a*) (*c*) (*c*) (*c*) (*b*) (*c*).

Horizontal strips and pairs showing varieties (*a*) and (*c*), or (*b*) and (*c*) *se-tenant* are scarce.

The earliest printing of the 1d. and 2½d. values was made on sheets with margin attached on two sides, the later printings being on sheets from which the margins had been removed. In this printing the vertical distances between the overprints are less than in later printings, so that in the lower horizontal rows of the sheet the overprint is near the top of the stamp.

The settings used on King George stamps and on the Kangaroo type are similar, but the latter stamps being smaller the overprints are closer together in the vertical rows.

PURPLE OVERPRINTS. We no longer differentiate between purple and black overprints in the above series. In our opinion the two colours are nowadays insufficiently distinct to warrant separation.

PRICES. The prices quoted for Nos. 65 to 101 apply to stamps with opts, Types 6 (*a*) or 6 (*c*). Stamps with opt Type 6 (*b*) are worth double. Vertical strips of three, showing (*a*), (*b*) and (*c*), are worth about five times the prices quoted for singles.

One Penny	N. W. PACIFIC ISLANDS.
(10)	(11)

1918 (23 May). *Nos.* 72 *and* 81 *surch locally with T* 10.

100 1d. on 5d. brown £120 £110
101 1d. on 1s. green £120 £110

Types 6 (*a*), (*b*), (*c*) occur on these stamps also.

1918–23. *Stamps of Australia optd with T* 11 ("P" *of* "PACIFIC" *over space between* "I" *and* "S" *of* "ISLANDS").

(i) *T* 5*a* (*King*). *W* 7. *P* 14

102 ½d. green 80 2·00
103 1d. carmine-red (Die I) 1·60 1·40
a. Substituted cliché £800
b. Rosine. Rough paper, locally gummed (perfd "OS") — £150
103*c* 1d. carmine-red (Die II) £225 65·00
d. Substituted cliché £800
e. Rosine. Rough paper, locally gummed (perfd "OS")
104 4d. yellow-orange (1919) 12·00 20·00
a. Line through "FOUR PENCE" £1100
105 5d. brown (1919) 5·00 14·00

(ii) *T* 1 (*Kangaroo*). *W* 9. *P* 12

106 2d. grey (Die I) (1919) 5·00 11·00
a. Die II 12·00 20·00
107 2½d. indigo (1919) 11·00 17·00
a. "1" of "½" omitted £5500 £4750
108 2½d. blue (1920) 5·00 13·00
109 3d. greenish olive (Die I) (1919) 9·50 16·00
a. Die II 32·00 48·00
ab. In pair with Die I £300
b. Light olive (Die II) (1923) 5·50 10·00
110 6d. ultramarine (1919) 7·50 15·00
111 6d. greyish ultramarine (1922) 40·00 55·00
112 9d. violet (1919) 12·00 30·00
113 1s. emerald 12·00 25·00
114 1s. pale blue-green 13·00 25·00
115 2s. brown (1919) 28·00 38·00
116 5s. grey and yellow (1919) 70·00 60·00
117 10s. grey and bright pink (1919) £200 £225
118 £1 brown and ultramarine (1922) £2750

(iii) *T* 5*a*. *W* 6*a of Australia* (*Mult Crown* A). *P* 14

119 ½d. green (1919) 40 2·25

Type 11 differs from Type 6 (*a*) in the position of the "P" of "PACIFIC", which is further to the left in Type 11*b*.

1921–22. *T* 5*a of Australia. W* 7. *Colour changes and new value. Optd with T* 11.

120 1d. bright violet (1922) 2·50 5·50
121 2d. orange 7·50 9·00
122 2d. scarlet (1922) 3·75 12·00
123 4d. violet (1922) 25·00 35·00
a. "FOUR PENCE" in thinner letters £750
124 4d. ultramarine (1922) 16·00 23·00
a. "FOUR PENCE" in thinner letters £750

TERRITORY OF NEW GUINEA

PRINTERS. See note at the beginning of Australia.

12 Native Village

(13)

(Des R. Harrison. Eng T. Harrison. Recess Note Printing Branch, Commonwealth Bank of Australia, Melbourne, from 1926 Note Ptg Branch, Reserve Bank of Australia, Melbourne)

1925–28. *P* 11.

125 12 ½d. orange 80 3·25
126 1d. green 1·25 3·25
126*a* 1½d. orange-vermilion (1926) 2·50 3·00
127 2d. claret 3·25 4·50
128 3d. blue 5·50 6·00
129 4d. olive-green 11·00 14·00
130 6d. dull yellow-brown 11·00 22·00
a. Olive-bistre (1927) 11·00 22·00
b. Pale yellow-bistre (1928) 12·00 22·00
131 9d. dull purple (*to* violet) 17·00 28·00
132 1s. dull blue-green 17·00 22·00
133 2s. brown-lake 28·00 38·00
134 5s. olive-bistre 55·00 75·00
135 10s. dull rose £130 £160
136 £1 dull olive-green £250 £275
125/36 *Set of* 13 £500 £600

1931 (8 June). *Air. Optd with T* 13. *P* 11.

137 12 ½d. orange 60 2·25
138 1d. green 1·25 2·25
139 1½d. orange-vermilion 1·40 4·00
140 2d. claret 1·60 7·00
141 3d. blue 2·75 5·00
142 4d. olive-green 3·50 7·50
143 6d. pale yellow-bistre 4·50 10·00
144 9d. violet 5·00 15·00
145 1s. dull blue-green 10·00 17·00
146 2s. brown-lake 14·00 25·00
147 5s. olive-bistre 32·00 48·00
148 10s. bright pink 70·00 85·00
149 £1 olive-grey £130 £160
137/49 *Set of* 13 £250 £350

14 Raggiana Bird of Paradise (Dates either side of value)

AIR MAIL

(15)

(Recess John Ash, Melbourne)

1931 (2 Aug). *Tenth Anniv of Australian Administration. T* **14** *(with dates). P* 11.
150 **14** 1d. green .. 45 50
151 1½d. vermilion .. 5·00 7·50
152 2d. claret .. 2·25 2·00
153 3d. blue .. 3·00 3·75
154 4d. olive-green .. 5·50 9·00
155 5d. deep blue-green .. 6·00 9·00
156 6d. bistre-brown .. 6·00 10·00
157 9d. violet .. 7·00 14·00
158 1s. pale blue-green .. 9·00 14·00
159 2s. brown-lake .. 13·00 24·00
160 5s. olive-brown .. 35·00 48·00
161 10s. bright pink .. 90·00 £120
162 £1 olive-grey .. £170 £200
150/62 .. *Set of* 13 £325 £425

1931 (2 Aug). *Air. Optd with T* **15**.
163 **14** ½d. orange .. 45 75
164 1d. green .. 1·00 1·50
165 1½d. vermilion .. 1·75 3·25
166 2d. claret .. 2·00 2·75
167 3d. blue .. 2·50 3·25
168 4d. olive-green .. 3·00 5·00
169 5d. deep blue-green .. 3·50 6·50
170 6d. bistre-brown .. 8·50 13·00
171 9d. violet .. 8·50 15·00
172 1s. pale blue-green .. 8·50 15·00
173 2s. dull lake .. 15·00 28·00
174 5s. olive-brown .. 25·00 40·00
175 10s. bright pink .. 80·00 £100
176 £1 olive-grey .. £140 £170
163/76 .. *Set of* 14 £275 £350

1932 (30 June)–**1934**. *T* **14** *(redrawn without dates). P* 11.
177 1d. green .. 50 50
178 1½d. claret .. 80 3·00
179 2d. vermilion .. 65 70
179*a* 2½d. green (14.9.34) .. 3·50 9·00
180 3d. blue .. 1·00 1·75
180*a* 3½d. aniline carmine (14.9.34) .. 8·00 9·00
181 4d. olive-green .. 1·40 2·50
182 5d. deep blue-green .. 2·00 2·00
183 6d. bistre-brown .. 1·60 3·25
184 9d. violet .. 8·50 16·00
185 1s. blue-green .. 4·50 10·00
186 2s. dull lake .. 9·00 17·00
187 5s. olive .. 27·00 40·00
188 10s. pink .. 70·00 80·00
189 £1 olive-grey .. 95·00 £100
177/89 .. *Set of* 15 £200 £250

1932 (30 June)–**34**. *Air. T* **14** *(redrawn without dates), optd with T* **15**. *P* 11.
190 ½d. orange .. 40 1·00
191 1d. green .. 40 1·00
192 1½d. claret .. 70 2·75
193 2d. vermilion .. 1·25 1·10
193*a* 2½d. green (14.9.34) .. 2·50 2·50
194 3d. blue .. 1·60 1·60
194*a* 3½d. aniline carmine (14.9.34) .. 4·00 4·00
195 4d. olive-green .. 3·00 4·00
196 5d. deep blue-green .. 4·25 7·50
197 6d. bistre-brown .. 3·25 8·50
198 9d. violet .. 6·50 8·50
199 1s. pale blue-green .. 6·50 8·00
200 2s. dull lake .. 11·00 17·00
201 5s. olive-brown .. 27·00 35·00
202 10s. pink .. 65·00 70·00
203 £1 olive-grey .. 90·00 70·00
190/203 .. *Set of* 16 £200 £250

Two sheets were reported of the ½d. without overprint but it is believed they were not issued.

16 Bulolo Goldfields

(Recess John Ash, Melbourne)

1935 (1 May). *Air. P* 11.
204 **16** £2 bright violet .. £250 £250
205 £5 emerald-green .. £700 £650

(17)

18

1935 (27 June). *Silver Jubilee. As Nos.* 177 *and* 179, *but shiny paper. Optd with T* **17**.
206 1d. green .. 1·00 1·00
207 2d. vermilion .. 1·75 2·25

(Recess John Ash, Melbourne)

1937 (18 May). *Coronation. P* 11.
208 **18** 2d. scarlet .. 50 30
209 3d. blue .. 50 30
210 5d. green .. 50 35
a. Re-entry (design completely duplicated) .. 42·00 45·00
211 1s. purple .. 75 70

(Recess John Ash, Melbourne)

1939 (1 Mar). *Air. Inscr "AIR MAIL POSTAGE" at foot. P* 11.
212 **16** ½d. orange .. 2·00 2·00
213 1d. green .. 80 1·25
214 1½d. claret .. 1·25 4·25
215 2d. vermilion .. 2·75 3·00
216 **16** 3d. blue .. 4·50 7·00
217 4d. yellow-olive .. 4·00 7·50
218 5d. deep green .. 2·75 3·25
219 6d. bistre-brown .. 5·00 8·50
220 9d. violet .. 6·50 13·00
221 1s. pale blue-green .. 8·50 12·00
222 2s. dull lake .. 32·00 45·00
223 5s. olive-brown .. 75·00 85·00
224 10s. pink .. £200 £225
225 £1 olive-green .. £120 £160
212/25 .. *Set of* 14 £400 £500

OFFICIAL STAMPS

Australian stamps perforated "O S" exist with overprint Type 11 for use in New Guinea. We do not list such varieties.

O S (O 1) **O S** (O 2)

1925–31. *Optd with Type* O **1**. *P* 11.
O1 **12** 1d. green .. 90 3·75
O2 1½d. orange-vermilion (1931) .. 5·50 10·00
O3 2d. claret .. 1·60 3·75
O4 3d. blue .. 2·00 4·25
O5 4d. olive-green .. 3·00 6·50
O6 6d. olive-bistre .. 8·00 18·00
a. Pale yellow-bistre (1931) .. 8·00 20·00
O7 9d. violet .. 8·00 20·00
O8 1s. dull blue-green .. 7·00 20·00
O9 2s. brown-lake .. 27·00 48·00
O1/9 .. *Set of* 9 55·00 £120

1931 (2 Aug). *Optd with Type* O **2**. *P* 11.
O10 **14** 1d. green .. 1·25 4·25
O11 1½d. vermilion .. 2·25 6·00
O12 2d. claret .. 2·25 5·50
O13 3d. blue .. 2·25 6·00
O14 4d. olive-green .. 2·25 8·50
O15 5d. deep blue-green .. 3·75 10·00
O16 6d. bistre-brown .. 7·50 15·00
O17 9d. violet .. 8·00 18·00
O18 1s. pale blue-green .. 12·00 20·00
O19 2s. brown-lake .. 35·00 55·00
O20 5s. olive-brown .. £120 £170
O10/20 .. *Set of* 11 £180 £275

1932 (30 June)–**34**. *T* **14** *(redrawn without dates), optd with Type* O **2**. *P* 11.
O21 1d. green .. 80 2·50
O22 1½d. claret .. 1·75 4·00
O23 2d. vermilion .. 1·75 3·50
O24 2½d. green (14.9.34) .. 2·75 5·50
O25 3d. blue .. 3·75 7·00
O26 3½d. aniline carmine (14.9.34) .. 3·75 8·50
O27 4d. olive-green .. 3·75 8·00
O28 5d. deep blue-green .. 3·75 8·50
O29 6d. bistre-brown .. 5·50 13·00
O30 9d. violet .. 11·00 22·00
O31 1s. pale blue-green .. 17·00 23·00
O32 2s. dull lake .. 42·00 60·00
O33 5s. olive-brown .. £120 £170
O21/33 .. *Set of* 13 £200 £300

Civil Administration in New Guinea was suspended in 1942, following the Japanese invasion. It is believed that the Japanese intended to issue various New Guinea stamps overprinted with Japanese characters and an anchor, but such issues were never made available for postal purposes.

On resumption, after the Japanese defeat in 1945, Australian stamps were used until the appearance of the issue for the combined territories of PAPUA & NEW GUINEA.

New Hebrides

Stamps of NEW SOUTH WALES were used by various Postal Agencies in the New Hebrides from 1891 onwards. Similar Postal Agencies supplying the stamps of NEW CALEDONIA were opened from 1903 onwards.

PRICES FOR STAMPS ON COVER TO 1945	
Nos. 1/8 (F1/5)	*from* × 10
No. 9	*from* × 2
Nos. 10/16 (F6/10)	*from* × 8
Nos. 18/28 (F11/32)	*from* × 6
Nos. 30/4 (F33/7)	*from* × 4
No. 35 (F32*a*)	—
Nos. 36/9	*from* × 3
Nos. 40/2 (F38/41)	*from* × 4
Nos. 43/51 (F42/52)	*from* × 5
Nos. 52/63 (F53/64)	*from* × 3
Nos. D1/10 (FD53/69)	*from* × 8

ANGLO-FRENCH CONDOMINIUM

The New Hebrides, an island group in the south-west Pacific, were recognised as an area of joint Anglo-French influence in 1878. The position was regularised by the Convention of 20 October 1906 which created a Condominium, the two nations having equal rights and shares in the administration of the islands.

Stamps inscribed in English or French were issued concurrently and had equal validity throughout the islands. A common currency was reflected in the face values from 1938.

Where common designs were used the main differences between stamps inscribed in English and those in French are as follows:
(a) Inscriptions in English or French.
(b) Position of cyphers. French issues normally have "RF" to the right or above the British royal cypher.
(c) French issues are without watermark, *unless otherwise stated.*

Inscriptions in English

Inscriptions in French

I. STAMPS INSCRIBED IN ENGLISH

NEW HEBRIDES.
CONDOMINIUM.
(1)

NEW HEBRIDES
CONDOMINIUM
(2)

1908 (29 Oct). *T* **23** *and* **24** *of Fiji optd with T* **1** *by Govt Printing Establishment, Suva. On the bicoloured stamps the word "FIJI" obliterated by a bar in the colour of the word. P* 14.

(a) Wmk Multiple Crown CA
1 ½d. green and pale green, **O** (No. 115) .. 60 2·75
1*a* ½d. green, **O** (No. 118) .. 40 2·00
2 1d. red, **O** .. 80 1·90
a. Opt omitted (in vert pair with normal) .. £4750
3 1s. green and carmine, **C** .. 16·00 22·00

(b) Wmk Crown CA
4 ½d. green and grey-green .. 48·00 60·00
5 2d. dull purple and orange .. 1·50 2·50
6 2½d. dull purple and blue/*blue* .. 1·50 2·50
7 5d. dull purple and green .. 5·00 8·50
8 6d. dull purple and carmine .. 5·00 8·50
9 1s. green and carmine .. £190 £240
1/9 .. *Set of* 9 £225 £275

1910 (15 Dec). *Types as last. Wmk Multiple Crown CA. P* 14. *Optd with T* **2** *by D.L.R.*
10 ½d. green, **O** .. 3·75 7·50
11 1d. red, **O** .. 8·00 8·50
12 2d. grey, **O** .. 1·00 3·00
13 2½d. bright blue, **O** .. 1·10 3·75
14 5d. dull purple and olive-green, **C** .. 1·40 5·00
15 6d. dull and deep purple, **C** .. 3·00 5·00
16 1s. black/*green*, **C** (R.) .. 3·00 7·00
10/16 .. *Set of* 7 19·00 35·00
10/16 Optd "Specimen" .. *Set of* 7 £425

3 Weapons and Idols

1d.
(4)

(Des J. Giraud. Recess D.L.R.)

1911 (25 July). *Wmk Mult Crown CA. P* 14.
18 **3** ½d. green .. 1·10 1·60
19 1d. red .. 1·60 2·00
20 2d. grey .. 3·25 3·75
21 2½d. ultramarine .. 1·60 3·75
24 5d. sage-green .. 2·00 3·75
25 6d. purple .. 3·00 4·00
26 1s. black/*green* .. 3·50 5·50
27 2s. purple/*blue* .. 11·00 15·00
28 5s. green/*yellow* .. 25·00 45·00
18/28 .. *Set of* 9 48·00 75·00
18/28 Optd "Specimen" .. *Set of* 9 £200

1920 (June)–**21**. *Surch with T* 4 *at Govt Printing Establishment, Suva.*

(a) On Nos. 24 *and* 26/8
30 **3** 1d. on 5d. sage-green (10.3.21) .. 22·00 32·00
a. Surch inverted .. £1000
31 1d. on 1s. black/*green* .. 4·00 12·00
32 1d. on 2s. purple/*blue* .. 4·00 12·00
33 1d. on 5s. green/*yellow* .. 4·00 12·00

(b) On No. F16
34 **3** 2d. on 40 c. red/*yellow* .. 4·00 12·00

(c) On No. F27
35 **3** 2d. on 40 c. red/*yellow* .. £180 £225

1921 (Sept–Oct). *Wmk Mult Script CA. P* 14.
36 **3** 1d. scarlet .. 2·50 5·00
37 2d. slate-grey .. 5·00 12·00
39 6d. purple .. 11·00 20·00
36/9 Optd "Specimen" .. *Set of* 3 80·00

1924 (1 May). *Surch as T* 4, *at Suva.*
40 **3** 1d. on ½d. green (No. 18) .. 2·00 11·00
41 1d. on 1d. scarlet (No. 36) .. 4·00 11·00
42 5d. on 2½d. ultramarine. (No. 21) .. 8·50 15·00
a. Surch inverted .. £900

5

(Recess D.L.R.)

1925 (June). *Wmk Mult Script CA. P* 14.
43 **5** ½d. (5 c.) black .. .. 50 1·60
44 1d. (10 c.) green .. .. 90 1·50
45 2d. (20 c.) slate-grey .. .. 1·25 1·50
46 2½d. (25 c.) brown .. .. 1·25 1·75
47 5d. (50 c.) ultramarine .. .. 1·75 2·25
48 6d. (60 c.) purple .. .. 3·50 6·50
49 1s. (1.25 fr.) black/*emerald* .. .. .. 3·50 6·50
50 2s. (2.50 fr.) purple/*blue* .. .. .. 8·50 12·00
51 5s. (6.25 fr.) green/*yellow* .. .. .. 16·00 23·00
43/51 .. .. *Set of* 9 32·00 50·00
43/51 Optd "Specimen" .. .. .. *Set of* 9 £225

CURRENCY. The currency used for the face values of issues to 1977 was an artificial, rather than an actual, monetary unit. The actual currencies in use being Australian dollars and the local franc.

6 Lopevi Is and Copra Canoe

(Des J. Kerhor. Recess B.W.)

1938 (1 June). *Gold Currency. Wmk Mult Script CA. P* 12.
52 **6** 5 c. blue-green .. .. 1·50 1·40
53 10 c. orange .. .. 1·50 1·10
54 15 c. bright violet .. .. 1·50 1·50
55 20 c. scarlet .. .. 1·60 2·50
56 25 c. reddish brown .. .. 1·60 2·50
57 30 c. blue .. .. 1·90 2·50
58 40 c. grey-olive .. .. 3·00 3·00
59 50 c. purple .. .. 3·00 2·00
60 1 f. red/*green* .. .. 7·00 7·50
61 2 f. blue/*green* .. .. 18·00 18·00
62 5 f. red/*yellow* .. .. 55·00 48·00
63 10 f. violet/*blue* .. .. £130 90·00
52/63 .. .. *Set of* 12 £200 £160
52/63 Perf "Specimen" .. .. .. *Set of* 12 £275

(Recess Waterlow)

1949 (10 Oct). *75th Anniv of Universal Postal Union. As T* **21** *of Antigua, but inscribed* "NEW HEBRIDES". *Wmk Mult Script CA. P* 13½–14.
64 10 c. red-orange 40 35
65 15 c. violet 85 40
66 30 c. ultramarine .. .. 1·25 80
67 50 c. purple .. .. 1·90 1·25

7 Outrigger Sailing Canoe

(Des C. Hertenberger (1 f. to 5 f.), R. Serres (others). Recess Waterlow)

1953 (30 Apr). *T* **7** *and similar horiz designs. Wmk Mult Script CA. P* 12½.
68 5 c. green 25 8
69 10 c. scarlet 25 10
70 15 c. yellow-ochre 25 15
71 20 c. ultramarine 25 20
72 25 c. olive 25 25
73 30 c. brown 35 30
74 40 c. blackish brown 40 30
75 50 c. violet 45 30
76 1 f. orange .. .. 2·50 1·75
77 2 f. reddish purple .. .. 8·00 9·50
78 5 f. scarlet .. .. 22·00 30·00
68/78 .. .. *Set of* 11 32·00 38·00
Designs:—5 to 20 c. Type **7**; 25 to 50 c. Native carving; 1 to 5 f. Two natives outside hut.

1953 (2 June). *Coronation. As No.* 47 *of Aden.*
79 10 c. black and carmine 40 75

10 Quirós's Caravel and Map

(Photo Harrison)

1956 (20 Oct). *50th Anniv of Condominium. T* **10** *and similar horiz design. Wmk Mult Script CA. P* 14½ × 14.
80 5 c. emerald 12 5
81 10 c. scarlet 20 5
82 20 c. deep bright blue 20 15
83 50 c. deep lilac 30 30
Designs:—5, 10 c. Type **10**; 20, 50 c. "Marianne", "Talking Drum" and "Britannia".

12 Port Vila: Iririki Islet

13 River Scene and Spear Fisherman

(Des H. Cheffer (T **12**), P Gandon (others). Recess Waterlow)

1957 (3 Sept). *Wmk Mult Script CA. T* **12/13** *and similar horiz design. P* 13½.
84 **12** 5 c. green 10 8
85 10 c. scarlet 12 8
86 15 c. yellow-ochre 15 12
87 20 c. ultramarine 20 15
88 **13** 25 c. olive 20 15
89 30 c. brown 20 15
90 40 c. sepia 30 25
91 50 c. violet 30 25
92 – 1 f. orange .. .. 1·50 1·00
93 – 2 f. mauve .. .. 8·00 5·00
94 – 5 f. black .. .. 20·00 15·00
84/94 .. .. *Set of* 11 28·00 20·00
Design:—1 to 5 f. Woman drinking from coconut.

1963 (2 Sept). *Freedom from Hunger. As No.* 76 *of Aden.*
95 60 c. green .. .. 1·50 35

15 Red Cross Emblem

(Des V. Whiteley. Litho B.W.)

1963 (2 Sept). *Red Cross Centenary. W* w **12**. *P* 13½.
96 **15** 15 c. red and black 50 15
97 45 c. red and blue 90 35

16 Exporting Manganese, Forari

17 Cocoa Beans

(Des V. Whiteley, from drawings by J. White (10 c., 20 c.), K. Penny (40 c.), C. Robin (3 f.). Photo Harrison. Des C. Robin (5 c., 1 f.), J. White (15 c.), G. Vasarhelyi (25 c., 5 f.), A. Larkins, Turrell and Thomas (30 c., 50 c., 2 f.). Recess Govt Printing Works, Paris)

1963 (25 Nov)–**72**. *T* **16/17** *and similar horiz designs. W* w **12** *(10 c., 20 c., 40 c., 3 f.) or no wmk (others). P* 14 *(3 f.),* 12½ *(10 c., 20 c., 40 c.) or* 13 *(others).*
98 5 c. lake, purple-brown and greenish blue (15.8.66) 20 25
*a. Lake and greenish blue** (25.2.72) .. 35·00 35·00
99 10 c. light brown, buff & emerald (16.8.65) .. 20 10
100 15 c. yellow-bistre, red-brown & deep violet .. 20 12
101 20 c. black, olive-grn & greenish bl (16.8.65) .. 45 15
102 25 c. reddish violet, orange-brown and crimson (15.8.66) 50 45
103 30 c. chestnut, bistre and violet 75 30
104 40 c. vermilion and deep blue (16.8.65) .. 90 1·40
105 50 c. green, yellow and greenish blue 75 35
106 1 f. red, black & deep bluish green (15.8.66) .. 2·50 2·00
107 2 f. black, brown-purple & yellow-olive .. 2·75 2·25
108 3 f. deep violet, orange-brown, emerald and black (16.8.65) .. .. .. 11·00 9·00
109 5 f. blue, deep blue and black (24.1.67) .. 20·00 16·00
98/109 .. .. *Set of* 12 35·00 29·00
Designs:—15 c. Copra; 20 c. Fishing from Palikulo Point; 25 c. Picasso Fish; 30 c. Nautilus shell; 40 c. Stingfish; 50 c. Blue-lined Surgeon (fish); 1 f. Cardinal Honeyeater; 2 f. Buff-bellied Flycatcher; 3 f. Whiteman Mountain Warbler; 5 f. White-collared Kingfisher.
*In No. 98*a* the globe is printed in the same colour as the centre, instead of in purple-brown.
See also No. 129.

28 I.T.U. Emblem

(Des M. Goaman. Litho Enschedé)

1965 (17 May). *I.T.U. Centenary. W* w **12**. *P* 11 × 11½.
110 **28** 15 c. scarlet and drab 35 15
111 60 c. blue and light red .. .. .. 1·50 40

29 I.C.Y. Emblem

(Des V. Whiteley. Litho Harrison)

1965 (24 Oct). *International Co-operation Year. W* w **12**. *P* 14½.
112 **29** 5 c. reddish purple and turquoise-green 15 8
113 55 c. deep bluish green and lavender .. 80 30

MINIMUM PRICE

The minimum price quoted is 5p which represents a handling charge rather than a basis for valuing common stamps. For further notes about prices see introductory pages.

30 Sir Winston Churchill and St. Paul's Cathedral in Wartime

(Des Jennifer Toombs. Photo Harrison)

1966 (24 Jan). *Churchill Commemoration. W* w **12**. *P* 14.
114 **30** 5 c. black, cerise, gold and new blue .. 30 10
115 15 c. black, cerise, gold and deep green .. 65 15
116 25 c. black, cerise, gold and brown .. 1·10 35
117 30 c. black, cerise, gold and bluish violet 1·25 40

31 Footballer's Legs, Ball and Jules Rimet Cup

(Des V. Whiteley. Litho Harrison)

1966 (1 July). *World Cup Football Championships. W* w **12** *(sideways). P* 14.
118 **31** 20 c. violet, yellow-green, lake & yell-brn 35 10
119 40 c. chocolate, blue-grn, lake & yell-brn 75 20

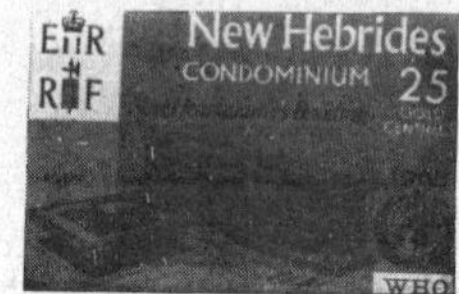

32 W.H.O. Building

(Des M. Goaman. Litho Harrison)

1966 (20 Sept). *Inauguration of W.H.O. Headquarters, Geneva. W* w **12** *(sideways). P* 14.
120 **32** 25 c. black, yellow-green and light blue .. 40 12
121 60 c. black, light purple and yellow-brown 1·00 25

33 "Education"

(Des Jennifer Toombs. Litho Harrison)

1966 (1 Dec). *20th Anniv of U.N.E.S.C.O. W* w **12** *(sideways). T* **33** *and similar horiz designs. P* 14.
122 15 c. slate-violet, red, yellow and orange .. 30 15
123 30 c. orange-yellow, violet and deep olive .. 65 35
124 45 c. black, bright purple and orange 85 45
Designs:—30 c. "Science"; 45 c. "Culture".

36 The Coast Watchers

(Des R. Granger Barrett. Photo Enschedé)

1967 (26 Sept). *25th Anniv of the Pacific War. T* **36** *and similar horiz designs. Multicoloured. W* w **12**. *P* 14 × 13.
125 15 c. Type **36** 20 15
126 25 c. Map of war zone, U.S. marine and Australian soldier 25 20
127 60 c. H.M.A.S. *Canberra* 50 35
128 1 f. "Flying Fortress" 65 75

1967 (5 Dec). *New value with W* w **12** *sideways.*
129 60 c. vermilion and deep blue (as No. 104) .. 80 70

40 Globe and Hemispheres

(Des and eng J. Combet. Recess Govt Printing Works, Paris)

1968 (23 May). *Bicentenary of Bougainville's World Voyage. T* **40** *and similar horiz designs. P* 13.
130 15 c. emerald, slate-violet and red 20 10
131 25 c. deep olive, maroon and ultramarine .. 35 15
132 60 c. bistre-brown, brown-pur & myrtle-grn .. 55 25
Designs:—25 c. Ships *La Boudeuse* and *L'Etoile*, and map; 60 c. Bougainville, ship's figure-head and bougainvillea flowers.

43 "Concorde" and Vapour Trails

45 Kauri Pine

(Des S. W. Moss (25 c.), R. Granger Barrett (60 c.). Litho D.L.R.)

1968 (9 Oct). *Anglo-French "Concorde" Project. T* **43** *and similar horiz design. W* w **12** *(sideways). P* 14.
133 25 c. lt blue, orange-red & deep violet-blue .. 1·75 90
134 60 c. red, black and bright blue .. .. 2·50 1·50
Design:—60 c. "Concorde" in flight.

(Des V. Whiteley. Litho Format)

1969 (30 June). *Timber Industry. W* w **12**. *P* 14½.
135 **45** 20 c. multicoloured (*shades*) 15 10
No. 135 was issued in small sheets of 9 (3 × 3) printed on a simulated wood-grain background and with a decorative border showing various stages of the local timber industry. There is a wide range of shades on the printing.

46 Cyphers, Flags and Relay Runner receiving Baton

48 Diver on Platform

(Des C. Haley. Photo Delrieu)

1969 (13 Aug). *Third South Pacific Games, Port Moresby. T* **46** *and similar horiz design. Multicoloured. P* 12½.
136 25 c. Type **46** 15 12
137 1 f. Cyphers, flags and relay runner passing baton 50 40

(Des V. Whiteley. Litho P.B.)

1969 (15 Oct). *Pentecost Island Land Divers. T* **48** *and similar vert designs. Multicoloured. W* w **12** *(sideways). P* 12½.
138 15 c. Type **48** 15 10
139 25 c. Diver jumping 20 20
140 1 f. Diver at end of fall 60 40

51 U.P.U. Emblem and New Headquarters Building

52 General de Gaulle

(Des and eng J. Gauthier. Recess Govt Ptg Wks, Paris)

1970 (20 May). *Inauguration of New U.P.U. Headquarters Building. P* 13.
141 **51** 1 f. 05, slate, red-orange & bright purple 55 60

(Des V. Whiteley. Photo Govt Ptg Wks, Paris)

1970 (20 July). *30th Anniv of New Hebrides' Declaration for the Free French Government. P* 13.
142 **52** 65 c. multicoloured 55 45
143 1 f. 10, multicoloured 85 65

35

(53)

54 "The Virgin and Child" (Bellini)

1970 (15 Oct). *As No. 101, but W* w **12** *(sideways) and surch with T* **53**.
144 35 c. on 20 c. black, ol-grn & greenish black .. 60 60

(Des V. Whiteley. Litho Harrison)

1970 (30 Nov). *Christmas. T* **54** *and similar vert design. Multicoloured. W* w **12** *(sideways). P* 14½ × 14.
145 15 c. Type **54** 15 10
146 50 c. "The Virgin and Child" (Cima) 30 20

1890-1970

IN MEMORIAM
9-11-70

(55)

1971 (19 Jan). *Death of General Charles de Gaulle. Nos.* 142/3 *optd with T* **55**, *vertical bars in black, inscriptions in gold.*
147 **52** 65 c. multicoloured 60 50
148 1 f. 10, multicoloured 90 75

56 Football

(Des G. Bétemps. Photo Delrieu)

1971 (13 July). *Fourth South Pacific Games, Papeete, French Polynesia. T* **56** *and similar multicoloured design. P* 12½.
149 20 c. Type **56** 20 15
150 65 c. Basketball (*vert*) 50 45

57 Kauri Pine, Cone and Arms of Royal Society

58 "The Adoration of the Shepherds" (detail, Louis le Nain)

(Des P. Powell. Litho Harrison)

1971 (7 Sept). *Royal Society Expedition to New Hebrides,* 1971. *W* w **12** *(sideways). P* 14½ × 14.
151 **57** 65 c. multicoloured 45 45

(Des G. Drummond. Litho Questa)

1971 (23 Nov). *Christmas. T* **58** *and similar vert design. Multicoloured. W* w **12**. *P* 14 × 13½.
152 25 c. Type **58** 25 25
153 50 c. "The Adoration of the Shepherds" (detail, Tintoretto) 30 30

59 "Drover" Mk III

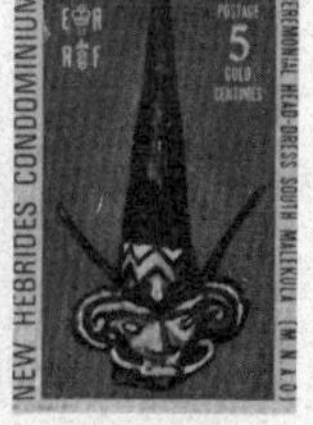

60 Ceremonial Headdress, South Malekula

(Des M. Goaman. Photo Delrieu)

1972 (29 Feb). *Aircraft. T* **59** *and similar horiz designs. Multicoloured. P* 13.
154 20 c. Type **59** 55 50
155 25 c. "Sandringham" flying-boat 70 40
156 30 c. D.H. "Dragon Rapide" 75 45
157 65 c. "Caravelle" .. .. 2·50 2·25

(Des Odette Baillais (bird designs), Pierrette Lambert (others). Photo Govt Printing Works, Paris)

1972 (24 July). *T* **60** *and similar vert designs. Multicoloured. P* 12½ × 13.
158 5 c. Type **60** 8 8
159 10 c. Baker's Pigeon 10 10
160 15 c. Gong and carving, North Ambrym 15 15
161 20 c. Red-headed Parrot Finch 25 25
162 25 c. *Cribraria fischeri* (shell) 25 25
163 30 c. *Oliva rubrolabiata* (shell) 30 30
164 35 c. Chestnut-bellied Kingfisher 40 40
165 65 c. *Strombus plicatus* (shell) 60 60
166 1 f. Gong (North Malekula) and carving (North Ambrym) .. .. 1·50 1·00
167 2 f. Palm Lorikeet .. .. 3·50 3·50
168 3 f. Ceremonial headdress, South Malekula (*different*) .. .. 4·50 5·00
169 5 f. Green snail shell .. .. 8·00 9·00
158/69 *and* 199 .. .. .. *Set of* 13 28·00 32·00

61 "Adoration of the Kings" (Spranger)

62 Royal and French Cyphers

(Des G. Drummond. Litho J.W.)

1972 (25 Sept). *Christmas. T* **61** *and similar vert design. Multicoloured. W* w **12**. *P* 14.
170 25 c. Type **61** 20 15
171 70 c. "The Virgin and Child in a Landscape" (Provoost) 35 35

(Des (from photographs by D. Groves) and photo Harrison)

1972 (20 Nov). *Royal Silver Wedding. Multicoloured; background colour given. W* w **12**. *P* 14 × 14½.
172 **62** 35 c. violet-black 30 20
173 65 c. yellow-olive 30 30

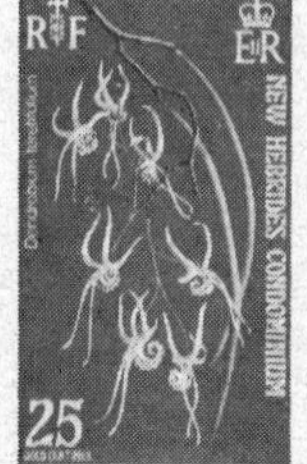

63 *Dendrobium teretifolium*

64 New Wharf at Vila

(Des Jennifer Toombs. Litho Questa)

1973 (26 Feb). *Orchids. T* **63** *and similar vert designs. Multicoloured. W* w **12** *(sideways). P* 14 × 14½.
174 25 c. Type **63** 50 20
175 30 c. *Ephemerantha comata* 60 30
176 35 c. *Spathoglottis petri* 70 35
177 65 c. *Dendrobium mohlianum* .. .. .. 1·60 1·50

(Des PAD Studio. Litho Questa)

1973 (14 May). *Opening of New Wharf at Vila. P* 14 × 14½ (25 c.) *or* 14½ × 14 (70 c.).
178 **64** 25 c. multicoloured 65 40
179 – 70 c. multicoloured .. .. .. 1·25 90
The 70 c. is as T **64**, but in a horizontal format.

65 Wild Horses

66 Mother and Child

(Des Pierrette Lambert. Photo Govt Printing Works, Paris)

1973 (13 Aug). *Tanna Island. T* **65** *and similar horiz design. Multicoloured. P* 13 × 12½.
180 35 c. Type **65** 60 35
181 70 c. Yasur Volcano .. .. 1·25 75

(Des Moutouh (35 c.), Tatin d'Avesnières (70 c.); adapted PAD Studio. Litho Questa)

1973 (19 Nov). *Christmas. T* **66** *and similar vert design. Multicoloured. W* w **12** *(sideways). P* 13½.
182 35 c. Type **66** 20 15
183 70 c. Lagoon scene 40 40

67 Pacific Pigeon

ROYAL VISIT
1974

(68)

(Des J. and H. Bregulla. Photo Govt Printing Works, Paris)

1974 (11 Feb). *Wild Life. T* **67** *and similar horiz designs. Multicoloured. P* 13 × 12½.

184 25 c. Type **67** — 95 — 55
185 35 c. Night Swallowtail (butterfly) — 1·50 — 1·25
186 70 c. Green Sea Turtle — 2·00 — 1·75
187 1 f. 15, Flying Fox — 3·25 — 2·50

1974 (11 Feb). *Royal Visit of Queen Elizabeth II. Nos.* 164 *and* 167 *optd with T* **68**.

188 35 c. Chestnut-bellied Kingfisher (R.) — 50 — 40
189 2 f. Palm Lorikeet — 2·25 — 2·00

69 Old Post Office

(Des Odette Baillais. Photo Govt Printing Works, Paris)

1974 (6 May). *Inauguration of New Post Office, Vila. T* **69** *and similar triangular design. Multicoloured. P* 12.

190 35 c. Type **69** — 35 — 40
a. *Tête-bêche* (pair). Nos. 190/1 — 1·25 — 1·60
191 70 c. New Post Office — 75 — 80

Nos. 190/1 were printed together, in *tête-bêche* pairs throughout the sheet.

70 Capt. Cook and Map

(Des J. Cooter. Litho J.W.)

1974 (1 Aug). *Bicentenary of Discovery. T* **70** *and similar horiz designs. Multicoloured. W w* **12** *(sideways on* 1 *f.* 15). *P* 11 (1 *f.* 15) *or* 13 *(others).*

192 35 c. Type **70** — 1·75 — 1·25
a. Horiz strip of 3. Nos. 192/4 — 5·00
193 35 c. William Wales and beach landing — 1·75 — 1·25
194 35 c. William Hodges and island scene — 1·75 — 1·25
195 1 f. 15, Capt Cook, map and H.M.S. *Resolution* (59 × 34 *mm*) — 4·00 — 4·00

Nos. 192/4 were printed together, *se-tenant*, in horizontal strips of 3 throughout the sheet forming a composite design.

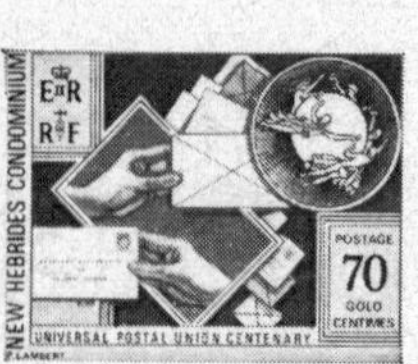

71 U.P.U. Emblem and Letters

72 "Adoration of the Magi" (Velazquez)

(Des Pierrette Lambert. Photo Govt Printing Works, Paris)

1974 (9 Oct). *Centenary of Universal Postal Union. P* 13 × 12½.

196 **71** 70 c. multicoloured — 55 — 65

(Des J. Cooter. Litho Questa)

1974 (14 Nov). *Christmas. T* **72** *and similar multicoloured design. W w* **12** *(sideways on* 70 *c.). P* 14 × 13½ (35 *c.) or* 13½ × 14 (70 *c.).*

197 35 c. Type **72** — 20 — 20
198 70 c. "The Nativity" (Gerard van Honthorst) (*horiz*) — 40 — 40

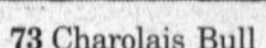

73 Charolais Bull

74 Canoeing

(Des and eng J. Pheulpin. Recess Govt Printing Works, Paris)

1975 (29 Apr). *P* 13 × 12½.

199 **73** 10 f. bistre-brown, green & dull ultram — 12·00 — 14·00

(Des J. Cooter. Litho Questa)

1975 (5 Aug). *World Scout Jamboree, Norway. T* **74** *and similar vert designs. Multicoloured. P* 13½.

200 25 c. Type **74** — 40 — 20
201 35 c. Preparing meal — 50 — 30
202 1 f. Map-reading — 1·50 — 85
203 5 f. Fishing — 8·00 — 5·50

75 "Pitti Madonna" (Michelangelo)

(Des PAD Studio. Litho Harrison)

1975 (11 Nov). *Christmas. Michelangelo's Sculptures. T* **75** *and similar vert designs. Multicoloured. W w* **12** *(sideways). P* 14½ × 14.

204 35 c. Type **75** — 25 — 20
205 70 c. "Bruges Madonna" — 45 — 40
206 2 f. 50, "Taddei Madonna" — 1·60 — 1·90

76 "Concorde"

(Des J. B. F. Chesnot. Typo Edila)

1976 (30 Jan). *First Commercial Flight of "Concorde". P* 13.

207 **76** 5 f. multicoloured — 14·00 — 7·50

77 Telephones of 1876 and 1976

78 Map of the Islands

(Des J. Gauthier. Photo Delrieu)

1976 (31 Mar). *Telephone Centenary. T* **77** *and similar vert designs. Multicoloured. P* 13½.

208 25 c. Type **77** — 35 — 25
209 70 c. Alexander Graham Bell — 85 — 75
210 1 f. 15, Satellite and Nouméa Earth Station — 1·40 — 1·10

(Des Odette Baillais. Photo Govt Printing Works, Paris)

1976 (29 June). *Constitutional Changes. T* **78** *and similar multicoloured designs. P* 13 (25 *c.) or* 13 × 12½ *(others).*

211 25 c. Type **78** — 30 — 30
212 1 f. View of Santo (36 × 26 *mm*) — 1·00 — 1·00
213 2 f. View of Vila (36 × 26 *mm*) — 1·75 — 1·75

No. 211 shows the incorrect longitude, 116°E instead of 166°E.

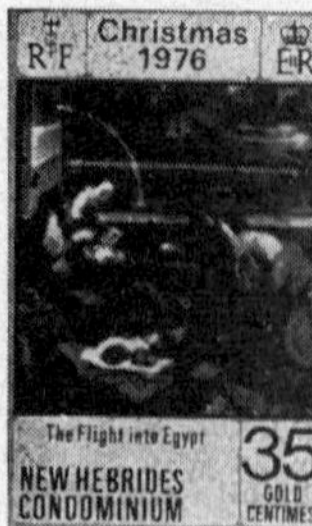

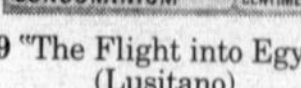

79 "The Flight into Egypt" (Lusitano)

80 Royal Visit, 1974

(Des J. Cooter. Litho Walsall)

1976 (8 Nov). *Christmas. T* **79** *and similar vert designs. Multicoloured. W w* **14**. *P* 13½.

214 35 c. Type **79** — 35 — 35
215 70 c. "Adoration of the Shepherds" — 70 — 70
216 2 f. 50, "Adoration of the Magi" — 1·75 — 1·75

Nos. 215/16 show retables by the Master of Santos-o-Novo.

(Des BG Studio. Litho Walsall)

1977 (7 Feb). *Silver Jubilee. T* **80** *and similar vert designs. Multicoloured. W w* **14**. *P* 13½.

217 35 c. Type **80** — 25 — 25
218 70 c. Imperial State Crown — 40 — 60
219 2 f. The Blessing — 85 — 1·40

(New Currency: 100 centimes=1 New Hebrides franc)

FNH (**81**) (5 f.) — FNH (**82**) (10 f., 20 f.) — FNH (**83**) (15 f.) — 25 FNH (**84**)

1977 (1 July). *Currency change. Surch by Govt. Ptg Works, Paris. Nos.* 220/3 *as T* **81/3**, *others as T* **84**.

220 5 f. on 5 c. Type **60** — 25 — 20
221 10 f. on 10 c. Baker's Pigeon — 45 — 35
222 15 f. on 15 c. Gong and carving — 55 — 50
223 20 f. on 20 c. Red-headed Parrot Finch — 70 — 55
224 25 f. on 25 c. *Cribraria fischeri* (shell) — 75 — 75
225 30 f. on 30 c. *Oliva rubrolabiata* (shell) — 85 — 75
226 35 f. on 35 c. Chestnut-bellied Kingfisher — 1·25 — 1·25
227 40 f. on 65 c. *Strombus plicatus* (shell) — 1·25 — 1·50
228 50 f. on 1 f. Gong and carving — 1·50 — 1·50
229 70 f. on 2 f. Palm Lorikeet — 2·50 — 2·50
230 100 f. on 3 f. Ceremonial headdress — 3·50 — 4·25
231 200 f. on 5 f. Green snail shell — 9·00 — 12·00
232 500 f. on 10 f. Type **73** — 22·00 — 26·00
220/32 *Set of* 13 — 40·00 — 48·00

FNH (**85**) (5 f.) — FNH (**86**) (10 f.) — FNH (**87**) (15 f.)

1977 (18 July–14 Sept). *Nos.* 158/60, 162/5 *and* 169 *surch by I.P.V., Port Vila, in typography with T* **85/7** *or similar surcharges.*

233 5 f. on 5 c. Type **60** (10.8.77) — 65 — 40
a. Surch double
234 10 f. on 10 c. Baker's Pigeon (10.7.77) — 50 — 20
235 15 f. on 15 c. Gong and carving (18.7.77) — 95 — 95
a. Short bar in surcharge (5.8.77) — 1·75 — 1·50
ab. Surch inverted
236 25 f. on 25 c. *Cribraria fischeri* (shell) (10.9.77) — 45·00 — 25·00
a. Surch "FHN" (R.5/1)
237 30 f. on 30 c. *Oliva rubrolabiata* (shell) (10.9.77) — 55·00 — 25·00
a. Surch "FHN" (R.5/1)
238 35 f. on 35 c. Chestnut-bellied Kingfisher (10.9.77) — 4·75 — 4·00
239 40 f. on 65 c. *Strombus plicatus* (shell) (12.9.77) — 4·75 — 4·00
240 200 f. on 5 f. Green snail shell (22.8.77) — 22·00 — 25·00
241 500 f. on 10 f. Type **73** (14.9.77) — 25·00 — 26·00
233/41 *Set of* 9 — £140 — £100

50 f. and 100 f. local surcharges were also prepared but these were not put on general sale, being available from the Philatelic Bureau only (*Price for set of* 2 *£50 mint, £60 used*).

Dates are those on which the various values were surcharged.

Surcharges on Nos. 236/41 are similar to Type **84**, but with new currency inscription as Type **86**.

89 Island of Erromango and Kauri Pine

90 "Tempi Madonna" (Raphael)

(Des L. Curtis. Litho J.W. (15, 30, 40 f.), Walsall (10, 35, 70, 500 f.), Questa (others))

1977 (6 Sept)–**78**. *Maps of the Islands. T* **89** *and similar vert designs. Multicoloured. W w* **14**. *P* 13 (15, 30, 40 *f.) or* 14 *(others).*

242 5 f. Type **89** — 15 — 10
243 10 f. Territory map and man splitting coconuts (9.5.78) — 25 — 20
244 15 f. Espiritu Santo and cattle (23.11.77) — 25 — 20
245 20 f. Efate and Vila P.O. — 30 — 30
246 25 f. Malekula and headdresses (23.11.77) — 35 — 40
247 30 f. Aoba, Maewo and pigs' tusks (23.11.77) — 45 — 50
248 35 f. Pentecost and land diver (9.5.78) — 50 — 60
249 40 f. Tanna and volcano (23.11.77) — 70 — 60
250 50 f. Shepherd Island and canoe — 70 — 70
251 70 f. Banks Island and dancers (9.5.78) — 1·75 — 1·40
252 100 f. Ambrym and idols — 1·75 — 1·60
253 200 f. Aneityum and baskets — 3·25 — 3·50
254 500 f. Torres Islands and archer fishing (9.5.78) — 8·00 — 9·00
242/54 *Set of* 13 — 17·00 — 17·00

(Des J.W. Litho Cartor S.A., France)

1977 (8 Dec). *Christmas. T* **90** *and similar vert designs. Multicoloured. W w* **14**. *P* 12.

255 10 f. Type **90** — 40 — 30
256 15 f. "The Flight into Egypt" (Gerard David) — 50 — 45
257 30 f. "Virgin and Child" (Batoni) — 75 — 80

OMNIBUS ISSUES

Details, together with prices for complete sets, of the various Omnibus issues from the 1935 Silver Jubilee series to date are included in a special section following Zululand at the end of the catalogue.

91 "Concorde" over New York

92 White Horse of Hanover

(Des BG Studio. Litho Rosenbaum Bros, Vienna)

1978 (9 May). *"Concorde" Commemoration. T* **91** *and similar horiz designs. Multicoloured. W w* **14** *(sideways). P* 13½.
258 10 f. Type **91** 65 65
259 20 f. "Concorde" over London 95 95
260 30 f. "Concorde" over Washington .. .. 1·25 1·25
261 40 f. "Concorde" over Paris .. .. .. 1·60 1·60

(Des Jennifer Toombs. Litho Questa)

1978 (2 June). *25th Anniv of Coronation. T* **92** *and similar vert designs. P* 15.
262 40 f. sepia, turquoise-blue and silver 80 80
a. Sheetlet. Nos. 262/4, each × 2 .. .. 4·50
263 40 f. multicoloured 80 80
264 40 f. sepia, turquoise-blue and silver 80 80
Designs:—No. 262, Type **92**. No. 263, Queen Elizabeth II; No. 264, Gallic Cock.
Nos. 262/4 were printed together in small sheets of 6, containing two *se-tenant* strips of 3 with horizontal gutter margin between.

93 "Madonna and Child"

11.1.79 FIRST ANNIVERSARY INTERNAL SELF-GOVERNMENT
10 FNH

(94)

(Des C. Abbott. Litho Questa)

1978 (1 Dec). *Christmas. Paintings by Dürer. T* **93** *and similar vert designs. Multicoloured. W w* **14**. *P* 14 × 13½.
265 10 f. Type **93** 20 20
266 15 f. "The Virgin and Child with St. Anne" .. 25 25
267 30 f. "Madonna of the Siskin" 50 50
268 40 f. "The Madonna of the Pear" 65 70

1979 (11 Jan). *1st Anniv of Internal Self-Government. As No.* 211 *surch as T* **94**.
269 **78** 10 f. on 25 c. multicoloured (blue background) 25 25
270 40 f. on 25 c. multicoloured (pale blue-green background) 85 85

95 1938 5 c. Stamp and Sir Rowland Hill

96 Chubwan Mask

(Des J.W. Litho Questa)

1979 (10 Sept). *Death Centenary of Sir Rowland Hill. T* **95** *and similar horiz designs showing stamps and Sir Rowland Hill. Multicoloured. W w* **14** *(sideways). P* 14.
271 10 f. Type **95** 20 20
272 20 f. 1969 25 c. Pentecost Island Land Divers commemorative 35 35
273 40 f. 1925 2d. (20 c.) 55 60
MS274 143 × 94 mm. No. 272 and as No. F286, but W w **14** (sideways) .. .. 1·00 1·00

(Des BG Studio. Litho Format)

1979 (16 Nov). *Festival of Arts. T* **96** *and similar vert designs. Multicoloured. W w* **14**. *P* 14.
275 5 f. Type **96** 10 10
276 10 f. Nal-Nal clubs and spears 15 15
277 20 f. Ritual puppet 30 40
278 40 f. Neqatmalow headdress 60 70

NEW INFORMATION

The editor is always interested to correspond with people who have new information that will improve or correct the Catalogue.

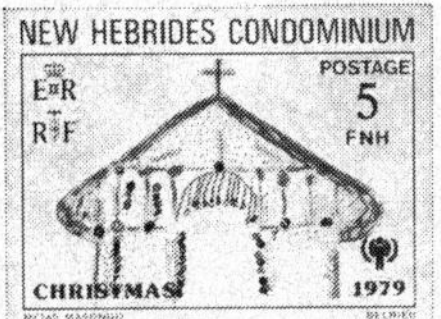

97 "Native Church" (Metas Masongo)

(Litho Delrieu)

1979 (4 Dec). *Christmas and International Year of the Child. Children's Drawings. T* **97** *and similar multicoloured designs. No wmk. P* 13.
279 5 f. Type **97** 10 10
280 10 f. "Priest and Candles" (Herve Rutu) .. 15 15
281 20 f. "Cross and Bible" (Mark Deards) (*vert*) .. 30 40
282 40 f. "Green Candle and Santa Claus" (Dev Raj) (*vert*) 60 70

98 White-bellied Honeyeater

(Des G. Drummond. Litho Walsall)

1980 (27 Feb). *Birds. T* **98** *and similar horiz designs. Multicoloured. W w* **14** *(sideways). P* 14.
283 10 f. Type **98** 35 35
284 20 f. Scarlet Robin 50 60
285 30 f. Yellow-fronted White Eye 85 85
286 40 f. Fan-tailed Cuckoo .. .. .. 1·00 1·00

POSTAGE DUE STAMPS

POSTAGE DUE (D 1)   POSTAGE DUE (D 2)   POSTAGE DUE (D 3)

1925 (June). *Optd with Type* D **1**, *by D.L.R.*
D1 **5** 1d. (10 c.) green .. .. 35·00 1·40
D2 2d. (20 c.) slate-grey .. .. .. 40·00 1·50
D3 3d. (30 c.) red .. .. 45·00 3·75
D4 5d. (50 c.) ultramarine .. .. .. 50·00 4·25
D5 10d. (1 f.) carmine/*blue* .. .. .. 55·00 5·50
D1/5 Optd "Specimen" .. .. *Set of* 5 £300

1938 (1 June). *Optd with Type* D **2**, *by B.W.*
D 6 **6** 5 c. blue-green .. .. 7·00 7·00
D 7 10 c. orange .. .. 8·00 7·50
D 8 20 c. scarlet .. .. 13·00 12·00
D 9 40 c. grey-olive .. .. 16·00 16·00
D10 1 f. red/*green* .. .. 42·00 42·00
D6/10 Perf "Specimen" .. .. *Set of* 5 £150

1953 (30 Apr). *Nos.* 68/9, 71, 74 *and* 76 *optd with Type* D **3**, *by Waterlow.*
D11 5 c. green .. .. 95 1·60
D12 10 c. scarlet .. .. 85 1·60
D13 20 c. ultramarine .. .. 1·75 3·50
D14 40 c. blackish brown .. .. 6·00 10·00
D15 1 f. orange .. .. 7·50 13·00

1957 (3 Sept). *Nos.* 84/5, 87, 90 *and* 92 *optd with Type* D **3**, *by Waterlow.*
D16 **12** 5 c. green 30 65
D17 10 c. scarlet 30 65
D18 20 c. ultramarine .. .. 1·25 1·50
D19 **13** 40 c. sepia .. .. 3·00 3·50
D20 – 1 f. orange .. .. 5·25 7·00

II. STAMPS INSCRIBED IN FRENCH

NOUVELLES HEBRIDES (F 1)   NOUVELLES-HEBRIDES (F 2)

1908 (21 Nov). *T* **15/17** *of New Caledonia optd with Types* F **1** *or* F **2** *(1 f.), by Govt Ptg Wks, Paris.*
F1 5 c. green .. .. 1·00 1·00
F2 10 c. carmine .. .. 1·25 1·25
F3 25 c. blue/*greenish* (R.) .. .. .. 1·60 1·60
F4 50 c. red/*orange* .. .. 2·25 2·25
F5 1 f. blue/*green* (R.) .. .. 5·00 5·00

CONDOMINIUM (F 3)   10c. (F 4)

1910 (Sept)–**11**. *Nos. F1/5 further optd with Type* F **3**, *or larger (1 f.), by Govt Ptg Wks, Paris.*
F 6 5 c. green 35 35
F 7 10 c. carmine 40 40
F 8 25 c. blue/*greenish* (R.) (1911) .. .. 80 1·00
F 9 50 c. red/*orange* (1911) .. .. .. 1·60 1·75
F10 1 f. blue/*green* (R.) .. .. 5·00 6·00
All the above were released in Paris on 16 March 1910. The 5 c., 10 c. and 1 f. were issued in New Hebrides in September but the 25 c. and 50 c. were not received until 1911 after the issue of the definitive stamps and they were placed in reserve, although some may have been issued on request.

1911 (12 July). *Wmk Mult Crown CA. P* 14.
F11 **3** 5 c. green 40 45
F12 10 c. carmine 35 45
F13 20 c. greyish slate 95 85
F14 25 c. ultramarine .. .. 1·60 1·60
F15 30 c. brown/*yellow* .. .. 1·60 1·60
F16 40 c. red/*yellow* .. .. 1·40 1·60
F17 **3** 50 c. sage-green .. .. 1·75 1·60
F18 75 c. orange .. .. 3·00 3·50
F19 1 f. red/*blue* .. .. 1·60 1·75
F20 2 f. violet .. .. 4·25 4·75
F21 5 f. red/*green* .. .. 7·00 9·50
F11/21 .. .. *Set of* 11 21·00 25·00

1913. *As last but wmk "R F" in sheet or without wmk.*
F22 **3** 5 c. green 75 85
F23 10 c. carmine 75 80
F24 20 c. greyish slate .. .. 1·00 1·25
F25 25 c. ultramarine .. .. 90 1·25
F26 30 c. brown/*yellow* .. .. 1·25 1·75
F27 40 c. red/*yellow* .. .. 8·50 9·00
F28 50 c. sage-green .. .. 5·50 6·00
F29 75 c. orange .. .. 5·50 7·50
F30 1 f. red/*blue* .. .. 3·00 3·25
F31 2 f. violet .. .. 5·00 6·50
F32 5 f. red/*green* .. .. 8·50 10·00
F22/32 .. .. *Set of* 11 35·00 42·00
The above were placed on sale in Paris on 29 April 1912.

1920–21. *Surch as Type* F **4**, *at Govt Printing Establishment, Suva, Fiji. (a) On stamps of* 1908–11 *(June* 1920*).*
F32*a* 5 c. on 50 c. red/*orange* (F4) £350 £350
F33 5 c. on 50 c. red/*orange* (F9) .. .. 1·25 1·60
F33*a* 10 c. on 25 c. blue/*greenish* (F8) 30 50

(*b*) *On stamps of* 1911–13 *(10.3.21)*
F34 **3** 5 c. on 40 c. red/*yellow* (F27) .. .. 16·00 20·00
F35 20 c. on 30 c. brown/*yellow* (F15) .. 5·50 7·50
F36 20 c. on 30 c. brown/*yellow* (F26) .. 8·50 13·00

(*c*) *On Inscr in English (10.3.21)*
F37 **3** 10 c. on 5d. sage-green (24) .. .. 5·50 7·50

1924 (1 May). *Stamps of* 1911–13 *surch as Type* F **4**, *at Suva.*
F38 **3** 10 c. on 5 c. green (F22) 40 60
F39 30 c. on 10 c. carmine (F23) 40 45
F40 50 c. on 25 c. ultramarine (F14) .. .. 8·00 11·00
F41 50 c. on 25 c. ultramarine (F25) .. .. 1·50 2·25

F 5

France Libre (F 6)

(Recess D.L.R.)

1925 (June). *Wmk "R F" in sheet or without wmk. P* 14.
F42 **F 5** 5 c. (½d.) black 50 70
F43 10 c. (1d.) green 35 35
F44 20 c. (2d.) greyish slate 35 35
F45 25 c. (2½d.) brown 35 35
F46 30 c. (3d.) red 35 35
F47 40 c. (4d.) red/*yellow* 55 65
F48 50 c. (5d.) ultramarine 60 80
F49 75 c. (7½d.) yellow-brown .. .. .. 85 1·40
F50 1 f. (10d.) carmine/*blue* .. .. .. 1·75 2·00
F51 2 f. (1/8) violet .. .. 2·50 3·25
F52 5 f. (4s.) carmine/*green* .. .. .. 4·50 6·00
F42/52 .. .. *Set of* 11 11·50 14·50
F42/52 Optd "Specimen" .. .. *Set of* 11 £250
In July 1929 a batch of mail was carried by aircraft from Port Vila to the French cruiser *Tourville* for sorting and forwarding at Nouméa, New Caledonia. Stamps of the above issue (including those with English inscriptions) were affixed to covers and handstamped "PAR AVION" before cancellation.

1938 (1 June). *Gold Currency. Wmk "R F" in sheet or without wmk. P* 12.
F53 **6** 5 c. blue-green 55 75
F54 10 c. orange 55 55
F55 15 c. bright violet 55 75
F56 20 c. scarlet 55 75
F57 25 c. reddish brown 85 95
F58 30 c. blue 70 80
F59 40 c. grey-olive .. .. 75 1·25
F60 50 c. purple 75 85
F61 1 f. lake/*pale green* (*shades*) .. .. 1·50 2·00
F62 2 f. blue/*pale green* (*shades*) .. .. 4·75 6·50
F63 5 f. red/*yellow* .. .. 12·00 15·00
F64 10 f. violet/*blue* .. .. 32·00 38·00
F53/64 .. .. *Set of* 12 50·00 60·00
F53/64 Optd "Specimen" .. .. *Set of* 12 £275

1941 (15 Apr). *Adherence to General de Gaulle. Optd with Type* F **6**, *at Nouméa, New Caledonia.*
F65 **6** 5 c. blue-green .. .. 3·75 4·00
F66 10 c. orange .. .. 3·75 4·00
F67 15 c. bright violet .. .. 4·25 4·75
F68 20 c. scarlet .. .. 4·50 5·00
F69 25 c. reddish brown .. .. 5·00 5·00
F70 30 c. blue .. .. 5·00 5·00
F71 40 c. grey-olive .. .. 5·00 5·00
F72 50 c. purple .. .. 5·00 5·00
F73 1 f. lake/*pale green* .. .. .. 7·00 7·50
F74 2 f. blue/*pale green* .. .. .. 7·50 8·00
F75 5 f. red/*yellow* .. .. 9·00 10·00
F76 10 f. violet/*blue* .. .. 12·00 13·00
F65/76 .. .. *Set of* 12 65·00 70·00

1949 (10 Oct). *75th Anniv of U.P.U. As Nos.* 64/7. *Wmk "R F" in sheet or without wmk. P* 13½.
F77 10 c. red-orange 60 50
F78 15 c. violet 90 80
F79 30 c. ultramarine .. .. 1·40 1·25
F80 50 c. purple .. .. 1·90 1·60

1953 (30 Apr). *As Nos.* 68/78. *Wmk "R F" in sheet or without wmk. P* 12½.
F81 **7** 5 c. green 5 5
F82 10 c. scarlet 12 12
F83 15 c. yellow-ochre 15 15
F84 20 c. ultramarine 30 30
F85 – 25 c. olive 30 30
F86 – 30 c. brown 55 55
F87 – 40 c. blackish brown 55 55
F88 – 50 c. violet 55 55
F89 – 1 f. orange .. .. 3·00 2·25

F90 – 2 f. reddish purple .. .. .. 10·00 11·00
F91 – 5 f. scarlet .. .. .. 24·00 28·00
F81/91 .. .. *Set of* 11 35·00 40·00

1956 (20 Oct). *Fiftieth Anniv of Condominium. As Nos.* 80/3. *Wmk "R F" in sheet or without wmk. P* 14½ × 14.
F92 **10** 5 c. emerald 45 45
F93 10 c. scarlet 45 45
F94 – 20 c. deep bright blue 65 65
F95 – 50 c. deep lilac .. .. .. 1·75 1·75

1957 (3 Sept). *As Nos.* 84/94. *Wmk "R F" in sheet or without wmk. P* 13½.
F 96 **12** 5 c. green 20 15
F 97 10 c. scarlet 25 15
F 98 15 c. orange-yellow 40 35
F 99 20 c. ultramarine 40 35
F100 **13** 25 c. yellow-olive 45 35
F101 30 c. brown 70 60
F102 40 c. sepia 70 60
F103 50 c. reddish violet 70 65
F104 – 1 f. red-orange .. .. .. 3·00 1·75
F105 – 2 f. mauve .. .. .. 9·00 8·50
F106 – 5 f. black .. .. .. 23·00 19·00
F96/106 .. .. *Set of* 11 35·00 29·00

F 7 Emblem and Globe **F 8** Centenary Emblem

(Des and eng J. Derrey. Recess Govt Ptg Wks, Paris)

1963 (2 Sept). *Freedom from Hunger. P* 13.
F107 **F 7** 60 c. deep bluish green and chestnut .. 4·00 2·75

(Des and eng J. Combet. Recess Govt Ptg Wks, Paris)

1963 (2 Sept). *Red Cross Centenary. P* 13.
F108 **F 8** 15 c. red, grey and orange .. .. 2·00 1·00
F109 45 c. red, grey and yellow-bistre .. 3·75 3·25

1963 (25 Nov)–**72**. *As Nos.* 98/109 *and* 129. *No wmk. P* 12½ (10, 20, 40, 60 *c.*), 14 (3 *f.*) *or* 13 (*others*).
F110 5 c. lake, purple-brown and greenish blue (15.8.66) 40 30
a. *Lake and greenish blue* (25.2.72) .. 35·00 35·00
F111 10 c. lt brown, buff & emerald* (16.8.65) .. 80 80
F112 10 c. lt brown, buff and emerald (5.8.68) .. 30 15
F113 15 c. yellow-bistre, red-brown & dp violet .. 45 25
F114 20 c. black, ol-green & grnsh bl* (16.8.65) .. 2·25 2·25
F115 20 c. black, ol-green & grnsh bl (5.8.68) .. 60 25
F116 25 c. reddish violet, orange-brown and crimson (15.8.66) 60 40
F117 30 c. chestnut, bistre and violet 90 50
F118 40 c. vermilion and deep blue* (16.8.65) .. 3·50 3·50
F119 50 c. green, yellow and greenish blue .. 1·00 60
F120 60 c. vermilion and deep blue (5.12.67) .. 1·50 80
F121 1 f. red, black & dp bluish grn (15.8.66) .. 2·00 1·25
F122 2 f. black, brown-purple & yellow-olive .. 5·00 3·75
F123 3 f. multicoloured* (16.8.65) .. .. 11·00 11·00
F124 3 f. multicoloured (5.8.68) .. .. 5·00 5·00
F125 5 f. blue, deep blue and black (24.1.67) .. 11·00 12·00
F110/25 .. .. *Set of* 16 42·00 38·00

*Normally all French New Hebrides issues have the "RF" inscription on the right to distinguish them from the British New Hebrides stamps which have it on the left. The stamps indicated by an asterisk have "RF" wrongly placed on the left.

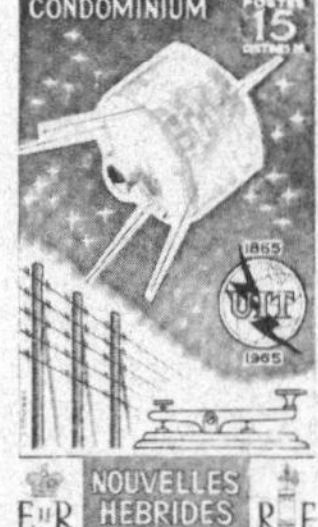

F 9 "Syncom" Communications Satellite, Telegraph Poles and Morse Key

(Des and eng J. Combet. Recess Govt Ptg Wks, Paris)

1965 (17 May). *Air. I.T.U. Centenary. P* 13.
F126 **F 9** 15 c. blue, emerald and red-brown .. 3·00 1·25
F127 60 c. cerise, slate and deep bluish green 6·50 5·00

1965 (24 Oct). *International Co-operation Year. As Nos.* 112/13. *P* 14½.
F128 **29** 5 c. dp reddish purple & turquoise-grn 30 15
F129 55 c. deep bluish green and lavender .. 1·60 90

1966 (24 Jan). *Churchill Commemoration. As Nos.* 114/17. *P* 14.
F130 **30** 5 c. black, cerise, gold and new blue .. 55 20
F131 15 c. black, cerise, gold and deep green .. 1·25 30
F132 25 c. black, cerise, gold and brown .. 1·75 70
F133 30 c. black, cerise, gold and bluish violet 2·00 75

1966 (1 July). *World Cup Football Championships. As Nos.* 118/19. *P* 14.
F134 **31** 20 c. violet, yellow-grn, lake & yell-brn .. 55 30
F135 40 c. chocolate, bl-grn, lake & yell-brn .. 85 60

1966 (20 Sept). *Inauguration of W.H.O. Headquarters, Geneva. As Nos.* 120/1. *P* 14.
F136 **32** 25 c. black, yellow-green and light blue 1·00 45
F137 60 c. black, mauve and yellow-ochre .. 2·25 75

1966 (1 Dec). *20th Anniv of U.N.E.S.C.O. As Nos.* 122/4. *P* 14.
F138 **33** 15 c. slate-violet, red, yellow and orange 75 25
F139 – 30 c. orange-yellow, violet & dp olive .. 1·25 70
F140 – 45 c. black, bright purple and orange .. 1·75 1·00

1967 (26 Sept). *25th Anniv of the Pacific War. As Nos.* 125/8. *P* 14 × 13.
F141 15 c. Type **36** 30 25
F142 25 c. War Zone map, U.S. marine and Australian soldier 55 40
F143 60 c. H.M.A.S. *Canberra* 95 85
F144 1 f. "Flying Fortress" .. .. .. 1·50 1·40

1968 (23 May). *Bicentenary of Bougainville's World Voyage. As Nos.* 130/2. *P* 13.
F145 **40** 15 c. emerald, slate-violet and red .. 20 20
F146 – 25 c. dp olive, maroon & ultramarine .. 40 40
F147 – 60 c. bistre-brn, brn-pur & myrtle-grn .. 90 90

1968 (9 Oct). *Anglo-French "Concorde" Project. As Nos.* 133/4. *P* 14.
F148 **43** 25 c. lt blue, orange-red & dp violet-bl .. 1·75 1·25
F149 – 60 c. red, black and bright blue .. .. 3·00 2·50

1969 (30 June). *Timber Industry. As No.* 135. *P* 14½.
F150 **45** 20 c. multicoloured (*shades*) 20 20

1969 (13 Aug). *3rd South Pacific Games, Port Moresby, Papua New Guinea. As Nos.* 136/7. *Multicoloured. P* 12½.
F151 25 c. Type **46** 25 25
F152 1 f. Runner passing baton, and flags .. 1·25 85

1969 (15 Oct). *Pentecost Island Land Divers. As Nos.* 138/40. *Multicoloured. P* 12½.
F153 15 c. Type **48** 30 30
F154 25 c. Diver jumping 40 40
F155 1 f. Diver at end of fall .. .. 1·40 1·40

1970 (20 May). *Inauguration of New U.P.U. Headquarters Building, Berne. As No.* 141. *P* 13.
F156 **51** 1 f. 05, slate, red-orange & brt purple .. 70 70

1970 (20 July). *30th Anniv of New Hebrides' Declaration for the Free French Government. As Nos.* 142/3. *P* 13.
F157 **52** 65 c. multicoloured 55 55
F158 1 f. 10, multicoloured .. .. .. 1·10 1·10

1970 (15 Oct). *No.* F115 *surch with T* **53**.
F159 35 c. on 20 c. black, ol-green & greenish blue 60 50

1970 (30 Nov). *Christmas. As Nos.* 145/6. *Multicoloured. P* 14½ × 14.
F160 15 c. Type **54** 15 12
F161 50 c. "The Virgin and Child" (G. Cima) .. 45 40

1971 (19 Jan). *Death of General Charles de Gaulle. Nos.* F157/8 *optd with T* **55**, *the vertical bars in black and inscriptions in gold.*
F162 **52** 65 c. multicoloured 75 55
a. Gold opt omitted .. ..
F163 1 f. 10, multicoloured .. .. .. 1·50 1·25
On No. F162a the vertical black bars are still present.

1971 (13 July). *4th South Pacific Games, Papeete, French Polynesia. As Nos.* 149/50. *Multicoloured. P* 12½.
F164 20 c. Type **56** 35 20
F165 65 c. Basketball (*vert*) 95 60

1971 (7 Sept). *Royal Society's Expedition to New Hebrides. As No.* 151. *P* 14½ × 14.
F166 **57** 65 c. multicoloured 50 50

1971 (23 Nov). *Christmas. As Nos.* 152/3. *Multicoloured. P* 14 × 13½.
F167 25 c. Type **58** 30 30
F168 50 c. "Adoration of the Shepherds" (J. Tintoretto) 45 45

1972 (29 Feb). *Aircraft. As Nos.* 154/7. *Multicoloured. P* 13.
F169 20 c. Type **59** 70 55
F170 25 c. "Sandringham" flying-boat 80 60
F171 30 c. DH "Dragon Rapide" 85 70
F172 65 c. "Caravelle" .. .. .. 2·75 2·75

1972 (24 July). *As Nos.* 158/69. *Multicoloured. P* 12½ × 13.
F173 5 c. Type **60** 10 8
F174 10 c. Baker's Pigeon 35 12
F175 15 c. Gong and carving, North Ambrym .. 20 15
F176 20 c. Red-headed Parrot Finch 50 25
F177 25 c. *Cribraria fischeri* (shell) 60 30
F178 30 c. *Oliva rubrolabiata* (shell) 60 30
F179 35 c. Chestnut-bellied Kingfisher 75 40
F180 65 c. *Strombus plicatus* (shell) 90 60
F181 1 f. Gong, North Malekula and carving, North Ambrym .. .. .. 1·50 1·50
F182 2 f. Palm Lorikeet .. .. .. 4·50 4·50
F183 3 f. Ceremonial headdress, South Malekula (*different*) .. .. .. 5·00 5·00
F184 5 f. Green snail shell .. .. .. 10·00 11·00
F173/84 *and* F213 .. .. *Set of* 13 38·00 38·00

1972 (25 Sept). *Christmas. As Nos.* 170/1. *Multicoloured. P* 14.
F185 25 c. Type **61** 40 25
F186 70 c. "Virgin and Child" (Provoost) 85 60

1972 (20 Nov). *Royal Silver Wedding. As Nos.* 172/3. *W w* **12**. *P* 14 × 14½.
F187 **62** 35 c. multicoloured 50 30
F188 65 c. multicoloured 75 45

1973 (26 Feb). *Orchids. As Nos.* 174/7. *Multicoloured. P* 14 × 14½.
F189 25 c. Type **63** 60 30
F190 30 c. *Ephemerantha comata* 65 40
F191 35 c. *Spathoglottis petri* 75 45
F192 65 c. *Dendrobium mohlianum* .. .. 2·50 2·25

1973 (14 May). *Opening of New Wharf, Vila. As Nos.* 178/9. *Multicoloured. P* 14 × 14½ (25 *c.*) *or* 14½ × 14 (70 *c.*).
F193 25 c. Type **64** 75 40
F194 70 c. View of wharf (*horiz*) .. .. 1·50 1·25

1973 (13 Aug). *Tanna Island. As Nos.* 180/1. *Multicoloured. P* 13 × 12½.
F195 35 c. Type **65** 90 65
F196 70 c. Yasur Volcano .. .. .. 1·75 1·25

1973 (19 Nov). *Christmas. As Nos.* 182/3. *Multicoloured. P* 14 × 13½.
F197 35 c. Type **66** 40 30
F198 70 c. Lagoon scene 85 65

1974 (11 Feb). *Wild Life. As Nos.* 184/7. *Multicoloured. P* 13 × 12½.
F199 25 c. Type **67** .. .. .. 1·25 60
F200 35 c. Night Swallowtail (butterfly) .. .. 1·90 1·10
F201 70 c. Green sea turtle .. .. .. 2·75 2·50
F202 1 f. 15, Flying fox .. .. .. 4·00 4·00

VISITE ROYALE
1974
(F 10)

1974 (11 Feb). *Royal Visit of Queen Elizabeth II. Nos.* F179 *and* F182 *optd with Type* F **10**.
F203 35 c. Chestnut-bellied Kingfisher (R.) .. 50 50
F204 2 f. Palm Lorikeet .. .. .. 3·25 3·75

1974 (6 May). *Inauguration of New Post Office, Vila. As Nos.* 190/1. *Multicoloured. P* 12.
F205 35 c. Type **69** 50 65
a. *Tête-bêche* (pair). Nos. F205/6 .. .. 1·10 1·50
F206 70 c. New Post Office 60 85

1974 (1 Aug). *Bicentenary of Discovery. As Nos.* 192/5. *Multicoloured. P* 11 (1 *f.* 15) *or* 13 × 13½ (*others*).
F207 35 c. Type **70** .. .. .. 2·25 1·75
a. Horiz strip of 3. Nos. F207/9 .. .. 6·50
F208 35 c. William Wales and beach landing .. 2·25 1·75
F209 35 c. William Hodges and island scene .. 2·25 1·75
F210 1 f. 15, Capt. Cook, *Resolution* and map of islands (64 × 39 *mm*) .. .. 5·50 6·00

1974 (9 Oct). *Centenary of Universal Postal Union. As No.* 196. *P* 13 × 12½.
F210a **71** 70 c. dp turquoise-blue, rosine & black 75 75

1974 (4 Nov). *Christmas. As Nos.* 197/8. *Multicoloured. P* 14 × 13½ (35 *c.*) *or* 13½ × 14 (70 *c.*).
F211 35 c. Type **72** 35 25
F212 70 c. "The Nativity" (G. van Honthorst) (*horiz*) 80 60

1975 (29 Apr). *As No.* 199. *P* 13 × 12½.
F213 **73** 10 f. bistre-brown, yellow-green & blue 14·00 17·00

1975 (5 Aug). *World Scout Jamboree, Norway. As Nos.* 200/3. *Multicoloured. P* 14 × 13½.
F214 25 c. Type **74** 55 20
F215 35 c. Preparing meal 75 30
F216 1 f. Map-reading .. .. .. 1·90 85
F217 5 f. Fishing .. .. .. 10·00 7·50

1975 (11 Nov). *Christmas. As Nos.* 204/6. *Multicoloured. P* 14½ × 14.
F218 35 c. Type **75** 30 30
F219 70 c. "Bruges Madonna" 60 60
F220 2 f. 50, "Taddei Madonna" .. .. 3·00 3·00

1976 (30 Jan). *First Commercial Flight of "Concorde". As No.* 207. *P* 13.
F221 **76** 5 f. multicoloured .. .. .. 14·00 8·50

1976 (31 Mar). *Telephone Centenary. As Nos.* 208/10. *Multicoloured. P* 13½.
F222 25 c. Type **77** 45 25
F223 70 c. Alexander Graham Bell .. .. 1·00 75
F224 1 f. 15, Satellite and Earth Station, Nouméa 1·60 1·40

1976 (29 June). *Constitutional Changes. As Nos.* 211/13. *Multicoloured. P* 13 (25 *c.*) *or* 13 × 12½ (*others*).
F225 25 c. Type **78** 50 30
F226 1 f. Luganville (36 × 26 *mm*) .. .. 1·50 1·00
F227 2 f. Vila (36 × 26 *mm*) .. .. .. 2·50 1·90
No. F225 shows the incorrect longitude, 116°E, instead of 166°E.
Nos. F226/7 exist with the inscription "PREMIERE ASSEMBLEE REPRESENTATIVE 1975" and the name of the city. These stamps were not available in the New Hebrides.

1976 (8 Nov). *Christmas. As Nos.* 214/16. *Multicoloured. P* 13½.
F228 35 c. Type **79** 35 35
F229 70 c. "Adoration of the Shepherds" 70 70
F230 2 f. 50, "Adoration of the Magi" .. .. 3·00 3·00

1977 (7 Feb). *Silver Jubilee. As Nos.* 217/19. *Multicoloured. P* 13½.
F231 35 c. Type **80** 35 20
F232 70 c. Imperial State Crown 60 35
F233 2 f. The Blessing .. .. .. 1·00 85

1977 (1 July). *Currency Change. Nos.* F173/84 *and* F214 *surch as T* **81/3** (*Nos.* F234/7) *or as T* **84** (*others*) *by Govt Ptg Wks, Paris.*
F234 5 f. on 5 c. Type **60** 25 20
F235 10 f. on 10 c. Baker's Pigeon 40 35
F236 15 f. on 15 c. Gong and carving, North Ambrym 50 45
F237 20 f. on 20 c. Red-headed Parrot Finch .. 80 65
F238 25 f. on 25 c. *Cribraria fischeri* (shell) .. 95 80
F239 30 f. on 30 c. *Oliva rubrolablata* (shell) .. 1·25 1·00
F240 35 f. on 35 c. Chestnut-bellied Kingfisher .. 1·60 1·25
F241 40 f. on 65 c. *Strombus plicatus* (shell) .. 1·75 1·50
F242 50 f. on 1 f. Gong, North Malekula, and carving, North Ambrym .. .. 1·75 1·75
F243 70 f. on 2 f. Palm Lorikeet .. .. 3·25 2·50
F244 100 f. on 3 f. Ceremonial headdress, South Malekula .. .. .. 4·00 4·25
F245 200 f. on 5 f. Green snail shell .. .. 11·00 12·00
F246 500 f. on 10 f. Type **73** .. .. 24·00 25·00
F234/46 .. .. *Set of* 13 45·00 48·00

1977 (18 July–14 Sept). *Nos.* F173/175, F177/180, F184 *and* F213 *surch by I.P.V., Port Vila, in typography with T* **85/7** *or similar surcharges.*
F247 5 f. on 5 c. Type **60** (10.8.77) .. .. 1·00 80
F248 10 f. on 10 c. Baker's Pigeon (20.7.77) .. 75 30
F249 15 f. on 15 c. Gong and carving (18.7.77) .. 1·25 95
a. Short bar in surcharge (5.8.77) .. 2·25 2·25
F250 25 f. on 25 c. *Cribraria fischeri* (shell) (10.9.77) .. .. 90·00 48·00
a. "FHN" for "FNH" (R.5/1) .. ..
F251 30 f. on 30 c. *Oliva rubrolabiata* (shell) (10.9.77) .. .. 90·00 45·00
a. "FHN" for "FNH" (R.5/1) .. ..
F252 35 f. on 35 c. Chestnut-bellied Kingfisher (10.9.77) .. .. 5·50 4·25
a. "NH" for "FNH" (R.4/2) .. ..
F253 40 f. on 65 c. *Strombus plicatus* (shell) (12.9.77) .. .. 6·00 4·50
F254 200 f. on 5 f. Green snail shell (22.8.77) .. 28·00 30·00
F255 500 f. on 10 f. Type **73** (14.9.77) .. .. 38·00 38·00
F247/55 .. .. *Set of* 9 £250 £150

Dates are those on which the various values were surcharged.

50 f., 70 f. and 100 f. local surcharges were also prepared, but were not put on general sale, being available from the Philatelic Bureau only.

1977 (7 Sept)–**78**. *Maps of the Islands. As Nos.* 242/54. *Multicoloured. P* 13 (10 *f.*, 30 *f.*, 40 *f.*) *or* 14 (*others*).
F256 5 f. Type **89** 15 10
F257 10 f. Territory map and man splitting coconuts (9.5.78) 25 20
F258 15 f. Espiritu Santo and cattle (23.11.77) .. 30 20
F259 20 f. Efate and Vila Post Office 45 30
F260 25 f. Malekula and headdresses (23.11.77) 60 40
F261 30 f. Aoba, Maewo and pigs' tusks (23.11.77) 70 45
F262 35 f. Pentecost and land diver (9.5.78) .. 85 60
F263 40 f. Tanna and volcano (23.11.77).. .. 1·25 75
F264 50 f. Shepherd Island and canoe .. .. 1·25 75
F265 70 f. Banks Island and dancers (9.5.78) .. 2·00 1·50
F266 100 f. Ambrym and idols .. .. .. 2·25 2·25
F267 200 f. Aneityum and baskets .. .. 4·50 5·00
F268 500 f. Torres Islands and archer fishing (9.5.78) .. .. 11·00 12·00
F256/68 .. .. *Set of* 13 23·00 22·00

1977 (8 Dec). *Christmas. As Nos.* 255/7. *Multicoloured. P* 12.
F269 10 f. Type **90**.. .. .. .. 30 30
F270 15 f. "The Flight into Egypt" (G. David) .. 50 50
F271 30 f. "Virgin and Child" (Pompeo Batoni) .. 1·10 90

1978 (9 May). *"Concorde". As Nos.* 258/61. *Multicoloured. P* 13½.
F272 10 f. Type **91**.. .. .. .. 75 65
F273 20 f. "Concorde" over London .. .. 1·10 95
F274 30 f. "Concorde" over Washington .. .. 1·60 1·25
F275 40 f. "Concorde" over Paris .. .. .. 1·90 1·60

1978 (2 June). *25th Anniv of Coronation. As Nos.* 262/4. *P* 15.
F276 **92** 40 f. sepia, turquoise-blue and silver .. 85 90
a. Sheetlet. Nos. F276/8 × 2 .. .. 4·75
F277 – 40 f. multicoloured 85 90
F278 – 40 f. sepia, turquoise-blue and silver .. 85 90

Nos. F276/278 were printed together in small sheets of 6, containing two *se-tenant* strips of 3, with horizontal gutter margin between.

1978 (1 Dec). *Christmas. As Nos.* 265/8. *Multicoloured. P* 14 × 13½.
F279 10 f. Type **93** 25 25
F280 15 f. "The Virgin and Child with St. Anne" .. 35 35
F281 30 f. "The Madonna with the Goldfinch" .. 60 70
F282 40 f. "The Madonna with the Child".. .. 70 80

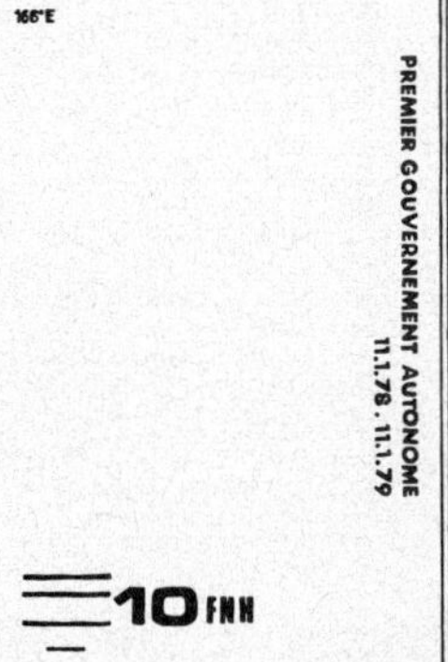

(F 11)

1979 (11 Jan). *1st Anniv of Internal Self-Government. As No.* F225 *surch as Type* **F 11**.
F283 **78** 10 f. on 25 c. multicoloured (blue background) 45 30
F284 40 f. on 25 c. multicoloured (pale blue-green background) .. .. .. 1·40 1·25

1979 (10 Sept). *Death Centenary of Sir Rowland Hill. As Nos.* 271/3. *Multicoloured. P* 14.
F285 10 f. Type **95**.. .. .. .. 35 35
F286 20 f. 1969 Land Divers 25 c. commemorative 55 55
F287 40 f. 1925 20 c. (2d.).. .. .. 75 75

For miniature sheet containing No. F286, see No. **MS**274.

1979 (16 Nov). *Festival of Arts. As Nos.* 275/8. *Multicoloured. P* 14.
F288 5 f. Type **96**.. .. .. .. 15 10
F289 10 f. Nal-Nal clubs and spears 25 12
F290 20 f. Ritual puppet 50 30
F291 40 f. Neqatmalow headdress 85 90

1979 (4 Dec). *Christmas and International Year of the Child. As Nos.* 279/82. *Multicoloured. P* 13.
F292 5 f. Type **97**.. .. .. .. 10 10
F293 10 f. "Priest and Candles" (Herve Rutu) .. 20 12
F294 20 f. "Cross and Bible" (Mark Deards) (*vert*). 40 30
F295 40 f. "Green Candle and Santa Claus" (Dev Raj) (*vert*) 75 60

1980 (27 Feb). *Birds. As Nos.* 283/6. *Multicoloured. P* 14.
F296 10 f. Type **98**.. .. .. .. 60 35
F297 20 f. Scarlet Robin 95 65
F298 30 f. Yellow-fronted White Eye .. .. 1·25 1·00
F299 40 f. Fan-tailed Cuckoo .. .. .. 1·60 1·60

POSTAGE DUE STAMPS

CHIFFRE TAXE	CHIFFRE TAXE	TIMBRE-TAXE
(FD 1)	(FD 2)	(FD 3)

1925 (June). *Optd with Type* FD **1**, *by D.L.R.*
FD53 F **5** 10 c. (1d.) green .. .. .. 22·00 1·90
FD54 20 c. (2d.) greyish slate .. .. 22·00 1·90
FD55 30 c. (3d.) red .. .. .. 22·00 1·90
FD56 50 c. (5d.) ultramarine .. .. 22·00 1·90
FD57 1 f. (10d.) carmine/*blue* .. .. 22·00 1·90
FD53/7 Optd "Specimen" .. .. *Set of* 5 £200

Although on sale in Paris, the Postmaster would not issue any in unused condition for about a year and most copies are cancelled-to-order.

1938 (1 June). *Optd with Type* FD **2**, *by Bradbury, Wilkinson.*
FD65 **6** 5 c. blue-green.. .. .. 4·50 4·75
FD66 10 c. orange .. .. .. 4·50 4·75
FD67 20 c. scarlet .. .. .. 7·00 7·50
FD68 40 c. grey-olive .. .. .. 14·00 15·00
FD69 1 f. lake/*pale green* .. .. 28·00 32·00
FD65/9 Optd "Specimen" .. .. *Set of* 5 £200

1941 (15 Apr). *Nos.* FD65/9 *optd with Type* F **6** *at Nouméa, New Caledonia.*
FD77 **6** 5 c. blue-green.. .. .. 6·00 6·00
FD78 10 c. orange .. .. .. 6·00 6·00
FD79 20 c. scarlet .. .. .. 6·00 6·00
FD80 40 c. grey-olive .. .. .. 6·00 6·00
FD81 1 f. lake/*pale green* .. .. 6·00 6·00

1953 (30 Apr). *Optd with Type* FD **3**, *by Waterlow.*
FD92 **7** 5 c. green .. .. .. 90 1·60
FD93 10 c. scarlet .. .. .. 90 1·60
FD94 20 c. ultramarine .. .. .. 2·50 4·00
FD95 – 40 c. blackish brown .. .. 7·00 11·00
FD96 – 1 f. orange .. .. .. 9·50 16·00

1957 (3 Sept). *Optd with Type* FD **3**, *by Waterlow.*
FD107 **12** 5 c. green 35 80
FD108 10 c. scarlet 35 80
FD109 20 c. ultramarine .. .. .. 1·00 1·75
FD110 **13** 40 c. sepia .. .. .. 3·50 6·00
FD111 – 1 f. red-orange .. .. .. 6·00 9·50

The New Hebrides Condominium became an independent republic, within the Commonwealth, on 30 July 1980 and was renamed VANUATU.

New Republic

The territory of this ephemeral State was part of Zululand, but was subsequently annexed to the South African Republic, as a new district, named Vrijheid. In January 1903 the territory was annexed to the Colony of Natal.

PRICES FOR STAMPS ON COVER
Nos. 1/95 *from* × 10

1

Printed with a rubber handstamp on paper bought in Europe and sent out ready gummed and perforated.

1886 (1 Jan)–**87**. *Various dates indicating date of printing. P* 11½.

A. *Without Arms.* (i) *Yellow Paper*
1 1 1d. black (9.1.86).. .. .. .. — £2500
2 1d. violet (9.1.86).. .. .. .. 10·00 12·00
3 2d. violet (9.1.86).. .. .. .. 10·00 15·00
a. "d" omitted (13.10.86) .. ..
4 3d. violet (13.1.86) .. .. .. 23·00
a. "d" omitted (13.10.86) .. ..
5 4d. violet (30.8.86) .. .. .. 35·00
6 6d. violet (21.5.86) .. .. .. 30·00
7 9d. violet (13.1.86) .. .. .. 30·00
8 1s. violet (30.8.86) .. .. .. 65·00
9 1/s. violet (13.10.86) £500
10 1/6 violet (30.8.86) .. .. .. 65·00
11 1s. 6d. violet (6.9.86) £500
a. "d" omitted (13.10.86) .. .. 85·00
12 2s. violet (30.8.86) .. .. .. 38·00
a. *Tête-bêche* (pair) (6.9.86) £475
13 2/6 violet (13.1.86) £150
14 2s. 6d. violet (20.2.86) .. .. .. 95·00
15 4s. violet (17.1.87) £400
16 5s. violet (1.86) .. .. .. 28·00 30·00
a. "5" omitted (in pair with normal) (7.3.86) £2000
17 1 5/6 violet (20.2.86) .. .. .. 35·00
18 5s. 6d. violet (20.2.86) £160
19 7/6 violet (13.1.86) £170
20 7s. 6d. violet (24.5.86) .. .. .. 95·00
21 10s. violet (6.9.86).. .. .. .. 95·00
22 10s. 6d. violet (7.1.86) £170
a. "d" omitted (1.86) .. .. .. 48·00
23 13s. violet (24.11.86) £400
24 £1 violet (13.1.86) £120
25 30s. violet (13.1.86) .. .. .. 95·00
a. *Tête-bêche* (pair) (24.11.86) £700

(ii) *Blue granite paper*
26 1 1d. violet (20.1.86) .. .. .. 13·00 14·00
a. "d" omitted (24.11.86) £375
27 2d. violet (24.1.86) .. .. .. 13·00 14·00
a. "d" omitted (24.11.86) £750
28 3d. violet (13.10.86) .. .. .. 16·00 18·00
a. *Tête-bêche* (pair) (13.10.86) £325
29 4d. violet (24.5.86) .. .. .. 13·00 16·00
30 6d. violet (24.5.86) .. .. .. 25·00 21·00
a. "6" omitted (in pair with normal) (24.5.86) £1500
31 9d. violet (6.9.86).. .. .. .. 24·00
32 1s. violet (7.3.86).. .. .. .. 28·00 30·00
a. *Tête-bêche* (pair) (21.5.86) £400
33 1s. 6d. violet (2.7.86) .. .. .. 35·00
a. *Tête-bêche* (pair) (6.9.86) £475
34 1/6 violet (13.10.86) £150
35 2s. violet (21.5.86) £120
36 2s. 6d. violet (19.8.86) £140
37 2/6 violet (19.8.86) £180
38 4s. violet (17.1.87) £200
39 5s. 6d. violet (13.1.86) £170
40 5/6 violet (13.1.86) £200
41 7/6 violet (13.1.86) £200
42 10s. violet (1.86) £200 £200
a. *Tête-bêche* (pair) (2.7.86) £500
43 10s. 6d. violet (7.1.86) £200
a. "d" omitted (2.7.86) £450
44 12s. violet (13.1.86) £300
45 13s. violet (17.1.87) £325
46 £1 violet (13.1.86) £250
47 30s. violet (13.1.86) £250

B. *With embossed Arms of New Republic.* (i) *Yellow paper*
48 1 1d. violet (20.1.86) .. .. .. 13·00 15·00
a. Arms inverted (20.1.86) .. .. 25·00 25·00
b. Arms *tête-bêche* (pair) (30.6.86 *or* 3.11.86) £100 £120
49 2d. violet (2.12.86) .. .. .. 13·00 15·00
a. Arms inverted (24.11.86) .. .. 23·00 28·00
50 4d. violet (2.12.86) .. .. .. 18·00 22·00
a. Arms inverted (12.86) .. .. 95·00 60·00
b. Arms *tête-bêche* (pair) (12.86) .. £250
51 6d. violet (2.12.86) .. .. .. 45·00

(ii) *Blue granite paper*
52 1 1d. violet (20.1.86) .. .. .. 14·00 16·00
a. Arms inverted (10.2.86) .. .. 35·00 40·00
b. Arms *tête-bêche* (pair) (3.11.86) ..
53 2d. violet (30.8.86) .. .. .. 14·00 16·00
a. Arms inverted (30.8.86) .. .. 48·00
b. Arms *tête-bêche* (pair) (2.12.86) .. £500

Stamps as Type **1** were produced as and when stocks were required, each printing including in its design the date on which it was prepared. The dates quoted above for Nos. 1/53 are those on which the various stamps first appeared. Details of the various printing dates are given below. From these dates it can be seen that some values share common printing dates, and, it is believed, that the different values were produced *se-tenant* within the same sheet, at least in some instances. A reported proof sheet in the Pretoria Postal Museum, on yellow paper and embossed, contains 4 examples of the 6d. value and 3 each of the 3d., 4d., 9d., 1s., 1/6, 2/-, 2/6, 3s., 4s., 5s., 5/6, 7/6, 10/-, 10/6, £1 and 30/-.

The significance, if any, of the two coloured papers and the use of the embossing machine have never been satisfactorily explained. Both the different papers and the embossing machine were introduced in January 1886, and occur throughout the period that the stamps with dates were used.

PRINTINGS

Date	*Paper*	*Face value*	*Cat. No.*	*Un.*	*Us.*
7 Jan 86	*Yellow*	10s. 6d.	22	£160	
	Blue	10s.	42		
		10s. 6d.	43	£450	
9 Jan 86	*Yellow*	1d.	1	—	£2500
		1d.	2	10·00	12·00
		2d.	3	10·00	15·00
13 Jan 86	*Yellow*	1d.	2	35·00	
		2d.	3	14·00	15·00
		3d.	4	40·00	
		9d.	7	£200	
		2/6	13	£160	
		7/6	19		
		£1	24	£130	
		30s.	25	95·00	
	Blue	5s. 6d.	39	£170	
		5/6	40	£200	
		7/6	41	£200	
		10s.	42	£400	
		10s. 6d.	43	£200	
		12s.	44	£300	
		£1	46	£250	
		30s.	47	£250	
20 Jan 86	*Blue*	1d.	26	£250	
	Yellow, embossed	1d.	48	32·00	
		1d.	48a	48·00	
	Blue, embossed	1d.	52	95·00	
Jan 20 86	*Blue*	1d.	26	23·00	
	Yellow, embossed	1d.	48a		
	Blue, embossed	1d.	52	£100	
24 Jan 86	*Blue*	1d.	26	18·00	
		2d.	27	30·00	
Jan 86	*Yellow*	5s.	16	28·00	30·00
		10s. 6d.	22a	80·00	
	Blue	10s.	42	£200	£200
10 Feb 86	*Yellow, embossed*	1d.	48		
		1d.	48a	48·00	
	Blue, embossed	1d.	52	£130	
		1d.	52a	35·00	
20 Feb 86	*Yellow*	2s. 6d.	14	£130	
		5/6	17	£120	
		5s. 6d.	18		

Date	Paper	Face value	Cat. No.	Un.	Us.
7 Mar 86	*Yellow*	1d.	2	£110	
		2s. 6d.	14	95·00	
		5s.	16	£200	85·00
		5s.	16a		
		5/6	17	35·00	
		5s. 6d.	18	£160	
	Blue	2d.	27	95·00	
		1s.	32		
17 Mar 86	*Yellow*	1d.	2	95·00	
	Yellow, embossed	1d.	48	48·00	
	Blue, embossed	1d.	52	95·00	
		1d.	52a	80·00	
26 Mar 86	*Blue, embossed*	1d.	52a	£130	
14 Apr 86	*Yellow*	1d.	2		
	Yellow, embossed	1d.	48	23·00	
		1d.	48a	£120	
	Blue, embossed	1d.	52	45·00	
24 Apr 86	*Yellow*	1d.	2	£100	
	Blue	2d.	27	28·00	
29 Apr 86	*Blue*	1s.	32	£110	
21 May 86	*Yellow*	6d.	6	£130	
	Blue	1d.	26	85·00	
		1s.	32	28·00	30·00
		1s.	32a	£400	
		2s.	35	£325	
23 May 86	*Blue, embossed*	1d.	52a	95·00	
24 May 86	*Yellow*	1d.	2	95·00	
		2d.	3	£120	
		5s.	16	70·00	
		7/6	19	£170	
		7s. 6d.	20	95·00	
	Blue	1d.	26	13·00	14·00
		2d.	27		
		4d.	29	85·00	
		6d.	30	£120	
		6d.	30a		
		1s.	32	£200	
		2s.	35	£120	
26 May 86	*Blue*	1d.	26	£110	
	Yellow, embossed	1d.	48	£250	
		1d.	48a	95·00	
	Blue, embossed	1d.	52	£130	
		1d.	52a	48·00	50·00
28 May 86	*Yellow, embossed*	1d.	48	32·00	
30 Jun 86	*Blue*	1d.	26		
Jun 30 86	*Blue*	1d.	26	15·00	16·00
	Yellow, embossed	1d.	48	14·00	16·00
		1d.	48a	25·00	28·00
		1d.	48b	£250	£275
	Blue, embossed	1d.	52	45·00	40·00
2 Jul 86	*Yellow*	6d.	6		
		9d.	7	95·00	95·00
	Blue	1s.	32		
		1s. 6d.	33	35·00	
		10s.	42	£400	
		10s.	42a	£500	
		10s. 6d.	43		
		10s. 6d.	43a		
7 Jul 86	*Yellow, embossed*	1d.	48	25·00	
		1d.	48a	95·00	95·00
	Blue, embossed	1d.	52	14·00	16·00
		1d.	52a	55·00	40·00
4 Aug 86	*Yellow, embossed*	1d.	48	55·00	
	Blue, embossed	1d.	52	35·00	
19 Aug 86	*Yellow*	2/6	13		
		2s. 6d.	14	£140	
	Blue	2s. 6d.	36	£140	
		2/6	37	£180	
30 Aug 86	*Yellow*	1d.	2	10·00	12·00
		2d.	3	11·00	
		3d.	4	23·00	
		4d.	5	48·00	
		6d.	6	32·00	
		9d.	7	48·00	
		1s.	8	65·00	
		1/6	10	65·00	
		2s.	12	95·00	
		2/6	13	£150	
	Blue	2d.	27	13·00	14·00
	Blue, embossed	2d.	53	42·00	
		2d.	53a	£110	
6 Sep 86	*Yellow*	1d.	2	12·00	
		2d.	3	8·50	9·00
		3d.	4	38·00	
		4d.	5	40·00	
		6d.	6	30·00	
		9d.	7	30·00	
		1s.	8	95·00	
		1/6	10	70·00	
		1s. 6d.	11	£500	
		2s.	12	£100	
		2s.	12a	£475	
		2/6	13	£150	
		5s.	16	£140	
		7s. 6d.	20	£200	
		10s.	21	95·00	
		£1	24	£120	
	Blue	6d.	30	20·00	21·00
		9d.	31	95·00	
		1s.	32	65·00	
		1s. 6d.	33	£140	
		1s. 6d.	33a	£475	
		2/6	37	£400	
		10s. 6d.	43		
13 Sep 86	*Yellow, embossed*	1d.	48	48·00	
		1d.	48a	48·00	
	Blue, embossed	1d.	52	85·00	
6 Oct 86	*Blue*	1d.	26	85·00	
	Yellow, embossed	1d.	48	23·00	18·00
	Blue, embossed	1d.	52	45·00	18·00
		1d.	52a	85·00	
13 Oct 86	*Yellow*	1d.	2	12·00	12·00
		2d.	3	10·00	11·00
		2d.	3a		
		3d.	4	23·00	25·00
		3d.	4a		
		4d.	5	35·00	
		6d.	6	30·00	32·00
		9d.	7	35·00	
		1s.	8	70·00	
		1/s.	9	£500	
		1/6	10	£150	
		1s. 6d.	11a	85·00	
		2s.	12	38·00	
		2/6	13	£160	
		5s.	16	42·00	
		10s.	21	95·00	£100
		10s. 6d.	22a	48·00	
		£1	24	£120	
	Blue	2d.	27	13·00	14·00
		3d.	28	16·00	18·00
		3d.	28a	£325	
		4d.	29	28·00	28·00
		1s.	32	28·00	
		1/6	34	£150	
		2s.	35	£120	
3 Nov 86	*Yellow*	1d.	2	28·00	
	Yellow, embossed	1d.	48	13·00	15·00
		1d.	48a	25·00	28·00
		1d.	48b	£100	£120
	Blue, embossed	1d.	52	14·00	
		1d.	52a	35·00	40·00
		1d.	52b		
13 Nov 86	*Yellow*	1d.	2	35·00	
24 Nov 86	*Yellow*	1d.	2	14·00	
		2d.	3	10·00	11·00
		3d.	4	30·00	32·00
		10s.	21	£200	
		13s.	23	£400	
		30s.	25	95·00	
		30s.	25a	£700	
	Blue	1d.	26	38·00	17·00
		1d.	26a	£375	
		2d.	27	18·00	
		2d.	27a		
		4d.	29	13·00	16·00
		6d.	30	20·00	21·00
		9d.	31	24·00	
		1s.	32	45·00	48·00
		1/6	34	£160	
		2s.	35	£140	
	Yellow, embossed	2d.	49	£160	
26 Nov 86	*Yellow*	1/6	10	£140	
2 Dec 86	*Yellow, embossed*	1d.	48	13·00	15·00
		1d.	48a	£160	
		2d.	49	13·00	15·00
		2d.	49a	23·00	28·00
2 Dec 86	*Yellow, embossed*	4d.	50	80·00	
		6d.	51	45·00	
	Blue, embossed	1d.	52	28·00	
		1d.	52a	£160	
		2d.	53	14·00	16·00
		2d.	53a	48·00	
		2d.	53b		
Dec 86	*Yellow, embossed*	4d.	50	18·00	22·00
		4d.	50a	93·00	60·00
		4d.	50b	£250	
		6d.	51	42·00	
4 Jan 87	*Yellow*	1d.	2	35·00	
		2d.	3	32·00	
		13s.	23	£400	
	Blue	1d.	26	13·00	14·00
		2d.	27	16·00	14·00
	Blue, embossed	2d.	53	42·00	
13 Jan 87	*Blue*	5/6	40	£400	
		7/6	41	£400	
17 Jan 87	*Yellow*	1d.	2	38·00	
		2d.	3	30·00	
		3d.	4	45·00	
		4s.	15	£200	
	Blue	1d.	26	75·00	
		4s.	38	£200	
		13s.	45	£325	
		30s.	47	£250	
20 Jan 87	*Blue*	2d.	27	32·00	
	Yellow, embossed	2d.	49	50·00	
		2d.	49a	£140	
	Blue, embossed	2d.	53	42·00	
		2d.	53a	95·00	
Jan 20 87	*Yellow, embossed*	1d.	48a	£400	

1887 (Feb–Mar). *As T* **1**, *but without date. With embossed Arms.*

(*a*) *Blue granite paper*

72	1d. violet	14·00	14·00
	a. Imperf between (pair)		
	b. Stamps *tête-bêche* (pair)	£325	
	c. Arms *tête-bêche* (pair)		
	d. Arms inverted	23·00	23·00
	e. Arms omitted	£110	£110
73	2d. violet	8·50	8·50
	a. Stamps *tête-bêche* (pair)	£325	
	b. Arms inverted	23·00	23·00
	c. Arms omitted	£110	95·00
74	3d. violet	13·00	13·00
	a. Stamps *tête-bêche* (pair)	£375	
	b. Arms *tête-bêche* (pair)		
	c. Arms inverted	48·00	48·00
75	4d. violet	13·00	13·00
	a. Stamps *tête-bêche* (pair)	£325	
	b. Arms *tête-bêche* (pair)	£275	
	c. Arms inverted	85·00	
76	6d. violet	13·00	13·00
	a. Arms inverted	85·00	
77	1/6 violet	14·00	14·00
	a. Arms inverted	80·00	

(*b*) *Yellow paper* (March 1887)

78	2d. violet (*arms omitted*)	13·00	
79	3d. violet	13·00	13·00
	a. Imperf between (pair)		
	b. Stamps *tête-bêche* (pair)	£325	£350
	c. Arms *tête-bêche* (pair)	£200	
	d. Arms inverted	23·00	23·00
	da. Double impression		
80	4d. violet	13·00	13·00
	a. Arms inverted	14·00	14·00
81	6d. violet	8·00	8·00
	a. Arms *tête-bêche* (pair)	£350	
	b. Arms inverted	42·00	42·00
	c. Arms omitted	80·00	
	ca. Double impression		
82	9d. violet	8·50	8·50
83	1s. violet	8·50	8·50
	a. Arms inverted	70·00	
84	1/6 violet	17·00	14·00
85	2s. violet	18·00	16·00
	a. Arms inverted	55·00	50·00
	b. Arms omitted	70·00	
86	2/6 violet	23·00	23·00
	a. Arms inverted	28·00	28·00
87	3s. violet	42·00	42·00
	a. Arms inverted	45·00	45·00
88	4s. violet	11·00	11·00
	a. Arms omitted (4*s*.)		
	b. Arms omitted (4/-)	£130	
89	5s. violet	13·00	13·00
	a. Imperf between (pair)		
	b. Arms inverted	—	80·00
90	5/6 violet	12·00	12·00
91	7/6 violet	14·00	17·00
	a. Arms *tête-bêche* (pair)		
	a. Arms inverted		
92	10s. violet	12·00	12·00
	a. Imperf between (pair)		
	b. Arms *tête-bêche* (pair)	£120	
	c. Arms inverted	23·00	
	d. Arms omitted	£110	45·00
93	10/6 violet	16·00	16·00
	a. Imperf between (pair)		
	b. Arms inverted		
94	£1 violet	45·00	45·00
	a. Stamps *tête-bêche* (pair)	£350	£375
	b. Arms inverted	55·00	
95	30s. violet	85·00	

New South Wales

PRICES FOR STAMPS ON COVER

Nos. 1/83	*from* × 2
Nos. 84/108	*from* × 3
Nos. 109/10	—
No. 110*b*	*from* × 3
Nos. 111/13	*from* × 2
No. 114	—
Nos. 115/24	*from* × 2
Nos. 125/6	—
Nos. 127/53	*from* × 2
Nos. 154/70	*from* × 3
Nos. 171/2	—
No. 173	*from* × 2
Nos. 174/81	—
Nos. 186/202	*from* × 2
Nos. 203/6	*from* × 10
Nos. 207/21	*from* × 5
Nos. 222/39	*from* × 6
Nos. 240/1	*from* × 2
Nos. 241*a*/3	*from* × 10
Nos. 244/52	—
Nos. 253/73	*from* × 10
Nos. 274/80	—
Nos. 281/4	*from* × 15
Nos. 285/7	*from* × 10
Nos. 287*c*/*d*	*from* × 2
Nos. 288/97	*from* × 10
Nos. 298/312	*from* × 12
Nos. 313/28	*from* × 10
No. 329	—
Nos. 330/45	*from* × 12
No. 346	—
Nos. 347/60	*from* × 12
No. O1	—
Nos. O2/12	*from* × 4
Nos. O13/18	—
Nos. O19/34	*from* × 20
Nos. O35/8	—
Nos. O39/47	*from* × 40
Nos. O48/53	—
Nos. O54/8	*from* × 20
No. O59	—
Nos. D1/7	*from* × 50
Nos. D8/10	—
Nos. D11/15	*from* × 50

1

2

(Eng Robert Clayton, Sydney)

1850 (1 Jan). *T* **1.** *Plate I. No clouds.* (*a*) *Soft yellowish paper.*

1	1d. crimson-lake	£4000	£500
2	1d. carmine	£3750	£450
3	1d. reddish rose	£3500	£425
4	1d. brownish red	£3750	£450

(*b*) *Hard bluish paper*

5	1d. pale red	£3750	£400
6	1d. dull lake	£3750	£400

1850 (Aug). *T* **2.** *Plate I, re-engraved by H. C. Jervis, commonly termed Plate II. With clouds.* (*a*) *Hard toned white to yellowish paper.*

7	1d. vermilion	£2000	£350
8	1d. dull carmine	£2000	£350
	a. No trees on hill (No. 7)	£4500	£500
	b. Hill unshaded (No. 8)	£4500	£500
	c. Without clouds (No. 15)	£4500	£500

(b) Hard greyish or bluish paper

9 1d. crimson-lake .. £2250 £350
10 1d. gooseberry-red .. £2750 £475
11 1d. dull carmine .. £1900 £300
12 1d. brownish red .. £1900 £300
a. No trees on hill (No. 7) .. £4500 £500
b. Hill unshaded (No. 8) .. £4500 £500
c. Without clouds (No. 15) .. £4500 £500

(c) Laid paper

13 1d. carmine .. £3500 £475
14 1d. vermilion .. £4000 £450
a. No trees on hill (No. 7) .. — £750
b. Hill unshaded (No. 8) .. — £750
c. Without clouds (No. 15) .. — £750

The varieties quoted with the letters "a", "b", "c" of course exist in each shade; the prices quoted are for the commonest shade, and the same applies to the following portions of this list.

The numbers given in brackets throughout indicate position on sheet.

3 4 A (Pl I)

Illustrations A, B, C, and D are sketches of the lower part of the inner circular frame, showing the characteristic variations of each plate.

(Eng John Carmichael)

1850 (1 Jan). *Plate I. Vertical-lined background. T* **3**.

(a) Early impressions, full details of clouds, etc.

15 2d. greyish blue .. £4500 £350
16 2d. deep blue .. — £400
a. Double lines on bale (No. 19) .. — £600

(b) Intermediate impressions

16*b* 2d. greyish blue .. £2750 £250
16*c* 2d. deep blue .. £3000 £275

T **4**. *(c) Later impressions, clouds, etc., mostly gone*

17 2d. blue .. £1900 £120
18 2d. dull blue .. £1500 £110

1850 (end Jan). *Stamps in the lower row partially retouched.*

19 2d. blue .. £2500 £190
20 2d. greyish blue .. £2250 £160

An interesting variety occurs on positions 9, 10, 11 and 19 in all five plates. It consists of ten loops of the engine-turning on each side of the design instead of the normal nine loops.

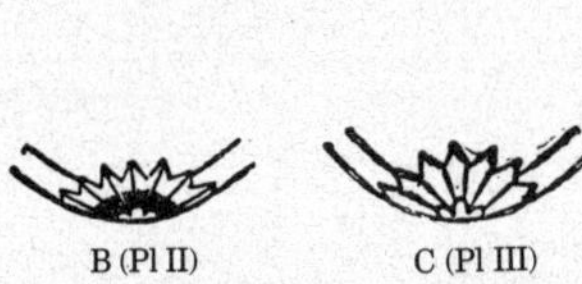

5 B (Pl II) C (Pl III)

(Plate entirely re-engraved by H. C. Jervis)

1850 (Apr). *T* **5**. *Plate II. Horizontal-lined background. Bale on left side supporting the seated figure, dated. Dot in centre of the star in each corner. (a) Early impressions.*

21 2d. indigo .. £3250 £275
22 2d. lilac-blue .. — £1000
23 2d. grey-blue .. £3250 £225
24 2d. bright blue .. £3250 £225
a. Fan as in Pl III, but with shading outside (No. 1) .. — £400
b. Fan as in Pl III, but without shading, and inner circle intersects the fan (No. 2) .. — £400
c. Pick and shovel omitted (No. 10) .. — £400
d. "CREVIT" omitted (No. 13) .. — £600
e. No whip (Nos. 4, 8, and 20) .. — £325

(b) Worn impressions

25 2d. dull blue .. £1600 £120
26 2d. Prussian blue .. £1700 £160
a. Fan as in Pl III, but with shading outside (No. 1) .. — £300
b. Fan as in Pl III, but without shading, and inner circle intersects the fan (No. 2) .. — £300
c. Pick and shovel omitted (No. 10) .. — £300
d. "CREVIT" omitted (No. 13) .. — £350
e. No whip (Nos. 4, 8, and 20) .. — £200

1850 (Aug). *Bottom row retouched with dots and dashes in lower spandrels.*

27 2d. Prussian blue .. £2250 £180
28 2d. dull blue .. £2000 £110
a. No whip (No. 20) .. — £250
b. "CREVIT" omitted (No. 13) .. — £300

(Plate re-engraved a second time by H. C. Jervis)

1850 (Sept). *Plate III. Bale not dated and single-lined, except Nos. 7, 10 and 12, which are double-lined. No dots in stars.*

29 2d. ultramarine .. £1900 £140
30 2d. deep blue .. £1800 £140
a. No whip (Nos. 15 and 19) .. — £225
b. Fan with 6 segments (No. 20) .. — £375
c. Double lines on bale (No. 7, 10, and 12) .. — £225

(Plate re-engraved a third time by H. C. Jervis)

1851 (Jan). *Plate IV. Double-lined bale, and circle in centre of each star. (a) Hard bluish grey wove paper.*

31 2d. ultramarine .. £2250 £140
32 2d. Prussian blue .. £1900 £110
33 2d. bright blue .. £2000 £120
a. Hill not shaded (No. 12) .. — £200
b. Fan with 6 segments (No. 20) .. — £200
c. No clouds (No. 22) .. — £200
d. Retouch (No. 13) .. — £275
e. No waves (Nos. 9 and 17) .. — £190

(b) Stout yellowish vertically laid paper

34 2d. ultramarine .. £2250 £140
35 2d. Prussian blue .. £2500 £120
a. Hill not shaded (No. 12) .. — £225
b. Fan with 6 segments (No. 20) .. — £225
c. No clouds (No. 22) .. — £225
d. Retouch (No. 13) .. — £300
e. No waves (Nos. 9 and 17) .. — £200
f. "PENOE" (No. 24)

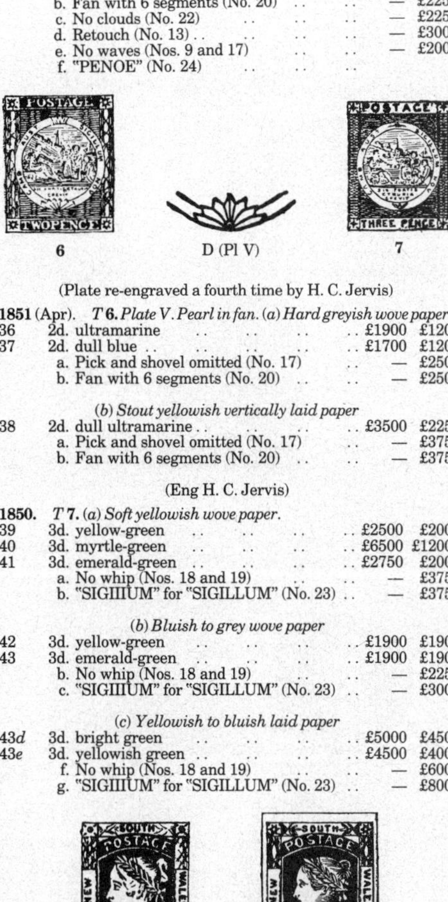

6 D (Pl V) 7

(Plate re-engraved a fourth time by H. C. Jervis)

1851 (Apr). *T* **6**. *Plate V. Pearl in fan. (a) Hard greyish wove paper.*

36 2d. ultramarine .. £1900 £120
37 2d. dull blue .. £1700 £120
a. Pick and shovel omitted (No. 17) .. — £250
b. Fan with 6 segments (No. 20) .. — £250

(b) Stout yellowish vertically laid paper

38 2d. dull ultramarine .. £3500 £225
a. Pick and shovel omitted (No. 17) .. — £375
b. Fan with 6 segments (No. 20) .. — £375

(Eng H. C. Jervis)

1850. *T* **7**. *(a) Soft yellowish wove paper.*

39 3d. yellow-green .. £2500 £200
40 3d. myrtle-green .. £6500 £1200
41 3d. emerald-green .. £2750 £200
a. No whip (Nos. 18 and 19) .. — £375
b. "SIGIIIUM" for "SIGILLUM" (No. 23) .. — £375

(b) Bluish to grey wove paper

42 3d. yellow-green .. £1900 £190
43 3d. emerald-green .. £1900 £190
b. No whip (Nos. 18 and 19) .. — £225
c. "SIGIIIUM" for "SIGILLUM" (No. 23) .. — £300

(c) Yellowish to bluish laid paper

43*d* 3d. bright green .. £5000 £450
43*e* 3d. yellowish green .. £4500 £400
f. No whip (Nos. 18 and 19) .. — £600
g. "SIGIIIUM" for "SIGILLUM" (No. 23) .. — £800

8 9

(Des A. W. Manning from sketch by W. T. Levine; eng on steel by John Carmichael, Sydney)

1851 (18 Dec)–**52**. *T* **8**. *Imperf. (a) Thick yellowish wove paper.*

44 1d. carmine .. £1700 £200
a. No leaves right of "SOUTH" .. — £400
b. Two leaves right of "SOUTH" .. — £400
c. "WALE" .. — £450

(b) Bluish medium wove paper (1852)

45 1d. carmine .. £1000 £140
46 1d. scarlet .. £1000 £140
47 1d. vermilion .. £900 £120
48 1d. brick-red .. £900 £120
a. No leaves right of "SOUTH" (Nos. 7 and 8) .. — £200
b. Two leaves right of "SOUTH" (No. 15) .. — £300
c. "WALE" (No. 9) .. — £300

(c) Thick vertically laid bluish paper (1852?)

49 1d. orange-brown .. £2750 £325
50 1d. claret .. £2750 £325
a. No leaves right of "SOUTH" .. — £500
b. Two leaves right of "SOUTH" .. — £500
c. "WALE" .. — £500

(Eng on steel by John Carmichael)

1851 (24 July). *T* **8**. *Plate I. Imperf. (a) Thick yellowish wove paper.*

51 2d. ultramarine .. £650 80·00

(b) Fine impressions, blue to greyish medium paper

52 2d. ultramarine .. £700 30·00
53 2d. chalky blue .. £600 30·00
54 2d. dark blue .. £600 30·00
55 2d. greyish blue .. £600 30·00

(c) Worn plate, blue to greyish medium paper

56 2d. ultramarine .. £425 30·00
57 2d. Prussian blue .. £425 30·00

(d) Worn plate, blue wove medium paper

58 2d. ultramarine .. £325 30·00
59 2d. Prussian blue .. £300 30·00

(Plate II eng H. C. Jervis)

1853 (Oct). *T* **9**. *Plate II. Stars in corners. Imperf.*

(a) Bluish medium to thick wove paper

60 2d. deep ultramarine .. £900 £130
61 2d. indigo .. £1000 £100
a. "WAEES" (No. 23) .. — £350

(b) Worn plate, hard blue wove paper

62 2d. deep Prussian blue .. £900 £100
a. "WAEES" (No. 23) .. — £325

1855 (Sept). *Plate III, being Plate I re-engraved by H. C. Jervis. Background of crossed lines. Imperf.*

(a) Medium bluish wove paper

63 2d. Prussian blue .. £450 55·00
a. "WALES" covered with wavy lines (No. 3) — £150

(b) Stout white wove paper

64 2d. Prussian blue .. £450 55·00
a. "WALES" covered with wavy lines (No. 3) — £190

(Eng John Carmichael)

1852 (3 Dec). *T* **8**. *Imperf. (a) Medium greyish blue wove paper.*

65 3d. deep green .. £1600 £225
66 3d. green .. £1300 £160
67 3d. dull yellow-green .. £1200 £120
a. "WAEES" (No. 37) .. — £400

(b) Thick blue wove paper

69 3d. emerald-green .. £1300 £225
71 3d. blue-green .. £1300 £225
a. "WAEES" (No. 37) .. — £600

1853 (Apr). *As T* **8**. *Fine background. Imperf.*

(a) Medium white wove paper

72 6d. vandyke-brown .. — £900
a. "WALLS" (No. 8) .. — £1500

(b) Medium bluish grey wove paper

73 6d. vandyke-brown .. £1700 £275
74 6d. yellow-brown .. £1800 £300
75 6d. chocolate-brown .. £1700 £275
76 6d. grey-brown .. £1600 £275
a. "WALLS" (No. 8) .. — £600

1853 (June). *Plate I re-engraved by H. C. Jervis. Coarse background. Imperf.*

77 6d. brown .. £1800 £325
78 6d. grey-brown .. £1700 £325

(Eng H. C. Jervis)

1853 (May). *Medium bluish paper. Imperf.*

79 8d. dull yellow .. £3250 £600
80 8d. orange-yellow .. £3250 £650
81 8d. orange .. £3500 £650
a. No bow at back of head (No. 9) .. — £1400
b. No leaves right of "SOUTH" (No. 21) .. — £1400
c. No lines in spandrel (Nos. 12, 22, and 32) .. — £900

10 13 14

NOTE. All watermarked stamps from No. 82 to No. 172 have double-lined figures, as T **10**.

1854 (Feb). *T* **8**. *Wmk* "1", *T* **10**. *Imperf. Yellowish wove paper.*

82 1d. red-orange .. £170 15·00
83 1d. orange-vermilion .. £170 15·00
a. No leaves right of "SOUTH" (Nos. 7 and 21) .. £325 85·00
b. Two leaves right of "SOUTH" (No. 15) .. £425 £120
c. "WALE" (No. 9) .. £425 £120

1854 (Jan). *Plate III. Wmk* "2". *Imperf.*

84 2d. ultramarine .. £100 10·00
85 2d. Prussian blue .. £100 10·00
86 2d. chalky blue .. £100 7·00
a. "WALES" partly covered .. £400 50·00

1854 (Mar). *Wmk* "3". *Imperf.*

87 3d. yellow-green .. £180 25·00
a. "WAEES" (No. 37) .. — £120
b. Error. Wmk "2" .. — £2250

(Eng John Carmichael)

1856 (1 Jan). *For Registered Letters. T* **13**. *No wmk. Imperf. Soft medium yellowish paper.*

88 (6d.) vermilion and Prussian blue .. £700 £170
a. Frame printed on back .. £2500 £1000
89 (6d.) salmon and indigo .. £700 £190
90 (6d.) orange and Prussian blue .. £700 £225
91 (6d.) orange and indigo .. £700 £200

1859 (Apr)–**60**. *Hard medium bluish wove paper, with manufacturer's wmk in sans-serif, double-lined capitals across sheet and only showing portions of letters on a few stamps in a sheet.*

(a) Imperf.

92 (6d.) orange and Prussian blue .. £700 £150
92*a* (6d.) vermilion and Prussian blue .. £850 £200

(b) P 12 (2.60)

93 (6d.) orange and Prussian blue .. £350 50·00
94 (6d.) orange and indigo .. £325 50·00

1860 (Feb)–**62**. *Coarse yellowish wove paper having the manufacturer's wmk in Roman capitals. (a) P* 12.

95 (6d.) rose-red and Prussian blue .. £250 40·00
96 (6d.) rose-red and indigo .. £325 90·00
97 (6d.) salmon and indigo

(b) P 13 (1862)

98 (6d.) rose-red and Prussian blue .. £225 55·00

1863 (May). *Yellowish wove paper. Wmk* "6". *P* 13.

99 (6d.) rose-red and Prussian blue .. 90·00 15·00
100 (6d.) rose-red and indigo .. £140 17·00
101 (6d.) rose-red and pale blue .. 65·00 15·00
a. Double impression of frame .. — £1500

(T **14**/**21** and **24** printed by the New South Wales Govt Ptg Dept from plates engraved by Perkins, Bacon & Co)

Two plates of the 2d. and 6d. were used. On Plate II of the 2d. the stamps are wider apart and more regularly spaced than on Plate I.

1856 (6 Apr). *Wmk "1". Imperf.*
102 14 1d. orange-vermilion £130 22·00
a. Error. Wmk "2"
103 1d. carmine-vermilion £130 22·00
104 1d. orange-red £130 22·00
a. Printed on both sides — £1400

1856 (7 Jan). *Plate I. Wmk "2". Imperf.*
105 14 2d. light ultramarine £140 8·00
106 2d. Prussian blue £130 8·00
107 2d. dull blue £130 8·00
108 2d. pale blue £130 8·00
a. Error. Wmk "1"
b. Error. Wmk "5" £450 60·00
c. Error. Wmk "8"

1858. *Plate I, retouched.*
109 14 2d. dull blue £1800 £450

1859 (3 Aug). *Lithographic transfer of Plate I.*
110 14 2d. pale cobalt-blue — £600
a. Retouched — £2500

1860 (Jan). *Plate II. Recess. Stamps printed wider apart.*
110*b* 14 2d. blue £350 12·00

1856 (10 Oct). *Wmk "3". Imperf.*
111 14 3d. yellow-green £700 £100
112 3d. bluish green £750 £100
113 3d. dull green £750 £100
a. Error, Wmk "2" — £2750
In the 3d. the value is in block letters on a white ground.

15

17

19

21

(6d. and 1s. des E. H. Corbould after sketches by T. W. Levinge)

1855 (1 Dec). *Wmk "5". Imperf.*
114 15 5d. dull green £1200 £550

1854 (Feb)–**59.** *Wmk "6". Imperf.*
115 17 6d. deep slate £450 32·00
116 6d. greenish grey £350 32·00
117 6d. slate-green £350 £100
a. Printed both sides
118 6d. bluish grey £400 55·00
119 6d. fawn £450 95·00
a. Error. Wmk "8" (15.8.59) £1500 £100
120 6d. grey £400 55·00
121 6d. olive-grey £400 32·00
122 6d. greyish brown £400 32·00
a. Error. Wmk "8" (15.8.59) £1500 £100

1855 (1 Dec). *Wmk "8". Imperf.*
125 19 8d. golden yellow £5500 £1300
126 8d. dull yellow-orange £5000 £1300

1854 (Feb). *Wmk "12". Imperf.*
127 21 1s. rosy vermilion £650 65·00
a. Error. Wmk "8" (20.6.57) £1900 £200
128 1s. pale red £650 65·00
129 1s. brownish red £700 75·00

1860 (Feb)–**63.** *Wmk double-lined figure of value. P* 12.
131 14 1d. orange-red £170 16·00
a. Imperf between (pair)
b. Double impression
132 1d. scarlet £100 16·00
133 2d. cobalt-blue (Pl I) £500 70·00
a. Retouched — £1600
134 2d. greenish blue (Pl II) 90·00 10·00
136 2d. Prussian blue (Pl II) 90·00 10·00
a. Error. Wmk "1" — £2750
b. Retouched (*shades*) — £500
137 2d. Prussian blue (Pl I) (3.61) £110 11·00
138 2d. dull blue (Pl I) £100 10·00
139 3d. yellow-green (1860) £1000 55·00
140 3d. blue-green £550 42·00
141 15 5d. dull green (1863) £100 36·00
142 5d. yellowish green (1863) £100 36·00
143 17 6d. grey-brown £275 45·00
144 6d. olive-brown £275 55·00
145 6d. greenish grey £350 45·00
146 6d. fawn £325 65·00
147 6d. mauve £300 35·00
148 6d. violet £275 16·00
a. Imperf between (pair)
149 19 8d. lemon-yellow — £1400
150 8d. orange £1700 £400
151 8d. red-orange £1700 £450
152 21 1s. brownish red £450 48·00
153 1s. rose-carmine £450 48·00
a. Imperf between (pair)
No. 133 was made by perforating a small remaining stock of No. 108. Nos. 137/8 were printed from the original plate after its return from London, where it had been repaired.

1862–72. *Wmk double-lined figure of value. (a) P* 13.
154 14 1d. scarlet (1862) 55·00 8·00
155 1d. dull red 55·00 8·00
156 3d. blue-green (12.62) 45·00 11·00
157 3d. yellow-green 50·00 8·50
a. Error. Wmk "6" (7.72) 50·00 12·00
158 14 3d. dull green 50·00 8·00
a. Error. Wmk "6" (7.72) 55·00 15·00
160 15 5d. bluish green 35·00 15·00
161 5d. bright yellow-green 38·00 24·00
162 5d. sea-green 38·00 17·00
162*a* 5d. dark bluish green 28·00 17·00
163 17 6d. reddish purple (Pl I, 7.62) 60·00 5·00
164 6d. mauve 60·00 5·00
165 6d. purple (Pl II, 1864) 55·00 4·50
a. Error. Wmk "5" (7.66) £350 25·00
b. Error. Wmk "12" (12.66) £275 20·00
166 6d. violet 55·00 6·00
167 6d. aniline mauve £900 £120
167*a* 19 8d. red-orange £140 55·00
167*b* 8d. yellow-orange £140 40·00
167*c* 8d. bright yellow £140 40·00
168 21 1s. rose-carmine 70·00 7·50
169 1s. carmine 70·00 8·00
170 1s. crimson-lake 70·00 8·00

(*b*) *Perf compound* 12 × 13
171 14 1d. scarlet — £1700
172 2d. dull blue £2000 £350

23

1864 (June). *W* **23.** *P* 13.
173 14 1d. pale red 36·00 16·00

24

25

(Des E. H. Corbould, R.I.)

1861–88. *W* **25.** *Various perfs.*
174 24 5s. dull violet, *p* 12 (1861) £1200 £325
a. Perf 13 (1861) £160 28·00
175 5s. royal purple, *p* 13 (1872) £275 45·00
176 5s. deep rose-lilac, *p* 13 (1875) 95·00 28·00
177 5s. deep purple, *p* 13 (1880) £150 40·00
a. Perf 10 (1882) £150 45·00
178 5s. rose-lilac, *p* 10 (1883) £110 40·00
179 5s. purple, *p* 12 (1885) — 45·00
a. Perf 10 × 12 (1885) — £120
180 5s. reddish purple, *p* 10 (1886) £110 40·00
a. Perf 12 × 10 (1887) £275 45·00
181 5s. rose-lilac, *p* 11 (1888) — £120
This value was replaced by Nos. 274, etc. in 1888 but reissued in 1897, *see* Nos. 297*c*/*e*.

26

28

29

(Printed by De La Rue & Co, Ltd, London and perf at Somerset House, London)

1862–65. *Surfaced paper. P* 14. (i) *W* **23.**
186 26 1d. dull red (Pl I, 4.64) 80·00 28·00

(ii) *No wmk*
187 26 1d. dull red (Pl II, 1.65) 60·00 28·00
188 28 2d. pale blue (3.62) 60·00 28·00

(Printed from the De La Rue plates in the Colony)

1862 (12 Apr). *Wmk double-lined "2". P* 13.
189 28 2d. blue 45·00 7·00
a. Perf 12 £120 12·00
b. Perf 12 × 13 £400

1864–65. *W* **23.** *P* 13.
190 26 1d. dark red-brown (Pl I) 70·00 14·00
191 1d. brownish red (Pl II) 18·00 1·50
192 1d. brick-red (Pl II) 18·00 1·50
a. Highly surfaced paper (1865) £180
194 28 2d. pale blue £110 3·50
Plates I and II were made from the same die; they can only be distinguished by the colour or by the marginal inscription.

1865–66. *Thin wove paper. No wmk. P* 13.
195 26 1d. brick-red 90·00 15·00
196 1d. brownish red 90·00 15·00
197 28 2d. pale blue 40·00 3·00

1863–69. *W* **29.** *P* 13.
198 26 1d. pale red (3.69) 70·00 11·00
199 28 2d. pale blue 7·50 50
a. Perf 12
200 2d. cobalt-blue 7·50 50
201 2d. Prussian blue 19·00 3·50

1862 (Sept). *Wmk double-lined "5". P* 13.
202 28 2d. dull blue 60·00 8·50

32

34

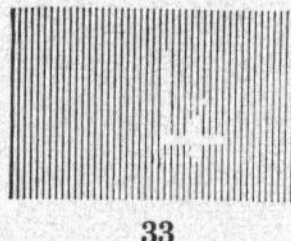
33

35

1867 (Sept)–**93.** *W* **33** *and* **35.**
203 32 4d. red-brown, *p* 13 28·00 3·00
204 4d. pale red-brown, *p* 13 28·00 3·00
205 34 10d. lilac, *p* 13 10·00 3·00
a. Imperf between (pair) £400
206 10d. lilac, *p* 11 (1893) 11·00 3·00
a. Perf 10 14·00 4·50
b. Perf 10 and 11, compound 18·00 7·50
c. Perf 12 × 11 £110 15·00

36

37

38

NINEPENCE
(39)

From 1871 to 1903 the 9d. is formed from the 10d. by a *black* surch. (T **39**), 15 mm long on Nos. 219 to 220h, and 13½ mm long on subsequent issues.

1871–84. *W* **36.**
207 26 1d. dull red, *p* 13 (8.71) 4·50 20
a. Imperf vert (horiz pair)
208 1d. salmon, *p* 13 4·50 20
a. Perf 10 £350 15·00
b. Perf 13 × 10 16·00 20
c. *Scarlet*. Perf 10 — £225
209 28 2d. Prussian-blue, *p* 13 (11.71) 5·50 20
a. Perf 11 × 12, comb £325 60·00
b. Imperf vert (horiz pair)
210 2d. pale blue, *p* 13 5·50 20
aa. "TWO PENCE" double impression at right
a. Perf 10 £325 22·00
b. Perf 13 × 10 6·00 20
c. Surfaced paper. Perf 13
211 14 3d. yellow-green (3.74), *p* 13 18·00 2·40
a. Perf 10 65·00 5·50
b. Perf 11 £200 £140
c. Perf 12 — £200
d. Perf 10 × 12 £200 32·00
e. Perf 12 × 11 £150 32·00
212 3d. bright green, *p* 10 £150 11·00
a. Perf 10 × 13 £130 15·00
213 32 4d. pale red-brown (8.77), *p* 13 40·00 6·00
214 4d. red-brown, *p* 13 40·00 6·00
a. Perf 10 £225 50·00
b. Perf 13 × 10 75·00 3·50
215 15 5d. bluish green (8.84), *p* 10 15·00 8·00
a. Perf 12 £300 £130
b. Perf 13 × 10
c. Perf 10 × 12 19·00 9·00
216 37 6d. bright mauve (1.72), *p* 13 30·00 1·00
a. Imperf between (horiz pair) — £450
217 6d. pale lilac, *p* 13 35·00 1·00
a. Perf 10 £225 12·00
b. Perf 13 × 10 55·00 1·90
c. Imperf between (horiz pair). Perf 13 × 10 — £500
218 19 8d. yellow (3.77), *p* 13 90·00 17·00
a. Perf 10 £300 24·00
b. Perf 13 × 10 £200 22·00
219 34 9d. on 10d. pale red-brown (8.71), *p* 13 18·00 4·50
220 9d. on 10d. red-brown, *p* 13 18·00 6·00
a. Perf 10 9·00 4·50
b. Perf 12 9·00 4·50
c. Perf 11 24·00 7·00
d. Perf 10 × 12 £300 £200
e. Perf 10 × 11 38·00 9·00
f. Perf 12 × 11 12·00 5·50
g. Perf 11 × 12, comb 12·00 5·50
h. In black and blue. Perf 11 £140
221 38 1s. black (4.76), *p* 13 80·00 2·50
a. Perf 10 £375 12·00
b. Perf 10 × 13 £200 4·50
c. Perf 11
d. Imperf between (horiz pair) — £750

Collectors should note that the classification of perforations is that adopted by the Royal Philatelic Society, London. "Perf 12" denotes the perforation formerly called "11½, 12" and "perf 13" that formerly called "12½, 13".

NEW INFORMATION

The editor is always interested to correspond with people who have new information that will improve or correct the Catalogue.

40 41

1882–93. W **40**.
222 **26** 1d. salmon, *p* 10 .. 9·00 20
a. Perf 13
b. Perf 10 × 13 .. 28·00 1·50
223 1d. orange *to* scarlet, *p* 13
a. Perf 10 .. 7·00 20
ab. Imperf between (horiz pair)
b. Perf 10 × 13 .. £120 6·00
c. Perf 10 × 12 .. £250 65·00
d. Perf 10 × 11 .. £450 £120
e. Perf 12 × 11 .. — £120
f. Perf 11 × 12, comb .. 4·50 25
h. Perf 11 .. — £130
224 **28** 2d. pale blue, *p* 13 .. £450 90·00
a. Perf 10 .. 8·00 25
b. Perf 13 × 10 .. 65·00 2·00
225 2d. Prussian blue, *p* 10 .. 17·00 25
a. Perf 13 × 10 .. 65·00 1·90
b. Perf 12 .. — £225
c. Perf 11 .. — £100
d. Perf 12 × 11 .. — £100
e. Perf 12 × 10 .. £225 65·00
f. Perf 10 × 11 .. £450 £100
g. Perf 11 × 12, comb .. 12·00 15
226 **14** 3d. yellow-green (1886), *p* 10 .. 5·00 80
a. Perf 10 × 12 .. £160 15·00
b. Perf 11 .. 5·00 80
c. Perf 12 × 11 .. 5·00 80
d. Perf 12 .. 9·00 1·00
e. Imperf between (horiz pair) .. £150
f. Imperf (pair) .. £130
227 3d. bluish green, *p* 10 .. 5·00 80
a. Perf 11 .. 5·00 80
b. Perf 10 × 11 .. 15·00 1·50
c. Perf 12 × 11 .. 5·00 1·00
d. Perf 12 × 10 .. 75·00 3·00
228 3d. emerald-green, *p* 10 (1893) .. 55·00 7·50
a. Perf 10 × 11 .. 55·00 3·00
b. Perf 12 × 10 .. 80·00 8·00
229 **32** 4d. red-brown, *p* 10 .. 28·00 2·00
a. Perf 10 × 12 .. — £130
b. Perf 11 × 12, comb .. 38·00 1·25
230 4d. dark brown, *p* 10 .. 38·00 2·75
a. Perf 12 .. — 35·00
b. Perf 10 × 12 .. — 90·00
c. Perf 11 × 12, comb .. 14·00 1·00
231 **15** 5d. dull green (1891), *p* 10 .. 12·00 90
a. Perf 11 × 10 .. 30·00 2·00
b. Perf 12 × 10 .. 80·00 3·50
232 5d. bright green, *p* 10 .. 32·00 4·50
a. Perf 11 .. — 4·50
b. Perf 10 × 11 .. 38·00 4·50
c. Perf 12 × 10 .. £150 6·50
233 5d. blue-green, *p* 10 .. 8·50 90
a. Perf 12 .. 11·00 90
b. Perf 11 .. 8·50 55
c. Perf 10 × 11 .. 24·00 1·60
d. Perf 11 × 12 or 12 × 11 .. 6·50 55
e. Imperf (pair) .. £275
234 **37** 6d. pale lilac, *p* 10 .. 30·00 1·00
a. Perf 10 × 13 or 13 × 10 .. — £300
b. Perf 10 × 12 .. 38·00 1·50
235 6d. mauve, *p* 10 .. 35·00 1·00
a. Perf 12 .. 80·00 2·50
b. Perf 11 .. 80·00 8·00
c. Perf 10 × 12 .. 32·00 1·00
d. Perf 11 × 12 or 12 × 11 .. 32·00 1·40
e. Perf 10 × 11 .. 55·00 1·00
f. Imperf between (horiz pair). Perf 12 × 10 .. — £650
236 **19** 8d. yellow, *p* 10 (1883) .. £100 15·00
a. Perf 12 .. £150 24·00
b. Perf 11 .. £100 17·00
c. Perf 10 × 12 .. £130 22·00
237 **38** 1s. black, *p* 10 .. 65·00 2·00
a. Perf 11 .. £200 9·00
b. Perf 10 × 12
c. Perf 10 × 13 .. — 11·00
d. Perf 11 × 12, comb .. 65·00 2·00

1886–87. W **41**.
238 **26** 1d. scarlet, *p* 10 .. 11·00 3·75
a. Perf 11 × 12, comb .. 2·00 90
239 **28** 2d. deep blue, *p* 10 .. 32·00 5·00
a. Perf 11 × 12, comb .. 12·00 95
b. Imperf

1891 (July). *Wmk* "10" *as T* **35**. *P* 10.
240 **14** 3d. green .. 12·00 80·00
241 3d. dark green .. 5·00 17·00

42 43

NOTE. The spacing between the Crown and "NSW" is 1 mm in T **42**, as against 2 mm in T **40**.

1903–8. W **42**.
241*a* **14** 3d. yellow-green, *p* 11 .. 6·00 90
b. Perf 12 .. 5·00 90
c. Perf 11 × 12 .. 5·00 90
242 3d. dull green, *p* 12 .. 19·00 1·75
a. Perf 11 × 12 .. 7·00 1·00
243 **15** 5d. dark blue-green, *p* 11 × 12 .. 5·00 90
a. Perf 11 .. 12·00 90
b. Perf 12 .. 19·00 3·50
c. Imperf (pair)

1885–86. W **41**. (i) *Overprinted* "POSTAGE", *in black*.
244 **43** 5s. green and lilac, *p* 13
a. Perf 10
b. Perf 12 × 10 .. £300 70·00
245 10s. claret and lilac, *p* 13
a. Perf 12 .. £400 £120
246 £1 claret and lilac, *p* 13 .. — £2000
a. Perf 12 .. £2000 £900

(ii) *Overprinted in blue*
247 **43** 10s. claret and mauve, *p* 10 .. £450 £100
a. Perf 12 .. £130 45·00
b. Perf 12 × 11 .. £225
248 £1 claret and rose-lilac, *p* 12 × 10 .. £2250

44

1894. *Overprinted* "POSTAGE" *in blue*. W **44**.
249 **43** 10s. claret and mauve, *p* 10 .. £200 38·00
249*a* 10s. claret and violet, *p* 12 .. £110 28·00
b. Perf 11 .. £100 28·00
c. Perf 12 × 11 .. £100 28·00
250 10s. aniline crimson & violet, *p* 12 × 11 £120 30·00
a. Perf 12 .. £140 40·00
250*b* £1 claret and violet, *p* 12 × 11

1903–04. *Optd* "POSTAGE" *in blue. Chalk-surfaced paper.* W **44**.
250*c* **43** 10s. aniline crimson & violet, *p* 12 × 11
251 10s. rosine and violet, *p* 12 (1904) .. £100 28·00
a. Perf 11 .. £120 28·00
b. Perf 12 × 11 .. £120 28·00
252 10s. claret and violet, *p* 12 × 11 (1904) .. £170 28·00

45 View of Sydney **46** Emu **47** Captain Cook

48 Queen Victoria and Arms of Colony **49** Superb Lyrebird **50** Kangaroo

1888–99. W **40**.
253 **45** 1d. lilac, *p* 11 × 12 .. 3·75 10
a. Perf 12 × 11½ .. 17·00 90
b. Perf 12 .. 5·00 10
c. Imperf (pair)
254 1d. mauve, *p* 11 × 12 .. 3·75 10
a. Perf 12 × 11½ .. 6·00 25
b. Perf 12 .. 5·50 25
c. Imperf between (pair). Perf 11 × 12
255 **46** 2d. Prussian blue, *p* 11 × 12 .. 3·00 10
a. Perf 12 × 11½ .. 7·00 10
b. Perf 12 .. 5·00 10
c. Imperf (pair) .. £100
d. Imperf between (horiz pair). Perf 11 × 12 .. £350
256 2d. chalky blue, *p* 11 × 12 .. 3·00 10
a. Perf 12 × 11½
b. Perf 12 .. 3·75 25
257 **47** 4d. purple-brown, *p* 11 × 12 .. 6·00 3·00
a. Perf 12 × 11½ .. 25·00 7·50
b. Perf 12 .. 21·00 3·25
c. Perf 11 .. £300 90·00
258 4d. red-brown, *p* 11 × 12 .. 6·00 3·00
a. Perf 12 × 11½ .. 10·00 2·75
b. Perf 12 .. 10·00 2·75
259 4d. orange-brown, *p* 12 × 11½ .. 10·00 2·75
260 4d. yellow-brown, *p* 12 × 11½ .. 7·50 3·00
261 **48** 6d. carmine, *p* 11 × 12 .. 20·00 2·50
a. Perf 12 × 11½ .. 25·00 3·00
b. Perf 12 .. 21·00 2·50
262 6d. emerald-green, *p* 11 × 12 (1898) .. 25·00 5·00
a. Perf 12 × 11½ .. 17·00 5·00
b. Perf 12 .. 17·00 5·00
262*c* 6d. orange-yellow, *p* 11 × 12 (1899) .. 13·00 3·00
d. Perf 12 × 11½ .. 12·00 2·50
e. Perf 12 .. 21·00 4·50
263 6d. yellow, *p* 12 × 11½ .. 13·00 1·25
264 **49** 8d. lilac-rose, *p* 11 × 12 .. 6·00 1·50
a. Perf 12 × 11½ .. 35·00 10·00
b. Perf 12 .. 6·00 1·75
265 8d. magenta, *p* 11 × 12 .. 75·00 9·00
a. Perf 12 × 11½ .. 6·00 1·75
b. Perf 12 .. 5·50 2·25
266 **34** 9d. on 10d. red-brown, *p* 11 × 12 (1897) 6·00 3·75
a. Perf 12 .. 9·00 5·00
b. Perf 11 .. 9·00 5·50
c. Double surcharge. Perf 11 .. £140 £120

268 **34** 10d. violet, *p* 11 × 12 (1897) .. 10·00 3·25
a. Perf 12 × 11½ .. 10·00 3·25
b. Perf 12 .. 13·00 4·00
c. Perf 11 .. 13·00 4·00
269 **50** 1s. maroon, *p* 11 × 12 (1889) .. 10·00 90
a. Perf 12 × 11½ .. 11·00 90
b. Perf 12 .. 17·00 90
270 1s. violet-brown, *p* 11 × 12 .. 10·00 90
a. Perf 12 × 11½ .. 35·00 1·25
b. Perf 12 .. 35·00 90
c. Imperf (pair) .. £550

All these perforations, with the exception of perf 11, are from comb machines.

1888. W **41**. *P* 11 × 12 *comb*.
271 **45** 1d. lilac .. 9·00
272 1d. mauve .. 7·50 10
273 **46** 2d. Prussian blue .. 40·00 3·00

51 Map of Australia **52** Capt. Arthur Phillip, first Governor and Lord Carrington, Governor in 1888

1888–89. W **25**. *P* 10.
274 **51** 5s. deep purple .. £225 50·00
275 5s. deep violet .. £200 48·00
276 **52** 20s. cobalt-blue .. £300 £125
274 & 276 Optd "Specimen" .. *Set of* 2 £225

53 54

1890. W **53**.
277 **51** 5s. lilac, *p* 10 .. £150 30·00
a. Perf 11 .. £225 40·00
aa. Imperf between (horiz pair)
b. Perf 12 .. £300 40·00
c. Perf 10 × 11 or 11 × 10 .. £225 30·00
278 5s. mauve, *p* 10 .. £225 30·00
a. Perf 11 .. £225 40·00

1890. W **54**.
279 **52** 20s. cobalt-blue, *p* 10 .. £225 90·00
a. Perf 11 .. £300 85·00
b. Perf 11 × 10
280 20s. ultramarine, *p* 11 .. £225 85·00
a. Perf 12 .. £325 £150
b. Perf 11 × 12 or 12 × 11 .. £225 85·00

55 Allegorical figure of Australia

Halfpenny

(56)

SEVEN-PENCE HALFPENNY

(57)

1890 (22 Dec). W **40**.
281 **55** 2½d. ultramarine, *p* 11 × 12 *comb* .. 55 30
a. Perf 12 × 11½, comb .. 45·00
b. Perf 12, comb .. 6·00 30

1891 (5 Jan). *Surch as T* **56** *and* **57**. W **40**.
282 **26** ½d. on 1d. grey, *p* 11 × 12 *comb* .. 50 30
a. Surch omitted
b. Surch double
283 **37** 7½d. on 6d. brown, *p* 10 .. 2·00 90
a. Perf 11 .. 2·00 90
b. Perf 12 .. 2·50 2·25
c. Perf 11 × 12 .. 2·25 2·00
d. Perf 10 × 12 .. 2·50 2·00
284 **38** 12½d. on 1s. red, *p* 10 .. 2·50 2·25
a. Perf 11 .. 2·75 2·00
b. Perf 11 × 12, comb .. 2·50 1·75
c. Perf 12 × 11½, comb .. 1·75 1·75
d. Perf 12, comb .. 3·25 1·75

58 Die I

1892 (21 Mar)–**99**. T **58**. *Die I. Narrow* "H" *in* "HALF". W **40**.
285 ½d. grey, *p* 10 .. 15·00 45
a. Perf 11 .. 90·00 5·00
b. Perf 10 × 12 .. 85·00 7·50
c. Perf 11 × 12 .. £100 10
d. Perf 12 .. £120 10

286 ½d. slate, *p* 11 × 12 (1897) 80 10
a. Perf 12 × 11½ 80 10
b. Perf 12 .. .. 80 10
c. Imperf between (horiz pair). Perf 11 × 12 £400
287 ½d. bluish green, *p* 11 × 12 (1899) .. .. 1·50 10
a. Perf 12 × 11½ 70 10
b. Perf 12 .. .. 80 10

The perforations 11 × 12, 12 × 11½, 12, are from comb machines.

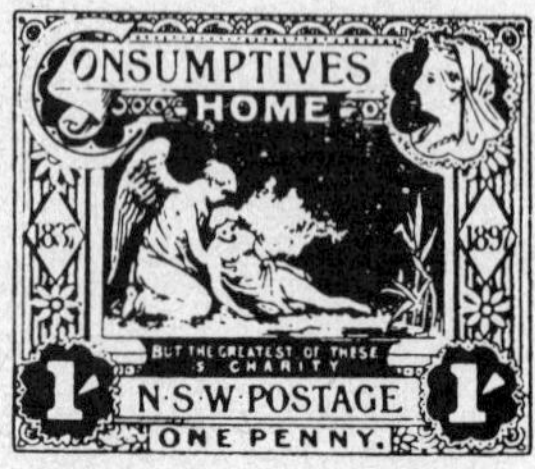

58*a*

58*b*

(Des Charles Taylor. Typo Govt Printing Office, Sydney)

1897. *Charity. T* **58***a and* **58***b. Wmk W* **40.** *P* 12 × 11 (1*d.*) *or* 11 (2½*d.*).
287*c* **58***a* 1d. (1s.) green and brown (22.6) .. 50·00 45·00
287*d* **58***b* 2½d. (2s. 6d.), gold, carmine & bl (28.6) £175 £175
287*c/d* Optd "Specimen" .. .. *Set of* 2 £325

These stamps, sold at 1s. and 2s. 6d. respectively, paid postage of 1d. and 2½d. only, the difference being given to a Consumptives' Home.

59

60

61

Dies of the 1d.

Die I

Die II

1d. Die I. The first pearl on the crown on the left side is merged into the arch, the shading under the fleur-de-lis is indistinct, the "S" of "WALES" is open.

Die II. The first pearl is circular, the vertical shading under the fleur-de-lis clear, the "S" of "WALES" not so open.

Dies of the 2½d.

Die I

Die II

2½d. Die I. There are 12 radiating lines in the star on the Queen's breast.

Die II. There are 16 radiating lines in the star and the eye is nearly full of colour.

1897–99. *W* 40.
288 **59** 1d. carmine (Die I), *p* 11 × 12 .. .. 1·75 10
a. Perf 12 × 11½ .. .. .. 2·00 10
289 1d. scarlet (Die I), *p* 11 × 12 .. .. 1·75 10
a. Perf 12 × 11½ .. .. .. 4·50 40
b. Perf 12 .. .. 4·50 50
ba. Imperf horiz (vert pair) .. ..
290 1d. rose-carmine (Die II), *p* 11 × 12 .. 1·75 10
a. Perf 12 × 11½ .. .. .. 1·50 10
b. Perf 12 .. .. 1·50 10
c. Imperf between (pair) £400
291 1d. salmon-red (Die II), *p* 12 × 11½ .. 1·75 10
a. Perf 12 .. .. 3·25 30
292 **60** 2d. deep dull blue, *p* 11 × 12 .. .. 1·75 10
a. Perf 12 × 11½ .. .. .. 1·75 10
b. Perf 12 .. .. 4·50 10
293 2d. cobalt-blue, *p* 11 × 12 .. .. 3·00 10
a. Perf 12 × 11½ .. .. .. 2·50 10
b. Perf 12 .. .. 3·00 10
294 **60** 2d. ultramarine, *p* 11 × 12 .. .. 2·50 10
a. Perf 12 × 11½ .. .. .. 1·75 10
b. Perf 12 .. .. 1·75 10
c. Imperf between (pair) .. ..
295 **61** 2½d. purple (Die I), *p* 12 × 11 .. .. 5·00 1·25
a. Perf 11½ × 12 .. .. .. 6·00 80
b. Perf 11 .. .. 6·00 1·75
296 2½d. deep violet (Die II), *p* 12 × 11 .. 3·50 80
a. Perf 11½ × 12 .. .. .. 6·00 1·25
b. Perf 12 .. .. 3·25 1·25
297 2½d. Prussian blue, *p* 12 × 11 .. .. 6·00
a. Perf 11½ × 12 .. .. .. 4·00 80
b. Perf 12 .. .. 3·25 80

The perforations 11 × 12, 12 × 11½ and 12 are from comb machines, the perforation 11 is from a single-line machine.

1897. *Reissue of T* **24.** *W* **25.** *P* 11.
297*c* 5s. reddish purple (*shades*) .. .. .. 30·00 12·00
ca. Imperf between (pair) £2750
d. Perf 12 .. .. 38·00 20·00
e. Perf 11 × 12 or 12 × 11 .. .. .. 30·00 19·00

1899 (Oct). *Chalk-surfaced paper. W* **40.** *P* 12 × 11½ *or* 11½ × 12 (2½*d.*), *comb.*
298 **58** ½d. blue-green (Die I) 90 10
a. Imperf (pair) .. .. .. 50·00 30·00
299 **59** 1d. carmine (Die II) 80 10
a. Imperf horiz (vert pair) .. ..
300 1d. scarlet (Die II) 80 10
301 1d. salmon-red (Die II) 80 10
a. Imperf (pair) .. .. .. 35·00 38·00
302 **60** 2d. cobalt-blue .. .. 1·75 10
a. Imperf (pair) .. .. .. 35·00
303 **61** 2½d. Prussian blue (Die II) .. .. 2·75 70
a. Imperf (pair) .. .. .. 40·00
303*b* **47** 4d. red-brown .. .. 6·00 2·75
c. Imperf (pair) £200
304 4d. orange-brown .. .. .. 6·00 2·75
305 **48** 6d. deep orange .. .. .. 8·00 90
a. Imperf (pair) £140
306 6d. orange-yellow .. .. .. 8·00 90
307 6d. emerald-green .. .. .. 35·00 1·50
a. Imperf (pair) £175
308 **49** 8d. magenta .. .. 6·00 2·00
309 **34** 9d. on 10d. dull brown .. .. .. 6·50 4·00
a. Surcharge double .. .. .. 90·00 70·00
b. Without surcharge .. .. .. 90·00
310 10d. violet .. .. 10·00 2·75
311 **50** 1s. maroon .. .. 9·00 80
312 1s. purple-brown .. .. .. 9·00 1·25
a. Imperf (pair) £150

62 Superb Lyrebird

63

1902. *Chalk-surfaced paper. W* **42.** *P* 12 × 11½ *or* 11½ × 12 (2½*d.*), *comb.*
313 **58** ½d. blue-green, (Die I) .. .. .. 2·75 10
a. Perf 12 × 11 .. .. .. 2·75
314 **59** 1d. carmine (Die II) 80 10
315 **60** 2d. cobalt-blue .. .. 1·50 10
316 **61** 2½d. dark blue (Die II) .. .. .. 2·75 10
317 **47** 4d. orange-brown .. .. .. 14·00 2·75
318 **48** 6d. yellow-orange .. .. .. 15·00 90
319 6d. orange .. .. 14·00 90
320 6d. orange-buff .. .. 14·00 90
321 **49** 8d. magenta .. .. 6·50 1·40
322 **34** 9d. on 10d. brownish orange .. .. 6·50 3·50
323 10d. violet .. .. 18·00 3·00
324 **50** 1s. maroon .. .. 10·00 80
325 1s. purple-brown .. .. .. 11·00 80
326 **62** 2s. 6d. green (Optd S. £35) .. .. 38·00 14·00

1903. *Wmk double-lined V over Crown. W w* **10.**
327 **63** 9d. brown & ultram, *p* 12¼ × 12½, *comb* (Optd S. £27) .. .. .. 7·50 1·75
328 9d. brown & dp blue, *p* 12¼ × 12½, *comb* .. .. 7·50 1·75
329 9d. brown and blue, *p* 11 .. .. .. £450 £275

Die II. Broad "H" in "HALF"

66

1905–10. *Chalk-surfaced paper. W* **66.** *P* 12 × 11½ *or* 11½ × 12 (2½*d.*) *comb, unless otherwise stated.*
330 **58** ½d. blue-green (Die I) .. .. .. 1·75 10
a. Perf 11½ × 11 .. .. ..
331 ½d. blue-green (Die II) 90 10
a. Perf 11½ × 11 .. .. .. 1·75
332 **59** 1d. rose-carmine (Die II) 75 10
a. Perf. 11½ × 11 .. .. .. 1·75
333 **60** 2d. deep ultramarine .. .. .. 1·75 10
b. Perf 11½ × 11 .. .. .. 2·00
333*d* 2d. milky blue (1910) .. .. .. 1·75 10
da. Perf 11 .. .. 60·00
db. Perf 11½ × 11 .. .. ..
334 **61** 2½d. Prussian blue (Die II) .. .. 2·75 80
335 **47** 4d. orange-brown .. .. .. 6·50 2·75
336 4d. red-brown .. .. 7·00 2·75
337 **48** 6d. dull yellow .. .. .. 11·00 1·00
a. Perf 11½ × 11 .. .. .. 19·00
338 6d. orange-yellow .. .. .. 11·00 90
a. Perf 11 × 11½ .. .. .. 25·00
339 **48** 6d. deep orange .. .. 8·00 90
a. Perf 11 .. .. £200
339*b* 6d. orange-buff .. .. 8·00 90
c. Perf 11½ × 11 .. .. .. 15·00 2·75
340 **49** 8d. magenta .. .. 6·50 1·75
341 8d. lilac-rose .. .. 6·50 2·00
342 **34** 10d. violet .. .. 13·00 2·75
a. Perf 11½ × 11 .. .. .. 12·00 2·50
b. Perf 11 .. .. 12·00 2·50
343 **50** 1s. maroon .. .. 8·00 85
344 1s. purple-brown (1908) .. .. .. 9·00 85
345 **62** 2s. 6d. blue-green .. .. .. 38·00 14·00
a. Perf 11½ × 11 .. .. .. 25·00 11·00
b. Perf 11 .. .. 28·00 15·00

67

1905 (Dec). *Chalk-surfaced paper. W* **67.** *P* 11.
346 **52** 20s. cobalt-blue .. .. £200 60·00
a. Perf 12 .. .. £200 60·00
b. Perf 11 × 12 or 12 × 11 .. .. £200 60·00

1906. *Wmk double-lined "A" and Crown, W w* **11.** *P* 12 × 12½, *comb.*
347 **63** 9d. brown and ultramarine .. .. 6·00 1·10
a. Perf 11 .. .. 42·00 35·00
348 9d. yellow-brown and ultramarine .. 6·00 90

1907 (July). *Wmk w* **11.** *P* 12 × 11½ *or* 11½ × 12 (2½*d.*), *comb, unless otherwise stated.*
349 **58** ½d. blue-green (Die I) .. .. .. 2·00 10
351 **59** 1d. dull rose (Die II) .. .. .. 1·75 10
352 **60** 2d. cobalt-blue .. .. 1·75 10
353 **61** 2½d. Prussian blue (Die II) .. .. 42·00
354 **47** 4d. orange-brown .. .. .. 7·00 2·25
355 **48** 6d. orange-buff .. .. .. 17·00 2·50
356 6d. dull yellow .. .. 15·00 2·50
357 **49** 8d. magenta .. .. 6·00 2·25
358 **34** 10d. violet, *p* 11 .. .. .. 18·00
359 **50** 1s. purple-brown .. .. .. 14·00 2·25
a. Perf 11 .. ..
360 **62** 2s. 6d. blue-green .. .. .. 42·00 20·00

OFFICIAL STAMPS

O S (O 1) O S (O 2) O S (O 3)

The space between the letters is normally 7 mm as illustrated, except on the 5d. and 8d. (11–11½ mm), 5s. (12 mm) and 20s. (14 mm). Later printings of the 3d., W **40**, are 5½ mm, and these are listed. Varieties in the settings are known on the 1d. (8 and 8½ mm), 2d. (8½ mm) and 3d. (9 mm).

Varieties of Type O 1 exist with "O" sideways.

Nos. O1/35 overprinted with Type O 1

1879. *Wmk double-lined "6". P* 13.
O1 **14** 3d. dull green .. .. — £450

1879 (Oct)–**85.** *W* **36.** *P* 13.
O 2 **26** 1d. salmon .. .. 8·50 2·00
a. Perf 10 (5.81) .. .. .. £200 30·00
b. Perf 13 × 10 (1881) .. .. 20·00 3·50
O 3 **28** 2d. blue .. .. 8·50 1·25
a. Perf 10 (7.81) .. .. .. £250 32·00
b. Perf 13 × 10 (1881) .. .. 20·00 2·50
c. Perf 10 × 13 (1881) .. .. 45·00 7·00
d. Perf 11 × 12 (11.84?) .. .. — £250
O 4 **14** 3d. dull green (R.) (12.79) .. .. — £225
O 5 3d. dull green (3.80) .. .. .. £300 45·00
a. Perf 10 (1881) .. .. ..
b. Yellow-green. Perf 10 (10.81) .. £160 25·00
c. Ditto. Perf 13 × 10 (1881) .. £160 25·00
d. Ditto. Perf 12 (4.85) £250
e. Ditto. Perf 12 × 10 (4.85) .. ..
O 6 **32** 4d. red-brown .. .. £160 7·50
a. Perf 10 (1881) .. .. .. — £225
b. Perf 13 × 10 (1881) £250 £300
c. Perf 10 × 13 (1881) .. .. £250 11·00
O 7 **15** 5d. green, *p* 10 (8.84) .. .. 14·00 7·50
O 8 **37** 6d. pale lilac .. .. £250 4·50
a. Perf 10 (1881) .. .. .. — 40·00
b. Perf 13 × 10 (1881) .. ..
O 9 **19** 8d. yellow (R.) (12.79) .. .. — £150
O10 8d. yellow (1880) .. .. .. — 9·00
a. Perf 10 (1881) .. .. .. £300 75·00
O11 **34** 9d. on 10d. brown, *p* 10 (1894) .. £300 1·50
O12 **38** 1s. black (R.) .. .. £225 7·50
a. Perf 10 (1881) .. .. .. — 16·00
b. Perf 13 × 10 (1881) .. .. — 9·00
c. Perf 10 × 13 (1881) .. .. — 45·00

Other stamps are known with red overprint but their status is in doubt.

1880–88. *Wmk "5/-", W* **25.** (*a*) *P* 13.
O13 **24** 5s. deep purple (15.2.80) .. .. £450 65·00
a. Royal purple .. .. .. — £350
b. Deep rose-lilac .. .. .. — £350

(*b*) *P* 10
O14 **24** 5s. deep purple (9.82) £450 £180
b. Rose-lilac (1883) £325 £120

(*c*) *P* 10 × 12
O15 **24** 5s. purple (10.86) .. .. ..

(*d*) *P* 12 × 10
O16 **24** 5s. reddish purple (1886) £350 £110

(*e*) *P* 12
O17 **24** 5s. purple .. .. — £180

(*f*) *P* 11
O18 **24** 5s. rose-lilac (1888) .. .. .. £180 42·00

1882–85. *W* **40.** *P* 10.
O19 **26** 1d. salmon .. .. 7·00 2·00
a. Perf 13 × 10 .. .. — £150
O20 1d. orange *to* scarlet .. .. .. 6·00 1·50
a. Perf 10 × 13 .. .. — £150
b. Perf 11 × 12, comb (1.84) .. .. 3·50 1·40
c. Perf 10 × 12 (4.85) .. .. .. — £130
d. Perf 12 × 11 (12.85) .. ..
O21 **28** 2d. blue .. .. 4·00 1·00
a. Perf 13 × 10 .. .. ..
b. Perf 10 × 13 .. .. £225 75·00
c. Perf 11 × 12, comb (1.84) .. .. 4·00 1·00
d. Ditto. Opt double .. .. ..
e. Perf 12 × 11 (12.85) .. ..
O22 **14** 3d. yellow-green (7 *mm*) .. .. 4·50 2·25
a. Perf 12 (4.85) £140 £100
b. Perf 12 × 10 (4.85) .. .. ..
O23 3d. bluish green (7 *mm*) .. .. 4·50 2·25
a. Perf 12 (4.85) £140 £100
b. Perf 12 × 10 (4.85) .. .. ..
c. Perf 10 × 11 (12.85) .. ..
O24 3d. yellow-green (5½ *mm*) .. .. 4·50 2·25
a. Perf 12 × 10 or 10 × 12 (4.85) .. 4·50 2·25
b. Perf 10 × 11 or 11 × 10 (12.85) ..
O25 3d. bluish green (5½ *mm*) .. .. 4·50 2·25
a. Perf 12 × 10 or 10 × 12 (4.85) .. 4·75 2·75
c. Perf 10 × 11 or 11 × 10 (12.85) .. 4·00 2·25
O26 **32** 4d. red-brown .. .. 25·00 2·50
a. Perf 11 × 12, comb (1.84) .. .. 7·00 2·25
b. Perf 10 × 12 (4.85) .. .. .. — 70·00
O27 4d. dark brown .. .. 11·00 2·25
a. Perf 11 × 12, comb (1.84) .. .. 7·00 2·25
b. Perf 12 (4.85) £250 £180
c. Perf 10 × 12 (4.85) £250 £110
O28 **15** 5d. dull green .. .. 8·50 4·00
a. Perf 12 × 10 (4.85) .. .. ..
O29 5d. blue-green .. .. 9·00 5·00
a. Perf 12 (4.85) £120
b. Perf 10 × 11 .. .. 9·00 5·00
O30 **37** 6d. pale lilac .. .. 14·00 1·75
a. Perf 11 (12.85) .. .. 15·00 1·50
O31 6d. mauve .. .. 14·00 1·75
a. Perf 12 (4.85) .. .. — 45·00
b. Perf 12 × 10 (4.85) .. .. .. 14·00 1·50
c. Perf 10 × 12 (4.85) .. .. .. 80·00 36·00
d. Perf 11 × 10 (12.85) .. .. .. 14·00 1·75
e. Perf 12 × 11 (12.85) .. .. .. 55·00 15·00
O32 **19** 8d. yellow .. .. 17·00 3·25
a. Perf 12 (4.85) .. .. £150 36·00
b. Perf 12 × 10 or 10 × 12 (4.85) .. 17·00 2·75
d. Perf 11 (12.85) .. .. 18·00 3·00
e. Ditto. Opt double .. .. ..
O33 **38** 1s. black (R.) .. .. 17·00 2·50
a. Perf 10 × 13 .. .. — 55·00
b. Perf 11 × 12, comb (1.84) .. .. 17·00 2·50
c. Ditto. Opt double .. .. ..

1886–87. *W* **41.** *P* 10.
O34 **26** 1d. scarlet .. .. 20·00 3·00
O35 **28** 2d. deep blue .. ..
a. Perf 11 × 12 .. ..

1887–89. *Nos.* 247/8 *overprinted in black.* (*a*) *With Type* O **1.**
O36 **43** 10s. claret and mauve, *p* 12 .. .. — £800

(*b*) *With Type* O **2** (April 1889)
O37 **43** 10s. claret and mauve, *p* 12 .. .. £1300 £600
a. Perf 10 .. .. £2250 £1500

(*c*) *With Type* O **3** (Jan 1887)
O38 **43** £1 claret and rose-lilac, *p* 12 × 10 .. £2500
a. Opt double .. .. ..

1888–89. *Optd as Type* O **1.** *P* 11 × 12. (i) *W* **40.**
O39 **45** 1d. mauve (5.88) .. .. .. 1·50 10
a. Perf 12 .. .. 1·50 10
O40 1d. lilac .. .. 1·50 10
a. Perf 12 .. .. 1·50 10
O41 **46** 2d. Prussian blue (9.88) .. .. 2·00 10
a. Perf 12 .. .. 2·00 10
O42 **47** 4d. purple-brown (10.88) .. .. 4·00 70
a. Perf 12 .. .. 5·50 70
b. Perf 11 .. ..
O43 4d. red-brown .. .. 4·00 70
a. Perf 12 .. .. 5·00 70
O44 **48** 6d. carmine (12.88) .. .. .. 4·50 85
a. Perf 12 .. .. 6·00 85
O45 **49** 8d. lilac-rose (3.89) .. .. .. 10·00 3·75
a. Perf 12 .. .. — 5·00
O46 **50** 1s. maroon (3.89) .. .. .. 8·00 1·25
a. Perf 12 .. .. 9·00 1·25
O47 1s. purple-brown .. .. .. 8·00 1·25
a. Perf 12 .. .. 8·00 1·25
b. Opt double .. .. ..

(ii) *W* **41** (1889)
O48 **45** 1d. mauve .. ..
O49 **46** 2d. blue .. ..

1888–89. *Optd as Type* O **1.** *W* **25.** *P* 10.
O50 **51** 5s. deep purple (R.) (4.89) £600 £450
O51 **52** 20s. cobalt-blue (11.88) £1200

1890–91. *Optd as Type* O **1.** *W* **53** (5s.) *or* **54** (20s.). *P* 10.
O52 **51** 5s. lilac (2.90) .. .. £150 42·00
a. Mauve .. .. £175 45·00
b. Dull lilac. Perf 12 .. .. .. £650
O53 **52** 20s. cobalt-blue (3.91) £1800

1891 (Jan)**–92.** *Nos.* 281/5 *optd as Type* O **1.** *W* **40.** *P* 11 × 12.
O54 **55** 2½d. ultramarine .. .. .. 2·75 1·50
O55 **26** ½d. on 1d. grey .. .. .. 16·00 8·50
O56 **37** 7½d. on 6d. brown, *p* 10 .. .. 17·00 7·50
O57 **38** 12½d. on 1s. red .. .. .. 17·00 7·50
O58 **58** ½d. grey (5.92) .. .. .. 2·50 1·75
a. Perf 10 .. .. 2·75 3·50
b. Perf 12 .. .. 2·50 2·00
c. Perf 12 × 11½ .. .. .. 4·00

1894 (30 June). *Optd as Type* O **1.** *Wmk* "**10**", *T* **35.**
O59 **34** 10d. lilac £150 £100
a. Perf 10 × 11 .. .. £225 £200

POSTAGE DUE STAMPS

D 1

(Dies eng by A. Collingridge. Typo Govt Printing Office, Sydney)

1891 (1 Jan)**–92.** *W* **40.** *P* 10.
D 1 **D 1** ½d. green (21.1.92) .. .. .. 2·50 2·00
D 2 1d. green .. .. 2·50 90
a. Perf 11 .. .. 2·75 90
b. Perf 12 .. .. 11·00 2·50
c. Perf 12 × 10 .. .. — 1·75
d. Perf 10 × 11 .. .. 5·00 90
e. Perf 11 × 12 or 12 × 11 .. .. 3·00 90
D 3 2d. green .. .. 4·50 80
a. Perf 11 .. .. 4·50 80
b. Perf 12 .. .. — 8·00
c. Perf 12 × 10 .. .. 12·00 3·00
d. Perf 10 × 11 .. .. 5·50 1·50
e. Perf 11 × 12 or 12 × 11 .. .. 4·50 80
D 4 3d. green .. .. 7·00 2·25
a. Perf 10 × 11 .. .. 7·00 2·25
D 5 4d. green .. .. 6·00 80
a. Perf 11 .. .. 7·00 80
b. Perf 10 × 11 .. .. 6·00 80
D 6 6d. green .. .. 11·00 2·00
D 7 8d. green .. .. 55·00 2·50
D 8 5s. green .. .. £120 30·00
a. Perf 11 .. .. £200 75·00
b. Perf 11 × 12 .. .. — £250
D 9 10s. green (early 1891) .. .. .. £180 45·00
a. Perf 12 × 10 .. .. £120 80·00
D10 20s. green (early 1891) .. .. .. £300 80·00
a. Perf 12 .. .. £300
b. Perf 12 × 10 .. .. £175 £100
D1/10 Optd "Specimen" .. .. *Set of* 10 £350

1900. *Chalk-surfaced paper. W* **40.** *P* 11.
D11 **D 1** ½d. emerald-green .. ..
D12 1d. emerald-green .. .. .. 2·50 1·25
a. Perf 12 .. .. 8·00 3·50
b. Perf 11 × 12 or 12 × 11 .. .. 2·25 90
D13 2d. emerald-green .. .. .. 4·50 1·40
a. Perf 12 .. .. — 10·00
b. Perf 11 × 12 or 12 × 11 .. .. 3·75 90
D14 3d. emerald-green, *p* 11 × 12 or 12 × 11 8·00 1·75
D15 4d. emerald-green .. .. .. 5·50 90

New South Wales now uses stamps of Australia.

New Zealand

During the years of the early settlement of New Zealand mail for Sydney, New South Wales, was routed through an unofficial postmaster at Kororareka. The first official post offices did not open until 1841 when the New South Wales authorities relinquished supervision of the postal service. The British G.P.O. was responsible for the operation of the overseas mails from 11 October 1841 until the postal service once again passed under colonial control in 1848.

For illustrations of handstamp types see BRITISH POST OFFICES ABROAD notes, following GREAT BRITAIN.

AUCKLAND

CROWNED-CIRCLE HANDSTAMPS

CC1 CC 1 AUCKLAND NEW ZEALAND (R.) (31.10.1846) .. .. *Price on cover* £300

NELSON

CROWNED-CIRCLE HANDSTAMPS

CC2 CC 1 NELSON NEW ZEALAND (R.) (31.10.1846) *Price on cover* £1100

NEW PLYMOUTH

CROWNED-CIRCLE HANDSTAMPS

CC3 CC 1 NEW PLYMOUTH NEW ZEALAND (R. *or* Black) (31.10.1846) .. *Price on cover* £1500

OTAGO

CROWNED-CIRCLE HANDSTAMPS

CC4 CC 2 OTAGO NEW ZEALAND (R.) (*circa* 1852) *Price on cover* £1500

PETRE

CROWNED-CIRCLE HANDSTAMPS

CC5 CC 1 PETRE NEW ZEALAND (R.) (31.10.1846) *Price on cover* £1500

PORT VICTORIA

CROWNED-CIRCLE HANDSTAMPS

CC6 CC 2 PORT VICTORIA NEW ZEALAND (R.) (*circa* 1852) .. .. *Price on cover* £1000

RUSSELL

CROWNED-CIRCLE HANDSTAMPS

CC7 CC 1 RUSSELL NEW ZEALAND (R.) (30.10.1846) *Price on cover* £1400

WELLINGTON

CROWNED-CIRCLE HANDSTAMPS

CC8 CC 1 WELLINGTON NEW ZEALAND (R.) (31.10.1846) .. .. *Price on cover* £500

A similar mark for Christchurch is only known struck, in black, as a cancellation after the introduction of adhesive stamps.

PRICES FOR STAMPS ON COVER TO 1945

Nos. 1/125	*from* × 2
Nos. 126/36	*from* × 3
Nos. 137/9	*from* × 2
No. 140	—
No. 141	*from* × 2
No. 142	—
Nos. 143/8	*from* × 2
Nos. 149/51	*from* × 10
Nos. 152/84	*from* × 2
Nos. 185/6	—
Nos. 187/203	*from* × 3
Nos. 205/7*e*	—
Nos. 208/13	*from* × 2
Nos. 214/16*j*	—
Nos. 217/70	*from* × 3
No. 271	—
Nos. 272/89	*from* × 3
Nos. 290/1	—
Nos. 292/312	*from* × 3
Nos. 313/51	*from* × 2
Nos. 353/74	*from* × 3
Nos. 375/7	—
Nos. 378/400	*from* × 3
Nos. 401/14	—
Nos. 415/*a*	*from* × 5
Nos. 416/17*a*	—
Nos. 418/*b*	*from* × 5
Nos. 418*c*/22*b*	—
Nos. 424/46	*from* × 2
Nos. 447/8	—
Nos. 449/50	*from* × 4
Nos. 452/69	*from* × 3
Nos. 470/666	*from* × 2
Nos. E1/5	*from* × 5
No. E6	*from* × 10
Nos. D1/8	*from* × 3
Nos. D9/16	*from* × 5
Nos. D17/20	*from* × 3
Nos. D21/47	*from* × 6
Nos. O1/24	*from* × 12
Nos. O59/66	*from* × 4
Nos. O67/8	—
Nos. O69/79	*from* × 5
Nos. O80/5	—
Nos. O86/91	*from* × 20
Nos. O92/99	*from* × 5
Nos. O100/11	*from* × 12
Nos. O112/13	—
Nos. O115/19	*from* × 15
Nos. O120/33	*from* × 10
Nos. O134/51	*from* × 4
Nos. P1/7	*from* × 8
Nos. L1/9	*from* × 6
Nos. L9*a*/12	—
Nos. L13/20	*from* × 10
Nos. L21/3	—
Nos. L24/41	*from* × 10
No. F1	—
No. F2	*from* × 5
Nos. F3/144	—
Nos. F145/58	*from* × 3
Nos. F159/68	—
Nos. F169/79	*from* × 3
Nos. F180/6	—
Nos. F187/90	*from* × 2
Nos. F191/203	*from* × 3
Nos. F204/11	—
Nos. F212/18	*from* × 2
Nos. A1/3	*from* × 2

1

2

(Eng by Humphreys. Recess P.B.)

1855 (18 July). *Wmk Large Star, W* w **1.** *Imperf.*
1 **1** 1d. dull carmine (*white paper*) .. £20000 £8000
2 2d. dull blue (*blued paper*) £9000 £550
3 1s. pale yellow-green (*blued paper*) .. £18000 £5250
a. Bisected (6d.) (on cover) .. .. † £25000

The 2d. and 2s. on white paper formerly listed are now known to be stamps printed on blued paper which have had the bluing washed out.

Nos. 3a and 6a. were used at Dunedin from March 1857 when the rate for ½ oz letters to Great Britain was reduced to 6d. All known examples are bisected vertically.

(Printed by J. Richardson, Auckland, N.Z.)

1855 (Dec). *First printing. Wmk Large Star. White paper. Imperf.*
3*b* **1** 1d. orange .. ..

1855 (Dec)**–57.** *No wmk. Blue paper. Imperf.*
4 **1** 1d. red £5000 £1400
5 2d. blue (3.56) £1800 £300
a. Without value .. ..
6 1s. green (9.57) £9000 £3500
a. Bisected (6d.) (on cover) .. .. † £15000

These stamps on blue paper may occasionally be found wmkd double-lined letters, being portions of the paper-maker's name.

1857 (Jan). *Wmk Large Star. White paper similar to the issue of July* 1855.
7 1 1d. dull orange .. .. — £12000

This stamp is in the precise shade of the 1d. of the 1858 printing by Richardson on *no wmk* white paper. An unsevered pair is known with Dunedin cancellation on a cover bearing arrival postmark of Auckland dated "19.1.1857".

1858–62. *Hard or soft white paper. No wmk.* (a) *Imperf.*
8 1 1d. dull orange (1858) £900 £300
8*a* 2d. deep ultramarine (1858) £1400 £650
9 2d. pale blue £700 £175
10 2d. blue £700 £175
11 2d. dull deep blue .. .. .. — £175
12 6d. bistre-brown (Aug 1859) £2000 £500
13 6d. brown £850 £300
14 6d. pale brown £850 £300
15 6d. chestnut £1800 £500
16 1s. dull emerald-green £5000 £1000
17 1s. blue-green £5000 £1200

(b) *Pin-roulette, about* 10
18 1 1d. dull orange .. .. — £4500
19 2d. blue .. .. — £4500
20 6d. brown .. .. — £4500
21 1s. blue-green .. .. — £6500

(c) *Serrated perf about* 16 *or* 18
22 1 1d. dull orange .. .. — £2750
23 2d. blue .. .. — £2750
24 6d. brown .. .. — £2750
25 6d. chestnut .. .. — £4750
26 1s. blue-green .. .. — £4750

(d) *Rouletted* 7
27 1 1d. dull orange £4250 £3000
28 2d. blue £5250 £2750
29 6d. brown £3500 £2750
a. Imperf between (pair) £10000 £9000
30 1s. dull emerald-green £5250 £3500
31 1s. blue-green £6500 £3500

(e) *P* 13 *at Dunedin* (1862)
31*a* 1 1d. dull orange .. .. — £2000
31*b* 2d. pale blue £2750 £1750
32 6d. pale brown .. ..

Other forms of separation, in addition to those shown above, are known, both on the stamps of this issue and on those of 1862. Some of the varieties are extremely rare, only single copies being known.

The 2d. in a distinctive deep bright blue on white paper wmkd. Large Star is believed by experts to have been printed by Richardson in 1861 or 1862. This also exists doubly printed and with serrated perf.

(Printed by John Davies at the G.P.O., Auckland, N.Z.)

1862 (Feb–Aug). *Wmk Large Star.* (a) *Imperf.*
33 1 1d. orange-vermilion £225 £110
34 1d. vermilion £275 £110
35 1d. carmine-vermilion £300 £140
36 2d. deep blue (Plate I) .. .. .. £200 55·00
37 2d. slate-blue (Plate I) £1200 £140
37*a* 2d. milky blue (Plate I, worn) .. ..
38 2d. pale blue (Plate I, worn) .. .. £125 65·00
39 2d. blue (*to* deep) (Plate I, very worn) .. £160 65·00
40 3d. brown-lilac £200 £100
41 6d. black-brown .. .. £500 70·00
42 6d. brown .. .. £500 70·00
43 6d. red-brown .. .. £400 60·00
44 1s. green £600 £150
45 1s. yellow-green £600 £140
46 1s. deep green £700 £175

Nos. 37*a*/38 show some signs of wear on right of Queen's head and shades of No. 39 show moderate to advanced states of wear.

(b) *Rouletted* 7 (6.62)
47 1 1d. orange-vermilion £3000 £600
48 1d. vermilion £1800 £600
48*a* 1d. carmine-vermilion .. .. .. — £700
49 2d. deep blue £1700 £400
50 2d. slate-blue £2750 £550
51 2d. pale blue £1500 £500
52 3d. brown-lilac £1700 £600
53 6d. black-brown £2000 £400
54 6d. brown £1700 £400
55 6d. red-brown £1700 £400
56 1s. green £1700 £500
57 1s. yellow-green £2750 £500
58 1s. deep green £2750 £600

(c) *Serrated perf* 14 *or* 16 (8.62)
59 1 1d. orange-vermilion .. .. .. — £750
60 2d. deep blue .. .. — £700
a. Imperf between (pair) £4000 £2000
61 2d. slate-blue .. ..
62 3d. brown-lilac .. .. — £1400
63 6d. black-brown .. .. — £1500
64 6d. brown .. .. — £1500
65 1s. yellow-green .. .. — £1700

(d) *Pin-perf* 10 (8.62)
66 1 2d. deep blue .. .. — £1700
67 6d. black-brown .. .. — £2750

The dates put to above varieties are the earliest that have been met with.

1862. *Wmk Large Star. P* 13 (*at Dunedin*).
68 1 1d. orange-vermilion £450 £150
69 1d. carmine-vermilion £450 £150
70 2d. deep blue (Plate I) .. .. .. £225 35·00
71 2d. slate-blue (Plate I) .. .. .. — £700
72 2d. blue (Plate I) .. .. £160 35·00
72*a* 2d. milky blue (Plate I) .. ..
73 2d. pale blue (Plate I) .. .. .. £160 35·00
74 3d. brown-lilac £450 £110
75 6d. black-brown £450 £100
a. Imperf between (horiz pair) ..
76 6d. brown .. .. £400 55·00
77 6d. red-brown .. .. £300 35·00
78 1s. dull green £300 £160
79 1s. deep green £400 £170
80 1s. yellow-green £400 £160

See also Nos. 110/125 and the note that follows these.

1862. *Pelure paper. No wmk.* (a) *Imperf.*
81 1 1d. orange-vermilion £4750 £1700
82 2d. ultramarine £2750 £750
83 2d. pale ultramarine £2750 £750
84 3d. lilac .. .. £25000 †
85 1 6d. black-brown £1000 £210
86 1s. deep green £4750 £800

The 3d. is known only unused.

(b) *Rouletted* 7
87 1 1d. orange-vermilion .. .. .. — £4000
88 6d. black-brown £2000 £450
89 1s. deep green £3500 £850

(c) *P* 13
90 1 1d. orange-vermilion £9500 £3000
91 2d. ultramarine £4500 £500
92 2d. pale ultramarine £4500 £500
93 6d. black-brown £3500 £300
94 1s. deep green £7000 £850

(d) *Serrated perf* 15
95 1 6d. black-brown .. .. — £3500

1863 (early). *Hard or soft white paper. No wmk.* (a) *Imperf.*
96 1 2d. dull deep blue (*shades*) £2000 £800

(b) *P* 13
96*a* 1 2d. dull deep blue (*shades*) £1500 £475

These stamps show slight beginnings of wear of the printing plate in the background to right of the Queen's ear, as one looks at the stamps. By the early part of 1864, the wear of the plate had spread, more or less, all over the background of the circle containing the head. The major portion of the stamps of this printing appears to have been consigned to Dunedin and to have been there perforated 13.

1864. *Wmk* "N Z", *W* **2.** (a) *Imperf.*
97 1 1d. carmine-vermilion £700 £200
98 2d. pale blue (Plate I worn) £750 £200
99 6d. red-brown £2000 £475
100 1s. green £850 £250

(b) *Rouletted* 7
101 1 1d. carmine-vermilion £4500 £2750
102 2d. pale blue (Plate I worn) £1300 £950
103 6d. red-brown £4250 £2750
104 1s. green £2750 £850

(c) *P* 13 (*at Dunedin*)
104*a* 1 1d. carmine-vermilion £5000 £3500
105 2d. pale blue (Plate I worn) £450 £160
106 1s. green £1000 £550
a. Imperf between (horiz pair) £7500

(d) *P* 12½ (*at Auckland*)
106*b* 1 1d. carmine-vermilion £3250 £1700
107 2d. pale blue (Plate I worn) .. .. £175 50·00
108 6d. red-brown .. .. £175 30·00
109 1s. yellow-green .. .. — £2000

1864–67. *Wmk Large Star. P* 12½ (*at Auckland*).
110 1 1d. carmine-vermilion (1864) .. .. 70·00 17·00
111 1d. pale orange-vermilion .. .. 70·00 17·00
a. Imperf (pair) £1200 £600
112 1d. orange .. .. £175 38·00
113 2d. pale blue (Plate I worn) (1864) .. 70·00 17·00
114 2d. deep blue (Plate II) (1866) .. .. 70·00 17·00
a. Imperf between (pair) .. .. — £2000
115 2d. blue (Plate II) .. .. 70·00 17·00
a. Retouched (Plate II) (1867) .. .. £120 19·00
c. Imperf (pair) (Plate II) £900 £900
d. Retouched. Imperf (pair) £1200 £1400
116 3d. brown-lilac (1864) £600 £500
117 3d. lilac .. .. 50·00 17·00
a. Imperf (pair) £1000 £600
118 3d. deep mauve .. .. £250 45·00
a. Imperf (pair) £1200 £600
119 4d. deep rose (1865) £1300 £250
120 4d. yellow (1865) .. .. 75·00 38·00
121 4d. orange £1000 £1000
122 6d. red-brown (1864) .. .. .. 70·00 17·00
122*a* 6d. brown .. .. 70·00 17·00
b. Imperf (pair) £650 £650
123 1s. deep green (1864) £375 £150
124 1s. green .. .. £250 60·00
125 1s. yellow-green .. .. £100 50·00

The above issue is sometimes difficult to distinguish from Nos. 68/80 because the vertical perforations usually gauge 12¾ and sometimes a full 13. However stamps of this issue invariably gauge 12½ horizontally, whereas the 1862 stamps measure a full 13.

The 1d., 2d. and 6d. were officially reprinted imperforate, without gum, in 1884 for presentation purposes. They can be distinguished from the errors listed by their shades which are pale orange, dull blue and dull chocolate-brown respectively, and by the worn state of the plates from which they were printed.

1871. *Wmk Large Star.* (a) *P* 10.
126 1 1d. brown .. .. £375 50·00

(b) *P* 12½ × 10
127 1 1d. deep brown .. .. — £650

(c) *P* 10 × 12½
128 1 1d. brown .. .. 85·00 17·00
a. Perf 12½ comp 10 (1 side) .. .. — 50·00
129 2d. deep blue (Plate II) .. .. .. — £4000
a. Perf 10* .. ..
130 2d. vermilion .. .. 90·00 17·00
a. Retouched .. .. £140 19·00
b. Perf 12½ comp 10 (1 side) .. .. — £250
c. Perf 10* .. ..
131 6d. deep blue £850 £425
a. Blue £675 £250
b. Imperf between (vert pair) .. .. — £3750
c. Perf 12½ comp 10 (1 side) £425 £160

(d) *P* 12½
132 1 1d. red-brown .. .. 90·00 17·00
a. Brown (shades, worn plate) .. .. 90·00 17·00
a. Imperf horiz (vert pair) .. .. — £2250
133 2d. orange .. .. 32·00 17·00
a. Retouched .. .. £110 40·00
134 2d. vermilion .. .. 80·00 17·00
a. Retouched .. .. £150 50·00
135 6d. blue .. .. 80·00 17·00
136 6d. pale blue .. .. 32·00 17·00

In or about 1872 both 1d. and 2d. stamps were printed on some paper having a wmk of script letters "W.T. & Co." (=Wiggins Teape & Co) in the sheet, and other paper with the name "T. H. Saunders" in double-lined capitals in the sheet; portions of these letters are occasionally found on stamps.

*Only one used copy each of Nos. 129a and 130c have been reported.

1872. *No wmk. P* 12½.
137 1 1d. brown .. .. £225 40·00
138 2d. vermilion .. .. 38·00 18·00
a. Retouched .. .. £150 18·00
139 4d. orange-yellow £120 £450

1872. *Wmk* "N Z", *W* **2.** *P* 12½.
140 1 1d. brown £12000 £2250
141 2d. vermilion .. .. £300 65·00
a. Retouched £600 £150

1872. *Wmk Lozenges, with* "INVICTA" *in double-lined capitals four times in the sheet. P* 12½.
142 1 2d. vermilion £2000 £850
a. Retouched £3250 £1100

3

4

(Des John Davies. Die eng on wood in Melbourne. Printed from electrotypes at Govt Ptg Office, Wellington)

1873 (1 Jan). (a) *Wmk* "NZ", *W* **2.**
143 3 ½d. pale dull rose (*p* 10) .. .. .. 60·00 14·00
144 ½d. pale dull rose (*p* 12½) .. .. £180 55·00
145 ½d. pale dull rose (*p* 12½ × 10) .. .. £110 42·00

(b) *No wmk*
146 3 ½d. pale dull rose (*p* 10) .. .. .. 60·00 20·00
147 ½d. pale dull rose (*p* 12½) .. .. £180 60·00
148 ½d. pale dull rose (*p* 12½ × 10) .. .. £150 55·00

As the paper used for Nos. 143/5 was originally intended for fiscal stamps which were more than twice as large, about one-third of the impressions fall on portions of the sheet showing no watermark, giving rise to varieties Nos. 146/8. In later printings of No. 151 a few stamps in each sheet are without watermark. These can be distinguished from No. 147 by the shade.

1875 (Jan). *Wmk Star, W* **4.**
149 3 ½d. pale dull rose (*p* 12½) .. .. 7·50 90
a. Imperf between (pair) £450 £275
150 ½d. dull pale rose (*p nearly* 12) .. .. 60·00 5·50

1892 (June). *Wmk* "*NZ and Star*", *W* **12***b*. *P* 12½.
151 3 ½d. bright rose (*shades*) .. .. .. 2·00 25
a. No wmk .. .. 3·75 2·25

5 6 7

8 9 10

11 12 12*a* 6 mm

12*b* 7 mm 12*c* 4 mm

(T **5/10** eng De La Rue. T **11** and **12** des, eng & plates by W. R. Bock. Typo Govt Ptg Office, Wellington)

1874 (1 Jan). *W* **12***a*. A. *White paper.* (a) *P* 12½.
152 5 1d. lilac .. .. 35·00 3·25
a. Imperf £400
153 6 2d. rose .. .. 35·00 1·60
154 7 3d. brown .. .. 75·00 45·00
155 8 4d. maroon .. .. £250 45·00
156 9 6d. blue .. .. £180 20·00
157 10 1s. green .. .. £1000 40·00

(b) *Perf nearly* 12
158 6 2d. rose £550 £180

(c) *Perf compound of* 12½ *and* 10
159 5 1d. lilac .. .. £150 40·00
160 6 2d. rose .. .. £350 60·00
161 7 3d. brown .. .. £150 50·00
162 8 4d. maroon .. .. £325 90·00
163 9 6d. blue .. .. £190 40·00
164 10 1s. green .. .. £1000 95·00
aa. Imperf between (vert pair) .. .. † —

(d) Perf nearly 12 × 12½

164*a*	**5**	1d. lilac	£650	£250
165	**6**	2d. rose	£650	£190

B. *Blued paper. (a) P 12½*

166	**5**	1d. lilac	65·00	29·00
167	**6**	2d. rose	90·00	29·00
168	**7**	3d. brown	£200	60·00
169	**8**	4d. maroon	£425	£100
170	**9**	6d. blue	£300	45·00
171	**10**	1s. green	£1000	£190

(b) Perf compound of 12½ and 10

172	**5**	1d. lilac	£180	45·00
173	**6**	2d. rose	£500	80·00
174	**7**	3d. brown	£130	55·00
175	**8**	4d. maroon	£450	£110
176	**9**	6d. blue	£300	90·00
177	**10**	1s. green	£1000	£200

1875. *Wmk Large Star, W* w **1**. *P* 12½.

178	**5**	1d. deep lilac	£450	75·00
179	**6**	2d. rose	£300	15·00

1878. *W* **12***a*. *P* 12 × 11½ *(comb).*

180	**5**	1d. mauve-lilac	25·00	2·00
181	**6**	2d. rose	25·00	1·75
182	**8**	4d. maroon	£120	35·00
183	**9**	6d. blue	70·00	16·00
184	**10**	1s. green	£110	27·00
185	**11**	2s. deep rose	£425	£375
186	**12**	5s. grey	£475	£375

This perforation is made by a horizontal "comb" machine, giving a gauge of 12 horizontally and about 11¾ vertically. Single specimens can be found apparently gauging 11½ all round or 12 all round, but these are all from the same machine. The perforation described above as "nearly 12" was from a single-line machine.

13 14 15

16 17 18

19 20 21

22

Description of Watermarks

W12a. 6 mm between "N Z" and star; broad irregular star; comparatively wide "N"; "N Z" 11½ mm wide.

W12b. 7 mm between "N Z" and star; narrower star; narrow "N"; "N Z" 10 mm wide.

W12*c*. 4 mm between "N Z" and star; narrow star; wide "N"; "N Z" 11½ mm wide.

Description of Papers

1882–88. Smooth paper with horizontal mesh. W **12***a*.
1888–98. Smooth paper with vertical mesh. *W* **12***b*.
1890–91. Smooth paper with vertical mesh. *W* **12***c*.
1898. Thin yellowish toned, coarse paper with clear vertical mesh. *W* **12***b*. Perf 11 only.

In 1899–1900 stamps appeared on medium to thick white coarse paper but we do not differentiate these (except where identifiable by shade) as they are more difficult to distinguish.

PAPER MESH. This shows on the back of the stamp as a series of parallel grooves, either vertical or horizontal. It is caused by the use of a wire gauze conveyor-belt during paper-making.

Description of Dies

1d.

Die 1

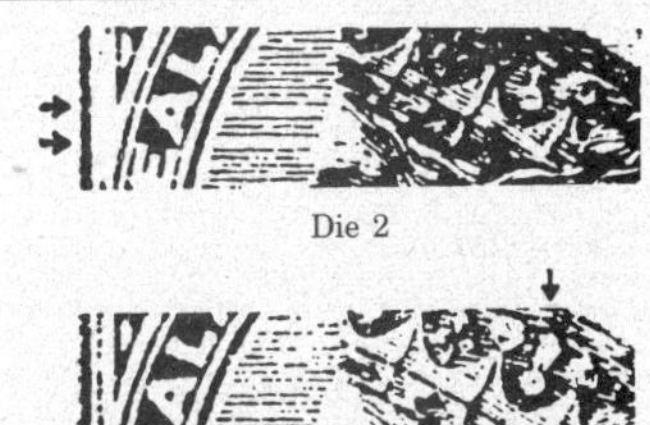

Die 2

Die 3

1882. Die 1. Background shading complete and heavy.

1886. Die 2. Background lines thinner. Two lines of shading weak or missing left of Queen's forehead.

1889. Die 3. Shading on head reduced; ornament in crown left of chignon clearer, with unshaded "arrow" more prominent.

2d.

Die 1

Die 2

Die 3

1882. Die 1. Background shading complete and heavy.

1886. Die 2. Weak line of shading left of forehead and missing shading lines below "TA".

1889. Die 3. As Die 2 but with comma-like white notch in hair below "&".

6d.

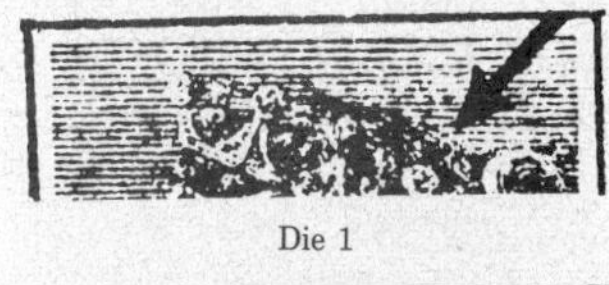

Die 1

Die 2

1882. Die 1. Shading heavy. Top of head merges into shading.

1892. Die 2. Background lines thinner. Shading on head more regular with clear line of demarcation between head and background shading.

(Des F. W. Sears (½d.), A. E. Cousins (2½d.), A. W. Jones (5d.); others adapted from 1874 issue by W. H. Norris. Dies eng A. E. Cousins (½d., 2½d., 5d.), W. R. Bock (others). Typo Govt Ptg Office)

1882–1900. *Inscr* "POSTAGE & REVENUE".

A. *W* **12***a*. *Paper with horiz mesh* (1.4.82–86). *(a) P* 12 × 11½

187	**14**	1d. rose *to* rose-red (Die 1)	35·00	4·00
		a. Imperf (pair)	£190	
		b. Imperf between (vert pair)		
		c. Die 2. *Pale rose to carmine-rose* (1886)	30·00	4·00
188	**15**	2d. lilac *to* lilac-purple (Die 1)	40·00	4·00
		a. Imperf (pair)	£225	
		b. Imperf between (vert pair)	£225	
		c. Die 2. *Lilac* (1886)	45·00	5·00
189	**17**	3d. yellow (1884)	45·00	4·50
190	**18**	4d. blue-green	48·00	4·50
191	**20**	6d. brown (Die 1)	60·00	4·50
192	**21**	8d. blue	65·00	45·00
193	**22**	1s. red-brown	75·00	12·00

(b) P 12½ (1884?)

193*a*	**14**	1d. rose *to* rose-red (Die 1)	£170	70·00

B. W **12***b*. *Paper with vert mesh* (1888–95). *(a) P* 12 × 11½ (1888–95)

194	**13**	½d. black (1.4.95)	25·00	48·00
195	**14**	1d. rose *to* rosine (Die 2)	30·00	3·50
		a. Die 3. *Rose to carmine* (1889)	30·00	3·50
196	**15**	2d. lilac (Die 2)	35·00	3·50
		a. Die 3. *Lilac to purple* (1889)	35·00	3·50
197	**16**	2½d. pale blue (1891)	32·00	5·50
		a. Ultramarine (green adverts) (1893)	42·00	12·00
198	**17**	3d. yellow	40·00	5·00
199	**18**	4d. green *to* bluish green	48·00	3·00
200	**19**	5d. olive-black (1.2.91)	40·00	14·00
		a. Imperf (pair)	£225	
201	**20**	6d. brown (Die 1)	55·00	2·75
		a. Die 2 (1892)	£110	50·00
202	**21**	8d. blue	65·00	45·00
203	**22**	1s. red-brown	75·00	6·50

(b) Perf compound of 12 and 12½ (1888–91)

204	**14**	1d. rose (Die 2)	£190	75·00
		a. Die 3 (1889)		

(c) P 12½ (1888–89)

205	**14**	1d. rose (Die 3) (1889)	£160	90·00
206	**15**	2d. lilac (Die 2)	£160	80·00
		a. Die 3. *Deep lilac* (1889)	£120	65·00
207	**16**	2½d. blue (1891)	£170	90·00

(d) Mixed perfs 12 × 11½ *and* 12½ (1891–93)

207*a*	**14**	1d. rose (Die 3)		
207*b*	**15**	2d. lilac (Die 3)		
207*c*	**18**	4d. green	—	50·00
207*d*	**19**	5d. olive-black	—	95·00
207*e*	**20**	6d. brown (Die 1)	—	£100
		ea. Die 2	—	£150

C. *W* **12***c*. *Paper with vert mesh* (1890). *(a) P* 12 × 11½

208	**14**	1d. rose (Die 3)	35·00	4·00
209	**15**	2d. purple (Die 3)	45·00	4·00
210	**16**	2½d. ultramarine (27.12)	38·00	6·00
211	**17**	3d. yellow	45·00	5·00
		a. Lemon-yellow	50·00	5·50
212	**20**	6d. brown (Die 1)	80·00	12·00
213	**22**	1s. deep red-brown	90·00	22·00

(b) P 12½

214	**14**	1d. rose (Die 3)	£170	£100
215	**15**	2d. purple (Die 3)	£180	90·00
216	**16**	2½d. ultramarine	£200	95·00

(c) Perf compound of 12 and 12½

216*a*	**20**	6d. brown (Die 1)	£180	£130

D. *Continuation of W* **12***b*. *Paper with vert mesh* (1891–1900)

(a) Perf compound of 10 and 12½ (1891–94)

216*b*	**14**	1d. rose (Die 3)	£150	70·00
216*c*	**15**	2d. lilac (Die 3)	£150	55·00
216*d*	**16**	2½d. blue (1893)	£130	60·00
216*e*	**17**	3d. yellow	£150	70·00
216*f*	**18**	4d. green	£170	£140
216*g*	**19**	5d. olive-black (1894)	£180	£170
216*h*	**20**	6d. brown (Die 1)	£190	£190
		i. Die 2 (1892)	£150	£150
216*j*	**22**	1s. red-brown	£170	£160

(b) P 10 (1891–95)

217	**13**	½d. black (1895)	2·50	15
218	**14**	1d. rose (Die 3)	4·00	10
		a. Carmine	5·00	1·25
		b. Imperf (pair)	£190	£190
		c. Imperf between (pair)	£225	
		d. Imperf horiz (vert pair)	£160	
		e. Mixed perfs 10 and 12½	£250	£120
219	**15**	2d. lilac (Die 3)	7·00	10
		a. Purple	9·00	15
		b. Imperf between (pair)	£140	
		c. Mixed perfs 10 and 12½	£200	90·00
220	**16**	2½d. blue (1892)	32·00	4·00
		a. Ultramarine	32·00	4·00
		b. Mixed perfs 10 and 12½	£170	80·00
221	**17**	3d. pale orange-yellow	35·00	5·00
		a. Orange	35·00	5·00
		b. Lemon-yellow	42·00	6·00
		c. Mixed perfs 10 and 12½	£160	£120
222	**18**	4d. green (1892)	45·00	2·50
		a. Blue-green (usually purple adverts)	45·00	3·50
		b. Mixed perfs 10 and 12½	£190	80·00
223	**19**	5d. olive-black (1893)	42·00	12·00
224	**20**	6d. brown (Die 1)	80·00	12·00
		a. Mixed perfs 10 and 12½		
		b. Die 2 (1892)	45·00	3·50
		ba. Black-brown	48·00	3·50
		c. Imperf (pair)	£200	
		d. Mixed perfs 10 and 12½	90·00	50·00
225	**21**	8d. blue *(adverts only)*	65·00	45·00
226	**22**	1s. red-brown	70·00	6·50
		a. Imperf between (pair)	£275	
		b. Mixed perfs 10 and 12½	£150	£100

(c) Perf compound of 11 and 10 (1895)

226*c*	**13**	½d. black	9·00	5·00
226*d*	**14**	1d. rose (Die 3)	18·00	3·75
226*e*	**20**	6d. brown (Die 2)	£160	70·00

(d) Perf compound of 10 and 11 (1895–97)

227	**13**	½d. black (1896)	3·25	15
		a. Mixed perfs 10 and 11	75·00	22·00
228	**14**	1d. rose (Die 3)	4·00	15
		a. Mixed perfs 10 and 11	80·00	40·00
229	**15**	2d. purple (Die 3)	7·50	12
		a. Mixed perfs 10 and 12	60·00	40·00
230	**16**	2½d. blue (1896)	32·00	4·00
		a. Ultramarine	32·00	4·00
		b. Mixed perfs 10 and 11	—	60·00
231	**17**	3d. lemon-yellow (1896)	35·00	5·00
232	**18**	4d. pale green (1896)	55·00	5·00
		a. Mixed perfs 10 and 11	—	75·00
233	**19**	5d. olive-black (1897)	40·00	12·00
234	**20**	6d. deep brown (Die 2) (1896)	45·00	3·50
		a. Mixed perfs 10 and 11		
235	**22**	1s. red-brown (1896)	70·00	8·00
		a. Mixed perfs 10 and 11	£130	70·00

(e) P 11 (1895–1900)

236	**13**	½d. black (1897)	2·50	15
		a. Thin coarse toned paper (1898)	20·00	50
		b. Ditto. Wmk sideways	—	£130

No.	Type	Description	Unused	Used
237	14	1d. rose (Die 3)	4·00	10
		a. Deep carmine	6·00	75
		b. Imperf between (pair)	£250	
		c. Deep carmine/thin coarse toned (1898)	8·00	75
		d. Ditto. Wmk sideways	—	£190
238	15	2d. mauve (Die 3)	7·00	12
		a. Purple	7·00	12
		b. Deep purple/thin coarse toned (1898)	10·00	55
		c. Ditto. Wmk sideways	—	£160
239	16	2½d. blue (1897)	32·00	4·00
		a. Thin coarse toned paper (1898)	38·00	9·00
240	17	3d. pale yellow (1897)	35·00	5·00
		a. Pale dull yellow/thin coarse toned (1898)	38·00	6·00
		b. Orange (1899)	35·00	5·00
		c. Dull orange-yellow (1900)	35·00	5·00
241	18	4d. yellowish green	35·00	2·25
		a. Bluish green (1897)	35·00	2·25
242	19	5d. olive-black/*thin coarse toned* (1899)	40·00	13·00
243	20	6d. brown (Die 2) (1897)	45·00	2·75
		a. Black-brown	45·00	2·75
		b. Brown/thin coarse toned (1898)	50·00	4·00
244	21	8d. blue (1898)	65·00	45·00
245	22	1s. red-brown (1897)	70·00	7·50

Only the more prominent shades have been included.

Stamps perf compound of 11 and 12½ exist but we do not list them as there is some doubt as to whether they are genuine.

In 1893 stamps were issued with commercial advertisements on the back. They are known on Nos. 195/200, 201a, 203, 205, 206a, 207*b*, 216*b*/*g* and 216*i*/*j* (most), 218/23 and 224b/226b (most).

For the ½d. and 2d. with double-lined watermark, see Nos. 292/3.

23 Mount Cook or Aorangi

24 Lake Taupo and Mount Ruapehu

25 Pembroke Peak, Milford Sound

26 Lake Wakatipu and Mount Earnslaw, inscribed "WAKITIPU"

27 Lake Wakatipu and Mount Earnslaw, inscribed "WAKATIPU"

28 Sacred Huia Birds

29 White Terrace, Rotomahana

30 Otira Gorge and Mount Ruapehu

31 Brown Kiwi

32 Maori War Canoe

33 Pink Terrace, Rotomahana

34 Kea and Kaka

35 Milford Sound

36 Mount Cook

(Recess Waterlow)

1898 (5 Apr). *No wmk. P* 12 *to* 14, 14, 15, *and* 16.

No.	Type	Description	Unused	Used
246	23	½d. purple-brown	3·25	45
		a. Imperf between (pair)	£500	£450
247		½d. purple-slate	3·25	45
248		½d. purple-black	4·50	2·00
249	24	1d. blue and yellow-brown	1·75	20
		a. Imperf between (pair)	£500	£450
		b. Imperf vert (horiz pair)	£375	£325
		c. Imperf horiz (vert pair)	£375	£325
250		1d. blue and brown	2·25	90
		a. Imperf between (pair)	£550	£450
251	25	2d. lake	20·00	25
		a. Imperf vert (horiz pair)	£375	£375
252		2d. rosy lake	20·00	25
		a. Imperf between (pair)	£500	£425
		b. Imperf vert (horiz pair)	£375	£375
253	26	2½d. sky-blue ("WAKITIPU")	5·50	16·00
254		2½d. blue ("WAKITIPU")	5·50	16·00
255	27	2½d. blue ("WAKATIPU")	9·50	1·75
256		2½d. deep blue ("WAKATIPU")	9·50	1·75
257	28	3d. yellow-brown	20·00	4·50
258	29	4d. bright rose	12·00	14·00
259		4d. lake-rose	14·00	15·00
260		4d. dull rose	12·00	14·00
261	30	5d. sepia	35·00	60·00
262		5d. purple-brown	22·00	11·00
263	31	6d. green	48·00	22·00
264		6d. grass-green	55·00	30·00
265	32	8d. indigo	27·00	14·00
266		8d. Prussian blue	27·00	14·00
267	33	9d. purple	26·00	15·00
268	34	1s. vermilion	40·00	15·00
269		1s. dull red	40·00	15·00
		a. Imperf between (pair)	£650	£550
270	35	2s. grey-green	90·00	55·00
		a. Imperf between (vert pair)	£650	£550
271	36	5s. vermilion	£225	£150
246/71		*Set of* 13	£450	£250

1899. *Printed by the Govt Printer at Wellington. Pirie paper. No wmk. P* 11.

No.	Type	Description	Unused	Used
272	27	2½d. blue	9·50	2·25
		a. Imperf between (pair)	£350	£350
		b. Imperf horiz (vert pair)	£250	£250
273		2½d. deep blue	9·50	2·25
274	28	3d. yellow-brown	14·00	65
		a. Imperf between (pair)	£475	£325
		b. Imperf vert (horiz pair)	£275	£250
275		3d. deep brown	14·00	65
		a. Imperf between (pair)	£475	£325
276	30	5d. purple-brown	17·00	2·75
277		5d. deep purple-brown	17·00	2·75
		a. Imperf between (pair)	£450	£400
278	31	6d. yellow-green	55·00	60·00
279		6d. deep green	48·00	48·00
280	32	8d. indigo	23·00	8·00
281		8d. Prussian blue	23·00	8·00
282	33	9d. deep purple	28·00	15·00
283		9d. rosy purple	23·00	9·00
284	34	1s. red	26·00	7·50
285		1s. dull orange-red	26·00	3·25
286		1s. dull brown-red	26·00	7·50
287		1s. bright red	32·00	16·00
288	35	2s. blue-green	70·00	35·00
289		2s. grey-green	70·00	35·00
290	36	5s. vermilion	£200	£130
291		5s. carmine-red	£300	£200
272/90		*Set of* 9	£350	£200

36*a*

1900. *Pirie paper. Wmk double-lined "NZ" and Star, W* **36*a***, *sideways. P* 11.

No.	Type	Description	Unused	Used
292	13	½d. black (Apr)	3·50	2·25
293	15	2d. bright purple (18 Apr)	7·00	2·25

37 White Terrace, Rotomahana

38*a*

38 Commemorative of the New Zealand Contingent in the South African War

(Recess Govt Ptg Office, Wellington. T **38** des J. Nairn)

1900–1. *W* **36*a***. *P* 11.

No.	Type	Description	Unused	Used
294	23	½d. deep green	3·00	10
294*a*		½d. green	3·00	10
		b. Imperf between (pair)	£250	£200
295		½d. yellow-green	3·00	10
296		½d. pale yellow-green	5·50	2·50
297	37	1d. lake	8·50	2·50
298		1d. crimson	6·00	10
299		1d. rose-red	6·00	10
		a. Imperf between (pair)	£500	£325
		b. Imperf vert (horiz pair)	£250	£200
299*c*	38	1½d. khaki*	£550	£425
300		1½d. brown	35·00	35·00
		a. Imperf vert (horiz pair)	£325	
		b. Imperf (pair)	£375	
301		1½d. chestnut	9·00	5·50
		a. Imperf vert (horiz pair)	£325	
		b. Imperf horiz (vert pair)	£425	
302		1½d. pale chestnut	9·00	5·50
		a. Imperf (pair)	£350	
303	38*a*	2d. dull violet	4·50	20
		a. Imperf between (pair)	£550	£375
304	38*a*	2d. mauve	6·50	1·25
305		2d. purple	5·00	20
		a. Imperf between (pair)	£375	

The above ½d. stamps are slightly smaller than those of the previous printing. A new plate was made to print 240 stamps instead of 120 as previously, and to make these fit the watermarked paper the border design was redrawn and contracted, the centre vignette remaining as before. The stamp varies in shade from *very deep green* to *pale yellow-green*. The 2d. stamp is also from a new and smaller plate.

*No. 299c is the rare first printing.

39 Lake Taupo and Mount Ruapehu

40

1900. *No wmk. P* 11.

No.	Type	Description	Unused	Used
307	39	4d. indigo and brown	8·00	1·75
308		4d. bright blue and chestnut	8·00	1·75
309		4d. deep blue and bistre-brown	8·00	1·75
310	31	6d. pale rose	30·00	3·00
		a. Imperf vert (horiz pair)	£350	
311		6d. rose-red	30·00	3·00
		a. Doubly printed	£275	
		b. Imperf between (pair)	£475	£475
		c. Imperf vert (horiz pair)	£170	
312		6d. scarlet	35·00	11·00
		a. Imperf vert (horiz pair)	£375	

(Des G. Bach. Recess Waterlow)

1901 (1 Jan). *Universal Penny Postage. No wmk. P* 12 *to* 16.

No.	Type	Description	Unused	Used
313	40	1d. carmine	8·00	3·00

(Recess Govt Ptg Office, Wellington)

1901 (Feb). *Pirie paper, thick and soft. W* **36*a***. (*a*) *P* 11.

No.	Type	Description	Unused	Used
314	40	1d. carmine-lake	15·00	6·50
315		1d. deep carmine	2·75	5
		a. Imperf between (pair)	£225	
316		1d. carmine	2·75	5
		a. Imperf between (pair)	£225	
		(*b*) *P* 14		
317	23	½d. green	9·00	2·50
318	40	1d. carmine	20·00	6·00
		a. Imperf between (pair)	£225	
		(*c*) *Perf compound of* 11 *and* 14		
319	23	½d. green	10·00	3·75
320		½d. deep green	10·00	3·75
321	40	1d. carmine	£250	£100
		(*d*) *P* 11 *and* 14 *mixed**		
322	23	½d. green	45·00	25·00
323	40	1d. carmine	£250	£110

*The term "mixed" is applied to stamps from sheets which were at first perforated 14, or 14 and 11 compound, and either incompletely or defectively perforated. These sheets were patched on the back with strips of paper, and re-perforated 11 in those parts where the original perforation was defective.

1901 (Dec). *Basted Mills, thin hard paper. W* **36*a***. (*a*) *P* 11.

No.	Type	Description	Unused	Used
324	23	½d. green	35·00	35·00
325	40	1d. carmine	50·00	40·00
		(*b*) *P* 14		
326	23	½d. green	20·00	7·00
		a. Imperf between (pair)	£325	
327	40	1d. carmine	16·00	1·50
		a. Imperf between (pair)	£325	
		(*c*) *Perf compound of* 11 *and* 14		
328	23	½d. green	16·00	14·00
329		½d. deep green	16·00	14·00
330	40	1d. carmine	12·00	1·75
		(*d*) *Mixed perfs*		
331	23	½d. green	75·00	75·00
332	40	1d. carmine	£100	80·00

1902 (Jan). *Cowan, thin hard paper. No wmk.* (*a*) *P* 11.

No.	Type	Description	Unused	Used
333	23	½d. green	£100	90·00
		(*b*) *P* 14		
334	23	½d. green	8·50	1·75
335	40	1d. carmine	14·00	1·00
		(*c*) *Perf compound of* 11 *and* 14		
336	23	½d. green	£100	£100
337	40	1d. carmine	£120	£120
		(*d*) *Mixed perfs*		
338	23	½d. green	£100	£100
339	40	1d. carmine	£140	£140

41 "Single" Wmk

1902 (Apr). *Cowan, thin hard paper. Wmk single-lined "NZ" and Star, W* **41**. (*a*) *P* 11.

No.	Type	Description	Unused	Used
340	23	½d. green	40·00	40·00
341	40	1d. carmine	£650	£500
		(*b*) *P* 14		
341*a*	23	½d. yellow-green	1·75	25
341*b*		½d. pale yellow-green	5·00	1·25

No.	Type	Description	Unused	Used
342	23	½d. green	1·75	20
		a. Imperf between (pair)	£150	
343		½d. deep green	2·25	30
		a. Imperf between (pair)	£150	
344	40	1d. carmine	2·25	5
		a. Imperf between (pair)	£170	
		b. Booklet pane of 6	£190	
345		1d. pale carmine	2·25	5
		a. Imperf between (pair)	£170	
		ab. Booklet pane of 6	£190	
345b		1d. deep carmine*	28·00	3·50
		ba. Booklet pane of 6	£600	
		(c) Perf compound of 11 and 14		
346	23	½d. green	8·50	14·00
347		½d. deep green	12·00	16·00
348	40	1d. carmine	£120	80·00
348a		1d. deep carmine*	£500	£375
		(d) Mixed perfs		
349	23	½d. green	17·00	17·00
350		½d. deep green	20·00	20·00
351	40	1d. carmine	20·00	20·00
351a		1d. pale carmine	20·00	20·00
351b		1d. deep carmine*	£325	£325

*Nos. 345b, 348a and 351b were printed from a plate made by Waterlow & Sons, known as the "Reserve" plate. The stamps do not show evidence of wearing and the area surrounding the upper part of the figure is more deeply shaded.

Nos. 344/5b with two or three sides imperf come from booklets.

A special plate was introduced in 1902 to print booklet panes and also had the minute dot (*see notes below No. 417a*), but a special characteristic of the booklet plate was that the pearl in the top left-hand corner was large.

1902–9. *W* **41** (*sideways on 3d., 5d., 6d., 8d., 1s. and 5s.*).

No.	Type	Description	Unused	Used
		(a) P 11 (1902–7)		
352	27	2½d. blue	11·00	9·00
353		2½d. deep blue (1905)	11·00	9·00
354	28	3d. yellow-brown	12·00	35
355		3d. bistre-brown	12·00	35
356		3d. pale bistre	15·00	2·50
357	39	4d. deep blue and deep brown/*bluish*	12·00	23·00
		a. Imperf vert (horiz pair)	£350	£375
358	30	5d. red-brown	15·00	5·50
359		5d. deep brown (1904)	15·00	2·50
360		5d. sepia (1906)	26·00	12·00
361	31	6d. rose	30·00	3·50
362		6d. rose-red	30·00	3·50
		a. Wmk upright	£350	£250
		b. Showing part of sheet wmk (7.02)*	32·00	18·00
363		6d. rose-carmine	30·00	3·50
		a. Imperf vert (horiz pair)	£300	£300
		b. Imperf horiz (vert pair)		
364		6d. bright carmine-pink (1905)	40·00	5·00
365		6d. scarlet	45·00	15·00
366	32	8d. blue	23·00	6·00
367		8d. steel-blue (1904)	23·00	6·00
		a. Imperf vert (horiz pair)	£325	£325
		b. Imperf horiz (vert pair)	£325	£325
368	33	9d. purple	23·00	8·00
369	34	1s. brown-red	25·00	3·25
370		1s. bright red	30·00	3·75
371		1s. orange-red	24·00	3·25
		a. Wmk W **12b** (1903?)	—	£1100
372		1s. orange-brown	30·00	4·25
373	35	2s. green	70·00	35·00
		a. No wmk. Laid paper	£160	£140
374		2s. blue-green (1907)	70·00	35·00
375	36	5s. deep red	£190	£120
		a. Wmk upright	£200	£130
376		5s. vermilion (1906)	£190	£120
		aa. Wmk upright	£200	£130
		(b) P 14 (1903–9)		
378	38	1½d. chestnut (1907)	8·50	22·00
379	38a	2d. grey-purple (1903)	5·00	35
380		2d. purple	5·00	35
		a. Imperf vert (horiz pair)	£325	£300
		b. Imperf horiz (vert pair)	£325	£300
381		2d. bright reddish purple	6·50	70
382	27	2½d. blue (1907)	8·00	1·75
383		2½d. deep blue	8·00	1·75
384	28	3d. bistre-brown	15·00	90
		a. Imperf vert (horiz pair)	£350	£250
385		3d. bistre (1906)	15·00	90
386		3d. pale yellow-bistre	20·00	7·50
387	39	4d. deep blue and deep brown/*bluish* (1903)	8·00	3·00
		a. Imperf vert (horiz pair)	£300	£250
		b. Imperf horiz (vert pair)	£300	£250
		c. Centre inverted	†	£20000
388		4d. blue and chestnut/*bluish* (1906)	8·00	90
389		4d. bl & ochre-brn/*bluish* (1909)	8·00	90
390	30	5d. black-brown	26·00	12·00
391		5d. red-brown (1906)	19·00	5·50
392	31	6d. bright carmine-pink (1906)	40·00	5·50
		a. Imperf vert (horiz pair)	£250	£250
393		6d. rose-carmine	40·00	6·00
394	32	8d. steel-blue (1907)	23·00	6·00
395	33	9d. purple (1906)	23·00	9·00
396	34	1s. orange-brown	32·00	4·50
397		1s. orange-red	27·00	4·50
398		1s. pale red (1907)	40·00	16·00
399	35	2s. green	48·00	20·00
400		2s. blue-green (1907)	50·00	20·00
401	36	5s. deep red	£190	£120
		a. Wmk upright	£200	£130
402		5s. dull red	£190	£120
		aa. Wmk upright	£200	£130
		(c) Perf compound of 11 and 14		
402a	38	1½d. chestnut	£450	£450
403	38a	2d. purple (1903)	£250	£250
403a	28	3d. bistre-brown	£450	£450
403b	39	4d. blue and yellow-brown	£300	£300
403c	30	5d. red-brown	£400	£400
404	31	6d. rose-carmine (1907)	£250	£200
404a	32	8d. steel-blue	£600	£600
404b	33	9d. purple	£800	£800
404c	36	5s. deep red	£1100	£1000
		(d) Mixed perfs		
405	38	1½d. chestnut	£450	£450
406	38a	2d. purple	£130	£130
407	28	3d. bistre-brown	£450	£450
408	39	4d. blue and chestnut/*bluish* (1904)	£250	£250
409		4d. blue and yellow-brown/*bluish*	£250	£250
409a	30	5d. red-brown	£375	£375
410	31	6d. rose-carmine	£250	£200
411		6d. bright carmine-pink	£250	£200
412	32	8d. steel-blue	£550	£550
413	33	9d. purple	£700	£700
413a	35	2s. blue-green	£600	£600
414	36	5s. vermilion	£1100	£1000

*No. 362b is on paper without general watermark, but showing the words "LISBON SUPERFINE" wmkd once in the sheet; the paper was obtained from Parsons Bros, an American firm with a branch at Auckland.

Two sizes of paper were used for the above stamps:—

(1) A sheet containing 240 wmks, with a space of 9 mm between each.

(2) A sheet containing 120 wmks, with a space of 24 mm between each vertical row.

Size (1) was used for the ½d., 1d., 2d., and 4d., and size (2) for 2½d., 5d., 9d., and 2s. The paper in each case exactly fitted the plates, and had the watermark in register, though in the case of the 4d., the plate of which contained only 80 stamps, the paper was cut up to print it. The 3d., 6d., 8d., and 1s. were printed on variety (1), but with watermark sideways: by reason of this, specimens from the margins of the sheets show parts of the words "NEW ZEALAND POSTAGE" in large letters, and some copies have no watermark at all. For the 1½d. and 5s. stamps variety (1) was also used, but two watermarks appear on each stamp.

1904. *Printed from new "dot" plates. W* **41**. *(a) P 14.*

No.	Type	Description	Unused	Used
415	40	1d. rose-carmine	3·00	10
415a		1d. pale carmine	3·00	10
		(b) Perf compound of 11 and 14		
416	40	1d. rose-carmine	£130	£130
		(c) Mixed perfs		
417	40	1d. rose-carmine	16·00	14·00
417a		1d. pale carmine	16·00	14·00

The above new plates have a minute dot between the stamps in the horizontal rows, but it is frequently cut out by the perforations. However, they can be further distinguished by the notes below.

In 1906 fresh printings were made from four new plates, two of which, marked in the margin "W1" and "W2", were supplied by Waterlow Bros and Layton, and the other two, marked "R1" and "R2", by W. R. Royle & Son. The intention was to note which pair of plates wore the best and produced the best results. They can be distinguished as follows:—

(a) (b) (c)

(d) (e) (f)

(a) Four o'clock flaw in rosette at top right corner. Occurs in all these plates but not in the original Waterlow plates.
(b) Pearl at right strong.
(c) Pearl at right weak.
(d) Dot at left and S-shaped ornament unshaded.
(e) S-shaped ornament with one line of shading within.
(f) As (e) but with line from left pearl to edge of stamp.

"Dot" plates comprise (a) and (d).
Waterlow plates comprise (a), (b) and (e).
Royle plates comprise (a), (c) and (e) and the line in (f) on many stamps but not all.

1906. *W* **41**. A. *Printed from new plates by Waterlow. (a) P 14.*

No.	Type	Description	Unused	Used
418	40	1d. deep rose-carmine	10·00	35
		aa. Imperf between (pair)	£200	
418a		1d. aniline carmine	9·00	40
		ab. Imperf between (pair)	£200	
418b		1d. rose-carmine	9·00	40
		(b) P 11		
418c	40	1d. aniline carmine	£325	£325
		(c) Perf compound of 11 and 14		
419	40	1d. rose-carmine	£300	£300
		(d) Mixed perfs		
419a	40	1d. deep rose-carmine	£325	£325
		B. *Printed from new plates by Royle. (a) P 14*		
419b	40	1d. rose-carmine	3·00	25
		c. Imperf between (vert pair)	£200	£200
419d		1d. bright rose-carmine	6·00	50
		(b) P 11		
419e	40	1d. bright rose-carmine	£225	£225
		(c) Perf compound of 11 and 14		
419f	40	1d. rose-carmine	85·00	85·00
		(d) Mixed perfs		
419g	40	1d. rose-carmine	£110	£110
		(e) P 14 × 14½ (comb) (May)		
419h	40	1d. bright rose-carmine	50·00	24·00
419i		1d. rose-carmine	50·00	24·00

Nos. 419h/i are known both with and without the small dot.
See also No. 441.

1905–6. *Stamps supplied to penny-in-the-slot machines. W* **41**.

(i) *"Dot" plates of* 1904. (ii) Waterlow *"reserve" plate of* 1902

No.	Type	Description	Unused	Used
		(a) Imperf top and bottom; zigzag roulette 9½ on one or both sides, two large holes at sides		
420	40	1d. rose-carmine (i)	£120	
420a		1d. deep carmine (ii)	£120	
		(b) As last but rouletted 14½		
420b	40	1d. rose-carmine (i)	£140	
420c		1d. deep carmine (ii)		
		(c) Imperf all round, two large holes each side		
421	40	1d. rose-carmine (i)	£180	
421a		1d. deep carmine (ii)	£140	
		(d) Imperf all round		
422	40	1d. deep carmine (ii)	£120	
		(e) Imperf all round. Two small indentations on back of stamp		
422a	40	1d. deep carmine (ii)	£130	£130
		(f) Imperf all round; two small pin-holes in stamp		
422b	40	1d. deep carmine (ii)	£130	£130

No. 421 *only* exists from strips of Nos. 420 or 420b (resulting from the use of successive coins) which have been separated by scissors. Similarly strips of Nos. 420a and 420c can produce single copies of No. 421a but this also exists in singles from a different machine.

Most used copies of Nos. 420/2 are forgeries and they should only be collected on cover.

42 Maori Canoe, *Te Arawa*

(Des L. J. Steele. Eng W. R. Bock. Typo Govt Ptg Office)

1906 (1–17 Nov). *New Zealand Exhibition, Christchurch. T* **42** *and similar horiz designs. W* **41**. *P* 14.

No.	Description	Unused	Used
424	½d. emerald-green	26·00	26·00
425	1d. vermilion	20·00	20·00
	a. Claret	£7000	£8000
426	3d. brown and blue	75·00	85·00
427	6d. pink and olive-green (17.11)	£180	£250

Designs:—1d. Maori art; 3d. Landing of Cook; 6d. Annexation of New Zealand.

The 1d. in claret was the original printing, which was considered unsatisfactory. One sheet was issued at the Exhibition P.O.

46

47 (T **28** reduced)

48 (T **31** reduced)

49 (T **34** reduced)

(New plates (except 4d.), supplied by Perkins Bacon. Recess (T **46** typo) by Govt Printer, Wellington)

1907–8. *Wmk single-lined "NZ" and Star, T* **41**. *(a) P* 14.

No.	Type	Description	Unused	Used
428	23	½d. green	13·00	4·00
		a. Imperf (pair)	85·00	
429		½d. yellow-green	8·50	2·00
429a		½d. deep yellow-green	4·50	90
430	47	3d. brown (1907)	38·00	17·00
431	48	6d. carmine-pink (1907)	42·00	7·00
432		6d. red	48·00	15·00
		(b) P 14 × 13, 13½ (comb)		
433	23	½d. green (1907)	10·00	2·75
434		½d. yellow-green	4·00	85
435	47	3d. brown	38·00	20·00
436		3d. yellow-brown	38·00	23·00
437	39	4d. blue and yellow-brown/*bluish*	27·00	20·00
438	48	6d. pink	£190	65·00
439	49	1s. orange-red (1907)	£130	40·00
		(c) P 14 × 15 (comb)		
440	23	½d. yellow-green (1907)	3·75	45
441	46	1d. carmine	24·00	50
442	47	3d. brown	38·00	8·00
443		3d. yellow-brown	38·00	8·00
445	48	6d. carmine-pink	42·00	7·00
446	49	1s. orange-red	£120	24·00
447		1s. deep orange-brown	£300	

The ½d. stamps of this 1907–8 issue have a minute dot in the margin between the stamps, where not removed by the perforation. (See note after No. 417a).

Stamps of T **47**, **48** and **49** also have a small dot as described in note after No. 417a.

Stamps T **46** are typographed but the design also differs from T **40**. The rosettes in the upper corners are altered and the lines on the globe diagonal instead of vertical. The paper is chalk-surfaced.

50

51

52

(Eng P.B. Typo in New Zealand)

1909 (8 Nov)–**12**. *Chalk-surfaced "De La Rue" paper. Toned gum. W* **41**. *P* 14 × 15, *comb.*

No.	Type	Description	Unused	Used
449	50	½d. yellow-green	2·50	15
		aa. Deep green	2·50	20
		a. Imperf (pair)	£140	
		b. Booklet pane. Five stamps plus label in position 1	£400	
		c. Ditto, but label in position 6	£400	
		d. Booklet pane of 6	£140	
		e. Ditto, but with coloured bars on selvedge (1912)	£140	

450 **51** 1d. carmine 90 5
a. Imperf (pair) £170
b. Booklet pane of 6 (1912) £110
c. Ditto, but with coloured bars on selvedge (1912) £110

½d. and 1d. stamps with blurred and heavy appearance are from booklets.

See also Nos. 520, etc.

(Eng W. R. Royle & Son, London, and recess-printed in New Zealand)

1909 (9 Nov)–**13.** *T* **52** *and similar types. W* **41.**

(*a*) *P 14 × 14½, comb machine*

452 2d. mauve .. .. 20·00 4·75
453 2d. deep mauve .. .. 22·00 4·75
454 3d. chestnut .. .. 22·00 70
455 4d. orange-red .. .. 28·00 22·00
456 4d. orange-yellow (1912) .. .. .. 25·00 5·00
457 5d. brown (1910) .. .. 16·00 80
458 5d. red-brown .. .. 14·00 80
459 6d. carmine (1910) .. .. 27·00 60
460 6d. deep carmine (29.10.13) .. .. .. 27·00 60
461 8d. indigo-blue .. .. 12·00 1·25
461*a* 8d. deep bright blue .. .. 15·00 1·50
462 1s. vermilion (1910) .. .. 48·00 5·00
452/62 .. .. .. *Set of* 8 £180 35·00

(*b*) *P 14, line machine**

463 3d. chestnut (1910) .. .. 27·00 3·00
464 4d. orange (1910) .. .. 22·00 11·00
465 5d. brown .. .. 18·00 3·25
466 5d. red-brown (15.9.11) .. .. .. 22·00 3·75
467 6d. carmine .. .. 35·00 7·50
469 1s. vermilion .. .. 48·00 7·50

*In addition to showing the usual characteristics of a line perforation, these stamps may be distinguished by their vertical perforation which measures 13.8. Nos. 452 to 462 generally measure vertically 14 to 14.3. An exception is 13.8 one vertical side but 14 the other.

See also No. 478 with sideways wmk.

AUCKLAND
EXHIBITION,
1913.

(59) 60

1913 (1 Dec). *Auckland Exhibition. T* **50, 51** *and* **52** *optd with T* **59.**

470 ½d. green .. .. 20·00 24·00
471 1d. carmine .. .. 24·00 26·00
472 3d. chestnut (*p* 14 × 14½) £160 £200
473 6d. carmine (*p* 14 × 14½) £170 £225

These overprinted stamps were only available for letters in New Zealand and to Australia.

1915–16. *T* **52** *and similar types.* (*a*) *W* **41.** *P* 14 × 13½.

474 3d. chestnut .. .. 50·00 45·00
a. Vert pair. P 14 × 13½ and 14 × 14½ .. £225 £275
475 5d. red-brown (1916) .. .. 15·00 1·75
a. Vert pair. P 14 × 13½ and 14 × 14½ .. 50·00 70·00
476 6d. carmine .. .. 50·00 45·00
a. Vert pair. P 14 × 13½ and 14 × 14½ .. £225 £275
477 8d. indigo-blue (3.16) .. .. .. 16·00 2·50
a. Vert pair. P 14 × 13½ and 14 × 14½ .. 50·00 70·00
477*b* 8d. deep bright blue (1916) .. .. .. 16·00 2·50
c. Vert pair. P 14 × 13½ and 14 × 14½ .. 50·00 70·00

All four values exist in complete sheets perf 14 × 14½ and the 3d. and 6d. also in full sheets perf 14 × 13½. The 3d., 5d. and 6d. also exist in two combinations: (*a*) five top rows perf 14 × 13½ with five bottom rows perf 14 × 14½ and (*b*) four top rows perf 14 × 13½ with six bottom rows perf 14 × 14½. The 8d. exists also as (*b*).

(*b*) *On paper with widely spaced wmk as used for 2½d. of pictorial issue and wmk sideways (see note after No. 414). P 14, line*

478 8d. indigo-blue (8.16) .. .. .. 13·00 22·00
a. No wmk .. .. 45·00 55·00

No. 478a must show no trace of the wmk.

(Des H. Linley Richardson, R.B.A.; plates made in London by P.B. and stamps recess-printed in New Zealand)

1915 (30 July)–**29.** *W* **41.** *P 14 × 14½, comb (See notes below).*

479 **60** 1½d. grey-slate .. .. 1·50 75
a. Perf 14 × 13½ .. .. 1·50 75
b. Vert pair, 479/9a .. .. .. 35·00 50·00
480 2d. bright violet .. .. 8·00 17·00
a. Perf 14 × 13½ .. .. 8·00 17·00
b. Vert pair, 480/80a .. .. .. 27·00 50·00
481 2d. yellow (15.1.16) .. .. .. 5·50 12·00
a. Perf 14 × 13½ .. .. 5·50 12·00
b. Vert pair, 481/1a .. .. .. 22·00 45·00
482 2½d. blue .. .. 10·00 5·00
a. Perf 14 × 13½ .. .. 6·00 3·50
b. Vert pair, 482/2a .. .. .. 42·00 65·00
483 3d. chocolate .. .. 8·00 70
a. Perf 14 × 13½ .. .. 8·00 60
b. Vert pair, 483/3a .. .. .. 38·00 55·00
484 4d. yellow .. .. 6·50 20·00
a. Perf 14 × 13½ .. .. 6·50 20·00
b. Vert pair, 484/4a .. .. .. 30·00 £120
485 4d. bright violet (7.4.16) .. .. .. 9·00 30
a. Perf 14 × 13½ .. .. 7·50 15
b. Imperf (pair) £950
c. Vert pair, 485/5a .. .. .. 38·00 65·00
486 4½d. deep green .. .. 18·00 13·00
a. Perf 14 × 13½ .. .. 16·00 10·00
b. Vert pair, 486/6a .. .. .. 55·00 65·00
487 5d. light blue (4.22) .. .. .. 20·00 12·00
a. Perf 14 × 13½ .. .. 11·00 60
b. Imperf (pair) £110 £120
488 5d. pale ultramarine .. .. .. 14·00 6·00
a. Perf 14 × 13½ .. .. 14·00 4·25
b. Vert pair, 488/8a (1929) .. .. 55·00 75·00
489 6d. carmine .. .. 8·50 60
a. Perf 14 × 13½ .. .. 8·50 30
b. Vert pair, 489/9a (1916) .. .. 80·00 £110
c. Imperf three sides (pair) £1200
d. Carmine-lake. P 14 × 13½ £500 £325
490 **60** 7½d. red-brown .. .. 22·00 25·00
a. Perf 14 × 13½ .. .. 14·00 14·00
b. Vert pair, 490/0a (10.20) .. .. 55·00 70·00
491 8d. indigo-blue (19.4.21) .. .. .. 13·00 26·00
a. Perf 14 × 13½ .. .. 13·00 24·00
b. Vert pair, 491/1a .. .. .. 38·00 70·00
492 8d. red-brown (*p* 14 × 13½) (2.22) .. 25·00 1·25
493 9d. sage-green .. .. 24·00 3·50
a. Perf 14 × 13½ .. .. 20·00 1·50
b. Vert pair, 493/3a .. .. .. 80·00 £100
c. Imperf three sides (pair) £1300
d. Imperf (pair) £1000
e. Yellowish olive. P 14 × 13½ (12.25) 28·00 9·00
494 1s. vermilion (1916) .. .. .. 17·00 60
a. Perf 14 × 13½ .. .. .. 20·00 95
b. Imperf (pair) £2250
c. Vert pair, 494/4a .. .. .. 90·00 £110
495 1s. pale orange-red .. .. .. 20·00 1·75
a. Imperf (pair) £325
b. Orange-brown £850 £425
479/95 .. .. *Set of* 15 £150 95·00

The 1½d., 2½d., 4½d. and 7½d. have value tablets as shown in T **60**. In the other values, the tablets are shortened, and the ornamental border at each side of the crown correspondingly extended.

Of this issue the 1½d., 2½d., 4d. (both), 4½d., 5d. (both), 6d., 7½d., 9d. and 1s. are known from sheets perforated 14 × 13½ throughout and the 4d. violet, 5d. (both), 6d. and 1s. from sheets perforated 14 × 14½ throughout.

All values from 1½d. to 1s. were also produced showing the use of the two different perforations within the same sheet as described beneath No. 477c. In most instances the top four rows were perforated 14 × 13½ and the bottom six 14 × 14½. For one printing of the 4d. violet and for all printings of the 5d. pale ultramarine with two perforations on the same sheet the arrangement differed in that the top five rows were perforated 14 × 14½ and the bottom five 14 × 13½.

Any stamps with the wmk with perforations measuring 14 × 14 or nearly must be classed as 14 × 14½, this being an irregularity of the comb machine, and not a product of the 14-line machine.

1916 (Mar–Aug). *On paper of pictorial issue, as No. 478 (wmk sideways on 2d., 3d., 6d.).*

496 **60** 1½d. grey-slate (*p* 14 × 14½) .. .. 1·25 1·50
a. No wmk .. .. 2·00 2·75
497 1½d. grey-slate (*p* 14 × 13½) .. .. 1·25 1·50
a. No wmk .. .. 2·00 2·75
b. Vert pair, 496/497 .. .. .. 20·00 30·00
c. As last. No wmk .. .. .. 28·00 45·00
498 2d. yellow (*p* 14) (June) .. .. .. 5·50 24·00
a. No wmk .. .. 26·00 48·00
499 3d. chocolate (*p* 14) (June) .. .. 6·00 2·75
a. No wmk .. .. 23·00 35·00
500 6d. carmine (*p* 14) (Aug) .. .. .. 7·00 25·00
a. No wmk .. .. 32·00 55·00

The "no wmk" varieties must show no trace of the wmk.

60*a*

60*b*

WAR STAMP

(61)

(Die eng W. R. Bock, Wellington. Typo in N.Z. from plates made locally)

1916 (Apr). *W* **41.** *P* 14 × 15.

501 **60*a*** 1½d. grey-black .. .. 7·50 35
502 1½d. black .. .. 7·50 35

Nos. 501 and 502 differ from No. 505 in many respects. The shading of the portrait is *diagonal* in the former and *horizontal* in the latter.

(Typo from steel plates by Perkins, Bacon & Co)

1915–19. *Chalk-surfaced "De La Rue" paper. Toned gum. W* **41.** *P* 14 × 15.

503 **60*b*** ½d. green (30.7.15) 90 5
a. Booklet pane of 6 with bars on selvedge .. .. .. 95·00
504 ½d. yellow-green .. .. 3·00 75
a. Very thick, hard, highly surfaced paper, white gum (12.15) .. .. 11·00 17·00
b. Booklet pane of 6 with bars on selvedge .. .. .. 80·00
505 1½d. slate (5.9.16) .. .. .. 6·50 15
506 1½d. orange-brown (9.18) .. .. .. 2·50 12
507 2d. yellow (9.16) .. .. 1·50 5
508 2d. pale yellow .. .. 3·50 75
509 3d. chocolate (5.19) .. .. .. 7·00 30

The first note after No. 495*b* also applies to *T* **60*b***.

Stamps from booklet panes have blurred, heavy impressions.

See also Nos. 519, etc.

1915 (24 Sept). *Optd with T* **61.** *P* 14 × 15.

510 **60*b*** ½d. green .. .. 1·50 25

62 "Peace" and Lion

63 "Peace" and Lion

(Plates by P.B., Waterlow and D.L.R. Des and typo D.L.R.)

1920 (27 Jan). *Victory. T* **62/3** *and similar designs. W* **41.** *P* 14.

511 ½d. green .. .. 2·25 75
a. Pale yellow-green .. .. .. 20·00 8·50
512 1d. carmine-red .. .. 2·25 25
a. Bright carmine .. .. 3·50 35
513 1½d. brown-orange .. .. 2·25 20
514 3d. chocolate .. .. 12·00 10·00
515 6d. violet .. .. 14·00 14·00
516 1s. orange-red .. .. 22·00 38·00
511/16 .. .. *Set of* 6 50·00 55·00

Designs: *Horiz (as T* **63**)—1½d. Maori chief. (*As T* **62**)—3d. Lion; 1s. King George V. *Vert (as T* **62**)—6d. "Peace" and "Progress".

The above stamps were placed on sale in London in November, 1919.

2d. 2d.

TWOPENCE

(68)

69

1922 (Mar). *Surch with T* **68.**

517 **62** 2d. on ½d. green (R.) .. .. .. 2·75 1·00

(Des and eng W. R. Bock. Typo at Wellington)

1923. *Restoration of Penny Postage. Chalky paper. Yellowish gum. W* **41.** *P* 14 × 15.

518 **69** 1d. carmine .. .. 1·50 20

"De La Rue" paper is chalk-surfaced and has a smooth finish. The watermark is as illustrated. The gum is toned and strongly resistant to soaking.

"Jones" paper is chalk-surfaced and has a coarser texture, is poorly surfaced and the ink tends to peel. The outline of the watermark commonly shows on the surface of the stamp. The gum is colourless or only slightly toned and washes off readily. Introduced in 1924.

"Cowan" paper is chalk-surfaced and is white and opaque. The watermark is usually smaller than in the "Jones" paper and is often barely visible. Introduced in 1925.

"Wiggins Teape" paper is chalk-surfaced and is thin and hard. It has a vertical mesh with a narrow watermark, whereas the other papers have a horizontal mesh and a wider watermark. Introduced in 1926.

1924–25. *W* **41.** *P* 14 × 15. (*a*) *"Jones" chalky paper, white gum.*

519 **60*b*** ½d. green .. .. 4·50 3·00
a. Booklet pane of 6 with bars on selvedge .. .. .. 85·00
520 **51** 1d. deep carmine .. .. .. 5·00 75
a. Pale carmine. Unsurfaced paper .. £275
b. Booklet pane of 6 with bars on selvedge .. .. .. 95·00
521 **69** 1d. carmine .. .. 3·50 1·00
522 **60*b*** 2d. dull yellow .. .. 4·50 10·00
523 3d. deep chocolate .. .. .. 14·00 3·50

Only one half-sheet of No. 520*a* is known, due to faulty manufacture.

(*b*) *Medium, unsurfaced paper, toned gum*

524 **51** 1d. rose-carmine (4.25) .. .. .. 13·00 35·00

(*c*) *Medium to thick chalky paper, toned gum. Wmk sideways*

526 **51** 1d. bright carmine (4.25) .. .. 2·50 8·50
a. No wmk .. .. 9·50 18·00
b. Imperf (pair) .. .. .. 50·00

Many stamps in the sheet of No. 526 are without watermark, while others show portions of "NEW ZEALAND POSTAGE" in double-lined capitals.

1925. *No wmk but bluish "NZ" and Star lithographed on back. P* 14 × 15.

527 **60*b*** ½d. apple-green 80 50
a. "NZ" and Star almost colourless .. 4·75
528 **51** 1d. rose-carmine 85 35
a. "NZ" and Star in black .. .. 8·00
b. "NZ" and Star colourless .. .. 20·00
529 **60*b*** 2d. yellow .. .. 4·75 17·00

1925–30. *W* **41.** (*a*) *"Cowan" thick, opaque chalky paper, white gum.*

530 **60*b*** ½d. green (*p* 14 × 15) 50 12
aa. Booklet pane of 6 with bars and adverts on selvedge .. .. 85·00
a. Perf 14 .. .. 60 30
ab. Booklet pane of 6, with bars on selvedge (1926) .. .. .. 45·00
ac. Ditto, but with adverts also on selvedge (1926) .. .. .. 45·00
531 **51** 1d. deep carmine (*p* 14 × 15) (8.25) .. 3·00 30
a. Imperf (pair) .. .. .. 60·00 70·00
b. Booklet pane of 6, bars and adverts on selvedge .. .. .. 45·00
532 **60*b*** 1½d. orange-brown (*p* 14) (1930) .. 8·50 8·50
a. Perf 14 × 15 .. .. .. 55·00 55·00
533 2d. yellow (*p* 14 × 15) .. .. .. 3·00 15
a. Perf 14 (1930) .. .. .. 3·25 15
534 3d. chocolate (*p* 14 × 15) .. .. 7·00 30
a. Perf 14 (1930) .. .. .. 9·50 90

Different adverts exist on booklet panes.

(*b*) *"Cowan" unsurfaced paper* (4.25)

535 **69** 1d. carmine-pink (*p* 14 × 15) .. .. 22·00 20·00

This is a medium soft paper similar to that on which the line-engraved stamps of T **60** were printed, with very shiny gum.

1926 (June)–**30.** *"Wiggins Teape" thin, hard, chalk-surfaced paper. W* **41.**

535*a* **51** 1d. rose-carmine (*p* 14 × 15) .. .. 9·50 3·00
535*b* **60*b*** 1½d. orange-brown (*p* 14) (1930) .. 27·00 40·00
535*c* 2d. yellow (*p* 14 × 15) .. .. .. 5·50 9·00
d. Perf 14 (7.27) .. .. .. 5·50 10·00

70 Exhibition Buildings

(Des H. L. Richardson. Eng and typo Govt Ptg Office, Wellington)

1925 (17 Nov). *Dunedin Exhibition. Thick "Cowan" chalky paper.* W **41.** *P* 14 × 15.

536	**70**	½d. yellow-green/*green*	2·75	7·50
537		1d. carmine/*rose*	2·75	5·00
538		4d. mauve/*pale mauve*	48·00	90·00
		a. "POSTAGF" at right	£190	£250

71

72

(Des H. L. Richardson; plates by Waterlow. Typo Wellington)

1926–30. *Chalky paper.* W **41.** *P* 14. (*a*) *"Jones" paper* (12.7.26).

539	**72**	2s. deep blue	60·00	40·00
540		3s. mauve	£120	£100
		(*b*) *"Cowan" paper*		
541	**71**	1d. rose-carmine (15.11.26)	40	5
		a. Imperf (pair)	45·00	
		b. Booklet pane of 6 with bars on selvedge	45·00	
		ba. Ditto, with adverts on selvedge also	45·00	
		c. Perf 14 × 15 (3.27)	45	5
		ca. Booklet pane of 6, with bars and adverts on selvedge (1934)	60·00	
542	**72**	2s. light blue (5.27)	55·00	14·00
543		3s. pale mauve (9.27)	£120	85·00
		(*c*) *"Wiggins Teape" paper* (6.30)		
543*a*	**71**	1d. rose-carmine	7·00	1·25

The 1d. value exists in a range of colours including scarlet and deep carmine to magenta but we have insufficient evidence to show that these were issued thus. There are also several shades of the issued stamp.

73 Nurse

74 Smiling Boy

(Typo Govt Printing Office, Wellington)

1929–30. *Anti-Tuberculosis Fund.* T **73** *and similar type.* W **41.** *P* 14. (*a*) *Inscribed* "HELP STAMP OUT TUBERCULOSIS".

544	1d. + 1d. scarlet (11.12.29)	15·00	15·00
	(*b*) *Inscribed* "HELP PROMOTE HEALTH"		
545	1d. + 1d. scarlet (29.10.30)	20·00	25·00

(Des L. C. Mitchell. Dies eng and plates made Royal Mint, London (1d.), Govt Ptg Office, Wellington from W. R. Bock die (2d.). Typo Govt Ptg Office, Wellington)

1931 (31 Oct). *Health Stamps.* W **41.** *P* 14½ × 14.

546	**74**	1d. + 1d. scarlet	£100	95·00
547		2d. + 1d. blue	£100	85·00

75 New Zealand Lake Scenery

FIVE PENCE

(76)

(Des L. C. Mitchell. Plates, Royal Mint, London. Typo Govt Ptg Office)

1931 (10 Nov). *Air.* W **41.** *P* 14 × 14½.

548	**75**	3d. chocolate	27·00	14·00
		a. Perf 14 × 15	£225	£425
549		4d. blackish purple	28·00	16·00
550		7d. brown-orange	32·00	14·00

1931 (18 Dec). *Air. Surch with* T **76.**

551	**75**	5d. on 3d. green (R.)	18·00	12·00

77 Hygeia, Goddess of Health

78 The Path to Health

(Des R. E. Tripe and W. J. Cooch. Eng H. T. Peat. Recess Govt Printing Office, Wellington)

1932 (18 Nov). *Health Stamp.* W **41.** *P* 14.

552	**77**	1d. + 1d. carmine	30·00	25·00

(Des J. Berry. Eng H. T. Peat. Recess Govt Printing Office, Wellington)

1933 (8 Nov). *Health Stamp.* W **41.** *P* 14.

553	**78**	1d. + 1d. carmine	14·00	18·00

TRANS-TASMAN
AIR MAIL
"FAITH IN AUSTRALIA."

(79)

80 Crusader

1934 (Feb). *Air.* T **75** *in new colour optd with* T **79.** W **41.** *P* 14 × 14½.

554	**75**	7d. light blue (B.)	42·00	48·00

(Des J. Berry. Recess D.L.R.)

1934 (26 Oct). *Health Stamp.* W **41.** *P* 14 × 13½.

555	**80**	1d. + 1d. carmine	9·00	16·00

81 Collared Grey Fantail

82 Brown Kiwi

83 Maori Woman

84 Maori Carved House

85 Mt Cook

86 Maori Girl

87 Mitre Peak

88 Swordfish

89 Harvesting

90 Tuatara Lizard

91 Maori Panel

92 Parson Bird

93 Capt. Cook at Poverty Bay

94 Mt Egmont

Die I Die II

(Des J. Fitzgerald (½d., 4d.), C. H. and R. J. G. Collins (1d.), M. Matthews (1½d.), H. W. Young (2d.), L. C. Mitchell (2½d., 3d., 8d., 1s., 3s.), W. J. Cooch and R. E. Tripe (5d.), T. I. Archer (6d.), I. F. Calder (9d.) and I. H. Jenkins (2s.). Litho Waterlow (9d.). Recess D.L.R. (remainder))

1935 (1 May). W **41.**

556	**81**	½d. bright green, *p* 14 × 13½	50	15
557	**82**	1d. scarlet (Die I), *p* 14 × 13½	50	10
		a. Perf 13½ × 14	35·00	16·00
		b. Die II. Perf 14 × 13½	3·25	75
		ba. Booklet pane of 6 with adverts on selvedge	25·00	
558	**83**	1½d. red-brown, *p* 14 × 13½	2·75	2·75
		a. Perf 13½ × 14	2·75	2·75
559	**84**	2d. orange, *p* 14 × 13½	1·25	30
560	**85**	2½d. chocolate and slate, *p* 13–14 × 13½	2·75	6·00
		a. Perf 13½ × 14	2·50	6·00
561	**86**	3d. brown, *p* 14 × 13½	12·00	60
562	**87**	4d. black and sepia, *p* 14	2·00	30
563	**88**	5d. ultramarine, *p* 13–14 × 13½	10·00	8·00
		a. Perf 13½ × 14	12·00	9·50
564	**89**	6d. scarlet, *p* 13½ × 14	2·75	70
565	**90**	8d. chocolate, *p* 14 × 13½	2·75	1·25
566	**91**	9d. scarlet and black, *p* 14 × 14½	12·00	2·75
567	**92**	1s. deep green, *p* 14 × 13½	9·00	2·50
568	**93**	2s. olive-green, *p* 13–14 × 13½	15·00	8·50
		a. Perf 13½ × 14	20·00	10·00
569	**94**	3s. chocolate & yell-brn, *p* 13–14 × 13½	20·00	27·00
		a. Perf 13½ × 14	14·00	25·00
556/69a		*Set of* 14	75·00	55·00

In the 2½d., 5d., 2s. and 3s. perf 13–14 × 13½ the horizontal perforations of each stamp are in two sizes, one half of each horizontal side measuring 13 and the other 14.

See also Nos. 577/90 and 630/1.

95 Bell Block Aerodrome

96 King George V and Queen Mary

(Des J. Berry. Eng Stamp Printing Office, Melbourne. Recess Govt Printing Office, Wellington)

1935 (4 May). *Air.* W **41.** *P* 14.

570	**95**	1d. carmine	40	20
571		3d. violet	3·50	3·75
572		6d. blue	7·50	4·00

(Frame by J. Berry. Recess B.W.)

1935 (7 May). *Silver Jubilee.* W **41.** *P* 11 × 11½.

573	**96**	½d. green	55	45
574		1d. carmine	55	20
575		6d. red-orange	20·00	32·00

97 "The Key to Health"

98 "Multiple Wmk"

(Des S. Hall. Recess John Ash, Melbourne)

1935 (30 Sept). *Health Stamp.* W **41.** *P* 11.

576	**97**	1d. + 1d. scarlet	2·25	2·75

WATERMARKS. In W 41 the wmk units are in vertical columns widely spaced and the sheet margins are unwatermarked or wmkd "NEW ZEALAND POSTAGE" in large letters.

In W 98 the wmk units are arranged alternately in horizontal rows closely spaced and are continued into the sheet margins.

(Litho Govt Ptg Office, Wellington (9d.). Recess Waterlow or D.L.R. (others))

1936–43. W **98.**

577	**81**	½d. bright green, *p* 14 × 13½	25	5
578	**82**	1d. scarlet (Die II), *p* 14 × 13½	25	5
579	**83**	1½d. red-brown, *p* 14 × 13½	1·50	1·25
580	**84**	2d. orange, *p* 14 × 13½	15	5
		a. Perf 12½† (6.41)	85	30
		c. Perf 14 (6.41)	2·25	1·25
		d. Perf 14 × 15 (6.41)	4·25	3·00
581	**85**	2½d. chocolate and slate, *p* 13–14 × 13½	1·25	3·00
		a. Perf 14	80	1·50
		b. Perf 14 × 13½ (1942)	1·00	2·25
582	**86**	3d. brown, *p* 14 × 13½	17·00	40
583	**87**	4d. black and sepia, *p* 14 × 13½	1·00	12
		a. Perf 12½* (1941)	4·25	70
		b. Perf 14, line (1941)	40·00	28·00
		c. Perf 14 × 14½ comb (7.42)	1·00	12
584	**88**	5d. ultramarine, *p* 13–14 × 13½	3·25	80
		a. Perf 12½*† (7.41, 1942)	8·50	1·50
		b. Perf 14 × 13½ (1942)	2·50	65
585	**89**	6d. scarlet, *p* 13½ × 14	1·25	10
		a. Perf 12½* (1941)	1·50	20
		b. Perf 14½ × 14 (1942)	80	10
586	**90**	8d. chocolate, *p* 14 × 13½ (*wmk sideways*)	2·00	75
		aa. Wmk upright (1939)	1·90	55
		a. Perf 12½* (*wmk sideways*) (1941)	1·75	60
		b. Perf 14 × 14½ (*wmk sideways*) (1943)	1·25	12
587	**91**	9d. red & gry, *p* 14 × 15 (*wmk sideways*)	14·00	1·50
		a. Red & grey-blk. Perf 13½ × 14 (1.3.38)	14·00	1·25
588	**92**	1s. deep green, *p* 14 × 13½	1·25	12
		a. Perf 12½* (11.41)	17·00	8·00
589	**93**	2s. olive-green, *p* 13–14 × 13½	9·50	1·25
		a. Perf 13½ × 14 (1938)	75·00	2·00
		b. Perf 12½*† (1941, 1942)	12·00	1·50
		c. Perf 14 × 13½ (1942)	8·50	85
590	**94**	3s. chocolate & yell-brn, *p* 13–14 × 13½	13·00	3·25
		a. Perf 12½* (1941)	25·00	20·00
		b. Perf 14 × 13½ (1942)	8·50	2·25
577/90b		*Set of* 14	50·00	7·75

*†Stamps indicated with an asterisk were printed and perforated by Waterlow; those having a dagger were printed by D.L.R. and perforated by Waterlow. No. 580d was printed by D.L.R. and perforated by Harrison and No. 583b was printed by Waterlow and perforated by D.L.R. These are all known as "Blitz perfs" because De La Rue were unable to maintain supplies after their works were damaged by enemy action. All the rest, except the 9d., were printed and perforated by D.L.R.

On stamps printed and perforated by De La Rue the perf 14 × 13½ varies in the sheet and is sometimes nearer 13½. 2d. perf 14 × 15 is sometimes nearer 14 × 14½.

2½d., 5d., 2s. and 3s. In perf 13–14 × 13½ one half the length of each horizontal perforation measures 13 and the other 14. In perf 14 × 13½ the horizontal perforation is regular.

4d. No. 583b is line-perf measuring 14 exactly and has a blackish sepia frame. No. 583c is a comb-perf measuring 14 × 14.3 or 14 × 14.2 and the frame is a warmer shade.

2s. No. 589a is comb-perf and measures 13.5 × 13.75.

For 9d. typographed, see Nos. 630/1.

99 N.Z. Soldier at Anzac Cove

100 Wool

(Des L. C. Mitchell. Recess John Ash, Melbourne)

1936 (27 Apr). *Charity. 21st Anniv of "Anzac" Landing at Gallipoli. W* **41**. *P* 11.
591 **99** ½d. + ½d. green . . . . 30 1·00
592 1d. + 1d. scarlet . . . . 30 1·00

(Des L. C. Mitchell. Recess John Ash, Melbourne)

1936 (1 Oct). *Congress of British Empire Chambers of Commerce, Wellington. Industries Issue. T* **100** *and similar horiz designs. W* **41**. *P* 11½.
593 ½d. emerald-green 15 25
594 1d. scarlet 15 20
595 2½d blue . . . . 2·25 6·00
596 4d. violet . . . . 2·00 5·50
597 6d. red-brown . . . . 1·75 4·75
Designs:—1d. Butter; 2½d. Sheep; 4d. Apples; 6d. Exports.

105 Health Camp

106 King George VI and Queen Elizabeth

(Des J. Berry. Recess John Ash, Melbourne)

1936 (2 Nov). *Health Stamp. W* **41**. *P* 11.
598 **105** 1d. + 1d. scarlet . . . . 80 2·75

(Recess B.W.)

1937 (13 May). *Coronation. W* **98**. *P* 14 × 13½.
599 **106** 1d. carmine 25 10
600 2½d. Prussian blue . . . . 75 1·25
601 6d. red-orange . . . . 1·00 1·00

107 Rock climbing

108 King George VI

108a

(Des G. Bull and J. Berry. Recess John Ash, Melbourne)

1937 (1 Oct). *Health Stamp. W* **41**. *P* 11.
602 **107** 1d. + 1d. scarlet . . . . 2·00 3·25

(Des W. J. Cooch. Recess B.W.)

1938–44. *W* **98**. *P* 14 × 13½.
603 **108** ½d. green (1.3.38) . . . . . . 1·75 5
604 ½d. brown-orange (10.7.41) 10 5
605 1d. scarlet (1.7.38) . . . . . . 2·00 5
606 1d. green (21.7.41) 10 5
607 **108a** 1½d. purple-brown (26.7.38) . . . . . . 11·00 1·60
608 1½d. scarlet (1.2.44) 15 5
609 3d. blue (26.9.41) 20 5
603/9 . . . . *Set of* 7 14·00 1·75
For other values see Nos. 680/89.

109 Children playing

110 Beach Ball

(Des J. Berry. Recess B.W.)

1938 (1 Oct). *Health Stamp. W* **98**. *P* 14 × 13½.
610 **109** 1d. + 1d. scarlet . . . . 1·25 1·60

(Des S. Hall. Recess Note Printing Branch, Commonwealth Bank of Australia, Melbourne)

1939 (16 Oct). *Health Stamps. Surcharged with new value. W* **41**. *P* 11.
611 **110** 1d. on ½d. + ½d. green . . . . . . 2·00 3·25
612 2d. on 1d. + 1d. scarlet . . . . . . 2·00 3·25

111 Arrival of the Maoris, 1350

115 Signing Treaty of Waitangi, 1840

(Des L. C. Mitchell (½d., 3d., 4d.); J. Berry (others). Recess B.W.)

1940 (2 Jan–8 Mar). *Centenary of Proclamation of British Sovereignty. T* **111**, **115** *and similar designs. W* **98**. *P* 14 × 13½ (2½d.), 13½ × 14 (5d.) *or* 13½ (*others*).
613 ½d. blue-green 30 5
614 1d. chocolate and scarlet 90 5
615 1½d. light blue and mauve 30 25
616 2d. blue-green and chocolate 90 5
617 2½d. blue-green and blue 45 35
618 3d. purple and carmine . . . . 2·25 40
619 4d. chocolate and lake . . . . 5·00 80
620 5d. pale blue and brown . . . . 3·75 3·50
621 6d. emerald-green and violet . . . . 5·00 45
622 7d. black and red . . . . 3·50 6·50
623 8d. black and red (8.3) . . . . 4·50 2·50
624 9d. olive-green and orange . . . . 9·00 3·00
625 1s. sage-green and deep green . . . . 11·00 2·75
613/25 . . . . *Set of* 13 42·00 19·00
Designs: *Horiz* (*as T* **111**)—1d. *Endeavour*, chart of N.Z., and Capt. Cook; 1½d. British Monarchs; 2d. Tasman with his ship and chart; 3d. Landing of immigrants, 1840; 4d. Road, Rail, Sea and Air Transport; 6d. *Dunedin* and "Frozen Mutton Route" to London; 7d., 8d. Maori council; 9d. Gold mining in 1861 and 1940. (*As T* **115**)—5d. H.M.S. *Britomar* at Akaroa, 1840. *Vert* (*as T* **111**)—1s. Giant Kauri tree.

1940 (1 Oct). *Health Stamps. As T* **110**, *but without extra surcharge. W* **41**. *P* 11.
626 **110** 1d. + ½d. blue-green . . . . . . 2·75 6·50
627 2d. + 1d. brown-orange . . . . . . 2·75 6·50

1D 1D

(**123**)

2,D

Inserted "2"

1941

(**124**)

1941. *Surch as T* **123**.
628 **108** 1d. on ½d. green (1.5.41) 15 5
629 **108a** 2d. on 1½d. purple-brown (4.41) 15 5
a. Inserted "2" £350 £250
The surcharge on No. 629 has only one figure, at top left, and there is only one square to obliterate the original value at bottom right.
The variety "Inserted 2" occurs on the 10th stamp, 10th row. It is identified by the presence of remnants of the damaged "2", and by the spacing of "2" and "D" which is variable and different from the normal.

(Typo Govt Printing Office, Wellington)

1941. *As T* **91**, *but smaller* (17½ × 20½ *mm*). *P* 14 × 15. (*a*) *W* **41**.
630 **91** 9d. scarlet and black (5.41) . . . . 45·00 4·75
(*b*) *W* **98**
631 **91** 9d. scarlet and black (29.9.41) . . . . 2·50 65

1941 (4 Oct). *Health Stamps. Nos. 626/7 optd with T* **124**.
632 **110** 1d. + ½d. blue-green . . . . . . 85 2·75
633 2d. + 1d. brown-orange . . . . . . 85 2·75

125 Boy and Girl on Swing

126 Princess Margaret

(Des S. Hall. Recess Note Printing Branch, Commonwealth Bank of Australia, Melbourne)

1942 (1 Oct). *Health Stamps. W* **41**. *P* 11.
634 **125** 1d. + ½d. blue-green 25 55
635 2d. + 1d. orange-red 25 55

(Des J. Berry. Recess B.W.)

1943 (1 Oct). *Health Stamps. T* **126** *and similar triangular design. W* **98**. *P* 12.
636 1d. + ½d. green 15 30
a. Imperf between (vert pair) £2500
637 2d. + 1d. red-brown 15 20
a. Imperf between (vert pair) £2500 £2500
Design:—2d. Queen Elizabeth II as Princess.

 TENPENCE 

(**128**)

1944 (1 May). *No. 615 surch with T* **128**.
662 10d. on 1½d. light blue and mauve 20 35

129 Queen Elizabeth II as Princess and Princess Margaret

130 Statue of Peter Pan, Kensington Gardens

(Recess B.W.)

1944 (9 Oct). *Health Stamps. W* **98**. *P* 13½.
663 **129** 1d. + ½d. green 10 20
664 2d. + 1d. blue 10 20

(Des J. Berry. Recess B.W.)

1945 (1 Oct). *Health Stamps. W* **98**. *P* 13½.
665 **130** 1d. + ½d. green and buff 5 10
666 2d. + 1d. carmine and buff 5 10

131 Lake Matheson

132 King George VI and Parliament House, Wellington

133 St. Paul's Cathedral

139 "St. George" (Wellington College War Memorial Window)

(Des J. Berry. Photo Harrison (1½d. and 1s.). Recess B.W. (1d. and 2d.) and Waterlow (others))

1946 (1 Apr). *Peace issue. T* **131/3**, **139** *and similar designs. W* **98** (*sideways on* 1½d.). *P* 13 (1d., 2d.), 14 × 14½ (1½d., 1s.), 13½ (*others*).
667 ½d. green and brown 10 15
668 1d. green 10 5
669 1½d. scarlet 10 12
670 2d. purple 15 5
671 3d. ultramarine and grey 20 10
672 4d. bronze-green and orange 20 30
673 5d. green and ultramarine 20 25
674 6d. chocolate and vermilion 20 12
675 8d. black and carmine 15 30
676 9d. blue and black 15 40
677 1s. grey-black 40 35
667/77 . . . . *Set of* 11 1·75 2·00
Designs: *Horiz* (*as T* **132**)—2d. The Royal Family. (*As T* **131**)—3d. R.N.Z.A.F. badge and aeroplanes; 4d. Army badge, tank and plough; 5d. Navy badge, war and trading ships; 6d. N.Z. coat of arms, foundry and farm; 9d. Southern Alps and Franz Josef Glacier. *Vert* (*as T* **139**)—1s. National Memorial Campanile.

142 Soldier helping Child over Stile

(Des J. Berry. Recess Waterlow)

1946 (24 Oct). *Health Stamps. W* **98**. *P* 13½.
678 **142** 1d. + ½d. green and orange-brown . . 5 10
a. Yellow-green and orange-brown . . 2·75 2·75
679 2d. + 1d. chocolate and orange-brown 5 10

144 King George VI

145 Statue of Eros

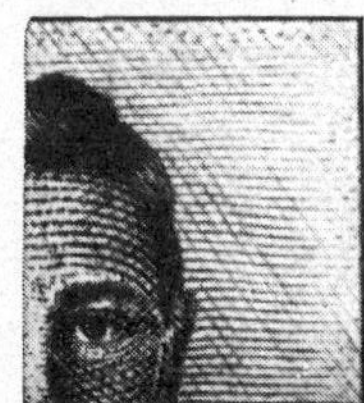
Plate 1

Plate 2

(Des W. J. Cooch. Recess T **108a**, B.W.; T **144**, D.L.R.)

1947–52. W **98** (*sideways on "shilling" values*). (*a*) *P* 14 × 13½.
680 **108a** 2d. orange 15 5
681 4d. bright purple 35 10
682 5d. slate 75 40
683 6d. carmine 50 5
684 8d. violet .. .. 1·00 15
685 9d. purple-brown .. .. 1·25 10
(*b*) *P* 14
686 **144** 1s. red-brown and carmine (Plate 1) .. 1·75 20
a. Wmk upright (Plate 1) 80 20
b. Wmk upright (Plate 2) .. .. 1·00 12
687 1s. 3d. red-brown and blue (Plate 2) .. 1·00 30
a. Wmk upright (14.1.52) .. .. 2·50 3·25
688 2s. brown-orange and green (Plate 1) .. 2·00 50
a. Wmk upright (Plate 1) .. .. 2·00 1·25
689 3s. red-brown and grey (Plate 2) .. 3·25 1·00
680/9 .. .. *Set of* 10 10·00 2·25

In head-plate 2 the diagonal lines of the background have been strengthened and result in the upper corners and sides appearing more deeply shaded.

(Des J. Berry. Recess Waterlow)

1947 (1 Oct). *Health Stamps. W* **98** (*sideways*). *P* 13½.
690 **145** 1d. + ½d. green 5 5
691 2d. + 1d. carmine 5 5

146 Port Chalmers, 1848

148 First Church, Dunedin

(Des J. Berry. Recess B.W.)

1948 (23 Feb). *Centennial of Otago. T* **146, 148** *and similar designs. W* **98** (*sideways on* 3d.). *P* 13½.
692 1d. blue and green 8 10
693 2d. green and brown 8 10
694 3d. purple 8 15
695 6d. black and rose 8 15

Designs: *Horiz*—2d. Cromwell, Otago; 6d. University of Otago.

150 Boy Sunbathing and Children Playing

151 Nurse and Child

(Des E. Linzell. Recess B.W.)

1948 (1 Oct). *Health Stamps. W* **98**. *P* 13½.
696 **150** 1d. + ½d. blue and green 5 5
697 2d. + 1d. purple and scarlet 5 5

1949 ROYAL VISIT ISSUE. Four stamps were prepared to commemorate this event: 2d. Treaty House, Waitangi; 3d. H.M.S. *Vanguard*; 5d. Royal portraits; 6d. Crown and sceptre. The visit did not take place and the stamps were destroyed, although a few examples of the 3d. later appeared on the market. A similar set was prepared in 1952, but was, likewise, not issued.

(Des J. Berry. Photo Harrison)

1949 (3 Oct). *Health Stamps. W* **98**. *P* 14 × 14½.
698 **151** 1d. + ½d. green 5 5
699 2d. + 1d. ultramarine 5 5
a. No stop below "D" of "1 D." .. 6·00 8·00

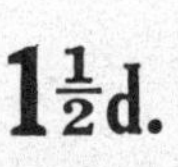

POSTAGE

(**152**)

153 Queen Elizabeth II and Prince Charles

1950 (28 July). *As Type* F **6**, *but without value, surch with T* **152**. *W* **98**. *Chalk-surfaced paper. P* 14.
700 F **6** 1½d. carmine 5 5

Originally issued with the watermark inverted, this later appeared with it upright.

(Des J. Berry and R. S. Phillips. Photo Harrison)

1950 (2 Oct). *Health Stamps. W* **98**. *P* 14 × 14½.
701 **153** 1d. + ½d. green 10 10
702 2d. + 1d. plum 10 10

154 Christchurch Cathedral

155 Cairn on Lyttleton Hills

(Des L. C. Mitchell (2d.), J. A. Johnstone (3d.) and J. Berry (others). Recess B.W.)

1950 (20 Nov). *Centennial of Canterbury, N.Z. T* **154/5** *and similar designs. W* **98** (*sideways on* 1d. *and* 3d.). *P* 13½.
703 1d. green and blue 8 12
704 2d. carmine and orange 10 10
705 3d. dark blue and blue 30 30
706 6d. brown and blue 15 25
707 1s. reddish purple and blue 45 90

Designs: *Vert* (*as T* **154**)—3d. John Robert Godley. *Horiz* (*as T* **155**)—6d. Canterbury University College; 1s. Aerial view of Timaru.

159 "Takapuna" class Yachts

(Des J. Berry and R. S. Phillips. Recess B.W.)

1951 (1 Nov). *Health Stamps. W* **98**. *P* 13½.
708 **159** 1½d. + ½d. scarlet and yellow 10 10
709 2d. + 1d. deep green and yellow 10 10

160 Princess Anne

161 Prince Charles

3D

(**162**)

(From photographs by Marcus Adams. Photo Harrison)

1952 (1 Oct). *Health Stamps. W* **98**. *P* 14 × 14½.
710 **160** 1½d. + ½d. carmine-red 12 15
711 **161** 2d. + 1d. brown 12 10

1952–53. *Nos.* 604 *and* 606 *surch as T* **162**.
712 **108** 1d. on ½d. brown-orange (11.9.53) .. 8 10
713 3d. on 1d. green (12.12.52*) 10 5

*Earliest known date used.

163 Buckingham Palace

164 Queen Elizabeth II

(Des L. C. Mitchell (1s. 6d.), J. Berry (others). Recess D.L.R. (2d., 4d.), Waterlow (1s. 6d.) Photo Harrison (3d., 8d.))

1953 (25 May). *Coronation. T* **163/4** *and similar designs. W* **98**. *P* 13.
714 2d. deep bright blue 15 15
715 3d. brown 15 5
716 4d. carmine .. .. 75 1·50
717 8d. slate-grey .. .. 70 1·00
718 1s. 6d. purple and ultramarine .. .. 1·60 2·50

Designs: *Horiz* (*as T* **163**)—4d. Coronation State Coach; 1s. 6d. St. Edward's Crown and Royal Sceptre. *Vert* (*as T* **164**)—8d. Westminster Abbey.

168 Girl Guides

169 Boy Scouts

(Des J. Berry. Photo Harrison)

1953 (7 Oct). *Health Stamps. W* **98**. *P* 14 × 14½.
719 **168** 1½d. + ½d. blue 10 8
720 **169** 2d. + 1d. deep yellow-green 10 15

No. 720 exists imperf three sides.

170 Queen Elizabeth II

171 Queen Elizabeth II and Duke of Edinburgh

(Des L. C. Mitchell. Recess Waterlow)

1953 (9 Dec). *Royal Visit. W* **98**. *P* 13 × 14 (*3d.*) *or* 13½ (*4d.*).
721 **170** 3d. dull purple 10 5
722 **171** 4d. deep ultramarine 10 20

172 **173** Queen Elizabeth II **174**

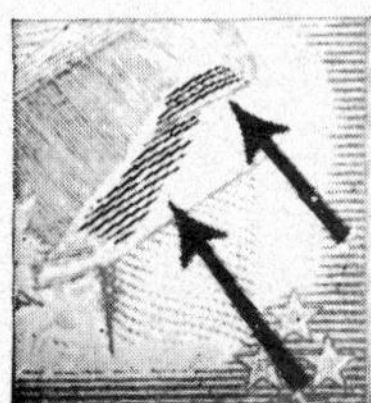
Die I

Die II

(Des L. C. Mitchell (T **172/3**), J. Berry (T **174**). Recess D.L.R. (T **173**), B.W. (others))

1953 (15 Dec)–**58.** *W* **98**. *P* 14 × 13½ (*T* **172**), 14 (*T* **173**) *or* 13½ (*T* **174**).
723 **172** ½d. slate-black (1.3.54) 12 12
724 1d. orange (1.3.54) 15 5
725 1½d. brown-lake 20 5
726 2d. bluish green (1.3.54) 20 5
727 3d. vermilion (1.3.54) 20 5
728 4d. blue (1.3.54) 40 15
729 6d. purple (1.3.54) .. .. 1·00 25
730 8d. carmine (1.3.54) 60 25
731 **173** 9d. brown and bright green (1.3.54) .. 60 10
732 1s. black & carm-red (Die I) (1.3.54) .. 65 5
a. Die II (1958) .. .. 60·00 9·00
733 1s. 6d. black and bright blue (1.3.54) .. 1·75 12
733*a* 1s. 9d. black and red-orange (1.7.57) .. 5·50 50
733*b* **174** 2s. 6d. brown (1.7.57) .. .. .. 40·00 5·50
734 3s. bluish green (1.3.54) .. .. 12·00 30
735 5s. carmine (1.3.54) .. .. .. 20·00 2·25
736 10s. deep ultramarine (1.3.54) .. .. 55·00 20·00
723/36 .. .. *Set of* 16 £120 27·00

1s. Dies I and II. The two dies of the Queen's portrait differ in the shading on the sleeve at right. The long lines running upwards from left to right are strong in Die I and weaker in Die II. In the upper part of the shading the fine cross-hatching is visible in Die I only between the middle two of the four long lines, but in Die II it extends clearly across all four lines.

In the lower part of the shading the strength of the long lines in Die I makes the cross-hatching appear subdued, whereas in Die II the weaker long lines make the cross-hatching more prominent.

Centre plates 1A, 1B and 2B are Die I; 3A and 3B are Die II.

For stamps as T **172** but with larger figures of value see Nos. 745/51.

1958 NEW PAPER. A new white opaque paper first came into use in August 1958 and was used for later printings of Nos. 733*a*, 745, 747/9, O159, O161, O163/4, O166 and L54. It is slightly thicker than the paper previously used, but obviously different in colour (white, against cream) and opacity (the previous paper being *relatively* transparent).

175 Young Climber and Mts Aspiring and Everest

(Des J. Berry. Recess; vignette litho B.W.)

1954 (4 Oct). *Health Stamps. W* **98**. *P* 13½.
737 **175** 1½d. + ½d. sepia and deep violet .. 10 12
738 2d. + 1d. sepia and blue-black .. 10 20

176 Maori Mail-carrier

177 Queen Elizabeth II

178 Douglas "DC 3" Airliner

(Des R. M. Conly (2d.), J. Berry (3d.), A. G. Mitchell (4d.). Recess D.L.R.)

1955 (18 July). *Centenary of First New Zealand Postage Stamps. W* **98.** *P* 14 (2*d.*), 14 × 14½ (3*d.*) *or* 13 (4*d.*).
739 **176** 2d. sepia and deep green 12 8
740 **177** 3d. brown-red 12 5
741 **178** 4d. black and bright blue 20 50

179 Children's Health Camps Federation Emblem

181 "The Whalers of Foveaux Strait"

180

(Des E. M. Taylor. Recess B.W.)

1955 (3 Oct). *Health Stamps. W* **98** *(sideways). P* 13½ × 13.
742 **179** 1½d. + ½d. sepia and orange-brown 15 50
743 2d. + 1d. red-brown and green 15 35
744 3d. + 1d. sepia and deep rose-red 20 20
a. Centre omitted

1955–59. *As Nos. 724/30 but larger figures of value and stars omitted from lower right corner.*
745 **180** 1d. orange (12.7.56) 35 5
746 1½d. brown-lake (1.12.55) 45 60
747 2d. bluish green (19.3.56) 30 5
748 3d. vermilion (1.5.56) 55 5
749 4d. blue (3.2.58) 2·25 25
750 6d. purple (20.10.55) 3·50 10
751 8d. chestnut (1.12.59) 3·75 5·50
745/51 *Set of* 7 10·00 6·00
See note *re* white opaque paper after No. 736. No. 751 exists only on white paper.

183 Takahe

(Des E. R. Leeming (2d.), L. C. Mitchell (3d.), M. R. Smith (8d.). Recess D.L.R.)

1956 (16 Jan). *Southland Centennial. T* **181, 183** *and similar design. W* **98.** *P* 13½ × 13 (8*d.*) *or* 13 × 12½ (*others*).
752 2d. deep blue-green 20 15
753 3d. sepia 15 5
754 8d. slate-violet and rose-red 1·50 2·40
Design: *Horiz*—3d. "Farming".

184 Children picking Apples

(Des L. C. Mitchell, after photo by J. F. Louden. Recess B.W.)

1956 (24 Sept). *Health Stamps. W* **98.** *P* 13 × 13½.
755 **184** 1½d. + ½d. purple-brown 15 50
a. Blackish brown 1·00 2·00
756 2d. + 1d. blue-green 15 35
757 3d. + 1d. claret 20 20

185 New Zealand Lamb and Map

186 Lamb, *Dunedin* and Modern Ship

(Des M. Goaman. Photo Harrison)

1957 (15 Feb). *75th Anniv of First Export of N.Z. Lamb. W* **98** *(sideways on 4d.). P* 14 × 14½ (4*d.*) *or* 14½ × 14 (8*d.*).
758 **185** 4d. blue 1·00 1·50
759 **186** 8d. deep orange-red 1·50 1·75

187 Sir Truby King

(Des M. R. Smith. Recess B.W.)

1957 (14 May). *50th Anniv of Plunket Society. W* **98.** *P* 13.
760 **187** 3d. bright carmine-red 10 5

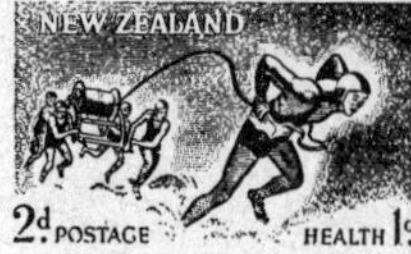

188 Life-savers in Action

189 Children on Seashore

(Des L. Cutten (2d.), L. C. Mitchell (3d.). Recess Waterlow)

1957 (25 Sept). *Health Stamps. W* **98** *(sideways). P* 13½.
761 **188** 2d. + 1d. black and emerald 15 15
762 **189** 3d. + 1d. ultramarine and rose-red 15 15
MS762*b* Two sheets each 112 × 96 mm with Nos. 761 and 762 in blocks of 6 (2 × 3). *Per pair* 14·00 18·00
MS762*c* As last but with wmk upright *Per pair* 25·00 42·00

2d
●

(190)

191 Girls' Life Brigade Cadet

192 Boys' Brigade Bugler

1958 (6 Jan). *No. 746 surch as T* **190.**
763 **180** 2d. on 1½d. brown-lake 8 5
a. Smaller dot in surch 8 5
b. Error. Surch on No. 725 (3.58) £110 £150
Diameter of dot on No. 763 is 4¼ mm; on No. 763a 3¾ mm.
Forgeries of No. 763b are known.

(Des J. Berry. Photo Harrison)

1958 (20 Aug). *Health Stamps. W* **98.** *P* 14 × 14½.
764 **191** 2d. + 1d. green 12 10
765 **192** 3d. + 1d. blue 12 10
MS765*a* Two sheets each 104 × 124 mm with Nos. 764/5 in blocks of 6 (3 × 2). *Per pair* 12·00 16·00

(Des J. E. Lyle. Eng F. D. Manley. Recess Commonwealth Bank of Australia Note Ptg Branch)

1958 (27 Aug). *30th Anniv of First Air Crossing of the Tasman Sea. As T* **120** *of Australia, but inscr* "NEW ZEALAND". *W* **98** *(sideways). P* 14 × 14½.
766 6d. deep ultramarine 30 40

193 Seal of Nelson

(Des M. J. Macdonald. Recess B.W.)

1958 (29 Sept). *Centenary of City of Nelson. W* **98.** *P* 13½ × 13.
767 **193** 3d. carmine 8 5

194 "Pania" Statue, Napier

195 Australian Gannets on Cape Kidnappers

(Des M. R. Smith (2d.), J. Berry (3d.), L. C. Mitchell (8d.). Photo Harrison)

1958 (3 Nov). *Centenary of Hawke's Bay Province. T* **194/5** *and similar design. W* **98** *(sideways on 3d.). P* 14½ × 14 (3*d.*) *or* 13½ × 14½ (*others*).
768 2d. yellow-green 12 8
769 3d. blue 20 5
770 8d. red-brown 1·90 2·50
Design:—*Vert* 8d. Maori sheep-shearer.

197 "Kiwi" Jamboree Badge

198 Careening H.M. Bark *Endeavour* at Ship Cove

(Des Mrs. S. M. Collins. Recess B.W.)

1959 (5 Jan). *Pan-Pacific Scout Jamboree. Auckland. W* **98.** *P* 13½ × 13.
771 **197** 3d. sepia and carmine 12 5

(Des G. R. Bull and G. R. Smith. Photo Harrison)

1959 (2 Mar). *Centenary of Marlborough Province. T* **198** *and similar horiz designs. W* **98** *(sideways). P* 14½ × 14.
772 2d. green 20 10
773 3d. deep blue 20 5
774 8d. light brown 1·90 2·50
Designs:—3d. Shipping wool, Wairau Bar, 1857; 8d. Salt industry, Grassmere.

201 Red Cross Flag

(Photo Harrison)

1959 (3 June). *Red Cross commemoration. W* **98** *(sideways). P* 14½ × 14.
775 **201** 3d. + 1d. red and ultramarine 10 10
a. Red Cross omitted £850

202 Grey Teal

203 New Zealand Stilt

(Des Display Section, G.P.O. Photo Harrison)

1959 (16 Sept). *Health Stamps. W* **98** *(sideways). P* 14 × 14½.
776 **202** 2d. + 1d. greenish yellow, ol & rose-red 15 20
777 **203** 3d. + 1d. black, pink and light blue 15 20
a. Pink ptg omitted 85·00
b. Pink ptg shifted to left (at least 2½ mm) 18·00
MS777*c*. Two sheets each 95 × 109 mm. with Nos. 776/7 in blocks of 6 (3 × 2). *Per pair* 8·50 18·00

204 "The Explorer"

205 "The Gold Digger"

(Des G. R. Bull and G. R. Smith. Photo Harrison)

1960 (16 May). *Centenary of Westland Province. T* **204/5** *and similar vert design. W* **98.** *P* 14 × 14½.
778 2d. deep dull green 20 10
779 3d. orange-red 20 8
780 8d. grey-black 1·75 3·25
Design:—8d. "The Pioneer Woman".

207 Manuka (Tea Tree)

214 National Flag

216 Trout

219 Taniwha (Maori Rock Drawing)

220 Butter Making

221 Tongariro National Park and Château   **221a** Tongariro National Park and Château

(Des Harrison (½d.), G. F. Fuller (1d., 3d., 6d.), A. G. Mitchell (2d., 4d., 5d., 8d., 3s., 10s., £1), P.O. Public Relations Division (7d.), P.O. Publicity Section (9d.), J. Berry (1s., 1s. 6d.), R. E. Barwick (1s. 3d.), J. C. Boyd (1s. 9d.), D. F. Kee (2s.), L. C. Mitchell (2s. 6d., 5s.). Photo D.L.R. (½d., 1d., 2d., 3d., 4d., 6d., 8d.) or Harrison (others))

1960 (11 July)–**66**. *T* **207, 214, 216, 219/21***a and similar designs. Ordinary or chalk-surfaced paper* (**C**). *W* **98** (*sideways on* 2½*d.,* 5*d.,* 1*s.,* 3*d.,* 1*s.* 6*d.,* 2*s.* 6*d.,* 3*s. and* 10*s.*). *P* 14 × 14½ (1*s.* 3*d.,* 1*s.* 6*d.,* 2*s.,* 5*s.,* £1) *or* 14½ × 14 (*others*).

781 **207** ½d. grey, green and cerise (1.9.60) .. 5 5
782 – 1d. orange, green, lake & brn (1.9.60) 5 5
b. Coil Perf 14½ × 13. Wmk sideways (11.63) 50 80
c. Chalky paper (1965?) 10 8
783 – 2d. carmine, black, yellow and green 12 5
784 – 2½d. red, yellow, blk & grn (**C**) (1.11.61) 25 5
785 – 3d. yellow, green, yellow-brown and deep greenish blue (1.9,60) .. 12 5
e. Coil. Perf 14½ × 13. Wmk sideways (3.10.63) 50 80
f. Chalky paper (1965?) 25 15
786 – 4d. purple, buff, yellow-green & lt blue 30 5
d. Chalky paper (1965?) .. .. £150 7·00
787 – 5d. yell, dp grn, blk & vio (**C**) (14.5.62) 40 5
788 – 6d. lilac, grn & dp bluish grn (1.9.60) 40 5
a. No wmk .. .. 17·00 12·00
c. Chalky paper (1966?) 30 40
788*c* – 7d. red, grn, yell & pale red (**C**) (16.3.66) 40 60
789 – 8d. rose-red, yell, grn & grey (1.9.60) 50 10
790 **214** 9d. red and ultramarine (1.9.60) .. 45 15
791 – 1s. brown and deep green 40 5
792 **216** 1s. 3d. carmine, sepia & brt bl (*shades*) .. .. 1·00 10
793 – 1s. 6d. olive-green and orange-brown 1·25 25
794 – 1s. 9d. bistre-brown .. .. .. 11·00 20
795 – 1s. 9d. orange-red, blue, green and yellow (**C**) (4.11.63) .. .. 4·75 50
796 **219** 2s. black and orange-buff .. .. 2·25 5
a. Chalky paper (1966) .. .. 2·00 1·25
797 **220** 2s. 6d. yellow and light brown .. 2·50 60
798 **221** 3s. blackish brown .. .. .. 35·00 1·75
799 **221a** 3s. bistre, blue and green (**C**) (1.4.64) 6·50 1·50
800 – 5s. blackish green .. .. .. 10·00 70
a. Chalky paper (1966) .. .. 7·00 4·25
801 – 10s. steel-blue .. .. 15·00 5·50
a. Chalky paper (1966) .. .. 7·00 10·00
802 – £1 deep magenta .. .. .. 12·00 16·00
781/802 .. .. *Set of* 23 85·00 25·00

Designs: *Vert* (*as T* **207**)—1d. Karaka; 2d. Kowhai Ngutu–kaka (Kaka Beak); 2½d. Titoki; 3d. Kowhai; 4d. Puarangi (Hibiscus); 5d. Matua Tikumu (Mountain Daisy); 6d. Pikiarero (Clematis); 7d. Koromiko; 8d. Rata. (*As T* **216**)—1s. 6d. Tiki. (*As T* **219**)—5s. Sutherland Falls; £1 Pohutu Geyser. *Horiz* (*as T* **214**)—1s. Timber industry—1s. 9d. Aerial top dressing. (*As T* **221**)—10s. Tasman Glacier.

MISSING COLOURS are known as following—½d. (green and grey), 1d. (orange), 2d. (black and yellow), 2½d. (red, yellow, green and red and green on same stamp), 3d. (yellow, green and brown), 4d. (purple, buff and yellow-green), 5d. (yellow), 6d. (lilac and green), 9d. (red). 1s. 3d. (carmine), and 2s. 6d. (yellow).

Nos. 782b and 785e were replaced by coils with upright watermark perf 15 × 14, in 1966.

CHALKY PAPER. The chalk-surfaced paper is not only whiter but also thicker, making the watermark difficult to see.

225 Sacred Kingfisher   **226** New Zealand Pigeon

(Des Display Section, G.P.O. Recess B.W.)

1960 (10 Aug). *Health Stamps. W* **98**. *P* 13½.
803 **225** 2d. + 1d. sepia and turquoise-blue .. 40 35
804 **226** 3d. + 1d. deep purple-brown and orange 45 40
MS804*b* Two sheets each 95 × 107 mm with Nos. 803 and 804 in blocks of 6. *P* 11½ × 11 *Per pair* 26·00 32·00

227 "The Adoration of the Shepherds" (Rembrandt)

(Photo Harrison)

1960 (1 Nov). *Christmas. W* **98**. *P* 12.
805 **227** 2d. red and deep brown/*cream* 25 10
a. Red omitted £300

228 Great Egret   **229** New Zealand Falcon

(Des Display Section, G.P.O. Recess B.W.)

1961 (2 Aug). *Health Stamps. W* **98**. *P* 13½.
806 **228** 2d. + 1d. black and purple 30 30
807 **229** 3d. + 1d. deep sepia and yellow-green 30 30
MS807*a* Two sheets each 97 × 121 mm with Nos. 806/7 in blocks of 6 (3 × 2) .. *Per pair* 18·00 22·00

2½d   2½d

(230)   (231)

232 "Adoration of the Magi" (Dürer)

1961 (1 Sept). *No.* 748 *surch with T* **230** (*wide setting*).
808 **180** 2½d. on 3d. vermilion 10 5
a. Narrow setting (T **231**) 10 5
b. Pair, wide and narrow .. .. 15·00 17·00

The difference in the settings is in the overall width of the new value, caused by two different spacings between the "2", "½" and "d".

(Photo Harrison)

1961 (16 Oct). *Christmas. W* **98** (*sideways*). *P* 14½ × 14.
809 **232** 2½d. multicoloured 20 5

233 Morse Key and Port Hills, Lyttelton

(Des A. G. Mitchell (3d.) and L. C. Mitchell (8d.). Photo Harrison)

1962 (1 June). *Telegraph Centenary. T* **233** *and similar horiz design. W* **98** (*sideways*). *P* 14½ × 14.
810 3d. sepia and bluish green 15 8
a. Green omitted £250
811 8d. black and brown-red .. .. .. 1·50 2·75
a. Imperf (pair) £550
b. Black omitted £225

Design:—8d. Modern teleprinter.

No. 811a comes from a sheet with the two top rows imperforate and the third row imperforate on three sides.

235 Red-fronted Parakeet   **236** Tieke Saddleback

(Des Display Section, G.P.O. Photo D.L.R.)

1962 (3 Oct). *Health Stamps. W* **98**. *P* 15 × 14.
812 **235** 2½d. + 1d. multicoloured 20 25
a. Orange omitted .. .. ..
813 **236** 3d. + 1d. multicoloured 20 25
a. Orange omitted £700
MS813*b* Two sheets each 96 × 101 mm with Nos. 812/3 in blocks of 6 (3 × 2) .. .. *Per pair* 22·00 30·00

237 "Madonna in Prayer" (Sassoferrato)

(Photo Harrison)

1962 (15 Oct). *Christmas. W* **98**. *P* 14½ × 14.
814 **237** 2½d. multicoloured 15 5

238 Prince Andrew **239**

(Design after photographs by Studio Lisa, London. Recess D.L.R.)

1963 (7 Aug). *Health Stamps. W* **98**. *P* 14.
815 **238** 2½d. + 1d. dull ultramarine (*shades*) .. 12 12
816 **239** 3d. + 1d. carmine 12 10
MS816*a* Two sheets each 93 × 100 mm with Nos. 815/16 in blocks of 6 (3 × 2) .. *Per pair* 18·00 22·00

240 "The Holy Family" (Titian)

(Photo Harrison)

1963 (14 Oct). *Christmas. W* **98** (*sideways*). *P* 12½.
817 **240** 2d. multicoloured 8 8
a. Imperf (pair) £130

241 Steam Locomotive "Pilgrim" and "DG" Diesel Electric Loco   **242** Diesel Express and Mt Ruapehu

(Des Commercial Art Section, N.Z. Railways. Photo D.L.R.)

1963 (25 Nov). *Railway Centenary. W* **98** (*sideways*). *P* 14.
818 **241** 3d. multicoloured 30 10
a. Blue (sky) omitted £180
819 **242** 1s. 9d. multicoloured .. .. 4·50 4·75
a. Red (value) omitted £500

1963 (3 Dec). *Opening of COMPAC (Trans-Pacific Telephone Cable). As T* **174** *of Australia but inscr* "NEW ZEALAND". *No wmk. P* 13½.
820 8d. red, blue, black and yellow .. .. 2·25 4·00

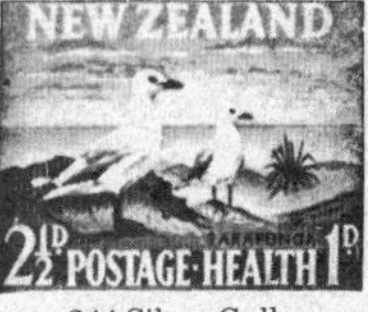

243 Road Map and Car Steering-wheel   **244** Silver Gulls

(Des L. C. Mitchell. Photo Harrison)

1964 (1 May). *Road Safety Campaign. W* **98**. *P* 15 × 14.
821 **243** 3d. black, ochre-yellow and blue .. 8 5

(Des Display Section G.P.O., after Miss T. Kelly. Photo Harrison)

1964 (5 Aug). *Health Stamps. T* **244** *and similar horiz design. Multicoloured. W* **98**. *P* 14½.
822 2½d. + 1d. Type **244** 12 20
823 3d. + 1d. Little Penguin 12 20
MS823*a* Two sheets each 171 × 84 mm with Nos. 822/3 in blocks of 8 (4 × 2) .. *Per pair* 35·00 45·00

246 Rev. S. Marsden taking first Christian service at Rangihoua Bay, 1814

7D
POSTAGE
(247)

(Des L. C. Mitchell. Photo Harrison)

1964 (12 Oct). *Christmas. W* **98** (*sideways*). *P* 14 × 13½.
824 **246** 2½d. multicoloured 8 8

1964 (14 Dec). *As Type* F **6**, *but without value, surch with T* **247**. *W* **98**. *Unsurfaced paper. P* 14 × 13½.
825 F **6** 7d. carmine-red 25 70

248 Anzac Cove

(Des R. M. Conly. Photo Harrison)

1965 (14 Apr). *50th Anniv of Gallipoli Landing. T* **248** *and similar horiz design. W* **98**. *P* 12½.
826 4d. yellow-brown 15 5
827 5d. green and red 15 45
Design:—5d. Anzac Cove and poppy.

250 I.T.U. Emblem and Symbols

(Photo Harrison)

1965 (17 May). *I.T.U. Centenary. W* **98**. *P* 14½ × 14.
828 **250** 9d. blue and pale chocolate . . . . 70 1·25

(From photograph by Karsh. Photo Note Ptg Branch, Reserve Bank of Australia)

1965 (24 May). *Churchill Commemoration. As T* **186** *of Australia but inscr* "NEW ZEALAND". *P* 13½.
829 7d. black, pale grey and light blue 25 55

251 Wellington Provincial Council Building

(Des from painting by L. B. Temple (1867). Photo Harrison)

1965 (26 July). *Centenary of Government in Wellington. W* **98** *(sideways). P* 14½ × 14.
830 **251** 4d. multicoloured 8 8

252 Kaka **253** Collared Grey Fantail (after Miss T. Kelly)

(Des Display Section, G.P.O. Photo Harrison)

1965 (4 Aug). *Health Stamps. W* **98**. *P* 14 × 14½.
831 **252** 3d. + 1d. multicoloured 20 25
832 **253** 4d. + 1d. multicoloured 20 25
a. Green ("POSTAGE HEALTH" and on leaves) omitted . . . . . . 70·00
MS832*b* Two sheets each 100 × 109 mm with Nos. 831/2 in blocks of 6 (3 × 2) . . *Per pair* 24·00 30·00

254 I.C.Y. Emblem **255** "The Two Trinities" (Murillo)

(Litho D.L.R.)

1965 (28 Sept). *International Co-operation Year. W* **98** *(sideways). P* 14.
833 **254** 4d. carmine-red and light yellow-olive 15 8

(Photo Harrison)

1965 (11 Oct). *Christmas. W* **98**. *P* 13½ × 14.
834 **255** 3d. multicoloured 8 5

256 Arms of New Zealand **259** "Progress" Arrowhead

(Des Display Section, G.P.O. Photo D.L.R.)

1965 (30 Nov). *11th Commonwealth Parliamentary Conference. T* **256** *and similar horiz designs. Multicoloured. P* 14.
835 4d. Type **256** 50 20
a. Blue (incl value) omitted £200
836 9d. Parliament House, Wellington and Badge 2·00 2·25
837 2s. Wellington from Mt Victoria . . . . 5·75 11·00

(Des Display Section, G.P.O. Photo Harrison)

1966 (5 Jan). *Fourth National Scout Jamboree, Trentham. W* **98**. *P* 14 × 15.
838 **259** 4d. gold and myrtle-green 15 10
a. Gold (arrowhead) omitted £400

260 New Zealand Bell Bird **262** "The Virgin with Child" (Maratta)

(Des Display Section, G.P.O. Photo Harrison)

1966 (3 Aug). *Health Stamps. T* **260** *and similar vert design. Multicoloured. W* **98** *(sideways). P* 14 × 14½.
839 3d. + 1d. Type **260** 15 30
840 4d. + 1d. Weka Rail 15 30
a. Deep brown (values and date) omitted . . £500
MS841 Two sheets each 107 × 91 mm. Nos. 839/40 in blocks of 6 (3 × 2) . . . . *Per pair* 18·00 22·00
In No. 840a besides the value, "1966" and "Weka" are also omitted and the bird, etc. appears as light brown.

(Photo Harrison)

1966 (3 Oct). *Christmas. W* **98** *(sideways). P* 14½.
842 **262** 3d. multicoloured 5 5

263 Queen Victoria and Queen Elizabeth II **264** Half-sovereign of 1867 and Commemorative Dollar Coin

(Des Display Section, G.P.O. Photo Harrison)

1967 (3 Feb). *Centenary of New Zealand Post Office Savings Bank. W* **98** *(sideways on 4d.). P* 14 × 14½.
843 **263** 4d. black, gold and maroon 12 10
844 **264** 9d. gold, silver, black, lt blue & dp grn 25 70

(New Currency. 100 cents = 1 dollar)

265 Manuka (Tea Tree) **266** Pohutu Geyser

1967 (10 July)–**70**. *Decimal Currency. Designs as* 1960–66 *issue, but with values inscr in decimal currency as T* **265**/**6**. *Chalky paper. W* **98** *(sideways on* 8 *c.,* 10 *c.,* 20 *c.,* 50 *c. and* $2). *P* 13½ × 14 (½ *c. to* 3 *c.,* 5 *c. and* 7 *c.*), 14½ × 14 (4 *c.,* 6 *c.,* 8 *c.,* 10 *c.,* 25 *c.,* 30 *c. and* $1) *or* 14 × 14½ (15 *c.,* 20 *c.,* 50 *c. and* $2).
845 **265** ½ c. pale blue, yellow-green and cerise 10 5
846 – 1 c. yellow, carmine, green & lt brown (as 1d.) 10 5
a. Booklet pane. Five stamps plus one printed label . . . . 1·25
847 – 2 c. carmine, black, yellow and green (as 2d.) 10 5

848 – 2½ c. yellow, green, yellow-brown and deep bluish green (as 3d.) . . 10 5
a. Deep bluish green omitted* . . £300
b. Imperf (pair)† . . 70·00
849 – 3 c. purple, buff, yellow-green and light greenish blue (as 4d.) . . 12 5
850 – 4 c. yellow, deep green, black and violet (as 5d.) 30 5
851 – 5 c. lilac, yellow-olive and bluish green (as 6d.) 35 5
852 – 6 c. red, green, yellow and light pink (as 7d.) 70 10
853 – 7 c. rose-red, yellow, green and grey (as 8d.) 85 10
854 **214** 8 c. red and ultramarine 85 10
a. Red omitted £150
855 – 10 c. brown and deep green (as 1s.) . . 80 45
856 – 15 c. olive-green and orange-brown (as 1s. 6d.) . . . . 2·25 1·25
857 **219** 20 c. black and buff . . . . 2·50 10
858 **220** 25 c. yellow and light brown . . . . 2·75 2·00
859 **221***a* 30 c. olive-yellow, green & greenish blue . . . . 3·50 60
a. No wmk (1970) . . . . 7·00 3·25
860 – 50 c. blackish green (as 5s.) . . . . 3·75 75
861 – $1 Prussian blue (as 10s.) . . . . 22·00 2·75
862 **266** $2 deep magenta . . . . 20·00 20·00
845/62 . . . . . . *Set of* 18 55·00 26·00

*This occurred on one horizontal row of ten, affecting the background colour so that the value is also missing. In the row above and the row below, the colour was partially omitted. The price is for a vertical strip.

The 2½ c. value has been seen with the yellow omitted, but only on a used example.

†This comes from a sheet of which the six right-hand vertical rows were completely imperforate and the top, bottom and left-hand margins had been removed.

The 4 c., 30 c. and 50 c. exist with PVA gum as well as gum arabic. No. 859a exists with PVA gum only.

For $4 to $10 in the "Arms" type, see under Postal Fiscal stamps.

See also Nos. 870, etc.

268 Running with Ball

(Des L. C. Mitchell. Photo Harrison)

1967 (2 Aug). *Health Stamps. Rugby Football. T* **268** *and similar multicoloured design. W* **98** *(sideways on* 2½ *c.). P* 14½ × 14 (2½ *c.*) *or* 14 × 14½ (3 *c.*).
867 2½ c. + 1 c. Type **268** 15 15
868 3 c. + 1 c. Positioning for a place-kick (*horiz*) 15 20
MS869 Two sheets; (*a*) 76 × 130 mm (867); (*b*) 130 × 76 mm (868). Containing blocks of six . . . . . . *Per pair* 18·00 22·00

270 Trawler and Catch **271** Brown Trout

276 Dairy Farm, Mt Egmont and Butter Consignment **277** Fox Glacier, Westland National Park

(Des Display Section, G.P.O. (7, 8, 10, 18, 20, 25 c. and 28 c. from photo), R. M. Conly (7½ c.). Litho B.W. (7, 8, 18, 20 c.) or photo D.L.R. (7½ c.) and Harrison (10, 25, 28 c.). Others (15 c., $2) as before)

1967–69. *T* **270**/**1**, **276**/**7** *and similar designs. Chalky paper (except* 7, 8, 18, 20 *c.). No wmk* (7, 8, 20 *c.*) *or W* **98** *(sideways on* 7½, 10, 15, 25 *c., upright on* 18, 28 *c.,* $2). *P* 13½ (7, 7½ *c.*), 13 × 13½ (8, 18, 20 *c.*), 14½ × 14 (10, 25 *c.*) *or* 14 × 14½ (15, 28 *c.,* $2).
870 7 c. multicoloured (3.12.69) . . . . 1·75 1·00
871 7½ c. multicoloured* (29.8.67) 50 70
a. Wmk upright (10.68) 70 80
872 8 c. multicoloured (8.7.69) . . . . 1·75 80
873 10 c. multicoloured (2.4.68) 60 5
a. Green (background) omitted . . £130
874 15 c. apple-green, myrtle-green and carmine (as No. 856†) (19.3.68) . . . . 1·25 35
875 18 c. multicoloured (8.7.69) . . . . 2·25 45
876 20 c. multicoloured (8.7.69) . . . . 2·25 30
877 25 c. multicoloured (10.12.68) . . . . 6·00 2·25
878 28 c. multicoloured (30.7.68) . . . . 1·50 10
879 $2 black, ochre & pale blue (as No. 862) (10.12.68) . . . . . . 65·00 24·00
870/79 . . . . . . *Set of* 10 75·00 27·00

Designs: *Horiz*—8 c. Apples and orchard; 10 c. Forest and timber; 18 c. Sheep and the "Woolmark"; 20 c. Consignments of beef and herd of cattle.

*No. 871 was originally issued to commemorate the introduction f the brown trout into New Zealand.

† No. 874 is slightly larger than No. 856, measuring 21 × 25 mm .nd the inscriptions and numerals differ in size.

278 "The Adoration of the Shepherds" (Poussin) 279 Mount Aspiring, Aurora Australis and Southern Cross 280 Sir James Hector (founder)

(Photo Harrison)

967 (3 Oct). *Christmas.* W **98** (*sideways*). P 13½ × 14.
'80 **278** 2½ c. multicoloured 5 5

(Des J. Berry. Litho D.L.R.)

'967 (10 Oct). *Centenary of the Royal Society of New Zealand.* W **98** (*sideways on* 4 c.). P 14 (4 c) *or* 13 × 14 (8 c.).
81 **279** 4 c. multicoloured 20 35
82 **280** 8 c. multicoloured 25 45

281 Open Bible 282 Soldiers and Tank

(Des Display Section, G.P.O. Litho D.L.R.)

968 (23 Apr). *Centenary of Maori Bible.* W **98**. P 13½.
83 **281** 3 c. multicoloured 10 5
a. Gold (inscr etc.) omitted .. .. 70·00

(Des L. C. Mitchell. Litho D.L.R.)

1968 (7 May). *New Zealand Armed Forces.* T **282** *and similar horiz designs. Multicoloured.* W **98** (*sideways*). P 14 × 13½.
384 4 c. Type **282** 45 20
385 10 c. Airmen, "Canberra" and "Kittyhawk" aircraft .. .. 1·40 80
86 28 c. Sailors and warships .. .. 2·50 3·75

285 Boy breasting Tape, and Olympic Rings 287 Placing Votes in Ballot Box

(Des L. C. Mitchell. Photo Harrison)

1968 (7 Aug). *Health Stamps.* T **285** *and similar horiz design. Multicoloured.* P 14½ × 14.
387 2½ c. + 1 c. Type **285** 15 15
388 3 c. + 1 c. Girl swimming and Olympic rings 15 15
MS889 Two sheets each 145 × 95 mm. Nos. 887/8 in blocks of six .. .. .. *Per pair* 16·00 18·00

(Des J. Berry. Photo Japanese Govt Ptg Bureau, Tokyo)

1968 (19 Sept). *75th Anniv of Universal Suffrage in New Zealand.* P 13.
390 **287** 3 c. ochre, olive-green and light blue .. 5 5

288 Human Rights Emblem 289 "The Nativity" (G. van Honthorst)

(Photo Japanese Govt Ptg Bureau, Tokyo)

1968 (19 Sept). *Human Rights Year.* P 13.
891 **288** 10 c. scarlet, yellow and deep green .. 30 75

(Photo Harrison)

1968 (1 Oct). *Christmas.* W **98** (*sideways*). P 14 × 14½.
392 **289** 2½ c. multicoloured 8 5

290 I.L.O. Emblem

(Photo Harrison)

1969 (11 Feb). *50th Anniv of International Labour Organization.* W **98** (*sideways*). P 14½ × 14.
893 **290** 7 c. black and carmine-red 45 85

291 Supreme Court Building, Auckland 292 Law Society's Coat of Arms

(Des R. M. Conly. Litho B.W.)

1969 (8 Apr). *Centenary of New Zealand Law Society.* T **291/2** *and similar design.* P 13½ × 13 (3 c.) *or* 13 × 13½ (*others*).
894 3 c. multicoloured (*shades*) 15 8
895 10 c. multicoloured .. .. 90 1·00
896 18 c. multicoloured (*shades*) .. .. .. 1·40 1·90
Design:—*Vert*—18 c. "Justice" (from Memorial Window in University of Canterbury, Christchurch).

295 Student being conferred with Degree

(Des R. M. Conly. Litho B.W.)

1969 (3 June). *Centenary of Otago University* T **295** *and similar multicoloured design.* P 13 × 13½ (3 c.) *or* 13½ × 13 (10 c.).
897 3 c. Otago University (*vert*) 15 12
898 10 c. Type **295** .. .. 65 1·00

296 Boys playing Cricket 298 Dr. Elizabeth Gunn (founder of First Children's Health Camp)

(Des R. M. Conly (4 c.); L. C. Mitchell (others). Litho B.W.)

1969 (6 Aug). *Health Stamps.* T **296** *and similar horiz design and* T **298**. P 12½ × 13 (*No.* 901) *or* 13 × 12½ (*others*).
899 2½ c. + 1 c. multicoloured 60 45
900 3 c. + 1 c. multicoloured 60 45
901 4 c. + 1 c. brown and ultramarine .. .. 70 1·40
MS902 Two sheets each 144 × 84 mm. Nos. 899/900 in blocks of six .. .. *Per pair* 27·00 28·00
Design:—3 c. Girls playing cricket.

299 Oldest existing House in New Zealand, and Old Stone Mission Store, Kerikeri

(Litho D.L.R.)

1969 (18 Aug). *Early European Settlement in New Zealand, and 150th Anniv of Kerikeri.* T **299** *and similar horiz design. Multicoloured.* W **98** (*sideways*). P 13 × 13½.
903 4 c. Type **299** 50 50
904 6 c. View of Bay of Islands .. .. .. 1·10 1·75

301 "The Nativity" (Federico Fiori (Barocci)) 302 Captain Cook, Transit of Venus and "Octant"

(Photo Harrison)

1969 (1 Oct). *Christmas.* P 13 × 14. A. W **98**. B. *No wmk.*

			A		B	
905	**301**	2½ c. multicoloured	8	8	8	8

(Des Eileen Mayo. Photo; portraits embossed Harrison)

1969 (9 Oct). *Bicentenary of Captain Cook's Landing in New Zealand.* T **302** *and similar horiz designs.* P 14½ × 14.
906 4 c. black, cerise and blue 75 35
907 6 c. slate-green, purple-brown & black .. 2·75 3·50
908 18 c. purple-brown, slate-green & black .. 4·75 4·75
909 28 c. cerise, black and blue .. .. .. 7·50 9·00
MS910 109 × 90 mm. Nos. 906/9 .. .. .. 30·00 30·00

Designs:—6 c. Sir Joseph Banks (naturalist) and outline of the *Endeavour*; 18 c. Dr. Daniel Solander (botanist) and his plant; 28 c. Queen Elizabeth II and Cook's chart, 1769.

The miniature sheet exists additionally inscribed on the selvedge at bottom. "A SOUVENIR FROM NEW ZEALAND STAMP EXHIBITION, NEW PLYMOUTH 6TH–11TH OCTOBER. 1969". These were not sold from Post Offices.

306 Girl, Wheat Field and C.O.R.S.O. Emblem 307 Mother feeding her Child, Dairy Herd and C.O.R.S.O. Emblem

(Des L. C. Mitchell. Photo Japanese Govt Printing Bureau, Tokyo)

1969 (18 Nov). *25th Anniv of C.O.R.S.O. (Council of Organizations for Relief Services Overseas).* P 13.
911 **306** 7 c. multicoloured .. .. .. 1·50 2·00
912 **307** 8 c. multicoloured .. .. .. 1·50 2·00

308 "Cardigan Bay" (champion trotter)

(Des L. C. Mitchell. Photo Courvoisier)

1970 (28 Jan). *Return of "Cardigan Bay" to New Zealand.* P 11½.
913 **308** 10 c. multicoloured 40 60

309 Red Admiral Butterfly 310 Queen Elizabeth II and New Zealand Coat of Arms

(Des Enid Hunter (½ c., 1 c., 2 c., 18 c., 20 c.), Eileen Mayo (2½ c. to 7 c.), D. B. Stevenson (7½ c., 8 c.), M. Cleverley (10 c., 15 c., 25 c., 30 c., $1, $2), M. V. Askew (23 c., 50 c.). Photo Harrison (½ c. to 20 c.), Enschedé (23 c., 50 c.), Courvoisier ($1, $2) or Litho B.W. (25 c., 30 c.))

1970 (12 Mar)–**76**. *Various designs at* T **309/10**. W **98** (*sideways on* 10, 15 *and* 20 c.) *or No wmk* (23 c., to $2).

(*a*) *Size as* T **309**. P 13½ × 13

914 ½ c. multicoloured (2.9.70) 15 20
915 1 c. multicoloured (2.9.70) 12 5
a. Wmk sideways (booklets) (6.7.71) .. 30 30
b. Booklet pane. No. 915a × 3 with three *se-tenant* printed labels (6.7.71) .. .. 1·75
916 2 c. multicoloured (2.9.70) 12 5
a. Black (inscr, etc.) omitted .. .. 85·00
917 2½ c. multicoloured (2.9.70) 40 8
918 3 c. black, brown and orange (2.9.70) .. 15 5
a. Wmk sideways (booklets) (6.7.71) .. 30 30
919 4 c. multicoloured (2.9.70) 20 5
a. Wmk sideways (booklets) (6.7.71) .. 30 30
920 5 c. multicoloured (4.11.70) 45 10
921 6 c. blackish grn, yell-grn & carm (4.11.70) 55 20
922 7 c. multicoloured (4.11.70) 70 25
923 7½ c. multicoloured (4.11.70) .. .. .. 1·25 1·75
924 8 c. multicoloured (4.11.70) 80 25

(*b*) *Size as* T **310**. *Various Perfs*

925 10 c. multicoloured (*p* 14½ × 14) 45 15
926 15 c. black, flesh and pale brown (*p* 13½ × 13) (20.1.71) .. .. 2·50 25
927 18 c. chestnut, black & apple-grn (*p* 13 × 13½) (20.1.71) .. .. 2·75 50
928 20 c. black & yell-brn (*p* 13½ × 13) (20.1.71) 2·75 60
929 23 c. multicoloured (*p* 13½ × 12½) (1.12.71) .. 1·00 20
930 25 c. multicoloured (*p* 13 × 13½) (1.9.71) .. 2·75 50
a. Perf 14 (11.76?) .. .. 1·25 40
931 30 c. multicoloured (*p* 13 × 13½) (1.9.71) .. 2·50 65
a. Perf 14 (9.76?) .. .. 4·00 2·25
932 50 c. multicoloured (*p* 13½ × 12½) (1.9.71) .. 1·50 35
933 $1 multicoloured (*p* 11½) (14.4.71) .. .. 2·50 80
934 $2 multicoloured (*p* 11½) (14.4.71) .. .. 4·75 2·75
914/34 .. .. *Set of* 21 24·00 8·50

Designs: *Vert*—½ c. Glade Copper Butterfly; 1 c. Type **309**; 2 c. Tussock Butterfly; 2½ c. Magpie Moth; 3 c. Lichen Moth; 4 c. Puriri Moth; 5 c. Scarlet Parrot Fish; 6 c. Sea Horses; 7 c. Leather Jacket (fish); 7½ c. Garfish; 8 c. John Dory (fish); 18 c. Maori Club; 25 c. Hauraki Gulf Maritime Park; 30 c. Mt Cook National Park. *Horiz*—10 c. Type **310**; 15 c. Maori fish hook; 20 c. Maori tattoo pattern; 23 c. Egmont National Park; 50 c. Abel Tasman National Park; $1 Geothermal Power; $2 Agricultural Technology.

Although issued as a definitive, No. 925 was put on sale on the occasion of the Royal Visit to New Zealand.

See also Nos. 1008, etc.

311 Geyser Restaurant

312 U.N. H.Q. Building

(Des M. Cleverley. Photo Japanese Govt Printing Bureau, Tokyo)

1970 (8 Apr). *World Fair, Osaka. T* **311** *and similar horiz designs. Multicoloured. P* 13.

935 7 c. Type **311** .. .. 1·25 1·75
936 8 c. New Zealand Pavilion .. .. 1·25 2·00
937 18 c. Bush Walk .. .. 2·75 2·25

(Des R. M. Conly (3 c.), L. C. Mitchell (10 c.). Litho D.L.R.)

1970 (24 June). *25th Anniv of United Nations. T* **312** *and similar vert design. P* 13½.

938 3 c. multicoloured 15 10
939 10 c. scarlet and yellow 50 60

Design:—10 c. Tractor on horizon.

313 Soccer

(Des L. C. Mitchell. Litho D.L.R.)

1970 (5 Aug). *Health Stamps. T* **313** *and similar multicoloured design. P* 13½.

940 2½ c. + 1 c. Netball (*vert*) 15 25
941 3 c. + 1 c. Type **313** 15 25
MS942 Two sheets: (*a*) 102 × 125 mm (940); (*b*) 125 × 102 mm (941), containing blocks of six *Per pair* 15·00 17·00

314 "The Virgin adoring the Child" (Correggio)

315 "The Holy Family" (stained glass window, Invercargill Presbyterian Church)

(Litho D.L.R.)

1970 (1 Oct). *Christmas. T* **314/15** *and similar design. P* 12½.

943 2½ c. multicoloured 12 5
944 3 c. multicoloured 12 5
 a. Green (inscr and value) omitted .. £120
945 10 c. black, orange and silver .. .. .. 65 1·10

Design: *Horiz*—10 c. Tower of Roman Catholic Church, Sockburn.

316 Chatham Islands Lily

(Des Eileen Mayo. Photo Japanese Govt Printing Bureau, Tokyo)

1970 (2 Dec). *Chatham Islands. T* **316** *and similar horiz design. Multicoloured. P* 13.

946 1 c. Type **316** 15 25
947 2 c. Albatross 25 35

317 Country Women's Institute Emblem

(Des L. C. Mitchell. Photo Japanese Govt Ptg Bureau, Tokyo)

1971 (10 Feb). *50th Anniversaries of Country Women's Institutes and Rotary International in New Zealand. T* **317** *and similar horiz design. Multicoloured. P* 13.

948 4 c. Type **317** 12 10
949 10 c. Rotary emblem and map of New Zealand 50 60

NEW INFORMATION

The editor is always interested to correspond with people who have new information that will improve or correct the Catalogue.

318 Racing Yacht

(Des J. Berry (5 c.), G. F. Fuller (8 c.). Litho B.W.)

1971 (3 Mar). *One Ton Cup Racing Trophy. T* **318** *and similar horiz design. Multicoloured. P* 13½ × 13.

950 5 c. Type **318** 25 25
951 8 c. One Ton Cup .. .. 60 1·00

319 Civic Arms of Palmerston North

(Des R. M. Conly. Photo Japanese Govt Ptg Bureau, Tokyo)

1971 (12 May). *City Centenaries. T* **319** *and similar horiz designs. Multicoloured. P* 13.

952 3 c. Type **319** 15 8
953 4 c. Arms of Auckland 20 15
954 5 c. Arms of Invercargill 40 60

320 Antarctica on Globe

321 Child on Swing

(Des Eileen Mayo. Photo Japanese Govt Ptg Bureau, Tokyo)

1971 (9 June). *Tenth Anniv of Antarctic Treaty. P* 13.

955 **320** 6 c. multicoloured .. .. 2·50 3·00

(Des Eileen Mayo. Photo Japanese Govt Ptg Bureau, Tokyo)

1971 (9 June). *25th Anniv of U.N.I.C.E.F. P* 13.

956 **321** 7 c. multicoloured .. .. 1·25 1·75

4c　　4c　　4c

(322)　　(322*a*)　　(322*b*)

T **322**. Photo, showing screening dots; thin bars, wide apart.
T **322***a*. Typo, without screening dots; thick bars, closer together.
T **322***b*. Typo; bars similar to T **322**.

1971–73. *No.* 917 *surcharged.*

(*a*) *In photogravure, by Harrison* (23.6.71*)

957 **322** 4 c. on 2½ c. multicoloured 30 10

(*b*) *Typographically, by Harrison* (13.7.72*)

957*a* **322***a* 4 c. on 2½ c. multicoloured 40 12
 ab. Albino surch £100
 ac. Surch double, one albino .. .. 15·00

(*c*) *Typographically, locally* (18.6.73*)

957*b* **322***b* 4 c. on 2½ c. multicoloured 30 10

*Earliest known postmarks.

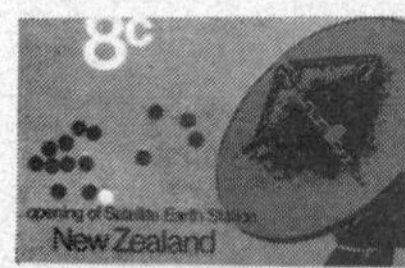

323 Satellite-tracking Aerial

(Des M. Cleverley. Photo Courvoisier)

1971 (14 July). *Opening of Satellite Earth Station. T* **323** *and similar horiz design. P* 11½.

958 8 c. black, drab-grey and vermilion .. .. 1·00 1·40
959 10 c. black, turquoise-grn & pale bluish vio .. 1·00 1·50

Design:—10 c. Satellite.

324 Girls playing Hockey

(Des L. C. Mitchell. Litho Harrison)

1971 (4 Aug). *Health Stamps. T* **324** *and similar horiz designs. Multicoloured. W* **98** (*sideways on* 5 c.). *P* 13½ × 13.

960 3 c. + 1 c. Type **324** 20 20
961 4 c. + 1 c. Boys playing hockey 20 25
962 5 c. + 1 c. Dental Health .. .. 80 1·10
MS963 Two sheets each 122 × 96 mm. Nos. 960/1 in blocks of six .. .. *Per pair* 17·00 20·00

325 "Madonna bending over the Crib" (Maratta)

326 "Tiffany" Rose

(Des Enid Hunter (10 c.), D. A. Hatcher (others). Photo Harrison)

1971 (6 Oct). *Christmas. T* **325** *and similar vert designs. Multicoloured. P* 13 × 13½.

964 3 c. Type **325** 15 10
965 4 c. "The Annunciation" (stained-glass window) (21½ × 38 *mm*) 15 5
966 10 c. "The Three Kings" (21½ × 38 *mm*) .. 90 1·40

(Des A. G. Mitchell. Photo Courvoisier)

1971 (3 Nov). *First World Rose Convention, Hamilton. T* **326** *and similar vert designs showing roses. Multicoloured. P* 11½.

967 2 c. Type **326** 20 20
968 5 c. "Peace" 40 30
969 8 c. "Chrysler Imperial" .. .. 80 1·00

327 Lord Rutherford and Alpha Particles

328 Benz (1895)

(Des M. Cleverley. Litho B.W.)

1971 (1 Dec). *Birth Centenary of Lord Rutherford* (*scientist*). *T* **327** *and similar horiz design. Multicoloured. P* 13½ × 13.

970 1 c. Type **327** 20 35
971 7 c. Lord Rutherford and formula .. .. 80 1·25

(Des A. G. Mitchell. Litho B.W.)

1972 (2 Feb). *International Vintage Car Rally. T* **328** *and similar horiz designs. Multicoloured. P* 14.

972 3 c. Type **328** 20 5
973 4 c. Oldsmobile (1904) 30 5
974 5 c. Ford "Model T" (1914) 45 15
975 6 c. Cadillac Service car (1915) 75 85
976 8 c. Chrysler (1924) .. .. 2·50 2·75
977 10 c. Austin "7" (1923) .. .. 2·50 2·75
972/7 .. .. *Set of* 6 5·00 6·00

329 Coat of Arms of Wanganui

330 Black Scree Cotula

(Des M. Cleverley. Litho Harrison)

1972 (5 Apr). *Anniversaries. T* **329** *and similar designs. P* 13 × 13½ (3, 5 *and* 8 c.) *or* 13½ × 13 (*others*).

978 3 c. multicoloured 12 10
979 4 c. red-orange, brown-bistre and black .. 15 10
980 5 c. multicoloured 25 15
981 8 c. multicoloured .. .. 2·50 3·25
982 10 c. multicoloured .. .. 2·50 3·25

Designs and Events: *Vert*—3 c. Type **329** (Centenary of Wanganui Council govt); 5 c. De Havilland DH89 "Rapide" *Dominie* and Boeing "737" (25th Anniv National Airways Corp); 8 c. French frigate and Maori palisade (Bicent of landing by Marion du Fresne). *Horiz*—4 c. Postal Union symbol (Tenth Anniv of Asian-Oceanic Postal Union); 10 c. Stone cairn (150th Anniv of New Zealand Methodist Church).

(Des Eileen Mayo. Litho Harrison)

1972 (7 June). *Alpine Plants. T* **330** *and similar vert designs. Multicoloured. P* 13½.

983 4 c. Type **330** 30 12
984 6 c. North Island Eidelweiss .. .. .. 1·40 1·40
985 8 c. Haast's Buttercup .. .. 2·50 2·75
986 10 c. Brown Mountain Daisy .. .. .. 3·50 4·00

331 Boy playing Tennis

332 "Madonna with Child" (Murillo)

(Des L. C. Mitchell. Litho Harrison)

972 (2 Aug). *Health Stamps. T* **331** *and similar vert design. P* 13 × 13½.
87 3 c. + 1 c. light grey and chestnut 20 20
88 4 c. + 1 c. light red-brown, grey and lemon 20 20
IS989 Two sheets each 107 × 123 mm. Nos. 987/8 in blocks of six .. .. .. *Per pair* 18·00 20·00
Design:—No. 988, Girl playing tennis.

(Des D. A. Hatcher. Photo Courvoisier)

972 (4 Oct). *Christmas. T* **332** *and similar vert designs. Multicoloured. P* 11½.
90 3 c. Type **332** 12 5
91 5 c. "The Last Supper" (stained-glass window, St. John's Church, Levin) 20 5
92 10 c. Pohutukawa flower .. .. .. 1·40 1·60

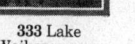

333 Lake Waikaremoana

334 Old Pollen Street

(Des D. A. Hatcher. Photo Courvoisier)

972 (6 Dec). *Lake Scenes. T* **333** *and similar vert designs. Multicoloured. P* 11½.
93 6 c. Type **333** .. .. 1·50 1·75
94 8 c. Lake Hayes .. .. 2·00 2·50
95 18 c. Lake Wakatipu .. .. 2·75 4·25
96 23 c. Lake Rotomahana .. .. 3·50 4·75

(Des Miss V. Jepsen (3 c.), B. Langford (others). Litho Harrison)

973 (7 Feb). *Commemorations. T* **334** *and similar horiz designs. Multicoloured (except 8 c.). P* 13½ × 13.
997 3 c. Type **334** 15 10
998 4 c. Coal-mining and pasture 20 8
999 5 c. Cloister 30 20
000 6 c. Forest, birds and lake 90 80
001 8 c. Rowers (light grey, indigo and gold) .. 1·00 1·50
002 10 c. Graph and people .. .. .. 1·40 2·00
97/1002 .. .. *Set of* 6 3·50 4·25
Events:—3 c. Centennial of Thames Borough; 4 c. Centennial of Westport Borough; 5 c. Centennial of Canterbury University; 6 c. 0th Anniv of Royal Forest and Bird Protection Society; 8 c. success of N.Z. Rowers in 1972 Olympics; 10 c. 25th Anniv of C.A.F.E.

335 Class "W" Locomotive

336 "Maori Woman and Child"

(Des R. M. Conly. Litho Harrison)

973 (4 Apr). *New Zealand Steam Locomotives. T* **335** *and similar horiz designs. Multicoloured. P* 14 × 14½.
003 3 c. Type **335** 60 10
004 4 c. Class "X" 70 10
005 5 c. Class "Ab" 80 15
006 10 c. Class "Ja" .. .. 3·50 3·75

973–76. *As Nos. 914 etc., but no wmk.*
008 1 c. multicoloured (7.9.73) 25 10
a. Booklet pane. No. 1008 × 3 with three se-tenant printed labels (8.74) .. .. 1·00
b. Red (wing markings) omitted .. ..
009 2 c. multicoloured (6.73?) 25 10
010 3 c. black, light brown and orange (1974) .. 40 20
011 4 c. multicoloured (7.9.73) 20 5
a. Bright green (wing veins) inverted .. £250
b. Purple-brown omitted £150
c. Orange-yellow omitted £150
d. Greenish blue (background) omitted .. £100
012 5 c. multicoloured (1973) .. .. .. 1·25 25
013 6 c. blackish green, yellow-green and rose-carmine (7.9.73) 40 25
014 7 c. multicoloured (1974) .. .. .. 1·75 90
015 8 c. multicoloured (1974) .. .. .. 2·25 1·00
a. Blue-green (background) omitted .. 80·00
017 10 c. multicoloured, *p* 13½ × 13 (6.73?) .. 30 5
a. Silver (Arms) omitted £120
b. Imperf (vert pair) £160
c. Deep blue (Queen's head, face value, etc.) omitted £140
018 15 c. blk, flesh & pale brn, *p* 13½ × 13 (2.8.76) 55 15
019 18 c. chestnut, black and apple-green (1974) .. 1·25 60
a. Black (inscr, etc.) omitted £150
020 20 c. black and yellow-brown (1974) .. .. 1·25 30
008/20 .. .. *Set of* 12 9·00 3·50

(Des and photo Courvoisier)

973 (6 June). *Paintings by Frances Hodgkins. T* **336** *and similar vert designs. Multicoloured. P* 11½.
027 5 c. Type **336** 50 12
028 8 c. "Hilltop" .. .. 1·40 1·75
029 10 c. "Barn in Picardy" .. .. .. 1·60 1·75
030 18 c. "Self Portrait Still Life" .. .. 2·50 3·00

337 Prince Edward

338 "Tempi Madonna" (Raphael)

(Des and litho Harrison)

1973 (1 Aug). *Health Stamps. P* 13 × 13½.
1031 **337** 3 c. + 1 c. dull yellowish green and reddish brown 25 25
1032 4 c. + 1 c. rose-red and blackish brown 25 25
MS1033 Two sheets each 96 × 121 mm with Nos. 1031/2 in blocks of 6 (3 × 2) .. *Per pair* 14·00 18·00

(Des A. G. Mitchell. Photo Enschedé)

1973 (3 Oct). *Christmas. T* **338** *and similar vert designs. Multicoloured. P* 12½ × 13½.
1034 3 c. Type **338** 15 5
1035 5 c. "Three Kings" (stained-glass window, St. Theresa's Church, Auckland) 20 5
1036 10 c. Family entering church .. .. .. 75 1·25

339 Mitre Peak

340 Hurdling

(Des D. A. Hatcher. Photo Enschedé)

1973 (5 Dec). *Mountain Scenery. T* **339** *and similar multicoloured designs. P* 13 × 13½ (6, 8 c.) *or* 13½ × 13 (*others*).
1037 6 c. Type **339** 90 90
1038 8 c. Mt Ngauruhoe .. .. 1·40 2·00
1039 18 c. Mt Sefton (*horiz*) .. .. .. 2·50 3·25
1040 23 c. Burnett Range (*horiz*) .. .. .. 3·00 3·25

(Des M. Cleverley. Litho Harrison)

1974 (9 Jan). *Tenth British Commonwealth Games, Christchurch. T* **340** *and similar vert designs.* 5 c. *black and violet-blue, others multicoloured. P* 13 × 14.
1041 4 c. Type **340** 15 5
1042 5 c. Ball-player 25 15
1043 10 c. Cycling 30 25
1044 18 c. Rifle-shooting .. .. 70 1·10
1045 23 c. Bowls .. .. 1·00 1·50
No. 1042 does not show the Games emblem, and commemorates the Fourth Paraplegic Games, held at Dunedin.

341 Queen Elizabeth II

342 "Spirit of Napier" Fountain

(Des D. A. Hatcher and A. G. Mitchell. Litho Harrison)

1974 (5 Feb). *New Zealand Day. Sheet* 131 × 74 *mm. containing T* **341** *and similar horiz designs, size* 37 × 20 *mm. Multicoloured. P* 13.
MS1046 4 c. × 5 Treaty House, Waitangi; Signing Waitangi Treaty; Type **341**; Parliament Buildings Extensions; Children in Class .. .. .. 1·75 2·50

(Des Miss V. Jepsen. Photo Courvoisier)

1974 (3 Apr). *Centenaries of Napier and U.P.U. T* **342** *and similar vert designs. Multicoloured. P* 11½.
1047 4 c. Type **342** 20 8
1048 5 c. Clock Tower, Berne 30 20
1049 8 c. U.P.U. Monument, Berne .. .. 1·00 1·60

343 Boeing Seaplane, 1919

344 Children, Cat and Dog

(Des R. M. Conly. Litho Harrison)

1974 (5 June). *History of New Zealand Airmail Transport. T* **343** *and similar horiz designs. Multicoloured. P* 14 × 13.
1050 3 c. Type **343** 30 10
1051 4 c. Lockheed "Electra", 1937 .. .. 35 15
1052 5 c. Bristol Freighter, 1958 .. .. .. 50 15
1053 23 c. Empire "S 30" flying-boat, 1940 .. .. 3·00 3·00

(Des B. Langford. Litho Harrison)

1974 (7 Aug). *Health Stamps. P* 13 × 13½.
1054 **344** 3 c. + 1 c. multicoloured 15 25
1055 – 4 c. + 1 c. multicoloured 20 25
1056 – 5 c. + 1 c. multicoloured .. .. 90 1·10
MS1057 145 × 123 mm. No. 1055 in block of ten 22·00 26·00
Nos. 1055/6 are as T **344**, showing children and pets.

345 "The Adoration of the Magi" (Konrad Witz)

346 Great Barrier Island

(Des Eileen Mayo. Photo Courvoisier)

1974 (2 Oct). *Christmas. T* **345** *and similar horiz designs. Multicoloured. P* 11½.
1058 3 c. Type **345** 12 5
1059 5 c. "The Angel Window" (stained-glass window, Old St. Pauls Church, Wellington) 20 5
1060 10 c. Madonna Lily .. .. 90 1·25

(Des D. A. Hatcher. Photo Enschedé)

1974 (4 Dec). *Off-shore Islands. T* **346** *and similar horiz designs. Multicoloured. P* 13½ × 13.
1061 6 c. Type **346** 50 40
1062 8 c. Stewart Island .. .. .. 1·00 1·25
1063 18 c. White Island .. .. 2·00 2·25
1064 23 c. The Brothers .. .. 2·50 2·75

347 Crippled Child

(Des Miss V. Jepsen (3 c., 5 c.), A. G. Mitchell (10 c., 18 c.). Litho Harrison)

1975 (5 Feb). *Anniversaries and Events. T* **347** *and similar horiz designs. Multicoloured. P* 13½.
1065 3 c. Type **347** 15 5
1066 5 c. Farming family 25 10
1067 10 c. I.W.Y. symbols .. .. 65 1·00
1068 18 c. Medical School Building, Otago University .. .. 85 1·50
Commemorations:—3 c. 40th Anniv of N.Z. Crippled Children Society; 5 c. 50th Anniv of Women's Division, Federated Farmers of N.Z.; 10 c. International Women's Year; 18 c. Centenary of Otago Medical School.

348 Scow *Lake Erie*

(Des R. M. Conly. Litho Harrison)

1975 (2 Apr). *Historic Sailing Ships. T* **348** *and similar horiz designs. P* 13½ × 13.
1069 4 c. black and red 20 5
1070 5 c. black and turquoise-blue 30 5
1071 8 c. black and yellow 60 45
1072 10 c. black and olive-yellow 60 50
1073 18 c. black and light brown .. .. .. 1·40 1·50
1074 23 c. black and slate-lilac .. .. .. 1·75 2·25
1069/74 .. .. *Set of* 6 4·25 4·25
Ships:—5 c. Schooner *Herald*; 8 c. Brigantine *New Zealander*; 10 c. Topsail schooner *Jessie Kelly*; 18 c. Barque *Tory*; 23 c. Full-rigged clipper *Rangitiki*.

349 Lake Summer Forest Park

(Des and photo Enschedé)

1975 (4 June). *Forest Park Scenes. T* **349** *and similar horiz designs. Multicoloured. P* 13.

1075	6 c. Type **349**	90	75
1076	8 c. North-west Nelson	1·25	1·50
1077	18 c. Kaweka	1·75	2·50
1078	23 c. Coromandel	2·25	3·00

350 Girl feeding Lamb

351 "Virgin and Child" (Zanobi Machiavelli)

(Des Margaret Chapman. Litho Harrison)

1975 (6 Aug). *Health Stamps. T* **350** *and similar horiz designs. Multicoloured. P* 13½ × 13.

1079	3 c. + 1 c. Type **350**	20	15
1080	4 c. + 1 c. Boy with hen and chicks	20	15
1081	5 c. + 1 c. Boy with duck and duckling	65	95
MS1082	123 × 146 mm. No. 1080 × 10	18·00	22·00

(Des Enid Hunter. Photo Harrison)

1975 (1 Oct). *Christmas. T* **351** *and similar horiz designs. Multicoloured. P* 13 × 13½ (3 *c.*) *or* 13½ × 13 (*others*).

1083	3 c. Type **351**	15	5
	a. Red omitted*		
1084	5 c. "Cross in Landscape" (stained-glass window, Greendale Church)	20	5
	a. Brown (face value) omitted	£150	
1085	10 c. "I saw three ships . . ." (carol)	1·00	1·25

*This occurred in the last two vertical rows of the sheet with the red partially omitted on the previous row.

Used copies of No. 1083 have been seen with the orange ("Christmas 1975") omitted.

352 "Sterling Silver"

353 Queen Elizabeth II (photograph by W. Harrison)

353*a* Maripi (knife)

353*b* Paua

353*c* "Beehive" (section of Parliamentary Buildings, Wellington)

(Des A. G. Mitchell (1 to 14 c.), I. Hulse (20 c. to $2), R. Conly ($5). Photo Harrison (1 to 10 c.), Courvoisier (11 to 14 c.), Heraclio Fournier (20 c. to $5))

1975 (26 Nov)–**81**. (*a*) *Vert designs as T* **352** *showing garden roses. Multicoloured. P* 14½ (6 *to* 8 *c.*) *or* 14½ × 14 (*others*).

1086	1 c. Type **352**	5	5
1087	2 c. "Lilli Marlene"	5	5
1088	3 c. "Queen Elizabeth"	40	12
	a. Perf 14½ (6.79)	15	5
1089	4 c. "Super Star"	10	5
1090	5 c. "Diamond Jubilee"	5	5
1091	6 c. "Cresset"	60	30
	a. Perf 14½ × 14 (8.76?)	5	5
1092	7 c. "Michele Meilland"	1·00	40
	a. Perf 14½ × 14 (6.76?)	8	5
1093	8 c. "Josephine Bruce"	1·00	40
	a. Perf 14½ × 14 (8.76?)	8	5
1094	9 c. "Iceberg"	15	5
	(*b*) *Type* **353**. *P* 14½ × 14 (7.12.77)		
1094*a*	10 c. multicoloured	75	40
	ab. Perf 14½ (2.79)	8	5
	(*c*) *Vert designs as T* **353*a*** *showing Maori artefacts. P* 11½ (24.11.76)		
1095	11 c. reddish brown, lemon & blackish brown	30	10
1096	12 c. reddish brown, lemon & blackish brown	30	10
1097	13 c. reddish brown, greenish blue and blackish brown	30	20
1098	14 c. reddish brown, lemon & blackish brown	30	10

Designs:—12 c. Putorino (flute); 13 c. Wahaika (club); 14 c. Kotiate (club).

	(*d*) *Horiz designs as T* **353*b*** *showing seashells. Multicoloured. P* 13		
1099	20 c. Type **353*b*** (29.11.78)	15	20
1100	30 c. Toheroa (29.11.78)	25	30
1101	40 c. Coarse Dosinia (29.11.78)	30	35
1102	50 c. Spiny Murex (29.11.78)	40	45
1103	$1 Scallop (26.11.79)	70	85
	a. Imperf between (vert pair)	£400	
1104	$2 Circular Saw (26.11.79)	1·40	1·75
	(*e*) *Type* **353*c***. *P* 13 (2.12.81)		
1105	$5 multicoloured	3·75	4·00
1086/1105	*Set of* 21	8·00	8·00

Faked "missing colour errors" exist of No. 1094*a*, involving parts of the portrait.

No. 1103a occurs on the top two rows of the sheet; the lower stamp being imperforate on three edges except for two perforation holes at the foot of each vertical side.

354 Family and League of Mothers Badge

(Des A. P. Derrick. Litho J.W.)

1976 (4 Feb). *Anniversaries and Metrication. T* **354** *and similar horiz designs. Multicoloured. P* 13½ × 14.

1110	6 c. Type **354**	15	5
1111	7 c. Weight, temperature, linear measure and capacity	15	5
1112	8 c. Ship, mountain and New Plymouth	40	10
1113	10 c. Two women shaking hands and Y.W.C.A. badge	35	40
1114	25 c. Map of the world showing cable links	80	1·40

Anniversaries:—6 c. League of Mothers, 50th Anniv; 7 c. Metrication; 8 c. Centenary of New Plymouth; 10 c. 50th Anniv of New Zealand Y.W.C.A.; 25 c. Centenary of link with International Telecommunications Network.

355 Gig

356 Purakaunui Falls

(Des G. F. Fuller. Litho Harrison)

1976 (7 Apr). *Vintage Farm Transport. T* **355** *and similar horiz designs. Multicoloured. P* 13½ × 13.

1115	6 c. Type **355**	20	20
1116	7 c. Thorneycroft lorry	30	5
1117	8 c. Scandi wagon	60	30
1118	9 c. Traction engine	45	50
1119	10 c. Wool wagon	60	60
1120	25 c. Cart	1·75	2·25
1115/20	*Set of* 6	3·50	3·50

(Des and photo Courvoisier)

1976 (2 June). *Waterfalls. T* **356** *and similar vert designs. Multicoloured. P* 11½.

1121	10 c. Type **356**	60	40
1122	14 c. Marakopa Falls	1·10	75
1123	15 c. Bridal Veil Falls	1·10	1·10
1124	16 c. Papakorito Falls	1·40	1·40

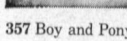

357 Boy and Pony

358 "Nativity" (Spanish carving)

(Des Margaret Chapman. Litho Harrison)

1976 (4 Aug). *Health Stamps. T* **357** *and similar vert designs. Multicoloured. P* 13 × 13½.

1125	7 c. + 1 c. Type **357**	20	25
1126	8 c. + 1 c. Girl and calf	20	25
1127	10 c. + 1 c. Girls and bird	55	80
MS1128	96 × 121 mm. Nos. 1125/7 × 2	7·00	9·00

(Des Margaret Chapman (18 c.), D. A. Hatcher (others). Photo Harrison)

1976 (6 Oct). *Christmas. T* **358** *and similar horiz designs. Multicoloured. P* 14 × 14½ (7 *c.*) *or* 14½ × 14 (*others*).

1129	7 c. Type **358**	20	5
1130	11 c. "Resurrection" (stained-glass window, St. Joseph's Catholic Church, Grey Lynn)	45	45
1131	18 c. Angels	90	90

359 Arms of Hamilton

360 Queen Elizabeth II

(Des P. L. Blackie. Litho Harrison)

1977 (19 Jan). *Anniversaries. T* **359** *and similar vert designs. Multicoloured. P* 13 × 13½.

1132	8 c. Type **359**	30	10
	a. Horiz strip of 3, Nos. 1132/4	90	
1133	8 c. Arms of Gisborne	30	10
1134	8 c. Arms of Masterton	30	10
1135	10 c. A.A. emblem	45	30
	a. Horiz pair. Nos. 1135/6	90	1·25
1136	10 c. Arms of the College of Surgeons	45	30

Events:—Nos. 1132/4, City Centenaries; No. 1135, 75th Anniv of the Automobile Association in New Zealand; No. 1136, 50th Anniv of Royal Australasian College of Surgeons.

Designs of each value were printed in the same sheet horizontally *se-tenant*.

(Des and photo Harrison from photographs by Warren Harrison)

1977 (23 Feb). *Silver Jubilee. Sheet* 178 × 82 *mm containing T* **360** *and similar vert designs showing different portraits. P* 14 × 14½.

MS1137	8 c. × 5 multicoloured	80	1·50
	a. Imperf	£1400	
	ab. Ditto, and silver omitted	£1800	
	b. Silver omitted	£550	

361 Physical Education and Maori Culture

(**362**)

(Des A. G. Mitchell. Litho Harrison)

1977 (6 Apr). *Education. T* **361** *and similar vert designs. Multicoloured. P* 13 × 13½.

1138	8 c. Type **361**	75	60
	a. Horiz strip of 5, Nos. 1138/42	3·25	
1139	8 c. Geography, science and woodwork	75	60
1140	8 c. Teaching the deaf, kindergarten and woodwork	75	60
1141	8 c. Tertiary and language classes	75	60
1142	8 c. Home science, correspondence school and teacher training	75	60

Nos. 1138/42 were printed horizontally *se-tenant* throughout the sheet.

1977 (Apr). *Coil Stamps. Nos.* 1010/11 *surch as T* **362** *by Govt Printer, Wellington.*

1143	7 c. on 3 c. Lichen Moth (19.4)	25	40
1144	8 c. on 4 c. Puriri Moth (21.4)	25	40

Forged "7 c." surcharges, similar to No. 1143, but in smaller type, are known applied to Nos. 918 and 1010.

363 Karitane Beach

364 Girl with Pigeon

(Des D. A. Hatcher. Photo Heraclio Fournier)

1977 (1 June). *Seascapes. T* **363** *and similar horiz designs. Multicoloured. P* 14½.

1145	10 c. Type **363**	30	15
1146	16 c. Ocean Beach, Mount Maunganui	45	55
1147	18 c. Piha Beach	55	55
1148	30 c. Kaikoura Coast	80	85

(Des A. P. Derrick. Litho Harrison)

1977 (3 Aug). *Health Stamps. T* **364** *and similar vert designs. Multicoloured. P* 13 × 13½.

1149	7 c. + 2 c. Type **364**	20	20
1150	8 c. + 2 c. Boy with frog	25	25
1151	10 c. + 2 c. Girl with butterfly	40	50
MS1152	97 × 120 mm. Nos. 1149/51 × 2	8·00	11·00

Stamps from the miniature sheet are without white border and together form a composite design.

365 "The Holy Family" (Correggio)

Des Margaret Chapman (23 c.), graphics for all values produced by printer. Photo Courvoisier)

977 (5 Oct). *Christmas. T* **365** *and similar vert designs. Multicoloured. P* 11½.
153 7 c. Type **365** 15 5
154 16 c. "Madonna and Child" (stained-glass window, St. Michael's and All Angels, Dunedin) 45 35
155 23 c. "Partridge in a Pear Tree" . . . . 95 1·00

366 Merryweather Manual Pump, 1860

367 Town Clock and Coat of Arms, Ashburton

(Des R. M. Conly. Litho Harrison)

977 (7 Dec). *Fire Fighting Appliances. T* **366** *and similar horiz designs. Multicoloured. P* 14 × 13.
156 10 c. Type **366** 20 15
157 11 c. 2-wheel hose, reel and ladder, 1880 . . 25 30
158 12 c. Shand Mason steam fire engine, 1873 . . 25 30
159 23 c. Chemical fire engine, 1888 . . . . 55 80

Des P. L. Blackie (No. 1162), Harrison (No. 1163), P. J. Durrant (others), Litho Harrison)

978 (8 Mar). *Centenaries. T* **367** *and similar multicoloured designs. P* 14.
160 10 c. Type **367** 25 5
a. Horiz pair. Nos. 1160/1 . . . . . . 50 70
161 10 c. Stratford and Mt Egmont 25 5
162 12 c. Early telephone 25 30
163 20 c. Bay of Islands (*horiz*) 45 65

Centenaries commemorated are those of the towns of Ashburton and Stratford, of the telephone in New Zealand, and of the Bay of Islands County.

The 10 c. values were printed together, *se-tenant*, in horizontal pairs throughout the sheet.

68 Students and vey Hall, Lincoln College

369

370 Maui Gas Drilling Platform

(Des A. P. Derrick. Litho Harrison)

978 (26 Apr). *Land Resources and Centenary of Lincoln College of Agriculture. T* **368** *and similar vert designs. Multicoloured. P* 14½.
164 10 c. Type **368** 15 10
165 12 c. Sheep grazing 25 25
166 15 c. Fertiliser ground spreading 30 30
167 16 c. Agricultural Field Days 30 30
168 20 c. Harvesting grain 45 50
169 30 c. Dairy farming 75 85
164/9 . . . . *Set of* 16 2·00 2·10

(Photo Harrison)

978 (3 May–9 June). *Coil Stamps. P* 14½ × 14 (10 c.) *or* 14 × 13 (*others*).
170 **369** 1 c. bright purple (9.6) 5 10
171 2 c. bright orange (9.6) 5 10
172 5 c. red-brown (9.6) 5 10
173 10 c. bright blue 8 15

(Des R. M. Conly. Litho Harrison)

978 (7 June). *Resources of the Sea. T* **370** *and similar vert designs. Multicoloured. P* 13 × 14.
174 12 c. Type **370** 20 15
175 15 c. Trawler 35 30
176 20 c. Map of 200 mile fishing limit 50 40
177 23 c. Marine mammals 60 50
178 35 c. Kingfish, snapper, grouper and squid . . 1·00 90

371 First Health Charity Stamp

372 "The Holy Family" (El Greco)

373 Sir Julius Vogel

(Des A. G. Mitchell. Litho Harrison)

1978 (2 Aug). *Health Stamps. Health Services Commemorations. T* **371** *and similar vert design. P* 13 × 14.
1179 10 c. + 2 c. black, red and gold 25 25
1180 12 c. + 2 c. multicoloured 25 30
MS1181 97 × 124 mm. Nos. 1179/80 × 3 . . . . 5·00 5·50

Designs and commemorations:—10 c. Type **371** (50th anniversary of health charity stamps); 12 c. Heart operation (National Heart Foundation).

(Des R. M. Conly. Photo Courvoisier)

1978 (4 Oct). *Christmas. T* **372** *and similar multicoloured designs. P* 11½.
1182 7 c. Type **372** 15 5
1183 16 c. All Saints' Church, Howick 45 45
1184 23 c. Beach scene 65 65

(Des A. G. Mitchell. Litho J.W.)

1979 (7 Feb). *Statesmen. T* **373** *and similar vert designs in sepia and drab. P* 13 × 13½.
1185 10 c. Type **373** 35 25
a. Horiz strip of 3, Nos. 1185/7 . . . . 1·00
1186 10 c. Sir George Grey 35 25
1187 10 c. Richard John Seddon 35 25

Nos. 1185/7 were printed together, *se-tenant*, in horizontal strips of 3 throughout the sheet.

Nos. 1185/7 have matt, almost invisible gum.

374 Riverlands Cottage, Blenheim

375 Whangaroa Harbour

(Des P. Leitch. Litho Enschedé)

1979 (4 Apr). *Architecture* (1*st series*). *T* **374** *and similar horiz designs. P* 13½ × 13.
1188 10 c. black, new blue and deep blue 12 12
1189 12 c. black, pale green and bottle green . . 20 20
1190 15 c. black and grey 20 25
1191 20 c. black, yellow-brown and sepia 30 35

Designs:—12 c. The Mission House, Waimate North; 15 c. "The Elms", Tauranga; 20 c. Provincial Council Buildings, Christchurch.

See also Nos. 1217/20 and 1262/5.

(Photo Heraclio Fournier)

1979 (6 June). *Small Harbours. T* **375** *and similar multicoloured designs. P* 13.
1192 15 c. Type **375** 25 20
1193 20 c. Kawau Island 30 35
1194 23 c. Akaroa Harbour (*vert*) 35 45
1195 35 c. Picton Harbour (*vert*) 55 65

376 Children with Building Bricks

(Des W. Kelsall. Litho J.W.)

1979 (6 June). *International Year of the Child. P* 14.
1196 **376** 10 c. multicoloured 15 10

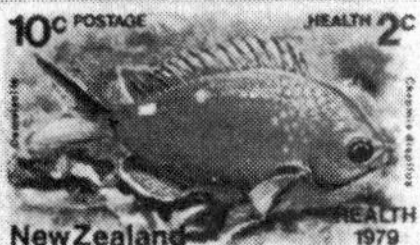

377 Demoiselle

4c

(**378**)

(Des P. Blackie (12 c.), G. Fuller (others). Litho Harrison)

1979 (25 July). *Health Stamps. Marine Life. T* **377** *and similar multicoloured designs. P* 13 × 13½ (12 c.) *or* 13½ × 13 (*others*).
1197 10 c. + 2 c. Type **377** 25 30
a. Horiz pair. Nos. 1197/8 . . . . . . 50 60
1198 10 c. + 2 c. Sea Urchin 25 30
1199 12 c. + 2 c. Fish and underwater cameraman (*vert*) 25 30
MS1200 144 × 72 mm. Nos. 1197/9, each × 2. P 14 × 14½ (12 c.) or 14½ × 14 (others) . . . . 4·00 5·50

Nos. 1197/8 were printed together, *se-tenant*, in horizontal pairs throughout the sheet.

1979 (31 Aug)–**80**. *Nos.* 1091a, 1092a, 1093a *and* 1094ab *surch as T* **378** *by Govt Printer, Wellington.*
1201 4 c. on 8 c. "Josephine Bruce" (24.9.79) . . 5 5
1202 14 c. on 10 c. Type **353** 25 20
1203 17 c. on 6 c. "Cresset" (9.10.79) 25 30
1203*a* 20 c. on 7 c. "Michele Meilland" (29.9.80) . . 20 20

379 "Madonna and Child" (sculpture by Ghiberti)

380 Chamber, House of Representatives

(Des D. Hatcher. Photo Courvoisier)

1979 (3 Oct). *Christmas. T* **379** *and similar vert designs. Multicoloured. P* 11½.
1204 10 c. Type **379** 20 5
1205 25 c. Christ Church, Russell 45 45
1206 35 c. Pohutukawa (tree) 65 65

(Des D. Hatcher. Litho J.W.)

1979 (26 Nov). *25th Commonwealth Parliamentary Conference, Wellington. T* **380** *and similar vert designs. Multicoloured. P* 13½.
1207 14 c. Type **380** 20 10
1208 20 c. Mace and Black Rod 35 35
1209 30 c. Wall hanging from the "Beehive" . . 50 60

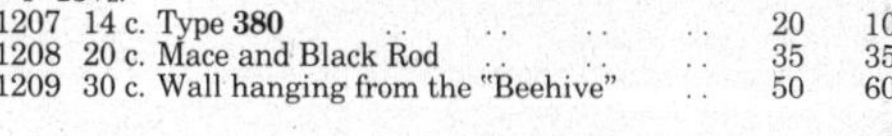

381 1855 1d. Stamp

(Des D. Hatcher (14 c. (all designs)), R. Conly (others). Litho Harrison)

1980 (17 Feb). *Anniversaries and Events. T* **381** *and similar designs. P* 13½ × 13 (14 c. (*all designs*)) *or* 14 (*others*).
1210 14 c. black, brown-red and yellow 20 20
a. Horiz strip of 3. Nos. 1210/12 60
ab. Black (inscription) omitted (*strip of* 3) . .
1211 14 c. black, deep turquoise-blue and yellow . . 20 20
1212 14 c. black, dull yellowish green and yellow . . 20 20
1213 17 c. multicoloured 25 25
1214 25 c. multicoloured 30 30
1215 30 c. multicoloured 35 35
1210/15 . . . . *Set of* 6 1·40 1·40
MS1216 146 × 96 mm. Nos. 1210/12. P 14½ × 14 (*sold at* 52 c.) . . . . 3·00 5·00

Designs and commemorations; (38 × 22 *mm*)—No. 1210, Type **381**; No. 1211, 1855 2d. stamp; No. 1212, 1855 1s. stamp (125th anniversary of New Zealand stamps). (40 × 23 *mm*)—No. 1213, Geyser, wood-carving and building (centenary of Rotorua (town)); No. 1214, *Earina autumnalis* and *thelymitra venosa* (International Orchid Conference, Auckland); No. 1215; Ploughing and Golden Plough Trophy (World Ploughing Championships, Christchurch).

The premium on No. **MS**1216 was used to help finance the "Zeapex 80" International Stamp Exhibition, Auckland.

Nos. 1210/12 were printed together, *se-tenant*, in horizontal strips of 3 throughout the sheet.

382 Ewelme Cottage, Parnell

383 Auckland Harbour

(Des P. Leitch. Litho Enschedé)

1980 (2 Apr). *Architecture* (2*nd series*). *T* **382** *and similar horiz designs. Multicoloured. P* 13½ × 12½.
1217 14 c. Type **382** 20 10
1218 17 c. Broadgreen, Nelson 30 30
1219 25 c. Courthouse, Oamaru 35 40
1220 30 c. Government Buildings, Wellington . . 40 45

(Des D. Hatcher. Photo Heraclio Fournier)

1980 (4 June). *Large Harbours. T* **383** *and similar horiz designs. Multicoloured. P* 13.
1221 25 c. Type **383** 30 30
1222 30 c. Wellington Harbour 35 35
1223 35 c. Lyttelton Harbour 45 45
1224 50 c. Port Chalmers 70 70

384 Surf-fishing

385 "Madonna and Child with Cherubim" (sculpture by Andrea della Robbia)

(Des Margaret Chapman. Litho Enschedé)

1980 (6 Aug). *Health Stamps. Fishing. T* **384** *and similar horiz designs. Multicoloured. P* 13 × 12½.
1225 14 c. + 2 c. Type **384** .. 25 30
a. Horiz pair. Nos. 1225/6 .. 50 60
1226 14 c. + 2 c. Wharf-fishing .. 25 30
1227 17 c. + 2 c. Spear-fishing .. 25 30
MS1228 148 × 75 mm. Nos. 1225/7 each × 2. P 13½ × 13 .. 2·25 2·50
Nos. 1225/6 were printed together, *se-tenant*, in horizontal pairs throughout the sheet.

(Des P. Durrant. Photo Courvoisier)

1980 (1 Oct). *Christmas. T* **385** *and similar vert designs. Multicoloured. P* 11½.
1229 10 c. Type **385** .. 15 5
1230 25 c. St. Mary's Church, New Plymouth .. 30 30
1231 35 c. Picnic scene .. 45 50

386 Te Heu Heu (chief)

387 Lt.-Col. the Hon W. H. A. Feilding and Borough of Feilding Crest

(Des R. Conly. Litho Heraclio Fournier)

1980 (26 Nov). *Maori Personalities. Vert designs as T* **386**. *Multicoloured. P* 12½ × 13.
1232 15 c. Type **386** .. 12 5
1233 25 c. Te Hau (chief) .. 20 8
1234 35 c. Te Puea (princess) .. 30 10
1235 45 c. Ngata (politician) .. 35 20
1236 60 c. Te Ata-O-Tu (warrior) .. 45 20

(Des R. Conly. Litho Harrison)

1981 (4 Feb). *Commemorations. T* **387** *and similar horiz design. P* 14½.
1237 20 c. multicoloured .. 25 25
1238 25 c. black and brown-ochre .. 30 30
Designs and Commemorations:—20 c. Type **387** (Centenary of Feilding (town)); 25 c. I.Y.D. emblem and cupped hands (International Year of the Disabled).

388 The Family at Play

389 Kaiauai River

(Des A. Derrick. Litho J.W.)

1981 (1 Apr). *"Family Life." T* **388** *and similar vert designs. Multicoloured. P* 13½ × 13.
1239 20 c. Type **388** .. 25 20
1240 25 c. The family, young and old .. 30 30
1241 30 c. The family at home .. 35 35
1242 35 c. The family at church .. 40 45

(Des D. Hatcher. Photo Heraclio Fournier)

1981 (3 June). *River Scenes. T* **389** *and similar multicoloured designs. P* 13½ × 13 (30, 35 c.) *or* 13 × 13½ (*others*).
1243 30 c. Type **389** .. 30 30
1244 35 c. Mangahao .. 35 40
1245 40 c. Shotover (*horiz*) .. 40 45
1246 60 c. Cleddau (*horiz*) .. 65 75

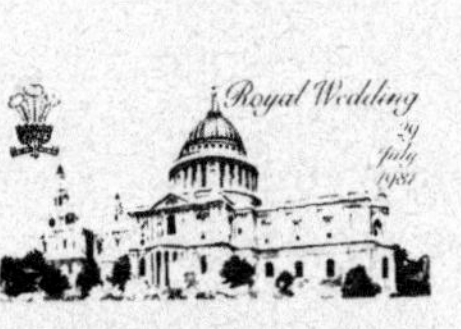

390 St. Paul's Cathedral

391 Girl with Starfish

(Des and litho Harrison)

1981 (29 July). *Royal Wedding. T* **390** *and similar horiz design. Multicoloured. P* 14½.
1247 20 c. Type **390** .. 20 20
a. Pair. Nos. 1247/8 .. 40 40
ab. Deep grey (inscriptions and date) omitted £750
1248 20 c. Prince Charles and Lady Diana Spencer 20 20
Nos. 1247/8 were printed together, *se-tenant*, in horizontal and vertical pairs throughout the sheet.

(Des P.O. Litho Harrison)

1981 (5 Aug). *Health Stamps. Children playing by the Sea. T* **391** *and similar vert designs. Multicoloured. P* 14½.
1249 20 c. + 2 c. Type **391** .. 25 35
a. Horiz pair. Nos. 1249/50 .. 50 70
1250 20 c. + 2 c. Boy fishing .. 25 35
1251 25 c. + 2 c. Children exploring rock pool .. 70 90
MS1252 100 × 125 mm. Nos. 1249/51, each × 2 .. 1·75 2·25
The 20 c. values were printed together, *se-tenant*, in horizontal pairs throughout the sheet, forming a composite design.
The stamps from No. **MS**1252 were printed together, *se-tenant*, in two horizontal strips of 3, each forming a composite design.

392 "Madonna Suckling the Child" (painting, d'Oggiono)

393 Tauranga Mission House

(Des Margaret Chapman. Photo Courvoisier)

1981 (7 Oct). *Christmas. T* **392** *and similar vert designs. Multicoloured. P* 11½.
1253 14 c. Type **392** .. 15 5
1254 30 c. St. John's Church, Wakefield .. 30 35
1255 40 c. Golden Tainui (flower) .. 40 45

(Des A. Derrick. Litho Walsall)

1982 (3 Feb). *Commemorations. T* **393** *and similar vert designs. Multicoloured. P* 14½.
1256 20 c. Type **393** .. 20 8
a. Horiz pair. Nos. 1256/7 .. 40 45
1257 20 c. Water tower, Hawera .. 20 8
1258 25 c. Cat .. 25 25
1259 30 c. *Dunedin* (sailing ship) .. 30 35
1260 35 c. Scientific research equipment .. 35 40
Commemorations:—No. 1256, Centenary of Tauranga (town); No. 1257, Centenary of Hawera (town); No. 1258, Centenary of S.P.C.A. (Society for the Prevention of Cruelty to Animals in New Zealand); No. 1259, Centenary of Frozen Meat Exports; No. 1260, International Year of Science.
The 20 c. values were printed together, *se-tenant*, in horizontal pairs throughout the sheet.

394 Map of New Zealand

395 Alberton, Auckland

(Des A. G. Mitchell. Litho Leigh-Mardon Ltd, Melbourne)

1982 (1 Apr–13 Dec). *P* 12½.
1261 **394** 24 c. pale yellowish green and ultram 30 20
a. Perf 14½ × 14 (13.12.82) .. 20 20

(Des P. Leitch. Litho Walsall)

1982 (7 Apr). *Architecture (3rd series). T* **395** *and similar horiz designs. Multicoloured. P* 14 × 14½.
1262 20 c. Type **395** .. 20 15
1263 25 c. Caccia Birch, Palmerston North .. 25 25
1264 30 c. Railway station, Dunedin .. 30 30
1265 35 c. Post Office, Ophir .. 35 40

396 Kaiteriteri Beach, Nelson (summer)

397 Labrador

(Des D. Hatcher. Photo Heraclio Fournier)

1982 (2 June). *"The Four Seasons". New Zealand Scenes. T* **396** *and similar horiz designs. Multicoloured. P* 13 × 13½.
1266 35 c. Type **396** .. 35 35
1267 40 c. St. Omer Park, Queenstown (Autumn) 40 40
1268 45 c. Mt Ngauruhoe, Tongariro National Park (Winter) .. 45 50
1269 70 c. Wairarapa farm (Spring .. 70 75

(Des R. Conly. Litho Enschedé)

1982 (4 Aug). *Health Stamps. Dogs. T* **397** *and similar ver designs. Multicoloured. P* 13 × 13½.
1270 24 c. + 2 c. Type **397** .. 25 2(
a. Horiz pair. Nos. 1270/1 .. 50 6(
1271 24 c. + 2 c. Border Collie .. 25 2(
1272 30 c. + 2 c. Cocker Spaniel .. 30 3!
MS1273 98 × 125 mm. Nos. 1270/2, each × 2. P 14 × 13½ .. 1·75 2·0
The 24 c. values were printed together, *se-tenant*, in horizonta pairs throughout the sheet.

398 "Madonna with Child and Two Angels" (paintings by Piero di Cosimo)

(Des Margaret Chapman. Photo Heraclio Fournier)

1982 (6 Oct). *Christmas. T* **398** *and similar vert designs. Multi-coloured. P* 14 × 13½.
1274 18 c. Type **398** .. 15 1!
1275 35 c. Rangiatea Maori Church, Otaki .. 30 3!
1276 45 c. Surf life-saving .. 45 5(

399 Nephrite

399*a* Grapes

(Des P. Durrant (1 c. to 9 c.), D. Little (others). Litho Leigh-Mardo Ltd. Melbourne)

1982 (1 Dec)–**83**. *Multicoloured. P* 14½ × 14. (*a*) *Minerals. T* **39** *and similar vert designs.*
1277 1 c. Type **399** .. 5
a. Perf 12½ .. 15 1
1278 2 c. Agate .. 5
a. Perf 12½ .. 1·00 1·0
1279 3 c. Iron Pyrites .. 5
1280 4 c. Amethyst .. 5
1281 5 c. Carnelian .. 5
1282 9 c. Native Sulphur .. 8 1

(*b*) *Fruits. T* **399***a* *and similar vert designs*
1283 10 c. Type **399***a* (7.12.83) .. 8 1
1284 20 c. Citrus Fruit (7.12.83) .. 15 2
1285 30 c. Nectarines (7.12.83) .. 25 3
1286 40 c. Apples (7.12.83) .. 30 3
1287 50 c. Kiwifruit (7.12.83) .. 40 4
1277/87 .. *Set of* 11 1·25 1·6

400 Old Arts Building, Auckland University

401 Queen Elizabeth II

(Des G. Emery (35 c.), P. Durrant (others). Litho Cambec Pres Melbourne (35 c.), J.W. (others))

1983 (2 Feb). *Commemorations. T* **400** *and similar vert design Multicoloured. P* 13 × 13½ (35 c.) *or* 14 × 13½ (*others*).
1303 24 c. Salvation Army Centenary logo .. 20 2
1304 30 c. Type **400** .. 25 3
1305 35 c. Stylised Kangaroo and Kiwi .. 30 3
1306 40 c. Rainbow Trout .. 35 4
1307 45 c. Satellite over Earth .. 40 4
Commemorations:—24 c. Centenary of Salvation Army; 30 Centenary of Auckland University; 35 c. Closer Economi Relationship agreement with Australia; 40 c. Centenary of intr duction of Rainbow Trout into New Zealand; 45 c. World Commun cations Year.

(Des P. Durrant. Litho Harrison)

1983 (14 Mar). *Commonwealth Day. T* **401** *and similar hor designs. Multicoloured. P* 13½.
1308 24 c. Type **401** .. 20 2
1309 35 c. Maori rock drawing .. 30 3
1310 40 c. Woolmark and wool-scouring symbols .. 35 4
1311 45 c. Coat of arms .. 40 5

402 "Boats, Island Bay" (Rita Angus)

403 Mt Egmont

(Des D. Hatcher. Litho Leigh-Mardon Ltd, Melbourne)

.983 (6 Apr). *Paintings by Rita Angus. T* **402** *and similar vert designs. Multicoloured. P* 14½.

.312 24 c. Type **402** 20 25
.313 30 c. "Central Otago Landscape" 25 30
.314 35 c. "Wanaka Landscape" 30 35
.315 45 c. "Tree" 40 45

(Des P. Durrant. Photo Heraclio Fournier)

.983 (1 June). *Beautiful New Zealand. T* **403** *and similar multicoloured designs. P* 13.

.316 35 c. Type **403** 30 35
.317 40 c. Cooks Bay 35 40
.318 45 c. Lake Matheson (*horiz*) 40 45
.319 70 c. Lake Alexandrina (*horiz*) 65 70

404 Tabby

405 "The Family of the Holy Oak Tree" (Raphael)

(Des R. Conly. Litho Harrison)

983 (3 Aug). *Health Stamps. Cats. T* **404** *and similar vert designs. Multicoloured. P* 14.

320 24 c. + 2 c. Type **404** 20 25
a. Horiz pair. Nos. 1320/1 .. .. .. 40 50
.321 24 c. + 2 c. Siamese 20 25
.322 30 c. + 2 c. Persian 25 30
MS1323 100 × 126 mm. Nos. 1320/2, each × 2 .. 1·25

The 24 c. values were printed together, *se-tenant*, in horizontal pairs throughout the sheet.

(Des R. Conly (45 c.), M. Wyatt (others). Photo Courvoisier)

.983 (5 Oct). *Christmas. T* **405** *and similar vert designs. Multicoloured. P* 12 × 11½.

.324 18 c. Type **405** 12 15
.325 35 c. St. Patrick's Church, Greymouth .. 30 35
.326 45 c. "The Glory of Christmas" (star and flowers) 40 45

406 Geology

(Des R. Conly. Litho Cambec Press, Melbourne)

984 (1 Feb). *Antarctic Research. T* **406** *and similar horiz designs. Multicoloured. P* 13½ × 13.

327 24 c. Type **406** 20 25
328 40 c. Biology 30 35
329 58 c. Glaciology 45 50
330 70 c. Meteorology 55 60
MS1331 126 × 110 mm. Nos. 1327/30 .. .. 1·50 1·60

07 *Mountaineer*, Lake Wakatipu

408 Mount Hutt

(Des M. Wyatt. Litho Cambec Press, Melbourne)

984 (4 Apr). *New Zealand Ferry Boats. T* **407** *and similar horiz designs. Multicoloured. P* 13½ × 13.

332 24 c. Type **407** 20 25
333 40 c. *Waikana*, Otago 30 35
334 58 c. *Britannia*, Waitemata 45 50
335 70 c. *Wakatere*, Firth of Thames 55 60

(Des D. Little. Litho Cambec Press, Melbourne)

984 (6 June). *Ski-slope Scenery. T* **408** *and similar horiz designs. Multicoloured. P* 13½ × 13.

336 35 c. Type **408** 30 35
337 40 c. Coronet Park 35 40
338 45 c. Turoa 40 45
339 70 c. Whakapapa 60 65

409 Hamilton's Frog

(Des A. G. Mitchell. Litho Cambec Press, Melbourne)

1984 (11 July). *Amphibians and Reptiles. T* **409** *and similar horiz designs. Multicoloured. P* 13½.

1340 24 c. Type **409** 20 25
a. Horiz pair. Nos. 1340/1 .. .. .. 40 50
1341 24 c. Great Barrier Skink 20 25
1342 30 c. Harlequin Gecko 25 30
1343 58 c. Otago Skink 50 55
1344 70 c. Gold-striped Gecko 60 65

Nos. 1340/1 were printed together, *se-tenant*, in horizontal pairs throughout the sheet.

410 Clydesdales ploughing Field

(Des Margaret Chapman. Litho Harrison)

1984 (1 Aug). *Health Stamps. Horses. T* **410** *and similar horiz designs. Multicoloured. P* 14½.

1345 24 c. + 2 c. Type **410** 25 30
a. Horiz pair. Nos. 1345/6 .. .. .. 50 60
1346 24 c. + 2 c. Shetland ponies 25 30
1347 30 c. + 2 c. Thoroughbreds 30 35
MS 1348 148 × 75 mm. Nos. 1345/7, each × 2 .. 1·40 1·50

Nos. 1345/6 were printed together, *se-tenant*, in horizontal pairs throughout the sheet.

411 "Adoration of the Shepherds" (Lorenzo di Credi)

(Des R. Conly (45 c.), P. Durrant (others). Photo Heraclio Fournier)

1984 (26 Sept). *Christmas. T* **411** *and similar multicoloured designs. P* 13½ × 14 (18 *c.*) *or* 14 × 13½ (*others*).

1349 18 c. Type **411** 15 20
1350 35 c. Old St. Paul's, Wellington (*vert*) .. 30 35
1351 45 c. "The Joy of Christmas" (*vert*) 40 45

412 Mounted Riflemen, South Africa, 1901

(Des R. Conly. Litho Harrison)

1984 (7 Nov). *New Zealand Military History. T* **412** *and similar horiz designs. Multicoloured. P* 15 × 14.

1352 24 c. Type **412** 20 25
1353 40 c. Engineers, France, 1917 .. .. .. 35 40
1354 58 c. Tanks of 2nd N.Z. Divisional Cavalry, North Africa, 1942 .. .. 50 55
1355 70 c. Infantryman in jungle kit, and 25-pounder gun, Korea and South-East Asia, 1950–72 .. .. 60 65
MS1356 122 × 106 mm. Nos. 1352/5 .. .. 1·60 1·75

413 St. John Ambulance Badge

(Des Lindy Fisher. Litho J.W.)

1985 (16 Jan). *Centenary of St. John Ambulance in New Zealand. P* 14.

1357 **413** 24 c. black, gold and bright rosine .. 20 25
1358 30 c. black, sil & bright ultram 25 30
1359 40 c. black and grey 35 40

The colours of the badge depicted are those for Bailiffs and Dames Grand Cross (24 c.), Knights and Dames of Grace (30 c.) and Serving Brothers and Sisters (40 c.).

ALTERED CATALOGUE NUMBERS

Any Catalogue numbers altered from the last edition are shown as a list in the introductory pages.

414 Nelson Horse-drawn Tram, 1862

(Des. R. Conly. Litho Cambec Press, Melbourne)

1985 (6 Mar). *Vintage Trams. T* **414** *and similar horiz designs. Multicoloured. P* 13½.

1360 24 c. Type **414** 20 25
1361 30 c. Graham's Town steam tram, 1871 .. 25 30
1362 35 c. Dunedin cable car, 1881 .. .. .. 30 35
1363 40 c. Auckland electric tram, 1902 .. .. 30 35
1364 45 c. Wellington electric tram, 1904 .. .. 35 40
1365 58 c. Christchurch electric tram, 1905 .. 45 50
1360/5 .. .. *Set of 6* 1·75 1·90

Index to New Zealand Stamp Designs from 1946

The following index is intended to facilitate the identification of all New Zealand stamps from 1946 onwards. Portrait stamps are usually listed under surnames only, views under the name of the town or city and other issues under the main subject or a prominent word and date chosen from the inscription. Simple abbreviations have occasionally been resorted to and when the same design or subject appears on more than one stamp, only the first of each series is indicated.

Abel Tasman National Park 932
Aerial Top Dressing 794
Agate 1278
Agricultural Field Days 1167
Agricultural Technology 934
Aircraft 671, 741, 1050
Airmen 885
Akaroa 1194
Alberton 1262
Alpine Plants 983
Amethyst 1280
Amphibians 1340
Andrew, Prince 815
Angus 1312
Anne, Princess 710
Antarctic Research 1327
Antarctic Treaty 955
Anzac 826
Apples 1286
Apples and Orchard 872
Army 1352
Ashburton 1160
Asian-Oceanic Postal Union 979
Auckland 953, 1221, 1363
Auckland University 1304
Automobile Assn 1135
Autumn 1267

Badge 671
Ball Player 1042
Bay of Islands 904, 981, 1163
Beach Scene 1184
Bellbird 839
Berne 1048
Birds 776, 803, 806, 812, 822, 831, 839, 947
Boeing Seaplane 1050
Bowls 1045
Boy and Frog 1150
Boy and Pony 1125
Boy Scouts 720, 771
Boys' Brigade 765
Bridal Veil Falls 1123
Bristol Freighter (aircraft) 1052
Britannia (ferry) 1334
Broadgreen 1218
Brown Trout 871
Burnett Range 1040
Butter Making 797, 858
Butterflies 914, 957, 1008, 1143

C.O.R.S.O. 911
Cable 820
Canterbury 703, 999
"Cardigan Bay" (horse) 913
Carnelian 1281
Cats 1320
Cattle and Ship loading 876
Charles, Prince 711
Chatham Islands 946
Child and Olympic Rings 887
Children and Pets 1054, 1079, 1125, 1149
Child Sunbathing 696
Children at Seaside 762, 1249
Children picking Apples 755
Children's Health Camps 742
Christchurch 1365
Christmas 805, 809, 814, 817, 824, 834, 842, 880, 892, 905, 943, 964, 990, 1034, 1058, 1083, 1129, 1153, 1182, 1204, 1229, 1253, 1274, 1324, 1349
Christmas Lily 1060
Church Tower and Cross 945
Churchill 829
Citrus Fruit 1284
Cleddau 1246
Coat of Arms 674, 700, 767, 825, 925, 952, 978, 1017
College of Surgeons 1136
Commonwealth Day 1308
Commonwealth Games 1041
Commonwealth Parliamentary Conf 835, 1207
Cook 906
Cooks Bay 1317
Coromandel 1078
Coronation 714
Coronet Park 1337
Correggio 943, 1153
Cosimo 1274
Country Women 948
Cricket 899
Crippled Children 1065
Cycling 1043

Dairy Farming 1169
Della Robbia 1229
Di Credi 1349
D'Oggiono 1253
Dogs 1270
Du Fresne 981
Dunedin 1264, 1362
Dürer 809

E.C.A.F.E. 1002
Economic Agreement with Australia 1305
Economy Zone 1176
Education 1138
Edward, Prince 1031
Egmont National Park 929
El Greco 1182
Elizabeth II 721, 723, 740, 745, 763, 808, **MS**1046, 1094a, **MS**1137, 1170, 1202
Elizabeth II and Duke of Edinburgh 722
Elizabeth II and Prince Charles 701
Empire "S. 30" (aircraft) 1053
Eros 690
Ewelme 1217
Expo '70 935

Family 1239
Family entering Church 1036
Farm Transport 1115
Feilding 1237
Fertiliser Groundspreading 1166
Fiori 905
Fire Engines 1156
First Christian Service 824
First Tasman Flight 766
Fish 792, 871, 920, 1012, 1178, 1197
Fishing 1225
Flag 790, 854
Flowers 781, 845, 946, 967, 983, 992, 1060, 1086, 1255
Football 941
Fox Glacier 878
Frozen Meat Exports 1259

George VI 680, 712
Geothermal Power 933
Girl and Butterfly 1151
Girl and Calf 1126
Girl and Pigeon 1149
Girl Guides 719
Girls and Bird 1127
Girls' Life Brigade 764
Gisborne 1133
Golden Tainui 1255
Gold-striped Gecko 1344
Government Buildings 1220
Graham's Town 1361
Grapes 1283
Great Barrier Island 1061
Great Barrier Skink 1341
Grey 1186
Greymouth 1325
Gunn 901

Hamilton 1132
Hamilton's Frog 1340
"Hark, the Herald Angels Sing" 1131
Harlequin Gecko 1342
Harvest of Grain 1168
Harvest of the Sea 1175
Hauraki Gulf 930
Hawera 1257
Hawke's Bay 768
Health 678, 690, 696, 698, 708, 710, 719, 737, 742, 755, 761, 764, 776, 803, 806, 812, 815, 822, 831, 839, 867, 887, 899, 940, 960, 987, 1031, 1054, 1079, 1125, 1149, 1197, 1225, 1249, 1270, 1320, 1345
Herald (ship) 1070
Hockey 960
Hodgkins 1027
Horses 1345
Howick 1183
Human Rights 891
Hurdling 1041

I.T.U. 828
"I saw Three Ships" 1085
International Co-operation Year 833
International Labour Organization 893
International Orchid Conference 1214
International Telecommunications Network 1114
International Women's Year 1067
International Year of Child 1196
International Year of Disabled 1238
International Year of Science 1260
Invercargill 954
Iron Pyrites 1279

Jamboree 771, 838
Jessie Kelly (ship) 1072

Kaiauai River 1243
Kaikoura Coast 1148
Kaka 831
Kakariki 812
Kangaroo and Kiwi 1305
Karearea 807
Karitane Beach 1145
Kawau 1193
Kaweka 1077
"Keep our Roads Safe" 821
Kereru 804
Kerikeri 903
King 760
Kiwifruit 1287
Korora 823
Kotare 803
Kotiate 1098
Kotuku 806

Lake Alexandrina 1319
Lake Erie (ship) 1069
Lake Matheson 1318
Lakes 993
Lake Summer 1075
Lamb Export Trade 758
Law Society 894
League of Mothers 1110
Life Savers 761
Life Saving 1276
Lincoln College 1164
Lockheed "Electra" (aircraft) 1051
Locomotives 1003
Lyttelton 1223

Mace and Black Rod 1208
Machiavelli 1083
Mangahao 1224
Maori Bible 883
Maori Club 927, 1019
Maori Fish Hook 926, 1018
Maori Mail Carrier 739
Maori Rock Drawing 796, 857
Maori Tattoo Pattern 928, 1020
Maori "Three Kings" 966
Map 1176, 1261
Marakopa Falls 1122
Maratta 842, 964
Marine Mammals 1177
Maripi 1095
Marlborough 772
Masterton 1134
Maui Gas 1174
Methodist Church 982
Metric 1111
Military History 1342
Minerals 1277
Mission House 1189
Mitre Peak 1037
Mountaineer (ferry) 1332
Mt Cook National Park 931
Mt Egmont 1316
Mt Hutt 1336
Mt Ngauruhoe 1038
Mt Sefton 1039
Mountain Climber 737
Murillo 834, 990

Napier 1047
National Airways 980
National Heart Foundation 1180
Native Sulphur 1282
Nativity Carving 1129
Nectarines 1285
Nelson 767, 1360
Nephrite 1277
Netball 940
New Plymouth 1112, 1230
New Zealand Day **MS**1046
New Zealander (ship) 1071
Ngata 1235
North West Nelson 1076
Nurse and Child 698

Oamaru 1219
Ocean Beach 1146
One Ton Cup 950
"Onward" 672
Ophir 1265
Orchid Conference 1214
Otago 692, 897, 1068
Otago Skink 1343

Palmerston North 952, 1263
Pan-Pacific Jamboree 771
Papakorito Falls 1124
Parliament House 668
Parliamentary Buildings 1105
"Partridge in a Peartree" 1155
Peace 667
Picnic Scene 1231
Picton 1195
Piha Beach 1147
Piwakawaka 832
Ploughing Championships 1215
Plunket Society 760
Poaka 777
Pohutu Geyser 802, 862, 879
Pohutukawa 992, 1206
Port Chalmers 1224
Poussin 880
"Progress through Co-operation" 1002
Provincial Council Buildings 1191
Purakaunui Falls 1121
Putorino 1096

Railways 818, 100
Rainbow Trout 130
Ranguatea Maori Church 127
Rangitiki (ship) 107
Raphael 1034, 132
Red Cross 77
Rembrandt 80
Reptiles 134
Riverlands Cottage 118
Rifle Shooting 104
Roses 967, 1086, 120
Rotary International 94
Rotorua 121
Royal Family 67
Royal Forest Society 100
Royal Society 88
Royal Visit 72
Royal Wedding 124
Rugby Football 86
Russell 120
Rutherford 97

Sailors 88
St. John Ambulance 135
St. Paul's Cathedral 66
Salvation Army 130
Sassoferrato 81
Satellite Earth Station 95
Savings Bank 84
School Dental Service 96
Sea and Resources 117
Seddon 118
Sheep and Wool 87
Sheep Grazing 116
Shells 109
Ships 673, 1069, 1085, 1175, 1259, 133
Shotover 124
Silver Jubilee **MS**113
Skiing 133
Society for Prevention of Cruelty to Animals 125
Soldier and Child 67
Soldiers 88
Southland 75
Spring 126
Stained Glass Windows 944, 965, 99 1035, 1059, 1084, 1130, 115
Stamp on Stamp 1179, 121
Stewart Island 106
Stratford 116
Summer 126
Sutherland Falls 800, 86

Tarapunga 82
Tasman Glacier 801, 86
Tauranga 125
Te Ata-O-Tu 123
Te Hau 123
Te Heu Heu 123
Te Puea 123
Telegraph 81
Telephone 116
Tennis 98
Tete 77
Thames Borough 99
The Brothers 106
"The Elms" 119
Tieke 81
Tiki 793, 856, 87
Timber 791, 855, 87
Titian 81
Tongariro 798, 85
Tory (ship) 107
Trams 136
Trawler and Fish 87
Turoa 133

U.N.I.C.E.F. 95
U.P.U. 104
United Nations 93
"Universal Suffrage" 89

Vintage Car Rally 97
Vogel 118
Von Houthorst 89

Wahaika 109
Waikana (ferry) 133
Wakatere (ferry) 133
Wakefield 125
Wall Hangings from the "Beehive" 120
Wanganui 97
Weka 84
Wellington 830, 1222, 1350, 136
Westland 77
Westport 99
Whakapapa 133
Whangaroa 119
White Island 106
Winter 126
Witz 105
Women's Division, Federated Farmers 106
World Communications Year 130
World Ploughing Championships 121

Y.W.C.A. 111
Yachts 708, 95

EXPRESS DELIVERY STAMPS

E 1

(Typo Govt Printing Office, Wellington)

1903 (9 Feb). *Value in first colour. W* **41**. *P* 11.
E1 E 1 6d. red and violet .. .. .. 30·00 18·00

1926–36. *Thick, white, opaque chalk-surfaced "Cowan" paper. W* **41**.

(*a*) *P* 14 × 14½
E2 E 1 6d. vermilion and bright violet .. 25·00 16·00

(*b*) *P* 14 × 15 (1936)
E3 E 1 6d. carmine and bright violet .. .. 26·00 27·00

1937–39. *Thin, hard, chalk-surfaced "Wiggins Teape" paper.*

(*a*) *P* 14 × 14½
E4 E 1 6d. carmine and bright violet .. .. 26·00 17·00

(*b*) *P* 14 × 15 (1939)
E5 E 1 6d. vermilion and bright violet .. 48·00 48·00

E 2 Express Mail Delivery Van

(Des J. Berry. Eng Stamp Ptg Office, Melbourne Recess Govt Ptg Office, Wellington)

1939 (16 Aug). *W* **41**. *P* 14.
E6 E 2 6d. violet .. .. 2·75 3·00

POSTAGE DUE STAMPS

D 1

(I)

N.Z.

(II)

3D. (*a*) Large "D"

5D. (*b*) Small "D"

(Typo Govt Printing Office, Wellington)

1899 (Dec). *W* **12***b*. *Coarse paper. P* 11.

I. Type I. *Circle of 14 ornaments, 17 dots over "N.Z.", "N.Z." large.*

(*a*) *Large "D"*
D1 D 1 ½d. carmine and green .. .. .. 9·00 14·00
a. No stop after "D" .. .. .. 65·00 75·00
D2 8d. carmine and green .. .. .. 60·00 75·00
D3 1s. carmine and green .. .. .. 65·00 60·00
D4 2s. carmine and green £120 £130

To avoid further subdivision the 1s. and 2s. are placed with the *pence* values, although the two types of "D" do not apply to the higher values.

(*b*) *Small "D"*
D6 D 1 5d. carmine and green .. .. .. 18·00 18·00
D7 6d. carmine and green .. .. .. 20·00 17·00
D8 10d. carmine and green .. .. .. 70·00 80·00

II. Type II. *Circle of 13 ornaments, 15 dots over "N.Z.", "N.Z." small.*

(*a*) *Large "D"*
D 9 D 1 ½d. vermilion and green .. .. 2·25 6·00
a. No stop after "D" .. .. .. 42·00 48·00
D10 1d. vermilion and green .. .. 7·00 1·00
D11 2d. vermilion and green .. .. 35·00 9·00
D12 3d. vermilion and green .. .. 14·00 3·50

(*b*) *Small "D"*
D14 D 1 1d. vermilion and green .. .. 8·00 1·25
D15 2d. vermilion and green .. .. 17·00 2·00
D16 4d. vermilion and green .. .. 20·00 7·50

D2

D3

(Des W. R. Bock. Typo Govt Printing Office)

1902 (28 Feb). *No wmk. P* 11.
D17 D 2 ½d. red and deep green .. .. 75 2·75

1904–08. *"Cowan" unsurfaced paper. W* **41** *(sideways). (a) P* 11.
D18 D 2 ½d. red and green (4.04) .. .. 1·25 1·00
a. Imperf between (pair) £350
D19 1d. red and green (5.12.05) .. 6·00 3·00
D20 2d. red and green (5.4.06) .. 90·00 90·00

(*b*) *P* 14
D21 D 2 1d. carmine and green (12.06) .. 4·50 50
a. Rose-pink and green (9.07) .. 3·75 25
D22 2d. carmine and green (10.06) .. 4·75 2·25
a. Rose-pink and green (6.08) .. 3·50 65

1913 (Jan)–**20.** *"De La Rue" chalky paper. Toned gum. W* **41**. *P* 14 × 15.
D23 D 2 ½d. carmine and green (6.19).. .. 2·50 1·00
D24 1d. carmine and green .. .. 3·50 20
D25 2d. carmine and green (8.20).. .. 5·00 1·75

1925 (May). *"Jones" chalky paper. White gum. W* **41**. *P* 14 × 15.
D26 D 2 ½d. carmine and green .. .. 25·00 25·00

1925 (July). *No wmk, but bluish "N Z" and Star lithographed on back. P* 14 × 15.
D27 D 2 ½d. carmine and green .. .. 1·75 10·00
D28 2d. carmine and green .. .. 2·25 9·00

1925 (Nov)–**35.** *"Cowan" thick, opaque chalky paper. W* **41**.

(*a*) *P* 14 × 15
D29 D 2 ½d. carmine and green (12.26) .. 2·50 3·25
D30 1d. carmine and green .. .. 5·00 1·25
D31 2d. carmine and green (6.26).. .. 6·50 4·00
D32 3d. carmine and green (6.35).. .. 23·00 20·00

(*b*) *P* 14
D33 D 2 ½d. carmine and green (10.28).. .. 9·50 12·00
D34 1d. rose and pale yellow-green (6.28) .. 3·25 30
D35 2d. carmine and green (10.29).. .. 6·50 1·75
D36 3d. carmine and green (5.28) .. .. 20·00 20·00

1937–38. *"Wiggins Teape" thin, hard chalky paper. W* **41**. *P* 14 × 15.
D37 D 2 ½d. carmine and yellow-green (2.38).. 7·00 12·00
D38 1d. carmine and yellow-green (1.37).. 7·00 3·25
D39 2d. carmine and yellow-green (6.37).. 7·00 5·00
D40 3d. carmine and yellow-green (11.37) 25·00 25·00

(Des J. Berry. Typo Govt Printing Office, Wellington)

1939–49. *P* 15 × 14. (*a*) *W* **41** *sideways* (16.8.39).
D41 D 3 ½d. turquoise-green .. .. .. 3·00 3·25
D42 1d. carmine .. .. .. 1·00 20
D43 2d. bright blue .. .. .. 4·00 2·75
D44 3d. orange-brown .. .. .. 8·50 11·00

(*b*) *W* **98** *sideways*
D45 D 3 1d. carmine (4.49) 55 30*
D46 2d. bright blue (12.46) .. .. 1·25 70
D47 3d. orange-brown (6.45) .. .. 7·00 4·50
a. Wmk upright (1943) .. .. 20·00 20·00

*The use of Postage Due stamps ceased in 1951, our used price for No. D45 being for stamps postmarked after this date (*price for examples clearly cancelled* 1949–51, £25).

OFFICIAL STAMPS

1892–1906. *Contemporary issues handstamped* "O.P.S.O." *diagonally. (a) Stamps of* 1873 *type. W* **12***b*. *P* 12½.
O 1 3 ½d. rose (V.) .. .. .. — £300

(*b*) *Stamps of* 1882–97 *optd in rose or magenta. W* **12***b*.
O 2 13 ½d. black (*p* 10).. .. .. — £120
a. Violet opt .. .. .. — £130
O 3 ½d. black (*p* 10 × 11) .. .. — £120
O 4 14 1d. rose (*p* 12 × 11½) .. .. — £130
O 5 1d. rose (*p* 11) .. .. .. — £130
O 6 15 2d. purple (*p* 11) .. .. .. — £225
O 7 2d. mauve-lilac (*p* 10) .. .. — £225
a. Violet opt .. .. ..
O 8 16 2½d. blue (*p* 11) .. .. .. — £160
O 9 2½d. ultramarine (*p* 10).. .. .. — £160
O10 2½d. ultramarine (*p* 10 × 11) .. .. — £160
O11 19 5d. olive-black (*p* 12 × 11½) .. .. — £250
O12 20 6d. brown (*p* 12 × 11½) .. .. — £300

(*c*) *Stamps of* 1898–1906 *optd in violet. P* 11. (i) *No wmk*
O13 23 ½d. green (*p* 14) (No. 334) .. .. — £110
O14 26 2½d. blue (*p* 12–16) .. .. — £275
O15 27 2½d. blue.. .. .. .. — £225
O16 39 4d. indigo and brown .. .. — £250
O17 30 5d. purple-brown .. .. .. — £300
a. Green opt .. .. .. — £275
O18 32 8d. indigo .. .. .. — £275

(ii) *W* **36***a*
O19 40 1d. carmine .. .. .. — £120

(iii) *W* **41** *(sideways on 3d., 1s.)*
O20 40 1d. carmine (*p* 14) (No. 344) .. .. — £120
a. Green opt .. .. .. — £120
O21 27 2½d. blue.. .. .. .. — £200
O22 28 3d. yellow-brown .. .. .. — £200
O23 34 1s. orange-red .. .. .. — £500
O24 35 2s. green .. .. .. — £500

The letters signify "On Public Service Only," and stamps so overprinted were used by the Post Office Department on official correspondence between the department and places abroad.

OFFICIAL.

(O 3)

1907–08. *Stamps of* 1902–7 *optd with Type* O **3** *(vertically upwards). W* **41** *(sideways on 3d., 6d., 1s., 5s. and £1). P* 14.
O59 23 ½d. yellow-green .. .. .. 5·00 1·00
O60 40 1d. carmine (Waterlow) .. .. 5·50 35
a. Perf compound of 11 and 14 .. £250 £190
b. Mixed perfs £250 £190
O60*c* 1d. carmine (Royle) .. .. 5·50 25
ca. Booklet pane of 6 (1908*) .. 20·00
d. Perf compound of 11 and 14 .. £170 £160
e. Mixed perfs £170 £160
O61 38*a* 2d. purple .. .. .. 6·50 1·25
O62 2d. bright purple .. .. .. 6·50 1·25
a. Mixed perfs £140 £140
O63 28 3d. bistre-brown .. .. .. 32·00 2·75
O64 31 6d. pink .. .. .. £110 15·00
a. Imperf vert (horiz pair) £500
b. Mixed perfs £325 £325
O65 34 1s. red .. .. .. 85·00 15·00
O66 35 2s. blue-green .. .. .. £120 55·00
a. Imperf between (pair) £700
b. Imperf vert (horiz pair) £400
O67 36 5s. deep red £275 £225
a. Wmk upright £650 £500
O68 F 4 £1 rose-pink (F89) (1908) £750 £700
O59/68 .. .. .. *Set of* 9 £1200 £900

*Though issued in 1908, a large quantity of booklets was mislaid and not utilized until they were found in 1930.

1908. *Optd as Type* O **3**. *W* **41**.
O69 23 ½d. green (*p* 14 × 15) .. .. 6·00 1·25
O70 46 1d. carmine (*p* 14 × 15) .. .. 40·00 1·00
O71 48 6d. pink (*p* 14 × 15) .. .. £110 24·00
O72 6d. pink (*p* 14 × 13, 13½) .. .. £140 30·00

1910–15. *Optd as Type* O **3**. *W* **41**. *P* 14 × 15 *(Nos.* O73/4*) or* 14 × 14½. *(others)*
O73 50 ½d. yellow-green .. .. .. 2·50 40
O74 51 1d. carmine .. .. .. 1·50 10
O76 52 3d. chestnut (1915) .. .. 20·00 1·50
a. Perf 14 × 13½ (1915) .. .. 60·00 70·00
b. Vert pair, Nos. O76/6a £300 £350
O77 – 6d. carmine (No. 459) .. .. 24·00 4·25
O78 – 6d. deep carmine (No. 460) .. 24·00 4·25
O79 – 1s. vermilion (No. 462) .. .. 65·00 22·00

1913–25. *Postal Fiscal stamps optd with Type* O **3**.

(i) *Chalk-surfaced "De La Rue" paper.* (*a*) *P* 14 (1913–14)
O80 F 4 2s. blue (30.9.14) .. .. 30·00 18·00
O81 5s. yellow-green (13.6.13) £100 £100
O82 £1 rose-carmine (1913) £750 £700

(*b*) *P* 14½ × 14, *comb* (1915)
O83 F 4 2s. deep blue (Aug) .. .. 30·00 18·00
a. No stop after "OFFICIAL" .. £120 £100
O84 5s. yellow-green (Jan).. .. .. £100 £100
a. No stop after "OFFICIAL" .. £275 £275

(ii) *Thick, white, opaque chalk-surfaced "Cowan" paper. P* 14½ × 14 (1925)
O85 F 4 2s. blue .. .. .. 65·00 65·00
a. No stop after "OFFICIAL" .. £160 £160

The overprint on these last and on No. O69 is from a new set of type, giving a rather sharper impression than Type O **3**, but otherwise resembling it closely.

1915–19. *Optd with Type* O **3**. *W* **41**. *P* 14 × 15.
O86 60*b* ½d. green (12.10.15) 50 10
O87 60*a* 1½d. grey-black (6.16) .. .. 7·00 4·50
O88 60*b* 1½d. slate (12.16) .. .. 2·25 70
O89 1½d. orange-brown (4.19) .. .. 2·75 60
O90 2d. yellow (4.17) .. .. .. 2·50 12
O91 3d. chocolate (11.19) .. .. 9·50 50
O86/91 .. .. .. *Set of* 6 22·00 6·00

See also Nos. O102, etc.

1916 (May). *Optd with Type* O **3**. *W* **41**. *P* 14 × 14½.
O92 52 8d. indigo-blue (R.) .. .. 18·00 23·00
a. Perf 14 × 13½ .. .. .. 18·00 23·00
b. Vert pair, Nos. O92/2a .. .. 50·00 75·00

1916–27. *Optd with Type* O **3**. *W* **41**. *P* 14 × 14½.
O93 60 3d. chocolate (5.16) .. .. 4·75 1·25
a. Perf 14 × 13½ .. .. .. 4·75 1·25
b. Vert pair, Nos. O93/3a .. .. 45·00 60·00
O94 4d. red-violet (*p* 14 × 13½) (4.25) .. 22·00 2·50
a. Perf 14 × 14½. *Violet* (4.27) .. 19·00 2·00
O95 6d. carmine (6.16) .. .. 6·50 85
a. Perf 14 × 13½ .. .. .. 6·50 75
b. Vert pair, Nos. O95 /5a .. .. 65·00 65·00
O96 8d. red-brown (*p* 14 × 13½) (8.22) .. £140 £140
O97 9d. sage-green (*p* 14 × 13½) (4.25) .. 60·00 40·00
O98 1s. vermilion (9.16) .. .. 12·00 3·00
a. Perf 14 × 13½ .. .. .. 20·00 10·00
b. Vert pair, Nos. O98/8a .. .. 75·00 £100
O99 1s. pale orange-red .. .. .. 22·00 7·00
O93/9.. .. .. .. *Set of* 7 £250 £180

1916 (July). *Optd with Type* O **3**. *On pictorial issue paper. W* **41** *sideways. P* 14
O100 60 3d. chocolate .. .. .. 3·50 4·00
a. No wmk .. .. .. 30·00 50·00

1924–34. *Optd with Type* O **3**. *P* 14 × 15.

(*a*) *"Jones" chalky paper. W* **41**. *White gum*
O102 60*b* ½d. green (1925) .. .. .. 3·00 1·50
O103 51 1d. deep carmine (1925) .. .. 5·00 1·25
O104 60*b* 3d. deep chocolate .. .. 18·00 3·50

(*b*) *No wmk. Bluish "N Z" and Star lithographed on back*
O105 51 1d. carmine-pink (1925) .. .. 4·25 5·00

(*c*) *"Cowan" thick, opaque, chalky paper. W* **41**. *White gum*
O106 60*b* ½d. green (1925) 50 10
a. Perf 14 (1929) 50 35
b. No stop after "OFFICIAL". Perf 14 12·00 12·00
O107 51 1d. deep carmine .. .. .. 4·00 1·25
O108 60*b* 1½d. orange-brown (*p* 14) (1929) .. 6·50 10·00
a. No stop after "OFFICIAL" .. 25·00 32·00
b. Perf 14 × 15 (1934) .. .. 17·00 20·00
O109 2d. yellow (*p* 14) (1931) .. .. 3·00 25
a. No stop after "OFFICIAL" .. 24·00 13·00
O110 3d. chocolate (1925) .. .. 8·50 70
a. No stop after "OFFICIAL" .. 26·00 15·00
b. Perf 14 (1930) .. .. .. 11·00 1·75
c. Do. No stop after "OFFICIAL" 32·00 18·00

1927–33. *Optd with Type* O **3**. *W* **41**. *P* 14.
O111 71 1d. rose-carmine .. .. .. 1·25 10
a. No stop after "OFFICIAL" .. 12·00 7·50
b. Perf 14 × 15 .. .. .. 1·75 10
O112 72 2s. light blue (No. 542) (2.28) .. £110 85·00
O113 F 6 5s. green (1933) £400 £400

Official (O 4)

Official (O 5)

1936–61. *Pictorial issue optd horiz or vert (2s.) with Type* O **4**.

(*a*) *W* **41** *(Single "N Z" and Star)*
O115 82 1d. scarlet (Die I) (*p* 14 × 13½) .. 60 10
a. Perf 13½ × 14 .. .. .. 40·00 27·00
O116 83 1½d. red-brown (*p* 13½ × 14) .. .. 9·00 14·00
a. Perf 14 × 13½ £3000
O118 92 1s. deep green (*p* 14 × 13½).. .. 8·50 12·00
O119 F 6 5s. green (*p* 14) (12.38) .. .. 28·00 12·00

The watermark of No. O119 is almost invisible.

Only 4 copies of No. O116a exist.

(b) W 98 (Mult "N Z" and Star)

O120 81 ½d. bright green, p 14 × 13½ (7.37) .. 2·00 2·00
O121 82 1d. scarlet (Die II), p 14 × 13½ (11.36) 85 8
O122 83 1½d. red-brown, p 14 × 13½ (7.36) .. 4·00 6·00
O123 84 2d. orange, p 14 × 13½ (1.38) .. 35 8
a. Perf 12½ (1942) .. .. .. 60·00 24·00
c. Perf 14 (1942) .. .. .. 5·00 5·50
O124 85 2½d. chocolate and slate, p 13–14 × 13½ (26.7.38) .. .. .. 7·50 13·00
a. Perf 14 (1938) .. .. .. 5·00 9·00
O125 86 3d. brown, p 14 × 13½ (1.3.38) .. 25·00 2·00
O126 87 4d. black and sepia, p 14 × 13½ (8.36) 2·50 60
a. Perf 14 (8.41) .. .. .. 2·50 60
b. Perf 12½ (1941) .. .. .. 1·75 90
c. Perf 14 × 14½ (10.42) .. .. 2·00 40
O127 89 6d. scarlet, p 13½ × 14 (12.37) .. 2·75 60
a. Perf 12½ (1941) .. .. .. 4·00 90
b. Perf 14½ × 14 (7.42) .. .. 1·75 40
O128 90 8d. chocolate, p 12½ (wmk sideways) (1942) .. .. .. 6·00 5·00
a. Perf 14 × 14½ (wmk sideways) (1945) .. .. .. 6·00 5·00
b. Perf 14 × 13½ .. .. .. † £1400
O129 91 9d. red and grey-black (G.) (No. 587a), p 13½ × 14 (1.3.38) .. 55·00 35·00
O130 9d. scarlet and black (Blk.) (No. 631), p 14 × 15 (1943) .. .. 23·00 23·00
O131 92 1s. deep green, p 14 × 13½ (2.37) .. 3·50 85
a. Perf 12½ (1942) .. .. .. 5·00 1·25
O132 93 2s. olive-green, p 13–14 × 13½ (5.37) 19·00 9·50
a. Perf 12½ (1942) .. .. .. 42·00 20·00
b. Perf 13½ × 14 (1939) .. .. 48·00 6·00
c. Perf 14 × 13½ (1944) .. .. 19·00 5·00
O133 F 6 5s. green, C, p 14 (3.43) .. .. 16·00 4·25
a. Perf 14 × 13½. Yellow-green, O (10.61) .. .. .. 15·00 8·00
O120/33 .. .. Set of 14 £150 85·00

The opt on No. O127a was sometimes applied at the top of the stamp, instead of always at the bottom, as on No. O127.

See notes on perforations after No. 590b.

1938–51. *Nos. 603 etc., optd with Type O 4.*

O134 108 ½d. green (1.3.38) .. .. .. 3·50 60
O135 ½d. brown-orange (1946) .. .. 1·25 65
O136 1d. scarlet (1.7.38) .. .. .. 4·00 20
O137 1d. green (10.7.41) 25 5
O138 108a 1½d. purple-brown (26.7.38) .. .. 35·00 18·00
O139 1½d. scarlet (2.4.51) .. .. .. 3·00 60
O140 3d. blue (16.10.41) 50 10
O134/40 .. .. Set of 7 42·00 18·00

1940 (2 Jan–8 Mar). *Centennial. Nos. 613, etc., optd with Type O 5.*

O141 ½d. blue-green (R.) 40 60
a. "ff" joined, as Type O 4 .. .. 24·00 22·00
O142 1d. chocolate and scarlet .. .. 1·25 10
a. "ff" joined, as Type O 4 .. .. 24·00 22·00
O143 1½d. light blue and mauve .. .. 1·00 2·00
O144 2d. blue-green and chocolate .. 1·50 10
a. "ff" joined, as Type O 4 .. .. 24·00 22·00
O145 2½d. blue-green and ultramarine .. 2·25 3·75
a. "ff" joined, as Type O 4 .. .. 24·00 22·00
O146 3d. purple and carmine (R.) .. .. 5·50 1·00
a. "ff" joined, as Type O 4 .. .. 24·00 22·00
O147 4d. chocolate and lake .. .. 17·00 1·75
a. "ff" joined, as Type O 4 .. .. 35·00 26·00
O148 6d. emerald-green and violet .. 15·00 2·50
a. "ff" joined, as Type O 4 .. .. 35·00 26·00
O149 8d. black and red (8.3) .. .. 15·00 12·00
a. "ff" joined, as Type O 4 .. .. 35·00 35·00
O150 9d. olive-green and vermilion .. 8·50 9·00
O151 1s. sage-green and deep green .. 32·00 8·00
O141/51 .. .. Set of 11 90·00 35·00

1947–49. *Nos. 680, etc., optd with Type O 4.*

O152 108a 2d. orange 50 5
O153 4d. bright purple .. .. .. 2·00 60
O154 6d. carmine .. .. .. 4·50 1·00
O155 8d. violet .. .. .. 8·00 6·50
O156 9d. purple-brown .. .. .. 11·00 9·00
O157 144 1s. red-brown and carmine (wmk upright) (Plate 1) .. .. 8·00 1·50
a. Wmk sideways (Plate 1) (1949) .. 8·00 2·50
b. Wmk upright (Plate 2) .. .. 16·00 4·50
O158 2s. brown-orange and green (wmk sideways) (Plate 1) .. .. 14·00 9·00
a. Wmk upright (Plate 1) .. .. 20·00 13·00
O152/8 .. .. Set of 7 42·00 25·00

6d

O 6 Queen Elizabeth II

(O 7)

(Des J. Berry. Recess B.W.)

1954 (1 Mar)–**63.** *W 98. P 14 × 13½.*

O159 O 6 1d. orange 20 15
O160 1½d. brown-lake .. .. .. 55 2·25
O161 2d. bluish green 40 15
O162 2½d. olive (1.3.63) .. .. .. 3·00 1·50
O163 3d. vermilion 30 10
O164 4d. blue 60 20
O165 9d. carmine .. .. .. 1·25 50
O166 1s. purple 95 10
O167 3s. slate (1.3.63) .. .. .. 35·00 45·00
O159/67 .. .. Set of 9 38·00 45·00

See note *re* white opaque paper after No. 736. Nos. O162 and O167 exist only on white paper.

1959 (1 Oct). *No. O160 surch with Type O 7.*

O168 O 6 6d. on 1½d. brown-lake .. .. 50 1·25

1961 (1 Sept). *No. O161 surch as Type O 7.*

O169 O 6 2½d. on 2d. bluish green .. .. 60 1·40

Owing to the greater use of franking machines by Government Departments, the use of official stamps was discontinued on 31 March 1965, but they remained on sale at the G.P.O. until 31 December 1965.

PROVISIONALS ISSUED AT REEFTON AND USED BY THE POLICE DEPARTMENT

1907 (Jan). *Current stamps of 1906, overwritten "Official," in red ink, and marked "Greymouth—PAID—3" inside a circular postmark stamp. P 14.*

P1 23 ½d. green £425 £600
P2 40 1d. carmine £425 £650
P3 38a 2d. purple £650 £800
P4 28 3d. bistre £550 £700
P5 31 6d. pink £750 £850
P6 34 1s. orange-red £1000 £1200
P7 35 2s. green .. .. — £5000

LIFE INSURANCE DEPARTMENT

L 1 Lighthouse L 2

(Des W. B. Hudson and J. F. Rogers; eng A. E. Cousins. Typo Govt Printing Office, Wellington)

1891–98. A. *W 12c. P 12 × 11½ (2.1.91).*

L 1 L 1 ½d. bright purple .. .. .. 45·00 7·00
L 2 1d. blue .. .. .. 45·00 9·00
a. Wmk 12b .. .. .. 85·00 18·00
L 3 2d. brown-red .. .. .. 80·00 4·00
a. Wmk 12b .. .. .. 90·00 9·00
L 4 3d. deep brown .. .. .. £190 35·00
L 5 6d. green .. .. .. £275 90·00
L 6 1s. rose £650 £190

B. *W 12b (1893–98). (a) P 10 (1893)*

L 7 L 1 ½d. bright purple .. .. .. 45·00 4·00
L 8 1d. blue .. .. .. 40·00 1·50
L 9 2d. lake .. .. .. 65·00 3·75

(b) *Perf compound of 11 and 10 (1896)*

L 9a L 1 ½d. bright purple .. .. .. 80·00 20·00
L 9b 1d. blue .. .. .. 45·00 9·00

(c) *Perf compound of 10 and 11 (1897)*

L10 L 1 ½d. bright purple .. .. .. — 50·00
L11 1d. blue

(d) *Mixed perfs 10 and 11 (1897)*

L12 L 1 2d. brown-red £550 £550

(e) *P 11 (1897–98)*

L13 L 1 ½d. bright purple .. .. .. 45·00 2·25
a. Thin coarse toned paper (1898) .. 43·00 4·50
L14 1d. blue .. .. .. 40·00 75
a. Thin coarse toned paper (1898) .. 45·00 90
L15 2d. brown-red .. .. .. 48·00 2·50
a. *Chocolate* .. .. .. 85·00 20·00
b. Thin coarse toned paper (1898) .. 50·00 3·00

1902–04. *W 41 (sideways). (a) P 11.*

L16 L 1 ½d. bright purple (1903) .. .. 45·00 2·50
L17 1d. blue (1902) .. .. .. 45·00 90
L18 2d. brown-red (1904) .. .. 60·00 3·50

(b) *Perf compound of 11 and 14*

L19 L 1 ½d. bright purple (1903) £1000
L20 1d. blue (1904) .. .. .. 75·00 9·00

Nos. L16/17 and L20 are known without watermark from the margins of the sheet.

1905–6. *Redrawn, with "V.R." omitted. W 41 (sideways). (a) P 11.*

L21 L 2 2d. brown-red (12.05) £1500 £120

(b) *P 14*

L22 L 2 1d. blue (1906) .. .. .. £140 25·00

(c) *Perf compound of 11 and 14*

L23 L 2 1d. blue (1906) £325 £150
a. Mixed perfs .. .. .. — £350

1913 (2 Jan)–**37.** *New values and colours. W 41.*

(a) *"De La Rue paper". P 14 × 15*

L24 L 2 ½d. green .. .. .. 3·50 60
a. *Yellow-green* .. .. .. 3·50 60
L25 1d. carmine .. .. .. 5·00 45
a. *Carmine-pink* .. .. .. 10·00 90
L26 1½d. black (1917) .. .. .. 22·00 4·25
L27 1½d. chestnut-brown (1919) .. .. 1·75 2·00
L28 2d. bright purple .. .. .. 24·00 10·00
L29 2d. yellow (1920) .. .. .. 3·50 2·25
L30 3d. yellow-brown .. .. .. 26·00 20·00
L31 6d. carmine-pink .. .. .. 20·00 15·00

(b) *"Cowan" paper.* (i) *P 14 × 15*

L31a L 2 ½d. yellow-green (1925) .. .. 4·25 1·25
L31b 1d. carmine-pink (1925) .. .. 10·00 1·75

(ii) *P 14*

L32 L 2 ½d. yellow-green (1926) .. .. 5·00 1·75
L33 1d. scarlet (1931) .. .. .. 8·00 1·25
L34 2d. yellow (1937) .. .. .. 3·25 2·50
L35 3d. brown-lake (1931) .. .. 18·00 17·00
L36 6d. pink (1925) .. .. .. 19·00 14·00

(c) *"Wiggins Teape" paper. P 14 × 15*

L36a L 2 ½d. yellow-green (3.37) .. .. 1·00 1·50
L36b 1d. scarlet (3.37) .. .. .. 3·25 45
L36c 6d. pink (7.37) .. .. .. 15·00 14·00

For descriptions of the various types of paper, see after No. 518.

In the 1½d. the word "POSTAGE" is in both the side-labels instead of at left only.

1944–47. *W 98. P 14 × 15.*

L37 L 2 ½d. yellow-green (7.47) .. .. 1·25 1·75
L38 1d. scarlet (6.44) .. .. .. 1·50 80
L39 L 2 2d. yellow (1946) .. .. .. 3·00 2·50
L40 3d. brown-lake (10.46) .. .. 8·50 7·00
L41 6d. pink (7.47) .. .. .. 7·00 10·00

L3 Castlepoint Lighthouse

L 6 Cape Campbell Lighthouse

(Des J. Berry. Recess B.W.).

1947 (1 Aug)–**65.** *Type L 3, L 6 and similar designs. W 98 (sideways on 1d., 2d., 2½d.). P 13½.*

L42 ½d. grey-green and orange-red .. .. 1·75 1·75
L43 1d. olive-green and pale blue 60 30
L44 2d. deep blue and grey-black 80 30
L45 2½d. black and bright blue (*white opaque paper*) (4.11.63) .. .. 7·50 8·50
L46 3d. mauve and pale blue .. .. 1·75 75
L47 4d. brown and yellow-orange .. .. 1·75 80
a. Wmk sideways (*white opaque paper*) (13.10.65) .. .. .. 7·50 10·00
L48 6d. chocolate and blue .. .. 1·75 2·00
L49 1s. red-brown and blue .. .. 1·75 2·00
L42/49 .. .. Set of 8 16·00 14·50

Designs: *Horiz* (*as Type* L 3)—1d Taiaroa lighthouse; 2d. Cape Palliser lighthouse; 6d. The Brothers lighthouse. *Vert* (*as Type* L 6)—3d. Eddystone lighthouse; 4d. Stephens Island lighthouse; 1s. Cape Brett lighthouse.

2c

10c

(L 11) (L 12)

1967 (10 July)–**68.** *Decimal currency. Stamps of 1947–65, surch as Type L 12 or L 11 (2 c.).*

L50 1 c. on 1d. (No. L43) .. .. .. 3·00 2·50
a. Wmk upright (*white opaque paper*) (10.5.68) .. .. .. 1·75 2·75
L51 2 c. on 2½d. (No. L45) .. .. .. 6·00 7·00
L52 2½ c. on 3d. (No. L46) .. .. .. 3·00 3·75
a. Wmk sideways (*white opaque paper*) (4.68?) .. .. .. 2·75 4·00
L53 3 c. on 4d. (No. L47a) .. .. .. 5·00 5·50
L54 5 c. on 6d. (No. L48) .. .. .. 3·25 4·50
L55 10 c. on 1s. (No. L49) .. .. .. 6·00 9·50
a. Wmk sideways (*white opaque paper*) .. 2·75 4·75
L50/55a .. .. Set of 6 19·00 25·00

See note *re* white opaque paper below No. 736.

No. L54 exists on both ordinary and whiter paper.

L 13 Moeraki Point Lighthouse

L 14 Puyesegur Point Lighthouse

(Des J. Berry. Litho B.W.)

1969 (27 Mar)–**77.** *Types L 13/14 and similar designs. No wmk. Chalk-surfaced paper (8, 10 c.), ordinary paper (others). P 14 (8, 10 c.) or 13½ (others).*

L56 ½ c. greenish yellow, red and deep blue .. 1·50 2·00
L57 2½ c. ultramarine, green and pale buff .. 1·00 1·25
L58 3 c. reddish brown and yellow 75 75
a. Chalk-surfaced paper (16.6.77) .. 45 60
L59 4 c. lt new blue, yellowish grn & apple-grn 1·00 1·00
a. Chalk-surfaced paper (16.6.77) .. 45 60
L60 8 c. multicoloured (17.11.76) 45 60
L61 10 c. multicoloured (17.11.76) 45 60
L62 15 c. black, light yellow and ultramarine .. 1·25 1·50
a. Perf 14. Chalk-surfaced paper (24.12.76) 90 1·25
L56/62a .. .. Set of 7 4·75 6·25

Designs: *Horiz*—4 c. Cape Egmont Lighthouse; *Vert*—3c. Baring Head Lighthouse; 8 c. East Cape; 10 c. Farewell Spit; 15 c. Dog Island Lighthouse.

25c

(L 16) L 17

1978 (8 Mar). *No. L 57 surch with Type L 16. Chalky paper.*

L63 L 14 25 c. on 2½ c. ultramarine, grn & buff 75 75

(Des A. G. Mitchell. Litho Harrison)

1981 (3 June). *P 14½.*

L64 L 17 5 c. multicoloured 5 5
L65 10 c. multicoloured 8 10
L66 20 c. multicoloured 15 20
L67 30 c. multicoloured 25 30
L68 40 c. multicoloured 30 35
L69 50 c. multicoloured 40 45
L64/9 .. .. Set of 6 1·10 1·25

POSTAL FISCAL STAMPS

As from 1 April 1882 fiscal stamps were authorised for postal use and conversely postage stamps became valid for fiscal use. Stamps in the designs of 1867 with "STAMP DUTY" above the Queen's head were withdrawn and although some passed through the mail quite legitimately they were mainly "philatelic" and we no longer list them. The issue which was specifically authorised in 1882 was the one which had originally been put on sale for fiscal use in 1880.

Although all fiscal stamps were legally valid for postage only values between 2s. and £1 were stocked at ordinary post offices. Other values could only be obtained by request from the G.P.O., Wellington or from offices of the Stamp Duties Department. Later the Arms types above £1 could also be obtained from the head post offices in Auckland, Christchurch, Dunedin and also a branch post office at Christchurch North where there was a local demand for them.

It seems sensible to list under Postal Fiscals the Queen Victoria stamps up to the £1 value and the Arms types up to the £5 because by 1931 the higher values were genuinely needed for postal purposes. Even the £10 was occasionally used on insured airmail parcels.

Although 2s. and 5s. values were included in the 1898 pictorial issue, it was the general practice for the Postal Department to limit the postage issues to 1s. until 1926 when the 2s. and 3s. appeared. These were then dropped from the fiscal issues and when in turn the 5s. and 10s. were introduced in 1953 and the £1 in 1960 no further printings of these values occurred in the fiscal series.

FORGED POSTMARKS. Our prices are for stamps with genuine postal cancellations. Beware of forged postmarks on stamps from which fiscal cancellations have been cleaned off.

Many small post offices acted as agents for government departments and it was the practice to use ordinary postal date-stamps on stamps used fiscally, so that when they are removed from documents they are indistinguishable from postally used specimens unless impressed with the embossed seal of the Stamp Duties Department.

Date-stamps very similar to postal date-stamps were sometimes supplied to offices of the Stamp Duties Department and it is not clear when this practice ceased. Prior to the Arms types the only sure proof of the postal use of off-cover fiscal stamps is when they bear a distinctive duplex, registered or parcel post cancellation, but beware of forgeries of the first two.

F 1

F 2

F 3

(Die eng W. R. Bock. Typo Govt Ptg Office)

1882 (Feb). *W* **12***a*. *P* 12 × 11½.

F1 F 1 1d. lilac .. £150 £300
F2 1d. blue .. 75·00 25·00

The 1d. fiscal was specifically authorised for postal use in February 1882 owing to a shortage of the 1d. Type **5** and pending the introduction of the 1d. Type **14** on 1 April.

The 1d. lilac fiscal had been replaced by the 1d. blue in 1878 but postally used copies with 1882 duplex postmarks are known although most postally used examples are dated from 1890 and these must have been philatelic.

(Des and dies eng W. R. Bock. Typo Govt Ptg Office)

1882 (early). *W* **12***a*. *P* 12 × 11½.

F3 F 2 1s. grey green ..
F4 F 3 1s. grey-green and red ..

Copies of these are known postally used in 1882 and although not specifically authorised for postal use it is believed that their use was permitted where there was a shortage of the 1s. postage stamp.

The 2s. value Type F **3** formerly listed is not known with 1882–83 postal date-stamps.

WMK TYPE F 5. The balance of the paper employed for the 1867 issue was used for early printings of Type F **4** introduced in 1880 before changing over to the "N Z" and Star watermark. The values we list with this watermark are known with 1882–83 postal date stamps. Others have later dates and are considered to be philatelic but should they be found with 1882–83 postal dates we would be prepared to add them to the list.

In the following list the 4d., 6d., 8d. and 1s. are known with early 1882 postal date-stamps and, like Nos. F3/4, it is assumed that they were used to meet a temporary shortage of postage stamps.

F 4

F 5

The 12s. 6d. value has the head in an oval (as Type **10**), and the 15s. and £1 values have it in a broken circle (as Type **7**).

(Dies eng W. R. Bock. Typo Govt Ptg Office)

1882 (1 Apr). *Type* F **4** *and similar types. "De La Rue" paper.*

A. *W* **12***a* (*6 mm*). (*a*) *P* 12 (1882)

F 5 4d. orange-red (*Wmk* F **5**) ..
F 6 6d. lake-brown ..
F 7 8d. green (*Wmk* F **5**) ..
F 8 1s. pink ..
F 9 2s. blue .. 45·00 4·50
F10 2s. 6d. grey-brown .. 80·00 4·50
a. Wmk F **5** ..
F11 5s. mauve .. £100 5·50
F12 4s. brown-rose .. £100 11·00
F13 5s. green .. £130 11·00
a. Yellow-green .. £130 11·00
F14 6s. rose .. £140 27·00
F15 7s. ultramarine .. £150 40·00
F16 7s. 6d. bronze-grey .. £150 45·00
F17 8s. deep blue .. £150 40·00
F18 9s. orange .. £140 45·00
F19 10s. brown-red .. £130 14·00
a. Wmk F **5**
F20 15s. green .. £170 45·00
F21 £1 rose-pink .. £170 45·00

(*b*) *P* 12½ (1886)

F22 2s. blue .. 45·00 4·50
F23 2s. 6d. grey-brown .. 80·00 4·50
F24 3s. mauve .. £100 5·50
F25 4s. purple-claret .. £100 11·00
a. Brown-rose .. £100 11·00
F26 5s. green .. £130 11·00
a. Yellow-green .. £130 11·00
F27 6s. rose .. £140 27·00
F28 7s. ultramarine .. £150 40·00
F29 8s. deep blue .. £150 40·00
F30 9s. orange .. £140 45·00
F31 10s. brown-red .. £130 14·00
F32 15s. green .. £170 45·00
F33 £1 rose-pink .. £170 45·00

B. *W* **12***b* (*7 mm*). *P* 12½ (1888)

F34 2s. blue .. 45·00 4·50
F35 2s. 6d. grey-brown .. 80·00 4·50
F36 3s. mauve .. £100 5·50
F37 4s. brown-rose .. £100 11·00
a. Brown-red .. £100 11·00
F38 5s. green .. £130 11·00
a. Yellow-green .. £130 11·00
F39 6s. rose .. £140 27·00
F40 7s. ultramarine .. £150 40·00
F41 7s. 6d. bronze-grey .. £150 45·00
F42 8s. deep blue .. £150 40·00
F43 9s. orange .. £140 45·00
F44 10s. brown-red .. £130 12·00
a. Maroon .. £130 12·00
F45 £1 pink .. £170 45·00

C. *W* **12***c* (*4 mm*). *P* 12½ (1890)

F46 2s. blue .. 70·00 11·00
F47 3s. mauve .. £140 27·00
F48 4s. brown-red .. £110 15·00
F49 5s. green .. £130 12·00
F50 6s. rose .. £150 27·00
F51 7s. ultramarine .. £160 40·00
F52 8s. deep blue .. £160 40·00
F53 9s. orange .. £140 45·00
F54 10s. brown-red .. £130 13·00
F55 15s. green .. £225 60·00

D. *Continuation of W* **12***b*. *P* 11 (1895–1901)

F56 2s. blue .. 27·00 5·50
F57 2s. 6d. grey-brown .. 80·00 4·50
a. Inscr "COUNTERPART" (1901)* .. £150 90·00
F58 3s. mauve .. £100 5·50
F59 4s. brown-red .. £100 10·00
F60 5s. yellow-green .. £130 12·00
F61 6s. rose .. £140 27·00
F62 7s. pale blue .. £150 40·00
F63 7s. 6d. bronze-grey .. £150 45·00
F64 8s. deep blue .. £150 40·00
F65 9s. orange .. £140 45·00
a. Imperf between (horiz pair) ..
F66 10s. brown-red .. £130 12·00
a. Maroon .. £130 12·00
F67 15s. green .. £170 45·00
F68 £1 rose-pink .. £170 45·00

*The plate normally printed in yellow and inscribed "COUNTERPART" just above the bottom value panel, was for use on the counterparts of documents but was issued in error in the colour of the normal fiscal stamp and accepted for use.

E. *W* **41** (*sideways*)

(i) *Unsurfaced "Cowan" paper*. (*a*) *P* 11 (1903)

F69 2s. 6d. grey-brown .. 80·00 4·50
F70 3s. mauve .. £100 5·50
F71 4s. orange-red .. £100 10·00
F72 6s. rose .. £140 27·00
F73 7s. pale blue .. £150 40·00
F74 8s. deep blue .. £140 40·00
F75 10s. brown-red .. £130 14·00
a. Maroon .. £130 14·00
F76 15s. green .. £170 45·00
F77 £1 rose-pink .. £170 45·00

(*b*) *P* 14 (1906)

F78 2s. 6d. grey-brown .. 80·00 4·50
F79 3s. mauve .. £100 5·50
F80 4s. orange-red .. £100 7·50
F81 5s. yellow-green .. 70·00 7·50
F82 6s. rose .. £140 27·00
F83 7s. pale blue .. £150 40·00
F84 7s. 6d. bronze-grey .. £150 45·00
F85 8s. deep blue .. £150 40·00
F86 9s. orange .. £140 45·00
F87 10s. maroon .. £130 12·00
F88 15s. green .. £170 45·00
F89 £1 rose-pink .. £170 45·00

(*c*) *P* 14½ × 14, *comb* (*clean-cut*) (1907)

F90 2s. blue .. 25·00 4·00
F91 2s. 6d. grey-brown .. 80·00 4·50
F92 3s. mauve .. £100 5·50
F93 4s. orange-red .. 90·00 7·50
F94 6s. rose .. £140 27·00
F95 10s. maroon .. £130 12·00
F96 15s. green .. £170 45·00
F97 £1 rose-pink .. £170 45·00

(ii) *Chalk-surfaced "De La Rue" paper*. (*a*) *P* 14 (1913)

F 98 2s. blue .. 25·00 4·00
F 99 2s. 6d. grey-brown .. 27·00 4·50
F100 3s. purple .. 70·00 5·50
F101 4s. orange-red .. 70·00 7·00
F102 5s. yellow-green .. 70·00 7·50
F103 6s. rose .. £100 14·00
F104 7s. pale blue .. £100 15·00
F105 7s. 6d. bronze-grey .. £150 45·00
F106 8s. deep blue .. £130 24·00
F107 9s. orange .. £140 45·00
F108 10s. maroon .. £130 12·00
F109 15s. green .. £170 40·00
F110 £1 rose-carmine .. £170 45·00

(*b*) *P* 14½ × 14, *comb* (1913–21)

F111 2s. deep blue .. 25·00 4·00
F112 2s. 6d. grey-brown .. 27·00 4·50
F113 3s. purple .. 70·00 5·50
F114 4s. orange-red .. 70·00 7·00
F115 5s. yellow-green .. 70·00 7·50
F116 6s. rose .. £100 14·00
F117 7s. pale blue .. £100 15·00
F118 8s. deep blue .. £130 24·00
F119 9s. orange .. £130 45·00
F120 10s. maroon .. £130 12·00
F121 12s. 6d. deep plum (1921) .. £1700 £450
F122 15s. green .. £170 40·00
F123 £1 rose-carmine .. £170 45·00

The "De La Rue" paper has a smooth finish and has toned gum which is strongly resistant to soaking.

(iii) *Chalk-surfaced "Jones" paper*. *P* 14½ × 14, *comb* (1924)

F124 2s. deep blue .. 25·00 4·00
F125 2s. 6d. deep grey-brown .. 27·00 4·50
F126 3s. purple .. 70·00 5·50
F127 5s. yellow-green .. 70·00 7·50
F128 10s. brown-red .. £130 12·00
F129 12s. 6d deep purple .. £1700 £450
F130 15s. green .. £170 40·00

The "Jones" paper has a coarser texture, is poorly surfaced and the ink tends to peel. The outline of the watermark commonly shows on the surface of the stamp. The gum is colourless or only slightly toned and washes off readily.

(iv) *Thick, opaque, chalk-surfaced "Cowan" paper*. *P* 14½ × 14, *comb* (1925–30)

F131 2s. blue .. 25·00 4·00
F132 2s. 6d. deep grey-brown .. 27·00 4·50
F133 3s. mauve .. £100 10·00
F134 4s. orange-red .. 70·00 7·00
F135 5s. yellow-green .. 70·00 7·50
F136 6s. rose .. £100 14·00
F137 7s. pale blue .. £100 15·00
F138 8s. deep blue .. £130 24·00
a. Error. Blue (as 2s.) (1930) ..
F139 10s. brown-red .. £130 12·00
F140 12s. 6d. blackish purple .. £1700 £450
F141 15s. green .. £170 40·00
F142 £1 rose-pink .. £170 45·00

The "Cowan" paper is white and opaque and the watermark, which is usually smaller than in the "Jones" paper, is often barely visible.

(v) *Thin, hard, chalk-surfaced "Wiggins Teape" paper*. *P* 14½ × 14, *comb* (1926)

F143 4s. orange-red .. 75·00 7·00
F144 £1 rose-pink .. £180 80·00

The "Wiggins Teape" paper has a vertical mesh with narrow watermark, whereas other chalk-surfaced papers with this perforation have a horizontal mesh and wider watermark.

F 6

35/-

(F 7)

(Des H. L. Richardson. Typo Govt Ptg Office)

1931–40. *As Type* F **6** (*various frames*). *W* **41**. *P* 14.

(i) *Thick, opaque, chalk-surfaced "Cowan" paper, with horizontal mesh* (1931–35)

F145 1s. 3d. lemon (4.31) .. 18·00 25·00
F146 1s. 3d. orange-yellow .. 5·00 2·50
F147 2s. 6d. deep brown .. 12·00 1·75
F148 4s. red .. 14·00 2·25
F149 5s. green .. 15·00 3·50
F150 6s. carmine-rose .. 22·00 5·50
F151 7s. blue .. 25·00 7·00
F152 7s. 6d. olive-grey .. 55·00 48·00
F153 8s. slate-violet .. 28·00 14·00
F154 9s. brown-orange .. 30·00 20·00
F155 10s. carmine-lake .. 24·00 5·00
F156 12s. 6d. deep plum (9.35) .. £140 £140
F157 15s. sage-green .. 60·00 15·00
F158 £1 pink .. 60·00 15·00
F159 25s. greenish blue .. £200 £275
F160 30s. brown (1935) .. £250 £120
F161 35s. orange-yellow .. £1800 £1800
F162 £2 bright purple .. £300 45·00
F163 £2 10s. red .. £200 £200
F164 £3 green .. £300 £150
F165 £3 10s. rose (1935) .. £1200 £950
F166 £4 light blue (1935) .. £300 £120
F167 £4 10s. deep olive-grey (1935) .. £1300 £1000
F168 £5 indigo-blue .. £325 90·00

(ii) *Thin, hard "Wiggins Teape" paper with vertical mesh* (1936–40)

(*a*) *Chalk-surfaced* (1936–39)

F169 1s. 3d. pale orange-yellow .. 3·75 60
F170 2s. 6d. dull brown .. 13·00 1·25
F171 4s. pale red-brown .. 16·00 2·00
F172 5s. green .. 18·00 4·25
F173 6s. carmine-rose .. 25·00 7·00
F174 7s. pale blue .. 28·00 10·00
F175 8s. slate-violet .. 38·00 20·00
F176 9s. brown-orange .. 45·00 22·00
F177 10s. pale carmine-lake .. 42·00 5·00
F178 15s. sage-green .. 75·00 16·00
F179 £1 pink .. 60·00 16·00
F180 30s. brown (1.39) .. £225 95·00
F181 35s. orange-yellow .. £2000 £2000
F182 £2 bright purple (1937) .. £300 55·00
F183 £3 green (1937) .. £300 £150
F184 £5 indigo-blue (1937) .. £375 £110

(*b*) *Unsurfaced* (1940)

F185 7s. 6d. olive-grey .. 90·00 90·00

Not all values listed above were stocked at ordinary post offices as some of them were primarily required for fiscal purposes but all were valid for postage.

1939. *No.* F161 *surch with Type* F **7**.

F186	35/- on 35s. orange-yellow	£375	£250

Because the 35s. orange-yellow could so easily be confused with the 1s. 3d. in the same colour it was surcharged.

1940 (June). *New values surch as Type* F **7**. *W* **41**. *"Wiggins Teape" chalk-surfaced paper. P* 14.

F187	3/6 on 3s. 6d. grey-green	12·00	5·00
F188	5/6 on 5s. 6d. lilac	24·00	20·00
F189	11/- on 11s. yellow	80·00	65·00
F190	22/- on 22s. scarlet	£190	£160

These values were primarily needed for fiscal use.

1940–58. *As Type* F **6** (*various frames*). *W* **98**.

(i) *P* 14. *"Wiggins Teape" chalk-surfaced paper with vertical mesh* (1940–56)

F191	1s. 3d. orange-yellow	3·75	30
F192	1s. 3d. yell & blk (*wmk inverted*) (14.6.55)	2·25	15
	b. Error. Yellow & bl (wmk inverted) (7.56)	7·00	7·00
F193	2s. 6d. deep brown	6·50	15
F194	4s. red-brown	7·50	25
F195	5s. green	12·00	50
F196	6s. carmine-rose	22·00	2·50
F197	7s. pale blue	25·00	5·50
F198	7s. 6d. olive-grey (*wmk inverted*) (21.12.50)	60·00	45·00
F199	8s. slate-violet	35·00	12·00
F200	9s. brown-orange (1.46)	35·00	15·00
F201	10s. carmine-lake	20·00	2·25
F202	15s. sage-green	45·00	17·00
F203	£1 pink	35·00	5·50
F204	25s. greenish blue (1946)	£275	£300
F205	30s. brown (1946)	£190	95·00
F206	£2 bright purple (1946)	65·00	24·00
F207	£2 10s. red (*wmk inverted*) (9.8.51) ..	£225	£190
F208	£3 green (1946)	80·00	45·00
F209	£3 10s. rose (11.48)	£1200	£1000
F210	£4 light blue (*wmk inverted*) (12.2.52) ..	£120	60·00
F211	£5 indigo-blue	£150	55·00

THREE SHILLINGS I.

THREE SHILLINGS II.

3s. 6d.

Type I. Broad serifed capitals

Type II. Taller capitals, without serifs

Surcharged

F212	3/6 on 3s. 6d. grey-green (I) (1942) ..	14·00	5·00
F213	3/6 on 3s. 6d. grey-green (II) (6.53) ..	30·00	30·00
F214	5/6 on 5s. 6d. lilac (1944)	22·00	9·00
F215	11/- on 11s. yellow (1942)	65·00	50·00
F216	22/- on 22s. scarlet (1945)	£190	£160

(ii) *P* 14 × 13½. *"Wiggins Teape" unsurfaced paper with horizontal mesh* (1956–58)

F217	1s. 3d. yellow and black (11.56)	2·25	20
F218	£1 pink (20.10.58)	45·00	24·00

No. F192b had the inscription printed in blue in error but as many as 378,000 were printed.

From about 1949–53 inferior paper had to be used and for technical reasons it was necessary to feed the paper into the machine in a certain way which resulted in whole printings with the watermark inverted for most values. These are fully listed in the *Elizabethan Catalogue*. In the above list the prices are for the cheapest form.

F 8

1967 (10 July). *Decimal currency. W* **98** (*sideways*). *Unsurfaced paper. P* 14.

F219	F **8**	$4 deep reddish violet	3·00	2·75
F220		$6 emerald	4·50	4·25
F221		$8 light greenish blue	6·00	5·50
F222		$10 deep ultramarine	7·50	7·00

The original printings were line perf on paper with the sideways watermark inverted ("N Z" to right of star when viewed from the front). From 1968 the stamps were comb perforated with the sideways watermark normal. The prices quoted are for the cheaper printings. Both are listed in the *Elizabethan Catalogue*.

ANTARCTIC EXPEDITIONS

KING EDWARD VII LAND

1908. *Shackleton Expedition. T* **40** *of New Zealand* (*p* 14), *optd* "King Edward VII Land" *in two lines, reading up*.

A1	1d. rose-carmine (No. 419*b* Royle) (G.) ..	£500	45·00
	a. Opt double	—	£1500
A1*b*	1d. rose-carmine (No. 418*b* Waterlow) (G.)	£1300	£800

A single used copy has been reported on the "dot" plate, No. 415.

VICTORIA LAND

1911. *Scott Expedition. Stamps of New Zealand optd* "VICTORIA LAND," *in two lines*.

A2	**50**	½d. green	£600	£600
A3	**51**	1d. carmine	45·00	55·00
		a. No stop after "LAND"	£450	£550

These issues were made under authority of the New Zealand Postal Department and, while not strictly necessary, they actually franked correspondence to New Zealand. They were sold to the public at a premium.

ROSS DEPENDENCY

This comprises a sector of the Antarctic continent and a number of islands. It was claimed by Great Britain on 30 July 1923 and soon afterward put under the jurisdiction of New Zealand.

1 H.M.S. *Erebus*

2 Shackleton and Scott

3 Map of Ross Dependency and New Zealand

4 Queen Elizabeth II

(Des E. M. Taylor (3d.), L. C. Mitcell (4d.), R. Smith (8d.), J. Berry (1s. 6d.). Recess D.L.R.)

1957 (11 Jan). *W* **98** *of New Zealand* (*Mult* N Z *and Star*). *P* 13 (1*s*. 6*d*.) *or* 14 (*others*).

1	**1**	3d. indigo	4·75	1·75
2	**2**	4d. carmine-red	4·75	1·75
3	**3**	8d. bright carmine-red & ultram (*shades*)	4·75	3·50
4	**4**	1s. 6d. slate-purple	8·00	4·00

(New Currency. 100 cents = 1 dollar)

5 H.M.S. *Erebus*

1967 (10 July). *Decimal currency. As Nos.* 1/4 *but with values inscr in decimal currency as T* **5**. *Chalky paper* (*except* 15 *c*.). *W* **98** *of New Zealand* (*sideways on* 7 *c*.). *P* 13 (15 *c*.) *or* 14 (*others*).

5	**5**	2 c. indigo (*shades*)	7·00	4·75
6	**2**	3 c. carmine-red	7·00	4·75
7	**3**	7 c. bright carmine-red and ultramarine	7·50	7·50
8	**4**	15 c. slate-purple	12·00	12·00

6 Great Skua

7 Scott Base

(Des M. Cleverley. Litho B.W.)

1972 (18 Jan)–**79**. *Horiz design as T* **6** (3 *to* 8 *c*.) *or* **7** (10, 18 *c*.). *Ordinary paper. P* 14½ × 14 (10, 18 *c*.) *or* 13 (*others*).

9	3 c. black, brownish grey and pale blue ..	85	85
	a. Chalk-surfaced paper (2.79)	55	55
10	4 c. black, royal blue and violet	60	60
	a. Chalk-surfaced paper (2.79)	35	40
11	5 s. black, brownish grey and rose-lilac ..	60	60
	a. Chalk-surfaced paper (2.79)	35	40
12	8 c. black, yellow-brown and brownish grey	70	85
	a. Chalk-surfaced paper (2.79)	45	55
13	10 c. black, turquoise-green and slate-green ..	1·00	1·25
	a. Perf 13½ × 13. Chalk-surfaced paper (2.79)	60	70
14	18 c. black, violet and bright violet	2·25	2·50
	a. Perf 13½ × 13. Chalk-surfaced paper (2.79)	75	1·10
9/14	.. .. *Set of* 6	5·50	6·00
9a/14a	.. .. *Set of* 6	2·75	3·25

Designs:—4 c. "Hercules" aeroplane at Williams Field; 5 c. Shackleton's Hut; 8 c. Supply ship H.M.N.Z.S. *Endeavour*; 18 c. Tabular ice floe.

8 Adelie Penguins

(Des R. Conly. Litho Asher and Co, Melbourne)

1982 (20 Jan). *Horiz designs as T* **8**. *Multicoloured. P* 15½.

15	5 c. Type **8**	5	5
16	10 c. Tracked vehicles	8	10
17	20 c. Scott Base	15	20
18	30 c. Field party	25	30
19	40 c. Vanda Station	30	35
20	50 c. Scott's hut, Cape Evans	40	45
15/20	.. .. *Set of* 6	1·10	1·25

TOKELAU

Formerly known as the Union Islands, and administered as part of the Gilbert & Ellice Islands Colony, they were transferred to New Zealand on 4 November 1925 and then administered by Western Samoa. The islands were finally incorporated in New Zealand on 1 January 1949 and became a dependency. The name Tokelau was adopted on 7 May 1946.

Stamps of GILBERT AND ELLICE ISLANDS were used in Tokelau from February 1911 until June 1926 when they were replaced by those of SAMOA. These were current until 1948.
The post office on Atafu opened in 1911, but the cancellations for the other two islands, Fakaofo and Nukunono, did not appear until 1926.

1 Atafu Village and Map

(Des J. Berry from photographs by T. T. C. Humphrey. Recess B.W.)

1948 (22 June). *T* 1 *and similar horiz designs. Wmk T* **98** *of New Zealand* (*Mult* N Z *and Star*). *P* 13½.

1		½d. red-brown and purple	15	35
2		1d. chestnut and green	30	55
3		2d. green and ultramarine	45	85

Designs:—1d. Nukunono hut and map; 2d. Fakaofo village and map.
Covers are known postmarked 16 June 1948, but this was in error for 16 July.

1953 (15 June*). *Coronation. As No.* 715 *of New Zealand, but inscr* "TOKELAU ISLANDS".

4	**164**	3d. brown	6·50	8·00

*This is the date of issue in Tokelau Islands but the stamps were released in New Zealand on 25 May.

ONE SHILLING

(4)

6D TOKELAU ISLANDS

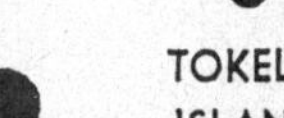

(5)

1956 (27 Mar). *No.* 1 *surch with T* 4 *by Govt Printer, Wellington.*

5	1	1s. on ½d. red-brown and purple	5·50	7·00

1966 (8 Nov). *Postal fiscal stamps of New Zealand* (*Type* **F 6**), *but without value, surch as T* 5 *by Govt Printer, Wellington. W* **98** *of New Zealand. P* 14.

6		6d. light blue	4·00	3·00
7		8d. light emerald	4·50	3·25
8		2s. light pink	5·75	4·75

(New Currency. 100 cents = 1 dollar (New Zealand))

1c (6)

5c TOKELAU ISLANDS (7)

1967 (10 July). *Decimal currency.*

(*a*) *Nos.* 1/3 *surch in decimal currency as T* 6 *by Govt Printer, Wellington*

9		1c. on 1d.	75	60
10		2 c. on 2d.	1·25	1·00
11		10 c. on ½d.	3·50	3·50

(*b*) *Postal Fiscal stamps of New Zealand* (*Type* **F 6**), *but without value, surch as T* 7 *by Govt Printer, Wellington. W* **98** *of New Zealand* (*sideways*). *P* 14 (*line or comb*)

12	**F 6**	3 c. reddish lilac	1·00	60
13		5 c. light blue	1·00	70
14		7 c. light emerald	1·50	1·25
15		20 c. light pink	3·50	3·00
9/15		*Set of* 7	11·00	10·00

8 British Protectorate (1877)

12 H.M.S. *Dolphin*, 1765

(Des New Zealand P.O. artists from suggestions by Tokelau Administration. Litho B.W.)

1969 (8 Aug). *History of Tokelau. T* 8 *and similar horiz designs. W* **98** *of New Zealand. P* 13 × 12½.

16		5 c. ultramarine, yellow and black	1·00	55
17		10 c. vermilion, yellow and black	1·50	1·00
18		15 c. green, yellow and black	2·50	1·75
19		20 c. yellow-brown, yellow and black	3·00	2·25

Designs:—10 c. Annexed to Gilbert and Ellice Islands, 1916; 15 c. New Zealand Administration, 1925; 20 c. New Zealand Territory, 1948.

1969 (1 Oct). *Christmas. As T* **301** *of New Zealand, but inscr* "TOKELAU ISLANDS". *W* **98** *of New Zealand. P* 13½ × 14½.

20	**301**	2 c. multicoloured	30	30

1970 (1 Oct). *Christmas. As T* **314** *of New Zealand but inscr* "TOKELAU ISLANDS". *P* 12½.

21	**341**	2 c. multicoloured	30	30

(Des D. B. Stevenson. Litho B.W.)

1970 (9 Dec). *Discovery of Tokelau. T* **12** *and similar multicoloured designs. P* 13½.

22	5 c. Type **12**	3·00	2·00
23	10 c. H.M.S. *Pandora*, 1791	3·75	2·50
24	25 c. *General Jackson*, 1835 (*horiz*)	7·50	6·00

13 Fan

14 Windmill Pump

(Des Enid Hunter. Litho Harrison)

1971 (20 Oct). *Various horiz designs as T* **13** *showing handicrafts. Multicoloured. P* 14.

25	1 c. Type **13**	20	20
26	2 c. Hand-bag	30	30
27	3 c. Basket	40	40
28	5 c. Hand-bag	65	65
29	10 c. Shopping-bag	1·00	1·00
30	15 c. Fishing box	3·50	3·50
31	20 c. Canoe	4·25	4·25
32	25 c. Fishing hooks	4·25	4·25
25/32	*Set of* 8	13·00	13·00

(Des A. G. Mitchell. Litho Questa)

1972 (6 Sept). *25th Anniversary of South Pacific Commission. T* **14** *and similar vert designs. Multicoloured. P* 14 × 13½.

33	5 c. Type **14**	1·25	1·00
34	10 c. Community well	1·75	1·40
35	15 c. Pest eradication	2·75	2·25
36	20 c. Flags of member nations	3·00	2·50

On No. 35 "PACIFIC" is spelt "PACFIC".

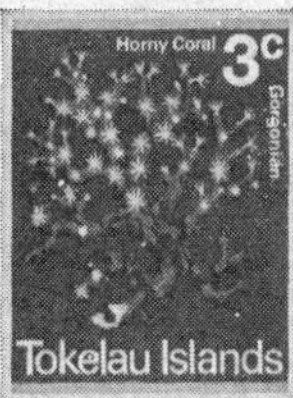

15 Horny Coral

16 Hump-back Cowrie

(Des Eileen Mayo. Litho B.W.)

1973 (12 Sept). *Coral. T* **15** *and similar vert designs. Multicoloured P.* 13.

37	3 c. Type **15**	2·25	1·75
38	5 c. Soft Coral	2·75	1·90
39	15 c. Mushroom Coral	5·00	3·50
40	25 c. Staghorn Coral	5·50	4·00

(Des G. F. Fuller. Litho Questa)

1974 (13 Nov). *"Shells of the Coral Reef". T* **16** *and similar horiz designs. Multicoloured. P* 14.

41	3 c. Type **16**	2·25	1·40
42	5 c. Tiger Cowrie	2·75	1·50
43	15 c. Mole Cowrie	4·75	3·50
44	25 c. Eyed Cowrie	5·75	5·00

17 Moorish Idol

18 Canoe Making

(Des Eileen Mayo. Litho Questa)

1975 (19 Nov). *Fishes. T* **17** *and similar vert designs. Multicoloured. P* 14.

45	5 c. Type **17**	2·25	75
46	10 c. Long-nosed Butterfly-fish	2·75	2·00
47	15 c. Lined Butterfly-fish	3·50	3·00
48	25 c. Red Fire-fish	4·75	3·75

(Des F. Paulo. Litho Questa)

1976 (27 Oct)–**81**. *T* **18** *and similar multicoloured designs showing local life. P* 14 × 13½ (9 c. *to* $1) *or* 13½ × 14 (*others*).

49	1 c. Type **18**	15	20
	a. Perf 14½ × 15 (15.7.81)	10	15
50	2 c. Reef fishing	15	20
51	3 c. Weaving preparation	25	25
	a. Perf 14½ × 15 (15.7.81)	10	15
52	5 c. Umu (kitchen)	40	40
	a. Perf 14½ × 15 (15.7.81)	10	15
53	9 c. Carving (*vert*)	15	15
	a. Perf 15 × 14½ (15.7.81)	15	20
54	20 c. Husking coconuts (*vert*)	30	30
	a. Perf 15 × 14½ (15.7.81)	20	30
55	50 c. Wash day (*vert*)	55	60
	a. Perf 15 × 14½ (15.7.81)	35	40
56	$1 Meal time (*vert*)	90	1·00
	a. Perf 15 × 14½ (15.7.81)	70	75
49/56	*Set of* 8	1·60	2·10

19 White Tern

20 Westminster Abbey

(Des F. Paulo. Litho Questa)

1977 (16 Nov). *Birds of Tokelau. T* **19** *and similar horiz designs. Multicoloured. P* 14½.

57	8 c. Type **19**	60	40
58	10 c. Turnstone	70	45
59	15 c. White-capped Noddy	1·00	70
60	30 c. Common Noddy	1·60	1·25

(Des Eileen Mayo. Litho Questa)

1978 (28 June). *25th Anniv of Coronation. T* **20** *and similar vert designs. Multicoloured. P* 14.

61	8 c. Type **20**	60	30
62	10 c. King Edward's Chair	70	35
63	15 c. Coronation regalia	90	65
64	30 c. Queen Elizabeth II	1·40	90

21 Canoe Race

22 Rugby

(Des F. Paulo. Photo Heraclio Fournier)

1978 (8 Nov). *Canoe Racing. T* **21** *and similar horiz designs showing races. P* 13½ × 14.

65	8 c. multicoloured	80	55
66	12 c. multicoloured	90	65
67	15 c. multicoloured	1·00	90
68	30 c. multicoloured	1·75	1·25

(Des F. Paulo. Photo Heraclio Fournier)

1979 (7 Nov). *Sports. T* **22** *and similar horiz designs. Multicoloured. P* 13½.

69	10 c. Type **22**	30	15
70	15 c. Cricket	70	50
71	20 c. Rugby (*different*)	70	55
72	30 c. Cricket (*different*)	1·00	70

23 Surfing

24 Pole Vaulting

(Des F. Paulo. Litho J.W.)

1980 (5 Nov). *Water Sports. T* **23** *and similar horiz designs. Multicoloured. P* 13.

73	10 c. Type **23**	15	15
74	20 c. Surfing (*different*)	20	20
75	30 c. Swimming	30	30
76	50 c. Swimming (*different*)	45	45

(Des F. Paulo. Photo Heraclio Fournier)

1981 (4 Nov). *Sports. T* **24** *and similar vert designs. Multicoloured. P* 14 × 13½.

77	10 c. Type **24**	15	15
78	20 c. Volleyball	25	25
79	30 c. Running	40	40
80	50 c. Volleyball (*different*)	50	50

(New Currency. 100 sene = 1 Samoan tola)

25 Wood Carving

26 Octopus Lure

(Des R. Conly. Litho Enschedé)

1982 (5 May). *Handicrafts. T* **25** *and similar vert designs. Multicoloured. P* 14 × 13½.

81	10 s. Type **25**	15	15
82	22 s. Bow-drilling sea shell	25	25
83	34 s. Bowl finishing	45	45
84	60 s. Basket weaving	65	65

(Des R. Conly. Litho Questa)

1982 (3 Nov). *Fishing Methods. T* **26** *and similar vert designs. Multicoloured. P* 14.

85	5 s. Type **26**	8	8
86	18 s. Multiple-hook fishing	20	20
87	23 s. Ruvettus fishing	25	25
88	34 s. Netting flying fish	40	40
89	63 s. Noose fishing	65	65
90	75 s. Bonito fishing	75	75
85/90	*Set of* 6	2·10	2·10

27 Outrigger Canoe **28** Javelin Throwing

(Des R. Conly. Litho Cambec Press, Melbourne)

1983 (4 May). *Transport. T* **27** *and similar horiz designs. Multicoloured. P* 13 × 13½.

91	5 s. Type **27**	5	8
92	18 s. Wooden whale boat	12	15
93	23 s. Aluminium whale boat	15	20
94	34 s. "Alia" fishing boat	25	30
95	63 s. M.V. *Frysna* (cargo ship)	45	50
96	75 s. McKinnon "Goose" flying boat	60	65
91/6	*Set of* 6	1·40	1·60

(Des R. Conly. Litho Questa)

1983 (2 Nov). *Traditional Pastimes. T* **28** *and similar horiz designs. Multicoloured. P* 14.

97	5 s. Type **28**	5	8
98	18 s. String game	12	15
99	23 s. Fire making	15	20
100	34 s. Shell throwing	25	30
101	63 s. Hand-ball game	45	50
102	75 s. Mass wrestling	60	65
97/102	*Set of* 6	1·40	1·60

29 Planting and Harvesting **30** Convict Tang ("Manini")

(Des R. Conly. Litho J.W.)

1984 (2 May). *Copra Industry. T* **29** *and similar vert designs. Multicoloured. P* 13½ × 13.

103	48 s. Type **29**	40	45
	a. Horiz strip of 5. Nos. 103/7	1·90	
104	48 s. Husking and splitting	40	45
105	48 s. Drying	40	45
106	48 s. Bagging	40	45
107	48 s. Shipping	40	45

Nos. 103/7 were printed together, *se-tenant*, in horizontal strips of 5 throughout the sheet.

(Des R. Conly. Litho B.D.T.)

1984 (5 Dec). *Fishes. T* **30** *and similar horiz designs. Multicoloured. P* 15 × 14.

108	1 s. Type **30**	5	5
109	2 s. Flying Fish ("Hahave")	5	5
110	5 s. Fire Wrasse ("Uloulo")	5	5
111	9 s. Unicorn Fish ("Ume ihu")	5	8
112	23 s. Napoleon Fish ("Lafilafi")	15	20
113	34 s. Red Snapper ("Fagamea")	25	30
114	50 s. Yellow Fin Tuna ("Kakahi")	35	40
115	75 s. Castor-oil Fish ("Palu po")	50	55
116	$1 Grey Shark ("Mokoha")	65	70
117	$2 Black Marlin ("Hakula")	1·25	1·40
108/17	*Set of* 10	3·00	3·25

Niger Coast Protectorate

OIL RIVERS PROTECTORATE

The British Consulate for the Bights of Benin and Biafra, having been established as early as 1849 on the island of Fernando Po, was permanently transferred to Old Calabar in 1882 following an upsurge in both trade and political activity.

A British protectorate was proclaimed over the coastal area in June 1885 and this was confirmed by the Congress of Berlin in the following year. In 1891 the administration was reorganised with a Consul-General at Old Calabar and Vice-Consuls at district stations.

The first post offices were opened in November 1891 at Old Calabar River, Bonny River, Brass River and Forcados River for which circular date stamps were eventually received from London, although usage in the early part of 1892 is rare.

From July 1892 local administrative handstamps, as Type Z 1, were used either as a cancellation or in conjunction with a circular date stamp struck across the adhesive.

Z 1

These oval handstamps are usually found on the 1892 overprinted issue, but the following are known on unoverprinted stamps of Great Britain:

1892

BENIN

Stamps of GREAT BRITAIN *cancelled with oval postmark, Type* Z 1, *inscribed* "BENIN".

Z1 2½d. purple/*blue* (V.)

BONNY

Stamps of GREAT BRITAIN *cancelled with oval postmark, Type* Z 1, *inscribed* "BONNY".

Z2 2½d. purple/*blue* (V.)

BRASS RIVER

Stamps of GREAT BRITAIN *cancelled with oval postmark, Type* Z 1, *inscribed* "BRASS".

Z3 2½d. purple/*blue* (Blk.)

OLD CALABAR RIVER

Stamps of GREAT BRITAIN *cancelled with oval postmark, Type* Z 1, *inscribed* "OLD CALABAR".

Z4 2½d. purple/*blue* (Blk.)

Stamps of GREAT BRITAIN *cancelled* "BRITISH VICE-CONSULATE OLD CALABAR" *within double-lined circle.*

Z5	2½d. purple/*blue* (V.)	£300
Z6	5d. dull purple and blue (V.)	

For later use of Type Z 1 and the circular Vice-Consulate marks see note beneath No. 6.

Z 2.

Unoverprinted stamps of Great Britain remained officially valid for postage in the Protectorate until 30 September 1892, but were available from post offices in the Niger Company Territories up to the end of 1899. The two areas were so closely linked geographically that offices in the Protectorate continued to accept letters franked with Great Britain stamps until the reorganisation of 1900. The listing below covers confirmed examples, known on cover or piece, the prices quoted being for the latter.

1892 *to* **1899**

Stamps of GREAT BRITAIN *cancelled with circular postmarks as Type* Z 2.

BENIN RIVER

Z 7	2d. green and carmine	
Z 8	2½d. purple/*blue*	
Z 9	3d. purple/*yellow*	
Z10	5d. dull purple and blue	
Z11	1s. green	

BONNY RIVER

Z12	½d. vermilion	
Z13	2½d. purple/*blue*	£150
Z14	5d. dull purple and blue	
Z15	6d. deep purple/*red*	

BRASS RIVER

Z16	1½d. dull purple and green	
Z17	2½d. purple/*blue*	£850
Z17*a*	2½d. purple/*blue* (squared-circle cancellation)	
Z18	6d. purple/*red*	£700

FORCADOS RIVER

Z19	1d. lilac	£525
Z20	2½d. purple/*blue*	
Z21	5d. dull purple and blue (m/s cancellation)	
Z22	10d. dull purple and carmine	

OLD CALABAR RIVER

Z23	½d. vermilion
Z24	1d. lilac
Z25	1½d. dull purple and green
Z26	2d. green and vermilion
Z27	2½d. purple/*blue*
Z28	5d. dull purple and blue
Z29	6d. purple/*red*
Z30	1s. green

OPOBO RIVER

Z31	2½d. purple/*blue*
Z32	10d. dull purple and carmine

Some later covers are known franked with G.B. stamps, but the origin of the stamps involved is uncertain.

PRICES FOR STAMPS ON COVER

Nos. 1/6	*from* × 6
Nos. 7/36	*from* × 2
Nos. 37/44	—
Nos. 45/50	*from* × 10
Nos. 51/6	*from* × 12
Nos. 57/65	*from* × 2
Nos. 66/73	*from* × 12

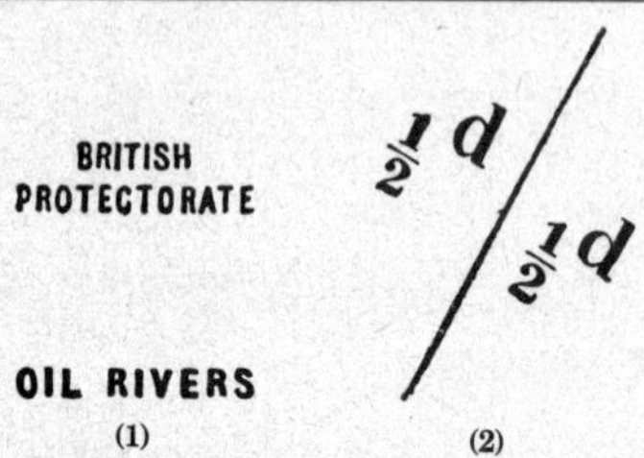

(1) (2)

1892 (20 July)–**94**. *Stamps of Great Britain optd by D.L.R. with T* 1.

1	**71**	½d. vermilion	4·50	5·00
2	**57**	1d. lilac	4·50	5·00
		a. Opt reversed "OIL RIVERS" at top	£4000	
		b. Bisected (½d.) (on cover)		† £2500
3	**73**	2d. green and carmine	7·00	7·00
		a. Bisected (1d.) (on cover)		† £5000
4	**74**	2½d. purple/*blue*	6·00	5·00
5	**78**	5d. dull purple & blue (No. 207*a* Die II)	8·00	9·50
		a. On No. 207 (Die I)		
6	**82**	1s. green	40·00	45·00
1/6		*Set of* 6	65·00	70·00
1/6 H/S "Specimen"		*Set of* 6	£500	

Nos. 2b and 3a were used at Bonny River during August and September 1894.

OVAL HANDSTAMPS. In addition to Nos. Z1/4 postmarks as Type Z 1 are also known used on the 1892–94 overprinted issue from the following offices:

Bakana (Nos. 2, 4/6)
Benin (Nos. 1/6)
Bonny (No. 2)
Brass (Nos. 3/5)
Buguma (Nos. 4 and 6)
Old Calabar (No. 4)
Opobo (Nos. 1/3)
Sombreiro River (Nos. 1/6)

The Vice-Consulate marks, as Nos. Z5/6, are also known struck on examples of No. 4 from Bonny, Forcados or Old Calabar.

Nos. 2 to 6 surcharged locally

1893 (3 Sept). *Issued at Old Calabar. Surch with T* 2 *and then bisected.*

7	½d. on half of 1d. (R.)	£150	£140
	a. Unsevered pair	£450	£425
	ab. Surch inverted and dividing line reversed (unsevered pair)	—	£3750
	b. Surch reversed (dividing line running from left to right)	—	£4250
	c. Straight top to "1" in "½"	£250	£250
	d. "½" omitted		
	e. Surch double (in pair with normal)	—	£1000
	f. *Se-tenant* pair. Nos. 7/8	—	£6000
8	½d. on half of 1d. (V.)	£4000	£3750
	a. Surch double (pair)	£7500	

The surcharge was applied in a setting covering one horizontal row at a time. Violet ink was used for the top row in the first sheet, but was then replaced with red.

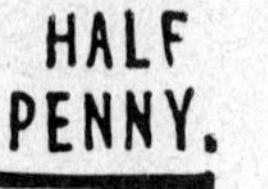

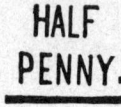

(3) (4)

1893 (Dec). *Issued at Old Calabar. Nos. 3/6 handstamped.*

(*a*) *With T* 3

9	½d. on 2d. (V.)	£275	£275
	a. Surch inverted	£2750	
	b. Surch diagonal (up or down)	£2250	
	c. Surch vertical (up or down)	£1200	
10	½d. on 2½d. (Verm.)	£6500	
	a. Surch in carmine	£10000	

(*b*) *With T* 4

11	½d. on 2½d. (G.)	£300	£300
	a. Surch double	£2000	

b. Surch diagonally inverted £1500
12 ½d. on 2½d. (Verm) £325 £325
13 ½d. on 2½d. (C.) £325 £325
a. Surch omitted (in pair)
14 ½d. on 2½d. (B.) £375 £375
15 ½d. on 2½d. (Blk.) £2250
a. Surch inverted
b. Surch diagonal inverted (up or down) £2250
16 ½d. on 2½d. (B.-Blk.) £1900

In T 3 "HALF" measures 9½ mm and "PENNY" 12½ mm with space 1½ mm between the words. Bar 14½ mm ending below the stop. The "F" is nearly always defective.

In T 4 "HALF" is 8½ mm, "PENNY" 12½ mm, spacing 2½ mm, and bar 16 mm, extending beyond the stop.

HALF PENNY.   HALF PENNY

5 (Stop after "N")   6 (No stop after "N")

(c) With T 5

17 ½d. on 2½d. (Verm.) £350 £350
a. Surch double — £1300
b. Surch vertical (up) — £2000

(d) With T 6

18 ½d. on 2d. (V.) £650 £500
19 ½d. on 2½d. (Verm.) £225 £200
a. Surch inverted £1200
b. Surch double — £1200
c. Surch diagonal (up or down) £1200
d. Surch omitted (in strip of 3) £5500
e. Surch vertical (up or down) £850
f. Surch diagonal, inverted (up or down) £1700

In T 5 the "P" and "Y" are raised, and the space between the words is about 4 mm. Bar is short, approx 13½ mm. T 6 is similar but without the stop after "N".

Half Penny   Half Penny

(7)   (8)

(e) With T 7

20 ½d. on 2d. (V.) £225 £225
a. Surch double — £5500
b. Surch vertical (up or down) £1500
c. Surch diagonal (up or down) £1400
d. Surch diagonal (inverted) £2750
21 ½d. on 2½d. (Verm.) £225 £200
a. Surch double £4000
b. Surch vertical (up or down) £1300
c. Surch inverted £1500
d. Surch diagonal (up or down) £1200
e. Surch diagonal, inverted (up) £3000
22 ½d. on 2½d. (B.) £4000 £3500
23 ½d. on 2½d. (C.)
24 ½d. on 2½d. (V.) £2250

(f) With T 8

25 ½d. on 2½d. (Verm.) £300 £325
a. Surch diagonal (up) £1600
26 ½d. on 2½d. (B.)
27 ½d. on 2½d. (G.) £275 £250
a. Surch double
28 ½d. on 2½d. (C.) — £700

In T 7 the "a" and "e" are narrow and have a short upward terminal hook. The "l" has a very small hook. The letters "nny" have curved serifs, and the distance between the words is 5½ mm.

In T 8 the "a" and "e" are wider. The "l" has a wider hook. The letters "nny" have straight serifs, and the distance between the words is 4¼ mm.

HALF PENNY.   HALF PENNY

(9)   (10)

(g) With T 9

29 ½d. on 2d. (V.) £300 £300
30 ½d. on 2d. (B.) £750 £700
a. Surch double
31 ½d. on 2½d. (Verm.) £450 £450
a. Surch double
32 ½d. on 2½d. (B.) £300 £300
33 ½d. on 2½d. (G.) £325 £325
a. Surch double (G.) £1100
b. Surch double (G. + Verm.)
34 ½d. on 2½d. (V.) £3500

(h) With T 10

35 ½d. on 2½d. (G.) £500 £500
36 ½d. on 2½d. (Verm.) £4000

One Shilling   5/-

(11)   (12)

(i) With T 11

37 1s. on 2d. (V.) £450 £400
a. Surch inverted £2500
b. Surch vertical (up or down) £2500
c. Surch diagonal (up or down) £2500
d. Surch diagonal, inverted (up or down) £2750
38 1s. on 2d. (Verm.) £550 £550
a. Surch inverted
b. Surch diagonal (up or down) £3750
c. Surch vertical (up or down) £3750
39 1s. on 2d. (Blk.) £5000
a. Surch inverted £8000
b. Surch vertical (up or down) £6500

There are two main types of the "One Shilling" surcharge:—

Type A. The "O" is over the "hi" of "Shilling" and the downstrokes of the "n" in "One", if extended, would meet the "ll" of "Shilling". The "g" is always raised. Type A is known in all three colours.

Type B. The "O" is over the first "i" of "Shilling" and the downstrokes of the "n" would meet the "li" of "Shilling". Type B is known in violet and vermilion.

There is a third, minor type of the black surcharge, but the differences are very slight.

Various types of the surcharges on Nos. 9 to 39 were printed on the same sheet, and different types in different colours may be found *se-tenant*. These are of great rarity.

(j) *As T 12*

40 5s. on 2d. (V.) £8000 £8000
a. Surch inverted
b. Surch vertical (up or down) £10000 £10000
c. Surch diagonal (down) £11000
41 10s. on 5d. (Verm.) £7000 £7500
a. Surch inverted £10000
b. Surch vertical (up or down) £9500
c. Surch diagonal (down)
42 20s. on 1s (V.) £38000
a. Surch inverted £80000
43 20s. on 1s. (Verm.) £65000
44 20s. on 1s. (Blk.)

NIGER COAST PROTECTORATE

The name of the protectorate was changed from 12 May 1893.

13

14

(Des G. D. Drummond. Recess Waterlow)

1893 (Nov (?))–**94**. *T* **13** (*with* "OIL RIVERS" *obliterated and* "NIGER COAST" *in top margin*). *Various frames. No wmk. Thick and thin papers. P* 14, 15, *and* 12 *to* 15 *in various combinations.*

45 ½d. vermilion 3·25 3·00
46 1d. pale blue 3·50 3·75
a. Bisected (½d.) (on cover) † £550
b. Dull blue 3·50 3·75
ba. Ditto. Bisected (½d.) (on cover) † £450
47 2d. green 9·50 10·50
a. Imperf between (pair) — £3000
b. Bisected (1d.) (on cover) † £700
48 2½d. carmine-lake 3·25 3·50
49 5d. grey-lilac 3·75 7·50
a. Lilac 4·75 9·50
50 1s. black 13·00 12·00
45/50 *Set of* 6 35·00 35·00

All values exist perf 14 and perf 15. There were three printings of each value, in June 1893, Jan 1894 and March 1894.

Nos. 46a, 46ba and 47b were used at Bonny River during August and September 1894.

(Recess Waterlow)

1894 (May). *T* **14** (*various frames*). *No wmk. P* 14, 15, 16 *and* 12 *to* 15 *in various combinations.*

51 ½d. yellow-green 1·40 1·60
a. Deep green 1·60 2·00
52 1d. orange-vermilion 5·50 5·50
a. Vermilion 2·00 2·75
b. Bisected diagonally (½d.) (on cover) † £500
53 2d. lake 2·00 2·25
a. Bisected diagonally (1d.) (on cover)
54 2½d. blue 3·00 2·50
a. Pale blue 2·50 2·00
55 5d. purple 2·75 3·25
a. Deep violet 3·25 4·25
56 1s. black 4·75 6·00
51/56 *Set of* 6 14·00 16·00

All values exist perf 15 and all except the 5d., perf 14. The 1d. is known perf 16.

Nos. 52b and 53a were used at Bonny River during August and September 1894.

½   1   ONE = = HALF PENNY

(15)   (16)   (17)

1894. *Provisionals. Issued at Opobo.*

(a) *Nos.* 46*b and* 46 *bisected vertically and surch with T* **15** (May–June)

57 "½" on half of 1d dull blue (R.) (May) £500 £225
a. Surch inverted (in strip of 3 with normals) £6000
58 "½" on half of 1d. pale blue (R.) (June) £750 £225
a. Surch *tête-bêche* (pair)
b. Surcharge inverted £2000

(b) *No.* 3 *bisected vertically and surch*

(i) *With T* **16** (12 *mm high*) (June-Oct)

59 "1" on half of 2d. (Verm.) £475 £350
a. Surch double £850 £800
b. Surch inverted — £800

(ii) *Smaller* "1" (4¾ *mm high*)

60 "1" on half of 2d. (C.) — £2000

(iii) *Smaller* "1" (3¾ *mm high*)

61 "1" on half on 2d. (C.)

Nos. 60 and 61 exist *se-tenant*. (*Price* £18000 *used.*)

(c) *No.* 52*a bisected, surch with T* **15** (Aug–Sept)

62 ½ on half of 1d. vermilion (Blk.) £900 £275
63 ½ on half of 1d. vermilion (V.) £900 £250
64 ½ on half of 1d. vermilion (B.) £900 £225
a. "½" double — £850

The stamp is found divided down the middle and also diagonally.

1894 (10 Aug). *Issued at Old Calabar. No.* 54 *surch with T* **17** *and two bars through value at foot.*

65 ½d. on 2½d. blue £225 £200
a. Surch double £1400 £1300
b. "OIE" for "ONE" £1300 £1000
c. Ditto. Surch double — £2000

There are eight types in the setting of T **17**.

(Recess Waterlow)

1897 (Mar)–**98**. *As T* **14** (*various frames*). *Wmk Crown CA. P* 14, 15 *and* 12 *to* 16 *in various combinations.*

66 ½d. green (7.97) 55 55
a. Sage-green 65 1·60
67 1d. orange-vermilion 1·25 1·25
a. Vermilion 1·40 1·25
b. Imperf between (pair)
68 2d. lake (7.97) 1·50 1·25
69 2½d. slate-blue (8.97) 1·75 2·75
a. Deep bright blue 1·75 2·25
70 5d. red-violet (1898) 4·75 13·00
a. Purple 4·75 13·00
71 6d. yellow-brown (6.98) 6·50 4·75
72 1s. black (1898) 7·50 10·00
73 2s. 6d. olive-bistre (6.98) 20·00 32·00
74 10s. deep violet (6.98) 75·00 £100
a. Bright violet (6.98) 80·00 £110
66/74 *Set of* 9 £110 £150
71, 73/4 Optd "Specimen" *Set of* 3 £225

Owing to a temporary shortage in Southern Nigeria, the above issue was again put into use during 1902, all stamps being perf 14, probably from the last printing made.

On 1 January 1900 the Niger Coast Protectorate together with the southern portion of the Niger Company Territories became the protectorate of SOUTHERN NIGERIA.

Niger Company Territories

Following the development of trade along the Niger, British commercial interests formed the United African Company in 1879 which became, in 1886, the Royal Niger Company. A charter was granted to the Company in the same year to administer territory along the Rivers Niger and Benue over which a British protectorate had been proclaimed. The Company's territories extended to the Niger delta to provide access to the interior.

Post Offices were opened at Akassa (1887), Burutu (1896), Lokoja (1898) and Abutshi (1899). The stamps of Great Britain were used from 1888.

On the establishment of postal services in 1887 the Company arranged with the British G.P.O. that unstamped mail marked with their handstamps would be delivered in Great Britain, the recipients only being charged the normal rate of postage from West Africa. This system was difficult to administer, however, so the British authorities agreed to the supply of G.B. stamps for use at the Company post offices.

Initially the stamps on such covers were left uncancelled until the mail arrived in the United Kingdom, the Company handstamp being struck elsewhere on the address side. This method continued to be used until early 1896, although a number of covers from the twelve months prior to that date do show the Company handstamp cancelling the stamps. Some of these covers were later recancelled on arrival in Great Britain. From May 1896 the postage stamps were cancelled in the Niger Territories.

In the following listings no attempt has been made to cover the use of the Company marks on the reverse of envelopes.

Dates given are those of earliest known postmarks. Colour of postmarks in brackets. Where two or more colours are given, price is for cheapest. Illustrations are reduced to two-thirds linear of the actual size.

Stamps of GREAT BRITAIN *cancelled as indicated below.*

ABUTSHI

1899 (4 Oct *to* 31 Dec). *Cancelled as T* **8**, *but inscribed* "THE ROYAL NIGER CO. C. & L. ABUTSHI" *with* "CUSTOMS (date) OFFICE" *in central oval.*

Z1 ½d. vermilion (V.) £200
Z2 1d. lilac (V.) £150
Z3 2½d. purple/*blue* (V.) £225
Z4 5d. dull purple and blue (V.) £250
Z5 10d. dull purple and carmine (V.) £300
Z6 2s. 6d. deep lilac (V.) £350

AKASSA

The listings for Nos. Z7/15 are for *covers* on which the Akassa handstamp appears on the front, but is *not* used as a cancellation for the G.B. stamps. Examples of Nos. Z16/26 occur, from 1895–96, with the handstamp struck on the front of the cover away from the stamps, or, from 1896, used as a cancellation. The prices quoted are for *single stamps* showing the cancellation; covers from either period being worth considerably more. On Nos. Z27/42 the handstamp was used as a cancellation and the prices quoted are for *single stamps.*

1   2

1888. *Cancelled as T* **3** *but with Maltese cross each side of* "AKASSA". *Size* 36 × 22 *mm.*
Z 7 6d. deep purple/*red* . . . .

1890 (24 June). *Size* 39 × 24 *mm.*
Z 8 **1** 2½d. Purple/*blue* (V.)
Z 9 3d. purple/*yellow*(V.)
Z10 5d. dull purple and blue (V.)
Z11 6d. deep purple/*red* (V.)
Z12 10d. dull purple and carmine (V.)
Z12*a* 1s. green (V.)
Z13 2s. lilac (V.)

1894.
Z14 **2** 1d. lilac (V.) (July) . . 65·00
Z15 2½d. purple/*lilac* (V.) (3 Oct)

THE ROYAL NIGER COMPANY
CHARTERED & LIMITED.
7- AUG. 98
POST OFFICE
AKASSA.

3 4

1895 (7 March). *Size* 39 × 25 *mm.*
Z16 **3** 2½d. purple/*blue* (V.)

1895 (1 June)–**99.**
Z17 **4** ½d. vermilion (V.) . . 22·00
Z18 1d. lilac (V.) . . 22·00
Z19 2d. green and vermilion (V.) . . £170
Z20 2½d. purple/*blue* (V.) . . 22·00
Z21 3d. purple/*yellow* (V.) . . £130
Z22 5d. dull purple and blue (V.) . . 23·00
Z23 6d. deep purple/*red* (V.) . . 50·00
Z24 9d. dull purple and blue (V.) . . £110
Z25 10d. dull purple and carmine (V.) . . 60·00
Z26 2s. 6d. deep lilac (V.) . . £110

1899 (20 May). *Cancelled as T* **4**, *but* "CUSTOMS DEPT" *in place of* "POST OFFICE".
Z27 1d. lilac (V.) . . £150
Z28 2½d. purple/*blue* (V.) . . £150

THE ROYAL NIGER COMPANY,
CHARTERED & LIMITED.
4 NOV.1889
POST OFFICE,
AKASSA.

5

1897 (Jan) *to* **1899** (Dec).
Z29 **5** ½d. vermilion (V.) . . 24·00
Z30 1d. lilac (V.) . . 23·00
a. "RECD" for year in postmark
Z31 2d. green and vermilion (V.) . . 55·00
Z32 2½d. purple/*blue* (V.) . . 32·00
a. "RECD" for year in postmark (1898)
Z33 3d. purple/*yellow* (V.) . . 90·00
Z34 4d. green and brown (V.) . . 60·00
Z35 4½d. green and carmine (V.) . . £425
Z36 5d. dull purple and blue (V.) . . 42·00
Z37 6d. deep purple/*red* (V.) . . 95·00
Z38 9d. dull purple and blue (V.) . . £140
Z39 10d. dull purple and carmine (V.) . . 60·00
Z40 1s. green (V.) . . £200
Z41 2s. 6d. deep lilac (V.) . . £120

1899 (9 Jan). *Cancelled as T* **7**, *but inscribed* "AKASSA".
Z42 5d. dull purple and blue (V.)

BURUTU

THE ROYAL NIGER COMPANY
CHARTERED & LIMITED.
31 MAR 1898
POST OFFICE.
BURUTU.

6

1897 (20 Jan) *to* **1898** (30 Oct). *Cancelled as T* **6**, "BURUTU" *in sans-serif caps. Size* 44 × 24 *mm.*
Z43 **6** ½d. vermilion (V.) . . 40·00
Z44 1d. lilac (V.) . . 40·00
Z45 1½d. dull purple and green (V.) . . £110
Z46 2d. green and carmine (V.) . . 60·00
Z47 2½d. purple/*blue* (V.) . . 23·00
Z48 3d. purple/*yellow* (V.) . . 75·00
Z49 4d. green and brown (V.) . . 50·00
Z50 5d. dull purple and blue (V.) . . 42·00
Z51 6d. deep purple/*red* (V.) . . 75·00
Z52 9d. dull purple and blue (V.) . . £110
Z53 10d. dull purple and carmine (V.) . . 60·00
Z54 1s. green (V.) . . £225
Z55 2s. 6d. lilac (V.) . . £100

The 2½d. is also known with this postmark in blue (6.9.97) and violet-black (Apr 1898) and the ½d., 2½d., 3d., 5d. and 10d. with it in black.

1898 *to* **1899.** *Cancelled as T* **4**, *but inscribed* "BURUTU" *in serifed caps. Size* 44 × 27 *mm.*
Z56 ½d. vermilion (V., Blk.) . . 42·00
Z57 1d. lilac (V., Blk.) . . 42·00
Z58 2d. green and vermilion (V.) . . £110
Z59 2½d. purple/*blue* (V., Blk.) . . 35·00
Z60 3d. purple/*yellow* (V.) . . 90·00
Z61 4d. green and brown (V.) . . 70·00
Z62 4½d. green and carmine (V.) . . £450
Z63 5d. dull purple and blue (V.) . . 45·00
Z64 6d. deep purple/*red* (V.) . . £110
Z65 9d. dull purple and blue (V.) . . £140
Z66 10d. dull purple and carmine (V., Blk.) . . 65·00
Z67 2s. 6d. lilac (V., Blk.) . . £150

7

1898 (9 July) *to* **1899** (Feb).
Z68 **7** 1d. lilac (V.)
Z69 2½d. purple/*blue* (V.) . . £180

1899 (20 May). *Cancelled as T* **4**, *but inscribed* "CUSTOM DEPT. BURUTU".
Z70 1d. lilac (V.)

There is some doubt as to the use of this cancellation for postal purposes.

LOKOJA

8

1899 (30 June *to* 31 Dec).
Z71 **8** ½d. vermilion (V.) . . 50·00
Z72 1d. lilac (V.) . . 45·00
Z73 2½d. purple/*blue* (V.) . . £150
Z74 5d. dull purple and blue (V.) . . £150
Z75 10d. dull purple and carmine (V.) . . £150
Z76 2s. 6d. deep lilac (V.)

AGENT GENERAL NIGER TERRITORIES

The listings for Nos. Z78/9 are for covers showing a handstamp struck on the address side, but *not* used as a cancellation for the G.B. stamp.

1894. *Cancelled as T* **8** *but inscribed* "AGENT GENERAL NIGER TERRITORIES".
Z78 2½d. purple/*blue* (V.) (3.10.94) . . 75·00

1895 (4 Aug). *Cancelled as T* **7** *but inscribed as last.*
Z79 2½d. purple/*blue* (V.) . . 75·00

It is now believed that these cancellations may have been used at Asaba.

The British Government purchased the Royal Niger Company territories and from 1 January 1900 they were incorporated into the protectorates of Northern and Southern Nigeria. Of the post offices listed above only Lokoja was then situated in Northern Nigeria, the remainder joining Niger Coast in forming Southern Nigeria.

A few later covers are known from the area franked with G.B. stamps, but the origin of the stamps involved is uncertain.

Nigeria

Nigeria was formed on 1 January 1914 from the former protectorates of Northern and Southern Nigeria.

PRICES FOR STAMPS ON COVER TO 1945	
Nos. 1/10	*from* × 3
Nos. 11/13	—
Nos. 15/24	*from* × 3
No. 25	—
Nos. 25*a*/9*d*	*from* × 3
No. 29*e*	—
Nos. 30/3	*from* × 3
Nos. 34/59	*from* × 2

CROWN COLONY

1

2

(Typo D.L.R.)

1914–27. *Wmk Mult Crown CA. Ordinary paper* (½d. *to* 2½d.) *or chalk-surfaced paper* (*others*). *P* 14.

A. *Die I.* (1.6.14–21)
1 **1** ½d. green . . 30 30
2 1d. carmine-red . . 35 25
a. Scarlet (6.17) . . 75 25
3 2d. grey . . 2·00 80
a. Slate-grey (1918) . . 2·75 85
4 2½d. bright blue . . 1·00 65
a. Dull blue (1915)
5 **2** 3d. purple/*yellow* (*white back*) . . 1·25 2·75
a. On yellow (*lemon back*) (8.15) . . 2·50 1·25
b. On deep yellow (*yellow back, thick paper*) (1915) . . 7·00 3·75
c. On pale yellow (*orange-buff back*) (12.20) . . 3·00 3·00
d. On pale yellow (*pale yellow back*) (1921) . . 3·50 2·00
6 **2** 4d. black and red/*yellow* (*white back*) . . 1·25 2·50
a. On yellow (*lemon back*) (8.15) . . 2·00 2·75
b. On deep yellow (*yellow back, thick paper*) (1915) . . 4·50 4·75
c. On pale yellow (*orange-buff back*) (1921) . . 2·75 3·00
d. On pale yellow (*pale yellow back*) (1921) . . 5·50 7·50
7 6d. dull and bright purple (*shades*) . . 2·00 2·00
8 **1** 1s. black /*pale blue-green* (*white back*) . . 1·60 2·25
a. On yellow-green (*white back*)
b. On pale blue-green (*yellow-green back*) (1915) . . 5·50 2·75
c. On pale blue-green (*blue-green back*) (1915) . . 2·00 2·25
d. On pale blue-green (*pale olive back*) (1918) . . 8·50 6·00
e. On emerald-green (*pale olive back*) (12.20) . . 4·50 6·00
f. On emerald-green (*emerald-green back*) (1921) . . 1·75 6·00
9 2s. 6d. black and red/*blue* . . 5·50 5·50
10 **2** 5s. green and red/*yellow* (*white back*) . . 8·00 13·00
a. On yellow (*lemon back*) (8.15) . . 13·00 16·00
b. On deep yellow (*yellow back, thick paper*) (1915) . . 14·00 18·00
c. On yellow (*orange-buff back*) (1921) . . 15·00 20·00
d. On pale yellow (*pale yellow back*) (1921) . . 20·00 26·00
11 **1** 10s. green and red/*blue-green* (*white back*) . . 32·00 35·00
a. On blue-green (*blue-green back*) (8.15) . . 32·00 35·00
b. On blue-green (*pale olive back*) (1918) . . £750 £900
c. On emerald green (*pale olive back*) (12.20) . . 48·00 48·00
d. On emerald-green (*emerald back*) (1921) . . 32·00 35·00
12 **2** £1 deep purple and black/*red* . . £160 £180

B. *Change to Die II* (19.1.27)
13 **2** £1 purple and black/*red* . . £180 £200
1/12 . . *Set of* 12 £190 £225
5/6, 8, 10/11 Optd "Specimen" (white backs) *Set of* 5 £250
1/12 Optd "Specimen" (coloured backs) *Set of* 12 £425

1921–32. *Wmk Mult Script CA. Ordinary paper* (½d. *to* 3d.) *or chalk-surfaced paper* (*others*). *P* 14.

A. *The basic issue. Die I for the* ½d., 1d., 2d., 2½d., 3d *and* 6d., *Die II remainder* (1921–26)
15 **1** ½d. green (1921) . . 50 40
16 1d. rose-carmine (1921) . . 30 20
17 2d. grey (5.21) . . 2·50 55
18 2½d. bright blue (5.21) . . 80 95
19 **2** 3d. bright violet (1.24) . . 3·50 3·50
20 4d. black and red/*pale yellow* (10.23) . . 65 65
21 6d. dull and bright purple (5.21) . . 3·50 3·00
22 **1** 1s. black/*emerald* (7.24) . . 1·25 75
23 2s. 6d. black and red/*blue* (8.25) . . 7·00 11·00
24 **2** 5s. green and red/*yellow* (10.26) . . 15·00 20·00
25 **1** 10s. green and red/*green* (4.26) . . 50·00 60·00
15/25 . . *Set of* 11 75·00 90·00
15/25 Optd "Specimen" *Set of* 11 £275

B. *Change to Die II* (1924–25)
25*a* **1** ½d. green (5.25) . . 30 35
25*b* 1d. rose-carmine (5.25) . . 30 20
25*c* 2d. grey (1924) . . 1·25 30
25*d* **2** 3d. bright violet (5.25) . . 3·25 2·50
25*e* 6d. dull and bright purple (7.24) . . 1·50 2·00

C. *New value and colours changed. Die II* (1927–31)
26 **2** 1½d. orange (1.4.31) . . 70 30
27 **1** 2d. chestnut (1.10.27) . . 1·75 1·75
28 2d. chocolate (1.7.28) . . 30 30
29 **2** 3d. bright blue (1.4.31) . . 2·50 3·00
26/7, 29 Optd/Perf "Specimen" *Set of* 3 95·00

D. *Reappearance of Die I* (*Key Plate* 23) (Mar to Aug 1932)
29*a* **1** 2d. chocolate (Mar) . . 3·75 1·00
29*b* **2** 4d. black and red/*pale yellow* . . 13·00 13·00
29*c* **1** 2s. 6d. black and red/*blue* . . 15·00 14·00
29*d* **2** 5s. green and red/*yellow* . . 35·00 42·00
29*e* **1** 10s. green and red/*green* . . 75·00 90·00

1935 (6 May). *Silver Jubilee. As Nos.* 91/4 *of Antigua but ptd by Waterlow. P* 11 × 12.
30 1½d. ultramarine and grey . . 45 30
31 2d. green and indigo . . 1·00 40
32 3d. brown and deep blue . . 1·75 1·90
33 1s. slate and purple . . 3·75 6·50
30/3 Perf "Specimen" *Set of* 4 65·00

3 Apapa Wharf

4 Fishing Village

5 Victoria-Buea Road

(Recess D.L.R.)

1936 (1 Feb). *Designs as T* **3**/**5**. *Wmk Mult Script CA.*

(*a*) *P* 11½ × 13
34 ½d. green . . 30 35
35 1d. carmine . . 30 25
36 1½d. brown . . 35 25
a. Perf 12½ × 13½ . . 16·00 1·25

37 2d. black 90 45
38 3d. blue .. .. 1·40 1·25
a. Perf 12½ × 13½ .. .. 45·00 16·00
39 4d. red-brown .. .. 1·75 3·00
40 6d. dull violet .. .. 1·40 1·40
41 1s. sage-green .. .. 4·00 5·50

(*b*) *P* 14

42 2s. 6d. black and ultramarine .. .. 8·00 12·00
43 5s. black and olive-green .. .. .. 15·00 20·00
44 10s. black and grey .. .. 55·00 60·00
45 £1 black and orange £110 £120
34/45 .. .. *Set of* 12 £180 £200
34/45 Perf "Specimen" .. .. *Set of* 12 £225

Designs: *Vert as T* 3/4—1d. Cocoa; 1½d. Tin dredger; 2d. Timber industry; 4d. Cotton ginnery; 6d. Habe minaret; 1s. Fulani Cattle. *Horiz as T* 5—5s. Oil Palms; 10s. River Niger at Jebba; £1, Canoe pulling.

1937 (12 May). *Coronation. As Nos.* 13/15 *of Aden, but printed by B.W. & Co. P* 11 × 11½.
46 1d. carmine 30 20
47 1½d. brown 35 25
48 3d. blue 65 70
46/8 Perf "Specimen" .. .. *Set of* 3 55·00

15 King George VI

16 Victoria-Buea Road

(Recess B.W. (T **15**), D.L.R. (others))

1938 (1 May)–**51**. *Designs as T* **15/16**. *Wmk Mult Script CA. P* 12 (*T* **15**) *or* 13 × 11½ (*others*).
49 **15** ½d. green 20 5
a. Perf 11½ (15.2.50) 20 10
50 1d. carmine .. .. 11·00 2·00
a. Rose-red (1941) 30 5
50*b* 1d. bright purple (1.12.44) 20 5
ba. Perf 11½ (15.2.50) 20 15
51 1½d. brown 25 5
a. Perf 11½ (15.11.50) 20 10
52 2d. black 25 30
52*aa* 2d. rose-red (1.12.44) 30 25
ab. Perf 11½ (15.2.50) 20 25
52*a* 2½d. orange (4.41) 25 45
53 3d. blue 20 5
53*a* 3d. black (1.12.44) 20 5
54 4d. orange .. .. 38·00 6·00
54*a* 4d. blue (1.12.44) 20 40
55 6d. blackish purple 25 5
a. Perf 11½ (17.4.51) 25 15
56 1s. sage-green 75 5
a. Perf 11½ (15.2.50) 45 10
57 1s. 3d. light blue (1940) 70 10
a. Perf 11½ (14.6.50) 70 25
b. Wmk sideways (Perf 11½) .. .. .. — £275
58 **16** 2s. 6d. black and blue .. .. .. 15·00 7·50
a. Perf 13½ (6.42) .. .. 2·00 1·75
ab. Perf 13½. *Black and deep blue* (1946) 15·00 11·00
b. Perf 14 (1942) .. .. 2·00 1·00
c. Perf 12 (15.8.51) .. .. 2·00 1·10
59 – 5s. black and orange .. .. 35·00 8·50
a. Perf 13½ (8.42) .. .. 3·75 1·60
b. Perf 14 (1948) .. .. 3·50 1·50
c. Perf 12 (19.5.49) .. .. 2·75 1·50
49/59c .. .. *Set of* 16 42·00 9·50
49/52*aa*, 53/9 Perf "Specimen" .. *Set of* 15 £180

Design: *Horiz as T* **16**—5s. R. Niger at Jebba.

1946 (21 Oct). *Victory. As Nos.* 28/9 *of Aden.*
60 1½d. chocolate 15 12
61 4d. blue 20 30
60/1 Perf "Specimen" .. .. *Set of* 2 55·00

1948 (20 Dec). *Royal Silver Wedding. As Nos.* 30/1 *of Aden.*
62 1d. bright purple 35 10
63 5s. brown-orange .. .. 8·50 12·00

1949 (10 Oct). *75th Anniv of Universal Postal Union. As Nos.* 114/17 *of Antigua.*
64 1d. bright reddish purple 30 15
65 3d. deep blue 65 45
66 6d. purple .. .. 1·10 1·25
67 1s. olive .. .. 1·60 1·75

1953 (2 June). *Coronation. As No.* 47 *of Aden but ptd by B.W.*
68 1½d. black and emerald 25 5

18 Old Manilla Currency

21 "Tin"

Type A
Gap in row of dots

Type B
Unbroken row of dots

Nos. 72*c*/*cc*. The original cylinder used was Type A (July 1956); later Type B (Sept 1957). The above illustrations will help classification, but two stamps per sheet of 60 of Type A show faint dots. However, one of these has the "2d." re-entry which does not exist in Type B sheets, and shades are distinctive.

24 Ife Bronze

26 Victoria Harbour

29 New and Old Lagos

(Des M. Fievet. Recess Waterlow)

1953 (1 Sept)–**57**. *T* **18, 21, 24, 26, 29** *and similar designs. Wmk Mult Script CA. P* 14.
69 **18** ½d. black and orange 12 5
70 – 1d. black and bronze-green 20 5
71 – 1½d. blue-green 30 8
72 **21** 2d. black and ochre (*shades*) 35 5
72*c* 2d. slate-violet (Type A) (23.7.56) .. 50 20
ca. Slate-blue (*shades*) (Type A) 75 5
cb. Bluish grey (Type B) (25.9.57) .. 45 5
cc. Grey (*shades*) (Type B) 40 5
73 – 3d. black and purple (*shades*) 30 5
b. Imperf (pair) £170
74 – 4d. black and blue 25 5
75 **24** 6d. orange-brown and black (*shades*) .. 25 5
76 – 1s. black and maroon 40 5
77 **26** 2s. 6d. black and green (*shades*) .. 2·75 10
78 – 5s. black and red-orange .. .. .. 2·75 50
79 – 10s. black and red-brown .. .. .. 3·75 1·00
80 **29** £1 black and violet .. .. 12·00 3·75
69/80 .. .. *Set of* 13 21·00 5·50

Designs: *Horiz* (*as T* **18**)—1d. Bornu horsemen; 1½d. "Groundnuts"; 3d. Jebba bridge and R. Niger; 4d. "Cocoa"; 1s. "Timber". (*As T* **26**)—5s. "Palm-oil"; 10s. "Hides and skins".

Nos. 72*c*/*cc* and Nos. 70 and 73 (from September 1958) were printed on rotary machines by a subsidiary company, Imprimerie Belge de Securité, in Belgium.

Nos. 72*ca* and 72*cc* were only available in Nigeria.

ROYAL VISIT
1956
(**30**)

31 Victoria Harbour

1956 (28 Jan). *Royal Visit. No.* 72 *optd with T* **30**.
81 **21** 2d. black and ochre 5 5
a. Opt inverted £140

(Recess Waterlow)

1958 (1 Dec). *Centenary of Victoria.* W w **12**. *P* 13½ × 14.
82 **31** 3d. black and purple 15 5

32 Lugard Hall

(Recess Waterlow)

1959 (14 Mar). *Attainment of Self-Government, Northern Region of Nigeria. T* **32** *and similar horiz design.* W w **12**. *P* 13½ (3d.) *or* 13½ × 14 (1s.).
83 3d. black and purple 5 5
84 1s. black and green 35 25

Design:—1s. Kano Mosque.

INDEPENDENT FEDERATION

34

35 Legislative Building

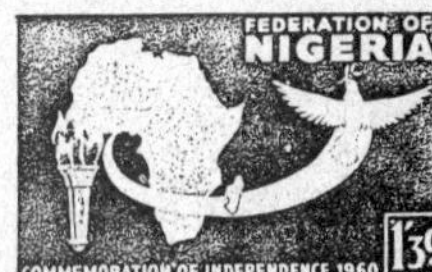

38 Dove, Torch and Map

(Des L. J. Wittington (1d.), R. Crawford (3d.), R. D. Baxter (6d.), J. White (1s. 3d.), Photo Waterlow)

1960 (1 Oct). *Independence. T* **35, 38** *and similar horiz designs.* W **34**. *P* 13½ (1s. 3d.) *or* 14 (*others*).
85 1d. black and scarlet 5 5
86 3d. black and greenish blue 8 5
87 6d. green and red-brown 12 10
88 1s. 3d. bright blue and yellow 30 20

Designs: (As *T* **35**)—3d. African paddling canoe; 6d. Federal Supreme Court.

39 Groundnuts

48 Central Bank

1961 (1 Jan). *T* **39, 48**, *and similar designs.* W **34**. *P* 15 × 14 (½*d. to* 1*s* 3*d.*) *or* 14½ (*others*).
89 ½d. emerald 5 5
90 1d. reddish violet 5 5
91 1½d. carmine-red 8 30
92 2d. deep blue 5 5
93 3d. deep green 5 5
94 4d. blue 8 12
95 6d. yellow and black 8 5
a. Yellow omitted .. .. — £190
96 1s. yellow-green 35 5
97 1s. 3d. orange 25 5
98 2s. 6d. black and yellow 90 12
99 5s. black and emerald .. .. 1·25 25
100 10s. black and ultramarine .. .. .. 2·50 90
101 £1 black and carmine-red .. .. .. 10·00 3·25
89/101 .. .. *Set of* 13 14·00 4·75

Designs: *Vert* (*as T* **39**)—1d. Coal mining; 1½d. Adult education; 2d. Pottery; 3d. Oyo carver; 4d. Weaving; 6d. Benin mask; 1s. Yellow-casqued Hornbill; 1s. 3d. Camel train. *Horiz* (*as T* **48**)—5s. Nigeria Museum; 10s. Kano airport; £1 Lagos railway station.

PRINTERS. The above and all following issues to No. 206 were printed in photogravure by Harrison & Sons, *except where otherwise stated.*

52 Globe and Railway Locomotive

56 Coat of Arms

(Des M. Goaman)

1961 (25 July). *Admission of Nigeria into U.P.U. T* **52** *and similar horiz designs.* W **34**. *P* 14½.
102 1d. red-orange and blue 5 5
103 3d. olive-yellow and black 10 5
104 1s. 3d. blue and carmine-red 35 15
105 2s. 6d. deep green and blue 55 55

Designs:—3d. Globe and mail-van; 1s. 3d. Globe and aircraft; 2s. 6d. Globe and ship.

(Des S. Bodo (3d.), R. Hopeman (4d.), C. Adesina (6d.), M. Shamir (1s. 6d.), B. Enweonwu (2s. 6d.))

1961 (1 Oct). *First Anniv of Independence. T* **56** *and similar designs.* W **34**. *P* 14½.
106 3d. multicoloured 8 5
107 4d. yellow-green and yellow-orange 12 15
108 6d. emerald-green 15 10
109 1s. 3d. grey, emerald and blue 30 20
110 2s. 6d. green and grey-blue 60 90

Designs: *Horiz*—4d. Natural resources and map; 6d. Nigerian Eagle; 1s. 3d. Eagles in flight; 2s. 6d. Nigerians and flag.

A used copy of No. 106 has been seen with both the silver (large "Y" appearing grey) and the yellow (appearing white) omitted.

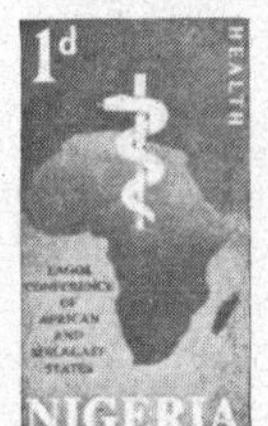

61 "Health"

66 Malaria Eradication Emblem and Parasites

(Des M. Shamir)

1962 (25 Jan). *Lagos Conference of African and Malagasy States. T* **61** *and similar vert designs. W* **34**. *P* 14 × 14½.

No.		Description		
111		1d. yellow-bistre	5	5
112		3d. deep reddish purple	8	5
113		6d. deep green	10	10
114		1s. brown	15	15
115		1s. 3d. blue	20	20

Designs:—3d. "Culture"; 6d. "Commerce"; 1s. "Communications"; 1s. 3d. "Co-operation".

1962 (7 Apr). *Malaria Eradication. T* **66** *and similar horiz designs. W* **34**. *P* 14½.

No.		Description		
116		3d. green and orange-red	5	5
117		6d. blue and bright purple	10	10
118		1s. 3d. magenta and violet-blue	30	20
119		2s. 6d. blue and yellow-brown	50	55

Designs:—6d. Insecticide spraying; 1s. 3d. Aerial spraying; 2s. 6d. Mother, child and microscope.

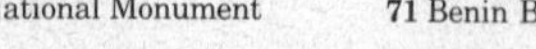

70 National Monument **71** Benin Bronze

(Des S. Bodo (3d.), B. Enweonwu (5s.))

1962 (1 Oct). *Second Anniv of Independence. W* **34**. *P* 14½ × 14 *(3d.) or* 14 × 14½ *(5s.).*

No.		Description		
120	**70**	3d. emerald and blue	8	5
		a. Emerald omitted		
121	**71**	5s. red, emerald and violet	1·50	1·50

72 Fair Emblem **73** "Cogwheels of Industry"

(Des M. Goaman (1d., 2s. 6d.), J. O. Gbagbeolu and M. Goaman (6d.), R. Hegeman (1s.))

1962 (27 Oct). *International Trade Fair, Lagos. W* **34**. *T* **72/3** *and similar designs. P* 14½.

No.		Description		
122		1d. olive-brown and orange-red	5	5
123		6d. carmine-red and black	10	8
124		1s. orange-brown and black	20	15
125		2s. 6d. ultramarine and yellow	55	45

Designs: *Horiz as T* **73**—1s. "Cornucopia of Industry"; 2s. 6d. Oilwells and tanker.

76 "Arrival of Delegates" **77** Mace as Palm Tree

(Des S. Akosile (2½d.), M. Goaman (others))

1962 (5 Nov). *Eighth Commonwealth Parliamentary Conference, Lagos. T* **76/77** *and similar design. W* **34**. *P* 14½.

No.		Description		
126		2½d. greenish blue	8	12
127		4d. indigo and rose-red	12	8
128		1s. 3d. sepia and lemon	30	25

Design: *Horiz*—4d. National Hall.

80 Tractor and Maize **81** Mercury Capsule and Kano Tracking Station

(Des M. Goaman)

1963 (21 Mar). *Freedom from Hunger. T* **80** *and similar design. W* **34**. *P* 14.

No.		Description		
129		3d. olive-green	20	5
130		6d. magenta	35	15

Design: *Vert*—3d. Herdsman.

(Des R. Hegeman)

1963 (21 June). *"Peaceful Use of Outer Space". T* **81** *and similar vert design. W* **34**. *P* 14½ × 14.

No.		Description		
131		6d. blue and yellow-green	12	8
132		1s. 3d. black and blue-green	30	25

Design:—1s. 3d. Satellite and Lagos Harbour.

83 Scouts shaking Hands

(Des S. Apostolou (3d.), G. Okiki (1s.))

1963 (1 Aug). *11th World Scout Jamboree, Marathon. T* **83** *and similar triangular-shaped design. W* **34**. *P* 14.

No.		Description		
133		3d. red and bronze-green	8	5
134		1s. black and red	30	25
MS134*a*		93 × 95 mm. Nos. 133/4	1·00	1·00
		ab. Red omitted (on 3d. value)	£200	

Design:—1s. Campfire.

85 Emblem and First Aid Team **88** President Azikiwe and State House

(Des M. Goaman)

1963 (1 Sept). *Red Cross Centenary. T* **85** *and similar horiz designs. W* **34**. *P* 14½.

No.		Description		
135		3d. red and deep ultramarine	12	5
136		6d. red and deep green	20	12
137		1s. 3d. red and deep sepia	60	45
MS137*a*		102 × 102 mm. No. 137 (block of four)	1·50	1·50

Designs:—6d. Emblem and "Hospital Services"; 1s. 3d. Patient and emblem.

(Des M. Shamir. Photo Govt Printer, Israel)

1963 (1 Oct). *Republic Day. T* **88** *and similar vert designs showing administrative buildings and President Azikiwe. P* 14 × 13.

No.		Description		
138		3d. yellow-olive and grey-green	8	5
139		1s. 3d. yellow-brown and sepia	20	20
		a. Yellow-brown (portrait) omitted		
140		2s. 6d. turquoise-blue and deep violet-blue	50	65

Designs:—1s. 3d. Federal Supreme Court Building; 2s. 6d. Parliament Building.

89 Charter and Broken Whip **90** "Freedom of Worship"

(Des S. Apostolou (3d.), Mrs. F. P. Effiong (others). Photo D.L.R.)

1963 (10 Dec). *15th Anniv of Declaration of Human Rights. T* **89/90** *and similar designs. W* **34**. *P* 13.

No.		Description		
141		3d. vermilion	5	5
142		6d. blue-green	10	5
143		1s. 3d. ultramarine	15	12
144		2s. 6d. bright purple	30	45

Designs: *Vert as T* **90**—1s. 3d. "Freedom from want"; 2s. 6d. "Freedom of speech".

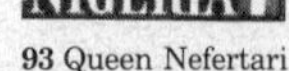

93 Queen Nefertari **94** Rameses II

(Des M. Shamir)

1964 (8 Mar). *Nubian Monuments Preservation. W* **34**. *P* 14½.

No.		Description		
145	**93**	6d. yellow-olive and emerald	15	8
146	**94**	2s. 6d. brown, deep olive and emerald	70	80

95 President Kennedy

(Des M. Shamir (1s. 3d.), M. Goaman (2s. 6d.), Mr. Bottiau (5s.). Photo Govt Printer, Israel (1s. 3d.); litho Lewin-Epstein, Bat Yam, Israel (others))

1964 (27 Aug). *President Kennedy Memorial Issue. T* **95** *and similar horiz designs. P* 13 × 14 *(1s. 3d.) or* 14 *(others).*

No.		Description		
147		1s. 3d. light violet and black	25	20
148		2s. 6d. black, red, blue and green	55	55
149		5s. black, deep blue, red and green	1·00	1·40
MS149*a*		154 × 135 mm. No. 149 (block of four). Imperf	6·00	6·00

Designs:—2s. 6d. President Kennedy and flags; 5s. President Kennedy (U.S. coin head) and flags.

98 President Azikiwe **99** Herbert Macaulay

(Des S. Apostolou (3d.), W. H. Irvine (others). Photo Govt Printer, Israel (3d.); Harrison (others))

1964 (1 Oct). *First Anniv of Republic. T* **98** *or* **99** *and similar vert design. P* 14 × 13 *(3d.) or* 14½ *(others).*

No.		Description		
150		3d. red-brown	5	5
151		1s. 3d. green	25	20
152		2s. 6d. deep grey-green	55	70

Design:—2s. 6d. King Jaja of Opobo.

101 Boxing Gloves

102 Hurdling

(Des A. Adalade (3d.), S. Medahunsi (6d.), M. Shamir (1s. 3d.), M. Goaman (2s. 6d.))

1964 (10 Oct). *Olympic Games, Tokyo. T* **101** *and similar designs, and T* **102**. *W* **34**. *P* 14 *(2s. 6d.) or* 14½ *(others).*

No.		Description		
153		3d. sepia and olive-green	8	5
154		6d. emerald and indigo	12	5
155		1s. 3d. sepia and yellow-olive	30	10
156		2s. 6d. sepia and chestnut	50	75
MS156*a*		102 × 102 mm. No. 156 (block of four). Imperf	3·00	3·00

Designs: *Horiz*—6d. High-jumping. *Vert*—1s. 3d. Running.

105 Scouts on Hill-top

(Des S. Apostolou (1d., 1s. 3d.), H. N. G. Cowham and Eagle Scout N. A. Lasisi (3d.), W. H. Irvine (6d.))

1965 (1 Jan). *50th Anniv of Nigerian Scout Movement. T* **105** *and similar vert designs. P* 14 × 14½.

No.		Description		
157		1d. brown	5	5
158		3d. red, black and emerald	15	5
159		6d. red, sepia and yellow-green	25	10
160		1s. 3d. bistre-brown, greenish yellow and black-green	50	75
MS160*a*		76 × 104 mm. No. 160 (block of four). Imperf	4·50	5·00

Designs:—3d. Scout badge on shield; 6d. Scout badges; 1s. 3d. Chief Scout and Nigerian scout.

109 "Telstar" 110 Solar Satellite

(Des M. Shamir. Photo Govt Printer, Israel)

1965 (1 Apr). *International Quiet Sun Years. P* 14 × 13.
161 **109** 6d. reddish violet and turquoise-blue . . 10 10
162 **110** 1s. 3d. green and reddish lilac 20 20

111 Native Tom-tom and Modern Telephone

(Des C. Botham (5s.), H. N. G. Cowham (others). Photo Enschedé)

1965 (2 Aug). *I.T.U. Centenary. T* **111** *and similar designs. P* 11½ × 11 (1s. 3d.) *or* 11 × 11½ (*others*).
163 3d. black, carmine and yellow-brown . . 15 5
164 1s. 3d. black, blue-green and chalky blue . . 1·25 1·00
165 5s. black, carmine, blue & brt greenish blue 3·75 4·00
Designs: *Vert*—1s. 3d. Microwave aerial. *Horiz*—5s. Telecommunications satellite and part of globe.

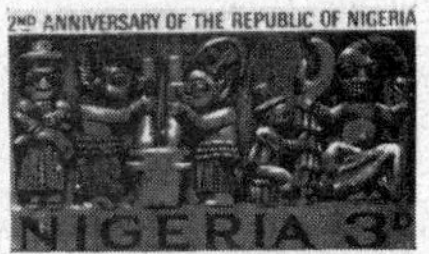

114 I.C.Y. Emblem and Diesel Locomotive 117 Carved Frieze

(Des W. H. Irvine. Photo D.L.R.)

1965 (1 Sept). *International Co-operation Year. T* **114** *and similar horiz designs. W* **34**. *P* 14 × 15.
166 3d. green, red and orange 45 5
167 1s. black, bright blue and lemon 80 40
168 2s. 6d. green, bright blue and yellow . . 3·75 4·00
Designs:—1s. Students and Lagos Teaching Hospital; 2s. 6d. Kainji (Niger) Dam.

(Des S. Apostolou (3d.), W. H. Irvine (others). Photo D.L.R.)

1965 (1 Oct). *2nd Anniv of Republic. T* **117** *and similar designs. P* 14 × 15 (3*d.*) *or* 15 × 14 (*others*).
169 3d. black, red and orange-yellow 10 5
170 1s. 3d. red-brown, dp green & lt ultramarine 45 25
171 5s. brown, blackish brown and light green . . 1·75 2·25
Designs: *Vert*—1s. 3d. Stone images at Ikom; 5s. Tada bronze.

120 Lion and Cubs 121 Elephants

132 Hippopotamus 133 Buffalo

(Des M. Fievet. Photo Harrison (1d., 2d., 3d., 4d. (No. 177a), 9d.) or Delrieu (others))

1965 (1 Nov)–**66**. *T* **120/1**, **132/3** *and similar designs. Without printer's imprint. Chalk-surfaced paper* (1*d.*, 2*d.*, 3*d.*, 4*d.*, 9*d.*). *P* 12 × 12½ (½*d.*, 6*d.*), 12½ × 12 (1½*d.*, 4*d.*), 14 × 13½ (1*d.*, 2*d.*, 3*d.*, 9*d.*) *or* 12½ (*others*).
172 ½d. multicoloured (1.11.65) 15 15
173 1d. multicoloured (1.11.65) 20 5
174 1½d. multicoloured (2.5.66) 70 85
175 2d. multicoloured (1.4.66) 45 5
176 3d. multicoloured (17.10.66) 50 5
177 4d. multicoloured (2.5.66) 50 30
a. Perf 14 × 13½ (1966) 20 5
178 6d. multicoloured (2.5.66) 50 5
179 9d. Prussian blue and orange-red (17.10.66) 55 30
180 1s. multicoloured (2.5.66) 65 5
181 1s. 3d. multicoloured (2.5.66) . . . . 2·25 15
182 2s. 6d. orange-brown, buff and brown (2.5.66) . . . . 1·00 30
183 5s. chestnut, light yellow and brown (2.5.66) 2·25 70
a. *Pale chestnut, yellow and brown-purple* (1966) . . . . 2·25 70
184 10s. multicoloured (2.5.66) . . . . . . 6·00 3·00
185 £1 multicoloured (2.5.66) . . . . . . 17·00 8·50
172/85 . . . . *Set of* 14 29·00 13·00
Designs: *Horiz* (*as T* **121**)—1½d. Splendid Sunbird; 2d. Village Weaver and Red-headed Malimbe; 3d. Cheetah; 4d. Leopards; 9d. Grey Parrots. (*As T* **133**)—1s. Blue-breasted Kingfishers; 1s. 3d. Crowned Cranes; 2s. 6d. Kobs; 5s. Giraffes. *Vert* (*as T* **120**)—6d. Saddle-bill Stork.
The 2d. and 3d. exist with PVA gum as well as gum arabic.
See also Nos. 220, etc.

The 1d., 3d., 4d. (No. 177a), 1s., 1s. 3d., 2s. 6d., 5s. and £1 values exist overprinted "F.G.N." (Federal Government of Nigeria) twice in black. They were prepared in November 1968 at the request of one of the State Governments for use as official stamps but the scheme was abandoned and meter machines were used instead. Some stamps held at Lagos Post Office were sold over the counter in error and passed through the post. The 3d., 4d. and 2s. 6d. exist used on official mail. The Director of Posts then decided to make limited stocks of all values, except the 1s., available from the Philatelic Bureau "in order not to create an artificial scarcity", but they had no postal validity.

COMMONWEALTH
P. M. MEETING
11. JAN. 1966

(134)

135 Y.M.C.A. Emblem and H.Q., Lagos

1966 (11 Jan). *Commonwealth Prime Ministers' Meeting, Lagos. No* 98 *optd with T* **134** *by the Nigerian Security Printing and Minting Co, Lagos, in red.*
186 **48** 2s. 6d. black and yellow 40 65

(Des S. B. Ajayi. Litho Nigerian Security Printing & Minting Co Ltd)

1966 (1 Sept). *Nigerian Y.W.C.A.'s Diamond Jubilee. P* 14.
187 **135** 4d. yellow-orange, ultramarine, orange-brown and yellow-green 8 5
188 9d. yellow-orange, ultramarine, brown and turquoise-green 20 25

137 Telephone Handset and Linesman 139 "Education, Science and Culture"

(Des S. B. Ajayi (4d.), N. Lasisi (1s. 6d.), B. Enweonwu (2s. 6d))

1966 (1 Oct). *Third Anniv of Republic. T* **137** *and similar designs. W* **34**. *P* 14½ × 14.
189 4d. green 12 5
190 1s. 6d. black, brown and reddish violet . . 60 75
191 2s. 6d. indigo, blue, yellow and green . . 1·60 2·50
Designs: *Vert*—4d. Dove and flag. *Horiz*—2s. 6d. Niger Bridge.

(Des V. Whiteley from sketch by B. Salisu)

1966 (4 Nov). *20th Anniv of U.N.E.S.C.O. W* **34** (*sideways*). *P* 14½ × 14.
192 **139** 4d. black, lake and orange-yellow . . 40 5
193 1s. 6d. black, lake and turquoise-green 1·50 1·75
194 2s. 6d. black, lake and rose-pink . . 2·50 3·75

140 Children drinking

(Des V. Whiteley, after M. O. Afamefuna (4d.), I. U. Anawanti (1s. 6d.) and S. Adeyemi (2s. 6d.))

1966 (1 Dec). *Nigerian Red Cross. T* **140** *and similar designs. W* **34**. *P* 14 × 14½ (1*s.* 6*d.*) *or* 14½ × 14 (*others*).
195 4d. + 1d. black, reddish violet and red . . 35 20
196 1s. 6d. + 3d. multicoloured . . . . . . 1·40 2·25
197 2s. 6d. + 3d. multicoloured . . . . . . 1·90 3·25
Designs: *Vert*—1s. 6d. Tending patient. *Horiz*—2s. 6d. Tending casualties, and badge.

143 Surveying

(Des M. Goaman)

1967 (1 Feb). *International Hydrological Decade. T* **143** *and similar multicoloured design. W* **34**. *P* 14½ × 14 (4*d.*) *or* 14 × 14½ (2*s.* 6*d.*).
198 4d. Type **143** 12 5
199 2s. 6d. Water gauge on dam (*vert*) . . . . 70 1·25

145 Globe and Weather Satellite 147 Eyo Masqueraders

(Des M. Shamir (4d.), S. Bodo (1s. 6d.))

1967 (23 Mar). *World Meteorological Day. T* **145** *and similar horiz design. W* **34**. *P* 14½ × 14.
200 4d. magenta and blue 12 5
201 1s. 6d. black, yellow and blue 50 70
Design:—1s. 6d. Passing storm and sun.

(Des G. A. Okiki (4d.), A. B. Saka Lawal (1s. 6d.), S. Bodo (2s. 6d.). Photo Enschedé)

1967 (1 Oct). *4th Anniv of Republic. T* **147** *and similar multicoloured designs. P* 11½ × 11 (2*s.* 6*d.*) *or* 11 × 11½ (*others*).
202 4d. Type **147** 20 5
203 1s. 6d. Crowd watching acrobat . . . . 1·40 1·50
204 2s. 6d. Stilt dancer (*vert*) . . . . . . 1·75 2·75

150 Tending Sick Animal 151 Smallpox Vaccination

(Des G. Drummond)

1967 (1 Dec). *Rinderpest Eradication Campaign. P* 14½ × 14.
205 **150** 4d. multicoloured 15 5
206 1s. 6d. multicoloured . . . . . . 70 1·25

PRINTERS AND PROCESS. Nos. 207/89 were printed in photogravure by the Nigerian Security Printing and Minting Co Ltd, *unless otherwise stated.*

(Des J. Owei. Litho)

1968 (7 Apr). *20th Anniv of World Health Organization. T* **151** *and similar horiz design. P* 14.
207 4d. magenta and black 12 5
208 1s. 6d. orange, lemon and black 60 80
Design:—1s. 6d. African and mosquito.

153 Chained Hands and Outline of Nigeria 155 Hand grasping at Doves of Freedom

(Des Jennifer Toombs)

1968 (1 July). *Human Rights Year. T* **153** *and similar design. P* 14.
209 4d. greenish blue, black and yellow 10 5
210 1s. 6d. myrtle-green, orange-red and black . . 45 70
Design: *Vert*—1s. 6d. Nigerian flag and Human Rights emblem.

(Des G. Vasarhelyi)

1968 (1 Oct). *5th Anniv of Federal Republic. P* 13½ × 14.
211 **155** 4d. multicoloured 10 5
212 1s. 6d. multicoloured 35 35

156 Map of Nigeria and Olympic Rings 158 G.P.O., Lagos

(Des J. Owei)

1968 (14 Oct). *Olympic Games, Mexico. T* **156** *and similar horiz design. P* 14.
213 4d. black, green and scarlet 10 5
214 1s. 6d. multicoloured 45 60
Design:—1s. 6d. Nigerian athletes, flag and Olympic rings.

(Des D.L.R.)

1969 (11 Apr). *Inauguration of Philatelic Service. P* 14.
215 **158** 4d. black and green 10 5
216 1s. 6d. black and blue 45 70

159 Yakubu Gowon and Victoria Zakari

(Des adapted from photo by Jackie Phillips. Litho)

1969 (20 Sept). *Wedding of General Gowon. P* 13 × 13½.
217 **159** 4d. chocolate and emerald 10 5
218 1s. 6d. black and emerald 35 50

1969–72. (*a*) *As No.* 173 *etc, but printed by Nigerian Security Printing and Mining Co Ltd. With printer's imprint* "N.S.P. & M. CO. LTD." *P* 13½ (6*d.*) *or P* 13 × 13½ (*others*).
220 1d. multicoloured 40 5
222 2d. multicoloured 55 5
a. Smaller imprint* (13.1.71) .. .. 1·10 35
223 3d. multicoloured (7.71) 60 10
a. Larger imprint* (22.10.71) .. .. 1·25 35
224 4d. multicoloured .. .. 1·25 5
a. Smaller imprint† .. ..
225 6d. multicoloured (1971) .. .. .. 1·00 20
226 9d. Prussian blue and orange-red (1970) .. 2·75 95
227 1s. multicoloured (8.71) .. .. .. 1·75 20
228 1s. 3d. multicoloured (1971).. .. .. 3·25 80
229 2s. 6d. multicoloured (1972).. .. .. 2·50 2·25
230 5s. multicoloured (1972) .. .. .. 2·50 3·00
220/30 .. .. *Set of* 10 15·00 7·00

*On No. 222a the designer's name measures 4¾ mm. On No. 223a the imprints measure 9 and 8½ mm respectively. The normal imprints on Nos. 222/3 both measure 5½ mm.

The date given for Nos. 222a and 223a are for the earliest known used copies.

†No. 224 has the left-hand imprint 6 mm long and the right-hand 5½ mm. On No. 224a the imprints are 5½ mm and 4½ mm respectively. The width of the design is also ½ mm smaller.

(*b*) *As Nos.* 222 *and* 224, *but redrawn, and printed by Enschedé. No printer's imprint; designer's name at right. P* 14½ × 13.
231 2d. multicoloured (9.70) .. .. .. 9·00 1·75
232 4d. multicoloured (3.71) .. .. .. 3·00 1·25

In the 2d. the face value is white instead of yellow, and in the 4d. the white lettering and value are larger.

160 Bank Emblem and "5th Anniversary"

161 Bank Emblem and Rays

(Des J. Owei (4d.), B. Salisu (1s. 6d.). Litho)

1969 (18 Oct). *Fifth Anniv of African Development Bank. P* 14.
233 **160** 4d. orange, black and blue 10 5
234 **161** 1s. 6d. lemon, black and plum .. 45 60

162 I.L.O. Emblem

164 Olumo Rock

(Des D. West)

1969 (15 Nov). *50th Anniv of International Labour Organisation. T* **162** *and similar horiz design. P* 14.
235 4d. black and bright reddish violet 10 5
236 1s. 6d. emerald and black 45 70
Design:—1s. 6d. World map and I.L.O. emblem.

(Des A. Onwudimegwu)

1969 (30 Dec). *International Year of African Tourism. T* **164** *and similar designs. P* 14.
237 4d. multicoloured 12 5
238 1s. black and bright emerald 35 30
239 1s. 6d. multicoloured 55 65
Designs: *Vert*—1s. Traditional musicians; 1s. 6d. Assob Falls.

167 Symbolic Tree

168 U.P.U. H.Q. Building

(Des E. Emokpae (4d., 1s., 2s.), B. Onobrakpeya (1s. 6d.). Photo Enschedé)

1970 (28 May). *"Stamp of Destiny"; End of Civil War. T* **167** *and similar designs. P* 11 × 11½ (2*s.*) *or* 11½ × 11 (*others*).
240 4d. gold, new blue and black.. .. .. 12 5
241 1s. multicoloured 30 20
242 1s. 6d. yellow-green and black 50 55
243 2s. multicoloured 65 85
Designs: *Vert*—1s. Symbolic Wheel; 1s. 6d. United Nigerians supporting Map. *Horiz*—2s. Symbolic Torch.

(Des A. Onwudimegwu)

1970 (29 June). *New U.P.U. Headquarters Building. P* 14.
244 **168** 4d. reddish violet and greenish yellow.. 10 5
245 1s. 6d. light greenish blue and deep blue 35 60

169 Scroll

170 Oil Rig

(Des A. Onwudimegwu)

1970 (1 Sept). *25th Anniv of United Nations. T* **169** *and similar vert design. P* 14.
246 4d. orange-brown, buff and black 10 5
247 1s. 6d. steel-blue, cinnamon and gold .. 35 40
Design:—1s. 6d. U.N. Building.

(Des E. Emokpae. Litho Enschedé)

1970 (30 Sept). *Tenth Anniv of Independence. T* **170** *and similar vert designs. Multicoloured. P* 13½ × 13.
248 2d. Type **170** 10 5
249 4d. University Graduate 15 8
250 6d. Durbar Horsemen 15 12
251 9d. Servicemen raising Flag.. .. .. 25 25
252 1s. Footballer 30 25
253 1s. 6d. Parliament Building.. .. .. 65 80
254 2s. Kainji Dam .. .. 80 1·10
255 2s. 6d. Agricultural Produce .. .. 95 1·40
248/55 .. .. *Set of* 8 3·00 3·75

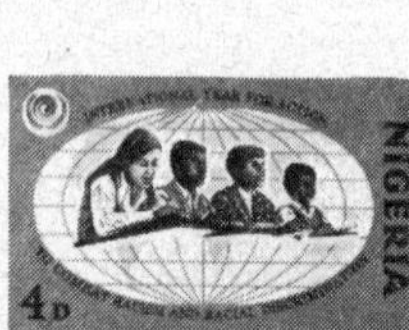

171 Children and Globe

172 Ibibio Face Mask

(Des E. Emokpae and A. Onwudimegwu. Photo Enschedé)

1971 (21 Mar). *Racial Equality Year. T* **171** *and similar multi-coloured designs. P* 13 × 13½ (4*d.*, 2*s.*) *or* 13½ × 13 (*others*).
256 4d. Type **171** 10 5
257 1s. Black and white men uprooting "Racism" (*vert*) 25 20
258 1s. 6d. The world in black and white (*vert*) .. 45 75
259 2s. Black and white men united .. .. 55 1·10

(Des A. Onwudimegwu)

1971 (30 Sept). *Antiquities of Nigeria. T* **172** *and similar vert designs. P* 13½ × 14.
260 4d. black and pale blue 12 5
261 1s. 3d. blackish brown and ochre 40 40
262 1s. 9d. emerald, sepia and olive-yellow .. 60 1·10
Designs:—1s. 3d. Benin bronze; 1s. 9d. Ife bronze.

173 Children and Symbol

174 Mast and Dish Aerial

(Des E. Emokpae)

1971 (11 Dec). *25th Anniv of U.N.I.C.E.F. T* **173** *and similar vert designs, each incorporating the U.N.I.C.E.F. symbol. P* 13½ × 14.
263 4d. multicoloured 12 5
264 1s. 3d. yellow-orange, orge-red & carm-lake 40 50
265 1s. 9d. pale greenish blue & dp greenish blue 60 1·10
Designs:—1s. 3d. Mother and child; 1s. 9d. Mother carrying child.

(Des A. Onwudimegwu)

1971 (30 Dec). *Opening of Nigerian Earth Satellite Station. T* **174** *and similar horiz designs. P* 14.
266 **174** 4d. multicoloured 15 5
267 – 1s. 3d. green, blue and black 65 70
268 – 1s. 9d. brown, orange and black .. 95 1·50
269 – 3s. mauve, black and magenta .. 1·60 2·25
Designs:—Nos. 267/9, as T **174**, but showing different views of the Satellite Station.

The 4d. has been seen on a cover from Ilorin, postmarked 23.12.71.

NEW INFORMATION

The editor is always interested to correspond with people who have new information that will improve or correct the Catalogue.

175 Trade Fair Emblem

176 Traffic

(Des E. Emokpae (4d.), A. Onwudimegwu (others). Litho D.L.R.)

1972 (23 Feb). *All-Africa Trade Fair. T* **175** *and similar designs. P* 13.
270 4d. multicoloured 10 5
271 1s. 3d. deep lilac, lemon and gold 40 50
272 1s. 9d. yellow-orange, orange-yellow & black 60 1·10
Designs: *Horiz*—1s. 3d. Map of Africa with pointers to Nairobi. *Vert*—1s. 9d. Africa on globe.

(Des A. Onwudimegwu (4d., 3s.), E. Emokpae (1s. 3d.), J. Owei (1s. 9d.). Litho D.L.R.)

1972 (23 June). *Change to Driving on the Right. T* **176** *and similar horiz designs. Multicoloured* (*except* 4*d.*). *P* 13.
273 4d. Type **176** (yellow-orge, dp chest & black) 15 5
274 1s. 3d. Roundabout .. .. 90 1·00
275 1s. 9d. Highway .. .. 1·10 1·50
276 3s. Road junction .. .. 2·50 3·50

177 Nok Style Terracotta Head

178 Hides and Skins

(Des G. Okiki (1s. 3d.), A. Aiyegbusi (others). Litho D.L.R.)

1972 (1 Sept). *All-Nigeria Arts Festival. T* **177** *and similar multi-coloured designs. P* 13.
277 4d. Type **177** 15 5
278 1s. 3d. Bronze pot from Igbo-Ukwu 65 85
279 1s. 9d. Bone harpoon (*horiz*).. .. .. 85 1·40

(New Currency. 100 kobo = 1 naira)

(Des E. Emokpae (8, 25, 30, 50 k., 1 n.), A. Onwudimegwu (others))

1973–74. *T* **178** *and similar designs. P* 14.

(*a*) *Photo. Left-hand imprint* 5¼ *mm long* (2 Jan†–2 Apr)
280 1 k. multicoloured (deep green foliage) .. 20 12
a. *Light emerald foliage** (2.4.73) 20 8
281 2 k. black, pale turquoise-blue and bright purple 35 10
282 5 k. multicoloured (emerald hills) .. 60 20
a. *Bright yellow-green hills** (2.4.73) .. 50 15
283 10 k. black, orange-yellow and lilac .. 70 20
284 12 k. black, pale emerald and deep cobalt .. 1·75 1·50
285 18 k. multicoloured .. .. 2·50 2·00
286 20 k. multicoloured .. .. 3·50 3·00
287 30 k. black, chrome-yellow and new blue .. 4·00 4·00
288 50 k. multicoloured (black background and figure) .. .. 5·00 2·75
a. *Deep chocolate background and figure** (2.4.73) .. .. 2·00 90
289 1 n. multicoloured .. .. 12·00 12·00
280/9 .. .. *Set of* 10 25·00 22·00

(*b*) *Litho. Left-hand imprint* 6 *mm long* (2 Apr 1973–74)
290 1 k. multicoloured (8.73) 10 5
291 2 k. black, pale turquoise-blue and bright purple (27.6.74)** 60 5
292 3 k. multicoloured 15 5
293 5 k. multicoloured (*shades*) (2.74) .. 30 10
294 7 k. multicoloured 30 10
295 8 k. multicoloured 40 15
296 10 k. black, orange-yellow and lilac (8.73) .. 55 15
297 12 k. black, green and cobalt (*shades*) .. 20 12
298 15 k. multicoloured 25 15
299 18 k. multicoloured 50 25
300 20 k. multicoloured 65 25
301 25 k. multicoloured 85 45
302 30 k. black, chrome-yellow and new blue .. 50 30
303 35 k. multicoloured 55 35
305 1 n. multicoloured (*shades*).. .. .. 1·25 1·10
306 2 n. multicoloured (*shades*).. .. .. 5·00 3·75
290/306 .. .. *Set of* 16 11·00 6·50

Designs: *Horiz*—2 k. Natural gas tanks; 3 k. Cement works; 5 k. Cattle-ranching; 7 k. Timber mill; 8 k. Oil refinery; 10 k. Leopards, Yankari Game Reserve; 12 k. New Civil Building; 15 k. Sugar-cane harvesting; 20 k. Vaccine production; 25 k. Modern wharf; 35 k. Textile machinery; 1 n. Eko Bridge; 2 n. Teaching Hospital, Lagos. *Vert*—18 k. Palm oil production; 30 k. Argungu Fishing Festival; 50 k. Pottery.

*On Nos. 280*a*, 282*a* and 288*a* other colours also differ, but the shades can best be identified by the distinctive features noted.

Used copies of No. 282*a* have been seen with orange omitted.

†Although First Day Covers of Nos. 280/9 were dated 1 January the stamps were not placed on sale until 2 January.

**This is the earliest known postmark date. No. 291 was not released by the Crown Agents in London until 11 September 1975.

Differences between printings:
1 k. In photogravure printings the stretched hide at left is in brownish black; on the litho stamps this hide is brown and yellow.

2 k. On the litho stamp the line of division between the black and pale blue colours of the gas tanks is a regular curve; on the photogravure printing it is horizontal and irregular. The litho stamp also has a wider mauve border at top.
5 k. The litho printing differs from the photogravure (Nos. 282/a) in having brown on the herdsman, instead of black.
10 k. The litho version has much less black on the leopards and tree trunk. It also shows black details at the left-hand end of the trunk, which do not appear on the photogravure version.
12 k. No. 284 is much darker than the litho version, especially within the building and amongst the trees at right.
18 k. The lithographed printing shows two oildrums in the foreground which are not present on the photogravure stamp.
20 k. The lithographed printing includes a brown plate not present on the photogravure version. This affects the colour of the chemist and apparatus.
30 k. No. 287 is much darker, with greater use of black in the design.
50 k. The litho version (No. 352) has solid shading on the potter's upper arm and lacks a black inner frame-line beneath the potter's wheel. No. 352 has a green printer's imprint at foot (instead of black) and its background is similar to that of No. 288a.
1 n. On the photogravure stamp the traffic is shown driving on the left. For the litho version the traffic is corrected to show it driving on the right.

See also Nos. 338/54.

PROCESS. From No. 307 onwards all stamps were lithographed by the Nigerian Security Printing and Minting Co Ltd.

179 Athlete

1973 (8 Jan). *Second All-African Games. Lagos. T* **179** *and similar multicoloured designs (except 5 k.). P* 13.
307 5 k. Type **179** (lt lilac, lt greenish bl & blk) .. 15 5
308 12 k. Football 50 60
309 18 k. Table-tennis .. .. 85 1·25
310 25 k. National Stadium (*vert*) .. .. .. 1·00 1·75

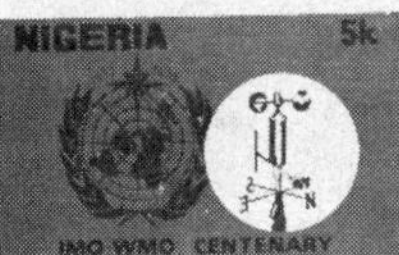

180 All-Africa House, Addis Ababa
181 Dr. Hansen

1973 (25 May). *Tenth Anniv of O.A.U. T* **180** *and similar vert designs. Multicoloured. P* 14.
311 5 k. Type **180** 15 5
312 18 k. O.A.U. flag 70 80
313 30 k. O.A.U. emblem and symbolic flight of ten stairs .. .. 1·10 1·40

(Des A. Onwudimegwu)

1973 (30 July). *Centenary of Discovery of Leprosy Bacillus. P* 14.
314 **181** 5 k. + 2 k. lt red-brown, flesh & black .. 25 35

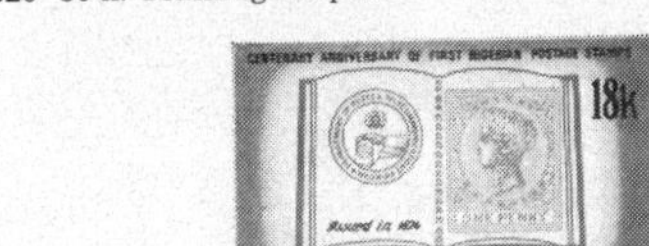

182 W.M.O. Emblem and Weather-vane
183 University Complex

(Des O. I. Oshiga)

1973 (4 Sept). *I.M.O./W.M.O. Centenary. P* 14.
315 **182** 5 k. multicoloured 15 5
316 30 k. multicoloured .. .. 1·25 1·75

(Des A. Onwudimegwu (5, 18 k.), C. Okechukwu (12 k.), O. I. Oshiga (30 k.))

1973 (17 Nov). *25th Anniv of Ibadan University. T* **183** *and similar multicoloured designs. P* 13½ × 14 (12 *k.*) *or* 14 × 13½ (*others*).
317 5 k. Type **183** 20 5
318 12 k. Students' population growth (*vert*) .. 45 45
319 18 k. Tower and students 70 75
320 30 k. Teaching Hospital .. .. 95 1·25

184 Lagos 1d. Stamp of 1874

(Des A. Onwudimegwu (30 k.), S. Eluare (others))

1974 (10 June). *Stamp Centenary. T* **184** *and similar horiz designs. P* 14 × 13½.
321 5 k. light emerald, yellow-orange and black 20 10
322 12 k. multicoloured 65 75
323 18 k. light yellowish green, mauve and black 95 1·25
324 30 k. multicoloured .. .. 1·90 2·75
Designs:—5 k. Graph of mail traffic growth; 12 k. Northern Nigeria £25 stamp of 1904; 30 k. Forms of mail transport.

185 U.P.U. Emblem on Globe
186 Starving and Well-fed Children

(Des S. Eluare (5 k.). A. Onwudimegwu (18 k.), O. I. Oshiga (30 k.))

1974 (9 Oct). *Centenary of Universal Postal Union. T* **185** *and similar horiz designs. P* 14.
325 5 k. lt greenish blue, yellow-orange & black 20 10
326 18 k. multicoloured .. .. 1·00 1·25
327 30 k. bistre-brown, lt greenish blue & black .. 1·90 2·50
Designs:—18 k. World transport map; 30 k. U.P.U. emblem and letters.

(Des A. Onwudimegwu (12 k.), S. Eluare (others))

1974 (25 Nov). *Freedom from Hunger Campaign. T* **186** *and similar designs. P* 14.
328 5 k. apple-green, buff and grey-black .. 15 10
329 12 k. multicoloured 60 70
330 30 k. multicoloured .. .. 1·60 2·25
Designs: *Horiz*—12 k. Poultry battery. *Vert*—30 k. Water-hoist.

187 Telex Network and Teleprinter
188 Queen Amina of Zaria

(Des S. Eluare)

1975 (3 July). *Inauguration of Telex Network. T* **187** *and similar vert designs. P* 13½ × 14.
331 5 k. black, yellow-orange & light olive-green 20 8
332 12 k. black, lemon and orange-brown 50 65
333 18 k. multicoloured .. .. 75 1·10
334 30 k. multicoloured .. .. 1·40 1·75
Nos. 332/4 are as T **187** but have the motifs arranged differently.

(Des A. Onwudimegwu)

1975 (18 Aug). *International Women's Year. P* 14.
335 **188** 5 k. deep olive, light yellow and azure .. 15 8
336 18 k. purple, pale blue and light mauve .. 80 1·10
337 30 k. multicoloured .. .. 1·40 1·75

189

1975–80*. *As Nos.* 290 *etc., but W* **189** (*sideways on* 50 *k.*).
338 1 k. multicoloured (6.4.77) 5 5
339 2 k. black, pale turq-bl & bright purple (9.75) 5 5
340 3 k. multicoloured (10.75) 5 5
341 5 k. multicoloured (1.76) 5 5
342 7 k. multicoloured (16.5.80) 12 8
343 8 k. multicoloured (12.76) 15 10
344 10 k. blk, orange-yell & lilac (*shades*) (7.4.76) 15 12
347 18 k. multicoloured (12.78) 30 35
348 20 k. multicoloured (9.79) 30 35
349 25 k. multicoloured (21.3.77) 40 45
352 50 k. multicoloured (2.9.77) 80 85
354 2 n. multicoloured (11.77) .. .. .. 3·00 3·25
338/54 .. .. *Set of* 12 5·00 5·25
*Earliest known dates of use.

190 Alexander Graham Bell
191 Child Writing

(Des A. Onwudimegwu)

1976 (10 Mar). *Telephone Centenary. T* **190** *and similar designs. W* **189** (*sideways on* 5 *and* 25 *k.*). *P* 13½.
355 5 k. multicoloured 15 10
356 18 k. multicoloured 80 90
357 25 k. royal blue, pale blue and blackish brown 1·40 1·75
a. No wmk .. .. 10·00
Designs: *Horiz*—18 k. Gong and modern telephone system. *Vert*—25 k. Telephones, 1876 and 1976.

(Des A. Onwudimegwu (5 k.), S. Eluare (18 k.), N. Lasisi (25 k.))

1976 (20 Sept). *Launching of Universal Primary Education. T* **191** *and similar designs. W* **189** (*sideways on* 18 *and* 25 *k.*). *P* 14.
358 5 k. lemon, light violet and bright mauve .. 15 10
359 18 k. multicoloured .. .. 70 1·00
360 25 k. multicoloured .. .. 1·25 1·75
Designs: *Vert*—18 k. Children entering school; 25 k. Children in class.

192 Festival Emblem

(Des O. I. Oshiga (5 k., 30 k.), A. Onwudimegwu (10 k., 12 k.), N. Lasisi (18 k.))

1976–77. *Second World Black and African Festival of Arts and Culture, Nigeria. T* **192** *and similar horiz designs. W* **189**. *P* 14.
361 5 k. gold and blackish brown (1.11.76) .. 15 10
362 10 k. lt red-brown, lt yellow & black (15.1.77) 35 40
363 12 k. multicoloured (15.1.77) 40 55
364 18 k. chrome-yellow, lt brown & blk (1.11.76) 60 80
365 30 k. magenta and black (15.1.77) .. .. 1·00 1·40
Designs:—10 k. National Arts Theatre; 12 k. African hair styles; 18 k. Musical instruments; 30 k. "Nigerian arts and crafts".

193 General Murtala Muhammed and Map of Nigeria
194 Scouts Saluting

(Des A. Onwudimegwu (5, 18 k.), O. I. Oshiga (30 k.))

1977 (12 Feb). *First Death Anniv of General Muhammed (Head of State). T* **193** *and similar vert designs. Multicoloured. W* **189** (*sideways on* 18 *and* 30 *k.*). *P* 14.
366 5 k. Type **193** 12 10
367 18 k. General in dress uniform 60 75
368 30 k. General in battle dress .. .. .. 95 1·25

(Des N. Lasisi (18 k.), A. Onwudimegwu (others))

1977 (2 Apr). *First All-Africa Scout Jamboree, Jos, Nigeria. T* **194** *and similar horiz designs. Multicoloured. W* **189** (*sideways on* 5 *k.*). *P* 14.
369 5 k. Type **194** 15 10
370 18 k. Scouts cleaning street 70 70
371 25 k. Scouts working on farm 85 95
372 30 k. Jamboree emblem and map of Africa .. 1·10 1·40

195 Trade Fair Complex

(Des S. Eluare (5 k.), A. Onwudimegwu (others))

1977 (27 Nov). *1st Lagos International Trade Fair. T* **195** *and similar horiz designs. W* **189**. *P* 14.
373 5 k. black, new blue and yellow-green .. 10 10
374 18 k. black, new blue and magenta 60 60
375 30 k. multicoloured 85 95
Designs:—18 k. Globe and Trade Fair emblem; 30 k. Weaving and basketry.

196 Map showing Nigerian Universities

(Des M. O. Shadare (5 k.), C. Okechukwu (12 k.), A. Onwudimegwu (18 k.), N. Lasisi (30 k.))

1978 (28 Apr). *Global Conference on Technical Co-operation between Developing Countries, Buenos Aires. T* **196** *and similar horiz designs. W* **189**. *P* 14.
376 5 k. multicoloured 10 10
377 12 k. multicoloured 35 35
378 18 k. multicoloured 50 50
379 30 k. yellow, bluish violet and black 85 85
Designs:—12 k. Map of West African highways and telecommunications; 18 k. Technologists undergoing training; 30 k. World map.

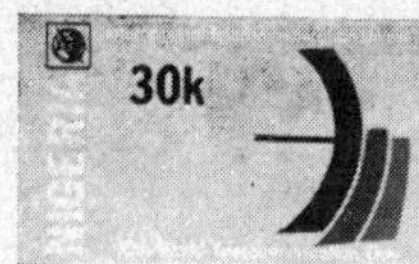

197 Microwave Antenna

1978 (17 May). *10th World Telecommunications Day. W* **189**. *P* 14.
380 **197** 30 k. multicoloured 85 85

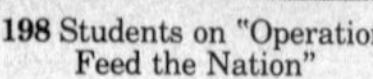
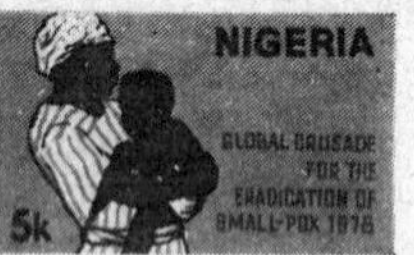

198 Students on "Operation Feed the Nation"

199 Mother with Infected Child

(Des J. Salisu (5 k.), N. Lasisi (18 k.), A. Onwudimegwu (30 k.))

1978 (7 July). *"Operation Feed the Nation" Campaign. T* **198** *and similar multicoloured designs. W* **189** *(sideways on 30 k.). P* 14.
381 5 k. Type **198** 10 10
382 18 k. Family backyard farm 35 40
383 30 k. Plantain farm (*vert*) 65 90

(Des G. Osuji (30 k.), N. Lasisi (others))

1978 (31 Aug). *Global Eradication of Smallpox. T* **199** *and similar designs. W* **189** *(sideways on 30 k.). P* 14.
384 5 k. black, orange-brown and rose-lilac .. 10 10
385 12 k. multicoloured 25 25
386 18 k. black, lake-brown and greenish yellow .. 40 45
387 30 k. black, silver and rose-pink 70 80
Designs: *Horiz*—12 k. Doctor and infected child; 18 k. Group of children being vaccinated. *Vert*—30 k. Syringe.

200 Nok Terracotta Human Figure, Bwari (900 B.C.–200 A.D.)

201 Anti-Apartheid Emblem

(Des local artists)

1978 (27 Oct). *Antiquities. T* **200** *and similar designs. W* **189** *(sideways on 5, 18 and 30 k.). P* 14.
388 5 k. black, new blue and carmine-red 10 10
389 12 k. multicoloured 35 35
390 18 k. black, greenish blue and carmine-red .. 50 50
391 30 k. multicoloured 85 85
Designs: *Horiz*—12 k. Igbo-Ukwu bronze snail shell, Igbo Isaiah (9th-century A.D.). *Vert*—18 k. Ife bronze statue of king (12th–15th century A.D.); 30 k. Benin bronze equestrian figure (about 1700 A.D.).

(Des A. Onwudimegwu)

1978 (10 Dec). *International Anti-Apartheid Year. W* **189** *(sideways). P* 14.
392 **201** 18 k. black, greenish yellow & vermilion 35 40

202 Wright Brothers and *Flyer*

203 Murtala Muhammed Airport

(Des A. Onwudimegwu)

1978 (28 Dec). *75th Anniv of Powered Flight. T* **202** *and similar horiz design. W* **189**. *P* 14.
393 5 k. multicoloured 10 10
394 18 k. black, ultramarine and light blue .. 45 45
Design:—18 k. Nigerian Air Force formation.

(Des A. Onwudimegwu)

1979 (15 Mar). *Opening of Murtala Muhammed Airport. W* **189**. *P* 14.
395 **203** 5 k. black, grey-blk & brt greenish blue 10 10

204 Child with Stamp Album

205 Mother and Child

1979 (11 Apr). *10th Anniv of National Philatelic Service. W* **189**. *P* 14.
396 **204** 5 k. multicoloured 10 10

1979 (28 June). *International Year of the Child. T* **205** *and similar multicoloured designs. W* **189** *(sideways on 25 k.). P* 14.
397 5 k. Type **205** 10 10
398 18 k. Children studying 40 45
399 25 k. Children playing (*vert*) 55 70

206 Trainee Teacher making Audio Visual Aid Materials

207 Necom House

(Des M. Shadare and O. Oshiga)

1979 (25 July). *50th Anniv of International Bureau of Education. T* **206** *and similar vert design. Multicoloured. W* **189** *(sideways). P* 14.
400 10 k. Type **206** 15 20
401 30 k. Adult education class 50 55

(Des A. Onwudimegwu)

1979 (20 Sept). *50th Anniv of Consultative Committee of International Radio. W* **189** *(sideways). P* 14.
402 **207** 10 k. multicoloured 20 20

208 Trainees of the Regional Aerial Survey School, Ile-Ife

(Des A. Onwudimegwu)

1979 (12 Dec). *21st Anniv of the Economic Commission for Africa. W* **189**. *P* 14.
403 **208** 10 k. multicoloured 20 20

209 Football, Cup and Map of Nigeria

210 Wrestling

(Des G. Akinola (10 k.), Mrs. O. Adeyeye (30 k.)

1980 (8 Mar). *African Cup of Nations Football Competition, Nigeria. T* **209** *and similar multicoloured design. W* **189** *(sideways on 30 k.). P* 14.
404 10 k. Type **209** 15 20
405 30 k. Footballer (*vert*) 50 55

(Des M. Shadare (10 k.), Mrs. O. Adeyeye (others))

1980 (19 July). *Olympic Games, Moscow. T* **210** *and similar designs. W* **189** *(sideways on 10, 20 and 45 k.). P* 14.
406 10 k. multicoloured 15 20
407 20 k. black and bright yellow-green 35 40
408 30 k. black, reddish orange and blue 55 65
409 45 k. multicoloured 75 85
Designs: *Vert*—20 k. Long jump; 45 k. Netball. *Horiz*—30 k. Swimming.

211 Figures supporting O.P.E.C. Emblem

212 Steam Locomotive

(Des G. Oluwasegun)

1980 (15 Sept). *20th Anniv of O.P.E.C. (Organization of Petroleum Exporting Countries). T* **211** *and similar design. W* **189** *(sideways on 45 k.). P* 14.
410 10 k. black, ultramarine and greenish yellow 15 20
411 45 k. black, deep turquoise-blue and magenta 75 80
Design: *Vert*—45 k. O.P.E.C. emblem on globe.

1980 (2 Oct). *25th Anniv of Nigerian Railway Corporation. T* **212** *and similar horiz designs. Multicoloured. W* **189**. *P* 14.
412 10 k. Type **212** 20 20
413 20 k. Loading goods train 55 55
414 30 k. Freight train 65 65

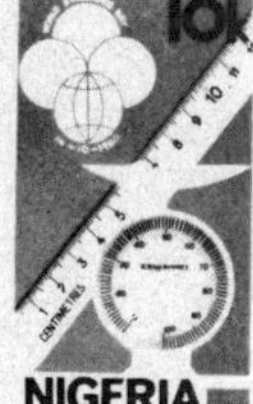

213 Metric Scales

214 "Communications" Symbols and Map of West Africa

(Des G. Akinola (10 k.), M. Shadare (30 k.))

1980 (14 Oct). *World Standards Day. T* **213** *and similar design. W* **189** *(sideways on 10 k.). P* 14.
415 10 k. red and black 15 20
416 30 k. multicoloured 50 55
Design: *Horiz*—30 k. Quality control.

1980 (5 Nov). *5th Anniv of E.C.O.W.A.S. (Economic Community of West African States). T* **214** *and similar horiz designs showing symbols of economic structure and map of West Africa. W* **189**. *P* 14.
417 10 k. black, yellow-orange and grey-olive .. 15 20
418 25 k. black, emerald and bright rose 45 50
419 30 k. black, greenish yellow and yellow-brown 55 60
420 45 k. black, turquoise-blue and bright blue .. 75 80
Designs:—25 k. "Transport"; 30 k. "Agriculture"; 45 k. "Industry".

215 Disabled Woman Sweeping

216 President launching "Green Revolution" (food production campaign)

(Des N. Lasisi (10 k.), G. Akinola (30 k.))

1981 (25 June). *International Year for Disabled Persons. T* **215** *and similar vert design. W* **189** *(sideways). P* 14.
421 10 k. multicoloured 15 15
422 30 k. black, chestnut and new blue 50 55
Design:—30 k. Disabled man filming.

(Des Mrs. A. Adeyeye (10 k.), G. Akinola (30 k.), S. Eluare (others))

1981 (16 Oct). *World Food Day. T* **216** *and similar designs. W* **189** *(sideways on 25 and 30 k.). P* 14.
423 10 k. multicoloured 15 15
424 25 k. black, greenish yellow and emerald .. 45 50
425 30 k. multicoloured 50 55
426 45 k. black, yellow-brown and orange-yellow 80 85
Designs: *Vert*—25 k. Food crops; 30 k. Harvesting tomatoes. *Horiz*—45 k. Pig farming.

217 Rioting in Soweto

218 "Preservation of Wildlife"

(Des G. Osuji)

1981 (10 Dec). *Anti-Apartheid Movement. T* **217** *and similar design. W* **189** *(sideways on 45 k.). P* 14.
427 30 k. multicoloured 50 55
428 45 k. black, vermilion and light green .. 80 85
Design: *Vert*—45 k. "Police brutality".

(Des G. Akinola)

1982 (22 Feb). *75th Anniv of Boy Scout Movement. T* **218** *and similar horiz design. Multicoloured. W* **189**. *P* 14.
429 30 k. Type **218** 50 55
430 45 k. Lord Baden-Powell taking salute .. 80 85

219 Early Innoculation

220 "Keep Your Environment Clean"

(Des G. Osuji (10 k.), C. Ogbebor (30 k.), N. Lasisi (45 k.))

1982 (24 Mar). *Centenary of Robert Koch's Discovery of Tubercle Bacillus. T* **219** *and similar designs. W* **189** *(sideways on 45 k.). P* 14.
431 10 k. multicoloured 20 15
432 30 k. grey-black, brown and turquoise-green .. 50 55
433 45 k. grey-black, light brown and bright green 80 85
Designs: *Horiz*—30 k. Technician and microscope. *Vert*—45 k. Patient being X-rayed.

(Des C. Ogbebor (10 k.), N. Lasisi (others))

1982 (10 June). *10th Anniv of U.N. Conference on Human Environment. T* **220** *and similar horiz designs. W* **189**. *P* 14.
434 10 k. multicoloured 15 15
435 20 k. yellow-orange, greenish grey and black . . 40 40
436 30 k. multicoloured 55 60
437 45 k. multicoloured 80 85
Designs:—20 k. "Check air pollution"; 30 k. "Preserve natural environment"; 45 k. "Reafforestation concerns all".

221 *Salamis parhassus*

222 Carving of "Male and Female Twins"

(Des G. Akinola)

1982 (15 Sept). *Nigerian Butterflies. T* **221** *and similar horiz designs. Multicoloured. W* **189**. *P* 14.
438 10 k. Type **221** 15 15
439 20 k. *Papilio zalmoxis* 40 40
440 30 k. *Pachylophus beckeri* 55 60
441 45 k. *Papilio hesperus* 80 85

(Des C. Ogbebor (10 k.), G. Akinola (20 k.), S. Eluare (30 k.), N. Lasisi (45 k.))

1982 (18 Nov). *25th Anniv of National Museum. T* **222** *and similar multicoloured designs. W* **189** *(sideways on 10, 30, 45 k.). P* 14.
442 10 k. Type **222** 15 15
443 20 k. Royal bronze leopard (*horiz*) 30 35
444 30 k. Soapstone seated figure 50 55
445 45 k. Wooden helmet mask 80 85

223 Three Generations

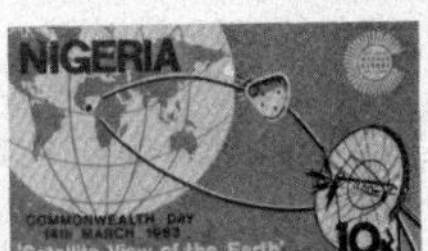

224 Satellite View of Globe

(Des G. Akinola)

1983 (8 Mar). *Family Day. T* **223** *and similar multicoloured design. W* **189** *(sideways on 30 k.). P* 14.
446 10 k. Type **223** 15 20
447 30 k. Parents with three children (*vert*) . . 50 55

(Des N. Lasisi (30 k.), C. Ogbebor (others))

1983 (14 Mar). *Commonwealth Day. T* **224** *and similar designs. W* **189** *(sideways on 30, 45 k.). P* 14.
448 10 k. yellow-brown and black 15 20
449 25 k. multicoloured 45 50
450 30 k. black, magenta and pale grey 50 55
451 45 k. multicoloured 80 85
Designs: *Horiz*—25 k. National Assembly Buildings. *Vert*—30 k. Drilling for oil; 45 k. Athletics.

225 Corps Members on Building Project

226 Postman on Bicycle

(Des Mrs. A. Adeyeye (25 k.), G. Akinola (others))

1983 (25 May). *10th Anniv of National Youth Service Corps. T* **225** *and similar multicoloured designs. W* **189** *(sideways on 25, 30 k.). P* 14.
452 10 k. Type **225** 15 20
453 25 k. On the assault-course (*vert*) 45 50
454 30 k. Corps members on parade (*vert*) 50 55

(Des N. Lasisi (25 k.), O. Ogunfowora (30 k.), Mrs. A. Adeyeye (others))

1983 (20 July). *World Communications Year. T* **226** *and similar multicoloured designs. W* **189** *(sideways on 10 k.). P* 14.
455 10 k. Type **226** 15 20
456 25 k. Newspaper kiosk (*horiz*) 45 50
457 30 k. Town crier blowing elephant tusk (*horiz*) 50 55
458 45 k. T.V. newsreader (*horiz*) 80 85

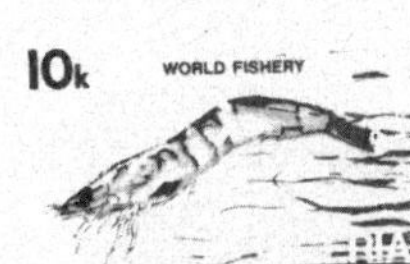

227 Pink Shrimp

228 On Parade

(Des Miss H. Toyu Woods (10 k.), G. Osuji (25 k.), Mrs. A. Adeyeye (30 k.), O. Ogunfowora (45 k.))

1983 (22 Sept). *World Fishery Resources. T* **227** *and similar horiz designs. W* **189**. *P* 14.
459 10 k. rose, new blue and black 15 20
460 25 k. multicoloured 45 50
461 30 k. multicoloured 50 55
462 45 k. multicoloured 80 85
Designs:—25 k. Long Neck Croaker; 30 k. Barracuda; 45 k. Fishing techniques.

(Des F. Nwaije (10 k.), Mrs A. Adeyeye (30 k.), G. Osuji (45 k.))

1983 (14 Oct). *Boys' Brigade Centenary and 75th Anniv of Movement in Nigeria. T* **228** *and similar multicoloured designs. W* **189** *(sideways on 10 k.). P* 14.
463 10 k. Type **228** 20 25
464 30 k. Members working on cassava plantation (*horiz*) 55 60
465 45 k. Skill training (*horiz*) . . . . . . 95 1·00

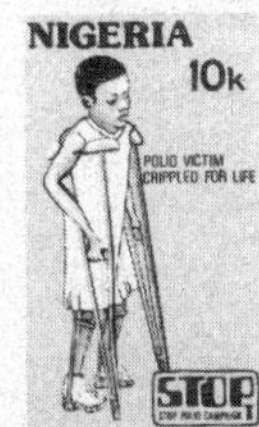

229 Crippled Child

230 Waterbuck

(Des S. Eluare (10 k.), G. Osuji (others))

1984 (29 Feb). *Stop Polio Campaign. T* **229** *and similar designs. W* **189** *(sideways on 10 k. and 30 k.). P* 14.
466 10 k. light blue, black and light brown . . 20 25
467 25 k. pale orange, black and greenish yellow . . 45 50
468 30 k. carmine-rose, black and orange-brown . . 55 60
Designs: *Horiz*—25 k. Child receiving vaccine. *Vert*—30 k. Healthy child.

(Des O. Ogunfowora (30 k.), Mrs. A. Adeyeye (45 k.), N. Lasisi (others))

1984 (25 May). *Nigerian Wildlife. T* **230** *and similar designs. W* **189** *(inverted on 30 k., sideways on 10 k., 45 k.). P* 14.
469 10 k. light green, light brown and black . . 20 25
470 25 k. multicoloured 45 50
471 30 k. yellow-brown, black and light green . . 55 60
472 45 k. new blue, pale orange and black 80 85
Designs: *Horiz*—25 k. Hartebeest; 30 k. Buffalo. *Vert*—45 k. African Golden Monkey.

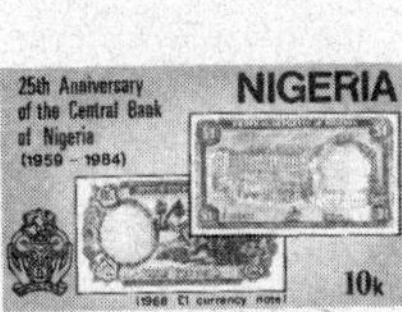

231 Obverse and Reverse of 1969 £1 Note

232 Boxing

1984 (2 July). *25th Anniv of Nigerian Central Bank. T* **231** *and similar horiz designs. W* **189** *(inverted on 30 k.). P* 14.
473 10 k. multicoloured 20 25
474 25 k. deep cinnamon, black and light green . . 45 50
475 30 k. light rose, black and grey-olive 55 60
Designs:—25 k. Central Bank; 30 k. Obverse and reverse of 1959 £5 note.

1984 (20 July). *Olympic Games, Los Angeles. T* **232** *and similar vert designs. Multicoloured. W* **189** *(sideways). P* 14.
476 10 k. Type **232** 20 25
477 25 k. Discus-throwing 45 50
478 30 k. Weightlifting 55 60
479 45 k. Cycling 80 85

233 Irrigation Project, Lesotho

234 Pin-tailed Whydah

(Des Mrs A. Adeyeye (10 k.), S. Eluare (25 k.), Miss H. Toyu Woods (30 k.), O. Ogunfowora (45 k.))

1984 (10 Sept). *20th Anniv of African Development Bank. T* **233** *and similar designs. W* **189** *(sideways on 10 k.). P* 14.
480 10 k. multicoloured 20 25
481 25 k. multicoloured 45 50
482 30 k. black, chrome yell & bright greenish bl 55 60
483 45 k. black, orange-brn & bright greenish bl . . 80 85
Designs: *Horiz*—25 k. Bomi Hills Road, Liberia; 30 k. School building project, Seychelles; 45 k. Coal mining, Niger.

1984 (24 Oct). *Rare Birds. T* **234** *and similar vert designs. Multicoloured. W* **189** *(sideways). P* 14.
484 10 k. Type **234** 20 25
485 25 k. Spur-winged Plover 45 50
486 30 k. Red Bishop 55 60
487 45 k. Francolin 80 85

POSTAGE DUE STAMPS

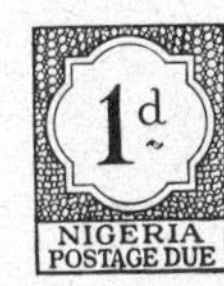

D 1

(Litho B.W.)

1959 (4 Jan). *Wmk Mult Script CA. P* 14½ × 14.
D1 D 1 1d. red-orange 10 20
D2 2d. red-orange 15 30
D3 3d. red-orange 25 40
D4 6d. red-orange . . . . 55 1·25
D5 1s. grey-black . . . . 1·40 2·25

1961 (1 Aug). *W* **34**. *P* 14½ × 14.
D 6 D 1 1d. red 8 15
D 7 2d. light blue 12 20
D 8 3d. emerald 20 30
D 9 6d. yellow 40 65
D10 1s. blue (*shades*) . . . . 65 1·75

(Typo Nigerian Security Printing & Minting Co)

1973 (3 May). *New Currency. No wmk. P* 12½ × 13½.
D11 D 1 2 k. red 5 5
D12 3 k. blue 5 8
D13 5 k. orange-yellow (*shades*) 8 8
D14 10 k. light apple-green (*shades*) 15 20

BIAFRA

The following stamps were issued by Biafra (the Eastern Region of Nigeria) during the civil war with the Federal Government, 1967–70.

They were in regular use within Biafra from the time when supplies of Nigerian stamps were exhausted; and towards the end of the conflict they began to be used on external mail carried by air via Libreville.

1 Map of Republic

2 Arms, Flag and Date of Independence

3 Mother and Child

(Typo and litho Mint, Lisbon)

1968 (5 Feb). *Independence. P* 12½.

1	1	2d. multicoloured	10	15
2	2	4d. multicoloured	15	25
3	3	1s. multicoloured	20	70

SOVEREIGN

BIAFRA

(4)

1968. *Nos.* 172/5 *and* 177/85 *of Nigeria optd as T* 4 (*without* "SOVEREIGN" *on* 10s.).

4	½d. multicoloured (No. 172)	40	75
5	1d. multicoloured (No. 173)	1·25	2·00
	a. Opt double	£110	
	b. Opt omitted (in pair with normal)	£250	
6	1½d. multicoloured (No. 174)	2·00	3·00
7	2d. multicoloured (No. 175)	15·00	22·00
8	4d. multicoloured (No. 177*a*)	15·00	22·00
9	6d. multicoloured (No. 178)	2·50	2·50
10	9d. Prussian blue and orange-red (No. 179)	75	95
11	1s. multicoloured (Blk. + R.) (No. 180)	48·00	70·00
12	1s. 3d. multicoloured (Blk. + R.) (No. 181)	30·00	40·00
13	2s. 6d. orange-brown, buff and brown (Blk. + R.) (No. 182)	1·75	3·25
	a. Red opt omitted	£120	
14	5s. chestnut, lt yell & brn (Blk. + R.) (No. 183)	2·25	4·00
	a. Red opt omitted	£120	
	b. Black opt omitted	£110	
	c. Pale chestnut, yellow & brn-pur (No. 183*a*)	2·25	4·00
15	10s. multicoloured (No. 184)	9·00	20·00
16	£1 multicoloured (Blk. + R.) (No. 185)	10·00	20·00
	a. Black ("SOVEREIGN BIAFRA") omitted	£125	
	b. Red (coat of arms) omitted	£125	
4/16	*Set of* 13	£120	£190

+5/-

BIAFRA - FRANCE
FRIENDSHIP 1968

SOVEREIGN
BIAFRA

(4*a*)

1968. *Nos.* 172/3 *of Nigeria surch as T* 4*a*.

16*c*	½d. + 5s. multicoloured	9·00
	ca. Surch double	75·00
	cb. Surch double, one inverted	50·00
	cd. "+ 5/-" omitted	
16*d*	1d. + £1 multicoloured	11·00
	da. Surch double	95·00
	db. Surch double, one inverted	50·00
	dc. "+ £1" omitted	75·00

5 Weapon Maintenance

8 Biafran Arms and Banknote

9 Orphaned Child

(Litho Mint, Lisbon)

1968 (30 May). *First Anniv of Independence. T* 5, 8/9 *and similar vert designs. P* 12½.

17	4d. multicoloured	8	8
18	1s. multicoloured	15	20
19	2s. 6d. multicoloured	40	70
20	5s. multicoloured	80	1·25
	a. Indigo (banknote) omitted	40·00	
21	10s. multicoloured	1·60	2·75

Designs:—1s. Victim of atrocity; 2s. 6d. Nurse and refugees.

+6D
HELP
BIAFRAN
CHILDREN

(10)

11 *Papilio dardanus* (butterfly) and *Lankesteria barteri* (plant)

1968 (30 May). *Nos.* 17/21 *surch as T* 10.

22	4d. + 2d. multicoloured	10	15
	a. Surch inverted	45·00	
23	1s. + 6d. multicoloured	25	40
	a. Surch inverted	40·00	
	b. Surch double	40·00	
	c. Surch omitted (in pair with normal)	£100	
24	2s. 6d. + 1s. multicoloured	50	85
25	5s. + 2s. 6d. multicoloured	1·00	2·25
	a. Surch inverted	40·00	
26	10s. + 2s. 6d. multicoloured	1·90	3·50
	a. Surch double	45·00	

1968 (2 Sept). *Butterflies and Plants. T* 11 *and similar horiz designs. Multicoloured. Litho. P* 14.

27	4d. Type 11	50	40
28	1s. 6d. *Papilio antimachus* and *Ipomoea involucrata*	85	90
29	2s. 6d. *Papilio zalmoxis* and *Haemanthus cinnabarinus*	1·40	1·40
30	5s. *Papilio hesperus* and *Clerodendrum splendens*	2·25	2·75

MEXICO OLYMPICS
1968

(15)

1968. *Olympic Games, Mexico. Nos.* 27/30 *optd with T* 15.

31	4d. Type 11	35	35
32	1s. 6d. *Papilio antimachus* and *Ipomoea involucrata*	65	85
	a. Opt inverted	85·00	
33	2s. 6d. *Papilio zalmoxis* and *Haemanthus cinnabarinus*	95	1·40
34	5s. *Papilio hesperus* and *Clerodendrum splendens*	1·60	2·50

16 Child in Chains and Globe

17 Pope Paul VI, Map of Africa and Papal Arms

1969 (30 May). *Second Anniv of Independence. Multicoloured; frame colours given. Litho. P* 13 × 13½.

35	16	2d. yellow-orange	20	45
36		4d. red-orange	25	55
		a. Green (wreath) and orange (Sun) omitted		
37		1s. new blue	50	1·25
38		2s. 6d. emerald	1·25	3·50

A miniature sheet with a face value of 10s. was also released.

1969 (25 Sept). *Visit of Pope Paul to Africa. T* 17 *and similar vert designs. Multicoloured. Litho. P* 13 × 13½.

39	4d. Type 17	40	55
40	6d. Pope Paul VI, Map of Africa and arms of the Vatican	55	1·25
41	9d. Pope Paul VI, map of Africa and St. Peter's Basilica, Vatican	75	1·90
42	3s. Pope Paul VI, map of Africa and Statue of St. Peter	2·25	5·50

A miniature sheet with a face value of 10s. was also released.

No. 42 has a magenta background. This value is also known with the background in brown-red or brown.

Biafra was overrun by Federal troops on 10 January 1970 and surrender took place on 15 January.

On 17 December the French Agency released a Christmas issue consisting of Nos. 39/42 overprinted "CHRISTMAS 1969 PEACE ON EARTH AND GOODWILL TO ALL MEN" together with the miniature sheet overprinted "CHRISTMAS 1969" and surcharged £1. Later Nos. 35/38 were released overprinted in red "SAVE BIAFRA 9TH JAN 1970" with a premium of 8d., 1s. 4d., 4s., and 10s. respectively together with the miniature sheet with a premium of £1. We have no evidence that these issues were actually put on sale in Biafra before the collapse, but it has been reported that the 4d. Christmas issue and 2d. + 8d. Save Biafra exist genuinely used before capitulation.

Nos. 40/41 have been seen surcharged "+ 10/–HUMAN RIGHTS" and the United Nations emblem but it is doubtful if they were issued.

Niue

PRICES FOR STAMPS ON COVER TO 1945

No. 1	*from* × 2
Nos. 2/5	*from* × 8
Nos. 6/7	—
Nos. 8/9	*from* × 30
Nos. 10/12	—
Nos. 13/31	*from* × 3
Nos. 32/7*c*	—
Nos. 38/47	*from* × 5
Nos. 48/9	—
No. 50	*from* × 15
Nos. 51/4	—
Nos. 55/61	*from* × 8
Nos. 62/8	*from* × 12
Nos. 69/71	*from* × 3
Nos. 72/4	*from* × 10
Nos. 75/8	*from* × 8
Nos. 79/88	—
Nos. 89/97	*from* × 2

NEW ZEALAND DEPENDENCY

Stamps of New Zealand overprinted

NIUE

(1)

1902 (4 Jan). *Handstamped with T* 1, *in green or bluish green. Waterlow paper. Wmk double-lined* "N Z" *and Star, W* 36*a. P* 11.

1	40	1d. carmine	£375	£375

A few overprints were made with a *greenish violet* ink. These occurred only in the first vertical row and part of the second row of the first sheet overprinted owing to violet ink having been applied to the pad (*Price* £1400 *un*).

NIUE.
½ PENI.

(2)

NIUE.
TAHA PENI.

3 1d.

NIUE.
2½ PENI.

(4)

1902 (4 Apr). *Type-set surcharges. T* 2, 3, *and* 4.

(i) *Waterlow paper. No wmk. P* 11

2	27	2½d. blue (R.)	1·25	2·50
		a. No stop after "PENI"	20·00	21·00
		b. Surch double		

(ii) *Basted Mills paper. Wmk double-lined* "N Z" *and Star, W* 36*a*

(*a*) *Perf* 14

3	23	½d. green (R.)	75	1·50
		a. Spaced "U" and "E"	3·50	4·50
		b. Surch inverted	£275	£300
4	40	1d. carmine (B.)	3·50	7·00
		a. Spaced "U" and "E"	14·00	16·00
		b. No stop after "PENI"	60·00	65·00
		c. Varieties a. and b. on same stamp	£100	£100

(*b*) *P* 11 *and* 14 *compound*

5	40	1d. carmine (B.)	75	1·40
		a. Spaced "U" and "E"	4·00	4·50
		b. No stop after "PENI"	9·50	12·00
		c. Varieties a. and b. on same stamp	55·00	60·00

(*c*) *Mixed perfs*

6	23	½d. green (R.)	£200
7	40	1d. carmine (B.)	£200

1902 (2 May). *Type-set surcharges, T* 2, 3. *Cowan paper. Wmk single-lined* "N Z" *and Star, W* 41. (*a*) *P* 14.

8	23	½d. green (R.)	65	80
		a. Spaced "U" and "E"	3·25	4·50
9	40	1d. carmine (B.)	50	65
		a. Surcharge double	£500	
		b. Spaced "U" and "E"	11·00	12·00
		c. No stop after "PENI"	10·00	17·00
		d. Varieties b. and c. on same stamp	32·00	35·00

(*b*) *Perf* 11 *and* 14 *compound*

10	23	½d. green (R.)	

(*c*) *Mixed perfs*

11	23	½d. green (R.)	£250
12	40	1d. carmine (B.)	£150
		a. Spaced "U" and "E"	

NIUE.

(5)

Tolu e Pene.

6 3d.

Ono e Pene.

7 6d.

Taha e Silenі.

8 1s.

1903 (2 July). *Optd with name at top, T* 5, *and values at foot, T* 6/8, *in blue. W* 41. *P* 11.

13	28	3d. yellow-brown	4·25	4·50
14	31	6d. rose-red	1·75	7·00
15	34	1s. brown-red ("Tahae" joined)	£750	
16		1s. bright red	10·00	12·00
		a. Orange-red	15·00	26·00

NIUE.
½ PENI.

(9)

NIUE.

(10)

1911 (30 Nov). *½d. surch with* **T 9**, *others optd at top as* **T 5** *and values at foot as* **T 7, 8. W 41.** *P* 14 × 14½.
17 **50** ½d. green (C.) 45 50
18 **52** 6d. carmine (B.) .. .. 4·00 7·50
19 1s. vermilion (B.) .. .. 9·50 20·00

1915 (Sept). *Surch as* **T 4. W 41.** *P* 14.
20 **27** 2½d. deep blue (C.) .. .. 2·50 5·50

1917 (Aug). *1d. surch as* **T 3**, *3d. optd as* **T 5** *with value as* **T 6. W 41.**
21 **51** 1d. carmine (*p* 14 × 15) (Br.) .. .. 2·00 3·50
a. No stop after "Peni" £100
22 **60** 3d. chocolate (*p* 14 × 14½) (B.) .. .. 60·00 75·00
a. No stop after "Pene" £450
b. Perf 14 × 13½ .. .. .. 85·00 95·00
c. Vert pair, Nos. 22/2b £180

1917–21. *Optd with* **T 10. W 41.** (*a*) *P* 14 × 15.
23 **60*b*** ½d. green (R.) (2.20) 50 60
24 **51** 1d. carmine (B.) (10.17) .. .. 60 1·25
25 **60*b*** 1½d. slate (R.) (11.17) .. .. 80 1·75
26 1½d. orange-brown (R.) (2.19) .. .. 70 1·75
27 3d. chocolate (B.) (6.19) .. .. 1·25 2·50
(*b*) *P* 14 × 14½
28 **60** 2½d. deep blue (R.) (10.20) .. .. 90 2·25
a. Perf 14 × 13½ .. .. .. 1·25 2·25
b. Vert pair, Nos. 28/a .. .. 15·00 22·00
29 3d. chocolate (B.) (10.17) .. .. 1·50 1·75
a. Perf 14 × 13½ .. .. .. 1·60 3·00
b. Vert pair, Nos. 29/a .. .. 25·00 32·00
30 6d. carmine (B.) (8.21) .. .. 3·75 6·50
a. Perf 14 × 13½ .. .. .. 4·00 7·50
b. Vert pair, Nos. 30/a .. .. 30·00 40·00
31 1s. vermilion (B.) (10.18) .. .. 4·25 8·00
a. Perf 14 × 13½ .. .. .. 6·00 8·00
b. Vert pair, Nos. 31/a .. .. 30·00 40·00
23/31 .. .. *Set of* 9 13·00 24·00

1918–29. *Postal Fiscal stamps as Type* **F 4** *of New Zealand optd with* **T 10. W 41** (*sideways*).
(i) *Chalk-surfaced "De La Rue" paper.* (*a*) *P* 14
32 5s. yellow-green (R.) (7.18) .. .. .. 60·00 75·00
(*b*) *P* 14½ × 14, *comb*
33 2s. deep blue (R.) (9.18) .. .. .. 19·00 26·00
34 2s. 6d. grey-brown (R.) (2.23) .. .. 19·00 26·00
35 5s. yellow-green (R.) (10.18) .. .. 20·00 35·00
36 10s. maroon (B.) (2.23) .. .. .. 70·00 90·00
37 £1 rose-carmine (B.) (2.23) £130 £150
(ii) *Thick, opaque, white chalk-surfaced "Cowan" paper. P* 14½ × 14
37*a* 5s. yellow-green (R.) (10.29) .. .. 20·00 35·00
37*b* 10s. brown-red (B.) (2.27) .. .. 70·00 90·00
37*c* £1 rose-pink (B.) (2.28) £130 £150

(Des, eng and ptd by P.B.)

1920 (23 Aug). *As* **T 9** *to* **14** *of Cook Islands but inscr "NIUE". No wmk. P* 14.
38 ½d. black and green .. .. .. 1·00 2·00
39 1d. black and dull carmine .. .. 1·10 1·50
40 1½d. black and red .. .. .. 1·50 2·75
41 3d. black and blue .. .. .. 85 2·75
42 6d. red-brown and green .. .. .. 1·60 5·00
43 1s. black and sepia .. .. .. 3·25 8·00
38/43 .. .. *Set of* 6 8·50 20·00

1925–27. *Pictorial stamps as* 1920 *and new values as* **T 16/17** *of Cook Islands, but inscr "NIUE".* **W 41.** *P* 14.
44 ½d. black and green (1927) .. .. 75 1·50
45 1d. black and deep carmine (1925) .. 55 90
46 2½d. black and blue (10.27) .. .. 1·00 3·00
47 4d. black and violet (10.27) .. .. 2·00 5·50

1927–28. *Admiral type of New Zealand optd as* **T 10. W 41.** *P* 14.
(*a*) *"Jones" paper*
48 **72** 2s. deep blue (2.27) (R.) .. .. 18·00 40·00
(*b*) *"Cowan" paper*
49 **72** 2s. light blue (R.) (2.28) .. .. 14·00 27·00

1931 (Apr). *No. 40 surch as* **T 18** *of Cook Is.*
50 2d. on 1½d. black and red 80 90

1931 (12 Nov). *Postal Fiscal stamps as Type* **F 6** *of New Zealand optd as* **T 10. W 41.** *Thick, opaque, chalk-surfaced "Cowan" paper. P* 14.
51 2s. 6d. deep brown (B.) .. .. .. 12·00 15·00
52 5s. green (R.) .. .. 24·00 40·00
53 10s. carmine-lake (B.) .. .. .. 35·00 50·00
54 £1 pink (B.) .. .. 55·00 75·00
See also Nos. 79/82 for different type of overprint.

(Des L. C. Mitchell. Recess P.B.)

1932 (16 Mar). *As* **T 20** *to* **26** *of Cook Is, but frames include "NIUE" as well as "COOK ISLANDS." No wmk. P* 13.
55 ½d. black and emerald .. .. .. 85 1·50
a. Perf 14 × 13 .. .. .. 65·00
56 1d. black and deep lake 60 25
57 2d. black and red-brown .. .. .. 60 1·25
a. Perf 13 and 14 mixed .. ..
58 2½d. black and slate-blue .. .. 3·25 4·75
59 4d. black and greenish blue .. .. 5·00 7·50
a. Perf 14 .. .. .. 5·00 5·50
60 6d. black and orange-vermilion .. .. 2·50 3·50
61 1s. black and purple (*p* 14) .. .. 3·75 5·50
55/61 .. .. *Set of* 7 15·00 20·00

(Recess-printed from Perkins, Bacon's plates at Govt Ptg Office, Wellington, N.Z.)

1932–36. *Pictorial types as* 1932, *but* **W 41.** *P* 14.
62 ½d. black and emerald 50 60
63 1d. black and deep lake 50 30
64 2d. black and yellow-brown (1.4.36) .. 40 50
65 2½d. black and slate-blue 50 85
66 4d. black and greenish blue 70 85
67 6d. black and red-orange (1.4.36) .. 90 70
68 1s. black and purple (1.4.36) .. .. 4·00 7·00
62/68 .. .. *Set of* 7 6·75 9·75

Imperforate proofs of No. 65 are known used on registered mail from Niue postmarked 30 August 1945 or 29 October 1945.
See also Nos. 89/97.

1935 (7 May). *Silver Jubilee. Designs as Nos.* 63, 65 *and* 67 (*colours changed*) *optd as* **T 27** *of Cook Is* (*wider vertical spacing on 6d.*). **W 41.** *P* 14.
69 1d. red-brown and lake .. .. .. 60 1·25
a. Narrow "K" in "KING" .. .. 3·25 12·00
b. Narrow "B" in JUBILEE .. .. 3·25 12·00
70 2½d. dull and deep blue (R.) .. .. 2·50 3·25
a. Narrow first "E" in "GEORGE" .. 5·50 12·00
b. Imperf between (vert pair) £550
71 6d. green and orange .. .. .. 5·50 7·50
a. Narrow "N" in "KING" .. .. 20·00 32·00
For illustrations of varieties, see Cook Islands.

NIUE
(13)

NIUE.
(14)

1937 (13 May). *Coronation Issue. Nos.* 599/601 *of New Zealand optd with* **T 13.**
72 1d. carmine 45 20
73 2½d. Prussian blue 55 25
74 6d. red-orange 75 45

1938 (2 May). *As* **T 29** *to* **31** *of Cook Is., but frames inscr. "NIUE COOK ISLANDS".* **W 41.** *P* 14.
75 1s. black and violet .. .. .. 3·25 4·00
76 2s. black and red-brown .. .. .. 5·00 7·00
77 3s. light blue and emerald-green .. .. 9·00 9·00

1940 (2 Sept). *As* **T 32** *of Cook Islands, but additionally inscr. "NIUE".* **W 98.** *P* 13½ × 14.
78 3d. on 1½d. black and purple 12 12

1941–67. *Postal Fiscal stamps as Type* **F 6** *of New Zealand with thin opt,* **T 14.** *P* 14.
(i) *Thin, hard, chalk-surfaced "Wiggins Teape" paper with vertical mesh* (1941–43). (*a*) **W 41**
79 2s. 6d. deep brown (B.) (4.41) .. .. 20·00 20·00
80 5s. green (R.) (4.41) £130 £130
81 10s. pale carmine-lake (B.) (6.42) £100 £120
82 £1 pink (B.) (2.43?) £140 £140
(*b*) **W 98** (1944–45)
83 2s. 6d. deep brown (B.) (3.45) .. .. 4·50 6·50
84 5s. green (R.) (11.44) .. .. .. 8·00 10·00
85 10s. carmine-lake (B.) (11.45) .. .. 30·00 38·00
86 £1 pink (B.) (6.42) .. .. .. 32·00 38·00
(ii) *Unsurfaced "Wiggins Teape" paper with horizontal mesh.* **W 98** (1957–67)
87 2s. 6d. deep brown (*p* 14 × 13½) (1.11.57) .. 3·25 3·25
88 5s. pale yellowish green (*wmk sideways*) (6.67) .. .. 55·00 65·00
Nos. 83/5 were later printed with the watermark inverted for technical reasons and the prices quoted are for the cheapest form. They are fully listed in the *Elizabethan Catalogue.*
No. 88 came from a late printing made to fill demands from Wellington, but no supplies were sent to Niue. It exists in both line and comb perf.

1944–46. *As* **T 20** *to* **25** *and* **29** *to* **31** *of Cook Is. but additionally inscr "NIUE".* **W 98** (*sideways on ½d., 1d., 1s. and 2s.*).
89 ½d. black and emerald 50 60
90 1d. black and deep lake 50 60
91 2d. black and red-brown 60 85
92 2½d. black and slate-blue (1946) 60 85
93 4d. black and greenish blue 60 90
94 6d. black and red-orange .. .. .. 1·00 2·00
95 1s. black and violet .. .. .. 2·50 5·00
96 2s. black and red-brown (1945) .. .. 4·50 7·00
97 3s. light blue and emerald-green (1945) .. 8·00 10·00
89/97 .. .. *Set of* 9 17·00 25·00

1946 (1 June). *Peace. Nos.* 668, 670, 674/5 *of New Zealand optd as* **T 14**, *but without stop* (*twice, reading up and down on 2d.*).
98 **132** 1d. green (Blk.) 10 10
99 – 2d. purple (B.) 12 12
100 – 6d. chocolate and vermilion (Blk.) 12 15
a. Opt double, one albino .. ..
101 **139** 8d. black and carmine (B.) 15 20
Nos. 102/112 are no longer used.

15 Map of Niue

16 Capt. Cook's *Resolution*

23 Bananas

24 Matapa Chasm

(Des J. Berry. Recess B.W.)

1950 (3 July). **T 15/16, 23/24** *and similar designs.* **W 98** *of New Zealand* (*sideways inverted on 1d., 2d., 3d., 4d., 6d. and 1s.*). *P* 13½ × 14 (*horiz*), 14 × 13½ (*vert*).
113 ½d. orange and blue 8 8
114 1d. brown and blue-green .. .. .. 1·25 20
115 2d. black and carmine 15 12
116 3d. blue and violet-blue 12 12
117 4d. olive-green and purple-brown 15 20
118 6d. green and brown-orange 25 15
119 9d. orange and brown 20 30
120 1s. purple and black 20 20
121 2s. brown-orange and dull green .. .. 4·00 3·50
122 3s. blue and black .. .. .. 5·00 4·50
113/22 .. .. *Set of* 10 10·00 8·50
Designs: *Horiz* (*as* **T 16**)—2d. Alofi landing; 3d. Native hut; 4d. Arch at Hikutavake; 6d. Alofi bay; 1s. Cave, Makefu. *Vert* (*as* **T 18**)—9d. Spearing fish.

1953 (25 May). *Coronation. As Nos.* 715 *and* 717 *of New Zealand, but inscr "NIUE".*
123 3d. brown 55 40
124 6d. slate-grey 95 60

(New Currency. 100 cents = 1 dollar)

1c
(25)

26

1967 (10 July–7 Aug). *Decimal currency.* (*a*) *Nos.* 113/22 *surch as* **T 25.**
125 ½ c. on ½d. 5 5
126 1 c. on 1d. 80 35
127 2 c. on 2d. 10 10
128 2½ c. on 3d. 10 10
129 3 c. on 4d. 10 12
130 5 c. on 6d. 15 20
131 8 c. on 9d. 20 20
132 10 c. on 1s. 25 25
133 20 c. on 2s. .. .. 2·00 2·00
134 30 c. on 3s. .. .. 2·50 2·75
125/34 .. .. *Set of* 10 5·50 5·50
(*b*) *Arms type of New Zealand without value, surch as in* **T 26. W 98** *of New Zealand* (*sideways*). *P* 14.
135 **26** 25 c. deep yellow-brown 75 90
a. Rough perf 11 .. .. .. 11·00 14·00
136 50 c. pale yellowish green .. .. 1·40 1·50
a. Rough perf 11 .. .. .. 12·00 16·00
137 $1 magenta .. .. 2·75 3·00
a. Rough perf 11 .. .. .. 15·00 18·00
138 $2 light pink .. .. 5·50 7·00
a. Rough perf 11 .. .. .. 18·00 26·00
The 25 c., $1 and $2 perf 14 exist both line and comb perforated. The 50 c. is comb perforated only. The perf 11 stamps resulted from an emergency measure in the course of printing.

1967 (3 Oct). *Christmas. As* **T 278** *of New Zealand, but inscr "NIUE".*
139 2½ c. multicoloured 10 12

1969 (1 Oct). *Christmas. As* **T 301** *of New Zealand, but inscr "NIUE".* **W 98** *of New Zealand. P* 13½ × 14½.
140 2½ c. multicoloured 10 12

27 "Pua"

37 Kalahimu

(Des Mrs. K. W. Billings. Litho Enschedé)

1969 (27 Nov). **T 27** *and similar vert designs. Multicoloured. P* 12½ × 13½.
141 ½ c. Type **27** 5 5
142 1 c. "Golden Shower" 8 8
143 2 c. Flamboyant 12 12
144 2½ c. Frangipani 12 12
145 3 c. Niue Crocus 12 12
146 5 c. Hibiscus 15 10
147 8 c. "Passion Fruit" 20 15
148 10 c. "Kampui" 30 20
149 20 c. Queen Elizabeth II (after Anthony Buckley) .. .. 1·75 1·50
150 30 c. Tapeu Orchid .. .. .. 3·00 2·50
141/150 .. .. *Set of* 10 5·50 4·50

(Des G. F. Fuller. Photo Enschedé)

1970 (19 Aug). *Indigenous Edible Crabs.* **T 37** *and similar horiz designs. Multicoloured. P* 13½ × 12½.
151 3 c. Type **37** 20 15
152 5 c. Kalavi 25 15
153 30 c. Unga 90 65

1970 (1 Oct). *Christmas. As* **T 314** *of New Zealand, but inscr "NIUE".*
154 2½ c. multicoloured 10 10

38 Native Canoe and Aircraft over Jungle

39 Spotted Triller

(Des L. C. Mitchell. Litho B.W.)

1970 (9 Dec). *Opening of Niue Airport.* **T 38** *and similar horiz designs. Multicoloured. P* 13½.
155 3 c. Type **38** 25 10
156 5 c. Ship, and aircraft over harbour 30 20
157 8 c. Aircraft over Airport 40 30

(Des A. G. Mitchell. Litho B.W.)

1971 (23 June). *Birds. T* **39** *and similar horiz designs. Multicoloured. P* 13½.
158 5 c. Type **39** 25 20
159 10 c. Purple-capped Fruit Dove 80 30
160 20 c. Blue-crowned Lory . . . . . . 1·00 60

1971 (6 Oct). *Christmas. As T* **325** *of New Zealand, but inscr* "NIUE".
161 3 c. multicoloured 10 10

40 Niuean Boy

41 Octopus Lure

(Des L. C. Mitchell. Litho Harrison)

1971 (17 Nov). *Niuean Portraits. T* **40** *and similar vert designs. Multicoloured. P* 13 × 14.
162 4 c. Type **40** 15 12
163 6 c. Girl with garland 20 12
164 9 c. Man 25 15
165 14 c. Woman with garland 40 40

(Des A. G. Mitchell. Litho B.W.)

1972 (3 May). *South Pacific Arts Festival, Fiji. T* **41** *and similar multicoloured designs. P* 13½.
166 3 c. Type **41** 15 15
167 5 c. War weapons 20 20
168 10 c. Sika throwing (*horiz*) 30 30
169 25 c. Vivi dance (*horiz*) 60 60

42 Alofi Wharf

(Des A. G. Mitchell. Litho Questa)

1972 (6 Sept). *25th Anniversary of South Pacific Commission. T* **42** *and similar horiz designs. Multicoloured. P* 14.
170 4 c. Type **42** 15 15
171 5 c. Medical Services 20 15
172 6 c. Schoolchildren 25 20
173 18 c. Dairy cattle 60 50

1972 (4 Oct). *Christmas. As T* **332** *of New Zealand but inscr* "NIUE".
174 3 c. multicoloured 10 10

43 Kokio

44 "Large Flower Piece" (Jan Brueghel)

(Des G. F. Fuller. Litho Harrison)

1973 (27 June). *Fishes. T* **43** *and similar horiz designs. Multicoloured. P* 14 × 13½.
175 8 c. Type **43** 45 45
176 10 c. Loi 50 50
177 15 c. Malau 65 65
178 20 c. Palu 70 70

(Des and litho Enschedé)

1973 (21 Nov). *Christmas. T* **44** *and similar vert designs showing flower studies by the artists listed. Multicoloured. P* 14 × 13½.
179 4 c. Type **44** 15 10
180 5 c. Bollongier 15 10
181 10 c. Ruysch 30 35

45 Capt. Cook and Bowsprit

46 King Fataaiki

(Des A. G. Mitchell. Litho Questa)

1974 (20 June). *Bicentenary of Capt. Cook's Visit. T* **45** *and similar horiz designs each showing Cook's portrait. Multicoloured. P* 13½ × 14.
182 2 c. Type **45** 40 30
183 3 c. Niue landing place 40 30
184 8 c. Map of Niue 65 65
185 20 c. Ensign of 1774 and Administration Building . . . . 1·00 1·10

SELF-GOVERNMENT

(Des A. G. Mitchell. Litho Questa)

1974 (19 Oct). *Self-Government. T* **46** *and similar multicoloured designs. P* 14 × 13½ (4 *and* 8 c.) *or* 13½ × 14 (*others*).
186 4 c. Type **46** 15 15
187 8 c. Annexation Ceremony, 1900 . . . . 25 25
188 10 c. Legislative Assembly Chambers (*horiz*) 25 25
189 20 c. Village meeting (*horiz*) 45 45

47 Decorated Bicycles

48 Children going to Church

(Des B. C. Strong. Litho D.L.R.)

1974 (13 Nov). *Christmas. T* **47** *and similar vert designs. P* 12½.
190 3 c. multicoloured 10 5
191 10 c. multicoloured 25 20
192 20 c. dull red-brown, slate and black . . 45 45
Designs:—10 c. Decorated motorcycles; 20 c. Motor transport to church.

(Des Enid Hunter. Litho Questa)

1975 (29 Oct). *Christmas. T* **48** *and similar horiz designs. Multicoloured. P* 14.
193 4 c. Type **48** 15 10
194 5 c. Child with balloons on bicycle 20 10
195 10 c. Balloons and gifts on tree 35 35

49 Hotel Buildings

50 Preparing Ground for Taro

(Des B. C. Strong. Litho Harrison)

1975 (19 Nov). *Opening of Tourist Hotel. T* **49** *and similar horiz design. Multicoloured. P* 13½ × 13.
196 8 c. Type **49** 15 15
197 20 c. Ground-plan and buildings 40 40

(Des A. G. Mitchell. Litho Questa)

1976 (3 Mar). *T* **50** *and similar horiz designs showing food gathering. Multicoloured. P* 13½ × 14.
198 1 c. Type **50** 5 5
199 2 c. Planting taro 8 8
200 3 c. Banana gathering 8 8
201 4 c. Harvesting taro 10 10
202 5 c. Gathering shell fish 15 10
203 10 c. Reef fishing 15 15
204 20 c. Luku gathering 35 35
205 50 c. Canoe fishing 90 90
206 $1 Coconut husking . . . . . . 1·75 1·75
207 $2 Uga gathering . . . . 3·25 3·25
198/207 . . . . *Set of* 10 6·00 6·00
See also Nos. 249/58 and 264/73.

51 Water

52 Christmas Tree, Alofi

(Des A. G. Mitchell. Litho Questa)

1976 (7 July). *Utilities. T* **51** *and similar vert designs. Multicoloured. P* 14.
208 10 c. Type **51** 20 15
209 15 c. Power 35 30
210 20 c. Telecommunications 40 35

(Des A. G. Mitchell. Litho Questa)

1976 (15 Sept). *Christmas. T* **52** *and similar horiz design. Multicoloured. P* 14.
211 9 c. Type **52** 25 20
212 15 c. Church Service, Avatele 35 30

53 Queen Elizabeth II and Westminster Abbey

(Des and photo Heraclio Fournier)

1977 (7 June). *Silver Jubilee. T* **53** *and similar horiz design. Multicoloured. P* 13½.
213 $1 Type **53** . . . . 3·00 2·50
214 $2 Coronation regalia . . . . 4·00 3·50
MS215 72 × 104 mm. Nos. 213/14 . . . . 7·00 7·00
Stamps from the miniature sheet have a blue border.

54 Child Care

55 "The Annunciation"

(Des R. M. Conly. Litho Questa)

1977 (29 June). *Personal Services. T* **54** *and similar horiz designs. Multicoloured. P* 14½.
216 10 c. Type **54** 15 12
217 15 c. School dental clinic 30 25
218 20 c. Care of the aged 35 25

(Des and photo Heraclio Fournier)

1977 (15 Nov). *Christmas. T* **55** *and similar vert designs showing paintings by Rubens. Multicoloured. P* 13.
219 10 c. Type **55** 25 15
220 12 c. "Adoration of the Magi" 25 15
221 20 c. "Virgin in a Garland 45 25
222 35 c. "The Holy Family" 70 55
MS223 82 × 129 mm. Nos. 219/22 . . . . 1·75 2·00

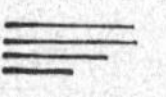

(**56**)

1977 (15 Nov). *Nos.* 198 *etc.,* 214, 216 *and* 218 *surch as T* **56** *by New Zealand Govt Printer.*
224 12 c. on 1 c. Type **50** 25 25
225 16 c. on 2 c. Planting taro 30 30
226 30 c. on 3 c. Banana gathering 50 40
227 35 c. on 4 c. Harvesting taro 55 45
228 40 c. on 5 c. Gathering shell fish 60 50
229 60 c. on 20 c. Luku gathering 85 75
230 70 c. on $1 Coconut husking 95 85
231 85 c. on $2 Uga gathering . . . . . . 1·25 1·00
232 $1.10 on 10 c. Type **54** . . . . . . 1·60 1·40
233 $2.60 on 20 c. Care of the aged . . . . 3·25 3·25
234 $3.20 on $2 Coronation regalia (Gold) . . 8·00 8·50
224/34 . . . . *Set of* 11 16·00 16·00

57 "An Island View in Atooi"

(Photo Heraclio Fournier)

1978 (18 Jan). *Bicentenary of Discovery of Hawaii. T* **57** *and similar horiz designs showing paintings by John Webber. Multicoloured. P* 13.
235 12 c. Type **57** 55 45
236 16 c. "View of Karakaooa, in Owhyhee" . . 65 55
237 20 c. "Offering before Capt. Cook in the Sandwich Islands" 70 60
238 30 c. "Tereoboo, King of Owhyhee bringing presents to Capt. Cook" 90 75
239 35 c. "Canoe in the Sandwich Islands, the rowers masked" . . . . 1·00 80
MS240 121 × 121 mm. Nos. 235/9 . . . . 4·25 4·25
Nos. 235/9 were each printed in small sheets of 6, including 1 *se-tenant* stamp-size label.

PRICES OF SETS

Set prices are given for many issues, generally those containing five stamps or more. Definitive sets include one of each value or major colour change, but do not cover different perforations, die types or minor shades. Where a choice is possible the set prices are based on the cheapest versions of the stamps included in the listings.

58 "The Deposition of Christ" (Caravaggio)

59 Flags of Niue and U.K.

(Photo Heraclio Fournier)

1978 (15 Mar). *Easter. Paintings from the Vatican Galleries. T* **58** *and similar vert design. Multicoloured. P* 13.
241 10 c. Type **58** 15 10
242 20 c. "The Burial of Christ" (Bellini) 30 25
MS243 102 × 68 mm. Nos. 241/2 .. .. .. 55 60

1978 (15 Mar). *Easter. Children's Charity. Designs as Nos.* 241/2 *in separate miniature sheets* 64 × 78 *mm, each with a face value of* 70 *c. +* 5 *c. P* 13.
MS244 As Nos. 241/2 .. .. *Set of* 2 *sheets* 2·25 2·50

(Photo Heraclio Fournier)

1978 (26 June). *25th Anniv of Coronation. T* **59** *and similar horiz designs. Multicoloured.* A. *White border.* B. *Turquoise-green border. P* 13.

		A		B	
245 $1.10 Type **59**		1·75	1·50	1·75	1·50
246 $1.10 Coronation portrait by Cecil Beaton		1·75	1·50	1·75	1·50
247 $1.10 Queen's personal flag for New Zealand		1·75	1·50	1·75	1·50
MS248 87 × 98 mm. Nos. 245/7		6·00	4·00		†

Nos. 245/7 were printed together in small sheets of 6, containing two *se-tenant* strips of 3, with horizontal gutter margin between. The upper strip has white borders, the lower turquoise-green.

(Litho Questa)

1978 (27 Oct). *Designs as Nos.* 198/207 *but margin colours changed and silver frame. P* 13½ × 14.
249 12 c. Type **50** 20 20
250 16 c. Planting taro 25 25
251 30 c. Banana gathering 40 40
252 35 c. Harvesting taro 45 45
253 40 c. Gathering shell fish 50 50
254 60 c. Reef fishing 65 65
255 75 c. Luku gathering 70 70
256 $1.10, Canoe fishing.. .. .. .. 1·40 1·40
257 $3.20, Coconut husking .. .. .. 3·00 3·25
258 $4.20, Uga gathering .. .. 4·00 4·25
249/58 .. .. *Set of* 10 10·50 11·00
See also Nos. 264/73.

60 "Festival of the Rosary"

(Des and photo Heraclio Fournier)

1978 (30 Nov). *Christmas. 450th Death Anniv of Dürer. T* **60** *and similar horiz designs. Multicoloured. P* 13.
259 20 c. Type **60** 40 25
260 30 c. "The Nativity" 50 40
261 35 c. "Adoration of the Magi" 55 45
MS262 143 × 82 mm. Nos. 259/61 .. .. 1·50 1·60
Nos. 259/61 were each printed in small sheets of 6.

1978 (30 Nov). *Christmas. Children's Charity. Designs as Nos.* 259/61 *in separate miniature sheets* 74 × 66 *mm., each with a face value of* 60 *c. +* 5 *c. P* 13.
MS263 As Nos. 259/61 .. .. *Set of* 3 *sheets* 2·50 2·75

(Litho Questa)

1979 (26 Feb–28 May). *Air. Designs as Nos.* 249/58 *but gold frames and additionally inscr* "AIRMAIL". *P* 13½ × 14.
264 15 c. Planting taro 20 20
265 20 c. Banana gathering 25 25
266 23 c. Harvesting taro 30 30
267 50 c. Canoe fishing 70 55
268 90 c. Reef fishing 85 85
269 $1.35, Type **50** (30.3) .. .. .. 1·25 1·50
270 $2.10, Gathering shell fish (30.3) .. .. 2·25 2·50
271 $2.60, Luku gathering (30.3) .. .. 3·00 3·25
272 $5.10, Coconut husking (28.5) .. .. 4·75 5·50
273 $6.35, Uga gathering (28.5).. .. .. 6·00 7·00
264/73 .. .. .. *Set of* 10 17·00 20·00

PRINTERS. The following stamps were printed in photogravure by Heraclio Fournier, Spain, *except where otherwise stated.*

61 "Pietà" (Gregorio Fernandez)

62 "The Nurse and Child" (Franz Hals)

1979 (2 Apr). *Easter. Paintings. T* **61** *and similar horiz design. Multicoloured. P* 13.
274 30 c. Type **61** 40 30
275 35 c. "Burial of Christ" (Pedro Roldan) .. 45 30
MS276 82 × 82 mm. Nos. 274/5 .. .. .. 90 1·00

1979 (2 Apr). *Easter. Children's Charity. Designs as Nos.* 274/5 *in separate miniature sheets* 86 × 69 *mm., each with a face value of* 70 *c. +* 5 *c. P* 13.
MS277 As Nos. 274/5 .. .. *Set of* 2 *sheets* 2·25 2·50

1979 (31 May). *International Year of the Child. Details of Paintings. T* **62** *and similar vert designs. Multicoloured. P* 14 × 13½.
278 16 c. Type **62** 25 20
279 20 c. "Child of the Duke of Osuna" (Goya) .. 30 25
280 30 c. "Daughter of Robert Strozzi" (Titian) .. 50 45
281 35 c. "Children eating Fruit" (Murillo) .. 50 50
MS282 80 × 115 mm. Nos. 278/81. P 13 .. .. 1·60 1·75

1979 (31 May). *International Year of the Child. Children's Charity. Designs as Nos.* 278/81 *in separate miniature sheets* 99 × 119 *mm, each with a face value of* 70 *c. +* 5 *c. P* 13.
MS283 As Nos. 278/81 .. .. *Set of* 4 *sheets* 3·50 4·00

63 Penny Black Stamp

64 Cook's Landing at Botany Bay

1979 (3 July). *Death Centenary of Sir Rowland Hill. T* **63** *and similar vert designs. Multicoloured. P* 14 × 13½.
284 20 c. Type **63** 25 30
285 20 c. Sir Rowland Hill and original Bath mail coach 25 30
286 30 c. Basel 1845 2½ r. stamp 40 45
287 30 c. Sir Rowland Hill and Alpine village coach 40 45
288 35 c. U.S.A. 1847 5 c. stamp 45 50
289 35 c. Sir Rowland Hill and first Transatlantic U.S.A. mail vessel 45 50
290 50 c. France 1849 20 c. stamp.. .. .. 60 65
291 50 c. Sir Rowland Hill and French Post Office railway van, 1849 .. .. .. 60 65
292 60 c. Bavaria 1849 1 k. stamp.. .. .. 70 80
293 60 c. Sir Rowland Hill and Bavarian coach with mail 70 80
284/93 .. .. *Set of* 10 4·50 5·00
MS294 143 × 149 mm. Nos. 284/93 .. .. 5·00 5·50
Nos. 284/5, 286/7, 288/9, 290/1 and 292/3 were each printed together, *se-tenant*, in horizontal pairs throughout the sheet forming composite designs.

1979 (30 July). *Death Bicentenary of Captain Cook. T* **64** *and similar horiz designs. Multicoloured. P* 14.
295 20 c. Type **64** 35 35
296 30 c. Cook's men during a landing on Erromanga 50 50
297 35 c. *Resolution* and *Discovery* in Queen Charlotte's Sound 55 55
298 75 c. Death of Captain Cook, Hawaii 95 95
MS299 104 × 80 mm. Nos. 295/8. P 13½.. .. 2·50 3·00

65 Launch of "Apollo 11"

66 "Virgin of Tortosa" (P. Serra)

1979 (27 Sept). *10th Anniv of Moon Landing. T* **65** *and similar vert designs. Multicoloured. P* 13½.
300 30 c. Type **65** 40 30
301 35 c. Lunar module on Moon 45 35
302 60 c. Helicopter, recovery ship and command module after splashdown 70 55
MS303 120 × 82 mm. Nos. 300/2 .. .. 1·50 1·60
Stamps from No. **MS**303 have the inscription in gold on a blue panel.

1979 (29 Nov). *Christmas. Paintings. T* **66** *and similar vert designs. Multicoloured. P* 13.
304 20 c. Type **66** 20 15
305 25 c. "Virgin with Milk" (R. di Mur) 25 20
306 30 c. "Virgin and Child" (S. di G. Sassetta) .. 30 30
307 50 c. "Virgin and Child" (J. Huguet) 45 40
MS308 95 × 113 mm. Nos. 304/7 .. .. .. 1·25 1·40

1979 (29 Nov). *Christmas. Children's Charity. Designs as Nos.* 304/7 *in separate miniature sheets,* 49 × 84 *mm, each with a face value of* 85 *c. +* 5 *c. P* 13.
MS309 As Nos. 304/7 .. .. *Set of* 4 *sheets* 4·00 4·25

HURRICANE
RELIEF
Plus 2c

(67)

68 "Pietà" (Bellini)

1980 (25 Jan). *Hurricane Relief. Various stamps surch as T* **67** *in black* (Nos. 310/19) *or silver* (320/30).

(*a*) *Nos.* 284/93 (*Death Centenary of Sir Rowland Hill*)
310 20 c. + 2 c. Type **63** 20 25
311 20 c. + 2 c. Sir Rowland Hill and original Bath mail coach 20 25
312 30 c. + 2 c. Basel 1845 2½ r. stamp 30 35
313 30 c. + 2 c. Sir Rowland Hill and Alpine village coach 30 35
314 35 c. + 2 c. U.S.A. 1847 5 c. stamp 35 40
315 35 c. + 2 c. Sir Rowland Hill and first Transatlantic U.S.A. mail vessel 35 40
316 50 c. + 2 c. France 1849 20 c. stamp 50 55
317 50 c. + 2 c. Sir Rowland Hill and French Post Office railway van, 1849.. .. .. 50 55
318 60 c. + 2 c. Bavaria 1849 1 k. stamp 60 65
319 60 c. + 2 c. Sir Rowland Hill and Bavarian coach with mail 60 65

(*b*) *Nos.* 295/8 (*Death Bicentenary of Captain Cook*)
320 20 c. + 2 c. Type **64** 20 25
321 30 c. + 2 c. Cook's men during a landing on Erromanga 30 35
322 35 c. + 2 c. *Resolution* and *Discovery* in Queen Charlotte's Sound 35 40
323 75 c. + 2 c. Death of Captain Cook, Hawaii .. 75 80

(*c*) *Nos.* 300/2 (*10th Anniv of Moon Landing*)
324 30 c. + 2 c. Type **65** 30 35
325 35 c. + 2 c. Lunar module on Moon 35 40
326 60 c. + 2 c. Helicopter, recovery ship and command module after splashdown .. 60 65

(*d*) *Nos.* 304/7 (*Christmas*)
327 20 c. + 2 c. Type **66** 20 25
328 25 c. + 2 c. "Virgin with Milk" (R. de Mur) .. 25 30
329 30 c. + 2 c. "Virgin and Child" (S. di G. Sassetta) 30 35
330 50 c. + 2c. "Virgin and Child" (J. Huguet) .. 50 55
310/30 .. .. *Set of* 21 7·50 8·00
On Nos. 310/19 "HURRICANE RELIEF" covers the two designs of each value.

1980 (2 Apr). *Easter. Paintings. T* **68** *and similar horiz designs showing "Pietà" paintings by various artists. Multicoloured. P* 13½ × 13.
331 25 c. Type **68** 30 25
332 30 c. Botticelli 35 30
333 35 c. Antony van Dyck 35 30
MS334 75 × 104 mm. As Nos. 331/3, but each with additional premium of "+ 2 c." .. .. .. 1·00 1·10
The premiums on No. **MS**334 were used to support Hurricane Relief.

1980 (2 Apr). *Easter. Hurricane Relief. Designs as Nos.* 331/3 *in separate miniature sheets,* 75 × 52 *mm, each with a face value of* 85 *c. +* 5 *c. P* 13 × 14.
MS335 As Nos. 331/3 .. .. *Set of* 3 *sheets* 2·75 3·00

69 Ceremonial Stool, New Guinea

1980 (30 July). *South Pacific Festival of Arts, New Guinea. T* **69** *and similar vert designs. Multicoloured. P* 13.
336 20 c. Type **69** 20 20
337 20 c. Ku-Tagwa plaque, New Guinea.. .. 20 20
338 20 c. Suspension hook, New Guinea 20 20
339 20 c. Ancestral board, New Guinea 20 20
340 25 c. Platform post, New Hebrides 25 25
341 25 c. Canoe ornament, New Ireland 25 25
342 25 c. Carved figure, Admiralty Islands .. 25 25
343 25 c. Female with child, Admiralty Islands .. 25 25
344 30 c. The God A'a, Rurutu (Austral Islands) .. 25 30
345 30 c. Statue of Tangaroa, Cook Islands .. 25 30
346 30 c. Ivory pendant, Tonga 25 30
347 30 c. Tapa (Hiapo) cloth, Niue.. .. .. 25 30
348 35 c. Feather box (Waka), New Zealand .. 30 35
349 35 c. Hei-Tiki amulet, New Zealand 30 35
350 35 c. House post, New Zealand 30 35
351 35 c. Feather image of god Ku, Hawaii .. 30 35
336/51 .. .. *Set of* 16 3·75 4·00

MS352 Four sheets, each 86 × 124 mm. (a) Nos. 336, 340, 344, 348; (b) Nos. 337, 341, 345, 349; (c) Nos. 338, 342, 346, 350; (d) Nos. 339, 343, 347, 351. Each stamp with an additional premium of 2 c. .. .. *Set of 4 sheets* 4·00 4·25
Nos. 336/9, 340/3, 344/7 and 348/51 were each printed together, *se-tenant*, in horizontal strips of 4 throughout the sheet.

NEW ZEALAND STAMP EXHIBITION

ZEAPEX'80 AUCKLAND

(70) (71)

1980 (22 Aug). *"Zeapex '80" International Stamp Exhibition, Auckland. Nos.* 284, 286, 288, 290 *and* 292 *optd with T* **70** *and Nos.* 285, 287, 289, 291 *and* 293 *optd with T* **71**, *both in black on silver background.*

353 20 c. Type **63** 20 20
354 20 c. Sir Rowland Hill and original Bath mail coach 20 20
355 30 c. Basel 1845 2½ r. stamp 30 30
356 30 c. Sir Rowland Hill and Alpine village coach 30 30
357 35 c. U.S.A. 1847 5 c. stamp 35 35
358 35 c. Sir Rowland Hill and first Transatlantic U.S.A. mail vessel 35 35
359 50 c. France 1849 20 c. stamp 45 45
360 50 c. Sir Rowland Hill and French Post Office railway van, 1849 .. .. .. 45 45
361 60 c. Bavaria 1849 1 k. stamp 55 55
362 60 c. Sir Rowland Hill and Bavarian coach with mail 55 55
353/62 .. .. *Set of* 10 3·50 3·50
MS363 143 × 149 mm. Nos. 353/62, each additionally surcharged "+ 2 c." .. .. 4·00 3·75

72 Queen Elizabeth the Queen Mother

73 100 Metre Dash

1980 (15 Sept). *80th Birthday of Queen Elizabeth the Queen Mother. P* 13.

364 **72** $1.10 multicoloured .. .. 1·75 1·75
MS365 55 × 80 mm. **72** $3 multicoloured .. .. 3·25 3·50
No. 364 was printed in small sheets of 6 including one *se-tenant* stamp-size label.

1980 (30 Oct). *Olympic Games, Moscow. T* **73** *and similar horiz designs. Multicoloured. P* 14 × 13½.

366 20 c. Type **73** 15 20
367 20 c. Allen Wells, Great Britain (winner of 100 metre dash) 15 20
368 25 c. } 400 metre freestyle (winner, Ines Diers, 20 25
369 25 c. } D.D.R.) 20 25
370 30 c. } Soling Class Yachting (winner, 25 30
371 30 c. } Denmark) 25 30
372 35 c. } Football (winner, Czechoslovakia) .. 30 35
373 35 c. } .. 30 35
366/73 .. .. *Set of* 8 1·60 2·00
MS374 119 × 128 mm. Nos. 366/73, each stamp including premium of 2 c. .. .. .. 2·10 2·25
Nos. 366/7, 368/9, 370/1 and 372/3 were each printed together, *se-tenant*, in horizontal pairs throughout the sheet, forming composite designs.

74 "The Virgin and Child"

75 *Phalaenopsis sp.*

1980 (28 Nov). *Christmas and 450th Death Anniv of Andrea del Sarto (painter). T* **74** *and similar vert designs showing different "The Virgin and Child" works. P* 13.

375 20 c. multicoloured 25 25
376 25 c. multicoloured 30 30
377 30 c. multicoloured 30 30
378 35 c. multicoloured 35 35
MS379 87 × 112 mm. Nos. 375/8 .. .. .. 1·10 1·25

1980 (28 Nov). *Christmas. Children's Charity. Designs as Nos.* 375/8 *in separate miniature sheets* 62 × 84 *mm, each with a face value of* 80 c. + 5 c. *P* 13.

MS380 As Nos. 375/8 .. .. *Set of 4 sheets* 3·00 3·25

1981 (2 Apr)–**82**. *Flowers* (1*st series*). *Horiz designs as T* **75**. *Multicoloured. P* 13.

381 2 c. Type **75** 5 5
382 2 c. Moth Orchid 5 5
383 5 c. *Euphorbia pulcherrima* 5 5
384 5 c. Poinsettia 5 5
385 10 c. *Thunbergia alata* 8 10
386 10 c. Black-eyed Susan 8 10
387 15 c. *Cochlospermum hibiscoides* 12 15
388 15 c. Buttercup Tree 12 15
389 20 c. *Begonia sp.* 15 20
390 20 c. Begonia 15 20
391 25 c. *Plumeria sp.* 20 25
392 25 c. Frangipani 20 25
393 30 c. *Strelitzia reginae* (26 May) 25 30
394 30 c. Bird of Paradise (26 May) 25 30
395 35 c. *Hibiscus syriacus* (26 May) 25 30
396 35 c. Rose of Sharon (26 May) 25 30
397 40 c. *Nymphaea sp.* (26 May) 30 35
398 40 c. Water Lily (26 May) 30 35
399 50 c. *Tibouchina sp.* (26 May) 40 45
400 50 c. Princess Flower (26 May) 40 45
401 60 c. *Nelumbo sp.* (26 May) 50 55
402 60 c. Lotus (26 May) 50 55
403 80 c. *Hybrid hibiscus* (26 May) 60 65
404 80 c. Yellow Hibiscus (26 May) 60 65
405 $1 Golden Shower Tree (*Cassia fistula*) (9.12.81) 80 85
406 $2 *Orchid var.* (9.12.81) .. .. .. 1·60 1·75
407 $3 *Orchid sp.* (9.12.81) .. .. .. 2·40 2·50
408 $4 *Euphorbia pulcherrima poinsettia* (15.1.82) .. .. 3·25 3·50
409 $6 *Hybrid hibiscus* (15.1.82) .. .. 4·75 5·00
410 $10 Scarlet Hibiscus (*Hibiscus rosasinensis*) (12.3.82) .. .. 8·00 8·50
381/410 .. .. *Set of* 30 24·00 26·00
The two designs of the 2 c. to 80 c. show different drawings of the same flower, one inscribed with its name in Latin, the other giving the common name. These were printed together, *se-tenant*, in horizontal and vertical pairs throughout the sheet.
Nos. 405/10 are larger, 47 × 33 mm.
See also Nos. 527/36.

76 "Jesus Defiled" (El Greco)

77 Prince Charles

1981 (10 Apr). *Easter. Details of Paintings. T* **76** *and similar horiz designs. Multicoloured. P* 14.

425 35 c. Type **76** 30 30
426 50 c. "Pietà" (Fernando Gallego) 50 50
427 60 c. "The Supper of Emmaus" (Jacopo da Pontormo) 55 55
MS428 69 × 111 mm. As Nos. 425/7, but each with charity premium of 2 c. P 13½ .. .. 1·40 1·60

1981 (10 Apr). *Easter. Children's Charity. Designs as Nos.* 425/7 *in separate miniature sheets* 78 × 86 *mm, each with a face value of* 80 c. + 5 c. *P* 13½ × 14.

MS429 As Nos. 425/7 .. .. *Set of 3 sheets* 2·50 2·75

1981 (26 June). *Royal Wedding. T* **77** *and similar vert designs. Multicoloured. P* 14.

430 75 c. Type **77** .. .. 1·25 1·25
431 95 c. Lady Diana Spencer .. .. .. 1·75 1·75
432 $1.20, Prince Charles and Lady Diana .. 2·00 2·00
MS433 78 × 85 mm. Nos. 430/2 .. .. .. 5·00 5·00
Nos. 430/2 were each printed in small sheets of 6, including one *se-tenant* stamp-size label.

78 Footballer Silhouettes

+5c

(79)

1981 (16 Oct). *World Cup Football Championship, Spain* (1982). *T* **78** *and similar horiz designs showing footballer silhouettes. P* 13.

434 30 c. blue-green, gold & new blue (Type **78**) .. 25 25
435 30 c. blue-green, gold and new blue (gold figure 3rd from left of stamp) 25 25
436 30 c. blue-green, gold and new blue (gold figure 4th from left) 25 25
437 35 c. new blue, gold and reddish orange (gold figure 3rd from left) 30 30
438 35 c. new blue, gold and reddish orange (gold figure 4th from left) 30 30
439 35 c. new blue, gold and reddish orange (gold figure 2nd from left) 30 30
440 40 c. reddish orange, gold and blue-green (gold figure 3rd from left, displaying close control) 35 40
441 40 c. reddish orange, gold and blue-green (gold figure 2nd from left) 35 40
442 40 c. reddish orange, gold and blue-green (gold figure 3rd from left, heading) 35 40
434/42 .. .. *Set of* 9 2·40 2·50
MS443 162 × 122 mm. 30 c. + 3 c., 35 c. + 3 c., 40 c. + 3 c. (each × 3). As Nos. 434/42 .. .. 3·00 3·00
The three designs of each value were printed together, *se-tenant*, in horizontal strips of 3 throughout the sheets.

1981 (3 Nov). *International Year for Disabled Persons. Nos.* 430/3 *surch as T* **79**.

444 75 c. + 5 c. Type **77** .. .. 2·25 2·00
445 95 c. + 5 c. Lady Diana Spencer .. .. 2·75 2·25
446 $1.20 + 5 c. Prince Charles and Lady Diana 3·75 2·75
MS447 78 × 85 mm. As Nos. 444/6, each surcharged "+ 10 c." .. .. 8·00 8·00
Nos. 444/6 have commemorative inscription overprinted on the sheet margins.

80 "The Holy Family with Angels"

81 Prince of Wales

1981 (11 Dec). *Christmas and 375th Birth Anniv of Rembrandt. T* **80** *and similar vert designs. Multicoloured. P* 14 × 13.

448 20 c. Type **79** 20 20
449 35 c. "Presentation in the Temple" 30 30
450 50 c. "Virgin and Child in Temple" 45 45
451 60 c. "The Holy Family" 55 55
MS452 79 × 112 mm. Nos. 448/51 .. .. .. 1·50 1·50

1982 (22 Jan). *Christmas. Children's Charity. Designs as Nos.* 448/51 *in separate miniature sheets* 66 × 80 *mm, each with a face value of* 80 c. + 5 c. *P* 14 × 13.

MS453 As Nos. 448/51 .. .. *Set of 4 sheets* 2·50 2·75

1982 (1 July). *21st Birthday of Princess of Wales. T* **81** *and similar horiz designs. Multicoloured. P* 14.

454 50 c. Type **81** 55 55
455 $1.25, Prince and Princess of Wales .. 1·25 1·25
456 $2.50, Princess of Wales .. .. .. 2·00 2·00
MS457 81 × 101 mm. Nos. 454/6 .. .. .. 3·75 4·00
Nos. 454/6 were each printed in small sheets of 6 including one *se-tenant* stamp-size label.
The stamps from No. **MS**457 are without white borders.

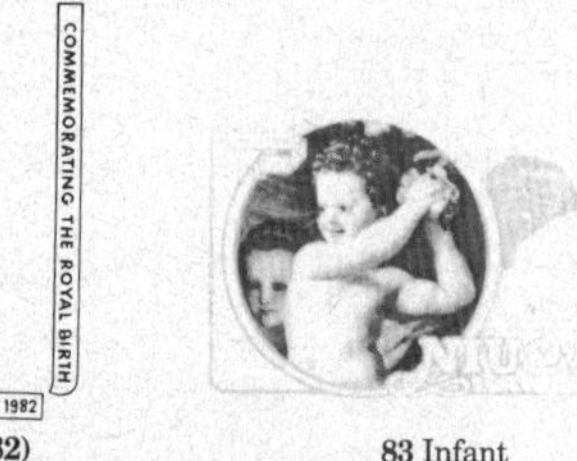

(82) **83** Infant

1982 (23 July). *Birth of Prince William of Wales* (1*st issue*). *Nos.* 430/3 *optd as T* **82**.

458 75 c. Type **77** (optd with T **82**) .. .. 2·25 1·75
a. Pair. Nos. 458/9 .. .. 4·50
459 75 c. Type **77** (optd "BIRTH OF PRINCE WILLIAM OF WALES 21 JUNE 1982") 2·25 1·75
460 95 c. Lady Diana Spencer (optd with T **82**) .. 3·25 2·50
a. Pair. Nos. 460/1 .. .. 6·50
461 95 c. Lady Diana Spencer (optd "BIRTH OF PRINCE WILLIAM OF WALES 21 JUNE 1982") .. .. 3·25 2·50
462 $1.20, Prince Charles and Lady Diana Spencer (optd with T **82**) .. .. 4·25 3·25
a. Pair. Nos. 462/3 .. .. 8·50
463 $1.20, Prince Charles and Lady Diana Spencer (optd "BIRTH OF PRINCE WILLIAM OF WALES 21 JUNE 1982") 4·25 3·25
458/63 .. .. *Set of* 6 18·00 14·00
MS464 78 × 85 mm. Nos. 430/2 each optd "PRINCE WILLIAM OF WALES 21 JUNE 1982" .. .. 8·50 6·50
Nos. 458/9, 460/1 and 462/3 were each printed *se-tenant* in small sheets of 6, containing three stamps overprinted with Type **82**, two with "BIRTH OF PRINCE WILLIAM OF WALES 21 JUNE 1982" and one stamp-size label.

1982 (10 Sept). *Birth of Prince William of Wales* (2*nd issue*). *Designs as Nos.* 454/7 *but with changed inscriptions. Multicoloured. P* 14.

465 50 c. Type **81** 55 55
466 $1.25, Prince and Princess of Wales .. 1·25 1·25
467 $2.50, Princess of Wales .. .. .. 2·00 2·00
MS468 81 × 101 mm. As Nos. 465/7 .. .. 3·75 4·00
Nos. 465/7 were each printed in small sheets of 6 including one *se-tenant*, stamp-size, label.

1982 (3 Dec). *Christmas. Paintings of Infants by Bronzino, Murillo and Boucher. T* **83** *and similar horiz designs. P* 13 × 14½.

469 40 c. multicoloured 35 40
470 52 c. multicoloured 45 50
471 83 c. multicoloured 80 85
472 $1.05, multicoloured .. .. 95 1·00
MS473 110 × 76 mm. Designs as Nos. 469/72 (*each* 31 × 27 *mm*), but without portrait of Princess and Prince William. P 13½ .. .. 2·50 2·75

ALTERED CATALOGUE NUMBERS

Any Catalogue numbers altered from the last edition are shown as a list in the introductory pages.

84 Prince and Princess of Wales with Prince William

85 Prime Minister Robert Rex

1982 (3 Dec). *Christmas. Children's Charity. Sheet* 72 × 58 *mm. P* 13 × 13½.
MS474 **84** 80 c. + 5 c. multicoloured 85 90
No. **MS**474 occurs with four different designs in the sheet margin.

1983 (14 Mar). *Commonwealth Day. T* **85** *and similar horiz designs. Multicoloured. P* 13.
475 70 c. Type **85** 65 70
476 70 c. *Resolution* and *Adventure* off Niue, 1774 65 70
477 70 c. Passion flower 65 70
478 70 c. Limes 65 70
Nos. 475/8 were issued together, *se-tenant*, in blocks of four throughout the sheet.

86 Scouts signalling

XV WORLD JAMBOREE CANADA
(87)

1983 (28 Apr). *75th Anniv of Boy Scout Movement and 125th Birth Anniv of Lord Baden-Powell. T* **86** *and similar vert designs. Multicoloured. P* 13.
479 40 c. Type **86** 35 40
480 50 c. Planting sapling 45 50
481 83 c. Map-reading 85 90
MS482 137 × 90 mm. As Nos. 479/81, but each with premium of 3 c. .. .. 1·60 1·75

1983 (14 July). *15th World Scout Jamboree, Alberta, Canada. Nos.* 479/82 *optd with T* **87**, *in black on silver background.*
483 40 c. Type **86** 35 40
484 50 c. Planting sapling 45 50
485 83 c. Map-reading 85 90
MS486 137 × 90 mm. As Nos. 483/5, but each with premium of 3 c. .. .. 1·60 1·75

88 Right Whale

1983 (15 Aug). *Protect the Whales. T* **88** *and similar horiz designs. Multicoloured. P* 13 × 14.
487 12 c. Type **88** 10 12
488 25 c. Fin Whale 20 25
489 35 c. Sei Whale 30 35
490 40 c. Blue Whale 35 40
491 58 c. Bowhead Whale 50 55
492 70 c. Sperm Whale 65 70
493 83 c. Humpback Whale 80 85
494 $1.05, Lesser Rorqual .. .. 95 1·00
495 $2.50, Grey Whale .. .. 2·10 2·25
487/95 .. .. *Set of* 9 5·50 6·00

89 Montgolfier Balloon, 1783

90 "The Garvagh Madonna"

1983 (14 Oct). *Bicentenary of Manned Flight. T* **89** *and similar horiz designs. Multicoloured.* (a) *Postage. P* 13½.
496 25 c. Type **89** 20 25
497 40 c. Wright Brothers' *Flyer*, 1903 .. .. .. 35 40
498 58 c. *Graf Zeppelin*, 1928 .. .. 50 55
499 70 c. Boeing "247", 1933 .. .. 65 70
500 82 c. "Apollo 8", 1968 .. .. 80 85
501 $1.05, Space shuttle *Columbia*, 1982 .. .. 95 1·00
496/501 .. .. *Set of* 6 3·00 3·25

(*b*) *Air. Inscr* "AIRMAIL"
MS502 118 × 130 mm. Nos. 496/501. P 13 .. 3·00 3·25

1983 (25 Nov). *Christmas. 500th Birth Anniv of Raphael. T* **90** *and similar vert designs. Multicoloured. P* 14 × 13½.
503 30 c. Type **90** 25 30
504 40 c. "Madonna of the Granduca" 30 35
505 58 c. "Madonna of the Goldfinch" 45 50
506 70 c. "The Holy Family of Francis I" 55 60
507 83 c. "The Holy Family with Saints" 65 70
MS508 120 × 114 mm. As Nos. 503/7 but each with a premium of 3 c. .. .. 2·25

1983 (30 Nov). *Various stamps surch as T* **200** *of Cook Islands.*

(*a*) *Nos.* 393/4, 399/404 *and* 407
509 52 c. on 30 c. *Strelitzia reginae* 40 45
510 52 c. on 30 c. Bird of Paradise 40 45
511 58 c. on 50 c. *Tibouchina sp.* 50 55
512 58 c. on 50 c. Princess Flower 50 55
513 70 c. on 60 c. *Nelumbo sp.* 55 60
514 70 c. on 60 c. Lotus 55 60
515 83 c. on 80 c. *Hybrid hibiscus* 70 75
516 83 c. on 80 c. Yellow Hibiscus 70 75
517 $3.70 on $3 *Orchid sp.* .. .. .. 3·00 3·25

(*b*) *Nos.* 431/2 *and* 455/6
518 $1.10 on 95 c. Lady Diana Spencer .. .. 3·00 2·25
a. Error. Surch on No. 458 .. .. .. 6·00 6·00
ab. Pair. Nos. 518a/b .. .. 15·00 15·00
b. Error. Surch on No. 459 .. .. .. 9·00 9·00
519 $1.10 on $1.25, Prince and Princess of Wales 2·25 2·00
520 $2.60 on $1.20, Prince Charles and Lady Diana .. .. 5·50 3·50
a. Error. Surch on No. 462 .. .. .. 6·00 6·00
ab. Pair. Nos. 520a/b .. .. 15·00 15·00
b. Error. Surch on No. 463 .. .. .. 9·00 9·00
521 $2.60 on $2.50, Princess of Wales .. .. 3·50 3·25
509/21 .. .. *Set of* 13 19·00 17·00

1983 (29 Dec). *Christmas. 500th Birth Anniv of Raphael. Children's Charity. Designs as Nos.* 503/7 *in separate miniature sheets,* 65 × 80 *mm, each with face value of* 85 *c.* + 5 *c. P* 13½.
MS522 As Nos. 503/7 .. .. *Set of* 5 *sheets* 3·00

91 Morse Key Transmitter

92 *Phalaenopsis sp.*

1984 (23 Jan). *World Communications Year. T* **91** *and similar vert designs. Multicoloured. P* 13 × 13½.
523 40 c. Type **91** 30 35
524 52 c. Wall-mounted phone 40 45
525 83 c. Communications satellite 60 65
MS526 114 × 90 mm. Nos. 523/5 .. .. .. 1·10 1·25

1984 (20 Feb–23 July). *Flowers (2nd series). Designs as Nos.* 381 *etc., but with gold frames and redrawn inscr as in T* **92**. *Multicoloured. P* 13 *(Nos.* 537/42*) or* 13 × 13½ *(others).*
527 12 c. Type **92** 10 12
528 25 c. *Euphorbia pulcherrima* 20 25
529 30 c. *Cochlospermum hibiscoides* 25 30
530 35 c. *Begonia sp.* 30 35
531 40 c. *Plumeria sp.* 30 35
532 52 c. *Strelitzia reginae* 40 45
533 58 c. *Hibiscus syriacus* 45 50
534 70 c. *Tibouchina sp.* 55 60
535 83 c. *Nelumbo sp.* 60 65
536 $1.05, *Hybrid hibiscus* 80 85
537 $1.75, *Cassia fistula* (10.5) .. .. .. 1·40 1·50
538 $2.30, *Orchid var.* (10.5) .. .. 1·75 1·90
539 $3.90, *Orchid sp.* (10.5) .. .. 3·00 3·25
540 $5 *Euphorbia pulcherrima poinsettia* (18.6) 3·75 4·00
541 $6.60, *Hybrid hibiscus* (18.6) .. .. .. 5·00 5·25
542 $8.30, *Hibiscus rosasinensis* (23.7) .. .. 6·25 6·50
527/42 .. .. *Set of* 16 22·50 24·00
Nos. 537/42 are larger, 39 × 31 mm.

93 Discus-throwing

94 Koala Bear

1984 (15 Mar). *Olympic Games, Los Angeles. T* **93** *and similar multicoloured designs showing ancient Greek sports. P* 14.
547 30 c. Type **93** 25 30
548 35 c. Sprinting (*horiz*) 30 35
549 40 c. Horse racing (*horiz*) 35 40
550 58 c. Boxing (*horiz*) 50 55
551 70 c. Javelin-throwing 60 65

1984 (24 Aug). *"Ausipex" International Stamp Exhibition, Melbourne.* (a) *Postage. Vert designs as T* **94** *showing Koala Bears. P* 14.
552 25 c. multicoloured 25 30
553 35 c. multicoloured 30 35
554 40 c. multicoloured 35 40
555 58 c. multicoloured 50 55
556 70 c. multicoloured 60 65

(*b*) *Air. Vert designs showing Kangaroos*
557 83 c. multicoloured 70 75
558 $1.05, multicoloured 90 95
559 $2.50, multicoloured .. .. 2·10 2·25
552/9 .. .. *Set of* 8 5·00 5·50
MS560 110 × 64 mm. $1.75, Wallaby; $1.75, Koala Bear. P 13½ .. .. 3·00 3·25

Norfolk Island

The stamps of TASMANIA were used in Norfolk Island from 1854 until 1856, such use being identified by the "72" numeral cancellation. From 1897 the stamps of NEW SOUTH WALES were in regular use, being replaced by issues for AUSTRALIA from 1913 to 1947.

AUSTRALIAN ADMINISTRATION

PRINTERS. Nos. 1 to 42 were printed at the Note Printing Branch Reserve Bank of Australia (until 14 Jan 1960, known as the Note Printing Branch, Commonwealth Bank) by recess. See note at the beginning of Australia *re* imprints.

1 Ball Bay

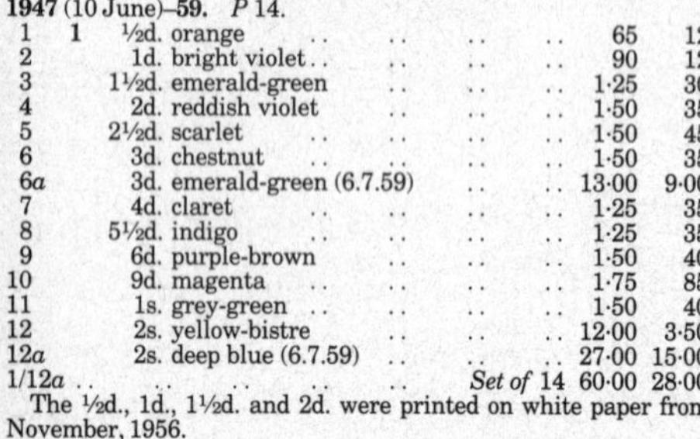

1947 (10 June)–**59.** *P* 14.

No.	Type	Description		
1	**1**	½d. orange	65	12
2		1d. bright violet	90	12
3		1½d. emerald-green	1·25	30
4		2d. reddish violet	1·50	35
5		2½d. scarlet	1·50	45
6		3d. chestnut	1·50	35
6*a*		3d. emerald-green (6.7.59)	13·00	9·00
7		4d. claret	1·25	35
8		5½d. indigo	1·25	35
9		6d. purple-brown	1·50	40
10		9d. magenta	1·75	85
11		1s. grey-green	1·50	40
12		2s. yellow-bistre	12·00	3·50
12*a*		2s. deep blue (6.7.59)	27·00	15·00
1/12*a*		.. .. *Set of* 14	60·00	28·00

The ½d., 1d., 1½d. and 2d. were printed on white paper from November, 1956.

NOTE. Stamps of T 1, perf 11, or in different colours, perf 11, are in the same category as those mentioned in Australia after No. 221.

2 Warder's Tower

3 Airfield

1953 (10 June). *T* **2/3** *and similar designs. P* 14½ × 15 (*vert*) *or* 15 × 14½ (*horiz*).

No.	Description		
13	3½d. brown-lake	5·00	2·00
14	6½d. deep green	5·00	2·25
15	7½d. deep blue	6·00	4·50
16	8½d. chocolate	12·00	6·50
17	10d. reddish violet	12·00	4·00
18	5s. sepia	48·00	20·00
13/18	.. .. *Set of* 6	80·00	35·00

Designs: *Horiz* (*as T* **3**)—7½d. First Governor's Residence; 5s. Bloody Bridge. *Vert* (*as T* **2**)—8½d. Barracks entrance; 10d. Salt house.

8 Norfolk Island Seal and Pitcairners Landing

1956 (8 June). *Centenary of Landing of Pitcairn Islanders on Norfolk Island. P* 15 × 14½.

No.	Type	Description		
19	**8**	3d. deep bluish green	2·00	1·50
20		2s. violet (*shades*)	5·00	4·50

Alternate stamps of the 2s. value were printed from a different die which is distinguishable by a dot in the bottom right corner.

7d   8d   NORFOLK ISLAND 5D

(9)   (10)   (11)

1958 (1 July). *Nos.* 15/16 *surch with T* **9/10**.

No.	Description		
21	7d. on 7½d. deep blue	4·00	3·50
22	8d. on 8½d. chocolate	5·00	3·50

1959 (7 Dec). 150*th Anniv of Australian Post Office. No.* 331 *of Australia surch with T* **11**.

No.	Description		
23	5d. on 4d. slate (R.)	2·00	60

12 *Hibiscus insularis*

14 White Tern

16 Red Hibiscus

17 Queen Elizabeth II and Cereus

21 Rose Apple

22 Red-tailed Tropic Bird

(Design recess; centre typo (T **21**))

1960–62. *T* **12, 14, 16/17, 21/2** *and similar designs. P* 14½ *or* 14½ × 14 (10*s*.).

No.	Description		
24	1d. bluish green (23.5.60)	20	10
25	2d. rose and myrtle-green (23.5.60)	25	15
26	3d. green (1.5.61)	1·25	30
27	5d. bright purple (20.6.60)	1·50	70
28	8d. red (20.6.60)	3·00	2·00
29	9d. ultramarine (23.5.60)	3·25	1·75
30	10d. brown and reddish violet (as No. 17) (27.2.61)	7·00	3·50
31	1s. 1d. carmine-red (16.10.61)	2·25	1·75
32	2s. sepia (1.5.61)	5·50	2·75
33	2s. 5d. deep violet (5.2.62)	2·50	1·50
34	2s. 8d. cinnamon and deep green (9.4.62) ..	6·00	2·25
35	5s. sepia and deep green (as No. 18) (27.2.61)	18·00	4·00
36	10s. emerald-green (14.8.61) (Optd S. £55) ..	50·00	35·00
24/36	.. .. *Set of* 13	90·00	50·00

Designs: *Vert* (*as T* **12**)—2d. *Lagunaria patersonii*; 5d. Lantana. (*As T* **21**); 1s. 1d. Fringed Hibiscus; 2s. 5d. Passion-flower. (*As T* **14**)—2s. Solanders Petrel.

Nos. 30 and 35 are redrawn.

The Specimen overprint on No. 36 is of similar status to those mentioned in the note at the beginning of Australia.

2/8

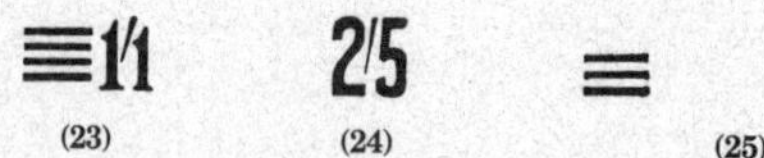

(23)   (24)   (25)

1960. *As Nos.* 13/15 *but colours changed, surch with T* **23/5**.

No.	Description		
37	1s. 1d. on 3½d. deep ultramarine (26.9.60)	10·00	7·00
38	2s. 5d. on 6½d. bluish green (26.9.60) ..	12·00	7·50
39	2s. 8d. on 7½d. sepia (29.8.60)	20·00	11·00

26 Queen Elizabeth II and Map

27 "Tweed Trousers" (*Atypichthys latus*)

1960 (24 Oct). *Introduction of Local Government. P* 14.

No.	Type	Description		
40	**26**	2s. 8d. reddish purple	35·00	25·00

1960 (21 Nov). *Christmas. As No.* 328 *of Australia.*

No.	Description		
41	5d. bright purple	2·50	1·75

1961 (20 Nov). *Christmas. As No.* 341 *of Australia.*

No.	Description		
42	5d. slate-blue	1·25	80

PRINTERS. All the following issues to No. 233 were printed in photogravure by Harrison and Sons, Ltd, London except issues which are in the same designs as Australia, *and where otherwise stated.*

1962–63. *Fishes. Horiz designs as T* **27**. *P* 14½ × 14.

No.	Description		
43	6d. sepia, yellow & dp bluish green (16.7.62)	2·00	1·00
44	11d. red-orange, brown and blue (25.2.63) ..	3·25	2·00
45	1s. blue, pink and yellow-olive (17.9.62) ..	2·00	1·00
46	1s. 3d. blue, red-brown and green (15.7.63)	5·00	2·50
47	1s. 6d. sepia, violet and light blue (6.5.63) ..	8·00	4·50
48	2s. 3d. dp blue, red & greenish yell (23.9.63)	9·50	5·00
43/8	.. .. *Set of* 6	27·00	14·50

Designs:—11d. "Trumpeter"; 1s. "Po'ov"; 1s. 3d. "Dreamfish"; 1s. 6d. "Hapoéka"; 2s. 3d. "Ophie" (*carangidae*).

1962 (19 Nov). *Christmas. As Nos.* 345 *of Australia.*

No.	Description		
49	5d. ultramarine	1·00	60

1963 (11 Nov). *Christmas. As No.* 361 *of Australia.*

No.	Description		
50	5d. red	1·00	60

33 Overlooking Kingston

37 Norfolk Pine

1964 (24 Feb–28 Sept). *Views. Horiz designs as T* **33**. *Multicoloured. P* 14½ × 14.

No.	Description		
51	5d. Type **33**	1·50	30
52	8d. Kingston	1·75	75
53	9d. The Arches (Bumboras) (11.5)	2·00	75
54	10d. Slaughter Bay (28.9)	6·00	90

(Photo Note Ptg Branch, Reserve Bank of Australia, Melbourne)

1964 (1 July). 50*th Anniv of Norfolk Island as Australian Territory. P* 13½.

No.	Type	Description		
55	**37**	5d. black, red and orange	50	15
56		8d. black, red and grey-green	1·00	40

1964 (9 Nov). *Christmas. As No.* 372 *of Australia.*

No.	Description		
57	5d. green, blue, buff and violet	75	45

1965 (14 Apr). 50*th Anniv of Gallipoli Landing. As T* **184** *of Australia, but slightly larger* (22 × 34½ *mm*). *Photo.*

No.	Description		
58	5d. sepia, black and emerald	45	15

1965 (25 Oct). *Christmas. Helecon paper. As No.* 381 *of Australia.*

No.	Description		
59	5d. multicoloured	20	10

(New Currency. 100 cents = $1 Australian)

38 *Hibiscus insularis*

39 Headstone Bridge

1966 (14 Feb). *Decimal currency. Various stamps surch in black on silver tablets, which vary slightly in size, obliterating old value as in T* **38**. *Surch typo.*

No.	Type	Description		
60	**38**	1 c. on 1d. bluish green (*value tablet* 4 × 5 *mm*)	30	12
		a. Value tablet larger, 5½ × 5½ mm	75	40
61	–	2 c. on 2d. rose and myrtle-green (No. 25)	25	10
62	**14**	3 c. on 3d. green	60	15
63	–	4 c. on 5d. bright purple (No. 27) ..	45	15
64	**16**	5 c. on 8d. red	50	15
65	–	10 c. on 10d. brown & reddish vio (No. 30)	1·25	45
66	–	15 c. on 1s. 1d. carmine-red (No. 31) ..	1·25	65
67	–	20 c. on 2s. sepia (No. 32)	4·00	1·50
68	–	25 c. on 2s. 5d. deep violet (No. 33) ..	2·00	1·75
69	**21**	30 c. on 2s. 8d. cinnamon and deep green	3·50	1·75
70	–	50 c. on 5s. sepia and deep green (No. 35)	6·00	2·75
71	**22**	$1 on 10s. emerald-green (*value tablet* 7 × 6½ *mm*)	6·00	4·75
		a. Value tablet smaller, 6½ × 4 mm	6·00	4·75
60/71		.. .. *Set of* 12	23·00	13·00

1966 (27 June). *Horiz designs as T* **39**. *Multicoloured. P* 14½ × 14.

No.	Description		
72	7 c. Type **39**	50	15
73	9 c. Cemetery Road	50	20

41 St. Barnabas' Chapel (interior)

42 St. Barnabas' Chapel (exterior)

1966 (23 Aug). *Centenary of Melanesian Mission. P* 14 × 14½.

No.	Type	Description		
74	**41**	4 c. multicoloured	25	15
75	**42**	25 c. multicoloured	55	25

43 Star over Philip Island

44 H.M.S. *Resolution*, 1774

(Des B.W.G. McCoy)

1966 (24 Oct). *Christmas. P* 14½.

No.	Type	Description		
76	**43**	4 c. multicoloured	10	10

(Des Harrison)

1967 (17 Apr)–**68.** *T* **44** *and similar horiz designs showing ships. Multicoloured. P* 14 × 14½.

No.	Description		
77	1 c. Type **44**	10	8
78	2 c. *La Boussole* and *L'Astrolabe*, 1788 ..	15	10
79	3 c. H.M. Brig *Supply*, 1788	15	12
80	4 c. H.M.S. *Sirius*, 1790	20	15
81	5 c. The *Norfolk*, 1798 (14.8.67)	20	20

82 7 c. H.M. Survey Cutter *Mermaid*, 1825 (14.8.67) 30 20
83 9 c. *Lady Franklin*, 1853 (14.8.67) 35 25
84 10 c. The *Morayshire*, 1856 (14.8.67) 40 30
85 15 c. *Southern Cross*, 1866 (18.3.68) .. .. 1·50 60
86 20 c. The *Pitcairn*, 1891 (18.3.68) .. .. 2·00 90
87 25 c. Norfolk whaleboat, 1895 (18.3.68) .. 2·75 1·00
88 30 c. H.M.C.S. *Iris*, 1907 (18.6.68) .. .. 5·50 2·50
89 50 c. The *Resolution*, 1926 (18.6.68) .. .. 7·00 3·50
90 $1 S.S. *Morinda*, 1931 (18.6.68) .. .. 11·00 7·00
77/90 .. .. *Set of* 14 28·00 15·00

1967 (7 June). *50th Anniv of Lions International. As No.* 411 *of Australia but colours changed.*
91 4 c. black, bluish green and olive-yellow .. 10 5

58 Prayer of John Adams and Candle

(Des B.G.W. McCoy)

1967 (16 Oct). *Christmas. P* 14.
92 **58** 5 c. black, light yellow-olive and red .. 10 5

1968 (5 Aug)–**71**. *Coil Stamps. As T* **199** *of Australia.*
93 3 c. black, light brown and vermilion .. 10 5
94 4 c. black, light brown and blue-green .. 10 5
95 5 c. black, light brown and deep violet .. 10 5
95*a* 6 c. black, lt brown & lake-brown (25.8.71) .. 25 25

59 "Skymaster" and "Lancastrian" Aircraft

60 Bethlehem Star and Flowers

(Des Harrison)

1968 (25 Sept). *21st Anniv of QANTAS Air Service, Sydney–Norfolk Island. P* 14.
96 **59** 5 c. bluish black, carmine-red & lt blue 10 10
97 7 c. blackish brown, carmine-red & turq 10 12

(Des Mrs. B. L. Laing)

1968 (24 Oct). *Christmas. P* 14 × 14½.
98 **60** 5 c. multicoloured 10 5

61 Captain Cook, Quadrant and Chart of Pacific Ocean

62 Van Diemen's Land, Norfolk Island and Sailing Ship

(Des V. Whiteley from sketch by J. G. Cowan)

1969 (3 June). *Captain Cook Bicentenary* (1st issue). *Observation of the transit of Venus across the Sun, from Tahiti. P* 14.
99 **61** 10 c. multicoloured 25 10
See also Nos. 118/19, 129, 152/5, 200/2 and 213/14.

(Des Mrs. A. Bathie and Mrs. M. J. McCoy)

1969 (29 Sept). *125th Anniv of the Annexation of Norfolk Island to Van Diemen's Land. P* 14 × 14½.
100 **62** 5 c. multicoloured 20 10
101 30 c. multicoloured 45 30

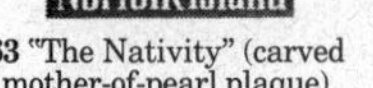

63 "The Nativity" (carved mother-of-pearl plaque)

64 New Zealand Grey Flyeater

(Des J. G. Cowan)

1969 (27 Oct). *Christmas. P* 14½ × 14.
102 **63** 5 c. multicoloured 10 10

(Des G. Mathews)

1970–71. *Birds. T* **64** *and similar multicoloured designs. Chalk-surfaced paper. P* 14.
103 1 c. Scarlet Robins (22.7.70) 15 10
104 2 c. Golden Whistler (24.2.71) 35 25
105 3 c. Type **64** (25.2.70) 35 20
106 4 c. Long-tailed Koels (25.2.70) 35 20
107 5 c. Red-fronted Parakeet (24.2.71) 50 45
108 7 c. Long-tailed Triller (22.7.70) 55 35
109 9 c. Island Thrush (25.2.70) 90 40
110 10 c. Boobook Owl (22.7.70) .. .. .. 1·50 60
111 15 c. Norfolk Island Pigeon (24.2.71) .. .. 3·25 1·75
112 20 c. White-chested White Eye (16.6.71) .. 3·50 1·75
113 25 c. Philip Island Parrots (22.7.70) .. .. 2·75 1·50
a. Error. Glazed, ordinary paper £225
114 30 c. Collared Grey Fantail (16.6.71) .. .. 5·00 3·00
115 45 c. Norfolk Island Starlings (25.2.70) .. 4·00 3·50
116 50 c. Crimson Rosella (24.2.71) .. .. 12·00 7·00
117 $1 Sacred Kingfisher (16.6.71) .. .. 15·00 12·00
103/17 .. .. *Set of* 15 45·00 30·00
Nos. 105, 106, 109, 112, 114, 115 and 117 are horizontal, and the remainder vertical designs.

65 Capt. Cook and Map of Australia

66 First Christmas Service, 1788

(Des R. Bates)

1970 (29 Apr). *Captain Cook Bicentenary* (2nd issue). *Discovery of Australia's East Coast. T* **65** *and similar horiz design. Multicoloured. P* 14.
118 5 c. Type **65** 25 15
119 10 c. H.M.S. *Endeavour* and aborigine .. 35 15

(Des R. Bates)

1970 (15 Oct). *Christmas. P* 14.
120 **66** 5 c. multicoloured 10 10

67 Bishop Patteson and Martyrdom of St. Stephen

68 Rose Window, St. Barnabas Chapel, Kingston

(Des R. Bates)

1971 (20 Sept). *Death Centenary of Bishop Patteson. T* **67** *and similar horiz designs. Multicoloured. P* 14 × 14½.
121 6 c. Type **67** 25 25
a. Pair. Nos. 121/2 .. .. .. 50 50
122 6 c. Bible, Martyrdom of St. Stephen and knotted palm-frond 25 25
123 10 c. Bishop Patteson and stained-glass .. 30 30
a. Pair. Nos. 123/4 .. .. .. 60 60
124 10 c. Cross and Bishop's Arms 30 30
Nos. 121/2 and 123/4 were printed in *se-tenant* pairs throughout the sheet.

(Des G. Hitch. Photo Heraclio Fournier, Spain)

1971 (25 Oct). *Christmas. P* 14 × 13½.
125 **68** 6 c. multicoloured 12 12

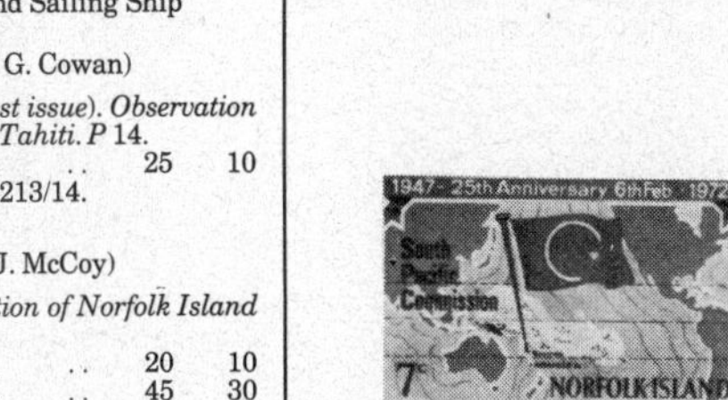

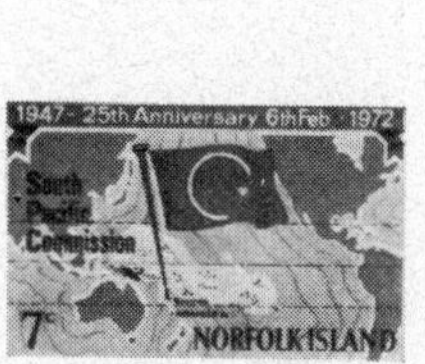

69 Map and Flag

70 "St. Mark" (stained-glass window, All Saints, Norfolk Is)

(Des G. Hitch)

1972 (7 Feb). *25th Anniv of South Pacific Commission. P* 14 × 14½.
126 **69** 7 c. multicoloured 50 30

(Des Mrs. M. J. McCoy)

1972 (16 Oct). *Christmas. P* 14.
127 **70** 7 c. multicoloured 12 12

71 Cross and Pines. (stained-glass window, All Saints Church)

72 *Resolution* in the Antarctic

(Des Harrison)

1972 (20 Nov). *Centenary of First Pitcairn-built Church. P* 14.
128 **71** 12 c. multicoloured 25 25

(Des G. Hitch)

1973 (17 Jan). *Captain Cook Bicentenary* (3rd issue). *Crossing of the Antarctic Circle. P* 14.
129 **72** 35 c. multicoloured .. .. .. 3·25 3·25

73 Child and Christmas Tree

74 Protestant Clergyman's Quarters

(Des B. W. McCoy (T **73**), R. Westwood (35 c.))

1973 (22 Oct). *Christmas. T* **73** *and similar vert design. Multicoloured. P* 14.
130 7 c. Type **73** 50 50
131 12 c. Type **73** 70 70
132 35 c. Fir trees and star .. .. .. 1·90 1·90

(Des G. Hitch)

1973 (19 Nov)–**75**. *Historic Buildings. T* **74** *and similar horiz designs. Multicoloured. P* 14 × 14½.
133 1 c. Type **74** 8 8
134 2 c. Royal Engineers' Office (1.5.74) 12 12
135 3 c. Double Quarters for Free Overseers (19.2.75) 25 12
136 4 c. Guard House (12.7.74) 20 15
137 5 c. Entrance to Pentagonal Gaol 25 15
138 7 c. Pentagonal Gaol (1.5.74) 35 25
139 8 c. Prisoners' Barracks (19.2.75) 50 35
140 10 c. Officers' Quarters, New Military Barracks 50 35
141 12 c. New Military Barracks (1.5.74) 50 40
142 14 c. Beach Stores (12.7.74) 60 45
143 15 c. The Magazine (19.2.75) 90 50
144 20 c. Entrance, Old Military Barracks (12.7.74) 80 65
145 25 c. Old Military Barracks (19.2.75) .. .. 1·40 90
146 30 c. Old Stores (Crankmill) (1.5.74) .. .. 1·50 1·25
147 50 c. Commissariat Stores .. .. .. 2·75 2·25
148 $1 Government House (12.7.74) .. .. 7·00 6·00
133/48 .. .. *Set of* 16 16·00 13·00

75 Royal Couple and Map

(Des Harrison)

1974 (8 Feb). *Royal Visit. P* 14 × 14½.
149 **75** 7 c. multicoloured 90 60
150 25 c. multicoloured .. .. .. 2·25 1·75

76 Chichester's *Madame Elijah*

(Des B. McCoy. Litho State Bank Note Printing Works, Helsinki)

1974 (28 Mar). *First Aircraft Landing on Norfolk Island. P* 14.
151 **76** 14 c. multicoloured .. .. .. 3·00 2·25

77 "Captain Cook" (engraving by J. Basire)

78 Nativity Scene (pearl-shell pew carving)

(Des C. I. Buffett. Litho Questa)

1974 (8 Oct). *Captain Cook Bicentenary* (4th issue). *Discovery of Norfolk Is. T* **77** *and similar vert designs. Multicoloured. P* 14.
152 7 c. Type **77** .. .. 1·75 1·10
153 10 c. "*Resolution*" (H. Roberts) .. .. 3·00 2·25
154 14 c. Norfolk Island Pine .. .. .. 3·25 2·50
155 25 c. "Norfolk Island flax" (G. Raper) .. .. 4·25 4·00

(Des G. Hitch)

1974 (18 Oct). *Christmas. P* 14½.
156 **78** 7 c. multicoloured 45 40
157 30 c. multicoloured .. .. .. 1·75 1·50

79 Norfolk Pine

(Manufactured by Walsall)

1974 (16 Dec). *Centenary of Universal Postal Union. T* **79** *and similar "island"-shaped designs. Multicoloured. Imperf* (*backing-paper roul* 20). *Self-adhesive.*

158 10 c. Type **79** . . . . 1·10 1·40
159 15 c. Offshore islands . . . . . . 1·25 1·50
160 35 c. Crimson Rosella and Sacred Kingfisher 2·00 3·00
161 40 c. Pacific map . . . . . . 2·50 4·25
MS162 106 × 101 mm. Map of Norfolk Is. cut-to-shape with reduced-size replicas of Nos. 158/61 26·00 26·00

80 H.M. Survey Cutter *Mermaid*

(Manufactured by Walsall)

1975 (18 Aug). *150th Anniv of Second Settlement. T* **80** *and similar "island"-shaped design. Multicoloured. Imperf* (*backing-paper roul* 20). *Self-adhesive.*

163 10 c. Type **80** 50 50
164 35 c. Kingston, 1835 (from painting by T. Seller) . . . . . . 1·00 1·00

81 Star on Norfolk Island Pine   82 Memorial Cross

(Des Harrison)

1975 (6 Oct). *Christmas. P* 14.

165 **81** 10 c. multicoloured 30 30
166 15 c. multicoloured 55 55
167 35 c. multicoloured . . . . . . 1·40 1·40

(Des Harrison)

1975 (24 Nov). *Centenary of St. Barnabas Chapel. T* **82** *and similar horiz design. Multicoloured. P* 14.

168 30 c. Type **82** 80 75
169 60 c. Laying foundation stone and Chapel in 1975 . . . . . . 1·50 1·25

83 Launching of *Resolution*   84 Whaleship *Charles W. Morgan*

(Des Harrison)

1975 (1 Dec). *50th Anniv of Launching of the "Resolution". T* **83** *and similar horiz design. Multicoloured. P* 14.

170 25 c. Type **83** 90 90
171 45 c. *Resolution* at sea . . . . . . 1·10 1·40

(Des Harrison)

1976 (5 July). *Bicentenary of American Revolution. T* **84** *and similar horiz designs. Multicoloured. P* 14.

172 18 c. Type **84** 50 50
173 25 c. Thanksgiving Service 75 75
174 40 c. "Flying Fortress" over Norfolk Is . . 1·25 1·25
175 45 c. California Quail . . . . . . 1·50 1·50

NEW INFORMATION

The editor is always interested to correspond with people who have new information that will improve or correct the Catalogue.

85 Tern and Sun   86 *Bassaris itea*

(Des Harrison)

1976 (4 Oct). *Christmas. P* 14.

176 **85** 18 c. multicoloured 50 50
177 25 c. multicoloured 75 75
178 45 c. multicoloured . . . . . . 1·25 1·25

(Des B. Hargreaves)

1976 (17 Nov)–**77**. *Butterflies and Moths. T* **86** *and similar horiz designs. Multicoloured. P* 14.

179 1 c. Type **86** 8 5
180 2 c. *Utetheisa pulchelloides vaga* (22.2.77) . . 10 5
181 3 c. *Agathia asterias jowettorum* (5.7.77) . . 10 5
182 4 c. *Cynthia kershawi* (5.7.77) 10 5
183 5 c. *Leucania loreyimima* 12 5
184 10 c. *Hypolimnas bolina nerina* 20 12
185 15 c. *Pyrrhorachis pyrrhogona subscrenulata* (22.2.77) 30 20
186 16 c. *Austrocarea iocephala millsi* 30 20
187 17 c. *Pseudocoremia christiani* (10.5.77) . . 35 20
188 18 c. *Cleora idiocrossa* 35 20
189 19 c. *Simplicia caeneusalis buffetti* (10.5.77) . . 35 25
190 20 c. *Austrocidaria ralstonae* (10.5.77) . . 40 25
191 30 c. *Hippotion scrofa* (22.2.77) 50 35
192 40 c. *Papilio ilioneus ilioneus* (10.5.77) . . 65 50
193 50 c. *Tiracola plagiata* (22.2.77) 80 65
194 $1 *Precis villida calybe* . . . . . . 1·75 1·75
195 $2 *Cepora perimale perimale* (5.7.77) . . 2·75 3·00
179/95 . . . . *Set of* 17 8·50 7·00

87 Queen's View, Kingston

(Des Harrison)

1977 (10 June). *Silver Jubilee. P* 14.

196 **87** 25 c. multicoloured 65 60

88 Hibiscus Flowers and Oil Lamp   89 Captain Cook (from a portrait by Nathaniel Dance)

(Des Mrs. M. J. McCoy)

1977 (4 Oct). *Christmas. P* 14 × 14½.

197 **88** 18 c. multicoloured 30 30
198 25 c. multicoloured 50 50
199 45 c. multicoloured 90 90

(Des Harrison)

1978 (18 Jan). *Captain Cook Bicentenary* (5*th issue*). *Discovery of Hawaii. T* **89** *and similar horiz designs. Multicoloured. P* 14½.

200 18 c. Type **89** 60 35
201 25 c. Discovery of Northern Hawaiian islands 75 60
202 80 c. British flag against island background . . 1·75 1·50

90 Guide Flag and Globe

(Manufactured by Walsall)

1978 (22 Feb). *50th Anniv of Girl Guides. T* **90** *and similar "island"-shaped designs. Multicoloured. Imperf* (*backing paper roul* 20). *Self-adhesive.*

203 18 c. Type **90** 35 35
204 25 c. Emblem and scarf badge 50 50
205 35 c. Emblem and Queen Elizabeth 70 70
206 45 c. Emblem and Lady Baden-Powell . . 90 90

91 St. Edward's Crown

(Des Harrison)

1978 (29 June). *25th Anniv of Coronation. T* **91** *and similar horiz design. Multicoloured. P* 14½.

207 25 c. Type **91** 50 50
208 70 c. Coronation regalia . . . . . . 1·25 1·25

92 View of Duncombe Bay with Scout at Camp Fire

(Des S. Jensen. Manufactured by Walsall)

1978 (22 Aug). *50th Anniv of Boy Scouts. T* **92** *and similar "island"-shaped designs. Multicoloured. Imperf* (*backing paper roul* 20). *Self-adhesive.*

209 20 c. Type **92** 35 35
210 25 c. View from Kingston and emblem . . 50 50
211 35 c. View of Anson Bay and Link Badge . . 70 70
212 45 c. Sunset scene and Lord Baden-Powell . . 90 90

93 Chart showing Route of Arctic Voyage   94 Poinsettia and Bible

(Des G. Hitch)

1978 (29 Aug). *Captain Cook Bicentenary* (6*th issue*). *Northernmost Voyages. T* **93** *and similar horiz design. Multicoloured. P* 14½.

213 25 c. Type **93** 50 50
214 90 c. "*Resolution* and *Discovery* in Pack Ice" (painting by Webber) . . . . 1·75 1·75

(Des Mrs. M. J. McCoy)

1978 (3 Oct). *Christmas. T* **94** *and similar vert designs. Multicoloured. P* 14½ × 14.

215 20 c. Type **94** 40 40
216 30 c. Native Oak and Bible 60 60
217 55 c. Hibiscus and Bible . . . . . . 1·00 1·00

95 Cook and Village of Staithes near Marton

(Des Harrison)

1978 (27 Oct). *250th Birth Anniv of Captain Cook. T* **95** *and similar horiz design. Multicoloured. P* 14½.

218 20 c. Type **95** 40 45
219 80 c. Cook and Whitby Harbour . . . . 1·60 1·75

96 *Resolution*   97 Assembly Building

(Des G. Hitch)

1979 (14 Feb). *Death Bicentenary of Captain Cook. T* **96** *and similar horiz designs. Multicoloured. P* 14.

220 20 c. Type **96** 70 55
 a. Pair. Nos. 220/1 . . . . . . 1·40 1·10
221 20 c. Cook (statue) 70 55
222 40 c. Cook's death 80 80
 a. Pair. Nos. 222/3 . . . . . . 1·60 1·60
223 40 c. Cook's death (*different*) 80 80

The 20 c. designs depict the *Resolution* and Cook's statue on a map showing the last voyage. The 40 c. designs show Cook's death from an aquatint by John Clevely.

Nos. 220/1 and 222/3 were each printed together, *se-tenant*, in horizontal pairs throughout the sheets, forming composite designs.

1979 (10 Aug). *First Norfolk Island Legislative Assembly.* P 14½ × 14.
224 **97** $1 multicoloured .. .. .. 1·50 1·40

98 Tasmania 1853 1d. Stamp and Sir Rowland Hill

1979 (27 Aug). *Death Centenary of Sir Rowland Hill. T* **98** *and similar horiz designs showing stamps and Sir Rowland Hill.* P 14 × 14½.
225 20 c. new blue and sepia 30 35
226 30 c. brown-red and olive-grey 40 45
227 55 c. violet and indigo 65 75
MS228 142 × 91 mm. No. 227. P 14 .. .. 80 90
Designs:—30 c. Penny Red; 55 c. 1d. "Ball Bay".

99 I.Y.C. Emblem and Map of Pacific showing Norfolk Island as Pine Tree

(Des Claire Walters. Litho Asher and Co, Melbourne)

1979 (25 Sept). *International Year of the Child.* P 15.
229 **99** 80 c. multicoloured .. .. .. 1·00 1·10

100 Emily Bay 101 Lions International Emblem

1979 (5 Nov).* *Christmas. T* **100** *and similar horiz designs showing different aspects of Emily Bay.* P 12½ × 13.
230 15 c. multicoloured 25 25
a. Horiz strip of 3. Nos. 230/2 90
231 20 c. multicoloured 35 35
232 30 c. multicoloured 40 40
MS233 152 × 83 mm. Nos. 230/2. P 14 × 14½ .. 2·00 1·75
Nos. 230/2 were printed together, *se-tenant*, in horizontal strips of 3 throughout the sheet, forming a composite design.
*Although released by the Crown Agents in London on 2 October the stamps were not released locally until 5 November.

(Des Norfolk Island Lions Club. Litho Asher and Co, Melbourne)

1980 (25 Jan). *Lions Convention.* P 15.
234 **101** 50 c. multicoloured 60 60

102 Rotary International Emblem

(Des E. Lenthall. Litho Asher and Co, Melbourne)

1980 (21 Feb). *75th Anniv of Rotary International.* P 15.
235 **102** 50 c. multicoloured 60 60
a. Black (face value and "NORFOLK ISLAND") omitted .. .. ..

103 "D.H. 60 (Gypsy Moth)" *Mme Elijah*

(Des G. Hitch. Litho Harrison)

1980 (25 Mar)–**81**. *Aeroplanes. Horiz designs as T* **103**. *Multicoloured.* P 14½ × 14.
236 1 c. Hawker Siddeley "H.S. 748" (3.3.81) .. 10 5
237 2 c. Type **103** 10 5
238 3 c. Curtis "P-40 Kittyhawk" 10 5
239 4 c. Chance Vought "F4U-1 Corsair" (19.8.80) 10 5
240 5 c. Grumman "TBF-1c Avenger" (19.8.80) .. 10 5
241 15 c. Douglas "SBD-5 Dauntless" (19.8.80) .. 20 20
242 20 c. Cessna "172" 25 25
243 25 c. Lockheed "Hudson" (3.3.81) 30 30
244 30 c. Lockheed "PV-1 Ventura" (13.1.81) .. 40 35
245 40 c. Avro "York" (3.3.81) 50 45
246 50 c. Douglas "DC-3" (13.1.81) 65 55
247 60 c. Avro "691 Lancastrian" (13.1.81) .. 75 65
248 80 c. Douglas "DC-4" (13.1.81) 95 85
249 $1 Beechcraft "Super King Air" (3.3.81) .. 1·25 1·10
250 $2 Fokker "F-27 Friendship" (19.8.80) .. 2·25 2·10
251 $5 Lockheed "C-130 Hercules" .. .. 5·00 5·50
236/51 .. .. *Set of* 16 11·50 11·00

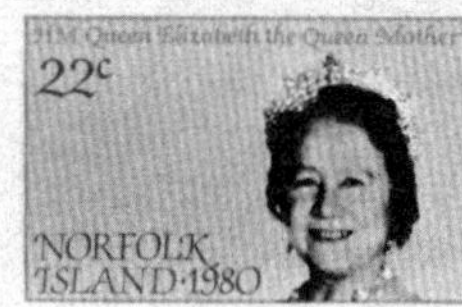

104 Queen Elizabeth the Queen Mother

(Des K. Williams. Litho Harrison)

1980 (4 Aug). *80th Birthday of Queen Elizabeth the Queen Mother.* P 14.
252 **104** 22 c. multicoloured 35 40
253 60 c. multicoloured 80 90

105 Red-tailed Tropic Birds

(Des K. Williams. Litho Harrison)

1980 (28 Oct). *Christmas. Birds. T* **105** *and similar horiz designs. Multicoloured.* P 14 × 14½.
254 15 c. Type **105** 55 55
a. Horiz strip of 3. Nos. 254/6 .. .. 1·50
255 22 c. White Terns 55 55
256 35 c. White-capped Noddys 55 55
257 60 c. White Terns (*different*) 75 75
Nos. 254/6 were printed together, *se-tenant*, in horizontal strips of 3 throughout the sheet.

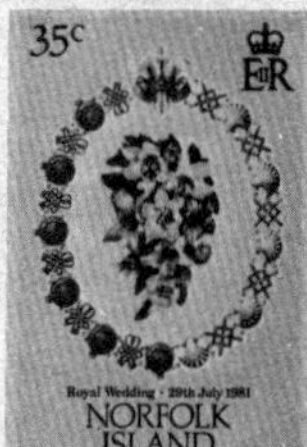

106 *Morayshire* and View of Norfolk Island 107 Wedding Bouquet from Norfolk Island

(Des Jennifer Toombs. Litho Harrison)

1981 (5 June). *125th Anniv of Pitcairn Islanders' Migration to Norfolk Island. T* **106** *and similar horiz designs. Multicoloured.* P 14½.
258 5 c. Type **106** 15 15
259 35 c. Islanders arriving ashore 55 55
260 60 c. View of new settlement 85 85
MS261 183 × 127 mm. Nos. 258/60 .. .. 1·50 1·50

(Des J.W. Litho Harrison)

1981 (22 July). *Royal Wedding. T* **107** *and similar vert designs. Multicoloured.* P 14.
262 35 c. Type **107** 50 50
263 55 c. Prince Charles at horse trials 80 80
264 60 c. Prince Charles and Lady Diana Spencer 90 90

108 Uniting Church of Australia 109 Pair of White-chested White Eyes

(Des K. Williams. Litho Harrison)

1981 (15 Sept). *Christmas. Churches. T* **108** *and similar horiz designs. Multicoloured.* P 14½ × 14.
265 18 c. Type **108** 25 25
266 24 c. Seventh Day Adventist Church 35 35
267 30 c. Church of the Sacred Heart 45 45
268 $1 St. Barnabas Chapel .. .. .. 1·25 1·25

(Des P. Slater. Litho Questa)

1981 (10 Nov). *White-chested White Eye ("Silvereye"). T* **109** *and similar horiz designs. Multicoloured.* P 14 × 14½.
269 35 c. Type **109** 45 40
a. Horiz strip of 5. Nos. 269/73 .. .. 2·25
270 35 c. Bird on nest 45 40
271 35 c. Bird with egg 45 40
272 35 c. Parents with chicks 45 40
273 35 c. Fledgelings 45 40
Nos. 269/73 were printed together, *se-tenant*, in horizontal strips of 5 throughout the sheet.

110 Aerial View of Philip Island

(Des local artist. Litho Harrison)

1982 (12 Jan). *Philip and Nepean Islands. T* **110** *and similar horiz designs. Multicoloured.* P 14 × 13½.
274 24 c. Type **110** 30 30
a. Horiz strip of 5. Nos. 274/8 .. .. 1·50
275 24 c. Close-up view of Philip Island landscape 30 30
276 24 c. Gecko (*Phyllodactylus guentheri*), Philip Island 30 30
277 24 c. Sooty Tern (*Sterna fuscata*), Philip Island 30 30
278 24 c. Philip Island Hibiscus (*Hibiscus insularis*) 30 30
279 35 c. Aerial view of Nepean Island 40 40
a. Horiz strip of 5. Nos. 279/83 .. .. 2·00
280 35 c. Close-up view of Nepean Island landscape 40 40
281 35 c. Gecko (*Phyllodactylus guentheri*), Nepean Island 40 40
282 35 c. White-masked Boobies (*Sula dactylatra*), Nepean Island 40 40
283 35 c. *Carpobrotus glaucescens* (flower), Nepean Island 40 40
274/83 .. .. *Set of* 10 3·50 3·50
The five designs of each value were printed together, *se-tenant*, in horizontal strips of 5 throughout the sheet.

111 Sperm Whale

(Des Jennifer Toombs. Litho Harrison)

1982 (23 Feb). *Whales. T* **111** *and similar horiz designs.* P 14½.
284 24 c. multicoloured 35 35
285 55 c. multicoloured 75 75
286 80 c. black, mauve and stone .. .. 1·00 1·00
Designs:—55 c. Southern Right Whale; 80 c. Humpback Whale.

112 *Diocet*, Wrecked 20 April 1873

(Litho Harrison)

1982 (18 May–27 July). *Shipwrecks. T* **112** *and similar horiz designs. Multicoloured.* P 14½ × 14.
287 24 c. H.M.S. *Sirius*, wrecked 19 March 1790 (27 July) 30 30
288 27 c. Type **112** 30 30
289 35 c. *Friendship*, wrecked 17 May 1835 (27 July) 40 40
290 40 c. *Mary Hamilton*, wrecked 6 May 1873 .. 50 50
291 55 c. *Fairlie*, wrecked 14 February 1840 (27 July) 65 70
292 65 c. *Warrigal*, wrecked 18 March 1918 .. 80 85
287/92 .. .. *Set of* 6 2·75 2·75

C-KURITY PAPER. The following issues up to No. 342 were all printed on this type of security paper, *unless otherwise stated.* It shows a pattern of blue fluorescent markings, resembling rosettes, on the reverse beneath the gum.

113 R.N.Z.A.F. "Hudson" dropping Christmas Supplies, 1942 114 50th (Queen's Own) Regiment

(Des A. Theobald. Litho Walsall)

1982 (7 Sept). *Christmas. 40th Anniv of first Supply-plane Landings on Norfolk Island (Christmas Day 1942). T* **113** *and similar horiz designs. Multicoloured.* P 14.
293 27 c. Type **113** 30 35
294 40 c. "Hudson" landing Christmas supplies, 1942 .. .. 45 50
295 75 c. Christmas, 1942 .. .. 90 95

(Des W. Fenton. Litho Questa)

1982 (9 Nov). *Military Uniforms. T* **114** *and similar vert designs. Multicoloured.* P 14½ × 14.
296 27 c. Type **114** 30 35
297 40 c. 58th (Rutlandshire) Regiment 45 50
298 55 c. 80th (Staffordshire Volunteers) Battalion Company 65 70
299 65 c. 11th (North Devonshire) Regiment .. 80 85

115 *Panaeolus papilionaceus* **116** Beechcraft "18" Aircraft

(Des Jane Thatcher. Litho Enschedé)

1983 (29 Mar). *Fungi. T* **115** *and similar vert designs. Multicoloured. P* 13½ × 13.

300 27 c. Type **115** 30 35
301 40 c. *Coprinus domesticus* 45 50
302 55 c. *Marasmius niveus* 65 70
303 65 c. *Cymatoderma elegans var. lamellatum* .. 80 85

(Des Walsall. Litho Format)

1983 (12 July). *Bicentenary of Manned Flight. T* **116** *and similar horiz designs. Multicoloured. P* 14½ × 14.

304 10 c. Type **116** 12 15
305 27 c. Fokker "F28 Fellowship" 30 35
306 45 c. French military "DC 4" 50 60
307 75 c. Sikorsky helicopter 90 95
MS308 105 × 100 mm. Nos. 304/7 .. .. 1·75 2·00

117 St. Matthew **118** Motor Ship *Chantik*

(Des McCombie-Skinner Studio. Litho Format)

1983 (13 Sept). *Christmas. 150th Birth Anniv of Sir Edward Burne-Jones. T* **117** *and similar vert designs showing stained-glass windows from St. Barnabas Chapel, Norfolk Island. Multicoloured. P* 14.

309 5 c. Type **117** 5 8
310 24 c. St. Mark 25 30
311 30 c. Jesus Christ 35 40
312 45 c. St. Luke 50 55
313 85 c. St. John .. .. 1·00 1·10

(Des G. Drummond. Litho Format)

1983 (15 Nov). *World Communications Year. ANZCAN Cable. T* **118** *and similar horiz designs. Multicoloured. Ordinary paper. P* 14½ × 14.

314 30 c. Type **118** 35 40
315 45 c. *Chantik* during in-shore operations .. 50 55
316 75 c. Cable ship *Mercury* 90 95
317 85 c. Diagram of cable route .. .. .. 1·00 1·10

119 Popwood **120** *Cheilodactylidae*

(Des I. Loe. Litho B.D.T.)

1984 (10 Jan–27 Mar). *Flowers. T* **119** *and similar vert designs. Multicoloured. P* 14.

318 1 c. Type **119** (27.3) 5 5
319 2 c. Strand Morning Glory 5 5
320 3 c. Native Phreatia 5 5
321 4 c. Philip Island Wisteria (27.3) 5 5
322 5 c. Norfolk Island Palm (27.3) 5 8
323 10 c. Evergreen 12 15
324 15 c. Bastard Oak (27.3) 20 25
325 20 c. Devil's Guts 25 30
326 25 c. White Oak 30 35
327 30 c. Ti (27.3) 35 40
328 35 c. Philip Island Hibiscus (27.3) 40 45
329 40 c. Native Wisteria 45 50
330 50 c. Native Jasmine 60 65
331 $1 Norfolk Island Hibiscus (27.3) .. .. 1·10 1·25
332 $3 Native Oberonia (27.3) .. .. .. 3·50 3·75
333 $5 Norfolk Island Pine .. .. 5·75 6·00
318/33 .. .. *Set of* 16 12·50 13·00

(Des Marg Towt. Litho Cambec Press, Melbourne)

1984 (17 Apr). *Reef Fishes. T* **120** *and similar horiz designs. Multicoloured. Ordinary paper. P* 13½ × 14.

334 30 c. Type **120** 40 45
335 45 c. *Pseudopeneus signatus* 60 65
336 75 c. *Acanthuridae* .. .. 1·00 1·10
337 85 c. *Chaeton ancinetus* .. .. 1·25 1·40

121 Owl with Eggs **122** 1953 7½d. and 1974 Cook Bicent 10 c. Stamps

(Des P. Slater. Litho Questa)

1984 (17 July). *Boobook Owl. T* **121** *and similar vert designs. Multicoloured. P* 14.

338 30 c. Type **121** 40 45
a. Horiz strip of 5. Nos. 338/42 .. .. 1·90
339 30 c. Fledgeling 40 45
340 30 c. Young owl on stump 40 45
341 30 c. Adult on branch 40 45
342 30 c. Owl in flight 40 45

Nos. 338/42 were printed together, *se-tenant*, in horizontal strips of 5 throughout the sheet.

(Des D. Miller. Litho Harrison)

1984 (18 Sept). *"Ausipex" International Stamp Exhibition, Melbourne. T* **122** *and similar horiz designs. Multicoloured. W w* **14** *(sideways). P* 14.

343 30 c. Type **122** 40 45
344 45 c. John Buffett commemorative postal stationery envelope 60 65
345 75 c. Design from Presentation Pack for 1982 Military Uniforms issue .. .. 1·00 1·10
MS346 151 × 93 mm. Nos. 343/5. P 14½ .. .. 2·10 2·25

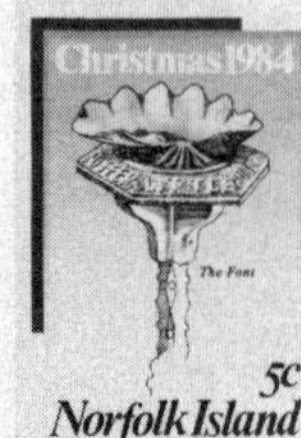

123 Font, Kingston Methodist Church **124** The Revd. Nobbs teaching Pitcairn Islanders

(Des R. Murphy. Litho Questa)

1984 (9 Oct). *Christmas. Centenary of Methodist Church on Norfolk Island. T* **123** *and similar vert designs. Multicoloured. W w* **14**. *P* 14.

347 5 c. Type **123** 8 10
348 24 c. Church service in Old Barracks, Kingston, late 1800's 35 40
349 30 c. The Revd. & Mrs. A. H. Phelps and sailing ship 40 45
350 45 c. The Revd. A. H. Phelps and First Congregational Church, Chester, U.S.A. .. 60 65
351 85 c. Interior of Kingston Methodist Church .. 1·25 1·40

(Des D. Hopkins. Litho B.D.T.)

1984 (6 Nov). *Death Centenary of the Revd. George Hunn Nobbs (leader of Pitcairn community). T* **124** *and similar vert designs. Multicoloured. W w* **14**. *P* 14 × 15.

352 30 c. Type **124** 40 45
353 45 c. The Revd. Nobbs with sick islander .. 60 65
354 75 c. Baptising baby .. .. 1·00 1·10
355 85 c. Presented to Queen Victoria, 1852 .. 1·25 1·40

125 *Fanny Fisher*

(Des O. Hopkins. Litho Cambec Press, Melbourne)

1985 (19 Feb). *19th-Century Whaling Ships* (*1st series*). *T* **125** *and similar horiz designs. Multicoloured. P* 13½ × 14.

356 5 c. Type **125** 8 10
357 33 c. *Costa Rica Packet* 35 40
358 50 c. *Splendid* 55 60
359 90 c. *Onward* .. .. 1·00 1·10

North Borneo

PRICES FOR STAMPS ON COVER TO 1945

No. 1	*from* × 100
Nos. 2/3	*from* × 10
Nos. 4/5	—
Nos. 6/19	*from* × 10
Nos. 19*b*/21*b*	—
Nos. 22/8	*from* × 50
Nos. 29/39	—
Nos. 40/8	*from* × 100
Nos. 49/50	—
Nos. 51/2	*from* × 10
No. 54	—
Nos. 55/65	*from* × 10
Nos. 66/79	*from* × 4
Nos. 81/6	—
Nos. 87/91	*from* × 12
Nos. 92/111	*from* × 4
Nos. 112/26	*from* × 10
Nos. 127/40	*from* × 6
Nos. 141/5	—
Nos. 146/57	*from* × 5
Nos. 158/79	*from* × 8
Nos. 181/5	—
Nos. 186/8	*from* × 10
Nos. 189/230	*from* × 4
Nos. 231/4	—
Nos. 235/49	*from* × 3
Nos. 250/2	—
Nos. 253/75	*from* × 12
Nos. 276/92	*from* × 7
Nos. 293/4	—
Nos. 295/300	*from* × 6
Nos. 301/2	—
Nos. 303/17	*from* × 3
Nos. 318/19	*from* × 20
Nos. 320/34	*from* × 3
Nos. D1/26	*from* × 20
Nos. D27/8	—
Nos. D29/35	*from* × 7
No. D35*a*	—
Nos. D36/65	*from* × 20
Nos. D66/70	*from* × 5

BRITISH NORTH BORNEO COMPANY ADMINISTRATION

PRINTERS. The stamps of this country up to 1894 were designed by T. Macdonald and printed in lithography by Blades, East and Blades, London.

1 8 Cents. **(2)** EIGHT CENTS **(3)**

1883. *P* 12.

1 1 2 c. red-brown .. .. 9·00 16·00
a. Imperf between (horiz pair) .. ..

The figure "2" varies in size.

1883. *No.* 1 *surch as T* **2** *or* **3**.

2 **2** 8 c. on 2 c. red-brown £600 £500
3 **3** 8 c. on 2 c. red-brown £300 £130
a. Surch double .. .. — £3000

Type **2** was handstamped and stamps without stop are generally forgeries. Type **3** was a setting of 50 (10 × 5) providing ten varieties; it normally has a stop which sometimes failed to print.

NOTE.—Prices are separately indicated (in a third price column, in brackets, or by notes below certain issues) for remainders of the stamps of North Borneo cancelled with black bars, where these exist. The issues since 1923 have not been thus cancelled.

It should be noted, however, that a postmark of this form was in use for postal purposes up to this period, and was used at one or two of the smaller post-offices until 1949. A small oval with five bars was used to mark railway mail during 1945/55 and also as a paquebot mark at Jesselton *c.* 1950.

4 **5** and Revenue **(6)**

1883. *P* 14.

4 4 50 c. violet .. .. .. 42·00 — 10·00
a. "ΓIFTY" (R.5/2) .. .. £200 — £100
5 5 $1 scarlet .. .. .. 30·00 — 7·50

1883. *P* 12.

6 1 4 c. pink .. .. 8·00 16·00
a. Imperf (horiz pair) .. .. .. † —
7 8 c. green .. .. 13·00 14·00

1886. *P* 14.

8	**1**	½ c. magenta	22·00	55·00
9		1 c. orange	95·00	£120
		a. Imperf (pair)	£200	
		b. Imperf horiz (vert pair)		
10		2 c. brown	6·00	6·00
		a. Imperf between (pair)	£225	
11		4 c. pink	7·50	17·00
12		8 c. green	7·50	17·00
		a. Imperf between (horiz pair)		
13		10 c. blue	7·50	15·00
		a. Imperf (pair)	£150	
8/13		.. .. *Set of* 6	£130	£200

Imperforate examples of the 4 c. pink are listed under No. 6a.

1886. *Nos.* 8 *and* 13 *optd with T* **6**.

14	½ c. magenta	35·00	60·00
15	10 c. blue	75·00	£100

3 CENTS (7) 5 CENTS (8) 3 CENTS Small "3" variety (R.3/4)

(Surchd by *North Borneo Herald*, Sandakan)

1886. *T* **1** *surch as T* **7/8.** (*a*) *P* 12.

16	**7**	3 c. on 4 c. pink	65·00	£150
		a. Small "3"	£2750	
17	**8**	5 c. on 8 c. green	£100	£160
		(*b*) *P* 14		
18	**7**	3 c. on 4 c. pink	32·00	75·00
		a. Small "3"	£850	
19	**8**	5 c. on 8 c. green	35·00	75·00
		a. Surch inverted	£1400	

9

10

11

12

13

1886–87. (*a*) *P* 14.

21*b*	**9**	½ c. magenta	4·75	7·50
22		½ c. rose	1·75	3·50
		a. Imperf (pair)	10·00	
23		1 c. orange-yellow	2·75	4·50
		a. Imperf between (vert pair)	£150	
		b. Imperf (pair)	9·00	
24		1 c. orange	85	2·25
		a. Imperf (pair)	6·00	
25		2 c. brown	1·25	2·25
		a. Imperf (pair)	6·00	
26		4 c. pink	85	2·50
		a. Imperf (pair)	6·00	
		b. Imperf between (horiz or vert pair)	£170	
		c. Imperf vert (horiz pair)		
		d. Error. 1 c. pink (centre stamp of strip of 3)	£100	£200
		da. Imperf between (pair)		
		db. Imperf (pair)	£1700	
27		8 c. green	1·75	3·00
		a. Imperf (pair)	8·50	
28		10 c. blue	3·25	7·00
		a. Imperf between (vert pair)	£180	
		b. Imperf (pair)	8·50	
29	**10**	25 c. indigo (c. £6)	38·00	
		a. Imperf between (vert pair)		
		b. Imperf (pair) (c. £10)	50·00	
30	**11**	50 c. violet (c. £7·50)	38·00	
		a. Imperf (pair) (c. £6)	40·00	
31	**12**	$1 scarlet (c. £6)	95·00	
		a. Imperf (pair) (c. £6)	55·00	
32	**13**	$2 sage-green (c. £15)	£120	
		a. Imperf (pair) (c. £13)	65·00	
21*b*/32		.. .. *Set of* 10	£275	
		(*b*) *P* 12		
34	**9**	½ c. magenta	80·00	£170
35		1 c. orange	48·00	75·00

14

15

16

17

1888. *T* **14/17** (**10** *to* **13** *redrawn*). *P* 14.

36	**14**	25 c. indigo	12·00	42·00	50
		a. Imperf (pair)	60·00	—	3·00
		b. Imperf vert (horiz pair) ..	†	†	£250
37	**15**	50 c. violet	18·00	65·00	50
		a. Imperf (pair)	65·00	—	3·00
		b. Chalky blue	†	75·00	†
38	**16**	$1 scarlet	18·00	60·00	50
		a. Imperf (pair)	65·00	—	3·00
39	**17**	$2 dull green	35·00	75·00	1·10
		a. Imperf (pair)	80·00	—	3·50

The new 25 c. has the inscription "BRITISH NORTH BORNEO" in taller capitals. In the 50 c. the "0" of the numerals "50" in the two upper corners is square-shaped at the top and bottom instead of being oval. The 1 dollar has 14 pearls instead of 13 at each side, and on the 2 dollars the word "BRITISH" measures 10½ to 11 mm in length in place of 12 mm.

18

1888–92. *P* 14.

40	**18**	½ c. magenta (1889)	2·25	3·00	—
		a. Imperf vert (horiz pair) ..			
		b. Rose	30	85	30
		ba. Imperf between (horiz pair) ..	£275		
41		1 c. orange (1892)	30	70	30
		a. Imperf vert (horiz pair) ..			
42		2 c. brown (1889)	3·50	2·75	30
		a. Imperf between (horiz pair) ..			
		b. Lake-brown	75	1·00	30
43		3 c. violet	1·10	1·75	30
		a. Printed triple, one inverted ..			
44		4 c. rose-pink (1889)	1·10	1·75	30
		a. Imperf between (pair) ..	—	£100	—
45		5 c. slate (1889)	1·10	1·75	30
		a. Imperf between (pair) ..			
46		6 c. lake (1892)	2·00	2·75	45
47		8 c. blue-green (1891)	2·00	2·75	45
		a. Yellow-green	4·00	5·50	45
		b. Printed triple, one inverted ..			
48		10 c. blue (1891)	2·00	2·75	50
		a. Imperf between (vert pair) ..	†	†	—
		b. Dull blue	2·10	2·50	50
		ba. Imperf between (horiz pair) ..			
		c. Printed double			
40*b*/8		.. .. *Set of* 9	9·50	14·50	

This set also exists imperf (*Price* £6 *per pair unused*; £4 *cancelled*).

These stamps were forged on several occasions. Most forgeries of the ½ c. value can be identified by reference to the top right-hand Chinese character which, on the forgeries, has a diagonal line joining the two top horizontal lines on its right-hand side.

19 20

1889. *P* 14.

49	**19**	$5 bright purple	48·00	70·00	6·00
		a. Imperf (pair)	32·00	—	16·00
50	**20**	$10 brown	80·00	£130	9·00
		a. Imperf (pair)	85·00	—	20·00
		b. "DOLLAPS" for "DOLLARS" (R.2/1)	£850	—	£325
		ba. Ditto. Imperf (pair)	£1200	—	£800

Two Cents. (21) 6 cents. (23) 1 cent. (22)

1890. *Surch as T* **21,** *in red.*

51	**14**	2 c. on 25 c. indigo	22·00	28·00
		a. Surch inverted	£225	£250
52		8 c. on 25 c. indigo	38·00	45·00

The first printing of Nos. 51/2 had the two lines of the surcharge 3.5 mm apart. On a second printing of both values this gap widened to 5 mm.

1891–92. *Surch with T* **22**.

54	**9**	6 c. on 8 c. green (1892)	£5000	£3500
		a. Large "s" in "cents"	£9000	
55	**18**	6 c. on 8 c. yellow-green	6·00	8·00
		a. Surch inverted	£175	£250
		b. "ɔents" for "cents"	£250	
		c. "cetns." for "cents"	£275	£300
		d. Large "s" in "cents"	85·00	85·00
56	**9**	6 c. on 10 c. blue	22·00	11·00
		a. Surch inverted	95·00	95·00
		b. Surch double	£600	
		c. Surch treble	£225	
		d. Large "s" in "cents."	65·00	65·00
57	**18**	6 c. on 10 c. blue	28·00	22·00
		a. Large "s" in "cents."	80·00	95·00

1892. *Surch as T* **23** ("Cents." *with capital* "C" *as in T* **21** *on No.* 65), *in red.*

63	**18**	1 c. on 4 c. rose-pink	10·00	13·00
		a. Surch double	£225	
		b. Surch on back and on front	—	£400
		ba. As b, but with surch double on front		
64		1 c. on 5 c. slate	5·00	5·00
65	**14**	8 c. on 25 c. indigo	70·00	85·00

24 Dyak Chief

25 Sambar Stag (*Cervus unicolor*)

26 Sago Palm

27 Great Argus Pheasant

28 Arms of the Company

29 Malay Dhow

30 Crocodile

31 Mount Kinabalu

32 Arms of the Company with Supporters

PERFORATION. There are a number of small variations in the perforation of the Waterlow issues of 1894 to 1922 which we believe to be due to irregularity of the pins rather than different perforators.

In the following lists, stamps perf 12, 12½, 13 or compound are described as perf 12–13, stamps perf 13½, 14 or compound are described as perf 13½–14 and those perf 14½, 15 or compound are listed as perf 14½–15. In addition the 13½–14 perforation exists compound with 14½–15 and with 12–13, whilst perf 15½–16 comes from a separate perforator.

(Recess Waterlow)

1894. *P* 14½–15.

66	**24**	1 c. black and olive-bistre	1·25	2·25
		a. Imperf between (horiz or vert pair)		
		b. Perf 13½–14	1·25	2·25
		c. Perf 13½–14, comp 14½–15 ..	8·50	12·00
		d. Perf 13½–14, comp 12–13	4·75	7·50
		e. Perf 12–13		
67		1 c. black and bistre-brown	1·00	2·25
		a. Perf 13½–14	1·25	2·25
		b. Perf 13½–14, comp 12–13	4·75	10·00
		c. Perf 12–13		
68	**25**	2 c. black and rose-lake	3·25	4·50
		a. Imperf between (horiz or vert pair)	£250	
		b. Perf 13½–14	14·00	17·00
69		2 c. black and lake	3·25	4·50
		a. Perf 13½–14	13·00	25·00
		b. Perf 13½–14, comp 12–13	5·00	7·50
		c. Imperf between (horiz pair) ..		
70	**26**	3 c. olive-green and mauve	2·10	4·50
		a. Imperf between (horiz pair) ..	£275	£300
		b. Bronze-green and mauve		
		c. Perf 13½–14		
71		3 c. olive-green and violet (*p* 13½–14)	4·50	9·00
		a. Imperf between (horiz pair) ..		

72 27 5 c. black and vermilion .. .. .. 4·50 9·00
a. Imperf between (horiz or vert pair) £275
b. Perf 13½–14 .. .. 15·00 32·00
c. Perf 13½–14, comp 12–13 .. .. — 32·00
d. Perf 13½–14, comp 14½–15 .. ..
e. Perf 12–13 .. ..
73 28 6 c. black and bistre-brown .. .. 14·00 25·00
a. Perf 13½–14 .. .. .. 4·00 8·00
b. Perf 13½–14, comp 12–13 .. .. — 19·00
c. Perf 13½–14, comp 14½–15 .. ..
d. Imperf between (horiz pair) ..
74 29 8 c. black and dull purple .. .. 2·25 6·00
a. Imperf between (vert pair) £275 £300
b. Perf 13½–14 .. .. .. 4·00 8·50
ba. Imperf between (vert pair) £275
d. Perf 13½–14, comp 12–13 .. ..
75 30 12 c. black and blue .. .. .. 23·00 38·00
a. Perf 13½–14 .. .. .. 23·00 38·00
b. Imperf between (horiz pair) (*canc*)
76 12 c. black and ultramarine .. .. 23·00 38·00
a. Perf 13½–14 .. .. .. 18·00 27·00
b. Imperf between (pair) .. ..
78 31 18 c. black and deep green .. .. 14·00 20·00
a. Perf 13½–14 .. .. .. 15·00 25·00
79 32 24 c. blue and rose-lake .. .. .. 16·00 25·00
a. Imperf between (vert pair) £275
b. Perf 13½–14 .. .. .. 16·00 25·00
c. Perf 13½–14, comp 14½–15 .. ..
66/79 .. .. *Set of* 9 60·00 £100

NOTE.—The prices in the used column are for postally used stamps with circular postmark. Stamps cancelled with bars can be supplied at about one-sixth of these prices.

32*a*

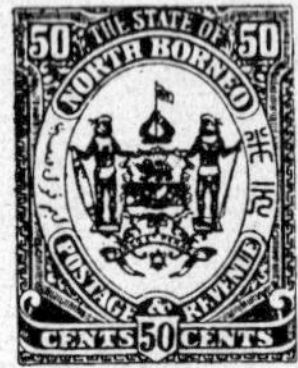
32*b*

32*c*

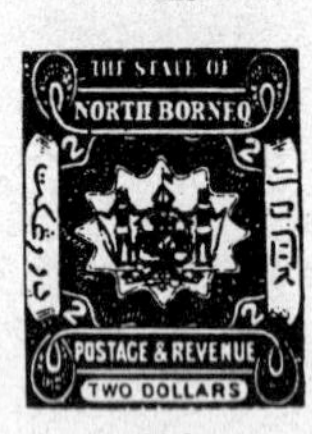
32*d*

(Litho Blades, East & Blades, London)

1894. *T* **32***a to* **32***d*, *and T* **19** *and* **20**, *but inscribed* "THE STATE OF NORTH BORNEO". *P* 14.
81 25 c. indigo .. .. 12·00 22·00 70
a. Imperf (pair) .. .. 13·00 — 2·75
b. Imperf between (horiz or vert pair) £500 — 60·00
c. Printed double, one inverted † † —
82 50 c. deep slate-purple .. .. .. 12·00 22·00 70
a. Imperf (pair) .. .. .. — — 2·50
b. Imperf between (horiz pair) ..
c. Printed double .. .. ..
d. Chalky blue .. .. ..
83 $1 scarlet .. .. 8·50 15·00 90
a. Perf 14 × 11 .. .. .. £120
b. Imperf (pair) .. .. .. 14·00 — 5·00
c. Printed both sides .. .. 15·00 — —
84 $2 dull green .. .. 17·00 35·00 90
a. Imperf (pair) .. .. .. — — 4·50
b. Printed double .. .. ..
85 $5 bright purple .. .. .. £110 £170 9·50
a. Imperf (pair) .. .. .. — — 14·00
b. Dull purple .. .. .. 50·00 90·00 3·50
86 $10 brown .. .. £110 £175 5·00
a. Imperf (pair) .. .. .. — — 11·00
81/6 .. .. *Set of* 6 £225 £300 —
81/6 Optd "Specimen" .. *Set of* 6 £120

For Nos. 81 to 83 in other colours, see Labuan 80*a*, 81*a* and 82*a*.

4

CENTS

(**33** (4 c. has 3½ mm between lines of surcharge))

(Surcharged by Waterlow)

1895 (June). *No.* 83 *surch as T* **33**.
87 4 cents on $1 scarlet .. .. 3·00 4·00 95
a. Surch double £300
88 10 cents on $1 scarlet .. .. 4·25 4·25 95
89 20 cents on $1 scarlet .. .. 6·00 6·50 95
90 30 cents on $1 scarlet .. .. 7·00 7·50 95
91 40 cents on $1 scarlet .. .. 7·50 8·50 1·10
87/91 Optd "Specimen" .. *Set of* 5 85·00

For 4 c. on $1 with wider spacing see No. 121.

No. 88 exists with the figures of the surcharge 2½ mm away from "CENTS". The normal setting has a space of 4 mm. Examples of the narrow setting have, so far, only been seen on cancelled-to-order stamps.

ALTERED CATALOGUE NUMBERS

Any Catalogue numbers altered from the last edition are shown as a list in the introductory pages.

34

35

36

37 Orang-Utan

38

39

40

41 Bruang or Honey-bear

42

43 Borneo Railway Train

44

45

(Recess Waterlow)

1897 (Mar)–**1902.** *T* **34** *to* **45**. *New frames. P* 13½–14.
92 1 c. black and bistre-brown .. .. 3·50 3·50
aa. Perf 16 .. ..
a. Perf 14½–15 .. .. .. 3·50 3·75
b. Perf 13½–14, comp 12–13 .. 14·00 17·00
c. Imperf between (horiz pair) (*canc*) ..
93 1 c. black and ochre .. .. .. 10·00 9·50
a. Perf 14½–15 .. .. .. 4·50 5·00
b. Perf 13½–14, comp 12–13 .. ..
c. Imperf between (horiz pair) .. ..
94 2 c. black and lake .. .. .. 5·00 2·75
a. Perf 14½–15 .. .. .. 5·00 2·75
b. Perf 13½–14, comp 12–13 .. — 7·00
c. Perf 12–13 .. ..
d. Imperf between (horiz pair) (*canc*) ..
95 2 c. black and green (1900) .. .. 7·00 3·25
a. Perf 14½–15 .. .. .. 8·50 7·00
b. Perf 13½–14, comp 12–13 .. 22·00 9·00
c. Perf 12–13 .. ..
d. Imperf between (pair) .. .. — £350
96 3 c. green and rosy mauve .. .. 6·00 6·50
a. Perf 14½–15 .. .. .. 13·00 15·00
b. Perf 13½–14, comp 12–13 .. 20·00 24·00
97 3 c. green and dull mauve (*p* 14½–15) .. 3·25 3·25
98 4 c. black and green (1900) .. .. 4·75 15·00
a. Perf 13½–14, comp 12–13 .. ..
99 4 c. black and carmine (1900) .. .. 5·50 4·75
a. Perf 16 .. .. 12·00 14·00
b. Perf 14½–15 .. .. .. 13·00 3·75
c. Perf 13½–14, comp 12–13 .. 6·50 11·00
d. Perf 12–13 .. ..
100 5 c. black and orange-vermilion .. .. 7·00 4·25
a. Perf 14½–15 .. .. .. 9·50 2·75
b. Perf 13½–14, comp 12–13 .. 10·00 6·50
c. Perf 12–13 .. ..
101 6 c. black and bistre-brown .. .. 10·00 4·00
a. Perf 14½–15 .. .. .. 5·50 3·75
102 8 c. black and brown-purple .. .. 8·50 12·00
a. Perf 16 .. .. 28·00 8·00
b. Perf 14½–15 .. .. .. 5·50 3·75
c. Imperf between (vert pair) .. ..
103 8 c. black and brown .. .. .. 5·00 6·50
a. Perf 14½–15 .. .. .. 10·00 12·00
b. Perf 16 .. ..
104 10 c. brown and slate-lilac (1902) .. 18·00 16·00
a. Imperf between (vert pair) .. ..
105 10 c. brown and slate-blue (1902) .. 27·00 24·00
106 12 c. black and dull blue .. .. 30·00 22·00
a. Imperf between (pair) .. .. — £150
b. Perf 14½–15 .. .. .. 30·00 22·00
c. Perf 13½–14, comp 12–13 .. 50·00 45·00
d. Perf 12–13 .. ..
107 16 c. green and chestnut (1902) .. 20·00 45·00
a. Perf 14½–15 .. .. .. 26·00 65·00
108 18 c. black and green (*p* 16) .. .. 7·00 9·00
a. Imperf vert (horiz pair) (*canc*) .. — 60·00
b. Imperf between (vert pair) .. ..
c. Imperf (pair) (*canc*) .. .. ..
109 24 c. blue and lake .. .. .. 8·50 22·00
a. Perf 13½–14, comp 12–13 .. 23·00 28·00
b. Perf 12–13 .. ..
92/109 (*one of each value*) .. *Set of* 12 £100 £120
92/109 (*excl.* 93, 97, 103/5, 107) Optd "Specimen" .. *Set of* 12 80·00

In the above the 18 c. has "POSTAL REVENUE" instead of "POSTAGE AND REVENUE" and the 24 c. has those words omitted. These stamps were replaced by others with corrected inscriptions; see Nos. 110 and 111.

NOTE.—Stamps cancelled-to-order can be supplied at about one-sixth the prices quoted above for postally used specimens, except in the case of some of the scarcer perforation varieties.

46

47

1897. *Corrected inscriptions. P* 13½–14.
110 46 18 c. black and green .. .. .. 20·00 12·00
a. Perf 14½–15 .. .. .. 25·00 12·00
b. Perf 13½–14, comp 12–13 .. ..
111 47 24 c. blue and lake .. .. .. 22·00 23·00
a. Perf 16 .. .. 27·00 28·00
b. Perf 14½–15 .. .. .. 20·00 23·00
c. Perf 13½–14, comp 12–13 .. ..
d. Perf 12–13 .. ..
110/11 Optd "Specimen" .. .. *Set of* 2 45·00

4 CENTS (**48**) (4½ mm between lines of surcharge)

BRITISH PROTECTORATE. (**49**)

4 cents (**50**)

1899. *Surch with T* **48**. (*a*) *P* 14½–15.
112 4 c. on 5 c. (No. 100*a*) .. .. ..
a. Perf 13½–14 .. .. .. 8·50 10·00
b. Perf 13½–14, comp 12–13 .. 26·00 20·00
113 4 c. on 6 c. (No. 101*a*) .. .. 16·00 20·00
a. Perf 13½–14 .. .. .. 7·50 13·00
114 4 c. on 8 c. (No. 102*b*) .. .. 11·00 10·00
115 4 c. on 12 c. (No. 106*b*) .. .. 11·00 13·00
a. Imperf between (pair) £300 £350
b. Perf 13½–14 .. .. ..
c. Perf 12–13 .. ..
d. Perf 13½–14, comp 12–13 ..
116 4 c. on 18 c. (No. 110*a*) .. .. 11·00 13·00
a. Perf 13½–14 .. .. ..
117 4 c. on 24 c. (No. 111*b*) .. .. 11·00 12·00
a. Perf 16 .. .. 30·00 40·00
b. Perf 13½–14 .. .. .. 15·00
c. Perf 13½–14, comp 12–13 .. 15·00
d. Perf 12–13 .. .. .. 11·00 12·00

(*b*) *P* 14
118 4 c. on 25 c. indigo (No. 81) .. .. 8·00 12·00
a. Imperf between (pair) £600
119 4 c. on 50 c. deep slate-purple (No. 82) .. 11·00 12·00
a. Chalky blue .. .. .. 22·00
121 4 c. on $1 scarlet (No. 83) .. .. 8·00 10·00
122 4 c. on $2 dull green (No. 84) .. .. 11·00 18·00
123 4 c. on $5 bright purple (No. 85) .. 60·00 80·00
a. Dull purple .. .. .. 30·00 40·00
124 4 c. on $10 brown (No. 86) .. .. 30·00 40·00
112/24 .. .. *Set of* 12 £140 £180
112/24 Optd "Specimen" .. *Set of* 12 £225

No. 121 differs only from No. 87 in having the "4" and "cents" wider apart.

Examples of the Kudat postmark dated "AU 15 1899" struck on Nos. 112/24 are generally considered to be faked.

The 1 c., 2 c. and 3 c. values of this set were also surcharged "4 CENTS" but were not issued. They exist overprinted "Specimen" (*price* £150 *the set of three*).

1899. *Surch as T* **48** *but* 8½ *mm between lines of surcharge. P* 14.
125 4 c. on $5 (No. 85) .. .. .. 15·00 18·00
126 4 c. on $10 (No. 86) .. .. .. 15·00 18·00

(Surcharged by Waterlow)

1901 (8 Oct)–**05.** *Optd as T* **49**. (*a*) *P* 13½–14.
127 1 c. (No. 92) (R.) .. .. .. 2·25 2·00
a. Perf 14½–15 .. .. .. 1·90 2·10
128 2 c. (No. 95) (R.) .. .. .. 2·50 2·25
a. Perf 16 .. .. 1·90 2·25
b. Perf 14½–15 .. .. .. 2·50 2·50
129 3 c. (No. 96) .. .. 1·10 2·25
a. Imperf between (vert pair) ..
b. Perf 14½–15 .. .. .. 5·50 2·00
c. Perf 13½–14, comp 14½–15 .. 17·00
130 4 c. (No. 99) (G.) .. .. .. 4·00 2·00
a. Perf 14½–15 .. .. .. 3·25 2·00
131 5 c. (No. 100) (G.) .. .. .. — 2·25
a. Perf 14½–15 .. .. .. 3·75 2·25
132 6 c. (No. 101) (R.) .. .. .. 15·00 17·00
a. No stop after "Protectorate" .. 65·00 65·00
b. Perf 16 .. .. 2·50 2·75
133 8 c. (No. 103) (B.) .. .. .. 3·75 3·75
a. No stop after "Protectorate" .. 4·50 12·00
b. Perf 13½–14, comp 12–13 .. 17·00 6·00
c. Imperf between (vert pair) ..
134 10 c. (No. 104) (R.) (7.02) .. .. 10·00 5·00
a. Perf 14½–15 .. .. .. 17·00 8·00
c. Perf 13½–14. No stop after "Protectorate" 95·00
d. Overprint double (c. £225) .. £250
e. On 10 c. (No. 105) .. ..
f. Imperf between (horiz pair) (*canc*) ..
135 12 c. (No. 106) (R.) .. .. .. 22·00 14·00

No.	Description		Unused	Used
136	16 c. (No. 107) (7.02)		14·00	8·50
	a. Perf 14½–15		14·00	8·50
	b. Perf 13½–14, comp 12–13		20·00	8·50
137	18 c. (No. 110) (R.)		8·00	9·50
	a. No stop after "Protectorate"			
	b. Perf 13½–14, comp 12–13			
138	24 c. (No. 111)		14·00	17·00
	a. Perf 14½–15		22·00	26·00
	b. Imperf between (horiz pair)			
	(*b*) *P* 14			
139	25 c. (No. 81) (R.) (c. 30p.)		4·00	11·00
	a. No stop after "Protectorate"		75·00	
	b. Overprints *tête-bêche* (pair)		£750	
	c. Overprint inverted		£325	
140	50 c. (No. 82) (R.) (c. 40p)		4·25	12·00
	a. No stop after "Protectorate"		35·00	48·00
	b. Chalky blue			
141	$1 (No. 83) (R.) (1.04)		17·00	28·00
142	$1 (No. 83) (c. £2·50)		13·00	22·00
	a. Imperf between (vert pair)		£300	
	b. Opt double (c. £250)			
	c. Opt triple			
143	$2 (No. 84) (R.) (1903) (c. £3·50)		32·00	45·00
	a. Opt double		£750	
144	$5 (No. 85*b*) (R.) (2.05) (c. £4)		65·00	£100
145	$10 (No. 86) (R.) (2.05) (c. £7)		£100	£120
	a. Opt inverted (c. £350)		£1000	
127/45		*Set of* 18	£275	£350
127/40 Optd "Specimen"		*Set of* 14	£250	

There was more than one setting of the overprint for some of the values. Full sheets of the 6 c. and 8 c. are known, without stop throughout.

NOTE.—Nos. 127/38 cancelled-to-order can be supplied at about one-sixth of the prices quoted for postally used specimens. Prices for Nos. 139/45, cancelled, are given in brackets.

1904–5. *Surch locally with T* **50.** (*a*) *P* 14½–15.

No.	Description		Unused	Used
146	4 c. on 5 c. (No. 100a)		9·50	15·00
	a. Surch omitted (in pair with normal)			
147	4 c. on 6 c. (No. 101a)		4·25	7·50
	a. Surch inverted		£180	
148	4 c. on 8 c. (No. 102b)		12·00	18·00
	a. Surch inverted		£225	
149	4 c. on 12 c. (No. 106b)		12·00	18·00
	a. Perf 13½–14		16·00	18·00
	b. Perf 13½–14, comp 12–13		23·00	27·00
	c. Surch omitted (in pair with normal)			
150	4 c. on 18 c. (No. 110a)		16·00	23·00
	a. Perf 13½–14			
151	4 c. on 24 c. (No. 111b)		16·00	23·00
	a. Perf 16		13·00	20·00
	b. Perf 13½–14		16·00	23·00
	c. Perf 12–13			
	(*b*) *P* 14			
152	4 c. on 25 c. (No. 81)		6·00	14·00
153	4 c. on 50 c. (No. 82)		6·00	14·00
154	4 c. on $1 (No. 83)		11·00	18·00
155	4 c. on $2 (No. 84)		14·00	22·00
156	4 c. on $5 (No. 85)		15·00	27·00
	a. Surch on No. 85*b*			
157	4 c. on $10 (No. 86)		15·00	27·00
	a. Surch inverted		£1000	
	b. Surch omitted (in pair with normal)			
146/57		*Set of* 12	£120	£200

51 Tapir

52 Traveller's-tree

53 Railway at Jesselton

54 The Sultan of Sulu, his staff and W. C. Cowie, first Chairman of the Company

55 Asiatic Elephant

56 Rhinoceros

57 Ploughing with Buffalo

58 Wild Boar

59 Palm Cockatoo

60 Rhinoceros Hornbill

61 Wild Bull

62 Dwarf Cassowary

(Recess Waterlow)

1909 (July)–**1922.** *Centres in black. P* 13½–14.

No.	Type	Description		Unused	Used	
158	**51**	1 c. chocolate-brown		2·75	70	25
		a. Perf 14½–15		5·00	3·25	—
159		1 c. brown		3·00	90	—
		a. Perf 14½–15		5·00	2·00	30
160	**52**	2 c. green		1·25	45	25
		a. Imperf between (pair)				
		b. Perf 14½–15		2·00	60	—
161	**53**	3 c. lake		1·75	1·00	25
162		3 c. rose-lake		2·50	60	30
		a. Perf 14½–15		24·00	—	55
163		3 c. green (1922)		5·50	80	—
164	**54**	4 c. scarlet		2·00	55	25
		a. Imperf between (vert pair)				
		b. Perf 14½–15		5·50	1·40	45
165	**55**	5 c. yellow-brown		4·25	1·25	30
		a. Perf 14½–15				
166		5 c. dark brown		4·50	1·25	—
167	**56**	6 c. olive-green		4·25	1·25	30
		a. Perf 14½–15		18·00	4·50	80
168		6 c. apple-green		9·00	1·60	—
169	**57**	8 c. lake		2·75	1·25	30
		a. Perf 14½–15				
170	**58**	10 c. greyish blue		13·00	2·25	30
		a. Perf 14½–15		13·00	7·00	—
171		10 c. blue		13·00	2·25	—
172		10 c. turquoise-blue		11·00	2·25	—
		a. Perf 14½–15		17·00	3·75	—
173	**59**	12 c. deep blue		11·00	1·60	45
		a. Perf 14½–15				
		b. Imperf vert (horiz pair)		†	†	—
173*c*		12 c. deep bright blue				
174	**60**	16 c. brown-lake		14·00	3·75	90
175	**61**	18 c. blue-green		38·00	45·00	1·60
176	**62**	24 c. maroon		16·00	3·50	80
		a. Deep lilac				
158/76			*Set of* 13	£100	60·00	—
158/76 Optd "Specimen"			*Set of* 13	£300		

For this issue perf 12½ see Nos. 277, etc.

(63)

64

65

1909 (Aug). *T* **61** *surch with T* **63.** *P* 13½–14.

No.	Description	Unused	Used	
177	20 c. on 18 c. blue-green (R.) (Optd S. £35)	3·50	1·60	50
	a. Perf 14½–15	£120	50·00	—

(Recess Waterlow)

1911. *P* 13½–14.

No.	Type	Description		Unused	Used
178	**64**	25 c. black and yellow-green		4·00	3·00
		a. Perf 14½–15		8·50	
		b. Imperf (pair)		30·00	
178*c*		25 c. black and blue-green			
179		50 c. black and steel-blue		7·50	4·00
		a. Perf 14½–15		15·00	13·00
		b. Imperf (pair)		45·00	
		c. Imperf between (horiz pair)			
180		$1 black and chestnut		14·00	4·75
		a. Perf 14½–15		23·00	12·00
		b. Imperf (pair)		45·00	
181		$2 black and lilac		26·00	11·00
182	**65**	$5 black and lake		48·00	38·00
		a. Imperf (pair)		70·00	
183		$10 black and brick-red		£110	85·00
		a. Imperf (pair)		75·00	
178/83			*Set of* 6	£190	£130
178/83 Optd "Specimen"			*Set of* 6	£200	

BRITISH

PROTECTORATE

(66)

2

cents

(67)

(68)

1912 (July). *Nos.* 85 *and* 86 *optd with T* **66**.

No.	Description		Unused	Used
184	$5 dull purple (R.) (c. £6)		£550	
185	$10 brown (R.) (c. £6)		£700	
	a. Opt inverted (*canc*)			

1916. *Stamps of* 1909–22 *surch as T* **67.** *P* 13½–14.

No.	Description		Unused	Used
186	2 c. on 3 c. black and rose-lake		5·50	6·00
	a. "s" inverted		85·00	85·00
	b. Surch double			
187	4 c. on 6 c. black and olive-green (R.)		5·50	6·00
	a. "s" inverted		85·00	85·00
	b. "s" inserted by hand		—	£350
	c. Perf 14½–15			
188	10 c. on 12 c. black and deep blue		8·50	11·00
	a. "s" inverted		90·00	90·00
186/8 Optd "Specimen"		*Set of* 3	£100	

1916 (May). *Stamps of* 1909–11 *optd with T* **68.** *P* 13½–14. *Centres in black.* (*a*) *Cross in vermilion.*

No.	Type	Description		Unused	Used
189	**51**	1 c. brown		7·50	16·00
190	**52**	2 c. green		25·00	38·00
		a. Perf 14½–15		30·00	48·00
191	**53**	3 c. rose-lake		18·00	25·00
192	**54**	4 c. scarlet		8·00	18·00
		a. Perf 14½–15		—	£100
193	**55**	5 c. yellow-brown		18·00	30·00
		a. Perf 14½–15			
194	**56**	6 c. apple-green		25·00	40·00
		a. Perf 14½–15			
195	**57**	8 c. lake		17·00	35·00
196	**58**	10 c. blue		32·00	50·00
197	**59**	12 c. deep blue		32·00	50·00
198	**60**	16 c. brown-lake		32·00	50·00
199	**61**	20 c. on 18 c. blue-green		32·00	50·00
200	**62**	24 c. dull mauve		50·00	60·00
		a. Imperf between (vert pair)			
201	**64**	25 c. green (*p* 14½–15)		£200	£300
189/201			*Set of* 13	£450	£650
		(*b*) *Cross in carmine*			
202	**51**	1 c. brown		17·00	30·00
		a. Perf 14½–15			
203	**52**	2 c. green		30·00	20·00
		a. Opt double		†	—
		b. Perf 14½–15			
204	**53**	3 c. rose-lake		20·00	35·00
205	**55**	5 c. yellow-brown		20·00	40·00
206	**56**	6 c. apple-green		18·00	35·00
		a. Perf 14½–15			
207	**57**	8 c. lake		18·00	35·00
208	**58**	10 c. blue		20·00	42·00
209	**59**	12 c. deep blue		32·00	55·00
210	**60**	16 c. brown-lake		38·00	65·00
211	**61**	20 c. on 18 c. blue-green		50·00	80·00
212	**62**	24 c. dull mauve		60·00	£110
213	**64**	25 c. green			
		a. Perf 14½–15		£350	£450
202/13			*Set of* 12	£600	£850

RED CROSS ✚

TWO CENTS
(69)

FOUR CENTS
(70)

1918. *Stamps of* 1909–11 *surch as T* **69.** *P* 13½–14.

No.	Type	Description		Unused	Used
		(*a*) *Lines of surcharge* 9 *mm apart*			
214	**51**	1 c. brown		1·60	6·50
		a. Imperf between (horiz pair)		£400	
215	**52**	2 c. green		1·00	3·75
		a. Imperf between (horiz or vert pair)		£400	
		b. Imperf (pair)			
		c. Perf 14½–15			
216	**53**	3 c. rose-red		2·75	7·00
		a. Imperf between (horiz pair)		£400	
		b. Perf 14½–15		20·00	38·00
217		3 c. dull rose-carmine		£130	
		a. Perf 14½–15		£160	
218	**54**	4 c. scarlet		1·00	3·25
		a. Surch inverted		£275	
219	**55**	5 c. deep brown		3·75	9·00
220		5 c. pale brown		3·75	13·00
221	**56**	6 c. olive-green		3·75	17·00
		a. Perf 14½–15		£130	
221*b*		6 c. apple-green			
		c. Perf 14½–15			
222	**57**	8 c. lake		3·50	7·00
		a. Inverted figure "3" for "C" in "CENTS"			
223	**58**	10 c. blue		3·50	12·00
224	**59**	12 c. deep bright blue		3·50	13·00
		a. Surch inverted		£500	
225	**60**	16 c. brown-lake		5·50	17·00
226	**62**	24 c. mauve		6·50	17·00
		(*b*) *Lines of surch* 13–14 *mm apart*			
227	**52**	2 c. green		38·00	48·00
228	**56**	6 c. olive-green		£180	£300
229	**64**	25 c. green		16·00	35·00
230		50 c. steel-blue		16·00	35·00
231		$1 chestnut		38·00	50·00
232		$2 lilac		55·00	70·00
233	**65**	$5 lake		£250	£400
234		$10 brick-red		£250	£400
214/34			*Set of* 17	£600	£1000

The above stamps were dispatched from London in three consignments, of which two were lost through enemy action at sea.

These stamps were sold at a premium of 2 c. per stamp, which went to the Red Cross Society.

1918. *Stamps of* 1909–11 *surch with T* **70**, *in red. P* 13½–14.

No.	Type	Description		Unused	Used
235	**51**	1 c. chocolate		75	3·50
		a. Imperf between (horiz pair)			
236	**52**	2 c. green		90	4·00
237	**53**	3 c. rose-lake		90	3·25
238	**54**	4 c. scarlet		75	4·00
239	**55**	5 c. brown		1·75	5·50
240	**56**	6 c. apple-green		1·60	7·50
		a. Imperf between (pair)		£650	
241	**57**	8 c. lake		2·00	7·50

No.	Type	Description	Unused	Used
242	**58**	10 c. turquoise-blue	2·75	14·00
242*a*		10 c. greenish blue	5·00	15·00
243	**59**	12 c. deep blue	5·00	11·00
		a. Opt double		
244	**60**	16 c. brown-lake	5·00	18·00
245	**62**	24 c. mauve	7·00	22·00
246	**64**	25 c. yellow-green	7·50	26·00
247		25 c. blue-green	22·00	55·00
248		50 c. steel-blue	16·00	32·00
		a. Perf 14½–15	55·00	
249		$1 chestnut	22·00	45·00
		a. Perf 14½–15	55·00	
250		$2 lilac	32·00	60·00
251	**65**	$5 lake	£200	£400
252		$10 brick-red	£200	£400
235/52		*Set of* 17	£450	£1000

Nos. 235/52 were sold at face, plus 4 c. on each stamp for Red Cross Funds.

MALAYA-BORNEO
EXHIBITION
1922.
(71)

THREE
CENTS
(72)

1922. *Stamps of* 1909–22 *optd as T* **71** *by Waterlow. P* 13½–14.

No.	Type	Description	Unused	Used
253	**51**	1 c. brown (R.)	3·75	12·00
		a. "BORHEO"	£350	£350
		b. "BORNEQ"	£275	£300
		c. Stop after "EXHIBITION."	35·00	
		d. Raised stop after "1922"		
		e. Perf 14½–15	5·50	15·00
		ea. "BORHEO"	£375	
		eb. "BORNEQ"		
		ec. Raised stop after "1922"	£120	
		ed. "EXHIBITICN." with stop	£700	
		ee. "MILAYA"		
		ef. Stop after "EXHIBITION."	35·00	
253*f*		1 c. brown (B.)(*p* 14½–15)	£600	
		fa. Vert pair, with and without opt	£1000	
		fb. Raised stop after "1922."	£700	
		fc. "BORHEO"	£1300	
		fd. "BORNEQ"	£1300	
		fe. "EXHIBITIOH"	£1300	
		ff. "EXHIBITICN." with stop	£1400	
		fg. "MILAYA"		
254		1 c. orange-brown (R.)	6·00	18·00
255	**52**	2 c. green (R.)	1·60	8·50
		a. Stop after "EXHIBITION."	16·00	
256	**53**	3 c. rose-lake (B.)	3·00	9·00
		a. Stop after "EXHIBITION."	25·00	
		b. "EXHIBITICN." with stop		
		c. Raised stop after "1922"		
257	**54**	4 c. scarlet (B.)	2·00	7·00
		a. Stop after "EXHIBITION."	17·00	
		b. Perf 14½–15		
		ba. Stop after "EXHIBITION."		
258	**55**	5 c. orange-brown (B.)	4·00	13·00
		a. Imperf between (vert pair)	£850	£700
		b. Stop after "EXHIBITION."	23·00	
		c. Opt double	£1750	
		d. Opt double (with stop)	£1300	
259		5 c. chestnut (B.)	7·00	23·00
		a. Stop after "EXHIBITION."		
260	**56**	6 c. apple-green (R.)	3·00	13·00
		a. Stop after "EXHIBITION."	22·00	
		b. Opt double	£1750	
		c. Opt double (with stop)		
261	**57**	8 c. dull rose (B.)	4·50	15·00
		a. Stop after "EXHIBITION."		
262		8 c. deep rose-lake (B.)	4·50	15·00
		a. Stop after "EXHIBITION."	28·00	
263	**58**	10 c. turquoise-blue (R.)	4·50	20·00
		a. Stop after "EXHIBITION."	28·00	
		b. Perf 14½–15	20·00	
		ba. Stop after "EXHIBITION."		
264		10 c. greenish blue (R.)	4·50	15·00
		a. Stop after "EXHIBITION."	30·00	
265	**59**	12 c. deep blue (R.)	5·00	20·00
		a. Stop after "EXHIBITION."	38·00	
266		12 c. deep bright blue (R.)	24·00	
		a. Stop after "EXHIBITION."	£130	
267	**60**	16 c. brown-lake (B.)	4·25	23·00
		a. Stop after "EXHIBITION."	30·00	
		b. Opt in red	£2000	
268	**61**	20 c. on 18 c. blue-green (B.)	8·00	27·00
		a. Stop after "EXHIBITION."	80·00	
269		20 c. on 18 c. blue-green (R.)	65·00	£130
		a. Stop after "EXHIBITION."	£200	£225
270	**62**	24 c. mauve (R.)	6·50	24·00
		a. Stop after "EXHIBITION."	35·00	
271		24 c. lilac (R.)	9·00	24·00
		a. Stop after "EXHIBITION."	38·00	
272		24 c. reddish lilac (R.)	18·00	45·00
		a. Stop after "EXHIBITION."	70·00	
273	**64**	25 c. blue-green (R.)	9·00	23·00
		a. Stop after "EXHIBITION."	40·00	
274		25 c. yellow-green (R.)	9·00	30·00
		a. Stop after "EXHIBITION."	40·00	
		b. Opt double	£750	
		c. Perf 14½–15	17·00	50·00
		ca. Stop after "EXHIBITION."	£200	
		cb. Opt double	£750	
275		50 c. steel-blue (R.)	7·00	26·00
		a. Stop after "EXHIBITION."	50·00	
		b. Perf 14½–15	32·00	
		ba. Stop after "EXHIBITION."	90·00	
253/75		*Set of* 14	60·00	£200
253/75 Optd "Specimen"		*Set of* 14	£500	

1923. *T* **54** *surch with T* **72**.

No.	Description	Unused	Used
276	3 c. on 4 c. black and scarlet	2·00	2·75
	a. Surch double		
276 Optd "Specimen"		65·00	

1925–28. *As* 1909–22. *Centres in black, and colour changed* (2 c.). *P* 12½.

No.	Type	Description	Unused	Used
277	**51**	1 c. chocolate-brown	75	1·00
		a. Imperf between (horiz pair)	£350	
278	**52**	2 c. claret	75	80
		a. Imperf between (horiz or vert pair)	†	—
279	**53**	3 c. green (1925)	3·50	2·50
		a. Imperf between (horiz pair)		
280	**54**	4 c. scarlet	1·60	35
		a. Imperf between (vert pair)	£300	
		b. Imperf between (horiz pair)	£500	
281	**55**	5 c. yellow-brown	2·50	1·75
		a. Imperf between (vert pair)		
282	**56**	6 c. olive-green	2·25	90
283	**57**	8 c. carmine	2·25	70
		a. Imperf between (horiz or vert pair)	£300	
284	**58**	10 c. turquoise-blue	2·25	95
		a. Imperf between (horiz or vert pair)	£400	
285	**59**	12 c. deep blue	2·50	1·50
286	**60**	16 c. red-brown	3·50	12·00
287	**61**	20 c. on 18 c. blue-green (R.)	4·50	4·25
288	**62**	24 c. violet	13·00	18·00
289	**64**	25 c. green	7·00	5·50
290		50 c. steel-blue	8·00	11·00
291		$1 chestnut	23·00	26·00
292		$2 mauve	40·00	42·00
293	**65**	$5 lake (1928)	65·00	75·00
294		$10 orange-red (1928)	£130	£150
277/94		*Set of* 18	£275	£325

73 Head of a Murut

76 Mount Kinabalu

(Eng J. A. C. Harrison. Recess Waterlow)

1931 (1 Jan). 50*th Anniv of British North Borneo Company. T* **73**, **76** *and similar designs. P* 12½.

No.	Description	Unused	Used
295	3 c. black and blue-green	3·00	2·00
296	6 c. black and orange	14·00	4·50
297	10 c. black and scarlet	8·50	9·00
298	12 c. black and ultramarine	6·50	7·00
299	25 c. black and violet	25·00	25·00
300	$1 black and yellow-green	28·00	38·00
301	$2 black and chestnut	40·00	55·00
302	$5 black and purple	80·00	£130
295/302	*Set of* 8	£180	£250
295/302 Optd "Specimen"	*Set of* 8	£350	

Designs: *Vert*—6 c. Orang-Utan; 10 c. Dyak warrior; $1 Badge of the Company; $5 Arms of the Company. *Horiz*—25 c. Clouded leopard; $2 Arms of the Company.

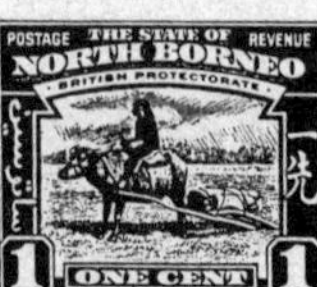

81 Buffalo Transport

82 Palm Cockatoo

(Eng J. A. C. Harrison. Recess Waterlow)

1939 (1 Jan). *T* **81/2** *and similar designs. P* 12½.

No.	Description	Unused	Used
303	1 c. green and red-brown	40	50
304	2 c. purple and greenish blue	50	35
305	3 c. slate-blue and green	40	50
306	4 c. bronze-green and violet	80	80
307	6 c. deep blue and claret	55	65
308	8 c. scarlet	50	45
309	10 c. violet and bronze-green	8·00	3·75
310	12 c. green and royal blue	1·25	2·40
	a. Green and blue	1·75	3·25
311	15 c. blue-green and brown	4·00	3·50
312	20 c. violet and slate-blue	4·75	3·50
313	25 c. green and chocolate	5·00	3·50
314	50 c. chocolate and violet	4·75	3·50
315	$1 brown and carmine	18·00	15·00
316	$2 violet and olive-green	70·00	60·00
317	$5 indigo and pale blue	£200	£160
303/17	*Set of* 15	£275	£225
303/17 Perf "Specimen"	*Set of* 15	£200	

Designs: *Vert*—3 c. Native; 4 c. Proboscis Monkey; 6 c. Mounted Bajaus; 10 c. Orang-Utan; 15 c. Dyak; $1, $2 Badge of the Company. *Horiz*—8 c. Eastern Archipelago; 12 c. Murut with blow-pipe; 20 c. River scene; 25 c. Native boat; 50 c. Mt Kinabalu; $5 Arms of the Company.

WAR TAX
(96)

WAR
TAX
(97)

1941 (24 Feb). *Nos.* 303/4 *optd with T* **96/7**.

No.	Description	Unused	Used
318	1 c. green and red-brown	12	40
319	2 c. purple and greenish blue	45	1·25

BRITISH MILITARY ADMINISTRATION

BMA
(98)

(99)

1945 (17 Dec). *Nos.* 303/17 *optd with T* **98**.

No.	Description	Unused	Used
320	1 c. green and red-brown	65	40
321	2 c. purple and greenish blue	65	40
322	3 c. slate-blue and green	30	40
323	4 c. bronze-green and violet	6·00	4·50
324	6 c. deep blue and claret	40	45
325	8 c. scarlet	60	95
326	10 c. violet and bronze-green	1·50	1·25
327	12 c. green and blue	60	95
	a. Green and royal blue		
328	15 c. blue-green and brown	60	95
329	20 c. violet and slate-blue	1·00	1·00
330	25 c. green and chocolate	1·40	1·25
331	50 c. chocolate and violet	2·25	2·50
332	$1 brown and carmine	14·00	14·00
333	$2 violet and olive-green	15·00	15·00
	a. Opt double	£1300	
334	$5 indigo and pale blue	13·00	14·00
320/34	*Set of* 15	50·00	50·00

These stamps and the similarly overprinted stamps of Sarawak were obtainable at all post offices throughout British Borneo (Brunei, Labuan, North Borneo and Sarawak), for use on local and overseas mail.

CROWN COLONY

1947 (1 Sept–22 Dec). *Nos.* 303 *to* 317 *optd with T* **99** *and bars obliterating words* "THE STATE OF" *and* "BRITISH PROTECTORATE".

No.	Description	Unused	Used
335	1 c. green and red-brown (15.12)	25	35
336	2 c. purple and greenish blue (22.12)	45	50
337	3 c. slate-blue and green (R.)(22.12)	25	45
338	4 c. bronze-green and violet	20	15
339	6 c. deep blue and claret (R.)(22.12)	25	40
340	8 c. scarlet	20	20
341	10 c. violet and bronze-green (15.12)	40	20
342	12 c. green and royal blue (22.12)	35	50
	a. Green and blue		
343	15 c. blue-green and brown (22.12)	35	45
344	20 c. violet and slate-blue (22.12)	35	45
345	25 c. green and chocolate (22.12)	35	35
346	50 c. chocolate and violet (22.12)	60	55
347	$1 brown and carmine (22.12)	60	75
348	$2 violet and olive-green (22.12)	2·50	3·75
349	$5 indigo and pale blue (R.) (22.12)	14·00	17·00
335/49	*Set of* 15	19·00	23·00
335/49 Perf "Specimen"	*Set of* 15	£250	

1948 (1 Nov). *Royal Silver Wedding. As Nos.* 30/1 *of Aden.*

No.	Description	Unused	Used
350	8 c. scarlet	35	40
351	$10 mauve	13·00	35·00

1949 (10 Oct). 75*th Anniv of Universal Postal Union. As Nos.* 114/17 *of Antigua.*

No.	Description	Unused	Used
352	8 c. carmine	40	35
353	10 c. brown	70	55
354	30 c. orange-brown	1·40	1·75
355	55 c. blue	1·50	1·75

100 Mount Kinabalu

102 Coconut Grove

(Photo Harrison)

1950 (1 July)–**52**. *T* **100**, **102** *and similar designs. Wmk Mult Script CA. Chalk-surfaced paper. P* 13½ × 14½ (*horiz*), 14½ × 13½ (*vert*).

No.	Description	Unused	Used
356	1 c. red-brown	12	30
357	2 c. blue	12	25
358	3 c. green	12	30
359	4 c. bright purple	12	25
360	5 c. violet	30	25
361	8 c. scarlet	30	30
362	10 c. maroon	20	30
363	15 c. ultramarine	30	30
364	20 c. brown	45	45
365	30 c. olive-brown	60	35
366	50 c. rose-carmine ("JESSLETON")	65	1·60
366*a*	50 c. rose-carmine ("JESSELTON") (1.5.52)	65	1·25
367	$1 red-orange	1·40	1·40
368	$2 grey-green	3·00	4·75
369	$5 emerald-green	7·00	11·00
370	$10 dull blue	26·00	40·00
356/70	*Set of* 16	38·00	55·00

Designs: *Horiz*—2 c. Native musical instrument; 8 c. Map; 10 c. Logging; 15 c. Native Prahu, Sandakan; 20 c. Bajau Chief; $2 Murut with blowpipe; $5 Net-fishing; $10 Arms of North Borneo. *Vert*—4 c. Hemp drying; 5 c. Cattle at Kota Belud; 30 c. Suluk craft, Lahad Datu; 50 c. Clock tower, Jesselton; $1 Bajau horsemen.

1953 (3 June). *Coronation. As No.* 47 *of Aden.*

No.	Description	Unused	Used
371	10 c. black and bright scarlet	30	40

115 Logging

(Photo Harrison)

1954 (1 Mar)–**57**. *Designs previously used for King George VI issue, but with portrait of Queen Elizabeth II as in T* **115**. *Chalk-surfaced paper. Wmk Mult Script CA. P* 14½ × 13½ (*vert*) *or* 13½ × 14½ (*horiz*).

No.	Description	Unused	Used
372	1 c. red-brown (1.10.54)	5	25
373	2 c. blue (1.6.56)	5	12
374	3 c. green (*shades*) (1.2.57)	25	40

375 4 c. bright purple (16.5.55) 12 5
376 5 c. reddish violet (1.7.54) 12 5
377 8 c. scarlet (1.10.54) 15 10
378 10 c. maroon 15 5
379 15 c. bright blue (16.5.55) 25 5
380 20 c. brown (3.8.54) 20 5
381 30 c. olive-brown (3.8.54) 35 5
382 50 c. rose-carmine ("JESSELTON") (*shades*) (10.2.56) 45 5
383 $1 red-orange (1.4.55) 95 25
384 $2 deep green (*shades*) (1.10.55) .. .. 2·50 2·50
385 $5 emerald-green (1.2.57) .. .. 13·00 13·00
386 $10 deep blue (1.2.57) .. .. 25·00 30·00
372/86 .. .. .. *Set of* 15 38·00 42·00

Designs: *Horiz*—1 c. Mount Kinabalu; 2 c. Native musical instrument; 8 c. Map; 15 c. Native prahu, Sandakan; 20 c. Bajau chief; $2 Murut with blowpipe; $5 Net-fishing; $10 Arms of North Borneo. *Vert*—3 c. Coconut grove; 4 c. Hemp drying; 5 c. Cattle at Kota Belud; 30 c. Suluk boat, Lahad Datu; 50 c. Clock Tower, Jesselton; $1 Bajau horseman.

Plate 2 of the 30 c., released 10 August 1960, had a finer, 250 screen, instead of the previous 200 (*price* £1.75 *mint*).

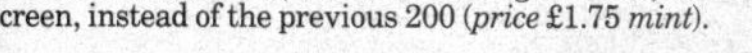

116 Borneo Railway, 1902

119 Arms of Chartered Company

(Recess Waterlow)

1956 (1 Nov). *75th Anniv of British North Borneo Co. T* **116, 119** *and similar designs. Wmk Mult Script CA. P* 13 × 13½ (*horiz*) *or* 13½ × 13 (*vert*).

387 10 c. black and rose-carmine 50 15
388 15 c. black and red-brown 30 15
389 35 c. black and bluish green 35 60
390 $1 black and slate 65 90

Designs: *Horiz*—15 c. Native prahu; 35 c. Mount Kinabalu.

120 Sambar Stag

121 Orang-utan

(Des Chong Yun Fatt. Recess Waterlow (until 1962), then D.L.R.)

1961 (1 Feb). *W w* **12**. *Horiz designs as T* **120** *or vert designs as T* **121**. *P* 13.

391 1 c. emerald and brown-red 5 5
392 4 c. bronze-green and orange 15 25
393 5 c. sepia and violet 15 5
394 6 c. black and blue-green 10 5
395 10 c. green and red 15 5
396 12 c. brown and grey-green 15 10
397 20 c. blue-green and ultramarine 40 5
398 25 c. grey-black and scarlet 30 20
399 30 c. sepia and olive 30 5
400 35 c. slate-blue and red-brown 30 15
401 50 c. emerald and yellow-brown 35 10
402 75 c. grey-blue and bright purple 75 50
403 $1 brown and yellow-green .. .. 2·00 35
404 $2 brown and slate .. .. .. 3·75 2·00
405 $5 emerald and maroon .. .. 14·00 10·00
406 $10 carmine and blue .. .. 22·00 22·00
391/406 .. .. .. *Set of* 16 40·00 32·00

Designs: *Horiz*—4 c. Honey bear; 5 c. Clouded Leopard; 6 c. Dusun woman with gong; 10 c. Map of Borneo; 12 c. Tembadau (wild bull); 20 c. Butterfly orchid; 25 c. Sumatran rhinoceros; 30 c. Murut with blow-pipe; 35 c. Mount Kinabalu; 50 c. Dusun and buffalo transport; 75 c. Bajau horsemen. *Vert*—$2 Rhinoceros Hornbill; $5 Crested Wood Partridge; $10 Arms of North Borneo.

1963 (4 June). *Freedom from Hunger. As No.* 76 *of Aden.*

407 12 c. ultramarine 65 20

POSTAL FISCALS

Three Cents. Revenue

(F 1) (Raised stop)

Ten Cents. Revenue

(F 2)

1886. *Regular issues surch as Type* F 1 *or* F 2.

F1 1 3 c. on 4 c. pink (No. 6) .. .. 30·00 45·00
a. Raised stop after "Cents" .. .. 70·00
F2 5 c. on 8 c. green (No. 7) .. .. 30·00 45·00
a. Raised stop after "Cents" .. .. 75·00
F3 4 10 c. on 50 c. violet (No. 4) .. .. 45·00 70·00
a. Surch double
b. No stop after "Cents" and stop after "Revenue." £130

POSTAGE DUE STAMPS

NOTE. Postage Due stamps cancelled-to-order can be supplied at about one-sixth of the prices quoted for postally used specimens. The issues since 1923 have not been thus cancelled.

POSTAGE DUE

(D 1)

1895 (1 Aug). *Stamps of* 1894 *optd with Type* D **1**. *P* 14½–15.

A. *Vertically* (*reading upwards*)

D 1 25 2 c. black and rose-lake .. .. 7·00 18·00
a. Opt double (*canc*) .. .. † £200
b. Opt reading downwards .. .. — £250
D 2 2 c. black and lake .. .. 4·25 6·00
a. Perf 13½–14
b. Opt omitted (in vert pair with normal) .. .. — £325
D 3 26 3 c. olive-green and mauve .. .. 3·50 7·50
a. Bronze-green and mauve
b. Opt reading downwards
D 3*c* 3 c. olive-green and violet
ca. Opt double (*canc*) .. .. † £350
cb. Perf 13½–14
D 4 27 5 c. black and vermilion .. .. 7·00 15·00
a. Printed double .. .. † —
b. Stop after "DUE." .. .. 35·00
c. Perf 13½–14 .. .. — 28·00
ca. Opt double
d. Perf 13½–14, comp 12–13 .. .. — 30·00
D 5 28 6 c. black and bistre-brown .. .. 6·50 16·00
a. Perf 13½–14 .. .. 3·75 13·00
b. Perf 12–13
c. Perf 13½–14, comp 12–13
d. Opt reading downwards
D 6 31 18 c. black and deep green .. .. 14·00 29·00
a. Opt reading downwards £300 £170
D3/4 & D6 Optd "Specimen" .. *Set of* 3 90·00

B. *Horizontally*

D 7 29 8 c. black and dull purple .. .. 7·50 18·00
a. Opt double
b. Perf 13½–14
ba. Opt inverted .. .. — 95·00
c. Perf 13½–14, comp 12–13
D 8 30 12 c. black and blue .. .. — 17·00
a. Opt double .. .. — £300
a. Perf 13½–14 .. .. 8·00 17·00
D 9 12 c. black and ultramarine (*p* 13½–14) 18·00
D10 31 18 c. black and deep green .. .. 12·00 28·00
a. Opt inverted £170 £350
b. Perf 13½–14 .. .. 16·00 26·00
ba. Opt double .. .. — £200
D11 32 24 c. blue and rose-lake .. .. — 28·00
a. Opt double
b. Perf 13½–14 .. .. 11·00
c. Perf 13½–14, comp 14½–15
D8 & D11 Optd "Specimen" .. *Set of* 2 50·00

1897. *Stamps of* 1897 *optd with Type* D **1**. *P* 14½–15.

A. *Vertically*

D12 2 c. black and lake .. .. 3·00 5·00
a. Perf 13½–14 .. .. 7·00

B. *Horizontally*

D13 2 c. black and lake .. .. 6·50 13·00
D14 8 c. black and brown-purple .. .. 6·50 13·00
a. Stop after "DUE." .. .. 14·00 23·00
D12 & D14 Optd "Specimen" .. *Set of* 2 45·00

1901. *Issue of* 1897–1902 *optd with Type* D **1**. *P* 13½–14.

A. *Vertically* (*reading upwards*)

D15 2 c. black and green .. .. 4·00 5·50
a. Perf 13½–14, comp 12–13 .. .. — 13·00
b. Perf 16
c. Perf 12–13
d. Opt reading downwards
D16 3 c. green and rosy mauve .. .. 4·00 5·50
a. Stop after "DUE." .. .. 14·00 23·00
b. Perf 14½–15 .. .. 2·00 3·50
c. Perf 13½–14, comp 14½–15
d. Opt double
e. Opt double. Stop after "DUE." £130
D17 3 c. green and dull mauve (*p* 14½–15) 3·75 5·50
a. Stop after "DUE." .. .. 12·00 20·00
b. Opt double. Stop after "DUE."
D18 4 c. black and carmine .. .. 3·50 4·75
a. Perf 14½–15
D19 5 c. black and orange-vermilion .. .. 5·00 6·00
a. Perf 14½–15 .. .. 5·50 8·00
b. Stop after "DUE." .. .. 20·00
D20 6 c. blk & bistre-brn (Optd "Specimen" £25) — 4·50
a. Perf 14½–15 .. .. 2·00 4·00
b. Perf 13½–14, comp 12–13
D20*c* 8 c. black and brown-purple (*p* 16)
D21 8 c. black and brown
a. Perf 14½–15 .. .. 2·25 4·00
ab. Opt reading downwards
D22 12 c. black and dull blue .. .. 9·00 13·00
a. Perf 14½–15
D23 18 c. black and green (No. 108)
a. Perf 16
D24 18 c. black and green (No. 110) .. .. 9·00 11·00
a. Perf 13½–14, comp 12–13 .. .. 9·00 11·00
D25 24 c. blue and lake (No. 109) .. .. — 6·50
D26 24 c. blue and lake
a. Perf 14½–15 .. .. 8·00 13·00

B. *Horizontally*

D27 2 c. black and green .. .. 14·00 25·00
D28 8 c. black and brown (*p* 14½–15) .. .. 19·00 35·00
a. Stop after "DUE." .. .. 42·00 65·00

An example of the 5 c. value, No. D19a, has been seen clearly postmarked 1899.

1902–5. *Stamps of* 1901–5 *optd* "British Protectorate," *further optd with Type* D **1**. *P* 13½–14. A. *Vertically* (1902).

D29 2 c. black and green (*p* 16) .. .. — £140
D30 3 c. green and rosy mauve .. .. 65·00 70·00
D31 5 c. black and orange-vermilion (*p* 14½–15) 75·00 70·00
D32 8 c. black and brown .. .. 75·00 70·00
D33 24 c. blue and lake .. .. — 55·00

B. *Horizontally, at top of stamp* (1904–5)

D34 2 c. black and green (*p* 14½–15) .. .. £120 50·00
a. Perf 16 .. .. 60·00 70·00
D35 4 c. black and carmine .. .. 75·00 19·00

C. *Horizontally, at centre of stamp* (1904–5)

D35*a* 1 c. black and bistre-brown
b. Perf 14½–15 .. .. £250
D36 2 c. black and green .. .. 1·25 75
a. Perf 14½–15 .. .. 50·00 45·00
D37 3 c. olive-green and rosy mauve .. .. 1·25 1·00
a. Perf 14½–15 .. .. 65·00 15·00
ab. "POSTAGE DUE" double
D38 4 c. black and carmine .. .. 3·50 2·50
a. "POSTAGE DUE" double .. .. 65·00
b. Perf 14½–15 .. .. 2·00 3·00
D39 5 c. black and orange-vermilion .. .. 2·50 1·60
a. Perf 14½–15 .. .. 6·50 7·50
D40 6 c. black and bistre-brown .. .. 4·00 3·00
a. "POSTAGE DUE" inverted .. .. — 90·00
b. "POSTAGE DUE" double .. .. † —
c. No stop after "PROTECTORATE"
d. Perf 16 .. .. 11·00 13·00
D41 8 c. black and brown .. .. 6·50 3·50
a. No stop after "PROTECTORATE" .. .. 28·00 20·00
D42 10 c. brown and slate-lilac .. .. 13·00 7·50
a. No stop after "PROTECTORATE"
D42*b* 10 c. brown and slate-blue .. .. 13·00 9·50
D43 12 c. black and blue .. .. 4·25 9·50
D44 16 c. green and chestnut .. .. 5·00 6·50
D45 18 c. black and green .. .. 3·75 6·50
a. "POSTAGE DUE" double .. .. — 45·00
b. Imperf between (vert pair)
D46 24 c. blue and lake .. .. 5·50 15·00
a. Perf 14½–15
b. "POSTAGE DUE" double .. .. — 75·00

D. *Horizontally. Optd locally, with stop after* "DUE." (1904–5)

D47 1 c. black and bistre-brown .. .. 4·00 19·00
a. With raised stop after "DUE." .. .. 6·50 19·00

No. D35*a*/b are usually found cancelled-to-order suggesting that they came from remainder stocks which were not issued, but we have also seen one unused example of No. D35*a* and two of No. D35b.

1920–31. *Stamps of* 1909–22, *optd with Type* D **1**. *P* 13½–14.

A. *Horizontally at top of stamp*

D48 4 c. black and scarlet (1920) .. .. 18·00 7·50

B. *Horizontally towards foot of stamp*

D49 2 c. black and green .. .. 4·00 7·50
a. Perf 14½–15 .. .. 3·75 6·00
D50 3 c. black and green .. .. 1·25 2·75
D51 4 c. black and scarlet .. .. 1·10 1·25
D52 5 c. black and yellow-brown .. .. 2·00 2·25
D53 6 c. black and olive-green .. .. 3·75 5·50
D53*a* 6 c. black and apple-green
D54 8 c. black and rose-lake .. .. 1·10 1·25
D55 10 c. black and turquoise-blue .. .. 4·25 7·00
a. Perf 14½–15 .. .. 35·00 48·00
D56 12 c. black and deep blue .. .. 8·00 13·00
D56*a* 16 c. black and red-brown .. .. 16·00 22·00
b. Black and brown-lake .. .. 8·50 20·00
D49 & D56*a* Optd "Specimen" .. *Set of* 2 40·00

Nos. D51/3 also exist with the overprint towards the centre of the stamp.

1926–31. *As* 1920–31, *but perf* 12½.

D57 2 c. black and claret .. .. 60 1·75
D58 3 c. black and green .. .. 1·00 2·50
D59 4 c. black and scarlet .. .. 60 1·25
D60 5 c. black and yellow-brown .. .. 2·50 5·50
D61 6 c. black and olive-green .. .. 2·50 3·00
D62 8 c. black and carmine .. .. 2·00 4·50
D63 10 c. black and turquoise-blue .. .. 3·75 9·00
D64 12 c. black and deep blue .. .. 6·00 12·00
D65 16 c. black and red-brown (1931) .. .. 10·00 18·00

Nos. D49/65 exist with two types of opt; A. Thick letters; pointed beard to "G". B. Thinner letters; "G" with square end to beard and "D" more open. No. D56*a* is Type B. and D56*b*, Type A.

D 2 Crest of the Company

(Recess Waterlow)

1939 (1 Jan). *P* 12½.

D66 D 2 2 c. brown .. .. 4·00 20·00
D67 4 c. scarlet .. .. 5·00 28·00
D68 6 c. violet .. .. 7·50 38·00
D69 8 c. green .. .. 11·00 45·00
D70 10 c. blue .. .. 18·00 48·00
D66/70 Perf "Specimen" .. *Set of* 5 £140

The stamps of North Borneo were withdrawn on 30 June 1964. For later issues see SABAH.

JAPANESE OCCUPATION OF NORTH BORNEO

The stamps listed under this heading were valid for use throughout British Borneo (i.e. in Brunei, Labuan, North Borneo and Sarawak).

PRICES FOR STAMPS ON COVER

Nos. J1/17	*from* × 4
Nos. J18/19	*from* × 5
Nos. J20/32	*from* × 25
Nos. J33/4	*from* × 2
Nos. J35/48	*from* × 4

1942 (June). *Stamps of North Borneo optd in one line as T* 1 *of Japanese Occupation of Brunei.* (*a*) *Nos.* 303/17.

J 1 1 c. green and red-brown .. .. 60·00 80·00
J 2 2 c. purple and greenish blue .. .. 48·00 70·00
J 3 3 c. slate-blue and green .. .. 48·00 70·00
J 4 4 c. bronze-green and violet .. .. 32·00 55·00

J 5		6 c. deep blue and claret	48·00	70·00
J 6		8 c. scarlet	48·00	70·00
J 7		10 c. violet and bronze-green	48·00	70·00
J 8		12 c. green and bright blue	70·00	£130
J 9		15 c. blue-green and brown	70·00	£130
J10		20 c. violet and slate-blue	70·00	£130
J11		25 c. green and chocolate	70·00	£130
J12		50 c. chocolate and violet	£120	£140
J13		$1 brown and carmine	80·00	£200
J14		$2 violet and olive-green	£150	£275
J15		$5 indigo and pale blue	£200	£375
		(*b*) *Nos.* 318 *and* 319 ("WAR TAX")		
J16		1 c. green and red-brown	70·00	55·00
J17		2 c. purple and greenish blue	80·00	55·00

1 Mt Kinabalu

2 Borneo Scene

(Litho G. Kolff, Batavia)

1943 (29 Apr). *P* 12½.

J18	1	4 c. red	9·00	10·00
J19	2	8 c. blue	9·00	10·00

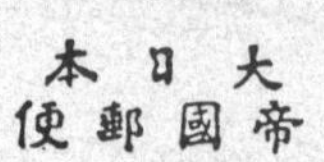

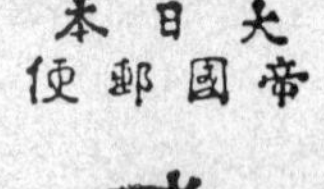

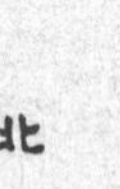

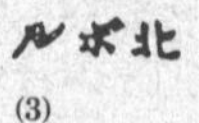
(3)

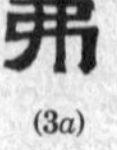
(3*a*)

("Imperial Japanese Postal Service North Borneo")

1944 (30 Sept). *Nos.* 303/15 *of North Borneo optd as T* 3.

J20		1 c. green and red-brown	1·25	2·00
J21		2 c. purple and greenish blue	1·25	2·00
J22		3 c. slate-blue and green	1·25	2·00
J23		4 c. bronze-green and violet	1·50	2·00
J24		6 c. deep blue and claret	1·75	2·00
J25		8 c. scarlet	3·25	3·00
J26		10 c. violet and bronze-green	1·75	3·00
J27		12 c. green and bright blue	1·50	3·00
J28		15 c. blue-green and brown	2·50	3·75
J29		20 c. violet and slate-blue	7·00	8·00
J30		25 c. green and chocolate	7·00	10·00
J31		50 c. chocolate and violet	15·00	20·00
J32		$1 brown and carmine	28·00	32·00

The spacing between the second and third lines of the overprint is 12 mm on the horizontal stamps, and 15 mm on the upright.

1944. *No.* J7 *with T* 3 *opt in addition.*

J32*a*	10 c. violet and bronze-green	£100	

The 2 c., 3 c., 8 c., 12 c. and 15 c. stamps of the 1942 issue are also known with Type 3 opt.

1945. *No.* J1 *surch with T* 3*a*.

J33	81	$2 on 1 c. green and red-brown	£1100	£1100

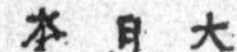

(4)

5 Girl War-worker

6 ("North Borneo")

1945 (?). *North Borneo No.* 315 *surch with T* 4.

J34	$5 on $1 brown and carmine	£1400	£1400

1945. *Contemporary stamps of Japan as T* 5 (*various subjects*) *optd with T* 6.

J35	1 s. red-brown (No. 391)	60	)
J36	2 s. scarlet (No. 318)	60	,0
J37	3 s. emerald-green (No. 319)	65	65
J38	4 s. yellow-green (No. 395)	65	65
J39	5 s. claret (No. 396)	90	1·10
J40	6 s. orange (No. 322)	1·10	1·60
J41	8 s. violet (No. 324)	1·10	1·60
J42	10 s. carmine and pink (No. 399)	1·40	1·60
J43	15 s. blue (No. 401)	1·40	1·75
J44	20 s. blue-slate (No. 328)	40·00	50·00
J45	25 s. brown and chocolate (No. 329)	32·00	32·00
J46	30 s. turquoise-blue (No. 330)	£125	80·00
J47	50 s. olive and bistre (No. 331)	27·00	35·00
J48	1 y. red-brown and chocolate (No. 332)	27·00	35·00

Designs:—2 s. General Nogi; 3 s. Hydro-electric Works; 4 s. Hyuga Monument and Mt Fuji; 5 s. Admiral Togo; 6 s. Garambi Lighthouse, Formosa; 8 s. Meiji Shrine; 10 s. Palms and map of S.E. Asia; 15 s. Airman; 20 s. Mt Fuji and cherry blossoms; 25 s. Horyu Temple; 30 s. Torii, Itsukushima Shrine at Miyajima; 50 s. Kinkaku Temple; 1 y. Great Buddha, Kamakura.

Northern Nigeria

PRICES FOR STAMPS ON COVER

Nos. 1/7	*from* × 3
Nos. 8/9	—
Nos. 10/16	*from* × 4
Nos. 17/19	—
Nos. 20/6	*from* × 3
No. 27	—
Nos. 28/37	*from* × 5
Nos. 38/9	—
Nos. 40/9	*from* × 5
Nos. 50/2	—

PRINTERS. All issues were typographed by De La Rue & Co.

1

2

1900 (Mar). *Wmk Crown CA. P* 14.

1	1	½d. dull mauve and green	65	1·50
2		1d. dull mauve and carmine	1·50	1·50
3		2d. dull mauve and yellow	3·00	6·00
4		2½d. dull mauve and ultramarine	7·00	9·00
5	2	5d. dull mauve and chestnut	13·00	20·00
6		6d. dull mauve and violet	12·00	14·00
7	1	1s. green and black	18·00	22·00
8		2s. 6d. green and ultramarine	65·00	
9		10s. green and brown	£200	
1/9		*Set of* 9	£300	
1/9 Optd "Specimen"		*Set of* 9	£275	

3

4

1902 (1 July). *Wmk Crown CA. P* 14.

10	3	½d. dull purple and green	40	65
11		1d. dull purple and carmine	50	45
12		2d. dull purple and yellow	1·00	1·75
13		2½d. dull purple and ultramarine	70	1·50
14	4	5d. dull purple and chestnut	2·50	5·00
15		6d. dull purple and violet	6·00	7·00
16	3	1s. green and black	5·00	6·00
17		2s. 6d. green and ultramarine	8·50	18·00
18		10s. green and brown	45·00	48·00
10/18		*Set of* 9	65·00	80·00
10/18 Optd "Specimen"		*Set of* 9	£250	

1904 (April). *Wmk Mult Crown CA. P* 14.

19	4	£25 green and carmine, **O**	£19000	

1905 (Aug–Oct). *Wmk Mult Crown CA. P* 14.

20	3	½d. dull purple and green, **OC** (Oct)	60	70
21		1d. dull purple and carmine, **OC**	75	30
22		2d. dull purple and yellow, **OC** (Oct)	1·25	2·25
23		2½d. dull purple and ultramarine, **O** (Oct)	4·00	4·25
24	4	5d. dull purple and chestnut, **OC** (Oct)	7·50	8·00
25		6d. dull purple and violet, **OC** (Oct)	7·00	8·50
26	3	1s. green and black, **OC** (Oct)	12·00	16·00
27		2s. 6d. green and ultramarine, **OC** (Oct)	17·00	18·00
20/7		*Set of* 8	45·00	50·00

1910 (Jan)–**11.** *Wmk Mult Crown CA. P* 14.

28	3	½d. green, **O** (4.10)	25	15
29		1d. carmine, **O** (1.10)	25	15
30		2d. grey, **O** (10.11)	1·10	2·00
31		2½d. blue, **O** (10.10)	1·00	2·00
32	4	3d. purple/*yellow*, **C** (9.11)	75	60
34		5d. dull purple and olive-green, **C** (2.11)	1·60	2·50
35		6d. dull purple and purple, **C** (11.10)	3·25	6·50
		a. Dull and bright purple (1911)	1·25	2·75
36	3	1s. black/*green*, **C** (11.10)	1·60	1·50
37		2s. 6d. black and red/*blue*, **C** (3.11)	11·00	10·00
38	4	5s. green and red/*yellow*, **C** (9.11)	23·00	24·00
39	3	10s. green and red/*green*, **C** (3.11)	38·00	45·00
28/39		*Set of* 11	70·00	80·00
28/39 Optd "Specimen"		*Set of* 11	£275	

5

6

1912. *Wmk Mult Crown CA. P* 14.

40	5	½d. deep green, **O**	25	25
41		1d. red, **O**	25	15
42		2d. grey, **O**	80	1·75
43	6	3d. purple/*yellow*, **C**	65	80
44		4d. black and red/*yellow*, **C**	60	60
45		5d. dull purple and olive-green, **C**	1·00	2·00
46		6d. dull and bright purple, **C**	1·25	1·90
47		9d. dull purple and carmine, **C**	1·25	2·75
48	5	1s. black/*green*, **C**	1·50	1·50
49		2s. 6d. black and red/*blue*, **C**	9·00	12·00
50	6	5s. green and red/*yellow*, **C**	22·00	30·00
51	5	10s. green and red/*green*, **C**	38·00	45·00
52	6	£1 purple and black/*red*, **C**	£150	£150
40/52		*Set of* 13	£200	£225
40/52 Optd "Specimen"		*Set of* 13	£350	

Since 1 January 1914, Northern Nigeria has formed part of NIGERIA.

Northern Rhodesia

PRICES FOR STAMPS ON COVER TO 1945

Nos. 1/21	*from* × 2
Nos. 22/4	*from* × 5
Nos. 25/45	*from* × 2
Nos. D1/4	*from* × 15

1

2

(Eng W. G. Fairweather. Recess Waterlow)

1925 (1 April)–**29.** *Wmk Mult Script CA. P* 12½.

1	1	½d. green	20	10
2		1d. brown	20	10
3		1½d. carmine-red	20	15
4		2d. yellow-brown	40	10
5		3d. ultramarine	1·00	45
6		4d. violet	1·25	65
7		6d. slate-grey	1·40	35
8		8d. rose-purple	7·00	12·00
9		10d. olive-green	7·00	12·00
10	2	1s. yellow-brown and black	2·75	1·25
11		2s. brown and ultramarine	14·00	16·00
12		2s. 6d. black and green	11·00	11·00
13		3s. violet and blue (1929)	22·00	21·00
14		5s. slate-grey and violet	22·00	18·00
15		7s. 6d. rose-purple and black	95·00	£110
16		10s. green and black	40·00	40·00
17		20s. carmine-red and rose-purple	£150	£160
1/17		*Set of* 17	£350	£375
1/17 Optd/Perf "Specimen"		*Set of* 17	£1000	

1935 (6 May). *Silver Jubilee. As Nos.* 91/4 *of Antigua.*

18	1d. light blue and olive-green	50	40
19	2d. green and indigo	90	80
	e. Horiz line from turret	6·00	
20	3d. brown and deep blue	2·75	3·50
21	6d. slate and purple	3·25	4·50
	a. Frame printed double, one albino	£1000	
18/21 Perf "Specimen"	*Set of* 4	70·00	

For illustration of plate variety see Omnibus section following Zululand.

1937 (12 May). *Coronation. As Nos.* 13/15 *of Aden, but ptd by B.W. P* 11 × 11½.

22	1½d. carmine	30	25
23	2d. buff	60	35
24	3d. blue	85	85
22/4 Perf "Specimen"	*Set of* 3	45·00	

3

4

(Recess Waterlow)

1938 (1 Mar)–**52.** *Wmk Mult Script CA. P* 12½.

25	3	½d. green	12	5
26		½d. chocolate (15.11.51)	30	70
		a. Perf 12½ × 14 (10.12.52)	25	60
27		1d. brown	12	5
		a. Chocolate (1948)	25	30
28		1d. green (15.11.51)	60	60
29		1½d. carmine-red	10·00	40
		a. Imperf between (horiz pair)	£7000	
30		1½d. yellow-brown (10.1.41)	12	5
31		2d. yellow-brown	48·00	2·50
32		2d. carmine-red (10.1.41)	25	5
33		2d. purple (1.12.51)	45	35
34		3d. ultramarine	25	5
35		3d. scarlet (1.12.51)	60	50
36		4d. dull violet	30	12
37		4½d. blue (5.5.52)	1·25	2·75
38		6d. grey	35	10
39		9d. violet (5.5.52)	1·75	2·75
40	4	1s. yellow-brown and black	45	10
41		2s. 6d. black and green	5·00	1·75
42		3s. violet and blue	6·00	7·00
43		5s. grey and dull violet	8·00	4·00
44		10s. green and black	10·00	7·00
45		20s. carmine-red and rose-purple	26·00	38·00
25/45		*Set of* 21	£110	60·00
25/45 Perf "Specimen"		*Set of* 15	£250	

1946 (26 Nov). *Victory. As Nos. 28/9 of Aden. P* 13½ × 14.

46		1½d. red-orange	20	15
		a. Perf 13½	75	75
47		2d. carmine	20	20
46/7 Perf "Specimen"		*Set of* 2	55·00	

1948 (1 Dec). *Royal Silver Wedding. As Nos.* 30/1 *of Aden, but inscr* "NORTHERN RHODESIA" *(recess 20s.).*

48		1½d. orange	30	15
49		20s. brown-lake	45·00	70·00

1949 (10 Oct). *75th Anniv of U.P.U. As Nos.* 114/17 *of Antigua.*

50		2d. carmine	25	35
51		3d. deep blue	1·25	1·25
52		6d. grey	1·25	1·25
53		1s. red-orange	1·50	1·75

5 Cecil Rhodes and Victoria Falls

(Recess D.L.R.)

1953 (30 May). *Birth Centenary of Cecil Rhodes. Wmk Mult Script CA. P* 12 × 11½.

54	5	½d. brown	15	30
55		1d. green	15	40
56		2d. mauve	15	20
57		4½d. blue	60	3·25
58		1s. orange and black	65	1·50

6 Arms of the Rhodesias and Nyasaland

(Recess Waterlow)

1953 (30 May). *Rhodes Centenary Exhibition. Wmk Mult Script CA. P* 14 × 13½.

59	6	6d. violet	15	15

1953 (2 June). *Coronation. As No.* 47 *of Aden.*

60		1½d. black and yellow-orange	15	15

7 8

(Recess Waterlow)

1953 (15 Sept). *Wmk Mult Script CA. P* 12½ × 14 *(pence values) or* 12½ × 13½ *(shilling values).*

61	7	½d. deep brown	15	5
62		1d. bluish green	15	5
63		1½d. orange-brown	25	5
64		2d. reddish purple	20	5
65		3d. scarlet	20	5
66		4d. slate-lilac	30	15
67		4½d. deep blue	30	60
68		6d. grey-black	40	5
69		9d. violet	40	40
70	8	1s. orange-brown and black	40	5
71		2s. 6d. black and green	2·50	3·50
72		5s. grey and dull purple	6·50	13·00
73		10s. green and black	11·00	19·00
74		20s. rose-red and rose-purple	20·00	35·00
61/74		*Set of* 14	38·00	65·00

For issues from 1954 to 1963, see RHODESIA AND NYASALAND.

9 Arms 10

(Photo Harrison)

1963 (10 Dec). *Arms black, gold and blue; portrait and inscriptions black; background colours below. P* 14½ (*T* **9**) *or* 13½ × 13 (*T* **10**).

75	9	½d. bright violet	5	12
		a. Value omitted	£170	
76		1d. light blue	15	5
		a. Value omitted	9·50	
77		2d. brown	15	5
78		3d. yellow	15	5
		a. Value omitted	48·00	
79		4d. green	20	12
		a. Value omitted	55·00	
80		6d. light olive-green	20	5
		a. Value omitted	£100	
81		9d. yellow-brown	30	12
		a. Value omitted	95·00	
82	9	1s. slate-purple	25	5
83		1s. 3d. bright purple	70	5
84	10	2s. orange	80	60
85		2s. 6d. lake-brown	90	80
86		5s. magenta	2·75	4·00
87		10s. mauve	6·50	8·00
88		20s. blue	15·00	23·00
		a. Value omitted	£600	
75/88		*Set of* 14	25·00	32·00

POSTAGE DUE STAMPS

D 1 D 2

(Typo D.L.R.)

1929–52. *Wmk Mult Script CA. P* 14.

D1	D 1	1d. grey-black	3·50	3·50
		a. *Black.* Chalky paper (22.1.52)	2·50	4·00
		b. Error. St. Edward's Crown W9*b*, C	50·00	
D2		2d. grey-black	3·50	4·50
D3		3d. grey-black	6·00	15·00
		aa. *Black,* Chalky paper (22.1.52)	6·50	15·00
		a. Error. Crown missing, W9*a*, C	70·00	
		b. Error. St. Edward's Crown, W9*b*, C	65·00	
D4		4d. grey-black	7·50	17·00
D1/4 Perf "Specimen"		*Set of* 4	70·00	

(Des D. Smith. Litho Govt Ptr, Lusaka)

1963 (10 Dec). *P* 12½.

D 5	D 2	1d. orange	20	40
D 6		2d. deep blue	25	50
D 7		3d. lake	35	80
D 8		4d. ultramarine	50	1·40
D 9		6d. purple	95	2·25
D10		1s. light emerald	2·50	6·00
		a. Imperf (vert pair)	£150	
		b. Block of four imperf horiz and imp between vert	£450	
D5/10		*Set of* 6	4·25	10·00

In all values the stamps in the right-hand vertical row of the sheet are imperforate on the right.

The stamps of Northern Rhodesia were withdrawn on 23 October 1964 when the territory attained independence. For later issues see ZAMBIA.

North-West Pacific Islands

(*see* New Guinea)

Nova Scotia

Organised postal services in Nova Scotia date from 1754 when the first of a series of Deputy Postmasters was appointed, under the authority of the British G.P.O. This arrangement continued until 1851 when the colony assumed responsibility for its postal affairs.

For illustrations of the handstamp types see BRITISH POST OFFICES ABROAD notes, following GREAT BRITAIN.

AMHERST

CROWNED-CIRCLE HANDSTAMPS

CC1 CC 1 AMHERST. N.S.(R) (25.2.1845) *Price on cover* £1250

ST. MARGARETS BAY

CROWNED-CIRCLE HANDSTAMPS

CC2 CC 1 ST. MARGARETS BAY. N.S.(R.) (30.4.1845) *Price on cover* £2250

Nos. CC1/2 were later used during temporary shortages of stamps, struck in red or black.

PRICES FOR STAMPS ON COVER

Nos. 1/8	*from* × 2
Nos. 9/29	*from* × 5

1 2

Crown and Heraldic Flowers of United Kingdom and Mayflower of Nova Scotia.

(Recess P.B.)

1851 (1 Sept)–**57.** *Bluish paper. Imperf.*

1	1	1d. red-brown (12.5.53)	£2750	£475
		a. Bisected (½d.) (on cover)	†	£50000
2	2	3d. deep blue	£1800	£350
		a. Bisected (1½d.) (on cover)	†	£3250
3		3d. bright blue	£1100	£170
		a. Bisected (1½d.) (on cover)	†	£3250
4		3d. pale blue (1857)	£900	£170
		a. Bisected (1½d.) (on cover)	†	£3250
5		6d. yellow-green	£4750	£500
		a. Bisected (3d.) (on cover)	†	£4000
6		6d. deep green (1857)	£10000	£950
		a. Bisected (3d.) (on cover)	†	£6000
		b. Quartered (1½d.) (on cover)	†	£38000
7		1s. cold violet	£19000	£9000
		a. Bisected (6d.) (on cover)	†	£42000
		b. Quartered (3d.) (on cover)	†	£55000
7*c*		1s. deep purple (1851)	£15000	£6500
		d. Watermarked	£20000	£9500
8		1s. purple (1857)	£14000	£3750
		a. Bisected (6d.) (on cover)	†	£32000

The watermark on No. 7d consists of the whole or part of a letter from the name "P. H. SAUNDERS" (the papermakers).

The stamps formerly catalogued on almost white paper are probably some from which the bluish paper has been discharged.

Reprints of all four values were made in 1890 on thin, hard, white paper. The 1d. is brown, the 3d. blue, the 6d. deep green, and the 1s. violet-black.

The 3d. bisects are only found used on cover to make up the 7½d. rate.

3 4 5

(Recess American Bank Note Co, New York)

1860–63. *P* 12. (*a*) *Yellowish paper.*

9	3	1 c. jet black	3·25	12·00
		a. Bisected (½ c.) (on cover)	†	£10000
10		1 c. grey-black	3·50	12·00
11		2 c. grey-purple	11·00	15·00
11*a*		2 c. purple	17·00	14·00
12		5 c. blue	£160	16·00
13		5 c. deep blue	£160	16·00
14	4	8½ c. deep green	3·00	
15		8½ c. yellow-green	3·00	
16		10 c. scarlet	14·00	18·00
17	5	12½ c. black	24·00	16·00
17*a*		12½ c. greyish black	—	16·00
		(*b*) *White paper*		
18	3	1 c. black	3·25	12·00
		a. Imperf between (horiz pair)	£150	
19		1 c. grey	3·25	12·00
20		2 c. dull purple	4·00	14·00
21		2 c. purple	4·00	14·00
22		2 c. grey-purple	4·00	14·00
		a. Bisected (1 c.) (on cover)	†	£4500
23		2 c. slate-purple	4·00	12·00
24		5 c. blue	£160	16·00
25		5 c. deep blue	£160	16·00
26	4	8½ c. deep green	16·00	27·00
27		10 c. scarlet	4·00	18·00
28		10 c. vermilion	5·00	18·00
		a. Bisected (5 c.) (on cover)	†	£1200
29	5	12½ c. black	19·00	22·00

Since 1868 Nova Scotia has used stamps of the Dominion of Canada.

Nyasaland Protectorate

PRICES FOR STAMPS ON COVER TO 1945

Nos. 1/9*a*	*from* × 5
Nos. 10/19	*from* ×—
No. 20	*from* × 5
Nos. 21/6	*from* × 4
Nos. 27/31	*from* ×—
Nos. 32/7	*from* × 5
Nos. 38/42	*from* ×—
Nos. 43/7	*from* × 8
Nos. 48/52	*from* ×—
No. 53	*from* × 15
No. 54	*from* × 2
Nos. 55/7*a*	*from* × 7
Nos. 57*d*/63	*from* × 3
Nos. 64/71	*from* ×—
Nos. 72/9	*from* × 3
Nos. 80/2	*from* ×—
Nos. 83/95	*from* × 4
Nos. 96/9	*from* ×—
Nos. 100/57	*from* × 2

By 1891 the territory west of Lake Nyasa was recognised as being under British protection and the southern, eastern and northern borders had been delineated with the Portuguese and German governments.

I. BRITISH CENTRAL AFRICA

A protectorate under the name "Nyassaland Districts" was declared on 14 May 1891, the title being changed to the "British Central Africa Protectorate" on 22 February 1893. Such a description had been in use for some time previously and the handwritten notice of 20 July 1891, announcing the introduction of postal services, described the area as "British Central Africa".

Until 1895 the British South Africa Company contributed to the revenues of the protectorate administration which, in return governed North Eastern Rhodesia. Stamps of the British South Africa Company overprinted "B.C.A." were used in both areas until 1895 and were retained for use in North Eastern Rhodesia until supplies were exhausted, probably in 1899.

B.C.A. (1) — B.C.A. FOUR SHILLINGS. (2) — ONE PENNY. (3)

1891 (April)–**1895.** *Stamps of Rhodesia optd as* T **1**. P 14, 14½.

No.	Type	Description	Unused	Used
1	1	1d. black	2·00	2·00
2	4	2d. sea-green and vermilion	1·50	2·50
		a. Bisected (1d.) (on cover)	†	£1800
3		4d. reddish chestnut and black	1·50	3·75
4	1	6d. ultramarine	40·00	25·00
5		6d. deep blue	6·00	8·00
6	4	8d. rose-lake and ultramarine	12·00	22·00
6a		8d. red and ultramarine	22·00	30·00
7	1	1s. grey-brown	11·00	11·00
8		2s. vermilion	20·00	26·00
9		2s. 6d. grey-purple	35·00	35·00
9a		2s. 6d. lilac	32·00	32·00
10	4	3s. brown and green (1895)	45·00	45·00
11		4s. grey-black and vermilion (2.93)	45·00	45·00
12	1	5s. orange-yellow	45·00	48·00
13		10s. deep green	85·00	95·00
14	2	£1 deep blue	£300	£350
15		£2 rose-red	£500	
16		£5 sage-green	£1100	
17		£10 brown	£2500	
1/14		*Set of* 13	£550	£600

The overprint varies on values up to 10s. Sets may be made with *thin* or *thick* letters.

1892 (Aug)–**93.** *Stamps of Rhodesia surch as* T **2**.

No.	Type	Description	Unused	Used
18	4	3s. on 4s. grey-black and vermilion (10.93)	£250	£250
19	1	4s. on 5s. orange-yellow	60·00	60·00

1895. *No.* 2 *surch at Cape Town with* T **3**.

No.	Type	Description	Unused	Used
20	4	1d. on 2d. sea-green and vermilion	10·00	24·00
		a. Surch double	£2750	£2000

Specimens are known with double surcharge, without stop after "PENNY". These are from a trial printing made at Blantyre, but it is believed that they were not issued to the public (*Price* £600 *un.*).

5 Arms of the Protectorate 6

(Litho D.L.R.)

1895. *No wmk.* P 14.

No.	Type	Description	Unused	Used
21	5	1d. black	4·00	4·00
22		2d. black and green	11·00	11·00
23		4d. black and reddish buff	18·00	22·00
24		6d. black and blue	20·00	10·00
25		1s. black and rose	25·00	20·00
26	6	2s. 6d. black and bright magenta	80·00	55·00
27		3s. black and yellow	65·00	22·00
28		5s. black and olive	75·00	48·00
29		£1 black and yellow-orange	£550	£225
30		£10 black and orange-vermilion	£2500	
31		£25 black and blue-green	£4500	£2250
21/8		*Set of* 8	£275	£170
21/9 Optd "Specimen"		*Set of* 9	£450	

Cancellations inscribed "BRITISH CENTRAL AFRICA" within a double-circle and with the name of a town across the centre or at foot were intended for use on stamps presented for the payment of the hut tax. Such marks can be found in black, violet or blue and are without date.

1896 (Feb). *Wmk Crown CA* (T **5**) *or CC* (*sideways*) (T **6**), P 14.

No.	Type	Description	Unused	Used
32	5	1d. black	5·00	4·75
33		2d. black and green	12·00	6·50
34		4d. black and orange-brown	15·00	17·00
35		6d. black and blue	12·00	9·00
36		1s. black and rose	15·00	11·00
37	6	2s. 6d. black and magenta	60·00	60·00
38		3s. black and yellow	30·00	18·00
39		5s. black and olive	70·00	70·00
40		£1 black and blue	£600	£300
41		£10 black and orange (Optd S. £200)	£2750	£1900
42		£25 black and green (Optd S. £450)	£6000	
32/9		*Set of* 8	£200	£180
32/40 Optd "Specimen"		*Set of* 9	£450	

7 — 8

1897 (Aug). T **7** (*wmk Crown CA*) *and* **8** (*wmk Crown CC*). P 14.

No.	Type	Description	Unused	Used
43	7	1d. black and ultramarine	1·25	50
44		2d. black and yellow	1·00	1·50
45		4d. black and carmine	5·50	4·00
46		6d. black and green	13·00	7·50
47		1s. black and dull purple	6·00	8·00
48	8	2s. 6d. black and ultramarine	28·00	28·00
49		3s. black and sea-green	£125	£125
50		4s. black and carmine	35·00	35·00
50a		10s. black and olive-green	55·00	65·00
51		£1 black and dull purple	£180	£120
52		£10 black and yellow (Optd S. £250)	£2500	£1200
43/51		*Set of* 10	£400	£350
43/51 Optd "Specimen"		*Set of* 10	£200	

ONE PENNY (9)

10

1898. *No.* 49 *surch with* T **9**, *in red.*

No.	Type	Description	Unused	Used
53	8	1d. on 3s. black and sea-green	7·50	8·50
		a. "PNNEY"	£1100	
		b. "PENN"	£600	
		c. Surch double	£600	£550

1898 (11 Mar). *Imperf.*

(*a*) *Setting I. The vertical frame lines of the stamps cross the space between the two rows of the sheet*

(i) *With the initials "J.G." or "J.T.G." on the back in black ink*

No.	Type	Description	Unused	Used
54	10	1d. vermilion and grey-blue	—	£450
		a. Without the initials	£1100	
		b. Without the initials and centre inverted	£5000	

(ii) *With a control number and letter or letters, printed in plain relief at the back*

No.	Type	Description	Unused	Used
55	10	1d. vermilion and grey-blue	—	48·00

(*b*) *Setting II. The vertical frame lines do not cross the space between the rows except at the extreme ends of the sheet. As No.* 55

No.	Type	Description	Unused	Used
55b	10	1d. vermilion and pale ultramarine	—	18·00
		c. Control on face	—	£3000
		d. Centre omitted (vert pair with normal)	£4250	
56		1d. vermilion and deep ultramarine	—	18·00
		a. Without Control at back	£650	42·00
		b. Control doubly impressed		

1898 (June). *Setting II.* P 12.

No.	Type	Description	Unused	Used
57	10	1d. vermilion and pale ultramarine	£600	8·50
57a		1d. vermilion and deep ultramarine	—	7·50
		b. Without Control at back	£650	32·00
		c. Two different Controls on back	—	£400

The two different settings of these stamps are each in 30 types, issued without gum.

1901. *Wmk Crown CA.* P 14.

No.	Type	Description	Unused	Used
57d	7	1d. dull purple and carmine-rose	95	1·10
57e		4d. dull purple and olive-green	6·50	6·50
58		6d. dull purple and brown	8·00	8·00
57d/58 Optd "Specimen"		*Set of* 3	£140	

11 — 12

(Typo D.L.R.)

1903–4. T **11** (*Wmk Crown CA*) *and* **12** (*Wmk Crown CC*). P 14.

No.	Type	Description	Unused	Used
59	11	1d. grey and carmine	2·00	40
60		2d. dull and bright purple	5·00	3·50
61		4d. grey-green and black	5·00	6·50
62		6d. grey and reddish buff	5·00	5·00
62a		1s. grey and blue	5·00	7·50
63	12	2s. 6d. grey-green and green	17·00	22·00
64		4s. dull and bright purple	32·00	40·00
65		10s. grey-green and black	45·00	55·00
66		£1 grey and carmine	£160	£130
67		£10 grey and blue (Optd S. £400)	£3000	£3000
59/66		*Set of* 9	£225	£225
59/66 Optd "Specimen"		*Set of* 9	£400	

1907. T **11**. *Wmk Mult Crown CA.* P 14.

No.	Type	Description	Unused	Used
68		1d. grey and carmine, C	1·25	1·25
69		2d. dull and bright purple, C	£5500	
70		4d. grey-green and black, C	£5500	
71		6d. grey and reddish buff, C	26·00	28·00

PRICES OF SETS

Set prices are given for many issues, generally those containing five stamps or more. Definitive sets include one of each value or major colour change, but do not cover different perforations, die types or minor shades. Where a choice is possible the set prices are based on the cheapest versions of the stamps included in the listings.

II. NYASALAND PROTECTORATE

The title of the Protectorate was changed again from 6 July 1907.

13 — 14

(Typo D.L.R.)

1908 (22 July). P 14. (*a*) *Wmk Crown CA.*

No.	Type	Description	Unused	Used
72	13	1s. black/*green*, C	2·25	4·00
		(*b*) *Wmk Mult Crown CA*		
73	13	½d. green, O	30	60
74		1d. carmine, O	35	25
75		3d. purple/*yellow*, C	1·75	3·00
76		4d. black and red/*yellow*, C	1·75	3·00
77		6d. dull purple and bright purple, C	4·25	6·00
78	14	2s. 6d. black and red/*blue*, C	25·00	30·00
79		4s. carmine and black, C	32·00	42·00
80		10s. green and red/*green*, C	50·00	70·00
81		£1 purple and black/*red*, C	£275	£325
82		£10 purple & ultram, C (Optd S.£450)	£5500	
72/81		*Set of* 10	£350	£425
72/81 Optd "Specimen"		*Set of* 10	£425	

15 — 16

(Typo D.L.R.)

1913 (1 Apr)–**1918.** T **15** *and* **16** (2s. 6d., *etc.*). *Wmk Mult Crown CA.* P 14.

No.	Type	Description	Unused	Used
83		½d. green, O	40	50
84		½d. blue-green, O (1918)	45	50
85		1d. carmine-red, O	75	55
86		1d. scarlet, O (1916)	45	45
87		2d. grey, O (1916)	1·40	50
88		2d. slate, O	1·75	70
89		2½d. bright blue, O	80	1·25
90		3d. purple/*yellow*, C (1914)	2·00	3·00
		a. On pale yellow	2·50	3·75
91		4d. black and red/*yellow*, C (*shades*)	2·40	2·50
		a. On pale yellow	3·25	4·50
92		6d. dull and bright purple, C	2·25	3·00
92a		6d. dull purple and bright violet, C	6·50	9·50
93		1s. black/*green*, C	4·50	4·50
		a. On blue-green, olive back	2·25	2·50
		b. On emerald back	2·40	4·00
94		2s. 6d. black and red/*blue*, C	8·50	13·00
95		4s. carmine and black, C	13·00	16·00
96		10s. green and red/*green*, C	45·00	55·00
97		10s. pale green and red/*green*, C	48·00	55·00
98		£1 purple and black/*red*, C	£100	£110
99		£10 purple and blue, C (Optd S.£250)	£2750	£2500
83/98		*Set of* 12	£160	£180
83/98 Optd "Specimen"		*Set of* 12	£400	

For stamps optd "N.F." see TANZANIA.

1921–30. T **15** *and* **16** (2s. *to* 10s.). *Wmk Mult Script CA.* P 14.

No.	Type	Description	Unused	Used
100		½d. green, O	55	25
101		1d. carmine, O	55	30
102		1½d. orange, O	12·00	12·00
103		2d. grey, O	60	55
105		3d. purple/*pale yellow*, C	2·75	1·75
106		4d. black and red/*yellow*, C	1·75	2·50
107		6d. dull and bright purple, C	3·25	3·25
108		1s. black/*emerald*, C (1930)	6·50	7·00
109		2s. purple and blue/*blue*, C	13·00	15·00
110		2s. 6d. black and red/*blue*, C (1924)	15·00	16·00
111		4s. carmine and black, C	11·00	12·00
112		5s. green and red/*yellow*, C (1929)	26·00	35·00
113		10s. green and red/*green*, C	55·00	60·00
100/13		*Set of* 13	£130	£150
100/13 Optd/Perf "Specimen"		*Set of* 13	£300	

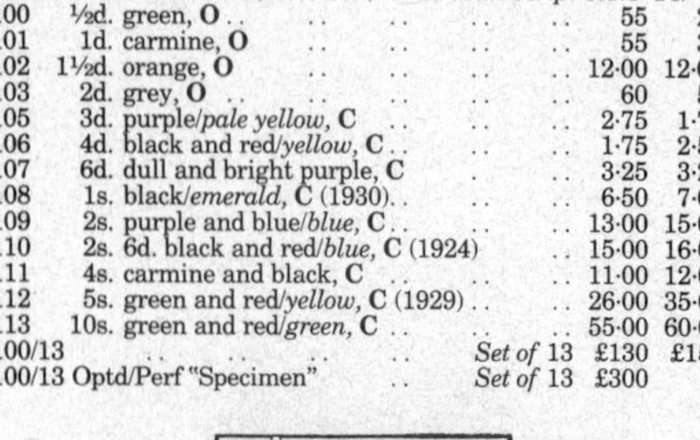

17 King George V and Symbol of the Protectorate

(Des Major H. E. Green. Recess Waterlow)

1934 (June)–**35.** *Wmk Mult Script CA.* P 12½.

No.	Type	Description	Unused	Used
114	17	½d. green	55	30
115		1d. brown	60	35
116		1½d. carmine	80	1·25
117		2d. pale grey	90	80
118		3d. blue	1·75	1·25
119		4d. bright magenta (20.5.35)	2·25	2·25
120		6d. violet	1·90	1·50
121		9d. olive-bistre (20.5.35)	4·00	10·00
122		1s. black and orange	4·00	8·50
114/22		*Set of* 9	15·00	24·00
114/22 Perf "Specimen"		*Set of* 9	£110	

1935 (6 May). *Silver Jubilee. As Nos.* 91/4 *of Antigua but ptd by Waterlow. P* 11 × 12.
123 1d. ultramarine and grey 40 40
124 2d. green and indigo .. .. 1·25 1·50
125 3d. brown and deep blue .. .. .. 4·25 7·00
126 1s. slate and purple .. .. 10·00 15·00
123/6 Perf "Specimen" .. .. *Set of* 4 60·00

1937 (12 May). *Coronation. As Nos.* 13/15 *of Aden, but ptd by B.W. P* 11 × 11½.
127 ½d. green 25 20
128 1d. brown 45 20
129 2d. grey-black 55 45
127/9 Perf "Specimen" .. .. *Set of* 3 45·00

18 Symbol of the Protectorate

19

(T **18** recess Waterlow; T **19** typo D.L.R.)

1938 (1 Jan)–**44.** *P* 12½ (*T* **18**) *or* 14 (*T* **19**).

(*a*) *Wmk Mult Script CA*
130 **18** ½d. green 55 15
130*a* ½d. brown (12.12.42) 15 20
131 1d. brown 55 10
131*a* 1d. green (12.12.42) 15 10
132 1½d. carmine .. .. 90 1·50
132*a* 1½d. grey (12.12.42) 35 60
133 2d. grey .. .. 1·00 35
133*a* 2d. carmine (12.12.42) 20 10
134 3d. blue 15 10
135 4d. bright magenta 35 50
136 6d. violet 45 25
137 9d. olive-bistre .. .. 65 1·50
138 1s. black and orange 65 60
139 **19** 2s. purple and blue/*blue*, **C** .. .. 5·50 4·50
140 2s. 6d. black and red/*blue*, **C** .. .. 6·50 5·00
141 5s. pale green and red/*yellow*, **C** .. 27·00 20·00
  a. Green and red/pale yellow, **O** (3.44) 45·00 30·00
142 10s. emerald and deep red/*pale green*, **C** 22·00 22·00
  a. Bluish green and brown-red/pale green, **O** (1.38) .. .. 65·00 45·00

(*b*) *Wmk Mult Crown CA*
143 **19** £1 purple and black/*red*, **C** .. .. 35·00 22·00
130/43 .. .. *Set of* 18 90·00 70·00
130/43 Perf "Specimen" .. .. *Set of* 18 £350

No. 141*a* has a yellow surfacing often applied in horizontal lines giving the appearance of laid paper.

The printer's archives record the despatch of No. 142*a* to Nyasaland in January 1938, but no used examples have been reported before 1945.

20 Lake Nyasa

21 King's African Rifles

(Recess B.W.)

1945 (1 Sept). *T* **20/1** *and similar designs. Wmk Mult Script CA (sideways on horiz designs). P* 12.
144 ½d. black and chocolate 10 10
145 1d. black and emerald 10 15
146 1½d. black and grey-green 10 12
147 2d. black and scarlet 12 10
148 3d. black and light blue 12 10
149 4d. black and claret 15 30
150 6d. black and violet 35 10
151 9d. black and olive .. .. 45 1·75
152 1s. indigo and deep green 35 10
153 2s. emerald and maroon .. .. .. 2·50 2·75
154 2s. 6d. emerald and blue .. .. .. 2·50 2·50
155 5s. purple and blue .. .. 3·25 3·50
156 10s. claret and emerald .. .. .. 6·00 7·50
157 20s. scarlet and black .. .. .. 18·00 26·00
144/57 .. .. *Set of* 14 30·00 40·00
144/57 Perf "Specimen" .. *Set of* 14 £250

Designs: *Horiz*—1½d., 6d. Tea estate; 2d., 1s., 10s. Map of Nyasaland; 4d., 2s. 6d. Tobacco; 9d. Type **20** ; 5s., 20s. Badge of Nyasaland. *Vert*—3d., 2s. Fishing Village.

1946 (16 Dec). *Victory. As Nos.* 28/9 *of Aden.*
158 1d. green 15 15
159 2d. red-orange 15 15
158/9 Perf "Specimen" .. .. *Set of* 2 55·00

27 Symbol of the Protectorate

28 Arms in 1891 and 1951

(Recess B.W.)

1947 (20 Oct). *Wmk Mult Script CA. P* 12.
160 **27** 1d. red-brown and yellow-green .. 20 10
160 Perf "Specimen" .. .. 55·00

1948 (15 Dec). *Royal Silver Wedding. As Nos.* 30/1 *of Aden.*
161 1d. green 15 15
162 10s. mauve .. .. 11·00 17·00

1949 (21 Nov). *75th Anniv of U.P.U. As Nos.* 114/17 *of Antigua.*
163 1d. blue-green 30 30
164 3d. greenish blue .. .. 1·40 1·00
165 6d. purple .. .. 1·50 1·00
166 1s. ultramarine .. .. 1·75 1·60

(Recess B.W.)

1951 (15 May). *Diamond Jubilee of Protectorate. Wmk Mult Script CA. P* 11 × 12.
167 **28** 2d. black and scarlet 15 40
168 3d. black and turquoise-blue 20 55
169 6d. black and violet 30 75
170 5s. black and indigo .. .. .. 1·75 6·00

1953 (30 May). *Rhodes Centenary Exhibition. As No.* 59 *of Northern Rhodesia.*
171 6d. violet 15 20

1953 (2 June). *Coronation. As No.* 47 *of Aden, but ptd by B.W.*
172 2d. black and brown-orange 12 12

29 Grading Cotton

(Recess B.W.)

1953 (1 Sept)–**54.** *Designs previously used for King George VI issue, but with portrait of Queen Elizabeth II as in T* **29.** *Wmk Mult Script CA. P* 12.
173 ½d. black and chocolate 12 40
  a. Perf 12 × 12½ (8.3.54) 10 15
174 1d. brown and bright green.. .. .. 15 5
175 1½d. black and deep grey-green 15 60
176 2d. black and yellow-orange 15 5
  a. Perf 12 × 12½ (8.3.54) 15 5
177 2½d. green and black 12 10
178 3d. black and scarlet 25 10
179 4½d. black and light blue 25 50
180 6d. black and violet 20 10
  a. Perf 12 × 12½ (8.3.54) 20 10
181 9d. black and deep olive .. .. .. 70 1·75
182 1s. deep blue and slate-green 30 12
183 2s. deep green and brown-red .. .. 2·25 2·75
184 2s. 6d. deep emerald and deep blue .. 2·25 3·75
185 5s. purple and Prussian blue .. .. 3·75 7·00
186 10s. carmine and deep emerald .. .. 9·00 13·00
187 20s. red and black .. .. 12·00 22·00
173a/87 .. .. *Set of* 15 28·00 48·00

Designs: *Horiz*—½d., 9d. Lake Nyasa; 1½d., 6d. Tea estate; 2d., 1s., 10s. Map of Nyasaland; 3d., 2s. 6d. Tobacco; 5s., 20s. Badge of Nyasaland. *Vert*—1d. Symbol of the protectorate; 4½d., 2s. Fishing village.

Stamps perf 12 × 12½ come from sheets comb-perforated 11.8 × 12.25. They were also issued in coils of 480 stamps made up from sheets.

For issues between 1954 and 1963, see RHODESIA AND NYASALAND.

30

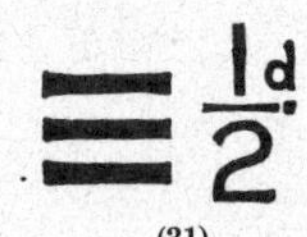

(31)

(Recess B.W.)

1963 (1 Nov). *T* **30,** *Revenue stamps optd* "POSTAGE", *or additionally surch as T* **31.** *P* 12.
188 ½d. on 1d. greenish blue 5 15
189 1d. green 8 5
190 2d. scarlet 8 20
191 3d. blue 10 5
192 6d. brown-purple 20 12
193 9d. on 1s. cerise 25 35
194 1s. purple 25 10
195 2s. 6d. black .. .. 70 1·75
196 5s. chocolate .. .. 1·25 2·50
197 10s. yellow-olive (*shades*) .. .. .. 3·25 6·00
198 £1 deep violet .. .. 5·00 8·00
188/98 .. .. *Set of* 11 10·00 17·00

32 Mother and Child

33 Chambo (fish)

34 Tea Industry

35 Nyala

(Des V. Whiteley. Photo Harrison)

1964 (1 Jan). *Designs as T* **32/5.** *P* 14½.
199 ½d. reddish violet 8 10
200 1d. black and green 10 10
201 2d. light red-brown 12 10
202 3d. red-brown, yellow-green & bistre-brown 12 10
203 4d. indigo and orange-yellow 30 20
204 6d. purple, yellow-green and light blue .. 15 10
205 1s. brown, turquoise-blue and pale yellow .. 20 10
206 1s. 3d. bronze-green and chestnut 30 20
207 2s. 6d. brown and blue 75 65
208 5s. blue, green, yellow and black .. .. 1·50 1·50
209 10s. green, orange-brown and black .. 4·25 3·75
210 £1 deep reddish purple and yellow .. 8·50 9·50
199/210 .. .. *Set of* 12 15·00 15·00

Designs: *As T* **32/3**—2d. Zebu Bull; 3d. Groundnuts; 4d. Fishing. *As T* **34**—1s. Timber; 1s. 3d. Turkish tobacco industry; 2s. 6d. Cotton industry; 5s. Monkey Bay, Lake Nyasa; 10s. Forestry, Afzelia.

POSTAGE DUE STAMPS

(Typo D.L.R.)

1950 (1 July). *As Type* D 1 *of Gold Coast, but inscr* "NYASALAND". *Wmk Mult Script CA. P* 14.
D1 1d. scarlet .. .. 2·00 3·75
D2 2d. ultramarine .. .. 5·00 8·50
D3 3d. green .. .. 8·00 11·00
D4 4d. purple .. .. 15·00 28·00
D5 6d. yellow-orange .. .. 24·00 48·00
D1/D5 .. .. *Set of* 5 48·00 90·00

The stamps of Nyasaland were withdrawn on 5 July 1964 when the territory attained independence. For later issues see MALAWI.

Orange Free State

PRICES FOR STAMPS ON COVER

Nos. 1/9	*from* × 12
Nos. 10/13	*from* × 10
Nos. 18/19	*from* × 12
No. 20	*from* × —
Nos. 21/42	*from* × 10
Nos. 48/51	*from* × 20
Nos. 52/138	*from* × 10
Nos. 139/51	*from* × 7
Nos. F1/17	*from* × —

INDEPENDENT REPUBLIC

1

(Typo D.L.R.)

1868 (1 Jan)–**94.** *P* 14.
1 **1** 1d. pale brown .. .. 2·25 45
2 1d. red-brown .. .. 2·25 45
3 1d. deep brown .. .. 2·75 50
4 6d. pale rose (1868) .. .. .. 9·00 3·50
5 6d. rose (1871) .. .. 3·50 3·00
6 6d. rose-carmine (1891) .. .. .. 9·50 12·00
7 6d. bright carmine (1894) .. .. .. 3·25 2·50
8 1s. orange-buff .. .. 40·00 6·00
9 1s. orange-yellow .. .. 5·00 2·25
  a. Double print .. .. — £2500

4 4 4 4

(2) (*a*) (*b*) (*c*) (*d*)

1877. *No.* 6 *surcharged T* **2** (*a*) *to* (*d*).
10 **1** 4 on 6d. rose-carmine (*a*) .. .. £150 35·00
  a. Surch inverted .. .. .. — £500
  b. Surch double (*a* + *c*) .. ..
  c. Surch double, one inverted (*a* + *c* inverted) .. .. .. — £1000
  d. Surch double one inverted (*a* inverted + *c*) .. ..
11 4 on 6d. rose-carmine (*b*) £900 £110
  a. Surch inverted .. .. .. — £700
  b. Surch double (*b* + *d*) .. ..
12 4 on 6d. rose-carmine (*c*) .. .. 60·00 25·00
  a. Surch inverted .. .. .. — £300
  b. Surch double .. .. ..
13 4 on 6d. rose-carmine (*d*) .. .. 80·00 30·00
  a. Surch inverted .. .. .. — £350

1878 (July). *P* 14.
18 1 4d. pale blue .. .. 5·50 2·25
19 4d. ultramarine .. .. 5·50 3·00
20 5s. green .. .. 11·00 8·00

1d. 1d. 1d. 1d. 1d. 1d.
(3) *(a)* *(b)* *(c)* *(e)* *(f)*

Type **3**: *(a)* Small "1" and "d." *(b)* Sloping serif. *(c)* Same size as *(b)*, but "1" with straighter horizontal serif. *(d)* Taller "1" with horizontal serif and antique "d". *(e)* Same size as *(d)* but with sloping serif and thin line at foot. *(f)* as *(d)* but with Roman "d".

1881 (19 May). *No.* 20 *surch T* **3** *(a) to (f) with heavy black bar cancelling the old value.*
21 1 1d. on 5s. green *(a)* .. .. .. 18·00 6·00
22 1d. on 5s. green *(b)* .. .. .. 10·00 7·00
a. Surch inverted .. .. .. — £400
b. Surch double .. .. .. — £400
23 1d. on 5s. green *(c)* .. .. .. 50·00 30·00
a. Surch inverted .. .. .. — £450
b. Surch double .. .. .. — £550
24 1d. on 5s. green *(d)* .. .. .. 15·00 10·00
a. Surch inverted £450 £400
b. Surch double .. .. .. — £450
25 1d. on 5s. green *(e)* £150 £175
a. Surch inverted .. .. .. — £1200
b. Surch double .. .. .. — £1000
26 1d. on 5s. green *(f)* .. .. .. 15·00 10·00
a. Surch inverted .. .. .. — £350
b. Surch double .. .. .. — £400

No. 21 was the first printing in one type only. Nos. 22 to 25 constitute the second printing about a year later, and are all found on the same sheet; and No. 26 the third printing of which about half have the stop raised.

Owing to defective printing, specimens may be found with the obliterating bar at the top of the stamps and others without the bar.

½d
(4)

1882 (Aug). *No.* 20 *surch with T* 4 *and with a thin black line cancelling old value.*
36 1 ½d. on 5s. green .. .. 2·25 2·50
a. Surch double £350 £300
b. Surch inverted .. ..

3d 3d 3d 3d 3d
(5) *(a)* *(b)* *(c)* *(d)* *(e)*

1882. *No.* 19 *surch with T* **5** *(a) to (e) with thin black line cancelling value.*
38 1 3d. on 4d. ultramarine *(a)* .. .. 25·00 20·00
a. Surch double .. .. .. — £500
39 3d. on 4d. ultramarine *(b)* .. .. 18·00 14·00
a. Surch double .. .. .. — £500
40 3d. on 4d. ultramarine *(c)* .. .. 18·00 14·00
a. Surch double .. .. .. — £500
41 3d. on 4d. ultramarine *(d)* .. .. 22·00 14·00
a. Surch double .. .. .. — £450
42 3d. on 4d. ultramarine *(e)* .. .. 95·00 60·00
a. Surch double .. .. .. — £550

1883–84. *P* 14.
48 1 ½d. chestnut 70 60
49 2d. pale mauve .. .. 1·25 60
50 2d. bright mauve .. .. 1·25 60
51 3d. ultramarine .. .. 2·25 2·00

For 1d. purple, see No. 68.

2d 2d
(6) *(a)* *(b)*

1888 (Sept–Oct). *No.* 51 *surch with T* **6** *(a) or (b).*
(a) Wide "2". (b) Narrow "2"
52 1 2d. on 3d. ultramarine *(a)* (Sept) .. 14·00 9·00
a. Surch inverted .. .. .. — £700
53 2d. on 3d. ultramarine *(b)* .. .. 4·25 2·25
a. Surch inverted .. .. .. — £300

A variety exists having "2" with a curly tail.

1d 1d Id
(7) *(a)* *(b)* *(c)*

1890 (Dec)–**91.** *Nos.* 51 *and* 19 *surch with T* **7** *(a) to (c).*
54 1 1d. on 3d. ultramarine *(a)* .. .. 1·10 1·10
a. Surch double .. .. .. 75·00
c. "1" and "d" wide apart £140 £110
55 1d. on 3d. ultramarine *(b)* .. .. 3·75 3·00
a. Surch double .. .. .. 95·00
57 1d. on 4d. ultramarine *(a)* .. .. 9·50 3·00
a. Surch double £110 £100
b. Surch double *(a + b)* £125
c. Surch triple .. .. ..
58 1d. on 4d. ultramarine *(b)* .. .. 35·00 32·00
a. Surch double £175
59 1d. on 4d. ultramarine *(c)* £400 £300
a. Surch double .. .. ..

The settings of the 1d. on 3d. and on 4d. are not identical. The variety *(c)* does not exist on the 3d.

2½d.
(8)

1892 (Oct). *No* 51 *surch with T* **8**.
67 1 2½d. on 3d. ultramarine .. .. .. 1·10 70
a. No stop after "d" .. .. .. 30·00

1894 (Sept). *Colour changed. P* 14.
68 1 1d. purple 45 45

½d ½d ½d
(9) *(a)* *(b)* *(c)*

½d ½d ½d ½d
(d) *(e)* *(f)* *(g)*

Types *(a)* and *(e)* differ from types *(b)* and *(f)* respectively, in the serifs of the "1", but owing to faulty overprinting this distinction is not always clearly to be seen.

1896 (Sept). *No.* 51 *surch with T* **9** *(a) to (g).*
69 1 ½d. on 3d. ultramarine *(a)* .. .. 1·25 1·60
70 ½d. on 3d. ultramarine *(b)* .. .. 3·00 3·25
71 ½d. on 3d. ultramarine *(c)* .. .. 3·25 3·25
72 ½d. on 3d. ultramarine *(d)* .. .. 3·25 3·25
73 ½d. on 3d. ultramarine *(e)* .. .. 3·00 3·25
74 ½d. on 3d. ultramarine *(f)* .. .. 3·00 3·00
75 ½d. on 3d. ultramarine *(g)* .. .. 1·75 2·25
a. Surch double .. .. .. 11·00 10·00
b. Surch triple .. .. ..

The double and triple surcharges are often different types, but are always type *(g)*, or in combination with type *(g)*.

Double surcharges in the same type, but without the "d" and bar, also exist, probably from a trial sheet prepared by the printer. Both mint and used examples are known.

Halve
Penny.

(10) 2½ **(11)**

1896. *No.* 51 *surch with T* **10**.
77 1 ½d. on 3d. ultramarine 45 55
(i) Errors in setting
78 1 ½d. on 3d. (no stop) .. .. .. 8·00 9·00
79 ½d. on 3d. ("Peuny") .. .. .. 8·50 9·00
80 ½d. on 3d. (no bar) .. .. .. 4·00 5·00
80*a* ½d. on 3d. (no bar or stop) £400
80*b* ½d. on 3d. (no bar and "Peuny") .. ..
(ii) Surch inverted
81 1 ½d. on 3d. .. .. 50·00
81*a* ½d. on 3d. (no stop) .. .. ..
81*b* ½d. on 3d. ("Peuny") .. .. ..
(iii) Surch double, one inverted
81c 1 ½d. on 3d. (Nos. 77 and 81) £225 £250
81*d* ½d. on 3d. (Nos. 77 and 81*a*) £450
81*e* ½d. on 3d. (Nos. 77 and 81*b*) £500
81*f* ½d. on 3d. (Nos. 81 and 78) .. ..
82 ½d. on 3d. (Nos. 81 and 79) .. .. — £425

Nos. 69 to 75 also exist surcharged as last but they are considered not to have been issued with authority.

1897 (1 Jan). *No.* 51 *surch with T* **11**. *(a) As in illustration. (b) With Roman "1" and antique "2" in fraction.*
83 1 2½d. on 3d. ultramarine *(a)* .. .. 1·10 1·10
83*a* 2½d. on 3d. ultramarine *(b)* .. .. £125 90·00

1897. *P* 14.
84 1 ½d. yellow (March) 45 45
85 ½d. orange 45 45
87 1s. brown (Aug) .. .. 3·25 2·25

The 6d. blue was prepared for use in the Orange Free State, but had not been brought into use when the stamps were seized in Bloemfontein. A few have been seen without the "V.R.I." overprint, but they were not authorized or available for postage. (*Price* £50.)

BRITISH OCCUPATION

V. R. I. V. R. I. V. R. I.

4d ½d ½d
31 (Level stops) **(32)** (Raised stops) **(33)**
Thin "V" Thick "V"

(Surch by Messrs Curling, Bloemfontein)

1900. *T* **1** *surch as T* **31/33** *(2½ on 3d. optd "V.R.I." only).*
(a) First printings surch as T **31** *with stops level* (March)
101 ½d. orange 80 50
a. No stop after "V" .. .. .. 12·00 12·00
b. No stop after "I" £150 £150
c. "½" omitted £150 £150
d. "I" omitted .. .. ..
e. "V.R.I." omitted £170
f. Value omitted £110
g. Small "½" .. .. .. 45·00 45·00
h. Surch double £125
102 1d. purple 45 45
a. Error. Brown £450 £350
b. No stop after "V" .. .. .. 10·00 10·00
c. No stop after "R" £150 £160
d. No stop after "I" .. .. ..
e. "1" omitted £150
f. "I" omitted .. .. .. 55·00 55·00
g. "I" and stop after "R" omitted .. .. 55·00 55·00
h. "V.R.I." omitted £170
i. "d" omitted £300
j. Value omitted .. .. .. 90·00
k. Inverted stop after "R" £160
l. Wider space between "1" and "d" .. £100 £100
m. "V" and "R" close £150
n. Pair, one without surch £275
o. "V" omitted .. .. ..
103 2d. bright mauve 45 45
a. No stop after "V" .. .. .. 8·00 8·00
b. No stop after "R" £300
c. No stop after "I" £300
d. "V.R.I." omitted £250
e. Value omitted .. .. ..
104 2½ on 3d. ultramarine *(a)* .. .. 3·00 2·75
a. No stop after "V" .. .. .. 55·00 55·00
105 2½ on 3d. ultramarine *(b)* £160 £160
106 3d. ultramarine 45 45
a. No stop after "V" .. .. .. 8·00 8·00
b. Pair, one without surch £300
c. "V.R.I." omitted .. .. ..
d. Value omitted .. .. ..
107 4d. ultramarine .. .. .. 2·75 2·75
a. No stop after "V" .. .. .. 35·00 35·00
108 6d. bright carmine .. .. .. 35·00 35·00
a. No stop after "V" £250 £275
b. "6" omitted £300 £300
109 6d. blue .. .. 1·10 1·00
a. No stop after "V" .. .. .. 17·00 17·00
b. "6" omitted .. .. .. 38·00 38·00
c. "V.R.I." omitted .. .. ..
110 1s. brown .. .. 2·00 2·00
a. Error. Orange-yellow £2000 £1500
b. No stop after "V" .. .. .. 20·00 20·00
c. "1" omitted £100 £100
d. "1" omitted and spaced stop after "s" .. £110
e. "V.R.I." omitted .. .. .. £150 80·00
f. Value omitted .. .. .. — £140
g. Raised stop after "s" .. .. 8·00 8·00
h. Wider space between "1" and "s" .. £150 £150
111 5s. green .. .. 17·00 17·00
a. No stop after "V" £180 £180
b. "5" omitted £700 £700
c. Inverted stop after "R" £400
d. Wider space between "5" and "s" .. £120 £120
e. Value omitted .. .. ..

All values are found with a rectangular stop instead of an oval stop after "R". Misplaced surcharges (upwards or sideways) also occur.

(b) Subsequent printings. (i) *Surch as T* **32**
112 ½d. orange 30 30
a. Raised and level stops mixed .. .. 1·40 1·60
b. Pair, one with level stops .. .. 6·50 8·00
c. No stop after "V" .. .. .. 2·00 2·00
d. No stop after "I" .. .. .. 18·00 18·00
e. "V" omitted £350
f. Small "½" .. .. .. 9·00 10·00
g. As a, and small "½" .. .. .. 9·00 10·00
i. Space between "V" and "R" .. ..
j. Value omitted .. .. ..
113 1d. purple 30 30
a. Raised and level stops mixed .. .. 1·25 1·40
b. Pair, one with level stops .. .. 13·00 13·00
c. No stop after "V" .. .. .. 4·00 4·00
d. No stop after "R" .. .. .. 10·00 10·00
e. No stop after "I" .. .. .. 9·00 10·00
f. No stops after "V" and "I" £425
g. Surch inverted £300
h. Surch double .. .. .. 90·00 80·00
i. Pair, one without surch £150
j. Short figure "1" £100 £100
k. Space between "V" and "R" .. .. 70·00 75·00
l. Space between "R" and "I" .. .. 90·00
m. Space between "1" and "d" £160
114 2d. bright mauve 45 45
a. Raised and level stops mixed .. .. 3·50 3·50
b. Pair, one with level stops .. .. 5·00 5·00
c. Surch inverted £350
d. "I" raised .. .. ..
e. Pair, one without surch .. ..
f. No stop after "V" .. .. ..
115 2½ on 3d. ultramarine *(a)* £180 £160
a. Raised and level stops mixed .. ..
116 2½ on 3d. ultramarine *(b)* £1000
117 3d. ultramarine 45 45
a. Raised and level stops mixed .. .. 4·50 4·50
b. Pair, one with level stops .. .. 11·00 11·00
c. No stop after "V" £140 £140
d. No stop after "R" .. .. .. — £500
e. "I" omitted £400
f. Surch double £400
g. Surch double, one diagonal £400
h. Ditto, diagonal surch, with mixed stops
118 4d. ultramarine .. .. .. 1·40 1·25
a. Raised and level stops mixed .. .. 4·75
b. Pair, one with level stops .. .. 11·00 11·00
119 6d. bright carmine .. .. .. 35·00 35·00
a. Raised and level stops mixed £140 £140
b. Pair, one with level stops £200
120 6d. blue .. .. 1·00 50
a. Raised and level stops mixed .. .. 4·75 4·75
b. Pair, one with level stops .. .. 11·00 11·00
c. No stop after "V" .. .. ..
d. No stop after "R" .. .. ..
121 1s. brown .. .. 1·00 1·00
a. Error. Orange-yellow £1200 £1200
b. Raised and level stops mixed .. .. 7·50
c. Pair, one with level stops .. .. 16·00 18·00
f. "s" omitted .. .. ..
g. "V.R.I." omitted .. .. ..
122 5s. green (Optd S.£40) .. .. .. 5·00 4·00
a. Raised and level stops mixed £250 £250
b. Pair, one with level stops £900
c. Short top to "5" .. .. .. 55·00 55·00

(ii) *Surch as T* **33**
123 ½d. orange 50 50
124 1d. purple 45 45
a. Inverted "1" for "I" .. .. .. 9·00 11·00
b. No stops after "R" and "I" .. .. 85·00 65·00
c. No stop after "R" .. .. .. 28·00 28·00
d. Surch double £300 £300
125 2d. bright mauve 60 70
a. Inverted "1" for "I" .. .. .. 11·00 11·00
126 2½ on 3d. ultramarine *(a)* £550 £650
127 2½ on 3d. ultramarine *(b)* .. ..
128 3d. ultramarine .. .. .. 1·00 1·10
a. Inverted "1" for "I" .. .. .. 70·00 45·00
b. Surch double .. .. ..
ba. Surch double, one diagonal .. ..

129 6d. bright carmine £375
130 6d. blue .. .. 3·25 4·00
131 1s. brown .. .. 3·50 4·50
132 5s. green .. .. 15·00 15·00

Stamps with thick "V" occur in certain positions in *later* settings of the type with stops above the line (T 32). *Earlier* settings with stops above the line have all stamps with thin "V".

Some confusion has previously been caused by the listing of certain varieties as though they occurred on stamps with thick "V", in fact they occur on stamps showing the normal thin "V", included in the settings which also contained the thick "V".

As small blocks of unsurcharged Free State stamps could be handed in for surcharging, varieties thus occur which are not found in the complete settings.

ORANGE RIVER COLONY

CROWN COLONY

ORANGE RIVER COLONY. (34) — 4d (35) — E. R. I. 6d (36)

1900 (10 Aug)–**02**. *Cape of Good Hope stamps (wmk Cabled Anchor. P 14) optd with T* **34** *by W. A. Richards and Sons, Cape Town.*
133 **17** ½d. green (13.10.00) 45 25
a. No stop .. .. 8·50 8·50
b. Opt double £550
134 1d. carmine (May 1902).. .. .. 60 60
a. No stop .. .. 11·00 11·00
135 **15** 2½d. ultramarine 60 60
a. No stop .. .. 28·00 28·00

In the ½d. and 2½d., the "no stop" after "COLONY" variety was the first stamp in the left lower pane. In the 1d. it is the twelfth stamp in the right lower pane on which the stop was present at the beginning of the printing but became damaged and soon failed to print.

1902 (14 Feb). *Surch with T* **35** *by "Bloemfontein Express".*
136 4d. on 6d. blue (No. 120) (R.) 60 60
a. No stop after "R". .. .. .. 25·00 25·00
c. Thick "V" .. .. 2·50 3·50
d. Thick "V" and inverted "1" for "I" .. 5·00 5·00

1902 (Aug). *Surch with T* **36**.
137 **1** 6d. blue .. .. 1·75 2·25
a. Surch double, one inverted ..
b. Wide space between "6" and "d" (R.4/2) .. .. 60·00 65·00

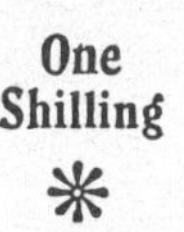

(37)

38 King Edward VII, Springbok and Gnu

1902 (Sept). *Surch with T* **37**.
138 **1** 1s. on 5s. green (O.) .. .. .. 3·50 4·50
a. Thick "V" .. .. 7·00 8·00
b. Short top to "5" .. .. 65·00 65·00
c. Surch double .. .. ..

(Typo D.L.R.)

1903 (3 Feb)–**04**. *Wmk Crown CA. P 14.*
139 **38** ½d. yellow-green (6.7.03) 75 40
140 1d. scarlet 50 20
141 2d. brown (6.7.03) .. .. .. 1·50 1·10
142 2½d. bright blue (6.7.03).. .. .. 75 60
143 3d. mauve (6.7.03) .. .. .. 1·50 80
144 4d. scarlet and sage-green (6.7.03) .. 4·75 2·75
a. "IOSTAGE" for "POSTAGE" .. £750 £600
145 6d. scarlet and mauve (6.7.03) .. 2·50 90
146 1s. scarlet and bistre (6.7.03) .. 8·00 2·25
147 5s. blue and brown (31.10.04) .. 55·00 27·00
139/47 .. .. *Set of* 9 70·00 32·00
139/47 Optd "Specimen" .. .. *Set of* 9 £225

No. 144a occurs on R.10/2 of the upper left pane.

Several of the above values are found with the overprint "C.S.A.R.", in black, for use by the Central South African Railways.

1905 (Nov)–**09**. *Wmk Mult Crown CA. P 14.*
148 **38** ½d. yellow-green (28.7.07) .. .. 1·00 30
149 1d. scarlet 65 30
150 4d. scarlet and sage-green (8.11.07) .. 3·50 1·50
a. "IOSTAGE" for "POSTAGE" .. £180 £150
151 1s. scarlet and bistre (2.09) .. .. 20·00 5·50

POSTAGE STAMPS

Postage stamps of Type 1 (tree), of several denominations, surcharged or unsurcharged, overprinted with Arms similar to above illustration, and in some cases surcharged in addition, were for use on postcards, the overprinting being done after the stamps were affixed to the cards.

FISCAL STAMPS USED FOR POSTAGE

The following were issued in 1878 (Nos. F1 and F3 in 1882) and were authorised for postal use between 1882 and 1886.

F 1

F 2

(Typo D.L.R.)

1882–86. *P 14.*
F 1 **F 1** 6d. pearl-grey .. .. 1·50 5·00
F 2 6d. purple-brown .. .. — 6·00
F 3 **F 2** 1s. purple-brown .. .. 2·50 8·00
F 4 1s. pearl-grey .. .. — 20·00
F 5 1s. 6d. blue .. .. 5·00 3·00
F 6 2s. magenta .. .. 5·00 3·00
F 7 3s. chestnut .. .. 6·00 20·00
F 8 4s. grey .. ..
F 9 5s. rose .. .. 7·00
F10 6s. green .. .. — 20·00
F11 7s. violet .. ..
F12 10s. orange .. .. 15·00 12·00
F13 £1 purple .. .. 22·00 15·00
F14 £2 red-brown .. .. 22·00
F14*a* £4 carmine .. ..
F15 £5 green .. .. 35·00 18·00

The 8s. yellow was prepared but we have no evidence of its use postally without surcharge Type F 3.

ZES PENCE.

(F 3)

1886. *Surch with Type* F 3.
F16 **F 2** 6d. on 4s. grey .. ..
F17 6d. on 8s. yellow .. .. .. 85·00

Postage stamps overprinted for use as Telegraph stamps and used postally are omitted as it is impossible to say with certainty which stamps were genuinely used for postal purposes.

Stamps of SOUTH AFRICA are now in use.

Pakistan

DOMINION

PAKISTAN (1) — PAKISTAN (2)

1947 (1 Oct). *Stamps of India, optd by litho at Nasik, as T* **1** *(3 p. to 12 a.) or* **2** *(14 a. and rupee values).*
1 **100a** 3 p. slate 5 5
2 ½ a. purple 5 5
3 9 p. green 5 5
4 1 a. carmine 5 5
5 **101** 1½ a. dull violet 5 5
6 2 a. vermilion 5 5
7 3 a. bright violet 5 5
8 3½ a. bright blue 20 60
9 **102** 4 a. brown 10 5
10 6 a. turquoise-green 15 5
11 8 a. slate-violet 20 5
12 12 a. lake 40 10
13 **103** 14 a. purple 40 35
14 **93** 1 r. grey and red-brown 40 10
a. Overprint omitted in pair with normal £400
b. Overprint inverted £100
15 2 r. purple and brown .. .. .. 1·00 35
16 5 r. green and blue .. .. .. 2·25 90
17 10 r. purple and claret .. .. .. 3·25 1·25
18 15 r. brown and green .. .. .. 22·00 42·00
19 25 r. slate-violet and purple .. .. 23·00 27·00
1/19 .. .. *Set of* 19 48·00 65·00

Numerous provisional "PAKISTAN" overprints, both hand-stamped and machine-printed, in various sizes and colours, on Postage and Official stamps, also exist.

These were made under authority of Provincial Governments, District Head Postmasters or Local Postmasters and are of considerable philatelic interest.

The 1 a. 3 p. (India No. 269) exists only as a local issue (*price, Karachi opt, 70p. unused; £1.25 used*).

The 12 a., as No. 12, but overprinted at Karachi exists with overprint inverted (*Price £60 unused*).

3 Constituent Assembly Building, Karachi

6 Crescent and Stars

(Des A. R. Chughtai (1 r.). Recess D.L.R.)

1948 (9 July). *Independence. T* **3**, **6** *and similar horiz designs. P* 13½ × 14 *or* 11½ *(1 r.).*
20 1½ a. ultramarine 10 5
21 2½ a. green 10 5
22 3 a. purple-brown 15 5
23 1 r. scarlet 50 15
a. Perf 14 × 13½ .. .. 3·25 3·50

Designs:—2½ a. Karachi Airport entrance; 3 a. Gateway to Lahore Fort.

7 Scales of Justice

8 Star and Crescent

9 Lloyds Barrage

10 Karachi Airport

13 Khyber Pass

(Recess Pakistan Security Ptg Corp Ltd, Karachi (P 13 and 13½), D.L.R. (others))

1948 (14 Aug)–**56**?. *T* **7**/**10**, **13** *and similar designs.*
24 **7** 3 p. red (*p* 12½) 5 5
a. Perf 13½ (1954?) 5 5
25 6 p. violet (*p* 12½) 5 5
a. Perf 13½ (1954?) 8 5
26 9 p. green (*p* 12½) 5 5
a. Perf 13½ (1954?) 10 5
27 **8** 1 a. blue (*p* 12½) 10 5
28 1½ a. grey-green (*p* 12½) 10 5
29 2 a. red (*p* 12½) 20 5
30 **9** 2½ a. green (*p* 14 × 13½) 25 60
31 **10** 3 a. green (*p* 14) 20 10
32 **9** 3½ a. bright blue (*p* 14 × 13½) 30 70
33 4 a. reddish brown (*p* 12½) 20 5
34 – 6 a. blue (*p* 14 × 13½) 30 15
35 – 8 a. black (*p* 12½) 30 10
36 **10** 10 a. scarlet (*p* 13½ × 14) .. .. .. 40 1·00
37 – 12 a. scarlet (*p* 14 × 13½) 40 15
38 – 1 r. ultramarine (*p* 13½ × 14) 50 5
a. Perf 13½ (1954?) .. .. .. 2·25 5
39 – 2 r. chocolate (*p* 13½ × 14) .. .. 4·00 10
a. Perf 13½ (1954?) .. .. .. 4·50 30
40 – 5 r. carmine (*p* 13½ × 14) .. .. 2·50 10
a. Perf 13½ (7.53) .. .. .. 4·00 20
41 **13** 10 r. magenta (*p* 14 × 13½) .. .. 4·00 4·50
a. Perf 12 .. .. 11·00 80
b. Perf 13 (1951) .. .. .. 9·00 65
42 15 r. blue-green (*p* 12) .. .. .. 5·00 8·00
a. Perf 14 × 13½ .. .. .. 9·00 12·00
b. Perf 13 (1956?) .. .. .. 9·50 10·00
43 25 r. violet (*p* 14 × 13½).. .. .. 11·00 15·00
a. Perf 12 .. .. 10·00 8·00
b. Perf 13 (1954) .. .. .. 14·00 11·00
24/43 .. .. *Set of* 20 26·00 18·00

Designs: *Vert (as T* **7**)—6 a., 8 a., 12 a. Karachi Port Trust. (*As T* **10**)—1 r., 2 r., 5 r. Salimullah Hostel, Dacca.

For 25 r. with W **98**, see No. 210.

14

(Recess D.L.R.)

1949 (11 Sept). *First Death Anniv of Mohammed Ali Jinnah. T* **14** *and similar type. P* 13½ × 14.
44 **14** 1½ a. brown .. .. 1·00 40
45 3 a. green .. .. 1·00 40
46 – 10 a. black .. .. 3·50 4·25

Design:—10 a. Inscription reads "QUAID-I-AZAM/MOHAMMAD ALI JINNAH" etc.

15 Star and Crescent

16 Karachi Airport

(Recess Pakistan Security Ptg Corp (P 13½), D.L.R. (others))

1949–53?. *Redrawn. Crescent moon with points to left as T* **15**/**16**.
47 **15** 1 a. blue (*p* 12½) 20 5
a. Perf 13½ (1953?) 25 5
48 1½ a. grey-green (*p* 12½) 20 5
a. Perf 13½ (1952?) 25 5
49 2 a. red (*p* 12½) 30 5
a. Perf 13½ (1953?) 30 5
50 **16** 3 a. green (*p* 13½ × 14) 60 55
51 – 6 a. blue (as No. 34) (*p* 14 × 13½) .. 1·00 15
52 – 8 a. black (as No. 35) (*p* 12½) .. .. 1·00 10
53 **16** 10 a. scarlet (*p* 13½ × 14) .. .. .. 1·50 40
54 – 12 a. scarlet (as No. 37) (*p* 14 × 13½) .. 2·25 20
47/54 .. .. *Set of* 8 6·25 1·25

17 Pottery

18 Aeroplane and Hour-glass

Two Types of 3½ a.:

I 

 II

19 Saracenic Leaf Pattern

20 Archway and Lamp

(Des A. R. Chughtai. Recess D.L.R., later printings, Pakistan Security Ptg Corp)

1951 (14 Aug)–**56.** *Fourth Anniv of Independence. P* 13.
55 **17** 2½ a. carmine 70 25
56 **18** 3 a. purple 40 5
57 **17** 3½ a. blue (I) 60 70
57*a* 3½ a. blue (II)(12.56) . . . . 1·25 60
58 **19** 4 a. green 35 5
59 6 a. brown-orange 35 5
60 **20** 8 a. sepia . . . . . . 1·50 5
61 10 a. violet 70 10
62 **18** 12 a. slate 60 5
55/62 . . . . . . *Set of* 9 5·75 1·40

The above and the stamps issued on the 14 August 1954, 1955 and 1956, are basically definitive issues, although issued on the Anniversary date of Independence.

21 "Scinde Dawk" stamp and Ancient and Modern Transport

(Recess D.L.R.)

1952 (14 Aug). *Centenary of "Scinde Dawk" Issue of India. P* 13.
63 **21** 3 a. deep olive/*yellow-olive* 60 40
64 12 a. deep brown/*salmon* . . . . 2·25 60

PRINTERS. All issues up to No. 219 were recess-printed by the Pakistan Security Printing Corporation, *unless otherwise stated*.

22 Kaghan Valley

23 Mountains, Gilgit

24 Tea Plantation, East Pakistan

1954 (14 Aug). *Seventh Anniv of Independence. T* **22**/**4** *and similar designs. P* 13½ (14 *a.,* 1 *r.,* 2 *r.*) *or* 13 (*others*).
65 6 p. reddish violet 5 5
66 9 p. blue 10 20
67 1 a. carmine 10 5
68 1½ a. red 10 5
69 14 a. deep green 40 5
70 1 r. green . . . . . . 1·25 5
71 2 r. red-orange . . . . . . 1·50 5
65/71 . . . . . . *Set of* 7 3·25 45

Designs: *As T* **22**—1½ a. Mausoleum of Emperor Jehangir, Lahore. *As T* **23**—1 a. Badshahi Mosque, Lahore. *As T* **24**—1 r. Cotton plants, West Pakistan; 2 r. Jute fields and river, East Pakistan.

29 View of K 2

1954 (25 Dec). *Conquest of K 2 (Mount Godwin-Austen). P* 13.
72 **29** 2 a. deep violet 20 10

30 Karnaphuli Paper Mill, Type I (Arabic fraction on left)

Type II (Arabic fraction on right)

1955 (14 Aug)–**56.** *Eighth Anniv of Independence. T* **30** *and similar horiz designs. P* 13.
73 2½ a. scarlet (I) 30 20
73*a* 2½ a. scarlet (II) (12.56) 40 25
74 6 a. deep ultramarine 40 5
75 8 a. deep reddish violet 55 5
76 12 a. carmine and orange 70 5

Designs:—6 a. Textile mill, West Pakistan; 8 a. Jute mill, East Pakistan; 12 a. Main Sui gas plant.

TENTH
ANNIVERSARY
UNITED NATIONS

24.10.55.

(34)

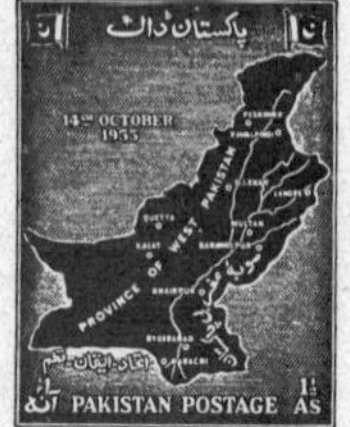

35 Map of West Pakistan

1955 (24 Oct). *Tenth Anniv of United Nations. Nos.* 68 *and* 76 *optd as T* **34**.
77 1½ a. red (B.) . . . . . . 1·75 4·25
78 12 a. carmine and orange (B.) . . . . 1·75 4·25

A second setting of T **34** exists in which "UNITED NATIONS" is 1 mm further to the left.

1955 (7 Dec). *West Pakistan Unity. P* 13½.
79 **35** 1½ a. myrtle-green 20 5
80 2 a. sepia 20 5
81 12 a. deep rose-red 80 20

REPUBLIC

36 Constituent Assembly Building, Karachi

(Litho D.L.R.)

1956 (23 Mar). *Republic Day. P* 13.
82 **36** 2 a. myrtle-green 12 5

37

38 Map of East Pakistan

1956 (14 Aug). *Ninth Anniv of Independence. P* 13½.
83 **37** 2 a. scarlet 5 5

1956 (15 Oct). *First Session of National Assembly of Pakistan at Dacca. P* 13½.
84 **38** 1½ a. myrtle-green 30 5
85 2 a. sepia 30 5
86 12 a. deep rose-red 75 20

39 Karnaphuli Paper Mill, East Bengal

40 Pottery

41 Orange Tree

1957 (23 Mar). *First Anniv of Republic. P* 13.
87 **39** 2½ a. scarlet 20 5
88 **40** 3½ a. blue 30 5
89 **41** 10 r. myrtle-green and yellow-orange . . 3·00 90

The above and No. 95 are primarily definitive issues, although issued on the Anniversary of Republic Day.

For 10 r. with W **98**, see No. 208.

42 Pakistani Flag

43 Pakistani Industries

(Litho D.L.R.)

1957 (10 May). *Centenary of Struggle for Independence (Indian Mutiny). P* 13.
90 **42** 1½ a. bronze-green 8 5
91 12 a. light blue 25 10

(Litho D.L.R.)

1957 (14 Aug). *Tenth Anniv of Independence. P* 13½ × 14.
92 **43** 1½ a. ultramarine 15 5
93 4 a. orange-red 35 25
94 12 a. mauve 50 40

44 Coconut Tree

45

1958 (23 Mar). *Second Anniv of Republic. P* 13.
95 **44** 15 r. red and deep reddish purple . . 6·00 4·00

This is a definitive issue, see note below No. 89.

See No. 209 for this stamp with W **98**.

(Photo Harrison)

1958 (21 Apr). *20th Death Anniv of Mohammed Iqbal (poet). P* 14½ × 14.
96 **45** 1½ a. yellow-olive and black 10 5
97 2 a. orange-brown and black 15 5
98 14 a. turquoise-blue and black 35 30

46 U.N. Charter and Globe

PAKISTAN
BOY SCOUT
2nd NATIONAL
JAMBOREE

CHITTAGONG
Dec. 58—Jan. 59

(47)

1958 (10 Dec). *Tenth Anniv of Declaration of Human Rights. P* 13.
99 **46** 1½ a. turquoise-blue 5 5
100 14 a. sepia 30 25

1958 (28 Dec). *Second Pakistan Boy Scouts National Jamboree, Chittagong. Nos.* 65 *and* 75 *optd with T* **47**.
101 6 p. reddish violet 12 5
102 8 a. deep reddish violet 20 20

REVOLUTION
DAY
Oct. 27, 1959

(48)

49 "Centenary of An Idea"

1959 (27 Oct). *Revolution Day. No.* 74 *optd with T* **48** *in red*.
103 6 a. deep ultramarine 8 8

1959 (19 Nov). *Red Cross Commemoration. Recess; cross typo. P* 13.
104 **49** 2 a. red and green 15 5
105 10 a. red and deep blue 85 30

50 Armed Forces Badge

51 Map of Pakistan

(Litho D.L.R.)

1960 (10 Jan). *Armed Forces Day. P* 13½ × 13.

No.	Type	Description	Unused	Used
106	50	2 a. red, ultramarine and blue-green	12	5
107		14 a. red and bright blue	35	15

1960 (23 Mar). *P* 13 × 13½.

No.	Type	Description	Unused	Used
108	51	6 p. deep purple	10	5
109		2 a. brown-red	15	5
110		8 a. deep green	25	5
111		1 r. blue	30	5

52 Uprooted Tree

53 Punjab Agricultural College

1960 (7 Apr). *World Refugee Year. P* 13.

No.	Type	Description	Unused	Used
112	52	2 a. rose-carmine	5	5
113		10 a. green	20	12

1960 (10 Oct). *Golden Jubilee of Punjab Agricultural College, Lyallpur. T* **53** *and similar horiz design. P* 12½ × 14.

No.	Type	Description	Unused	Used
114		2 a. slate-blue and carmine-red	10	5
115		8 a. bluish green and reddish violet	30	20

Design:—8 a. College arms.

55 "Land Reforms, Rehabilitation and Reconstruction"

56 Caduceus

(Des M. H. Hanjra. Photo D.L.R.)

1960 (27 Oct). *Revolution Day. P* 13 × 13½.

No.	Type	Description	Unused	Used
116	55	2 a. green, pink and brown	5	5
		a. Green and pink omitted	9·00	
117		14 a. green, yellow and ultramarine	25	15

(Photo D.L.R.)

1960 (16 Nov). *Centenary of King Edward Medical College, Lahore. P* 13.

No.	Type	Description	Unused	Used
118	56	2 a. yellow, black and blue	12	5
119		14 a. emerald, black and carmine	45	25

57 "Economic Co-operation"

58 Zam-Zama Gun, Lahore ("Kim's Gun," after Rudyard Kipling)

1960 (5 Dec). *International Chamber of Commerce C.A.F.E.A. Meeting, Karachi. P* 13.

No.	Type	Description	Unused	Used
120	57	14 a. orange-red	20	15

(Centre typo, background recess Pakistan Security Ptg Corp)

1960 (24 Dec). *Third Pakistan Boy Scouts National Jamboree, Lahore. P* 12½ × 14.

No.	Type	Description	Unused	Used
121	58	2 a. carmine, yellow & dp bluish green	15	8

(New Currency. 100 paisa=1 rupee)

1 PAISA

(59)

1961 (1 Jan–14 Feb). *Nos. 24a, 67/8, 83 and 108/9, surch as T* **59**. *Nos. 123/4 and 126 surch by Pakistan Security Ptg Corp and others by the Times Press, Karachi.*

No.	Description	Unused	Used
122	1 p. on 1½ a. red (10.1)	5	5
123	2 p. on 3 p. red	5	5
124	3 p. on 6 p. deep purple	5	5
	a. "PASIA" for "PAISA"	2·50	
125	7 p. on 1 a. carmine (14.2)	10	10
126	13 p. on 2 a. brown-red (14.2)	10	5
	a. "PAIS" for "PAISA"	2·50	
127	13 p. on 2 a. scarlet (14.2)	10	5
122/7	*Set of* 6	40	30

No. 122. Two settings were used, the first with figure "1" 2½ mm tall and the second 3 mm.

On the 1 p. with tall "1" and the 13 p. (No. 127), the space between the figures of value and "P" of "PAISA" varies between 1½ mm and 3 mm.

See also Nos. 262/4.

ERRORS. In the above issue and the corresponding official stamps we have listed errors in the stamps surcharged by the Pakistan Security Printing Corp but have not included the very large number of errors which occurred in the stamps surcharged by the less experienced Times Press. This was a very hurried job and there was no time to carry out the usual checks. It is also known that some errors were not issued to the public but came on the market by other means.

NOTE. Stamps in the old currency were also *handstamped* with new currency equivalents and issued in various districts but these local issues are outside the scope of this catalogue.

60 Khyber Pass

61 Shalimar Gardens, Lahore

62 Chota Sona Masjid (gateway)

(*a*) (*b*) (*c*)

Types (*a*) and (*b*) show the first letter in the top right-hand inscription; (*a*) wrongly engraved, "SH" (*b*) corrected to "P".

On Nos. 131/2 and 134 the corrections were made individually on the plate, so that each stamp in the sheet may be slightly different.

Type (*c*) refers to No. 133a only.

1961–63. *No wmk. P* 13 (*T* **62**) *or* 14 (*others*).

No.	Type	Description	Unused	Used
		(*a*) *Inscribed* "SHAKISTAN" *in Bengali*		
128	60	1 p. violet (1.1.61)	5	5
129		2 p. rose-red (1.1.61)	5	5
130		5 p. ultramarine (23.3.61)	10	5
		(*b*) *Inscribed* "PAKISTAN" *in Bengali*		
131	60	1 p. violet	5	5
132		2 p. rose-red	5	5
133		3 p. reddish purple (27.10.61)	5	5
		a. Re-engraved. First letter of Bengali inscription as Type (*c*) (1963)	5	5
134		5 p. ultramarine	5	5
135		7 p. emerald (23.3.61)	10	5
136	61	10 p. brown (14.8.61)	10	5
137		13 p. slate-violet (14.8.61)	10	5
138		25 p. deep blue (1.1.62)	40	5
139		40 p. deep purple (1.1.62)	40	5
140		50 p. deep bluish green (1.1.62)	25	5
141		75 p. carmine-red (23.3.62)	40	5
142		90 p. yellow-green (1.1.62)	40	5
143	62	1 r. vermilion (7.1.63)	1·50	5
144		1 r. 25, reddish violet (27.10.61)	75	15
144*a*		2 r. orange (7.1.63)	2·00	20
144*b*		5 r. green (7.1.63)	4·25	60
128/44*b*		*Set of* 19	10·00	1·50

See also Nos. 170/81 and 204/7.

(63)

64 Warsak Dam and Power Station

1961 (12 Feb). *Lahore Stamp Exhibition. Optd with T* **63**.

No.	Type	Description	Unused	Used
145	51	8 a. deep green (R.)	20	30

1961 (1 July). *Completion of Warsak Hydro-Electric Project. P* 12½ × 14.

No.	Type	Description	Unused	Used
146	64	40 p. black and blue	20	10

65 Narcissus

66 Ten Roses

1961 (2 Oct). *Child Welfare Week. P* 14.

No.	Type	Description	Unused	Used
147	65	13 p. turquoise-blue	12	5
148		90 p. bright purple	40	20

1961 (4 Nov). *Co-operative Day. P* 13.

No.	Type	Description	Unused	Used
149	66	13 p. rose-red and deep green	25	5
150		90 p. rose-red and blue	50	15

67 Police Crest and "Traffic Control"

68 Locomotive "Eagle" of 1861

(Photo D.L.R.)

1961 (30 Nov). *Police Centenary. P* 13.

No.	Type	Description	Unused	Used
151	67	13 p. silver, black and blue	20	5
152		40 p. silver, black and red	60	15

(Des M. Thoma. Photo D.L.R.)

1961 (31 Dec). *Railway Centenary. T* **68** *and similar horiz design. P* 14.

No.	Type	Description	Unused	Used
153		13 p. green, black and yellow	35	5
154		50 p. yellow, black and green	60	20

Design:—50 p. Diesel locomotive and tracks forming "1961".

(70)

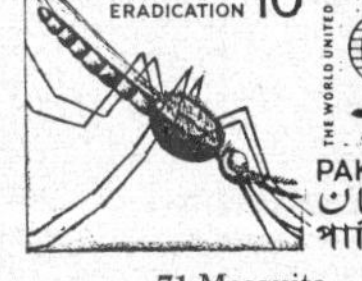

71 Mosquito

1962 (6 Feb). *First Karachi–Dacca Jet Flight. No. 87 surch with T* **70**.

No.	Type	Description	Unused	Used
155	39	13 p. on 2½ a. scarlet (R.)	15	12

(Photo D.L.R.)

1962 (7 Apr). *Malaria Eradication. T* **71** *and similar horiz design. P* 14.

No.	Type	Description	Unused	Used
156		10 p. black, yellow and red	15	10
157		13 p. black, greenish yellow and red	15	10

Design:—13 p. Mosquito pierced by blade.

73 Pakistan Map and Jasmine

(Photo Courvoisier)

1962 (8 June). *New Constitution. P* 12.

No.	Type	Description	Unused	Used
158	73	40 p. yellow-green, bluish green and grey	25	20

74 Football

78 Marble Fruit Dish and Bahawalpuri Clay Flask

1962 (14 Aug). *Sports. T* **74** *and similar horiz designs. P* 12½ × 14.

No.	Type	Description	Unused	Used
159		7 p. black and blue	10	5
160		13 p. black and green	15	5
161		25 p. black and purple	25	5
162		40 p. black and orange-brown	1·40	60

Designs:—13 p. Hockey; 25 p. Squash; 40 p. Cricket.

1962 (10 Nov). *Small Industries. T* **78** *and similar vert designs. P* 13.

No.	Type	Description	Unused	Used
163		7 p. brown-lake	10	5
164		13 p. deep green	65	10
165		25 p. reddish violet	15	5
166		40 p. yellow-green	15	15
167		50 p. deep red	15	15

Designs:—13 p. Sports equipment; 25 p. Camel-skin lamp and brassware; 40 p. Wooden powderbowl and basket-work; 50 p. Inlaid cigarette-box and brassware.

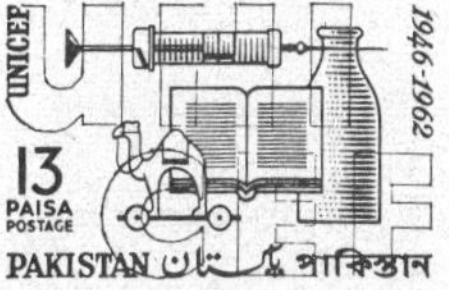

83 "Child Welfare"

(Des M. Thoma. Photo D.L.R.)

1962 (11 Dec). *16th Anniv of U.N.I.C.E.F. P* 14.

No.	Type	Description	Unused	Used
168	83	13 p. black, light blue and maroon	5	5
169		40 p. black, yellow and turquoise-blue	10	5

Nos. 170, etc. Nos. 131/42

1962–70. *As T* 60/1 *but with redrawn Bengali inscription at top right. No wmk.*

170 **60** 1 p. violet (1963) 5 5
171 2 p. rose-red (1964) 5 5
a. Imperf (pair) . . . . 6·00
172 3 p. reddish purple (1970) 5 5
173 5 p. ultramarine (1963) 5 5
174 7 p. emerald (1964) 5 5
175 **61** 10 p. brown (1963) 5 5
176 13 p. slate-violet 5 5
176*a* 15 p. bright purple (31.12.64) 10 5
ab. Imperf (pair) . . . . 6·00
176*b* 20 p. myrtle-green (26.1.70) 20 5
ba. Imperf (pair) . . . . 6·00
177 25 p. deep blue (1963) 10 5
178 40 p. deep purple (1964) 15 5
a. Imperf (pair) . . . . 10·00
179 50 p. deep bluish green (1964) 15 5
180 75 p. carmine-red (1964) 20 5
181 90 p. yellow-green (1964) 20 5
170/81 . . . . . . *Set of* 14 1·25 60

Other values in this series and the high values (Nos. 204/10) are known imperforate but we are not satisfied as to their status.

U.N.FORCE W. IRIAN

(84)

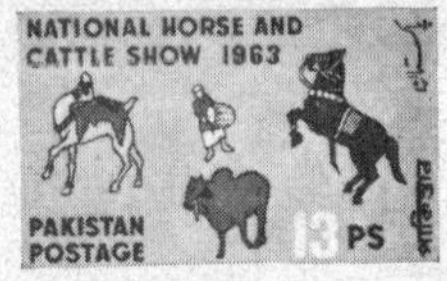

85 "Dancing" Horse, Camel and Bull

1963 (15 Feb). *Pakistan U.N. Force in West Irian. No.* 176 *optd with T* 84.

182 **61** 13 p. slate-violet (R.) 15 5

(Des S. Jahangir. Photo Courvoisier)

1963 (13 Mar). *National Horse and Cattle Show. P* 11½.

183 **85** 13 p. blue, sepia and cerise 15 5

86 Wheat and Tractor

1963 (21 Mar). *Freedom from Hunger. T* 86 *and similar horiz design. P* 12½ × 14.

184 13 p. orange-brown 30 10
185 50 p. bistre-brown 90 55

Design:—50 p. Rice.

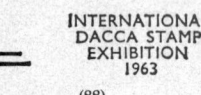

13 PAISA

INTERNATIONAL
DACCA STAMP
EXHIBITION
1963

(88)

89 Centenary Emblem

1963 (23 Mar). *2nd International Stamp Exhibition, Dacca. No.* 109 *surch with T* 88.

186 **51** 13 p. on 2 a. brown-red 25 20

1963 (25 June). *Centenary of Red Cross. Recess; cross typo. P* 13.

187 **89** 40 p. red and deep olive 60 15

90 Paharpur

100 YEARS OF P.W.D.
OCTOBER, 1963
13

(94)

1963 (16 Sept). *Archaeological Series. T* 90 *and similar designs. P* 14 × 12½ (13 *p.*) *or* 12½ × 15 (*others*).

188 7 p. ultramarine 8 5
189 13 p. sepia 10 5
190 40 p. carmine 20 15
191 50 p. deep reddish violet 40 20

Designs: *Vert*—13 p. Moenjodaro; *Horiz*—40 p. Taxila; 50 p. Mainamati.

1963 (7 Oct). *Centenary of Public Works Department. No.* 133 *surch with T* 94.

192 **60** 13 p. on 3 p. reddish purple 10 5

95 Ataturk's Mausoleum

1963 (10 Nov). *25th Death Anniv of Kemal Atatürk. P* 13½.

193 **95** 50 p. red 12 10

96 Globe and U.N.E.S.C.O. Emblem

(Photo D.L.R.)

1963 (10 Dec). *15th Anniv of Declaration of Human Rights. P* 14.

194 **96** 50 p. brown, red and ultramarine . . 15 8

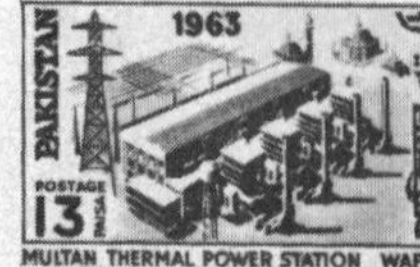

97 Thermal Power Installations

1963 (25 Dec). *Completion of Multan Thermal Power Station. P* 12½ × 14.

195 **97** 13 p. ultramarine 10 5

98 Multiple Star and Crescent

99 Temple of Thot, Queen Nefertari and Maids

1963–79. *As Nos.* 43*b*, 89, 95 *and* 143/44*b*, *but W* **98**.

204 **62** 1 r. vermilion 15 5
205 1 r. 25, reddish violet (1964) 30 10
a. *Purple* (1975?) 30 10
ab. Imperf (pair) . . . . 7·00
206 2 r. orange (1964) 30 10
a. Imperf (pair) . . . . 16·00
207 5 r. green (1964) 70 25
208 **41** 10 r. myrtle-green & yellow-orge (1968) 3·00 2·50
a. Imperf (pair)
b. Wmk sideways . . . .
209 **44** 15 r. red and deep reddish purple (*wmk sideways*) (20.3.79) . . . . . . 6·00 5·00
210 **13** 25 r. violet (1968) . . . . 8·50 8·50
a. Wmk sideways . . . .
ab. Imperf (pair) . . . . 15·00
204/10 . . . . *Set of* 7 17·00 15·00

Other values exist imperforate but we are not satisfied as to their status.

1964 (30 Mar). *Nubian Monuments Preservation. T* 99 *and similar horiz design. P* 13 × 13½.

211 13 p. turquoise-blue and red 10 5
212 50 p. bright purple and black 35 15

Design:—50 p. Temple of Abu Simbel.

101 "Unisphere" and Pakistan Pavilion

103 Shah Abdul Latif's Mausoleum

1964 (22 Apr). *New York World's Fair. T* 101 *and similar design. P* 12½ × 14 (13 *p.*) *or* 14 × 12½ (1 *r.* 25).

213 13 p. ultramarine 5 5
214 1 r. 25, ultramarine and red-orange . . 30 30

Design: *Vert*—1 r. 25, Pakistan Pavilion on "Unisphere".

1964 (25 June). *Death Bicentenary of Shah Abdul Latif of Bhit. P* 13½ × 13.

215 **103** 50 p. bright blue and carmine-lake . . 15 10

104 Mausoleum of Quaid-i-Azam

105 Mausoleum

1964 (11 Sept). *16th Death Anniv of Mohammed Ali Jinnah (Quaid-i-Azam). P* 13½ (15 *p.*) *or* 13 (50 *p.*).

216 **104** 15 p. emerald-green 12 5
217 **105** 50 p. bronze-green 20 10

106 Bengali and Urdu Alphabets

107 University Building

1964 (5 Oct). *Universal Children's Day. P* 13.

218 **106** 15 p. brown 8 5

1964 (21 Dec). *First Convocation of the West Pakistan University of Engineering and Technology, Lahore. P* 12½ × 14.

219 **107** 15 p. chestnut 8 5

PROCESS. All the following issues were lithographed by the Pakistan Security Printing Corporation, *unless otherwise stated.*

108 "Help the Blind"

109 "I.T.U. Emblem and Symbols

(Des A. Chughtai)

1965 (28 Feb). *Blind Welfare. P* 13.

220 **108** 15 p. ultramarine and yellow 10 5

1965 (17 May). *I.T.U. Centenary. Recess. P* 12½ × 14.

221 **109** 15 p. reddish purple 70 15

110 I.C.Y. Emblem

1965 (26 June). *International Co-operation Year. P* 13 × 13½.

222 **110** 15 p. black and light blue 35 5
223 50 p. green and yellow 75 40

111 "Co-operation"

112 Globe and Flags of Turkey, Iran and Pakistan

1965 (21 July). *First Anniv of Regional Development Co-operation Pact. P* 13½ × 13 (15 *p.*) *or* 13 (50 *p.*).

224 **111** 15 p. multicoloured 8 5
225 **112** 50 p. multicoloured 20 10

113 Soldier and Tanks

1965 (25 Dec). *Pakistan Armed Forces. T* 113 *and similar horiz designs. Multicoloured. P* 13½ × 13.

226 7 p. Type **113** 15 5
227 15 p. Naval officer and destroyer 20 5
228 50 p. Pilot and "F-104" Starfighters 50 25

MINIMUM PRICE

The minimum price quoted is 5p which represents a handling charge rather than a basis for valuing common stamps. For further notes about prices see introductory pages.

116 Army, Navy and Air Force Crests

117 Atomic Reactor, Islamabad

1966 (13 Feb). *Armed Forces Day. P* 13½ × 13.
229 **116** 15 p. royal blue, dull grn, brt blue & buff 15 5

1966 (30 Apr). *Inauguration of Pakistan's First Atomic Reactor. Recess. P* 13.
230 **117** 15 p. black 5 5

118 Bank Crest

119 Children

1966 (25 Aug). *Silver Jubilee of Habib Bank. P* 12½ × 14.
231 **118** 15 p. blue-green, yellow-orange & sepia 5 5

1966 (3 Oct). *Universal Children's Day. P* 13½.
232 **119** 15 p. black, red and pale yellow 5 5

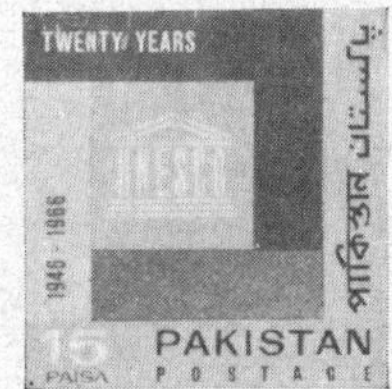

120 U.N.E.S.C.O. Emblem

1966 (24 Nov). *20th Anniv of U.N.E.S.C.O. P* 14.
233 **120** 15 p. multicoloured 45 20

121 Flag, Secretariat Building and President Ayub

1966 (29 Nov). *Islamabad (new capital). P* 13.
234 **121** 15 p. deep bluish green, chestnut, light blue and bistre-brown 5 5
235 50 p. deep bluish green, chestnut, light blue and black 12 10

122 Avicenna

123 Mohammed Ali Jinnah

1966 (3 Dec). *Foundation of Health and Tibbi Research Institute. P* 13 × 13½.
236 **122** 15 p. dull green and salmon 10 5
a. Imperf (pair) .. .. .. 55·00

1966 (25 Dec). *90th Birth Anniv of Mohammed Ali Jinnah. T* **123** *and similar design bearing same portrait but in different frame. Litho and recess. P* 13.
237 **123** 15 p. black, orange and greenish blue .. 5 5
238 – 50 p. black, purple and ultramarine .. 12 15

ALTERED CATALOGUE NUMBERS

Any Catalogue numbers altered from the last edition are shown as a list in the introductory pages.

124 Tourist Year Emblem

125 Emblem of Pakistan T.B. Association

1967 (1 Jan). *International Tourist Year. P* 13½ × 13.
239 **124** 15 p. black, light blue and yellow-brown 5 5

1967 (10 Jan). *Tuberculosis Eradication Campaign. P* 13½ × 13.
240 **125** 15 p. red, sepia and chestnut 12 5

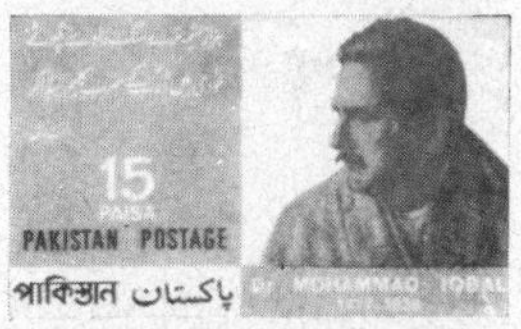

126 Scout Salute and Badge

127 "Justice"

1967 (29 Jan). *4th National Scout Jamboree. Photo. P* 12½ × 14.
241 **126** 15 p. light orange-brown and maroon .. 25 12

1967 (17 Feb). *Centenary of West Pakistan High Court. P* 13.
242 **127** 15 p. black, slate, light red and slate-blue 15 8

128 Dr. Mohammed Iqbal (philosopher)

1967 (21 Apr). *Iqbal Commemoration. P* 13.
243 **128** 15 p. sepia and light red 10 5
244 1 r. sepia and deep green 20 25

129 Hilal-i-Isteqlal Flag

1967 (15 May). *Award of Hilal-i-Isteqlal (for Valour) to Lahore, Sialkot, and Sargodha. P* 13.
245 **129** 15 p. multicoloured 15 5

130 "20th Anniversary"

1967 (14 Aug). *20th Anniv of Independence. Photo. P* 13.
246 **130** 15 p. red and deep bluish green 15 5

131 "Rice Exports"

132 Cotton Plant, Yarn and Textiles

1967 (26 Sept). *Pakistan Exports. T* 131/2 *and similar design. Photo. P* 13 × 13½.
247 10 p. yellow, deep bluish green and deep blue 8 5
248 15 p. multicoloured 10 5
a. Pale orange (top panel) omitted .. .. 10·00
249 50 p. multicoloured 15 15
Design: *Vert as T* 132—50 p. Raw jute, bale and bags.

134 Clay Toys

1967 (2 Oct). *Universal Children's Day. P* 13.
250 **134** 15 p. multicoloured 10 5

135 Shah and Empress of Iran and Gulistan Palace, Teheran

1967 (26 Oct). *Coronation of Shah Mohammed Riza Pahlavi and Empress Farah of Iran. Recess and litho. P* 13.
251 **135** 50 p. purple, blue and light yellow-ochre 15 15

136 "Each For All–All For Each"

1967 (4 Nov). *Co-operative Day. P* 13.
252 **136** 15 p. multicoloured 10 5

137 Mangla Dam

1967 (23 Nov). *Indus Basin Project. P* 13.
253 **137** 15 p. multicoloured 15 10

138 Crab pierced by Sword

139 Human Rights Emblem

1967 (26 Dec). *The Fight Against Cancer. P* 13.
254 **138** 15 p. red and black 10 10

1968 (31 Jan). *Human Rights Year. Photo. P* 14 × 13.
255 **139** 15 p. red and deep turquoise-blue .. 8 8
256 50 p. red, yellow and silver-grey 25 25

140 Agricultural University, Mymensingo

141 W.H.O. Emblem

1968 (28 Mar). *First Convocation of East Pakistan Agricultural University. Photo. P* 13½ × 13.
257 **140** 15 p. multicoloured 10 8

1968 (7 Apr). *20th Anniv of World Health Organization. Photo. P* 14 × 13.
258 **141** 15 p. green and orange-red 8 5
259 50 p. red-orange and indigo 25 20

142 Kazi Nazrul Islam (poet, composer and patriot)

1968 (25 June). *Nazrul Islam Commemoration. Recess and litho. P* 13.
260 **142** 15 p. sepia and pale yellow 12 5
261 50 p. sepia and pale rose-red 25 20
Nos. 260/1 with a two-line inscription giving the wrong date of birth ("1889") were prepared but not issued. Some are known to have been released in error.

4 PAISA
(143)

1968 (18 July–Aug). *Nos.* 56, 74 *and* 61 *surch as T* **143**.
262 4 p. on 3 a. purple 5 5
263 4 p. on 6 a. deep ultramarine (R.) (Aug) . . 5 5
264 60 p. on 10 a. violet (R.) 30 35
a. Surch in black 40 45

144 Children running with Hoops

1968 (7 Oct). *Universal Children's Day. P* 13.
265 **144** 15 p. multicoloured 10 5

145 "National Assembly"

1968 (27 Oct). *"A Decade of Development". T* **145** *and similar horiz designs. P* 13.
266 10 p. multicoloured 10 10
267 15 p. multicoloured 12 10
268 50 p. multicoloured 35 30
269 60 p. light blue, dull purple and vermilion . . 35 30
Designs:—15 p. Industry and agriculture; 50 p. Army, Navy and Air Force; 60 p. Minaret and atomic reactor plant.

149 Chittagong Steel Mill

1969 (7 Jan). *Pakistan's First Steel Mill, Chittagong. P* 13.
270 **149** 15 p. grey, light blue & pale yellow-olive 5 5

150 "Family" **151** Olympic Gold Medal and Hockey Player

1969 (14 Jan). *Family Planning. P* 13½ × 13.
271 **150** 15 p. bright purple & pale greenish blue 5 5

1969 (30 Jan). *Olympic Hockey Champions. Photo. P* 13½.
272 **151** 15 p. black, gold, deep green & pale blue 15 8
273 1 r. black, gold, dp green & flesh-pink . . 50 40

152 Mirza Ghalib and Lines of Verse

1969 (15 Feb). *Death Centenary of Mirza Ghalib (poet). P* 13.
274 **152** 15 p. multicoloured 10 8
275 50 p. multicoloured 20 25
The lines of verse on No. 275 are different from those in T **152**.

153 Dacca Railway Station

1969 (27 Apr). *First Anniv of New Dacca Railway Station. P* 13.
276 **153** 15 p. multicoloured 30 15

154 I.L.O. Emblem and "1919–1969" **155** Mughal Miniature (Pakistan)

1969 (15 May). *50th Anniv of International Labour Organisation. P* 13½.
277 **154** 15 p. buff and bluish green 10 5
278 50 p. cinnamon and cerise 20 20

1969 (21 July). *Fifth Anniv of Regional Co-operation for Development. T* **155** *and similar vert designs. Multicoloured. P* 13.
279 20 p. Type **155** 20 10
280 50 p. Safav miniature (Iran) 35 15
281 1 r. Ottoman miniature (Turkey) 45 40

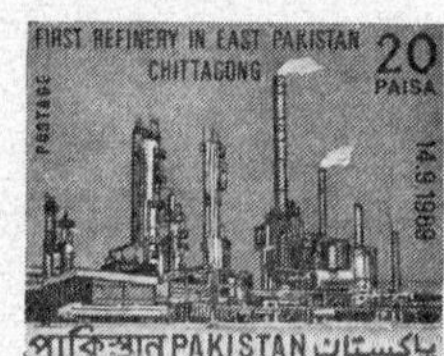

158 Eastern Refinery, Chittagong

1969 (14 Sept). *First Oil Refinery in East Pakistan. Photo. P* 13½ × 13.
282 **158** 20 p. multicoloured 10 8

159 Children playing Outside "School"

1969 (6 Oct). *Universal Children's Day. Photo. P* 13.
283 **159** 20 p. multicoloured 12 12

160 Japanese Doll and P.I.A. Air Routes

1969 (1 Nov). *Inauguration of P.I.A. Pearl Route, Dacca–Tokyo. P* 13½ × 13.
284 **160** 20 p. multicoloured 10 5
a. Yellow and pink omitted . . . . 7·00
285 50 p. multicoloured 25 30
a. Yellow and pink omitted . . . . 7·00

161 "Reflection of Light" Diagram

1969 (4 Nov). *Millenary Commemorative of Ibn-al-Haitham (physicist). Photo. P* 13.
286 **161** 20 p. black, lemon and light blue . . 12 10

162 Vickers "Vimy" and Karachi Airport **163** Flags, Sun Tower and Expo Site Plan

1969 (2 Dec). *50th Anniv of First England–Australia Flight. Photo. P* 13½ × 13.
287 **162** 50 p. multicoloured 40 35

1970 (15 Mar). *World Fair, Osaka. P* 13.
288 **163** 50 p. multicoloured 20 25

164 New U.P.U. H.Q. Building

1970 (20 May). *New U.P.U. Headquarters Building. P* 13½ × 13.
289 **164** 20 p. multicoloured 10 5
290 50 p. multicoloured 35 30
The above, in a miniature sheet, additionally inscr "U.P.U. Day 9th Oct, 1971", were put on sale on that date in very limited numbers.

165 U.N. H.Q. Building

1970 (26 June). *25th Anniv of United Nations. T* **165** *and similar horiz design. Multicoloured. P* 13 × 13½.
291 20 p. Type **165** 8 5
292 50 p. U.N. emblem 30 30

167 I.E.Y. Emblem, Book and Pen

1970 (6 July). *International Education Year. P* 13.
293 **167** 20 p. multicoloured 12 8
294 50 p. multicoloured 35 25

168 Saiful Malook Lake (Pakistan)

1970 (21 July). *Sixth Anniv of Regional Co-operation for Development. T* **168** *and similar square designs. Multicoloured. P* 13.
295 20 p. Type **168** 15 10
296 50 p. Seeyo-Se-Pol Bridge, Esfahan (Iran) . . 25 12
297 1 r. View from Fethiye (Turkey) 40 35

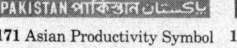

171 Asian Productivity Symbol **172** Dr. Maria Montessori

1970 (18 Aug). *Asian Productivity Year. Photo. P* 12½ × 14.
298 **171** 50 p. multicoloured 15 15

1970 (31 Aug). *Birth Centenary of Dr. Maria Montessori (educationist). P* 13.
299 **172** 20 p. multicoloured 10 10
300 50 p. multicoloured 20 15

173 Tractor and Fertilizer Factory

1970 (12 Sept). *Tenth Near East F.A.O. Regional Conference, Islamabad. P* 13.
301 **173** 20 p. bright green, and orange-brown 10 8

174 Children and Open Book **175** Pakistan Flag and Text

1970 (5 Oct). *Universal Children's Day. Photo. P* 13.
302 **174** 20 p. multicoloured 10 8

1970 (7 Dec). *General Elections for National Assembly. P* 13½ × 13.
303 **175** 20 p. green and bluish violet 12 12

1970 (17 Dec). *General Elections for Provincial Assemblies. As No.* 303, *but inscr* "PROVINCIAL ASSEMBLIES 17TH DEC., 1970".
304 **175** 20 p. green and pale magenta 12 12

176 Conference Crest and burning Al-Aqsa Mosque

1970 (26 Dec). *Conference of Islamic Foreign Ministers. Karachi. P* 13.
305 **176** 20 p. multicoloured 12 10

177 Coastal Embankments

1971 (25 Feb). *Coastal Embankments in East Pakistan Project. P* 13.
306 **177** 20 p. multicoloured 15 12

178 Emblem and United Peoples of the World **180** Chaharbagh School (Iran)

179 Maple Leaf Cement Factory, Daudkhel

1971 (21 Mar). *Racial Equality Year. P* 13.
307 **178** 20 p. multicoloured 12 12
308 50 p. multicoloured 20 25

1971 (1 July). *20th Anniv of Colombo Plan. P* 13.
309 **179** 20 p. brown, black and reddish violet . . 10 12

1971 (21 July). *Seventh Anniv of Regional Co-operation for Development. T* **180** *and similar horiz designs. Multicoloured. P* 13.
310 10 p. Selimiye Mosque (Turkey) 12 12
311 20 p. Badshahi Mosque (Lahore) 20 20
312 50 p. Type **180** 45 30

181 Electric Locomotive and Boy with Toy Train

1971 (4 Oct). *Universal Children's Day. P* 13.
313 **181** 20 p. multicoloured 20 15

182 Horseman and Symbols

1971 (15 Oct). *2500th Anniv of Persian Monarchy. P* 13.
314 **182** 10 p. multicoloured 12 12
315 20 p. multicoloured 20 25
316 50 p. multicoloured 30 35
The above exist in a miniature sheet, but only a very limited quantity was placed on sale.

183 Hockey-player and Trophy

1971 (24 Oct). *World Cup Hockey Tournament, Barcelona. P* 13.
317 **183** 20 p. multicoloured 20 20

184 Great Bath, Moenjodaro

1971 (4 Nov). *25th Anniv of U.N.E.S.C.O. and Campaign to save the Moenjodaro Excavations. P* 13.
318 **184** 20 p. multicoloured 15 15

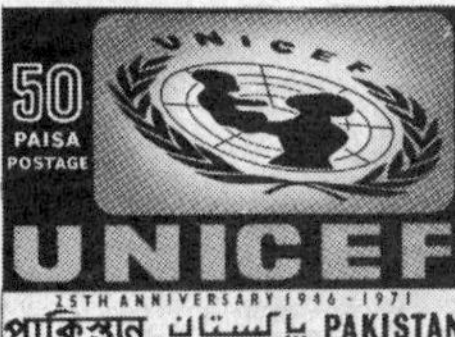

185 U.N.I.C.E.F. Symbol

1971 (11 Dec). *25th Anniv of U.N.I.C.E.F. P* 13.
319 **185** 50 p. multicoloured 25 25

186 King Hussein and Jordanian Flag

1971 (25 Dec). *50th Anniv of Hashemite Kingdom of Jordan. P* 13.
320 **186** 20 p. multicoloured 15 12

187 Badge of Hockey Federation and Trophy **188** Reading Class

1971 (31 Dec). *Hockey Championships Victory. P* 13.
321 **187** 20 p. multicoloured 20 20

1972 (15 Jan). *International Book Year. P* 13½.
322 **188** 20 p. multicoloured 15 15

INDEPENDENT OF THE BRITISH COMMONWEALTH

On 30 January 1972 Pakistan left the Commonwealth.
For the convenience of collectors we continue to list later issues in this volume.

189 View of Venice

1972 (7 Feb). *U.N.E.S.C.O. Campaign to Save Venice. P* 13.
323 **189** 20 p. multicoloured 20 20

190 E.C.A.F.E. Emblem and Discs **191** Human Heart

1972 (28 Mar). *25th Anniv of E.C.A.F.E. (Economic Commission for Asia and the Far East). P* 13.
324 **190** 20 p. multicoloured 12 15

1972 (7 Apr). *World Health Day. P* 13 × 13½.
325 **191** 20 p. multicoloured 20 20

192 "Only One Earth" **193** "Fisherman" (Cevat Dereli)

1972 (5 June). *U.N. Conference on the Human Environment, Stockholm. P* 13 × 13½.
326 **192** 20 p. multicoloured 20 20

1972 (21 July). *Eighth Anniv of Regional Co-operation for Development. T* **193** *and similar vert designs. Multicoloured. P* 13.
327 10 p. Type **193** 10 10
328 20 p. "Iranian Woman" (Behzad) 15 15
329 50 p. "Will and Power" (A. R. Chughtai) . . 35 35
a. Brown-ochre (border) omitted . . . . 15·00

194 Mohammed Ali Jinnah and Tower **195** Donating Blood

1972 (14 Aug). *25th Anniv of Independence. T* **194** *and similar horiz designs. Multicoloured. P* 13 (*10 and 60 p.*) *or* 14 × 12½ (*20 p.*).
330 10 p. Type **194** 5 5
331 20 p. "Land Reform" (*74 × 23½ mm*) 12 20
332 20 p. "Labour Reform" (*74 × 23½ mm*) .. 12 20
333 20 p. "Education Policy" (*74 × 23½ mm*) .. 12 20
334 20 p. "Health Policy" (*74 × 23½ mm*) .. 12 20
335 60 p. National Assembly Building (*46 × 28 mm*) 25 25
330/5 .. .. *Set of* 6 70 1·00
Nos. 331/4 were printed horizontally *se-tenant* throughout the sheet.

1972 (6 Sept). *National Blood Transfusion Service. P* 13½×12½.
336 **195** 20 p. multicoloured 15 12

196 People and Squares

1972 (16 Sept). *Centenary of Population Census. P* 13½.
337 **196** 20 p. multicoloured 12 12

197 Children from Slums

1972 (2 Oct). *Universal Children's Day. P* 13.
338 **197** 20 p. multicoloured 12 12

198 People and Open Book

1972 (23 Oct). *Education Week. P* 13.
339 **198** 20 p. multicoloured 20 15

199 Nuclear Power Plant

1972 (28 Nov). *Inauguration of Karachi Nuclear Power Plant. P* 13.
340 **199** 20 p. multicoloured 12 15

200 Copernicus in Observatory

1973 (19 Feb). *500th Birth Anniv of Nicholas Copernicus* (*astronomer*). *P* 13.
341 **200** 20 p. multicoloured 20 20

201 Moenjodaro Excavations

202 Elements of Meteorology

1973 (23 Feb). *50th Anniv of Moenjodaro Excavations. P* 13 × 13½.
342 **201** 20 p. multicoloured 20 20

1973 (23 Mar). *I.M.O./W.M.O. Centenary. P* 13.
343 **202** 20 p. multicoloured 20 20

203 Prisoners-of-war

1973 (18 Apr). *Prisoners-of-war in India. P* 13.
344 **203** 1 r. 25, multicoloured 55 45

204 National Assembly Building and Constitution Book

1973 (21 Apr). *Constitution Week. P* 12½ × 13½.
345 **204** 20 p. multicoloured 20 20

205 Badge and State Bank Building

1973 (1 July). *25th Anniv of Pakistan State Bank. P* 13.
346 **205** 20 p. multicoloured 12 15
347 1 r. multicoloured 30 35

206 Lut Desert Excavations (Iran)

207 Constitution Book and Flag

1973 (21 July). *9th Anniv of Regional Co-operation for Development. T* **206** *and similar vert designs. Multicoloured. P* 13 × 13½.
348 20 p. Type **206** 15 15
349 60 p. Main Street, Moenjodaro (Pakistan) .. 25 25
350 1 r. 25, Mausoleum of Antiochus I (Turkey) 40 40

1973 (14 Aug). *Independence Day and Enforcement of the Constitution. P* 13.
351 **207** 20 p. multicoloured 15 15

208 Mohammed Ali Jinnah (Quaid-i-Azam)

209 *Wallago attu*

1973 (11 Sept). *25th Death Anniv of Mohammed Ali Jinnah. P* 13.
352 **208** 20 p. light emerald, pale yellow and black 15 15

1973 (24 Sept). *Fishes. T* **209** *and similar horiz designs. Multicoloured. P* 13½.
353 10 p. Type **209** 30 30
354 20 p. *Labeo rohita* 35 35
355 60 p. *Tilapia mossambica* 40 40
356 1 r. *Catla catla* 40 40
Nos. 353/6 were printed within one sheet, horizontally *se-tenant*.

210 Children's Education

1973 (1 Oct). *Universal Children's Day. P* 13.
357 **210** 20 p. multicoloured 12 15

211 Harvesting

1973 (15 Oct). *Tenth Anniv of World Food Programme. P* 13.
358 **211** 20 p. multicoloured 20 20

212 Ankara and Kemal Atatürk

1973 (29 Oct). *50th Anniv of Turkish Republic. P* 13.
359 **212** 50 p. multicoloured 25 25

213 Boy Scout

214 "Basic Necessities"

1973 (11 Nov). *National Silver Jubilee Scout Jamboree. P* 13.
360 **213** 20 p. multicoloured 25 25

1973 (16 Nov). *25th Anniv of Declaration of Human Rights. P* 13.
361 **214** 20 p. multicoloured 20 20

215 Al-Biruni and Nandana Hill

216 Dr. Hansen, Microscope and Bacillus

1973 (26 Nov). *Al-Biruni Millennium Congress. P* 13.
362 **215** 20 p. multicoloured 20 20
363 1 r. 25, multicoloured 50 65

1973 (29 Dec). *Centenary of Hansen's Discovery of Leprosy Bacillus. P* 13.
364 **216** 20 p. multicoloured 25 25

217 Family and Emblem

218 Conference Emblem

1974 (1 Jan). *World Population Year. P* 13.
365 **217** 20 p. multicoloured 10 10
366 1 r. 25, multicoloured 30 40

1974 (22 Feb). *Islamic Summit Conference, Lahore. T* **218** *and similar design. P* 14 × 12½ (*20 p.*) *or* 13 (*65 p.*).
367 20 p. Type **218** 10 10
368 65 p. Emblem on "Sun" (*42 × 30 mm*) .. 30 40
MS369 102 × 102 mm. Nos. 367/8. Imperf .. 3·25 3·75

219 Units of Weight and Measurement

220 "Chand Chauthai" Carpet, Pakistan

1974 (1 July). *Adoption of International Weights and Measures System. P* 13.
370 **219** 20 p. multicoloured 15 15

1974 (21 July). *Tenth Anniv of Regional Co-operation for Development. Vert designs as T* **220** *showing carpets from member countries. Multicoloured. P* 13.
371 20 p. Type **220** 15 15
372 60 p. Persian carpet, 16th-century 45 45
373 1 r. 25, Anatolian carpet, 15th-century .. 65 80

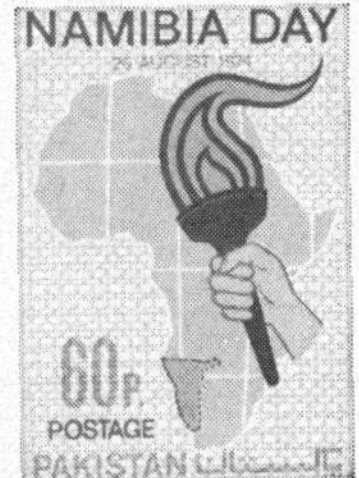

221 Hands protecting Sapling **222** Torch and Map

1974 (9 Aug). *Tree Planting Day. P* 13.
374 **221** 20 p. multicoloured 25 20

1974 (26 Aug). *Namibia Day. P* 13.
375 **222** 60 p. multicoloured 30 35

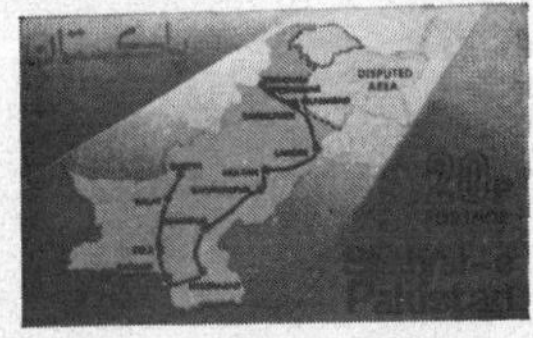

223 Highway Map

1974 (23 Sept). *Shahrah-e-Pakistan (Pakistan Highway). P* 13.
376 **223** 20 p. multicoloured 25 20

224 Boy at Desk **225** U.P.U. Emblem

1974 (7 Oct). *Universal Children's Day. P* 13.
377 **224** 20 p. multicoloured 25 20

1974 (9 Oct). *Centenary of Universal Postal Union. T* **225** *and similar vert design. Multicoloured. P* 13 × 13½ *(20 p.) or* 13 *(2 r. 25).*
378 20 p. Type **225** 20 20
379 2 r. 25, U.P.U. emblem, aeroplane and mail-wagon (30 × 41 *mm*) .. .. .. 1·25 1·60
MS380 100 × 101 mm. Nos. 378/9. Imperf .. 5·50 7·50

226 Liaquat Ali Khan **227** Dr. Mohammed Iqbal (poet and philosopher)

1974 (16 Oct). *Liaquat Ali Khan (First Prime Minister of Pakistan). P* 13 × 13½.
381 **226** 20 p. black and light vermilion 25 20

1974 (9 Nov). *Birth Centenary of Dr. Iqbal* (1977) *(1st issue). P* 13.
382 **227** 20 p. multicoloured 25 20
See also Nos. 399, 433 and 445/9.

228 Dr. Schweitzer and River Scene

1975 (14 Jan). *Birth Centenary of Dr. Albert Schweitzer. P* 13.
383 **228** 2 r. 25, multicoloured 80 80

229 Tourism Year Symbol

1975 (15 Jan). *South East Asia Tourism Year. P* 13.
384 **229** 2 r. 25, multicoloured 55 60

230 Assembly Hall, Flags and Prime Minister Bhutto

(Des A. Salahuddin)

1975 (22 Feb). *First Anniv of Islamic Summit Conference, Lahore. P* 13.
385 **230** 20 p. multicoloured 15 10
386 1 r. multicoloured 40 40

231 "Scientific Research" **232** "Globe" and Algebraic Symbol

(Des A. Salahuddin (20 p.), M. Ahmed (2 r. 25))

1975 (15 June). *International Women's Year. T* **231** *and similar horiz design. Multicoloured. P* 13.
387 20 p. Type **231** 20 20
388 2 r. 25, Girl teaching woman ("Adult Education") .. .. 80 1·10

1975 (14 July). *International Congress of Mathematical Sciences, Karachi. P* 13.
389 **232** 20 p. multicoloured 25 20

233 Pakistani Camel-skin Vase **234** Sapling and Dead Trees

(Des I. Gilani)

1975 (21 July). *Eleventh Anniv of Regional Co-operation for Development. T* **233** *and similar multicoloured designs. P* 13.
390 20 p. Type **233** 20 20
391 60 p. Iranian tile *(horiz)* 40 40
392 1 r. 25, Turkish porcelain vase 65 65

1975 (9 Aug). *Tree Planting Day. P* 13 × 13½.
393 **234** 20 p. multicoloured 25 20

235 Black Partridge **236** "Today's Girls"

(Des A. Salahuddin)

1975 (30 Sept). *Wildlife Protection (1st series). P* 13.
394 **235** 20 p. multicoloured 30 25
395 2 r. 25, multicoloured .. .. 1·75 1·75

See also Nos. 400/1, 411/12, 417/18, 493/6, 560, 572/3, 581/2, 599, 600, 605 and 621/2.

1975 (6 Oct). *Universal Children's Day. P* 13.
396 **236** 20 p. multicoloured 25 20

237 Hazrat Amir Khusrau, Sitar and Tabla

(Des A. Salahuddin)

1975 (24 Oct). *700th Birth Anniv of Hazrat Amir Khusrau (poet and musician). P* 13½ × 12½.
397 **237** 20 p. multicoloured 15 20
398 2 r. 25, multicoloured .. .. 75 1·25

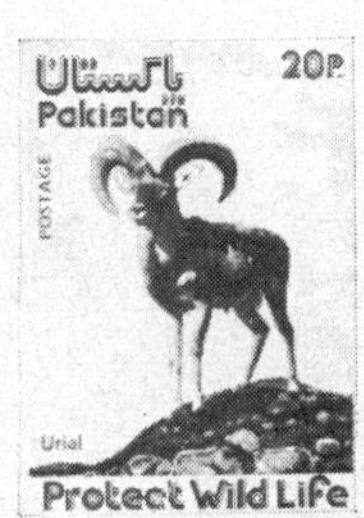

238 Dr. Mohammed Iqbal **239** Urial (wild sheep)

(Des A. Salahuddin)

1975 (9 Nov). *Birth Centenary of Dr. Iqbal* (1977) *(2nd issue). P* 13.
399 **238** 20 p. multicoloured 25 20

(Des M. Ahmed)

1975 (31 Dec). *Wildlife Protection (2nd series). P* 13.
400 **239** 20 p. multicoloured 30 25
401 3 r. multicoloured .. .. 2·00 1·90

240 Moenjodaro Remains **241** Dome and Minaret of Rauza-e-Mubarak

(Des A. Salahuddin)

1976 (29 Feb). *"Save Moenjodaro" (1st series). T* **240** *and similar vert designs. Multicoloured. P* 13.
402 10 p. Type **240** 55 55
403 20 p. Remains *(different)* 65 65
404 65 p. The Citadel 65 65
405 3 r. Well inside a house 65 65
406 4 r. The "Great Bath" 75 75

Nos. 402/6 were printed horizontally *se-tenant* within the sheet, the five stamps forming a composite design of the excavations.
See also Nos. 414 and 430.

(Des A. Ghani. Photo)

1976 (3 Mar). *International Congress on Seerat. P* 13 × 13½.
407 **241** 20 p. multicoloured 20 20
408 3 r. multicoloured .. .. 1·00 1·25

242 Alexander Graham Bell and Telephone Dial

(Des M. M. Saeed. Photo)

1976 (10 Mar). *Telephone Centenary. P* 13.
409 **242** 3 r. multicoloured .. .. 1·25 1·50

243 College Arms within "Sun"

(Des A. Salahuddin)

1976 (15 Mar). *Centenary of National College of Arts, Lahore. P* 13.
410 **243** 20 p. multicoloured 20 20

244 Common Peafowl

(Des A. Salahuddin)

1976 (31 Mar). *Wildlife Protection* (*3rd series*). *P* 13.
411 **244** 20 p. multicoloured 30 25
412 3 r. multicoloured .. .. .. 1·75 2·00

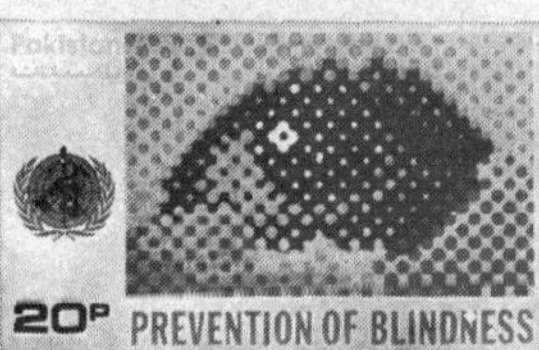

245 Human Eye

(Des M. M. Saeed)

1976 (7 Apr). *Prevention of Blindness. P* 13.
413 **245** 20 p. multicoloured 25 20

246 Unicorn and Ruins

(Des I. Gilani)

1976 (31 May). *"Save Moenjodaro"* (*2nd series*). *P* 13.
414 **246** 20 p. multicoloured 25 20

247 Jefferson Memorial **248** Ibex

(Des I. Gilani (90 p.), A. Salahuddin (4 r.))

1976 (4 July). *Bicentenary of American Revolution. T* **247** *and similar horiz design. Multicoloured. P* 13 (90 *p.*) *or* 13½ (4 *r.*).
415 90 p. Type **247** 50 25
416 4 r. "Declaration of Independence" (47 × 36 *mm*) .. .. 3·00 3·50

(Des M. Ahmed)

1976 (12 July). *Wildlife Protection* (*4th series*). *P* 13.
417 **248** 20 p. multicoloured 30 25
418 3 r. multicoloured .. .. .. 1·75 2·00

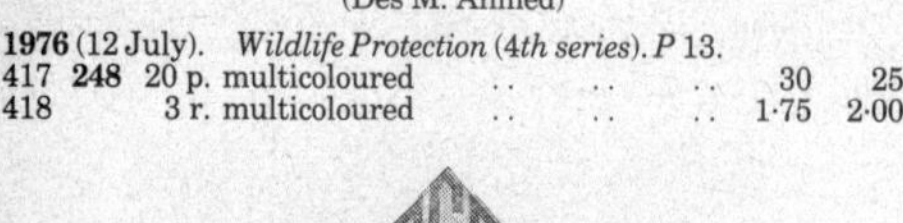

249 Mohammed Ali Jinnah

(Des A. Salahuddin)

1976 (21 July). *Twelfth Anniv of Regional Co-operation for Development. T* **249** *and similar diamond-shaped designs. Multicoloured. P* 14.
419 20 p. Type **249** 25 25
420 65 p. Reza Shah the Great (Iran) 25 25
421 90 p. Kemal Atatürk (Turkey) 25 25

Nos. 419/21 were printed vertically *se-tenant* throughout the sheet.

250 Urdu Text **251** Mohammed Ali Jinnah and Wazir Mansion

1976 (14 Aug). *Birth Centenary of Mohammed Ali Jinnah* (*1st issue*). *P* 13. (*a*) *Type* **250**.
422 5 p. black, new blue and yellow 20 20
423 10 p. black, yellow and magenta 20 20
424 15 p. black and violet-blue 20 20
425 1 r. black, yellow and new blue 30 30

(*b*) *Multicoloured designs as T* **251**, *different buildings in the background*
426 20 p. Type **251** 20 20
427 40 p. Sind Madressah 20 20
428 50 p. Minar Qarardad-e-Pakistan 20 20
429 3 r. Mausoleum 45 50
422/9 .. .. *Set of* 8 1·75 1·75

Nos. 422/9 were printed in *se-tenant* blocks of 8 throughout the sheet.

See also No. 436.

252 Dancing-girl, Ruins and King Priest

(Des A. Salahuddin)

1976 (31 Aug). *"Save Moenjodaro"* (*3rd series*). *P* 14.
430 **252** 65 p. multicoloured 35 20

253 U.N. Racial Discrimination Emblem

(Des A. Salahuddin)

1976 (15 Sept). *U.N. Decade to Combat Racial Discrimination. P* 12½ × 13½.
431 **253** 65 p. multicoloured 20 20

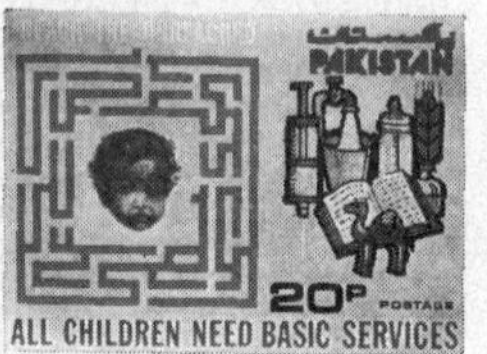

254 Child in Maze and Basic Services

(Des M. Ahmed)

1976 (4 Oct). *Universal Children's Day. P* 13.
432 **254** 20 p. multicoloured 15 10

Stamps commemorating the visit of King Khalid of Saudi Arabia and showing the Islamabad Mosque were prepared for release on 11 October 1976, but withdrawn before issue. Some are known to have been released in error.

255 Verse from "Allama Iqbal" **256** Mohammed Ali Jinnah giving Scout Salute

(Des M. A. Javed)

1976 (9 Nov). *Birth Centenary of Dr. Iqbal* (1977) (*3rd issue*). *P* 13.
433 **255** 20 p. multicoloured 10 10

(Des I. Gilani)

1976 (20 Nov). *Quaid-i-Azam Centenary Jamboree. P* 13½.
434 **256** 20 p. multicoloured 20 15

257 Children Reading **258** Mohammed Ali Jinnah

(Des M. Ahmed)

1976 (15 Dec). *Children's Literature. P* 13.
435 **257** 20 p. multicoloured 15 5

(Litho and embossed Cartor S.A., France)

1976 (25 Dec). *Birth Centenary of Mohammed Ali Jinnah* (*2nd issue*). *P* 12½.
436 **258** 10 r. emerald and gold .. .. .. 2·25 2·50

259 Rural Family **260** Turkish Vase, 1800 B.C.

(Des M. Ahmed)

1977 (14 Apr). *Social Welfare and Rural Development Year. P* 13.
437 **259** 20 p. multicoloured 10 5

(Des A. Salahuddin)

1977 (21 July). *13th Anniv of Regional Co-operation for Development. T* **260** *and similar horiz designs. P* 13.
438 20 p. red-orange, violet-blue and black .. 15 5
439 65 p. multicoloured 20 15
440 90 p. multicoloured 30 30

Designs:—60 p. Pakistani toy bullock cart, Moenjodaro; 90 p. Pitcher with spout, Sialk Hill, Iran.

261 Forest **262** Desert Scene

(Des A. Ahmed)

1977 (9 Aug). *National Tree Plantation Campaign. P* 13.
441 **261** 20 p. multicoloured 10 5

(Des M. A. Javed)

1977 (5 Sept). *U.N. Conference on Desertification, Nairobi. P* 13.
442 **262** 65 p. multicoloured 20 12

263 "Water for the Children of the World" **264** Aga Khan III

(Des A. Salahuddin)

1977 (3 Oct). *Universal Children's Day. P* 13½ × 12½.
443 **263** 50 p. multicoloured 25 12

(Des A. Rauf)

1977 (2 Nov). *Birth Centenary of Aga Khan III. P* 13.
444 **264** 2 r. multicoloured 55 55

NEW INFORMATION

The editor is always interested to correspond with people who have new information that will improve or correct the Catalogue.

265 Iqbal and Spirit of the Poet Roomi (from painting by Behzad)
266 The Holy "Khana-Kaaba" (House of God, Mecca)

(Des A. Ahmed)

1977 (9 Nov). *Birth Centenary of Dr. Mohammed Iqbal (4th issue). T* **265** *and similar vert designs. Multicoloured. P* 13.
445 20 p. Type **265** 25 25
446 65 p. Iqbal looking at Jamaluddin Afghani and Saeed Haleem Pasha at prayer (Behzad) 25 25
447 1 r. 25, Urdu verse 30 30
448 2 r. 25, Persian verse.. .. .. .. 35 35
449 3 r. Iqbal 40 40

Nos. 445, 448/9, 447 and 446 (in that order) were issued in horizontal *se-tenant* strips of 5.

(Des I. Gilani)

1977 (21 Nov). *Haj (pilgrimage to Mecca). P* 14.
450 **266** 65 p. multicoloured 30 20

267 Rheumatic Patient and Healthy Man
268 Woman in Costume of Rawalpindi-Islamabad

(Des T. Hameed)

1977 (19 Dec). *World Rheumatism Year. P* 13.
451 **267** 65 p. turquoise-blue, black and yellow .. 30 20

(Des A. Salahuddin)

1978 (5 Feb). *Indonesia–Pakistan Economic and Cultural Co-operation Organization. P* 12½ × 13½.
452 **268** 75 p. multicoloured 30 20

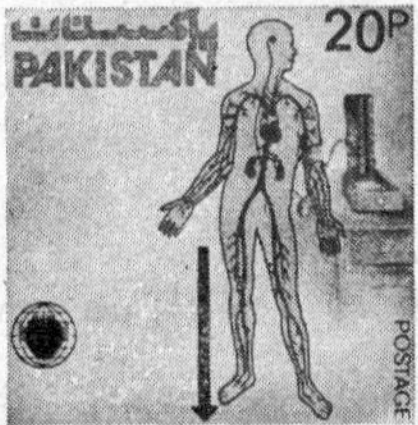

269 Human Body and Sphygmomanometer
270 Henri Dunant

(Des A. Salahuddin)

1978 (20 Apr). *World Hypertension Month. P* 13.
453 **269** 20 p. multicoloured 15 10
454 – 2 r. multicoloured 60 60

The 2 r. value is as T **269**, but has the words "Down with high blood pressure" instead of the Urdu inscription at bottom left.

(Des A. Salahuddin)

1978 (8 May). *150th Birth Anniv of Henri Dunant (founder of Red Cross). P* 14.
455 **270** 1 r. black, new blue and vermilion .. 20 20

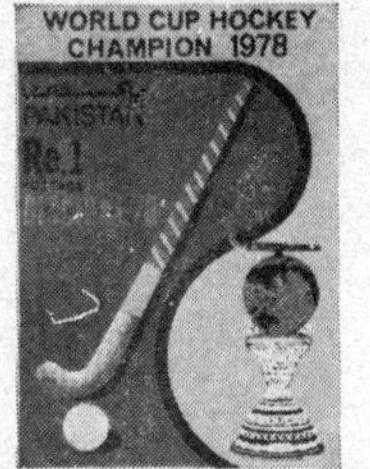

271 Red Roses (Pakistan)
272 "Pakistan, World Cup Hockey Champions"

(Des A. Salahuddin)

1978 (21 July). *14th Anniv of Regional Co-operation for Development. T* **271** *and similar vert designs. Multicoloured. P* 13½.
456 20 p. Type **271** 10 10
457 90 p. Pink roses (Iran).. .. .. .. 20 20
458 2 r. Yellow rose (Turkey) 25 25

Nos. 456/8 were printed together, *se-tenant*, in horizontal strips of 3 throughout the sheet.

(Des M. Munawar)

1978 (26 Aug). *"Riccione '78" International Stamp Fair. T* **272** *and similar vert design. Multicoloured. P* 13.
459 1 r. Type **272** 12 12
460 2 r. Fountain at Piazza Turismo 25 25

273 Cogwheels within Globe Symbol
274 St. Patrick's Cathedral

(Des A. Salahuddin)

1978 (3 Sept). *U.N. Technical Co-operation amongst Developing Countries Conference. P* 13.
461 **273** 75 p. multicoloured 15 10

(Des A. Salahuddin)

1978 (29 Sept). *Centenary of St. Patrick's Cathedral, Karachi. T* **274** *and similar vert design. Multicoloured. P* 13.
462 1 r. Type **274** 12 12
463 2 r. Stained glass window 25 25

275 Minar-i-Qarardad-e-Pakistan
276 Tractor

276a Mausoleum of Ibrahim Khan

Two Dies of 75 p. value:

Die I

Die II

Die I. Size of design 26½ × 21½ mm. Figures of value large; "p" small. Plough does not touch left-hand frame.

Die II. Size of design 25½ × 21 mm. Smaller figures; larger "p". Plough touches left-hand frame.

(Des A. Salahuddin. Litho (10, 25, 40, 50, 90 p.), recess (others))

1978 (7 Nov)–**81.** *No wmk* (2 *to* 90 *p.*) *or W* **90** (1 *to* 5 *r.*). *P* 14 × 13½ (2 *to* 5 *p.*), 13½ × 14 (10 *to* 90 *p.*) *or* 13 (1 *to* 5 *r.*).
464 **275** 2 p. deep grey-green 5 5
465 3 p. black 5 5
a. Imperf (pair) .. .. .. 5·00
466 5 p. deep ultramarine 5 5
467 **276** 10 p. new blue & greenish bl (7.10.79) .. 5 5
468 20 p. deep yellow-green (25.3.79) .. 5 5
469 25 p. dp green & dull magenta (19.3.79) 5 5
470 40 p. new blue and magenta (16.12.78) 5 5
471 50 p. slate-lilac & turq-green (19.3.79) .. 5 5
472 60 p. black (16.12.78) 5 5
a. Imperf (pair) .. .. .. 5·00
473 75 p. dull vermilion (I) (16.12.78) .. 60 5
a. Imperf (pair) .. .. .. 16·00
b. Die II (1980) 8 5
ba. Imperf (pair) .. .. .. 7·00
474 90 p. magenta and new blue (16.12.78) 10 5
475 **276a** 1 r. bronze-green (2.8.80) 10 5
a. Imperf (pair) .. .. .. 20·00
476 1 r. 50, red-orange (17.11.79) .. 15 5
a. Imperf (pair) .. .. .. 6·00
477 **276a** 2 r. carmine-red (17.11.79) 20 10
a. Imperf (pair) .. .. .. 7·00
478 3 r. blue-black (4.6.80) 30 30
a. Imperf (pair) .. .. .. 9·00
479 4 r. black (1.1.81) 40 40
a. Imperf (pair) .. .. ..
480 5 r. sepia (1.1.81) 50 50
a. Imperf (pair) .. .. ..

The remaining values as Type **276** printed in recess, are from Die II.

GUM. Later printings of the 10 p., 20 p. and 25 p. values (Nos. 467/9) occur with matt, almost invisible gum of a PVA type, instead of the gum arabic used previously.

277 Emblem and "United Races" Symbol
278 Maulana Mohammad Ali Jauhar

(Des M. Munawar)

1978 (20 Nov). *International Anti-Apartheid Year. P* 13.
481 **277** 1 r. multicoloured 15 15

(Des A. Salahuddin)

1978 (10 Dec). *Birth Centenary of Maulana Mohammad Ali Jauhar (patriot). P* 13.
482 **278** 50 p. multicoloured 10 10

279 "Tornado", "Rapide" and Wright *Flyer*

(Des A. Salahuddin)

1978 (24 Dec). *75th Anniv of Powered Flight. T* **279** *and similar diamond-shaped designs. Multicoloured. P* 13.
483 65 p. Type **279** 20 20
484 1 r. "Phantom F4F", "Tri-star" and Wright *Flyer* 20 20
485 2 r. "X15", Tu. "104" and Wright *Flyer* .. 30 35
486 2 r. 25, Mig "15", "Concorde" and Wright *Flyer* 35 40

Nos. 483/6 were printed together, *se-tenant*, in blocks of 4 throughout the sheet.

280 "Holy Koran illuminating Globe" and Raudha-e-Mubarak (mausoleum)
281 "Aspects of A.P.W.A."

(Des A. Salahuddin)

1979 (10 Feb). *"12th Rabi-ul-Awwal" (Prophet Mohammed's birthday). P* 13.
487 **280** 20 p. multicoloured 10 10

(Des M. Saeed)

1979 (25 Feb). *30th Anniv of A.P.W.A. (All Pakistan Women's Association). P* 13.
488 **281** 50 p. multicoloured 10 10

OMNIBUS ISSUES

Details, together with prices for complete sets, of the various Omnibus issues from the 1935 Silver Jubilee series to date are included in a special section following Zululand at the end of the catalogue.

282 Tippu Sultan Shaheed of Mysore

(Des A. Rauf)

1979 (23 Mar). *Pioneers of Freedom. T* **282** *and similar diamond-shaped designs. Multicoloured. W* **98.** *P* 14.
490 10 r. Type **282** 90 90
491 15 r. Sir Syed Ahmad Khan .. .. .. 1·25 1·25
492 25 r. Altaf Hussain Hali .. .. .. 2·25 2·10

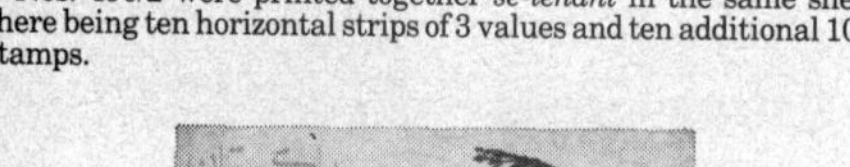

Nos. 490/2 were printed together *se-tenant* in the same sheet: there being ten horizontal strips of 3 values and ten additional 10 r. stamps.

283 Himalayan Monal Pheasant

(Des M. Ahmed)

1979 (17 June). *Wildlife Protection* (5*th series*). *Pheasants. T* **283** *and similar horiz designs. Multicoloured. P* 13.
493 20 p. Type **283** 5 5
494 25 p. Kalij 5 5
495 40 p. Koklass 10 10
496 1 r. Cheer 25 15

284 "Pakistan Village Scene" (Ustad Bakhsh)

(Des A. Rauf)

1979 (21 July). 15*th Anniv of Regional Co-operation for Development. Paintings. T* **284** *and similar horiz designs. Multicoloured. P* 14 × 12½.
497 40 p. Type **284** 15 15
498 75 p. "Iranian Goldsmith" (Kamal al Molk) .. 15 15
499 1 r. 60, "Turkish Harvest" (Namik Ismail) .. 20 20
Nos. 497/9 were printed together, *se-tenant*, in vertical strips of 3 throughout the sheet.

285 Guj Embroidered Shirt (detail)

1979 (23 Aug). *Handicrafts* (1*st series*). *T* **285** *and similar horiz designs. Multicoloured. P* 14 × 12½.
500 40 p. Type **285** 15 15
501 1 r. Enamel inlaid brass plate 20 20
502 1 r. 50, Baskets 25 25
503 2 r. Chain-stitch embroidered rug (detail) .. 30 35
Nos. 500/3 were printed together, *se-tenant*, in blocks of 4 throughout the sheet.
See also Nos. 578/9, 595/6 and 625/8.

286 Children playing on Climbing Frame

(Des A. Rauf)

1979 (10 Sept). *S.O.S. Children's Village, Lahore* (*orphanage*). *P* 13.
504 **286** 50 p. multicoloured 10 5

287 "Island" (Z. Maloof)

(Des A. Salahuddin)

1979 (22 Oct). *International Year of the Child. Children's Paintings. T* **287** *and similar horiz designs. Multicoloured. P* 14 × 12½.
505 40 p. Type **287** 15 15
506 75 p. "Playground" (R. Akbar) 25 25
507 1 r. "Fairground" (M. Azam) 25 25
508 1 r. 50, "Hockey Match" (M. Tayyab) .. 30 30
MS509 79 × 64 mm. 2 r. "Child looking at Faces in the Sky" (M. Mumtaz) (*vert*). Imperf .. .. 3·25 3·25
Nos. 505/8 were printed together, *se-tenant*, in blocks of 4 throughout the sheet.
Examples of No. **MS**509 are known overprinted in gold for the "PHILEXFRANCE" International Stamp Exhibition in 1982. The Pakistan Post Office has declared such overprints to be bogus.

288 Warrior attacking Crab

CUSTOMS CENTENARY 1878 1978
Re.1 POSTAGE
PAKISTAN

289 Pakistan Customs Emblem

(Des A. Salahuddin)

1979 (12 Nov). *Fight Against Cancer. P* 14.
510 **288** 40 p. black, greenish yellow and magenta 10 5

(Des A. Salahuddin)

1979 (10 Dec). *Centenary of Pakistan Customs Service. P* 13 × 13½.
511 **289** 1 r. multicoloured 15 12

290 Boeing "747 (Jumbo)" and Douglas "DC-3" Airliners

291 Islamic Pattern

(Des A. Salahuddin)

1980 (10 Jan). 25*th Anniv of Pakistan International Air Lines. P* 13.
512 **290** 1 r. multicoloured 15 12

(Des and litho Secura, Singapore)

1980 (15 Jan–10 Mar). *Matt, almost invisible PVA gum. P* 12.
513 **291** 10 p. slate-green and orange-yellow .. 5 5
514 15 p. slate-green and bright yellow-green 5 5
515 25 p. violet and brown-red (10.3) .. 5 5
516 35 p. carmine & brt yellow-green (10.3) .. 5 5
517 – 40 p. rosine and olive-sepia 5 5
518 – 50 p. violet and dull yellow-green (10.3) 5 5
519 – 80 p. brt yellow-green & black (10.3) .. 8 10
513/19 .. .. *Set of* 7 35 35
The 40 to 80 p. values also show different Islamic patterns, the 40 p. being horizontal and the remainder vertical.

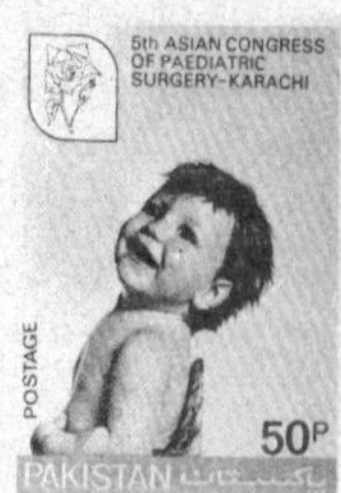

292 Young Child

293 Conference Emblem

(Des M. Saeed)

1980 (16 Feb). 5*th Asian Congress of Paediatric Surgery, Karachi. P* 13.
530 **292** 50 p. multicoloured 10 5

(Des A. Salahuddin)

1980 (17 May). 11*th Islamic Conference of Foreign Ministers, Islamabad. P* 13.
531 **293** 1 r. multicoloured 15 15

294 Karachi Port

(Des A. Salahuddin)

1980 (15 July). *Centenary of Karachi Port Authority. P* 13 × 13½.
532 **294** 1 r. multicoloured 15 12

RICCIONE 80

(**295**)

296 College Emblem with Old and New Buildings

1980 (30 Aug). *"Riccione 80" International Stamp Exhibition. Nos.* 505/8 *optd with T* **295** *in red.*
533 40 p. Type **287** 5 5
534 75 p. "Playground" (R. Akbar) 8 10
535 1 r. "Fairground" (M. Azam) 10 15
536 1 r. 50, "Hockey Match" (M. Tayyab) .. 15 20

(Des M. Munawar)

1980 (18 Sept). 75*th Anniv of Command and Staff College, Quetta. P* 13.
537 **296** 1 r. multicoloured 10 12

WORLD TOURISM CONFERENCE
MANILA 80

(**297**)

1980 (27 Sept). *World Tourism Conference, Manila. No.* 496 *optd with T* **297**.
538 1 r. Cheer 10 12

298 Birth Centenary Emblem

(Des A. Salahuddin)

1980 (5 Oct). *Birth Centenary of Hafiz Mahmood Shairani. P* 13.
539 **298** 40 p. multicoloured 5 5

299 Shalimar Gardens, Lahore

(Des A. Salahuddin)

1980 (23 Oct). *Aga Khan Award for Architecture. P* 13.
540 **299** 2 r. multicoloured 20 30

300 Rising Sun

301 Money Order Form

(Des S. Ahmed (40 p.), J. Sultana (2 r.), A. Salahuddin (others))

1980 (10 Nov). 1400*th Anniv of Hegira* (1*st issue*). *T* **300** *and similar multicoloured designs. P* 14 (2 *r.*) *or* 13 (*others*).
541 40 p. Type **300** 5 5
542 2 r. Ka'aba and symbols of Moslem achievement (34 × 34 *mm*) 25 30

543 3 r. Holy Koran illuminating World (31 × 54 *mm*) 30 40
MS544 106 × 84 mm. 4 r. Candles. Imperf .. 45 60
See also No. 549.

(Des A. Ahmed)

1980 (20 Dec). *Centenary of Money Order Service. P* 13.
545 **301** 40 p. multicoloured 5 5

302 Postcards encircling Globe

303 Heinrich von Stephan and U.P.U. Emblem

(Des A. Ahmed)

1980 (27 Dec). *Centenary of Postcard Service. P* 13.
546 **302** 40 p. multicoloured 5 5

(Des J. Sultana)

1981 (7 Jan). *150th Birth Anniv of Heinrich von Stephan (founder of U.P.U.). P* 13.
547 **303** 1 r. multicoloured 10 12

304 Aircraft and Airmail Letters

(Des J. Sultana)

1981 (15 Feb). *50th Anniv of Airmail Service. P* 13.
548 **304** 1 r. multicoloured 10 12

305 Mecca

306 Conference Emblem and Afghan Refugees

1981 (7 Mar). *1400th Anniv of Hegira (2nd issue). P* 13.
549 **305** 40 p. multicoloured 5 5

(Des Z. Akhlaq (Nos. 550 and 552), A. Ahmed (Nos. 551 and 553), M. Jafree (No. 554))

1981 (29 Mar). *Islamic Summit Conference (1st issue). T* **306** *and similar multicoloured designs. P* 13.
550 40 p. Type **306** 5 5
551 40 p. Conference emblem encircled by flags and Afghan refugees (28 × 58 *mm*) 5 5
552 1 r. Type **306** 12 12
553 1 r. As No. 551 .. .. 12 12
554 2 r. Conference emblem and map showing Afghanistan (48 × 32 *mm*) 20 25

307 Conference Emblem

308 Kemal Atatürk

(Des A. Salahuddin (Nos. 555, 557), A. Irani (Nos. 556, 558))

1981 (20 Apr). *Islamic Summit Conference (2nd issue). T* **307** *and similar multicoloured design. P* 13.
555 40 p. Type **307** 5 5
556 40 p. Conference emblem and flags (28 × 46 *mm*) 5 5
557 85 p. Type **307** 12 12
558 85 p. As No. 556 .. .. 12 12

(Des A. Salahuddin)

1981 (19 May). *Birth Centenary of Kemal Atatürk (Turkish statesman). P* 13.
559 **308** 1 r. multicoloured 10 12

309 Green Turtle

310 Dome of the Rock

(Des Jamal. Litho Secura, Singapore)

1981 (20 June). *Wildlife Protection (6th series). Matt, almost invisible PVA gum. P* 12 × 11½.
560 **309** 40 p. multicoloured 5 5

(Des A. Salahuddin)

1981 (25 July). *Palestinian Welfare. P* 13.
561 **310** 2 r. multicoloured 25 25

311 Malubiting West

(Litho Secura, Singapore)

1981 (20 Aug). *Karakoram Range Mountain Peaks. T* **311** *and similar multicoloured designs. Matt, almost invisible PVA gum. P* 14 × 13½.
562 40 p. Type **311** 5 5
563 40 p. Malubiting West (24 × 31 *mm*) 5 5
564 1 r. Haramosh 10 10
565 1 r. Haramosh (24 × 31 *mm*) 10 10
566 1 r. 50, K6 .. .. 15 15
567 1 r. 50, K6 (24 × 31 *mm*) 15 15
568 2 r. K2, Broad Peak, Gasherbrum 4 and Gasherbrum 2 .. .. 15 20
569 2 r. K2 (24 × 31 *mm*) 15 20
562/9 .. .. *Set of* 8 80 90
The two designs of each value were printed together, *se-tenant*, in horizontal pairs throughout the sheet.

312 Pakistan Steel "Furnace No. 1"

313 Western Tragopan

(Des A. Ahmed)

1981 (31 Aug). *First Firing of Pakistan Steel "Furnace No. 1", Karachi. P* 13.
570 **312** 40 p. multicoloured 5 5
571 2 r. multicoloured 15 20

(Litho Secura, Singapore)

1981 (15 Sept). *Wildlife Protection (7th series). Matt, almost invisible PVA gum. P* 14.
572 **313** 40 p. multicoloured 5 5
573 – 2 r. multicoloured 20 20
The 2 r. value is as Type **313** but the background design shows a winter view.

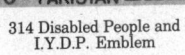

314 Disabled People and I.Y.D.P. Emblem

315 World Hockey Cup below flags of participating Countries

(Des M. Saeed)

1981 (12 Dec). *International Year for Disabled Persons. P* 13.
574 **314** 40 p. multicoloured 5 5
575 2 r. multicoloured 20 20

(Des A. Salahuddin)

1982 (31 Jan). *Pakistan—World Cup Hockey Champions. T* **315** *and similar vert design. Multicoloured. P* 13.
576 1 r. Type **315** 12 10
577 1 r. World Hockey Cup above flags of participating countries 12 10

316 Camel Skin Lamp

317 Chest X-Ray of Infected Person

(Des A. Salahuddin. Litho Secura, Singapore)

1982 (20 Feb). *Handicrafts (2nd series). T* **316** *and similar vert design. Multicoloured. P* 14.
578 1 r. Type **316** 12 10
579 1 r. Hala pottery 12 10
See also Nos. 595/6.

(Des A. Ahmed)

1982 (24 Mar). *Centenary of Robert Koch's Discovery of Tubercle Bacillus. P* 13.
580 **317** 1 r. multicoloured 12 10

318 Indus Dolphin

(Des A. Salahuddin. Litho Secura, Singapore)

1982 (24 Apr). *Wildlife Protection (8th series). P* 12 × 11½.
581 **318** 40 p. multicoloured 5 5
582 – 1 r. multicoloured 15 10
The 1 r. value is as Type **318** but the design is reversed.

319 "Apollo–Soyuz" Link-up, 1975

(Des A. Salahuddin)

1982 (7 June). *Peaceful Uses of Outer Space. P* 13.
583 **319** 1 r. multicoloured 12 10

320 Sukkur Barrage

(Des A. Salahuddin)

1982 (17 July). *50th Anniv of Sukkur Barrage. P* 13.
584 **320** 1 r. multicoloured 12 10

321 Pakistan National Flag and Stylised Sun

RICCIONE — 82.
(322)

(Des A. Ahmed)

1982 (14 Aug). *Independence Day. T* **321** *and similar vert design. Multicoloured. P* 13.
585 40 p. Type **321** 5 5
586 85 p. Map of Pakistan and stylised torch .. 8 8

1982 (28 Aug). *"Riccione 82" International Stamp Exhibition. No. 584 optd with T* **322**.
587 **320** 1 r. multicoloured 8 10

323 Arabic Inscription and University Emblem

(Des Syed Tanwir Rizvi)

1982 (14 Oct). *Centenary of the Punjab University. P* 13½ × 13.
588 **323** 40 p. multicoloured 5 5

324 Scout Emblem and Tents

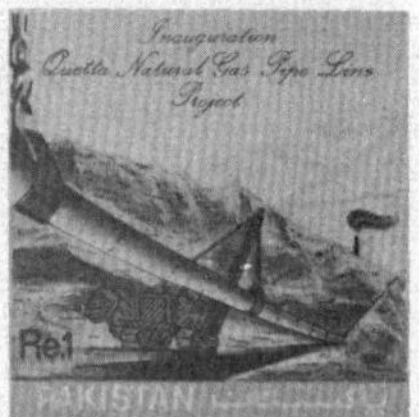

325 Laying Pipeline

(Des M. Saeed)

1982 (23 Dec). *75th Anniv of Boy Scout Movement. P* 13.
589 **324** 2 r. multicoloured 25 25

(Des A. Salahuddin)

1983 (6 Jan). *Inauguration of Quetta Natural Gas Pipeline Project. P* 13.
590 **325** 1 r. multicoloured 10 12

326 Common Peacock (*Papilio polyctor*)

(Litho Secura, Singapore)

1983 (15 Feb). *Butterflies. T* **326** *and similar horiz designs. Multicoloured. Matt, almost invisible PVA gum. P* 13½.
591 40 p. Type **326** 10 5
592 50 p. Common Rose (*Polydorus aristolchiae*) .. 10 5
593 60 p. Plain Tiger (*Danaus chrysippus*) .. 10 5
594 1 r. 50, Lemon Butterfly (*Papilio demoleus*) 20 30

(Litho Secura, Singapore)

1983 (9 Mar). *Handicrafts* (*3rd series*). *Vert designs as T* **316.** *Multicoloured. Matt, almost invisible PVA gum. P* 14.
595 1 r. Five flower motif needlework, Sind .. 10 12
596 1 r. Straw mats 10 12

327 School of Nursing and University Emblem

(Des A. Salahuddin)

1983 (16 Mar). *Presentation of Charter to Aga Khan University, Karachi. P* 13½ × 13.
597 **327** 2 r. multicoloured 20 25
No. 597 was issued in sheets of 8 (2 × 4), each horizontal pair being separated by a different *se-tenant* label showing views of the University.

328 Yak Caravan crossing Zindiharam-Darkot Pass, Hindu Kush

(Des A. Salahuddin)

1983 (28 Apr). *Trekking in Pakistan. P* 13.
598 **328** 1 r. multicoloured 10 12

OMNIBUS ISSUES

Details, together with prices for complete sets, of the various Omnibus issues from the 1935 Silver Jubilee series to date are included in a special section following Zululand at the end of the catalogue.

329 Marsh Crocodile

(Litho Secura, Singapore)

1983 (19 May). *Wildlife Protection* (*9th series*). *Matt, almost invisible PVA gum. P* 13½.
599 **329** 3 r. multicoloured 30 35

330 Chinkara (antelope)

331 Floral Design

(Litho Secura, Singapore)

1983 (20 June). *Wildlife Protection* (*10th series*). *Matt, almost invisible PVA gum. P* 14 × 13½.
600 **330** 1 r. multicoloured 10 12

(Des A. Ahmed)

1983 (14 Aug). *36th Anniv of Independence. T* **331** *and similar vert design. Multicoloured. P* 13.
601 60 p. Type **331** 5 5
602 4 r. Hand holding flaming torch 40 45

332 Traditional Weaving, Pakistan

(Des A. Salahuddin)

1983 (19 Aug). *Indonesian–Pakistan Economic and Cultural Co-operation Organization, 1969–1983. T* **332** *and similar horiz design. Multicoloured. P* 13.
603 2 r. Type **332** 20 25
604 2 r. Traditional weaving, Indonesia 20 25

333 "Siberian Cranes" (Great White Cranes) (Sir Peter Scott)

1983 (8 Sept). *Wildlife Protection* (*11th series*). *P* 13.
605 **333** 3 r. multicoloured 30 35

334 W.C.Y. Emblem

1983 (9 Oct). *World Communications Year. T* **334** *and similar multicoloured design. P* 13 (2 *r.*) *or* 14 (3 *r.*).
606 2 r. Type **334** 20 25
607 3 r. W.C.Y. emblem (*different*) (33 × 33 *mm*) 30 35

335 Farm Animals

336 Agricultural Produce and Fertiliser Factory

(Des A. Salahuddin)

1983 (24 Oct). *World Food Day. T* **335** *and similar horiz designs. Multicoloured. P* 13.
608 3 r. Type **335** 30 35
609 3 r. Fruit 30 35
610 3 r. Crops 30 35
611 3 r. Sea food 30 35
Nos. 608/11 were printed together, *se-tenant*, in horizontal strips of four throughout the sheet.

(Des J. Sultana)

1983 (24 Oct). *National Fertiliser Corporation. P* 13 × 13½.
612 **336** 60 p. multicoloured 5 5

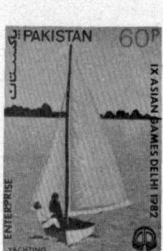

337 Lahore, 1852

338 Winner of "Enterprise" Event

(Des A. Salahuddin)

1983 (13 Nov). *National Stamp Exhibition, Lahore. T* **337** *and similar vert designs showing panoramic view of Lahore in* 1852. *Multicoloured. P* 13 × 13½.
613 60 p. Musti Durwaza Dharmsala 5 5
614 60 p. Khabgha 5 5
615 60 p. Type **337** 5 5
616 60 p. Summan Burj Hazuri 5 5
617 60 p. Flower Garden, Samadhi Northern Gate 5 5
618 60 p. Budda Darya, Badshahi Masjid 5 5
613/18 .. .. *Set of* 6 30 30
Nos. 613/18 were printed together, *se-tenant* in sheets of twelve, containing two horizontal strips of six.

(Des J. Sultana)

1983 (31 Dec). *Yachting Champions, Asian Games, Delhi. T* **338** *and similar vert design. Multicoloured. P* 13.
619 60 p. Type **338** 5 5
620 60 p. Winner of "OK" Dinghy event 5 5

339 Snow Leopard

(Litho Secura, Singapore)

1984 (21 Jan). *Wildlife Protection* (*12th series*). *Matt, almost invisible PVA gum. P* 14.
621 **339** 40 p. multicoloured 5 5
622 1 r. 60, multicoloured 20 25

340 Jahangir Khan (World Squash Champion)

341 P.I.A. Airliner

1984 (17 Mar). *Squash. P* 13.
623 **340** 3 r. multicoloured 35 40

(Des A. Salahuddin)

1984 (29 Apr). *20th Anniv of Pakistan International Airways' Service to China. P* 13.
624 **341** 3 r. multicoloured 35 40

342 Glass-work

343 Attock Fort

(Des A. Salahuddin. Litho Secura, Singapore)

1984 (31 May). *Handicrafts (4th series).* T **342** *and similar designs showing glass-work in Sheesh Mahal, Lahore Fort. P* 13½.

625 1 r. multicoloured (blue frame) 10 12
626 1 r. multicoloured (red frame) 10 12
627 1 r. multicoloured (green frame) (*horiz*) 10 12
628 1 r. multicoloured (violet frame) (*horiz*) 10 12

(Des J. Sultana)

1984 (16 June–1 Nov). *Forts.* T **343** *and similar horiz designs. P* 11.

629 5 p. brownish black and brown-purple (1.11.84) 5 5
630 10 p. brownish black and rose-red (25.9.84) 5 5
631 20 p. black and bright reddish violet 5 5
632 60 p. blackish brown and light brown 5 8

Design:—5 p. Kot Diji Fort; 10 p. Rohtas Fort; 60 p. Lahore Fort.
Numbers have been reserved for future additions to this set.

344 Shah Rukn i Alam's Tomb, Multan

1984 (26 June). *Aga Khan Award for Architecture. P* 13.

647 **344** 60 p. multicoloured 8 10

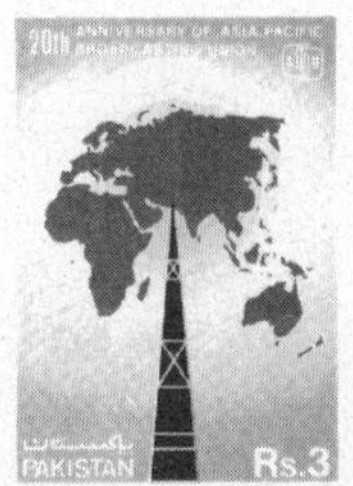

345 Radio Mast and Map of World

1984 (1 July). *20th Anniv of Asia–Pacific Broadcasting Union. P* 13.

648 **345** 3 r. multicoloured 35 40

346 Wrestling

(Des A. Salahuddin)

1984 (31 July). *Olympic Games, Los Angeles.* T **346** *and similar horiz designs. Multicoloured. P* 13.

649 3 r. Type **346** 35 40
650 3 r. Boxing 35 40
651 3 r. Athletics 35 40
652 3 r. Hockey 35 40
653 3 r. Yachting 35 40

347 Jasmine (National flower) and Inscription

(Des M. Munawar)

1984 (14 Aug). *Independence Day.* T **347** *and similar horiz design. Multicoloured. P* 13.

654 60 p. Type **347** 5 8
655 4 r. Symbolic torch 45 50

OFFICIAL STAMPS

PAKISTAN

(O 1)

1947. *Official stamps of India, Nos.* O143/50, *optd as Type* O **1** *and Nos.* O138/41 *optd as* T **2** *by litho, at Nasik.*

O 1 O **20** 3 p. slate 5 5
O 2 ½ a. purple 8 5
O 3 9 p. green 8 15
O 4 1 a. carmine 8 5
O 5 1½ a. dull violet 8 5
O 6 2 a. vermilion 15 5
O 7 2½ a. bright violet 30 45
O 8 4 a. brown 20 10
O 9 8 a. slate-violet 30 20
O10 **93** 1 r. grey and red-brown 50 15
O11 2 r. purple and brown 1·50 60
O12 5 r. green and blue 7·00 9·00
O13 10 r. purple and claret 16·00 25·00
O1/13 *Set of* 13 24·00 32·00

See note after No. 19. The 1 a. 3 p. (India, No. O146*a*) exists only as a local issue (*price*, Karachi opt, £2 *un.*, £2·25 *us.*).

SERVICE (O 2) **SERVICE** (O 3) **SERVICE** (O 4)

NOTE. Apart from a slight difference in size, Types O **2** and O **3** can easily be distinguished by the difference in the shape of the "c". Type O **4** is taller and thinner in appearance.

PRINTERS. Type O **2** was overprinted by De La Rue and Types O **3** and O **4** by the Pakistan Security Ptg Corp.

1948 (14 Aug)–54? *Optd with Type* O **2**.

O14 **7** 3 p. red (No. 24) 10 5
O15 6 p. violet (No. 25) (R.) 10 5
O16 9 p. green (No. 26) (R.) 10 5
O17 **8** 1 a. blue (No. 27) (R.) 60 5
O18 1½ a. grey-green (No. 28) (R.) 60 5
O19 2 a. red (No. 29) 85 5
O20 **10** 3 a. green (No. 31) 75 1·00
O21 **9** 4 a. reddish brown (No. 33) 60 5
O22 – 8 a. black (No. 35) (R.) 60 90
O23 – 1 r. ultramarine (No. 38) 1·00 15
O24 – 2 r. chocolate (No. 39) 2·00 1·00
O25 – 5 r. carmine (No. 40) 2·50 2·75
O26 **13** 10 r. magenta (No. 41) 8·50 12·00
a. Perf 12 (10.10.51) 8·50 12·00
b. Perf 13 (1954?) 9·00 15·00
O14/26 *Set of* 13 17·00 16·00

1949. *Optd with Type* O **2**.

O27 1 a. blue (No. 47) (R.) 30 5
O28 1½ a. grey-green (No. 48) (R.) 30 5
a. Opt inverted — 23·00
O29 2 a. red (No. 49) 70 5
a. Opt omitted (in pair with normal)
O30 3 a. green (No. 50) 1·75 2·25
O31 8 a. black (No. 52) (R.) 3·00 3·25

1951 (14 Aug). *4th Anniv of Independence. As Nos.* 56, 58 *and* 60, *but inscr* "SERVICE" *instead of* "PAKISTAN POSTAGE".

O32 **18** 3 a. purple 55 90
O33 **19** 4 a. green 45 8
O34 **20** 8 a. sepia 1·75 70

1953. *Optd with Type* O **3**.

O35 3 p. red (No. 24a) 5 5
O36 6 p. violet (No. 25a) (R.) 8 5
O37 9 p. green (No. 26a) (R.) 10 5
O38 1 a. blue (No. 47a) (R.) 12 5
O39 1½ a. grey-green (No. 48a) (R.) 12 5
O40 2 a. red (No. 49a) (1953?) 15 5
O41 1 r. ultramarine (No. 38a) 1·75 20
O42 2 r. chocolate (No. 39a) 1·75 30
O43 5 r. carmine (No. 40a) 4·25 80
O44 10 r. magenta (No. 41b) (date?) 7·50 13·00
O35/44 *Set of* 10 14·00 13·00

1954 (14 Aug). *Seventh Anniv of Independence. Nos.* 65/71 *optd with Type* O **3**.

O45 6 p. reddish violet (R.) 10 10
O46 9 p. blue (R.) 15 60
O47 1 a. carmine 15 10
O48 1½ a. red 15 10
O49 14 a. deep green (R.) 45 70
O50 1 r. green (R.) 50 20
O51 2 r. red-orange 1·25 60
O45/51 *Set of* 7 2·50 2·25

1955 (14 Aug). *Eighth Anniv of Independence. No.* 75 *optd with Type* O **3**.

O52 8 a. deep reddish violet (R.) 15 10

1957 (Jan)–59. *Nos.* 65/71 *optd with Type* O **4**.

O53 6 p. reddish violet (R.) 5 5
a. Opt inverted † —
O54 9 p. blue (R.) (1.59) 5 25
a. Opt inverted
O55 1 a. carmine 5 5
a. Opt inverted
O56 1½ a. red 5 5
a. Opt double
O57 14 a. deep green (R.) (2.59) 40 70
O58 1 r. green (R.) (4.58) 40 10
O59 2 r. red-orange (4.58) 2·00 30
O53/9 *Set of* 7 2·75 1·25

1958 (Jan)–61. *Optd with Type* O **4**.

O60 **7** 3 p. red (No. 24a) 5 5
O61 – 5 r. carmine (No. 40a) (7.59) 2·75 1·25
O62 **41** 10 r. myrtle-green and yellow-orange (No. 89) (R.) (1961) 6·00 4·75
a. Opt inverted

1958 (Jan)–61. *Nos.* 74/5 *optd with Type* O **4**.

O63 6 a. deep ultramarine (R.) (4.61) 20 20
O64 8 a. deep reddish violet (R.) 20 5

1959 (Aug). *No.* 83 *optd with Type* O **4**.

O65 **37** 2 a. scarlet 5 5

1961 (Apr). *Nos.* 110/11 *optd with Type* O **4**.

O66 **51** 8 a. deep green 20 10
O67 1 r. blue 20 10
a. Opt inverted 5·00

NEW CURRENCY. In addition to the local *handstamped* surcharges mentioned in the note above No. 122, the following *typographed* surcharges were made at the Treasury at Mastung and issued in the Baluchi province of Kalat: 6 p. on 1 a. (No. O55), 9 p. on 1½ a. (No. O56) and 13 p. on 2 a. (No. O65). They differ in that the surcharges are smaller and "PAISA" is expressed as "Paisa". Being locals they are outside the scope of this catalogue.

1961. *Optd with Type* O **4**.

O68 1 p. on 1½ a. (No. 122) 5 5
a. Optd with Type O **3** 40 40
O69 2 p. on 3 p. (No. 123) (1.1.61) 5 5
a. Surch double
b. Optd with Type O **3** 1·25 1·25
O70 3 p. on 6 p. (No. 124) 5 5
O71 7 p. on 1 a. (No. 125) 5 5
a. Optd with Type O **3** 1·50 1·50
O72 13 p. on 2 a. (No. 126) 5 5
O73 13 p. on 2 a. (No. 127) 5 5
O68/73 *Set of* 6 25 25

No. O68 exists with small and large "1" (see note below Nos. 122/7, etc.).

ERRORS. See note after No. 127.

SERVICE

(O 5)

1961–63. *Nos.* 128/44*b optd with Type* O **4** (*rupee values*) *or* O **5** (*others*). (*a*) *Inscribed* "SHAKISTAN".

O74 1 p. violet (R.) (1.1.61) 5 5
O75 2 p. rose-red (R.) (12.1.61) 5 5
O76 5 p. ultramarine (R.) (23.3.61) 10 10

(*b*) *Inscribed* "PAKISTAN"

O77 1 p. violet (R.) 5 5
O78 2 p. rose-red (R.) 5 5
O79 3 p. reddish purple (R.) (27.10.61) 5 5
O80 5 p. ultramarine (R.) 5 5
O81 7 p. emerald (R.) (23.3.61) 5 5
O82 10 p. brown (R.) 5 5
a. Opt inverted
O83 13 p. slate-violet (R.) (14.2.61) 10 5
O85 40 p. deep purple (R.) (1.1.62) 10 5
O86 50 p. deep bluish green (R.) (1.1.62) 15 5
a. Opt double † —
O87 75 p. carmine-red (R.) (23.3.62) 20 5
a. Opt double
O88 1 r. vermilion (7.1.63) 35 5
a. Opt double
b. Opt as Type O **3**
c. Opt inverted
O89 2 r. orange (7.1.63) 1·25 50
O90 5 r. green (R.) (7.1.63) 2·75 2·00
O74/90 *Set of* 16 5·00 3·00

1963–78? *Nos.* 170, *etc., optd with Type* O **5**, *in red.*

O 91 1 p. violet 5 5
O 92 2 p. rose-red (1965) 5 5
a. Opt inverted
b. Albino opt
c. Opt double, one albino
O 93 3 p. reddish purple (1967) 5 5
a. Opt double
b. Opt inverted
O 94 5 p. ultramarine 5 5
a. Opt inverted
ab. Vert pair, top stamp without opt, lower with opt inverted
O 95 7 p. emerald (date?) 80 5
O 96 10 p. brown (1965) 5 5
a. Opt inverted
O 97 13 p. slate-violet 5 5
O 98 15 p. bright purple (31.12.64) 5 5
O 99 20 p. myrtle-green (26.1.70) 5 5
a. Opt double 20·00
O100 25 p. deep blue (1977) 15 5
O101 40 p. deep purple (1972?) 15 5
O102 50 p. deep bluish green (1965) 10 5
O103 75 p. carmine-red (date?) 30 10
O104 90 p. yellow-green (5.78?) 30 25
O91/104 *Set of* 14 1·90 80

1968–(?). *Nos.* 204, 206 *and* 207 *optd with Type* O **4**.

O105 **62** 1 r. vermilion 30 8
a. Opt inverted 8·00
O107 2 r. orange (date?) 45 15
a. Opt inverted
O108 5 r. green (R.) (date?) 1·00 65
a. Opt inverted

1979–80? *Nos.* 464/72, 473*b and* 475/8 *optd as Type* O **5** *in black* (2 *r.*) *or in red* (*reading vertically downwards on* 2, 3 *and* 5 *p.*) (*others*).

O109 **275** 2 p. deep grey-green 5 5
O110 3 p. black 5 5
O111 5 p. deep ultramarine 5 5
a. Opt reading upwards
b. Vert pair, top stamp without opt
O112 **276** 10 p. new blue and greenish blue 5 5
O113 20 p. deep yellow-green 5 5
O114 25 p. deep green and dull magenta 5 5
O115 40 p. new blue and magenta 5 5
a. Opt inverted
b. Albino opt 10·00
O116 50 p. slate-lilac and turquoise-green 5 5
O117 60 p. black 5 5
O118 75 p. dull vermilion (Die II) (1980) 8 8
O119 **276***a* 1 r. bronze-green (1980) 10 10
O120 1 r. 50, red-orange (1979) 15 15
O121 2 r. carmine-red (1979) 20 25
O122 3 r. blue-black (1980) 30 30
O109/22 *Set of* 14 75 75

(Des and litho Secura, Singapore)

1980 (15 Jan–10 Mar). *As Nos.* 513/19 *but inscr* "SERVICE". *P* 12.

No.	Type	Description	Unused	Used
O125	**291**	10 p. slate-green and orange-yellow ..	5	5
O126		15 p. slate-green & brt yellow-green ..	5	5
O127		25 p. violet and brown-red (10 Mar) ..	5	5
O128		35 p. carmine & brt yell-grn (10 Mar) ..	5	5
O129	–	40 p. rosine and olive-sepia	5	5
O130	–	50 p. violet & dull yell-green (10 Mar)	5	5
O131	–	80 p. brt yellow-green & blk (10 Mar) ..	8	10
O125/31		.. .. *Set of* 7	20	20

BAHAWALPUR

PRICES FOR STAMPS ON COVER TO 1945

Nos. O1/2	*from* × 30
Nos. O7/13	*from* × 5
Nos. O14/18	*from* × 30

(1)

1947 (15 Aug). *Nos.* 265/8, 269*a*/77 *and* 259/62 *of India optd locally with T* 1.

No.	Type	Description	Unused
1	**100*a***	3 p. slate (R.)	3·00
2		½ a. purple	3·00
3		9 p. green (R.)	3·00
4		1 a. carmine	3·00
5	**101**	1½ a. dull violet (R.)	4·00
6		2 a. vermilion	4·00
7		3 a. bright violet (R.)	4·00
8		3½ a. bright blue (R.)	4·00
9	**102**	4 a. brown	5·00
10		6 a. turquoise-green (R.)	5·00
11		8 a. slate-violet (R.)	5·00
12		12 a. lake	5·00
13	**103**	14 a. purple	35·00
14	**93**	1 r. grey and red-brown	15·00
15		2 r. purple and brown (R.)	£200
16		5 r. green and blue (R.)	£225
17		10 r. purple and claret	£250
1/17		.. .. *Set of* 17	£700

Nos. 1/17 were issued during the interim period, following the implementation of the Indian Independence Act, during which time Bahawalpur was part of neither of the two Dominions created. The Amir acceded to the Dominion of Pakistan on 3 October 1947 and these overprinted stamps of India were then withdrawn.

The stamps of Bahawalpur only had validity for use within the state. For external mail Pakistan stamps were used.

PRINTERS. All the following issues were recess-printed by De La Rue & Co, Ltd, London.

2 Amir Muhammad Bahawal Khan I Abbasi

3

1948. *Bicentenary Commemoration. W* 3 (*sideways*). *P* 12½ × 11½.

No.	Type	Description	Unused	Used
18	**2**	½ a. black and carmine	20	1·75

4 H.H. the Amir of Bahawalpur

5 The Tombs of the Amirs

6 Mosque in Sadiq-Garh

7 Fort Derawar, from the Lake

8 Nur-Mahal Palace

9 The Palace, Sadiq-Garh

10 H.H. the Amir of Bahawalpur

11 Three Generations of Rulers; H.H. the Amir in centre

1948 (1 Apr). *W* 3 (*sideways on vert designs*). *P* 12½ (*T* 4), 11½ × 12½ (*T* 5, 7, 8 *and* 9), 12½ × 11½ (*T* 6 *and* 10) *or* 13½ × 14 (*T* 11).

No.	Type	Description	Unused
19	**4**	3 p. black and blue	20
20		½ a. black and claret	20
21		9 p. black and green	20
22		1 a. black and carmine	20
23		1½ a. black and violet	20
24	**5**	2 a. green and carmine	20
25	**6**	4 a. orange and brown	25
26	**7**	6 a. violet and blue	30
27	**8**	8 a. carmine and violet	35
28	**9**	12 a. green and carmine	45
29	**10**	1 r. violet and brown	60
30		2 r. green and claret	1·00
31		5 r. black and violet	2·25
32	**11**	10 r. scarlet and black	5·00

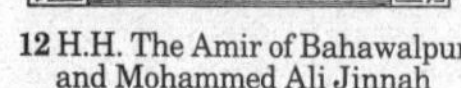

12 H.H. The Amir of Bahawalpur and Mohammed Ali Jinnah

13 Soldiers of 1848 and 1948

1948 (3 Oct). *First Anniv of Union of Bahawalpur with Pakistan. W* 3. *P* 13.

No.	Type	Description	Unused	Used
33	**12**	1½ a. carmine and blue-green	10	1·00

1948 (15 Oct). *Multan Campaign Centenary. W* 3. *P* 11½.

No.	Type	Description	Unused	Used
34	**13**	1½ a. black and lake	20	1·75

1948. *As Nos.* 29/32, *but colours changed.*

No.	Type	Description	Unused
35	**10**	1 r. deep green and orange	20
36		2 r. black and carmine	30
37		5 r. chocolate and ultramarine	50
38	**11**	10 r. red-brown and green	85

14 Irrigation

17 U.P.U. Monument, Berne

1949 (3 Mar). *Silver Jubilee of Accession of H.H. the Amir of Bahawalpur. T* 14 *and similar horiz designs. W* 3. *P* 14.

No.	Description	Unused
39	3 p. black and ultramarine	5
40	½ a. black and brown-orange	5
41	9 p. black and green	5
42	1 a. black and carmine	5

Designs:—½ a. Wheat; 9 p. Cotton; 1 a. Sahiwal bull.

1949 (10 Oct). *75th Anniv of Universal Postal Union. W* 3. *P* 13.

No.	Type	Description	Unused	Used
43	**17**	9 p. black and green	25	2·50
		a. Perf 17½ × 17	1·25	4·50
44		1 a. black and magenta	25	2·50
		a. Perf 17½ × 17	1·25	4·50
45		1½ a. black and orange	25	2·50
		a. Perf 17½ × 17	1·25	4·50
46		2½ a. black and blue	25	2·50
		a. Perf 17½ × 17	1·25	4·50

OFFICIAL STAMPS

O 1 Panjnad Weir

O 2 Camel and Calf

O 3 Blackbuck Antelope

O 4 Eastern White Pelicans

O 5 Juma Masjid Palace, Fort Derawar

O 6 Temple at Pattan Munara

1945 (1 Jan). *Various horizontal pictorial designs, with red Arabic opt. W* 3. *P* 14.

No.	Type	Description	Unused	Used
O1	**O 1**	½ a. black and green	95	2·00
O2	**O 2**	1 a. black and carmine	1·60	1·50
O3	**O 3**	2 a. black and violet	2·50	2·50
O4	**O 4**	4 a. black and olive-green	5·00	4·75
O5	**O 5**	8 a. black and brown	3·00	5·50
O6	**O 6**	1 r. black and orange	3·00	5·50

Stamps without overprint must be regarded as being ordinary revenue stamps, unless found *se-tenant* with overprinted stamps.

O 7 Baggage Camels

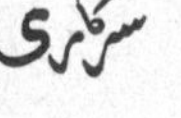

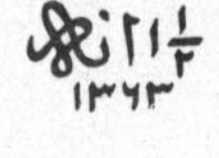

(O 8)

1945 (10 Mar). *Red Arabic opt. No wmk. P* 14.

No.	Type	Description	Unused	Used
O7	**O 7**	1 a. black and brown	25·00	32·00

1945 (Mar–June). *Surch as Type* O 8 (*at Security Printing Press, Nasik*) *instead of red Arabic opt. No wmk. P* 14.

No.	Type	Description	Unused	Used
O11	**O 5**	½ a. on 8 a. black and purple	4·25	1·75
O12	**O 6**	1½ a. on 1 r. black and orange	9·00	2·50
O13	**O 1**	1½ a. on 2 r. black and blue (1 June) ..	16·00	3·50

SERVICE

(O 9)

O 10 H.H. the Amir of Bahawalpur

1945. *Optd with Type* O 9 (*by D.L.R.*) *instead of red Arabic opt. No wmk. P* 14.

No.	Type	Description	Unused	Used
O14	**O 1**	½ a. black and carmine	1·00	2·25
O15	**O 2**	1 a. black and carmine	1·75	2·50
O16	**O 3**	2 a. black and orange	3·50	7·50

1945. *P* 14.

No.	Type	Description	Unused	Used
O17	**O 10**	3 p. black and blue	25	1·25
O18		1½ a. black and violet	1·25	4·50

O 11 Allied Banners

(Des E. Meronti. Recess, background litho)

1946 (May). *Victory. P* 14.

No.	Type	Description	Unused	Used
O19	**O 11**	1½ a. green and grey	1·25	1·25

NEW INFORMATION

The editor is always interested to correspond with people who have new information that will improve or correct the Catalogue.

1948. *Nos.* 19, 22, 24/5 *and* 35/8 *optd as Nos.* O1/6.

O20 4 3 p. black and blue (R.) .. .. .. 10 2·00
O21 1 a. black and carmine (Blk.) .. .. 10 2·00
O22 5 2 a. green and carmine (Blk.) .. .. 10 3·00
O23 6 4 a. orange and brown (Blk.) .. .. 10 3·00
O24 10 1 r. deep green and orange (R.) .. .. 15 4·00
O25 2 r. black and carmine (R.) .. .. 25 6·00
O26 5 r. chocolate and ultramarine (R.) .. 40 10·00
O27 11 10 r. red-brown and green (R.) .. .. 75 15·00

1949 (10 Oct). *75th Anniv of Universal Postal Union. Nos.* 43/6 *optd as Nos.* O1/6.

O28 17 9 p. black and green .. .. .. 15 4·50
a. Perf 17½ × 17 .. .. .. 1·75 9·00
O29 1 a. black and magenta .. .. .. 15 4·50
a. Perf 17½ × 17 .. .. .. 1·75 9·00
O30 1½ a. black and orange .. .. .. 15 4·50
a. Perf 17½ × 17 .. .. .. 1·75 9·00
O31 2½ a. black and blue .. .. .. 15 4·50
a. Perf 17½ × 17 .. .. .. 1·75 9·00

Since 1949 only Pakistan stamps have been used in Bahawalpur for both internal and external mail.

Palestine

The stamps of TURKEY were used in Palestine from 1865.
In addition various European Powers, and Egypt, maintained post offices at Jerusalem (Austria, France, Germany, Italy, Russia), Jaffa (Austria, France, Egypt, France, Germany, Russia) and Haifa (Austria, France) using their own stamps or issues specially prepared for Levant post offices. All foreign post offices had closed by the time of the British Occupation.

PRICES FOR STAMPS ON COVER TO 1945

No. 1	*from* × 4
No. 2	*from* × 2
Nos. 3/4	*from* × 5
Nos. 5/15	*from* × 4
Nos. 16/29	*from* × 3
Nos. 30/42	*from* × 2
No. 43	—
Nos. 44/57	*from* × 2
Nos. 58/9	—
Nos. 60/8	*from* × 3
Nos. 69/70	—
Nos. 71/89	*from* × 3
Nos. 90/103	*from* × 4
Nos. 104/11	*from* × 8
Nos. D1/5	*from* × 25
Nos. D6/20	*from* × 10

BRITISH MILITARY OCCUPATION

Valid also for use in Transjordan, Cilicia, Northern Egypt and Syria.

1

(2)

3

"E.E.F." = Egyptian Expeditionary Force

(Litho Typographical Dept, Survey of Egypt, Giza, Cairo)

1918 (10 Feb). *Wmk Royal Cypher in column* (W **100** *of Great Britain*). *Ungummed. Roul* 20.

1 1 1 p. indigo (Optd S. £550) £250 £175
a. Deep blue £225 £150
b. Blue £250 £175

Control: A 18. (*Prices, corner block of* 4; No. 1, £1200. No. 1*a*, £1100. No. 1*b*, £1200.)

1918 (16 Feb). *As last* (*ungummed*), *surch with T* **2**.

2 1 5 m. on 1 p. cobalt-blue (Optd S. £550) .. £140 £800
a. "MILLILMES" (No. 10 in sheet) .. £2750

Control: B 18 A. (*Corner block*, £1500.)

1918 (5 Mar). *As No.* 1 *but colour changed. With gum.*

3 1 1 p. ultramarine .. .. 3·50 3·50

Control: C 18. (*Corner block*, £75.)

1918 (5 Mar *and* 13 May). *No.* 3 *surch with T* **2**.

4 1 5 m. on 1 p. ultramarine .. .. .. 7·00 6·00
a. Arabic surch wholly or partly missing (No. 11 in sheet) £400

Controls: C 18 B (Mar). (*Corner block*, £750.)
D 18 C (May). (*Corner block*, £175.)

(Typo Stamping Dept, Board of Inland Revenue, Somerset House, London)

1918 (16 July–27 Dec). *Wmk Royal Cypher in column. P* 15 × 14.

5 3 1 m. sepia 30 30
a. Deep brown 35 35
6 2 m. blue-green 30 30
a. Deep green 40 40
7 3 m. yellow-brown (17 Dec) 40 40
a. Chestnut .. .. .. 10·00 7·00
8 4 m. scarlet 40 40
9 5 m. yellow-orange (25 Sept) 40 30
a. Orange 60 50
10 3 1 p. deep indigo (9 Nov) 40 15
11 2 p. pale olive 75 75
a. Olive .. .. .. 1·00 1·00
12 5 p. purple .. .. .. 2·00 3·00
13 9 p. ochre (17 Dec) .. .. .. 3·00 4·50
14 10 p. ultramarine (17 Dec) .. .. 3·00 4·50
15 20 p. pale grey (27 Dec) .. .. .. 8·50 16·00
a. Slate-grey .. .. .. 15·00 22·00
5/15 .. .. *Set of* 11 20·00 30·00

There are two sizes of the design of this issue:
19 × 23 mm. 1, 2, and 4 m., and 2 and 5 p.
18 × 21½ mm. 3 and 5 m., and 1, 9, 10 and 20 p.
There are numerous minor plate varieties in this issue, such as stops omitted in "E.E.F.", malformed Arabic characters, etc.

Originally issued by the Military Authorities for use of the civil population in occupied enemy territories (including at one time or another, a large part of Asia Minor), these stamps were used in Palestine until superseded by the following issue. They were demonetised on 1 May, 1922.

CIVIL ADMINISTRATION UNDER BRITISH HIGH COMMISSIONER

Palestine was placed under civil administration by a British High Commissioner on 1 July 1920.

فلسطين PALESTINE פלשתינה א״י (4) — فلسطين PALESTINE פלשתינה א״י (5) — فلسطين PALESTINE פלשתינה א״י (6)

Differences:—
T **5**. 20 mm vert and 7 mm between English and Hebrew.
T **6**. 19 mm and 6 mm respectively.

(Optd at Greek Orthodox Convent, Jerusalem)

1920 (1 Sept). *Optd with T* **4** (*Arabic* 8 *mm long*). (*a*) *P* 15 × 14.

16 3 1 m. sepia .. .. 1·75 1·75
17 2 m. blue-green .. .. .. 8·00 4·00
18 3 m. chestnut .. .. .. 4·00 4·00
a. Opt inverted £500 £600
19 4 m. scarlet .. .. .. 1·60 1·90
20 5 m. yellow-orange .. .. .. 6·00 4·00
21 1 p. deep indigo (Sil.) .. .. .. 1·75 1·50
22 2 p. deep olive .. .. .. 1·75 2·25
23 5 p. deep purple .. .. .. 8·00 16·00
24 9 p. ochre .. .. 9·00 20·00
25 10 p. ultramarine .. .. .. 10·00 19·00
26 20 p. pale grey .. .. .. 15·00 30·00

(*b*) *P* 14

27 3 2 m. blue-green .. .. .. 1·75 2·00
28 3 m. chestnut .. .. .. 38·00 45·00
29 5 m. orange .. .. .. 1·75 1·25
16/29 .. .. .. *Set of* 14 £100 £145

Two settings of T **4** are known to specialists, the first being used for all values perf 15 × 14 except the 1 p. and the second for all values in both perfs.
Apart from minor varieties due to broken type, there are three major errors which are rare in some values. These are (*a*) two Hebrew characters at left transposed (all values of first setting only); (*b*) diamond-shaped dot over the Arabic "t" making the word read "Faleszin" for "Falestin" (2 p. to 20 p. of first setting and 1 m. and 3 m. perf 15 × 14, and 5 m. perf 14 of second setting); (*c*) "B" for final "E" of "PALESTINE" (2 p. to 20 p. of first setting and all values of second setting except 3 m. perf 14).
Faulty registration of the overprint in this issue has resulted in numerous misplaced overprints, either vertically or horizontally, which are not of great importance with the exception of Nos. 21 and 29 which exist with the overprint out of sequence, i.e. Hebrew/Arabic/English or English/Arabic/Hebrew or English/Hebrew only. Also all values are known with Arabic/English only.

1920 (22 Sept)–**21**. *Optd with T* **5*** (*Arabic* 10 *mm long*).

(*a*) *P* 15 × 14

30 3 1 m. sepia (27.12.20) .. .. .. 75 1·00
a. Opt inverted .. .. .. £400 †
31 2 m. blue-green (27.12.20) .. .. 3·00 4·00
32 3 m. yellow-brown (27.12.20) .. .. 75 1·00
33 4 m. scarlet (27.12.20) .. .. 1·00 1·50
34 5 m. yellow-orange .. .. .. 3·00 1·00
35 1 p. deep indigo (Silver) (21.6.21) .. £650 17·00
36 2 p. olive (21.6.21) .. .. .. 60·00 26·00
37 5 p. deep purple (21.6.21) .. .. 25·00 10·00

(*b*) *P* 14

38 3 1 m. sepia £550 £650
39 2 m. blue-green .. .. .. 3·00 4·00
40 4 m. scarlet .. .. .. 65·00 80·00
41 5 m. orange .. .. .. £110 14·00
a. Yellow-orange .. .. .. 2·00 1·75
42 1 p. deep indigo (Silver) .. .. 28·00 2·50
43 5 p. purple £200 £375
30/43 (*cheapest*) .. .. *Set of* 8 £110 50·00

*In this setting the Arabic and Hebrew characters are badly worn and blunted, the Arabic "S" and "T" are joined (i.e. there is no break in the position indicated by the arrow in our illustration); the letters of "PALESTINE" are often irregular or broken; and the space between the two groups of Hebrew characters varies from 1 mm to over 1¾ mm. (*For clear, sharp overprint, see Nos.* 47/59.)
The dates of issue given are irrespective of the perforations, i.e. one or both perfs could have been issued on the dates shown.
Nos. 31 and 39 exist with any one line of the overprint both partly and almost completely missing.

1920 (6 Dec). *Optd with T* **6**. (*a*) *P* 15 × 14.

44 3 3 m. yellow-brown .. .. .. 35·00 42·00
44*a* 5 m. yellow-orange £12000 £7500

(*b*) *P* 14

45 3 1 m. sepia .. .. 30·00 35·00
46 5 m. orange .. .. £500 35·00

1921 (29 May–4 Aug). *Optd as T* **5**†. (*a*) *P* 15 × 14.

47 3 1 m. sepia (23.6) .. .. .. 4·50 3·00
48 2 m. blue-green (23.6) .. .. .. 8·00 5·00
49 3 m. yellow-brown (23.6) .. .. .. 25·00 4·00
a. "PALESTINE" omitted £1750
50 4 m. scarlet (23.6) .. .. .. 20·00 4·50
51 5 m. yellow-orange .. .. .. 22·00 2·00
52 1 p. deep indigo (Silver) (July) .. 20·00 1·00
53 2 p. olive (4.8) .. .. .. 30·00 8·50
54 5 p. purple (4.8) .. .. .. 25·00 15·00
55 9 p. ochre (4.8) .. .. .. 45·00 £120
56 10 p. ultramarine (4.8) .. .. 45·00 20·00
57 20 p. pale grey (4.8) .. .. .. 90·00 65·00
47/57 .. .. .. *Set of* 11 £325 £245

(*b*) *P* 14

58 3 1 m. sepia .. .. — £2500
59 20 p. pale grey £9000 £2750

†In this setting the Arabic and Hebrew characters are sharp and pointed as in T **6**; there is usually a break between the Arabic "S" and "T" though this is sometimes filled with ink; and the whole overprint is much clearer. The space between the two groups of Hebrew characters is always 1¾ mm.

فلسطين PALESTINE פלשתינה א״י (7) — فلسطين PALESTINE פלשתינה א״י (8)

1921 (Sept–Oct). *Optd with T* **7** ("PALESTINE" *in sans-serif letters*) *by Stamping Dept, Board of Inland Revenue, Somerset House, London. Wmk Royal Cypher in column. P* 15 × 14.

60 3 1 m. sepia 30 25
61 2 m. blue-green 30 30
62 3 m. yellow-brown 30 20
63 4 m. scarlet 40 50
64 5 m. yellow-orange 55 25
65 1 p. bright turquoise-blue 80 25
66 2 p. olive .. .. 1·25 55
67 5 p. deep purple .. .. .. 4·75 6·00
68 9 p. ochre .. .. 11·00 13·00
69 10 p. ultramarine .. .. .. 13·00 £400
70 20 p. pale grey .. .. .. 50·00 £850
60/70 .. .. .. *Set of* 11 75·00

(Printed and optd by Waterlow & Sons from new plates)

1922 (Sept–Nov). *T* **3** (*redrawn*), *optd with T* **8**. *Wmk Mult Script CA.* (*a*) *P* 14.

71 3 1 m. sepia 30 15
a. Deep brown 35 15
b. Opt inverted .. .. .. — £7500
c. Opt double £250 £325
72 2 m. yellow 50 35
a. Orange-yellow .. .. .. 1·75 95
73 3 m. greenish blue 50 15
74 4 m. carmine-pink 35 30
75 5 m. orange 50 15
76 6 m. blue-green 80 50
77 7 m. yellow-brown .. .. .. 1·00 50
78 8 m. scarlet 80 35
79 1 p. grey .. .. 1·00 25
80 13 m. ultramarine 90 25
81 2 p. olive .. .. 2·00 60
a. Opt inverted £400 £400
b. Ochre .. .. .. £100 7·50
82 5 p. deep purple .. .. .. 6·00 2·00
82*a* 9 p. ochre £850 £250
83 10 p. light blue .. .. .. 24·00 9·00
a. "E.F.F." for "E.E.F." in bottom panel £600 £500
84 20 p. bright violet .. .. .. £120 90·00

(*b*) *P* 15 × 14

86 3 5 p. deep purple .. .. .. 32·00 4·00
87 9 p. ochre .. .. 14·00 13·00
88 10 p. light blue .. .. .. 10·00 4·50
a. "E.F.F." for "E.E.F." in bottom panel £500 £400
89 20 p. bright violet .. .. .. 14·00 12·00
71/89 (*cheapest*) .. .. *Set of* 15 50·00 35·00
71/89 Optd "Specimen" .. .. *Set of* 15 £550

Most values can be found on thin paper.
In this issue the design of all denominations is the same size, 18 mm × 21½ mm. Varieties may be found with one or other of the stops between "E.E.F." missing.

BRITISH MANDATE TO THE LEAGUE OF NATIONS

The League of Nations granted a mandate to Great Britain for the administration of Palestine on 29 September 1923.

9 Rachel's Tomb

10 Dome of the Rock

11 Citadel, Jerusalem

12 Sea of Galilee

(Des F. Taylor. Typo Harrison)

1927 (1 June)–**45**. *Wmk Mult Script CA. P* 13½ × 14½ (*2 m. to 20 m.*) *or* 14.

No.	Type	Description	Unused	Used
90	**9**	2 m. greenish blue (14.8.27)	12	12
91		3 m. yellow-green	12	12
92	**10**	4 m. rose-pink (14.8.27)	2·00	70
93	**11**	5 m. orange (14.8.27)	12	12
		a. From coils. Perf 14½ × 14 (1936)	4·00	5·00
		b. Yellow (12.44)	20	20
		c. Yellow. From coils. Perf 14½ × 14 (1945)	6·00	6·00
94	**10**	6 m. pale green (14.8.27)	1·50	1·00
		a. Deep green	15	15
95	**11**	7 m. scarlet (14.8.27)	2·50	50
96	**10**	8 m. yellow-brown (14.8.27)	10·00	5·00
97	**9**	10 m. slate (14.8.27)	15	10
		a. Grey. From coils. Perf 14½ × 14 (11.38)	5·00	5·50
		b. Grey (1944)	10	10
98	**10**	13 m. ultramarine	3·50	30
99	**11**	20 m. dull olive-green (14.8.27)	25	12
		a. Bright olive-green (12.44)	20	10
100	**12**	50 m. deep dull purple (14.8.27)	90	15
		a. Bright purple (12.44)	90	15
101		90 m. bistre (14.8.27)	50·00	50·00
102		100 m. turquoise-blue (14.8.27)	1·00	15
103		200 m. deep violet (14.8.27)	6·00	2·50
		a. Bright violet (1928)	11·00	6·00
		b. Blackish violet (12.44)	1·25	90
90/103*b*		*Set of* 14	65·00	50·00
90/103 H/S "Specimen"		*Set of* 14	£425	

Three sets may be made of the above issue; one on thin paper, one on thicker paper with a ribbed appearance, and another on thick white paper without ribbing.

2 m. stamps in the grey colour of the 10 m. exist as also 50 m. stamps in blue, but it has not been established whether they were issued.

1932 (1 June)–**44**. *New values and colours. Wmk Mult Script CA. P* 13½ × 14½ (*4 m. to 15 m.*) *or* 14.

No.	Type	Description	Unused	Used
104	**10**	4 m. purple (1.11.32)	12	12
105	**11**	7 m. deep violet	12	12
106	**10**	8 m. scarlet	12	12
107		13 m. bistre (1.8.32)	20	12
108		15 m. ultramarine (1.8.32)	35	12
		a. Grey-blue (12.44)	20	12
		b. Greenish blue	20	12
109	**12**	250 m. brown (15.1.42)	1·50	1·50
110		500 m. scarlet (15.1.42)	3·00	2·00
111		£P1 black (15.1.42)	5·00	2·50
104/11		*Set of* 8	10·00	6·00
104/11 Perf "Specimen"		*Set of* 8	£525	

POSTAL FISCALS

Type-set stamps inscribed "O.P.D.A." (= Ottoman Public Debt Administration) or "H.J.Z." (Hejaz Railway); British 1d. stamps (No. 336); and Palestine stamps overprinted with one or other of the above groups of letters, or with the word "Devair", with or without surcharge of new value, are fiscal stamps. They are known used as postage stamps, alone, or with other stamps to make up the correct rates, and were passed by the postal authorities, although they were not definitely authorised for postal use.

POSTAGE DUE STAMPS

D 1

D 2 (MILLIEME)

D 3 (MIL)

(Typo Greek Orthodox Convent, Jerusalem)

1923 (1 Apr). *P* 11.

No.	Type	Description	Unused	Used
D1	D **1**	1 m. yellow-brown	25·00	35·00
		a. Imperf (pair)	£500	
		b. Imperf between (horiz pair)	£700	
D2		2 m. blue-green	10·00	10·00
		a. Imperf (pair)	£550	
D3		4 m. scarlet	12·00	15·00
D4		8 m. mauve	6·00	6·50
		a. Imperf (pair)	£200	
		b. Imperf between (horiz pair)	—	£1800
D5		13 m. steel blue	7·50	7·50
		a. Imperf between (horiz pair)	£700	

Perfectly centred and perforated stamps of this issue are worth considerably more than the above prices, which are for average specimens.

(Types D **2/3**. Typo D.L.R.)

1924 (1 Dec). *Wmk Mult Script CA. P* 14.

No.	Type	Description	Unused	Used
D 6	D **2**	1 m. deep brown	90	1·25
D 7		2 m. yellow	1·00	1·25
D 8		4 m. green	1·10	1·25
D 9		8 m. scarlet	1·60	80
D10		13 m. ultramarine	2·50	2·50
D11		5 p. violet	5·00	1·75
D6/11		*Set of* 6	11·00	8·00
D6/11 Optd "Specimen"		*Set of* 6	£325	

1928 (1 Feb)–**45**. *Wmk Mult Script CA. P* 14.

No.	Type	Description	Unused	Used
D12	D **3**	1 m. brown	30	30
		a. Perf 15 × 14 (1944)	10·00	15·00
D13		2 m. yellow	30	35
D14		4 m. green	40	35
		a. Perf 15 × 14 (1945)	9·50	13·00
D15		6 m. orange-brown (10.33)	80	80
D16		8 m. carmine	55	50
D17		10 m. pale grey	55	50
D18		13 m. ultramarine	90	1·00
D19		20 m. pale olive-green	1·10	90
D20		50 m. violet	1·25	1·00
D12/20		*Set of* 9	5·50	5·00
D12/20 Perf (D15) or Optd (others) "Specimen"		*Set of* 9	£300	

The British Mandate terminated on 14 May 1948. Later issues of stamps and occupation issues will be found listed under Gaza, Israel and Jordan in Part 19 (*Middle East*) of this catalogue.

Papua (British New Guinea)

Stamps of QUEENSLAND were used in British New Guinea (Papua) from at least 1885 onwards. Post Offices were opened at Daru (1894), Kulumadau (Woodlarks) (1899), Nivani (1899), Port Moresby (1885), Samarai (1888), Sudest (1899) and Tamata (1899). Stamps were usually cancelled "N.G." (at Port Moresby from 1885) or "BNG" (without stops at Samarai or with stops at the other offices) from 1888. Queensland stamps were replaced in Papua by the issue of 1901.

PRICES FOR STAMPS ON COVER

Nos. 1/7	*from* × 3
No. 8	—
Nos. 9/14*a*	*from* × 3
Nos. 14*c*/21	*from* × 2
No. 22	—
Nos. 23/9*a*	*from* × 2
No. 29*b*	—
Nos. 30/2	*from* × 4
Nos. 34/8*b*	*from* × 3
No. 38*c*	—
Nos. 38*d*/65	*from* × 3
Nos. 66/71	*from* × 2
Nos. 72/4	—
Nos. 75/91	*from* × 3
Nos. 92/8	*from* × 6
Nos. 99/109	*from* × 3
Nos. 110/11	—
Nos. 112/14	*from* × 3
No. 115	—
Nos. 116/28	*from* × 3
Nos. 130/53	*from* × 2
Nos. 154/7	*from* × 5
Nos. 158/67	*from* × 3
No. 168	*from* × 2
Nos. O1/12	*from* × 5

1 Lakatoi (Native Canoe) with Hanuabada Village in Background

2 (Horizontal)

(Recess D.L.R.)

1901 (1 July)–**05**. *Wmk Mult Rosettes, W* **2**. *P* 14.

No.	Type	Description	Unused	Used
		I. *Thick paper. Wmk horizontal*		
1	**1**	½d. black and yellow-green	6·00	8·00
2		1d. black and carmine	4·50	6·50
3		2d. black and violet	7·00	7·00
4		2½d. black and ultramarine	13·00	16·00
5		4d. black and sepia	32·00	32·00
6		6d. black and myrtle-green	30·00	32·00
7		1s. black and orange	70·00	80·00
8		2s. 6d. black and brown (1905)	£750	£750
		II. *Thick paper. Wmk vertical*		
9	**1**	½d. black and yellow-green	4·00	4·50
10		1d. black and carmine	4·00	4·00
11		2d. black and violet	4·00	4·50
12		2½d. black and ultramarine	9·50	15·00
13		4d. black and sepia	45·00	48·00
14		6d. black and myrtle-green	55·00	70·00
14*a*		1s. black and orange	55·00	70·00
14*b*		2s. 6d. black and brown	£1100	£1100
		III. *Thin paper. Wmk horizontal*		
14*c*	**1**	½d. black and yellow-green	£140	£130
14*d*		2½d. black and ultramarine	£170	£150
14*e*		2½d. black and dull blue	£180	£160
		IV. *Thin paper. Wmk vertical*		
15	**1**	½d. black and yellow-green	8·00	10·00
16		1d. black and carmine	48·00	48·00
17		2d. black and violet	40·00	20·00
18		2½d. black and ultramarine	£170	£150
18*a*		2½d. black and dull blue	£170	£150
19		4d. black and sepia	£110	£120
20		6d. black and myrtle-green	£350	£375
21		1s. black and orange	£350	£375
22		2s. 6d. black and brown	£750	£750
1/22		*Set of* 8	£800	£800

The sheets of the ½d., 2d., and 2½d. show a variety known as "white leaves" on R. 4/5 while the 2d. and 2½d. (both R6/2) and the ½d. and 1s. (both R. 6/3) show what is known as the "unshaded leaves" variety.

Papua.
(3)

Papua.
(4)

1906–7. A. *Optd with T* **3** (*large opt*), *at Port Moresby* (8 Nov 1906).

No.	Type	Description	Unused	Used
		I. *Thick paper. Wmk horizontal*		
23	**1**	4d. black and sepia	£225	£225
24		6d. black and myrtle-green	24·00	30·00
25		1s. black and orange	18·00	24·00
26		2s. 6d. black and brown	£160	£170
		II. *Thick paper. Wmk vertical*		
27	**1**	2½d. black and ultramarine	6·50	12·00
28		4d. black and sepia	£190	£190
29		6d. black and myrtle-green	22·00	27·00
29*a*		1s. black and orange	£325	£325
29*b*		2s. 6d. black and brown	£1600	£1600
		III. *Thin paper. Wmk vertical*		
30	**1**	½d. black and yellow-green	6·00	8·00
31		1d. black and carmine	9·00	8·50
32		2d. black and violet	4·50	5·50
23/32 (*cheapest*)		*Set of* 8	£375	£375

B. *Optd with T* **4** (*small opt*), *at Brisbane* (May–June 1907)

No.	Type	Description	Unused	Used
		I. *Thick paper. Wmk horizontal*		
34	**1**	½d. black and yellow-green	29·00	45·00
35		2½d. black and ultramarine	65·00	85·00
36		1s. black and orange	60·00	75·00
37		2s. 6d. black and brown	42·00	48·00
		a. Opt reading downwards	£1300	
		c. Opt double (horiz)	—	£1300
		d. Opt triple (horiz)	—	£1100
		II. *Thick paper. Wmk vertical*		
38	**1**	2½d. black and ultramarine	5·50	8·00
		a. Opt double		
38*b*		1s. black and orange	60·00	65·00
38*c*		2s. 6d. black and brown	£1300	£1400
		III. *Thin paper. Wmk horizontal*		
38*d*	**1**	½d. black and yellow-green	75·00	75·00
39		2½d. black and ultramarine	13·00	24·00
		a. Opt double		
39*b*		2½d. black and dull blue	80·00	80·00
		IV. *Thin paper. Wmk vertical*		
40	**1**	½d. black and yellow-green	4·00	5·50
		a. Opt double	£1900	
41		1d. black and carmine	5·50	6·00
		a. Opt reading upwards	£500	£500
42		2d. black and violet	5·00	3·50
42*a*		2½d. black and ultramarine		
43		4d. black and sepia	26·00	32·00
44		6d. black and myrtle-green	23·00	35·00
		a. Opt double	£1700	£1800
45		1s. black and orange	38·00	42·00
		a. Opt double, one diagonal		
46		2s. 6d. black and brown	38·00	48·00
34/46 (*cheapest*)		*Set of* 8	£130	£160

In the setting of this overprint Nos. 10, 16, and 21 have the "p" of "Papua" with a defective foot or inverted "d" for "p", and in No. 17 the "pua" of "Papua" is a shade lower than the first "a".

No. 37a comes from a single sheet on which the overprints were sideways. Examples exist showing one, two or four complete or partial overprints.

PRINTERS. All the following issues were printed at Melbourne. See notes at beginning of Australia.

5 Large "PAPUA"

B

C

Three types of the 2s. 6d.:—
A. Thin top to "2" and small ball. Thin "6" and small ball. Thick uneven stroke.
B. Thin top to "2" and large, well shaped ball. Thin "6" and large ball. Very thick uneven stroke.
C. Thick top to "2" and large, badly shaped ball. Thick "6" and uneven ball. Thin even line.

Type A is not illustrated as the stamp is distinguishable by perf and watermark.

The litho stones were prepared from the engraved plates of the 1901 issue, value for value except the 2s. 6d. for which the original plate was mislaid. No. 48 containing Type A was prepared from the original ½d. plate with the value inserted on the stone and later a fresh stone was prepared from the 1d. plate and this contained Type B. Finally, the original plate of the 2s. 6d. was found and a third stone was prepared from this, and issued in 1911. These stamps show Type C.

6 Small "PAPUA"

(Litho Government Printing Office, Melbourne, from transfers from original engraved plates)

1907–10. *Wmk Crown over A, W w* **11**.

No.	Type	Description	Unused	Used
		A. *Large* "PAPUA". (*a*) *Wmk upright. P* 11		
47	**5**	½d. black and yellow-green (11.07)	1·25	2·25
		(*b*) *Wmk sideways. P* 11		
48	**5**	2s. 6d. black and chocolate (A) (12.09)	48·00	60·00
		B. *Small* "PAPUA"		
		I. *Wmk upright.* (*a*) *P* 11 (1907–8)		
49	**6**	1d. black and rose (6.08)	4·00	3·50
50		2d. black and purple (10.08)	5·00	5·00
51		2½d. black and bright ultramarine (7.08)	12·00	18·00
		a. Black and pale ultramarine	5·00	6·00

52 6 4d. black and sepia (20.1.07) .. .. 5·00 5·50
53 6d. black and myrtle-green (4.08) .. 11·00 15·00
54 1s. black and orange (10.08) .. .. 14·00 18·00

(b) P 12½ (1907–9)

55 6 2d. black and purple (10.08) .. .. 5·50 5·50
56 2½d. black and bright ultramarine (7.08) 22·00 35·00
a. Wmk sideways .. .. ..
b. Black and pale ultramarine .. 14·00 20·00
57 4d. black and sepia (20.1.07) .. .. 7·00 7·00
58 1s. black and orange (1.09) .. .. 42·00 60·00

II. *Wmk sideways*. (a) *P* 11 (1909–10)

59 6 ½d. black and yellow-green (12.09) .. 3·50 4·00
a. Black and deep green (1910) .. 27·00 40·00
60 1d. black and carmine (1.10) .. .. 8·00 8·50
61 2d. black and purple (1.10) .. .. 4·50 3·25
62 2½d. black and dull blue (1.10) .. .. 5·50 6·00
63 4d. black and sepia (1.10) .. .. 5·00 6·00
64 6d. black and myrtle-green (11.09) .. 13·00 10·00
65 1s. black and orange (3.10) .. .. 38·00 48·00

(b) P 12½ (1909–10)

66 6 ½d. black and yellow-green (12.09) .. 1·60 2·25
a. Black and deep green (1910) .. 27·00 35·00
67 1d. black and carmine (12.09).. .. 5·50 4·75
68 2d. black and purple (1.10) .. .. 3·00 2·25
69 2½d. black and dull blue (1.10).. .. 10·00 15·00
70 6d. black and myrtle-green (11.09) .. £1200 £1100
71 1s. black and orange (3.10) .. .. 14·00 25·00

(c) *Perf compound of* 11 *and* 12½

72 6 ½d. black and yellow-green £1500 £1500
73 2d. black and purple £700
74 4d. black and sepia £2000

(Litho Commonwealth Stamp Printing Office, Melbourne, by J. B. Cooke, from new stones madde by fresh transfers)

1910 (Sept)–**11**. *Large* "PAPUA". *W w* **11** (*upright*). *P* 12½.
75 5 ½d. black and green (12.10) .. .. 3·50 3·25
76 1d. black and carmine .. .. .. 5·50 3·00
77 2d. black and dull purple (*shades*) (12.10) .. .. 4·25 4·00
a. "C" for "O" in "POSTAGE" (R.4/3) 55·00 65·00
78 2½d. black and blue-violet (10.10) .. 4·50 10·00
79 4d. black and sepia (10.10) .. .. 3·75 8·00
80 6d. black and myrtle-green .. .. 9·00 9·00
81 1s. black and deep orange (12.10) .. 13·00 16·00
82 2s. 6d. black and brown (B) .. .. 45·00 60·00
83 2s. 6d. black and brown (C) (1911) .. 45·00 60·00
75/83 .. .. *Set of* 8 80·00 £100

A variety showing a white line or "rift" in clouds occurs on R. 5/3 in Nos. 49/74 and the "white leaves" variety mentioned below No. 22 occurs on the 2d. and 2½d. values in both issues. They are worth about four times the normal price.

8

ONE PENNY

(9)

(Typo J. B. Cooke)

1911–15. *Printed in one colour. W* **8** (*sideways*).

(a) *P* 12½ (1911–12)

84 6 ½d. yellow-green .. .. 70 1·50
a. Green .. .. 45 1·25
85 1d. rose-pink .. .. 1·40 50
86 2d. bright mauve .. .. 1·00 1·10
87 2½d. bright ultramarine .. .. .. 5·50 7·50
a. Dull ultramarine .. .. .. 5·50 7·50
88 4d. pale olive-green .. .. .. 4·50 8·00
89 6d. orange-brown .. .. .. 5·00 8·00
90 1s. yellow .. .. 11·00 14·00
91 2s. 6d. rose-carmine .. .. .. 32·00 40·00
84/91 .. .. *Set of* 8 55·00 70·00

(b) *P* 14

92 6 1d. rose-pink (6.15) .. .. .. 11·00 8·50
a. Pale scarlet .. .. 4·00 3·50

1917. *Above issue surch with T* **9** *at Port Moresby*.
93 6 1d. on ½d. yellow-green .. .. .. 1·10 1·60
a. Green .. .. 80 1·25
94 1d. on 2d. bright mauve .. .. .. 9·50 9·50
95 1d. on 2½d. ultramarine .. .. .. 2·50 3·50
96 1d. on 4d. pale olive-green .. .. 2·50 4·75
97 1d. on 6d. orange-brown .. .. .. 10·00 12·00
98 1d. on 2s. 6d. rose-carmine .. .. 4·50 9·00
93/98 .. .. *Set of* 6 27·00 35·00

(Typo J. B. Cooke (1916–18), T. S. Harrison (1918–26), A. J. Mullett (No. 101*a* only) (1926–27), or John Ash (1927–31))

1916–31. *Printed in two colours. W* **8** (*sideways*). *P* 14.
99 6 ½d. myrtle and apple green (Harrison and Ash) (1919) 45 35
a. Myrtle and pale olive-green (1927) 40 65
100 1d. black and carmine-red (1916) 1·40 60
a. Grey-black and red (1918).. 1·60 25
b. Intense black and red (Harrison) (1926) .. .. 1·90 95
101 1½d. pale grey-blue (*shades*) and brown (1925) 80 30
a. Cobalt and light brown (Mullett) (1927) .. .. 6·00 3·25
b. Bright blue and bright brown (1929) 1·25 50
c. "POSTACE" at right (R. 1/1) (all ptgs) .. .. .. *From* 35·00 38·00
102 2d. brown-purple and brown-lake (1919) .. .. 2·00 1·50
a. Deep brown-purple and lake (1931) 12·00 2·00
b. Brown-purple and claret (1931) .. 3·50 1·50
103 2½d. myrtle and ultramarine (1919) .. 3·50 6·50
104 6 3d. black and bright blue-green (1916) 1·50 1·75
a. Error. Black and deep greenish Prussian blue* £400 £400
b. Sepia-black and bright blue-green (Harrison) .. .. 20·00 15·00
c. Black and blue-green (1927) .. 2·50 2·75
105 4d. brown and orange (1919) .. .. 5·00 6·50
a. Light brown and orange (1927) .. 5·50 12·00
106 5d. bluish slate and pale brown (1931) 4·75 9·00
107 6d. dull and pale purple (1919) .. 2·75 4·50
a. Dull purple and red-purple (1927) 4·00 7·50
b. "POSTACE" at left (R.6/2) (all ptgs) .. .. *From* 65·00 75·00
108 1s. sepia and olive (1919) .. .. 4·00 6·00
a. Brown and yellow-olive (1927) .. 4·25 7·00
109 2s. 6d. maroon and pale pink (1919) .. 24·00 30·00
a. Maroon and bright pink (shades) (1927) .. .. 24·00 35·00
110 5s. black and deep green (1916) .. 45·00 45·00
111 10s. green and pale ultramarine (1925) £190 £200
99/111 .. .. *Set of* 13 £250 £275

*Beware of similar shades produced by removal of yellow pigment.

The printers of the various shades can be determined by their dates of issue. The Ash printings are on whiter paper.

For 9d. and 1s 3d. values, see Nos. 127/8.

AIR MAIL

(10)

(11)

1929 (Oct)–**30**. *Air. Optd with T* **10** *by Govt Printer, Port Moresby*.

(a) *Cooke printing. Yellowish paper*

112 6 3d. black and bright blue-green .. 3·00 5·00
a. Opt omitted in vert pair with normal £2250

(b) *Harrison printing. Yellowish paper*

113 6 3d. sepia-black and bright blue-green 55·00 60·00

(c) *Ash printing. White paper*

114 6 3d. black and blue-green .. .. 2·50 4·00
a. Opt omitted in horiz pair with normal £3250
b. Ditto, but vert pair.. .. .. £2750
c. Opt vertical, on back £2750
d. Opts *tête-bêche* (pair) £1700

1930 (15 Sept). *Air. Optd with T* **11**, *in carmine by Govt Printer, Port Moresby*. (a) *Harrison printings. Yellowish paper.*

115 6 3d. sepia-black and bright blue-green £400
116 6d. dull and pale purple .. .. 7·00 12·00
a. "POSTACE" at left (R. 6/2) .. 70·00 £100
117 1s. sepia and olive .. .. .. 18·00 32·00
a. Opt inverted £2250

(b) *Ash printings. White paper*

118 6 3d. black and blue-green .. .. 85 2·75
119 6d. dull purple and red-purple.. .. 5·50 10·00
a. "POSTACE" at left (R6/2).. .. 65·00 £100
120 1s. brown and yellow-olive .. .. 7·50 13·00

5d.

TWO PENCE

(12)

FIVE PENCE

(13)

1931 (1 Jan). *Surch with T* **12** *by Govt Printer, Port Moresby*.

(a) *Mullett printing*

121 6 2d. on 1½d. cobalt and light brown .. 25·00 38·00
a. "POSTACE" at right (R. 1/1) .. £170

(b) *Ash printing*

122 6 2d. on 1½d. bright blue and bright brown .. .. 2·50 3·00
a. "POSTACE" at right (R. 1/1) .. 45·00 55·00

1931. *Surch as T* **13** *by Govt Printer, Port Moresby*.

(a) *Cooke printing*

123 6 1s. 3d. on 5s. black and deep green .. 4·50 8·00

(b) *Harrison printing. Yellowish paper*

124 6 9d. on 2s. 6d. maroon and pale pink (Dec) 4·50 9·00

(c) *Ash printings. White paper*

125 6 5d. on 1s. brown and yellow-olive (26.7) 1·60 3·25
126 9d. on 2s. 6d. maroon and bright pink 4·75 11·00

(Typo J. Ash)

1932. *W* **15** *of Australia* (*Mult* "C of A"). *P* 11.
127 5 9d. lilac and violet .. .. .. 7·00 16·00
128 1s. 3d. lilac and pale greenish blue .. 12·00 23·00
127/8 Optd "Specimen" .. .. *Set of* 2 £550

15 Motuan Girl

18 Greater Bird of Paradise

20 Native Mother and Child

22 Papuan Motherhood

(Des F. E. Williams (2s., £1 and frames of other values), E. Whitehouse (2d., 4d., 6d., 1s., and 10s.); remaining centres from photos by Messrs F. E. Williams and Gibson. Recess J. Ash (all values) and W. C. G. McCracken (½d., 1d., 2d., 4d.))

1932 (14 Nov). *T* **15**, **18**, **20**, **22** *and similar designs. No wmk. P* 11.
130 ½d. black and orange 35 90
a. Black and buff (McCracken) .. .. 26·00 26·00
131 1d. black and green 40 30
132 1½d. black and lake .. .. .. 1·40 4·25
133 2d. red .. .. 3·50 55
134 3d. black and blue .. .. .. 4·00 7·50
135 4d. olive-green .. .. 4·50 8·00
136 5d. black and slate-green .. .. 3·50 4·75
137 6d. bistre-brown .. .. .. 5·50 7·00
138 9d. black and violet .. .. .. 10·00 15·00
139 1s. dull blue-green .. .. .. 6·00 12·00
140 1s. 3d. black and dull purple .. .. 14·00 20·00
141 2s. black and slate green .. .. 14·00 20·00
142 2s. 6d. black and rose-mauve .. .. 24·00 35·00
143 5s. black and olive-brown .. .. 45·00 48·00
144 10s. violet £100 £100
145 £1 black and olive-grey £225 £200
130/145 .. .. *Set of* 16 £425 £450

Designs: *Vert* (*as T* **15**)—1d. A Chieftain's son; 1½d. Tree-houses; 3d. Papuan dandy; 5d. Masked dancer; 9d. Papuan shooting fish; 1s. 3d. Lakatoi; 2s. Papuan art; 2s. 6d. Pottery making; 5s. Native policeman; £1 Delta house. (*As T* **18**)—1s. *Dubu*—or ceremonial platform. *Horiz* (*as T* **20**)—10s. Lighting a fire.

31 Hoisting the Union Jack

32 Scene on H.M.S. *Nelson*

(Recess J. Ash)

1934 (6 Nov). *50th Anniv of Declaration of British Protectorate. P* 11.
146 31 1d. green .. .. 1·75 2·50
147 32 2d. scarlet .. .. 2·50 2·50
148 31 3d. blue.. .. .. 7·00 7·00
149 32 5d. purple .. .. 13·00 14·00

HIS MAJESTY'S JUBILEE.

1910 1935

(33)

HIS MAJESTY'S JUBILEE. 1910 — 1935

(34)

MAJESTY'S

Normal

MAJESTY'S

"Accent" flaw (R. 5/4)

1935 (9 July). *Silver Jubilee. Nos.* 131, 133/4 *and* 136 *optd with T* **33** *or* **34** (*2d.*).
150 1d. black and green 50 90
a. "Accent" flaw .. .. 20·00 24·00
151 2d. scarlet .. .. 95 1·25
152 3d. black and blue .. .. 2·75 3·50
a. "Accent" flaw .. .. 35·00 45·00
153 5d. black and slate-green .. .. .. 9·50 11·00
a. "Accent" flaw .. .. 50·00 55·00

35

36 Port Moresby

(Recess J. Ash)

1937 (14 May). *Coronation. P* 11.
154 35 1d. green 30 15
155 2d. scarlet 30 15
156 3d. blue.. .. .. 45 20
157 5d. purple 50 35

(Recess J. Ash)

1938 (6 Sept). *Air. 50th Anniv of Declaration of British Possession. P* 11.
158 36 2d. rose-red .. .. 3·50 3·25
159 3d. bright blue .. .. 4·00 3·50
160 5d. green .. .. 5·50 5·50
161 8d. brown-lake .. .. 13·00 12·00
162 1s. mauve .. .. 25·00 15·00

37 Natives poling Rafts

(Recess J. Ash)

1939 (6 Sept). *Air. P* 11.
163 **37** 2d. rose-red .. .. 3·00 2·50
164 3d. bright blue .. .. 3·75 3·75
165 5d. green .. .. 5·00 2·75
166 8d. brown-lake .. .. 8·50 6·50
167 1s. mauve .. .. 12·00 10·00

(Recess W. C. G. McCracken)

1941 (2 Jan). *Air. P* 11½.
168 **37** 1s. 6d. olive-green .. .. 48·00 42·00
163/168 .. .. *Set of* 6 70·00 60·00

OFFICIAL STAMPS

STAMPS PERFORATED "OS". Postage stamps perforated "OS" were also used for official purposes. We do not list such varieties separately, but can supply when in stock.

(O 1)

(Typo T. S. Harrison (1d. and 2s. 6d.) and J. Ash)

1931 (29 July)–**32**. *Optd with Type* O 1. *W* 8 *or W* 15 *of Australia* (*9d., 1s. 3d.*). *P* 14 *or* 11 (*9d., 1s. 3d.*).
O 1 **6** ½d. myrtle and apple-green .. .. .. 80 2·25
O 2 1d. grey-black and red .. .. .. 1·75 4·00
 a. Intense black and red .. .. .. 85 2·75
O 3 1½d. bright blue and bright brown .. .. 1·60 4·75
 a. "POSTACE" at right .. .. .. 45·00 55·00
O 4 2d. brown-purple and claret .. .. .. 1·75 5·00
O 5 3d. black and blue-green .. .. .. 1·75 7·00
O 6 4d. light brown and orange .. .. .. 2·00 7·00
O 7 5d. bluish slate and pale brown .. .. 4·50 10·00
O 8 6d. dull purple and red-purple .. .. 5·50 8·50
 a. "POSTACE" at left .. .. .. 70·00 90·00
O 9 9d. lilac and violet (1932) .. .. .. 17·00 28·00
O10 1s. brown and yellow-olive .. .. .. 9·00 14·00
O11 1s. 3d. lilac & pale greenish blue (1932) 25·00 42·00
O12 2s. 6d. maroon and pale pink (Harrison) .. .. 25·00 42·00
 a. Maroon and bright pink (Ash) .. 25·00 42·00
O1/12 .. .. *Set of* 12 85·00 £160

Civil Administration, in Papua, was suspended in 1942; on resumption, after the Japanese defeat in 1945, Australian stamps were used until the appearance of the issue of the combined territories of PAPUA & NEW GUINEA.

Papua New Guinea

AUSTRALIAN TRUST TERRITORY

The name of the combined territory was changed from "Papua and New Guinea" to "Papua New Guinea" at the beginning of 1972.

SPECIMEN OVERPRINTS. These come from specimen sets in which the lower values were cancelled-to-order, but stamps above the value of 10s. were overprinted "Specimen". These overprints are listed as they could be purchased from the Post Office.

1 Tree Kangaroo

2 Buka Head-dresses

3 Native Youth

14 Map of Papua and New Guinea

15 Papuan shooting Fish

(Recess Note Printing Branch, Commonwealth Bank, Melbourne)

1952 (30 Oct)–**58**. *T* 1/3, 14/15 *and similar designs. P* 14.
1 ½d. emerald 30 10
2 1d. deep brown 20 5
3 2d. blue 35 10
4 2½d. orange .. .. 1·75 40
5 3d. deep green .. .. 1·50 5
6 3½d. carmine-red 60 5
6*a* 3½d. black (2.6.58) .. .. 9·50 4·25
7 6½d. dull purple (*shades*) .. .. 3·25 20
8 7½d. blue .. .. 12·00 10·00
9 9d. brown .. .. 8·00 1·00
10 1s. yellow-green .. .. 3·75 25
11 1s. 6d. deep green .. .. 12·00 1·25
12 2s. indigo .. .. 10·00 25
13 2s. 6d. brown-purple .. .. 9·00 70
14 10s. blue-black .. .. 90·00 23·00
15 £1 deep brown .. .. £120 24·00
1/15 .. .. *Set of* 16 £250 60·00
14/15 Optd "Specimen" .. .. .. *Set of* 2 £150

Designs: *Vert* (*as T* 1/3)—2½d. Greater Bird of Paradise; 3d. Native policeman; 3½d. Papuan head-dress. (*As T* 15)—6½d. Kiriwina Chief House; 7½d. Kiriwina yam house; 1s. 6d. Rubber tapping; 2s. Sepik dancing masks. *Horiz* (*as T* 14)—9d. Copra making; 1s. Lakatoi; 2s. 6d. Native shepherd and flock.

(16) (17)

1957 (29 Jan). *Nos* 4 *and* 10 *with T* **16** *or T* **17**.
16 4d. on 2½d. orange 30 10
17 7d. on 1s. yellow-green 70 15

18 Cacao Plant

19 Klinki Plymill

20 Cattle

21 Coffee Beans

(Recess Note Ptg Branch, Commonwealth Bank, Melbourne)

1958 (2 June)–**60**. *New values. P* 14.
18 **18** 4d. vermilion 90 5
19 5d. green (10.11.60) .. .. 1·25 5
20 **19** 7d. bronze-green .. .. 10·00 25
21 8d. deep ultramarine (10.11.60) .. .. 2·50 3·00
22 **20** 1s. 7d. red-brown .. .. 50·00 38·00
23 2s. 5d. vermilion (10.11.60) .. .. .. 8·00 7·00
24 **21** 5s. crimson and olive-green .. .. .. 12·00 1·75
18/24 .. .. *Set of* 7 75·00 45·00

(22)

23 Council Chamber, Port Moresby

1959 (1 Dec). *No.* 1 *surch with T* **22**.
25 **1** 5d. on ½d. emerald 30 5

(Photo Harrison)

1961 (10 Apr). *Reconstitution of Legislative Council. P* 15 × 14.
26 **23** 5d. deep green and yellow .. .. .. 3·00 45
27 2s. 3d. deep green and light salmon .. .. 25·00 14·00

24 Female, Goroka, New Guinea

26 Female Dancer

28 Traffic Policeman

(Des Pamela M. Prescott, Recess Note Ptg Branch, Reserve Bank of Australia, Melbourne)

1961 (26 July)–**62**. *T* **24**, **26**, **28** *and similar designs. P* 14½ × 14 (*1d., 3d., 3s.*) *or* 14 × 14½ (*others*).
28 1d. lake 60 5
29 3d. indigo 30 5
30 1s. bronze-green .. .. 8·00 30
31 2s. maroon .. .. 1·25 30
32 3s. deep bluish green (5.9.62) .. .. .. 2·00 1·50

Designs:—*Vert* (*as T* **24**)—3d. Tribal Elder, Tari, Papua. (*As T* **26**)—2s. Male dancer.

29 Campaign Emblem

30 Map of South Pacific

(Recess Note Ptg Branch, Reserve Bank of Australia, Melbourne)

1962 (7 Apr). *Malaria Eradication. P* 14.
33 **29** 5d. carmine-red and light blue 90 20
34 1s. red and sepia .. .. 4·50 2·00
35 2s. black and yellow-green .. .. .. 9·00 5·50

(Des Pamela M. Prescott. Recess Note Ptg Branch, Reserve Bank of Australia, Melbourne)

1962 (9 July). *Fifth South Pacific Conference, Pago Pago. P* 14½ × 14.
36 **30** 5d. scarlet and light green .. .. 1·25 20
37 1s. 6d. deep violet and light yellow .. 7·00 4·00
38 2s. 6d. deep green and light blue .. 7·00 6·50

31 Throwing the Javelin

33 Runners

(Des G. Hamori. Photo Courvoisier)

1962 (24 Oct). *Seventh British Empire and Commonwealth Games, Perth. T* **31**, **33** *and similar design. P* 11½.
39 5d. brown and light blue 30 15
 a. Pair. Nos. 39/40 .. .. 2·00 2·00
40 5d. brown and orange 30 15
41 2s. 3d. brown and light green .. .. .. 6·00 4·50

Design: (*As T* **31**)—5d. High jump.
Nos. 39/40 are arranged together *se-tenant* in sheets of 100.

34 Raggiana Bird of Paradise

35 Golden Opossum

36 Rabaul

37 Queen Elizabeth II

(Des S. T. Cham (10s.), A. Buckley (photo) (£1). Photo Harrison (£1), Courvoisier (others)).

1963. *P* 14½ (£1) *or* 11½ (*others*).
42 **34** 5d. yellow, chestnut and sepia (27 Mar) .. 70 5
43 **35** 6d. red, yellow-brown and grey (27 Mar) .. 1·00 1·25
44 **36** 10s. multicoloured (13 Feb) .. .. 28·00 20·00
45 **37** £1 sepia, gold and blue-green (3 July) .. 22·00 8·00
44/5 Optd "Specimen" .. .. .. *Set of* 2 £110

1963 (1 May). *Red Cross Centenary. As No.* 351 *of Australia.*
46 5d. red, grey-brown and bluish green .. 60 12

38 Waterfront, Port Moresby

(Des J. McMahon (8d.), Pamela M. Prescott (2s. 3d.). Recess Note Ptg Branch, Reserve Bank of Australia, Melbourne)

1963 (8 May). *T* **38** *and similar horiz design. P* 14 × 13½.
47 **38** 8d. green 75 25
48 – 2s. 3d. ultramarine .. .. 1·00 50

Design:—2s. 3d. Piaggio "P-166" Aircraft landing at Tapini.

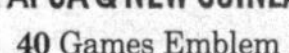

40 Games Emblem **41** Watam Head

(Des Pamela M. Prescott. Recess Note Ptg Branch, Reserve Bank of Australia, Melbourne)

1963 (14 Aug). *First South Pacific Games, Suva. P* 13½ × 14½.
49 **40** 5d. bistre 25 5
50 1s. deep green 75 70

(Des Pamela M. Prescott. Photo Courvoisier)

1964 (5 Feb). *Native Artefacts. T* **41** *and similar vert designs. Multicoloured. P* 11½.
51 11d. Type **41** . . . . 1·50 20
52 2s. 5d. Watam Head (*different*) . . . . 2·00 1·25
53 2s. 6d. Bosmun Head . . . . . . 2·00 35
54 5s. Medina Head . . . . 3·50 60

45 Casting Vote **46** "Health Centres"

(Photo Courvoisier)

1964 (4 Mar). *Common Roll Elections. P* 11½.
55 **45** 5d. brown and drab 25 5
56 2s. 3d. brown and pale blue . . . . 1·00 1·00

(Recess Note Ptg Branch, Reserve Bank of Australia, Melbourne)

1964 (5 Aug). *Health Services. T* **46** *and similar vert designs. P* 14.
57 5d. violet 20 5
58 8d. bronze-green 35 20
59 1s. blue 35 15
60 1s. 2d. brown-red 60 75
Designs:—8d. "School health"; 1s. "Infant, child and maternal health"; 1s. 2d. "Medical training".

50 Striped Gardener Bowerbird **51** Emperor of Germany Bird of Paradise

(Photo Courvoisier)

1964 (28 Oct)–**65**. *Vert designs as T* **50** (*1d. to 8d.*) *or* **51** (*others*). *Multicoloured; background colours given. P* 11½ (*1d. to 8d.*) *or* 12 × 11½ (*1s. to 10s.*).
61 1d. pale olive-yellow (20.1.65) 40 5
62 3d. light grey (20.1.65) 50 10
63 5d. pale red (20.1.65) 55 5
64 6d. pale green 75 20
65 8d. lilac 80 30
66 1s. salmon . . . . 1·00 20
67 2s. light blue (20.1.65) . . . . . . 1·75 50
68 2s. 3d. light green (20.1.65) . . . . 1·75 1·50
69 3s. pale yellow (20.1.65) . . . . . . 2·75 2·50
70 5s. cobalt (20.1.65) . . . . . . 18·00 7·00
71 10s. pale drab (Optd S. £140) . . . . 17·00 10·00
61/71 . . . . *Set of* 11 40·00 20·00
Designs:—3d. Adelbert Bowerbird; 5d. Blue Bird of Paradise; 6d. Lawes' Parotia; 8d. Black-billed Sicklebill; 2s. Brown Sicklebill; 2s. 3d. Lesser Bird of Paradise; 3s. Magnificent Bird of Paradise; 5s. Twelve-wired Bird of Paradise; 10s. Magnificent Riflebird.

61 Canoe Prow

(Des Pamela M. Prescott. Photo Courvoisier)

1965 (24 Mar). *Sepik Canoe Prows in Port Moresby Museum. T* **61** *and similar horiz designs showing carved prows. P* 11½.
72 4d. multicoloured 60 10
73 1s. 2d. multicoloured . . . . . . 3·00 2·00
74 1s. 6d. multicoloured . . . . . . 1·25 20
75 4s. multicoloured . . . . 3·75 1·25

1965 (14 Apr). *50th Anniv of Gallipoli Landing. As T* **184** *of Australia, but slightly larger* (22 × 34½ *mm*). *Photo.*
76 2s. 3d. sepia, black and emerald 80 25

65 Urban Plan and Native House

(Des G. Hamori. Photo Courvoisier)

1965 (7 July). *Sixth South Pacific Conference, Lae. T* **65** *and similar horiz design. P* 11½.
77 6d. multicoloured 10 5
78 1s. multicoloured 15 10
No. 78 is similar to T **65** but with the plan on the right and the house on the left. Also "URBANISATION" reads downwards.

66 Mother and Child **67** Globe and U.N. Emblem

(Photo Courvoisier)

1965 (13 Oct). *20th Anniv of U.N.O. T* **66/7** *and similar vert design. P* 11½.
79 6d. sepia, blue and pale turquoise-blue . . 10 5
80 1s. orange-brown, blue & dp reddish violet . . 20 20
81 2s. blue, blue-green and light yellow-olive . . 25 20
Design:—2s. U.N. Emblem and globes.

69 Blue Emperor **71** New Guinea Birdwing

(Photo Courvoisier)

1966 (14 Feb–12 Oct). *Decimal Currency. Butterflies. Vert designs as T* **69** (*1 to 5 c.*), *or horiz as T* **71** (*others*). *Multicoloured. P* 11½.
82 1 c. Type **69** 15 5
83 3 c. White-banded Map Butterfly 30 12
84 4 c. Mountain Swallowtail 35 12
85 5 c. Port Moresby Terinos 35 5
86 10 c. Type **71** 50 5
86*a* 12 c. Blue Crow (12.10) . . . . . . 2·50 2·50
87 15 c. Euchenor Butterfly . . . . . . 5·00 1·50
88 20 c. White-spotted Parthenos . . . . 3·75 40
89 25 c. Orange Jezebel . . . . 6·50 1·50
90 50 c. New Guinea Emperor . . . . . . 14·00 3·00
91 $1 Blue Spotted Leaf-wing . . . . . . 5·50 4·00
92 $2 Paradise Birdwing . . . . . . 12·00 7·50
82/92 . . . . *Set of* 12 45·00 18·00

80 "Molala Harai" **84** Throwing the Discus

(Des Rev. H. A. Brown. Photo Courvoisier)

1966 (8 June). *Folklore. Elema Art* (*1st series*). *T* **80** *and similar vert designs. P* 11½.
93 2 c. black and carmine 15 5
94 7 c. black, light yellow and light blue . . 20 5
95 30 c. black, carmine and apple-green 40 30
96 60 c. black, carmine and yellow . . . . 2·00 1·25
Designs:—7 c. "Marai"; 30 c. "Meavea Kivovia"; 60 c. "Toivita Tapaivita".
Nos. 93/6 were supplementary values to the decimal currency definitive issue.
See also Nos. 152/5 and 342/5.

(Photo Courvoisier)

1966 (31 Aug). *South Pacific Games, Nouméa. T* **84** *and similar vert designs. Multicoloured. P* 11½.
97 5 c. Type **84** 15 5
98 10 c. Football 30 15
99 20 c. Tennis 35 15

87 *Mucuna novoguineensis* **91** "Fine Arts"

(Des Mrs. D. Pearce. Photo Courvoisier)

1966 (7 Dec). *Flowers. T* **87** *and similar vert designs. Multicoloured. P* 11½.
100 5 c. Type **87** 15 5
101 10 c. *Tecomanthe dentrophila* 20 20
102 20 c. *Rhododendron macgregoriae* 40 35
103 60 c. *Rhododendron konori* . . . . . . 90 1·25

(Des G. Hamori. Photo Courvoisier)

1967 (8 Feb). *Higher Education. T* **91** *and similar horiz designs. Multicoloured. P* 12½ × 12.
104 1 c. Type **91** 5 5
105 3 c. "Surveying" 5 5
106 4 c. "Civil Engineering" 5 5
107 5 c. "Science" 5 5
108 20 c. "Law" 35 35

96 *Sagra speciosa* **100** Laloki River

(Des Pamela M. Prescott. Photo Courvoisier)

1967 (12 Apr). *Fauna Conservation* (*Beetles*). *T* **96** *and similar vert designs. Multicoloured. P* 11½.
109 5 c. Type **96** 15 5
110 10 c. *Eupholus schoenherri* 30 15
111 20 c. *Sphingnotus albertisi* 65 20
112 25 c. *Cyphogastra albertisi* 65 20

(Des G. Wade. Photo Courvoisier)

1967 (28 June). *Laloki River Hydro-Electric Scheme, and "New Industries". T* **100** *and similar vert designs. Multicoloured. P* 12½.
113 5 c. Type **100** 10 5
114 10 c. Pyrethrum 20 10
115 20 c. Tea Plant 35 20
116 25 c. Type **100** 35 20

103 Air Attack at Milne Bay **107** Papuan Lory

(Des R. Hodgkinson (2 c.), F. Hodgkinson (5 c.), G. Wade (20 c., 50 c.). Photo Courvoisier)

1967 (30 Aug). *25th Anniv of the Pacific War. T* **103** *and similar multicoloured designs. P* 11½.
117 2 c. Type **103** 5 10
118 5 c. Kokoda Trail (*vert*) 5 5
119 20 c. The Coast Watchers 30 25
120 50 c. Battle of the Coral Sea . . . . 1·40 70

(Des T. Walcot. Photo Courvoisier)

1967 (29 Nov). *Christmas. Territory Parrots. T* **107** *and similar vert designs. Multicoloured. P* 12½.
121 5 c. Type **107** 20 5
122 7 c. Pesquet's Parrot 25 25
123 20 c. Dusky Lory 90 25
124 25 c. Edward's Fig Parrot . . . . . . 1·00 15

111 Chimbu Head-dresses **112**

(Des P. Jones. Photo Courvoisier)

1968 (21 Feb). *"National Heritage". T* **111/12** *and similar multicoloured designs. P* 12 × 12½.
125 5 c. Type **111** 10 5
126 10 c. Southern Highlands Head-dress (*horiz*) . . 15 10
127 20 c. Western Highlands Head-dress (*horiz*) . . 35 25
128 60 c. Type **112** . . . . 1·50 70

115 *Hyla thesaurensis*

119 Human Rights Emblem and Papuan Head-dress (abstract)

(Des and photo Courvoisier)

1968 (24 Apr). *Fauna Conservation (Frogs). T* **115** *and similar horiz designs. Multicoloured. P* 11½.

129 5 c. Type **115** 15 5
130 10 c. *Hyla iris* 25 20
131 15 c. *Ceratobatrachas guentheri* 45 35
132 20 c. *Nyctimystes narinosa* 80 50

(Des G. Hamori. Litho Enschedé)

1968 (26 June). *Human Rights Year. T* **119** *and similar horiz design. Multicoloured. P* 13½ × 12½.

133 5 c. Type **119** 12 5
134 10 c. Human Rights in the World (abstract) .. 20 15

121 Leadership (abstract)

123 Egg Cowry

(Des G. Hamori. Litho Enschedé)

1968 (26 June). *Universal Suffrage. T* **121** *and similar horiz design. Multicoloured. P* 13½ × 12½.

135 20 c. Type **121** 30 25
136 25 c. Leadership of the Community (abstract) 35 35

(Des P. Jones. Photo Courvoisier)

1968–69. *Seashells. Multicoloured designs as T* **123**. *P* 12 × 12½ ($2), 12½ × 12 (1 *c. to* 20 *c.*) *or* 11½ (*others*).

137 1 c. Type **125** (29.1.69) 5 5
138 3 c. Laciniated Conch (30.10.68) 30 8
139 4 c. Lithograph Cone (29.1.69) 20 10
140 5 c. Marbled Cone (28.8.68) 25 5
141 7 c. Episcopal Mitre (29.1.69) 35 5
142 10 c. Red Volute (30.10.68) 55 10
143 12 c. Areola Bonnet (29.1.69) .. .. .. 2·00 60
144 15 c. Scorpion Conch (30.10.68) .. .. 1·00 40
145 20 c. Fluted Clam (28.8.68) .. .. .. 1·25 30
146 25 c. Chocolate Flamed Venus Shell (28.8.68) 1·25 60
147 30 c. Giant Murex (28.8.68) .. .. .. 2·00 75
148 40 c. Chambered Nautilus (30.10.68) .. .. 2·25 95
149 60 c. Pacific Triton (28.8.68) .. .. .. 3·50 80
150 $1 Emerald Snail (30.10.68) .. .. 7·00 2·75
151 $2 Glory of the Sea (*vert*) (29.1.69) .. .. 20·00 9·00
137/51 .. .. *Set of* 15 38·00 15·00

The 1, 5, 7, 15, 40, 60 c. and $1 exist with PVA gum as well as gum arabic.

138 Tito Myth

140 Luvuapo Myth

139 Iko Myth

141 Miro Myth

(Des from native motifs by Rev. H. A. Brown. Litho Enschedé)

1969 (9 Apr). *Folklore. Elema Art (2nd series). P* 12½ × 13½ × *Roul* 9 *between se-tenant pairs.*

152 **138** 5 c. black, yellow and red 10 5
a. Pair. Nos. 152/3 .. .. .. 20 20
153 **139** 5 c. black, yellow and red 10 5
154 **140** 10 c. black, grey and red 20 30
a. Pair. Nos. 154/5 .. .. .. 40 60
155 **141** 10 c. black, grey and red 20 30

Nos. 152/3 and 154/5 were issued in vertical *se-tenant* pairs, separated by a line of roulette.

142 "Fireball" Class Yacht

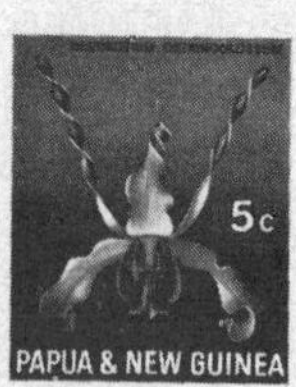

145 *Dendrobium ostinoglossum*

(Des J. Fallas. Recess Note Ptg Branch, Reserve Bank of Australia)

1969 (25 June). *Third South Pacific Games, Port Moresby. T* **142** *and similar designs. P* 14 × 14½ (5 *c.*) *or* 14½ × 14 (*others*).

156 5 c. black 20 5
157 10 c. deep bluish violet 25 20
158 20 c. myrtle-green 45 45

Designs: *Horiz*—10 c. Swimming pool, Boroko; 20 c. Games arena, Konedobu.

(Des P. Jones. Photo Courvoisier)

1969 (27 Aug). *Flora Conservation (Orchids). T* **145** *and similar vert designs. Multicoloured. P* 11½.

159 5 c. Type **145** 45 5
160 10 c. *Dendrobium lawesii* 65 40
161 20 c. *Dendrobium pseudofrigidum* .. .. 1·60 60
162 30 c. *Dendrobium conanthum* .. .. .. 1·90 40

149 Bird of Paradise

150 Native Potter

(Des G. Hamori. Photo Note Ptg Branch, Reserve Bank of Australia)

1969 (24 Sept)–**71**. *Coil stamps. P* 15 × *imperf.*

162*a* **149** 2 c. blue, black and red (1.4.71) .. 15 10
163 5 c. bright green, brown and red-orange 15 5

(Des G. Hamori. Photo Courvoisier)

1969 (24 Sept). 50*th Anniv of International Labour Organization. P* 11½.

164 **150** 5 c. multicoloured 10 5

151 Tareko

155 Prehistoric Ambun Stone

(Des G. Hamori. Photo Courvoisier)

1969 (29 Oct). *Musical Instruments. T* **151** *and similar horiz designs. P* 12½ × 12.

165 5 c. multicoloured 25 5
166 10 c. black, olive-green and pale yellow .. 40 25
167 25 c. black, yellow and brown 70 45
168 30 c. multicoloured 80 60

Designs:—10 c. Garamut; 25 c. Iviliko; 30 c. Kundu.

(Des R. Bates. Photo Courvoisier)

1970 (11 Feb). *"National Heritage". T* **155** *and similar horiz designs. Multicoloured. P* 12½ × 12.

169 5 c. Type **155** 20 5
170 10 c. Masawa canoe of Kula Circuit 45 30
171 25 c. Torres' Map, 1606 .. .. 1·25 60
172 30 c. H.M.S. *Basilisk* .. .. 1·50 95

159 King of Saxony Bird of Paradise

(Des T. Walcot. Photo Courvoisier)

1970 (13 May). *Fauna Conservation (Birds of Paradise). T* **159** *and similar vert designs. Multicoloured. P* 12 × 11½.

173 5 c. Type **159** .. .. 1·00 15
174 10 c. King Bird of Paradise .. .. .. 1·75 1·25
175 15 c. Raggiana Bird of Paradise .. .. 2·50 2·00
176 25 c. Sickle-crested Bird of Paradise .. .. 3·00 1·90

163 McDonnell Douglas "DC-6B" and Mt Wilhelm

164 Lockheed "Electra" and Mt Yule

165 Boeing "727" and Mt Giluwe

166 Fokker "Friendship" and Manam Island

(Des D. Gentleman. Photo Harrison)

1970 (8 July). *Australian and New Guinea Air Services. T* **163/6** *and similar horiz designs. Multicoloured. P* 14½ × 14.

177 5 c. Type **163** 30 10
a. Block of 4. Nos. 177/80 .. .. .. 1·25
178 5 c. Type **164** 30 10
179 5 c. Type **165** 30 10
180 5 c. Type **166** 30 10
181 25 c. McDonnell Douglas "DC-3" and Matupi Volcano .. .. 1·25 1·25
182 30 c. Boeing "707" and Hombrom's Bluff .. 1·25 1·25
177/82 .. .. *Set of* 6 3·25 2·50

Nos. 177/80 were issued together, *se-tenant*, in blocks of 4 throughout the sheet.

169 N. Miklouho-Maclay (scientist) and Effigy

170 Wogeo Island Food Bowl

(Des D. Gentleman. Photo Courvoisier)

1970 (19 Aug). 42*nd ANZAAS (Australian-New Zealand Association for the Advancement of Science) Congress, Port Moresby. T* **169** *and similar horiz designs. P* 11½.

183 5 c. multicoloured 15 5
184 10 c. multicoloured 40 20
185 15 c. multicoloured .. .. 1·00 40
186 20 c. multicoloured .. .. 1·10 30

Designs:—10 c. B. Malinowski (anthropologist) and native hut; 15 c. T. Salvadori (ornithologist) and Dwarf Cassowary; 20 c. F. R. R. Schlechter (botanist) and flower.

(Des P. Jones. Photo Courvoisier)

1970 (28 Oct). *Native Artefacts. T* **170** *and similar multicoloured designs. P* 12½ × 12 (30 *c.*) *or* 12 × 12½ (*others*).

187 5 c. Type **170** 12 5
188 10 c. Lime Pot 50 25
189 15 c. Aibom Sago Storage Pot 60 30
190 30 c. Manus Island Bowl (*horiz*) .. .. 1·25 90

171 Eastern Highlands Dwelling

172 Spotted Cuscus

(Des G. Wade. Photo Courvoisier)

1971 (27 Jan). *Native Dwellings. T* **171** *and similar vert designs showing dwellings from the places given. Multicoloured. P* 11½.

191 5 c. Type **171** 15 5
192 7 c. Milne Bay 30 30
193 10 c. Purari Delta 40 25
194 40 c. Sepik .. .. 1·75 1·50

(Des R. Bates. Photo Courvoisier)

1971 (31 Mar). *Fauna Conservation. T* **172** *and similar multi-coloured designs. P* 11½.

195 5 c. Type **172** 30 5
196 10 c. Brown and White Striped Possum .. 60 35
197 15 c. Feather-tailed Possum .. .. .. 1·50 2·00
198 25 c. Spiny Ant-Eater (*horiz*) .. .. .. 2·00 2·00
199 30 c. Goodfellow's Tree-climbing Kangaroo (*horiz*) .. .. 2·00 1·50

MINIMUM PRICE

The minimum price quoted is 5p which represents a handling charge rather than a basis for valuing common stamps. For further notes about prices see introductory pages.

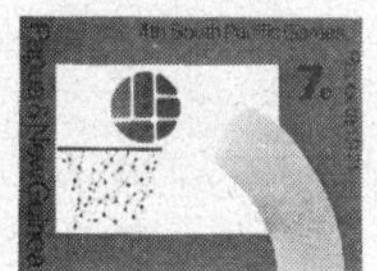

173 "Basketball" — 174 Bartering Fish for Vegetables

(Des G. Hamori, Litho D.L.R.)

1971 (9 June). *Fourth South Pacific Games, Papeete, Tahiti. T* **173** *and similar horiz designs. Multicoloured. P* 13½ × 14.

200 7 c. Type **173** 20 5
201 14 c. "Sailing" 50 40
202 21 c. "Boxing" 55 75
203 28 c. "Athletics" 65 85

(Des G. Wade. Photo Courvoisier)

1971 (18 Aug). *Primary Industries. T* **174** *and similar vert designs. Multicoloured. P* 11½.

204 7 c. Type **174** 15 5
205 9 c. Man stacking yams 55 75
206 14 c. Vegetable market 70 55
207 30 c. Highlanders cultivating garden .. .. 1·50 1·00

175 Sia Dancer — 176 Papuan Flag over Australian Flag

(Des Bette Hays. Photo Courvoisier)

1971 (27 Oct). *Native Dancers. T* **175** *and similar multicoloured designs. P* 11½.

208 7 c. Type **175** 35 5
209 9 c. Urasena dancer 45 45
210 20 c. Siassi Tubuan dancers (*horiz*) .. .. 1·50 1·60
211 28 c. Sia dancers (*horiz*) .. .. 1·75 1·75

(Des R. Bates. Photo Courvoisier)

1972 (26 Jan). *Constitutional Development. T* **176** *and similar horiz design. P* 12½ × 12.

212 **176** 7 c. multicoloured 50 10
a. Pair. Nos. 212/13 .. .. 1·00 1·00
213 – 7 c. multicoloured 50 10

Design:—No. 213, Crest of Papua New Guinea and Australian coat of arms.

Nos. 212/13 were printed vertically *se-tenant* within the sheet.

177 Map of Papua New Guinea and Flag of South Pacific Commission — 178 Turtle

(Des R. Bates. Photo Courvoisier)

1972 (26 Jan). *25th Anniv of South Pacific Commission. T* **177** *and similar horiz design. P* 12½ × 12.

214 **177** 15 c. multicoloured .. .. 1·00 80
a. Pair. Nos. 214/15 .. .. 2·00 2·00
215 – 15 c. multicoloured .. .. 1·00 80

Design:—No. 215, Man's face and flag of the Commission.

Nos. 214/15 were printed vertically *se-tenant* within the sheet.

(Des R. Bates. Photo Courvoisier)

1972 (17 Mar). *Fauna Conservation (Reptiles). T* **178** *and similar horiz designs. Multicoloured. P* 11½.

216 7 c. Type **178** 40 5
217 14 c. Rainforest Dragon .. .. 1·60 1·75
218 21 c. Green Python .. .. 1·90 2·00
219 30 c. Salvador's Monitor .. .. 2·25 1·90

179 Curtiss "Seagull MF6" Aircraft and *Eureka* — 180 New National Flag

(Des Major L. G. Halls. Photo Courvoisier)

1972 (7 June). *50th Anniv of Aviation. T* **179** *and similar horiz designs. Multicoloured. P* 11½.

220 7 c. Type **179** 50 5
221 14 c. De Havilland "37" and native porters .. 2·25 2·00
222 20 c. Junkers "G-31" and gold dredge .. 2·50 2·00
223 25 c. Junkers "F-13" and mission church .. 2·50 2·00

(Des R. Bates. Photo Courvoisier)

1972 (16 Aug). *National Day. T* **180** *and similar vert designs. Multicoloured. P* 11½.

224 7 c. Type **180** 40 5
225 10 c. Native drum 80 65
226 30 c. Blowing conch-shell .. .. 1·00 80

181 Rev. Copland King — 182 Mt Tomavatur Station

(Des G. Wade. Photo Courvoisier)

1972 (25 Oct). *Christmas (Missionaries). T* **181** *and similar horiz designs. Multicoloured. P* 11½.

227 7 c. Type **181** 70 40
228 7 c. Rev. Dr. Flierl 70 40
229 7 c. Bishop Verjus 70 40
230 7 c. Pastor Ruatoka 70 40

(Des R. Bates. Photo Courvoisier)

1973 (24 Jan). *Completion of Telecommunications Project, 1968–72. T* **182** *and similar horiz designs. Multicoloured. P* 12½ *(Nos. 231/4) or* 11½ *(others).*

231 7 c. Type **182** 80 45
a. Block of 4. Nos. 231/4 .. .. .. 3·25
232 7 c. Mt Kerigomma Station 80 45
233 7 c. Sattelburg Station 80 45
234 7 c. Wideru Station 80 45
235 9 c. Teleprinter (36 × 26 *mm*) 80 65
236 30 c. Network Map (36 × 26 *mm*) .. .. 2·50 2·50
231/6 .. .. *Set of* 6 6·00 4·25

Nos. 231/4 were printed in *se-tenant* blocks of four within the sheet.

183 Queen Carola's Parotia — 184 Wood Carver

(Des W. Cooper. Photo Courvoisier)

1973 (30 Mar). *Birds of Paradise. T* **183** *and similar vert designs. Multicoloured. P* 11½.

237 7 c. Type **183** .. .. 1·25 70
238 14 c. Goldie's Bird of Paradise .. .. .. 2·50 2·00
239 21 c. Ribbon-tailed Bird of Paradise (18 × 49 *mm*) .. .. 3·00 2·75
240 28 c. Princess Stephanie's Bird of Paradise (18 × 49 *mm*) .. .. 4·25 3·50

(Des R. Bates. Photo Courvoisier)

1973 (13 June)–**74**. *T* **184** *and similar horiz designs. Multicoloured. P* 11½.

241 1 c. Type **184** 10 5
242 3 c. Wig-makers (23.1.74) 20 8
243 5 c. Mt Bagana (22.8.73) 15 10
244 6 c. Pig Exchange (7.8.74) 50 50
245 7 c. Coastal village 20 12
246 8 c. Arawe mother (23.1.74) 35 15
247 9 c. Fire dancers 25 15
248 10 c. Tifalmin hunter (23.1.74) 35 15
249 14 c. Crocodile hunters (22.8.73) 45 30
250 15 c. Mt Elimbari 50 30
251 20 c. Canoe-racing (23.1.74) 85 40
252 21 c. Making sago (22.8.73) 65 45
253 25 c. Council House 70 45
254 28 c. Menyamya bowmen (22.8.73) 80 60
255 30 c. Shark-snaring (22.8.73) .. .. .. 1·00 75
256 40 c. Fishing canoes .. .. 1·50 1·00
257 60 c. Tapa cloth-making (23.1.74) .. .. .. 2·50 1·50
258 $1 Asaro Mudmen (23.1.74) .. .. .. 7·50 5·50
259 $2 Enga "Sing Sing" (7.8.74) .. .. .. 14·00 10·00
241/59 .. .. *Set of* 19 29·00 20·00

185 Stamps of German New Guinea, 1897

(Des R. Bates. Photo (1 c.), litho and recess (6 c.) or litho (7 c.) State Printing Works, Berlin. Photo and recess D.L.R. (9 c.). Recess and typo Reserve Bank of Australia (25 and 30 c.))

1973 (24 Oct). *75th Anniv of Papua New Guinea Stamps. T* **185** *and similar horiz designs. Chalky paper* (25, 30 c.). *P* 13½ (1, 6, 7 c.), 14 × 13½ *(9 c.) or* 14 × 14½ *(25, 30 c.).*

260 1 c. multicoloured 8 15
261 6 c. indigo, new blue and silver 30 35
262 7 c. multicoloured 35 35
263 9 c. multicoloured 45 50
264 25 c. orange and gold .. .. 1·50 2·50
265 30 c. plum and silver .. .. 1·75 2·75
260/65 .. .. *Set of* 6 4·00 6·00

Designs: *As T* 185—6 c. 2 mark stamp of German New Guinea, 1900; 7 c. Surcharged registration label of New Guinea, 1914. 46 × 35 *mm*.—9 c. Papua 1s. stamp, 1901. 45 × 38 *mm*—25 c. ½d. stamp of New Guinea, 1925; 30 c. Papua 10s. stamp, 1932.

SELF-GOVERNMENT

186 Native Carved Heads — 187 Queen Elizabeth II (from photograph by Karsh)

(Des G. Wade. Photo Courvoisier)

1973 (5 Dec). *Self-Government. P* 11½.

266 **186** 7 c. multicoloured 50 40
267 10 c. multicoloured .. .. 90 1·10

(Des and photo Harrison)

1974 (22 Feb). *Royal Visit. P* 14 × 14½.

268 **187** 7 c. multicoloured 45 35
269 30 c. multicoloured .. .. 2·25 2·50

188 Blyth's Hornbill — 189 *Dendrobium bracteosum*

(Des T. Nolan. Photo Courvoisier)

1974 (12 June). *Birds' Heads. T* **188** *and similar multicoloured designs. P* 11½ *(10 c.) or* 12 *(others).*

270 7 c. Type **188** .. .. 2·00 1·00
271 10 c. Double-wattled Cassowary (33 × 49 *mm*) 3·00 3·25
272 30 c. New Guinea Harpy Eagle .. .. .. 7·00 9·00

(Des T. Nolan. Photo Courvoisier)

1974 (20 Nov). *Flora Conservation. T* **189** *and similar vert designs. Multicoloured. P* 11½.

273 7 c. Type **189** 60 5
274 10 c. *D. anosmum* .. .. 1·25 50
275 20 c. *D. smillieae* .. .. 1·90 1·25
276 30 c. *D. insigne* .. .. 2·50 1·75

190 Motu Lagatoi — 191 1-toea Coin

(Des G. Wade. Photo Courvoisier)

1975 (26 Feb). *National Heritage—Canoes. T* **190** *and similar horiz designs. Multicoloured. P* 11½.

277 7 c. Type **190** 30 5
278 10 c. Tami two-master morobe 60 60
279 25 c. Aramia racing canoe .. .. 1·40 1·60
280 30 c. Buka canoe .. .. 1·40 1·40

(New Currency. 100 toea = 1 kina)

(Des G. Wade. Photo Courvoisier)

1975 (21 Apr). *New Coinage. T* **191** *and similar multicoloured designs. P* 11½.

281 1 t. Type **191** 5 5
282 7 t. New 2 t. and 5 t. coins (45 × 26 *mm*) .. 40 5
283 10 t. New 10 t. coin 60 30
284 20 t. New 20 t. coin .. .. 1·40 80
285 1 k. New 1 k. coin (45 × 26 *mm*) .. .. 6·50 6·50

192 *Ornithoptera alexandrae* — 193 Boxing

(Des R. Bates. Photo Courvoisier)

1975 (11 June). *Fauna Conservation (Birdwing Butterflies). T* **192** *and similar vert designs. Multicoloured. P* 11½.

286	7 t. Type **192**	50	5
287	10 t. *O. victoriae regis*	80	45
288	30 t. *O. allottei*	1·75	1·50
289	40 t. *O. chimaera*	2·25	1·90

(Des R. Bates. Photo Courvoisier)

1975 (2 Aug). *Fifth South Pacific Games, Guam. T* **193** *and similar vert designs. Multicoloured. P* 11½.

290	7 t. Type **193**	25	5
291	20 t. Running	70	65
292	25 t. Basketball	85	80
293	30 t. Swimming	1·00	85

INDEPENDENT

194 Map and National Flag

(Des and photo Courvoisier)

1975 (10 Sept). *Independence. T* **194** *and similar horiz design. Multicoloured. P* 11½.

294	7 t. Type **194**	35	10
295	30 t. Map and National emblem	90	1·00
MS296	116 × 58 mm. Nos. 294/5	1·50	1·50

195 M.V. *Bulolo* **196** Rorovana Carvings

(Des R. Bates. Photo Courvoisier)

1976 (21 Jan). *Ships of the 1930s. T* **195** *and similar horiz designs. Multicoloured. P* 11½.

297	7 t. Type **195**	35	5
298	15 t. M.V. *Macdhui*	55	40
299	25 t. M.V. *Malaita*	95	95
300	60 t. S.S. *Montoro*	3·00	3·50

(Des R. Bates. Photo Courvoisier)

1976 (17 Mar). *Bougainville Art. T* **196** *and similar horiz designs. Multicoloured. P* 11½.

301	7 t. Type **196**	30	5
302	20 t. Upe hats	75	85
303	25 t. Kapkaps	85	95
304	30 t. Canoe paddles	1·10	1·25

197 Rabaul House **198** Landscouts

(Des G. Wade. Photo Courvoisier)

1976 (9 June). *Native Dwellings. T* **197** *and similar horiz designs. Multicoloured. P* 11½.

305	7 t. Type **197**	35	5
306	15 t. Aramia house	55	30
307	30 t. Telefomin house	1·50	70
308	40 t. Tapini house	1·60	90

(Des R. Bates. Photo Courvoisier)

1976 (18 Aug). *50th Anniversaries of Survey Flight and Scouting in Papua New Guinea. T* **198** *and similar horiz designs. Multicoloured. P* 11½.

309	7 t. Type **198**	30	5
310	10 t. D. H. floatplane	40	20
311	15 t. Seascouts	75	75
312	60 t. Floatplane on water	2·25	2·50

199 Father Ross and New Guinea Highlands

(Des R. Bates. Photo Courvoisier)

1976 (28 Oct). *William Ross Commemoration. P* 11½.

313	**199**	7 t. multicoloured	45	15

ALTERED CATALOGUE NUMBERS

Any Catalogue numbers altered from the last edition are shown as a list in the introductory pages.

200 Clouded Rainbow Fish

(Des P. Jones. Photo Courvoisier)

1976 (28 Oct). *Fauna Conservation (Tropical Fish). T* **200** *and similar horiz designs. Multicoloured. P* 11½.

314	5 t. Type **200**	35	5
315	15 t. Emperor or Imperial Angel Fish	95	55
316	30 t. Freckled Rock Cod	1·90	1·00
317	40 t. Threadfin Butterfly Fish	2·00	1·25

201 Man from Kundiawa **202** Headdress, Wasara Tribe

(Des R. Bates. Litho Questa (1, 2 k.) or photo Courvoisier (others))

1977 (12 Jan)–**78**. *T* **201/2** *and similar multicoloured designs showing headdresses. P* 14 (1, 2 *k.*) *or* 11½ (*others*).

318	1 t. Type **201** (29.3.78)	5	5
319	5 t. Masked dancer, Abelam area of Maprik (29.3.78)	10	5
320	10 t. Headdress from Koiari (7.6.78)	20	15
321	15 t. Woman with face paint, Hanuabada (29.3.78)	25	25
322	20 t. Orokaiva dancer (7.6.78)	35	30
323	25 t. Haus Tambaran dancer, Abelam area of Maprik (29.3.78)	40	40
324	30 t. Asaro Valley headdress (29.3.78)	45	45
325	35 t. Singsing costume, Garaina (7.6.68)	60	50
326	40 t. Waghi Valley headdress (29.3.78)	60	55
327	50 t. Trobriand Island dancer (7.6.78)	90	75
328	1 k. Type **202**	1·50	1·50
329	2 k. Headdress, Mekeo tribe	3·00	3·00
318/29	*Set of* 12	7·50	7·00

Sizes:—1, 5, 20 t. 25 × 31 *mm;* 35, 40 t. 23 × 38 *mm;* 1 k. 28 × 35 *mm;* 2 k. 33 × 23 *mm;* others 26 × 26 *mm.*

203 National Flag and Queen Elizabeth II **204** White-breasted Ground Pigeon

(Des and photo Harrison)

1977 (16 Mar). *Silver Jubilee. Horiz designs showing Queen Elizabeth as T* **203**. *Multicoloured. P* 14½ × 14.

330	7 t. Type **203**	25	5
	a. Silver (face value and inscr) omitted	£450	
331	15 t. National emblem	45	60
332	35 t. Map of P.N.G.	85	1·00

(Des W. Cooper. Photo Courvoisier)

1977 (8 June). *Fauna Conservation (Birds). T* **204** *and similar horiz designs. Multicoloured. P* 11½.

333	5 t. Type **204**	15	5
334	7 t. Victoria Crowned Pigeon	20	5
335	15 t. Pheasant Pigeon	45	45
336	30 t. Orange-fronted Fruit Dove	1·40	85
337	50 t. Banded Imperial Pigeon	2·25	1·40

205 Guides and Gold Badge **206** Kari Marupi Myth

(Des R. Bates. Litho Questa)

1977 (10 Aug). *50th Anniv of Guiding in Papua New Guinea. Horiz designs showing badge as T* **205**. *Multicoloured. P* 14½.

338	7 t. Type **205**	25	5
339	15 t. Guides mapping	40	20
340	30 t. Guides washing	70	50
341	35 t. Guides cooking	85	60

(Des Rev. H. A. Brown. Litho Enschedé)

1977 (19 Oct). *Folklore. Elema Art (3rd series). T* **206** *and similar vert designs. P* 13½ × 13.

342	7 t. multicoloured	20	5
343	20 t. multicoloured	65	30
344	30 t. orange-red, light blue and black	90	65
345	35 t. orange-red, yellow and black	90	65

Designs:—20 t. Savoripi clan myth; 30 t. Oa-Laea myth; 35 t. Oa-Iriarapo myth.

207 Blue-tailed Skink **208** *Roboastra arika*

(Des T. Nolan. Photo Courvoisier)

1978 (25 Jan). *Fauna Conservation (Skinks). T* **207** *and similar horiz designs. Multicoloured. P* 11½.

346	10 t. Type **207**	35	5
347	15 t. Green Tree Skink	40	20
348	35 t. Crocodile Skink	65	55
349	40 t. New Guinea Blue-tongued Skink	85	70

(Des B. Twigden. Photo Courvoisier)

1978 (29 Aug). *Sea Slugs. T* **208** *and similar horiz designs. Multicoloured. P* 11½.

350	10 t. Type **208**	35	5
351	15 t. *Chromodoris fidelis*	40	25
352	35 t. *Flabellina macassarana*	80	80
353	40 t. *Chromodoris trimarginata*	85	85

209 Present Day Royal Papua New Guinea Constabulary **210** Ocarina

(Des R. Bates. Photo Harrison)

1978 (26 Oct). *History of Royal Papua New Guinea Constabulary. T* **209** *and similar horiz designs showing uniformed police and constabulary badges. Multicoloured. P* 14½.

354	10 t. Type **209**	30	5
355	15 t. Mandated New Guinea Constabulary, 1921–1941	50	15
356	20 t. British New Guinea Armed Constabulary, 1890–1906	55	40
357	25 t. German New Guinea Police, 1899–1914	65	45
358	30 t. Royal Papua and New Guinea Constabulary, 1906–1964	90	60

(Des R. Bates. Litho Questa)

1979 (24 Jan). *Musical Instruments. T* **210** *and similar multicoloured designs. P* 14½ × 14 (7, 28 *t.*) *or* 14 × 14½ (*others*).

359	7 t. Type **210**	15	5
360	20 t. Musical bow (*horiz*)	45	30
361	28 t. Launut	60	50
362	35 t. Nose flute (*horiz*)	75	70

211 East New Britain Canoe **212** Katudababila (waist belt)

(Des G. Wade. Litho Questa)

1979 (28 Mar). *Traditional Canoe Prows and Paddles. T* **211** *and similar vert designs. Multicoloured. P* 14½.

363	14 t. Type **211**	35	30
364	21 t. Sepik war canoe	50	45
365	25 t. Trobriand Islands canoe	60	50
366	40 t. Milne Bay canoe	1·00	85

(Des R. Bates. Photo Courvoisier)

1979 (6 June). *Traditional Currency. T* **212** *and similar horiz designs. Multicoloured. P* 12½ × 12.

367	7 t. Type **212**	12	5
368	15 t. Doga (chest ornament)	25	30
369	25 t. Mwali (armshell)	40	55
370	35 t. Soulava (necklace)	60	75

213 *Oenetus sp.* **214** "The Right to Affection and Love"

(Des T. Nolan. Photo Courvoisier)

1979 (29 Aug). *Fauna Conservation. Moths. T* **213** *and similar multicoloured designs. P* 11½.

No.	Description	Unused	Used
371	7 t. Type **213**	20	5
372	15 t. *Celerina vulgaris*	35	25
373	20 t. *Alcidis aurora* (*vert*)	45	40
374	25 t. *Phyllodes conspicillator*	55	50
375	30 t. *Nyctalemon patroclus* (*vert*)	70	60

(Des G. Wade. Litho Enschedé)

1979 (24 Oct). *International Year of the Child. T* **214** *and similar vert designs. Multicoloured. P* 13½ × 13.

No.	Description	Unused	Used
376	7 t. Type **214**	15	5
377	15 t. "The right to adequate nutrition and medical care"	30	30
378	30 t. "The right to play"	55	55
379	60 t. "The right to a free education"	1·00	1·10

215 "Post Office Service"

216 Detail from Betrothal Ceremony Mural, Minj District, Western Highlands Province

(Des G. Wade. Litho Enschedé)

1980 (23 Jan). *Admission to U.P.U.* (1979). *T* **215** *and similar horiz designs. Multicoloured. P* 13 × 13½.

No.	Description	Unused	Used
380	7 t. Type **215**	12	5
381	25 t. "Wartime mail"	40	40
382	35 t. U.P.U. emblem	55	60
383	40 t. "Early postal services"	65	70

(Des W. Tubun. Photo Courvoisier)

1980 (26 Mar). *South Pacific Festival of Arts. T* **216** *and similar vert designs showing different details from mural of betrothal ceremony, Minj District, Western Highlands Province. P* 11½.

No.	Description	Unused	Used
384	20 t. black, greenish yellow and pale orange	30	30
	a. Strip of 5. Nos. 384/8	1·40	
385	20 t. multicoloured (two figures—left-hand black and yellow; right-hand black, yellow and red)	30	30
386	20 t. multicoloured (two figures—left-hand black and orange; right-hand black)	30	30
387	20 t. multicoloured (two figures, one behind the other)	30	30
388	20 t. multicoloured (one figure)	30	30

Nos. 384/8 were printed together, *se-tenant*, in horizontal strips of 5 throughout the sheet.

217 Family being Interviewed

(Des R. Bates. Litho Questa)

1980 (4 June). *National Census. T* **217** *and similar horiz designs. Multicoloured. P* 14 × 13½.

No.	Description	Unused	Used
389	7 t. Type **217**	20	5
390	15 t. Population symbol	35	25
391	40 t. Figures and map of Papua New Guinea	80	60
392	50 t. Heads symbolising population growth	85	75

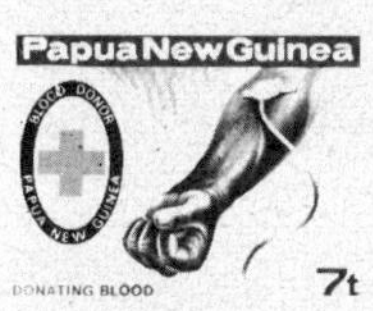

218 Donating Blood

219 Bonon

(Des R. Bates. Litho Questa)

1980 (27 Aug). *Red Cross Blood Bank. T* **218** *and similar horiz designs. Multicoloured. P* 14½.

No.	Description	Unused	Used
393	7 t. Type **218**	15	5
394	15 t. Receiving transfusion	25	30
395	30 t. Map of Papua New Guinea showing blood transfusion centres	50	50
396	60 t. Blood and its components	85	90

(Des Dr. E. Lindgren (35 t.), T. Nolan (others). Photo Courvoisier)

1980 (29 Oct). *Mammals. T* **219** *and similar multicoloured designs. P* 11½.

No.	Description	Unused	Used
397	7 t. Type **219**	10	5
398	30 t. Native Spotted Cat (*vert*)	50	50
399	35 t. Tube-nosed Bat (*vert*)	55	55
400	45 t. Mumut	65	65

220 White-headed Kingfisher

221 Native Mask

(Des W. Peckover. Photo Courvoisier)

1981 (21 Jan). *Kingfishers. T* **220** *and similar multicoloured designs. P* 11½.

No.	Description	Unused	Used
401	3 t. Type **220**	10	5
402	7 t. Forest Kingfisher	15	10
403	20 t. Sacred Kingfisher	45	40
404	25 t. White-tailed Kingfisher (26 × 46 *mm*)	55	45
405	60 t. Blue-winged Kookaburra	1·25	1·00

(Des R. Bates. Photo Note Ptg Branch, Reserve Bank of Australia)

1981 (21 Jan). *Coil stamps. Vert designs as T* **221**. *P* 15 × *imperf.*

No.	Description	Unused	Used
406	2 t. reddish violet and orange	5	5
407	5 t. cerise and blue-green	8	10

Design:—5 t. Hibiscus flower.

222 Mortar Team

223 M.A.F. (Missionary Aviation Fellowship) Aeroplane

(Des T. Reilly (15 t.), R. Bates (others). Litho Enschedé)

1981 (25 Mar). *Defence Force. T* **222** *and similar horiz designs. Multicoloured. P* 13 × 13½.

No.	Description	Unused	Used
408	7 t. Type **222**	15	5
409	15 t. Aeroplane and aircrew	30	25
410	40 t. P.N.G.S. *Aitape* and seamen	70	65
411	50 t. Medical team examining children	75	75

(Des G. Wade. Litho Questa)

1981 (17 June). *"Mission Aviation". T* **223** *and similar vert designs. Multicoloured. P* 14.

No.	Description	Unused	Used
412	10 t. Type **223**	20	20
413	15 t. Catholic mission aeroplane	25	25
414	20 t. S.I.L. (Summer Institute of Linguistics) helicopter	35	35
415	30 t. Lutheran mission aeroplane	55	55
416	35 t. S.D.A. (Seventh Day Adventist Church) aeroplane	65	65

224 Scoop Net Fishing

225 *Forcartia buhleri*

(Des G. Wade. Litho Questa)

1981 (26 Aug). *Fishing. T* **224** *and similar horiz designs. Multicoloured. P* 14.

No.	Description	Unused	Used
417	10 t. Type **224**	15	15
418	15 t. Kite fishing	30	30
419	30 t. Rod fishing	50	50
420	60 t. Scissor net fishing	95	85

(Des P. Jones. Photo Courvoisier)

1981 (28 Oct). *Land Snail Shells. T* **225** *and similar horiz designs. Multicoloured. P* 11½ × 12.

No.	Description	Unused	Used
421	5 t. Type **225**	10	10
422	15 t. *Naninia citrina*	30	35
423	20 t. *Papuina adonis* and *papuina hermione*	40	45
424	30 t. *Papustyla hindei* and *papustyla novaepommeraniae*	60	65
425	40 t. *Rhynchotrochus strabo*	80	90

226 Lord Baden-Powell and Flag-raising Ceremony

227 Yangoru and Boiken Bowls, East Sepik

(Des G. Wade. Photo Courvoisier)

1982 (20 Jan). *75th Anniv of Boy Scout Movement. T* **226** *and similar horiz designs. Multicoloured. P* 11½.

No.	Description	Unused	Used
426	15 t. Type **226**	35	35
427	25 t. Scout leader and camp	50	50
428	35 t. Scout, and hut building	65	65
429	50 t. Percy Chaterton, and Scouts administering first aid	85	85

(Des R. Bates. Litho Questa)

1982 (24 Mar). *Native Pottery. T* **227** *and similar multicoloured designs. P* 14 (10, 20 *t.*) *or* 14½ (*others*).

No.	Description	Unused	Used
430	10 t. Type **227**	20	15
431	20 t. Utu cooking pot and small Gumalu pot, Madang	40	40
432	40 t. Wanigela pots, Northern District (37 × 23 *mm*)	65	65
433	50 t. Ramu Valley pots, Madang (37 × 23 *mm*)	85	85

228 "Eat Healthy Foods"

229 *Stylophora sp*

(Des G. Wade, Litho J.W.)

1982 (21 May). *Food and Nutrition. T* **228** *and similar horiz designs. Multicoloured. P* 14½ × 14.

No.	Description	Unused	Used
434	10 t. Type **228**	20	15
435	15 t. Protein foods	35	35
436	30 t. Protective foods	65	65
437	40 t. Energy foods	75	75

(Des Courvoisier or W. Peckover (5 k.). Photo Courvoisier)

1982 (21 July)–**84**. (*a*). *Corals. Multicoloured designs as T* **229**. *P* 11½.

No.	Description	Unused	Used
438	1 t. Type **229**	5	5
439	3 t. *Dendrophyllia sp.* (*vert*) (12.1.83)	5	8
440	5 t. *Acropora humilis*	8	10
441	10 t. *Dendronephthya sp.* (*vert*) (12.1.83)	15	20
442	15 t. *Distichopora sp*	25	30
443	20 t. *Isis sp.* (*vert*) (9.11.83)	30	35
444	25 t. *Acropora sp.* (*vert*) (9.11.83)	40	45
445	30 t. *Dendronephthya sp.* (*diff*) (*vert*) (12.1.83)	50	55
446	35 t. *Stylaster elegans* (*vert*) (9.11.83)	55	60
447	40 t. *Antipathes sp.* (*vert*) (12.1.83)	65	70
448	45 t. *Turbinarea sp.* (*vert*) (9.11.83)	70	75
449	1 k. *Xenia sp*	1·75	1·90
450	3 k. *Distichopora sp.* (*vert*) (12.1.83)	4·75	5·00
	(*b*) *Bird of Paradise. Multicoloured square design,* 33 × 33 *mm*		
451	5 k. *Paradisaea raggiana* (15.8.84)	8·00	8·25
438/51	*Set of* 14	16·00	17·00

230 Missionaries landing on Beach

231 Athletics

(Des B. To Una. Photo Courvoisier)

1982 (15 Sept). *Centenary of Catholic Church in Papua New Guinea. Mural on wall of Nordup Catholic Church, East New Britain. T* **230** *and similar vert designs. Multicoloured. P* 11½.

No.	Description	Unused	Used
457	10 t. Type **230**	15	20
	a. Horiz strip of 3. Nos. 457/9	40	
458	10 t. Missionaries talking to natives	15	20
459	10 t. Natives with slings and spears ready to attack	15	20

Nos. 457/9 come in *se-tenant* strips of 3 horizontally throughout the sheet, each strip forming a composite design.

(Des R. Bates. Litho Questa)

1982 (6 Oct). *Commonwealth Games and "Anpex 82" Stamp Exhibition, Brisbane. T* **231** *and similar horiz designs. Multicoloured. P* 14½.

No.	Description	Unused	Used
460	10 t. Type **231**	15	15
461	15 t. Boxing	25	25
462	45 t. Rifle-shooting	65	70
463	50 t. Bowls	70	75

232 National Flag

(Des Walsall. Litho Harrison)

1983 (9 Mar). *Commonwealth Day. T* **232** *and similar horiz designs. Multicoloured. P* 14.

No.	Description	Unused	Used
464	10 t. Type **232**	15	20
465	15 t. Basket-weaving and cabbage-picking	25	30
466	20 t. Crane hoisting roll of material	30	35
467	50 t. Lorries and ships	70	75

233 Transport Communications

234 *Chelonia depressa*

(Des G. Wade. Litho J.W.)

1983 (7 Sept). *World Communications Year. T* **233** *and similar horiz designs. Multicoloured. P* 14.

468	10 t. Type **233**	15	20
469	25 t. "Postal service"	40	45
470	30 t. "Telephone service"	45	50
471	60 t. "Transport service"	85	90

(Des R. Bates. Photo Courvoisier)

1984 (8 Feb). *Turtles. T* **234** *and similar horiz designs. Multicoloured. P* 11½.

472	5 t. Type **234**	8	10
473	10 t. *Chelonia mydas*	15	20
474	15 t. *Eretmochelys imbricata*	25	30
475	20 t. *Lepidochelys olivacea*	30	35
476	25 t. *Caretta caretta*	40	45
477	40 t. *Dermochelys coriacea*	60	65
472/7	*Set of* 6	1·60	1·75

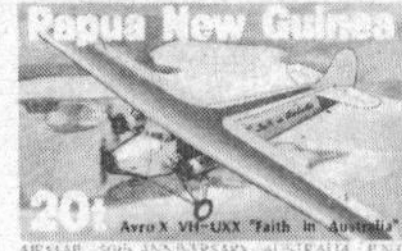

235 Avro "X VH-UXX" *Faith in Australia*

(Des T. Reilly. Litho Format)

1984 (9 May). *50th Anniv of First Airmail Australia-Papua New Guinea. T* **235** *and similar horiz designs. Multicoloured. P* 14½ × 14.

478	20 t. Type **235**	35	40
479	25 t. "DH86B VH-UYU" *Carmania*	45	50
480	40 t. Westland "Widgeon VH-UGI"	75	80
481	60 t. Consolidated "Catalina NC777" *Guba*	1·10	1·25

236 Parliament House

237 Ceremonial Shield and Club, Central Province

(Des A. Brennan, adapted G. Vasarhelyi. Litho Harrison)

1984 (7 Aug). *Opening of New Parliament House. P* 13½ × 14.

482	**236**	10 t. multicoloured	20	25

(Des The Revd. A. H. Brown. Photo Courvoisier)

1984 (21 Sept). *Ceremonial Shields. T* **237** *and similar vert designs. Multicoloured. Granite paper. P* 11½.

483	10 t. Type **237**	20	25
484	20 t. Ceremonial shield, West New Britain	35	40
485	30 t. Ceremonial shield, Madang Province	55	60
486	50 t. Ceremonial shield, East Sepik	90	95

238 H.M.S. *Nelson* at Port Moresby, 1884

239 Fergusson Island

(Des R. Bates, Litho Format)

1984 (6 Nov). *Centenary of Protectorate Proclamations for British New Guinea and German New Guinea. T* **238** *and similar horiz designs. Multicoloured. P* 14½ × 14.

487	10 t. Type **238**	20	25
	a. Horiz pair. Nos. 487/8	40	50
488	10 t. Papua New Guinea flag and Port Moresby, 1984	20	25
489	45 t. Papua New Guinea flag and Rabaul, 1984	85	90
	a. Horiz pair. Nos. 489/90	1·75	1·75
490	45 t. S.M.S. *Elisabeth* at Rabaul, 1884	85	90

The two designs for each value were issued together, *se-tenant*, as horizontal pairs throughout the sheets, each pair forming a composite picture.

(Des R. Bates. Photo Courvoisier)

1985 (6 Feb). *Tourist Scenes. T* **239** *and similar multicoloured designs. Granite paper. P* 11½.

491	10 t. Type **239**	15	20
492	25 t. Sepik River	40	45
493	40 t. Chimbu Gorge (*horiz*)	60	65
494	60 t. Dali Beach, Vanimo (*horiz*)	90	95

OMNIBUS ISSUES

Details, together with prices for complete sets, of the various Omnibus issues from the 1935 Silver Jubilee series to date are included in a special section following Zululand at the end of the catalogue.

POSTAGE DUE STAMPS

POSTAL CHARGES

6d.

IXIXIXIXIX

(D 1)

POSTAL CHARGES

3s.

(D 2)

1960 (1 Mar). *Postage stamps surcharged. (a) No.* 8 *with Type* D **1**.

D1	6d. on 7½d. blue (R.)	£500	£225
	a. Surch double	£1800	£1200
	(*b*) *Nos.* 1, 4, 6*a*, 7/8 *as Type* D **2**		
D2	1d. on 6½d. maroon	14·00	6·50
D3	3d. on ½d. emerald (B.)	15·00	7·00
	a. Surch double	£225	
D4	6d. on 7½d. blue (R.)	23·00	14·00
	a. Surch double	£225	
D5	1s. 3d. on 3½d. black (O.)	24·00	16·00
D6	3s. on 2½d. orange	38·00	30·00

Of No. D1a, only a few copies are known from a sheet used at Goroka.

D 3

(Typo Note Ptg Branch, Reserve Bank of Australia, Melbourne)

1960 (2 June). *W* **15** *of Australia. P* 14.

D 7	D **3**	1d. orange	45	35
D 8		3d. yellow-brown	70	45
D 9		6d. blue	75	50
D10		9d. deep red	90	1·50
D11		1s. light emerald	90	60
D12		1s. 3d. violet	1·75	1·75
D13		1s. 6d. pale blue	7·50	6·00
D14		3s. yellow	8·00	2·25
D7/14		*Set of* 8	19·00	12·00

The use of Postal Charge stamps was discontinued on 12 February 1966, but they remained on sale at the Philatelic Bureau until 31 August 1966.

Pitcairn Islands

CROWN COLONY

Stamps of NEW ZEALAND were used by a Postal Agency operating on Pitcairn Islands from June 1927 until October 1940.

PRICES FOR STAMPS ON COVER TO 1945
Nos. 1/8 *from* × 2

1 Cluster of Oranges

2 Christian on *Bounty* and Pitcairn Island

(Recess B.W. (1d., 3d., 4d., 8d. and 2s. 6d.), and Waterlow (others))

1940 (15 Oct)–**51**. *T* **1/2** *and similar horiz designs. Wmk Mult Script CA. P* 11½ × 11 (*1d., 3d., 4d., 8d. and 2s. 6d.*) *or* 12½ (*others*).

1	½d. orange and green	40	45
2	1d. mauve and magenta	40	45
3	1½d. grey and carmine	45	50
4	2d. green and brown	1·60	1·00
5	3d. yellow-green and blue	1·50	1·40
5*a*	4d. black and emerald-green (1.9.51)	17·00	13·00
6	6d. brown and grey-blue	2·50	2·00
6*a*	8d. olive-green and magenta (1.9.51)	17·00	14·00
7	1s. violet and grey	1·75	2·25
8	2s. 6d. green and brown	11·00	8·00
1/8	*Set of* 10	48·00	38·00
1/8 (ex. *a* Nos.) Perf "Specimen"	*Set of* 8	£400	

Designs:—1½d. John Adams and his house; 2d. Lt. Bligh and *Bounty*; 3d. Pitcairn Islands and Pacific Ocean; 4d. *Bounty* Bible; 6d. H.M. Armed Vessel *Bounty*; 8d. School, 1949; 1s. Fletcher Christian and Pitcairn Island; 2s. 6d. Christian on *Bounty* and Pitcairn Coast.

1946 (2 Dec). *Victory. As Nos.* 28/9 *of Aden.*

9	2d. brown	70	35
10	3d. blue	75	45
9/10 Perf "Specimen"	*Set of* 2	80·00	

1949 (1 Aug). *Royal Silver Wedding. As Nos.* 30/1 *of Aden.*

11	1½d. scarlet	1·00	1·00
12	10s. mauve	£110	£120

1949 (10 Oct). *75th Anniv of Universal Postal Union. As Nos.* 114/17 *of Antigua.*

13	2½d. red-brown	10·00	7·50
14	3d. deep blue	12·00	8·50
15	6d. deep blue-green	13·00	11·00
16	1s. purple	14·00	12·00

1953 (2 June). *Coronation. As No.* 47 *of Aden, but ptd by B.W.*

17	4d. black and deep bluish green	2·50	6·50

9 *Cordyline terminalis*

10 Pitcairn Island Map

(Recess D.L.R.)

1957 (2 July)–**58**. *T* **9/10** *and similar designs. Wmk Mult Script CA. P* 13 × 12½ (*horiz*) *or* 12½ × 13 (*vert*).

18	½d. green and reddish lilac (*shades*)	60	35
19	1d. black and olive-green (*shades*)	70	50
20	2d. brown and greenish blue	60	40
21	2½d. deep brown and red-orange	60	50
22	3d. emerald and deep ultramarine	75	50
23	4d. scarlet and deep ultramarine (I)	1·75	1·75
23*a*	4d. carmine-red and deep ultramarine (II) (5.11.58)	6·50	3·50
24	6d. pale buff and indigo	2·25	1·25
25	8d. deep olive-green and carmine-lake	2·00	1·50
26	1s. black and yellowish brown	2·00	1·50
27	2s. green and red-orange	38·00	22·00
28	2s. 6d. ultramarine and lake (*shades*)	25·00	15·00
18/28	*Set of* 12	70·00	40·00

Designs: *Vert*—2d. John Adams and *Bounty* Bible; 2s. Island wheelbarrow. *Horiz*—2½d. Handicrafts: Bird model; 3d. Bounty Bay; 4d. Pitcairn School; 6d. Pacific Ocean map; 8d. Inland scene; 1s. Handicrafts: Ship model; 2s. 6d. Launching new whaleboat.

Nos. 23/*a*. Type I is inscribed "PITCAIRN SCHOOL"; Type II "SCHOOLTEACHER'S HOUSE".

See also No. 33

20 Pitcairn Island and Simon Young

(Des H. E. Maud. Photo Harrison)

1961 (15 Nov). *Centenary of Return of Pitcairn Islanders from Norfolk Island. T* **20** *and similar horiz designs. W* w **12**. *P* 14½ × 13½.
29 3d. black and yellow .. .. 1·50 90
30 6d. red-brown and blue .. .. 2·00 1·00
31 1s. red-orange and blue-green .. .. .. 2·50 1·25
Designs:—6d. Norfolk Island and Pitcairn Islands; 1s. Migrant schooner *Mary Ann*.

1963 (4 June). *Freedom from Hunger. As No.* 76 *of Aden.*
32 2s. 6d. ultramarine .. .. 38·00 15·00

1963 (4 Dec). *As No.* 18 *but wmk* w **12**.
33 **9** ½d. green and reddish purple .. .. 55 1·00

1963 (9 Dec). *Red Cross Centenary. As Nos.* 147/8 *of Antigua.*
34 2d. red and black .. .. 2·50 1·40
35 2s. 6d. red and blue .. .. 15·00 11·00

23 Pitcairn Is Longboat

24 Queen Elizabeth II (after Anthony Buckley)

(Des M. Farrar Bell. Photo Harrison)

1964 (5 Aug)–**65**. *T* **23/4** *and similar horiz designs. Multicoloured. W* w **12**. *P* 14 × 14½.
36 ½d. Type **23** 5 12
37 1d. The *Bounty* 30 15
38 2d. "Out from Bounty Bay" 40 20
39 3d. Great Frigate Bird 40 20
40 4d. White Tern 40 20
41 6d. Pitcairn Warbler 45 25
42 8d. Red-footed Booby 45 35
43 10d. Red-tailed Tropic Birds 50 40
44 1s. Henderson Island Crake 50 40
45 1s. 6d. Stephen's Lory .. .. 11·00 2·50
46 2s. 6d. Murphy's Petrel .. .. 11·00 3·50
47 4s. Henderson Island Fruit Dove .. .. 11·00 4·00
48 8s. Type **24** (5.4.65) .. .. 6·00 7·00
36/48 .. .. *Set of* 13 38·00 17·00

1965 (17 May). *I.T.U. Centenary. As Nos.* 166/7 *of Antigua.*
49 1d. mauve and orange-brown .. .. .. 1·25 40
50 2s. 6d. turquoise-green and bright blue .. 22·00 12·00

1965 (25 Oct). *International Co-operation Year. As Nos.* 168/9 *of Antigua.*
51 1d. reddish purple and turquoise-green .. 1·00 40
52 1s. 6d. deep bluish green and lavender .. 20·00 10·00

1966 (24 Jan). *Churchill Commemoration. As Nos.* 170/3 *of Antigua.*
53 2d. new blue .. .. 2·25 75
54 3d. deep green .. .. 5·50 1·50
55 6d. brown .. .. 12·00 5·50
56 1s. bluish violet .. .. 16·00 8·00

1966 (1 Aug). *World Cup Football Championships. As Nos.* 176/7 *of Antigua.*
57 4d. violet, yellow-green, lake & yell-brn 3·00 1·50
58 2s. 6d. chocolate, blue-green, lake & yell-brn 10·00 4·50

1966 (20 Sept). *Inauguration of W.H.O. Headquarters, Geneva. As Nos.* 178/9 *of Antigua.*
59 8d. black, yellow-green and light blue .. 7·00 3·50
60 1s. 6d. black, light purple and yellow-brown 11·00 4·00

1966 (1 Dec). *20th Anniv of U.N.E.S.C.O. As Nos.* 196/8 *of Antigua.*
61 ½d. slate-violet, red, yellow and orange .. 25 30
62 10d. orange-yellow, violet and deep olive .. 6·00 3·25
63 2s. black, bright purple and orange .. .. 12·00 4·25

36 Mangarevan, *circa* 1325

(Des V. Whiteley. Photo Harrison)

1967 (1 Mar). *Bicentenary of Discovery of Pitcairn Islands. T* **36** *and similar horiz designs. Multicoloured. W* w **12**. *P* 14½.
64 ½d. Type **36** 5 5
65 1d. P. F. de Quiros and *San Pedro y Pablo*, 1606 .. .. 10 8
66 8d. *San Pedro* and *Los Tres Reyes*, 1606 .. 40 30
67 1s. Carteret and H.M.S. *Swallow*, 1767 .. 50 40
68 1s. 6d. *Hercules*, 1819 .. .. 50 50

(New Currency. 100 cents = 1 New Zealand dollar)

½c

(**41** *Bounty* Anchor)

1967 (10 July). *Decimal currency. Nos.* 36/48 *surch in decimal currency by die-stamping in gold as T* **41**.
69 ½ c. on ½d. multicoloured 5 5
70 1 c. on 1d. multicoloured 30 15
71 2 c. on 2d. multicoloured 35 15
72 2½ c. on 3d. multicoloured 35 20
73 3 c. on 4d. multicoloured 40 25
74 5 c. on 6d. multicoloured 40 30
75 10 c. on 8d. multicoloured 50 40
76 15 c. on 10d. multicoloured .. .. .. 1·25 80
77 20 c. on 1s. multicoloured .. .. .. 1·75 1·50
78 25 c. on 1s. 6d. multicoloured .. .. 4·50 2·00
79 30 c. on 2s. 6d. multicoloured .. .. 6·00 3·00
80 40 c. on 4s. multicoloured .. .. .. 9·00 3·50
81 45 c. on 8s. multicoloured .. .. .. 12·00 4·00
69/81 .. .. *Set of* 13 32·00 15·00
The ½ c. and 1 c. exist with PVA gum as well as gum arabic.

42 Bligh and *Bounty*'s Launch

1967 (7 Dec). *150th Death Anniv of Admiral Bligh. T* **42** *and similar horiz designs. P* 13½ × 13.
82 1 c. turq-blue, black and royal blue (*shades*) 10 30
83 8 c. black, yellow and magenta 70 40
84 20 c. black, brown and pale buff 70 40
Designs:—8 c. Bligh and followers cast adrift; 20 c. Bligh's tomb.

45 Human Rights Emblem

(Des G. Hamori. Litho D.L.R.)

1968 (4 Mar). *Human Rights Year. P* 13½ × 13.
85 **45** 1 c. multicoloured 10 10
86 2 c. multicoloured 35 20
87 25 c. multicoloured 65 40

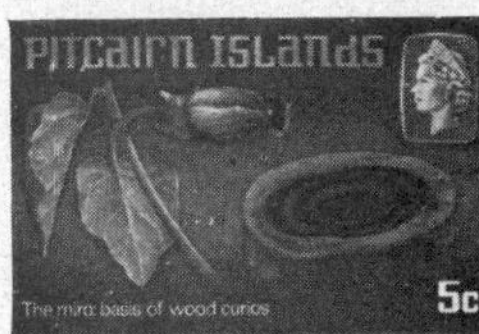

46 Miro Wood and Flower

(Des Jennifer Toombs. Photo Harrison)

1968 (19 Aug). *Handicrafts (1st series). T* **46** *and similar designs. W* w **12** (*sideways on vert designs*). *P* 14 × 13½ (5, 10 c.) *or* 13½ × 14 (*others*).
88 5 c. multicoloured 90 65
89 10 c. bronze-green, brown and orange .. 1·00 70
90 15 c. deep bluish violet, chocolate and salmon 1·25 75
91 20 c. multicoloured .. .. 1·25 80
Designs: *Horiz*—10 c. Flying Fish model. *Vert*—15 c. "Hand" vases; 20 c. Woven baskets.
See also Nos. 207/10.

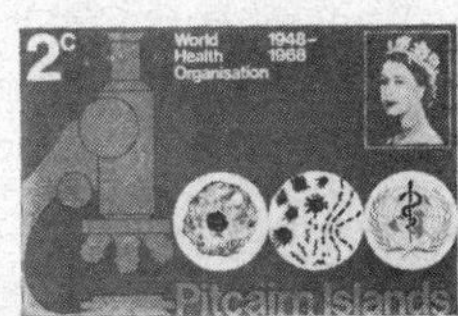

50 Microscope and Slides

(Des Jennifer Toombs. Litho D.L.R.)

1968 (25 Nov). *20th Anniv of World Health Organisation. T* **50** *and similar horiz design. W* w **12** (*sideways*). *P* 14.
92 2 c. black, turquoise-blue and ultramarine .. 35 20
93 20 c. black, orange and bright purple .. 1·25 75
Design:—20 c. Hypodermic syringe and jars of tablets.

52 Pitcairn Island

62 "Flying Fox" Cable System

(Des Jennifer Toombs. Litho Questa (50 c., $1), D.L.R. (others))

1969 (17 Sept)–**75**. *T* **52**, **62** *and similar designs. Chalk-surfaced paper. W* w **12** (*upright on* 3 c., 25 c., *sideways on* $1 *and horiz designs*). *P* 14½ × 14 (50 c.), 14 ($1) *or* 13 (*others*).
94 1 c. multicoloured 35 20
a. Glazed, ordinary paper (9.8.71) 65 50
95 2 c. multicoloured 25 20
96 3 c. multicoloured 25 20
97 4 c. multicoloured 30 25
98 5 c. multicoloured 30 25
99 6 c. multicoloured 30 25
100 8 c. multicoloured 45 30
101 10 c. multicoloured .. .. 6·00 3·00
a. Glazed, ordinary paper (9.8.71) .. .. 2·00 2·75
102 15 c. multicoloured .. .. 1·40 90
a. Queen's head omitted £400
103 20 c. multicoloured .. .. 1·40 1·00
104 25 c. multicoloured .. .. 1·50 1·10
105 30 c. multicoloured .. .. 1·75 1·75
106 40 c. multicoloured .. .. 3·00 2·25
106*a* 50 c. multicoloured (*glazed, ordinary paper*) (2.1.73) .. .. 10·00 6·00
106*b* $1 multicoloured (*glazed, ordinary paper*) (21.4.75) .. .. 17·00 14·00
94/106*b* .. .. *Set of* 15 35·00 28·00
Designs: *Horiz*—2 c. Captain Bligh and *Bounty* chronometer; 4 c. Plans and drawing of *Bounty*; 5 c. Breadfruit containers and plant; 6 c. Bounty Bay; 8 c. Pitcairn longboat; 10 c. Ship landing point; 15 c. Fletcher Christian's Cave; 20 c. Thursday October Christian's House; 30 c. Radio Station, Taro Ground; 40 c. *Bounty* Bible; 50 c. Pitcairn Coat of Arms. *Vert*—3 c. *Bounty* anchor; $1 Queen Elizabeth II.
See also No. 133.

65 Lantana

69 Auntie and Ann (grouper)

(Des Jennifer Toombs. Litho D.L.R.)

1970 (23 Mar). *Flowers. T* **65** *and similar vert designs. Multicoloured. W* w **12**. *P* 14.
107 1 c. Type **65** 20 20
108 2 c. "Indian Shot" 80 55
109 5 c. Pulau .. .. 2·50 1·75
110 25 c. Wild Gladiolus .. .. 10·00 8·00

(Des Jennifer Toombs. Photo Harrison)

1970 (12 Oct). *Fishes. T* **69** *and similar horiz designs. Multicoloured. W* w **12**. *P* 14.
111 5 c. Type **69** .. .. 3·00 1·75
112 10 c. Dream Fish (rudder fish) .. .. .. 3·00 2·00
113 15 c. Elwyn's Trousers (wrasse) .. .. 3·50 2·25
114 20 c. Whistling Daughter (wrasse) .. .. 3·75 3·00

ROYAL VISIT 1971

(**70**)

71 Polynesian Rock Carvings

1971 (22 Feb). *Royal Visit. No.* 101 *optd with T* **70**, *in silver.*
115 10 c. multicoloured .. .. 8·00 12·00

(Des Jennifer Toombs. Litho A & M)

1971 (3 May). *Polynesian Pitcairn. T* **71** *and similar multicoloured designs. W* w **12** (*sideways on* 10 *and* 15 *c.*). *P* 13½.
116 5 c. Type **71** .. .. 2·50 1·50
117 10 c. Polynesian artefacts (*horiz*) .. .. 3·00 2·00
118 15 c. Polynesian stone fish-hook (*horiz*) .. 3·25 2·00
119 20 c. Polynesian stone deity .. .. .. 3·75 3·00

72 Commission Flag

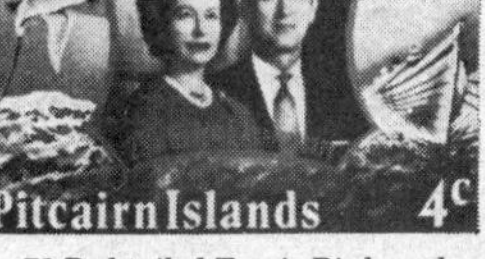

73 Red-tailed Tropic Birds and Longboat

(Des Jennifer Toombs. Litho Questa)

1972 (4 Apr). *25th Anniv of South Pacific Commission. T* **72** *and similar horiz designs. Multicoloured* (*except* 4 c.). W w **12** (*sideways on* 4 c.). *P* 14.

120 4 c. dp blue, blue-violet & brt yellow (T **72**) .. 2·25 1·75
121 8 c. Young and Elderly (Health) .. .. 2·25 2·25
122 18 c. Junior School (Education) .. .. 3·00 2·50
123 20 c. Goods store (Economy) .. .. .. 4·00 3·00

(Des (from photographs by D. Groves) and photo Harrison)

1972 (20 Nov). *Royal Silver Wedding. Multicoloured; background colour given.* W w **12**. *P* 14 × 14½.

124 **73** 4 c. slate-green 75 75
125 20 c. bright blue .. .. 1·00 1·25

74 Rose-apple

75 Horn-shell and Mitres

(Des Jennifer Toombs. Litho J.W.)

1973 (25 June). *Flowers. T* **74** *and similar vert designs. Multicoloured.* W w **12** (*sideways*). *P* 14.

126 4 c. Type **74** .. .. 1·50 75
127 8 c. Mountain-apple .. .. 2·25 1·25
128 15 c. "Lata" .. .. 3·50 2·25
129 20 c. "Dorcas-flower" .. .. 3·75 2·50
130 35 c. Guava .. .. 4·50 3·50

1973 (14 Nov). *Royal Wedding. As Nos.* 165/6 *of Anguilla. Centre multicoloured.* W w **12** (*sideways*). *P* 13½.

131 10 c. bright mauve 50 40
132 25 c. emerald 60 50

1974 (4 Feb). *As No.* 94 *but wmk upright. Glazed, ordinary paper.*

133 **52** 1 c. multicoloured .. .. .. 1·40 1·90

134/46 Catalogue numbers vacant.

(Des Jennifer Toombs. Litho Questa)

1974 (15 Apr). *Shells. T* **75** *and similar horiz designs. Multicoloured.* W w **12**. *P* 14.

147 4 c. Type **75** .. .. 2·25 1·25
148 10 c. Dove-shell .. .. 3·00 2·00
149 18 c. Limpet and False Limpet .. .. 3·75 2·75
150 50 c. Lucine shell .. .. 5·50 4·00
MS151 130 × 121 mm. Nos. 147/50 .. .. 13·00 12·00

76 Island Post Office

(Des Jennifer Toombs. Litho Questa)

1974 (22 July). *Centenary of Universal Postal Union. T* **76** *and similar horiz designs.* W w **12** (*sideways*). *P* 14.

152 4 c. multicoloured 75 50
153 20 c. bright purple, light cinnamon and black 1·00 1·25
154 35 c. multicoloured .. .. 1·25 1·50

Designs:—20 c. Pre-stamp letter, 1922; 35 c. Mailship and Pitcairn longboat.

77 Churchill and Text "Lift up your Hearts . . ."

(Des Jennifer Toombs. Litho Questa)

1974 (30 Nov). *Birth Centenary of Sir Winston Churchill. T* **77** *and similar horiz design.* W w **14** (*sideways*). *P* 14½.

155 20 c. blackish olive, apple-green & dp slate .. 2·00 1·75
156 35 c. sepia, greenish yellow and deep slate .. 2·25 1·90

Design:—35 c. Text "Give us the tools . . .".

78 H.M.S. *Seringapatam*, 1830

(Des Jennifer Toombs. Litho Walsall)

1975 (22 July). *Mailboats. T* **78** *and similar horiz designs. Multicoloured.* W w **14** (*sideways*). *P* 14.

157 4 c. Type **78** 95 50
158 10 c. The *Pitcairn*, 1890 .. .. .. 1·60 90
159 18 c. R.M.S. *Athenic*, 1904 .. .. .. 2·50 1·75
160 50 c. S.S. *Gothic*, 1948 .. .. 4·25 3·50
MS161 145 × 110 mm. Nos. 157/60 .. .. 15·00 13·00

79 Pitcairn Wasp

80 Fletcher Christian

(Des Jennifer Toombs. Litho Questa)

1975 (9 Nov). *Pitcairn Insects. T* **79** *and similar horiz designs. Multicoloured.* W w **12** (*sideways*). *P* 14.

162 4 c. Type **79** .. .. 1·00 70
163 6 c. Grasshopper .. .. 1·25 85
164 10 c. Moths .. .. 1·75 1·40
165 15 c. Devil's Needle .. .. 2·25 2·00
166 20 c. Banana Moth .. .. 2·50 2·75

(Des Jennifer Toombs. Litho J.W.)

1976 (4 July). *Bicentenary of American Revolution. T* **80** *and similar vert designs. Multicoloured.* W w **14**. *P* 13½.

167 5 c. Type **80** 75 60
a. Horiz pair. Nos. 167 and 169 .. .. 2·50 2·10
168 10 c. H.M.S. *Bounty* 95 75
a. Horiz pair. Nos. 168 and 170 .. .. 3·00 2·50
169 30 c. George Washington .. .. .. 1·75 1·50
170 50 c. *Mayflower* .. .. 2·25 1·75

The 5 and 30 c. and 10 and 50 c. values were each printed together, *se-tenant*, in horizontal pairs throughout the sheets.

81 Chair of Homage

82 The Island's Bell

(Des Jennifer Toombs. Litho J.W.)

1977 (6 Feb). *Silver Jubilee. T* **81** *and similar vert designs. Multicoloured.* W w **14**. *P* 13.

171 8 c. Prince Philip's visit, 1971 .. .. 65 55
172 20 c. Type **81** 85 90
173 50 c. Enthronement .. .. 1·00 1·40

(Des Jennifer Toombs. Litho Walsall)

1977 (12 Sept)–**81**. *Various multicoloured designs as T* **82**. W w **14** (*upright on* 1 *c.,* 9 *c.,* 70 *c. and* $2; *sideways on others*). *P* 14.

174 1 c. Type **82** 5 5
175 2 c. Building a longboat 5 5
176 5 c. Landing cargo 5 5
177 6 c. Sorting supplies 5 5
178 9 c. Cleaning wahoo (fish) 10 10
179 10 c. Cultivation 10 10
179*a* 15 c. Sugar Mill (1.10.81) 20 20
180 20 c. Grating coconut and bananas 20 20
181 35 c. The Island church 35 35
182 50 c. Fetching miro logs, Henderson Is. .. 45 45
182*a* 70 c. Burning obsolete stamp issues (1.10.81) 70 70
183 $1 Prince Philip, Bounty Bay and Royal Yacht *Britannia* 85 95
184 $2 Queen Elizabeth II (photograph by Reginald Davis) .. .. 1·75 2·00
174/84 .. .. *Set of* 13 4·50 4·75

The 1 c., 9 c., 70 c. and $2 are vertical designs, the remainder horizontal.

83 Building a *Bounty* Model

84 Coronation Ceremony

(Des E. W. Roberts. Litho Questa)

1978 (9 Jan). *"Bounty Day". T* **83** *and similar horiz designs. Multicoloured.* W w **14** (*sideways*). *P* 14½.

185 6 c. Type **83** .. .. 1·00 75
186 20 c. The model at sea .. .. 2·00 1·40
187 35 c. Burning the model .. .. 2·25 1·60
MS188 166 × 122 mm. Nos. 185/7 .. .. 12·00 10·00

(Des Jennifer Toombs. Litho Cartor S.A., France)

1978 (9 Oct). *25th Anniv of Coronation. Sheet* 94 × 78 *mm.* W w **14**. *P* 12.

MS189 **84** $1.20, multicoloured .. .. .. 4·50 5·00

85 Harbour before Development

(Des J.W. Litho Bruder Rosenbaum, Vienna)

1978 (18 Dec). *"Operation Pallium" (Harbour Development Project). T* **85** *and similar horiz designs. Multicoloured.* W w **14** (*sideways*). *P* 13½.

190 15 c. Type **85** 65 60
191 20 c. Unloading *Sir Geraint* 75 65
192 30 c. Work on the jetty 80 70
193 35 c. Harbour after development 85 75

86 John Adams and Diary Extract

(Des Jennifer Toombs. Litho Questa)

1979 (5 Mar). *150th Death Anniv of John Adams (mutineer from the "Bounty"). T* **86** *and similar horiz design. Multicoloured.* W w **14** (*sideways*). *P* 14.

194 35 c. Type **86** 90 90
195 70 c. John Adams' grave and diary extract .. 1·25 1·25

87 Pitcairn's Island sketched from H.M.S. *Amphitrite*

(Des Jennifer Toombs. Litho Questa)

1979 (12 Sept). *19th-century Engravings. T* **87** *and similar horiz designs.* W w **14** (*sideways*). *P* 14.

196 6 c. black, brown-ochre and stone 25 25
197 9 c. black, violet and pale violet 35 35
198 20 c. black, brt green & pale yellowish green 60 55
199 70 c. black, scarlet and pale rose .. .. 1·25 1·00

Designs:—9 c. Bounty Bay and Village of Pitcairn; 20 c. Lookout Ridge; 70 c. Church and School House.

88 Taking Presents to the Square

(Des and litho J.W.)

1979 (28 Nov). *Christmas and International Year of the Child. T* **88** *and similar horiz designs. Multicoloured.* W w **14** (*sideways*). *P* 13.

200 6 c. Type **88** 25 20
201 9 c. Decorating trees with the presents .. 35 35
202 20 c. Chosen men distribute the gifts 50 50
203 35 c. Carrying presents home 60 60
MS204 198 × 73 mm. Nos. 200/3. P 13½ × 14 .. 4·00 4·00

89 Loading Mail from Supply Ship to Longboats

(Des Jennifer Toombs. Litho Format)

1980 (6 May). *"London 1980" International Stamp Exhibition. Sheet* 120 × 135 *mm containing T* **89** *and similar horiz designs. Multicoloured.* W w **14** (*sideways*). *P* 14½.

MS205 35 c. Type **89**; 35 c. Mail being conveyed by "Flying Fox" (hoisting mechanism) to the Edge; 35 c. Tractor transporting mail from the Edge to Adamstown; 35 c. Mail being off-loaded at Post Office .. 1·75 2·25

90 Queen Elizabeth the Queen Mother

(Des Harrison. Litho Questa)

1980 (4 Aug). *80th Birthday of Queen Elizabeth the Queen Mother. W* w **14** *(sideways). P* 14.
206 **90** 50 c. multicoloured .. .. .. 1·10 1·10

(Des Jennifer Toombs. Litho Questa)

1980 (29 Sept). *Handicrafts (2nd series). Multicoloured designs as T* **46**. *W* w **14** *(sideways on 9 and 20 c.). P* 14.
207 9 c. Turtles (wood carvings) 30 20
208 20 c. Pitcairn wheelbarrow (wood carving) .. 30 35
209 35 c. Gannet (wood carving) *(vert)* 30 45
210 40 c. Woven bonnet and fan *(vert)* 30 50

91 Part of Adamstown

(Des BG Studio. Litho Rosenbaum Bros, Vienna)

1981 (22 Jan). *Landscapes. T* **91** *and similar horiz designs. Multicoloured. W* w **14** *(sideways). P* 13½.
211 6 c. Type **91** 10 10
212 9 c. Big George 15 15
213 20 c. Christian's Cave, Gannets Ridge .. 20 20
214 35 c. Radio Station from Pawala Valley Ridge 40 40
215 70 c. Tatrimoa 70 70

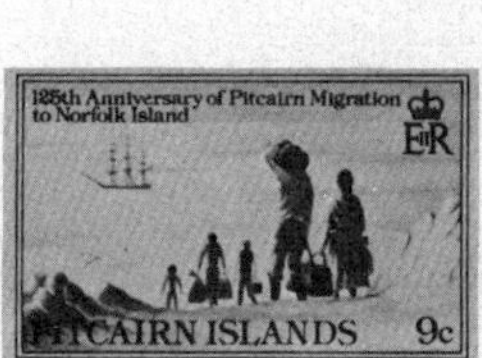

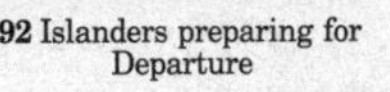

92 Islanders preparing for Departure

93 Prince Charles as Colonel-in-Chief, Cheshire Regiment

(Des Jennifer Toombs. Litho Heraclio Fournier)

1981 (3 May). *125th Anniv of Pitcairn Islanders' Migration to Norfolk Island. T* **92** *and similar horiz designs. Multicoloured. P* 13 × 14.
216 9 c. Type **92** 25 20
217 35 c. View of Pitcairn Island from *Morayshire* 60 45
218 70 c. *Morayshire* 85 75

(Des J.W. Litho Format)

1981 (22 July). *Royal Wedding. T* **93** *and similar vert designs. Multicoloured. W* w **14**. *P* 14.
219 20 c. Wedding bouquet from Pitcairn Islands 25 25
220 35 c. Type **93** 40 40
221 $1.20, Prince Charles and Lady Diana Spencer .. .. 1·00 1·10

94 Lemon

95 Pitcairn Islands Coat of Arms

(Des Daphne Padden. Litho Harrison)

1982 (23 Feb). *Fruit. T* **94** *and similar horiz designs. Multicoloured. W* w **14** *(sideways). P* 14½.
222 9 c. Type **94** 10 10
223 20 c. Pomegranate 20 20
224 35 c. Avocado 30 30
225 70 c. Pawpaw 60 65

(Des Jennifer Toombs. Litho Harrison)

1982 (1 July). *21st Birthday of Princess of Wales. T* **95** *and similar vert designs. Multicoloured. W* w **14**. *P* 14½ × 14.
226 6 c. Type **95** 5 5
227 9 c. Princess at Royal Opera House, Covent Garden, December 1981 .. .. .. 8 10
228 70 c. Balcony Kiss 60 65
229 $1.20, Formal portrait .. .. .. 1·00 1·10

96 Raphael's Angels

(Des Leslie McCombie. Litho Walsall)

1982 (19 Oct). *Christmas. T* **96** *and similar designs showing Raphael's Angels. W* w **14** *(sideways on* 15 c. *and* 20 c.*). P* 13½ × 14 (15 c., 20 c.) *or* 14 × 13½ *(others).*
230 15 c. black, silver and pink 15 15
231 20 c. black, silver and pale lemon 20 20
232 50 c. yellow-brown, silver and stone 45 45
233 $1 black, silver and cobalt 85 85
The 50 c. and $1 are vertical designs.

97 Radio Operator

(Des Jennifer Toombs. Litho Harrison)

1983 (14 Mar). *Commonwealth Day. T* **97** *and similar horiz designs. Multicoloured. W* w **14** *(sideways). P* 13½.
234 6 c. Type **97** 5 8
235 9 c. Postal clerk 8 10
236 70 c. Fisherman 60 65
237 $1.20, Artist .. .. 1·00 1·10

98 *Topaz* sights Smoke on Pitcairn

(Des Jennifer Toombs. Litho B.D.T.)

1983 (14 June). *175th Anniv of Folger's Discovery of the Settlers. T* **98** *and similar horiz designs. Multicoloured. W* w **14** *(sideways). P* 14.
238 6 c. Type **98** 10 10
239 20 c. Three islanders approach the *Topaz* .. 20 25
240 70 c. Capt. Mayhew Folger welcomed by John Adams 60 65
241 $1.20, Folger presented with *Bounty* chronometer .. .. 1·00 1·10

99 Hattie-Tree

(Des Jennifer Toombs. Litho B.D.T.)

1983 (6 Oct). *Trees of Pitcairn Islands. T* **99** *and similar horiz designs. Multicoloured. W* w **14** *(sideways). P* 13½.
242 35 c. Type **99** 30 35
a. Pair. Nos. 242/3 .. .. 60 70
243 35 c. Leaves from Hattie-Tree 30 35
244 70 c. Pandanus 65 70
a. Pair. Nos. 244/5 .. .. 1·25 1·40
245 70 c. Pandanus and basket weaving 65 70
The two designs of each value were printed together, *se-tenant*, in horizontal and vertical pairs throughout the sheet.

100 *Pseudojuloides atavai*

(Des C. Abbott. Litho Format)

1984 (11 Jan). *Fishes. T* **100** *and similar horiz designs. Multicoloured. W* w **14** *(sideways). P* 14½.
246 1 c. Type **100** 5 5
247 4 c. *Halichoeres melasmapomus* 5 5
248 6 c. *Scarus longipinnis* 5 5
249 9 c. *Variola louti* 8 10
250 10 c. *Centropyge hotumatua* 8 10
251 15 c. *Stegastes emeryi* 12 15
252 20 c. *Chaetodon smithi* 15 20
253 35 c. *Xanthichthys mento* 25 30
254 50 c. *Chrysiptera galba* 40 45
255 70 c. *Genicanthus spinus* 55 60
256 $1 *Myripristis tiki* 75 80
257 $1.20, *Anthias ventralis* 90 95
258 $2 *Pseudocaranx dentex* .. .. .. 1·50 1·60
246/58 .. .. *Set of* 13 4·50 5·00

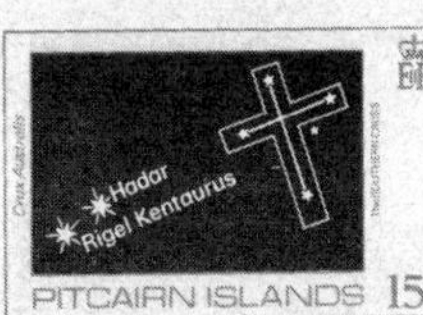

101 "Southern Cross"

(Des J. Cooter. Litho Walsall)

1984 (14 May). *Night Sky. T* **101** *and similar horiz designs. W* w **14** *(sideways). P* 14.
259 15 c. deep violet-blue, pale rose-lilac and gold 12 15
260 20 c. deep violet-blue, bright yell-grn & gold 20 25
261 70 c. deep violet-blue, yellow-ochre and gold .. 60 65
262 $1 deep violet-blue, pale blue and gold .. 85 90
Constellations:—20 c. "Southern Fish"; 70 c. "Lesser Dogs"; $1 "The Virgin".

102 Aluminium Longboat

103 "H.M.S. *Portland* standing off Bounty Bay" (J. Linton Palmer)

(Des C. Abbott. Litho Enschedé)

1984 (21 Sept). *"Ausipex" International Stamp Exhibition, Melbourne. Sheet* 134 × 86 *mm containing T* **102** *and similar horiz design. Multicoloured. W* w **14** *(sideways). P* 13½ × 14.
MS263 50 c. Type **102**; $2 Traditional-style wooden longboat .. .. 2·25 2·40

(Des Jennifer Toombs. Litho Questa)

1985 (16 Jan). *19th-Century Paintings (1st series). T* **103** *and similar horiz designs. Multicoloured. W* w **14** *(sideways). P* 13½ × 14 ($2) *or* 14 *(others).*
264 6 c. Type **103** 5 8
265 9 c. "Christian's Look Out" (J. Linton Palmer) 8 10
266 35 c. "The Golden Age" (J. Linton Palmer) .. 25 30
267 $1 "A View of the Village" (William Smyth) (48 × 31 *mm*) .. .. 1·50 1·60

Prince Edward Island

PRICES FOR STAMPS ON COVER

Nos. 1/4	*from* × 2
Nos. 5/6	—
Nos. 7/8	*from* × 3
Nos. 9/20	*from* × 4
Nos. 21/6	*from* × 2
Nos. 27/31	*from* × 4
Nos. 32/3	*from* × 40
Nos. 34/45	*from* × 4
Nos. 46/7	*from* × 3

1

2

3

4

5

6

(Typo Charles Whiting, London)

1861 (1 Jan). *Yellowish toned paper. (a) P* 9.

1	**1**	2d. rose	£160	£100
		a. Imperf between (horiz pair)	£3000	
		b. Imperf horiz (vert pair)		
		c. Bisected (1d.) (on cover)		
2		2d. rose-carmine	£160	£100
3	**2**	3d. blue	£350	£175
		a. Bisected (1½d.) (on cover)		
		b. Double print	£1300	
4	**3**	6d. yellow-green	£475	£250
		(b) Rouletted		
5	**1**	2d. rose	£1700	

The 2d. and 3d., perf 9, were authorised to be bisected and used for half their normal value.

1862. *Yellowish toned paper. P* 11.

6	**4**	1d. brown-orange	23·00	50·00
7	**6**	9d. bluish lilac (29.3.62)	40·00	16·00
8		9d. dull mauve	40·00	16·00

1863–68. *Yellowish toned paper. (a) P* 11½ × 12.

9	**4**	1d. yellow-orange	8·50	13·00
		a. Bisected (½d.) (on cover)	†	£900
		b. Imperf between (horiz pair)	£200	
10		1d. orange-buff	11·00	12·00
11		1d. yellow	12·00	13·00
12	**1**	2d. rose	6·00	8·50
		a. Imperf vert (horiz pair)		
		b. Bisected (1d.) (on cover)	†	£1200
13		2d. deep rose	7·00	11·00
14	**2**	3d. blue	8·50	12·00
		a. Imperf horiz (vert pair)		
		b. Bisected (1½d.) (on cover)		
15		3d. deep blue	8·50	8·00
16	**5**	4d. black (1867)	12·00	15·00
		a. Imperf vert (horiz pair)		
		b. Bisected (2d.) (on cover)	†	£1000
17	**3**	6d. yellow-green (15.12.66)	17·00	17·00
		a. Bisected (3d.) (on cover)		
18		6d. blue-green (1868)	17·00	17·00
19	**6**	9d. lilac	16·00	16·00
20		9d. reddish mauve	16·00	16·00
		a. Imperf vert (horiz pair)	£300	
		b. Bisected (4½d.) (on cover)	†	£1100
		(b) Perf compound of 11 *and* 11–12½		
21	**4**	1d. yellow-orange	£150	60·00
22	**1**	2d. rose	£150	60·00
23	**2**	3d. blue	£170	60·00
24	**5**	4d. black	£190	£180
25	**3**	6d. yellow-green	£170	£180
26	**6**	9d. reddish mauve	£180	£180

1870. *Coarse, wove bluish white paper. P* 11½–12.

27	**1**	2d. rose	7·00	8·50
28		2d. rose-pink	5·50	8·00
		a. "TWC"	65·00	
		b. Imperf between (horiz pair)	£110	
29	**2**	3d. pale blue	6·00	8·50
30		3d. blue	6·00	8·50
		a. Imperf between (horiz pair)	£250	
31	**5**	4d. black	3·00	26·00
		a. Imperf between (horiz pair)	£110	
		b. Bisected (2d.) (on cover)	†	£1300
		c. Perf compound 11 and 11½–12		

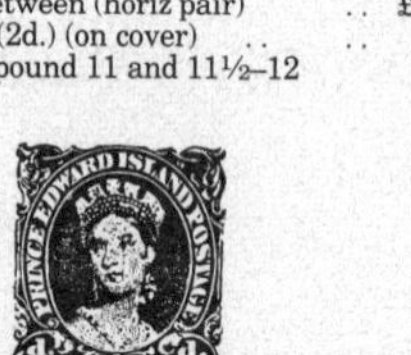
7

(Recess British-American Bank Note Co., Montreal and Ottawa)

1870 (1 June). *P* 12.

32	**7**	4½d. (3d. stg), yellow-brown	13·00	26·00
33		4½d. (3d. stg), deep brown	13·00	26·00

8

9

10

11

12

13

(Typo Charles Whiting, London)

1872 (1 Jan). *(a) P* 11½–12.

34	**8**	1 c. orange	1·60	8·50
35		1 c. yellow-orange	1·60	7·00
36		1 c. brown-orange	2·50	8·50
37	**10**	3 c. rose	3·25	7·00
		a. Stop between "PRINCE. EDWARD"	18·00	20·00
		b. Bisected (1½ c.) (on cover)		
		c. Imperf horiz (vert pair)	£300	
		(b) Perf 12 *to* 12¼, *large holes*		
38	**9**	2 c. blue	8·00	24·00
		a. Bisected (1 c.) (on cover)		
39	**11**	4 c. yellow-green	1·50	15·00
40		4 c. deep green	2·50	10·00
		a. Bisected (2 c.) (on cover)	†	£1900
41	**12**	6 c. black	1·60	10·00
		a. Bisected (3 c.) (on cover)	†	£700
		b. Imperf between (horiz pair)	£190	
		c. Imperf vert (horiz pair)		
42	**13**	12 c. reddish mauve	1·60	20·00
		(c) P 12½–13, *smaller holes*		
43	**8**	1 c. orange	12·00	
44		1 c. brown-orange	1·60	7·50
45	**10**	3 c. rose	8·50	8·50
		a. Stop between "PRINCE. EDWARD"	50·00	55·00
45*b*	**12**	6 c. black	—	£250
		(d) Perf compound of (a) and (c) 11½–12 × 12½–13		
46	**8**	1 c. orange	30·00	32·00
47	**10**	3 c. rose	32·00	32·00
		a. Stop between "PRINCE. EDWARD"	£170	£180

The stamps were withdrawn 1 July 1873, when the Colony became a Province of the Dominion of Canada.

Qatar

An independent Arab Shaikhdom, with a British postal administration until 23 May 1963.

There was no postal service from Qatar until 20 May 1950. Prior to this date the few foreign residents made their own arrangements for their mail to be carried to Bahrain for onward transmission through the postal services.

The first organised post from the capital, Doha, was an extension of the work in the state by the British Political Officer. From 20 May 1950 British residents were able to send mail via his office. The first two sendings had the Bahrain stamps supplied cancelled by a circular office stamp, but later batches, up to the introduction of the first Doha postmark in July 1950, had the stamps cancelled on arrival at Bahrain.

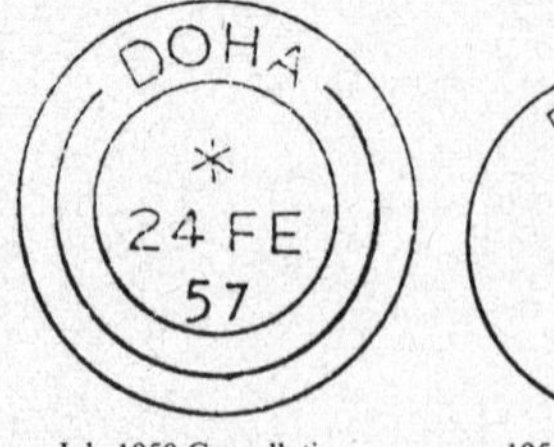

July 1950 Cancellation

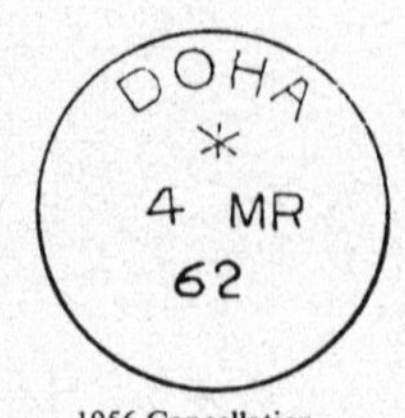

1956 Cancellation

The Post Office became a separate entity in August 1950 when its services were made available to the general public. After initially using the Bahrain surcharges on Great Britain the supply of stamps for the Qatar office was switched to the British Postal Agencies in Eastern Arabia surcharges.

The circular cancellation, dating from July 1950, continued to be used until replaced by a slightly smaller version in early 1956.

A further post office was opened on 1 February 1956 at the Umm Said oil terminal, using its own cancellation.

Both offices were issued with standard oval Registered handstamps, Doha in 1950 and Umm Said in 1956.

1956 Umm Said Cancellation

All stamps to 1960 surcharged in issues of Great Britain

QATAR NP 1 NP (1)

QATAR 3 NP NP (2)

QATAR 75 NP (3)

1957 (1 Apr)–**59**. *(a) T* **154/60** *(St Edward's Crown wmk, W* **165**) *surch as T* **1** *to* **3**.

1	**1**	1 n.p. on 5d. brown	5	10
2	**2**	3 n.p. on ½d. orange-red	12	30
3		6 n.p. on 1d. ultramarine	12	30
4		9 n.p. on 1½d. green	12	12
5		12 n.p. on 2d. light red-brown	20	30
6	**1**	15 n.p. on 2½d. carmine-red (I)	15	15
7	**2**	20 n.p. on 3d. deep lilac (B.)	15	55
8	**1**	25 n.p. on 4d. ultramarine	45	80
9		40 n.p. on 6d. reddish purple	40	5
		a. Deep claret (21.7.59)	80	15
10		50 n.p. on 9d. bronze-green	95	45
11	**3**	75 n.p. on 1s. 3d. green	1·50	1·25
12		1 r. on 1s. 6d. grey-blue	2·50	15
1/12		*Set of* 12	6·00	3·50

QATAR 2 RUPEES I

QATAR 2 RUPEES II

(4)

QATAR 5 RUPEES I

QATAR 5 RUPEES II

(5)

QATAR 10 RUPEES I

QATAR 10 RUPEES II

(6)

Type I (**4/6**). Type-set overprints. Bold thick letters with sharp corners and straight edges. Bars close together and usually slightly longer than in Type II.

Type II (**4/6**). Plate-printed overprints. Thinner letters, rounded corners and rough edges. Bars wider apart.

(b) Nos. 536/8 *surch with T* **4/6**

			I (1.4.57)		II (18.9.57)	
13	**166**	2 r. on 2s. 6d. black-brown	6·50	2·50	10·00	6·00
14	**167**	5 r. on 5s. rose-red	14·00	5·50	20·00	16·00
15	**168**	10 r. on 10s. ultramarine	26·00	15·00	80·00	£130

QATAR
15 NP

(7)

1957 (1 Aug). *World Scout Jubilee Jamboree. Nos.* 557/9 *surch in two lines as T* **7** (15 *n.p.*) *or in three lines (others).*

16	15 n.p. on 2½d. carmine-red	75	45
17	25 n.p. on 4d. ultramarine	90	80
18	75 n.p. on 1s. 3d. green	1·25	1·00

1960 (26 Apr–28 Sept). *Q.E.II (Mult Crowns wmk, W* **179**) *surch as T* **1** *or* **2**.

20	**2**	3 n.p. on ½d. orange-red (28.9)	90	1·75
21		6 n.p. on 1d. ultramarine (21.6)	1·50	3·25
22		9 n.p. on 1½d. green (28.9)	1·00	1·75
23		12 n.p. on 2d. light red-brown (28.9)	4·25	7·50

No.	Type	Description	Unused	Used
24	1	15 n.p. on 2½d. carmine-red (II)	35	5
25	2	20 n.p. on 3d. deep lilac (B.) (28.9)	35	20
26	1	40 n.p. on 6d. deep claret (21.6)	60	25
20/6		*Set of* 7	8·00	13·00

8 Shaikh Ahmad bin Ali al Thani

9 Peregrine Falcon

10 Dhow

11 Oil Derrick

12 Mosque

(Des O. C. Meronti (T **8**), M. Goaman (T **9**), M. Farrar Bell (T **10**), J. Constable and O. C. Meronti (T **11/12**). Photo Harrison, (T **8/10**). Recess D.L.R. (T **11/12**))

1961 (2 Sept). *P* 14½ (5 *n.p. to* 75 *n.p.*) *or* 13 (1 *r. to* 10 *r.*).

No.	Type	Description	Unused	Used
27	**8**	5 n.p. carmine	5	5
28		15 n.p. black	8	5
29		20 n.p. reddish purple	10	5
30		30 n.p. deep green	12	5
31	**9**	40 n.p. red	50	5
32		50 n.p. sepia	60	5
33	**10**	75 n.p. ultramarine	60	15
34	**11**	1 r. scarlet	60	5
35		2 r. ultramarine	1·50	50
36	**12**	5 r. bronze-green	2·75	1·50
37		10 r. black	6·50	3·25
27/37		*Set of* 11	12·00	5·00

The Qatar Post Department took over the postal services on 23 May 1963. Later stamp issues will be found listed in Part 19 (*Middle East*) of this catalogue.

Queensland

Stamps of NEW SOUTH WALES were used in Queensland from 26 January 1860, until 1 November 1860. The stamps so used were the 1d., 2d. and 3d. diademed heads, the large square 6d., 8d. and 1s., and the "registered" stamp.

PRICES FOR STAMPS ON COVER

Nos. 1/3	*from* × 2
Nos. 4/56	*from* × 3
Nos. 57/8	—
Nos. 59/73	*from* × 4
Nos. 74/82	*from* × 2
Nos. 83/109	*from* × 3
Nos. 110/13	*from* × 2
Nos. 116/17	*from* × 3
Nos. 118/27	—
Nos. 128/50	*from* × 4
Nos. 151/65	—
Nos. 166/78	*from* × 10
Nos. 179/83	*from* × 4
Nos. 184/206	*from* × 15
No. 207	—
Nos. 208/54	*from* × 15
Nos. 256/64	*from* × 10
Nos. 264*a*/*b*	*from* × 2
Nos. 265/6	*from* × 20
Nos. 267/9	*from* × 5
Nos. 270/80*a*	—
Nos. 281/5	*from* × 10
Nos. 286/308	*from* × 12
No. 309	—
Nos. F1/37	—

1

2 Large Star

3 Small Star

(Dies eng W. Humphrvs. Recess P.B.)

1860 (1 Nov). *W* **2**. *Imperf.*

No.	Type	Description	Unused	Used
1	**1**	1d. carmine-rose	£2250	£800
2		2d. blue	£5000	£1700
3		6d. green	£3500	£800

1860 (Nov). *W* **2**. *Clean-cut perf* 14–15½.

No.	Type	Description	Unused	Used
4	**1**	1d. carmine-rose (1.11)	£1300	£300
5		2d. blue (1.11)	£400	£120
		a. Imperf between (pair)		
6		6d. green (15.11)	£450	65·00

1860–61. *W* **3**. *Clean-cut perf* 14–15½.

No.	Type	Description	Unused	Used
7	**1**	2d. blue	£450	£100
		a. Imperf between (horiz pair)	—	£750
8		3d. brown (15.4.61)	£250	50·00
		a. Re-entry		
		b. Retouch (R. 2/8)		
9		6d. green	£500	55·00
10		1s. violet (15.11.60)	£475	70·00
11		"REGISTERED" (6d.) olive-yellow (1.61)	£325	70·00
		a. Imperf between (pair)	£2750	

The perforation of the 3d. is that known as "intermediate between clean-cut and rough".

The 3d. re-entry shows doubling of the left-hand arabesque and the retouch has redrawn spandrel dots under "EN" of "PENCE", a single dot in the centre of the circle under "E" and the bottom outer frame liner closer to the spandrel's frame line.

1861 (July (?)). *W* **3**. *Clean-cut perf* 14.

No.	Type	Description	Unused	Used
12	**1**	1d. carmine-rose	£100	28·00
13		2d. blue	£325	38·00

1861 (Sept). *W* **3**. *Rough perf* 14–15½.

No.	Type	Description	Unused	Used
14	**1**	1d. carmine-rose	65·00	28·00
15		2d. blue	90·00	28·00
		a. Imperf between (pair)		
16		3d. brown	38·00	23·00
		a. Imperf between (pair)	£1400	
		b. Re-entry		
		c. Retouch (R. 2/8)		
17		6d. deep green	£200	27·00
18		6d. yellow-green	£200	27·00
19		1s. violet	£325	80·00
20		"REGISTERED" (6d.) orange-yellow	25·00	32·00

(Printed and perforated in Brisbane)

1862–67. *Thick toned paper. No wmk.* (*a*) *P* 13 (1862–63).

No.	Type	Description	Unused	Used
21	**1**	1d. Indian red (16.12.62)	£350	80·00
22		1d. orange-vermilion (2.63)	60·00	12·00
		a. Imperf (pair)	—	£200
		b. Imperf between (pair)		
23		2d. blue (16.12.62)	40·00	9·00
24		2d. pale blue	£100	27·00
		a. Imperf (pair)	—	£190
		b. Imperf between (horiz pair)	—	£850
25		3d. brown	55·00	24·00
		a. Re-entry		
		b. Retouch (R. 2/8)		
26		6d. apple-green (17.4.63)	90·00	12·00
27		6d. yellow-green	80·00	12·00
		a. Imperf between (horiz pair)	—	£950
28		6d. blue-green	£120	27·00
		a. Imperf (pair)	—	£250
29		1s. grey (14.7.63)	£140	16·00
		a. Imperf betwen (horiz pair)	—	£850
		b. Imperf betwen (vert pair)		

The top or bottom row of perforation was sometimes omitted from the sheet, resulting in stamps perforated on three sides only.

(*b*) *P* 12½ × 13 (1867)

No.	Type	Description	Unused	Used
30	**1**	1d. orange-vermilion	60·00	27·00
31		2d. blue	48·00	20·00
32		3d. brown	65·00	20·00
		a. Re-entry		
		b. Retouch (R. 2/8)		
33		6d. apple-green	—	27·00
34		6d. yellow-green	—	27·00
35		1s. grey	£170	32·00
		a. Imperf between (horiz pair)		

The previously listed stamps perforated 13 round holes come from the same perforating machine as Nos. 21/9 after the pins had been replaced. The holes vary from rough to clean-cut.

1864–65. *W* **3**. (*a*) *P* 13.

No.	Type	Description	Unused	Used
44	**1**	1d. orange-vermilion (1.65)	65·00	17·00
		a. Imperf between (horiz pair)	£375	
45		2d. pale blue (1.65)	48·00	17·00
46		2d. deep blue	48·00	17·00
		a. Imperf between (vert pair)	£850	
		b. Bisected (1d.) (on cover)	†	£1800
47		6d. yellow-green (1.65)	£140	17·00
48		6d. deep green	£160	17·00
49		"REGISTERED" (6d.) orge-yell (21.6.64)	65·00	30·00
		a. Double printed	£750	
		b. Imperf		

(*b*) *P* 12½ × 13

No.	Type	Description	Unused	Used
50	**1**	1d. orange-vermilion	95·00	40·00
50*a*		2d. deep blue		

1866 (24 Jan). *Wmk* "QUEENSLAND/POSTAGE—POSTAGE/STAMPS—STAMPS" *in three lines in script capitals with double wavy lines above and below the wmk and single wavy lines with projecting sprays between each line of words. There are ornaments* ("*fleurons*") *between* "POSTAGE" "POSTAGE" *and between* "STAMPS" "STAMPS". *Single stamps only show a portion of one or two letters of this wmk.* (*a*) *P* 13.

No.	Type	Description	Unused	Used
51	**1**	1d. orange-vermilion	£130	25·00
52		2d. blue	42·00	17·00

(*b*) *P* 12½ × 13

No.	Type	Description	Unused	Used
52*a*	**1**	1d. orange-vermilion		
52*b*		2d. blue		

1866 (24 Sept). *Lithographed on thick paper. No wmk. P* 13.

No.	Type	Description	Unused	Used
53	**1**	4d. slate	£150	15·00
		a. Re-entry		
		b. Retouch (R. 2/8)		
55		4d. lilac	90·00	7·00
		a. Re-entry		
		b. Retouch (R. 2/8)		
56		4d. reddish lilac	90·00	14·00
		a. Re-entry		
		b. Retouch (R. 2/8)		
57		5s. bright rose	£180	60·00
58		5s. pale rose	£180	35·00
		a. Imperf between (vert pair)	—	£500

The 4d. is from a transfer taken from the 3d. die, and the 5s. was taken from the 1s. die, the final "s" being added. The alteration in the values was made by hand on the stone, and there are many varieties, such as tall and short letters in "FOUR PENCE", some of the letters of "FOUR" smudged out, and differences in the position of the two words.

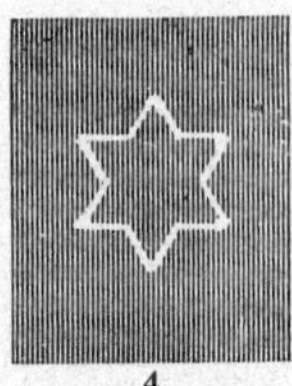

4

1868–74. *Wmk small truncated Star*, W **4** *on each stamp, and the word* "QUEENSLAND" *in single-lined Roman capitals four times in each sheet.* (*a*) *P* 13.

No.	Type	Description	Unused	Used
59	**1**	1d. orange-vermilion (18.1.71)	60·00	3·50
60		2d. pale blue	42·00	3·50
61		2d. blue (3.4.68)	35·00	1·75
62		2d. bright blue	42·00	1·75
63		2d. greenish blue	80·00	1·75
64		2d. dark blue	42·00	1·75
		a. Imperf		
65		3d. olive-green (27.2.71)	80·00	4·50
		a. Re-entry		
		b. Retouch (R. 2/8)		
66		3d. greenish grey	95·00	4·75
		a. Re-entry		
		b. Retouch (R. 2/8)		
67		3d. brown	80·00	4·75
		a. Re-entry		
		b. Retouch (R. 2/8)		
68		6d. yellow-green (10.11.71)	£130	6·50
69		6d. green	£130	9·00
70		6d. deep green	£170	15·00
71		1s. greenish grey (13.11.72)	£375	32·00
72		1s. brownish grey	£375	32·00
73		1s. mauve (19.2.74)	£200	22·00

(*b*) *P* 12 (about Feb 1874)

No.	Type	Description	Unused	Used
74	**1**	1d. orange-vermilion	£250	24·00
75		2d. blue	—	35·00
76		3d. greenish grey	—	£180
		a. Re-entry		
		b. Retouch (R. 2.8)		
77		3d. brown	£250	£160
		a. Re-entry		
		b. Retouch (R. 2/8)		
78		6d. green	£850	40·00
79		1s. mauve	—	40·00

(*c*) *P* 13 × 12

No.	Type	Description	Unused	Used
80	**1**	1d. orange-vermilion	—	£150
81		2d. blue	£850	40·00
82		3d. greenish grey		

Reprints were made in 1895 of all five values on the paper of the regular issue, and perforated 13; the colours are:—1d. orange and orange-brown, 2d. dull blue and bright blue, 3d. deep brown, 6d. yellow-green, 1s. red-violet and dull violet. The "Registered" was also reprinted with these on the same paper, but perforated 12. One sheet of the 2d. reprint is known to have had the perforations missing between the fourth and fifth vertical rows.

5

6

(4d., litho. Other values recess)

1868–78. *Wmk Crown and Q*, W **5**. (*a*) *P* 13 (1868–75).

No.	Type	Description	Unused	Used
83	**1**	1d. orange-vermilion (10.11.68)	50·00	4·50
		a. Imperf		
84		1d. pale rose-red (4.11.74)	48·00	8·50
85		1d. deep rose-red	95·00	9·00
86		2d. pale blue (4.11.74)	48·00	1·75
87		2d. deep blue (20.11.68)	38·00	4·50
		a. Imperf (pair)	£275	
		b. Imperf between (vert pair)		
88		3d. brown (11.6.75)	70·00	12·00
		a. Re-entry		
		b. Retouch (R. 2/8)		
89		4d. yellow (1.1.75)	£750	40·00
90		6d. deep green (9.4.69)	£120	9·00
91		6d. yellow-green	95·00	6·50
92		6d. pale apple-green (1.1.75)	£160	9·00
		a. Imperf	£160	
93		1s. mauve	—	29·00

(*b*) *P* 12 (1876–78)

No.	Type	Description	Unused	Used
94	**1**	1d. deep orange-vermilion	48·00	4·00
95		1d. pale orange-vermilion	50·00	4·00
		a. Imperf between (vert pair)		
96		1d. rose-red	55·00	9·00
97		1d. flesh	70·00	9·00
98		2d. pale blue	95·00	15·00
99		2d. bright blue	19·00	80
100		2d. deep blue	25·00	1·50
101		3d. brown	60·00	9·00
		a. Re-entry		
		b. Retouch (R. 2/8)		
102		4d. yellow	£600	17·00
103		4d. buff	£600	14·00
104		6d. deep green	£140	7·00
105		6d. green	£130	4·25
106		6d. yellow-green	£140	4·50
107		6d. apple-green	£140	7·00
108		1s. mauve	40·00	9·00
109		1s. purple	£140	5·00
		a. Imperf between (pair)		

(c) P 13 × 12 or 12 × 13

110	1	1d. orange-vermilion	—	75·00
110*a*		1d. rose-red		
111		2d. deep blue	£1100	£110
112		4d. yellow		
113		6d. deep green	—	£130

(d) P 12½ × 13

114	1	1d. orange-vermilion		
115		2d. deep blue		
115*a*		6d. yellow-green		

(e) P 12½

115*b*	1	2d. deep blue		

Reprints exist of the 1d., 2d., 3d., 6d. and 1s. on thicker paper, Wmk *W* **6**, and in different shades from the originals.

1879. *No wmk. P* 12.

116	1	6d. pale emerald-green	£160	20·00
		a. Imperf between (horiz pair)	—	£475
117		1s. mauve (*fiscal-cancel* £5)	95·00	40·00

No. 117 has a very indistinct lilac *burelé* band at back.

Nos. 116/17 can be found showing portions of a papermaker's watermark, either T. H. Saunders & Co or A. Pirie & Sons.

1881. *Lithographed from transfers from the* 1s. *die. Wmk Crown and Q*, *W* **6**. *P* 12.

118	1	2s. pale blue (6 Apr)	60·00	15·00
119		2s. blue (*fiscal-cancel* £3)	55·00	15·00
		a. Imperf vert (horiz pair)		
120		2s. deep blue (*fiscal-cancel* £3)	75·00	15·00
121		2s. 6d. dull scarlet (28 Aug)	£110	18·00
122		2s. 6d. bright scarlet (*fiscal-cancel* £3) ..	90·00	
123		5s. pale yellow-ochre (28 Aug)	£100	17·00
124		5s. yellow-ochre (*fiscal-cancel* £4) ..	£100	17·00
125		10s. reddish brown (Mar)	£350	90·00
		a. Imperf	£375	
126		10s. bistre-brown	£350	90·00
127		20s. rose (*fiscal-cancel* £6)	£700	£100

Of the 2s. and 20s. stamps there are five types of each, and of the other values ten types of each.

Beware of fiscally used copies that have been cleaned and provided with forged postmarks.

7

Die I

Die II

Dies I and II often occur in the same sheet.

Die I. The whole horizontal inner line of the triangle in the upper right-hand corner merges into the outer white line of the oval above the "L".

Die II. The same line is short and does not touch the inner oval.

1879–80. *Typo. P* 12. *(a) Wmk Crown and Q*, *W* **5**.

128	7	1d. reddish brown (Die I)	65·00	8·00
		a. Die II	£100	8·00
		ab. "QOEENSLAND"		
129		1d. orange-brown (Die I)	£100	8·00
130		2d. blue (Die I)	48·00	3·00
		a. "PENGE" (R. 12/6)		
		b. "QUEENSbAND" (R. 5/6)		
		c. "QU" joined		
131		4d. orange-yellow	£300	24·00

(b) No wmk, with lilac burelé band on back

132	7	1d. reddish brown (Die I)	£275	35·00
		a. Die II	£300	65·00
		ab. "QOEENSLAND"	—	£1400
133		2d. blue (Die I)	£350	17·00
		a. "PENGE" (R. 12/6)	£3250	£600
		b. "QUEENSbAND" (R. 5/6)		

(c) Wmk Crown and Q, *W* **6**

134	7	1d. reddish brown (Die I)	32·00	5·00
		a. Imperf between (pair)	—	£140
		b. Die II	40·00	5·00
		ba. "QOEENSLAND"	£100	
		bb. Imperf between (pair)	—	£120
135		1d. dull orange (Die I)	9·00	3·00
		a. Die II	9·00	3·00
		ab. "QOEENSLAND"	50·00	18·00
136		1d. scarlet (Die I)	10·00	1·50
		a. Die II	11·00	1·90
		ab. "QOEENSLAND"	80·00	24·00
137		2d. blue (Die I)		
		a. "PENGE"		
		b. "QUEENSbAND"		
		c. Die II	24·00	2·50
138		2d. grey-blue (Die I)	20·00	70
		a. "PENGE"	—	60·00
		b. "QUEENSbAND"		
		c. Die II		
139		2d. bright blue (Die I)	28·00	80
		a. "PENGE"		
		b. "QUEENSbAND"		
		c. Imperf between (pair)	£375	
		d. Die II		
140		2d. deep blue (Die I)		
		a. "PENGE"		
		b. "QUEENSbAND"		
		c. Die II	24·00	4·50
141		4d. orange-yellow	£110	9·00
		a. Imperf between (pair)		
142		6d. deep green	45·00	3·50
		a. Imperf between (pair)		
143		6d. yellow-green	50·00	3·50
144		1s. deep violet	42·00	3·50
145		1s. pale lilac	40·00	5·00

The variety "QO" is No. 48 in the first arrangement, and No. 44 in a later arrangement on the sheets.

All these values have been seen imperf and unused, but we have no evidence that any of them were used in this condition.

The above were printed in sheets of 120, from plates made up of 30 groups of four electrotypes. There are four different types in each group, and two such groups of four are known of the 1d. and 2d., thus giving eight varieties of these two values. There was some resetting of the first plate of the 1d., and there are several plates of the 2d.; the value in the first plate of the latter value is in thinner letters, and in the last plate three types in each group of four have the "TW" of "TWO" joined, the letters of "PENCE" are larger and therefore much closer together, and in one type the "O" of "TWO" is oval, that letter being circular in the other types.

(8)

9

10

1880 (21 Feb). *Surch with T* **8**.

151	7	½d. on 1d. (No. 134) (Die I)	£130	70·00
		a. Die II	£400	£325
		ab. "QOEENSLAND"	£750	£700

Examples with "Half-penny" reading downwards are forged surcharges.

1882–86. *Recess. P* 12. *(a) Thin paper. W* **5** *twice sideways*.

152	9	2s. bright blue	70·00	17·00
153		2s. 6d. vermilion	60·00	20·00
154		5s. rose	45·00	19·00
155		10s. brown	£110	32·00
156		£1 deep green	£250	£100
		a. Re-entry (R. 1/2)		
		b. Retouch (R. 6/4)		

(b) Thin paper. W **6** *twice sideways*

157	9	2s. 6d. vermilion	50·00	24·00
158		5s. rose	48·00	17·00
159		10s. brown	£200	40·00
160		£1 deep green	£190	48·00
		a. Re-entry (R. 1/2)		
		b. Retouch (R. 6/4)		

(c) Thick paper. W **10**

161	9	2s. bright blue	85·00	20·00
162		2s. 6d. vermilion	45·00	19·00
163		5s. rose	38·00	20·00
164		10s. brown	£100	32·00
165		£1 deep green	£190	45·00
		a. Re-entry (R. 1/2)		
		b. Retouch (R. 6/4)		

The re-entry on the £1 shows as a double bottom frame line and the retouch occurs alongside the bottom left numeral.

See also Nos. 270/1.

11

12

In T **12** the shading lines do not extend entirely across, as in T **11**, thus leaving a white line down the front of the throat and point of the bust.

1882–83. *W* **6**. *(a) P* 12.

166	11	1d. pale vermilion-red	3·00	20
		a. Double print		
167		1d. deep vermilion-red	3·00	20
168		2d. blue	4·25	12
		a. Imperf between (horiz pair) ..		
169		4d. pale yellow	17·00	1·25
		a. "PENGE" for "PENCE" (R. 8/1) ..	£120	40·00
		b. "EN" joined in "PENCE" (R. 4/6) ..		
170		6d. green	7·00	70
171		1s. violet	16·00	1·75
172		1s. lilac	10·00	1·75
173		1s. deep mauve	10·00	1·25
174		1s. pale mauve	11·00	1·25
		a. Imperf	†	—

(b) P 9½ × 12

176	11	1d. pale red	40·00	14·00
177		2d. blue	£180	22·00
178		1s. mauve	80·00	17·00

The above were printed from plates made up of groups of four electrotypes as previously. In the 1d. the words of value are followed by a full stop. There are four types of the 4d., 6d., and 1s., eight types of the 1d., and twelve types of the 2d.

1887–89. *W* **6**. *(a) P* 12.

179	12	1d. vermilion-red	2·75	20
180		2d. blue	5·00	20
		a. Oval white flaw on Queen's head behind diadem (R. 12/5)		
181		2s. deep brown	55·00	23·00
182		2s. pale brown	50·00	20·00

(b) P 9½ × 12

183	12	2d. blue	£140	19·00

These are from new plates; four types of each value grouped as before. The 1d. is without stop. In all values No. 2 in each group of four has the "L" and "A" of "QUEENSLAND" joined at the foot, and No. 3 of the 2d. has "P" of word "PENCE" with a long downstroke.

The 2d. is known bisected and used as a 1d. value.

13

14

1890–94. *W* **6** *(sideways on* ½*d.). P* 12½, 13 *(comb machine)*.

184	13	½d. pale green	2·75	50
185		½d. deep green	2·75	50
186		½d. deep blue-green	3·00	50
187	12	1d. vermilion-red	2·00	15
		a. Imperf	23·00	23·00
		b. Oval broken by tip of bust (R. 10/3)		
188		2d. blue (old plate)	4·00	15
189		2d. pale blue (old plate)	3·50	15
190		2d. pale blue (retouched plate) ..	3·25	30
		a. "FWO" for "TWO" (R. 8/7)		
191	14	2½d. carmine	9·00	55
192	12	3d. brown	7·50	1·40
193	11	4d. yellow	14·00	95
		a. "PENGE" for "PENCE" (R. 8/1) ..	45·00	
		b. "EN" joined in "PENCE" (R. 4/6) ..		
194		4d. orange	16·00	95
		a. "PENGE" for "PENCE" (R. 8/1) ..	50·00	20·00
		b. "EN" joined in "PENCE" (R. 4/6) ..		
195		4d. lemon	17·00	1·10
		a. "PENGE" for "PENCE" (R. 8/1) ..	60·00	
		b. "EN" joined in "PENCE" (R. 4/6) ..		
196		6d. green	7·50	1·00
197	12	2s. red-brown	40·00	5·50
198		2s. pale brown	40·00	6·00

This issue is perforated by a new vertical comb machine, gauging about 12¾ × 12¾. The 3d. is from a plate similar to those of the last issue, No. 2 in each group of four types having "L" and "A" joined at the foot. The ½d. and 2½d. are likewise in groups of four types, but the differences are very minute. In the retouched plate of the 2d. the letters "L" and "A" no longer touch in No. 2 of each group and the "P" in No. 3 is normal.

1894–95. A. *Thick paper. W* **10**. *(a) P* 12½, 13.

202	12	1d. vermilion-red	2·50	12
		a. Oval broken by tip of bust (R. 10/3)		
203		1d. red-orange	2·25	12
		a. Oval broken by tip of bust (R. 10/3)		
204		2d. blue (retouched plate)	3·00	20
		a. "FWO" for "TWO" (R. 8/7)		

(b) P 12

205	11	1s. mauve	10·00	2·75

B. *Unwmkd paper; with blue burelé band at back. P* 12½, 13

206	12	1d. deep vermilion-red	2·00	12
		a. Oval broken by tip of bust (R. 10/3)		
		b. "PE" of "PENNY" omitted (R. 1/2)		

C. *Thin paper. Crown and Q faintly impressed. P* 12½, 13

207	12	2d. blue (retouched plate)	5·00	
		a. "FWO" for "TWO" (R. 8/7)		

15

16

17

18

1895–96. A. *W* **6** *(sideways on* ½*d.). (a) P* 12½, 13.

208	15	½d. green	95	45
209		½d. deep green	95	45
		a. Printed both sides	55·00	
210	16	1d. orange-red	1·90	20
211		1d. pale red	1·75	20
212		2d. blue	2·75	35
213	17	2½d. carmine	8·00	2·75
214		2½d. rose	8·00	2·75
215	18	5d. purple-brown	10·00	2·50

(b) P 12

217	16	1d. red		
218		2d. blue	—	4·50

B. *Thick paper. W* **10** *(sideways) (part only on each stamp)*.

(a) P 12½, 13

219	15	½d. green	95	45
220		½d. deep green	95	45

(b) P 12

221	15	½d. green	9·00	
222		½d. deep green	9·00	

C. *No wmk; with blue burelé band at back. (a) P* 12½, 13

223	15	½d. green	95	
		a. Without *burelé* band	40·00	
224		½d. deep green	1·00	

(b) P 12

225	15	½d. green	11·00	
		a. Without *burelé* band	40·00	

Nos. 223a and 225a are from the margins of the sheet.

D. *Thin paper, with Crown and Q faintly impressed. P* 12½, 13

227	15	½d. green	1·40	50
228	16	1d. orange-red	3·00	30

19

1896. *W* **6.** *P* 12½, 13.

229	**19**	1d. vermilion	1·75	30

20 21 22

23 24 25

Die I Die II

Two Dies of 4d.:

Die I. Serif of horizontal bar on lower right 4d. is clear of vertical frame line.
Die II. Serif joins vertical frame line.

1897–1907. *Figures in all corners.* *W* **6** (*sideways on* ½*d*). *P* 12½, 13.

231	**20**	½d. deep green	2·50	1·75
		a. Perf 12	—	90·00
232	**21**	1d. orange-vermilion	1·00	12
233		1d. vermilion	1·00	12
234		2d. blue	1·25	12
		a. Cracked plate		
235		2d. deep blue	1·25	12
		a. Cracked plate		
236	**22**	2½d. rose	15·00	5·00
237		2½d. purple/*blue*	7·00	65
238		2½d. brown-purple/*blue*	7·00	65
239		2½d. slate-*blue*	12·00	2·50
240	**21**	3d. brown	10·00	95
241		3d. deep brown	8·00	70
242		3d. reddish brown (1906)	8·00	80
243		3d. grey-brown (1907)	9·50	80
244		4d. yellow (Die I)	8·00	80
		a. Die II		
245		4d. yellow-buff (Die I)	8·00	80
		a. Die II		
246	**23**	5d. purple-brown	6·00	65
247		5d. dull brown (1906)	7·00	1·40
248		5d. black-brown (1907)	7·00	1·75
249	**21**	6d. green	6·00	1·10
250		6d. yellow-green	6·00	1·25
251	**24**	1s. pale mauve	12·00	1·00
252		1s. dull mauve	12·00	1·00
253		1s. bright mauve	13·00	2·00
254	**25**	2s. turquoise-green	32·00	5·00

The 1d. perf 12 × 9½ was not an authorised issue.

The cracked plate variety on the 2d. developed during 1901 and shows as a white break on the Queen's head and neck.

1899. *W* **6** (*a*) *Zigzag roulette in black.* (*b*) *The same but plain.* (*c*) *Roulette* (*a*) *and also* (*b*). (*d*) *Roulette* (*b*) *and perf* 12½, 13. (*e*) *Roulette* (*a*) *and perf* 12½, 13. (*f*) *Compound of* (*a*), (*b*), *and perf* 12½, 13.

256	**21**	1d. vermilion (*a*)	4·50	2·75
257		1d. vermilion (*b*)	2·25	75
258		1d. vermilion (*c*)	4·25	
259		1d. vermilion (*d*)	2·75	1·60
260		1d. vermilion (*e*)	55·00	
261		1d. vermilion (*f*)	75·00	

26 27

1899–1906. *W* **6.** *P* 12½, 13.

262	**26**	½d. deep green	80	15
263		½d. grey-green	80	15
264		½d. pale green (1906)	80	15

Stamps of T **26** without wmk, are proofs.

1900. *Charity. T* **27** *and horiz design showing Queen Victoria in medallion inscr* "PATRIOTIC FUND 1900". *W* **6.** *P* 12.

264*a*		1d. (6d.) claret	75·00	75·00
264*b*		2d. (1s.) violet	£170	£170

These stamps, sold at 6d. and 1s. respectively, paid postage of 1d. and 2d. only, the difference being contributed to a Patriotic Fund.

28

QUEENSLAND (*a*) QUEENSLAND (*b*)

Two types of the word "QUEENSLAND"

Dates on T **28** are those of the establishment of the colonies.

(Eng and typo in Melbourne, Victoria)

1903. *W* w **10.** *P* 12½.

265	**28**	9d. brown and ultramarine (*a*)	9·50	1·75
266		9d. brown and ultramarine (*b*)	9·50	1·75

1903. *W* **6.** *P* 12.

267	**26**	½d. green	1·00	25
268	**21**	1d. vermilion	2·25	70
269		2d. blue	—	3·25

Nos. 267/9 can be found with rough or clean cut holes from this comb machine. A perf 12½ line machine was also used, but stamps from it are difficult to distinguish.

1905. *Recess. W* **10.** *P* 12½, 13 (*irregular line*).

270	**9**	2s. 6d. vermilion	85·00	32·00
271		£1 deep green	£550	£300
		a. Re-entry (R. 1/2)		
		b. Retouch (R. 6/4)		

29

1905–10. *Litho.* A. *W* **6**, *twice sideways.* (*a*) *P* 12 (1905–6).

272	**9**	5s. rose (7.06)	80·00	65·00
273		£1 deep green (7.11.05)	£300	90·00
		a. Re-entry (R. 1/2)		
		b. Retouch (R. 6/4)		
		(*b*) *P* 12½, 13 (*irregular line*)		
274	**9**	£1 deep green (7.06)	£400	90·00
		a. Re-entry (R. 1/2)		
		b. Retouch (R. 6/4)		
		B. *W* **29**, *twice sideways. P* 12½, 13 (*irregular line*) (1907–10)		
275	**9**	2s. 6d. vermilion	55·00	26·00
276		2s. 6d. dull orange (1910)	75·00	32·00
277		5s. rose	50·00	26·00
278		5s. deep rose	50·00	32·00
279		10s. deep brown	£110	35·00
280		£1 bluish green	£225	80·00
		a. Re-entry (R. 1/2)		
		b. Retouch (R. 6/4)		
280*c*		£1 deep green	£350	£250
		ca. Re-entry (R. 1/2)		
		cb. Retouch (R. 6/4)		

The lithographic stone used for Nos. 272/80c took the full sheet of 30 so the varieties on the £1 recess-printed version also appear on the stamps printed by lithography.

30 32

Redrawn types of T **21**

T **30**. The head is redrawn, the top of the crown is higher and touches the frame, as do also the back of the chignon and the point of the bust. The forehead is filled in with lines of shading, and the figures in the corners appear to have been redrawn also.

T **32**. The forehead is plain (white instead of shaded), and though the top of the crown is made higher, it does not touch the frame; but the point of the bust and the chignon still touch The figure in the right lower corner does not touch the line below, and has not the battered appearance of that in the first redrawn type. The stamps are very clearly printed, the lines of shading being distinct.

1906 (Sept). *W* **6.** *P* 12½, 13 (*comb*).

281	**30**	2d. dull blue (*shades*)	2·50	70

1907–12. *Wmk Crown and double-lined A, W* w **11**.

		(*a*) *P* 12 × 12½.		
282	**28**	9d. brown and ultramarine (*a*)	22·00	2·50
283		9d. brown and ultramarine (*b*)	11·00	2·00
283*a*		9d. pale brown and blue (*a*)		
284		9d. pale brown and blue (*b*)	11·00	2·25
		(*b*) *P* 11 (1912)		
285	**28**	9d. brown and blue (*b*)	—	£180

1907–09. *W* **29.** (*a*) *P* 12½, 13 (*comb*).

286	**26**	½d. deep green	80	15
287		½d. deep blue-green	80	15
288	**21**	1d. vermilion	95	12
		a. Imperf (pair)	£150	
289	**30**	2d. dull blue	1·40	12
289*a*		2d. bright blue (3.08)	7·50	2·00
290	**32**	2d. bright blue (4.08)	1·50	12
291	**21**	3d. pale brown (8.08)	10·00	70
292		3d. bistre-brown	9·50	75
293		4d. yellow (Die I)	9·50	1·25
		a. Die II		
294		4d. grey-black (Die I) (4.09)	9·00	1·00
		a. Die II		
295	**23**	5d. dull brown	6·50	1·10
295*a*		5d. sepia (12.09)	9·50	1·90
296	**21**	6d. yellow-green	8·50	1·10
297		6d. bright green	9·00	1·50
298	**24**	1s. violet (1908)	13·00	1·60
299		1s. bright mauve	14·00	1·50
300	**25**	2s. turquoise-green (8.08)	38·00	5·00

Stamps of this issue also exist with the irregular line perforation 12½, 13. This was used when the comb perforation was under repair.

		(*b*) *P* 13 × 11 *to* 12½		
301	**26**	½d. deep green		
302	**21**	1d. vermilion	95	12
303	**32**	2d. blue	1·75	55
304	**21**	3d. bistre-brown	4·25	75
305		4d. grey-black	12·00	
306	**23**	5d. dull brown	8·00	
307	**21**	6d. yellow-green	8·50	
308	**23**	1s. violet	18·00	

The perforation (*b*) is from a machine introduced to help cope with the demands caused by the introduction of penny postage. The three rows at top (or bottom) of the sheet show varieties gauging 13 × 11½, 13 × 11, and 13 × 12 respectively, these are obtainable in strips of three showing the three variations.

Many values of the 1907–09 issue were subsequently produced by lithography.

1911. *W* **29.** *Perf irregular compound,* 10½ *to* 12½.

309	**21**	1d. vermilion		

This was from another converted machine, formerly used for perforating Railway stamps. The perforation was very unsatisfactory and only one or two sheets were sold.

POSTAL FISCALS

Authorised for use from 1 January 1880 until 1 July 1892

CANCELLATIONS. Beware of stamps which have had pen-cancellations cleaned off and then had faked postmarks applied. Used prices quoted are for postally used examples between the above dates.

F 1 F 2

1866–68. A. *No wmk. P* 13.

F 1	**F 1**	1d. blue	18·00	2·75
F 2		6d. deep violet	18·00	20·00
F 3		1s. blue-green	23·00	5·00
F 4		2s. brown	70·00	35·00
F 5		2s. 6d. dull red	70·00	22·00
F 6		5s. yellow	£170	26·00
F 7		10s. green	£325	65·00
F 8		20s. rose	£375	£120
		B. *Wmk* F **2.** *P* 13		
F 9	**F 1**	1d. blue	7·00	20·00
F10		6d. deep violet	18·00	25·00
F11		6d. blue	18·00	6·00
F12		1s. blue-green	23·00	6·00
F13		2s. brown	70·00	12·00
F13*a*		5s. yellow	£170	25·00
F14		10s. green	£325	60·00
F15		20s. rose	£370	£120

F 3 F 4 F 5

1871–2. *P* 12 *or* 13. A. *Wmk Large Crown and Q, as W* **10.**

F16	**F 3**	1d. mauve	5·00	2·25
F17		6d. red-brown	12·00	6·50
F18		1s. green	18·00	6·50
F19		2s. blue	29·00	6·50
F20		2s. 6d. brick-red	40·00	13·00
F21		5s. orange-brown	85·00	13·00
F22		10s. brown	£170	50·00
F23		20s. rose	£325	£110
		B. *No wmk. Blue burelé band at back*		
F24	**F 3**	1d. mauve	7·50	3·25
F25		6d. red-brown	14·00	7·00
F26		6d. mauve	16·00	8·00
F27		1s. green	23·00	8·50
F28		2s. blue	35·00	50·00
F29		2s. 6d. vermilion	65·00	20·00
F30		5s. yellow-brown	£100	25·00
F31		10s. brown	£190	70·00
F32		20s. rose	£300	85·00

1878–9. A. *No wmk. Lilac burelé band at back. P* 12.

F33	F 4	1d. violet	—	9·00

B. *Wmk Crown and Q, W* **5**. *P* 12

F34	F 4	1d. violet	11·00	5·50

Stamps as Type F **5** were not issued until 1 July 1892. The existence of postal cancellations on such issues was unauthorised.

Queensland now uses Australian stamps.

Rhodesia

Stamps of BECHUANALAND were used in Rhodesia, at Bulawayo from August 1888 until 1892.

PRICES FOR STAMPS ON COVER TO 1945

Nos. 1/7	*from* × 5
Nos. 8/13	—
Nos. 14/17	*from* × 2
Nos. 18/24	*from* × 10
Nos. 25/6	—
Nos. 27/8	*from* × 7
Nos. 29/35	*from* × 10
Nos. 36/7	—
Nos. 41/6	*from* × 6
Nos. 47/50	—
Nos. 51/3	*from* × 2
Nos. 58/64	*from* × 3
Nos. 66/72	*from* × 8
Nos. 73/4	—
Nos. 75/87	*from* × 6
Nos. 88/93*a*	—
Nos. 94/9	*from* × 3
Nos. 100/10	*from* × 5
Nos. 111/13*e*	—
Nos. 114/18	*from* × 7
Nos. 119/60*a*	*from* × 2
Nos. 160*b*/6*b*	—
Nos. 167/78	*from* × 2
Nos. 179/81*a*	—
Nos. 182/5*a*	*from* × 2
Nos. 186/208	*from* × 3
Nos. 209/41	*from* × 2
Nos. 242/54*a*	—
Nos. 255/77	*from* × 2
Nos. 278/9c	—
Nos. 280/1	*from* × 7
Nos. 282/310	*from* × 2
Nos. 311/22	—

A. ISSUES FOR THE BRITISH SOUTH AFRICA COMPANY TERRITORY

1

2

½d.

(3)

(Recess B.W.)

1892 (2 Jan). *Thin wove paper. P* 14, 14½.

1	**1**	1d. black	8·00	3·00
2		6d. ultramarine	45·00	20·00
3		6d. deep blue	17·00	6·50
4		1s. grey-brown	25·00	18·00
5		2s. vermilion	35·00	25·00
6		2s. 6d. grey-purple	27·00	25·00
7		2s. 6d. lilac	27·00	25·00
8		5s. orange-yellow	50·00	48·00
9		10s. deep green	80·00	90·00
10	**2**	£1 deep blue	£175	£130
11		£2 rose-red*	£475	£150
12		£5 sage-green	£1800	£450
13		£10 brown	£3250	£700
1/10		*Set of* 10	£425	£350

*For later printing of the £2 see No. 74.

Nos. 3 and 7 came from later printings.

Great caution is needed in buying the high values in either used or unused condition, many stamps offered being revenue stamps cleaned and re-gummed or with forged postmarks.

The following sheet watermarks are known in the issues of 1892 and 1892–94. (1) William Collins, Sons & Co's paper watermarked with the firm's monogram, and "PURE LINEN WOVE BANK" in double-lined capitals. (2) As (1) with "EXTRA STRONG" and "139" added. (3) Paper by Wiggins, Teape & Co, watermarked "W T & Co" in script letters in double-lined wavy border. (4) The same firm's paper, watermarked "1011" in double-lined figures. (5) "WIGGINS TEAPE & CO LONDON" in double-lined block capitals. Many values can also be found on a slightly thicker paper without wmk, but single specimens are not easily distinguishable.

1892 (2 Jan).* *Nos.* 2 *and* 4 *surch as T* **3**.

14	**1**	½d. on 6d. ultramarine	80·00	£110
15		2d. on 6d. ultramarine	75·00	£130
16		4d. on 6d. ultramarine	95·00	£180
17		8d. on 1s. grey-brown	£100	£225

*This, being the date when postal services commenced, is the earliest date when these stamps could have been used, but it has not been established when supplies arrived.

Caution is needed in buying these surcharges as both forged surcharges and forged postmarks exist.

4

5 (ends of scrolls behind legs of springboks)

(T **4**. Centre recess; value B.W.)

1892 (2 Jan)–**94**. *Thin wove paper (wmks as note after No.* 13). *P* 14, 14½.

18	**4**	½d. dull blue and vermilion	2·75	2·50
19		½d. deep blue and vermilion	2·75	2·50
20		2d. sea-green and vermilion	5·00	2·50
21		3d. grey-black and green (8.92)	5·00	3·50
22		4d. chestnut and black	5·00	3·50
23		8d. rose-lake and ultramarine	5·00	4·00
24		8d. red and ultramarine	5·00	4·00
25		3s. brown and green (1894)	60·00	55·00
26		4s. grey-black and vermilion (1893)	32·00	35·00
18/26		*Set of* 8	£110	95·00

(Recess P.B. from the Bradbury, Wilkinson plates)

1895? *Thick soft wove paper. P* 12½.

27	**4**	2d. green and red	22·00	7·00
28		4d. yellow-brown and black	22·00	9·00
		a. Imperf (pair)	£1200	

(Centre recess; value typo P.B.)

1896–97. *Wove paper. P* 14.

(*a*) *Die I. Plates* 1 *and* 2.

Small dot to the right of the tail of the right-hand supporter in the coat of arms. Body of lion only partly shaded.

29	**5**	1d. scarlet and emerald	4·50	2·25
		a. Carmine-red and emerald		
30		2d. brown and mauve	4·50	2·25
31		3d. chocolate and ultramarine	2·25	2·25
32		4d. ultramarine and mauve		
		a. Imperf between (pair)		
		b. Blue and mauve	3·50	3·50
33		6d. mauve and pink	35·00	4·25
34		8d. green and mauve/*buff*	2·75	1·75
		a. Imperf between (pair		
		b. Imperf (pair)	£1400	
35		1s. green and blue	7·00	3·25
36		3s. green and mauve/*blue*	30·00	30·00
		a. Imperf (pair)	£1600	
37		4s. orange-red and blue/*green*	28·00	22·00
29/37		*Set of* 9	£110	65·00

(*b*) *Die II. Plates* 3 *and* 4

No dot. Body of lion heavily shaded all over.

41	**5**	½d. slate and violet	1·25	2·25
42		1d. scarlet and emerald	1·25	2·25
43		2d. brown and mauve	3·50	4·00
44		4d. ultramarine and mauve	32·00	9·00
		a. Blue and mauve	2·50	1·25
46		6d. mauve and rose	2·50	1·50
47		2s. indigo and green/*buff*	17·00	3·75
48		2s. 6d. brown and purple/*yellow*	20·00	23·00
49		5s. chestnut and emerald	30·00	26·00
50		10s. slate and vermilion/*rose*	70·00	65·00
41/50		*Set of* 9	£130	£120

One Penny

(6)

THREE PENCE.

(7)

(Surchd by *Bulawayo Chronicle*)

1896 (April). *Matabele Rebellion provisionals. Surch with T* **6** *and* **7**.

51	**6**	1d. on 3d. (No. 21)	£550	£650
		a. "P" in "Penny" inverted	£6000	
		b. "y" in "Penny" inverted		
52		1d. on 4s. (No. 26)	£550	£450
		a. "P" in "Penny" inverted	£6000	
		b. "y" in "Penny" inverted	£6000	
		c. Single bar through original value	£1000	£1300
53	**7**	3d. on 5s. (No. 8)	£275	£375
		a. "R" in "THREE" inverted	£8500	
		b. "T" in "THREE" inverted	£8500	

Nos. 51 and 52 occur in two settings, one with 9¾ mm between value and upper bar, the other with 11 mm between value and upper bar.

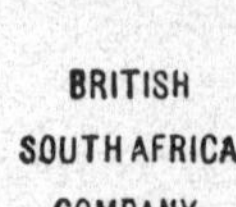

(8)

9 (Ends of scrolls between legs of springboks)

1896 (22 May). *Cape of Good Hope stamps optd by Argus Printing Co Cape Town, with T* **8**. *Wmk Anchor* (3*d. wmk Crown CA*). *P* 14.

58	**6**	½d. grey-black (No. 48*a*)	5·50	7·50
59	**17**	1d. rose-red (No. 58)	5·50	7·50
60	**6**	2d. deep bistre (No. 50*a*)	7·50	7·50
61		3d. pale claret (No. 40)	30·00	38·00
62		4d. blue (No. 51)	12·00	12·00
		a. "COMPANY," omitted	£8500	
63	**4**	6d. deep purple (No. 52*a*)	40·00	50·00
64	**6**	1s. yellow-ochre (No. 65)	80·00	£110
58/64		*Set of* 7	£160	£200

(Recess Waterlow)

1897. *P* 13½ *to* 16.

66	**9**	½d. grey-black and purple	1·60	2·00
67		1d. scarlet and emerald	2·75	3·00
68		2d. brown and mauve	2·00	2·00
69		3d. brown-red and slate-blue	2·00	1·50
		a. Imperf between (pair)	£1100	
70		4d. ultramarine and claret	2·75	2·50
		a. Imperf between (pair)	£3500	£3500
71		6d. dull purple and pink	2·50	4·50
72		8d. green and mauve/*buff*	5·50	3·00
		a. Imperf between (pair)	—	£900
73		£1 black and red-brown/*green*	£500	£275

(Recess Waterlow, from the Bradbury plate)

1897 (Jan). *P* 15.

74	**2**	£2 rosy red	£1800	£400

10

11

12

(Recess Waterlow)

1898–1908. *P* 13½ *to* 15½.

75	**10**	½d. dull bluish green	50	12
		a. Yellow-green (1904)	60	12
		aa. Imperf between (pair)	£600	
		ab. Imperf (pair)	£550	
76		½d. deep green (*shades*) (1908)	20·00	30
77		1d. rose (*shades*)	50	12
		a. Imperf (pair)	£650	£660
		b. Imperf between (pair)	£600	
78		1d. red (*shades*) (1905)	1·40	12
		a. Imperf between (pair)	£325	
		b. Imperf (pair)	£500	
79		2d. brown	1·25	15
80		2½d. dull blue (*shades*)	2·25	25
		a. Imperf between (pair)	£500	£500
		b. Grey-blue (*shades*) (1903)	3·50	40
81		3d. claret	3·75	1·75
		a. Imperf between (pair)	£700	
82		4d. olive	3·25	40
		a. Imperf between (pair)	£800	
83		6d. reddish purple	3·75	2·50
		a. Reddish mauve (1902)	7·50	7·00
84	**11**	1s. bistre	4·25	2·75
		a. Imperf between (pair)	£2000	
		b. Deep olive-bistre (1907)	£250	
		bc. Imperf (pair)	£2000	
		bd. Imperf between (horiz pair)	£2250	
		c. Bistre brown (1908)	14·00	6·00
		d. Brownish yellow (1908)	8·00	3·25
85		2s. 6d. bluish grey (11.06)	11·00	3·50
		a. Imperf between (pair)	£900	£600
		b. Imperf (vert pair)	—	£5000
86		3s. deep violet (1902)	7·00	3·25
		a. Deep bluish violet (1908)	16·00	7·00
87		5s. brown-orange	20·00	7·00
88		7s. 6d. black (11.01)	30·00	27·00
89		10s. grey-green	15·00	8·00
90	**12**	£1 greyish red-purple (*p* 15½) (7.01)	£160	32·00
		a. Perf 14. *Blackish purple* (1902)	£160	32·00
91		£2 brown (5.08)	80·00	20·00
92		£5 deep blue (7.01)	£4000	£2250
93		£10 lilac (7.01)	£4000	£2250
93*a*		£20 yellow-bistre (1901?)	£7500	
75/90		*Set of* 14	£200	80·00
80/1, 85/6, 88/93 Perf "Specimen"		*Set of* 10	£900	

A £100 cherry-red, perf 13½, was issued in June 1901, three examples being known with fiscal cancellations.

13 Victoria Falls

RHODESIA.

(14)

(Recess Waterlow)

1905 (13 July). *Visit of British Association and Opening of Victoria Falls Bridge. P* 13½ *to* 15.

94	**13**	1d. red	2·50	2·50
95		2½d. deep blue	7·50	7·50
96		5d. claret (Optd S. £125)	17·00	20·00
97		1s. blue-green	18·00	22·00
		a. Imperf (pair)	£7500	
		b. Imperf vert (horiz pair)	£8000	
		c. Imperf horiz (vert pair)	£10000	
98		2s. 6d. black	£100	£130
99		5s. violet	80·00	85·00
94/99		*Set of* 6	£200	£250
94/9 Perf (5d.) or Optd (others) "Specimen"		*Set of* 6	£300	

1909 (15 Apr)–**12**. *Optd as T* **14**. *P* 13½ *to* 15.

100	**10**	½d. green *to* deep green	30	12
		a. No stop	27·00	20·00
		b. Yellow-green (1911)	27·00	27·00
101		1d. carmine-rose	35	12
		a. No stop	30·00	19·00
		b. Imperf between (pair)	£300	
		c. Deep carmine-rose	35	12
		cd. Imperf between (pair)	£350	

No.	Type	Description	Unused	Used
102	10	2d. brown	1·60	1·25
		a. No stop	30·00	28·00
103		2½d. pale dull blue	55	40
		a. No stop	18·00	18·00
104		3d. claret	1·60	75
		a. No stop	55·00	45·00
105		4d. olive	2·50	90
		a. No stop	42·00	45·00
106		6d. dull purple	6·00	3·25
		a. No stop	42·00	30·00
		b. *Reddish purple*	3·00	1·25
107	11	1s. deep brownish bistre	4·00	1·25
		a. No stop	42·00	28·00
108		2s. 6d. bluish grey	13·00	7·00
		a. No stop	42·00	45·00
109		3s. deep violet	12·00	10·00
110		5s. orange	22·00	14·00
		a. No stop	45·00	48·00
111		7s. 6d. black	28·00	14·00
112		10s. dull green	18·00	16·00
		a. No stop	£170	£180
113	12	£1 grey-purple	90·00	48·00
		a. Vertical pair, one without opt	£8500	
		b. Overprint in violet	£225	£225
113c		£2 brown (*bluish paper*)	£3000	£250
113d		£2 rosy brown (*p* 14½ × 15) (1921)	£3000	£275
113e		£5 deep blue (*bluish paper*)	£4500	£1500
100/113		*Set of* 14	£170	£100
100/13 Perf "Specimen"		*Set of* 14	£350	

In some values the no stop variety occurs in every stamp in a vertical row of a sheet, in other values only once in a sheet. Other varieties, such as no serif to the right of apex of "A", no serif to top of "E", etc., exist in some values.

RHODESIA. 5d

(15)

RHODESIA. TWO SHILLINGS.

(16)

1909 (April)–**11**. *Surch as T* **15** *and* **16** (2s.), *in black.*

No.	Type	Description	Unused	Used
114	10	5d. on 6d. reddish purple	6·00	6·00
		a. Surcharge in violet	65·00	
115		5d. on 6d. dull purple	6·50	6·50
116	11	7½d. on 2s. 6d. bluish grey	4·50	4·00
		a. Surcharge in violet	8·50	7·00
		ab. Surch double	†	—
117		10d. on 3s. deep violet	12·00	12·00
		a. Surcharge in violet	4·00	4·00
118		2s. on 5s. orange	11·00	11·00
114/18 Perf "Specimen"		*Set of* 4	£170	

In the 7½d. and 10d. surcharges, the bars are spaced as in T **16**.

17

18

(Recess Waterlow)

1910 (11 Nov)–**13**. (*a*) *P* 14.

No.	Type	Description	Unused	Used
119	17	½d. yellow-green	4·00	60
		a. Imperf (pair)	£3750	£4500
120		½d. bluish green	7·00	60
121		½d. olive-green	17·00	1·25
122		½d. dull green	55·00	50·00
123		1d. bright carmine	4·00	20
		a. Imperf between (pair)	£15000	
124		1d. carmine-lake	15·00	30
125		1d. rose-red	5·00	20
126		2d. black and grey	15·00	4·50
127		2d. black-purple and slate-grey	£225	£600
128		2d. black and slate-grey	17·00	4·50
129		2d. black and slate	15·00	4·50
130		2d. black and grey-black	20·00	8·50
131		2½d. ultramarine	14·00	10·00
131a		2½d. bright ultramarine	12·00	10·00
132		2½d. dull blue	14·00	10·00
133		2½d. chalky blue	14·00	10·00
134		3d. purple and ochre	13·00	5·50
135		3d. purple and yellow-ochre	15·00	5·50
136		3d. magenta and yellow-ochre	75·00	65·00
137		3d. violet and ochre	85·00	70·00
138		4d. greenish black and orange	90·00	50·00
139		4d. brown-purple and orange	60·00	32·00
140		4d. black and orange	12·00	10·00
141		5d. purple-brown and olive-green	20·00	18·00
141a		5d. purple-brown and olive-yellow	20·00	40·00
		ab. Error. Purple-brown and ochre	£700	£190
143		5d. lake-brown and olive	£130	60·00
143a		5d. lake-brown and green	£18000	£2500
144		6d. red-brown and mauve	14·00	10·00
145		6d. brown and purple	14·00	7·00
145a		6d. bright chestnut and mauve	£750	80·00
146		8d. black and purple	£3250	
147		8d. dull purple and purple	£140	50·00
148		8d. greenish black and purple	£150	38·00
149		10d. scarlet and reddish mauve	32·00	70·00
150		10d. carmine and deep purple	£500	70·00
151		1s. grey-black and deep blue-green	24·00	15·00
151a		1s. black and deep blue-green		
152		1s. black and pale blue-green	17·00	8·00
152a		1s. purple-black and blue-green	£275	35·00
153		2s. black and ultramarine	50·00	35·00
154		2s. black and dull blue	£500	42·00
154a		2s. purple-black and ultramarine	£5000	£550
155		2s. 6d. black and lake	£500	£500
155a		2s. 6d. black and crimson	£500	£500
156		2s. 6d. sepia and deep crimson	£600	£600
156a		2s. 6d. bistre-brown and crimson	£900	£900
157		2s. 6d. black and rose-carmine	£500	£500
158		3s. green and violet (*shades*)	£120	£130
158a	17	3s. bright green and magenta	£900	£550
159		5s. vermilion and deep green	£250	£275
160		5s. scarlet and pale yellow-green	£300	£325
160a		5s. crimson and yellow-green	£275	£300
160b		7s. 6d. carmine and pale blue	£900	£900
161		7s. 6d. carmine and light blue	£900	£900
162		7s. 6d. carmine and bright blue	£1100	£1100
163		10s. deep myrtle and orange	£800	£400
164		10s. blue-green and orange	£750	£400
165		£1 carmine-red and bluish black	£1200	£500
166		£1 rose-scarlet and bluish black	£1300	£500
166a		£1 crimson and slate-black	£1400	£850
		b. Error. Scarlet and reddish mauve	£8500	

(*b*) *P* 15

No.	Type	Description	Unused	Used
167	17	½d. blue-green	£275	15·00
168		½d. yellow-green	£375	15·00
169		½d. apple-green	£600	27·00
170		1d. carmine	£350	11·00
170a		1d. carmine-lake	£450	11·00
170b		1d. rose-carmine	£375	11·00
171		2d. black and grey-black	£550	25·00
171a		2d. black and grey	£550	25·00
171b		2d. black and slate	£550	25·00
172		2½d. ultramarine (*shades*)	£140	80·00
173		3d. purple and yellow-ochre	£1400	80·00
173a		3d. claret and pale yellow-ochre	£1300	80·00
174		4d. black and orange (*shades*)	50·00	80·00
175		5d. lake-brown and olive-green	£900	£100
176		6d. brown and mauve	£1000	80·00
177		1s. black and blue-green (*shades*)	£900	70·00
178		2s. black and dull blue	£1200	£700
179		£1 red and black	£12000	£5000

(*c*) *P* 15 × 14 *or* 14 × 15

No.	Type	Description	Unused	Used
179a	17	½d. yellow-green	£6000	£5500
179b		1d. carmine	†	—
180		3d. purple and ochre	£2750	£500
181		4d. black and orange	£600	
181a		1s. black and blue-green	£10000	£5000

(*d*) *P* 13½

No.	Type	Description	Unused	Used
182	17	½d. yellow-green	£325	28·00
182a		½d. green	£325	28·00
183		1d. bright carmine	£2500	50·00
184		2½d. ultramarine (*shades*)	28·00	30·00
185		8d. black and purple (*shades*)	£120	£300
185a		8d. grey-purple and dull purple	£250	£300
119/185 Optd "Specimen" perf 14 except 2½d. and 8d. perf 13½		*Set of* 18	£3250	

Plate varieties in T **17** are:—½d., double dot below "D" in right-hand value tablet (*from* £600 *un.*, £500 *used*); 2d. to £1 excluding 2½d., straight stroke in Queen's right ear known as the "gash in ear" variety (*from* 3 *to* 8 *times normal*).

Stamps from the above and the next issue are known compound perf with 14 or 15 on one side only or on adjoining sides but we no longer list them.

(Recess Waterlow)

1913 (1 Sept)–**22**. *No wmk.* (i) *From single working plates.*

(*a*) *P* 14.

No.	Type	Description	Unused	Used
186	18	½d. blue-green	2·75	25
		a. Imperf between (pair)	£500	£500
187		½d. deep green	1·00	12
188		½d. yellow-green	2·50	20
		a. Imperf between (pair)	£500	£500
188b		½d. dull green	2·00	12
189		½d. bright green	3·00	12
190		1d. rose-carmine	1·00	12
		a. Imperf between (pair)	£500	£500
191		1d. carmine-red (*shades*)	2·50	12
		a. Imperf between (pair)	£800	
192		1d. brown-red	1·50	12
193		1d. red	1·50	12
194		1d. scarlet	6·50	30
		a. Imperf between (horiz pair)	£800	
195		1d. rose-red	1·00	12
196		1d. crimson	£500	19·00
197		1½d. brown-ochre (1919)	1·00	12
		a. Imperf between (pair)	£500	£500
198		1½d. bistre-brown (1917)	1·40	12
		a. Imperf between (pair)	£500	£500
199		1½d. drab-brown (1917)	1·40	12
		a. Imperf between (pair)	£550	
200		2½d. deep blue	2·50	3·25
201		2½d. bright blue	2·50	3·25

(*b*) *P* 15

No.	Type	Description	Unused	Used
202	18	½d. blue-green	5·00	3·50
203		½d. green	5·00	3·50
204		1d. carmine-red	£325	£225
		a. Imperf between (pair)	£4000	
204b		1d. rose-red	£375	£250
205		1d. brown-red	1·25	2·25
206		1½d. bistre-brown (1919)	8·00	5·50
206a		1½d. drab-brown	8·00	5·50
207		2½d. deep blue	11·00	11·00
208		2½d. bright blue	11·00	11·00

(*c*) *P* 14 × 15

No.	Type	Description	Unused	Used
208a	18	½d. green	£1200	£190

(*d*) *P* 15 × 14

No.	Type	Description	Unused	Used
208b	18	½d. green	£1200	£190
208c		1½d. drab-brown		

(*e*) *P* 13½

No.	Type	Description	Unused	Used
208d	18	1d. red (*shades*)	—	£750

Die I

Die II

Die III

The remaining values were printed from double, i.e. head and duty, plates. There are at least four different head plates made from three different dies, which may be distinguished as follows:—

Die I. The King's left ear is neither shaded nor outlined; no outline to top of cap. Shank of anchor in cap badge is complete.

Die II. The ear is shaded all over, but has no outline. The top of the cap has a faint outline. Anchor as Die I.

Die III. The ear is shaded and outlined; a heavy continuous outline round the cap. Shank of anchor is broken just below the lowest line which crosses it.

(ii) *Printed from double plates. Head Die* I. (*a*) *P* 14.

No.	Type	Description	Unused	Used
209	18	2d. black and grey	3·75	3·00
210		3d. black and yellow	18·00	3·75
211		4d. black and orange-red	3·50	7·50
212		5d. black and green	3·50	5·00
213		6d. black and mauve	£125	20·00
213a		8d. violet and green		
214		2s. black and brown	25·00	20·00

(*b*) *P* 15

No.	Type	Description	Unused	Used
215	18	3d. black and yellow	4·50	4·50
216		4d. black and orange-red	90·00	10·00
217		6d. black and mauve	3·25	2·75
217a		8d. violet and green		
218		2s. black and brown	10·00	13·00

(iii) *Head Die* II. (*a*) *P* 14

No.	Type	Description	Unused	Used
219	18	2d. black and grey	4·50	2·50
220		2d. black and brownish grey	9·00	2·50
221		3d. black and deep yellow	9·50	2·00
222		3d. black and yellow	16·00	1·40
223		3d. black and buff	2·75	1·50
224		4d. black and orange-red	4·50	2·00
225		4d. black and deep orange-red	3·75	2·00
226		5d. black and grey-green	5·50	7·50
227		5d. black and bright green	4·25	7·50
228		6d. black and mauve	7·50	1·75
229		6d. black and purple	13·00	2·25
230		8d. violet and green	9·50	10·00
231		10d. blue and carmine-red	8·00	11·00
232		1s. black and greenish blue	8·50	8·50
233		1s. black and turquoise-blue	3·50	4·25
234		2s. black and brown	20·00	7·50
235		2s. black and yellow-brown	38·00	15·00
236		2s. 6d. indigo and grey-brown	22·00	9·00
236a		2s. 6d. pale blue and brown	29·00	11·00
236b		3s. brown and blue	38·00	45·00
237		3s. chestnut and bright blue	38·00	45·00
238		5s. blue and yellow-green	65·00	30·00
239		5s. blue and blue-green	38·00	30·00
240		7s. 6d. blackish purple and slate-black	£170	£170
241		10s. crimson and yellow-green	£190	£180
242		£1 black and purple	£700	£800
243		£1 black and violet	£800	£900

(*b*) *P* 15

No.	Type	Description	Unused	Used
244	18	2d. black and grey	2·50	3·50
245		4d. black and deep orange-vermilion	£550	£275
246		8d. violet and green	£170	£160
247		10d. blue and red	4·50	8·00
248		1s. black and greenish blue	5·50	3·00
249		2s. 6d. indigo and grey-brown	20·00	23·00
250		3s. chocolate and blue	£850	£250
251		5s. blue and yellow-green	50·00	45·00
251a		5s. blue and blue-green	£750	
252		7s. 6d. blackish purple and slate-black	60·00	80·00
253		10s. red and green	£225	£300
254		£1 black and purple	£1000	£1300
254a		£1 black and deep purple	£1500	£1500
186/254a Optd "Specimen" (various Dies and Perfs)		*Set of* 19	£1900	

(iv) *Head Die* III. *Toned paper, yellowish gum.* (*a*) *P* 14

No.	Type	Description	Unused	Used
255	18	2d. black and brownish grey	5·00	2·75
256		2d. black and grey-black	1·90	1·40
		a. Imperf between (pair)	£3250	£3750
257		2d. black and grey	2·00	1·90
258		2d. black and sepia	6·00	2·50
259		3d. black and yellow	2·50	1·40
260		3d. black and ochre	2·50	1·40
261		4d. black and orange-red	6·00	1·90
262		4d. black and dull red	4·50	2·50
263		5d. black and pale green	3·00	4·25
		a. Imperf between (pair)	£4500	
264		5d. black and green	3·00	4·25
265		6d. black and reddish mauve	3·25	2·25
266		6d. black and dull mauve	2·75	2·25
		a. Imperf between (pair)		
267		8d. mauve and dull blue-green	12·00	12·00
		a. Imperf vert (horiz pair)		
268		8d. mauve and greenish blue	12·00	12·00
269		10d. indigo and carmine	8·00	11·00
270		10d. blue and red	6·00	9·50
271		1s. black and greenish blue	3·50	2·40
272		1s. black and pale blue-green	3·50	2·40
272a		1s. black and light blue	7·50	4·50
272b		1s. black and green	30·00	13·00
273		2s. black and brown	8·50	8·50
		aa. Imperf between (vert pair)	—	£12000
273a		2s. black and yellow-brown	£350	40·00
274		2s. 6d. dp ultramarine & grey-brn	17·00	17·00
274a		2s. 6d. pale blue and pale bistre-brown (*shades*)	50·00	20·00
274b		3s. chestnut and light blue	£140	45·00
275		5s. deep blue and blue-green (*shades*)	40·00	30·00
276		5s. blue & pale yell-grn (*shades*)	40·00	30·00
276a		7s. 6d. maroon and slate-black	£650	£700
277		10s. carmine-lake and yellow-green	£375	£225
278		£1 black and bright purple	£700	£800
279		£1 black and deep purple	£700	£800
279a		£1 black and violet-indigo	£700	£800
279b		£1 black and deep violet	£700	£750

(*b*) *P* 15

No.	Type	Description	Unused	Used
279c	18	2d. black and brownish grey	£4500	£1300

Half Penny

(19)

Half-Penny.

(20)

1917 (15 Aug). *No. 190 surch at the Northern Rhodesian Administrative Press, Livingstone, with T* **19**, *in violet or violet-black.*

280 **18** ½d. on 1d. rose-carmine (*shades*) 1·75 4·00
a. Surch inverted £1500 £1500
b. Letters "n n" spaced wider 5·50 8·50
c. Letters "n y" spaced wider 3·00 6·00

The setting was in two rows of 10 repeated three times in the sheet.

The two colours of the surcharge occur on the same sheet.

1917 (22 Sept). *No. 190 surch as T* **20** (*new setting with hyphen, and full stop after* "Penny"), *in deep violet.*

281 **18** ½d. on 1d. rose-carmine (*shades*) 95 2·00

1922–24. *New printings on white paper with clear white gum.*

(i) *Single working plates.* (*a*) *P* 14

282 **18** ½d. dull green (1922) 2·50 12
a. Imperf between (pair) £1200
283 ½d. deep blue-green (1922) 1·50 45
284 1d. bright rose (1922) 1·75 80
285 1d. bright rose-scarlet (1923) 1·40 65
a. Imperf between (pair) £1200
286 1d. aniline red (8.24) 25·00 2·25
287 1½d. brown-ochre (1923) 1·60 40
a. Imperf between (pair) £850

(*b*) *P* 15

288 **18** ½d. dull green (1923) 12·00 7·50
289 1d. bright rose-scarlet (1923) 17·00 18·00
290 1½d. brown-ochre (1923) 15·00 8·50

(ii) *Double plates. Head Die* III. (*a*) *P* 14

291 **18** 2d. black and grey-purple (1922) 1·40 90
292 2d. black and slate-purple (1923) 2·25 1·00
293 3d. black & yellow (1922) 4·50 7·00
294 4d. black & orange-vermilion (1922–3) 6·50 5·50
295 6d. jet-black and lilac (1922–3) 2·00 1·25
296 8d. mauve and pale blue-green (1922) 13·00 13·00
297 8d. violet and grey-green (1923) 13·00 13·00
298 10d. bright ultramarine and red (1922) 7·00 10·00
299 10d. brt ultramarine & carm-red (1923) 7·00 10·00
300 1s. black and dull blue (1922–3) 2·00 2·00
a. Imperf between (pair) £4000
301 2s. black and brown (1922–3) 9·50 9·50
302 2s. 6d. ultramarine and sepia (1922) 18·00 18·00
303 2s. 6d. violet-blue & grey-brown (1923) 13·00 13·00
304 3s. red-brown & turquoise-bl (1922) 18·00 15·00
305 3s. red-brown and grey-blue (1923) 35·00 28·00
306 5s. brt ultramarine and emerald (1922) 55·00 35·00
307 5s. deep blue and bright green (1923) 55·00 35·00
308 7s. 6d. brown-purple and slate (1922) £140 £160
309 10s. crimson and brt yellow-green (1922) £130 £140
310 10s. carmine and yellow-green (1923) £130 £160
311 £1 black and deep magenta (1922) £600 £650
311*a* £1 black and magenta (1923) £600 £650

(*b*) *P* 15 (1923)

312 **18** 2d. black and slate-purple 26·00
313 4d. black and orange-vermilion 26·00
314 6d. jet-black and lilac 26·00
315 8d. violet and grey-green 26·00
316 10d. bright ultramarine & carmine-red 42·00
317 2s. black and dull blue 42·00
318 2s. black and brown 90·00
319 2s. 6d. violet-blue and grey-brown 95·00
320 3s. red-brown and grey-blue £120
321 5s. deep blue and bright green £140
322 £1 black and magenta £750

The 1922 printing shows the mesh of the paper very clearly through the gum. In the 1923 printing the gum is very smooth and the mesh of the paper is not so clearly seen. Where date is given as "(1922–23)" two printings were made, which do not differ sufficiently in colour to be listed separately.

Nos. 312/22 were never sent out to Rhodesia but only issued in London. Any used copies could, therefore, only have been obtained by favour.

In 1924 Rhodesia was divided into NORTHERN and SOUTHERN RHODESIA and between 1954 and 1964 these were merged in the Central African Federation (*see* RHODESIA AND NYASALAND). In 1964 there were again separate issues for Northern and Southern Rhodesia but after Northern Rhodesia became independent and was renamed Zambia, Southern Rhodesia was renamed RHODESIA in October 1964.

B. ISSUES FOR THE FORMER SOUTHERN RHODESIA

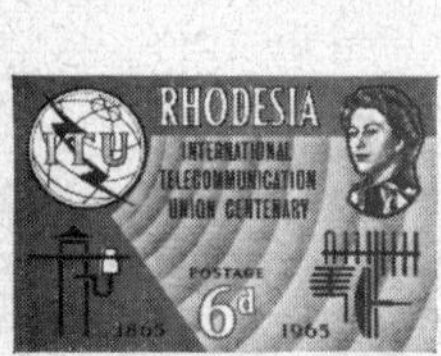

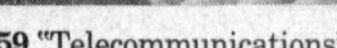
59 "Telecommunications"

60 Bangala Dam

(Des V. Whiteley. Photo Harrison)

1965 (17 May). *I.T.U. Centenary. P* 14½.

351 **59** 6d. violet and light yellow-olive 2·00 60
352 1s. 3d. violet and lilac 3·25 1·75
353 2s. 6d. violet and light brown 8·00 11·00

(Des V. Whiteley. Photo Harrison)

1965 (19 July). *Water Conservation. T* **60** *and similar vert designs. Multicoloured. P* 14.

354 3d. Type **60** 30 5
355 4d. Irrigation canal 1·75 1·25
356 2s. 6d. Cutting sugar cane 6·00 6·50

63 Sir Winston Churchill, Quill, Sword and Houses of Parliament

(Des H. Baxter. Photo Harrison)

1965 (16 Aug). *Churchill Commemoration. P* 14½.

357 **63** 1s. 3d. black and bright blue 1·50 1·75

UNILATERAL DECLARATION OF INDEPENDENCE

Independence was declared by Rhodesia on 11 November 1965 but this was not recognised by the British Government. Following a conference in London during 1979 it was agreed that the British Government should resume control, pending elections to be held in February 1980.

After the elections Rhodesia became an independent republic within the Commonwealth on 18 April 1980, as ZIMBABWE.

64 Coat of Arms

(Des Col. C. R. Dickenson. Litho Mardon Printers, Salisbury)

1965 (8 Dec). *"Independence". P* 11.

358 **64** 2s. 6d. multicoloured 35 45
a. Imperf (pair) £300

INDEPENDENCE
11th November
1965

INDEPENDENCE
11th November 1965 = 5/-

(**65**) (**66**)

1966 (17 Jan). (*a*) *Nos. 92/105 of Southern Rhodesia optd with T* **65** *or larger* (5s. *to* £1).

359 ½d. yellow, yellow-green and light blue 5 5
a. Pair, one stamp without opt.
360 1d. reddish violet and yellow-ochre 8 5
361 2d. yellow and deep violet 10 5
362 3d. chocolate and pale blue 12 5
363 4d. yellow-orange and deep green 15 5
364 6d. carmine-red, yellow & dp dull green 20 5
365 9d. red-brown, yellow and olive-green 35 10
a. Opt double 70·00
366 1s. blue-green and ochre 35 5
a. Opt double 80·00
367 1s. 3d. red, violet and yellow-green 1·25 10
368 2s. blue and ochre 2·50 2·25
369 2s. 6d. ultramarine and vermilion 1·00 40
370 5s. light brown, bistre-yellow & lt blue 40·00 24·00
a. Opt double £160
371 10s. black, yellow-ochre, lt bl & carm-red 7·00 4·00
372 £1 brown, yell-green, buff & salmon-pink 6·00 6·50

(*b*) *No. 357 surch with T* **66**

373 5s. on 1s. 3d. black and bright blue (R.) 60·00 £100
359/73 *Set of* 15 £110 £120

Owing to the existence of forgeries, No. 370a should only be purchased when accompanied by a certificate of genuineness.

67 Emeralds

68 Zeederberg Coach, *circa* 1895

(Des V. Whiteley. Photo Harrison)

1966 (9 Feb). *As Nos. 92/105 of Southern Rhodesia, but inscr* "RHODESIA" *as T* **67**. *Some designs and colours changed. P* 14½ (1d. *to* 4d.), 13½ × 13 (6d. *to* 2s. 6d.) *or* 14½ × 14 (5s. *to* £1).

374 – 1d. reddish violet and yellow-ochre 8 5
375 – 2d. yell-orge and dp grn (as No. 96) 8 5
a. Yellow-orange omitted £325
376 – 3d. chocolate and pale blue 10 5
a. Chocolate omitted £325
b. Pale blue omitted £325
377 **67** 4d. emerald and sepia 15 5
378 **50** 6d. carmine-red, yellow & dp dull grn 20 5
379 – 9d. yellow and deep violet (as No. 94) 25 25
380 **45** 1s. yellow, yellow-green and light blue 35 5
381 – 1s. 3d. blue and ochre (as No. 101) 60 25
382 – 1s. 6d. red-brn, yell & olive-grn (as No. 98) 1·00 35
383 – 2s. red, violet and yell-grn (as No. 100) 1·25 1·00
384 – 2s. 6d. blue, vermilion & turquoise-bl 1·00 55
385 **56** 5s. light brown, bistre-yellow & lt blue 2·25 2·00
386 – 10s. black, yell-ochre, lt bl & carm-red 10·00 10·00
387 **58** £1 brown, yell-green, buff & salmon-pk 27·00 19·00
374/87 *Set of* 14 40·00 30·00

Nos. 379/80 are in larger format, as T **50**.

No. 376a occurred in the bottom row of a sheet and No. 376b in the top two rows of a sheet.

For stamps printed by lithography, see Nos. 397/407.

PRINTERS. All the following stamps were printed by lithography by Mardon Printers, Salisbury.

(Des V. Whiteley (Nos. 388/90))

1966 (2 May). *28th Congress of Southern Africa Philatelic Federation* ("*Rhopex*"). *T* **68** *and similar horiz designs. P* 14½.

388 3d. multicoloured 1·25 50
389 9d. grey-buff, sepia and grey-green 1·25 1·50
390 1s. 6d. pale blue and black 2·00 2·25
391 2s. 6d. salmon-pink, pale dull grn & blk 2·50 3·00
MS392 126 × 84 mm. Nos. 388/91 30·00 32·00

Designs:—9d. Sir Rowland Hill; 1s. 6d. The Penny Black; 2s. 6d. Rhodesian stamp of 1892 (No. 12).

69 De Havilland "Rapide" (1946) **70** Kudu

1966 (1 June). *20th Anniv of Central African Airways. T* **69** *and similar horiz designs. P* 14½ × 14.

393 6d. black, blue, yellow and green 1·25 1·25
394 1s. 3d. blue, yellow-orange, black and green 2·00 1·25
395 2s. 6d. black, blue, yellow and green 6·00 8·00
396 5s. black and blue 8·50 12·00

Aircraft:—1s. 3d. Douglas "DC3." (1953); 2s. 6d. Vickers "Viscount" (1956); 5s. Modern jet.

1966–69. *As Nos. 374/87 but litho. P* 14½ (1d. *to* 2s.) *or* 14½ × 14 (*others*).

397 1d. reddish violet and yellow-ochre (*shades*) (2.6.66) 20 25
398 2d. orange and green (1.11.67) 50 40
399 3d. chocolate-brn & pale grnsh bl (29.1.68) 50 15
400 4d. emerald, bistre-brown & drab (21.9.66) 45 25
401 6d. carmine-red, yell & ol-grey (1.11.66) 60 40
402 9d. yellow and light violet (20.11.67) 90 90
403 1s. 3d. blue and ochre (1.11.66) 3·50 1·90
404 2s. dull red, violet & sage-green (18.7.66) 12·00 10·00
405 5s. yellow-brown, deep bistre-yellow and light blue (25.6.66) 22·00 14·00
406 10s. black, buff, lt bl & carm-red (10.8.66) 60·00 80·00
407 £1 pale brown, yellow-green, brown-ochre and salmon (10.8.66) 65·00 90·00
397/407 *Set of* 11 £150 £180

In addition to the change in printing process from photogravure to lithography and the difference in perforation in the 6d. to 2s. values (14½ instead of 13½ × 13) and shade variations, the oval portrait frame is larger (and in some values thicker) in the 1d. to 2s., and in the 1s. 3d. the Queen's head is also larger.

Trial printings exist of the 5s., 10s., and £1 values on a slightly thinner paper. These are rare.

1967–68. *Dual Currency Issue. As Nos.* 376, 380 *and* 382/4 *but value in decimal currency in addition as in T* **70**. *P* 14½. *White gum* (*No.* 408) *or cream gum* (*others*).

408 3d./2½ c. chocolate-brown and pale greenish blue (15.3.67) 60 25
409 1s./10 c. yell, grn & greenish bl (1.11.67) 1·25 1·25
410 1s. 6d./15 c. red-brown, yellow and yellow-green (11.3.68) 16·00 5·00
411 2s./20 c. dull red, viol and sage-grn (11.3.68) 25·00 18·00
412 2s. 6d./25 c. ultramarine-blue, vermilion and bright turquoise-blue (9.12.68) 65·00 80·00

71 Dr. Jameson (administrator)

(Des from painting by F. M. Bennett)

1967 (17 May). *Famous Rhodesians* (1*st issue*) *and 50th Death Anniv of Dr. Jameson. P* 14½.

413 **71** 1s. 6d. multicoloured 1·25 1·50

See also Nos. 426, 430, 457, 458, 469, 480, 488 and 513.

72 Soapstone Sculpture (Joram Mariga)

1967 (12 July). *Tenth Anniv of Opening of Rhodes National Gallery. T* **72** *and similar vert designs. P* 14½ × 14 (3d., 9d.) *or* 14 (*others*).

414 3d. reddish chestnut, yellow-olive and black 50 20
415 9d. lt greenish blue, dp olive-brown & black 90 75
a. Perf 13½ 13·00 17·00
416 1s. 3d. multicoloured 1·40 1·75
417 2s. 6d. multicoloured 1·75 2·25

Designs:—9d. "The Burgher of Calais" (detail, Rodin); 1s. 3d. "The Knight" (stamp design wrongly inscr) (Roberto Crippa); 2s. 6d. "John the Baptist" (M. Tossini).

73 Baobab Tree

1967 (6 Sept). *Nature Conservation. T* **73** *and similar designs. P* 14½.

418	4d. light brown and black	55	70
419	4d. yellow-olive and black	55	70
420	4d. deep grey and black	55	70
421	4d. yellow-orange and black	55	70

Designs: *Horiz*—No. 418, Type **73**; No. 419, White Rhino; No. 420, Elephants. *Vert*—No. 421, Wild Gladiolus.

74 Wooden Hand Plough

(Des Rose Martin)

1968 (26 Apr). *15th World Ploughing Contest, Norton, Rhodesia. T* **74** *and similar horiz designs. P* 14½.

422	3d. pale orange, orange-verm & lake-brown	35	10
423	9d. multicoloured	75	60
424	1s. 6d. multicoloured	1·25	1·50
425	2s. 6d. multicoloured	1·50	2·00

Designs:—9d. Early wheel plough; 1s. 6d. Steam powered tractor, and ploughs; 2s. 6d. Modern tractor, and plough.

75 Alfred Beit (national benefactor)

76 Raising the Flag, Bulawayo, 1893

(Des from painting by A. Haywood)

1968 (15 July). *Famous Rhodesians (2nd issue). P* 14½.

426	**75**	1s. 6d. pale orange, black and brown	1·00	1·25

(Des Rose Martin)

1968 (4 Nov). *75th Anniv of Matabeleland. T* **76** *and similar vert designs. P* 14½.

427	3d. pale orange, red-orange and black	50	20
428	9d. multicoloured	1·00	1·00
429	1s. 6d. pale turquoise-green, deep emerald and blackish green	1·25	1·75

Designs:—9d. View and coat of arms of Bulawayo; 1s. 6d. Allan Wilson (combatant in the Matabele War).

77 Sir William Henry Milton (administrator)

(Des from painting by S. Kendrick)

1969 (15 Jan). *Famous Rhodesians (3rd issue). P* 14½.

430	**77**	1s. 6d. multicoloured	1·00	1·25

78 2 ft Gauge Locomotive (1899)

(Des Rose Martin)

1969 (22 May). *70th Anniv of Opening of Beira-Salisbury Railway. T* **78** *and similar horiz designs showing locomotives. Multicoloured. P* 14½.

431	3d. Type **78**	1·00	25
432	9d. Steam loco (1904)	2·00	1·50
433	1s. 6d. Articulated loco (1950)	8·00	6·00
434	2s. 6d. Diesel-electric (1955)	11·00	11·00

79 Low Level Bridge

(Des Rose Martin)

1969 (18 Sept). *Bridges of Rhodesia. T* **79** *and similar horiz designs. Multicoloured. P* 14½.

435	3d. Type **79**	85	25
436	9d. Mpudzi bridge	1·60	1·25
437	1s. 6d. Umniati bridge	6·00	5·50
438	2s. 6d. Birchenough bridge	7·00	8·50

(New Currency. 100 cents = 1 dollar)

80 Harvesting Wheat

81 Devil's Cataract, Victoria Falls

(Des from colour-transparencies (3, 6 c.), Rose Martin (others))

1970 (17 Feb)–**73.** *Decimal Currency. T* **80/1** *and similar horiz designs. P* 14½.

439	1 c. multicoloured	10	5
	a. Booklet pane of 4	40	
440	2 c. multicoloured	10	5
441	2½ c. multicoloured	10	5
	a. Booklet pane of 4	40	
441*c*	3 c. multicoloured (1.1.73)	1·90	20
	ca. Booklet pane of 4	7·50	
442	3½ c. multicoloured	20	5
	a. Booklet pane of 4	1·00	
442*b*	4 c. multicoloured (1.1.73)	1·90	30
	ba. Booklet pane of 4	7·50	
443	5 c. multicoloured	25	10
443*b*	6 c. multicoloured (1.1.73)	3·50	1·25
443*c*	7½ c. multicoloured (1.1.73)	7·00	3·25
444	8 c. multicoloured	3·00	90
445	10 c. multicoloured	60	10
446	12½ c. multicoloured	70	25
446*a*	14 c. multicoloured (1.1.73)	14·00	4·75
447	15 c. multicoloured	3·00	40
448	20 c. multicoloured	3·00	35
449	25 c. multicoloured	3·25	1·25
450	50 c. turquoise and ultramarine	4·50	3·00
451	$1 multicoloured	15·00	15·00
452	$2 multicoloured	35·00	35·00
439/52	*Set of* 19	85·00	60·00

Designs: *Size as T* **80**—2 c. Pouring molten metal; 2½ c. Zimbabwe Ruins; 3 c. Articulated lorry; 3½ c. and 4 c. Statute of Cecil Rhodes; 5 c. Mine headgear. *Size as T* **81**—6 c. Hydrofoil *Seaflight*; 7½ c. As 8 c.; 10 c. Yachting on Lake McIlwaine; 12½ c. Hippo in river; 14 c. and 15 c. Kariba Dam; 20 c. Irrigation canal. *As T* **80/1** *but larger* (31 × 26 *mm*)—25 c. Bateleurs; 50 c. Radar antenna and Vickers "Viscount"; $1 "Air Rescue"; $2 Rhodesian flag.

82 Despatch Rider, *circa* 1890

(Des Rose Martin)

1970 (1 July). *Inauguration of Posts and Telecommunications Corporation. T* **82** *and similar horiz designs. Multicoloured. P* 14½.

453	2½ c. Type **82**	60	30
454	3½ c. Loading mail at Salisbury airport	1·40	75
455	15 c. Constructing telegraph line, *circa* 1890	3·25	3·00
456	25 c. Telephone and modern telecommunications equipment	4·75	6·00

83 Mother Patrick (Dominican nurse and teacher)

(Des Rose Martin from photograph)

1970 (16 Nov). *Famous Rhodesians (4th issue). P* 14½.

457	**83**	15 c. multicoloured	2·00	2·00

84 Frederick Courteney Selous (big-game hunter, explorer and pioneer)

(Des from painting by L. C. Dickinson)

1971 (1 Mar). *Famous Rhodesians (5th issue). P* 14½.

458	**84**	15 c. multicoloured	2·00	2·00

NEW INFORMATION

The editor is always interested to correspond with people who have new information that will improve or correct the Catalogue.

85 Hoopoe

86 Porphyritic Granite

(Des from photographs by Peter Ginn)

1971 (1 June). *Birds of Rhodesia (1st series). T* **85** *and similar multicoloured designs. P* 14½.

459	2 c. Type **85**	1·25	20
460	2½ c. Half-collared Kingfisher (*horiz*)	1·25	20
461	5 c. Golden-breasted Bunting	4·00	2·00
462	7½ c. Carmine Bee Eater	4·50	2·75
463	8 c. Red-eyed Bulbul	4·50	3·50
464	25 c. Senegal Wattled Plover (*horiz*)	10·00	8·00
459/64	*Set of* 6	23·00	15·00

See also Nos. 537/42.

(Des from photographs by University of Rhodesia and Dept of Geological Survey)

1971 (30 Aug). *"Granite 71" Geological Symposium. T* **86** *and similar vert designs. Multicoloured. P* 14.

465	2½ c. Type **86**	80	5
466	7½ c. Muscovite mica seen through microscope	2·00	1·25
467	15 c. Granite seen through microscope	3·75	4·50
468	25 c. Geological map of Rhodesia	4·50	6·50

87 Dr. Robert Moffat (missionary)

1972 (14 Feb). *Famous Rhodesians (6th issue). P* 14½.

469	**87**	13 c. multicoloured	1·75	1·75

88 Bird ("Be Airwise")

89 "The Three Kings"

(Des C. Lawton)

1972 (17 July). *"Prevent Pollution". T* **88** *and similar horiz designs. Multicoloured. P* 14½.

470	2½ c. Type **88**	40	5
471	3½ c. Antelope ("Be Countrywise")	70	20
472	7 c. Fish ("Be Waterwise")	1·40	1·50
473	13 c. City ("Be Citywise")	1·90	2·75

1972 (28 Aug). *"Rhophil '72". As Nos.* 439a, 441a *and* 442a *with commemorative inscr in margins. Each* 66 × 78 *mm.*

MS474	1 c. multicoloured	3·75	3·75
MS475	2½ c. multicoloured	3·75	3·75
MS476	3½ c. multicoloured	3·75	3·75

(Des Rose Martin)

1972 (18 Oct). *Christmas. P* 14.

477	**89**	2 c. multicoloured	12	5
478		5 c. multicoloured	90	60
479		13 c. multicoloured	90	1·10

90 Dr. David Livingstone

91 W.M.O. Emblem

1973 (2 Apr). *Famous Rhodesians (7th issue). P* 14.

480	**90**	14 c. multicoloured	1·75	2·00

(Des S. J. Ivey)

1973 (2 July). *I.M.O./W.M.O. Centenary. P* 14.

481	**91**	3 c. multicoloured	20	5
482		14 c. multicoloured	1·75	2·00
483		25 c. multicoloured	2·75	3·50

92 Arms of Rhodesia

1973 (10 Oct). *50th Anniv of Responsible Government. P* 14.

No.	Type	Description	Mint	Used
484	**92**	2½ c. multicoloured	30	5
485		4 c. multicoloured	60	35
486		7½ c. multicoloured	1·60	1·60
487		14 c. multicoloured	3·00	5·00

93 George Pauling (construction engineer)

(Des P. Birch)

1974 (15 May). *Famous Rhodesians* (8*th issue*). *P* 14.

No.	Type	Description	Mint	Used
488	**93**	14 c. multicoloured	2·25	2·25

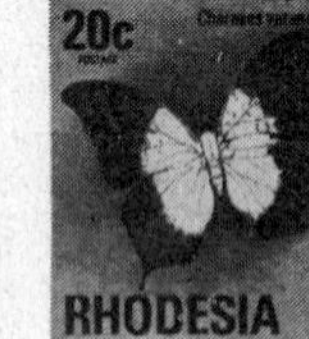

94 Kudu **95** Thunbergia **96** Pearl Charaxes

(Des J. Huntly)

1974 (14 Aug)–**76**. *Various vert designs as T* **94/6**. *Multicoloured. P* 14½ (1 *to* 14 *c.*) *or* 14 (*others*). (*a*) *Antelopes. Size as T* **94**.

No.	Description	Mint	Used
489	1 c. Type **94**	10	5
490	2½ c. Eland	90	5
	a. Booklet pane of 4	3·50	
491	3 c. Roan Antelope	10	5
	a. Booklet pane of 4	70	
492	4 c. Reedbuck	10	5
	a. Booklet pane of 4	70	
493	5 c. Bushbuck	20	5
	(*b*) *Wild Flowers. Size as T* **95**		
494	6 c. Type **95**	40	10
495	7½ c. Flame Lily	3·50	1·25
496	8 c. As 7½ c. (1.7.76)	40	15
497	10 c. Devil Thorn	25	20
498	12 c. Hibiscus (1.7.76)	70	45
499	12½ c. Pink Sabi Star	5·00	1·75
500	14 c. Wild Pimpernel	6·50	2·00
501	15 c. As 12½ c. (1.7.76)	70	45
502	16 c. As 14 c. (1.7.76)	70	45
	(*c*) *Butterflies. Size as T* **96**		
503	20 c. Type **96**	90	45
504	24 c. Yellow Pansy (1.7.76)	1·75	50
505	25 c. As 24 c.	7·50	2·75
506	50 c. Queen Purple Tip	90	80
507	$1 Large Striped Swordtail	1·50	1·50
508	$2 Guinea Fowl Butterfly	2·00	2·75
489/508	*Set of* 20	30·00	14·00

97 Collecting Mail **98** Thomas Baines (artist)

(Des M. Chase)

1974 (20 Nov). *Centenary of Universal Postal Union. T* **97** *and similar horiz designs. Multicoloured. P* 14.

No.	Description	Mint	Used
509	3 c. Type **97**	30	5
510	4 c. Sorting mail	60	20
511	7½ c. Mail delivery	1·50	1·00
512	14 c. Weighing parcel	2·25	2·50

(Des from self-portrait)

1975 (12 Feb). *Famous Rhodesians* (9*th issue*). *P* 14.

No.	Type	Description	Mint	Used
513	**98**	14 c. multicoloured	2·00	2·00

99 *Euphorbia confinalis* **100** Prevention of Head Injuries

(Des Nancy Abrey)

1975 (16 July). *International Succulent Congress, Salisbury* ("*Aloe* '75"). *T* **99** *and similar vert designs. Multicoloured. P* 14½.

No.	Description	Mint	Used
514	2½ c. Type **99**	20	5
515	3 c. *Aloe excelsa*	20	5
516	4 c. *Hoodia lugardii*	40	20
517	7½ c. *Aloe ortholopha*	90	70
518	14 c. *Aloe musapana*	2·50	1·50
519	25 c. *Aloe saponaria*	3·50	2·50
514/19	*Set of* 6	7·00	4·50

(Des Val Bond)

1975 (15 Oct). *Occupational Safety. T* **100** *and similar horiz designs. Multicoloured. P* 14.

No.	Description	Mint	Used
520	2½ c. Type **100**	30	5
521	4 c. Bandaged hand and gloved hand	80	15
522	7½ c. Broken glass and eye	1·60	1·40
523	14 c. Blind man and welder with protective mask	2·50	2·50

8c

101 Telephones, 1876 and 1976 (**102**)

(Des M. Chase)

1976 (10 Mar). *Telephone Centenary. T* **101** *and similar vert design. P* 14.

No.	Description	Mint	Used
524	3 c. grey-black and pale blue	12	5
525	14 c. brownish black and light stone	60	70

Design:—14 c. Alexander Graham Bell.

1976 (1 July). *Nos.* 495, 500 *and* 505 *surch as T* **102**.

No.	Description	Mint	Used
526	8 c. on 7½ c. Flame Lily	50	30
527	16 c. on 14 c. Wild Pimpernel	60	50
528	24 c. on 25 c. Yellow Pansy	1·50	2·00

103 Roan Antelope **104** Msasa

(Des N. Pedersen)

1976 (21 July). *Vulnerable Wildlife. T* **103** *and similar horiz designs. Multicoloured. P* 14.

No.	Description	Mint	Used
529	4 c. Type **103**	35	5
530	6 c. Brown Hyena	45	20
531	8 c. Wild Dog	65	70
532	16 c. Cheetah	75	1·25

(Des Nancy Abrey)

1976 (17 Nov). *Trees of Rhodesia. T* **104** *and similar vert designs. Multicoloured. P* 14.

No.	Description	Mint	Used
533	4 c. Type **104**	20	5
534	6 c. Red Mahogany	30	10
535	8 c. Mukwa	40	55
536	16 c. Rhodesian Teak	55	85

105 Common Bulbul **106** "Lake Kyle" (Joan Evans)

(Des B. Finch)

1977 (16 Mar). *Birds of Rhodesia* (2*nd series*). *T* **105** *and similar vert designs. Multicoloured. P* 14.

No.	Description	Mint	Used
537	3 c. Type **105**	20	5
538	4 c. Yellow-mantled Whydah	20	5
539	6 c. Cape Longclaw	25	20
540	8 c. Eastern Long-tailed Shrike	45	30
541	16 c. Lesser Blue-eared Glossy Starling	75	70
542	24 c. Green Wood Hoopoe	95	90
537/42	*Set of* 6	2·50	2·00

1977 (20 July). *Landscape Paintings. T* **106** *and similar horiz designs. Multicoloured. P* 14.

No.	Description	Mint	Used
543	3 c. Type **106**	15	5
544	4 c. "Chimanimani Mountains" (Joan Evans)	15	5
545	6 c. "Rocks near Bonsor Reef", (Alice Balfour)	20	10
546	8 c. "A Dwala near Devil's Pass" (Alice Balfour)	40	30
547	16 c. "Zimbabwe" (Alice Balfour)	50	60
548	24 c. "Victoria Falls" (Thomas Baines)	60	80
543/8	*Set of* 6	1·75	1·75

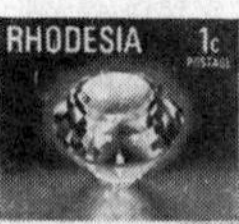

107 Virgin and Child **108** Fair Spire

(Des Dianne Deudney)

1977 (16 Nov). *Christmas. P* 14.

No.	Type	Description	Mint	Used
549	**107**	3 c. multicoloured	10	5
550		6 c. multicoloured	15	10
551		8 c. multicoloured	25	12
552		16 c. multicoloured	40	65

1978 (15 Mar). *Trade Fair Rhodesia, Bulawayo. T* **108** *and similar vert design. Multicoloured. P* 14.

No.	Description	Mint	Used
553	4 c. Type **108**	15	5
554	8 c. Fair Spire (*different*)	25	25

109 Morganite **110** Rhinoceros

111 Odzani Falls

(Des N. Pedersen (1 to 17 c.), D. Myles (21 c. to $2))

1978 (16 Aug). *Multicoloured.*

No.	Description	Mint	Used
	(*a*) *Horiz designs as T* **109** *showing gemstones. P* 14½		
555	1 c. Type **109**	10	5
556	3 c. Amethyst	15	5
557	4 c. Garnet	15	5
558	5 c. Citrine	15	5
559	7 c. Blue Topaz	20	5
	(*b*) *Horiz designs as T* **110** *showing wild animals. P* 14½		
560	9 c. Type **110**	20	5
561	11 c. Lion	20	12
562	13 c. Warthog	20	12
563	15 c. Giraffe	20	15
564	17 c. Zebra	25	5
	(*c*) *Horiz designs as T* **111** *showing waterfalls. P* 14		
565	21 c. Type **111**	25	30
566	25 c. Goba Falls	30	40
567	30 c. Inyangombi Falls	40	30
568	$1 Bridal Veil Falls	1·00	1·75
569	$2 Victoria Falls	1·25	2·00
555/69	*Set of* 15	4·00	4·50

112 Wright *Flyer*

(Des C. Herbert)

1978 (18 Oct). *75th Anniv of Powered Flight. T* **112** *and similar horiz designs. Multicoloured. P* 14.

No.	Description	Mint	Used
570	4 c. Type **112**	10	5
571	5 c. Blériot "XI"	12	5
572	7 c. Vickers "Vimy" *Silver Queen* II	15	15
573	9 c. "A.W. 15 Atalanta"	15	15
574	17 c. Vickers "Viking 1B"	30	40
575	25 c. Boeing "720B"	35	70
570/5	*Set of* 6	1·00	1·40

POSTAGE DUE STAMPS

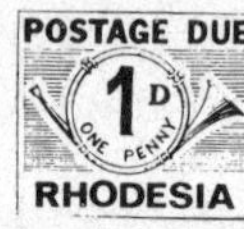

D 2 D 3 Zimbabwe Bird (soapstone sculpture)

(Typo Printing and Stationery Dept, Salisbury)

1965 (17 June). *Roul* 9.

No.	Type	Description	Mint	Used
D1	D 2	1d. orange-red (*roul* 5)	1·25	5·00
		a. Roul 9	95	1·75
D2		2d. deep blue	95	4·50
D3		4d. green	1·00	4·50
D4		6d. plum	2·25	5·00

The 2d. has a stop below the "D".

(Litho Mardon Printers, Salisbury)

1966 (15 Dec). *P* 14½.

D 5	D 3	1d. red	1·40	1·40
D 6		2d. bluish violet	1·75	1·75
D 7		4d. pale green	2·00	2·50
D 8		6d. reddish violet	2·25	2·50
D 9		1s. red-brown	2·75	3·00
D10		2s. black	3·75	5·00
D5/10		*Set of* 6	12·50	14·50

1970 (17 Feb)–**73**. *Decimal Currency. As Type* D 3, *but larger* (26 × 22½ *mm*). *P* 14½.

D11	D 3	1 c. bright green	55	60
D12		2 c. ultramarine	55	60
D13		5 c. bright reddish violet	70	70
D14		6 c. pale lemon (7.5.73)	1·00	1·00
D15		10 c. cerise	1·10	1·50

For later issues see ZIMBABWE.

Rhodesia & Nyasaland

Stamps for the Central African Federation of Northern and Southern Rhodesia and Nyasaland Protectorate.

1

2

3 Queen Elizabeth II

(Recess Waterlow)

1954 (1 July)–**56**. *P* 13½ × 14 (*T* 1), 13½ × 13 (*T* 2) *or* 14 × 13½ (*T* 3).

1	1	½d. red-orange	12	5
		a. Coil stamp. Perf 12½ × 14 (6.2.56)	35	1·25
2		1d. ultramarine	12	5
		a. Coil stamp. Perf 12½ × 14. *Deep blue* (*shades*) (1.10.55)	35	1·25
3		2d. bright green	15	5
3*a*		2½d. ochre (15.2.56)	85	5
4		3d. carmine-red	30	5
5		4d. red-brown	60	20
6		4½d. blue-green	30	40
7		6d. bright reddish purple (*shades*)	45	5
8		9d. violet	1·00	75
9		1s. grey-black	80	5
10	2	1s. 3d. red-orange and ultramarine	2·00	15
11		2s. deep blue and yellow-brown	5·00	75
12		2s. 6d. black and rose-red	6·00	80
13		5s. violet and olive-green	12·00	2·00
14	3	10s. dull blue-green and orange	28·00	20·00
15		£1 olive-green and lake	45·00	42·00
1/15		*Set of* 16	90·00	60·00

Nos. 1a and 2a printed on rotary machines by subsidiary company, Imprimerie Belge de Securité, in Belgium.

4 Aeroplane over Victoria Falls

5 Livingstone and Victoria Falls

(Des J. E. Hughes (3d.), V. E. Horne (1s.). Recess Waterlow)

1955 (15 June). *Centenary of Discovery of Victoria Falls. P* 13½ (3*d*.) *or* 13 (1*s*.).

16	4	3d. ultramarine & dp turquoise-grn	15	25
17	5	1s. purple and deep blue	40	1·00

6 Tea Picking

10 Rhodes's Grave

11 Lake Bangweulu

12*a* Rhodesian Railway Trains

19 Federal Coat of Arms

(Des M. Kinsella (9d.). Recess Waterlow (½d., 1d., 2d., 1s.) until 1962, then D.L.R., D.L.R. (2½d., 4d., 6d., 9d., 2s., 2s. 6d.) and B.W. (others))

1959 (12 Aug)–**62**. *T* 6, 10/11, 12*a*, 19 *and similar designs. P* 13½ × 14 (½*d*., 1*d*., 2*d*.), 14½ (2½*d*., 4*d*., 6*d*., 9*d*., 2*s*., 2*s*. 6*d*.), 14 × 13½ (3*d*.), 13½ × 13 (1*s*.), 14 (1*s*. 3*d*.) *or* 11 (*others*).

18	½d. black and light emerald	12	12
	a. Coil stamp. Perf 12½ × 14	40	1·50
19	1d. carmine-red and black	12	5
	a. Coil stamp (*shades*). Perf 12½ × 14	40	1·50
	ac. Carmine-red (centre) omitted	£200	
20	2d. violet and yellow-brown	25	5
21	2½d. purple and grey-blue	25	40
22	3d. black and blue	15	5
	a. Centre omitted	£350	
23	4d. maroon and olive	40	5
24	6d. ultramarine and deep myrtle-green	35	5
24*a*	9d. orge-brown & reddish violet (15.5.62)	1·25	1·75
25	1s. light green and ultramarine	60	5
26	1s. 3d. emerald and deep chocolate	1·75	5
27	2s. grey-green and carmine	4·00	75
28	2s. 6d. light blue and yellow-brown	5·50	45
29	5s. deep chocolate and yellow-green	11·00	2·75
30	10s. olive-brown and rose-red	35·00	16·00
31	£1 black and deep violet	45·00	38·00
18/31	*Set of* 16	95·00	55·00

Designs: *Vert* (*as T* 6)—1d. V.H.F. mast; 2d. Copper mining; 2½d. Fairbridge Memorial. (*As T* 11)—6d. Eastern Cataract, Victoria Falls. *Horiz* (*as T* 12*a*)—1s. Tobacco; 1s. 3d. Lake Nyasa; 2s. Chirundu Bridge; 2s. 6d. Salisbury Airport. (*As T* 19)—5s. Rhodes Statue; 10s. Mlanje.

20 Kariba Gorge, 1955

(Photo Harrison (3d., 6d.), D.L.R. (others))

1960 (17 May). *Opening of Kariba Hydro-Electric Scheme. T* 20 *and similar horiz designs. P* 14½ × 14 (3*d*., 6*d*.) *or* 14 (*others*).

32	3d. blackish green and red-orange	25	5
	a. Red-orange omitted		
33	6d. brown and yellow-brown	70	30
34	1s. slate-blue and green	1·75	90
35	1s. 3d. light blue and orange-brown (*shades*)	3·00	80
36	2s. 6d. deep slate-purple and orange-red	9·00	9·00
37	5s. reddish violet and turquoise-blue	17·00	28·00
32/37	*Set of* 6	29·00	35·00

Designs:—6d. 330 kV power lines; 1s. Barrage wall; 1s. 3d. Barrage and lake; 2s. 6d. Interior of power station; 5s. Barrage wall and Queen Mother (top left).

26 Miner Drilling

(Des V. Whiteley. Photo Harrison)

1961 (8 May). *Seventh Commonwealth Mining and Metallurgical Congress. T* 26 *and similar horiz design. P* 15 × 14.

38	6d. olive-green and orange-brown	1·50	45
39	1s. 3d. black and light blue	2·00	1·25

Design:—1s. 3d. Surface installations, Nchanga Mine.

28 D.H. "Hercules" on Rhodesian Airstrip

31 Tobacco Plant

1962 (6 Feb). *30th Anniv of First London-Rhodesia Airmail Service. T* 28 *and similar horiz designs. P* 14½ × 14.

40	6d. bronze-green and vermilion	40	25
41	1s. 3d. light blue, black and yellow	1·00	60
42	2s. 6d. rose-red and deep violet	9·50	10·00

Designs:—1s. 3d. Empire "C" class flying-boat taking off from Zambesi; 2s. 6d. "Comet" at Salisbury airport.

(Des V. Whiteley. Photo Harrison)

1963 (18 Feb). *World Tobacco Congress, Salisbury. T* 31 *and similar vert designs. P* 14 × 14½.

43	3d. green and olive-brown	20	5
44	6d. green, brown and blue	40	65
45	1s. 3d. chestnut and indigo	1·00	75
46	2s. 6d. yellow and brown	3·75	5·00

Designs:—6d. Tobacco field; 1s. 3d. Auction floor; 2s. 6d. Cured tobacco.

35 Red Cross Emblem

(Photo Harrison)

1963 (6 Aug). *Red Cross Centenary. P* 14½ × 14.

47	35	3d. red	35	10

36 African "Round Table" Emblem

(Des V. Whiteley. Photo Harrison)

1963 (11 Sept). *World Council of Young Men's Service Clubs, Salisbury. P* 14½ × 14.

48	36	6d. black, gold and yellow-green	40	50
49		1s. 3d. black, gold, yell-grn & lilac	1·00	1·10

POSTAGE DUE STAMPS

The 1d. and 2d. (Nos. 2/3) exist with a rubber-stamped "POSTAGE DUE" cancellation. In the absence of proper labels these values were used as postage dues at the Salisbury G.P.O. but according to the G.P.O. the handstamp was intended as a cancellation and not as an overprint (although "unused" examples of the 1d. are known). Its use was discontinued at the end of August 1959.

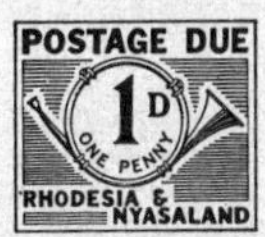

D 1

(Typo Federal Printing and Stationery Dept, Salisbury)

1961 (19 Apr). *P* 12½.

D1	D 1	1d. vermilion	1·25	2·50
		a. Imperf between (horiz pair)	£180	
D2		2d. deep violet-blue	1·50	3·00
D3		4d. green	2·25	4·00
D4		6d. purple	2·75	7·00

The 2d. has a stop below the "D".

The stamps of the Federation were withdrawn on 19 February 1964 when all three constituent territories had resumed issuing their own stamps.

Sabah

(*formerly* North Borneo)

SABAH (136) **SABAH** (137)

1964 (1 July). *Nos.* 391/406 *of North Borneo* (*D.L.R. printings*), *optd. Cents values optd with T* 136, *dollar values with T* 137.

408	1 c. emerald and brown-red	5	5
409	4 c. bronze-green and orange	12	10
410	5 c. sepia and violet (*shades*)	12	5
411	6 c. black and blue-green	10	5
412	10 c. green and red	12	5
413	12 c. brown and grey-green	12	5
414	20 c. blue-green and ultramarine	35	5
415	25 c. grey-black and scarlet	35	60
416	30 c. sepia and olive	35	5
417	35 c. slate-blue and red-brown	45	20
418	50 c. emerald and yellow-brown	45	10
419	75 c. grey-blue and bright purple	95	55
420	$1 brown and yellow-green	2·50	50
421	$2 brown and slate	3·25	2·75
422	$5 emerald and maroon	10·00	9·50
423	$10 carmine and blue	18·00	17·00
408/23	*Set of* 16	32·00	28·00

Old stocks bearing Waterlow imprints of the 4 c., 5 c., 20 c. and 35 c. to $10 were used for overprinting, but in addition new printings of all values by De La Rue using the original plates with the De La Rue imprint replacing the Waterlow imprint were specially made for overprinting.

ALTERED CATALOGUE NUMBERS

Any Catalogue numbers altered from the last edition are shown as a list in the introductory pages.

138 *Vanda hookeriana*

139 Great Orange Tip

1965 (15 Nov). *As Nos.* 166/72 *of Johore, but with Arms of Sabah inset as in T* **138**. W w **13** (*upright*).

No.		Description	Unused	Used
424		1 c. multicoloured	8	10
425		2 c. multicoloured	8	10
426		5 c. multicoloured	12	5
427		6 c. multicoloured	20	5
428		10 c. multicoloured	20	5
429		15 c. multicoloured (*shades*)	55	12
430		20 c. multicoloured	80	20
424/30		*Set of* 7	1·75	65

The 5 c. to 15 c. exist with PVA gum as well as gum arabic.
The higher values used with this issue were Nos. 20/27 of Malaysia.

1970 (20 Nov). *As No.* 428, *but W w* **13** (*sideways*).

No.		Description	Unused	Used
431		10 c. multicoloured	65	90

1971 (1 Feb)–**78**. *As Nos.* 175/87 *of Johore but with Arms of Sabah, as in T* **139**. (*a*) *Litho by Bradbury, Wilkinson.*

No.		Description	Unused	Used
432		1 c. multicoloured	5	20
433		2 c. multicoloured	5	20
434		5 c. multicoloured	15	5
435		6 c. multicoloured	15	5
436		10 c. multicoloured	15	5
437		15 c. multicoloured	30	12
438		20 c. multicoloured	35	12
432/8		*Set of* 7	1·10	70

(*b*) *Photo by Harrison* (1977–78)

No.		Description	Unused	Used
439		1 c. multicoloured	10	20
440		2 c. multicoloured	12	25
441		5 c. multicoloured	1·50	90
442		10 c. multicoloured	15	12
443		15 c. multicoloured	40	40

For differences between litho and photo printings, see after Johore No. 187.
The higher values used with this issue were Nos. 64/71 of Malaysia.

140 *Hibiscus rosa-sinensis*

1979 (30 Apr). *As Nos.* 188/94 *of Johore but with Arms of Sabah as in T* **140**.

No.		Description	Unused	Used
444		1 c. *Rafflesia hasseltii*	5	5
445		2 c. *Pterocarpus indicus*	5	5
446		5 c. *Lagerstroemia speciosa*	5	5
447		10 c. *Durio zibethinus*	8	5
448		15 c. Type **140**	10	5
449		20 c. *Rhododendron scortechinii*	15	5
450		25 c. *Phaeomeria speciosa*	15	5
444/50		*Set of* 7	55	20

For higher values used in conjunction with this series see Nos. 190/7 of Malaysia.

St. Helena

CROWN COLONY

PRICES FOR STAMPS ON COVER TO 1945

Nos. 1/2*a*	*from* × 10
Nos. 3/5	*from* × 4
Nos. 6/45	*from* × 10
Nos. 46/52	*from* × 4
Nos. 53/67	*from* × 3
No. 71	—
Nos. 72/86	*from* × 3
Nos. 87/8	*from* × 10
Nos. 89/95	*from* × 3
No. 96	—
Nos. 97/110	*from* × 3
Nos. 111/13	—
Nos. 114/40	*from* × 2

1

ONE PENNY

(2)

FOUR PENCE

(3)

(Recess P.B.)

Wmk Large Star, W w 1

1856 (1 Jan). *Imperf.*

No.	Type	Description	Unused	Used
1	1	6d. ..	£550	£225

1861 (April (?)). (*a*) *Clean-cut perf* 14 *to* 16.

No.	Type	Description	Unused	Used
2	1	6d. blue	£1000	£200
		(*b*) *Rough perf* 14 *to* 16		
2*a*	1	6d. blue	£350	£150

NOTE: The issues which follow consist of 6d. stamps, T **1**, printed in various colours and (except in the case of the 6d. values) surcharged with a new value, as T **2** to **10**, *e.g.* stamps described as "1d." are, in fact, 1d. on 6d stamps, and so on.
The numbers in the Type column below refer to the *types of the lettering* of the surcharged value.

(Printed by D.L.R. from P.B. plate)

Two Types of Bar on 1d. value:
A. Bar 16–17 mm long.
B. Bar 18½–19 mm long.

1863 (July). *Wmk Crown CC. Surch as T* **2/3** *with thin bar approximately the same length as the words. Imperf.*

No.	Type	Description	Unused	Used
3	2	1d. lake (Type A)	£110	£140
		a. Surch double	£3000	£1500
		b. Surch omitted	£9500	
4		1d. lake (Type B)	£110	£140
		a. Vert pair. Nos. 3/4	£1200	
5	3	4d. carmine (*bar* 15½–16½ *mm*)	£500	£250
		a. Surch double	£6000	£6000

ONE PENNY (4 (A))

ONE PENNY (4 (B))

ONE PENNY (4 (C))

TWO PENCE (5)

THREE PENCE (6)

FOUR PENCE (7)

ONE SHILLING (8)

FIVE SHILLINGS (9)

Three Types of Bar:
A. Thin bar (16½ to 17 mm) nearly the same length as the words.
B. Thick bar (14 to 14½ mm) much shorter than the words, except on the 2d. (Nos. 9, 22, 28) where it is nearly the same length.
C. Long bar (17 to 18 mm) same length as the words.

1864–80. *Wmk Crown CC. 6d. as T* 1, *without surcharge.*

No.	Type	Description	Unused	Used
		(*a*) *P* 12½ (1864–73)		
6	4	1d. lake (Type A) (1864)	22·00	23·00
		a. Surch double		
7		1d. lake (Type B) (1868)	48·00	45·00
		a. Surch double		
		b. Imperf	£2500	
8		1d. lake (Type C) (1871)	13·00	13·00
		a. Surch in blue-black	£750	£550
9	5	2d. yellow (Type B) (1868)	45·00	48·00
		a. Imperf	£6000	
10		2d. yellow (Type C) (1873)	48·00	15·00
		a. Surch in blue-black	£4500	£2750
11	6	3d. deep dull purple (Type B) (1868)	42·00	42·00
		a. Surch double	—	£4500
		b. Imperf	£700	
		c. *Light purple*	£2750	£750
12		3d. deep dull purple (Type A) (1873)	48·00	45·00
13	7	4d. carmine (Type A) (1864)	48·00	35·00
		a. Surch double	—	£4500
14	7	4d. carmine (Type B) (*words* 18 *mm long*) (1868)	48·00	38·00
		a. Surch double	—	£4000
		b. Surch double (18 + 19 *mm widths*)	£9000	£9000
		c. Imperf	£6000	
15		4d. carmine-rose (Type B) (*words* 19 *mm long*) (1868)	£130	£100
		a. Surch omitted	†	—
16	–	6d. dull blue (1871)	£400	85·00
		a. Ultramarine (1873)	£250	75·00
17	8	1s. deep yellow-green (Type A) (1864)	55·00	22·00
		a. Surch double	—	£18000
18		1s. deep yellow-green (Type B) (1868)	£225	95·00
		a. Surch double	£9000	
		b. Imperf	£10000	
		c. Surch omitted*	£9000	
19		1s. deep green (Type C) (1871)	£150	15·00
		a. Surch in blue-black		
20	9	5s. orange (Type B) (1868)	35·00	45·00
		a. Yellow	£250	£200
		(*b*) *P* 14 × 12½ (1876)		
21	4	1d. lake (Type B)	27·00	15·00
22	5	2d. yellow (Type B)	45·00	32·00
23		3d. purple (Type B)	£140	50·00
24		4d. carmine (Type B) (*words* 16½ *mm long*)	48·00	32·00
25	–	6d. milky blue	£140	24·00
26	8	1s. deep green (Type C)	£225	25·00
		(*c*) *P* 14 (1880)		
27	4	1d. lake (Type B)	28·00	12·00
28	5	2d. yellow (Type B)	35·00	18·00
29	–	6d. milky blue	£110	30·00
30	8	1s. yellow-green (Type B)	25·00	12·00

The only known copy of No. 15a is in the Royal Collection, although a second badly damaged example may exist.
*No. 18c is from a sheet of the 1s. with surcharge misplaced, the fifth row of 12 stamps being thus doubly surcharged and the tenth row without surcharge.

2½d

(10)

11

12

1884–94. *Wmk Crown CA. T* **1** *surch. Bars similar to Type* B *above* (*except* 2½*d., T* **10**, *and the* 1*s., in which the bar is nearly the same length as the words*). *The* 6*d. as before without surcharge. P* 14.

No.	Type	Description	Unused	Used
34	–	½d. green (*words* 17 *mm*) (1884)	2·00	3·25
		a. "N" and "Y" spaced		
35	–	½d. emerald (*words* 17 *mm*) (1885)	6·00	6·00
		a. "N" and "Y" spaced	£700	
		b. Surch double	£1000	
		ba. Ditto. "N" and "Y" spaced*		
36	–	½d. deep green (*words* 14½ *mm*) (1893)	1·75	2·00
37	4	1d. red (1887)	3·25	3·00
38		1d. pale red (1890)	3·25	3·00
39	5	2d. yellow (1894)	3·25	3·75
40	10	2½d. ultramarine (1893)	3·50	6·00
		a. Surch double	£9000	
		b. Stamp doubly printed	£4000	
41	6	3d. deep mauve (1887)	3·50	4·50
		a. Surch double	—	£9000
42		3d. deep reddish lilac (1887)	6·00	7·00
		a. Surch double	£4500	£5500
43	7	4d. pale brown (*words* 16½ *mm*) (1890)	8·00	12·00
43*a*		4d. sepia (*words* 17 *mm*) (1894)	13·00	8·00
44	–	6d. grey (1887)	13·00	10·00
45	8	1s. yellow-green (1894)	20·00	13·00
		a. Surch double	£4750	
40/1, 43, 44 Optd "Specimen"		*Set of* 4	£110	

Examples of the above are sometimes found showing no watermark; these are from the bottom row of the sheet, which had escaped the watermark, the paper being intended for stamps of a different size to Type 1.
Some are found without bar and others with bar at top of stamp, due to careless overprinting.
Of the 2½d. with double surcharge only six copies exist, and of the 2½d. double printed, one row of 12 stamps existed on one sheet only.
*No. 35ba. No. 35a occurs on stamp No. 216 in the sheet. In No. 35ba only one of the two surcharges shows the variety.

CANCELLATIONS. Nos. 36/45 and No. 20, have been sold cancelled with a violet diamond-shaped grill with four interior bars extending over two stamps. These cannot be considered as *used* stamps, and they are consequently not priced in the list.
This violet obliteration is easily removed and many of these remainders have been cleaned and offered as unused; some are repostmarked with a date and name in thin type rather larger than the original, a usual date being "Ap. 4.01."

(Typo D.L.R.)

1890–97. *Wmk Crown CA. Plate I for the* 1½*d. Plate II for the other values* (*for differences see Seychelles*). *P* 14.

No.	Type	Description	Unused	Used
46	11	½d. green (1897)	2·75	4·25
47		1d. carmine (1896)	4·75	4·00
48		1½d. red-brown and green (1890)	4·25	5·50
49		2d. orange-yellow (1896)	5·00	8·50
50		2½d. ultramarine (1896)	8·00	11·00
51		5d. mauve (1896)	20·00	25·00
52		10d. brown (1896)	28·00	30·00
46/52		*Set of* 7	65·00	80·00
46/52 Optd "Specimen"		*Set of* 7	£350	

The note below No. 45a *re* violet diamond-shaped grill cancellation also applies to Nos. 46/52.

1902. *Wmk Crown CA. P* 14.

No.	Type	Description	Unused	Used
53	12	½d. green (Mar)	1·00	1·50
54		1d. carmine (24 Feb)	2·75	3·75
53/4 Optd "Specimen"		*Set of* 2	90·00	

13 Government House

14 The Wharf

(Typo D.L.R.)

1903 (May). *Wmk Crown CC. P* 14.
55 **13** ½d. brown and grey-green . . . . 1·75 2·25
 a. Bluish paper £160 £110
56 **14** 1d. black and carmine . . . . 1·75 2·00
 a. Bluish paper £160 £110
57 **13** 2d. black and sage-green . . . . 10·00 9·50
 a. Bluish paper £160 £110
58 **14** 8d. black and brown . . . . 21·00 30·00
59 **13** 1s. brown and brown-orange . . . . 21·00 30·00
60 **14** 2s. black and violet . . . . 38·00 48·00
55/60 . . *Set of* 6 85·00 £110
55/60 Optd "Specimen" *Set of* 6 £250

A printing of the 1d. value in Type **14** in red only on Mult Crown CA paper was made in 1911, but not sold to the public. Examples are known overprinted "SPECIMEN" (*Price* £550).

15

(Typo D.L.R.)

1908 (May). *P* 14. (*a*) *Wmk Mult Crown CA.*
64 **15** 2½d. blue, **O** . . . . 1·90 3·00
66 4d. black and red/*yellow*, **OC** . . 1·90 4·00
67 6d. dull and deep purple, **OC** . . 3·50 8·50
(*b*) *Wmk Crown CA*
71 **15** 10s. green and red/*green*, **C** . . £300 £400
64/71 Optd "Specimen" *Set of* 4 £300

16

17

(Typo D.L.R.)

1912–16. *Wmk Mult Crown CA. P* 14.
72 **16** ½d. black and green . . . . 90 1·50
73 **17** 1d. black and carmine-red . . . . 1·10 1·25
 a. Black and scarlet (1916) . . 24·00 27·00
74 1½d. black and dull orange (1913) . . 3·00 4·25
75 **16** 2d. black and greyish slate . . 3·00 3·50
76 **17** 2½d. black and bright blue . . 3·00 5·00
77 **16** 3d. black and purple/*yellow* (1913) . . 3·00 5·00
78 **17** 8d. black and dull purple . . 12·00 25·00
79 **16** 1s. black and black/*green* . . 17·00 23·00
80 **17** 2s. black and blue/*blue* . . 38·00 50·00
81 3s. black and violet (1913) . . 60·00 80·00
72/81 . . *Set of* 10 £130 £180
72/81 Optd "Specimen" *Set of* 10 £300

No. 73*a* is on thicker paper than 73.

18

19

(Typo D.L.R.)

1912. *Wmk Mult Crown CA. P* 14.
83 **18** 4d. black and red/*yellow*, **C** . . 3·50 14·00
84 6d. dull and deep purple, **C** . . 3·75 13·00
83/4 Optd "Specimen" *Set of* 2 75·00

1913. *Wmk Mult Crown CA. P* 14.
85 **19** 4d. black and red/*yellow*, **O** . . 4·25 6·00
86 6d. dull and deep purple, **O** . . 9·50 20·00
85/6 Optd "Specimen" *Set of* 2 90·00

The split "A" variety illustrated above No. 86 of Gambia also occurs on Nos. 85/6 (*Prices*: 4d. £60, 6d. £100 *un*).

WAR TAX

ONE PENNY

(20)

(21)

1916 (Sept). *As No. 73a, on thin paper, surch with T* **20**.
87 **17** 1d. + 1d. black and scarlet . . 50 1·40
 a. Surch double . . — £6000
87 Optd "Specimen" . . 65·00

1919. *No. 73 on thicker paper, surch with T* **21**.
88 **17** 1d. + 1d. black and carmine-red (*shades*) (Optd S. £65) . . 45 1·40

1922 (Jan). *Printed in one colour. Wmk Mult Script CA. P* 14.
89 **17** 1d. green . . 80 5·50
90 1½d. rose-scarlet . . 7·50 16·00
91 **16** 3d. bright blue . . 13·00 26·00
89/91 Optd "Specimen" *Set of* 3 95·00

22 Badge of St. Helena

PLATE FLAWS ON THE 1922–37 ISSUE. Many constant plate varieties exist on both the vignette and duty plates of this issue.

The three major varieties are illustrated and listed below with prices for mint examples. Fine used stamps showing these flaws are worth a considerable premium over the mint prices quoted.

a. Broken mainmast. Occurs on R.2/1 of all sheets from the second printing onwards. It does not appear on Nos. 93/6 and 112/13 as these stamps only exist from the initial printing invoiced in May 1922.

b. Torn flag. Occurs on R.4/6 of all sheets from printings up to and including that invoiced in December 1922. The flaw was retouched for the printing invoiced in December 1926 and so does not occur on Nos. 99e, 103 and 107/10.

c. Cleft rock. Occurs on R.5/1 of all sheets from the second printing onwards. It does not appear on Nos. 93/6 and 112/13 as these stamps only exist from the initial printing invoiced in May 1922.

(Des T. Bruce. Typo D.L.R.)

1922 (June)–**37.** *P* 14. (*a*) *Wmk Mult Crown CA.*
92 **22** 4d. grey and black/*yellow*, **C** (2.23) . . 3·50 6·00
 a. Broken mainmast . . 80·00
 b. Torn flag . . 80·00
 c. Cleft rock . . 80·00
93 1s. 6d. grey and green/*blue-green*, **C** . . 22·00 35·00
 b. Torn flag . . £350
94 2s. 6d. grey and red/*yellow*, **C** . . 35·00 48·00
 b. Torn flag . . £400
95 5s. grey and green/*yellow*, **C** . . 48·00 65·00
 b. Torn flag . . £450
96 £1 grey and purple/*red*, **C** . . £600 £850
 b. Torn flag . . £1500
92/6 Optd "Specimen" *Set of* 5 £900

The paper of No. 93 is bluish on the surface with a full green back.

(*b*) *Wmk Mult Script CA*
97 **22** ½d. grey and black, **C** (2.23) . . 55 55
 a. Broken mainmast . . 25·00
 b. Torn flag . . 50·00
 c. Cleft rock . . 25·00
98 1d. grey and green, **C** . . 75 60
 a. Broken mainmast . . 25·00
 b. Torn flag . . 25·00
 c. Cleft rock . . 25·00
99 **22** 1½d. rose-red, **C** (2.23) . . 2·00 4·00
 a. Broken mainmast . . 80·00
 b. Torn flag . . 80·00
 c. Cleft rock . . 80·00
 d. Carmine-rose . . 14·00 20·00
 da. Broken mainmast . . £200
 db. Torn flag . . £200
 dc. Cleft rock . . £200
 e. Deep carmine-red (1937) . . 80·00 £110
 ea. Broken mainmast . . £500
 ec. Cleft rock . . £500
100 2d. grey and slate, **C** (2.23) . . 1·25 1·25
 a. Broken mainmast . . 50·00
 b. Torn flag . . 50·00
 c. Cleft rock . . 50·00
101 3d. bright blue, **C** (2.23) . . 1·25 2·25
 a. Broken mainmast . . 50·00
 b. Torn flag . . 60·00
 c. Cleft rock . . 50·00
103 5d. green and carmine/*green*, **C** (1927) . . 2·75 4·25
 a. Broken mainmast . . £100
 c. Cleft rock . . £100
104 6d. grey and bright purple, **C** . . 1·90 4·75
 a. Broken mainmast . . £100
 b. Torn flag . . 90·00
 c. Cleft rock . . 90·00
105 8d. grey and bright violet, **C** (2.23) . . 4·50 7·50
 a. Broken mainmast . . £150
 b. Torn flag . . £150
 c. Cleft rock . . £120
106 1s. grey and brown, **C** . . 4·00 7·50
 a. Broken mainmast . . £150
 b. Torn flag . . £120
 c. Cleft rock . . £100
107 1s. 6d. grey and green/*green* (1927) . . 12·00 23·00
 a. Broken mainmast . . £200
 c. Cleft rock . . £200
108 2s. purple and blue/*blue*, **C** (1927) . . 12·00 23·00
 a. Broken mainmast . . £200
 c. Cleft rock . . £200
109 2s. 6d. grey and red/*yellow* (1927) . . 15·00 26·00
 a. Broken mainmast . . £200
 c. Cleft rock . . £200
110 5s. grey and green/*yellow* (1927) . . 35·00 48·00
 a. Broken mainmast . . £350
 c. Cleft rock . . £350
111 7s. 6d. grey and yellow-orange, **C** . . 70·00 £110
 a. Broken mainmast . . £500
 b. Torn flag . . £500
 c. Cleft rock . . £500
112 10s grey and olive-green, **C** . . £130 £150
 b. Torn flag . . £700
113 15s. grey and purple/*blue*, **C** . . £1500 £1900
 b. Torn flag . . £2750
97/112 . . *Set of* 15 £275 £350
97/113 Optd "Specimen" . . *Set of* 16 £1200

23 Lot and Lot's Wife

24 The "Plantation"

30 St. Helena

32 Badge of St. Helena

(Recess B.W.)

1934 (23 April). *Centenary of British Colonisation. T* **23/4, 30, 32** *and similar horiz designs. Wmk Mult Script CA. P* 12.
114 ½d. black and purple . . 60 1·50
115 1d. black and green . . 1·40 2·00
116 1½d. black and scarlet . . 2·75 4·00
117 2d. black and orange . . 3·75 4·25
118 3d. black and blue . . 6·50 8·00
119 6d. black and light blue . . 11·00 13·00
120 1s. black and chocolate . . 20·00 30·00
121 2s. 6d. black and lake . . 45·00 70·00
122 5s. black and chocolate . . 85·00 £110
123 10s. black and purple . . £300 £350
114/123 . . *Set of* 10 £450 £550
114/23 Perf "Specimen" *Set of* 10 £500

Design:—1½d. Map of St. Helena; 2d. Quay at Jamestown; 3d. James Valley; 6d. Jamestown; 1s. Munden's Promontory; 5s. High Knoll.

1935 (6 May). *Silver Jubilee. As Nos. 91/4 of Antigua.*
124 1½d. deep blue and carmine . . 75 1·60
 e. Horiz line from turret . . 7·00
125 2d. ultramarine and grey . . 2·25 2·50
 e. Horiz line from turret . . 15·00
126 6d. green and indigo . . 9·00 9·00
127 1s. slate and purple . . 17·00 20·00
124/7 Perf "Specimen" *Set of* 4 85·00

For illustration of plate variety see Omnibus section following Zululand.

1937 (19 May). *Coronation. As Nos. 13/15 of Aden.*
128 1d. green . . 35 40
129 2d. orange . . 75 45
130 3d. bright blue . . 90 60
128/30 Perf "Specimen" *Set of* 3 55·00

33 Badge of St. Helena

(Recess Waterlow)

1938 (12 May)–**44.** *Wmk Mult Script CA. P* 12½.

No.	Description		
131	**33** ½d. violet	25	20
132	1d. green	24·00	16·00
132*a*	1d. yellow-orange (8.7.40)	25	20
133	1½d. scarlet	25	20
134	2d. red-orange	30	20
135	3d. ultramarine	90·00	42·00
135*a*	3d. grey (8.7.40)	45	35
135*b*	4d. ultramarine (8.7.40)	50	40
136	6d. light blue	70	40
136*a*	8d. sage-green (8.7.40)	3·00	2·25
	b. Olive-green (24.5.44)	5·50	6·00
137	1s. sepia	1·25	1·25
138	2s. 6d. maroon	6·50	6·00
139	5s. chocolate	10·00	13·00
140	10s. purple	22·00	27·00
131/140	*Set of* 14	£140	£100
131/40 Perf "Specimen"	*Set of* 14	£275	

See also Nos. 149/51.

1946 (21 Oct). *Victory. As Nos.* 28/9 *of Aden.*

No.	Description		
141	2d. red-orange	20	25
142	4d. blue	20	30
141/2 Perf "Specimen"	*Set of* 2	60·00	

1948 (20 Oct). *Royal Silver Wedding. As Nos.* 30/1 *of Aden.*

No.	Description		
143	3d. black	40	40
144	10s. violet-blue	23·00	45·00

1949 (10 Oct). *75th Anniv of Universal Postal Union. As Nos.* 114/17 *of Antigua.*

No.	Description		
145	3d. carmine	60	55
146	4d. deep blue	1·75	1·60
147	6d. olive	2·25	2·00
148	1s. blue-black	3·00	3·00

1949 (1 Nov). *Wmk Mult Script CA. P* 12½.

No.	Description		
149	**33** 1d. black and green	65	1·50
150	1½d. black and carmine	70	1·50
151	2d. black and scarlet	70	1·50

1953 (2 June). *Coronation. As No.* 47 *of Aden.*

No.	Description		
152	3d. black and deep reddish violet	85	1·25

34 Badge of St. Helena   35 Heart-shaped Waterfall

(Recess D.L.R.)

1953 (4 Aug). *Horiz designs as T* **34**, *and T* **35**. *Wmk Mult Script CA. P* 14.

No.	Description		
153	½d. black and bright green	25	20
154	1d. black and deep green	25	20
155	1½d. black and reddish purple (*shades*)	60	50
156	2d. black and claret	60	35
157	2½d. black and red	60	25
158	3d. black and brown	80	15
159	4d. black and deep blue	65	35
160	6d. black and deep lilac	65	25
161	7d. black and grey-black	90	85
162	1s. black and carmine	65	35
163	2s. 6d. black and violet	8·00	5·50
164	5s. black and deep brown	18·00	12·00
165	10s. black and yellow-orange	45·00	40·00
153/65	*Set of* 13	70·00	55·00

Designs:—1d. Flax plantation; 2d. Lace-making; 2½d. Drying flax; 3d. St. Helena Sand Plover; 4d. Flagstaff and The Barn; 6d. Donkeys carrying flax; 7d. Island map; 1s. The Castle; 2s. 6d. Cutting flax; 5s. Jamestown; 10s. Longwood House.

45 Stamp of 1856

(Recess D.L.R.)

1956 (3 Jan). *St. Helena Stamp Centenary. Wmk Mult Script CA. P* 11½.

No.	Description		
166	**45** 3d. Prussian blue and carmine	15	10
167	4d. Prussian blue and reddish brown	20	15
168	6d. Prussian blue & dp reddish purple	25	35

46 Arms of East India Company

(Recess Waterlow)

1959 (5 May). *Tercentenary of Settlement. T* **46** *and similar horiz designs. W* w **12**. *P* 12½ × 13.

No.	Description		
169	3d. black and scarlet	15	10
170	6d. light emerald and slate-blue	65	35
171	1s. black and orange	70	40

Designs:—6d. *London* off James Bay; 1s. Commemoration Stone.

ST. HELENA
Tristan Relief
9d +

(49)

1961 (12 Oct). *Tristan Relief Fund. Nos.* 46 *and* 49/51 *of Tristan da Cunha surch as T* **49** *by Govt Printer, Jamestown.*

No.	Description		
172	2½ c. + 3d. black and brown-red		
173	5 c. + 6d. black and blue		
174	7½ c. + 9d. black and rose-carmine		
175	10 c. + 1s. black and light brown		
172/5	*Set of* 4	£4500	£1250

The above stamps were withdrawn from sale on 19 October, 434 complete sets having been sold.

50 Cunning Fish

51 Yellow Canary

53 Queen Elizabeth II   63 Queen Elizabeth II with Prince Andrew (after Cecil Beaton)

(Des V. Whiteley. Photo Harrison)

1961 (12 Dec)–**65.** *T* **50/1**, **53**, **63** *and similar designs. W* w **12**. *P* 11½ × 12 (*horiz*), 12 × 11½ (*vert*) *or* 14½ × 14 (£1).

No.	Description		
176	1d. brt blue, dull violet, yellow & carmine	10	5
	a. Chalky paper (4.5.65)	45	12
177	1½d. yellow, green, black and light drab	30	12
178	2d. scarlet and grey	15	5
179	3d. light blue, black, pink and deep blue	25	10
	a. Chalky paper (30.11.65)	65	20
180	4½d. yellow-green, green, brown and grey	60	25
181	6d. red, sepia and light yellow-olive	60	25
	a. Chalky paper (30.11.65)	80	35
182	7d. red-brown, black and violet	45	30
183	10d. brown-purple and light blue	45	30
184	1s. greenish yellow, bluish green & brown	45	30
185	1s. 6d. grey, black and slate-blue	6·00	3·50
186	2s. 6d. red, pale yellow and turquoise, C	4·00	2·25
187	5s. yellow, brown and green	8·50	4·25
188	10s. orange-red, black and blue	17·00	9·50
189	£1 chocolate and light blue	28·00	22·00
	a. Chalky paper (30.11.65)	32·00	30·00
176/89 (*cheapest*)	*Set of* 14	60·00	38·00

Designs: *Horiz* (*as T* **50**)—2d. Brittle Starfish; 7d. Trumpet Fish; 10d. Feather Starfish; 2s. 6d. Orange Starfish; 10s. Deep-water Bull's-eye. *Vert* (*as T* **51**)—4½d. Red-wood Flower; 6d. Madagascan Red Fody; 1s. Gum-wood Flower; 1s. 6d. White Tern; 5s. Night-blooming Cereus.

1963 (4 June). *Freedom from Hunger. As No.* 76 *of Aden.*

No.	Description		
190	1s. 6d. ultramarine	6·50	1·75

1963 (2 Sept). *Red Cross Centenary. As Nos.* 147/8 *of Antigua.*

No.	Description		
191	3d. red and black	90	35
192	1s. 6d. red and blue	5·50	3·00

FIRST LOCAL POST
4th JANUARY 1965

(64)

65 Badge of St. Helena

1965 (4 Jan). *First Local Post. Nos.* 176, 179, 181 *and* 185 *optd with T* **64.**

No.	Description		
193	1d. bright blue, dull violet, yellow & carmine	20	10
194	3d. light blue, black, pink and deep blue	20	10
195	6d. red, sepia and light yellow-olive	20	15
196	1s. 6d. grey, black and slate-blue	20	15

1965 (17 May). *I.T.U. Centenary. As Nos.* 166/7 *of Antigua.*

No.	Description		
197	3d. blue and grey-brown	80	30
198	6d. bright purple and bluish green	95	40

1965 (15 Oct). *International Co-operation Year. As Nos.* 168/9 *of Antigua.*

No.	Description		
199	1d. reddish purple and turquoise-green	35	15
200	6d. deep bluish green and lavender	1·90	55

1966 (24 Jan). *Churchill Commemoration. As Nos.* 170/3 *of Antigua.*

No.	Description		
201	1d. new blue	20	10
202	3d. deep green	75	30
203	6d. brown	1·25	60
204	1s. 6d. bluish violet	2·25	1·25

1966 (1 July). *World Cup Football Championships. As Nos.* 176/7 *of Antigua.*

No.	Description		
205	3d. violet, yellow-green, lake & yellow-brn	90	25
206	6d. chocolate, blue-green, lake & yellow-brn	1·40	50

1966 (20 Sept). *Inauguration of W.H.O. Headquarters, Geneva. As Nos.* 178/9 *of Antigua.*

No.	Description		
207	3d. black, yellow-green and light blue	70	25
208	1s. 6d. black, light purple and yellow-brown	3·50	1·25

1966 (1 Dec). *20th Anniv of U.N.E.S.C.O. As Nos.* 196/8 *of Antigua.*

No.	Description		
209	3d. slate-violet, red, yellow and orange	1·75	45
210	6d. orange-yellow, violet and deep olive	2·75	70
211	1s. 6d. black, bright purple and orange	4·50	2·50

(Des W. H. Brown. Photo Harrison)

1967 (5 May). *New Constitution. W* w **12** (*sideways*). *P* 14½ × 14.

No.	Description		
212	**65** 1s. multicoloured	40	20
213	2s. 6d. multicoloured	55	30
	a. Red (ribbon, etc.) omitted	£275	

66 Fire of London

(Des M. Goaman. Recess D.L.R.)

1967 (4 Sept). *300th Anniv of Arrival of Settlers after Great Fire of London. T* **66** *and similar horiz designs. W* w **12**. *P* 13.

No.	Description		
214	1d. carmine-red and black (*shades*)	15	10
215	3d. ultramarine and black	25	15
216	6d. slate-violet and black	25	15
217	1s. 6d. olive-green and black	40	25

Designs:—3d. East Indiaman *Charles*; 6d. Settlers landing at Jamestown; 1s. 6d. Settlers clearing scrub.

70 Interlocking Maps of Tristan and St. Helena

(Des Jennifer Toombs. Photo Harrison)

1968 (4 June). *30th Anniv of Tristan da Cunha as a Dependency of St. Helena. T* **70** *and similar horiz design. W* w **12**. *P* 14 × 14½.

No.	Description		
218	**70** 4d. purple and chocolate	25	10
219	– 8d. olive and brown	30	20
220	**70** 1s. 9d. ultramarine and chocolate	30	25
221	– 2s. 3d. greenish blue and brown	35	25

Design:—8d., 2s. 3d. Interlocking maps of St. Helena and Tristan.

72 Queen Elizabeth and Sir Hudson Lowe

(Des M. Farrar Bell. Litho D.L.R.)

1968 (4 Sept). *150th Anniv of the Abolition of Slavery in St. Helena. T* **72** *and similar horiz design. Multicoloured. W* w **12** (*sideways*). *P* 13 × 12½.

No.	Description		
222	3d. Type **72**	30	15
223	9d. Type **72**	45	25
224	1s. 6d. Queen Elizabeth and Sir George Bingham	60	30
225	2s. 6d. As 1s. 6d.	75	30

74 Blue Gum Eucalyptus and Road Construction

(Des Sylvia Goaman. Litho P.B.)

1968 (4 Nov). *Horiz designs as T* **74**. *Multicoloured. W* w **12** *(sideways). P* 13½.

226	½d. Type **74**	8	8
227	1d. Cabbage-tree and electricity development	8	8
228	1½d. St. Helena Redwood and dental unit	10	10
229	2d. Scrubweed and pest control	10	10
230	3d. Tree-fern and flats in Jamestown	12	10
231	4d. Blue gum Eucalyptus, pasture and livestock improvement	20	20
232	6d. Cabbage-tree and schools broadcasting	20	20
233	8d. St. Helena Redwood and country cottages	25	25
234	10d. Scrubweed and new school buildings	30	30
235	1s. Tree-fern and reafforestation	35	30
236	1s. 6d. Blue gum Eucalyptus and heavy lift crane	70	1·25
237	2s. 6d. Cabbage-tree and Lady Field Children's Home	90	1·50
238	5s. St. Helena Redwood and agricultural training	2·00	2·75
239	10s. Scrubweed and New General Hospital	4·25	6·00
240	£1 Tree-fern and lifeboat *John Dutton*	17·00	18·00
226/40	*Set of* 15	24·00	28·00

See also No. 274 for distinct shade of £1 value.

89 Brig *Perseverance*

93 W.O. and Drummer of the 53rd Foot, 1815

(Des J.W. Litho P.B.)

1969 (19 Apr). *Mail Communications. T* **89** *and similar horiz designs. Multicoloured. W* w **12** *(sideways). P* 13½.

241	4d. Type **89**	55	25
242	8d. R.M.S. *Dane*	1·00	35
243	1s. 9d. S.S. *Llandovery Castle*	1·25	45
244	2s. 3d. R.M.S. *Good Hope Castle*	1·40	55

(Des R. North. Litho Format)

1969 (3 Sept). *Military Uniforms. T* **93** *and similar vert designs. Multicoloured. W* w **12**. *P* 14.

245	6d. Type **93**	75	40
246	8d. Officer and Surgeon, 20th Foot, 1816	1·10	55
247	1s. 8d. Drum Major, 66th Foot, 1816, and Royal Artillery Officer, 1820	2·00	1·00
248	2s. 6d. Private, 91st Foot, and 2nd Corporal, Royal Sappers and Miners, 1832	2·75	1·50

97 Dickens, Mr. Pickwick and Job Trotter (*Pickwick Papers*)

(Des Jennifer Toombs. Litho P.B.)

1970 (9 June). *Death Centenary of Charles Dickens. T* **97** *and similar horiz designs each incorporating a portrait of Dickens. Multicoloured. Chalk-surfaced paper. W* w **12** *(sideways). P* 13½ × 13.

249	4d. Type **97**	40	20
	a. Shiny unsurfaced paper	40	35
250	8d. Mr. Bumble and Oliver (*Oliver Twist*)	60	30
	a. Shiny unsurfaced paper	70	55
251	1s. 6d. Sairey Gamp and Mark Tapley (*Martin Chuzzlewit*)	1·10	50
	a. Shiny unsurfaced paper	1·25	1·25
252	2s. 6d. Jo and Mr. Turveydrop (*Bleak House*)	1·40	95
	a. Shiny unsurfaced paper	1·75	1·75

Supplies sent to St. Helena were on paper with a dull surface which reacts to the chalky test and with PVA gum. Crown Agents supplies were from a later printing on shiny paper which does not respond to the chalky test and with gum arabic.

98 "Kiss of Life"

99 Officer's Shako Plate (20th Foot)

(Des Jennifer Toombs. Litho J.W.)

1970 (15 Sept). *Centenary of British Red Cross. T* **98** *and similar horiz designs. W* w **12** *(sideways). P* 14.

253	6d. bistre, vermilion and black	25	20
254	9d. turquoise-green, vermilion and black	40	30
255	1s. 9d. pale grey, vermilion and black	60	40
256	2s. 3d. pale lavender, vermilion and black	65	50

Designs:—9d. Nurse with girl in wheelchair; 1s. 9d. Nurse bandaging child's knee; 2s. 3d. Red Cross emblem.

(Des J.W. Litho Questa)

1970 (2 Nov). *Military Equipment* (1st issue). *T* **99** *and similar vert designs. Multicoloured. W* w **12**. *P* 12.

257	4d. Type **99**	1·25	40
258	9d. Officer's Breast-plate (66th Foot)	2·75	1·25
259	1s. 3d. Officer's Full Dress Shako (91st Foot)	3·00	1·50
260	2s. 11d. Ensign's Shako (53rd Foot)	3·50	2·00

See also Nos. 281/4, 285/8 and 291/4.

100 Electricity Development

101 St. Helena holding the "True Cross"

(Litho P.B.)

1971 (15 Feb). *Decimal Currency. Designs as Nos.* 227/40, *but with values inscr in decimal currency as in T* **100**. *W* w **12** *(sideways). P* 13½.

261	½p. multicoloured	5	10
262	1p. multicoloured (as 1½d.)	8	10
263	1½p. multicoloured (as 2d.)	10	10
264	2p. multicoloured (as 3d.)	80	60
265	2½p. multicoloured (as 4d.)	12	15
266	3½p. multicoloured (as 6d.)	15	20
267	4½p. multicoloured (as 8d.)	20	25
268	5p. multicoloured (as 10d.)	25	30
269	7½p. multicoloured (as 1s.)	35	55
270	10p. multicoloured (as 1s. 6d.)	40	60
271	12½p. multicoloured (as 2s. 6d.)	50	85
272	25p. multicoloured (as 5s.)	2·00	1·50
273	50p. multicoloured (as 10s.)	2·75	2·75
274	£1 multicoloured†	19·00	20·00
261/74	*Set of* 14	24·00	25·00

†Although the design of No. 274 in no way differs from that of No. 240, it was reprinted specially for decimalisation, and differs considerably in shade from No. 240, as do others from their counterparts in the 1968 set.

The main differences in No. 274 are in the mountain which is blue rather than pinkish blue and in the sea which is light blue instead of greenish blue.

See also No. 309.

(Des R. Granger Barrett. Litho Questa)

1971 (5 Apr). *Easter. W* w **12**. *P* 14 × 14½.

275	**101**	2p. multicoloured	30	20
276		5p. multicoloured	45	25
277		7½p. multicoloured	60	40
278		12½p. multicoloured	90	55

102 Napoleon (after painting by J.-L. David) and Tomb on St. Helena

(Des J.W. Litho Questa)

1971 (5 May). *150th Death Anniv of Napoleon, T* **102** *and similar vert design. Multicoloured. W* w **12**. *P* 13½.

279	2p. Type **102**	70	45
280	34p. "Napoleon at St. Helena" (H. Delaroche)	7·00	5·25

(Des J.W. Litho Questa)

1971 (10 Nov). *Military Equipment* (2nd issue). *Multicoloured designs as T* **99**. *W* w **12**. *P* 14.

281	1½p. Artillery Private's hanger	1·50	75
282	4p. Baker rifle and socket bayonet	3·50	2·25
283	6p. Infantry Officer's sword	3·50	2·50
284	22½p. Baker rifle and sword bayonet	4·75	3·50

(Des and litho J.W.)

1972 (19 June). *Military Equipment* (3rd issue). *Multicoloured designs as T* **99**. *W* w **12**. *P* 14.

285	2p. multicoloured	90	45
286	5p. reddish lilac, new blue and black	2·75	2·00
287	7½p. multicoloured	2·75	2·25
288	12½p. pale olive-sepia, brown and black	3·50	2·50

Designs:—2p. Royal Sappers and Miners breast-plate, post 1823; 5p. Infantry sergeant's spontoon, *circa* 1830; 7½p. Royal Artillery officer's breast-plate, *circa* 1830; 12½p. English military pistol, *circa* 1800.

103 St. Helena Sand Plover and White Tern

(Des (from photograph by D. Groves) and photo Harrison)

1972 (20 Nov). *Royal Silver Wedding. Multicoloured; background colour given. W* w **12**. *P* 14 × 14½.

289	**103**	2p. slate-green	30	30
290		16p. lake-brown	55	60

(Des J.W. Litho Questa)

1973 (20 Sept). *Military Equipment* (4th issue). *Multicoloured designs as T* **99**. *W* w **12** *(sideways). P* 14.

291	2p. Other Rank's shako, 53rd Foot, 1815	1·75	85
292	5p. Band and Drums sword, 1830	3·75	2·75
293	7½p. Royal Sappers and Miners Officer's hat, 1830	4·25	3·25
294	12½p. General's sword, 1831	5·50	4·25

1973 (14 Nov). *Royal Wedding. As Nos.* 165/6 *of Anguilla.*

295	2p. violet-blue	20	20
296	18p. light emerald	35	35

104 *Westminster* and *Claudine* beached, 1849

(Des J.W. Litho Questa)

1973 (17 Dec). *Tercentenary of East India Company Charter. T* **104** *and similar horiz designs. Multicoloured. W* w **12**. *P* 14.

297	1½p. Type **104**	90	50
298	4p. *True Briton*, 1790	1·40	1·25
299	6p. *General Goddard* in action, 1795	1·40	1·25
300	22½p. *Kent* burning in the Bay of Biscay, 1825	3·50	4·25

105 U.P.U. Emblem and Ships

(Des J.W. Litho Questa)

1974 (15 Oct). *Centenary of Universal Postal Union. T* **105** *and similar horiz design. Multicoloured. W* w **12** *(sideways on* **MS**303). *P* 14.

301	5p. Type **105**	40	40
302	25p. U.P.U. emblem and letters	1·10	1·10
MS303	89 × 84 mm. Nos. 301/2	1·75	1·90

106 Churchill in Sailor Suit, and Blenheim Palace

107 Capt. Cook and H.M.S. *Resolution*

(Des Jennifer Toombs. Litho Questa)

1974 (30 Nov). *Birth Centenary of Sir Winston Churchill. T* **106** *and similar horiz design. W* w **14** *sideways (Nos. 304/5) or W* w **12** *sideways* (**MS**306). *P* 14.

304	5p. multicoloured	45	35
305	25p. black, flesh and reddish purple	95	1·10
MS306	108 × 93 mm. Nos. 304/5	1·60	2·00

Design:—25p. Churchill and River Thames.

(Des J. Cooter. Litho Questa)

1975 (14 July). *Bicentenary of Capt. Cook's Return to St. Helena. T* **107** *and similar horiz design. Multicoloured. W* w **14** *(sideways on* 25p.). *P* 13½.

307	5p. Type **107**	1·50	90
308	25p. Capt. Cook and Jamestown	3·50	2·25

(Litho Questa)

1975 (13 Aug). *As No.* 264 *but whiter paper. P* 14.

309	2p. multicoloured	1·00	1·50

108 *Mellissia begonifolia* (tree)

109 £1 Note

(Des Jennifer Toombs. Litho J.W.)

1975 (20 Oct). *Centenary of Publication of "St. Helena" by J. C. Melliss. T* **108** *and similar multicoloured designs. W* w **14** *(sideways on 12 and 25p.). P* 13.

310	2p. Type **108**	25	15
311	5p. *Mellissius adumbratus* (beetle)	45	35
312	12p. St. Helena Sand Plover (*horiz*)	1·10	1·10
313	25p. *Scorpaenia mellissii* (fish) (*horiz*) ..	1·25	1·25

(Des V. Whiteley Studio. Litho J.W.)

1976 (15 Mar). *First Issue of Currency Notes. T* **109** *and similar horiz design. Multicoloured. W* w **12** *(sideways). P* 13½.

314	8p. Type **109**	75	50
315	33p. £5 Note	2·00	1·90

110 1d. Stamp of 1863

(Des C. Abbott. Litho J.W.)

1976 (4 May). *Festival of Stamps, London. T* **110** *and similar designs. W* w **14** *(sideways on 5 and 25p.). P* 13½.

316	5p. light red-brown, black and light flesh ..	35	30
317	8p. black, green and pale dull green ..	50	45
318	25p. multicoloured	80	70

Designs: *Vert*—8p. 1d. stamp of 1922. *Horiz*—25p. Mail carrier *Good Hope Castle*.

For miniature sheet containing No. 318 see Ascension No. **MS**218.

111 "High Knoll, 1806" (Capt. Barnett)

(Des C. Abbott. Litho Questa)

1976 (14 Sept)–**82.** *Aquatints and Lithographs of St. Helena. T* **111** *and similar horiz designs. Multicoloured. W* w **14** *(sideways). P* 13½ *(£1, £2) or* 14 *(others).*

A. *On ordinary paper without imprint date*

B. *On cream paper with imprint date* ("1982")

		A		B	
319	1p. Type **111**	10	10	10	10
320	3p. "The Friar Rock, 1815" (G. Bellasis)	15	15	†	
321	5p. "The Column Lot, 1815" (G. Bellasis)	15	15	†	
322	6p. "Sandy Bay Valley, 1809" (H. Salt)	15	15	†	
323	8p. "Scene from Castle Terrace, 1815" (G. Bellasis) ..	20	20	†	
324	9p. "The Briars, 1815" ..	20	20	†	
325	10p. "Plantation House, 1821" (J. Wathen)	50	50	25	30
326	15p. "Longwood House, 1821" (J. Wathen)	35	35	†	
327	18p. "St. Paul's Church" (V. Brooks)	35	35	†	
328	26p. "St. James's Valley, 1815" (Capt. Hastings)	55	55	†	
329	40p. "St. Matthew's Church, 1860" (V. Brooks)	80	80	†	
330	£1 "St. Helena, 1815" (G. Bellasis)	2·00	2·00	†	
	a. Gold omitted	£750	—	†	
331	£2 "Sugar Loaf Hill, 1821" (J. Wathen)	6·00	6·50	4·00	4·50
319/31	.. .. .. *Set of* 13	10·50	11·00	†	

The £1 and £2 are larger, 47 × 34 mm.

Dates of issue: Without imprint—14.9.76, 1, 3, 5, 8, 10, 18, 26, 40p., £1; 23.11.76, 6, 9, 15p., £2. With imprint—10.5.82, 1, 10p., £2.

112 Duke of Edinburgh paying Homage

(Des M. Shamir. Litho J.W.)

1977 (7 Feb). *Silver Jubilee. T* **112** *and similar horiz designs. Multicoloured. W* w **14** *(sideways). P* 13.

332	8p. Royal visit, 1947	35	35
333	15p. Queen's sceptre with dove	50	45
334	26p. Type **112**	55	50

113 Halley's Comet (from Bayeux Tapestry)

114 Sea Lion

(Des C. Abbott. Litho Questa)

1977 (23 Aug). *Tercentenary of Halley's Visit. T* **113** *and similar horiz designs. Multicoloured. W* w **14** *(sideways). P* 14.

335	5p. Type **113**	45	30
336	8p. Late 17th-century sextant	60	40
337	27p. Halley and Halley's Mount, St. Helena ..	1·25	90

(Des Jennifer Toombs. Litho Questa)

1978 (2 June). *25th Anniv of Coronation. T* **114** *and similar vert designs. P* 15.

338	25p. agate, cerise and silver	80	80
	a. Sheetlet. Nos. 338/40 × 2	4·25	
339	25p. multicoloured	80	80
340	25p. agate, cerise and silver	80	80

Designs:—No. 338, Black Dragon of Ulster; No. 339, Queen Elizabeth II; No. 340, Type **114**.

Nos. 338/40 were printed together in small sheets of 6, containing two *se-tenant* strips of 3, with horizontal gutter margin between.

115 Period Engraving of St. Helena

(Des J.W. Litho Questa)

1978 (14 Aug). *Wreck of the "Witte Leeuw". T* **115** *and similar horiz designs. Multicoloured. W* w **14** *(sideways). P* 14½.

341	3p. Type **115**	15	15
342	5p. Chinese porcelain	20	20
343	8p. Bronze cannon	30	30
344	9p. Chinese porcelain (*different*)	35	35
345	15p. Pewter mug and ceramic flasks	55	55
346	20p. Dutch East Indiaman	70	70
341/6	.. .. *Set of* 6	2·00	2·00

116 *Discovery*

117 Sir Rowland Hill

(Des and litho (25p. also embossed) Walsall)

1979 (19 Feb). *Bicentenary of Captain Cook's Voyages, 1768–79. T* **116** *and similar vert designs. Multicoloured. P* 11.

347	3p. Type **116**	25	15
348	8p. Cook's portable observatory	45	35
349	12p. *Pharnaceum acidum* (based on sketch by Joseph Banks)	55	45
350	25p. Flaxman/Wedgwood medallion of Captain Cook	1·00	1·00

(Des J.W. Litho Questa)

1979 (20 Aug). *Death Centenary of Sir Rowland Hill. T* **117** *and similar designs. W* w **14** *(sideways on 8 to 32p.). P* 14.

351	5p. multicoloured	25	20
352	8p. multicoloured	35	25
353	20p. multicoloured	70	65
354	32p. black, magenta and deep mauve	90	85

Designs: *Horiz*—8p. 1965 1d. 1st Local Post stamp; 20p. 1863 1d. on 6d. stamp; 32p. 1902 1d. stamp.

118 R. F. Seal's Chart of 1823 showing the Elevation of the Coastline

(Des G. Vasarhelyi. Litho Questa)

1979 (10 Dec). *150th Anniv of the Inclined Plane. T* **118** *and similar designs. W* w **14** *(sideways on 5 and 8p.). P* 14.

355	5p. black, brownish grey and stone	35	25
356	8p. black, brownish grey and stone	45	30
357	50p. multicoloured	1·40	1·40

Designs: *Horiz*—8p. The Inclined Plane in 1829. *Vert*—50p. The Inclined Plane in 1979.

119 Napoleon's Tomb, 1848 120 East Indiaman

(Des J.W. Litho Questa)

1980 (23 Feb). *Centenary of Empress Eugenie's Visit. T* **119** *and similar horiz designs. W* w **14** *(sideways). P* 14.

358	5p. gold, reddish brown and pale red-brown	30	25
359	8p. gold, reddish brown and pale bistre ..	45	35
360	62p. gold, reddish brown & pale orange-brn ..	1·75	1·75
MS361	180 × 110 mm. Nos. 358/60	2·25	2·50

Designs:—8p. Landing at St. Helena; 62p. At the tomb of Napoleon.

(Des C. Abbott. Litho Format)

1980 (6 May). *"London 1980" International Stamp Exhibition. T* **120** *and similar vert designs. Multicoloured. W* w **14**. *P* 14½.

362	5p. Type **120**	25	30
363	8p. *Dolphin* postal stone	30	40
364	47p. Postal stone outside Castle entrance, Jamestown	1·40	1·50
MS365	111 × 120 mm. Nos. 362/4	1·75	2·00

121 Queen Elizabeth the Queen Mother

(Des and litho Harrison)

1980 (18 Aug*). *80th Birthday of Queen Elizabeth the Queen Mother. W* w **14** *(sideways). P* 14.

366	**121**	24p. multicoloured	65	65

*This is the local date of issue; the Crown Agents released the stamp on 4 August.

122 The Briars, 1815

(Des C. Abbott. Litho Questa)

1980 (17 Nov). *175th Anniv of Wellington's Visit. T* **122** *and similar multicoloured design. W* w **14** *(sideways on 9p.). P* 14.

367	9p. Type **122**	45	35
368	30p. "Wellington" (Goya) (*vert*)	80	65

Nos. 367/8 were each printed in small sheets of 10 stamps.

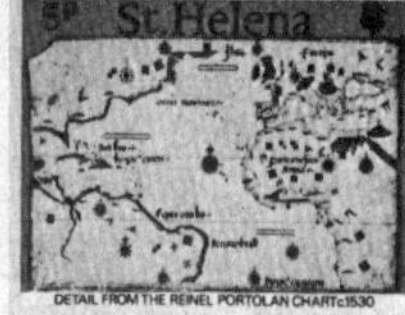

123 Redwood

124 Detail from Reinel Portolan Chart, *circa* 1530

(Des Daphne Padden. Litho Enschedé)

1981 (5 Jan). *Endemic Plants. T* **123** *and similar horiz designs. Multicoloured. W* w **14** *(sideways). P* 13½.

369	5p. Type **123**	25	20
370	8p. Old Father Live Forever	35	25
371	15p. Gumwood	40	40
372	27p. Black Cabbage	65	65

(Des Harrison. Litho Walsall)

1981 (22 May). *Early Maps. T* **124** *and similar horiz designs. W* w **14** *(sideways). P* 14 × 14½.

373	5p. multicoloured	25	20
374	8p. black, brown-lake and grey	40	35
375	20p. multicoloured	55	60
376	30p. multicoloured	70	80
MS377	114 × 83 mm. 24p. black and grey ..	70	95

Designs:—8p. John Thornton's Map of St. Helena, *circa* 1700; 20p. Map of St. Helena, 1815; 30p. Map of St. Helena, 1817; miniature sheet, Part of Gastaldi's map of Africa, 16th-century.

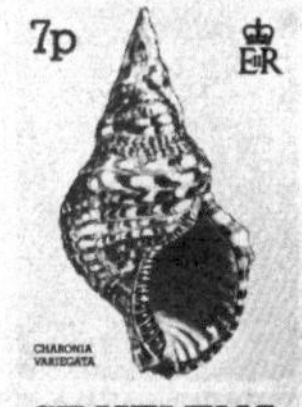

125 Prince Charles as Royal Navy Commander

126 *Charonia Variegata*

(Des J.W. Litho Questa)

1981 (22 July). *Royal Wedding. T* **125** *and similar vert designs. Multicoloured. W* w **14**. *P* 14.

378 14p. Wedding bouquet from St. Helena .. 40 40
379 29p. Type **125** 50 45
380 32p. Prince Charles and Lady Diana Spencer 65 60

(Des J.W. Litho Walsall)

1981 (10 Sept). *Seashells. T* **126** *and similar vert designs. Multicoloured. W* w **14**. *P* 14.

381 7p. Type **126** 35 20
382 10p. *Cypraea spurca sanctaehelenae* 40 25
383 25p. *Janthina janthina* 70 60
384 53p. *Pinna rudis* .. .. 1·40 1·25

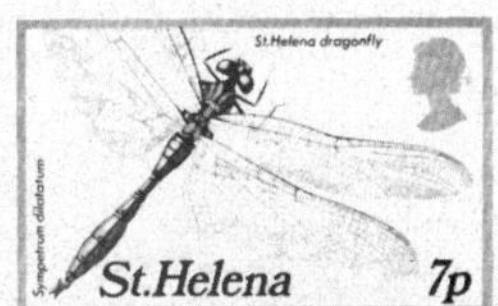

127 Traffic Duty

128 St. Helena Dragonfly

(Des BG Studio. Litho Questa)

1981 (5 Nov). *25th Anniv of Duke of Edinburgh Award Scheme. T* **127** *and similar vert designs. Multicoloured. W* w **14**. *P* 14.

385 7p. Type **127** 35 25
386 11p. Signposting 40 30
387 25p. Animal care 65 70
388 50p. Duke of Edinburgh, in Guards' uniform, on horse-back .. .. 1·40 1·60

(Des C. Abbott. Litho Questa)

1982 (4 Jan). *Insects* (*1st series*). *T* **128** *and similar horiz designs. Multicoloured. W* w **14** (*sideways on* 7, 10 *and* 25*p*., *inverted on* 32*p*.). *P* 14½.

389 7p. Type **128** 30 25
390 10p. Burchell's Beetle 40 35
391 25p. Cockroach Wasp 70 60
392 32p. World's largest earwig (45 × 27 *mm*) .. 80 75

See also Nos. 411/14.

129 Charles Darwin

130 Prince and Princess of Wales at Balmoral, Autumn 1981

(Des L. Curtis. Litho Questa)

1982 (19 Apr). *150th Anniv of Charles Darwin's Voyage. T* **129** *and similar horiz designs. Multicoloured. W* w **14** (*sideways*). *P* 14.

393 7p. Type **129** 30 20
394 14p. Flagstaff Hill and Darwin's hammer .. 45 35
395 25p. Ring-necked Pheasant and Chukar Partridge 75 60
396 29p. *Beagle* off St. Helena 95 75

(Des C. Abbott. Litho Format)

1982 (1 July). *21st Birthday of Princess of Wales. T* **130** *and similar vert designs. Multicoloured. W* w **14**. *P* 13½ × 14 (7, 55*p*.) *or* 13½ (*others*).

397 7p. St. Helena coat of arms 15 12
398 11p. Type **130** 25 20
399 29p. Bride on Palace Balcony 60 60
a. Perf 13½ × 14 .. .. 30·00 10·00
b. Imperf (pair) £475
400 55p. Formal portrait .. .. 1·10 1·25

1st PARTICIPATION
COMMONWEALTH GAMES 1982

(131)

132 Lord Baden-Powell

1982 (25 Oct). *Commonwealth Games, Brisbane. Nos.* 326 *and* 328 *optd with T* **131**.

401 15p. "Longwood House, 1821" (G. Wathen) .. 30 30
402 26p. "St. James's Valley, 1815" (Capt. Hastings) 55 55

(Des L. McCombie. Litho Walsall)

1982 (29 Nov). *75th Anniv of Boy Scout Movement. T* **132** *and similar designs. W* w **14** (*inverted on* 3*p*., 29*p*.; *sideways on* 11*p*., 59*p*.). *P* 14.

403 3p. lake-brown, grey and orange-yellow .. 12 12
404 11p. lake-brown, grey & bright yellow-green 25 25
405 29p. lake-brown, grey and reddish orange .. 60 60
406 59p. lake-brown, grey & bright yellow-green 1·25 1·25

Designs: *Horiz*—11p. Boy Scout (drawing by Lord Baden-Powell); 59p. Camping at Thompsons Wood. *Vert*—29p. Canon Walcott.

133 King and Queen Rocks

134 *Coriolus versicolor*

(Des C. Abbott. Litho B.D.T.)

1983 (14 Jan). *Views of St. Helena by Roland Svensson. T* **133** *and similar multicoloured designs. W* w **14** (*sideways on* 29*p*., 59*p*.). *P* 14.

407 7p. Type **133** 15 20
408 11p. Turk's Cap 20 25
409 29p. Coastline from Jamestown (*horiz*) .. 55 60
410 59p. Mundens Point (*horiz*) .. .. .. 1·25 1·40

(Des C. Abbott. Litho Questa)

1983 (22 Apr). *Insects* (*2nd series*). *Horiz designs as T* **128**. *Multicoloured. W* w **14** (*sideways*). *P* 14½.

411 11p. Death's-head Hawk-moth 30 35
412 15p. Saldid-shore bug 35 40
413 29p. Click beetle 55 60
414 59p. Weevil .. .. 1·25 1·40

(Des Garden Studio. Litho Format)

1983 (16 June). *Fungi. T* **134** *and similar multicoloured designs. W* w **14** (*sideways on* 29*p*.). *P* 14.

415 11p. Type **134** 20 25
416 15p. *Pluteus brunneisucus* 30 35
417 29p. *Polyporus induratus* (*horiz*) 55 60
418 59p. *Coprinus angulatus* .. .. .. 1·25 1·40

135 Java Sparrow

136 Birth of St. Helena

(Des J.W. Litho Questa)

1983 (12 Sept). *Birds. T* **135** *and similar vert designs. Multicoloured. W* w **14**. *P* 14.

419 7p. Type **135** 15 20
420 15p. Madagascan Red Fody 30 35
421 33p. Common Waxbill 65 70
422 59p. Yellow Canary .. .. 1·25 1·40

(Des Jennifer Toombs. Litho Questa)

1983 (17 Oct). *Christmas. Life of St. Helena* (*1st series*). *T* **136** *and similar vert design. Multicoloured. W* w **14**. *P* 14 × 13½.

423 10p. Type **136** 25 25
a. Sheetlet Nos. 423/4, each ×5 .. .. 3·00
424 15p. St. Helena being taken to convent .. 35 35

Nos. 423/4 were printed together in small sheets of 10, containing horizontal strips of 5 for each value separated by a horizontal gutter margin.

See also Nos. 450/3.

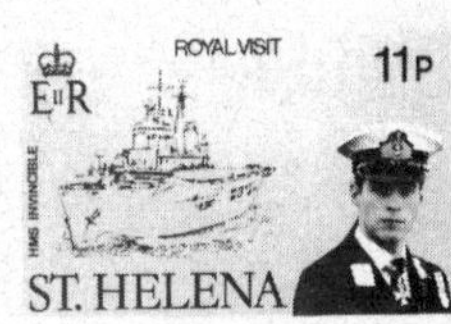

137 1934 ½d. Stamp

138 Prince Andrew and H.M.S. *Invincible*

(Des C. Abbott. Litho Questa)

1984 (3 Jan). *150th Anniv of St. Helena as a British Colony. T* **137** *and similar square designs showing values of the* 1934 *Centenary of British Colonisation issue. Multicoloured. W* w **14** (*sideways*). *P* 13½.

425 1p. Type **137** 5 5
426 3p. 1934 1d. stamp 5 8
427 6p. 1934 1½d. stamp 10 12
428 7p. 1934 2d. stamp 12 15
429 11p. 1934 3d. stamp 20 25
430 15p. 1934 6d. stamp 25 30
431 29p. 1934 1s. stamp 50 55
432 33p. 1934 5s. stamp 55 60
433 59p. 1934 10s. stamp .. .. 1·10 1·25
434 £1 1934 2s. 6d. stamp .. .. 1·75 1·90
435 £2 St. Helena Coat of Arms .. .. .. 3·50 3·75
425/35 .. .. *Set of* 11 7·50 8·00

(Des D. Bowen. Litho Format)

1984 (4 Apr). *Visit of Prince Andrew. T* **138** *and similar horiz design. Multicoloured. W* w **14** (*sideways*). *P* 14.

436 11p. Type **138** 25 25
437 60p. Prince Andrew and H.M.S. *Herald* .. 1·25 1·40

139 *St. Helena*

140 Twopenny Coin and Donkey

(Des A. Theobald. Litho Questa)

1984 (14 May). *250th Anniv of "Lloyd's List"* (*newspaper*). *T* **139** *and similar vert designs. Multicoloured. W* w **14**. *P* 14½ × 14.

438 10p. Type **139** 20 25
439 18p. Solomons Facade (local agent) 35 40
440 25p. Lloyd's Coffee House, London 50 55
441 50p. S.S. *Papanui* .. .. 1·00 1·10

(Des G. Drummond. Litho Format)

1984 (23 July). *New Coinage. T* **140** *and similar horiz designs. Multicoloured. W* w **14** (*sideways*). *P* 14.

442 10p. Type **140** 20 25
443 15p. Five pence coin and Wire Bird 30 35
444 29p. Penny coin and Yellowfin Tuna 60 65
445 50p. Ten pence coin and Arum Lily .. .. 1·00 1·10

141 Mrs. Rebecca Fuller (former Corps Secretary)

(Des L. Curtis. Litho Walsall)

1984 (12 Oct). *Centenary of Salvation Army on St. Helena. T* **141** *and similar multicoloured designs. W* w **14** (*sideways on* 11*p*., 25*p*.). *P* 14.

446 7p. Type **141** 15 20
447 11p. Meals-on-wheels service (*horiz*) 20 25
448 25p. Salvation Army Citadel, Jamestown (*horiz*) 50 55
449 60p. Salvation Army band at Jamestown Clock Tower .. .. 1·25 1·40

(Des Jennifer Toombs. Litho Questa)

1984 (9 Nov). *Christmas. Life of St. Helena* (*2nd series*). *Vert designs as T* **136**. *Multicoloured. W* w **14**. *P* 14.

450 6p. St. Helena visits prisoners 12 15
451 10p. Betrothal of St. Helena 20 25
452 15p. Marriage of St. Helena to Constantius .. 30 35
453 33p. Birth of Constantine 65 70

St. Kitts-Nevis

ST. CHRISTOPHER

The first recorded postal marking for St. Christopher dates from 1746, although it is probable that a branch of the British G.P.O. operated on the island before that date.

Stamps of Great Britain were used between May 1858 and the end of March 1860 when control of the postal services passed to the local authorities. In the years which followed, prior to the introduction of St. Christopher stamps in April 1870, a circular "PAID" handstamp was used on overseas mail.

For illustrations of the postmark types see BRITISH POST OFFICES ABROAD notes, following GREAT BRITAIN.

BASSETERRE

Stamps of GREAT BRITAIN *cancelled* "A 12" *as Type* **2**.

1858 *to* **1860.**

Z1	1d. rose-red (1857), *perf* 14	
Z2	2d. blue (1858) (Plate No. 7)	£900
Z3	4d. rose (1857)	£300
Z4	6d. lilac (1856)	£180
Z5	1s. green (1856)	£900

PRICES FOR STAMPS ON COVER

Nos. 1/5	*from* × 5
Nos. 6/8	*from* × 10
Nos. 9/10	*from* × 4
Nos. 11/21	*from* × 3
Nos. 22/3	*from* × 6
Nos. 24/8	—
Nos. R1/6	—

1

Halfpenny
(2)

FOUR PENCE
(3)

(Typo D.L.R.)

1870 (1 April)–**76.** *Wmk Crown CC.* (*a*) *P* 12½.

1	1	1d. dull rose	42·00	38·00
		a. Wmk sideways	£225	£180
2		1d. magenta	26·00	26·00
3		1d. pale magenta	30·00	28·00
4		6d. green	80·00	18·00
5		6d. yellow-green	80·00	28·00
		(*b*) *P* 14 (1875–6)		
6	1	1d. magenta	80·00	15·00
		a. Bisected diag or vert (½d.) (on cover)	†	£750
7		1d. pale magenta	55·00	14·00
8		6d. green	25·00	15·00
		a. Imperf between (pair)		
		b. Wmk sideways	£250	

1879 (Nov). *New values. Wmk Crown CC. P* 14.

9	1	2½d. red-brown	£170	£170
10		4d. blue	£150	27·00
		a. Wmk sideways		

1882–90. *Wmk Crown CA. P* 14.

11	1	½d. dull green	1·25	1·40
		a. Wmk sideways		
12		1d. dull magenta	£350	90·00
		a. Bisected diagonally (½d.) (on cover)		
13		1d. carmine-rose	1·00	1·25
		a. Bisected (½d.) (on cover)		
14		2½d. pale red-brown	£170	75·00
15		2½d. deep red-brown	£180	80·00
16		2½d. ultramarine (1884)	3·50	4·25
17		4d. blue	£400	50·00
18		4d. grey (1884)	2·50	3·00
19		6d. olive-brown (1890)	£170	£160
20		1s. mauve (1887)	£170	£150
21		1s. bright mauve	£180	£160
19/20 Optd "Specimen"		*Set of* 2	£150	

1885 (March). *No.* 13 *bisected and No.* 8 *surch with T* **2** (*diag*) *and T* **3** *respectively.*

22	½d. on half of 1d. carmine-rose	24·00	32·00
	a. Unsevered pair	£110	£120
	ab. Ditto, one surch inverted		
	b. Surch inverted	£400	£325
	c. Surch double		
23	4d. on 6d. green	40·00	55·00
	a. Full stop after "PENCE"	85·00	95·00
	b. Surch double	£1600	

ONE PENNY.
(4)

4d.
(5)

On Types **4**, **5** and **7** the cancelling bar at foot was applied by hand, using a pen and ruler.

1886 (June). *No.* 8 *surch with T* **4** *or* **5**.

24	1	1d. on 6d. green	16·00	28·00
		a. Surch inverted	£4750	
		b. Surch double	—	£1100
25		4d. on 6d. green	48·00	90·00
		a. No stop after "d"	£180	£200
		b. Surch double	£1400	£1600

No. 24b is only known penmarked or with violet handstamp.

1887 (May). *Surch with T* **4**.

26	1	1d. on ½d. dull green	32·00	38·00

ONE PENNY.
(7)

1888 (May). *No.* 16 *surch.*

		(*a*) *As T* **4** *but without bar through old value*		
27	1	1d. on 2½d. ultramarine	£8000	£8000
		(*b*) *With T* **7**		
28	1	1d. on 2½d. ultramarine	35·00	42·00
		a. Surch inverted	£6500	£4250

The 1d. of Antigua was used provisionally in St. Christopher in 1890, and can be distinguished by the postmark, which is "A 12" in place of "A02" (*price from £160 used*).

REVENUE STAMPS USED FOR POSTAGE

Saint Christopher
(R 1)

SAINT KITTS NEVIS REVENUE
(R 2)

1883. *Nos.* F6 *and* F8 *of Nevis optd with Type* R **1**, *in violet. Wmk Crown CA. P* 14.

R1	1d. lilac-mauve	£200	
R2	6d. green	40·00	55·00

1885. *Optd with Type* R **2**. *Wmk Crown CA. P* 14.

R3	1	1d. rose	1·25	4·25
R4		3d. mauve	4·50	15·00
R5		6d. orange-brown	1·75	15·00
R6		1s. olive	1·40	15·00

Other fiscal stamps with overprints as above also exist, but none of these was ever available for postal purposes.

The stamps for St. Christopher were superseded by the general issue for Leeward Islands on 31 October 1890.

Stamps for St. Kitts, issued from 1980 onwards will be found listed after those for the combined colony.

NEVIS

Little is known concerning the early postal affairs of Nevis, but it is recorded that the British G.P.O. was to establish a branch office on the island under an Act of Parliament, passed in 1710, although arrangements may not have been finalised for a number of years afterwards. Nevis appears as "a new office" in the P.O. Accounts of 1787.

Stamps of Great Britain were used on the island from May 1858 until the colonial authorities assumed control of the postal service on 1 May 1860. Between this date and the introduction of Nevis stamps in 1861 No. CC1 was again used on overseas mail.

For illustrations of the handstamp and postmark types see BRITISH POST OFFICES ABROAD notes, following GREAT BRITAIN.

CHARLESTOWN

CROWNED-CIRCLE HANDSTAMPS

CC1 CC **5** NEVIS (R.) (9.1852) .. *Price on cover* £1600

No. CC1, but struck in black, was later used in the 1880's on several occasions when there were shortages of adhesive stamps.

Stamps of GREAT BRITAIN *cancelled* "A 09" *as Type* **2**.

1858 *to* **1860.**

Z1	1d. rose-red (1857), *perf* 14	£375
Z2	2d. blue (1858) (Plate Nos. 7, 8)	
Z3	4d. rose (1857)	£300
Z4	6d. lilac (1856)	£275
Z5	1s. green (1856)	

PRICES FOR STAMPS ON COVER

Nos. 1/22	*from* × 8
Nos. 23/4	*from* × 4
Nos. 25/34	*from* × 6
Nos. 35/6	*from* × 7
Nos. F1/8	*from* × 12

1

2

3

4

The designs on the stamps refer to a medicinal spring on the island

(Recess Nissen & Parker, London)

1861. *P* 13. (*a*) *Blued paper.*

1	1	1d. dull rose	£140	95·00
2	2	4d. rose	£450	£140
3	3	6d. grey-lilac	£400	£180
4	4	1s. green	£650	£150
		(*b*) *Greyish paper*		
5	1	1d. dull lake	25·00	25·00
6	2	4d. rose	65·00	48·00
7	3	6d. grey	48·00	35·00
8	4	1s. green	£130	48·00

1866. *White paper. P* 15.

9	1	1d. pale red	19·00	20·00
10		1d. deep red	19·00	20·00
11	2	4d. orange	95·00	19·00
12		4d. deep orange	95·00	19·00
13	4	1s. blue-green	£140	26·00
14		1s. yellow-green	£800	£100
		a. Laid paper	£10000	£3250
		b. No. 9 on sheet with crossed lines on hill	£3500	£500
		c. Ditto. On laid paper		

(Lithographed by transfer from the engraved plates Nissen and Parker, London)

1876. *P* 15.

15	1	1d. pale rose-red	10·00	12·00
		a. Imperf (pair)	£200	
16		1d. deep rose-red	11·00	13·00
17		1d. vermilion-red	12·00	13·00
		a. Bisected (on cover)	†	£650
18	2	4d. orange-yellow	£140	27·00
		a. Imperf between (vert pair)	£3000	
19	3	6d. grey	£180	£170
20	4	1s. pale green	35·00	80·00
		a. Imperf		
		b. Imperf between (strip of three)	£3000	
		c. No. 9 on sheet with crossed lines on hill	£225	
21		1s. deep green	35·00	90·00

With one exception, resulting from a stone which was not retouched, No. 9 on the sheet of the 1s. *deep* green, has not the distinct "crossed lines on hill" of Nos. 14b, 20c and F5a, but traces of the lines are visible.

RETOUCHES. 1d. Lithograph.

i. No. 1 on sheet. Top of hill over kneeling figure redrawn by five thick lines and eight small slanting lines	£140	£150
ii. No. 1 on sheet. Another retouch. Three series of short vertical strokes behind the kneeling figure	£140	£150
iii. No. 3 on sheet. Right upper corner star and border below star retouched	£140	£150
iv. No. 9 on sheet. Retouch in same position as on No. 3 but differing in detail	£140	£150
v. No. 12 on sheet. Dress of standing figure retouched by a number of horizontal and vertical lines	£140	£150

1878. *Litho. P* 11½.

22	1	1d. vermilion-red	15·00	35·00
		a. Bisected (on cover)	†	£650
		b. Imperf (pair)	£180	
		c. Imperf between (pair)		

5 (Die I)

NEVIS. ½d.
(6)

(Typo D.L.R.)

1879–80. *Wmk Crown CC. P* 14.

23	5	1d. lilac-mauve (1880)	25·00	22·00
		a. Bisected (½d.) (on cover)	†	£400
24		2½d. red-brown	85·00	75·00

1882–90. *Wmk Crown CA. P* 14.

25	5	½d. dull green (1883)	3·00	3·50
26		1d. lilac-mauve	65·00	25·00
		a. Bisected (½d.) on cover	†	£400
27		1d. carmine (1884)	3·00	3·25
		a. Dull rose	13·00	10·00
28		2½d. red-brown	85·00	55·00
29		2½d. ultramarine (1884)	4·50	4·50
30		4d. blue	£275	55·00
31		4d. grey (1884)	3·75	3·75
32		6d. green (1883)	£350	£350
33		6d. chestnut (1888)	22·00	35·00
34		1s. pale violet (1890)	85·00	90·00
33, 34 Optd "Specimen"		*Set of* 2	£140	

1883. *No.* 26 *bisected vertically and surch with T* **6**.

35	½d. on half 1d. lilac-mauve (V.)	£275	26·00
	a. Surch double	—	£275
	b. Surch on half "REVENUE" stamp No. F6	—	£500
36	½d. on half 1d. lilac-mauve	£250	25·00
	a. Surch double	—	£275
	b. Unsevered pair	£650	
	ba. Surch on right half only		
	c. Surch on half "REVENUE" stamp No. F6	—	£500

FISCALS USED FOR POSTAGE

Revenue REVENUE

(F 1) (F 2)

1882. *(a) Stamps of* 1876 *optd with Type* F 1.

No.	Description	Unused	Used
F1	1d. bright red	15·00	
F2	1d. rose	15·00	7·00
F3	4d. orange	25·00	
F4	6d. grey	45·00	
F5	1s. green	65·00	
	a. No. 9 on sheet with crossed lines on hill		
	(b) Nos. 26, 30 and 32 optd with Type F 2		
F6	1d. lilac-mauve	11·00	11·00
F7	4d. blue	8·50	12·00
F8	6d. green	8·50	13·00

The retouches listed for the 1d. *lithograph* also occur on No. F1 (*Price from* £110).

The stamps of Nevis were superseded by the general issue for Leeward Islands on 31 October 1890. Stamps for Nevis were again issued in 1980 and will be found listed after those for the combined colony.

ST. KITTS-NEVIS

CROWN COLONY

Stamps for the combined colony were introduced in 1903, and were used concurrently with the general issues of Leeward Islands.

PRICES FOR STAMPS ON COVER TO 1945

Nos. 1/9	*from* × 3
No. 10	—
Nos. 11/20	*from* × 3
No. 21	—
Nos. 22/3	*from* × 15
Nos. 24/34	*from* × 3
Nos. 35/6	—
Nos. 37/47	*from* × 2
Nos. 47*a*/*b*	—
Nos. 48/57	*from* × 2
Nos. 58/60	—
Nos. 61/4	*from* × 2
Nos. 65/7	*from* × 5
Nos. 68/77*c*	*from* × 2

1 Christopher Columbus

2 Medicinal Spring

(Typo D.L.R.)

1903. *Wmk Crown CA. P* 14.

No.	Type	Description	Unused	Used
1	1	½d. dull purple and deep green	3·00	2·25
2	2	1d. grey-black and carmine	3·50	60
3	1	2d. dull purple and brown	4·75	10·00
4		2½d. grey-black and blue	13·00	9·00
5	2	3d. deep green and orange	5·00	10·00
6	1	6d. grey-black and bright purple	7·00	12·00
7		1s. grey-green and orange	7·50	12·00
8	2	2s. deep green and grey-black	13·00	14·00
9	1	2s. 6d. grey-black and violet	23·00	35·00
10	2	5s. dull purple and sage-green	38·00	55·00
1/10		*Set of* 10	£100	£140
1/10 Optd "Specimen"		*Set of* 10	£180	

1905–18. *Wmk Mult Crown CA. P* 14.

No.	Type	Description	Unused	Used
11	1	½d. dull purple and deep green, O	5·50	7·00
12		½d. grey-green, O (1907)	80	1·00
		a. Dull blue-green, O	40	1·25
13	2	1d. grey-black and carmine, C	1·50	1·25
14		1d. carmine, O (1907)	1·60	55
		a. Scarlet, O	75	55
15	1	2d. dull purple and brown, OC	1·60	2·75
16		2½d. grey-black and blue, O	17·00	9·50
17		2½d. bright blue, O (1907)	1·60	1·90
18	2	3d. deep green and orange, OC	3·25	3·75
19	1	6d. grey-black and deep violet, O	12·00	20·00
		a. Grey-black & dp purple, C (1908)	9·00	15·00
		b. Grey-black & brt purple, C (1916)	9·00	15·00
20		1s. grey-green and orange, OC (1909)	5·00	17·00
21	2	5s. dull purple & sage-grn, C (11.18)	35·00	60·00
11/21		*Set of* 11	70·00	£110
12, 14, 17 Optd "Specimen"		*Set of* 3	90·00	

WAR TAX (3) WAR STAMP (3*a*)

1916 (Oct). *Optd with T* 3. *Wmk Mult Crown CA. P* 14.

No.	Type	Description	Unused	Used
22	1	½d. green (Optd S. £55)	20	30
		a. Grey-green	15	30

1918 (Aug). *Special printing, optd with T* 3*a*. *Wmk Mult Crown CA. P* 14.

No.	Type	Description	Unused	Used
23	1	1½d. orange (Optd S. £65)	20	35

4

5

(Typo D.L.R.)

1920–22. *Wmk Mult Crown CA (sideways). P* 14.

No.	Type	Description	Unused	Used
24	4	½d. blue-green, O	1·00	1·00
25	5	1d. carmine, O	90	1·00
26	4	1½d. orange-yellow, O	90	1·25
27	5	2d. slate-grey, O	3·25	4·50
28	4	2½d. ultramarine, O	1·60	3·25
29	5	3d. purple/*yellow,* C	1·60	5·50
30	4	6d. dull purple and bright mauve, C	3·25	8·00
31	5	1s. grey and black/*green,* C	2·40	6·50
32	4	2s. dull purple and blue/*blue,* C	10·00	15·00
33	5	2s. 6d. grey and red/*blue,* C	12·00	22·00
34	4	5s. green and red/*pale yellow,* C	17·00	40·00
35	5	10s. green and red/*green,* C	32·00	55·00
36	4	£1 purple and black/*red,* C (1922)	£225	£350
24/36		*Set of* 13	£275	£450
24/36 Optd "Specimen"		*Set of* 13	£500	

1921–9. *Wmk Mult Script CA (sideways). P* 14.

No.	Type	Description	Unused	Used
37	4	½d. blue-green, O	30	50
		a. Yellow-green, O	2·50	1·40
38	5	1d. rose-carmine, O	35	40
39		1d. deep violet, O (1922)	1·40	40
		a. Pale violet, O (1929)	50	30
40	4	1½d. red, O (1925)	1·25	2·50
40*a*		1½d. red-brown, O (1929)	50	50
41	5	2d. slate-grey, O (1922)	50	70
42	4	2½d. pale bright blue, O (1922)	1·40	5·50
43		2½d. brown, O (1922)	1·25	4·00
44		2½d. ultramarine, C (1927)	1·25	3·50
		a. Ultramarine, O (1927)	2·50	1·60
45	5	3d. dull ultramarine, O (1922)	1·25	2·75
45*a*		3d. purple/*yellow,* C (1926)	1·60	2·75
46	4	6d. dull and bright purple, C (1924)	2·50	4·50
46*a*	5	1s. black/*green,* C (1929)	6·50	8·00
47	4	2s. purple and blue/*blue,* C (1922)	6·50	13·00
47*a*	5	2s. 6d. black and red/*blue,* C (1927)	15·00	24·00
47*b*	4	5s. green and red/*yellow,* C (1929)	25·00	42·00
37/47*b*		*Set of* 16	60·00	£100
37/47*b* Optd/Perf "Specimen"		*Set of* 16	£500	

No. 38 is overprinted "Specimen". A later printing exists perforated "Specimen" (*Price* £110).

6 Old Road Bay and Mount Misery

(Typo D.L.R.)

1923. *Tercentenary of Colony. Chalk-surfaced paper. P* 14.

No.	Type	Description	Unused	Used
		(a) Wmk Mult Script CA (sideways)		
48	6	½d. black and green	2·00	4·00
49		1d. black and bright violet	2·00	3·00
50		1½d. black and scarlet	4·50	7·50
51		2d. black and slate-grey	3·50	5·00
52		2½d. black and brown	6·50	13·00
53		3d. black and ultramarine	7·00	14·00
54		6d. black and bright purple	12·00	23·00
55		1s. black and sage-green	18·00	30·00
56		2s. black and blue/*blue*	38·00	55·00
57		2s. 6d. black and red/*blue*	75·00	85·00
58		10s. black and red/*emerald*	£275	£375
		(b) Wmk Mult Crown CA (sideways)		
59	6	5s. black and red/*pale yellow*	£140	£275
60		£1 black and purple/*red*	£1800	£2500
48/60		*Set of* 13	£2250	£3000
48/60 Optd "Specimen"		*Set of* 13	£1800	

1935 (6 May). *Silver Jubilee. As Nos.* 91/4 *of Antigua, but ptd by Waterlow. P* 11 × 12.

No.	Description	Unused	Used
61	1d. deep blue and scarlet	50	50
62	1½d. ultramarine and grey	60	1·50
63	2½d. brown and deep blue	1·50	2·25
64	1s. slate and purple	7·00	11·00
61/4 Perf "Specimen"	*Set of* 4	70·00	

1937 (12 May). *Coronation. As Nos.* 13/15 *of Aden.*

No.	Description	Unused	Used
65	1d. scarlet	35	30
66	1½d. buff	35	30
67	2½d. bright blue	50	60
65/7 Perf "Specimen"	*Set of* 3	50·00	

Nos. 61/7 are inscribed "ST. CHRISTOPHER AND NEVIS".

7 King George VI

8 King George VI and Medicinal Spring

9 King George VI and Christopher Columbus

10 King George VI and Anguilla Island

(Typo; centre litho (T **10**). D.L.R.)

1938 (15 Aug)–**48.** *Wmk Mult Script CA (sideways on T* **8** *and* **9**). *P* 14 (*T* **7** *and* **10**) *or* 13 × 12 (*T* **8**/**9**).

No.	Type	Description	Unused	Used
68	7	½d. green	35	15
		a. Blue-green (1943)	25	15
69		1d. scarlet	70	40
		a. Carmine (1943)	40	12
		b. Rose-red (1947)	40	12
70		1½d. orange	25	10
71	8	2d. scarlet and grey, O	13·00	2·75
		aa. Carmine and deep grey, C	15·00	9·00
		a. Perf 14. *Scar & pale grey,* OC (1941)	60	35
		ab. Perf 14. *Scarlet & dp grey,* O (1943)	16·00	6·50
72	7	2½d. ultramarine	90	50
		a. Bright ultramarine (1943)	30	12
73	8	3d. dull purple and scarlet, O	2·25	1·25
		aa. Rose-lilac and carmine-red, C (1940)	4·50	2·50
		a. Perf 14. *Dull pur & scar,* CO (1942)	60	35
		ab. Reddish mve & scar-verm, C (1948)	27·00	15·00
		ac. Reddish lilac and scarlet, O (1948)	27·00	12·00
74	9	6d. green and bright purple, O	4·00	1·50
		a. Perf 14. *Green & dp claret,* C (1942)	24·00	13·00
		ab. Perf 14. *Green and purple,* OC	1·00	45
75	8	1s. black and green, O	4·00	1·40
		a. Perf 14, OC (1943)	70	45
76		2s. 6d. black and scarlet, O	15·00	10·00
		a. Perf 14, CO (1942)	4·75	3·00
77	9	5s. green and scarlet, O	40·00	26·00
		a. Perf 14, CO (1942)	9·00	4·00
77*b*	10	10s. black and ultramarine (1.9.48)	20·00	25·00
77*c*		£1 black and brown (1.9.48)	35·00	40·00
68/77*c*		*Set of* 12	65·00	65·00
68/77 Perf "Specimen"		*Set of* 10	£140	

1946 (1 Nov). *Victory. As Nos.* 28/9 *of Aden.*

No.	Description	Unused	Used
78	1½d. red-orange	15	15
79	3d. carmine	15	15
78/9 Perf "Specimen"	*Set of* 2	60·00	

1949 (3 Jan). *Royal Silver Wedding. As Nos.* 30/1 *of Aden.*

No.	Description	Unused	Used
80	2½d. ultramarine	15	15
81	5s. carmine	5·00	8·00

1949 (10 Oct). *75th Anniv of Universal Postal Union. As Nos.* 114/17 *of Antigua.*

No.	Description	Unused	Used
82	2½d. ultramarine	40	25
83	3d. carmine-red	60	75
84	6d. magenta	1·00	1·25
85	1s. blue-green	1·50	1·50

ANGUILLA ANGUILLA

TERCENTENARY 1650-1950 (11)

TERCENTENARY 1650—1950 (12)

1950 (10 Nov). *Tercentenary of British Settlement in Anguilla. T* **7** *optd as T* **11** *and T* **8**/**9**, *perf* 13 × 12, *optd as T* **12**.

No.	Type	Description	Unused	Used
86	7	1d. bright rose-red	10	12
87		1½d. orange	10	12
		a. Error. Crown missing, W 9*a*	£500	
		b. Error. St. Edward's Crown, W 9*b*	£375	
88		2½d. bright ultramarine	12	12
89	8	3d. dull purple and scarlet	10	15
90	9	6d. green and bright purple	10	25
91	8	1s. black and green (R.)	12	30
86/91		*Set of* 6	60	95

Nos. 87*a*/*b* occur on a row in the watermark, in which the crowns and letters "CA" alternate.

(New Currency. 100 cents = 1 West Indian dollar)

1951 (16 Feb). *Inauguration of B.W.I. University College. As Nos.* 118/19 *of Antigua.*

No.	Description	Unused	Used
92	3c. black and yellow-orange	20	20
93	12c. turquoise-green and magenta	25	35

ST. CHRISTOPHER, NEVIS AND ANGUILLA

LEGISLATIVE COUNCIL

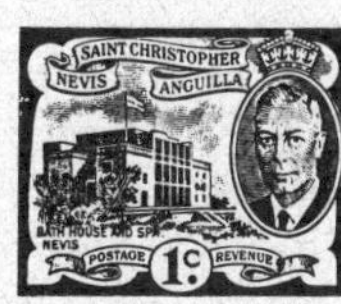

13 Bath House and Spa

14 Map of the Islands

1952 (14 June). *Vert designs as T* **14** (3, 12 *c.*) *or horiz as* **13** (*others*). *Wmk Mult Script CA. P* 12½.

No.	Description	Unused	Used
94	1 c. deep green and ochre	20	30
95	2 c. green	30	35
96	3 c. carmine-red and violet	10	30
97	4 c. scarlet	30	35
98	5 c. bright blue and grey	30	30
99	6 c. ultramarine	35	40
100	12 c. deep blue and reddish brown	40	40
101	24 c. black and carmine-red	50	50
102	48 c. olive and chocolate	2·50	2·25
103	60 c. ochre and deep green	2·25	2·75
104	$1.20, deep green and ultramarine	6·00	4·50
105	$4.80, green and carmine	17·00	35·00
94/105	*Set of* 12	27·00	42·00

Designs:—2 c. Warner Park; 4 c. Brimstone Hill; 5 c. Nevis from the sea, North; 6 c. Pinney's Beach; 12 c. Sir Thomas Warner's Tomb; 24 c. Old Road Bay; 48 c. Sea Island cotton; 60 c. The Treasury; $1.20, Salt pond; $4.80, Sugar factory.

1953 (2 June). *Coronation. As No. 47 of Aden.*
106 2 c. black and bright green 10 10

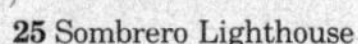

25 Sombrero Lighthouse   **26** Map of Anguilla and Dependencies

(Recess Waterlow (until 1961), then D.L.R.)

1954 (1 Mar)–**57.** *Designs previously used for King George VI issue, but with portrait of Queen Elizabeth II as in T* **25/6** *or new values and designs* (½ c., 8 c., $2.40). *Wmk Mult Script CA. P* 12½.
106*a* ½ c. deep olive (3.7.56) 5 5
107 1 c. deep green and ochre (*shades*) 5 5
 b. Imperf vert (horiz strip of three) .. † —
108 2 c. green (*shades*) 5 5
109 3 c. carmine-red and violet (*shades*) .. 8 5
110 4 c. scarlet 8 5
111 5 c. bright blue and grey 10 5
112 6 c. ultramarine (*shades*) 10 5
112*a* 8 c. grey-black (1.2.57) .. .. 1·40 15
113 12 c. deep blue and red-brown 12 5
114 24 c. black and carmine-red (1.12.54) .. 20 5
115 48 c. olive-bistre and chocolate (1.12.54) .. 75 50
116 60 c. ochre and deep green (1.12.54) .. 1·50 1·00
117 $1.20, dp green & ultram (*shades*) (1.12.54) 4·75 2·50
117*a* $2.40, black and red-orange (1.2.57) .. 15·00 15·00
118 $4.80, green and carmine (1.12.54) .. 20·00 20·00
106*a*/18 .. .. *Set of* 15 40·00 35·00
Design: *Horiz*—½ c., $1.20 Salt Pond; 1 c. Bath House and Spa; 2 c. Warner Park; 4 c. Brimstone Hill; 5 c. Nevis from the sea, North; 6 c. Pinney's Beach; 24 c. Old Road Bay; 48 c. Sea Island cotton; 60 c. The Treasury; $4.80, Sugar factory. *Vert*—3 c. Map of the islands; 12 c. Sir Thomas Warner's Tomb.

Stamps of St. Christopher, Nevis and Anguilla were in concurrent use with the stamps inscribed "LEEWARD ISLANDS" until 1 July 1956, when the general Leeward Islands stamps were withdrawn.

27 Alexander Hamilton and View of Nevis

(Des Eva Wilkin. Recess Waterlow)

1957 (11 Jan). *Birth Bicentenary of Alexander Hamilton. Wmk Mult Script CA. P* 12½.
119 **27** 24 c. green and deep blue 15 15

1958 (22 Apr). *Inauguration of British Caribbean Federation. As Nos.* 135/7 *of Antigua.*
120 3 c. deep green 15 10
121 6 c. blue 25 40
122 12 c. scarlet 30 15

MINISTERIAL GOVERNMENT

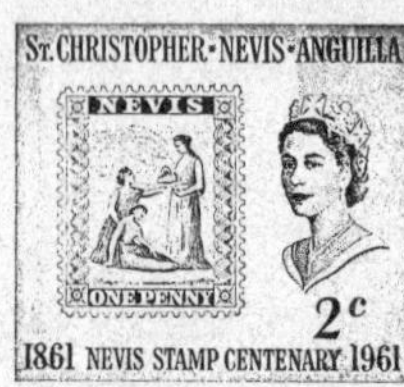

28 One Penny Stamp of 1861

(Recess Waterlow)

1961 (15 July). *Nevis Stamp Centenary. T* **28** *and similar horiz designs. W w* **12**. *P* 14.
123 2 c. red-brown and green 10 15
124 8 c. red-brown and deep blue 20 15
125 12 c. black and carmine-red 25 15
126 24 c. deep bluish green and red-orange .. 35 25
Designs:—8 c. Fourpence stamp of 1861; 12 c. Sixpence stamp of 1861; 24 c. One shilling stamp of 1861.

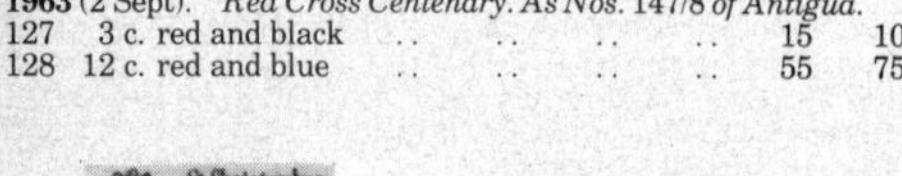

1963 (2 Sept). *Red Cross Centenary. As Nos.* 147/8 *of Antigua.*
127 3 c. red and black 15 10
128 12 c. red and blue 55 75

32 New Lighthouse, Sombrero   **33** Loading Sugar Cane, St. Kitts

(Des V. Whiteley. Photo Harrison)

1963 (20 Nov). *Vert designs as T* **32** (2, 3, 15, 25, 60 *c.*, $1, $5) *or horiz as* **33** (*others*) *in sepia and light blue* (½ *c.*), *greenish yellow and blue* ($1) *or multicoloured* (*others*). *W w* **12** (*upright*). *P* 14.
129 ½ c. Type **32** 5 5
130 1 c. Type **33** 5 5
131 2 c. Pall Mall Square, Basseterre 5 5
 a. White fountain and Church .. .. 90·00
132 3 c. Gateway, Brimstone Hill Fort, St. Kitts 5 5
133 4 c. Nelson's Spring, Nevis 5 5
134 5 c. Grammar School, St. Kitts 8 5
135 6 c. Crater, Mt Misery, St. Kitts 10 5
136 10 c. Hibiscus 15 5
137 15 c. Sea Island cotton, Nevis 35 5
138 20 c. Boat building, Anguilla 30 5
139 25 c. White-crowned Pigeon (*shades*) .. 50 20
140 50 c. St. George's Church Tower, Basseterre .. 60 40
141 60 c. Alexander Hamilton .. .. .. 1·50 45
142 $1 Map of St. Kitts-Nevis .. .. 3·00 1·50
143 $2.50, Map of Anguilla .. .. .. 5·50 4·50
144 $5 Arms of St. Christopher, Nevis and Anguilla .. .. 8·00 9·00
129/144 .. .. *Set of* 16 18·00 15·00
The 1, 4, 5, 6, 10 and 20 c. values exist with PVA gum as well as gum arabic.
See also Nos. 166/71.

ARTS FESTIVAL ST KITTS 1964

(**48**)

49 Festival Emblem

1964 (14 Sept). *Arts Festival. Nos.* 132 *and* 139 *optd as T* **48**.
145 3 c. Gateway, Brimstone Hill Fort, St Kitts 5 5
 a. Opt double .. ..
146 25 c. White-crowned Pigeon 15 15

1965 (17 May). *I.T.U. Centenary. As Nos.* 166/7 *of Antigua.*
147 2 c. bistre-yellow and rose-carmine 8 5
148 50 c. turquoise-blue and yellow-olive 70 45

1965 (15 Oct). *International Co-operation Year. As Nos.* 168/9 *of Antigua.*
149 2 c. reddish purple and turquoise-green .. 10 5
150 25 c. deep bluish green and lavender 20 20

1966 (24 Jan). *Churchill Commemoration. As Nos.* 170/3 *of Antigua.*
151 ½ c. new blue 5 5
152 3 c. deep green 20 10
153 15 c. brown 55 40
154 25 c. bluish violet 75 55

1966 (4 Feb). *Royal Visit. As Nos.* 174/5 *of Antigua.*
155 3 c. black and ultramarine 10 5
156 25 c. black and magenta 30 25

1966 (1 July). *World Cup Football Championships. As Nos.* 176/7 *of Antigua.*
157 6 c. violet, yellow-green, lake & yellow-brn .. 10 5
158 25 c. chocolate, blue-green, lake & yell-brn .. 20 20

(Photo Harrison)

1966 (15 Aug). *Arts Festival. P* 14 × 14½.
159 **49** 3 c. black, buff, emerald-green and gold 5 5
160 25 c. black, buff, emerald-green and silver 15 15

1966 (20 Sept). *Inauguration of W.H.O. Headquarters, Geneva. As Nos.* 178/9 *of Antigua.*
161 3 c. black, yellow-green, and light blue .. 5 5
162 40 c. black, light purple, and yellow-brown .. 30 20

1966 (1 Dec). *20th Anniv of U.N.E.S.C.O. As Nos.* 196/8 *of Antigua.*
163 3 c. slate-violet, red, yellow and orange .. 5 5
164 6 c. orange-yellow, violet and deep olive .. 10 10
165 40 c. black, bright purple and orange .. 50 35

ASSOCIATED STATEHOOD

1967–69. *As Nos.* 129, 131/2, 137, 139 *and* 142 *but wmk sideways.*
166 **20** ½ c. sepia and light blue (9.1.69) .. 5 12
167 – 2 c. multicoloured (27.6.67) 12 5
168 – 3 c. multicoloured (16.7.68) 12 5
169 – 15 c. multicoloured (16.7.68) 70 40
170 – 25 c. multicoloured (16.7.68) .. .. 1·25 50
171 – $1 greenish yell & bl (*shades*) (16.7.68) 3·75 4·00
166/71 .. .. *Set of* 6 5·50 4·50
The 2 c. and $1 values exist with PVA gum as well as gum arabic.
Nos. 172/81 vacant.

50 Government Headquarters, Basseterre   **53** John Wesley and Cross

(Des V. Whiteley. Photo Harrison)

1967 (1 July). *Statehood. T* **50** *and similar horiz designs. Multicoloured. W w* **12**. *P* 14½ × 14.
182 3 c. Type **50** 5 5
183 10 c. National Flag 8 8
184 25 c. Coat of Arms 15 15

(Litho D.L.R.)

1967 (1 Dec). *West Indies Methodist Conference. T* **53** *and similar vert designs. P* 13 × 13½.
185 3 c. black, cerise and reddish violet 5 5
186 25 c. black, light greenish blue and blue .. 15 10
187 40 c. black, yellow and orange 25 25
Designs:—25 c. Charles Wesley and Cross; 40 c. Thomas Coke and Cross.

56 "Herald" Aircraft over Merchant Ship   **57** Dr. Martin Luther King

(Des and litho D.L.R.)

1968 (30 July). *Caribbean Free Trade Area. W w* **12** (*sideways*). *P* 13.
188 **56** 25 c. multicoloured 15 10
189 50 c. multicoloured 30 15

(Des G. Vasarhelyi. Litho Enschedé)

1968 (30 Sept). *Martin Luther King Commemoration. W w* **12**. *P* 12 × 12½.
190 **57** 50 c. multicoloured 15 20

58 "Mystic Nativity" (Botticelli)   **60** Tarpon

(Des and photo Harrison)

1968 (27 Nov). *Christmas. Paintings. T* **58** *and similar vert design. Multicoloured. W w* **12** (*sideways*). *P* 14½ × 14.
191 12 c. Type **58** 8 5
192 25 c. "The Adoration of the Magi" (Rubens) .. 12 12
193 40 c. Type **58** 20 20
194 50 c. As 25 c. 20 25

(Des G. Drummond. Photo Harrison)

1969 (25 Feb). *Fishes. T* **60** *and similar horiz designs. W w* **12**. *P* 14 × 14½.
195 6 c. multicoloured 10 10
196 12 c. black, turquoise-green & greenish blue 20 15
197 40 c. multicoloured 45 25
198 50 c. multicoloured 50 30
Designs:—12 c. Garfish; 40 c. Horse-eye Jack; 50 c. Redsnapper.

64 The Warner Badge and Islands   **67** "The Adoration of the Kings" (Mostaert)

(Des V. Whiteley. Litho Format)

1969 (1 Sept). *Sir Thomas Warner Commemoration. T* **64** *and similar horiz designs. Multicoloured. W w* **12** (*sideways*). *P* 13½ × 14.
199 20 c. Type **64** 15 15
200 25 c. Sir Thomas Warner's tomb 15 15
201 40 c. Charles I's commission 20 25

(Des Enschedé. Litho B.W.)

1969 (17 Nov). *Christmas. Paintings. T* **67** *and similar vert design. Multicoloured. W w* **12** (*sideways*). *P* 13½.
202 10 c. Type **67** 8 5
203 25 c. Type **67** 12 15
204 40 c. "The Adoration of the Kings" (Geertgen) 25 30
205 50 c. As 40 c. 25 30

73 Portuguese Caravels (16th-cent)

(Des and litho J.W.)

1970 (2 Feb–8 Sept). *Designs as T* **73** *in black, pale orange and emerald* (½ c.) *or multicoloured* (*others*). *W* w **12** (*upright on vert designs, sideways on horiz designs*). *P* 14.

206 ½ c. Pirates and treasure at Frigate Bay (*vert*) 5 5
207 1 c. English two-decker warship, 1650 (*vert*) 8 5
208 2 c. Naval flags of colonizing nations (*vert*) .. 15 5
209 3 c. Rapier hilt (17th-century) (*vert*).. .. 15 5
210 4 c. Type **73** 15 5
211 5 c. Sir Henry Morgan and fireships, 1669 .. 20 5
212 6 c. L'Ollonois and pirate carrack (16th-century) 20 5
213 10 c. 17th-century smugglers' ship 25 5
214 15 c. "Piece-of-eight" (*vert*) (I) .. .. .. 1·00 40
214*a* 15 c. "Piece-of-eight" (*vert*) (II) (8.9.70) .. 40 20
215 20 c. Cannon (17th-century) 35 20
216 25 c. Humphrey Cole's Astrolabe, 1574 (*vert*) 40 15
217 50 c. Flintlock pistol (17th-century) 85 80
218 60 c. Dutch flute (17th-century) (*vert*).. .. 2·75 90
219 $1 Captain Bartholomew Roberts and his crew's death warrant (*vert*) .. .. 2·75 1·10
220 $2.50, Railing piece (16th-century) .. .. 4·25 4·50
221 $5 Drake, Hawkins and sea battle .. .. 8·00 7·50
206/221 .. .. *Set of* 17 19·00 14·00

Nos. 214/*a*. Type I, coin inscribed "HISPANIANUM"; Type II, corrected to "HISPANIARUM". No. 214*a* also differs considerably in shade from No. 214.

See also Nos. 269/80 and 322/31.

85 Graveyard Scene (*Great Expectations*)

(Des Jennifer Toombs. Litho B.W.)

1970 (1 May). *Death Centenary of Charles Dickens. T* **85** *and similar designs. W* w **12** (*sideways on horiz designs*). *P* 13.

222 4 c. bistre-brown, gold and deep blue-green .. 10 5
223 20 c. bistre-brown, gold and reddish purple .. 25 20
224 25 c. bistre-brown, gold and olive-green .. 25 25
225 40 c. bistre-brown, gold and ultramarine .. 50 60

Designs: *Horiz*—20 c. Miss Havisham and Pip (*Great Expectations*). *Vert*—25 c. Dickens's Birthplace; 40 c. Charles Dickens.

86 Local Steel Band

(Des V. Whiteley. Litho Enschedé)

1970 (1 Aug). *Festival of Arts. T* **86** *and similar horiz designs. Multicoloured. W* w **12** (*sideways*). *P* 13½.

226 20 c. Type **86** 15 15
227 25 c. Local String Band 15 15
228 40 c. Scene from *A Midsummer Night's Dream* 30 30

87 1d. Stamp of 1870 and Post Office, 1970

88 "Adoration of the Shepherds" (detail) (Frans van Floris)

(Des J. Cooter. Litho J.W.)

1970 (14 Sept). *Stamp Centenary. T* **87** *and similar horiz designs. W* w **12** (*sideways*). *P* 14½.

229 ½ c. green and rose 5 5
230 20 c. deep blue, green and rose 25 15
231 25 c. brown-purple, green and rose 25 15
232 50 c. scarlet, green and black .. .. .. 1·10 1·60

Designs:—20 c., 25 c. 1d. and 6d. Stamps of 1870; 50 c. 6d. Stamp of 1870 and early postmark.

(Des Enschedé. Litho Format)

1970 (16 Nov). *Christmas. T* **88** *and similar vert design. Multicoloured. W* w **12**. *P* 14.

233 3 c. Type **88** 5 5
234 20 c. "The Holy Family" (Van Dyck) 15 10
235 25 c. As 20 c. 15 15
236 40 c. Type **88** 25 35

89 Monkey Fiddle

(Des Sylvia Goaman. Litho Format)

1971 (1 Mar). *Flowers. T* **89** *and similar horiz designs. Multicoloured. W* w **12** (*sideways*). *P* 14½.

237 ½ c. Type **89** 5 5
238 20 c. Tropical Mountain Violet 25 15
239 30 c. Trailing Morning Glory 45 45
240 50 c. Fringed Epidendrum 60 60

90 Royal Poinciana

(Des Enschedé. Litho J.W.)

1971 (1 June). *Phillipe de Poincy Commemoration. T* **90** *and similar multicoloured designs. W* w **12** (*sideways on* 20 *and* 30 *c.*). *P* 13½.

241 20 c. Type **90** 25 20
242 30 c. Château de Poincy 35 35
243 50 c. De Poincy's badge (*vert*) 50 55

91 The East Yorks

92 "Crucifixion" (Massys)

(Des V. Whiteley. Litho Walsall)

1971 (1 Sept). *Siege of Brimstone Hill*, 1782. *T* **91** *and similar horiz designs. Multicoloured. W* w **12** (*sideways*). *P* 14½.

244 ½ c. Type **91** 5 5
245 20 c. Royal Artillery 65 40
246 30 c. French infantry 85 50
247 50 c. The Royal Scots .. .. 1·25 1·00

(Des J. Cooter. Litho J.W.)

1972 (1 Apr). *Easter. W* w **12**. *P* 14 × 13½.

248 **92** 4 c. multicoloured 5 5
249 20 c. multicoloured 20 10
250 30 c. multicoloured 30 45
251 40 c. multicoloured 40 50

93 "Virgin and Child" (Borgognone)

94 Brown Pelicans

(Des J. Cooter. Litho J.W.)

1972 (2 Oct). *Christmas. T* **93** *and similar multicoloured designs. W* w **12** (*sideways on vert designs*). *P* 14.

252 3 c. Type **93** 5 5
253 20 c. "Adoration of the Kings" (J. Bassano) (*horiz*) 20 10
254 25 c. "Adoration of the Shepherds" (Domenichino) 25 25
255 40 c. "Virgin and Child" (Fiorenzo di Lorenzo)

(Des (from photograph by D. Groves) and photo Harrison)

1972 (20 Nov). *Royal Silver Wedding. Multicoloured; background colour given. W* w **12**. *P* 14 × 14½.

256 **94** 20 c. carmine 25 30
257 25 c. bright blue 25 30

95 Landing on St. Christopher, 1623

96 "The Last Supper" (Titian)

(Des J.W. Litho Questa)

1973 (28 Jan). *350th Anniv of Sir Thomas Warner's landing on St. Christopher. T* **95** *and similar horiz designs. Multicoloured. W* w **12**. *P* 13½.

258 4 c. Type **95** 35 15
259 25 c. Growing tobacco 90 55
260 40 c. Building fort at Old Road .. .. 1·75 1·25
261 $2.50, Warner's ship .. .. 3·00 2·25

(Des J. Cooter. Litho Walsall)

1973 (16 Apr). *Easter. T* **96** *and similar multicoloured designs showing paintings of "The Last Supper" by the artists listed. W* w **12** (*sideways on* $2.50). *P* 13½ × 14 ($2.50) *or* 14 × 13½ (*others*).

262 4 c. Type **96** 8 5
263 25 c. Ascr to Roberti 45 30
264 $2.50, Juan de Juanes (*horiz*) .. .. 2·25 2·50

VISIT OF
H. R. H. THE PRINCE OF WALES 1973
(97)

1973 (31 May). *Royal Visit. Nos.* 258/61 *optd with T* **97** *by Questa.*

265 4 c. Type **95** 20 20
266 25 c. Growing tobacco 30 30
267 40 c. Building fort at Old Road 40 40
268 $2.50, Warner's ship .. .. 1·25 1·50

(Des J.W. Litho Harrison ($10), J.W. (others))

1973 (12 Sept)–**74.** *As Nos.* 206, 208/9, 211/13, 214*a*/17, 219 *and new horiz design* ($10), *but W* w **12** (*sideways on vert designs, upright on horiz designs*).

269 ½ c. Pirates and treasure at Frigate Bay .. 5 20
270 2 c. Naval flags of colonizing nations .. 20 25
271 3 c. Rapier hilt 20 25
272 5 c. Sir Henry Morgan and fireships, 1669 .. 35 25
273 6 c. L'Ollonois and pirate carrack (16th-century) 35 40
274 10 c. 17th-century smugglers' ship 40 45
275 15 c. "Piece-of-eight" (II) 65 75
276 20 c. Cannon (17th-century) 75 95
277 25 c. Humphrey Cole's Astrolabe, 1574 .. 80 1·00
278 50 c. Flintlock pistol (17th-century) .. .. 1·10 1·50
279 $1 Captain Bartholomew Roberts and his crew's death warrant .. .. .. 2·50 3·00
280 $10 "The Apprehension of Blackbeard" (Edward Teach) (16.11.74) .. .. 18·00 15·00
269/80 .. .. *Set of* 12 23·00 22·00

Nos. 281/4 vacant.

99 Harbour Scene and 2d. Stamp of 1903

(Des V. Whiteley Studio. Litho Enschedé)

1973 (1 Oct). *70th Anniv of First St. Kitts-Nevis Stamps. T* **99** *and similar horiz designs. Multicoloured. W* w **12** (*sideways*). *P* 13 × 13½.

285 4 c. Type **99** 8 5
286 25 c. Sugar-mill and 1d. stamp of 1903 .. 30 20
287 40 c. Unloading boat and ½d. stamp of 1903 70 65
288 $2.50, Rock-carvings and 3d. stamp of 1903 4·50 3·50
MS289 144 × 95 mm. Nos. 285/8 .. .. 9·00 9·50

1973 (14 Nov). *Royal Wedding. As Nos.* 165/6 *of Anguilla.*

290 25 c. light emerald 15 10
291 40 c. brown-ochre 20 15

100 "Madonna and Child" (Murillo)

101 "Christ carrying the Cross" (S. del Piombo)

(Des J. Cooter. Litho Format)

1973 (1 Dec). *Christmas. T* **100** *and similar multicoloured designs showing "The Holy Family" by the artists listed.* W w **12** (*sideways on* $1). *P* 13½.
292 4 c. Type **100** 5 5
293 40 c. Mengs 30 20
294 60 c. Sassoferrato 50 50
295 $1 Filippino Lippi (*horiz*) 50 60

(Des J. Cooter. Litho D.L.R.)

1974 (8 Apr). *Easter. T* **101** *and similar multicoloured designs.* W w **12** (*sideways on* $2.50). *P* 13½.
296 4 c. Type **101** 8 8
297 25 c. "The Crucifixion" (Goya) 25 20
298 40 c. "The Trinity" (Ribera) 35 30
299 $2.50, "The Deposition" (Fra Bartolomeo) (*horiz*) .. .. 2·25 2·75

102 University Centre, St. Kitts

103 Hands reaching for Globe

(Des G. Drummond. Litho Questa)

1974 (1 June). *25th Anniv of University of West Indies. T* **102** *and similar horiz design. Multicoloured.* W w **12** (*sideways*). *P* 13½.
300 10 c. Type **102** 10 5
301 $1 As Type **102** but showing different buildings 50 70
MS302 99 × 95 mm. Nos. 301/2 .. .. 75 1·00

(Des Jennifer Toombs. Litho Questa)

1974 (5 Aug). *Family Planning. T* **103** *and similar designs.* W w **12** (*sideways on* 25 *c. and* $2.50). *P* 14.
303 4 c. orange-brown, new blue and black 5 5
304 25 c. multicoloured 25 25
305 40 c. multicoloured 40 40
306 $2.50, multicoloured .. .. 2·75 3·25
Designs: *Horiz*—25 c. Instruction by nurse; $2.50, Emblem and globe on scales. *Vert*—40 c. Family group.

104 Churchill as Army Lieutenant

105 Aeroplane and Map

(Des PAD Studio. Litho Questa)

1974 (30 Nov). *Birth Centenary of Sir Winston Churchill. T* **104** *and similar vert designs. Multicoloured.* W w **12**. *P* 13½.
307 4 c. Type **104** 5 5
308 25 c. Churchill as Prime Minister 25 20
309 40 c. Churchill as Knight of the Garter 35 40
310 60 c. Churchill's statue, London 45 45
MS311 99 × 148 mm. Nos. 307/10 .. .. .. 1·25 1·50

(Des J.W. Litho Questa)

1974 (16 Dec). *Opening of Golden Rock Airport, St. Kitts. Sheets* 98 × 148 *mm.* W w **12**. *P* 13½.
MS312 **105** 40 c.multicoloured 30 50
MS313 45 c.multicoloured 30 50

106 "The Last Supper" (Doré)

107 E.C.C.A. H.Q. Buildings, Basseterre

(Des PAD Studio. Litho Questa)

1975 (24 Mar). *Easter. T* **106** *and similar vert designs showing paintings by Doré. Multicoloured.* W w **12**. *P* 14½.
314 4 c. Type **106** 5 5
315 25 c. "Christ Mocked" 15 10
316 40 c. "Jesus falling beneath the Cross" 20 20
317 $1 "The Erection of the Cross" 60 75

(Des J. Cooter. Litho Enschedé)

1975 (2 June*). *Opening of East Caribbean Currency Authority's Headquarters. T* **107** *and similar horiz designs.* W w **14** (*sideways*). *P* 13 × 13½.
318 12 c. multicoloured 10 10
319 25 c. multicoloured 20 20
320 40 c. light vermilion, silver and grey-black .. 30 30
321 45 c. multicoloured 30 30
Designs:—25 c. Specimen one-dollar banknote; 40 c. Half-dollar of 1801 and current 4-dollar coin; 45 c. Coins of 1801 and 1960.
*This is the local date of issue; the Crown Agents released the stamps on 28 April.

1975–77. *As Nos.* 207, 209/13, 214*a*/15 *and* 218/19 *but* W w **14** (*sideways on* 4, 5, 6, 10, 20 *and* 60 *c.*).
A. *White, ordinary paper.*
B. *Cream, chalk-surfaced paper.*

		A		B	
332	1 c. English two-decker war-ship, 1650	†		20	20
323	3 c. Rapier hilt (17th-century)	20	12	40	40
324	4 c. Type **73**	20	12	40	40
325	5 c. Sir Henry Morgan and fireships, 1669	30	25	50	50
326	6 c. L'Ollonois and pirate carrack (16th-century)	45	15	55	60
327	10 c. 17th-century smugglers' ship	45	20	70	50
328	15 c. "Piece-of-eight" (II) ..	55	25	90	90
329	20 c. Cannon (17th-century) ..	90	90	1·00	1·00
330	60 c. Dutch flute (17th-century)	2·75	1·75	†	
331	$1 Captain Bartholomew Roberts and his crew's death warrant	†		3·75	2·75
323A/30A	.. .. *Set of* 8	5·25	3·25		
322B/31B	.. .. *Set of* 9			7·50	6·50

Dates of issue: Ordinary paper–5, 6 and 20 c. 11.6.75; others 11.6.76. Chalk-surfaced paper–5, 15 c. and $1 16.8.77; others 17.5.77
Nos. 332/7 vacant.

108 Evangeline Booth (Salvation Army General)

109 Golfer

(Des Jennifer Toombs. Litho Questa)

1975 (15 Sept). *International Women's Year. T* **108** *and similar vert designs. Multicoloured.* W w **12**. *P* 14.
338 4 c. Type **108** 5 5
339 25 c. Sylvia Pankhurst 20 20
340 40 c. Marie Curie 30 30
341 $2.50, Lady Annie Allen (teacher and guider) .. .. 2·25 2·25

(Des Sue Lawes. Litho Questa)

1975 (1 Nov). *Opening of Frigate Bay Golf Course.* W w **14** (*sideways*). *P* 13½.
342 **109** 4 c. black and rose-red 5 5
343 25 c. black and greenish yellow 25 15
344 40 c. black and light emerald 40 25
345 $1 black and new blue.. .. .. .. 1·40 95

110 "St. Paul" (Pier Francesco Sacchi)

111 "Crucifixion" (detail)

(Des J.W. Litho Questa)

1975 (1 Dec). *Christmas. T* **110** *and similar vert designs showing details from paintings in the National Gallery, London. Multicoloured.* W w **14**. *P* 13½.
346 25 c. Type **110** 20 15
347 40 c. "St James" (Bonifazio di Pitati) 30 30
348 45 c. "St. John the Baptist" (Mola) 30 30
349 $1 "St. Mary" (Raphael) 75 80

(Des J. Cooter. Litho Questa)

1976 (14 Apr). *Easter. Stained-glass Windows. T* **111** *and similar vert designs. Multicoloured.* W w **14**. *P* 14 × 13½ (4 *c.*) *or* 14 (*others*).
350 4 c. Type **111** 5 5
a. Strip of 3. Nos. 350/2 15
351 4 c. } "Crucifixion" 5 5
352 4 c. } 5 5
353 25 c. "Last Supper" 15 15
354 40 c. "Last Supper" (*different*).. .. .. .. 25 25
355 $1 "Baptism of Christ" 65 65
350/5 .. .. *Set of* 6 1·00 1·00
Nos. 350/2 were printed horizontally *se-tenant*, together forming a composite design, No. 350 being the left-hand stamp.
Nos. 353/5 are smaller, 27 × 35 mm.

1976 (8 July). *West Indian Victory in World Cricket Cup. As Nos.* 559/60 *of Barbados.*
356 12 c. Map of the Caribbean 80 35
357 40 c. Prudential Cup .. .. 1·60 90
MS358 95 × 80 mm. Nos. 356/7 .. .. 3·75 4·00

112 Crispus Attucks and the Boston Massacre

113 "The Nativity" (Sforza Book of Hours)

(Des J.W. Litho Questa)

1976 (26 July). *Bicentenary of American Revolution. T* **112** *and similar horiz designs. Multicoloured.* W w **14** (*sideways*). *P* 13½.
359 20 c. Type **112** 20 20
360 40 c. Alexander Hamilton and Battle of Yorktown 35 45
361 45 c. Jefferson and Declaration of Independence 35 45
362 $1 Washington and the Crossing of the Delaware .. .. 85 1·00

(Des Jennifer Toombs. Litho Questa)

1976 (1 Nov). *Christmas. T* **113** *and similar vert designs. Multicoloured.* W w **14**. *P* 14.
363 20 c. Type **113** 20 10
364 40 c. "Virgin and Child with St. John" (Pintoricchio) 30 20
365 45 c. "Our Lady of Good Children" (Ford Maddox-Brown) 35 30
366 $1 "Little Hands Outstretched to Bless" (Margaret Tarrant) 85 65

114 Royal Visit, 1966

115 "Christ on the Cross" (Niccolo di Liberatore)

(Des J.W. Litho Questa)

1977 (7 Feb). *Silver Jubilee. T* **114** *and similar vert designs. Multicoloured.* W w **14**. *P* 13½.
367 50 c. Type **114** 25 35
368 55 c. The Sceptre 25 35
369 $1.50, Bishops paying homage 55 75

(Des G. Hutchins. Litho Questa)

1977 (14 Apr*). *Easter. T* **115** *and similar designs showing paintings from the National Gallery, London. Multicoloured.* W w **14** (*sideways on* 50 *c.*). *P* 14.
370 25 c. Type **115** 20 10
371 30 c. "The Resurrection" (imitator of Mantegna) 25 20
372 50 c. "The Resurrection" (Ugolino da Siena) (*horiz*) 35 35
373 $1 "Christ Rising from the Tomb" (Gaudenzio Ferrari) 60 60
*This is the local release date; the Crown Agents released the stamps ten days earlier.

116 Estridge Mission

117 Laboratory Instruments

(Des Jennifer Toombs. Litho Cartor S.A., France)

1977 (27 June). *Bicentenary of Moravian Mission. T* **116** *and similar horiz designs.* W w **14** (*sideways*). *P* 12½.
374 4 c. black, greenish blue and new blue 5 5
375 20 c. black, brt mauve & brt reddish violet .. 20 20
376 40 c. black, yellow and yellow-orange 30 30
Designs:—20 c. Mission symbol; 40 c. Basseterre Mission.

(Des G. Hutchins. Litho Questa)

1977 (11 Oct). *75th Anniv of Pan-American Health Organization. T* **117** *and similar vert designs.* W w **14**. *P* 14.

377 3 c. multicoloured 5 5
378 12 c. multicoloured 15 10
379 20 c. multicoloured 20 15
380 $1 red-brown, bright orange and black .. 85 70

Designs:—12 c. Fat cells, blood cells and nerve cells; 20 c. "Community participation in health"; $1 Inoculation.

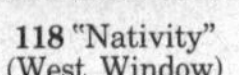

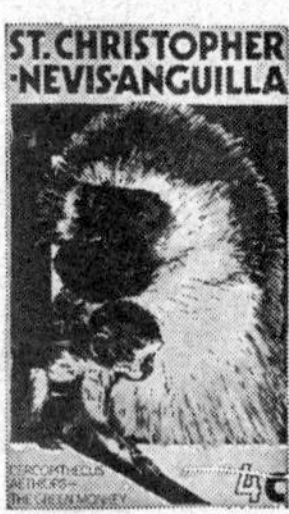

118 "Nativity" (West Window)

119 Parent Monkey with Vervet

(Des Jennifer Toombs. Litho Rosenbaum Bros, Vienna)

1977 (15 Nov). *Christmas. Vert designs as T* **118** *showing stained-glass windows from Chartres Cathedral. Multicoloured.* W w **14** *(inverted). P* 13½.

381 4 c. Type **118** 10 10
382 6 c. "Three Magi" (West window) 10 8
383 40 c. "La Belle Verriere" 25 25
384 $1 "Virgin and Child" (Rose window) .. 60 60

(Des BG Studio. Litho Questa)

1978 (15 Apr). *The Green Monkey. T* **119** *and similar vert design.* W w **14**. *P* 14½.

385 **119** 4 c. yellow-brown, rosine and black .. 8 8
386 – 5 c. multicoloured 8 8
387 **119** 55 c. yellow-brown, apple-green & black 40 25
388 – $1.50, multicoloured .. .. .. 1·10 1·00

Design:—5 c., $1.50, Monkeys on branch.

120 Falcon of Edward III

121 Tomatoes

(Des C. Abbott. Litho Questa)

1978 (2 June). *25th Anniv of Coronation. T* **120** *and similar vert designs. P* 15.

389 $1 olive-brown and vermilion 35 45
a. Sheetlet. Nos. 389/91 × 2 .. .. 1·90
390 $1 multicoloured 35 45
391 $1 olive-brown and vermilion 35 45

Designs:—No. 389, Type **120**; No. 390, Queen Elizabeth II; No. 391, Pelican.

(Des BG Studio. Litho D.L.R.)

1978 (8 Sept). *Horiz designs as T* **121**. *Multicoloured.* W w **14** *(sideways). P* 14½ × 14.

392 1 c. Type **121** 5 5
393 2 c. Defence Force band 5 5
394 5 c. Radio and T.V. station 8 8
395 10 c. Technical college 10 10
396 12 c. T.V. assembly plant 10 10
397 15 c. Sugar cane harvesting 12 12
398 25 c. Crafthouse (craft centre) 15 15
399 30 c. Cruise ship 20 20
400 40 c. Lobster and sea crab 25 25
401 45 c. Royal St. Kitts Hotel and golf course .. 30 30
402 50 c. Pinney's Beach, Nevis 30 30
403 55 c. New runway at Golden Rock 30 30
404 $1 Cotton picking 45 45
405 $5 Brewery .. .. 2·25 2·25
406 $10 Pineapples and peanuts .. .. .. 6·00 6·00
392/406 .. .. *Set of* 15 9·50 9·50

122 Investiture

123 Wise Man with Gift of Gold

(Des L. Curtis. Litho Rosenbaum Bros, Vienna)

1978 (9 Oct). *50th Anniv of Boy Scout Movement on St. Christopher and Nevis. T* **122** *and similar vert designs. Multicoloured.* W w **14**. *P* 13½.

407 5 c. Type **122** 5 5
408 10 c. Map reading 10 8
409 25 c. Pitching tent 25 20
410 40 c. Cooking 45 35
411 50 c. First aid 55 45
412 55 c. Rev. W. A. Beckett (founder of scouting in St. Kitts) 60 50
407/12 .. .. *Set of* 6 1·75 1·50

(Des Jennifer Toombs. Litho Walsall)

1978 (1 Dec). *Christmas. T* **123** *and similar vert designs. Multicoloured.* W w **14**. *P* 13½.

413 5 c. Type **123** 5 5
414 15 c. Wise Man with gift of Frankincense .. 10 10
415 30 c. Wise Man with gift of Myrrh 20 25
416 $2.25, Wise Men paying homage to the infant Jesus .. .. 1·00 1·50

124 *Canna coccinea*

125 St. Christopher 1870–76 1d. Stamp and Sir Rowland Hill

(Des Daphne Padden. Litho Questa)

1979 (19 Mar). *Flowers (1st series). T* **124** *and similar vert designs. Multicoloured.* W w **14**. *P* 14.

417 5 c. Type **124** 5 5
418 30 c. *Heliconia bihai* 35 15
419 55 c. *Ruellia tuberosa* 55 35
420 $1.50, *Gesneria ventricosa* .. .. .. 1·25 85

See also Nos. 430/3.

(Des J.W. Litho Walsall)

1979 (2 July). *Death Centenary of Sir Rowland Hill. T* **125** *and similar horiz designs showing stamps and portrait. Multicoloured.* W w **14** *(sideways). P* 14½ × 14.

421 5 c. Type **125** 5 5
422 15 c. 1970 Stamp Centenary 50 c. commemorative 10 5
423 50 c. Great Britain 1841 2d. 30 30
424 $2.50, St. Kitts-Nevis 1923 300th Anniversary of Colony £1 commemorative .. 1·10 1·25

126 "The Woodman's Daughter"

127 Nevis Lagoon

(Des BG Studio. Litho Format)

1979 (12 Nov). *Christmas and International Year of the Child. Paintings by Sir John Millais. T* **126** *and similar vert designs. Multicoloured.* W w **14**. *P* 13½.

425 5 c. Type **126** 5 5
426 25 c. "Cherry Ripe" 15 15
427 30 c. "The Rescue" 15 15
428 55 c. "Bubbles" 30 30
MS429 100 × 68 mm. $1 "Christ in the House of His Parents" 50 50

(Des J. Cooter. Litho Questa)

1980 (4 Feb). *Flowers (2nd series). Vert designs as T* **124**. *Multicoloured.* W w **14** *(inverted). P* 14.

430 4 c. *Clerodendrum aculeatum* 5 5
431 55 c. *Inga laurina* 30 30
432 $1.50, *Epidendrum difforme* 80 70
433 $2 *Salvia serotina* .. .. 1·10 1·10

(Des and litho Secura, Singapore)

1980 (6 May). *"London 1980" International Stamp Exhibition. T* **127** *and similar multicoloured designs.* W w **14** *(sideways, on 5 and 55 c., inverted on 30 c.). P* 13.

434 5 c. Type **127** 5 5
435 30 c. Fig Tree Church (*vert*) 15 15
436 55 c. Nisbet Plantation 35 35
437 $3 "Nelson" (Fuger) (*vert*) .. .. .. 1·25 1·40
MS438 107 × 77 mm 75 c. Detail of "Nelson Falling" (D. Dighton). P 13½ × 13 .. .. 70 80
a. Wmk sideways .. .. 40·00

OFFICIAL STAMPS

OFFICIAL

(O 1)

1980 (3 Mar). *Nos. 396, 398 and 400/6 optd with Type* O **1**.

O1 12 c. T.V. assembly plant .. .. .. 1·25 75
O2 25 c. Crafthouse (craft centre) 15 15
O3 40 c. Lobster and sea crab 50 40
O4 45 c. Royal St. Kitts Hotel and golf course .. 45 30
O5 50 c. Pinney's Beach, Nevis 30 30
O6 55 c. New runway at Golden Rock 30 30
O7 $1 Cotton picking .. .. 3·00 2·00
O8 $5 Brewery .. .. 2·25 2·25
O9 $10 Pineapples and Peanuts .. .. .. 4·50 3·50
O1/9 .. .. *Set of* 9 12·00 9·50

From 23 June 1980 St. Kitts and Nevis had separate postal authorities, each with their own issues.

ST. KITTS

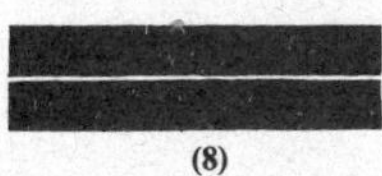

(8)

1980 (23 June). *As Nos. 394/406 of St. Christopher, Nevis and Anguilla optd with T* **8**. *A.* W w **14** *(sideways). B. No wmk.*

		A		B	
29	5 c. Radio and T.V. station ..	20	20	5	5
30	10 c. Technical college ..	25	25	5	5
31	12 c. T.V. assembly plant ..	1·00	1·00	†	
32	15 c. Sugar cane harvesting ..	20	20	5	5
33	25 c. Crafthouse (craft centre) ..	20	20	8	10
34	30 c. Cruise ship ..	20	20	10	12
35	40 c. Lobster and sea crab ..	50	50	12	15
36	45 c. Royal St. Kitts Hotel and golf course ..	25	25	†	
37	50 c. Pinney's Beach, Nevis ..	20	25	†	
38	55 c. New runway at Golden Rock ..	20	25	20	25
39	$1 Cotton picking ..	40	40	40	40
40	$5 Brewery ..	2·00	2·00	3·50	3·00
41	$10 Pineapples and peanuts ..	3·75	4·00	6·00	6·00
29A/41A	.. *Set of* 13	8·50	9·00		
29B/41B	.. *Set of* 10			9·50	9·00

9 H.M.S. *Vanguard*, 1762

10 Queen Elizabeth the Queen Mother

(Litho Secura, Singapore)

1980 (8 Aug). *Ships. T* **9** *and similar horiz designs. Multicoloured.* W w **14** *(sideways). P* 13 × 13½.

42 4 c. Type **9** 5 5
a. Opt omitted £175
43 10 c. H.M.S. *Boreas*, 1787 .. .. .. 5 5
a. Opt omitted £200
44 30 c. H.M.S. *Druid*, 1827 .. .. .. 20 15
a. Opt omitted £200
45 55 c. H.M.S. *Winchester*, 1831 .. .. .. 40 30
a. Opt inverted £200
b. Opt omitted £200
46 $1.50, Harrison Line *Philosopher*, 1857 .. 70 60
a. Opt omitted £200
47 $2 Harrison Line S.S. *Contractor*, 1930 .. 90 80
a. Opt double £175
42/7 .. .. *Set of* 6 2·10 1·75

Nos. 42/7 are overprinted "ST. KITTS" and have the previous combined inscription obliterated.

(Des and litho Format)

1980 (4 Sept). *80th Birthday of Queen Elizabeth the Queen Mother.* W w **14**. *P* 13½.

48 **10** $2 multicoloured 90 85

No. 48 was printed in sheets containing two *se-tenant* stamp-size labels.

11 The Three Wise Men

(Des Walsall. Litho Questa)

1980 (10 Nov). *Christmas. T* **11** *and similar horiz designs. Multicoloured.* W w **14** *(sideways). P* 14½ × 14.

49 5 c. Type **11** 5 5
50 15 c. The Shepherds 5 5
51 30 c. Bethlehem 12 15
52 $4 Nativity scene .. .. 1·60 1·75

12 Purple-throated Carib

13 Bananaquit

(Des Jennifer Toombs. Litho Questa)

1981 (5 Feb)–**82**. *Birds. Vert designs as T* **12** (1 *to* 10 c.) *or horiz as T* **13** (15 c. *to* $10). *Multicoloured.* W w **14** (*sideways on* 1 *to* 10 c.). *P* 13½ × 14 (1 *to* 10 c.) *or* 14 (15 c. *to* $10).
A. *Without imprint date*
B. *With imprint date ("1982") at foot of design*

No.	Description	A		B	
53	1 c. Magnificent Frigate Bird	5	5	5	5
54	4 c. Brown Crested Flycatcher	5	5	5	5
55	5 c. Type **12**	10	10	10	10
56	6 c. Burrowing Owl	10	10	10	10
57	8 c. Purple Martin	10	10	10	10
58	10 c. Yellow-crowned Night Heron	10	10	10	10
59	15 c. Type **13**	10	10	10	10
60	20 c. Scaly-breasted Thrasher	15	15	15	15
61	25 c. Grey Kingbird	15	15	15	15
62	30 c. Green-throated Carib	15	15	15	15
63	40 c. Turnstone	20	20	20	20
64	45 c. Black-faced Grassquit	25	25	25	25
65	50 c. Cattle Egret	30	30	30	30
66	55 c. Brown Pelican	30	30	30	30
67	$1 Lesser Antillean Bullfinch	45	50	45	50
68	$2.50, Zenaida Dove	1·10	1·25	1·10	1·25
69	$5 American Kestrel	2·25	2·50	2·25	2·50
70	$10 Antillean Crested Hummingbird	4·50	4·75	4·50	4·75
53/70	*Set of* 18	9·50	10·00	9·50	10·00

Dates of issue: Without imprint—5.2.81, 5 c. and 10 c. to $10; 30.5.81, 1, 4, 6, 8 c. With imprint—8.6.82, 1 c. to $10.

14 Battalion Company Sergeant, 3rd Regt of Foot ("The Buffs"), *circa* 1801

15 Miriam Pickard (first Guide Commissioner)

(Des G. Vasarhelyi. Litho Format)

1981 (5 Mar). *Military Uniforms* (1*st series*). *T* **14** *and similar vert designs. Multicoloured.* W w **14**. *P* 14½.

No.	Description		
71	5 c. Type **14**	5	5
72	30 c. Battalion Company Officer, 45th Regt of Foot, 1796–97	15	15
73	55 c. Battalion Company Officer, 9th Regt of Foot, 1790	35	30
74	$2.50, Grenadier, 38th Regt of Foot, 1751	1·10	1·10

See also Nos. 110/13.

(Des D. Shults. Litho Questa)

1981 (23 June–14 Dec). *Royal Wedding. Horiz designs as T* **26/27** *of Kiribati. Multicoloured.* (a) W w **14**. *P* 14.

No.	Description		
75	55 c. *Saudadoes*	25	25
	a. Sheetlet. No 75 × 6 and No. 76	2·00	
76	55 c. Prince Charles and Lady Diana Spencer	80	80
77	$2.50, *Royal George*	1·00	1·00
	a. Sheetlet No. 77 × 6 and No. 78	8·00	
78	$2.50, As No. 76	2·00	2·00
79	$4 *Britannia*	1·60	1·60
	a. Sheetlet. No. 79 × 6 and No. 80	13·00	
80	$4 As No. 76	3·00	3·00
MS81	120 × 109 mm. $5 As No. 76. Wmk sideways. P 12 (14 Dec)	6·00	2·00

(*b*) *Booklet stamps. No wmk. P* 12 (19 Nov)

No.	Description		
82	55 c. As No. 76	30	30
	a. Booklet pane. No. 82 × 4	1·00	
83	$2.50, As No. 78	1·10	1·25
	a. Booklet pane. No. 83 × 2	2·25	

Nos. 75/80 were printed in sheetlets of seven stamps of the same face value, each containing six of the "Royal Yacht" design and one of the larger design showing Prince Charles and Lady Diana.

Nos. 82/3 come from $9.40 stamp booklets.

(Des Jennifer Toombs. Litho Walsall)

1981 (21 Sept). *50th Anniv of St. Kitts Girl Guide Movement. T* **15** *and similar vert designs. Multicoloured.* W w **14**. *P* 14.

No.	Description		
84	5 c. Type **15**	5	5
85	30 c. Lady Baden-Powell's visit, 1964	15	15
86	55 c. Visit of Princess Alice, 1960	30	35
87	$2 Thinking-Day parade, 1980's	85	90

16 Stained-glass Windows

17 Admiral Samuel Hood

(Des Jennifer Toombs. Litho Format)

1981 (30 Nov). *Christmas. T* **16** *and similar vert designs showing stained-glass windows.* W w **14**. *P* 13 × 14.

No.	Description		
88	5 c. multicoloured	5	5
89	30 c. multicoloured	15	15
90	55 c. multicoloured	30	35
91	$3 multicoloured	1·25	1·40

1982 (15 Mar). *Bicentenary of Brimstone Hill Siege. T* **17** *and similar horiz designs.* W w **14** (*sideways*). *P* 14.

No.	Description		
92	15 c. multicoloured	10	10
93	55 c. multicoloured	30	35
MS94	96 × 71 mm. $5 black, red-orange & yell-brn	2·00	2·25

Designs:—55 c. Marquis De Bouillé; $5 Battle scene.

18 Alexandra, Princess of Wales, 1863

ROYAL BABY

(19)

(Des D. Shults and J. Cooter. Litho Format)

1982 (22 June). *21st Birthday of Princess of Wales. T* **18** *and similar vert designs. Multicoloured.* W w **14**. *P* 13½ × 14.

No.	Description		
95	15 c. Type **18**	10	5
96	55 c. Coat of arms of Alexandra of Denmark	40	35
97	$6 Diana, Princess of Wales	3·25	2·75

1982 (12 July). *Birth of Prince William of Wales. Nos.* 95/7 *optd with T* **19**

No.	Description		
98	15 c. Type **18**	10	5
	a. Opt inverted	48·00	
99	55 c. Coat of arms of Alexandra of Denmark	40	35
100	$6 Diana, Princess of Wales	3·25	2·75

20 Naturalist Badge

21 Santa with Christmas Tree and Gifts

(Des Philatelists (1980) Ltd. Litho Questa)

1982 (18 Aug). *75th Anniv of Boy Scout Movement. T* **20** *and similar vert designs. Multicoloured.* W w **14**. *P* 14 × 13½.

No.	Description		
101	5 c. Type **20**	5	5
102	55 c. Rescuer badge	30	35
103	$2 First Aid badge	1·00	1·00

(Des Marcel Frazer (5 c.), Sinclair Herbert (55 c.), Marijka Grey ($1.10), Gary Bowrin ($3). Litho Format)

1982 (20 Oct). *Christmas. Children's Paintings. T* **21** *and similar horiz designs. Multicoloured.* W w **14** (*sideways*). *P* 14 × 13½.

No.	Description		
104	5 c. Type **21**	5	5
105	55 c. The Inn	30	35
106	$1.10, Three Kings	55	60
107	$3 Annunciation	1·40	1·50

22 Cruise Ship *Stella Oceanis* at Basseterre

23 Sir William Smith (founder)

(Des G. Drummond. Litho Format)

1983 (14 Mar). *Commonwealth Day. T* **22** *and similar horiz design. Multicoloured.* W w **14** (*sideways*). *P* 14.

No.	Description		
108	55 c. Type **22**	30	35
109	$2 R.M.S. *Queen Elizabeth 2* at Basseterre	95	1·00

(Des G. Vasarhelyi. Litho Format)

1983 (25 May). *Military Uniforms* (2*nd series*). *Vert designs as T* **14**. *Multicoloured.* W w **14**. *P* 14½.

No.	Description		
110	15 c. Light Company Private, 15th Regt of Foot, *circa* 1814	5	8
111	30 c. Battalion Company Officer, 15th Regt of Foot, *circa* 1780	15	20
112	55 c. Light Company Officer, 5th Regt of Foot, *circa* 1822	30	35
113	$2.50, Battalion Company Officer, 11th Regt of Foot, *circa* 1804	1·10	1·25

(Des J. Cooter. Litho Format)

1983 (27 July). *Centenary of the Boys' Brigade. T* **23** *and similar vert designs. Multicoloured.* W w **14**. *P* 13½.

No.	Description		
114	10 c. Type **23**	5	8
115	45 c. B.B. members on steps of Sandy Point Methodist Church	20	25
116	50 c. Brigade drummers	25	30
117	$3 Boys' Brigade badge	1·40	1·50

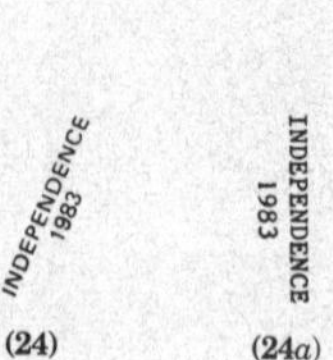

(24) **(24*a*)**

25 Montgolfier Balloon, 1783

1983 (19 Sept). *Nos.* 55, 59/63 *and* 66/70 *optd with T* **24**.
A. *No imprint date*
B. *With imprint date*

No.	Description	A		B	
118	5 c. Type **12**	5	5	10	10
	a. Opt inverted	†		60·00	—
	b. Optd with T **24*a*** (local opt)	15·00	15·00	10·00	4·00
	ba. Opt inverted (reading upwards)	55·00	—	50·00	—
119	15 c. Type **13**	1·00	1·00	10	5
	a. Opt double	†		50·00	—
120	20 c. Scaly-breasted Thrasher	†		12	8
121	25 c. Grey Kingbird	†		15	12
	a. Opt inverted	†		65·00	—
122	30 c. Green-throated Carib	20·00	20·00	20	15
123	40 c. Turnstone	†		25	20
124	55 c. Brown Pelican	50	50	30	30
	a. Opt inverted	†		50·00	—
125	$1 Lesser Antillean Bullfinch	8·00	8·00	50	50
126	$2.50, Zenaida Dove	2·25	2·25	1·25	1·25
127	$5 American Kestrel	3·00	3·00	2·25	2·50
128	$10 Antillean Crested Hummingbird	6·50	6·50	4·50	5·00
118A/28A	*Set of* 8	37·00	37·00		
118B/28B	*Set of* 11			8·75	9·00

(Des A. Theobald. Litho Format)

1983 (28 Sept). *Bicentenary of Manned Flight. T* **25** *and similar multicoloured designs.* W w **15** (*sideways on Nos.* 130/3). *P* 14.

No.	Description		
129	10 c. Type **25**	5	8
130	45 c. Sikorsky *Russian Knight* biplane (*horiz*)	20	25
131	50 c. Lockheed "Tristar" (*horiz*)	25	30
132	$2.50, Bell "XS-1" (*horiz*)	1·10	1·25
MS133	108 × 145 mm. Nos. 129/32	1·60	

26 Star over West Indian Town

27 Parrot in Tree

(Des Jennifer Toombs. Litho Format)

1983 (7 Nov). *Christmas. T* **26** *and similar horiz designs. Multicoloured.* W w **15** (*sideways*). *P* 14.

No.	Description		
134	15 c. Type **26**	8	10
135	30 c. Shepherds watching Star	15	20
136	55 c. Mary and Joseph	30	35
137	$2.50, The Nativity	1·10	1·25
MS138	130 × 130 mm. Nos. 134/7. Wmk upright	1·75	1·90

(Des Court House Studio. Litho Format)

1984 (30 Jan). *Batik Designs* (1*st series*). T **27** *and similar vert designs.* W w **15**. *P* 14 × 13½.

No.	Description		
139	45 c. multicoloured	20	25
140	50 c. multicoloured	25	30
141	$1.50, new blue, bistre-yellow & brt mag	70	75
142	$3 multicoloured	1·40	1·50

Designs:—50 c. Man under coconut tree; $1.50, Women with fruit; $3 Butterflies.

See also Nos. 169/72.

28 Cushion Star

(Des G. Drummond. Litho J.W.)

1984 (4 July). *Marine Wildlife. T* **28** *and similar multicoloured designs.* W w **15** (*sideways on* 5 c. *to* 75 c.). *P* 14.

143	5 c. Type **28**	5	5
144	10 c. Red File Shell	5	5
145	15 c. Red-lined Cleaning Shrimp	10	12
146	20 c. Bristolworm	12	15
147	25 c. Flamingo Tongue	15	20
148	30 c. Christmas Tree Worm	20	25
149	40 c. Pink-tipped Anemone	25	30
150	50 c. Smallmouth Grunt	30	35
151	60 c. Glasseye Snapper	35	40
152	75 c. Reef Squirrelfish	45	50
153	$1 Sea Fans and Flamefish (*vert*)	60	65
154	$2.50, Reef Butterflyfish (*vert*)	1·00	1·60
155	$5 Blackbar Soldierfish (*vert*)	3·00	3·25
156	$10 Cocoa Damselfish (*vert*)	6·00	6·50
143/56	*Set of* 14	11·75	12·75

29 Agriculture

(Des G. Vasarhelyi. Litho Questa)

1984 (15 Aug). *25th Anniv of 4-H Organisation. T* **29** *and similar horiz designs. Multicoloured.* W w **15** (*sideways*). *P*. 14.

157	30 c. Type **29**	20	25
158	55 c. Animal husbandry	35	40
159	$1.10, The 4-H Pledge	75	80
160	$3 On parade	2·00	2·10

30 Construction of Royal St. Kitts Hotel

(Des K. Tatem (15 c.), Tessa Wattley (30 c.), Myrna Elcock and L. Freeman ($1.10), A. Williams ($3), adapted Jennifer Toombs. Litho Format)

1984 (18 Sept). *First Anniv of Independence of St. Kitts-Nevis. T* **30** *and similar multicoloured designs.* W w **15** (*sideways on* 15, 30 *c.*). *P* 14.

161	15 c. Type **30**	12	15
162	30 c. Independence celebrations	20	25
163	$1.10, National Anthem and aerial view (*vert*)	75	80
164	$3 "Dawn of a New Day" (*vert*)	2·00	2·10

31 Opening Presents

(Des Jennifer Toombs. Litho Questa)

1984 (1 Nov). *Christmas. T* **31** *and similar horiz designs. Multicoloured.* W w **15** (*sideways*). *P* 14.

165	15 c. Type **31**	12	15
166	60 c. Singing carols	40	45
167	$1 Nativity play	70	75
168	$2 Leaving church on Christmas Day	1·40	1·50

(Des Court House Studio. Litho Format)

1985 (6 Feb). *Batik Designs* (2*nd series*). *Horiz designs as T* **27**. W w **15** (*sideways*). *P* 13½ × 14.

169	15 c. black, bright green and light green	8	10
170	40 c. black, bright greenish blue and bright new blue	25	30
171	60 c. black, orange-vermilion and vermilion	35	40
172	$3 black, lake-brown and orange-brown	1·75	1·90

Designs:—15 c. Country bus; 40 c. Donkey cart; 60 c. Rum shop, and man on bicycle; $3 S.V. *Polynesia* (tourist yacht).

OFFICIAL STAMPS

1980 (23 June). *Nos. 32/41 additionally optd with Type* o **1** *of St. Christopher, Nevis and Anguilla. A.* W w **14** (*sideways*). B. *No wmk.*.

		A		B	
O 1	15 c. Sugar cane harvesting	5	5	†	
O 2	25 c. Crafthouse (craft centre)	8	10	12	12
O 3	30 c. Cruise ship	10	12	15	15
O 4	40 c. Lobster and sea crab	12	15	50·00	50·00
O 5	45 c. Royal St. Kitts Hotel and golf course	15	20	†	
O 6	50 c. Pinney's Beach, Nevis	20	25	†	
O 7	55 c. New runway at Golden Rock	20	25	25	25
	a. Opt inverted	75·00	—	†	
O 8	$1 Cotton picking	40	40	40	40
O 9	$5 Brewery	2·00	2·25	2·25	2·50
O10	$10 Pineapples and peanuts	3·75	4·00	4·50	5·00
	a. Opt inverted	£100	—	†	
O1/10	*Set of* 10	6·50	7·00		
O2/10	*Set of* 7			55·00	55·00

OFFICIAL

(O 1)

1981 (5 Feb). *Nos. 59A/70A optd with Type* O **1**.

O11	15 c. Type **13**	5	5
O12	20 c. Scaly-breasted Thrasher	5	5
O13	25 c. Grey Kingbird	10	10
O14	30 c. Green-throated Carib	10	10
O15	40 c. Turnstone	15	15
O16	45 c. Black-faced Grassquit	20	20
O17	50 c. Cattle Egret	20	20
O18	55 c. Brown Pelican	25	25
O19	$1 Lesser Antillean Bullfinch	45	45
O20	$2.50, Zenaida Dove	1·00	1·00
O21	$5 American Kestrel	1·90	2·00
O22	$10 Antillean Crested Hummingbird	4·00	4·25
O11/22	*Set of* 12	7·50	8·00

1983 (2 Feb). *Nos. 75/80 optd with Type* O **1** (55 *c.*) *or surch also* (*others*).

O23	45 c. on $2.50, *Royal George* (New Blue)	25	25
	a. Sheetlet No. O23 × 6 and No. O24	1·40	
	b. Surch double	35·00	
	c. Albino surch	30·00	
	f. Deep ultramarine surch	50	
	fd. Surch inverted	30·00	
	fe. Surch inverted (horiz pair)	65·00	
O24	45 c. on $2.50, Prince Charles and Lady Diana Spencer (New Blue)	25	25
	b. Surch double	90·00	
	c. Albino surch	65·00	
	f. Deep ultramarine surch	75	
	fd. Surch inverted	65·00	
O25	55 c. *Saudadoes* (New Blue)	30	30
	a. Sheetlet No. O25 × 6 and No. O26	1·75	
	b. Opt double	35·00	
	c. Albino opt	30·00	
	d. Opt inverted	25·00	
	e. Opt inverted (horiz pair)	60·00	
	f. Deep ultramarine opt	60	
	fd. Opt inverted	30·00	
	fe. Opt inverted (horiz pair)	65·00	
O26	55 c. Prince Charles and Lady Diana Spencer (New Blue)	30	30
	b. Opt double	90·00	
	c. Albino opt	75·00	
	d. Opt inverted	65·00	
	f. Deep ultramarine opt	90	
	fd. Opt inverted	65·00	
O27	$1.10 on $4 *Britannia* (Blk.)	60	70
	a. Sheetlet. No. O27 × 6 and No. O28	3·50	
	b. Surch double	30·00	
	f. Deep ultramarine surch	20·00	
O28	$1.10 on $4 Prince Charles and Lady Diana Spencer (Blk.)	60	70
	b. Surch double	75·00	
	f. Deep ultramarine surch	55·00	
O23/8	*Set of* 6	2·10	2·25

Nos. O23fe, O25e and O25fe show the surcharge or overprint intended for the large design, inverted and struck across a horizontal pair of the smaller. Nos. O24fd, O26d and O26fd each show two inverted surcharges or overprints intended for a horizontal pair of the smaller design.

NEVIS

(7)

8 Nevis Lighter

1980 (23 June). *Nos. 394/406 of St. Christopher, Nevis and Anguilla optd with T* **7**.

37	5 c. Radio and T.V. Station	5	5
38	10 c. Technical college	5	5
39	12 c. T.V. assembly plant	50	50
40	15 c. Sugar cane harvesting	10	5
41	25 c. Crafthouse (craft centre)	12	10
	a. No wmk	10·00	10·00
42	30 c. Cruise ship	20	12
43	40 c. Lobster and sea crab	1·00	1·00
44	45 c. Royal St. Kitts Hotel and golf course	1·00	1·00
45	50 c. Pinney's Beach, Nevis	75	75
46	55 c. New runway at Golden Rock	25	25
47	$1 Picking cotton	1·00	1·00
	a. No wmk	30·00	30·00
48	$5 Brewery	1·75	1·75
49	$10 Pineapples and peanuts	3·50	3·50
37/49	*Set of* 13	9·50	9·50

1980 (4 Sept). *80th Birthday of Queen Elizabeth the Queen Mother. As T* **10** *of St. Kitts, but inscr* "NEVIS".

50	$2 multicoloured	75	80

No. 50 was printed in sheets including two *se-tenant* stamp-size labels.

(Des Jennifer Toombs. Litho Questa)

1980 (8 Oct). *Boats. T* **8** *and similar multicoloured designs.* W w **14** (*sideways on* 5, 30 *and* 55 *c.*). *P* 14.

51	5 c. Type **8**	5	5
52	30 c. Local fishing boat	25	25
53	55 c. *Caona*	35	35
54	$3 Windjammer's S.V. *Polynesia* (39 × 53 *mm*)	1·00	1·60
	a. Perf 12 (booklets)	1·00	1·60
	ab. Booklet pane of 3	3·00	

No. 54a comes from $12.30 stamp booklets containing No. 53 × 6 and one pane as No. 54ab. In this pane each stamp is surrounded by white margins, the pane being divided in three by vertical roulettes.

9 Virgin and Child

(Des Jennifer Toombs. Litho Format)

1980 (20 Nov). *Christmas. T* **9** *and similar vert designs. Multicoloured.* W w **14**. *P* 14.

55	5 c. Type **9**	5	5
56	30 c. Angel	12	15
57	$2.50, The Three Wise Men	95	1·00

10 Charlestown Pier

11 New River Mill

(Des Jennifer Toombs. Litho Questa)

1981 (5 Feb)–**82**. *Horiz designs as T* **10** (5, 10 *c.*) *or T* **11** (15 *c. to* $10). *Multicoloured.* W w **14**. *P* 14 × 13½ (5, 10 *c.*) *or* 14 (*others*).
A. *No imprint date*
B. *With imprint date* ("1982") *at foot of design* (9.6.82.)

		A		B	
58	5 c. Type **10**	5	5	5	5
59	10 c. Court House and Library	5	5	5	5
60	15 c. Type **11**	8	5	8	5
61	20 c. Nelson Museum	10	10	10	10
62	25 c. St. James' Parish Church	12	12	12	12
63	30 c. Nevis Lane	15	15	15	15
64	40 c. Zetland Plantation	20	20	20	20
65	45 c. Nisbet Plantation	20	25	20	25
66	50 c. Pinney's Beach	25	25	25	25
67	55 c. Eva Wilkin's Studio	25	30	25	30
68	$1 Nevis at dawn	50	45	50	45
69	$2.50, Ruins of Fort Charles	1·25	1·10	1·25	1·10
70	$5 Old Bath House	2·50	2·25	2·50	2·25
71	$10 Beach at Nisbet's	5·00	4·50	5·00	4·50
58/71	*Set of* 14	9·50	9·00	9·50	9·00

(Des D. Shults. Litho Questa)

1981 (23 June–14 Dec). *Royal Wedding. Horiz designs as T* **26/27** *of Kiribati. Multicoloured.* (*a*) W w **14**. *P* 14.

72	55 c. *Royal Caroline*	25	30
	a. Sheetlet. No. 72 × 6 and No. 73	2·00	
73	55 c. Prince Charles and Lady Diana Spencer	50	50
74	$2 *Royal Sovereign*	75	80
	a. Sheetlet No. 74 × 6 and No. 75	6·00	

75 $2 As No. 73 . . 1·50 1·50
76 $5 *Britannia* . . 1·90 2·00
a. Sheetlet. No. 76 × 6 and No. 77 . . 14·00
77 $5 As No. 73 . . 3·00 3·00
MS78 120 × 109 mm. $4.50, As No. 73, Wmk sideways. P 12 (14 Dec). . . 4·00 2·00

(*b*) *Booklet stamps. No wmk. P* 12 (19 Nov).
79 55 c. As No. 72 . . 25 30
a. Booklet pane. No. 79 × 4 . . 1·00
80 $2 As No. 75 . . 1·00 1·25
a. Booklet pane. No. 80 × 2 . . 2·00

Nos. 72/7 were printed in sheetlets of seven stamps of the same face value, each containing six of the "Royal Yacht" design and one of the larger design showing Prince Charles and Lady Diana.

Nos. 79/80 come from $8.40 stamp booklets.

12 Zebra

13 Caroline of Brunswick, Princess of Wales, 1793

(Des Jennifer Toombs. Litho Questa)

1982 (16 Feb). *Butterflies* (1st *series*). *T* **12** *and similar horiz designs. Multicoloured. W* w **14** (*sideways*). *P* 14.
81 5 c. Type **12** . . 5 5
82 30 c. Malachite . . 15 15
83 55 c. Southern Dagger Tail . . 25 25
84 $2 Large Orange Sulphur . . 90 90
See also Nos. 105/8.

(Des D. Shults and J. Cooter. Litho Format)

1982 (22 June). *21st Birthday of Princess of Wales. T* **13** *and similar vert designs. Multicoloured. W* w **14**. *P* 13½ × 14.
85 30 c. Type **13** . . 40 20
86 55 c. Coat of arms of Caroline of Brunswick . . 55 35
87 $5 Diana, Princess of Wales . . 2·25 1·90

1982 (12 July). *Birth of Prince William of Wales. Nos.* 85/7 *optd with T* **19** *of St. Kitts.*
88 30 c. Type **13** . . 40 20
89 55 c. Coat of arms of Caroline of Brunswick . . 55 35
90 $5 Diana, Princess of Wales . . 2·25 1·90

14 Cyclist

(Des Philatelists (1980) Ltd. Litho Questa)

1982 (18 Aug). *75th Anniv of Boy Scout Movement. T* **14** *and similar horiz designs. Multicoloured. W* w **14** (*sideways*). *P* 13½ × 14.
91 5 c. Type **14** . . 5 5
92 30 c. Athlete . . 15 15
93 $2.50, Camp cook . . 1·25 1·25

15 Santa Claus

16 Tube Sponge

(Des Eugene Seabrookes (15 c.), Kharenzabeth Glasgow (30 c.), Davia Grant (£1.50), Leonard Huggins ($2.50); adapted Jennifer Toombs. Litho Format)

1982 (25 Oct). *Christmas. Children's Paintings. T* **15** *and similar multicoloured designs. W* w **14** (*sideways on* $1.50 *and* $2.50). *P* 13½ × 14 (15 *c*., 30 *c*.) *or* 14 × 13½ (*others*).
94 15 c. Type **15** . . 5 5
95 30 c. Carollers . . 15 15
96 $1.50, Decorated house and local band (*horiz*) 70 70
97 $2.50, Adoration of the Shepherds (*horiz*) . . 1·25 1·25

(Des G. Drummond. Litho Format)

1983 (12 Jan). *Corals. T* **16** *and similar vert designs. Multicoloured. W* w **14**. *P* 14.
98 15 c. Type **16** . . 5 8
99 30 c. Stinging coral . . 15 20
100 55 c. Flower coral . . 30 30
101 $3 Sea Rod and Red Fire Sponge . . 1·40 1·50
MS102 82 × 115 mm. Nos. 98/101 . . 1·75 2·00

17 H.M.S. *Boreas* off Nevis

(Des G. Drummond. Litho Format)

1983 (14 Mar). *Commonwealth Day. T* **17** *and similar horiz design. Multicoloured. W* w **14** (*sideways*). *P* 14.
103 55 c. Type **17** . . 25 30
104 $2 Capt. Horatio Nelson and H.M.S. *Boreas* at anchor . . 95 1·00

(Des Jennifer Toombs. Litho Format)

1983 (8 June). *Butterflies* (2*nd series*). *Multicoloured designs as T* **12**. *W* w **14** (*sideways on* 30 *c. and* $2). *P* 14.
105 30 c. Tropical Chequered Skipper . . 20 20
106 55 c. Caribbean Buckeye (*vert*) . . 25 30
107 $1.10, Common Long-tailed Skipper (*vert*) . . 50 55
108 $2 The "Mimic" . . 95 1·00

INDEPENDENCE 1983 (**18**)

INDEPENDENCE 1983 (**18*a***)

19 Montgolfier Balloon, 1783

1983 (19 Sept). *Nos.* 58 *and* 60/71 *optd with T* **18**.
A. *No imprint date*
B. *With imprint date.*

		A		B	
109	5 c. Type **10**	†		5	5
	a. Vert pair, lower stamp without opt.				
	b. Optd with T **18*a*** (local opt)	18·00	20·00	10·00	4·00
	ba. Opt T **18*a*** inverted	†		65·00	—
110	15 c. Type **11**	35·00	35·00	5	5
111	20 c. Nelson Museum	12·00	12·00	8	10
112	25 c. St. James' Parish Church	12·00	12·00	10	12
113	30 c. Nevis Lane	2·00	2·00	12	15
	a. Opt inverted	†		55·00	—
114	40 c. Zetland Plantation	1·00	1·00	15	20
115	45 c. Nisbet Plantation	†		20	25
116	50 c. Pinney's Beach	†		20	25
117	55 c. Eva Wilkin's Studio	1·00	1·00	25	30
	a. Opt double	†		55·00	—
118	$1 Nevis at dawn	1·50	1·50	40	45
119	$2.50, Ruins of Fort Charles	2·00	2·00	1·00	1·10
120	$5 Old Bath House	3·50	3·50	2·10	2·25
121	$10 Beach at Nisbet's	7·00	7·00	4·25	4·50
110A/121A	*Set of* 11	85·00	85·00		
109B/121B	*Set of* 13			8·00	9·00

(Des A. Theobald. Litho Format)

1983 (28 Sept). *Bicentenary of Manned Flight. T* **19** *and similar multicoloured designs. W* w **15** (*sideways on* 45 *c. to* $2.50). *P* 14.
122 10 c. Type **19** . . 5 8
123 45 c. Sikorsky "S-38", flying boat (*horiz*) 20 25
124 50 c. Beechcraft "Twin Bonanza" (*horiz*) 25 30
125 $2.50, B. Ae. "Sea Harrier" (*horiz*) . . 1·10 1·25
MS126 118 × 145 mm. Nos. 109/12. Wmk sideways 1·60 1·75

20 Mary praying over Holy Child

(Des Jennifer Toombs. Litho Format)

1983 (7 Nov). *Christmas. T* **20** *and similar horiz designs. Multicoloured. W* w **15** (*sideways*). *P* 14.
127 5 c. Type **20** . . 5 8
128 30 c. Shepherds with flock . . 15 20
129 55 c. Three Angels . . 30 35
130 $3 Boy with two girls . . 1·75 1·90
MS131 135 × 149 mm. Nos. 127/30 . . 2·00 2·10

21 County of Oxford (1945)

22 Boer War

(Des J. W. Litho Format)

1983 (10 Nov). *Leaders of the World. Railway Locomotives* (1*st series*). *T* **21** *and similar horiz designs, the first in each pair showing technical drawings and the second the locomotive at work. P* 12½.
132 55 c. multicoloured . . 25 30
a. Vert pair. Nos. 132/3 . . 50 60
133 55 c. multicoloured . . 25 30
134 $1 bright crimson, new blue and black . . 45 50
a. Vert pair. Nos. 134/5 . . 90 1·00
135 $1 multicoloured . . 45 50
136 $1 magenta, new blue and black . . 45 50
a. Vert pair. Nos. 136/7 . . 90 1·00
137 $1 multicoloured . . 45 50
138 $1 bright crimson, black and greenish yellow 45 50
a. Vert pair. Nos. 138/9 . . 90 1·00
139 $1 multicoloured . . 45 50
140 $1 multicoloured . . 45 50
a. Vert pair. Nos. 140/1 . . 90 1·00
141 $1 multicoloured . . 45 50
142 $1 greenish yellow, black and new blue . . 45 50
a. Vert pair. Nos. 142/3 . . 90 1·00
143 $1 multicoloured . . 45 50
144 $1 greenish yellow, black & brt magenta . . 45 50
a. Vert pair. Nos. 144/5 . . 90 1·00
145 $1 multicoloured . . 45 50
146 $1 multicoloured . . 45 50
a. Vert pair. Nos. 146/7 . . 90 1·00
147 $1 multicoloured . . 45 50
132/47 . . *Set of* 16 6·25 6·75

Designs:—Nos. 132/3, *County of Oxford* (1945), 134/5, *Evening Star* (1960); 136/7, Stanier "Class 5" (1934); 138/9, *Pendennis Castle* (1924); 140/1, *Winston Churchill* (1946); 142/3, *Mallard* (1935); 144/5, *Britannia* (1951); 146/7, *King George V* (1927).

Nos. 132/3, 134/5, 136/7, 138/9, 140/1, 142/3, 144/5 and 146/7 were printed together, *se-tenant* in vertical pairs throughout the sheets.

See also Nos. 214/26.

(Des Court House Studio. Litho Format)

1984 (11 Apr). *Leaders of the World. British Monarchs* (1*st series*). *T* **22** *and similar vert designs. Multicoloured. P* 12½.
148 5 c. Type **22** . . 5 5
a. Horiz pair. Nos. 148/9 . . 10 12
149 5 c. Queen Victoria . . 5 5
150 50 c. Queen Victoria at Osborne House . . 35 40
a. Horiz pair. Nos. 150/1 . . 70 80
151 50 c. Osborne House . . 35 40
152 60 c. Battle of Dettingen . . 40 45
a. Horiz pair. Nos. 152/3 . . 80 90
153 60 c. George II . . 40 45
154 75 c. George II at the Bank of England . . 50 55
a. Horiz pair. Nos. 154/5 . . 1·00 1·10
155 75 c. Bank of England . . 50 55
156 $1 Coat of Arms of George II . . 70 75
a. Horiz pair. Nos. 156/7 . . 1·40 1·50
157 $1 George II (*different*) . . 70 75
158 $3 Coat of Arms of Queen Victoria . . 2·00 2·10
a. Horiz pair. Nos. 158/9 . . 4·00 4·25
159 $3 Queen Victoria (*different*) . . 2·00 2·10
148/59 . . *Set of* 12 7·25 8·00

Nos. 148/9, 150/1, 152/3, 154/5, 156/7 and 158/9 were printed together, *se-tenant* in horizontal pairs throughout the sheet.

See also Nos. 231/6.

23 Golden Rock Inn

(Des Jennifer Toombs. Litho J.W.)

1984 (16 May). *Tourism.* (1*st series*). *T* **23** *and similar horiz designs. Multicoloured. W* w **15** (*sideways*). *P* 14.
160 55 c. Type **23** . . 40 45
161 55 c. Rest Haven Inn . . 40 45
162 55 c. Cliffdwellers Hotel . . 40 45
163 55 c. Pinney's Beach Hotel . . 40 45
See also Nos. 245/8.

24 Early Seal of Colony

(Des G. Drummond. Litho Format)

1984 (8 June). *W* w **15** (*sideways*). *P* 14.
164 **24** $15 dull scarlet . . 9·00 9·50

25 Cadillac

(Des J. W. Litho Format)

1984 (25 July). *Leaders of the World. Automobiles* (1*st series*). *T* **25** *and similar horiz designs, the first in each pair showing technical drawings and the second paintings. P* 12½.
165 1 c. greenish yellow, black and magenta . . 5 5
a. Vert pair. Nos. 165/6 . . 5 5

166 1 c. multicoloured 5 5
167 5 c. new blue, magenta and black 5 5
a. Vert pair. Nos. 167/8 . . . . . . 8 10
168 5 c. multicoloured 5 5
169 15 c. multicoloured 12 15
a. Vert pair. Nos. 169/70 . . . . . . 25 30
170 15 c. multicoloured 12 15
171 35 c. magenta, greenish yellow and black . . 25 30
a. Vert pair. Nos. 171/2 . . . . . . 50 60
172 35 c. multicoloured 25 30
173 45 c. new blue, magenta and black 30 35
a. Vert pair. Nos. 173/4 . . . . . . 60 70
174 45 c. multicoloured 30 35
175 55 c. multicoloured 40 45
a. Vert pair. Nos. 175/6 . . . . . . 80 90
176 55 c. multicoloured 40 45
177 $2.50, magenta, black and greenish yellow 1·75 1·90
a. Vert pair. Nos. 177/8 . . . . . . 3·50 3·75
178 $2.50, multicoloured . . . . . . 1·75 1·90
179 $3 new blue, greenish yellow and black . . 2·00 2·10
a. Vert pair. Nos. 179/80 . . . . . . 4·00 4·25
180 $3 multicoloured . . . . . . 2·00 2·10
165/80 . . . . . . *Set of* 16 8·75 9·50

Designs:—Nos. 165/6, Cadillac "V16 Fleetwood Convertible" (1932); 167/8, Packard "Twin Six Touring Car" (1916); 169/70, Daimler, "2 Cylinder" (1886); 171/2, Porsche "911 S Targa" (1970); 173/4, Benz "Three Wheeler" (1885); 175/6, M.G. "TC" (1947); 177/8, Cobra "Roadster 289" (1966), 179/80, Aston Martin "DB6 Hardtop" (1966).

Nos. 165/6, 167/8, 169/70, 171/2, 173/4, 175/6, 177/8 and 179/80 were printed together, *se-tenant* in vertical pairs throughout the sheet.

See also Nos. 203/10.

26 Carpentry

27 Yellow Bell

(Des Jennifer Toombs. Litho Questa)

1984 (1 Aug). *10th Anniv of Culturama Celebrations.* ***T* 26** *and similar horiz designs. Multicoloured.* **W w 15** (*sideways*). *P* 14.
181 30 c. Type **26** 20 25
182 55 c. Grass mat and basket-making 40 45
183 $1 Pottery-firing 70 75
184 $3 Culturama Queen and dancers . . . . 2·00 2·10

(Des Jennifer Toombs. Litho Format)

1984 (8 Aug). *Flowers.* ***T* 27** *and similar vert designs. Multicoloured.* **W w 15.** *P* 14.
185 5 c. Type **27** 5 5
186 10 c. Plumbago 5 8
187 15 c. Flamboyant 10 12
188 20 c. Eyelash Orchid 12 15
189 30 c. *Bougainvillea* 20 25
190 40 c. *Hibiscus sp.* 25 30
191 50 c. Night-blooming Cereus 30 35
192 55 c. Yellow Mahoe 35 40
193 60 c. Spider-lily 35 40
194 75 c. Scarlet Cordia 45 50
195 $1 Shell-ginger 60 65
196 $3 Blue Petrea . . . . 1·75 1·90
197 $5 Coral Hibiscus . . . . 3·00 3·25
198 $10 Passion Flower . . . . 6·00 6·50
185/98 . . . . . . *Set of* 14 12·25 13·25

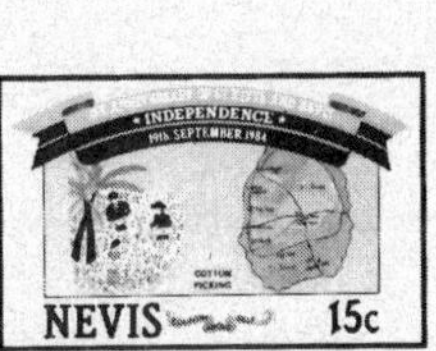

28 Cotton-picking and Map

29 C.P. Mead

(Des A. Grant (15 c.), Tracy Watkins (55 c.), C. Manners ($1.10), D. Grant ($3), adapted Court House Advertising. Litho Format)

1984 (18 Sept). *First Anniv of Independence of St. Kitts-Nevis.* ***T* 28** *and similar horiz designs. Multicoloured.* **W w 15** (*sideways*). *P* 14.
199 15 c. Type **28** 12 15
200 55 c. Alexander Hamilton's birthplace . . 40 45
201 $1.10, Local agricultural produce 80 85
202 $3 Nevis Peak and Pinneys Beach . . . . 2·00 2·10

(Des J. W. Litho Format)

1984 (23 Oct). *Leaders of the World. Automobiles (2nd series). Horiz designs as* ***T* 25**, *the first in each pair showing technical drawings and the second paintings. P* 12½.
203 5 c. black, pale new blue and yellow-brown 5 5
a. Vert pair. Nos. 203/4 . . . . . . 8 10
204 5 c. multicoloured 5 5
205 30 c. black, pale turquoise-green & lake-brn . . 20 25
a. Vert pair. Nos. 205/6 . . . . . . 40 45
206 30 c. multicoloured 20 25
207 50 c. black, pale drab and red-brown 35 40
a. Vert pair. Nos. 207/8 . . . . . . 70 80
208 50 c. multicoloured 35 40
209 $3 black, grey-brown and dull green . . 2·00 2·10
a. Vert pair. Nos. 209/10 . . . . . . 4·00 4·25
210 $3 multicoloured . . . . 2·00 2·10
203/10 . . . . . . *Set of* 8 4·50 5·00

Designs:—Nos. 203/4, Lagonda "Speed Model" touring car (1929); 205/6, Jaguar "E-Type" 4.2 litre (1967); 207/8, Volkswagen "Beetle" (1947); 209/10, Pierce Arrow "V12" (1932).

Nos. 203/10 were issued in a similar sheet format to Nos. 165/80.

(Des Court House Studio. Litho Format)

1984 (23 Oct). *Leaders of the World. Cricketers (1st series).* ***T* 29** *and similar vert designs, the first in each pair showing a head portrait and the second the cricketer in action. P* 12½.
211 5 c. multicoloured 5 5
a. Horiz pair. Nos. 211/12 . . . . . . 8 10
212 5 c. multicoloured 5 5
213 25 c. multicoloured 15 20
a. Horiz pair. Nos. 213/14 . . . . . . 30 40
214 25 c. multicoloured 15 20
215 55 c. multicoloured 40 45
a. Horiz pair. Nos. 215/16 . . . . . . 80 90
216 55 c. multicoloured 40 45
217 $2.50, multicoloured . . . . . . 1·75 1·90
a. Horiz pair. Nos. 217/18 . . . . . . 3·00 3·75
218 $2.50, multicoloured . . . . . . 1·75 1·40
211/18 . . . . . . *Set of* 8 4·25 4·50

Designs:—Nos. 211/12, C. P. Mead; 213/14, J. B. Statham; 215/16, Sir Learie Constantine; 217/18, Sir Leonard Hutton.

Nos. 211/12, 213/14, 215/16 and 217/18 were printed together, *se-tenant*, in horizontal pairs throughout the sheets.

See also Nos. 237/44.

(Des J. W. Litho Format)

1984 (29 Oct). *Leaders of the World. Railway Locomotives (2nd series). Horiz designs as* ***T* 21** *the first in each pair showing technical drawings and the second the locomotive at work. P* 12½.
219 5 c. multicoloured 5 5
a. Vert pair. Nos. 219/20 . . . . . . 8 10
220 5 c. multicoloured 5 5
221 10 c. multicoloured 8 10
a. Vert pair. Nos. 221/2 . . . . . . 15 20
222 10 c. multicoloured 8 10
223 60 c. multicoloured 40 45
a. Vert pair. Nos. 223/4 . . . . . . 80 90
224 60 c. multicoloured 40 45
225 $2.50, multicoloured . . . . . . 1·75 1·90
a. Vert pair. Nos. 225/6 . . . . . . 3·50 3·75
226 $2.50, multicoloured . . . . . . 1·75 1·90
219/26 . . . . . . *Set of* 8 4·00 4·00

Designs:—Nos. 219/20, J.N.R. Class EF81 (1968); 221/2, P.O. Class 5500 (1927); 223/4, S.N.C.F. Class 240P (1940); 225/6, J.N.R. *Shin-Kansen* (1964).

Nos. 219/26 were issued in a similar format to Nos. 132/47.

30 Fifer and Drummer from Honeybees Band

(Des Jennifer Toombs. Litho Questa)

1984 (2 Nov). *Christmas. Local Music.* ***T* 30** *and similar horiz designs. Multicoloured.* **W w 15** (*sideways*). *P* 14.
227 15 c. Type **30** 12 15
228 40 c. Guitar and "barhow" players from Canary Birds Band 30 35
229 60 c. Shell All Stars steel band 40 45
230 $3 Organ and choir, St. John's Church, Fig Tree . . . . 2·00 2·10

(Des Court House Studio. Litho Format)

1984 (20 Nov). *Leaders of the World. British Monarchs (2nd series). Vert designs as* ***T* 22.** *Multicoloured. P* 12½.
231 5 c. King John and Magna Carta 5 8
a. Horiz pair. Nos. 231/2 . . . . . . 8 12
232 5 c. Barons and King John 5 8
233 55 c. King John 35 40
a. Horiz pair Nos. 233/4 . . . . . . 70 80
234 55 c. Newark Castle 35 40
235 $2 Coat of arms . . . . 1·40 1·50
a. Horiz pair. Nos. 235/6 . . . . . . 2·75 3·00
236 $2 King John (*different*) . . . . . . 1·40 1·50
231/6 . . . . . . *Set of* 6 3·25 3·50

Nos. 231/6 were issued in a similar sheet format to Nos. 148/59.

(Des Court House Studio. Litho Format)

1984 (20 Nov). *Leaders of the World. Cricketers (2nd series). Vert designs as* ***T* 29**, *the first in each pair listed showing a head portrait and the second the cricketer in action. P* 12½.
237 5 c. multicoloured 5 8
a. Horiz pair. Nos. 237/8 . . . . . . 8 12
238 5 c. multicoloured 5 8
239 15 c. multicoloured 12 15
a. Horiz pair. Nos. 239/40 . . . . . . 25 30
240 15 c. multicoloured 12 15
241 55 c. multicoloured 35 40
a. Horiz pair. Nos. 241/2 . . . . . . 70 80
242 55 c. multicoloured 35 40
243 $2,50, multicoloured . . . . . . 1·75 1·90
a. Horiz pair. Nos. 243/4 . . . . . . 3·50 3·75
244 $2.50, multicoloured . . . . . . 1·75 1·90
237/44 . . . . . . *Set of* 8 4·00 4·50

Designs:—Nos. 237/8, J. D. Love; 239/40, S. J. Dennis; 241/2, B. W. Luckhurst; 243/4, B. L. D'Oliveira.

Nos. 237/44 were issued in a similar sheet format to Nos. 211/18.

(Des Jennifer Toombs. Litho Format)

1985 (12 Feb). *Tourism (2nd series). Horiz designs as* ***T* 23.** *Multicoloured.* **W w 15** (*sideways*). *P* 14.
245 $1.20, Croney's Old Manor Hotel 75 80
246 $1.20, Montpelier Plantation Inn 75 80
247 $1.20, Nisbet's Plantation Inn 75 80
248 $1.20, Zetland Plantation Inn 75 80

OFFICIAL STAMPS

1980 (30 July). *Nos. 40/9 additionally optd with Type* **O 1** *of St. Christopher, Nevis and Anguilla.*
O 1 15 c. Sugar cane havesting 5 5
O 2 25 c. Crafthouse (craft centre) 8 10
a. Optd on No. 41a . . . . 35·00 35·00
O 3 30 c. Cruise ship 10 12
O 4 40 c. Lobster and sea crab 12 15
O 5 45 c. Royal St. Kitts Hotel and golf course . . 20 25
a. Opt inverted . . . . 75·00
O 6 50 c. Pinney's Beach, Nevis 20 25
a. Opt inverted £100
O 7 55 c. New runway at Golden Rock 20 25
a. Opt double . . . . 70·00
O 8 $1 Picking cotton 40 45
O 9 $5 Brewery . . . . 2·40 2·50
a. Opt inverted £110
O10 $10 Pineapples and peanuts . . . . 4·75 5·00
O1/10 . . . . . . *Set of* 10 8·50 9·00

1981 (Feb). *Nos. 60A/71A optd with Type* **O 1** *of St. Kitts.*
O11 15 c. New River Mill 5 5
O12 20 c. Nelson Museum 8 10
O13 25 c. St. James' Parish Church 10 12
O14 30 c. Nevis Lane 12 15
O15 40 c. Zetland Plantation 15 20
O16 45 c. Nisbet Plantation 20 25
O17 50 c. Pinney's Beach 20 25
O18 55 c. Eva Wilkin's Studio 25 30
O19 $1 Nevis at dawn 40 45
O20 $2.50, Ruins of Fort Charles . . . . 1·00 1·10
O21 $5 Old Bath House . . . . 2·10 2·75
O22 $10 Beach at Nisbet's . . . . . . 4·25 4·50
O11/22 . . . . . . *Set of* 12 8·00 9·00

1983 (2 Feb). *Nos. 72/7 optd with Type* **O 1** *of St. Kitts (55 c.) or surch also (others).*
O23 45 c. on $2 *Royal Sovereign* (New Blue) . . 20 25
a. Sheetlet. No. O23 × 6 and No. O24 . . 1·40
b. Surch inverted . . . . 28·00
c. Surch inverted (horiz pair) . . . . 70·00
d. Albino surch . . . . 28·00
da. Albino surch inverted . . . .
e. Horiz pair, one without surch . .
f. Deep ultramarine surch 40 50
fb. Surch inverted . . . . 30·00
fc. Surch inverted (horiz pair) . . . . 70·00
O24 45 c. on $2 Prince Charles and Lady Diana Spencer (New Blue) 20 25
b. Surch inverted . . . . 65·00
d. Albino surch . . . . 55·00
f. Deep ultramarine surch 40 50
fb. Surch inverted . . . . 75·00
O25 55 c. *Royal Caroline* (New Blue) 20 25
a. Sheetlet. No. O25 × 6 and No. O26 . . 1·40
d. Albino opt . . . . 25·00
db. Albino opt inverted . . . . . . 25·00
dc. Albino opt inverted (horiz pair) . . 35·00
f. Deep ultramarine opt 75
fb. Opt inverted . . . . 28·00
fc. Opt inverted (horiz pair) . . . . 60·00
ff. Opt double . . . . 35·00
O26 55 c. Prince Charles and Lady Diana Spencer (New Blue) 25 25
d. Albino opt . . . . 50·00
db. Albino opt inverted . . . . . . 55·00
f. Deep ultramarine opt . . . . . . 1·00
fb. Opt inverted . . . . 60·00
ff. Opt double . . . . 70·00
O27 $1.10 on $5 *Britannia* (Blk.) 45 50
a. Sheetlet. No. O27 × 6 and No. O28 . . 3·00
d. Albino surch . . . . 30·00
f. deep ultramarine surch . . . . 28·00
fb. Surch inverted . . . . 35·00
fc. Surch inverted (horiz pair) . . . . 70·00
O28 $1.10 on $5 Prince Charles and Lady Diana Spencer (Blk.) 55 60
d. Albino surch . . . . 55·00
f. Deep ultramarine surch . . . . 70·00
fb. Surch inverted . . . . 85·00
O23/28 . . . . . . *Set of* 6 1·75 1·75

Nos. O23c, O23fc, O25dc, O25fc and O27fc show the surcharge or overprint intended for the large design inverted and struck across a horizontal pair of the smaller. Nos. O24b, O24fb, O26db, O26fb and O28fb each show two inverted surcharges intended for a horizontal pair of the smaller design.

St. Lucia

Although a branch office of the British G.P.O. was not opened at Castries, the island capital, until 1844 some form of postal arrangements for overseas mails existed from at least 1841 when the issue of a Ship Letter handstamp is recorded.

The stamps of Great Britain were used on the island from May 1858 until the end of April 1860 when the local authorities assumed responsibility for the postal service. No. CC1 was again used on overseas mail between 1 May and the introduction of St. Lucia stamps in December 1860.

For illustrations of the handstamp and postmark types see BRITISH POST OFFICES ABROAD notes, following GREAT BRITAIN.

CASTRIES

CROWN-CIRCLE HANDSTAMPS

CC1 CC1 ST. LUCIA (R.) (1.5.1844) *Price on cover* £900

No. CC1 was utilised, struck in black, during a shortage of 1d. stamps in 1904. *Price on cover* £275.

Stamps of GREAT BRITAIN *cancelled* "A 11" *as Type* **2**.

1858 *to* **1860**

No.	Description	Price
Z1	1d. rose-red (1857), *perf* 14	£1400
Z2	2d. blue (1855)	
Z3	4d. rose (1857)	£325
Z4	6d. lilac (1856)	£200
Z5	1s. green (1856)	£750

PRICES FOR STAMPS ON COVER TO 1945	
Nos. 1/8	*from* × 5
Nos. 9/10	†
Nos. 11/24	*from* × 6
Nos. 25/30	*from* × 3
Nos. 31/6	*from* × 2
Nos. 39/42	*from* × 3
Nos. 43/50	*from* × 5
Nos. 51/2	—
Nos. 53/62	*from* × 3
No. 63	*from* × 4
Nos. 64/75	*from* × 3
Nos. 76/7	—
Nos. 78/88	*from* × 3
No. 89	*from* × 4
No. 90	*from* × 20
Nos. 91/112	*from* × 3
Nos. 113/24	*from* × 2
Nos. 125/7	*from* × 10
Nos. 128/41	*from* × 2
Nos. D1/2	*from* × 20
Nos. D3/6	*from* × 30
Nos. F1/28	—

CROWN COLONY

1

Half
penny

(2)

(Recess P.B.)

1860 (18 Dec). *Wmk Small Star, W* w **2**. *P* 14 *to* 16.

No.	Type	Description	Unused	Used
1	1	(1d.) rose-red	£120	£120
		a. Imperf vert (horiz pair)		
		b. Double impression	£1300	
2		(4d.) blue	£400	£325
		a. Deep blue		
		b. Imperf vert (horiz pair)		
3		(6d.) green	£475	£425
		a. Imperf vert (horiz pair)		
		b. Deep green	£500	£425

(Recess D.L.R.)

1863. *Wmk Crown CC. P* 12½.

No.	Type	Description	Unused	Used
5	1	(1d.) lake	55·00	80·00
		b. Brownish lake	75·00	75·00
7		(4d.) indigo	£175	£150
8		(6d.) emerald-green	£300	£325
		Prepared for use, but not issued. Surch as T **2**		
9	1	½d. on (6d.) emerald-green	40·00	
10		6d. on (4d.) indigo	£1400	

1864 (19 Nov)–**76**. *Wmk Crown CC.* (*a*) *P* 12½.

No.	Type	Description	Unused	Used
11	1	(1d.) black	18·00	17·00
		a. Intense black	17·00	16·00
12		(4d.) yellow	£120	40·00
		b. Lemon-yellow	£2000	
		c. Chrome-yellow	£130	40·00
		d. Olive-yellow	£250	70·00
13		(6d.) violet	70·00	38·00
		a. Mauve	£150	38·00
		b. Deep lilac	90·00	40·00
14		(1s.) brown-orange	£275	40·00
		b. Orange	£200	40·00
		c. Pale orange	£150	40·00
		ca. Imperf between (horiz pair)		
		(*b*) *P* 14		
15	1	(1d.) black (6.76)	17·00	17·00
		a. Imperf between (horiz pair)		
16		(4d.) yellow (6.76)	60·00	32·00
		a. Olive-yellow	£130	80·00
17		(6d.) mauve (6.76)	60·00	40·00
		a. Pale lilac	60·00	32·00
		b. Violet	£170	60·00
18		(1s.) orange (10.76)	£225	40·00
		a. Deep orange	£180	35·00

HALFPENNY

(3)

2½ PENCE

(4)

5

1881 (Sept). *Surch with T* **3** *or* **4**. *Wmk Crown CC. P* 14

No.	Type	Description	Unused	Used
23	1	½d. green	35·00	40·00
24		2½d. brown-red	21·00	21·00

The 1d. black is known surcharged "1d." in violet ink by hand, but there is no evidence that this was done officially.

1882–84. *Surch as T* **3**. *Wmk Crown CA.* (*a*) *P* 14

No.	Type	Description	Unused	Used
25	1	½d. green (1882)	20·00	22·00
26		1d. black (C.)	20·00	20·00
		a. Bisected (on cover)	†	—
27		4d. yellow	£170	40·00
28		6d. violet	35·00	35·00
29		1s. orange	£225	£160
		(*b*) *P* 12		
30	1	4d. yellow	£475	35·00

Deep blue stamps, wmk Crown CA, perf 14 or 12, are fiscals from which the overprint "THREE PENCE—REVENUE", or "REVENUE", has been fraudulently removed.

(Typo D.L.R.)

1883 (6 July)–**86**. *Wmk Crown CA. Die* 1. *P* 14.

No.	Type	Description	Unused	Used
31	5	½d. dull green	3·25	3·25
32		1d. carmine-rose	23·00	15·00
33		2½d. blue	13·00	2·25
34		4d. brown (1885)	18·00	2·50
35		6d. lilac (1886)	£300	£275
36		1s. orange-brown (1885)	£500	£175

We no longer list imperforate examples of stamps appearing between 1863 and 1887 as there is no evidence that these were ever issued.

1886–87. *Wmk Crown CA. Die* I. *P* 14.

No.	Type	Description	Unused	Used
39	5	1d. dull mauve	3·50	7·50
40		3d. dull mauve and green	32·00	19·00
41		6d. dull mauve and blue (1887)	9·00	14·00
42		1s. dull mauve and red (1887)	38·00	25·00
39/42 Optd "Specimen"		*Set of* 4	£120	

1891–98. *Wmk Crown CA. Die* II. *P* 14.

No.	Type	Description	Unused	Used
43	5	½d. dull green	50	50
44		1d. dull mauve	90	30
45		2d. ultramarine and orange (1898)	2·25	2·75
46		2½d. ultramarine	3·00	45
47		3d. dull mauve and green	4·50	5·50
48		4d. brown	3·50	4·00
49		6d. dull mauve and blue	8·50	11·00
50		1s. dull mauve and red	4·50	8·50
51		5s. dull mauve and orange	32·00	48·00
52		10s. dull mauve and black	65·00	75·00
43/52		*Set of* 10	£110	£140
45, 51, 52 Optd "Specimen"		*Set of* 3	£150	

For description and illustration of differences between Die I and Die II see Introduction.

ONE
HALF
PENNY

(6)

$\frac{1}{2}d$

(7)

ONE
PENNY

(8)

N

Normal "N"

N

Thick "N"

Three types of T **8**

I. All letters "N" normal.
II. Thick diagonal stroke in first "N".
III. Thick diagonal stroke in second "N".

1891–92 (*a*) *Stamps of Die* I *surch.*

No.	Type	Description	Unused	Used
53	6	½d. on 3d. dull mauve and green	50·00	50·00
		a. Small "A" in "HALF"	80·00	80·00
		b. Small "O" in "ONE"	80·00	80·00
54	7	½d. on half 6d. dull mauve and blue	15·00	15·00
		a. No fraction bar	£140	£140
		b. Surch sideways	£325	
		c. Surch double	£350	£400
		d. "2" in fraction omitted	£275	£450
		e. Thick "1" with sloping serif	£130	£130
		f. Surch triple	£550	
		g. Figure "1" used as fraction bar	£375	£250
55	8	1d. on 4d. brown (I) (12.91)	18·00	18·00
		a. Surch double	£150	
		b. Surch inverted	£650	£600
		c. Type II	22·00	22·00
		ca. Surch double	£150	
		cb. Surch inverted	—	£600
		d. Type III	22·00	22·00
		(*b*) *Stamp of Die* II *surch*		
56	6	½d. on 3d. dull mauve and green	32·00	29·00
		a. Surch double	£650	£600
		b. Surch inverted	£1600	£600
		c. Small "O" in "ONE"	£130	£130
		d. Small "A" in "HALF"	£130	£130
		e. "ONE" misplaced ("O" over "H")	£130	£130

9

10

(Typo D.L.R.)

1902–3. *Wmk Crown CA. P* 14.

No.	Type	Description	Unused	Used
58	9	½d. dull purple and green	1·00	1·25
59		1d. dull purple and carmine	1·75	80
60		2½d. dull purple and ultramarine	8·00	8·50
61	10	3d. dull purple and yellow	7·50	8·50
62		1s. green and black	9·50	10·00
58/62 Optd "Specimen"		*Set of* 5	£130	

11 The Pitons

(Recess D.L.R.)

1902 (15 Dec). *400th Anniv of Discovery by Columbus. Wmk Crown CC, sideways. P* 14

No.	Type	Description	Unused	Used
63	11	2d. green and brown	6·50	9·00
63 Optd "Specimen"			£110	

This stamp was formerly thought to have been issued on 16 December but it has been seen on a postcard clearly postmarked 15 December.

1904–10. *Wmk Mult Crown CA. P* 14.

No.	Type	Description	Unused	Used
64	9	½d. dull purple and green, **CO**	55	60
65		½d. green, **O** (1907)	70	45
66		1d. dull purple and carmine, **CO**	80	25
67		1d. carmine, **O** (1907)	70	25
68		2½d. dull purple and ultramarine, **CO**	4·50	5·50
69		2½d. blue, **O** (1907)	4·00	4·50
70	10	3d. dull purple and yellow, **O**	5·50	7·50
71		3d. purple/*yellow*, **C** (1909)	2·50	6·00
72		6d. dull purple and violet, **CO** (1905)	8·00	8·50
		a. Dull and bright purple, **C** (1907)	7·00	9·00
73		6d. dull purple, **C** (1910)	12·00	15·00
74		1s. green and black, **C** (1905)	11·00	12·00
75		1s. black/*green*, **C** (1909)	9·50	10·00
76		5s. green and carmine, **O** (1905)	28·00	40·00
77		5s. green and red/*yellow*, **C** (1907)	32·00	45·00
64/77		*Set of* 14	£110	£140
65, 67, 69, 71/2*a*, 75/7 Optd "Specimen"		*Set of* 9	£225	

12

13

14

15

16

(Typo D.L.R.)

1912–20. *Wmk Mult Crown CA. P* 14.

No.	Type	Description	Unused	Used
78	12	½d. deep green, **O**	50	40
		a. Yellow-green, **O** (1916)	45	25
79		1d. carmine-red, **O**	1·90	12
		a. Scarlet, **O** (1916)	1·75	12
		b. Rose-red, **O**	1·75	40
80	13	2d. grey, **O**	3·00	5·50
		a. Slate-grey, **O** (1916)	7·50	10·00
81	12	2½d. ultramarine, **O**	2·40	3·25
		a. Bright blue, **O** (1918)	2·25	3·25
		b. Deep bright blue, **O**	6·00	6·00
82	15	3d. purple/*yellow*, **C**	1·25	2·75
		a. On pale yellow (Die I)	6·00	8·50
		b. On pale yellow (Die II)	6·00	11·00
83	14	4d. black and red/*yellow*, **C**	1·60	4·00
		a. White back (Optd S £25)	1·40	4·00
84	15	6d. dull and bright purple, **C**	3·75	7·50
		a. Grey-purple and purple, **C** (1918)	8·00	11·00
85		1s. black/*green*, **C**	4·50	7·50
		a. On blue-green, olive back	6·00	8·00
86		1s. orange-brown, **C** (1920)	3·50	9·00
87	16	2s. 6d. black and red/*blue*, **C**	15·00	22·00
88	15	5s. green and red/*yellow*, **C**	35·00	48·00
78/88		*Set of* 11	65·00	£100
78/88 Optd "Specimen"		*Set of* 11	£170	

WAR
TAX

(17)

WAR TAX

(18)

1916 (June). *Optd locally with T* **17**.

No.	Type	Description	Unused	Used
89	12	1d. scarlet	2·75	5·00
		a. Opt double	£350	£375
		b. Carmine	19·00	22·00

For the overprinting with Type **17** the top margin of the sheet was folded beneath the top row of stamps so that marginal examples from this row show an inverted albino impression of the overprint in the top margin.

1916 (Sept). *Optd in London with T* **18**.

No.	Type	Description	Unused	Used
90	12	1d. scarlet (Optd S. £50)	15	25

1921—26. *Wmk Mult Script CA. P 14.*
91 **12** ½d. green, O 25 20
92 1d. rose-carmine, O 1·75 5·00
93 1d. deep brown, O (1922) 35 25
94 **14** 1½d. dull carmine, O (1922) 40 75
95 **13** 2d. slate-grey, O 35 30
96 **12** 2½d. bright blue, O 1·75 2·25
97 2½d. orange, O (1925) 8·00 11·00
98 2½d. dull blue, O (1926) 2·25 3·25
99 **15** 3d. bright blue, O (1922) 4·50 8·50
a. Dull blue, O (1926) 1·75 3·25
100 3d. purple/*yellow,* C (1926) 70 2·75
a. Deep purple/yellow, C 3·00 5·50
101 **14** 4d. black and red/*yellow,* C (1924) 90 3·50
102 **15** 6d. grey-purple and purple, C 2·40 6·00
103 1s. orange-brown, C 2·40 6·50
104 **16** 2s. 6d. black and red/*blue,* C(1924) 12·00 25·00
105 **15** 5s. green and red/*pale yellow,* C (1923) 25·00 38·00
91/105 *Set of* 15 55·00 £100
91/105 Optd "Specimen" *Set of* 15 £275

1935 (6 May). *Silver Jubilee. As Nos.* 91/4 *of Antigua.*
109 ½d. black and green 35 45
e. Horiz line from turret 3·00
110 2d. ultramarine and grey 70 1·40
111 2½d. brown and deep blue 1·60 2·75
e. Horiz line from turret 8·00
112 1s. slate and purple 6·00 7·50
109/12 Perf "Specimen" *Set of* 4 70·00
For illustration of plate variety see Omnibus section following Zululand.

19 Port Castries

20 Columbus Square, Castries

21 Ventine Falls

25 The Badge of the Colony

(Recess D.L.R.)

1936 (1 Mar-Apr). *T* **19/21, 25** *and similar designs. Wmk Mult Script CA. P* 14 *or* 13 × 12 (1*s. and* 10*s.*).
113 **19** ½d. black and bright green 40 45
a. Perf 13 × 12 (8.4.36) 35 1·25
114 **20** 1d. black and brown 30 30
a. Perf 13 × 12 (8.4.36) 2·00 2·75
115 **21** 1½d. black and scarlet 55 45
a. Perf 12 × 13 12·00 3·00
116 **19** 2d. black and grey 35 45
117 **20** 2½d. black and blue 45 50
118 **21** 3d. black and dull green 1·75 1·60
119 **19** 4d. black and red-brown 85 1·60
120 **20** 6d. black and orange 1·25 1·75
121 – 1s. black and light blue 1·75 4·00
122 – 2s. 6d. black and ultramarine 12·00 20·00
123 – 5s. black and violet 17·00 26·00
124 **25** 10s. black and carmine 75·00 £100
113/124 *Set of* 12 £100 £140
113/24 Perf "Specimen" *Set of* 12 £225
Designs: *Vert* (*as T* **21**) 2s. 6d. Inniskilling monument. *Horiz* (*as T* **19**) 1s. Fort Rodney, Pigeon Island; 5s. Government House.

1937 (12 May). *Coronation. As* Nos. 13/15 *of Aden, but ptd by B. W. P* 11 × 11½.
125 1d. violet 20 20
126 1½d. carmine 30 20
127 2½d. blue 30 20
125/27 Perf "Specimen" *Set of* 3 55·00

26 King George VI

27 Columbus Square

28 Government House

31 Device of St. Lucia

(Recess Waterlow (T **26** and **30**), D.L.R. (T **27/8**) and B.W. (T **29** and **31**))

1938 (22 Sept)–**48.** *T* **26/8, 31** *and similar designs. Wmk Mult Script CA* (*sideways on* 2*s.*).
128 **26** ½d. green (*p* 14½ × 14) 20 12
a. Perf 12½ (1943) 12 12
129 1d. violet (*p* 14½ × 14) 90 25
a. Perf 12½ (1938) 12 20
129*b* 1d. scarlet (*p* 12½) (1947) 12 15
c. Perf 14½ × 14 (1948) 12 15
130 1½d. scarlet (*p* 14½ × 14) 25 12
a. Perf 12½ (1943) 15 30
131 2d. grey (*p* 14½ × 14) 12 35
a. Perf 12½ (1943) 12 12
132 2½d. ultramarine (*p* 14½ × 14) 12 12
a. Perf 12½ (1943) 12 12
132*b* 2½d. violet (*p* 12½) (1947) 20 15
133 3d. orange (*p* 14½ × 14) 20 12
a. Perf 12½ (1943) 15 12
133*b* 3½d. ultramarine (*p* 12½) (1947) 30 35
134 **27** 6d. claret (*p* 13½) 1·00 75
a. Carmine-lake (*p* 13½) (1945) 2·00 1·00
aa. Perf 12 *Claret* (1948) 1·25 1·25
134*b* **26** 8d. brown (*p* 12½) (1946) 75 50
135 **28** 1s. brown (*p* 13½) 65 65
a. Perf 12 (1948) 1·00 1·25
136 – 2s. blue and purple (*p* 12) 2·75 1·40
136*a* **26** 3s. bright purple (*p* 12½) (1946) 8·50 6·00
137 – 5s. black and mauve (*p* 12½) 6·00 5·00
138 **31** 10s. black/*yellow* (*p* 12) 7·00 10·00
141 **26** £1 sepia (*p* 12½) (1946) 25·00 28·00
128a/141 *Set of* 17 48·00 48·00
128/41 Perf "Specimen" *Set of* 17 £300
Designs: *Horiz* (*as T* **28**): 2s. The Pitons; 5s. Loading bananas.

1946 (8 Oct). *Victory. As Nos.* 28/9 *of Aden.*
142 1d. lilac 20 15
143 3½d. blue 25 15
142/3 Perf "Specimen" *Set of* 2 50·00

1948 (26 Nov). *Royal Silver Wedding. As Nos.* 30/1 *of Aden.*
144 1d. scarlet 25 15
145 £1 purple-brown 24·00 40·00

(New Currency. 100 cents=1 West Indian dollar)

32 King George VI

33 Device of St. Lucia

(Recess Waterlow (**32**), B.W. (**33**))

1949 (1 Oct)–**50.** *Value in cents or dollars. Wmk Mult Script CA. P* 12½ (1 *c. to* 16 *c.*), 11 × 11½ (*others*).
146 **32** 1 c. green 15 12
a. Perf 14 (1949) 45 45
147 2 c. magenta 15 12
a. Perf 14½ × 14 (1949) 1·10 1·25
148 3 c. scarlet 15 15
149 4 c. grey 15 12
a. Perf 14½ × 14 — £1400
150 5 c. violet 15 12
151 6 c. orange 15 12
152 7 c. ultramarine 15 12
153 12 c. claret 40 45
a. Perf 14½ × 14 (1950) £275 £150
154 16 c. brown 35 25
155 **33** 24 c. light blue 40 30
156 48 c. olive-green 2·25 1·10
157 $1.20, purple 2·75 7·00
158 $2.40, blue-green 7·50 26·00
159 $4.80, rose-carmine 15·00 30·00
146/159 *Set of* 14 26·00 60·00

1949 (10 Oct). *75th Anniv of Universal Postal Union. As Nos.* 114/17 *of Antigua.*
160 5 c. violet 25 35
161 6 c. orange 40 50
162 12 c. magenta 40 60
163 24 c. blue-green 75 1·00

1951 (16 Feb). *Inauguration of B.W.I. University College. As* Nos. 118/19 *of Antigua.*
164 3 c. black and scarlet 20 15
165 12 c. black and deep carmine 30 20

34 Phoenix rising from Burning Buildings

NEW 1951 CONSTITUTION
(**35**)

(Flames typo, rest recess B.W.)

1951 (19 June). *Reconstruction of Castries. Wmk Mult Script CA. P* 13½ × 13.
166 **34** 12 c. red and blue 20 30

1951 (25 Sept). *New Constitution. Optd with T* **35** *by Waterlow. P* 12½.
167 **32** 2 c. magenta 12 30
168 4 c. grey 12 30
169 5 c. violet 12 30
170 12 c. claret 15 45

1953 (2 June). *Coronation. As No.* 47 *of Aden.*
171 3 c. black and scarlet 8 8

36 Queen Elizabeth II

37 Device of St. Lucia

(Recess Waterlow (T **36**), until 1960, then D.L.R. B.W. (T **37**))

1953 (28 Oct)–**54.** *Wmk Mult Script CA. P* 14½ × 14 (*T* **36**) *or* 11 × 11½ (*T* **37**).
172 **36** 1 c. green (1.4.54) 5 5
173 2 c. magenta 5 5
174 3 c. red (2.9.54) 5 5
175 4 c. slate (7.1.54) 8 5
176 5 c. violet (*shades*) (1.4.54) 12 5
177 6 c. orange (*shades*) (2.9.54) 12 5
178 8 c. lake (2.9.54) 12 5
179 10 c. ultramarine (*shades*) (2.9.54) 15 5
180 15 c. red-brown (*shades*) (2.9.54) 30 5
181 **37** 25 c. deep turquoise-blue (2.9.54) 40 10
182 50 c. deep olive-green (2.9.54) 1·00 60
183 $1 bluish green (2.9.54) 3·25 1·75
184 $2.50, carmine (2.9.54) 12·00 9·50
172/84 *Set of* 13 16·00 11·00

1958 (22 Apr). *Inauguration of British Caribbean Federation. As Nos.* 135/7 *of Antigua.*
185 3 c. deep green 15 12
186 6 c. blue 15 25
187 12 c. scarlet 20 30

MINISTERIAL GOVERNMENT

38 Columbus's *Santa Maria* off the Pitons

39 Stamp of 1860

(Recess Waterlow)

1960 (1 Jan). *New Constitution for the Windward and Leeward Islands. W w* **12.** *P* 13.
188 **38** 8 c. carmine-red 15 10
189 10 c. red-orange 20 15
190 25 c. deep blue 35 40

(Recess Waterlow)

1960 (18 Dec). *Stamp Centenary. W w* **12.** *P* 13½.
191 **39** 5 c. rose-red and ultramarine 15 10
192 16 c. deep blue and yellow-green 25 25
193 25 c. green and carmine-red 25 25

1963 (4 June). *Freedom from Hunger. As No.* 76 *of Aden.*
194 25 c. bluish green 40 20

1963 (2 Sept). *Red Cross Centenary. As Nos.* 147/8 *of Antigua.*
195 4 c. red and black 15 10
196 25 c. red and blue 40 55

40 Queen Elizabeth II **41**
(after A. C. Davidson-Houston)

42 Fishing Boats

43 Castries Harbour

44 Vigie Beach

45 Queen Elizabeth II

(Des V. Whiteley. Photo Harrison)

1964 (1 Mar). *Designs as T* **40/5**, W w **12**. *P* 14½ (*T* **40**), *others* 14½ × 14 (*vert or* 14 × 14½ (*horiz*).
197 1 c. crimson 5 5
198 2 c. bluish violet 5 5
199 4 c. turquoise-green (*shades*) 8 5
200 5 c. Prussian blue 8 5
201 6 c. yellow-brown 10 10
202 8 c. multicoloured 10 5
203 10 c. multicoloured 12 5
204 12 c. multicoloured 15 15
205 15 c. multicoloured 20 15
206 25 c. multicoloured 35 20
207 35 c. blue and buff .. .. 1·75 40
208 50 c. multicoloured .. .. 1·90 60
209 $1 multicoloured .. .. 2·75 1·40
210 $2.50, multicoloured .. .. 3·50 3·75
197/210 .. .. *Set of* 14 10·00 6·00
Designs:—1 to 6 c. Type **40**; 8, 10 c. Type **41**. *Horiz as T* **42/3**—15 c. Pigeon Island; 25 c. Reduit Beach; 50 c. The Pitons.
See also No. 249.

1964 (23 April). *400th Birth Anniv of William Shakespeare. As No. 164 of Antigua.*
211 10 c. blue-green 10 10

1965 (17 May). *I.T.U. Centenary. As Nos. 166/7 of Antigua.*
212 2 c. mauve and magenta 10 5
213 50 c. lilac and light olive-green .. .. .. 1·25 50

1965 (25 Oct). *International Co-operation Year. As Nos. 168/9 of Antigua.*
214 1 c. reddish purple and turquoise-green .. 5 5
215 25 c. deep bluish green and lavender 20 20

1966 (24 Jan). *Churchill Commemoration. As Nos. 170/3 of Antigua.*
216 4 c. new blue 5 5
217 6 c. deep green 15 10
218 25 c. brown 30 25
219 35 c. bluish violet 40 35

1966 (4 Feb). *Royal Visit. As Nos. 174/5 of Antigua.*
220 4 c. black and ultramarine 10 5
221 25 c. black and magenta 40 35

1966 (1 July). *World Cup Football Championships, England. As Nos. 176/7 of Antigua.*
222 4 c. violet, yellow-green, lake & yellow-brn .. 10 5
223 25 c. chocolate, blue-green, lake & yellow-brn 20 20

1966 (20 Sept). *Inauguration of W.H.O. Headquarters, Geneva. As Nos. 178/9 of Antigua.*
224 4 c. black, yellow-green and light blue .. 8 5
225 25 c. black, light purple and yellow-brown .. 25 20

1966 (1 Dec). *20th Anniv of U.N.E.S.C.O. As Nos. 196/8 of Antigua.*
226 4 c. slate-violet, red, yellow and orange .. 10 5
227 12 c. orange-yellow, violet and deep olive .. 25 20
228 25 c. black, bright purple and orange 50 40

ASSOCIATED STATEHOOD

STATEHOOD
1st MARCH 1967
(49)

STATEHOOD
1st MARCH 1967
(50)

51 Map of St. Lucia

(Optd by Art Printery, Castries from dies supplied by Harrison. Photo Harrison (No. 240))

1967 (7 Mar). *Statehood. (a) Postage. Nos.* 198 *and* 200/9 *optd with T* **49** (2, 5, 6 *c.*) *or T* **50** (*others*) *in red.*
229 2 c. bluish violet 20 20
a. Horiz pair, one without opt .. ..
230 5 c. Prussian blue 10 5
a. Opt inverted .. .. 45·00
231 6 c. yellow-brown 10 5
232 8 c. multicoloured 20 15
233 10 c. multicoloured 25 15
234 12 c. multicoloured 30 15
235 15 c. multicoloured .. .. 1·25 90
236 25 c. multicoloured .. .. 1·50 1·00
237 35 c. blue and buff .. .. 2·25 1·75
238 50 c. multicoloured .. .. 2·25 2·25
239 $1 multicoloured .. .. 2·50 2·50
229/39 .. .. *Set of* 11 10·00 8·00

(*b*) *Air. P* 14½ × 14.
240 **51** 15 c. new blue 10 5
Overprinted 1 c. and $2.50 stamps were prepared for issue but were not put on sale over the post office counter. Later, however, they were accepted for franking (*Price for set of* 2 £15 *mint*, £18 *used*).

52 "Madonna and Child with the Infant Baptist" (Raphael)

53 Batsman and Sir Frederick Clarke (Governor)

(Des and photo Harrison)

1967 (16 Oct). *Christmas.* W w **12** (*sideways*). *P* 14½.
241 **52** 4 c. multicoloured 5 5
242 25 c. multicoloured 15 15

(Des V. Whiteley. Photo Harrison)

1968 (8 Mar). *M.C.C.'s West Indies Tour.* W w **12** (*sideways*). *P* 14½ × 14.
243 **53** 10 c. multicoloured 20 15
244 35 c. multicoloured 60 50

54 "The Crucified Christ with the Virgin Mary, Saints and Angels" (Raphael)

55 "Noli me tangere" (detail by Titian)

(Des and photo Harrison)

1968 (25 Mar). *Easter.* W w **12** (*sideways*). *P* 14 × 14½.
245 **54** 10 c. multicoloured 5 5
246 **55** 15 c. multicoloured 5 5
247 **54** 25 c. multicoloured 10 10
248 **55** 35 c. multicoloured 15 15

1968 (14 May)*. *As No.* 205 *but* W w **12** (*sideways*).
249 15 c. multicoloured 15 15
*This is the London release date. Stamps from this printing were available some months earlier on St. Lucia.

56 Dr. Martin Luther King

57 "Virgin and Child in Glory" (Murillo)

(Des V. Whiteley. Litho D.L.R.)

1968 (4 July). *Martin Luther King Commemoration.* W w **12**. *P* 13½ × 14.
250 **56** 25 c. blue, black and flesh 10 10
251 35 c. violet-black, black and flesh .. 15 15

(Des and photo Harrison)

1968 (17 Oct). *Christmas. Paintings. T* **57** *and similar vert design. Multicoloured.* W w **12** (*sideways*). *P* 14½ × 14.
252 5 c. Type **57** 5 5
253 10 c. "Madonna with Child" (Murillo) .. 8 8
254 25 c. Type **57** 12 12
255 35 c. As 10 c. 20 20

59 Purple-throated Carib

(Des V. Whiteley. Litho Format)

1969 (10 Jan). *Birds. T* **59** *and similar horiz design. Multicoloured.* W w **12** (*sideways*). *P* 14.
256 10 c. Type **59** 20 5
257 15 c. St. Lucia Amazon 25 10
258 25 c. Type **59** 35 20
259 35 c. As 15 c. 40 25

61 "Head of Christ Crowned with Thorns" (Reni)

62 "Resurrection of Christ" (Sodoma)

(Des and photo Harrison)

1969 (20 Mar). *Easter.* W w **12** (*sideways*). *P* 14½ × 14.
260 **61** 10 c. multicoloured 5 5
261 **62** 15 c. multicoloured 10 8
262 **61** 25 c. multicoloured 15 12
263 **62** 35 c. multicoloured 20 20

63 Map showing "CARIFTA" Countries

(Des J. Cooter. Photo Harrison)

1969 (29 May). *First Anniv of CARIFTA (Caribbean Free Trade Area). T* **63** *and similar horiz designs. Multicoloured.* W w **12**. *P* 14.
264 5 c. Type **63** 5 5
265 10 c. Type **63** 5 5
266 25 c. Handclasp and names of CARIFTA countries 15 15
267 35 c. As 25 c. 20 20

65 Emperor Napoleon and Empress Josephine

66 "Virgin and Child" (P. Delaroche)

(Des and litho Enschedé)

1969 (22 Sept). *Birth Bicentenary of Napoleon Bonaparte. P* 14 × 13.
268 **65** 15 c. multicoloured 15 10
269 25 c. multicoloured 20 12
270 35 c. multicoloured 20 20
271 50 c. multicoloured 30 35

(Des J. W. Photo Harrison)

1969 (27 Oct). *Christmas. Paintings. T* **66** *and similar vert design. Multicoloured.* W w **12** (*sideways*). *P* 14½ × 14.
272 5 c. Type **66** 5 5
273 10 c. "Holy Family" (Rubens) 5 5
274 25 c. Type **66** 15 15
275 35 c. As 10 c. 20 25

68 House of Assembly

69 "The Sealing of the Tomb" (Hogarth)

(Des J. Cooter ($10), Sylvia and M. Goaman (others). Litho Questa ($10), Format (others))

1970 (2 Feb)–**73**. *T* **68** *and similar designs. Multicoloured.* W w **12** (*sideways on* 1 *c. to* 35 *c. and* $10). *P* 14.
276 1 c. Type **68** 5 5
277 2 c. Roman Catholic Cathedral 10 8
278 4 c. The Boulevard, Castries 12 8
279 5 c. Castries Harbour 12 8
280 6 c. Sulphur springs 12 8
281 10 c. Vigie Airport 20 8
282 12 c. Reduit Beach 20 10
283 15 c. Pigeon Island 25 10
284 25 c. The Pitons and yacht 40 15

285 35 c. Marigot Bay 50 25
286 50 c. Diamond Waterfall (*vert*) 70 60
287 $1 Flag of St. Lucia (*vert*) .. .. .. 1·25 70
288 $2.50, St. Lucia Coat of Arms (*vert*). .. .. 3·75 2·25
289 $5 Queen Elizabeth II (*vert*). .. .. 6·50 6·50
289*a* $10 Map of St. Lucia (*vert*) (3.12.73) .. .. 12·00 15·00
276/89*a* .. .. *Set of* 15 24·00 23·00
See also Nos. 367/8 and 395/8.

(Des V. Whiteley. Litho Enschedé)

1970 (7 Mar). *Easter. Triptych by Hogarth. T* **69** *and similar multicoloured designs. W* w **12** *(sideways). Roul.* 9 × *P* 12½.
290 25 c. Type **69** 40 45
a. Strip of 3. Nos. 290/2 .. .. .. 1·40
291 35 c. "The Three Marys at the Tomb". 50 55
292 $1 "The Ascension" (39 × 55 *mm*) 65 80
Nos. 290/2 were issued in sheets of 30 (6 × 5) containing the Hogarth Triptych spread over all three values of the set. This necessitated a peculiar arrangement with the $1 value (which depicts the centre portion of the triptych) 10 mm higher than the other values in the *se-tenant* strip.

72 Charles Dickens and Dickensian Characters

(Des V. Whiteley. Litho B.W.)

1970 (8 June). *Death Centenary of Charles Dickens. W* w **12** *(sideways). P* 14.
293 **72** 1 c. multicoloured 5 5
294 25 c. multicoloured 40 20
295 35 c. multicoloured 50 35
296 50 c. multicoloured 60 50

73 Nurse and Emblem

(Des R. Granger Barrett. Litho J.W.)

1970 (18 Aug). *Centenary of British Red Cross. T* **73** *and similar horiz design. Multicoloured. W* w **12** *(sideways). P* 14.
297 10 c. Type **73** 10 5
298 15 c. Flags of Great Britain, Red Cross and St. Lucia 15 10
299 25 c. Type **73** 25 15
300 35 c. As 15 c. 30 25

74 "Madonna with the Lilies" (Luca della Robbia)
75 "Christ on the Cross" (Rubens)

(Des P. B. Litho and embossed Walsall)

1970 (16 Nov). *Christmas. P*11.
301 **74** 5 c. multicoloured 5 5
302 10 c. multicoloured 10 5
303 35 c. multicoloured 25 30
304 40 c. multicoloured 25 30

(Des and litho Enschedé)

1971 (29 Mar). *Easter. T* **75** *and similar vert design. Multicoloured. W* w **12**. *P* 13½ × 13.
305 10 c. Type **75** 5 5
306 15 c. "Descent from the Cross" (Rubens) .. 10 5
307 35 c. Type **75** 20 20
308 40 c. As 15 c. 20 20

76 Moule à Chique Lighthouse

(Des J. W. Litho Questa)

1971 (1 May). *Opening of Beane Field Airport. T* **76** *and similar horiz design. Multicoloured. W* w **12** *(sideways). P* 14½ × 14.
309 5 c. Type **76** 5 5
310 25 c. Aircraft landing at Beane Field.. .. 30 30

77 Morne Fortune

78 Morne Fortune, Modern View

(Des V. Whiteley. Litho Questa)

1971 (10 Aug.). *Old and New Views of St. Lucia. T* **77/8** *and similar horiz designs. Multicoloured. W* w **12** *(sideways). P* 13½ × 13.
311 5 c. Type **77** 5 5
312 5 c. Type **78** 5 5
313 10 c. } Castries city 10 5
314 10 c. } .. 10 5
315 25 c. } Pigeon Island 25 25
316 25 c. } .. 25 25
317 50 c. } View from grounds of Govt House .. 55 75
318 50 c. } .. 55 75
311/18 .. .. *Set of* 8 1·75 2·00
Each value of this issue was printed horizontally and vertically *se-tenant* in two designs showing respectively old and new views of St. Lucia.
The old views are taken from paintings by J. H. Caddy.

79 "Virgin and Child with Two Angels" (Verrocchio)
80 "St. Lucia" (Dolci School) and Coat of Arms

(Des J. Cooter. Litho J.W.)

1971 (15 Oct). *Christmas. T* **79** *and similar vert designs. Multicoloured. W* w **12**. *P* 14.
319 5 c. Type **79** 5 5
320 10 c. "Virgin and Child, St. John the Baptist and an Angel" (Morando) 10 5
321 35 c. "Madonna and Child" (Battista).. .. 30 35
322 40 c. Type **79** 40 55

(Des and litho Harrison)

1971 (13 Dec). *National Day. W* w **12**. *P* 14 × 14½.
323 **80** 5 c. multicoloured 5 5
324 10 c. multicoloured 10 5
325 25 c. multicoloured 25 25
326 50 c. multicoloured 45 55

81 "The Dead Christ Mourned" (Carracci)

(Des G. Drummond. Litho Questa)

1972 (15 Feb). *Easter. T* **81** *and similar horiz design. Multicoloured. W* w **12**. *P* 14.
327 10 c. Type **81** 10 10
328 25 c. "Angels weeping over the dead Christ" (Guercino) 25 30
329 35 c. Type **81** 30 25
330 50 c. As 25 c. 45 50

82 Science Block and Teachers' College

(Des P. Powell. Litho Questa)

1972 (18 Apr). *Morne Educational Complex. T* **82** *and similar horiz designs. Multicoloured. W* w **12**. *P* 14.
331 5 c. Type **82** 5 5
332 15 c. University Centre 10 10
333 25 c. Secondary School 15 20
334 35 c. Technical College 30 35

83 Steamship Stamp and Map

Des J. Cooter. Litho Questa)

1972 (22 June). *Centenary of First Postal Service by St. Lucia Steam Conveyance Co Ltd. T* **83** *and similar horiz designs. W* w **12**. *P* 14.
335 5 c. multicoloured 10 5
336 10 c. ultramarine, mauve and black 15 10
337 35 c. light rose-carmine, pale greenish blue and black 45 25
338 50 c. multicoloured .. .. 1·25 1·40
Designs:—10 c. Steamship stamp and Castries Harbour; 35 c. Steamship stamp and Soufrière; 50 c. Steamship stamps.

84 "The Holy Family" (Sebastiano Ricci)

(Des J. Cooter. Litho J.W.)

1972 (18 Oct). *Christmas. W* w **12** *(sideways). P* 14½.
339 **84** 5 c. multicoloured 5 5
340 10 c. multicoloured 5 5
341 35 c. multicoloured 25 25
342 40 c. multicoloured 35 35

85 Arms and St. Lucia Amazon
86 Week-day Headdress

(Des (from photograph by D. Groves) and photo Harrison)

1972 (20 Nov). *Royal Silver Wedding. Multicoloured; background colour given. W* w **12**. *P* 14 × 14½.
343 **85** 15 c. carmine 20 20
344 35 c. yellow-olive.. .. .. .. 20 20

(Des Sylvia Goaman. Litho A. & M.)

1973 (1 Feb). *Local Headdresses. T* **86** *and similar vert designs. Multicoloured. W* w **12**. *P* 13.
345 5 c. Type **86** 5 5
346 10 c. Formal style 10 10
347 25 c. Unmarried girl's style 25 20
348 50 c. Ceremonial style.. .. .. .. 55 60

87 Coat of Arms
88 H.M.S. *St. Lucia*

(Des and litho Harrison)

1973–76. *Coil Stamps. P* 14½ × 14.
A. *W* w **12** *upright* (19.4.73). B. *W* w **12** *sideways* (1976).

			A		B	
349	**87**	5 c. olive-green	10	10	5	5
350		10 c. new blue	15	15	5	8
351		25 c. lake-brown	15	15	†	

(Des R. Granger Barrett. Litho Questa)

1973 (24 May). *Historic Ships. T* **88** *and similar horiz designs. Multicoloured. W* w **12**. *P* 13½ × 14.
352 15 c. Type **88** 30 15
353 35 c. H.M.S. *Prince of Wales* 55 25
354 50 c. *Oliph Blossom* 90 50
355 $1 H.M.S. *Rose* .. .. 1·10 85
MS356 122 × 74 mm. Nos. 352/5 .. .. .. 2·50 4·00

89 Plantation and Flower

90 "The Virgin with Child" (Maratta)

(Des PAD Studio. Litho Walsall)

1973 (26 July). *Banana Industry. T* **89** *and similar horiz designs. Multicoloured. W* w **12**. *P* 14.

357 5 c. Type **89** 10 8
358 15 c. Aerial spraying 20 12
359 35 c. Boxing plant 45 25
360 50 c. Loading a boat 85 65

(Des J. Cooter. Litho Walsall)

1973 (17 Oct). *Christmas. T* **90** *and similar vert designs. Multicoloured. W* w **12** (*sideways*). *P* 13½.

361 5 c. Type **90** 5 5
362 15 c. "Madonna in the Meadow" (Raphael) .. 10 5
363 35 c. "The Holy Family" (Bronzino) 35 15
364 50 c. "Madonna of the Pear" (Dürer) 60 75

1973 (14 Nov). *Royal Wedding. As Nos.* 165/6 *of Anguilla.*

365 40 c. grey-green 15 15
366 50 c. rosy lilac 15 15

1974 (15 Mar). *As Nos.* 277/8 *but wmk upright.*

367 2 c. Roman Catholic Cathedral 80 80
368 4 c. The Boulevard, Castries .. .. .. 1·10 1·40

91 "The Betrayal"

92 3-Escalins Coins, 1798

(Des J. Cooter. Litho D.L.R.)

1974 (1 Apr). *Easter. T* **91** *and similar horiz designs showing paintings by Ugolino da Siena. Multicoloured. W* w **12** (*sideways on Nos.* 369/72, *upright on* **MS**373). *P* 13.

369 5 c. Type **91** 5 5
370 35 c. "The Way to Calvary" 25 15
371 80 c. "The Deposition" 60 65
372 $1 "The Resurrection" 70 80
MS373 180 × 140 mm. Nos. 369/72 .. .. 2·00 2·50

(Des J. Cooter. Litho Format)

1974 (20 May). *Coins of Old St. Lucie. T* **92** *and similar vert designs. Multicoloured. W* w **12** (*sideways*). *P* 14 × 13½.

374 15 c. Type **92** 15 10
375 35 c. 6-escalins coins, 1798 .. .. .. 35 30
376 40 c. 2-livres 5-sols coins, 1813 .. .. 35 30
377 $1 6-livres 15-sols coins, 1813 .. .. 95 1·10
MS378 151 × 115 mm. Nos. 374/7 .. .. 2·00 2·75

93 Baron de Laborie

94 "Virgin and Child" (Andrea del Verrocchio)

(Des J. W. Litho Questa)

1974 (29 Aug). *Past Governors of St. Lucia. T* **93** *and similar vert designs. Multicoloured. W* w **12** (*sideways on Nos.* 379/82, *upright on* **MS**383). *P* 14.

379 5 c. Type **93** 5 5
380 35 c. Sir John Moore 30 20
381 80 c. Sir Dudley Hill 60 65
382 $1 Sir Frederick Clarke 80 85
MS383 153 × 117 mm. Nos. 379/82 .. .. 2·25 2·75

(Des PAD Studio. Litho D.L.R.)

1974 (18 Nov). *Christmas. T* **94** *and similar vert designs. Multicoloured. W* w **12**. *P* 13 × 13½.

384 5 c. Type **94** 5 5
385 35 c. "Virgin and Child" (Andrea della Robbia) 20 10
386 80 c. "Madonna and Child" (Luca della Robbia) 50 65
387 $1 "Virgin and Child" (Rossellino) 65 75
MS388 92 × 140 mm. Nos. 384/7 .. .. .. 1·75 2·00

95 Churchill and Montgomery

96 "Christ on the Cross" (School of Van der Weyden)

(Des PAD Studio. Litho Format)

1974 (30 Nov). *Birth Centenary of Sir Winston Churchill. T* **95** *and similar horiz design. Multicoloured. W* w **12** (*sideways*). *P* 14.

389 5 c. Type **95** 10 10
390 $1 Churchill and Truman 55 70

(Des J. Cooter. Litho Questa)

1975 (27 Mar). *Easter. T* **96** *and similar vert designs. Multicoloured. W* w **12**. *P* 13½.

391 5 c. Type **96** 5 5
392 35 c. "Noli me tangere" (Romano) 20 10
393 80 c. "Calvary" (Gallego) 50 65
394 $1 "Noli me tangere" (Correggio) 60 75

1975 (28 July). *As Nos.* 278 *etc. but W* w **14** (*sideways*).

395 4 c. The Boulevard, Castries 60 60
396 5 c. Castries Harbour 70 70
397 10 c. Vigie Airport 90 90
398 15 c. Pigeon Island .. .. 1·50 1·50

97 "Nativity" (French Book of Hours)

98 Naval Vessel *Hanna*

1975 (12 Dec). *Christmas. T* **97** *and similar vert designs. Multicoloured. W* w **12**. *P* 14½.

399 5 c. Type **97** 5 5
400 10 c. } Epiphany scene .. 10 10
401 10 c. } (stained-glass window) .. 10 10
402 10 c. } .. 10 10
403 40 c. "Nativity" (Hastings Book of Hours) .. 45 45
404 $1 "Virgin and Child with Saints" (Borgognone) .. .. 1·25 1·25
399/404 .. .. *Set of* 6 1·75 1·75
MS405 105 × 109 mm. Nos. 399 and 403/4 .. 1·75 1·90

Nos. 400/2 were printed horizontally *se-tenant* within the sheet to form the composite design listed.

(Des J. W. Litho Format)

1976 (26 Jan). *Bicentenary of American Revolution. T* **98** *and similar horiz designs showing ships. Multicoloured. P* 14½.

406 ½ c. Type **98** 5 5
407 1 c. Mail Packet *Prince of Orange* 8 5
408 2 c. H.M.S. *Edward* 10 5
409 5 c. Merchantman *Millern* 30 5
410 15 c. Lugger *Surprise* 60 20
411 35 c. H.M.S. *Serapis* .. .. 1·10 50
412 50 c. Frigate *Randolph* .. .. 1·25 65
413 $1 Frigate *Alliance* .. .. 2·25 1·40
406/13 .. .. *Set of* 8 5·00 2·75
MS414 142 × 116 mm. Nos. 410/13. P 13 .. .. 5·00 5·00

99 Laughing Gull

100 H.M.S. *Ceres*

(Des J.W. Litho Questa)

1976 (17 May)–**79**. *T* **99** *and similar vert designs. Multicoloured. Ordinary paper. W* w **12** (1 c.), *W* w **14** (*others*). *P* 14.

415 1 c. Type **99** 10 5
416 2 c. Little Blue Heron 20 5
417 4 c. Belted Kingfisher 25 8
418 5 c. St. Lucia Amazon 25 8
419 6 c. St. Lucia Oriole 25 8
420 8 c. Brown Trembler 25 10
421 10 c. American Kestrel 25 10
422 12 c. Red-billed Tropic Bird 30 10
423 15 c. Moorhen 30 12
424 25 c. Common Noddy 35 20
a. Chalk-surfaced paper (7.79) 50 20
425 35 c. Sooty Tern 50 25
a. Chalk-surfaced paper (1979) .. .. 2·00 2·00
426 50 c. Osprey 70 35
427 $1 White-breasted Trembler 95 55
428 $2.50, St. Lucia Black Finch .. .. 1·75 1·75
429 $5 Red-necked Pigeon .. .. 3·50 3·50
430 $10 Caribbean Elaenia .. .. 6·50 6·50
a. Chalk-surfaced paper (7.79) .. .. 7·50 7·50
415/30a .. .. *Set of* 16 15·00 12·00

1976 (19 July). *West Indian Victory in World Cricket Cup. As Nos.* 559/60 *of Barbados.*

431 50 c. Caribbean map .. .. 1·25 70
432 $1 Prudential Cup .. .. 1·50 1·25
MS433 92 × 79 mm. Nos. 431/2 .. .. .. 3·25 3·25

(Des J. Cooter. Litho Walsall)

1976 (4 Sept). *Royal Navy Crests. T* **100** *and similar vert designs. Multicoloured. W* w **14** (*inverted*). *P* 14.

434 10 c. Type **100** 15 5
435 20 c. H.M.S. *Pelican* 25 15
436 40 c. H.M.S. *Ganges* 45 35
437 $2 H.M.S. *Ariadne* .. .. 1·75 2·50

101 "Madonna and Child" (Murillo)

102 Queen Elizabeth II

(Des J. Cooter. Litho Questa)

1976 (15 Nov). *Christmas. T* **101** *and similar vert designs. Multicoloured. W* w **14**. *P* 13½.

438 10 c. Type **101** 10 5
439 20 c. "Madonna and Child with Angels" (Costa) 25 12
440 50 c. "Madonna and Child Enthroned" (Isenbrandt) 45 30
441 $2 "Madonna and Child with St. John" (Murillo) .. .. 1·00 1·10
MS442 105 × 93 mm. $2.50, As Type **101** .. 1·40 1·75

(Des Daphne Padden. Litho Questa)

1977 (7 Feb). *Silver Jubilee. W* w **14** (*sideways*). *P* 14.

443 **102** 10 c. multicoloured 15 5
444 20 c. multicoloured 20 15
445 40 c. multicoloured 30 25
446 $2 multicoloured .. .. 85 1·10
MS447 128 × 95 mm. **102** $2.50 multicoloured 1·10 1·25

103 Scouts from Tapion School

104 "Nativity" (Giotto)

(Des J. W. Litho Format)

1977 (17 Oct). *Caribbean Boy Scout Jamboree. T* **103** *and similar vert designs. Multicoloured. P* 14½.

448 ½ c. Type **103** 5 5
449 1 c. Sea scouts 5 5
450 2 c. Scout from Micoud 5 5
451 10 c. Two scouts from Tapion School 15 15
452 20 c. Venture scouts 25 25
453 50 c. Scout from Gros Islet 50 50
454 $1 Sea scouts in boat 90 90
448/54 .. .. *Set of* 7 1·75 1·75
MS455 75 × 85 mm. $2.50, As $1 .. .. .. 2·25 2·50

(Des J. W. Litho Questa)

1977 (31 Oct). *Christmas. T* **104** *and similar vert designs. Multicoloured. P* 14.

456 ½ c. Type **104** 5 5
457 1 c. "Perugia triptych" (Fra Angelico) .. 5 5
458 2 c. "Virgin and Child" (El Greco) 5 5
459 20 c. "Madonna of the Rosary" (Caravaggio) .. 15 5
460 50 c. "Adoration of the Magi" (Velazquez) .. 30 30
461 $1 "Madonna of Carmel" (Tiepolo) 50 60
462 $2.50, "Adoration of the Magi" (Tiepolo) .. 90 1·25
456/62 .. .. *Set of* 7 1·75 2·00

105 "Susan Lunden"

106 Yeoman of the Guard and Life Guard

(Des C. Abbott. Litho Harrison)

1977 (28 Nov). *400th Birth Anniv of Rubens. T* **105** *and similar vert designs. Multicoloured.* W w **14** *(sideways). P* 14 × 15.
463 10 c. Type **105** 10 5
464 35 c. "The Rape of the Sabine Women" (detail) 25 15
465 50 c. "Ludovicus Nonnius" 35 20
466 $2.50, "Minerva protects Pax from Mars" (detail) .. .. 1·00 1·10
MS467 145 × 120 mm. Nos. 463/6 .. .. .. 1·75 2·00

(Des J. W. Litho Questa)

1978 (2 June). *25th Anniv of Coronation. T* **106** *and similar horiz designs. Multicoloured. P* 14.
468 15 c. Type **106** 12 10
469 20 c. Groom and postillion 15 12
470 50 c. Footman and coachman 35 30
471 $3 State trumpeter and herald .. .. .. 1·40 1·40
MS472 114 × 88 mm. $5 Master of the Horse and Gentleman-at-Arms .. .. 2·00 2·00
Nos. 468/71 also exist perf 12 (*Price for set of* 4 £1.75 *mint or used*) from additional sheetlets of 3 stamps and one label. Stamps perforated 14 are from normal sheets of 50.

107 Queen Angelfish

(Des G. Vasarhelyi. Litho Format)

1978 (19 June). *Fishes. T* **107** *and similar horiz designs. Multicoloured. P* 15.
473 10 c. Type **107** 10 10
474 20 c. Foureye Butterflyfish 20 15
475 50 c. French Angelfish 45 35
476 $2 Yellowtail Damselfish .. .. 1·25 1·50
MS477 155 × 89 mm. $2.50, Rock Beauty .. 1·75 1·90

108 French Grenadier and Map of the Battle **109** The Annunciation

(Des J. W. Litho Questa)

1978 (29 Nov). *Bicentenary of Battle of Cul-de-Sac. T* **108** *and similar horiz designs. Multicoloured. P* 14
478 10 c. Type **108** 10 5
479 30 c. British Grenadier officer and map of St. Lucia (Bellin), 1762 .. .. .. 25 10
480 50 c. Coastline from Gros Islet to Cul-de-Sac and British fleet opposing French landings 40 25
481 $2.50, General James Grant, 1798, and Light Infantrymen of 46th Regiment .. .. 1·75 1·40

(Des Jennifer Toombs. Litho Questa)

1978 (4 Dec). *Christmas. T* **109** *and similar horiz design. Multicoloured.* W w **14**. *P* 14.
482 30 c. Type **109** 15 15
483 50 c. Type **109** 25 25
484 55 c. The Nativity 30 30
485 80 c. As 55 c. 50 50

INDEPENDENT

110 Hewanorra International Air Terminal

(Des J. W. Litho Questa)

1979 (22 Feb). *Independence. T* **110** *and similar horiz designs. Multicoloured.* W w **14** *(sideways). P* 14.
486 10 c. Type **110** 10 5
487 30 c. New coat of arms 15 10
488 50 c. Government House and Sir Allen Lewis (first Governor-General) 25 15
489 $2 French, St. Lucia and Union flags on map of St. Lucia 75 95
MS490 127 × 80 mm. Nos. 486/9 .. .. .. 1·10 1·50

111 Popes Paul VI and John Paul I

(Des J.W. Litho Harrison)

1979 (28 May). *Pope Paul VI Commemoration. T* **111** *and similar horiz designs. Multicoloured.* W w **14** (sideways). *P* 14½ × 14.
491 10 c. Type **111** 5 5
492 30 c. President Sadat of Egypt with Pope Paul 20 15
493 50 c. Pope Paul with Secretary-General U Thant 35 25
494 55 c. Pope Paul and Prime Minister Golda Meir of Israel 40 30
495 $2 Martin Luther King received in audience by Pope Paul .. .. 1·00 80

112 Dairy Farming

(Des G. Drummond. Litho Format)

1979 (2 July). *Agriculture Diversification. T* **112** *and similar horiz designs. Multicoloured.* W w **14** *(sideways). P* 14.
496 10 c. Type **112** 5 5
497 35 c. Fruit and vegetables 20 10
498 50 c. Water conservation 30 25
499 $3 Copra industry .. .. 1·10 1·25

113 Lindbergh and Flying-boat **114** "A Prince of Saxony" (Cranach the Elder)

(Des L. Curtis. Litho Walsall)

1979 (2 Oct). *50th Anniv of Lindbergh's Inaugural Airmail Flight via St. Lucia. T* **113** *and similar horiz designs.* W w **14** *(sideways). P* 14.
500 10 c. black, Indian red and pale orange .. 5 5
501 30 c. multicoloured 12 15
502 50 c. multicoloured 20 25
503 $2 multicoloured 90 95
Designs:—30 c. Flying boat and route map; 50 c. Arrival at La Toc, September, 1929; $2 Letters on first flight.

(Litho Questa)

1979 (6 Dec). *International Year of the Child. Paintings. T* **114** *and similar vert designs. Multicoloured. P.* 14.
504 10 c. Type **114** 5 5
505 50 c. "The Infanta Margarita" (Velazquez) .. 15 15
506 $2 "Girl playing Badminton" (Chardin) .. 75 80
507 $2.50, "Mary and Francis Wilcox" (Stock) .. 95 1·00
MS508 113 × 94 mm. $5 "Two Children" (Picasso) 1·90 2·00

115 Notice of Introduction of Penny Post **116** "Madonna and Child" (Bernardino Fungai)

(Des J.W. Litho Questa)

1979 (10 Dec). *Death Centenary of Sir Rowland Hill. T* **115** *and similar vert designs. Multicoloured. P* 14.
509 10 c. Type **115** 5 5
510 50 c. Original stamp sketch 20 30
511 $2 1860 1d. stamp 60 65
512 $2.50, Penny Black stamp 70 75
MS513 111 × 85 mm. $5 Sir Rowland Hill .. 1·60 2·00
Nos. 509/12 also exist perf 12 (*price for set of* 4 £1·40 *mint or used*) from additional sheetlets of 5 stamps and one label. Stamps perforated 14 are from normal sheets of 40.

(Des R. Vigurs. Litho Walsall)

1980 (14 Jan). *Christmas* (1979) *and International Year of the Child. T* **116** *and similar vert designs showing "Madonna and Child" paintings by various artists. Multicoloured.* W w **14**. *P* 14.
514 10 c. Type **116** 5 5
515 50 c. Carlo Dolci 20 20
516 $2 Titian 75 80
517 $2.50, Giovanni Bellini 90 95
MS518 94 × 120 mm. Nos. 514/17 .. .. .. 1·90 2·00

117 St. Lucia Steam Conveyance **118** Mickey Mouse astride Rocket

(Des G. Drummond. Litho Questa)

1980 (6 May). *"London 1980" International Stamp Exhibition. T* **117** *and similar horiz designs. Multicoloured.* W w **14** *(sideways). P* 14.
519 10 c. Type **117** 5 5
520 30 c. S.S. *Assistance* 1d. postmark of 1879 .. 15 10
521 50 c. Postage due handstamp of 1929 .. .. 20 15
522 $2 Crowned-circle paid stamp of 1844 .. 70 80
MS523 85 × 76 mm. Nos. 519/22 .. .. .. 1·00 1·10

(Litho Format)

1980 (29 May). *10th Anniv of Moon Landing* (1979). *Walt Disney Cartoon Characters. T* **118** *and similar multicoloured designs showing characters in space scenes. P* 11.
524 ½ c. Type **118** 5 5
525 1 c. Donald Duck being towed by rocket (*horiz*) 5 5
526 2 c. Minnie Mouse on Moon 5 5
527 3 c. Goofy hitching lift to Mars 5 5
528 4 c. Goofy and moondog (*horiz*) 5 5
529 5 c. Pluto burying bone on Moon (*horiz*) .. 5 5
530 10 c. Donald Duck and love-sick martian (*horiz*) 5 5
531 $2 Donald Duck paddling spaceship (*horiz*) 1·25 1·25
532 $2.50, Mickey Mouse driving moonbuggy (*horiz*) .. .. 1·40 1·40
524/32 .. .. *Set of* 9 2·50 2·50
MS533 102 × 127 mm. $5 Goofy leaping from space-ship on to Moon. P 13½ .. .. .. 2·25 2·50

119 Queen Elizabeth the Queen Mother

(Litho Questa)

1980 (4 Aug). *80th Birthday of Queen Elizabeth the Queen Mother. P* 14.
534 **119** 10 c. multicoloured 10 10
535 $2.50, multicoloured .. .. 1·75 1·75
MS536 85 × 65 mm. **119** $3 multicoloured .. 1·75 2·10

120 Hawker Siddeley "HS 748"

(Des A. Theobald. Litho Harrison)

1980 (11 Aug). *Transport. Horiz designs as T* **120**. *Multicoloured.* W w **14** (*sideways on* 5 *c. to* $1). *P* 14½ × 14.
537 5 c. Type **120** 5 5
538 10 c. McDonnell Douglas "DC-10" airliner .. 5 5
539 15 c. Local bus 10 12
540 20 c. Refrigerator ship 10 10
541 25 c. "Islander" aeroplane 12 12
542 30 c. Pilot boat 15 15
543 50 c. Boeing "727" airliner 30 35
544 75 c. Cruise ship 45 50
545 $1 Lockheed "Tristar" airliner 50 55
546 $2 Cargo liner .. .. 1·00 90
547 $5 Boeing "707" airliner .. .. 3·00 3·25
548 $10 *Queen Elizabeth 2* (liner) .. .. .. 5·00 4·50
537/48 .. .. *Set of* 12 9·75 9·50
For stamps with watermark W w **15** see Nos. 690/8.

121 Shot-putting **122** Coastal Landscape within Cogwheel

(Des M. Diamond. Litho Questa)

1980 (22 Sept). *Olympic Games, Moscow. T* **121** *and similar horiz designs. Multicoloured. P* 14.

549	10 c. Type **121**	5	5
550	50 c. Swimming	20	20
551	$2 Gymnastics	80	85
552	$2.50, Weight-lifting	90	95
MS553	108 × 83 mm. $5 Athletes with Olympic Torch	1·90	2·00

(Des BG Studio. Litho Questa)

1980 (30 Sept). *75th Anniv of Rotary International. T* **122** *and similar vert designs showing different coastal landscapes within cogwheels. P* 14.

554	10 c. multicoloured	5	5
555	50 c. multicoloured	25	15
556	$2 greenish black, carmine & greenish yell	85	85
557	$2.50, multicoloured	95	95
MS558	103 × 106 mm. $5 multicoloured	1·90	200

123 Sir Arthur Lewis

(Des J. W. Litho Questa)

1980 (23 Oct). *Nobel Prize Winners. T* **123** *and similar vert designs. Multicoloured. P* 14.

559	10 c. Type **123**	5	5
560	50 c. Martin Luther King Jnr.	20	15
561	$2 Ralph Bunche	80	90
562	$2.50, Albert Schweitzer	90	1·00
MS563	115 × 91 mm. $5 Albert Einstein	1·90	2·00

1980
HURRICANE

$1.50 RELIEF

(124)

1980 (3 Nov). *Hurricane Relief. Nos.* 539/40 *and* 543 *surch with T* **124**.

564	$1.50 on 15 c. Local bus	60	65
565	$1.50 on 20 c. Refrigerator ship	60	65
566	$1.50 on 50 c. Boeing "727" airliner	60	65

125 "The Nativity" (Giovanni Battista)

126 Agouti

(Des J. Cooter. Litho Questa)

1980 (1 Dec). *Christmas. Paintings. T* **125** *and similar vert designs. Multicoloured. W w* 14. *P* 14 × 13½.

567	10 c. Type **125**	5	5
568	30 c. "Adoration of the Kings" (Pieter the Elder)	20	10
569	$2 "Adoration of the Shepherds" (ascribed to Murillo)	1·10	1·25
MS570	102 × 88 mm. $1 × 3, Angel with people of St. Lucia (*composite design*) (*each* 30 × 75 *mm*). P 14½ × 14	1·50	1·60

(Des G. Drummond. Litho Questa)

1981 (19 Jan). *Wildlife. T* **126** *and similar vert designs. Multicoloured. P* 14.

571	10 c. Type **126**	10	10
572	50 c. St. Lucia Amazon	30	30
573	$2 Purple-throated Carib	1·00	1·10
574	$2.50, Fiddler Crab	1·25	1·40
MS575	103 × 87 mm. $5 Monarch Butterfly	2·40	2·50

127 Prince Charles at Balmoral

128 Lady Diana Spencer

(Des J. W. Litho Questa)

1981 (23 June). *Royal Wedding. T* **127** *and similar vert designs. Multicoloured. P* 14.

576	25 c. Prince Charles and Lady Diana Spencer	20	25
577	50 c. Clarence House	25	30
578	$4 Type **127**	1·75	1·90
MS579	96 × 82 mm. $5 Glass Coach and coachman	2·25	2·50

Nos. 576/8 also exist perforated 12 (*price for set of* 3 £2.10 *mint or used*) from additional sheetlets of five stamps and one label. These stamps have changed background colours.

(Manufactured by Walsall)

1981 (23 June). *Royal Wedding. Booklet stamps. T* **128** *and similar vert designs. Multicoloured. Roul* 5 × *imperf* Self-adhesive.*

580	50 c. Type **128**	20	20
	a. Booklet pane. Nos. 580/1 each × 3	3·00	
581	$2 Prince Charles	80	80
582	$5 Prince Charles and Lady Diana Spencer	3·00	3·00
	a. Booklet pane of 1	3·00	

*The 50 c. and $2 values were each separated by various combinations of rotary knife (giving a straight edge) and roulette. The $5 value exists only with straight edges.

129 "The Cock"

130 "Industry"

(Des J.W. Litho Questa)

1981 (20 July). *Birth Centenary of Picasso. T* **129** *and similar vert designs. Multicoloured. P* 13½ × 14.

583	30 c. Type **129**	20	20
584	50 c. "Man with an Ice-Cream"	25	25
585	55 c. "Woman dressing her Hair"	25	25
586	$3 "Seated Woman"	1·40	1·50
MS587	128 × 102 mm. $5 "Night Fishing at Antibes"	2·25	2·50

(Des Walsall. Litho Format)

1981 (28 Sept). *25th Anniv of Duke of Edinburgh Award Scheme. T* **130** *and similar vert designs. Multicoloured. W w* **14**. *P* 14½.

588	10 c. Type **130**	5	5
589	35 c. "Community service"	20	20
590	50 c. "Physical recreation"	25	25
591	$2.50, Duke of Edinburgh speaking at Caribbean Conference, 1975	1·25	1·40

131 Louis Braille

132 "Portrait of Fanny Travis Cochran" (Cecilia Beaux)

(Des J.W. Litho Questa)

1981 (10 Nov). *International Year for Disabled Persons. Famous Disabled People. T* **131** *and similar horiz designs. Multicoloured. P* 14.

592	10 c. Type **131**	5	5
593	50 c. Sarah Bernhardt	25	25
594	$2 Joseph Pulitzer	1·00	1·10
595	$2.50, Henri de Toulouse-Lautrec	1·25	1·40
MS596	115 × 90 mm. $5 Franklin Delano Roosevelt	2·25	2·50

(Des BG Studio. Litho Questa)

1981 (1 Dec). *Decade for Women. Paintings. T* **132** *and similar vert designs. Multicoloured. P* 14.

597	10 c. Type **132**	5	5
598	50 c. "Women with Dove" (Marie Laurencin)	25	25
599	$2 "Portrait of a Young Pupil of David" (Aimee Duvivier)	1·00	1·10
600	$2.50, "Self-portrait" (Rosalba Carriera)	1·25	1·40
MS601	104 × 78 mm. $5 "Self-portrait" (Elizabeth Vigee-le-Brun)	2·25	2·50

133 "The Adoration of the Magi" (Sfoza)

134 1860 1d. Stamp

(Des BG Studio. Litho Format)

1981 (15 Dec). *Christmas Paintings. T* **133** *and similar vert designs. Multicoloured. W w* **14**. *P* 14.

602	10 c. Type **133**	5	5
603	30 c. "The Adoration of the Kings" (Orcanga)	15	15
604	$1.50, "The Adoration of the Kings" (Gerard)	75	75
605	$2.50, "The Adoration of the Kings" (Foppa)	1·25	1·40

(Des J.W. Litho Questa)

1981 (29 Dec). *First Anniv of U.P.U. Membership. T* **134** *and similar horiz designs. Multicoloured. P* 14.

606	10 c. Type **134**	5	5
607	30 c. 1969 First anniversary of Caribbean Free Trade Area 25 c. commemorative	15	15
608	50 c. 1979 Independence $2 commemorative	25	25
609	$2 U.P.U. emblem with U.P.U. and St. Lucia flags	1·00	1·25
MS610	128 × 109 mm. $5 U.P.U. Headquarters, Berne, and G.P.O. Building, Castries	1·75	1·90

135 Scene from Football Match

(Des Clover Mill. Litho Format)

1982 (15 Feb). *World Cup Football Championship, Spain. T* **135** *and similar horiz designs showing scenes from different matches. P* 15.

611	10 c. multicoloured	5	5
612	50 c. multicoloured	25	25
613	$2 multicoloured	1·00	1·10
614	$2.50, multicoloured	1·25	1·40
MS615	104 × 84 mm. $5 multicoloured	2·25	2·50

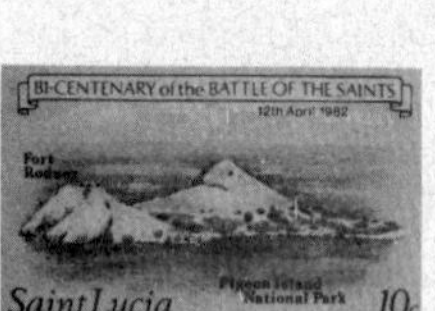

136 Pigeon Island National Park

137 Map-reading

(Des J. Cooter. Litho Format)

1982 (13 Apr). *Bicentenary of Battle of the Saints. T* **136** *and similar horiz designs. Multicoloured. W w* **14**. *P* 14.

616	10 c. Type **136**	5	5
617	35 c. Battle scene	20	20
618	50 c. Rodney (English admiral) and De Grasse (French admiral)	25	25
619	$2.50, Map of the Saints, Martinique and St. Lucia	1·25	1·40
MS620	125 × 75 mm. Nos. 616/19	1·75	2·00

(Litho Questa)

1982 (4 Aug). *75th Anniv of Boy Scout Movement. T* **137** *and similar vert designs. Multicoloured. W w* **14**. *P* 14.

621	10 c. Type **137**	5	5
622	50 c. First Aid practice	25	25
623	$1.50, Camping	75	80
624	$2.50, Campfire singsong	1·25	1·40

138 Leeds Castle

139 "Adoration of the Kings" (detail, Jan Brueghel)

(Des PAD Studio. Litho Questa)

982 (1 Sept). *21st Birthday of Princess of Wales. T* **138** *and similar vert designs. Multicoloured. P* 14½ × 14.
25 50 c. Type **138** .. 30 25
26 $2 Princess Diana boarding aircraft .. 1·00 95
27 $4 Wedding .. 2·00 1·90
IS628 102 × 75 mm. $5 Princess of Wales .. 2·10 2·25

(Des PAD Studio. Litho Harrison)

982 (10 Nov). *Christmas. T* **139** *and similar vert designs depicting details from paintings. Multicoloured. W w* **14.** *P* 14.
29 10 c. Type **139** .. 5 8
30 30 c. "Nativity" (Lorenzo Costa) .. 15 15
31 50 c. "Virgin and Child" (Fra Filippo Lippi) .. 25 25
32 80 c. "Adoration of the Shepherds" (Nicolas Poussin) .. 40 50

140 The Pitons

141 Crown Agents Headquarters, Millbank, London

(Des D. Bowen. Litho Questa)

983 (14 Mar). *Commonwealth Day. T* **140** *and similar horiz designs. Multicoloured. W w* **14** *(sideways). P* 14.
33 10 c. Type **140** .. 5 5
34 30 c. Tourist beach .. 15 20
35 50 c. Banana harvesting .. 20 25
36 $2 Flag of St. Lucia .. 95 1·00

(Des L. Curtis. Litho Questa)

983 (1 Apr). *150th Anniv of Crown Agents. T* **141** *and similar vert designs. Multicoloured. W w* **14.** *P* 14.
37 10 c. Type **141** .. 5 5
38 15 c. Road construction .. 5 8
39 50 c. Road network map .. 20 25
40 $2 First St. Lucia stamp .. 95 1·00

142 Communications at Sea

(Des J.W. Litho Format)

1983 (12 July). *World Communications Year. T* **142** *and similar horiz designs. Multicoloured. P* 14½.
641 10 c. Type **142** .. 5 5
642 50 c. Communications in the air .. 20 25
643 $1.50, T.V. transmission via satellite .. 70 75
644 $2.50, Computer communications .. 1·10 1·25
MS645 107 × 88 mm. $5 Weather satellite .. 2·50 2·75

143 Longspine Squirrelfish

(Des G. Drummond. Litho Format)

1983 (23 Aug). *Coral Reef Fishes. T* **143** *and similar horiz designs. Multicoloured. P* 14½.
646 10 c. Type **143** .. 5 5
647 50 c. Banded Butterflyfish .. 20 25
648 $1.50, Blackbar Soldierfish .. 70 75
649 $2.50, Yellowtail Snapper .. 1·10 1·25
MS650 122 × 97 mm. $5 Red Hind .. 2·50 2·75

144 *Duke of Sutherland* (1930)

145 "The Niccolini-Cowper Madonna"

(Des J.W. Litho Format)

1983 (14 Oct). *Leaders of the World. Railway Locomotives (1st series). T* **144** *and similar horiz designs, the first in each pair showing technical drawings and the second the locomotive at work. P* 12½.
651 35 c. multicoloured .. 15 20
a. Vert pair. Nos. 651/2 .. 30 40
652 35 c. multicoloured .. 15 20
653 35 c. multicoloured .. 15 20
a. Vert pair. Nos. 653/4 .. 30 40
654 35 c. multicoloured .. 15 20
655 50 c. multicoloured .. 25 30
a. Vert pair. Nos. 655/6 .. 50 60
656 50 c. multicoloured .. 25 30
657 50 c. multicoloured .. 25 30
a. Vert pair. Nos. 657/8 .. 50 60
658 50 c. multicoloured .. 25 30
659 $1 multicoloured .. 45 50
a. Vert pair. Nos. 659/60 .. 90 1·00
660 $1 multicoloured .. 45 50
661 $1 multicoloured .. 45 50
a. Vert pair. Nos. 661/2 .. 90 1·00
662 $1 multicoloured .. 45 50
663 $2 multicoloured .. 95 1·00
a. Vert pair. Nos. 663/4 .. 1·90 2·00
664 $2 multicoloured .. 95 1·00
665 $2 multicoloured .. 95 1·00
a. Vert pair. Nos. 665/6 .. 1·90 2·00
666 $2 multicoloured .. 95 1·00
651/66 .. *Set of* 16 6·50 7·00

Designs:—Nos. 651/2, *Duke of Sutherland* (1930); 653/4, *City of Glasgow* (1940); 655/6, *Lord Nelson* (1926); 657/8, *Leeds United* (1928); 659/60, *Bodmin* (1945); 661/2, *Eton* (1930); 663/4, *Flying Scotsman* (1923); 665/6, *Rocket* (1829).

Nos. 651/2, 653/4, 655/6, 657/8, 659/60, 661/2, 663/4 and 665/6 were printed together, *se-tenant*, in vertical pairs throughout the sheets.

See also Nos. 715/26 and 761/76.

(Litho Format)

1983 (21 Nov). *Christmas. 500th Birth Anniv of Raphael. T* **145** *and similar vert designs showing details of Raphael paintings. Multicoloured. W w* **14.** *P* 14.
667 10 c. Type **145** .. 5 5
668 30 c. "The Holy Family with a Palm Tree" .. 15 20
669 50 c. "The Sistine Madonna" .. 25 30
670 $5 "The Alba Madonna" .. 2·50 2·75

146 George III

147 Clarke & Co's Drug Store

(Des Court House Studio. Litho Format)

1984 (13 Mar). *Leaders of the World. British Monarchs. T* **146** *and similar vert designs. Multicoloured. P* 12½.
671 5 c. Battle of Waterloo .. 5 5
a. Horiz pair. Nos. 671/2 .. 8 10
672 5 c. Type **146** .. 5 5
673 10 c. George III at Kew .. 8 10
a. Horiz pair. Nos. 673/4 .. 15 20
674 10 c. Kew Palace .. 8 10
675 35 c. Coat of Arms of Elizabeth I .. 25 30
a. Horiz pair. Nos. 675/6 .. 50 60
676 35 c. Elizabeth I .. 25 30
677 60 c. Coat of Arms of George III .. 40 45
a. Horiz pair. Nos. 677/8 .. 80 90
678 60 c. George III (*different*) .. 40 45
679 $1 Elizabeth I at Hatfield .. 70 75
a. Horiz pair. Nos. 679/80 .. 1·40 1·50
680 $1 Hatfield Palace .. 70 75
681 $2.50, Spanish Armada .. 1·75 1·90
a. Horiz pair. Nos. 681/2 .. 3·50 3·75
682 $2.50, Elizabeth I (*different*) .. 1·75 1·90
671/82 .. *Set of* 12 5·75 6·25

Nos. 671/2, 673/4, 675/6, 677/8, 679/80 and 681/2 were printed together in *se-tenant* horizontal pairs throughout the sheets.

(Des J. Cooter. Litho Questa)

1984 (6 Apr). *Historic Buildings. T* **147** *and similar multi-coloured designs. W w* **15** *(sideways on 45 c. to $2.50). P* 14 × 13½ *(10 c.) or* 13½ × 14 *(others).*
683 10 c. Type **147** .. 8 10
684 45 c. Colonial architecture (*horiz*) .. 30 35
685 65 c. Colonial "chattel" house (*horiz*) .. 45 50
686 $2.50, Treasury after 1906 earthquake (*horiz*) 1·75 1·90

1984 (15 May). *As Nos.* 540/42, 545/6 *and* 548, *but W w* **15** *(sideways on 20 c. to $1). P* 14½ × 14.
690 20 c. Refrigerator ship .. 12 15
691 25 c. "Islander" aeroplane .. 15 20
692 30 c. Pilot boat .. 20 25
695 $1 Lockheed "Tristar" airliner .. 60 65
696 $2 Cargo liner .. 1·25 1·40
698 $10 *Queen Elizabeth II* (liner) .. 6·00 6·50
690/8 .. *Set of* 6 7·50 8·25

148 Logwood

(Des J. Cooter. Litho Format)

1984 (12 June). *Forestry Resources. T* **148** *and similar multi-coloured designs. W w* **15** *(inverted on 65 c., sideways on others). P* 14 × 13½ *(65 c.) or* 13½ × 14 *(others).*
699 10 c. Type **148** .. 8 10
700 45 c. Calabash .. 30 35
701 65 c. Gommier (*vert*) .. 45 50
702 $2.50, Raintree .. 1·75 1·90

149 Bugatti Type "57SC Atlantic Coupe"

(Des J.W. Litho Format)

1984 (25 June). *Leaders of the World. Automobiles (1st series). T* **149** *and similar horiz designs, the first in each pair showing technical drawings and the second paintings. P* 12½.
703 5 c. black, reddish lavender and lemon .. 5 5
a. Vert pair. Nos. 703/4 .. 8 10
704 5 c. multicoloured .. 5 5
705 10 c. black, azure and rose-carmine .. 8 10
a. Vert pair. Nos. 705/6 .. 15 20
706 10 c. multicoloured .. 8 10
707 $1 black, pale green and orange-brown .. 70 75
a. Vert pair. Nos. 707/8 .. 1·40 1·50
708 $1 multicoloured .. 70 75
709 $2.50, black, pale flesh and slate-blue .. 1·75 1·90
a. Vert pair. Nos. 709/10 .. 3·50 3·75
710 $2.50, multicoloured .. 1·75 1·90
703/10 .. *Set of* 8 4·50 5·00

Designs:—Nos. 703/4, Bugatti Type "57SC Atlantic Coupe"; 705/6, Chevrolet "Bel Air Convertible"; 707/8, Alfa Romeo "1750 GS (Zagato)"; 709/10, Duesenberg "S J Roadster".

Nos. 703/4, 705/6, 707/8 and 709/10 were printed together, *se-tenant*, in vertical pairs throughout the sheets.

See also Nos. 745/60.

150 Pygmy Gecko

151 Men's Volleyball

(Des Jennifer Toombs. Litho Format)

1984 (8 Aug). *Endangered Wildlife. T* **150** *and similar horiz designs. Multicoloured. W w* **15** *(sideways). P* 14.
711 10 c. Type **150** .. 8 10
712 45 c. Maria Island Ground Lizard .. 30 35
713 65 c. Green Iguana .. 45 50
714 $2.50, Couresse Snake .. 1·75 1·90

(Des J.W. Litho Format)

1984 (21 Sept). *Leaders of the World. Railway Locomotives (2nd series). Horiz designs as T* **144**, *the first in each pair showing technical drawings and the second the locomotive at work. P* 12½.
715 1 c. multicoloured .. 5 5
a. Vert pair. Nos. 715/16 .. 5 5
716 1 c. multicoloured .. 5 5
717 15 c. multicoloured .. 12 15
a. Vert pair. Nos. 717/18 .. 25 30
718 15 c. multicoloured .. 12 15
719 50 c. multicoloured .. 35 40
a. Vert pair. Nos. 719/20 .. 70 80
720 50 c. multicoloured .. 35 40
721 75 c. multicoloured .. 50 55
a. Vert pair. Nos. 721/2 .. 1·00 1·10
722 75 c. multicoloured .. 50 55
723 $1 multicoloured .. 70 75
a. Vert pair. Nos. 723/4 .. 1·40 1·50
724 $1 multicoloured .. 70 75
725 $2 multicoloured .. 1·40 1·50
a. Vert pair. Nos. 725/6 .. 2·75 3·00
726 $2 multicoloured .. 1·40 1·50
715/26 .. *Set of* 12 5·50 6·00

Designs:—Nos. 715/16, *Taw* (1897); 717/18, "Crocodile 1.C.C.1." (1920); 719/20, *The Countess* (1903); 721/2, Class "GE6/6 C.C." (1921); 723/4, Class "P8" (1906); 725/6, *Der Adler* (1835).

Nos. 715/26 were issued in a similar sheet format to Nos. 651/66.

(Des Court House Studio. Litho Format)

1984 (21 Sept). *Leaders of the World. Olympic Games, Los Angeles. T* **151** *and similar vert designs. Multicoloured. P* 12½.
727 5 c. Type **151** .. 5 5
a. Horiz pair. Nos. 727/8 .. 8 10
728 5 c. Women's volleyball .. 5 5
729 10 c. Women's hurdles .. 8 10
a. Horiz pair. Nos. 729/30 .. 15 20
730 10 c. Men's hurdles .. 8 10
731 65 c. Show jumping .. 45 50
a. Horiz pair. Nos. 731/2 .. 90 1·00
732 65 c. Dressage .. 45 50
733 $2.50, Women's gymnastics .. 1·75 1·90
a. Horiz pair. Nos. 733/4 .. 3·50 3·75
734 $2.50, Men's gymnastics .. 1·75 1·90
727/34 .. *Set of* 8 4·00 4·50

Nos. 727/8, 729/30, 731/2, 733/4 were printed together, *se-tenant*, in horizontal pairs throughout the sheets.

Examples of No. 537 exist overprinted "RUMBRIDGE PACK R.F.C./1984 TOUR". This was a private souvenir, connected with a tour to St. Lucia by an English rugby club in October 1984. It was not sold by the St. Lucia Post Office or Philatelic Bureau.

152 Glass of Wine and Flowers 153 Slaves preparing Manioc

(Des G. L. Vasarhelyi. Litho Format)

1984 (31 Oct). *Christmas. T* **152** *and similar vert designs. Multi-coloured. W* w **15.** *P* 14.

735 10 c. Type **152** 8 10
736 35 c. Priest and decorated altar 25 30
737 65 c. Nativity scene 45 50
738 $3 Holy Family .. .. 2·00 2·10
MS739 147 × 77 mm. Nos. 735/8 .. .. .. 2·75 3·00

(Des J. Cooter. Litho Format)

1984 (12 Dec). *150th Anniv of Abolition of Slavery. T* **153** *and similar vert designs. Each black and yellow-ochre. W* w **15.** *P* 14 × 13½.

740 10 c. Type **153** 8 10
741 35 c. Sifting and cooking cassava flour .. 25 30
742 55 c. Cooking pot, and preparing tobacco .. 35 40
743 $5 Stripping tobacco leaves for twist tobacco 3·50 3·75
MS744 154 × 110 mm. As Nos. 740/3, but without dates and side inscription and with the face values in different positions .. .. 4·00 4·25

(Des Artists International (65 c.), J.W. (others). Litho Format)

1984 (19 Dec). *Leaders of the World. Automobiles (2nd series). Horiz designs as T* **149**, *the first in each pair showing technical drawings and the second paintings. P* 12½.

745 10 c. black, pale green and lake-brown .. 8 10
a. Vert pair. Nos. 745/6 .. .. .. 15 20
746 10 c. multicoloured 8 10
747 30 c. black, azure and bright yellow-green .. 20 25
a. Vert pair. Nos. 747/8 .. .. .. 40 50
748 30 c. multicoloured 20 25
749 55 c. black, greenish yellow and orange-brown 35 40
a. Vert pair. Nos. 749/50 .. .. .. 70 80
750 55 c. multicoloured 35 40
751 65 c. black, grey and brown-lilac 45 50
a. Vert pair. Nos. 751/2 .. .. .. 90 1·00
752 65 c. multicoloured 45 50
753 75 c. black, pale cinnamon, & orange-verm 50 55
a. Vert pair. Nos. 753/4 .. .. .. 1·00 1·10
754 75 c. multicoloured 50 55
755 $1 black, pale cinnamon and dull violet-blue 70 75
a. Vert pair. Nos. 755/6 .. .. .. 1·40 1·50
756 $1 multicoloured 70 75
757 $2 black, pale green and orange-red .. 1·40 1·50
a. Vert pair. Nos. 757/8 .. .. .. 2·75 3·00
758 $2 multicoloured .. .. 1·40 1·50
759 $3 black, pale cinnamon & orange-verm 2·00 2·10
a. Vert pair. Nos. 759/60 .. .. .. 4·00 4·25
760 $3 multicoloured .. .. 2·00 2·10
745/60 .. .. *Set of* 16 10·00 11·00

Designs:—Nos. 745/6, Panhard and Levassor; 747/8, N.S.U. "RO-80" Saloon; 749/50, Abarth "Bialbero"; 751/2, TVR "Vixen 2500M"; 753/4, Ford "Mustang" Convertible; 755/6, Ford "Model T"; 757/8, Aston Martin" DB3S"; 759/60, Chrysler "Imperial CG Dual Cowl" Phaeton.

Nos. 745/60 were issued in a similar sheet format to Nos. 703/10.

(Des T. Hadler (5, 15, 35 c.), J.W. (others). Litho Format)

1985 (4 Feb). *Leaders of the World. Railway Locomotives (3rd series). Horiz designs as T* **144**, *the first in each pair showing technical drawings and the second the locomotive at work. P* 12½.

761 5 c. multicoloured 5 5
a. Vert pair. Nos. 761/2 5
762 5 c. multicoloured 5 5
763 15 c. multicoloured 8 10
a. Vert pair. Nos. 763/4 15
764 15 c. multicoloured 8 10
765 35 c. multicoloured 20 25
a. Vert pair. Nos. 765/6 40
766 35 c. multicoloured 20 25
767 60 c. multicoloured 35 40
a. Vert pair. Nos. 767/8 70
768 60 c. multicoloured 35 40
769 75 c. multicoloured 45 50
a. Vert pair. Nos. 769/70 40
770 75 c. multicoloured 45 50
771 $1 multicoloured 60 65
a. Vert pair. Nos. 771/2 .. .. .. 1·25
772 $1 multicoloured 60 65
773 $2 multicoloured .. .. 1·25 1·40
a. Vert pair. Nos. 773/4 .. .. .. 2·50
774 $2 multicoloured .. .. 1·25 1·40
775 $2.50, multicoloured .. .. .. 1·50 1·60
a. Vert pair. Nos. 775/6 .. .. .. 3·00
776 $2.50, multicoloured .. .. .. 1·50 1·60
761/76 .. .. *Set of* 16 8·00 9·00

Designs:—Nos. 761/2, J.N.R. Class "C53" (1928); 763/4, India Class "Heavy L" (1885); 765/6, Q.G.R. Class "B18¼" (1926); 767/8, *Owain Glyndwr* (1923); 769/70, *Lion* (1838); 771/2, Coal engine (1873); 773/4, No. 2238, Class "Q6" (1921); 775/6, Class "H" (1920).

Nos. 761/76 are in the same sheet format as Nos. 651/66.

OMNIBUS ISSUES

Details, together with prices for complete sets, of the various Omnibus issues from the 1935 Silver Jubilee series to date are included in a special section following Zululand at the end of the catalogue.

154 Girl Guide Badge in Shield and Crest of St. Lucia

(Des Court House Studio. Litho Questa)

1985 (21 Feb). *75th Anniv of Girl Guide Movement and 60th Anniv of Guiding in St. Lucia. W* w **15.** *P* 14.

777 **154** 10 c. multicoloured 5 8
778 35 c. multicoloured 20 25
779 65 c. multicoloured 35 40
780 $3 multicoloured .. .. .. 1·75 1·90

POSTAGE DUE STAMPS

D 1

No. **No.**

Normal Wide fount

(Type-set Government Printing Office)

1930. *Each stamp individually handstamped with different number. No wmk. No gum. Rough perf* 12. *(a) Horizontally laid paper.*

D1 D 1 1d. black/*blue* .. .. 2·25 3·00
a. Wide, wrong fount "No." .. .. 6·00 6·00
b. Missing stop after "ST" .. .. 8·50 8·50
c. Missing stop after "LUCIA" .. .. 8·50 8·50
d. Handstamped number double .. 50·00

(b) Wove paper

D2 D 1 2d. black/*yellow* .. .. 4·50 6·00
a. Wide, wrong fount "No." .. .. 9·00 10·00
b. Imperf between (vert pair) £3500
c. Missing stop after "ST" .. .. 9·50 11·00
d. Incorrect number with correction above .. .. 50·00

It is believed that there were three settings of the 1d. and two of the 2d., the same type being used for both values.

For the initial setting of the 1d. the wide "No." variety occurs on the last four stamps in the bottom row of the sheet of 60 (6 × 10). In later settings first the second and then later the first stamps in the same row were changed to show the variety. Nos. D1b and D2c occur on R.5/3 and No. D1c on R.9/2.

Some sheets from the initial printing of the 1d. show a paper-maker's watermark, "KINGSCLERE" in double-lined capitals above a crown, across a number of stamps.

The sheets had all outer edges, except that at the left, imperforate. It would appear that they were bound into books from which they could be detached, using the perforations at the left-hand edge.

The handstamped numbers were applied at the Post Office, using numbering machines. Each value had its own sequence of numbers and it is possible to recognise, by minor differences in fount, the use of two such machines. This is especially noticeable on examples of Nos. D1d and D2d where the corrections are often applied using a second machine. No. D2d shows the incorrect number partly erased and a correction struck across it.

D 2

D 3

D 4 St. Lucia Coat of Arms

(Typo D.L.R.)

1933–47. *Wmk Mult Script CA. P* 14.

D3 D 2 1d. black .. .. 2·00 2·75
D4 2d. black .. .. 3·00 4·25
D5 4d. black (28.6.47) .. .. .. 3·25 6·50
D6 8d. black (28.6.47) .. .. .. 3·50 8·50
D3/6 Perf "Specimen" .. .. *Set of* 4 £130

1949 (1 Oct)–**52.** *Value in cents. Wmk Mult Script CA. Typo. P* 14.

D 7 D 3 2 c. black .. .. 1·60 2·50
a. Chalky paper (27.11.52) 20 75
ab. Error. Crown missing, W 9*a* .. 32·00
ac. Error. St. Edward's Crown, W 9*b* .. 22·00
D 8 4 c. black .. .. 2·50 3·50
a. Chalky paper (27.11.52) .. .. 35 1·00
ab. Error. Crown missing, W 9*a* .. 35·00
ac. Error. St. Edward's Crown, W 9*b* .. 24·00
D 9 8 c. black .. .. 3·50 6·00
a. Chalky paper (27.11.52) .. .. 90 2·50
ac. Error. St. Edward's Crown, W 9*b* .. 55·00
D10 16 c. black .. .. 10·00 13·00
a. Chalky paper (27.11.52) .. .. 1·40 4·75
ac. Error. St. Edward's Crown, W 9*b* .. 60·00

1965 (9 Mar). *As Nos. D7/8 but wmk* w **12.** *Unsurfaced pape*[r]. *P* 14.

D11 D 3 2 c. black .. .. 65 2·5
D12 4 c. black .. .. 80 3·0

Nos. D9a, D10a and D11/12 exist overprinted as T **49** in red *(Pric*[e] *for set of* 4 £150 *mint).*

(Des L. Curtis. Litho Format)

1981 (4 Aug). *W* w **14.** *P* 14.

D13 D 4 5 c. brown-purple 5
D14 15 c. emerald 10 1
D15 25 c. red-orange 15 2
D16 $1 deep ultramarine 60 6

OFFICIAL STAMPS

OFFICIAL

(O 1)

1983 (13 Oct). *Nos. 537/48 optd with Type* O **1.**

O 1 5 c. Type **120** 5
O 2 10 c. McDonnell Douglas "DC-10" airliner .. 5
O 3 15 c. Local bus 10 1
O 4 20 c. Refrigerator ship 12 1
O 5 25 c. "Islander" aeroplane 15 2
O 6 30 c. Pilot boat 20 2
O 7 50 c. Boeing "727" airliner 30 3
O 8 75 c. Cruise ship 45 5
O 9 $1 Lockheed "Tristar" airliner 60 6
O10 $2 Cargo liner .. .. 1·25 1·4
O11 $5 Boeing "707" airliner .. .. 3·00 3·2
O12 $10 *Queen Elizabeth 2* (liner) .. .. 6·00 6·5
O1/12 .. .. *Set of* 12 11·00 12·0

POSTAL FISCAL STAMPS

Nos. F1/28 were authorised for postal use from 14 April 1885.

CANCELLATIONS. Many used examples of the Postal Fisca[l] stamps have had previous pen cancellations removed before bein[g] used postally.

SHILLING STAMP (F 1) One Penny Stamp (F 2) HALFPENNY Stamp (F 3)

1881. *Wmk Crown CC. P* 14. *(a) Surch as Type* F **1.**

F1 1 ONE PENNY STAMP, black (C.) .. 26·00 30·0
a. Surch inverted £700 £70
b. Surch double £650 £70
F2 FOUR PENNY STAMP, yellow .. 50·00 60·0
a. Bisected (2d.) (on cover) .. ..
F3 SIX PENCE STAMP, mauve .. .. 90·00 £10
F4 SHILLING STAMP, orange .. .. 50·00 60·0
a. "SHILEING" £650
b. "SHILDING" £650 £70

(b) Surch as Type F **2**

F 7 1 One Penny Stamp, black (R.) .. .. 26·00 30·0
a. Surch double £700
F 8 Four Pence Stamp, yellow .. .. 40·00 45·0
F 9 Six Pence Stamp, mauve .. .. 40·00 45·0
F10 Shilling Stamp, orange .. .. 42·00 60·0

(c) Surch as Type F **3**

F11 1 Halfpenny Stamp, green .. .. 26·00 30·0
a. "Stamp" double £450 £45
F12 One Shilling Stamp, orange *(wmk Crown CA)* .. .. 45·00 50·0
a. "Stamp" double £450 £50

FOUR PENCE REVENUE (F 4) Revenue (F 5) REVENUE (F 6)

1882. *Wmk Crown CA. Surch as Type* F **4.** *(a) P* 14.

F13 1 1d. black (C.) .. .. 14·00 15·00
a. Imperf. (pair) £1100
F14 2d. pale blue .. .. 6·50 9·00
a. Imperf (pair) .. .. ..
F15 3d. deep blue (C.) .. .. .. 24·00 32·00
F16 4d. yellow .. .. 6·00 8·00
F17 6d. mauve .. .. 15·00 20·00

(b) P 12

F18 1 1d. black (C.) .. .. 15·00 20·00
F19 3d. deep blue (C.) .. .. .. 20·00 20·00
F20 1s. orange .. .. 20·00 23·00

1883. *Nos. 25, 26, 30 and 32 optd locally as Type* F **5.**

(a) Word 11 mm long

F21 1d. black (C.) .. .. 12·00 23·00
a. Opt inverted .. .. ..
b. Opt double £250 £350

(b) Word 13 mm

F22 1d. black (C.) .. .. — 26·00

(c) Word 15½ mm

F23 ½d. green .. .. — 29·00
a. "Revenue" double .. .. .. — £225
F24 1d. black (C.) .. .. 11·00 13·00
a. "Revenue" double £130
b. "Revenue" triple £250
c. "Revenue" double, one inverted .. £250 £300
F25 1d. rose (No. 30) .. .. .. — 23·00
F26 4d. yellow .. .. — 30·00

1884–85. *Optd with Type* F **6.** *Wmk Crown CA. P* 14.

F27 5 1d. slate (C.) .. .. 6·50 10·00
a. Imperf (pair) .. .. ..
F28 1d. dull mauve (Die I) (1885) .. .. 6·50 7·50

St. Vincent

Although postal markings for St. Vincent are recorded as early as 1793 it was not until 1852 that the British G.P.O. opened a branch office at Kingstown, the island's capital.

The stamps of Great Britain were used between May 1858 and the end of April 1860. From 1 May in that year the local authorities assumed responsibility for the postal services and fell back on the use of No. CC1 until the introduction of St. Vincent stamps in 1861.

For illustration of the handstamp and postmark types see BRITISH POST OFFICES ABROAD notes, following GREAT BRITAIN.

KINGSTOWN

CROWNED-CIRCLE HANDSTAMPS

CC1 CC 1 ST. VINCENT (R.) (30.1.1852) *Price on cover* £750

Stamps of GREAT BRITAIN cancelled "A 10" *as Type* **2**.

1858 *to* **1860**.
Z1 1d. rose-red (1857), *perf* 14 .. .. £550
Z2 2d. blue (1855) .. ..
Z3 4d. rose (1857) £350
Z4 6d. lilac (1856) £250
Z5 1s. green (1856) £950

PRICES FOR STAMPS ON COVER TO 1945

Nos. 1/2	*from* × 3
Nos. 3/7	*from* × 5
No. 8	—
No. 9	*from* × 5
No. 10	—
Nos. 11/19	*from* × 4
Nos. 20/1	*from* × 3
Nos. 22/5	*from* × 4
Nos. 26/8	—
Nos. 29/31	*from* × 5
No. 32	—
Nos. 33/5	*from* × 2
Nos. 36/8	*from* × 4
Nos. 39/41	*from* × 6
Nos. 42/5	*from* × 4
No. 46	*from* × 12
Nos. 47/54	*from* × 4
Nos. 55/8	*from* × 8
No. 59	*from* × 10
No. 60	*from* × 6
Nos. 61/3	*from* × 8
Nos. 67/75	*from* × 3
Nos. 76/84	*from* × 2
Nos. 85/92	*from* × 3
No. 93	—
Nos. 94/8	*from* × 3
Nos. 99/107	*from* × 2
Nos. 108/19	*from* × 3
No. 120	—
No. 121	*from* × 3
No. 122	*from* × 5
No. 123	—
No. 124	*from* × 5
Nos. 126/9	*from* × 10
Nos. 131/45	*from* × 3
Nos. 146/8	*from* × 6
Nos. 149/59	*from* × 2

CROWN COLONY

1

(2)

3

(**T 1, 3** and **7** recess P.B.)

1861 (8 May). *No wmk.* (a) *Intermediate perf* 14 *to* 16.
1 1 1d. rose-red £7000 £600
a. Imperf vert (horiz pair) .. ..
2 6d. deep yellow-green £5500 £300

(b) *Rough perf* 14 *to* 16
3 1 1d. rose-red .. .. 26·00 18·00
a. Imperf vert (horiz pair) £350
b. Imperf (pair) £250

1862 (Sept). *No wmk. Rough perf* 14 *to* 16.
4 1 6d. deep green .. .. .. 65·00 18·00
a. Imperf between (horiz pair) .. £900
b. Imperf (pair) £300

1863–68. *No wmk.* (a) *P* 11 *to* 12½.
5 1 1d. rose-red (3.63) .. .. .. 30·00 20·00
6 4d. deep blue (*shades*) (1866) £350 £110
a. Imperf between (horiz pair) ..
7 6d. deep green (7.68) .. .. .. £200 70·00
8 1s. slate-grey (8.66) £1500 £1100

(b) *P* 14 *to* 16
9 1 1s. slate-grey (*shades*) £300 £125

(c) *P* 11 *to* 12½ × 14 *to* 16
10 1 1d. rose-red £2750 £1300
11 1s. slate-grey (*shades*) £225 £120

1869. *Colours changed. No wmk. P* 11 *to* 12½.
12 1 4d. yellow £350 £150
13 1s. indigo .. .. £325 90·00
14 1s. brown £375 £160

1871 (Apr). *Wmk Small Star, Type* w **2**. *Rough perf* 14 *to* 16.
15 1 1d. black .. .. 28·00 16·00
a. Imperf between (vert pair) £4500
16 6d. deep green .. .. £250 85·00

1872. *Colour changed. W* w **2**. *P* 11 *to* 12½.
17 1 1s. deep rose-red £750 £140

1872–75. *W* w **2**. (a) *Perf about* 15.
18 1 1d. black (*shades*) (1872) .. .. 26·00 12·00
19 6d. dull blue-green (*shades*) (1873) .. £600 38·00
a. Deep blue-green (1875) .. .. £600 42·00

(b) *P* 11 *to* 12½ × 15
20 1 1s. lilac-rose (1873) £5000 £400

No. 19*a* always has the watermark sideways and Nos. 16 and 19 normally have it upright but are known with it sideways.

1875. *Colour changed. W* w **2**. *P* 11 to 12½.
21 1 1s. claret £600 £250

1876–78. *W* w **2**. (a) *P* 11 *to* 12½ × 15.
22 1 1d. black (*shades*) (1876) .. .. 40·00 8·00
a. Imperf between (horiz pair) .. — £3000
23 6d. pale green (1877) .. .. .. £500 70·00
24 1s. vermilion (2.77) £700 £140
a. Imperf vert (horiz pair) .. ..

(b) *P* 11 to 12½
25 1 4d. deep blue (7.77) .. .. .. £450 90·00

(c) *Perf about* 15
26 1 6d. pale green (3.77) £1500 £450
a. Light yellow-green (1878) .. .. £550 35·00
27 1s. vermilion (1878?) .. .. .. — £5500
a. Imperf .. .. — £1800

Nos. 23 and 26 always have the watermark sideways but No. 26*a* always has the watermark upright.

1880 (May). *No.* 19*a divided vertically by a line of perforation gauging* 12, *and surch locally as T* **2**.
28 1 1d. on half 6d. bright blue-green (R.) .. £300 £200
a. Unsevered pair £900 £550

1880 (June). *W* w **2**. *P* 11 *to* 12½.
29 1 1d. olive-green .. .. 85·00 10·00
30 6d. bright green .. .. £275 65·00
31 1s. bright vermilion .. .. .. £850 65·00
a. Imperf between (horiz pair) ..
32 3 5s. rose-red £1500 £1500
a. Imperf .. ..

d
1
2
(4)

ONE PENNY
(5)

4d
(6)

1881. *Nos.* 30/31 *surch locally. No.* 33 *is divided vertically like No.* 28.
33 4 ½d. on half 6d. bright green (R.) (1.9) £160 £160
a. Unsevered pair £375 £375
b. Fraction bar omitted (pair with and without bar) £3250 £4000
34 5 1d. on 6d. bright green (30.11) .. £375 £225
35 6 4d. on 1s. bright vermilion (28.11) .. £1200 £650

Three unused single copies of No. 33 are known with the surcharge omitted.

ST VINCENT
HALF PENNY
7

2½ PENCE
(8)

1d
2½ PENCE
(9)

1881 (Dec). *W* w **2**. *P* 11 *to* 12½.
36 7 ½d. orange (*shades*) .. .. .. 7·00 4·50
37 1 1d. drab (*shades*) .. .. .. £800 9·50
38 4d. bright blue £1400 £100
a. Imperf between (horiz pair) .. ..

(Recess D.L.R. from Perkins, Bacon plates)

1882 (Nov)–**83.** *No.* 40 *is surch with T* **8**. *Wmk Crown CA. P* 14.
39 1 1d. drab .. .. 16·00 3·75
40 2½d. on 1d. lake (1883) .. .. .. 7·00 2·00
41 4d. ultramarine .. .. .. £300 30·00
a. Dull ultramarine £950 £350

1883–84. *Wmk Crown CA. P* 12.
42 7 ½d. green (1884) .. .. 28·00 20·00
43 1 4d. ultramarine-blue .. .. .. £250 17·00
a. Grey-blue £1000 £300
44 6d. bright green £400 £300
45 1s. orange-vermilion .. .. .. 45·00 38·00

The ½d. orange, 1d. rose-red, 1d. milky blue (without surcharge) and 5s. carmine-lake which were formerly listed are now considered to be colour trials. They are, however, of great interest. (*Prices un.* ½d. £900, 1d. red £900, 1d. blue £1200, 5s. £1500.)

1885 (Mar). *No.* 40 *surch locally as in T* **9**.
46 1 1d. on 2½d. on 1d. lake .. .. 8·50 9·50

Stamps with three cancelling bars instead of two are considered to be proofs.

1885–93. *No.* 49 *is surch with T* **8**. *Wmk Crown CA. P* 14.
47 7 ½d. green 80 25
a. Deep green .. .. 2·25 50
48 1 1d. rose-red .. .. 1·90 80
a. Rose (1886) .. .. 4·25 1·50
b. Red (1887) .. .. 1·40 45
c. Carmine-red (1889) .. .. .. 22·00 3·75
49 2½d. on 1d. milky blue (1889) .. .. 22·00 4·25
50 4d. red-brown .. .. £800 22·00
51 4d. purple-brown (1886) .. .. .. 22·00 4·00
a. Chocolate (1887) .. .. .. 20·00 3·25
52 6d. violet (1888) .. .. 70·00 80·00
53 3 5s. lake (1888) .. .. 26·00 32·00
a. Brown-lake (1893) .. .. .. 28·00 30·00
49, 51*a*, 52 Optd "Specimen" .. *Set of* 3 75·00

2½d.
(10)

5
PENCE
(11)

1890. *No.* 51*a surch with T* **10**.
54 1 2½d. on 4d. chocolate .. .. .. 48·00 55·00
a. No fraction bar £200 £200

1890–93. *No.* 55 *is surch with T* **8**. *Colours changed. Wmk Crown CA. P* 14.
55 1 2½d. on 1d. grey-blue (1890) .. .. 8·50 1·40
a. Blue (1893) 75 55
56 4d. yellow (1893) (Optd S. £28) .. 1·90 3·00
57 6d. dull purple (1891) .. .. .. 2·25 3·50
58 1s. orange (1891) .. .. .. 5·50 8·00
a. Red-orange (1892) .. .. .. 8·50 12·00

1892. *No.* 51*a surch with T* **11**, *in purple.*
59 1 5d. on 4d. chocolate (Optd S. £30) .. 7·00 9·00

Some letters are known double due to loose type, the best known being the first "E", but they are not constant.

FIVE PENCE
(12)

13

14

1893–94. *Surch with T* **12**. *Wmk Crown CA. P* 14.
60 1 5d. on 6d. carmine-lake (Optd S. £45) .. 9·00 14·00
a. Deep lake (1893) .. .. .. 1·50 1·90
b. Lake (1894) .. .. 2·75 4·25
c. Surch double .. .. — £3750

(Recess D.L.R.)

1897 (13 July). *New values. Wmk Crown CA. P* 14.
61 1 2½d. blue .. .. 3·00 5·50
62 5d. sepia .. .. 7·50 13·00
61/2 Optd "Specimen" .. .. *Set of* 2 80·00

1897 (6 Oct). *Surch as T* **12**. *Wmk Crown CA. P* 14.
63 1 3d. on 1d. mauve (Optd S. £50) .. .. 7·50 10·00
a. Red-mauve .. .. 9·50 14·00

(Typo D.L.R.)

1899. *Wmk Crown CA. P* 14.
67 13 ½d. dull mauve and green .. .. 80 1·25
68 1d. dull mauve and carmine .. .. 3·00 90
69 2½d. dull mauve and blue .. .. 5·00 6·50
70 3d. dull mauve and olive .. .. 5·00 8·50
71 4d. dull mauve and orange .. .. 4·00 11·00
72 5d. dull mauve and black .. .. 8·00 12·00
73 6d. dull mauve and brown .. .. 14·00 22·00
74 14 1s. green and carmine .. .. .. 20·00 30·00
75 5s. green and blue .. .. .. 70·00 95·00
67/75 .. .. *Set of* 9 £120 £170
67/75 Optd "Specimen" .. .. *Set of* 9 £225

15

16

(Typo D.L.R.)

1902. *Wmk Crown CA. P* 14.
76 15 ½d. dull purple and green 70 65
77 1d. dull purple and carmine 75 35
78 16 2d. dull purple and black .. .. 3·25 4·00
79 15 2½d. dull purple and blue .. .. 5·00 7·00
80 3d. dull purple and olive .. .. 6·50 5·00
81 6d. dull purple and brown .. .. 9·00 13·00
82 16 1s. green and carmine .. .. .. 14·00 22·00
83 15 2s. green and violet .. .. .. 25·00 28·00
84 16 5s. green and blue .. .. .. 42·00 55·00
76/84 .. .. *Set of* 9 95·00 £120
76/84 Optd "Specimen" .. .. *Set of* 9 £150

1904–11. *Wmk Mult Crown CA. P* 14.
85 15 ½d. dull purple and green, **OC** (1905) .. 70 80
86 1d. dull purple and carmine, **OC** .. 3·75 90
88 2½d. dull purple and blue, **C** (1906) .. 7·50 14·00
89 6d. dull purple and brown, **C** (1905) .. 9·50 14·00
90 16 1s. green and carmine, **OC** (1906) .. 9·50 14·00
91 15 2s. purple and bright blue/*blue*, **C** (3.09?) .. .. 25·00 38·00

92 16 5s. green and red/*yellow*, C (3.09?) .. 32·00 45·00
93 £1 purple and black/*red*, C (1911) .. £350 £400
85/93 .. *Set of* 8 £400 £475
91/3 Optd "Specimen" .. *Set of* 3 £300

17 18

(Recess D.L.R.)

1907–08. *Wmk Mult Crown CA. P* 14.
94 **17** ½d. green (2.7.07) .. 80 90
95 1d. carmine (26.4.07) .. 2·50 70
96 2d. orange (5.08) .. 1·90 4·50
97 2½d. blue (8.07) .. 7·00 9·00
98 3d. violet (1.6.07) .. 8·50 15·00
94/8 Optd "Specimen" .. *Set of* 5 £120

1909. *No dot below "d". Wmk Mult Crown CA. P* 14.
99 **18** 1d. carmine (3.09) .. 1·25 70
100 6d. dull purple (16.1.09) .. 11·00 19·00
101 1s. black/*green* (16.1.09) .. 7·50 9·50
99/101 Optd "Specimen" .. *Set of* 3 75·00

1909 (Nov)–**11.** *T* **18**, *redrawn (dot below "d", as in T* **17**). *Wmk Mult Crown CA. P* 14.
102 ½d. green (31.10.10) .. 65 55
103 1d. carmine .. 50 30
104 2d. grey (3.8.11) .. 2·00 3·50
105 2½d. ultramarine (25.7.10) .. 2·00 3·75
106 3d. purple/*yellow* .. 3·00 3·25
107 6d. dull purple .. 3·50 7·50
102/7 .. *Set of* 6 10·50 17·00
102 and 104/6 Optd "Specimen" .. *Set of* 4 95·00

19

ONE PENNY.

(20)

(Recess D.L.R.)

1913 (1 Jan)–**17.** *Wmk Mult Crown CA. P* 14.
108 **19** ½d. green .. 35 35
109 1d. red .. 60 25
a. Rose-red .. 75 25
b. Scarlet (1.17) .. 2·00 2·50
110 2d. grey .. 4·00 7·00
a. Slate .. 2·50 4·75
111 2½d. ultramarine .. 70 1·00
112 3d. purple/*yellow* .. 1·75 5·00
a. On lemon .. 3·50 8·00
b. On pale yellow .. 2·75 7·00
113 4d. red/*yellow* .. 1·00 2·50
114 5d. olive-green (7.11.13) .. 2·75 11·00
115 6d. claret .. 2·75 4·50
116 1s. black/*green* .. 4·00 4·50
117 1s. bistre (1.5.14) .. 5·00 9·00
118 **18** 2s. blue and purple .. 10·00 20·00
119 5s. carmine and myrtle .. 20·00 32·00
120 £1 mauve and black .. £100 £120
108/20 .. *Set of* 13 £130 £190
108/20 Optd "Specimen" .. *Set of* 13 £350

Nos. 118/20 are from new centre and frame dies, the motto "PAX ET JUSTITIA" being slightly over 7 mm long, as against just over 8 mm in Nos. 99 to 107. Nos. 139/41 are also from the new dies.

1915. *Surch with T* **20**.
121 **19** 1d. on 1s. black/*green* (R.) .. 2·50 9·00
a. "ONE" omitted .. £800
b. "ONE" double .. £800
c. "PENNY" and bar double .. £750

The spacing between the two words varies from 7¾ mm to 10 mm.

WAR STAMP. (21) WAR STAMP. (22) WAR STAMP (24)

1916 (June). *Optd locally with T* **21**. *(a) First and second settings; words 2 to 2½ mm apart.*
122 **19** 1d. red .. 1·40 2·75
a. Opt double .. £140 £140
b. Comma for stop .. 7·00 9·50

In the first printing every second stamp has the comma for stop. The second printing of this setting has full stops only. These two printings can therefore only be distinguished in blocks or pairs.

(b) Third setting; words only 1½ mm apart
123 **19** 1d. red .. 42·00
a. Opt double .. £1100

Stamps of the first setting are offered as this rare one. Care must be taken to see that the distance between the lines is not over 1½ mm.

(c) Fourth setting; optd with T **22**. *Words 3½ mm apart*
124 **19** 1d. carmine-red .. 1·25 2·00
a. Opt double .. £200

1916 (Aug)–**18.** *T* **19**, *new printing, optd with T* **24**.
126 1d. carmine-red (Optd S. £70) .. 35 50
127 1d. pale rose-red .. 25 50
128 1d. deep rose-red .. 20 50
129 1d. pale scarlet (1918) .. 20 50

1921–32. *Wmk Mult Script CA. P* 14.
131 **19** ½d. green .. 25 20
132 1d. carmine .. 25 25
a. Red .. 25 15
132*b* **19** 1½d. brown (1932) .. 60 35
133 2d. grey .. 30 25
133*a* 2½d. bright blue (1926) .. 60 45
134 3d. bright blue .. 3·00 6·50
135 3d. purple/*yellow* (1926) .. 1·25 2·25
135*a* 4d. red/*yellow* (1930) .. 1·75 5·00
136 5d. sage-green .. 1·60 5·00
137 6d. claret (1.11.27) .. 2·25 4·50
138 1s. bistre-brown .. 2·75 6·00
a. Ochre (1927) .. 4·00 11·00
139 **18** 2s. blue and purple .. 9·00 16·00
140 5s. carmine and myrtle .. 15·00 30·00
141 £1 mauve and black (1928) .. £110 £130
131/41 .. *Set of* 14 £130 £190
131/41 Optd/Perf "Specimen" .. *Set of* 14 £250

1935 (6 May). *Silver Jubilee. As Nos.* 91/4 *of Antigua but ptd by Waterlow. P* 11 × 12.
142 1d. deep blue and scarlet .. 55 45
143 1½d. ultramarine and grey .. 75 70
144 2½d. brown and deep blue .. 2·00 2·25
145 1s. slate and purple .. 4·50 8·50
142/5 Perf "Specimen" .. *Set of* 4 60·00

1937 (12 May). *Coronation. As Nos.* 13/15 *of Aden but ptd by B.W. P* 11 × 11½.
146 1d. violet .. 35 20
147 1½d. carmine .. 55 35
148 2½d. blue .. 65 75
146/8 Perf "Specimen" .. *Set of* 3 45·00

25

26 Young's Island and Fort Duvernette

27 Kingstown and Fort Charlotte

28 Bathing Beach at Villa

29 Victoria Park, Kingstown

(Recess B.W.)

1938 (11 Mar)–**47.** *Wmk Mult Script CA. P* 12.
149 **25** ½d. blue and green .. 15 12
150 **26** 1d. blue and lake-brown .. 12 12
151 **27** 1½d. green and scarlet .. 20 12
152 **25** 2d. green and black .. 70 60
153 **28** 2½d. blue-black and blue-green .. 12 30
153*a* **29** 2½d. green and purple-brown (1947) .. 12 12
154 **25** 3d. orange and purple .. 15 12
154*a* **28** 3½d. blue-black and blue-green (1947) .. 40 40
155 **25** 6d. black and lake .. 50 50
156 **29** 1s. purple and green .. 50 50
157 **25** 2s. blue and purple .. 3·50 1·25
157*a* 2s. 6d. red-brown and blue (1947) .. 2·25 6·50
158 5s. scarlet and deep green .. 7·00 4·00
158*a* 10s. violet and brown (1947) .. 7·50 11·00
159 £1 purple and black .. 20·00 22·00
149/59 .. *Set of* 15 40·00 42·00
149/59 Perf "Specimen" .. *Set of* 15 £250

1946 (15 Oct). *Victory. As Nos.* 28/9 *of Aden.*
160 1½d. carmine .. 25 12
161 3½d. blue .. 25 12
160/1 Perf "Specimen" .. *Set of* 2 50·00

1948 (30 Nov). *Royal Silver Wedding. As Nos.* 30/1 *of Aden.*
162 1½d. scarlet .. 25 15
163 £1 bright purple .. 22·00 28·00

No. 163 was originally printed in black, but the supply of these was stolen in transit. A few examples exist, some perforated "Specimen".

(New Currency. 100 cents=1 West Indian dollar)

1949 (26 Mar)–**52.** *Value in cents and dollars. Wmk Mult Script CA. P* 12.
164 **25** 1 c. blue and green .. 20 15
164*a* 1 c. green and black (10.6.52) .. 25 15
165 **26** 2 c. blue and lake-brown .. 25 15
166 **27** 3 c. green and scarlet .. 30 20
166*a* **25** 3 c. orange and purple (10.6.52) .. 25 20
167 4 c. green and black .. 25 25
167*a* 4 c. blue and green (10.6.52) .. 25 15
168 **29** 5 c. green and purple-brown .. 25 15
169 **25** 6 c. orange and purple .. 30 25
169*a* **27** 6 c. green and scarlet (10.6.52) .. 25 15
170 **28** 7 c. blue-black and blue-green .. 60 50
170*a* 10 c. blue-black and blue-green (10.6.52) .. 60 50
171 **25** 12 c. black and lake .. 60 50
172 **29** 24 c. purple and green .. 65 65
173 **25** 48 c. blue and purple .. 2·50 2·25
174 60 c. red-brown and blue .. 3·00 2·25
175 $1.20, scarlet and deep green .. 6·00 6·50
176 $2.40, violet and brown .. 10·00 13·00
177 $4.80, purple and black .. 22·00 24·00
164/77 .. *Set of* 19 45·00 48·00

1949 (10 Oct). *75th Anniv of Universal Postal Union. As Nos.* 114/17 *of Antigua.*
178 5 c. blue .. 35 20
179 6 c. purple .. 50 35
180 12 c. magenta .. 75 70
181 24 c. blue-green .. 1·75 1·25

1951 (16 Feb). *Inauguration of B.W.I. University College. As Nos.* 118/19 *of Antigua.*
182 3 c. deep green and scarlet .. 40 35
183 12 c. black and purple .. 50 45

1951 (21 Sept). *New Constitution. Optd with T* **34** *of Dominica, by B.W.*
184 **27** 3 c. green and scarlet .. 25 60
185 **25** 4 c. green and black .. 25 60
186 **29** 5 c. green and purple-brown .. 20 60
187 **25** 12 c. black and lake .. 25 60

1953 (2 June). *Coronation. As No.* 47 *of Aden.*
188 4 c. black and green .. 60 30

30

31

(Recess Waterlow (until 1961), then D.L.R.)

1955 (16 Sept). *Wmk Mult Script CA. P* 13½ × 14 *(T* **30**) *or* 14 *(T* **31**).
189 **30** 1 c. orange (*shades*) .. 10 10
190 2 c. ultramarine (*shades*) .. 10 5
191 3 c. slate .. 12 5
192 4 c. brown .. 15 5
193 5 c. scarlet .. 15 5
194 10 c. reddish violet (*shades*) .. 20 5
195 15 c. deep blue .. 45 15
196 20 c. green .. 50 10
197 25 c. black-brown .. 50 20
198 **31** 50 c. red-brown (*shades*) .. 1·75 1·50
199 $1 myrtle-green (*shades*) .. 7·00 3·50
200 $2.50, deep blue (*shades*) .. 35·00 19·00
189/200 .. *Set of* 12 40·00 21·00

See also Nos. 207/20 and **MS**633.

1958 (22 Apr). *Inauguration of British Caribbean Federation. As Nos.* 135/7 *of Antigua.*
201 3 c. deep green .. 40 30
202 6 c. blue .. 55 55
203 12 c. scarlet .. 80 55

MINISTERIAL GOVERNMENT

1963 (4 June). *Freedom from Hunger. As No.* 76 *of Aden.*
204 8 c. reddish violet .. 1·75 1·00

1963 (2 Sept). *Red Cross Centenary. As Nos.* 147/8 *of Antigua.*
205 4 c. red and black .. 75 40
206 8 c. red and blue .. 1·25 85

(Recess D.L.R.)

1964–65. *As 1955 but wmk w* **12**. *(a) P* 12½ *(14 Jan–Feb 1964).*
207 **30** 10 c. deep lilac .. 55 55
208 15 c. deep blue .. 2·25 1·75
209 20 c. green (24.2.64*) .. 28·00 12·00
210 25 c. black-brown .. 6·00 2·50
211 **31** 50 c. chocolate .. 8·00 12·00

(b) P 13 × 14 *(T* **30**) *or* 14 *(T* **31**)
212 **30** 1 c. orange (15.12.64) .. 12 12
213 2 c. blue (15.12.64) .. 25 12
214 3 c. slate (15.12.64) .. 1·25 50
215 5 c. scarlet (15.12.64) .. 50 20
216 10 c. deep lilac (15.12.64) .. 60 20
217 15 c. deep blue (9.11.64) .. 2·00 80
218 20 c. green (1964) .. 1·25 55
219 25 c. black-brown (20.10.64) .. 5·50 2·75
220 **31** 50 c. chocolate (18.1.65) .. 18·00 15·00
212/20 .. *Set of* 9 26·00 18·00

*This is the earliest known date recorded in St. Vincent although it may have been put on sale on 14.1.64.

32 Scout Badge and Proficiency Badges

33 Tropical Fruits

(Des V. Whiteley. Litho Harrison)

1964 (23 Nov). *50th Anniv of St. Vincent Boy Scouts Association. W w* **12**. *P* 14½.
221 **32** 1 c. yellow-green and chocolate .. 5 5
222 4 c. blue and brown-purple .. 5 5
223 20 c. yellow and black-violet .. 35 10
224 50 c. red and bronze-green .. 75 60

(Des V. Whiteley. Photo Harrison)

1965 (23 Mar). *Botanic Gardens Bicentenary. T* **33** *and similar multicoloured designs. W w* **12**. *P* 14½ × 13½ *(horiz) or* 13½ × 14½ *(vert).*

225	1 c. Type **33**	5	5
226	4 c. Breadfruit and the *Providence*	10	5
227	25 c. Doric Temple and pond *(vert)*	40	35
228	40 c. Talipot Palm and Doric Temple *(vert)*	85	65

1965 (17 May). *I.T.U. Centenary. As Nos.* 166/7 *of Antigua.*

229	4 c. light blue and light olive-green	50	15
230	48 c. ochre-yellow and orange	2·75	1·60

37 Boat-building, Bequia (inscr "BEOUIA")

(Des M. Goaman. Photo Harrison)

1965 (16 Aug)–**67**. *T* **37** *and similar multicoloured designs. W w* **12**. *P* 14½ × 13½ *(horiz designs) or* 13½ × 14½ *(vert).*

231	1 c. Type **37** ("BEOUIA")	15	10
231*a*	1 c. Type **37** ("BEQUIA") (27.6.67)	15	10
232	2 c. Friendship Beach, Bequia	12	5
233	3 c. Terminal Building, Arnos Vale Airport	15	5
234	4 c. Woman with bananas *(vert)*	1·00	30
235	5 c. Crater Lake	15	5
236	6 c. Carib Stone *(vert)*	15	5
237	8 c. Arrowroot *(vert)*	30	5
238	10 c. Owia Salt Pond	30	5
239	12 c. Deep water wharf	35	10
240	20 c. Sea Island cotton *(vert)*	40	5
241	25 c. Map of St. Vincent and islands *(vert)*	50	20
242	50 c. Breadfruit *(vert)*	1·25	75
243	$1 Baleine Falls *(vert)*	4·50	1·25
244	$2.50, St. Vincent Amazon *(vert)*	13·00	7·50
245	$5 Arms of St. Vincent *(vert)*	20·00	12·00
231/45	*Set of* 16	38·00	20·00

The 1 c. (No. 231*a*), 2 c., 3 c., 5 c. and 10 c. exist with PVA gum as well as gum arabic.

See also No. 261.

1966 (24 Jan). *Churchill Commemoration. As Nos.* 170/3 *of Antigua.*

246	1 c. new blue	5	5
247	4 c. deep green	45	10
248	20 c. brown	2·50	90
249	40 c. bluish violet	5·00	1·75

1966 (4 Feb). *Royal Visit. As Nos.* 174/5 *of Antigua.*

250	4 c. black and ultramarine	1·50	25
251	25 c. black and magenta	5·50	2·00

1966 (20 Sept). *Inauguration of W.H.O. Headquarters, Geneva. As Nos.* 178/9 *of Antigua.*

252	4 c. black, yellow-green and light blue	65	10
253	25 c. black, light purple and yellow-brown	2·50	1·25

1966 (1 Dec). *20th Anniv of U.N.E.S.C.O. As Nos.* 196/8 *of Antigua.*

254	4 c. slate-violet, red, yellow and orange	60	10
255	8 c. orange-yellow, violet and deep olive	1·00	40
256	25 c. black, bright purple and orange	2·75	1·25

38 Coastal View of Mount Coke Area

(Des and photo Harrison)

1967 (1 Dec). *Autonomous Methodist Church. T* **38** *and similar horiz designs. Multicoloured. W w* **12**. *P* 14 × 14½.

257	2 c. Type **38**	5	5
258	8 c. Kingstown Methodist Church	15	10
259	25 c. First Licence to perform marriages	40	20
260	35 c. Conference Arms	50	30

1968 (20 Feb). *As No.* 234, *but W w* **12** *sideways.*

261	4 c. Woman with bananas	30	20

The above exists with PVA gum as well as gum arabic.

39 Meteorological Institute

(Des G. Vasarhelyi. Photo Harrison)

1968 (28 May). *World Meteorological Day. W w* **12**. *P* 14 × 14½.

262	**39**	4 c. multicoloured	5	5
263		25 c. multicoloured	25	15
264		35 c. multicoloured	30	25

40 Dr. Martin Luther King and Cotton Pickers

(Des V. Whiteley. Litho D.L.R.)

1968 (28 Aug). *Martin Luther King Commemoration. W w* **12** *(sideways). P* 13.

265	**40**	5 c. multicoloured	5	5
266		25 c. multicoloured	20	15
267		35 c. multicoloured	25	25

41 Speaker addressing Demonstrators

42 Scales of Justice and Human Rights Emblem

(Des V. Whiteley. Photo Enschedé)

1968 (1 Nov). *Human Rights Year. P* 13 × 14 (3 *c.*) *or* 14 × 13 (35 *c.*).

268	**41**	3 c. multicoloured	5	5
269	**42**	35 c. royal blue and turquoise-blue	35	20

43 Male Masquerader

44 Steel Bandsman

(Des V. Whiteley. Litho Format)

1969 (17 Feb). *St. Vincent Carnival. T* **43/4** *and similar designs. P* 14.

270	1 c. multicoloured	5	5
271	5 c. red and deep chocolate	15	8
272	8 c. multicoloured	20	12
273	25 c. multicoloured	30	20

Designs: *Horiz*—8 c. Carnival Revellers. *Vert*—25 c. Queen of Bands.

METHODIST
CONFERENCE
MAY
1969
(47)

1969 (14 May). *Methodist Conference. Nos.* 257/8, 241 *and* 260 *optd with T* **47**.

274	2 c. multicoloured	10	15
275	8 c. multicoloured	45	50
276	25 c. multicoloured	50	50
277	35 c. multicoloured	9·00	12·00

48 "Strength in Unity"

49 Map of "CARIFTA" Countries

(Des J. Cooter. Litho D.L.R.)

1969 (1 July). *First Anniv of CARIFTA (Caribbean Free Trade Area). W w* **12** *(sideways on T* **48**). *P* 13.

278	**48**	2 c. black, pale buff and red	5	5
279	**49**	5 c. multicoloured	10	5
280	**48**	8 c. black, pale buff and pale green	20	20
281	**49**	25 c. multicoloured	50	50

ASSOCIATED STATEHOOD

50 Flag of St. Vincent

(Des V. Whiteley, based on local designs. Photo Harrison)

1969 (27 Oct). *Statehood. T* **50** *and similar horiz designs. W w* **12**. *P* 14 × 14½.

282	4 c. multicoloured	10	5
283	10 c. multicoloured	40	25
284	50 c. grey, black and orange	60	30

Designs:—10 c. Battle scene with insets of Petroglyph and Carib chief Chatoyer; 50 c. Carib House with maces and scales.

51 Green Heron

(Des J.W. Photo Harrison)

1970 (12 Jan)–**71**. *T* **51** *and similar multicoloured designs. Chalk-surfaced paper. W w* **12** *(sideways on* 1, 2, 3, 6, 8, 20, 25 *c.*, $1, $2.50 *and upright on others). P* 14.

285	½ c. House Wren *(vert)*	10	15
286	1 c. Type **51**	35	30
	a. Glazed, ordinary paper (9.8.71)	10	15
287	2 c. Lesser Antillean Bullfinches	12	8
288	3 c. St. Vincent Amazons	15	8
289	4 c. Rufous-throated Solitaire *(vert)*	15	8
290	5 c. Red-necked Pigeon *(vert)*	2·25	50
	a. Glazed, ordinary paper (9.8.71)	60	30
291	6 c. Bananaquits	25	15
292	8 c. Purple-throated Carib	25	15
293	10 c. Mangrove Cuckoo *(vert)*	30	20
294	12 c. Common Black Hawk *(vert)*	40	25
295	20 c. Bare-eyed Thrush	60	35
296	25 c. Hooded Tanager	70	40
297	50 c. Blue Hooded Euphonia	90	90
298	$1 Barn Owl *(vert)*	5·50	3·00
299	$2.50, Yellow-bellied Elaenia *(vert)*	8·50	5·00
300	$5 Ruddy Quail Dove	16·00	9·50
285/300	*Set of* 16	32·00	19·00

See also Nos. 361/8 and 396/8.

52 "DHC-6" Twin Otter

(Des R. Granger Barrett. Litho Enschedé)

1970 (13 Mar). *20th Anniv of Regular Air Services. T* **52** *and similar horiz designs. Multicoloured. W w* **12** *(sideways). P* 14 × 13.

301	5 c. Type **52**	15	5
302	8 c. Grumman "Goose"	40	20
303	10 c. Hawker Siddeley "HS-748"	50	25
304	25 c. Douglas "DC-3"	1·25	1·00

53 "Children's Nursery"

54 "Angel and the Two Marys at the Tomb" (stained-glass window)

(Des R. Granger Barrett. Photo Harrison)

1970 (1 June). *Centenary of British Red Cross. T* **53** *and similar horiz designs. Multicoloured. W w* **12**. *P* 14.

305	3 c. Type **53**	10	5
306	5 c. "First Aid"	15	5
307	12 c. "Voluntary Aid Detachment"	25	15
308	25 c. "Blood Transfusion"	45	35

(Des L. Curtis. Litho J.W.)

1970 (7 Sept). *150th Anniv of St. George's Cathedral, Kingstown. T* **54** *and similar multicoloured designs. W w* **12** *(sideways on horiz designs). P* 14.

309	½ c. Type **54**	5	5
310	5 c. St. George's Cathedral *(horiz)*	10	5
311	25 c. Tower, St. George's Cathedral	30	15
312	35 c. Interior, St. George's Cathedral *(horiz)*	40	20
313	50 c. Type **54**	50	55

55 "The Adoration of the Shepherds" (Le Nain)

(Des J. Cooter. Litho Questa)

1970 (23 Nov). *Christmas. T* **55** *and similar vert design. Multicoloured. W* w **12** (*sideways on* 25 *c.,* 50 *c.*). *P* 14.

314	8 c. "The Virgin and Child" (Bellini)	15	10
315	25 c. Type **55**	25	15
316	35 c. As 8 c.	45	20
317	50 c. Type **55**	65	65

56 New Post Office and 6d. Stamp of 1861

(Des J. Cooter. Litho Questa)

1971 (29 Mar). *110th Anniv of First St. Vincent Stamps. T* **56** *and similar horiz design. Multicoloured. W* w **12** (*sideways*). *P* 14.

318	2 c. Type **56**	10	8
319	4 c. 1d. Stamp of 1861 and New Post Office	15	8
320	25 c. Type **56**	30	20
321	$1 As 4 c.	1·50	1·60

57 Trust Seal and Wildlife

58 "Madonna appearing to St. Anthony" (Tiepolo)

(Des G. Drummond. Litho J.W.)

1971 (4 Aug). *St. Vincent's National Trust. T* **57** *and similar horiz design. Multicoloured. W* w **12** (*sideways*). *P* 13½ × 14.

322	12 c. Type **57**	30	20
323	30 c. Old Cannon, Fort Charlotte	70	40
324	40 c. Type **57**	1·25	75
325	45 c. As 30 c.	1·40	90

(Des J. Cooter. Litho Questa)

1971 (6 Oct). *Christmas. T* **58** *and similar horiz design. Multicoloured. W* w **12** (*sideways on* 10 *c. and* $1). *P* 14½ × 14 (10 c., $1) *or* 14 × 14½ (5 c., 25 c.).

326	5 c. Type **58**	15	5
327	10 c. "The Holy Family on the Flight into Egypt" (detail, Pietro da Cortona)	20	5
328	25 c. Type **58**	55	30
329	$1 As 10 c.	1·75	2·00

59 Careening

60 Private, Grenadier Company, 32nd Foot (1764)

(Des J. Cooter. Litho J.W.)

1971 (25 Nov). *The Grenadines of St. Vincent. T* **59** *and similar vert designs. Multicoloured. W* w **12**. *P* 13½.

330	1 c. Type **59**	5	10
331	5 c. Seine fishermen	20	10
332	6 c. Map of the Grenadines	20	10
333	15 c. Type **59**	40	30
334	20 c. As 5 c.	60	40
335	50 c. As 6 c.	1·50	1·50
330/5	*Set of* 6	2·75	2·25
MS336	177 × 140 mm. Nos. 330/5	12·00	11·00

(Des and litho J.W.)

1972 (14 Feb). *Military Uniforms. T* **60** *and similar vert designs. Multicoloured. W* w **12**. *P* 14 × 13½.

337	12 c. Type **60**	1·10	60
338	30 c. Officer, Battalion Company, 31st Foot (1772)	2·50	1·75
339	50 c. Private, Grenadier Company, 6th Foot (1772)	3·75	2·75

61 Breadnut Fruit

62 Candlestick Cassia

(Des P. Powell. Litho Questa)

1972 (16 May). *Fruit. T* **61** *and similar vert designs. Multicoloured. W* w **12** (*sideways*). *P* 13½.

340	3 c. Type **61**	10	5
341	5 c. Pawpaw	20	5
342	12 c. Plumrose or Roseapple	1·40	90
343	25 c. Mango	2·50	1·60

(Des Sylvia Goaman. Litho B.W.)

1972 (31 July). *Flowers. T* **62** *and similar vert designs. Multicoloured. P* 13 ($1) *or* 13½ × 14 (*others*).

344	1 c. Type **62**	5	10
345	30 c. Lobster Claw	80	40
346	40 c. White Trumpet	1·00	40
347	$1 Soufriere tree	2·50	1·75

63 Sir Charles Brisbane and Coat of Arms

(Des Jennifer Toombs. Litho J.W.)

1972 (29 Sept). *Birth Bicentenary of Sir Charles Brisbane. T* **63** *and similar horiz designs. W* w **12** (*sideways*). *P* 13½.

348	20 c. yellow-ochre, gold and red-brown	80	30
349	30 c. light yellow, light mauve and black	1·25	45
350	$1 multicoloured	4·00	3·50
MS351	171 × 111 mm. Nos. 348/50 (*sold at* $2)	9·00	10·00

Designs:—30 c. H.M.S. *Arethusa*; $1 H.M.S. *Blake*.

64 Arrowroot and Breadfruit

(Des (from photograph by D. Groves) and photo Harrison)

1972 (20 Nov). *Royal Silver Wedding. Multicoloured; background colour given. W* w **12**. *P* 14 × 14½.

352	**64**	30 c. red-brown	50	25
353		$1 myrtle-green	1·00	25

65 Sighting St. Vincent

66 "The Last Supper" (French Stained-glass Window)

(Des J. Cooter. Litho Enschedé)

1973 (31 Jan). *475th Anniv of Columbus's Third Voyage to the West Indies. T* **65** *and similar triangular designs. Multicoloured. W* w **12**. *P* 13½.

354	5 c. Type **65**	40	15
355	12 c. Caribs watching Columbus's fleet	75	40
356	30 c. Christopher Columbus	2·00	1·75
357	50 c. *Santa Maria*	3·00	2·25

(Des J. Cooter. Litho Questa)

1973 (19 Apr). *Easter. T* **66** *and similar vert designs. Multicoloured. W* w **12** (*sideways*). *P* 14 × 13½.

358	**66**	15 c. multicoloured	35	30
		a. Horiz strip of 3. Nos. 358/60	2·10	
359	–	60 c. multicoloured	90	60
360	–	$1 multicoloured	1·00	75

Nos. 358, 360 and 359 were printed, in that order, horizontally *se-tenant* throughout a sheet of 45 stamps, and form a composite design of "The Last Supper".

1973 (13 June–23 Nov). *As Nos.* 285 *etc, but W* w **12** *upright on* 2, 3, 6, 20 *c. and sideways on others. Glazed paper.*

361	2 c. Lesser Antillean Bullfinches (23.11)	20	15
362	3 c. St. Vincent Amazons (23.11)	20	15
363	4 c. Rufous-throated Solitaire (*vert*) (23.11)	25	15
364	5 c. Red-necked Pigeon (*vert*)	50	30
365	6 c. Bananaquits (23.11)	40	25
366	10 c. Mangrove Cuckoo (*vert*) (23.11)	55	20
367	12 c. Common Black Hawk (*vert*) (23.11)	95	60
368	20 c. Bare-eyed Thrush (23.11)	1·50	75
361/8	*Set of* 8	4·00	2·25

For the 1 c. value with watermark upright see Grenadines of St. Vincent No. 3a.

67 William Wilberforce and Poster

68 P.P.F. Symbol

(Des Jennifer Toombs. Litho D.L.R.)

1973 (11 July). *140th Death Anniv of William Wilberforce. T* **67** *and similar horiz designs. Multicoloured. W* w **12**. *P* 14 × 13½.

369	30 c. Type **67**	75	40
370	40 c. Slaves cutting cane	90	60
371	50 c. Wilberforce and medallion	1·25	90

(Des PAD Studio. Litho Walsall)

1973 (3 Oct). *21st Anniv of International Planned Parenthood Federation. T* **68** *and similar vert design. Multicoloured. W* w **12** (*sideways*). *P* 14.

372	12 c. Type **68**	40	30
373	40 c. "IPPF" and symbol	1·10	1·00

1973 (14 Nov). *Royal Wedding. As Nos.* 165/6 *of Anguilla.*

374	50 c. deep blue	65	30
375	70 c. grey-green	65	30

69 Administrative Block, Mona

(Des PAD Studio. Litho Questa)

1973 (13 Dec). *25th Anniv of West Indies University. T* **69** *and similar multicoloured designs. W* w **12** (*sideways on* $1). *P* 14.

376	5 c. Type **69**	10	5
377	10 c. University Centre, Kingstown	15	10
378	30 c. Aerial view, Mona University	40	40
379	$1 University coat of arms (*vert*)	1·40	1·10

30c

■ ■

(70)

71 "The Descent from the Cross" (Sansovino)

1973 (15 Dec). *Nos.* 297, 292 *and* 298 *surch in half sheets with T* **70**, *by the Govt Printer, St. Vincent.*

380	30 c. on 50 c. multicoloured	50	30
	a. Surch double	30·00	
	b. Surch double (on front) and single inverted (on reverse)	75·00	
	c. Surch double, one inverted	75·00	
	d. Surch inverted		
381	40 c. on 8 c. multicoloured	60	40
	a. Surch double	35·00	
	b. Surch inverted	£125	
382	$10 on $1 multicoloured	24·00	10·00
	a. Surch double	95·00	
	b. Surch inverted	£110	
	c. Surch double, one inverted	£110	

SPECIMEN STAMPS. From No. 383 onwards the stamps of St. Vincent exist overprinted "SPECIMEN", these being produced for publicity purposes.

(Des PAD Studio. Litho Enschedé)

1974 (10 Apr). *Easter. T* **71** *and similar vert designs showing sculptures. Multicoloured.* W w **12** *(sideways).* P 14 × 13½.

No.	Description		
383	5 c. Type **71**	5	5
384	30 c. "The Deposition" (English, 14th-century)	20	10
385	40 c. "Pieta" (Fernandez)	25	20
386	$1 "The Resurrection" (French, 16th-century)	75	90

72 *Istra*

(Des J.W. Litho Questa)

1974 (28 June). *Cruise Ships. T* **72** *and similar horiz designs. Multicoloured.* W w **12** *(sideways).* P 14.

No.	Description		
387	15 c. Type **72**	20	10
388	20 c. *Oceanic*	30	20
389	30 c. *Alexander Pushkin*	40	30
390	$1 *Europa*	1·40	80
MS391	134 × 83 mm. Nos. 387/90	2·50	2·50

73 U.P.U. Emblem

(Des J.W. Litho Questa)

1974 (25 July). *Centenary of Universal Postal Union. T* **73** *and similar horiz designs. Multicoloured.* W w **12**. P 14.

No.	Description		
392	5 c. Type **73**	5	5
393	12 c. Globe within posthorn	15	5
394	60 c. Map of St. Vincent and hand-cancelling	35	35
395	90 c. Map of the World	45	55

74 Royal Tern

75 Scout Badge and Emblems

(Des J.W. Litho Questa)

1974 (29 Aug). *T* **74** *and similar vert designs. Multicoloured. Glazed paper.* W w **12** *(sideways on* 40 c. *and* $10). P 14.

No.	Description		
396	30 c. Type **74**	70	45
397	40 c. Brown Pelican	90	60
398	$10 Magnificent Frigate Bird	30·00	21·00

(Des Sylvia Goaman. Litho Enschedé)

1974 (9 Oct). *Diamond Jubilee of Scout Movement in St. Vincent.* W w **12**. P 13 × 13½.

No.	Type	Description		
399	**75**	10 c. multicoloured	15	5
400		25 c. multicoloured	25	10
401		45 c. multicoloured	50	40
402		$1 multicoloured	1·00	60

76 Sir Winston Churchill

77 The Shepherds

(Des C. Abbott. Litho Questa)

1974 (28 Nov). *Birth Centenary of Sir Winston Churchill. T* **76** *and similar vert designs. Multicoloured.* W w **12**. P 14.

No.	Description		
403	25 c. Type **76**	10	10
404	35 c. Churchill in military uniform	20	15
405	45 c. Churchill in naval uniform	30	25
406	$1 Churchill in air-force uniform	60	50

(Des Jennifer Toombs. Litho Enschedé)

1974 (5 Dec). *Christmas. T* **77** *and similar vert designs.* W w **12**. P 12 × 12½.

No.	Type	Description		
407	**77**	3 c. violet-blue and black	5	5
		a. Horiz strip of 4. Nos. 407/10	20	
408	–	3 c. violet-blue and black	5	5
409	–	3 c. violet-blue and black	5	5
410	–	3 c. violet-blue and black	5	5
411	**77**	8 c. apple-green and black	15	12
412	–	35 c. rose and deep maroon	40	15
413	–	45 c. olive-bistre and brown-black	50	45
414	–	$1 lavender and slate-black	1·00	75
407/14		*Set of* 8	2·00	1·50

Designs:—Nos. 408, 412 Mary and crib; Nos. 409, 413 Joseph, ox and ass; Nos. 410, 414 The Magi.

Nos. 407/10 were issued horizontally *se-tenant* within the sheet, together forming a composite design of the Nativity.

78 Faces

(Des G. Drummond. Litho D.L.R.)

1975 (7–27 Feb). *Kingstown Carnival. T* **78** *and similar horiz designs. Multicoloured.* W w **12**. P 14 × 13½.

No.	Description		
415	1 c. Type **78**	5	5
	a. Booklet pane. No. 415 × 2 plus printed label (27.2)	35	
	b. Booklet pane. Nos. 415, 417 and 419 (27.2)	1·25	
416	15 c. Pineapple women	20	15
	a. Booklet pane. Nos. 416, 418 and 420 (27.2)	2·25	
417	25 c. King of the Bands	30	25
418	35 c. Carnival dancers	40	15
419	45 c. Queen of the Bands	50	25
420	$1.25, "African Splendour"	1·25	1·00
415/20	*Set of* 6	2·40	1·60
MS421	146 × 128 mm. Nos. 415/20	3·50	4·50

79 French Angelfish

Two types of $2.50:

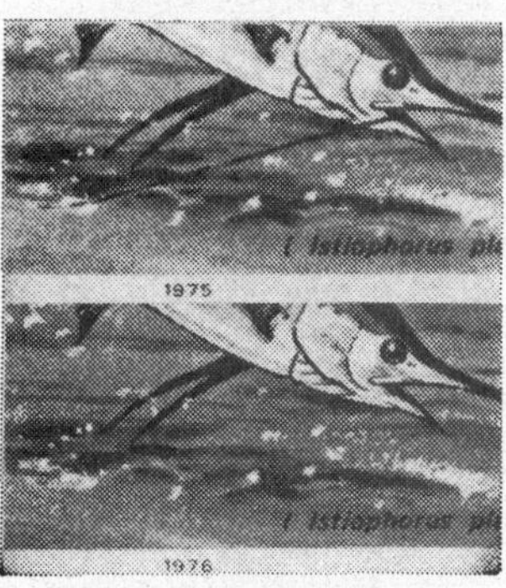

Type I. Fishing-line attached to fish's mouth. Imprint "1975".
Type II. Fishing-line omitted. Imprint "1976".

(Des G. Drummond. Litho Questa)

1975 (10 Apr)–**76**. *T* **79** *and similar horiz designs. Multicoloured.* W w **14** *(sideways).* P 14½.

No.	Description		
422	1 c. Type **79**	12	12
423	2 c. Spotfin Butterfly-fish	15	10
424	3 c. Horse-eyed Jack	15	10
425	4 c. Mackerel	20	10
426	5 c. French Grunt	20	10
427	6 c. Spotted Goatfish	20	10
428	8 c. Ballyhoo	20	12
429	10 c. Sperm Whale	30	10
430	12 c. Humpback Whale	40	20
431	15 c. Cowfish	70	30
432	15 c. Skipjack (14.10.76)	2·00	35
433	20 c. Queen Angelfish	40	15
434	25 c. Princess Parrotfish	45	10
435	35 c. Red Hind	50	10
436	45 c. Atlantic Flying Fish	65	10
437	50 c. Porkfish	65	10
438	70 c. "Albacore" or Yellowfin Tuna (14.10.76)	2·25	70
439	90 c. Pompano (14.10.76)	2·25	70
440	$1 Queen Triggerfish	1·25	40
441	$2.50, Sailfish (I)	4·75	4·50
	a. Type II (12.7.76)	4·00	2·25
442	$5 Dolphin Fish	7·00	2·75
443	$10 Blue Marlin	10·00	9·00
422/43	*Set of* 22	30·00	16·00

Some of the above issue exist with different dates in the imprint at the foot of each stamp.

MINIMUM PRICE

The minimum price quoted is 5p which represents a handling charge rather than a basis for valuing common stamps. For further notes about prices see introductory pages.

80 Cutting Bananas

(Des G. Drummond. Litho Questa)

1975 (26 June). *Banana Industry. T* **80** *and similar horiz designs. Multicoloured.* W w **12** *(sideways).* P 13½.

No.	Description		
447	25 c. Type **80**	25	15
448	35 c. Packaging Station, La Croix	40	25
449	45 c. Cleaning and boxing	50	40
450	70 c. Shipping bananas aboard *Geeste Tide*	80	60

81 Snorkel Diving

(Des G. Drummond. Litho Questa)

1975 (31 July). *Tourism. T* **81** *and similar horiz designs. Multicoloured.* W w **14** *(sideways).* P 13½.

No.	Description		
451	15 c. Type **81**	12	12
452	20 c. Aquaduct Golf Course	20	15
453	35 c. Steel Band at Mariner's Inn	35	25
454	45 c. Sunbathing at Young Island	45	35
455	$1.25, Yachting Marina	2·00	1·50

82 George Washington, John Adams, Thomas Jefferson and James Madison

(Des G. Drummond. Litho Questa)

1975 (11 Sept). *Bicentenary of American Revolution. T* **82** *and similar horiz designs.* P 14.

No.	Description		
456	½ c. black and lavender	5	5
457	1 c. black and light emerald	5	5
458	1½ c. black and light magenta	5	5
459	5 c. black and bright yellow-green	12	5
460	10 c. black and light violet-blue	15	5
461	25 c. black and dull orange-yellow	25	8
462	35 c. black and light greenish blue	40	20
463	45 c. black and bright rose	50	25
464	$1 black and light orange	85	60
465	$2 black and light yellow-olive	1·50	1·25
456/65	*Set of* 10	3·50	2·50
MS466	179 × 156 mm. Nos. 456/65	5·50	4·00

Presidents:—1 c. Monroe, Quincy Adams, Jackson, van Buren; 1½ c. W. Harrison, Tyler, Polk, Taylor; 5 c. Fillmore, Pierce, Buchanan, Lincoln; 10 c. Andrew Johnson, Grant, Hayes, Garfield; 25 c. Arthur, Cleveland, B. Harrison, McKinley; 35 c. Theodore Roosevelt, Taft, Wilson, Harding; 45 c. Coolidge, Hoover, Franklin Roosevelt, Truman; $1 Eisenhower, Kennedy, Lyndon Johnson, Nixon; $2 Pres. Ford and White House.

Nos. 456/65 were each issued in sheets of ten stamps and two *se-tenant* labels.

83/4 "Shepherds"

(Des Jennifer Toombs. Litho Harrison)

1975 (4 Dec). *Christmas. T* **83/4** *and similar triangular designs.* P 13½ × 14. A. W w **12** *(upright).* B. W w **12** *(sideways).*

No.	Description	A		B	
467	3 c. black and magenta	5	5	5	5
	a. Block of 4. Nos. 467/70	20	20	20	20
468	3 c. black and magenta	5	5	5	5
469	3 c. black and magenta	5	5	5	5
470	3 c. black and magenta	5	5	5	5
471	8 c. black & lt greenish blue	8	8	8	8
	a. Pair. Nos. 471/2	15	15	15	15
472	8 c. black & lt greenish blue	8	8	8	8
473	35 c. black and yellow	20	20	20	20
	a. Pair. Nos. 473/4	40	40	40	40

			A		B	
474	35 c. black and yellow	..	20	20	20	20
475	45 c. black and yellow-green	..	25	25	25	25
	a. Pair. Nos. 475/6	..	50	50	50	50
476	45 c. black and yellow-green	..	25	25	25	25
477	$1 black and bright lilac	..	65	65	65	65
	a. Pair. Nos. 477/8	..	1·25	1·25	1·25	1·25
478	$1 black and bright lilac	..	65	65	65	65
467/78	.. .. .. *Set of* 12		2·25	2·25	2·25	2·25

Designs:—No. 467, "Star of Bethlehem"; 468, "Holy Trinity"; 469, As T **83**; 470, "Three Kings"; 471/2, As 467; 473/4, As 468; 475/6, T **83/4**; 477/8 As 470. The two designs of each denomination (Nos. 471/8) differ in that the longest side is at the foot or at the top as shown in T **83/4**.

Each denomination was printed in sheets of 16, the designs being *se-tenant* and so arranged that the watermark comes upright, inverted, sideways right and sideways left.

85 Carnival Dancers

(Des G. Drummond. Litho Questa)

1976 (19 Feb). *Kingstown Carnival. T* **85** *and similar horiz designs. Multicoloured.* W w **14** (*sideways*). *P* 13½.

479 1 c. Type **85** 5 5
a. Booklet pane. Nos. 479 and 480 plus printed label .. 25
480 2 c. Humpty-Dumpty people .. 5 5
a. Booklet pane. Nos. 480/2 .. 65
481 5 c. Smiling faces .. 10 5
482 35 c. Dragon worshippers .. 35 25
a. Booklet pane. Nos. 482/4 .. 2·25
483 45 c. Carnival tableaux .. 60 45
484 $1.25, Bumble-Bee dancers .. 1·40 1·10
479/84 .. *Set of* 6 2·25 1·75

70¢

(86)

87 Blue-headed Hummingbird and Yellow Hibiscus

1976 (8 Apr). *Nos.* 424 *and* 437 *surch as T* **86**.

485 70 c. on 3 c. Horse-eyed Jack .. 1·25 1·25
a. Surch inverted .. 50·00
486 90 c. on 50 c. Porkfish .. 1·40 1·40
a. Surch inverted .. 50·00

(Des G. Drummond. Litho Walsall)

1976 (20 May). *Hummingbirds and Hibiscuses. T* **87** *and similar vert designs. Multicoloured.* W w **14** (*inverted*). *P* 13½.

487 5 c. Type **87** .. 30 5
488 10 c. Antillean Crested Hummingbird and Pink Hibiscus .. 50 20
489 35 c. Purple-throated Carib and White Hibiscus .. 1·25 80
a. No wmk .. 60·00
490 45 c. Blue-headed Hummingbird and Red Hibiscus .. 1·50 1·00
491 $1.25, Green-throated Carib and Peach Hibiscus .. 9·50 6·00

1976 (16 Sept). *West Indian Victory in World Cricket Cup. As Nos.* 559/60 *of Barbados.*

492 15 c. Map of the Caribbean .. 75 35
493 45 c. Prudential Cup .. 2·00 1·25

88 St Mary's Church, Kingstown

(Des G. Drummond. Litho Questa)

1976 (18 Nov). *Christmas. T* **88** *and similar horiz designs. Multicoloured.* W w **14** (*sideways*). *P* 14.

494 35 c. Type **88** .. 35 25
495 45 c. Anglican Church, Georgetown .. 35 20
496 50 c. Methodist Church, Georgetown .. 40 25
497 $1.25, St. George's Cathedral, Kingstown .. 1·00 85

89 Barrancoid Pot-stand

(Des G. Vasarhelyi. Litho J.W.)

1976 (16 Dec). *National Trust. T* **89** *and similar horiz designs. Multicoloured.* W w **14** (*sideways*). *P* 13½.

498 5 c. Type **89** .. 5 5
499 45 c. National Museum .. 40 30
500 70 c. Carib sculpture .. 60 40
501 $1 Ciboney petroglyph .. 90 65

90 William I, William II, Henry I and Stephen

(Des G. Vasarhelyi. Litho J.W.)

1977 (7 Feb). *Silver Jubilee. T* **90** *and similar horiz designs. Multicoloured. P* 13½. (*a*) *W w* **14** (*sideways*). *From sheets.*

502 ½ c. Type **90** .. 5 5
503 1 c. Henry II, Richard I, John, Henry III .. 5 5
504 1½ c. Edward I, Edward II, Edward III, Richard II .. 5 5
505 2 c. Henry IV, Henry V, Henry VI, Edward IV .. 5 5
506 5 c. Edward V, Richard III, Henry VII, Henry VIII .. 10 5
507 10 c. Edward VI, Lady Jane Grey, Mary I, Elizabeth I .. 12 5
508 25 c. James I, Charles I, Charles II, James II 20 15
509 35 c. William III, Mary II, Anne, George I .. 30 20
510 45 c. George II, George III, George IV .. 35 25
511 75 c. William IV, Victoria, Edward VII .. 45 35
512 $1 George V, Edward VIII, George VI .. 55 45
513 $2 Elizabeth II leaving Westminster Abbey .. 95 70
502/13 .. *Set of* 12 2·75 2·40
MS514 170 × 146 mm. Nos. 502/13. P 14½ × 14 4·00 4·00

(*b*) *No wmk. From booklets*

515 ½ c. Type **90** .. 2·75 2·75
a. Booklet pane. Nos. 515/18 *se-tenant* .. 11·00
516 1 c. As No. 503 .. 2·75 2·75
517 1½ c. As No. 504 .. 2·75 2·75
518 2 c. As No. 505 .. 2·75 2·75
519 5 c. As No. 506 .. 2·75 2·75
a. Booklet pane. Nos. 519/22 *se-tenant* .. 11·00
520 10 c. As No. 507 .. 2·75 2·75
521 25 c. As No. 508 .. 2·75 2·75
522 35 c. As No. 509 .. 2·75 2·75
523 45 c. As No. 510 .. 2·75 2·75
a. Booklet pane. Nos. 523/6 *se-tenant* .. 11·00
524 75 c. As No. 511 .. 2·75 2·75
525 $1 As No. 512 .. 2·75 2·75
526 $2 As No. 513 .. 2·75 2·75
515/26 .. *Set of* 12 29·00 29·00

Nos. 502/13 were each issued in sheets of ten stamps and two *se-tenant* labels.

91 Grant of Arms

(Des G. Drummond. Litho Questa)

1977 (12 May). *Centenary of Windward Is Diocese. T* **91** *and similar horiz designs. Multicoloured.* W w **14** (*sideways*). *P* 13½.

527 15 c. Type **91** .. 12 5
528 35 c. Bishop Berkeley and mitres .. 25 20
529 45 c. Map and arms of diocese .. 30 20
530 $1.25, St. George's Cathedral and Bishop Woodroffe .. 1·00 95

CARNIVAL 1977

JUNE 25TH-JULY 5TH

(92)

1977 (2 June). *Kingstown Carnival. Nos.* 426, 429, 432/3 *and* 440 *optd with T* **92**.

531 5 c. French Grunt .. 15 12
a. Red opt .. 60·00
532 10 c. Sperm Whale (R.) .. 25 15
a. Optd double (R. and Blk.) .. 60·00
533 15 c. Skipjack (R.) .. 30 25
a. Black opt .. 50·00
534 20 c. Queen Angel Fish (R.) .. 45 30
a. Opt inverted .. 35·00
b. Black opt .. 55·00
535 $1 Queen Triggerfish .. 1·90 1·40
a. Red opt .. 60·00

93 Guide and Emblem

CARIBBEAN VISIT 1977

(94)

(Des PAD Studio. Litho J.W.)

1977 (1 Sept). *50th Anniv of St. Vincent Girl Guides. T* **93** *and similar vert designs. The* $2 *value is additionally optd.* "1930–1977". *Multicoloured.* W w **14**. *P* 13½.

536 5 c. Type **93** .. 5 5
537 15 c. Early uniform, ranger, guide and brownie 25 12
538 20 c. Early uniform and guide .. 30 15
539 $2 Lady Baden-Powell .. 1·75 1·40
a. Optd dates omitted .. 60·00

1977 (27 Oct). *Royal Visit. No.* 513 *optd with T* **94**.

540 $2 Queen Elizabeth leaving Westminster Abbey .. 1·25 1·00

95 Map of St. Vincent

96 Opening Verse and Scene

(Des G. Drummond. Litho Questa)

1977–78. *Provisionals.* W w **12**. *P* 14½ × 14.

541 **95** 20 c. blk, dull violet-bl & pale bl (31.1.78) 25 20
542 40 c. black, dull orange & flesh (30.11.77) 45 45
a. Black (value) omitted .. 50·00
543 40 c. black, magenta and salmon (31.1.78) 40 35

Nos. 541/3 were printed in 1974, without value, for provisional use; they were locally surcharged before going on sale.

(Des Jennifer Toombs. Litho Enschedé)

1977 (1 Dec). *Christmas. Scenes and Verses from the carol "While Shepherds Watched their Flocks by Night". T* **96** *and similar vert designs. Multicoloured.* W w **14**. *P* 13 × 11.

544 5 c. Type **96** .. 5 5
545 10 c. Angel consoling shepherds .. 5 5
546 15 c. View of Bethlehem .. 10 5
547 25 c. Nativity scene .. 15 15
548 50 c. Throng of Angels .. 40 30
549 $1.25, Praising God .. 90 60
544/9 .. *Set of* 6 1·50 1·00
MS550 150 × 170 mm. Nos. 544/9. P 13½ .. 1·75 1·75

97 Painted Lady and *Bougainvillea glabra var. alba*

(Des Daphne Padden. Litho Walsall)

1978 (6 Apr). *Butterflies and Bougainvilleas. T* **97** *and similar horiz designs. Multicoloured.* W w **14** (*sideways*). *P* 14.

551 5 c. Type **97** .. 10 5
552 25 c. Silver Spot and "Golden Glow" .. 30 12
553 40 c. Red Anartia and "Mrs. McLean" .. 40 20
554 50 c. The Mimic and "Cyphen" .. 55 35
555 $1.25, Giant Hairstreak and "Thomasii" .. 1·25 80

(Des G. Drummond. Litho J.W.)

1978 (2 June). *25th Anniv of Coronation. Horiz designs as Nos.* 422/5 *of Montserrat. Multicoloured.* W w **14** (*sideways*). *P* 13.

556 40 c. Westminster Abbey .. 30 15
557 50 c. Gloucester Cathedral .. 40 20
558 $1.25, Durham Cathedral .. 60 35
559 $2.50, Exeter Cathedral .. 1·00 65
MS560 130 × 102 mm. Nos. 556/9. P 13½ × 14 .. 2·00 1·60

Nos. 556/9 were each printed in sheets of ten stamps and two *se-tenant* labels.

98 Rotary International Emblem and Motto

99 "Co-operation in Education Leads to Mutual Understanding and Respect"

(Des G. Hutchins. Litho Questa)

1978 (13 July). *International Service Clubs. T* **98** *and similar horiz designs showing club emblems and mottoes. Multicoloured.* W w **14** (*sideways*). *P* 14½.

561 40 c. Type **98** .. 40 20
562 50 c. Lions International .. 45 25
563 $1 Jaycees .. 80 80

(Des G. Hutchins. Litho Questa)

1978 (7 Sept). *10th Anniv of Project School to School (St. Vincent-Canada school twinning project). T* **99** *and similar multicoloured design showing flags and blackboard.* W w **14** (*sideways on* $2). *P* 14.
564 40 c. Type **99** 20 20
565 $2 "Co-operation in Education Leads to the Elimination of Racial Intolerance" (*horiz*) 1·10 1·10

100 Arnos Vale Airport

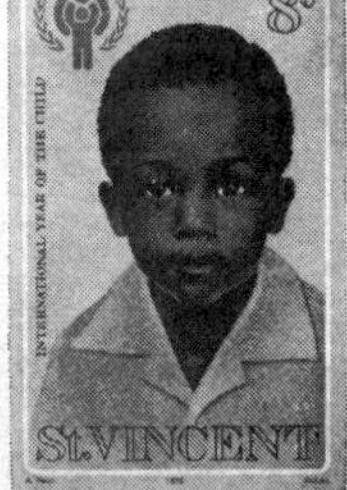

101 Young Child

(Des G. Drummond. Litho Questa)

1978 (19 Oct). *75th Anniv of Powered Flight. T* **100** *and similar horiz designs. Multicoloured.* W w **14** (*sideways*). *P* 14½ × 14.
566 10 c. Type **100** 10 8
567 40 c. Wilbur Wright landing *Flyer* 35 25
568 50 c. Orville Wright in *Flyer* 40 30
569 $1.25, Orville Wright and *Flyer* airborne .. 1·00 75

(Des A. Paish. Litho Questa)

1979 (14 Feb). *International Year of the Child. T* **101** *and similar vert designs showing portraits of young children.* W w **14**. *P* 14 × 13½.
570 8 c. black, gold and pale yellow-green .. 10 8
571 20 c. black, gold and pale rose-lilac 20 12
572 50 c. black, gold and pale violet-blue 75 35
573 $2 black, gold and flesh .. .. .. 3·25 1·10

10c+5c

SOUFRIERE
RELIEF
FUND 1979

(102)

103 Sir Rowland Hill

(Des G. Drummond. Litho Questa)

1979 (17 Apr). *Soufrière Eruption Relief Fund. Designs as T* **95** *but surchd as T* **102** *by Reliance Printery, Kingstown.* W w **12**. *P* 14½ × 14.
574 10 c. + 5 c. violet-blue and pale rose-lilac .. 10 15
575 50 c. + 25 c. yellow-brown and buff 35 50
576 $1 + 50 c. reddish brown and brownish grey 65 70
577 $2 + $1 deep green and apple-green .. 1·25 1·25

(Des J.W. Litho Harrison)

1979 (31 May). *Death Centenary of Sir Rowland Hill. T* **103** *and similar horiz designs. Multicoloured.* W w **14** (*sideways*). *P* 14.
578 40 c. Type **103** 20 20
579 50 c. Penny Black and Twopenny Blue stamps 30 30
580 $3 1861 1d. and 6d. stamps .. .. .. 1·25 1·25
MS581 170 × 123 mm. Nos. 578/80, 594/5 and 599 (see footnote after No. 601) .. .. .. 3·00 3·25
Nos. 578/80 were each printed in sheets including two *se-tenant* stamp-size labels.

104 First and Latest Buccament Postmarks and Map of St. Vincent

ST VINCENT AND
THE GRENADINES
AIR SERVICE 1979

(105)

(Des J.W. Litho Harrison)

1979 (31 May–1 Sept). *St. Vincent Post Offices. Horiz designs as T* **104** *showing first and latest postmarks and map of St. Vincent. Multicoloured.* W w **14** (*sideways*). *P* 14.
582 1 c. Type **104** 5 5
583 2 c. Sion Hill 5 5
584 3 c. Cumberland 5 5
585 4 c. Questelles 10 5
586 5 c. Layou 10 5
587 6 c. New Ground 10 5
588 8 c. Mesopotamia 10 5
589 10 c. Troumaca 10 5
590 12 c. Arnos Vale 15 5
591 15 c. Stubbs 15 5
592 20 c. Orange Hill 15 10
593 25 c. Calliaqua 15 12
594 40 c. Edinboro 25 20
595 50 c. Colonarie 30 25
596 80 c. Biabou 40 35
597 $1 Chateaubelair 50 50
598 $2 Head P.O., Kingstown 85 90
599 $3 Barrouallie .. .. 1·25 1·40
600 $5 Georgetown .. .. 2·10 2·25
601 $10 Kingstown .. .. 4·25 4·75
582/601 .. .. *Set of* 20 10·00 10·00
Dates of issue:—40, 50 c., $3 (from No. **MS**581 and booklets only) 31.5.79; others, and 40, 50 c., $3 from sheets, 1.9.79.
See also Nos. **MS**581 and **MS**637.

1979 (6 Aug). *Opening of St. Vincent and the Grenadines Air Service. No. 566 optd with T* **105**, *in red, by Reliance Printery, Kingstown.*
602 10 c. Type **100** 10 8

INDEPENDENT

106 National Flag and *Ixora coccinea* (flower)

(Des J.W. Litho Enschedé)

1979 (27 Oct). *Independence. T* **106** *and similar horiz designs. Multicoloured.* W w **14** (*sideways*). *P* 12½ × 12.
603 20 c. Type **106** 10 10
604 50 c. House of Assembly and *Ixora stricta* (flower) 25 25
605 80 c. Prime Minister R. Milton Cato and *Ixora williamsii* (flower) 40 40

INDEPENDENCE 1979

(107)

1979 (27 Oct). *Independence. Nos. 422, 425/30, 432, 434, 437/40, 441a and 443 optd with T* **107**, *by Letchworth Press, Barbados.*
606 1 c. Type **79** 5 5
607 4 c. Mackerel 10 10
608 5 c. French Grunt 10 10
609 6 c. Spotted Goatfish 10 10
610 8 c. Ballyhoo 12 12
611 10 c. Sperm Whale 15 15
612 12 c. Humpback Whale 15 15
613 15 c. Skipjack 15 15
614 25 c. Princess Parrotfish 20 20
615 50 c. Porkfish 35 35
616 70 c. "Albacore" or Yellowfin Tuna 45 45
617 90 c. Pompano 50 50
618 $1 Queen Triggerfish 50 50
619 $2.50, Sailfish (II) .. .. 1·25 1·25
a. Opt inverted £150
b. Optd on Type I (No. 441) .. .. .. 9·00 9·00
620 $10 Blue Marlin .. .. 4·75 4·75
606/20 .. .. *Set of* 15 8·00 8·00

108 Virgin and Child

109 Jack Spaniard and Oleander

(Des Jennifer Toombs. Litho Questa)

1979 (1 Nov). *Christmas. Scenes and Verses from the carol "Silent Night". T* **108** *and similar horiz designs. Multicoloured.* W w **14** (*sideways*). *P* 13½.
621 10 c. Type **108** 5 5
622 20 c. Jesus in manger 10 10
623 25 c. Shepherds 12 12
624 40 c. Angel 20 20
625 50 c. Angels with infant Jesus 25 25
626 $2 Nativity scene 80 80
621/6 .. .. *Set of* 6 1·40 1·40
MS627 151 × 170 mm. Nos. 621/6 .. .. 1·60 1·60

(Des J.W. Litho Walsall)

1979 (13 Dec). *Flowers and Insects. T* **109** *and similar vert designs showing insects and different varieties of Oleander flower. Multicoloured.* W w **14**. *P* 14.
628 5 c. Type **109** 5 5
629 10 c. Labelle 5 5
630 25 c. Praying Mantis 15 12
631 50 c. Green Guava Beetle 30 25
632 $2 Citrus Weevil .. .. 1·00 90

(Des and litho D.L.R.)

1980 (28 Feb). *Centenary of St. Vincent "Arms" Stamps. Sheet 116 × 72 mm containing designs as T* **31**. W w **14** (*sideways*). *P* 14 × 13½.
MS633 116 × 72 mm. 50 c. reddish brown; $1 deep grey-green; $2.50 deep blue .. .. .. 1·60 1·75

110 Queen Elizabeth II

(Des J.W. Litho Harrison)

1980 (24 Apr). *"London 1980" International Stamp Exhibition. T* **110** *and similar horiz designs. Multicoloured.* W w **14** (*sideways*). *P* 14.
634 80 c. Type **110** 30 30
635 $1 Great Britain 1954 3d. and St. Vincent 1954 5 c. definitive stamps 40 40
636 $2 Unadopted postage stamp design of 1971 80 80
MS637 165 × 115 mm. Nos. 596/8 and 634/6 .. 3·00 3·00
Nos. 634/6 were each printed in sheets containing 2 *se-tenant* stamp-size labels.

111 Steel Band

112 Football

(Des G. Drummond. Litho Questa)

1980 (12 June). *Kingstown Carnival. T* **111** *and similar horiz design. Multicoloured.* W w **14** (*sideways*). *P* 13½ × 14.
638 20 c. Type **111** 10 10
a. Pair. Nos. 638/9 .. .. 20 20
639 20 c. Steel band (*different*) 10 10
Nos. 638/9 were printed together, *se-tenant*, in horizontal and vertical pairs throughout the sheet.

(Des Polygraphic. Litho Rosenbaum Bros, Vienna)

1980 (7 Aug). *"Sport for All". T* **112** *and similar vert designs. Multicoloured.* W w **14** (*inverted*). *P* 13½.
640 10 c. Type **112** 5 5
641 60 c. Cycling 25 20
642 80 c. Basketball 30 30
643 $2.50, Boxing .. .. 1·00 1·00

HURRICANE
RELIEF
50¢

(113)

114 Agouti

1980 (7 Aug). *Hurricane Relief. Nos. 640/3 surch with T* **113**. W w **14** (*upright*).
644 10 c. + 50 c. Type **112** 25 30
645 60 c. + 50 c. Cycling 50 60
646 80 c. + 50 c. Basketball 55 65
647 $2.50 + 50 c. Boxing .. .. 1·25 1·25

(Des L. Curtis. Litho Questa)

1980 (2 Oct). *Wildlife. T* **114** *and similar horiz designs. Multicoloured.* W w **14** (*sideways*). *P* 14 × 14½.
648 25 c. Type **114** 12 12
649 50 c. Giant Toad 25 25
650 $2 Mongoose .. .. 95 1·00

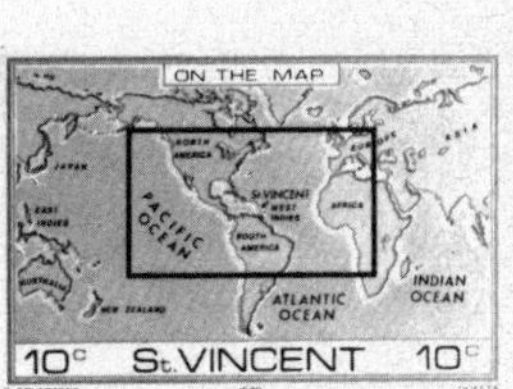

115 Map of World showing St. Vincent

116 *Ville de Paris*

(Des G. Drummond. Litho Questa)

1980 (4 Dec). *St. Vincent "On the Map". T* **115** *and similar designs depicting maps showing St. Vincent. Multicoloured.* W w **14** (*sideways*). *P* 13½ × 14.
651 10 c. Type **115** 5 5
652 50 c. Western hemisphere 25 25
563 $1 Central America 50 55
654 $2 St. Vincent .. .. 95 1·00
MS655 143 × 95 mm. No. 654. P 12 .. .. 95 1·00

(Des J.W. Litho Rosenbaum Bros, Vienna)

1981 (19 Feb). *Sailing Ships. T* **116** *and similar vert designs. Multicoloured.* W w **14**. *P* 13½.
656 50 c. Type **116** 25 25
657 60 c. *Ramillies* 30 35
658 $1.50, *Providence* 70 75
659 $2 R.M.S.P. *Dee* .. .. 95 1·00

117 Arrowroot Cultivation

(Des G. Drummond. Litho Format)

1981 (21 May). *Agriculture. T* **117** *and similar horiz designs. Multicoloured.* W w **14** *(sideways). P* 14.

660 25 c. Type **117** 10 12
a. Pair. Nos. 660/1 .. .. 20 25
661 25 c. Arrowroot processing 10 12
662 50 c. Banana cultivation 20 25
a. Pair. Nos. 662/3 .. .. 40 50
663 50 c. Banana export packaging station .. 20 25
664 60 c. Coconut plantation 25 30
a. Pair. Nos. 664/5 .. .. 50 60
665 60 c. Copra drying frames 25 30
666 $1 Cocoa cultivation 50 45
a. Pair. Nos. 666/7 .. .. 1·00 90
667 $1 Cocoa beans and sun drying frames .. 50 45
660/7 .. .. *Set of* 8 1·90 2·00

The two designs of each value were printed together, *se-tenant*, in horizontal and vertical pairs throughout the sheet.

(Des D. Shults. Litho Questa)

1981 (17 July–26 Nov). *Royal Wedding. Horiz designs as T* **26/27** *of Kiribati. Multicoloured. (a)* W w **15**. *P* 14.

668 60 c. *Isabella* 25 25
a. Sheetlet. No. 668 × 6 and No. 669 .. 2·00
669 60 c. Prince Charles and Lady Diana Spencer 70 70
670 $2.50, *Alberta* (tender) .. .. .. 1·00 1·00
a. Sheetlet. No. 670 × 6 and No. 671 .. 8·00
671 $2.50, As No. 669 .. .. 2·25 2·25
672 $4 *Britannia* .. .. 1·60 1·75
a. Sheetlet. No. 672 × 6 and No. 673 .. 12·00
673 $4 As No. 669 .. .. 3·50 3·50
MS674 120 × 109 mm. $5 As No. 669. Wmk sideways. P 12 (26 Nov) .. .. 2·00 2·00

(b) Booklet stamps. No wmk. P 12 (26 Nov)

675 60 c. As No. 668 .. .. 25 25
a. Booklet pane. No. 675 × 4 .. .. 1·00
676 $2.50, As No. 671 .. .. 1·25 1·25
a. Booklet pane. No. 676 × 2 .. .. 2·50

Nos. 668/73 were printed in sheetlets of seven stamps of the same face value, each containing six of the "Royal Yacht" design and one of the larger design showing Prince Charles and Lady Diana.

Nos. 675/6 come from $9.80 stamp booklets.

118 Kingstown General Post Office **119**

(Des G. Drummond. Litho Questa)

1981 (1 Sept). *U.P.U. Membership.* W w **14** *(sideways). P* 14.

677 **118** $2 multicoloured .. .. .. 95 1·00
a. Horiz pair. Nos. 677/8 .. .. 1·90 2·00
678 **119** $2 multicoloured .. .. .. 95 1·00

Nos. 677/8 were printed together, *se-tenant*, in horizontal pairs throughout the sheet, forming a composite design.

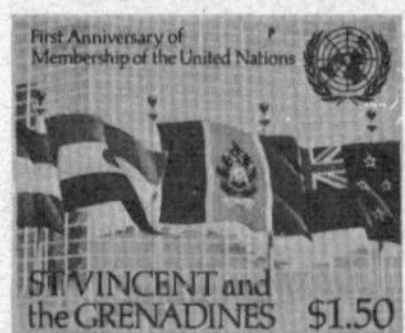

120 St. Vincent Flag with Flags of other U.N. Member Nations

(Des L. Curtis. Litho Format)

1981 (11 Sept). *First Anniv of U.N. Membership. T* **120** *and similar horiz design. Multicoloured.* W w **14** *(sideways). P* 13½ × 14.

679 $1.50, Type **120** 70 75
680 $2.50, Prime Minister Robert Milton Cato .. 1·25 1·40

Nos. 679/80 are inscribed "ST. VINCENT and the GRENADINES" and were each printed in small sheets of 6 including one *se-tenant* stamp-size label.

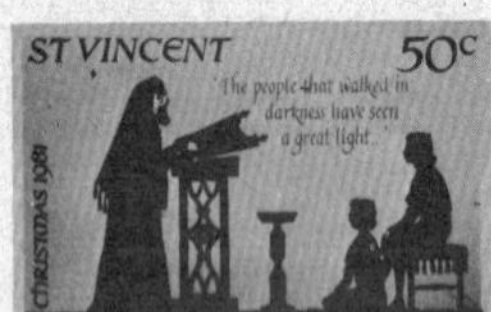

121 Silhouettes of Figures at Old Testament Reading, and Bible Extract

(Des Jennifer Toombs. Litho Security Printers (M), Malaysia)

1981 (19 Nov). *Christmas. T* **121** *and similar horiz designs showing silhouettes of figures. Multicoloured.* W w **14** *(sideways). P* 12.

681 50 c. Type **121** 25 25
682 60 c. Madonna, and angel 25 30
683 $1 Madonna, and Bible extract 50 55
684 $2 Joseph and Mary travelling to Bethlehem 95 1·00
MS685 129 × 127 mm. Nos. 681/4. P 13½ .. 1·90 2·00

122 Sugar Boilers

(Des L. Curtis. Litho Format)

1982 (5 Apr). *First Anniv of Re-introduction of Sugar Industry. T* **122** *and similar horiz designs. Multicoloured.* W w **14** *(sideways). P* 14.

686 50 c. Type **122** 25 25
687 60 c. Sugar drying plant 25 30
688 $1.50, Sugar mill machinery 70 75
689 $2 Crane loading sugar cane .. .. 95 1·00

123 Butterfly Float **124** Augusta of Saxe-Gotha, Princess of Wales, 1736

(Des G. Vasarhelyi. Photo Heraclio Fournier)

1982 (10 June). *Carnival* 1982. *T* **123** *and similar multicoloured designs. P* 13½.

690 50 c. Type **123** 25 25
691 60 c. Angel dancer *(vert)* 25 30
692 $1.50, Winged dancer *(vert)* 70 75
693 $2 Eagle float .. .. 95 1·00

(Des D. Shults and J. Cooter. Litho Format)

1982 (1 July). *21st Birthday of Princess of Wales. T* **124** *and similar vert designs. Multicoloured.* W **24** *of Kiribati. P* 13½ × 14.

694 50 c. Type **124** 35 25
695 60 c. Coat of arms of Augusta of Saxe-Gotha 35 30
696 $6 Diana, Princess of Wales .. .. 3·00 2·75

125 Scout Emblem **126** De Havilland "Moth", 1932

(Des L. Curtis. Litho Questa)

1982 (15 July). *75th Anniv of Boy Scout Movement. T* **125** *and similar vert design. Multicoloured.* W w **14**. *P* 14.

697 $1.50, Type **125** 70 75
698 $2.50, 75th anniv emblem .. .. .. 95 1·00

1982 (19 July). *Birth of Prince William of Wales. Nos.* 694/6 *optd with T* **19** *of St. Kitts.*

699 50 c. Type **124** 30 25
700 60 c. Coat of arms of Augusta of Saxe-Gotha .. 35 30
a. Opt inverted .. .. 65·00
701 $6 Diana, Princess of Wales .. .. 3·00 2·75

(Des A. Theobald. Litho Questa)

1982 (29 July). *50th Anniv of Airmail Service. T* **126** *and similar horiz designs. Multicoloured.* W w **14** *(sideways). P* 14.

702 50 c. Type **126** 25 25
703 60 c. Grumman "Goose", 1952 .. .. 25 30
704 $1.50, Hawker-Siddeley "748", 1968 .. 70 75
705 $2 Britten-Norman "Trislander", 1982 .. 95 1·00

127 M.V. *Geestport*

(Des G. Drummond. Litho Format)

1982 (27 Dec). *Cruise Ships. T* **127** *and similar horiz designs. Multicoloured.* W w **14** *(sideways). P* 14.

706 45 c. Type **127** 25 25
707 60 c. *Stella Oceanic* 30 35
708 $1.50, M.V. *The Victoria* 70 75
709 $2 *Queen Elizabeth 2* .. .. .. 95 1·00

128 *Pseudocorynactis caribbeorum*

(Des McCombie-De Bay. Litho Security Printers (M), Malaysia)

1983 (10 Feb). *Marine Life. T* **128** *and similar multicoloured designs.* W w **14** *(sideways on 60 c., $1.50, $2). P* 12.

710 50 c. Type **128** 25 25
711 60 c. *Actinoporus elegans (vert)* 30 35
712 $1.50, *Arachnanthus nocturnus (vert)* .. 70 75
713 $2 *Hippocampus reidi (vert)* .. .. .. 95 1·00

45¢ ■

129 Satellite View of St. Vincent **(130)**

(Des R. Vigurs. Litho Questa)

1983 (14 Mar). *Commonwealth Day. T* **129** *and similar horiz designs. Multicoloured.* W w **14** *(sideways). P* 14.

714 45 c. Type **129** 25 25
715 60 c. Flag of St. Vincent 30 35
716 $1.50, Prime Minister R. Milton Cato .. 70 75
717 $2 Harvesting bananas .. .. .. 95 1·00

Nos. 714/17 are inscribed "St. Vincent & The Grenadines".

1983 (26 Apr). *No.* 681 *surch with T* **130** *by Reliance Printery, Kingstown.*

718 45 c. on 50 c. Type **121** 20 25

131 Symbolic Handshake **132** Sir William Smith (founder)

(Des J.W. Litho Security Printers (M), Malaysia)

1983 (6 July). *10th Anniv of Treaty of Chaguaramas. T* **131** *and similar vert designs. Multicoloured.* W w **14** *(sideways). P* 11½ × 12.

719 45 c. Type **131** 25 25
720 60 c. Commerce emblem 30 35
721 $1.50, Caribbean map 70 75
722 $2 Flags of member countries and map of St. Vincent .. .. 95 1·00

(Des L. Curtis. Litho Security Printers (M), Malaysia)

1983 (6 Oct). *Centenary of Boys' Brigade. T* **132** *and similar vert designs. Multicoloured.* W w **14**. *P* 12 × 11½.

723 45 c. Type **132** 25 25
724 60 c. On parade 30 35
725 $1.50, Craftwork 70 75
726 $2 Community service .. .. .. 95 1·00

133 Ford "Model T" (1908)

(Des J.W. Litho Format)

1983 (25 Oct). *Leaders of the World. Automobiles (1st series). T* **133** *and similar horiz designs, the first in each pair showing technical drawings and the second paintings. P* 12½.

727 10 c. multicoloured 5 5
a. Vert pair. Nos. 727/8 .. .. .. 10 10
728 10 c. multicoloured 5 5
729 60 c. multicoloured 30 35
a. Vert pair. Nos. 729/30 .. .. .. 60 70
730 60 c. multicoloured 30 35
731 $1.50, multicoloured 75 80
a. Vert pair. Nos. 731/2 .. .. .. 1·50 1·60
732 $1.50, multicoloured 75 80
733 $1.50, multicoloured 75 80
a. Vert pair. Nos. 733/4 .. .. .. 1·50 1·60
734 $1.50, multicoloured 75 80
735 $2 multicoloured .. .. 95 1·00
a. Vert pair. Nos. 735/6 .. .. .. 1·90 2·00
736 $2 multicoloured .. .. 95 1·00
737 $2 multicoloured .. .. 95 1·00
a. Vert pair. Nos. 737/8 .. .. .. 1·90 2·00
738 $2 multicoloured .. .. 95 1·00
727/38 .. .. *Set of* 12 6·75 7·25

Designs:—Nos. 727/8, Ford "Model T" (1908); 729/30, Supercharged Cord "812" (1937); 731/2, Citroen "Open Tourer" (1937); 733/4, Mercedes Benz "300SL Gull-Wing" (1954); 735/6, Rolls-Royce "Phantom I" (1925); 737/8, Ferrari "Boxer 512BB" (1976).

Nos. 727/8, 729/30, 731/2, 733/4, 735/6 and 737/8 were printed together, *se-tenant*, in vertical pairs throughout the sheets.

See also Nos. 820/9.

134 Appearance of the Nativity Star

(Des Jennifer Toombs. Litho Security Printers (M), Malaysia)

1983 (15 Nov). *Christmas. T* **134** *and similar horiz designs showing the Shepherds. W w* **14.** *P* 12.

739 10 c. Type **134** 5 5
740 50 c. Message of the Angel 30 35
741 $1.50, The Heavenly Host 70 75
742 $2.40, Worshipping Jesus .. .. .. 1·10 1·25
MS743 130 × 130 mm. Nos. 739/42. Wmk sideways 2·10 2·25

135 *King Henry VIII*

(Des J.W. Litho Format)

1983 (8 Dec). *Leaders of the World. Railway Locomotives* (1st *series*). *T* **135** *and similar horiz designs, the first in each pair showing technical drawings and the second the locomotive at work. P* 12½.

744 10 c. multicoloured 5 5
a. Vert pair. Nos. 744/5 .. .. .. 10 10
745 10 c. multicoloured 5 5
746 10 c. multicoloured 5 5
a. Vert pair. Nos. 746/7 .. .. .. 10 10
747 10 c. multicoloured 5 5
748 25 c. multicoloured 12 15
a. Vert pair. Nos. 748/9 .. .. .. 25 30
749 25 c. multicoloured 12 15
750 50 c. multicoloured 25 30
a. Vert pair. Nos. 750/1 .. .. .. 50 60
751 50 c. multicoloured 25 30
752 60 c. multicoloured 30 35
a. Vert pair Nos. 752/3 .. .. .. 60 70
753 60 c. multicoloured 30 35
754 75 c. multicoloured 40 45
a. Vert pair. Nos. 754/5 .. .. .. 80 90
755 75 c. multicoloured 40 45
756 $2.50, multicoloured .. .. 1·25 1·40
a. Vert pair. Nos. 756/7 .. .. .. 2·50 2·75
757 $2.50, multicoloured .. .. 1·25 1·40
758 $3 multicoloured .. .. 1·50 1·75
a. Vert pair. Nos. 758/9 .. .. .. 3·00 3·50
759 $3 multicoloured .. .. 1·50 1·75
744/59 .. .. *Set of* 16 7·00 8·00

Designs:—Nos. 744/5, *King Henry VIII* (1927); 746/7, *Royal Scots Grey* (1961); 748/9, *Hagley Hall* (1928); 750/1, *Sir Lancelot* (1926); 752/3, B12 Class (1912); 754/5, Deeley "Compound" (1902); 756/7, *Cheshire* (1927); 758/9, Bullied "Austerity" (1942).

Nos. 744/59 were issued in a similar sheet format to Nos. 727/38.

See also Nos. 792/807 and 834/41.

136 Fort Duvernette

(Des Walsall. Litho Questa)

1984 (13 Feb). *Fort Duvernette. T* **136** *and similar horiz designs. Multicoloured. W w* **15** (*sideways*). *P* 14 × 14½.

760 35 c. Type **136** 15 20
761 45 c. Soldiers on fortifications 20 25
762 $1 Cannon facing bay 45 50
763 $3 Map of St. Vincent and mortar .. .. 1·40 1·50

137 White Frangipani

(Des J. Cooter. Litho Harrison)

1984 (2 Apr). *Flowering Trees and Shrubs. T* **137** *and similar horiz designs. Multicoloured. W w* **14** (*sideways*). *P* 13½ × 14.

764 5 c. Type **137** 5 5
765 10 c. Genip 5 5
766 15 c. Immortelle 10 12
767 20 c. Pink Poui 12 15
768 25 c. Buttercup 15 20
769 35 c. Sandbox 20 25
770 45 c. Locust 30 35
771 60 c. Colville's Glory 35 40
772 75 c. Lignum Vitae 45 50
773 $1 Golden Shower 60 65
774 $5 Angelin .. .. 3·00 3·25
775 $10 Roucou .. .. 6·00 6·50
764/75 .. .. *Set of* 12 10·50 11·25

138 Trench Warfare, First World War

139 Musical Fantasy Costume

(Des Court House Studio. Litho Format)

1984 (25 Apr). *Leaders of the World. British Monarchs. T* **138** *and similar vert designs. Multicoloured. P* 12½.

776 1 c. Type **138** 5 5
a. Horiz pair. Nos. 776/7 .. .. .. 5 5
777 1 c. George V and trenches 5 5
778 5 c. Battle of Bannockburn 5 5
a. Horiz pair. Nos. 778/9 .. .. .. 8 10
779 5 c. Edward II and battle 5 5
780 60 c. George V 40 45
a. Horiz pair. Nos. 780/1 .. .. .. 80 90
781 60 c. York Cottage, Sandringham 40 45
782 75 c. Edward II 50 55
a. Horiz pair. Nos. 782/3 .. .. .. 1·00 1·10
783 75 c. Berkeley Castle 50 55
784 $1 Coat of arms of Edward II 70 75
a. Horiz pair. Nos. 784/5 .. .. .. 1·40 1·50
785 $1 Edward II (*different*) 70 75
786 $4 Coat of arms of George V .. .. 2·75 3·00
a. Horiz pair. Nos. 786/7 .. .. .. 5·50 6·00
787 $4 George V and Battle of Jutland .. .. 2·75 3·00
776/87 .. .. *Set of* 12 8·00 8·50

Nos. 776/7, 778/9, 780/1, 782/3, 784/5 and 786/7 were printed together, *se-tenant*, in horizontal pairs throughout the sheets, each pair forming a composite design.

(Des G. Vasarhelyi. Litho Questa)

1984 (25 June). *Carnival* 1984. *T* **139** *and similar horiz designs showing Carnival costumes. Multicoloured. W w* **15** (*sideways*). *P* 14.

788 35 c. Type **139** 25 30
789 45 c. African princess 30 35
790 $1 Market woman 70 75
791 $3 Carib hieroglyph .. .. 2·00 2·10

(Des J.W. Litho Format)

1984 (27 July). *Leaders of the World. Railway Locomotives* (2nd *series*). *Horiz designs as T* **135**, *the first in each pair showing technical drawings and the second the locomotive at work. P* 12½.

792 1 c. multicoloured 5 5
a. Vert pair. Nos. 792/3 .. .. .. 5 5
793 1 c. multicoloured 5 5
794 2 c. multicoloured 5 5
a. Vert pair. Nos. 794/5 .. .. .. 5 5
795 2 c. multicoloured 5 5
796 3 c. multicoloured 5 5
a. Vert pair. Nos. 796/7 .. .. .. 5 5
797 3 c. multicoloured 5 5
798 50 c. multicoloured 35 40
a. Vert pair. Nos. 798/9 .. .. .. 70 75
799 50 c. multicoloured 35 40
800 75 c. multicoloured 50 55
a. Vert pair. Nos. 800/1 .. .. .. 1·00 1·10
801 75 c. multicoloured 50 55
802 $1 multicoloured 70 75
a. Vert pair. Nos. 802/3 .. .. .. 1·40 1·50
803 $1 multicoloured 70 75
804 $2 multicoloured .. .. 1·40 1·50
a. Vert pair. Nos. 804/5 .. .. .. 2·75 3·00
805 $2 multicoloured .. .. 1·40 1·50
806 $3 multicoloured .. .. 2·00 2·10
a. Vert pair. Nos. 806/7 .. .. .. 4·00 4·25
807 $3 multicoloured .. .. 2·00 2·10
792/807 .. .. *Set of* 16 9·00 9·50

Designs:—Nos. 792/3, Liberation Class (1945); 794/5, Dreadnought Class (1967); 796/7, No. 242A1 (1946); 798/9, Dean Goods Class (1883); 800/1, Hetton Colliery No. 1 (1822); 802/3, *Penydarren* (1804); 804/5, *Novelty* (1829); 806/7, Class 44 (1925).

Nos. 792/807 were issued in a similar sheet format to Nos. 727/38.

140 Slaves tilling Field

141 Judo

(Des G. Vasarhelyi. Litho Questa)

1984 (1 Aug). 150*th Anniv of Emancipation of Slaves on St. Vincent. T* **140** *and similar horiz designs. Multicoloured. W w* **15** (*sideways*). *P* 14.

808 35 c. Type **140** 25 30
809 45 c. Sugar-cane harvesting 30 35
810 $1 Cutting sugar-cane 70 75
811 $3 William Wilberforce and African slave caravan .. .. 2·00 2·10

(Des Court House Studio. Litho Format)

1984 (30 Aug). *Leaders of the World. Olympic Games, Los Angeles. T* **141** *and similar vert designs. Multicoloured. P* 12½.

812 1 c. Type **141** 5 5
a. Horiz pair. Nos. 812/13 .. .. .. 5 5
813 1 c. Weightlifting 5 5
814 3 c. Pursuit cycling 5 5
a. Horiz pair. Nos. 814/15 .. .. .. 5 5
815 3 c. Cycle road-racing 5 5
816 60 c. Women's backstroke swimming 40 45
a. Horiz pair. Nos. 816/17 .. .. .. 80 90
817 60 c. Men's butterfly swimming 40 45
818 $3 Sprint start .. .. 2·00 2·10
a. Horiz pair. Nos. 818/19 .. .. .. 4·00 4·25
819 $3 Finish of long distance race .. .. 2·00 2·10
812/19 .. .. *Set of* 8 4·25 4·75

Nos. 812/13, 814/15, 816/17 and 818/19 were printed together, *se-tenant*, in horizontal pairs throughout the sheets.

(Des J.W. Litho Format)

1984 (22 Oct). *Leaders of the World. Automobiles* (2nd *series*). *Horiz designs as T* **133**, *the first in each pair showing technical drawings and the second paintings. P* 12½.

820 5 c. black, drab and bright green 5 5
a. Vert pair. Nos. 820/1 .. .. .. 8 10
821 5 c. multicoloured 5 5
822 20 c. black, pink and pale new blue 15 20
a. Vert pair. Nos. 822/3 .. .. .. 30 40
823 20 c. multicoloured 15 20
824 55 c. black, pale green and lake-brown .. 40 45
a. Vert pair. Nos. 824/5 .. .. .. 80 90
825 55 c. multicoloured 40 90
826 $1.50, black, pale turq-grn & turq-grn .. 1·00 1·10
a. Vert pair. Nos. 826/7 .. .. .. 2·00 2·25
827 $1.50, multicoloured .. .. 1·00 1·10
828 $2.50, black, turquoise-green and lilac .. 1·75 1·90
a. Vert pair. Nos. 828/9 .. .. .. 3·50 3·75
829 $2.50, multicoloured .. .. 1·75 1·90
820/9 .. .. *Set of* 10 6·00 6·50

Designs:—Nos. 820/1, Austin-Healey "Sprite" (1958); 822/3, Maserati "Ghibli Coupe" (1971); 824/5, Pontiac "GTO" (1964); 826/7, Jaguar "D-Type" (1957); 828/9, Ferrari "365 GTB4 Daytona" (1970).

Nos. 820/9 were issued in a similar sheet format to Nos. 727/38.

142 Grenadier, 70th Regt of Foot, 1773

143 N. S. Taylor

(Des J. Cooter. Litho Questa)

1984 (12 Nov). *Military Uniforms. T* **142** *and similar vert designs. Multicoloured. W w* **15.** *P* 14.

830 45 c. Type **142** 30 35
831 60 c. Grenadier, 6th Regt of Foot, 1775 .. 40 45
832 $1.50, Grenadier, 3rd Regt of Foot, 1768 .. 1·00 1·10
833 $2 Battalion Company officer, 14th Regt of Foot, 1780 .. .. 1·40 1·50

(Des J.W. Litho Format)

1984 (21 Nov). *Leaders of the World. Railway Locomotives* (3rd *series*). *Horiz designs as T* **135**, *the first in each pair showing technical drawings and the second the locomotive at work. Multicoloured. P* 12½.

834 5 c. multicoloured 5 8
a. Vert pair. Nos. 834/5 .. .. .. 8 12
835 5 c. multicoloured 5 8
836 40 c. multicoloured 30 35
a. Vert pair. Nos. 836/7 .. .. .. 60 70
837 40 c. multicoloured 30 35
838 75 c. multicoloured 50 55
a. Vert pair. Nos. 838/9 .. .. .. 1·00 1·10
839 75 c. multicoloured 50 55
840 $2.50, multicoloured .. .. 1·75 1·90
a. Vert pair. Nos. 840/1 .. .. .. 3·50 3·75
841 $2.50, multicoloured .. .. 1·75 1·90
834/41 .. .. *Set of* 8 4·50 5·25

Designs:—Nos. 834/5, Rhodesian Railways Class 20 (1954); 836/7, *Southern Maid* (1928); 838/9, *Prince of Wales* (1911); 840/1, German Class 05 (1935).

Nos. 834/41 were issued in a similar sheet format to Nos. 727/38.

(Des Court House Studio. Litho Format)

1985 (7 Jan). *Leaders of the World. Cricketers. T* **143** *and similar vert designs, the first in each pair showing a head portrait and the second the cricketer in action. P* 12½.

842 5 c. multicoloured 5 5
a. Horiz pair. Nos. 842/3 5
843 5 c. multicoloured 5 5
844 35 c. multicoloured 20 25
a. Horiz pair. Nos. 844/5 40
845 35 c. multicoloured 20 25
846 50 c. multicoloured 30 35
a. Horiz pair. Nos. 846/7 60
847 50 c. multicoloured 30 35
848 $3 multicoloured .. .. 1·75 1·90
a. Horiz pair. Nos. 848/9 .. .. .. 3·50
849 $3 multicoloured .. .. 1·75 1·90
842/9 .. .. *Set of* 8 4·25 4·75

Designs:—Nos. 842/3, N. S. Taylor; 844/5, T. W. Graveney; 846/7, R. G. D. Willis; 848/9, S. D. Fletcher.

Nos. 842/3, 844/5, 846/7, and 848/9 were printed together, *se-tenant*, in vertical pairs throughout the sheets.

144 Eye Lash Orchid

(Des G. Drummond. Litho Format)

1985 (31 Jan). *Orchids. T* **144** *and similar vert designs. Multicoloured. W* w **15.** *P* 14.

850	35 c. Type **144**	20	25
851	45 c. *Ionopsis utricularioides*	25	30
852	$1 *Epidendrum secundum*	60	65
853	$3 *Oncidium altissimum*	1·75	1·90

OFFICIAL STAMPS

OFFICIAL

(O 1)

1982 (11 Oct). *Nos. 668/73 optd with Type* O **1**.

O1	60 c. *Isabella*	25	30
	a. Sheetlet. No. O1 × 6 and No. O2 . .	2·00	
	b. Opt double		
	c. Albino opt	12·00	
O2	60 c. Prince Charles and Lady Diana Spencer	50	50
	b. Opt double		
	c. Albino opt	35·00	
O3	$2.50, *Alberta* (tender)	1·00	1·10
	a. Sheetlet. No. O3 × 6 and No. O4 . .	8·00	
	b. Opt inverted	30·00	
	c. Opt inverted (horiz pair)	80·00	
O4	$2.50, Prince Charles and Lady Diana Spencer	1·50	1·50
	b. Opt inverted	95·00	
O5	$4 *Britannia*	1·75	1·90
	a. Sheetlet. No. O5 × 6 and No. O6 . .	13·00	
	b. Opt double		
	c. Albino opt	20·00	
	d. Opt inverted		
	e. Opt inverted (horiz pair)		
O6	$4 Prince Charles and Lady Diana Spencer	2·25	2·25
	b. Opt double		
	c. Albino opt	55·00	
	d. Opt inverted		
O1/6	. . . . . . *Set of* 6	7·00	7·00

Nos. O3c and O5e show the long overprint, intended for Nos. O4 or O6, inverted and struck across a horizontal pair of Nos. O3 or O5. Nos. O4b and O6d show two examples of Type O **1** inverted on the same stamp.

POSTAL FISCAL STAMPS

The following were primarily intended for the payment of passport fees, but were also valid for postal purposes and are frequently found used on parcels.

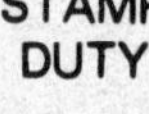

(F 1)

F **2** St. Vincent Coat of Arms

1980 (Feb). *Stamps as T* **95**, *without value, surch as Type* F **1**. *W* w **12**. *P* 14½ × 14.

F1	$5 deep lavender and azure	3·00	2·50
F2	$10 light green and apple green	6·50	5·50
F3	$20 reddish purple and pale rose-lilac . .	12·50	12·00

(Des Harrison. Recess D.L.R.)

1980 (19 May). *W* w **14**. *P* 14 × 13.

F4	F **2** $5 chalky blue	3·00	3·25
F5	$10 deep green	6·00	6·50
F6	$20 brown-red	10·50	11·00

1984 (22 May). *As No.* F6, *but W* w **15.** *P* 12.

F9	F **2** $20 brown-red	11·00	11·50

GRENADINES OF ST. VINCENT

A group of islands south of St. Vincent which includes Bequia, Mustique, Canouan and Union.

For stamps inscribed "The Grenadines of St. VINCENT" issued by St. Vincent in 1971, see under St. Vincent Nos. 330/6.

Stamps of the Grenadines of St. Vincent exist overprinted "SPECIMEN", these being produced for publicity purposes.

1973 (14 Nov). *Royal Wedding. As Nos.* 165/6 *of Anguilla.*

1	25 c. light green	20	15
2	$1 ochre	40	25

GRENADINES
OF

(1)

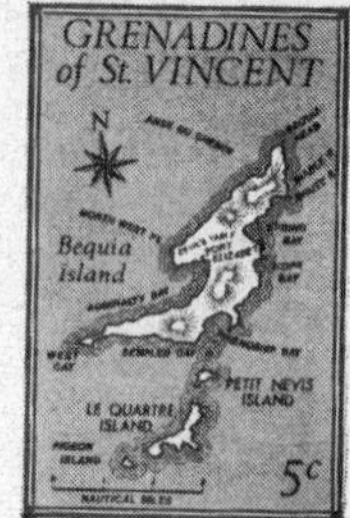

2 Map of Bequia

1974 (24 Apr). *Stamps of St. Vincent. T* **51** *etc. optd in litho with T* **1** *by Harrison & Sons. Glazed paper. W* w **12** (*sideways on* 4, 5, 10, 12, 50 *c. and* $5).

3	1 c. Green Heron	5	5
	a. Opt omitted	50·00	
	b. Albino opt	45·00	
4	2 c. Lesser Antillean Bullfinches	12	12
5	3 c. St. Vincent Amazons	75	75
6	4 c. Rufous-throated Solitaire	12	8
7	5 c. Red-necked Pigeon	12	8
8	6 c. Bananaquits	15	10
9	8 c. Purple-throated Carib	15	10
10	10 c. Mangrove Cuckoo	15	10
11	12 c. Common Black Hawk	20	12
	a. Opt double	£125	
12	20 c. Bare-eyed Thrush	35	20
13	25 c. Hooded Tanager	40	20
14	50 c. Blue-hooded Euphonia	70	40
	a. Albino opt	80·00	
15	$1 Barn Owl	1·50	1·10
16	$2.50, Yellow-billed Elaenia	5·50	3·00
17	$5 Ruddy Quail Dove	12·00	7·00
3/17	. . . . . . *Set of* 15	20·00	12·00

(Des G. Drummond. Litho Enschedé)

1974 (9 May). *Maps* (*1st series*). *T* **2** *and similar vert designs. W* w **12** (*sideways*). *P* 13 × 12½.

18	5 c. black, light dull green and deep dull green	10	5
19	15 c. multicoloured	20	12
20	20 c. multicoloured	30	15
21	30 c. black, light rose-lilac and lake . .	40	15
22	40 c. black, lavender and deep ultramarine . .	50	25
23	$1 black, cobalt and bright ultramarine . .	90	75
18/23	. . . . . . *Set of* 6	2·25	1·25

Maps:—15 c. The Grenadines and Prune Island (inset); 20 c. Mayreau Island and Tobago Cays; 30 c. Mustique Island; 40 c. Union Island; $1 Canouan Island.

Nos. 18/23 were each issued in sheets of ten stamps and two *se-tenant* labels.

See also Nos. 85/8.

**GRENADINES
OF**

(3)

4 Boat-building

1974 (7 June). *Nos. 361/2 of St. Vincent optd in typo with T* **3** *by Govt Printer, St. Vincent. Glazed paper. W* w **12**.

24	2 c. Lesser Antillean Bullfinches	40	30
25	3 c. St. Vincent Amazons	40	30
	a. Opt double	45·00	
	b. Albino opt	11·00	
	c. Chalky paper. Wmk sideways (No. 288)	40·00	30·00

1974 (25 July). *Centenary of Universal Postal Union. As Nos.* 392/5 *of St. Vincent but colours and face-values changed and inscr* "Grenadines of St. Vincent".

26	2 c. U.P.U. emblem	5	5
27	15 c. Globe within posthorn	15	5
28	40 c. Map of St. Vincent and hand-cancelling	30	20
29	$1 Map of the world	45	40

(Des G. Drummond. Litho Questa)

1974. *Bequia Island* (*1st series*). *T* **4** *and similar horiz designs. Multicoloured. P* 14. (*a*) *W* w **12** (*sideways*) (26.9.74).

30	5 c. Type **4**	4·00	2·75
31	30 c. Careening at Port Elizabeth	20	20
32	35 c. Admiralty Bay	25	25
33	$1 Fishing boat race	55	40
	(*b*) *W* w **14** (*sideways*) (12.74)		
34	5 c. Type **4**	20	10

No. 34 differs in shade from No. 30, notably in the shirt of the man at right, which is red on No. 34 instead of purple.

Nos. 30/4 were each issued in sheets of ten stamps and two *se-tenant* labels.

See also Nos. 185/8.

5 Music Volute (imprint at foot showing designer, date and printer)

(Des R. Granger Barrett. Litho Questa)

1974 (27 Nov)–**77.** *Shells and Molluscs. Horiz designs as T* **5.** *Multicoloured. W* w **14** (*sideways*). *P* 14.

A. *No imprint.* B. *Imprint at foot*

		A		B	
35	1 c. Atlantic Thorny Oyster . .	5	5	†	
36	2 c. Zigzag Scallop	5	5	†	
37	3 c. Reticulated Helmet . .	5	5	†	
38	4 c. Type **5**	8	8	8	8
39	5 c. Amber Pen Shell	8	8	8	8
40	6 c. Angular Triton	8	8	8	8
41	8 c. Flame Helmet	12	8	10	8
42	10 c. Caribbean Olive	12	8	10	8
	a. Corrected imprint	†		15	10
43	12 c. Common Sundial	12	10	†	
44	15 c. Glory of the Atlantic Cone	25	20	30	15
45	20 c. Flame Auger	30	35	30	20
	a. Corrected imprint	†		30	15
46	25 c. King Venus	25	20	30	15
47	35 c. Long-spined Star-shell . .	40	30	35	25
	a. Corrected imprint	†		45	25
48	45 c. Speckled Tellin	45	30	†	
49	50 c. Rooster Tail Conch . .	50	35	45	30
50	$1 Green Star Shell	1·50	75	1·00	60
51	$2.50, Incomparable Cone . .	2·75	1·50	3·25	1·25
52	$5 Rough File Clam	6·00	3·50	6·50	3·00
52*a*	$10 Measled Cowrie	11·00	4·50	†	
35A/52*a*A	. . . . *Set of* 19	22·00	11·00		
38B/52B	. . . . *Set of* 13			12·00	5·50

Dates of issue: 27.11.74, Nos. 35A/52A; 12.7.76, Nos. 52aA, 38B/42B, 45B, 47B and 49B/50B; 2.6.77, Nos. 42a, 44B, 45a, 46B, 47a, 51B, 52B.

On Nos. 42a, 44B, 45a, 46B, 47a, 51B and 52B the designer's name is correctly spelt as "R. Granger Barrett". Previously the last name had been spelt "Barratt".

1974 (28 Nov). *Birth Centenary of Sir Winston Churchill. As Nos.* 403/6 *of St. Vincent but colours and face-values changed and inscr* "GRENADINES OF ST. VINCENT".

53	5 c. Type **75**	5	5
54	40 c. As 35 c.	25	20
55	50 c. As 45 c.	30	15
56	$1 As $1	60	40

6 Cotton House, Mustique

(Des G. Drummond. Litho Questa)

1975 (27 Feb). *Mustique Island. T* **6** *and similar horiz designs. Multicoloured. W* w **14** (*sideways*). *P* 14.

57	5 c. Type **6**	5	5
58	35 c. "Blue Waters", Endeavour Bay . .	25	20
59	45 c. Endeavour Bay	30	20
60	$1 "Les Jolies Eaux", Gelliceaux Bay . .	75	60

Nos. 57/60 were each issued in sheets of ten stamps and two *se-tenant* labels.

7 Soldier Martinique

(Des G. Drummond. Litho Questa)

1975 (15 May). *Butterflies. T* **7** *and similar horiz designs. Multicoloured. W* w **14** (*sideways*). *P* 14.

61	3 c. Type **7**	20	10
62	5 c. Silver-spotted Flambeau	25	10
63	35 c. Gold Rim	80	20
64	45 c. Bright Blue and Donkey's Eye . .	1·25	40
65	$1 Biscuit	2·25	70

8 Resort Pavilion

(Des G. Drummond. Litho Harrison)

1975 (24 July). *Petit St. Vincent. T* **8** *and similar horiz designs. Multicoloured. W* w **14** (*sideways*). *P* 14.

66	5 c. Type **8**	10	5
67	35 c. The Harbour	40	20
68	45 c. The Jetty	90	50
69	$1 Sailing in coral lagoon	1·25	60

Nos. 66/9 were each issued in sheets of ten stamps and two *se-tenant* labels.

9 Ecumenical Church, Mustique

(Des G. Drummond. Litho Questa)

1975 (20 Nov). *Christmas. T* **9** *and similar horiz designs. Multicoloured.* W w **12** (*sideways*). *P* 14.

70 5 c. Type **9** 5 5
71 25 c. Catholic Church, Union Island 25 20
72 50 c. Catholic Church, Bequia 40 35
73 $1 Anglican Church, Bequia 70 50

10 Sunset Scene

(Des G. Drummond. Litho J.W.)

1976 (26 Feb). *Union Island* (1*st series*). *T* **10** *and similar horiz designs. Multicoloured.* W w **14** (*sideways*). *P* 13½.

74 5 c. Type **10** 10 10
75 35 c. Customs and Post Office, Clifton .. 25 15
76 45 c. Anglican Church, Ashton 35 20
77 $1 Mailboat, Clifton Harbour .. .. 1·00 60

Nos. 74/7 were each issued in sheets of ten stamps and two *se-tenant* labels.

See also Nos. 242/5.

11 Staghorn Coral

(Des G. Drummond. Litho Questa)

1976 (13 May). *Corals. T* **11** *and similar horiz designs. Multicoloured.* W w **14** (*sideways*). *P* 14.

78 5 c. Type **11** 5 5
79 35 c. Elkhorn coral 25 15
80 45 c. Pillar coral 35 20
81 $1 Brain coral .. .. 1·00 80

12 25 c. Bicentennial Coin

(Des J. Cooter. Litho Questa)

1976 (15 July). *Bicentenary of American Revolution. T* **12** *and similar horiz designs.* W w **14** (*sideways*). *P* 13½.

82 25 c. silver, black and light violet-blue .. 25 10
83 50 c. silver, black and light rose-red .. 60 35
84 $1 silver, black and mauve 95 55

Designs:—50 c. Half-dollar coin; $1 One dollar coin.

Nos. 82/4 were each issued in sheets of ten stamps and two *se-tenant* labels.

(Des G. Drummond. Litho Questa)

1976 (23 Sept). *Maps* (2*nd series*). *Vert designs as T* **2**, *showing various islands as detailed below.* W w **14**. *P* 13½.

A. Bequia — D. Mustique — F. Prune
B. Canouan — E. Petit St. Vincent — G. Union
C. Mayreau

To indicate individual islands, use the above letters as a suffix to the following catalogue numbers.

85 5 c. black, myrtle-green and pale emerald .. 10 10
 a. Booklet pane. Nos. 85/6 and 88 plus printed label 45
 b. Booklet pane. Nos. 85 × 2 and 86 plus printed label 30
86 10 c. black, ultramarine and greenish blue .. 10 10
 a. Booklet pane. Nos. 86 × 2 and 87 plus printed label 40
87 35 c. black, red-brown and bright rose .. 20 20
 a. Booklet pane. Nos. 87 × 2 and 88 plus printed label 65
88 45 c. black, scarlet and yellow-orange .. 25 25
85/8 .. .. *Set of* 4 (*one island*) 60 60
85/8 .. .. .. *Set of* 28 (*seven islands*) 4·00 4·00

Nos. 85/8 were only issued in $2.50 stamp booklets.

13 Station Hill School and Post Office

(Des G. Drummond. Litho Questa)

1976 (2 Dec). *Mayreau Island. T* **13** *and similar horiz designs. Multicoloured.* W w **14** (*sideways*). *P* 14.

89 5 c. Type **13** 5 5
90 35 c. Church at Old Wall 20 15
91 45 c. La Sourciere Anchorage 30 20
92 $1 Saline Bay 65 60

Nos. 89/92 were each issued in sheets of ten stamps and two *se-tenant* labels.

14 Coronation Crown Coin

(Des G. Vasarhelyi. Litho Questa)

1977 (3 Mar). *Silver Jubilee. T* **14** *and similar horiz designs. Multicoloured.* W w **14** (*sideways*). *P* 14.

93 25 c. Type **14** 45 35
94 50 c. Silver Wedding Crown 55 40
95 $1 Silver Jubilee Crown 65 50

Nos. 93/5 were each issued in sheets of ten stamps and two *se-tenant* labels.

15 Fiddler Crab

(Des BG Studio. Litho Questa)

1977 (19 May). *Crustaceans. T* **15** *and similar horiz designs. Multicoloured.* W w **14** (*sideways*). *P* 14.

96 5 c. Type **15** 5 5
97 35 c. Ghost crab 30 15
98 50 c. Blue crab 40 20
99 $1.25, Spiny lobster 90 70

16 Snorkel Diving

(Des G. Drummond. Litho Questa)

1977 (25 Aug). *Prune Island. T* **16** *and similar horiz designs. Multicoloured.* W w **14** (*sideways*). *P* 14½.

100 5 c. Type **16** 5 5
101 35 c. Palm Island Resort 20 15
102 45 c. Casuarina Beach 30 20
103 $1 Palm Island Beach Club 70 60

Nos. 100/3 were each issued in sheets of ten stamps and two *se-tenant* labels.

17 Mustique Island

(Des G. Drummond. Litho Questa)

1977 (31 Oct). *Royal Visit. Previously unissued stamps without face values, locally surch with new inscription.* W w **12**. *P* 14½ × 14.

104 **17** 40 c. turquoise-green and blue-green (Blk. (value) and R.) 25 20
105 $2 yellow-ochre and yellow-brown (R. (value) and B.) .. .. .. 1·00 70

18 The Clinic, Charlestown

(Des G. Drummond. Litho Harrison)

1977 (8 Dec). *Canouan Island* (1*st series*). T **18** *and similar horiz designs. Multicoloured.* W w **14**. *P* 14½.

106 5 c. Type **18** 5 5
107 35 c. Town jetty, Charlestown 20 15
108 45 c. Mailboat arriving at Charlestown .. 30 20
109 $1 Grand Bay 70 60

Nos. 106/9 were each issued in sheets of ten stamps and two *se-tenant* labels.

See also Nos. 307/10.

19 Tropical Mockingbird

(Des J.W. Litho Enschedé)

1978 (11 May). *Birds and their Eggs. Horiz designs as T* **19**. *Multicoloured.* W w **14** (*sideways*). *P* 12½ × 12.

110 1 c. Type **19** 5 5
111 2 c. Mangrove Cuckoo 5 5
112 3 c. Osprey 10 5
113 4 c. Smooth-billed Ani 10 5
114 5 c. House Wren 10 5
115 6 c. Bananaquit 10 5
116 8 c. Carib Grackle 10 5
117 10 c. Yellow-bellied Elaenia 10 5
118 12 c. Collared Plover 15 5
119 15 c. Cattle Egret 15 5
120 20 c. Red-footed Booby 15 5
121 25 c. Red-billed Tropic Bird 20 5
122 40 c. Royal Tern 25 15
123 50 c. Brown-crested Flycatcher 25 20
124 80 c. Purple Gallinule 35 30
125 $1 Broad-winged Hawk 45 50
126 $2 Scaly-breasted Ground Dove 80 75
127 $3 Laughing Gull .. .. 1·25 1·25
128 $5 Common Noddy .. .. 2·25 1·75
129 $10 Grey Kingbird .. .. 4·50 3·50
110/29 .. .. *Set of* 20 10·00 8·00

See also Nos. **MS**155 and **MS**170.

(Des G. Drummond. Litho J.W.)

1978 (2 June). *25th Anniv of Coronation. Horiz designs as Nos. 422/5 of Montserrat. Multicoloured.* W w **14** (*sideways*). *P* 13.

130 5 c. Worcester Cathedral 5 5
131 40 c. Coventry Cathedral 30 20
132 $1 Winchester Cathedral 70 40
133 $3 Chester Cathedral .. .. 1·60 1·00
MS134 130 × 102 mm. Nos. 130/3. P 13½ × 14 .. 2·40 1·50

Nos. 130/3 were each issued in sheets of ten stamps and two *se-tenant* labels.

20 Green Turtle

21 Three Kings following Star

(Des R. Granger Barrett. Litho Walsall)

1978 (20 July). *Turtles. T* **20** *and similar horiz designs. Multicoloured.* W w **14** (*sideways*). *P* 14.

135 5 c. Type **20** 5 5
136 40 c. Hawksbill turtle 25 25
137 50 c. Leatherback turtle 30 35
138 $1.25, Loggerhead turtle 75 75

(Des Jennifer Toombs. Litho Questa)

1978 (2 Nov). *Christmas. Scenes and Verses from the Carol "We Three Kings of Orient Are". T* **21** *and similar vert designs. Multicoloured.* W w **14**. *P* 14 × 13½.

139 5 c. Type **21** 5 5
140 10 c. King with gift of Gold 5 5
141 25 c. King with gift of Frankincense 15 10
142 50 c. King with gift of Myrrh 25 20
143 $2 Three Kings paying homage to infant Jesus 85 80
MS144 154 × 175 mm. Nos. 139/43 .. .. .. 1·75 1·40

22 Sailing Yachts

23 False Killer Whale

(Des G. Drummond. Litho Questa)

1979 (25 Jan). *National Regatta. T* **22** *and similar vert designs showing sailing yachts.* W w **14**. *P* 14.
145 5 c. multicoloured 5 5
146 40 c. multicoloured 25 25
147 50 c. multicoloured 35 35
148 $2 multicoloured .. .. 1·25 1·25

(Des L. Curtis. Litho Questa)

1979 (8 Mar). *Wildlife. Horiz designs as T* **114** *of St. Vincent. Multicoloured.* W w **14** (*sideways*). *P* 14 × 14½.
149 20 c. Green Iguana 10 10
150 40 c. Manicou 20 20
151 $2 Red-legged Tortoise 90 80
Nos. 149/51 were each printed in four panes of 12 throughout the sheet, each pane including two *se-tenant* labels.

(Des J.W. Litho. Enschedé)

1979 (21 May). *Death Centenary of Sir Rowland Hill. Horiz designs as T* **103** *of St. Vincent. Multicoloured.* W w **14** (*sideways*). *P* 12½ × 12.
152 80 c. Sir Rowland Hill 35 40
153 $1 Great Britain 1d. and 4d. stamps of 1858 with "A10" (Kingstown, St. Vincent) postmark 40 45
154 $2 St. Vincent ½d. and 1d. stamps of 1894 with Bequia postmark 80 65
MS155 165 × 115 mm. Nos. 124/6 and 152/4 .. 3·75 3·25
Nos. 152/4 were each printed in sheets including two *se-tenant* stamp-size labels.

1979 (24 Oct). *International Year of the Child. As Nos.* 570/3 *of St. Vincent.*
156 6 c. black, silver and pale blue 5 5
157 40 c. black, silver and salmon 15 15
158 $1 black, silver and buff 40 35
159 $3 black, silver and lilac .. .. .. 1·25 1·00

(Des J.W. Litho Enschedé)

1979 (27 Oct). *Independence. Horiz designs as T* **106** *of St. Vincent. Multicoloured.* W w **14** (*sideways*). *P* 12½ × 12.
160 5 c. National flag and *Ixora salici-folia* (flower) 5 5
161 40 c. House of Assembly and *Ixora odorata* (flower) 15 15
162 $1 Prime Minister R. Milton Cato and *Ixora javanica* (flower) 45 45

(Des R. Granger Barrett. Litho Walsall)

1980 (31 Jan). *Whales and Dolphins. T* **23** *and similar horiz designs. Multicoloured.* W w **14** (*sideways*). *P* 14.
163 10 c. Type **23** 5 5
164 50 c. Spinner Dolphin 25 20
165 90 c. Bottle Nosed Dolphin 45 40
166 $2 Blackfish 90 65

(Des J.W. Litho Enschedé)

1980 (24 Apr). *"London 1980" International Stamp Exhibition. Horiz designs as T* **110** *of St. Vincent. Multicoloured.* W w **14** (*sideways*). *P* 12½ × 12.
167 40 c. Queen Elizabeth II 30 35
168 50 c. St. Vincent 1965 2 c. definitive 30 35
169 $3 1973 25 c. and Royal Wedding commemoratives .. .. 1·10 1·25
MS170 165 × 115 mm. Nos. 122/3, 127 and 167/9 2·75 3·25
Nos. 167/9 were printed in sheets including 2 *se-tenant* stamp-size labels.

(Des Polygraphic. Litho Rosenbaum Bros, Vienna)

1980 (7 Aug). *"Sport for All". Vert designs as T* **112** *of St. Vincent. Multicoloured.* W w **14**. *P* 13½.
171 25 c. Running 12 12
172 50 c. Sailing 25 25
173 $1 Long jumping 45 50
174 $2 Swimming 80 90

1980 (7 Aug). *Hurricane Relief. Nos.* 171/4 *surch with T* **113** *of St. Vincent.*
175 25 c.+50 c. Running 35 40
176 50 c.+50 c. Sailing 45 50
177 $1+50 c. Long jumping 65 75
178 $2+50 c. Swimming .. .. 1·00 1·25

24 Scene and Verse from the Carol "De Borning Day"

25 Post Office, Port Elizabeth

(Des Jennifer Toombs. Litho Questa)

1980 (13 Nov). *Christmas. T* **24** *and similar vert designs showing scenes and verses from the carol "De Borning Day".* W w **14**. *P* 14 × 13½.
179 5 c. multicoloured 5 5
180 50 c. multicoloured 25 25
181 60 c. multicoloured 30 30
182 $1 multicoloured 40 45
183 $2 multicoloured 80 80
MS184 159 × 178 mm. Nos. 179/83 .. .. 2·00 2·10

(Des G. Drummond. Litho Questa)

1981 (19 Feb). *Bequia Island* (2*nd series*). *T* **25** *and similar horiz designs. Multicoloured.* W w **14** (*sideways*). *P* 14½ × 14.
185 50 c. Type **25** 25 25
186 60 c. Moonhole 30 30
187 $1.50, Fishing boats, Admiralty Bay .. 70 75
188 $2 *Friendship Rose* at jetty .. .. .. 95 1·00
The $2 value was originally printed with the country name in black and the face value in white. A quantity of these were stolen in transit before issue and the remainder were not placed on sale, the stamp being reprinted with the inscriptions in red.
Nos. 185/8 were each printed in sheets including two *se-tenant* stamp-size labels.

26 Ins. Cannaouan (map of Windward Islands by R. Ottens, *circa* 1765)

27 Bar Jack

(Des J. Cooter. Litho Format)

1981 (2 Apr). *Details from Early Maps. T* **26** *and similar horiz designs. Multicoloured.* W w **14** (*sideways*). *P* 13½.
189 50 c. Type **26** 30 30
a. Pair. Nos. 189/90 .. .. 60 60
190 50 c. Cannouan Is. (chart by J. Parsons, 1861) 30 30
191 60 c. Ins. Moustiques (map of Windward Islands by R. Ottens, *circa* 1765) .. 35 35
a. Pair. Nos. 191/2 .. .. 70 70
192 60 c. Mustique Is. (chart by J. Parsons, 1861) 35 35
193 $2 Ins. Bequia (map of Windward Islands by R. Ottens, *circa* 1765) 95 95
a. Pair. Nos. 193/4 .. .. 1·90 1·90
194 $2 Bequia Is. (map surveyed in 1763 by T. Jefferys) 95 95
189/94 .. .. *Set of* 6 3·00 3·00
The two designs of each value were printed together, *se-tenant*, in horizontal and vertical pairs throughout the sheet.

(Des D. Shults. Litho Questa)

1981 (17 July–26 Nov). *Royal Wedding. Horiz designs as T* **26/27** *of Kiribati. Multicoloured.* (a) W w **15**. *P* 14.
195 50 c. *Mary* 20 25
a. Sheetlet. No. 195 × 6 and No. 196 .. 2·00
196 50 c. Prince Charles and Lady Diana Spencer 80 80
197 $3 *Alexandra* .. .. 1·25 1·25
a. Sheetlet. No. 197 × 6 and No. 198 .. 8·50
198 $3 As No. 196 .. .. 3·00 3·00
199 $3.50, *Britannia* .. .. 1·40 1·40
a. Sheetlet. No. 199 × 6 and No. 200 .. 9·50
200 $3.50, As No. 196 .. .. 3·00 3·00
MS201 120 × 109 mm. $5 As No. 196. Wmk sideways. P 12 (26 Nov) .. .. 2·00 2·00
(*b*) *Booklet stamps. No wmk. P* 12 (26 Nov)
202 50 c. As No. 195 .. .. 20 25
a. Booklet pane. No. 202 × 4 80
203 $3 As No. 198 .. .. 1·50 1·60
a. Booklet pane. No. 203 × 2 .. .. 3·00
Nos. 195/200 were printed in sheetlets of seven stamps of the same face value, each containing six of the "Royal Yacht" design and one of the larger design showing Prince Charles and Lady Diana.
Nos. 202/3 come from $10 stamp booklets.

(Des N. Weaver. Litho Questa)

1981 (9 Oct). *Game Fish. T* **27** *and similar horiz designs. Multicoloured.* W w **14** (*sideways*). *P* 14.
204 10 c. Type **27** 15 10
205 50 c. Tarpon 35 25
206 60 c. Cobia 40 30
207 $2 Blue Marlin .. .. 1·25 1·00

28 H.M.S. *Experiment*

29 Prickly Pear Fruit

(Des J. Cooter. Litho Security Printers (M), Malaysia)

1982 (28 Jan). *Ships. Horiz designs as T* **28**. *Multicoloured.* W w **14**. *P* 13½ × 13.
208 1 c. Type **28** 5 5
209 3 c. S.S. *Lady Nelson* 5 5
210 5 c. Brig *Daisy* 5 5
211 6 c. Carib canoe 5 5
212 10 c. *Hairoun Star* 5 8
213 15 c. M.T.S. *Jupiter* 10 12
214 20 c. S.Y. *Christina* 12 15
215 25 c. R.M.S.P. *Orinoco* 15 20
216 30 c. H.M.S. *Lively* 20 25
217 50 c. C.S.S. *Alabama* 30 35
218 60 c. S.S. *Denmark* 35 40
219 75 c. *Santa Maria* 45 50
220 $1 C.S.S. *Baffin* 60 65
221 $2 *Queen Elizabeth 2* .. .. .. 1·25 1·40
222 $3 R.Y. *Britannia* .. .. 1·75 1·90
223 $5 M.V. *Geeststar* .. .. 3·00 3·25
224 $10 *Grenadines Star* .. .. 6·00 6·50
208/24 .. .. *Set of* 17 13·00 14·00

(Des G. Drummond. Litho Harrison)

1982 (5 Apr). *Prickly Pear Cactus. T* **29** *and similar vert designs. Multicoloured.* W w **14**. *P* 14.
225 10 c. Type **29** 5 5
226 50 c. Prickly Pear flower buds 25 25
227 $1 Flower of Prickly Pear Cactus 45 50
228 $2 Prickly Pear Cactus .. .. 95 1·00

30 Anne Neville, Princess of Wales, 1470

31 Old and New Uniforms

(Des D. Shults and J. Cooter. Litho Format)

1982 (1 July). *21st Birthday of Princess of Wales. T* **30** *and similar vert designs. Multicoloured.* W w **15**. *P* 13½ × 14.
229 50 c. Type **30** 35 25
230 60 c. Coat of arms of Anne Neville 40 30
231 $6 Diana, Princess of Wales .. .. .. 3·00 2·50

(Des L. Curtis. Litho W.S. Cowell Ltd)

1982 (15 July). *75th Anniv of Boy Scout Movement. T* **31** *and similar vert design. Multicoloured.* W w **14** (*inverted*). *P* 14½.
232 $1.50, Type **31** 70 75
233 $2.50, Lord Baden-Powell .. .. .. 1·10 1·25

ROYAL BABY

BEQUIA

(**32**)

33 Silhouette Figures of Mary and Joseph

1982 (19 July). *Birth of Prince William of Wales. Nos.* 229/31 *optd with various island names as T* **32**.
A. Bequia B. Canouan C. Mayreau
D. Mustique E. Union Island
To indicate individual islands, use the above letters as a suffix to the following catalogue numbers.
234 50 c. Type **30** 35 25
a. Opt C (Mayreau) inverted .. .. 85·00
b. Opt D (Mustique) inverted .. .. 80·00
235 60 c. Coat of arms of Anne Neville 40 30
a. Opt D (Mustique) inverted .. .. 85·00
b. Opt E (Union Island) inverted .. .. 85·00
c. Opt E (Union Island) double £150
236 $6 Diana, Princess of Wales .. .. .. 3·00 2·50

(Des Jennifer Toombs. Litho Security Printers (M), Malaysia)

1982 (18 Nov). *Christmas. T* **33** *and similar horiz designs showing silhouettes of figures. Multicoloured.* W w **14**. *P* 13½.
237 10 c. Type **33** 5 8
238 $1.50, Animals in stable 70 75
239 $2.50, Mary and Joseph with baby Jesus .. 1·10 1·25
MS240 168 × 99 mm. Nos. 237/9 .. .. .. 1·75 2·00

45¢

(**34**)

35 Power Station, Clifton

1983 (26 Apr). *No.* 123 *surch with T* **34** *by Reliance Printery, Kingstown.*
241 45 c. on 50 c. Brown-crested Flycatcher .. 20 25

(Des G. Drummond. Litho Security Printers (M), Malaysia)

1983 (12 May). *Union Island* (2*nd series*). *T* **35** *and similar horiz designs. Multicoloured.* W w **14**. *P* 13½.
242 50 c. Type **35** 20 25
243 60 c. Sunrise, Clifton harbour 30 35
244 $1.50, Junior Secondary School, Ashton .. 70 75
245 $2 Frigate Rock and Conch Shell Beach .. 95 1·00
Nos. 242/5 were each printed in sheets including two *se-tenant* stamp-size labels.

36 British Man-of-war

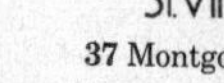

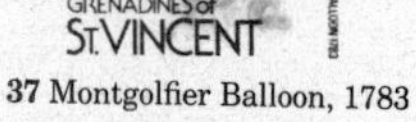

37 Montgolfier Balloon, 1783

(Des and litho J.W.)

1983 (15 Sept). *Bicentenary of Treaty of Versailles. T* **36** *and similar vert designs. Multicoloured. W* w **14.** *P* 14½.

246	45 c. Type **36**	20	25
247	60 c. American man-of-war	30	35
248	$1.50, Soldiers carrying U.S. flags	70	75
249	$2 British troops in battle	95	1·00

(Des A. Theobald. Litho Format)

1983 (15 Sept). *Bicentenary of Manned Flight. T* **37** *and similar multicoloured designs. W* w **14** (*sideways on Nos.* 251/53). *P* 14.

250	45 c. Type **37**	20	25
251	60 c. Ayres "Turbo-thrush Commander" (*horiz*)	30	35
252	$1.50, Lebaudy "1" dirigible (*horiz*)	70	75
253	$2 Space shuttle *Columbia* (*horiz*)	95	1·00
MS254	110 × 145 mm. Nos. 250/3. Wmk sideways	2·10	2·25

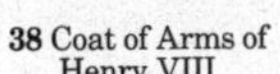

38 Coat of Arms of Henry VIII

39 Quarter Dollar and Half Dollar, 1797

(Des Court House Studio. Litho Format)

1983 (25 Oct). *Leaders of the World. British Monarchs. T* **38** *and similar vert designs. Multicoloured. P* 12½.

255	60 c. Type **38**	35	40
	a. Horiz pair. Nos. 255/6	70	80
256	60 c. Henry VIII	35	40
257	60 c. Coat of Arms of James I	35	40
	a. Horiz pair. Nos. 257/8	70	80
258	60 c. James I	35	40
259	75 c. Henry VIII	40	45
	a. Horiz pair. Nos. 259/60	80	90
260	75 c. Hampton Court	40	45
261	75 c. James I	40	45
	a. Horiz pair. Nos. 261/2	80	90
262	75 c. Edinburgh Castle	40	45
263	$2.50, The *Mary Rose*	1·40	1·50
	a. Horiz pair. Nos. 263/4	2·75	3·00
264	$2.50, Henry VIII and Portsmouth harbour	1·40	1·50
265	$2.50, Gunpowder Plot	1·40	1·50
	a. Horiz pair. Nos. 265/6	2·75	3·00
266	$2.50, James I and the Gunpowder Plot	1·40	1·50
255/66	*Set of* 12	7·75	8·50

Nos. 255/6, 257/8, 259/60, 261/2, 263/4 and 265/6 were printed together, *se-tenant*, in horizontal pairs throughout the sheets.

(Des J. Cooter. Litho Walsall)

1983 (1 Dec). *Old Coinage. T* **39** *and similar vert designs. Multicoloured. W* w **14.** *P* 14.

267	20 c. Type **39**	12	15
268	45 c. Nine Bitts, 1811–14	25	30
269	75 c. Twelve Bitts and Six Bitts, 1811–14	40	45
270	$3 Sixty-six Shillings, 1798	1·75	1·90

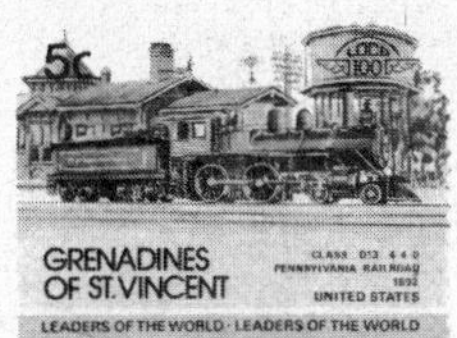

40 Class "D 13"

(Des J.W. Litho Format)

1984 (15 Mar). *Leaders of the World. Railway Locomotives* (1st *series*). *T* **40** *and similar horiz designs, the first in each pair showing technical drawings and the second the locomotive at work. P* 12½.

271	5 c. multicoloured	5	5
	a. Vert pair. Nos. 271/2	8	10
272	5 c. multicoloured	5	5
273	10 c. multicoloured	8	10
	a. Vert pair. Nos. 273/4	15	20
274	10 c. multicoloured	8	10
275	15 c. multicoloured	12	20
	a. Vert pair. Nos. 275/6	25	40
276	15 c. multicoloured	12	20
277	35 c. multicoloured	25	30
	a. Vert pair. Nos. 277/8	50	60
278	35 c. multicoloured	25	30
279	45 c. multicoloured	30	35
	a. Vert pair. Nos. 279/80	60	70
280	45 c. multicoloured	30	35
281	60 c. multicoloured	40	45
	a. Vert pair. Nos. 281/2	80	90
282	60 c. multicoloured	40	45
283	$1 multicoloured	70	75
	a. Vert pair. Nos. 283/4	1·40	1·50
284	$1 multicoloured	70	75
285	$2.50, multicoloured	1·75	1·90
	a. Vert pair. Nos. 285/6	3·50	3·75
286	$2.50, multicoloured	1·75	1·90
271/86	*Set of* 16	6·50	7·25

Designs:—Nos. 271/2, Class "D 13"; 273/4, High Speed Train "125"; 275/6, Class "T 9"; 277/8, *Claud Hamilton*; 279/80, Class "J"; 281/2, Class "D 16"; 283/4, *Lode Star*; 285/6, *Blue Peter*.

Nos. 271/2, 273/4, 275/6, 277/8, 279/80, 281/2, 283/4 and 285/6 were printed together, *se-tenant* in vertical pairs throughout the sheet.

See also Nos. 311/26 and Nos. 351/9.

41 Spotted Eagle Ray

(Des G. Drummond. Litho Format)

1984 (26 Apr). *Reef Fishes. T* **41** *and similar horiz designs. Multicoloured. W* w **15.** *P* 14.

287	45 c. Type **41**	30	35
288	60 c. Queen Trigger Fish	40	45
289	$1.50, White Spotted File Fish	1·00	1·10
290	$2 Schoolmaster	1·40	1·50

42 R. A. Woolmer

43 Junior Secondary School

(Des Court House Studio. Litho Format)

1984 (16 Aug). *Leaders of the World. Cricketers* (1st *series*). *T* **42** *and similar vert designs, the first in each pair showing a portrait and the second the cricketer in action. P* 12½.

291	1 c. multicoloured	5	5
	a. Horiz pair. Nos. 291/2	5	5
292	1 c. multicoloured	5	5
293	3 c. multicoloured	5	5
	a. Horiz pair. Nos. 293/4	5	5
294	3 c. multicoloured	5	5
295	5 c. multicoloured	5	5
	a. Horiz pair. Nos. 295/6	8	10
296	5 c. multicoloured	5	5
297	30 c. multicoloured	20	25
	a. Horiz pair. Nos. 297/8	40	50
298	30 c. multicoloured	20	25
299	60 c. multicoloured	40	45
	a. Horiz pair. Nos. 299/300	80	90
300	60 c. multicoloured	40	45
301	$1 multicoloured	70	75
	a. Horiz pair. Nos. 301/2	1·40	1·50
302	$1 multicoloured	70	75
303	$2 multicoloured	1·40	1·50
	a. Horiz pair. Nos. 303/4	2·75	3·00
	ab. Imperf (horiz pair)		
304	$2 multicoloured	1·40	1·50
305	$3 multicoloured	2·00	2·10
	a. Horiz pair. Nos. 305/6	4·00	4·25
306	$3 multicoloured	2·00	2·10
291/306	*Set of* 16	8·00	9·00

Designs:—Nos. 293/4, K. S. Ranjitsinhji; 295/6, W. R. Hammond; 297/8, D. L. Underwood; 299/300, W. G. Grace; 301/2, E. A. E. Baptiste; 303/4, A. P. E. Knott; 305/6, L. E. G. Ames.

See also Nos. 331/7.

(Des G. Drummond. Litho Questa)

1984 (3 Sept). *Canouan Island* (2nd *series*). *T* **43** *and similar horiz designs. Multicoloured. W* w **15** (*sideways*). *P* 14.

307	35 c. Type **43**	25	30
308	45 c. Police Station	30	35
309	$1 Post Office	70	75
310	$3 Anglican Church	2·00	2·10

(Des J.W. Litho Format)

1984 (9 Oct). *Leaders of the World. Railway Locomotives* (2nd *series*). *Horiz designs as T* **40**, *the first in each pair showing technical drawings and the second the locomotive at work. P* 12½.

311	1 c. multicoloured	5	5
	a. Vert pair. Nos. 311/12	5	5
312	1 c. multicoloured	5	5
313	5 c. multicoloured	5	5
	a. Vert pair. Nos. 313/14	8	10
314	5 c. multicoloured	5	5
315	20 c. multicoloured	15	20
	a. Vert pair. Nos. 315/16	30	40
316	20 c. multicoloured	15	20
317	35 c. multicoloured	25	30
	a. Vert pair. Nos. 317/18	50	60
318	35 c. multicoloured	25	30
319	60 c. multicoloured	40	45
	a. Vert pair. Nos. 319/20	80	90
320	60 c. multicoloured	40	45
321	$1 multicoloured	70	75
	a. Vert pair. Nos. 321/2	1·40	1·50
322	$1 multicoloured	70	75
323	$1.50, multicoloured	1·00	1·10
	a. Vert pair. Nos. 323/4	2·00	2·25
324	$1.50, multicoloured	1·00	1·10
325	$3 multicoloured	2·00	2·25
	a. Vert pair. Nos. 325/6	4·00	4·50
326	$3 multicoloured	2·00	2·25
311/26	*Set of* 16	8·50	9·25

Designs:—Nos. 311/12, Class "C62" (1948); 313/14, Class "V" (1903); 315/16, *Catch-Me-Who-Can* (1808); 317/18, Class "E10" (1948); 319/20, *J.B. Earle* (1904); 321/2, *Lyn* (1898); 323/4, *Talyllyn* (1865); 325/6, *Cardean* (1906).

Nos. 311/26 were issued in a similar sheet format to Nos. 271/86.

44 Lady of the Night

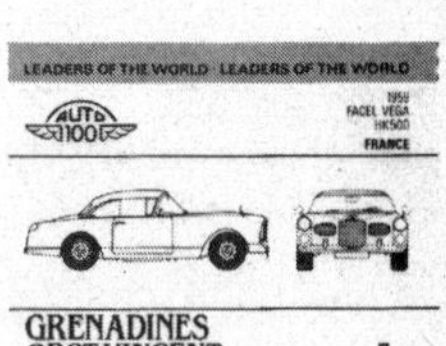

45 Facel "Vega HK500"

(Des Jennifer Toombs. Litho Questa)

1984 (15 Oct). *Night-blooming Flowers. T* **44** *and similar vert designs. Multicoloured. W* w **15.** *P* 14.

327	35 c. Type **44**	25	30
328	45 c. Four o'clock	30	35
329	75 c. Mother-in-Law's Tongue	50	55
330	$3 Queen of the Night	2·00	2·10

(Des Court House Studio. Litho Format)

1984 (28 Nov). *Leaders of the World. Cricketers* (2nd *series*). *Vert designs as T* **42**, *the first in each pair listed showing a head portrait and the second the cricketer in action. P* 12½.

331	5 c. multicoloured	5	5
	a. Horiz pair. Nos. 331/2	8	8
332	5 c. multicoloured	5	5
333	30 c. multicoloured	20	25
	a. Horiz pair. Nos. 333/4	40	50
334	30 c. multicoloured	20	25
335	$1 multicoloured	70	75
	a. Horiz pair. Nos. 335/6	1·40	1·50
336	$1 multicoloured	70	75
337	$2.50, multicoloured	1·75	1·90
	a. Horiz pair. Nos. 337/8	3·50	3·75
338	$2.50, multicoloured	1·75	1·90
331/8	*Set of* 8	4·75	5·25

Designs:—Nos. 331/2, S. F. Barnes; 333/4, R. Peel; 335/6, H. Larwood; 337/8, Sir John Hobbs.

Nos. 331/8 were issued in a similar sheet format to Nos. 291/306.

(Des J.W. Litho Format)

1984 (28 Nov). *Leaders of the World. Automobiles. T* **45** *and similar horiz designs, the first in each pair showing technical drawings and the second paintings. P* 12½.

339	5 c. black, azure and dull yellow-green	5	5
	a. Vert pair. Nos. 339/40	8	8
340	5 c. multicoloured	5	5
341	25 c. black, pale lilac and pink	15	20
	a. Vert pair. Nos. 341/2	30	40
342	25 c. multicoloured	15	20
343	50 c. black, pale blue and pale orange	35	40
	a. Vert pair. Nos. 343/4	70	80
344	50 c. multicoloured	35	40
345	$3 black, stone and brown lake	2·00	2·25
	a. Vert pair. Nos. 345/6	4·00	4·50
346	$3 multicoloured	2·00	2·25
339/46	*Set of* 8	4·50	5·25

Designs:—Nos. 339/40, Facel "Vega HK500"; 341/2, B.M.W. "328"; 343/4, Frazer-Nash "TT Replica 1.5L"; 345/6, Buick "Roadmaster Riviera".

Nos. 339/40, 341/2, 343/4 and 345/6 were printed together, *se-tenant*, in vertical pairs throughout the sheets.

46 The Three Wise Men and Star

(Des Jennifer Toombs. Litho Format)

1984 (3 Dec). *Christmas. T* **46** *and similar horiz designs. Multicoloured. W* w **15** (*sideways*). *P* 14½.

347	20 c. Type **46**	15	20
348	45 c. Journeying to Bethlehem	30	35
349	$3 Presenting gifts	2·00	2·10
MS350	177 × 107 mm. Nos. 347/9. Wmk inverted	2·40	2·50

(Des J.W. Litho Format)

1985 (31 Jan). *Leaders of the World. Railway Locomotives* (3rd *series*). *Horiz designs as T* **40**, *the first in each pair showing technical drawings and the second the locomotive at work. P* 12½.

351	1 c. multicoloured	5	5
	a. Vert pair. Nos. 351/2	5	
352	1 c. multicoloured	5	5
353	15 c. multicoloured	8	10
	a. Vert pair Nos. 353/4	15	
354	15 c. multicoloured	8	10
355	75 c. multicoloured	45	50
	a. Vert pair. Nos. 355/6	90	
356	75 c. multicoloured	45	50
357	$3 multicoloured	1·75	1·90
	a. Vert pair. Nos. 357/8	3·50	
358	$3 multicoloured	1·75	1·90
351/8	*Set of* 8	4·25	
MS359	142 × 122 mm. Nos. 355/8. W w **15.**	4·00	4·50

Designs:—Nos. 351/2, P.L.M. "Grosse C" (1898); 353/4, Class "C12" (1932); 355/6, Class "D50" (1923); 357/8, *Fire Fly* (1840).

Nos. 351/8 were issued in a similar sheet format to Nos. 271/86.

Appendix

The following issues for individual islands in the Grenadines group fall outside the criteria for full listing as detailed on page VIII of the General Catalogue Information in this edition.

BEQUIA

1984

Leaders of the World. Railway Locomotives (1st *series*). *Two designs*

for each value, the first showing technical drawings and the second the locomotive at work. 1, 5, 10, 25, 35, 45 c., $1.50, $2, *each* × 2.
Grenadines of St. Vincent 1982 *Ships definitives* (*Nos.* 208/24) *optd* "BEQUIA". 1, 3, 5, 6, 10, 15, 20, 25, 30, 50, 60, 75 c., $1, $2, $3, $5, $10.
Leaders of the World. Automobiles (1*st series*). *Two designs for each value, the first showing technical drawings and the second the car in action.* 5, 40 c., $1, $1.50, *each* × 2.
Leaders of the World. Olympic Games, Los Angeles. 1, 10, 60 c., $3, *each* × 2.
Leaders of the World. Railway Locomotives (2*nd series*). *Two designs for each value, the first showing technical drawings and the second the locomotive at work.* 1, 5, 10, 35, 75 c., $1, $2.50, $3, *each* × 2.
Leaders of the World. Automobiles (2*nd series*). *Two designs for each value, the first showing technical drawings and the second the car in action.* 5, 10, 20, 25, 75 c., $1, $2.50, $3, *each* × 2.

1985

Leaders of the World. Railway Locomotives (3*rd series*). *Two designs for each value, the first showing technical drawings and the second the locomotive at work.* 25, 55, 60 c., $2, *each* × 2.
Leaders of the World. Dogs. 25, 35, 55 c., $2, *each* × 2.

UNION ISLAND

1984

Leaders of the World. British Monarchs. Two designs for each value, forming a composite picture. 1, 5, 10, 20, 60 c., $3, *each* × 2.
Leaders of the World. Railway Locomotives (1*st series*). *Two designs for each value, the first showing technical drawings and the second the locomotive at work.* 5, 60 c., $1, $2.
Grenadines of St. Vincent 1982 *Ships definitives* (*Nos.* 208/24) *optd* "UNION ISLAND". 1, 3, 5, 6, 10, 15, 20, 25, 30, 50, 60, 75 c., $1, $2, $3, $5, $10.
Leaders of the World. Cricketers. Two designs for each value, the first showing a portrait and the second the cricketer in action. 1, 10, 15, 55, 60, 75 c., $1.50, $3, *each* × 2.
Leaders of the World. Railway Locomotives (2*nd series*). *Two designs for each value, the first showing technical drawings and the second the locomotive at work.* 5, 10, 20, 25, 75 c., $1, $2.50, $3, *each* × 2.

1985

Leaders of the World. Automobiles. Two designs for each value, the first showing technical drawings and the second the car in action. 1, 50, 75 c., $2.50, *each* × 2.
Leaders of the World. Birth Bicent of John J. Audubon (ornithologist). Birds. 15, 50 c., $1, $1.50, *each* × 2.
Leaders of the World. Railway Locomotives (3*rd series*). *Two designs for each value, the first showing technical drawings and the second the locomotive at work.* 5, 50, 60 c., $2, *each* × 2.

OFFICIAL STAMPS

1982 (11 Oct). *Nos.* 195/200 *optd with Type* O **1** *of St. Vincent.*

No.	Description	Unused	Used
O1	50 c. *Mary*	20	25
	a. Sheetlet. No. O1 × 6 and No. O2	1·75	
	b. Opt double		
	c. Albino opt	5·00	
	d. Horiz pair, one without opt		
O2	50 c. Prince Charles and Lady Diana Spencer	55	55
	b. Opt double		
	c. Albino opt	20·00	
O3	$3 *Alexandra*	1·25	1·40
	a. Sheetlet. No. O3 × 6 and No. O4	9·00	
	b. Opt double		
	c. Albino opt	10·00	
O4	$3 Prince Charles and Lady Diana Spencer	1·75	1·75
	b. Opt double		
	c. Albino opt	30·00	
O5	$3.50, *Britannia*	1·40	1·50
	a. Sheetlet. No. O5 × 6 and No. O6	10·00	
	c. Albino opt	12·00	
O6	$3.50, Prince Charles and Lady Diana Spencer	2·00	2·00
	c. Albino opt	35·00	
O1/6	*Set of* 6	6·50	7·00

Samoa

PRICES FOR STAMPS ON COVER TO 1945

Nos. 1/20 are very rare used on cover.

Nos. 21/40	*from* × 20
Nos. 41/8	*from* × 100
Nos. 49/56	*from* × 4
Nos. 57/64	*from* × 12
Nos. 65/8	*from* × 2
Nos. 69/97	*from* × 20
Nos. 101/9	*from* × 3
Nos. 110/14	—
Nos. 115/21	*from* × 3
Nos. 122/32	—
Nos. 134/64	*from* × 3
Nos. 165/76	—
Nos. 177/214	*from* × 2

INDEPENDENT KINGDOM OF SAMOA

1

(Des H. H. Glover. Litho S. T. Leigh & Co, Sydney, N.S.W.)

1877 (1 Oct)–**80.**

A. 1*st state: line above* "X" *in* "EXPRESS" *not broken. P* 12½

No.	Type	Description	Unused	Used
1	1	1d. ultramarine	£200	85·00
2		3d. deep scarlet	£225	85·00
3		6d. bright violet	£200	85·00
		a. Pale lilac	£250	85·00

B. 2*nd state: line above* "X" *broken, and dot between top of* "M" *and* "O" *of* "SAMOA". *P* 12½ (1878–79)

No.	Type	Description	Unused	Used
4	1	1d. ultramarine	80·00	75·00
5		3d. bright scarlet	£200	85·00
6		6d. bright violet	£130	75·00
7		1s. dull yellow	£120	75·00
		a. Line above "X" not broken	£100	80·00
		b. Perf 12 (1879)	60·00	75·00
		c. Orange-yellow	75·00	80·00
8		2s. red-brown	£200	£140
		a. Chocolate	£200	£275
9		5s. green	£700	£950

C. 3*rd state: line above* "X" *repaired, dot merged with upper right serif of* "M" (1879). (*a*) *P* 12½

No.	Type	Description	Unused	Used
10	1	1d. ultramarine	75·00	65·00
11		3d. vermilion	85·00	80·00
12		6d. lilac	90·00	75·00
13		2s. brown	£150	£120
		a. Chocolate	£150	£120
14		5s. green	£400	£500
		a. Line above "X" not repaired		

(*b*) *P* 12

No.	Type	Description	Unused	Used
15	1	1d. blue	20·00	30·00
		a. Deep blue	28·00	60·00
		b. Ultramarine	24·00	30·00
16		3d. vermilion	35·00	50·00
		a. Carmine-vermilion	35·00	60·00
17		6d. bright violet	35·00	38·00
		a. Deep violet	35·00	70·00
18		2s. deep brown	£100	£140
19		5s. yellow-green	£375	£500
		a. Deep green	£350	£450
		b. Line above "X" not repaired (Nos. 29, 30)		

D. 4*th state: spot of colour under middle stroke of* "M". *P* 12 (1880)

No.	Type	Description	Unused	Used
20	1	9d. orange-brown	40·00	80·00

Originals exist imperf, but are not known used in this state.

On sheets of the 1d., 1st state, at least eight stamps have a stop after "PENNY". In the 2nd state, three stamps have the stop, and in the 3rd state, only one.

In the 1st state, all the stamps, 1d., 3d. and 6d., were in sheets of 20 and also the 1d. in the 3rd state.

All values in the 2nd state and all values except the 1d. in the 3rd state were in sheets of 10.

As all sheets of all printings of the originals were imperf at the outer edges, the only stamps which can have perforations on all four sides are Nos. 1 to 3*a*, 10 and 15 to 15*b*, all other originals being imperf on one or two sides.

The perf 12 stamps, which gauge 11.8, are generally very rough but later the machine was repaired and the 1d., 3d. and 6d. are known with clean-cut perforations.

Remainders, in sheets of 21, of the 1d. and 6d., the 2*d. rose* (which was never *issued*), and of the 3d., in sheets of 12, and of the 9d., 1s., 2s. and 5s. (probably also in sheets of 12), were found in the Samoan post office when this service closed down in 1881. The remainders are rare in complete sheets, but of very little value as singles, compared with the originals.

Reprints of all values, in sheets of 40, were made after the originals had been withdrawn from sale. These are practically worthless.

The majority of both reprints and remainders are in the 4th state as the 9d. with the spot of colour under the middle stroke of the "M", but a few stamps (both remainders and reprints) do not show this, while on some it is very faint.

There are three known types of forgery, one of which is rather dangerous, the others being crude.

2 Palm Trees

3 King Malietoa Laupepa

4*a* 6 mm

4*b* 7 mm

4*c* 4 mm

Description of Watermarks

(These are the same as W **12***a*/*c* of New Zealand)

W **4***a*. 6 mm between "N Z" and star; broad irregular star; comparatively wide "N"; "N Z" 11½ mm wide.

W **4***b*. 7 mm between "N Z" and star; narrower star; narrow "N"; "N Z" 10 mm wide.

W **4***c*. 4 mm between "N Z" and star; narrow star; wide "N"; "N Z" 11 mm wide.

(Des A. E. Cousins (T **3**). Dies eng W. R. Bock and A. E. Cousins (T **2**) or A. E. Cousins (T **3**). Typo Govt Ptg Office, Wellington)

1886–1900. (i) *W* **4***a*. (*a*) *P* 12½ (Oct–Nov 1886).

No.	Type	Description	Unused	Used
21	2	½d. purple-brown	11·00	16·00
22		1d. yellow-green	5·50	11·00
23		2d. dull orange	6·00	6·00
24		4d. blue	7·50	7·50
25		1s. rose-carmine	25·00	7·50
		a. Bisected (2½d.) (on cover)*	†	£250
26		2s. 6d. reddish lilac	35·00	25·00

(*b*) *P* 12 × 11½ (July–Nov 1887)

No.	Type	Description	Unused	Used
27	2	½d. purple-brown	80·00	
28		1d. yellow-green	95·00	25·00
29		2d. yellow	75·00	£140
30		4d. blue	£200	£175
31		6d. brown-lake	13·00	6·00
32		1s. rose-carmine	—	£120
33		2s. 6d. reddish lilac	£190	

(ii) *W* **4***c*. *P* 12 × 11½ (May 1890)

No.	Type	Description	Unused	Used
34	2	½d. purple-brown	70·00	27·00
35		1d. green	25·00	27·00
36		2d. brown-orange	60·00	19·00
37		4d. blue	£100	4·75
38		6d. brown-lake	£175	11·00
39		1s. rose-carmine	—	11·00
40		2s. 6d. reddish lilac	—	7·50

(iii) *W* **4***b*. (*a*) *P* 12 × 11½ (1890–92)

No.	Type	Description	Unused	Used
41	2	½d. pale purple-brown	70	1·75
		a. Blackish purple	70	1·50
42		1d. myrtle-green (5.90)	5·50	1·40
		a. Green	5·50	1·40
		b. Yellow-green	5·50	1·40
43		2d. dull orange (5.90)	6·00	2·00
44	3	2½d. rose (11.92)	£175	3·50
		a. Pale rose	£175	3·50
45	2	4d. blue	£175	7·50
46		6d. brown-lake	£100	7·50
47		1s. rose-carmine	£175	3·50
48		2s. 6d. slate-lilac	—	3·50

(*b*) *P* 12½ (Mar 1891–92)

No.	Type	Description	Unused	Used
49	2	½d. purple-brown		
50		1d. green		
51		2d. orange-yellow	—	80·00
52	3	2½d. rose (1.92)	1·40	3·50
53	2	4d. blue	—	£350
54		6d. brown-purple	—	£600
55		1s. rose-carmine	—	£300
56		2s. 6d. slate-lilac		

(*c*) *P* 11 (1895–1900)

No.	Type	Description	Unused	Used
57	2	½d. purple-brown	65	1·40
		a. Deep purple-brown	65	1·40
		b. Blackish purple (1900)	65	35·00
58		1d. green	1·25	1·75
		a. Bluish green (1897)	1·25	1·75
		b. Deep green (1900)	1·25	22·00
59		2d. pale yellow	25·00	35·00
		a. Orange (1896)	25·00	35·00
		b. Bright yellow (1.97)	4·75	3·50
		c. Pale ochre (10.97)	4·00	70
		d. Dull orange (1900)	4·75	
60	3	2½d. rose	70	3·50
		a. Deep rose-carmine (1900)	1·10	42·00
61	2	4d. blue	5·75	1·50
		a. Deep blue (1900)	70	50·00
62		6d. brown-lake	4·75	3·00
		a. Brown-purple (1900)	1·75	60·00
63		1s. rose	3·50	4·75
		a. Dull rose-carmine/toned (5.98)	1·50	35·00
		b. Carmine (1900)	1·50	
64		2s. 6d. purple	50·00	9·50
		a. Reddish lilac (wmk inverted) (1897)	5·75	9·50
		b. Deep purple/toned (wmk reversed) (5.98)	4·75	9·50
		ba. Imperf between (vert pair)	£500	
		c. Slate-violet	£120	

*Following a fire on 1 April 1895 which destroyed stocks of all stamps except the 1s. value perf 12½, this was bisected and used as a 2½d. stamp for overseas letters between April and May 1895, and was cancelled in blue or black. Fresh supplies of the 2½d. did not arrive until July 1895, although other values were available from 23 May.

Bisects of the 1s. perf 11 are known on cover cancelled in black in May and June 1895 and were later made to fill a philatelic demand; these are found on piece and are cancelled in black only (*price* £7).

The dates given relate to the earliest dates of printing in the various watermarks and perforations and not to issue dates.

The perf 11 issues (including those later surcharged or overprinted), are very unevenly perforated owing to the large size of the pins. Evenly perforated copies are extremely hard to find.

For the 2½d. black, see Nos. 81/2 and for the ½d. green and 1d. red-brown, see Nos. 88/9.

FIVE PENCE (5) — FIVE PENCE (6) — 5d (7)

1893 (Nov–Dec). *Handstamped singly, at Apia.*

(*a*) *In two operations*

65 5 5d. on 4d. blue (37) 28·00 27·00
a. Bars omitted — £350
66 5d. on 4d. blue (45) 48·00 90·00
67 6 5d. on 4d. blue (37) 70·00 90·00
68 5d. on 4d. blue (45) 75·00

(*b*) *In three operations* (Dec)

69 7 5d. on 4d. blue (37) (R.) 8·00 12·00
a. Stop after "d" £250 50·00
b. Bars omitted
70 5d. on 4d. blue (45) (R.) 8·00 35·00

In Types **5** and **6** the bars obliterating the original value vary in length from 13½ to 16½ mm and can occur with either the thick bar over the thin one or vice versa.

Double handstamps exist but we do not list them.

No. 69a came from a separate handstamp which applied the "5d." at one operation. Where the "d" was applied separately its position in relation to the "5" naturally varies.

8

Surcharged 1½d. (9) — R 3d. (10)

The "R" in Type **10** indicates use for registration fee.

(Des and die eng A. E. Cousins. Typo New Zealand Govt Ptg Office)

1894–1900. *W* **4***b* (*sideways*). (*a*) *P* 11½ × 12.

71 8 5d. dull vermilion (3.94) 8·00 3·00
a. Dull red 8·00 3·00

(*b*) *P* 11

72 8 5d. dull red (1895) 8·00 6·00
a. Deep red (1900) 1·40 13·00

1895–1900. *W* **4***b*.

(i) *Handstamped with T* **9** *or* **10**. (*a*) *P* 12 × 11½ (26.1.95)

73 2 1½d. on 2d. dull orange (B.) 3·00 3·00
74 3d. on 2d. dull orange 8·50 5·75

(*b*) *P* 11 (6.95)

75 2 1½d. on 2d. orange (B.) 1·50 1·50
a. Pair, one without handstamp
b. On 2d. yellow 75·00 60·00
76 3d. on 2d. orange 3·00 6·00
a. On 2d. yellow 75·00 60·00

(ii) *Surch printed**. *P* 11

77 2 1½d. on 2d. orange-yellow (B.)

(iii) *Handstamped as T* **9** *or* **10**.† *P* 11 (1896)

78 2 1½d. on 2d. orange-yellow (B.) 1·50 16·00
79 3d. on 2d. orange-yellow 3·00 42·00
a. Imperf between (vert pair) £400
b. Pair, one without handstamp

(iv) *Surch typo as T* **10**. *P* 11 (Feb 1900)

80 2 3d. on 2d. deep red-orange (G.) 2·00 £130

*It is believed that this was type-set from which clichés were made and set up in a forme and then printed on a hand press. This would account for the clear indentation on the back of the stamp and the variation in the position on the stamps which probably resulted from the clichés becoming loose in the forme.

†In No. 78 the "2" has a serif and the handstamp is in pale greenish blue instead of deep blue. In No. 79 the "R" is slightly narrower. In both instances the stamp is in a different shade.

A special printing in a distinctly different colour was made for No. 80 and the surcharge is in green.

Most of the handstamps exist double.

1896 (Aug). *Printed in the wrong colour. W* **4***b*. (*a*) *P* 10 × 11.

81 3 2½d. black 1·25 3·75

(*b*) *P* 11

82 3 2½d. black £250 75·00
a. Mixed perfs 10 and 11

Surcharged 2½d. (11) — PROVISIONAL GOVT. (12)

1898–99. *W* **4***b*. *P* 11. (*a*) *Handstamped as T* **11** (10.98).

83 2 2½d. on 1s. dull rose-carmine/*toned* 8·00 16·00

(*b*) *Surch as T* **11** (1899)

84 2 2½d. on 1d. bluish green (R.) 70 2·00
a. Surch inverted — £350
85 2½d. on 1s. dull rose-carmine/*toned* (R.) 3·50 8·00
a. Surch double £350
86 2½d. on 1s. dull rose-carmine/*toned* (Blk.) 3·50 8·00
87 2½d. on 2s. 6d. deep purple/*toned* 4·75 9·50

The typographed surcharge was applied in a setting of nine, giving seven types differing in the angle and length of the fractional line, the type of stop, etc.

1899. *Colours changed. W* **4***b*. *P* 11.

88 2 ½d. dull blue-green 65 1·40
a. Deep green 65 1·40
89 1d. deep red-brown 55 1·10

1899–1900. *Provisional Government. New printings optd with T* **12** (*longer words and shorter letters on* 5d.). *W* **4***b*. *P* 11.

90 2 ½d. dull blue-green (R.) 25 40
a. Yellowish green (1900) 25 40
91 1d. chestnut (B.) 40 45
92 2d. dull orange (R.) 30 45
a. Orange-yellow (1900) 40 55
93 4d. deep dull blue (R.) 45 60
94 8 5d. dull vermilion (B.) 75 90
a. Red (1900) 75 90
95 2 6d. brown-lake (B.) 1·40 1·40
96 1s. rose-carmine (B.) 3·00 3·50
97 2s. 6d. reddish purple (R.) 6·00 7·50

The Samoan group of islands was partitioned in 1899: Western Samoa (Upolu, Savaii, Apolima and Manono) to Germany and Eastern Samoa (Tutuila, the Manu'a Is and Rose Is) to the United States. German issues of 1900–14 will be found listed in Part 7 (*Germany*) of this catalogue, there were no U.S. issues.

The German Islands of Samoa surrendered to the New Zealand Expeditionary Force on 29 August 1914 and were administered by New Zealand until 1962.

WESTERN SAMOA

NEW ZEALAND OCCUPATION

G.R.I. 1d. (13) — G.R.I. 1 Shillings. (14)

(Surch *Samoanische Zeitung*, Apia)

1914 (Sept). *German Colonial issue* (*ship*) (*no wmk*) *surch as T* **13** *or* **14** (*mark values*).

101 ½d. on 3 pf. brown 8·50 8·50
a. Surch double £500 £300
b. No fraction bar 40·00 30·00
c. Comma after "I" £600 £500
d. "1" to left of "2" in "½" 35·00 23·00
102 ½d. on 5 pf. green 23·00 12·00
a. No fraction bar 40·00 35·00
c. Comma after "I" £350 £170
d. Surch double £450 £300
e. "1" to left of "2" in "½" 40·00 45·00
103 1d. on 10 pf. carmine 95·00 40·00
a. Surch double £350 £300
104 2½d. on 20 pf. ultramarine 28·00 12·00
a. No fraction bar 40·00 38·00
b. "1" to left of "2" in "½" 40·00 40·00
c. Surch inverted £550 £500
d. Comma after "I" £450 £325
e. Surch double £550 £500
105 3d. on 25 pf. black and red/*yellow* 50·00 25·00
a. Surch double £400 £250
b. Comma after "I" £3500 £750
106 4d. on 30 pf. black and orange/*buff* 95·00 60·00
107 5d. on 40 pf. black and carmine £110 70·00
108 6d. on 50 pf. black and purple/*buff* 55·00 25·00
a. Surch double £450 £500
b. Inverted "9" for "6" £120 £100
109 9d. on 80 pf. black and carmine/*rose* £190 95·00
110 "1 shillings" on 1 m. carmine £3000 £2750
111 "1 shilling" on 1 m. carmine £9500 £7000
112 2s. on 2 m. blue £2750 £2750
113 3s. on 3 m. violet-black £1400 £1200
a. Surch double £4500 £4750
114 5s. on 5 m. carmine and black £1000 £950
a. Surch double £9500 £10000

The ½d. to 9d. were surcharged in a vertical setting of 10.

No. 108b is distinguishable from 108, as the "d" and the "9" are not in a line, and the upper loop of the "9" turns downwards to the left.

UNAUTHORISED SURCHARGES. Examples of the 2d. on 20 pf., 3d. on 30 pf., 3d. on 40 pf., 4d. on 40 pf., 6d. on 80 pf., 2s. on 3 m. and 2s. on Marshall Islands 2 m., together with a number of errors not listed above, were produced by the printer on stamps supplied by local collectors. These were not authorised by the New Zealand Military Administration.

SAMOA. (15)

1914 (29 Sept). *Stamps of New Zealand, T* **50, 51, 52** *and* **27**, *optd as T* **15**, *but opt only* 14 *mm long on all except* 2½*d. Wmk "N Z" and Star, W* **41**.

115 ½d. yellow-green (R.) (*p* 14 × 15) 35 45
116 1d. carmine (B.) (*p* 14 × 15) 35 30
117 2d. mauve (R.) (*p* 14 × 14½) 95 1·10
118 2½d. deep blue (R.) (*p* 14) 2·00 2·25
119 6d. carmine (B.) (*p* 14 × 14½) 2·25 2·50
a. Perf 14 × 13½ 14·00 15·00
b. Vert pair. Nos. 119/19a 26·00 30·00
120 6d. pale carmine (B.) (*p* 14 × 14½) 10·00 9·50
121 1s. vermilion (B.) (*p* 14 × 14½) 6·50 9·00

1914–24. *Postal Fiscal stamps as Type* F **4** *of New Zealand optd with T* **15**. *W* **41** (*sideways*). *Chalk-surfaced "De La Rue" paper.*

(*a*) *P* 14 (Nov 1914–17)

122 2s. blue (R.) (9.17) 80·00 £100
123 2s. 6d. grey-brown (B.) (9.17) 6·00 8·50
124 5s. yellow-green (R.) 9·00 12·00
125 10s. maroon (B.) 20·00 28·00
126 £1 rose-carmine (B.) 60·00 80·00

(*b*) *P* 14½ × 14, *comb* (1917–24)

127 2s. deep blue (R.) (3.18) 6·00 8·00
128 2s. 6d. grey-brown (B.) (10.24) 75·00 90·00
129 3s. purple (R.) (6.23) 9·00 20·00
130 5s. yellow-green (R.) (9.17) 10·00 13·00
131 10s. maroon (B.) (3.18) 22·00 32·00
132 £1 rose-carmine (B.) (3.18) 60·00 70·00

We no longer list the £2 value as it is doubtful if this was used for postal purposes.

See also Nos. 165/6*d*.

1916–19. *King George V stamps of New Zealand optd as T* **15**, *but* 14 *mm long.* (*a*) *T* **60***b*. *Typo. P* 14 × 15.

134 ½d. yellow-green (R.) 30 30
135 1½d. slate (R.) (1917) 45 35
136 1½d. orange-brown (R.) (1919) 30 75
137 2d. yellow (R.) (14.2.18) 50 30
138 3d. chocolate (B.) (1919) 1·10 2·50

(*b*) *T* **60**. *Recess. P* 14 × 14½, *etc.*

139 2½d. blue (R.) 90 90
a. Perf 14 × 13½ 55 80
b. Vert pair. Nos. 139/9a 9·00 10·00
140 3d. chocolate (B.) (1917) 55 1·25
a. Perf 14 × 13½ 1·10 1·60
b. Vert pair. Nos. 140/40a 8·50 12·00
141 6d. carmine (B.) (5.5.17) 1·75 2·40
a. Perf 14 × 13½ 1·75 4·00
b. Vert pair. Nos. 141/1a 9·50 13·00
142 1s. vermilion (B.) 3·75 10·00
a. Perf 14 × 13½ 2·75 3·50
b. Vert pair. Nos. 142/2a 12·00 22·00

LEAGUE OF NATIONS MANDATE

Administered by New Zealand.

1920 (July). *Victory. T* **62** *to* **67** *of New Zealand, optd as T* **15**, *but* 14 *mm long.*

143 ½d. green (R.) 70 90
144 1d. carmine (B.) 70 75
145 1½d. brown-orange (R.) 1·25 2·25
146 3d. chocolate (B.) 1·75 5·50
147 6d. violet (R.) 4·00 6·50
148 1s. orange-red (B.) 8·00 11·00
143/8 *Set of* 6 15·00 24·00

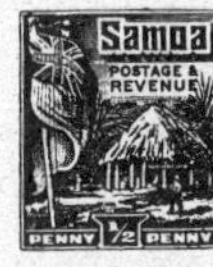

16 Native Hut

SILVER JUBILEE OF KING GEORGE V 1910-1935. (17)

(Eng B.W. Recess-printed at Wellington, N.Z.)

1921 (23 Dec). *W* **41** *of New Zealand.* (*a*) *P* 14 × 14½.

149 16 ½d. green 50 1·40
150 1d. lake 35 50
151 1½d. chestnut 40 2·50
152 2d. yellow 50 1·90

(*b*) *P* 14 × 13½

153 16 ½d. green 65 1·40
154 1d. lake 45 30
155 1½d. chestnut 5·50 7·50
156 2d. yellow 4·00 65
157 2½d. grey-blue 80 3·00
158 3d. sepia 1·40 3·25
159 4d. violet 1·40 3·25
160 5d. light blue 1·50 5·00
161 6d. bright carmine 2·25 5·00
162 8d. red-brown 3·25 9·00
163 9d. olive-green 3·25 9·00
164 1s. vermilion 5·00 13·00
153/64 *Set of* 12 25·00 55·00

1925–28. *As Nos.* 127/32, *but thick, opaque, white chalk-surfaced "Cowan" paper.*

165 2s. blue (R.) (12.25) 80·00 85·00
166 2s. 6d. deep grey-brown (B.) (10.28) 60·00 80·00
166*a* 3s. mauve (R.) (9.25) 45·00 50·00
166*b* 5s. yellow-green (R.) (11.26) 14·00 18·00
ba. Opt at top of stamp £650
166*c* 10s. brown-red (B.) (12.25) 24·00 30·00
166*d* £1 rose-pink (B.) (11.26) 50·00 75·00

1926–27. *T* **72** *of New Zealand, optd with T* **15**, *in red.*

(*a*) *"Jones" paper*

167 2s. deep blue (11.26) 6·50 12·00
168 3s. mauve (10.26) 9·00 17·00

(*b*) *"Cowan" paper*

169 2s. light blue (10.11.27) 12·00 20·00
170 3s. pale mauve (10.11.27) 40·00 60·00

1932 (Aug). *Postal Fiscal stamps as Type* F **6** *of New Zealand optd with T* **15**. *W* **41**. *Thick, opaque, white chalk-surfaced "Cowan" paper. P* 14.

171 2s. 6d. deep brown (B.) 15·00 22·00
172 5s. green (R.) 24·00 32·00
173 10s. carmine-lake (B.) 35·00 55·00
174 £1 pink (B.) 55·00 70·00
175 £2 bright purple (R.) £275
176 £5 indigo-blue (R.) £900

The £2 and £5 values were primarily for fiscal use.

1935 (7 May). *Silver Jubilee. Optd with T* **17**. *P* 14 × 13½.

177 16 1d. lake 35 60
a. Perf 14 × 14½ 75·00 85·00
178 2½d. grey-blue 1·10 2·00
179 6d. bright carmine 5·50 7·00

18 Samoan Girl

19 Apia

21 Chief and Wife

25 Lake Lanuto'o

(Recess D.L.R.)

1935 (7 Aug). *T* **18/19, 21, 25** *and similar designs. W* **41** *of New Zealand ("N Z" and Star).*

(*a*) *P* 14 × 13½, (*b*) *P* 13½ × 14 *or* (*c*) *P* 14

180 ½d. green (*a*) 25 35
181 1d. black and carmine (*b*) 25 20
182 2d. black and orange (*c*) 70 50
a. Perf 13½ × 14 .. .. 2·75 3·00
183 2½d. black and blue (*a*) 25 20
184 4d. slate and sepia (*b*) 70 45
185 6d. bright magenta (*b*) 50 50
186 1s. violet and brown (*b*) 70 55
187 2s. green and purple-brown (*a*) .. .. .. 1·75 1·40
188 3s. blue and brown-orange (*a*) .. .. .. 3·25 4·00
180/8 .. .. *Set of* 9 7·50 7·50

Designs: *Horiz*—2d. River scene; 4d. Canoe and house; 6d. R. L. Stevenson's home "Vailima"; 1s. Stevenson's Tomb. *Vert* (*as T* **25**)—3s. Falefa Falls.

See also Nos. 200/3.

WESTERN
SAMOA.
(27)

1935–42. *Postal Fiscal stamps as Type* F **6** *of New Zealand optd with T* **27**. *W* **41**. *P* 14.

(*a*) *Thick, opaque chalk-surfaced "Cowan" paper* (7.8.35)

189 2s. 6d. deep brown (B.) .. .. 7·50 13·00
190 5s. green (B.) .. .. 12·00 18·00
191 10s. carmine-lake (B.) .. .. 29·00 38·00
192 £1 pink (B.) .. .. 60·00 85·00
193 £2 bright purple (R.) £170 £225
194 £5 indigo-blue (R.).. .. .. £450 £475

(*b*) *Thin, hard chalk-surfaced "Wiggins, Teape" paper* (1941–42)

194*a* 5s. green (B.) (6.42) .. .. 35·00 42·00
194*b* 10s. pale carmine-lake (B.) (6.41) .. .. 48·00 65·00
194*c* £2 bright purple (R.) (2.42) £250 £300
194*d* £5 indigo-blue (R.) (2.42) £375 £450

The £2 and £5 values were primarily for fiscal use.

See also Nos. 207/14.

28 Coastal Scene

31 Robert Louis Stevenson

(Des J. Berry (1d. and 1½d.). L. C. Mitchell (2½d. and 7d.). Recess B.W.)

1939 (29 Aug). *25th Anniv of New Zealand Control. T* **28, 31** *and similar horiz designs. W* **98** *of New Zealand. P* 13½ × 14 *or* 14 × 13½ (*7d.*).

195 1d. olive-green and scarlet 40 35
196 1½d. light blue and red-brown 55 60
197 2½d. red-brown and blue .. .. .. 2·00 2·25
198 7d. violet and slate-green .. .. .. 4·75 4·00

Designs:—1½d. Western Samoa; 2½d. Samoan dancing party.

32 Samoan Chief

33 Apia Post Office

(Recess B.W.)

1940 (2 Sept). *W* **98** *of New Zealand* (*Mult "N Z" and Star*). *P* 14 × 13½.

199 **32** 3d. on 1½d. brown 12 12

T **32** was not issued without surcharge.

(T **33**. Des L. C. Mitchell. Recess B.W.)

1944–49. *As Nos.* 180, 182/3 *and T* **33**. *W* **98** *of New Zealand* (*Mult "N Z" and Star*) (*sideways on* 2½*d.*). *P* 14 *or* 13½ × 14 (*5d.*).

200 ½d. green .. .. 45 1·25
202 2d. black and orange .. .. 2·00 3·00
203 2½d. black and blue (1948) .. .. .. 3·00 7·50
205 5d. sepia and blue (8.6.49) .. .. .. 70 1·25

1945–48. *Postal Fiscal stamps as Type* F **6** *of New Zealand optd with T* **27**. *W* **98**. *Thin hard, chalk-surfaced "Wiggins Teape" paper. P* 14.

207 2s. 6d. deep brown (B.) (6.45) .. .. 2·50 5·50
208 5s. green (B.) (5.45) .. .. .. 6·00 7·50
209 10s. carmine-lake (B.) (4.46) .. .. 20·00 20·00
210 £1 pink (B.) (6.48) .. .. .. 80·00 90·00
211 30s. brown (8.48) £160 £200
212 £2 bright purple (R.) (11.47) £160 £200
213 £3 green (8.48) £225 £300
214 £5 indigo-blue (R.) (1946) £450 £600

The £2 to £5 values were mainly used for fiscal purposes. The £5 also exists from a printing in May 1953 with the watermark inverted.

See also Nos. 232/5.

WESTERN
SAMOA
(34)

1946 (1 June). *Peace Issue. Stamps of New Zealand optd with T* 34 (*reading up and down at sides on 2d.*).

215 **132** 1d. green 12 10
216 **134** 2d. purple (B.) 12 10
217 **138** 6d. chocolate and vermilion 12 10
218 **139** 8d. black and carmine (B.) 12 10

UNITED NATIONS TRUST TERRITORY

Administered by New Zealand.

35 Making Siapo Cloth

42 Thatching a Native Hut

43 Preparing Copra

44 Samoan Chieftainess

(Recess B.W.)

1952 (10 Mar). *T* **35, 42/4** *and similar designs. W* **98** *of New Zealand* (*sideways on 1s. and 3s.*). *P* 13 (*½d., 2d., 5d. and 1s.*) *or* 13½ (*others*).

219 ½d. claret and orange-brown.. .. .. 10 20
220 1d. olive-green and green 10 10
221 2d. carmine-red 12 10
222 3d. pale ultramarine and indigo 30 10
223 5d. brown and deep green .. .. .. 1·25 80
224 6d. pale ultramarine and rose-magenta .. 40 15
225 8d. carmine 30 35
226 1s. sepia and blue 30 15
227 2s. yellow-brown .. .. 3·25 1·75
228 3s. chocolate and brown-olive .. .. 6·50 4·00
219/28 .. .. *Set of* 10 11·00 7·00

Designs: *Horiz* (*as T* **43**)—1d. Native houses and flags; 3d. Malifa Falls (wrongly inscribed "Aleisa Falls"); 6d. Bonito fishing canoe; 8d. Cacao harvesting. *Vert* (*as T* **35**)—2d. Seal of Samoa.

1953 (25 May). *Coronation. As designs of New Zealand, but inscr "WESTERN SAMOA".*

229 **164** 2d. brown 45 25
230 **166** 6d. slate-grey 95 80

WESTERN

SAMOA
(45)

1955 (14 Nov). *Postal Fiscal stamps as Type* F **6** *of New Zealand optd with T* **45**. *W* **98**. *Chalk-surfaced "Wiggins, Teape" paper. P* 14.

232 5s. green (B.).. .. .. 14·00 16·00
233 10s. carmine-lake (B.) .. .. .. 18·00 24·00
234 £1 pink (B.) .. .. 35·00 40·00
235 £2 bright purple (R.) .. .. .. 75·00 £130

The £2 value was mainly used for fiscal purposes.

46 Native Houses and Flags

47 Seal of Samoa

(Recess B.W.)

1958 (21 Mar). *Inauguration of Samoan Parliament. T* **46/7** *and similar horiz design. W* **98** *of New Zealand* (*sideways*). *P* 13½ × 13 (*6d.*) *or* 13½ (*others*).

236 4d. cerise 20 20
237 6d. deep reddish violet 20 15
238 1s. deep ultramarine 25 20

Design:—1s. Map of Samoa, and the Mace.

INDEPENDENT

Samoa became independent on 1 January 1962.

49 Samoan Fine Mat

50 Samoa College

(Litho B.W.)

1962 (2 July). *Independence. T* **49/50** *and similar designs. W* **98** *of New Zealand* (*sideways on horiz stamps*). *P* 13½.

239 1d. brown and rose-carmine 5 5
240 2d. brown, green, yellow and red 8 5
241 3d. brown, blue-green and blue 10 5
242 4d. magenta, yellow, blue and black .. 25 10
243 6d. yellow and blue 25 10
244 8d. bluish green, yellow-green and blue .. 25 10
245 1s. brown and bluish green 30 10
246 1s. 3d. yellow-green and blue 90 60
247 2s. 6d. red and ultramarine .. .. .. 2·00 1·50
248 5s. ultramarine, yellow, red and drab .. 4·75 3·75
239/48 .. .. *Set of* 10 8·00 5·50

Designs: *Horiz*—3d. Public library; 4d. Fono House; 6d. Map of Samoa; 8d. Airport; 1s. 3d. "Vailima"; 2s. 6d. Samoan flag; 5s. Samoan seal. *Vert*—1s. Samoan orator.

See Nos. 257/62.

59 Seal and Joint Heads of State

60 Signing the Treaty

(Des L. C. Mitchell. Photo Harrison)

1963 (1 Oct). *First Anniv of Independence. W* **98** *of New Zealand. P* 14.

249 **59** 1d. deep sepia and green 5 5
250 4d. deep sepia and blue.. .. .. 8 5
251 8d. deep sepia and rose-pink 15 10
252 2s. deep sepia and orange 30 30

(Des L. C. Mitchell. Photo Enschedé)

1964 (1 Sept). *2nd Anniv of New Zealand–Samoa Treaty of Friendship. P* 13½.

253 **60** 1d. multicoloured 5 5
254 8d. multicoloured 15 10
255 2s. multicoloured 25 25
256 3s. multicoloured 30 35

61 Kava Bowl

1965 (4 Oct)–**66?** *As Nos.* 239, 241/5, *but W* **61** (*sideways on horiz designs*).

257 1d. brown and rose-carmine 40 40
258 3d. brown, blue-green and blue (1966?) .. 27·00 9·00
259 4d. magenta, yellow, blue and black .. 35 20
260 6d. yellow and blue 40 25
261 8d. bluish green, yellow-green and blue .. 35 30
262 1s. brown and bluish green 50 35
257/62 .. .. *Set of* 6 27·00 9·50

62 Red-tailed Tropic Bird

63 Flying Fish

(Des L. C. Mitchell. Photo Harrison)

1965 (29 Dec). *Air. W* **61** (*sideways*). *P* 14½.

263 **62** 8d. black, red-orange and blue.. .. 45 10
264 **63** 2s. black and blue .. .. .. 1·00 40

64 Aerial View of Deep Sea Wharf

(Des Tecon Co (U.S.A.). Photo Enschedé)

966 (2 Mar). *Opening of First Deep Sea Wharf, Apia. T* **64** *and similar horiz design. Multicoloured. W* **61** *(sideways). P* 13½.

65 1d. Type **64** 5 5
66 8d. Aerial view of wharf and bay 20 10
67 2s. As 8d. 50 20
68 3s. Type **64** 70 25

66 W.H.O. Building

(Des M. Goaman. Photo D.L.R.)

1966 (4 July). *Inauguration of W.H.O. Headquarters, Geneva. T* **66** *and similar horiz design. W* **61** *(sideways). P* 14.

269 3d. yellow-ochre, blue and light slate-lilac .. 20 10
270 4d. blue, yellow, green & light orange-brown 25 10
271 6d. reddish lilac, emerald and yellow-olive .. 30 15
272 1s. blue, yellow, green and turquoise-green 50 20

Designs:—3d., 6d. Type **66**; 4d., 1s. W.H.O. Building on flag.

HURRICANE RELIEF
6d

(68)

1966 (1 Sept). *Hurricane Relief Fund. No. 261 surch with T* **68** *by Bradbury, Wilkinson.*

273 **54** 8d.+6d. bluish green, yellow-grn & blue 15 15

69 Hon. Tuatagaloa L. S. (Minister of Justice)

(Des and photo Harrison)

1967 (16 Jan). *Fifth Anniv of Independence. T* **69** *and similar horiz designs. W* **61** *(sideways). P* 14½ × 14.

274 3d. sepia and bluish violet 8 5
275 8d. sepia and light new blue.. .. .. 15 10
276 2s. sepia and olive 25 20
277 3s. sepia and magenta 35 25

Designs:—8d. Hon. F. C. F. Nelson (minister of Works, Marine and Civil Aviation); 2s. Hon. To'omata T. L. (minister of Lands); Hon. Fa'alava'au G. (minister of Post Office, Radio and Broadcasting).

73 Samoan Fales (houses), 1890

(Des V. Whiteley. Photo Harrison)

1967 (16 May). *Centenary of Mulinu'u as Seat of Government. T* **73** *and similar horiz design. Multicoloured. W* **61**. *P* 14½ × 14.

278 8d. Type **73** 10 10
279 1s. Fono (Parliament) House, 1967 .. .. 10 10

(New Currency. 100 sene or cents=1 tala or dollar)

75 Carunculated Honeyeater

76 Black-breasted Honeyeater

(Des V. Whiteley. Litho Format ($2, $4). Photo Harrison (others))

1967 (10 July)–**69**. *Decimal currency. Multicoloured designs as T* **75** *(1 s. to $1) or* **76** *($2, $4). W* **61** *(sideways). P* 13½ *($2, $4) or* 14 × 14½ *(others).*

280 1 s. Type **75** 5 5
281 2 s. Pacific Pigeon 8 5
282 3 s. Samoan Starling 10 5
283 5 s. White-vented Flycatcher 12 5
284 7 s. Red-headed Parrot Finch 15 5
285 10 s. Purple Swamphen 25 5
286 20 s. Barn Owl .. .. 2·00 90
287 25 s. Tooth-billed Pigeon .. .. .. 1·75 65
288 50 s. Island Thrush .. .. 1·75 80
289 $1 Samoan Fantail .. .. 3·50 2·75
289*a* $2 Type **76** (14.7.69) .. .. .. 11·00 11·00
289*b* $4 Savaii White Eye (6.10.69) .. .. 38·00 42·00
280/9*b* .. .. *Set of* 12 55·00 55·00

85 Nurse and Child

(Des G. Vasarhelyi. Photo D.L.R.)

1967 (27 Nov). *South Pacific Health Service. T* **85** *and similar horiz designs. Multicoloured. P* 14.

290 3 s. Type **85** 8 5
291 7 s. Leprosarium 12 5
292 20 s. Mobile X-ray Unit 40 25
293 25 s. Apia Hospital 50 25

89 Thomas Trood

93 Cocoa

(Des M. Farrar-Bell. Litho B.W.)

1968 (15 Jan). *6th Anniv of Independence. T* **89** *and similar horiz designs. Multicoloured. P* 13½.

294 2 s. Type **89** 5 5
295 7 s. Dr. Wilhelm Solf 10 5
296 20 s. J. C. Williams 25 20
297 25 s. Fritz Marquardt 30 25

(Des Jennifer Toombs. Photo Enschedé)

1968 (15 Feb). *Agricultural Development. T* **93** *and similar vert designs. W* **61**. *P* 13 × 12½.

298 3 s. deep red-brown, yellow-green and black 5 5
299 5 s. myrtle-green, greenish yellow & lt brn .. 10 5
300 10 s. scarlet, blackish brown and olive-yellow 15 10
301 20 s. yellow-bistre, yellow and blackish olive .. 25 25

Designs:—5 s. Breadfruit; 10 s. Copra; 20 s. Bananas.

97 Women weaving Mats

(Des G. Vasarhelyi. Photo Harrison)

1968 (22 Apr). *21st Anniv of the South Pacific Commission. T* **97** *and similar horiz designs. Multicoloured. W* **61**. *P* 14½ × 14.

302 7 s. Type **97** 15 5
303 20 s. Palm trees and bay 30 20
304 25 s. Sheltered cove 40 30

1928-1968
KINGSFORD-SMITH
TRANSPACIFIC FLIGHT
20
SENE

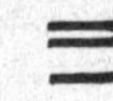

(100)

1968 (13 June). *40th Anniv of Kingsford Smith's Trans-Pacific Flight. No. 285 surch with T* **100**.

305 20 s. on 10 s. Purple Swamphen 30 20

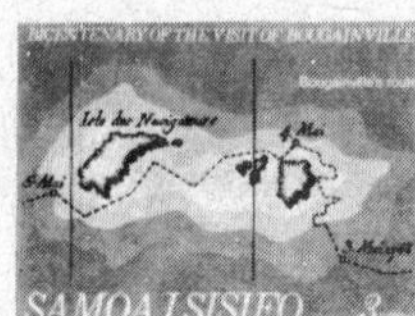

101 Bougainville's Route

(Des Jennifer Toombs. Litho B.W.)

1968 (17 June). *Bicentenary of Bougainville's Visit to Samoa. T* **101** *and similar horiz designs. W* **61** *(sideways). P* 14.

306 3 s. new blue and black 10 5
307 7 s. light ochre and black 15 10
308 20 s. multicoloured 65 45
309 25 s. multicoloured 85 50

Designs:—7 s. Louis de Bougainville; 20 s. Bougainvillea flower; 25 s. Ships *La Boudeuse* and *L'Etoile*.

105 Globe and Human Rights Emblem

106 Dr. Martin Luther King

(Des G. Vasarhelyi. Photo Harrison)

1968 (26 Aug). *Human Rights Year. W* **61**. *P* 14.

310 **105** 7 s. greenish blue, brown and gold .. 10 5
311 20 s. orange, green and gold 20 15
312 25 s. violet, green and gold 20 20

(Des and litho D.L.R.)

1968 (23 Sept). *Martin Luther King Commemoration. W* **61**. *P* 14½ × 14.

313 **106** 7 s. black and olive-green 10 5
314 20 s. black and bright purple 15 15

107 Polynesian Version of Madonna and Child

108 Frangipani—*Plumeria acuminata*

(Des and litho D.L.R.)

1968 (14 Oct). *Christmas. W* **61**. *P* 14.

315 **107** 1 s. multicoloured 5 5
316 3 s. multicoloured 5 5
317 20 s. multicoloured 25 15
318 30 s. multicoloured 30 20

(Des J.W. Litho Format)

1969 (20 Jan). *Seventh Anniv of Independence. T* **108** *and similar multicoloured designs. P* 14½.

319 2 s. Type **108** 10 10
320 7 s. Hibiscus *(vert)* 30 10
321 20 s. Red-Ginger *(vert)* 80 30
322 30 s. "Moso'oi" .. .. 1·00 40

109 R. L. Stevenson and *Treasure Island*

110 Weightlifting

(Des Jennifer Toombs. Litho D.L.R.)

1969 (21 Apr). *75th Death Anniv of Robert Louis Stevenson. Horiz designs, each showing portrait as in T* **109**. *Multicoloured. W* **61** *(sideways). P* 14.

323 3 s. Type **109** 15 10
324 7 s. *Kidnapped* 20 10
325 20 s. *Dr. Jekyll and Mr. Hyde* 65 35
326 22 s. *Weir of Hermiston* 80 45

(Des J. Mason. Photo Note Ptg Branch, Reserve Bank of Australia)

1969 (21 July). *Third South Pacific Games, Port Moresby. T* **110** *and similar vert designs. P* 13½.

327 3 s. black and sage-green 8 8
328 20 s. black and light blue 20 15
329 22 s. black and dull orange 20 15

Designs:—20 s. Yachting; 22 s. Boxing.

113 U.S. Astronaut on the Moon and the Splashdown near Samoan Islands

(Des J. Mason. Photo Note Ptg Branch, Reserve Bank of Australia)

1969 (24 July). *First Man on the Moon. P* 13½.
330 **113** 7 s. multicoloured 20 15
331 20 s. multicoloured 20 20

114 "Virgin with Child" (Murillo)

(Des and photo Heraclio Fournier)

1969 (6 Oct). *Christmas. T* **114** *and similar vert designs. Multicoloured. P* 14.
332 1 s. Type **114** 5 5
333 3 s. "The Holy Family" (El Greco) 5 5
334 20 s. "The Nativity" (El Greco) 25 20
335 30 s. "The Adoration of the Magi" (detail, Velazquez) 35 30
MS336 116 × 126 mm. Nos. 332/5 .. .. 1·50 1·50

115 Seventh Day Adventists' Sanatorium, Apia

(Des V. Whiteley. Litho Format)

1970 (19 Jan). *Eighth Anniv of Independence. T* **115** *and similar designs. W* **61** (*sideways on* 2, 7 *and* 22 *s.*). *P* 14.
337 2 s. yellow-brown, pale slate and black .. 5 5
338 7 s. violet, buff and black 10 5
339 20 s. rose, lilac and black 30 20
340 22 s. olive-green, cinnamon and black .. 35 25

Designs: *Horiz*—7 s. Rev. Father Violette and Roman Catholic Cathedral, Apia; 22 s. John Williams, 1797–1839, and London Missionary Society Church, Sapali'i. *Vert*—20 s. Mormon Church of Latter Day Saints, Tuasivi-on-Safotulafai.

119 Wreck of S.M.S. *Adler*

(Des J.W. Litho Questa)

1970 (27 Apr). *Great Apia Hurricane of* 1889. *T* **119** *and similar horiz designs. Multicoloured. W* **61** (*sideways*). *P* 13½.
341 5 s. Type **119** 55 25
342 7 s. U.S.S. *Nipsic* 60 25
343 10 s. H.M.S. *Calliope* .. .. .. 1·00 60
344 20 s. Apia after the hurricane .. .. .. 2·25 2·00

120 Sir Gordon Taylor's *Frigate Bird III*

(Des R. Honisett. Photo. Note Ptg Branch, Reserve Bank of Australia)

1970 (27 July). *Air. Aircraft. T* **120** *and similar horiz designs. Multicoloured. P* 13½ × 13.
345 3 s. Type **120** 20 5
346 7 s. Polynesian Airlines "DC-3" 45 5
347 20 s. Pan-American "Samoan Clipper" .. 1·50 60
348 30 s. Air Samoa Britten-Norman "Islander" .. 2·00 1·10

121 Kendal's Chronometer and Cook's Sextant

122 "Peace for the World" (F. B. Eccles)

(Des J. Berry. Litho Questa)

1970 (14 Sept). *Cook's Exploration of the Pacific. T* **121** *and similar designs. W* **61** (*sideways on* 30 *s.*). *P* 14.
349 1 s. carmine, silver and black 20 12
350 2 s. multicoloured 35 25
351 20 s. black, bright blue and gold .. .. 4·00 2·25
352 30 s. multicoloured .. .. .. 5·50 3·50

Designs: *Vert*—2 s. Cook's statue, Whitby; 20 s. Cook's head. *Horiz* (83 × 25 *mm*)—30 s. Cook, H.M.S. *Endeavour* and island.

(Des from paintings. Photo Heraclio Fournier)

1970 (26 Oct). *Christmas. T* **122** *and similar vert designs. Multicoloured. P* 13.
353 2 s. Type **122** 5 5
354 3 s. "The Holy Family" (W. E. Jahnke) .. 5 5
355 20 s. "Mother and Child" (F. B. Eccles) .. 35 25
356 30 s. "Prince of Peace" (Meleane Fe'ao) .. 50 35
MS357 111 × 158 mm. Nos. 353/6 .. .. 1·90 2·25

123 Pope Paul VI

124 Native and Tree

(Des J. Cooter. Litho Format)

1970 (29 Nov). *Visit of Pope Paul to Samoa. W* **61**. *P* 14 × 14½.
358 **123** 8 s. black and grey-blue 20 10
359 20 s. black and plum 45 20

(Des G. Drummond from sketches by the American Timber Co. Litho Questa)

1971 (1 Feb). *Timber Industry. T* **124** *and similar multicoloured designs. P* 13½.
360 3 s. Type **124** 5 5
361 8 s. Bulldozer in clearing (*horiz*) 15 5
362 20 s. Log in sawmill (*horiz*) 45 35
363 22 s. Floating logs and harbour 45 35

125 Canoe (fautasi) in Apia Harbour and first stamps of Samoa and U.S.A.

(*Half-sized illustration. Actual size* 84 × 26 *mm*)

(Des E. Roberts. Photo Courvoisier)

1971 (12 Mar). *"Interpex" Stamp Exhibition, New York. Sheet* 138 × 80 *mm. P* 11½.
MS364 **125** 70 s. multicoloured .. .. .. 2·50 2·75

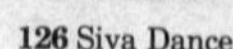

126 Siva Dance

127 "Queen Salamasina"

(Des and litho J.W.)

1971 (9 Aug). *Tourism. T* **126** *and similar horiz designs. Multicoloured. W* **61** (*sideways*). *P* 14.
365 5 s. Type **126** 40 15
366 7 s. Samoan cricket .. .. .. 1·10 80
367 8 s. Hideaway Hotel .. .. .. 1·10 70
368 10 s. Aggie Grey and her hotel .. .. 1·10 80

(Des Jennifer Toombs. Litho J.W.)

1971 (20 Sept). *Myths and Legends of Old Samoa* (1*st series*). *T* **127** *and similar vert designs from carvings by S. Ortquist. Multicoloured. W* **61** (*sideways*). *P* 14 × 13½.
369 3 s. Type **127** 10 10
370 8 s. "Lu and his Sacred Hens" 20 15
371 10 s. "God Tagaloa fishes Samoa from the sea" 30 20
372 22 s. "Mount Vaea and the Pool of Tears" .. 65 50

See also Nos. 426/9.

128 "The Virgin and Child" (Bellini)

129 Map and Scales of Justice

(Des J. Cooter. Litho J.W.)

1971 (4 Oct). *Christmas. T* **128** *and similar design. W* **61**. *P* 14 × 13½.
373 **128** 2 s. multicoloured 5
374 3 s. multicoloured 5
375 – 20 s. multicoloured 45 3
376 – 30 s. multicoloured 70 5

Design: *Vert*—20 s., 30 s. "The Virgin and Child with St. Ann and John the Baptist" (Leonardo da Vinci).

(Des E. Roberts. Photo Courvoisier)

1972 (10 Jan). *First South Pacific Judicial Conference*. *P* 11½ × 11.
377 **129** 10 s. multicoloured 30 2

Issued on matt, almost invisible gum.

130 Asau Wharf, Savaii

131 Flags of Member Countries

(Des V. Whiteley. Litho A. & M.)

1972 (10 Jan). *Tenth Anniv of Independence. T* **130** *and similar horiz designs. Multicoloured. W* **61** (*sideways*). *P* 13.
378 1 s. Type **130** 5 5
379 8 s. Parliament Building 20 15
380 10 s. Mothers' Centre 25 20
381 22 s. "Vailima" Residence and rulers 35 40

(Des V. Whiteley. Litho Questa)

1972 (17 Mar). *25th Anniv of South Pacific Commission. T* **131** *and similar multicoloured designs. W* **61** (*sideways on* 8 *s. and* 10 *s.*). *P* 14 × 13½ (3 *and* 7 *s.*) *or* 13½ × 14 (*others*).
382 3 s. Type **131** 10 5
383 7 s. Flag and Afoafouvale Misimoa (Gen Sec) 15 15
384 8 s. H.Q. building, Nouméa (*horiz*) 15 15
385 10 s. Flags and area map (*horiz*) 20 25

132 Expedition Ships

133 Bull Conch

(Des J. Berry; adapted J. Cooter. Litho Questa)

1972 (14 June). *250th Anniv of sighting of Western Samoa by Jacob Roggeveen. T* **132** *and similar horiz designs. Multicoloured. W* **61** (*sideways, except* 2 *s.*). *P* 14½.
386 2 s. Type **132** 15 10
387 8 s. Ships in storm 60 20
388 10 s. Ships passing island 65 25
389 30 s. Route of Voyage (85 × 25 *mm*) .. .. 2·75 2·00

(Des Format ($5) or J.W. (others). Litho Format ($5), Questa (others))

1972 (18 Oct)–**76**. *T* **133** *and similar multicoloured designs. W* **61** (*sideways, on* 1 *s. to* 50 *s.*). *White, ordinary paper. P* 13½ (*$1 to* $5) *or* 14½ (*others*).
390 1 s. Type **133** 20 5
a. Cream, chalk-surfaced paper (30.11.76) 30 30
391 2 s. Rhinoceros Beetle 20 5
a. Cream, chalk-surfaced paper (30.11.76) 30 30
392 3 s. Skipjack (fish) 30 5
393 4 s. Painted Crab 30 10
a. Cream, chalk-surfaced paper (30.11.76) 40 30
394 5 s. Butterfly Fish 35 10
a. Cream, chalk-surfaced paper (30.11.76) 45 30
395 7 s. Samoan Monarch (butterfly) 60 10
396 10 s. Triton Shell 50 15
397 20 s. Jewel Beetle 95 30
398 50 s. Spiny Lobster .. .. .. 2·00 75

99 $1 Hawkmoth (29 × 45 *mm*) .. .. 3·50 1·75
99*a* $2 Green Turtle (29 × 45 *mm*) (18.6.73) .. 4·50 4·00
99*b* $4 Black Marlin (29 × 45 *mm*) (27.3.74) .. 4·75 7·00
99*c* $5 Green Tree Lizard (29 × 45 *mm*) (30.6.75) 5·00 7·50
90/9*c* .. .. *Set of* 13 21·00 20·00

134 "The Ascension" **135** Erecting a Tent

(Des PAD Studio. Litho Harrison)

1972 (1 Nov). *Christmas. Stained-glass Windows in Apia. T* **134** *and similar vert designs. Multicoloured.* W **61.** *P* 14 × 14½.
400 1 s. Type **134** 5 5
401 4 s. "The Blessed Virgin and Infant Christ" 12 5
402 10 s. "St. Andrew blessing Samoan canoe" .. 30 10
403 30 s. "The Good Shepherd" .. .. .. 1·10 85
MS404 70 × 159 mm. Nos. 400/3 .. .. .. 1·75 1·90

(Des G. Drummond. Litho Format)

1973 (29 Jan). *Boy Scout Movement. T* **135** *and similar horiz designs. Multicoloured.* W **61** (*sideways*). *P* 14.
405 2 s. Saluting the flag 5 5
406 3 s. First-aid 5 5
407 8 s. Type **135** 20 10
408 20 s. Samoan action-song 75 85

136 Hawker Siddeley "748"

(Des E. Roberts. Photo Courvoisier)

1973 (9 Mar). *Air. T* **136** *and similar horiz designs showing aircraft at Faleolo Airport. Multicoloured. P* 11½.
409 8 s. Type **136** 15 15
410 10 s. H.S. "748" in flight 20 15
411 12 s. H.S. "748" on runway 25 25
412 22 s. B.A.C. 1-11 .. .. 45 50
Issued on matt, almost invisible gum.

137 Apia General Hospital **138** Mother and Child, and Map

(Des C. Abbott. Litho Questa)

1973 (20 Aug). *25th Anniv of W.H.O. T* **137** *and similar vert designs. Multicoloured.* W **61.** *P* 14.
413 2 s. Type **137** 8 5
414 8 s. Baby clinic 25 10
415 20 s. Filariasis research 65 45
416 22 s. Family welfare 65 50

(Des W. E. Jahnke (3 s.), Fiasili Keil (4 s.), E. Coter (others); adapted Jennifer Toombs. Litho J.W.)

1973 (15 Oct). *Christmas. T* **138** *and similar vert designs. Multicoloured.* W **61.** *P* 14.
417 3 s. Type **138** 8 5
418 4 s. Mother and child, and village .. 10 5
419 10 s. Mother and child, and beach .. 25 10
420 30 s. Samoan stable 95 95
MS421 144 × 103 mm. Nos. 417/20 .. .. 1·75 1·90

139 Boxing

(Des G. Drummond. Litho Questa)

1974 (24 Jan). *Commonwealth Games, Christchurch. T* **139** *and similar horiz designs. Multicoloured.* W **61** (*sideways*). *P* 14.
422 8 s. Type **139** 15 15
423 10 s. Weightlifting 20 20
424 20 s. Bowls 40 40
425 30 s. Athletics stadium 75 75

(Des Jennifer Toombs. Litho Questa)

1974 (13 Aug). *Myths and Legends of Old Samoa (2nd series). Vert designs as T* **127** *from carvings by S. Ortquist. Multicoloured.* W **61.** *P* 14 × 13½.
426 2 s. Tigilau and sacred dove 5 5
427 8 s. Pili, his sons and fishing net 20 15
428 20 s. Sina and the origin of the coconut .. 65 40
429 30 s. The warrior, Nafanua 90 80

140 Mail-van at Faleolo Airport

(Des E. Roberts. Photo Heraclio Fournier)

1974 (4 Sept). *Centenary of Universal Postal Union. T* **140** *and similar horiz designs. Multicoloured. P* 13 × 12½ (50 s.) *or* 13 (*others*).
430 8 s. Type **140** 15 10
431 20 s. Ship at Apia Wharf 45 40
432 22 s. Early Post Office, Apia, and letter .. 50 45
433 50 s. William Willis and sailing-raft (87 × 29 *mm*) .. .. 1·25 1·50
MS434 140 × 82 mm. No. 433 .. .. .. 2·25 2·75
The stamp in No. **MS**434 has a coloured margin, whereas that of No. 433 is white.

141 "Holy Family" (Sebastiano)

(Des PAD Studio. Litho Enschedé)

1974 (18 Nov). *Christmas. T* **141** *and similar horiz designs. Multicoloured.* W **61** (*sideways*). *P* 13 × 13½.
435 3 s. Type **141** 5 5
436 4 s. "Virgin and Child with Saints" (Lotto) .. 5 5
437 10 s. "Madonna and Child with St. John" (Titian) 20 10
438 30 s. "Adoration of the Shepherds" (Rubens) .. 80 90
MS439 128 × 87 mm. Nos. 435/8 .. .. 1·50 1·60

142 Winged Passion Flower

(Des J.W. Litho Questa)

1975 (15 Jan). *Tropical Flowers. T* **142** *and similar multicoloured designs.* W **61** (*sideways on* 8 *and* 30 *s.*). *P* 14.
440 8 s. Type **142** 20 10
441 20 s. Gardenia (*vert*) 50 45
442 22 s. *Barringtonia samoensis* (*vert*) 55 50
443 30 s. Malay apple 85 85

143 *Joyita* loading at Apia **144** "Pate" Drum

(Des E. Roberts. Photo Heraclio Fournier)

1975 (14 Mar). *"Interpex 1975" Stamp Exhibition, New York, and "Joyita Mystery". T* **143** *and similar horiz designs. Multicoloured. P* 13½.
444 1 s. Type **143** 5 5
445 8 s. *Joyita* sails for Tokelau Islands 20 20
446 20 s. Taking to rafts 45 45
447 22 s. *Joyita* abandoned 60 60
448 50 s. Discovery of *Joyita* north of Fiji .. .. 1·25 1·25
MS449 150 × 100 mm. Nos. 444/8. Imperf .. 2·75 3·25

(Des Iosua To'afa; adapted L. Curtis. Litho Harrison)

1975 (30 Sept). *Musical Instruments. T* **144** *and similar vert designs. Multicoloured.* W **61** (*sideways*). *P* 14.
450 8 s. Type **144** 15 10
451 20 s. "Lali" drum 40 30
452 22 s. "Logo" drum 40 30
453 30 s. "Pu" shell horn 70 50

145 "Mother and Child" (Meleane Fe'ao) **146** "The Boston Massacre, 1770" (Paul Revere)

(Des local artists; adapted G. Vasarhelyi. Litho Walsall)

1975 (25 Nov). *Christmas. T* **145** *and similar vert designs. Multicoloured.* W **61** (*inverted*). *P* 14.
454 3 s. Type **145** 5 5
455 4 s. "The Saviour" (Polataia Tuigamala) .. 5 5
456 10 s. "A Star is Born" (Iosua To'afa) 25 10
457 30 s. "Madonna and Child" (Ernesto Coter) .. 70 80
MS458 101 × 134 mm. Nos. 454/7 .. .. 1·50 1·50

(Des J. Cooter. Litho Walsall)

1976 (20 Jan). *Bicentenary of American Revolution. T* **146** *and similar horiz designs. Multicoloured.* W **61** (*sideways*). *P* 13½.
459 7 s. Type **146** 25 25
460 8 s. "The Declaration of Independence" (Trumbull) 25 25
461 20 s. "The Ship that Sank in Victory, 1779" (Ferris) 90 90
462 22 s. "Pitt addressing the Commons, 1782" (R. A. Hickel) 90 90
463 50 s. "The Battle of Princetown" (Mercer) .. 2·00 2·00
MS464 160 × 125 mm. Nos. 459/63 .. .. 6·50 7·00

147 Mullet Fishing

(Des V. Whiteley Studio. Litho Harrison)

1976 (27 Apr). *Fishing. T* **147** *and similar horiz designs. Multicoloured.* W **61.** *P* 14.
465 10 s. Type **147** 20 15
466 12 s. Fish traps 25 15
467 22 s. Samoan fishermen 50 30
468 50 s. Net fishing .. .. 1·40 1·10

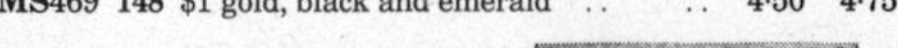

148 Paul Revere's Ride

(Des J. Berry. Photo Heraclio Fournier)

1976 (29 May). *"Interphil" Stamp Exhibition. Sheet* 120 × 80 *mm. P* 13.
MS469 **148** $1 gold, black and emerald .. .. 4·50 4·75

149 Boxing **150** Mary and Joseph going to Bethlehem

(Des C. Abbott. Litho Questa)

1976 (21 June). *Olympic Games, Montreal. T* **149** *and similar horiz designs. Multicoloured.* W **61** (*sideways*). *P* 14.
470 10 s. Type **149** 15 10
471 12 s. Wrestling 20 15
472 22 s. Javelin 45 30
473 50 s. Weightlifting .. .. 1·10 1·00

(Des C. Abbott. Litho Questa)

1976 (18 Oct). *Christmas. T* **150** *and similar vert designs. Multicoloured.* W **61.** *P* 13½.
474 3 s. Type **150** 5 5
475 5 s. The Shepherds 5 5

476 22 s. The Holy Family 35 30
477 50 s. The Magi .. .. 1·10 1·10
MS478 124 × 115 mm. Nos. 474/7 .. .. 2·00 2·00

151 Queen Elizabeth and View of Apia

(Des BG Studio. Litho Questa)

1977 (11 Feb). *Silver Jubilee and Royal Visit. T* **151** *and similar horiz designs. Multicoloured. W* **61** *(sideways). P* 13½.
479 12 s. Type **151** 20 20
480 26 s. Presentation of Spurs of Chivalry .. 45 50
481 32 s. Queen and Royal Yacht *Britannia* .. 55 55
482 50 s. Queen leaving Abbey 70 80

152 Map of Flight Route

(Des C. Abbott. Litho Walsall)

1977 (20 May). *50th Anniv of Lindbergh's Transatlantic Flight. Horiz desig ıs showing the "Spirit of St. Louis". Multicoloured. W* **61** *(sideways). P* 14.
483 22 s. Type **152** 35 20
484 24 s. In flight 45 30
485 26 s. Landing 45 30
486 50 s. Col. Lindbergh .. .. 1·00 1·10
MS487 194 × 93 mm. Nos. 483/6 .. .. .. 3·50 3·50

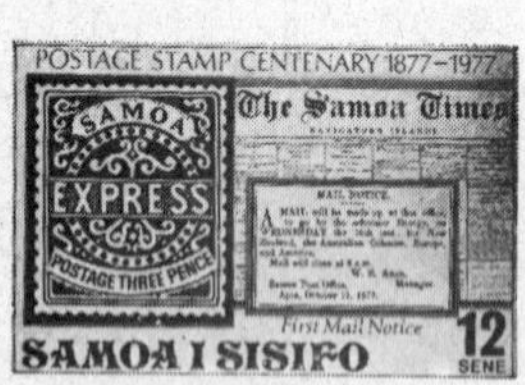

153 3d. Express Stamp and First Mail Notice

154 "Samoan Nativity" (P. Feata)

(Des J. Cooter. Litho Questa)

1977 (29 Aug). *Stamp Centenary. T* **153** *and similar horiz designs. W* **61** *(sideways). P* 13½.
488 12 s. lemon, red and sepia 30 20
489 13 s. multicoloured 30 20
490 26 s. multicoloured 55 40
491 50 s. multicoloured .. .. 1·00 1·10
Designs:—13 s. Early cover and 6d. Express; 26 s. Apia Post Office and 1d. Express; 50 s. Schooner *Energy,* 1877, and 6d. Express.

(Designs adapted by J.W. Litho Questa)

1977 (11 Oct). *Christmas. T* **154** *and similar vert designs. Multicoloured. W* **61**. *P* 14.
492 4 s. Type **154** 5 5
493 6 s. "The Offering" (E. Saofaiga) 10 5
494 26 s. "Madonna and Child" (F. Tupou) .. 40 35
495 50 s. "Emmanuel" (M. Sapa'u) 85 80
MS496 117 × 159 mm. Nos. 492/5 .. .. 1·60 1·75

155 Apia Automatic Telephone Exchange

(Des J.W. Litho Questa)

1977 (28 Oct*). *Telecommunications Project. T* **155** *and similar horiz designs. Multicoloured. W* **61** *(sideways). P* 14.
497 12 s. Type **155** 20 15
498 13 s. Mulinuu Radio Terminal 20 15
499 26 s. Old and new telephones 50 45
500 50 s. "Global communication" 90 90
*The above were originally scheduled for release on 11 July and were put on sale by the Crown Agents in England on that date.

156 Polynesian Airlines Boeing "737"

(Des E. Roberts. Litho Heraclio Fournier)

1978 (21 Mar). *Aviation Progress. T* **156** *and similar horiz designs. Multicoloured. P* 14.
501 12 s. Type **156** 25 15
502 24 s. Wright brothers' *Flyer* 50 40
503 26 s. Kingsford Smith's *Southern Cross* .. 50 40
504 50 s. "Concorde" .. .. 1·10 85
MS505 150 × 120 mm. Nos. 501/4 .. .. 2·25 2·50

157 Hatchery, Aleipata

158 Pacific Pigeon

(Des J.W. Litho Questa)

1978 (14 Apr). *Hawksbill Turtle Conservation Project. T* **157** *and similar horiz design. Multicoloured. W* **61** *(sideways). P* 14½ × 14.
506 24 s. Type **157** 50 50
507 $1 Turtle .. .. 1·75 1·75

(Des Jennifer Toombs. Litho Questa)

1978 (21 Apr). *25th Anniv of Coronation. T* **158** *and similar vert designs. P* 15.
508 26 s. black, brown and deep magenta 35 40
a. Sheetlet. Nos. 508/10 × 2 .. .. 1·90
509 26 s. multicoloured 35 40
510 26 s. black, brown and deep magenta 35 40
Designs:—No. 508, King's Lion; No. 509, Queen Elizabeth II; No. 510, Type **158**.
Nos. 508/10 were printed together in small sheets of 6, containing two *se-tenant* strips of 3, with horizontal gutter margin between.

159 Flags of Western Samoa and Canada with Canadian National Tower

160 Captain Cook

(Des BG Studio. Litho Walsall)

1978 (9 June). *"Capex '78" International Stamp Exhibition, Toronto. Sheet* 119 × 79 *mm. W* **61**. *P* 14½.
MS511 **159** $1 blue, red and black .. .. .. 3·00 3·50

(Des J. Berry. Litho Harrison)

1978 (28 Aug). *250th Birth Anniv of Captain Cook. T* **160** *and similar vert designs. Multicoloured. W* **61**. *P* 14½ × 14.
512 12 s. Type **160** 30 15
513 24 s. Cook's cottage, Gt Ayton, Yorkshire .. 70 50
514 26 s. Old drawbridge over the river Esk, Whitby 80 50
515 50 s. H.M.S. *Resolution* .. .. 1·25 1·50

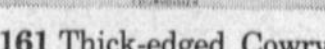

161 Thick-edged Cowry

162 "Madonna on the Crescent"

(Photo Courvoisier)

1978 (15 Sept)–**80**. *Shells. Horiz designs as T* **161**. *Multicoloured. P* 12½.
516 1 s. Type **161** 5 5
517 2 s. Isabella cowry 5 5
518 3 s. Money cowry 5 5
519 4 s. Eroded cowry 10 5
520 6 s. Honey cowry 10 5
521 7 s. Banded cowry 10 5
522 10 s. Globe cowry 12 10
523 11 s. Mole cowry 12 10
524 12 s. Children's cowry 12 10
525 13 s. Flag cone (20.11.78) 15 12
526 14 s. Soldier cone (20.11.78) 15 12
527 24 s. Cloth-of-gold cone (20.11.78) 25 20
528 26 s. Lettered cone (20.11.78) 30 25
529 50 s. Tiled cone (20.11.78) 45 40
530 $1 Black Marble cone (20.11.78) 95 75
530*a* $2 Marlin-spike auger (18.7.79) .. .. 1·50 1·60
530*b* $3 Scorpion Spider Conch (18.7.79) .. 2·25 2·50
530*c* $5 Common Harp (26.8.80) .. .. 4·25 4·50
516/30c .. .. *Set of* 18 10·00 10·00
Issued on matt, almost invisible gum.

(Des C. Abbott. Litho Questa)

1978 (6 Nov). *Christmas. Woodcuts by Dürer. T* **162** *and simila vert designs. W* **61**. *P* 14.
531 4 s. black and yellow-brown 5
532 6 s. black and turquoise-blue 10
533 26 s. black and bright blue 40 2
534 50 s. black and bright violet 85 8
MS535 103 × 154 mm. Nos. 531/4 .. .. 1·40 1·6
Designs:—6 s. "Nativity"; 26 s. "Adoration of the Magi"; 50 "Annunciation".

163 Boy with Coconuts

164 *Charles W. Morgan*

(Des G. Drummond. Litho Questa)

1979 (10 Apr). *International Year of the Child. T* **163** *and simila horiz designs. Multicoloured. W* **61** *(sideways). P* 14.
536 12 s. Type **163** 25 1
537 24 s. White Sunday 45 4
538 26 s. Children at pump 50 4
539 50 s. Young girl with ukulele .. .. .. 1·00 1·0

(Des J. Cooter. Litho Format)

1979 (29 May). *Sailing Ships (1st series). T* **164** *and similar hori designs. Multicoloured. W* **61** *(sideways). P* 13½.
540 12 s. Type **164** 25 15
541 14 s. *Lagoda* 30 20
542 24 s. *James T. Arnold* 50 35
543 50 s. *Splendid* .. .. 1·00 85
See also Nos. 561/4 and 584/7.

165 Launch of "Apollo 11"

166 Sir Rowland Hill (statue) and Penny Black

(Des J.W. Litho Questa)

1979 (20 June). *10th Anniv of Moon Landing. T* **165** *and similar designs in chocolate and dull vermilion* (12 *s.*) *or multicoloured (others). W* **61** *(sideways on* 14, 26 *s. and* $1). *P* 14½ × 14 (12, 24, 50 *s.*) *or* 14 × 14½ *(others).*
544 12 s. Type **165** 20 20
545 14 s. Lunar module and astronaut on Moon (*horiz*) 25 25
546 24 s. View of Earth from Moon 40 40
547 26 s. Astronaut on Moon (*horiz*) 40 40
548 50 s. Lunar and Command modules in Space 70 70
549 $1 Command module after splash-down (*horiz*) .. .. 1·50 1·50
544/9 .. .. *Set of* 6 3·00 3·00
MS550 90 × 130 mm. No. 549 .. .. .. 1·75 1·90
No. **MS**550 is inscribed "Spashdown" in error.

(Des and litho J.W.)

1979 (27 Aug). *Death Centenary of Sir Rowland Hill. T* **166** *and similar vert designs. Multicoloured. W* **61**. *P* 14.
551 12 s. Type **166** 20 20
552 24 s. Two-penny Blue with "Maltese Cross" postmark 35 35
553 26 s. Sir Rowland Hill and Penny Black .. 35 35
554 $1 Two-penny Blue and Sir Rowland Hill (statue) .. .. 90 1·00
MS555 128 × 95 mm. Nos. 551/4 .. .. .. 1·75 2·00

167 Anglican Church, Apia

(Des A. Peake. Photo Courvoisier)

1979 (22 Oct). *Christmas. Churches. T* **167** *and similar horiz designs. P* 11½.
556 4 s. black and pale blue 5 5
557 6 s. black and bright yellow-green 10 5
558 26 s. black and yellow-ochre 35 35
559 50 s. black and reddish lilac 60 65
MS560 150 × 124 mm. Nos. 556/9 .. .. 1·00 1·25
Designs:—6 s. Congregational Christian, Leulumoega; 26 s. Methodist, Piula; 50 s. Protestant, Apia.
Issued on matt, almost invisible gum.

(Des J. Cooter. Litho Format)

1980 (22 Jan). *Sailing Ships (2nd series). Horiz designs as T* **164**. *Multicoloured. W* **61** *(sideways). P* 13½.
561 12 s. *William Hamilton* 15 15
562 14 s. *California* 20 20
563 24 s. *Liverpool II* 35 35
564 50 s. *Two Brothers* 70 70

168 "Equipment for a Hospital"

Des M. Goaman (12, 50 s.), E. Roberts (others). Photo Heraclio Fournier)

1980 (26 Mar). *Anniversaries. T* **168** *and similar horiz designs. Multicoloured. P* 13½ × 14.

565 12 s. Type **168** 15 15
566 13 s. John Williams, dove with olive twig and commemorative inscription 15 15
567 14 s. Dr. Wilhelm Solf (instigator), flag and commemorative inscription 20 20
568 24 s. Cairn Monument 30 30
569 26 s. Williams Memorial, Savai'i 30 30
570 50 s. Paul P. Harris (founder) 60 60
565/70 . . . . . . *Set of* 6 1·50 1·50

Commemorations:—12, 50 s. 75th anniversary of Rotary International; 13, 26 s. 150th anniversary of John Williams' (missionary) arrival in Samoa; 14, 24 s. 80th anniversary of raising of German flag.

169 Samoan Village Scene

(Des J.W. Litho Walsall)

1980 (6 May). *"London 1980" International Stamp Exhibition. Sheet* 140 × 81 *mm. W* **61** *(sideways). P* 14.

MS571 **169** $1 multicoloured . . . . . . 1·25 1·50

170 Queen Elizabeth the Queen Mother

(Des Harrison. Litho Questa)

1980 (4 Aug). *80th Birthday of Queen Elizabeth the Queen Mother. P* 14.

572 **170** 50 s. multicoloured 85 75

171 1964 2nd Anniversary of New Zealand–Samoa Treaty of Friendship 2 s. Commemorative and "Zeapex '80" Emblem

(Des E. Roberts. Photo Heraclio Fournier)

1980 (23 Aug). *"Zeapex '80" International Stamp Exhibition, Auckland. Sheet* 130 × 80 *mm. P* 14.

MS573 **171** $1 multicoloured . . . . . . 1·60 2·00

172 Afiamalu Satellite Earth Station

(Des and photo Courvoisier)

1980 (1 Sept). *Afiamalu Satellite Earth Station. T* **172** *and similar horiz designs. Multicoloured. P* 11½.

574 12 s. Type **172** 15 15
575 14 s. Satellite station (*different*) 20 20
576 24 s. Satellite station and map of Savai'i and Upolu 30 30
577 50 s. Satellite and globe 60 60

173 Afiamalu Satellite Earth Station 24 s. Commemorative Stamp and "Sydpex 80" Emblem

(Des E. Roberts. Litho Sprintpak, Mayne Nickless Ltd, Australia)

1980 (29 Sept). *"Sydpex 80" International Stamp Exhibition, Sydney. Sheet* 130 × 80 *mm. Imperf.*

MS578 **173** $2 multicoloured . . . . . . 2·25 2·75

174 "The Saviour" (J. Poynton)

175 President Franklin D. Roosevelt and Hyde Park (family home)

(Des G. Vasarhelyi. Litho Format)

1980 (28 Oct). *Christmas. Paintings. T* **174** *and similar vert designs. Multicoloured. W* **61**. *P* 13½.

579 8 s. Type **174** 8 5
580 14 s. "Madonna and Child" (Lealofi F. Siaopo) 15 10
581 27 s. "Nativity" (Pasila Feata) 25 20
582 50 s. "Yuletide" (R. P. Aiono) 50 60
MS583 90 × 105 mm. Nos. 579/82 . . . . 95 1·10

(Des J. Cooter. Litho Format)

1981 (26 Jan). *Sailing Ships (3rd series). Horiz designs as T* **164**. *Multicoloured. P* 13½.

584 12 s. *Ocean* 20 15
585 18 s. *Horatio* 30 25
586 27 s. H.M.S. *Calliope* 45 45
587 32 s. H.M.S. *Calypso* 50 60

(Des J.W. Litho Format)

1981 (29 Apr). *International Year for Disabled Persons. President Franklin D. Roosevelt Commemoration. T* **175** *and similar horiz designs. Multicoloured. P* 14.

588 12 s. Type **175** 15 15
589 18 s. Roosevelt's inauguration, 4 March 1933 25 25
590 27 s. Franklin and Eleanor Roosevelt . . 35 35
591 32 s. Roosevelt's Lend-lease Bill (Atlantic convoy, 1941) 40 40
592 38 s. Roosevelt the philatelist 45 45
593 $1 Campobello House (summer home) . . 1·00 1·00
588/93 . . . . . . *Set of* 6 2·40 2·40

176 Hotel Tusitala

177 Wedding Bouquet from Samoa

(Des and litho Walsall)

1981 (29 June). *Tourism. T* **176** *and similar horiz designs. Multicoloured. W* **61** *(sideways). P* 14½ × 14.

594 12 s. Type **176** 15 15
595 18 s. Apia Harbour 25 25
596 27 s. Aggie Grey's Hotel 30 30
597 32 s. Preparation for Ceremonial Kava . . 40 40
598 54 s. Piula water pool 65 65

(Des J.W. Litho Walsall)

1981 (22 July). *Royal Wedding. T* **177** *and similar vert designs. Multicoloured. W* **61**. *P* 14.

599 18 s. Type **177** 30 25
600 32 s. Prince Charles as Colonel-in-Chief, Gordon Highlanders 40 40
601 $1 Prince Charles and Lady Diana Spencer 95 1·10

178 Tattooing Instruments

179 Black Marlin

(Des E. Roberts. Litho Cambec Press, Melbourne)

1981 (29 Sept). *Tattooing. T* **178** *and similar horiz designs. Multicoloured. P* 13½.

602 12 s. Type **178** 20 20
a. Horiz strip of 4. Nos. 602/5 . . . . 1·50
603 18 s. First stage of tattooing 25 25
604 27 s. Progressive stage 30 30
605 $1 Completed tattoo 90 90

Nos. 602/5 were printed together, *se-tenant*, in horizontal strips of 4 throughout the sheet.

(Des E. Roberts. Litho Cambec Press, Melbourne)

1981 (9 Oct). *"Philatokyo '81" International Stamp Exhibition, Tokyo. Sheet* 130 × 80 *mm. P* 14 × 13½.

MS606 **179** $2 multicoloured . . . . . . 1·75 2·00

180 *Thespesia populnea*

181 George Washington's Pistol

(Des and litho J.W.)

1981 (30 Nov). *Christmas. Flowers. T* **180** *and similar vert designs. Multicoloured. W* **61**. *P* 13½.

607 11 s. Type **180** 15 12
608 15 s. Copper Leaf 20 15
609 23 s. *Allamanda cathartica* 30 25
610 $1 Mango . . . . 1·00 1·00
MS611 86 × 120 mm. Nos. 607/10 . . . . 1·60 1·75

(Des J.W. Litho Format)

1982 (26 Feb). *250th Birth Anniv of George Washington. T* **181** *and similar horiz designs, each in black, ochre and stone. P* 13½.

612 23 s. Type **181** 30 30
613 25 s. Mount Vernon (Washington's house) . . 30 30
614 34 s. George Washington 40 40
MS615 104 × 103 mm. $1 Washington taking Oath of Office as President . . . . . . 95 1·00

182 "Shipping Services"

(Des E. Roberts. Litho Cambec Press, Melbourne)

1982 (24 May). *20th Anniv of Independence. T* **182** *and similar horiz designs. Multicoloured. P* 13½ × 14.

616 18 s. Type **182** 20 25
617 23 s. "Air services" 30 35
618 25 s. N.P.F. (National Provident Fund) Building, Apia 30 35
619 $1 "Telecommunications" . . . . . . 95 1·00

183 Scouts map-reading and "75"

184 Boxing

(Des J.W. Litho Walsall)

1982 (20 July). *75th Anniv of Boy Scout Movement. T* **183** *and similar horiz designs. Multicoloured. W* **61** *(sideways). P* 14½.

620 5 s. Type **183** 5 5
621 38 s. Scout salute and "75" 40 40
622 44 s. Scout crossing river by rope, and "75" . . 50 50
623 $1 "Tower" of Scouts and "75" . . . . 1·00 1·00
MS624 93 × 81 mm. $1 As No. 623 but with portrait of Lord Baden-Powell replacing emblem (47 × 35 *mm*). P 11 . . . . 1·00 1·10

(Des Garden Studio. Litho Walsall)

1982 (20 Sept). *Commonwealth Games, Brisbane. T* **184** *and similar vert designs. Multicoloured. W w* **14**. *P* 14½.

625 23 s. Type **184** 25 25
626 25 s. Hurdling 25 25
627 34 s. Weightlifting 35 35
628 $1 Bowling . . . . 95 1·00

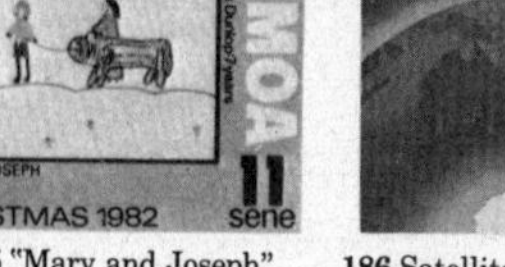

185 "Mary and Joseph" (Emma Dunlop)

186 Satellite View of Australasia

(Des J.W. Litho Questa)

1982 (15 Nov). *Christmas. Children's Pictures. T* **185** *and similar horiz designs. Multicoloured. W* **61** *(sideways). P* 14 × 14½.

629 11 s. Type **185** 12 10
630 15 s. "Mary, Joseph and baby Jesus" (Marie Tofaeono) 15 15
631 38 s. "Madonna and Child" (Ralph Laban and Fetalaiga Fareni) 40 40
632 $1 "Mother and Child" (Panapa Pouesi) . . 95 1·00
MS633 130 × 119 mm. Nos. 629/32 . . . . 1·60 1·75

(Des Walsall. Litho Enschedé)

1983 (23 Feb). *Commonwealth Day. T* **186** *and similar horiz designs. Multicoloured.* W w **14** (*sideways*). *P* 13 × 13½.
634 14 s. Type **186** 12 15
635 29 s. Flag of Samoa 25 30
636 43 s. Harvesting copra 35 40
637 $1 Head of State Malietoa Tanumafili II .. 80 85

187 Douglas "DC-1"

(Des J.W. Litho Questa)

1983 (7 June). *Bicentenary of Manned Flight and 50th Anniv of Douglas Commercial Aircraft. Sheet,* 215 × 113 *mm, containing horiz designs as T* **187**. *Multicoloured.* W w **14** (*sideways*). *P* 14.
MS638 32 s. × 10, each design showing a different Douglas aircraft from the "DC-1" to the "DC-10" .. 2·50 2·75

188 Pole-vaulting **189** Lime

(Des McCombie Skinner Studio. Litho Format)

1983 (31 Aug). *South Pacific Games. T* **188** *and similar vert designs. Multicoloured.* W w **14**. *P* 14 × 14½.
639 8 s. Type **188** 8 10
640 15 s. Netball 12 15
641 25 s. Tennis 15 20
642 32 s. Weight-lifting 25 30
643 35 s. Boxing 25 30
644 46 s. Football 35 40
645 48 s. Golf 35 40
646 56 s. Rugby 40 45
639/46 .. .. *Set of* 8 1·75 2·00

(Des E. Roberts. Litho Enschedé)

1983 (28 Sept)–**84**. *Fruit. T* **189** *and similar vert designs. Multicoloured.* W w **14** (*inverted on* 1 *s.*). *P* 13½ ($2 *to* $5) *or* 14 × 13½ (*others*).
647 1 s. Type **189** 5 5
648 2 s. Star fruit 5 5
649 3 s. Mangosteen 5 5
650 4 s. Lychee 5 5
651 7 s. Passion fruit 5 5
652 8 s. Mango 5 5
653 11 s. Pawpaw 5 8
654 13 s. Pineapple 8 10
655 14 s. Breadfruit 8 10
656 15 s. Banana 10 12
657 21 s. Cashew Nut (30.11.83) 15 20
658 25 s. Guava (30.11.83) 15 20
659 32 s. Water Melon (30.11.83) 20 25
660 48 s. Sasalapa (30.11.83) 30 35
661 56 s. Avocado (30.11.83) 40 45
662 $1 Coconut (30.11.83) 60 75
663 $2 Vi Apple (11.4.84) .. .. .. 1·25 1·40
664 $4 Grapefruit (11.4.84) .. .. .. 2·50 2·75
665 $5 Orange (11.4.84) .. .. 3·25 3·50
647/65 .. .. *Set of* 19 8·00 9·50
Nos. have been reserved for future additions to this set.

190 On Parade **191** Togitogiga Falls, Upolu

(Des Brian Melton Studio. Litho Format)

1983 (10 Oct). *Centenary of Boys' Brigade. Sheet* 120 × 83 *mm.* W w **14**. *P* 14.
MS668 **190** $1 multicoloured 80 85

(Litho Format)

1984 (15 Feb). *Scenic Views. T* **191** *and similar horiz designs. Multicoloured.* W w **14** (*sideways*). *P* 14.
669 25 s. Type **191** 15 20
670 32 s. Lano Beach, Savai'i 25 30
671 48 s. Mulinu'u Point, Upolu 40 45
672 56 s. Nu'utele Island 45 50

SAMOA 32s

19th U.P.U. CONGRESS
HAMBURG 1984

192 Apia Harbour (**193**)

(Des Jennifer Toombs. Litho Questa)

1984 (24 May). *250th Anniv of "Lloyd's List" (newspaper). T* **192** *and similar vert designs. Multicoloured.* W w **14**. *P* 14 × 14½.
673 32 s. Type **192** 25 30
674 48 s. Apia hurricane, 1889 .. .. 40 45
675 60 s. M.V. *Forum Samoa* 45 50
676 $1 S.S. *Matua* 75 80

1984 (7 June). *Universal Postal Union Congress, Hamburg. No.* 662 *optd with T* **193**.
677 $1 Coconut 75 80

194 Olympic Stadium

(Des Garden Studio. Litho Format)

1984 (26 June). *Olympic Games, Los Angeles. T* **194** *and similar horiz designs. Multicoloured.* W w **14** (*sideways*). *P* 14½.
678 25 s. Type **194** 20 25
679 32 s. Weightlifting 25 30
680 48 s. Boxing 40 45
681 $1 Running 75 80
MS682 170 × 120 mm. Nos. 678/81 .. .. .. 1·50 1·60

195 Nomad "N24" Aircraft

(Des E. Roberts. Litho Walsall)

1984 (21 Sept). *"Ausipex" International Stamp Exhibition, Melbourne. Sheet* 131 × 80 mm. W w **14** (*sideways*). *P* 14.
MS683 **195** $2.50, multicoloured .. .. 1·90 2·00

196 "Faith"

(Litho Walsall)

1984 (7 Nov). *Christmas. "The Three Virtues" (Raphael). T* **196** *and similar horiz designs. Multicoloured.* W w **14** (*sideways*). *P* 14.
684 25 s. Type **196** 20 25
685 35 s. "Hope" 25 30
686 $1 "Charity" 75 80
MS687 63 × 76 mm. Nos. 684/6 .. .. .. 1·25 1·40

197 *Dendrobium biflorum*

(Des Jennifer Toombs. Litho Format)

1985 (23 Jan). *Orchids. T* **197** *and similar vert designs. Multicoloured.* *P* 14.
688 48 s. Type **197** 30 35
689 56 s. *Dendrobium vaupelianum Kraenzl* 40 45
690 67 s. *Glomera montana* 45 50
691 $1 *Spathoglottis plicata* 70 75

NEW INFORMATION

The editor is always interested to correspond with people who have new information that will improve or correct the Catalogue.

Sarawak

Sarawak was placed under British protection in 1888. It was ceded to Great Britain on 1 July 1946 and was administered as a Crown Colony until 16 September 1963 when it became a state of the Federation of Malaysia.

Stamps of INDIA were used in Sarawak from *circa* 1859. They were replaced by Sarawak issues from 1869, although these were only valid for "local" postage as far as Singapore. Mail for further afield needed a combination of Sarawak and STRAITS SETTLEMENTS stamps, a stock of the latter being kept by the Sarawak Post Office. This arrangement continued until 1897.

PRICES FOR STAMPS ON COVER TO 1945

No. 1	—
Nos. 2/7	*from* × 50
Nos. 8/21	*from* × 4
Nos. 22/6	*from* × 5
No. 27	*from* × 40
Nos. 28/35	*from* × 5
Nos. 36/47	*from* × 8
No. 48	†
No. 49	*from* × 10
Nos. 50/61	*from* × 6
No. 62	†
Nos. 63/71	*from* × 4
Nos. 72/3	*from* × 8
Nos. 74/5	—
Nos. 76/90	*from* × 7
Nos. 91/105	*from* × 5
Nos. 106/25	*from* × 3
Nos. 126/45	*from* × 2

BROOKE FAMILY ADMINISTRATION

Sir James Brooke. 1842–11 June 1868
Sir Charles Brooke. 11 June 1868–17 May 1917

UNUSED PRICES. Nos. 1/7, 27 and 32/5 in unused condition are normally found to be without gum. Prices in the unused column are for stamps in this state. Examples of these issues with original gum are worth considerably more.

1 Sir James Brooke **2** Sir Charles Brooke

The initials in the corners of T **1** and **2** stand for "James (Charles) Brooke, Rajah (of) Sarawak".

(T **1** and **2**. Die eng Wm. Ridgway. Litho Maclure, Macdonald & Co, Glasgow)

1869 (1 Mar). *P* 11.
1 **1** 3 c. brown/*yellow* .. .. 40·00 £200
Specimens are known printed from the engraved die in orange-brown on orange surface-coloured paper, and perf 12. These were submitted to the Sarawak authorities as examples of the stamps and exist both with and without obliterations.

1871 (1 Jan). *P* 11 (*irregular*).
2 **2** 3 c. brown/*yellow* .. .. 2·00 4·00
a. Stop after "THREE". .. .. .. 22·00 35·00
b. Imperf between (vert pair) £225
c. Imperf between (horiz pair) £275
The "stop" variety, No. 2a, which occurs on stamp No. 97 in the sheet, is of no more philatelic importance than any of the numerous other variations, such as narrow first "A" in "SARAWAK" (No. 17) and "R" with long tail in left lower corner (No. 90), but it has been accepted by collectors for many years, and we therefore retain it. The papermaker's wmk "L N L" appears once or twice in sheets of No. 2.
Specimens are known, recess-printed, similar to those mentioned in the note after No. 1.

TWO CENTS

Copies of No. 2 surcharged as above were first reported in 1876 but following the discovery of dies for forgeries and faked postmarks in 1892 it was concluded that the issue was bogus, especially as the availability of the 2 c. of 1875 made it unnecessary to issue a provisional. It has now been established that a 2 c. postal rate was introduced from 1 August 1874 for the carriage of newspapers. Moreover one example is known with a stop after "CENTS." and showing other minor differences from the forgery illustrated. This stamp could be genuine and if others come to light we will reconsider listing it.

1875 (1 Jan). *P* 11½–12.
3 **2** 2 c. mauve/*lilac* (*shades*) .. .. .. 3·50 6·50
4 4 c. red-brown/*yellow* .. .. .. 4·00 5·00
a. Imperf between (vert pair) £350
5 6 c. green/*green* .. .. 4·00 5·00
6 8 c. bright blue/*blue* .. .. .. 5·00 6·00
7 12 c. red/*pale rose* .. .. 9·00 11·00
Nos. 3, 4, 6 and 7 have the watermark "L N L" in the sheet, as No. 2. No. 5 is watermarked "L N T".
All values exist imperf and can be distinguished from the proofs by shade and impression. Stamps rouletted, pin-perf, or roughly perf 6½ to 7 are proofs clandestinely perforated.

The 12 c. "laid" paper, formerly listed, is not on a true laid paper, he "laid" effect being accidental and not consistent.

The lithographic stones for Nos. 3 to 7 were made up from strips f five distinct impressions hence there are five types of each value iffering mainly in the lettering of the tablets of value. There are laws on nearly every individual stamp, from which they can be plated.

4 Sir Charles Brooke

(Typo D.L.R.)

1888 (10 Nov)–**1897**. *No wmk. P* 14.

8 4 1 c. purple and black (6.6.92) .. .. 1·25 1·40
9 2 c. purple and carmine .. .. .. 2·50 1·40
a. Purple and rosine (1897) .. .. 3·75 2·25
10 3 c. purple and blue (11.88) .. .. 1·25 1·40
11 4 c. purple and yellow (10.11.88) .. .. 12·00 20·00
12 5 c. purple and green (12.6.91) .. .. 7·50 4·50
13 6 c. purple and brown (11.11.88) .. .. 10·00 22·00
14 8 c. green and carmine .. .. .. 4·50 4·75
a. Green and rosine (1897) .. .. 10·00 7·50
15 10 c. green and purple (12.6.93) .. .. 18·00 13·00
16 12 c. green and blue (11.11.88) .. .. 4·00 6·50
17 16 c. green and orange (28.12.97) .. .. 22·00 30·00
18 25 c. green and brown (19.11.88) .. .. 22·00 26·00
19 32 c. green and black (28.12.97) .. .. 22·00 35·00
20 50 c. green (26.7.97) .. .. .. 23·00 35·00
21 $1 green and black (2.11.97) .. .. 35·00 48·00
8/21 .. .. *Set of* 14 £170 £225

Prepared for use but not issued

21*a* $2 green and blue £300
21*b* $5 green and violet £300
21*c* $10 green and carmine £300

On No. 21 the value is in black on an uncoloured ground.

The tablet of value in this and later similar issues is in the second colour given.

One Cent. (5) one cent. (6)

2C. (7) 5c (8) 5C. (9)

1889 (3 Aug)–**92**. *T* 4 *surch. P* 14.

22 5 1 c. on 3 c. (12.1.92) .. .. .. 25·00 25·00
a. Surch double £300 £225
23 6 1 c. on 3 c. (2.92) .. .. .. 5·00 8·00
a. No stop after "cent" .. .. 65·00
24 7 2 c. on 8 c. (3.8.89) .. .. .. 4·00 7·50
a. Surch double £225
b. Surch inverted £1200
c. Surch omitted (in pair with normal) £1100
25 8 5 c. on 12 c. (17.2.91) .. .. .. 20·00 24·00
a. No stop after "C" .. .. .. 20·00 23·00
b. "C" omitted £200
c. Surch double £750
d. Surch double, one vertical £1000
e. Surch omitted (in pair with normal)
26 9 5 c. on 12 c. (17.2.91) .. .. .. 60·00 80·00
a. No stop after "C" .. .. .. 60·00 70·00
b. "C" omitted £275 £225
c. Surch double £650

ONE CENT (10)

1892 (23 May). *No.* 2 *surch with T* 10.

27 2 1 c. on 3 c. brown/*yellow* .. .. .. 1·10 1·50
a. Stop after "THREE." .. .. 15·00 20·00
b. Imperf between (vert pair) £350
c. Surch double £250

Varieties with part of the surcharge missing are due to gum on the face of the unsurcharged stamps receiving part of the surcharge, which was afterwards washed off.

11

12

13 Sir Charles Brooke 14

(Die eng Wm. Ridgway. Recess P.B.)

1895 (1 Jan–Sept). *No wmk. P* 11½–12.

28 11 2 c. brown-red .. .. 5·50 8·50
a. Imperf between (vert pair) £200
b. Imperf between (horiz pair) £225
c. Second ptg. Perf 12½ (Sept) .. .. 3·50 5·50
ca. Perf 12½. Imperf between (horiz pair) £225
29 12 4 c. black .. .. 5·50 4·50
a. Imperf between (horiz pair) £180
30 13 6 c. violet .. .. 6·50 9·00
31 14 8 c. green .. .. 8·50 10·00

Stamps of these types, printed in wrong colours, are trials and these, when surcharged with values in "pence", are from waste sheets that were used by Perkins, Bacon & Co as trial paper when preparing an issue of stamps for British South Africa.

4 CENTS. (15)

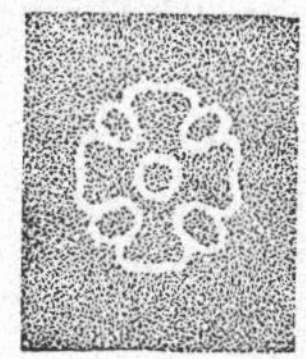

16

1899. *Surch as T* 15.

32 2 2 c. on 3 c. brown/*yellow* (19.9.99) .. 1·75 3·50
a. Stop after "THREE" .. .. .. 35·00
b. Imperf between (vert pair) £550
33 2 c. on 12 c. red/*pale rose* (29.6.99) .. 2·75 5·00
a. Surch inverted £650 £750
34 4 c. on 6 c. green/*green* (R.) (16.11.99) .. 23·00 32·00
35 4 c. on 8 c. bright blue/*blue* (R.) (29.6.99) 4·00 7·50

A variety of surcharge with small "S" in "CENTS" may be found in the 2 c. on 12 c. and 4 c. on 8 c. and a raised stop after "CENTS" on the 4 c. on 6 c.

The omission of parts of the surcharge is due to gum on the surface of the stamps (see note after No. 27).

(Typo D.L.R.)

1899 (10 Nov)–**1908**. *Inscribed* "POSTAGE POSTAGE." *No wmk. P* 14.

36 4 1 c. grey-blue and rosine (1.1.01) 65 45
a. Grey-blue and red 65 20
b. Ultramarine and rosine .. .. 2·50 40
c. Dull blue and carmine .. .. 3·75 3·75
37 2 c. green (16.12.99) 40 25
38 3 c. dull purple (1.2.08) .. .. .. 1·75 20
39 4 c. rose-carmine (10.11.99) .. .. 3·50 1·60
a. Aniline carmine .. .. .. 2·75 20
40 8 c. yellow and black (6.12.99) .. .. 3·50 2·25
41 10 c. ultramarine (10.11.99) .. .. 3·75 90
42 12 c. mauve (16.12.99) .. .. .. 4·00 2·50
a. Bright mauve (1905) .. .. 9·50 5·50
43 16 c. chestnut and green (16.12.99) .. 4·00 3·75
44 20 c. bistre and bright mauve (4.00) .. 6·50 6·50
45 25 c. brown and blue (16.12.99) .. .. 5·50 8·50
46 50 c. sage-green and carmine (16.12.99) .. 13·00 18·00
47 $1 rose-carmine and green (16.12.99) .. 24·00 35·00
a. Rosine and pale green .. .. 35·00 42·00
36/47 .. .. *Set of* 12 60·00 70·00

Prepared for use but not issued

48 4 5 c. olive-grey and green .. .. .. 18·00

The figures of value in the $1 are in colour on an uncoloured ground.

1902. *Inscribed* "POSTAGE POSTAGE". *W* **16**. *P* 14.

49 4 2 c. green .. .. 11·00 6·50

Sir Charles Vyner Brooke. 17 May 1917–1 July 1946

17 Sir Charles Vyner Brooke

ONE cent (18)

(Typo D.L.R.)

1918 (26 Mar). *No wmk. Chalky paper. P* 14.

50 17 1 c. slate-blue and red 25 30
a. Dull blue and carmine 50 50
51 2 c. green 50 45
52 3 c. brown-purple .. .. .. 1·25 1·40
53 4 c. rose-carmine .. .. .. 1·40 1·25
a. Rose-red .. .. 1·25 1·75
54 8 c. yellow and black .. .. .. 4·25 13·00
55 10 c. blue (*shades*) .. .. .. 2·25 4·50
56 12 c. purple .. .. 3·50 4·75
57 16 c. chestnut and green .. .. .. 5·00 4·75
58 20 c. olive and violet (*shades*) .. .. 3·50 4·25
59 25 c. brown and bright blue .. .. 4·00 5·50
60 50 c. olive-green and carmine .. .. 6·00 7·50
61 $1 bright rose and green .. .. 12·00 17·00
50/61 .. .. *Set of* 12 40·00 60·00
50/61 Optd "Specimen" .. .. *Set of* 12 £190

Prepared for use but not issued

62 17 1 c. slate-blue and slate .. .. .. 35·00

On the $1 the figures of value are in colour on an uncoloured ground.

1922–23. *New colours and values. No wmk. Chalk-surfaced paper. P* 14.

63 17 2 c. purple (5.3.23) .. .. .. 40 1·00
64 3 c. dull green (23.3.22) 40 60
65 4 c. brown-purple (10.4.23) 40 25
66 5 c. yellow-orange .. .. .. 40 1·25
67 6 c. claret (1.22) .. .. 90 1·40
68 8 c. bright rose-red .. .. .. 2·50 6·00
69 17 10 c. black (1923) .. .. 2·25 2·75
70 12 c. bright blue (12.22) .. .. .. 7·00 13·00
a. Pale dull blue .. .. .. 5·50 10·00
71 30 c. ochre-brown and slate .. .. 4·25 7·00
63/71 .. .. *Set of* 9 15·00 27·00

1923 (Jan). *Surch as T* **18**. *(a) First printing. Bars* 1¼ *mm apart.*

72 17 1 c. on 10 c. dull blue .. .. .. 16·00 32·00
a. "cnet" for "cent" £300 £500
73 2 c. on 12 c. purple .. .. .. 5·50 14·00
a. Thick, narrower "W" in "TWO" .. 16·00 29·00

(b) Second printing. Bars ¾ *mm apart*

74 17 1 c. on 10 c. blue .. .. 75·00 £120
a. "en" of "cent" scratched out and "ne" overprinted £2500
75 2 c. on 12 c. purple .. .. .. 45·00 60·00
a. Thick, narrower "W" in "TWO" .. £100

In the 2 c. on 12 c. the words of the surcharge are about 7½ mm from the bars.

Variety 74a arose from a native printer "correcting" an already correct surcharge in the second printing in the endeavour exactly to reproduce the "cnet" error of the first printing.

The thick "W" variety occurs on all stamps of the last two horizontal rows of the first printing (12 stamps per sheet), and in the last two vertical rows of the second (20 stamps per sheet).

1928 (Apr)–**29**. *W* **16** *(Multiple). Chalk-surfaced paper. P* 14.

76 17 1 c. slate-blue and carmine 45 45
77 2 c. bright purple 45 40
78 3 c. green .. .. 45 1·40
79 4 c. brown-purple .. .. .. 1·50 15
80 5 c. yellow-orange (5.8.29) .. .. 2·00 3·25
81 6 c. claret 70 40
82 8 c. bright rose-red .. .. .. 2·25 4·50
83 10 c. black .. .. 1·25 2·25
84 12 c. bright blue .. .. .. 2·25 4·25
85 16 c. chestnut and green .. .. 2·25 3·75
86 20 c. olive-bistre and violet .. .. 2·25 3·50
87 25 c. brown and bright blue .. .. 3·00 6·50
88 30 c. bistre-brown and slate .. .. 5·00 5·00
89 50 c. olive-green and carmine .. .. 5·00 7·00
90 $1 bright rose and green .. .. 13·00 20·00
76/90 .. .. *Set of* 15 38·00 55·00
76/90 Optd/Perf "Specimen" .. *Set of* 15 £250

In the $1 the value is as before.

19 Sir Charles Vyner Brooke

20

(Recess Waterlow)

1932 (1 Jan). *W* **20**. *P* 12½.

91 19 1 c. indigo 75 50
92 2 c. green 75 50
93 3 c. violet .. .. 2·25 1·25
94 4 c. red-orange 75 40
95 5 c. deep lake .. .. 2·50 2·00
96 6 c. scarlet .. .. 3·00 6·00
97 8 c. orange-yellow .. .. .. 3·50 5·00
98 10 c. black .. .. 3·00 4·75
99 12 c. deep ultramarine .. .. .. 3·00 4·75
100 15 c. chestnut .. .. 3·50 6·00
101 20 c. red-orange and violet .. .. 3·50 6·00
102 25 c. orange-yellow and chestnut .. 4·50 7·50
103 30 c. sepia and vermilion .. .. 4·50 9·00
104 50 c. carmine-red and olive-green .. 6·50 9·00
105 $1 green and carmine .. .. .. 12·00 18·00
91/105 .. .. *Set of* 15 48·00 70·00
91/105 Perf "Specimen" .. .. *Set of* 15 £200

21 Sir Charles Vyner Brooke

BMA (22)

(Recess B.W.)

1934 (1 May)–**41**. *No wmk. P* 12.

106 21 1 c. purple 20 12
107 2 c. green 15 12
107*a* 2 c. black (1.3.41) .. .. .. 75 1·40
108 3 c. black 15 12
108*a* 3 c. green (1.3.41) 50 70
109 4 c. bright purple 30 15
110 5 c. violet 15 12
111 6 c. carmine 20 40
111*a* 6 c. lake-brown (1.3.41) .. .. 70 1·90
112 8 c. red-brown 20 20
112*a* 8 c. carmine (1.3.41) 45 50
113 10 c. scarlet 65 65
114 12 c. blue 35 65
114*a* 12 c. orange (1.3.41) .. .. .. 65 3·00
115 15 c. orange .. .. 40 2·50
115*a* 15 c. blue (1.3.41) .. .. .. 65 3·00
116 20 c. olive-green and carmine 90 90
117 25 c. violet and orange .. .. .. 50 1·00
118 30 c. red-brown and violet .. .. 70 1·40
119 50 c. violet and scarlet .. .. .. 1·75 1·50
120 $1 scarlet and sepia .. .. .. 1·75 2·00
121 $2 bright purple and violet .. .. 4·00 10·00
122 $3 carmine and green .. .. .. 7·00 13·00
123 $4 blue and scarlet .. .. .. 11·00 16·00

124 **21** $5 scarlet and red-brown .. .. .. 22·00 29·00
125 $10 black and yellow .. .. .. 38·00 48·00
106/25 .. .. *Set of* 26 80·00 £120
106/25 Perf "Specimen" .. .. *Set of* 26 £450

For the 3 c. green, wmkd Mult Script CA, see No. 152a.

BRITISH MILITARY ADMINISTRATION

1945 (17 Dec). *Optd with T* **22**.

126 **21** 1 c. purple 20 20
127 2 c. black (R.) 20 20
a. Opt double .. .. .. † —
128 3 c. green 20 25
129 4 c. bright purple 20 25
130 5 c. violet (R.) 40 50
131 6 c. lake-brown 60 75
132 8 c. carmine .. .. 6·00 5·50
133 10 c. scarlet 60 75
134 12 c. orange .. .. 80 2·50
135 15 c. blue .. .. 1·00 40
136 20 c. olive-green and carmine .. .. 1·25 1·75
137 25 c. violet and orange (R.) .. .. 1·50 2·00
138 30 c. red-brown and violet .. .. 1·50 3·25
139 50 c. violet and scarlet .. .. 1·75 40
140 $1 scarlet and sepia .. .. .. 3·50 3·00
141 $2 bright purple and violet .. .. 11·00 6·50
142 $3 carmine and green .. .. 17·00 22·00
143 $4 blue and scarlet .. .. .. 25·00 28·00
144 $5 scarlet and red-brown .. .. 55·00 60·00
145 $10 black and yellow (R.) .. .. 90·00 85·00
126/45 .. .. .. *Set of* 20 £190 £200

These stamps, and the similarly overprinted stamps of North Borneo, were obtainable at all post offices throughout British Borneo (Brunei, Labuan, North Borneo and Sarawak), for use on local and overseas mail.

23 Sir James Brooke, Sir Charles Vyner Brooke and Sir Charles Brooke

(24)

(Recess B.W.)

1946 (18 May). *Centenary Issue. P* 12.

146 **23** 8 c. lake 20 30
147 15 c. blue 40 70
148 50 c. black and scarlet .. .. .. 80 1·75
149 $1 black and sepia .. .. .. 1·75 7·50
146/9 Perf "Specimen" .. .. *Set of* 4 90·00

CROWN COLONY

1947 (16 Apr). *Optd with T* **24**, *typo by B.W. in blue-black or red. Wmk Mult Script CA. P* 12.

150 **21** 1 c. purple 15 15
151 2 c. black (R.) 15 15
152 3 c. green (R.) 15 15
a. Albino opt £900
153 4 c. bright purple 20 25
154 6 c. lake-brown 20 40
155 8 c. carmine 15 15
156 10 c. scarlet 20 35
157 12 c. orange 15 45
158 15 c. blue (R.) 15 40
159 20 c. olive-green and carmine (R.) .. 35 70
160 25 c. violet and orange (R.) 30 35
161 50 c. violet and scarlet (R.) 20 30
162 $1 scarlet and sepia .. .. .. 70 1·25
163 $2 bright purple and violet .. .. 1·75 5·50
164 $5 scarlet and red-brown .. .. 4·50 5·50
150/64 .. .. .. *Set of* 15 8·00 14·50
150/64 Perf "Specimen" .. *Set of* 15 £275

No. 152a shows an uninked impression of T **24**.

1948 (25 Oct). *Royal Silver Wedding. As Nos.* 30/1 *of Aden.*

165 8 c. scarlet 40 30
166 $5 brown .. .. 17·00 27·00

1949 (19 Oct). *75th Anniv of Universal Postal Union. As Nos.* 114/17 *of Antigua.*

167 8 c. carmine 60 50
168 15 c. deep blue .. .. 1·50 1·50
169 25 c. deep blue-green .. .. .. 1·75 1·60
170 50 c. violet .. .. 2·75 3·50

25 *Troides Brookiana*

26 Tarsier

(Recess; Arms typo B.W.)

1950 (3 Jan). *T* **25/6** *and similar designs. Wmk Mult Script CA. P* 11½ × 11 (*horiz*) *or* 11 × 11½ (*vert*).

171 1 c. black 30 30
172 2 c. red-orange 35 40
173 3 c. green 35 35
174 4 c. chocolate 35 15
175 6 c. turquoise-blue 35 20
176 8 c. scarlet 35 15
177 10 c. orange .. .. 90 1·60
178 12 c. violet 95 60
179 15 c. blue 70 15
180 20 c. purple-brown and red-orange .. 70 15
181 25 c. green and scarlet 75 15
182 50 c. brown and violet 90 20
183 $1 green and chocolate .. .. .. 3·00 85
184 $2 blue and carmine .. .. .. 10·00 5·00
185 $5 black, yellow, red and purple .. 17·00 5·50
171/85 .. .. *Set of* 15 32·00 14·00

Designs: *Horiz*—8 c. Dayak Dancer; 10 c. Scaly ant eater; 12 c. Kenyah boys; 15 c. Fire-making; 20 c. Kelemantan rice barn; 25 c. Pepper vines; $1 Kelabit smithy; $2 Map of Sarawak; $5 Arms of Sarawak. *Vert*—3 c. Kayan tomb; 4 c. Kayan girl and boy; 6 c. Bead work; 50 c. Iban woman.

40 Map of Sarawak

(Recess B.W.)

1952 (1 Feb). *Wmk Mult Script CA. P* 11½ × 11.

186 **40** 10 c. orange 15 12

1953 (3 June). *Coronation. As No.* 47 *of Aden.*

187 10 c. black and deep violet-blue 35 50

41 Logging

44 Malabar Pied Hornbill

51 Queen Elizabeth II

52 Queen Elizabeth II (after Annigoni)

(Des M. Thoma (1, 2 c.), R. Turrell (4 c.), J. D. Hughes (6, 12 c.), A. Hakim bin Moliti (8 c.), J. Woodcock (10 c.), J. Browning (15 c.), G. Gundersen (20 c.), K. Munich (25 c.). Recess, Arms typo ($5). B.W.)

1955 (1 June)–**57**. *T* **41, 44, 51/2** *and similar designs. Wmk Mult Script CA. P* 11 × 11½ (1 c., 2 c., 4 c.), 12 × 13 (30 c., 50 c., $1, $2) *or* 11½ × 11 (*others*).

188 **41** 1 c. green (1.10.57) 5 20
189 – 2 c. red-orange (1.10.57) 20 10
190 – 4 c. lake-brown (*shades*) (1.10.57) .. 35 5
191 **44** 6 c. greenish blue (1.10.57) 30 5
192 – 8 c. rose-red (1.10.57) 15 5
193 – 10 c. deep green (1.10.57) 15 5
194 – 12 c. plum (1.10.57) 65 10
195 – 15 c. ultramarine (1.10.57) 40 10
196 – 20 c. olive and brown (1.10.57) .. 40 5
197 – 25 c. sepia and green (1.10.57) .. 50 10
198 **51** 30 c. red-brown and deep lilac .. 70 5
199 50 c. black and carmine (1.10.57) .. 75 5
200 **52** $1 myrtle-green & orge-brn (1.10.57) .. 1·75 30
201 $2 violet and bronze-green (1.10.57) .. 3·25 1·50
202 – $5 multicoloured (1.10.57) .. .. 15·00 3·75
188/202 .. .. .. *Set of* 15 23·00 6·00

Designs: *Horiz*—8 c. Shield with spears; 10 c. Kenyah ceremonial carving; 12 c. Barong panau; 15 c. Turtles; 20 c. Melanan basket-making; 25 c. Astana, Kuching; $5 Arms of Sarawak. *Vert* (*as T* **41**)—2 c. Young Orang-Utan; 4 c. Kayan dancing; 50 c. Queen Elizabeth II; $2 Queen Elizabeth II (after Annigoni).

1963 (4 June). *Freedom from Hunger. As No.* 76 *of Aden.*

203 12 c. sepia 80 40

STATE OF MALAYSIA

1964–65. *As* 1955–57 *but wmk* w **12**. *Perfs as before.*

204 **41** 1 c. green (8.9.64) 5 25
205 – 2 c. red-orange (17.8.65) .. .. 40 1·75
206 **44** 6 c. greenish blue (8.9.64) 30 70
207 – 10 c. deep green (8.9.64) 30 15
208 – 12 c. plum (8.9.64) .. .. .. 80 1·50
209 – 15 c. ultramarine (17.8.65) .. .. 1·25 3·25
210 – 20 c. olive and brown (9.6.64) 60 40
211 – 25 c. deep sepia and bluish green (8.9.64) 90 2·50
204/11 .. .. .. *Set of* 8 4·25 9·50

53 *Vanda hookeriana*

54 Blue Pansy Butterfly

1965 (15 Nov). *As Nos.* 166/72 *of Johore but with Arms of Sarawak inset as in T* **53**.

212 1 c. multicoloured 8 12
213 2 c. multicoloured 8 12
a. Black (country name and shield) omitted 50·00
214 5 c. multicoloured 12 5
215 6 c. multicoloured 15 5
a. Black (country name and shield) omitted 50·00
216 10 c. multicoloured (*shades*) 20
217 15 c. multicoloured 55
218 20 c. multicoloured 80 1
212/18 .. .. *Set of* 7 1·75 5

The 1 c., 6 c., 10 c. and 15 c. exist with PVA gum as well as gum arabic.

No. 213a was formerly listed with Trengganu No. 101 but there is evidence that it was issued in Sarawak.

A used example of No. 218 is known with the bright purple (blooms) omitted.

The higher values used with this issue were Nos. 20/27 of Malaysia.

(Litho B.W.)

1971 (1 Feb). *As Nos.* 175/81 *of Johore but with Arms of Sarawak inset as in T* **54**.

219 1 c. multicoloured 5 1
220 2 c. multicoloured 5 1
221 5 c. multicoloured 15
222 6 c. multicoloured 15
223 10 c. multicoloured 20
224 15 c. multicoloured 30 1
225 20 c. multicoloured 35 1
219/25 .. .. *Set of* 7 1·10 6

The higher values used with this issue were Nos. 64/71 of Malaysia.

55 Blue Pansy Butterfly (different crest at right)

56 *Rhododendron scortechinii*

(Photo Harrison)

1977 (12 Feb)–**78**. *As Nos.* 219/21 *and* 223/5 *but ptd in photogravure showing new State Crest as T* **55**.

226 1 c. multicoloured (1978) .. .. .. 1·50 1·0
227 2 c. multicoloured (1978) 12 1
228 5 c. multicoloured 15 1
230 10 c. multicoloured (4.4.77) 15 1
231 15 c. multicoloured (19.4.77) 30 3
232 20 c. multicoloured (1978) 80 5
226/32 .. .. *Set of* 6 2·75 2·0

1979 (30 Apr). *As Nos.* 188/94 *of Johore but with Arms of Sarawak as in T* **56**.

233 1 c. *Rafflesia hasseltii* 5 5
234 2 c. *Pterocarpus indicus* 5 5
235 5 c. *Lagerstroemia speciosa* 5 5
236 10 c. *Durio zibethinus* 5 5
237 15 c. *Hibiscus rosa-sinensis* 10 5
238 20 c. Type **56** 12 5
239 25 c. *Phaeomeria speciosa* 15 5
233/9 .. .. *Set of* 7 50 2

For higher values used in conjunction with this series see Nos. 190/7 of Malaysia.

JAPANESE OCCUPATION OF SARAWAK

The stamps listed under this heading were valid for use throughout North Borneo, (i.e. in Brunei, Labuan, North Borneo and Sarawak).

PRICES FOR STAMPS ON COVER	
Nos. J1/21	*from* × 6
Nos. J22/6	—

府政國帝本日大

(1)

("Imperial Japanese Government")

1942. *Stamps of Sarawak optd with T* **1** *in violet.*

J 1 **21** 1 c. purple .. .. 8·00 9·00
J 2 2 c. green .. .. 21·00 24·00
J 3 2 c. black .. .. 21·00 24·00
J 4 3 c. black .. .. 45·00 50·00
J 5 3 c. green .. .. 15·00 17·00
J 6 4 c. bright purple .. .. .. 9·00 9·00
J 7 5 c. violet .. .. 11·00 12·00
J 8 6 c. carmine .. .. 16·00 16·00
J 9 6 c. lake-brown .. .. 13·00 15·00
J10 8 c. red-brown .. .. 45·00 50·00
J11 8 c. carmine .. .. 50·00 55·00
J12 10 c. scarlet .. .. 12·00 13·00
J13 12 c. blue .. .. 22·00 24·00
J14 12 c. orange .. .. 45·00 55·00
J15 15 c. orange .. .. 45·00 50·00
J16 15 c. blue .. .. 18·00 24·00
J17 20 c. olive-green and carmine .. .. 9·00 14·00
J18 25 c. violet and orange .. .. .. 9·00 14·00
J19 30 c. red-brown and violet .. .. 9·00 14·00
J20 50 c. violet and scarlet .. .. .. 14·00 15·00
J21 $1 scarlet and sepia .. .. .. 16·00 22·00
J22 $2 bright purple and violet .. .. 42·00 45·00
J23 $3 carmine and green £275 £425
J24 $4 blue and scarlet .. .. .. 45·00 60·00
J25 $5 scarlet and red-brown .. .. 40·00 50·00
J26 $10 black and yellow .. .. .. 55·00 75·00

The overprint, being handstamped, exists inverted on all values.

Stamps of T **21** optd with Japanese symbols within an oval frame are revenue stamps, while the same stamps overprinted with three Japanese characters between two vertical double rules, were used as seals.

Seychelles

We no longer list the 6d. lilac (1862) (Plate No. 3) with obliter-
tion "B 64" as there is no evidence that British stamps were sold
n the Seychelles.

Stamps of MAURITIUS were used at Victoria on Mahé Island from 11 December 1861 until 1890, being cancelled "B 64". No further post offices were opened until 1901.

PRICES FOR STAMPS ON COVER TO 1945

Nos. 1/8	*from* × 8
Nos. 9/21	*from* × 20
Nos. 22/5	*from* × 5
Nos. 26/7	*from* × 7
Nos. 28/36	*from* × 4
Nos. 37/40	*from* × 20
Nos. 41/5	*from* × 5
Nos. 46/81	*from* × 4
Nos. 82/131	*from* × 3
Nos. 132/4	*from* × 10
Nos. 135/49	*from* × 3

DEPENDENCY OF MAURITIUS

PRINTERS. Nos. 1 to 123 were typographed by De La Rue & Co.

1

Die I

Die II

In Die I there are lines of shading in the middle compartment of the diadem which are absent from Die II.

1890 (5 April)–**92.** *Wmk Crown CA. P* 14. (i) *Die* I.

1 1 2 c. green and carmine .. .. .. 1·25 6·00
2 4 c. carmine and green .. .. .. 5·50 8·50
3 8 c. brown-purple and blue .. .. .. 3·00 6·00
4 10 c. ultramarine and brown .. .. .. 3·75 7·00
5 13 c. grey and black .. .. .. 4·50 9·00
6 16 c. chestnut and blue .. .. .. 3·25 3·75
7 48 c. ochre and green .. .. .. 17·00 20·00
8 96 c. mauve and carmine .. .. .. 32·00 45·00
1/8 .. .. *Set of* 8 65·00 95·00
1/8 Optd "Specimen" .. .. *Set of* 8 £200

(ii) *Die* II (1892)

9 1 2 c. green and rosine .. .. .. 85 1·25
10 4 c. carmine and green .. .. .. 90 1·25
11 8 c. brown-purple and ultramarine .. 2·25 2·50
12 10 c. bright ultramarine and brown .. 3·00 3·00
13 13 c. grey and black .. .. .. 2·25 2·25
14 16 c. chestnut and ultramarine .. .. 11·00 10·00
9/14 .. .. *Set of* 6 18·00 18·00

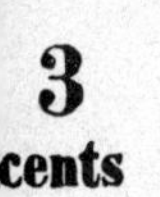

(2)

18 CENTS

(3)

4

1893 (1 Jan). *Surch locally as T* 2.

15 3 c. on 4 c. (No. 10).. .. .. .. 75 1·10
a. Surch inverted £500 £550
b. Surch double £600
c. Surch omitted (in pair with normal) .. £4500
16 12 c. on 16 c. (No. 6).. .. .. .. 1·75 2·25
a. Surch inverted £550
b. Surch double £4000 £5500
17 12 c. on 16 c. (No. 14) .. .. .. 1·75 2·25
a. Surch double .. ..
18 15 c. on 16 c. (No. 6).. .. .. .. 8·00 11·00
a. Surch inverted £400 £400
b. Surch double £550 £550
19 15 c. on 16 c. (No. 14) .. .. .. 5·00 2·25
a. Surch inverted £600 £600
b. Surch double £800 £800
c. Surch treble £2000
20 45 c. on 48 c. (No. 7).. .. .. .. 7·50 5·00
21 90 c. on 96 c. (No. 8).. .. .. .. 22·00 24·00
15/21 .. .. *Set of* 7 42·00 42·00

Nos. 15, 16, 18, 19 and 20 exist with "cents" omitted and with "cents" above value and are due to misplacement of the surcharge. No. 17 exists with surcharge omitted in pair with normal due to misplacement sideways.

1893 (Nov). *New values. Die* II. *Wmk Crown CA. P* 14.

22 1 3 c. dull purple and orange 50 50
23 12 c. sepia and green .. .. .. 90 1·40
24 1 15 c. sage-green and lilac .. .. 2·75 2·75
25 45 c. brown and carmine.. .. .. 18·00 20·00
22/25 Optd "Specimen" .. .. *Set of* 4 80·00

1896 (1 Aug). *No.* 25 *surch as T* 3.

26 1 18 c. on 45 c. brown and carmine .. 4·00 4·25
a. Surch double £950 £950
b. Surch treble £1200
27 36 c. on 45 c. brown and carmine .. 11·00 18·00
a. Surch double £950
26/27 H/S "Specimen" .. .. *Set of* 2 80·00

1897–1900. *Colours changed and new values. Die* II. *Wmk Crown CA. P* 14.

28 1 2 c. orange-brown and green (1900) 40 1·25
29 6 c. carmine (1900) .. .. .. 1·75 1·75
30 15 c. ultramarine (1900) .. .. .. 4·00 3·25
31 18 c. ultramarine .. .. 2·25 4·00
32 36 c. brown and carmine .. .. .. 16·00 13·00
33 4 75 c. yellow and violet (1900) .. .. 26·00 35·00
34 1 r. bright mauve and deep red .. .. 14·00 10·00
35 1 r. 50, grey and carmine (1900) .. 40·00 55·00
36 2 r. 25, bright mauve and green (1900) 45·00 55·00
28/36 .. .. *Set of* 9 £130 £160
28/36 Optd "Specimen" .. .. *Set of* 9 £200

3 cents

(5)

6 cents

(5*a*)

1901. *Nos.* 12, 14, 32 *and* 11 *surch locally with T* 5 *or* 5*a*.

37 3 c. on 10 c. (10.01) .. .. 70 1·90
a. Surch double £650
38 3 c. on 16 c. (8.01) .. .. 70 2·50
a. Surch inverted £600 £600
b. Surch double £500
c. "3 cents" omitted £550 £550
39 3 c. on 36 c. (21.6.01) .. .. .. 70 1·90
a. Surch double £850 £1200
b. "3 cents" omitted £500 £650
40 6 c. on 8 c. (8.01) .. .. 70 2·25
a. Surch inverted £850 £850
37/40 H/S "Specimen" .. .. *Set of* 4 £120

1902 (June). *Surch locally as T* 5.

41 1 2 c. on 4 c. (No. 10) .. .. .. 2·50 5·50
42 4 30 c. on 75 c. (No. 33) .. .. .. 4·00 12·00
a. Narrow "0" in "30" .. .. .. 22·00 42·00
43 30 c. on 1 r. (No. 34) .. .. .. 4·00 12·00
a. Narrow "0" in "30" .. .. .. 22·00 42·00
b. Surch double £600
44 45 c. on 1 r. (No. 34) .. .. .. 6·00 13·00
45 45 c. on 2 r. 25, (No. 36) .. .. .. 13·00 20·00
a. Narrow "5" in "45" .. .. .. 70·00 90·00
41/5 H/S "Specimen" .. .. *Set of* 5 £140

6

7

3 cents

(8)

1903 (26 May). *Wmk Crown CA. P* 14.

46 6 2 c. chestnut and green 30 75
47 3 c. dull green .. .. 1·25 1·25
48 6 c. carmine 80 25
49 12 c. olive-sepia and dull green .. .. 1·50 85
50 15 c. ultramarine .. .. 2·25 3·00
51 18 c. sage-green and carmine .. .. 4·50 8·50
52 30 c. violet and dull green .. .. .. 6·50 8·50
53 45 c. brown and carmine .. .. .. 7·50 10·00
54 7 75 c. yellow and violet .. .. .. 9·00 16·00
55 1 r. 50, black and carmine .. .. 35·00 45·00
56 2 r. 25, purple and green .. .. .. 26·00 45·00
46/56 .. .. *Set of* 11 85·00 £130
46/56 Optd "Specimen" .. .. *Set of* 11 £250

1903. *Surch locally with T* 8.

57 6 3 c. on 15 c. ultramarine (3.7) .. .. 1·75 4·00
58 3 c. on 18 c. sage-green and carmine (2.9) 5·00 11·00
59 3 c. on 45 c. brown and carmine (21.7) .. 1·50 5·50
57/9 H/S "Specimen" .. .. *Set of* 3 £120

CROWN COLONY

The Seychelles became a Separate Crown Colony by Letters Patent dated 31 August 1903.

1906. *Wmk Mult Crown CA. P* 14.

60 6 2 c. chestnut and green .. .. .. 40 1·00
61 3 c. dull green 70 70
62 6 c. carmine 80 25
63 12 c. olive-sepia and dull green .. .. 3·00 70
64 15 c. ultramarine .. .. 1·60 4·00
65 18 c. sage-green and carmine .. .. 3·00 5·50
66 30 c. violet and dull green .. .. .. 6·50 7·50
67 45 c. brown and carmine .. .. .. 4·00 8·00
68 7 75 c. yellow and violet .. .. .. 14·00 22·00
69 1 r. 50, black and carmine .. .. 24·00 28·00
70 2 r. 25, purple and green .. .. .. 30·00 35·00
60/70 .. .. *Set of* 11 80·00 £100

9

10

1912–13. *Wmk Mult Crown CA. P* 14.

71 9 2 c. chestnut and green 25 90
72 3 c. green 35 35
73 6 c. aniline carmine .. .. .. 8·00 5·00
a. Carmine-red .. .. 2·25 25
74 12 c. olive-sepia and dull green .. .. 1·00 4·50
75 15 c. ultramarine .. .. 2·00 1·00
76 18 c. sage-green and carmine .. .. 1·25 5·00
77 30 c. violet and green .. .. .. 5·00 1·40
78 45 c. brown and carmine .. .. .. 3·00 7·00
79 10 75 c. yellow and violet .. .. .. 6·00 7·50
80 1 r. 50, black and carmine .. .. 6·50 2·40
81 2 r. 25, rose-purple and green .. .. 32·00 32·00
a. Bright purple and green .. .. 28·00 15·00
71/81*a* .. .. *Set of* 11 48·00 40·00
71/81 Optd "Specimen" .. .. *Set of* 11 £225

The split "A" variety illustrated above No. 86 of Gambia also occurs on Nos. 71/81 (*Prices about three times normal*).

The 2 c., 3 c. and 15 c. were issued in April 1912, the 6 c. in June 1913 and the remainder in January 1913.

11

12

13

1917–22. *Wmk Mult Crown CA. P* 14.

82 11 2 c. chestnut and green, **O** 15 90
83 3 c. green, **O** 25 20
84 12 5 c. deep brown, **O** (1920) .. .. 35 1·00
85 11 6 c. carmine, **O** 45 20
a. Rose, **O** *(1919)* .. .. .. 3·00 40
86 12 c. grey, **O** (1919) .. .. .. 35 2·50
87 15 c. ultramarine, **O** .. .. .. 55 2·25
88 18 c. purple/*yellow*, **C** (1919) .. .. 2·25 6·50
a. On orange-buff (1920) .. .. .. 12·00 20·00
b. On pale yellow (Die II) (1922) .. .. 2·00 7·00
89 13 25 c. black and red/*yellow*, **C** .. .. 3·25 7·00
a. On orange-buff (1920) .. .. .. 26·00 35·00
b. On pale yellow (Die II) (1922) .. .. 3·25 5·00
90 11 30 c. dull purple and olive, **C** .. .. 4·50 7·00
91 45 c. dull purple and orange, **C** (1919) .. 3·25 7·50
92 13 50 c. dull purple and black, **C** (1920) .. 4·50 7·50
93 75 c. black/*blue-green* (*olive back*), **C** .. 3·50 8·00
a. On emerald back (Die II) (1922) .. 5·00 11·00
94 1 r. dull purple and red, **C** (1920) .. 15·00 18·00
95 1 r. 50, reddish purple and blue/*blue*, **C** 17·00 25·00
a. Blue-pur & bl/blue, **C** (Die II) (1922) 11·00 23·00
96 2 r. 25, yellow-green and violet, **C** .. 32·00 50·00
97 5 r. green and blue, **C** (1920) .. .. 50·00 75·00
82/97 .. .. *Set of* 16 £120 £190
82/97 Optd "Specimen" .. .. *Set of* 16 £325

1921–32. *Wmk Mult Script CA. P* 14.

98 11 2 c. chestnut and green, **O** 20 25
99 3 c. green, **O** 25 30
100 3 c. black, **O** (1922) 50 60
101 4 c. green, **O** (1922) 50 35
102 4 c. sage-green and carmine, **O** (1928) .. 3·25 7·50
103 12 5 c. deep brown, **O** .. .. .. 1·75 3·00
104 11 6 c. carmine, **O** .. .. 80 2·50
105 6 c. deep mauve, **O** (1922) 35 15
106 13 9 c. red, **O** (1927) .. .. .. 1·25 2·75
107 11 12 c. grey (Die II), **O** .. .. .. 1·00 50
108 12 c. carmine-red, **O** (1922) 60 35
109 12 c. grey (Die I), **O** (1932) .. .. 2·75 2·50
110 15 c. bright blue, **O** .. .. .. 4·00 12·00
111 15 c. yellow, **O** (1922) .. .. .. 1·25 4·75
112 18 c. purple/*pale yellow*, **C** (1925) .. 2·50 5·00
113 13 20 c. bright blue, **O** (1922) .. .. 2·25 2·00
a. Dull blue, **O** *(1926)* .. .. .. 4·00 2·00
114 11 25 c. black and red/*pale yellow*, **C** (1925) 1·90 5·50
115 30 c. dull purple and olive, **C** .. .. 1·60 6·00
116 45 c. dull purple and orange, **C** .. .. 1·60 7·00
117 13 50 c. dull purple and black, **C** .. .. 1·90 5·50
118 75 c. black/*emerald*, **C** (1924) .. .. 9·50 15·00
119 1 r. dull purple and red (Die II), **C** .. 12·00 20·00
120 1 r. dull purple and red (Die I), **C** (1932) 18·00 23·00
121 1 r. 50, purple and blue/*blue*, **C** (1924) .. 13·00 15·00
122 2 r. 25, yellow-green and violet, **C** .. 15·00 22·00
123 5 r. yellow-green and blue, **C** .. .. 48·00 60·00
98/123 .. .. *Set of* 24 £120 £180
98/123 Optd "Specimen" .. .. *Set of* 24 £450

The 3 c. green and 12 c. grey (Die II) were reissued in 1927. "Specimens" of these also exist.

1935 (6 May). *Silver Jubilee. As Nos.* 91/4 *of Antigua but ptd by B.W. P* 11 × 12.

128 6 c. ultramarine and grey-black 55 40
a. Extra flagstaff £150
b. Short extra flagstaff .. .. .. 60·00
129 12 c. green and indigo .. .. .. 1·60 55
a. Extra flagstaff £2000 £2500
b. Short extra flagstaff .. .. .. 75·00
130 20 c. brown and deep blue .. .. .. 1·90 90
a. Extra flagstaff £150
b. Short extra flagstaff .. .. .. 60·00
131 1 r. slate and purple .. .. .. 3·50 8·00
a. Extra flagstaff £120
b. Short extra flagstaff .. .. .. 50·00
128/31 Perf "Specimen" .. .. *Set of* 4 75·00

For illustrations of plate varieties see Omnibus section following Zululand.

1937 (12 May). *Coronation. As Nos.* 13/15 *of Aden, but ptd by B.W. P* 11 × 11½.

132 6 c. sage-green 30 15
133 12 c. orange 35 15
134 20 c. blue 60 50
132/4 Perf "Specimen" .. .. *Set of* 3 45·00

14 Coco-de-mer Palm

15 Giant Tortoise

16 Fishing Pirogue

(Photo Harrison)

1938 (1 Jan)–**49.** *Wmk Mult Script CA. P* 14½ × 13½ (*vert*) *or* 13½ × 14½ (*horiz*).

No.	Type	Description	Unused	Used
135	**14**	2 c. purple-brown, **CO** (10.2.38)	12	12
136	**15**	3 c. green, **C**	1·40	60
136*a*		3 c. orange, **CO** (8.8.41)	30	25
137	**16**	6 c. orange, **C**	1·60	95
137*a*		6 c. greyish green, **C** (8.8.41)	80	30
		b. Green, **OC** (11.42)	25	10
138	**14**	9 c. scarlet, **C** (10.2.38)	2·00	3·25
138*a*		9 c. grey-blue, **CO** (8.8.41)	20	20
		b. Dull blue, **OC** (19.11.45)	80	40
139	**15**	12 c. reddish violet, **C**	9·00	1·25
139*a*		15 c. brown-carmine, **C** (8.8.41)	60	50
		b. Brown-red, **O** (11.42)	35	30
139*c*	**14**	18 c. carmine-lake, **CO** (8.8.41)	35	15
		d. Rose-carmine, **C** (5.4.49)	30	15
140	**16**	20 c. blue, **C**	16·00	6·50
140*a*		20 c. brown-ochre, **CO** (8.8.41)	30	20
141	**14**	25 c. brown-ochre, **C**	27·00	15·00
142	**15**	30 c. carmine, **C** (10.2.38)	28·00	15·00
142*a*		30 c. blue, **CO** (8.8.41)	30	25
143	**16**	45 c. chocolate, **C** (10.2.38)	35	25
		a. Purple-brown, **OC** (11.42)	35	25
144	**14**	50 c. deep reddish violet, **CO** (10.2.38)	30	15
144*a*		50 c. bright lilac, **C** (13.6.49)	30	25
145	**15**	75 c. slate-blue, **C** (10.2.38)	60·00	50·00
145*a*		75 c. deep slate-lilac, **CO** (8.8.41)	50	35
146	**16**	1 r. yellow-green, **C** (10.2.38)	80·00	60·00
146*a*		1 r. grey-black, **CO** (8.8.41)	60	30
147	**14**	1 r. 50, ultramarine, **CO** (10.2.38)	1·25	1·50
148	**15**	2 r. 25, olive, **CO** (10.2.38)	1·40	2·00
149	**16**	5 r. red, **CO** (10.2.38)	5·00	4·50
135/49		*Set of* 25	£200	£140
135/49 (*excl* 144*a*) Perf "Specimen"		*Set of* 24	£375	

The stamps on ordinary paper appeared in 1942–43.

1946 (23 Sept). *Victory. As Nos.* 28/9 *of Aden.*

No.	Description	Unused	Used
150	9 c. light blue	12	12
151	30 c. deep blue	20	20
150/1 Perf "Specimen"	*Set of* 2	48·00	

1948 (5 Nov). *Royal Silver Wedding. As Nos.* 30/1 *of Aden.*

No.	Description	Unused	Used
152	9 c. ultramarine	15	50
153	5 r. carmine	7·50	13·00

1949 (10 Oct). 75*th Anniv of Universal Postal Union. As Nos.* 114/17 *of Antigua, but inscr* "SEYCHELLES" (*recess*).

No.	Description	Unused	Used
154	18 c. bright reddish purple	20	20
155	50 c. purple	70	60
156	1 r. grey	70	65
157	2 r. 25, olive	1·75	1·60

17 Sail-fish

18 Map of Indian Ocean

(Photo Harrison)

1952 (3 Mar). *Various designs as T* **14/16** *but with new portrait and crown as in T* **17/18.** *Chalk-surfaced paper. Wmk Mult Script CA. P* 14½ × 13½ (*vert*) *or* 13½ × 14½ (*horiz*).

No.	Type	Description	Unused	Used
158	**17**	2 c. lilac	25	30
		a. Error. Crown missing, W **9***a*	70·00	
		b. Error. St. Edward's Crown, W **9***b*	50·00	
159	**15**	3 c. orange	25	30
		a. Error. Crown missing, W **9***a*	70·00	
		b. Error. St. Edward's Crown, W **9***b*	50·00	
160	**14**	9 c. chalky blue	25	30
		a. Error. Crown missing, W **9***a*	70·00	
		b. Error. St. Edward's Crown, W **9***b*	50·00	
161	**16**	15 c. deep yellow-green	40	30
		a. Error. Crown missing, W **9***a*	80·00	
		b. Error. St. Edward's Crown, W **9***b*	60·00	
162	**18**	18 c. carmine-lake	40	30
		a. Error. Crown missing, W **9***a*	80·00	
		b. Error. St. Edward's Crown, W **9***b*	60·00	
163	**16**	20 c. orange-yellow	50	40
		a. Error. Crown missing, W **9***a*	£100	
		b. Error. St. Edward's Crown, W **9***b*	80·00	
164	**15**	25 c. vermilion	50	50
		a. Error. Crown missing, W **9***a*	£110	
		b. Error. St. Edward's Crown, W **9***b*	90·00	
165	**17**	40 c. ultramarine	60	45
		a. Error. Crown missing, W **9***a*	£120	
		b. Error. St. Edward's Crown, W **9***b*	£100	
166	**16**	45 c. purple-brown	60	45
		a. Error. Crown missing, W **9***a*	£140	
		b. Error. St. Edward's Crown, W **9***b*	£110	
167	**14**	50 c. reddish violet	60	50
		a. Error. Crown missing, W **9***a*	£140	
		b. Error. St. Edward's Crown, W **9***b*	£110	
168	**18**	1 r. grey-black	1·25	90
		b. Error. St. Edward's Crown, W **9***b*	£180	
169	**14**	1 r. 50, blue	2·75	5·00
		b. Error. St. Edward's Crown, W **9***b*	£250	
170	**15**	2 r. 25, brown-olive	3·00	5·00
		b. Error. St. Edward's Crown, W **9***b*	£300	
171	**18**	5 r. red	4·75	8·50
		b. Error. St. Edward's Crown, W **9***b*	£350	
172	**17**	10 r. green	10·00	19·00
158/72		*Set of* 15	23·00	38·00

See *Introduction* re the watermark errors.

1953 (2 June). *Coronation. As No.* 47 *of Aden.*

No.	Description	Unused	Used
173	9 c. black and deep bright blue	15	60

19 Sail-fish

20 "Flying Fox" (fruit bat)

(Photo Harrison)

1954 (1 Feb)–**57.** *Designs previously used for King George VI issue, but with portrait of Queen Elizabeth II, as in T* **19** *and T* **20**. *Chalk-surfaced paper. Wmk Mult Script CA. P* 14½ × 13½ (*vert*) *or* 13½ × 14½ (*horiz*).

No.	Type	Description	Unused	Used
174	**19**	2 c. lilac	10	10
175	–	3 c. orange	10	10
175*a*	**20**	5 c. violet (25.10.57)	15	20
176	–	9 c. chalky blue	10	10
176*a*	–	10 c. chalky blue (*shades*) (15.9.56)	30	15
177	–	15 c. deep yellow-green	20	15
178	–	18 c. crimson	15	20
179	–	20 c. orange-yellow	20	20
180	–	25 c. vermilion	20	20
180*a*	–	35 c. crimson (15.9.56)	65	50
181	**19**	40 c. ultramarine	35	35
182	–	45 c. purple-brown	50	30
183	–	50 c. reddish violet	30	30
183*a*	–	70 c. purple-brown (15.9.56)	1·25	1·25
184	–	1 r. grey-black	60	60
185	–	1 r. 50, blue	2·25	3·50
186	–	2 r. 25, brown-olive	4·00	5·50
187	—	5 r. red	13·00	11·00
188	**19**	10 r. green	25·00	18·00
174/88		*Set of* 19	45·00	38·00

Designs: *Horiz*—15 c., 20 c., 45 c., 70 c. Fishing pirogue; 18 c., 35 c., 1 r., 5 r. Map of Indian Ocean. *Vert*—3 c., 25 c., 2 r. 25, Giant Tortoise; 9 c., 50 c., 1 r. 50, Coco de Mer Palm.

21 "La Pierre de Possession"

5 cents

(**22**)

(Photo Harrison)

1956 (15 Nov). *Bicentenary of "La Pierre de Possession". Wmk Mult Script CA. P* 14½ × 13½.

No.	Type	Description	Unused	Used
189	**21**	40 c. ultramarine	20	20
190		1 r. black	30	35

191 191a 191 191b 191 191c

1957 (16 Sept). *No.* 182 *surch with T* **22**.

No.	Description	Unused	Used
191	5 c. on 45 c. purple-brown	12	15
	a. Italic "e"	3·00	
	b. Italic "s"	3·00	
	c. Italic "c"	2·50	
	d. Thick bars omitted	£300	
	e. Surch double	£140	

23 Mauritius 6d. Stamp with Seychelles "B 64" Cancellation

(Recess: cancellation typo B.W.)

1961 (11 Dec). *Centenary of First Seychelles Post Office. W* w **12.** *P* 11½.

No.	Type	Description	Unused	Used
193	**23**	10 c. blue, black and purple	10	10
194		35 c. blue, black and myrtle-green	20	15
195		2 r. 25, blue, black and orange-brown	55	75

24 Black Parrot

29 Anse Royale Bay

40 Colony's Badge

(Des V. Whiteley. Photo Harrison)

1962 (21 Feb)–**68.** *T* **24, 29, 40** *and similar designs. W* w **12** (*upright*). *P* 13½ × 14½ (*horiz designs and* 10 *r.*) *or* 14½ × 13½ (*others*).

No.	Description	Unused	Used
196	5 c. multicoloured	5	5
197	10 c. multicoloured	5	5
198	15 c. multicoloured	8	10
199	20 c. multicoloured	10	10
200	25 c. multicoloured	10	10
200*a*	30 c. multicoloured (15.7.68)	1·60	90
201	35 c. multicoloured	1·50	2·25
202	40 c. multicoloured	25	25
203	45 c. multicoloured (1.8.66)	2·00	1·50
204	50 c. multicoloured	30	25
205	70 c. ultramarine and light blue	3·25	4·00
206	75 c. multicoloured (1.8.66)	1·50	2·00
207	1 r. multicoloured	45	35
208	1 r. 50, multicoloured	1·40	3·50
209	2 r. 25, multicoloured	2·25	2·75
210	3 r. 50, multicoloured	2·75	5·00
211	5 r. multicoloured	4·50	5·00
212	10 r. multicoloured	18·00	18·00
196/212	*Set of* 18	35·00	42·00

Designs: *Vert* (*as T* **24**)—10 c. Vanilla vine; 15 c. Fisherman; 20 c. Denis Island lighthouse; 25 c. Clock Tower, Victoria; 50 c. Cascade Church; 70 c. Sail-fish; 75 c. Coco-de-Mer palm. *Horiz* (*as T* **29**)—30 c., 35 c. Anse Royale Bay; 40 c. Government House; 45 c. Fishing pirogue; 1 r. Cinnamon; 1r. 50, Copra; 2r. 25 Map; 3r. 50, Land settlement; 5 r. Regina Mundi convent.

The 1 r. exists with PVA gum as well as gum arabic, but the 30 c. exists with PVA gum only.

See also Nos. 233/7.

For stamps of the above issue overprinted "B.I.O.T" see under British Indian Ocean Territory.

1963 (4 June). *Freedom from Hunger. As No.* 76 *of Aden.*

No.	Description	Unused	Used
213	70 c. reddish violet	1·25	55

1963 (16 Sept). *Red Cross Centenary. As Nos.* 147/8 *of Antigua.*

No.	Description	Unused	Used
214	10 c. red and black	30	10
215	75 c. red and blue	1·50	80

(**41**)

42 Flying Fox

1965 (15 Apr). *Nos.* 201 *and* 205 *surch as T* 41.

No.	Description	Unused	Used
216	45 c. on 35 c. multicoloured	20	15
217	75 c. on 70 c. ultramarine and light blue	30	30

1965 (1 June). *I.T.U. Centenary. As Nos.* 166/7 *of Antigua.*

No.	Description	Unused	Used
218	5 c. orange and ultramarine	20	10
219	1 r. 50, mauve and apple-green	1·50	65

1965 (25 Oct). *International Co-operation Year. As Nos.* 168/9 *of Antigua.*

No.	Description	Unused	Used
220	5 c. reddish purple and turquoise-green	15	8
221	40 c. deep bluish green and lavender	45	30

1966 (24 Jan). *Churchill Commemoration. As Nos.* 170/3 *of Antigua.*

No.	Description	Unused	Used
222	5 c. new blue	15	10
223	15 c. deep green	50	15
224	75 c. brown	1·50	45
225	1 r. 50, bluish violet	2·25	75

1966 (1 July). *World Cup Football Championships. As Nos.* 176/7 *of Antigua.*

No.	Description	Unused	Used
226	15 c. violet, yellow-green, lake & yellow-brn	15	10
227	1 r. chocolate, blue-green, lake & yellow-brn	50	25

1966 (20 Sept). *Inauguration of W.H.O. Headquarters, Geneva. As Nos.* 178/9 *of Antigua.*

No.	Description	Unused	Used
228	20 c. black, yellow-green and light blue	20	10
229	50 c. black, light purple and yellow-brown	45	20

1966 (1 Dec). 20*th Anniv of U.N.E.S.C.O. As Nos.* 196/8 *of Antigua.*

No.	Description	Unused	Used
230	15 c. slate-violet, red, yellow and orange	25	10
231	1 r. orange-yellow, violet and deep olive	90	30
232	5 r. black, bright purple and orange	3·50	2·75

1967–69. *As Nos. 196/7, 204 and new values as T* **42** *but wmk* w **12** *(sideways).*

233 5 c. multicoloured (7.2.67) 35 15
234 10 c. multicoloured (4.6.68) 25 10
235 50 c. multicoloured (13.5.69) .. .. .. 1·50 1·00
236 60 c. red, blue & blackish brn (15.7.68) .. 1·00 1·00
237 85 c. ultramarine and light blue (as No. 205) (15.77.68) 90 90

The 10 c. exists with PVA gum as well as gum arabic, but the 50 c. to 85 c. exist with PVA gum only.

UNIVERSAL
ADULT
SUFFRAGE
1967

(43)

44 Cowrie Shells

1967 (18 Sept). *Universal Adult Suffrage. As Nos.* 198 *and* 206, *but* W w **12** *(sideways), and Nos.* 203 *and* 210 *(wmk upright), optd with T* **43**.

238 15 c. multicoloured 8 8
239 45 c. multicoloured 12 12
240 75 c. multicoloured 15 20
241 3 r. 50, multicoloured 35 50

(Des V. Whiteley. Photo Harrison)

1967 (4 Dec). *International Tourist Year. T* **44** *and similar horiz designs. Multicoloured.* W w **12**. *P* 14 × 13.

242 15 c. Type **44** 20 10
243 40 c. Cone Shells 25 10
244 1 r. Arthritic Spider Conch 35 15
245 2 r. 25, Subulate Auger and Triton Shells .. 90 75

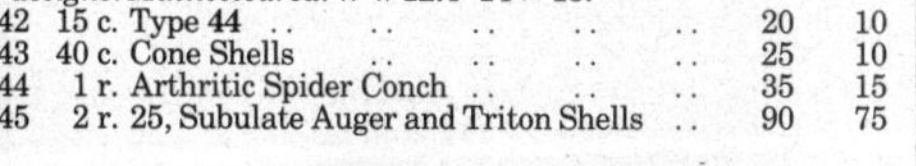

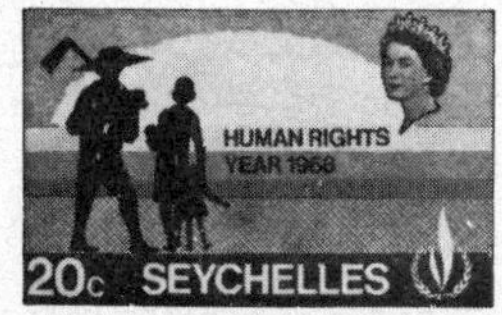

= 30

(48)

49 Farmer with Wife and Children at Sunset

1968 (16 Apr). *Nos.* 202/3 *and as No.* 206 *surch as T* **48** (30 c.) *or with* "CENTS" *added, and three bars (others).* W w **12** *(sideways on No.* 248).

246 30 c. on 40 c. multicoloured 15 10
247 60 c. on 45 c. multicoloured 25 20
248 85 c. on 75 c. multicoloured 35 25

(Des Mary Hayward. Litho Harrison)

1968 (2 Sept). *Human Rights Year.* W w **12.** *P* 14½ × 13½.

249 **49** 20 c. multicoloured 8 8
250 50 c. multicoloured 12 12
251 85 c. multicoloured 15 15
252 2 r. 25, multicoloured 25 40

50 Expedition landing at Anse Possession

54 Apollo Launch

(Des Mary Hayward. Litho and die-stamped Harrison)

1968 (30 Dec). *Bicentenary of First Landing on Praslin. T* **50** *and similar multicoloured designs.* W w **12** *(sideways on* 50 c., 85 c.). *P* 14.

253 20 c. Type **50** 15 10
254 50 c. Vessels at anchor (*vert*) 30 20
255 85 c. Coco-de-Mer and Black Parrot (*vert*) .. 35 25
256 2 r. 25, Vessels under sail .. .. .. 2·25 1·50

(Des V. Whiteley. Litho Format)

1969 (9 Sept). *First Man on the Moon. T* **54** *and similar horiz designs. Multicoloured.* W w **12** *(sideways on horiz designs). P* 13½.

257 5 c. Type **54** 10 8
258 20 c. Module leaving Mother-ship for Moon .. 25 15
259 50 c. Astronauts and Space Module on Moon .. 35 40
260 85 c. Tracking station 40 45
261 2 r. 25, Moon craters with Earth on the "Horizon" .. .. 85 1·25

59 Picault's Landing, 1742

60 Badge of Seychelles

(Des Mary Hayward. Litho Enschedé)

1969 (3 Nov)–**75.** *Horiz designs as T* **59/60.** *Multicoloured.* W w **12** *(sideways). Slightly toned paper. P* 13 × 12½.

262 5 c. Type **59** 8 5
263 10 c. U.S. satellite-tracking station 10 10
a. Whiter paper (8.3.73) 30 30
264 15 c. *Königsberg I* at Aldabra, 1914† 25 12
a. Whiter paper (8.3.73) 55 55
265 20 c. Fleet re-fuelling off St. Anne, 1939–45 .. 25 12
a. Whiter paper (13.6.74) 70 70
266 25 c. Exiled Ashanti King Prempeh 20 20
a. Whiter paper (8.3.73) 55 55
267 30 c. Laying Stone of Possession, 1756 .. 1·00 1·50
268 40 c. As 30 c. (11.12.72) .. .. .. 90 1·00
a. Whiter paper (13.6.74) .. .. .. 1·40 1·40
269 50 c. Pirates and treasure 35 20
a. Whiter paper (13.6.74) .. .. .. 1·00 1·00
270 60 c. Corsairs attacking merchantman .. 1·00 1·50
271 65 c. As 60 c. (11.12.72) .. .. .. 1·50 2·00
a. Whiter paper (13.8.75) .. .. .. 2·00 2·50
272 85 c. Impression of proposed airport .. .. 1·25 1·50
273 95 c. As 85 c. (11.12.72) .. .. .. 1·75 2·00
a. Whiter paper (13.6.74) .. .. .. 2·25 2·25
274 1 r. French Governor capitulating to British naval officer, 1794 .. .. .. 60 40
a. Whiter paper (8.3.73) .. .. .. 1·00 70
275 1 r. 50, *Sybille* and *Chiffone* in battle, 1801 2·00 2·50
a. Whiter paper (8.3.73) .. .. .. 3·00 3·75
276 3 r. 50, Visit of the Duke of Edinburgh, 1956 1·75 2·50
a. Whiter paper (13.8.75) .. .. .. 2·75 4·25
277 5 r. Chevalier Queau de Quincy .. .. 1·75 1·75
278 10 r. Indian Ocean chart, 1574 .. .. 3·25 4·25
279 15 r. Type **60** .. .. 5·50 9·00
262/79 .. .. *Set of* 18 21·00 28·00
263a/76a .. .. *Set of* 11 14·00 16·00

†The design is incorrect in that it shows *Königsberg II* and the wrong date ("1915").

The stamps on the whiter paper are highly glazed, producing shade variations and are easily distinguishable from the original printings on toned paper.

74 White Terns, Ship and Island

(Des A. Smith; adapted V. Whiteley. Litho D.L.R.)

1970 (27 Apr). *Bicentenary of First Settlement, St. Anne Island. T* **74** *and similar horiz designs. Multicoloured.* W w **12** *(sideways). P* 14.

280 20 c. Type **74** 35 12
281 50 c. Flying Fish, ship and island 40 20
282 85 c. Compass and chart 45 35
283 3 r. 50, Anchor on sea-bed .. .. .. 1·00 1·10

78 Girl and Optician's Chart

79 Pitcher Plant

(Des A. Smith. Litho Questa)

1970 (4 Aug). *Centenary of British Red Cross. T* **78** *and similar multicoloured designs.* W w **12** *(sideways on horiz designs). P* 14.

284 20 c. Type **78** 10 10
285 50 c. Baby, scales and milk bottles 15 10
286 85 c. Woman with child and umbrella (*vert*) .. 20 15
287 3 r. 50, Red Cross local H.Q. building .. 1·25 1·25

(Des G. Drummond. Litho J.W.)

1970 (29 Dec). *Flowers. T* **79** *and similar vert designs. Multicoloured.* W w **12.** *P* 14.

288 20 c. Type **79** 55 50
289 50 c. Wild Vanilla .. .. 1·00 70
290 85 c. Tropic-Bird Orchid .. .. .. 2·00 1·25
291 3 r. 50, Vare Hibiscus .. .. .. 7·00 6·50
MS292 81 × 133 mm. Nos. 288/91. Wmk inverted 20·00 22·00

80 Seychelles "On the Map"

81 Piper "Navajo"

(Des and litho J.W.)

1971 (18 May). *"Putting Seychelles on the Map". Sheet* 152 × 101 *mm.* W w **12** *(sideways). P* 13½.

MS293 **80** 5 r. multicoloured .. .. .. 12·00 15·00

(Des and litho J.W.)

1971 (28 June). *Airport Completion. T* **81** *and similar multi-coloured designs showing aircraft.* W w **12** *(sideways on horiz designs). P* 14 × 14½ *(5, 20 and 60 c.) or* 14½ *(others).*

294 5 c. Type **81** 10 10
295 20 c. Westland "Wessex" 20 20
296 50 c. "Catalina" flying-boat (*horiz*) 40 30
297 60 c. Grumman "Albatross" 45 40
298 85 c. Short "G" Class flying-boat (*horiz*) .. 65 60
299 3 r. 50, Vickers Supermarine "Walrus" (*horiz*) 6·50 6·50
294/9 .. .. *Set of* 6 7·50 7·50

82 Santa Claus delivering Gifts (Jean-Claude Waye Hive)

(83)

(Des Jennifer Toombs. Litho A. & M.)

1971 (12 Oct). *Christmas. Drawings by local children. T* **82** *and similar horiz designs. Multicoloured.* W w **12** *(sideways). P* 13½.

300 10 c. Type **82** 15 5
301 15 c. Santa Claus seated on turtle (Edison Thérésine) 20 20
302 3 r. 50, Santa Claus landing on island (Isabelle Tirant) .. .. 1·10 1·50

1971 (21 Dec). *Nos.* 267, 270 *and* 272 *surch in grey as T* **83**.

303 40 c. on 30 c. Laying Stone of Possession, 1756 50 60
304 65 c. on 60 c. Corsairs attacking merchantman 70 95
305 95 c. on 85 c. Impression of proposed airport .. 90 1·25

ROYAL VISIT 1972

(84)

85 Seychelles Brush Warbler

1972 (20 Mar). *Royal Visit. Nos.* 265 *and* 277 *optd with T* **84**.

306 20 c. Fleet re-fuelling off St. Anne, 1939–45 .. 15 20
307 5 r. Chevalier Queau de Quincy (Gold) .. 2·50 3·00

(Des R. Gillmor. Litho Questa)

1972 (24 July). *Rare Seychelles Birds. T* **85** *and similar vert designs. Multicoloured.* W w **12** *(sideways). P* 13½.

308 5 c. Type **85** 12 10
309 20 c. Bare-legged Scops Owl 40 30
310 50 c. Seychelles Blue Pigeon .. .. .. 1·00 90
311 65 c. Seychelles Magpie Robin .. .. .. 1·25 1·00
312 95 c. Seychelles Paradise Flycatcher .. .. 2·25 2·25
313 3 r. 50, Seychelles Kestrel .. .. .. 8·50 9·00
308/13 .. .. *Set of* 6 12·00 12·00
MS314 144 × 162 mm. Nos. 308/13 .. .. 22·00 22·00

86 Fireworks Display

87 Giant Tortoise and Sailfish

(Des V. Whiteley. Litho Questa)

1972 (18 Sept). *"Festival '72". T* **86** *and similar multicoloured designs.* W w **12** *(sideways on 10 and 25 c.). P* 14.

315 10 c. Type **86** 8 8
316 15 c. Pirogue race (*horiz*) 10 10
317 25 c. Floats and costumes 15 20
318 5 r. Water skiing (*horiz*) .. .. .. 1·75 2·40

(Des (from photograph by D. Groves) and photo Harrison)

1972 (20 Nov). *Royal Silver Wedding. Multicoloured; background colour given.* W w **12.** *P* 14 × 14½.

319 **87** 95 c. turquoise-blue 25 30
320 1 r. 50, red-brown 25 40

1973 (14 Nov). *Royal Wedding. As Nos.* 165/6 *of Anguilla.*

321 95 c. ochre 15 15
322 1 r. 50, dull deep blue 20 25

88 Soldier Fish

(Des G. Drummond. Litho Questa)

1974 (5 Mar). *Fishes. T* **88** *and similar horiz designs. Multicoloured. W* w **12**. *P* 14½ × 14.

323 20 c. Type **88** 15 10
324 50 c. File Fish 30 25
325 95 c. Butterfly Fish 55 65
326 1 r. 50, Gaterin .. .. 1·25 1·75

89 Globe and Letter

(Des Sylvia Goaman. Litho Enschedé)

1974 (9 Oct). *Centenary of Universal Postal Union. T* **89** *and similar horiz designs. Multicoloured.* W w **12** (*sideways*). *P* 12½ × 12.

327 20 c. Type **89** 10 10
328 50 c. Globe and radio beacon 25 25
329 95 c. Globe and postmark 45 70
330 1 r. 50, Emblems within "UPU" .. .. .. 60 1·00

90 Sir Winston Churchill

VISIT OF
Q.E. II

(**91**)

(Des G. Vasarhelyi. Litho Questa)

1974 (30 Nov). *Birth Centenary of Sir Winston Churchill. T* **90** *and similar horiz design. Multicoloured.* W w **12**. *P* 14.

331 95 c. Type **90** 50 65
332 1 r. 50, Profile portrait 60 75
MS333 81 × 109 mm. Nos. 331/2 .. .. .. 1·50 2·00

1975 (8 Feb). *Visit of R.M.S. "Queen Elizabeth II". Nos.* 265a, 269a, 273a *and* 275a *optd with T* **91**.

334 20 c. Fleet re-fuelling off St. Anne, 1939–45 .. 12 25
335 50 c. Pirates and treasure 30 45
336 95 c. Impression of proposed airport (Sil.) .. 50 85
337 1 r. 50, *Sybille* and *Chiffone* in battle, 1801 .. 75 1·25

INTERNAL
SELF-GOVERNMENT
OCTOBER
1975

(**92**)

93 Queen Elizabeth I

1975 (1 Oct). *Internal Self-Government. Nos.* 265a, 271a, 274a *and* 276a *optd with T* **92** *in gold, by Enschedé.*

338 20 c. Fleet re-fuelling off St. Anne, 1939–45 .. 12 25
339 65 c. Corsairs attacking merchantman .. 35 45
340 1 r. French Governor capitulating to British naval officer, 1794 .. .. .. 45 65
341 3 r. 50, Visit of Duke of Edinburgh, 1956 .. 1·60 2·50

(Des C. Abbott. Litho Walsall)

1975 (15 Dec). *International Women's Year. T* **93** *and similar vert designs. Multicoloured.* W w **14** (*inverted*). *P* 13½.

342 10 c. Type **93** 5 5
343 15 c. Gladys Aylward 8 8
344 20 c. Elizabeth Fry 10 8
345 25 c. Emmeline Pankhurst 10 8
346 65 c. Florence Nightingale 25 20
347 1 r. Amy Johnson 40 35
348 1 r. 50, Joan of Arc 50 60
349 3 r. 50, Eleanor Roosevelt .. .. 1·75 2·00
342/9 .. .. *Set of* 8 2·75 3·00

MINIMUM PRICE

The minimum price quoted is 5p which represents a handling charge rather than a basis for valuing common stamps. For further notes about prices see introductory pages.

94 Map of Praslin and Postmark

95 First Landing, 1609 (inset portrait of Premier James Mancham)

(Des J.W. Litho Questa)

1976 (30 Mar). *Rural Posts. T* **94** *and similar vert designs showing maps and postmarks. Multicoloured.* W w **14**. *P* 14.

350 20 c. Type **94** 15 15
351 65 c. La Digue 40 45
352 1 r. Mahé with Victoria postmark 60 60
353 1 r. 50, Mahé with Anse Royale postmark .. 80 1·25
MS354 166 × 127 mm. Nos. 350/3 .. .. .. 3·25 4·25

INDEPENDENT

(Des G. Drummond. Litho J.W.)

1976 (29 June). *Independence. T* **95** *and similar vert designs. Multicoloured.* W w **12** (*sideways*). *P* 13½.

355 20 c. Type **95** 10 8
356 25 c. The Possession Stone 10 8
357 40 c. First settlers, 1770 .. .. 15 12
358 75 c. Chevalier Queau de Quincy 30 30
359 1 r. Sir Bickham Sweet-Escott 40 30
360 1 r. 25, Legislative Building 65 65
361 1 r. 50, Seychelles badge 75 75
362 3 r. 50, Seychelles flag .. .. 1·90 1·90
355/62 .. .. *Set of* 8 4·00 3·75

96 Flags of Seychelles and U.S.A.

(Des and litho J.W.)

1976 (12 July). *Seychelles Independence and American Independence Bicentenary. T* **96** *and similar horiz design. Multicoloured.* W w **12** (*sideways*). *P* 13½.

363 1 r. Type **96** 30 25
364 10 r. Statehouses of Seychelles and Philadelphia .. .. 3·75 3·25

97 Swimming

98 Seychelles Paradise Flycatcher

(Des J.W. Litho Questa)

1976 (26 July). *Olympic Games, Montreal. T* **97** *and similar horiz designs.* W w **14** (*sideways*). *P* 14.

365 20 c. ultramarine, cobalt and sepia 10 5
366 65 c. bottle-green, apple-green and grey-black 15 10
367 1 r. chestnut, blue-green and grey-black .. 25 15
368 3 r. 50, crimson, rose and grey-black .. .. 90 1·10

Designs:—65 c. Hockey; 1 r. Basketball; 3 r. 50, Football.

(Des Mrs. R. Fennessy. Litho Questa)

1976–77. *Fourth Pan-African Ornithological Congress, Seychelles. T* **98** *and similar multicoloured designs.* W w **14** (*sideways on Nos.* 370/1). *P* 14. *A. Ordinary paper* (8.11.76). *B. Chalky paper* (7.3.77).

	A		B	
369 20 c. Type **98**	15	8	15	8
370 1 r. 25, Seychelles Sunbird (*horiz*) ..	65	65	65	65
371 1 r. 50, Seychelles Brown White Eye (*horiz*)	80	80	80	80
372 5 r. Black Parrot	2·25	2·25	2·25	2·25
MS373 161 × 109 mm. Nos. 369/72	4·00	4·25	†	
a. 5 r. value in miniature sheet imperf	£550			

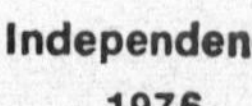

(**99**)

100 Inauguration of George Washington

1976 (22 Nov). *Independence. Nos.* 265a, 269, 271a, 273a, 274a, 276a *and* 277/9 *optd with T* **99** (*No.* 271 *additionally surch.*). W w **12** (*sideways*).

374 20 c. Fleet re-fuelling off St. Anne, 1939–45 .. 15 25
375 50 c. Pirates and treasure 30 30
376 95 c. Impression of proposed airport 45 45
377 1 r. French Governor capitulating to British naval officer, 1794 .. .. .. 45 45
378 3 r. 50, Visit of Duke of Edinburgh, 1956 .. 2·50 2·50
a. Opt inverted .. .. 75·00
b. On No. 276 .. .. 3·00 3·00
379 5 r. Chevalier Queau de Quincy .. .. 2·75 3·00
380 10 r. Indian Ocean chart, 1574 .. .. 5·00 7·00
381 15 c. Type **60** .. .. 8·00 9·00
382 25 r. on 65 c. Corsairs attacking merchantman 12·00 15·00
374/82 .. .. *Set of* 9 28·00 35·00

(Des Jennifer Toombs. Litho Questa)

1976 (21 Dec). *Bicentenary of American Revolution. T* **100** *and similar horiz designs. P* 14 × 13½.

383 1 c. crimson and light rose 5 5
384 2 c. violet and light lilac 5 5
385 3 c. bright blue and azure 5 5
386 4 c. chestnut and light yellow 5 5
387 5 c. emerald and light yellow-green 5 5
388 1 r. 50, sepia and cinnamon 35 35
389 3 r. 50, dp turquoise-blue & pale blue-green .. 90 90
390 5 r. chestnut and light yellow .. .. 1·25 1·25
391 10 r. chalky blue and azure .. .. .. 2·40 2·40
383/91 .. .. *Set of* 9 4·50 4·50
MS392 141 × 141 mm. 25 r. plum and magenta 6·00 6·50

Designs:—2 c. Jefferson and Louisiana Purchase; 3 c. William Seward and Alaska Purchase; 4 c. Pony Express, 1860; 5 c. Lincoln's Emancipation Proclamation; 1 r. 50 Transcontinental Railroad, 1869; 3 r. 50 Wright Brothers flight, 1903; 5 r. Henry Ford's assembly-line, 1913; 10 r. J. F. Kennedy and 1969 Moon-landing; 25 r. Signing Independence Declaration, 1776.

101 Silhouette of the Islands

102 Cruiser *Aurora* and Flag

(Des G. Hutchins (Nos. 395/8), J.W. (others). Litho Questa)

1977 (5 Sept). *Silver Jubilee. T* **101** *and similar multicoloured designs.* W w **14** (*sideways on* 20 *and* 40 *c.*, 5 *and* 10 *r.*). *P* 14.

393 20 c. Type **101** 5 5
394 40 c. Silhouette (*different*) 5 5
395 50 c. The Orb (*vert*) 8 10
396 1 r. St. Edward's Crown (*vert*) 15 20
397 1 r. 25, Ampulla and Spoon (*vert*) 20 25
398 1 r. 50, Sceptre with Cross (*vert*) 25 30
399 5 r. Silhouette (*different*) .. .. .. 90 1·00
400 10 r. Silhouette (*different*) .. .. .. 1·75 2·00
393/400 .. .. *Set of* 8 3·00 3·50
MS401 133 × 135 mm. 20 c., 50 c., 1 r., 10 r. all wmk sideways .. .. 2·25 2·50

(Litho State Printing Works, Moscow)

1977 (7 Nov). 60*th Anniv of Russian October Revolution. P* 12 × 12½.

402 **102** 1 r. 50, multicoloured 35 40
MS403 101 × 129 mm. No. 402 .. .. .. 35 40

103 Coral Scene

(Des G. Drummond. Litho Walsall (40 c., 1 r., 1 r. 25, 1 r. 50), J.W. (others))

1977–84. *Multicoloured designs as T* **103**. *Rupee values show* "Re" *or* "Rs". *W* w **14** (*sideways on* 10, 20, 50 *and* 75 *c.*). *P* 14½ × 14 (40 *c.*, 1 *r.*, 1 *r.* 25, 1 *r.* 50), 13 (5, 10, 15, 20 *r.*) *or* 14 (*others*).

A. *No imprint*. B. *Imprint date at foot*

	A		B	
404 5 c. Reef Fish	5	5	†	
405 10 c. Hawksbill Turtle	5	5	5	5
406 15 c. Coco-de-Mer	5	5	5	5
407 20 c. Wild Vanilla Orchid ..	5	5	5	5
408 25 c. Tiger Butterfly	5	5	5	5
409 40 c. Type **103**	8	5	8	10
410 50 c. Giant Tortoise	10	5	8	10
411 75 c. Crayfish	15	10	15	20
412 1 r. Madagascan Red Fody ..	35	12	40	30
413 1 r. 25, White Tern	45	15	†	
414 1 r. 50, Flying Fox	50	20	60	50
415 3 r. 50, Green Gecko	75	80	†	
416 5 r. Octopus	1·00	60	†	
417 10 r. Giant Tiger Cowrie ..	1·75	1·75	†	
418 15 r. Pitcher Plant	2·75	3·00	†	
419 20 r. Coat of arms	3·50	3·75	†	
404A/19A .. .. *Set of* 16	10·50	10·00		
405B/14B .. .. *Set of* 9			1·40	1·25

Dates of issue: Without imprint 10.11.77, 40 c., 1 r. to 1 r. 50; 6.2.78, 10, 20, 50, 75 c., 5 r., 20 r.; 10.4.78, others. With imprint 14.3.80, 10, 15, 25, 40, 50, 75, 1 r., 1 r. 50; 5.84, 20 c.

The 40 c., 1 r., 1 r. 25 and 1 r. 50 values are horizontal designs, 31 × 27 mm; the 5, 10, 15 and 20 r. are vertical, 28 × 36 mm; the others are horizontal, 29 × 25 mm.

For rupee values showing face value as "R" see Nos. 487/94.

104 St. Roch Roman Catholic Church, Bel Ombre

(Des G. Drummond. Litho Walsall)

977 (5 Dec). *Christmas. T* **104** *and similar horiz designs. Multicoloured.* W w **14** *(sideways). P* 13½ × 14.
20 20 c. Type **104** 5 5
21 1 r. Anglican cathedral, Victoria 20 10
22 1 r. 50, Roman Catholic cathedral, Victoria 25 20
23 5 r. St. Mark's Anglican church, Praslin . . 1·00 1·25

105 Liberation Day ringed on Calendar

106 Stamp Portraits of Edward VII, George V and George VI

(Des local artists; adapted L. Curtis. Litho Questa)

978 (5 June). *Liberation Day. T* **105** *and similar vert designs. Multicoloured.* W w **14**. *P* 14 × 13½.
24 40 c. Type **105** 10 5
25 1 r. 25, Hands holding bayonet, torch and flag 25 20
26 1 r. 50, Fisherman and farmer 30 30
27 5 r. Soldiers and rejoicing people . . . . 1·00 1·25

(Des G. Drummond. Litho Questa)

978 (21 Aug). *25th Anniv of Coronation. T* **106** *and similar vert designs. Multicoloured.* W w **14**. *P* 14.
28 40 c. Type **106** 10 5
29 1 r. 50, Victoria and Elizabeth II 35 35
30 3 r. Queen Victoria Monument 70 75
31 5 r. Queen's Building, Victoria . . . . 1·00 1·10
MS432 87 × 129 mm. Nos. 428/31 . . . . 2·25 2·25

107 Gardenia

(Des G. Hutchins. Litho Questa)

978 (16 Oct). *Wildlife. T* **107** *and similar horiz designs. Multicoloured.* W w **14** *(sideways). P* 13½ × 14.
33 40 c. Type **107** 10 8
34 1 r. 25, Seychelles Magpie Robin 50 45
35 1 r. 50, Seychelles Paradise Flycatcher . . 55 50
36 5 r. Green Turtle . . . . 1·25 1·25

108 Possession Stone

109 Seychelles Fody

(Des G. Hutchins. Litho Questa)

978 (15 Dec). *Bicentenary of Victoria. T* **108** *and similar horiz designs. Multicoloured.* W w **14** *(sideways). P* 13½ × 14.
37 20 c. Type **108** 10 8
38 1 r. 25, Plan of 1782 "L'Etablissement" . . 35 35
39 1 r. 50, Clock Tower 40 40
40 5 r. Bust of Pierre Poivre . . . . . . 1·25 1·50

(Des G. Drummond. Litho Questa)

979 (27 Feb). *Birds (1st series). T* **109** *and similar vert designs. Multicoloured.* W w **14**. *P* 14.
41 2 r. Type **109** 50 50
a. Horiz strip of 5. Nos. 441/5 . . . . 2·25
42 2 r. Striated Heron 50 50
43 2 r. Thick-billed Bulbul 50 50
44 2 r. Seychelles Cave Swiftlet 50 50
45 2 r. Grey-headed Lovebird 50 50
Nos. 441/5 were printed together, *se-tenant*, in horizontal strips of 5 throughout the sheet.
See also Nos. 463/7, 500/4 and 523/7.

110 Patrice Lumumba

111 1978 5 r. Liberation Day Commemorative and Sir Rowland Hill

(Des G. Vasarhelyi. Litho Questa)

1979 (5 June). *African Liberation Heroes. T* **110** *and similar vert designs.* W w **14**. *P* 14 × 14½.
446 40 c. black, deep violet and lilac 10 5
447 2 r. black, blue and pale blue 35 35
448 2 r. 25, black, reddish brown & orange-brn . . 45 45
449 5 r. black, bronze-green and dull green . . 1·00 1·10
Designs:—2 r. Kwame Nkrumah; 2 r. 25, Dr. Eduardo Mondlane; 5 r. Hamilcar Cabral.

(Des J.W. Litho Questa)

1979 (27 Aug). *Death Centenary of Sir Rowland Hill. T* **111** *and similar vert designs showing stamps and Sir Rowland Hill. Multicoloured.* W w **14**. *P* 14.
450 40 c. Type **111** 10 8
451 2 r. 25, 1972 50 c. Rare Birds commemorative 40 50
452 3 r. 1962 50 c. definitive 60 65
MS453 112 × 88 mm. 5 r. 1892 4 c. definitive. Wmk inverted . . . . 1·00 1·25

112 Child with Book

113 The Herald Angel

(Des BG Studio. Litho Questa)

1979 (26 Oct). *International Year of the Child. T* **112** *and similar multicoloured designs.* W w **14** *(sideways on 40 c. and 2 r. 25). P* 14½.
454 40 c. Type **112** 5 5
455 2 r. 25, Children of different races 40 45
456 3 r. Young child with ball (*vert*) 55 60
457 5 r. Girl with glove-puppet (*vert*) 80 85
Nos. 454/7 were each printed in sheets including two *se-tenant* stamp-size labels.

(Des J. Cooter. Litho Walsall)

1979 (3 Dec). *Christmas. T* **113** *and similar multicoloured designs.* W w **14** *(sideways on 3 r.). P* 14½ × 14 *(3 r.) or* 14 × 14½ *(others).*
458 20 c. Type **113** 5 5
459 2 r. 25, The Virgin and Child 40 45
460 3 r. The Three Kings (*horiz*) 55 60
MS461 87 × 75 mm. 5 r. The Flight into Egypt (*horiz*) (wmk sideways). P 14½ × 14 . . . . 75 80

R.1.10

(114)

115 Seychelles Kestrel

1979 (7 Dec). *As No.* 415 *but with imprint, surch with T* **114**.
462 1 r. 10 on 3 r. 50, Green Gecko 20 30

(Des G. Drummond. Litho Questa)

1980 (29 Feb). *Birds (2nd series). Seychelles Kestrel. T* **115** *and similar vert designs. Multicoloured.* W w **14** *(inverted). P* 14.
463 2 r. Type **115** 50 50
a. Horiz strip of 5. Nos. 463/7 . . . . 2·25
464 2 r. Pair of Seychelles Kestrels 50 50
465 2 r. Seychelles Kestrel with eggs 50 50
466 2 r. Seychelles Kestrel on nest with chick . . 50 50
467 2 r. Seychelles Kestrel chicks in nest . . 50 50
Nos. 463/7 were printed together, *se-tenant*, in horizontal strips of 5 throughout the sheet.

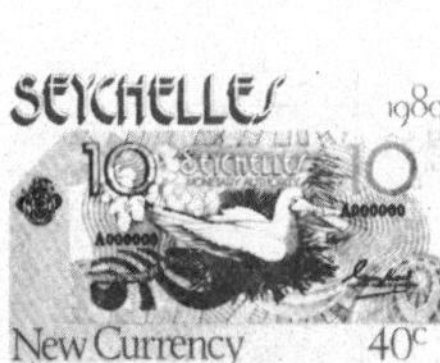

116 10 Rupees Banknote

117 Sprinting

(Des B. Grout. Litho Questa)

1980 (18 Apr). *"London 1980" International Stamp Exhibition. New Currency. T* **116** *and similar multicoloured designs showing banknotes.* W w **14** *(sideways on 40 c. and 1 r. 50). P* 14.
468 40 c. Type **116** 5 5
469 1 r. 50, 25 rupees 20 20
470 2 r. 25, 50 rupees (*vert*) 30 30
471 5 r. 100 rupees (*vert*) 70 70
MS472 119 × 102 mm. Nos. 468/71 (wmk sideways) 1·40 1·40

(Des J.W. Litho Questa)

1980 (13 June). *Olympic Games, Moscow. T* **117** *and similar vert designs. Multicoloured.* W w **14**. *P* 14 × 14½.
473 40 c. Type **117** 10 5
474 2 r. 25, Weightlifting 35 35
475 3 r. Boxing 50 50
476 5 r. Yachting 75 75
MS477 90 × 121 mm. Nos. 473/6 . . . . 1·75 1·90

118 "Jumbo Jet" Airliner

119 Female Palm

(Des A. Theobald. Litho Questa)

1980 (22 Aug). *International Tourism Conference, Manila. T* **118** *and similar horiz designs. Multicoloured.* W w **14** *(sideways). P* 14.
478 40 c. Type **118** 10 10
479 2 r. 25, Bus 45 45
480 3 r. Cruise liner 65 65
481 5 r. Launch 90 90

(Des L. Curtis. Litho Harrison)

1980 (14 Nov). *Coco-de-Mer (palms). T* **119** *and similar vert designs. Multicoloured.* W w **14**. *P* 14.
482 40 c. Type **119** 10 10
483 2 r. 25, Male Palm 45 45
484 3 r. Artefacts 65 65
485 5 r. Fisherman's gourd 90 90
MS486 82 × 140 mm. Nos. 482/5 . . . . 1·90 2·00

1981 (9 Jan). *As Nos.* 412/14, 415 *(but new value), and* 416/19 *all with face values redrawn to show* "R" *instead of* "Re" *or* "Rs".
487 1 r. Madagascan Red Fody 20 25
488 1 r. 10, Green Gecko 20 25
489 1 r. 25, White Tern 25 30
490 1 r. 50, Flying Fox 30 35
491 5 r. Octopus . . . . 1·10 1·25
492 10 r. Giant Tiger Cowrie . . . . . . 2·25 2·50
493 15 r. Pitcher Plant . . . . 3·25 3·50
494 20 r. Coat of arms . . . . 4·50 4·75
487/94 . . . . *Set of* 8 10·50 12·00
Nos. 487/94 were printed with imprint date ("1980") at foot.

120 Vasco da Gama's *San Gabriel*, 1497

121 Male White Tern

(Des J.W. Litho Format)

1981 (27 Feb). *Ships. T* **120** *and similar horiz designs. Multicoloured.* W w **14** *(sideways). P* 14½ × 14.
495 40 c. Type **120** 10 10
496 2 r. 25, Mascarenhas' caravel, 1505 . . . . 50 55
497 3 r. 50, Darwin's H.M.S. *Beagle*, 1831 . . 80 85
498 5 r. R.M.S. *Queen Elizabeth 2*, 1968 . . . . 1·10 1·25
MS499 141 × 91 mm. Nos. 495/98 . . . . 2·25 2·50

(Des G. Drummond. Litho Questa)

1981 (10 Apr). *Birds (3rd series). White Tern. T* **121** *and similar vert designs. Multicoloured.* W w **14**. *P* 14.
500 2 r. Type **121** 50 50
a. Horiz strip of 5. Nos. 500/4 . . . . 2·25

501	2 r. Pair of White Terns	50	50
502	2 r. Female White Tern	50	50
503	2 r. Female White Tern on nest, and egg ..	50	50
504	2 r. White Tern and chick	50	50

Nos. 500/4 were printed together, *se-tenant*, in horizontal strips of 5 throughout the sheet.

(Des D. Shults. Litho Questa)

1981 (23 June–16 Nov). *Royal Wedding. Horiz designs as T* **26/27** *of Kiribati. Multicoloured. (a) W* w **15**. *P* 14.

505	1 r. 50, *Victoria and Albert I*	25	30
	a. Sheetlet. No. 505 × 6 and No. 506 ..	2·00	
506	1 r. 50, Prince Charles and Lady Diana Spencer	60	60
507	5 r. *Cleveland*	90	95
	a. Sheetlet. No. 507 × 6 and No. 508 ..	6·00	
508	5 r. As No. 506	2·25	2·50
509	10 r. *Britannia*	1·75	1·90
	a. Sheetlet. No. 509 × 6 and No. 510 ..	13·00	
510	10 r. As No. 506	3·00	3·00
MS511	120 × 109 mm. 7 r. 50, As No. 506. Wmk sideways. P 12 (16 Nov).	1·50	1·50

(*b*) *Booklet stamps. No wmk. P* 12 (16 Nov)

512	1 r. 50, As No. 505	25	30
	a. Booklet pane. No. 512 × 4	1·00	
513	5 r. As No. 508	1·00	1·25
	a. Booklet pane. No. 513 × 2	2·00	

Nos. 505/10 were printed in sheetlets of seven stamps of the same face value, each containing six of the "Royal Yacht" design and one of the larger design showing Prince Charles and Lady Diana.

Nos. 512/13 come from 22 r. stamp booklets.

122 Britten-Norman "Islander"

123 Flying Foxes (Roussettes) in Flight

(Litho Harrison)

1981 (27 July). *10th Anniv of Opening of Seychelles International Airport. Aircraft. T* **122** *and similar horiz designs. Multicoloured. W* w **14** (*sideways*). *P* 14½.

514	40 c. Type **122**	10	10
515	2 r. 25, Britten-Norman "Trislander" ..	45	50
516	3 r. 50, BAC (Vickers) "VC10" airliner ..	70	75
517	5 r. Boeing "747" airliner	1·00	1·10

(Litho Format)

1981 (9 Oct). *Flying Fox (Roussette)*. T **123** *and similar vert designs. Multicoloured. W* w **14**. *P* 14.

518	40 c. Type **123**	10	10
519	2 r. 25, Flying Fox (Roussette) eating ..	45	50
520	3 r. Roussette climbing across tree branch ..	70	70
521	5 r. Roussette hanging from tree branch ..	1·00	1·10
MS522	95 × 130 mm. Nos. 518/21	2·25	2·50

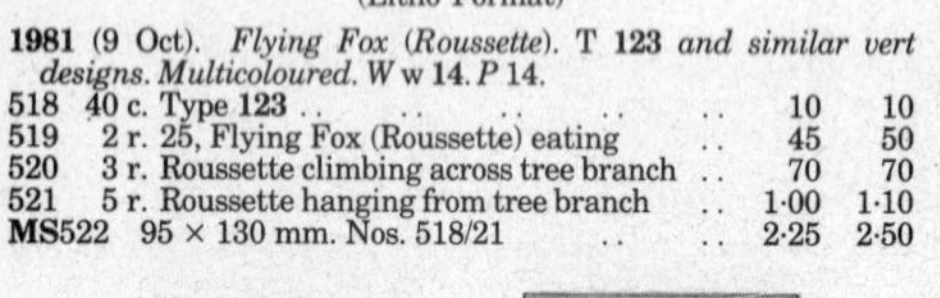

124 Chinese Little Bittern (male)

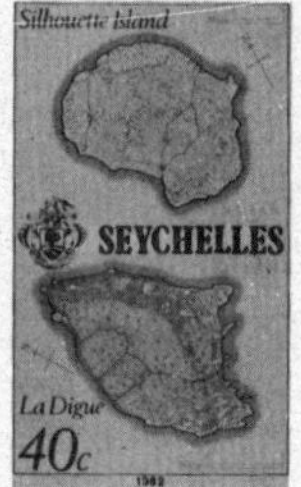

125 Silhouette Island and La Digue

(Des G. Drummond. Litho Questa)

1982 (4 Feb). *Birds (4th series). Chinese Little Bittern. T* **124** *and similar vert designs. Multicoloured. W* w **14**. *P* 14.

523	3 r. Type **124**	70	65
	a. Horiz strip of 5. Nos. 523/7 ..	3·25	
524	3 r. Chinese Little Bittern (female) ..	70	65
525	3 r. Hen on nest	70	65
526	3 r. Nest and eggs	70	65
527	3 r. Hen with chicks	70	65

Nos. 523/7 were printed together, *se-tenant*, in horizontal strips of 5 throughout the sheet.

(Des J. Cooter. Litho Format)

1982 (22 Apr). *Modern Maps. T* **125** *and similar vert designs. Multicoloured. W* w **14**. *P* 14½.

528	40 c. Type **125**	10	10
529	1 r. 50, Denis and Bird Islands	35	35
530	2 r. 75, Praslin	65	65
531	7 r. Mahé	1·75	1·75
MS532	92 × 128 mm. Nos. 528/31	2·50	2·75

126 "Education"

(Des PAD Studio. Litho Harrison)

1982 (5 June). *5th Anniv of Liberation. T* **126** *and similar horiz designs. Multicoloured. W* w **14** (*sideways*). *P* 14.

533	40 c. Type **126**	10	10
534	1 r. 75, "Health"	35	35
535	2 r. 75, "Agriculture"	65	65
536	7 r. "Construction"	1·75	1·75
MS537	128 × 120 mm. Nos. 533/6. P 14½ ..	2·50	2·75

127 Tourist Board Emblem

128 Tata Bus

(Des and litho Harrison)

1982 (1 Sept). *Tourism. T* **127** *and similar horiz designs. Multicoloured. W* w **14** (*sideways*). *P* 14.

538	1 r. 75, Type **127**	35	35
539	1 r. 75, Northolme Hotel	35	35
540	1 r. 75, Reef Hotel	35	35
541	1 r. 75, Barbarous Beach Hotel	35	35
542	1 r. 75, Coral Strand Hotel	35	35
543	1 r. 75, Beau Vallon Bay Hotel	35	35
544	1 r. 75, Fisherman's Cove Hotel	35	35
545	1 r. 75, Mahé Beach Hotel	35	35
538/45	.. .. *Set of* 8	2·50	2·50

(Des C. Abbott. Litho Harrison)

1982 (18 Nov). *Land Transport. T* **128** *and similar horiz designs. Multicoloured. W* w **14** (*sideways*). *P* 14.

546	20 c. Type **128**	8	8
547	1 r. 75, Mini-moke	35	35
548	2 r. 75, Ox-cart	60	60
549	7 r. Truck	1·60	1·60

129 Radio Seychelles Control Room

(Des A. Theobald. Litho Questa)

1983 (25 Feb). *World Communications Year. T* **129** *and similar horiz designs. Multicoloured. W* w **14** (*sideways*). *P* 14.

550	40 c. Type **129**	8	10
551	2 r. 75, Satellite Earth Station	45	50
552	3 r. 50, Radio Seychelles Television control room	70	75
553	5 r. Postal services sorting office	1·00	1·10

130 Agricultural Experimental Station

(Des L. Curtis. Litho Questa)

1983 (14 Mar). *Commonwealth Day. T* **130** *and similar horiz designs. Multicoloured. W* w **14** (*sideways*). *P* 14.

554	40 c. Type **130**	8	10
555	2 r. 75, Food processing plant	45	50
556	3 r. 50, Unloading fish catch	70	75
557	7 r. Seychelles flag	1·40	1·50

131 Denis Island Lighthouse

(Des Harrison. Litho Format)

1983 (14 July). *Famous Landmarks. T* **131** *and similar horiz designs. Multicoloured. W* w **14** (*sideways*). *P* 14 × 13½.

558	40 c. Type **131**	8	10
559	2 r. 75, Victoria Hospital	50	55
560	3 r. 50, Supreme Court	70	75
561	7 r. State House	1·40	1·50
MS562	110 × 98 mm. Nos. 558/61	2·75	3·00

132 *Royal Vauxhall* Balloon, 1836

(Des A. Theobald. Litho Harrison)

1983 (15 Sept). *Bicentenary of Manned Flight. T* **132** *and simil*[...] *horiz designs. Multicoloured. W* w **14** (*sideways*). *P* 14.

563	40 c. Type **132**	8	1
564	1 r. 75, De Havilland "D.H.50J"	35	4
565	2 r. 75, Grumman "Albatross" flying boat ..	50	5
566	7 r. Swearingen "Merlin"	1·40	1·7

133 "DC 10" Aircraft

134 Swamp Plant and Moorhen

(Des Park Advertising. Litho Walsall)

1983 (26 Oct). *1st International Flight of Air Seychelles. W* w 1[...] (*sideways*). *P* 14.

567	**133**	2 r. multicoloured	40	4

(Des L. Curtis. Litho Questa)

1983 (17 Nov). *Centenary of Visit to Seychelles by Marianne Nort*[...] (*botanic artist*). *T* **134** *and similar vert designs. Multicoloure*[...] *W* w **14**. *P* 14.

568	40 c. Type **134**	8	1
569	1 r. 75, *Wormia flagellaria*	35	4
570	2 r. 75, Asiatic Pancratium	50	5
571	7 r. Pitcher Plant	1·40	1·5
MS572	90 × 121 mm. Nos. 568/71	2·25	2·5

50c ▬

(135)

1983 (28 Dec). *Nos.* 505/10 *surch as T* **135**.

573	50 c. on 1 r. 50, *Victoria and Albert I*	10	1
	a. Sheetlet. No. 573 × 6 and No. 574 ..	70	
	b. Albino surch	33·00	
	c. Surch double, one albino	35·00	
	d. Surch double, one inverted	55·00	
	e. Surch double, one in 2 r. 25 value ..	45·00	
574	50 c. on 1 r. 50, Prince Charles and Lady Diana Spencer	10	1
	b. Albino surch	75·00	
	c. Surch double, one albino	85·00	
	d. Surch double, one inverted	£125	
	e. Surch double, one in 2 r. 25 value ..	£110	
575	2 r. 25 on 5 r. *Cleveland*	50	5
	a. Sheetlet. No. 575 × 6 and No. 576 ..	3·50	
576	2 r. 25 on 5 r. As No. 574	50	5
577	3 r. 75 on 10 r. *Britannia*	80	8
	a. Sheetlet. No. 577 × 6 and No. 578 ..	5·50	
	b. Albino surch	30·00	
	c. Surch double	90·00	
578	3 r. 75 on 10 r. As No. 574	80	8
	b. Albino surch	65·00	
	c. Surch double	£225	
573/8	.. .. *Set of* 6	2·50	2·7

136 Coconut Vessel

137 Victoria Port

(Des Jennifer Toombs. Litho Format)

1984 (29 Feb). *Traditional Handicrafts. T* **136** *and similar hori*[...] *designs. Multicoloured. W* w **14** (*sideways*). *P* 14.

579	50 c. Type **136**	12	1
580	2 r. Scarf and doll	50	5
581	3 r. Coconut-fibre roses	75	8
582	10 r. Carved fishing boat and doll	2·50	2·7

(Des C. Collins. Litho Questa)

1984 (21 May). *25th Anniv of "Lloyd's List"* (*newspaper*). *T* **137** *and similar vert designs. Multicoloured. W* w **14**. *P* 14½ × 14.

583	50 c. Type **137**	12	1
584	2 r. Steam ship	50	5
585	3 r. Cruise Liner	75	8
586	10 r. Loss of R.F.A. *Ennerdale*	2·50	2·7

138 Old S.P.U.P. Office

(Des D. Miller. Litho B.D.T.)

84 (2 June). *20th Anniv of Seychelles People's United Party. T* **138** *and similar multicoloured designs. W* w **14** (*sideways on* 50 *c.*, 3 *r.*). *P* 14.

7	50 c. Type **138**	12	15
8	2 r. Liberation statue (*vert*)	50	55
9	3 r. New S.P.U.P. office	75	80
0	10 r. President René (*vert*)	2·50	2·75

139 1949 U.P.U. 2 r. 25 Stamp

(Des M. Joyce. Litho Harrison)

84 (18 June). *Universal Postal Union Congress, Hamburg. Sheet* 70 × 85 *mm. W* w **14** (*sideways*). *P* 14½.

MS591 **139** 5 r. yellow-olive, flesh and black .. 1·25 1·40

140 Long Jumping

(Des L. Curtis. Litho Questa)

84 (28 July). *Olympic Games, Los Angeles. T* **140** *and similar horiz designs. Multicoloured. W* w **14** (*sideways*). *P* 14.

2	50 c. Type **140**	12	15
3	2 r. Boxing	50	55
4	3 r. Swimming	75	80
5	10 r. Weightlifting	2·50	2·75
S596	100 × 100 mm. Nos. 592/5	3·75	4·00

141 Sub-aqua Diving

(Des A. Theobald. Litho Questa)

84 (24 Sept). *Water Sports. T* **141** *and similar horiz designs. Multicoloured. W* w **14** (*sideways*). *P* 14.

97	50 c. Type **141**	12	15
98	2 r. Paragliding	50	55
99	3 r. Sailing	75	80
00	10 r. Water-skiing	2·50	2·75

142 Humpback Whale

(Des A. Jardine. Litho Questa)

984 (19 Nov). *Whale Conservation. T* **142** *and similar horiz designs. Multicoloured. W* w **14** (*sideways*). *P* 14.

01	50 c. Type **142**	12	15
02	2 r. Sperm Whale	50	55
03	3 r. Right Whale	75	80
04	10 r. Blue Whale	2·50	2·75

POSTAGE DUE STAMPS

D 1

(Frame recess, value typo B.W.)

951 (1 Mar). *Wmk Mult Script CA. P* 11½.

1	D 1	2 c. scarlet and carmine	1·25	2·00
2		3 c. scarlet and green	1·25	2·00
3		6 c. scarlet and bistre	1·25	1·50
4		9 c. scarlet and orange	1·50	2·00
5		15 c. scarlet and violet	2·00	4·75
6		18 c. scarlet and blue	2·00	5·00
7		20 c. scarlet and brown	2·25	5·00
8		30 c. scarlet and claret	2·25	5·50
1/8		*Set of* 8	12·00	25·00

964 (7 July)–**65**. *As* 1951 *but W* w **12**.

9	D 1	2 c. scarlet and carmine	65	1·75
10		3 c. scarlet and green (14.9.65)	1·75	2·50

(Litho Walsall)

1980 (29 Feb). *Design as Type* D 1 *but redrawn, size* 18 × 22 *mm. W* w **14** (*sideways*). *P* 14.

D11	5 c. rosine and magenta	5	5
D12	10 c. rosine and deep blue-green	5	5
D13	15 c. rosine and bistre	5	5
D14	20 c. rosine and orange-brown	5	5
D15	25 c. rosine and bright violet	5	5
D16	75 c. rosine and maroon	15	20
D17	80 c. rosine and deep grey-blue	15	20
D18	1 r. rosine and deep reddish purple	20	25
D11/18	*Set of* 8	65	75

ZIL ELWANNYEN SESEL

(SEYCHELLES OUTER ISLANDS)

For use from Aldabra, Coetivy, Farquhar and the Amirante Islands, served by the M.V. *Cinq-Juin* travelling post office.

I Inscr "ZIL ELOIGNE SESEL"

1 Reef Fish

2 *Cinq Juin*

1980 (20 June)–**81**. *Designs as Nos.* 404/11 (*with imprint*) *and* 487/94 *of Seychelles but inscr.* "ZIL ELOIGNE SESEL" *as in T* **1**. *W* w **14** (*sideways on* 10, 20, 50, 75 *c.*). *P* 14½ × 14 (40 *c.*, 1 *r.*, 1 *r.* 25, 1*r.* 50), 13½ (5, 10, 15, 20 *r.*) *or* 14 (*others*).

1	5 c. Type **1**	5	5
2	10 c. Hawksbill Turtle	5	5
3	15 c. Coco-de-Mer	10	5
4	20 c. Wild Vanilla	10	5
5	25 c. Butterfly on flower	15	5
6	40 c. Coral scene	15	10
7	50 c. Giant Tortoise	15	10
8	75 c. Crayfish	20	15
9	1 r. Madagascan Red Fody	25	20
10	1 r. 10, Green Gecko	30	25
11	1 r. 25, White Tern	35	35
12	1 r. 50, Flying Fox	35	35
13	5 r. Octopus	80	90
	a. Perf 13 (1981)	75	80
14	10 r. Giant Tiger Cowrie	1·50	2·00
	a. Perf 13 (1981)	1·50	1·75
15	15 r. Pitcher Plant	2·25	2·75
	a. Perf 13 (1981)	2·25	2·50
16	20 r. Seychelles coat of arms	3·50	3·75
	a. Perf 13 (1981)	3·50	3·75
1/16	*Set of* 16	9·00	10·00

Nos. 1/12 exist with imprint dates of either "1980" or "1981", Nos. 13/16 with "1980" only and Nos. 13a/16a "1981" only.

(Des L. Curtis. Litho Walsall)

1980 (24 Oct). *Establishment of Travelling Post Office. T* **2** *and similar horiz designs. Multicoloured. W* w **14** (*sideways*). *P* 14.

17	1 r. 50, Type **2**	60	55
18	2 r. 10, Hand-stamping covers	75	70
19	5 r. Map of Zil Eloigne Sesel	1·25	1·25

Nos. 17/19 were printed in sheets including two *se-tenant* stamp-size labels.

The original version of No. 19 incorrectly showed the Agalega Islands as Seychelles territory. A corrected version was prepared prior to issue and stamps in the first type were intended for destruction. Mint examples are known, however, originating, it is believed, from supplies sent to at least one overseas dealer by mistake. Such stamps are not listed as they were not available from Seychelles post offices or valid for postage.

3 Yellowfin Tuna

(Des G. Drummond. Litho Rosenbaum Bros, Vienna)

1980 (28 Nov). *Marine Life. T* **3** *and similar horiz designs. Multicoloured. W* w **14**. *P* 14.

20	1 r. 50, Type **3**	50	50
21	2 r. 10, Blue Marlin (fish)	60	60
22	5 r. Sperm Whale	1·10	1·10

Nos. 20/2 were printed in sheets including two *se-tenant* stamp-size labels.

(Des D. Shults. Litho Questa)

1981 (23 June–16 Nov). *Royal Wedding. Horiz designs as T* **26/27** *of Kiribati. Multicoloured.* (*a*) *W* w **15**. *P* 14.

23	40 c. *Royal Escape*	10	10
	a. Sheetlet. No. 23 × 6 and No. 24	1·00	
24	40 c. Prince Charles and Lady Diana Spencer	50	50
25	5 r. *Victoria and Albert II*	75	80
	a. Sheetlet. No. 25 × 6 and No. 26	6·00	
26	5 r. As No. 24	2·25	2·25
27	10 r. *Britannia*	1·50	1·60
	a. Sheetlet. No. 27 × 6 and No. 28	12·00	
28	10 r. As No. 24	4·50	4·50
MS29	120 × 109 mm. 7 r. 50, As No. 24. Wmk sideways. P 12 (16 Nov)	1·50	1·50

(*b*) *Booklet stamps. No wmk. P* 12 (16 Nov)

30	40 c. As No. 23	25	30
	a. Booklet pane. No. 30 × 4	1·00	
31	5 r. As No. 26	75	85
	a. Booklet pane. No. 31 × 2	1·50	

Nos. 23/8 were printed in sheetlets of seven stamps of the same face value, each containing six of the "Royal Yacht" design and one of the larger design showing Prince Charles and Lady Diana.

Nos. 30/1 come from 13 r. 20 stamp booklets.

4 Wright's Skink

(Des and litho Walsall)

1981 (11 Dec). *Wildlife (1st series). T* **4** *and similar horiz designs. Multicoloured.* W w **14** *(sideways). P* 14.

32	1 r. 40, Type **4**	40	40
33	2 r. 25, Tree Frog	50	50
34	5 r. Robber Crab	1·00	1·10

See also Nos. 45/7.

5 *Cinq Juin* ("Communications")

(Des L. Curtis. Litho Harrison)

1982 (11 Mar). *Island Development. Ships. T* **5** *and similar horiz designs.* W w **14**. *P* 14 × 14½.

35	1 r. 75, black and orange	40	50
36	2 r. 10, black and turquoise-blue	50	60
37	5 r. black and bright scarlet	1·00	1·10

Designs:—2 r. 10, *Junon* ("fisheries protection"); 5 r. Drilling Ship *Diamond M. Dragon*.

II Inscr "ZIL ELWAGNE SESEL"

6 *Paulette*

(Des L. Curtis. Litho Harrison)

1982 (22 July). *Local Mail Vessels. T* **6** *and similar horiz designs. Multicoloured.* W w **14** *(sideways). P* 14.

38	40 c. Type **6**	10	10
39	1 r. 75, *Janette*	35	35
40	2 r. 75, *Lady Esme*	50	50
41	3 r. 50, *Cinq Juin*	55	55

7 Birds flying over Island **8** Red Land Crab

(Des Harrison. Litho Format)

1982 (19 Nov). *Aldabra, World Heritage Site. T* **7** *and similar horiz designs. Multicoloured.* W w **14** *(sideways). P* 14.

42	40 c. Type **7**	15	15
43	2 r. 75, Map of the atoll	65	65
44	7 r. Giant Tortoises	1·40	1·40

(Des G. Drummond. Litho Questa)

1983 (25 Feb). *Wildlife (2nd series). T* **8** *and similar horiz designs. Multicoloured.* W w **14** *(sideways). P* 14 × 14½.

45	1 r. 75, Type **8**	35	40
46	2 r. 75, Black Terrapin	45	55
47	7 r. Madagascar Green Gecko	1·40	1·50

9 Map of Poivre Island and Île du Sud **10** Aldabra Warbler

(Des J. Cooter. Litho Format)

1983 (27 Apr). *Island Maps. T* **9** *and similar vert designs. Multicoloured.* W w **14**. *P* 14.

48	40 c. Type **9**	10	10
49	1 r. 50, Île des Roches	30	35
50	2 r. 75, Astove Island	45	55
51	7 r. Coëtivy Island	1·40	1·50
MS52	93 × 129 mm. Nos. 48/51	2·10	2·40

(Des G. Drummond. Litho Harrison)

1983 (13 July). *Birds. T* **10** *and similar multicoloured designs.* W w **14** *(sideways on 5 c. to 2 r. 75). P* 14.

53	5 c. Type **10**	5	5
54	10 c. Zebra Dove	5	5
55	15 c. Madagascar Nightjar	5	5
56	20 c. Madagascar Cisticola	5	5
57	25 c. Madagascar White Eye	5	8
58	40 c. Mascarene Fody	10	12
59	50 c. White-throated Rail	12	15
60	75 c. Black Bulbul	15	20
61	2 r. Western Reef Heron	45	50
62	2 r. 10, Souimanga Sunbird	45	50
63	2 r. 50, Madagascar Turtle Dove	55	60
64	2 r. 75, Sacred Ibis	60	65
65	3 r. 50, Black Coucal *(vert)*	75	80
66	7 r. Seychelles Kestrel *(vert)*	1·50	1·60
67	15 r. Comoro Blue Pigeon *(vert)*	3·50	3·75
68	20 r. Greater Flamingo *(vert)*	4·50	4·75
53/68	.. .. *Set of* 16	11·50	12·25

11 Windsurfing

(Des G. Wilby. Litho Questa)

1983 (27 Sept). *Tourism. T* **11** *and similar horiz designs. Multicoloured.* W w **14** *(sideways). P* 14.

69	50 c. Type **11**	10	12
70	2 r. Hotel	40	45
71	3 r. View of beach	60	65
72	10 r. Islands at sunset	2·00	2·10

1983 (16–28 Dec). *Nos. 23/8 surch as T* **135** *of Seychelles.*

73	30 c. on 40 c. *Royal Escape*	5	8
	a. Sheetlet. No. 73 × 6 and No. 74	40	
	b. Surch double	50·00	
	c. Error. Surch 50 c. (as Seychelles No. 573)	60·00	
74	30 c. on 40 c. Prince Charles and Lady Diana Spencer	5	8
	b. Surch double	£125	
	c. Error. Surch 50 c. (as Seychelles No. 574)	£140	
75	2 r. on 5 r. *Victoria and Albert II* (28.12.83) ..	45	50
	a. Sheetlet. No. 75 × 6 and No. 76	3·25	
	b. Albino surch	40·00	
	c. Surch double	75·00	
76	2 r. on 5 r. As No. 74 (28.12.83)	45	50
	b. Albino surch	65·00	
	c. Surch double	£200	
77	3 r. on 10 r. *Britannia* (28.12.83)	65	70
	a. Sheetlet. No. 77 × 6 and No. 78	4·50	
78	3 r. on 10 r. As No. 74 (28.12.83)	65	70
73/8	.. .. *Set of* 6	2·00	2·25

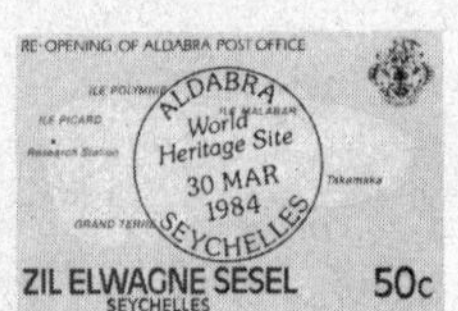

12 Map of Aldabra and Commemorative Postmark

(Des L. Curtis. Litho Questa)

1984 (30 Mar). *Re-opening of Aldabra Post Office. T* **12** *and similar horiz designs. Multicoloured.* W w **14** *(sideways). P* 14.

79	50 c. Type **12**	12	15
80	2 r. 75, Aldabra Rail	70	75
81	3 r. Giant Tortoise	75	80
82	10 r. Red-footed Booby	2·50	2·75

13 Fishing from Boat

(Des L. Curtis. Litho Walsall)

1984 (31 May). *Game Fishing. T* **13** *and similar multicoloured designs.* W w **14** *(sideways on 50 c., 10 r.). P* 14.

83	50 c. Type **13**	12	15
84	2 r. Hooked fish *(vert)*	50	55
85	3 r. Weighing catch *(vert)*	75	80
86	10 r. Fishing from boat *(different)*	2·50	2·75

14 Giant Hermit Crab **15** Constellation of "Orion"

(Des G. Drummond. Litho Format)

1984 (24 Aug). *Crabs. T* **14** *and similar horiz designs. Multicoloured.* W w **14** *(sideways). P* 14½.

87	50 c. Type **14**	12	15
88	2 r. Fiddler Crabs	50	55
89	3 r. Sand Crab	75	80
90	10 r. Spotted Pebble Crab	2·50	2·75

(Des A. Theobald. Litho Format)

1984 (16 Oct). *The Night Sky. T* **15** *and similar vert designs. Multicoloured.* W w **14**. *P* 14.

91	50 c. Type **15**	12	[illegible]
92	2 r. "Cygnus"	50	[illegible]
93	3 r. "Virgo"	75	[illegible]
94	10 r. "Scorpio"	2·50	[illegible]

III Inscr ZIL ELWANNYEN SESEL

16 *Lenzites elegans*

(Des G. Drummond. Litho Walsall)

1985 (31 Jan). *Fungi. T* **16** *and similar vert designs. Multicoloured.* W w **14**. *P* 14.

95	50 c. Type **16**	10	[illegible]
96	2 r. *Xylaria telfairei*	45	[illegible]
97	3 r. *Lentinus sajor-caju*	65	[illegible]
98	10 r. *Hexagonia tenuis*	2·25	[illegible]

Sierra Leone

PRICES FOR STAMPS ON COVER TO 1945

Nos. 1/3	*from* × 10
Nos. 4/15	*from* × 4
Nos. 16/26	*from* × 5
Nos. 27/34	*from* × 10
Nos. 35/7	*from* × 5
No. 38	—
No. 39	*from* × 8
Nos. 41/52	*from* × 3
No. 53	—
No. 54	*from* × 20
Nos. 55/71	*from* × 2
Nos. 73/84	*from* × 3
No. 85	—
Nos. 86/97	*from* × 3
No. 98	—
Nos. 99/110	*from* × 3
No. 111	—
Nos. 112/26	*from* × 2
Nos. 127/30	—
Nos. 131/45	*from* × 2
Nos. 146/8	—
Nos. 155/66	*from* × 2
No. 167	—
Nos. 168/78	*from* × 2
Nos. 179/80	—
Nos. 181/4	*from* × 3
Nos. 185/7	*from* × 5
Nos. 188/200	*from* × 2

CROWN COLONY AND PROTECTORATE

PRINTERS. All issues of Sierra Leone until 1932 were typographed by De La Rue & Co. Ltd, London.

1

2

HALF
PENNY

(3)

1859 (21 Sept)–**74.** *No wmk. P* 14.
1 1 6d. dull purple .. £180 38·00
2 6d. grey-lilac (1865) .. £180 32·00
3 6d. reddish lilac (1874) .. 35·00 20·00

1872. *No wmk. P* 12½.
4 1 6d. reddish violet .. £200 50·00

The paper used for the 6d. value often shows varying degrees of blueing, caused by a chemical reaction.

The 6d., imperf, is believed to be a proof (*Price*, £100).

1872–73. *Wmk Crown CC. P* 12½. (a) *Wmk sideways* (April 1872).
7 2 1d. rose-red .. 35·00 22·00
8 3d. buff .. 65·00 25·00
9 4d. blue .. 90·00 27·00
10 1s. green .. £110 27·00

(b) *Wmk upright* (Sept 1873)
11 2 1d. rose-red .. 28·00 18·00
12 2d. magenta .. 70·00 32·00
13 3d. saffron-yellow .. £450 £100
14 4d. blue .. £160 48·00
15 1s. green .. £250 £100

1876–77. *Wmk Crown CC. P* 14.
16 2 ½d. brown .. 2·50 5·50
17 1d. rose-red .. 13·00 10·00
18 1½d. lilac (1877) .. 12·00 4·75
19 2d. magenta .. 22·00 4·75
20 3d. buff .. 20·00 5·50
21 4d. blue .. 50·00 6·00
22 1s. green .. 35·00 9·50
16/22 .. *Set of* 7 £140 42·00

1883 (June–26 Sept). *Wmk Crown CA. P* 14.
23 2 ½d. brown .. 17·00 20·00
24 1d. rose-red (26.9.83) .. £200 35·00
25 2d. magenta .. 26·00 6·50
26 4d. blue .. £750 28·00

1884 SIERRA 5s. LEONE SURCHARGE. From 2 June 1884 the administration decided that, as a temporary measure, revenue and fiscal duties were to be paid with ordinary postage stamps. At that time there was no postage value higher than 1s., so a local surcharge, reading "SIERRA 5s. LEONE" was applied to No. 22. Until its withdrawal on 1 March 1885 this surcharge was valid for both fiscal and postal purposes, although no postal cover or piece has yet been found.

Remainders of the surcharge were cancelled by a horizontal red brush stroke.

1884 (July)–**93.** *Wmk Crown CA. P* 14.
27 2 ½d. dull green .. 35 20
28 1d. carmine .. 1·40 35
a. Rose-carmine (1885?) .. 28·00 8·50
29 1½d. pale violet (1893) .. 2·00 5·00
30 2d. grey .. 6·00 2·25
31 2½d. ultramarine (1891) .. 7·00 45
32 3d. yellow (1892) .. 2·25 3·50
33 4d. brown .. 2·25 2·25
34 1s. red-brown (1888) .. 13·00 8·00
27/34 .. *Set of* 8 30·00 20·00
27/8, 30/1, 33/4 (*perf* 14) Optd "Specimen" .. *Set of* 6 £250
27/8, 30, 33 (*perf* 12) Optd "Specimen" .. *Set of* 4 £300

1885–96. *Wmk Crown CC. P* 14.
35 1 6d. dull violet (1885) .. 48·00 19·00
a. Bisected (3d.) (on cover) .. † £1600
36 6d. brown-purple (1890) .. 17·00 14·00
37 6d. purple-lake (1896) .. 5·50 8·00
36 Optd "Specimen" .. 45·00

1893. *Surch with T* 3. *P* 14. (a) *Wmk Crown CC.*
38 2 ½d. on 1½d. lilac .. £350 £400
a. "PFNNY" .. £1800 £2250

(b) *Wmk Crown CA*
39 2 ½d. on 1½d. pale violet .. 4·25 5·00
a. Surch inverted .. £110 £110
b. "PFNNY" .. 80·00 80·00
ba. Ditto. Surch inverted .. £1300

The 6d. fiscal, inscribed "STAMP DUTY" as Type 6, surcharged "ONE-PENNY" is known used for postage between June and August 1894, but no official sanction for such usage can be found in *The Royal Gazette*.

4

5

1896–97. *Wmk Crown CA. P* 14.
41 4 ½d. dull mauve and green (1897) .. 65 50
42 1d. dull mauve and carmine .. 65 35
43 1½d. dull mauve and black (1897) 2·75 4·25
44 2d. dull mauve and orange .. 2·50 3·00
45 2½d. dull mauve and ultramarine .. 1·60 1·00
46 5 3d. dull mauve and slate .. 8·00 7·00
47 4d. dull mauve and carmine (1897) .. 6·50 9·50
48 5d. dull mauve and black (1897) 7·00 10·00
49 6d. dull mauve (1897) .. 9·50 10·00
50 1s. green and black .. 10·00 11·00
51 2s. green and ultramarine .. 25·00 25·00
52 5s. green and carmine .. 42·00 48·00
53 £1 purple/*red* .. £150 £225
41/53 .. *Set of* 13 £250 £325
41/53 Optd "Specimen" .. *Set of* 13 £325

6

POSTAGE
AND
REVENUE

(7)

1897 (Mar). *Wmk CA over Crown, w* 7. (a) *Optd with T* 7. *P* 14.
54 6 1d. dull purple and green .. 1·60 1·75
a. Opt double .. £650 £750

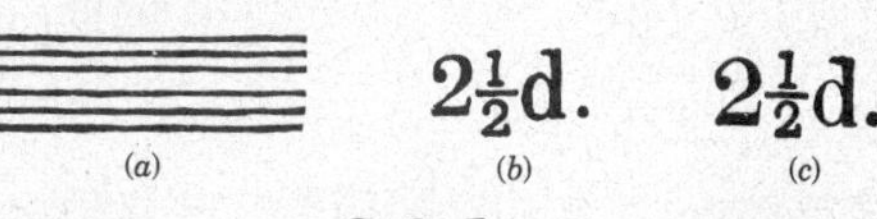

2½d. (a)

2½d. (b)

2½d. (c)

2½d. (d)

2½d. (e)

2½d. (f)

(b) *Surch in addition with "2½d." below T* 7. *Original value cancelled by* 6 *bars*
55 6 2½d. on 3d. dull purple and green (*a*) .. 8·00 8·00
a. Surch double
b. Surch double ((*a*) + (*c*)) .. £4750
c. Surch double ((*a*) + (*d*))
56 2½d. on 3d. dull purple and green (*c*) .. 35·00 42·00
57 2½d. on 3d. dull purple and green (*d*) .. 90·00 £110
58 2½d. on 3d. dull purple and green (*e*) .. £200 £225
59 2½d. on 6d. dull purple and green (*a*) .. 14·00 13·00
60 2½d. on 6d. dull purple and green (*c*) .. 65·00 75·00
61 2½d. on 6d. dull purple and green (*d*) .. £160 £180
62 2½d. on 6d. dull purple and green (*e*) .. £325 £350

The 2½d. on 3d. and 2½d. on 6d. are printed in sheets containing two settings of thirty, of which there are twenty-two of (*a*), five of (*c*), two of (*d*), and one of (*e*).

Two copies are known of No. 55a, five of 55b (of which two are in the Royal collection), and two of 55c (of which one is in the Royal collection). The Royal collection also contains one copy of the 2½d. (*a*) with 2½d. (*e*) on 3d. but this is probably unique.

POSTAGE AND
REVENUE

(8)

(c) *As before, but optd with T* 8. *The surcharge "2½d." is above T* 8, *and there are only* 5 *bars cancelling original value instead of* 6
63 6 2½d. on 1s. dull lilac (*a*) .. 80·00 60·00
64 2½d. on 1s. dull lilac (*b*) .. £1200 £1200
65 2½d. on 1s. dull lilac (*c*) .. £600 £700
66 2½d. on 1s. dull lilac (*d*) .. £350 £400
66*a* 2½d. on 1s. dull lilac (*f*) .. £1200 £1200
67 2½d. on 2s. dull lilac (*a*) .. £800 £900
68 2½d. on 2s. dull lilac (*b*) .. £12000
69 6 2½d. on 2s. dull lilac (*c*) .. £6000
70 2½d. on 2s. dull lilac (*d*) .. £5000
71 2½d. on 2s. dull lilac (*f*) .. £12000

The setting was rearranged to surch Nos. 63/71, so that in the pane of thirty there were twenty-two examples of (*a*), one of (*b*), two of (*c*), four of (*d*) and one of (*f*).

9

10

1903. *Wmk Crown CA. P* 14.
73 9 ½d. dull purple and green .. 2·25 2·00
74 1d. dull purple and rosine .. 50 40
75 1½d. dull purple and black .. 1·75 3·75
76 2d. dull purple and brown-orange .. 4·00 6·50
77 2½d. dull purple and ultramarine .. 5·00 5·50
78 10 3d. dull purple and grey .. 5·00 7·00
79 4d. dull purple and rosine .. 6·00 7·50
80 5d. dull purple and black .. 6·50 7·50
81 6d. dull purple .. 8·00 7·50
82 1s. green and black .. 13·00 13·00
83 2s. green and ultramarine .. 22·00 18·00
84 5s. green and carmine .. 28·00 38·00
85 £1 purple/*red* .. £275 £325
73/85 .. *Set of* 13 £325 £400
73/85 Optd "Specimen" .. *Set of* 13 £450

1904–5. *Wmk Mult Crown CA. P* 14.
86 9 ½d. dull purple and green, C (1904) .. 4·00 90
87 1d. dull purple and rosine, OC (1904) .. 50 35
88 1½d. dull purple and black, C .. 2·00 4·00
89 2d. dull purple and brown-orange, C .. 2·75 2·75
90 2½d. dull purple and ultramarine, C .. 3·25 2·50
91 10 3d. dull purple and grey, C .. 7·00 4·00
92 4d. dull purple and rosine, C .. 3·25 2·75
93 5d. dull purple and black, C .. 7·50 7·50
94 6d. dull purple, C .. 2·50 2·75
95 1s. green and black, C .. 7·50 8·50
96 2s. green and ultramarine, C .. 14·00 14·00
97 5s. green and carmine, C .. 28·00 32·00
98 £1 purple/*red*, C .. £250 £325
86/98 .. *Set of* 13 £300 £375

1907–10. *Wmk Mult Crown CA. P* 14.
99 9 ½d. green, O (1907) .. 45 30
100 1d. carmine, O .. 2·75 30
a. Red, O (1907) .. 45 25
101 1½d. orange, O (1910) .. 30 2·00
102 2d. greyish slate, O .. 1·00 1·50
103 2½d. blue, O (1907) .. 80 1·40
104 10 3d. purple/*yellow*, OC .. 2·00 2·75
105 4d. black and red/*yellow*, C .. 1·50 1·10
106 5d. purple and olive-green, C .. 2·75 3·25
107 6d. dull and bright purple, C .. 3·00 4·00
108 1s. black/*green*, C .. 5·00 4·50
109 2s. purple and bright blue/*blue*, C .. 15·00 11·00
110 5s. green and red/*yellow*, C .. 27·00 32·00
111 £1 purple and black/*red*, C .. £160 £225
99/111 .. *Set of* 13 £200 £250
99/111 Optd "Specimen" .. *Set of* 13 £375

11

12

13

14

1912–16. *Wmk Mult Crown CA. P* 14.
112 11 ½d. blue-green, O .. 65 40
a. Yellow-green .. 55 50
b. Deep green .. 1·60 65
113 1d. carmine-red, O .. 60 15
a. Scarlet (1916) .. 55 30
b. Rose-red .. 90 20
114 1½d. orange, O .. 85 85
a. Orange-yellow .. 1·60 95
115 2d. greyish slate, O .. 70 15
116 2½d. deep blue, O .. 4·75 1·60
a. Ultramarine .. 95 85
116*b* 14 3d. purple/*yellow*, C .. 1·40 2·50
ba. On pale yellow .. 2·50 3·25
117 12 4d. black and red-*yellow*, O .. 1·25 2·00
a. On lemon .. 3·75 5·00
b. On pale yellow (Die II) .. 70 1·90
118 5d. purple and olive-green, O .. 90 2·25
119 6d. dull and bright purple, C .. 3·25 3·25
120 13 7d. purple and orange, C .. 1·50 3·50
121 9d. purple and black, C .. 4·75 4·25
122 12 10d. purple and red, C .. 2·50 5·00
124 14 1s. black/*green*, C .. 3·00 3·50
a. On blue-green, green back .. 1·90 2·75
125 2s. blue and purple/*blue*, C .. 7·00 3·75
126 5s. red and green/*yellow*, C .. 11·00 17·00
127 10s. red and green/*green*, C .. 25·00 30·00
a. Carmine and blue-green/green .. 30·00 35·00
b. Carmine and yellow-green/green .. 30·00 35·00

128 **14** £1 black and purple/*red*, **C** .. .. 80·00 £110
129 £2 blue and dull purple, **C** (S. £110) .. £400 £450
130 £5 orange and green, **C** (S. £250) .. £1000
112/28 .. .. *Set of* 17 £130 £170
112/28 Optd "Specimen" .. .. *Set of* 17 £425

1921–28. *Wmk Mult Script CA. P* 14.
131 **11** ½d. dull green, **O** 35 15
a. Bright green 80 35
132 1d. bright violet, **O** (Die I) (1924) 80 40
a. Die II (1926) 50 10
133 1½d. scarlet, **O** (1925) 50 45
134 2d. grey, **O** (1922) 50 10
135 2½d. ultramarine, **O** 55 65
136 **12** 3d. bright blue, **O** (1922) 50 25
137 4d. black and red/*pale yellow*, **O** (1925) 1·75 1·25
138 5d. purple and olive-green, **O** 75 90
139 6d. grey-purple and bright purple, **C** .. 1·75 1·25
140 **13** 7d. purple and orange, **C** (1928) .. 2·00 5·00
141 9d. purple and black, **C** (1922) .. 3·00 4·00
142 **12** 10d. purple and red, **C** (1926) .. .. 3·00 5·00
143 **14** 1s. black/*emerald*, **C** (1925) .. .. 1·75 2·50
144 2s. blue and dull purple/*blue*, **C** .. 6·50 6·50
145 5s. red and green/*yellow*, **C** (1927) .. 10·00 20·00
146 10s. red and green/*green*, **C** (1927) .. 35·00 48·00
147 £2 blue and dull purple, **C** (1923) (Optd S. £110) £475 £500
148 £5 orange and green, **C** (1923) (Optd S. £300) £1100
131/146 .. .. .. *Set of* 16 60·00 85·00
131/46 Optd "Specimen" .. .. *Set of* 16 £350

15 Rice Field

16 Palms and Cola Tree

1932 (1 Mar). *Wmk Mult Script CA. (a) Recess Waterlow. P* 12½.
155 **15** ½d. green 30 35
156 1d. violet 15 15
157 1½d. carmine .. .. 45 1·25
a. Imperf between (horiz pair) ..
158 2d. brown 45 40
159 3d. blue 55 75
160 4d. orange .. .. 85 1·00
161 5d. bronze-green .. .. .. 85 1·25
162 6d. light blue .. .. 1·25 1·60
163 1s. lake .. .. 2·50 4·50

(*b*) *Recess B.W. P* 12.
164 **16** 2s. chocolate .. .. .. 8·50 11·00
165 5s. deep blue .. .. .. 15·00 18·00
166 10s. green .. .. .. 32·00 50·00
167 £1 purple .. .. .. 80·00 £120
155/167 .. .. .. *Set of* 13 £130 £190
155/67 Perf "Specimen" .. .. *Set of* 13 £225

17 Arms of Sierra Leone

20 Old Slave Market, Freetown

27 African Elephant

28 King George V

(Des Father F. Welch. Recess B.W.)

1933 (2 Oct). *Centenary of Abolition of Slavery and of Death of William Wilberforce. T* **17, 20, 27/8** *and similar designs. Wmk Mult Script CA (sideways on horiz designs). P* 12.
168 ½d. green 55 90
169 1d. black and brown 35 15
170 1½d. chestnut .. .. .. 3·25 5·50
171 2d. purple .. .. 2·25 40
172 3d. blue .. .. 1·60 3·25
173 4d. brown .. .. 5·00 10·00
174 5d. green and chestnut .. .. 8·50 18·00
175 6d. black and brown-orange .. 10·00 12·00
176 1s. violet .. .. 10·00 14·00
177 2s. brown and light blue .. .. 32·00 38·00
178 5s. black and purple £150 £225
179 10s. black and sage-green £180 £275
180 £1 violet and orange £550 £700
168/180 .. .. .. *Set of* 13 £900 £1200
168/80 Perf "Specimen" .. *Set of* 13 £1000

Designs: *Vert*—1d. "Freedom"; 1½d. Map of Sierra Leone; 4d. Government sanatorium. *Horiz*—3d. Native fruit seller; 5d. Bullom canoe; 6d. Punting near Banana; 1s. Government buildings; 2s. Bunce Island; £1 Freetown harbour.

1935 (6 May). *Silver Jubilee. As Nos.* 91/4 *of Antigua, but ptd by B.W. P* 11 × 12.
181 1d. ultramarine and grey-black 25 15
a. Extra flagstaff .. .. .. 22·00
b. Short extra flagstaff .. .. 14·00
c. Lightning conductor .. .. 12·00
182 3d. brown and deep blue .. .. .. 85 1·25
a. Extra flagstaff .. .. .. 24·00
c. Lightning conductor .. .. 14·00
183 5d. green and indigo .. .. .. 1·40 3·75
a. Extra flagstaff .. .. .. 60·00
c. Lightning conductor .. .. 30·00
184 1s. slate and purple .. .. .. 3·25 3·25
a. Extra flagstaff £110
c. Lightning conductor .. .. 40·00
181/4 Perf "Specimen" .. *Set of* 4 60·00

For illustrations of plate varieties see Omnibus section following Zululand.

1937 (12 May). *Coronation. As Nos.* 13/15 *of Aden, but ptd by B.W. P* 11 × 11½.
185 1d. orange 50 30
186 2d. purple 50 45
187 3d. blue 60 90
185/7 Perf "Specimen" .. .. *Set of* 3 45·00

30 Freetown from the Harbour

31 Rice Harvesting

(Recess Waterlow)

1938 (1 May)–**44.** *Wmk Mult Script CA (sideways). P* 12½.
188 **30** ½d. black and blue-green 15 10
189 1d. black and lake 15 5
a. Imperf between (pair) .. .. — £1600
190 **31** 1½d. scarlet .. .. .. 9·00 20
190*a* 1½d. mauve (1.2.41) 15 5
191 2d. mauve .. .. 18·00 1·25
191*a* 2d. scarlet (1.2.41) 15 10
192 **30** 3d. black and ultramarine 15 5
193 4d. black and red-brown (20.6.38) .. 45 30
194 **31** 5d. olive-green (20.6.38) .. .. 85 1·00
195 6d. grey (20.6.38) 40 10
196 **30** 1s. black and olive-green (20.6.38) .. 50 20
196*a* **31** 1s. 3d. yellow-orange (1944) 45 30
197 **30** 2s. black and sepia (20.6.38) .. 1·50 60
198 **31** 5s. red-brown (20.6.38) .. .. 3·25 1·75
199 10s. emerald-green (20.6.38) .. .. 9·00 5·50
200 **30** £1 deep blue (20.6.38) .. .. 17·00 13·00
188/200 .. .. .. *Set of* 16 55·00 22·00
188/200 Perf "Specimen" .. .. *Set of* 16 £225

1946 (1 Oct). *Victory. As Nos.* 28/9 *of Aden.*
201 1½d. lilac 15 15
202 3d. ultramarine 20 15
201/2 Perf "Specimen" .. .. *Set of* 2 40·00

1948 (1 Dec). *Royal Silver Wedding. As Nos.* 30/1 *of Aden.*
203 1½d. bright purple 25 15
204 £1 indigo .. .. 18·00 20·00

1949 (1 Dec). *75th Anniv of U.P.U. As Nos.* 114/17 *of Antigua.*
205 1½d. purple 15 20
206 3d. deep blue 70 40
207 6d. grey 70 65
208 1s. olive 75 90

1953 (2 June). *Coronation. As No.* 47 *of Aden but ptd by B.W.*
209 1½d. black and purple 15 10

32 Cape Lighthouse **33** Cotton Tree, Freetown

(Recess Waterlow)

1956 (2 Jan)–**61.** *Designs as T* **32/3**. *Wmk Mult Script CA. P* 13½ × 13 (*horiz*) *or* 14 (*vert*).
210 ½d. black and deep lilac 12 20
211 1d. black and olive 12 5
212 1½d. black and ultramarine 12 40
213 2d. black and brown 20 5
214 3d. black and bright blue 25 5
a. Perf 13 × 13½ .. .. .. 1·60 2·25
215 4d. black and slate-blue 25 20
216 6d. black and violet 25 5
217 1s. black and scarlet 30 5
218 1s. 3d. black and sepia 90 8
219 2s. 6d. black and chestnut .. .. 2·25 60
220 5s. black and deep green .. .. 1·25 45
221 10s. black and bright reddish purple .. 4·25 4·75
a. Black and purple (19.4.61) .. .. 9·50 20·00
222 £1 black and orange .. .. .. 14·00 12·00
210/22 .. .. .. *Set of* 13 22·00 17·00

Designs: *Horiz*—1d. Queen Elizabeth II Quay; 1½d. Piassava workers; 4d. Iron ore production, Marampa; 6d. Whale Bay, York Village; 1s. 3d. Aeroplane and map; 10s. Law Courts, Freetown; £1, Government House. *Vert*—3d. Rice harvesting; 1s. Bullom Boat; 2s. 6d. Orugu Bridge; 5s. Kuranko Chief.

INDEPENDENT

45 Palm Fruit Gathering

46 Licensed Diamond Miner

52

(Des K. Penny (½d., 1s.), Messrs Thoma, Turrell and Larkins (1d., 3d., 6d., 2s. 6d.), W. G. Rumley (1½d., 5s.), J. H. Vandi (2d., 10s.), R. A. Sweet (4d., 1s 3d.), J. White (£1). Recess B.W.)

1961 (27 Apr). *Independence. T* **45/6** *and similar designs. W* **52**. *P* 13½.
223 ½d. chocolate and deep bluish green .. 5 5
224 1d. orange-brown and myrtle-green .. 5 5
225 1½d. black and emerald 5 5
226 2d. black and ultramarine 5 5
227 3d. orange-brown and blue 5 5
228 4d. turquoise-blue and scarlet .. 5 5
229 6d. black and purple 10 5
230 1s. chocolate and yellow-orange .. 12 5
231 1s. 3d. turquoise-blue and violet .. 20 10
232 2s. 6d. deep green and black 40 25
233 5s. black and red .. .. .. 1·00 1·00
234 10s. black and green .. .. .. 2·00 2·00
235 £1 carmine-red and yellow .. .. 4·50 5·00
223/235 .. .. .. *Set of* 13 8·00 8·00

Designs: *Vert*—1½d., 5s. Bundu mask; 2d., 10s. Bishop Crowther and Old Fourah Bay College; 1s. Palm fruit gathering; £1, Forces Bugler. *Horiz*—3d., 6d. Sir Milton Margai; 4d., 1s. 3d. Lumley Beach, Freetown; 2s. 6d. Licensed diamond miner.

53 Royal Charter, 1799

55 Old House of Representatives, Freetown, 1924

(Des C. P. Rang (3d., 4d.), F. H. Burgess (1s. 3d.). Recess B.W.)

1961 (25 Nov). *Royal Visit. T* **53, 55** *and similar designs. W* **52**. *P* 13½.
236 3d. black and rose-red 8 8
237 4d. black and violet 10 10
238 6d. black and yellow-orange 12 10
239 1s. 3d. black and blue 30 20

Designs: *Vert*—4d. King's Yard Gate, Freetown, 1817. *Horiz*—1s. 3d. H.M. Yacht *Britannia* at Freetown.

57 Campaign Emblem

(Recess B.W.)

1962 (7 Apr). *Malaria Eradication. W* **52**. *P* 11 × 11½.
240 **57** 3d. carmine-red 5 5
241 1s. 3d. deep green 15 10

58 Fireball Lily

59 Jina-gbo

(Des M. Goaman. Photo Harrison)

1963 (1 Jan). *Flowers. Vert designs as T* **58** (½d., 1½d., 3d., 4d., 1s., 2s. 6d., 5s., 10s.) *or horiz as T* **59** (*others*). *Multicoloured. W* **52** (*sideways on vert designs*). *P* 14.
242 ½d. Type **58** . . 5 5
243 1d. Type **59** . . 5 5
244 1½d. Stereospermum . . 10 10
245 2d. Black-eyed Susan . . 10 5
246 3d. Beniseed . . 10 5
247 4d. Blushing Hibiscus . . 12 5
248 6d. Climbing Lily . . 12 5
249 1s. Beautiful Crinum . . 20 5
250 1s. 3d. Blue Bells . . 25 25
251 2s. 6d. Broken Hearts . . 70 45
252 5s. Ra-ponthi . . 1·50 1·25
253 10s. Blue Plumbago . . 3·00 2·75
254 £1 African Tulip Tree . . 11·00 8·00
242/254 . . *Set of* 13 16·00 12·00

71 Threshing Machine and Corn Bins

(Des V. Whiteley. Recess B.W.)

1963 (21 Mar). *Freedom from Hunger. T* **71** *and similar horiz design. W* **52**. *P* 11½ × 11.
255 3d. black and yellow-ochre . . 15 5
256 1s. 3d. sepia and emerald-green . . 40 20
Design:—1s. 3d. Girl with onion crop.

2ND YEAR OF INDEPENDENCE 19 PROGRESS 63 DEVELOPMENT 3d. (73)

2nd Year Independence Progress Development 1963 10d. (74)

(Optd by Govt Printer, Freetown)

1963 (27 Apr). *Second Anniv of Independence. Surch or optd as T* **73**/**4**. (*a*) *Postage*.
257 3d. on ½d. black & deep lilac (No. 210) (R.) 5 5
a. Small "c" in "INDEPENDENCE" 4·00 4·00
258 4d. on 1½d. black & ultram (No. 212) (Br.) . . 5 5
259 6d. on ½d. black & deep lilac (No. 210) (O.) 8 5
a. Small "c" in "INDEPENDENCE" . . 6·00 6·00
260 10d. on 3d. black & bright blue (No. 214) (R.) 20 12
261 1s. 6d. on 3d. black & brt bl (No. 214) (V.) . . 25 12
262 3s. 6d. on 3d. black & brt bl (No. 214) (Ult.) 40 30

(*b*) *Air. Additionally optd* "AIR MAIL"
263 7d. on 1½d. black & ultram (No. 212) (C.) . . 10 10
264 1s. 3d. on 1½d. blk & ultram (No. 212) (R.) 12 12
265 2s. 6d. black and chestnut (No. 219) (V.) . . 50 40
266 3s. on 3d. black & bright blue (No. 214) (B.) 50 40
267 6s. on 3d. black & bright blue (No. 214) (R.) 75 80
268 11s. on 10s. black and bright reddish purple (No. 221) (C.) . . 1·75 2·25
269 11s. on £1 black and orange (No. 222) (C.) . . £600 £250
257/268 . . *Set of* 12 4·25 4·25

75 Centenary Emblem

(Des M. Goaman. Recess B.W.)

1963 (1 Nov). *Centenary of Red Cross. T* **75** *and similar vert designs. W* **52**. *P* 11 × 11½.
270 3d. red and violet . . 15 10
271 6d. red and black . . 20 15
272 1s. 3d. red and deep bluish green . . 35 20
Designs:—6d. Red Cross emblem; 1s. 3d. Centenary emblem.

1853–1859–1963 Oldest Postal Service Newest G.P.O. in West Africa 1s. (78)

1853–1859–1963 Oldest Postage Stamp Newest G.P.O. in West Africa AIRMAIL (79)

1963 (4 Nov). *Postal Commemorations. Optd or surch by Govt Printer, Freetown*. (*a*) *Postage. As T* **78**.
273 3d. black and bright blue (No. 214) . . 5 5
274 4d. on 1½d. black and ultram (No. 212) (C.) 5 5
275 9d. on 1½d. black and ultram (No. 212) (V.) 12 5
276 1s. on 1s. 3d. turq-blue & vio (No. 231) (C.) . . 15 5
277 1s. 6d. on ½d. blk & dp lilac (No. 210) (Mag.) 20 15
278 2s. on 3d. black & bright blue (No. 214) (Br.) 30 30

(*b*) *Air. As T* **79**
279 7d. on 3d. black and rose-red (No. 236) (Br.) 10 10
280 1s. 3d. black and blue (No. 239) (C.) . . 12 15
281 2s. 6d. on 4d. turquoise-blue & scar (No. 228) 40 40
282 3s. on 3d. black and rose-red (No. 236) (V.) . . 40 50
283 6s. on 6d. black & yell-orge (No. 238) (Ult.) 65 75
284 £1 black and orange (No. 222) (R.) . . 10·00 14·00
273/284 . . *Set of* 12 11·00 15·00

The events commemorated are: 1853, "First Post Office"; 1859, "First Postage Stamps"; and 1963, "Newest G.P.O." in West Africa. Nos. 273, 278 have the opt. in five lines; Nos. 279, 282 in six lines (incl "AIRMAIL").

80 Lion Emblem and Map **81** Globe and Map

(Recess and litho Walsall Lithographic Co, Ltd)

1964 (10 Feb). *World's Fair, New York. Imperf. Self-Adhesive.*

(*a*) *Postage. T* **80**
285 1d. multicoloured . . 5 5
286 3d. multicoloured . . 5 5
a. Lion omitted
287 4d. multicoloured . . 5 5
288 6d. multicoloured . . 5 5
289 1s. multicoloured . . 5 5
a. "POSTAGE 1/-" omitted . . 35·00
290 2s. multicoloured . . 15 15
291 5s. multicoloured . . 30 30
a. "POSTAGE 5/-" omitted . . 35·00

(*b*) *Air. T* **81**
292 7d. multicoloured . . 5 5
293 9d. multicoloured . . 5 5
a. "AIR MAIL 9d." omitted
294 1s. 3d. multicoloured . . 10 5
a. "AIR MAIL 1/3" omitted . . 35·00
295 2s. 6d. multicoloured . . 15 15
296 3s. 6d. multicoloured . . 20 20
a. "AIR MAIL 3/6" omitted
297 6s. multicoloured . . 30 35
a. "AIR MAIL 6/–" omitted . . 40·00
298 11s. multicoloured . . 50 65
a. "AIR MAIL 11/-" omitted . . 42·00
285/298 . . *Set of* 14 1·90 2·00

Nos. 285/98 were issued in sheets of 30 (6 × 5) on green (postage) or yellow (airmail) backing paper with the emblems of Samuel Jones & Co. Ltd, self-adhesive paper-makers, on the back.

WARNING. These and later self-adhesive stamps should be kept on their backing paper except commercially used, which should be retained on cover or piece.

82 Inscription and Map **83** Pres. Kennedy and Map

(Recess and litho Walsall)

1964 (11 May). *President Kennedy Memorial Issue. Imperf. Self-adhesive.* (*a*) *Postage. Green backing paper.*
299 **82** 1d. multicoloured . . 5 5
300 3d. multicoloured . . 5 5
301 4d. multicoloured . . 5 5
302 6d. multicoloured . . 5 5
303 1s. multicoloured . . 5 5
304 2s. multicoloured . . 15 10
305 5s. multicoloured . . 40 30

(*b*) *Air. Yellow backing paper*
306 **83** 7d. multicoloured . . 5 5
307 9d. multicoloured . . 5 5
308 1s. 3d. multicoloured . . 10 5
309 2s. 6d. multicoloured . . 15 20
310 3s. 6d. multicoloured . . 25 30
311 6s. multicoloured . . 40 50
312 11s. multicoloured . . 55 70
299/312 . . *Set of* 14 2·10 2·25

(New Currency. 100 cents = 1 leone)

3c (84) AIRMAIL 7c (85) LE 1·00 (86)

1964–66. *Decimal currency. Various stamps surch locally.*

(i) *First issue* (4.8.64). (*a*) *Postage. Surch as T* **84**
313 1 c. on 6d. multicoloured (No. 248) (R.) . . 5 5
314 2 c. on 3d. black and rose-red (No. 236) . . 5 5
315 3 c. on 3d. multicoloured (No. 246) . . 5 5
a. Surch inverted
316 5 c. on ½d. chocolate and deep bluish green (No. 223) (B.) . . 8 5
317 8 c. on 3d. black & yell-ochre (No. 255) (R.) . . 10 5
318 10 c. on 1s. 3d. multicoloured (No. 250) (R.) . . 10 5
319 15 c. on 1s. multicoloured (No. 249) . . 15 5
320 25 c. on 6d. black & yell-orge (No. 238) (V.) . . 30 35
321 50 c. on 2s. 6d. dp green & blk (No. 232) (O.) . . 60 60

(*b*) *Air. As T* **85** *or* **86** (*Nos.* 326/7)
322 7 c. on 1s. 3d. sepia and emerald-green (No. 256) (B.) . . 10 5
323 20 c. on 4d. turquoise-blue & scarlet (No. 228) 25 15
324 30 c. on 10s. black and green (No. 234) (R.) . . 35 40
325 40 c. on 5s. black and red (No. 233) (B.) . . 50 50
326 1 l. on 1s. 3d. multicoloured (No. 308) (R.) . . 1·25 1·50
327 2 l. on 11s. multicoloured (No. 312) . . 2·50 3·25
313/327 . . *Set of* 15 6·00 6·50

1c (87) TWO LEONES Le 2·00 (88)

(ii) *Second issue* (20.1.65). *Surch as T* **87** *or* **88** (*Nos.* 332/3)

(*a*) *Postage*
328 1 c. on 3d. orange-brown and blue (No. 227) 5 5
329 2 c. on 1d. multicoloured (No. 299) . . 5 5
330 4 c. on 3d. multicoloured (No. 300) . . 5 5
a. Error. 4 c. on 1d. (No. 299)
331 5 c. on 2d. multicoloured (No. 245) . . 10 5
332 1 l. on 5s. multicoloured (No. 252) (Gold) 2·50 2·50
333 2 l. on £1 carmine-red & yell (No. 235) (B.) . . 4·25 4·25
a. Surch double (B. + Blk.) . . — 50·00

(*b*) *Air*
334 7 c. on 7d. multicoloured (No. 306) (R.) . . 15 15
335 60 c. on 9d. multicoloured (No. 307) . . 85 85
328/335 . . *Set of* 8 7·00 7·00

(iii) *Third issue* (4.65). *Surch in figures* (*various sizes*). (*a*) *Postage*
336 1 c. on 1½d. black & emerald (No. 225) (R.) 5 5
337 2 c. on 3d. multicoloured (No. 300) . . 8 8
338 2 c. on 4d. multicoloured (No. 287) . . 8 8
339 3 c. on 1d. multicoloured (No. 243) . . 8 5
340 3 c. on 2d. black and ultram (No. 226) (R.) . . 5 5
341 5 c. on 1s. 3d. turq-bl & violet (No. 231) (R.) . . 10 10
a. Surch inverted
342 15 c. on 6d. multicoloured (No. 302) . . 80 70
343 15 c. on 1s. multicoloured (No. 303) (R.) 1·25 1·25
344 20 c. on 6d. black and purple (No. 229) (R.) 30 30
345 25 c. on 6d. multicoloured (No. 248) (R.) 35 35
346 50 c. on 3d. orange-brn & blue (No. 227) (R.) . . 80 80
347 60 c. on 5s. multicoloured (No. 291) (V.) . . 2·50 2·50
348 1 l. on 4d. multicoloured (No. 301) (R.) 3·50 3·50
349 2 l. on £1 carmine-red & yell (No. 235) (B.) . . 5·00 5·00

(*b*) *Air*
350 7 c. on 9d. multicoloured (No. 293) . . 12 12
336/350 . . *Set of* 15 14·00 14·00

2c (89) TWO Leones (90)

(iv) *Fourth issue* (9.11.65). *Surch as T* **89**. (*a*) *Postage*
351 **80** 1 c. on 6d. multicoloured (V.) . . 3·25 7·00
352 1 c. on 2s. multicoloured (V.) . . 3·25 7·00
353 **82** 1 c. on 2s. multicoloured (V.) . . 3·25 7·00
354 1 c. on 5s. multicoloured (V.) . . 3·25 7·00

(*b*) *Air*
355 **81** 2 c. on 1s. 3d. multicoloured . . 3·25 7·00
356 **83** 2 c. on 1s. 3d. multicoloured . . 3·25 7·00
357 2 c. on 3s. 6d. multicoloured . . 3·25 7·00
358 **81** 3 c. on 7d. multicoloured . . 3·25 7·00
359 **83** 3 c. on 9d. multicoloured . . 3·25 7·00
360 **81** 5 c. on 2s. 6d. multicoloured . . 3·25 7·00
361 **83** 5 c. on 2s. 6d. multicoloured . . 3·25 7·00
362 **81** 5 c. on 3s. 6d. multicoloured . . 3·25 7·00
363 5 c. on 6s. multicoloured . . 3·25 7·00
364 **83** 5 c. on 6s. multicoloured . . 3·25 7·00
351/364 . . *Set of* 14 40·00 90·00

(v) *Fifth issue* (28.1.66). *Air. No.* 374 *further surch with T* **90**
365 2 l. on 30 c. on 6d. multicoloured . . 8·00 5·00

IN MEMORIAM TWO GREAT LEADERS 2c

(**91** Margai and Churchill)

1965 (19 May). *Sir Milton Margai and Sir Winston Churchill Commemoration. Nos.* 242/3, 245/50 *and* 252/4 *surch as T* **91** *on horiz designs or with individual portraits on vert designs as indicated.*

(*a*) *Postage*
366 2 c. on 1d. Type **59** . . 5 5
367 3 c. on 3d. Beniseed (Margai) . . 5 5
368 10 c. on 1s. Beautiful Crinum (Churchill) . . 10 5
369 20 c. on 1s. 3d. Blue Bells . . 30 10
370 50 c. on 4d. Blushing Hibiscus (Margai) . . 60 45
371 75 c. on 5s. Ra-ponthi (Churchill) . . 1·75 1·50

(*b*) *Air. Additionally optd* "AIR MAIL"
372 7 c. on 2d. Black-eyed Susan . . 10 5
373 15 c. on ½d. Type **58** (Margai) . . 30 15

374 30 c. on 6d. Climbing Lily (O. and W.) .. 60 30
375 1 l. on £1 African Tulip Tree .. .. 3·50 2·25
376 2 l. on 10s. Blue Plumbago (Churchill) .. 8·00 6·00
a. Surch value omitted £160
366/376 .. .. *Set of* 11 13·00 10·00

92 Cola Plant and Nut

93 Arms of Sierra Leone

94 Inscription and Necklace

(Des M. Meers. Manufactured by Walsall Lithographic Co, Ltd)

1965 (Nov). *Imperf. Self-adhesive.*

A. *Embossed on silver foil, backed with paper bearing advertisements. Emerald, olive-yellow and carmine; denominations in colours given. Postage.*

377 **92** 1 c. emerald 15 10
378 2 c. carmine 15 10
379 3 c. olive-yellow 15 10
380 4 c. silver/*emerald* 20 12
381 5 c. silver/*carmine* 20 12

B. *Typo and embossed on cream paper backed with advertisements*

(*a*) *Postage*

382 **93** 20 c. multicoloured 80 35
383 50 c. multicoloured .. .. .. 2·00 1·40

(*b*) *Air*

384 **93** 40 c. multicoloured .. .. .. 1·75 1·40

C. *Foil-backed and litho, with advertisements on white paper backing (see footnote). Air*

385 **94** 7 c. multicoloured 30 15
386 15 c. multicoloured 75 50
377/386 .. .. *Set of* 10 5·75 4·00

The above stamps were issued in single form with attached tabs to remove the backing paper, with the exception of No. 385 which was in sheets of 25 bearing a single large advertisement on the back.

For other stamps in Type **92** see Nos. 421/31 and 435/42*a*. For 10 c. stamps in Type **93** see Nos. 433/*a*.

2c
FIVE YEARS
INDEPENDENCE
1961-1966
(95)

15c
AIRMAIL
FIVE YEARS
INDEPENDENCE
1961-1966
(96)

1966 (27 Apr). *Fifth Anniv of Independence. Various stamps surch.*

(*a*) *Postage. As T* **95**

387 1 c. on 6d. multicoloured (No. 248) .. 5 5
388 2 c. on 4d. multicoloured (No. 247) .. 5 5
389 3 c. on 1½d. black & ultram (No. 212) (B.) .. 5 5
390 8 c. on 1s. multicoloured (No. 249) (B.) .. 12 12
391 10 c. on 2s. 6d. multicoloured (No. 251) (B.) .. 15 12
392 20 c. on 2d. black and brown (No. 213) (B.) .. 25 25

(*b*) *Air. As T* **96**

393 7 c. on 3d. red and violet (No. 270) 10 12
394 15 c. on 1s. multicoloured (No. 249) 25 12
395 25 c. on 2s. 6d. multicoloured (No. 251) .. 50 70
396 50 c. on 1½d. multicoloured (No. 244) .. 90 1·00
397 1 l. on 4d. multicoloured (No. 247) .. .. 1·50 1·90
387/397 .. .. *Set of* 11 3·50 4·25

The inscription on No. 387 is in larger type.

97 Lion's Head

98 Map of Sierra Leone

(Des and embossed Walsall)

1966 (12 Nov). *First Sierra Leone Gold Coinage Commemoration. Circular designs, embossed on gold foil, backed with paper bearing advertisements. Imperf.* (*a*) *Postage.*

(i) *¼ golde coin. Diameter 1½ in.*

398 **97** 2 c. magenta and yellow-orange .. 5 5
399 **98** 3 c. emerald and bright purple 5 5

(ii) *½ golde coin. Diameter 2⅛ in.*

400 **97** 5 c. vermilion and ultramarine .. 8 8
401 **98** 8 c. turquoise-blue and black 12 12

(iii) *1 golde coin. Diameter 3¼ in.*

402 **97** 25 c. violet and emerald 35 35
403 **98** 1 l. orange and cerise .. .. .. 2·50 2·50

(*b*) *Air.* (i) *¼ golde coin. Diameter 1½ in.*

404 **98** 7 c. red-orange and cerise 10 10
405 **97** 10 c. cerise and greenish blue 15 12

(ii) *½ golde coin. Diameter 2⅛ in.*

406 **98** 15 c. orange and cerise 25 25
407 **97** 30 c. bright purple and black 40 45

(iii) *1 golde coin. Diameter 3¼ in.*

408 **98** 50 c. bright green and purple 75 75
409 **97** 2 l. black and emerald .. .. .. 4·50 4·50
398/409 .. .. *Set of* 12 8·50 8·50

12½
(99)

17½
(100)

=17½
(101)

1967 (2 Dec). *Decimal Currency Provisionals. Surch as T* **99** (*Nos. 410/13*), *T* **100** (*Nos. 415/17*) *or T* **101** (*others*). (*a*) *Postage.*

410 6½ c. on 75 c. on 5s. mult (No. 371) (R.) .. 15 15
411 7½ c. on 75 c. on 5s. mult (No. 371) (S.) .. 15 15
412 9½ c. on 50 c. on 4d. mult (No. 370) (G.) .. 20 20
413 12½ c. on 20 c. on 1s. 3d. multicoloured (No. 369) (V.) 25 25
414 17½ c. on 50 c. multicoloured (No. 383) .. 1·75 1·75
415 17½ c. on 1 l. on 4d. mult (No. 348) (B.) .. 1·75 1·75
416 18½ c. on 1 l. on 4d. multicoloured (No. 348) 1·75 1·75
417 18½ c. on 60 c. on 5s. multicoloured (No. 347) 5·50 5·50
418 25 c. on 50 c. multicoloured (No. 383) .. 70 70

(*b*) *Air*

419 11½ c. on 40 c. multicoloured (No. 384) .. 20 20
420 25 c. on 40 c. multicoloured (No. 384) .. 70 70
410/20 .. .. *Set of* 11 12·00 12·00

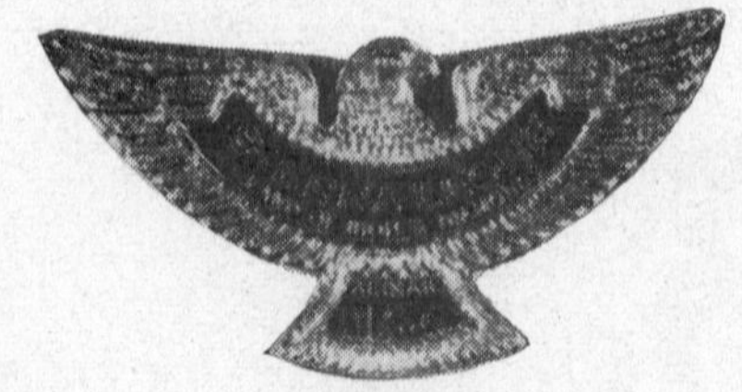

102 Eagle

(Manufactured by Walsall)

1967 (2 Dec)–**69**. *Decimal Currency. Imperf. Self-adhesive.*

(*a*) *Postage. As T* **92**, *but embossed on white paper, backed with paper bearing advertisements. Background colours given first, and value tablet colours in brackets*

421 **92** ½ c. carmine-red (carmine/*white*) .. 10 10
422 1 c. carmine (carmine/*white*) 10 5
423 1½ c. orange-yellow (green/*white*) .. 15 12
424 2 c. carmine-red (green/*white*) 25 10
425 **92** 2½ c. apple-green (yellow/*white*) .. 30 25
426 3 c. carmine-red (white/*carmine*) .. 20 10
427 3½ c. reddish purple (white/*green*) .. 30 30
428 4 c. carmine-red (white/*green*) 30 12
429 4½ c. dull green (green/*white*) 30 30
430 5 c. carmine (yellow/*white*) 30 12
431 5½ c. brown-red (green/*white*) 30 30

(*b*) *Air. T* **102** *embossed on black paper, backed with paper bearing advertisements; or,* (*No.* 433), *as T* **93**, *typo and embossed on cream paper, also with advertisements*

432 **102** 9½ c. red and gold/*black* 40 40
432*a* 9½ c. blue and gold/*black* (10.9.69) .. 50 55
433 **93** 10 c. multicoloured (red frame) .. 45 45
433*a* 10 c. mult (black frame) (10.9.69) .. 55 55
434 **102** 15 c. green and gold/*black* 70 80
434*a* 15 c. red and gold/*black* (10.9.69) .. 80 90
421/34*a* .. .. .. *Set of* 17 5·25 5·00

The ½, 1½, 2, 2½, 3, 3½ and 5 c. also exist without advertisements.

The footnote below Nos. 377/86 also applies here.

Although only released for collectors on 2 December, the 5 c. was known to be in use locally in February and the 3 c. in March. The 1 c. and 2 c. were also released locally some months earlier.

See also Nos. 538/44.

1968. *No advertisements on back, and colours in value tablet reversed. Background colours given first, and value tablet colours in brackets.*

435 **92** ½ c. carmine-red (white/*green*) 5 5
436 1 c. carmine (white/*carmine*) 15 12
437 2 c. carmine (white/*green*) .. .. 1·25 1·25
438 2½ c. apple-green (white/*yellow*) .. 1·75 1·75
439 3 c. carmine-red (carmine/*white*) .. 55 55

On Nos. 435 and 438, the figure "½" is larger than in Nos. 421 and 425.

It is believed that the ½ c. was released in February, the 2½ c. in April and the others in March.

The 1 c. also exists with advertisements on the backing paper.

The footnote below Nos. 377/86 also applies here.

1968–69. *No advertisements on back, colours changed and new value* (7 c.). *Background colours given first, and value tablet colours in brackets.* (*a*) *Postage.*

440 **92** 2 c. pink (white/*brown-lake*) 40 40
441 2½ c. deep bluish green (white/*orange*) .. 40 40
442 3½ c. olive-yellow (blue/*white*) 55 55

(*b*) *Air*

442*a* **92** 7 c. yellow (carmine/*white*) (10.9.69) 90 80
435/42*a* .. .. *Set of* 9 5·50 5·25

On Nos. 441/2 the fraction "½" is larger than in Nos. 425 and 427.

It is believed that the 3½ c. was released in March 1968 and the 2 and 2½ c. in May 1968.

The 2 c. also exists with advertisements on the backing paper.

The footnote below Nos. 377/86 also applies here.

103 Outline Map of Africa

(Litho Walsall)

1968 (25 Sept). *Human Rights Year. Each value comes in six types, showing different territories in yellow, as below. Imperf. Self-adhesive.*

A. Portuguese Guinea. D. Rhodesia.
B. South Africa. E. South West Africa.
C. Mozambique. F. Angola.

To indicate yellow territory use above letters as suffix to the following catalogue numbers.

(*a*) *Postage*

Each Territory

443 **103** ½ c. multicoloured 5 5
444 2 c. multicoloured 8 8
445 2½ c. multicoloured 8 8
446 3½ c. multicoloured 8 8
447 10 c. multicoloured 15 15
448 11½ c. multicoloured 20 20
449 15 c. multicoloured 25 25

(*b*) *Air*

450 **103** 7½ c. multicoloured 12 12
451 9½ c. multicoloured 20 20
452 14½ c. multicoloured 25 25
453 18½ c. multicoloured 30 30
454 25 c. multicoloured 40 40
455 1 l. multicoloured .. .. .. 9·50 6·50
456 2 l. multicoloured .. .. .. 18·00 14·00
443/56 Each territory .. .. *Set of* 14 27·00 20·00
443/56 Six territories .. .. *Set of* 84 £160 £120

Nos. 443/56 were issued in sheets of 30 (6 × 5) on backing paper depicting diamonds or the coat of arms on the reverse. The six types occur once in each horizontal row.

PRICES OF SETS

Set prices are given for many issues, generally those containing five stamps or more. Definitive sets include one of each value or major colour change, but do not cover different perforations, die types or minor shades. Where a choice is possible the set prices are based on the cheapest versions of the stamps included in the listings.

OLYMPIC PARTICIPATION
MEXICO 1968
POSTAGE
*6½
(104)

1968 (30 Nov). *Mexico Olympics Participation.*

(*a*) *Postage. No.* 383 *surch or optd* (*No.* 461) *as T* **104**

No.	Type	Description		
457	**93**	6½ c. on 50 c. multicoloured	12	12
458		17½ c. on 50 c. multicoloured	35	35
459		22½ c. on 50 c. multicoloured	45	45
		a. Surch double	£170	
460		28½ c. on 50 c. multicoloured	55	60
461		50 c. multicoloured	95	1·00

(*b*) *Air. No.* 384 *surch or optd* (*No.* 466) *as T* **104**, *in red*

No.	Type	Description		
462	**93**	6½ c. on 50 c. multicoloured	12	12
		a. Surch double	£190	
463		17½ c. on 40 c. multicoloured	35	35
464		22½ c. on 40 c. multicoloured	45	45
465		28½ c. on 40 c. multicoloured	55	60
466		40 c. multicoloured	90	1·00
457/66		*Set of* 10	4·25	4·50

105 1859 6d.

111 1965 15 c. Self-adhesive

(Litho Walsall)

1969 (1 Mar). *Fifth Anniv of World's First Self-adhesive Postage Stamps. Reproductions of earlier issues. Multicoloured. Imperf. Self-adhesive.* (*a*) *Postage. Vert designs.*

No.	Description		
467	1 c. Type **105**	5	5
468	2 c. 1965 2 c. self-adhesive	5	5
469	3½ c. 1961 Independence 2 c. commemorative	5	5
470	5 c. 1965 20 c. self-adhesive	12	12
471	12½ c. 1948 Royal Silver Wedding £1 commemorative	30	30
472	1 l. 1923 £2	3·50	3·50

(*b*) *Air. Horiz designs*

No.	Description		
473	7½ c. Type **111**	20	20
474	9½ c. 1967 9½ c. self-adhesive	20	15
475	20 c. 1964 1s. 3d. self-adhesive	40	40
476	30 c. 1964 President Kennedy Memorial 6s. commemorative self-adhesive	55	55
477	50 c. 1933 Centenary of Abolition of Slavery £1 commemorative	1·75	1·75
478	2 l. 1963 2nd Anniversary of Independence 11s. commemorative	17·00	17·00
467/478	*Set of* 12	22·00	22·00

Nos. 467 and 473 were issued with tabs as note under Nos. 377/86 and No. 474 exists with tabs and also in the normal version on backing paper.

All values are on white backing paper with advertisements printed on the reverse.

117 Ore-Ship, Globe and Flags of Sierra Leone and Japan

118 Ore-Ship, Map of Europe and Africa and Flags of Sierra Leone and Netherlands

The 3½ c., 9½ c., 2 l. and 10 c., 50 c., 1 l. are as T **118** but show respectively the flags of Great Britain and West Germany instead of the Netherlands.

(Litho Walsall)

1969 (10 July). *Pepel Port Improvements. Imperf. Self-adhesive, backed with paper bearing advertisements.* (*a*) *Postage.*

No.	Type	Description		
479	**117**	1 c. multicoloured	5	5
480	**118**	2 c. multicoloured	5	5
481	–	3½ c. multicoloured	8	8
482	–	10 c. multicoloured	12	12
483	**118**	18½ c. multicoloured	25	25
484	–	50 c. multicoloured	85	85

(*b*) *Air*

No.	Type	Description		
485	**117**	7½ c. multicoloured	10	10
486	–	9½ c. multicoloured	15	15
487	**117**	15 c. multicoloured	25	25
488	**118**	25 c. multicoloured	35	35
489	–	1 l. multicoloured	1·75	1·75
490	–	2 l. multicoloured	4·25	4·25
479/90		*Set of* 12	7·50	7·50

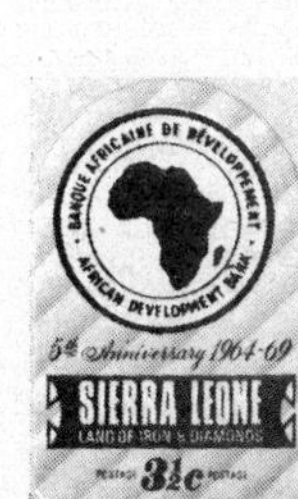

119 African Development Bank Emblem

120 Boy Scouts Emblem in "Diamond"

(Litho and embossed Walsall)

1969 (10 Sept). *Fifth Anniv of African Development Bank. Self-adhesive, backed with paper bearing advertisements. Imperf.*

(*a*) *Postage*

No.	Type	Description		
491	**119**	3½ c. deep green, gold and blue	30	30

(*b*) *Air*

No.	Type	Description		
492	**119**	9½ c. bluish violet, gold and apple-green	55	55

(Litho Walsall)

1969 (6 Dec). *Boy Scouts Diamond Jubilee. T* **120** *and similar design. Imperf. Self-adhesive, backed with paper bearing advertisements.*

(*a*) *Postage*

No.	Type	Description		
493	**120**	1 c. multicoloured	5	5
494		2 c. multicoloured	8	8
495		3½ c. multicoloured	12	12
496		4½ c. multicoloured	15	15
497		5 c. multicoloured	15	15
498		75 c. multicoloured	9·00	7·00

(*b*) *Air*

No.	Type	Description		
499	–	7½ c. multicoloured	35	30
500	–	9½ c. multicoloured	45	35
501	–	15 c. multicoloured	70	50
502	–	22 c. multicoloured	1·25	90
503	–	55 c. multicoloured	7·50	6·00
504	–	3 l. multicoloured	85·00	70·00
493/504		*Set of* 12	95·00	75·00

Design: *Octagonal Shape* (65 × 51 *mm*)—Nos. 499/504 Scout saluting, Baden-Powell and badge.

(121)

1970 (28 Mar). *Air. No.* 443 *surch as T* 121.

No.	Type	Description		*Each Territory*
505	**103**	7½ c. on ½ c. multicoloured (G.)	20	15
506		9½ c. on ½ c. multicoloured (P.)	20	20
507		15 c. on ½ c. multicoloured (B.)	40	30
508		28 c. on ½ c. multicoloured (G.)	70	65
509		40 c. on ½ c. multicoloured (B.)	1·25	1·40
510		2 l. on ½ c. multicoloured (Sil.)	7·00	7·50
505/10 Each Territory		*Set of* 6	9·00	9·00
505/10 Six Territories		*Set of* 36	50·00	50·00

122 Expo Symbol and Maps of Sierra Leone and Japan

(Litho Walsall)

1970 (22 June). *World Fair, Osaka. T* **122** *and similar design. Imperf. Self-adhesive, backed with paper bearing advertisements.*

(*a*) *Postage*

No.	Type	Description		
511	**122**	2 c. multicoloured	5	5
512		3½ c. multicoloured	5	5
513		10 c. multicoloured	12	12
514		12½ c. multicoloured	15	15
515		20 c. multicoloured	25	25
516		45 c. multicoloured	75	75

(*b*) *Air*

No.	Type	Description		
517	–	7½ c. multicoloured	10	10
518	–	9½ c. multicoloured	12	12
519	–	15 c. multicoloured	20	20
520	–	25 c. multicoloured	50	50
521	–	50 c. multicoloured	1·00	1·00
522	–	3 l. multicoloured	8·50	8·50
511/22		*Set of* 12	11·00	11·00

Design: *Chrysanthemum shape* (43 × 42 *mm*)—Nos. 517/22 Maps of Sierra Leone and Japan.

123 Diamond

124 Palm Nut

(Litho and embossed Walsall)

1970 (3 Oct). *Imperf. Self-adhesive, backed with paper bearing advertisements.*

No.	Type	Description		
523	**123**	1 c. multicoloured	5	5
524		1½ c. multicoloured	5	5
525		2 c. multicoloured	10	5
526		2½ c. multicoloured	10	5
527		3 c. multicoloured	12	8
528		3½ c. multicoloured	15	10
529		4 c. multicoloured	15	12
530		5 c. multicoloured	20	12
531	**124**	6 c. multicoloured	20	12
532		7 c. multicoloured	25	15
533		8½ c. multicoloured	30	20
534		9 c. multicoloured	30	20
535		10 c. multicoloured	35	25
536		11½ c. multicoloured	40	30
537		18½ c. multicoloured	60	50

1970 (3 Oct). *Air. As T* **102**, *but embossed on white paper. Backed with paper bearing advertisements.*

No.	Type	Description		
538	**102**	7½ c. gold and red	30	20
539		9½ c. rose and bright green	35	25
540		15 c. pink and greenish blue	45	35
541		25 c. gold and purple	75	60
542		50 c. bright green and orange	1·75	1·50
543		1 l. royal blue and silver	4·50	4·50
544		2 l. ultramarine and gold	9·00	9·00
523/44		*Set of* 22	18·00	17·00

126 "Jewellery Box" and Sewa Diadem

(Litho and embossed Walsall)

1970 (30 Dec). *Diamond Industry. T* **126** *and similar design. Imperf (backing paper roul 20). Self-adhesive, backed with paper bearing advertisements. (a) Postage.*

545	**126**	2 c. multicoloured	10	10
546		3½ c. multicoloured	12	12
547		10 c. multicoloured	25	25
548		12½ c. multicoloured	30	30
549		40 c. multicoloured	90	80
550		1 l. multicoloured	6·50	4·00
		(b) Air		
551	–	7½ c. multicoloured	20	20
552	–	9½ c. multicoloured	25	25
553	–	15 c. multicoloured	40	40
554	–	25 c. multicoloured	75	75
555	–	75 c. multicoloured	3·50	2·75
556	–	2 l. multicoloured	18·00	15·00
545/556		*Set of* 12	28·00	23·00

Design: *Horiz* (63 × 61 *mm*)—Nos. 551/6, Diamond and curtain.

127 "Traffic Changeover"

10c
AIRMAIL
(128)

1971 (1 Mar). *Changeover to Driving on the Right of the Road. Imperf (backing paper roul 20). Self-adhesive, backed with paper bearing advertisements. (a) Postage.*

557	**127**	3½ c. yellow-orange, ultram & blk	45	35
		(b) Air		
558	**127**	9½ c. ultramarine, yell-orge & blk	1·10	1·25

1971 (1 Mar). *Air. Surch as T* **128**, *in red (No. 559), blue (Nos. 560 and 562) or black (others).*

559	10 c. on 2d. black and ultramarine (No. 226)	55	30
560	20 c. on 1s. chocolate & yell-orge (No. 230)	85	60
561	50 c. on 1d. multicoloured (No. 243)	1·75	1·50
562	70 c. on 30 c. multicoloured (No. 476)	2·75	2·75
563	1 l. on 30 c. multicoloured (No. 476)	3·75	3·75

REPUBLIC

129 Flag and Lion's Head

130 Pres. Siaka Stevens

(Manufactured by Walsall)

1971 (27 Apr). *Tenth Anniv of Independence. T* **129** *and similar design. Imperf. Self-adhesive, backed with paper bearing advertisements. (a) Postage.*

564	**129**	2 c. multicoloured	5	5
565		3½ c. multicoloured	8	8
566		10 c. multicoloured	15	15
567		12½ c. multicoloured	20	20
568		40 c. multicoloured	70	70
569		1 l. multicoloured	2·50	2·50
		(b) Air		
570	–	7½ c. multicoloured	12	12
571	–	9½ c. multicoloured	15	15
572	–	15 c. multicoloured	25	25
573	–	25 c. multicoloured	35	35
574	–	75 c. multicoloured	2·25	2·25
575	–	2 l. multicoloured	7·00	7·00
564/75		*Set of* 12	12·00	12·00

Design: *"Map" shaped as T* **129**—Nos. 570/5, Bugles and lion's head.

(Litho D.L.R.)

1972 (5 Dec)–**78.** *Multicoloured; colour of background given. P* 13.
A. *Glazed ordinary paper.*
B. *Chalk-surfaced paper* (1975–78).

			A		B	
576	**130**	1 c. light rose-lilac	5	5	5	5
577		2 c. lavender (*shades*)	8	5	12	5
578		4 c. cobalt	10	5	15	5
579		5 c. light cinnamon	10	5	15	5
580		7 c. light rose	12	8	20	8
581		10 c. olive-bistre	15	10	20	10
582		15 c. pale yellow-green	25	15	35	15
583		18 c. yellow-ochre	25	20	35	20
584		20 c. pale greenish blue	30	20	40	20
585		25 c. orange-ochre	35	25	45	25
586		50 c. light turquoise-green	90	65	1·40	80
587		1 l. bright reddish mauve (*shades*)	1·75	1·25	2·50	2·00
588		2 l. orange-salmon	4·00	4·00	5·50	6·00
589		5 l. light stone	9·00	8·50	12·00	13·00
576/89		*Set of* 14	16·00	14·00	21·00	21·00

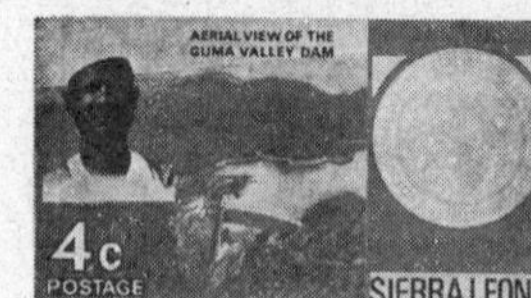

131 Guma Valley Dam and Bank Emblem

(Litho D.L.R.)

1975 (14 Jan). *Tenth Anniv of African Development Bank* (1974). *P* 13½ × 13. *(a) Postage.*

590	**131**	4 c. multicoloured	42·00	26·00
		(b) Air		
591	**131**	15 c. multicoloured	1·00	80

132 Opening Ceremony

(Litho D.L.R.)

1975 (25 Aug). *Opening of New Congo Bridge and President Stevens' 70th Birthday. P* 12½ × 13. *(a) Postage.*

592	**132**	5 c. multicoloured	6·00	5·50
		(b) Air		
593	**132**	20 c. multicoloured	70	60

133 Presidents Tolbert and Stevens, and Handclasp

(Litho D.L.R.)

1975 (3 Oct). *1st Anniv of Mano River Union. P* 12½ × 13. *(a) Postage.*

594	**133**	4 c. multicoloured	75	1·00
		(b) Air		
595	**133**	15 c. multicoloured	35	40

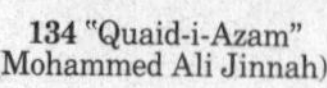

134 "Quaid-i-Azam" (Mohammed Ali Jinnah)

135 Queen Elizabeth II

(Litho Pakistan Security Printing Corporation)

1977 (28 Jan). *Birth Centenary of Mohammed Ali Jinnah (Quaid-i-Azam). P* 13.

596	**134**	30 c. multicoloured	90	95

(Des A. Larkins. Litho De La Rue, Colombia)

1977 (28 Nov). *Silver Jubilee. P* 12½ × 12.

597	**135**	5 c. multicoloured	10	10
598		1 l. multicoloured	1·40	1·60

136 College Buildings

137 St. Edward's Crown and Sceptres

(Des A. Larkins. Litho De La Rue, Colombia)

1977 (19 Dec). *150th Anniv of Fourah Bay College. T* **136** *and similar vert design. Multicoloured. P* 12 × 12½ (5 c.) *or* 12½ × 12 (20 c.).

599	5 c. Type **136**	8	8
600	20 c. The old college	35	35

(Des L. Curtis. Litho Harrison)

1978 (14 Sept). *25th Anniv of Coronation. T* **137** *and similar vert designs. Multicoloured. P* 14½ × 14.

601	5 c. Type **137**	8	8
602	50 c. Queen Elizabeth II in Coronation Coach	75	85
603	1 l. Queen Elizabeth II and Prince Philip	1·25	1·40

138 Fig Tree Blue

139 Young Child's Face

(Des J. Cooter. Litho Questa)

1979 (9 Apr). *Butterflies* (1*st series*). *T* **138** *and similar horiz designs. Multicoloured. P* 14½ × 14.

604	5 c. Type **138**	10	8
605	15 c. Narrow Blue-banded Swallowtail	25	20
606	25 c. Pirate	40	35
607	1 l. African Giant Swallowtail	2·00	2·25

See also Nos. 646/9.

(Des BG Studio. Litho Walsall)

1979 (13 Aug). *International Year of the Child and 30th Anniv of S.O.S. International (child distress organisation). T* **139** *and similar vert designs. Multicoloured. W w* **14**. *P* 14 × 13½.

608	5 c. Type **139**	10	8
609	27 c. Young child with baby	50	50
610	1 l. Mother with young child	1·90	1·90
MS611	114 × 84 mm. No. 610. Wmk sideways	1·75	1·90

140 Presidents Stevens (Sierra Leone) and Tolbert (Liberia), Dove with Letter and Bridge

(Des L. Curtis. Litho Questa)

1979 (3 Oct). *5th Anniv of Mano River Union and 1st Anniv of Postal Union. W w* **14** *(sideways). P* 13½ × 14.

612	**140**	5 c. sepia, orange and greenish yellow	8	8
613		22 c. sepia, orge-yell & brt reddish violet	25	25
614		27 c. sepia, light blue and orange	30	30
615		35 c. sepia, blue-green and orange-red	35	35
616		1 l. sepia, brt reddish violet & lt blue	1·25	1·25
MS617		144 × 73 mm. No. 616	1·50	1·75

141 Great Britain 1848 10d. Stamp

142 Knysna Touraco

(Des J.W. Litho Walsall)

1979 (19 Dec). *Death Centenary of Sir Rowland Hill. T* **141** *and similar vert designs showing stamps. W w* **14**. *P* 14 × 14½.

618	10 c. black, orange-brown and new blue	15	12
619	15 c. black, brown-ochre and greenish blue	25	20
620	50 c. black, carmine and greenish yellow	60	70
MS621	90 × 99 mm. 1 l. black, carm-red & flesh	1·40	1·40

Designs:—15 c. 1872 4d.; 50 c. 1961 £1 Independence commemorative; 1 l. 1912 £1.

(Des J.W. Litho Format)

1980 (29 Jan)–**82**. *Birds. Multicoloured designs as T* **142**. *W w* **14** (*sideways on* 1, 2, 3, 5, 7 *c*., 1, 2 *and* 5 *l*.). *P* 14.

A. *No imprint*. B. *Imprint date at foot*

		A		B	
622	1 c. Type **142**	10	10	10	10
623	2 c. Olive-bellied Sunbird	10	10	10	10
624	3 c. Western Black-headed Oriole	15	10	5	5
625	5 c. Spur-winged Goose	15	10	10	10
626	7 c. Didric Cuckoo	15	10	5	8
627	10 c. Grey Parrot (*vert*)	20	12	15	12
628	15 c. Blue Quail (*vert*)	30	25	25	25
629	20 c. African Wood Owl (*vert*)	35	30	35	30
630	30 c. Great Blue Turaco (*vert*)	45	40	45	40
631	40 c. Blue-breasted Kingfisher (*vert*)	50	40	50	40
632	50 c. Black Crake (*vert*)	60	60	50	50
633	1 l. Hartlaub's Duck	90	95	50	55
634	2 l. Black Bee Eater	2·00	2·25	1·75	2·00
635	5 l. Barrow's Bustard	4·50	5·00	4·25	4·75
622/35	*Set of* 14	9·50	9·50	8·00	8·50

Dates of issue: No Imprint—29.1.80. With Imprint—21.12.81 5, 10, 15, 30, 40, 50 c., 1 l., 2 l., 5 l.; 15.3.82 1, 2, 3, 20 c.; 11.10.82 7 c.

For similar stamps, but without watermark, see Nos. 760/73.

143 Paul P. Harris (founder), President Stevens of Sierra Leone and Rotary Emblem

(Des BG Studio. Litho Walsall)

1980 (23 Feb). *75th Anniv of Rotary International. W w* **14** (*sideways*). *P* 13½.

636	**143**	5 c. multicoloured	5	5
637		27 c. multicoloured	25	25
638		50 c. multicoloured	50	50
639		1 l. multicoloured	95	95

144 *Maria*, 1884

145 Organisation for African Unity Emblem

(Des L. Dunn. Litho Walsall)

1980 (6 May). *"London 1980" International Stamp Exhibition. Mail Ships. T* **144** *and similar horiz designs. Multicoloured. W w* **14** (*sideways*). *P* 14.

640	6 c. Type **144**	5	5
641	31 c. *Tarquah*, 1902	35	35
642	50 c. *Aureol*, 1951	70	60
643	1 l. *Africa Palm*, 1974	1·25	1·00

(Des L. Curtis. Litho Questa)

1980 (1 July). *African Summit Conference, Freetown. W w* **14**. *P* 14 × 14½.

644	**145**	20 c. black, light blue and bright purple	15	20
645		1 l. black, bright purple and light blue	90	95

146 Small Striped Swordtail

147 Arrival at Freetown Airport

(Des I. Loe. Litho Questa)

1980 (6 Oct). *Butterflies* (2*nd series*). *T* **146** *and similar vert designs. Multicoloured. W w* **14**. *P* 13½.

646	5 c. Type **146**	10	5
647	27 c. Pearl Charaxes	40	30
648	35 c. White Barred Charaxes	45	35
649	1 l. Zaddach's Forester	1·40	1·60

(Des L. Curtis. Litho Format)

1980 (5 Dec). *Tourism. T* **147** *and similar vert designs. Multicoloured. W w* **14**. *P* 13½.

650	6 c. Type **147**	5	5
651	26 c. Welcome to tourists	25	25
652	31 c. Freetown cotton tree	30	30
653	40 c. Beinkongo Falls	40	40
654	50 c. Sports facilities	50	50
655	1 l. Forest elephant	95	95
650/5	*Set of* 6	2·25	2·25

148 Servals

149 Soldiers (Defence)

(Des P. Oxenham. Litho Questa)

1981 (28 Feb). *Wild Cats. T* **148** *and similar horiz designs. Multicoloured. W w* **14** (*sideways*). *P* 13½ × 14.

656	6 c. Type **148**	5	5
	a. Horiz pair. Nos. 656/7	10	10
657	6 c. Serval cubs	5	5
658	31 c. African Golden Cats	30	30
	a. Horiz pair. Nos. 658/9	60	60
659	31 c. African Golden Cat cubs	30	30
660	50 c. Leopards	45	45
	a. Horiz pair. Nos. 660/1	90	90
661	50 c. Leopard cubs	45	45
662	1 l. Lions	80	80
	a. Horiz pair. Nos. 662/3	1·60	1·60
663	1 l. Lion cubs	80	80
656/63	*Set of* 8	2·75	2·75

The two designs of each value were printed together, *se-tenant*, in horizontal pairs throughout the sheet, forming composite designs.

(Des G. Hutchins. Litho Walsall)

1981 (18 Apr). *20th Anniv of Independence and 10th Anniv of Republic. National Services. T* **149** *and similar multicoloured designs. W w* **14** (*sideways on* 31 *c. and* 1 *l.*). *P* 14½.

664	6 c. Type **149**	5	5
665	31 c. Nurses administering first aid, and ambulance (Health) (*horiz*)	30	30
666	40 c. Controlling traffic (Police Force)	35	35
667	1 l. Patrol boat (Coastguard) (*horiz*)	95	95

150 Wedding Bouquet from Sierra Leone

151 Sandringham

(Des J.W. Litho Harrison)

1981 (22 July). *Royal Wedding* (1*st issue*). *T* **150** *and similar vert designs. Multicoloured. W w* **14**. *P* 14.

668	31 c. Type **150**	40	35
669	45 c. Prince Charles as helicopter pilot	50	50
670	1 l. Prince Charles and Lady Diana Spencer	85	90

(Des J.W. Litho Format)

1981 (9 Sept–30 Nov). *Royal Wedding* (2*nd issue*). *T* **151** *and similar vert designs. Multicoloured.* (*a*) *Sheet stamps. P* 12.

671	35 c. Type **151**	40	30
672	60 c. Prince Charles in outdoor clothes	65	55
673	1 l. 50, Prince Charles and Lady Diana Spencer	1·25	1·40
MS674	96 × 83 mm. 3 l. Royal Landau. P 14	2·75	

(*b*) *Booklet stamps. P* 14 (30 Nov)

675	70 c. Type **51**	75	80
	a. Booklet pane. Nos. 675/6 × 2 plus two printed labels	3·00	
676	1 l. 30, As 60 c.	1·00	1·00
677	2 l. As 1 l. 50	3·25	3·25
	a. Booklet pane of 1	3·25	

Nos. 671/3 were each printed in small sheets of 6 including one *se-tenant* stamp-size label.

152 "Physical Recreation"

153 Pineapples

(Des BG Studio. Litho Questa)

1981 (30 Sept). *25th Anniv of Duke of Edinburgh Award Scheme and President's Award Scheme Publicity. T* **152** *and similar vert designs. Multicoloured. W w* **14**. *P* 14.

678	6 c. Type **152**	5	5
679	31 c. "Community service"	30	25
680	1 l. Duke of Edinburgh	1·10	90
681	1 l. President Siaka Stevens	1·10	90

(Des BG Studio. Litho Questa)

1981 (16 Oct). *World Food Day* (1*st issue*). *T* **153** *and similar vert designs. Multicoloured. W w* **14**. *P* 14.

682	6 c. Type **153**	5	5
683	31 c. Groundnuts	25	25
684	50 c. Cassava fruits	45	45
685	1 l. Rice plants	90	90

154 Groundnuts

(Litho Format)

1981 (2 Nov). *World Food Day* (2*nd issue*). *Agricultural Industry. T* **154** *and similar horiz designs. Multicoloured. P* 14½.

686	6 c. Type **154**	5	5
687	31 c. Cassava	25	25
688	50 c. Rice	45	45
689	1 l. Pineapples	90	90

155 Scouts with Cattle

50c 50c

(**156**)

(Des M. Diamond. Litho Questa)

1982 (23 Aug). *75th Anniv of Boy Scout Movement. T* **155** *and similar horiz designs. Multicoloured. P* 14.

690	20 c. Type **155**	20	15
691	50 c. Scouts picking flowers	45	40
692	1 l. Lord Baden-Powell	90	90
693	2 l. Scouts fishing	1·90	2·00
MS694	101 × 70 mm. 3 l. Scouts raising flag	2·75	3·25

1982 (30 Aug). *Nos.* 668/7 *surch as T* **156**.

695	50 c. on 31 c. Type **150**	40	40
696	50 c. on 35 c. Type **151**	40	40
697	50 c. on 45 c. Prince Charles as helicopter pilot	40	40
698	50 c. on 60 c. Prince Charles in outdoor clothes	40	40
699	90 c. on 1 l. Prince Charles and Lady Diana Spencer	75	75
700	2 l. on 1 l. 50, Prince Charles and Lady Diana Spencer	1·50	1·50
695/700	*Set of* 6	3·75	3·75
MS701	95 × 83 mm. 3 l. 50 on 3 l. Royal Landau	3·00	3·25

157 Heading

158 Prince and Princess of Wales

(Des PAD Studio. Litho Questa)

1982 (7 Sept). *World Cup Football Championship, Spain. T* **157** *and similar vert designs. Multicoloured. P* 14.

702	20 c. Type **157**	20	15
703	30 c. Dribbling	30	25
704	1 l. Tackling	95	95
705	2 l. Goalkeeping	1·90	2·00
MS706	92 × 75 mm. 3 l. Shooting	2·75	3·00

Nos. 702/5 were each printed in small sheets of 6 including one, *se-tenant*, stamp-sized label.

(Des PAD Studio. Litho Questa)

1982 (15 Sept). *21st Birthday of Princess of Wales. T* **158** *and similar vert designs. Multicoloured. P* 14½ × 14.

707	31 c. Caernarvon Castle	35	35
708	50 c. Type **158**	50	50
709	2 l. Princess of Wales	1·75	1·75
MS710	103 × 75 mm. 3 l. Princess of Wales (*different*)	2·75	3·00

Nos. 707/9 also exist in sheetlets of 5 stamps and 1 label.

1982 (15 Oct). *Birth of Prince William of Wales. Nos.* 707/10 *optd with T* **171** *of Antigua*.

711	31 c. Caernarvon Castle	35	35
712	50 c. Type **158**	50	50
713	2 l. Princess of Wales	1·75	1·75
MS714	103 × 75 mm. 3 l. Princess of Wales (*different*)	2·75	3·00

Nos. 711/13 also exist in sheetlets of 5 stamps and 1 label.

OMNIBUS ISSUES

Details, together with prices for complete sets, of the various Omnibus issues from the 1935 Silver Jubilee series to date are included in a special section following Zululand at the end of the catalogue.

159 Washington with Troops

160 Temptation of Christ

(Des C. Mill. Litho Questa)

1982 (30 Oct). *250th Birth Anniv of George Washington. T* **159** *and similar multicoloured designs. P* 14.
715 6 c. Type **159** 8 8
716 31 c. Portrait of Washington (*vert*) 25 25
717 50 c. Washington with horse 45 45
718 1 l. Washington standing on battlefield (*vert*) 90 90
MS719 103 × 71 mm. 2 l. Washington at home .. 2·00 2·25

(Des N. Waldman Studio. Litho Questa)

1982 (18 Nov). *Christmas. Stained-glass Windows. T* **160** *and similar vert designs. Multicoloured. P* 13½ × 14.
720 6 c. Type **160** 5 5
721 31 c. Baptism of Christ 20 20
722 50 c. Annunciation 40 40
723 1 l. Nativity 90 90
MS724 74 × 104 mm. 2 l. Mary and Joseph .. 1·60 1·75

WORLD CUP WINNERS

ITALY (3)

vs.

W. GERMANY (1)

(161)

162 Long Snouted Crocodile

1982 (2 Dec). *World Cup Football Championship Winners. Nos.* 702/6 *optd with T* **161**.
725 20 c. Type **157** 15 20
726 30 c. Dribbling 25 30
727 1 l. Tackling 80 85
728 2 l. Goalkeeping .. .. 1·60 1·75
MS729 91 × 75 mm. 3 l. Shooting .. .. .. 2·40 2·75

(Des G. Drummond. Litho Questa)

1982 (10 Dec). *Death Centenary of Charles Darwin. T* **162** *and similar horiz designs. Multicoloured. P* 14.
730 6 c. Type **162** 10 5
731 31 c. Rainbow Lizard 30 30
732 50 c. River Turtle 45 50
733 1 l. Chameleon .. .. 95 1·00
MS734 90 × 70 mm. 2 l. Royal Python (*vert*) .. 1·75 1·90

163 Diogenes

(Des Design Images. Litho Questa)

1983 (28 Jan). *500th Birth Anniv of Raphael. Details from painting "The School of Athens". T* **163** *and similar multicoloured designs. P* 13½.
735 6 c. Type **163** 5 5
736 31 c. Euclid, Ptolemy, Zoroaster, Raphael and Sodoma 25 30
737 50 c. Euclid and his pupils 40 45
738 2 l. Pythagoras, Francesco Maria della Rovere and Heraclitus .. .. 1·60 1·75
MS739 101 × 126 mm. 3 l. Plato and Aristotle (*vert*) 2·40 2·50

164 Agricultural Training

165 Map of Africa and Flag of Sierra Leone

(Litho Questa)

1983 (14 Mar). *Commonwealth Day. T* **164** *and similar horiz designs. Multicoloured. P* 14.
740 6 c. Type **164** 8 8
741 10 c. Tourism development 10 10
742 50 c. Broadcasting training 45 45
743 1 l. Airport services 90 90

(Des M. Diamond. Litho J.W.)

1983 (29 Apr). *25th Anniv of Economic Commission for Africa. P* 13.
744 **165** 1 l. multicoloured 55 60

166 Chimpanzees in Tree

(Des J. Iskowitz. Litho Questa)

1983 (19 May). *Endangered Species. T* **166** *and similar multicoloured designs. P* 14.
745 6 c. Type **166** 5 5
746 10 c. Three Chimpanzees (*vert*) 5 8
747 31 c. Chimpanzees swinging in tree (*vert*) .. 15 20
748 60 c. Group of Chimpanzees 55 60
MS749 115 × 80 mm. 3 l. African Elephant .. 1·10 1·25

167 Traditional Communications

168 Montgolfier Balloon, Paris, 1783

(Des R. Sauber. Litho Questa)

1983 (14 July). *World Communications Year. T* **167** *and similar horiz designs. Multicoloured. P* 14.
750 6 c. Type **167** 5 5
751 10 c. Mail via Mano River 5 8
752 20 c. Satellite ground station 10 12
753 1 l. English packet, *circa* 1805 .. .. .. 55 60
MS754 115 × 85 mm. 2 l. Telecommunications .. 1·10 1·25

(Des Artists International. Litho Questa)

1983 (31 Aug). *Bicentenary of Manned Flight. T* **168** *and similar multicoloured designs. P* 14.
755 6 c. Type **168** 5 5
756 20 c. *Deutschland* airship, Berlin, 1879 (*horiz*) 10 12
757 50 c. *Norge I*, North Pole, 1926 (*horiz*) .. 30 35
758 1 l. *Cape Sierra* sport balloon, Freetown, 1983 55 60
MS759 115 × 85 mm. 2 l. Airship of 21st century 1·10 1·25

1983 (Oct). *Birds. As Nos. 622B/35B but without wmk.*
760 1 c. Type **142** 5 5
761 2 c. Olive-bellied Sunbird 5 5
763 5 c. Spur-winged Goose 5 5
765 10 c. Grey Parrot (*vert*) 5 8
766 15 c. Blue Quail (*vert*) 8 10
767 20 c. African Wood Owl (*vert*) 10 12
768 30 c. Great Blue Turaco (*vert*) 15 20
769 40 c. Blue-breasted Kingfisher (*vert*) 20 25
770 50 c. Black Crake (*vert*) 30 35
772 2 l. Black Bee Eater .. .. 1·10 1·25
773 5 l. Barrow's Bustard .. .. 2·75 3·00
760/73 .. .. *Set of* 11 4·50 5·00

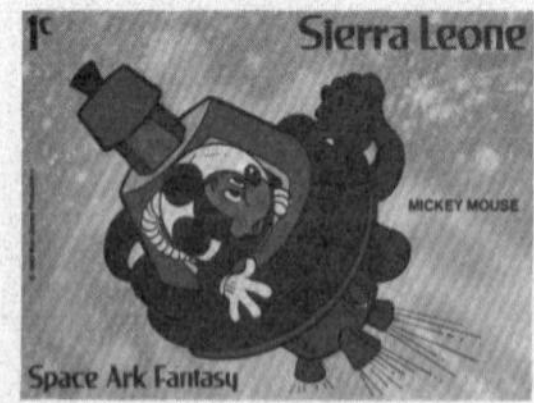

169 Mickey Mouse

(Litho Format)

1983 (18 Nov). *Space Ark Fantasy. T* **169** *and similar horiz designs featuring Disney cartoon characters. Multicoloured. P* 13½.
774 1 c. Type **169** 5 5
775 1 c. Huey, Dewey and Louie 5 5
776 3 c. Goofy in spaceship 5 5
777 3 c. Donald Duck 5 5
778 10 c. Ludwig von Drake 5 8
779 10 c. Goofy 5 8
780 2 l. Mickey Mouse and Giraffe in spaceship 1·10 1·25
781 3 l. Donald Duck floating in space .. .. 1·60 1·75
774/81 .. .. *Set of* 8 2·75 3·00
MS782 140 × 116 mm. 5 l. Mickey Mouse leaving spaceship .. .. 2·75 3·00

First Decade of The Mano River Union 1973-1983
6c
SIERRA LEONE

170 Graduates from Union Training Programme

(Des G. Vasarhelyi. Litho Format)

1984 (8 Feb). *10th Anniv of the Mano River Union. T* **170** *and similar horiz designs. Multicoloured. P* 15.
783 6 c. Type **170** 5 5
784 25 c. Intra-Union trade 8 10
785 31 c. Member Presidents on map 10 12
786 41 c. Signing ceremony marking Guinea's accession 12 15
MS787 75 × 113 mm. No. 786 .. .. .. 12 15

171 Gymnastics

172 "Apollo 11" Lift-off

(Des J. Iskowitz. Litho Questa)

1984 (27 Mar). *Olympic Games, Los Angeles. T* **171** *and similar horiz designs. Multicoloured. P* 14.
788 90 c. Type **171** 30 35
789 1 l. Hurdling 30 35
790 3 l. Javelin-throwing 90 95
MS791 104 × 71 mm. 7 l. Boxing .. .. .. 2·10 2·25

(Des J. Iskowitz. Litho Questa)

1984 (14 May). *15th Anniv of First Moonwalk. T* **172** *and similar multicoloured designs. P* 14.
792 50 c. Type **172** 15 20
793 75 c. Lunar module 25 30
794 1 l. 25, First Moonwalk 40 45
795 2 l. 50, Lunar exploration 80 85
MS796 99 × 69 mm. 5 l. Family watching Moonwalk on television (*horiz*) .. .. 1·50 1·60

173 "Concorde"

(Des S. David. Litho Walsall)

1984 (19 June). *Universal Postal Union Congress, Hamburg. T* **173** *and similar horiz design. Multicoloured. P* 14.
797 4 l. Type **173** .. .. 1·25 1·40
MS798 100 × 70 mm. 4 l. Heinrich von Stephan (founder of U.P.U.) .. .. 1·25 1·40

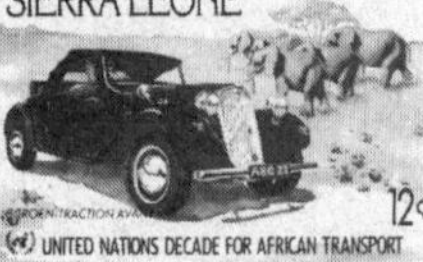

174 Citroen "Traction Avante"

25c

(175)

(Des S. David. Litho Format)

1984 (16 July). *United Nations Decade for African Transport. T* **174** *and similar horiz designs. Multicoloured. P* 14½ × 15.
799 12 c. Type **174** 5 5
800 60 c. Locomobile 20 25
801 90 c. A.C. "Ace" 30 35
802 1 l. Vauxhall "Prince Henry" 30 35
803 1 l. 50, Delahaye "135" 45 50
804 2 l. Mazda "1105" 60 65
799/804 .. .. *Set of* 6 1·75 1·90
MS805 107 × 75 mm. 6 l. Volkswagen "Beetle". P 15 .. .. 1·75 1·90

1984 (3 Aug). *Surch as T* **175**. (*a*) *On Nos.* 625, 627 *and* 634. *A. No imprint. B. Imprint date at foot.*

		A		B	
806	25 c. on 10 c. Grey Parrot (*vert*)	4·00	4·00	3·50	3·50
807	40 c. on 10 c. Grey Parrot (*vert*)	4·00	4·00	3·50	3·50
808	50 c. on 2 l. Black Bee Eater	4·00	4·00	3·50	3·50
809	70 c. on 5 c. Spur-winged Goose	4·00	4·00	3·50	3·50
810	10 l. on 5 c. Spur-winged Goose	8·00	8·00	8·00	8·00

(*b*) *On Nos.* 763, 765 *and* 772
811 25 c. on 10 c. Grey Parrot (*vert*) 8 10
812 40 c. on 10 c. Grey Parrot (*vert*) 12 15
813 50 c. on 2 l. Black Bee Eater 15 20
814 70 c. on 5 c. Spur-winged Goose 25 30
815 10 l. on 5 c. Spur-winged Goose .. .. 3·50 3·75

Nos. 806B/10B exist with either "1981" or "1982" imprint dates.

Singapore

A Crown Colony until the end of 1957. From 1 August 1958, an internally self-governing territory designated the State of Singapore. From 16 September 1963, part of the Malaysian Federation until 9 August 1965, when it became an independent republic within the Commonwealth.

Stamps in the Crown Colony Victory design were prepared for Singapore in 1946, but not issued. Examples of the 8 c. carmine are known to exist.

CROWN COLONY

1948 (1 Sept)–**52.** *As T* **58** *of Straits Settlements, but inscr* "SINGAPORE" *at foot. Wmk Mult Script CA. Chalk-surfaced paper. (a) P* 14.

No.	Description		Unused	Used
1	1 c. black		12	5
2	2 c. orange		15	5
3	3 c. green		20	5
4	4 c. brown		20	10
5	6 c. grey		25	10
6	8 c. scarlet (1.10.48)		25	10
7	10 c. purple		20	5
8	15 c. ultramarine (1.10.48)		90	5
9	20 c. black and green (1.10.48)		1·75	20
10	25 c. purple and orange (1.10.48)		90	5
11	40 c. red and purple (1.10.48)		4·50	4·50
12	50 c. black and blue (1.10.48)		2·00	5
13	$1 blue and purple (1.10.48)		9·00	40
14	$2 green and scarlet (25.10.48)		48·00	1·50
15	$5 green and brown (1.10.48)		£100	1·50
1/15		*Set of* 15	£150	8·00

(*b*) *P* 17½ × 18

No.	Description		Unused	Used
16	1 c. black (21.5.52)		50	50
17	2 c. orange (31.10.49)		70	35
19	4 c. brown (1.7.49)		70	5
19*a*	5 c. bright purple (1.9.52)		1·75	25
21	6 c. grey (10.12.52)		70	10
21*a*	8 c. green (1.9.52)		3·25	90
22	10 c. purple (9.2.50)		50	5
22*a*	12 c. scarlet (1.9.52)		3·25	2·00
23	15 c. ultramarine (9.2.50)		2·00	5
24	20 c. black and green (31.10.49)		2·50	45
24*a*	20 c. bright blue (1.9.52)		3·25	5
25	25 c. purple and orange (9.2.50)		80	5
25*a*	35 c. scarlet and purple (1.9.52)		3·25	90
26	40 c. red and purple (24.5.51)		15·00	8·50
27	50 c. black and blue (9.2.50)		2·75	5
28	$1 blue and purple (31.10.49)		8·50	20
	a. Error. St. Edward's Crown, W 9*b*		£650	
29	$2 green and scarlet (24.5.51)		95·00	1·75
	a. Error. St. Edward's Crown, W 9*b*		£650	
30	$5 green and brown (19.12.51)		£120	1·75
16/30		*Set of* 18	£250	16·00

Nos. 28a and 29a occur on rows in the watermark in which the crowns and letters "CA" alternate.

1948 (25 Oct). *Royal Silver Wedding. As Nos.* 30/1 *of Aden.*

No.	Description	Unused	Used
31	10 c. violet	75	10
32	$5 brown	95·00	27·00

1949 (10 Oct). *75th Anniv of Universal Postal Union. As Nos.* 114/17 *of Antigua.*

No.	Description	Unused	Used
33	10 c. purple	75	5
34	15 c. deep blue	3·25	1·40
35	25 c. orange	3·75	1·25
36	50 c. blue-black	5·50	2·50

1953 (2 June). *Coronation. As No.* 47 *of Aden.*

No.	Description	Unused	Used
37	10 c. black and reddish purple	75	8

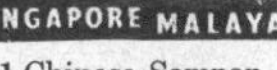

1 Chinese Sampan

2 Raffles Statue

3 Singapore River

4 Arms of Singapore

(Des Dr. C. A. Gibson-Hill, except 25 c., 30 c., 50 c. and $5 (from photographs, etc.). Photo Harrison (1 c. to 50 c.). Recess (centre typo on $5) B.W. (others))

1955 (4 Sept). *Designs as T* **1/4**. *Wmk Mult Script CA. P* 13½ × 14½ (1 *c. to* 50 *c.*) *or* 14 (*others*).

No.	Description		Unused	Used
38	1 c. black		8	25
39	2 c. yellow-orange		50	40
40	4 c. brown		25	5
41	5 c. bright purple		25	10
42	6 c. deep grey-blue		25	10
43	8 c. turquoise-blue		55	45
44	10 c. deep lilac		65	5
45	12 c. rose-carmine		70	1·00
46	20 c. ultramarine (*shades*)		70	5
47	25 c. orange-red and bluish violet (*shades*)		75	5
48	30 c. violet and brown-purple		1·25	5
49	50 c. blue and black		1·25	5
50	$1 blue and deep purple		12·00	10
51	$2 blue-green and scarlet		32·00	70
52	$5 yellow, red, brown and slate-black		45·00	2·75
38/52		*Set of* 15	85·00	5·50

Designs: *Horiz as T* 1—2 c. Malay Kolek; 4 c. Twa-Kow; 5 c. Lombok sloop; 6 c. Trengganu Pinas; 8 c. Palari; 10 c. Timber Tongkong; 12 c. Hainan trader; 20 c. Cocos-Keeling schooner; 25 c. "Argonaut" aircraft; 30 c. Oil tanker; 50 c. M.S. *Chusan.*

Plate 2A and 2B of the 10 c. (12 April 1960) and the blue "3A" and "3B" plates of the 50 c. "3A–2A", "3B–2B" (part of the 24 January 1961 issue and later printings) were printed with a finer screen (250 dots per inch, instead of the normal 200) (*Price* 10 c., £1.25 *un.*, 20*p us.* 50 *c.*, £1.50 *un.*, 5*p us.*).

INTERNAL SELF-GOVERNMENT

16 The Singapore Lion

17 State Flag

(Photo Harrison)

1959 (1 June). *New Constitution. W w* **12**. *P* 11½ × 12.

No.	Type	Description		Unused	Used
53	**16**	4 c. yellow, sepia and rose-red		30	20
54		10 c. yellow, sepia and reddish purple		40	15
55		20 c. yellow, sepia and bright blue		1·25	1·75
56		25 c. yellow, sepia and green		1·25	1·10
57		30 c. yellow, sepia and violet		1·75	1·75
58		50 c. yellow, sepia and deep slate		2·50	1·75
53/8			*Set of* 6	6·50	6·00

(Litho Enschedé)

1960 (3 June). *National Day. W w* **12** (*sideways*). *P* 13½.

No.	Type	Description	Unused	Used
59	**17**	4 c. red, yellow and blue	15	12
60		10 c. red, yellow and grey	30	5

18 Clasped Hands

(Photo Enschedé)

1961 (3 June). *National Day. W w* **12**. *P* 13½.

No.	Type	Description	Unused	Used
61	**18**	4 c. black, brown and pale yellow	15	12
62		10 c. black, deep green and pale yellow	30	5

19 *Arachnis "Maggie Oei"* (orchid)

20 Sea-Horse

21 Six-banded Barb

24 *Vanda "Tan Chay Yan"* (orchid)

26*a* Black-naped Tern

30 White-rumped Shama

(Photo Harrison (orchids, fish and 15 c. bird) D.L.R. (birds, except 15 c.))

1962 (31 Mar)–**66.** *T* **19/21**, **24**, **26*a***, **30** *and similar designs. Orchid and bird designs multicoloured; background colours given. W w* **12**. *P* 12½ (i), 14½ × 13½ (ii), 13½ × 14½ (iii), 13½ × 13 (iv) *or* 13 × 13½ (v).

No.	Description		Unused	Used
63	1 c. mauve (i) (10.3.63)		5	25
64	2 c. brown and green (ii)		8	15
65	4 c. black and orange-red (iii)		10	5
	a. Black omitted		60·00	
66	5 c. red and black (iii)		12	5
	a. Red omitted		60·00	
67	6 c. black and greenish yellow (ii)		12	5
68	8 c. pale turquoise-blue (i) (10.3.63)		55	1·00
69	10 c. red-orange and black (iii)		15	5
	a. Red-orange omitted		55·00	
70	12 c. salmon (i) (10.3.63)		55	80
70*a*	15 c. bright blue (i) (9.11.66)		1·00	5
71	20 c. orange and blue (ii)		30	5
	a. Orange omitted		75·00	
72	25 c. black and orange (iii)		35	5
73	30 c. stone (i) (10.3.63)		1·00	5
74	50 c. apple-green (iv) (10.3.63)		95	5
75	$1 yellow (iv) (10.3.63)		7·00	20
76	$2 grey-blue (iv) (10.3.63)		13·00	90
77	$5 cobalt (v) (10.3.63)		26·00	2·50
63/77		*Set of* 16	45·00	5·50

Designs: *Horiz* (*as T* **21**)—5 c. Clown fish; 10 c. Harlequin; 25 c. Two-spot Gourami. (*As T* **30**)—$1 White-breasted Kingfisher. *Vert* (*as T* **20**)—6 c. Archer fish; 20 c. Butterfly fish. (*As T* **24**)—12 c. *Grammaphotyllum speciosum* (orchid); 30 c. *Vanda "Miss Joaquim"* (orchid). (*As T* **26*a***)—$2 Yellow-bellied Sunbird; $5 White-bellied Sea Eagle.

The 15 c., 30 c., $2 and $5 exist with PVA gum as well as gum arabic.

See also Nos. 83/88.

34 "The Role of Labour in Nation-Building"

35 Blocks of Flats, Singapore

(Photo Courvoisier)

1962 (3 June). *National Day. P* 11½ × 12.

No.	Type	Description	Unused	Used
78	**34**	4 c. yellow, rose-carmine and black	15	15
79		10 c. yellow, blue and black	30	5

(Photo Harrison)

1963 (3 June). *National Day. W w* **12**. *P* 12½.

No.	Type	Description	Unused	Used
80	**35**	4 c. orange-red, black, blue & turq-blue	15	15
81		10 c. orange-red, blk, yell-olive & turq–bl	30	5

36 Dancers in National Costume

37 Workers

(Photo Harrison)

1963 (8 Aug). *South East Asia Cultural Festival. W w* **12**. *P* 14 × 14½.

No.	Type	Description	Unused	Used
82	**36**	5 c. multicoloured	15	10

INDEPENDENT REPUBLIC

1966 (1 Mar)–**67.** *As Nos.* 63, 66, 69, 72, 74/5, *but W w* **12** (*sideways*). *Orchid, fish and bird designs multicoloured; background colours given.*

No.	Description		Unused	Used
83	1 c. mauve (22.2.67)		5	40
84	5 c. red and black (30.5.67)		25	5
85	10 c. red-orange and black (30.5.67)		25	5
86	25 c. black and orange (9.66*)		45	15
87	50 c. apple-green (1.3.66*)		1·00	85
	a. Imperf (pair)		£200	
88	$1 yellow (18.5.67)		6·50	3·25
83/8		*Set of* 6	7·75	4·25

*The 25 and 50 c. values were not released in London until 30.5.67 and 9.6.66. The 25 c. value, however, is known used in September 1966 and the 50 c. on 1.3.66.

The 1 c. and 25 c. exist with PVA gum as well as gum arabic.

(Photo D.L.R.)

1966 (9 Aug). *First Anniv of Republic. W w* **12** (30 *c.*) *or no wmk* (*others*). *P* 12½ × 13.

No.	Type	Description	Unused	Used
89	**37**	15 c. multicoloured	40	12
90		20 c. multicoloured	60	45
91		30 c. multicoloured	80	50

38 Flag Procession

(Photo D.L.R.)

1967 (9 Aug). *National Day. P* 14 × 14½.

No.	Type	Description	Unused	Used
92	**38**	6 c. rosine, brown and slate	20	15
93		15 c. reddish purple, brown and slate	40	10
94		50 c. bright blue, brown and slate	1·00	70

Nos. 92/4 are respectively inscribed "Build a Vigorous Singapore" in Chinese, Malay and Tamil in addition to the English inscription.

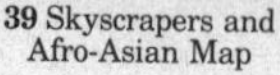

39 Skyscrapers and Afro-Asian Map

40 Symbolical Figure wielding Hammer, and Industrial Outline of Singapore

(Photo D.L.R.)

1967 (7 Oct). *2nd Afro-Asian Housing Congress. P* 14 × 13.

95 **39** 10 c. multicoloured 25 12
 a. Opt omitted £100 £100
96 25 c. multicoloured 50 90
97 50 c. multicoloured 80 70

The above were originally scheduled for release in 1966, and when finally issued were overprinted with the new date and a black oblong obliterating the old date.

(Photo Harrison)

1968 (9 Aug). *National Day. Inscription at top in Chinese* (6 c.), *Malay* (15 c.) *or Tamil* (50 c.). *P* 13½ × 14.

98 **40** 6 c. orange-red, black and gold 25 15
99 15 c. apple-green, black and gold .. 35 12
100 50 c. greenish blue, black and gold .. 80 70

41 Half check Pattern

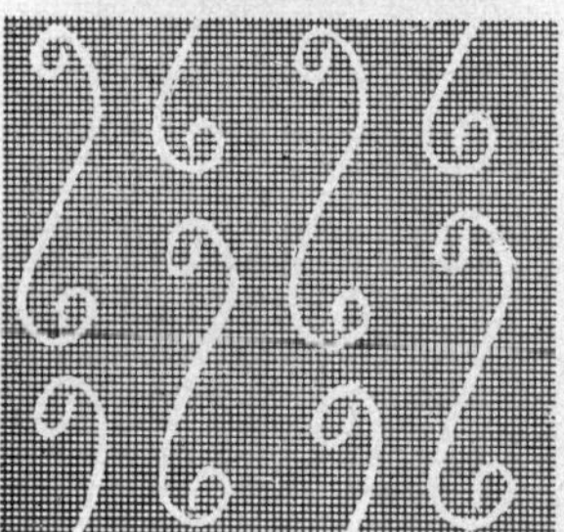

42 Scrolled "S" multiple

43 Mirudhangam

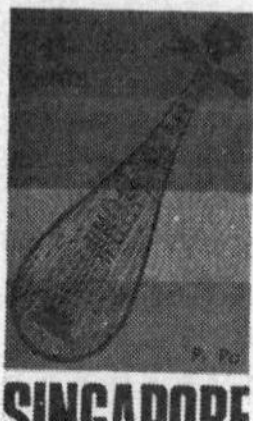

44 Pi Pa

45 Sword Dance

51 Dragon Dance

(Photo D.L.R. (5 c. to $1), Japanese Govt Printing Bureau, Tokyo (others))

1968–73. *T* 43/5, 51 *and similar designs.* 5 *c. to* $1: *Chalk-surfaced paper; W* 41; *P* 14. *Others: Ordinary paper; W* 42 *upright* (1 c., $5) *or sideways* (4 c., $2, $10); *P* 13½.

101 1 c. multicoloured (10.11.69) 12 30
102 4 c. multicoloured (10.11.69) 30 40
103 5 c. multicoloured (29.12.68) 8 5
 a. Glazed unsurfaced paper (16.12.70) .. 2·25 1·00
 b. Chalky paper. Perf 13 (27.6.73) .. .. 1·25 70
104 6 c. black, lemon and orange (1.12.68) .. 10 8
105 10 c. multicoloured (29.12.68) 10 5
 a. Glazed unsurfaced paper (16.12.70) .. 2·25 1·00
 b. Chalky paper. Perf 13 (12.9.73) .. .. 1·50 70
106 15 c. multicoloured (29.12.68) 30 5
107 20 c. multicoloured (1.12.68) 15 8
 a. Perf 13 (12.9.73) .. .. .. 1·60 1·50
108 25 c. multicoloured (29.12.68) 40 30
 a. Perf 13 (27.6.73) .. .. .. 2·25 2·25
109 30 c. multicoloured (1.12.68) 30 15
 a. Perf 13 (12.9.73) .. .. .. 2·25 2·25
110 50 c. blk, orge-red & lt yell-brown (1.12.68) .. 50 30
 a. Perf 13 (12.9.73) .. .. .. 2·75 3·25
111 75 c. multicoloured (1.12.68) 70 35
112 $1 multicoloured (29.12.68) 80 45
 a. Perf 13 (12.9.73) .. .. .. 5·00 6·00
113 $2 multicoloured (10.11.69) .. .. 3·50 90
114 $5 multicoloured (10.11.69) .. .. 9·00 3·00
115 $10 multicoloured (6.12.69) .. .. 30·00 8·00
101/15 .. .. *Set of* 15 42·00 13·00
103b/12a .. .. .. *Set of* 7 15·00 15·00

Designs: *Vert* (*as T* 45)—6 c. Lion dance; 10 c. Bharatha Natyam; 15 c. Tari Payong; 20 c. Kathak Kali; 25 c. Lu Chih Shen and Lin Chung; 50 c. Tari Lilin; 75 c. Tarian Kuda Kepang; $1 Yao Chi. (*As T* 44)—$2, Rebab; $10 Ta Ku. *Horiz* (*as T* 43)—$5 Vina.

58 E.C.A.F.E. Emblem

59 "100000" and Slogan as Block of Flats

(Des Eng Siak Loy. Photo Japanese Govt Ptg Bureau, Tokyo)

1969 (15 Apr). *25th Plenary Session of the U.N. Economic Commission for Asia and the Far East. P* 13.

116 **58** 15 c. black, silver and pale blue 40 15
117 30 c. black, silver and red 90 80
118 75 c. black, silver and violet-blue .. 1·75 2·00

(Des Tay Siew Chiah. Litho B.W.)

1969 (20 July). *Completion of "*100,000 *Homes for the People" Project. P* 13½.

119 **59** 25 c. black and emerald 90 50
120 50 c. black and deep blue .. .. 1·25 90

60 Aircraft over Silhouette of Singapore Docks

61 Sea Shells

(Des Eng Siak Loy and Han Kuan Cheng. Litho B.W.)

1969 (9 Aug). *150th Anniv of Founding of Singapore. T* **60** *and similar vert designs. P* 14 × 14½.

121 15 c. black, vermilion and yellow 50 20
122 30 c. black, blue and new blue 85 60
123 75 c. multicoloured .. .. .. 2·50 3·00
124 $1 black and vermilion .. .. 3·25 3·00
125 $5 vermilion and black .. .. 35·00 42·00
126 $10 black and bright green .. .. 48·00 48·00
121/6 .. .. .. *Set of* 6 80·00 90·00
MS127 120 × 120 mm. Nos. 121/6. P 13½ .. £325 £350

Designs:—30 c. U.N. emblem and outline of Singapore; 75 c. Flags and outline of Malaysian Federation; $1 Uplifted hands holding crescent and stars; $5 Tail of Japanese aircraft and search-light beams; $10 Bust from statue of Sir Stamford Raffles.

(Des Tay Siew Chiah (15 c.), Eng Siak Loy (others). Litho Rosenbaum Bros, Vienna)

1970 (15 Mar). *World Fair, Osaka. T* **61** *and similar vert designs. Multicoloured. P* 13½.

128 15 c. Type **61** 90 15
129 30 c. Tropical fish .. .. .. 1·75 90
130 75 c. Greater Flamingo and Helmeted Hornbill 4·75 3·75
131 $1 Orchid .. .. 4·75 6·00
MS132 94 × 154 mm. Nos. 128/31 .. .. 20·00 21·00

62 "Kindergarten"

63 Soldier charging

(Des Choy Weng Yang. Litho B.W.)

1970 (1 July). *Tenth Anniv of People's Association. T* **62** *and similar square designs. P* 13½.

133 15 c. agate and bright orange 50 12
134 50 c. ultramarine and yellow-orange .. 1·40 1·40
135 75 c. bright purple and black .. .. 2·25 2·75

Designs:—50 c. "Sport"; 75 c. "Culture".

(Des Choy Weng Yang. Litho Rosenbaum Bros, Vienna)

1970 (9 Aug). *National Day. T* **63** *and similar vert designs. Multicoloured. P* 13½.

136 15 c. Type **63** 70 10
137 50 c. Soldier on assault course .. .. 2·75 2·25
138 $1 Soldier jumping .. .. .. 3·75 4·25

64 Sprinters

(Des Choy Weng Yang. Photo Japanese Govt Ptg Bureau, Tokyo)

1970 (23 Aug). *Festival of Sports. T* **64** *and similar horiz designs. P* 13 × 13½.

139 10 c. magenta, black and ultramarine .. 90 90
 a. Horiz strip of 4. Nos. 139/42 .. 4·50
140 15 c. black, ultramarine and red-orange .. 1·25 1·25
141 25 c. black, red-orange and bright green .. 1·40 1·50
142 50 c. black, bright green and magenta .. 1·50 1·75

Designs:—15 c. Swimmers; 25 c. Tennis-players; 50 c. Racing-cars.

Nos. 139/42 were issued together *se-tenant* in horizontal strips of four within the sheet.

65 Ship of Neptune Oriental Lines

(Des W. Lee. Litho Rosenbaum Bros, Vienna)

1970 (1 Nov). *Singapore Shipping. T* **65** *and similar horiz designs. P* 12.

143 15 c. multicoloured .. .. .. 1·10 55
144 30 c. yellow-ochre and ultramarine .. .. 3·25 3·75
145 75 c. yellow-ochre and vermilion .. .. 5·00 6·00

Designs:—30 c. Container berth; 75 c. Ship-building.

66 Country Names forming Circle

(Des W. Lee. Litho D.L.R.)

1971 (1 Jan). *Commonwealth Heads of Government Meeting, Singapore. T* **66** *and similar horiz designs. Multicoloured. P* 14 ($1) *or* 15 × 14½ (*others*).

146 15 c. Type **66** 60 12
147 30 c. Flags in circle .. .. .. 1·10 65
148 75 c. Commonwealth flags .. .. 2·50 2·75
149 $1 Commonwealth flags linked to Singapore (63 × 61 *mm*) .. .. .. 3·00 3·75

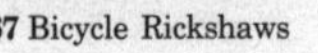

67 Bicycle Rickshaws

68 Chinese New Year

(Des Eng Siak Loy (15, 20 and 30 c.), W. Lee (others). Litho B.W.)

1971 (4 Apr). *Visit A.S.E.A.N. Year* (*A.S.E.A.N.* = *Association of South East Asian Nations*). *T* **67** *and similar designs. P* 13 × 13½ (50, 75 c.) *or* 11½ (*others*).

150 15 c. black, deep bluish violet and orange .. 30 15
151 20 c. indigo, orange and turquoise-blue .. 45 35
152 30 c. vermilion and deep maroon 75 70
153 50 c. multicoloured .. .. .. 2·25 3·25
154 75 c. multicoloured .. .. .. 3·00 4·00

Designs: *As T* **67**—20 c. Houseboat "village" and boats; 30 c. Bazaar. *Horiz* (68 × 18 *mm*)—50 c. Modern harbour skyline; 75 c. Religious buildings.

(Des W. Lee. Litho Rosenbaum Bros, Vienna)

1971 (9 Aug). *Singapore Festivals. T* **68** *and similar vert designs. Multicoloured. P* 14.

155 15 c. Type **68** 55 15
156 30 c. Hari Raya .. .. 1·50 1·50
157 50 c. Deepavali .. .. 2·50 3·00
158 75 c. Christmas .. .. 2·75 3·75
MS159 150 × 125 mm. Nos. 155/8 .. .. 21·00 21·00

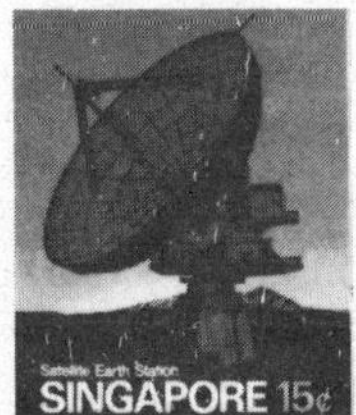

69 "Dish" Aerial

(Des W. Lee. Litho B.W.)

1971 (23 Oct). *Opening of Satellite Earth Station. P* 13½.
160 **69** 15 c. multicoloured .. .. 2·50 75
161 – 30 c. multicoloured .. .. 7·00 7·00
a. Block of 4. Nos. 161/4 .. .. 28·00
162 – 30 c. multicoloured .. .. 7·00 7·00
163 – 30 c. multicoloured .. .. 7·00 7·00
164 – 30 c. multicoloured .. .. 7·00 7·00

Designs:—Nos. 161/4 were printed in *se-tenant* blocks of four throughout the sheet, the four stamps forming a composite design similar to T **69**. They can be identified by the colour of the face value which is: yellow (No. 161), green (No. 162), magenta (No. 163) or orange (No. 164).

70 "Singapore River and Fort Canning, 1843–7" (Lieut. E. A. Porcher)

(Des W. Lee. Litho B.W.)

1971 (5 Dec). *Art. T* **70** *and similar horiz designs. Multicoloured. P* 12½ × 13 (50 *c. and* $1) *or* 13 (*others*).
165 10 c. Type **70** 75 60
166 15 c. "The Padang, 1851" (J. T. Thomson) .. 1·50 1·25
167 20 c. "Singapore Waterfront, 1848–9" .. 1·75 1·60
168 35 c. "View from Fort Canning, 1846" (J. T. Thomson) .. .. 3·75 3·75
169 50 c. "View from Mt Wallich, 1857" (P. Carpenter) (69 × 47 *mm*) .. .. .. 5·50 6·00
170 $1 "Singapore Waterfront, 1861" (W. Gray) (69 × 47 *mm*) .. .. 10·00 12·00
165/70 .. .. *Set of* 6 21·00 23·00

71 One Dollar of 1969

(Des W. Lee. Litho B.W.)

1972 (4 June). *Coins. T* **71** *and similar horiz designs. P* 13½.
171 15 c. orange, black and deep green 45 15
172 35 c. black and vermilion .. .. .. 1·00 1·25
173 $1 yellow, black and bright blue .. .. 3·25 4·25

Designs:—15 c. One-cent coin of George V; $1 One hundred and fifty dollar gold coin of 1969.

72 "Moon Festival" (Seah Kim Joo)

73 Lanterns and Fish

(Des W. Lee. Litho State Bank Note Printing Works, Helsinki)

1972 (9 July). *Contemporary Art. T* **72** *and similar multicoloured designs. P* 12½.
174 15 c. Type **72** 40 20
175 35 c. "Complimentary Forces" (Thomas Yeo) (36 × 54 *mm*) .. .. 1·25 1·50
176 50 c. "Rhythm in Blue" (Yusman Aman) (36 × 54 *mm*) .. .. 2·00 2·25
177 $1 "Gibbons" (Chen Wen Hsi) .. .. 3·75 4·75

(Des Eng Siak Loy. Litho State Bank Note Printing Works, Helsinki)

1972 (9 Aug). *National Day. T* **73** *and similar vert designs symbolising Festivals. Multicoloured. P* 12½.
178 15 c. Type **73** 40 15
179 35 c. Altar and candles .. .. .. 85 1·00
180 50 c. Jug, bowl and gifts .. .. .. 1·25 1·75
181 75 c. Candle .. .. 2·00 2·75

74 Student Welding

75 *Maria Rickmers*

(Des Eng Siak Loy. Photo Kultura, Budapest)

1972 (1 Oct). *Youth. T* **74** *and similar horiz designs. P* 12.
182 15 c. multicoloured 40 10
183 35 c. multicoloured .. .. 90 1·25
184 $1 red-orange, blue-violet & yellowish grn 2·75 3·50

Designs:—35 c. Sport; $1 Dancing.

(Des Choy Weng Yang (Nos. 185/7), Eng Siak Loy (**MS**188). Litho Harrison)

1972 (17 Dec). *Shipping. T* **75** *and similar multicoloured designs. P* 14 × 14½.
185 15 c. *Neptune Ruby* (42 × 29 *mm*) 70 30
186 75 c. Type **75** .. .. 3·75 4·00
187 $1 Chinese junk .. .. 5·00 5·25
MS188 152 × 84 mm. Nos. 185/7 .. .. .. 14·00 17·00

76 P.Q.R. Slogan

77 Jurong Bird Park

(Des W. Lee. Litho B.W.)

1973 (25 Feb). *"Prosperity through Quality and Reliability" Campaign. T* **76** *and similar vert designs. P* 14.
189 **76** 15 c. multicoloured 30 12
190 – 35 c. multicoloured 75 75
191 – 75 c. multicoloured .. .. 1·25 1·90
192 – $1 multicoloured .. .. 1·60 2·50

Nos. 190/2 show various P.Q.R. emblems.

(Des Han Kuan Cheng. Litho Harrison)

1973 (29 Apr). *Singapore Landmarks. T* **77** *and similar vert designs. P* 12½.
193 15 c. black and red-orange 45 12
194 35 c. black and myrtle-green 90 90
195 50 c. black and red-brown .. .. .. 1·75 2·00
196 $1 black and purple .. .. 3·00 3·50

Designs:—35 c. National Theatre; 50 c. City Hall; $1 Fullerton Building and Singapore River.

78 Aircraft Tail-fins

79 "Culture"

(Des W. Lee. Litho B.W.)

1973 (24 June). *Aviation. T* **78** *and similar horiz designs. Multicoloured. P* 13½ × 13.
197 10 c. Type **78** 25 8
198 35 c. Emblem of Singapore Airlines and destinations 75 75
199 75 c. Emblem on tail-fin .. .. .. 1·25 1·60
200 $1 Emblems encircling the globe .. .. 1·90 2·25

(Des Eng Siak Loy. Litho Harrison)

1973 (9 Aug). *National Day. T* **79** *and similar vert designs. P* 13½.
201 **79** 10 c. orange and black .. .. .. 1·25 55
a. Block of 4. Nos. 201/4 .. .. 6·00
202 – 35 c. orange and black .. .. .. 1·50 1·25
203 – 50 c. orange and black .. .. .. 1·75 1·50
204 – 75 c. orange and black .. .. .. 2·00 1·75

Nos. 201/4 were printed in *se-tenant* blocks of four within the sheet, and form a composite design representing Singapore's culture.

80 Athletics, Judo and Boxing

81 Agave

82 Mangosteen

(Des C. Lim. Photo Heraclio Fournier)

1973 (1 Sept). *Seventh S.E.A.P.* Games. T* **80** *and similar designs. P* 14 (10 *to* 35 *c.*) *or* 13 × 14 (*others*).
205 10 c. gold, silver and indigo 25 10
206 15 c. gold and grey-black 50 20
207 25 c. gold, silver and black 65 45
208 35 c. gold, silver and deep blue .. .. 1·10 75
209 50 c. multicoloured .. .. 1·75 1·90
210 $1 silver, royal blue and yellow-green .. 3·25 4·50
205/10 .. .. *Set of* 6 7·00 7·00
MS211 130 × 111 mm. Nos. 205/10. P 13 × 14 .. 9·00 10·00

Designs: *As T* **80**—15 c. Cycling, weight-lifting, pistol-shooting and sailing; 25 c. Footballs; 35 c. Table-tennis bat, shuttlecock, tennis ball and hockey stick. *Horiz* (41 × 25 *mm*):—50 c. Swimmers; $1 Stadium.

*S.E.A.P. = South East Asian Peninsula.

(Des W. Lee (1 c. to 75 c.), Eng Siak Loy (others). Photo Heraclio Fournier)

1973. *Various multicoloured designs as T* **81/2**. *With fluorescent security markings.*

(*a*) *Stylized flowers and plants, size as T* **81**. *P* 13 (30.9.73)
212 1 c. Type **81** 5 5
213 5 c. *Coleus blumei* 5 5
a. Booklet pane. Nos. 213 × 4, 214 × 4, 216 × 2 *se-tenant* .. .. 2·00
214 10 c. *Vinca rosea* 12 5
215 15 c. *Helianthus angustifolius* 15 5
216 20 c. *Licuala grandis* 25 10
217 25 c. *Wedelia trilobata* 30 5
218 35 c. *Chrysanthemum frutescens* 50 20
219 50 c. *Costus malortieanus* 65 10
220 75 c. *Gerbera jamesonii* 90 25

(*b*) *Fruits, size as T* **82**. *P* 12½ × 13 (1.11.73)
221 $1 Type **82** .. .. 1·50 30
222 $2 Jackfruit .. .. 3·25 1·25
223 $5 Coconut .. .. 6·50 2·75
224 $10 Pineapple .. .. 14·00 9·00
212/24 .. .. *Set of* 13 25·00 13·00

83 Tiger and Orang-utans

84 Multicolour Guppy

(Des Eng Siak Loy. Litho B.W.)

1973 (16 Dec). *Singapore Zoo. T* **83** *and similar vert designs. Multicoloured. P* 13.
225 5 c. Type **83** 25 5
226 10 c. Leopard and gazelles 45 20
227 35 c. Panther and deer .. .. .. 1·75 1·75
228 75 c. Horse and lion .. .. 2·75 3·25

(Des Eng Siak Loy. Photo Heraclio Fournier)

1974 (21 Apr). *Tropical Fish. T* **84** *and similar vert designs. Multicoloured. P* 14.
229 5 c. Type **84** 20 5
230 10 c. Half Black Guppy 40 15
231 35 c. Multicolour Guppy (*different*) .. .. 1·10 1·40
232 $1 Black Guppy .. .. 2·75 3·75

85 Scout Badge within "9"

86 U.P.U. Emblem and Multiple "Centenary"

(Des W. Lee. Litho Harrison)

1974 (9 June). *Ninth Asia-Pacific Scout Conference. P* 13½ × 14½.
233 **85** 10 c. multicoloured 25 10
234 75 c. multicoloured .. .. .. 1·25 1·25

(Des W. Lee. Litho Harrison)

1974 (7 July). *Centenary of Universal Postal Union. T* **86** *and similar vert designs. P* 14 × 13½.
235 10 c. orange-brown, purple-brown and gold .. 25 10
236 35 c. new blue, deep blue and gold 70 85
237 75 c. multicoloured .. .. 1·60 2·25

Designs:—35 c. U.P.U. emblem and multiple U.N. symbols; 75 c. U.P.U. emblem and multiple peace doves.

87 Family Emblem

88 "Tree and Sun" (Chia Keng San)

(Des Eng Siak Loy. Litho B.W.)

1974 (9 Aug). *World Population Year. T* **87** *and similar horiz designs. Multicoloured. P* 12½ × 13½.

238 10 c. Type **87** 15 5
239 35 c. Male and female symbols 70 80
a. Emerald (male symbol) omitted .. .. 90·00
240 75 c. World population map .. .. .. 1·60 1·90

(Des Eng Siak Loy. Photo Heraclio Fournier)

1974 (1 Oct). *Universal Children's Day. T* **88** *and similar vert designs showing children's paintings. Multicoloured. P* 13½.

241 5 c. Type **88** 20 5
242 10 c. "My Daddy and Mummy" (Angeline Ang) 35 10
243 35 c. "A Dump Truck" (Si-Hoe Yeen Joong) .. 1·75 1·75
244 50 c. "My Aunt" (Raymond Teo) .. .. 2·25 2·75
MS245 138 × 100 mm. Nos. 241/4. P 13 .. .. 4·75 5·00

89 Street Scene

(Des Loy Chin. Litho Secura, Singapore)

1975 (26 Jan). *Singapore Views. T* **89** *and similar horiz designs. Multicoloured. P* 13½.

246 15 c. Type **89** 30 10
247 20 c. Singapore River 50 40
248 $1 "Kelong" (fish-trap) .. .. .. 2·75 4·00

90 Emblem and Lighters' Prows

91 Satellite Earth Station, Sentosa

(Des Choy Weng Yang. Litho Secura, Singapore)

1975 (10 Mar). *Ninth Biennial Conference of International Association of Ports and Harbours, Singapore. T* **90** *and similar horiz designs. Multicoloured. P* 13½.

249 5 c. Type **90** 10 5
250 25 c. Freighter and ship's wheel 40 40
251 50 c. Oil-tanker and flags 75 85
252 $1 Container-ship and propellers .. .. 1·25 2·00

(Des Sim Tong Khern. Photo Heraclio Fournier)

1975 (29 June). *"Science and Industry". T* **91** *and similar multicoloured designs. P* 13½.

253 10 c. Type **91** 25 5
254 35 c. Oil refineries (*vert*) 75 90
255 75 c. "Medical Sciences" .. .. .. 1·75 2·00

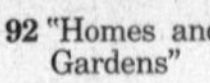

92 "Homes and Gardens"

93 Crowned Cranes

(Des Tay Siew Chiah. Litho Secura, Singapore)

1975 (9 Aug). *Tenth National Day. T* **92** *and similar square designs. Multicoloured. P* 13½.

256 10 c. Type **92** 20 5
257 35 c. "Shipping and Ship-building" 75 75
258 75 c. "Communications and Technology" .. 1·90 2·25
259 $1 "Trade, Commerce and Industry" .. 2·10 2·50

(Des Eng Siak Loy. Litho Harrison)

1975 (5 Oct). *Birds. T* **93** *and similar vert designs. Multicoloured. P* 14½ × 13½.

260 5 c. Type **93** 25 5
261 10 c. Great Indian Hornbill 45 5
262 35 c. White-breasted Kingfisher and White-collared Kingfisher .. .. .. 2·00 1·75
263 $1 Sulphur-crested Cockatoo and Blue and Yellow Macaw .. .. 5·00 6·00

94 "Equality"

95 Yellow Flame

(Des Tay Siew Chiah. Litho Secura, Singapore)

1975 (7 Dec). *International Women's Year. T* **94** *and similar square designs. Multicoloured. P* 13½.

264 10 c. Type **94** 25 8
265 35 c. "Development" .. .. 1·50 1·25
266 75 c. "Peace" .. .. 2·75 3·25
MS267 128 × 100 mm. Nos. 264/6 .. .. 4·50 5·00

(Des Tay Siew Chiah. Litho Secura, Singapore)

1976 (18 Apr). *Wayside Trees. T* **95** *and similar vert designs. Multicoloured. P* 13½.

268 10 c. Type **95** 25 8
269 35 c. Cabbage Tree 65 75
270 50 c. Rose of India .. .. 1·10 1·25
271 75 c. Variegated Coral Tree .. .. .. 1·60 2·50

96 *Arachnis hookeriana* × *Vanda* Hilo Blue

97 Festival Symbol and Band

(Des Eng Siak Loy. Litho Secura, Singapore)

1976 (20 June). *Singapore Orchids. T* **96** *and similar vert designs. Multicoloured. P* 13½.

272 10 c. Type **96** 35 8
273 35 c. *Arachnis Maggie Oei* × *Vanda insignis* 1·00 75
274 50 c. *Arachnis Maggie Oei* × *Vandu* Rodman 2·00 1·75
275 75 c. *Arachnis hookeriana* × *Vanda* Dawn Nishimura .. .. 2·75 3·50

(Des Han Kuan Cheng. Litho Harrison)

1976 (9 Aug). *Tenth Anniv of Singapore Youth Festival. Horiz designs showing festival symbol as T* **97**. *Multicoloured. P* 12½.

276 10 c. Type **97** 20 8
277 35 c. Athletes 60 60
278 75 c. Dancers .. .. 1·40 1·40

98 "Queen Elizabeth Walk"

(Des H. Weepaul. Litho Secura, Singapore)

1976 (14 Nov). *Paintings of Old Singapore, circa* 1905–10, *by A. L. Watson. T* **98** *and similar horiz designs. Multicoloured. With fluorescent security markings. P* 14.

279 10 c. Type **98** 30 10
280 50 c. "The Padang" .. .. 1·75 1·75
281 $1 "Raffles Place" .. .. 3·25 3·50
MS282 164 × 91 mm. Nos. 279/81. P 13½ .. 6·50 6·50

99 Chinese Costume

100 Radar, Missile and Soldiers

(Des Margaret Heng. Litho Harrison)

1976 (19 Dec). *Bridal Costumes. T* **99** *and similar vert designs. Multicoloured. P* 14.

283 10 c. Type **99** 25 5
284 35 c. Indian costume .. .. 1·00 90
285 75 c. Malay costume .. .. 1·75 1·90

(Des Eng Siak Loy. Litho Harrison)

1977 (12 Mar). *Tenth Anniv of National Service. T* **100** *and similar vert designs. Multicoloured. P* 14.

286 10 c. Type **100** 30 5
287 50 c. Tank and soldiers .. .. 1·25 90
288 75 c. Soldiers, wireless operators, pilot and aircraft .. .. 2·00 1·75

101 Lyrate Cockle

102 Spotted Hermit Crab

(Des Tay Siew Chiah. Litho Secura, Singapore)

1977. *Multicoloured designs as T* **101/2**. *With fluorescent security markings. P* 13. (*a*) *Shells as T* **101** (9.4.77).

289 1 c. Type **101** 5 5
290 5 c. Folded Scallop 5 5
a. Booklet pane. Nos. 290 × 4 and 291 × 8 *se-tenant* .. .. 1·00
291 10 c. Marble Cone 10 5
a. Imperf (pair) .. ..
292 15 c. Scorpion Conch 30 5
293 20 c. Amplustre Bubble 35 5
294 25 c. Spiral Babylon 40 5
295 35 c. Regal Thorny Oyster 60 20
296 50 c. Winged Frog Shell 75 5
297 75 c. Troschel's Murex .. .. 1·00 15

(*b*) *Fish and Crustaceans as T* **102** (4.6.77)

298 $1 Type **102** .. .. 1·50 15
299 $2 Stingray .. .. 1·75 50
300 $5 Cuttlefish .. .. 3·50 2·25
301 $10 Lionfish .. .. 7·50 5·50
289/301 .. .. *Set of* 13 16·00 8·00

103 Shipbuilding

104 Keyhole and Banknotes

(Des W. Lee. Litho Secura, Singapore)

1977 (1 May). *Labour Day. T* **103** *and similar horiz designs. Multicoloured. P* 13 × 12½.

302 10 c. Type **103** 15 5
303 50 c. Building construction 85 60
304 75 c. Road construction .. .. .. 1·25 1·00

(Des Tay Siew Chiah. Litho Secura, Singapore)

1977 (16 July). *Centenary of Post Office Savings Bank. T* **104** *and similar vert designs. Multicoloured. P* 13.

305 10 c. Type **104** 15 5
306 35 c. On-line banking service 75 50
307 75 c. GIRO service .. .. 1·60 1·25

105 Flags of Member Nations

106 "Chingay Procession" (Liang Yik Yin)

(Des Eng Siak Loy. Litho Secura, Singapore)

1977 (8 Aug). *Tenth Anniv of A.S.E.A.N. (Association of South-East Asian Nations). T* **105** *and similar vert designs. Multicoloured. P* 14.

308 10 c. Type **105** 15 5
309 35 c. "Agriculture" 60 50
310 75 c. "Industry" .. .. 1·25 1·10

(Des H. Weepaul. Litho Secura, Singapore)

1977 (1 Oct). *Children's Art. T* **106** *and similar horiz designs. Multicoloured. P* 12½.

311 10 c. Type **106** 20 5
312 35 c. "At the Bus Stop" (Chong Khing Ann) .. 75 50
313 75 c. "Playground" (Yap Li Hwa) .. .. 1·60 1·40
MS314 160 × 97 mm. Nos. 311/13 .. .. 2·75 2·75

107 "Life Sciences"

108 Botanical Gardens and Esplanade, Jurong Bird Park

(Des Tay Siew Chiah. Litho Format)

1977 (10 Dec). *Singapore Science Centre. T* **107** *and similar vert designs. Multicoloured. P* 14.
315 10 c. Type **107** 10 5
316 35 c. "Physical sciences" 45 30
317 75 c. "Science and technology" .. .. 1·00 85
318 $1 Singapore Science Centre .. .. 1·25 1·00

(Des C. Kiat. Litho Harrison)

1978 (22 Apr). *Parks and Gardens. T* **108** *and similar multicoloured designs. P* 14½.
319 10 c. Type **108** 15 5
320 35 c. Lagoon, East Coast Park (*vert*) 45 30
321 75 c. Botanical Gardens (*vert*) 75 50

109 Red-whiskered Bulbul

111 Map of South East Asia showing Cable Network

110 Thian Hock Keng Temple

(Des Eng Siak Loy. Litho Secura, Singapore)

1978 (1 July). *Singing Birds. T* **109** *and similar vert designs. Multicoloured. P* 13½.
322 10 c. Type **109** 25 5
323 35 c. Oriental White Eye 70 40
324 50 c. White-rumped Shama 90 55
325 75 c. White-crested Laughing Thrush and Melodious Laughing Thrush .. .. 1·25 1·00

(Des Eng Siak Loy. Litho Secura, Singapore)

1978 (9 Aug). *National Monuments. T* **110** *and similar horiz designs. Multicoloured. P* 13½.
326 10 c. Type **110** 15 12
327 10 c. Hajjah Fatimah Mosque 15 12
328 10 c. Armenian Church 15 12
329 10 c. Sri Mariamman Temple 15 12
MS330 173 × 86 mm. 35 c. × 4, as Nos. 326/9 .. 2·75 2·75
Stamps from No. **MS**330 are similar in design to Nos. 326/9 but have no borders and the inscriptions are slightly larger.

(Des J. Heng. Litho Secura, Singapore)

1978 (3 Oct). *A.S.E.A.N. (Association of South East Asian Nations) Submarine Cable Network* (1*st issue*). *Completion of Philippines–Singapore section. P* 13½ (*around design as well as stamp*).
331 **111** 10 c. multicoloured 10 5
332 35 c. multicoloured 40 40
333 50 c. multicoloured 50 50
334 75 c. multicoloured .. .. 80 1·00
See also Nos. 385/8 and 458/62.

112 *Neptune Spinel*

(Des Paul Wee Hui Hong. Litho Secura, Singapore)

1978 (18 Nov). *10th Anniv of Neptune Orient Shipping Lines. T* **112** *and similar horiz designs. Multicoloured. P* 13½.
335 10 c. Type **112** 15 5
336 35 c. *Neptune Aries* 40 40
337 50 c. *Anro Temasek* 45 45
338 75 c. *Neptune Pearl* .. .. 80 1·00

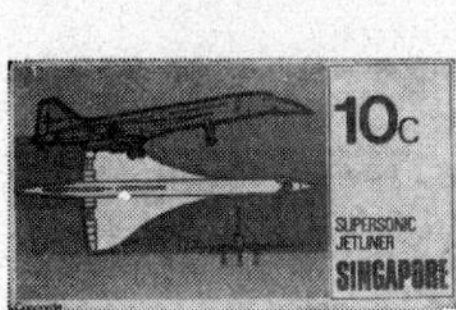

113 "Concorde"

114 10 Kilometre Marker

(Des Paul Wee Hui Hong. Litho Secura, Singapore)

1978 (16 Dec). *Aviation. T* **113** *and similar horiz designs. Multicoloured. P* 13.
339 10 c. Type **113** 15 5
340 35 c. Boeing "747B" 35 20
341 50 c. Vickers "Vimy" 50 30
342 75 c. Wright Brothers' *Flyer* 1 .. .. .. 70 75

(Des W. Lee. Litho Secura, Singapore)

1979 (24 Feb). *Metrication. T* **114** *and similar vert designs. Multicoloured. P* 13½.
343 10 c. Type **114** 8 5
344 35 c. Tape measure 20 20
345 75 c. Weighing scales 45 45

115 Vanda Hybrid

116 Envelope with new Singapore Postcode

(Des Paul Wee Hui Hong. Litho Harrison)

1979 (14 Apr). *Orchids. T* **115** *and similar designs showing different varieties of Vanda Hybrid. P* 14½ × 14 (10, 35 *c.*) *or* 14 × 14½ (*others*).
346 10 c. multicoloured 15 5
347 35 c. multicoloured 35 20
348 50 c. multicoloured (*vert*) 50 30
349 75 c. multicoloured (*vert*) 70 45

(Des Paul Wee Hui Hong. Litho Secura, Singapore)

1979 (1 July). *Postal Code Publicity. P* 13.
350 **116** 10 c. multicoloured 8 5
351 – 50 c. multicoloured 30 30
The 50 c. design is as Type **116**, but the envelope is addressed to the Philatelic Bureau, General Post Office and has the postcode "Singapore 0104".

117 Early Telephone and Overhead Cables

118 "Lantern Festival" (Eng Chun-Ngan)

(Des Eng Siak Loy. Litho J.W.)

1979 (5 Oct). *Centenary of Telephone Service. T* **117** *and similar horiz designs. P* 13.
352 10 c. yellow-brown and new blue 8 5
353 35 c. bright orange, blue and reddish violet .. 20 25
354 50 c. blue, dp turquoise-grn & yellowish grn .. 35 35
355 75 c. yellowish green and bright orange .. 50 70
Designs:—35 c. Telephone dial and world map; 50 c. Modern telephone and city scene; 75 c. Latest computerised telephone and circuit diagram.

(Des Han Kuan Cheng. Litho Secura, Singapore)

1979 (10 Nov). *International Year of the Child. Children's Drawings. T* **118** *and similar horiz designs. Multicoloured. P* 12½ × 13.
356 10 c. Type **118** 10 5
357 35 c. "Singapore Harbour" (Wong Chien Chien) 30 20
358 50 c. "Use Your Hands" (Leong Choy Yeen) .. 40 25
359 75 c. "Soccer" (Tan Cheong Hin) 60 45
MS360 154 × 98 mm. Nos. 356/9 .. .. .. 1·50 1·25

119 View of Gardens

120 Hainan Junk

(Des Eng Siak Loy. Litho Secura, Singapore)

1979 (15 Dec). *120th Anniv of Botanic Gardens. T* **119** *and similar horiz designs showing different views of the gardens. P* 13 × 13½.
361 10 c. multicoloured 8 5
a. Imperf (pair)
362 50 c. multicoloured 40 40
363 $1 multicoloured 75 80

(Des Eng Siak Loy. Litho J.W.)

1980 (5 Apr)–**83**. *Ships. Multicoloured designs as T* **120**. *Ordinary paper* (1 *c.*, 10 *c.*), *phosphorised paper* ($1 *to* $10) *and ordinary or phosphorised paper* (*others*). *P* 14 (1 *to* 75 *c.*) *or* 13½ ($1 *to* $10).
364 1 c. Type **120** (26.4.80) 5 5
365 5 c. Clipper (26.4.80) 5 5
366 10 c. Fujian Junk (26.4.80) 8 5
p. One phosphor band (12.83) 8 5
367 15 c. Golekkan (26.4.80) 10 5
368 20 c. Palari (26.4.80) 15 5
369 25 c. East Indiaman (26.4.80) 20 5
370 35 c. Galleon (26.4.80) 25 5
371 50 c. Caravel (26.4.80) 40 15
372 75 c. Jiangsu Trader (26.4.80) 55 25
373 $1 Coaster (42 × 25 *mm*) 70 45
a. Imperf (pair) £200
374 $2 Oil Tanker (42 × 25 *mm*) .. .. 1·40 90
375 $5 Screw Steamer (42 × 25 *mm*) .. .. 3·50 3·25
376 $10 Paddle Wheel Steamer (42 × 25 *mm*) .. 7·00 7·50
364/76 .. .. *Set of* 13 13·00 11·50

MINIMUM PRICE

The minimum price quoted is 5p which represents a handling charge rather than a basis for valuing common stamps. For further notes about prices see introductory pages.

121 Straits Settlements 1867 1½ c. Stamp and Map of Singapore, 1843

122 C.P.F. Emblem and "Keys to Retirement Benefits"

(Des Paul Wee Hui Hong. Litho Secura, Singapore)

1980 (6 May). *"London 1980" International Stamp Exhibition. T* **121** *and similar vert designs. Multicoloured. P* 13.
377 10 c. Type **121** 20 5
378 35 c. Straits Settlements 1906 $500 stamp and treaty between Johore and British Colony of Singapore 35 20
379 $1 1948 $2 stamp and map of Malaysia .. 70 60
380 $2 1969 150th Anniversary of Singapore $10 commemorative and letter to Col. Addenbrooke from Sir Stamford Raffles .. 1·25 95
MS381 148 × 104 mm. Nos. 377/80 .. .. 2·75 3·00

(Des Paul Wee Hui Hong. Litho Secura, Singapore)

1980 (1 July). *25th Anniv of Central Provident Fund Board. T* **122** *and similar vert designs showing C.P.F. emblem. Multicoloured. P* 13 × 12½.
382 10 c. Type **122** 10 5
383 50 c. "C.P.F. savings for home ownership" .. 40 25
384 $1 "C.P.F. savings for old-age" 75 70

123 Map of South East Asia showing Cable Network

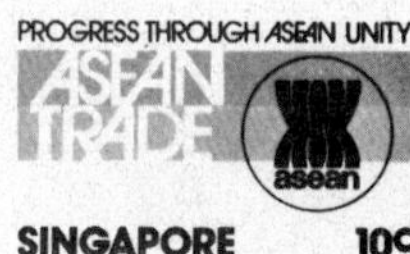

124 A.S.E.A.N. Trade Fair Emblem

(Des J. Heng. Litho Secura, Singapore)

1980 (8 Aug). *A.S.E.A.N. (Association of South East Asian Nations) Submarine Cable Network* (2*nd issue*). *Completion of Indonesia–Singapore Section. P* 13½ (*around design as well as stamp*).
385 **123** 10 c. multicoloured 10 5
386 35 c. multicoloured 40 20
387 50 c. multicoloured 50 30
388 75 c. multicoloured 65 75

(Des Paul Wee Hui Hong. Litho Secura, Singapore)

1980 (3 Oct). *A.S.E.A.N. (Association of South East Asian Nations) Trade Fair. P* 12½ × 13.
389 **124** 10 c. multicoloured 5 5
390 35 c. multicoloured 30 20
391 75 c. multicoloured 60 65

125 Ixora

126 International Currency Symbols

(Des S. Tan and Chua Ban Har. Litho J.W.)

1980 (8 Nov). *National Tree Planting Day. Flowers. T* **125** *and similar horiz designs. Multicoloured. P* 13½ × 13.
392 10 c. Type **125** 5 5
393 35 c. Allamanda 40 25
394 50 c. Sky Vine 50 35
395 75 c. Bougainvillea 60 65

(Des Paul Wee Hui Hong. Litho Secura, Singapore)

1981 (24 Jan). *10th Anniv of Monetary Authority of Singapore. P* 14.
396 **126** 10 c. black, vermilion & greenish yellow 5 5
397 35 c. multicoloured 30 20
398 75 c. multicoloured 55 60

(**127**)

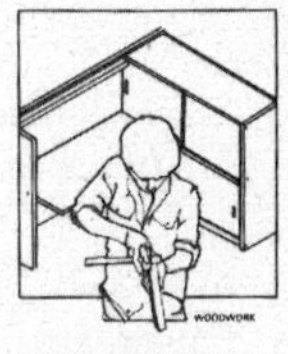

128 Woodwork

1981 (4 Mar). *No. 65 surch with T* **127**.
399 **21** 10 c. on 4 c. black and orange-red .. 5 5

(Des Sng Tong Beng. Litho J.W.)

1981 (11 Apr). *Technical Training. T* **128** *and similar vert designs. Multicoloured. P* 13 × 13½.
400 10 c. Type **128** 5 5
401 35 c. Building construction 25 20
402 50 c. Electronics 40 30
403 75 c. Precision machining 50 60

129 Figures representing various Sports

130 "The Rights to Environmental Aids"

(Des Lim Ching San. Litho J.W.)

1981 (25 Aug). *"Sports for All". T* **129** *and similar vert designs showing figures representing various sports. P* 14.
404 10 c. multicoloured 5 5
405 75 c. multicoloured 55 45
406 $1 multicoloured 75 75

(Des Chua Ban Har. Litho Harrison)

1981 (24 Nov). *International Year for Disabled Persons. T* **130** *and similar vert designs. Multicoloured. One centre phosphor band (10 c.) or phosphorised paper (others). P* 14½.
407 10 c. Type **130** 5 5
408 35 c. "The right to social integration" 30 20
409 50 c. "The right to education" 45 35
410 75 c. "The right to work" 70 70
Nos. 407/10 were printed with phosphor bands or on phosphorised paper similar to that used on contemporary Great Britain issues.

131 Control Tower and Passenger Terminal Building, Changi Airport

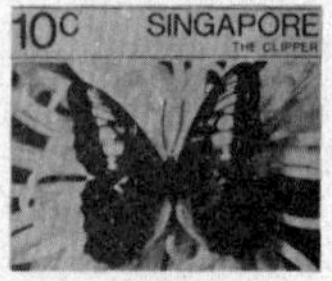

132 Clipper

(Des J. Heng. Litho Secura, Singapore Ltd)

1981 (29 Dec). *Opening of Changi Airport. P* 14 × 13½.
411 **131** 10 c. multicoloured 5 5
412 35 c. multicoloured 20 20
413 50 c. multicoloured 30 30
414 75 c. multicoloured 50 50
415 $1 multicoloured 65 75
MS416 154 × 105 mm. Nos. 411/15 .. .. 2·50 3·25
The five values show different background emblems representing the Parks and Recreation Dept, Public Works Dept, Telecommunications Authority, Port of Singapore and Dept of Civil Aviation.

(Des Eng Siak Loy. Litho J.W.)

1982 (3 Mar). *Butterflies. T* **132** *and similar horiz designs. Multicoloured. One centre phosphor band (10 c.) or phosphorised paper (others). P* 14½.
417 10 c. Type **132** 5 5
418 50 c. Blue Glassy Tiger 35 25
419 $1 Raja Brooke's Birdwing 70 80

133 A.S.E.A.N. Emblem

134 Football and Stylised Player

(Des Paul Wee Hui Hong. Litho Secura, Singapore)

1982 (14 June). *15th Anniv of A.S.E.A.N. (Association of South East Asian Nations). One centre phosphor band (10 c.) or phosphorised paper (others). P* 14½ × 14.
420 **133** 10 c. multicoloured 5 5
421 35 c. multicoloured 20 25
422 – 50 c. multicoloured 30 30
423 – 75 c. multicoloured 45 50
The 50 and 75 c. values are as Type **133**, but are inscribed "15th ASEAN Ministerial Meeting".

(Des Paul Wee Hui Hong. Litho Secura, Singapore)

1982 (9 July). *World Cup Foodball Championship, Spain. T* **134** *and similar vert designs. One centre phosphor band (10 c.) or phosphorised paper (others). P* 12.
424 10 c. black, bright blue and greenish blue .. 5 5
425 75 c. multicoloured 45 50
426 $1 multicoloured 65 70
Designs:—75 c. Football and World Cup, Asian Zone Four emblem; $1 Football and globe.

135 Sultan Shoal Lighthouse, 1896

136 Yard Gantry Cranes

(Des Eng Siak Loy. Litho Secura, Singapore)

1982 (7 Aug). *Lighthouses of Singapore. T* **135** *and similar horiz designs. Multicoloured. One centre phosphor band (10 c.) or phosphorised paper (others). P* 12.
427 10 c. Type **135** 5 5
428 75 c. Horsburgh Lighthouse, 1855 .. .. 45 50
429 $1 Raffles Lighthouse, 1855 .. .. 65 70
MS430 148 × 104 mm. Nos. 427/9 .. .. 1·40 1·50
No. **MS**430 was printed on plain paper without phosphor.

(Des Goh Seng Lim. Litho Secura, Singapore)

1982 (15 Sept). *10th Anniv of Container Terminal. T* **136** *and similar horiz designs. Multicoloured. One centre phosphor band (10 c.) or phosphorised paper (others). P* 13½.
431 10 c. Type **136** 5 5
432 35 c. Computer 20 25
433 50 c. Freightlifter 30 30
434 75 c. Straddle carrier 45 50

137 Scouts on Parade

138 Productivity Movement Slogans

(Des Poh Siew Wah. Litho Secura, Singapore)

1982 (15 Oct). *75th Anniv of Boy Scout Movement. T* **137** *and similar vert designs. Multicoloured. One centre phosphor band (10 c.) or phosphorised paper (others). P* 14 × 13.
435 10 c. Type **137** 5 5
436 35 c. Scouts hiking 20 25
437 50 c. Scouts building tower 30 30
438 75 c. Scouts canoeing 45 50

(Des M. Gan. Litho Secura, Singapore)

1982 (17 Nov). *Productivity Movement. T* **138** *and similar diamond-shaped designs. One centre phosphor band (10 c.) or phosphorised paper (others). P* 13½.
439 10 c. orange and emerald 5 5
440 35 c. yellow-ochre and deep dull blue 20 25
441 50 c. maroon, bistre-yellow and brownish grey 30 35
442 75 c. maroon and lemon 45 50
Designs:—35 c. Family and housing ("Benefits of Productivity"); 50 c. Works meeting ("Quality Control Circles"); 75 c. Aspects of Singapore business ("Everybody's Business").

139 Commonwealth Logo and Country Names

140 Soccer

(Des Eng Siak Loy. Litho Secura, Singapore)

1983 (14 Mar). *Commonwealth Day. One centre phosphor band (10 c.) or phosphorised paper (others). P* 13 × 13½.
443 **139** 10 c. multicoloured 5 5
444 35 c. multicoloured 20 25
445 75 c. multicoloured 45 50
446 $1 multicoloured 65 70

(Des Lim Ching San. Litho Secura, Singapore)

1983 (28 May). *12th South-East Asia Games. T* **140** *and similar vert designs. Multicoloured. One centre phosphor band (10 c.) or phosphorised paper (others). P* 13½ × 13.
447 10 c. Type **140** 5 5
448 35 c. Racket games 20 25
449 75 c. Athletics 45 50
450 $1 Swimming 65 70

141 Policeman and Family

142 1977 ASEAN Stamps and Statue of King Chulalongkorn

(Des Lim Ching San. Litho J.W.)

1983 (24 June). *Neighbourhood Watch Scheme. T* **141** *and similar horiz designs. Multicoloured. One centre phosphor band (10 c.) or phosphorised paper (others). P* 13½ × 14.
451 10 c. Type **141** 5 5
452 35 c. Policeman and children 20 25
453 75 c. Policeman and inhabitants with linked arms 45 50

(Des Sylvia Tan and Ko Hui-Huy. Litho J.W.)

1983 (4 Aug). *Bangkok International Stamp Exhibition. T* **142** *and similar vert designs. Multicoloured. One centre phosphor band (10 c.), phosphorised paper (35 c., $1) or ordinary paper (miniature sheet). P* 14.
454 10 c. Type **142** 5 5
455 35 c. 1980 ASEAN stamps and map of South-East Asia 20 25
456 $1 1982 ASEAN stamps and signatures of Heads of State 60 65
MS457 147 × 104 mm. Nos. 454/6 .. .. 85 1·00

143 Map of South-East Asia showing Cable Network

(Des J. Heng. Litho Secura, Singapore)

1983 (27 Sept). *A.S.E.A.N. (Association of South-East Asian Nations) Submarine Cable Network (3rd issue). Completion of Malaysia-Singapore-Thailand section. One centre phosphor band (10 c.), phosphorised paper (35 c. to 75 c.) or ordinary paper (miniature sheet). P* 13½ *(around design as well as stamp).*
458 **143** 10 c. multicoloured 5 5
459 35 c. multicoloured 20 25
460 50 c. multicoloured 30 35
461 75 c. multicoloured 45 50
MS462 146 × 100 mm. Nos. 331, 388, 458/61 .. 1·60 1·75

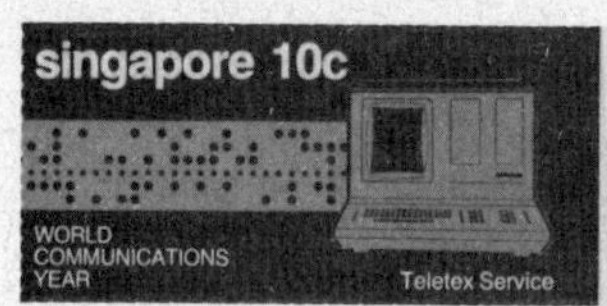

144 Teletex Service

(Des Sylvia Tan and Ko Hui-Huy. Litho Enschedé)

1983 (10 Nov). *World Communications Year. T* **144** *and similar horiz designs. Phosphorised paper. P* 12½ × 13.
463 10 c. greenish yellow, light emerald and black 5 5
464 35 c. greenish yellow, brt rose-red & chocolate 20 25
465 75 c. bright yellow-green, greenish blue and deep violet-blue 45 50
466 $1 greenish yell, olive-brn & brownish blk 50 55
Designs:—35 c. World telephone numbering plan; 75 c. Satellite transmission; $1 Sea communications.

145 Slaty-breasted Rail

146 House of Tan Yeok Nee

(Des Poh Siew Wah. Litho Harrison)

1984 (15 Mar). *Coastal Birds. T* **145** *and similar horiz designs. Multicoloured. One centre phosphor band (10 c.) or phosphorised paper (others). P* 14½ × 13½.
467 10 c. Type **145** 8 10
468 35 c. Black Bittern 30 35
469 50 c. Brahminy Kite 40 45
470 75 c. Common Moorhen 60 65

(Des Poh Siew Wah. Litho Secura, Singapore)

1984 (7 June). *National Monuments. T* **146** *and similar vert designs. Multicoloured. One centre phosphor band* (10 c.) *or phosphorised paper* (*others*). *P* 12.
471 10 c. Type **146** 8 10
472 35 c. Thong Chai building . . 30 35
473 50 c. Telok Ayer market . . 40 45
474 $1 Nagore Durgha shrine . . 80 85

147 1970 $1 National Day Stamp **148** Schoolchildren

(Des P. Hong. Litho Secura, Singapore)

1984 (9 Aug–23 Nov). *"25 Years of Nation Building." T* **147** *and similar vert designs showing various Singapore stamps. Multicoloured. One centre phosphor band* (10 c.) *or phosphorised paper* (*others*). *P* 14 × 14½.
475 10 c. Type **147** . . 8 10
476 35 c. 1981 $1 "Sports for All" stamp . . 30 35
477 50 c. 1969 25 c. "100,000 Homes for the People" stamp . . 40 45
478 75 c. 1976 10 c. Wayside Trees stamp . . 60 65
479 $1 1981 $1 Opening of Changi Airport stamp 80 85
480 $2 1981 10 c. Monetary Authority stamp . . 1·75 1·90
475/80 . . *Set of* 6 3·50 3·75
MS481 132 × 106 mm. Nos. 475/80. P 12½ (23 Nov) 3·75 4·00

No. **MS**481 is on ordinary paper without a phosphor band on the 10 c. stamp.

(Des Lim Ching San. Litho Secura)

1984 (26 Oct). *"Total Defence". T* **148** *and similar vert designs. One centre phosphor band. P* 12.
482 10 c. brown and orange-vermilion . . 8 10
a. Horiz strip of 5. Nos. 482/6 . . 40
483 10 c. brown, yellow-olive and new blue . . 8 10
484 10 c. brown, bright violet and pale salmon . . 8 10
485 10 c. brown, orange-brown and mauve . . 8 10
486 10 c. brown, yellow and yellow-olive . . 8 10

Designs:—No. 482, Type **148**; 483, People of Singapore; 484, Industrial workers; 485, Civil Defence first aid worker; 486, Anti-aircraft gun crew.

Nos. 482/6 were printed together, *se-tenant*, in horizontal strips of five throughout the sheet.

POSTAGE DUE STAMPS

The postage due stamps of Malayan Postal Union were in use in Singapore until replaced by the following issues.

D 1 D 2

(Litho B.W.)

1968 (1 Feb). *W w* **12**. *P* 9.
D1 D 1 1 c. green . . 15 30
D2 2 c. red . . 15 30
D3 4 c. yellow-orange . . 40 65
D4 8 c. chocolate . . 25 40
D5 10 c. magenta . . 50 80
D6 12 c. slate-violet . . 60 85
D7 20 c. new blue . . 2·00 2·75
D8 50 c. drab . . 3·75 4·50
D1/8 . . *Set of* 8 7·00 9·50

The 10, 12 and 20 c. exist on both white and toned paper; the rest on toned paper only.

1973. *White paper. W w* **12**. *P* 13 × 13½.
D 9 D 1 10 c. bright magenta (27.4) . . 55 1·00
D10 50 c. sage-green (24.8) . . 2·75 5·50

1977–78. *White paper. No wmk. P* 12½ × 13.
D11 D 1 1 c. green . . 18·00 20·00
D12 4 c. yellow-orange . . 18·00 20·00
D13 10 c. bright magenta . . 18·00 20·00
D14 20 c. new blue . . 23·00 25·00
D15 50 c. sage-green . . 35·00 40·00

(Litho Secura, Singapore)

1978 (25 Sept)–**81**. *No wmk. P* 13.
D16 D 2 1 c. blue-green . . 20 30
a. Perf 12 × 11½ (1981) 5 5
D17 4 c. pale orange . . 15 20
a. Perf 12 × 11½ (1981) 5 5
D18 10 c. cerise . . 25 35
a. Perf 12 × 11½ (1981) 8 10
D19 20 c. light blue . . 35 40
a. Perf 12 × 11½ (1981) 15 20
D20 50 c. yellow-green . . 65 80
a. Perf 12 × 11½ (1981) 40 45

Solomon Islands

(*formerly* British Solomon Islands)

PRICES FOR STAMPS ON COVER TO 1945	
Nos. 1/7	*from* × 5
Nos. 8/36	*from* × 3
Nos. 37/8	—
Nos. 39/51	*from* × 3
No. 52	—
Nos. 53/6	*from* × 2
Nos. 57/9	*from* × 6
Nos. 60/72	*from* × 2
Nos. D1/8	*from* × 5

BRITISH PROTECTORATE

1 2

(Des C. M. Woodford. Litho W. E. Smith & Co, Sydney)

1907 (14 Feb). *No wmk. P* 11.
1 1 ½d. ultramarine . . 12·00 22·00
2 1d. rose-carmine . . 30·00 35·00
3 2d. indigo . . 30·00 35·00
a. Imperf between (horiz pair) . . £7500
4 2½d. orange-yellow . . 35·00 38·00
a. Imperf between (vert pair) . . £4000
b. Imperf between (horiz pair) . . £4000 £4000
5 5d. emerald-green . . 55·00 80·00
6 6d. chocolate . . 70·00 70·00
a. Imperf between (vert pair) . . £3000
7 1s. bright purple . . £100 £100
1/7 . . *Set of* 7 £300 £350

Three types exist of the ½d. and 2½d., and six each of the other values, differing in minor details.

(Recess D.L.R.)

1908 (1 Nov)–**11**. *Wmk Mult Crown CA* (*sideways*). *P* 14.
8 2 ½d. green . . 80 1·50
9 1d. red . . 1·90 2·40
10 2d. greyish slate . . 2·50 3·25
11 2½d. ultramarine . . 3·00 5·00
11*a* 4d. red/*yellow* (3.11) . . 5·50 12·00
12 5d. olive . . 13·00 10·00
13 6d. claret . . 11·00 10·00
14 1s. black/*green* . . 16·00 18·00
15 2s. purple/*blue* (3.10) . . 35·00 48·00
16 2s. 6d. red/*blue* (3.10) . . 50·00 90·00
17 5s. green/*yellow* (3.10) . . £120 £140
8/17 . . *Set of* 11 £225 £300
8/17 Optd "Specimen" . . *Set of* 11 £350

The ½d. and 1d. were issued in 1913 on rather thinner paper and with brownish gum.

3 4

(T **3** and **4**. Typo D.L.R.)

1913. *Inscribed* "POSTAGE POSTAGE". *Wmk Mult Crown CA. P* 14.
18 3 ½d. green (1.4) . . 2·00 3·75
19 1d. red (1.4) . . 2·50 10·00
20 3d. purple/*yellow* (27.2) . . 3·00 8·00
a. On orange-buff . . 4·00 18·00
21 11d. dull purple and scarlet (27.2) . . 10·00 17·00
18/21 Optd "Specimen" . . *Set of* 4 70·00

1914–23. *Inscribed* "POSTAGE REVENUE". *Wmk Mult Crown CA. P* 14.
22 4 ½d. green, **O** . . 1·25 4·00
23 ½d. yellow-green, **O** (1917) . . 1·50 5·00
24 1d. carmine-red, **O** . . 1·25 2·00
25 1d. scarlet, **O** (1917) . . 3·00 6·50
26 2d. grey, **O** . . 2·50 8·50
27 2½d. ultramarine, **O** . . 3·00 7·00
28 3d. purple/*pale yellow*, **C** (1.23) . . 22·00 35·00
29 4d. black and red/*yellow*, **C** . . 8·50 8·00
30 5d. dull purple and olive-green, **C** . . 15·00 22·00
31 5d. brown-purple and olive-green, **C** . . 15·00 24·00
32 6d. dull and bright purple, **C** . . 8·00 18·00
33 1s. black/*green*, **C** . . 9·00 14·00
a. On blue-green, olive back . . 9·00 17·00
34 2s. purple and blue/*blue*, **C** . . 12·00 20·00
35 2s. 6d. black and red/*blue*, **C** . . 17·00 26·00
36 5s. green and red/*yellow*, **C** . . 32·00 40·00
a. On orange-buff (1920) . . 35·00 48·00
37 10s. green and red/*green*, **C** . . £100 £140
38 £1 purple and black/*red*, **C** . . £250 £300
22/38 . . *Set of* 14 £450 £550
22/38 Optd "Specimen" . . *Set of* 14 £600

Variations in the coloured papers are mostly due to climate and do not indicate separate printings.

1922–31. *Wmk Mult Script CA. P* 14.
39 4 ½d. green, **O** (10.22) . . 55 1·75
40 1d. scarlet, **O** (8.23) . . 9·00 9·00
41 1d. dull violet, **O** (1927) . . 1·25 3·50
42 3 1½d. bright scarlet, **O** (1924) . . 2·00 55
43 4 2d. slate-grey, **O** (4.23) . . 1·50 3·50
44 3d. pale ultramarine, **O** (11.23) . . 1·25 3·25
45 4d. black and red/*yellow*, **C** (1927) . . 2·75 6·50
45*a* 4½d. red-brown, **O** (1931) . . 6·00 12·00
46 5d. dull purple and olive-green, **C** . . 3·50 11·00
47 6d. dull and bright purple, **C** . . 3·50 8·00
48 1s. black/*emerald*, **C** . . 4·50 8·50
49 2s. purple and blue/*blue*, **C** (1927) . . 12·00 27·00
50 2s. 6d. black and red/*blue*, **C** . . 17·00 32·00
51 5s. green and red/*pale yellow*, **C** . . 28·00 45·00
52 10s. green and red/*emerald*, **C** (1925) . . £130 £180
39/52 . . *Set of* 15 £200 £325
39/52 Optd/Perf "Specimen" . . *Set of* 15 £425

1935 (6 May). *Silver Jubilee. As Nos.* 91/4 *of Antigua.*
53 1½d. deep blue and carmine . . 80 1·00
e. Horiz line from turret . . 7·00
54 3d. brown and deep blue . . 3·75 7·00
55 6d. light blue and olive-green . . 7·00 10·00
56 1s. slate and purple . . 8·00 11·00
e. Horiz line from turret . . 40·00
53/6 Perf "Specimen" . . *Set of* 4 60·00

For illustration of plate variety see Omnibus section following Zululand.

1937 (13 May). *Coronation Issue. As Nos.* 13/15 *of Aden but ptd by B.W. P* 11 × 11½.
57 1d. violet . . 45 50
58 1½d. carmine . . 50 50
59 3d. blue . . 80 70
57/9 Perf "Specimen" . . *Set of* 3 48·00

5 Spears and Shield **6** Native Constable and Chief

8 Canoe House **9** Roviana Canoe

(Recess D.L.R. (2d., 3d., 2s. and 2s. 6d.), Waterlow (others))

1939 (1 Feb)–**1951**. *T* **5/6, 8/9** *and similar designs. Wmk Mult Script CA. P* 13½ (2*d.*, 3*d.*, 2*s. and* 2*s.* 6*d.*) *or* 12½ (*others*).
60 ½d. blue and blue-green . . 15 50
61 1d. brown and deep violet . . 25 35
62 1½d. blue-green and carmine . . 70 70
63 2d. orange-brown and black . . 55 70
a. Perf 12 (7.11.51) . . 55 1·50
64 2½d. magenta and sage-green . . 1·00 90
a. Imperf between (vert pair) . . £6000
65 3d. black and ultramarine . . 90 90
a. Perf 12 (29.11.51) . . 45 1·60
66 4½d. green and chocolate . . 12·00 17·00
67 6d. deep violet and reddish purple . . 60 60
68 1s. green and black . . 1·50 1·25
69 2s. black and orange . . 12·00 7·00
70 2s. 6d. black and violet . . 22·00 11·00
71 5s. emerald-green and scarlet . . 20·00 11·00
72 10s. sage-green and magenta (27.4.42) . . 14·00 23·00
60/72 . . *Set of* 13 75·00 65·00
60/72 Perf "Specimen" . . *Set of* 13 £175

Designs: *Horiz* (*as T* **9**)—1½d. Artificial Island, Malaita; 1s. Breadfruit; 5s. Malaita canoe. (*As T* **8**)—3d. Roviana canoes; 2s. Tinakula volcano; 2s. 6d. Common Scrub Hen. *Vert* (*as T* **6**)—4½d., 10s. Native house, Reef Islands; 6d. Coconut plantation.

1946 (15 Oct). *Victory. As Nos.* 28/9 *of Aden.*
73 1½d. carmine . . 30 25
74 3d. blue . . 35 30
73/4 Perf "Specimen" . . *Set of* 2 42·00

1949 (14 Mar). *Royal Silver Wedding. As Nos.* 30/1 *of Aden.*
75 2d. black . . 75 40
76 10s. magenta . . 27·00 25·00

1949 (10 Oct). *75th Anniv of Universal Postal Union. As Nos.* 114/17 *of Antigua.*
77 2d. red-brown . . 1·10 50
78 3d. deep blue . . 2·25 75
79 5d. deep blue-green . . 2·75 1·25
80 1s. blue-black . . 4·50 1·50

1953 (2 June). *Coronation. As No.* 47 *of Aden.*
81 2d. black and grey-black . . 50 90

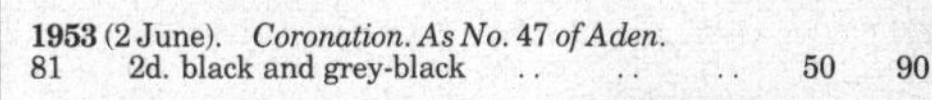

17 Ysabel Canoe **18** Roviana Canoe

24 Native Constable and Chief   **25** Arms of the Protectorate

(Des Miss I. R. Stinson (½d.), R. Bailey (2½d.), R. A. Sweet (5d., 1s., 1s. 3d.), Capt. J. Brett Hilder (6d., 8d., 9d., 5s.). Recess B.W. (½d., 2½d., 5d., 6d., 8d., 9d., 1s., 1s. 3d., 5s.), D.L.R. (1d., 2d., 2s.), Waterlow (1½d., 3d., 2s. 6d., 10s., £1), until 1962, then D.L.R.)

1956 (1 Mar)–**60**. *T* **17/18, 24/5** *and similar horiz designs. Wmk Mult Script CA. P* 12 (*1d., 2d., 2s.*), 13 (*1½d., 3d., 2s. 6d., 10s., £1*) *or* 11½ (*others*).

82	½d. orange and purple	12	25
83	1d. yellow-green and red-brown	20	10
84	1½d. slate-green and carmine-red (*shades*)	20	25
85	2d. deep brown and dull green	25	15
86	2½d. black and blue	30	40
87	3d. blue-green and red	30	15
88	5d. black and blue	60	1·25
89	6d. black and turquoise-green	70	40
90	8d. bright blue and black	40	20
90*a*	9d. emerald and black (28.1.60)	3·75	1·25
91	1s. slate and yellow-brown (*shades*)	95	60
91*a*	1s. 3d. black and blue (*shades*) (28.1.60)	5·00	2·25
92	2s. black and carmine	4·50	2·50
93	2s. 6d. emerald & bright purple (*shades*)	5·00	1·25
94	5s. red-brown	9·00	5·50
95	10s. sepia	14·00	11·00
96	£1 black and blue (5.11.58)	45·00	40·00
82/96	*Set of* 17	80·00	60·00

Designs: (*As T* **17**)—5d., 1s. 3d. Map; 6d. Trading Schooner; 1s. Voyage of H.M.S. *Swallow*, 1767; 2s. 6d. Common Scrub Hen; 5s. Mendaña and Ship. (*As T* **25**)—1d. Roviana canoe; 1½d. Artificial Island, Malaita; 2d. Canoe house; 3d. Malaita Canoe; 8d., 9d. Henderson airfield, Guadalcanal; 2s. Tinakula Volcano.

LEGISLATIVE COUNCIL

32 Great Frigate Bird

(Litho Enschedé)

1961 (19 Jan). *New Constitution,* 1960. *W* w **12** (*sideways*). *P* 13 × 12½.

97	**32**	2d. black and turquoise-green	10	10
98		3d. black and rose-carmine	10	10
99		9d. black and reddish purple	25	30

1963 (4 June). *Freedom from Hunger. As No.* 76 *of Aden.*
100 1s. 3d. ultramarine .. 7·00 1·50

1963 (2 Sept). *Red Cross Centenary. As Nos.* 147/8 *of Antigua.*
101 2d. red and black .. 1·25 25
102 9d. red and blue .. 4·25 2·25

1963–64. *As Nos.* 83/5, 87, 89, 90*a and* 91*a*/3, *but wmk* w **12**.

103	1d. yellow-green and red-brown (9.7.64)	70	50
104	1½d. slate-green and red (9.7.64)	70	60
105	2d. deep brown and dull green (9.7.64)	60	35
106	3d. lt blue-grn & scar (*shades*) (16.11.63)	90	45
107	6d. black and turquoise (7.7.64)	1·75	1·25
108	9d. emerald and black (7.7.64)	60	1·00
109	1s. 3d. black and blue (7.7.64)	2·25	2·50
110	2s. black and carmine (9.7.64)	4·25	5·50
111	2s. 6d. emerald & reddish purple (9.7.64)	15·00	17·00
103/111	*Set of* 9	24·00	26·00

2 c ☰

33 Makira Food Bowl   (**48**)

(Des M. Farrar-Bell. Litho D.L.R.)

1965 (24 May). *Horiz designs as T* **33**. *W* w **12**. *P* 13 × 12½.

112	½d. black, deep slate-blue and light blue	5	12
113	1d. black, orange and yellow	30	10
114	1½d. black, blue and yellow-green	30	12
115	2d. black, ultramarine and light blue	40	12
116	2½d. black, light brown & pale yellow-brown	15	15
117	3d. black, green and light green	15	10
118	6d. black, magenta and yellow-orange	40	12
119	9d. brownish blk, dp bluish grn & pale yell	50	20
120	1s. black, chocolate and magenta	80	20
121	1s. 3d. black and rose-red	3·00	2·00
122	2s. black, bright purple and lilac	5·00	2·75
123	2s. 6d. black, olive-brown and light brown	1·50	1·50
124	5s. black, ultramarine and violet	9·00	5·50
125	10s. black, olive-green and yellow	12·00	7·00
126	£1 black, deep reddish violet and pink	16·00	12·00
112/126	*Set of* 15	45·00	29·00

Designs:—1d. *Dendrobium veratrifolium* (orchid); 1½d. Scorpion Shell; 2d. Blyth's Hornbill; 2½d. Ysabel shield; 3d. Rennellese club; 6d. Moorish Idol; 9d. Lesser Frigate Bird; 1s. *Dendrobium macrophyllum* (orchid); 1s. 3d. *Dendrobium spectabilis* (orchid); 2s. Sanford's Sea Eagle; 2s. 6d. Malaita belt; 5s. *Ornithoptera victoreae* (butterfly); 10s. Ducorp's Cockatoo; £1, Western canoe figurehead.

1965 (28 June). *I.T.U. Centenary. As Nos.* 166/7 *of Antigua.*
127 2d. orange-red and turquoise-blue .. 45 15
128 3d. turquoise-blue and olive-brown .. 50 15

1965 (25 Oct). *International Co-operation Year. As Nos.* 168/9 *of Antigua.*
129 1d. reddish purple and turquoise-green .. 30 10
130 2s. 6d. deep bluish green and lavender .. 1·75 35

1966 (24 Jan). *Churchill Commemoration. As Nos.* 170/3 *of Antigua.*

131	2d. new blue	20	10
132	9d. deep green	75	15
133	1s. 3d. brown	95	20
134	2s. 6d. bluish violet	1·75	45

(New Currency. 100 cents = 1 Australian dollar)

1966–67. *Decimal Currency. Nos.* 112/26 *variously surch as T* **48** *by De La Rue. A. Wmk upright. B. Wmk sideways.*

		A		B	
135	1 c. on ½d.	5	5	5	5
136	2 c. on 1d.	10	5	10	5
137	3 c. on 1½d. (*shades*)	10	5	12	5
138	4 c. on 2d.	12	5	12	5
139	5 c. on 6d.	15	5	12	5
140	6 c. on 2½d.	15	5	15	5
141	7 c. on 3d. (*shades*)	20	5	15	5
142	8 c. on 9d.	25	5	20	5
143	10 c. on 1s. (*shades*)	35	5	50	5
144	12 c. on 1s. 3d.	†		80	10
145	13 c. on 1s. 3d.	50	25	90	50
146	14 c. on 3d.	†		75	20
147	20 c. on 2s.	1·00	35	1·25	35
148	25 c. on 2s. 6d.	1·00	50	1·25	35
149	35 c. on 2d.	†		2·75	50
	a. Surch omitted (horiz pair with normal)	†		—	—
	b. Surch value only omitted	†		—	—
150	50 c. on 5s. (R.)	5·00	3·00	5·50	2·50
151	$1 on 10s.	6·00	4·75	5·50	3·00
152	$2 on £1	7·50	9·00	7·50	8·50
135A/152A	*Set of* 15	20·00	16·00		
135B/152B	*Set of* 18			25·00	15·00

Dates of issue: 1967—1 March, 12 c., 14 c., 35 c. 1966—14 February. All watermark upright. 1966—All other watermark sideways.

The positions of the bars in the surcharge vary considerably from stamp to stamp within the sheets.

The stamps with sideways watermark are all from new printings and in some instances there are marked shade variations from Nos. 112/26 which were used for making Nos. 135A/152A.

1966 (1 July). *World Cup Football Championships. As Nos.* 176/7 *of Antigua.*
153 8 c. violet, yellow-green, lake & yellow-brn .. 50 15
154 35 c. chocolate, blue-green, lake & yellow-brn 1·50 35

1966 (20 Sept). *Inauguration of W.H.O. Headquarters, Geneva. As Nos.* 178/9 *of Antigua.*
155 3 c. black, yellow-green and light blue .. 35 12
156 50 c. black, light purple and yellow-brown .. 2·50 70

1966 (1 Dec). *20th Anniv of U.N.E.S.C.O. As Nos.* 196/8 *of Antigua.*
157 3 c. slate-violet, red, yellow and orange .. 40 15
158 25 c. orange-yellow, violet and deep olive .. 1·40 40
159 $1 black, bright purple and orange .. 6·50 3·25

49 Henderson Field

(Des V. Whiteley. Photo Harrison)

1967 (28 Aug). *25th Anniv of Guadalcanal Campaign (Pacific War). T* **49** *and similar horiz design. Multicoloured. W* w **12**. *P* 14 × 14½.
160 8 c. Type **49** .. 15 10
161 35 c. Red Beach landings .. 55 25

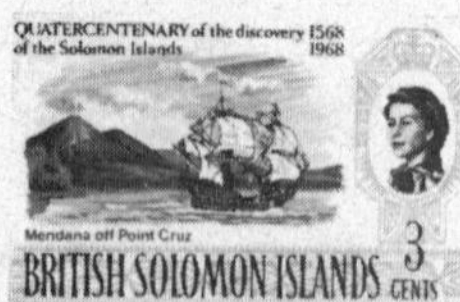

51 Mendaña off Point Cruz

(Des V. Whiteley. Photo Harrison)

1968 (7 Feb). *Quatercentenary of the Discovery of Solomon Is. T* **51** *and similar horiz designs. Multicoloured. W* w **12**. *P* 14.

162	3 c. Type **51**	30	10
163	8 c. Arrival of missionaries	40	15
164	35 c. Pacific Campaign, World War II	1·50	70
165	$1 Proclamation of the Protectorate	3·25	1·25

55 Vine Fishing

(Des R. Granger Barrett. Photo Harrison)

1968 (20 May)–**71**. *Horiz designs as T* **55**. *Chalk-surfaced paper. W* w **12** (*inverted on No.* 167a). *P* 14½.

166	1 c. turquoise-blue, black and brown	5	5
	a. Glazed, ordinary paper (9.8.71)	70	70
167	2 c. apple-green, black and brown	10	5
	a. Glazed, ordinary paper (9.8.71)	70	70
168	3 c. green, myrtle-green and black	12	5
	a. Glazed, ordinary paper (9.8.71)	70	70
169	4 c. bright purple, black and brown	12	5
	a. Glazed, ordinary paper (9.8.71)	70	70
170	6 c. multicoloured	15	5
171	8 c. multicoloured	25	10
	a. Glazed, ordinary paper (9.8.71)	1·50	1·60
172	12 c. yellow-ochre, brown-red and black	65	30
	a. Glazed, ordinary paper (9.8.71)	2·25	2·50
173	14 c. orange-red, chocolate and black	70	50
174	15 c. multicoloured	80	45
	a. Glazed, ordinary paper (9.8.71)	2·50	3·00
175	20 c. bright blue, red and black	1·50	65
	a. Glazed, ordinary paper (9.8.71)	4·25	4·50
176	24 c. rose-red, black and yellow	90	70
177	35 c. multicoloured	1·60	1·60
178	45 c. multicoloured	2·25	2·25
179	$1 violet-blue, light green and black	8·00	6·50
180	$2 multicoloured	11·00	12·00
166/80	*Set of* 15	25·00	23·00
166a/75a	*Set of* 8	12·00	13·00

Designs:—2 c. Kite fishing; 3 c. Platform fishing; 4 c. Net fishing; 6 c. Gold Lip shell diving; 8 c. Night fishing; 12 c. Boat building; 14 c. Cocoa; 15 c. Road building; 20 c. Geological survey; 24 c. Hauling timber; 35 c. Copra; 45 c. Harvesting rice; $1, Honiara Port; $2, Internal air service.

The stamps on glazed, ordinary paper exist with PVA gum only. The 1 c. to 12 c. and 20 c. on chalk-surfaced paper exist with PVA gum as well as gum arabic, but the others exist with gum arabic only.

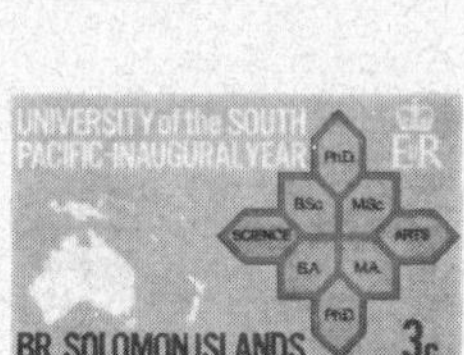

70 Map of Australasia and Diagram   **71** Basketball Player

(Des R. Gates. Litho Enschedé)

1969 (10 Feb). *Inaugural Year of the South Pacific University. P* 12½ × 12.

181	**70**	3 c. multicoloured	8	5
182		12 c. multicoloured	25	15
183		35 c. multicoloured	35	20

(Des J. Cooter. Photo Harrison)

1969 (13 Aug). *Third South Pacific Games, Port Moresby. T* **71** *and similar vert designs. Multicoloured. W* w **12** (*sideways*). *P* 14½ × 14.

184	3 c. Type **71**	8	5
185	8 c. Footballer	20	10
186	14 c. Sprinter	35	20
187	45 c. Rugby player	1·00	65
MS188	126 × 120 mm. Nos. 184/7	10·00	10·00

Stamps from the miniature sheets differ slightly from those in the ordinary sheets, particularly the 14 c. value, which has a shadow below the feet on the runner. The footballer and rugby player on the 8 c. and 45 c. values also have shadows below their feet, but these are more pronounced than on the stamps from the ordinary sheets.

75 South Sea Island with Star of Bethlehem   **76** Southern Cross, "PAX" and Frigatebird (stained glass window)

(Des L. Curtis. Photo Harrison)

1969 (21 Nov). *Christmas. W* w **12** (*sideways*). *P* 14½ × 14.

189	**75**	8 c. black, violet and turquoise-green	40	15
190	**76**	35 c. multicoloured	1·10	50

77 "Paid" Stamp, New South Wales 1896–1906 2d. Stamp and 1906–07 Tulagi Postmark

(Des G. Drummond. Litho B.W.)

1970 (15 Apr). *Inauguration of New G.P.O. Honiara. T* **77** *and similar horiz designs. W* w **12** (*sideways*). *P* 13.
191 7 c. light magenta, deep blue and black .. 50 20
192 14 c. sage-green, deep blue and black .. 85 40

193 18 c. multicoloured 90 50
194 23 c. multicoloured .. .. 1·10 65
Designs:—14 c. 1906–07 2d. stamp and C. M. Woodford; 18 c. 1910–14 5s. stamp and Tulagi postmark, 1913; 23 c. New G.P.O., Honiara.

81 Coat of Arms

83 British Red Cross H.Q., Honiara

(Des V. Whiteley. Photo Harrison)

1970 (15 June). *New Constitution. T* **81** *and similar design. W* w **12** *(sideways on 18 c.). P* 14½ × 14 *(18 c.) or* 14 × 14½ *(35 c.).*
195 18 c. multicoloured 60 40
196 35 c. pale apple-green, deep blue and ochre .. 1·25 1·00
Design: *Horiz*—35 c. Map.

(Des L. Curtis. Litho Questa)

1970 (17 Aug). *Centenary of British Red Cross. T* **83** *and similar horiz design. W* w **12** *(sideways). P* 14 × 14½.
197 3 c. multicoloured 25 15
198 35 c. blue, vermilion and black .. .. 1·50 1·10
Design:—35 c. Wheelchair and map.

86 Reredos (Altar Screen)

(Des L. Curtis. Litho J.W.)

1970 (19 Oct). *Christmas. T* **86** *and similar design. W* w **12** *(sideways on 45 c.). P* 14 × 13½ *(8 c.) or* 13½ × 14 *(45 c.).*
199 8 c. ochre and bluish violet 40 15
200 45 c. chestnut, yellow-orange & blackish brn 1·50 80
Design: *Vert*—8 c. Carved angel.

87 La Perouse and *La Boussole*

(Des J.W. Litho Questa)

1971 (28 Jan). *Ships and Navigators* (1st series). *T* **87** *and similar horiz designs. Multicoloured. W* w **12** *(sideways). P* 14.
201 3 c. Type **87** 65 20
202 4 c. Astrolabe and Polynesian Reed Map .. 75 20
203 12 c. Abel Tasman and the *Heemskerk* .. 1·75 90
204 35 c. Te puki canoe .. .. 3·50 2·50
See also Nos. 215/18, 236/9, 254/7 and 272/5.

88 J. Atkin, Bishop Patteson and S. Taroaniara

(Des J.W. Litho Questa)

1971 (5 April). *Death Centenary of Bishop Patteson. T* **88** *and similar multicoloured designs. W* w **12** *(sideways on 2 c., 4 c.). P* 14½ × 14 *(2 c., 4 c.) or* 14 × 14½ *(others).*
205 2 c. Type **88** 15 8
206 4 c. Last Landing at Nukapu 30 15
207 14 c. Memorial Cross and Nukapu *(vert)* .. 50 20
208 45 c. Knotted Leaf and Canoe *(vert)* 70 65

89 Torch Emblem and Boxers

90 Melanesian Lectern

(Des C. Debenham. Litho Questa)

1971 (9 Aug). *Fourth South Pacific Games, Tahiti. T* **89** *and similar horiz designs. Multicoloured. W* w **12** *(sideways). P* 14.
209 3 c. Type **89** 15 10
210 8 c. Emblem and footballers 30 15
211 12 c. Emblem and runner 30 25
212 35 c. Emblem and skin-diver 75 60

(Des C. Abbott. Litho A. & M.)

1971 (15 Nov). *Christmas. T* **90** *and similar vert design. Multicoloured. W* w **12**. *P* 13½.
213 9 c. Type **90** 35 25
214 45 c. "United we Stand" (Margarita Bara) .. 1·00 1·00

(Des J.W. Litho Questa)

1972 (1 Feb). *Ships and Navigators* (2nd series). *Horiz designs as T* **87**. *Multicoloured. W* w **12** *(sideways). P* 14.
215 4 c. Bougainville and *La Boudeuse* 30 12
216 9 c. Horizontal planisphere and ivory backstaff 60 50
217 15 c. Philip Carteret and H.M.S. *Swallow* .. 85 70
218 45 c. Malaita canoe .. .. 3·75 3·25

91 *Cupha woodfordi*

(Des R. Granger Barrett. Litho Questa)

1972 (3 July)–**73**. *T* **91** *and similar horiz designs. Multicoloured. W* w **12** *(upright on $5, sideways on others). P* 14.
219 1 c. Type **91** 15 15
220 2 c. *Ornithoptera priamus urvillanus* .. 25 20
221 3 c. *Vindula sapor* 25 20
222 4 c. *Papilio ulysses orsippus* 25 25
223 5 c. Great Trevally 25 20
224 8 c. Little Bonito 40 45
225 9 c. Sapphire Demoiselle 50 45
226 12 c. *Costus speciosus* .. .. 1·25 70
227 15 c. Orange Anemone Fish .. .. .. 1·25 75
228 20 c. *Spathoglottis plicata* .. .. .. 2·75 1·40
229 25 c. *Ephemerantha comata* .. .. .. 2·75 1·50
230 35 c. *Dendrobium cuthbertsonii* .. .. 3·25 2·00
231 45 c. *Heliconia salomonica* .. .. .. 3·50 3·00
232 $1 Blue Finned Triggerfish .. .. 7·00 6·00
233 $2 *Ornithoptera allotti* .. .. .. 14·00 14·00
233*a* $5 Great Frigate Bird (2.7.73) .. .. 12·00 12·00
219/33*a* .. .. *Set of* 16 42·00 38·00
The 1 to 4 c. and $2 are butterflies; the 5 to 9 c., 15 c. and $1 are fishes; the 12 c. and 20 to 45 c. are flowers and the $5 a bird.

92 Greetings and Message Drum

(Des (from photograph by D. Groves) and photo Harrison)

1972 (20 Nov). *Royal Silver Wedding. Multicoloured; background colour given. W* w **12**. *P* 14 × 14½.
234 **92** 8 c. rose-carmine 20 20
235 45 c. deep yellow-olive 40 40

(Des J.W. Litho Questa)

1973 (9 Mar). *Ships and Navigators* (3rd series). *Horiz designs as T* **87**. *Multicoloured. W* w **12**. *P* 14.
236 4 c. D'Entrecasteaux and the *Recherche* .. 30 20
237 9 c. Ship's hour-glass and chronometer .. 60 50
238 15 c. Lt. Shortland and the *Alexander* .. 90 80
239 35 c. Tomoko (war canoe) .. .. .. 3·75 3·50

93 Pan Pipes

(Des and litho J.W.)

1973 (1 Oct). *Musical Instruments. T* **93** *and similar horiz designs. Multicoloured. W* w **12**. *P* 13½.
240 4 c. Type **93** 15 12
241 9 c. Castanets 40 30
242 15 c. Bamboo flute 50 40
243 35 c. Bauro gongs 90 80
244 45 c. Bamboo band .. .. 1·25 1·10

1973 (14 Nov). *Royal Wedding. As Nos.* 165/6 *of Anguilla.*
245 4 c. deep grey-blue 8 8
246 35 c. bright blue 40 40

94 "Adoration of the Kings" (Jan Brueghel)

(Des PAD Studio. Litho Questa)

1973 (26 Nov). *Christmas. T* **94** *and similar designs showing "Adoration of the Kings" by the artists listed. Multicoloured. W* w **12** *(sideways on 22 c.). P* 13½ *(45 c.) or* 14 *(others).*
247 8 c. Type **94** 35 30
248 22 c. Pieter Brueghel *(vert)* .. .. .. 1·00 1·00
249 45 c. Botticelli (48 × 35 *mm*) .. .. .. 1·40 1·25

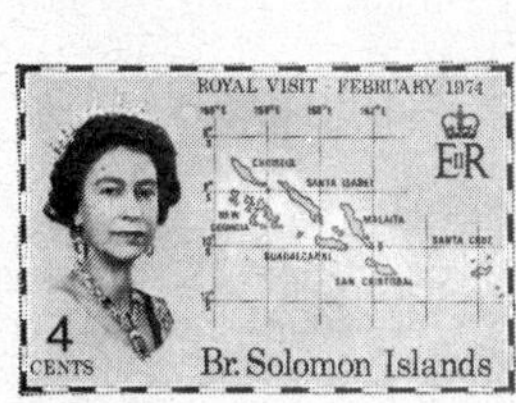

95 Queen Elizabeth II and Map

96 "Postman"

(Des G. Drummond. Litho Questa)

1974 (18 Feb). *Royal Visit. W* w **12**. *P* 13½.
250 **95** 4 c. multicoloured 20 10
251 9 c. multicoloured 40 35
252 15 c. multicoloured 70 70
253 35 c. multicoloured .. .. 1·75 2·50

(Des and litho J.W.)

1974 (15 May). *Ships and Navigators* (4th series). *Horiz designs as T* **87**. *Multicoloured. W* w **12** *(sideways). P* 14.
254 4 c. Commissioner landing from S.S. *Titus* .. 30 20
255 9 c. Radar scanner 50 45
256 15 c. Natives being transported to a "Blackbirder" 90 70
257 45 c. Lieut. John F. Kennedy's P.T. 109 .. 3·75 2·50

(Des Jennifer Toombs. Litho Questa)

1974 (29 Aug). *Centenary of Universal Postal Union. T* **96** *and similar designs showing Origami figures. W* w **12** *(sideways on 9 and 45 c.). P* 14.
258 4 c. light yellow-green, deep green and black 20 15
259 9 c. light olive-bistre, lake-brown and black 35 20
260 15 c. mauve, purple and black 55 30
261 45 c. cobalt, dull ultramarine and black .. 1·10 1·10
Designs: *Horiz*—9 c. Carrier-pigeon; 45 c. Pegasus. *Vert*—15 c. St. Gabriel.

97 "New Constitution" Stamp of 1970

(Des R. Granger Barrett. Litho Questa)

1974 (16 Dec). *New Constitution. T* **97** *and similar horiz design. W* w **14** *(sideways). P* 14.
262 **97** 4 c. multicoloured 20 15
263 – 9 c. dull rose-red, black & lt yell-ochre 40 35
264 – 15 c. dull rose-red, blk & lt greenish yell 65 65
265 **97** 35 c. multicoloured .. .. 1·25 1·40
MS266 134 × 84 mm. Nos. 262/5 .. .. .. 4·50 4·50
Design:—9 c., 15 c. "New Constitution" stamp of 1961 (inscr "1960").

98 Golden Whistler

(Des G. Drummond. Litho Questa)

1975 (7 Apr). *Birds. T* **98** *and similar horiz designs. Multicoloured. W* w **12**. *P* 14.
267 1 c. Type **98** 45 45
268 2 c. Common Kingfisher 50 50
269 3 c. Red-bibbed Fruit Dove 55 55
270 4 c. Little Button Quail 55 55
271 $2 Duchess Lorikeet .. .. .. 15·00 13·50
See also Nos. 305/20.

(Des and litho J.W.)

1975 (29 May). *Ships and Navigators* (5th series). *Horiz designs as T* **87**. *Multicoloured. W* w **12**. *P* 13½.
272 4 c. M.V. *Walande* 30 15
273 9 c. M.V. *Melanesian* 60 30
274 15 c. M.V. *Marsina* 90 55
275 45 c. S.S. *Himalaya* .. .. 2·75 2·50

99 800-Metres Race

(Des PAD Studio. Litho Walsall)

1975 (4 Aug). *Fifth South Pacific Games, Guam. T* **99** *and similar horiz designs. Multicoloured. W w* **14** *(sideways). P* 13½.

276	4 c. Type **99**	20	10
277	9 c. Long-jump	30	15
278	15 c. Javelin-throwing	45	30
279	45 c. Football	1·25	1·25
MS280	130 × 95 mm. Nos. 276/9	4·50	4·50

100 Christmas Scene and Candles **(101)**

(Des G. Vasarhelyi. Litho Questa)

1975 (13 Oct). *Christmas. T* **100** *and similar horiz designs. Multicoloured. W w* **12** *(sideways). P* 14.

281	15 c. Type **100**	60	35
282	35 c. Shepherds, angels and candles	1·25	90
283	45 c. The Magi and candles	1·75	1·25
MS284	140 × 130 mm. Nos. 281/3	4·50	4·00

1975 (12 Nov). *Nos. 267/70, 223/32, 271 and 233a with obliterating bar as T* **101** *over* "BRITISH".

285	1 c. Type **98**	20	25
286	2 c. Common Kingfisher	25	25
287	3 c. Red-bibbed Fruit Dove	25	25
288	4 c. Little Button Quail	25	25
289	5 c. Great Trevally	30	25
290	8 c. Little Bonito	50	45
291	9 c. Sapphire Demoiselle	50	45
292	12 c. *Costus speciosus*	1·25	75
293	15 c. Orange Anemone Fish	1·25	90
294	20 c. *Spathoglottis plicata*	2·25	1·25
295	25 c. *Ephemerantha comata*	2·25	1·50
296	35 c. *Dendrobium cuthbertsonii*	3·25	1·75
297	45 c. *Heliconia salomonica*	3·50	3·00
298	$1 Blue Finned Triggerfish	5·50	5·00
299	$2 Duchess Lorikeet	11·00	12·00
300	$5 Great Frigate Bird	20·00	22·00
285/300	*Set of* 16	48·00	45·00

SELF-GOVERNMENT

102 Ceremonial Food-bowl

(Des J. Cooter. Litho Questa)

1976 (12 Jan). *Artefacts (1st series). T* **102** *and similar multicoloured designs. W w* **12** *(upright on 35 c.; sideways on others). P* 14.

301	4 c. Type **102**	15	10
302	15 c. Chieftains' money	35	20
303	35 c. Nguzu-nguzu (canoe protector spirit) (*vert*)	90	70
304	45 c. Nguzu-nguzu canoe prow	1·25	80

See also Nos. 337/40, 353/6 and 376/9.

103 Golden Whistler

(Des G. Drummond. Litho Questa)

1976 (8 Mar–6 Dec). *Nos. 267/71 with new country inscr (omitting* "BRITISH") *as T* **103**, *and new values. Multicoloured. W w* **14** *(sideways). P* 14.

305	1 c. Type **103**	20	20
306	2 c. Common Kingfisher	25	25
307	3 c. Red-bibbed Fruit Dove	25	25
308	4 c. Little Button Quail	30	25
309	5 c. Black and White Fantail	30	25
310	6 c. Golden Cowrie	40	30
311	10 c. Glory of the Sea Cone	50	30
312	12 c. Rainbow Lory	60	40
313	15 c. Pearly Nautilus	65	40
314	20 c. Venus Comb Murex	80	45
315	25 c. Commercial Trochus	85	50
316	35 c. Melon or Baler Shell	1·00	70
317	45 c. Orange Spider Conch	1·50	1·25
318	$1 Pacific Triton	3·50	3·00
319	$2 Duchess Lorikeet	7·00	7·00
320	$5 Great Frigate Bird (6.12)	11·00	11·00
305/20	*Set of* 16	26·00	24·00

104 Coastwatchers, 1942 **105** Alexander Graham Bell

(Des J. Cooter. Litho Walsall)

1976 (24 May). *Bicentenary of American Revolution. T* **104** *and similar horiz designs. Multicoloured. W w* **14** *(sideways). P* 14.

321	6 c. Type **104**	30	20
322	20 c. *Amagiri* ramming PT109 and Lt. J. F. Kennedy	1·25	60
323	35 c. Henderson Airfield	2·00	1·10
324	45 c. Map of Guadalcanal	2·50	1·25
MS325	95 × 115 mm. Nos. 321/4	6·50	5·50

(Des P. Powell. Litho Harrison)

1976 (26 July). *Telephone Centenary. T* **105** *and similar vert designs. W w* **14** *(sideways). P* 14½ × 14.

326	6 c. multicoloured	20	15
327	20 c. multicoloured	40	30
328	35 c. brown-orange, lt orange & lt vermilion	75	60
329	45 c. multicoloured	80	80

Designs:—20 c. Radio telephone via satellite; 35 c. Ericson's magneto telephone; 45 c. Stick telephone and first telephone.

106 B.A.C. "1–11" **107** The Communion Plate

(Des and litho Walsall)

1976 (13 Sept). *50th Anniv of First Flight to Solomon Islands. T* **106** *and similar horiz designs. Multicoloured. W w* **14** *(sideways). P* 14.

330	6 c. Type **106**	25	15
331	20 c. Britten-Norman "Islander"	50	30
332	35 c. "Dakota DC3"	1·00	80
333	45 c. De Havilland "DH50A"	1·10	1·25

(Des Jennifer Toombs. Litho Questa)

1977 (7 Feb). *Silver Jubilee. T* **107** *and similar vert designs. Multicoloured. W w* **14**. *P* 13½.

334	6 c. Queen's visit, 1974	15	12
335	35 c. Type **107**	40	65
336	45 c. The Communion	55	90

108 Carving from New Georgia **109** Spraying Roof and Mosquito

(Des J. Cooter. Litho Questa)

1977 (9 May). *Artefacts (2nd series). T* **108** *and similar vert designs showing carvings. W w* **14**. *P* 14.

337	6 c. multicoloured	20	12
338	20 c. multicoloured	40	40
339	35 c. slate-black, grey and rose-red	70	70
340	40 c. multicoloured	80	90

Designs:—20 c. Sea adaro (spirit); 35 c. Shark-headed man; 45 c. Man from Ulawa or Malaita.

(Des G. Vasarhelyi. Litho Questa)

1977 (27 July). *Malaria Eradication. T* **109** *and similar horiz designs. Multicoloured. W w* **14** *(sideways). P* 14.

341	6 c. Type **109**	30	20
342	20 c. Taking blood samples	60	40
343	35 c. Microscope and map	90	75
344	45 c. Delivering drugs	1·00	95

110 The Shepherds **111** Feather Money

(Des M. and G. Shamir. Litho Questa)

1977 (12 Sept). *Christmas. T* **110** *and similar vert designs. Multicoloured. W w* **14**. *P* 14.

345	6 c. Type **110**	20	12
346	20 c. Mary and Jesus in stable	40	20
347	35 c. The Three Kings	75	75
348	45 c. "The Flight into Egypt"	85	1·00

(Des D.L.R. Litho Harrison)

1977 (24 Oct). *Introduction of Solomon Islands Coins and Banknotes. T* **111** *and similar horiz designs. Multicoloured. W w* **14**. *P* 14 × 14½.

349	6 c. Type **111**	20	15
	a. Horiz pair. Nos. 349/50	40	30
350	6 c. New currency coins	20	15
351	45 c. New currency notes	90	1·00
	a. Horiz pair. Nos. 351/2	1·75	2·00
352	45 c. Shell money	90	1·00

The two designs of each value were printed in horizontal *se-tenant* pairs throughout their sheets.

112 Figure from Shortland Island **113** Sandford Eagle

(Des J. Cooter. Litho Questa)

1978 (11 Jan). *Artefacts (3rd series). T* **112** *and similar vert designs. W w* **14**. *P* 14.

353	6 c. multicoloured	20	10
354	20 c. multicoloured	40	30
355	35 c. deep brown, black and orange	75	65
356	45 c. multicoloured	85	80

Designs:—20 c. Ceremonial shield; 35 c. Santa Cruz ritual figure; 45 c. Decorative combs.

(Des Jennifer Toombs. Litho Questa)

1978 (21 Apr). *25th Anniv of Coronation. T* **113** *and similar vert designs. Multicoloured. P* 15.

357	45 c. black, vermilion and silver	55	60
	a. Sheetlet. Nos. 357/9 × 2	3·00	
358	45 c. multicoloured	55	60
359	45 c. black, vermilion and silver	55	60

Designs:—No. 357, King's Dragon; No. 358, Queen Elizabeth II; No. 359, Type **113**.

Nos. 357/9 were printed together in small sheets of 6, containing two *se-tenant* strips of 3, with horizontal gutter margin between.

INDEPENDENT

114 National Flag **115** John

(Des L. Curtis. Litho Questa)

1978 (7 July). *Independence. T* **114** *and similar vert designs. Multicoloured. W w* **14**. *P* 14.

360	6 c. Type **114**	15	10
361	15 c. Governor-General's flag	30	20
362	35 c. The Cenotaph, Honiara	65	70
363	45 c. National coat of arms	80	90

(Des J.W. Litho Questa)

1978 (4 Oct). *450th Death Anniv of Dürer. Details from his Painting "Four Apostles". T* **115** *and similar vert designs. Multicoloured. W w* **14**. *P* 14.

364	6 c. Type **115**	15	12
365	20 c. Peter	30	35
366	35 c. Paul	65	75
367	45 c. Mark	80	1·00

116 Firelighting

117 *Discovery*

(Des K. G. Watkinson; adapted J.W. Litho Questa)

1978 (15 Nov). *50th Anniv of Scouting in Solomon Islands. T* **116** *and similar horiz designs. Multicoloured. W* w **14** *(sideways). P* 14.

368 6 c. Type **116** 20 12
369 20 c. Camping 40 35
370 35 c. Solomon Islands Scouts . . . . 1·00 75
371 45 c. Canoeing . . . . 1·25 1·00

(Des and litho (45 c. also embossed) Walsall)

1979 (16 Jan). *Bicentenary of Captain Cook's Voyages,* 1768–79. *T* **117** *and similar vert designs. P* 11.

372 8 c. multicoloured 30 20
373 18 c. multicoloured 50 40
374 35 c. black, yellowish green and silver . . 80 80
375 45 c. multicoloured . . . . 1·25 95

Designs:—18 c. "Captain Cook" (Nathaniel Dance); 35 c. Sextant; 45 c. Flaxman/Wedgwood medallion of Captain Cook.

118 Fish Net Float

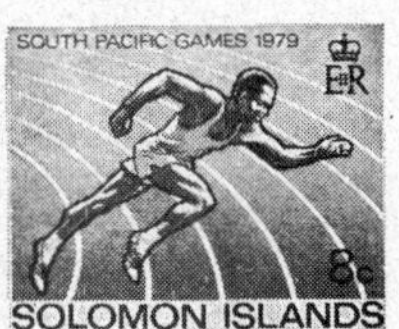

119 Running

(Des J. Cooter. Litho Questa)

1979 (21 Mar). *Artefacts (4th series). T* **118** *and similar designs. W* w **14** *(sideways on 8 and 35 c.). P* 14.

376 8 c. multicoloured 15 10
377 20 c. multicoloured 30 20
378 35 c. black, grey and rose 60 60
379 45 c. black, chestnut and apple-green. . . . 85 80

Designs: *Vert*—20 c. Armband of shell money; 45 c. Forehead ornament. *Horiz*—35 c. Ceremonial food bowl.

(Des L. Curtis. Litho Format)

1979 (4 June). *South Pacific Games, Fiji. T* **109** *and similar horiz designs. Multicoloured. W* w **14** *(sideways). P* 13½.

380 8 c. Type **119** 15 15
381 20 c. Hurdling 35 35
382 35 c. Football 50 50
383 45 c. Swimming 75 75

120 1908 6d. Stamp

121 Sea Snake

(Des J.W. Litho Format)

1979 (16 Aug). *Death Centenary of Sir Rowland Hill. T* **120** *and similar vert designs showing stamps. W* w **14**. *P* 14.

384 8 c. carmine and pale rose 15 15
385 20 c. deep mauve and pale mauve 40 40
386 35 c. multicoloured 55 55
MS387 121 × 121 mm. 45 c. rosine, deep dull green and pink 80 85

Designs:—20 c. Great Britain 1856 6d.; 35 c. 1978 45 c. Independence commemorative; 45 c. 1922 10s.

(Des L. Curtis. Litho Enschedé)

1979 (18 Sept)–**83**. *Reptiles. Vert designs as T* **121**. *Multicoloured. W* w **14**. *P* 13½ × 13.

A. *No imprint*. B. *Imprint date at foot*.

		A		B	
388	1 c. Type **121**	5	5	†	
389	3 c. Red-banded Tree Snake	5	5	†	
390	4 c. Whip Snake	5	5	†	
391	6 c. Pacific Boa	5	8	†	
392	8 c. Skink	8	10	†	
393	10 c. Gecko (*Lepidodactylus lugubris*)	12	15	†	
394	12 c. Monitor	12	15	12	15
395	15 c. Anglehead	15	20	†	
396	20 c. Giant Toad	25	30	†	
397	25 c. Marsh Frog	30	35	30	35
398	30 c. Horned Frog	35	40	35	40
399	35 c. Tree Frog	40	45	†	
399*a*	40 c. Burrowing Snake	†		45	50
400	45 c. Guppy's Snake	50	55	†	
400*a*	50 c. Tree Gecko	†		55	60
401	$1 Large Skink	1·10	1·25	1·10	1·25
402	$2 Guppy's Frog	2·25	2·40	†	
403	$5 Estuarine Crocodile . .	5·50	5·75	5·50	5·75
403*a*	$10 Hawksbill Turtle	†		11·00	11·50
388/403	. . . . *Set of* 16	10·50	11·25		
394/403*a*	. . . . *Set of* 8			17·50	18·00

Dates of issue:—18.9.79, Nos. 388A/403A; 25.1.82, Nos. 401B, 403B; 27.8.82, Nos. 394B, 397B; 20.9.82, No. 403*a*; 24.1.83, Nos. 399aB, 400aB; 31.8.83, No. 398B.

122 "Madonna and Child" (Morando)

123 H.M.S. *Curacao*, 1839

(Des BG Studio. Litho Questa)

1979 (15 Nov). *Christmas. International Year of the Child. T* **122** *and similar vert designs showing "Madonna and Child" paintings by various artists. Multicoloured. W* w **14**. *P* 14 × 14½.

404 4 c. Type **122** 5 5
405 20 c. Luini 25 25
406 35 c. Bellini 40 40
407 50 c. Raphael 55 55
MS408 92 × 133 mm. Nos. 404/7 . . . . . . 1·50 1·60

(Des L. Curtis. Litho Questa)

1980 (23 Jan). *Ships and Crests (1st series). T* **123** *and similar horiz designs. Multicoloured. W* w **14** *(sideways). P* 14.

409 8 c. Type **123** 20 10
410 20 c. H.M.S. *Herald*, 1854 . . . . . . 45 30
411 35 c. H.M.S. *Royalist*, 1889 . . . . . . 65 45
412 45 c. H.M.S. *Beagle*, 1878 . . . . . . 80 60

See also Nos. 430/3.

124 Steel Fishery Training Vessel

(Des G. Hutchins. Litho Secura, Singapore)

1980 (27 Mar). *Fishing. Ancillary Craft. T* **124** *and similar horiz designs. Multicoloured. W* w **14** *(sideways). P* 13½.

413 8 c. Type **124** 15 10
414 20 c. F.R.P. Fishery Training Vessel 30 25
415 45 c. Refrigerated Fish Carrier 50 50
416 80 c. Research Vessel . . . . 1·00 1·10

125 *Comliebank* (cargo-ship) and 1935 Tulagi Registered Letter Postmark

(Des A. Theobald. Litho Questa)

1980 (6 May). *"London 1980" International Stamp Exhibition. Mail-carrying Transport. T* **125** *and similar horiz designs. Multicoloured. W* w **14** *(sideways). P* 14½ × 14.

417 45 c. Type **125** 50 55
a. Sheetlet. Nos. 417/20 . . . . . . 1·75
418 45 c. Douglas "C-47" aeroplane (U.S. Army Postal Service, 1943) 50 55
419 45 c. B.A.C. "1-11" airliner and 1979 Honiara postmark 50 55
420 45 c. *Corabank* (ferry) and 1979 Auki postmark 50 55

Nos. 417/20 were printed together as a sheetlet containing a *se-tenant* block of 4.

126 Queen Elizabeth the Queen Mother

127 Angel with Trumpet

(Des Harrison. Litho Questa)

1980 (4 Aug). *80th Birthday of Queen Elizabeth the Queen Mother. W* w **14** *(sideways). P* 14.

421 **126** 45 c. multicoloured 80 80

(Des C. Abbott. Litho Walsall)

1980 (2 Sept). *Christmas. T* **127** *and similar vert designs. Multicoloured. W* w **14**. *P* 14½ × 14.

422 8 c. Type **127** 10 10
423 20 c. Angel with fiddle. 25 25
424 45 c. Angel with trumpet (*different*) 50 55
425 80 c. Angel with lute 80 90

128 *Parthenos sylvia*

129 Francisco Antonio Maurelle

(Des J. Cooter. Litho Secura, Singapore)

1980 (12 Nov). *Butterflies (1st series). T* **128** *and similar horiz designs. Multicoloured. W* w **14** *(sideways. P* 13½.

426 8 c. Type **128** 10 10
427 20 c. *Delias schoenbergi* 25 25
428 45 c. *Jamides cephion* 40 45
429 80 c. *Ornithoptera victoriae* . . . . . . 1·00 1·00

See also Nos. 456/9.

(Des L. Curtis. Litho Questa)

1981 (14 Jan). *Ships and Crests (2nd series). Horiz designs as T* **123**. *Multicoloured. W* w **14** *(sideways). P* 14.

430 8 c. H.M.S. *Mounts Bay* 12 10
431 20 c. H.M.S. *Charybdis* 25 25
432 45 c. H.M.S. *Hydra* 50 50
433 $1 H.M.Y. *Britannia* . . . . 1·25 1·25

(Des J. Cooter. Litho Questa)

1981 (23 Mar). *Bicentenary of Maurelle's Visit and Production of Bauche's Chart,* 1791 *(No.* **MS**438). *T* **129** *and similar designs. Wmk CA Diagonal (sideways on 8 c. and $1). P* 13½ × 14 *(8 c., $1) or* 14 × 13½ *(others).*

434 8 c. black, deep brown and greenish yellow . . 15 10
435 10 c. black, vermilion and stone 15 12
436 45 c. multicoloured 60 65
437 $1 multicoloured . . . . 1·25 1·40
MS438 126 × 91 mm. 25 c. × 4, each black, vermilion and stone (wmk sideways). P 14½ . . . . 1·25 1·40

Designs: *Horiz*—10 c. Bellin's map of 1742 showing route of *La Princesa*; 45 c. *La Princesa. Vert*—$1 Spanish compass cards, 1745 and 1757. No. **MS**438, "Chart of a part of the South Sea" (*each stamp* 44 × 28 *mm*).

Stamps in No. **MS**438 were printed to form a composite design.

130 Netball

131 Prince Charles as Colonel-in-Chief, Royal Regiment of Wales

(Des R. Granger Barrett. Litho Security Printers (M), Malaysia)

1981 (7 July). *Mini South Pacific Games. T* **130** *and similar vert designs. Multicoloured. W* w **14**. *P* 12.

439 8 c. Type **130** 10 10
440 10 c. Tennis 12 12
441 25 c. Running 30 35
442 30 c. Football 35 40
443 45 c. Boxing 55 60
MS444 102 × 67 mm $1 Stylised athletes (wmk sideways) . . . . 1·25 1·40

(Des and litho J.W.)

1981 (22 July). *Royal Wedding. T* **131** *and similar vert designs. Multicoloured. W* w **14**. *P* 13½ × 13.

445 8 c. Wedding bouquet from Solomon Islands 10 10
446 45 c. Type **131** 55 60
447 $1 Prince Charles and Lady Diana Spencer 1·25 1·40

132 "Music"

133 Primitive Church

(Des BG Studio. Litho Questa)

1981 (28 Sept). *25th Anniv of Duke of Edinburgh Award Scheme. T* **132** *and similar vert designs. Multicoloured. W* w **14**. *P* 14.

448 8 c. Type **132** 10 10
449 25 c. "Handicrafts" 30 30
450 45 c. "Canoeing" 70 70
451 $1 Duke of Edinburgh .. .. 1·40 1·40

(Des BG Studio. Litho Format)

1981 (12 Oct). *Christmas. Churches. T* **133** *and similar horiz designs. W* w **14** *(sideways). P* 14.

452 8 c. black, buff and cobalt 10 10
453 10 c. multicoloured 12 12
454 25 c. black, buff and dull green 35 30
455 $2 multicoloured .. .. 2·25 2·25

Designs:—10 c. St. Barnabas Anglican Cathedral, Honiara; 25 c. Early church; $2 Holy Cross Cathedral, Honiara.

(Des J. Cooter. Litho Secura, Singapore)

1982 (5 Jan). *Butterflies (2nd series). Horiz designs as T* **128**. *Multicoloured. W* w **14** *(sideways). P* 13½ × 13.

456 10 c. Autumn Leaf or Leafwing (*Doleschallia bisaltide*) 15 12
457 25 c. Tailless Swallowtail (*Papilio bridgei hecataeus*) 35 35
458 35 c. *Taenaris phorcas* 40 40
a. Wmk inverted .. .. 40·00
459 $1 Blue Triangle or Common Bluebottle (*Graphium sarpedon*) .. .. .. 1·50 1·50

No. 458a shows a change of watermark position from sideways to inverted.

50 CENTS SURCHARGE
CYCLONE RELIEF FUND
1982

(134)

135 Pair of Sanford's Sea Eagles constructing Nest

1982 (3 May). *Cyclone Relief Fund. No. 447 surch with T* **134** *in red.*

460 $1 + 50 c. Prince Charles and Lady Diana Spencer .. .. 2·50 2·50

(Des N. Arlott. Litho Walsall)

1982 (15 May). *Sanford's Sea Eagle. T* **135** *and similar vert designs. Multicoloured. W* w **14**. *P* 14.

461 12 c. Type **135** 20 20
a. Horiz strip of 5. Nos. 461/5 .. .. 1·10
462 12 c. Egg and chick 20 20
463 12 c. Hen feeding chicks 20 20
464 12 c. Fledgelings 20 20
465 12 c. Young bird in flight 20 20
466 12 c. Pair of birds and village dwellings .. 20 20
461/6 .. .. *Set of* 6 1·10 1·10

Nos. 461/6 were printed together, *se-tenant*, in various combinations throughout sheets also including one stamp-size label.

136 Wedding Portrait

137 Flags of Solomon Islands and United Kingdom

(Des Jennifer Toombs. Litho Walsall)

1982 (1 July). *21st Birthday of Princess of Wales. T* **136** *and similar vert designs. Multicoloured. W* w **14**. *P* 14½ × 14.

467 12 c. Solomon Islands coat of arms 15 15
468 40 c. Lady Diana Spencer at Broadlands, May 1981 .. .. 50 55
469 50 c. Type **136** 55 60
470 $1 Formal portrait .. .. 1·10 1·25

(Des Studio 53. Litho Questa)

1982 (11 Oct). *Royal Visit (Nos. 471/2,* **MS475**) *and Commonwealth Games, Brisbane (Nos. 473/4,* **MS476**). *T* **137** *and similar square designs. Multicoloured. W* w **14** *(sideways). P* 14.

471 12 c. Type **137** 15 15
a. Pair. Nos. 471/2 .. .. .. 30 30
472 12 c. Queen and Prince Philip 15 15
473 25 c. Running 30 35
a. Pair. Nos. 473/4 .. .. .. 60 70
474 25 c. Boxing 30 35
MS475 123 × 123 mm. Nos. 471/2 and $1 Royal Yacht *Britannia* .. .. 1·25 1·40
MS476 123 × 123 mm. Nos. 473/4 and $1 Royal Yacht *Britannia* .. .. 1·60 1·75

Nos. 471/2 and 473/4 were each printed in small sheets of 10, including 2 *se-tenant*, stamp-size, labels, the two stamp designs appearing *se-tenant*, both horizontally and vertically.

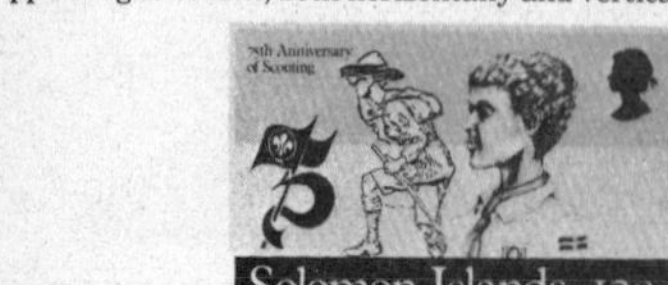

138 Boy Scouts

(Des McCombie Skinner. Litho Format)

1982 (4 Nov). *75th Anniv of Boy Scout Movement (Nos. 477, 479, 481, 483) and Centenary of Boys' Brigade (others). T* **138** *and similar horiz designs. Multicoloured. W* w **14** *(sideways). P* 14.

477 12 c. Type **138** 15 15
478 12 c. Boys' Brigade cadets 15 15
479 25 c. Lord Baden-Powell 30 35
480 25 c. Sir William Smith 30 35
481 35 c. Type **138** 35 40
482 35 c. As No. 478 .. .. 35 40
483 50 c. As No. 479 .. .. 60 65
484 50 c. As No. 480 .. .. 60 65
477/84 .. .. *Set of* 8 2·50 2·75

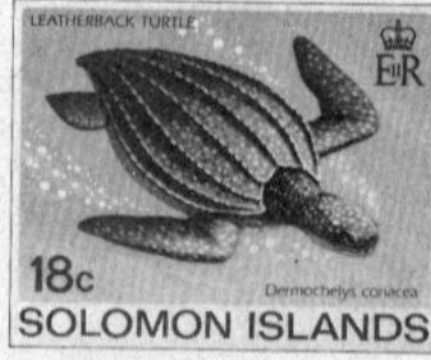

139 Leatherback Turtle

(Des L. Curtis. Litho Format)

1983 (5 Jan). *Turtles. T* **139** *and similar horiz designs. Multicoloured. W* w **14** *(sideways). P* 14½.

485 18 c. Type **139** 25 25
486 35 c. Loggerhead turtle 40 45
487 45 c. Pacific Ridley turtle 55 60
488 50 c. Green turtle 60 65

140 *Oliva vidum, Conus generalis* and *Murex tribulus*

(Des W. Fenton. Litho Questa)

1983 (14 Mar). *Commonwealth Day. Shells. T* **140** *and similar horiz designs. Multicoloured. W* w **14** *(sideways). P* 14.

489 12 c. Type **140** 15 20
490 35 c. Romu, Kurila, Kakadu and money belt .. 40 45
491 45 c. Shells from "Bride-price" necklaces .. 55 60
492 50 c. *Trochus niloticus* polished and in its natural state 60 65

141 Montgolfier Balloon

(Des A. Theobald. Litho Format)

1983 (30 June). *Bicentenary of Manned Flight. T* **141** *and similar horiz designs. Multicoloured. W* w **14** *(sideways). P* 14.

493 30 c. Type **141** 35 40
494 35 c. R.A.A.F. Lockheed "Hercules" 40 45
495 40 c. Wright brothers' *Flyer III* 50 55
496 45 c. Space shuttle *Columbia* 55 60
497 50 c. Beechcraft "Baron-Solair" 60 65

142 Weto Dancers

(Des J.W. Litho Format)

1983 (25 Aug). *Christmas. T* **142** *and similar horiz designs. Multicoloured. W* w **14** *(sideways). P* 14.

498 12 c. Type **142** 15 20
499 15 c. Custom wrestling 20 25
500 18 c. Girl dancers 20 25
501 20 c. Devil dancers 20 25
502 25 c. Bamboo band 30 35
503 35 c. Gilbertese dancers 40 45
504 40 c. Pan pipers 50 55
505 45 c. Girl dancers 55 60
506 50 c. Cross surrounded by flowers 60 65
498/506 .. .. *Set of* 9 2·75 3·25
MS507 153 × 112 mm. Nos. 498/506 .. 2·75 3·25

Stamps from No. **MS**507 are without the inscription, "Christmas 1983", shown on Nos. 498/506.

143 Earth Satellite Station

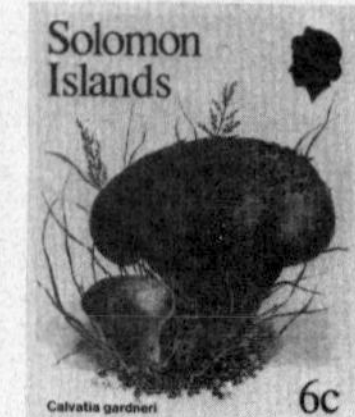

144 *Calvatia gardneri*

(Des Jennifer Toombs. Litho Format)

1983 (19 Dec). *World Communications Year. T* **143** *and similar horiz designs. Multicoloured. W* w **14** *(sideways). P* 14.

508 12 c. Type **143** 15 20
509 18 c. Ham radio operator 20 25
510 25 c. 1908 2½d. Canoe stamp 30 35
511 $1 1908 6d. Canoe stamp .. .. .. 1·10 1·25
MS512 131 × 103 mm. No. 511 .. .. .. 1·10 1·25

(Des Gillian Tomblin. Litho Enschedé)

1984 (30 Jan). *Fungi. T* **144** *and similar vert designs. Multicoloured. W* w **14**. *P* 13½.

513 6 c. Type **144** 5 8
514 18 c. *Marasmiellus inoderma* 20 25
a. Booklet pane of 6 .. .. .. 1·25
515 35 c. *Pycnoporus sanguineus* 40 45
a. Booklet pane of 6 .. .. .. 2·50
516 $2 *Filoboletus manipularis* .. .. .. 2·40 2·50

Booklet panes Nos. 514a and 515a were from special sheets providing blocks of 6 (3 × 2) with vertical margins at both the left and right of each pane.

145 Cross surrounded by Flowers

146 *Olivebank*, 1892

(Des J.W. Litho Format)

1984 (16 Apr). *Visit of Pope John Paul II. W* w **14** *(sideways). P* 14.

517 **145** 12 c. multicoloured 15 20
518 50 c. multicoloured 65 70

(Des Studio 53. Litho Questa)

1984 (21 Apr). *250th Anniv of "Lloyd's List" (newspaper). T* **146** *and similar vert designs. Multicoloured. W* w **14**. *P* 14.

519 12 c. Type **146** 15 20
520 15 c. S.S. *Tinhow*, 1906 .. .. .. 20 25
521 18 c. *Oriana* at Point Cruz, Honiara 25 30
522 $1 Point Cruz, Honiara .. .. .. 1·25 1·40

(Des Jennifer Toombs. Litho Format)

1984 (18 June). *Universal Postal Union Congress, Hamburg. As No.* **MS**512 *but with changed sheet inscriptions and U.P.U. logo in margin. Multicoloured. W* w **14** *(sideways). P* 14.

MS523 $1 1908 6d. Canoe stamp .. .. .. 1·25 1·40

147 Village Drums

148 Solomon Islands Flag and Torch-bearer

(Des McCombie Skinner Studio. Litho Questa)

1984 (2 July). *20th Anniv of Asia-Pacific Broadcasting Union. T* **147** *and similar horiz designs. Multicoloured. W* w **14** *(sideways). P* 13½ × 14.

524 12 c. Type **147** 15 20
525 45 c. Radio City, Guadalcanal 60 65
526 60 c. S.I.B.C. studios, Honiara 75 80
527 $1 S.I.B.C. Broadcasting House .. .. 1·25 1·40

(Des McCombie Skinner Studio. Litho Format)

1984 (4 Aug–22 Sept). *Olympic Games, Los Angeles. T* **148** *and similar multicoloured designs. W* w **14** *(sideways on 25 c. to $1). P* 14 × 13½ *(12 c.) or* 13½ × 14 *(others).*

528 12 c. Type **148** 15 20
529 25 c. Lawson Tama Stadium, Honiara (*horiz*) 30 35
a. Booklet pane Nos. 529/30, each × 2 (22.9.84) .. .. 1·90
530 50 c. Honiara Community Centre (*horiz*) .. 65 70
531 95 c. Alick Wickham inventing crawl stroke, Bronte Baths, New South Wales, 1898 (*horiz*) (22.9.84) .. .. 1·25 1·40
a. Booklet pane of 1 .. .. 1·25
532 $1 Olympic Stadium, Los Angeles (*horiz*) .. 1·25 1·40

No. 531 only exists from $3·95 stamp booklets.

149 Little Pied Cormorant

(Des I. Loe. Litho Questa)

1984 (21 Sept). *"Ausipex" International Stamp Exhibition, Melbourne. Birds. T* **149** *and similar vert designs. Multicoloured. W w* **14**. *P* 14½.

No.	Description	Unused	Used
533	12 c. Type **149**	15	20
534	18 c. Australian Grey Duck	25	30
535	35 c. Nankeen Night-heron	45	50
536	$1 Dollarbird	1·25	1·40
MS537	130 × 96 mm. Nos. 533/6	2·00	2·25

POSTAGE DUE STAMPS

D 1

(Typo B.W.)

1940 (1 Sept). *Wmk Mult Script CA. P* 12.

No.	Type	Description	Unused	Used
D1	D 1	1d. emerald-green	3·25	5·50
D2		2d. scarlet	3·75	6·00
D3		3d. brown	5·00	8·50
D4		4d. blue	7·50	9·50
D5		5d. grey-green	8·00	14·00
D6		6d. purple	9·00	15·00
D7		1s. violet	15·00	26·00
D8		1s. 6d. turquoise-green	30·00	55·00
D1/8		*Set of* 8	75·00	£130
D1/8 Perf "Specimen"		*Set of* 8	£150	

Somaliland Protectorate

Stamps of EGYPT were used in Somaliland Protectorate for some years prior to the withdrawal of the Egyptian garrisons in 1884. From this date until 1903 the stamps of INDIA were used at Berbera and Zaila (established 1 January 1887).

The Protectorate Post Office was established on 1 June 1903, when control of British Somaliland was transferred from the Indian Government to the British Foreign Office.

PRICES FOR STAMPS ON COVER TO 1945

Nos. 1/11	*from* × 12
Nos. 12/13	—
Nos. 18/22	*from* × 8
Nos. 23/4	—
Nos. 25/30	*from* × 10
Nos. 32/59	*from* × 8
Nos. 60/72	*from* × 4
Nos. 73/85	*from* × 3
Nos. 86/9	*from* × 2
Nos. 90/2	*from* × 5
Nos. 93/104	*from* × 3
Nos. 105/16	*from* × 4
Nos. O1/13	*from* × 3
No. O14	—

BRITISH
SOMALILAND

(1)

2

3

SETTINGS OF TYPE 1

In all printings the ½, 1, 2, 2½, 3, 4, 8, 12 a. and 1 r. values were overprinted from a setting of 240 (2 panes 12 × 10, one above the other), covering the entire sheet at one operation.

The 6 a., which was in sheets of 320 (4 panes, each 8 × 10), had a modified setting of 160, applied twice to each sheet.

The high values were overprinted in sheets of 96 (8 panes, each 4 × 3).

The settings for the low value stamps contained two slightly different styles of overprint, identified by the position of "B" of "BRITISH". Type A shows this letter over the "M" of "SOMALILAND" and Type B over the "OM".

For the first printing with the overprint at the top of the design the 240 position setting showed all the stamps in the upper pane and 63 in the lower as Type A, with the remaining 57 as Type B. When the setting was used for the printing with overprint at foot it was amended slightly so that one of the Type A examples in the upper pane became a Type B.

The 6 a. value with overprint at top shows 250 examples of Type A and 70 as Type B in each sheet. This proportion altered in the printing with overprint at foot to 256 as Type A and 64 as Type B.

OVERPRINT VARIETIES

Missing second "I" in "BRITISH"—Occurs on the stamps with overprint at top from R.2/6 of the upper pane and R.5/1 of the lower, although it is believed that the example on the 2½ a. (No. 4a) only occurs from the second position. On the later printing with overprint at foot a similar error can be found on R.7/12 of the upper pane. Some examples of both these errors show traces of the letter remaining, but the prices quoted are for stamps with it completely omitted.

Figure "1" for first "I" in "BRITISH"—Occurs on R.6/4 of the upper pane for all printings of the 240 impression setting. In addition it has been reported from R.7/12 of the Queen Victoria 2½, 12 a. and 1 r. with overprint at foot. Both versions of the 6 a. show the variety on R.6/4 of the upper left and upper right panes.

Curved overprint—Occurs on R.3/4 of the top right-hand pane of the high values.

"SUMALILAND"—Occurs on R.2/9 of the upper pane for all low values with the overprint at foot, except the 6 a. A similar variety occurs on the high values from the same series on R.1/3 of the top left pane.

"SOMAL.LAND"—Occurs on R.7/5 of the lower pane from the 240 impression setting with the overprint at foot. In addition the Edwardian values of this series also have an example on R.6/7. The 6 a. has examples of the flaw on R.6/9 and R.7/5 of both the lower right and left panes. A similar variety occurs on the high values from the same series at R.3/4 of the third pane in the left-hand column.

1903 (1 June). *Stamps of India optd with T* 1, *at top of stamp, in Calcutta.*

No.	Type	Description	Unused	Used
1	**23**	½ a. yellow-green	75	3·00
		a. "BRIT SH"	£160	
2	**25**	1 a. carmine	85	3·00
		a. "BRIT SH"	£160	£225
		b. "BR1TISH"	£140	
3	**27**	2 a. pale violet	70	70
		a. "BRIT SH"	£250	
		b. "BR1TISH"	£250	
		c. Opt double	£600	
4	**36**	2½ a. ultramarine	2·25	5·50
		a. "BRIT SH"	£325	
		b. "BR1TISH"	£275	
5	**28**	3 a. brown-orange	1·75	4·50
		a. "BRIT SH"	£350	
		b. "BR1TISH"	£300	
6	**29**	4 a. slate-green	2·25	6·00
		a. "BR1TISH"	£300	
7	**21**	6 a. olive-bistre	3·25	6·50
		a. "BR1TISH"	£225	
8	**31**	8 a. dull mauve	3·25	7·00
		a. "BR1TISH"	£350	
9	**32**	12 a. purple/*red*	4·50	9·00
		a. "BR1TISH"	£350	
10	**37**	1 r. green and carmine	7·50	13·00
		a. "BR1TISH"	£375	
11	**38**	2 r. carmine and yellow-brown	19·00	25·00
		a. Curved opt	75·00	
12		3 r. brown and green	20·00	30·00
		a. Curved opt	£110	
13		5 r. ultramarine and violet	25·00	38·00
		a. Curved opt	£125	
1/13		*Set of* 13	80·00	£140

1903 (1 Sept–2 Nov). *Stamps of India optd with T* 1, *at bottom of stamp, in Calcutta. (a) On issues of Queen Victoria.*

No.	Type	Description	Unused	Used
18	**36**	2½ a. ultramarine (2.11)	2·50	6·50
		a. "BR1TISH"	£180	
		b. "SUMALILAND"	£225	
		c. "SOMAL.LAND"	£225	
19	**21**	6 a. olive-bistre (2.11)	2·25	5·00
		a. "BR1TISH"	£200	
		b. "SOMAL.LAND"	£120	
20	**32**	12 a. purple/*red* (2.11)	6·50	12·00
		a. "BR1TISH"	£200	
		b. "SUMALILAND"	£300	
		c. "SOMAL.LAND"	£300	
21	**37**	1 r. green and carmine (2.11)	7·00	12·00
		a. "BR1TISH"	£250	
		b. "SUMALILAND"	£400	
		c. "SOMAL.LAND"	£400	
22	**38**	2 r. carmine and yellow-brown (2.11)	42·00	55·00
		a. Curved opt	£225	
		b. "SUMALILAND"	£300	
		c. "SOMAL.LAND"	£300	
23		3 r. brown and green (2.11)	48·00	60·00
		a. Opt double (one albino), both inverted	£400	
		b. Curved opt	£225	
		c. "SUMALILAND"	£300	
		d. "SOMAL.LAND"	£300	
24		5 r. ultramarine and violet (2.11)	38·00	50·00
		a. "SUMALILAND"	£250	
		b. "SOMAL.LAND"	£250	
		(b) On issues of King Edward VII		
25	**42**	½ a. green	75	1·10
		a. "BRIT SH"	£275	
		b. "BR1TISH"	75·00	
		c. "SUMALILAND"	75·00	
		d. "SOMAL.LAND"	18·00	
26	**43**	1 a. carmine (8.10)	75	75
		a. "BRIT SH"	£200	
		b. "BR1TISH"	80·00	
		c. "SUMALILAND"	80·00	
		d. "SOMAL.LAND"	20·00	
27	**44**	2 a. violet (2.11)	2·50	3·50
		a. "BRIT SH"	£750	
		b. "BR1TISH"	£200	
		c. "SUMALILAND"	£200	
		d. "SOMAL.LAND"	35·00	
28	**46**	3 a. orange-brown (2.11)	2·50	4·50
		a. "BR1TISH"	£225	
		b. "SUMALILAND"	£225	
		c. "SOMAL.LAND"	35·00	
29	**47**	4 a. olive (2.11)	2·50	4·75
		a. "BR1TISH"	£250	
		b. "SUMALILAND"	£250	
		c. "SOMAL.LAND"	40·00	
30	**49**	8 a. mauve (2.11)	3·75	6·00
		a. "BR1TISH"	£250	
		b. "SUMALILAND"	£250	
		c. "SOMAL.LAND"	50·00	
18/30		*Set of* 13	£140	£200

(Typo D.L.R.)

1904 (15 Feb–3 Sept). *(a) Wmk Crown CA. P* 14.

No.	Type	Description	Unused	Used
32	**2**	½ a. dull green and green	60	3·50
33		1 a. grey-black and red (3.9)	90	4·25
34		2 a. dull and bright purple (3.9)	2·25	3·50
35		2½ a. bright blue (3.9)	2·50	6·00
36		3 a. chocolate and grey-green (3.9)	2·50	6·00
37		4 a. green and black (3.9)	3·25	6·00
38		6 a. green and violet (3.9)	6·00	8·50
39		8 a. grey-black and pale blue (3.9)	6·00	11·00
40		12 a. grey-black and orange-buff (3.9)	10·00	13·00
		(b) Wmk Crown CC. P 14		
41	**3**	1 r. green (3.9)	16·00	23·00
42		2 r. dull and bright purple (3.9)	32·00	45·00
43		3 r. green and black (3.9)	38·00	48·00
44		5 r. grey-black and red (3.9)	40·00	55·00
32/44		*Set of* 13	£140	£200
32/44 Optd "Specimen"		*Set of* 13	£225	

1905 (July)–**11**. *Wmk Mult Crown CA. P* 14.

No.	Type	Description	Unused	Used
45	**2**	½ a. dull green and green, **O**	70	3·50
46		1 a. grey-black and red, **OC** (10.7.05)	1·00	2·75
47		2 a. dull and bright purple, **O**	4·00	7·00
48		2½ a. bright blue, **O**	5·00	10·00
49		3 a. chocolate and grey-green, **OC**	3·25	9·00
50		4 a. green and black, **OC**	3·75	10·00
51		6 a. green and violet, **OC**	3·75	10·00
52		8 a. grey-black and pale blue, **O**	4·50	10·00
		a. Black and blue, **C** (27.1.11)	28·00	45·00
53		12 a. grey-black and orange-buff, **O**	4·50	11·00
		a. Blk & orge-brn, **C** (9.11.11)	15·00	32·00

1909 (30 Apr–May). *Wmk Mult Crown CA. P* 14.

No.	Type	Description	Unused	Used
58	**2**	½ a. bluish green, **O** (May)	4·75	7·50
59		1 a. red, **O** (Optd S. £20)	4·75	4·50
45/59		*Set of* 11	35·00	75·00

4 5

(Typo D.L.R.)

1912 (Nov)–**19.** *Wmk Mult Crown CA. P* 14.
60 **4** ½ a. green, **O** (11.13) .. .. 25 1·25
61 1 a. red, **O** .. .. 80 1·25
a. Scarlet, **O** (1917) .. .. .. 3·00 2·75
62 2 a. dull and bright purple, **C** (12.13) .. 4·50 6·50
a. Dull purple and violet-purple, **C** (4.19) .. .. 6·00 10·00
63 2½ a. bright blue, **O** (10.13) .. .. 1·25 3·50
64 3 a. chocolate and grey-green, **C** (10.13) 1·25 3·50
65 4 a. green and black, **C** (12.12).. .. 1·50 4·75
66 6 a. green and violet, **C** (4.13) .. .. 1·50 3·00
67 8 a. grey-black and pale blue, **C** (10.13) 2·40 6·50
68 12 a. grey-black and orange-buff, **C** (10.13) .. .. 2·40 7·50
69 **5** 1 r. green, **C** .. .. 4·00 7·50
70 2 r. dull purple and purple, **C** (4.19) .. 15·00 28·00
71 3 r. green and black, **C** (4.19) .. .. 28·00 42·00
72 5 r. black and scarlet, **C** (4.19).. .. 40·00 60·00
60/72 .. .. *Set of* 13 90·00 £160
60/72 Optd "Specimen" .. .. *Set of* 13 £190

1921. *Wmk Mult Script CA. P* 14.
73 **4** ½ a. blue-green, **O** .. .. .. 25 1·75
74 1 a. carmine-red, **O** 25 70
75 2 a. dull and bright purple, **C** .. .. 80 1·40
76 2½ a. bright blue, **O** .. .. .. 1·00 3·50
77 3 a. chocolate and green, **C** .. .. 2·25 6·50
78 4 a. green and black, **C**.. .. .. 2·50 3·75
79 6 a. green and violet, **C**.. .. .. 1·50 5·50
80 8 a. grey-black and pale blue, **C** .. 2·75 5·50
81 12 a. grey-black and orange-buff, **C** .. 6·50 15·00
82 **5** 1 r. dull green, **C** .. .. .. 7·00 18·00
83 2 r. dull purple and purple, **C** .. .. 17·00 30·00
84 3 r. dull green and black, **C** .. .. 24·00 45·00
85 5 r. black and scarlet, **C** .. .. 48·00 75·00
73/85 .. .. *Set of* 13 £100 £190
73/85 Optd "Specimen" .. .. *Set of* 13 £190

1935 (6 May). *Silver Jubilee. As Nos.* 91/4 *of Antigua but ptd by Waterlow. P* 11 × 12.
86 1 a. deep blue and scarlet .. .. .. 1·60 2·00
87 2 a. ultramarine and grey .. .. .. 1·60 3·25
88 3 a. brown and deep blue .. .. .. 2·50 6·00
89 1 r. slate and purple .. .. .. 6·50 10·00
86/9 Perf "Specimen" .. .. *Set of* 4 60·00

1937 (13 May). *Coronation. As Nos.* 13/15 *of Aden.*
90 1 a. scarlet 10 25
91 2 a. grey-black 20 45
92 3 a. bright blue .. .. 50 1·10
90/2 Perf "Specimen" .. .. *Set of* 3 35·00

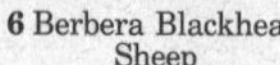

6 Berbera Blackhead Sheep

7 Greater Kudu Antelope

8 Somaliland Protectorate

(Des H. W. Claxton. Recess Waterlow)

1938 (10 May). *Portrait to left. Wmk Mult Script CA. P* 12½.
93 **6** ½ a. green 35 60
94 1 a. scarlet 35 60
95 2 a. maroon 30 75
96 3 a. bright blue .. .. 1·75 2·40
97 **7** 4 a. sepia .. .. 1·75 2·40
98 6 a. violet .. .. 1·10 3·00
99 8 a. grey .. .. 1·75 3·75
100 12 a. red-orange .. .. 2·00 4·50
101 **8** 1 r. green .. .. 8·50 18·00
102 2 r. purple .. .. 7·00 17·00
103 3 r. bright blue .. .. 7·00 17·00
104 5 r. black .. .. 11·00 17·00
a. Imperf between (horiz pair) .. £3250
93/104 .. .. *Set of* 12 38·00 80·00
93/104 Perf "Specimen" .. .. *Set of* 12 95·00

Following the Italian Occupation during 1940–41 the stamps of ADEN were used at Berbera from 1 July 1941 until 26 April 1942.

9 Berbera Blackhead Sheep

5 Cents (10) 1 Shilling (11)

(Recess Waterlow)

1942 (27 Apr). *As T* **6/8** *but with full-face portrait of King George VI, as in T* **9.** *Wmk Mult Script CA. P* 12½.
105 **9** ½ a. green 12 15
106 1 a. scarlet 12 15
107 2 a. maroon 50 45
108 3 a. bright blue 12 35
109 **7** 4 a. sepia 12 35
110 6 a. violet 20 35
111 8 a. grey 25 35
112 12 a. red-orange 35 45
113 **8** 1 r. green .. .. 90 1·00
114 2 r. purple .. .. 3·00 3·00
115 3 r. bright blue .. .. 3·50 4·00
116 5 r. black .. .. 4·50 6·00
105/16 .. .. .. *Set of* 12 12·50 15·00
105/16 Perf "Specimen" .. .. *Set of* 12 £130

1946 (15 Oct). *Victory. As Nos.* 28/9 *of Aden. P* 13½ × 14.
117 1 a. carmine 15 35
a. Perf 13½ .. .. 2·75 20·00
118 3 a. blue 15 35
117/18 Perf "Specimen" .. *Set of* 2 30·00

1949 (28 Jan). *Royal Silver Wedding. As Nos.* 30/1 *of Aden.*
119 1 a. scarlet 10 10
120 5 r. black .. .. 4·00 7·50

1949 (10 Oct). *75th Anniv of U.P.U. As Nos.* 114/17 *of Antigua and surch with new values.*
121 1 a. on 10 c. carmine 15 20
122 3 a. on 30 c. deep blue (R.) 45 45
123 6 a. on 50 c. purple 55 50
124 12 a. on 1s. red-orange 75 80

1951 (2 Apr). *1942 issue surch as T* **10/11.**
125 5 c. on ½ a. green 12 12
126 10 c. on 2 a. maroon 12 12
127 15 c. on 3 a. bright blue 12 15
128 20 c. on 4 a. sepia 12 15
129 30 c. on 6 a. violet 25 35
130 50 c. on 8 a. grey 30 25
131 70 c. on 12 a. red-orange 35 40
132 1s. on 1 r. green 40 40
133 2s. on 2 r. purple .. .. .. 80 3·25
134 2s. on 3 r. bright blue .. .. 1·00 3·25
135 5s. on 5 r. black (R.) .. .. 6·00 6·00
125/35 .. .. .. *Set of* 11 8·50 13·00
At least one cover is known postmarked 1 April, in error, at Burao.

1953 (2 June). *Coronation. As No.* 47 *of Aden.*
136 15 c. black and green 15 30

12 Camel and Gurgi

13 Askari

(Recess B.W.)

1953 (15 Sept)–**58.** *T* **12/13** *and similar horiz designs. Wmk Mult Script CA. P* 12½.
137 **12** 5 c. slate-black 5 5
138 **13** 10 c. red-orange (*shades*) 30 10
139 **12** 15 c. blue-green 20 5
140 20 c. scarlet 20 5
141 **13** 30 c. reddish brown 30 5
142 – 35 c. blue 45 10
143 – 50 c. brown and rose-carmine .. 45 10
144 – 1s. light blue 40 10
145 – 1s. 30 c. ultramarine and black (1.9.58) 2·50 3·25
146 – 2s. brown and bluish violet .. .. 3·75 2·75
147 – 5s. red-brown and emerald .. .. 5·00 8·00
148 – 10s. brown and reddish violet .. .. 5·50 12·00
137/48 .. .. .. *Set of* 12 17·00 24·00
Designs:—35 c., 2s. Somali Stock Dove; 50 c., 5s. Martial Eagle; 1s. Berbera Blackhead Sheep; 1s. 30 c. Sheikh Isaaq's Tomb; 10s. Taleh Fort.

OPENING OF THE LEGISLATIVE COUNCIL 1957 (19)

LEGISLATIVE COUNCIL UNOFFICIAL MAJORITY, 1960 (20)

1957 (21 May). *Opening of Legislative Council. Nos.* 140 *and* 144 *optd with T* **19.**
149 20 c. scarlet 5 5
150 1s. light blue 10 10

1960 (5 Apr). *Legislative Council's Unofficial Majority. Nos.* 140 *and* 145 *optd as T* **20.**
151 20 c. scarlet 5 5
152 1s. 30, ultramarine and black 15 15

OFFICIAL STAMPS

SERVICE

BRITISH SOMALILAND (O 1)

BRITISH SOMALILAND (O 2)

O.H.M.S. (O 3)

SETTING OF TYPE O 1

The 240 impression setting used for the Official stamps differs considerably from that on the contemporary postage issue with overprint at foot, although the "BR1TISH" error can still be found on R.6/4 of the upper pane. The Official setting is recorded as consisting of 217 overprints as Type A and 23 as Type B.

OVERPRINT VARIETIES

Figure "1" for first "I" in "BRITISH". Occurs on R.6/4 of the upper pane as for the postage issue.
"BRITIS H"—Occurs on R.8, stamps 4 and 10 of the lower pane.

1903 (1 June). *Official stamps of India, 1883–1900, optd with Type* O 1 *in Calcutta.*
O1 **23** ½ a. yellow-green .. .. .. 6·50 35·00
a. "BR1TISH" £400
b. "BRITIS H" £100
O2 **25** 1 a. carmine .. .. .. 8·50 10·00
a. "BR1TISH" £400
b. "BRITIS H" £100
O3 **27** 2 a. pale violet .. .. .. 11·00 40·00
a. "BR1TISH" £500
b. "BRITIS H" £125
O4 **31** 8 a. dull mauve.. .. .. 28·00 £325
a. "BR1TISH" £750
b. "BRITIS H" £160
O5 **37** 1 r. green and carmine .. .. 28·00 £250
a. "BR1TISH" £750
b. "BRITIS H" £160
The 8 a. is known with the stop omitted after the "M" of "O.H.M.S.".

SETTING OF TYPE O 2

This 240 impression setting of "BRITISH SOMALILAND" also differs from that used to prepare the postage issue with overprint at foot, although many of the errors from the latter still occur in the same positions for the Official stamps. The setting used for Nos. O6/9*f* contained 180 overprints as Type A and 60 as Type B.

OVERPRINT VARIETIES

Missing second "I" in "BRITISH"—Occurs R.7/12 of upper pane as for the postage issue.
Figure "1" for first "I" in "BRITISH"—Occurs R.6/4 of upper pane as for the postage issue.
"SUMALILAND"—Occurs R.2/9 of the upper pane as for the postage issue.
"SOMAL.LAND"—Occurs R.6/7 of the lower pane as for the postage issue.

SERVICE

(O 2*a*)

"SERVICE" in wrong fount (Type O **2***a*)—Occurs R.1/7 of lower pane.

1903. *Prepared for use, but not issued. Postage stamps of India, Queen Victoria 1892 issue* (1 *r.*) *or King Edward VII 1902 issue (others), optd with Type* O **2** *in Calcutta.*
O6 **42** ½ a. green .. .. 1·25
a. "BRIT SH" .. .. .. 90·00
b. "BR1TISH" .. .. .. 40·00
c. "SUMALILAND" .. .. 40·00
d. "SOMAL.LAND" .. .. 20·00
e. "SERVICE" as Type O **2***a* .. 30·00
O7 **43** 1 a. carmine .. .. .. 1·25
a. "BRIT SH" .. .. .. 90·00
b. "BR1TISH" .. .. .. 40·00
c. "SUMALILAND" .. .. 40·00
d. "SOMAL.LAND" .. .. 20·00
e. "SERVICE" as Type O **2***a* .. 30·00
O8 **44** 2 a. violet .. .. .. 2·50
a. "BRIT SH" £130
b. "BR1TISH" .. .. .. 50·00
c. "SUMALILAND" .. .. 50·00
d. "SERVICE" as Type O **2***a* .. 35·00
O9 **49** 8 a. mauve .. .. .. 24·00
a. "BRIT SH" £1400
b. "BR1TISH" £400
c. "SUMALILAND" £400
d. "SERVICE" as Type O **2***a* .. £225
O9*f* **37** 1 r. green and carmine .. .. 26·00
fa. "BRIT SH" £1400
fb. "BR1TISH" £400
fc. "SUMALILAND" £400
fd. "SOMAL.LAND" £200
fe. "SERVICE" as Type O **2***a* .. £225
Used examples of the four lower values are known, but there is no evidence that such stamps did postal duty.

SETTING OF TYPE O 3

The anna values were overprinted in sheets of 120 (2 panes 6 × 10) from a setting matching the pane size. The full stop after the "M" on the fifth vertical column was either very faint or completely omitted. The prices quoted are for stamps with the stop missing; examples with a partial stop are worth much less.
The 1 r. value was overprinted from a separate setting of 60 which did not show the "missing stop" varieties.

1904 (1 Sept)–**05.** *Stamps of Somaliland Protectorate optd with Type* O **3.** *P* 14. (*a*) *Wmk Crown CA.*
O10 **2** ½ a. dull green and green .. .. 7·00 42·00
a. No stop after "M" £500

O11	2	1 a. grey-black and carmine	10·00	15·00
		a. No stop after "M"	£400	£500
O12		2 a. dull and bright purple	£120	55·00
		a. No stop after "M"	£1400	£650
O13		8 a. grey-black and pale blue	75·00	£140
		a. No stop after "M"	£500	
		(b) Wmk Mult Crown CA		
O14	2	2 a. dull and bright purple, **O** (7.05?)	75·00	£450
		a. No stop after "M"	£1200	
		(c) Wmk Crown CC		
O15	3	1 r. green	£150	£450
O10/13, O15 Optd "Specimen"		*Set of* 5	£250	

All Somaliland Protectorate stamps were withdrawn from sale on 25 June 1960 and until the unification on 1 July, issues of Italian Somalia together with Nos. 353/5 of Somalia Republic were used. Later issues will be found listed in Part 14 (*Africa since Independence N–Z*) of this catalogue.

South Africa

The following territories combined to form the Union of South Africa in 1910 (of which they became provinces) and their issues are listed in alphabetical order in this Catalogue:—

CAPE OF GOOD HOPE (incl Griqualand West)
NATAL (incl New Republic and Zululand)
ORANGE FREE STATE
TRANSVAAL

PRICES FOR STAMPS ON COVER TO 1945

Nos. 1/2	*from* × 3
Nos. 3/15	*from* × 4
Nos. 16/17	—
Nos. 18/21	*from* × 6
Nos. 26/32	*from* × 2
No. 33	*from* × 4
Nos. 34/110	*from* × 1
Nos. D1/7	*from* × 4
Nos. D8/33	*from* × 6
Nos. O1/33	*from* × 4

UNION OF SOUTH AFRICA

Although South Africa is now a republic, outside the British Commonwealth, all its stamp issues are listed together here purely as a matter of convenience to collectors.

1

(Des H. S. Wilkinson. Recess D.L.R.)

1910 (4 Nov). *Opening of Union Parliament. Inscribed bilingually. Wmk Multiple Rosettes. P* 14.

1	1	2½d. deep blue (H/S S. £475)	9·00	6·50
2		2½d. blue	6·00	3·00

The deep blue shade is generally accompanied by a blueing of the paper.

The price quoted for the "Specimen" handstamp is for the small italic type with capital and lower case letters.

2

3

4 Springbok's Head

(Typo D.L.R.)

1913 (1 Sept)–**24**. *Inscribed bilingually. W* **4**. *(a) P* 14.

3	2	½d. green	35	5
		a. Stamp doubly printed	£8500	
		b. Blue-green	1·60	12
		c. Yellow-green	1·75	12
4		1d. rose-red (*shades*)	60	5
		a. Carmine-red	90	5
		b. Scarlet (*shades*)	75	12
5		1½d. chestnut (*shades*) (23.8.20)	80	10
		a. *Tête-bêche* (pair)	3·50	8·00
6	3	2d. dull purple	1·50	10
		a. Deep purple	3·00	10
7		2½d. bright blue	2·50	1·10
		a. Deep blue	5·00	2·40
8		3d. black and orange-red	4·00	30
		a. Black and dull orange-red	6·00	70
9		3d. ultramarine (*shades*) (10.22)	4·00	1·40
10		4d. orange-yellow and olive-green	9·00	45
		a. Orange-yellow and sage-green	7·00	40
11		6d. black and violet	5·50	15
		a. Black and bright violet	7·50	15
12		1s. orange	17·00	55
		a. Orange-yellow	25·00	55
13		1s. 3d. violet (*shades*) (1.10.20)	20·00	14·00
14		2s. 6d. purple and green	65·00	4·00

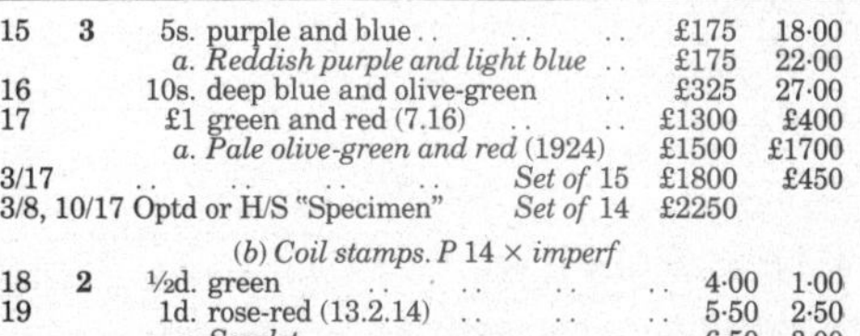

15	3	5s. purple and blue	£175	18·00
		a. Reddish purple and light blue	£175	22·00
16		10s. deep blue and olive-green	£325	27·00
17		£1 green and red (7.16)	£1300	£400
		a. Pale olive-green and red (1924)	£1500	£1700
3/17		*Set of* 15	£1800	£450
3/8, 10/17 Optd or H/S "Specimen"		*Set of* 14	£2250	
		(b) Coil stamps. P 14 × *imperf*		
18	2	½d. green	4·00	1·00
19		1d. rose-red (13.2.14)	5·50	2·50
		a. Scarlet	6·50	3·00
20		1½d. chestnut (15.11.20)	6·00	3·75
21	3	2d. dull purple (7.10.21)	6·00	3·50

The 6d. exists with "Z" of "ZUID" wholly or partly missing due to wear of plate (*Price wholly missing*, £65 *un*, £35 *us*).

5

(Eng A. J. Cooper. Litho *Cape Times* Ltd)

1925 (25 Feb). *Air. Inscr bilingually. P* 12.

26	5	1d. carmine	6·50	10·00
27		3d. ultramarine	13·00	14·00
28		6d. magenta	18·00	25·00
29		9d. green	38·00	48·00

Beware of forgeries of all values.

INSCRIPTIONS. From 1926 until 1951 (also Nos. 167 and 262/5), most issues were inscribed in English and Afrikaans alternately throughout the sheets.

As we only stock these in *se-tenant* pairs, unused and used, we no longer quote for single used copies and they must be considered to be worth very much less than half the prices quoted for pairs. Prices are for horizontal pairs, vertical pairs being worth about 50% less.

Similarly, the War Effort bantam stamps (Nos. 96/103), and Nos. 124 and D30/3 are priced for units of two or three as the case may be.

PRICES for Nos. 30/135 are for horizontal pairs, *unless otherwise indicated.*

6 Springbok

7 Van Riebeeck's Ship

8 Orange Tree

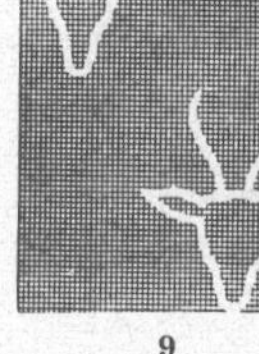

9

(Typo first by Waterlow, later by Govt Printer, Pretoria)

1926 (1 Jan)–**27**. *W* **9**. *P* 14½ × 14.

30	6	½d. black and green	2·00	1·50
		a. Missing "1" in "½"	£1100	
		b. Perf 13½ × 14 (1927)	90·00	25·00
		ba. *Tête-bêche* (pair)	£1000	
31	7	1d. black and carmine	2·00	1·10
		a. Perf 13½ × 14 (1927)	90·00	25·00
		aa. *Tête-bêche* (pair)	£1000	
32	8	6d. green and orange (1.5.26)	30·00	16·00

No. 30a exists in Afrikaans only. Nos. 30b and 31a are from booklets of Pretoria-printed stamps.

For ½d. with pale grey centre, see No. 126.

For rotogravure printing see Nos. 42, etc.

10 "Hope"

(Recess B.W.)

1926 (1 Jan). *T* **10**. *Inscribed in English* (E) *or Afrikaans* (A). *W* **9**. *Imperf.*

			Single stamps E		A	
33		4d. grey-blue (*shades*)	1·60	1·00	1·60	1·00

In this value the English and Afrikaans inscriptions are on separate sheets.

This stamp is known with private perforations or roulettes.

11 Union Buildings, Pretoria

12 Groot Schuur

12*a* A Native Kraal

13 Gnus

14 Ox-wagon inspanned

15 Ox-wagon outspanned

16 Cape Town and Table Bay

(Recess B.W.)

1927 (1 Mar)–**28**. *W* **9**. *P* 14 (*early ptgs*) *or* 14 × 13½ (*from* 1930 *onwards*).

34	11	2d. grey and maroon	20·00	20·00
35	12	3d. black and red	25·00	25·00
35*a*	12*a*	4d. brown (23.3.28)	32·00	42·00
36	13	1s. brown and deep blue	45·00	45·00
37	14	2s. 6d. green and brown	£170	£250
38	15	5s. black and green	£275	£550
39	16	10s. bright blue and brown	£225	£200
		a. Centre inverted		
34/9		*Set of* 7	£750	£900
34/9 H/S "Specimen"		*Set of* 7	£1200	

17 D.H. "Moth"

(Typo Govt Ptg Wks, Pretoria)

1929 (16 Aug). *Air. Inscribed bilingually. No wmk. P* 14 × 13½.

			Un single	*Us single*
40	17	4d. green	5·00	3·75
41		1s. orange	24·00	20·00

PRINTER. All the following issues, except *where stated otherwise*, are printed by rotogravure (the design having either plain lines or a dotted screen) by the Government Printer, Pretoria.

I II

The two types of the 1d. differ in the spacing of the horizontal lines in the side panels:—Type I close; Type II wide. The Afrikaans had the spacing of the words POSSEEL-INKOMSTE close in Type I and more widely spaced in Type II.

1930–45. *T* **6** *to* **8** *and* **11** *to* **14** *redrawn,* "SUIDAFRIKA" (*in one word*) *on Afrikaans stamps. W* **9**. *P* 15 × 14 (½d., 1d., *and* 6d.) *or* 14.

42		½d. black and green (1.31)	1·75	1·75
		a. Two English or two Afrikaans stamps *se-tenant* (vert pair)	50·00	
		b. *Tête-bêche*	£950	
43		1d. black and carmine (I) (5.30)	2·75	70
		a. *Tête-bêche*	£950	
		b. Frame omitted (*single stamp*)	£500	
43*c*		1d. black and carmine (II) (8.32)	15·00	2·25
44		2d. slate-grey and lilac (5.31)	14·00	3·25
		a. *Tête-bêche*	£1800	
		b. Frame omitted (*single stamp*)	£650	
44*c*		2d. blue and violet (1.9.38)	£140	45·00
45		3d. black and red (11.31)	48·00	45·00
45*a*		3d. blue (10.33)	7·50	3·00
46		4d. brown (19.11.32)	48·00	28·00
46*a*		4d. brown (*shades*) (*again redrawn*) (1936)	5·00	3·50
47		6d. green and orange (5.31)	23·00	3·25
48		1s. brown and deep blue (14.9.32)	55·00	22·00
49		2s. 6d. green and brown (24.12.32)	£140	£100
49*a*		2s. 6d. blue and brown (1945)	22·00	14·00
42/9*a*		*Set of* 13	£475	£250

For similar designs with "SUID-AFRIKA" hyphenated, see Nos. 54 etc. and Nos. 114 etc.

The 1d. (Type I) exists without watermark from a trial printing (*Price* £80 *un*).

The Rotogravure printings may be distinguished from the preceding Typographed and Recess printed issues by the following tests:—

TYPO ROTO

R R

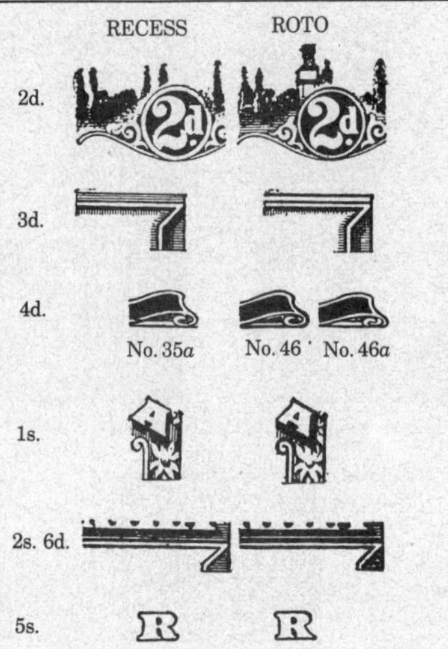

ROTOGRAVURE:

½d., 1d. and 6d. Leg of "R" in "AFR" ends squarely on the bottom line.

2d. The newly built War Memorial appears to the left of the value.

3d. Two fine lines have been removed from the top part of the frame.

4d. No. 46. The scroll is in solid colour.
No. 46a. The scroll is white with a crooked line running through it. (No. 35a. The scroll is shaded by the diagonal lines.)

1s. The shading of the last "A" partly covers the flower beneath.

2s. 6d. The top line of the centre frame is thick and leaves only one white line through it and the name.

5s. (Nos. 64/a). The leg of the "R" is straight.

Rotogravure impressions are generally coarser.

18 Church of the Vow

19 "The Great Trek"

20 A Voortrekker

21 Voortrekker Woman

1933 (3 May)–**36**. *Voortrekker Memorial Fund. W* **9**. *P* 14.

50	**18**	½d. +½d. black and green (15.1.36) ..	3·25	3·00
51	**19**	1d. +½d. grey-black and pink ..	3·75	3·00
52	**20**	2d. +1d. grey-green and purple	5·00	5·00
53	**21**	3d. +1½d. grey-green and blue ..	11·00	11·00

22 Gold Mine

22a Groot Schuur

I

II

III

Dies of 6d.

23 Groot Constantia

1933–48. "SUID-AFRIKA" (*hyphenated*) *on Afrikaans stamps. W* **9**. *P* 15 × 14 (*½d., 1d. and 6d.*) *or* 14 (*others*).

54	**6**	½d. grey and green (9.36) ..	2·50	1·25
		a. Coil stamp. Perf 13½ × 14 (1935) ..	20·00	22·00
56	**7**	1d. grey and carmine (*shades*) (19.4.34)	60	35
		aa. Imperf (pair)	£225	
		a. Grey and bright rose-carmine (1948)	55	40
		b. Coil stamp. Perf 13½ × 14 (1935) ..	24·00	26·00
		c. Frame omitted (*single stamp*) ..	£100	
57	**22**	1½d. green and bright gold (12.11.36) ..	3·00	1·40
		a. Shading omitted from mine dump (in pair with normal)	70·00	
		b. Blue-green and dull gold (8.40) ..	5·00	1·60
58	**11**	2d. blue and violet (11.38)	45·00	25·00
58a		2d. grey and dull purple (5.41)	6·50	4·25
59	**22a**	3d. ultramarine (2.40)	2·25	60
61	**8**	6d. green and vermilion (I) (10.37) ..	45·00	13·00
61a		6d. green and vermilion (II) (6.38) ..	11·00	4·50
61b		6d. green and red-orange (III) (11.46) ..	7·50	4·25
62	**13**	1s. brown and chalky blue (2.39) ..	12·00	4·00
		a. Frame omitted (*single stamp*) ..	£400	
64	**15**	5s. black and green (10.33)	85·00	24·00
		a. Black and blue-green (9.44) ..	27·00	13·00
64b	**23**	10s. blue and sepia (8.39)	65·00	25·00
		ba. Blue and blackish brown (8.39) ..	40·00	10·00
54/64ba (*only one 6d.*)		*Set of* 10	£130	60·00

The ½d. and 1d. coil stamps may be found in blocks emanating from the residue of the large rolls which were cut into sheets and distributed to Post Offices.

1d. Is printed from Type II. Frames of different sizes exist due to reductions made from time to time for the purpose of providing more space for the perforations.

3d. In No. 59 the frame is unscreened and composed of solid lines. Centre is diagonally screened. Scrolls above "3d." are clear lined, light in the middle and dark at sides.

6d. Die I. Green background lines faint. "SUID-AFRIKA" 16¼ mm long.

Die II. Green background lines heavy. "SUID-AFRIKA" 17 mm long. "S" near end of tablet. Scroll open.

Die III. Scroll closed up and design smaller (18 × 22 mm).

Single specimens of the 1930 issue inscribed in English may be distinguished from those listed above as follows:—

½d. and 1d. Centres in varying intensities of black instead of grey.

2d. The letters of "SOUTH AFRICA" are wider and thicker.

3d. The trees are shorter and the sky is lined.

6d. The frame is pale orange.

1s. The frame is greenish blue.

For similar designs, but printed in screened rotogravure, see Nos. 114 to 122a.

24

24a

1937–40. *W* **9**. *P* 15 × 14.

64c	**24**	½d. grey and green	3·00	1·25
		d. Grey and blue-green (1940)	75	25

The lines of shading in T **24** are all horizontal and thicker than in T **6**. In Nos. 64c and 64d the design is composed of solid lines. For stamps with designs composed of dotted lines, see No. 114. Later printings of No. 64d have a smaller design.

1935 (1 May). *Silver Jubilee. Inscr bilingually. W* **9**. *P* 15 × 14.

65	**24a**	½d. black and blue-green	2·25	4·00
66		1d. black and carmine	2·50	3·75
67		3d. blue	30·00	48·00
68		6d. green and orange	50·00	60·00

In stamps with English at top the ½d., 3d. and 6d. have "SILWER JUBILEUM" to left of portrait, and "POSTAGE REVENUE" or "POSTAGE" (3d. and 6d.) in left value tablet. In the 1d., "SILVER JUBILEE" is to the left of portrait. In alternate stamps the positions of English and Afrikaans inscriptions are reversed.

JIPEX

1936

(24b)

25

1936 (2 Nov). *Johannesburg International Philatelic Exhibition. Optd with T* **24b**.

			Un sheet	*Us sheet*
MS69	**6**	½d. grey and green (No. 54)	5·50	10·00
MS70	**7**	1d. grey and carmine (No. 56)	4·00	7·00

Issued each in miniature sheet of six stamps with marginal advertisements.

1937 (12 May). *Coronation. W* **9** (*sideways*). *P* 14.

71	**25**	½d. grey-black and blue-green	25	40
72		1d. grey-black and carmine	35	40
73		1½d. orange and greenish blue	50	65
74		3d. ultramarine	1·75	1·10
75		1s. red-brown and turquoise-blue ..	5·00	3·00
		a. Hyphen omitted on Afrikaans stamp (R.2/13)	30·00	

26 Voortrekker Ploughing

27 Wagon crossing Drakensberg

28 Signing of Dingaan–Retief Treaty

29 Voortrekker Monument

1938 (14 Dec). *Voortrekker Centenary Memorial Fund. W* **9**. *P* 14 (*Nos. 76/7*) *or* 15 × 14 (*others*).

76	**26**	½d. + ½d. blue and green	4·00	4·00
77	**27**	1d. + 1d. blue and carmine	5·00	5·00
78	**28**	1½d. + 1½d. chocolate and blue-green ..	9·00	9·50
79	**29**	3d. + 3d. bright blue	9·50	11·00

30 Wagon Wheel

31 Voortrekker Family

(Des W. H. Coetzer)

1938 (14 Dec). *Voortrekker Commemoration. W* **9**. *P* 15 × 14.

80	**30**	1d. blue and carmine	2·75	1·75
81	**31**	1½d. greenish blue and brown	3·50	1·75

32 Old Vicarage, Paarl, now a museum

33 Symbol of the Reformation

34 Huguenot Dwelling, Drakenstein Mountain Valley

1939 (17 July). *250th Anniv of Huguenot Landing in South Africa and Huguenot Commemoration Fund. W* **9**. *P* 14 (*Nos. 82/3*) *or* 15 × 14 (*No.* 84).

82	**32**	½d. +½d. brown and green	4·50	3·75
83	**33**	1d. +1d. green and carmine	6·00	4·50
84	**34**	1½d. +1½d. blue-green and purple ..	7·00	7·50

34a Gold Mine

1941 (Aug). *W* **9** (*sideways*). *P* 14 × 15.

87	**34a**	1½d. blue-green and yellow-buff (*shades*)	55	12
		a. Yellow-buff (centre) omitted ..	£700	

35 Infantry

36 Nurse and Ambulance

37 Airman

38 Sailor, Destroyer and Lifebelts

39 Women's Auxiliary Services

40 Artillery

41 Electric Welding

42 Tank Corps

1941–42. *War Effort. W* **9** *(sideways on 2d., 4d., 6d.). P* 14 *(2d., 4d., 6d.) or* 15 × 14 *(others). (a) Inscr alternately.*

88	**35**	½d. green (19.11.41)	75	45
		a. Blue-green (7.42)	2·00	1·25
89	**36**	1d. carmine (3.10.41)	75	35
90	**37**	1½d. myrtle-green (12.1.42)	35	25
91	**39**	3d. blue (1.8.41)	4·50	4·50
92	**40**	4d. orange-brown (20.8.41)	7·00	4·50
		a. Red-brown (6.42)	20·00	14·00
93	**41**	6d. red-orange (3.9.41)	5·50	4·00

(b) Inscr bilingually

			Un single	*Us single*
94	**38**	2d. violet (15.9.41)	60	10
95	**42**	1s. brown (27.10.41)	3·00	1·40
88/95 ..		.. .. *Set of* 6 *pairs and* 2 *singles*	20·00	14·00

43 Infantry

44 Nurse

45 Airman

46 Sailor

47 Women's Auxiliary Services

48 Electric Welding

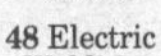

49 Heavy Gun in Concrete Turret

50 Tank Corps

Unit *(pair)*

Unit *(triplet)*

1942–44. *War Effort. Reduced sizes. In pairs perf* 14 (P) *or strips of three, perf* 15 × 14 (T), *subdivided by roulette* 6½. *W* **9** *(sideways on 3d., 4d. and 1s.). (a) Inscr alternately.*

			Un unit	*Us unit*
96	**43**	½d. blue-green (T) (10.42)	90	35
		a. Green (3.43)	2·50	90
		b. Greenish blue (7.44)	2·00	80
		c. Roulette omitted	£175	
97	**44**	1d. carmine-red (T) (5.1.43)	90	35
		a. Bright carmine (3.44)	1·00	35
		b. Roulette omitted	£175	
98	**45**	1½d. red-brown (P) (8.42)	90	25
		a. Roulette 13 (12.42)	2·25	2·25
		b. Roulette omitted	£175	
99	**46**	2d. violet (P) (2.43)	1·25	50
		a. Reddish violet (6.43)	1·50	65
		b. Roulette omitted	£250	
100	**47**	3d. blue (T) (10.42)	4·75	3·00
101	**48**	6d. red-orange (P) (10.42)	3·00	2·50
		(b) Inscr bilingually		
102	**49**	4d. slate-green (T) (10.42)	5·50	4·00
103	**50**	1s. brown (P) (11.42)	5·50	1·50
96/103		.. .. *Set of* 8	20·00	11·00

51 Signaller

52

53

1943 (2 Jan)–**46.** *W* **9.** *P* 15 × 14.

104	**51**	1s. 3d. olive-brown	7·50	4·50
		a. Blackish brown (5.46)	5·50	4·00

1943. *Coil stamps. Redrawn. In single colours with plain background. W* **9.** *P* 15 × 14.

105	**52**	½d. blue-green (18.2.43)	80	1·10
106	**53**	1d. carmine (9.43)	80	1·00

54 Union Buildings, Pretoria

1945–46. *Redrawn. W* **9.** *P* 14.

107	**54**	2d. slate and violet (3.45)	5·00	4·00
		a. Slate and bright violet (shades) (1946)	2·00	3·00

In Nos. 107 and 107*a* the Union Buildings are shown at a different angle from Nos. 58 and 58*a*. Only the centre is screened i.e., composed of very small square dots of colour arranged in straight diagonal lines. For whole design screened and colours changed, see No. 116. No. 107*a* also shows "2" of "2d." clear of white circle at top.

55 "Victory"

56 "Peace"

57 "Hope"

1945 (3 Dec). *Victory. W* **9.** *P* 14.

108	**55**	1d. brown and carmine	25	30
109	**56**	2d. slate-blue and violet	25	40
110	**57**	3d. deep blue and blue	25	60

58 King George VI

59 King George VI and Queen Elizabeth

60 Queen Elizabeth II as Princess, and Princess Margaret

1947 (17 Feb). *Royal Visit. W* **9.** *P* 15 × 14.

111	**58**	1d. black and carmine	12	15
112	**59**	2d. violet	15	20
113	**60**	3d. blue	15	25

5s.

1947–54. "SUID-AFRIKA" *hyphenated on Afrikaans stamps. Printed from new cylinders with design in screened rotogravure. W* **9.** *P* 15 × 14 *(½d., 1d. and 6d.) or* 14 *(others).*

114	**24**	½d. grey and green (1947)	70	25
115	**7**	1d. grey and carmine (1.9.50)	60	20
116	**54**	2d. slate-blue and purple (3.50) ..	80	35
117	**22*a***	3d. dull blue (4.49)	1·50	70
117*a*		3d. blue (3.51)	1·50	50
		b. Deep blue (1954)	50·00	40·00
118	**12*a***	4d. brown (22.8.52)	1·60	1·50
119	**8**	6d. green and red-orange (III) (1.50) ..	2·75	80
		a. Green and brown-orange (III) (1951)	2·50	90
120	**13**	1s. brown and chalky blue (1.50) ..	5·50	1·50
		a. Blackish brown & deep ultram (4.52)	15·00	8·00
121	**14**	2s. 6d. green and brown (8.49)	14·00	13·00
122	**15**	5s. black and pale blue-green (I) (9.49)	32·00	22·00
122*a*		5s. black & dp yellow-green (II) (1.54) ..	65·00	40·00
114/22		.. .. *Set of* 9	55·00	35·00

In screened rotogravure the design is composed of very small squares of colour arranged in straight diagonal lines.

½d. Size 17¾ × 21¾ mm. Early printings have only the frame screened.

1d. Size 18 × 22 mm. For smaller, redrawn design, see No. 135.

2d. For earlier issue with centre only screened, and in different colours, see Nos. 107/*a*.

3d. No. 117. Whole stamp screened with irregular grain. Scrolls above "3d." solid and toneless. Printed from two cylinders.

No. 117*a*/*b*. Whole stamp diagonally screened. Printed from one cylinder. Clouds more pronounced.

4d. Two groups of white leaves below name tablet and a clear white line down left and right sides of stamp.

61 Gold Mine

62 King George VI and Queen Elizabeth

1948 (1 Apr). *W* **9.** *In pair, perf* 14, *sub-divided by roulette* 6½.

			Un unit of 4	*Us unit*
124	**61**	1½d. blue-green and yellow-buff ..	50	90

1948 (26 Apr). *Silver Wedding. W* **9.** *P* 14.

125	**62**	3d. blue and silver	50	25

(Typo Government Printer, Pretoria)

1948 (July). *W* **9.** *P* 14½ × 14.

126	**6**	½d. pale grey and blue-green	30	50

This was an economy printing made from the old plates of the 1926 issue for the purpose of using up a stock of cut paper. For the original printing in black and green, see No. 30.

63 *Wanderer* entering Durban

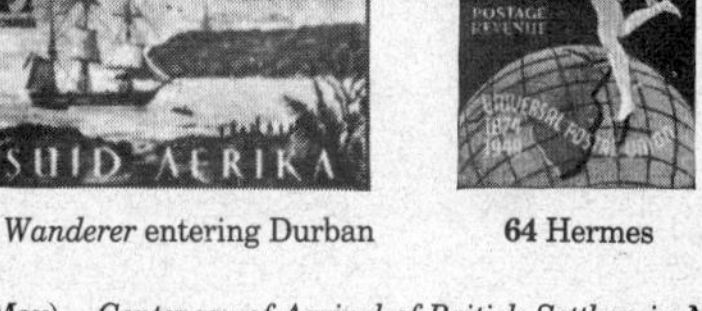

64 Hermes

1949 (2 May). *Centenary of Arrival of British Settlers in Natal. W* **9.** *P* 15 × 14.

127	**63**	1½d. claret	25	20

1949 (1 Oct). *75th Anniv of Universal Postal Union. As T* **64** *inscr* "UNIVERSAL POSTAL UNION" *and* "WERELDPOSUNIE" *alternately. W* **9** *(sideways). P* 14 × 15.

128	**64**	½d. blue-green	60	50
129		1½d. brown-red	75	65
130		3d. bright blue	1·75	1·75

65 Wagons approaching Bingham's Berg

(Des W. H. Coetzer)

1949 (1 Dec). *Inauguration of Voortrekker Monument, Pretoria. T* **65** *and similar horiz designs. W* **9.** *P* 15 × 14.

		Un single	*Us single*
131	1d. magenta	10	8
132	1½d. blue-green	10	8
133	3d. blue	10	10

Designs:—1½d. Voortrekker Monument, Pretoria; 3d. Bible, candle and Voortrekkers.

68 Union Buildings, Pretoria

1950 (Apr). *W* **9** *(sideways). P* 14 × 15.

134	**68**	2d. blue and violet	30	30

1951 (22 Feb). *As No.* 115, *but redrawn with the horizon clearly defined. Size reduced to* 17¼ × 21¼ *mm.*

135	**7**	1d. grey and carmine	40	20

PRICES. All later issues except Nos. 167 and 262/5 are inscribed bilingually and prices are for single copies, unused and used.

69 Seal and Monogram

70 "Maria de la Quellerie" (D. Craey)

1952 (14 Mar). *Tercentenary of Landing of Van Riebeeck. T* **69/70** *and similar designs. W* **9** *(sideways on* 1d. *and* 4½d.*). P* 14 × 15 *(*1d. *and* 4½d.*) or* 14 × 15 *(others).*

136 ½d. brown-purple and olive-grey 15 20
137 1d. deep blue-green 10 5
138 2d. deep violet 25 5
139 4½d. blue 25 25
140 1s. brown 75 15

Designs: *Horiz*—2d. Arrival of Van Riebeeck's ships; 1s. "Landing at the Cape" (C. Davidson Bell). *Vert*—4½d. "Jan van Riebeeck" (D. Craey).

SATISE **SADIPU**

(74) (75)

76 Queen Elizabeth II

1952 (26 Mar). *South African Tercentenary International Stamp Exhibition. No.* 137 *optd with T* **74** *and No.* 138 *with T* **75**.

141 1d. deep blue-green 25 30
142 2d. deep violet 25 30

1953 (2 June). *Coronation. W* **9** *(sideways). P* 14 × 15.

143 **76** 2d. deep violet-blue 20 5
a. *Ultramarine* 20 5

77

1953 (1 Sept). *Centenary of First Cape of Good Hope Stamp. T* **77** *and similar horiz design. W* **9**. *P* 15 × 14.

144 1d. sepia and vermilion 10 5
145 4d. deep blue and light blue 10 5

Design:—4d. "Cape Triangular" 4d. stamp.

79 Merino Ram

80 Springbok

81 Aloes

1953 (1 Oct). *W* **9**. *P* 14.

146 **79** 4½d. slate-purple and yellow 70 30
147 **80** 1s. 3d. chocolate .. .. 2·25 15
148 **81** 1s. 6d. vermilion and deep blue-green 2·50 30

82 Arms of Orange Free State and Scroll

1954 (23 Feb). *Centenary of Orange Free State. W* **9**. *P* 15 × 14.

149 **82** 2d. sepia and pale vermilion 10 5
150 4½d. purple and slate 30 80

ALTERED CATALOGUE NUMBERS

Any Catalogue numbers altered from the last edition are shown as a list in the introductory pages.

83 Warthog

92 Springbok

93 Gemsbok

1954 (14 Oct). *T* **83, 92/3** *and similar designs. W* **9** *(sideways on large vert designs). P* 15 × 14 *(*½d. *to* 2d.*),* 14 *(others).*

151 ½d. deep blue-green 5 5
152 1d. brown-lake 5 5
153 1½d. sepia 12 5
154 2d. plum 12 5
155 3d. chocolate and turquoise-blue 12 5
156 4d. indigo and emerald 50 5
157 4½d. blue-black and grey-blue .. .. .. 1·50 1·50
158 6d. sepia and orange 70 5
159 1s. deep brown and pale chocolate 85 5
160 1s. 3d. brown and bluish green .. .. 1·40 5
161 1s. 6d. brown and rose .. .. 2·50 60
162 2s. 6d. brown-black and apple-green .. 4·25 20
163 5s. black-brown and yellow-orange .. .. 16·00 90
164 10s. black and cobalt .. .. 23·00 4·50
151/64 .. .. *Set of* 14 45·00 7·25

Designs: *Vert (as T* **83**)—1d. Gnu; 1½d. Leopard; 2d. Zebra. *(As T* **93**)—3d. Rhinoceros; 4d. Elephant; 4½d. Hippopotamus; 1s. Kudu; 2s. 6d. Nyala; 5s. Giraffe; 10s. Sable Antelope. *Horiz (as T* **92**)—6d. Lion.

See also Nos. 170/7 and 185/97.

97 President Kruger

98 President M. Pretorius

1955 (21 Oct). *Centenary of Pretoria. W* **9** *(sideways). P* 14 × 15.

165 **97** 3d. slate-green 25 8
166 **98** 6d. maroon 40 20

99 A. Pretorius, Church of the Vow and Flag

100 Settlers' Block-wagon and House

1955 (1 Dec). *Voortrekker Covenant Celebrations, Pietermaritzburg. W* **9**. *P* 14.

		Un pair	*Us pair*
167 **99**	2d. blue and magenta	55	2·00

1958 (1 July). *Centenary of Arrival of German Settlers in South Africa. W* **9**. *P* 14.

168 **100** 2d. chocolate and pale purple 10 5

101 Arms of the Academy

1959 (1 May). *50th Anniv of the South African Academy of Science and Art, Pretoria. W* **9**. *P* 15 × 14.

169 **101** 3d. deep blue and turquoise-blue .. 12 5
a. Deep blue printing omitted .. £650

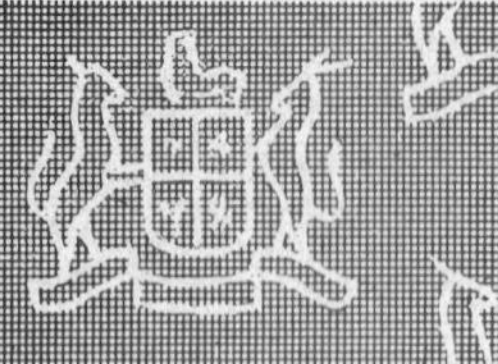

102 Union Coat of Arms

1 s 1 s

I II

1959–60. *As Nos.* 151/2, 155/6, 158/9 *and* 162/3, *but W* **102**.

170 ½d. deep greenish blue (12.60) .. .. 25 1·75
171 1d. brown-lake (I) (10.59) 8 5
a. Redrawn. Type II (10.60) 12 5
172 3d. chocolate and turquoise-blue (9.59) .. 25 5
173 4d. indigo and emerald (1.60) 80 20
174 6d. sepia and orange (2.60) .. .. 1·75 20
175 1s. deep brown and pale chocolate (11.59) .. 2·75 15
176 2s. 6d. brown-black & apple-green (12.59) .. 8·00 5·50
177 5s. black-brown & yellow-orange (10.60) .. 22·00 30·00
170/7 .. .. *Set of* 8 32·00 35·00

Nos. 171/a. In Type II "1d. Posgeld Postage" is more to the left in relation to "South Africa", with "1" almost central over "S" instead of to right as in Type I.

103 Globe and Antarctic Scene

1959 (16 Nov). *South African National Antarctic Expedition. W* **102**. *P* 14 × 15.

178 **103** 3d. blue-green and orange 25 5

104 Union Flag

106 "Wheel of Progress"

1960 (2 May). *50th Anniv of Union of South Africa. T* **104, 106** *and similar designs. W* **102** *(sideways on* 4d. *and* 6d.*). P* 14 × 15 *(*4d., 6d.*) or* 15 × 14 *(others).*

179 4d. orange-red and blue 30 8
180 6d. red, brown and light green 35 8
181 1s. deep blue and light yellow 60 10
182 1s. 6d. black and light blue .. .. .. 3·25 2·75

Designs: *Vert*—6d. Union Arms. *Horiz*—1s. 6d. Union Festival emblem.

See also No. 190, 192/3.

108 Locomotives of 1860 and 1960

1960 (2 May). *Centenary of South African Railways. W* **102**. *P* 15 × 14.

183 **108** 1s. 3d. deep blue .. .. 3·25 75

109 Prime Ministers Botha, Smuts, Hertzog, Malan, Strijdom and Verwoerd

1960 (31 May). *Union Day. W* **102**. *P* 15 × 14.

184 **109** 3d. brown and pale brown 10 5
a. Pale brown omitted* £950

*This is due to a rectangular piece of paper adhering to the background cylinder, resulting in R.2/1 missing the colour completely and six adjoining stamps having it partially omitted. The item in block of eight is probably unique.

(New Currency. 100 cents=1 rand)

1961 (14 Feb). *As previous issues but with values in cents and rand. W* **102** *(sideways on* 3½ c., 7½ c., 20 c., 50 c., 1 r.*). P* 15 × 14 *(*½ c., *to* 2½ c., 10 c.*),* 14 × 15 *(*3½ c., 7½ c.*) or* 14 *(others).*

185 ½ c. deep bluish green (as 151) 5 10
186 1 c. brown-lake (as 152) 8 5
187 1½ c. sepia (as 153) 10 12
188 2 c. plum (as 154) 10 12
189 2½ c. brown (as 184) 8 5
190 3½ c. orange-red and blue (as 179) 15 40
191 5 c. sepia and orange (as 158) 20 20
192 7½ c. red, brown and light green (as 180) .. 35 70
193 10 c. deep blue and light yellow (as 181) .. 35 15
194 12½ c. brown and bluish green (as 160) .. 1·40 1·40
195 20 c. brown and rose (as 161) .. .. 2·50 2·50
196 50 c. black-brown & orange-yellow (as 163) 10·00 10·00
197 1 r. black and cobalt (as 164) .. .. 22·00 19·00
185/97 .. .. *Set of* 13 35·00 32·00

REPUBLIC

110 African Pygmy Kingfisher

111 Kafferboom Flower

112 Afrikander Bull

113 Pouring Gold

114 Groot Constantia

115 Burchell's Gonolek

116 Baobab Tree

117 Maize

118 Cape Town Castle Entrance

119 Protea

120 Secretary Bird

121 Cape Town Harbour

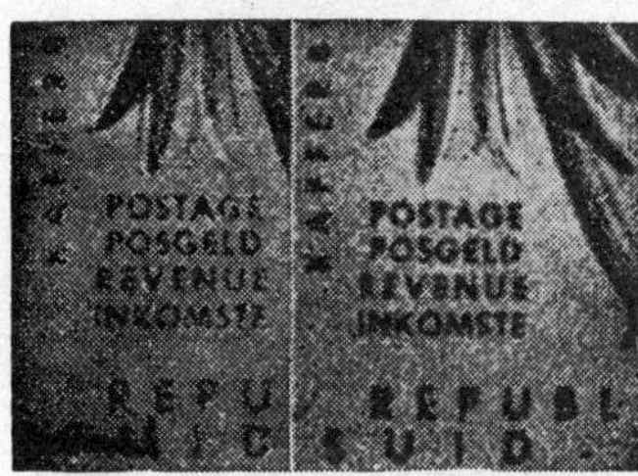

122 Strelitzia

Three types of 1 c.

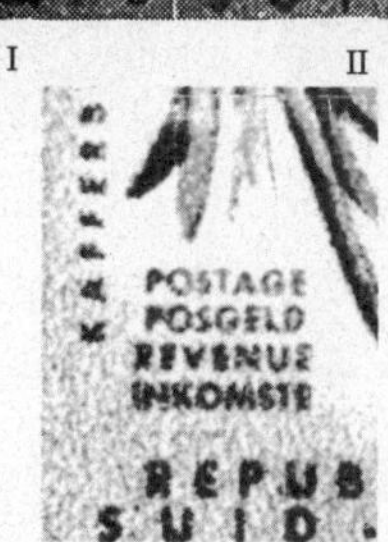

I II

III

Type I. Lowest point of flower between "OS" of "POSTAGE". Right-hand petal over "E".
Type II. Flower has moved fractionally to the right so that lowest point is over "S" of "POSTAGE". Right-hand petal over "E".
Type III. Lowest point directly over "O". Right-hand petal over "G".

Two types of 2½ c.

In Type I the lines of the building are quite faint. In Type II all lines of the building have been strengthened by re-engraving.

(Des Mrs. T. Campbell (½ c., 3 c., 1 r.); Miss N. Desmond (1 c.); De La Rue (2½ c., 5 c., 12½ c.); H. L. Prager (50 c.); Govt. Ptg Dept artist (others))

1961 (31 May)–**63**. *Unsurfaced paper*. *W* **102** (*sideways on* ½ *c*., 1½ *c*., 2½ *c*., 5 *c. to* 20 *c*.). *P* 14 × 15 (½ *c*., 1½ *c*.), 15 × 14 (1 *c*.), *or* 14 (*others*).

198	**110**	½ c.	bright blue, carmine and brown	8	5
			a. Perf 14 (3.63)	10	5
199	**111**	1 c.	red and olive-grey (I)	8	5
			a. Type II (1.62)	12	5
			b. Type III (coils) (5.63)	20	10
200	**112**	1½ c.	brown-lake and light purple ..	12	5
201	**113**	2 c.	ultramarine and yellow.. ..	12	5
202	**114**	2½ c.	violet and green (I)	20	5
			a. Type II. *Deep violet and green* (9.61)	20	5
203	**115**	3 c.	red and deep blue	1·00	5
204	**116**	5 c.	yellow and greenish blue ..	50	5
205	**117**	7½ c.	yellow-brown and light green ..	80	8
206	**118**	10 c.	sepia and green	90	10
207	**119**	12½ c.	red, yellow and black-green ..	2·25	20
208	**120**	20 c.	turquoise-blue, carm & brn-orge	4·75	30
209	**121**	50 c.	black and bright blue	32·00	3·50
210	**122**	1 r.	orange, olive-green and light blue	28·00	3·50
198/210			.. .. *Set of* 13	65·00	6·00

No. 198 was issued in coils on 18.5.63 with the spurs of the branch strengthened.

1961–74 *Definitives*

Key to designs, perfs, watermarks, papers and phosphors

Value	*Type*	*Perf*	*W* **102.** *Ordinary*	*No wmk. Ordinary*	*W* **127.** *Chalky*
½ c.	**110**	14 × 15	198	—	—
		14	198a	—	—
1 c.	**111** (I)	15 × 14	199	211	—
	(II)		199a	211a	227
	(III)		199b	—	—
1½ c.	**112**	14 × 15	200	—	228
2 c.	**113**	14	201	212	229
2½ c.	**114** (I)	14	202	—	—
	(II)		202a	213	230/*a*
3 c.	**115**	14	203	214	—
5 c.	**116**	14	204	215	231
7½ c.	**117**	14	205	216	232
10 c.	**118**	14	206	217	233
12½ c.	**119**	14	207	—	—
20 c.	**120**	14	208	218	234/*a*
50 c.	**121**	14	209	219	235
1 r.	**122**	14	210	—	236

Redrawn Designs

			W **127** *Upright. Plain or phosphorised*	*W* **127** *Tête-bêche. Phos frame*	*No wmk. Phosphorised Glossy*	*Chalky*
½ c.	**130***a*	14	238	—	—	—
		14 × 15	238b	—	—	—
1 c.	**131**	15 × 14	239	—	—	—
		13½ × 14	239a	—	—	—
1½ c.	**132**	14 × 15	240	284	—	—
		14 × 13½	240	—	—	—
2 c.	**133**	14	241	285	315a	—
		12½	—	—	315	315b
2½ c.	**134**	14	242	286	—	—
3 c.	**135**	14	243	287	—	—
		12½	—	—	316	316a
4 c.	**134**	14	243*b*	288	—	—
5 c.	**136**	14	244	289	318a	—
		12½	—	—	318	318,b
6 c.	**137**	14	—	290	—	—
		12½	—	—	—	319
7½ c.	**137**	14	245	291	—	—
9 c.	**139**	14	245*a*	292	—	—
		12½	—	—	320	—
10 c.	**138**	14	246	293	321a	—
		12½	—	—	321	321b
12½ c.	**139**	14	247/*a*	294	—	—
15 c.	**140**	14	248	295	—	—
20 c	**141**	14	249	296	—	—
		12½	—	—	323	323a
50 c.	**142**	14	250	—	—	—
		12½	—	—	324	324a
1 r.	**143**	14	251	—	—	—
		12½	—	—	325	—

New Designs

			W **127** *Tête-bêche. Plain or phosphorised*	*W* **127** *Tête-bêche. Phos-frame*	*No wmk. Phosphorised Glossy*	*Chalky*
½ c.	**168**	14 × 13½	276	282	—	—
		14 × 14½	276a	—	313	—
		14 × 15	—	282a	—	—
1 c.	**169**	13½ × 14	277	283	—	—
		14	—	—	314	—
4 c.	**182**	14	310/*a*	—	—	—
		12½	—	—	317/*b*	317c
15 c.	**182***a*	14	311	—	—	—
		12½	—	—	—	322

1961 (Aug)–**63**. *As Nos*. 199, 201/6 *and* 208/9 *but without wmk*.

211	**111**	1 c.	red and olive-grey (I)	25	5
			a. Type II (9.62)	25	5
212	**113**	2 c.	ultramarine and yellow (8.63) ..	70	5
213	**114**	2½ c.	deep violet and green (II) (*shades*)	25	5
214	**115**	3 c.	red and deep blue (10.61) ..	45	5
215	**116**	5 c.	yellow and greenish blue (12.61) ..	50	5
216	**117**	7½ c.	yellow-brown and light green (3.62)	1·25	10
217	**118**	10 c.	sepia and green (*shades*) (11.61) ..	1·25	12
218	**120**	20 c.	turq-blue, carm & brn-orge (4.63)	12·00	60
219	**121**	50 c.	black and bright blue (8.62) ..	20·00	3·00
211/19			.. .. *Set of* 9	32·00	3·50

123 Blériot Monoplane and Boeing 707 Airliner over Table Mountain

124 Folk-dancers

1961 (1 Dec). *50th Anniv of First South African Aerial Post*. *W* **102** (*sideways*). *P* 14 × 15.

220	**123**	3 c.	blue and red	40	5

(Des K. Esterhuysen)

1962 (1 Mar). *50th Anniv of Volkspele* (*folk-dancing*) *in South Africa*. *W* **102** (*sideways*). *P* 14 × 15.

221	**124**	2½ c.	orange-red and brown	20	5

125 The *Chapman*

1962 (20 Aug). *Unveiling of Precinct Stone, British Settlers Monument, Grahamstown*. *W* **102.** *P* 15 × 14.

222	**125**	2½ c.	turquoise-green and purple ..	40	5
223		12½ c.	blue and deep chocolate ..	3·50	2·25

126 Red Disa (orchid), Castle Rock and Gardens

(Des M. F. Stern)

1963 (14 Mar). *50th Anniv of Kirstenbosch Botanic Gardens, Cape Town*. *P* 13½ × 14.

224	**126**	2½ c.	multicoloured	30	5
			a. Red (orchid, etc) omitted ..	£850	

127 (normal version)

128 Centenary Emblem and Nurse

129 Centenary Emblem and Globe

1963 (30 Aug). *Centenary of Red Cross*. *Chalk-surfaced paper*. *Wmk* **127** (*sideways on* 2½ *c*.). *P* 14 × 13½ (2½ *c*.) *or* 15 × 14 (12½ *c*.).

225	**128**	2½ c.	red, black and reddish purple ..	30	5
226	**129**	12½ c.	red and indigo	3·75	1·50
			a. Red cross omitted.. ..	£850	

1963–67. *As* 1961–3 *but chalk-surfaced paper and W* **127** (*sideways on* 1½ *c*., 2½ *c*., 5 *c*., 7½ *c*., 10 *c*., 20 *c*.). *P* 15 × 14 (1 *c*.), 14 × 15 (1½ *c*.), *or* 14 (*others*).

227	**111**	1 c.	red and olive-grey (II) (9.63) ..	8	5
228	**112**	1½ c.	brown-lake and light purple (1.67)	1·75	30
229	**113**	2 c.	ultramarine and yellow (11.64) ..	15	5
230	**114**	2½ c.	violet and green (II) (10.63) ..	12	5
			a. *Bright reddish violet and emerald* (II) (3.66)	45	20
231	**116**	5 c.	yellow and greenish blue (9.66) ..	1·40	5
232	**117**	7½ c.	yellow-brown & brt grn (23.2.66)	10·50	15
233	**118**	10 c.	sepia-brn & lt emer (*shades*) (9.64)	55	5
234	**120**	20 c.	turq-blue, carm & brn-orge (7.64)	2·25	15
			a. *Dp turq-blue, carm & flesh* (20.7.65)	2·25	15
235	**121**	50 c.	black and ultramarine (4.66) ..	30·00	4·75
236	**122**	1 r.	orange, lt green & pale blue (7.64)	55·00	23·00
227/36			.. .. *Set of* 10	90·00	26·00

In the 2½ c. (No. 230*a*), 5 c., 7½ c., 10 c. (Jan 1967 printing only) and 50 c. the watermark is indistinct but they can easily be distinguished from the stamps without watermark by their shades and the chalk-surfaced paper which is appreciably thicker and whiter.

130 Assembly Building, Umtata

1963 (11 Dec). *First Meeting of Transkei Legislative Assembly*. *Chalk-surfaced paper*. *W* **127**. *P* 15 × 14.

237	**130**	2½ c.	sepia and light green	30	5

130a African Pygmy Kingfisher

131 Kafferboom Flower

132 Afrikander Bull

133 Pouring Gold

134 Groot Constantia

135 Burchell's Gonolek

136 Baobab Tree

137 Maize

138 Cape Town Castle Entrance

139 Protea

140 Industry

141 Secretary Bird

142 Cape Town Harbour

143 Strelitzia

(15 c. des C. E. F. Skotnes)

Redrawn types.

½ c. "½C" larger and "REPUBLIEK VAN REPUBLIC OF" smaller.

3 c. and 12½ c. Inscriptions and figures of value larger.

Others. "SOUTH AFRICA" and "SUID-AFRIKA" larger and bolder. The differences vary in each design but are easy to see by comparing the position of the letters of the country name with "REPUBLIC OF" and "REPUBLIEK VAN".

1964–72. *As 1961–63 but designs redrawn and new values (4 c., 9 c. and 15 c.). Chalk-surfaced paper.* W **127** *(sideways on all values to 20 c. except 1 and 3 c.).* P 14 × 15 (1½ c.), 15 × 14 (1 c.) *or* 14 *(others).*

238	**130a**	½ c. bright blue, carmine and brown (*shades*) (21.5.64)	5	5
		a. Imperf (pair)	£250	
		b. Perf 14 × 15. *Bright blue, carmine and yellow-brown* (6.7.67)	12	5
239	**131**	1 c. red and olive-grey (9.3.67)	12	5
		a. Perf 13½ × 14 (7.68)	30	5
240	**132**	1½ c. dull red-brown and light purple (*shades*) (21.9.67)	12	5
		c. Perf 14 × 13½. *Red-brown and light purple* (14.8.69)	30	10
241	**133**	2 c. ultramarine & yell (*shades*) (8.1.68)	20	5
242	**134**	2½ c. violet and green (*shades*) (19.4.67)	25	5
243	**135**	3 c. red and deep blue (*shades*) (11.64)	30	5
243b	**134**	4 c. violet and green (10.71)	75	20
244	**136**	5 c. yellow and greenish blue (*shades*) (14.2.68)	55	5
245	**137**	7½ c. yellow-brown & brt grn (26.7.67)	80	5
245a	**139**	9 c. red, yellow and slate-green (2.72)	6·00	90
246	**138**	10 c. sepia and green (*shades*) (10.6.68)	70	10
247	**139**	12½ c. red, yellow and black-green (3.64)	1·50	8
		a. *Red, pale yellow & bl-grn* (2.2.66)	1·50	10
248	**140**	15 c. black, lt ol-yell & red-orge (1.3.67)	2·75	25
249	**141**	20 c. turquoise-blue, carmine and brown-orange (*shades*) (2.68)	4·00	15
250	**142**	50 c. black and bright blue (17.6.68)	6·50	50
251	**143**	1 r. orange, light green & lt blue (6.65)	10·00	1·50
238/51		*Set of* 16	32·00	3·50

WATERMARK. Two forms of the watermark Type **127** exist in the above issue: the normal Type **127** (sometimes indistinct), and a very faint *tête-bêche* watermark, i.e. alternately facing up and down, which was introduced in mid-1967. As it is extremely difficult to distinguish these on single stamps we do not list it.

The ½ (both perfs), 1, 2, 2½, 3, 15 c. and 1 r. are known in both forms, the 1½, 4, 5, 7½, 9, 10, 20 and 50 c. only in the *tête-bêche* form, and the 12½ c. Type **127** only.

GUM. The 2, 3, 5, 20, 50 c. and 1 r. exist with PVA gum as well as gum arabic.

PHOSPHORISED PAPER. From October 1971 onwards phosphor bands (see Nos. 282/96) gave way to phosphorised paper which cannot be distinguished from non-phosphor stamps without the aid of a lamp. For this reason we do not distinguish these printings in the above issue, but some are slightly different shades which are listed in the *Elizabethan Catalogue* and all have PVA gum.

The 4 c. and 9 c. are on phosphorised paper only and differ from Nos. 288 and 292 by the lack of phosphor bands.

145 "Springbok" Badge of Rugby Board

147 Calvin

1964 (8 May). *75th Anniv of South African Rugby Board. Chalk-surfaced paper.* T **145** *and similar horiz design.* W **127** *(sideways on 2½ c.).* P 14 × 15 (2½ c.) *or* 15 × 14 (12½ c.).

252	2½ c. yellow-brown and deep green	15	5
253	12½ c. black and light yellow-green	5·50	4·25

Design:—12½ c. Rugby footballer.

1964 (10 July). *400th Death Anniv of Calvin (Protestant reformer). Chalk-surfaced paper.* W **127** *(sideways).* P 14 × 13½.

254	**147**	2½ c. cerise, violet and brown	15	5

148 Nurse's Lamp

149 Nurse holding Lamp

I. Screened base to lamp II. Clear base to lamp

1964 (12 Oct). *50th Anniv of South African Nursing Association. Chalk-surfaced paper.* W **127** *(sideways on 2½ c.).* P 14 × 15 (2½ c.) *or* 15 × 14 (12½ c.).

255	**148**	2½ c. ultramarine and dull gold (Type I)	20	5
256		2½ c. brt blue & yellow-gold (Type II)	30	10
		a. *Ultramarine and dull gold*	25	5
257	**149**	12½ c. bright blue and gold	3·50	2·25
		a. Gold omitted	£700	

150 I.T.U. Emblem and Satellites

1965 (17 May). *I.T.U. Centenary.* T **150** *and similar horiz design. Chalk-surfaced paper.* W **127**. P 15 × 14.

258	2½ c. orange and blue	50	5
259	12½ c. brown-purple and green	3·50	2·75

Design:—12½ c. I.T.U. emblem and symbols.

152 Pulpit in Groote Kerk, Cape Town

153 Church Emblem

1965 (21 Oct). *Tercentenary of Nederduites Gereformeerde Kerk (Dutch Reformed Church) in South Africa. Chalk-surfaced paper* W **127** *(sideways on 2½ c., inverted on 12½ c.).* P 14 × 15 (2½ c.) *or* 15 × 14 (12½ c.).

260	**152**	2½ c. brown and light yellow	15	5
261	**153**	12½ c. black, light orange and blue	3·00	2·00

154 Diamond 155 Bird in flight

(Des C. E. F. Skotnes)

1966 (31 May). *Fifth Anniv of Republic.* T **154/5** *and similar designs. Chalk-surfaced paper.* W **127** *(sideways on* 1 c., 3 c.). P 14 × 13½ (1 c.), 13½ × 14 (2½ c.), 14 × 15 (3 c.) *or* 15 × 14 (7½ c.).

		Un pair	*Us pair*
262	1 c. black, bluish green and olive-yellow	35	35
263	2½ c. blue, deep blue and yellow-green	90	1·25
264	3 c. red, greenish yellow and red-brown	4·75	4·75
265	7½ c. blue, ultramarine and yellow	5·50	6·00

Designs: *Vert*—3 c. Maize plants. *Horiz*—7½ c. Mountain landscape.

Nos. 262/5 exist on Swiss-made paper with *tête-bêche* watermark from a special printing made for use in presentation albums for delegates to the U.P.U. Congress in Tokyo in 1969, as supplies of the original Harrison paper were by then exhausted (*Set of 4 pairs price £140 mint*).

158 Verwoerd and Union Buildings, Pretoria

(Des from portrait by Dr. Henkel)

1966 (6 Dec). *Verwoerd Commemoration.* T **158** *and similar designs. Chalk-surfaced paper.* W **127** *(sideways on* 3 c.). P 14 × 15 (3 c.) *or* 15 × 14 (*others*).

266	2½ c. blackish brown and turquoise	12	5
267	3 c. blackish brown and yellow-green	15	5
268	12½ c. blackish brown and greenish blue	2·00	95

Designs: *Vert*—3 c. "Dr. H. F. Verwoerd" (I. Henkel). *Horiz*—12½ c. Verwoerd and map of South Africa.

161 "Martin Luther" (Cranach the Elder)

162 Wittenberg Church Door

1967 (31 Oct). *450th Anniv of Reformation.* W **127** ((*sideways*), *normal on* 2½ c., *tête-bêche on* 12½ c.). P 14 × 15.

269	**161**	2½ c. black and rose-red	15	5
270	**162**	12½ c. black and yellow-orange	3·00	2·50

163 "Profile of Pres. Fouché" (I. Henkel)

164 Portrait of Pres. Fouché

1968 (10 Apr). *Inauguration of President Fouché.* W **127** *(sideways).* P 14 × 15.

271	**163**	2½ c. chocolate and pale chocolate	15	5
272	**164**	12½ c. deep blue and light blue	2·75	2·00

No. 272 also exists with the watermark *tête-bêche* (*Price un £2.75; used £2*).

165 Hertzog in 1902

1968 (21 Sept). *Inauguration of General Hertzog Monument, Bloemfontein. T* **165** *and similar designs. W* **127** (*tête-bêche on* 2½ *c., inverted on* 3 *c., sideways on* 12½ *c.*). *P* 14 × 13½ (12½ *c.*) *or* 13½ × 14 (*others*).

273 2½ c. black, brown and olive-yellow .. 15 5
274 3 c. black, red-brown, red-orange and yellow 20 5
275 12½ c. black, red and yellow-orange .. .. 3·00 2·00
Designs: *Horiz*—3 c. Hertzog in 1924. *Vert*—12½ c. Hertzog Monument.

168 Natal Kingfisher

169 Kafferboom Flower

1969. *W* **127** (*tête-bêche, sideways on* ½ *c.*). *P* 14 × 13½ (½ *c.*) *or* 13½ × 14 (1 *c.*).

276 **168** ½ c. new bl, carm-red & yell-ochre (1.69) 10 5
a. Coil. Perf 14 × 14½ (5.69) .. .. 1·40 45
277 **169** 1 c. rose-red and olive-brown (1.69) .. 10 5
See also Nos. 282/3 and 313/14.

170 Springbok and Olympic Torch

171 Professor Barnard and Groote Schuur Hospital

1969 (15 Mar). *South African Games, Bloemfontein. W* **127** (*tête-bêche, sideways*). *P* 14 × 13½.

278 **170** 2½ c. black, blue-black, red & sage-grn 15 5
279 12½ c. black, blue-blk, red & cinnamon .. 2·50 2·00

1969 (7 July). *World's First Heart Transplant and 47th South African Medical Association Congress. T* **171** *and similar horiz design. W* **127** (*tête-bêche*). *P* 13½ × 14 (2½ *c.*) *or* 15 × 14 (12½ *c.*).

280 2½ c. plum and rose-red 15 5
281 12½ c. carmine-red and royal blue .. .. 3·25 2·25
Design:—12½ c. Hands holding heart.

1969–71. *As* 1964–72 *issue, Nos.* 276/7, *and new value* (6 *c.*), *but with phosphor bands printed horizontally and vertically between the stamp designs, over the perforations, thus producing a frame effect. W* **127** *arranged tête-bêche* (*upright on* 1, 2 *and* 3 *c., sideways on others*). *P* 14 × 13½ (½, 1½ *c.*), 13½ × 14 (1 *c.*), *or* 14 (*others*).

282 **168** ½ c. new blue, carmine-red and yellow-ochre (1.70) 15 15
a. Coil. Perf 14 × 15 (2.71) .. .. 1·50 65
283 **169** 1 c. rose-red and olive-brown (12.69) .. 15 5
284 **132** 1½ c. red-brown and light purple (12.69) 20 5
285 **133** 2 c. ultram & yellow (*shades*) (11.69) .. 25 5
286 **134** 2½ c. violet and green (*shades*) (1.70) .. 25 5
287 **135** 3 c. red and deep blue (30.9.69) .. 45 5
288 **134** 4 c. violet and green (1.3.71) 50 10
289 **136** 5 c. yellow and greenish blue (17.11.69) 60 5
290 **137** 6 c. yellow-brown & brt green (3.5.71) 1·00 20
291 7½ c. yellow-brown & brt grn (17.11.69) 2·50 15
292 **139** 9 c. red, yellow & black-grn (17.5.71) 1·75 30
293 **138** 10 c. brown and pale green (1.70) .. 1·75 12
294 **139** 12½ c. red, yellow and black-green (2.5.70) .. .. 5·50 75
295 **140** 15 c. blk, lt olive-yell & red-orge (1.70) 2·75 90
296 **141** 20 c. turquoise-blue, carmine and brown-orange (*shades*) (18.2.70) .. 4·75 30
282/96 .. .. *Set of* 15 20·00 3·00
No. 286 exists on normal RSA wmk as well as RSA *tête-bêche* wmk.
The 1, 2, 2½, 3, 10, 15 and 20 c. exist with PVA gum as well as gum arabic, but the 4, 6 and 9 c. exist with PVA gum only.
For stamps without wmk, see Nos. 313, etc.

173 Mail Coach

174 Transvaal Stamp of 1869

1969 (6 Oct). *Centenary of First Stamps of South African Republic (Transvaal). Phosphor bands on all four sides* (2½ *c.*). *W* **127** (*tête-bêche, sideways on* 12½ *c.*). *P* 13½ × 14 (2½ *c.*) *or* 14 × 13½ (12½ *c.*).

297 **173** 2½ c. yellow, indigo and yellow-brown 25 5
298 **174** 12½ c. emerald, gold and yellow-brown 3·25 2·00

PHOSPHOR FRAME. Nos. 299/306 have phosphor applied on all four sides as a frame.

175 "Water 70" Emblem

177 "The Sower"

1970 (14 Feb). *Water 70 Campaign. T* **175** *and similar design. W* **127** (*tête-bêche* (*sideways on* 2½ *c.*)). *P* 14 × 13½ (2½ *c.*) *or* 13½ × 14 (3 *c.*).

299 2½ c. green, bright blue and chocolate .. 15 5
300 3 c. Prussian blue, royal blue and buff .. 25 12
Design: *Horiz*—3 c. Symbolic waves.

1970 (24 Aug). 150*th Anniv of Bible Society of South Africa. T* **177** *and similar horiz design* (*gold die-stamped on* 12½ *c.*). *W* **127** (*tête-bêche, sideways on* 2½ *c.*). *P* 14 × 13½ (2½ *c.*) *or* 13½ × 14 (12½ *c.*).

301 2½ c. multicoloured 15 5
302 12½ c. gold, black and blue .. .. .. 3·00 2·75
Design:—12½ c. "Biblia" and open book.

178 J. G. Strijdom and Strijdom Tower

179 Map and Antarctic Landscape

1971 (22 May). *"Interstex" Stamp Exhibition, Cape Town. P* 14 × 13½.
A. *W* **127** (*sideways tête-bêche*). B. *W* **102** (*sideways*).

		A		B	
303 **178**	5 c. light greenish blue, black and pale yellow	25	10	1·75	2·50

1971 (22 May). *Tenth Anniv of Antarctic Treaty. W* **127** (*tête-bêche*). *P* 13½ × 14.

304 **179** 12½ c. blue-black, greenish bl & orge-red 5·00 4·50

180 "Landing of British Settlers, 1820" (T. Baines)

1971 (31 May). *Tenth Anniv of the Republic of South Africa. T* **180** *and similar design. W* **127** (*tête-bêche sideways on* 4 *c.*). *P* 13½ × 14 (2 *c.*) *or* 14 × 13½ (4 *c.*).

305 2 c. pale flesh and brown-red.. .. .. 20 10
306 4 c. green and black 25 10
Design: *Vert*—4 c. Presidents Steyn and Kruger and Treaty of Vereeniging Monument.
No. 306 exists with PVA gum as well as gum arabic.

PHOSPHORISED PAPER. All issues from here are on phosphorised paper *unless otherwise stated.*

181 View of Dam

(Des C. Bridgeford (4 c.), C. Lindsay (others))

1972 (4 Mar). *Opening of Hendrik Verwoerd Dam. T* **181** *and similar horiz designs. Multicoloured. W* **127** (*tête-bêche*). *P* 13½ × 14.

307 4 c. Type **181** 20 5
308 5 c. Aerial view of Dam 25 5
309 10 c. Dam and surrounding country (58 × 21 *mm*) .. .. 2·00 1·25

182 Sheep

182*a* Lamb

(Des K. Esterhuysen (4 c.), H. Botha (15 c.))

1972 (15 May–Oct). *W* **127** (*tête-bêche*). *P* 14.

310 **182** 4 c. olive-brn, yell, pale bl & slate-bl .. 25 5
a. Grey-olive, yellow, bright blue and slate-blue (10.72) 25 5
311 **182*a*** 15 c. pale stone, deep blue and dull blue 1·40 30
Other shades exist of the 4 c.
See also Nos. 317 and 322.

183 Black and Siamese Cats

184 Transport and Industry

1972 (19 Sept). *Centenary of Societies for the Prevention of Cruelty to Animals. W* **127** (*sideways tête-bêche*). *P* 14 × 13½.

312 **183** 5 c. multicoloured 65 10

1972–74. *As Nos.* 310/11 *and* 282 *etc. but no wmk. P* 14 × 14½ (½ *c.*), 14 (1 *c.*) *or* 12½ (*others*). *Phosphorised, glossy paper.*

313 **168** ½ c. bright blue, scarlet and yellow-ochre (coil) (6.73) .. .. .. 6·50 3·50
314 **169** 1 c. rose-red and olive-brown (1.74) .. 5 5
315 **133** 2 c. blue and orange-yellow (11.72) .. 15 5
a. Perf 14. *Deep ultramarine and orange-yellow* (coil) (7.73) .. .. 3·25 2·00
b. Chalky paper (17.7.74) 15 15
316 **135** 3 c. scarlet and deep blue (8.5.73) .. 30 5
a. Chalky paper (18.2.74) 60 30
317 **182** 4 c. grey-blue, yellow, blue and bluish slate* (1.10.73) 25 12
a. Olive-sepia, yellow, azure and slate-blue (18.2.74) 25 10
*b. Lavender-brown, pale yellow, blue and bluish slate** (26.7.74).. .. 25 20
c. Chalky paper* (22.8.74) 60 45
318 **136** 5 c. orge-yell & greenish bl (4.10.73) .. 60 10
a. Perf 14. *Yellow and light greenish blue* (coil) (7.73) .. .. .. 5·00 2·75
b. Chalky paper (5.74) 85 40
319 **137** 6 c. yellow-brown and bright green (*chalky paper*) (22.7.74) .. .. 1·25 60
320 **139** 9 c. red, yell & grn-blk (*shades*) (6.73) 1·75 30
321 **138** 10 c. reddish brown & brt grn (8.5.73) .. 75 12
a. Perf 14 (coil) (6.73) .. .. 7·00 4·00
b. Chalky paper (17.7.74) 95 70
322 **182*a*** 15 c. pale stone, deep blue and dull blue (*chalky paper*) (4.9.74) .. .. 2·00 2·00
323 **141** 20 c. turquoise-blue, rose-carmine and orange-buff (8.5.73) .. .. 3·25 35
a. Chalky paper (5.74) .. .. 3·75 1·00
324 **142** 50 c. black and bright blue (6.73) .. 5·50 1·00
a. Chalky paper (22.7.74) .. .. 7·00 2·75
325 **143** 1 r. orange, lt green & lt bl (8.10.73) .. 15·00 3·00
a. Orange omitted .. .. ..
313/25 .. .. *Set of* 13 32·00 10·00
*On these stamps the colours are known to vary within the sheet.
No. 314 also differs in that the central design has been moved down about 1 mm.
Nos. 317/c also differ from No. 310 by measuring 26¼ × 21 mm instead of 27¼ × 21¾ mm.

(Des J. Hoekstra (4 c.), M. Barnett (others))

1973 (1 Feb). 50*th Anniv of ESCOM (Electricity Supply Commission). T* **184** *and similar vert designs. Multicoloured. P* 12 × 12½ (4 *c.*) *or* 12½ (*others*).

326 4 c. Type **184** 20 5
327 5 c. Pylon (21 × 28 *mm*) 30 10
328 15 c. Cooling Towers (21 × 28 *mm*) .. .. 3·00 2·25

185 University Coat of arms

187 C. J. Langenhoven

186 Rescuing Sailors

(Des P. de Wet (15 c.), H. Meiring (others))

1973 (2 Apr). *Centenary of University of South Africa. T* **185** *and similar designs. W* **127** (*tête-bêche*) (5 *c.*) *or no wmk* (*others*). *P* 12 × 12½ (5 *c.*) *or* 12½ (*others*).

329 4 c. multicoloured 20 5
330 5 c. multicoloured 30 12
331 15 c. black and gold .. .. .. 3·00 2·25
Designs: *Horiz* (37 × 21 *mm*)—5 c. University Complex, Pretoria. *Vert* (*As T* **185**)—15 c. Old University Building, Cape Town.

WATERMARK. All issues from this date are on unwatermarked paper, *unless otherwise stated.*

(Des M. Barnett)

1973 (2 June). *Bicentenary of Rescue by Wolraad Woltemade. T* **186** *and similar horiz designs. P* 11½ × 12½.
332 4 c. lt red-brown, lt yellow-green and black .. 25 5
333 5 c. yellow-olive, light yellow-green & black 40 10
334 15 c. red-brown, light yellow-green and black 5·00 3·50
Designs:—5 c. *De Jong Thomas* foundering; 15 c. *De Jong Thomas* breaking up and sailors drowning.

(Des J. Mostert)

1973 (1 Aug). *Birth Centenary of C. J. Langenhoven (politician and composer of national anthem). T* **187** *and similar designs. P* 12½ (4 *and* 5 *c.) or* 11½ × 12½ (15 *c.).*
335 **187** 4 c. multicoloured 25 5
336 – 5 c. multicoloured 35 10
337 – 15 c. multicoloured .. .. .. 5·00 3·25
Nos. 336/7 are as T **187** but with motifs rearranged. The 5 c. is vert, 21 × 38 mm, and the 15 c. is horiz, 38 × 21 mm.

188 Communications Map

(Des C. Webb)

1973 (1 Oct). *World Communications Day. P* 12½.

(*a*) *No wmk. Glossy paper*
338 **188** 15 c. multicoloured .. .. .. 2·25 1·60

(*b*) *W* **127** (*tête-bêche*). *Chalky paper*
339 **188** 15 c. multicoloured .. .. .. 2·50 3·50

189 Restored Buildings

190 Burgerspond (obverse and reverse)

(Des W. Jordaan)

1974 (14 Mar). *Restoration of Tulbagh. T* **189** *and similar multicoloured design. P* 12½.
340 4 c. Type **189** 20 8
341 5 c. Restored Church Street (58 × 21 *mm*) .. 30 20

(Des P. de Wet. Litho)

1974 (6 Apr). *Centenary of the Burgerspond (coin). P* 12½ × 12.
342 **190** 9 c. brown, orange-red & pale yell-olive 70 70

191 Dr. Malan

192 Congress Emblem

(Des I. Henkel)

1974 (22 May). *Birth Centenary of Dr. D. F. Malan (Prime Minister). P* 12½ × 12.
343 **191** 4 c. blue and light blue 20 5

(Des Ingrid Paul)

1974 (13 June). 15*th World Sugar Congress, Durban. P* 12 × 12½.
344 **192** 15 c. deep ultramarine and silver .. 1·40 1·00

193 "50" and Radio Waves

(Des Ingrid Paul)

1974 (13 July). 50*th Anniv of Broadcasting in South Africa. P* 12 × 12½.
345 **193** 4 c. red and black 20 8

194 Monument Building

(Des G. Cunningham)

1974 (13 July). *Inauguration of British Settlers' Monument, Grahamstown. P* 12 × 12½.
346 **194** 5 c. red and black 20 10

195 Stamps of the South African Provinces

(Des K. Esterhuysen)

1974 (9 Oct). *Centenary of Universal Postal Union. P* 12½.
347 **195** 15 c. multicoloured .. .. .. 1·50 1·25

196 Iris

197 Bokmakierie Shrikes

(Des E. de Jong. Recess and photo)

1974 (20 Nov)–**75**. *Multicoloured. Glossy paper* (2, 3, 4, 6, 7, 30 *c. and* 1 *r.) or chalk-surfaced paper (others). P* 12½ (1 *to* 25 *c.) or* 12 × 12½ (*others*).

(*a*) *Vert designs as T* **196** *showing flowers, or horiz designs showing birds or fish*
348 1 c. Type **196** 5 5
349 2 c. Wild Heath 15 5
a. Chalk-surfaced paper (2.75) 8 5
350 3 c. Geranium 15 5
a. Chalk-surfaced paper (*shades*) (6.75) .. 10 5
ab. Imperf (pair) £200
351 4 c. Arum Lily 20 5
a. Chalk-surfaced paper (2.75) 12 5
352 5 c. Cape Gannet 20 5
353 6 c. Galjoen (fish) 25 5
354 7 c. Zebra Fish 25 5
355 9 c. Angel Fish 30 5
356 10 c. Moorish Idol 30 5
357 14 c. Roman (fish) 35 5
358 15 c. Greater Double-collared Sunbird .. 40 5
359 20 c. Yellow-billed Hornbill 50 10
360 25 c. Barberton Daisy 60 10

(*b*) *Horiz designs as T* **197**
361 30 c. Type **197** .. .. 7·00 40
362 50 c. Stanley Cranes .. .. 2·50 45
363 1 r. Bateleurs .. .. 7·00 3·50
348/63 *Set of* 16 18·00 4·50
A used block of 4 and a single on cover of No. 351 have been seen with the yellow omitted.

1974 (20 Nov)–**76**. *Coil stamps. As Nos.* 348/9, 352 *and* 356 *but photo, colours changed. Glossy paper. P* 12½.
370 1 c. reddish violet and pink 25 15
a. Perf 14. Chalk-surfaced paper (12.75) .. 25 15
371 2 c. bronze-green and yellow-ochre 35 15
a. Chalk-surfaced paper (7.75) 35 15
b. Perf 14. Chalk-surfaced paper (11.76?) .. 35 20
372 5 c. black and light slate-blue 55 20
373 10 c. deep violet-blue and light blue .. .. 1·60 75
a. Perf 14. Chalk-surfaced paper (4.76) .. 1·40 75

198 Voortrekker Monument and Encampment

(Des J. Hoekstra)

1974 (6 Dec). 25*th Anniv of Voortrekker Monument, Pretoria. P* 12½.
374 **198** 4 c. multicoloured 25 20

199 SASOL Complex

200 President Diederichs

(Des C. Webb)

1975 (26 Feb). 25*th Anniv of SASOL (South African Coal, Oil and Gas Corporation Ltd). P* 11½ × 12½.
375 **199** 15 c. multicoloured .. .. .. 1·75 1·40

(Des J. L. Booysen. Recess (4 c.) or photo (15 c.))

1975 (19 Apr). *Inauguration of the State President. P* 12½ × 11½.
376 **200** 4 c. agate and gold 12 8
377 15 c. royal blue .. .. .. 1·40 1·25

201 Jan Smuts

202 "Dutch East Indiaman, Table Bay"

(Des J. Hoekstra. Recess and photo)

1975 (24 May). *Jan Smuts Commemoration. P* 12½ × 11½.
378 **201** 4 c. black and olive-black 15 10

(Des J. Hoekstra. Photo (Nos. 379/82) or litho (**MS**383))

1975 (18 June). *Death Centenary of Thomas Baines (painter). T* **202** *and similar horiz designs. Multicoloured. P* 11½ × 12½.
379 5 c. Type **202** 30 8
380 9 c. "Cradock, 1848" 65 35
381 15 c. "Thirsty Flat, 1848" .. .. .. 1·25 75
382 30 c. "Pretoria, 1874" .. .. 2·25 2·25
MS383 120 × 95 mm. Nos. 379/82 . .. .. 4·25 5·25

203 Gideon Malherbe's House, Paarl

(Des P. de Wet. Recess and photo)

1975 (14 Aug). *Centenary of Genootskap van Regte Afrikaners (Afrikaner Language Movement). P* 12½.
384 **203** 4 c. multicoloured 15 5

204 "Automatic Sorting"

205 Title Page of *Die Afrikaanse Patriot*

(Des J. Sampson)

1975 (11 Sept). *Postal Mechanisation. P* 12½ × 11½.
385 **204** 4 c. multicoloured 15 5

(Des K. Esterhuysen. Recess and photo (4 c.). Des P. de Wet. Litho (5 c.))

1975 (10 Oct). *Inauguration of the Language Monument, Paarl. T* **205** *and similar vert design. P* 12½ × 11½.
386 4 c. black, pale stone and bright orange .. 15 8
387 5 c. multicoloured 20 10
Design:—5 c. "Afrikaanse Taalmonument".

206 Table Mountain

(Des P. Bosman and J. Hoekstra. Litho)

1975 (13 Nov). *Tourism. T* **206** *and similar horiz designs. Multicoloured. P* 12½.
388 15 c. Type **206** .. .. 2·25 2·00
a. Block of 4. Nos. 388/91 .. .. .. 8·00
389 15 c. Johannesburg .. .. 2·25 2·00
390 15 c. Cape Vineyards .. .. 2·25 2·00
391 15 c. Lions in Kruger National Park .. .. 2·25 2·00
Nos. 388/91 were printed together, *se-tenant*, in blocks of 4 throughout the sheet.

207 Globe and Satellites

(Des J. Hoekstra. Litho)

1975 (3 Dec). *Satellite Communication. P* 12½.
392 **207** 15 c. multicoloured 70 60

208 Bowls

(209)

(Des J. Maskew. Litho)

976. *Sporting Commemorations. T* **208** *and similar vert designs. P* 12½ × 11½.
93 15 c. black and light sage-green (18.2) .. 60 60
94 15 c. black and bright yellow-green (15.3) .. 95 70
95 15 c. black and pale yellow-olive (16.8) .. 60 60
96 15 c. black and apple-green (2.12) 60 55
MS397 161 × 109 mm. Nos. 393/6 (2.12) .. .. 3·25 3·50
Designs:—No. 393, Type **208** (World Bowls Championships, ohannesburg); No. 394, Batsman (Centenary of Organised Cricket in South Africa); No. 395, Polo player; No. 396, Gary Player golfer).

976 (6 Apr). *South Africa's Victory in World Bowls Championships. No.* 393 *optd with T* **209** *in gold.*
98 **208** 15 c. black and light sage-green 60 75

210 "Picnic under a Baobab Tree"

(Des J. Hoekstra. Photo (4 c.) or litho (others and **MS**403))

1976 (20 Apr). *Birth Centenary of Erich Mayer (painter). T* **210** *and similar horiz designs. Multicoloured. P* 11½ × 12½.
399 4 c. Type **210** 25 8
a. Imperf (pair) £150
400 10 c. "Foot of the Blaawberg" 55 20
401 15 c. "Harbeespoort Dam" 95 95
402 20 c. "Street scene, Doornfontein" .. .. 1·40 1·40
MS403 121 × 95 mm. Nos. 399/402 .. .. 3·75 4·25

211 Cheetah

212 "Emily Hobhouse" (H. Naude)

(Des P. Bosman. Photo (3 c.) or litho (others))

1976 (5 June). *World Environmental Day. T* **211** *and similar horiz designs. Multicoloured. P* 11½ × 12½.
404 3 c. Type **211** 20 8
405 10 c. Black Rhino 80 35
406 15 c. Bontebok .. .. 1·25 1·00
407 20 c. Mountain Zebra .. .. 1·75 1·75

(Des J. Hoekstra)

1976 (8 June). *50th Death Anniv of Emily Hobhouse (welfare worker). P* 12½ × 11½.
408 **212** 4 c. multicoloured 15 8

213 Early Mailship

214 Family with Globe

(Des K. Esterhuysen. Litho)

1976 (5 Oct). *Ocean Mail Service Centenary. P* 11½ × 12½.
409 **213** 10 c. multicoloured 75 60
a. Imperf (horiz pair) £200

(Des I. Ross)

1976 (6 Nov). *Family Planning and Child Welfare. P* 12½ × 11½.
410 **214** 4 c. chestnut and light salmon 15 8

215 Glasses of Wine

216 Dr. Jacob du Toit

(Des H. Botha. Litho)

1977 (14 Feb). *International Wine Symposium, Cape Town. P* 12½ × 11½.
411 **215** 15 c. multicoloured 70 65

(Des J. Hoekstra)

1977 (21 Feb). *Birth Centenary of J. D. du Toit (theologian and poet). P* 12½ × 11½.
412 **216** 4 c. multicoloured 12 8

217 Palace of Justice

218 *Protea repens*

(Des H. Meiring)

1977 (18 May). *Centenary of Transvaal Supreme Court. P* 11½ × 12½.
413 **217** 4 c. red-brown 12 8

(Des D. Findlay. Photo (1, 2, 3 c. (No. 416), 4, 5, 8, 10 to 20 c. (Nos. 425/a) and coil stamps) or litho (others))

1977 (27 May)–82. *Vert designs as T* **218** *showing Proteas or other Succulents. Multicoloured. (a) Sheet stamps. P* 12½.
414 1 c. Type **218** 5 5
415 2 c. *P punctata* 10 5
416 3 c. *P neriifolia* (photo) (p 12½) 10 5
416*a* 3 c. *P neriifolia* (litho) (p 14 × 13½) (1.10.79) 10 5
417 4 c. *P longifolia* 10 5
a. Imperf (pair) £100
418 5 c. *P cynaroides* 10 5
a. Perf 14 × 13½ (4.3.81) 10 5
419 6 c. *P canaliculata* 25 5
a. Black (face value and inscr at foot) omitted £120
b. Perf 14 × 13½ (25.10.79*) 20 5
420 7 c. *P lorea* 25 5
a. Perf 14 × 13½ (19.9.80) 20 10
421 8 c. *P mundii* 30 5
a. Perf 14 × 13½ (10.7.81) 15 10
422 9 c. *P roupelliae* 25 5
a. Perf 14 × 13½ (22.12.78) .. .. 3·50 1·00
423 10 c. *P aristata* 25 5
a. Perf 14 × 13½ (12.1.82) 25 5
424 15 c. *P eximia* 30 5
425 20 c. *P magnifica* (photo) 45 10
a. Perf 14 × 13½ (16.2.78) .. .. .. 1·75 1·75
425*b* 20 c. *P magnifica* (litho) (p 14 × 13½) (24.5.82) 45 15
426 25 c. *P grandiceps* 50 10
a. Perf 14 × 13½ (3.6.80) 40 15
427 30 c. *P amplexicaulis* 55 15
a. Perf 14 × 13½ (19.10.80) 50 30
428 50 c. *Leucospermum cordifolium* 90 35
a. Perf 14 × 13½ (9.10.80) 75 50
429 1 r. *Paranomus reflexus* .. .. .. 1·75 80
a. Perf 14 × 13½ (30.7.80) .. .. .. 1·75 95
430 2 r. *Orothamnus zeyheri* .. .. .. 3·50 2·50
a. Perf 14 × 13½ (22.5.81) .. .. .. 3·00 2·25

(*b*) *Coil stamps. Imperf* × *perf* 14
431 1 c. *Leucadendron argenteum* 10 10
432 2 c. *Mimetes cucullatus* 15 10
433 5 c. *Serruria florida* 15 10
434 10 c. *Leucadendron sessile* 30 20
414/34 .. .. *Set of* 21 8·75 4·00
*Sheets dated 15 August 1979.
Later printings of the coil stamps come with every fifth stamp numbered on the back.

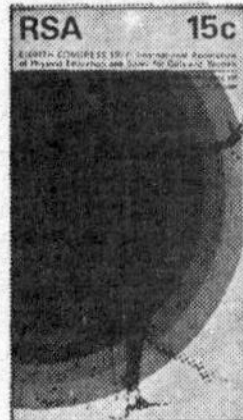

219 Gymnast

220 Metrication Symbol on Globe

(Des D. Cowie. Litho)

1977 (15 Aug). *Eighth Congress of International Association of Physical Education and Sports for Girls and Women. P* 12½ × 11½.
435 **219** 15 c. black, salmon-red and yellow .. 45 30

(Des L. Wilsenach. Litho)

1977 (15 Sept). *Metrication. P* 12 × 12½.
436 **220** 15 c. multicoloured 45 30

221 Atomic Diagram

(Des R. Sargent. Litho)

1977 (8 Oct). *Uranium Development. P* 12 × 12½.
437 **221** 15 c. multicoloured 45 30

222 National Flag

(Des J. Hoekstra)

1977 (11 Nov). *50th Anniv of National Flag. P* 12 × 12½.
438 **222** 5 c. multicoloured 12 8

223 Walvis Bay, 1878

(Des A. H. Barrett. Litho)

1978 (10 Mar). *Centenary of Annexation of Walvis Bay. P* 12½.
439 **223** 15 c. multicoloured 60 60

224 Dr. Andrew Murray

225 Steel Rail

(Des J. Hoekstra. Litho)

1978 (9 May). *150th Birth Anniv of Dr. Andrew Murray (church statesman). P* 12½ × 12.
440 **224** 4 c. multicoloured 12 8

(Des H. Botha. Litho)

1978 (5 June). *50th Anniv of I.S.C.O.R. (South African Iron and Steel Industrial Corporation). P* 12½.
441 **225** 15 c. multicoloured 30 25

226 Richards Bay

(Des A. H. Barrett. Litho)

1978 (31 July). *Harbours. T* **226** *and similar horiz design. Multicoloured. P* 12½.
442 15 c. Type **226** 45 30
a. Pair. Nos. 442/3 .. .. 90 1·25
443 15 c. Saldanhabaai 45 30
Nos. 442/3 were printed together, *se-tenant*, in horizontal and vertical pairs throughout the sheet.

227 "Shepherd's Lonely Dwelling, Riversdale"

228 Pres. B. J. Vorster

(Des G. Mynhardt. Litho)

1978 (21 Aug). *125th Birth Anniv of J. E. A. Volschenk (painter). T* **227** *and similar horiz designs. Multicoloured. P* 12½.
444 10 c. Type **227** 25 20
445 15 c. "Clouds and Sunshine, Laneberg Range, Riversdale" 60 30

446 20 c. "At the Foot of the Mountain" 85 60
447 25 c. "Evening on the Veldt" .. .. .. 1·10 1·10
MS448 124 × 90 mm. Nos. 444/7 .. .. .. 2·75 3·25

(Des A. H. Barrett. Litho)

1978 (10 Oct). *Inauguration of President Vorster. P* 14 × 13½.
449 **228** 4 c. brown-purple and gold 50 15
a. Perf 12½ × 12 .. .. .. 15 5
450 15 c. dull violet and gold.. .. .. 40 35

229 Golden Gate

(Des A. H. Barrett. Litho)

1978 (13 Nov). *Tourism. T* **229** *and similar horiz designs. Multi-coloured. P* 12½.
451 10 c. Type **229** 25 15
452 15 c. Blyde River Canyon 60 35
453 20 c. Amphitheatre, Drakensberg 85 70
454 25 c. Cango Caves .. .. 1·10 1·00

230 Dr. Wadley (inventor) and Tellurometer

(Des A. H. Barrett. Litho)

1979 (12 Feb). *25th Anniv of Tellurometer (radio distance measurer). P* 12½.
455 **230** 15 c. multicoloured 30 25

231 1929 4d. Airmail Stamp

(Des G. Mynhardt. Litho)

1979 (30 Mar). *50th Anniv of Stamp Production in South Africa. P* 14.
456 **231** 15 c. green, cream and slate 30 25

232 "Save Fuel"

(Des A. H. Barrett)

1979 (2 Apr). *Fuel Conservation. P* 12 × 12½.
457 **232** 4 c. black and vermilion 15 5
a. Pair. Nos. 457/8 .. .. 30 30
458 – 4 c. black and vermilion 15 5
No. 458 is as T **232** but has face value and country initials in bottom left-hand corner, and Afrikaans inscription above English.
Nos. 457/8 were printed together, *se-tenant*, in horizontal and vertical pairs throughout the sheet.

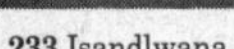

233 Isandlwana **234** "Health Care"

(Des A. H. Barrett. Litho)

1979 (25 May). *Centenary of Zulu War. T* **233** *and similar horiz designs in black and rose-red, showing drawings. P* 14.
459 4 c. Type **233** 15 5
460 15 c. Ulundi 55 55
461 20 c. Rorke's Drift 65 65
MS462 125 × 90 mm. Nos. 459/61. P 12½ .. 3·00 3·50

(Des J. Hoekstra. Litho)

1979 (19 June). *Health Year. P* 12½ × 12.
463 **234** 4 c. multicoloured 15 5
a. Perf 14 × 13½ 45 15

235 Children looking at Candle

(Des G. Mynhardt. Litho)

1979 (13 Sept). *50th Anniv of Christmas Stamp Fund. P* 14.
464 **235** 4 c. multicoloured 8 5

236 University of Cape Town **237** "Gary Player"

(Des G. Mynhardt. Litho)

1979 (1 Oct). *50th Anniv of University of Cape Town. P* 13½ × 14.
465 **236** 4 c. multicoloured 25 15
a. Perf 12 × 12½ 15 5

(Des H. de Klerk. Litho)

1979 (4 Oct). *"Rosafari 1979" World Rose Convention, Pretoria. T* **237** *and similar vert designs. Multicoloured. P* 14 × 13½.
466 4 c. Type **237** 15 5
467 15 c. "Prof. Chris Barnard" 40 40
468 20 c. "Southern Sun" 50 50
469 25 c. "Soaring Wings" 65 65
MS470 100 × 125 mm. Nos. 466/9 .. .. 1·75 2·00

238 University of Stellenbosch **239** F.A.K. Emblem

(Des A. H. Barrett. Litho)

1979 (8 Nov). *300th Anniv of Stellenbosch (oldest town in South Africa). T* **238** *and similar horiz design. Multicoloured. P* 14.
471 4 c. Type **238** 10 5
472 15 c. Rhenish Church on the Braak 30 30

(Des J. Hoekstra)

1979 (18 Dec). *50th Anniv of F.A.K. (Federation of Afrikaans Cultural Societies). P* 12½ × 12.
473 **239** 4 c. multicoloured 10 5

240 "Still-life with Sweet Peas" **241** "Cullinan II"

(Des G. Mynhardt. Litho)

1980 (6 May). *Paintings by Pieter Wenning. T* **240** *and similar multicoloured design. P* 14 × 13½.
474 5 c. Type **240** 10 5
475 25 c. "House in the Suburbs, Cape Town" (44½ × 37 *mm*) 55 45
MS476 94 × 121 mm. Nos. 474/5 .. .. 1·75 1·90

(Des A. H. Barrett. Litho)

1980 (12 May). *World Diamond Congresses, Johannesburg. T* **241** *and similar vert design. Multicoloured. P* 14.
477 15 c. Type **241** 40 30
478 20 c. "Cullinan I (Great Star of Africa)" .. 50 40

NEW INFORMATION

The editor is always interested to correspond with people who have new information that will improve or correct the Catalogue.

242 C. L. Leipoldt **243** University of Pretoria

(Des J. Hoekstra. Litho)

1980 (3 Sept). *Birth Centenary of C. L. Leipoldt (poet). P* 14 × 13½.
479 **242** 5 c. multicoloured 10

(Des P. de Wet. Litho)

1980 (9 Oct). *50th Anniv of University of Pretoria. P* 14 × 13½.
480 **243** 5 c. multicoloured 10

244 "Marine with Shipping" (Willem van de Velde)

(Des G. Mynhardt. Litho)

1980 (3 Nov). *Paintings from South African National Gallery, Capetown. T* **244** *and similar multicoloured designs. P* 14.
481 5 c. Type **244** 10 5
482 10 c. "Firetail and his Trainer" (George Stubbs) 20 15
483 15 c. "Lavinia" (Thomas Gainsborough) (*vert*) 30 25
484 20 c. "Classical Landscape" (Pieter Post) .. 40 30
MS485 126 × 90 mm. Nos. 481/4 .. .. .. 1·40 1·60

245 Joubert, Kruger and M. Pretorius (Triumvirate Government) **246** Boers advancing up Amajuba Mountain

(Des A. H. Barrett. Litho)

1980 (15 Dec). *Centenary of Paardekraal Monument (cairn commemorating formation of Boer Triumvirate Government). T* **245** *and similar multicoloured design. P* 14 × 13½ (5 *c.*) *or* 13½ × 14 (10 *c.*).
486 5 c. Type **245** 5 5
487 10 c. Paardekraal Monument (*vert*) 15 15

(Des Diana Arbuthnot. Litho)

1981 (27 Feb). *Centenary of Battle of Amajuba. T* **246** *and similar multicoloured design. P* 13½ × 14 (5 *c.*) *or* 14 × 13½ (15 *c.*).
488 5 c. Type **246** 5 5
489 15 c. British troops defending hill (*horiz*) .. 25 25

247 Ballet *Raka*

(Des H. Botha. Litho)

1981 (23 May). *Opening of State Theatre, Pretoria. T* **247** *and similar horiz design. Multicoloured. P* 14.
490 20 c. Type **247** 25 30
491 25 c. Opera *Aida* 30 35
MS492 110 × 90 mm. Nos. 490/1 .. .. .. 60 70

248 Former Presidents C. R. Swart, J. J. Fouché, N. Diederichs and B. J. Vorster

(Des A. H. Barrett. Litho)

1981 (30 May). *20th Anniv of Republic. T* **248** *and similar design. P* 14.
493 5 c. black, grey-olive and bistre 5 5
494 15 c. multicoloured 20 20
Design: (28 × 22 *mm*)—15 c. President Marais Viljoen.

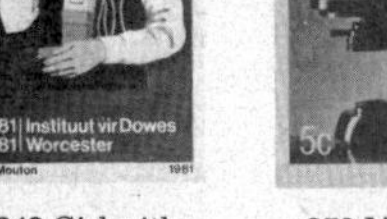
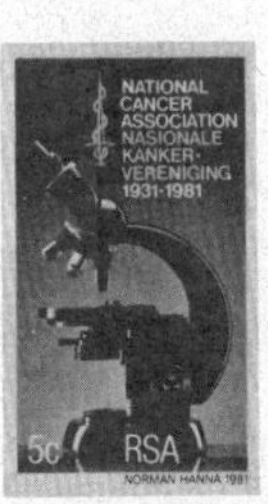
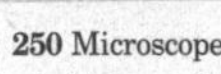
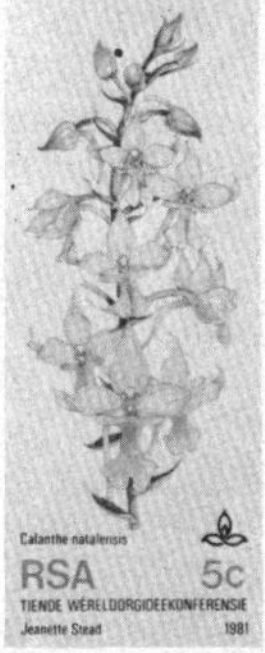

249 Girl with Hearing Aid **250** Microscope **251** *Calanthe natalensis*

(Des Mare Mouton. Litho)

1981 (12 June). *Centenary of Institutes for Deaf and Blind, Worcester. T* **249** *and similar vert design. Multicoloured. P* 13½ × 14.
495 5 c. Type **249** 5 5
496 15 c. Boy reading braille 20 25

(Des N. Hanna. Litho)

1981 (10 July). *50th Anniv of National Cancer Association. P* 13½ × 14.
497 **250** 5 c. multicoloured 5 5

(Des Jeanette Stead. Litho)

1981 (11 Sept). *Tenth World Orchid Conference, Durban. T* **251** *and similar vert designs. Multicoloured. P* 14.
498 5 c. Type **251** 5 5
499 15 c. *Eulophia speciosa* 25 25
500 20 c. *Disperis fanniniae* 30 35
501 25 c. *Disa uniflora* 40 40
MS502 120 × 91 mm. Nos. 498/501 .. .. 1·00 1·25

252 Voortrekkers in Uniform **253** Lord Baden-Powell **254** Dr. Robert Koch

(Des J. Hoekstra. Litho)

1981 (30 Sept). *50th Anniv of Voortrekker Movement (Afrikaans cultural youth organization). P* 14.
503 **252** 5 c. multicoloured 5 5

(Des J. Meyer. Litho)

1982 (22 Feb). *75th Anniv of Boy Scout Movement. P* 13½ × 14.
504 **253** 15 c. multicoloured 20 15

(Des J. Meyer. Litho)

1982 (24 Mar). *Centenary of Discovery of Tubercle Bacillus by Dr. Robert Koch. P* 13½ × 14.
505 **254** 20 c. multicoloured 20 20

255 Submarine **256** Old Provost, Grahamstown

(Des A. H. Barrett. Litho)

1982 (2 Apr). *25th Anniv of Simonstown as South African Navy Base. T* **255** *and similar horiz designs. Multicoloured. P* 14.
506 8 c. Type **255** 10 10
507 15 c. Strike craft 15 15
508 20 c. Minesweeper 25 25
509 25 c. Harbour patrol boats 30 30
MS510 125 × 90 mm. Nos. 506/9 .. .. 90 1·00

(Des A. H. Barrett. Recess (Nos. 511, 512*b*, 513/14, 515*a*, 516*a*, 521, 522*a* and 524/7), photo (Nos. 528/31) or litho (others))

1982 (15 July)–**84**. *South African Architecture. Designs as T* **256**.

(*a*) *Sheet stamps. P* 14
511 1 c. reddish brown (*recess*) 5 5
511*a* 1 c. reddish brown (*litho*) (2.4.84) 5 5
512 2 c. yellow-olive (*litho*) 5 5
512*a* 2 c. deep green (*litho*) (9.5.83) 5 5
512*b* 2 c. bottle green (*recess*) (28.11.83) 5 5
513 3 c. violet 5 5
514 4 c. brown-olive 5 5
515 5 c. carmine (*litho*) 5 5
515*a* 5 c. brown-purple (*recess*) (11.11.83) 5 5
516 6 c. deep blue-green (*litho*) 5 5
516*a* 6 c. blackish green (*recess*) (9.8.84) 5 5
517 7 c. dull yellowish green 5 8
518 8 c. greenish blue 8 10
518*a* 8 c. indigo (3.1.83) 5 8
519 9 c. deep mauve 5 8
520 10 c. Venetian red 10 12
520*a* 10 c. purple-brown (26.1.83) 8 10
520*b* 11 c. cerise (2.4.84) 8 10
521 15 c. deep violet-blue 12 15
522 20 c. vermilion (*litho*) 20 25
522*a* 20 c. brownish black (*recess*) (15.6.83) .. 15 20
523 25 c. bistre 20 25
524 30 c. agate 25 30
525 50 c. deep turquoise-blue (*shades*) 40 45
526 1 r. deep violet 80 85
527 2 r. deep carmine .. .. 1·50 1·75
511/27 .. .. *Set of* 18 (*one of each value*) 3·75 4·25
Designs: (28 × 20 *mm*)—2 c. Tuynhuys, Cape Town; 3 c. Appèlhof, Bloemfontein; 4 c. Raadsaal, Pretoria; 5 c. Cape Town Castle; 6 c. Goewermentsgebou, Bloemfontein; 7 c. Drostdy, Graaff-Reinet; 8 c. Leeuwenhof, Cape Town; 9 c. Libertas, Pretoria; 10 c. City Hall, Pietermaritzburg; 11 c. City Hall, Kimberley; 15 c. Matjesfontein; 20 c. Post Office, Durban; 25 c. Melrose House, Pretoria. (45 × 28 *mm*)—30 c. Old Legislative Assembly Building, Pietermaritzburg; 50 c. Raadsaal, Bloemfontein; 1 r. Houses of Parliament, Cape Town; 2 r. Uniegebou, Pretoria.

(*b*) *Coil stamps. P* 14 × *imperf*
528 1 c. brown 5 5
529 2 c. yellow-green 5 5
530 5 c. lake-brown 5 5
531 10 c. light brown 8 10
Designs: (28 × 20 *mm*)—1 c. Drostdy, Swellendam; 2 c. City Hall, East London; 5 c. Head Post Office, Johannesburg; 10 c. Morgenster, Somerset West.

257 Bradysaurus **258** Gough Island Base

(Des Sheila Nowers. Litho)

1982 (1 Dec). *Karoo Fossils. T* **257** *and similar horiz designs. Multicoloured. P* 14.
532 5 c. Type **257** 10 10
533 15 c. Lystrosaurus 25 25
534 20 c. Euparkeria 30 30
535 25 c. Thrinaxodon 35 40
MS536 107 × 95 mm. Nos. 532/5 .. .. .. 95 1·10

(Des D. Thorpe. Litho)

1983 (19 Jan). *Weather Stations. T* **258** *and similar horiz designs. Multicoloured. P* 13½ × 14.
537 8 c. Type **258** 10 10
538 20 c. Marion Island base 30 30
539 25 c. Taking meteorological readings 30 35
540 40 c. Launching weather balloon, Sanae .. 50 55

259 Class S2 Light Shunting Locomotive **260** Rugby

(Des H. Botha. Litho)

1983 (27 Apr). *Steam Railway Locomotives. T* **259** *and similar horiz designs. Multicoloured. P* 14.
541 10 c. Type **259** 12 15
542 20 c. Class 16E express loco 25 30
543 25 c. Class 6H loco 30 35
544 40 c. Class 15F main-line loco 50 55

(Des Sheila Nowers. Litho)

1983 (20 July). *Sport in South Africa. T* **260** *and similar multicoloured designs. P* 14.
545 10 c. Type **260** 12 15
546 20 c. Soccer (*horiz*) 25 30
547 25 c. Yachting 30 35
548 40 c. Horse-racing (*horiz*) 50 55

261 Plettenberg Bay **262** Thomas Pringle

(Des A. H. Barrett. Litho)

1983 (12 Oct). *Tourism. Beaches. T* **261** *and similar horiz designs. Multicoloured. P* 14.
549 10 c. Type **261** 12 15
550 20 c. Durban 25 30
551 25 c. West coast 30 35
552 40 c. Clifton 50 55
MS553 128 × 90 mm. Nos. 549/52 .. .. 1·10 1·25

(Des J. van Ellinckhuijzen. Litho)

1984 (24 Feb). *South African English Authors. T* **262** *and similar vert designs. P* 14.
554 10 c. olive-brown, yellow-brown and grey .. 12 15
555 20 c. olive-brown, deep bluish green and grey 25 30
556 25 c. olive-brown, deep brown-rose and grey .. 30 35
557 40 c. olive-brown, olive-ochre and grey .. 50 55
Designs:—20 c. Pauline Smith; 25 c. Olive Schreiner; 40 c. Sir Percy Fitzpatrick.

263 Manganese

(Des H. Botha. Litho)

1984 (8 June). *Strategic Minerals. T* **263** *and similar horiz designs. Multicoloured. P* 14.
558 11 c. Type **263** 10 12
559 20 c. Chromium 20 25
560 25 c. Vanadium 25 30
561 30 c. Titanium 25 30

264 Bloukrans River Bridge **265** Preamble to the Constitution in English

(Des D. Bagnall. Litho)

1984 (24 Aug). *South African Bridges. T* **264** *and similar horiz designs. Multicoloured. P* 14.
562 11 c. Type **264** 10 12
563 25 c. Durban four level interchange 25 30
564 30 c. Mfolozi rail bridge 25 30
565 45 c. Gouritz River bridge 40 45

(Des G. Mynhardt. Litho)

1984 (3 Sept). *New Constitution. T* **265** *and similar vert designs. P* 14.
566 11 c. stone, black and bistre 10 12
a. Horiz pair. Nos. 566/7 .. .. .. 20 25
567 11 c. stone, black and bistre 10 12
568 25 c. stone, deep claret and bistre 25 30
569 30 c. multicoloured 25 30
Designs:—No. 567, Preamble to the Constitution in Afrikaans; 568, Last two lines of National Anthem; 569, South African coat of arms.
Nos. 566/7 were printed together, *se-tenant*, in horizontal pairs.

266 Pres. P. W. Botha **267** Pro Patria Medal

1984 (2 Nov). *Inauguration of President Botha. Litho. P* 14.
570 **266** 11 c. multicoloured 10 12
571 25 c. multicoloured 25 30

(Des B. Jackson. Litho)

1984 (9 Nov). *Military Decorations. T* **267** *and similar vert designs. Multicoloured. P* 14.
572 11 c. Type **267** 10 12
573 25 c. De Wet Decoration 25 30
574 30 c. John Chard Decoration 25 30
575 45 c. Honoris Crux (Diamond) Decoration .. 40 45
MS576 71 × 116 mm. Nos. 572/5 .. .. .. 1·00 1·10

MINIMUM PRICE

The minimum price quoted is 5p which represents a handling charge rather than a basis for valuing common stamps. For further notes about prices see introductory pages.

POSTAGE DUE STAMPS

D 1

UNION OF SOUTH AFRICA (A)

UNION OF SOUTH AFRICA (B)

(Typo D.L.R.)

1914–22. *Inscribed bilingually. Lettering as* A. *W* **4.** *P* 14.

			Un single	Used single
D1	D 1	½d. black and green (19.3.15)	60	1·25
D2		1d. black and scarlet (19.3.15)	50	12
D3		2d. black and reddish violet (12.12.14)	3·75	25
		a. Black and bright violet (1922)	4·25	25
D4		3d. black and bright blue (2.2.15)	1·50	75
D5		5d. black and sepia (19.3.15)	3·50	7·00
D6		6d. black and slate (19.3.15)	6·00	7·50
D7		1s. red and black (19.3.15)	70·00	90·00

There are interesting minor varieties in some of the above values, e.g. ½d. to 3d., thick downstroke to "d"; 1d., short serif to "1"; raised "d"; 2d., forward point of "2" blunted; 3d., raised "d"; very thick "d".

(Litho Govt Printer, Pretoria)

1922. *Lettering as* A. *No wmk. Rouletted.*

D 8	D 1	½d. black and bright green (6.6.22)	50	1·25
D 9		1d. black and rose-red (3.10.22)	55	65
D10		1½d. black and yellow-brown (3.6.22)	1·00	1·40

(Litho Govt Printer, Pretoria)

1922–26. *Type* D 1 *redrawn. Lettering as* B. *P* 14.

D11	½d. black and green (1.11.22)	25	70
D12	1d. black and rose (16.5.23)	25	15
D13	1½d. black and yellow-brown (12.1.24)	25	80
D14	2d. black and pale violet (16.5.23)	45	45
	a. Imperf (pair)	£140	
	b. Black and deep violet	2·75	1·25
D15	3d. black and blue (3.7.26)	6·00	5·00
D16	6d. black and slate (9.23)	7·50	7·50

The locally printed stamps, perf 14, differ both in border design and in figures of value from the rouletted stamps. All values except the 3d. and 6d. are known with closed "G" in "POSTAGE" usually referred to as the "POSTADE" variety. This was corrected in later printings.

D 2

D 3

D 4

(Typo Pretoria)

1927–28. *Inscribed bilingually. No wmk. P* 13½ × 14.

D17	D 2	½d. black and green	25	60
D18		1d. black and carmine	25	15
D19		2d. black and mauve	1·75	30
		a. Black and purple	3·50	1·40
D20		3d. black and blue	5·00	5·50
D21		6d. black and slate	5·00	6·00

1932–42. *Type* D 2 *redrawn.* W **9.** *P* 15 × 14.

(a) Frame roto, value typo

D22	½d. black and blue-green (1934)	80	60
D23	2d. black and deep purple (10.4.33)	2·75	30

(b) Whole stamp roto

D25	1d. black and carmine (3.34)	25	15
D26	2d. black and deep purple (1940)	1·75	15
	a. Thick (double) "2d."	15·00	10·00
D27	3d. black and Prussian blue (3.8.32)	5·50	4·75
D28	3d. deep blue and blue (1935)	3·50	60
	a. Indigo and milky blue (1942)	4·00	90
D29	6d. green and brown-ochre (7.6.33)	11·00	4·00
	a. Green and bright orange (1938)	5·00	1·50

In No. D26 the value, when magnified, has the meshed appearance of a photogravure screen, whereas in No. D23 the black of the value is solid.

1943–47. *Inscr bilingually. Roto.* W **9.** *In units of three, perf* 15 × 14 *subdivided by roulette* 6½.

			Un unit	Us unit
D30	D 3	½d. blue-green (1947)	2·50	6·50
D31		1d. carmine	2·25	2·75
D32		2d. dull violet	4·00	4·75
		a. Bright violet	11·00	12·00
D33		3d. indigo (1945)	12·00	20·00

1948–49. *New figure of value and capital "D". Whole stamp roto.* W **9.** *P* 15 × 14.

D34	D 4	½d. black and blue-green	1·75	1·25
D35		1d. black and carmine	1·75	90
D36		2d. black and violet (1949)	2·25	1·25
		a. Thick (double) "2d."	20·00	10·00
D37		3d. deep blue and blue	5·00	5·50
D38		6d. green and bright orange	7·00	7·50

1950–58. *As Type* D 4, *but* "SUID-AFRIKA" *hyphenated. Whole stamp roto.* W **9.** *P* 15 × 14.

D39	1d. black and carmine (5.50)	50	25
D40	2d. black and violet (*shades*)(4.51)	50	25
	a. Thick (double) "2d."	7·00	4·00
D41	3d. deep blue and blue (5.50)	2·25	1·25
D42	4d. deep myrtle-green and emerald (2.58)	1·75	2·25
D43	6d. green and bright orange (1951)	5·50	3·75
D44	1s. black-brown and purple-brown (2.58)	6·50	7·00
D39/44	*Set of* 6	15·00	13·50

D 5

D 6 Afrikaans at top

D 7 English at top

1961 (14 Feb). *Values in cents as Type* D **5.** *Whole stamp roto.* W **102.** *P* 15 × 14.

D45	1 c. black and carmine	20	65
D46	2 c. black and violet	25	65
D47	4 c. deep myrtle-green and emerald	80	2·00
D48	5 c. deep blue and blue	2·00	2·25
D49	6 c. green and orange-red	2·75	3·75
D50	10 c. sepia and brown-lake	6·50	7·50
D45/50	*Set of* 6	11·00	15·00

1961 (31 May)–**69.** *Roto.* W **102.** *P* 15 × 14.

D51	D 6	1 c. black and carmine	40	60
D52	D 7	1 c. black and carmine (6.62)	40	50
D53		2 c. black and deep reddish violet	40	55
D54	D 6	4 c. dp myrtle-green & light emerald	70	85
D54*a*	D 7	4 c. dp myrtle-grn & lt emerald (6.69)	90	1·00
D55		5 c. deep blue and grey-blue	2·00	2·75
D56		5 c. black and grey-blue (6.62)	1·75	2·00
D57	D 6	6 c. deep green and red-orange	2·25	3·00
D58	D 7	10 c. sepia and purple-brown	3·25	3·25
D51/8		*Set of* 9	11·00	13·00

1967 (Dec)–**71.** *Roto.* W **127** (*tête-bêche*). *P* 15 × 14.

D59	D 6	1 c. black and carmine	20	25
D60	D 7	1 c. black and carmine	20	25
D61	D 6	2 c. black and deep reddish violet	30	30
		a. Perf 14	5·00	5·00
D62	D 7	2 c. black and deep reddish violet	30	30
		a. Perf 14	5·00	5·00
D62*b*		4 c. deep myrtle-green and light emerald (6.69)*	5·00	5·50
D62*c*	D 6	4 c. deep myrtle-green and light emerald (6.69)*	75·00	65·00
D63		4 c. black and pale green (4.71)	1·50	1·75
		a. Perf 14	5·00	5·00
D64	D 7	4 c. black and pale green (4.71)	1·50	1·75
		a. Perf 14	5·00	5·00
D65	D 6	5 c. black and deep blue	60	50
D66	D 7	5 c. black and deep blue	60	50
D67	D 6	6 c. green and orange-red (1968)	80	1·10
D68	D 7	6 c. green and orange-red (1968)	80	1·10
D69	D 6	10 c. black and purple-brown	1·50	2·25
		a. Black and brown-lake (12.69)	1·50	2·25
D70	D 7	10 c. black and purple-brown	1·50	2·25
		a. Black and brown-lake (12.69)	1·50	2·25
D59/70*a* *except* D62*b/c*		*Set of* 12	8·50	10·50

Nos. D59/70 were printed in two panes, one with inscriptions as Type D **6** and the other as Type D **7**.

*Nos. D62*b/c* were part of a printing of No. D54/*a*. Most were printed on paper with the Arms watermark, but some were printed on RSA paper with the watermark upright and faint. Most of these were spoiled but a few sheets were issued in Types D **7** and D **6**, the latter being very scarce.

D 8

1972 (22 Mar). *English at right* (1, 4 *and* 8 c.) *or at left* (*others*). W **127** (*sideways tête-bêche*). *Phosphorised paper. P* 14 × 13½.

D71	D 8	1 c. deep yellowish green	40	50
D72		2 c. bright orange	60	65
D73		4 c. plum	1·10	1·25
D74		6 c. chrome-yellow	1·60	1·90
		a. Phosphorised glossy paper	1·75	2·50
D75		8 c. ultramarine	2·00	2·50
D76		10 c. bright scarlet	2·50	3·00
D71/6		*Set of* 6	7·50	9·00

The 6 c. also exists on non-phosphor glossy paper.

The use of Postage Due stamps ceased in 1975.

OFFICIAL STAMPS

OFFICIAL. OFFISIEEL. (O 1)

OFFISIEEL OFFICIAL (O 2)

(Approximate measurements between lines of opt are shown in mm in brackets)

1926 (1 Dec). *Optd vertically upwards, with stops, as Type* O 1.

(a) On 1913 issue (singles)

O1	3	2d. Nos. 6/6a (12½)	11·00	2·50

(b) On 1926 issue (pairs)

O2	6	½d. No. 30 (12½)	3·50	5·00
O3	7	1d. No. 31 (12½)	2·00	3·25
O4	8	6d. No. 32 (12½)	£550	75·00

This overprint is found on the ½d., 1d. and 6d. values of both the London and Pretoria printings. The London printings of the ½d. and 1d. stamps are considerably scarcer than the Pretoria, but the 6d. Pretoria printing is scarcer still.

1928–29. *Optd vertically upwards, as Type* O 1, *but without stops.*

O5	11	2d. No. 34 (17½)	2·75	4·50
O6		2d. No. 34 (19) (1929)	2·75	4·25
O7	8	6d. No. 32 (11½)	12·00	14·00

1929. *Typographed stamps optd with Type* O 2.

O 8	6	½d. No. 30 (13½)	90	1·25
		a. Stop after "OFFISIEEL" on English stamp	14·00	14·00
		b. Ditto. On Afrikaans stamp	14·00	14·00
O 9	7	1d. No. 31 (13½)	1·75	2·25
O10	8	6d. No. 32 (13½)	6·00	11·00
		a. Stop after "OFFISIEEL" on English stamp	28·00	35·00
		b. Ditto. On Afrikaans stamp	28·00	35·00

1930–47. *Rotogravure stamps* ("SUIDAFRIKA" *in one word*) *optd with Type* O 2.

O11	6	½d. No. 42 (9½–12) (1931)	90	1·50
		a. Stop after "OFFISIEEL" on English stamp	14·00	14·00
		b. Ditto. On Afrikaans stamp	14·00	14·00
O12		½d. No. 42 (12½) (1932)	1·75	2·25
O13	7	1d. No. 43 (12½ and 13½)	2·25	2·75
		a. Stop after "OFFISIEEL" on English stamp	14·00	15·00
		b. Ditto. On Afrikaans stamp	14·00	15·00
		c. Opt double	£225	
O14		1d. No. 43c (12½) (1932)	3·50	4·00
O15	11	2d. No. 44 (21) (1931)	6·00	10·00
O15*a*		2d. No. 44c (20½) (1939)	30·00	40·00
O16	8	6d. No. 47 (12½)	7·00	7·00
		a. Stop after "OFFISIEEL" on English stamp	25·00	25·00
		b. Ditto. On Afrikaans stamp	25·00	25·00
O17	13	1s. No. 48 (19) (1932)	20·00	24·00
O18		1s. No. 48 (21) (1938)	20·00	24·00
O19	14	2s. 6d. No. 49 (18) (1933)	32·00	38·00
O20		2s. 6d. No. 49 (21) (1939)	32·00	38·00
O20*a*		2s. 6d. No. 49*a* (19½–20) (1946)	32·00	38·00
		ab. Diaeresis on second "E" (1947)	£500	

Nos. O8a/b, O10a/b, O11a/b, O13a/b and O16a/b. The pairs include one stamp with variety and the other normal. In No. O20ab the variety occurs on both the English and Afrikaans stamps.

1932–33. *Recess-printed stamps optd with Type* O 2.

O21	13	1s. No. 36 (17½, 18 and 20½)	22·00	30·00
		a. Stop after "OFFICIAL" on Afrikaans stamp	£100	£120
O22	14	2s. 6d. No. 37 (17½ and 18)	35·00	45·00
		a. Stop after "OFFICIAL" on Afrikaans stamp	£130	£140

Nos. O21a and O22a. The pairs include one stamp with variety and the other normal.

OFFICIAL OFFISIEEL (O 3)

OFFICIAL OFFISIEEL (O 4)

1935–51. *Rotogravure stamps* ("SUID-AFRIKA" *hyphenated*).

(a) Optd with Type O 2 *("OFFICIAL" at right)*

O23	6	½d. No. 54 (12½) (1937)	2·00	3·50
O24	24	½d. No. 64c (11 and 12½) (1938)	2·00	2·50
O24*a*		½d. No. 64*d* (12) (1948)	75	2·50
O24*b*		½d. No. 114 (11) (1949)	1·00	2·50
O25	7	1d. No. 56 (11½–13)	65	80
O26	22	1½d. No. 57 (20) (1937)	3·00	4·25
O26*a*		1½d. No. 57*a* (20) (1942)	5·00	5·50
O26*b*	34*a*	1½d. No. 87 (14½) (1947)	1·75	2·50
		ba. Diaeresis on second "E" (1946?)	65·00	65·00
O26*c*		1½d. No. 87 (16) (1950)	2·00	2·25
O27	11	2d. No. 58 (20) (1938)	10·00	15·00
O27*a*	54	2d. No. 107 (20) (1947)	2·25	2·75
		ab. Diaeresis on second "E" (1947)	£160	£160
O27*b*		2d. No. 107*a* (20) (1949)	2·75	4·00
O28	8	6d. No. 61 (12 and 13) (1938)	35·00	24·00
O28*a*		6d. No. 61*a* (11½–13) (1940)	8·00	9·00
O28*b*		6d. No. 61*b* (12) (1947)	7·50	9·00
O29	13	1s. No. 62 (20) (1940)	12·00	12·00
		aa. Diaeresis on second "E" (1946?)	£600	£600
O29*a*		1s. No. 120 (17½–18½) (1950)	6·50	11·00
O29*b*	15	5s. No. 64*a* (20) (1951)	35·00	40·00
O29*c*	23	10s. No. 64*b* (19½) (1950)	45·00	45·00

(b) Optd with Type O 3 *("OFFICIAL" at left)*

O30	15	5s. No. 64*a* (18) (1940)	40·00	50·00
O31	23	10s. No. 64*b* (19) (1940)	55·00	55·00

The pairs of Nos. O26ba, and O29aa include one stamp with variety and one normal.

No. O27ab occurs on two horizontal pairs in the sheet and can therefore be found on stamps inscribed in either language.

1944. *Optd with Type* O 4 *reading up and down and with diaeresis over the second* "E" *of* "OFFISIEEL".

O32	24	½d. No. 64*d* (10)	4·00	3·00

OFFISIEEL OFFICIAL (O 5)

OFFICIAL OFFISIEEL (O 6)

1944. *Optd with Type* O **5** *reading upwards* ("OFFICIAL" *at right*).

O33	**11**	2d. No. 58*a* (18½)	1·50	1·75

1949–50. *Optd with Type* O **6** *reading upwards* ("OFFICIAL" *at left*).

O34	**34*a***	1½d. No. 87 (16)	4·00	4·50
O35	**68**	2d. No. 134 (16) (1950)	£650	£750

OFFISIEEL OFFICIAL

(O **7**)

1950–54. *Optd as Type* O **7**.

O35*a*	**24**	½d. No. 64*d* (10) (1951)	60	1·25
O35*b*		½d. No. 114 (10) (1953)	70	1·50
O36	**7**	1d. No. 56*a* (10)	1·25	2·75
O36*a*		1d. No. 115 (10) (1951)	1·25	1·50
O36*b*		1d. No. 135 (10) (1952)	90	1·50
O37	**34*a***	1½d. No. 87 (14½) (1951)	1·25	2·00
O38	**68**	2d. No. 134 (14½)	1·25	1·75
		a. Opt inverted		
O39	**8**	6d. No. 119 (10)	1·50	3·00
O39*a*		6d. No. 119*a* (10) (1951)	1·75	2·50
O40	**13**	1s. No. 120 (19)	4·00	6·50
O40*a*		1s. No. 120*a* (19) (1953)	65·00	85·00
O41	**14**	2s. 6d. No. 121 (19)	10·00	24·00
O41*a*	**15**	5s. No. 64*a* (19) (1951)	22·00	38·00
O41*b*		5s. No. 122 (19) (1953)	26·00	42·00
O41*c*		5s. No. 122*a* (19) (1954)	35·00	55·00
O42	**23**	10s. No. 64*ba* (19)	45·00	48·00

On No. O36*a* the overprint is thicker.

The use of official stamps ceased in January 1955.

South Arabia

The stamps of the Aden States surcharged in fils and dinars and with the word "ADEN" obliterated and replaced by "SOUTH ARABIA" (or commemorative inscription also) are listed under the Aden States.

South Arabian Federation

Comprising Aden and most of the territories of the former Western Aden Protectorate plus one from the Eastern Aden Protectorate.

(Currency. 100 cents=1 shilling)

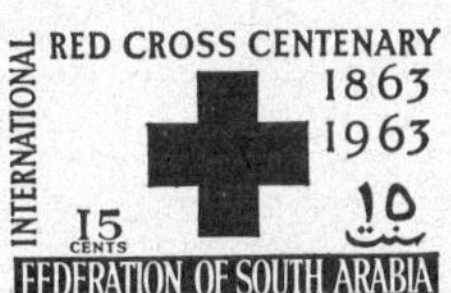

1 Red Cross Emblem

1963 (25 Nov). *Red Cross Centenary. W* w **12**. *P* 13½.

1	**1**	15 c. red and black	15	15
2		1s. 25, red and blue	45	45

(New Currency. 1000 fils=1 dinar)

2 Federal Crest 3 Federal Flag

(Des V. Whiteley. Photo Harrison)

1965 (1 Apr). *P* 14½ × 14 (*T* **2**) *or* 14½ (*T* **3**).

3	**2**	5 f. blue	5	5
4		10 f. violet-blue	5	5
5		15 f. turquoise-green	5	5
6		20 f. green	5	5
7		25 f. yellow-brown	8	5
8		30 f. yellow-bistre	8	5
9		35 f. chestnut	10	5
10		50 f. red	12	5
11		65 f. yellow-green	25	20
12		75 f. crimson	25	10
13	**3**	100 f. multicoloured	30	10
14		250 f. multicoloured	65	25
15		500 f. multicoloured	1·75	60
16		1 d. multicoloured	3·00	2·25
3/16		*Set of* 14	6·00	3·50

4 I.C.Y. Emblem

(Des V. Whiteley. Litho Harrison)

1965 (24 Oct). *International Co-operation Year. W* w **12**. *P* 14½.

17	**4**	5 f. reddish purple and turquoise-green	5	5
18		65 f. deep bluish green and lavender	30	10

5 Sir Winston Churchill and St. Paul's Cathedral in Wartime

(Des Jennifer Toombs. Photo Harrison)

1966 (24 Jan). *Churchill Commemoration. No wmk. P* 14.

19	**5**	5 f. black, cerise, gold and new blue	5	5
20		10 f. black, cerise, gold and deep green	15	5
21		65 f. black, cerise, gold and brown	45	15
22		125 f. black, cerise, gold and bluish violet	75	85

6 Footballer's Legs, Ball and Jules Rimet Cup

(Des V. Whiteley. Litho Harrison)

1966 (1 July). *World Cup Football Championship, England. No wmk. P* 14.

23	**6**	10 f. violet, yellow-green, lake & yell-brn	5	5
24		50 f. chocolate, blue-grn, lake & yell-brn	25	10

7 W.H.O. Building

(Des M. Goaman. Litho Harrison)

1966 (20 Sept). *Inauguration of W.H.O. Headquarters, Geneva. No wmk. P* 14.

25	**7**	10 f. black, yellow-green and light blue	10	5
26		75 f. black, light purple and yellow-brown	35	20

8 "Education"

9 "Science"

10 "Culture"

(Des Jennifer Toombs. Litho Harrison)

1966 (15 Dec). *20th Anniv of U.N.E.S.C.O. No wmk. P* 14.

27	**8**	10 f. slate-violet, red, yellow and orange	10	5
28	**9**	65 f. orange-yellow, vio & dp olive	30	45
29	**10**	125 f. black, bright purple and orange	65	90

The South Arabian Federation became fully independent on 30 November 1967. Later issues for this area will be found listed in Part 19 (*Middle East*) of this catalogue under YEMEN, PEOPLE'S DEMOCRATIC REPUBLIC.

South Australia

PRICES FOR STAMPS ON COVER

Nos. 1/3	*from* × 3
No. 4	†
Nos. 5/12	*from* × 2
Nos. 13/18	*from* × 3
Nos. 19/43	*from* × 4
Nos. 44/9*b*	—
Nos. 50/110	*from* × 3
No. 111	—
Nos. 112/34	*from* × 6
Nos. 135/45	*from* × 3
Nos. 146/66	*from* × 5
Nos. 167/77	*from* × 10
Nos. 178/80	—
Nos. 181/94	*from* × 12
Nos. 195/208	—
Nos. 229/34	*from* × 12
No. 235	—
Nos. 236/44	*from* × 8
Nos. 245/60	*from* × 15
Nos. 262/7	*from* × 20
Nos. 268/75	*from* × 30
Nos. 276/9	—
Nos. 280/8	*from* × 30
Nos. 289/92	—
Nos. 293/304	*from* × 15
No. 305	—
Nos. O1/13	—
Nos. O14/36	*from* × 20
Nos. O37/42	*from* × 5
Nos. O43/6	*from* × 50
Nos. O47/9	—
Nos. O50/3	*from* × 30
No. O54	*from* × 15
Nos. O55/71	*from* × 50
Nos. O72/85	*from* × 75
Nos. O86/7	—

1 2 Large Star

(Eng Wm Humphrys. Recess P.B.)

1855. *Printed in London. W* **2**. *Imperf.*

1	**1**	1d. dark green (26.10.55)	£2500	£300
2		2d. rose-carmine (*shades*) (1.1.55)	£800	£125
3		6d. deep blue (26.10.55)	£2000	£150

Prepared and sent to the Colony, but not issued

4	**1**	1s. violet	£4500	

A printing of 500,000 of these 1s. stamps was made and delivered, but as the colour was liable to be confused with that of the 6d. stamp, the stock was destroyed on 5 June 1857.

NOTE. Proofs of the 1d. and 6d. without wmk exist, and these are found with forged star watermarks added, and are sometimes offered as originals.

For reprints of the above and later issues, see note after No. 194.

1856–58. *Printed by Govt Ptr, Adelaide, from Perkins, Bacon plates. W* **2**. *Imperf.*

5	**1**	1d. deep yellow-green (15.6.58)	£5000	£450
6		1d. yellow-green (11.10.58)	—	£550
7		2d. orange-red (23.4.56)	—	£130
8		2d. blood-red (14.11.56)	£1200	£110
		a. Printed on both sides		
9		2d. red (*shades*) (29.10.57)	£650	55·00
		a. Printed on both sides	—	£750
10		6d. slate-blue (7.57)	£2000	£225
11		1s. red-orange (8.7.57)	—	£500
12		1s. orange (11.6.58)	£3750	£400

1858–59. *W* **2**. *Rouletted. (This first rouletted issue has the same colours as the local imperf issue).*

13	**1**	1d. yellow-green (8.1.59)	£475	45·00
14		1d. light yellow-green (18.3.59)	£475	50·00
		a. Imperf between (pair)		
15		2d. red (17.2.59)	£110	18·00
		a. Printed on both sides		
17		6d. slate-blue (12.12.58)	£375	25·00
18		1s. orange (18.3.59)	£800	35·00
		a. Printed on both sides	—	£1000

3 4 (5)

1860–69. *Second rouletted issue, printed in colours only found rouletted or perforated. Surch with T* **5** *(Nos.* 35/7*). W* **2**.

No.	Type	Description	Unused	Used
19	1	1d. bright yellow-green (22.4.61)	45·00	25·00
20		1d. dull blue-green (17.12.63)	40·00	23·00
21		1d. sage-green	50·00	27·00
22		1d. pale sage-green (27.5.65)	40·00	
23		1d. deep green (1864)	£225	65·00
24		1d. deep yellow-green (1869)	90·00	
24*a*		2d. pale red	60·00	4·00
		b. Printed on both sides	—	£375
25		2d. pale vermilion (3.2.63)	48·00	4·00
26		2d. bright vermilion (19.8.64)	38·00	2·75
		a. Imperf between (horiz pair)	£700	£300
27	3	4d. dull violet (24.1.67)	48·00	17·00
28	1	6d. violet-blue (19.3.60)	£140	6·00
29		6d. greenish blue (11.2.63)	65·00	4·00
30		6d. dull ultramarine (25.4.64)	60·00	4·00
		a. Imperf between (horiz pair)	—	£300
31		6d. violet-ultramarine (11.4.68)	£150	6·00
32		6d. dull blue (26.8.65)	£100	6·50
		a. Imperf between (pair)	—	£600
33		6d. Prussian blue (7.9.69)	£550	50·00
33*a*		6d. indigo	—	55·00
34	4	9d. grey-lilac (24.12.60)	42·00	9·00
		a. Imperf between (horiz pair)		
35		10d. on 9d. orange-red (B.) (20.7.66)	90·00	24·00
36		10d. on 9d. yellow (B.) (29.7.67)	£140	20·00
37		10d. on 9d. yellow (Blk.) (14.8.69)	£1500	30·00
		a. Surch inverted at the top	—	£3000
		b. Printed on both sides	—	£800
		c. Roul × perf 10	†	—
38	1	1s. yellow (25.10.61)	£450	28·00
		a. Imperf between (vert pair)		
39		1s. grey-brown (10.4.63)	£150	16·00
40		1s. dark grey-brown (26.5.63)	£130	16·00
41		1s. chestnut (25.8.63)	£140	11·00
42		1s. lake-brown (27.3.65)	£110	12·00
		a. Imperf between (horiz pair)	—	£400
43	3	2s. rose-carmine (24.1.67)	£150	25·00
		a. Imperf between (vert pair)	—	£750

1868–71. *Remainders of old stock subsequently perforated by the* 11½–12½ *machine.*

(*a*) *Imperf stamps. P* 11½–12½

No.	Type	Description	Unused	Used
44	1	2d. pale vermilion (Feb 1868)	—	£1400
45		2d. vermilion (18.3.68)	—	£1500

(*b*) *Rouletted stamps. P* 11½–12½

No.	Type	Description	Unused	Used
46	1	1d. bright green (9.11.69)	—	£550
47		2d. pale vermilion (15.8.68)	—	£500
48		6d. Prussian blue (8.11.69)	—	£225
		aa. Horiz pair perf all round, roul between		
48*a*		6d. indigo		
49	4	9d. grey-lilac (29.3.71)	£1800	£190
		a. Perf × roulette	—	£180
49*b*	1	1s. lake-brown (23.5.70)		

1867–70. *W* **2.** *P* 11½–12½ × *roulette.*

No.	Type	Description	Unused	Used
50	1	1d. pale bright green (2.11.67)	£160	18·00
51		1d. bright green (1868)	£120	18·00
52		1d. grey-green (26.1.70)	£160	20·00
		a. Imperf between (horiz pair)		
53		1d. blue-green (29.11.67)	£200	30·00
54	3	4d. dull violet (July 1868)	£1700	£130
55		4d. dull purple (1869)	—	90·00
56	1	6d. bright pale blue (29.5.67)	£550	19·00
57		6d. Prussian blue (30.7.67)	£500	19·00
		a. Printed on both sides		
58		6d. indigo (1.8.69)	£650	24·00
59	4	10d. on 9d. yellow (B.) (2.2.69)	£700	30·00
		a. Printed on both sides	—	£550
60	1	1s. chestnut (April 1868)	£300	15·00
61		1s. lake-brown (3.3.69)	£300	15·00

NOTE. The stamps perf 11½, 12½, or compound of the two, are here combined in one list, as both perforations are on the one machine, and all the varieties *may* be found in each sheet of stamps. This method of classifying the perforations by the machines is by far the most simple and convenient.

3-PENCE

(6)

7 (=Victoria *W* **20**)

1868–79. *Surch with T* **6** *(Nos.* 66/8*). W* **2.** *P* 11½–12½.

No.	Type	Description	Unused	Used
62	1	1d. pale bright green (8.2.68)	£150	18·00
63		1d. grey-green (18.2.68)	£120	40·00
64		1d. dark green (20.3.68)	50·00	17·00
		a. Printed on both sides		
65		1d. deep yellow-green (28.6.72)	45·00	18·00
66	3	3d. on 4d. Prussian blue (Blk.) (7.2.71)	—	£700
67		3d. on 4d. sky-blue (Blk.) (12.8.70)	£275	9·00
		a. Imperf		
		b. Rouletted	—	£500
68		3d. on 4d. deep ultramarine (Blk.) (9.72)	65·00	6·00
		a. Surch double (10.9.74)	—	£3500
		b. Additional surch on back	—	£2400
		c. Surch omitted (26.4.74)	£14000	£9000
70		4d. dull purple (1.2.68)	55·00	15·00
		a. Imperf between (horiz pair)		
71		4d. dull violet (1868)	50·00	8·00
72	1	6d. bright pale blue (23.2.68)	£300	11·00
73		6d. Prussian blue (29.9.69)	90·00	6·00
		a. Perf 11½ × imperf (horiz pair)		
74		6d. indigo (1869)	£120	17·00
75	4	9d. claret (7.72)	90·00	8·00
76		9d. bright mauve (1.11.72)	90·00	8·00
		a. Printed on both sides	—	£300
77		9d. red-purple (15.1.74)	40·00	8·00
78		10d. on 9d. yellow (B.) (15.8.68)	£1000	24·00
		a. Error. Wmk Crown and S A (1868)	—	£1200
79	4	10d. on 9d. yellow (Blk.) (13.9.69)	£200	27·00
80	1	1s. lake-brown (9.68)	£150	11·00
81		1s. chestnut (8.10.72)	£110	16·00
82		1s. dark red-brown	90·00	11·00
83		1s. red-brown (6.1.69)	£100	11·00
84	3	2s. pale rose-pink (10.10.69)	£950	£150
85		2s. deep rose-pink (8.69)	—	£100
86		2s. crimson-carmine (16.10.69)	70·00	18·00
87		2s. carmine (1869)	60·00	10·00
		a. Printed on both sides	—	£300

1870–71. *W* **2.** *P* 10.

No.	Type	Description	Unused	Used
88	1	1d. grey-green (6.70)	£120	15·00
89		1d. pale bright green (9.8.70)	£120	15·00
90		1d. bright green (1871)	£100	15·00
91	3	3d. on 4d. dull ultramarine (R.) (6.8.70)	£325	50·00
92		3d. on 4d. pale ultram (Blk.) (14.2.71)	£250	12·00
93		3d. on 4d. ultramarine (Blk.) (14.8.71)	£100	16·00
93*a*		3d. on 4d. Prussian blue (Blk.) (16.12.71)		
94		4d. dull lilac (1870)	£110	10·00
95		4d. dull purple (1871)	£100	10·00
96	1	6d. bright blue (19.6.70)	£180	17·00
97		6d. indigo (11.10.71)	£225	16·00
98		1s. chestnut (4.1.71)	£150	19·00

1870–73. *W* **2.** *P* 10 × 11½–12½, 11½–12½ × 10, *or compound.*

No.	Type	Description	Unused	Used
99	1	1d. pale bright green (11.10.70)	£140	14·00
		a. Printed on both sides		
100		1d. grey-green	£130	15·00
101		1d. deep green (19.6.71)	75·00	10·00
102	3	3d. on 4d. pale ultram (Blk.) (9.11.70)	£175	30·00
103		4d. dull lilac (11.5.72)	—	18·00
104		4d. slate-lilac (5.3.73)	£120	18·00
105	1	6d. Prussian blue (2.3.70)	£140	8·00
106		6d. bright Prussian blue (26.10.70)	£150	10·00
107	4	10d. on 9d. yellow (Blk.) (1.70)	£110	14·00
108	1	1s. chestnut (17.6.71)	—	32·00
109	3	2s. rose-pink (24.4.71)	—	£170
110		2s. carmine (2.3.72)	£120	25·00

1871 (17 July). *W* **7.** *P* 10.

No.	Type	Description	Unused	Used
111	3	4d. dull lilac	£1500	£250
		a. Printed on both sides		

8 Broad Star

8 PENCE

(9)

1876–1900. *W* **8.** *Surch with T* **9** *(Nos.* 118/21*).* (*a*) *P* 11½–12½.

No.	Type	Description	Unused	Used
112	3	3d. on 4d. ultramarine (1.6.79)	50·00	14·00
		a. Surch double	—	£1400
113		4d. violet-slate (15.3.79)	90·00	11·00
114		4d. plum (16.4.80)	40·00	6·00
115		4d. deep mauve (8.6.82)	40·00	5·00
116	1	6d. indigo (2.12.76)	90·00	4·50
		a. Imperf between (horiz pair)		
117		6d. Prussian blue (7.78)	55·00	4·00
118	4	8d. on 9d. brown-orange (7.76)	48·00	4·50
119		8d. on 9d. burnt umber (1880)	55·00	4·50
120		8d. on 9d. brown (9.3.80)	55·00	4·50
		a. Imperf between (vert pair)	£350	
121		8d. on 9d. grey-brown (10.5.81)	48·00	6·00
		a. Surch double	—	£350
122		9d. purple (9.3.80)	30·00	6·00
		a. Printed on both sides	—	£200
123		9d. rose-lilac (21.8.80)	8·00	2·00
124		9d. rose-lilac (*large holes*) (26.5.00)	8·00	2·25
125	1	1s. red-brown (3.11.77)	42·00	2·75
		a. Imperf between (horiz pair)	—	£250
126		1s. reddish lake-brown (1880)	40·00	3·00
127		1s. lake-brown (9.1.83)	45·00	2·75
128		1s. Vandyke brown (1891)	60·00	8·00
129		1s. dull brown (1891)	38·00	2·75
130		1s. chocolate (*large holes*) (6.5.97)	24·00	3·00
		a. Imperf vert (horiz pair)	£250	
131		1s. sepia (*large holes*) (22.5.00)	24·00	3·00
		a. Imperf between (vert pair)	£150	
132	3	2s. carmine (15.2.77)	25·00	4·00
		a. Imperf between (horiz pair)	—	£400
		b. Imperf (pair)		
133		2s. rose-carmine (1885)	32·00	6·00
134		2s. rose-carmine (*large holes*) (6.12.98)	30·00	5·50

The perforation with larger, clean-cut holes resulted from the fitting of new pins to the machine.

(*b*) *P* 10

No.	Type	Description	Unused	Used
135	1	6d. Prussian blue (11.11.79)	80·00	12·00
136		6d. bright blue (1879)	£100	11·00
136*a*		1s. reddish lake-brown	£225	

(*c*) *P* 10 × 11½–12½, 11½–12½ × 10, *or compound*

No.	Type	Description	Unused	Used
137	3	4d. violet-slate (21.5.79)	£100	10·00
138		4d. dull purple (4.10.79)	22·00	2·00
139	1	6d. Prussian blue (29.12.77)	48·00	2·50
140		6d. bright blue	70·00	5·50
141		6d. bright ultramarine	35·00	1·75
142		1s. reddish lake-brown (9.2.85)	75·00	9·00
143		1s. dull brown (29.6.86)	90·00	10·00
144	3	2s. carmine (27.12.77)	40·00	5·00
145		2s. rose-carmine (1887)	35·00	4·50
		a. Imperf between (horiz pair)	—	£400

MINIMUM PRICE

The minimum price quoted is 5p which represents a handling charge rather than a basis for valuing common stamps. For further notes about prices see introductory pages.

10

11

12

1901–2. *Wmk Crown SA (wide), W* **10.** *P* 11½–12½ *(large holes).*

No.	Type	Description	Unused	Used
146	4	9d. claret (1.2.02)	9·00	9·00
147	1	1s. dark brown (12.6.01)	20·00	9·00
148		1s. dark reddish brown (1902)	20·00	10·00
		a. Imperf between (vert pair)		
149		1s. red-brown (aniline) (18.7.02)	22·00	11·00
150	3	2s. crimson (29.8.01)	25·00	12·00
151		2s. carmine	19·00	8·00

(Plates and electrotypes by D.L.R. Printed in Adelaide)

1868–76. *W* **10.** (*a*) *Rouletted.*

No.	Type	Description	Unused	Used
152	12	2d. deep brick-red (8.68)	38·00	3·25
153		2d. pale orange-red (5.10.68)	35·00	2·75
		a. Printed on both sides	—	£200
		b. Imperf between (horiz pair)	—	£225

(*b*) *P* 11½–12½

No.	Type	Description	Unused	Used
154	11	1d. blue-green (10.1.75)	65·00	11·00
155	12	2d. pale orange-red (5.5.69)	£850	£190

(*c*) *P* 11½–12½ × *roulette*

No.	Type	Description	Unused	Used
156	12	2d. pale orange-red (20.8.69)	—	£120

(*d*) *P* 10 × *roulette*

No.	Type	Description	Unused	Used
157	12	2d. pale orange-red (7.5.70)	£250	20·00

(*e*) *P* 10

No.	Type	Description	Unused	Used
158	11	1d. blue-green (4.75)	18·00	3·50
159	12	2d. brick-red (4.70)	9·00	25
160		2d. orange-red (1.7.70)	8·00	20
		a. Printed on both sides	—	£160

(*f*) *P* 10 × 11½–12½, 11½–12½ × 10, *or compound*

No.	Type	Description	Unused	Used
161	11	1d. blue-green (27.8.75)	38·00	10·00
162	12	2d. brick-red (19.1.71)	£400	6·00
163		2d. orange-red (3.2.71)	—	8·50
		a. Imperf (8.76)		

1869. *Wmk Large Star, W* **2.** (*a*) *Rouletted.*

No.	Type	Description	Unused	Used
164	12	2d. orange-red (13.3.69)	38·00	11·00

(*b*) *P* 11½–12½ × *roulette*

No.	Type	Description	Unused	Used
165	12	2d. orange-red (1.8.69)	—	90·00

(*c*) *P* 11½–12½

No.	Type	Description	Unused	Used
165*a*	12	2d. orange-red (7.69)		

1871 (15 July). *Wmk V and Crown, W* **7.** *P* 10.

No.	Type	Description	Unused	Used
166	12	2d. brick-red	40·00	12·00

13

HALF-

PENNY

(14)

1876–85. *Wmk Crown SA (close), W* **13.** (*a*) *P* 10.

No.	Type	Description	Unused	Used
167	11	1d. blue-green (9.2.76)	4·50	1·25
168		1d. yellowish green (11.78)	4·75	1·25
169		1d. deep green (11.79)	5·00	1·25
		a. Imperf between (horiz pair)		
170	12	2d. orange-red (8.76)	4·50	12
171		2d. dull brick-red (21.5.77)	4·50	12
172		2d. blood-red (31.10.79)	£170	3·00
173		2d. pale red (4.85)	4·50	12

(*b*) *P* 10 × 11½–12½, *or* 11½–12½ × 10, *or compound*

No.	Type	Description	Unused	Used
174	11	1d. deep green (11.2.80)	18·00	2·25
175		1d. blue-green (2.3.80)	8·00	1·90
176	12	2d. orange-red (4.9.77)	£120	3·00
177		2d. brick-red (6.80)	£120	3·00

(*c*) *P* 11½–12½

No.	Type	Description	Unused	Used
178	11	1d. blue-green (2.84)	—	£110
179	12	3d. orange-red (14.9.77)	—	£110
180		2d. blood-red (1.4.80)	—	£110

For stamps perf 15, see Nos. 238/40.

1882 (1 Jan). *Surch with T* **14.** *W* **13.** *P* 10.

No.	Type	Description	Unused	Used
181	11	½d. on 1d. green	7·00	2·50

15

16

17

18

1883–95. W **13.** (*a*) *P* 10.
182 **15** ½d. chocolate (1.3.83) .. .. .. 2·25 40
a. Imperf between (horiz pair) ..
183 ½d. Venetian red (4.4.89) .. .. 2·00 35
184 ½d. brown (1895) .. .. .. 2·25 35
185 **16** 3d. sage-green (12.86) .. .. .. 8·00 1·10
186 3d. olive-green (6.6.90) .. .. .. 8·00 1·50
187 3d. deep green (12.4.93) .. .. 5·50 60
188 **17** 4d. pale violet (3.90) .. .. .. 7·00 95
189 4d. aniline violet (3.1.93) .. .. 9·00 1·00
190 **18** 6d. pale blue (4.87) .. .. .. 7·00 1·40
191 6d. blue (5.5.87) .. .. .. 8·50 60
(*b*) *P* 10 × 11½–12½, 11½–12½ × 10, *or compound*
192 **15** ½d. pale brown (25.9.91) .. .. 11·00 1·25
193 ½d. dark brown (9.9.92) .. .. .. 4·00 95
a. Imperf between (horiz pair) ..
(*c*) *P* 11½–12½
194 **15** ½d. Venetian red (12.10.90) .. .. 5·50 75

In 1884, and in later years, reprints on paper wmkd Crown SA, W **10**, were made of Nos. 1, 2, 3, 4, 12, 13, 14, 15, 19, 24, 27, 28, 32, 33, 34, 35, 36, 37, 38, 40, 43, 44, 49*a*, 53, 65, 67, 67 with surch in red, 70, 71, 72, 73, 78, 79, 81, 83, 86, 90, 118, 119, 120, 121, 122, 155, 158, 159, 164, 181, 182. They are optd with the word "REPRINT".

For stamps perf 15, see Nos. 236/7 and 242/4.

19

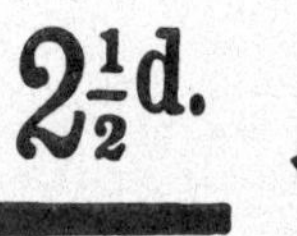

(20)

(21)

(Plates and electrotypes by D.L.R. Printed in Adelaide)

1886–96. *T* **19** (*inscr* "POSTAGE & REVENUE"). **W 13.** *Parts of two or more wmks, on each stamp, sometimes sideways.* A. *Perf* 10. B. *Perf* 11½–12½ (*small or large holes*).

		A		B	
195	2s. 6d. mauve	25·00	8·00	†	
	a. Dull violet	†		24·00	6·00
	b. Bright aniline violet	†		25·00	7·00
196	5s. rose-pink	40·00	12·00	32·00	12·00
	a. Rose-carmine ..	†		35·00	14·00
197	10s. green	£110	35·00	80·00	35·00
198	15s. brownish yellow ..	£225	—	£275	£120
199	£1 blue	£200	90·00	£150	80·00
200	£2 Venetian red ..	£450	£200	£450	£200
201	50s. dull pink	£600	£250	£600	—
202	£3 sage green	£700	—	£700	—
203	£4 lemon	£900	—	£800	—
204	£5 grey	£1500	—	£1600	—
205	£5 brown (1896) ..	†		£1600	£1000
206	£10 bronze	£2250	£700	£1700	£700
207	£15 silver	£4500	—	£4500	—
208	£20 claret	£5000	—	£5000	—

Variations exist in the length of the words and shape of the letters of the value inscription.

The 2s. 6d. dull violet, 5s. rose-pink, 10s., £1 and £5 brown exist perf 11½–12½ with either large or small holes; the 2s. 6d. aniline, 5s. rose-carmine, 15s., £2 and 50s. with large holes only and the remainder only with small holes.

Stamps perforated 11½–12½ small holes, are, generally speaking, rather rarer than those with the 1895 (large holes) gauge.

Stamps perf 10 were issued on 20 Dec 1886. Stamps perf 11½–12½ (small holes) are known with earliest dates covering the period from June 1890 to Feb 1896. Earliest dates of stamps with large holes range from July 1896 to May 1902.

1891 (1 Jan). *Colours changed and surch with T* **20/21.** **W 13.**
(*a*) *P* 10
229 **17** 2½d. on 4d. pale green (Br.) .. .. 4·50 2·50
a. Fraction bar omitted .. .. 90·00 75·00
230 2½d. on 4d. deep green (Br.) .. .. 5·00 1·75
a. "2" and "½" closer together .. 20·00 18·00
b. Fraction bar omitted .. ..
c. Imperf between (horiz pair) ..
d. Imperf between (vert pair) .. .. — £325
231 **18** 5d. on 6d. pale brown (C.) .. .. 11·00 3·25
232 5d. on 6d. dark brown (C.) .. .. 11·00 3·00
a. No stop after "5D" £150
(*b*) *P* 10 × 11½–12½ *or* 11½–12½ × 10
233 **17** 2½d. on 4d. pale green (Br.) .. .. 6·00 3·00
234 2½d. on 4d. deep green (Br.) .. .. 6·00 3·00
(*c*) *P* 11½–12½
235 **17** 2½d. on 4d. green (Br.) .. .. .. 25·00 40·00

1893–4. *Surch with T* **20** (*No.* 241). **W 13.** *P* 15.
236 **15** ½d. pale brown (1.93) .. .. .. 2·50 30
237 ½d. dark brown .. .. .. 2·50 30
a. Perf 12½ between (pair) .. £120 28·00
b. Imperf between (horiz pair) .. 80·00
238 **11** 1d. green (8.5.93) .. .. .. 3·00 1·25
239 **12** 2d. pale orange (9.2.93) .. .. 5·50 12
240 2d. orange-red .. .. .. 6·00 12
a. Imperf between (vert pair) .. £150
241 **17** 2½d. on 4d. green (14.10.93) .. .. 7·00 2·00
a. "2" and "½" closer .. .. 30·00 19·00
b. Fraction bar omitted .. ..
242 4d. purple (1.1.94) .. .. .. 10·00 2·00
243 4d. slate-violet .. .. .. 10·00 1·75
244 **18** 6d. blue (20.11.93) .. .. .. 19·00 3·50

22

23

24 G.P.O., Adelaide

(Des Tannenberg, Melbourne; plates by D.L.R. Typo Sands and McDougall, Adelaide)

1894 (1 Mar). **W 13.** *P* 15.
245 **22** 2½d. violet-blue .. .. .. 9·00 1·00
246 **23** 5d. brown-purple .. .. .. 10·00 1·25

1895–99. **W 13.** *P* 13.
247 **15** ½d. pale brown (9.95) .. .. 2·50 30
248 ½d. deep brown (19.3.97) .. .. 2·50 30
249 **11** 1d. pale green (11.1.95) .. .. 4·00 1·25
250 1d. green .. .. .. 4·00 1·25
a. Imperf between (vert pair) .. ..
251 **12** 2d. pale orange (19.1.95) .. .. 3·50 12
252 2d. orange-red (9.5.95) .. .. 3·50 10
253 **22** 2½d. violet-blue (11.2.95) .. .. 4·00 45
254 **16** 3d. pale olive-green (26.7.97) .. 5·00 55
255 3d. dark olive-green (27.11.99) .. 5·00 50
256 **17** 4d. violet (21.1.96) .. .. 6·00 40
257 **23** 5d. brown-purple (1.96) .. .. 6·50 50
258 5d. purple .. .. .. 6·50 45
259 **18** 6d. pale blue (3.96) .. .. 7·00 40
260 6d. blue .. .. .. 7·00 40

The 1d. in pale green, formerly listed under No. 261 as redrawn with slightly thicker lettering, is now accepted as resulting from a printing from a worn plate.

(½d. Typo D.L.R.)

1898–1906. **W 13.**

A. *Perf* 13 (1898–1903). B. *Perf* 12 × 11½ (*comb*) (1904–6)

			A		B	
262	**24**	½d. yellow-green	1·00	20	1·25	12
263	**11**	1d. rosine	2·00	12	5·00	12
264		1d. scarlet	2·75	12	3·00	12
		a. Deep red	2·50	12	†	
265	**12**	2d. bright violet ..	2·00	12	2·75	12
266	**22**	2½d. indigo	4·50	45	5·50	45
267	**23**	5d. dull purple ..	†		7·00	85

Earliest dates: Perf 13. ½d., 27 Dec 1899; 1d. rosine, 8 August 1899; 1d. scarlet, 23 December 1903; 2d. 10 October 1899; 2½d. 25 March 1898.

Perf 12 × 11½. ½d. July 1905; 1d. rosine, 2 February 1904; 1d. scarlet, 25 July 1904; 2d. 11 October 1904; 2½d. 4 July 1906; 5d. January 1905.

25

The measurements given indicate the length of the value inscription in the bottom label. The dates are those of the earliest known postmarks.

1902–4. *As T* **19**, *but top tablet as T* **25** (*thin* "POSTAGE"). **W 13.**
(*a*) *P* 11½–12½
268 3d. olive-green (18½ mm) (1.8.02) .. 2·75 35
269 4d. red-orange (17 mm) (29.11.02) .. 4·50 70
270 6d. blue-green (16–16½ mm) (29.11.02) .. 5·50 70
271 8d. ultramarine (19 mm) (25.4.02) .. 7·50 1·90
272 8d. ultramarine (16½ mm) (22.3.04) .. 7·50 1·90
a. "EIGNT" £1000 £1300
273 9d. rosy lake (19.9.02) .. .. 7·00 1·00
a. Imperf between (vert pair) .. £190
b. Imperf between (horiz pair) ..
274 10d. dull yellow (29.11.02) .. .. 8·50 2·00
275 1s. brown (18.8.02) .. .. .. 10·00 1·75
a. Imperf between (horiz pair) ..
b. Imperf between (vert pair) .. £550
c. "POSTAGE" and value in red-brown 45·00 20·00
276 2s. 6d. pale violet (19.9.02) .. .. 32·00
a. Bright violet (2.2.03) .. .. 25·00 7·00
277 5s. rose (17.10.02) .. .. .. 55·00 40·00
278 10s. green (1.11.02) .. .. .. £100 60·00
279 £1 blue (1.11.02) £250 £140
(*b*) *P* 12
280 3d. olive-green (20 mm) (15.4.04) .. 3·50 70
a. "POSTAGE" omitted; value below "AUSTRALIA" £300
281 4d. orange-red (17½–18 mm) (18.2.03) .. 5·00 70
282 6d. blue-green (15 mm) (14.11.03) .. 14·00 2·25
283 9d. rosy lake (2.12.03) .. .. 15·00 3·00

26

V X

In Type X the letters in the bottom line are slightly larger than in Type V, especially the "A", "S" and "P".

Y Z

In Type Z the letters "S" and "G" are more open than in Type Y. Nos. 196/*a* and 277 are similar to Type Y with all letters thick and regular and the last "S" has the top curve rounded instead of being slightly flattened.

1904–11. *As T* **19**, *but top tablet as T* **26** (*thick* "POSTAGE"). **W 13.** *P* 12.
284 6d. blue-green (27.4.04) .. .. 4·50 70
285 8d. bright ultramarine (4.7.05) .. .. 8·00 2·00
a. Value closer (15¼ mm) .. .. 16·00
b. Dull ultramarine (2.4.08) .. .. 9·00 2·25
ba. Ditto. Value closer (15¼ mm) .. 24·00
286 9d. rosy lake (17–17¼ mm) (18.7.04) .. 7·00 1·00
a. Value 16½–16¾ mm (2.06) .. 15·00 3·50
b. Brown-lake. Perf 12½ small holes (6.6.11) 10·00
287 10d. dull yellow (8.07) .. .. .. 15·00 3·00
a. Imperf between (horiz pair) .. £225 £160
b. Imperf between (vert pair) .. ..
288 1s. brown (12.4.04) .. .. .. 9·00 1·75
a. Imperf between (vert pair) .. £130
b. Imperf between (horiz pair) .. £180
289 2s. 6d. bright violet (V.) (14.7.05) .. 38·00 6·00
a. Dull violet (X) (8.06) .. .. 38·00 6·00
290 5s. rose-scarlet (Y) (8.04) .. .. 45·00 25·00
a. Scarlet (Z) (8.06) .. .. 45·00 25·00
b. Pale rose. Perf 12½ (small holes) (Z) (7.10) 60·00 28·00
291 10s. green (26.8.08) £120 £150
292 £1 blue (29.12.04) £170 £125
a. Perf 12½ (small holes) (7.10) .. £150 £100

The "value closer" variety on the 8d. occurs six times in the sheet of 60. The value normally measures 16½ mm but in the variety it is 15¼ mm.

The 9d., 5s. and £1, perf 12½ (small holes), are late printings made in 1910–11 to use up the Crown SA paper.

No. 286*b* has the value as Type C of the 9d. on Crown over A paper.

27

1905–11. W **27.** *P* 12 × 11½ (*new comb machine*).
293 **24** ½d. pale green (4.07) .. .. .. 1·00 20
a. Yellow-green .. .. .. 1·10 12
294 **11** 1d. rosine (2.12.05) .. .. .. 1·90 12
a. Scarlet (4.11) .. .. .. 1·75 12
295 **12** 2d. bright violet (2.2.06) .. .. 2·50 12
aa. Imperf between (pair) .. ..
a. Mauve (4.08) .. .. .. 1·60 12
296 **22** 2½d. indigo-blue (14.9.10) .. .. 7·00 95
297 **23** 5d. brown-purple (11.3.08) .. .. 7·50 1·40

Three types of the 9d., perf 12½, distinguishable by the distance between "NINE" and "PENCE".

A. Distance 1¾ mm. B. Distance 2¼ mm. C. Distance 2½ mm.

1906–12. *T* **19** ("POSTAGE" *thick as T* **26**). **W 27.** *P* 12 *or* 12½ (*small holes*).
298 3d. sage-green (19 mm) (26.6.06) .. 4·00 70
a. Imperf between (horiz pair) .. .. — £500
b. Perf 12½. *Sage-green* (17 mm) (9.12.09) 4·50 70
c. Perf 12½. *Deep olive* (20 mm) (7.10) .. 17·00 3·25
d. Perf 12½. *Yellow-olive* (14 mm) (16.12.11) 8·00 80
da. Perf 12½. *Bright olive-green* (19–19¾ mm) (5.12) .. .. .. 7·50 70
e. Perf 11 (17 mm) (10.7.11) £180 £180
299 4d. orange-red (10.9.06) .. .. 6·00 1·25
a. Orange .. .. .. 7·50 1·10
b. Perf 12½. *Orange* (27.10.09) .. 6·00 1·10
300 6d. blue-green (1.9.06) .. .. 7·00 75
a. Perf 12½ (21.4.10) .. .. 5·50 55
ab. Perf 12½. Imperf between (vert pair) £275 £250
301 8d. bright ultramarine (*p* 12½) (8.09) .. 10·00 3·00
a. Value closer (8.09) .. .. 28·00 24·00
302 9d. brown-lake (3.2.06) .. .. 10·00 1·50
a. Imperf between (vert pair) .. £180
aa. Imperf between (horiz pair) .. £200
b. Deep lake (9.5.08) .. .. 24·00 3·00
c. Perf 12½. *Lake* (A) (5.9.09) .. 11·00 3·00
d. Perf 12½. *Lake* (B) (7.09) .. 12·00 3·00
e. Perf 12½. *Brown-lake* (C) .. 17·00 5·00
ea. Perf 12½. *Deep lake.* Thin paper (C) .. 14·00 3·00
f. Perf 11 (1909) .. .. .. — £160
303 1s. brown (30.5.06) .. .. .. 11·00 2·50
a. Imperf between (horiz pair) .. £150
b. Perf 12½ (10.3.10) .. .. 8·00 1·00
304 2s. 6d. bright violet (X) (10.6.09) .. 30·00 6·00
a. Perf 12½. *Pale violet* (X) (6.10) .. 30·00 7·00
ab. Perf 12½. *Deep purple* (X) (5.11.12) .. 35·00 5·50
305 5s. bright rose (*p* 12½) (Z) (24.4.11) .. 65·00

The "value closer" variety of the 8d. occurred 11 times in the sheet of 60 in the later printing only. On No. 301 the value measures 16½ mm while on No. 301a it is 15¼ mm.

The 1s. brown, perf compound of 11½ and 12½, formerly listed is now omitted, as it must have been perforated by the 12 machine, which in places varied from 11½ to 13.

OFFICIAL STAMPS

A. Departmentals

Following suspected abuses involving stamps supplied for official use it was decided by the South Australian authorities that such supplies were to be overprinted with a letter, or letters, indicating the department of the administration to which the stamps had been invoiced.

The system was introduced on 1 April 1868 using overprints struck in red. Later in the same year the colour of the overprints was amended to blue, and, during the latter months of 1869, to black.

In 1874 the Postmaster-General recommended that this somewhat cumbersome system be replaced by a general series of "O.S." overprints with the result that the separate accounting for the Departmentals ceased on 30 June of that year. Existing stocks continued to be used, however, and it is believed that much of the residue was passed to the Government Printer to pay postage on copies of the *Government Gazette*.

We are now able to provide a check list of these most interesting issues based on the definitive work, *The Departmental Stamps of South Australia* by A. R. Butler, FRPSL, RDP, published by the Royal Philatelic Society, London in 1978.

No attempt has been made to assign the various overprints to the catalogue numbers of the basic stamps, but each is clearly identified by both watermark and perforation. The colours are similar to those of the contemporary postage stamps, but there can be shade variations. Errors of overprint are recorded in footnotes, but not errors occurring on the basic stamps used.

Most departmental overprints are considered to be scarce to rare in used condition, with unused examples, used multiples and covers being regarded as considerable rarities.

Forgeries of a few items do exist, but most can be readily identified by comparison with genuine examples. A number of forged overprints on stamps not used for the genuine issues also occur.

A. (Architect)

Optd in red with stop. *W* **2.** 2d. (*roul*), 4d. (*p* 11½–12½), 6d. (*roul*), 1s. (*roul*)
Optd in red without stop. *W* **2.** *Roul.* 1d., 6d., 1s.
Optd in black. (*a*) *W* **2.** 4d. (*p* 11½–12½), 4d. (*p* 10), 4d. (*p* 10 × 11½–12½), 6d. (*p* 11½–12½), 2s. (*roul*)
(*b*) *W* **10.** 2d. D.L.R. (*roul*), 2d. D.L.R. (*p* 10)

A.G. (Attorney–General)

Optd in red. *W* **2.** *Roul.* 1d., 2d., 6d., 1s.
Optd in blue. (*a*) *W* **2.** *Roul.* 6d.
(*b*) *W* **10.** *Roul.* 2d. D.L.R.
Optd in black. (*a*) *W* **2.** 1d. (*p* 11½–12½ × *roul*), 4d. (*p* 11½–12½), 4d. (*p* 10), 6d. (*p* 11½–12½ × *roul*), 6d. (*p* 11½–12½), 1s. (*p* 11½–12½ × *roul*), 1s. (*p* 10)
(*b*) *W* **10.** 2d. D.L.R. (*roul*), 2d. D.L.R. (*p* 10)

A.O. (Audit Office)

Optd in red. *W* **2.** 2d. (*roul*), 4d. (*p* 11½–12½), 6d. (*roul*)
Optd in blue. (*a*) *W* **2.** *P* 11½–12½. 1d., 6d.
(*b*) *W* **10.** *Roul.* 2d. D.L.R.
Optd in black. (*a*) *W* **2.** 1d. (*p* 11½–12½), 1d. (*p* 10), 1d. (*p* 10 × 11½–12), 2d. D.L.R. (*roul*), 4d. (*p* 11½–12½), 4d. (*p* 10 × 11½–12½), 6d. (*roul*), 6d. (*p* 11½–12½), 1s. (*p* 10), 1s. (*p* 11½–12½ × *roul*)
(*b*) *W* **7.** *P* 10. 4d.
(*c*) *W* **10.** 2d. D.L.R. (*roul*), 2d. D.L.R. (*p* 10)

B.D. (Barracks Department)

Optd in red. *W* **2.** *Roul.* 2d., 6d., 1s.

B.G. (Botanic Garden)

Optd in black. (*a*) *W* **2.** 1d. (*p* 11½–12½ × *roul*), 1d. (*p* 11½–12½), 1d. (*p* 10), 1d. (*p* 10 × 11½–12½), 2d. D.L.R. (*roul*), 6d. (*roul*), 6d. (*p* 11½–12½ × *roul*), 6d. (*p* 11½–12½), 6d. (*p* 10), 1s. (*p* 11½–12½ × *roul*), 1s. (*p* 11½–12½), 1s. (*p* 10 × 11½–12½)
(*b*) *W* **7.** *P* 10. 2d. D.L.R.
(*c*) *W* **10.** 2d. D.L.R. (*roul*), 2d. D.L.R. (*p* 10)

B.M. (Bench of Magistrates)

Optd in red. *W* **2.** *Roul.* 2d.
Optd in black. *W* **10.** *Roul.* 2d. D.L.R.

C. (Customs)

Optd in red. *W* **2.** 1d. (*roul*), 2d. (*roul*), 4d. (*p* 11½–12½), 6d. (*roul*), 1s. (*roul*)
Optd in blue. (*a*) *W* **2.** *Roul.* 1d., 4d., 6d., 1s., 2s.
(*b*) *W* **10.** *Roul.* 2d. D.L.R.
Optd in black. (*a*) *W* **2.** 1d. (*roul*), 1d. (*p* 10), 1d. (*p* 10 × 11½–12½), 2d. D.L.R. (*p* 10 × 11½–12½), 4d. (*p* 11½–12½), 4d. (*p* 10), 4d. (*p* 10 × 11½–12½), 6d. (*roul*), 6d. (*p* 11½–12½), 6d. (*p* 10), 1s. (*p* 11½–12½ × *roul*), 1s. (*p* 11½–12½), 2s. (*roul*)
(*b*) *W* **7.** *P* 10. 2d. D.L.R.
(*c*) *W* **10.** 2d. D.L.R. (*roul*), 2d. D.L.R. (*p* 10 × *roul*), 2d. D.L.R. (*p* 10), 2d. D.L.R. (*p* 10 × 11½–12½)

The 2d. (*W* **10.** *Roul*) with black overprint is known showing the error "G" for "C".

C.D. (Convict Department)

Optd in red. *W* **2.** 2d. (*roul*), 4d. (*p* 11½–12½), 6d. (*roul*), 1s. (*roul*)
Optd in black. (*a*) *W* **2.** 1d. (*p* 11½–12½ × *roul*), 2d. D.L.R. (*roul*), 2d. D.L.R. (*p* 11½–12½), 2d. D.L.R. (*p* 11½–12½ × *roul*), 4d. (*p* 11½–12½), 6d. (*p* 11½–12½ × *roul*), 1s. (*p* 11½–12½ × *roul*)
(*b*) *W* **10.** *Roul.* 2d. D.L.R.

C.L. (Crown Lands)

Optd in red. *W* **2.** 2d. (*roul*), 4d. (*p* 11½–12½), 6d. (*roul*), 1s. (*roul*)
Optd in blue. (*a*) *W* **2.** *Roul.* 4d., 6d.
(*b*) *W* **10.** *Roul.* 2d. D.L.R.
Optd in black. (*a*) *W* **2.** 2d. D.L.R. (*roul*), 4d. (*p* 11½–12½), 4d. (*p* 10), 4d. (*p* 10 × 11½–12½), 6d. (*roul*), 6d. (*p* 11½–12½), 1s. (*p* 11½–12½ × *roul*), 1s. (*p* 11½–12½), 2s. (*roul*), 2s. (*p* 11½–12½)
(*b*) *W* **7.** *P* 10. 2d. D.L.R., 4d.
(*c*) *W* **10.** 2d. D.L.R. (*roul*), 2d. D.L.R. (*p* 10), 2d. D.L.R. (*p* 10 × 11½–12½)

The 2s. (*W* **2.** *P* 11½–12½) with black overprint is known showing the stop omitted after "L".

C.O. (Commissariat Office)

Optd in red. *W* **2.** 2d. (*roul*), 4d. (*p* 11½–12½), 6d. (*roul*), 1s. (*roul*)
Optd in black. (*a*) *W* **2.** 4d. (*p* 11½–12½), 4d. (*p* 10), 4d. (*p* 10 × 11½–12½), 6d. (*p* 11½–12½), 1s. (*p* 11½–12½), 2s. (*p* 11½–12½)
(*b*) *W* **10.** 2d. D.L.R. (*roul*), 2d. D.L.R. (*p* 10)

The 2s. (*W* **2.** *P* 11½–12½) with black overprint is known showing the stop omitted after "O".

C.P. (Commissioner of Police)

Optd in red. *W* **2.** 2d. (*roul*), 4d. (*p* 11½–12½), 6d. (*roul*)

C.S. (Chief Secretary)

Optd in red. *W* **2.** 2d. (*roul*), 4d. (*p* 11½–12½), 6d. (*roul*), 1s. (*roul*)
Optd in blue. (*a*) *W* **2.** *Roul.* 4d., 6d.
(*b*) *W* **10.** *Roul.* 2d. D.L.R.
Optd in black. (*a*) *W* **2.** 2d. D.L.R. (*roul*), 4d. (*roul*), 4d. (*p* 11½–12½ × *roul*), 4d. (*p* 11½–12½), 4d. (*p* 10), 4d. (*p* 10 × 11½–12½), 6d. (*p* 11½–12½ × *roul*), 6d. (*p* 11½–12½), 6d. (*p* 10), 6d. (*p* 10 × 11½–12½), 1s. (*p* 11½–12½ × *roul*), 1s. (*p* 11½–12½), 1s. (*p* 10), 1s. (*p* 10 × 11½–12½), 2s. (*p* 10 × 11½–12½)
(*b*) *W* **7.** *P* 10. 4d.
(*c*) *W* **10.** 2d. D.L.R. (*roul*), 2d. D.L.R. (*p* 10)

C.Sgn. (Colonial Surgeon)

Optd in red. *W* **2.** 2d. (*roul*), 4d. (*p* 11½–12½), 6d. (*roul*)
Optd in black. (*a*) *W* **2.** 2d. D.L.R. (*roul*), 4d. (*p* 11½–12½), 4d. (*p* 10), 4d. (*p* 10 × 11½–12½), 6d. (*roul*), 6d. (*p* 11½–12½), 1s. (*p* 11½–12½ × *roul*)
(*b*) *W* **10.** 2d. D.L.R. (*roul*), 2d. D.L.R. (*p* 11½–12½ × *roul*), 2d. D.L.R. (*p* 10)

Two types of overprint exist on the 2d. D.L.R. (*W* **10.** *Roul*), the second type having block capitals instead of the serifed type used for the other values.

D.B. (Destitute Board)

Optd in red. *W* **2.** 1d. (*roul*), 2d. (*roul*), 4d. (*p* 11½–12½), 6d. (*roul*), 1s. (*roul*)
Optd in blue. (*a*) *W* **2.** *Roul.* 2d. D.L.R., 6d.
(*b*) *W* **10.** *Roul.* 2d. D.L.R.
Optd in black. (*a*) *W* **2.** 1d. (*p* 11½–12½), 4d. (*p* 11½–12½), 4d. (*p* 10), 6d. (*p* 10 × 11½–12½), 1s. (*p* 10)
(*b*) *W* **10.** 2d. D.L.R. (*roul*), 2d. D.L.R. (*p* 10), 2d. D.L.R. (*p* 10 × 11½–12½)

The 2d. D.L.R. (*W* **10.** *P* 10) with black overprint is known showing the stop omitted after "D".

D.R. (Deeds Registration)

Optd in red. *W* **2.** *Roul*, 2d., 6d.

E. (Engineer)

Optd in red. *W* **2.** 2d. (*roul*), 4d. (*p* 11½–12½), 6d. (*roul*), 1s. (*roul*)
Optd in blue. (*a*) *W* **2.** *Roul.* 1s.
(*b*) *W* **10.** *Roul.* 2d. D.L.R.
Optd in black. (*a*) *W* **2.** 4d. (*p* 11½–12½ × *roul*), 4d. (*p* 11½–12½), 4d. (*p* 10), 4d. (*p* 10 × 11½–12½), 6d. (*p* 11½–12½), 6d. (*p* 10 × 11½–12½), 1s. (*p* 11½–12½ × *roul*). 1s. (*p* 11½–12½), 1s. (*p* 10 × 11½–12½), 2s. (*p* 10 × 11½–12½)
(*b*) *W* **7.** *P* 10. 4d.
(*c*) *W* **10.** 2d. D.L.R. (*roul*), 2d. D.L.R. (*p* 10)

E.B. (Education Board)

Optd in red. *W* **2.** 2d. (*roul*), 4d. (*p* 11½–12½), 6d. (*roul*)
Optd in blue. (*a*) *W* **2.** *Roul.* 4d., 6d.
(*b*) *W* **10.** *Roul.* 2d. D.L.R.
Optd in black. (*a*) *W* **2.** 2d. D.L.R. (*roul*), 4d. (*roul*), 4d. (*p* 11½–12½), 4d. (*p* 10), 4d. (*p* 10 × 11½–12½), 6d. (*p* 11½–12½ × *roul*), 6d. (*p* 11½–12½)
(*b*) *W* **7.** *P* 10. 2d. D.L.R.
(*c*) *W* **10.** 2d. D.L.R. (*roul*), 2d. D.L.R. (*p* 10), 2d. D.L.R. (*p* 10 × 11½–12½)

G.F. (Gold Fields)

Optd in black. (*a*) *W* **2.** *Roul.* 6d.
(*b*) *W* **10.** 2d. D.L.R. (*p* 10 × *roul*), 2d. D.L.R. (*p* 10)

G.P. (Government Printer)

Optd in red. *W* **2.** *Roul.* 1d., 2d., 6d., 1s.
Optd in blue. (*a*) *W* **2.** *Roul.* 1d., 6d., 1s., 2s.
(*b*) *W* **10.** *Roul.* 2d. D.L.R.
Optd in black. (*a*) *W* **2.** 1d. (*roul*), 1d. (*p* 11½–12½ × *roul*), 1d. (*p* 11½–12½), 1d. (*p* 10), 1d. (*p* 10 × 11½–12½), 6d. (*p* 11½–12½ × *roul*), 1s. (*p* 10), 1s. (*p* 10 × 11½–12½), 2s. (*roul*), 2s. (*p* 11½–12½), 2s. (*p* 10 × 11½–12½)
(*b*) *W* **10.** 2d. D.L.R. (*roul*), 2d. D.L.R. (*p* 10)

The 1d. (*W* **2.** *Roul*) with red overprint is known showing "C.P." instead of "G.P.".

G.S. (Government Storekeeper)

Optd in red. *W* **2.** *Roul.* 2d., 6d., 1s.

G.T. (Goolwa Tramway)

Optd in red. *W* **2.** 1d. (*roul*), 2d. (*roul*), 4d. (*p* 11½–12½), 6d. (*roul*), 1s. (*roul*)
Optd in black. (*a*) *W* **2.** 2d. D.L.R. (*roul*), 4d. (*p* 11½–12½)
(*b*) *W* **10.** 2d. D.L.R. (*roul*), 2d. D.L.R. (*p* 10)

The 2d. and 6d. (both *W* **2.** *Roul*) with red overprint are known showing the stop omitted after "T". The 1s. (*W* **2.** *Roul*) with red overprint is known showing "C.T." instead of "G.T.".

H. (Hospitals)

Optd in black. (*a*) *W* **7.** *P* 10. 2d. D.L.R.
(*b*) *W* **10.** 2d. D.L.R. (*p* 10), 2d. D.L.R. (*p* 10 × 11½–12½)

H.A. (House of Assembly)

Optd in red. *W* **2.** 1d. (*roul*), 2d. (*roul*), 4d. (*p* 11½–12½), 6d. (*roul*), 1s. (*roul*)
Optd in black. (*a*) *W* **2.** 1d. (*p* 11½–12½), 1d. (*p* 10), 1d. (*p* 10 × 11½–12½), 4d. (*p* 11½–12½), 4d. (*p* 10), 6d. (*roul*), 6d. (*p* 11½–12½), 1s. (*p* 11½–12½ × *roul*), 1s. (*p* 11½–12½)
(*b*) *W* **10.** 2d. D.L.R. (*roul*), 2d. D.L.R. (*p* 10)

I.A. (Immigration Agent)

Optd in red. *W* **2.** 1d. (*roul*), 2d. (*roul*), 4d. (*p* 11½–12½), 6d. (*roul*)

I.E. (Intestate Estates)

Optd in black. W **10.** *P* 10. 2d. D.L.R.

I.S. (Inspector of Sheep)

Optd in red. *W* **2.** *Roul.* 2d., 6d.
Optd in blue. *W* **2.** *P* 11½–12½. 6d.
Optd in black. (*a*) *W* **2.** 2d. D.L.R. (*roul*), 6d. (*p* 11½–12½ × *roul*)
(*b*) *W* **10.** 2d. D.L.R. (*roul*), 2d. D.L.R. (*p* 10)

L.A. (Lunatic Asylum)

Optd in red. *W* **2.** 1d. (*roul*), 2d. (*roul*), 4d. (*p* 11½–12½), 6d. (*roul*), 1s. (*roul*)
Optd in black. (*a*) *W* **2.** 4d. (*p* 11½–12½), 4d. (*p* 10), 4d. (*p* 10 × 11½–12½), 6d. (*p* 11½–12½ × *roul*), 6d. (*p* 11½–12½), 1s. (*p* 11½–12½), 2s. (*roul*)
(*b*) *W* **10.** 2d. D.L.R. (*roul*), 2d. D.L.R. (*p* 10)

L.C. (Legislative Council)

Optd in red. *W* **2.** *Roul.* 2d., 6d.
Optd in black. (*a*) *W* **2.** *Roul.* 6d.
(*b*) *W* **10.** 2d. D.L.R. (*roul*), 2d. D.L.R. (*p* 10 × *roul*)

The 2d. and 6d. (both *W* **2.** *Roul*) with red overprint are known showing the stop omitted after "C".

L.L. (Legislative Librarian)

Optd in red. *W* **2.** 2d. (*roul*), 4d. (*p* 11½–12½), 6d. (*roul*)
Optd in black. (*a*) *W* **2.** *P* 11½–12½. 6d.
(*b*) *W* **10.** *P* 10. 2d. D.L.R.

The 2d. and 6d. (both *W* **2.** *Roul*) with red overprint are known showing the stop omitted from between the two letters.

L.T. (Land Titles)

Optd in red. *W* **2.** 2d. (*roul*), 4d. (*p* 11½–12½), 6d. (*roul*), 1s. (*roul*)
Optd in blue. *W* **10.** *Roul.* 2d. D.L.R.
Optd in black. (*a*) *W* **2.** 4d. (*p* 11½–12½), 4d. (*p* 10), 4d. (*p* 10 × 11½–12½), 6d. (*p* 11½–12½ × *roul*), 6d. (*p* 11½–12½), 6d. (*p* 10), 6d. (*p* 10 × 11½–12½)
(*b*) *W* **7.** *P* 10. 2d. D.L.R.
(*c*) *W* **10.** 2d. D.L.R. (*roul*), 2d. D.L.R. (*p* 10)

The 2d. and 6d. (both *W* **2.** *Roul*) with red overprint are known showing the stop omitted after "T".

M. (Military)

Optd in red. *W* **2.** *Roul.* 2d., 6d., 1s.
Optd in black. *W* **2.** 6d. (*p* 11½–12½ × *roul*), 1s. (*p* 11½–12½ × *roul*), 2s. (*roul*)

M.B. (Marine Board)

Optd in red. *W* **2.** 1d. (*roul*), 2d. (*roul*), 4d. (*roul*), 4d. (*p* 11½–12½), 6d. (*roul*), 1s. (*roul*)
Optd in black. (*a*) *W* **2.** 1d. (*roul*), 1d. (*p* 11½–12½), 2d. D.L.R. (*roul*), 4d. (*p* 11½–12½ × *roul*), 4d. (*p* 11½–12½), 4d. (*p* 10), 4d. (*p* 10 × 11½–12½), 6d. (*roul*), 6d. (*p* 11½–12½), 6d. (*p* 10), 6d. (*p* 10 × 11½–12½), 1s. (*p* 11½–12½ × *roul*), 1s. (*p* 11½–12½), 1s. (*p* 10), 1s. (*p* 10 × 11½–12½)
(*b*) *W* **7.** *P* 10. 2d. D.L.R., 4d.
(*c*) *W* **10.** 2d. D.L.R. (*roul*), 2d. D.L.R. (*p* 10)

M.R. (Manager of Railways)

Optd in red. *W* **2.** *Roul.* 2d., 6d.
Optd in black. (*a*) *W* **2.** 1d. (*p* 11½–12½), 1d. (*p* 10), 2d. D.L.R. (*roul*), 4d. (*roul*), 4d. (*p* 11½–12½), 6d. (*roul*), 6d. (*p* 11½–12½ × *roul*), 6d. (*p* 11½–12½), 10d. on 9d. (*roul*), 1s. (*roul*), 1s. (*p* 11½–12½ × *roul*), 2s. (*p* 11½–12½), 2s. (*p* 10 × 11½–12½)
(*b*) *W* **10.** 2d. D.L.R. (*roul*), 2d. D.L.R. (*p* 10), 2d. D.L.R. (*p* 10 × 11½–12½)

M.R.G. (Main Roads Gambierton)

Optd in red without stops. *W* **2.** *Roul.* 2d., 6d.
Optd in blue without stops. *W* **10.** *Roul.* 2d. D.L.R.
Optd in black without stops. *W* **10.** 2d. D.L.R. (*roul*), 2d. D.L.R. (*p* 10)
Optd in black with stops. *W* **10.** 2d. D.L.R. (*roul*), 2d. D.L.R. (*p* 10)

The 2d. D.L.R. (*W* **10.** *P* 10) with black overprint is known showing the stops omitted after "M" and "R".

N.T. (Northern Territory)

Optd in black. (*a*) *W* **2.** *P* 11½–12½. 1d., 3d. on 4d., 4d., 6d., 1s.
(*b*) *W* **10.** 2d. D.L.R. (*roul*), 2d. D.L.R. (*p* 10)

O.A. (Official Assignee)

Optd in red. *W* **2.** 2d. (*roul*), 4d. (*p* 11½–12½)
Optd in blue. *W* **10.** *Roul.* 2d. D.L.R.
Optd in black. (*a*) *W* **2.** 4d. (*p* 11½–12½), 4d. (*p* 10)
(*b*) *W* **7.** *P* 10. 2d. D.L.R.
(*c*) *W* **10.** 2d. D.L.R. (*roul*), 2d. D.L.R. (*p* 10 × *roul*), 2d. D.L.R. (*p* 10)

P. (Police)

Optd in blue. (*a*) *W* **2.** *Roul.* 6d.
(*b*) *W* **10.** *Roul.* 2d. D.L.R.
Optd in black. (*a*) *W* **2.** 6d. (*p* 11½–12½ × *roul*), 6d. (*p* 11½–12½), 6d. (*p* 10)
(*b*) *W* **7.** *P* 10. 2d. D.L.R.
(*c*) *W* **10.** 2d. D.L.R. (*roul*), 2d. D.L.R. (*p* 11½–12½), 2d. D.L.R. (*p* 11½–12½ × *roul*), 2d. D.L.R. (*p* 10 × *roul*), 2d. D.L.R. (*p* 10), 2d. D.L.R. (*p* 10 × 11½–12½)

P.A. (Protector of Aborigines)

Optd in red. *W* **2.** *Roul.* 2d., 6d.
Optd in black. (*a*) *W* **2.** *Roul.* 2d. D.L.R., 6d.
(*b*) *W* **10.** 2d. D.L.R. (*roul*), 2d. D.L.R. (*p* 10)

P.O. (Post Office)

Optd in red. *W* **2.** *Roul.* 1d., 2d., 6d., 1s.
Optd in blue. *W* **2.** *Roul.* 2d., 2d. D.L.R.
Optd in black. (*a*) *W* **2.** 1d. (*p* 10 × 11½–12½), 2d. D.L.R. (*roul*), 4d. (*p* 11½–12½), 6d. (*roul*), 6d. (*p* 11½–12½), 1s. (*p* 11½–12½ × *roul*), 1s. (*p* 11½–12½), 1s. (*p* 10), 1s. (*p* 10 × 11½–12½)
(*b*) *W* **10.** 2d. D.L.R. (*roul*), 2d. D.L.R. (*p* 10 × *roul*), 2d. D.L.R. (*p* 10)

The 6d. (*W* **2.** *Roul*) with red overprint is known showing the stop omitted after "O", but with two stops after "P".

P.S. (Private Secretary)

Optd in red. *W* **2.** 1d. (*roul*), 2d. (*roul*), 4d. (*p* 11½–12½), 6d. (*roul*), 1s. (*roul*)
Optd in black. (*a*) *W* **2.** 1d. (*p* 11½–12½ × *roul*), 1d. (*p* 11½–12½), 1d. (*p* 10), 3d. (*in black*) on 4d. (*p* 11½–12½), 3d. (*in red*) on 4d. (*p* 10), 3d. (*in black*) on 4d. (*p* 10), 4d. (*p* 11½–12½), 4d. (*p* 10), 4d. (*p* 10 × 11½–12½), 6d. (*roul*), 6d. (*p* 11½–12½ × *roul*), 6d. (*p* 11½–12½), 6d. (*p* 10), 9d. (*roul*), 9d. (*p* 11½–12½), 10d. on 9d. (*p* 10 × 11½–12½), 1s. (*p* 11½–12½ × *roul*), 2s. (*p* 11½–12½)
(*b*) *W* **7.** *P* 10. 2d. D.L.R.
(*c*) *W* **10.** 2d. D.L.R. (*roul*), 2d. D.L.R. (*p* 10)

P.W. (Public Works)

Optd in red without stop after "W". *W* **2.** *Roul.* 2d., 6d., 1s.
Optd in black. (*a*) *W* **2.** 2d. D.L.R. (*roul*), 4d. (*p* 10), 6d. (*roul*), 6d. (*p* 11½–12½), 1s. (*p* 11½–12½ × *roul*)
(*b*) *W* **10.** 2d. D.L.R. (*roul*), 2d. D.L.R. (*p* 10)

R.B. (Road Board)

Optd in red. *W* **2.** 1d. (*roul*), 2d. (*roul*), 4d. (*p* 11½–12½), 6d. (*roul*), 1s. (*roul*)
Optd in blue without stops. *W* **10.** *Roul.* 2d. D.L.R.

Optd in black. (*a*) *W* **2**. 1d. (*p* 11½–12½ × *roul*), 1d. (*p* 10), 4d. (*p* 10), 2s. (*roul*)
(*b*) *W* **7**. *P* 10. 2d. D.L.R.
(*c*) *W* **10**. 2d. D.L.R. (*roul*), 2d. D.L.R. (*p* 10)

The 6d. (*W* **2**. *Roul*) with red overprint is known showing the stop omitted after "B".

R.G. (Registrar-General)

Optd in red. *W* **2**. *Roul*. 2d., 6d., 1s.
Optd in blue. (*a*) *W* **2**. *P* 11½–12½ × *roul*. 6d.
(*b*) *W* **10**. 2d. D.L.R. (*roul*), 2d. D.L.R. (*p* 11½–12½ × *roul*)
Optd in black. (*a*) *W* **2**. 2d. D.L.R. (*roul*), 6d. (*p* 10), 6d. (*p* 10 × 11½–12½), 1s. (*p* 11½–12½ × *roul*), 1s. (*p* 10)
(*b*) *W* **7**. *P* 10. 2d. D.L.R.
(*c*) *W* **10**. 2d. D.L.R. (*roul*), 2d. D.L.R. (*p* 10 × *roul*), 2d. D.L.R. (*p* 10), 2d. D.L.R. (*p* 10 × 11½–12½)

S. (Sheriff)

Optd in red. *W* **2**. *Roul*. 2d., 6d.
Optd in blue. (*a*) *W* **2**. *P* 11½–12½ × *roul*. 6d.
(*b*) *W* **10**. *Roul*. 2d. D.L.R.
Optd in black. (*a*) *W* **2**. 4d. (*p* 11½–12½), 4d. (*p* 10), 6d. (*roul*), 6d. (*p* 11½–12½), 6d. (*p* 10)
(*b*) *W* **10**. 2d. D.L.R. (*roul*), 2d. D.L.R. (*p* 10 × *roul*), 2d. D.L.R. (*p* 10), 2d. D.L.R. (*p* 10 × 11½–12½)

S.C. (Supreme Court)

Optd in red. *W* **2**. *Roul*. 2d., 6d.
Optd in black. *W* **10**. *P* 10. 2d. D.L.R.

S.G. (Surveyor-General)

Optd in red. *W* **2**. 2d. (*roul*), 4d. (*p* 11½–12½), 6d. (*roul*)
Optd in blue. (*a*) *W* **2**. *Roul*. 4d.
(*b*) *W* **10**. *Roul*. 2d. D.L.R.
Optd in black. (*a*) *W* **2**. 2d. D.L.R. (*roul*), 4d. (*p* 11½–12½), 4d. (*p* 10), 4d. (*p* 10 × 11½–12½), 6d. (*p* 11½–12½ × *roul*), 6d. (*p* 11½–12½), 6d. (*p* 10), 6d. (*p* 10 × 11½–12½)
(*b*) *W* **7**. *P* 10. 2d. D.L.R.
(*c*) *W* **10**. 2d. D.L.R. (*roul*), 2d. D.L.R. (*p* 10 × *roul*), 2d. D.L.R. (*p* 10)

S.M. (Stipendiary Magistrate)

Optd in red. *W* **2**. 1d. (*roul*), 2d. (*roul*), 4d. (*roul*), 4d. (*p* 11½–12½), 6d. (*roul*), 1s. (*roul*)
Optd in blue. (*a*) *W* **2**. *Roul*. 2d., 4d., 6d.
(*b*) *W* **10**. *Roul*. 2d. D.L.R.
Optd in black. (*a*) *W* **2**. 1d. (*p* 11½–12½), 1d. (*p* 10), 2d. D.L.R. (*roul*), 4d. (*roul*), 4d. (*p* 11½–12½ × *roul*), 4d. (*p* 11½–12½), 4d. (*p* 10), 4d. (*p* 10 × 11½–12½), 6d. (*p* 11½–12½ × *roul*), 6d. (*p* 11½–12½), 6d. (*p* 10), 6d. (*p* 10 × 11½–12½), 1s. (*p* 11½–12½ × *roul*)
(*b*) *W* **7**. *P* 10. 2d. D.L.R.
(*c*) *W* **10**. 2d. D.L.R. (*roul*), 2d. D.L.R. (*p* 10 × *roul*), 2d. D.L.R. (*p* 10), 2d. D.L.R. (*p* 10 × 11½–12½)

The 2d. and 4d. (both *W* **2**. *Roul*) with red overprint are known showing the stop omitted after "M".

S.T. (Superintendent of Telegraphs)

Optd in red. *W* **2**. *Roul*. 2d., 6d.
Optd in blue. *W* **10**. 2d. D.L.R. (*roul*), 2d. D.L.R. (*p* 11½–12½)
Optd in black. (*a*) *W* **2**. *Roul*. 2d. D.L.R., 6d.
(*b*) *W* **7**. *P* 10. 2d. D.L.R.
(*c*) *W* **10**. 2d. D.L.R. (*roul*), 2d. D.L.R. (*p* 10 × *roul*), 2d. D.L.R. (*p* 10)

The 2d. and 6d. (both *W* **2**. *Roul*) with red overprint (2d., 6d.) or black overprint (6d.) are known showing the stop omitted after "T".

T. (Treasury)

Optd in red. *W* **2**. 1d. (*roul*), 2d. (*roul*), 4d. (*p* 11½–12½ × *roul*), 6d. (*roul*), 1s. (*roul*)
Optd in blue. (*a*) *W* **2**. *Roul*. 1d., 4d., 6d., 2s.
(*b*) *W* **10**. *Roul*. 2d. D.L.R.
Optd in black. (*a*) *W* **2**. 1d. (*p* 10), 2d. D.L.R. (*roul*), 4d. (*roul*), 4d. (*p* 11½–12½), 6d. (*roul*), 6d. (*p* 11½–12½), 1s. (*p* 11½–12½ × *roul*), 1s. (*p* 10 × 11½–12½), 2s. (*roul*), 2s. (*p* 11½–12½), 2s. (*p* 10 × 11½–12½)
(*b*) *W* **7**. *P* 10. 2d. D.L.R.
(*c*) *W* **10**. 2d. D.L.R. (*roul*), 2d. D.L.R. (*p* 10)

T.R. (Titles Registration)

Optd in black. (*a*) *W* **2**. 4d. (*p* 11½–12½), 4d. (*p* 10 × 11½–12½), 6d. (*p* 11½–12½), 6d. (*p* 10 × 11½–12½), 1s. (*p* 11½–12½)
(*b*) *W* **10**. *P* 10. 2d. D.L.R.

V. (Volunteers)

Optd in red. *W* **2**. *Roul*. 2d., 6d., 1s.
Optd in black. (*a*) *W* **2**. *Roul*. 6d.
(*b*) *W* **7**. *P* 10. 2d. D.L.R.
(*c*) *W* **10**. 2d. D.L.R. (*roul*), 2d. D.L.R. (*p* 10 × *roul*), 2d. D.L.R. (*p* 10)

The 2d. (*W* **10**. *P* 10 × *roul*) overprinted in black is only known showing the stop omitted after "V".

VA. (Valuator of Runs)

Optd in black without stop after "V". (*a*) *W* **2**. *P* 10. 4d.
(*b*) *W* **10**. *P* 10. 2d. D.L.R.

VN. (Vaccination)

Optd in black without stop after "V". *W* **2**. *P* 10. 4d.

W. (Waterworks)

Optd in red. *W* **2**. *Roul*. 2d.
Optd in black. (*a*) *W* **2**. *P* 11½–12½. 6d., 2s.
(*b*) *W* **10**. 2d. D.L.R. (*roul*), 2d. D.L.R. (*p* 10)

The 2d. (*W* **2**. *Roul*) with red overprint is known showing the stop omitted after "W".

B. General

O.S. (O 1)   **O.S** (O 2)

1874–77. *Optd with Type* O **1**. *W* **2**. (*a*) *P* 10.
O 1 **3** 4d. dull purple (18.2.74) £950 £250

(*b*) *P* 11½–12½ × 10.
O 2 **1** 1d. green (2.1.74) .. .. — 75·00
O 3 **3** 4d. dull violet (12.2.75) .. .. 32·00 4·50
O 4 **1** 6d. Prussian blue (20.10.75) .. .. — 8·00
O 4*a* **3** 2s. rose-pink .. ..
O 5 2s. carmine (3.12.76) .. .. — 75·00

(*c*) *P* 11½–12½
O 6 **1** 1d. deep yellow-green (30.1.74) .. — 16·00
a. Printed on both sides ..
O 7 **3** 3d. on 4d. ultramarine (26.6.77) .. £650 £175
a. No stop after "S" .. — £200
O 8 4d. dull violet (13.7.74) .. .. 23·00 5·00
a. No stop after "S" .. — 14·00
O 9 **1** 6d. bright blue (31.8.75) .. .. 45·00 11·00
a. "O.S." double .. — 21·00
O10 6d. Prussian blue (27.3.74) .. .. 35·00 4·50
a. No stop after "S" .. — 15·00
O11 **4** 9d. red-purple (22.3.76) .. .. £180 50·00
a. No stop after "S" .. £225
O12 **1** 1s. red-brown (5.8.74) .. .. 32·00 5·00
a. "O.S." double .. — 15·00
b. No stop after "S" .. 40·00 12·00
O13 **3** 2s. crimson-carmine (13.7.75) .. .. 48·00 8·50
a. No stop after "S" ..
b. No stops .. — 25·00
c. Stops at top of letters ..

1876–85. *Optd with Type* O **1**. *W* **8**. (*a*) *P* 10.
O14 **1** 6d. bright blue (1879) .. .. 50·00 8·00

(*b*) *P* 10 × 11½–12½, 11½–12½ × 10, *or compound*
O15 **3** 4d. violet-slate (24.1.78) .. .. 50·00 6·00
O16 4d. plum (29.11.81) .. .. 24·00 2·25
O17 4d. deep mauve .. .. 16·00 2·00
a. No stop after "S" .. — 15·00
b. No stop after "O" ..
c. "O.S." double ..
d. "O.S." inverted .. — 75·00
O18 **1** 6d. bright blue (1877) .. .. 22·00 2·50
a. "O.S." inverted ..
b. No stop after "O" ..
O19 6d. bright ultramarine (27.3.85) .. 20·00 2·00
a. "O.S." inverted ..
b. "O.S." double ..
c. "O.S." double, one inverted ..
d. No stop after "S" ..
e. No stops after "O" & "S" ..
O20 1s. red-brown (27.3.83) .. .. 22·00 4·00
a. "O.S." inverted ..
b. No stop after "O" ..
c. No stop after "S" ..
O21 **3** 2s. carmine (16.3.81) .. .. 25·00 4·25
a. "O.S." inverted .. — 75·00
b. No stop after "S" ..

(*c*) *P* 11½–12½
O22 **3** 3d. on 4d. ultramarine .. ..
O23 4d. violet-slate (14.3.76) .. .. £120 6·00
O24 4d. deep mauve (19.8.79) .. .. 32·00 2·00
a. "O.S." inverted ..
b. "O.S." double, one inverted ..
c. No stop after "S" ..
O25 **1** 6d. Prussian blue (6.77) .. .. 25·00 3·00
a. "O.S." double .. — 17·00
b. "O.S." inverted ..
O26 **4** 8d. on 9d. brown (9.11.76) .. .. £275 75·00
a. "O.S." double .. £450
b. "O" only .. — £150
O26*c* 9d. purple .. £700
O27 **1** 1s. red-brown (12.2.78) .. .. 15·00 3·00
a. "O.S." inverted .. £110 50·00
b. No stop after "S" .. £140
O28 1s. lake-brown (8.11.83) .. .. 13·00 2·50
O29 **3** 2s. rose-carmine (12.8.85) .. .. 30·00 4·25
a. "O.S." double .. — 40·00
b. "O.S." inverted .. — 42·00
c. No stop after "S" .. — 15·00

1891–1903. *Optd with Type* O **2**. (*a*) *W* **8**. *P* 11½–12½.
O30 **1** 1s. lake-brown (18.4.91) .. .. 15·00 8·00
O31 1s. Vandyke brown .. .. 18·00 5·00
O32 1s. dull brown (2.7.96) .. .. 15·00 3·50
a. No stop after "S" ..
O33 1s. sepia (*large holes*) (4.1.02) .. .. 11·00 2·50
a. "O.S." double ..
b. No stop after "S" ..
O34 **3** 2s. carmine (26.6.00) .. .. 32·00 6·00
a. No stop after "S" ..

(*b*) *W* **8**. *P* 10 × 11½–12½
O35 **3** 2s. rose-carmine (9.11.95) .. .. 23·00 4·00
a. No stop after "S" .. 40·00
b. "O.S." double ..

(*c*) *W* **10**. *P* 11½–12½
O36 **1** 1s. dull brown (7.3.03) .. .. 15·00 2·50

1874–76. *Optd with Type* O **1**. *W* **10**. (*a*) *P* 10.
O37 **11** 1d. blue-green (30.9.75) .. .. 55·00 15·00
a. "O.S." inverted ..
b. No stop after "S" ..
O38 **12** 2d. orange-red (18.2.74) .. .. 8·00 30
a. No stop after "S" ..
b. "O.S." double ..

(*b*) *P* 10 × 11½–12½, 11½–12½ × 10, *or compound*
O39 **11** 1d. blue-green (16.9.75) .. ..
a. No stop after "S" ..
O40 **12** 2d. orange-red (27.9.76) .. .. — 3·75

(*c*) *P* 11½–12½
O41 **11** 1d. blue-green (13.8.75) .. .. — 12·00
a. "O.S." inverted ..
b. No stop after "S" ..
O42 **12** 2d. orange-red (20.5.74) .. .. — 80·00

1876–80. *Optd with Type* O **1**. *W* **13**. (*a*) *P* 10.
O43 **11** 1d. blue-green (2.10.76) .. .. 3·50 12
a. "O.S." inverted .. — 24·00
b. "O.S." double .. 25·00 20·00
c. "O.S." double, one inverted ..
d. No stops .. — 12·00
e. No stop after "S" .. — 7·00
f. No stop after "O" ..
O44 **11** 1d. deep green .. .. 4·50 15
a. "O.S." double .. — 22·00
O45 **12** 2d. orange-red (21.9.77) .. .. 4·00 12
a. "O.S." double .. 28·00 15·00
b. "O.S." inverted .. — 10·00
c. "O.S." double, both inverted .. — 50·00
d. "O.S." double, one inverted ..
e. No stop after "O" .. — 8·00
f. No stop after "S" ..
g. No stops after "O" & "S" ..
O46 2d. brick-red .. .. 23·00 65

(*b*) *P* 10 × 11½–12½, 11½–12½ × 10, *or compound*
O47 **11** 1d. deep green (14.8.80) .. .. — 18·00
a. "O.S." double ..
O48 **12** 2d. orange-red (6.4.78) .. .. 35·00 6·00
a. "O.S." inverted ..
b. No stop after "S" ..

(*c*) *P* 11½–12½
O49 **12** 2d. orange-red (15.7.80) .. .. — 60·00

1882 (20 Feb). *No.* O43 *surch with T* **14**. *W* **13**. *P* 10.
O50 **11** ½d. on 1d. blue-green .. .. 12·00 3·00
a. "O.S." inverted ..

1888–91. *Optd with Type* O **1**. *W* **13**. *P* 10.
O51 **17** 4d. violet (24.1.91) .. .. 7·00 70
O52 **18** 6d. blue (15.11.88) .. .. 4·50 50
a. "O.S." double ..
b. No stop after "S" ..

1891. *As No.* O51 *surch with T* **20**. *W* **13**. (*a*) *P* 10.
O53 **17** 2½d. on 4d. green (1.8.91) .. .. 24·00 3·25
a. "2" and "½" closer .. — 35·00
b. No stop after "S" ..
c. "O.S." omitted (in pair with normal)
d. "O.S." inverted ..
e. "O.S." double ..

(*b*) *P* 10 × 11½–12½, 11½–12½ × 10, *or compound*
O54 **17** 2½d. on 4d. green (1.10.91) .. .. 27·00 7·00

(*c*) *P* 11½–12½
O54*a* **17** 2½d. on 4d. green (1.6.91) ..

1891–95. *Optd with Type* O **2**. *W* **13**. (*a*) *P* 10.
O55 **15** ½d. brown (2.5.94) .. .. 5·50 2·00
a. No stop after "S" ..
O56 **11** 1d. green (22.4.91) .. .. 4·50 12
a. "O.S." double .. 28·00
b. No stop after "S" .. — 4·50
c. "O.S." in blackish blue .. £150 2·75
d. "O.S." double, one inverted ..
O57 **12** 2d. orange-red (22.4.91) .. .. 4·00 12
a. No stop after "S" .. — 6·00
b. "O.S." double ..
O58 **17** 2½d. on 4d. green (18.8.94) .. .. 16·00 1·60
a. No stop after "S" .. — 10·00
b. "O.S." inverted .. £100
c. "2" and "½" closer .. 45·00 15·00
d. Fraction bar omitted ..
O59 4d. pale violet (13.2.91) .. .. 5·50 60
a. "O" only .. — 30·00
b. "O.S." double ..
c. No stop after "S" ..
O60 4d. aniline violet (31.8.93) .. .. 7·00 50
a. No stop after "S" ..
b. "O.S." double ..
O61 **18** 5d. on 6d. brown (2.12.91) .. .. 25·00 4·00
a. No stop after "S" .. 45·00 10·00
b. No stop after "5D" .. £150
O62 6d. blue (4.4.93) .. .. 3·50 50
a. No stop after "S" ..
b. "O.S." in blackish blue ..

(*b*) *P* 10 × 11½–12½
O63 **15** ½d. pale brown (26.3.95) .. .. 6·00 1·90
O64 **17** 2½d. on 4d. green (17.9.95) .. .. — 30·00
a. "O.S." double ..

(*c*) *P* 11½–12½
O65 **15** ½d. Venetian red (13.6.91) .. .. 13·00 2·50

1893–1901. *Optd with Type* O **2**. *W* **13**. *P* 15.
O66 **15** ½d. pale brown (8.6.95) .. .. 4·00 1·25
O67 **11** 1d. green (8.9.94) .. .. 3·00 12
a. No stop after "S" ..
b. "O.S." double ..
O68 **12** 2d. orange-red (16.6.94) .. .. 4·00 12
a. "O.S." double .. — 12·00
b. "O.S." inverted .. — 7·00
O68*c* **22** 2½d. violet-blue .. .. 7·00 75
O69 **17** 4d. slate-violet (4.4.95) .. .. 8·00 75
a. "O.S." double .. — 10·00
O70 **23** 5d. purple (29.3.01) .. .. 12·00 1·75
O71 **18** 6d. blue (20.9.93) .. .. 4·50 50

1895–1901. *Optd with Type* O **2**. *W* **13**. *P* 13.
O72 **15** ½d. brown (17.5.98) .. .. 5·50 1·50
a. Opt triple, twice sideways ..
O73 **11** 1d. green (20.5.95) .. .. 5·00 12
a. No stop after "S" .. 19·00 6·00
O74 **12** 2d. orange (11.2.96) .. .. 3·75 12
a. No stop after "S" .. — 6·00
b. "O.S." double ..
O75 **22** 2½d. violet-blue (5.7.97) .. .. 5·50 45
a. No stop after "S" ..
O76 **17** 4d. violet (12.96) .. .. 5·00 45
a. No stop after "S" .. 14·00 5·50
b. "O.S." double .. 13·00 8·00
O77 **23** 5d. purple (29.9.01) .. .. 8·00 1·90
a. No stop after "S" ..
O78 **18** 6d. blue (13.9.99) .. .. 5·50 60
a. No stop after "S" .. 12·00

O. S.

(O 3)

1899–1901. *Optd with Type* O **3**. *W* **13**. *P* 13.
O80 **24** ½d. yellow-green (12.2.00) .. .. 4·00 30
a. No stop after "S" ..
b. "O.S." inverted .. 25·00

O81 11 1d. rosine (22.9.99) 2·75 30
a. "O.S." inverted — 15·00
b. "O.S." double
c. No stop after "S" — 9·00
O82 12 2d. bright violet (1.6.00) 4·50 35
a. "O.S." inverted 17·00 17·00
b. "O.S." double
c. No stop after "S" 17·00
O83 22 2½d. indigo (2.10.01) 5·00 70
a. "O.S." inverted — 16·00
b. No stop after "S" 27·00
O84 17 4d. violet (18.11.00) 4·00 12
a. "O.S." inverted 40·00
b. No stop after "S" 11·00
O85 18 6d. blue (8.10.00) 4·50 45
a. No stop after "S" 12·00

1891 (May). *Optd as Type* O **3** *but wider.* W **13**. P 10.
O86 19 2s. 6d. pale violet £1800 £1400
O87 5s. pale rose £1800 £1400
Only one sheet (60) of each of these stamps was printed.

South Australia now uses the stamps of AUSTRALIA.

South Georgia

As South Georgia remained a dependency of the Falkland Islands the stamps are listed under FALKLAND ISLANDS DEPENDENCIES.

South West Africa

(*formerly* German S. W. Africa)

The stamps of Germany were used in the colony from July 1886 until the introduction of issues for GERMAN SOUTH-WEST AFRICA in May 1897. Following occupation by South African forces in 1914–15 the issues of SOUTH AFRICA were used, being replaced by the overprinted issues in 1923.

Walvis (or Walfish) Bay, the major anchorage on the South West Africa coast, was claimed by Great Britain as early as 1796. In 1878 the 430 sq mile area around the port, together with a number of offshore islands, was annexed to Cape Province, passing to the Union of South Africa in 1910.

Stamps of the Cape of Good Hope and South Africa were used at Walfish Bay, often cancelled with numeral obliterator 300, until the enclave was transferred to the South West Africa administration on 1 October 1922.

The Walfish Bay territory reverted to South Africa on 30 August 1977 and from that date the stamps of South Africa were, once again, in use.

PRICES FOR STAMPS ON COVER TO 1945

Nos. 1/133	*from* × 2
Nos. D1/5	*from* × 10
Nos. D6/51	*from* × 20
Nos. O1/4	*from* × 3
Nos. O5/20	*from* × 15
No. O21	—
No. O22	*from* × 15

INSCRIPTIONS. Most of the postage stamps up to No. 140 are inscribed alternately in English and Afrikaans throughout the sheets and the same applies to all the Official stamps and to Nos. D30/33.

PRICES for Nos. 1/140 are for horizontal pairs, *unless otherwise indicated.*

South West / Africa. (1)   Zuid-West / Afrika. (2)

1923. *Stamps of South Africa, T* **2** *and* **3**, *typo with T* **1** *and* **2** *alternately.* I. *14 mm between lines of typo overprint.* (2 Jan).
1 ½d. green 1·00 1·50
a. "Wes" for "West" £110
b. "Afr ica" (R.20/2) £100
2 1d. rose-red 1·25 1·50
a. Opt inverted £650
b. "Wes" for "West" £250
c. "Af.rica" for "Africa" £225
d. Opt double £600
e. "Afr ica" (R.20/2) 95·00
3 2d. dull purple 1·60 3·00
a. Opt inverted £550
4 3d. ultramarine 7·50 11·00
5 4d. orange-yellow and sage-green 8·50 12·00
6 6d. black and violet 11·00 15·00
7 1s. orange-yellow 23·00 28·00
8 1s. 3d. pale violet 35·00 42·00
a. Opt inverted £250
9 2s. 6d. purple and green £125 £150
10 5s. purple and blue £400 £400
11 10s. blue and olive-green £3000 £3000
12 £1 green and red £2500 £2500
1/12 *Set of* 12 £5500 £5750
1/12 Optd "Specimen" *Set of 12 singles* £3000

Minor varieties, due to wear of type including broken "t" in West," may be found. Varieties showing one line of overprint only, or lower line above upper line, due to misplacement, may also be found. All values may be found with faint stop after "Afrika," and the ½d., 1d., 2d. and 3d. occasionally without stop.

14 mm between lines, but opt lithographed in shiny ink
12*a* ½d. green 4·00 7·50
12*b* 4d. orange-yellow and sage-green 35·00 40·00
12*c* 6d. black and violet 30·00 40·00
12*d* 1s. orange-yellow 85·00 95·00
12*e* 1s. 3d. pale violet £120 £140
12*f* 2s. 6d. purple and green £325 £350
12*a*/12*f* *Set of* 6 £500 £600

II. *10 mm between lines of typo overprint* (May 1923)
13 5s. purple and blue £375 £350
a. "Afrika" without stop £2250
14 10s. blue and olive-green £1500 £1300
a. "Afrika" without stop £3000 £3000
15 £1 green and red £2500 £2500
a. "Afrika" without stop £5500

Zuidwest / Afrika. (3)   South West / Africa. (4)

1923–24. *Stamps of South Africa, T* **2** *and* **3**, *optd as T* **3** (*"Zuidwest" in one word, without hyphen*) *and* **4** *alternately.*

III. "South West" *14 mm long;* "Zuidwest" *11 mm long; 14 mm between lines of opt* (Aug-Sept, 1923)
16 ½d. green (9.24) 2·00 3·25
a. "outh" for "South" £1300
17 1d. rose-red 2·00 2·75
a. "outh" for "South" £1300
18 2d. dull purple 2·75 2·75
a. Opt double £850
19 3d. ultramarine 3·50 5·00
20 4d. orange-yellow and sage-green 5·00 7·00
21 6d. black and violet 10·00 14·00
22 1s. orange-yellow 13·00 20·00
23 1s. 3d. pale violet 28·00 35·00
24 2s. 6d. purple and green 75·00 90·00
25 5s. purple and blue £125 £150
26 10s. blue and olive-green £375 £500
27 £1 green and red £650 £750
16/27 *Set of* 12 £1100 £1400

Two sets may be made with this overprint, one with bold lettering, and the other with thinner lettering and smaller stops.

IV. "South West" *16 mm long;* "Zuidwest" *12 mm long; 14 mm between lines of opt* (July 1924)
28 2s. 6d purple and green £150 £200

VI. "South West" *16 mm long**; "Zuidwest" *12 mm long; 9½ mm between lines of opt* (Dec. 1924)
29 ½d. green 3·25 5·50
30 1d. rose-red 1·25 2·25
31 2d. dull purple 2·25 2·75
32 3d. ultramarine 3·25 5·00
a. Deep bright blue 80·00 80·00
33 4d. orange-yellow and sage-green 6·00 8·50
34 6d. black and violet 6·50 9·00
35 1s. orange-yellow 11·00 15·00
36 1s. 3d. pale violet 14·00 17·00
37 2s. 6d. purple and green 48·00 60·00
38 5s. purple and blue 90·00 £150
39 10s. blue and olive-green £150 £150
40 £1 green and red £650 £700
40*a* £1 pale olive-green and red £550 £700
29/40*a* *Set of* 12 £750 £1200
35, 39/40 H/S "Specimen" *Set of* 3 £1100

*Two sets with this overprint may be made one with "South West" 16 mm long, and the other 16½ mm the difference occurring in the spacing between the words. No. 40*a* only exists with the latter spacing.

Suidwes / Afrika. (5)   South West / Africa. (6)

1926. *Pictorial types of South Africa optd with T* **5** (*on stamps inscr in Afrikaans*) *and* **6** (*on stamps inscr in English*) *sideways, alternately in black.*
41 ½d. black and green 1·60 3·75
42 1d. black and carmine 1·60 3·50
43 6d. green and orange 32·00 48·00

SOUTH WEST AFRICA (7)   SUIDWES-AFRIKA (8)

1926. *Triangular stamps of South Africa, imperf, optd with T* **7** (E.) *or T* **8** (A.).

Single stamps
E A
44 10 4d. grey-blue 1·40 2·25 1·40 2·25

1927. *As Nos.* 41/3, *but Afrikaans opt on stamp inscr in English and vice versa.*
45 ½d. black and green 1·60 2·75
a. "Africa" without stop £130
46 1d. black and carmine 1·60 2·75
a. "Africa" without stop £190
47 6d. green and orange 14·00 20·00
a. "Africa" without stop £130

SOUTH WEST AFRICA (9)   S.W.A. (10)   S.W.A. (11)

1927. *As No.* 44E, *but overprint T* **9**.
Single stamps
48 4d. grey-blue (Optd S. £120) 12·00 16·00

1927. *Pictorial stamps of South Africa optd alternately as T* **5** *and* **6**, *in blue, but with lines of overprint spaced* 16 *mm.*
49 2d. grey and purple 5·00 8·00
50 3d. black and red 6·50 9·50
51 1s. brown and blue 17·00 28·00
52 2s. 6d. green and brown 60·00 70·00
53 5s. black and green £100 £140
54 10s. blue and bistre-brown £150 £225
49/54 *Set of* 6 £300 £425
49/51, 54 H/S "Specimen" *Set of* 4 £1200

A variety of Nos. 49, 50, 51 and 54, with spacing 16½ mm between lines of overprint, occurs in one vertical row of each sheet.

1927. *As No.* 44, *but perf* 11½ *by John Meinert, Ltd, Windhoek.*
Single stamps
E A
55 4d. grey-blue 1·75 2·50 1·75 2·50
a. Imperf between (pair) 24·00 — 24·00 —
55 Optd "Specimen" £120 £120

1927–30. *Optd with T* **10**. (*a*) *T* **3** *of South Africa.*
Single stamps
56 1s. 3d. pale violet (H/S S. £150) 6·00 6·50
a. Without stop after "A" £250
57 £1 pale olive-green and red 350 £350
a. Without stop after "A" £2000 £1800

(*b*) *Pictorial stamps of South Africa*
Un pair *Us pair*
58 ½d. black and green 1·50 2·50
a. Without stop after "A" 60·00
b. "S.W.A." opt above value 4·00 7·50
c. As b, in vert pair, top stamp without opt £325
59 1d. black and carmine 1·50 2·50
a. Without stop after "A" 60·00
b. "S.W.A." opt at top (30.4.30) 3·50 6·50
c. As b. in vert pair, top stamp without opt £250
60 2d. grey and purple 4·50 6·00
a. Without stop after "A" £130
b. Opt double, one inverted £750 £800
61 3d. black and red 7·00 10·00
a. Without stop after "A" £130
62 4d. brown (1928) 15·00 23·00
a. Without stop after "A" £130
63 6d. green and orange 18·00 22·00
a. Without stop after "A" £130
64 1s. brown and blue 22·00 26·00
a. Without stop after "A" £1300
65 2s. 6d. green and brown 55·00 70·00
a. Without stop after "A" £300
66 5s. black and green £100 £120
a. Without stop after "A" £325
67 10s. blue and bistre-brown £225 £250
a. Without stop after "A" £500
58/67 *Set of* 10 £400 £450
58/61, 63/7 H/S "Specimen" *Set of* 9 £1500

The overprint is normally found at the base of the ½d., 1d., 6d., 1s. 3d. and £1 values and at the top of the remainder.

1930. *Nos.* 42 *and* 43 *of South Africa* (*rotogravure printing*), *optd with T* **10**.
68 ½d. black and green 3·75 7·50
69 1d. black and carmine 3·75 7·50

1930 (27 Nov). *Air. T* **17** *of South Africa optd.* (*a*) *As T* **10**.
Un single *Us single*
70 4d. green (*first printing*) 12·00 16·00
a. No stop after "A" of "S.W.A." £100 £110
b. Later printings 12·00 20·00
71 1s. orange (*first printing*) 90·00 £120
a. No stop after "A" of "S.W.A." £500 £550
b. Later printings 28·00 38·00

First printing: Thick letters, blurred impression. Stops with rounded corners.

Later printings: Thinner letters, clear impression. Clean cut, square stops.

(*b*) *As T* **11** (12.30)
72 4d. green 4·00 6·50
a. Opt double £120
b. Opt inverted £110
73 1s. orange 7·50 12·00

12 Kori Bustard

13 Cape Cross

14 Bogenfels

15 Windhoek

16 Waterberg

17 Luderitz Bay

18 Bush Scene

19 Elands

20 Zebra and Gnus

21 Herero Huts

22 Welwitschia Plant

23 Okuwahaken Falls

24 Monoplane over Windhoek

25 Biplane over Windhoek

(Recess B.W.)

1931 (5 Mar). *T* **12** *to* **25** *(inscr alternately in English and Afrikaans).* W **9** *of South Africa. P* 14 × 13½. *(a) Postage.*

No.	Description	Un	Us
74	½d. black and emerald	55	80
75	1d. indigo and scarlet	55	70
76	2d. blue and brown	75	1·75
77	3d. grey-blue and blue	1·00	2·00
78	4d. green and purple	1·50	3·25
79	6d. blue and brown	2·25	3·75
80	1s. chocolate and blue	4·50	6·50
81	1s. 3d. violet and yellow	7·50	11·00
82	2s. 6d. carmine and grey	18·00	22·00
83	5s. sage-green and red-brown	27·00	38·00
84	10s. red-brown and emerald	75·00	85·00
85	20s. lake and blue-green	£150	£170
	(b) Air		
86	3d. brown and blue	32·00	38·00
87	10d. black and purple-brown	55·00	75·00
74/87	*Set of* 14	£325	£400

26

(Recess B.W.)

1935 (1 May). *Silver Jubilee. Inscr bilingually.* W **9** *of South Africa. P* 14 × 13½.

No.	Type	Description	*Un single*	*Us single*
88	**26**	1d. black and scarlet	70	65
89		2d. black and sepia	1·25	75
90		3d. black and blue	11·00	14·00
91		6d. black and purple	7·00	8·50

1935–36. *Voortrekker Memorial Fund. T* **18** *to* **21** *of South Africa optd with T* **10**.

No.	Description	Un	Us
92	½d. + ½d. olive-green and green	1·60	3·50
	a. Opt inverted	£180	
93	1d. + ½d. grey-black and pink	2·25	3·00
94	2d. + 1d. grey-green and purple	7·00	7·50
	a. Without stop after "A"	£180	
	b. Opt double	£150	
95	3d. + 1½d. grey-green and blue	14·00	17·00
	a. Without stop after "A"	£180	

27 Mail Tr...

28

(Recess B.W.)

1937 (1 Mar). W **9** *of South Africa. P* 14 × 13½.

No.	Type	Description	Un	Us
96	**27**	1½d. purple-brown	2·75	1·25

(Recess B.W.)

1937 (12 May). *Coronation.* W **9** *of South Africa. P* 13½ × 14.

No.	Type	Description	Un	Us
97	**28**	½d. black and emerald	45	35
98		1d. black and scarlet	45	30
99		1½d. black and orange	55	30
100		2d. black and brown	60	40
101		3d. black and blue	65	60
102		4d. black and purple	85	65
103		6d. black and yellow	1·10	1·25
104		1s. black	1·60	1·90
97/104		*Set of* 8	5·50	5·00

1938 (14 Dec). *Voortrekker Centenary Memorial. Nos.* 76 *to* 79 *of South Africa optd as T* **11**.

No.	Description	Un	Us
105	½d. + ½d. blue and green	2·00	4·00
106	1d. + 1d. blue and carmine	2·25	3·50
107	1½d. + 1½d. chocolate and blue-green	5·50	10·00
108	3d. + 3d. bright blue	13·00	16·00

1938 (14 Dec). *Voortrekker Commemoration. Nos.* 80/1 *of South Africa optd as T* **11**.

No.	Description	Un	Us
109	1d. blue and carmine	2·25	3·50
110	1½d. greenish blue and brown	5·00	6·00

1939 (17 July). 250*th Anniv of Landing of Huguenots in South Africa and Huguenot Commemoration Fund. Nos.* 82/4 *of South Africa optd as T* **11**.

No.	Description	Un	Us
111	½d. + ½d. brown and green	3·00	3·75
112	1d. + 1d. green and carmine	4·00	4·50
113	1½d. + 1½d. blue-green and purple	5·50	9·00

SWA	SWA	SWA	S W A
(29)	(30)	(31)	(32)

1941–42. *War Effort. Nos.* 88/95 *of South Africa optd with T* **29** *or* **30** *(3d. and 1s.). (a) Inscr alternately.*

No.	Description	Un	Us
114	½d. green	60	1·00
	a. Blue-green (1942)	55	80
115	1d. carmine	45	65
116	1½d. myrtle-green (1942)	45	65
117	3d. blue	2·50	3·00
118	4d. orange-brown	4·75	3·25
	a. Red-brown	7·50	9·00
119	6d. red-orange	2·50	3·00
	(b) Inscr bilingually	*Un single*	*Us single*
120	2d. violet	50	35
121	1s. brown	1·25	1·10
114/21	*Set of* 6 *pairs and* 2 *singles*	11·50	11·50

1943–44. *War Effort (reduced sizes). Nos.* 96 *to* 103 *of South Africa, optd with T* **29** *(1½d. and 1s., No.* 129*), or T* **31** *(others).*

No.	Description	*Un unit*	*Us unit*
	(a) Inscr alternately		
122	½d. blue-green (T)	55	60
	a. Green	1·00	1·25
	b. Greenish blue	60	60
123	1d. carmine-red (T)	60	60
	a. Bright carmine	60	60
124	1½. red-brown (P)	70	45
125	2d. violet (P)	60	55
	a. Reddish violet	75	75
126	3d. blue (T)	2·50	3·00
127	6d. red-orange (P)	2·50	2·25
	a. Opt inverted	£350	
	(b) Inscr bilingually		
128	4d. slate-green (T)	3·00	3·50
	a. Opt inverted	£250	
129	1s. brown (opt T **29**) (P)	5·00	5·00
	a. Opt inverted	£300	
	b. Opt T **31** (1944)	2·50	2·75
	c. Opt T **31** inverted	£300	£250
122/9b	*Set of* 8	11·50	12·50

The "units" referred to above consist of pairs (P) or triplets (T).

No. 127 exists with another type of opt as Type **31**, but with broader "s", narrower "w" and more space between the letters.

1943 (15 Jan). *No.* 104 *of South Africa, optd with T* **29**.

No.	Description	Un	Us
130	1s. 3d. olive-brown	5·00	3·50

1945. *Victory. Nos.* 108/10 *of South Africa optd with T* **30**.

No.	Description	Un	Us
131	1d. brown and carmine	25	30
	a. Opt inverted	£180	
132	2d. slate-blue and violet	30	35
133	3d. deep blue and blue	55	75

1947 (17 Feb). *Royal Visit. Nos.* 111/13 *of South Africa optd as T* **31**, *but* 8½ × 2 *mm.*

No.	Description	Un	Us
134	1d. black and carmine	15	15
135	2d. violet	20	30
136	3d. blue	20	30

1948 (26 Apr). *Royal Silver Wedding. No.* 125 *of South Africa, optd as T* **31**, *but* 4 × 2 *mm.*

No.	Description	Un	Us
137	3d. blue and silver	60	60

1949 (1 Oct). 75*th Anniv of U.P.U. Nos.* 128/30 *of South Africa optd as T* **30**, *but* 13 × 4 *mm.*

No.	Description	Un	Us
138	½d. blue-green	90	80
139	1½d. brown-red	90	80
140	3d. bright blue	1·50	1·25

1949 (1 Dec). *Inauguration of Voortrekker Monument, Pretoria. Nos.* 131/3 *of South Africa optd with T* **32**.

No.	Description	Un	Us
141	1d. magenta	10	8
142	1½d. blue-green	15	12
143	3d. blue	15	30

1952 (14 Mar). *Tercentenary of Landing of Van Riebeeck. Nos.* 136/40 *of South Africa optd as T* **30**, *but* 8 × 3½ *mm* (1d., 4½d.) *or* 11 × 4 *mm (others).*

No.	Description	Un	Us
144	½d. brown-purple and olive-grey	10	20
145	1d. deep blue-green	10	5
146	2d. deep violet	50	5
147	4½d. blue	50	1·00
148	1s. brown	1·25	30

PRINTERS. The following stamps were printed by the Government Printer, Pretoria, in photogravure (Nos. 149/234) or lithography (subsequent issues), *unless stated otherwise.*

33 Queen Elizabeth II and *Catophracies Alexandri*

1953 (2 June). *Coronation. T* **33** *and similar horiz designs.* W **9** *of South Africa. P* 14.

No.	Description	Un	Us
149	1d. bright carmine	75	10
150	2d. deep bluish green	75	10
151	4d. magenta	1·60	1·60
152	6d. dull ultramarine	1·75	1·75
153	1s. deep orange-brown	1·75	1·25

Designs:—2d. *Bauhinia macrantha*, 4d. *Caralluma nebrownii*, 6d. *Gloriosa virescens*, 1s. *Rhigozum tricholotum.*

34 "Two Bucks" (rock painting)

36 "Rhinoceros Hunt" (rock painting)

38 Karakul Lamb

39 Ovambo Woman blowing Horn

(Des O. Schroeder (1d, to 4d.), M. Vandenschen (4½d. to 10s.))

1954 (15 Nov). *T* **34, 36, 38/9** *and similar designs.* W **9** *of South Africa (sideways on vert designs). P* 14.

No.	Description	Un	Us
154	1d. brown-red	20	5
155	2d. deep brown	35	5
156	3d. dull purple	65	5
157	4d. blackish olive	1·25	10
158	4½d. deep blue	1·25	20
159	6d. myrtle-green	1·25	10
160	1s. deep mauve	1·25	15
161	1s. 3d. cerise	4·00	85
162	1s. 6d. purple	4·00	90
163	2s. 6d. bistre-brown	6·50	1·50
164	5s. deep bright blue	15·00	7·00
165	10s. deep myrtle-green	40·00	32·00
154/65	*Set of* 12	65·00	38·00

Designs: *Vert (as T* **34**)–2d. "White Lady" (rock painting). *(As T* **38**)–2s. 6d. Lioness; 5s. Gemsbok; 10s. Elephant. *(As T* **39**)–1s. Ovambo woman; 1s. 3d. Herero woman; 1s. 6d. Ovambo girl. *Horiz (as T* **36**)–4d. "White Elephant and Giraffe" (rock painting).

1960 *As Nos.* 154/7, 162, *but* W **102** *of South Africa (sideways on vert designs). P* 14.

No.	Description	Un	Us
166	1d. brown-red	40	30
167	2d. deep brown	70	40
168	3d. dull purple	1·25	70
169	4d. blackish olive	4·25	4·25
170	1s. 6d. purple	19·00	18·00

(New Currency. 100 cents=1 rand)

46 G.P.O. Windhoek

47 Finger Rock

48 Mounted Soldier Monument

49 Quivertree

50 S.W.A. House, Windhoek

50a Lesser Flamingoes and Swakopmund Lighthouse

51 Fishing Industry

52 Lesser Flamingo

53 German Lutheran Church, Windhoek

54 Diamond

55 Fort Namutoni

55a Hardap Dam

56 Topaz

57 Tourmaline

58 Heliodor

1961 (14 Feb)–**63**. *Unsurfaced paper.* W **102** *of South Africa (sideways on vert designs). P* 14.

171	**46**	½ c. brown and pale blue	12	5
172	**47**	1 c. sepia and reddish lilac	12	5
173	**48**	1½ c. slate-violet and salmon	20	5
174	**49**	2 c. deep green and yellow	40	5
175	**50**	2½ c. red-brown and light blue	35	5
176	**50a**	3 c. ultramarine and rose-red (1.10.62)	1·50	10
177	**51**	3½ c. indigo and blue-green	70	15
178	**52**	5 c. scarlet and grey-blue	1·60	5
179	**53**	7½ c. sepia and pale lemon	80	25
180	**54**	10 c. blue and greenish yellow	1·75	20
181	**55**	12½ c. indigo and lemon	1·00	30
182	**55a**	15 c. chocolate and light blue (16.3.63)	7·00	2·50
183	**56**	20 c. brown and red-orange	4·00	50
184	**57**	50 c. deep bluish green & yellow-orge	6·50	1·75
185	**58**	1 r. yellow, maroon and blue	14·00	8·50
171/185		*Set of* 15	35·00	13·00

See also Nos. 186/91, 202/16, 224/6 and 240.

1962–66. *As No.* 171, *etc., but without watermark.*

186	**46**	½ c. brown and pale blue (8.62)	40	30
187	**48**	1½ c. slate-violet and salmon (9.62)	70	30
188	**49**	2 c. deep green and yellow (5.62)	1·25	20
189	**50**	2½ c. red-brown and light blue (1964)	2·00	30
190	**51**	3½ c. indigo and blue-green (1966)	3·50	3·50
191	**52**	5 c. scarlet and grey-blue (9.62)	2·50	35
186/91		*Set of* 6	9·25	4·50

59 "Agricultural Development"

60 Centenary Emblem and Map

61 Centenary Emblem and part of Globe

1963 (16 Mar). *Opening of Hardap Dam.* W **102** *of South Africa (sideways). P* 14.

192	**59**	3 c. chocolate and light green	75	25

1963 (30 Aug). *Centenary of Red Cross. P* 14.

193	**60**	7½ c. red, black and light blue	6·00	3·75
194	**61**	15 c. red, black and orange-brown	10·00	8·00

62 Interior of Assembly Hall

63 Calvin

1964 (14 May). *Opening of Legislative Assembly Hall, Windhoek.* W **102** *of South Africa. P* 14.

195	**62**	3 c. ultramarine and salmon	75	10

1964 (1 Oct). 400*th Death Anniv of Calvin (Protestant reformer). P* 14.

196	**63**	2½ c. brown-purple and gold	45	12
197		15 c. deep bluish green and gold	3·00	1·75

64 Mail Runner of 1890

65 Kurt von François (founder)

66 Dr. H. Vedder

(Des D. Aschenborn)

1965 (18 Oct). 75*th Anniv of Windhoek. Chalk-surfaced paper.* W **127** *of South Africa (sideways). P* 14.

198	**64**	3 c. sepia and scarlet	50	20
199	**65**	15 c. red-brown and blue-green	3·00	1·75

1966 (4 July). 90*th Birth Anniv of Dr. H. Vedder (philosopher and writer). Chalk-surfaced paper.* W **127** *of South Africa (sideways). P* 14.

200	**66**	3 c. blackish green and salmon	50	20
201		15 c. deep sepia and light blue	2·75	1·75

Nos. 200/1 exist on Swiss-made paper with *tête-bêche* watermark from a special printing made for use in presentation albums for delegates to the U.P.U. Congress in Tokyo in 1969, as supplies of the original Harrison paper were by then exhausted (*Set of* 2 *price* £17 *mint*).

1966–72. *As* 1961–66 *but chalk-surfaced paper and* W **127** *of South Africa* (sideways on vert designs).*

202	**46**	½ c. brown and pale blue (1967)	45	5
203	**47**	1 c. sepia and light reddish lilac (*shades*) (1967)	35	5
204	**48**	1½ c. slate-violet and salmon (1968)	1·00	20
205	**49**	2 c. deep bluish green and yellow	65	10
206	**50**	2½ c. dp red-brown & lt turq-bl (*shades*)	40	5
207	**50a**	3 c. ultramarine and rose-red (1970)	1·50	20
208	**51**	3½ c. indigo and blue-green (1967)	3·50	1·75
209	**50**	4 c. dp red-brown & lt turq-bl (1.4.71)	2·00	70
210	**52**	5 c. scarlet and grey-blue (1968)	2·00	10
211	**53**	6 c. sepia and greenish yellow (31.8.71)	6·00	3·50
212		7½ c. sepia and pale lemon (1967)	2·50	1·25
213	**55**	9 c. indigo and greenish yellow (1.7.71)	6·50	4·00
214	**54**	10 c. brt blue & greenish yellow (6.70)	4·00	1·25
		a. Whiter background† (9.72)	3·75	40
215	**55a**	15 c. chocolate and light blue (1.72)	6·50	3·50
216	**56**	20 c. brown and red-orange (1968)	5·50	85
202/16		*Set of* 15	38·00	15·00

*The watermark in this issue is indistinct but the stamps can be distinguished from the stamps without watermark by their shades and the chalk-surfaced paper which is appreciably thicker and whiter. The 1, 1½, 3, 4, 5, 6, 9, 10, 15 and 20 c. are known only with the watermark *tête-bêche* but the ½ c. and 2½ c. exist with both forms, the remainder being as illustrated.

† No. 214a, printed from sheets, has a much whiter background around the value and behind "SOUTH WEST AFRICA" compared with No. 214, which was issued in coils only.

See also Nos. 224/6 and 240.

67 Camelthorn Tree

(Des D. Aschenborn (2½ c., 3 c.), Govt Printer, Pretoria (15 c.))

1967 (6 Jan). *Verwoerd Commemoration. Chalk-surfaced paper. T* **67** *and similar designs.* W **127** *of South Africa (sideways on vert designs). P* 14.

217		2½ c. black and emerald-green	35	15
218		3 c. brown and new blue	45	20
219		15 c. blackish brown and reddish purple	3·75	2·50

Designs: *Vert.*—3 c. Waves breaking against rock; 15 c. Dr. H. F. Verwoerd.

70 President Swart

71 President and Mrs. Swart

1968 (2 Jan). *Swart Commemoration. Chalk-surfaced paper.* W **127** *of South Africa (tête-bêche, sideways). P* 14 × 15.

220	**70**	3 c. orange-red, black and turquoise-blue		
		G. Inscribed in German	45	15
		A. Inscribed in Afrikaans	45	15
		E. Inscribed in English	45	15
221	**71**	15 c. red, blackish olive and dull green (*shades*)		
		G. Inscribed in German	2·75	1·75
		A. Inscribed in Afrikaans	2·75	1·75
		E. Inscribed in English	2·75	1·75
220/1		*Set of* 2 *values in strips of three*	16·00	
		Set of 6 *singles*	8·50	5·00

The three languages appear, *se-tenant*, both horizontally and vertically, throughout the sheet.

1970 (14 Feb). *Water* 70 *Campaign. As Nos.* 299/300 *of South Africa, but without phosphor band and inscr* "SWA".

222	2½ c. green, bright blue and chocolate	55	25
223	3 c. Prussian blue, royal blue and buff	60	30

72 G.P.O., Windhoek

73 "Red Sand-dunes, Eastern South West Africa"

1970–71. *As Nos.* 202 *and* 204/5 *but* "POSGELD INKOMSTE" *omitted and larger figure of value as in T* **72**. W **127** *of South Africa (tête-bêche, sideways on* 1½ *and* 2 *c.).*

224	**72**	½ c. brown and pale blue (6.70)	1·25	30
225	–	1½ c. slate-violet and salmon (1.6.71)	8·00	7·50
226	–	2 c. deep bluish green and lemon (11.70)	1·50	25

1970 (24 Aug). 150*th Anniv of Bible Society of South Africa. As Nos.* 301/2 *of South Africa, but inscr* "SWA".

228	2½ c. multicoloured	1·00	25
229	12½ c. gold, black and blue	9·00	6·50

No. 228 has a phosphor frame, probably added in error.

A mint example of No. 229 exists with a second, blind, impression of the die-stamped features.

1971 (31 May). *"Interstex" Stamp Exhibition, Cape Town. As No.* 303A *of South Africa, but without phosphor frame and inscr* "SWA".

230	5 c. light greenish blue, black and pale yellow	7·00	3·25

1971 (31 May). *Tenth Anniv of Antarctic Treaty. As No.* 304 *of South Africa, but without phosphor frame, and inscr* "SWA".

231	12½ c. blue-black, greenish blue & orge-red	45·00	25·00

1971 (31 May). *Tenth Anniv of the South African Republic. As Nos.* 305/6 *of South Africa, but without phosphor frame, and inscr* "SWA".

232	2 c. pale flesh and brown-red	3·25	85
233	4 c. green and black	4·25	90

1972 (19 Sept). *Centenary of S.P.C.A. As No.* 312 *of South Africa, but inscr* "SWA".

234	5 c. multicoloured	1·75	70

WATERMARK. All issues from this date are on unwatermarked paper.

(Lettering by E. de Jong)

1973 (1 May). *Scenery. T* **73** *and similar multicoloured designs showing paintings by Adolph Jentsch. P* 11½ × 12½ (10 *and* 15 *c.) or* 12½ × 11½ *(others).*

235	2 c. Type **73**	1·00	75
236	4 c. "After the Rain"	2·00	1·25
237	5 c. "Barren Country"	2·50	1·50
238	10 c. "Schaap River" (*vert*)	4·00	3·50
239	15 c. "Namib Desert" (*vert*)	6·00	4·75

1973 (28 May). *As Nos.* 207 *but without wmk. Phosphorised paper.*

240	**50a**	3 c. ultramarine and rose-red	90	1·25

No. 240 is also distinguishable in that the lettering of "SOUTH WEST AFRICA" is whiter.

74 *Sarcocaulon rigidum*

75 *Euphorbia virosa*

(Des D. Findlay)

1973 (1 Sept)–**79**. *Succulents. Various multicoloured designs as T* **74/5**. *Phosphorised glossy paper (original printing of all values) or ordinary paper* (1, 2, 3, 4, 5, 9, 10, 15, 20, 30, 50 c.).

(*a*) *As T* **74**. *P* 12½.

241	1 c. Type **74**	15	5
	a. Black (face value, etc.) omitted	£120	
242	2 c. *Lapidaria margaretae*	20	5
	a. Perf 14 × 13½ (4.8.79)	20	20
243	3 c. *Titanopsis schwantesii*	20	5
	a. Black (face value, etc.) omitted	£120	
	b. Perf 14 × 13½ (8.8.79)	25	20
244	4 c. *Lithops karasmontana*	25	5
245	5 c. *Caralluma lugardii*	25	5
	a. Black (face value, etc.) omitted	£120	
	b. Perf 14 × 13½ (12.12.79)	40	40
246	6 c. *Dinteranthus microspermus*	35	10
247	7 c. *Conophytum gratum*	35	10
248	9 c. *Huernia oculata*	50	15

249 10 c. *Gasteria pillansii* 50 15
 a. Black (face value, etc.) omitted .. ..
 b. Perf 14 × 13½ (13.8.79) 70 70
250 14 c. *Stapelia pedunculata* 60 25
251 15 c. *Fenestraria aurantiaca* 65 25
252 20 c. *Decabelone grandiflora* 75 30
253 25 c. *Hoodia bainii* 80 35

(*b*) *As T* **75**. *P* 11½ × 12½ (30 *c.*, 1 *r.*) *or* 12½ × 11½ (50 *c.*)
254 30 c. Type **75** 85 50
 a. Perf 13½ × 14 (27.12.79) .. .. 1·75 1·75
255 50 c. *Pachypodium namaquanum* (*vert*) .. 2·00 2·25
 a. Perf 14 × 13½ (18.12.79) .. .. 2·50 2·50
256 1 r. *Welwitschia bainesii* .. .. .. 3·75 3·00
241/56 .. .. *Set of* 16 11·00 7·00

1973 (1 Sept)–**80**. *Coil stamps. As Nos.* 241/2 *and* 245 *but photo, colours changed. P* 14.
257 1 c. black and light mauve 15 15
 a. Chalk-surfaced paper (7.76?) 20 12
 b. Imperf × perf 14. Chalk-surfaced paper (1980) 30 30
258 2 c. black and yellow 15 15
 a. Chalk-surfaced paper (7.76?) 20 12
 b. Imperf × perf 14. Chalk-surfaced paper (1.79) 30 20
259 5 c. black and light rose-red 35 25
 a. Imperf × perf 14. Chalk-surfaced paper (8.2.78) 35 30

Coils of Nos. 257b, 258b and 259a come with every fifth stamp numbered on the reverse.

76 Chat-shrike

77 Giraffe, Antelope and Spoor

(Des D. Findlay)

1974 (13 Feb). *Rare Birds. T* **76** *and similar vert designs. Multicoloured. P* 12½ × 11½.
260 4 c. Type **76** .. .. 1·50 65
261 5 c. Peach-faced Lovebirds .. .. .. 2·00 95
262 10 c. Damaraland Rock Jumper .. .. .. 5·00 3·00
263 15 c. Rüppell's Parrots .. .. .. 9·00 7·50

(Des O. Schröder)

1974 (10 Apr). *Twyfelfontein Rock-engravings. T* **77** *and similar multicoloured designs. P* 11½ × 12½ (15 *c.*) *or* 12½ × 11½ (*others*).
264 4 c. Type **77** .. .. 1·25 50
265 5 c. Elephant, hyena, antelope and spoor .. 1·50 80
 a. Black (value and "SWA") omitted .. £190
266 15 c. Kudu Cow (38 × 21 *mm*) .. .. 6·50 4·25

78 Cut Diamond

79 Wagons and Map of the Trek

(Des M. Barnett)

1974 (30 Sept). *Diamond Mining. T* **78** *and similar vert design. Multicoloured. P* 12½ × 11½.
267 10 c. Type **78** .. .. 3·00 2·00
268 15 c. Diagram of shore workings .. .. 4·00 3·00

(Des K. Esterhuysen)

1974 (13 Nov). *Centenary of Thirstland Trek. P* 11½ × 12½.
269 **79** 4 c. multicoloured 60 50

80 Peregrine Falcon

81 Kolmannskop (ghost town)

(Des D. Findlay)

1975 (19 Mar). *Protected Birds of Prey. T* **80** *and similar vert designs. Multicoloured. P* 12½ × 11½.
270 4 c. Type **80** .. .. 1·25 55
271 5 c. Verreaux's Eagle .. .. 1·50 70
272 10 c. Martial Eagle .. .. 4·50 3·25
273 15 c. Egyptian Vulture .. .. 6·00 5·00

(Des A. H. Barrett)

1975 (23 July). *Historic Monuments. T* **81** *and similar horiz designs. Multicoloured. P* 11½ × 12½.
274 5 c. Type **81** 35 15
275 9 c. "Martin Luther" (steam tractor) 70 60
276 15 c. Kurt von Francois and Old Fort, Windhoek .. .. 1·25 80

82 "View of Lüderitz"

(Des J. Hoekstra)

1975 (15 Oct). *Otto Schröder. T* **82** *and similar horiz designs showing his paintings. Multicoloured. P* 11½ × 12½.
277 15 c. Type **82** 75 55
 a. Block of 4. Nos. 277/80 .. .. .. 4·00
278 15 c. "View of Swakopmund" 75 55
279 15 c. "Harbour Scene" 75 55
280 15 c. "Quayside, Walvis Bay" 75 55
MS281 122 × 96 mm. Nos. 277/80 .. .. 4·00 5·00

Nos. 277/80 were printed together, in *se-tenant* blocks of four within the sheet.

83 Elephants

(Des H. Pager)

1976 (31 Mar). *Prehistoric Rock Paintings. T* **83** *and similar horiz designs. Multicoloured. P* 11½ × 12½.
282 4 c. Type **83** 45 20
283 10 c. Rhinoceros 75 60
284 15 c. Antelope .. .. 1·00 80
285 20 c. Man with bow and arrow .. .. 1·40 1·00
MS286 121 × 95 mm. Nos. 282/5 .. .. 3·50 4·25

84 Schwerinsburg

(Des H. Pager)

1976 (14 May). *Castles. T* **84** *and similar horiz designs. Multicoloured. P* 11½ × 12½.
287 Type **84** 60 35
288 15 c. Schloss Duwisib 85 55
289 20 c. Heynitzburg .. .. 1·25 70

85 Dassie

(Des D. Findlay)

1976 (16 July). *Fauna Conservation. T* **85** *and similar horiz designs. Multicoloured. P* 11½ × 12½.
290 4 c. Type **85** 40 20
291 10 c. Dik-Dik .. .. 1·25 60
292 15 c. Tree Squirrel .. .. 2·00 1·10

86 The Augustineum, Windhoek

(Des H. Pager)

1976 (17 Sept). *Modern Buildings. T* **86** *and similar horiz design. P* 11½ × 12½.
293 15 c. black and yellow 50 35
294 20 c. black and light yellow 60 40

Design:—20 c. Katutura Hospital, Windhoek.

87 Ovambo Water Canal System

(Des A. H. Barrett)

1976 (19 Nov). *Water and Electricity Supply. T* **87** *and similar horiz design. Multicoloured. P* 11½ × 12½.
295 15 c. Type **87** 50 35
296 20 c. Ruacana Falls Power Station 60 45

88 Coastline near Pomona

(Des A. H. Barrett)

1977 (29 Mar). *Namib Desert. T* **88** *and similar horiz designs. Multicoloured. P* 12½.
297 4 c. Type **88** 35 30
298 10 c. Bush and dunes, Sossusvlei 60 60
299 15 c. Plain near Brandberg 95 75
300 20 c. Dunes, Sperr Gebiet .. .. .. 1·25 90

89 Kraal

(Des A. H. Barrett)

1977 (15 July). *The Ovambo People. T* **89** *and similar horiz designs. P* 11½ × 12½.
301 4 c. multicoloured 15 12
302 10 c. black, dull orange and cinnamon .. 40 30
303 15 c. multicoloured 50 50
304 20 c. multicoloured 65 65

Designs—10 c. Grain baskets; 15 c. Pounding grain; 20 c. Women in tribal dress.

90 Terminal Buildings

(Des H. Pager and A. H. Barrett)

1977 (22 Aug). *J. G. Strijdom Airport, Windhoek. P* 12½.
305 **90** 20 c. multicoloured 60 60

91 Drostdy, Lüderitz

92 Side-winding Adder

(Des A. H. Barrett)

1977 (4 Nov). *Historic Houses. T* **91** *and similar horiz designs. Multicoloured. P* 12 × 12½.
306 5 c. Type **91** 15 12
307 10 c. Woermannhaus, Swakopmund 40 40
308 15 c. Neu-Heusis, Windhoek 45 40
309 20 c. Schmelenhaus, Bethanie 65 55
MS310 122 × 96 mm. Nos. 306/9 .. .. 2·00 2·50

(Des D. Findlay)

1978 (6 Feb). *Small Animals. T* **92** *and similar horiz designs. Multicoloured. P* 12½.
311 4 c. Type **92** 20 10
312 10 c. Golden Sand-mole 40 30
313 15 c. Palmato Gecko 60 45
314 20 c. Namaqua Chameleon 75 55

93 Ostrich Hunting

(Des A. H. Barrett)

1978 (14 Apr). *The Bushmen. T* **93** *and similar horiz designs in light grey-brown, stone and black. P* 12 × 12½.
315 4 c. Type **93** 15 10
316 10 c. Woman carrying fruit 25 25
317 15 c. Hunters kindling fire 45 45
318 20 c. Woman with musical instrument .. 55 55

94 Lutheran Church, Windhoek

ALGEMENE
STEMREG

(**95**)

(Des A. H. Barrett)

1978 (16 June). *Historical Churches. T* **94** *and similar horiz designs. P* 12½.
319 4 c. grey-black and cinnamon 15 10
320 10 c. grey-black and ochre 25 25

321 15 c. grey-black and light brown-rose .. 35 35
322 20 c. grey-black and light grey-blue 45 45
MS323 125 × 90 mm. Nos. 319/22 .. .. 1·40 1·50
Designs:—10 c. Lutheran Church, Swakopmund; 15 c. Rhenish Mission Church, Otjimbingwe; 20 c. Rhenish Missionary Church, Keetmanshoop.

1978 (1 Nov). *Universal Suffrage. Designs as Nos.* 244/5, 249 *and* 251/3 *optd with T* **95** *(or similar inscr in English or German).*
324 4 c. *Lithops karasmontana* .. ..
A. Opt in Afrikaans.. .. .. .. 10 10
E. Opt in English 10 10
G. Opt in German 10 10
325 5 c. *Caralluma lugardii* .. ..
A. Opt in Afrikaans.. .. .. .. 10 10
E. Opt in English 10 10
G. Opt in German 10 10
326 10 c. *Gasteria pillansii*.. .. .. ..
A. Opt in Afrikaans.. .. .. .. 20 20
E. Opt in English 20 20
G. Opt in German 20 20
327 15 c. *Fenestraria aurantiaca* .. .. ..
A. Opt in Afrikaans.. .. .. .. 30 35
E. Opt in English 30 35
G. Opt in German 30 35
328 20 c. *Decabelone grandiflora* .. .. ..
A. Opt in Afrikaans.. .. .. .. 35 40
E. Opt in English 35 40
G. Opt in German 35 40
329 25 c. *Hoodia bainni* .. ..
A. Opt in Afrikaans.. .. .. .. 40 45
E. Opt in English 40 45
G. Opt in German 40 45
324/9 .. .. *Set of* 18 *(6 strips of 3)* 4·00 4·25
Nos. 324A/G, 325A/G, 326A/G, 327A/G, 328A/G and 329A/G were each printed together, *se-tenant*, in horizontal and vertical strips of 3 throughout the sheets.

96 Greater Flamingo

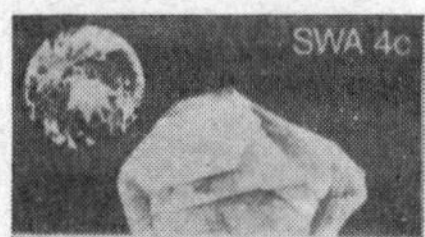

97 Silver Topaz

(Des D. Findlay)

1979 (5 Apr). *Water Birds. T* **96** *and similar vert designs. Multicoloured. P* 14.
330 4 c. Type **96** 15 10
331 15 c. White-breasted Cormorant 40 40
332 20 c. Chestnut-banded Sand Plover 50 50
333 25 c. Eastern White Pelican 55 55

(Des H. Botha)

1979 (26 Nov). *Gemstones. T* **97** *and similar horiz designs. Multicoloured. P* 14.
334 4 c. Type **97** 20 10
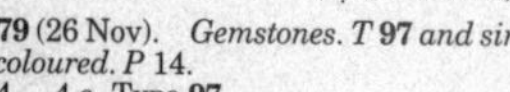
335 15 c. Aquamarine 40 40
336 20 c. Malachite 50 50
337 25 c. Amethyst 60 60

98 Killer Whale

99 Black-nosed Impala (*Aepyceros petersi*)

(Des A. H. Barrett)

1980 (25 Mar). *Whales. T* **98** *and similar multicoloured designs. P* 14.
338 4 c. Type **98** 20 5
339 5 c. Humpback Whale (38 × 22 *mm*) .. 20 10
340 10 c. Southern Right Whale (38 × 22 *mm*) .. 35 30
341 15 c. Sperm Whale (58 × 22 *mm*) 60 60
342 20 c. Fin Whale (58 × 22 *mm*) 80 80
343 25 c. Blue Whale (88 × 22 *mm*) .. .. 1·10 1·10
338/43 .. .. *Set of* 6 2·75 2·75
MS344 202 × 95 mm. Nos. 338/43 .. .. 4·00 4·25

(Des P. Bosman)

1980 (25 June). *25th Anniv of Division of Nature Conservation and Tourism. Antelopes. T* **99** *and similar horiz designs. Multicoloured. P* 14.
345 5 c. Type **99** 15 8
346 10 c. Tsessebe (*Demaliscus lunatus*) 30 15
347 15 c. Roan Antelope (*Hippotragus equinus*) .. 50 30
348 20 c. Sable Antelope (*Hippotragus niger*) .. 60 35

ALTERED CATALOGUE NUMBERS

Any Catalogue numbers altered from the last edition are shown as a list in the introductory pages.

100 Black-backed Jackal (*Canis mesomelas*)

101 Suricate (*Suricata suricatta*)

(Des P. Bosman)

1980 (1 Oct)–**84**. *Wildlife. Multicoloured designs as T* **100**. *P* 14.
349 1 c. Type **100** 5 5
350 2 c. Cape Hunting-dog (*Lycaon pictus*) .. 5 5
351 3 c. Brown Hyena (*Hyaena brunnea*) .. 5 5
352 4 c. Springbuck (*Antidorcas marsupialis*) .. 5 5
353 5 c. Gemsbok (*Oryx gazella*) 5 5
354 6 c. Greater Kudu (*Tragelaphus strepsiceros*) 5 5
355 7 c. Hartmann's Mountain Zebra (*Equus. zebra hartmannae*) (*horiz*) 5 5
356 8 c. Crested Porcupine (*Hystrix africae-australis*) (*horiz*) 5 8
357 9 c. Honey-badger (*Mellivora capensis*) (*horiz*) 5 8
358 10 c. Cheetah (*Acinonyx jubatus*) (*horiz*) .. 8 10
358*a* 11 c. Blue Wildebeest (*Connochaetes taurinus*) (2.4.84) 8 10
359 15 c. Hippopotamus (*Hippopotamus amphibius*) (*horiz*) 12 15
360 20 c. Eland (*Taurotragus oryx*) (*horiz*) .. 15 20
361 25 c. Black Rhinoceros (*Diceros bicornis*) (*horiz*) 20 25
362 30 c. Lion (*Panthera leo*) (*horiz*) 25 30
363 50 c. Giraffe (*Giraffa camelopardalis*) .. 40 45
364 1 r. Leopard (*Panthera pardus*) 80 85
365 2 r. African Elephant (*Loxodonta africano*).. 1·50 1·75
349/65 .. .. *Set of* 18 3·50 4·00

(Des P. Bosman. Photo)

1980 (1 Oct). *Coil stamps. Wildlife. Vert designs as T* **101**. *Imperf × perf* 14.
366 1 c. yellow-brown 5 5
367 2 c. deep dull blue 5 5
368 5 c. yellow-olive 5 5
Designs:—2 c. Vervet Monkey (*Cercopithecus pygerythrus*); 5 c. Chacma Baboon (*Papio ursinus*).

102 Von Bach

(Des A. H. Barrett)

1980 (25 Nov). *Water Conservation. Dams. T* **102** *and similar horiz designs. Multicoloured. P* 14.
369 5 c. Type **102** 10 10
370 10 c. Swakoppoort 20 15
371 15 c. Naute 30 30
372 20 c. Hardap 35 35

103 View of Fish River Canyon

104 *Aloe erinacea*

(Des A. H. Barrett)

1981 (20 Mar). *Fish River Canyon. T* **103** *and similar horiz designs showing various views of canyon. P* 14.
373 5 c. multicoloured 10 10
374 15 c. multicoloured 25 25
375 20 c. multicoloured 35 35
376 25 c. multicoloured 40 40

(Des D. Findlay)

1981 (14 Aug). *Aloes. T* **104** *and similar vert designs. Multicoloured. P* 14 × 13½.
377 5 c. Type **104** 10 5
378 15 c. *Aloe viridiflora* 25 25
379 20 c. *Aloe pearsonii* 35 35
380 25 c. *Aloe littoralis* 35 35

105 Paul Weiss-Haus

(Des A. H. Barrett)

1981 (16 Oct). *Buildings of Lüderitz (town). T* **105** *and similar horiz designs. Multicoloured. P* 14.
381 5 c. Type **105** 5 5
382 15 c. Deutsche Afrika Bank 20 20
383 20 c. Schroederhaus 30 30
384 25 c. Altes Postamt 30 35
MS385 125 × 90 mm. Nos. 381/4 .. .. 85 90

106 Salt Pan

107 Kalahari Starred Tortoise (*Psammobates oculifer*)

(Des A. H. Barrett)

1981 (4 Dec). *Salt Industry. T* **106** *and similar horiz designs. Multicoloured. P* 14.
386 5 c. Type **106** 5 5
387 15 c. Dumping and washing 20 20
388 20 c. Loading by conveyor 25 30
389 25 c. Dispatch to refinery 30 35

(Des A. H. Barrett)

1982 (12 Mar). *Tortoises. T* **107** *and similar horiz designs. Multicoloured. P* 14.
390 5 c. Type **107** 5 5
391 15 c. Leopard Tortoise (*Geochelone pardalis*) .. 20 20
392 20 c. Angulate Tortoise (*Chersina angulata*) .. 25 30
393 25 c. Speckled Padloper (*Homopus signatus*) .. 30 35

108 Mythical Sea-monster

(Des Sheila Nowers)

1982 (28 May). *Discoverers of South West Africa. Bartolomeu Dias. T* **108** *and similar horiz designs. Multicoloured. P* 14.
394 15 c. Type **108** 20 20
395 20 c. Bartolomeu Dias and map of Africa showing voyage 25 30
396 25 c. Dias' caravel 30 35
397 30 c. Dias erecting commemorative cross, Angra das Voltas, 25 July 1488.. .. 35 40

109 Brandberg

110 Otjikaeva Head-dress of Herero Woman

(Des A. H. Barrett)

1982 (3 Aug). *Mountains of South West Africa. T* **109** *and similar horiz designs. Multicoloured. P* 13½ × 14.
398 6 c. Type **109** 8 8
399 15 c. Omatako 20 20
400 20 c. Die Nadel 25 30
401 25 c. Spitzkuppe 30 35

(Des A. H. Barrett)

1982 (15 Oct). *Traditional Head-dresses of South West Africa. (1st series). T* **110** *and similar vert designs. Multicoloured. P* 14.
402 6 c. Type **110** 8 8
403 15 c. Ekori head-dress of Himba 20 20
404 20 c. Oshikoma hair-piece and iipando plaits of Ngandjera 30 30
405 25 c. Omhatela head-dress of Kwanyama .. 30 35
See also Nos. 427/30.

111 Fort Vogelsang

112 Searching for Diamonds, Kolmanskop, 1908

(Des J. van Ellinckhuijzen)

1983 (16 Mar). *Centenary of Lüderitz. T* **111** *and similar designs. P* 14.
406 6 c. brownish black and deep carmine-red .. 5 8
407 20 c. brownish black and yellow-brown .. 25 30
408 25 c. brownish black and chestnut 30 35

409 30 c. brownish black and brown-purple .. 35 40
410 40 c. brownish black and bright green .. 50 55

Designs: *Vert* (23 × 29 *mm*)—20 c. Chief Joseph Fredericks; 30 c. Heinrich Vogelsang (founder); 40 c. Adolf Lüderitz (colonial promoter). *Horiz* (*As T* **111**)—25 c. Angra Pequena.

(Des J. van Ellinckhuijzen)

1983 (8 June). *75th Anniv of Discovery of Diamonds. T* **112** *and similar designs. P* 13½ × 14 (10, 20 c.) *or* 14 × 13½ (*others*).

411 10 c. deep brown and pale stone 12 15
412 20 c. maroon and pale stone 25 30
413 25 c. Prussian blue and pale stone 30 35
414 40 c. brownish black and pale stone 50 55

Designs: *Horiz* (34 × 19 *mm*)—20 c. Digging for diamonds, Kolmanskop, 1908. *Vert* (19 × 26 *mm*)—25 c. Sir Ernest Oppenheimer (industrialist); 40 c. August Stauch (prospector).

113 "Zebras drinking" (J. van Ellinckhuijzen)

114 The Rock Lobster

1983 (1 Sept). *Painters of South West Africa. T* **113** *and similar horiz designs. Multicoloured. P* 13½ × 14.

415 10 c. Type **113** 12 15
416 20 c. "Rossing Mountain" (H. Henckert) .. 25 30
417 25 c. "Stampeding Buffalo" (F. Krampe) .. 30 35
418 40 c. "Erongo Mountains" (J. Blatt) 50 55

(Des J. van Ellinckhuijzen)

1983 (23 Nov). *Lobster Industry. T* **114** *and similar horiz designs. Multicoloured. P* 13½ × 14.

419 10 c. Type **114** 12 15
420 20 c. Mother ship and fishing dinghies .. 25 30
421 25 c. Netting lobsters from dinghy 30 35
422 40 c. Packing lobsters 50 55

115 Hohenzollern House

(Des A. H. Barrett)

1984 (8 Mar). *Historic Buildings in Swakopmund. T* **115** *and similar horiz designs. P* 14.

423 10 c. grey-black and orange-brown 10 12
424 20 c. grey-black and new blue 20 25
425 25 c. grey-black and yellow-green 25 30
426 30 c. grey-black and ochre 25 30

Designs:—20 c. Railway Station; 25 c. Imperial District Bureau; 30 c. Ritterburg.

(Des A. H. Barrett)

1984 (25 May). *Traditional Head-dresses of South West Africa (2nd series). Multicoloured designs as T* **110**. *P* 14.

427 11 c. Eendjushi head-dress of Kwambi .. 10 12
428 20 c. Bushman woman 20 25
429 25 c. Omulenda head-dress of Kwaluudhi .. 25 30
430 30 c. Mbukushu women 25 30

116 Map and German Flag

117 Sweet Thorn

(Des J. van Ellinckhuijzen)

1984 (7 Aug). *Centenary of German Colonisation. T* **116** *and similar horiz designs. Multicoloured. P* 14 × 14½.

431 11 c. Type **116** 10 12
432 25 c. Raising the German flag, 1884 .. .. 25 30
433 30 c. German Protectorate boundary marker 25 30
434 45 c. S.M.S. *Elizabeth* and S.M.S. *Leipzig* .. 40 45

(Des Eva-Maria Linsmayer)

1984 (22 Nov). *Spring in South West Africa. T* **117** *and similar vert designs. Multicoloured. P* 14.

435 11 c. Type **117** 10 12
436 25 c. Camel Thorn 25 30
437 30 c. Hook Thorn 25 30
438 45 c. Candle-pod Acacia 40 45

NEW INFORMATION

The editor is always interested to correspond with people who have new information that will improve or correct the Catalogue.

POSTAGE DUE STAMPS

Postage Due stamps of Transvaal or South Africa overprinted

1923. *Optd with T* **1** *and* **2** *alternately.*

I. 14 *mm between lines of overprint.* (*a*) *On stamps of Transvaal*

		Un pair	*Us pair*
D1	5d. black and violet	3·75	9·50
	a. "Wes" for "West"	85·00	
	b. "Afrika" (no stop)	45·00	
D2	6d. black and red-brown	7·00	12·00
	a. "Wes" for "West"	£100	
	b. "Afrika" (no stop)	65·00	
	(*b*) *On South Africa stamps* (*De La Rue printing*)		
D3	2d. black and violet	5·50	7·50
	a. "Wes" for "West"	80·00	80·00
	b. "Afrika" (no stop)	90·00	
D4	3d. black and blue	3·00	6·50
	a. "Wes" for "West"	65·00	
D5	6d. black and slate	10·00	17·00
	a. "Wes" for "West"	50·00	
	(*c*) *On South Africa stamps* (*Pretoria printing*)		
	(i) *Type* D **1** (A). *Rouletted*		
D6	1d. black and rose	1·75	3·75
	a. "Wes" for "West"	45·00	
	b. "Afrika" (no stop)	45·00	
	c. Unrouletted between (pair)	£500	
D7	1½d. black and yellow-brown	1·00	3·00
	a. "Wes" for "West"	45·00	
	b. "Afrika" (no stop)	38·00	
	(ii) *Type* D **1** (B). *P* 14		
D8	½d. black and green	90	2·50
	a. Opt inverted	£250	
	b. Opt double	£180	£180
	c. "Wes" for "West"	40·00	
	d. "Afrika" (no stop)	40·00	
D9	2d. black and violet	1·75	4·00
	a. "Wes" for "West"	50·00	
	b. "Afrika" (no stop)	50·00	

The "Wes" variety occurs in the English overprint only, in some printings.

A variety of Nos. D1, D4, D5 and D9 with spacing 15 mm between lines of overprint occurs on four stamps in each pane of certain printings of this setting.

Nos. D1, D4, D6, D7 and D9 exist with 2 mm spacing between "South" and "West", and also with 2½ mm; Nos. D2, D3 and D8 only with 2 mm spacing; and No. D5 only with 2½ mm.

II. 10 *mm between lines of overprint.* (*a*) *On stamp of Transvaal*

D10	5d. black and violet	40·00	60·00
	(*b*) *On South Africa stamps* (*De La Rue printing*)		
D11	2d. black and violet	3·75	6·50
	a. "Afrika" (no stop)	60·00	
D12	3d. black and blue	3·75	6·50
	a. "Afrika" (no stop)	45·00	
	(*c*) *On South Africa stamp* (*Pretoria printing*). *Type* D **1** (A), *rouletted*		
D13	1d. black and rose (July 1923)	£2000	

1923–27. *Optd as T* **3** ("*Zuidwest*" *in one word without hyphen*) *and* **4**.

III. "South West" 14 *mm long;* "*Zuidwest*" 11 *mm long;* 14 *mm between lines of overprint* (Sept 1923). (*a*) *On stamp of Transvaal*

D14	6d. black and red-brown	8·50	17·00
	(*b*) *On South Africa stamps* (*Pretoria printing*) *Type* D **1** (A)		
	(i) *Rouletted*		
D15	1d. black and rose	1·75	4·00
	(ii) *P* 14		
D16	½d. black and green	1·75	3·50
D17	1d. black and rose	1·75	3·50

IV. "South West" 16 *mm long;* "*Zuidwest*" 12 *mm long;* 14 *mm between lines of overprint.* (*a*) *On stamp of Transvaal*

D17*a*	5d. black and violet	£200	£275
	(*b*) *On South Africa stamps* (*Pretoria printing*). *Type* D **1** (B). *P* 14		
D18	½d. black and green	1·25	2·75
D19	1d. black and rose	1·75	3·75
D20	6d. black and slate	2·25	7·00
	a. "Afrika" (no stop)	£140	
	V. *As* IV, *but* 12 *mm between lines of overprint*		
	(*a*) *On stamp of Transvaal*		
D21	5d. black and violet	2·75	7·50
	(*b*) *On South Africa stamp* (*De La Rue printing*)		
D22	3d. black and blue	6·00	7·50
	(*c*) *On South Africa stamps* (*Pretoria printing*). *Type* D **1** (B). *P* 14		
D23	½d. black and green	1·75	3·75
D24	1½d. black and yellow-brown	1·75	3·75
	VI. *As* IV, *but* 9½ *mm between lines of overprint*		
	(*a*) *On stamp of Transvaal*		
D25	5d. black and violet	1·75	3·50
	a. "Africa" (no stop)	42·00	
	(*b*) *On South Africa stamp* (*De La Rue printing*)		
D26	3d. black and blue	2·75	5·50
	(*c*) *On South Africa stamps* (*Pretoria printing*). *Type* D **1** (B). *P* 14		
D27	½d. black and green	1·00	2·75
D28	1d. black and rose	90	1·75
	a. "Africa" (no stop)	55·00	
D29	1½d. black and yellow-brown	90	2·25
	a. "Africa" (no stop)	45·00	
D30	2d. black and violet	1·25	2·25
	a. "Africa" (no stop)	45·00	
D31	3d. black and blue	1·25	2·50
	a. "Africa" (no stop)	45·00	
D32	6d. black and slate	3·75	9·50
	a. "Africa" (no stop)	70·00	

In Nos. D18/25, D29, D31 and D32, "South West" is 16 mm long, and in Nos. D26 and D27, 16½ mm long. Nos. D28 and D30 exist in both 16 mm and 16½ mm varieties. (*See note after* No. 40*a*.) In Nos. D20, D29, D31 and D32 a variety with "South West" 16½ mm long occurs once only in each sheet of 120 stamps (in certain printings only, in the case of D20), and similarly Nos. D28 and D30 occur with the two measurements on the same sheet from certain printings.

Suidwes	South West
Afrika.	Africa.
(D 1)	(D 2)

1927. *Optd as Types* D **1** *and* D **2**, *alternately.* 12 *mm between lines of overprint.* (*a*) *On stamp of Transvaal.*

D33	5d. black and violet	8·50	16·00
	(*b*) *On South Africa stamps* (*Pretoria printing*). *Type* D **1**, *redrawn.* *P* 14		
D34	1½d. black and yellow-brown	55	2·00
	a. "Africa" (no stop)	32·00	
D35	2d. black and pale violet	65	1·75
	a. "Africa" (no stop)	32·00	
D36	2d. black and deep violet	75	2·25
	a. "Africa" (no stop)	32·00	
D37	3d. black and blue	3·25	6·50
	a. "Africa" (no stop)	50·00	
D38	6d. black and slate	4·25	8·00
	a. "Africa" (no stop)	85·00	
	(*c*) *On South Africa stamp* (*Pretoria printing*). *Type* D **2**. *P* 14		
D39	1d. black and carmine	70	2·25
	a. "Africa" (no stop)	7·00	

1928–29. *Optd with T* **10**. *On South Africa stamps* (*Pretoria printing*). *P* 14. (*a*) *Type* D **1**, *redrawn.*

		Un single	*Us single*
D40	3d. black and blue	60	2·75
	a. Without stop after "A"	16·00	
D41	6d. black and slate	1·75	3·75
	(*b*) *Type* D **2**		
D42	½d. black and green	30	1·25
D43	1d. black and carmine	40	1·00
	a. Without stop after "A"	25·00	
D44	2d. black and mauve	50	1·50
D45	3d. black and blue	85	3·00
D46	6d. black and slate	1·50	6·00
	a. Without stop after "A"	12·00	

D 3

D 4

D 5

(Litho B.W.)

1931 (23 Feb). *Inscribed bilingually.* **W 9** *of South Africa. P* 12.

D47 D **3**	½d. black and green	60	1·75
D48	1d. black and scarlet	60	1·25
D49	2d. black and violet	70	1·40
D50	3d. black and blue	1·50	8·00
D51	6d. black and slate	3·75	17·00

PRINTER. The following issues have been printed by the South African Government Printer, Pretoria.

1959 (18 May). *Centre typo; frame roto.* **W 9** *of South Africa. P* 15 × 14.

D52 D **4**	1d. black and scarlet	50	2·00
D53	2d. black and reddish violet	85	2·50
D54	3d. black and blue	1·50	7·00

1960 (Dec). *As Nos.* D52 *and* D54 *but* **W 102** *of South Africa.*

D55	1d. black and scarlet	3·25	5·50
D56	3d. black and blue	3·25	5·50

1961 (14 Feb). *As Nos.* D52 *etc, but whole stamp roto, and value in cents.* **W 102** *of South Africa.*

D57	1 c. black and blue-green	20	75
D58	2 c. black and scarlet	20	75
D59	4 c. black and reddish violet	30	1·00
D60	5 c. black and light blue	40	1·50
D61	6 c. black and green	55	2·25
D62	10 c. black and yellow	1·00	3·25
D57/62	*Set of* 6	2·40	8·50

1972 (22 Mar). **W 127** (*sideways tête-bêche*). *Phosphorised chalk-surfaced paper. P* 14 × 13½.

D63 D **5**	1 c. emerald	30	1·00
D64	8 c. ultramarine	1·75	3·00

The use of Postage Due stamps ceased in April 1975.

OFFICIAL STAMPS

OFFICIAL		OFFISIEEL	
South West	Africa.	Suidwes	Afrika.
(O 1)		(O 2)	

1926 (Dec). *Nos.* 30, 31, 6 *and* 32 *of South Africa optd with Type* O **1** *on English stamp and* O **2** *on Afrikaans stamp alternately.*

		Un pair	*Us pair*
O1	½d. black and green	65·00	85·00
O2	1d. black and carmine	65·00	85·00
O3	2d. dull purple	£140	£140
O4	6d. green and orange	85·00	85·00

OFFICIAL OFFISIEEL

S.W.A. S.W.A.

(O 3) (O 4)

1929 (May). *Nos. 30, 31, 32 and 34 of South Africa optd with Type O 3 on English stamp and O 4 on Afrikaans stamp.*

O5	½d. black and green ..	75	3·00
O6	1d. black and carmine	75	3·00
O7	2d. grey and purple ..	1·75	3·75
	a. Pair, stamp without stop after "OFFICIAL" ..	4·50	8·50
	b. Pair, stamp without stop after "OFFISIEEL" ..	4·50	8·50
	c. Pair comprising a and b ..	14·00	25·00
O8	6d. green and orange	2·50	7·00

Types O 3 and O 4 are normally spaced 17 mm between lines on all except the 2d. value, which is spaced 13 mm.

Except on No. O7, the words "OFFICIAL" or "OFFISIEEL" normally have no stops after them.

OFFICIAL S.W.A. OFFISIEEL S.W.A.

(O 5) (O 6)

OFFICIAL. S.W.A. OFFISIEEL. S.W.A.

(O 7) (O 8)

1929 (Aug). *Nos. 30, 31 and 32 of South Africa optd with Types O 5 and O 6, and No. 34 with Types O 7 and O 8, languages to correspond.*

O 9	½d. black and green ..	40	3·00
O10	1d. black and carmine	45	3·00
O11	2d. grey and purple ..	1·00	4·75
	a. Pair, one stamp without stop after "OFFICIAL" ..	3·00	14·00
	b. Pair, one stamp without stop after "OFFISIEEL" ..	3·00	14·00
	c. Pair consisting of a and b ..	14·00	40·00
O12	6d. green and orange	2·25	10·00

OFFICIAL OFFISIEEL

(O 9) (O 10)

1931. *English stamp optd with Type O 9 and Afrikaans stamp with Type O 10 in red.*

			Un pair	*Us pair*
O13	12	½d. black and emerald ..	90	3·50
O14	13	1d. indigo and scarlet ..	70	3·50
O15	14	2d. blue and brown	60	3·50
O16	17	6d. blue and brown	1·50	8·00

OFFICIAL OFFISIEEL

(O 11) (O 12)

1938 (1 July). *English stamp optd with Type O 11 and Afrikaans with Type O 12 in red.*

O17	27	1½d. purple-brown	6·00	11·00

OFFICIAL OFFISIEEL

(O 13) (O 14)

1945–50. *English stamp optd with Type O 13, and Afrikaans stamp with Type O 14 in red.*

O18	12	½d. black and emerald ..	90	3·00
O19	13	1d. indigo and scarlet (1950) ..	90	3·00
		a. Opt double ..	£425	
O20	27	1½d. purple-brown	3·25	7·50
O21	14	2d. blue and brown (1947?)	£375	£500
O22	17	6d. blue and brown	2·50	8·00

OFFICIAL OFFISIEEL

(O 15) (O 16)

1951 (16 Nov)–**52.** *English stamp optd with Type O 15 and Afrikaans stamp with Type O 16, in red.*

O23	12	½d. black and emerald (1952) ..	75	2·50
O24	13	1d. indigo and scarlet ..	65	2·50
		a. Opts transposed	22·00	32·00
O25	27	1½d. purple-brown	4·50	8·00
		a. Opts transposed	25·00	35·00
O26	14	2d. blue and brown	65	3·25
		a. Opts transposed	20·00	38·00
O27	17	6d. blue and brown	3·00	11·00
		a. Opts transposed	20·00	45·00

The above errors refer to stamps with the English overprint on Afrikaans stamp and *vice versa.*

The use of official stamps ceased in January 1955.

Southern Cameroons

The following issue, although ordered by the Southern Cameroons authorities, was also on sale in Northern Cameroons, until the latter joined Nigeria. The stamps therefore can be found with Nigerian postmarks.

CAMEROONS U.K.T.T.

(1)

1960 (1 Oct)–**61.** *Nos. 69/71, 72 cb/cc and 73/80 of Nigeria optd with T 1, in red.*

1	18	½d. black and orange ..	5	20
2	19	1d. black and bronze-green	5	5
		a. Grey-blk & dull bronze-grn (19.9.61)	10	20
3	20	1½d. blue-green ..	10	15
4	21	2d. grey ..	10	15
		aa. bluish grey ..	18·00	10·00
		a. Pale grey (19.9.61) ..	10	25
5	22	3d. black and deep lilac..	15	5
6	23	4d. black and blue	12	40
7	24	6d. orange-brown and black (*p* 14)	12	10
		a. Perf 13 × 13½ (19.9.61)	20	60
8	25	1s. black and maroon ..	25	10
9	26	2s. 6d. black and green	80	1·50
10	27	5s. black and red-orange	1·25	3·00
11	28	10s. black and red-brown	3·25	9·00
12	29	£1 black and violet	10·00	21·00
1/12		.. *Set of* 12	15·00	32·00

Nos. 2, 4 and 4*aa* were overprinted on stamps printed by Waterlows' subsidiary, Imprimerie Belge de Securité.

Nos. 2a, 4a and 7a were from new printings produced by De La Rue instead of Waterlow.

The above stamps were withdrawn on 30 September 1961, when Southern Cameroons became part of the independent republic of Cameroun.

Southern Nigeria

The Colony and Protectorate of Southern Nigeria was formed on 1 January 1900 by the amalgamation of Niger Coast Protectorate with the southern part of the Niger Territories. Lagos was incorporated into the territory on 16 February 1906.

The stamps of NIGER COAST PROTECTORATE were used in Southern Nigeria until the introduction of Nos. 1/9, and also during a shortage of these values in mid-1902. The issues of LAGOS were utilized throughout Southern Nigeria after 16 February 1906 until supplies were exhausted.

PRICES FOR STAMPS ON COVER

Nos. 1/7	*from* × 4
Nos. 8/9	—
Nos. 10/18	*from* × 3
Nos. 19/20	—
Nos. 21/30	*from* × 3
Nos. 31/2	—
Nos. 33/42	*from* × 3
Nos. 43/4	—
Nos. 45/53	*from* × 3
Nos. 55/6	—

PRINTERS. All issues of Southern Nigeria were typographed by De La Rue & Co, Ltd, London.

1

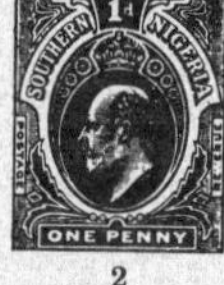

2

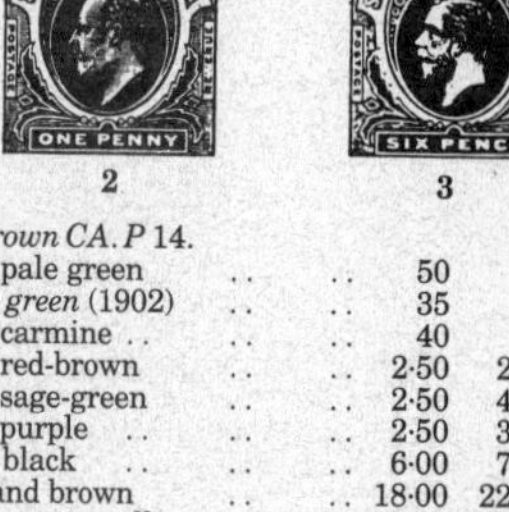

3

1901 (Mar)–**02.** *Wmk Crown CA. P 14.*

1	1	½d. black and pale green	50	75
		a. Black and green (1902)	35	50
2		1d. black and carmine ..	40	50
3		2d. black and red-brown	2·50	2·75
4		4d. black and sage-green	2·50	4·00
5		6d. black and purple ..	2·50	3·50
6		1s. green and black	6·00	7·00
7		2s. 6d. black and brown	18·00	22·00
8		5s. black and orange-yellow	45·00	70·00
9		10s. black and purple/*yellow*	90·00	£120
1/9		.. *Set of* 9	£150	£200
1/9 Optd "Specimen"		.. *Set of* 9	£180	

1903 (Mar)–**04.** *Wmk Crown CA. P 14.*

10	2	½d. grey-black and pale green ..	50	30
11		1d. grey-black and carmine	90	30
12		2d. grey-black and chestnut	1·00	90
13		2½d. grey-black and blue (1904)..	3·00	1·75
14		4d. grey-black and olive-green..	1·75	3·25
15		6d. grey-black and purple	6·50	9·00
16		1s. green and black	7·50	7·00
17		2s. 6d. grey-black and brown	9·00	14·00
		a. Grey and yellow-brown	50·00	65·00
18		5s. grey-black and yellow	38·00	48·00
19		10s. grey-black and purple/*yellow*	38·00	50·00
20		£1 green and violet	£225	£300
10/20		.. *Set of* 11	£300	£400
10/20 Optd "Specimen"		.. *Set of* 11	£300	

1904 (June)–**08.** *Wmk Mult Crown CA. P 14.*

21	2	½d. grey-black and pale green, **OC**	30	20
22		1d. grey-black and carmine, **OC**	45	20
23		2d. grey-black and chestnut, **O**	1·25	70
		a. Pale grey and chestnut (1907)	1·75	60
24		2½d. grey-black and bright blue, **O** (1905)	80	85
25		3d. orange-brown and bright purple, **C** (1907) (Optd S. £18)	5·50	2·50
26		4d. grey-black & olive-green, **OC** (1905)	8·00	5·00
		a. Grey-black & pale olive-grn, **C** (1907)	4·75	8·00
27		6d. grey-black and bright purple, **OC** ..	2·75	1·75
28		1s. grey-green and black, **OC** ..	2·00	1·50
29		2s. 6d. grey-black and brown, **OC** (1905)	13·00	9·50
30		5s. grey-black and yellow, **OC** (1905) ..	23·00	24·00
31		10s. grey-black & purple/*yellow*, **C** (1908)	65·00	80·00
32		£1 green and violet, **OC** (1905)	85·00	£120
21/32		.. *Set of* 12	£180	£225

I

II

Die I. Thick "1"; small "d".
Die II. Thinner "1"; larger "d".

1907–11. *Colours changed. Ordinary paper (½d. to 2½d.) or chalk-surfaced paper (others). Wmk Mult Crown CA. P 14.*

33	2	½d. pale green ..	55	25
		a. Blue-green (1910) ..	25	25
34		1d. carmine (I) ..	70	20
		a. Die II. *Carmine-red* (1910)..	25	10
35		2d. greyish slate (1909)	1·00	70
36		2½d. blue (1909) ..	1·00	2·75
37		3d. purple/*yellow* (1909)	1·00	65
38		4d. black and red/*yellow* (1909)	1·00	1·00
39		6d. dull purple and purple (1909)	4·50	3·00
		a. Dull purple and bright purple (1911)	6·50	2·25
40		1s. black/*green* (1909) ..	3·75	1·25
41		2s. 6d. black and red/*blue* (1909)	5·00	2·50
42		5s. green and red/*yellow* (1909)	23·00	26·00
43		10s. green and red/*green* (1909)..	40·00	45·00
44		£1 purple and black/*red* (1909)	95·00	£120
33/44		.. *Set of* 12	£160	£180
33/44 Optd "Specimen"		.. *Set of* 12	£325	

It was formerly believed that the plate used for printing the head was retouched in 1907 but the fact that the 1d. Die II, which did not appear until 1910, only exists in the first state of the head threw some doubts on this theory. Specialists now recognise that two dies of the head existed and that plates from both were used in Southern Nigeria.

The differences are very small and we refrain from listing them until more research is done, both in this country and in others where they may have been used. The differences are illustrated below:

A

B

In Head A the fifth line of shading on the king's cheek shows as a line of dots and the lines of shading up to the king's hair are broken in places. In Head B the lines of shading are more regular, especially the fifth line.

The following stamps are known:

Ordinary colours: 21 ordinary and chalky, A; 22 ordinary and chalky, A; 23, A; 23*a*, B; 24, A; 25, B; 26 ordinary and chalky, A; 27 ordinary, A; 27 chalky, B; 28 ordinary, A; 28 chalky, B; 29 ordinary, A; 29 chalky, A and B; 30 ordinary, A; 30 chalky, B; 31, B; 32 ordinary, A; 32 chalky, B.

New colours: 33, A and B; 33*a*, B; 34, A and B; 34*a*, A; 35/44, B.

1912. *Wmk Mult Crown CA. P 14.*

45	3	½d. green	30	15
46		1d. red ..	60	10
47		2d. grey ..	75	80
48		2½d. bright blue ..	1·60	1·90
49		3d. purple/*yellow*	95	60
50		4d. black and red/*yellow*	1·50	2·00
51		6d. dull and bright purple	1·75	1·00
52		1s. black/*green* ..	2·50	1·25
53		2s. 6d. black and red/*blue*	8·50	9·50
54		5s. green and red/*yellow*	14·00	18·00
55		10s. green and red/*green*	40·00	45·00
56		£1 purple and black/*red*	90·00	£120
45/56		.. *Set of* 12	£150	£180
45/56 Optd "Specimen"		.. *Set of* 12	£325	

On 1 January 1914 Southern Nigeria became part of NIGERIA.

PRICES OF SETS

Set prices are given for many issues, generally those containing five stamps or more. Definitive sets include one of each value or major colour change, but do not cover different perforations, die types or minor shades. Where a choice is possible the set prices are based on the cheapest versions of the stamps included in the listings.

Southern Rhodesia

PRICES FOR STAMPS ON COVER TO 1945
Nos. 1/61 *from* × 2

SELF-GOVERNMENT

1

2 King George V

3 Victoria Falls

(Recess Waterlow)

1924 (1 Apr)–**29.** *P* 14.

No.	Type	Description	Unused	Used
1	1	½d. blue-green	50	20
		a. Imperf between (horiz pair)	£650	£600
		b. Imperf between (vert pair)	£700	£650
		c. Imperf vert (horiz pair)	£800	
2		1d. bright rose	50	15
		a. Imperf between (horiz pair)	£750	£600
		b. Imperf between (vert pair)	£750	
		c. Perf 12½ (coil) (1929)	12·00	40·00
3		1½d. bistre-brown	70	30
		a. Imperf between (horiz pair)	£7000	
		b. Imperf between (vert pair)	£2000	
4		2d. black and purple-grey	1·25	60
		a. Imperf between (horiz pair)	£4000	
5		3d. blue	2·50	2·25
6		4d. black and orange-red	2·50	3·75
7		6d. black and mauve	2·50	2·50
		a. Imperf between (horiz pair)	£5500	
8		8d. purple and pale green	15·00	20·00
9		10d. blue and rose	15·00	20·00
10		1s. black and light blue	4·50	4·50
11		1s. 6d. black and yellow	25·00	30·00
12		2s. black and brown	27·00	27·00
13		2s. 6d. blue and sepia	48·00	60·00
14		5s. blue and blue-green	95·00	95·00
1/14		*Set of* 14	£200	£250

Prices for "imperf between" varieties are for adjacent stamps from the same pane and not for those separated by wide gutter margins between vertical or horizontal pairs, which come from the junction of two panes.

(T **2** recess by B.W.; T **3** typo by Waterlow)

1931 (1 April)–**37.** *T* **2** (*line perf* 12 *unless otherwise stated*) *and* **3** (*comb perf* 15 × 14). (*The* 11½ *perf is comb.*).

No.	Type	Description	Unused	Used
15	2	½d. green	25	30
		a. Perf 11½ (1933)	40	15
		b. Perf 14 (1935)	50	20
16		1d. scarlet	40	20
		a. Perf 11½ (1933)	80	15
		b. Perf 14 (1935)	40	20
16c		1½d. chocolate (1933)	32·00	45·00
		d. Perf 11½ (1.4.32)	1·00	45
17	3	2d. black and sepia	4·50	4·00
18		3d. deep ultramarine	14·00	15·00
19	2	4d. black and vermilion	2·75	70
		a. Perf 11½ (1935)	15·00	5·00
		b. Perf 14 (10.37)	32·00	26·00
20		6d. black and magenta	3·00	60
		a. Perf 11½ (1933)	12·00	75
		b. Perf 14 (1936)	20·00	1·25
21		8d. violet and olive-green	4·50	6·50
		a. Perf 11½ (1934)	18·00	23·00
21b		9d. vermilion and olive-green (1.9.34)	13·00	14·00
22		10d. blue and scarlet	10·00	6·50
		a. Perf 11½ (1933)	11·00	13·00
23		1s. black and greenish blue	7·00	2·00
		a. Perf 11½ (1935)	26·00	13·00
		b. Perf 14 (10.37)	£140	£100
24		1s. 6d. black and orange-yellow	20·00	18·00
		a. Perf 11½ (1936)	48·00	48·00
25		2s. black and brown	20·00	13·00
		a. Perf 11½ (1933)	55·00	35·00
26		2s. 6d. blue and drab	35·00	35·00
		a. Perf 11½ (1933)	48·00	38·00
27		5s. blue and blue-green	70·00	80·00
		a. Printed on gummed side	£2750	
15/27		*Set of* 15	£190	£180

No. 16c was issued in booklets only.

PRINTERS. All stamps from Types **4** to **29** were recess-printed by Waterlow and Sons, Ltd, London, except where otherwise stated.

4

1932 (1 May). *P* 12½.

No.	Type	Description	Unused	Used
29	4	2d. green and chocolate	2·75	30
30		3d. deep ultramarine	7·00	1·90
		a. Imperf horiz (vert pair)	£6000	£6500
		b. Imperf between (vert pair)		

5 Victoria Falls

1935 (6 May). *Silver Jubilee. P* 11 × 12.

No.	Type	Description	Unused	Used
31	5	1d. olive and rose-carmine	75	40
32		2d. emerald and sepia	2·00	1·90
33		3d. violet and deep blue	9·00	14·00
34		6d. black and purple	11·00	12·00

1935–41. *Inscr* "POSTAGE AND REVENUE".

No.	Type	Description	Unused	Used
35	4	2d. green and chocolate (*p* 12½)	2·75	3·25
		a. Perf 14 (1941)	75	10
35b		3d. deep blue (*p* 14) (1938)	95	25

6 Victoria Falls and Railway Bridge

7 King George VI

1937 (12 May). *Coronation. P* 12½.

No.	Type	Description	Unused	Used
36	6	1d. olive and rose-carmine	45	25
37		2d. emerald and sepia	60	60
38		3d. violet and blue	3·75	5·50
39		6d. black and purple	2·25	2·00

1937 (25 Nov). *P* 14.

No.	Type	Description	Unused	Used
40	7	½d. green	20	5
41		1d. scarlet	20	5
42		1½d. red-brown	20	5
43		4d. red-orange	35	5
44		6d. grey-black	45	5
45		8d. emerald-green	1·50	90
46		9d. pale blue	1·25	50
47		10d. purple	1·60	2·00
48		1s. black and blue-green	80	5
		a. Double print of frame	£225	
49		1s. 6d. black and orange-yellow	6·50	2·00
50		2s. black and brown	7·50	2·00
51		2s. 6d. ultramarine and purple	7·50	2·25
52		5s. blue and blue-green	20·00	2·25
40/52		*Set of* 13	42·00	11·00

8 British South Africa Co's Arms

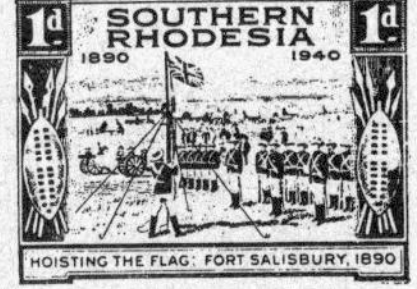
9 Fort Salisbury, 1890

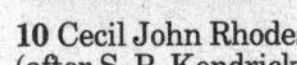
10 Cecil John Rhodes (after S. P. Kendrick)

15 Lobengula's Kraal and Govt House, Salisbury

(Des Mrs. L. E. Curtis (½d., 1d., 1½d., 3d.), Mrs I. Mount (others))

1940 (3 June). *British South Africa Company's Golden Jubilee. T* **8/10, 15** *and similar designs. P* 14.

No.	Type	Description	Unused	Used
53		½d. slate-violet and green	8	5
54		1d. violet-blue and scarlet	10	5
55		1½d. black and red-brown	10	8
56		2d. green and bright violet	60	30
57		3d. black and blue	55	30
58		4d. green and brown	1·00	70
59		6d. chocolate and green	1·00	1·25
60		1s. blue and green	1·25	1·75
53/60		*Set of* 8	4·25	4·00

Designs: *Horiz* (*as T* **8**)—2d. Fort Victoria; 3d. Rhodes makes peace. *Vert* (*as T* **10**)—4d. Victoria Falls Bridge; 6d. Statue of Sir Charles Coghlan.

16 Mounted Pioneer

17 Queen Elizabeth II when Princess and Princess Margaret

(Roto South African Govt Printer, Pretoria)

1943 (1 Nov). *50th Anniv of Occupation of Matabeleland. W* **9** *of South Africa* (*Mult Springbok*) *sideways. P* 14.

No.	Type	Description	Unused	Used
61	16	2d. brown and green	10	8

1947 (1 Apr). *Royal Visit. T* **17** *and similar horiz design. P* 14.

No.	Type	Description	Unused	Used
62		½d. black and green	8	5
63		1d. black and scarlet	8	5

Design:—1d. King George VI and Queen Elizabeth.

19 Queen Elizabeth

20 King George VI

21 Queen Elizabeth II when Princess

22 Princess Margaret

1947 (8 May). *Victory. P* 14.

No.	Type	Description	Unused	Used
64	19	1d. carmine	5	5
65	20	2d. slate	8	8
66	21	3d. blue	10	12
67	22	6d. orange	12	15

(Recess B.W.)

1949 (10 Oct). *75th Anniv of Universal Postal Union. As Nos.* 115/16 *of Antigua.*

No.	Type	Description	Unused	Used
68		2d. slate-green	75	40
69		3d. blue	1·40	2·50

23 Queen Victoria, Arms and King George VI

1950 (12 Sept). *Diamond Jubilee of Southern Rhodesia. P* 14.

No.	Type	Description	Unused	Used
70	23	2d. green and brown	8	8

24 "Medical Services"

27 "Water Supplies"

(Des A. R. Winter (2d.), Mrs. J. M. Enalim (others))

1953 (15 Apr). *Birth Centenary of Cecil Rhodes. T* **24, 27** *and similar horiz designs. P* 14.

No.	Type	Description	Unused	Used
71		½d. pale blue and sepia	15	40
72		1d. chestnut and blue-green	15	5
73		2d. grey-green and violet	20	5
74		4½d. deep blue-green & deep ultramarine	1·50	2·75
75		1s. black and red-brown	2·50	1·00

Designs:—1d. "Agriculture"; 2d. "Building"; 1s. "Transport".

No. 74 also commemorates the Diamond Jubilee of Matabeleland.

1953 (30 May). *Rhodes Centenary Exhibition, Bulawayo. As No.* 59 *of Northern Rhodesia but without watermark.*

No.	Type	Description	Unused	Used
76		6d. violet	35	50

30 Queen Elizabeth II

(Recess D.L.R.)

1953 (1 June). *Coronation. P* 12 × 12½.

No.	Type	Description	Unused	Used
77	30	2s. 6d. carmine	5·50	7·00

31 Sable Antelope

33 Rhodes's Grave

34 Farm Worker

42 Basket Maker

43 Balancing Rocks

44 Coat of Arms

(Recess, centre typo (4d.), B.W.)

1953 (31 Aug). *T* **31, 33/4, 42/4** *and similar designs. P* 13½ × 14 (2*d*., 6*d*., 5*s*.), 14 (10*s*., £1) *or* 14 × 13½ (*others*).

No.	Value	Description	Unused	Used
78	½d.	grey-green and claret	15	20
79	1d.	green and brown	15	5
80	2d.	deep chestnut and reddish violet	15	5
81	3d.	chocolate and rose-red	30	30
82	4d.	red, green and indigo	50	8
83	4½d.	black and deep bright blue	75	1·00
84	6d.	brown-olive & deep turquoise-green	75	12
85	9d.	deep blue and reddish brown	1·50	1·60
86	1s.	reddish violet and light blue	75	15
87	2s.	purple and scarlet	5·00	4·75
88	2s. 6d.	yellow-olive and orange-brown	7·00	5·50
89	5s.	yellow-brown and deep green	20·00	15·00
90	10s.	red-brown and olive	32·00	38·00
91	£1	rose-red and black	40·00	65·00
78/91		*Set of* 14	£100	£120

Designs: *Vert* (*as T* **31**) 1d. Tobacco planter. (*As T* **33**) 6d. Baobab tree. *Horiz* (*as T* **34**)—4d. Flame Lily; 4½d. Victoria Falls; 9d. Lion; 1s. Zimbabwe Ruins; 2s. Birchenough Bridge; 2s. 6d. Kariba Gorge.

For issues from 1954 to 1963 see under RHODESIA AND NYASALAND.

45 Maize

50 Flame Lily

56 Cattle

58 Coat of Arms

(Des V. Whiteley. Photo Harrison)

1964 (19 Feb). *T* **45, 50, 56, 58** *and similar horiz designs. P* 14½ (½*d. to* 4*d.*), 13½ × 13 (6*d. to* 2*s.* 6*d.*) *or* 14½ × 14 (*others*).

No.	Value	Description	Unused	Used
92	½d.	yellow, yellow-green and light blue	5	12
93	1d.	reddish violet and yellow-ochre	8	5
	a.	Reddish violet omitted	£450	
94	2d.	yellow and deep violet	8	5
95	3d.	chocolate and pale blue	10	5
96	4d.	yellow-orange and deep green	15	5
97	6d.	carmine-red, yellow and deep dull green	40	5
98	9d.	red-brown, yellow and olive-green	1·25	80
99	1s.	blue-green and ochre	70	5
	a.	blue-green (Queen and emeralds) omitted	£700	
100	1s. 3d.	red, violet and yellow-green	3·00	5
101	2s.	blue and ochre	2·75	75
102	2s. 6d.	ultramarine and vermilion	2·75	70
	a.	Vermilion omitted	£200	
103	5s.	light brown, bistre-yellow & light blue	5·00	2·50
104	10s.	black, yell-ochre, lt blue & carmine-red	19·00	11·00
105	£1	brown, yellow-green, buff & salmon-pink	28·00	24·00
92/105		*Set of* 14	55·00	35·00

Designs: (*As T* **45**)—1d. Buffalo; 2d. Tobacco; 3d. Kudu; 4d. Citrus. (*As T* **50**)—9d. Ansellia Orchid; 1s. Emeralds; 1s. 3d. Aloe; 2s. Lake Kyle; 2s. 6d. Tiger Fish. (*As T* **56**)—10s. Helmet Guinea-fowl.

Nos. 92 and 93 exist in coils constructed from normal sheets.

See also Nos. 359/72 of Rhodesia.

POSTAGE DUE STAMPS

SOUTHERN RHODESIA

(D 1)

1951 (1 Oct)–52? *Postage Due stamps of Great Britain optd with Type* D **1**.

No.	Type	Value	Description	Unused	Used
D1	D 1	½d.	emerald (No. D27)	3·50	4·25
D2		1d.	violet-blue (No. D36)	2·00	1·00
D3		2d.	agate (No. D29)	4·50	3·50
D4		3d.	violet (No. D30)	3·00	1·75
D5		4d.	blue (No. D38)	1·75	2·00
D6		4d.	dull grey-green (No. D31) (1952?)	£110	£180
D7		1s.	deep blue (No. D33)	3·50	2·25
D1/5, 7			*Set of* 6	16·00	13·00

In October 1964 Southern Rhodesia was renamed Rhodesia. Issues after this date will be found listed under RHODESIA.

Sri Lanka

(*formerly* Ceylon)

REPUBLIC

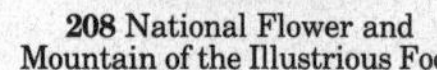

208 National Flower and Mountain of the Illustrious Foot

209 Map of World with Buddhist Flag

(Des L. D. P. Jayawardena. Litho D.L.R.)

1972 (22 May). *Inauguration of the Republic of Sri Lanka. P* 13.

No.	Type	Description	Unused	Used
591	**208**	15 c. multicoloured	15	8

(Des L. D. P. Jayawardena. Litho Harrison)

1972 (26 May). *Tenth Conference of the World Fellowship of Buddhists. P* 14 × 13.

No.	Type	Description	Unused	Used
592	**209**	5 c. multicoloured	5	5

This stamp was scheduled for release in May 1971, and when finally released had the year "1972" additionally overprinted in red. Sheets are known without this overprint but their status has not been established.

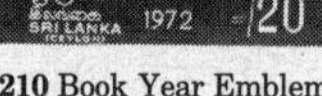

210 Book Year Emblem

211 Imperial Angelfish

(Des L. D. P. Jayawardena. Photo Pakistan Security Printing Corp)

1972 (8 Sept). *International Book Year. P* 13.

No.	Type	Description	Unused	Used
593	**210**	20 c. light yellow-orange and lake-brown	20	20

(Des G. D. Kariyawasam. Litho Rosenbaum Bros, Vienna)

1972 (12 Oct). *T* **211** *and similar horiz designs showing fish. Multicoloured. P* 13 × 13½.

No.	Value	Description	Unused	Used
594	2 c.	Type **211**	5	5
	a.	Plum colour omitted	6·00	
595	3 c.	Green Chromide	5	5
596	30 c.	Skipjack	10	5
597	2 r.	Black Ruby Barb	35	60

On No. 594a the stripes of the fish are in green instead of plum.

212 Memorial Hall

(Des R. B. Mawilmada. Litho D.L.R.)

1973 (17 May). *Opening of Bandaranaike Memorial Hall. P* 14.

No.	Type	Description	Unused	Used
598	**212**	15 c. light cobalt and deep grey-blue	10	5

213 King Vessantara giving away his Children

214 Bandaranaike Memorial Conference Hall

(Des P. Wanigatunga. Litho D.L.R.)

1973 (3 Sept). *Rock and Temple Paintings. T* **213** *and similar vert designs. Multicoloured. P* 13½ × 14.

No.	Value	Description	Unused	Used
599	35 c.	Type **213**	5	5
600	50 c.	The Prince and the Grave-digger	10	5
601	90 c.	Bearded old man	25	30
602	1 r. 55,	Two female figures	40	50
MS603		115 × 141 mm. Nos. 599/602	1·25	1·50

(Des and litho Harrison)

1974 (6 Sept). *20th Commonwealth Parliamentary Conference, Colombo. P* 14½.

No.	Type	Description	Unused	Used
604	**214**	85 c. multicoloured	20	20

215 Prime Minister Bandaranaike

216 "UPU" and "100"

(Des and photo Harrison)

1974 (25 Sept). *P* 14½.

No.	Type	Description	Unused	Used
605	**215**	15 c. multicoloured	15	5
		a. Red (face value) omitted	8·00	
		b. Pale blue (background) omitted	8·00	

(Des P. Jayatillake. Litho German Bank Note Ptg Co, Leipzig)

1974 (9 Oct). *Centenary of Universal Postal Union. P* 13½ × 13.

No.	Type	Description	Unused	Used
606	**216**	50 c. multicoloured	45	35

217 Sri Lanka Parliament Building

218 Sir Ponnambalam Ramanathan (politician)

(Litho Toppan Printing Co, Japan)

1975 (1 Apr). *Inter-Parliamentary Meeting. P* 13.

No.	Type	Description	Unused	Used
607	**217**	1 r. multicoloured	30	25

(Des A. Rasiah. Litho Toppan Ptg Co, Japan)

1975 (4 Sep). *Ramanathan Commemoration. P* 13.

No.	Type	Description	Unused	Used
608	**218**	75 c. multicoloured	30	20

219 D. J. Wimalasurendra (engineer)

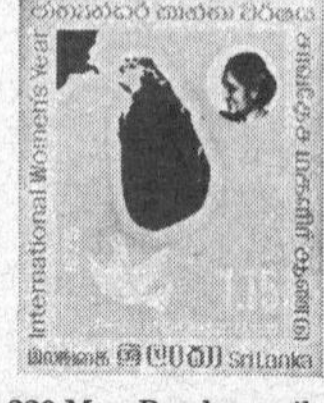

220 Mrs. Bandaranaike, Map and Dove

(Des A. Dharmasiri. Litho Toppan Ptg Co, Japan)

1975 (17 Sept). *Wimalasurendra Commemoration. P* 13.

No.	Type	Description	Unused	Used
609	**219**	75 c. blue-black and new blue	30	20

(Des B. U. Ananda Somatilaka. Litho Toppan Ptg Co, Japan)

1975 (22 Dec). *International Women's Year. P* 13.

No.	Type	Description	Unused	Used
610	**220**	1 r. 15, multicoloured	45	45

OMNIBUS ISSUES

Details, together with prices for complete sets, of the various Omnibus issues from the 1935 Silver Jubilee series to date are included in a special section following Zululand at the end of the catalogue.

221 Ma-ratmal 222 Mahaweli Dam

(Des and litho Toppan Ptg Co, Japan)

1976 (1 Jan). *Indigenous Flora. T* **221** *and similar vert designs. Multicoloured. P* 13.
611 25 c. Type **221** . . 8 5
a. Imperf (pair) . . 55·00
612 50 c. Binara . . 10 5
613 75 c. Daffodil orchid . . 12 12
614 10 r. Diyapara . . 3·00 3·75
MS615 153 × 153 mm. Nos. 611/14 . . 3·75 4·50

A used example of No. 613 has been seen with the yellow printing apparently omitted. This results in the leaves appearing blue instead of green.

(Des R. B. Mawilmada. Litho German Bank Note Ptg Co, Leipzig)

1976 (8 Jan). *Diversion of the Mahaweli River. P* 13 × 12½.
616 **222** 85 c. turquoise, violet-blue and azure . . 25 20

223 Dish Aerial 224 Conception of the Buddha

(Des P. A. Miththapala. Litho German Bank Note Ptg Co, Leipzig)

1976 (6 May). *Opening of Satellite Earth Station, Padukka. P* 14 × 13½.
617 **223** 1 r. multicoloured . . 40 45

(Des P. Wanigatunga. Litho Toppan Ptg Co, Japan)

1976 (7 May). *Vesak. T* **224** *and similar horiz designs showing paintings from the Dambava Temple. Multicoloured. P* 13.
618 5 c. Type **224** . . 5 5
619 10 c. King Suddhodana and the astrologers . . 5 5
620 1 r. 50, The astrologers being entertained . . 20 20
621 2 r. The Queen in a palanquin . . 25 25
622 2 r. 25, Royal procession . . 30 35
623 5 r. Birth of the Buddha . . 70 80
618/23 . . *Set of* 6 1·40 1·50
MS624 161 × 95 mm. Nos. 618/23 . . 2·75 3·50

225 Blue Sapphire 226 Prime Minister Mrs. S. Bandaranaike

(Des State Gem Corporation. Litho Toppan Ptg Co, Japan)

1976 (16 June). *Gems of Sri Lanka. T* **225** *and similar horiz designs. Multicoloured. P* 12 × 12½.
625 60 c. Type **225** . . 30 5
626 1 r. 15, Cat's Eye . . 50 25
627 2 r. Star sapphire . . 70 60
628 5 r. Ruby . . 1·50 2·25
MS629 152 × 152 mm. Nos. 625/8 . . 3·50 4·00

(Photo Harrison)

1976 (4 Aug). *Non-aligned Summit Conference, Colombo. P* 14 × 14½.
630 **226** 1 r. 15, multicoloured . . 20 20
631 2 r. multicoloured . . 35 35

227 Statue of Liberty 228 Bell, Early Telephone and Telephone Lines

(Des A. Harischandra. Litho German Bank Note Ptg Co, Leipzig)

1976 (29 Nov). *Bicentenary of American Revolution. P* 13½.
632 **227** 2 r. 25, cobalt and indigo . . 55 55

(Des A. Harischandra. Litho German Bank Note Ptg Co, Leipzig)

1976 (21 Dec). *Telephone Centenary. P* 13.
633 **228** 1 r. multicoloured . . 20 20

229 Maitreya (pre-carnate Buddha) 230 Kandyan Crown

(Des P. Wanigatunga. Litho German Bank Note Ptg Co, Leipzig)

1977 (1 Jan). *Centenary of Colombo Museum. T* **229** *and similar vert designs showing statues. Multicoloured. P* 12½.
634 50 c. Type **229** . . 12 5
635 1 r. Sundara Murti Swami (Tamil psalmist) 25 15
636 5 r. Tara (goddess) . . 1·00 1·50

(Des R. B. Mawilmada. Litho Toppan Ptg Co, Japan)

1977 (18 Jan). *Regalia of the Kings of Kandy. T* **230** *and similar vert design. Multicoloured. P* 13.
637 1 r. Type **230** . . 35 20
638 2 r. Throne and footstool . . 65 70

231 Sri Rahula Thero (poet) 232 Sir Ponnambalam Arunachalam (social reformer)

(Des S. Dissanayaka. Litho Toppan Ptg Co, Japan)

1977 (23 Feb). *Sri Rahula Commemoration. P* 13.
639 **231** 1 r. multicoloured . . 25 25

(Litho Toppan Ptg Co, Japan)

1977 (10 Mar). *Ponnambalam Arunachalam Commemoration. P* 13.
640 **232** 1 r. multicoloured . . 25 25

233 Brass Lamps 234 Siddi Lebbe (author and educationalist

(Des A. Harischandra. Litho Toppan Ptg Co, Japan)

1977 (7 Apr). *Handicrafts. T* **233** *and similar vert designs. Multicoloured. P* 13.
641 20 c. Type **233** . . 5 5
642 25 c. Jewellery box . . 5 5
643 50 c. Caparisoned elephant . . 10 5
644 5 r. Mask . . 1·00 1·50
MS645 205 × 89 mm. Nos. 641/4 . . 1·75 2·25

(Des Sarasvati Rockwood. Litho Toppan Ptg Co, Japan)

1977 (11 June). *Siddi Lebbe Commemoration. P* 13½.
646 **234** 1 r. multicoloured . . 25 25

235 Girl Guide 236 Parliament Building and "Wheel of Life"

(Des and litho Asher & Co, Melbourne)

1977 (13 Dec). *60th Anniv of Sri Lanka Girl Guides Association. P* 14½ × 15.
647 **235** 75 c. multicoloured . . 45 25

(Des R. B. Mawilmada. Photo Enschedé)

1978 (4 Feb). *Election of New President. P* 12 × 12½.
648 **236** 15 c. gold, brt yellow-green & emerald . . 20 5

No. 648 was re-issued on 7 September 1978, additionally dated "1978.09.07" to mark the Promulgation of the Constitution for the Democratic Socialist Republic of Sri Lanka. This re-issue was only available on First Day Covers (*Price on F.D.C. £2*).

See also Nos. 680/*a*.

237 Youths Running 238 Prince Siddhartha's Renunciation

(Des M. Dissanayake. Litho Asher & Co, Melbourne)

1978 (27 Apr). *National Youth Service Council. P* 15 × 14½.
649 **237** 15 c. multicoloured . . 15 5

(Des P. Wanigatunga. Litho Metal Box Singapore Ltd)

1978 (16 May). *Vesak. Rock Carvings from Borobudur Temple. T* **238** *and similar horiz design in buff, brown and ultramarine. P* 13.
650 15 c. Type **238** . . 10 5
651 50 c. Prince Siddhartha shaving his hair . . 30 20

•05

(239) 240 Veera Puran Appu

1978 (18 May–20 Nov). *Nos.* 559, 601/2, 605 *and* 648/9 *surch as T* **239**.
652 5 c. on 90 c. Bearded old man (26.6.) . . 5 5
a. Surch inverted . . 12·00
653 10 c. on 35 c. Type **213** . . 5 5
a. Surch inverted . . 12·00
654 25 c. on 15 c. Type **215** (20.11) . . 60 20
655 25 c. on 15 c. Type **236** (20.11) . . 60 20
a. Surch inverted . . 10·00
656 25 c. on 15 c. Type **237** (Blk. and Pink) (20.11) 60 20
a. Surch and obliterating square inverted . . 9·00
ab. Surch only inverted . . 8·50
657 1 r. on 1 r. 55, Two female figures (17.11) . . 40 15
a. Surch inverted
652/7 . . *Set of* 6 1·90 75

No. 656 has the surcharge applied in black on a pink square, previously printed over the original face value.

(Des A. Dharmasiri. Litho Metal Box Singapore Ltd)

1978 (8 Aug). *130th Death Anniv of Veera Puran Appu (revolutionary). P* 13.
658 **240** 15 c. multicoloured . . 15 10

SRI LANKA

15

241 *Troides helena darsius* (242)

(Des G. Ratnavira. Litho J.W.)

1978 (28 Nov). *Butterflies. T* **241** *and similar vert designs. Multicoloured. P* 14 × 13½.
659 25 c. Type **241** . . 5 5
660 50 c. *Cethosia nietneri nietneri* . . 5 5
661 5 r. *Kallima philarchus philarchus* . . 30 20
662 10 r. *Papilio polymnestor parinda* . . 55 55
MS663 203 × 147 mm. Nos. 659/62 . . 2·50 2·75

1979 (22 Mar). *No.* 486 *of Ceylon surch with T* **242** *in black and turquoise-blue.*
664 15 c. on 10 c. myrtle-green . . 15 5
a. Surch double . . 12·00
b. Turq-blue surch omitted . . 20·00

Type **242** shows only part of the turquoise-blue section of the overprint ("SRI LANKA"), which also includes a rectangle obliterating the original face value. The new value is printed on this rectangle in black.

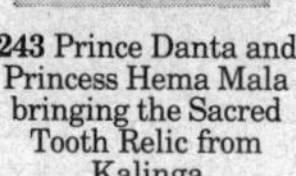

243 Prince Danta and Princess Hema Mala bringing the Sacred Tooth Relic from Kalinga

244 Piyadasa Sirisena

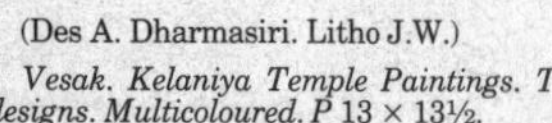

(Des A. Dharmasiri. Litho J.W.)

1979 (3 May). *Vesak. Kelaniya Temple Paintings. T* **243** *and similar vert designs. Multicoloured. P* 13 × 13½.

665 25 c. Type **243** 5 5
666 1 r. Theri Sanghamitta bringing the Bodhi Tree branch to Sri Lanka 12 12
667 10 r. King Kirti Sri Rajasinghe offering fan of authority to the Sangha Raja . . . . 95 1·10
MS668 120 × 80 mm. Nos. 665/7 . . . . . . 1·40 1·75

(Des P. Jayatillake. Litho Toppan Ptg Co, Japan)

1979 (22 May). *Piyadasa Sirisena (writer) Commemoration. P* 13.

669 **244** 1 r. 25, multicoloured 20 20

245 Wrestlers

246 Dudley Senanayake

(Des R. B. Mawilmada. Litho Metal Box Singapore Ltd)

1979 (28 May). *Wood Carvings from Embekke Temple. T* **245** *and similar vert design. P* 14.

670 20 r. chocolate, ochre and deep green . . 95 1·00
671 50 r. agate, bistre-yellow and deep green . . 2·50 2·50
Design:—50 r. Dancer.

(Photo Heraclio Fournier)

1979 (19 June). *Dudley Senanayake (former Prime Minister) Commemoration. P* 14.

672 **246** 1 r. 25, bottle green 15 20

247 Mother with Child

248 Ceylon 1857 6d. Stamp and Sir Rowland Hill

(Des A. Dharmasiri and R. Mawilmada. Litho Metal Box Singapore Ltd)

1979 (31 July). *International Year of the Child. T* **247** *and similar horiz designs. Multicoloured. P* 12½.

673 5 c. Type **247** 5 5
674 3 r. Superimposed heads of children of different races 35 45
675 5 r. Children playing 45 55

(Des A. Dharmasiri. Litho Toppan Ptg Co, Japan)

1979 (27 Aug). *Death Centenary of Sir Rowland Hill. P* 13.

676 **248** 3 r. multicoloured 25 30

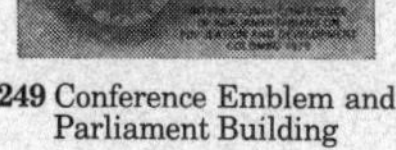

249 Conference Emblem and Parliament Building

250 Airline Emblem on Aircraft Tail-fin

(Des A. Harischandra. Litho Toppan Ptg Co, Japan)

1979 (28 Aug). *International Conference of Parliamentarians on Population and Development, Colombo. P* 13.

677 **249** 2 r. multicoloured 10 20

(Des S. Saparamadu. Litho Metal Box Singapore Ltd)

1979 (1 Sept). *Inauguration of "Airlanka" Airline. P* 12½.

678 **250** 3 r. black, deep blue-green & vermilion 15 25

251 Coconut Tree

252 Swami Vipulananda

(Des G. Wathuwalagedara. Litho Metal Box Singapore Ltd)

1979 (10 Sept). *10th Anniv of Asian and Pacific Coconut Community. P* 14.

679 **251** 2 r. multicoloured 15 25

1979 (10 Oct)–**81**. *Design as No. 648 but smaller,* 21 × 24 *mm. P* 12½ × 13.

680 **236** 25 c. gold, brt yellow-green & emerald . . 5 5
680*a* 50 c. gold, brt yell-grn & emer (6.8.81) . . 10 5

(Des R. B. Mawilmada. Litho Metal Box Singapore Ltd)

1979 (18 Nov). *Swami Vipulananda (philosopher) Commemoration. P* 12½.

681 **252** 1 r. 25, multicoloured 20 20

253 Inscription and Crescent

254 "The Great Teacher" (Institute emblem)

(Des Q. V. Saldin. Litho Metal Box Singapore Ltd)

1979 (22 Nov). *1500th Anniv of the Hegira (Mohammedan religion). P* 12½.

682 **253** 3 r. 75, black, deep green and blue-green 35 40

(Des H. P. Rupasinghe. Litho Metal Box Singapore Ltd)

1979 (29 Nov). *50th Anniv of Institute of Ayurveda (school of medicine). P* 13 × 12½.

683 **254** 15 c. multicoloured 12 10

255 Ceylon Blue Magpie

256 Rotary International Emblem and Map of Sri Lanka

(Des G. Ratnavira. Litho German Bank Note Ptg Co, Leipzig)

1979 (13 Dec). *Birds. T* **255** *and similar vert designs. Multicoloured. P* 13½ × 14.

684 10 c. Type **255** 5 5
685 15 c. Ceylon Hanging Parrot 5 5
686 75 c. Ceylon Whistling Thrush 5 5
687 1 r. Ceylon Spurfowl 5 5
688 5 r. Yellow-fronted Barbet 30 35
689 10 r. Yellow-tufted Bulbul 55 60
684/9 . . . . *Set of* 6 95 1·00
MS690 151 × 151 mm. Nos. 684/9 . . . . 2·00 2·50

(Des A. Harischandra. Litho Metal Box Singapore Ltd)

1979 (27 Dec). *50th Anniv of Sri Lanka Rotary Movement and 75th Anniv of Rotary International. P* 14.

691 **256** 1 r. 50, multicoloured 25 30

257 A. Ratnayake

.35

(258)

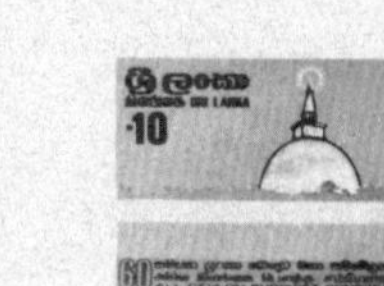

259 Tank and Stupa (symbols of Buddhist culture)

(Photo Govt Ptg Works, Rome)

1980 (7 Jan). *80th Birth Anniv of A. Ratnayake (politician). P* 13½.

692 **257** 1 r. 25, deep grey-green 15 20

1980 (17 Mar). *No. 680 surch with T* **258.**

693 **236** 35 c. on 25 c. gold, brt yell-grn & emer . . 15 15
a. Surch ".33" (R. 6/1) . . . . . . 15·00

(Des R. B. Mawilmada. Photo Govt Ptg Works, Rome)

1980 (25 Mar). *60th Anniv of All Ceylon Buddhist Congress. T* **259** *and similar horiz design showing symbols of Buddhist culture. Multicoloured. P* 13½.

694 10 c. Type **259** 5 5
695 35 c. Bo-leaf wheel and fan 10 10

260 Colonel Olcott

261 Patachara's Journey through Forest

(Des S. Senevirante. Litho J.W.)

1980 (17 May). *Centenary of Arrival of Colonel Olcott (campaigner for Buddhism). P* 14.

696 **260** 2 r. multicoloured 15 15

(Des A. Dharmasiri. Litho Metal Box Singapore Ltd)

1980 (23 May). *Vesak. Details from Temple Paintings, Purvaramaya, Kataluwa. T* **261** *and similar horiz design. Multicoloured. P* 13½.

697 35 c. Type **261** 5 5
698 1 r. 60, Patachara crossing river 8 10

262 George E. de Silva

263 Dalada Maligawa

(Des A. Rasiah. Litho German Bank Note Ptg Co, Leipzig)

1980 (8 June). *George E. de Silva (politician) Commemoration. P* 13.

699 **262** 1 r. 60, multicoloured 12 10

(Des A. Dharmasiri and R. B. Mawilmada. Litho Metal Box Singapore Ltd)

1980 (25 Aug). *U.N.E.S.C.O.—Sri Lanka Cultural Triangle Project. T* **263** *and similar horiz designs. P* 13.

700 35 c. claret 5 5
701 35 c. grey 5 5
702 35 c. rose-carmine 5 5
703 1 r. 60, olive-green 8 10
704 1 r. 60, slate-green 8 10
705 1 r. 60, sepia 8 10
700/5 . . . . *Set of* 6 25 30
MS706 215 × 115 mm. Nos. 700/5 . . . . 45 55
Designs: No. 701, Dambulla; No. 702, Alahana Pirivena; No. 703, Jetavanarama; No. 704, Abhayagiri; No. 705, Sigiri.

264 Co-operation Symbols

265 Lanka Mahila Samiti Emblem

(Des R. B. Mawilmada. Litho Metal Box Singapore Ltd)

1980 (1 Oct). *50th Anniv of Co-operative Department. P* 13.

707 **264** 20 c. multicoloured 10 5

(Des R. B. Mawilmada. Photo Govt Ptg Works, Rome)

1980 (7 Nov). *50th Anniv of Lanka Mahila Samiti (Rural Women's Movement). P* 14 × 13.

708 **265** 35 c. violet, rosine and yellow 5 5

266 The Holy Family

267 Colombo Public Library

(Des L. Priyantha Silva. Litho Metal Box Singapore Ltd)

1980 (20 Nov). *Christmas. T* **266** *and similar vert design. Multicoloured. P* 12 × 11½.

709 35 c. Type **266** 5 5
710 3 r. 75, The Three Wise Men 25 35
MS711 125 × 75 mm. Nos. 709/10. P 13½ . . 40 50

(Des P. Jayatillake. Litho Toppan Ptg Co, Japan)

1980 (17 Dec). *Opening of Colombo Public Library. P* 12 × 12½.

712 **267** 35 c. multicoloured 5 5

268 Flag of Walapane Disawa

269 Fishing Cat

(Des Mrs. J. L. M. Fernando. Litho Toppan Ptg Co, Japan)

1980 (18 Dec). *Ancient Flags. T* **268** *and similar horiz designs. P* 13.
713 10 c. black, green and brown-purple 5 5
714 25 c. black, greenish yellow and brown-purple 5 5
715 1 r. 60, black, greenish yellow & brn-purple 15 20
716 20 r. black, greenish yellow and brown-purple 1·40 1·60
MS717 215 × 140 mm. Nos. 713/16 .. .. 1·50 1·75
Designs:—25 c. Flag of the Gajanayaka, Huduhumpola, Kandy; 1 r. 60, Sinhala royal flag; 20 r. Sinhala royal flag, Ratnapura.

(Des L. Ranasinghe. Litho J.W.)

1981 (10 Feb). *Animals. T* **269** *and similar horiz designs. Multi-coloured. P* 13½ × 14.
718 2 r. 50, Type **269** 12 15
719 3 r. Golden Palm Cat 15 20
720 4 r. Mouse Deer 25 30
721 5 r. Rusty-spotted Cat 35 45
MS722 165 × 89 mm. Nos. 718/21 .. .. 1·00 1·50
Nos. 718/21 are previously unissued stamps surcharged as in T **269**.

270 Heads and Houses on Map of Sri Lanka

271 Sri Lanka Light Infantry Regimental Badge

(Des D. Hemaratna. Litho Toppan Ptg Co, Japan)

1981 (2 Mar). *Population and Housing Census. P* 12½ × 12.
723 **270** 50 c. multicoloured 10 5

(Des D. Karunaratne. Litho Metal Box Singapore Ltd)

1981 (1 Apr). *Centenary of Sri Lanka Light Infantry. P* 12 × 11½.
724 **271** 2 r. multicoloured 20 20

272 Panel from "The Great Stupa" in Honour of the Buddha, Sanci, India, 1st-century A.D.

273 St. John Baptist de la Salle

(Des P. Jayatillake. Litho German Bank Note Ptg Co, Leipzig)

1981 (5 May). *Vesak. T* **272** *and similar vert designs. P* 13 × 13½.
725 35 c. black, blackish green and sage-green .. 5 5
726 50 c. multicoloured 5 5
727 7 r. black and flesh 40 45
MS728 147 × 108 mm. Nos. 725/7. P 13 × 14. .. 80 90
Designs:—50 c. Silk banner representing a Bodhisattva from "Thousand Buddhas", Tun-Huang, Central Asia; 7 r. Bodhisattva from Fondukistan, Afghanistan.

(Des Grant Kenyon and Eckhardt Ltd. Litho State Printing Works, Moscow)

1981 (15 May). 300*th Anniv of De La Salle Brothers (Religious Order of the Brothers of the Christian Schools). P* 12½ × 12.
729 **273** 2 r. brt rose, deep violet-blue & new blue 15 15

274 Rev. Polwatte Sri Buddadatta

275 Dr. Al-Haj T. B. Jayah

(Des G. Fernando. Litho Metal Box Singapore Ltd)

1981 (22 May). *National Heroes. T* **274** *and similar vert designs, each showing scholar, writer and Buddhist campaigner. P* 12.
730 50 c. bistre 5 5
731 50 c. brown-rose 5 5
732 50 c. deep mauve 5 5
Designs:—No. 731, Rev. Mohottiwatte Gunananda; No. 732, Dr. Gnanaprakasar.

(Des P. Jayatillake. Litho Metal Box Singapore Ltd)

1981 (31 May). *Dr. Al-Haj T. B. Jayah (statesman) Commemoration. P* 12.
733 **275** 50 c. grey-green 5 5

276 Dr. N. M. Perera

277 Stylised Disabled Person and Globe

(Des P. Jayatillake. Litho Metal Box Singapore Ltd)

1981 (6 June). *Dr. N. M. Perera (campaigner for social reform) Commemoration. P* 12.
734 **276** 50 c. rose-red 5 5

(Des A. Adhikari. Litho State Printing Works, Moscow)

1981 (19 June). *International Year for Disabled Persons. P* 12 × 12½.
735 **277** 2 r. vermilion, black and grey 10 12

278 Hand placing Vote into Ballot Box

(Des J. Vincent (50 c.), R. Mawilmada (7 r.). Litho State Printing Works, Moscow)

1981 (7 July). 50*th Anniv of Universal Franchise. T* **278** *and similar multicoloured design. P* 12½ × 12 (50 c.) *or* 12 × 12½ (7 r.)
736 50 c. Type **278** 5 5
737 7 r. Ballot box, and people forming map of Sri Lanka (*vert*) 35 40

279 T. W. Rhys Davids (founder)

280 Federation Emblem and "25"

(Des P. Jayatillake. Litho State Printing Works, Moscow)

1981 (14 July). *Centenary of Pali Text Society. P* 12½ × 12.
738 **279** 35 c. stone, dp brown & orange-brown .. 5 5

(Des R. Mawilmada. Litho Secura, Singapore)

1981 (21 July). 25*th Anniv of All Ceylon Buddhist Students' Federation. P* 13½.
739 **280** 2 r. black, greenish yellow & dull verm 10 12

281 "Plan for Happiness"

282 Dove Symbol with Acupuncture Needle and "Yin-Yang" (Chinese universe duality emblem)

(Des D. Wijesinghe. Litho Secura, Singapore)

1981 (25 Sept). *Population and Family Planning. P* 13½ × 13.
740 **281** 50 c. multicoloured 5 5

(Des F. Perera. Litho State Printing Works, Moscow)

1981 (20 Oct). *World Acupuncture Congress. P* 12 × 12½.
741 **282** 2 r. black, yellow and red-orange .. 15 15

283 Union and Sri Lanka Flags

284 "Conserve our Forests"

(Des and litho J.W.)

1981 (21 Oct). *Royal Visit. P* 14.
742 **283** 50 c. multicoloured 5 5
743 5 r. multicoloured 25 30
MS744 165 × 90 mm. Nos. 742/3 .. .. .. 30 35

(Des Ravi Advertising. Litho German Bank Note Co, Leipzig)

1981 (27 Nov). *Forest Conservation. T* **284** *and similar horiz designs. P* 13.
745 35 c. multicoloured 5 5
746 50 c. olive-brown and stone 5 5
747 5 r. multicoloured 25 30
MS748 180 × 90 mm. Nos. 745/7. P 14 × 13 .. 40 50
Designs:—50 c. "Plant a tree"; 5 r Jak (tree).

285 Sir James Peiris

286 F. R. Senanayaka

(Des P. Jayatillake. Litho Metal Box Singapore Ltd)

1981 (20 Dec). *Birth Centenary of Sir James Peiris (politician). P* 12.
749 **285** 50 c. light brown 5 5

(Des M. Katugampola. Litho J.W.)

1982 (1 Jan). *Birth Centenary of F. R. Senanayaka (national hero). P* 14.
750 **286** 50 c. olive-brown 5 5

287 Philip Gunawardhane

288 Department of Inland Revenue Building, Colombo

(Des P. Jayatillake. Litho J.W.)

1982 (11 Jan). 10*th Death Anniv of Philip Gunawardhane (politician). P* 14.
751 **287** 50 c. cerise 5 5

(Des S. Mallikerachchi. Litho J.W.)

1982 (9 Feb). 50*th Anniv of Department of Inland Revenue. P* 14.
752 **288** 50 c. black, blue-black & reddish orange 5 5

289 Rupavahini Emblem

290 Cricketer and Ball

(Des G. Arthasad. Litho J.W.)

1982 (15 Feb). *Inauguration of Rupavahini (national television service). P* 14.
753 **289** 2 r. 50, lemon, purple-brown and grey 12 15

(Des R. Mawilmada. Litho J.W.)

1982 (17 Feb). *First Sri Lanka–England Cricket Test Match, Colombo. P* 14.
754 **290** 2 r. 50, multicoloured 12 15

291 *Obsbeckia wightiana*

292 Mother breast-feeding Child

(Des P. Jayatillake. Litho Security Printers (M), Malaysia)

1982 (1 Apr). *Flowers. T* **291** *and similar horiz designs. Multi-coloured. P* 12.

755	35 c. Type **291**	5	5
756	2 r. *Mesua nagassarium*	12	15
757	7 r. *Rhodomyrtus tomentosa*	40	40
758	20 r. *Phaius tancarvilleae*	1·10	1·25
MS759	180 × 110 mm. Nos. 755/8	1·60	1·75

(Des A. Ratnapala. Litho Pakistan Security Printing Corp)

1982 (6 Apr). *Food and Nutrition Policy Planning. P* 13.

760 **292**	50 c. multicoloured	5	5

293 Conference Emblem

294 King Vessantara giving away magical, rain-making White Elephant

(Des M. Hussain. Litho J.W.)

1982 (21 Apr). *World Hindu Conference. P* 14.

761 **293**	50 c. multicoloured	5	5

(Des A. Dharmasiri. Litho J.W.)

1982 (23 Apr). *Vesak. Legend of Vessantara Jataka. Details of Cloth Painting from Arattana Rajamaha Vihara (temple), Hanguranketa, District of Nuwara Eliya. T* **294** *and similar horiz designs. Multicoloured. P* 14.

762	35 c. Type **294**	5	5
763	50 c. King Vessantara with family in Vankagiri Forest	5	5
764	2 r. 50, Vessantara giving away his children as slaves	15	15
765	5 r. Vessantara and family returning to Jetuttara in royal chariot	30	40
MS766	160 × 115 mm. Nos. 762/5	60	70

295 Parliament Buildings, Sri Jayawardanapura

296 Dr. C. W. W. Kannangara

(Des M. Katugampola. Litho J.W.)

1982 (29 Apr). *Opening of Parliament Building Complex, Sri Jayawardanapura, Kotte. P* 14.

767 **295**	50 c. multicoloured	5	5

(Des M. Katugampola. Litho State Printing Works, Moscow)

1982 (22 May). *Dr. C. W. W. Kannangara ("Father of Free Education") Commemoration. P* 12 × 12½.

768 **296**	50 c. yellow-olive	5	5

297 Lord Baden-Powell

298 Dr. G. P. Malalasekara

(Des W. Rohana. Litho State Printing Works, Moscow)

1982 (24 May). *125th Birth Anniv of Lord Baden-Powell. P* 12½ × 12.

769 **297**	50 c. multicoloured	10	5

(Des A. Rasiah. Litho State Printing Works, Moscow)

1982 (26 May). *Dr. G. P. Malalasekara (founder of World Fellowship of Buddhists) Commemoration. P* 12 × 12½.

770 **298**	50 c. deep bluish green	5	5

299 Wheel encircling Globe

300 Wildlife

(Des A. Ratnapala. Litho State Printing Works, Moscow)

1982 (1 June). *World Buddhist Leaders Conference. P* 12½ × 12.

771 **299**	50 c. multicoloured	5	5

(Des U. Karunaratna. Litho State Printing Works, Moscow)

1982 (5 June). *World Environment Day. P* 12½ × 12.

772 **300**	50 c. multicoloured	10	5

301 Sir Waitialingam Duraiswamy

(Des A. Rasiah. Litho State Printing Works, Moscow)

1982 (14 June). *Sir Waitialingam Duraiswamy (statesman and educationalist) Commemoration. P* 12 × 12½.

773 **301**	50 c. blackish brown and brown	5	5

302 Y.M.C.A. Emblem

(Des R. Mawilmada. Litho State Printing Works, Moscow)

1982 (24 June). *Centenary of Colombo Y.M.C.A. P* 11½ × 11.

774 **302**	2 r. 50, multicoloured	12	15

303 Rev. Weliwita Sri Saranankara Sangharaja

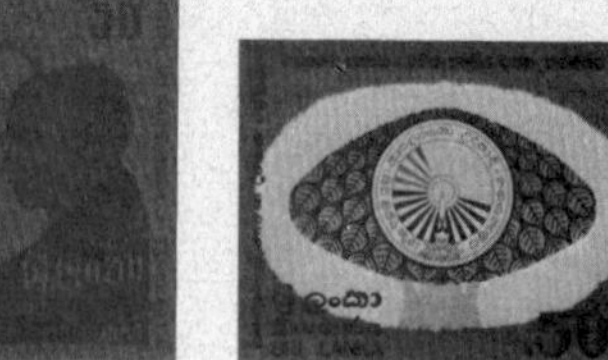

304 Maharagama Sasana Sevaka Samithiya Emblem

(Des M. Katugampola. Litho State Printing Works, Moscow)

1982 (5 July). *Rev. Weliwita Sri Saranankara Sangharaja (Buddhist leader) Commemoration. P* 12 × 12½.

775 **303**	50 c. brown and yellow-orange	5	5

(Des A. Ratnapala. Litho Toppan Ptg Co, Japan)

1982 (4 Aug). *Silver Jubilee of Maharagama Sasana Sevaka Samithiya (Buddhist Social Reform Movement). P* 12 × 12½.

776 **304**	50 c. multicoloured	5	5

305 Dr. Robert Koch

306 Sir John Kotelawala

(Des W. Rohana. Litho Toppan Ptg Co, Japan)

1982 (21 Sept). *Centenary of Robert Koch's Discovery of Tubercle Bacillus. P* 12 × 12½.

777 **305**	50 c. multicoloured	5	5

(Des A. Rasiah. Litho State Printing Works, Moscow)

1982 (2 Oct). *2nd Death Anniv of Sir John Kotelawala. P* 12 × 12½.

778 **306**	50 c. deep olive	5	5

307 Eye Donation Society and Lions Club Emblems

308 1859 4d. Dull Rose and 1948 15 c. Independence Commemorative

(Des Grant Kenyon and Eckhardt Ltd. Litho State Printing Works, Moscow)

1982 (16 Nov). *World-Wide Sight Conservation Project. P* 12 × 12½.

779 **307**	2 r. 50, multicoloured	15	20

(Des D. Karunaratne. Litho Security Printers (M), Malaysia)

1982 (2 Dec). *125th Anniv of First Postage Stamps. T* **308** *and similar horiz design. Multicoloured. P* 13 × 13½.

780	50 c. Type **308**	5	8
781	2 r. 50, 1859 1s. 9d. green and 1981 50 c. "Just Society" stamp	15	20
MS782	159 × 84 mm. Nos. 780/1 (*sold at* 5 *r.*)	25	30

309 Sir Oliver Goonetilleke

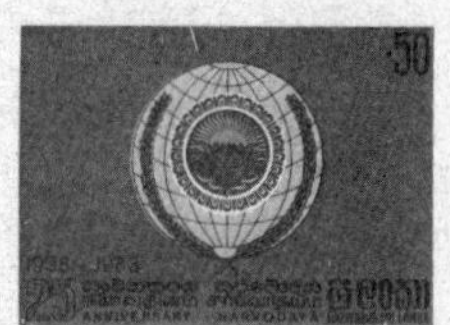

310 Sarvodaya Emblem

(Des A. Ratnapala. Litho State Printing Works, Moscow)

1982 (17 Dec). *4th Death Anniv of Sir Oliver Goonetilleke (statesman). P* 12 × 12½.

783 **309**	50 c. olive-grey, bistre-brown and black	5	8

(Des P. Gunasinghe. Litho Secura, Singapore)

1983 (1 Jan). *25th Anniv of Sarvodaya Movement. P* 13 × 13½.

784 **310**	50 c. multicoloured	5	8

311 Morse Key, Radio Aerial and Radio Amateur Society Emblem

312 Customs Co-operation Council Emblem and Sri Lanka Flag

(Des W. Rohana. Litho Secura, Singapore)

1983 (17 Jan). *Amateur Radio Society. P* 13 × 13½.

785 **311**	2 r. 50, multicoloured	15	20

(Des W. Rohana. Litho Secura, Singapore)

1983 (26 Jan). *30th Anniv of International Customs Day. P* 12 × 11½.

786 **312**	50 c. multicoloured	5	8
787	5 r. multicoloured	25	30

313 Bottlenose Dolphin

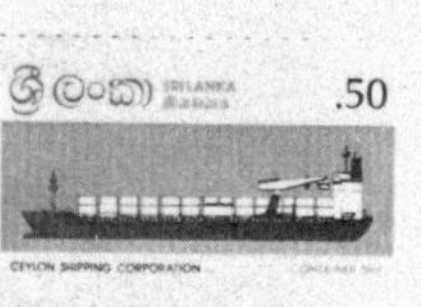

314 Container Ship

(Des G. Ratnavira. Litho Harrison)

1983 (22 Feb). *Marine Mammals. T* **313** *and similar horiz designs. P* 14½ × 14.

788	50 c. black, new blue and grey-green	5	8
789	2 r. multicoloured	10	12

790 2 r. 50, black, deep grey-blue and deep bluish grey 15 20
791 10 r. multicoloured 55 60
Designs:—2 r. Dugongs; 2 r. 50, Humpback Whale; 10 r. Great Sperm Whale.

(Des Vision Ltd. Litho Security Printers (M), Malaysia)

1983 (1 Mar). *Ships of the Ceylon Shipping Corporation. T* **314** *and similar horiz designs. Multicoloured. P* 11½ × 12.
792 50 c. Type **314** 5 8
793 2 r. 50, Map of routes 15 20
794 5 r. Conventional cargo ship 25 30
795 20 r. Oil tanker .. .. 1·10 1·25

315 Woman with I.W.D. Emblem and Sri Lanka Flag

316 Waterfall

(Des R. Mawilmada. Litho Secura, Singapore)

1983 (8 Mar). *International Women's Day. T* **315** *and similar vert design. Multicoloured. P* 13.
796 50 c. Type **315** 5 8
797 5 r. Woman, emblem, map and symbols of progress 25 30

(Des S. Lankatilake. Litho Secura, Singapore)

1983 (14 Mar). *Commonwealth Day. T* **316** *and similar horiz designs. Multicoloured. P* 13.
798 50 c. Type **316** 5 8
799 2 r. 50, Tea plucking 15 20
800 5 r. Harvesting rice 25 30
801 20 r. Decorated elephants .. .. 1·10 1·25

317 Lions Club International Badge

318 "The Dream of Queen Mahamaya"

(Des U. Karunaratna. Litho J.W.)

1983 (7 May). *25th Anniv of Lions Club International in Sri Lanka. P* 14.
802 **317** 2 r. 50, multicoloured 15 20

(Des A. Dharmasiri. Litho Toppan Ptg Co, Japan)

1983 (13 May). *Vesak. Life of Prince Siddhartha from murals by George Keyt and Gotami Vihara. T* **318** *and similar vert designs. Multicoloured. P* 12½ × 12.
803 35 c. Type **318** 5 5
804 50 c. "Prince Siddhartha given to Maha Brahma" 5 8
805 5 r. "Prince Siddhartha and the Sleeping Dancers" 25 30
806 10 r. "The Meeting with Mara" 55 60
MS807 150 × 90 mm. Nos. 803/6 .. .. .. 90 1·00

319 First Telegraph Transmission Colombo to Galle, 1858

320 Henry Woodward Amarasuriya (philanthropist)

(Des W. Rohana. Litho Toppan Ptg Co, Japan)

1983 (17 May). *125th Anniv of Telecommunications in Sri Lanka (2 r.) and World Communications Year (10 r.). T* **319** *and similar horiz design. Multicoloured. P* 12 × 12½.
808 2 r. Type **319** 10 12
809 10 r. World Communications Year emblem .. 55 60

(Litho Security Printers (M), Malaysia (No. 810), Pakistan Security Printing Corp (others))

1983 (22 May). *National Heroes. T* **320** *and similar vert designs. P* 12 × 11½ *(No. 810) or* 13 *(others).*
810 50 c. bright emerald 5 8
811 50 c. new blue 5 8
812 50 c. magenta 5 8
813 50 c. turquoise-green 5 8
Designs:—No. 811, Father Simon Perera (historian); No. 812, Charles Lorenz (lawyer and newspaper editor); No. 813, Noordeen Abdul Cader (first President of All-Ceylon Muslim League).

321 Family and Village

322 Caravan of Bulls

(Des K. Gunasiri and U. Karunaratna. Litho Toppan Ptg Co, Japan)

1983 (23 June). *Gam Udawa (Village Re-awakening Movement). T* **321** *and similar horiz design. Multicoloured. P* 12 × 12½.
814 50 c. Type **321** 5 8
815 5 r. Village view 25 30

(Des A. Rasiah (35 c., 2 r.), D. Hemaratna (2 r. 50), U. Karunaratna (5 r.). Litho State Printing Office, Budapest)

1983 (22 Aug). *Transport. T* **322** *and similar horiz designs. Multicoloured. P* 12
816 35 c. Type **322** 5 8
817 2 r. Steam train 10 12
818 2 r. 50, Ox and cart 15 20
819 5 r. Ford motor car 25 30

323 Sir Tikiri Banda Panabokke

324 C. W. Thamotheram Pillai

(Des and litho Harrison)

1983 (2 Sept). *20th Death Anniv of Adigar Sir Tikiri Banda Panabokke. P* 14 × 14½.
820 **323** 50 c. Indian red 5 8

(Des and litho Pakistan Security Printing Corp)

1983 (1 Oct). *C. W. Thamotheram Pillai (Tamil scholar) Commemoration. P* 13.
821 **324** 50 c. orange-brown 5 8

325 Arabi Pasha

326 Reverend Thero

(Des and litho Pakistan Security Printing Corp)

1983 (13 Nov). *Centenary of the Exile to Ceylon of Arabi Pasha (Egyptian nationalist). P* 13 × 13½.
822 **325** 50 c. green 5 8

(Des and litho Harrison)

1983 (25 Nov). *Reverend Thero (scholar) Commemoration. P* 14 × 14½.
823 **326** 50 c. red-brown 5 8

327 Mary praying over Jesus and St. Joseph welcoming Shepherds

328 Sri Lanka Wood Pigeon

(Des P. de Silva. Litho German Bank Note Co, Leipzig)

1983 (30 Nov). *Christmas. P* 12½ × 13.
824 **327** 50 c. multicoloured 5 8
825 5 r. multicoloured 25 30
MS826 85 × 141 mm. Nos. 824/5 .. .. .. 30 35

(Des G. Ratnavira. Litho Format)

1983 (15 Dec). *Birds. T* **328** *and similar designs. Multicoloured. P* 14 × 14½.
827 25 c. Type **328** 5 5
828 35 c. Large Sri Lanka White-eye 5 5
829 2 r. Sri Lanka Dusky-blue Flycatcher 12 15
830 20 r. Ceylon Coucal .. .. 1·10 1·25
MS831 183 × 93 mm. Nos. 827/30 .. .. .. 1·10 1·25

329 Paddy Field, Globe and F.A.O. Emblem

(Des R. Mawilmada. Litho State Ptg Works, Moscow)

1984 (2 Feb). *World Food Day. P* 12½ × 12.
832 **329** 3 r. multicoloured 15 20

330 Modern Tea Warehouse

331 Students and University

(Des M. Ratnapala. Litho State Ptg Works, Moscow)

1984 (31 Jan). *Centenary of the Colombo Tea Auctions. T* **330** *and similar horiz designs. Multicoloured. P* 12½ × 12.
833 1 r. Type **330** 5 5
834 2 r. Logo 12 15
835 5 r. Girl picking tea 30 35
836 10 r. Auction in progress 65 70

(Des R. Mawilmada. Litho Security Printers (M), Malaysia)

1984 (10 Feb). *4th Anniv of Mahapola Scheme for Development and Education. T* **331** *and similar vert designs. Multicoloured. P* 12.
837 60 c. Type **331** 5 5
838 1 r. Teacher with Gnana Darsana class 5 5
839 5 r. 50, Student with books and microscope .. 35 40
840 6 r. Mahapola lamp symbol 40 45

332 King Daham Sonda instructing Angels

333 Development Programme Logo

(Des A. Dharmasiri. Litho D.L.R)

1984 (27 Apr). *Vesak. The Story of King Daham Sonda from Ancient Casket Paintings. T* **332** *and similar horiz designs. Multicoloured. A. P* 14. *B. P* 13 × 13½.

		A		B	
841	35 c. Type **332**	5	5	25	15
842	60 c. Elephant paraded with gift of gold	5	5	20	10
843	5 r. King Daham Sonda leaps into mouth of God Sakra ..	30	35	45	40
844	10 r. God Sakra carrying King Daham Sonda	65	70	65	70
MS845	154 × 109 mm. Nos. 841/4. P 13	1·00	1·10		

(Des R. Mawilmada. Litho Harrison)

1984 (5 May). *Sri Lanka Lions Clubs' Development Programme. P* 14 × 14½.
846 **333** 60 c. multicoloured 5 5

334 Dodanduwe Siri Piyaratana Tissa Mahanayake Thero (Buddhist scholar)

335 Association Emblem

(Litho State Ptg Works, Moscow)

1984 (22 May). *National Heroes. T* **334** *and similar vert designs. P* 12 × 12½.
847 60 c. yellow-bistre 5 5
848 60 c. yellow-green 5 5
849 60 c. emerald-green 5 5
850 60 c. red 5 5
851 60 c. deep yellow-brown 5 5

Designs:—No. 847, Type **334**; 848, G. P. Wickremarachchi (physician); 849, Sir Mohamed Macan Markar (politician); 850, Dr. W. Arthur de Silva (philanthropist); 851, K. Balasingham (lawyer).

(Des A. Harischandra. Litho Govt Printing Bureau, Tokyo)

1984 (16 June). *Centenary of Public Service Mutual Provident Association. P* 13 × 13½.
852 **335** 4 r. 60, multicoloured 25 30

337 World Map showing A.P.B.U. Countries

336 Sri Lanka Village

(Des S. Herath. Litho State Ptg Wks, Moscow)

1984 (23 June). 6*th Anniv of "Gam Udawa" (Village Reawakening Movement). P* 12 × 12½.
853 **336** 60 c. multicoloured 5 5

(Des G. Arthasad. Litho State Ptg Wks, Moscow)

1984 (30 June). 20*th Anniv of Asia-Pacific Broadcasting Union. P* 12½ × 12.
854 **337** 7 r. multicoloured 40 45

338 Drummers and Elephant carrying Royal Instructions

339 Vanda Memoria Ernest Soysa (orchid)

(Des R. Mawilmada. Litho State Ptg Wks, Moscow)

1984 (11 Aug). *Esala Perahera (Procession of the Tooth), Kandy. T* **338** *and similar horiz designs. Multicoloured. P* 12½ × 12.
855 4 r. 60, Type **338** 25 30
a. Horiz strip of 4 Nos. 855/8 .. .. 1·00
856 4 r. 60, Dancers and elephants 25 30
857 4 r. 60, Elephant carrying Tooth Relic .. 25 30
858 4 r. 60, Custodian of the Sacred Tooth and attendants 25 30
MS859 223 × 108 mm. Nos. 855/8 .. .. 1·00 1·10

Nos. 855/8 were printed together, *se-tenant*, in horizontal strips of 4 throughout the sheet, forming a composite design.

(Des G. Ratnavira. Litho D.L.R.)

1984 (28 Aug). 50*th Anniv of Ceylon Orchid Circle. T* **339** *and similar vert designs, showing orchids. Multicoloured.* A. *P* 14. B. *P* 13½ × 13.

		A		B	
860	60 c. Type **339**	5	5	10	10
861	4 r. 60, *Acanthephippium bicolor*	25	30	60	50
862	5 r. *Vanda tessellata var. rufescens*	30	35	40	40
863	10 r. *Anoectochilus setaceus* ..	65	70	†	
MS864	155 × 110 mm. Nos. 860/3. P 13	1·25	1·40		

340 Symbolic Athletes and Stadium

341 D. S. Senanayake, Temple and Fields

(Des M. Heenkenda. Litho Govt Printing Bureau, Tokyo)

1984 (5 Oct). *National School Games. P* 13½ × 13.
865 **340** 60 c. black, grey and bright new blue .. 5 5

(Des L. Jayawardena (35 c.), G. Fernando (60 c.), N. Lasantha (4 r. 60), R. Mawilmada (6 r.). Litho J.W.)

1984 (20 Oct). *Birth Centenary of D. S. Senanayake (former Prime Minister). T* **341** *and similar horiz designs. Multicoloured. P* 14.
866 35 c. Type **341** 5 5
867 60 c. Senanayake and statue 5 5
868 4 r. 60, Senanayake and irrigation project .. 30 35
869 6 r. Senanayake and House of Representatives 40 45

Stellaland

PRICES FOR STAMPS ON COVER
The issues of Stellaland are rare on cover

1 Arms of the Republic

(Litho by Van der Sandt, de Villiers & Co, Cape Town)

1884 (Feb). *P* 12.
1 **1** 1d. red £170
a. Imperf between (pair) £1400
2 3d. orange .. .. 10·00
a. Imperf between (pair) £300
3 4d. blue .. .. 10·00
a. Imperf between (pair) £300
4 6d. lilac-mauve .. .. 10·00
a. Imperf between (pair) £650
5 1s. green .. .. 25·00

1885 (Oct). *Surch* "**Twee**" *in violet-lake.*
6 **1** 2d. on 4d. blue £2000

No date stamps were employed in Stellaland, the stamps being pen-cancelled with the initials of the postal official and date, but a date stamp was used on arrival at Barkly West or Kimberley.

Stellaland, with surrounding territory, was proclaimed the British Bechuanaland Colony on 30 September 1885. Its stamps were withdrawn and superseded by British Bechuanaland stamps on 2 December 1885. It is now part of South Africa.

Sudan

ANGLO-EGYPTIAN CONDOMINIUM

An Egyptian post office was opened at Suakin in 1867 and the stamps of Egypt, including postage dues and the official (No. O64), were used in the Sudan until replaced by the overprinted "SOUDAN" issue of 1897.

Cancellations have been identified from eleven post offices, using the following postmark types:

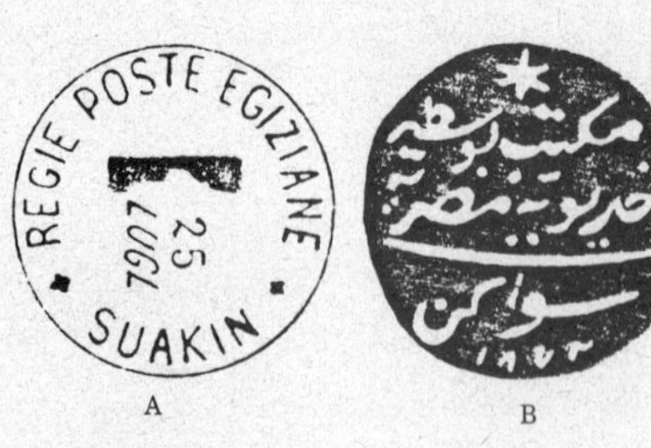

A B

C

D

E

F

G

H

I

J

K

L

BERBER (*spelt* BARBAR). *Open* 1873 *to* 1884. *Postmark type* G.
DABROUSSA. *Open* 1889? *onwards. Postmark as type* J *but with* 11 *bars in arcs.*
DONGOLA. *Open* 1873 *to* 1885 *and* 1896 *onwards. Postmark types* F, G, K, L.
GEDAREF. *Open* ? *Postmark type* H.
KASSALA. *Open* 1875 *to* 1885. *Postmark type* G.
KHARTOUM. *Open* 1873 *to* 1884. *Postmark types* E (*spelt* KARTUM), G (*spelt* HARTUM), I (*with or without line of Arabic above date*).
KORTI. *Open* 1884/5 *and* 1897. *Postmark type* K.
SUAKIN. *Open* 1867 *onwards. Postmark types* A, B, C (*spelt* SUAKIM), D (*spelt* SUAKIM *and also with year replaced by concentric arcs*), I (*spelt* SOUAKIN), J (*spelt* SAWAKIN, *number of bars differs*).
TANI. *Open* 1885. *Postmark type* K.
TOKAR. *Open* 1891 *onwards. Postmark type* J (7 *bars in arcs*).
WADI HALFA. *Open* 1873 *onwards. Postmark types* F (*spelt* WADI HALFE), G (*spelt* WADI HALFE), I, J (*number of bars differs*).
WADI HALFA CAMP. *Open* 1896 *onwards. Postmark type* I.

Official records also list post offices at the following locations, but no genuine postal markings from them have yet been reported: Chaka, Dara, Debeira, El Abiad, El Fasher, El Kalabat, Faras, Fashoda, Fazogl, Ishkeit, Kalkal, Karkok, Mesellemia, Sara, Sennar and Taoufikia (not to be confused with the town of the same name in Egypt.

M

The post office at Kassala was operated by Italy from 1894 until 896, using stamps of Eritrea cancelled with postmark type M.

From the last years of the nineteenth century until 1912 that art of Sudan lying south of the 5 degree North latitude line was dministered by Uganda (the area to the east of the Nile) or by elgium (the area to the west of the Nile, known as the Lado nclave).

Stamps of Uganda or East Africa and Uganda were used at ondokoro and Nimuli between 1901 and 1911, usually cancelled vith circular date stamps or, probably in transit at Khartoum, by lozenge-shaped grid of 18 × 17 dots.

Stamps of Belgian Congo were used from the Lado Enclave etween 1897 and 1909, although no local postmarks were upplied, examples being initially cancelled in manuscript.

PRICES FOR STAMPS ON COVER TO 1945

Nos. 1/9	*from* × 8
Nos. 10/17	*from* × 6
Nos. 18/29	*from* × 5
Nos. 30/95	*from* × 2
Nos. D1/11	*from* × 30
Nos. O1/3	—
Nos. O4/22	*from* × 15
Nos. A1/16	*from* × 6

(1)

1895 (1 Mar). *Nos. 54b, 55a, 57/a, 58a, 59, 60, 62a and 63 of Egypt optd as T* **1** *by Govt Ptg Wks, Bûlâq, Cairo.*

No.	Description		Unused	Used
1	1 m. pale brown	..	90	1·25
	a. Opt inverted	..	£275	
	b. Deep brown	..	1·25	2·00
3	2 m. green	..	1·60	2·00
4	3 m. orange-yellow	..	1·60	1·75
5	5 m. rose-carmine	..	3·00	3·00
	a. Opt inverted	..	£325	
6	1 p. ultramarine	..	5·00	5·50
7	2 p. orange-brown	..	18·00	12·00
8	5 p. slate	..	20·00	12·00
	a. Opt double	..		
9	10 p. mauve	..	18·00	22·00
1/9	..	*Set of* 8	60·00	55·00

Numerous forgeries exist including some which show the characteristics of the varieties mentioned below.

There are six varieties of the overprint on each value most of which can be supplied in vertical strips at double the catalogue price.

In some printings the large dot is omitted from the left-hand Arabic character on one stamp in the pane of 60.

The overprint was frequently misplaced, and pairs may be found with and without it, and also with the overprint diagonal.

PRINTERS. All stamps of Sudan were printed by De La Rue & Co, Ltd, London, *except where otherwise stated.*

2 Arab Postman

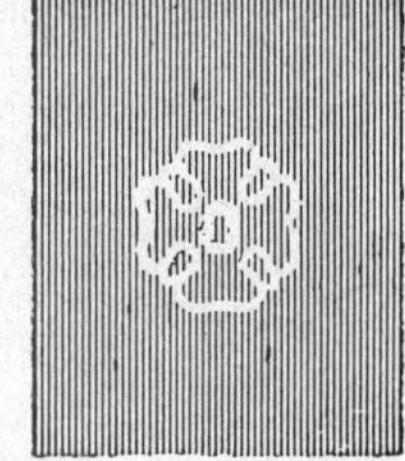

3

(Des E. A. Stanton. Typo)

1898 (1 Mar). *W* **3**. *P* 14.

No.	Type	Description	Unused	Used
10	2	1 m. brown and pink	40	25
11		2 m. green and brown	1·00	1·00
12		3 m. mauve and green	1·00	1·40
13		5 m. carmine and black	75	25
14		1 p. blue and brown	3·25	2·75
15		2 p. black and blue	8·00	4·00
16		5 p. brown and green	9·50	6·50
17		10 p. black and mauve	12·00	4·50
10/17		*Set of* 8	32·00	18·00

ALTERED CATALOGUE NUMBERS

Any Catalogue numbers altered from the last edition are shown as a list in the introductory pages.

4

5 Milliemes

(5)

1902–21. *W* **4**. *P* 14.

No.	Type	Description	Unused	Used
18	2	1 m. brown and carmine (5.05)	20	8
19		2 m. green and brown (11.02)	40	20
20		3 m. mauve and green (7.03)	75	35
21		4 m. blue and bistre (20.1.07)	90	1·75
22		4 m. vermilion and brown (10.07)	1·25	1·10
23		5 m. scarlet and black (12.03)	1·40	8
24		1 p. blue and brown (12.03)	1·60	25
25		2 p. black and blue (2.08)	10·00	2·00
26		2 p. purple and orange-yell, **C** (22.12.21)	1·75	1·75
27		5 p. brown and green, **OC** (2.08)	6·00	70
28		10 p. black and mauve, **OC** (2.11)	11·00	1·25
18/28		*Set of* 11	32·00	8·50

1903 (Sept). *No. 16 surch at Khartoum with T* **5**, *in blocks of* 30.

No.	Description	Unused	Used
29	5 m. on 5 pi. brown and green	2·25	6·50
	a. Surch inverted	£275	£250

6

7

1921–23. *Chalk-surfaced paper. Typo. W* **4**. *P* 14.

No.	Type	Description	Unused	Used
30	6	1 m. black and orange (4.2.22)	60	85
31		2 m. yellow-orange and chocolate (1922)	3·00	1·75
		a. Yellow and chocolate (1923)	3·50	2·00
32		3 m. mauve and green (25.1.22)	1·75	1·75
33		4 m. green and chocolate (21.3.22)	2·00	1·10
34		5 m. olive-brown and black (4.2.22)	1·25	8
35		10 m. carmine and black (1922)	1·25	10
36		15 m. bright blue and chestnut (14.12.21)	2·00	1·50
30/36		*Set of* 7	10·50	6·50

1927–41. *W* **7**. *P* 14.

No.	Type	Description	Unused	Used
37	6	1 m. black and orange, **CO**	5	5
38		2 m. orange and chocolate, **CO**	10	5
39		3 m. mauve and green, **CO**	15	5
40		4 m. green and chocolate, **CO**	20	5
41		5 m. olive-brown and black, **CO**	20	5
42		10 m. carmine and black, **CO**	20	5
43		15 m. bright blue and chestnut, **CO**	20	5
44	2	2 p. purple and orange-yellow, **CO**	20	5
44*a*		3 p. red-brown and blue, **CO** (1.1.40)	60	10
44*b*		4 p. ultramarine and black, **C** (2.11.36)	60	5
45		5 p. chestnut and green, **CO**	70	5
45*a*		6 p. greenish blue and black, **CO** (2.11.36)	1·25	25
45*b*		8 p. emerald and black, **CO** (2.11.36)	1·50	35
46		10 p. black and reddish purple, **C** (2.11.36)	90	10
		a. Black and bright mauve, **O** (1941)	2·25	40
46*b*		20 p. pale blue and blue, **CO** (17.10.35)	1·75	20
37/46*b*		*Set of* 15	7·75	1·25

The ordinary paper of this issue is thick, smooth and opaque and is a wartime substitute for chalk-surface paper.

For similar stamps, but with different Arabic inscriptions, see Nos. 96/111.

AIR MAIL (8) **AIR MAIL** (9) **AIR** Extended foot to "R" (R.5/12)

1931 (15 Feb–Mar). *Air. Stamps of* 1927 *optd with T* **8** *or* **9** (2 *p.*).

No.	Description	Unused	Used
47	5 m. olive-brown and black (Mar)	1·25	1·75
48	10 m. carmine and black	1·25	3·00
49	2 p. purple and orange-yellow	1·75	3·75
	a. Extended foot to "R"	16·00	

2½ 2½

10 Statue of Gen. Gordon

AIR MAIL

(11)

1931 (1 Sept)–**37**. *Air. Recess. W* **7** (*sideways*). *P* 14.

No.	Type	Description	Unused	Used
49*b*	10	3 m. green and sepia (1.1.33)	3·00	4·75
50		5 m. black and green	1·25	50
51		10 m. black and carmine	2·00	90
52		15 m. red-brown and sepia	80	30
		a. Perf 11½ × 12½ (1937)	1·75	35
53		2 p. black and orange	50	25
		a. Perf 11½ × 12½ (1937)	9·00	13·00
53*b*		2½ p. magenta and blue (1.1.33)	2·25	35
		c. Perf 11½ × 12½ (1936)	1·25	90
		ca. Aniline magenta and blue	3·75	3·75
54	10	3 p. black and grey	1·25	50
		a. Perf 11½ × 12½ (1937)	3·75	2·75
55		3½ p. black and violet	2·25	2·50
		a. Perf 11½ × 12½ (1937)	7·00	11·00
56		4½ p. red-brown and grey	10·00	14·00
57		5 p. black and ultramarine	3·00	1·90
		a. Perf 11½ × 12½ (1937)	3·00	1·75
57*b*		7½ p. green and emerald (17.10.35)	4·75	5·00
		c. Perf 11½ × 12½ (1937)	4·50	7·50
57*d*		10 p. brown and greenish blue (17.10.35)	8·50	2·25
		e. Perf 11½ × 12½ (1937)	4·50	8·50
49*b*/57*e*		*Set of* 12	30·00	30·00

1932 (18 July). *Air. No.* 44 *surch with T* **11**.

No.	Description	Unused	Used
58	2½ p. on 2 p. purple and orange-yellow	6·00	6·50

12 Gen. Gordon (after C. Ouless)

13 Gordon Memorial College, Khartoum

14 Gordon Memorial Service, Khartoum (after R. C. Woodville)

1935 (1 Jan). *50th Death Anniv of General Gordon, Recess. W* **7**. *P* 14.

No.	Type	Description	Unused	Used
59	12	5 m. green	60	20
60		10 m. yellow-brown	75	55
61		13 m. ultramarine	2·00	4·50
62		15 m. scarlet	1·25	75
63	13	2 p. blue	1·50	75
64		5 p. orange-vermilion	3·00	1·75
65		10 p. purple	9·50	7·00
66	14	20 p. black	26·00	35·00
67		50 p. red-brown	60·00	70·00
59/67		*Set of* 9	95·00	£110

7½ PIASTRES
فروش ٧ ½

(15)

5 MILLIEMES
٥ مليمات

(16)

1935. *Air. Surch as T* **15.**

No.	Type	Description	Unused	Used
68	10	15 m. on 10 m. black and carmine (Apr)	1·00	50
		a. Surch double	£600	£650
69		2½ p. on 3 m. green and sepia (Apr)	1·90	4·75
		a. Second arabic letter from left missing	£110	£110
		b. Small "½"	9·00	14·00
70		2½ p. on 5 m. black and green (Apr)	1·25	2·25
		a. Second Arabic letter from left missing	60·00	60·00
		b. Small "½"	6·50	9·00
		c. Surch inverted	£600	£650
		d. Ditto with variety a.		
		e. Ditto with variety b.		
71		3 p. on 4½ p. red-brown and grey (Apr)	3·00	7·50
72		7½ p. on 4½ p. red-brown and grey (Mar)	7·00	14·00
73		10 p. on 4½ p. red-brown and grey (Mar)	6·00	14·00
68/73		*Set of* 6	18·00	38·00

Nos. 69a and 70a occur in position 49 of the sheet of 50; the small "½" variety occurs in positions 17, 27, 32, 36, 41, 42 and 46.

The 15 m. on 10 m. and the 7½ p. on 4½ p. surcharged in red and the 2½ p. on 3 m. and 2½ p. on 5 m. in green are from proof sheets; the latter two items being known cancelled. A 7¼ p. on 4½ p. also exists from a proof sheet.

1938 (1 July). *Air. Surch as T* **16**.

No.	Type	Description	Unused	Used
74	10	5 m. on 2½ p. (*p* 11½ × 12½)	50	25
75		3 p. on 3½ p. (*p* 14)	7·50	10·00
		a. Perf 11½ × 12½	£325	£375
76		3 p. on 7½ p. (*p* 14)	1·25	2·75
		a. Perf 11½ × 12½	£325	£375
77		5 p. on 10 p. (*p* 14)	1·75	3·00
		a. Perf 11½ × 12½	£325	£400

A 5 p. on 2½ p., perf 11½ × 12½, exists either mint or cancelled from a trial printing.

5 Mills.

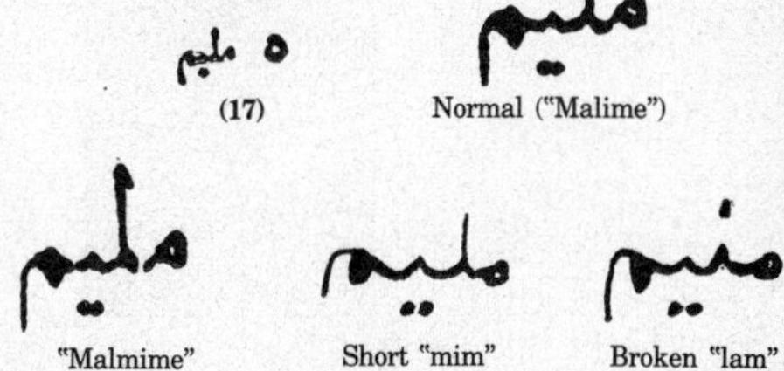

(17) Normal ("Malime")

"Malmime" Short "mim" Broken "lam"

1940 (25 Feb). *Surch with T* **17** *by McCorquodale (Sudan) Ltd, Khartoum.*

No.	Type	Description	Unused	Used
78	6	5 m. on 10 m. carmine and black	15	40
		a. "Malmime"	12·00	13·00
		b. Two dots omitted	12·00	13·00
		c. Short "mim"	12·00	13·00
		d. Broken "lam"	12·00	13·00

The "Malmime" error occurs on Row 5, stamp 1 of the two left-hand panes. Nos. 78b/d all occur on the two right-hand panes, the missing dots on Row 8, stamp 6; the short "mim" on Row 3, stamp 1; and the broken "lam" on Row 6, stamp 2.

A variety known as "Inserted 5" occurs in the bottom right-hand pane, Row 4, stamp 5, of some sheets. It is said that the "5" was damaged and became a hyphen and dots which were replaced by a hand-inserted "5". This "inserted 5" is usually dropped and not completely upright.

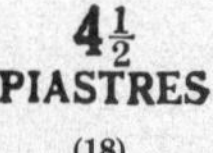

4½ PIASTRES (18)

4½ Piastres (19)

1940–1. *Surch as T* **18** *or* **19** *at Khartoum.*
79 **6** 4½ p. on 5 m. olive-brown & blk (9.2.41) .. 15·00 4·00
80 **2** 4½ p. on 8 p. emerald and black (12.12.40) 9·00 5·50

20 Tuti Island, R. Nile, near Khartoum

21 Tuti Island, R. Nile near Khartoum

(Des Miss H. M. Hebbert. Litho Security Printing Press, Nasik, India)

1941 (25 Mar–10 Aug). *P* 14 × 13½ (*T* **20**) *or P* 13½ × 14 (*T* **21**).
81 **20** 1 m. slate and orange (10.8) 10 70
82 2 m. orange and chocolate (10.8) 25 70
83 3 m. mauve and green (10.8) 25 12
84 4 m. green and chocolate (10.8) 15 25
85 5 m. olive-brown and black (10.8) .. 15 5
86 10 m. carmine and black (10.8) .. .. 4·50 2·25
87 15 m. bright blue and chestnut 15 5
88 **21** 2 p. purple and orange-yellow (10.8) .. 3·00 1·40
89 3 p. red-brown and blue 70 5
90 4 p. ultramarine and black 60 10
91 5 p. chestnut and green (10.8) .. .. 4·00 4·50
92 6 p. greenish blue and black (10.8) .. 8·00 1·50
93 8 p. emerald and black (10.8) .. .. 7·00 1·50
94 10 p. slate and purple (10.8) .. .. 24·00 2·25
95 20 p. pale blue and blue (10.8) .. .. 32·00 23·00
81/95 .. .. *Set of* 15 75·00 35·00

22 23

1948 (1 Jan). *Arabic inscriptions below camel altered. Typo. W* **7**. *P* 14
96 **22** 1 m. black and orange, **C** 5 25
97 2 m. orange and chocolate, **C** 10 15
98 3 m. mauve and green, **C** 10 5
99 4 m. deep green and chocolate, **C** .. 10 5
100 5 m. olive-brown and black, **C** 20 5
101 10 m. rose-red and black, **C** 20 5
a. Centre inverted .. .. ..
102 15 m. ultramarine and chestnut, **C** .. 20 5
103 **23** 2 p. purple and orange-yellow, **C** .. 75 12
104 3 p. red-brown and deep blue, **C** .. 75 15
105 4 p. ultramarine and black, **C** 80 40
106 5 p. brown-orange and deep green, **C** .. 1·25 35
107 6 p. greenish blue and black, **C**.. .. 80 55
108 8 p. bluish green and black, **O** .. .. 90 1·00
109 10 p. black and mauve, **OC** .. .. 1·50 80
110 20 p. pale blue and deep blue, **O**.. .. 2·75 50
a. Perf 13, **C** .. .. .. 17·00 25·00
111 50 p. carmine and ultramarine, **C** .. 5·00 1·50
96/111 .. .. *Set of* 16 14·00 5·25

For similar stamps, but with different Arabic inscriptions, see Nos. 37/46*a*.

24 25

1948 (1 Oct). *Golden Jubilee of "Camel Postman" design. Chalk-surfaced paper. Typo. W* **7**. *P* 13.
112 **24** 2 p. black and light blue 15 10

1948 (Dec). *Opening of Legislative Assembly, Chalk-surfaced paper. Typo. W* **7**. *P* 13.
113 **25** 10 m. rose-red and black 15 5
114 5 p. brown-orange and deep green .. 15 10

26 Blue Nile Bridge, Khartoum

(Des Col. W. L. Atkinson (2½ p., 6 p.), G. R. Wilson (3 p.), others from photographs. Recess)

1950 (1 July). *Air. T* **26** *and similar horiz designs. W* **7**. *P* 12.
115 2 p. black and blue-green .. .. .. 1·25 15
116 2½ p. light blue and red-orange 50 35
117 3 p. reddish purple and blue 70 20
118 3½ p. purple-brown and yellow-brown .. 90 1·50
119 4 p. brown and light blue 70 75
120 4½ p. black and ultramarine .. .. .. 2·50 2·75
a. Black and steel-blue .. .. .. 2·50 3·00
121 6 p. black and carmine 85 60
122 20 p. black and purple .. .. .. 3·00 2·75
115/122 .. .. *Set of* 8 9·00 8·00

Designs:—2½ p. Kassala Jebel; 3 p. Sagia (water wheel); 3½ p. Port Sudan; 4 p. Gordon Memorial College; 4½ p. Nile Post Boat; 6 p. Suakin; 20 p. G.P.O., Khartoum.

34 Ibex **35** Cotton Picking

(Des Col. W. L. Atkinson (1 m., 2 m., 4 m., 5 m., 10 m., 3 p., 3½ p., 20 p.), Col. E. A. Stanton (50 p.) others from photographs. Typo)

1951 (1 Sept). *Designs as T* **34/5**. *Chalk-surfaced paper. W* **7**. *P* 14 *(millieme values) or* 13 *(piastre values).*
123 1 m. black and orange 5 20
124 2 m. black and bright blue 5 5
125 3 m. black and green.. .. .. .. 20 40
126 4 m. black and yellow-green.. .. .. 5 5
127 5 m. black and purple (*shades*) 5 5
128 10 m. black and pale blue 5 5
129 15 m. black and chestnut (*shades*) 10 5
130 2 p. deep blue and pale blue (*shades*) .. 12 5
131 3 p. brown and pale ultramarine (*shades*) .. 25 5
132 3½ p. bright green and red-brown (*shades*) .. 25 5
133 4 p. blue and black (*shades*).. .. .. 25 5
134 5 p. orange-brown and yellow-green .. 25 5
135 6 p. blue and black (*shades*).. .. .. 45 10
136 8 p. blue and brown (*shades*) 85 25
137 10 p. black and green.. .. .. .. 1·25 15
138 20 p. blue-green and black .. .. .. 2·75 40
139 50 p. carmine and black .. .. .. 4·25 1·25
123/139 .. .. *Set of* 17 10·00 2·75

Designs: *Vert as T* **34**—2 m. Whale-headed Stork; 3 m. Giraffe; 4 m. Baggara girl; 5 m. Shilluk warrior; 10 m. Hadendowa; 15 m. Policeman. *Horiz as T* **35**—3 p. Ambatch canoe; 3½ p. Nuba wrestlers; 4 p. Weaving; 5 p. Saluka farming; 6 p. Gum tapping; 8 p. Darfur chief; 10 p. Stack Laboratory; 20 p. Nile lechwe. *Vert as T* **35**—50 p. Camel postman.

SELF-GOVERNMENT

51 Camel Postman

1954 (9 Jan). *Self-Government. Chalk-surfaced paper. Typo. W* **7**. *P* 13.
140 **51** 15 m. orange-brown and bright green .. 15 5
141 3 p. blue and indigo 20 20
142 5 p. black and reddish purple 20 20

Stamps as Type **51**, but dated "1953" were released in error at the Sudan Agency in London. They had no postal validity. (*Price per set £14 un*).

Later issues of Sudan as an independent republic will be found in Part 14 (*Africa since Independence N–Z*) of this catalogue.

POSTAGE DUE STAMPS

1897 (1 Mar). *Type* D **3** *of Egypt, optd with T* **1** *at Bûlâq.*
D1 2 m. green .. .. 1·40 3·00
D2 4 m. maroon .. .. 1·40 3·00
a. Bisected (2 m.) (on cover) .. .. † —
D3 1 p. ultramarine .. .. 2·75 5·00
D4 2 p. orange .. .. 5·50 11·00
a. Bisected (1 p.) (on cover).. .. .. † —

In some printings the large dot is omitted from the left-hand Arabic character on one stamp in the pane.

No. D1 has been recorded used as a bisect.

D 1 Gunboat *Zafir* D 2

1901 (1 Jan). *Typo. W* **4**. *P* 14.
D5 D **1** 2 m. black and brown, **OC** 25 60
D6 4 m. brown and green, **OC** 60 90
D7 10 m. green and mauve, **OC** .. .. 1·50 1·25
D8 20 m. ultramarine and carmine, **CO** .. 2·00 2·75

Nos. D6 and D8 exist used as bisects.

1927–30. *W* **7**. *P* 14.
D 9 D **1** 2 m. black and brown, **C** (1930) .. 60 60
D10 4 m. brown and green, **C** 70 90
D11 10 m. green and mauve, **CO** .. .. 1·25 1·90

1948 (1 Jan). *Arabic inscriptions at foot altered. Chalk-surfaced paper. Typo. W* **7**. *P* 14.
D12 D **2** 2 m. black and brown-orange .. .. 80 2·00
D13 4 m. brown and green .. .. .. 1·75 3·75
D14 10 m. green and mauve .. .. .. 3·25 1·75
D15 20 m. ultramarine and carmine.. .. 7·00 7·50

OFFICIAL STAMPS

1900 (8 Feb). *5 mils of* 1897 *punctured* "S G" *by hand. The* "S" *has* 14 *and the* "G" 12 *holes.*
O1 5 m. rose-carmine .. .. 40·00 20·00

1901 (Jan). *1 m. wmk Quatrefoil, punctured as No.* O1.
O2 1 m. brown and pink .. .. 35·00 25·00

Nos. O1/2 are found with the punctured "SG" inverted, reversed or inverted and reversed.

O.S.G.S. (O 1) ("On Sudan Government Service") **O.S.G.S.** (O 2)

1902. *No.* 10 *optd at Khartoum as Type* O **1** *in groups of* 30 *stamps.*
O3 **2** 1 m. brown and pink .. .. .. 2·00 2·25
a. Oval "O" (No. 19) .. .. .. 65·00
b. Round stops. (Nos. 25 to 30) .. 7·50 8·50
c. Opt inverted £300
d. Ditto and oval "O" £2000
e. Ditto and round stops £550
f. Opt double £300
g. Ditto and round stops £750
h. Ditto and oval "O" .. .. ..

1903–12. *T* **2** *optd as Type* O **2**, *by D.L.R. in sheets of* 120 *stamps.*

(i) *Wmk Quatrefoil* (3.06)
O 4 10 p. black and mauve .. .. .. 4·50 4·25
a. Malformed "O" .. .. ..

(ii) *Wmk Mult Star and Crescent*
O 5 1 m. brown and carmine (9.04) 30 15
a. Opt double .. .. ..
b. Malformed "O" .. .. ..
O 6 3 m. mauve and green (2.04) 85 30
a. Opt double .. .. ..
b. Malformed "O" .. .. ..
O 7 5 m. scarlet and black (1.1.03) 85 10
a. Malformed "O" .. .. ..
O 8 1 p. blue and brown (1.1.03) .. .. 1·40 15
a. Malformed "O" .. .. ..
O 9 2 p. black and blue (1.1.03) .. .. 3·25 35
a. Malformed "O" .. .. ..
O10 5 p. brown and green (1.1.03) .. .. 1·40 65
a. Malformed "O" .. .. ..
O11 10 p. black and mauve (9.12) .. .. 2·75 6·00
a. Malformed "O" .. .. ..
O4/11.. .. .. *Set of* 8 14·00 11·00

The malformed "O" is slightly flattened on the left-hand side and occurs on position 7 of the lower pane.

S.G. (O 3) **S.G.** (O 4) Thick **S.G.** (O 5) Thin

1936 (19 Sept)–**46.** *Nos.* 37/43 *optd with Type* O **3**, *and* 44/46*a with Type* O **4**. *W* **7**. *P* 14.
O12 **6** 1 m. black and orange, **O** (22.11.46) .. 12 40
a. Opt double .. .. † —
O13 2 m. orange and chocolate, **O** (4.45) .. 10 30
O14 3 m. mauve and green, **C** (1.37).. .. 20 5
O15 4 m. green and chocolate, **C** 20 20
O16 5 m. olive-brown and black, **CO** (3.40) .. 15 5
O17 10 m. carmine and black, **C** (6.46) .. 30 5
O18 15 m. bright blue and chestnut, **CO** (21.6.37) 35 10
O19 **2** 2 p. purple and orange-yellow, **CO** (4.37) 50 10
O19*a* 3 p. red-brown and blue, **O** (4.46) .. 50 50
O19*b* 4 p. ultramarine and black, **CO** (4.46) .. 50 30
O20 5 p. chestnut and green, **CO** 75 30
O20*a* 6 p. greenish blue and black, **O** (4.46) .. 1·50 60
O20*b* 8 p. emerald and black, **O** (4.46) .. 1·75 1·75
O21 10 p. black and reddish purple, **C** (10.37) 2·50 1·10
a. Black and bright mauve, **O** (1941) .. 3·25 1·25
O22 20 p. pale blue and blue, **O** (6.46) .. 3·75 4·75
O12/22 .. .. *Set of* 15 12·00 9·50

1948 (1 Jan). *Nos.* 96/102 *optd with Type* O **3**, *and* 103/111 *with Type* O **4**.
O23 **22** 1 m. black and orange 5 30
O24 2 m. orange and chocolate 10 5
O25 3 m. mauve and green 12 20
O26 4 m. deep green and chocolate 12 8
O27 5 m. olive-brown and black 12 5
O28 10 m. rose-red and black 12 10
O29 15 m. ultramarine and chestnut 15 5
O30 **23** 2 p. purple and orange-yellow 20 5
O31 3 p. red-brown and deep blue 25 5
O32 4 p. ultramarine and black 40 10
a. Perf 13 .. .. 11·00 14·00
O33 5 p. brown-orange and deep green .. 50 20
O34 6 p. greenish blue and black 50 20
O35 8 p. bluish green and black 55 35
O36 10 p. black and mauve 85 50
O37 20 p. pale blue and deep blue .. .. 3·00 80
O38 50 p. carmine and ultramarine .. .. 12·00 5·00
O23/38 .. .. *Set of* 16 17·00 7·25

1950 (1 July). *Air. Optd with Type* O **4**.

No.	Description	Un	Us
O39	2 p. black and blue-green (R.)	1·75	90
O40	2½ p. light blue and red-orange	1·25	1·00
O41	3 p. reddish purple and blue	1·25	70
O42	3½ p. purple-brown and yellow-brown	1·25	2·50
O43	4 p. brown and light blue	1·25	1·75
O44	4½ p. black and ultramarine (R.)	2·75	4·25
	a. Black and steel-blue	2·75	5·00
O45	6 p. black and carmine (R.)	1·50	2·25
O46	20 p. black and purple (R.)	6·00	9·50
O39/46	*Set of* 8	15·00	21·00

1951 (1 Sept)–**58**. *Nos.* 123/9 *optd with Type* O **3**, *and* 130/9 *with Type* O **4**.

No.	Description	Un	Us
O47	1 m. black and orange (R.)	5	40
O48	2 m. black and bright blue (R.)	5	5
O49	3 m. black and green (R.)	55	1·25
O50	4 m. black and yellow-green (R.)	5	5
O51	5 m. black and purple (R.)	5	5
O52	10 m. black and pale blue (R.)	8	5
O53	15 m. black and chestnut (R.)	10	5
O54	2 p. deep blue and pale blue (*shades*)	12	5
	a. Opt inverted	£350	
O55	3 p. brown & dp ultramarine (*shades*)	35	5
O56	3½ p. bright green & red-brown (*shades*)	25	5
O57	4 p. blue and black (*shades*)	25	5
O58	5 p. orange-brown and yellow-green	25	5
O59	6 p. blue and black (*shades*)	25	5
O60	8 p. blue and brown (*shades*)	45	10
O61	10 p. black and green (R.)	70	30
O61*a*	10 p. black and green (Blk.) (1958)	2·50	20
O62	20 p. blue-green and black	1·75	45
	a. Opt inverted	—	£250
O63	50 p. carmine and black	4·00	2·00
O47/63	*Set of* 18	11·00	4·25

ARMY SERVICE STAMPS

ARMY OFFICIAL (A 1)

ARMY OFFICIAL (A 2)

Army Service (A 3)

1905 (Jan). T **2** *optd at Khartoum as Types* A **1** *or* A **2**. *Wmk Mult Star and Crescent.* (i) "ARMY" *reading up.*

No.	Description	Un	Us
A1	1 m. brown and carmine (A 1)	1·90	85
	a. "!" for "I"	17·00	10·00
	b. Opt Type A **2**	12·00	5·50

(ii) *Overprint horizontal*

No.	Description	Un	Us
A2	1 m. brown and carmine (A 1)	£200	
	a. "!" for "I"	£2250	
	b. Opt Type A **2**	£1400	

The horizontal overprint exists with either "ARMY" or "OFFICIAL" reading the right way up. It did not fit the stamps, resulting in misplacements where more than one whole overprint appears, or when the two words are transposed.

(iii) "ARMY" *reading down*

No.	Description	Un	Us
A3	1 m. brown and carmine (A 1)	26·00	26·00
	a. "!" for "I"	£375	£400
	b. Opt Type A **2**	£275	£300

1905 (Nov). *As No* A 1, *but wmk Quatrefoil,* W **3**.

No.	Description	Un	Us
A4	1 m. brown and pink (A 1)	75·00	70·00
	a. "!" for "I"	—	£1500
	b. Opt Type A **2**	£900	

The 29th stamp in each setting of 30 (Nos. A1–A4) has an exclamation mark for first "I" in "OFFICIAL" while the 6th and 12th stamps are Type A **2**.

Two varieties of the 1 millieme

A. 1st Ptg. 14 mm between lines of opt.

B. Later Ptgs. 12 mm between lines.

All other values are Type B.

1906 (Jan)–**11**. T **2** *optd as Type* A **3**.

(i) *Wmk Mult Star and Crescent,* W **4**

No.	Description	Un	Us
A 5	1 m. brown and carmine (Type A)	£120	£100
A 6	1 m. brown and carmine (Type B)	1·50	30
	a. Opt double	—	£450
	b. Opt inverted	£300	£300
	c. Pair, one without opt		
	d. "Service" omitted	—	£3000
	e. "A" for "A" in "Army"	£150	£150
A 7	2 m. green and brown	4·25	1·25
	a. Pair, one without opt	£1500	
	b. "Army" omitted	£1600	
A 8	3 m. mauve and green	5·00	65
	a. Opt inverted	£1600	
A 9	5 m. scarlet and black	1·40	20
	a. Opt. double	£190	£190
	b. Opt inverted	—	£160
	c. "Amry"	—	£2000
	d. "A" for "A" in "Army"	—	£250
	e. Opt double, one inverted	£550	£250
A10	1 p. blue and brown	3·25	25
	a. "Army" omitted	£1700	£1700
A11	2 p. black and blue (1.09)	9·00	8·00
A12	5 p. brown and green (5.08)	42·00	17·00
A13	10 p. black and mauve (5.11)	£325	£450
A6/10 Optd "Specimen"	*Set of* 5	£400	

There were a number of printings of these Army Service stamps; the earlier are as Type A 3; the 1908 printing has a narrower "A" in "Army" and the 1910–11 printings have the tail of the "y" in "Army" much shorter.

(ii) *Wmk Quatrefoil,* W **3**

No.	Description	Un	Us
A14	2 p. black and blue	16·00	5·50
A15	5 p. brown and green	50·00	55·00
A16	10 p. black and mauve	60·00	65·00
A14/16 Optd "Specimen"	*Set of* 3	£375	

Between 1912 and 1935 a number of stamps have been issued punctured "S.G." (Sudan Government) or "AS" (Army Service), but we no longer list such items.

Swaziland

PRICES FOR STAMPS ON COVER TO 1945

Nos. 1/10	—
Nos. 11/20	*from* × 4
Nos. 21/4	*from* × 5
Nos. 25/7	*from* × 10
Nos. 28/38	*from* × 4
Nos. 39/41	*from* × 5
Nos. D1/2	*from* × 30

TRIPARTITE GOVERNMENT

Following internal unrest and problems caused by the multitude of commercial concessions granted by the Swazi king the British and Transvaal governments intervened during 1889 to establish a tripartite administration under which the country was controlled by their representatives, acting with the agent of the Swazi king.

The Pretoria government had previously purchased the concession to run the postal service and, on the establishment of the tripartite administration, provided overprinted Transvaal stamps for use from the post offices opened at Bremersdorp, Darkton and Embekelweni.

Swazieland
(1)

1889 (18–20 Oct). *Stamps of Transvaal (South African Republic) optd with* T **1**, *in black.* (*a*) *P* 12½ × 12.

No.	Type	Description	Un	Us
1	**18**	1d. carmine	14·00	15·00
		a. Opt inverted	£425	£450
2		2d. olive-bistre	65·00	13·00
		a. Opt inverted	—	£900
		b. "Swazielan"	£900	£650
3		1s. green	12·00	13·00
		a. Opt inverted	£400	£425

(*b*) *P* 12½

No.	Type	Description	Un	Us
4	**18**	½d. grey	8·50	10·00
		a. Opt inverted	£400	£425
		b. "Swazielan"	£750	£600
		c. "Swazielan" inverted	—	£1600
5		2d. olive-bistre	12·00	12·00
		a. Opt inverted	£425	£450
		b. "Swazielan"	£425	£450
		c. "Swazielan" inverted	£1200	£1200
		d. Opt double	£1750	
6		6d. blue	15·00	22·00
7		2s. 6d. buff (20 Oct)	80·00	£100
8		5s. slate-blue (20 Oct)	85·00	£100
		a. Opt inverted	£1600	£1600
		b. "Swazielan"	£4000	
		c. "Swazielan" inverted		
9		10s. fawn (20 Oct)	£1800	£1200

The variety without "d" occurs on the left-hand bottom corner stamp in each sheet of certain printings.

1892 (Aug). *Optd in carmine. P* 12½.

No.	Type	Description	Un	Us
10	**18**	½d. grey	8·00	10·00
		a. Opt inverted	£400	
		b. Opt double	£400	£400
		c. Pair, one without opt	—	£425

A printing of the above with stop after "Swazieland" was made in July 1894 but these were not issued.

After further negotiations in 1894 the British and Transvaal governments agreed that Swaziland would become a protectorate of the Transvaal in February 1895. The overprinted stamps were withdrawn on 7 November 1894 and replaced by ordinary issues of the Transvaal.

Shortly after the outbreak of the Boer War in 1899 the Transvaal administration withdrew from Swaziland and there was no postal service from the area until the country became a British Protectorate in March 1902. From that date, until the introduction of the 1933 definitives, the post offices listed below used Transvaal or South Africa stamps.

The following post offices or postal agencies existed in Swaziland before 1933. Dates given are those on which it is generally accepted that the offices were first opened. Some were subsequently closed before the end of the period.

Bremersdorp (1889)	Mankaiana (1913)
Darkton (1889)	Mbabane (*previously* Embabaan) (1905)
Dwaleni (1918)	M'dimba (1898)
Embabaan (1895)	Mhlotsheni (1910)
Embekelweni (1889)	Mooihoek (1918)
Ezulweni (1910)	Motshane (1929)
Forbes Reef (1906)	Nomahasha (1904)
Goedgegun (1925)	Nsoko (1927)
Hlatikulu (1903)	Piggs Peak (1899)
Hluti (1912)	Sandhlan (1903)
Ivy (1912)	Sicunusa (1913)
Kubuta (1926)	Stegi (1910)
Mahamba (1899)	Umkwakweni (1898)
Malkerns (1914)	White Umbuluzi (1925)
Malomba (1928)	

BRITISH PROTECTORATE

2 King George V

3 King George VI

(Des Rev. C. C. Tugman. Recess D.L.R.)

1933 (2 Jan). *Wmk Mult Script CA. P* 14.

No.	Type	Description	Un	Us
11	**2**	½d. green	25	40
12		1d. carmine	35	15
13		2d. brown	40	45
14		3d. blue	55	60
15		4d. orange	1·25	1·60
16		6d. bright purple	1·50	2·50
17		1s. olive	2·50	6·00
18		2s. 6d. bright violet	20·00	35·00
19		5s. grey	48·00	70·00
20		10s. sepia	£170	£190
11/20		*Set of* 10	£225	£250
11/20 Perf "Specimen"		*Set of* 10	£250	

The ½d., 1d., 2d. and 6d. values exist overprinted "OFFICIAL", but authority for their use was withdrawn before any were actually used. However, some stamps had already been issued to the Secretariat staff before instructions were received to invalidate their use (*Price* £3750 *per set un*).

1935 (4 May). *Silver Jubilee. As Nos.* 91/4 *of Antigua, but ptd by B.W. P* 11 × 12.

No.	Description	Un	Us
21	1d. deep blue and scarlet	40	40
	a. Extra flagstaff	40·00	
	b. Short extra flagstaff	12·00	
	c. Lightning conductor	10·00	
22	2d. ultramarine and grey-black	60	70
	a. Extra flagstaff	50·00	
	c. Lightning conductor	12·00	
23	3d. brown and deep blue	1·25	2·25
	a. Extra flagstaff	40·00	
	b. Short extra flagstaff	12·00	
24	6d. slate and purple	1·50	3·25
	a. Extra flagstaff	50·00	
	b. Short extra flagstaff	15·00	
	c. Lightning conductor	12·00	
21/4 Perf "Specimen"	*Set of* 4	48·00	

For illustrations of plate varieties see Omnibus section following Zululand.

1937 (12 May). *Coronation. As Nos.* 13/15 *of Aden, but ptd by B.W. P* 11 × 11½.

No.	Description	Un	Us
25	1d. carmine	30	15
26	2d. yellow-brown	35	20
27	3d. blue	40	25
25/7 Perf "Specimen"	*Set of* 3	32·00	

(Recess D.L.R.)

1938 (1 Apr)–**54**. *Wmk Mult Script CA. P* 13½ × 13.

No.	Type	Description	Un	Us
28	**3**	½d. green	20	25
		a. Perf 13½ × 14 (1.43)	15	20
		b. Perf 13½ × 14. *Bronze-green* (2.50)	25	35
29		1d. rose-red	35	15
		a. Perf 13½ × 14 (1.43)	15	15
30		1½d. light blue	70	30
		a. Perf 14 (1941)	40	45
		b. Perf 13½ × 14 (1.43)	20	20
31		2d. yellow-brown	70	35
		a. Perf 13½ × 14 (1.43)	15	12
32		3d. ultramarine	80	50
		a. Deep blue (10.38)	85	50
		b. Perf 13½ × 14. *Ultramarine* (1.43)	40	50
		c. Perf 13½ × 14. *Light ultram* (10.46)	70	60
		d. Perf 13½ × 14. *Deep blue* (10.47)	50	50
33		4d. orange	85	65
		a. Perf 13½ × 14 (1.43)	40	45
34		6d. deep magenta	1·00	55
		a. Perf 13½ × 14 (1.43)	40	1·00
		b. Perf 13½ × 14. *Reddish purple* (*shades*) (7.44)	60	30
		c. Perf 13½ × 14. *Claret* (13.10.54)	70	55
35		1s. brown-olive	2·25	65
		a. Perf 13½ × 14 (1.43)	50	25
36		2s. 6d. bright violet	5·50	3·50
		a. Perf 13½ × 14. *Violet* (1.43)	2·00	2·00
		b. Perf 13½ × 14. *Reddish violet* (10.47)	2·75	2·50
37		5s. grey	10·00	7·00
		a. Perf 13½ × 14. *Slate* (1.43)	40·00	25·00
		b. Perf 13½ × 14. *Grey* (5.44)	15·00	7·00
38		10s. sepia	25·00	12·00
		a. Perf 13½ × 14 (1.43)	9·00	6·00
28/38a		*Set of* 11	21·00	15·00
28/38 Perf "Specimen"		*Set of* 11	£120	

The above perforations vary slightly from stamp to stamp, but the average measurements are respectively: 13.3 × 13.2 comb (13½ × 13), 14.2 line (14) and 13.3 × 13.8 comb (13½ × 14).

Swaziland
(4)

1945 (3 Dec). *Victory. Nos.* 108/10 *of South Africa optd with* T **4**.

No.	Description	*Un pair*	*Us pair*
39	1d. brown and carmine	10	15
40	2d. slate-blue and violet	15	15
41	3d. deep blue and blue	15	20

1947 (17 Feb). *Royal Visit. As Nos.* 32/5 *of Basutoland.*

No.	Description	*Un*	*Us*
42	1d. scarlet	8	5
43	2d. green	8	5
44	3d. ultramarine	10	8
45	1s. mauve	10	10
42/5 Perf "Specimen"	*Set of* 4	80·00	

1948 (1 Dec). *Royal Silver Wedding. As Nos.* 30/1 *of Aden.*

No.	Description	Un	Us
46	1½d. ultramarine	20	15
47	10s. purple-brown	16·00	18·00

1949 (10 Oct). *75th Anniv of Universal Postal Union. As Nos.* 114/17 *of Antigua.*

No.	Description	Un	Us
48	1½d. blue	15	12
49	3d. deep blue	50	35
50	6d. magenta	70	65
51	1s. olive	75	1·00

1953 (3 June). *Coronation. As No.* 47 *of Aden.*

No.	Description	Un	Us
52	2d. black and yellow-brown	15	20

5 Havelock Asbestos Mine

7 Swazi Married Woman

(Recess B.W.)

1956 (2 July). *T* **5**, **7** *and similar designs. Wmk Mult Script CA. P* 13 × 13½ (*horiz*) *or* 13½ × 13 (*vert*).

53	½d. black and orange	8	5
54	1d. black and emerald	10	5
55	2d. black and brown	12	5
56	3d. black and rose-red	15	5
57	4½d. black and deep bright blue	25	15
58	6d. black and magenta	30	5
59	1s. black and deep olive	30	5
60	1s. 3d. black and sepia	90	35
61	2s. 6d. emerald and carmine-red	1·50	80
62	5s. deep lilac and slate-black	3·00	1·75
63	10s. black and deep lilac	6·00	6·50
64	£1 black and turquoise-blue	16·00	23·00
53/64	*Set of* 12	26·00	30·00

Designs: *Horiz*—1d., 2s. 6d. A Highveld view; 1s. Type **5**. *Vert*—3d., 1s. 3d. Swazi courting couple; 4½d., 5s. Swazi warrior; 6d., £1. Greater Kudu Antelope; 10s. Type **7**.

(New Currency. 100 cents = 1 rand)

½c (11) 1c (12) 2c (13) 3½c (14)

2½c (I) 2½c (II) 4c (I) 4c (II)

5c (I) 5c (II) 25c (I) 25c (II)

50c (I) 50c (II) 50c (III)

R1 (I) R1 (II) R1 (III) R2 (I) R2 (II)

1961 (14 Feb–May). *Nos.* 53/64 *surch as T* **11** *to* **14**.

65	½ c. on ½d.	60	1·25
	a. Surch inverted	£120	
66	1 c. on 1d.	5	5
	a. Surch double	£190	
67	2 c. on 2d.	12	5
68	2½ c. on 2d.	10	5
69	2½ c. on 3d. (Type I)	15	10
	a. Type II	20	25
70	3½ c. on 2d. (May)	10	5
71	4 c. on 4½d. (Type I)	15	15
	a. Type II	15	15
72	5 c. on 6d. (Type I)	12	5
	a. Type II	12	10
73	10 c. on 1s.	5·00	4·50
	a. Surch double (vert pair)*	£190	
74	25 c. on 2s. 6d. (Type I)	75	90
	a. Type II (central)	1·00	1·25
	b. Type II (bottom left)	95·00	£120
75	50 c. on 5s. (Type I)	80	1·00
	a. Type II	6·50	6·50
	b. Type III	£250	£325
76	1 r. on 10s. (Type I)	1·50	2·00
	a. Type II	7·50	8·50
	b. Type III	30·00	45·00
77	2 r. on £1 (Type I)	13·00	14·00
	a. Type II (middle left)	12·00	12·00
	b. Type II (bottom)	27·00	45·00
65/77a	*Set of* 13	19·00	20·00

*No. 73a is best collected as a vertical pair, due to the fall of the second surcharge.

No. 74b has the thin Type II surcharge at bottom left, in similar position to the thicker Type I, No. 74, with which it should not be confused.

No. 77b has the surcharge centrally placed at bottom. No. 77a has it at middle left, above "KUDU".

No. 66 with surcharge central (instead of bottom left) and No. 75a bottom left (instead of middle left) are believed to be from trial sheets released with the normal stocks. They do not represent separate printings. (No. 66 *price* £35 *un*).

(Recess B.W.)

1961. *As* 1956 *issue, but with values in cents and rands. Wmk Mult Script CA. P* 13 × 13½ (*horiz*) *or* 13½ × 13 (*vert*).

78	½ c. black and orange (as ½d.) (14.2)	5	15
79	1 c. black and emerald (as 1d.) (14.2)	10	8
80	2 c. black and brown (as 2d.) (10.9)	12	20
81	2½ c. black and rose-red (as 3d.) (14.2)	15	10
82	4 c. black & dp bright bl (as 4½d.) (10.9)	20	25
83	5 c. black and magenta (as 6d.) (10.9)	30	10
84	10 c. black and deep olive (as 1s.) (14.2)	30	10
85	12½ c. black and sepia (as 1s 3d.) (14.2)	90	50
86	25 c. emerald and carmine-red (as 2s 6d.) (1.8)	1·50	1·25
87	50 c. deep lilac & slate-blk (as 5s.) (10.9)	2·25	2·25
88	1 r. black and deep lilac (as 10s.) (10.9)	4·00	4·25
89	2 r. black and turquoise-blue (as £1) (1.8)	14·00	14·00
78/89	*Set of* 12	22·00	21·00

15 Swazi Shields

16 Battle Axe

(Des Mrs. C. Hughes. Photo Enschedé)

1962 (24 Apr). *Various designs as T* **15/16**. *W* w **12**. *P* 14 × 13 (*horiz*) *or* 13 × 14 (*vert*).

90	½ c. black, brown and yellow-brown	5	5
91	1 c. yellow-orange and black	5	5
92	2 c. deep bluish green, black and yellow-olive	8	5
93	2½ c. black and vermilion (*shades*)	8	5
94	3½ c. yellow-green and deep grey	8	5
95	4 c. black and turquoise-green (*shades*)	10	5
96	5 c. black, red and orange-red	25	5
97	7½ c. deep brown and buff (*shades*)	20	15
98	10 c. black and light blue	20	5
99	12½ c. carmine and grey-olive	45	70
100	15 c. black and bright purple	45	60
101	20 c. black and green	50	60
102	25 c. black and bright blue	60	70
103	50 c. black and rose-red	2·75	2·75
104	1 r. emerald and ochre	3·25	2·75
105	2 r. carmine-red and ultramarine	9·00	6·50
90/105	*Set of* 16	16·00	13·00

Designs: *Vert*—2 c. Forestry; 2½ c. Ceremonial headdress; 3½ c. Musical instrument; 4 c. Irrigation; 5 c. Long-tailed Whydah; 7½ c. Rock paintings; 10 c. Secretary Bird; 12½ c. Pink Arum; 15 c. Swazi married woman; 20 c. Malaria control; 25 c. Swazi warrior; 1 r. Aloes. *Horiz*—50 c. Southern Ground Hornbill; 2 r. Msinsi in flower.

1963 (4 June). *Freedom from Hunger. As No.* 76 *of Aden.*

106	15 c. reddish violet	65	30

1963 (2 Sept). *Red Cross Centenary. As Nos.* 147/8 *of Antigua.*

107	2½ c. red and black	10	10
108	15 c. red and blue	50	30

31 Train and Map

(Des R. A. H. Street. Recess B.W.)

1964 (5 Nov). *Opening of Swaziland Railway. W* w **12**. *P* 11½.

109	**31**	2½ c. emerald-green and purple	15	5
110		3½ c. turquoise-blue & deep yellow-ol	15	10
111		15 c. red-orange and deep chocolate	30	20
112		25 c. olive-yellow and deep ultram	50	30

1965 (17 May). *I.T.U. Centenary. As Nos.* 166/7 *of Antigua.*

113	2½ c. light blue and bistre	15	5
114	15 c. bright purple and rose	50	25

1965 (25 Oct). *International Co-operation Year. As Nos.* 168/9 *of Antigua.*

115	½ c. reddish purple and turquoise-green	5	5
116	15 c. deep bluish green and lavender	50	25

1966 (24 Jan). *Churchill Commemoration. As Nos.* 170/3 *of Antigua.*

117	½ c. new blue	5	5
118	2½ c. deep green	25	5
119	15 c. brown	90	30
120	25 c. bluish violet	1·25	55

1966 (1 Dec). 20*th Anniv of U.N.E.S.C.O. As Nos.* 196/8 *of Antigua.*

121	2½ c. slate-violet, red, yellow and orange	15	5
122	7½ c. orange-yellow, violet and deep olive	30	20
123	15 c. black, bright purple and orange	55	45

PROTECTED STATE

32 King Sobhuza II and Map

33 King Sobhuza II

(Des and photo Harrison)

1967 (25 Apr). *Protected State. W* w **12** (*sideways on hor* *designs*). *P* 14½.

124	**32**	2½ c. multicoloured	5	
125	**33**	7½ c. multicoloured	10	1
126	**32**	15 c. multicoloured	15	1
127	**33**	25 c. multicoloured	20	2

34 Students and University

(Des V. Whiteley. Photo Harrison)

1967 (7 Sept). *First Conferment of University Degrees. P* 14 × 14½.

128	**34**	2½ c. sepia, ultramarine & lt yellow-orge	5	
129		7½ c. sepia, ultramarine & lt greenish bl	10	1
130		15 c. sepia, ultramarine and rose	15	1
131		25 c. sepia, ultramarine and light violet	20	2

35 Inclawa Ceremony

36 Reed Dance

(Des Mrs. G. Ellison. Photo Harrison)

1968 (5 Jan). *Traditional Customs. P* 14.

132	**35**	3 c. silver, vermilion and black	5	
133	**36**	10 c. silver, light brown, orange and black	15	1
134	**35**	15 c. gold, vermilion and black	20	2
135	**36**	25 c. gold, light brown, orange and black	25	2

3c

(37)

38 Cattle Ploughing

1968 (1 May). *No.* 96 *surch with T* **37**.

136	3 c. on 5 c. black, red and orange-red	5	5

INDEPENDENT

(Des Mrs. G. Ellison. Photo Enschedé)

1968 (6 Sept). *Independence. T* **38** *and similar horiz designs. W* w **12** (*sideways*). *P* 14 × 12½.

137	3 c. multicoloured	5	5
	a. Imperf (pair)	£110	
138	4½ c. multicoloured	15	15
	a. Imperf (pair)	£110	
139	17½ c. yellow, green, black and gold	20	20
140	25 c. slate, black and gold	70	70
MS141	180 × 162 mm. Nos. 137/40 each × 5	14·00	16·00
	a. Error. Imperf	£1200	

Designs:—4½ c. Overhead cable carrying asbestos; 17½ c. Cutting sugar cane; 25 c. Iron ore mining and railway map.

Nos. 137/40 were printed in sheets of 50, but also in miniature sheets of 20 (4 × 5) containing *se-tenant* strips of each value.

INDEPENDENCE 1968

(42)

43 Porcupine

1968 (6 Sept). *Nos.* 90/105 *optd as T* **42**, *and No.* 93 *additionally surch* 3 *c., by Enschedé.* (*a*) *Wmk upright.*

142	½ c. black, brown and yellow-brown	5	5
	a. Brown omitted	£150	
	b. Albino opt	40·00	
143	1 c. yellow-orange and black	5	5
144	2 c. dp bluish green, black & yellow-ol	5	5
145	2½ c. black and vermilion (*shades*)	5	5
146	3 c. on 2½ c. black and vermilion (*shades*)	5	5
147	3½ c. yellow-green and deep grey	12	5
148	4 c. black and turquoise-green (*shades*)	10	5
149	5 c. black, red and orange-red	30	5
150	7½ c. deep brown and buff	20	10
151	10 c. black and light blue	25	5
152	12½ c. carmine and grey-olive	25	30
153	15 c. black and bright purple	25	30
154	20 c. black and green	50	70
155	25 c. black and bright blue	45	50
156	50 c. black and rose-red	1·50	1·75
157	1 r. emerald and ochre	2·75	3·25
158	2 r. carmine-red and ultramarine	7·00	8·00

(b *Wmk sideways*

59	50 c. black and rose-red	1·50	1·50
60	2 r. carmine-red and ultramarine	6·50	6·50
42/60	*Set of* 19	19·00	21·00

The 2½ c., 3½ c., 5 c., 12½ c., 50 c. (No. 156) and 2 r. (No. 158) xist with gum arabic only, the 1 c., 2 c., 3 c., 4 c., and 15 c. with oth gum arabic and PVA gum and the remainder with PVA gum nly.

(Des and litho D.L.R.)

969 (1 Aug)–**75**. *T* **43** *and similar designs showing animals. Multicoloured. W* w **12** (*sideways on* 3 *c.,* 3½ *c.,* 1 *r.,* 2 *r.*). *P* 13 × 13½ (3 *c.,* 3½ *c.*), 12½ × 13 (1 *r.,* 2 *r.*) *or* 13 × 12½ (*others*).

61	½ c. Caracal (African Lynx)	5	5
62	1 c. Type **43**	10	5
63	2 c. Crocodile	20	5
	a. Perf 12½ × 12 (29.9.75)	65	70
64	3 c. Lion	30	10
65	3½ c. African Elephant	30	10
66	5 c. Bush pig	30	5
67	7½ c. Impala	35	10
68	10 c. Chacma Baboon	40	10
69	12½ c. Ratel (Honey Badger)	70	70
70	15 c. Leopard	1·25	70
71	20 c. Blue Wildebeest	95	80
72	25 c. White Rhinoceros	1·40	1·00
73	50 c. Burchell's Zebra	1·50	2·00
174	1 r. Waterbuck (*vert*)	4·00	5·00
175	2 r. Giraffe (*vert*)	8·50	10·00
161/75	*Set of* 15	18·00	19·00

Nos. 161/73 are horizontal as Type **43** but the 3 c. and 3½ c. are arger, 35 × 24½ mm.

No. 163a was printed by the D.L.R. works in Bogotá, Colombia.

See also Nos. 219/20 and 229.

44 King Sobhuza II and Flags

45 King Sobhuza II, U.N. Building and Emblem

(Des D.L.R. Litho P.B.)

1969 (24 Sept). *Admission of Swaziland to the United Nations. W* w **12** (*sideways*). *P* 13½.

176	**44**	3 c. multicoloured	5	5
177	**45**	7½ c. multicoloured	15	10
178	**44**	12½ c. multicoloured	30	30
179	**45**	25 c. multicoloured	45	45

46 Athlete, Shield and Spears

47 *Bauhinia galpinii*

(Des L. Curtis. Litho Format)

1970 (16 July). *Ninth Commonwealth Games, Edinburgh. T* **46** *and similar vert designs. Multicoloured. W* w **12**. *P* 14.

180	3 c. Type **46**	5	5
181	7½ c. Runner	20	15
182	12½ c. Hurdler	35	35
183	25 c. Procession of Swaziland competitors	40	40

(Des L. Curtis from "Wild Flowers of Natal" by Dr. W. G. Wright. Litho Questa)

1971 (1 Feb). *Flowers. T* **47** *and similar vert designs. Multicoloured. W* w **12**. *P* 14½.

184	3 c. Type **47**	25	10
185	10 c. *Crocosmia aurea*	60	25
186	15 c. *Gloriosa superba*	90	35
187	25 c. *Watsonia densiflora*	1·25	70

48 King Sobhuza II in Ceremonial Dress

49 UNICEF emblem

(Des L. Curtis. Litho Format)

1971 (22 Dec). *Golden Jubilee of Accession of King Sobhuza II. T* **48** *and similar vert designs. Multicoloured. W* w **12**. *P* 14.

188	3 c. Type **48**	5	5
189	3½ c. Sobhuza II in medallion	5	5
190	7½ c. Sobhuza II attending Incwala ceremony	30	30
191	25 c. Sobhuza II and aides at opening of Parliament	55	85

(Des Sylvia Goaman. Litho J.W.)

1972 (17 Apr). *25th Anniv of UNICEF. W* w **12** (*sideways*). *P* 13½.

192	**49**	15 c. black and bright lilac	40	40
193	–	25 c. black and yellow-olive	60	60

The 25 c. value is as T **49**, but the inscription is rearranged.

50 Local Dancers

(Des G. Drummond. Litho Questa)

1972 (11 Sept). *Tourism. T* **50** *and similar horiz designs. Multicoloured. W* w **12**. *P* 13½ × 14.

194	3½ c. Type **50**	10	5
195	7½ c. Swazi beehive hut	15	15
196	15 c. Ezulwini Valley	55	55
197	25 c. Fishing, Usutu River	1·00	1·00

51 Spraying Mosquitoes

(Des PAD Studio. Litho Questa)

1973 (21 May). *25th Anniv of W.H.O. T* **51** *and similar horiz design. Multicoloured. W* w **12**. *P* 14.

198	3½ c. Type **51**	12	12
199	7½ c. Anti-malaria vaccination	20	20

52 Mining

(Des G. Drummond. Litho Questa)

1973 (21 June). *Natural Resources. T* **52** *and similar horiz designs. Multicoloured. W* w **12**. *P* 13½.

200	3½ c. Type **52**	20	5
201	7½ c. Cattle	35	35
202	15 c. Water	40	25
203	25 c. Rice	50	50

53 Coat of Arms

54 Flags and Mortar-board

(Des J.W. Litho Walsall)

1973 (7 Sept). *Fifth Anniv of Independence. T* **53** *and similar horiz designs. Multicoloured* (*except* 3 *c.*). *W* w **12**. *P* 14.

204	3 c. Type **53** (salmon and black)	12	10
205	10 c. King Sobhuza II saluting	30	25
206	15 c. Parliament Buildings	40	40
207	25 c. National Somhlolo Stadium	50	50

(Des P. Powell. Litho Format)

1974 (29 Mar). *Tenth Anniv of University of Botswana, Lesotho and Swaziland. T* **54** *and similar vert designs. Multicoloured. W* w **12** (*sideways*). *P* 14.

208	7½ c. Type **54**	20	20
209	12½ c. University campus	30	30
210	15 c. Map of Southern Africa	40	40
211	25 c. University badge	50	50

55 King Sobhuza as College Student

56 New Post Office, Lobamba

(Des Mary Nelson; adapted PAD Studio. Litho Enschedé)

1974 (22 July). *75th Birthday of King Sobhuza II. T* **55** *and similar vert designs. Multicoloured. W* w **12**. *P* 13 × 10½.

212	3 c. Type **55**	8	5
213	9 c. King Sobhuza in middle-age	20	20
214	50 c. King Sobhuza at 75 years of age	1·10	1·10

(Des R. Granger Barrett. Litho Questa)

1974 (9 Oct). *Centenary of Universal Postal Union. T* **56** *and similar horiz designs. Multicoloured. W* w **12** (*sideways*). *P* 14.

215	4 c. Type **56**	15	5
216	10 c. Mbabane Temporary Post Office, 1902	40	35
217	15 c. Carrying mail by cableway	55	55
218	25 c. Mule-drawn mail-coach	65	70

(New Currency. 100 cents = 1 lilangeni (*plural* emalangeni))

1975 (2 Jan). *New currency. As Nos.* 174/5 *but inscr in emalangeni. W* w **12** (*upright*). *P* 12½ × 13.

219	1 e. Waterbuck	3·00	3·00
220	2 e. Giraffe	5·50	5·50

57 Umcwasho Ceremony

58 Control Tower, Matsapa Airport

(Des PAD Studio. Litho Kynoch Press)

1975 (20 Mar). *Swazi Youth. T* **57** *and similar multicoloured designs. W* w **12** (*sideways on* 3, 10 *and* 25 *c.*). *P* 14.

221	3 c. Type **57**	8	5
222	10 c. Butimba (hunting party)	20	15
223	15 c. Lusekwane (sacred shrub) (*horiz*)	35	35
224	25 c. Goina Regiment	50	55

(Des V. Whiteley Studio. Litho Questa)

1975 (18 Aug). *Tenth Anniv of Internal Air Service. T* **58** *and similar horiz designs. Multicoloured. W* w **14** (*sideways*). *P* 14.

225	4 c. Type **58**	30	20
226	5 c. Fire engine	30	20
227	15 c. Douglas "Dakota"	1·50	1·25
228	25 c. Hawker Siddeley "748"	2·00	2·00

(Litho De La Rue, Bogotá, Colombia)

1975 (29 Sept). *As No.* 164 *but W* w **12** *upright*.

229	3 c. Lion	1·50	1·25

3c

(59)

1975 (15 Nov). *Nos.* 167 *and* 169 *surch as T* **59**.

230	3 c. on 7½ c. Impala	45	45
231	6 c. on 12½ c. Ratel	65	65

60 Elephant Symbol

(Des Mary-Jane Rostami. Litho Questa)

1975 (22 Dec). *International Women's Year. T* **60** *and similar designs. W* w **14** (*sideways on* 4 *and* 5 *c.*). *P* 14.

232	4 c. light bluish grey, black & light brt blue	12	10
233	5 c. multicoloured	12	10

234 15 c. multicoloured 50 40
235 25 c. multicoloured 65 50
Designs: *Horiz*—5 c. Queen Labotsibeni. *Vert*—15 c. Craftswoman; 25 c. "Women in Service".

61 African Black-headed Oriole

(Des C. Abbott. Litho Questa)

1976 (2 Jan)–78. *Birds.* *T* **61** *and similar multicoloured designs.* W w **14** (*sideways on* 1 c., 3 c., 2 e.). *Chalk-surfaced paper. P* 14.
236 1 c. Type **61** 15 15
237 2 c. African Green Pigeon (*vert*) 20 12
238 3 c. Green-winged Pytilia 25 20
239 4 c. Violet Starling (*vert*) 25 10
a. Ordinary paper (31.7.78) 45 40
240 5 c. Black-headed Heron (*vert*) 25 12
241 6 c. Stonechat (*vert*) 25 12
242 7 c. Chorister Robin Chat (*vert*) 25 20
243 10 c. Four-coloured Bush-shrike (*vert*) .. 35 25
244 15 c. Black-collared Barbet (*vert*) 70 55
245 20 c. Grey Heron (*vert*) 85 60
246 25 c. Giant Kingfisher (*vert*) 85 65
247 30 c. Verreaux's Eagle (*vert*) 85 70
248 50 c. Red Bishop (*vert*) .. .. .. 1·25 1·00
a. Ordinary paper (31.7.78) .. .. 90 1·00
249 1 e. Pin-tailed Whydah (*vert*) .. .. 2·25 2·75
a. Ordinary paper (31.7.78) .. .. 1·75 2·50
250 2 e. Lilac-breasted Roller .. .. .. 4·00 4·75
a. Ordinary paper (31.7.78) .. .. 3·50 4·50
236/50a .. .. *Set of* 15 10·00 10·50

62 Blindness from Malnutrition

63 Marathon

(Des Jennifer Toombs. Litho Questa)

1976 (15 June). *Prevention of Blindness. T* **62** *and similar horiz designs. Multicoloured.* W w **14** (*sideways*). *P* 14.
251 5 c. Type **62** 15 12
252 10 c. Infected retina 30 25
253 20 c. Blindness from trachoma 60 60
254 25 c. Medicines 70 70

(Des PAD Studio. Litho Walsall)

1976 (17 July). *Olympic Games, Montreal. T* **63** *and similar vert designs. Multicoloured.* W w **14** (*inverted*). *P* 14.
255 5 c. Type **63** 12 10
256 6 c. Boxing 15 12
257 20 c. Football 45 55
258 25 c. Olympic torch and flame 50 60

64 Footballer Shooting

65 Alexander Graham Bell and Telephone

(Des J.W. Litho Questa)

1976 (13 Sept). *F.I.F.A. Membership. T* **64** *and similar vert designs. Multicoloured.* W w **14**. *P* 14.
259 4 c. Type **64** 15 10
260 6 c. Heading 15 12
261 20 c. Goalkeeping 60 55
262 25 c. Player about to shoot 65 65

(Des J.W. Litho Walsall)

1976 (22 Nov). *Telephone Centenary. T* **65** *and similar horiz designs.* W w **14** (*sideways*). *P* 14.
263 4 c. multicoloured 10 8
264 5 c. multicoloured 12 10
265 10 c. multicoloured 20 20
266 15 c. multicoloured 35 35
267 20 c. multicoloured 40 45
Nos. 264/7 are as T **65**, but show different telephones.

66 Queen Elizabeth II and King Sobhuza II

(Des Walsall. Litho Questa)

1977 (7 Feb). *Silver Jubilee. T* **66** *and similar horiz designs. Multicoloured.* W w **14** (*sideways*). *P* 13½.
268 20 c. Type **66** 35 35
269 25 c. Coronation Coach at Admiralty Arch .. 35 40
270 50 c. Queen in coach 50 70

67 Matsapa College

(Des J. Cooter. Litho Questa)

1977 (2 May). *50th Anniv of Police Training. T* **67** *and similar multicoloured designs.* W w 14 (*upright on* 20 c., *sideways on others*). *P* 14.
271 5 c. Type **67** 10 10
272 10 c. Uniformed police and land rover .. 25 25
273 20 c. Police badge (*vert*) 45 45
274 25 c. Dog handling 55 55

68 Animals and Hunters

(Des BG Studio. Litho Questa)

1977 (8 Aug). *Rock Paintings. T* **68** *and similar horiz designs. Multicoloured.* W w **14** (*sideways*). *P* 14.
275 5 c. Type **68** 15 10
276 10 c. Four dancers in a procession 20 25
277 15 c. Man with cattle 35 35
278 20 c. Four dancers 40 40
MS279 103 × 124 mm. Nos. 275/8 .. .. 1·25 1·40

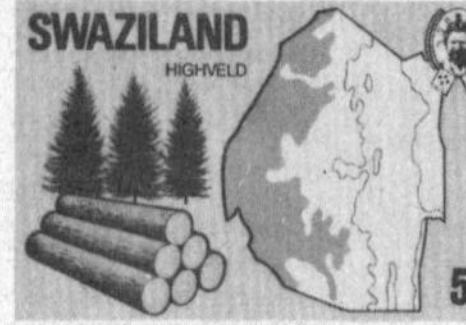

69 Timber, Highveld Region

70 Timber, Highveld Region

(Des L. Curtis. Litho D.L.R.)

1977 (17 Oct). *Maps of the Regions. T* **69** *and similar horiz designs. Multicoloured.* W w 14 (*sideways*). *P* 13½.
280 5 c. Type **69** 12 10
281 10 c. Pineapple, Middleveld 25 20
282 15 c. Orange and Lemon, Lowveld 45 35
283 20 c. Cattle, Lubombo region 55 45
MS284 87 × 103 mm. Four 25 c. designs as T **70**, together forming a composite map of Swaziland .. 2·25 2·50

71 Cabbage Tree

(Des Jennifer Toombs. Litho Walsall)

1978 (12 Jan). *Trees of Swaziland. T* **71** *and similar hor designs. Multicoloured* (*except* 5 c.). W w **14** (*sideways*). *P* 13½.
285 5 c. Type **71** (apple-green, ochre and black) .. 12
286 10 c. Marula 30
287 20 c. Kiaat 50
288 25 c. Lucky bean-tree 60

72 Rural Electrification at Lobamba

73 Elephant

(Des G. Drummond. Litho Questa)

1978 (6 Mar). *Hydro-electric Power. T* **72** *and similar hor designs.* W w **14** (*sideways*). *P* 13½.
289 5 c. black and buff 12 1
290 10 c. black and light green 30 2
291 20 c. black and pale blue 50 4
292 25 c. black and magenta 60 5
Designs:—10 c. Edwaleni Power Station; 20 c. Switchgea Magudza Power Station; 25 c. Turbine Hall, Edwaleni.

(Des C. Abbott. Litho Questa)

1978 (2 June). *25th Anniv of Coronation. T* **73** *and similar ve designs. P* 15.
293 25 c. chalky blue, black and sage-green .. 25 3
a. Sheetlet. Nos. 293/5 × 2 .. .. .. 1·50
294 25 c. multicoloured 25 2
295 25 c. chalky blue, black and sage-green .. 25 3
Designs:—No. 293, Queen's Lion; No. 294, Queen Elizabeth I No. 295, Type **73**.
Nos. 293/5 were printed together in small sheets of 6, containin two *se-tenant* strips of 3, with horizontal gutter margin between.

74 Clay Pots

(Des C. Abbott. Litho Questa)

1978 (24 July). *Handicrafts* (1*st series*). *T* **74** *and similar hori designs. Multicoloured.* W w **14** (*sideways*). *P* 13½ × 14.
296 5 c. Type **74** 10 8
297 10 c. Basketwork 20 15
298 20 c. Wooden utensils 40 30
299 30 c. Wooden pot 55 50
See also Nos. 310/13.

75 Defence Force

(Des BG Studio. Litho Questa)

1978 (6 Sept). *10th Anniv of Independence. T* **75** *and similar hori designs. Multicoloured.* W w **14** (*sideways*). *P* 14.
300 4 c. Type **75** 8 8
301 6 c. The King's Regiment 8 8
302 10 c. Tinkabi tractor (agricultural development) 15 15
303 15 c. Water-pipe laying (self-help scheme) .. 25 25
304 25 c. Sebenta adult literacy scheme 35 40
305 50 c. Fire emergency service 65 70
300/5 .. .. *Set of* 6 1·40 1·50

76 Archangel Gabriel appearing before Shepherds

77 Prospecting at Phophonyane

(Des V. Whiteley Studio. Litho Harrison)

1978 (12 Dec). *Christmas. T* **76** *and similar horiz designs. Multicoloured.* W w **14**. *P* 14½ × 14.
306 5 c. Type **76** 8 8
307 10 c. Three Wise Men paying homage to infant Jesus 15 10

308 15 c. Archangel Gabriel warning Joseph .. 20 20
309 25 c. Flight into Egypt 30 30

(Des C. Abbott. Litho Walsall)

1979 (10 Jan). *Handicrafts (2nd series). Horiz designs as T* **74**. *Multicoloured. W w* **14** *(sideways). P* 13½.
310 5 c. Sisal bowls .. 5 5
311 15 c. Pottery .. 25 25
312 20 c. Basket work .. 30 35
313 30 c. Hide shield .. 35 45

(Des L. Curtis. Litho Questa)

1979 (27 Mar). *Centenary of Discovery of Gold in Swaziland. T* **77** *and similar vert designs. W w* **14**. *P* 14.
314 5 c. gold and deep ultramarine .. 15 10
315 15 c. gold and deep brown .. 40 35
316 25 c. gold and deep green .. 65 50
317 50 c. gold and carmine-red .. 1·00 1·00
Designs:—15 c. Early 3-stamp battery mill; 25 c. Cyanide tanks at Piggs Peak; 50 c. Pouring off molten gold.

78 "Girls at the Piano"

(Des BG Studio. Litho Questa)

1979 (8 May). *International Year of the Child. Paintings by Renoir. T* **78** *and similar horiz designs. Multicoloured. W w* **14** *(sideways). P* 13½.
318 5 c. Type **78** .. 5 5
319 15 c. "Madame Charpentier and her Children" 25 25
320 25 c. "Girls picking Flowers" .. 40 35
321 50 c. "Girl with Watering Can" .. 70 75
MS322 123 × 135 mm. Nos. 318/21 .. 1·40 1·50

79 1933 1d. Carmine Stamp and Sir Rowland Hill

(Des J.W. Litho Walsall)

1979 (17 July). *Death Centenary of Sir Rowland Hill. T* **79** *and similar horiz designs showing stamps and portrait of Sir Rowland Hill. Multicoloured. W w* **14** *(sideways). P* 14½ × 14.
323 10 c. 1945 3d. Victory commemorative .. 20 20
324 20 c. Type **79** .. 40 40
325 25 c. 1968 25 c. Independence commemorative 40 50
MS326 115 × 90 mm. 50 c. 1956 6d. Great Kudu Antelope definitive .. 90 1·00

80 Obverse and Reverse of 5 Cents

(Des G. Hutchins. Litho Walsall)

1979 (6 Sept). *Coins. T* **80** *and similar horiz designs. W w* **14** *(sideways). P* 13½.
327 5 c. black and light brown .. 10 10
328 10 c. black and new blue .. 15 15
329 20 c. black and yellowish green .. 30 30
330 50 c. black and yellow-orange .. 65 65
331 1 e. black and cerise .. 1·40 1·40
Designs:—10 c. Obverse and reverse of 10 cents; 20 c. Obverse and reverse of 20 cents; 50 c. Reverse of 50 cents; 1 e. Reverse of 1 lilangeni.

81 Big Bend Post Office

(Des J. Cooter. Litho Questa)

1979 (22 Nov). *Post Office Anniversaries. T* **81** *and similar designs. W w* **14** *(sideways on 5, 20 and 50 c.). P* 13½.
332 5 c. multicoloured .. 8 8
333 15 c. multicoloured .. 25 25
334 20 c. black, sage-green and magenta .. 30 30
335 50 c. multicoloured .. 75 75
Designs and commemorations: *Horiz*—5 c. Type **81** (25th anniversary of Posts and Telecommunications Services); 20 c. 1949 75th anniversary of U.P.U. 1s. commemorative stamp (10th anniversary of U.P.U. membership); 50 c. 1974 centenary of U.P.U. 25 c. commemorative stamp (10th anniversary of U.P.U. membership). *Vert*—15 c. Microwave antenna. Mount Ntondozi (25th anniversary of Posts and Telecommunications Services).

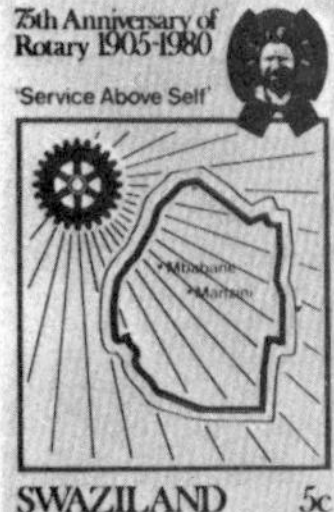

82 Map of Swaziland **83** *Brunsvigia radulosa*

(Des BG Studio. Litho Walsall)

1980 (23 Feb). *75th Anniv of Rotary International. T* **82** *and similar vert designs in gold and bright blue. W w* **14**. *P* 13½.
336 5 c. Type **82** .. 10 8
337 15 c. Vitreous cutter and optical illuminator .. 30 30
338 50 c. Scroll .. 85 85
339 1 e. Rotary Headquarters, Evanston, U.S.A. 1·75 1·75

(Des BG Studio. Litho Secura, Singapore)

1980 (28 Apr)–**83**. *Flowers. Multicoloured designs as T* **83**. A. *Without imprint date below design. P* 13½. B. *With imprint date. P* 12 (12.83).

		A		B	
340	1 c. Type **83**	5	5	5	5
341	2 c. *Aloe suprafoliata*	5	5	5	5
342	3 c. *Haemanthus magnificus*	5	5	†	
343	4 c. *Aloe marlothii*	5	5	5	5
344	5 c. *Dicoma zeyheri*	5	5	†	
345	6 c. *Aloe kniphofioides*	5	5	5	5
346	7 c. *Cyrtanthus bicolor*	5	5	†	
347	10 c. *Eucomis autumnalis*	10	12	8	10
348	15 c. *Leucospermum gerrardii*	12	15	†	
349	20 c. *Haemanthus multiflorus*	20	25	15	20
350	30 c. *Acridocarpus natalitius*	25	30	†	
351	50 c. *Adenium swazicum*	40	45	†	
352	1 e. *Protea simplex*	80	85	†	
353	2 e. *Calodendrum capense*	1·50	1·75	†	
354	5 e. *Gladiolus ecklonii*	4·00	4·25	†	
340A/54A	*Set of* 15	7·00	7·50	†	
340B/9B	*Set of* 6			40	45

Nos. 347/51 are horizontal, 42 × 25 mm, and Nos. 352/4 vertical, 28 × 38 mm.

84 Mail Runner

(Des A. Theobald. Litho Walsall)

1980 (6 May). *"London 1980" International Stamp Exhibition. T* **84** *and similar horiz designs. Multicoloured. W w* **14** *(sideways). P* 14.
355 10 c. Type **84** .. 12 15
356 20 c. Post Office mail truck .. 25 30
357 25 c. Mail sorting office .. 30 35
358 50 c. Ropeway conveying mail at Bulembu .. 70 75

85 Yellow Fish

(Des and litho Walsall)

1980 (25 Aug). *River Fishes. T* **85** *and similar horiz designs. Multicoloured. W w* **14** *(sideways). P* 13½.
359 5 c. Type **85** .. 5 5
360 10 c. Silver Barbel .. 12 12
361 15 c. Tiger Fish .. 20 20
362 30 c. Squeaker Fish .. 40 40
363 1 e. Bream .. 1·40 1·40

86 Oribi

(Des G. Drummond. Litho Harrison)

1980 (1 Oct). *Wildlife Conservation. T* **86** *and similar multicoloured designs. W w* **14** *(sideways on* 5 *and* 50 *c.). P* 14.
364 5 c. Type **86** .. 5 5
365 10 c. Nile Crocodile (*vert*) .. 12 12
366 50 c. Pangolin .. 80 80
367 1 e. Leopard (*vert*) .. 1·60 1·75

87 Public Bus Service

(Des G. Hutchins. Litho Format)

1981 (5 Jan). *Transport. T* **87** *and similar horiz designs. Multicoloured. W w* **14** *(sideways). P* 14½.
368 5 c. Type **87** .. 5 5
369 25 c. Royal Swazi National Airways .. 35 35
370 30 c. Swaziland United Transport .. 40 40
371 1 e. Swaziland Railway .. 2·00 2·00

88 Mantenga Falls **89** Prince Charles on Hike

(Des L. Curtis. Litho Format)

1981 (16 Mar). *Tourism. T* **88** *and similar horiz designs. Multicoloured. W w* **14** *(sideways). P* 14.
372 5 c. Type **88** .. 5 5
373 15 c. Mananga Yacht Club .. 15 20
374 30 c. White Rhinoceros in Mlilwane Game Sanctuary .. 40 40
375 1 e. Roulette wheel, playing cards and dice ("casinos") .. 1·40 1·60

(Des J.W. Litho Walsall)

1981 (21 July). *Royal Wedding. T* **89** *and similar vert designs. Multicoloured. W w* **14**. *P* 14.
376 10 c. Wedding bouquet from Swaziland .. 25 20
377 25 c. Type **89** .. 40 30
378 1 e. Prince Charles and Lady Diana Spencer 1·10 1·25

90 Installation of King Sobhuza II, 22 December 1921 **91** "Physical Recreation"

(Des J.W. Litho Harrison)

1981 (24 Aug). *Diamond Jubilee of King Sobhuza II. T* **90** *and similar horiz designs. Multicoloured. W w* **14** *(sideways). P* 14½.
379 5 c. Type **90** .. 5 5
380 10 c. Royal visit, 1947 .. 12 12
381 15 c. King Sobhuza II and Coronation of Queen Elizabeth II, 1953 .. 20 20
382 25 c. King Sobhuza taking Royal Salute, Independence, 1968 .. 30 30
383 30 c. King Sobhuza in youth .. 35 35
384 1 e. King Sobhuza and Parliament Buildings 1·25 1·25
379/84 .. *Set of* 6 2·00 2·00

(Des BG Studio. Litho Questa)

1981 (5 Nov). *25th Anniv of Duke of Edinburgh Award Scheme. T* **91** *and similar vert designs. Multicoloured. W w* **14**. *P* 14.
385 5 c. Type **91** .. 5 5
386 20 c. "Expeditions" .. 30 30
387 50 c. "Skills" .. 80 80
388 1 e. Duke of Edinburgh in ceremonial dress 1·60 1·60

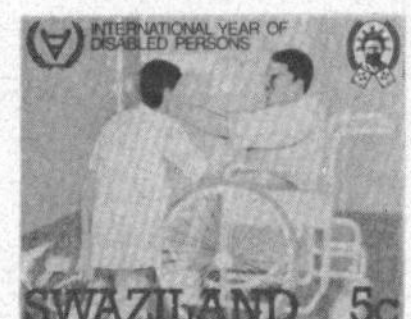

92 Disabled Person in Wheelchair

(Des and litho Walsall)

1981 (16 Dec). *International Year for the Disabled. T* **92** *and similar multicoloured designs.* W w **14** (*sideways on* 5 c. *and* 1 e.). *P* 14 × 14½ (5 c., 1 e.) *or* 14½ × 14 (*others*).

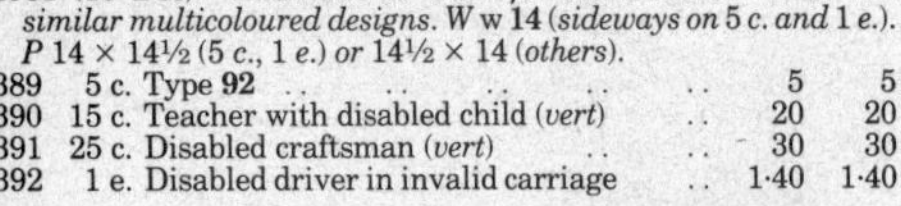

No.	Description	Unused	Used
389	5 c. Type **92**	5	5
390	15 c. Teacher with disabled child (*vert*)	20	20
391	25 c. Disabled craftsman (*vert*)	30	30
392	1 e. Disabled driver in invalid carriage	1·40	1·40

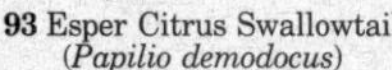

93 Esper Citrus Swallowtail (*Papilio demodocus*)

94 Man holding a Flower, after discarding Cigarettes

(Des I. Loe. Litho Rosenbaum Bros, Vienna)

1982 (6 Jan). *Butterflies* (*1st series*). *T* **93** *and similar horiz designs. Multicoloured.* W w **14** (*sideways*). *P* 14.

No.	Description	Unused	Used
393	5 c. Type **93**	10	5
394	10 c. Godart Green-veined Charaxes (*Charaxes candiope*)	20	10
395	50 c. Linnaeus Narrow Green or Blue-banded Swallowtail (*Papilio nireus*)	90	75
396	1 e. Bois Duval Angled Grass Yellow (*Eurema desjardinsii*)	1·75	1·75

(Des PAD Studio. Litho Format)

1982 (27 Apr). *Pan-African Conference on Smoking and Health. T* **94** *and similar vert design. Multicoloured.* W w **14**. *P* 14.

No.	Description	Unused	Used
397	5 c. Type **94**	8	8
398	10 c. Smoker and non-smoker climbing stairs	15	15

95 Male Fishing Owl

96 Swaziland Coat of Arms

(Des G. Drummond. Litho J.W.)

1982 (16 June). *Wildlife Conservation* (*1st series*). *Pel's Fishing Owl. T* **95** *and similar vert designs. Multicoloured.* W w **14**. *P* 13½ × 13.

No.	Description	Unused	Used
399	35 c. Type **95**	45	50
	a. Horiz strip of 5. Nos. 399/403	2·00	
400	35 c. Female Fishing Owl at nest	45	50
401	35 c. Pair of Fishing Owls	45	50
402	35 c. Fishing Owl, nest and egg	45	50
403	35 c. Adult Fishing Owl with youngster	45	50

Nos. 399/403 were printed together, *se-tenant*, in horizontal and vertical strips of 5 throughout the sheet.

See also Nos. 425/9 and Nos. 448/52.

(Des C. Abbott. Litho W. S. Cowells Ltd)

1982 (1 July). *21st Birthday of Princess of Wales. T* **96** *and similar vert designs. Multicoloured.* W w **14**. *P* 14½.

No.	Description	Unused	Used
404	5 c. Type **96**	5	5
405	20 c. Princess leaving Eastleigh Airport, Southampton, August 1981	25	25
406	50 c. Bride at Buckingham Palace	55	60
407	1 e. Formal portrait	1·25	1·40

97 Irrigation

(Des G. Hutchins. Litho Walsall)

1982 (1 Sept). *Sugar Industry. T* **97** *and similar horiz designs. Multicoloured.* W w **14** (*sideways*). *P* 14 × 14½.

No.	Description	Unused	Used
408	5 c. Type **97**	5	5
409	20 c. Harvesting	25	25
410	30 c. Mhlume mills	35	35
411	1 e. Sugar transportation by train	1·25	1·40

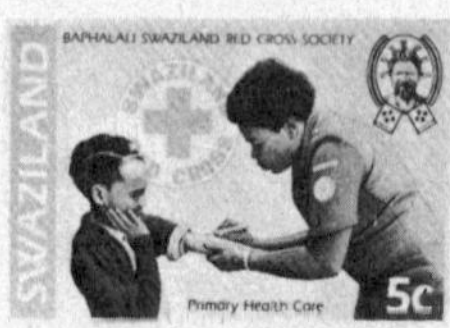

98 Nurse with Child

(Des L. Curtis. Litho Questa)

1982 (9 Nov). *Swaziland Red Cross Society* (*Baphaladi*). *T* **98** *and similar horiz designs. Multicoloured.* W w **14** (*sideways*). *P* 14.

No.	Description	Unused	Used
412	5 c. Type **98**	8	8
413	20 c. Juniors carrying stretcher	25	25
414	50 c. Disaster relief	55	60
415	1 e. Henri Dunant (founder of Red Cross)	1·25	1·40

99 Taking the Oath

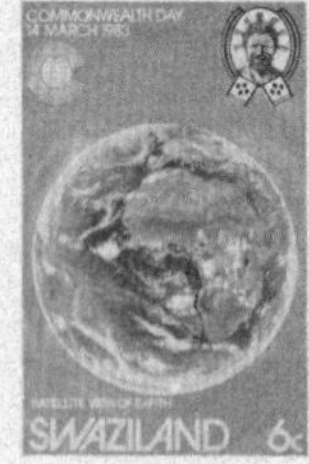

100 Satellite View of Earth

(Des B. Melton. Litho Format)

1982 (6 Dec). *75th Anniv of Boy Scout Movement. T* **99** *and similar horiz designs. Multicoloured.* W w **14** (*sideways*). *P* 14 × 13½.

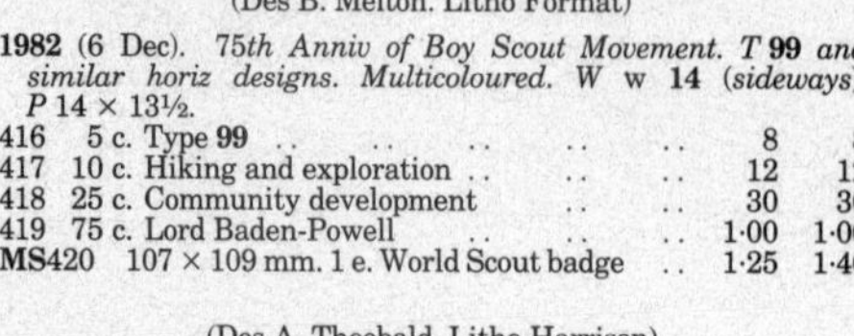

No.	Description	Unused	Used
416	5 c. Type **99**	8	8
417	10 c. Hiking and exploration	12	12
418	25 c. Community development	30	30
419	75 c. Lord Baden-Powell	1·00	1·00
MS420	107 × 109 mm. 1 e. World Scout badge	1·25	1·40

(Des A. Theobald. Litho Harrison)

1983 (14 Mar). *Commonwealth Day. T* **100** *and similar multicoloured designs.* W w **14** (*sideways on* 50 c., 1 e.). *P* 14.

No.	Description	Unused	Used
421	6 c. Type **100**	5	8
422	10 c. King Sobhuza II	12	15
423	50 c. Swazi woman and beehive huts (*horiz*)	60	65
424	1 e. Spraying sugar crops (*horiz*)	1·25	1·40

(Des G. Drummond. Litho J.W.)

1983 (16 May). *Wildlife Conservation* (*2nd series*). *Lammergeier. Vert designs as T* **95**. *Multicoloured.* W w **14**. *P* 13½ × 13.

No.	Description	Unused	Used
425	35 c. Adult male	45	50
	a. Horiz strip of 5. Nos. 425/9	2·00	
426	35 c. Pair	45	50
427	35 c. Nest and egg	45	50
428	35 c. Female at nest	45	50
429	35 c. Adult bird with fledgling	45	50

Nos. 425/9 were printed together, *se-tenant*, in horizontal strips of 5 throughout the sheet.

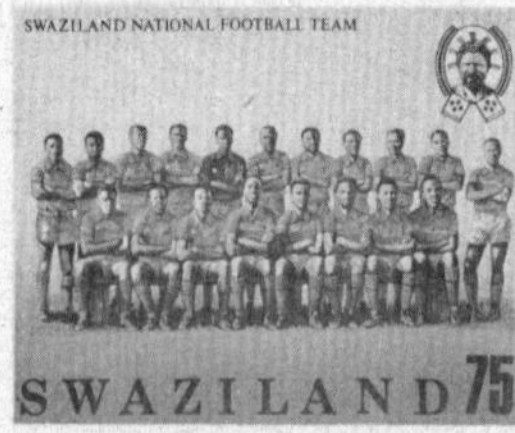

101 Swaziland National Football Team

102 Montgolfier Balloon

(Des G. Vasarhelyi. Litho Format)

1983 (20 Aug). *Tour of Swaziland by English Football Clubs. Three sheets,* 101 × 72 *mm, each containing one* 75 c. *stamp as T* **101**. *Multicoloured.* W w **14** (*sideways*). *P* 13½.

MS430 75 c. Type **101**; 75 c. Tottenham Hotspur; 75 c. Manchester United . . *Set of 3 sheets* 2·75 3·00

(Des. D. Hartley-Marjoram. Litho Format)

1983 (22 Aug). *Bicentenary of Manned Flight. T* **102** *and similar multicoloured designs.* W w **14** (*sideways on* 10 c. *to* 50 c.). *P* 14.

No.	Description	Unused	Used
431	5 c. Type **102**	5	8
432	10 c. Wright brothers' *Flyer* (*horiz*)	12	15
433	25 c. Fokker "Fellowship" (*horiz*)	30	35
434	50 c. Bell "X-1" (*horiz*)	60	65
MS435	73 × 73 mm. 1 e. Space shuttle *Columbia*	1·25	1·40

103 Dr. Albert Schweitzer (Peace Prize, 1952)

(Des G. Vasarhelyi. Litho Harrison)

1983 (21 Oct). *150th Birth Anniv of Alfred Nobel. T* **103** *and similar horiz designs. Multicoloured.* W w **14** (*sideways*). *P* 14.

No.	Description	Unused	Used
436	6 c. Type **103**	8	8
437	10 c. Dag Hammarskjöld (Peace Prize, 1961)	12	15
438	50 c. Albert Einstein (Physics Prize, 1921)	65	70
439	1 e. Alfred Nobel	1·40	1·50

NEW INFORMATION

The editor is always interested to correspond with people who have new information that will improve or correct the Catalogue.

104 Maize

(Des Jennifer Toombs. Litho Harrison)

1983 (29 Nov). *World Food Day. T* **104** *and similar horiz designs. Multicoloured.* W w **14** (*sideways*). *P* 14.

No.	Description	Unused	Used
440	6 c. Type **104**	5	5
441	10 c. Rice	12	1
442	50 c. Cattle herding	60	6
443	1 e. Ploughing	1·40	1·5

105 Women's College

106 Male on Ledge

(Des C. Abbott. Litho Format)

1984 (12 Mar). *Education. T* **105** *and similar horiz designs. Multicoloured.* W w **14** (*sideways*). *P* 14.

No.	Description	Unused	Used
444	5 c. Type **105**	5	5
445	15 c. Technical Training School	12	15
446	50 c. University	45	50
447	1 e. Primary school	40	95

(Des G. Drummond. Litho J.W.)

1984 (18 May). *Wildlife Conservation.* (*3rd series*) *Bald Ibis. T* **106** *and similar vert designs. Multicoloured.* W w **14**. *P* 13½ × 13.

No.	Description	Unused	Used
448	35 c. Type **106**	30	35
	a. Horiz strip of 5. Nos. 448/52	1·40	
449	35 c. Male and female	30	35
450	35 c. Bird and egg	30	35
451	35 c. Female on nest of eggs	30	35
452	35 c. Adult and fledgling	30	35

Nos. 448/52 were printed together, *se-tenant*, in horizontal strips of 5 throughout the sheet.

107 Mule-drawn Passenger Coach

(Des A. Theobald. Litho Walsall)

1984 (15 June). *Universal Postal Union Congress, Hamburg. T* **107** *and similar horiz designs. Multicoloured.* W w **14** (*sideways*). *P* 14½.

No.	Description	Unused	Used
453	7 c. Type **107**	8	10
454	15 c. Ox-drawn post wagon	12	15
455	50 c. Mule-drawn mail coach	45	50
456	1 e. Bristol to London mail coach	90	95

108 Running

(Des Harrison. Litho Walsall)

1984 (27 July). *Olympic Games, Los Angeles. T* **108** *and similar horiz designs. Multicoloured.* W w **14** (*sideways*). *P* 14.

No.	Description	Unused	Used
457	7 c. Type **108**	8	10
458	10 c. Swimming	10	12
459	50 c. Shooting	45	50
460	1 e. Boxing	90	95
MS461	100 × 70 mm. Nos. 457/60	1·50	1·60

109 Suillus bovinus

(Des J. Spencer. Litho Format)

1984 (19 Sept). *Fungi.* **T 109** *and similar multicoloured designs.* W w **14** (*sideways on* 10 c., 1 e.). *P* 14.

No.	Description	Unused	Used
462	10 c. Type **109** ..	10	12
463	15 c. *Langermannia gigantea* (*vert*)	12	15
464	50 c. *Coriolus versicolor* (*vert*) ..	45	50
465	1 e. *Boletus edulis*	90	95

110 King Sobhuza opening Railway, 1964

(Des W. Fenton. Litho Walsall)

1984 (5 Nov). *20th Anniv of Swaziland Railways.* **T 110** *and similar horiz designs. Multicoloured.* W w **14** (*sideways*). *P* 14.

No.	Description	Unused	Used
466	10 c. Type **110** ..	10	12
467	25 c. Type "15A" locomotive at Siweni Yard ..	25	30
468	30 c. Container loading, Matsapha Station ..	25	30
469	1 e. Locomotive No. 268 leaving Alto Tunnel	90	95
MS470	144 × 74 mm. Nos. 466/9 ..	1·50	1·60

POSTAGE DUE STAMPS

D 1

Postage Due
2d

(D 2)

D 3

(Typo D.L.R.)

1933 (2 Jan)–**57**. *Wmk Mult Script CA. P* 14.

No.	Type	Description	Unused	Used
D1	D 1	1 d. carmine, **O** ..	30	1·75
		a. Deep carmine, **C** (24.10.51) ..	20	1·50
		ac. Error. St Edward's Crown, W **9*b***, **C**	45·00	
D2		2d. pale violet, **O**	1·75	6·00
		a. Chalky paper (22.2.57)	1·75	6·00
D1/2 Perf "Specimen"		*Set of* 2	40·00	

1961 (8 Feb). *No.* 55 *surch with Type* **D 2**.

No.	Type	Description	Unused	Used
D3	7	2d. on 2d. ..	9·00	10·00

Another 2d. on 2d. Postage Due, with small surcharge as Type D **5**, was produced *after the currency change*, to meet the philatelic demand (*Price* 40*p unused*).

(Typo D.L.R.)

1961 (14 Feb). *Chalk-surfaced paper. Wmk Mult Script CA. P* 14.

No.	Type	Description	Unused	Used
D4	D 3	1 c. carmine	15	45
D5		2 c. violet	25	55
D6		5 c. green	60	1·25

Postage Due
1c

(D 4)

Postage Due
1c

(D 5)

1961. *No.* 55 *surcharged.* A. *As Type* **D 4**. (14 Feb).

No.	Type	Description	Unused	Used
D 7	7	1 c. on 2d.	2·25	3·00
D 8		2 c. on 2d.	2·25	3·00
D 9		5 c. on 2d.	2·25	3·00

B. *As Type* **D 5**. (Date?)

No.	Type	Description	Unused	Used
D10	7	1 c. on 2d.	1·90	2·75
D11		2 c. on 2d.	80	1·40
D12		5 c. on 2d.	2·50	3·00

D 6

(Des and litho B.W.)

1971 (1 Feb). *W w* **12**. *P* 11½.

No.	Type	Description	Unused	Used
D13	D 6	1 c. bright rose-red	20	40
D14		2 c. purple	30	55
D15		5 c. dull green	60	1·25

1977 (17 Jan). *W w* **14** (*sideways*). *P* 11½.

No.	Type	Description	Unused	Used
D16	D 6	1 c. rose-red	40	75
D17		2 c. purple	60	95
D18		5 c. dull green	1·00	1·75

(Litho Harrison)

1978 (20 Apr). *W w* **14**. *P* 14½ × 14.

No.	Type	Description	Unused	Used
D19	D 6	1 c. carmine	5	5
D20		2 c. purple	5	5
D21		5 c. blue-green	5	8

Tanzania

(*formerly* Tanganyika)

The stamps of GERMANY were used in the colony between October 1890 and July 1893 when issues for GERMAN EAST AFRICA were provided.

PRICES FOR STAMPS ON COVER TO 1945

The Mafia Island provisionals (No. M1/52) are very rare used on cover.

Nos. N1/5	*from* × 2
Nos. 45/59	*from* × 3
Nos. 60/2	—
Nos. 63/73	*from* × 3
Nos. 74/86	*from* × 8
Nos. 87/8	—
Nos. 89/92	*from* × 5
Nos. 93/106	*from* × 3
No. 107	—

MAFIA ISLAND

BRITISH OCCUPATION

Mafia Island was captured by the British from the Germans in December 1914. Letters were first sent out unstamped, then with stamps handstamped with Type M 1. Later the military were supplied with handstamps by the post office in Zanzibar. These were used to produce Nos. M11/52.

G.R.
MAFIA

(M 1)

(M 3)

1915 (Jan). *German East Africa Yacht types, handstamped with Type* M **1**. *Wmk Lozenges, or no wmk* (1 *r.,* 2 *r.*). A. *In black.* B. *In violet.*

No.	Description	A	B
M 1	2½ h. brown	£325	£275
M 2	4 h. green ..	£325	£275
M 3	7½ h. carmine	£325	£250
	a. Pair, one without handstamp	†	£950
M 4	15 h. ultramarine ..	£450	£275
	a. Pair, one without handstamp	†	£950
M 5	20 h. black and red/*yellow* ..	£450	£275
M 6	30 h. black and carmine	£500	£275
	a. Pair, one without handstamp	†	£950
M 7	45 h. black and mauve	£550	£500
M 8	1 r. carmine	£2500	£2250
M 9	2 r. green ..	£3000	£2750
M10	3 r. blue-black and red	£3750	£2750

Prices are for unused examples.

A few contemporary Zanzibar stamps (1, 3, 6 and 15 c.) are known with the above handstamp.

1915 (July). *German East Africa Yacht types with handstamped four-line surcharge* "G.R.—POST—6 CENTS—MAFIA" *in black, green or violet. Wmk Lozenges or no wmk* (1 *r.,* 2 *r.*).

No.	Description	Unused	Used
M11	6 c. on 2½ h. brown ..	£400	£500
M12	6 c. on 4 h. green	£400	£500
M13	6 c. on 7½ h. carmine	£400	£500
M14	6 c. on 15 h. ultramarine	£400	£500
M15	6 c. on 20 h. black and red/*yellow*	£400	£500
M16	6 c. on 30 h. black and carmine	£500	£550
M17	6 c. on 45 h. black and mauve	£500	£600
M18	6 c. on 1 r. carmine		
	a. Surch double	£2250	
M19	6 c. on 2 r. green		
M20	6 c. on 3 r. blue-black and red		

The 5, 20 and 40 pesa values of the 1900 Yacht issue are also known with the above surcharge as are the contemporary 1 c. and 6 c. Zanzibar stamps.

1915 (Sept). (*a*) *German East African fiscal stamps.* "Statistik des Waaren-Verkehrs" (*Trade Statistical Charge*) *overprinted in bluish green,* "O.H.B.M.S. Mafia" *in a circle, as Type* M **3**.

No.	Description	Unused	Used
M21	24 pesa, vermilion/*buff*	£160	£190
M22	12½ heller, drab	£160	£190
M23	25 heller, dull green..	£160	£190
M24	50 heller, slate	£160	£190
M25	1 rupee, lilac	£160	£190

(*b*) *German East African* "Ubersetzungs- Gebühren" (*Translation Fee*) *stamp, overprinted as before*

No.	Description	Unused	Used
M26	25 heller, grey	£300	£325

G. R
POST
MAFIA

(M 4)

G. R.
Post
MAFIA.

(M 5)

(*c*) *Stamps as above, but with further opt as Type* M **4**, *in green*

No.	Description	Unused	Used
M27	24 pesa, vermilion/*buff*	£160	£180
M28	12½ heller, drab	£160	£180
M29	25 heller, dull green	£160	£180
M30	50 heller, slate	£160	£180
M31	1 rupee, lilac	£160	£180
M32	25 heller, grey (No. M26) ..	£170	

1915 (Sept). *Stamps of Indian Expeditionary Forces* (*India optd* "I.E.F.") *with a further opt Type* M **4** *handstruck in green, greenish black or dull blue.*

No.	Type	Description	Unused	Used
M33	55	3 p. grey	9·50	11·00
		a. Pair, one stamp without opt	—	£140
M34	56	½ a. green	12·00	13·00
M35	57	1 a. carmine	15·00	16·00
M36	59	2 a. mauve	20·00	25·00
M37	61	2½ a. ultramarine	22·00	30·00
M38	62	3 a. orange-brown	25·00	25·00
M39	63	4 a. olive	35·00	40·00
M40	65	8 a. purple	55·00	65·00
M41	66	12 a. dull claret	£110	£150
M42	67	1 r. brown and green ..	£130	£170
M33/M42		*Set of* 10	£400	£500

All values exist with the overprint inverted, and several are known with overprint double or sideways.

1916 (Oct). *Stamps of Indian Expeditionary Forces* (*India optd* "I.E.F.") *with further opt Type* M **5** *handstruck in green, greenish black or dull blue.*

No.	Type	Description	Unused	Used
M43	55	3 p. grey	40·00	40·00
M44	56	½ a. green	40·00	40·00
M45	57	1 a. carmine ..	42·00	42·00
M46	59	2 a. mauve	42·00	42·00
M47	61	2½ a. ultramarine	45·00	45·00
M48	62	3 a. orange-brown	48·00	48·00
M49	63	4 a. olive	50·00	50·00
M50	65	8 a. purple	55·00	55·00
M51	66	12 a. dull claret	65·00	65·00
M52	67	1 r. brown and green ..	70·00	70·00

Stamps with handstamp inverted are known.

NYASA-RHODESIAN FORCE

This issue was sanctioned for use by the Nyasa-Rhodesian Force in conquered territory in German East Africa.

N. F.

(N 1)

1916. **T 15** *of Nyasaland optd with Type* N **1** *by Govt Printer, Zomba.*

No.	Type	Description	Unused	Used
N1	15	½d. green	1·10	4·00
N2		1d. scarlet	90	2·50
N3		3d. purple/*yellow*	5·00	14·00
		a. Opt double ..	£6500	£6000
N4		4d. black and red/*yellow*	19·00	35·00
N5		1s. black/*green*	18·00	32·00
N1/5 Optd "Specimen"		*Set of* 5	£375	

Of No. N3a only six copies were printed, these being the bottom row on one pane issued at M'bamba Bay F.P.O., German East Africa.

This overprint was applied in a setting of 60 (10 rows of 6) and the following minor varieties occur on all values: small stop after "N" (No. 1); broken "F" (No. 21); very small stop after "F" (No. 35); no serifs at top left and bottom of "N" (No. 55).

TANGANYIKA

BRITISH OCCUPATION OF GERMAN EAST AFRICA

G.E.A. (1) **G. E. A.** (2) **G.E.A.** (3)

1917–21. *Stamps of Kenya, Uganda and Tanganyika optd with* **T 1** *and* **2**. *Wmk Mult Crown CA. Ordinary paper* (1 *c. to* 15 *c.*) *or chalk-surfaced paper* (*others*).

No.	Type	Description	Unused	Used
45	3	1 c. black (R.) ..	20	55
46		1 c. black (Verm)	8·50	11·00
47		3 c. green	20	30
48		6 c. scarlet	20	30
49		10 c. orange	20	30
50		12 c. slate-grey ..	30	1·25
51		15 c. bright blue ..	30	1·10
52		25 c. black and red/*yellow*	60	1·50
		a. On pale-yellow (1921) (Optd S. £35)	95	2·75
53		50 c. black and lilac	80	2·75
54		75 c. black/*blue-green, olive-back* (R.)	1·10	3·00
		a. On emerald back (Optd S. £42)	2·25	5·50
55	4	1 r. black/*green* (R.)	1·75	5·50
		a. On emerald back	2·75	6·50
56		2 r. red and black/*blue* ..	4·75	10·00
57		3 r. violet and green	7·50	13·00
58		4 r. red and green/*yellow*	13·00	19·00
59		5 r. blue and dull purple	18·00	25·00
60		10 r. red and green/*green*	45·00	70·00
		a. On emerald back	50·00	80·00
61		20 r. black and purple/*red*	75·00	£110
62		50 r. carmine and green (S. £150)	£500	£500
45/61		*Set of* 16	£150	£250
45/61 Optd "Specimen"		*Set of* 16	£450	

Early printings of the rupee values exist with very large stop after the "E" in "G.E.A." (R. 5/3). There are round stops after "E" varieties, which in one position of later printings became a small stop.

1921. *As* 1917–22 *but wmk Mult Script CA.*

No.	Type	Description	Unused	Used
63	3	12 c. slate-grey, **O**	1·75	4·00
64		15 c. bright blue, **O**	30	1·40
65		50 c. black and dull purple, **C**	6·50	15·00
66	4	2 r. red and black/*blue*, **C**	32·00	55·00
67		3 r. violet and green, **C** ..	38·00	60·00
68		5 r. blue and dull purple, **C**	40·00	60·00
63/8		*Set of* 6	£110	£180
63/8 Optd "Specimen"		*Set of* 6	£225	

1922. **T 3** *of Kenya optd by the Government printer at Dar-es-Salaam with* **T 3**. *Wmk Mult Script CA.*

No.	Description	Unused	Used
72	1 c. black (R.) ..	20	1·50
73	10 c. orange-yellow	30	2·75

BRITISH MANDATED TERRITORY

4

5

(Recess B.W.)

1922. *Head in black. Wmk Mult Script CA. (a) P* 15 × 14.

74	4	5 c. slate-purple	50	35
75		10 c. green	30	35
76		15 c. carmine-red	55	10
77		20 c. orange	45	10
78		25 c. black	3·50	5·50
79		30 c. blue	2·00	2·50
80		40 c. yellow-brown	2·25	3·00
81		50 c. slate-grey	2·25	2·75
82		75 c. yellow-bistre	5·00	7·50

(*b*) *P* 14. A. *Wmk sideways*. B. *Wmk upright*

			A		B	
83	5	1s. green	3·00	4·25	3·00	4·25
84		2s. purple	6·50	8·50	5·50	10·00
85		3s. black	7·50	16·00	†	
86		5s. scarlet	12·00	23·00	12·00	23·00
87		10s. deep blue	40·00	55·00	35·00	55·00
88		£1 yellow-orange	75·00	£100	65·00	90·00
74/88		.. .. *Set of* 15 (*incl* 85A)			£130	£200
74/88 Optd "Specimen"		*Set of* 15			£425	

In the £1 stamp the words of value are on a curved scroll running across the stamp above the words "POSTAGE AND REVENUE".

1925. *As* 1922. *Frame colours changed.*

89	4	5 c. green	50	90
90		10 c. orange-yellow	1·75	1·00
91		25 c. blue	5·50	7·50
92		30 c. purple	1·40	4·00
89/92 Optd "Specimen"		.. *Set of* 4	90·00	

6

7

(Typo D.L.R.)

1927–31. *Head in black. Wmk Mult Script CA. P* 14.

93	6	5 c. green	20	10
94		10 c. yellow	25	10
95		15 c. carmine-red	20	10
96		20 c. orange-buff	50	10
97		25 c. bright blue	65	75
98		30 c. dull purple	1·25	1·25
98*a*		30 c. bright blue (1931)	6·50	75
99		40 c. yellow-brown	1·25	2·25
100		50 c. grey	70	40
101		75 c. olive-green	4·25	7·50
102	7	1s. green, **O**	2·00	1·00
103		2s. deep purple, **O**	4·50	2·00
104		3s. black, **O**	8·00	14·00
105		5s. carmine-red, **C**	8·50	10·00
106		10s. deep blue, **C**	30·00	45·00
107		£1 brown-orange, **C**	85·00	£110
93/107		.. .. .. *Set of* 16	£140	£180
93/107 Optd/Perf "Specimen"		*Set of* 16	£250	

For issues between 1935 and 1961 see KENYA, UGANDA AND TANGANYIKA.

INDEPENDENT REPUBLIC

8 Teacher and Pupils

9 District Nurse and Child

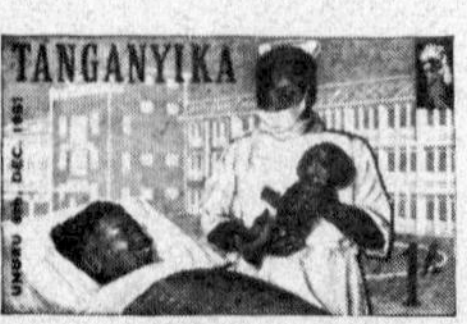
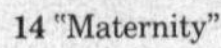

14 "Maternity"

15 Freedom Torch over Mt Kilimanjaro

(Des V. Whiteley. Photo Harrison)

1961 (9 Dec). *Independence. T* **8/9**, **14/15** *and similar designs. P* 14 × 15 (5 *c.*, 30 *c.*), 15 × 14 (10 *c.*, 15 *c.*, 20 *c.*, 50 *c.*) *or* 14½ (*others*).

108	5 c. sepia and light apple-green	5	5
109	10 c. deep bluish green	5	5
110	15 c. sepia and blue	5	5
	a. Blue omitted	£130	
111	20 c. orange-brown	5	5
112	30 c. black, emerald and yellow	8	5
	a. Inscr "UHURU 196"	£250	£100
113	50 c. black and yellow	10	5
114	1s. brown, blue and olive-yellow	20	5
115	1s. 30, red, yell, blk, brown & blue (*shades*) ..	45	5
116	2s. blue, yellow, green and brown	50	12
117	5s. deep bluish green and orange-red ..	1·25	50
118	10s. black, reddish purple and light blue ..	4·75	3·00
	a. Reddish purple (diamond) omitted ..	75·00	
119	20s. red, yellow, black, brown & green ..	8·50	11·00
108/19	.. .. *Set of* 12	15·00	14·00

Designs: *Vert* (*as T* **9**)—15 c. Coffee-picking; 20 c. Harvesting maize; 50 c. Serengeti lions. *Horiz* (*as T* **8**)—30 c. Tanganyikan flag. (*As T* **14**)—2s. Dar-es-Salaam waterfront; 5s. Land tillage; 10s. Diamond and mine. *Vert*—20s. Type **15**.

No. 112a. The missing "1" in "1961" occurs on emerald Plate 1C, R. 10/10. The "1" was later inserted but it is, however, very slightly shorter and the figure is more solid than normal.

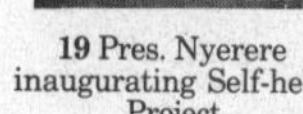

19 Pres. Nyerere inaugurating Self-help Project

20 Hoisting Flag on Mt Kilimanjaro

(Photo Harrison)

1962 (9 Dec). *Inauguration of Republic. Vert designs as T* **19/20**. *P* 14½.

120	30 c. emerald	5	5
121	50 c. yellow, black, green, red and blue ..	5	5
122	1s. 30, multicoloured	15	10
123	2s. 50, black, red and blue	30	45

Designs:—1s. 30, Presidential emblem; 2s. 50, Independence Monument.

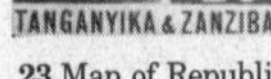

23 Map of Republic

24 Torch and Spear Emblem

(Des M. Goaman. Photo Harrison)

1964 (7 July). *United Republic of Tanganyika and Zanzibar Commemoration. P* 14 × 14½.

124	**23**	20 c. yellow-green and light blue ..	5	5
125	**24**	30 c. blue and sepia	5	5
126		1s. 30, orange-brown and ultramarine	15	10
127	**23**	2s. 50, purple and ultramarine ..	30	45

Despite the inscription on the stamps the above issue was only on sale in Tanganyika and had no validity in Zanzibar.

TANZANIA

The United Republic of Tanganyika and Zanzibar, formed 26 April 1964, was renamed the United Republic of Tanzania on 29 October 1964.

Issues to No. 176, except Nos. Z142/5, were also valid in Kenya and Uganda.

25 Hale Hydro-Electric Scheme

26 Tanzanian Flag

27 National Servicemen

33 Dar-es-Salaam Harbour

38 Arms of Tanzania

(Des V. Whiteley. Photo Harrison)

1965 (9 Dec). *T* **25/7**, **33**, **38** *and similar designs. P* 14 × 14½ (5 … 10 *c.*, 20 *c.*, 50 *c.*, 65 *c.*), 14½ × 14 (15 *c.*, 30 *c.*, 40 *c.*), *or* … (*others*).

128	5 c. ultramarine and yellow-orange ..	5	
129	10 c. black, greenish yellow, green & blue ..	5	
130	15 c. multicoloured	5	
131	20 c. sepia, grey-green and greenish blue ..	8	
132	30 c. black and red-brown	10	
133	40 c. multicoloured	25	2…
134	50 c. multicoloured	25	
135	65 c. green, red-brown and blue	65	1·…
136	1s. multicoloured	40	
137	1s. 30, multicoloured	1·50	2…
138	2s. 50, blue and orange-brown	2·75	9…
139	5s. lake-brown, yellow-green and blue ..	2·50	8…
140	10s. olive-yellow, olive-green and blue ..	3·25	2·…
141	20s. multicoloured	8·00	11·…
128/41	.. .. *Set of* 14	18·00	15·…

Designs: *Horiz* (*as T* **25**)—20 c. Road-building; 50 c. Zebra… Manyara National Park; 65 c. Mt Kilimanjaro, *Vert* (… *T* **27**)—30 c. Drum, spear, shield and stool; 40 c. Giraffes, Mikur… National Park. *Horiz* (*As T* **33**)—1s. 30, Skull of *Zinjanthropus* an… excavations, Olduvai Gorge; 2s. 50, Fishing; 5s. Sisal industry; 10… State House, Dar-es-Salaam.

Z 39 Pres. Nyerere and First Vice-Pres. Karume within Bowl of Flame

Z 40 Hands supporting Bowl of Flame

(Des J. Ahmed (Type **Z 39**), G. Vasarhelyi (Type **Z 40**). Photo Enschedé)

1966 (26 April). *2nd Anniv of United Republic. P* 14 × 13.

Z142	**Z 39**	30 c. multicoloured	5	
Z143	**Z 40**	50 c. multicoloured	5	
Z144		1s. 30, multicoloured	20	1…
Z145	**Z 39**	2s. 50, multicoloured	45	1·0…

Nos. Z142/5 were on sale in Zanzibar only.

39 Cardinal

40 Mud Skipper

41 Scorpion Fish

(Des Rena Fennessy. Photo Harrison)

1967 (9 Dec)–**73**. *Designs as T* **39/41**. *Chalk-surfaced paper P* 14 × 15 (5 *c. to* 70 *c.*) *or* 14½ (*others*).

142	5 c. magenta, yellow-olive and black ..	5	5
	a. Glazed, ordinary paper (22.1.71) ..	10	10
143	10 c. brown and bistre	5	5
	a. Glazed, ordinary paper (27.9.72) ..	10	10
144	15 c. grey, turquoise-blue and black	5	5
	a. Glazed, ordinary paper (22.1.71) ..	10	10
145	20 c. brown and turquoise-green	5	5
	a. Glazed, ordinary paper (16.7.73) ..	15	15
146	30 c. sage-green and black	8	5
	a. Glazed, ordinary paper (3.5.71)	25	12
147	40 c. yellow, chocolate and bright green ..	12	12
	a. Glazed, ordinary paper (10.2.71) ..	20	12
148	50 c. multicoloured	12	5
	a. Glazed, ordinary paper (10.2.71) ..	20	10
149	65 c. orange-yellow, bronze-green and black	2·75	3·00
150	70 c. multicoloured (15.9.69)	1·25	1·75
	a. Glazed, ordinary paper (22.1.71) ..	2·50	2·50
151	1s. orange-brown, slate-blue and maroon ..	30	5
	a. Glazed, ordinary paper (3.2.71)	30	5
152	1s. 30, multicoloured	1·50	5
153	1s. 50, multicoloured (15.9.69)	1·50	50
	a. Glazed, ordinary paper (27.9.72) ..	1·75	15
154	2s. 50, multicoloured	1·50	45
	a. Glazed, ordinary paper (27.9.72) ..	1·75	15
155	5s. greenish yellow, black & turquoise-grn	2·50	1·25
	a. Glazed, ordinary paper (3.2.71)	3·00	20
156	10s. multicoloured	4·00	1·60
	a. Glazed, ordinary paper (3.2.71) (*shades*)	4·00	30
157	20s. multicoloured	9·00	4·50
	a. Glazed, ordinary paper (3.2.71)	9·00	40
142/57	.. .. *Set of* 16	22·00	12·00
142a/57a	.. .. *Set of* 14	21·00	4·00

Designs: *Horiz as T* **39/40**—15 c. White Spotted Puffer; 20 c. Sea Horses; 30 c. Bat Fish; 40 c. Sweetlips; 50 c. Blue Club-nosed Wrasse; 65 c. Bennett's Butterfly; 70 c. Striped Grouper. *Horiz as T* **41**—1s. 30, Powder Blue Surgeon; 1s. 50, Fusilier; 2s 50, Red Snapper; 5s. Moorish Idol; 10s. Picasso Fish; 20s. Squirrel Fish.

On chalk-surfaced paper all values except the 30 c., exist with PVA gum as well as gum arabic, but the 70 c. and 1s. 50 exist with PVA gum only. Stamps on glazed, ordinary paper come only with PVA gum.

53 *Papilio hornimani*

54 *Euphaedra neophron*

80c
(55)

(Des Rena Fennessy. Photo Harrison)

1973 (10 Dec). *Various vert designs as T* **53/4**.

(*a*) *Size as T* **53**. *P* 14½ × 14
158 5 c. light yellow-olive, lt violet-blue & black 5 5
159 10 c. multicoloured 10 5
160 15 c. light violet-blue and black 10 5
161 20 c. reddish cinnamon, orange-yellow & blk 15 5
162 30 c. yellow, orange and black (*shades*) .. 15 5
163 40 c. multicoloured 20 5
164 50 c. multicoloured 20 5
165 60 c. lt grey-brown, lemon & reddish brown .. 40 5
166 70 c. turquoise-green, pale orange and black .. 25 5

(*b*) *Size as T* **54**. *P* 14
167 1s. multicoloured 25 15
168 1s. 50, multicoloured 55 25
169 2s. 50, multicoloured 70 35
170 5s. multicoloured 90 80
171 10s. multicoloured .. .. 2·00 2·00
172 20s. multicoloured .. .. 3·75 4·00
158/72 .. .. *Set of* 15 8·75 7·25

Butterflies:—10 c. *Colotis ione*; 15 c. *Amauris makuyuensis*; 20 c. *Libythea laius*; 30 c. *Danaus chrysippus*; 40 c. *Sallya rosa*; 50 c. *Axiocerses styx*; 60 c. *Eurema hecabe*; 70 c. *Acraea insignis*; 1s. *Euphaedra neophron*; 1s. 50, *Precis octavia*; 2s. 50, *Charaxes eupale*; 5s. *Charaxes pollux*; 10s. *Salamis parhassus*; 20s. *Papilio ophidicephalus*.

Nos. 159 and 164 exist in coils, constructed from normal sheets.

1975 (17 Nov). *Nos.* 165, 168/9 *and* 172 *surch as T* **55**.
173 80 c. on 60 c. *Eurema hecabe* 55 35
174 2s. on 1s. 50, *Precis octavia* .. .. .. 1·25 1·00
175 3s. on 2s. 50, *Charaxes eupale* .. .. 11·00 11·00
176 40s. on 20s. *Papilio ophidicephalus* .. .. 8·00 8·00

1976 (15 Apr). *Telecommunications Development. As Nos.* 56/60 *of Kenya but inscr* "TANZANIA".
177 50 c. Microwave Tower 15 5
178 1s. Cordless switchboard 25 5
179 2s. Telephones 40 35
180 3s. Message Switching Centre 50 50
MS181 120 × 120 mm. Nos. 177/80 .. .. 1·50 1·50

1976 (5 July). *Olympic Games, Montreal. As Nos* 61/5 *of Kenya but inscr* "TANZANIA".
182 50 c. Akii Bua, Ugandan hurdler 15 5
183 1s. Filbert Bayi, Tanzanian runner .. 30 5
184 2s. Steve Muchoki, Kenyan boxer 65 40
185 3s. Olympic flame and East African flags .. 85 60
MS186 129 × 154 mm. Nos. 182/5 .. .. 5·00 4·00

1976 (4 Oct). *Railway Transport. As Nos.* 66/70 *of Kenya but inscr* "TANZANIA".
187 50 c. Tanzania-Zambia Railway 25 5
188 1s. Nile Bridge, Uganda 40 5
189 2s. Nakuru Station, Kenya .. .. .. 1·10 50
190 3s. Class A locomotive, 1896 .. .. 1·40 75
MS191 154 × 103 mm. Nos. 187/90 .. .. 4·00 2·50

1977 (10 Jan). *Game Fish of East Africa. As Nos.* 71/5 *of Kenya but inscr* "TANZANIA".
192 50 c. Nile Perch 20 5
193 1s. Tilapia 35 5
194 3s. Sailfish .. .. 1·00 40
195 5s. Black Marlin .. .. 1·75 70
MS196 153 × 129 mm. Nos. 192/5 .. .. 3·00 1·50

1977 (15 Jan). *Second World Black and African Festival of Arts and Culture, Nigeria. As Nos* 76/80 *of Kenya but inscr* "TANZANIA".
197 50 c. Maasai Manyatta (village), Kenya .. 15 5
198 1s. "Heartbeat of Africa" (Ugandan dancers) 30 5
199 2s. Makonde sculpture 65 50
200 3s. "Early Man and Technology" (skinning animal) 85 75
MS201 132 × 190 mm. Nos. 197/200 .. .. 3·00 2·50

1977 (5 Apr). *25th Anniv of Safari Rally. As Nos* 81/5 *of Kenya but inscr* "TANZANIA".
202 50 c. Rally-car and villagers 15 5
203 1s. Pres. Kenyatta starting rally 25 10
204 2s. Car fording river 70 85
205 5s. Car and elephants .. .. .. 1·50 2·00
MS206 126 × 93 mm. Nos. 202/5 .. .. 3·50 3·25

1977 (30 June). *Centenary of Ugandan Church. As Nos.* 86/90 *of Kenya but inscr* "TANZANIA".
207 50 c. Canon Kivebulaya 15 5
208 1s. Modern Namirembe Cathedral 30 5
209 2s. The first Cathedral 90 50
210 5s. Early congregation, Kigezi .. .. 2·00 1·50
MS211 126 × 89 mm. Nos. 207/10 .. .. 3·00 2·50

1977 (26 Sept). *Endangered Species. As Nos.* 96/101 *of Kenya but inscr* "TANZANIA".
212 50 c. Pancake Tortoise 20 5
213 1s. Nile Crocodile 35 15
214 2s. Hunter's Hartebeest .. .. .. 1·25 55
215 3s. Red Colobus monkey .. .. .. 2·00 1·00
216 5s. Dugong .. .. 2·50 2·00
MS217 127 × 101 mm. Nos. 213/16 .. .. 6·50 4·00

56 Prince Philip and President Nyerere

(Des G. Vasarhelyi. Litho Questa)

1977 (23 Nov). *Silver Jubilee. T* **56** *and similar horiz designs. Multicoloured. P* 14 × 13½.
218 50 c. Type **56** 15 5
219 5s. Pres. Nyerere with Queen and Prince Philip 90 70
220 10s. Jubilee emblem and Commonwealth flags 1·40 1·50
221 20s. The Crowning .. .. 2·50 2·75
MS222 128 × 102 mm. Nos. 218/21 .. .. 4·50 4·50

57 Improvements in Rural Living Standards

(Des N. P. Ndembo. Litho B.W.)

1978 (5 Feb). *First Anniv of Chama Cha Mapinduzi (New Revolutionary Party). T* **57** *and similar horiz designs. P* 13½ × 14.
223 50 c. multicoloured 10 5
224 1s. multicoloured 20 5
225 3s. multicoloured 80 70
226 5s. black, light green and greenish yellow .. 1·10 1·00
MS227 142 × 106 mm. Nos. 223/6 .. .. 2·00 1·90

Designs:—1s. Flag raising ceremony, Zanzibar; 3s. Handing over of TANU headquarters, Dodoma; 5s. Chairman Julius Nyerere.

1978 (17 Apr). *World Cup Football Championship, Argentina. As Nos.* 122/6 *of Kenya but inscr* "TANZANIA".
228 50 c. Joe Kadenge and forwards 15 5
229 1s. Mohamed Chuma and cup presentation 30 5
230 2s. Omari Kidevu and goalmouth scene .. 75 55
231 3s. Polly Ouma and forwards 90 70
MS232 136 × 81 mm. Nos. 228/31 .. .. 2·00 1·75

25th ANNIVERSARY CORONATION
2nd JUNE 1953
(58)

25th ANNIVERSARY CORONATION
2nd JUNE 1953
(59)

1978 (2 June). *25th Anniv of Coronation. Nos.* 218/22. A. *Optd as T* **58**. *P* 14 × 13½. B. *Optd as T* **59**. *P* 12 × 11½.

		A		B	
233	50 c. Type **56**	8	5	8	5
234	5s. Pres. Nyerere with Queen and Prince Philip	80	80	80	80
235	10s. Jubilee emblem and Commonwealth flags	1·50	1·50	1·50	1·50
236	20s. The Crowning	2·25	2·25	2·25	2·25
MS237	128 × 102 mm. Nos. 233/6 ..	4·50	5·50	4·50	5·50

60 "Do not Drink and Drive"

61 Lake Manyara Hotel

(Des J.W. Litho B.W.)

1978 (1 July). *Road Safety. T* **60** *and similar vert designs. P* 13½ × 13.
238 50 c. multicoloured 15 5
239 1s. multicoloured 30 5
240 3s. orange-red, black and light brown .. 90 70
241 5s. multicoloured .. .. 1·40 1·10
MS242 92 × 129 mm. Nos. 238/41. P 14 .. .. 2·50 2·50

Designs:—1s. "Show courtesy to young, old and crippled"; 3s. "Observe the Highway Code"; 5s. "Do not drive a faulty vehicle".

(Des M. Raza. Litho B.W.)

1978 (11 Sept). *Game Lodges. T* **61** *and similar horiz designs. Multicoloured. P* 13½ × 13.
243 50 c. Type **61** 10 5
244 1s. Lobo Wildlife Lodge 20 10
245 3s. Ngorongoro Crater Lodge 45 45
246 5s. Ngorongoro Wildlife Lodge 75 75
247 10s. Mafia Island Lodge .. .. .. 1·75 1·90
248 20s. Mikumi Wildlife Lodge .. .. 3·25 3·50
243/8 .. .. *Set of* 6 6·00 6·00
MS249 118 × 112 mm. Nos. 243/8 .. .. 8·00 9·00

62 "Racial Suppression"

(Des local artist; adapted G. Hutchins. Litho Harrison)

1978 (24 Oct). *International Anti-Apartheid Year. T* **62** *and similar vert designs. P* 14½ × 14.
250 50 c. multicoloured 10 5
251 1s. black, yellowish green and yellow .. 20 5
252 2s. 50, multicoloured 55 55
253 5s. multicoloured .. .. 85 1·00
MS254 127 × 132 mm. Nos. 250/3 .. .. 2·00 2·00

Designs:—1s. "Racial division"; 2s. 50, "Racial harmony"; 5s. "Fall of suppression and rise of freedom".

63 Fokker "Friendship"

(Des J. Mzinga; adapted J.W. Litho Walsall)

1978 (28 Dec). *75th Anniv of Powered Flight. T* **63** *and similar horiz designs. Multicoloured. P* 13½.
255 50 c. Type **63** 10 5
256 1s. "Dragon" on Zanzibar Island, 1930's .. 20 5
257 2s. "Concorde" 45 50
258 5s. Wright brothers' *Flyer*, 1903 .. .. 85 1·00
MS259 133 × 97 mm. Nos. 255/8 .. .. 1·50 1·60

64 Corporation Emblem

(Des local artists; adapted BG Studio. Litho Harrison)

1979 (3 Feb). *1st Anniv of Tanzania Posts and Telecommunications Corporation. T* **64** *and similar horiz design. Multicoloured. P* 14½ × 14.
260 50 c. Type **64** 10 10
261 5s. Headquarters buildings 75 80
MS262 82 × 97 mm. Nos. 260/1 .. .. 1·25 1·25

65 Pres. Nyerere (patron of National I.Y.C. Committee) with Children

30c
(66)

(Des J. Mzinga. Litho B.W.)

1979 (25 June). *International Year of the Child. T* **65** *and similar horiz designs. Multicoloured. P* 14½.
263 50 c. Type **65** 8 5
264 1s. Day care centre 15 5
265 2s. "Immunisation" (child being vaccinated) 30 40
266 5s. National I.Y.C. Committee emblem .. 65 85
MS267 127 × 91 mm. Nos. 263/6 .. .. 1·50 1·50

1979 (Sept*). *Nos.* 159 *and* 166 *surch as T* **66** (*No.* 269 *has horiz bar through original value*).
268 10 c. + 30 c. multicoloured 10 10
269 50 c. on 70 c. turquoise-green, pale orge & bl. 10 10

The face value of No. 268 was 40 c.; the 30 c. surcharge being added to the original 10 c., which was not obliterated. This method was adopted because of difficulties during the actual surcharging. On No. 269 the 70 c. face value is obliterated by a bar.

* The earliest known postmark date for No. 268 is 15 September and for No. 269 12 September.

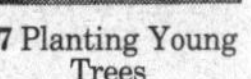

67 Planting Young Trees

68 Mwenge Satellite Earth Station

(Des J. Mzinga. Litho J.W.)

1979 (24 Sept). *Forest Preservation. T* **67** *and similar vert designs. Multicoloured. P* 14 × 14½.
270 50 c. Type **67** 10 5
271 1s. Replacing dead trees with saplings .. 20 5
272 2s. Rainfall cycle 40 40
273 5s. Forest fire warning 75 95

(Des and litho J.W.)

1979 (14 Dec). *Opening of Mwenge Satellite Earth Station. P* 13½.
274 **68** 10 c. multicoloured 5 5
275 40 c. multicoloured 8 8
276 50 c. multicoloured 10 10
277 1s. multicoloured 20 20

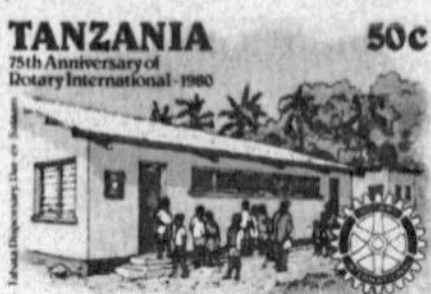

69 Tabata Dispensary, Dar-es-Salaam

(Litho J.W.)

1980 (10 Apr). *75th Anniv of Rotary International. T* **69** *and similar horiz designs. Multicoloured. P* 13.
278 50 c. Type **69** 8 5
279 1s. Ngomvu Village water project 15 5
280 5s. Flying Doctor service (plane donation) .. 70 80
281 20s. Torch and 75th Anniversary emblem .. 2·75 3·00
MS282 120 × 101 mm. Nos. 278/81. P 14 .. .. 3·50 3·75

70 Zanzibar 1896 2 r. Stamp and 1964 25 c. Definitive

(Des J.W. Litho Questa)

1980 (21 Apr). *Death Centenary of Sir Rowland Hill* (1979). *T* **70** *and similar multicoloured designs. P* 14.
283 40 c. Type **70** 10 5
284 50 c. Tanganyika 1962 Independence 50 c. commemorative and man attaching stamp to letter (*vert*) 12 5
285 10s. Tanganyika 1922 25 c. stamp and 1961 1s. 30, definitive .. .. 1·50 1·60
286 20s. Penny Black and Sir Rowland Hill (*vert*) 2·50 3·00
MS287 158 × 120 mm. Nos. 283/6 .. .. 4·00 4·25

'LONDON 1980'
PHILATELIC EXHIBITION

(71)

1980 (5 May). *"London 1980" International Stamp Exhibition. Nos.* 283/7 *optd with T* **71**.
288 40 c. Type **71** 10 10
289 50 c. Tanganyika 1962 Independence 50 c. commemorative and man attaching stamp to letter 12 12
290 10s. Tanganyika 1922 25 c. stamp and 1961 1s. 30, definitive .. .. 1·50 1·60
291 20s. Penny Black and Sir Rowland Hill .. 2·50 3·00
MS292 158 × 120 mm. Nos. 288/91 .. .. 3·00 3·25

District 920 - 55th Annual Conference, Arusha, Tanzania

(72)

1980 (23 June). *Annual Conference of District* 920, *Rotary International, Arusha. Nos.* 278/82 *optd as T* **72**.
293 50 c. Type **69** 12 10
294 1s. Ngomvu Village water project 15 10
295 5s. Flying Doctor service (plane donation) .. 65 70
296 20s. Torch and 75th Anniversary of Rotary International Emblem .. .. .. 2·25 2·50
MS297 120 × 101 mm. Nos. 293/6 .. .. 3·00 3·25

73 Conference, Tanzanian Posts and Telecommunications Corporation and U.P.U. Emblems

(Des and litho J.W.)

1980 (1 July). *P.A.P.U. (Pan-African Postal Union) Plenipotentiary Conference, Arusha. P* 13.
298 **73** 50 c. black and bright violet 10 5
299 1s. black and ultramarine 15 5
300 5s. black and orange-red 70 75
301 10s. black and blue-green .. .. 1·25 1·60

74 Gidamis Shahanga (marathon)

(Litho J.W.)

1980 (18 Aug). *Olympic Games, Moscow. T* **74** *and similar horiz designs. Multicoloured. P* 13.
302 50 c. Type **74** 10 5
a. Horiz strip of 4. Nos. 302/5 .. .. 3·50
303 1s. Nzael Kyomo (sprints) 15 5
304 10s. Zakayo Malekwa (javelin) .. .. 1·25 1·25
305 20s. William Lyimo (boxing) .. .. .. 2·25 2·25
MS306 172 × 117 mm. Nos. 302/305. P 14 .. 3·50 3·50

Nos. 302/305 were printed either in separate sheets or together, *se-tenant*, in horizontal strips of 4 throughout the sheet.

75 Spring Hare

76 Impala

(Des Rena Fennessy. Litho B.W.)

1980 (1 Oct). *Wildlife. Multicoloured designs. P* 14.

(*a*) *Horiz as T* **75**
307 10 c. Type **75** 5 5
308 20 c. Genet 5 5
309 40 c. Mongoose 5 5
310 50 c. Ratel 5 5
311 75 c. Rock Hyrax 8 5
312 80 c. Leopard 8 5

(*b*) *Horiz as T* **76**
313 1s. Type **76** 10 5
314 1s. 50, Giraffe 15 12
315 2s. Zebra 20 25
316 3s. Buffalo 30 35
317 5s. Lion 45 50
318 10s. Rhinoceros .. .. 95 1·00
319 20s. Elephant .. .. 1·90 2·00
320 40s. Cheetah .. .. 3·75 4·00
307/20 .. .. *Set of* 14 7·50 7·50

77 Ngorongoro Conservation Area Authority Emblem

ROYAL WEDDING
H.R.H. PRINCE CHARLES
29th JULY 1981

(78)

(Des D. Kyungu. Litho J.W.)

1981 (2 Feb). *60th Anniv of Ngorongoro and Serengeti National Parks. T* **77** *and similar horiz designs. P* 13.
321 50 c. multicoloured 5 5
322 1s. black, gold and deep blue-green .. 10 5
323 5s. multicoloured 55 60
324 20s. multicoloured .. .. 2·10 2·25

Designs:—1s. Tanzania National Parks emblem; 5s. Friends of the Serengeti emblem; 20s. Friends of Ngorongoro emblem.

1981 (29 July). *Royal Wedding. Nos.* 220/1 *optd with T* **78**.
325 10s. Jubilee emblem and Commonwealth flags 1·75 1·75
326 20s. Crowning .. .. 3·25 3·25
MS327 88 × 97 mm. Nos. 325/6 .. .. 10·00 10·00

79 Mail Runner

(Des D. Kyungu. Litho State Printing Works, Moscow)

1981 (21 Oct). *Commonwealth Postal Administrations Conference, Arusha. T* **79** *and similar horiz designs. Multicoloured. P* 12½ × 12.
328 50 c. Type **79** 10 5
329 1s. Letter sorting 15 12
330 5s. Letter Post symbols 60 70
331 10s. Flags of Commonwealth nations .. 1·10 1·25
MS332 130 × 100 mm. Nos. 328/31 .. .. 1·75 2·00

80 Morris Nyunyusa (blind drummer)

(Des and litho Harrison)

1981 (30 Nov). *International Year for Disabled Persons. T* **80** *and similar horiz designs. Multicoloured. P* 14.
333 50 c. Type **80** 10 5
334 1s. Mgulani Rehabilitation Centre, Dar-es-Salaam 15 12
335 5s. Aids for disabled persons 60 70
336 10s. Disabled children cleaning school compound .. .. 1·10 1·25

81 President Mwalimu Julius K. Nyerere

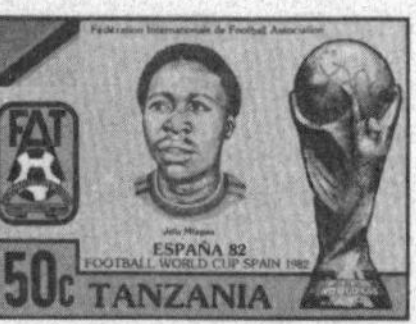

82 Ostrich

(Litho J.W.)

1982 (13 Jan). *20th Anniv of Independence. T* **81** *and similar horiz designs. Multicoloured. P* 13 × 13½.
337 50 c. Type **81** 10 5
338 1s. Electricity plant, Mtoni 15 12
339 3s. Sisal industry 45 50
340 10s. "Universal primary education" .. .. 1·10 1·25
MS341 120 × 85 mm. Nos. 337/40 .. .. 1·60 1·75

(Des and litho J.W.)

1982 (25 Jan). *Birds. T* **82** *and similar vert designs. Multicoloured. P* 13½ × 13.
342 50 c. Type **82** 15 5
343 1s. Secretary Bird 20 10
344 5s. Kori Bustard 75 80
345 10s. Saddle-bill Stork .. .. 1·40 1·60

83 Jella Mtaga

(Des P. Ndembo. Litho J.W.)

1982 (2 June). *World Cup Football Championship, Spain. T* **83** *and similar horiz designs. Multicoloured. P* 14.
346 50 c. Type **83** 10 5
347 1s. Football stadium 15 12
348 10s. Diego Maradona .. .. 1·25 1·40
349 20s. FIFA emblem .. .. 2·25 2·40
MS350 130 × 100 mm. Nos. 346/9 .. .. 3·25 3·50

84 "Jade" of Seronera with Cubs

(Des and litho Harrison)

1982 (15 July). *Animal Personalities. T* **84** *and similar horiz designs. Multicoloured. P* 14.
351 50 c. Type **84** 10 5
352 1s. Female Golden Jackal and cubs (incorrectly inscr "Wild dog") 15 12
353 5s. "Fifi" and two sons of "Gombe" (chimpanzees) 70 80
354 10s. "Bahati" of Lake Manyara with twins, "Rashidi" and "Ramadhani" (elephants) .. 1·40 1·50
MS355 120 × 89 mm. Nos. 351/4. P 14½ .. .. 2·10 2·25

85 Brick-laying

86 Ploughing Field

(Des P. Ndembo. Litho J.W.)

1982 (25 Aug). *75th Anniv of Boy Scout Movement. T* **85** *and similar horiz designs. Multicoloured. P* 14.
356 50 c. Type **85** 10 5
357 1s. Camping 15 12
358 10s. Tracing signs .. .. 1·25 1·40
359 20s. Lord Baden-Powell .. .. .. 2·25 2·50
MS360 130 × 100 mm. Nos. 356/9 .. .. 3·25 3·50

(Des P. Ndembo. Litho J.W.)

1982 (16 Oct). *World Food Day. T* **86** *and similar horiz designs. Multicoloured. P* 14.
361 50 c. Type **86** 5 8
362 1s. Dairy farming 10 12
363 5s. Maize farming 55 60
364 10s. Grain storage .. .. 1·10 1·25
MS365 129 × 99 mm. Nos. 361/4 .. .. 2·00 2·10

87 Immunization

(Des P. Ndembo. Litho State Printing Works, Moscow)

1982 (1 Dec). *Centenary of Robert Koch's Discovery of Tubercle Bacillus. T* **87** *and similar horiz designs. Multicoloured. P* 12½ × 12.

366	50 c. Type **87**	5	8
367	1s. Dr. Robert Koch	10	12
368	5s. International Union Against TB emblem	55	60
369	10s. World Health Organization emblem	1·10	1·25

88 Letter Post

(Litho State Printing Works, Moscow)

1983 (3 Feb). *5th Anniv of Posts and Telecommunications Corporation. T* **88** *and similar horiz designs. Multicoloured. P* 12.

370	50 c. Type **88**	5	8
371	1s. Training institute	10	12
372	5s. Satellite communications	55	60
373	10s. U.P.U., I.T.U. and T.P.T.C.C. (Tanzania Posts and Telecommunications Corporation) emblems	1·10	1·25
MS374	126 × 96 mm. Nos. 370/3	1·75	2·00

89 Pres. Mwalimu Julius Nyerere

(Litho J.W.)

1983 (14 Mar). *Commonwealth Day. T* **89** *and similar horiz designs. Multicoloured. P* 14.

375	50 c. Type **89**	5	8
376	1s. Athletics and boxing	10	12
377	5s. Flags of Commonwealth countries	55	60
378	10s. Pres. Nyerere and members of British Royal Family	1·10	1·25
MS379	121 × 100 mm. Nos. 375/8	1·75	2·00

90 Eastern and Southern African Management Institute, Arusha, Tanzania

(Des P. Ndembo. Litho State Ptg Wks, Moscow)

1983 (12 Sept). *25th Anniv of the Economic Commission for Africa. T* **90** *and similar horiz designs. Multicoloured. P* 12½ × 12.

380	50 c. Type **90**	5	8
381	1s. 25th Anniversary inscription and U.N. logo	10	12
382	5s. Mineral collections	55	60
383	10s. E.C.A. Silver Jubilee logo and O.A.U. flag	1·10	1·25
MS384	132 × 102 mm. Nos. 380/3	1·75	2·00

91 Telephone Cables

(Des P. Ndembo. Litho J.W.)

1983 (17 Oct). *World Communications Year. T* **91** *and similar horiz designs. Multicoloured. P* 14.

385	50 c. Type **91**	5	8
386	1s. W.C.Y. logo	10	12
387	5s. Postal service	55	60
388	10s. Microwave tower	1·10	1·25
MS389	102 × 92 mm. Nos. 385/8	1·75	2·00

ALTERED CATALOGUE NUMBERS

Any Catalogue numbers altered from the last edition are shown as a list in the introductory pages.

92 Bagamoyo Boma

(Des J. de Silva and P. Ndembo. Litho State Ptg Wks, Moscow)

1983 (12 Dec). *Historical Buildings. T* **92** *and similar horiz designs. Multicoloured. P* 12½ × 12.

390	1s. Type **92**	10	12
391	1s. 50, Beit el Ajaib, Zanzibar	15	20
392	5s. Anglican Cathedral, Zanzibar	55	60
393	10s. Original German Government House and present State House, Dar-es-Salaam	1·10	1·25
MS394	130 × 100 mm. Nos. 390/3	1·90	2·00

93 Sheikh Abeid Amani Karume (founder of Afro-Shirazi Party)

(Des P. Ndembo. Litho J.W.)

1984 (18 June). *20th Anniv of Zanzibar Revolution. T* **93** *and similar horiz designs. Multicoloured. P* 14.

395	1s. Type **93**	10	12
396	1s. 50, Clove farming	15	20
397	5s. Symbol of Industrial Development	55	60
398	10s. New housing schemes	1·10	1·25
MS399	130 × 100 mm. 15s. M.V. *Mapinduzi* and map	1·50	1·60

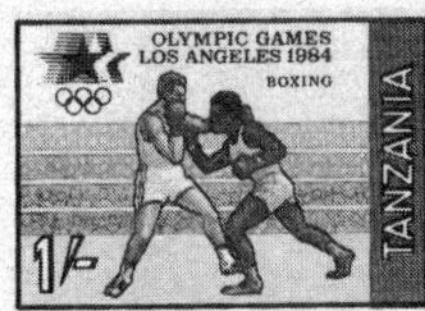

94 Boxing

(Des P. Ndembo. Litho State Ptg Wks, Moscow)

1984 (6 Aug). *Olympic Games, Los Angeles. T* **94** *and similar horiz designs. Multicoloured. P* 12½ × 12.

400	1s. Type **94**	10	12
401	1s. 50, Running	15	20
402	5s. Basketball	55	60
403	20s. Football	2·00	2·10
MS404	130 × 100 mm. Nos. 400/3	2·75	3·00

95 Icarus in Flight

(Des P. Ndembo. Litho J.W.)

1984 (15 Nov). *40th Anniv of International Civil Aviation Organization. T* **95** *and similar horiz designs. Multicoloured. P* 13 × 12½.

405	1s. Type **95**	10	12
406	1s. 50, Aircraft and air traffic controller	15	20
407	5s. Aircraft undergoing maintenance	55	60
408	10s. I.C.A.O. badge	1·10	1·25
MS409	130 × 100 mm. Nos. 405/8	1·90	2·00

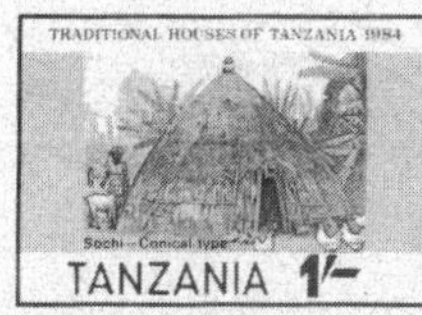

96 Sochi – Conical House

(Des P. Ndembo. Litho State Ptg Wks, Moscow)

1984 (20 Dec). *Traditional Houses. T* **96** *and similar horiz designs. Multicoloured. P* 12½ × 12.

410	1s. Type **96**	8	10
411	1s. 50, Isyenga – circular type	12	15
412	5s. Tembe – flatroofed type	45	50
413	10s. Banda – coastal type	90	95
MS414	129 × 99 mm. Nos. 410/13	1·50	1·60

OFFICIAL STAMPS

OFFICIAL (O 1) OFFICIAL (O 2) (3½ mm tall)

1961 (9 Dec). *Nos.* 108/14 *and* 117 *optd with Type* O **1** (10, 15, 20, 50 *c. or larger* (17 *mm*) 5, 30 *c.*) *or with Type* O **2** (1*s. or larger* (22 *mm*) 5*s.*).

O1	5 c. sepia and light apple-green	5	5
O2	10 c. deep bluish green	5	5
O3	15 c. sepia and blue	5	5
O4	20 c. orange-brown	5	5
O5	30 c. black, emerald and yellow	8	5
O6	50 c. black and yellow	10	5
O7	1s. brown, blue and olive-yellow	15	5
O8	5s. deep bluish green and orange-red	1·00	1·10
O1/8	*Set of* 8	1·25	1·25

(Opt photo Harrison)

1965 (9 Dec). *Nos.* 128/132, 134, 136, 139 *optd as Types* O **1** (15 *c.*, 30 *c. or larger* (17 *mm*) 5 *c.*, 10 *c.*, 20 *c.*, 50 *c.*), *or with* O **2** (1*s.*, 5*s.*).

O 9	5 c. ultramarine and yellow-orange	5	5
O10	10 c. black, greenish yellow, green & blue	5	5
O11	15 c. multicoloured	5	5
O12	20 c. sepia, grey-green and greenish blue	5	5
O13	30 c. black and red-brown	8	5
O14	50 c. multicoloured	15	5
O15	1s. multicoloured	30	10
O16	5s. lake-brown, yellow-green and blue	1·50	1·50
O9/16	*Set of* 8	2·00	1·75

OFFICIAL (O 3) (3 mm tall)

(Opt litho Govt Printer, Dar-es-Salaam)

1967 (10–18 Nov). *Nos.* 134, 136 *and* 139 *optd as No.* O14 (50 *c.*) *or with Type* O **3** (*others*).

O17	50 c. multicoloured (18.11)		
O18	1s. multicoloured (18.11)	7·00	2·50
O19	5s. lake-brown, yellow-green and blue	9·00	4·50

The issue dates given are for the earliest known postmarked copies.

Nos. O9/16 were overprinted by Harrison in photogravure and Nos. O17/19 have litho overprints by the Government Printer, Dar-es-Salaam. On No. O17 the overprint is the same size (17 mm long) as on No. O14.

1967 (9 Dec)–**71**. *Nos.* 142/6, 148, 151 *and* 155 *optd as Type* O **1**, *but larger* (*measuring* 17 *mm*) (5 *c. to* 50 *c.*) *or as Type* O **2** (1*s. and* 5*s.*). *Chalk-surfaced paper.*

O20	5 c. magenta, yellow-olive and black	5	5
	a. Glazed, ordinary paper (22.1.71)	15	15
O21	10 c. brown and bistre	5	5
O22	15 c. grey, turquoise-blue and black	5	5
	a. Glazed, ordinary paper (22.1.71)	15	15
O23	20 c. brown and turquoise-green	8	5
O24	30 c. sage-green and black	10	5
O25	50 c. multicoloured	12	5
	a. Glazed, ordinary paper (22.1.71)	30	15
O26	1s. orange-brown, slate-blue and maroon	25	25
	a. Glazed, ordinary paper (3.2.71)	50	20
O27	5s. greenish yellow, black & turquoise-grn	1·50	1·75
	a. Glazed, ordinary paper (3.2.71)	2·25	2·75
O20/7	*Set of* 8	2·00	2·10

The chalk-surfaced paper exists with both PVA gum and gum arabic, but the glazed, ordinary paper exists PVA gum only.

OFFICIAL (O 4) OFFICIAL (O 5)

1970 (10 Dec)–**73**. *Nos.* 142/8, 151 *and* 155 *optd locally by letterpress as Type* O 4 (5 *to* 50 *c.*) *or as Type* O **2** *but measuring* 28 *mm* (1*s. and* 5*s.*). (*a*) *Chalk-surfaced paper.*

O28	5 c. magenta, yellow-olive and black	8	5
	a. "OFFCIAL" (R.7/6)		
O29	10 c. brown and bistre	10	5
	a. "OFFCIAL" (R.7/6)		
O30	20 c. brown and turquoise-green	20	15
O31	30 c. sage-green and black	25	20

(*b*) *Glazed, ordinary paper* (1973)

O32	5 c. magenta, yellow-olive and black		
	a. "OFFCIAL" (R.7/6)		
O33	10 c. brown and bistre		
	a. "OFFCIAL" (R.7/6)		
O34	15 c. grey, turquoise-blue and black		
	a. "OFFCIAL" (R.7/6)		
O35	20 c. brown and turquoise-green		
O36	40 c. yellow, chocolate and bright green		
	a. Opt double		
	b. "OFFICIA" (R.10/9 and 10)		
O37	50 c. multicoloured		
	a. "OFFCIAL" (R.7/6)		
O38	1s. orange-brown, slate-blue and maroon		
	a. Opt double		
O39	5s. greenish yellow, black & turquoise-grn		

The letterpress overprint can be distinguished from the photogravure by its absence of screening dots and the overprint showing through to the reverse, apart from the difference in length.

1973 (10 Dec). *Nos.* 158/9, 161, 163/4 *and* 166/70 *optd with Type* O **1** (5 *to* 70 *c.*) *or Type* O **5** (*others*).

O40	5 c. light yellow-olive, lt violet-blue & black	5	5
O41	10 c. multicoloured	5	5
O42	20 c. reddish cinnamon, orange-yellow & blk	10	5
O43	40 c. multicoloured	15	8
O44	50 c. multicoloured	15	8
O45	70 c. turquoise-green, pale orange and black	20	10
O46	1s. multicoloured	20	12
O47	1s. 50, multicoloured	40	30
	a. Pair, one without opt	†	—
O48	2s. 50, multicoloured	55	65
O49	5s. multicoloured	1·00	1·40
O40/9	*Set of* 10	2·50	2·50

No. O47a is due to a paper fold and comes from a sheet used at Kigoma in 1974.

1977 (Feb). *Nos.* 159, 161 *and* 163/4 *optd locally by letterpress as Type* O **3**.

No.	Description		
O50	10 c. multicoloured		
	a. "OFFCIAL" (R. 7/6)		
O51	20 c. multicoloured		
	a. "OFFCIAL" (R. 7/6)		
O52	40 c. multicoloured		
	a. "OFFCIAL" (R. 7/6)		
O53	50 c. multicoloured		
	a. "OFFCIAL" (R. 7/6)		
	b. Opt inverted		

OFFICIAL

(O **6**)

OFFICIAL

(O **7**)

1980 (Nov). *Nos.* 307/12 *optd with Type* O **6**, *and Nos.* 313 *and* 315/17 *optd with Type* O **7**.

No.	Description		
O54	10 c. Type **75**	5	5
O55	20 c. Genet	5	5
O56	40 c. Mongoose	5	5
O57	50 c. Ratel	5	5
O58	75 c. Rock Hyrax	8	10
O59	80 c. Leopard	8	10
O60	1s. Type **76**	10	12
O61	2s. Zebra	20	25
O62	3s. Buffalo	30	35
O63	5s. Lion	45	50
O54/63	*Set of* 10	1·25	1·50

On the 10, 50 c., 2 and 5s. values the overprint reads downwards, on the others it reads upwards.

POSTAGE DUE STAMPS

Postage Due stamps of Kenya and Uganda were issued for provisional use as such in Tanganyika on 1 July 1933. The postmark is the only means of identification.

The Postage Due stamps of Kenya, Uganda and Tanganyika were used in Tanganyika until 2 January 1967.

D 1

(Litho D.L.R.)

1967 (3 Jan). *P* 14 × 13½.

No.	Type	Description		
D1	D 1	5 c. scarlet	35	65
D2		10 c. green	45	75
D3		20 c. deep blue	70	1·25
D4		30 c. red-brown	70	1·60
D5		40 c. bright purple	70	2·00
D6		1s. orange	1·50	3·25
D1/6		*Set of* 6	4·00	8·50

1969–71. *As Nos.* D1/6, *but perf* 14 × 15.
A. *Chalk-surfaced paper* (19.12.69).
B. *Glazed, ordinary paper* (13.7.71).

No.	Type	Description	A		B	
D 7	D 1	5 c. scarlet	25	65	40	80
D 8		10 c. green (*shades*)	25	65	40	80
D 9		20 c. deep blue	35	1·00	55	1·25
D10		30 c. red-brown (*shades*)	40	1·40	60	1·60
D11		40 c. bright purple	50	1·75	1·25	2·75
D12		1s. orange	†		1·75	5·00
D7B/12B		*Set of* 6			4·50	11·00

The stamps on chalk-surfaced paper exist only with gum arabic, but the stamps on glazed paper exist only with PVA gum.

1973 (12 Dec). *As Nos.* D1/6, *but glazed ordinary paper. P* 15.

No.	Type	Description		
D13	D 1	5 c. scarlet	25	60
D14		10 c. emerald	25	60
D15		20 c. deep blue	40	85
D16		30 c. red-brown	45	1·50
D17		40 c. bright mauve	55	1·75
D18		1s. bright orange	1·25	3·00
D13/18		*Set of* 6	2·75	7·50

(Litho Questa)

1978 (31 July). *Chalky paper. P* 13½ × 14.

No.	Type	Description		
D19	D 1	5 c. brown-red	5	5
D20		10 c. emerald	5	5
D21		20 c. steel-blue	5	5
D22		30 c. red-brown	5	5
D23		40 c. bright purple	5	5
D24		1s. bright orange	10	12
D19/24		*Set of* 6	30	35

Tasmania

PRICES FOR STAMPS ON COVER

Nos. 1/4	*from* × 2
Nos. 5/12	*from* × 3
No. 13	—
Nos. 14/23	*from* × 2
No. 24	—
Nos. 25/83	*from* × 3
Nos. 84/106	*from* × 6
Nos. 107/9	—
Nos. 110/29	*from* × 3
Nos. 130/40	*from* × 4
Nos. 141/4	—
Nos. 145/50	*from* × 3
Nos. 151/3	—
Nos. 154/69	*from* × 6
Nos. 170/6*a*	—
Nos. 177/82	*from* × 20
Nos. 183/200	*from* × 10
Nos. 201/7	*from* × 15
Nos. 209/15	*from* × 6
Nos. 216/22	*from* × 15
Nos. 223/5	—
Nos. 226/7	*from* × 15
Nos. 229/36	*from* × 20
Nos. 237/60	*from* × 10
No. 261	—
Nos. F1/25	—
Nos. F26/9	*from* × 15

1

2

3

(Eng C. W. Coard. Recess H. and C. Best at the office of the *Courier* Newspaper)

1853 (1 Nov). *No wmk. Imperf. Twenty-four varieties in four rows of six each.*

(*a*) *Medium soft yellowish paper with all lines clear and distinct*

No.	Type	Description		
1	1	1d. pale blue	£3250	£800
2		1d. blue	£3250	£800

(*b*) *Thin hard white paper with lines of the engraving blurred and worn*

No.	Type	Description		
3	1	1d. pale blue	£3000	£750
4		1d. blue	£3000	£750

1853–54. *No wmk. Imperf. In each plate there are twenty-four varieties in four rows of six each.*

(*a*) *Plate I. Finely engraved. All lines in network and background thin, clear, and well defined.* (1853)

(i) *First state of the plate, brilliant colours*

No.	Type	Description		
5	2	4d. bright red-orange	£2500	£650
		a. Double impression		
6		4d. bright brownish orange	—	£850

(ii) *Second state of plate, with blurred lines and worn condition of the central background*

No.	Type	Description		
7	2	4d. red-orange	£2250	£375
8		4d. orange	£2000	£350
9		4d. pale orange	—	£350

(*b*) *Plate II. Coarse engraving, lines in network and background thicker and blurred* (1854)

No.	Type	Description		
10	2	4d. orange	£1800	£325
		a. Double print, one albino		
11		4d. dull orange	£1800	£325
12		4d. yellowish orange	£1800	£325
13		4d. red-orange (*laid paper*)	£3000	

No. 13 is from a proof sheet and is only known unused. The paper has wide vertical laid lines.

In the 4d. Plate I, the outer frame-line is thin all round. In Plate II it is, by comparison with other parts, thicker in the lower left angle.

In 1879 reprints were made of the 1d. in blue and the 4d., Plate I, in brownish yellow, on thin, tough, white wove paper, and perforated 11½. In 1887, a reprint from the other plate of the 4d. was made in reddish brown and in black, and in 1889 of the 1d. in blue and in black, and of the 4d. (both plates) in yellow and in black on white card, imperforate. As these three plates were defaced after the stamps had been superseded, all these reprints show two thick strokes across the Queen's Head.

(Eng W. Humphrys after water-colour sketch by E. Corbould. Recess P.B.)

1855 (Aug). *Wmk Large Star*, W w 1. *Imperf.*

No.	Type	Description		
14	3	1d. carmine	£4750	£950
15		2d. deep green	£1600	£550
16		2d. green	£1600	£600
17		4d. deep blue	£1400	85·00
18		4d. blue	£1300	95·00

There is a proof of the 1d. on thick, no wmk, paper that is sometimes sold as the issued stamp.

(Printed by H. and C. Best, of Hobart)

1856–57. *No wmk. Imperf.*

No.	Type	Description		
19	3	1d. pale brick-red (4.56)	£5000	£550
20		2d. dull emerald-green (1.57)	£6000	£700
21		4d. deep blue (5.57)	£650	85·00
22		4d. blue	£550	85·00
23		4d. pale blue	—	£120

1856 (Nov). *Pelure paper. No wmk. Imperf.*

No.	Type	Description		
24	3	1d. deep red-brown	£2500	£550

4

7

8

1857 (Aug)–**60**. *Wmk double-lined numerals* "1", "2" *or* "4" *as* W **4**. *Imperf.*

No.	Type	Description		
25	3	1d. deep red-brown	£400	23·00
26		1d. pale red-brown	£275	18·00
27		1d. brick-red	£150	17·00
28		1d. dull vermilion	80·00	17·00
29		1d. carmine	80·00	17·00
		a. Double print	—	£130
30		2d. dull emerald-green	—	70·00
31		2d. deep green	£180	32·00
32		2d. green	—	30·00
		a. Double print	—	£160
33		2d. yellow-green	£200	60·00
34		2d. slate-green	£120	50·00
35		4d. blue	£100	17·00
		a. Double print	—	£160
36		4d. pale blue	£100	12·00
37		4d. bright blue	£100	17·00
		a. Printed on both sides		
		b. Double print	—	£130
38		4d. very deep blue	—	75·00
		a. Double print	—	£160
39		4d. cobalt-blue	—	60·00

CANCELLATIONS. Beware of early Tasmanian stamps with pen-cancellations cleaned off and faked postmarks applied.

(Recess P.B.)

1858 (Jan). (*a*) *Wmk double-lined numerals* "6" *or* "12". *Imperf.*

No.	Type	Description		
40	7	6d. dull lilac	£650	70·00
41	8	1s. bright vermilion	£500	80·00
42		1s. dull vermilion	—	60·00

(*b*) *Prepared for use, but not issued. Wmk Large Star. Imperf*

No.	Type	Description		
43	7	6d. lilac	£700	

(Plates by P.B. Typo in the Colony)

1860–67. *Wmk double-lined* "6". *Imperf.*

No.	Type	Description		
44	7	6d. dull slate-grey (3.60)	£325	60·00
45		6d. grey	—	65·00
46		6d. grey-violet (4.63)	£130	60·00
		a. Double print	—	£130
47		6d. dull bluish (2.65)	£140	48·00
48		6d. bluish purple	£275	55·00
49		6d. reddish mauve (1867)	£750	£225

In 1871 reprints were made of the 6d. (in mauve) and the 1s. on white wove paper, and perforated 11½. They are found with or without "REPRINT". In 1889 they were again reprinted on white card, imperforate and perforated 12. These later impressions are also found with or without "REPRINT".

1864–70. *Double-line numeral watermarks. Various local roulettes and perforations.*

(*a*) *Roughly punctured roulette about* 8, *by J. Walch, at Hobart* (1864)

No.	Type	Description		
50	3	1d. brick-red	—	£150
51		1d. carmine	£275	£100
52		4d. pale blue	—	£140
53	7	6d. dull lilac	—	£170
54	8	1s. vermilion	—	£500

(*b*) *Pin-perf* 5½ *to* 9½ *at Longford, near Launceston* (Mar 1867)

No.	Type	Description		
55	3	1d. carmine	£275	70·00
56		4d. bright blue	—	£160
57	7	6d. grey-violet	—	£150
58		6d. reddish mauve	—	£425
59	8	1s. vermilion		

(*c*) *Pin-perf* 13½ *to* 14½ (1867?)

No.	Type	Description		
60	3	1d. brick-red	—	£190
61		1d. dull vermilion	—	£190
62		1d. carmine		
63		2d. yellow-green	—	£275
64		4d. pale blue	—	£160
65	7	6d. grey-violet	—	£375
66	8	1s. vermilion		

(*d*) *Oblique roulette* 10, 10½ (1866?)

No.	Type	Description		
67	3	1d. brick-red	—	£325
68		1d. carmine	£850	£275
69		2d. yellow-green	—	£425
70		4d. bright blue	—	£375
71	7	6d. grey-violet	—	£600

(*e*) *Oblique roulette* 14 *to* 15, *used at Deloraine* (1867?)

No.	Type	Description		
72	3	1d. brick-red	—	£375
73		1d. dull vermilion	—	£375
74		1d. carmine	—	£375
75		2d. yellow-green	—	£425
76		4d. pale blue	—	£325
77	7	6d. grey-violet	–	£600
78	8	1s. vermilion	—	£750

(*f*) *Serrated perf* 19 (1868–69)

No.	Type	Description		
79	3	1d. carmine (*pen-cancel* £9)	£200	£100
80		2d. yellow-green	—	£200
81		4d. deep blue	£500	95·00
82		4d. cobalt-blue	—	95·00
83	7	6d. bluish purple	—	£375

1864–80. *Double-line numeral watermarks.*

I. *Perforated by J. Walch and Sons, Hobart.* (*a*) *P* 10

No.	Type	Description		
84	3	1d. brick-red	45·00	18·00
85		1d. vermilion	45·00	18·00
86		1d. deep carmine	42·00	18·00
87		1d. pale carmine	45·00	18·00
88		2d. sage-green	£250	£120
89		2d. yellow-green	£200	70·00
90		4d. blue	80·00	9·50
91		4d. pale blue	80·00	9·50
		a. Double print	—	£110

No.	Type	Description	Unused	Used
92	**7**	6d. grey-violet	£150	13·00
93		6d. dull bluish	80·00	16·00
94		6d. bluish purple	—	18·00
95		6d. reddish mauve	£300	60·00
96	**8**	1s. vermilion	90·00	19·00

(*b*) *P* 11½ *to* 12

No.	Type	Description	Unused	Used
96*a*	**3**	1d. vermilion	45·00	
97		1d. deep carmine	35·00	6·50
98		1d. pale carmine	38·00	13·00
99		2d. pale yellow-green	£160	38·00
100		2d. deep yellow-green	£100	38·00
101		4d. blue	70·00	13·00
102		4d. deep blue	70·00	11·00
103		4d. cobalt-blue	—	28·00
104	**7**	6d. bluish purple	£120	18·00
105		6d. reddish mauve	70·00	32·00
106	**8**	1s. vermilion	95·00	28·00
		a. Double print	—	£150

(*c*) *Perf compound* 10 × 11½, 12

No.	Type	Description	Unused	Used
107	**3**	1d. deep carmine	£1300	
108		4d. blue	—	£900

(*d*) *Wmk double-lined* "2". *P* 12½–10 (Nov 1869)

No.	Type	Description	Unused	Used
109	**3**	1d. carmine (*pen-cancel* £50)	—	£1000

II. *Perforated by R. Harris, Launceston. P* 12½, 12

No.	Type	Description	Unused	Used
110	**3**	1d. brick-red	45·00	23·00
111		1d. vermilion	42·00	17·00
112		1d. deep carmine	25·00	6·50
113		2d. sage-green	£200	£100
114		2d. yellow-green	£225	80·00
115		4d. bright blue	£130	35·00
116		4d. blue	£130	35·00
117	**7**	6d. dull bluish	£160	40·00
118		6d. bluish purple	£170	40·00
119		6d. reddish mauve	£350	90·00
120	**8**	1s. vermilion	£180	65·00

III. *Perforated by the Government at Hobart.* (*a*) *P* 11, 11½ (1871–80)

No.	Type	Description	Unused	Used
121	**7**	6d. dull mauve	70·00	19·00
122		6d. bright mauve	65·00	19·00
		a. Imperf between (pair)	—	£425
123		6d. dull purple (3.75)	65·00	19·00
		a. Imperf (pair)	—	£400
124		6d. bright purple	65·00	28·00
		a. Double print	—	£110
		b. Imperf between (horiz pair)	£750	
125		6d. lilac-purple	70·00	38·00
126	**8**	1s. dull vermilion	75·00	38·00
		a. Imperf between (horiz pair)		
127		1s. brownish vermilion	65·00	38·00

(*b*) *P* 12

No.	Type	Description	Unused	Used
128	**7**	6d. bright purple	80·00	16·00
129		6d. dull claret	24·00	11·00

All stamps perforated by the "Walch" machine gauge over 11½ and under 12, while those of the Government machine gauge 11½ or under.

11

12

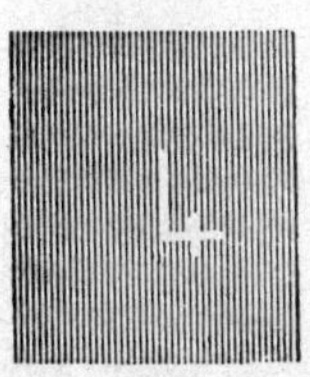

13

14

(Plates by D.L.R. Typo in the Colony)

1870–71. *Wmk single lined numerals.* W **12, 13,** *or* **14.** (*a*) *P* 12.

No.	Type	Description	Unused	Used
130	**11**	1d. rose-red (10)	27·00	8·50
131		1d. deep rose-red (10)	45·00	6·50
132		1d. rose-red (4)	40·00	8·50
133		2d. yellow-green (2)	38·00	4·50
134		2d. blue-green (2)	42·00	4·50
135		4d. blue (4)	£700	£400
136		10d. black (10)	11·00	6·00

(*b*) *P* 11½

No.	Type	Description	Unused	Used
137	**11**	1d. rose-red (10)	£900	
138		2d. yellow-green (2)	80·00	6·50
139		2d. blue-green (2)	32·00	3·25
		a. Double print		
140		10d. black (10)	18·00	10·00

(*c*) *Imperf* (*pairs*)

No.	Type	Description	Unused	Used
141	**11**	1d. rose-red (4)	—	£160
142		1d. rose-red (10)	£190	£190
143		2d. green (2)		
144		10d. black (10)	£110	

The above were printed on paper borrowed from New South Wales.

15

16

1871–79. *W* **15**. (*a*) *P* 12.

No.	Type	Description	Unused	Used
145	**11**	1d. rose	60·00	5·50
146		1d. carmine	65·00	7·00
147		2d. green (11.72)	£400	95·00
148		3d. red-brown	60·00	14·00
149		3d. deep red-brown	60·00	14·00
150		4d. buff (8.8.76)	£225	15·00
151		9d. pale blue	28·00	
152		5s. purple	£225	
153		5s. mauve	£150	

(*b*) *P* 11½

No.	Type	Description	Unused	Used
154	**11**	1d. rose	3·25	50
155		1d. bright rose	3·25	50
156		1d. vermilion (4.73)	£200	65·00
157		1d. carmine	4·50	50
158		1d. pink	4·50	50
159		2d. deep green (11.72)	12·00	50
160		2d. yellow-green (12.75)	£110	1·50
161		2d. blue-green	20·00	50
162		3d. pale red-brown	30·00	3·25
163		3d. deep red-brown	30·00	3·75
		a. Imperf between (pair)		
164		3d. purple-brown (1.78)	30·00	3·25
165		3d. brownish purple	30·00	3·25
166		4d. ochre	42·00	5·50
167		4d. buff (8.8.76)	35·00	6·50
168		4d. pale yellow	35·00	5·50
169		9d. blue	13·00	5·00
170		5s. purple (*pen cancel* £2.50)	£130	17·00
171		5s. mauve	£110	17·00

(*c*) *Imperf* (*pairs*)

No.	Type	Description	Unused	Used
172	**11**	1d. rose (*pen cancel* £25)		
173		2d. green	—	£150
174		3d. pale red-brown	£120	
175		3d. purple-brown	—	£275
176		9d. blue	£120	
176*a*		5s. purple		

See also Nos. 209/15.

(Typo D.L.R.)

1878 (28 Oct). *W* **16**. *P* 14.

No.	Type	Description	Unused	Used
177	**11**	1d. carmine	2·75	25
178		1d. rose-carmine	2·75	25
179		1d. scarlet	2·75	25
180		2d. pale green	3·00	25
181		2d. green	3·00	25
182		8d. dull purple-brown	11·00	2·50

In 1871 the 1d., 2d., 3d., 4d. blue, 9d., 10d. and 5s., T **11** were reprinted on soft white wove, and perforated 11½; and in 1879 the 4d. yellow and 8d. were reprinted on thin, tough, white wove. All nine varieties are found with and without "REPRINT". In 1889 the 4d. blue was also reprinted on white card imperforate, and perforated 12. The 5s. has been reprinted in *mauve* on white card, perforated 12. These later impressions, like those of 1871 and 1879, are found with or without "REPRINT".

1880–91. *Colonial print. W* **16**. (*a*) *P* 12.

No.	Type	Description	Unused	Used
183	**11**	½d. orange (1889)	2·00	1·50
184		½d. deep orange	1·90	1·25
185		1d. pink (1889)	11·00	2·50
		a. Imperf (pair)	90·00	£100
186		1d. rosine	4·00	1·75
187		1d. dull rosine	6·50	2·75
		a. Imperf (pair)	65·00	
188		3d. red-brown (1880)	6·00	1·75
		a. Imperf (pair)	80·00	
		b. Imperf between (pair)	£450	
189		4d. deep yellow (1883)	50·00	10·00
190		4d. chrome-yellow	70·00	10·00
		a. Printed both sides	£180	

(*b*) *P* 11½

No.	Type	Description	Unused	Used
192	**11**	½d. orange (8.3.89)	1·90	90
193		½d. deep orange	1·90	1·10
194		1d. dull red (14.2.89)	3·50	1·10
195		1d. vermilion-red (4.80)	2·75	1·10
196		3d. red-brown (1.83)	8·00	2·50
197		4d. deep yellow (1.83)	25·00	5·00
198		4d. chrome-yellow	25·00	6·00
199		4d. olive-yellow	90·00	18·00
200		4d. buff	26·00	6·50

Halfpenny

(17)

d. 2½

(18) (2¼ mm between "d", and "2")

d. 2½

(19) (3½ mm between "d" and "2")

1889–91. *W* **16**. (*a*) *Surch locally with T* **17**. *P* 14.

No.	Type	Description	Unused	Used
201	**11**	½d. on 1d. scarlet (1.1.89)	6·00	2·75
		a. "al" in "Half" reading down	£700	£450

A minor variety has broken "p" in "Halfpenny".

(*b*) *Surch locally with T* **18**. *P* 11½

No.	Type	Description	Unused	Used
204	**11**	2½d. on 9d. pale blue	5·00	1·90
		b. Surch double, one inverted	£200	£200
205		2½d. on 9d. deep blue	5·75	2·50

(*c*) *Surch locally with T* **19**. *P* 12

No.	Type	Description	Unused	Used
207	**11**	2½d. on 9d. pale blue	4·50	1·90
		a. Blue surch		

There is a reprint of the 2½d. on 9d. on stout white wove paper, perf 12, overprinted "REPRINT".

1891. *Colonial print. Reissue with W* **15**. (*a*) *P* 12.

No.	Type	Description	Unused	Used
209	**11**	½d. orange	12·00	6·00
		a. Imperf (pair)	60·00	
210		1d. dull rosine	14·00	6·00
211		1d. rosine	25·00	10·00
212		4d. bistre	13·00	4·50

(*b*) *P* 11½

No.	Type	Description	Unused	Used
213	**11**	½d. orange	12·00	4·00
214		½d. brown-orange	10·00	3·75
215		1d. rosine	10·00	4·00

20

21

21*a*

(Typo D.L.R.)

1892–99. *W* **16**. *P* 14.

No.	Type	Description		Unused	Used
216	**20**	½d. orange and mauve		1·25	30
217	**21**	2½d. purple		2·25	1·00
218	**20**	5d. pale blue and brown		4·50	1·40
219		6d. violet and black		5·00	1·10
220	**21*a***	10d. purple-lake and deep green		9·00	4·25
221	**20**	1s. rose and green		6·00	1·75
222		2s. 6d. brown and blue		20·00	5·00
223		5s. lilac and red		22·00	11·00
224		10s. mauve and brown		65·00	22·00
225		£1 green and yellow		£550	£160
216/25			*Set of* 10	£650	£180
216/25 Optd "Specimen"			*Set of* 10	£225	

1896. *Colonial print. W* **16**. *P* 12.

No.	Type	Description	Unused	Used
226	**11**	4d. pale bistre	12·00	5·50
227		9d. pale blue	6·50	1·75
		a. Blue	7·00	2·75

22 Lake Marion

23 Mount Wellington

24 Hobart

25 Tasman's Arch

26 Spring River, Port Davey

27 Russell Falls

28 Mount Gould, Lake St. Clair

29 Dilston Falls

30

DIFFERENCES BETWEEN LITHOGRAPHED AND TYPOGRAPHED ISSUES

Lithographed	Typographed
General appearance fine.	*Comparatively crude and coarse appearance.*
½d. All "V over Crown" wmk.	All "Crown over A" wmk.
1d. The shading on the path on the right bank of the river consists of very fine dots. In printings from worn stones the dots hardly show.	The shading on the path is coarser, consisting of large dots and small patches of colour.
The shading on the white mountain is fine (or almost absent in many stamps).	The shading on the mountain is coarse, and clearly defined.

2d. Three rows of windows in large building on shore, at extreme left, against inner frame.	Two rows of windows.
3d. Clouds very white. Stars in corner ornaments have long points. Shading of corner ornaments is defined by a coloured outer line.	Clouds dark. Stars have short points. Shading of ornaments terminates against white background.
4d. Lithographed only.	—
6d. No coloured dots at base of waterfall. Outer frame of value tablets is formed by outer line of design.	Coloured dots at base of waterfall. Thick line of colour between value tablets and outer line. Small break in inner frame below second "A" of "TASMANIA".

(Recess D.L.R.)

1899 (Dec)–**1900**. *W* **30**. *P* 14.
229 **22** ½d. deep green .. 1·25 20
230 **23** 1d. bright lake .. 1·25 12
231 **24** 2d. deep violet .. 1·75 12
232 **25** 2½d. indigo .. 10·00 4·50
233 **26** 3d. sepia .. 7·50 1·00
234 **27** 4d. deep orange-buff .. 12·00 1·50
235 **28** 5d. bright blue .. 13·00 3·75
236 **29** 6d. lake .. 17·00 2·00
229/36 Optd "Specimen" .. *Set of* 8 £225

(Litho Government Printing Office, Melbourne)

1902–3. *Transfers from London plates. Wmk V over Crown,* W w **10** (*sideways on ½d., 2d.*). *P* 12½.
237 **22** ½d. green (1903) .. 1·25 20
a. Perf 11 .. 3·25 25
b. Perf comp of 12½ and 11 .. 50·00 35·00
238 **23** 1d. carmine-red .. 1·50 12
239 **24** 2d. violet .. 95 12
a. Perf 11 .. 95 20
b. Perf comp of 12½ and 11 .. 55·00 35·00
c. *Purple* .. 95 12
ca. *Purple*. Perf 11 .. 3·25 12
237/9 Optd "Specimen" .. *Set of* 3 £120

As the V and Crown paper was originally prepared for stamps of smaller size, portions of two or more watermarks appear on each stamp.

The ½d. and 2d. may be found with wmk upright, the normal position in these values being sideways.

We only list the main groups of shades in this and the following issues. There are variations of shade in all values, particularly in the 2d. where there is a wide range, also in the 1d. in some issues.

(Typo Govt Ptg Office, Melbourne)

1902–3. *Plates made at Govt Printing Office.* W w **10**. *P* 12½.

(*a*) *Wmk sideways* (Oct 1902)
240 **23** 1d. pale red (*to rose*) .. 1·75 12
a. Perf 11 .. 12·00 12
b. Perf comp of 12½ and 11 .. £150 35·00

Stamps from this printing with wmk upright, are scarce, especially perf 11.

(*b*) *Wmk upright* (April 1903)
241 **23** 1d. rose-red .. 1·25 12
a. Perf 11 .. 7·00 12
b. Perf comp of 12½ and 11 .. £150 35·00
c. *Deep carmine-red* .. 50·00 55
ca. *Deep carmine-red*. Perf 11 .. — 13·00
cb. *Deep carmine-red*. Perf comp of 12½ and 11 ..

(Litho Govt Ptg Office, Melbourne)

1905 (Sept)–**12**. *Transfers from London plates. Wmk Crown over A,* W w **11** (*sideways on horiz stamps*). *P* 12½.
242 **24** 2d. purple .. 2·75 12
a. Perf 11 .. 6·00 12
b. Perf comp of 12½ and 11 .. 13·00 2·40
c. Perf comp of 12½ and 12 .. — 38·00
d. Perf comp of 11 and 12 ..
e. *Dull purple* .. 2·00
ea. *Dull purple*. Perf 11 .. 8·50 25
243 **26** 3d. brown .. 7·00 65
a. Perf 11 .. 9·00 90
b. Perf comp of 12½ and 11 .. 38·00
244 **27** 4d. orange-buff (1907) .. 12·00 1·50
a. Perf 11 .. 11·00 1·40
b. Perf comp of 12½ and 11 .. £160
c. *Brown-ochre* (wmk sideways). Perf 11 (1907) .. 24·00 6·50
d. *Orange-yellow* (1912) .. 15·00 2·10
da. *Orange-yellow*. Perf 11 (1912) .. 14·00
245 **29** 6d. lake .. 21·00 3·00
a. Perf 11 .. 24·00 3·50
b. Perf comp of 12½ and 11 .. £130

Stamps with perf compound of 12½ and 12 or 11 and 12 are found on sheets which were sent from Melbourne incompletely perforated. The line of perforation gauging 12 was done at the Government Printing Office, Hobart.

(Typo Govt Ptg Office, Melbourne)

1905–11. *Plates made at Govt Printing Office. Wmk Crown over A,* W w **11** (*sideways on horiz designs*). *P* 12½.
246 **22** ½d. yellow-green (1909) .. 1·25 20
a. Perf 11 (1908) .. 1·25 20
b. Perf comp of 12½ and 11 .. 30·00
c. Perf comp of 11 and 12 ..
247 **23** 1d. rose-red .. 1·25 12
a. Perf 11 .. 1·25 12
b. Perf comp of 12½ and 11 .. 1·50 70
c. Perf comp of 12½ and 12 .. 30·00 4·50
d. Perf comp of 11 and 12 .. 42·00
e. *Bright rose* .. — 12
ea. *Bright rose*. Perf 11 .. 2·50 12
f. *Crimson* (1910) ..
fa. *Crimson*. Perf 11 .. — 20
fb. *Crimson*. Perf comp of 12½ and 12 ..
248 **24** 2d. purple .. 2·00 12
a. Perf 11 .. 2·40 12
b. *Dull violet* .. 2·00 20
ba. *Dull violet*. Perf 11 .. 2·00 12
bb. *Dull violet*. Perf comp of 12½ and 11 14·00 5·50
bc. *Dull violet*. Perf comp of 12½ and 12
bd. *Dull violet*. Perf comp of 11 and 12 .. 70·00 38·00
c. *Bright violet* (1910) .. 7·00 35
ca. *Bright violet*. Perf 11 .. 7·00 30
249 **26** 3d. brown (1909) .. 6·50 90
a. Perf 11 .. 6·75 1·25
b. Perf comp of 12½ and 11 .. £130
250 **29** 6d. dull lake (1911) .. 15·00 3·25
a. Perf 11 .. 15·00 2·75
b. Perf comp of 12½ and 11 .. £130

The note after No. 245 *re* perfs compound with perf 12 also applies here.

The ½d. and 2d. are found with wmk upright and the 1d. with wmk sideways, each perf 12½ or 11.

Stamps showing blotchy or defective impression often with shading appearing as solid colour, are from worn typographed plates, with the exception of Nos. 244*d* and 244*da*.

(Typo Govt Ptg Office, Melbourne)

1911. *New plate.* W w **11** (*sideways*). *P* 12½.
251 **24** 2d. bright violet .. 1·75 12
a. Perf 11 .. 2·00 20
b. Perf comp of 12½ and 11 .. 70·00

Stamps from this plate differ from Nos. 248*c* and 248*ca* in the width of the design (33 to 33¾ mm, against just over 32 mm), in the taller, bolder letters of "TASMANIA", in the slope of the mountain in the left background, which is clearly outlined in white, and in the outer vertical frame-line at left, which appears "wavy". Compare Nos. 252, etc., which are always from this plate.

ONE PENNY
(31)

1½d.
(32)

1912 (Oct). *No. 251 surch with T* **31**. *P* 12½.
252 **24** 1d. on 2d. bright violet (R.) .. 1·00 12
a. Perf 11 .. 1·75 25
b. Perf comp of 12½ and 11 .. — 85·00

(Typo Govt Ptg Office, Melbourne)

1912 (Dec). *Thin paper, white gum* (*as Victoria,* 1912). W w **11** (*sideways on 3d.*). *P* 12½.
253 **23** 1d. crimson .. 3·25 12
a. Perf 11 .. 4·00 12
b. Perf comp of 12½ and 11 ..
254 **26** 3d. brown .. 17·00 17·00

1903–5. *Wmk V over Crown,* W w **10**. *P* 12½.
255 **11** 9d. blue .. 7·00 2·50
a. Perf 11 .. 7·50 2·75
b. Perf comp of 12½ and 11 .. — £375
c. *Pale blue* .. 7·50 2·75
d. *Bright blue* .. 7·50 3·00
e. *Ultramarine* .. £350
f. *Indigo* .. £130
256 **20** 1s. rose and green .. 8·50 3·00
a. Perf 11 .. 18·00
255/6 Optd "Specimen" .. *Set of* 2 £100

1904 (29 Dec). *No. 218* (*W* **16**) *surch with T* **32**.
257 **20** 1½d. on 5d. pale blue & brn (Optd S. £28) 1·75 90

Stamps with inverted surcharge or without surcharge *se-tenant* with stamps with normal surcharge were obtained irregularly and were not issued for postal use.

1906–13. *Wmk Crown over A,* W w **11**. *P* 12½.
258 **11** 8d. purple-brown (1907) .. 14·00 3·00
a. Perf 11 .. 14·00 2·75
259 9d. blue (1907) .. 7·00 2·00
a. Perf 11 .. 7·00 2·00
b. Perf comp of 12½ and 11 (1909) .. 42·00
c. Perf comp of 12½ and 12 (1909) .. 90·00
d. Perf comp of 11 and 12 .. £180
260 **20** 1s. rose and green (1907) .. 8·50 1·50
a. Perf 11 (1907) .. 8·50 4·00
b. Perf comp of 12½ and 11 .. 12·00
c. Perf comp of 12½ and 12 .. 35·00
261 10s. mauve and brown (1906) .. 95·00 35·00
a. Perf 11 .. £150
b. Perf comp of 12½ and 12 .. £140

The note after No. 245 *re* perfs compound with perf 12, also applies here.

POSTAL FISCALS

Authorised for use in 1882

CLEANED STAMPS. Beware of postal fiscal stamps with pen-cancellations removed.

F 1

F 2

F 3

F 4

(Recess Alfred Bock, Hobart)

1863. *Wmk double-lined* "1", *W* **4**. *Imperf.*
F1 F **1** 3d. green .. 40·00 32·00
F2 F **2** 2s. 6d. carmine .. 45·00 32·00
F3 F **3** 5s. sage-green .. 45·00 38·00
F4 5s. brown .. £120 £100
F5 F **4** 10s. salmon .. £100 95·00
F6 10s. orange .. £150 95·00

1864. *Wmk double-lined* "1", *W* **4**. (*a*) *P* 10.
F 7 F **1** 3d. green .. 24·00 13·00
F 8 F **2** 2s. 6d. carmine .. 25·00
F 9 F **3** 5s. brown .. 40·00
F10 F **4** 10s. orange .. 25·00

(*b*) *P* 12
F11 F **1** 3d. green .. 29·00 17·00
F12 F **2** 2s. 6d. carmine .. 29·00 24·00
F13 F **3** 5s. sage-green .. 19·00 16·00
F14 5s. brown .. 50·00
F15 F **4** 10s. salmon .. 19·00 17·00
F16 10s. orange-brown .. 27·00 24·00

(*c*) *P* 12½, 13
F17 F **1** 3d. green .. 48·00
F18 F **2** 2s. 6d. carmine .. 48·00
F19 F **3** 5s. brown .. 60·00
F20 F **4** 10s. orange-brown .. 40·00

(*d*) *P* 11½
F21 F **1** 3d. green ..
F22 F **2** 2s. 6d. lake .. 25·00 22·00
F23 F **3** 5s. sage-green .. 19·00 13·00
F24 F **4** 10s. salmon .. 34·00 27·00

In 1879, the 3d., 2s. 6d., 5s. (brown), and 10s. (orange) were reprinted on thin, tough, white paper, and are found with or without "REPRINT". In 1889 another reprint was made on white card, imperforate and perforated 12. These are also found with or without "REPRINT".

F 5 Duck-billed Platypus

REVENUE
(F **6**)

(Typo D.L.R.)

1880. *W* **16**. *P* 14.
F25 F **5** 1d. slate .. 8·00 3·25
F26 3d. chestnut .. 9·00 2·25
F27 6d. mauve .. 30·00 2·00
F28 1s. rose-pink .. 38·00 3·25

All values are known imperf, but not used.

Reprints are known of the 1d. in *deep blue* and the 6d. in lilac. The former is on yellowish white, the latter on white card. Both values also exist on wove paper, perf 12, with the word "REPRINT".

1888. *W* **16**. *P* 11½, 12.
F29 F **2** 2s. 6d. lake .. 15·00 11·00
a. Imperf between (horiz pair) .. £450

1900 (Nov). *Optd with Type* F **6**. A. *Types* F **2** *and* F **4**. *W* **16**.
F30 2s. 6d. carmine (*imperf*) .. £170
a. "REVFNUE" .. £250
F31 2s. 6d. carmine (*p* 12) .. £160
a. "REVFNUE" ..
b. Opt inverted ..
c. "REVFNUE" inverted ..
F32 10s. salmon (*p* 12) ..
a. "REVFNUE" ..
F33 10s. salmon (*W* **4**, *p* 12) ..
a. "REVFNUE" ..

B. *Type* F **5**. *W* **16**. *P* 14
F34 3d. chestnut .. 13·00
a. Double opt, one vertical ..

C. *Type* F **5**. *Lithographed. P* 12. (*a*) *Thin transparent paper. W* **15**
F35 1d. blue .. 65·00

(*b*) *Thick paper. W* **16**
F36 1d. blue .. 12·00
a. Imperf between (horiz pair) .. £300
b. "REVENUE" inverted .. £100
c. "REVENUE" double .. £275
d. *Pale blue* .. 12·00
F37 2d. chestnut .. 13·00
a. Value omitted .. £180
b. Value double .. £225
F38 6d. mauve .. 42·00
a. Double print .. £200
F39 1s. pink .. 75·00

It is doubtful if Nos. F35 to F39 were authorised for postage, though some are known duly postmarked. No. F37 is somewhat different in design from Type F **5**.

D. *T* **20**. *W* **16**. *P* 14
F40 £1 green and yellow .. £180
a. Opt double, one vertical .. £325

The authorisation for the above issues to be used for postal purposes was withdrawn from 1 December 1900 although examples continued to be used "unofficially" until at least 1903, the postal authorities inserting notices in the *Government Gazette* during 1902 in an attempt to end such usage.

Tasmania now uses the stamps of AUSTRALIA.

Togo

ANGLO-FRENCH OCCUPATION

The stamps of GERMANY were used in the colony from March 1888 until June 1897 when issues for TOGO were provided.

PRICES FOR STAMPS ON COVER

Nos. 1/22	*from* × 2
Nos. 23/33	—
Nos. 34/58	*from* × 3

Stamps of German Colonial issue Types A and B 1900 and 1909–14 (5 pf. and 10 pf.)

TOGO
Anglo-French
Occupation
(1)

Half penny
(2)

1914 (28 Sept). *Optd with T* **1**. *Wide setting. Lines 3 mm apart.*
1 3 pf. brown .. .. £130 95·00
2 5 pf. green .. .. £130 95·00
3 10 pf. carmine (Wmk Lozenges) £150 £120
a. Opt inverted .. .. — £5000
b. Opt *tête-bêche* in vert pair .. .. .. — £6500
c. No wmk .. .. — £4750
4 20 pf. ultramarine .. .. 28·00 19·00
5 25 pf. black and red/*yellow* .. .. .. 28·00 23·00
6 30 pf. black and orange/*buff* .. .. .. 28·00 23·00
7 40 pf. black and carmine £300 £225
8 50 pf. black and purple/*buff* £8500 £7000
9 80 pf. black and carmine/*rose* £325 £250
10 1 m. carmine £5000 £3000
11 2 m. blue £7500 £5500
a. "Occupation" double £10000 £10000
b. Opt inverted £9500

1914 (1 Oct). *Nos.* 1 *and* 2 *surch as T* **2**.
12 ½d. on 3 pf. brown £425 £275
a. Thin "y" in "penny" £650 £475
13 1d. on 5 pf. green £425 £275
a. Thin "y" in "penny" £650 £475

TOGO
Anglo-French
Occupation
(3)

TOGO
Anglo-French
Occupation
Half penny
(4)

1914 (Oct). (*a*) *Optd with T* **3**. *Narrow Setting. Lines 2 mm apart.*
14 3 pf. brown £650 £550
a. "Occupation" omitted £2500
15 5 pf. green £600 £550
16 10 pf. carmine £1300 £1300
17 20 pf. ultramarine .. .. 14·00 12·00
a. "TOG" £5000 £5000
18 25 pf. black and red/*yellow* .. .. .. 19·00 19·00
a. "TOG" £10000
19 30 pf. black and orange/*buff* .. .. .. 19·00 19·00
20 40 pf. black and carmine £650 £700
21 50 pf. black and purple/*buff* £7500 £5000
22 80 pf. black and carmine/*rose* £600 £650
23 1 m. carmine £7000 £3750
24 2 m. blue £7000 £6500
25 3 m. violet-black .. .. — £20000
26 5 m. lake and black .. .. — £20000

(*b*) *Narrow setting, but including value, as T* **4**
27 ½d. on 3 pf. brown .. .. 26·00 23·00
a. "TOG" £425 £200
b. Thin "y" in "penny" .. .. .. 55·00 38·00
28 1d. on 5 pf. green .. .. 6·50 6·50
a. "TOG" .. .. £130 65·00
b. Thin "y" in "penny" .. .. .. 15·00 15·00

SETTINGS

Wide setting, *3 mm apart.* The overprint on the 3 pf. to 80 pf. was set up in five rows of 10, repeated twice on each sheet. There are many minor varieties.

The *tête-bêche* opt on the 10 pf. is due to the sheet being turned round after the upper 50 stamps had been overprinted so that vertical pairs from the two middle rows have the opt *tête-bêche*.

In the 20 pf. one half of a sheet was overprinted with the wide setting (3 mm), and the other half with the narrow setting (2 mm), so that vertical pairs from the middle of the sheet show the two varieties of the overprint.

Narrow setting, *2 mm apart.* In the ½d. on 3 pf. brown, the 1d. on 5 pf. green and the 20 pf. blue stamp No. 37 in each setting has the error "TOG".

The ½d. on 3 pf. and 1d. on 5 pf. have the following variety in each of setting of 50:—

Thin dropped "y" with small serifs on Nos. 1, 2, 11, 21, 31, 41 and 42.

TOGO
Anglo-French
Occupation
(6)

TOGO
ANGLO-FRENCH
OCCUPATION
(7)

TOGO
ANGLO-FRENCH
OCCUPATION
(8)

1915 (7 Jan). *Optd as T* **6**. *The words* "Anglo-French" *measure* 15 *mm instead of* 16 *mm as in T* **3**.
29 3 pf. brown £4500 £2500
30 5 pf. green £200 £130
31 10 pf. carmine £200 £130
a. No wmk .. ..
32 20 pf. ultramarine £1700 £475
32*a* 40 pf. black and carmine .. .. .. † —
33 50 pf. black and purple/*buff* £6500 £5000

This printing was made on another lot of German Togo stamps, found at Sansane-Mangu.

The setting is in groups of 25 (5 × 5), repeated four times on a sheet.

The fifth stamp in each setting has a broken second "O" in "TOGO", resembling a badly formed "U".

The German Colonial stamps overprinted "Togo Occupation franco-anglaise" will be found in Part 6 (*France*) of this catalogue.

Stamps of Gold Coast overprinted

1915 (May). *Stamps of Gold Coast, optd locally with T* **7** ("OCCUPATION" 14½ *mm long*).
34 **9** ½d. green 25 40
g. Opt double .. .. 50·00 60·00
35 **10** 1d. red 25 30
g. Opt double .. .. 55·00 65·00
h. Opt inverted .. .. 45·00 50·00
ha. Ditto. "TOGO" omitted .. ..
36 **11** 2d. greyish slate 30 40
37 **9** 2½d. bright blue 40 55
38 **11** 3d. purple/*yellow* 65 80
a. White back .. .. 3·25 4·50
40 6d. dull and bright purple .. .. .. 65 1·75
41 **9** 1s. black/*green* .. .. 1·25 2·00
g. Opt double £110
42 2s. purple and blue/*blue* .. .. .. 3·50 6·50
43 **11** 2s. 6d. black and red/*blue* .. .. .. 4·50 6·00
44 **9** 5s. green and red/*yellow* (*white back*) .. 8·00 12·00
45 10s. green and red/*green* .. .. .. 20·00 27·00
46 20s. purple and black/*red* .. .. .. 55·00 75·00
34/46 .. .. *Set of* 12 85·00 £120

Varieties (*Nos. indicate positions in pane*).
A. *Small* "F" *in* "FRENCH" (25, 58 *and* 59).
B. *Thin* "G" *in* "TOGO" (24).
C. *No hyphen after* "ANGLO" (5).
D. *Two hyphens after* "ANGLO" (5).
E. "CUPATION" *for* "OCCUPATION" (33).
F. "CCUPATION" *for* "OCCUPATION" (57).

Prices are for unused. Used are worth more

		A	B	C	D	E	F
34	½d.	1·50	3·00	1·75	†	65·00	32·00
35	1d.	1·75	4·25	2·50	†	†	55·00
	h. Inverted ..	£300	£350	£350	†	†	†
36	2d.	1·75	5·50	45·00	25·00	†	50·00
37	2½d.	2·50	6·00	22·00	30·00	†	50·00
38	3d.	2·50	6·00	28·00	†	†	55·00
	a. White back ..	14·00	40·00	†	†	†	†
40	6d.	4·25	5·50	†	†	†	90·00
41	1s.	4·25	6·00	†	†	†	50·00
42	2s.	15·00	20·00	38·00	†	†	£100
43	2s. 6d.	16·00	25·00	48·00	†	†	£225
44	5s.	19·00	35·00	60·00	†	†	90·00
45	10s.	42·00	70·00	†	†	†	£175
46	20s.	85·00	£110	†	†	†	£175

1916 (Apr). *London opt T* **8** ("OCCUPATION" 15 *mm long*). *Heavy type and thicker letters showing through on back.*
47 **9** ½d. green 15 25
48 **10** 1d. red 15 20
49 **11** 2d. greyish slate 35 45
50 **9** 2½d. bright blue 45 60
51 **11** 3d. purple/*yellow* 55 85
52 6d. dull and bright purple .. .. .. 55 1·00
53 **9** 1s. black/*green* .. .. 1·25 1·50
a. On blue-green, olive back .. .. .. 3·25 4·00
b. On emerald back .. .. .. 75·00 £100
54 2s. purple and blue/*blue* .. .. .. 3·75 5·00
55 **11** 2s. 6d. black and red/*blue* .. .. .. 4·50 5·50
56 **9** 5s. green and red/*yellow* .. .. .. 7·50 10·00
a. On orange buff .. .. .. 7·00 13·00
57 10s. green and red/*green* .. .. .. 20·00 27·00
a. On blue-green, olive back .. .. 13·00 17·00
58 20s. purple and black/*red* .. .. .. 55·00 70·00
47/58 .. .. *Set of* 12 80·00 £100
47/58 Optd "Specimen" .. .. *Set of* 12 £700

Tokelau Islands

see after New Zealand

Tonga

The Tongan Post Office was established in 1885 and FIJI 2d. and 6d. stamps are recorded in use until the arrival of Nos. 1/4.

PRICES FOR STAMPS ON COVER TO 1945

Nos. 1/4	*from* × 20
Nos. 5/9	*from* × 10
Nos. 10/28	*from* × 5
Nos. 29/32	*from* × 4
Nos. 33/7	*from* × 5
Nos. 38/54	*from* × 4
Nos. 55/63	*from* × 6
Nos. 64/70	*from* × 3
Nos. 71/87	*from* × 2

The Official stamps, Nos. O1/10, are very rare used on cover.

PROTECTORATE KINGDOM

King George I, 1845–93

1 King George I

2

(Eng Bock and Cousins. Plates made and typo Govt Ptg Office, Wellington)

1886–88. *W* **2**. *P* 12½ (*line*) *or* 12 × 11½ (*comb*)*.
1 **1** 1d. carmine (*p* 12½) (27.8.86) .. .. 80·00 14·00
a. Perf 12½ × 10 .. .. ..
b. Perf 12 × 11½ (15.7.87) .. .. 10·00 7·50
ba. Pale carmine (*p* 12 × 11½) .. .. 16·00 12·00
2 2d. pale violet (*p* 12½) (27.8.86) .. .. 17·00 11·00
a. Bright violet .. .. 30·00 11·00
b. Perf 12 × 11½ (15.7.87) .. .. 10·00 8·00
ba. Bright violet (*p* 12 × 11½) .. .. 11·00 8·00
3 6d. blue (*p* 12½) (9.10.86) .. .. 15·00 5·50
a. Perf 12 × 11½ (15.10.88) .. .. 14·00 5·50
ab. Dull blue (*p* 12 × 11½) .. .. 9·00 5·50
4 1s. pale green (*p* 12½) (9.10.86) .. .. 40·00 10·00
a. Deep green (*p* 12½) .. .. .. 45·00 7·00
b. Perf 12 × 11½ (15.10.88) .. .. 23·00 8·00
ba. Deep green (*p* 12 × 11½) .. .. 23·00 7·00

*See note after New Zealand, No. 186.

FOUR
PENCE.
(3)

EIGHT
PENCE.
(4)

(Surch Messrs Wilson & Horton, Auckland, N.Z.)

1891 (10 Nov). *Nos.* 1b *and* 2b *surch.*
5 **3** 4d. on 1d. carmine .. .. .. 5·00 9·00
a. No stop after "PENCE" .. .. 38·00 55·00
6 **4** 8d. on 2d. violet .. .. .. 30·00 38·00
a. Short "T" in "EIGHT" .. .. 55·00 65·00

No. 5a occurred on R. 6/8 and 9, R. 10/11, all from the righthand pane.

1891 (23 Nov). *Optd with stars in upper right and lower left corners. P* 12½.
7 **1** 1d. carmine .. .. 35·00 35·00
a. Three stars £125
b. Four stars £175
c. Five stars £325
d. Perf 12 × 11½ £110
da. Three stars £225
db. Four stars £275
dc. Five stars £500
8 2d. violet .. .. 35·00 35·00
a. Perf 12 × 11½ £110

1892 (15 Aug). *W* **2**. *P* 12 × 11½.
9 **1** 6d. yellow-orange .. .. 11·00 16·00

5 Arms of Tonga

6 King George I

(Dies eng A. E. Cousins. Typo at Govt Printing Office, Wellington, N.Z.)

1892 (10 Nov). *W* **2**. *P* 12 × 11½.
10 **5** 1d. pale rose .. .. 13·00 16·00
a. Bright rose .. .. 12·00 16·00
b. Bisected diag (½d.) (on cover) .. .. † £550
11 **6** 2d. olive .. .. 9·50 15·00
12 **5** 4d. chestnut .. .. 20·00 25·00
13 **6** 8d. bright mauve .. .. 45·00 55·00
14 1s. brown .. .. 38·00 45·00

½d.
(7)

2½d.
(8)

FIVE
PENCE.
(9)

7½d.
(10)

1893. *Printed in new colours and surch with T* **7/10** *by Govt Printing Office, Wellington.* (*a*) *In carmine. P* 12½ (21 Aug).
15 **5** ½d. on 1d. bright ultramarine .. .. 23·00 23·00
a. Surch omitted .. .. ..
16 **6** 2½d. on 2d. green .. .. .. 14·00 14·00
17 **5** 5d. on 4d. orange .. .. .. 11·00 15·00
18 **6** 7½d. on 8d. carmine .. .. .. 35·00 42·00

(*b*) *In black. P* 12 × 11½ (Nov)
19 **5** ½d. on 1d. dull blue .. .. .. 32·00 40·00
20 **6** 2½d. on 2d. green .. .. .. 17·00 17·00
a. Surch double .. .. .. — £550

SURCHARGE.
HALF-PENNY
(11)

SURCHARGE.
2½d.
(12)

(Surch at the *Star* Office, Auckland, N.Z.)

1894 (June). *Surch with T* **11** *or* **12**.

No.	Type	Description	Unused	Used
21	**5**	½d. on 4d. chestnut (B.)	3·50	7·50
		a. "SURCHARCE"	7·50	12·00
22	**6**	½d. on 1s. brown	3·50	11·00
		a. "SURCHARCE"	9·50	13·00
		b. Surch double	£400	
		c. Surch double with "SURCHARCE"	£500	
23		2½d. on 8d. bright mauve	6·00	11·00
		a. No stop after "SURCHARGE"	22·00	28·00
24		2½d. on 1s. green (No. 4*a*)	22·00	22·00
		a. No stop after "SURCHARGE"	48·00	
		b. Perf 12 × 11½	15·00	20·00
		ba. No stop after "SURCHARGE"	40·00	

Nos. 21/4 were surcharged in panes of 60 (6 × 10) with Nos. 21a and 22a occurring on R. 2/6, R. 4/6, R. 5/6, R. 9/1 and R. 10/6.

(Design resembling No. 11 litho and surch at *Star* Office, Auckland, N.Z.)

1895 (May). *As T* **6** *surch as T* **11** *and* **12**. *No wmk. P* 12.

No.	Type	Description	Unused	Used
25	**11**	1d. on 2d. pale blue (C.)	22·00	22·00
26	**12**	1½d. on 2d. pale blue (C.)	30·00	27·00
		a. Perf 12 × 11	27·00	26·00
27		2½d. on 2d. pale blue (C.)*	38·00	38·00
		a. No stop after "SURCHARGE"	£200	
28		7½d. on 2d. pale blue (C.)	£125	
		a. Perf 12 × 11	48·00	45·00

*The 2½d. on 2d. is the only value which normally has a stop after the word "SURCHARGE".

King George II, 1893–1918

13 King George II

Half Penny

VAEU OE PENI

(14)

(Litho *Star* Office, Auckland, N.Z.)

1895 (16 Aug). *No wmk. P* 12.

No.	Type	Description	Unused	Used
29	**13**	1d. olive-green	14·00	15·00
		a. Bisected diagonally (½d.) (on cover)	†	£450
		b. Imperf between (pair)	—	£5000
30		2½d. rose	20·00	24·00
		a. Stop (flaw) after "POSTAGE"	45·00	45·00
31		5d. blue	12·00	18·00
		a. Perf 12 × 11	15·00	20·00
		b. Perf 11	£325	
32		7½d. orange-yellow	14·00	23·00
		a. Yellow	14·00	23·00

1895 (Sept). *T* **13** *redrawn and surch. No wmk. P* 12.

No.	Type	Description	Unused	Used
33	**11**	½d. on 2½d. vermilion	27·00	30·00
		a. "SURCHARCE"	60·00	
		b. Stop after "POSTAGE"	75·00	
34		1d. on 2½d. vermilion	20·00	25·00
		a. Stop after "POSTAGE"	45·00	
35	**12**	7½d. on 2½d. vermilion	45·00	45·00
		a. Stop after "POSTAGE"	75·00	

In the ½d. surcharge there is a stop after "SURCHARGE" and not after "PENNY". In the 1d. and 7½d. the stop is after the value only.

1896 (May). *Nos.* 26a *and* 28a *with typewritten surcharge* "Half-Penny-" *in violet, and Tongan surcharge in black.*

(A) *Tongan surch reading downwards.*
(B) *Tongan surch reading upwards.*

No.	Type	Description	A		B	
36	**6**	½d. on 1½d. on 2d.	£110	—	£140	—
		a. Perf 12	£120	—	£140	£120
		ab. "Haalf" (*p* 12)	†		£500	—
		c. "H" double	†		—	—
37		½d. on 7½d. on 2d.	18·00	22·00	18·00	22·00
		a. "Hafl" for "Half"	£425	£425	†	
		b. "Hafl" ("Penny" omitted)	£500	—	†	
		c. "PPenny"	£180	—	†	
		d. Stops instead of hyphens	£180	—	£275	—
		e. "Halyf"	—	—	†	
		f. "Half-Penny-" inverted	£750	—	†	
		g. No hyphen after "Penny"	—	—	†	
		h. "Hwlf"	†		—	—
		j. "Penny" double	†		—	—
		k. "Penny" twice, with "Half" on top of upper "Penny"	†		—	—
		l. Capital "P" over small "p"	—	—	†	
		m. Perf 12	—	—	£250	—
		ma. No hyphen after "Half" (*p* 12)	—	—	†	

There are variations in the relative positions of the words "Half" and "Penny", both vertically and horizontally.

15 Arms

16 Ovava Tree, Kana-Kubolu

17 King George II

18 Prehistoric Trilith at Haamonga

19 Bread Fruit

20 Coral

21 View of Haapai

22 Red Shining Parrot

23 View of Vavau Harbour

I No sword hilt

II Top of hilt showing

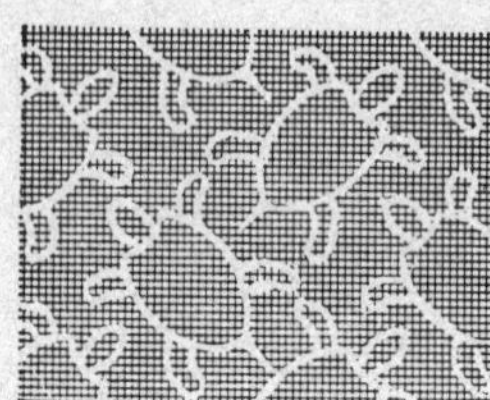

24 Tortoises

(Recess D.L.R.)

1897 (1 June). *W* **24**. *P* 14.

No.	Type	Description	Unused	Used
38	**15**	½d. indigo	50	55
39	**16**	1d. black and scarlet	50	35
40	**17**	2d. sepia and bistre (I)	3·00	1·90
41		2d. sepia and bistre (II)	13·00	5·00
42		2d. grey and bistre (II)	2·00	1·50
43		2½d. black and blue	1·75	1·50
		a. No fraction bar in "½"	60·00	60·00
44	**18**	3d. black and yellow-green	1·50	2·25
45	**19**	4d. green and purple	5·00	5·00
46	**17**	5d. black and orange	6·00	6·00
47	**20**	6d. red	5·00	2·75
48	**17**	7½d. black and green	6·00	9·00
		a. Centre inverted	£3000	
49		10d. black and lake	10·00	12·00
50		1s. black and red-brown	7·00	7·00
		a. No hyphen before "TAHA"	£140	£140
51	**21**	2s. black and ultramarine	18·00	20·00
52	**22**	2s. 6d. deep purple	27·00	25·00
53	**23**	5s. black and brown-red	22·00	22·00
38/53		*Set of* 14	£100	£100

The 1d., 3d. and 4d. are known bisected and used for half their value.

T - L

1 June, 1899.

(25)

26 Queen Salote

1899 (1 June). *Royal Wedding. Optd with T* **25** *at* "Star" *Office, Auckland, N.Z.*

No.	Type	Description	Unused	Used
54	**16**	1d. black and scarlet	22·00	35·00
		a. "1889" for "1899"	£200	£200

The Letters "T L" stand for Taufa'ahau, the King's family name, and Lavinia, the bride.

Queen Salote, 1918–65

Die I

Die II

(Recess D.L.R.)

1920–37. *W* **24**. *P* 14.

No.	Type	Description	Unused	Used
55	**15**	½d. yellow-green (1934)	20	85
56	**26**	1½d. grey-black (1935)	35	2·00
57		2d. slate-purple and violet	1·90	4·25
57*a*		2d. black and dull purple (Die I) (1924)	2·00	1·40
		b. Die II (1937)	2·75	2·00
58		2½d. black and blue	1·90	7·50
59		2½d. bright ultramarine (1934)	45	1·00
60		5d. black and orange-vermilion	3·00	4·00
61		7½d. black and yellow-green	1·25	2·00
62		10d. black and lake	3·00	4·50
63		1s. black and red-brown	2·25	3·50
55/63		*Set of* 10	14·50	28·00
55/63 Optd/Perf "Specimen"		*Set of* 9	70·00	

In Die II the ball of the "2" is larger and the word "PENI-E-UA" is re-engraved and slightly shorter; the "U" has a spur on the left side.

TWO PENCE

PENI-E-UA

(27)

TWO PENCE

PENI-E-UA

(28)

1923 (20 Oct)–**24.** *Nos.* 46 *and* 48 *to* 53 *surch as T* **27** (*vert stamps*) *or* **28** (*horiz stamps*).

No.	Type	Description	Unused	Used
64		2d. on 5d. black and orange (B.)	1·40	1·75
65		2d. on 7½d. black and green (B.)	15·00	20·00
66		2d. on 10d. black and lake (B.)	11·00	18·00
67		2d. on 1s. black and red-brown (B.)	23·00	24·00
		a. No hyphen before "TAHA"	£275	
68		2d. on 2s. black and ultramarine (R.)	3·50	8·00
69		2d. on 2s. 6d. deep purple (R.)	5·00	6·00
70		2d. on 5s. black and brown-red (R.)	3·00	4·00
64/70		*Set of* 7	55·00	75·00

29 Queen Salote

(Recess D.L.R.)

1938 (12 Oct). *20th Anniv of Queen Salote's Accession. Tablet at foot dated* "1918–1938". *W* **24**. *P* 14.

No.	Type	Description	Unused	Used
71	**29**	1d. black and scarlet	55	1·50
72		2d. black and purple	3·25	2·00
73		2½d. black and ultramarine	3·25	3·00
71/3 Perf "Specimen"		*Set of* 3	65·00	

For Silver Jubilee issue in a similar design, see Nos. 83/87.

Die III

(Recess D.L.R.)

1942–49. *Wmk Mult Script CA* (*sideways on* 5s.). *P* 14.

No.	Type	Description	Unused	Used
74	**15**	½d. yellow-green	12	60
75	**16**	1d. black and scarlet	25	50
76	**26**	2d. black and purple (Die II)	20	40
		a. Die III (4.49)	6·50	5·00

77	**26**	2½d. bright ultramarine	20	35
78	**18**	3d. black and yellow-green	25	30
79	**20**	6d. red	40	65
80	**26**	1s. black and red-brown	40	85
81	**22**	2s. 6d. deep purple	10·00	12·00
82	**23**	5s. black and brown-red	11·00	15·00
74/82		*Set of* 9	21·00	27·00
74/82 Perf "Specimen"		*Set of* 9	£100	

In Die III the foot of the "2" is longer than in Die II and extends towards the right beyond the curve of the loop; the letters of "PENI-E-UA" are taller and differently shaped.

UANIMA TA'U 'OE PULE 'A 'ENE 'AFIO 1918-1943

30

(Recess D.L.R.)

1944 (25 Jan). *Silver Jubilee of Queen Salote's Accession. As T* **29**, *but inscr* "1918–1943" *at foot, as T* **30**. *Wmk Mult Script CA. P* 14.

83	1d. black and carmine	12	20
84	2d. black and purple	12	20
85	3d. black and green	12	20
86	6d. black and orange	12	35
87	1s. black and brown	12	40
83/7 Perf "Specimen"	*Set of* 5	70·00	

1949 (10 Oct). *75th Anniv of Universal Postal Union. As Nos.* 114/17 *of Antigua.*

88	2½d. ultramarine	30	15
89	3d. olive	50	60
90	6d. carmine-red	55	40
91	1s. red-brown	60	60

31 Queen Salote **33**

32 Queen Salote

(Photo Waterlow)

1950 (1 Nov). *Queen Salote's Fiftieth Birthday. Wmk Mult Script CA. P* 12½.

92	**31**	1d. carmine	15	35
93	**32**	5d. green	30	60
94	**33**	1s. violet	35	70

34 Map

35 Palace, Nuku'alofa

(Recess Waterlow)

1951 (2 July). *50th Anniv of Treaty of Friendship between Great Britain and Tonga. T* **34/5** *and similar designs. Wmk Mult Script CA. P* 12½ (3d.), 13 × 13½ (½d.), 13½ × 13 (*others*).

95	½d. green	25	35
96	1d. black and carmine	20	40
97	2½d. green and brown	30	60
98	3d. yellow and bright blue	60	60
99	5d. carmine and green	60	60
100	1s. yellow-orange and violet	60	60
95/100	*Set of* 6	2·25	2·75

Designs: *Horiz*—2½d. Beach scene; 5d. Flag; 1s. Arms of Tonga and G.B. *Vert*—3d. H.M.N.Z.S. *Bellona.*

40 Royal Palace, Nuku'alofa

43 Swallows' Cave, Vava'u

52 Queen Salote

53 Arms of Tonga

(Des J. Berry. Centre litho, frame recess (£1), recess (others) B.W.)

1953 (1 July). *T* **40**, **43**, **52/3** *and similar designs. W* **24**. *P* 11 × 11½ (*vert*) *or* 11½ × 11 (*horiz*).

101	1d. black and red-brown	5	5
102	1½d. blue and emerald	5	5
103	2d. deep turquoise-green and black	20	5
104	3d. blue and deep bluish green	20	5
105	3½d. yellow and carmine-red	20	10
106	4d. yellow and deep rose-carmine	35	10
107	5d. blue and red-brown	25	12
108	6d. black and deep blue	25	10
109	8d. emerald and deep reddish violet	30	10
110	1s. blue and black	30	5
111	2s. sage-green and brown	45	60
112	5s. orange-yellow and slate-lilac	5·00	3·50
113	10s. yellow and black	5·50	4·00
114	£1 yellow, scarlet, ultramarine & dp brt bl	9·50	9·00
101/14	*Set of* 14	20·00	16·00

Designs: *Horiz* (*as T* **40**)—1½d. Shore fishing with throw-net; 2d. Ketches and canoe; 3½d. Map of Tongatapu; 4d. Vava'u Harbour; 5d. Post Office, Nuku'alofa; 6d. Aerodrome, Fua'amotu; 8d. Nuku'alofa wharf; 2s. Lifuka, Ha'apai; 5s. Mutiny of the *Bounty*. *Vert* (*as T* **43**)—1s. Map of Tonga Islands.

54 Stamp of 1886

55 Whaler and Longboat

(Des D. M. Bakeley. Photo Harrison)

1961 (1 Dec). *75th Anniv of Tongan Postal Service. T* **54/5** *and similar horiz designs. W* **24**. *P* 14½ × 13½.

115	1d. carmine and brown-orange	15	10
116	2d. ultramarine	25	10
117	4d. blue-green	20	10
118	5d. violet	35	12
119	1s. red-brown	50	12

Designs:—4d. Queen Salote and Post Office, Nuku'alofa; 5d. Mail steamer; 1s. Mailplane over Tongatapu.

1862
TAU'ATĀINA
EMANCIPATION
1962

(59)

60 "Protein Foods"

1962 (7 Feb). *Centenary of Emancipation. Nos.* 101, 104, 107/10, 112, 117 *optd with T* **59** (*No.* 126 *surch also*), *in red, by R. S. Wallbank, Govt Printer.*

120	1d. black and red-brown	15	12
121	4d. blue-green	25	20
122	5d. blue and red-brown	25	20
123	6d. black and deep blue	30	25
124	8d. emerald and deep reddish violet	45	30
125	1s. blue and black	35	30
	a. Opt inverted	£325	£190
126	2s. on 3d. blue and deep bluish green	80	80
	a. Missing fraction-bar in surch	10·00	
127	5s. orange-yellow and slate-lilac	1·25	1·50
	a. Opt inverted	£160	
120/127	*Set of* 8	3·50	3·25

(Des M. Goaman. Photo Harrison)

1963 (4 June). *Freedom from Hunger. W* **24**. *P* 14 × 14½.

128	**60**	11d. ultramarine	30	20

61 Coat of Arms

62 Queen Salote

63 Queen Salote

(Des Ida West. Die-cut Walsall)

1963 (17 June). *First Polynesian Gold Coinage Commemoration. Circular designs. Embossed on gold foil, backed with paper, inscr overall* "TONGA THE FRIENDLY ISLANDS". *Imperf.*

(*a*) *Postage.* ¼ *koula coin. Diameter* 1⅝ *in.*

129	**61**	1d. carmine	5	5
130	**62**	2d. deep blue	8	8
131	**61**	6d. blue-green	12	12
132	**62**	9d. bright purple	15	15
133	**61**	1s. 6d. violet	20	25
134	**62**	2s. light emerald	30	35

(*b*) *Air.* (i) ½ *koula coin. Diam* 2⅛ *in.*

135	**63**	10d. carmine	20	20
136	**61**	11d. blue-green	20	20
137	**63**	1s. 1d. deep blue	20	20

(ii) 1 *koula coin. Diam* 3⅛ *in.*

138	**63**	2s. 1d. bright purple	30	35
139	**61**	2s. 4d. light emerald	35	40
140	**63**	2s. 9d. violet	40	45
129/140 *and* O17		*Set of* 13	5·00	6·50

Examples of a 9d. Postage value in the design of the 1s. 6d. exists, but these have been identified as proofs.

64 Red Cross Emblem

(Des V. Whiteley. Litho B.W.)

1963 (7 Oct). *Red Cross Centenary. W* **24**. *P* 13½.

141	**64**	2d. red and black	10	5
142		11d. red and blue	30	15

65 Queen Salote

66 Map of Tongatapu

(Des M. Meers. Die-cut Walsall)

1964 (19 Oct). *Pan-Pacific South-East Asia Woman's Association Meeting, Nuku'alofa. Embossed on gold foil, backed with paper inscr overall* "TONGA THE FRIENDLY ISLANDS". *Imperf.*

(a) Postage

No.	Type	Description	Unused	Used
143	65	3d. pink	5	5
144		9d. light blue	10	12
145		2s. yellow-green	20	25
146		5s. lilac	35	50

(b) Air

No.	Type	Description	Unused	Used
147	66	10d. blue-green	10	12
148		1s. 2d. black	15	20
149		3s. 6d. cerise	25	35
150		6s. 6d. violet	45	60
143/150		*Set of* 8	1·50	2·00

(67)

1965 (18 Mar). *"Gold Coin" stamps of* 1963 *surch as T* **67** *by Walsall Lithographic Co. New figures of value in gold; obliterating colours shown in brackets. (a) Postage.*

No.	Type	Description	Unused	Used
151	61	1s. 3d. on 1s. 6d. violet (R.)	15	15
152	62	1s. 9d. on 9d. bright purple (W.)	20	20
153	61	2s. 6d. on 6d. blue-green (R.)	30	35
154		5s. on 1d. carmine	14·00	14·00
155	62	5s. on 2d. deep blue	2·50	2·75
156		5s. on 2s. light emerald	1·00	1·25

(b) Air

No.	Type	Description	Unused	Used
157	63	2s. 3d. on 10d. carmine	25	30
158	61	2s. 9d. on 11d. blue-green (W.)	30	35
159	63	4s. 6d. on 2s. 1d. bright purple (R.)	10·00	10·00
160	61	4s. 6d. on 2s. 4d. light emerald (R.)	10·00	10·00
161	63	4s. 6d. on 2s. 9d. violet (R.)	10·00	10·00
151/161 *and* O18		*Set of* 12	48·00	48·00

King Taufa'ahau IV, 16 December 1965

1866-1966
TUPOU COLLEGE
& SECONDARY
EDUCATION

(68)

AIRMAIL
1866 CENTENARY 1966
TUPOU COLLEGE
&
SECONDARY EDUCATION
10d XX

(69)

1966 (18 June). *Centenary of Tupou College and Secondary Education. Nos.* 115/16 *and* 118/19 *optd or surch. (a) Postage. As T* **68**.

No.	Description	Unused	Used
162	1d. carmine and brown-orange (P.)	5	5
163	3d. on 1d. carmine and brown-orange (P.)	5	5
164	6d. on 2d. ultramarine (R.)	10	5
165	1s. 2d. on 2d. ultramarine (R.)	15	15
166	2s. on 2d. ultramarine (R.)	20	20
167	3s. on 2d. ultramarine (R.)	25	25

(b) Air. As T **69**

No.	Description	Unused	Used
168	5d. violet	10	5
169	10d. on 1d. carmine and brown-orange	12	5
170	1s. red-brown	15	5
171	2s. 9d. on 2d. ultramarine	30	30
	a. Sideways "X"	5·50	
172	3s. 6d. on 5d. violet	35	35
	a. Sideways "X"	5·50	
173	4s. 6d. on 1s. red-brown	35	35
	a. Sideways "X"	5·50	
162/173 *and* O19/20	*Set of* 14	4·00	3·75

(70)

(71)

1966 (16 Dec). *Queen Salote Commemoration. "Women's Association" stamps of* 1964 *optd as T* **70**/1, *or surch also, by Walsall Lithographic Co. Inscriptions and new figures of value in first colour and obliterating shapes in second colour given.*

(a) Postage. Optd as T **70**

No.	Type	Description	Unused	Used
174	65	3d. (silver and ultramarine)	5	5
175		5d. on 9d. (silver and black)	5	5
176	65	9d. (silver and black)	10	10
177		1s. 7d. on 3d. (silver and ultramarine)	20	20
178		3s. 6d. on 9d. (silver and black)	40	40
179		6s. 6d. on 3d. (silver and ultramarine)	70	70

(b) Air. Optd as T **71**

No.	Type	Description	Unused	Used
180	66	10d. (silver and black)	12	12
181		1s. 2d. (black and gold)	15	15
182		4s. on 10d. (silver and black)	45	45
183		5s. 6d. on 1s. 2d. (black and gold)	60	60
184		10s. 6d. on 1s. 2d. (gold and black)	1·10	1·10
174/184		*Set of* 11	3·50	3·50

(New Currency. 100 seniti = 1 pa'anga)

1 SENITI 1

(72)

10
Seniti
10

(73)

1967 (25 Mar). *Decimal currency. Various stamps surch as T* **72/3**.

No.	Description	Unused	Used
185	1 s. on 1d. (No. 101)	5	5
186	2 s. on 4d. (No. 106)	5	5
187	3 s. on 5d. (No. 107)	5	5
188	4 s. on 5d. (No. 107)	30	30
189	5 s. on 3½d. (No. 105)	8	8
190	6 s. on 8d. (No. 109)	10	10
191	7 s. on 1½d. (No. 102)	12	12
192	8 s. on 6d. (No. 108)	12	12
193	9 s. on 3d. (No. 104)	15	15
194	10 s. on 1s. (No. 110)	15	15
195	11 s. on 3d. on 1d. (No. 163)	20	20
196	21 s. on 3s. on 2d. (No. 167)	35	35
197	23 s. on 1d. (No. 101)	35	35
198	30 s. on 2s. (No. 111)* (R.)	1·75	1·75
199	30 s. on 2s. (No. 111)* (R.)	2·00	2·00
200	50 s. on 6d. (No. 108) (R.)	1·25	1·25
201	60 s. on 2d. (No. 103) (R.)	1·75	1·75
185/201 *and* O21	*Set of* 18	10·00	10·00

The above surcharges come in a variety of types and sizes. *No. 198 has the surcharged value expressed horizontally; No. 199 has the figures "30" above and below "SENITI".

74 Coat of Arms (reverse)

75 King Taufa'ahau IV (obverse)

(Die-cut Walsall)

1967 (4 July). *Coronation of King Taufa'ahau IV. Circular designs. Embossed on palladium foil, backed with paper inscr overall* "The Friendly Islands Tonga", *etc. Imperf.*

Sizes

(a) Diameter 1½ *in.*	*(d) Diameter* $2\frac{3}{10}$ *in.*
(b) Diameter $1\frac{7}{10}$ *in.*	*(e) Diameter* $2\frac{7}{10}$ *in.*
(c) Diameter 2 *in.*	*(f) Diameter* $2\frac{9}{10}$ *in.*

(a) Postage

No.	Type	Description	Unused	Used
202	74	1 s. orange and greenish blue *(b)*	5	5
203	75	2 s. greenish blue and deep magenta *(c)*	5	5
204	74	4 s. emerald and bright purple *(d)*	8	8
205	75	15 s. turquoise and violet *(e)*	25	25
206	74	28 s. black and bright purple *(a)*	50	50
207	75	50 s. carmine-red and ultramarine *(c)*	85	85
208	74	1 p. blue and carmine *(f)*	1·50	1·50

(b) Air

No.	Type	Description	Unused	Used
209	75	7 s. carmine-red and black *(b)*	10	10
210	74	9 s. brown-purple and emerald *(c)*	12	12
211	75	11 s. greenish blue and orange *(d)*	15	15
212	74	21 s. black and emerald *(e)*	30	30
213	75	23 s. bright purple and light emerald *(a)*	40	40
214	74	29 s. ultramarine and emerald *(c)*	50	50
215	75	2 p. bright purple and orange *(f)*	2·00	2·00
202/15		*Set of* 14	6·00	6·00

The commemorative coins depicted in reverse (Type **74**) are inscribed in various denominations as follows: 1 s.—"20 SENITI"; 4 s.—"PA'ANGA"; 9 s.—"50 SENITI"; 21 s.—"TWO PA'ANGA"; 28 s.—"QUARTER HAU"; 29 s.—"HALF HAU"; 1 p. "HAU".

The
Friendly Islands
welcome the
United States
Peace Corps
S

(76)

1967 (15 Dec). *Arrival of U.S. Peace Corps in Tonga. As Nos.* 101/14, *but imperf in different colours and surch as T* **76**.

(a) Postage.

No.	Description	Unused	Used
216	1 s. on 1d. black and orange-yellow	5	5
217	2 s. on 2d. ultramarine and carmine-red	5	5
218	3 s. on 3d. chestnut and yellow	5	5
219	4 s. on 4d. reddish violet and yellow	5	5
220	5 s. on 5d. green and yellow	10	5
221	10 s. on 1s. carmine-red and yellow	20	10
222	20 s. on 2s. claret and new blue	35	35
223	50 s. on 5s. sepia and orange-yellow	65	65
224	1 p. on 10s. orange-yellow	1·25	1·25

(b) Air

No.	Description	Unused	Used
225	11 s. on 3½d. ultramarine (R.)	20	20
226	21 s. on 1½d. emerald	40	40
227	23 s. on 3½d. ultramarine	45	45
216/27 *and* O26/8	*Set of* 15	6·50	6·50

On Nos. 219 and 224 the opt is smaller, and in four lines instead of five. On Nos. 216/20 the surcharge takes the form of an alteration to the currency name as in T **76**.

2 SENITI 2

(77)

10
SENITI
10

(78)

1968 (6 Apr). *Various stamps surch as T* **77/8**.

(a) Postage

No.	Description	Unused	Used
228	1 s. on 1d. (No. 101) (R.)	5	5
229	2 s. on 4d. (No. 106)	5	5
230	3 s. on 3d. (No. 104) (B.)	5	5
231	4 s. on 5d. (No. 107) (R.)	5	5
232	5 s. on 2d. (No. 103) (R.)	5	5
233	6 s. on 6d. (No. 108) (R.)	8	8
234	7 s. on 1½d. (No. 102) (R.)	10	10
235	8 s. on 8d. (No. 109) (R.)	10	12
236	9 s. on 3½d. (No. 105)	20	20
237	10 s. on 1s. (No. 110) (R.)	20	20
238	20 s. on 5s. (No. 112) (R.)	45	45
239	2 p. on 2s. (No. 111) (R.)	4·00	4·00

(b) Air. Surch as T **78** *with* "AIRMAIL" *added*

No.	Description	Unused	Used
240	11 s. on 10s. (No. 113) (R.)	25	25
241	21 s. on 10s. (No. 113) (R.)	50	50
242	23 s. on 10s. (No. 113) (R.)	50	50
228/42 *and* O22/5	*Set of* 19	13·00	14·00

H.M'S BIRTHDAY
4 JULY 1968

(79)

Friendly Islands
Field & Track Trials
South Pacific Games
Port Moresby
1969
S

(80)

1968 (4 July). *50th Birthday of King Taufa'ahua IV. Nos.* 202/15 *optd as T* **79**. *(a) Postage.*

No.	Type	Description	Unused	Used
243	74	1 s. orange and greenish blue *(b)* (R.)	5	5
244	75	2 s. greenish blue & dp magenta *(b)* (B.)	5	5
245	74	4 s. emerald and bright purple *(d)* (R.)	8	8
246	75	15 s. turquoise and violet *(e)* (B.)	20	20
247	74	28 s. black and bright purple *(a)* (R.)	45	45
248	75	50 s. carmine-red and ultramarine (c) (B.)	80	80
249	74	1 p. blue and carmine *(f)* (R.)	1·75	1·75

(b) Air

No.	Type	Description	Unused	Used
250	75	7 s. carmine-red and black *(b)* (B.)	10	10
251	74	9 s. brown-purple and emerald *(c)* (R.)	12	12
252	75	11 s. greenish blue and orange *(d)* (B.)	15	15
253	74	21 s. black and emerald *(e)* (R.)	35	35
		a. Opt (gold only) double	£275	
254	75	23 s. bright purple & lt emerald *(a)* (B.)	35	35
255	74	29 s. ultramarine and emerald *(c)* (R.)	55	55
256	75	2 p. bright purple and orange *(f)* (B.)	3·75	3·75
243/56 *and* O29/32		*Set of* 18	14·00	14·00

The overprints vary in size, but are all crescent-shaped as Type **79** and inscribed "H.M'S BIRTHDAY 4 JULY 1968" (Type **79**) or "HIS MAJESTY'S 50th BIRTHDAY" (others).

1968 (19 Dec). *South Pacific Games Field and Track Trials, Port Moresby, New Guinea. Nos.* 101/14, *but imperf, in different colours and surch as T* **80**. *(a) Postage.*

No.	Description	Unused	Used
257	5 s. on 5d. green and yellow (R.)	8	8
258	10 s. on 1s. carmine-red and yellow	12	15
259	15 s. on 2s. claret and new blue	20	25
260	25 s. on 2d. ultramarine and carmine-red	35	35
261	50 s. on 1d. black and orange-yellow	65	65
262	75 s. on 10s. orange-yellow (G.)	1·00	1·00

(b) Air

No.	Description	Unused	Used
263	6 s. on 6d. black and yellow*	10	10
264	7 s. on 4d. reddish violet and yellow	10	10
265	8 s. on 8d. black and greenish yellow	12	12
	a. Surch 11½ mm as on 6d.	†	90·00
266	9 s. on 1½d. emerald	15	15

267 11 s. on 3d. chestnut and yellow 15 15
268 21 s. on 3½d. ultramarine 30 30
269 38 s. on 5s. sepia and orange-yellow .. 45 45
270 1 p. on 10s. orange-yellow .. .. .. 1·25 1·25
257/70 *and* O33/4 .. .. .. *Set of* 16 6·00 6·00
*On No. 263 the surcharge is smaller (11½ mm wide).

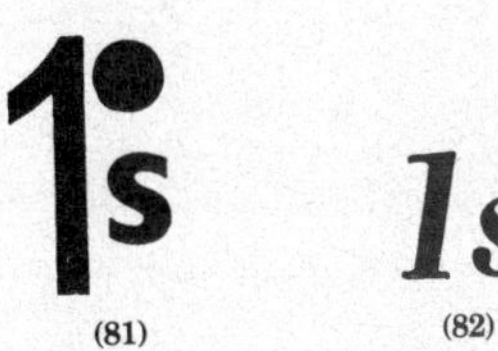

(81) (82)

1969. *Emergency Provisionals. Various stamps (Nos. 273/6 are imperf and in different colours) surch as T* **81** *or* **82**. *(a) Postage.*
271 1 s. on 1s. 2d. on 2d. ultramarine (No. 165) .. 30 30
272 1 s. on 2s. on 2d. ultramarine (No. 166) .. 30 30
273 1 s. on 6d. black and yellow (as No. 108) .. 15 15
274 2 s. on 3½d. ultramarine (as No. 105) .. 20 20
275 3 s. on 1½d. emerald (as No. 102) 20 20
276 4 s. on 8d. black & greenish yell (as No. 109) 25 25

(b) Air. Nos. 171/3 surch with T **82**
277 1 s. on 2s. 9d. on 2d. ultramarine 30 30
a. Sideways "X" .. .. 4·75
278 1 s. on 3s. 6d. on 5d. violet 30 30
a. Sideways "X" .. .. 4·75
279 1 s. on 4s. 6d. on 1s. red-brown 30 30
a. Sideways "X" .. .. 4·75
271/9 .. .. *Set of* 9 2·10 2·10

SELF-ADHESIVE ISSUES. From No. 280 all stamps are manufactured by Walsall Security Printers Ltd and are self-adhesive. The backing paper is separated by roulette or perforations (from No. 780 onwards), and shows on its reverse the words "*TONGA where time begins*", or, from No. 568 onwards, various texts or illustrations. This also applies to the Official stamps.

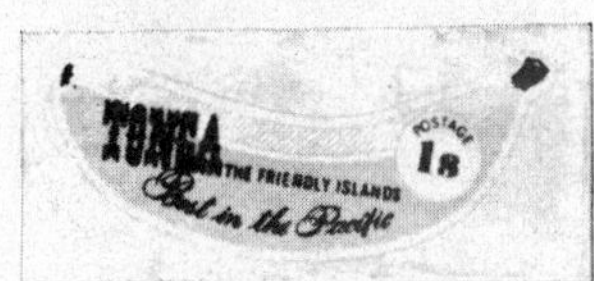

83 Banana

1969 (21 Apr). *Coil stamps.*
280 **83** 1 s. scarlet, black and greenish yellow .. 20 20
281 2 s. brt green, black & greenish yellow .. 30 30
282 3 s. violet, black and greenish yellow .. 35 35
283 4 s. ultramarine, black & greenish yell 45 45
284 5 s. bronze-green, black & greenish yell 55 55
Nos. 280/4 were produced in rolls of 200, each even stamp having a number applied to the front of the backing paper, with the usual inscription on the reverse.
See also Nos. 325/9, 413/17 and 675/89.

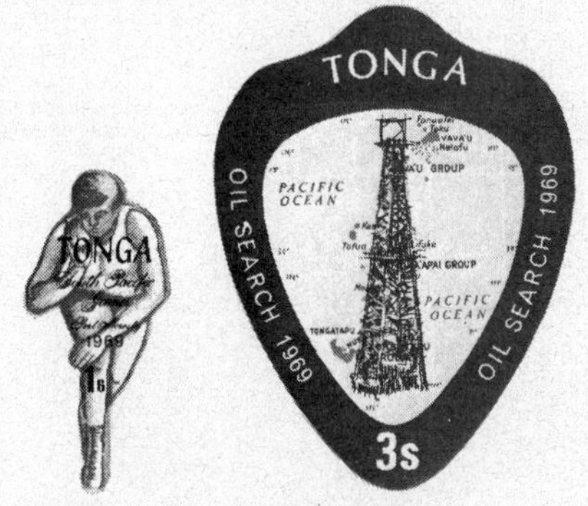

84 Putting the Shot **86** Oil Derrick and Map

1969 (13 Aug). *Third South Pacific Games, Port Moresby. T* **84** *and similar design. (a) Postage.*
285 **84** 1 s. black, red and buff 5 5
286 3 s. bright green, red and buff 8 8
287 6 s. blue, red and buff 10 10
288 10 s. bluish violet, red and buff 15 15
289 30 s. blue, red and buff 50 50

(b) Air
290 – 9 s. black, violet and orange 15 15
291 – 11 s. black, ultramarine and orange .. 15 15
292 – 20 s. black, bright green and orange .. 30 30
293 – 60 s. black, cerise and orange .. .. 1·50 1·50
294 – 1 p. black, blue-green and orange .. 2·00 2·00
285/94 *and* O35/6 .. .. .. *Set of* 12 7·00 7·00
Design:—9, 11, 20, 60 s., 1 p. Boxing.

1969 (23 Dec). *First Oil Search in Tonga. T* **86** *and similar vert design.*

(a) Postage
295 **86** 3 s. multicoloured 5 5
296 7 s. multicoloured 12 12
297 20 s. multicoloured 40 40
298 25 s. multicoloured 50 50
299 35 s. multicoloured 80 80

(b) Air
300 – 9 s. multicoloured 20 20
301 – 10 s. multicoloured 20 20
302 – 24 s. multicoloured 45 45
303 – 29 s. multicoloured 60 60
304 – 38 s. multicoloured 90 90
295/304 *and* O37/8 .. .. .. *Set of* 12 8·50 8·50
Design:—Nos. 300/4, Oil derrick and island of Tongatapu.

87 Members of the British and Tongan Royal Families

1970 (7 Mar). *Royal Visit. T* **87** *and similar design. Multicoloured.*

(a) Postage
305 **87** 3 s. multicoloured 10 10
306 5 s. multicoloured 15 15
307 10 s. multicoloured 30 30
308 25 s. multicoloured 80 80
309 50 s. multicoloured .. .. .. 1·50 1·50

(b) Air
310 – 7 s. multicoloured 20 20
311 – 9 s. multicoloured 25 25
312 – 24 s. multicoloured 80 80
313 – 29 s. multicoloured 90 90
314 – 38 s. multicoloured .. .. .. 1·25 1·25
305/14 *and* O39/41 .. .. .. *Set of* 13 14·00 14·00
Design:—Nos. 310/14, Queen Elizabeth II and King Taufa'ahau Tupou IV.

89 Book, Tongan Rulers and Flag

1970 (4 June). *Entry into British Commonwealth. T* **89** *and similar design. (a) Postage.*
315 **89** 3 s. multicoloured 5 5
316 7 s. multicoloured 15 15
317 15 s. multicoloured 30 30
318 25 s. multicoloured 40 40
319 50 s. multicoloured 70 70

(b) Air
320 – 9 s. turquoise-blue, gold and scarlet .. 15 15
321 – 10 s. bright purple, gold and greenish blue 20 20
322 – 24 s. olive-yellow, gold and green .. 40 40
323 – 29 s. new blue, gold and orange-red .. 45 45
324 – 38 s. deep orange-yellow, gold & brt emer 60 60
315/24 *and* O42/4 .. .. .. *Set of* 13 6·00 6·00
Design: "*Star*" *shaped* (44 × 51 *mm*)—Nos. 320/4, King Taufa'ahau Tupou IV.

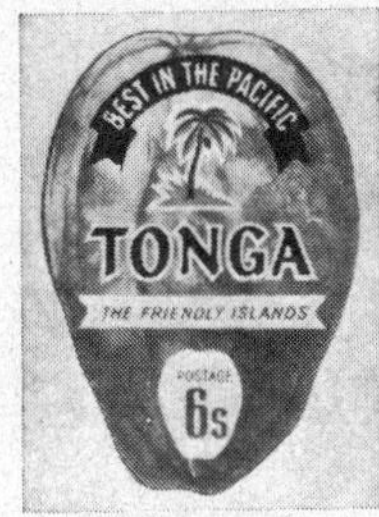

90 Coconut

1970 (9 June). *Coil stamps. (a) As T* **83** *but colours changed.*
325 **83** 1 s. greenish yellow, bright purple & blk 15 15
326 2 s. greenish yellow, ultramarine & black 20 20
327 3 s. greenish yellow, chocolate and black 25 25
328 4 s. greenish yellow, emerald and black 25 25
329 5 s. greenish yellow, orge-red & bl .. 30 30

(b) T **90**. *Multicoloured; colour of face value given*
330 **90** 6 s. rose-carmine 35 35
331 7 s. bright purple 40 40
332 8 s. bluish violet 45 45
333 9 s. turquoise 55 55
334 10 s. pale orange 55 55
325/34 .. .. *Set of* 10 3·00 3·00
Nos. 325/34 and O45/54 were produced in rolls of 200, each even stamp having a number applied to the front of the backing paper, with the usual inscription on the reverse.

91 "Red Cross"

(Litho (postage) or litho and die-stamped (air))

1970 (17 Oct). *Centenary of British Red Cross. T* **91** *and similar "cross" shaped design. (a) Postage.*
335 **91** 3 s. vermilion, black and light green .. 5 5
336 7 s. vermilion, black and ultramarine .. 15 15
337 15 s. vermilion and bright purple .. 30 30
338 25 s. vermilion, black and turquoise-blue 50 50
339 75 s. vermilion and deep red-brown .. 2·25 2·25

(b) Air
340 – 9 s. vermilion and silver 20 20
341 – 10 s. vermilion and bright purple .. 20 20
342 – 18 s. vermilion and green 35 35
343 – 38 s. vermilion and ultramarine .. 1·00 1·00
344 – 1 p. vermilion and turquoise-blue .. 2·75 2·75
335/44 *and* O55/7 .. .. .. *Set of* 13 12·00 12·00
Design: *As T* **91**—Nos. 340/4 as Nos. 335/9 but with inscription rearranged and coat of arms omitted.
On Nos. 335/6 and 338 the black colour is produced as a composite of the other two colours used.

(92)

(93)

1971 (30 Jan). *Fifth Death Anniv of Queen Salote. Nos. 174/84 surch as T* **92/3**. *Obliterating shapes in black; inscriptions and figures of value in colour given. (a) Postage. Surch as T* **92**.
345 **65** 2 s. on 5d. on 9d. (silver) 10 10
346 3 s. on 9d. (orange-red) 10 10
347 5 s. on 3d. (bright green) 15 15
348 15 s. on 3s. 6d. on 9d. (orange-brown) .. 45 45
a. Surch double .. .. .. — 30·00
349 25 s. on 6s. 6d. on 3d. (purple) 80 80
350 50 s. on 1s. 7d. on 3d. (gold) .. .. 1·75 1·75

(b) Air. Surch as T **93**
351 **66** 9 s. on 10d. (silver) 30 30
352 24 s. on 4s. on 10d. (orange-brown) .. 80 80
353 29 s. on 5s. 6d. on 1s. 2d. (orange-red) .. 90 90
354 38 s. on 10s. 6d. on 1s. 2d. (bright green) 1·40 1·40
345/54 *and* O58/61 .. .. .. *Set of* 14 15·00 15·00

(94)

HONOURING
JAPANESE
POSTAL
CENTENARY
1871-1971
15s
(95)

1971 (17 Apr). *"Philatokyo 1971" Stamp Exhibition. As Nos. 101/2, 106 and 109/11, but imperf, colours changed and surch as T* **94** *(Nos. 355/6, 358/61 and 363), as T* **95** *(Nos. 357, 362) or with similar surcharge in four lines (No. 364). (a) Postage.*
355 3 s. on 8d. blk & greenish yellow (Blk. & R.) 5 5
356 7 s. on 4d. reddish violet & yellow (Blk. & R.) 15 15
357 15 s. on 1s. carmine, red and yellow .. 30 30
358 25 s. on 1d. black & orange-yellow (Blk. & R.) 50 50
359 75 s. on 2s. claret & new blue (Blk. & R.) 1·60 1·60

(b) Air. Additionally surch "AIRMAIL"
360 9 s. on 1½d. emerald (Blk. and R.) .. 20 20
361 10 s. on 4d. reddish violet & yellow (Blk. & R.) 20 20
362 18 s. on 1s. carmine-red and yellow (V.) 35 35
363 38 s. on 1d. black & orange-yellow (Blk. & R.) 80 80
364 1 p. on 2s. claret and new blue .. .. 2·25 2·25
355/64 *and* O62/4 .. .. .. *Set of* 13 11·00 11·00

96 Wristwatch

97 Pole-vaulter

1971 (20 July)–**72**. *Air. Backed with paper bearing advertisements.*

365	**96**	14 s. multicoloured	55	55
365*a*		17 s. multicoloured (20.7.72)	65	65
366		21 s. multicoloured	75	75
366*a*		38 s. multicoloured (20.7.72)	1·10	1·10
365/6*a* *and* O65/6*a*		.. .. .. *Set of* 8	5·50	5·50

1971 (20 July). *Fourth South Pacific Games, Tahiti.* T **97** *and similar design. (a) Postage.*

367	**97**	3 s. multicoloured	8	8
368		7 s. multicoloured	15	12
369		15 s. multicoloured	30	30
370		25 s. multicoloured	45	45
371		50 s. multicoloured	1·00	1·00
		(b) Air		
372	–	9 s. multicoloured	20	20
373	–	10 s. multicoloured	20	20
374	–	24 s. multicoloured	55	55
375	–	29 s. multicoloured	70	70
376	–	38 s. multicoloured	90	90
367/76 *and* O67/9		.. .. .. *Set of* 13	9·00	9·00

Design: *Horiz*—Nos. 372/6, High-jumper.

98 Medal of Merit (reverse)

99 Child

1971 (30 Oct). *Investiture of Royal Tongan Medal of Merit.* T **98** *and similar "medal" shaped design. Multicoloured; colour of medal given.*

		(a) Postage		
377	**98**	3 s. gold	8	8
378		24 s. silver	45	45
379	–	38 s. brown	70	70
		(b) Air		
380	–	10 s. gold	25	25
381	–	75 s. silver	1·50	1·50
382	**98**	1 p. brown	1·90	1·90
377/82 *and* O70/2		.. .. .. *Set of* 9	8·00	8·00

Design: *As T* **98**—Nos. 379/81, Obverse of the Medal of Merit.

1971 (31 Dec). *25th Anniv of UNICEF.* T **99** *and similar design.*

		(a) Postage		
383	**99**	2 s. multicoloured	5	5
384		4 s. multicoloured	8	8
385		8 s. multicoloured	15	15
386		16 s. multicoloured	30	30
387		30 s. multicoloured	60	60
		(b) Air		
388	–	10 s. multicoloured	20	20
389	–	15 s. multicoloured	30	30
390	–	25 s. multicoloured	45	45
391	–	50 s. multicoloured	90	90
392	–	1 p. multicoloured	1·75	1·75
383/92 *and* O73/5		.. .. .. *Set of* 13	8·00	8·00

Design: *Vert* (21 x 42 *mm*)—Nos. 388/92, Woman.

100 Map of South Pacific, and *Olovaha*

1972 (14 Apr). *Merchant Marine Routes.* T **100** *and similar design.*

		(a) Postage		
393	**100**	2 s. multicoloured	5	5
394		10 s. multicoloured	20	20
395		17 s. multicoloured	40	40
396		21 s. multicoloured	50	50
397		60 s. multicoloured	2·00	2·00
		(b) Air		
398	–	9 s. multicoloured	20	20
399	–	12 s. multicoloured	25	25
400	–	14 s. multicoloured	30	30
401	–	75 s. multicoloured	2·25	2·25
402	–	90 s. multicoloured	2·75	2·75
393/402 *and* O76/8		.. .. .. *Set of* 13	13·00	13·00

Design:—Nos. 398/402, Map of South Pacific and *Niuvakai.*

101 ¼ Hau Coronation Coin

1972 (15 July). *Fifth Anniv of Coronation.* T **101** *and similar design.*

		(a) Postage		
403	**101**	5 s. multicoloured	10	10
404		7 s. multicoloured	12	12
405		10 s. multicoloured	15	15
406		17 s. multicoloured	25	25
407		60 s. multicoloured	1·00	1·00
		(b) Air		
408	–	9 s. multicoloured	15	15
409	–	12 s. multicoloured	20	20
410	–	14 s. multicoloured	25	25
411	–	21 s. multicoloured	35	35
412	–	75 s. multicoloured	1·50	1·50
403/12 *and* O79/81		.. .. .. *Set of* 13	8·50	8·50

Design (47 × 41 *mm*):—Nos. 408/12, as T **101**, but with coins above inscription instead of beneath it.

102 Water Melon

1972 (30 Sept). *Coil stamps. (a) As T* **83**, *but inscription altered, omitting "Best in the Pacific", and colours changed.*

413	**83**	1 s. light yellow, scarlet and black ..	10	10
414		2 s. light yellow, ultramarine and black	15	15
415		3 s. light yellow, yellow-green and black	20	20
416		4 s. light yellow, royal blue and black ..	20	20
417		5 s. light yellow, reddish brn & bl ..	20	20
		(b) As T **90** *but colours changed. Colour of face value given*		
418	**90**	6 s. dull orange	20	20
419		7 s. ultramarine	25	25
420		8 s. bright magenta	25	25
421		9 s. brown-orange	25	25
422		10 s. bright new blue	30	30
		(c) T **102**. *Colour of face value given*		
423	**102**	15 s. new blue	45	45
424		20 s. reddish orange	60	60
425		25 s. chocolate	70	70
426		40 s. yellow-orange	1·50	1·50
427		50 s. lemon	1·75	1·75
413/27		.. .. .. *Set of* 15	6·50	6·50

Nos. 413/27 and O82/96 were produced in rolls, each even stamp having a number applied to the front of the backing paper, with the usual inscription on the reverse.

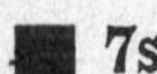

NOVEMBER 1972
INAUGURAL
Internal Airmail
Nuku'alofa — Vava'u

(103)

1972 (2 Nov). *Inaugural Internal Airmail. No. 398 surch with T* **103**.

428		7 s. on 9 s. multicoloured	3·50	2·50

104 Hoisting Tongan Flag

1972 (9 Dec). *Proclamation of Sovereignty over Minerva Reefs.* T **104** *and similar design. (a) Postage.*

429	**104**	5 s. multicoloured	10	10
430		7 s. multicoloured	10	12
431		10 s. multicoloured	15	20
432		15 s. multicoloured	25	30
433		40 s. multicoloured	80	80
		(b) Air		
434	–	9 s. multicoloured	15	15
435	–	12 s. multicoloured	20	25
436	–	14 s. multicoloured	25	30
437	–	38 s. multicoloured	75	75
438	–	1 p. multicoloured	2·00	2·00
429/38 *and* O97/9		.. .. .. *Set of* 13	8·00	8·00

Design: *Spherical* (52 *mm diameter*)—Nos. 434/8, Proclamation in Govt Gazette.

105 Coins around Bank

1973 (30 Mar). *Foundation of Bank of Tonga.* T **105** *and similar design. (a) Postage.*

439	**105**	5 s. multicoloured	10	10
440		7 s. multicoloured	12	12
441		10 s. multicoloured	15	15
442		20 s. multicoloured	35	35
443		30 s. multicoloured	50	50
		(b) Air		
444	–	9 s. multicoloured	20	20
445	–	12 s. multicoloured	25	25
446	–	17 s. multicoloured	35	35
447	–	50 s. multicoloured	1·10	1·10
448	–	90 s. multicoloured	1·75	1·75
439/48 *and* O100/2		.. .. .. *Set of* 13	9·00	9·00

Design: *Horiz* (64 × 52 *mm*)—Nos. 444/8, Bank and banknotes.

106 Handshake and Scout in Canoe

1973 (29 June). *Silver Jubilee of Scouting in Tonga.* T **106** *and similar design. (a) Postage.*

449	**106**	5 s. multicoloured	15	10
450		7 s. multicoloured	20	12
451		15 s. multicoloured	70	40
452		21 s. multicoloured	85	50
453		50 s. multicoloured	3·25	1·75
		(b) Air		
454	–	9 s. multicoloured	35	25
455	–	12 s. multicoloured	50	30
456	–	14 s. multicoloured	70	50
457	–	17 s. multicoloured	80	60
458	–	1 p. multicoloured	11·00	5·50
449/58 *and* O103/5		.. .. .. *Set of* 13	85·00	42·00

Design: *Square* (53 × 53 *mm*)—Nos. 454/8, Scout badge.

MINIMUM PRICE

The minimum price quoted is 5p which represents a handling charge rather than a basis for valuing common stamps. For further notes about prices see introductory pages.

107 Excerpt from Cook's Log-book

1973 (2 Oct). *Bicentenary of Capt. Cook's Visit to Tonga. T* **107** *and similar design. (a) Postage.*

459 **107** 6 s. multicoloured 20 20
460 8 s. multicoloured 25 25
461 11 s. multicoloured 40 40
462 35 s. multicoloured .. .. .. 2·50 2·50
463 40 s. multicoloured .. .. .. 2·50 2·50

(b) Air

464 – 9 s. multicoloured 30 30
465 – 14 s. multicoloured 55 55
466 – 29 s. multicoloured .. .. .. 2·25 2·25
467 – 38 s. multicoloured .. .. .. 2·50 2·50
468 – 75 s. multicoloured .. .. .. 5·00 5·00
459/68 *and* O106/8 .. .. *Set of* 13 27·00 27·00

Design: *Vert*—Nos. 464/8, The *Resolution*.

(108) 109 Red Shining Parrot

1973 (19 Dec). *Commonwealth Games, Christchurch, New Zealand. Various stamps optd as T* **108** *(No. 474 optd "AIRMAIL" in addition). (a) Postage.*

469 5 s. on 50 s. (No. 371) (Blk. and Gold) .. 10 10
470 12 s. on 38 s. (No. 379) (R. and Silver) . .. 25 25
471 14 s. on 75 s. (No. 381) (R. and Gold) 25 25
472 20 s. on 1 p. (No. 382) (Blk. and Gold) . .. 40 40
473 50 s. on 24 s. (No. 378) (Blk. and Silver) .. 95 95

(b) Air

474 7 s. on 25 s. (No. 370) (Blk. and Silver) .. 12 12
475 9 s. on 38 s. (No. 376) (V.) 15 15
476 24 s. (No. 374) 50 50
477 29 s. on 9 s. (No. 454) (B.) 60 60
478 40 s. on 14 s. (No. 456) 90 90
469/78 *and* O109/11 .. .. .. *Set of* 13 8·00 8·00

1974 (20 Mar). *Air.*

479 **109** 7 s. multicoloured 15 15
480 9 s. multicoloured 20 20
481 12 s. multicoloured 25 25
482 14 s. multicoloured 30 30
483 17 s. multicoloured 35 35
484 29 s. multicoloured 60 60
485 38 s. multicoloured 80 80
486 50 s. multicoloured .. .. .. 1·00 1·00
487 75 s. multicoloured .. .. .. 1·60 1·60
479/87 .. .. *Set of* 9 4·75 4·75

Nos. 479/87 and O112/20 were produced in rolls, each stamp having a number applied to the front of the backing paper, with the usual inscription on the reverse.

110 "Stamped Letter"

1974 (20 June). *Centenary of Universal Postal Union. T* **110** *and similar design. (a) Postage.*

488 **110** 5 s. multicoloured 12 10
489 10 s. multicoloured 20 15
490 15 s. multicoloured 30 25
491 20 s. multicoloured 40 35
492 50 s. multicoloured .. .. .. 1·75 1·50

(b) Air

493 – 14 s. multicoloured 30 25
494 – 21 s. multicoloured 55 45
495 – 60 s. multicoloured .. .. .. 2·00 1·75

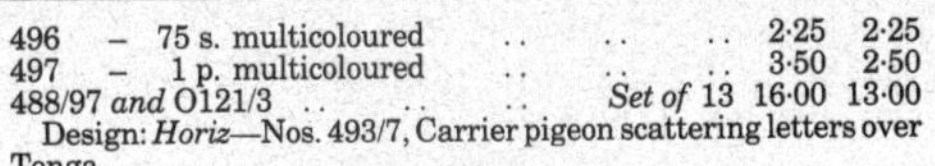
496 – 75 s. multicoloured .. .. 2·25 2·25
497 – 1 p. multicoloured .. .. 3·50 2·50
488/97 *and* O121/3 .. .. *Set of* 13 16·00 13·00

Design: *Horiz*—Nos. 493/7, Carrier pigeon scattering letters over Tonga.

111 Girl Guide Badges

1974 (11 Sept). *Tongan Girl Guides. T* **111** *and similar design.*

(a) Postage

498 **111** 5 s. multicoloured 20 20
499 10 s. multicoloured 40 40
500 20 s. multicoloured 90 90
501 40 s. multicoloured .. .. .. 1·90 1·90
502 60 s. multicoloured .. .. .. 2·50 2·50

(b) Air

503 – 14 s. multicoloured 65 65
504 – 16 s. multicoloured 65 65
505 – 29 s. multicoloured .. .. .. 1·25 1·25
506 – 31 s. multicoloured .. .. .. 1·50 1·50
507 – 75 s. multicoloured .. .. .. 3·50 3·50
498/507 *and* O124/6 .. .. *Set of* 13 21·00 21·00

Design: *Vert*—Nos. 503/7, Girl Guide leaders.

112 Sailing Ship

1974 (11 Dec). *Establishment of Royal Marine Institute. T* **112** *and similar design. (a) Postage.*

508 **112** 5 s. multicoloured 20 20
509 10 s. multicoloured 40 40
510 25 s. multicoloured 75 75
511 50 s. multicoloured .. .. .. 1·75 1·75
512 75 s. multicoloured .. .. .. 2·50 2·50

(b) Air

513 – 9 s. multicoloured 40 40
514 – 14 s. multicoloured 65 65
515 – 17 s. multicoloured 75 75
516 – 60 s. multicoloured .. .. .. 2·25 2·25
517 – 90 s. multicoloured .. .. .. 3·75 3·75
508/17 *and* O127/9 .. .. *Set of* 13 18·00 18·00

Design: *Horiz* (51 × 46 *mm*)—Nos. 513/17, Tongan Bulk Tanker, *James Cook*.

113 Dateline Hotel, Nuku'alofa

1975 (11 Mar). *South Pacific Forum and Tourism. T* **113** *and similar vert designs. (a) Postage.*

518 **113** 5 s. multicoloured 8 8
519 10 s. multicoloured 12 12
520 15 s. multicoloured 20 20
521 30 s. multicoloured 45 45
522 1 p. multicoloured .. .. .. 1·60 1·60

(b) Air

523 – 9 s. multicoloured 12 12
524 – 12 s. multicoloured 15 15
525 – 14 s. multicoloured 20 20
526 – 17 s. multicoloured 20 20
527 – 38 s. multicoloured 55 55
518/27 *and* O130/2 .. .. *Set of* 13 8·00 8·00

Designs (46 × 60 *mm*):—9, 12, 14 s. Beach; 17, 38 s. Surf and sea.

114 Boxing

1975 (11 June). *Fifth South Pacific Games, Guam. T* **114** *and similar "star"-shaped design. (a) Postage.*

528 **114** 5 s. multicoloured 8 8
529 10 s. multicoloured 15 15
530 20 s. multicoloured 30 30
531 25 s. multicoloured 35 35
532 65 s. multicoloured .. .. .. 1·10 1·10

(b) Air

533 – 9 s. multicoloured 15 15
534 – 12 s. multicoloured 20 20
535 – 14 s. multicoloured 20 20
536 – 17 s. multicoloured 25 25
537 – 90 s. multicoloured .. .. .. 1·50 1·50
528/37 *and* O133/5 .. .. *Set of* 13 7·50 7·50

Design (37 × 43 *mm*):—Nos. 533/7, Throwing the Discus.

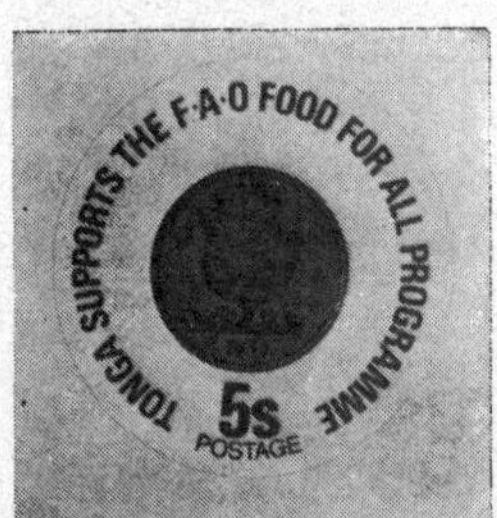

115 Commemorative Coin

1975 (3 Sept). *F.A.O. Commemoration. T* **115** *and similar designs.*

(a) Postage

538 5 s. multicoloured 10 10
539 20 s. multicoloured 35 35
540 50 s. new blue, black and silver 90 90
541 1 p. ultramarine, black and silver .. .. 1·90 1·90
542 2 p. black and silver .. .. 4·00 4·00

(b) Air

543 12 s. multicoloured 25 25
544 14 s. multicoloured 25 25
545 25 s. vermilion, black and silver 40 40
546 50 s. bright magenta, black and silver 90 90
547 1 p. black and silver .. .. 1·90 1·90
538/47 .. .. *Set of* 10 10·00 10·00

Nos. 539/47 are as T **115** but show different coins. Nos. 542 and 544 are horiz, size 75 × 42 mm.

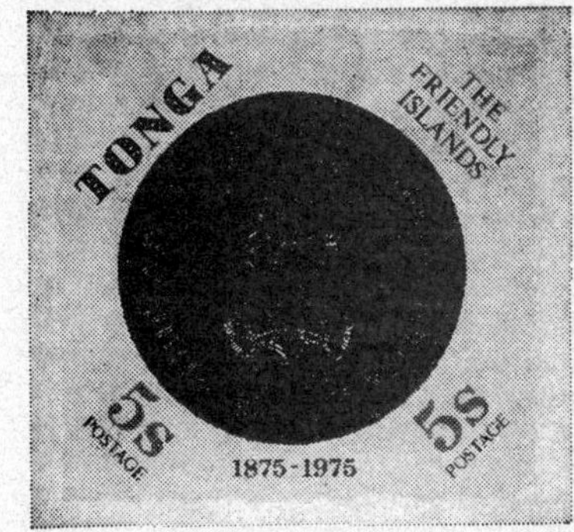

116 Commemorative Coin

1975 (4 Nov). *Centenary of Tongan Constitution. T* **116** *and similar designs showing coinage. Multicoloured. (a) Postage.*

548 5 s. Type **116** 8 8
549 10 s. King George I 15 15
550 20 s. King Taufa'ahau IV 30 30
551 50 s. King George II 80 80
552 75 s. Tongan arms .. .. 1·75 1·75

(b) Air

553 9 s. King Taufa'ahau IV 15 15
554 12 s. Queen Salote 20 20
555 14 s. Tongan arms 20 20
556 38 s. King Taufa'ahau IV 60 60
557 1 p. Four monarchs .. .. 2·00 2·00
548/57 *and* O136/8 .. .. *Set of* 13 8·50 8·50

Sizes:—60 × 40 mm, Nos. 549 and 551; 76 × 76 mm, Nos. 552 and 557; 57 × 56 mm, others.

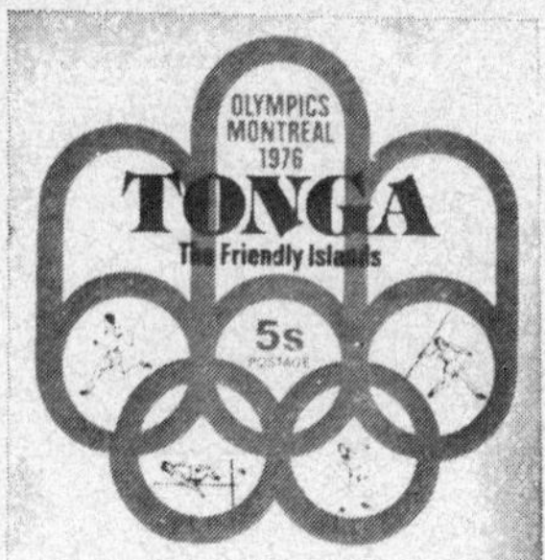

117 Montreal Logo

1976 (24 Feb). *First Participation in Olympic Games. (a) Postage.*

No.	Type	Description	Unused	Used
558	**117**	5 s. vermilion, black and blue	12	12
559		10 s. vermilion, black and emerald	25	25
560		25 s. vermilion, black and bistre	65	65
561		35 s. vermilion, black and mauve	75	75
562		70 s. vermilion, black and olive-yellow	2·00	2·00
(b) Air. Montreal logo optd on Girl Guide stamps (Nos. 500 etc)				
563	**111**	12 s. on 20 s. multicoloured	30	30
564	–	14 s. on 16 s. multicoloured	30	30
565	–	16 s. multicoloured	35	35
566	**111**	38 s. on 40 s. multicoloured	1·00	1·00
567	–	75 s. multicoloured	2·25	2·25
558/67 *and* O139/41		*Set of* 13	13·00	13·00

118 Signatories of Declaration of Independence

1976 (26 May). *Bicentenary of American Revolution. T* **118** *and similar horiz designs showing signatories to the Declaration of Independence. (a) Postage.*

No.	Type	Description	Unused	Used
568	**118**	9 s. multicoloured	40	30
569	–	10 s. multicoloured	40	30
570	–	15 s. multicoloured	70	60
571	–	25 s. multicoloured	1·25	1·00
572	–	75 s. multicoloured	4·25	3·75
(b) Air				
573	–	12 s. multicoloured	50	40
574	–	14 s. multicoloured	60	50
575	–	17 s. multicoloured	80	70
576	–	38 s. multicoloured	2·25	2·00
577	–	1 p. multicoloured	6·00	5·00
568/77 *and* O142/4		*Set of* 13	24·00	21·00

119 Nathaniel Turner and John Thomas (Methodist missionaries)

1976 (25 Aug). *150th Anniv of Christianity in Tonga. T* **119** *and similar design. (a) Postage.*

No.	Type	Description	Unused	Used
578	**119**	5 s. multicoloured	15	15
579		10 s. multicoloured	25	25
580		20 s. multicoloured	40	40
581		25 s. multicoloured	45	45
582		85 s. multicoloured	1·90	1·90
(b) Air. Design showing Missionary Ship "Triton" (45 × 59 mm)				
583	–	9 s. multicoloured	25	25
584	–	12 s. multicoloured	30	30
585	–	14 s. multicoloured	35	35
586	–	17 s. multicoloured	40	40
587	–	38 s. multicoloured	1·00	1·00
578/87 *and* O145/7		*Set of* 13	10·00	10·00

OMNIBUS ISSUES

Details, together with prices for complete sets, of the various Omnibus issues from the 1935 Silver Jubilee series to date are included in a special section following Zululand at the end of the catalogue.

120 Emperor Wilhelm I and King George Tupou I

1976 (1 Nov). *Centenary of Treaty of Friendship with Germany.*

No.	Type	Description	Unused	Used
(a) Postage				
588	**120**	9 s. multicoloured	20	20
589		15 s. multicoloured	30	30
590		22 s. multicoloured	40	40
591		50 s. multicoloured	90	90
592		73 s. multicoloured	1·40	1·40
(b) Air. Circular design (52 mm diameter) showing Treaty Signing				
593	–	11 s. multicoloured	25	25
594	–	17 s. multicoloured	40	40
595	–	18 s. multicoloured	40	40
596	–	31 s. multicoloured	60	60
597	–	39 s. multicoloured	70	70
588/97 *and* O148/50		*Set of* 13	9·50	9·50

121 Queen Salote and Coronation Procession

1977 (7 Feb). *Silver Jubilee. (a) Postage.*

No.	Type	Description	Unused	Used
598	**121**	11 s. multicoloured	2·50	1·00
599		20 s. multicoloured	1·75	70
600		30 s. multicoloured	2·00	1·00
601		50 s. multicoloured	3·00	2·00
602		75 s. multicoloured	4·00	2·50
(b) Air. Square design (59 × 59 mm) showing Queen Elizabeth and King Taufa'ahau				
603	–	15 s. multicoloured	1·25	60
604	–	17 s. multicoloured	1·50	70
605	–	22 s. multicoloured	30·00	8·00
606	–	31 s. multicoloured	1·75	1·00
607	–	39 s. multicoloured	2·00	1·25
598/607 *and* O151/3		*Set of* 13	55·00	20·00

122 Tongan Coins

1977 (4 July). *Tenth Anniv of King's Coronation. (a) Postage.*

No.	Type	Description	Unused	Used
608	**122**	10 s. multicoloured	30	25
609		15 s. multicoloured	50	40
610		25 s. multicoloured	70	60
611		50 s. multicoloured	1·50	1·25
612		75 s. multicoloured	2·00	1·75
(b) Air. Oval design (64 × 46 mm) showing 1967 Coronation Coin				
613	–	11 s. multicoloured	30	25
614	–	17 s. multicoloured	50	40
615	–	18 s. multicoloured	50	40
616	–	39 s. multicoloured	1·00	90
617	–	1 p. multicoloured	3·00	2·50
608/17 *and* O154/6		*Set of* 13	14·00	12·00

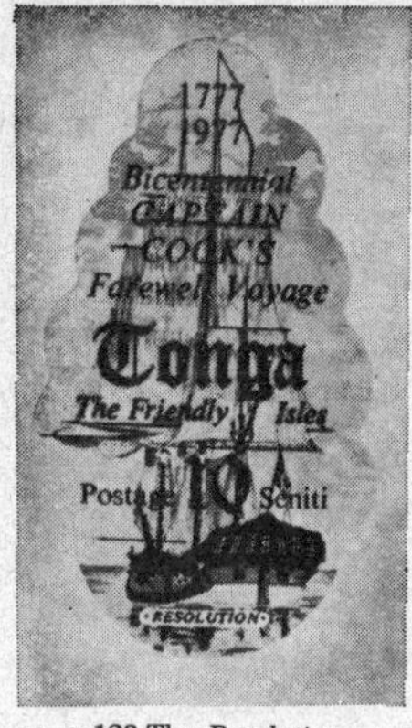

123 The *Resolution*

1977 (28 Sept). *Bicentenary of Capt. Cook's Last Voyage.*

No.	Type	Description	Unused	Used
(a) Postage.				
618	**123**	10 s. multicoloured	60	60
619		17 s. multicoloured	95	95
620		25 s. multicoloured	1·75	1·75
621		30 s. multicoloured	2·00	2·00
622		40 s. multicoloured	2·50	2·50
(b) Air. Horiz design (52 × 46 mm) showing coin and extract from Cook's journal				
623	–	15 s. multicoloured	90	90
624	–	22 s. multicoloured	1·60	1·60
625	–	31 s. multicoloured	2·00	2·00
626	–	50 s. multicoloured	3·00	3·00
627	–	1 p. multicoloured	6·00	6·00
618/27 *and* O157/9		*Set of* 13	30·00	29·00

124 Humpback Whale

(125)

1977 (16 Dec). *Whale Conservation. (a) Postage.*

No.	Type	Description	Unused	Used
628	**124**	15 s. black, grey and bright blue	50	40
629		22 s. black, grey and dull green	65	55
630		31 s. black, grey and orange	80	70
631		38 s. black, grey and bright lilac	1·10	95
632		64 s. black, grey and red-brown	1·75	1·50
(b) Air. Hexagonal design (66 × 51 mm) showing Sei and Fin Whales				
633	–	11 s. multicoloured	45	35
634	–	17 s. multicoloured	60	50
635	–	18 s. multicoloured	60	50
636	–	39 s. multicoloured	1·25	1·00
637	–	50 s. multicoloured	1·60	1·40
628/37 *and* O160/2		*Set of* 13	14·00	12·00

1978 (17 Feb). *Various stamps surch as T* **125**. *(a) Postage.*

No.	Type	Description	Unused	Used
638	**115**	15 s. on 5 s. multicoloured	80	85
639	**119**	15 s. on 5 s. multicoloured (Br.)	80	85
640	**117**	15 s. on 10 s. verm, blk & emerald (G.)	80	85
641	**119**	15 s. on 10 s. multicoloured	80	85
642	**121**	15 s. on 11 s. multicoloured (Blk. & Sil.)	1·75	1·75
643	**114**	15 s. on 20 s. multicoloured	80	85
644	–	15 s. on 38 s. mult (No. O133) (V.)	80	85
(b) Air				
645	–	17 s. on 9 s. multicoloured (No. 533)	80	85
646	–	17 s. on 9 s. multicoloured (583) (V.)	80	85
647	–	17 s. on 12 s. multicoloured (534) (V.)	80	85
648	–	17 s. on 12 s. mult (573) (R. & Gold)	80	85
649	–	17 s. on 18 s. mult (595) (Olive & Br.)	80	85
650	–	17 s. on 38 s. multicoloured (527) (G.)	80	85
651	–	17 s. on 38 s. multicoloured (556) (B.)	80	85
652	–	1 p. on 35 s. mult (O151) (Silver & B.)	20·00	20·00
653	–	1 p. on 38 s. mult (576) (B. & Gold)	5·00	5·50
654	–	1 p. on 75 s. mult (572) (G. & Sil.)	5·00	5·50
638/54		*Set of* 17	38·00	35·00

The surcharges on Nos. 638/9 are formed by adding a figure "1" to the existing face value.

The surcharge on No. 644 includes the word "POSTAGE".

126 Flags of Canada and Tonga

1978 (5 May). *Commonwealth Games, Edmonton.* (a) *Postage.*

No.	Type	Description	Unused	Used
655	126	10 s. blue, red and black	20	15
656		15 s. multicoloured	30	25
657		20 s. turquoise-green, black and red	45	35
658		25 s. red, blue and black	50	40
659		45 s. black and red	1·00	90
		(b) *Air. Leaf-shaped design* (39 × 40 *mm*) *showing Maple Leaf*		
660	–	17 s. black and red	40	30
661	–	35 s. black, red and blue	70	60
662	–	38 s. black, red and turquoise-green	85	75
663	–	40 s. black, red and green	90	80
664	–	65 s. black, red and chestnut	1·60	1·40
655/64 *and* O163/5		*Set of* 13	9·50	8·00

127 King Taufa'ahau Tupou IV

1978 (4 July). *60th Birthday of King Taufa'ahau Tupou IV.*

(a) *Postage*

No.	Type	Description	Unused	Used
665	127	2 s. black, deep blue and cobalt	5	5
666		5 s. black, deep blue and rose-pink	10	10
667		10 s. black, deep blue and mauve	20	20
668		25 s. black, deep blue and brownish grey	45	40
669		75 s. black, deep blue and yellow-ochre	1·40	1·25
		(b) *Air. Star-shaped design* (44 × 51 *mm*) *showing portrait of King*		
670	–	11 s. black, dp blue & greenish yellow	20	20
671	–	15 s. black, deep blue and cinnamon	30	25
672	–	17 s. black, deep blue and bright lilac	35	30
673	–	39 s. black, dp blue & turquoise-green	75	65
674	–	1 p. black, deep blue and pink	2·00	1·75
665/74 *and* O166/8		*Set of* 13	8·00	7·50

128 Banana

1978 (29 Sept)–**82.** (a) *Coil stamps. Designs as T* **128** *showing bananas (the number coinciding with the face value).*

No.	Description	Unused	Used
675	1 s. black and greenish yellow	5	5
676	2 s. deep blue and greenish yellow	5	5
677	3 s. purple-brown, yellow and greenish yellow	5	5
678	4 s. deep blue, yellow and greenish yellow	5	5
679	5 s. vermilion, yellow and greenish yellow	5	5
	(b) *Coil stamps. Coconut-shaped design* (18 × 26 *mm*)		
680	6 s. purple, emerald and bistre-brown	10	10
681	7 s. greenish blue, emerald and light brown	12	12
682	8 s. vermilion, emerald and light brown	12	12
683	9 s. deep mauve, emerald and light brown	15	15
684	10 s. emerald and light brown	15	15
	(c) *Coil stamps. Pineapple-shaped design* (17 × 30 *mm*)		
684*a*	13 s. deep mauve, emerald and cinnamon (17.12.82)	20	20
685	15 s. blue-green, orange-brown and emerald	25	25
686	20 s. brown, orange-brown and emerald	30	30
687	30 s. magenta, orange-brown and emerald	40	40
688	50 s. black, orange-brown and emerald	70	70
689	1 p. purple, orange-brown and emerald	1·50	1·50
	(d) *Mixed fruit oval design* (55 × 29 *mm*)		
689*a*	2 p. multicoloured (17.12.82)	2·75	2·75
689*b*	3 p. multicoloured (17.12.82)	3·75	3·75
675/89*b*	*Set of* 18	9·50	9·50

Nos. 675/89 and O169/83 were produced in rolls, each even stamp having a number applied to the backing paper, with the usual inscription on the reverse.

129 Whale

1978 (15 Dec). *Endangered Wildlife Conservation. T* **129** *and similarly shaped designs. Multicoloured.* (a) *Postage.*

No.	Description	Unused	Used
690	15 s. Type **129**	30	30
691	18 s. Bat	35	35
692	25 s. Turtle	45	45
693	28 s. Red Shining Parrot	50	50
694	60 s. Type **129**	1·10	1·10
	(b) *Air*		
695	17 s. Type **129**	35	35
696	22 s. As 18 s.	40	40
697	31 s. As 25 s.	55	55
698	39 s. As 28 s.	70	70
699	45 s. Type **129**	85	85
690/9 *and* O184/6	*Set of* 13	8·50	8·50

130 Metrication Symbol

1979 (16 Feb). *Decade of Progress. T* **130** *and other multi-angular designs in ultramarine and gold (31 s.) or multicoloured (others).*

(a) *Postage*

No.	Description	Unused	Used
700	5 s. Type **130**	8	10
701	11 s. Map of South Pacific Islands	15	20
702	18 s. "Building wall of progress" with the assistance of the United States Peace Corps	25	30
703	22 s. New churches	35	40
704	50 s. Map showing air routes	70	75
	(b) *Air*		
705	15 s. As 50 s.	20	25
706	17 s. As 11 s.	25	30
707	31 s. Rotary International emblem	40	45
708	39 s. Government offices	55	60
709	1 p. "Communications"	1·40	1·50
700/9 *and* O187/9	*Set of* 13	6·50	7·00

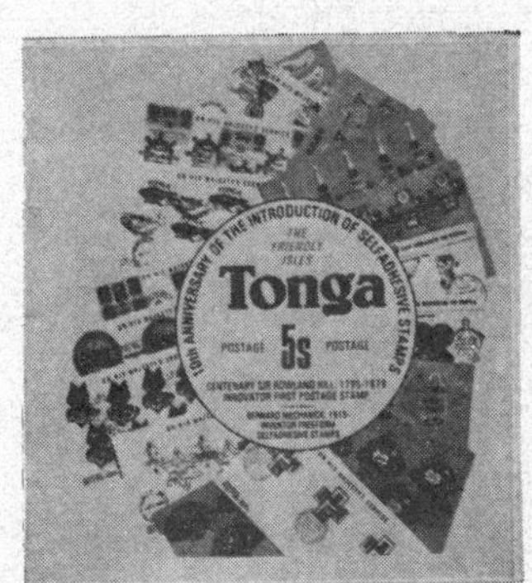

131 Various Envelopes bearing Self-adhesive Stamps

1979 (1 June). *Death Centenary of Sir Rowland Hill and 10th Anniv of Tongan Self-adhesive Stamps.* (a) *Postage.*

No.	Type	Description	Unused	Used
710	131	5 s. multicoloured	10	10
711		10 s. multicoloured	20	20
712		25 s. multicoloured	55	55
713		50 s. multicoloured	1·00	1·00
714		1 p. multicoloured	2·00	2·00
		(b) *Air. Multi-angular design* (53 × 53 *mm*) *showing various self-adhesive stamps*		
715	–	15 s. multicoloured	30	30
716	–	17 s. multicoloured	35	35
717	–	18 s. multicoloured	35	35
718	–	31 s. multicoloured	60	60
719	–	39 s. multicoloured	75	75
710/19 *and* O190/2		*Set of* 13	9·00	9·00

132

(Des R. Edge and K. Jones)

1979 (17 Aug)–**82.** *Air. Coil stamps.*

No.	Type	Description	Unused	Used
720	132	5 s. black and cobalt	5	5
721		11 s. black and bright blue	15	20
722		14 s. black and violet	15	20
723		15 s. black and mauve	20	25
724		17 s. black and bright magenta	20	25
725		18 s. black and bright rose-red	20	25
726		22 s. black and orange-vermilion	25	30
726*a*		29 s. black and rose (17.12.82)	30	35
727		31 s. black and orange-yellow	35	40
727*a*		32 s. black and yellow-ochre (17.12.82)	35	40
728		39 s. black and bright yellow-green	50	55
728*a*		47 s. black and light brown (17.12.82)	45	50
729		75 s. black and bright blue-green	90	95
730		1 p. black and emerald	1·25	1·40
720/30		*Set of* 14	4·75	5·50

Nos. 720/30 and O193/203 were produced in rolls, each even stamp having a number applied to the backing paper, with the usual inscription on the reverse.

133 Rain Forest, Island of 'Eua

1979 (23 Nov). *Views as seen through the Lens of a Camera.*

(a) *Postage*

No.	Type	Description	Unused	Used
731	133	10 s. multicoloured	20	20
732		18 s. multicoloured	30	30
733		31 s. multicoloured	45	45
734		50 s. multicoloured	75	75
735		60 s. multicoloured	85	85
		(b) *Air. Design as T* **133** *but showing Isle of Kao*		
736	–	5 s. multicoloured	10	10
737	–	15 s. multicoloured	25	25
738	–	17 s. multicoloured	30	30
739	–	39 s. multicoloured	60	60
740	–	75 s. multicoloured	1·10	1·10
731/40 *and* O204/6		*Set of* 13	7·00	7·00

134 King George Tupou I, Admiral Du Bouzet and Map of Tonga

(135)

1980 (9 Jan). *125th Anniv of France–Tonga Treaty of Friendship.*

(a) *Postage*

No.	Type	Description	Unused	Used
741	134	7 s. multicoloured	10	12
742		10 s. multicoloured	15	20
743		14 s. multicoloured	20	25
744		50 s. multicoloured	70	75
745		75 s. multicoloured	1·00	1·10
		(b) *Air. Design as T* **134** *but showing King George Tupou I, Napoleon III and "L'Aventure" (sailing ship)*		
746	–	15 s. multicoloured	20	25
747	–	17 s. multicoloured	25	30
748	–	22 s. multicoloured	35	40
749	–	31 s. multicoloured	40	45
750	–	39 s. multicoloured	55	60
741/50 *and* O207/9		*Set of* 13	6·50	7·00

1980 (30 Apr). *Olympic Games, Moscow. Nos.* 710/19 *surch or optd only (No. 755) as T* **135** *in black on silver background.*

(a) *Postage*

No.	Type	Description	Unused	Used
751	131	13 s. on 5 s. multicoloured	20	25
752		20 s. on 10 s. multicoloured	30	35
753		25 s. multicoloured	35	40
754		33 s. on 50 s. multicoloured	45	50
755		1 p. multicoloured	1·40	1·50
		(b) *Air*		
756	–	9 s. on 15 s. multicoloured	15	20
757	–	16 s. on 17 s. multicoloured	25	30
758	–	29 s. on 18 s. multicoloured	40	45
759	–	32 s. on 31 s. multicoloured	45	50
760	–	47 s. on 39 s. multicoloured	65	70
751/60 *and* O210/12		*Set of* 13	6·50	7·00

136 Scout at Camp-fire

1980 (30 Sept). *South Pacific Scout Jamboree, Tonga and 75th Anniv of Rotary International.* (a) *Postage.*

No.	Type	Description	Unused	Used
761	136	9 s. multicoloured	25	25
762		13 s. multicoloured	40	40

763 **136** 15 s. multicoloured 40 40
764 30 s. multicoloured 65 65

(b) Air. Design as T **136** *showing Scout activities and Rotary emblem*

765 – 29 s. multicoloured 70 70
766 – 32 s. multicoloured 70 70
767 – 47 s. multicoloured 95 95
768 – 1 p. multicoloured 2·00 2·00
761/8 *and* O214/15 *Set of* 10 9·50 9·50

9

(137)

138 Red Cross and Tongan Flags, with Map of Tonga

1980 (3 Dec)–**82.** *Various stamps surch as T* **137**. *(a) Postage.*

769 **117** 9 s. on 35 s. vermilion, black and mauve 12 15
770 **119** 13 s. on 20 s. multicoloured 15 20
771 13 s. on 25 s. multicoloured 15 20
772 – 19 s. on 25 s. multicoloured (No. 571) 25 30
773 **114** 1 p. on 65 s. multicoloured 1·25 1·40
773*a* – 5 p. on 25 s. multicoloured (No. O214) (B.) (4.1.82) 4·75 5·00
773*b* – 5 p. on 2 p. multicoloured (No. O215) (B.) (4.1.82) 4·75 5·00
ba. Stamp omitted (centre stamp of strip of 3)

(b) Air

774 – 29 s. on 14 s. multicoloured (No. 585) 35 40
775 – 29 s. on 39 s. multicoloured (No. 597) 35 40
776 – 32 s. on 12 s. multicoloured (No. 554) 40 45
777 – 32 s. on 14 s. multicoloured (No. 574) 40 45
778 – 47 s. on 12 s. multicoloured (No. 524) 55 60
779 – 47 s. on 12 s. multicoloured (No. 584) 55 60
769/79 *and* O216 *Set of* 14 15·00 16·00

On No. 773ba the centre stamp in a vertical strip of 3 became detached so that the surcharge was applied to the white backing paper.

1981 (9 Sept). *International Year for Disabled Persons.*

(a) Postage. P 14½ × 14.

780 **138** 2 p. multicoloured 2·25 2·40
781 3 p. multicoloured 3·00 3·25

(b) Air. Vert design (25 × 33 mm) showing Red Cross flag and map depicting Tongatapu and Eua. P 13½

782 – 29 s. multicoloured 35 40
783 – 32 s. multicoloured 40 45
784 – 47 s. multicoloured 55 60

139 Prince Charles and King Taufa'ahau Tupou IV

1981 (21 Oct). *Royal Wedding and Centenary of Treaty of Friendship between Tonga and Great Britain. T* **139** *and similar vert designs. Multicoloured. P* 13½.

785 13 s. Type **139** 45 45
786 47 s. Prince Charles and Lady Diana Spencer 75 75
787 1 p. 50, Prince Charles and Lady Diana (*different*) 2·25 2·25
a. Imperf backing paper (pair)
788 3 p. Prince and Princess of Wales after wedding ceremony 4·50 4·50

140 Report of Printing in *Missionary Notices*

1981 (25 Nov). *Christmas. 150th Anniv of first Books Printed in Tonga. T* **140** *and similar horiz designs. Multicoloured. P* 13½.

789 9 s. Type **140** 20 20
790 13 s. *Missionary Notices* report (*different*) 25 25
791 32 s. Type in chase 60 60
792 47 s. Bible class 90 90

141 Landing Scene

1981 (25 Nov). *Bicentenary of Maurelle's Discovery of Vava'u. T* **141** *and similar horiz designs. Multicoloured. P* 14 × 14½.

793 9 s. Type **141** 25 25
794 13 s. Map of Vava'u 40 40
795 47 s. *La Princesa* 1·75 1·75
796 1 p. *La Princesa* (*different*) 4·00 4·00
MS797 100 × 78 mm. As No. 796. Imperf 4·00 4·00

The stamp from No. **MS**797 is as No. 796 but without inscription at foot of design.

142 Battle Scene

1981 (16 Dec). *175th Anniv of Capture of "Port au Prince" (ship). T* **142** *and similar horiz designs in black and new blue. P* 13½.

798 9 s. Type **142** 40 40
799 32 s. Battle scene (*different*) 45 45
800 47 s. Map of Ha'apai Group 60 60
801 47 s. Native canoes preparing to attack 60 60
802 1 p. *Port au Prince* 1·25 1·25

The 47 s. values were printed together, *se-tenant*, in horizontal and vertical pairs throughout the sheet.

143 Baden-Powell at Brownsea Island, 1907

CYCLONE RELIEF

T$1+50s
POSTAGE & RELIEF

(144)

1982 (22 Feb). *75th Anniv of Boy Scout Movement and 125th Birth Anniv of Lord Baden-Powell. T* **143** *and similar vert designs. P* 13½.

803 29 s. Type **143** 35 40
804 32 s. Baden-Powell on his charger "Black Prince" 40 45
805 47 s. Baden-Powell at Imperial Jamboree, 1924 55 60
806 1 p. 50, Cover of first *Scouting for Boys* journal 1·60 1·75
807 2 p. 50, Newsboy, 1900 and Mafeking Siege 3d. stamp 3·50 3·75

1982 (14 Apr). *Cyclone Relief. No. 788 optd with T* **144** *in silver.*

808 1 p. + 50 s. on 3 p. Prince and Princess of Wales after wedding ceremony 8·00 6·50
a. Imperf backing paper (pair) £200

145 Ball Control

146 M.V. *Olovaha*

1982 (7 July). *World Cup Football Championship, Spain. T* **145** *and similar vert designs. Multicoloured. P* 13½.

809 32 s. Type **145** 40 45
810 47 s. Goalkeeping 55 60
811 75 s. Heading 90 95
812 1 p. 50, Shooting 1·75 1·75

1982 (11 Aug). *Inter-Island Transport. T* **146** *and similar horiz design. Multicoloured. P* 14 × 14½.

813 9 s. Type **146** 10 10
814 13 s. Type **146** 15 15
815 47 s. SPIA "Twin Otter" 55 60
816 1 p. As 47 s. 1·25 1·40

147 Mail Boat

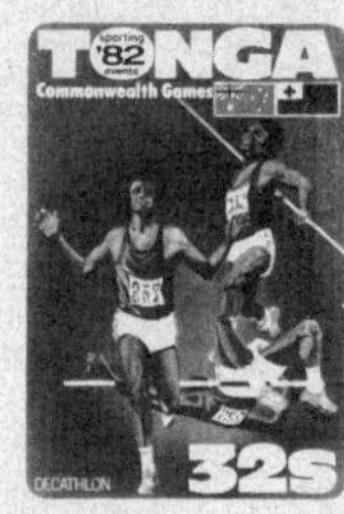

148 Decathlon

1982 (29 Sept). *Tin Can Mail Centenary. T* **147** *and similar vert designs. P* 13½ × 14.

817 13 s. multicoloured 15 15
818 32 s. multicoloured 40 45
819 47 s. multicoloured 55 60
820 2 p. black and pale turquoise-green 2·40 2·50
MS821 135 × 90 mm. Nos. 817/19. Imperf 1·25 1·40
MS822 135 × 89 mm. As No. 820 but with gold inscriptions. Imperf 2·50 2·75

Designs:—32 s. Mail boat and ship; 47 s. Collecting Tin Can mail; 2 p. Map of Niuafo'ou.

1982 (25 Oct). *Commonwealth Games, Brisbane. T* **148** *and similar multicoloured design. P* 13½.

823 32 s. Type **148** 40 45
824 1 p. 50, Tongan Police band at opening ceremony (*horiz*) 1·90 2·00

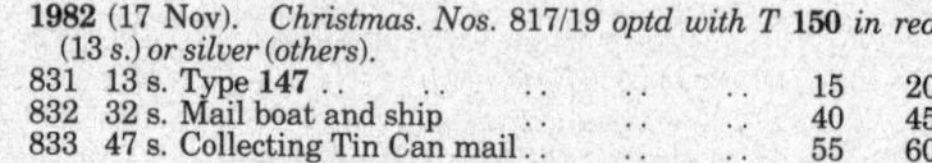

149 Pupils

(150)

1982 (25 Oct). *Tonga College Centenary. T* **149** *and similar multicoloured designs. P* 13½ *(Nos. 825/6) or* 14 × 14½ *(others).*

825 5 s. Type **149** (Tongan inscription) 12 10
826 5 s. Type **149** (English inscription) 12 10
827 29 s. School crest and monument (Tongan inscr) (29 × 22 *mm*) 65 65
828 29 s. As No. 827, but inscr in English 65 65
829 29 s. King George Tupou I (founder) and school (Tongan inscr) (29 × 22 *mm*) 65 65
830 29 s. As No. 829, but inscr in English 65 65
825/30 *Set of* 6 2·50 2·50

Nos. 825/6 were printed together, *se-tenant*, in pairs and Nos. 827/30 in blocks of four throughout the sheets.

1982 (17 Nov). *Christmas. Nos. 817/19 optd with T* **150** *in red (13 s.) or silver (others).*

831 13 s. Type **147** 15 20
832 32 s. Mail boat and ship 40 45
833 47 s. Collecting Tin Can mail 55 60

151 H.M.S. *Resolution*, and S. S. *Canberra*

1983 (22 Feb). *Sea and Air Transport. T* **151** *and similar horiz designs. Multicoloured. P* 14.

834 29 s. Type **151** (sage-green background) 35 40
835 32 s. Type **151** (buff background) 40 45
836 47 s. Montgolfier's balloon and "Concorde" (pale blue background) 55 60
837 1 p. 50, As No. 836 (lilac background) 1·90 2·00
MS838 120 × 165 mm. 2 p. 50, S.S. *Canberra* and "Concorde" 3·00 3·25

152 Globe and Inset of Tonga

153 SPIA DH "Twin Otter"

1983 (14 Mar). *Commonwealth Day. T* **152** *and similar horiz designs. Multicoloured. P* 14.

839 29 s. Type **152** 35 40
840 32 s. Tongan dancers 6·50 2·50
841 47 s. Fishing boats 55 60
842 1 p. 50, King Taufa'ahau Tupou IV and flag 1·90 2·00

1983 (11 May). *Inauguration of Niuafo'ou Airport. T* **153** *and similar horiz design. Multicoloured. P* 14 × 14½.

843 32 s. Type **153** 35 40
844 47 s. Type **153** 40 45
845 1 p. SPIA Boeing "707" 1·25 1·40
846 1 p. 50, As 1 p. 1·90 2·00

154 "Intelsat IV" Satellite

155 Obverse and Reverse of Pa'anga Banknote

1983 (22 June). *World Communications Year. T* **154** *and similar multicoloured designs. P* 11 (2 *p.*) *or* 14 × 14½ (*others*).

847 29 s. Type **154** 35 40
848 32 s. "Intelsat IVA" satellite .. 40 45
849 75 s. "Intelsat V" satellite .. 90 95
850 2 p. Moon post cover (45 × 32 *mm*) .. 2·40 2·50

1983 (3 Aug). *10th Anniv of Bank of Tonga. P* 14.

851 **155** 1 p. multicoloured .. 1·25 1·40
852 2 p. multicoloured .. 2·50 2·75

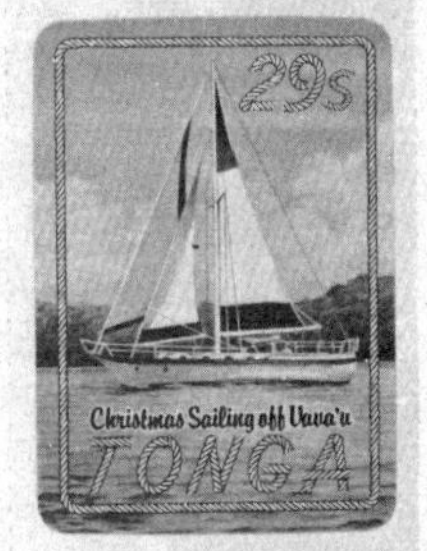

156 Early Printing Press

157 Yacht off Coast

(Des A. Benjamin and R. Edge)

1983 (22 Sept). *Printing in Tonga. T* **156** *and similar vert designs. Multicoloured. P* 14.

853 13 s. Type **156** .. 15 20
854 32 s. Arrival of W. Woon .. 40 45
855 1 p. Early Tongan print .. 1·25 1·40
856 2 p. *The Tonga Chronicle* .. 2·50 2·75

1983 (17 Nov). *Christmas. Yachting off Vava'u. T* **157** *and similar vert designs. Multicoloured. P* 11.

857 29 s. Type **157** .. 35 40
858 32 s. View of yacht from cave .. 40 45
859 1 p. 50, Anchored yacht .. 1·90 2·00
860 2 p. 50, Yacht off coast (*different*) .. 2·75 3·00

158 Abel Tasman

159 *Swainsonia casta*

(Des R. Edge)

1984 (12 Mar). *Navigators and Explorers of the Pacific. T* **158** *and similar horiz designs. P* 14.

861 32 s. deep dull green and black .. 40 45
862 47 s. reddish violet and black .. 60 65
863 90 s. light brown and black .. 1·10 1·25
864 1 p. 50, royal blue and black .. 2·00 2·10

Designs:—47 s. Samuel Wallis; 90 s. William Bligh; 1 p. 50, James Cook.

1984 (10 Apr–17 Sept). *Marine Life. T* **159** *and similar multicoloured designs. P* 14 (1, 2, 3, 5 *p.*) *or* 14½ (*others*).

865 1 s. Type **159** .. 5 5
866 2 s. *Porites sp* (26.6.84) .. 5 5
867 3 s. *Holocentrus ruber* (18.5.84) .. 5 5
868 5 s. *Cyprae mappa viridis* .. 5 8
869 6 s. *Dardanus megistos* (crab) (17.9.84) .. 5 8
870 9 s. *Stegostoma fasciatum* (18.5.84) .. 10 12
871 10 s. *Conus bullatus* .. 10 12
872 13 s. *Pterois volitans* (18.5.84) .. 15 20
873 15 s. *Conus textile* .. 15 20
874 20 s. *Dascyllus aruanus* (18.5.84) .. 20 25
875 29 s. *Conus aulicus* .. 30 35
876 32 s. *Acanthurus leucosternon* (18.5.84) .. 35 40
877 47 s. *Lambis truncata* .. 50 55
878 1 p. *Millepora dichotama* (26.6.84) .. 1·10 1·25
879 2 p. *Birgus latro* (crab) (17.9.84) .. 2·10 2·25
880 3 p. *Chicoreus palma-rosae* .. 3·25 3·50
881 5 p. *Thunnus albacares* (18.5.84) .. 5·25 5·50
865/81 .. *Set of* 17 12·50 13·25

Nos. 878/81 are horizontal, 38 × 23 mm.

160 Printer checking Newspaper

161 U.S.A. Flag and Running

1984 (26 June). *20th Anniv of* Tonga Chronicle (*newspaper*). *Die-cut.*

882 **160** 3 s. grey-brown and bright blue .. 5 5
a. Sheetlet of 12 .. 50
883 32 s. grey-brown and vermilion .. 40 45
a. Sheetlet of 12 .. 4·75

Nos. 882/3 were each printed in sheetlets of 12, the designs being superimposed on a reproduction of the front page from the first edition. This was printed in grey and is in Tongan for the 3 s. and English for the 32 s.

(Des R. Edge)

1984 (23 July). *Olympic Games, Los Angeles. T* **161** *and similar horiz designs, each showing U.S. flag. Each printed in black, scarlet-vermilion and bright new blue. P* 14 × 14½.

884 29 s. Type **161** .. 35 40
885 47 s. Javelin-throwing .. 60 65
886 1 p. 50, Shot-putting .. 2·00 2·10
887 3 p. Olympic torch .. 3·75 4·00

162 Sir George Airy and Dateline on World Map

163 Australia 1914 Kookaburra 6d. Stamp

(Des R. Edge)

1984 (20 Aug). *Centenary of International Dateline. T* **162** *and similar horiz design. Multicoloured. P* 14.

888 47 s. Type **162** .. 60 65
889 2 p. Sir Sandford Fleming and Map of Pacific time zones .. 2·50 2·75

1984 (17 Sept). *"Ausipex" International Stamp Exhibition, Melbourne. T* **163** *and similar vert design. Multicoloured. P* 14.

890 32 s. Type **163** .. 40 45
891 1 p. 50, Tonga 1897 Parrot 2s. 6d. stamp .. 2·00 2·10
MS892 90 × 100 mm. As Nos. 890/1, but without exhibition logo and with "TONGA" and face values in gold. Die-cut .. 2·40 2·50

Examples of No. **MS**892 without face values are Exhibition Banquet souvenirs without postal validity.

164 Beach at Sunset ("Silent Night")

(Des R. Edge)

1984 (12 Nov). *Christmas. Carols. T* **164** *and similar vert designs. Multicoloured. P* 14.

893 32 s. Type **164** .. 45 45
894 47 s. Hut and palm trees ("Away in a Manger") 60 65
895 1 p. Sailing boats ("I Saw Three Ships") .. 1·25 1·40

Nos. 893/5 were each issued in sheets of 20 stamps with 5 labels, in the central vertical row, showing progressive stages of the design.

OFFICIAL STAMPS

G.F.B.

(O 1)

(O 2)

(G.F.B. = Gaue Faka Buleaga = On Government Service)

1893 (13 Feb). *Optd with Type* O 1 *by Govt Printing Office, Wellington, N.Z. W* **2**. *P* 12 × 11½.

O1 **5** 1d. ultramarine (C.) .. 8·00 18·00
a. Bisected diagonally (½d.) (on cover)
O2 **6** 2d. ultramarine (C.) .. 15·00 25·00
O3 **5** 4d. ultramarine (C.) .. 35·00 55·00
O4 **6** 8d. ultramarine (C.) .. 75·00 £100
O5 1s. ultramarine (C.) .. 85·00 £120

Above prices are for stamps in good condition and colour. Faded and stained stamps from the remainders are worth much less.

1893 (Dec). *Nos* O1 *to* O5 *variously surch with new value, sideways as Type* O **2**.

O 6 **5** ½d. on 1d. ultramarine .. 12·00 18·00
O 7 **6** 2½d. on 2d. ultramarine .. 12·00 18·00
O 8 **5** 5d. on 4d. ultramarine .. 12·00 18·00
O 9 **6** 7½d. on 8d. ultramarine .. 15·00 25·00
a. "D" of "7½D." omitted
b. Surch double .. £700
O10 10d. on 1s. ultramarine .. 15·00 25·00

OFFICIAL AIR MAIL
1862
TAU'ATAINA
EMANCIPATION
1962

(O 3)

OFFICIAL
AIRMAIL
40
SENITI

(O 4)

1962 (7 Feb). *Air. Centenary of Emancipation. Nos.* 112/14, 116 *and* 118/19 *optd with Type* O **3** *in red by* R. S. Wallbank, *Govt Printer.*

O11 – 2d. ultramarine .. — 6·00
a. "OFFICIAI" .. — 11·00
b. "MAII" .. — 11·00
O12 – 5d. violet .. — 6·50
a. "OFFICIAI" .. — 12·00
b. "MAII" .. — 12·00
O13 – 1s. red-brown .. — 3·75
a. "OFFICIAI" .. — 11·00
b. "MAII" .. — 11·00
c. Opt double
ca. "OFFICIAI"
cb. "MAII"
O14 – 5s. orange-yellow and slate-lilac .. — 55·00
a. "MAII" .. — 75·00
O15 **52** 10s. yellow and black .. — 22·00
a. "MAII"
O16 **53** £1 yellow, scar, ultram & dp brt blue .. — 35·00
a. "MAII"
O11/O16 .. *Set of* 6 £225 £120

SET PRICES. Official Stamps from here onwards are included in the complete set prices given with any corresponding Postage issues.

1963 (15 July). *Air. First Polynesian Gold Coinage Commemoration. As T* **63** *but inscr* "OFFICIAL AIRMAIL". 1 *koula coin* (*diam* 3⅛ *in.*). *Imperf.*

O17 **63** 15s. black .. 3·00 4·50

1965 (18 Mar). *No.* O17 *surch as T* **67**.

O18 **63** 30s. on 15s. black .. 4·00 4·00

1966 (18 June). *Air. Centenary of Tupou College and Secondary Education. No.* 117 *surch with* "OFFICIAL AIRMAIL" *and new value, with commemorative inscription as in T* **69** *but in italic capital letters.*

O19 10s. on 4d. blue-green .. 1·00 1·00
a. Surch inverted .. — £150
O20 20s. on 4d. blue-green .. 1·40 1·40

1967 (25 Mar). *Air. Decimal currency. No.* 112 *surch* "OFFICIAL AIRMAIL ONE PA'ANGA" *in three lines, in red.*

O21 1 p. on 5s. .. 2·25 2·25
a. "AIRMAIL" above "OFFICIAL" .. 95·00

No. O21a occurred once in a number of sheets until it was corrected.

1967 (4 July). *Air. No.* 114 *surch in various denominations as Type* O **4**.

O22 **53** 40 s. on £1 .. 80 90
O23 60 s. on £1 .. 1·40 1·50
O24 1 p. on £1 .. 2·00 2·25
O25 2 p. on £1 .. 4·00 4·25

Nos. O22/5 were first used on 4 July 1967, but supplies of unused stamps were not made available until April 1968.

The Friendly Islands
welcome the
United States
Peace Corps Official Airmail 30s

(O 5)

Friendly Islands
Trials
Field & Track
South Pacific
Games
Port Moresby
1969
T$ 1·00
OFFICIAL
AIRMAIL

(O 6)

1967 (15 Dec). *Air. Arrival of U.S. Peace Corps in Tonga. As No.* 114, *but imperf, and background colour changed, and surch as Type* O **5**.

O26 **53** 30 s. on £1 yellow, scarlet, ultramarine and emerald-green .. 60 60

O27 **53** 70 s. on £1 yellow, scarlet, ultramarine and emerald-green 1·00 1·00
O28 1 p. 50, on £1 yellow, scarlet, ultramarine and emerald-green 1·90 1·90

1968 (4 July). *50th Birthday of King Taufa'ahua IV. No. 207 surch.* "HIS MAJESTY'S 50th BIRTHDAY" (*as T* **79**), "OFFICIAL AIRMAIL" *and new value.*
O29 **75** 40 s. on 50 s. (Turq.) 70 70
O30 60 s. on 50 s. (G.) 1·10 1·10
O31 1 p. on 50 s. (V.) 1·75 1·75
O32 2 p. on 50 s. (P.) 3·50 3·50

1968 (19 Dec). *Air. South Pacific Games Field and Track Trials, Port Moresby, New Guinea. As No.* 114, *but imperf, background colour changed and surch as Type* O **6**.
O33 **53** 20 s. on £1 yellow, scarlet, ultramarine and emerald-green 30 30
O34 1 p. on £1 yellow, scarlet, ultramarine and emerald-green 1·25 1·25

1969 (13 Aug). *Air. Third South Pacific Games, Port Moresby. Design as Nos.* 290/4.
O35 70 s. carmine-red, bright green and turquoise 1·40 1·40
O36 80 s. carmine-red, orange and turquoise 1·50 1·50

OFFICIAL AIRMAIL
1969 OIL SEARCH 90s

(O 7)

Royal Visit
MARCH
1970
OFFICIAL
AIRMAIL
T$1·25

(O 8)

1969 (23 Dec). *Air. First Oil Search in Tonga. As No.* 114 *but imperf, background colour changed to emerald-green, and surch as Type* O **7**.
O37 **53** 90 s. on £1 multicoloured 2·50 2·50
a. "1966" for "1969"
O38 1 p. 10 on £1 multicoloured (R.) 2·75 2·75
a. "1966" for "1969"
No. O38 is surch as Type O **7**, but without "OFFICIAL AIRMAIL".

1970 (7 Mar). *Royal Visit. As No.* 110 *but imperf, colours changed, and surch as Type* O **8**.
O39 75 s. on 1s. carmine-red and yellow 2·50 2·50
O40 1 p. on 1s. carmine-red and yellow (B.) 3·00 3·00
O41 1 p. 25 on 1s. carmine-red & yellow (G.) 3·50 3·50

OFFICIAL
Commonwealth
Member
JUNE 1970
50s
AIRMAIL

(O 9)

1970 (4 June). *Entry into British Commonwealth. As No.* 112 *but imperf, background colour changed, and surch as Type* O **9**.
O42 50 s. on 5s. orange-yellow and sepia 70 70
O43 90 s. on 5s. orange-yellow and sepia (R.) 1·00 1·00
O44 1 p. 50 on 5s. orange-yellow & sepia (G.) 1·75 1·75

1970 (4 June). *As Nos.* 325/34, *but inscr.* "OFFICIAL POST". *Colour of* "TONGA" *given for* 6 *to* 10 *s.*
O45 **83** 1 s. greenish yellow, brt purple & blk 15 15
O46 2 s. greenish yellow, ultram & black 20 20
O47 3 s. greenish yellow, chocolate & blk 25 25
O48 4 s. greenish yellow, emerald and black 25 25
O49 5 s. greenish yellow, orange-red & blk 30 30
O50 **90** 6 s. ultramarine 35 35
O51 7 s. deep mauve 40 40
O52 8 s. gold 45 45
O53 9 s. bright carmine 55 55
O54 10 s. silver 55 55
O45/54 *Set of* 10 3·00 3·00
The note after No. 334 also applies here.
See also Nos. O82/91.

Centenary
British Red Cross
1870-1970
OFFICIAL AIRMAIL
30s

(O 10)

1970 (17 Oct). *Centenary of British Red Cross. As Nos.* 102 *and* 112 *but imperf, colours changed and surch as Type* O **10**.
O55 30 s. on 1½d. emerald (Blk. and R.) 70 70
O56 80 s. on 5s. orange-yellow & sepia (B. & R.) 2·25 2·25
O57 90 s. on 5s. orange-yellow & sepia (B. & R.) 2·25 2·25

OFFICIAL AIRMAIL 20s

1965 IN MEMORIAM 1970

(O 11)

PHILATOKYO '71

(O 12)

1971 (30 Jan). *Air. Fifth Death Anniv of Queen Salote. As No.* 113, *but imperf, colours changed and optd as Type* O **11**.
O58 **52** 20 s. on 10s. orange-yellow 70 70
O59 30 s. on 10s. orange-yellow 90 90
O60 50 s. on 10s. orange-yellow 1·75 1·75
O61 2 p. on 10s. orange-yellow 6·50 6·50

1971 (17 Apr). *Air. "Philatokyo 1971" Stamp Exhibition. Unissued Red Cross surcharges on No.* 107, *but imperf, colours changed and additionally surch as Type* O **12**.
O62 30 s. on 5d. green and yellow (B. & R.) 75 75
O63 80 s. on 5d. green and yellow (Blk. & R.) 2·25 2·25
O64 90 s. on 5d. green and yellow (P. & R.) 2·50 2·50

1971 (20 July)–**72**. *Air. As Nos.* 365/6*a*, *but inscr* "OFFICIAL AIRMAIL".
O65 **96** 14 s. multicoloured 55 55
O65*a* 17 s. multicoloured (20.7.72) 65 65
O66 21 s. multicoloured 75 75
O66*a* 38 s. multicoloured (20.7.72) 1·10 1·10

O **13** Football

1971 (20 July). *Air. Fourth South Pacific Games, Tahiti.*
O67 O **13** 50 s. multicoloured 95 95
O68 90 s. multicoloured 1·75 1·75
O69 1 p. 50, multicoloured 2·50 2·50

INVESTITURE 1971
OFFICIAL 60s AIRMAIL

(O 14)

(*Illustration reduced. Actual size* 61 × 13 *mm*)

1971 (30 Oct). *Air. Investiture of Royal Tongan Medal of Merit. Nos.* 315, 318 *and* 316 *surch as Type* O **14**.
O70 **89** 60 s. on 3 s. multicoloured 90 90
O71 80 s. on 25 s. multicoloured 1·25 1·25
O72 1 p. 10 on 7 s. multicoloured 1·75 1·75

O **15** "UNICEF" and Emblem

1971 (31 Dec). *Air. 25th Anniv of UNICEF.*
O73 O **15** 70 s. multicoloured 1·25 1·25
O74 80 s. multicoloured 1·40 1·40
O75 90 s. multicoloured 1·50 1·50

1972 (14 Apr). *Air. Merchant Marine Routes. Design similar to T* **100**, *but inscr* "OFFICIAL AIRMAIL".
O76 20 s. multicoloured 50 50
O77 50 s. multicoloured 1·75 1·75
O78 1 p. 20, multicoloured 3·25 3·25
Design:—Nos. O76/8, Map of South Pacific, and *Aoniu*.

1972 (15 July). *Air. Fifth Anniv of Coronation. Design similar to T* **101**, *but inscr* "OFFICIAL AIRMAIL".
O79 50 s. multicoloured 1·10 1·10
O80 70 s. multicoloured 1·40 1·40
O81 1 p. 50, multicoloured 3·00 3·00
Design (47 × 57 *mm*):—Nos. O79/81, As T **101**, but with different background.

1972 (30 Sept). *As Nos.* 413/27, *but inscr* "OFFICIAL POST".

(*a*) *As Nos.* 413/17
O82 **83** 1 s. light yellow, scarlet and black 10 10
O83 2 s. light yellow, dp blue-green & black 15 15
O84 3 s. light yellow, yellow-green and black 20 20
O85 4 s. light yellow and black 20 20
O86 5 s. light yellow and black 20 20

(*b*) *As Nos.* O50/4, *but colours changed. Colour of* "TONGA" *given*
O87 **90** 6 s. light green 20 2
O88 7 s. light green 25 2
O89 8 s. light green 25 2
O90 9 s. light green 25 2
O91 10 s. light green 30 3

(*c*) *As Nos.* 423/7. *Colour of face value given*
O92 **102** 15 s. new blue 45 45
O93 20 s. reddish orange 60 60
O94 25 s. chocolate 70 70
O95 40 s. yellow-orange 1·50 1·50
O96 50 s. royal blue 1·75 1·75
O82/96 *Set of* 15 6·50 6·50
The note after No. 427 also applies here.

1972 (9 Dec). *Air. Proclamation of Sovereignty over Minerva Reefs. Design similar to T* **104**, *but inscr* "OFFICIAL AIRMAIL".
O97 25 s. multicoloured 40 40
O98 75 s. multicoloured 1·25 1·25
O99 1 p. 50, multicoloured 2·50 2·50
Design: *Horiz* (64 × 39 *mm*)—Nos. O97/9, Flags and map.

TONGA
1973
ESTABLISHMENT
BANK OF TONGA
40s
OFFICIAL AIRMAIL

(O 16)

1973 (30 Mar). *Air. Foundation of Bank of Tonga. No.* 396 *surch as Type* O **16**.
O100 **100** 40 s. on 21 s. mult (Blk. & G.) 1·00 1·00
O101 85 s. on 21 s. multicoloured (B. & G.) 1·90 1·90
O102 1 p. 25 on 21 s. multicoloured (Br.) 2·50 2·50

30s
SILVER JUBILEE
TONGAN SCOUTING
1948 - 1973

(O 17)

1973 (29 June). *Silver Jubilee of Scouting in Tonga. Nos.* O76, O74 *and* 319 *variously optd in silver (Nos.* O103/4) *or silver and gold (No.* O105).
O103 – 30 s. on 20 s. multicoloured 10·00 3·50
O104 O **15** 80 s. multicoloured 25·00 11·00
O105 **89** 1 p. 40 on 50 s. multicoloured 40·00 24·00

1973 (2 Oct). *Air. Bicentenary of Capt. Cook's Visit. Design similar to T* **107**, *but inscr* "OFFICIAL AIRMAIL".
O106 25 s. multicoloured 1·75 1·75
O107 80 s. multicoloured 5·00 5·00
O108 1 p. 30, multicoloured 6·50 6·50
Design: *Horiz* (52 × 45 *mm*)—Nos. O106/8, Bulk Tanker *James Cook*.

1974
Commonwealth
Games
Christchurch
OFFICIAL AIRMAIL
50s

(O 18)

1973 (19 Dec). *Air. Commonwealth Games. Nos.* O67/9 *optd with Type* O **18**, *in blue.*
O109 O **13** 50 s. multicoloured 90 90
O110 90 s. multicoloured 1·60 1·60
O111 1 p. 50, multicoloured 2·25 2·25

O **19** Dove of Peace

1974 (20 Mar). *Air.*
O112 O **19** 7 s. turq-grn, reddish vio & orge-red 15 15
O113 9 s. turq-grn, reddish vio & red-brn 20 20
O114 12 s. turq-grn, reddish vio & yell-orge 30 30

O115 O 19 14 s. turquoise-green, reddish violet and bistre-yellow 30 30
O116 17 s. multicoloured 35 35
O117 29 s. multicoloured 60 60
O118 38 s. multicoloured 80 80
O119 50 s. multicoloured .. .. .. 1·00 1·00
O120 75 s. multicoloured .. .. .. 1·60 1·60
O112/120 .. .. *Set of* 9 4·75 4·75

1974 (20 June). *Air. Centenary of Universal Postal Union. Design similar to T* **110**, *but inscr* "OFFICIAL AIRMAIL".
O121 25 s. dp red-orange, lt yellow-green & black 1·00 70
O122 35 s. lemon, magenta and black .. .. 1·50 95
O123 70 s. deep orange, bright blue and black .. 3·50 2·50
Design: *Square* (40 × 40 *mm*)—Letters "UPU".

1974 (11 Sept). *Air. Tongan Girl Guides. Design similar to T* **111**, *but inscr* "OFFICIAL AIRMAIL".
O124 45 s. multicoloured .. .. 2·25 2·25
O125 55 s. multicoloured .. .. 2·50 2·50
O126 1 p. multicoloured .. .. 5·00 5·00
Design: *Oval* (35 × 52 *mm*)—Lady Baden-Powell.

1974 (11 Dec). *Air. Establishment of Royal Marine Institute. Designs similar to T* **112** *but inscr* "Official Airmail".
O127 30 s. multicoloured .. .. 1·25 1·25
O128 35 s. multicoloured .. .. 1·50 1·50
O129 80 s. multicoloured .. .. 3·50 3·50
Designs: *Horiz* (61 × 43 *mm*)—30 s., 35 s. Badge and handclasp. *Horiz* (64 × 55 *mm*)—80 s. Badge and Tongan banknotes.

1975 (11 Mar). *Air. South Pacific Forum and Tourism. Designs similar to T* **113** *but inscr* "OFFICIAL AIRMAIL".
O130 50 s. multicoloured .. .. 1·10 1·10
O131 75 s. multicoloured .. .. 1·75 1·75
O132 1 p. 25, multicoloured .. .. .. 2·50 2·50
Designs: (49 × 43 *mm*)—50 s. Jungle arch; others, Sunset scene.

1975 (11 June). *Air. Fifth South Pacific Games. Design similar to T* **114** *but inscr* "OFFICIAL AIRMAIL".
O133 38 s. multicoloured 60 60
O134 75 s. multicoloured .. .. 1·25 1·25
O135 1 p. 20, multicoloured .. .. .. 2·00 2·00
Design: *Oval* (51 × 27 *mm*):—Runners on track.

O **20** Tongan Monarchs

1975 (4 Nov). *Air. Centenary of Tongan Constitution.*
O136 O **20** 17 s. multicoloured 40 40
O137 60 s. multicoloured .. .. .. 1·25 1·25
O138 90 s. multicoloured .. .. .. 1·75 1·75

1976 (24 Feb). *Air. First Participation in Olympic Games. Design similar to T* **117** *but inscr* "OFFICIAL AIRMAIL".
O139 45 s. multicoloured .. .. 1·75 1·75
O140 55 s. multicoloured .. .. 2·00 2·00
O141 1 p. multicoloured .. .. 3·25 3·25
Design: *Oval* (36 × 53 *mm*)—Montreal logo.

1976 (26 May). *Air. Bicentenary of American Revolution. Designs as T* **118** *showing signatories to the Declaration of Independence. Inscr* "OFFICIAL AIRMAIL".
O142 20 s. multicoloured .. .. 1·25 95
O143 50 s. multicoloured .. .. 2·75 2·50
O144 1 p. 15, multicoloured .. .. .. 6·50 5·50

1976 (25 Aug). *Air. 150th Anniv of Christianity in Tonga. Hexagonal design* (65 × 52 *mm*) *showing Lifuka Chapel.*
O145 65 s. multicoloured .. .. 1·40 1·40
O146 85 s. multicoloured .. .. 1·75 1·75
O147 1 p. 15, multicoloured .. .. .. 2·50 2·50

1976 (1 Nov). *Air. Centenary of Treaty of Friendship with Germany. Rectangular design* (51 × 47 *mm*) *showing text.*
O148 30 s. multicoloured 60 60
O149 60 s. multicoloured .. .. 1·40 1·40
O150 1 p. 25, multicoloured .. .. .. 2·75 2·75

1977 (7 Feb). *Air. Silver Jubilee. Vert design* (57 × 66 *mm*) *showing flags of Tonga and the U.K.*
O151 35 s. multicoloured .. .. 7·00 1·50
O152 45 s. multicoloured .. .. 1·75 1·00
O153 1 p. 10, multicoloured .. .. .. 2·25 1·50

1977 (4 July). *Air. Tenth Anniv of King's Coronation. Square design* (50 × 50 *mm*) *showing 1967 Coronation Coin.*
O154 20 s. multicoloured 80 70
O155 40 s. multicoloured .. .. 1·60 1·40
O156 80 s. multicoloured .. .. 3·00 2·50

1977 (28 Sept). *Air. Bicentenary of Capt. Cook's Last Voyage. Rectangular design* (52 × 46 *mm*) *showing text.*
O157 20 s. multicoloured .. .. 1·75 1·60
O158 55 s. on 20 s. multicoloured .. .. .. 4·00 3·50
O159 85 s. on 20 s. multicoloured .. .. .. 6·00 5·50
The face values of Nos. O158/9 are surcharged on the stamps, the original face value being incorrect.

1977 (16 Dec). *Air. Whale Conservation. Hexagonal design* (66 × 51 *mm*) *showing Blue Whale.*
O160 45 s. multicoloured .. .. 1·40 1·25
O161 65 s. multicoloured .. .. 2·10 1·90
O162 85 s. multicoloured .. .. 2·50 2·25

1978 (5 May). *Air. Commonwealth Games, Edmonton. "Teardrop" design* (35 × 52 *mm*) *showing Games Emblem.*
O163 30 s. black, blue and red 55 45
O164 60 s. black, red and blue .. .. .. 1·25 1·00
O165 1 p. black, red and blue .. .. .. 1·75 1·60

1978 (4 July). *Air. 60th Birthday of King Taufa'ahau Tupou IV. Medal-shaped design* (21 × 45 *mm*) *showing portrait of King.*
O166 26 s. black, vermilion and yellow 45 35
O167 85 s. black, light brown and yellow .. .. 1·40 1·25
O168 90 s. black, bright violet and yellow.. .. 1·50 1·40

1978 (29 Sept). *Coil stamps.* (a) *Designs similar to Nos.* 675/9 *but inscr* "OFFICIAL POST".
O169 1 s. purple and greenish yellow 5 5
O170 2 s. brown and greenish yellow 5 5
O171 3 s. carmine, yellow and greenish yellow .. 5 5
O172 4 s. brown, yellow and greenish yellow .. 5 5
O173 5 s. blue-green, yellow and greenish yellow 5 5

(b) *Designs similar to Nos.* 680/4 *but inscr* "OFFICIAL POST"
O174 6 s. yellow-brown, emerald and light brown 10 10
O175 7 s. blue-black, emerald and light brown .. 12 12
O176 8 s. magenta, emerald and light brown 12 12
O177 9 s. red-brown, emerald and light brown .. 15 15
O178 10 s. deep green, emerald and light brown .. 15 15

(c) *Designs similar to Nos.* 685/9 *but inscr* "OFFICIAL POST"
O179 15 s. grey-black, orange-brown and emerald 25 25
O180 20 s. vermilion, orange-brown and emerald 30 30
O181 30 s. emerald and orange-brown 40 40
O182 50 s. new blue, orange-brown and emerald .. 70 70
O183 1 p. reddish violet, orange-brown & emer .. 1·50 1·50
O169/83 .. .. *Set of* 15 3·50 3·50

1978 (15 Dec). *Air. Endangered Wildlife Conservation. Designs as Nos.* 690/2 *but inscr* "OFFICIAL AIRMAIL".
O184 40 s. Type **129** 70 70
O185 50 s. Bat 95 95
O186 1 p. 10, Turtle .. .. 2·00 2·00

1979 (16 Feb). *Air. Decade of Progress. Designs similar to Nos.* 700/9 *but inscr* "OFFICIAL AIRMAIL".
O187 38 s. Tonga Red Cross emblem 55 60
O188 74 s. As No. 702 .. .. 1·00 1·10
O189 80 s. As No. 701 .. .. 1·10 1·25

1979 (1 June). *Air. Death Centenary of Sir Rowland Hill and 10th Anniv of Tongan Self-adhesive Stamps. Hand-shaped design* (45 × 53 *mm*) *showing self-adhesive stamps being removed from backing paper.*
O190 45 s. multicoloured 90 90
O191 65 s. multicoloured .. .. 1·25 1·25
O192 80 s. multicoloured .. .. 1·60 1·60

O **21** Blue-crowned Lory with foliage

O **22** Blue-crowned Lory without foliage

1979 (17 Aug). *Air. Coil stamps.*
O193 O **21** 5 s. mult (face value in black) .. 5 5
O194 11 s. multicoloured 15 20
O195 14 s. multicoloured 15 20
O196 15 s. multicoloured 20 25
O197 17 s. multicoloured 20 25
O198 18 s. multicoloured 20 25
O199 22 s. multicoloured 25 30
O200 31 s. multicoloured 35 40
O201 39 s. multicoloured 50 55
O202 75 s. multicoloured 90 95
O203 1 p. multicoloured .. .. .. 1·25 1·40
See also No. O213.

1979 (23 Nov). *Air. Views as seen through the Lens of a Camera. Design as T* **133** *but showing Niuatoputapu and Tafahi.*
O204 35 s. multicoloured 55 55
O205 45 s. multicoloured 65 65
O206 1 p. multicoloured .. .. 1·50 1·50

1980 (9 Jan). *Air. 125th Anniv of France-Tonga Treaty of Friendship. Design as T* **134** *but showing the Establishment of the Principle of Religious Freedom in the Pacific Islands.*
O207 40 s. multicoloured 55 60
O208 55 s. multicoloured 80 85
O209 1 p. 25, multicoloured .. .. .. 1·75 1·90

1980 (30 Apr). *Air. Olympic Games, Moscow. Nos.* O190/2 *surch as T* **135** *in black on silver background.*
O210 26 s. on 45 s. multicoloured 35 40
O211 40 s. on 65 s. multicoloured 55 60
O212 1 p. 10, on 1 p. multicoloured .. .. 1·60 1·75

1980 (May). *No.* O193 *redrawn without foliage as Type* O **22**.
O213 O **22** 5 s. mult (face value in magenta) ..

1980 (30 Sept). *Air. South Pacific Scout Jamboree, Tonga and 75th Anniv of Rotary International. Design showing Scout camp and Rotary emblem.*
O214 25 s. multicoloured 60 60
O215 2 p. multicoloured .. .. 3·75 3·75

T$2 **OFFICIAL** OFFICIAL

(O 23) (O 24) (O 25)

1980 (3 Dec). *Air. No.* O145 *surch with Type* O **23**.
O216 2 p. on 65 s. multicoloured .. .. .. 2·50 2·75

1983 (22 Feb–Mar). *Nos.* 834/6 *handstamped with Type* O **24** (29 *s.*, 32 *s.*) *or optd with Type* O **25** (47 *s.*).
O217 29 s. Type **151** .. .. 2·50 2·50
O218 32 s. Type **151** .. .. 3·25 3·25
O219 47 s. Montgolfier's balloon and "Concorde" (Mar) .. .. 4·50 4·50

OFFICIAL ***OFFICIAL***

(O **26**) (O **27**)

1984 (10 Apr–17 Sept). *Nos.* 865/79 *optd with Type* O **26** (1, 5, 10, 15, 29, 47 *s.*) *or with Type* O **27** (*others*).
O220 1 s. Type **159** 5 5
O221 2 s. *Porites sp* (26.6.84) 5 5
O222 3 s. *Holocentrus ruber* (18.5.84) 5 5
O223 5 s. *Cypraea mappa viridis* 5 5
O224 6 s. *Dardanus megistos* (17.9.84) 5 8
O225 9 s. *Stegostoma fasciatum* (18.5.84) .. 10 12
O226 10 s. *Conus bullatus* 10 12
O227 13 s. *Pterois volitans* (18.5.84) 15 20
O228 15 s. *Conus textile* 15 20
O229 20 s. *Dascyllus aruanus* (18.5.84) 20 25
O230 29 s. *Conus aulicus* 30 35
O231 32 s. *Acanthurus leucosternon* (18.5.84) .. 35 40
O232 47 s. *Lambis truncata* 50 55
O233 1 p. *Millepora dichotama* (26.6.84) .. .. 1·10 1·25
O234 2 p. *Birgus latro* (17.9.84) .. .. .. 2·10 2·25
O220/34 .. .. *Set of* 15 4·75 5·25

NIUAFO'OU

The following stamps were provided for the remote island of Niuafo'ou and were not valid for postage in the remainder of Tonga.

T$1

NIUAFO'OU
KINGDOM OF TONGA

1 Map of Niuafo'ou (2)

(Des and litho Walsall)

1983 (11 May). (*a*) *P* 14.

No.	Type	Description	Unused	Used
1	1	1 s. pale stone, black and rosine	5	5
2		2 s. pale stone, black and light emerald	5	5
3		3 s. pale stone, black & dull ultram	5	5
4		3 s. pale stone, black and chestnut	5	5
5		5 s. pale stone, black and deep magenta	5	5
6		6 s. pale stone, black and greenish blue	5	8
7		9 s. pale stone, black & dull yell-grn	8	10
8		10 s. pale stone, black & dull ultram	12	15
9		13 s. pale stone, black and light emerald	15	20
10		15 s. pale stone, black and chestnut	15	20
11		20 s. pale stone, black and greenish blue	20	25
12		29 s. pale stone, black and deep magenta	30	35
13		32 s. pale stone, black & dull yellow-green	35	40
14		47 s. pale stone, black and rosine	50	55

(*b*) *No.* 820 *of Tonga surch* (*No.* 15) *with T* **2** *by lithography or optd only* (*No.* 16) *by typography. P* 13½.

No.	Type	Description	Unused	Used
15		1 p. on 2 p. pale turquoise-green & black (V.)	1·10	1·25
		a. Deep mauve surch in typography	10·00	10·00
16		2 p. pale turquoise-green (Gold)	2·25	2·40
1/16		*Set of* 16	5·00	6·00

Most examples of No. 15 have the surcharge printed by lithography. A small quantity did, however, receive a typography surcharge in a different shade to form No. 15a. In addition to the colour the typography printing can be identified by the white rims to the letters and figures. All examples of No. 16 were printed by typography.

1983 (11 May). *Inauguration of Niuafo'ou Airport. As T* **153** *of Tonga. P* 14 × 14½.

No.	Type	Description	Unused	Used
17		29 s. multicoloured	1·25	1·25
18		1 p. multicoloured	3·75	4·00

3s

(3)

4 Eruption of Niuafo'ou

1983 (30 May). *As T* 1, *but without value, surch with T* 3 *by Tonga Government Printer.*

No.	Type	Description	Unused	Used
19		3 s. pale stone, black and royal blue	5	5
20		5 s. pale stone, black and royal blue	5	5
21		32 s. pale stone, black and royal blue	35	40
		a. Surch inverted	£600	
22		2 p. pale stone, black and royal blue	2·25	2·40
		a. Surch inverted	£125	

(Des R. Edge. Litho Walsall)

1983 (29 Sept). *25th Anniv of Re-settlement. T* **4** *and similar horiz designs. Multicoloured. P* 14.

No.	Type	Description	Unused	Used
23		5 s. Type **4**	5	5
24		29 s. Lava flow	35	40
25		32 s. Islanders fleeing to safety	40	45
26		1 p. 50, Evacuation by boat	1·90	2·00

5 Purple Swamphen

6 Green Turtle

(Des N. Arlott. Litho Walsall)

1983 (15 Nov). *Birds of Niuafo'ou. T* **5** *and similar designs. P* 11 (1 *p.*, 2 *p.*), 14 (20 *s. to* 47 *s.*) *or* 14½ (*others*).

No.	Type	Description	Unused	Used
27		1 s. black and deep mauve	5	5
28		2 s. black and bright blue	5	5
29		3 s. black and blue-green	5	5
30		5 s. black and yellow	5	5
31		6 s. black and red-orange	5	8
32		9 s. multicoloured	10	12
33		10 s. multicoloured	10	12
34		13 s. multicoloured	15	20
35		15 s. multicoloured	15	20
36		20 s. multicoloured	20	25
37		29 s. multicoloured	30	35
38		32 s. multicoloured	35	40
39		47 s. multicoloured	50	55
40		1 p. multicoloured	1·10	1·25
41		2 p. multicoloured	2·10	2·25
27/41		*Set of* 15	4·75	5·25

Designs: *Vert* (22 × 29 *mm*)—2 s. White-collared Kingfisher; 3 s. Red-headed Parrotfinch; 5 s. Banded Rail; 6 s. Niuafo'ou Megapode; 9 s. Giant Forest Honeyeater; 10 s. Purple Swamphen (*different*) (22 × 36 *mm*)—29 s. Red-headed Parrotfinch (*different*); 32 s. White-collared Kingfisher (*different*) (29 × 42 *mm*)—1 p. As 10 s. *Horiz* (29 × 22 *mm*)—13 s. Banded Rail (*different*); 15 s. Niuafo'ou Megapode (*different*); (36 × 22 *mm*)—20 s. As 13 s.; 47 s. As 15 s.; (42 × 29 *mm*)—2 p. As 15 s.

(Des R. Edge. Litho Walsall)

1984 (7 Mar). *Wildlife and Nature Reserve. T* **6** *and similar multi-coloured designs. P* 14.

No.	Type	Description	Unused	Used
42		29 s. Type **6**	40	45
43		32 s. Flying Fox (*vert*)	40	45
44		47 s. Humpback Whale	60	65
45		1 p. 50, Niuafo'ou Megapode (*vert*)	2·00	2·10

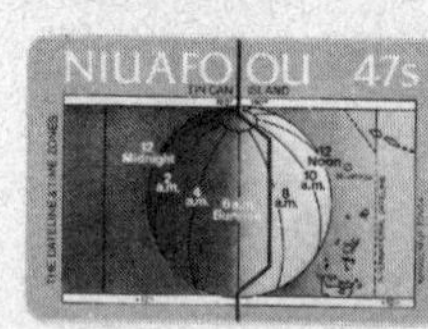

7 Diagram of Time Zones

8 Australia 1913 £2 Kangaroo Definitive

(Des R. Edge. Litho Walsall)

1984 (20 Aug). *Centenary of International Dateline. T* **7** *and similar horiz design. Multicoloured. P* 14.

No.	Type	Description	Unused	Used
46		47 s. Type **7**	60	65
47		2 p. Location map showing Niuafo'ou	2·50	2·75

1984 (17 Sept). *"Ausipex" International Stamp Exhibition, Melbourne. T* **8** *and similar vert design. Multicoloured. P* 14.

No.	Type	Description	Unused	Used
48		32 s. Type **8**	40	45
49		1 p. 50, Niuafo'ou 1983 10 s. map definitive	2·00	2·10
MS50		90 × 100 mm. As Nos. 48/9, but without exhibition logo and with face value at foot. Die cut.	2·40	2·50

Examples of No. **MS**50 without face values are Exhibition Banquet souvenirs without postal validity.

Transjordan

PRICES FOR STAMPS ON COVER

Nos. 1/88*a*	*from* × 10
Nos. 89/142	*from* × 5
Nos. 143/243	*from* × 3
Nos. D112/24	*from* × 5
Nos. D159/248	*from* × 3
No. O117	*from* × 5

Transjordan was part of the Turkish Empire from 1516 to 1918. The area was overrun by British and Arab forces, organised by Colonel T. E. Lawrence, in September 1918, and as Occupied Enemy Territory (East), became part of the Syrian state under the Emir Faisal, who was king of Syria from 11 March to 24 July 1920. On 25 April 1920 the Supreme Council of the Allies assigned to the United Kingdom a mandate to administer both Palestine and Transjordan, as the area to the east of the Jordan was called. The mandate came into operation on 29 September 1923. During 1920 the stamps of the Arab Kingdom of Syria were in use.

BRITISH MANDATED TERRITORY

(1000 milliemes = 100 piastres = £1 Egyptian)

"EAST". Where the word "East" appears in the Arabic overprints it is not used in its widest sense but as implying the land or government "East of Jordan".

شرقي الاردن ("East of Jordan") (1)

شرقي الاردن (1*a*)

(Optd at Greek Orthodox Convent, Jerusalem)

1920 (Nov). *T* **3** *of Palestine optd with T* **1**. (*a*) *P* 15 × 14.

No.	Type	Description	Unused	Used
1	1	1 m. sepia	25	50
		a. Opt inverted	£110	
2		2 m. blue-green	2·75	4·00
		a. Silver opt	£120	£140
3		3 m. yellow-brown	40	50
		a. Opt Type 1*a*	£800	
4		4 m. scarlet	40	50
5		5 m. yellow-orange	40	90
6		2 p. olive	1·50	2·75
		a. Opt Type 1*a*	£900	
7		5 p. deep purple	12·00	18·00
		a. Opt Type 1*a*	£850	
8		9 p. ochre	£1100	£1200
1/7		*Set of* 7	16·00	25·00

(*b*) *P* 14

No.	Type	Description	Unused	Used
9	1	1 m. sepia	15	40
		a. Opt inverted	£110	
10		2 m. blue-green	15	40
		a. Silver opt	£130	
11		3 m. yellow-brown	3·50	6·00
12		4 m. scarlet	7·00	12·00
13		5 m. orange	40	60
14		1 p. deep indigo (Silver)	70	1·50
15		2 p. deep olive	80	2·00
16		5 p. purple	1·60	4·00
17		9 p. ochre	3·00	10·00
18		10 p. ultramarine	3·50	10·00
19		20 p. pale grey	6·00	20·00
9/19		*Set of* 11	24·00	60·00

Emir Abdullah, 1 April 1921–22 May 1946

Abdullah, a son of the King of the Hejaz, was made Emir of Transjordan in 1921. On 26 May 1923 Transjordan was recognised as an autonomous state and on 20 February 1928 it was accorded a degree of independence.

عشر القرش ("Tenth of a piastre") (2)

القرش ("Piastre") (3)

1922 (Nov). *Nos.* 1/19 *additionally handstamped with steel dies at Amman as T* **2** *or* **3**. (*a*) *P* 15 × 14.

No.	Type	Description	Unused	Used
20	2	1/10 p. on 1 m. sepia	18·00	35·00
		a. Red surch	50·00	35·00
		b. Violet surch	50·00	50·00
21		2/10 p. on 2 m. blue-green	20·00	20·00
		a. Error. Surch "3/10" for "2/10"	80·00	
		b. Red surch	45·00	40·00
		c. Violet surch	55·00	50·00
22		3/10 p. on 3 m. yellow-brown	6·00	6·00
		a. Pair, one without surch	£450	
		b. Opt Type 1*a*	£1000	
		c. Violet surch	35·00	35·00
23		4/10 p. on 4 m. scarlet	48·00	48·00
24		5/10 p. on 5 m. yellow-orange	£150	65·00
		a. Violet surch	£200	£100
25	3	2 p. on 2 p. olive	£160	50·00
		aa. Opt Type 1*a*	£1000	
		a. Red surch	£180	60·00
		b. Violet surch	£225	80·00
26		5 p. on 5 p. deep purple	35·00	60·00
		a. Opt Type 1*a*	£1000	
27		9 p. on 9 p. ochre	£180	£200
		a. Red surch	80·00	90·00

(*b*) *P* 14

No.	Type	Description	Unused	Used
28	2	1/10 p. on 1 m. sepia	12·00	15·00
		a. Red surch	30·00	25·00
		b. Violet surch	£300	£350
29		2/10 p. on 2 m. blue-green	18·00	18·00
		a. Error. Surch "3/10" for "2/10"	55·00	50·00
		b. Red surch	45·00	35·00
		c. Violet surch	40·00	40·00

30 2 5/10 p. on 5 m. orange .. .. .. £180 40·00
a. Violet surch .. .. ..
31 3 1 p. on 1 p. deep indigo (R.) .. .. £130 30·00
a. Violet surch £250
32 9 p. on 9 p. ochre (R.) £250 £275
33 10 p. on 10 p. ultramarine £700 £750
34 20 p. on 20 p. pale grey £600 £650

T 3 of Palestine (perf 15 × 14) similarly surch

35 3 10 p. on 10 p. ultramarine £1800 £2000
36 20 p. on 20 p. pale grey £1800 £2000

T 2 reads "tenths of a piastre". T 3 reads "the piastre", both with Arabic figures below. These surcharges were supplied in order to translate the Egyptian face values of the stamps into terms intelligible to the local population, *i.e.* tenths of a piastre (= milliemes) and piastres of the Turkish gold pound; but the actual face value of the stamps remained unchanged.

Being handstamped the surcharge may be found either at the top or bottom of the stamp, and exists double on most values.

("Arab Government of the East, April 1921")
(4)

1922 (Dec). *Stamps of* 1920, *handstamped with a steel die as T* 4, *in red-purple, violet or black.* (a) P* 15 × 14.

37 4 1 m. sepia (R.P.) .. .. .. 22·00 22·00
a. Violet opt .. .. .. 25·00 25·00
b. Black opt .. .. .. 17·00 17·00
38 2 m. blue-green (R.P.) .. .. 17·00 17·00
a. Violet opt .. .. .. 15·00 15·00
b. Black opt .. .. .. 12·00 12·00
39 3 m. yellow-brown (R.P.) .. .. 20·00 20·00
a. Opt Type 1*a* £1250
b. Violet opt .. .. .. 4·00 4·00
c. Black opt .. .. .. 5·00 5·00
40 4 m. scarlet (R.P.) .. .. .. 35·00 40·00
a. Violet opt .. .. .. 35·00 40·00
b. Black opt .. .. .. 35·00 35·00
41 5 m. yellow-orange (R.P.) .. .. 30·00 8·00
a. Violet opt .. .. .. 12·00 10·00
42 2 p. olive (No. 6) (R.P.) .. .. 30·00 18·00
a. Violet opt .. .. .. 20·00 12·00
b. Black opt .. .. .. 8·00 6·00
c. On No. 6a (R.P.) £750
d. On No. 6a (V.) £800 £600
43 5 p. deep purple (R.P.) .. .. 40·00 60·00
aa. Pair, one without opt £950
a. Violet opt .. .. .. 30·00 45·00
44 9 p. ochre (R.P.) £200 £225
a. Violet opt £120 £150
ab. Opt Type 1*a* £1500
b. Black opt .. .. .. 50·00 75·00

(b) P 14

45 4 1 m. sepia (R.P.) .. .. .. 7·00 9·00
a. Pair, one without opt £650
b. Violet opt .. .. .. 18·00 12·00
c. Black opt .. .. .. 12·00 11·00
46 2 m. blue-green (R.P.) .. .. 20·00 20·00
a. Violet opt .. .. .. 4·00 4·00
b. Black opt .. .. .. 5·00 5·00
46*c* 3 m. yellow-brown (V.) £400 £200
47 5 m. orange (R.P.) .. .. .. £275 65·00
a. Violet opt .. .. .. 20·00 15·00
48 1 p. deep indigo (R.P.) .. .. 20·00 10·00
a. Violet opt .. .. .. 15·00 9·00
49 2 p. olive (V.) .. .. .. 60·00 65·00
50 5 p. purple (R.P.) .. .. .. 70·00 80·00
a. Violet opt .. .. .. 80·00 90·00
51 9 p. ochre (V.) £400 £450
52 10 p. ultramarine (R.P.) £800 £900
a. Violet opt £800 £900
53 20 p. pale grey (R.P.) £800 £950
a. Violet opt £850 £950

*The ink of the "black" overprint is not a true black, but is caused by a mixture of inks from different ink-pads. The colour is, however, very distinct from either of the others. Other values may exist with "black" overprint.

Most values are known with inverted and/or double overprints.

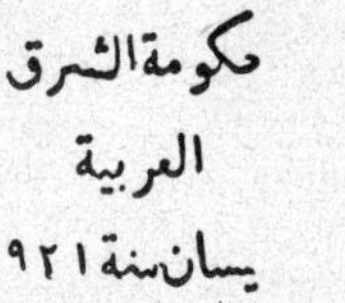

("Arab Government of the East, April 1921")
(5)

1923 (1 Mar). *Stamps of* 1920, *with typographed overprint, T* 5.

(a) P 15 × 14

54 5 1 m. sepia (Gold) £1500 £1500
55 2 m. blue-green (Gold) .. .. 17·00 20·00
56 3 m. yellow-brown (Gold) .. .. 10·00 12·00
a. Opt double £200
b. Opt inverted £225
c. Black opt .. .. .. 60·00 70·00
57 4 m. scarlet .. .. .. 8·00 9·00
58 5 m. yellow-orange .. .. .. 40·00 35·00
59 2 p. olive (No. 6) (Gold) .. .. 12·00 12·00
a. Black opt £300
b. On No. 6a (Gold) £750 £550
60 5 p. deep purple (No. 7) (Gold) .. 30·00 60·00
a. Opt inverted £375
b. On No. 7a £750
ba. Ditto. Gold opt inverted .. £750

(b) P 14

62 5 1 m. sepia (Gold) .. .. .. 15·00 20·00
a. Opt inverted £200

63 5 2 m. blue-green (Gold) .. .. 10·00 12·00
a. Opt inverted £275
b. Opt double £300
64 5 m. orange .. .. .. 8·00 8·00
65 1 p. deep indigo (Gold) .. .. 10·00 12·00
a. Opt double £350 £350
b. Black opt £400 £450
66 9 p. ochre .. .. .. 35·00 80·00
67 10 p. ultramarine (Gold) .. .. 45·00 £100
68 20 p. pale grey (Gold) .. .. 45·00 £100
a. Opt inverted £400
b. Opt double £400
c. Opt double, one inverted .. £400
d. 2nd and 3rd lines of opt omitted .. £700
e. Opt double, one gold, one black, latter inverted £650
f. Black opt £400
fa. Black opt inverted £450
fb. Black opt double, one inverted .. £500

There are numerous constant minor varieties in this overprint in all values.

Same overprint on stamp of Palestine, T 3

69 5 5 m. orange £1300 £1700

In this variety the overprint, T 1 of Jordan, has been applied to the stamp, but is not inked, so that it is hardly perceptible.

(6)

(7)

(8)

(9)

1923 (April–Oct). *Stamps of the preceding issues further surch by means of handstamps. (a) Issue of Nov* 1920.

70 – 2½/10ths p. on 5 m. (13) (B.–Blk.) .. £100 £100
a. Black surch £100 £100
b. Violet surch £100 £100

(b) Stamp of Palestine

71 6 5/10 p. on 3 m. (7) £4500

(c) Issue of Nov 1922

72 6 5/10 p. on 3 m. (22) £4000
73 5/10 p. on 5 p. (26) (V.) .. .. 50·00 60·00
73*b* 5/10 p. on 9 p. (27a) £120 £140
74 7 ½ p. on 5 p. (26) .. .. .. 70·00 80·00
75 ½ p. on 9 p. (27) £4500
a. On No. 27a £120 £180
76 ½ p. on 9 p. (32) .. .. .. — £5000
77 8 1 p. on 5 p. (26) .. .. .. 60·00 80·00

(d) Issue of Dec 1922

78 6 5/10 p. on 3 m. (39) .. .. .. 85·00 £100
a. On No. 39a £400
b. On No. 39b .. .. .. 40·00 50·00
c. Without numeral of value .. £110
79 5/10 p. on 5 p. (43a) .. .. .. 4·00 7·00
c. Pair, one without surch .. £300
79*d* 5/10 p. on 9 p. (44b) .. .. .. — £800
e. Surch on No. 44a .. .. — £900
80 7 ½ p. on 2 p. (42) .. .. .. 80·00 £100
b. On No. 42a .. .. .. 80·00 £110
c. On No. 42b .. .. .. 60·00 £110
e. On No. 42b. Pair, one without surch £600
f. On No. 42c £300
81 ½ p. on 5 p. (43a) £1800
82 ½ p. on 5 p. (50) £1500
83 8 1 p. on 5 p. (43) £1800
b. On No. 43a £1200 £1300

(e) Issue of 1 *March* 1923

84 6 5/10 p. on 3 m. (56) .. .. .. 25·00 30·00
85 7 ½ p. on 9 p. (*p* 15 × 14) .. .. 60·00 £120
86 ½ p. on 9 p. (66) £100
87 9 1 p. on 10 p. (67) £1200 £1300
a. Violet surch £1500
88 2 p. on 20 p. (68) .. .. .. 40·00 70·00
88*a* 2 p. on 20 p. (68f) £1500

The handstamp on No. 88 has an Arabic "2" in place of the "1" shown in the illustration of Type 9.

Being handstamped many of the above exist inverted or double.

TYPES OF SAUDI ARABIA. The following illustrations are repeated here for convenience from Saudi Arabia.

11

20

21

22

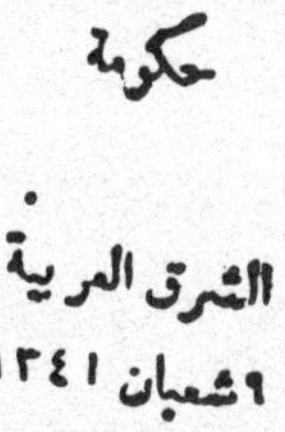

("Arab Government of the East, 9 Sha'ban 1341")
(10)

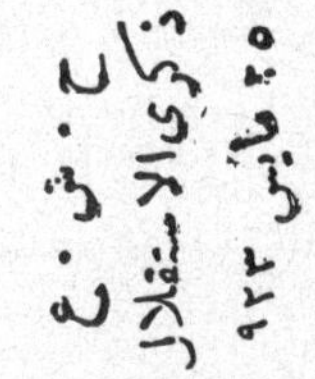

("Arab Government of the East. Commemoration of Independence, 25 May 1923")
(11)

It should be noted that as Arabic is read from right to left, the overprint described as reading downwards appears to the English reader as though reading upwards. Our illustration of Type 11 shows the overprint reading downwards.

1923 (April). *Stamps of Saudi Arabia. T* 11, *with typographed opt, T* 10.

89 10 ⅛ p. chestnut .. .. .. 1·25 1·00
a. Opt double £140
b. Opt inverted £110
90 ½ p. scarlet .. .. .. 1·25 1·00
91 1 p. blue 80 80
a. Opt inverted £100 £120
92 1½ p. lilac .. .. .. 1·00 1·25
a. Opt double £160
b. Top line omitted .. .. — £160
c. Pair, one without opt £200
93 2 p. orange .. .. .. 1·25 1·75
94 3 p. brown .. .. .. 2·00 2·50
a. Opt inverted £170
b. Opt double £170
c. Pair, one without opt £225
95 5 p. olive .. .. .. 4·00 5·00
89/95 .. .. .. *Set of* 7 11·00 13·00

On same stamps, surcharged with new values (Saudi Arabia, Nos. 47 *and* 49)

96 10 ¼ p. on ⅛ p. chestnut .. .. 4·00 5·00
a. Opt and surch inverted £150
b. Ditto. but 2nd and 3rd lines of opt omitted £180
97 10 p. on 5 p. olive .. .. .. 12·00 18·00

In this setting, the first line of the overprint measures 9 mm, the second 18½–19½ mm, and the third, 19–21 mm. On 35 stamps out of the setting of 36 the Arabic "9" (right-hand character in bottom line) is widely spaced from the rest of the inscription. Minor varieties of this setting exist on all values.

For later setting, varying from the above, see Nos. 121/4.

1923 (25 May). *T* 3 *of Palestine optd with T* 11, *reading up or down, in black or gold. A. Reading downwards. B. Reading upwards.*

		A		B	
98 11 1 m. (Blk.)		17·00	17·00	65·00	70·00
a. Opt double, one inverted (Blk.) ..		£600	£600	†	
b. Gold opt		80·00	90·00	70·00	75·00
c. Opt double, one inverted (Gold) ..		£600	—	†	
d. Opt double (Blk. + Gold) ..		£600	£600	†	
99 2 m. (Blk.)		28·00	35·00	45·00	50·00
100 3 m. (Blk.)		10·00	12·00	75·00	80·00
101 4 m. (Blk.)		10·00	12·00	25·00	32·00
102 5 m. (Blk.)		35·00	40·00	†	
103 1 p. (Gold)		£600	—	35·00	40·00
a. Opt double		£600	£600	—	—
b. Black opt		†		—	—
104 2 p. (Blk.)		30·00	50·00	—	—
105 5 p. (Gold)		45·00	50·00	£600	£400
a. Opt double		£550	—	†	
106 9 p. (Blk.)		60·00	80·00	35·00	40·00
107 10 p. (Blk.)		45·00	70·00	£500	—
108 20 p. (Blk.)		£500	—	45·00	65·00

The 9 and 10 p. are perf 14, all the other values being perf 15 × 14.

An error reading "933" instead of "923" occurs as No. 2 in the setting of 24, on all values.

No. 107A *surch with T* 9

109 9 1 p. on 10 p. ultramarine £5000

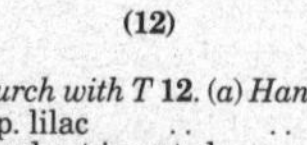

(12)

1923 (Sept). *No.* 92 *surch with T* 12. *(a) Handstamped.*

110 12 ½ p. on 1½ p. lilac .. .. .. 6·00 6·00
a. Surch and opt inverted .. .. 50·00
b. Opt double .. .. .. 50·00
c. Opt double, one inverted .. .. 50·00 60·00
d. Pair, one without opt £120

This handstamp is known inverted; double; double, one inverted; and omitted in pair with normal.

(b) Typographed

111 12 ½ p. on 1½ p. lilac .. .. .. 30·00 30·00
a. Surch inverted £150
b. Surch double £200
c. Pair, one without surch £300

حكومة حكومة
الشرق العربية الشرق العربية
٩ شعبان ١٣٤١ ٩ شعبان ١٣٤١

(13*a*) (13*b*)
("Arab Government of the East, 9 Sha'ban, 1341")

These two types differ in the spacing of the characters and in the position of the bottom line which is to the left of the middle line in T 13*a* and centrally placed in T 13*b*.

1923 (Oct). *T* **11** *of Saudi Arabia handstamped as T* **13***a or* **13***b*.
112 **13*a*** ½ p. scarlet .. .. 4·00 5·00
113 **13*b*** ½ p. scarlet .. .. 4·00 5·00

د ٠ ق ٠ ج

ملك العرب

حكومة الشرق العربية ١ ج ٠ ث ٣٤٣

(**15** "Arab Government of the East") ("Commemorating the coming of His Majesty the King of the Arabs" and date)
(**16**)

1924 (Jan). *T* **11** *of Saudi Arabia with typographed opt T* **15**.
114 **15** ½ p. scarlet .. .. 6·00 8·00
a. Opt inverted £150
115 1 p. blue £100 £100
116 1½ p. lilac £180
The ½ p. exists with thick, brown gum, which tints the paper, and with white gum and paper.

1924 (18 Jan). *Visit of King Hussein of Hejaz. T* **11** *of Saudi Arabia optd with T* **15** *and with further typographed opt T* **16**.

A. *In Black*. B. *In Gold*

		A		B	
117 **16** ½ p. scarlet	..	1·00	1·00	2·00	2·00
a. Type **15** omitted	..	£100	—	†	
b. Type **16** inverted	..	£150	—	†	
c. Imperf between (pr)	..	50·00	—	—	—
118 1 p. blue	..	1·25	1·25	2·00	2·00
a. Type **15** omitted	..	£100	—	†	
b. Both opts inverted	..	£100	—	£200	—
d. Imperf between (pr)	..	†		—	—
119 1½ p. lilac	..	1·50	1·50	2·00	2·00
a. Type **15** inverted	..	75·00	—	£100	—
120 2 p. orange	..	2·00	2·00	2·50	2·50

The spacing of the lines of the overprint varies considerably, and a variety dated "432" for "342" occurs on the twelfth stamp in each sheet.

1924 (Mar–May). *T* **11** *of Saudi Arabia optd as T* **10** (*new setting*).*
121 ½ p. scarlet .. .. 2·00 2·00
a. Opt inverted .. .. 75·00
122 ½ p. maroon .. .. 4·50 2·00
a. Opt inverted .. .. 85·00
123 1 p. blue .. .. 3·00 2·00
a. Opt double .. .. 95·00
124 1½ p. lilac .. .. 5·00 6·00
*This setting is from fresh type, the first line measuring 8¾ mm, the second nearly 20 mm and third 18¼ mm.
On all stamps in this setting (except Nos. 1, 9, 32 and 33) the Arabic "9" is close to the rest of the inscription.
The dots on the character "Y" (the second character from the left in the second line) are on many stamps vertical (:) instead of horizontal (..).
There are many errors. In the third line, No. 24 of the setting reads "Shabál", and No. 27 reads "Shabn" (instead of "Sha'an").
On some sheets of the ½ p. (both colours), the right hand character, "H", in the first line, was omitted from the second stamp in the first row of the sheet.

حكومة الشرق العربي ١٣٤٢ حكومة الشرق العربي سنة ١٣٤٣

("Government of the Arab East, 1342")
(**17**)
("Government of the Arab East, 1343")
(**18**)

1924 (Sept–Nov). *T* **11** *of Saudi Arabia with type-set opt as T* **17**.
125 **17** ⅛ p. chestnut 35 15
a. Opt inverted £100
126 ¼ p. green 30 30
a. Tête-bêche (pair) .. .. .. 6·00 8·00
b. Opt inverted .. .. 75·00
127 ½ p. scarlet 30 30
128 ½ p. maroon .. .. 1·00 60
129 1 p. blue .. .. 2·00 1·50
a. Imperf between (horiz pair) .. 75·00
130 1½ p. lilac .. .. 2·50 2·50
131 2 p. orange .. .. 2·00 2·00
132 **17** 3 p. brown-red .. .. 1·50 1·50
a. Opt inverted .. .. 55·00
b. Opt double .. .. 55·00
133 5 p. olive .. .. 2·00 2·50
134 10 p. brown-purple and mauve (R.) .. 4·00 5·00
a. Centre inverted .. .. ..
b. Black opt £130
125/34 .. .. *Set of* 10 21·00 24·00
Varieties may be found with dates "1242" or "1343", with "1" or "2" inverted, and other errors exist.

1925 (Aug). *T* **20/22** *of Saudi Arabia with lithographed opt T* **18**.
135 **18** ⅛ p. chocolate 25 25
a. Imperf between (horiz pair) .. 75·00 £110
136 ¼ p. ultramarine 25 25
137 ½ p. carmine 35 35
138 1 p. green 35 35
139 1½ p. orange 50 80
140 2 p. blue .. .. 70 1·25
a. Opt treble £100 £120
141 3 p. sage-green (R.) .. .. .. 1·00 2·00
a. Imperf between (horiz pair) .. 80·00 £120
b. Black opt £100 £120
142 5 p. chestnut .. .. 2·00 4·00
135/42 .. .. *Set of* 8 5·00 9·00
The whole series exists imperforate and (except the 1 and 2 p.) with inverted overprint, both perf and imperf.

شرق الاردن

("East of the Jordan")
(**19**)

22 Emir Abdullah

23 Emir Abdullah

(Opt typo by Waterlow)

1925 (1 Nov). *Stamps of Palestine,* 1922 (*without the three-line Palestine opt*), *optd with T* **19**. *Wmk Mult Script CA*. (*a*) *P* 14.
143 **19** 1 m. deep brown 10 15
144 2 m. yellow 10 15
145 3 m. greenish blue 10 15
146 4 m. carmine-pink 10 15
147 5 m. orange 10 15
a. Yellow-orange .. .. 30·00 18·00
148 6 m. blue-green 15 20
149 7 m. yellow-brown 15 20
150 8 m. scarlet 20 30
151 13 m. ultramarine 40 60
152 1 p. grey 40 40
153 2 p. olive 60 70
a. Olive-green .. .. 90·00 25·00
154 5 p. deep purple .. .. 2·50 3·00
155 9 p. ochre .. .. 4·00 4·50
156 10 p. light blue .. .. 5·00 6·00
a. Error. "E.F.F." in bottom panel .. £650 £550
157 20 p. bright violet .. .. 10·00 12·00
143/57 .. .. *Set of* 15 23·00 28·00
143/57 Optd "Specimen" .. .. *Set of* 15 90·00

(*b*) *P* 15 × 14
157*a* **19** 9 p. ochre £1100 £1200
158 10 p. blue .. .. 60·00 70·00
158*a* 20 p. bright violet £1100 £850

(New Currency. 1000 milliemes = £1 Palestinian)

(Recess Perkins, Bacon & Co)

1927 (1 Nov)–**29**. *New Currency. Wmk Mult Script CA. P* 14.
159 **22** 2 m. greenish blue 15 10
160 3 m. carmine-pink 20 12
161 4 m. green 50 30
162 5 m. orange 25 15
163 10 m. scarlet 50 25
164 15 m. ultramarine 40 25
165 20 m. olive-green 50 50
166 **23** 50 m. purple .. .. 1·75 2·00
167 90 m. bistre .. .. 4·50 4·50
168 100 m. blue .. .. 6·00 5·00
169 200 m. violet .. .. 14·00 10·00
170 500 m. brown (1929) .. .. .. 45·00 30·00
171 1000 m. slate-grey (1929) .. .. .. 80·00 50·00
159/71 .. .. *Set of* 13 £140 90·00
159/71 Optd/perf "Specimen" .. *Set of* 13 £125

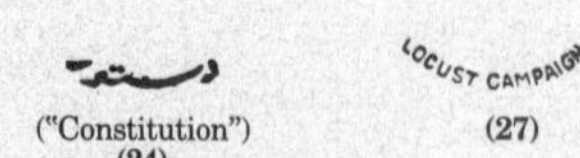

("Constitution")
(**24**)

(**27**)

(Optd at Cairo)

1928 (1 Sept). *New Constitution of* 20 *February* 1928. *Optd with T* **24**.
172 **22** 2 m. greenish blue 50 50
173 3 m. carmine-pink 60 60
174 4 m. green 60 60
175 5 m. orange 60 60
176 10 m. scarlet 90 80
177 15 m. ultramarine .. .. 1·00 1·00
178 20 m. olive-green .. .. 3·00 3·00
179 **23** 50 m. purple .. .. 5·00 3·50
180 90 m. bistre .. .. 10·00 10·00
181 100 m. blue .. .. 16·00 16·00
182 200 m. violet .. .. 40·00 40·00
172/82 .. .. *Set of* 11 70·00 70·00

(Optd at Alexandria by Whitehead, Morris & Co)

1930 (1 Apr). *Locust Campaign. Optd as T* **27**.
183 **22** 2 m. greenish blue 75 75
a. Opt inverted £180
184 **22** 3 m. carmine-pink 80 80
185 4 m. green 60 60
186 5 m. orange .. .. 6·00 6·00
a. Opt double £300 £325
b. Pair, one without bottom line .. £350
187 10 m. scarlet 55 55
188 15 m. ultramarine 80 80
a. Opt inverted £160 £225
189 20 m. olive-green 85 85
190 **23** 50 m. purple .. .. 4·00 4·00
191 90 m. bistre .. .. 9·00 9·00
192 100 m. blue .. .. 11·00 11·00
193 200 m. violet .. .. 26·00 26·00
194 500 m. brown .. .. 65·00 65·00
a. "C" of "LOCUST" omitted £500 £500
183/94 .. .. *Set of* 12 £125 £125

28

29

(Re-engraved with figures of value at left only. Recess Perkins, Bacon)

1930 (1 June)–**39**. *Wmk Mult Script CA. P* 14.
194*b* **28** 1 m. red-brown (6.2.34) 15 15
c. Perf 13½ × 13 (1939) 60 30
195 2 m. greenish blue 15 15
a. Perf 13½ × 13. *Bluish green* (1939) 60 30
196 3 m. carmine-pink 15 15
196*a* 3 m. green (6.2.34) 15 15
b. Perf 13½ × 13 (1939) .. .. 2·00 1·50
197 4 m. green 20 15
197*a* 4 m. carmine-pink (6.2.34) 50 15
b. Perf 13½ × 13 (1939) .. .. 6·00 3·00
198 5 m. orange 25 15
a. Coil stamp. P 13½ × 14 (1936) .. 6·00 1·50
b. Perf 13½ × 13 (1939) .. .. 13·00 2·00
199 10 m. scarlet 40 15
a. Perf 13½ × 13 (1939) .. .. 21·00 2·75
200 15 m. ultramarine 50 25
a. Coil stamp. P 13½ × 14 (1936) .. 6·00 2·00
b. Perf 13½ × 13 (1939) .. .. 2·50 1·50
201 20 m. olive-green .. .. .. 1·00 30
a. Perf 13½ × 13 (1939) .. .. 16·00 6·00
202 **29** 50 m. purple .. .. .. 1·25 1·00
203 90 m. bistre .. .. .. 2·00 1·50
204 100 m. blue .. .. .. 3·00 2·25
205 200 m. violet .. .. .. 7·50 7·00
206 500 m. brown .. .. .. 11·00 7·00
207 £P1 slate-grey .. .. .. 25·00 16·00
194*b*/207 .. .. .. *Set of* 16 50·00 36·00
194*b*/207 Perf "Specimen" .. *Set of* 16 75·00
For stamps perf 12 see Nos. 230/43, and for T **28** lithographed, perf 13½, see Nos. 222/9.

30 Mushetta

31 Threshing Scene

32 The Khazneh at Petra

33 Emir Abdullah

(Vignettes from photographs; frames des Yacoub Sukker. Recess Bradbury, Wilkinson)

1933 (1 Feb). *As T* **30** (*various designs*) *and T* **31/3**. *Wmk Mult Script CA. P* 12.
208 1 m. black and maroon 40 40
209 2 m. black and claret 40 40
210 3 m. blue-green 50 60
211 4 m. black and brown 60 70
212 5 m. black and orange 80 80
213 10 m. carmine .. .. .. 1·25 1·25
214 15 m. blue .. .. .. 1·75 1·25
215 20 m. black and sage-green .. .. 2·50 2·50
216 50 m. black and purple .. .. 5·50 5·50
217 90 m. black and yellow .. .. 7·50 7·50
218 100 m. black and blue .. .. 10·00 10·00
219 200 m. black and violet .. .. 32·00 32·00
220 500 m. scarlet and red-brown .. .. 95·00 95·00
221 £P1 black and yellow-green £375 £325
208/21 .. .. .. *Set of* 14 £500 £450
208/21 Perf "Specimen" .. .. *Set of* 14 £350
Designs: *As T* **30**—2 m. Nymphaeum, Jerash; 3 m. Kasr Kharana; 4 m. Kerak Castle; 5 m. Temple of Artemis, Jerash; 10 m. Ajlun Castle; 20 m. Allenby Bridge over the Jordan.
The 90 m., 100 m. and 200 m. are similar to the 3 m., 5 m. and 10m. respectively, but are larger (33½ × 23½ mm). The 500 m. is similar to T **32**, but larger (23½ × 33½ mm).

(Litho Survey Dept, Cairo)

942 (18 May). *T* **28**, *but with Arabic characters above portrait and in top left circle modified as in T* **34**. *No wmk. P* 13½.

22	**34**	1 m. red-brown	20	15
23		2 m. green	20	20
24		3 m. yellow-green	25	20
25		4 m. carmine-pink	35	25
26		5 m. yellow-orange	40	20
27		10 m. scarlet	60	45
28		15 m. blue	1·00	45
29		20 m. olive-green	1·75	1·00
22/9		*Set of* 8	4·00	2·50

(Recess Bradbury, Wilkinson)

943 (1 Jan)–44. *Wmk Mult Script CA. P* 12.

30	**28**	1 m. red-brown	8	8
31		2 m. bluish green	8	8
32		3 m. green	8	5
33		4 m. carmine-pink	8	5
34		5 m. orange	8	5
35		10 m. red	12	10
36		15 m. blue	25	20
37		20 m. olive-green (5.44)	25	20
38	**29**	50 m. purple (5.44)	45	30
39		90 m. bistre (5.44)	1·00	60
240		100 m. blue (5.44)	1·50	70
241		200 m. violet (5.44)	3·00	2·00
242		500 m. brown (5.44)	7·00	6·00
243		£P1 slate-grey (5.44)	20·00	10·00
230/43		*Set of* 14	30·00	18·00

Nos. 237/43 were released in London by the Crown Agents about May 1944 but were not put on sale in Transjordan until 26 August 1946.

POSTAGE DUE STAMPS

حكومة

مستحق

الشرق العربية

مستحق — ٩ شعبان ١٣٤١

(D 1 "Due") (D 2)

1923 (Sept). *Issue of April, 1923, with opt T* **10**, *with further typographed opt Type* D **1** (*the 3 p. with handstamped surch as T* **12** *at top*).

D112	½ p. on 3 p. brown	6·50	7·50
	a. "Due" inverted	30·00	32·00
	b. "Due" double	30·00	40·00
	ba. "Due" double, one inverted	£100	
	c. Arabic "t" & "h" transposed	90·00	
	ca. As c, inverted	£200	
	d. Surch at foot of stamp	25·00	
	da. Ditto, but with var. c	£120	
	e. Surch omitted	£150	
D113	1 p. blue	5·00	5·50
	a. Type **10** inverted	50·00	
	b. "Due" inverted	22·00	20·00
	c. "Due" double	24·00	
	d. "Due" double, one inverted	£100	
	e. Arabic "t" & "h" transposed	60·00	
	f. "Due" omitted (in vertical pair)	£150	
D114	1½ p. lilac	5·00	5·50
	a. "Due" inverted	22·00	22·00
	b. "Due" double	24·00	
	ba. "Due" double, one diagonal	50·00	
	c. Arabic "t" & "h" transposed	60·00	
	ca. As c, inverted	£120	
	d. "Due" omitted (in pair)	£150	
D115	2 p. orange	5·00	6·00
	a. "Due" inverted	28·00	28·00
	b. "Due" double	32·00	
	ba. "Due" double, one diagonal	60·00	
	c. "Due" treble	£100	
	d. Arabic "t" & "h" transposed	60·00	
	e. Arabic "h" omitted	60·00	

The variety, Arabic "t" and "h" transposed, occurred on No. 2 in the first row of all values in the first batch of sheets printed. The variety, Arabic "h" omitted, occurred on every stamp in the first three rows of at least three sheets of the 2 p.

Handstamped in four lines as Type D **2** *and surch as on No.* D112

D116	½ p. on 3 p. brown	20·00	25·00
	a. Opt and surch inverted	£100	
	b. Opt double	£100	
	c. Surch omitted	£110	
	d. Opt inverted. Surch normal, but at foot of stamp	60·00	
	e. Opt omitted and opt inverted (pair)	£140	
	f. "Due" double, one inverted	80·00	
	g. "Due" double, one larger	90·00	
	h. Surch double	£120	

حكومة

الشرق العربية

مستحق

٩ شعبان ١٣٤١

مستحق

شرق الاردن

(D 3) ("Due. East of the Jordan") (D 4)

1923 (Oct). *T* **11** *of Saudi Arabia handstamped with Type* D **3**.

D117	½ p. scarlet	60	60
D118	1 p. blue	80	80
D119	1½ p. lilac	1·00	1·25
D120	2 p. orange	1·40	1·60
D121	3 p. brown	2·50	3·00
	a. Pair, one without handstamp	£150	
D122	5 p. olive	4·00	5·00
D117/22	*Set of* 6	10·00	12·00

There are three types of this handstamp, differing in some of the Arabic characters. They occur inverted, double etc.

1923 (Nov). *T* **11** *of Saudi Arabia with opt similar to Type* D **4** *but first three lines typo and fourth handstruck.*

D123	1 p. blue	24·00	
D124	5 p. olive	6·00	

(Opt typo by Waterlow)

1925 (Nov). *Stamps of Palestine* 1922 (*without the three-line Palestine opt*), *optd with Type* D **4**. *P* 14.

D159	1 m. deep brown	20	40
D160	2 m. yellow	30	40
D161	4 m. carmine-pink	40	60
D162	8 m. scarlet	80	1·25
D163	13 m. ultramarine	1·00	1·40
D164	5 p. deep purple	2·75	4·00
	a. Perf 15 × 14	18·00	20·00
D159/64	*Set of* 6	5·00	7·00
D159/64 Optd "Specimen"	*Set of* 6	60·00	

مستحق

١ مليم (1 m.) (D **5**) — ٢ مليم (2 m.) — ٤ مليم (4 m.)

٨ مليم (8 m.) — ١٣ مليم (13 m.) — ٥ قروش (5 p.)

(Surch typo at Jerusalem)

1926. *Postage stamps of* 1 *November* 1925, *surch "Due" and new value as Type* D **5**. *Bottom line of surcharge differs for each value as illustrated.*

D165	1 m. on 1 m. deep brown	1·00	1·25
D166	2 m. on 1 m. deep brown	1·00	1·25
D167	4 m. on 3 m. greenish blue	1·10	1·40
D168	8 m. on 3 m. greenish blue	1·25	1·40
D169	13 m. on 13 m. ultramarine	1·75	2·25
D170	5 p. on 13 m. ultramarine	1·75	2·25
D165/70	*Set of* 6	7·00	9·00

١ مستحق ١

(D 6 "Due") D 7 D 8

(Surch at Cairo)

1929 (1 Jan). *Nos.* 159 *etc. optd only or surch in addition as Type* D **6**.

D183	**22**	1 m. on 3 m. carmine-pink	20	20
D184		2 m. greenish blue	30	30
		a. Pair, one without surch	£140	
D185		4 m. on 15 m. ultramarine	40	40
		a. Surch inverted	70·00	£150
D186		10 m. scarlet	50	60
D187	**23**	20 m. on 100 m. blue	1·50	1·50
		a. Vert pair, one without surch	£160	
D188		50 m. purple	2·50	2·50
		a. Pair, one without surch	£250	
D183/8		*Set of* 6	5·00	5·00

(Recess Perkins, Bacon)

1929 (1 Apr)–**39**. *Wmk Mult Script CA. P* 14.

D189	D **7**	1 m. red-brown	20	20
		a. Perf 13½ × 13 (1939)	40·00	40·00
D190		2 m. orange-yellow	20	25
D191		4 m. green	20	25
D192		10 m. scarlet	50	70
D193		20 m. olive-green	60	80
D194		50 m. blue	1·00	1·25
D189/94		*Set of* 6	2·50	3·00
D189/94 Perf "Specimen"		*Set of* 6	50·00	

(Litho Survey Dept, Cairo)

1942 (22 Dec). *Redrawn. Top line of Arabic in taller lettering. No wmk. P* 13½.

D230	D **8**	1 m. red-brown	25	25
D231		2 m. orange-yellow	50	25
D232		10 m. scarlet	50	60

(Recess Bradbury, Wilkinson)

1944. *Wmk Mult Script CA. P* 12.

D244	D **7**	1 m. red-brown	10	10
D245		2 m. orange-yellow	10	10
D246		4 m. green	15	10
D247		10 m. carmine	40	30
D248		20 m. olive-green	1·00	80

OFFICIAL STAMP

(حكومة)

الشرق العربي

١٣٤٢

("Arab Government of the East, 1342" = 1924) (O 1)

1924. *T* **11** *of Saudi Arabia with typographed opt, Type* O **1**.

O117	½ p. scarlet	20·00	80·00

By treaty of 22 March 1946 with the United Kingdom, Transjordan was proclaimed an independent kingdom on 25 May 1946.

Later issues are listed under JORDAN in Part 19 (*Middle East*) of this catalogue.

Transvaal

(*formerly* South African Republic)

PRICES FOR STAMPS ON COVER

Nos. 1/6 are rare used on cover.

Nos. 7/85	*from* × 20
Nos. 86/155	*from* × 3
Nos. 156/62	*from* × 6
Nos. 163/9	*from* × 5
Nos. 170/225	*from* × 10
Nos. 226/34	*from* × 20
Nos. 235/7	—
Nos. 238/43	*from* × 12
Nos. 244/55	*from* × 4
Nos. 256/7	*from* × 6
Nos. 258/9	—
Nos. 260/76	*from* × 20
Nos. D1/7	*from* × 20

The issues for Pietersburg, Lydenburg, Rustenburg, Schweizer Renecke, Volksrust and Wolmaransstad are very rare when on cover.

FIRST REPUBLIC

For the 1d., 3d., 6d. and 1s. stamps, T **1** and **2**, two plates of each value were made, each plate consisting of forty stamp blocks, arranged in five rows of eight in a row.

The two plates of a value were sometimes, but not always, used together, producing a sheet of eighty stamps in two panes of forty each.

One block was inverted in the original left-hand plate of the 6d. and also of the 1s. In the panes of the printed stamps this was No. 25 on the right-hand pane in the 6d. and No. 1 on the right pane of the 1s. From this cause arose the *tête-bêche* varieties of these two values in some of the printings; and later, when these stamps were overprinted, an inverted surcharge is found whenever these panes were so treated. In addition to this in the case of the 1d., 3d., 6d., and 1s. stamps it is known that at least one sheet of each of these values must have been printed with the whole surcharge inverted.

Many unauthorised imitations of these three values were made in Germany, but, with the exception of certain impressions of the 1s. value in yellow-green on soft medium paper, they all differ from the originals in some parts of the design, particularly in the eagle and the ribbon bearing the motto under the coat of arms. To this class belong forgeries of the 1d., in red or black, in which the numerals in the top corners are enclosed in a white frame.

The exception—the 1s., in yellow-green, above mentioned—was once regarded as genuine and catalogued, but it has been proved by Mr. J. N. Luff (see his articles, "Otto's Printings," in Vols. XXXIII and XXXIV of the *Philatelic Record*; it is his "surreptitious printing J") that these were printed from an unauthorised small plate of four subjects, on each of which were certain flaws that can be easily identified in the impressions. They somewhat resemble the 1s. stamps of 1876–7, but the paper is smoother and firmer and the printing clearer.

1

2

3

(Typo Adolph Otto in Gustrow, Mecklenburg-Schwerin)

1869. *Thin paper, clear and distinct impressions.* (*a*) *Imperf.*

1	**1**	1d. brown-lake	£225	
		a. Orange-red	£225	
2		6d. bright ultramarine	£130	
		a. Pale ultramarine	£110	£120
3		1s. deep green	£450	
		a. *Tête-bêche* (pair)	£8000	

(*b*) *Fine roulette,* 15½ *to* 16

4	**1**	1d. brown-lake	55·00	
		a. Brick-red	48·00	
		b. Orange-red	48·00	
		c. Vermilion	48·00	
5		6d. bright ultramarine	48·00	
		a. Pale ultramarine	48·00	

6 1 1s. deep green .. .. 70·00
a. *Yellow-green* .. .. 60·00
b. *Emerald-green* .. .. 60·00

These stamps were printed from two sets of plates, one with the stamps spaced 1¼ to 1½ mm apart, the other with the stamps spaced 2½ to 3½ mm apart. The former are rouletted close to the design of all the four sides, and on the 1d. of that printing the outer frame-lines do not join at the right lower corner.

(Typo as last, in Germany)

1871 (July). *Thin paper, clear and distinct impressions. Fine roulette, 15½ to 16.*
7 2 3d. pale reddish lilac .. .. 70·00 65·00
a. *Deep lilac* .. .. 75·00 65·00

These fine rouletted stamps and all subsequent printings are from the plates which were subsequently sent to South Africa.

Imperf specimens of the 3d. pale reddish lilac were sent out to South Africa, but there is no evidence that they were issued for postal use. They are without the small dot on the left leg of the eagle which is always found in the issued stamps. They also exist *tête-bêche* (*price for un pair* £3250).

(Typo M. J. Viljoen at Pretoria)

1870 (4 April). *Thin gummed paper from Germany. Impressions coarse and defective. (a) Imperf.*
8 1 1d. dull rose-red .. .. 50·00
a. *Reddish pink* .. .. 50·00
b. *Carmine-red* .. .. 48·00
9 6d. dull ultramarine £160
a. *Tête-bêche* (pair) £5500

(*b*) *Fine roulette, 15½ to 16*
10 1 1d. carmine-red £700 £200
11 6d. dull ultramarine .. .. £170 85·00

(*c*) *Wide roulette, 6½*
12 1 1d. carmine-red .. .. — £850

1870. *Thick, hard paper, yellow streaky gum. (a) Imperf* (26 April).
13 1 1d. pale rose-red .. .. 40·00
a. *Carmine-red* .. .. 48·00 55·00
14 1s. yellow-green .. .. 55·00 55·00
a. *Tête-bêche* (pair) £7500

(*b*) *Fine roulette, 15½ to 16* (10 May)
15 1 6d. ultramarine .. .. 55·00 55·00
a. *Tête-bêche* (pair) £6500 £5500
16 1s. yellow-green £525 £525

1870 (24 May). *Thick hard paper, thin yellow smooth gum. Fine roulette, 15½ to 16.*
17 1 1d. carmine-red .. .. 70·00

1870 (4 July). *Medium paper, blotchy heavy printing and whitish gum. Fine roulette, 15½ to 16.*
18 1 1d. rose-red .. .. 32·00 32·00
a. *Carmine-red* .. .. 32·00 32·00
b. *Crimson*. From over-inked plate .. £120
19 6d. ultramarine .. .. 55·00 55·00
a. *Tête-bêche* (pair) .. ..
b. *Deep ultram*. From over-inked plate £400 £150
20 1s. deep green .. .. 65·00 55·00
a. From over-inked plate £400 £150

Nos. 18*b*, 19*b* and 20a were printed from over-inked plates, giving heavy, blobby impressions.

(Typo J. P. Borrius, at Potchefstroom)

1870 (Sept).

I. *Stout paper, but with colour often showing through, whitish gum*

(*a*) *Imperf*
21 1 1d. black £110 £110

(*b*) *Fine roulette, 15½ to 16*
22 1 1d. black .. .. 10·00 12·00
a. *Grey-black* .. .. 10·00 12·00
23 6d. blackish blue .. .. 85·00 35·00
a. *Dull blue* .. .. 55·00 32·00

II. *Thin transparent paper. Fine roulette, 15½ to 16*
24 1 1d. bright carmine .. .. £130 45·00
25 1d. black £140 £525
26 6d. ultramarine .. .. 60·00 35·00
27 1s. green .. .. 60·00 35·00

1872 (Dec).

I. *Thinnish opaque paper, clear printing. Fine roulette, 15½ to 16*
28 1 1d. reddish pink .. .. 48·00 29·00
a. *Carmine-red* .. .. 48·00 29·00
29 2 3d. grey-lilac .. .. 65·00 29·00
30 1 6d. ultramarine .. .. 45·00 21·00
a. *Pale ultramarine* .. .. 48·00 21·00
31 1s. yellow-green .. .. 48·00 21·00
a. *Green* .. .. 48·00 21·00
aa. Bisected (6d.) (on cover) .. .. †

II. *Thickish wove paper. (a) Fine roulette, 15½ to 16*
32 1 1d. dull rose .. .. £400 55·00
a. *Brownish rose* .. .. £475 85·00
b. Printed on both sides .. ..
33 6d. milky blue .. .. £130 27·00
a. *Deep dull blue* .. .. 65·00 26·00
aa. Imperf (pair) £525
ab. Imperf between (horiz pair) .. £475

(*b*) *Wide roulette, 6½*
34 1 6d. dull blue .. ..

III. *Very thick dense paper. Fine roulette, 15½ to 16*
35 1d. dull rose .. .. £475 95·00
a. *Brownish rose* .. .. — 75·00
36 6d. dull ultramarine .. .. £160 48·00
a. *Bright ultramarine* .. .. .. £170 48·00
37 1s. yellow-green £700 £550

(Typo in Germany from a new plate made by A. Otto at Gustrow)

1874 (30 Sept). *Thin smooth paper, clearly printed. Fine roulette, 15½ to 16.*
38 3 6d. bright ultramarine .. .. .. 45·00 17·00
a. Bisected (3d.) (on cover) .. .. †

Reprints of this stamp, both unused and with forged postmarks, are in a *duller* shade of colour than the originals, and the paper is rather thicker. Reprints also exist in fancy colours.

(Typo P. Davis & Son, Pietermaritzburg)

1874 (Sept). *P 12½. (a) Thin transparent paper.*
39 1 1d. pale brick-red .. .. 60·00 29·00
a. *Brownish red* .. .. 55·00 29·00
40 6d. deep blue .. .. 80·00 29·00

(*b*) *Thicker opaque paper*
41 1 1d. pale red .. .. 95·00 55·00
42 6d. blue .. .. 75·00 35·00
a. Imperf between (pair) .. ..
b. *Deep blue* .. .. 70·00 35·00

(Typo The Stamp Commission, Pretoria)

1875 (29 April). *Very thin soft opaque (semi-pelure).*

(*a*) *Imperf*
43 1 1d. orange-red .. .. £110 35·00
a. Pin-perf .. ..
44 2 3d. lilac .. .. 70·00 35·00
45 1 6d. blue .. .. 65·00 32·00
a. *Milky blue* .. .. £110 32·00
aa. *Tête-bêche* (pair) £6000
ab. Pin-perf .. ..

(*b*) *Fine roulette, 15½ to 16*
46 1 1d. orange-red £375 £120
47 2 3d. lilac £400 £130
48 1 6d. blue £375 £120

(*c*) *Wide roulette, 6½*
49 1 1d. orange-red .. .. — £140
50 2 3d. lilac .. .. — £200
51 1 6d. blue .. .. — £110
a. *Bright blue* .. .. — £110
b. *Milky blue* .. .. — £110

1876(?). *Very thin hard transparent paper (pelure). (a) Imperf.*
52 1 1d. brownish red .. .. 35·00 16·00
a. *Orange-red* .. .. 32·00 16·00
b. *Dull red* .. .. 32·00 32·00
53 2 3d. lilac .. .. 35·00 32·00
a. *Deep lilac* .. .. 45·00 32·00
54 1 6d. pale blue .. .. 32·00 32·00
a. *Blue* .. .. 32·00 16·00
aa. *Tête-bêche* (pair) .. .. .. — £4750
b. *Deep blue* .. .. 32·00 16·00

(*b*) *Fine roulette, 15½ to 16*
55 1 1d. orange-red £250 £110
a. *Brown-red* £250 £110
56 2 3d. lilac .. .. £325 95·00
57 1 6d. blue .. .. £140 85·00
a. *Deep blue* .. .. £140 95·00

(*c*) *Wide roulette, 6½*
58 1 1d. orange-red £700 £140
a. *Bright red* .. .. — £120
59 2 3d. lilac .. .. — £170
60 1 6d. deep blue .. .. £700 75·00

(*d*) *Pin-perf*
61 1 1d. dull red £400 £225
62 2 3d. lilac .. .. — £225
63 1 6d. blue .. .. — £200

1876. *Stout hard-surfaced paper.*

I. *Smooth, nearly white, gum. (a) Imperf*
64 1 1d. bright red .. .. 14·00 9·50
65 2 3d. lilac £400
66 1 6d. bright blue .. .. 65·00 13·00
a. *Tête-bêche* (pair) .. .. .. — £4750
b. *Pale blue* .. .. 65·00 14·00

(*b*) *Fine roulette, 15½ to 16*
67 1 1d. bright red £400 £140
68 2 3d. lilac £225
69 1 6d. bright blue .. .. — £140

(*c*) *Wide roulette, 6½*
70 1 1d. bright red £400 £140
71 6d. pale blue .. .. — £200

II. *Deep brown gum, staining the paper*
72 1 6d. deep blue (*imperf*) .. .. .. 35·00 11·00
a. *Tête-bêche* (pair) .. .. .. — £3500
73 6d. deep blue (*fine roulette*) .. .. — £400
74 6d. deep blue (*wide roulette*) £475 £225

1876–7.

I. *Coarse soft white paper, printed in the colours that were overprinted in July 1877. (a) Imperf*
75 1 1d. brick-red .. .. 70·00 38·00
76 6d. deep blue .. .. £130 38·00
a. *Milky blue* .. .. £250 65·00
77 1s. yellow-green .. .. £200 70·00
a. Bisected (6d.) (on cover) .. .. †

(*b*) *Fine roulette, 15½ to 16*
78 1 1d. brick-red .. .. — £250
79 6d. deep blue .. .. — £130
80 1s. yellow-green £550 £250

(*c*) *Wide roulette, 6½*
81 1 1d. brick-red .. .. — £300
81*a* 6d. deep blue .. ..
82 1s. yellow-green .. ..

(*d*) *Fine × wide roulette*
83 1 1d. brick-red £550 £250

II. *Hard thick coarse yellowish paper*
84 1 1d. brick-red (*imperf*) .. .. ..
85 1d. brick-red (*wide roulette*) .. ..

See also Nos. 171/4.

FIRST BRITISH OCCUPATION

V. R. V. R.

TRANSVAAL. TRANSVAAL.
(4) (5)

T 4 is the normal overprint, but in some printings No. 11 on the pane has a wider-spaced overprint, as T 5.

1877 (July). *Optd with T 4 in red. (a) Imperf.*
86 2 3d. lilac (*semi-pelure*) £1100 £22
a. Opt Type 5 .. ..
87 3d. lilac (*pelure*) £1100 £14
a. Opt Type 5 .. .. £4750
b. Opt on back £3000
c. Opt double, in red and in black .. £4750
88 1 6d. blue £1300 £15
a. Opt inverted or *tête-bêche* pair .. — £425
b. Opt double £3500
c. Opt Type 5 .. .. £4250
d. *Deep blue* .. .. — £22
89 1s. yellow-green £450 £13
a. Bisected (6d.) (on cover) .. .. † £120
b. Opt inverted or *tête-bêche* pair .. — £325
c. Opt Type 5 .. .. £3000

(*b*) *Fine roulette, 15½ to 16*
90 2 3d. lilac (*pelure*) .. .. — £110
91 1 6d. blue .. .. — £110
92 1s. yellow-green £1000 £45
a. Opt Type 5 .. ..

(*c*) *Wide roulette, 6½*
93 2 3d. lilac (*pelure*) .. .. — £110
a. Opt Type 5 .. ..
94 1 6d. blue .. .. — £110
a. Opt Type 5 .. ..
95 1s. yellow-green £2750 £100
a. Opt inverted or *tête-bêche* pair .. — £250

In the above, the stamps overprinted are the 3d. of the issues o April 1875 and 1876 and the 6d. and 1s. of 1876–77.

1877. *Optd with T 4 in black.*

I. *Pelure paper*
96 1 1d. orange-red (*imperf*) .. .. .. £160 85·0
97 1d. orange-red (*fine roulette*) .. .. — £100

II. *Hard-surfaced paper*
98 1 1d. bright red (*imperf*) .. .. .. 13·00 13·0
a. Opt inverted £475 £400
b. Opt Type 5 .. .. £750 £800
99 1d. bright red (*fine roulette*) .. .. £130 38·0
a. Opt inverted .. ..
b. Opt double .. ..
100 1d. bright red (*wide roulette*) £475 £140

III. *Coarse soft paper. (a) Imperf*
101 1 1d. brick-red (5.77) .. .. 13·00 13·00
a. Opt double .. .. — £900
b. Opt Type 5 .. ..
102 2 3d. lilac .. .. 55·00 22·00
a. Opt inverted .. ..
b. *Deep lilac* .. .. £130 65·00
103 1 6d. dull blue .. .. 70·00 22·00
a. Opt double £2750
b. Opt inverted £1200 £140
c. *Tête-bêche* (pair) .. .. .. — £3000
d. Opt Type 5 .. .. — £1000
da. Opt Type 5 inverted .. .. ..
e. *Blue* (*bright to deep*) .. .. .. £140 17·00
ea. Bright blue, opt inverted .. .. — £475
f. Pin-perf .. .. — £450
104 1s. yellow-green .. .. 65·00 32·00
a. Opt inverted £850 £140
b. *Tête-bêche* (pair) .. .. .. — £3000
c. Opt Type 5 .. .. £2750 £900
d. Bisected (on cover) .. .. .. † £900

(*b*) *Fine roulette, 15½ to 16*
105 1 1d. brick-red .. .. 55·00 55·00
106 2 3d. lilac .. .. £130 48·00
107 1 6d. dull blue .. .. £140 32·00
a. Opt inverted .. .. — £550
b. Opt Type 5 .. .. £3500
108 1s. yellow-green .. .. £140 70·00
a. Opt inverted £800 £375
b. Opt Type 5 .. .. — £2500

(*c*) *Wide roulette, 6½*
109 1 1d. brick-red £550 £130
a. Opt Type 5 .. ..
110 2 3d. lilac .. .. — £475
111 1 6d. dull blue .. .. — £1100
a. Opt inverted .. .. — £3000
112 1s. yellow-green .. .. £325 95·00
a. Opt inverted £1100 £475

1877 (31 Aug). *Optd with T 4 in black.*
113 1 6d. blue/*rose* (*imperf*) .. .. .. 45·00 32·00
a. Bisected (3d.) (on cover) .. .. †
b. Opt inverted .. .. 45·00 32·00
c. *Tête-bêche* (pair) £2500
d. Opt omitted £2750
114 6d. blue/*rose* (*fine roulette*) .. .. £140 55·00
a. Opt inverted .. .. £400 48·00
b. *Tête-bêche* (pair) .. .. ..
c. Opt omitted .. ..
115 6d. blue/*rose* (*wide roulette*) .. ..
a. Opt inverted .. ..
b. Opt omitted .. ..

V. R. *V. R.*

Transvaal Transvaal
(6) (7)

1877 (July). I. *Optd with T 6 in black. (a) Imperf.*
116 1 1d. red/*blue* .. .. 35·00 17·00
a. "Transvral" .. .. — £2500
b. Opt double £3000
c. Opt inverted £600 £300
d. Opt omitted .. ..
117 1d. red/*orange* .. .. 7·00 8·00
a. Pin-perf .. ..
b. Printed both sides .. .. ..

18 2 3d. mauve/*buff* .. .. 17·00 17·00
a. Opt inverted .. — £550
b. Pin-perf
19 1 6d. blue/*green* .. .. 55·00 23·00
a. Deep blue/green .. 70·00 27·00
b. Broken "Y" for "V" in "V.R."
c. Small "V" in "Transvaal"
d. Stop in front of "R" (= V..R). .. — £550
e. *Tête-bêche* (pair) .. — £3000
f. Opt inverted .. — £700
g. Pin-perf
20 6d. blue/*blue* .. 35·00 17·00
a. *Tête-bêche* (pair) .. — £2750
b. Opt inverted .. — £700
c. Opt omitted .. — £1600
d. Opt double .. — £2500
e. Pin-perf
f. Bisected (3d.) (on cover) .. † £475

(b) *Fine roulette*, 15½ *to* 16

21 1 1d. red/*blue* .. 55·00 27·00
a. "Transvral" .. — £2750
22 1d. red/*orange* .. 21·00 17·00
a. Imperf between (pair)
23 2 3d. mauve/*buff* .. 70·00 17·00
a. Imperf between (pair)
b. Opt inverted .. — £2500
24 1 6d. blue/*green* .. 55·00 14·00
a. Bisected (3d.) (on cover) .. † £450
b. *Tête-bêche* (pair)
c. Opt inverted .. — £475
d. Opt omitted .. — £3000
e. Stop in front of "R" (= V..R). .. — £1000
25 6d. blue/*blue* .. £170 38·00
a. Bisected (3d.) (on cover) .. † £450
b. Imperf between (pair)
c. Opt inverted .. — £900
d. Opt omitted .. — £2500

(c) *Wide roulette*, 6½

126 1 1d. red/*orange* .. £200 85·00
127 2 3d. mauve/*buff* .. — 85·00
128 1 6d. blue/*green* .. — £850
129 6d. blue/*blue* .. — £200
a. Opt inverted

II. *Optd with T* 7 *in black.* (a) *Imperf*

130 1 1d. red/*orange* .. 32·00 23·00
131 2 3d. mauve/*buff* .. 32·00 21·00
a. Pin-perf about 9 .. — £550
132 1 6d. blue/*blue* .. 70·00 17·00
a. *Tête-bêche* (pair) .. £7500
b. Opt inverted .. — £300

(b) *Fine roulette*, 15½ *to* 16

133 1 1d. red/*orange* .. — 95·00
134 2 3d. mauve/*buff* .. £120 85·00
a. Imperf between (pair)
135 1 6d. blue/*blue* .. — 85·00
a. Opt inverted .. — £800

(c) *Wide roulette*, 6½

136 1 1d. red/*orange* .. — £200
137 2 3d. mauve/*buff* .. — £250
138 1 6d. blue/*blue* .. — £250
a. Opt inverted

1879 (18 April). I. *Optd with T* **6** *in black.*

139 2 3d. mauve/*green* (*imperf*) .. £120 21·00
a. Pin-perf
b. Opt inverted .. — £1500
c. Opt double
140 3d. mauve/*green* (*fine roulette*) .. £525 £140
141 3d. mauve/*green* (*wide roulette*) .. — £225

II. *Optd with T* 7 *in black*

142 2 3d. mauve/*green* (*imperf*) .. 70·00 16·00
a. Opt inverted .. — £1500
b. Opt omitted .. — £2750
c. Printed both sides
143 3d. mauve/*green* (*fine roulette*) .. £475 £140
144 3d. mauve/*green* (*wide roulette*) .. — £250

V. R.
Transvaal
(8)

V. R.
Transvaal
(8a)

9

1879 (Aug-Sept). *Optd with T* **8** *in black.* (a) *Imperf.*

145 1 1d. red/*yellow* .. 32·00 27·00
a. Small "T", Type 8*a* .. £200 £140
b. Red/orange .. 27·00 20·00
ba. Small "T", Type 8*a* .. £150 £140
146 2 3d. mauve/*green* .. £225 16·00
a. Small "T", Type 8*a* .. £250 £140
147 3d. mauve/*blue* .. 29·00 20·00
a. Small "T", Type 8*a* .. £160 65·00

(b) *Fine roulette*, 15½ *to* 16

148 1 1d. red/*yellow* .. — £200
a. Small "T", Type 8*a* .. £800 £525
b. Red/orange .. — £375
ba. Small "T", Type 8*a*
149 2 3d. mauve/*green* .. £700 £225
a. Small "T", Type 8*a*
150 3d. mauve/*blue* .. — £150
a. Small "T", Type 8*a* .. — £600

(c) *Wide roulette*, 6½

151 1 1d. red/*yellow* .. — £800
a. Small "T", Type 8*a*
b. Red/orange
ba. Small "T", Type 8*a*
152 2 3d. mauve/*green*
a. Small "T", Type 8*a*
153 3d. mauve/*blue*

(d) *Pin-perf, about* 17

154 1 1d. red/*yellow* .. — £525
a. Small "T", Type 8*a*
155 2 3d. mauve/*blue*

(Recess B.W.)

1878 (26 Aug)–**80**. *P* 14, 14½.

156 9 ½d. vermilion (1880) .. 16·00 21·00
157 1d. pale red-brown .. 4·00 3·00
a. Brown-red .. 3·00 2·25
158 3d. dull rose .. 4·00 2·25
a. Claret .. 6·50 4·00
159 4d. sage-green .. 8·50 4·25
160 6d. olive-black .. 4·00 3·00
a. Black-brown .. 5·00 2·25
161 1s. green .. 55·00 35·00
162 2s. blue .. £100 60·00

The above prices are for specimens perforated on all four sides. Stamps from margins of sheets, with perforations absent on one or two sides, can be supplied for about 30% less.

1 Penny (10) 1 Penny (11) 1 Penny (12)

1 Penny (13) 1 Penny (14)

1 PENNY (15) 1 Penny (16)

1879 (22 April). *No.* 160*a surch with T* **10** *to* **16**.

A. *In black.* B. *In red.*

			A		B	
163 10	1d. on 6d.		£150	45·00	£400	£140
164 11	1d. on 6d.		60·00	32·00	£140	£100
165 12	1d. on 6d.		£130	45·00	£300	£140
166 13	1d. on 6d.		60·00	45·00	£140	£100
167 14	1d. on 6d.		£400	£120	—	—
168 15	1d. on 6d.		32·00	20·00	90·00	50·00
169 16	1d. on 6d.		£140	65·00	£400	£150

SECOND REPUBLIC

EEN PENNY
(17)

1882. *No.* 159 *surch with T* **17**.

170 9 1d. on 4d. sage-green .. 3·00 2·00
a. Surch inverted .. £300

1883. *Re-issue of T* **1** *and* **2**. *P* 12.

171 1 1d. grey (*to* black) .. 1·25 75
172 2 3d. grey-black (*to* black)/*rose* .. 6·00 2·25
a. Bisected (1d.) (on cover) .. † £475
173 3d. pale red .. 3·00 1·00
a. Bisected (1d.) (on cover)
b. Chestnut .. 15·00 2·25
c. Vermilion .. 13·00 2·50
174 1 1s. green (*to* deep) .. 7·50 1·50
a. Bisected (6d.) (on cover) .. † £225
b. *Tête-bêche* (pair) .. £300 75·00

Reprints are known of Nos. 172, 173, 173*b* and 173*c*. The paper of the first is *bright rose* in place of *dull rose*, and the impression is brownish black in place of grey-black to deep black. The reprints on white paper have the paper thinner than the originals, and the gum yellowish instead of white. The colour is a dull deep orange-red.

18

REPRINTS. Reprints of the general issues 1885–93, 1894–95, 1895–96 and 1896–97 exist in large quantities. They cannot readily be distinguished from genuine originals except by comparison with used stamps, but the following general characteristics may be noted. The reprints are all perf 12½, large holes; the paper is whiter than that usually employed for the originals and their colours lack the lustre of those of the genuine stamps.

Forged surcharges have been made on these reprints.

(Des J. Vurtheim. Typo Enschedé)

1885 (13 Mar)–**1893**. *P* 12½.

175 18 ½d. grey .. 10 10
a. Perf 13½ .. 1·75 55
b. Perf 12½ × 12 .. 80 10
ba. Perf 11½ × 12
176 1d. carmine .. 10 10
a. Perf 12½ × 12 .. 35 10
aa. Perf 11½ × 12 .. 3·50 2·00
b. Rose .. 10 10
ba. Perf 12½ × 12 .. 10 10
177 2d. brown-purple (*p* 12½ × 12) .. 20 10
178 2d. olive-bistre (1887) .. 20 10
a. Perf 12½ × 12 .. 1·75 10
179 2½d. mauve (*to* bright) (1893) .. 55 10
180 3d. mauve (*to* bright) .. 55 25
a. Perf 12½ × 12 .. 3·00 55
aa. Perf 11½ × 12 .. 12·00 9·50
181 4d. bronze-green .. 95 25
a. Perf 13½ .. 2·00 55
b. Perf 12½ × 12 .. 7·00 55
ba. Perf 11½ × 12 .. £140 55·00
182 6d. pale dull blue .. 55 10
a. Perf 13½ .. 2·00 55
b. Perf 12½ × 12 .. 3·00 15
ba. Perf 11½ × 12
183 18 1s. yellow-green .. 1·40 35
a. Perf 13½ .. 7·00 3·00
b. Perf 12½ × 12 .. 3·50 20
184 2s. 6d. orange-buff (*to* buff) .. 2·00 1·10
a. Perf 12½ × 12 .. 4·00 2·75
185 5s. slate .. 3·00 1·40
a. Perf 12½ × 12 .. 3·75 1·25
186 10s. fawn .. 12·00 1·40
187 £5 deep green (1892)* .. £2000 £170

The variety, perf 11½ × 12 in the 1d., 3d., 4d. and 6d. is from sheets perforated with the 12½ × 12 machine.

*Most examples of No. 187 on the market are either forgeries or reprints.

HALVE PENNY (19) HALVE PENNY (20)

1885. *Surch with T* **19** *or* **20** (*No.* 189).

A. *Reading down.* B. *Reading up.*

		A		B	
188 2	½d. on 3d. (No. 173)	80	80	80	80
189 18	½d. on 3d. (No. 180a)	80	80	†	
	a. "PRNNY"	22·00	—	†	
	b. 2nd "N" inverted	50·00	—	†	
	c. Perf 11½ × 12	3·00	—	†	
190 1	½d. on 1s. (No. 174)	3·00	3·50	3·00	3·50
	a. *Tête-bêche* (pair)	†		—	£150

No. 188 was issued on 22 May, No. 189 on 28 September and No. 190 in August.

In sheets of Nos. 188 and 190 one half-sheet had the surch reading upwards and the other half-sheet downwards.

HALVE PENNY Z.A.R (21) TWEE PENCE Z. A. R. (22)

1885 (1 Sept). *No.* 160*a surch in red.*

191 21 ½d. on 6d. black-brown .. 5·25 5·75
192 22 2d. on 6d. black-brown .. 95 95

2d (23) 2d (24)

1887 (15 Jan). *T* **18** *surch. P* 12½ × 12.

193 23 2d. on 3d. mauve .. 1·50 1·50
a. Surch double .. — £140
b. Perf 11½ × 12 .. 2·75 2·75
194 24 2d. on 3d. mauve .. 55 55
a. Surch double .. — £160
b. Perf 11½ × 12 .. 2·00 2·00

Halve Penny (25) 1 Penny (26)

2½ Pence (27) 2½ Pence (28)

Two varieties of surcharge:
A. Vertical distance between bars 12½ mm.
B. Distance 13½ mm.

1893. *T* **18** *surch. P* 12½. (a) *In red.*

195 25 ½d. on 2d. olive-bistre (A) (27 May) .. 50 55
a. Surch inverted (A) .. 1·10 1·10
b. Variety B .. 90 90
ba. Variety B, inverted .. 3·75

(b) *In black*

196 25 ½d. on 2d. olive-bistre (A) (2 July) .. 50 50
a. Surch inverted (A) .. 3·00 3·00
b. Extra surch on back inverted (A) .. £120
c. Variety B .. 70 70
ca. Variety B, inverted .. — 8·00
cb. Extra surch on back inverted (B) ..

197 **26** 1d. on 6d. blue (A) (26 Jan) 10 10
a. Surch double (A) .. .. .. 38·00 32·00
b. Surch inverted (A) .. .. .. 90 1·00
c. Variety B 35 35
ca. Variety B inverted .. .. .. 2·75 2·75
cb. Variety B double .. .. .. — 50·00
d. Pair with and without surch £100
198 **27** 2½d. on 1s. green (A) (2 Jan) 40 35
a. "2/½" for "2½" .. .. .. 15·00 15·00
b. Surch inverted (A) .. .. .. 1·00 1·10
ba. Surch inverted and "2/½" for "2½" £140
c. Extra surch on back inverted (A) ..
d. Variety B 75 90
da. Variety B, inverted .. .. 4·50 5·25
199 **28** 2½d. on 1s. green (A) (24 June) 95 90
a. Surch double (A) .. .. .. 23·00 23·00
b. Surch inverted (A) .. .. .. 4·50 4·50
c. Variety B .. .. .. 3·50 3·50
ca. Variety B, double .. ..
cb. Variety B, inverted .. ..

29 (Wagon with shafts)

30 (Wagon with pole)

1894–95. *P* 12½.
200 **29** ½d. grey 10 10
201 1d. carmine 10 10
202 2d. olive-bistre 10 10
203 6d. pale dull blue 50 40
204 1s. yellow-green .. .. .. 2·40 2·75
For note *re* reprints, see below T **18**.

1895–96. *P* 12½.
205 **30** ½d. pearl-grey 10 10
a. Lilac-grey 10 10
206 1d. rose-red 10 10
207 2d. olive-bistre 10 10
208 3d. mauve 15 10
209 4d. olive-black 65 55
210 6d. pale dull blue 40 12
211 1s. yellow-green 70 65
212 5s. slate .. .. 2·75 3·00
212*a* 10s. pale chestnut .. .. .. 3·75 1·25
For note *re* reprints, see below T **18**.

Halve
Penny

(31)

1d. 1d.

(**32**—Round dot) (**32*a***—Square dot)

1895 (July–Aug). *Nos.* 211 *and* 179 *surch.*
213 **31** ½d. on 1s. green (R.) 10 10
a. Surch spaced 55 65
b. "Pennij" for "Penny" .. .. 35·00
c. Surch inverted .. .. .. 3·00 2·75
d. Surch double .. .. .. 42·00
214 **32** 1d. on 2½d. bright mauve (G.) 10 10
a. Surch inverted .. .. .. 14·00 11·00
b. Surch double .. ..
c. Surch on back only .. ..
d. Type **32*a*** 95 95
da. Type **32*a*** inverted .. .. .. 38·00
The normal surcharge on No. 213 is spaced 3 mm between "Penny" and the bars; on No. 213a 4 mm approx. Copies may be found in which one or both of the bars have failed to print.

33

34

1895 (July). *Fiscal stamp optd* "POSTZEGEL". *P* 11½.
215 **33** 6d. bright rose (G.) 50 65
a. Imperf between (pair) .. ..

(Litho The Press Printing and Publishing Works, Pretoria)

1895 (6 Sept). *Introduction of Penny Postage. P* 11.
215*b* **34** 1d. red (pale *to* deep) 35 15
ba. Imperf between (pair) .. .. 15·00 12·00

1896–97. *P* 12½.
216 **30** ½d. green 10 10
217 1d. rose-red and green 10 10
218 2d. brown and green 10 10
219 2½d. dull blue and green 10 10
220 3d. purple and green 10 10
221 4d. sage-green and green 10 10
222 **30** 6d. lilac and green 10 10
223 1s. ochre and green 20 10
224 2s. 6d. dull violet and green 50 50
For note *re* reprints, see below T **18**.

SECOND BRITISH OCCUPATION

FORGERIES. The forgeries of the "V.R.I." and "E.R.I." overprints most often met with can be recognised by the fact that the type used is perfect and the three stops are always in alignment with the bottom of the letters. In the genuine overprints, which were made from old type, it is impossible to find all three letters perfect and all three stops perfect and in exact alignment with the bottom of the letters.

V. R. I. **(35)** E. R. I. **(36)** E. R. I. Half Penny **(37)**

1900 (18 June). *Optd with T* **35**.
226 **30** ½d. green 12 12
f. "V.I.R." £500
227 1d. rose-red and green 12 12
f. No stop after "R" and "I" .. .. 40·00 40·00
228 2d. brown and green 40 12
f. "V.I.R." £500
229 2½d. dull blue and green 12 12
230 3d. purple and green 12 12
231 4d. sage-green and green 40 20
f. "V.I.R." £500
232 6d. lilac and green 50 20
233 1s. ochre and green 55 40
234 2s. 6d. dull violet and green .. .. 1·10 90
235 5s. slate .. .. 2·00 2·00
236 10s. pale chestnut .. .. .. 4·00 4·00
237 **18** £5 green* .. .. ..
234/7 Optd "Specimen" .. .. *Set of* 4 £200
The error "V.I.R." occurred on stamp No. 34 in the first batch of stamps to be overprinted—a few sheets of the ½d., 2d. and 4d. The error was then corrected and stamps showing it are very rare.
*Most examples of No. 237 on the market are forgeries.

Varieties.
A. No stop after "V". B. No stop after "R".
C. No stop after "I". D. Overprint inverted.
E. Overprint double.

		A	B	C	D	E
226	½d.	7·00	4·50	3·00	3·00	—
227	1d.	7·00	4·50	1·75	3·00	30·00
228	2d.	9·50	†	12·00	4·75	—
229	2½d.	9·00	—	6·00	3·00	†
230	3d.	10·00	17·00	11·00	28·00	†
231	4d.	17·00	20·00	9·00	9·00	†
232	6d.	5·75	10·00	7·50	7·50	†
233	1s.	5·75	—	10·00	9·00	30·00
234	2s. 6d.	9·00	23·00	†	†	†
235	5s.	—	†	†	†	†
236	10s.	28·00	†	28·00	†	†
237	£5	—	†	†	†	†

The above prices are for unused. Used are worth the same, or rather more in some cases.

1901–2. *Optd with T* **36**.
238 **30** ½d. green (7.01) 10 10
239 1d. rose-red and green (20.3.01) .. 10 10
a. "E" of opt omitted .. .. .. 45·00
240 3d. purple and green (6.02) 55 55
241 4d. sage-green and green (6.02) .. 55 65
242 2s. 6d. dull violet and green (10.02) .. 3·00 3·50

1901 (July). *Surch with T* **37**.
243 **30** ½d. on 2d. brown and green 10 10
a. No stop after "E" .. .. 38·00

38 (POSTAGE REVENUE)

39 (POSTAGE POSTAGE)

(Typo D.L.R.)

1902 (1 April)–**1903.** *Wmk Crown CA. P* 14.
244 **38** ½d. black and bluish green 25 10
245 1d. black and carmine 25 10
246 2d. black and purple 65 10
247 2½d. black and blue 90 50
248 3d. black and sage-green (1903) .. 1·25 20
249 4d. black and brown (1903) .. .. 1·50 50
250 6d. black amd orange-brown 90 35
251 1s. black and sage-green .. .. 3·50 1·10
252 2s. black and brown .. .. .. 11·00 9·00
253 **39** 2s. 6d. magenta and black .. .. 4·50 3·75
254 5s. black and purple/*yellow* .. .. 7·50 5·50
255 10s. black and purple/*red* .. .. 16·00 13·00
244/55 .. .. .. *Set of* 12 45·00 30·00
244/55 Optd "Specimen" .. .. *Set of* 12 £250
The colour of the "black" centres varies from brownish grey or grey to black.

1903. *Wmk Crown CA. P* 14.
256 **39** 1s. grey-black and red-brown .. .. 1·50 75
257 2s. grey-black and yellow .. .. 4·75 4·50
258 £1 green and violet .. .. .. 55·00 45·00
259 £5 orange-brown and violet £1200 £400
256/9 Optd "Specimen" .. .. *Set of* 4 £500

1904–9. *Wmk Mult Crown CA. P* 14.
260 **38** ½d. black and bluish green, **O** 80 10
261 1d. black and carmine, **O** 70 10
262 **38** 2d. black and purple, **C** (1906) 90 1
263 2½d. black and blue, **CO** (1905) 90 6
264 3d. black and sage-green, **C** (1906) .. 75 1
265 4d. black and brown, **C** (1906) 90 2
266 6d. black and orange, **O** (1905) .. .. 1·25 2
a. Black and brown-orange, **C** 95 2
267 **39** 1s. black and red-brown, **O** (1905) .. 1·25 2
268 2s. black and yellow, **O** (1906) .. .. 3·25 1·5
269 2s. 6d. magenta and black, **O** (1909) .. 6·00 1·7
270 5s. black and purple/*yellow*, **O** .. .. 7·50 1·7
271 10s. black and purple/*red*, **O** (1907) .. 17·00 3·0
272 £1 green and violet, **OC** (1908) .. .. 55·00 9·5
260/72 .. .. *Set of* 13 85·00 17·0
There is considerable variation in the "black" centres as in th previous issue.

1905–9. *Wmk Mult Crown CA. P* 14.
273 **38** ½d. yellow-green 25 1
a. Deep green (1908) 35 1
274 1d. scarlet 25
a. Wmk Cabled Anchor, T **13** of Cape of Good Hope .. .. .. — £60
275 2d. purple (1909) .. .. .. 1·00 1
276 2½d. bright blue (1909) .. .. .. 3·25 1·7
273/6 Optd "Specimen" .. .. *Set of* 4 80·00
A 2d. grey, T **38**, was prepared for use but not issued. It exist overprinted "Specimen", *price* £225.
The monocoloured ½d. and 1d. are printed from new combine plates. These show a slight alteration in that the frame does no touch the crown.
Many of the King's Head stamps are found overprinted or perfor ated "C.S.A.R.", for use by the Central South African Railways.

FISCALS WITH POSTAL CANCELLATIONS

Various fiscal stamps are found apparently postally used, bu these were used on telegrams not on postal matter.

POSTAGE DUE STAMPS

D 1

(Typo D.L.R.)

1907. *Wmk Mult Crown CA. P* 14.
D1 **D 1** ½d. black and blue-green .. .. 75 1·25
D2 1d. black and scarlet 75 50
D3 2d. brown-orange .. .. .. 75 1·25
D4 3d. black and blue .. .. .. 2·50 1·75
D5 5d. black and violet .. .. .. 1·50 3·50
D6 6d. black and red-brown .. .. 3·25 3·50
D7 1s. scarlet and black .. .. .. 3·25 4·75
D1/7 .. .. *Set of* 7 11·50 15·00

Transvaal now uses the stamps of SOUTH AFRICA.

PIETERSBURG

Authorised by President Kruger and in use until 9 April 1901, when British troops entered the town.

PRICES. Genuinely used copies are very rare. Stamps cancelled by favour exist and are worth the same as the unused prices quoted.
The issued stamps are initialled by the Controller but three sheets of the ½d. were stuck together and this resulted in some being issued without initials. The 1d., 2d., 4d. and 1s. values without initials must be regarded as proofs and are worth about £5 each.
Sheets of the 6d. without initials are believed to be remainders, some being overprinted "PHILATELIC CONGRESS PRETORIA OCTOBER 1934" and affixed to menus for the Congress dinner.

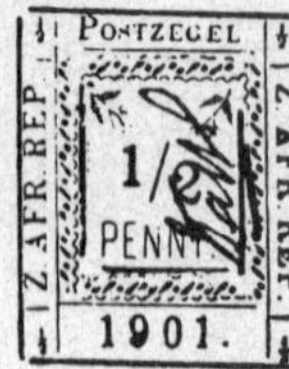

P 1

P 2

P 3

TYPES P 1/3. Each value was printed in sheets of 24 (6 × 4) of which the first two horizontal rows were as Type P **1**, the third row as Type P **2** and the fourth as Type P **3**.

(Type-set *De Zoutpansberg Wachter* Press, Pietersburg)

1901 (20 Mar (1*d.*)–3 Apr (*others*)). A. *Imperf.*

(*a*) *Controller's initials in black*
1 **P 1** ½d. black/*green* .. .. 15·00
e. Controller's initials omitted .. 95·00
2 **P 2** ½d. black/*green* .. .. 45·00
d. Controller's initials omitted .. 95·00

3 P 3 ½d. black/*green* .. .. 45·00
d. Controller's initials omitted .. 95·00
4 P 1 1d. black/*red* .. .. 3·50
5 P 2 1d. black/*red* .. .. 5·50
6 P 3 1d. black/*red* .. .. 7·00
7 P 1 2d. black/*orange* .. .. 6·00
8 P 2 2d. black/*orange* .. .. 14·00
9 P 3 2d. black/*orange* .. .. 22·00
10 P 1 4d. black/*blue* .. .. 5·50
11 P 2 4d. black/*blue* .. .. 9·50
12 P 3 4d. black/*blue* .. .. 32·00
13 P 1 6d. black/*green* .. .. 9·50
14 P 2 6d. black/*green* .. .. 15·00
15 P 3 6d. black/*green* .. .. 40·00
16 P 1 1s. black/*yellow* .. .. 8·00
17 P 2 1s. black/*yellow* .. .. 14·00
18 P 3 1s. black/*yellow* .. .. 25·00

(*b*) *Controller's initials in red*

19 P 1 ½d. black/*green* .. .. 15·00
20 P 2 ½d. black/*green* .. .. 35·00
21 P 3 ½d. black/*green* .. .. 40·00

B. *P* 11½. (*a*) *Controller's initials in red*

22 P 1 ½d. black/*green* .. .. 5·50
c. Imperf vert (horiz pair) .. .. 95·00
23 P 2 ½d. black/*green* .. .. 17·00
c. Imperf vert (horiz pair) £120
24 P 3 ½d. black/*green* .. .. 12·00
b. Imperf vert (horiz pair) £120

(*b*) *Controller's initials in black*

25 P 1 1d. black/*red* .. .. 2·00
m. Imperf vert (horiz pair) .. .. 55·00
n. Imperf between (vert pair: No. 25 + No. 26) .. ..
o. Imperf horiz (vert pair) .. ..
26 P 2 1d. black/*red* .. .. 2·75
f. Imperf vert (horiz pair) .. .. 80·00
g. Imperf horiz (vert pair: No. 26 + No. 27) .. ..
27 P 3 1d. black/*red* .. .. 4·00
f. Imperf vert (horiz pair) .. .. 80·00
28 P 1 2d. black/*orange* .. .. 5·50
29 P 2 2d. black/*orange* .. .. 8·00
30 P 3 2d. black/*orange* .. .. 14·00

CONSTANT VARIETIES

Rows 1 *and* 2 *are as Type* P 1, *Row* 3 *as Type* P 2 *and Row* 4 *as Type* P 3.

½d. *value*
First printing—Imperf
R.1/2 No stop after left "AFR" .. .. (No. 1a) 80·00
R.1/3 "⅓" at top left, no bar over lower right "½" .. .. (No. 1b) 80·00
R.1/6 No stop after date .. .. (No. 1c)
R.2/5 "BEP" at left, no stop after date .. (No. 1d) 80·00
R.3/3 "AFB" at left .. .. (No. 2a) 80·00
R.3/4 "POSTZEGEI" .. .. (No. 2b) 80·00
R.3/6 No bar over lower right "½" .. .. (No. 2c) 80·00
R.4/1 No stop after right "AFR" .. .. (No. 3a) 80·00
R.4/4 No stop after left "Z", no bar under top right "½" .. .. (No. 3b) 80·00
R.4/5 "POSTZECEL AER" at left .. .. (No. 3c) 80·00

Second printing
R.1/4 No stop after right "AFR" .. *Imperf* (No. 19a) 95·00
Perf (No. 22a) 55·00
R.2/1 Left side of inner frame too high *Imperf* (No. 19b) 95·00
Perf (No. 22b) 55·00
R.3/5 Centre figures "½" level .. *Imperf* (No. 20a) 75·00
Perf (No. 23a) 55·00
R.3/6 No stop after right "AFR" .. *Imperf* (No. 20b) 75·00
Perf (No. 23b) 55·00
R.4/6 Hyphen between right "AFR" and "REP" .. .. *Imperf* (No. 21a) 75·00
Perf (No. 24a) 55·00

Third printing—Imperf
R.1/1 & 4 Top left "½" inverted, no stop after right "AFR" .. .. (No. 19c) 95·00
R.1/2 Top right "½" inverted .. .. (No. 19d) £120
R.1/3 "⅓" at lower right .. .. .. (No. 19e) £120
R.1/5 "POSTZFGEL" .. .. (No. 19f) £120
R.1/6 Left spray inverted, "AFB" at right .. (No. 19g) £120
R.2/1 "REB" at left, left side of inner frame too high .. .. (No. 19h) £120
R.2/2 "BEP" at left .. .. (No. 19i) £120
R.2/3 "POSTZEOEL" .. .. (No. 19j) £120
R.2/4 "AER" at right .. .. (No. 19k) £120
R.2/5 No stop after date .. .. .. (No. 19l)
R.3/1 "⅓" at top left, "PE" of "PENNY" spaced (No. 20c) £120
R.3/2 Right spray inverted .. .. .. (No. 20d) £120
R.3/3 Top left "½" inverted .. .. .. (No. 20e) £120
R.4/3 "⅓" at top right .. .. .. (No. 21b) £120
R.4/4 Lower left "½" inverted .. .. (No. 21c) £120
R.4/5 "¼" at top left .. .. (No. 21d) £120

1d. *value*
First printing
R.1/2 Inverted "1" at lower left, first "1" of date dropped .. .. .. *Imperf* (No. 4a) 45·00
Perf (No. 25a) 29·00
R.1/3 No bar under top left "1" .. *Imperf* (No. 4b) 45·00
Perf (No. 25b) 29·00
R.1/4 No bar over lower right "1" .. *Imperf* (No. 4c) 45·00
Perf (No. 25c)
R.1/5 "POSTZFGEL" .. .. *Imperf* (No. 4d) 45·00
Perf (No. 25d) 29·00
R.1/6 "AFB" at right .. .. .. *Imperf* (No. 4e) 45·00
Perf (No. 25e) 29·00
R.2/1 "REB" at left .. .. .. *Imperf* (No. 4f) 45·00
Perf (No. 25f) 29·00
R.2/2 "BEP" at left .. .. .. *Imperf* (No. 4g) 45·00
Perf (No. 25g) 29·00
R.2/3 "POSTZEOEL" .. .. *Imperf* (No. 4h) 45·00
Perf (No. 25h) 29·00
R.2/4 "AER" at right .. .. .. *Imperf* (No. 4i) 45·00
Perf (No. 25i) 29·00
R.2/5 No stop after date .. .. *Imperf* (No. 4j) 45·00
Perf (No. 25j) 29·00
R.2/6 No stop after "PENNY" .. *Imperf* (No. 4k) 45·00
Perf (No. 25k) 29·00
R.3/2 Right spray inverted .. .. *Imperf* (No. 5a) 45·00
Perf (No. 26a) 29·00
R.3/3 No bar over lower left "1" .. *Imperf* (No. 5b) 45·00
Perf (No. 26b) 29·00
R.3/4 No stop after left "Z" .. .. *Imperf* (No. 5c) 45·00
Perf (No. 26c) 29·00
R.3/6 "POSTZEGFL", no stop after right "AFR" .. .. *Imperf* (No. 5d) 45·00
Perf (No. 26d) 29·00
R.4/1 No stop after right "AFR" .. *Imperf* (No. 6a) 45·00
Perf (No. 27a) 29·00
R.4/2 & 6 Left spray inverted .. .. *Imperf* (No. 6b) 29·00
Perf (No. 27b) 17·00
R.4/3 "POSTZEGEI" .. .. .. *Imperf* (No. 6c) 45·00
Perf (No. 27c) 29·00
R.4/4 No bar under top right "1" .. *Imperf* (No. 6d) 45·00
Perf (No. 27d) 29·00

Second printing
R.1/2 First "1" in date dropped .. *Imperf* (No. 4l) 45·00
Perf (No. 25l) 29·00
R.3/6 No stop after right "AFR" .. *Imperf* (No. 5e) 45·00
Perf (No. 26e) 29·00
R.4/5 Dropped "P" in "PENNY" .. *Imperf* (No. 6e) 45·00
Perf (No. 27e) 29·00

2d. *value*
First printing—Imperf
R.1/1 "1" at lower right .. .. (No. 7a) 60·00
R.1/2 No stop after left "AFR" (*on small part of printing*) .. .. (No. 7b) £120
R.1/3 No bar over lower right "2" (*on small part of printing*) .. .. .. (No. 7c) £120
R.1/3 "PENNY" for "PENCE" .. .. (No. 7d) 60·00
R.1/5 "POSTZFGEL" .. .. (No. 7e) 60·00
R.1/6 "AFB" at right .. .. (No. 7f) 60·00
R.2/1 "REB" at left .. .. (No. 7g) 60·00
R.2/2 "AFB" at left .. .. (No. 7h) 60·00
R.2/3 "POSTZEOEL" .. .. (No. 7i) 60·00
R.2/4 "AER" at right .. .. (No. 7j) 60·00
R.2/5 No stop after date .. .. .. (No. 7k) 60·00
R.2/6 No stop after date, vertical line after "POSTZEGEL" .. .. (No. 7l) 60·00
R.3/2 Right spray inverted .. .. .. (No. 8a) 60·00
R.3/3 No bar over lower left "2" .. .. (No. 8b) 60·00
R.3/4 Centre "2" inverted, no stop after left "Z" (No. 8c) 60·00
R.3/6 "POSTZEGFL", no stop after right "AFR" .. .. (No. 8d) 60·00
R.4/1 Centre "2" wider, no stop after right "AFR" (*occurs on second printing also*) (No. 9a) 60·00
R.4/2 Centre "2" wider, left spray inverted .. (No. 9b) 60·00
R.4/3 "POSTZEGEI" .. .. (No. 9c) 60·00
R.4/4 No bar under top right "2" .. .. (No. 9d) 60·00
R.4/5 "1" at lower left, "P" in "PENCE" dropped .. .. (No. 9e) 60·00
R.4/6 Left spray inverted .. .. .. (No. 9f) 60·00

Second printing
R.1/2 First "1" in date dropped .. *Imperf* (No. 7m) 60·00
Perf (No. 28a) 40·00
R.2/1 No stop after left "REP" .. *Imperf* (No. 7n) 60·00
Perf (No. 28b) 40·00
R.3/4 No stop after left "Z" .. .. *Imperf* (No. 8e) 60·00
R.3/6 No stop after right "AFR" .. *Imperf* (No. 8f) 60·00
Perf (No. 29a) 40·00
R.4/1 Centre 2 wider, no stop after right "AFR" (*occurs on first printing also*) .. .. *Imperf* (No. 9a) 60·00
Perf (No. 30a) 40·00
R.4/2 Centre "2" wider .. .. *Imperf* (No. 9g) 60·00
Perf (No. 30b) 40·00
R.4/5 "P" in "PENCE" dropped .. *Imperf* (No. 9h) 60·00
Perf (No. 30c) 40·00

4d. *value*
First printing
R.1/2 No stop after left "AFR' .. .. (No. 10a) 60·00
R.1/3 No bar over lower right "4" .. .. (No. 10b) 60·00
R.1/3 "PENNY" for "PENCE" (*on small part of printing*) .. .. (No. 10c) £120
R.1/5 "POSTZFGEL" .. .. (No. 10d) 60·00
R.1/6 "AFB" at right .. .. (No. 10e) 60·00
R.2/1 "REB" at left .. .. (No. 10f) 60·00
R.2/2 "AFB" at left .. .. (No. 10g) 60·00
R.2/3 "POSTZEOEL" .. .. (No. 10h) 60·00
R.2/4 "AER" at right .. .. (No. 10i) 60·00
R.2/5 No stop after date .. .. .. (No. 10j) 60·00
R.3/2 Right spray inverted .. .. .. (No. 11a) 60·00
R.3/3 No bar over lower left "4" (*on small part of printing*) .. .. (No. 11b) £120
R.3/4 No stop after left "Z" .. .. .. (No. 11c) 60·00
R.3/6 "POSTZEGFL" .. .. (No. 11d) 60·00
R.4/1 Centre "4" wider, no stop after right "AFR" .. .. (No. 12a) 60·00
R.4/2 Centre "4" wider, left spray inverted .. (No. 12b) 60·00
R.4/3 "POSTZEGEI" .. .. (No. 12c) 60·00
R.4/4 No bar under top right "4" .. .. (No. 12d) 60·00
R.4/5 "AER" at left, "P" in "PENCE" dropped (No. 12e) 60·00
R.4/6 Left spray inverted .. .. .. (No. 12f) 60·00

Second printing
R.2/1 Left inner frame too high .. .. (No. 10k) 60·00
R.4/1–2 Centre "4" wider .. .. .. (No. 12g) 40·00
R.4/5 "P" in "PENCE" dropped .. .. (No. 12h) 60·00

6d. *value*
First printing
R.1/2 No stop after left "AFR" .. .. (No. 13a) 75·00
R.1/3 No bar over lower right "6" .. .. (No. 13b) 95·00
R.1/3 "PENNY" for "PENCE" (*on small part of printing*) .. .. (No. 13c) £120
R.1/5 "POSTZFGEL" .. .. (No. 13d) 75·00
R.1/6 "AFB" at right .. .. (No. 13e) 75·00
R.2/1 "REB" at left .. .. (No. 13f) 75·00
R.2/2 "AFB" at left .. .. (No. 13g) 75·00
R.2/3 "POSTZEOEL" .. .. (No. 13h) 75·00
R.2/4 "AER" at right .. .. (No. 13i) 75·00
R.2/5 No stop after date .. .. .. (No. 13j) 75·00
R.3/2 Right spray inverted .. .. .. (No. 14a) 75·00
R.3/4 Centre "6" inverted, no stop after left "Z" (*on small part of printing*) .. .. .. (No. 14b) £120
R.3/4 No stop after left "Z" .. .. .. (No. 14c) 90·00
R.3/6 "POSTZEGFL" .. .. (No. 14d) 75·00
R.4/1 Centre "6" wider, no stop after right "AFR" .. .. (No. 15a) 75·00
R.4/2 Centre "6" wider, left spray inverted .. (No. 15b) 75·00
R.4/3 "POSTZEGEI" .. .. (No. 15c) 75·00
R.4/4 No bar under top right "6" .. .. (No. 15d) 75·00
R.4/5 "AER" at left, "P" in "PENCE" dropped (No. 15e) 75·00
R.4/6 Left spray inverted .. .. .. (No. 15f) 75·00

Second printing
R.2/1 Left inner frame too high, no stop after left "REP" .. .. (No. 13k) 75·00
R.4/1–2 Centre "6" wider .. .. .. (No. 15g) 55·00
R.4/5 "P" in "PENCE" dropped .. .. (No. 15h)

1s. *value*
R.1/2 No stop after left "AFR" .. .. (No. 16a) 55·00
R.1/3 No bar over lower right "1" .. .. (No. 16b) 55·00
R.2/5 No stop after date .. .. .. (No. 16c) 55·00
R.3/4 "POSTZEGEI", no stop after left "Z" .. (No. 17a) 55·00
R.4/1 No stop after right "AFR" .. .. (No. 18a) 55·00
R.4/4 No bar under top right "1" .. .. (No. 18b) 55·00
R.4/5 "AER" at left .. .. (No. 18c) 55·00

LOCAL BRITISH OCCUPATION ISSUES DURING THE SOUTH AFRICAN WAR 1900–2

Stamps of the Transvaal Republic, unless otherwise stated, variously overprinted or surcharged.

LYDENBURG

V.R.I.
3d.
(L 1)

1900 (Sept). *No.* 217 *surch with Type* L 1, *others optd* "V.R.I" *only.*
1 **30** ½d. green .. .. 75·00 55·00
2 1d. rose-red and green .. .. .. 60·00 55·00
3 2d. brown and green £600 £450
4 2½d. blue and green .. .. .. — £500
5 3d. on 1d. rose-red and green .. .. 60·00 45·00
6 3d. purple and green .. .. ..
7 4d. sage-green and green £1300 £450
8 6d. lilac and green £1300 £350
9 1s. ochre and green £2000

Only one genuine copy of No. 6 (unused) is known.
Type **34** surcharged "V.R.I. 1d." is now considered by experts to be bogus.

RUSTENBURG

1900 (23 June). *Handstamped* **V.R.** *in violet.*
1 **30** ½d. green .. .. 90·00 60·00
2 1d. rose-red and green .. .. .. 70·00 45·00
3 2d. brown and green .. .. .. £150 60·00
4 2½d. blue and green .. .. .. 90·00 50·00
5 3d. purple and green .. .. .. £130 60·00
6 6d. lilac and green £400 £225
7 1s. ochre and green £700 £500
8 2s. 6d. dull violet and green .. .. — £3000

SCHWEIZER RENECKE

BESIEGED
(SR 1)

1900 (Aug). *Handstamped with Type* SR 1 *in black, reading vert up or down.* (*a*) *On stamps of Transvaal.*
1 **30** ½d. green .. .. † £225
2 1d. rose-red and green .. .. .. † £225
3 2d. brown and green .. .. .. † £300
4 6d. lilac and green .. .. .. † £750

(*b*) *On stamps of Cape of Good Hope*
5 **17** ½d. green .. .. † £400
6 1d. carmine .. .. † £400

This was a siege issue, authorised by the commander of the British troops in the town shortly after 19 August and exhausted by the end of September 1900. All stamps were cancelled with the dated circular town postmark ("Schweizer Reneke, Z.A.R."), usually after having been stuck on paper before use. Unused, without the postmark, do not exist.

VOLKSRUST

1902 (Mar). *Optd* "V.R.I.", *T* **35**. *P* 12.
1 **33** 1d. pale blue .. .. — 30·00
2 6d. dull carmine .. .. — 32·00
3 1s. olive-bistre .. .. — 45·00
4 1s. 6d. brown .. .. — 48·00
5 2s. 6d. dull purple .. .. — 48·00

These are the normal Transvaal Revenue stamps of the period, authorised for postal use in Volksrust.

WOLMARANSSTAD

Cancelled V-R-I. (L 3)
Cancelled V-R-I. (L 4)

1900 (June). *Optd with Type* L 3.
1 **30** ½d. green (B.) £200
a. Opt inverted .. ..
2 1d. rose-red and green (B.) £140
3 2d. brown and green (B.) .. ..
4 2½d. blue and green (R.) £800
a. Opt in blue .. .. ..
5 3d. purple and green (B.) £1500
6 4d. sage-green and green (B.) .. £1600
7 6d. lilac and green (B.) £1600
8 1s. ochre and green (B.) .. ..

1900 (July). *Optd with Type* L 4.
9 **34** 1d. red (B.) £150 £160

Trinidad and Tobago

TRINIDAD

CROWN COLONY

The first post office was established at Port of Spain in 1800 to deal with overseas mail. Before 1851 there was no post office inland service, although a privately-operated one along the coast did exist, for which rates were officially fixed (see No. 1). During 1851 the colonial authorities established an inland postal system which commenced operation on 14 August. Responsibility for the overseas mails passed to the local post authorities in 1858.

No. CC1 is recorded in the G.P.O. Record Book on 21 March 1852 and most examples are found used with the early Britannia 1d. stamps to indicate prepayment of the additional overseas rate in cash or, later, to show that letters were fully franked with adhesive stamps. This is the normal usage of the handstamp and commands little, if any premium over the cover price quoted below for the stamps involved. The use of the handstamp without an adhesive is rare.

For illustrations of the handstamp types see BRITISH POST OFFICES ABROAD notes, following GREAT BRITAIN.

PORT OF SPAIN

CROWNED-CIRCLE HANDSTAMPS

CC1 CC 6 TRINIDAD (R.) (*without additional adhesive stamp*) (21.3.52) . . . . *Price on cover* £500

PRICES FOR STAMPS ON COVER	
No. 1	*from* × 2
Nos. 2/12	*from* × 5
No. 13	—
Nos. 14/20	*from* × 2
Nos. 25/30	—
Nos. 31/44	*from* × 3
No. 45	—
Nos. 46/59	*from* × 3
Nos. 60/3	*from* × 4
Nos. 64/8	*from* × 3
Nos. 69/85	*from* × 12
No. 87	—
Nos. 88/90	*from* × 15
Nos. 91/7	*from* × 10
Nos. 98/102	*from* × 5
No. 103	—
Nos. 104/5	*from* × 15
Nos. 106/12	*from* × 8
No. 113	—
Nos. 114/21	*from* × 4
Nos. 122/4	—
No. 125	*from* × 10
Nos. 126/30	*from* × 5
No. 131	—
Nos. 132/43	*from* × 3
Nos. 144/5	—
Nos. 146/8	*from* × 3
Nos. D1/17	*from* × 12

1

2 Britannia

1847 (24 Apr). *Litho. Imperf.*
1 1 (5 c.) blue £11000 £7000

The "LADY McLEOD" stamps were issued in April 1847, by David Bryce, owner of the S.S. *Lady McLeod*, and sold at five cents each for the prepayment of the carriage of letters by his vessel between Port of Spain and San Fernando.

Used examples are pen-cancelled or have a corner skimmed off.

(Recess P.B.)

1851 (14 Aug)–**1856**. *No value expressed. Imperf. Blued paper.*
2 2 (1d.) purple-brown (1851) . . . . 5·25 40·00
3 (1d.) blue *to* deep blue (1851) . . . . 4·50 28·00
4 (1d.) deep blue (1853)* . . . . £150 65·00
5 (1d.) grey (1851) . . . . 23·00 32·00
6 (1d.) brownish grey (1853) . . . . 20·00 35·00
7 (1d.) brownish red (1853) . . . . £300 45·00
8 (1d.) brick-red (1856) . . . . £100 45·00

*No. 4 shows the paper deeply and evenly blued, especially on the back. It has more the appearance of having been printed on blue paper rather than on white paper that has become blued.

1854–57. *Imperf. White paper.*
9 2 (1d.) deep purple (1854) . . . . 11·00 40·00
10 (1d.) dark grey (1854) . . . . 18·00 55·00
11 (1d.) blue (? date) . . . .
12 (1d.) rose-red (1857) . . . . £1500 45·00

PRICES. Prices quoted for the unused of most of the above issues and Nos. 25 and 29 are for "remainders" with original gum, found in London. Old colours that have been out to Trinidad are of much greater value.

3 Britannia 4

The following provisional issues were lithographed in the Colony (from die engraved by Charles Petit), and brought into use to meet shortages of the Perkins Bacon stamps during the following periods:

(1) Sept 1852–May 1853; (2) March 1855–June 1855; (3) Dec 1856–Jan 1857; (4) Oct 1858–Jan 1859; (5) March 1860–June 1860.

1852–60. *No value expressed. Imperf.*

A. *First Issue* (Sept 1852). *Fine impression; lines of background clear and distinct.* (i) *Yellowish paper*
13 3 (1d.) blue £8500 £2000

(ii) *Bluish cartridge paper* (Feb 1853)
14 3 (1d.) blue . . . . . . — £2250

B. *Second issue* (March 1855). *Thinner paper. Impression less distinct than before*
15 3 (1d.) pale blue *to* greenish blue . . . . — £900

C. *Third issue* (December 1856). *Background often of solid colour, but with clear lines in places*
16 3 (1d.) bright blue *to* deep blue . . . . — £1200

D. *Fourth issue* (October 1858). *Impression less distinct, and rarely showing more than traces of background lines*
17 3 (1d.) very deep greenish blue . . . . — £650
18 (1d.) slate-blue £4000 £650

E. *Fifth issue* (March 1860). *Impression shows no (or hardly any) background lines*
19 3 (1d.) grey *to* bluish grey £4000 £450
20 (1d.) red (*shades*) . . . . 11·00 £450

In the worn impression of the fourth and fifth issues, the impression varies according to the position on the stone. Generally speaking, stamps of the fifth issue have a flatter appearance and cancellations are often less well defined. The paper of both these issues is thin or very thin. In all issues except 1853 (Feb) the gum tends to give the paper a toned appearance.

Stamps in the slate-blue shade (No. 18) also occur in the fifth issue, but are not readily distinguishable.

(Recess P.B.)

1859 (9 May). *Imperf.*
25 4 4d. grey-lilac . . . . 55·00 £225
28 6d. deep-green . . . . — £425
29 1s. indigo . . . . 60·00 £275
30 1s. purple-slate . . . .

No. 30 may be of unissued status.

1859 (Sept). (*a*) *Pin-perf* 12½.
31 2 (1d.) rose-red . . . . £500 30·00
32 (1d.) carmine-lake . . . . £500 30·00
33 4 4d. dull lilac . . . . — £700
34 4d. dull purple . . . . — £700
35 6d. yellow-green £1800 £150
36 6d. deep green £1800 £130
37 1s. purple-slate £2750 £850

(*b*) *Pin-perf* 13½–14
38 2 (1d.) rose-red . . . . 65·00 16·00
39 (1d.) carmine-lake . . . . £110 13·00
40 4 4d. dull lilac . . . . £650 60·00
40*a* 4d. brownish purple . . . . 60·00 80·00
41 4d. dull purple . . . . £200 80·00
42 6d. yellow-green . . . . £300 60·00
43 6d. deep green . . . . £250 55·00
43*a* 6d. bright yellow-green . . . . 60·00 70·00
b. Imperf between (vert pair) £3500
44 1s. purple-slate . . . . — £550

(*c*) *Compound pin-perf* 13½–14 × 12½
45 2 (1d.) carmine-lake . . . .
45*a* 4 4d. dull purple . . . . † —

PRICES. The Pin-perf stamps are very scarce with perforations on all sides and the prices quoted above are for good average specimens.

The note after No. 12 also applies to Nos. 38, 40*a*, 43*a*, 46, 47 and 50.

1860 (Aug). *Clean-cut perf* 14–16½.
46 2 (1d.) rose-red . . . . 70·00 20·00
a. Imperf vert (horiz pair) £1900
b. Imperf between (vert pair) . . . .
47 4 4d. brownish lilac . . . . 85·00 45·00
48 4d. lilac . . . . — £225
49 6d. bright yellow-green . . . . £200 70·00
50 6d. deep green £150 £120

1861 (June). *Rough perf* 14–16½.
52 2 (1d.) rose-red . . . . 50·00 12·00
53 (1d.) rose . . . . 50·00 11·00
54 4 4d. brownish lilac . . . . £140 18·00
55 4d. lilac . . . . £350 18·00
a. Imperf . . . .
56 6d. yellow-green . . . . £150 35·00
57 6d. deep green . . . . £350 26·00
58 1s. indigo £600 £130
59 1s. deep bluish purple £750 £225

(Recess D.L.R.)

1862–63. *Thick paper.* (*a*) *P* 11½, 12.
60 2 (1d.) crimson-lake . . . . 45·00 10·00
61 4 4d. deep purple . . . . 45·00 22·00
62 6d. deep green . . . . £500 22·00
63 1s. bluish slate . . . . £600 65·00

(*b*) *P* 11½, 12, *compound with* 11
63*a* 2 (1d.) crimson-lake . . . . — £350
63*b* 4 6d. deep green . . . . — £4000

(*c*) *P* 13 (1863)
64 2 (1d.) lake . . . . 18·00 15·00
65 4 6d. emerald-green . . . . £275 35·00
67 1s. bright mauve £2500 £225

(*d*) *P* 12½ (1863)
68 2 (1d.) lake . . . . 9·50 10·00

1863–75. *Wmk Crown CC. P* 12½.
69 2 (1d.) lake . . . . 13·00 3·25
a. Wmk sideways . . . . 55·00 5·50
70 (1d.) rose . . . . 13·00 1·60
a. Imperf (pair) . . . .
71 (1d.) scarlet . . . . 12·00 1·25
72 (1d.) carmine . . . . 13·00 1·50
73 4 4d. bright violet . . . . 45·00 7·00
74 4 4d. pale mauve . . . . £110 7·5
75 4d. dull lilac . . . . 20·00 8·0
77 6d. emerald-green . . . . 25·00 9·0
78 6d. deep green . . . . £200 7·5
80 6d. yellow-green . . . . 20·00 4·0
81 6d. apple-green . . . . 20·00 4·5
82 6d. blue-green . . . . 28·00 4·5
83 1s. bright deep mauve . . . . 90·00 5·5
84 1s. lilac-rose . . . . 55·00 4·5
85 1s. mauve (aniline) . . . . 45·00 5·5

The 1s. in a purple-slate shade is a colour changeling.

5

(Typo D.L.R.)

1869. *Wmk Crown CC. P* 12½.
87 5 5s. rose-lake . . . . 60·00 45·00

1872. *Colours changed. Wmk Crown CC. P* 12½.
88 4 4d. grey . . . . 38·00 4·00
89 4d. bluish grey . . . . 38·00 4·00
90 1s. chrome-yellow . . . . 60·00 2·25

1876. *Wmk Crown CC.* (*a*) *P* 14.
91 2 (1d.) lake . . . . 2·50 65
a. Bisected (½d.) (on cover) . . . . † £375
92 (1d.) rose-carmine . . . . 3·25 1·00
93 (1d.) scarlet . . . . 17·00 1·00
94 4 4d. bluish grey . . . . 22·00 1·75
95 6d. bright yellow-green . . . . 22·00 1·60
96 6d. deep yellow-green . . . . 25·00 1·40
97 1s. chrome-yellow . . . . 25·00 4·00

(*b*) *P* 14 × 12½
97*a* 4 6d. yellow-green . . . . — £4000

HALFPENNY (6) **ONE PENNY** (7)

1879–82. *Surch with T* 6 *or* 7. *P* 14.

(*a*) *Wmk Crown CC* (June 1879)
98 2 ½d. lilac . . . . 4·00 4·50
99 ½d. mauve . . . . 4·50 4·50
a. Wmk sideways . . . . 17·00 17·00

(*b*) *Wmk Crown CA* (1882)
100 2 ½d. lilac . . . . £200 28·00
101 1d. rosy carmine . . . . 7·00 75
a. Bisected (½d.) (on cover) . . . . † £275

1882. *Wmk Crown CA. P* 14.
102 4 4d. bluish grey . . . . 60·00 4·50

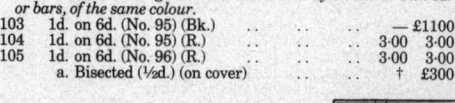

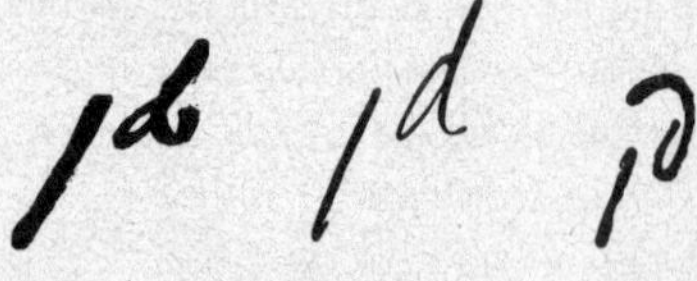
(8) Various styles

1882 (9 May). *Surch by hand in various styles as T* 8 *in red or black ink and the original value obliterated by a thick or thin bar or bars, of the same colour.*
103 1d. on 6d. (No. 95) (Bk.) . . . . — £1100
104 1d. on 6d. (No. 95) (R.) . . . . 3·00 3·00
105 1d. on 6d. (No. 96) (R.) . . . . 3·00 3·00
a. Bisected (½d.) (on cover) . . . . † £300

10

11 Britannia

12 Britannia

(Typo D.L.R.)

1883–94. *P* 14. (*a*) *Wmk Crown CA.*
106 10 ½d. dull green 50 30
107 1d. carmine . . . . 1·25 30
a. Bisected (½d.) (on cover) . . . . † £150
108 2½d. bright blue . . . . 3·00 30
110 4d. grey . . . . 2·75 60
111 6d. olive-black (1884) . . . . 2·75 3·00
112 1s. orange-brown (1884) . . . . 4·75 3·00

(*b*) *Wmk Crown CC*
113 5 5s. maroon (1894) . . . . 12·00 16·00
106/13 . . . . *Set of* 7 24·00 21·00
106/12 Optd "Specimen" . . . . *Set of* 6 £200

Two types of 1d. value:

ONE PENNY (I) (round "o") **ONE PENNY** (II) (oval "o")

(Typo D.L.R.)

896 (17 Aug)–**1900**. *P* 14. (*a*) *Wmk Crown CA*.
14 **11** ½d. dull purple and green 30 20
15 1d. dull purple and rose (I) 60 20
16 1d. dull purple and rose (II) (1900) .. 48·00 1·50
17 2½d. dull purple and blue .. .. 1·25 50
18 4d. dull purple and orange .. .. 3·00 4·75
19 5d. dull purple and mauve .. .. 3·75 4·75
20 6d. dull purple and black .. .. 3·50 4·50
21 1s. green and brown .. .. .. 4·50 5·00

(*b*) *Wmk CA over Crown*
22 **12** 5s. green and brown, **O** .. .. 28·00 40·00
23 10s. green and ultramarine, **O** .. 90·00 95·00
24 £1 green and carmine, **OC** .. .. 85·00 90·00
14/24 .. .. *Set of* 10 £200 £225
14/24 Optd "Specimen" .. .. *Set of* 10 £150

No. 119, surcharged "3d." was prepared for use but not issued. It exists overprinted "Specimen", *price* £100.

Collectors are warned against apparently postally used copies of this issue which bear "REGISTRAR-GENERAL" obliterations and are of very little value.

13 Landing of Columbus

(Recess D.L.R.)

1898. *Discovery of Trinidad Commemoration. Wmk Crown CC. P* 14.
125 **13** 2d. brown and dull violet .. .. 2·25 90
125 Optd "Specimen" .. .. 50·00

1901–06. *Colours changed. Wmk Crown CA or CA over Crown* (5s.). *P* 14.
126 **11** ½d. grey-green, **O** (1902) 45 35
127 1d. black/*red*, **O** (II) 70 10
a. Value omitted £9000
128 2½d. purple and blue/*blue*, **O** (1902) .. 3·25 80
129 4d. green and blue/*buff*, **OC** (1902) .. 1·60 2·75
130 1s. black and blue/*yellow*, **O** (1903) .. 6·50 4·50
131 **12** 5s. lilac and mauve, **O** .. .. 22·00 28·00
a. Deep purple and mauve, **OC** (1906) 22·00 28·00
126/31 .. .. *Set of* 6 32·00 32·00
126/31 Optd "Specimen" .. .. *Set of* 6 £120

A pane of sixty of No. 127a was found in a post office in Trinidad but not more than nine copies are believed to have been sold, and the rest withdrawn.

1904–09. *Wmk Mult Crown CA. P* 14.
132 **11** ½d. grey-green, **OC** 65 35
133 ½d. blue-green, **O** (1906) .. .. 2·25 80
134 1d. black/*red*, **OC** (II) 65 15
135 1d. rose-red, **O** (1907) 70 15
136 2½d. purple and blue/*blue*, **C** .. .. 7·00 2·25
137 2½d. blue, **O** (1906) .. .. .. 1·00 30
138 4d. grey and red/*yellow*, **C** (1906) .. 1·90 4·75
a. Black and red/yellow, **C** .. .. 7·00 9·00
139 6d. dull purple and black, **C** (1905) .. 8·00 10·00
140 6d. dull and bright purple, **C** (1906) .. 4·50 5·50
141 1s. black and blue/*yellow*, **C** .. .. 7·50 7·50
142 1s. purple and blue/*golden yellow*, **C** .. 7·50 8·50
143 1s. black/*green*, **C** (1906) .. .. 1·90 2·50
144 **12** 5s. deep purple and mauve, **C** (1907) .. 27·00 35·00
145 £1 green and carmine, **C** (1907) .. 90·00 90·00
132/45 .. .. *Set of* 14 £140 £150
135/43 Optd "Specimen" .. .. *Set of* 6 £100

No. 135 is from a new die, the letters of "ONE PENNY" being short and thick, while the point of Britannia's spear breaks the uppermost horizontal line of shading in the background.

14 15 16

(Typo D.L.R.)

1909. *Wmk Mult Crown CA. P* 14.
146 **14** ½d. green, **O** 35 15
147 **15** 1d. rose-red, **O** 35 12
148 **16** 2½d. blue, **O** .. .. 2·50 2·50
146/8 Optd "Specimen" .. .. *Set of* 3 50·00

TOBAGO

Although early postal markings are recorded from 1805 onwards it was not until 1841 that the British G.P.O. established a branch office at Scarborough, the island capital, to handle the overseas mail.

The stamps of Great Britain were in use from May 1858 to the end of March 1860 when the control of the postal service passed to the local authorities.

From 1 April 1860 Nos. CC1/2 were again used on overseas mail, pending the introduction of Tobago stamps in 1879.

For illustrations of the handstamp and postmark types see BRITISH POST OFFICES ABROAD notes, following GREAT BRITAIN.

SCARBOROUGH

CROWNED-CIRCLE HANDSTAMPS
CC1 CC **2** TOBAGO (R.) (31.10.1851) *Price on cover* £600
CC2 CC **6** TOBAGO (R.) (*recorded* 1875)
.. .. .. *Price on cover* £800

Stamps of GREAT BRITAIN *cancelled* "A 14" *as Type* **2**.

1858 *to* **1860**.
Z 1 1d. rose-red (1857), *perf* 14 .. .. .. £650
Z 2 4d. rose (1857) £225
Z 3 6d. lilac (1856) £200
Z 4 1s. green (1856) £700

PRICES FOR STAMPS ON COVER	
Nos. 1/4	*from* × 25
Nos. 5/7	—
Nos. 8/12	*from* × 10
Nos. 13/19	*from* × 6
Nos. 20/4	*from* × 30
Nos. 26/33	*from* × 25

CANCELLATIONS. Beware of early stamps of Tobago with fiscal endorsements removed and forged wide "A 14" postmarks added.

1 2

2½ PENCE
(3)

(T **1** and **2**. Typo D.L.R.)

1879 (1 Aug). *Fiscal stamps issued provisionally pending the arrival of stamps inscr* "POSTAGE". *Wmk Crown CC. P* 14.
1 **1** 1d. rose .. .. 35·00 35·00
2 3d. blue .. .. 38·00 32·00
3 6d. orange .. .. 20·00 27·00
4 1s. green .. .. £350 48·00
a. Bisected (6d.) (on cover) .. ..
5 5s. slate £550 £500
6 £1 mauve £5000

The stamps were introduced for fiscal purposes on 1 July 1879.

Stamps of T **1**, watermark Crown CA, are fiscals which were never admitted to postal use.

1880 (Nov). *No. 3 bisected vertically and surch with pen and ink*.
7 **1** 1d. on half of 6d. orange £2000 £150

1880 (20 Dec). *Wmk Crown CC. P* 14.
8 **2** ½d. purple-brown .. .. .. 14·00 14·00
9 1d. Venetian red .. .. .. 26·00 14·00
a. Bisected (½d.) (on cover) .. .. † £1200
10 4d. yellow-green .. .. .. £180 20·00
a. Bisected (2d.) (on cover) .. .. † £1200
b. Malformed "CE" in "PENCE" .. £900 £400
11 6d. stone .. .. £225 90·00
12 1s. yellow-ochre .. .. .. 60·00 25·00

For illustration of Nos. 10b, 18a, 22b, 30a, 31a and 33b see above No. 4 of Dominica.

1883 (Apr). *No. 11 surch with T* **3**.
13 **2** 2½d. on 6d. stone .. .. .. 11·00 4·00
a. Surch double £2500 £1200
b. Large "2" with long tail £100 £110

"SLASH" FLAW. Stamps as Type **2** were produced from Key and Duty plates. On the Key plate used for consignments between 2 October 1892 and 16 December 1896, damage in the form of a large cut or "slash" shows after the "E" of "POSTAGE".

After 1896 an attempt was made to repair the "slash". This resulted in its disappearance, but left an incomplete edge to the circular frame at right.

1882–84. *Wmk Crown CA. P* 14.
14 **2** ½d. purple-brown (1882) .. .. 2·00 7·00
15 1d. Venetian red (1882) .. .. 2·40 2·40
a. Bisected diag (½d.) (on cover) ..
16 2½d. dull blue (1883] .. .. .. 3·75 2·75
a. Bright blue .. .. .. 1·25 1·50
b. Ultramarine .. .. .. 1·25 1·00
c. "Slash" flaw .. .. .. 8·50 20·00
ca. "Slash" flaw repaired .. .. 50·00
18 4d. yellow-green (1882) .. .. £170 90·00
a. Malformed "CE" in "PENCE" .. £800 £400
19 6d. stone (1884).. .. .. .. £550 £475

1885–96. *Colours changed and new value. Wmk Crown CA. P* 14.
20 **2** ½d. dull green (1886) 25 30
a. "Slash" flaw .. .. .. 9·00 20·00
ab. "Slash" flaw repaired .. .. 13·00
21 1d. carmine (1889) 35 25
a. "Slash" flaw .. .. .. 5·00 10·00
ab. "Slash" flaw repaired .. .. 22·00
22 4d. grey (1885) .. .. 85 1·00
a. Imperf (pair) £1600
b. Malformed "CE" in "PENCE" .. 50·00 80·00
c. "Slash" flaw .. .. .. 50·00 85·00
ca. "Slash" flaw repaired .. .. 65·00
23 6d. orange-brown (1886) .. .. 1·75 3·50
a. "Slash" flaw .. .. .. 50·00 85·00
ab. "Slash" flaw repaired .. .. 75·00
24 **2** 1s. olive-yellow (1894) .. .. .. 2·50 6·50
a. Pale olive-yellow .. .. ..
b. "Slash" flaw .. .. .. 60·00 £120
ba. "Slash" flaw repaired .. .. 85·00
c. Error. Orange-brown (1896) .. 5·00
20, 21 and 23 Optd "Specimen" .. *Set of* 3 £170

½ PENNY (4)　　2½ PENCE (5)　　½d POSTAGE (6)

1886–89. *Nos.* 16, 19 *and* 23 *surch as T* **4**.
26 ½d. on 2½d. dull blue (4.86) .. .. 2·00 4·75
a. Figure further from word .. .. 14·00 17·00
b. Surch double £1300 £1100
c. Surch omitted. Vert pair with No. 26 .. £8000
d. Ditto with No. 26a £15000
27 ½d. on 6d. stone (1.86) .. .. .. 3·50 9·00
a. Figure further from word .. .. 35·00 45·00
b. Surch inverted £1200
c. Surch double £1500
28 ½d. on 6d. orange-brown (8.87) .. .. 45·00 50·00
a. Figure further from word £225 £250
b. Surch double .. .. .. — £1000
29 1d. on 2½d. dull blue (7.89) .. .. 14·00 14·00
a. Figure further from word .. .. 70·00 75·00

The surcharge is in a setting of 12 (two rows of 6) repeated five times in the pane. Nos. 7, 9 and 10 in the setting have a raised "P" in "PENNY", and No. 10 also shows the wider spacing between figure and word.

1891–92. *No.* 22 *surch with T* **4** *or* **5**.
30 ½d. on 4d. grey (3.92) .. .. .. 8·50 15·00
a. Malformed "CE" in "PENCE" £350 £500
b. Surch double £1800
31 2½d. on 4d. grey (8.91) .. .. .. 6·00 8·00
a. Malformed "CE" in "PENCE" £300 £400
b. Surch double £1800

1896. *Fiscal stamp* (*T* **1**, *value in second colour, wmk Crown CA, P* 14), *surch with T* **6**.
33 ½d. on 4d. lilac and carmine .. .. 8·00 10·00
a. Space between "½" and "d" .. .. 15·00 20·00
b. Malformed "CE" in "PENCE" £275 £300

From 1896 until 1913 Trinidad stamps were used in Tobago.

TRINIDAD AND TOBAGO

PRICES FOR STAMPS ON COVER	
Nos. 149/55	*from* × 3
Nos. 156/7	—
Nos. 174/89	*from* × 10
Nos. 206/56	*from* × 2
Nos. D18/25	*from* × 12

17 18

(Typo D.L.R.)

1913–23. *Wmk Mult Crown CA. P* 14.
149 **17** ½d. green, **O** 45 15
a. Yellow-green (1915) 90 40
b. Blue-green (*thick paper*) (1917) .. 70 35
c. Blue-green/bluish (3.18) .. .. 7·00 7·00
150 1d. bright red, **O** 40 35
a. Red (*thick paper*) (1916) 25 10
b. Pink (1918).. .. .. .. 4·50 80
c. Carmine-red (5.18) 25 10
151 2½d. ultramarine, **O** .. .. .. 2·50 70
a. Bright blue (*thick paper*) (1916) .. 2·00 85
b. Bright blue (*thin paper*) (1918) .. 3·50 1·40
152 4d. black and red/*yellow*, **OC** .. .. 1·10 1·90
a. White back (12.13) (Optd S. £16) .. 3·25 4·25
b. On lemon (1917) .. .. .. 15·00
c. On pale yellow (Optd S. £16) (1923) 3·75 6·50
153 6d. dull and reddish purple, **C**.. .. 4·25 3·25
a. Dull and deep purple (1918) .. 2·75 3·75
b. Dull purple and mauve (2.18) .. 3·50 4·00
154 1s. black/*green*, **O** .. .. .. 2·75 3·50
a. White back (Optd S. £16) .. .. 1·50 3·50
b. On blue-green, olive back .. .. 2·75 3·75
c. On emerald back (Optd S. £16) .. 2·75 2·75
155 **18** 5s. dull purple and mauve, **C** (1914) .. 20·00 25·00
a. Deep purple and mauve (1918) .. 20·00 25·00
b. Lilac and violet .. .. .. 25·00 32·00
c. Dull purple and violet .. .. 30·00 38·00
d. Brown-purple and violet .. .. 22·00 32·00
156 £1 grey-green and carmine, **C** (1914).. 90·00 £110
a. Deep yellow-green and carmine (1918) .. .. .. 90·00 £110
149/56 .. .. *Set of* 8 £110 £130
149/56 Optd "Specimen" .. .. *Set of* 8 £140

No. 156*a* is from a plate showing background lines very worn.

18*a*

1914 (18 Sept). *Red Cross Label authorised for use as ½d. stamp. Typo. P* 11–12.
157 18*a* (½d.) Red .. .. 12·00 £180
The above was authorised for internal use on one day only, to raise funds for the Red Cross. The used price is for stamp on cover.

19. 10. 16.

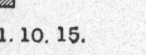

21. 10. 15.

(19)

(19*a*)

1915 (21 Oct). *Optd with T* **19**. *Cross in red with outline and date in black.*
174 **17** 1d. red 35 45
a. Cross 2 mm to right .. .. 12·00 12·00
b. "1" of "15" forked foot .. .. 5·50 7·50
c. Broken "0" in "10" .. .. .. 9·00 9·50
The varieties occur in the following positions on the *pane* of 60: a. No. 11. b. No. 42. c. No. 45. Variety a. is only found on the right-hand pane.

1916 (19 Oct). *Optd with T* **19***a*. *Cross in red with outline and date in black.*
175 **17** 1d. scarlet 25 40
a. No stop after "16" .. .. .. 5·00 6·00
b. "19.10.16" omitted .. .. ..
No. 175a appears on stamp No. 36 on the right-hand pane only.

FORGERIES. Beware of forgeries of the "War Tax" errors listed below. There are also other unlisted errors which are purely fakes.

WAR TAX (19*b*) WAR TAX (20) WAR TAX (21) WAR TAX (22)

1917 (2 Apr). *Optd with T* **19***b*.
176 **17** 1d. red 20 40
a. Opt inverted £140
b. Scarlet 25 55

1917 (May). *Optd with T* **20**.
177 **17** ½d. green 15 15
a. Pair, one without opt £150
178 1d. red 20 20
a. Pair, one without opt £150
b. Scarlet 25 15
ba. Opt double .. .. 80·00
The varieties without overprint were caused by the type being shifted over towards the left so that one stamp in the lowest row of each pane escaped.

1917 (21 June). *Optd with T* **21**.
179 **17** ½d. yellow-green 55 75
a. Pale green 50 70
b. Deep green 60 85
180 1d. red 15 15
Pairs are known of the 1d. stamps, one stamp without the overprint. This was caused by a shifting of the type to the left-hand side, but only a few stamps on the right-hand vertical row escaped the overprint and such pairs are very rare.

1917 (21 July–Sept). *Optd with T* **22**.
181 **17** ½d. yellow-green .. .. .. 1·40 2·00
a. Deep green 15 40
182 1d. red (Sept) 15 15

WAR TAX (23) WAR TAX (24) WAR TAX (25) War Tax (26)

1917 (1 Sept). *Optd with T* **23** *(closer spacing between lines of opt).*
183 **17** ½d. deep green 20 35
a. Pale yellow-green .. .. ..
184 1d. red .. .. 5·50 8·00

1917 (31 Oct). *Optd with T* **24**.
185 **17** 1d. scarlet 15 30
a. Opt inverted .. .. 70·00

1918 (7 Jan). *Optd with T* **25**.
186 **17** 1d. scarlet 15 15
a. Opt double £130
b. Opt inverted .. .. 80·00

1918 (13 Feb–May). *Optd with T* **26**.
187 **17** ½d. bluish green 15 30
a. Pair, one without opt £350
188 1d. scarlet 15 25
a. Opt double .. .. 80·00
b. Rose-red (1.5.18) 25 30

1918 (14 Sept). *New printing as T* **26**, *but 19 stamps on each sheet have the letters of the word "Tax" wider spaced, the "x" being to the right of "r" of "War" instead of under it. Thick bluish paper.*
189 **17** 1d. scarlet ("Tax" spaced) .. .. 75 1·25
a. Opt double £140

1921–22. *Wmk Mult Script CA. P* 14.
206 **17** ½d. green, **O** 35 60
207 1d. scarlet, **O** 20 25
208 1d. brown, **O** (17.2.22) 25 25
209 2d. grey, **O** (17.2.22) .. .. .. 2·00 2·00
210 2½d. bright blue, **O** .. .. .. 90 3·00
211 3d. bright blue, **O** (17.2.22) .. .. 2·50 3·00
212 6d. dull and bright purple, **C** .. .. 3·50 4·75
213 **18** 5s. dull purple and purple, **C** (1921) .. 28·00 45·00
214 5s. deep purple and purple, **C** (1922) .. 28·00 45·00
215 £1 green and carmine, **C** .. .. 80·00 £130
206/15 .. .. *Set of* 9 £110 £170
206/15 Optd "Specimen" .. .. *Set of* 9 £200

27

(Typo D.L.R.)

1922–28. *P* 14. *(a) Wmk Mult Crown CA.*
216 **27** 4d. black and red/*pale yellow*, **C** 70 80
217 1s. black/*emerald*, **C** .. .. .. 3·00 3·25

(b) Wmk Mult Script CA
218 **27** ½d. green, **O** 15 10
219 1d. brown, **O** 20 10
220 1½d. bright rose, **O** 55 15
a. Scarlet 30 20
222 2d. grey, **O** 40 30
223 3d. blue, **O** 95 40
224 4d. black and red/*pale yellow*, **C** (1928) 2·25 2·50
225 6d. dull purple and bright magenta, **C** 5·50 10·00
226 6d. green and red/*emerald*, **C** (1924) .. 2·25 1·00
227 1s. black/*emerald*, **C** .. .. .. 2·25 1·40
228 5s. dull purple and mauve, **C** .. .. 16·00 20·00
229 £1 green and bright rose, **C** .. .. 95·00 £140
216/29 .. .. *Set of* 13 £110 £160
216/29 Optd "Specimen" .. .. *Set of* 13 £225

(New Currency. 100 cents = 1 dollar)

28 First Boca

29 Imperial College of Tropical Agriculture

(Recess B.W.)

1935 (1 Feb)–**37.** *T* **28/9** *and similar horiz designs. Wmk Mult Script CA (sideways). P* 12.
230 1 c. blue and green 45 15
a. Perf 12½ (1936) 12 12
231 2 c. ultramarine and yellow-brown 55 35
a. Perf 12½ (1936) 20 15
232 3 c. black and scarlet 20 15
a. Perf 12½ (1936) 25 15
233 6 c. sepia and blue 70 45
a. Perf 12½ (1937) 35 70
234 8 c. sage-green and vermilion 50 65
235 12 c. black and violet 55 60
a. Perf 12½ (1937) .. .. 70 1·25
236 24 c. black and olive-green .. .. .. 1·40 1·00
a. Perf 12½ (1937) .. .. 3·00 2·75
237 48 c. deep green .. .. 8·00 10·00
238 72 c. myrtle-green and carmine .. .. 16·00 18·00
230/8 .. .. *Set of* 9 25·00 28·00
230/8 Perf "Specimen" .. .. *Set of* 9 90·00
Designs:—3 c. Mt Irvine Bay, Tobago; 6 c. Discovery of Lake Asphalt; 8 c. Queen's Park, Savannah; 12 c. Town Hall, San Fernando; 24 c. Government House; 48 c. Memorial Park; 72 c. Blue Basin.

1935 (6 May). *Silver Jubilee. As Nos.* 91/4 *of Antigua but ptd by B.W. P* 11 × 12.
239 2 c. ultramarine and grey-black 20 20
a. Extra flagstaff .. .. 30·00
b. Short extra flagstaff .. .. .. 10·00
c. Lightning conductor .. .. .. 10·00
240 3 c. deep blue and scarlet 20 30
a. Extra flagstaff .. .. 45·00
c. Lightning conductor .. .. .. 14·00
241 6 c. brown and deep blue .. .. .. 60 1·75
a. Extra flagstaff .. .. 70·00
b. Short extra flagstaff .. .. .. 18·00
c. Lightning conductor .. .. .. 18·00
242 24 c. slate and purple .. .. 2·50 3·25
a. Extra flagstaff .. .. 60·00
c. Lightning conductor .. .. .. 17·00
239/42 Perf "Specimen" .. .. *Set of* 4 45·00
For illustrations of plate varieties see Omnibus section following Zululand.

1937 (12 May). *Coronation. As Nos.* 13/15 *of Aden.*
243 1 c. green 12 10
244 2 c. yellow-brown 30 15
245 8 c. orange 55 50
243/5 Perf "Specimen" .. .. *Set of* 3 32·00

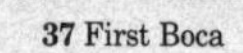

37 First Boca

47 King George VI

1938 (2 May)–**44.** *T* **37** *and similar horiz designs, and T* **47**. *Wmk Mult Script CA (sideways on* 1 *c. to* 60 *c.)*

(a) P 11½ × 11
246 1 c. blue and green 10
247 2 c. blue and yellow-brown 10
248 3 c. black and scarlet .. .. 15·00 5
248*a* 3 c. green and purple-brown (1941) 10
249 4 c. chocolate .. .. 9·00 1·7
249*a* 4 c. scarlet (1941) 40 2
249*b* 5 c. magenta (1.5.41) 15
250 6 c. sepia and blue 25
251 8 c. sage-green and vermilion 40 1
252 12 c. black and purple .. .. 3·50 9
a. Black and slate-purple (1944) 80 1
253 24 c. black and olive-green 70 2
254 60 c. myrtle-green and carmine .. .. 3·75 9

(b) T **47**. *P* 12
255 $1.20, blue-green (1.40) .. .. .. 4·25 5
256 $4.80, rose-carmine (1.40) .. .. .. 30·00 12·0
246/56 .. .. *Set of* 14 60·00 15·0
246/56 *exc* 249*b* Perf "Specimen" .. *Set of* 13 £140
Designs:—2 c. Imperial College of Tropical Agriculture; 3 c. Mt Irvine Bay, Tobago; 4 c. Memorial Park; 5 c. G.P.O. and Treasury, 6 c. Discovery of Lake Asphalt; 8 c. Queen's Park, Savannah; 12 c Town Hall, San Fernando; 24 c. Government House; 60 c. Blue Basin.

1946 (1 Oct). *Victory. As Nos.* 28/9 *of Aden.*
257 3 c. chocolate 15 12
258 6 c. blue 15 12
257/8 Perf "Specimen" .. .. *Set of* 2 27·00

1948 (22 Nov). *Silver Wedding. As Nos.* 30/1 *of Aden (recess* $4.80).
259 3 c. red-brown 12 12
260 $4.80, carmine .. .. 18·00 24·00

1949 (10 Oct). *75th Anniv of Universal Postal Union. As Nos.* 114/17 *of Antigua.*
261 5 c. bright reddish purple 25 15
262 6 c. deep blue 50 45
263 12 c. violet 60 50
264 24 c. olive 80 80

1951 (16 Feb). *University College of B.W.I. As Nos.* 118/19 *of Antigua.*
265 3 c. green and red-brown 20 15
266 12 c. black and reddish violet 35 25

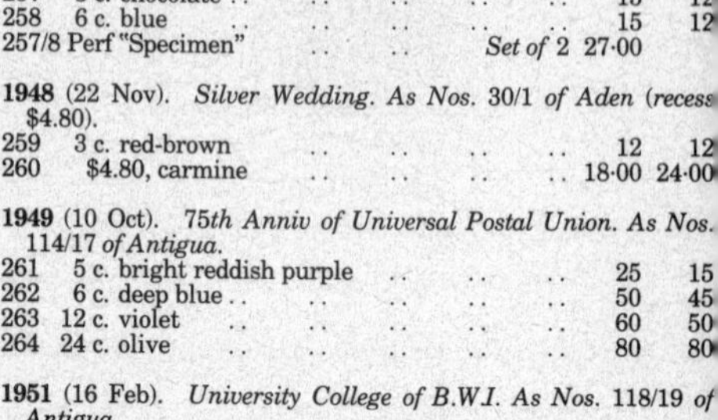

48 First Boca

49 Mt Irvine Bay, Tobago

(Recess B.W.)

1953 (20 Apr)–**55.** *Designs previously used for King George VI issue, but with portrait of Queen Elizabeth II as in T* **48** *(1 c., 2 c., 12 c.) or* **49** *(other values). Wmk Mult Script CA. P* 12 *(dollar values) or* 11½ × 11 *(others).*
267 1 c. blue and green (*shades*) 15 5
268 2 c. indigo and orange-brown 15 5
269 3 c. deep emerald and purple-brown 15 5
270 4 c. scarlet 20 5
271 5 c. magenta 30 5
272 6 c. brown and greenish blue 30 5
273 8 c. deep yellow-green and orange-red .. 30 5
274 12 c. black and purple 30 5
275 24 c. black and yellow-olive (*shades*) .. 30 5
276 60 c. blackish green and carmine .. .. 2·50 30
277 $1.20, bluish green .. .. 1·40 65
a. Perf 11½ (19.1.55) .. .. .. 1·25 30
278 $4.80, cerise .. .. 9·50 13·00
a. Perf 11½ (16.11.55) .. .. .. 9·50 7·00
267/78a .. .. *Set of* 12 14·00 7·25
Designs: *Horiz*—2 c. Imperial College of Tropical Agriculture; 4 c. Memorial Park; 5 c. G.P.O. and Treasury; 6 c. Discovery of Lake Asphalt; 8 c. Queen's Park, Savannah; 12 c. Town Hall, San Fernando; 24 c. Government House; 60 c. Blue Basin. *Vert* (18 × 21 *mm*)—$1.20, $4.80, Queen Elizabeth II.

1953 (3 June). *Coronation. As No.* 47 *of Aden.*
279 3 c. black and green 8 8

ONE CENT

(50)

1956 (20 Dec). *No.* 268 *surch with T* **50**.
280 1 c. on 2 c. indigo and orange-brown 45 70

1958 (22 Apr). *Inauguration of British Caribbean Federation. As Nos.* 135/7 *of Antigua.*
281 5 c. deep green 12 5
282 6 c. blue 12 12
283 12 c. scarlet 12 10

PRINTERS. Nos. 284 to 354 were printed in photogravure by Harrison & Sons, *unless otherwise stated.*

PRICES OF SETS

Set prices are given for many issues, generally those containing five stamps or more. Definitive sets include one of each value or major colour change, but do not cover different perforations, die types or minor shades. Where a choice is possible the set prices are based on the cheapest versions of the stamps included in the listings.

51 Cipriani Memorial

52 Queen's Hall

53 White-tailed Goldenthroat

54 Map of Trinidad and Tobago

(Des V. Whiteley (1, 2, 12, 35, 60 c., $4.80), J. Matthews (5 c.), H. Baxter (6, 8, 10, 15 c.), M. Goaman (25 c., 50 c., $1.20))

1960 (24 Sept)–**65**. *Designs as T* **51/4**. *W* w **12** (*upright*). *P* 13½ × 14½ (1 c., 60 c., $1.20, $4.80) *or* 14½ × 13½ (*others*).

284	1 c. stone and black	5	5
285	2 c. bright blue (*shades*)	5	5
286	5 c. chalky blue	8	5
287	6 c. red-brown (*shades*)	8	5
288	8 c. yellow-green	10	5
289	10 c. deep lilac	10	5
290	12 c. vermilion	12	5
291	15 c. orange	1·25	45
291*a*	15 c. orange (15.9.64)	75	5
292	25 c. rose-carmine and deep blue	35	5
293	35 c. emerald and black	35	5
294	50 c. yellow, grey and blue	45	5
295	60 c. vermilion, yellow-green and indigo ..	60	20
	a. Perf 14½ (12.65*)	£120	30·00
296	$1.20, multicoloured	4·00	1·00
297	$4.80, apple-green and pale blue	8·50	4·25
284/97	.. .. .. *Set of* 15	15·00	6·00

Designs: *Vert as T* **51**—60 c. Anthurium Lilies. *Horiz as T* **52**–5 c. Whitehall; 6 c. Treasury Building; 8 c. Governor-General's House; 10 c. General Hospital, San Fernando; 12 c. Oil refinery; 15 c. (No. 291), Crest; 15 c. (No. 291*a*), Coat of arms; 25 c. Scarlet Ibis; 35 c. Pitch Lake; 50 c. Mohammed Jinnah Mosque.

*This is the earliest date reported to us. It comes from an unannounced printing which was despatched to Trinidad on 3 December 1964.

The 2, 5, 6, 12 and 25 c. exist with PVA gum as well as gum arabic.

See also No. 317.

65 Scouts and Gold Wolf Badge

1961 (4 Apr). *Second Caribbean Scout Jamboree. Design multicoloured; background colours below. W* w **12**. *P* 13½ × 14½.

298	**65**	8 c. light green	15	10
299		25 c. light blue	25	15

INDEPENDENT

66 "Buccoo Reef" (painting by Carlisle Chang)

71 "Protein Foods"

1962 (31 Aug). *Independence. T* **66** *and similar horiz designs. W* w **12**. *P* 14½.

300	5 c. bluish green	5	5
301	8 c. grey	12	15
302	25 c. reddish violet	15	5
303	35 c. brown, yellow, green and black ..	30	10
304	60 c. red, black and blue	50	60

Designs:—8 c. Piarco Air Terminal; 25 c. Hilton Hotel, Port-of-Spain; 35 c. Greater Bird of Paradise and map; 60 c. Scarlet Ibis and map.

(Des M. Goaman)

1963 (4 June). *Freedom from Hunger. W* w **12**. *P* 14 × 13½.

305	**71**	5 c. brown-red	10	5
306		8 c. yellow-bistre	20	10
307		25 c. violet-blue	35	12

72 Jubilee Emblem

1964 (15 Sept). *Golden Jubilee of Trinidad and Tobago Girl Guides' Association. W* w **12**. *P* 14½ × 14.

308	**72**	6 c. yellow, ultramarine and rose-red ..	5	5
309		25 c. yellow, ultramarine and bright blue	15	10
310		35 c. yellow, ultramarine & emerald-grn	25	20

73 I.C.Y. Emblem

(Litho State Ptg Wks, Vienna)

1965 (15 Nov). *International Co-operation Year. P* 12.

311	**73**	35 c. red-brown, dp green & ochre-yell ..	40	10

74 Eleanor Roosevelt, Flag and U.N. Emblem

1965 (10 Dec). *Eleanor Roosevelt Memorial Foundation. W* w **12**. *P* 13½ × 14.

312	**74**	25 c. black, red and ultramarine ..	10	10

75 Parliament Building

FIFTH YEAR OF
INDEPENDENCE
31st AUGUST 1967

(**79**)

1966 (8 Feb). *Royal Visit. T* **75** *and similar horiz designs. Multicoloured. W* w **12** (*sideways*). *P* 13½ × 14½.

313	5 c. Type **75**	15	5
314	8 c. Map, H.M. Yacht *Britannia* and Arms ..	80	50
315	25 c. Map and flag	85	45
316	35 c. Flag and panorama	90	55

1966 (15 Nov). *As No.* 284 *but W* w **12** (*sideways*).

317	1 c. stone and black	5	5

No. 317 exists with PVA gum as well as gum arabic.

1967 (31 Aug). *Fifth Year of Independence. Nos.* 288/9, 291*a and* 295 *optd as T* **79**.

318	8 c. yellow-green	5	5
319	10 c. deep lilac	5	5
320	15 c. orange	5	5
321	60 c. vermilion, yellow-green and indigo ..	20	20

On No. 321 the overprint is in five lines.

80 Musical Instruments

81 Calypso King

1968 (17 Feb). *Trinidad Carnival. Horiz designs as T* **80** (15 *and* 25 c.), *or vert designs as T* **81** (35 *and* 60 c.). *Multicoloured. P* 12.

322	5 c. Type **80**	5	5
323	10 c. Type **81**	5	5
324	15 c. Steel band	5	5
325	25 c. Carnival procession	5	5
326	35 c. Carnival King	10	10
327	60 c. Carnival Queen	20	20
322/7	.. .. *Set of* 6	45	45

86 Doctor giving Eye-Test

87 Peoples of the World and Emblem

1968 (7 May). *20th Anniv of World Health Organization. W* w **12** (*sideways*). *P* 14.

328	**86**	5 c. red, blackish brown and gold ..	5	5
329		25 c. orange, blackish brown and gold ..	10	5
330		35 c. bright blue, black and gold	15	10

1968 (5 Aug). *Human Rights Year. W* w **12** (*sideways*). *P* 13½ × 14.

331	**87**	5 c. cerise, black and greenish yellow ..	5	5
332		10 c. new blue, black and greenish yellow	5	5
333		25 c. apple-green, black & greenish yell ..	10	10

88 Cycling

(Des G. Vasarhelyi. Islands additionally die-stamped in gold (5 c. to 35 c.))

1968 (14 Oct). *Olympic Games, Mexico. T* **88** *and similar horiz designs. Multicoloured. W* w **12**. *P* 14.

334	5 c. Type **88**	5	5
335	15 c. Weightlifting	10	5
336	25 c. Relay-racing	12	5
337	35 c. Sprinting	15	10
338	$1.20, Maps of Mexico and Trinidad ..	75	65

93 Cocoa Beans

94 Green Hermit

(Des G. Vasarhelyi. Queen's profile die-stamped in gold (G.) or silver (S.), also the Islands on 20, 25 c.)

1969–72. *Designs as T* **93/4**. *W* w **12** (*sideways on* 1 *to* 8 c., 40 c., 50 c.). *P* 14 × 14½ ($2.50, $5) *or* 14 (*others*).

A. *Chalk-surfaced paper* (1.4.69)
B. *Glazed, ordinary paper* (24.3.72*)

		A		B	
339	1 c. multicoloured (S.)	5	5	5	5
	a. Queen's head omitted ..	60·00	—	†	
340	3 c. multicoloured (G.)	5	5	5	5
341	5 c. mult (*shades*) (G.)	15	5	15	5
	a. Queen's head omitted ..	†		—	—
	b. Imperf (pair)	†		£175	—
	ba. Ditto and Queen's head omitted	†		£275	—
342	6 c. multicoloured (G.)	5	5	5	5
	a. Queen's head omitted ..	£100	—	†	
	b. Imperf (pair)	£250	—	†	
343	8 c. multicoloured (S.)	8	5	†	
344	10 c. multicoloured (G.)	25	5	25	5
345	12 c. mult (*shades*) (S.)	12	5	20	12
346	15 c. multicoloured (S.)	12	5	20	12
	a. Queen's head omitted ..	£350	—	†	
347	20 c. scarlet, black & grey (G.) ..	20	5	30	20
348	25 c. scarlet, blk & new bl (S.) ..	20	12	30	20
	a. Silver (Queen's head and island) omitted	†		75·00	—
349	30 c. multicoloured (S.)	25	12	30	25
350	40 c. multicoloured (G.)	1·00	25	1·50	60
351	50 c. multicoloured (S.)	45	20	95	70
352	$1 multicoloured (G.)	1·00	40	1·25	1·00
	a. Gold (Queen's head) omitted	90·00	—	—	—
353	$2.50, multicoloured (G.) ..	1·50	1·75	†	
	a. Perf 14 (1972)	20·00	15·00	†	
354	$5 multicoloured (G.)	3·00	3·00	†	
	a. Gold (Queen's head) omitted	—	—	†	
	b. Perf 14 (1972)	40·00	35·00	†	
339A/54A	.. .. *Set of* 16	7·50	5·50	†	
339B/52B	.. .. *Set of* 13	†		5·00	3·00

Designs: *Horiz as T* **93**—3 c. Sugar refinery; 5 c. Rufous-vented Chachalaca; 6 c. Oil refinery; 8 c. Fertilizer plant; 40 c. Scarlet Ibis; 50 c. Maracas Bay; $2.50, Fishing; $5, Red House. *Vert as T* **94**—12 c. Citrus fruit; 15 c. Arms of Trinidad and Tobago; 20, 25 c. Flag and outline of Trinidad and Tobago; 30 c. Chaconia plant; $1, Poui tree.

*This was the date of receipt at the G.P.O.; the dates of issue are not known.

The listed missing die-stamped heads have the heads completely omitted and, except for No. 352a which results from a shift, show a blind impression of the die. They should not be confused with stamps from sheets containing a row of partially missing heads progressing down to mere specks of foil. The 20 c. value also exists with the gold omitted from the map only. We have also seen stamps with an additional "blind" profile cutting into the rear of the head but without a second die-stamped impression. Varieties of this nature are outside the scope of this catalogue.

See also Nos. 432/4 and 473.

108 Captain A. A. Cipriani (labour leader) and Entrance to Woodford Square

(Photo State Ptg Works, Vienna)

1969 (1 May). *50th Anniv of International Labour Organization. T* **108** *and similar horiz design. P* 12.
355 6 c. black, gold and carmine-red 8 8
356 15 c. black, gold and new blue 10 10
Design:—15 c. Arms of Industrial Court and entrance to Woodford Square.

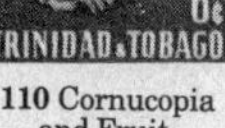

110 Cornucopia and Fruit

111 Map showing "CARIFTA" Countries

(Des and photo State Ptg Works, Vienna)

1969 (1 Aug). *First Anniv of CARIFTA (Caribbean Free Trade Area). T* **110/11** *and similar multicoloured designs. P* 13½.
357 6 c. Type **110** 5 5
358 10 c. British and member nations' flags (*horiz*) 5 5
359 30 c. Type **111** 25 10
360 40 c. Boeing "727" in flight (*horiz*) 30 15

114 Space Module landing on Moon

(Des G. Vasarhelyi. Litho D.L.R.)

1969 (2 Sept). *First Man on the Moon. T* **114** *and similar multicoloured designs. P* 14.
361 6 c. Type **114** 5 5
362 40 c. Space module and astronauts on Moon (*vert*) 30 10
363 $1 Astronauts seen from inside space module 75 65
The above were released by the Philatelic Agency in the U.S.A. on 1 September, but not sold locally until 2 September.

117 Parliamentary Chamber, Flags and Emblems

(Photo Harrison)

1969 (23 Oct*). *15th Commonwealth Parliamentary Association Conference, Port-of-Spain. T* **117** *and similar horiz designs. Multicoloured. W w* **12**. *P* 14½ × 13½.
364 10 c. Type **117** 8 5
365 15 c. J.F. Kennedy College 10 5
366 30 c. Parliamentary maces 20 10
367 40 c. Cannon and emblem 20 20
*This was the local release date; the Philatelic Agency in New York released the stamps ten days earlier.

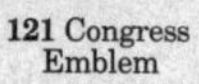

121 Congress Emblem

122 Emblem and Islands at Daybreak

(Photo Rosenbaum Bros, Vienna)

1969 (3 Nov). *International Congress of the Junior Chamber of Commerce. T* **121/2** *and similar vert design. P* 13½.
368 6 c. black, red and gold 5 5
369 30 c. gold, lake and light blue 15 15
370 40 c. black, gold and ultramarine 20 15
Design:—40 c. Emblem, palm-trees and ruin.
The above were released by the Philatelic Agency in the U.S.A. on 2 November, but not sold locally until 3 November.

ALTERED CATALOGUE NUMBERS

Any Catalogue numbers altered from the last edition are shown as a list in the introductory pages.

124 "Man in the Moon"

129 Statue of Gandhi

(Des V. Whiteley. Litho Questa)

1970 (6 Feb). *Carnival Winners. T* **124** *and similar multicoloured designs. W w* **12** *(sideways on 40 c.). P* 14.
371 5 c. Type **124** 5 5
372 6 c. "City beneath the Sea" 5 5
373 15 c. "Antelope" God Bamibara 5 5
374 30 c. "Chanticleer" Pheasant Queen of Malaya 15 10
375 40 c. Steel Band of the Year (*horiz*) 15 10
The above were released by the Philatelic Agency in the U.S.A. on 2 February, but not sold locally until 6 February.

(Photo State Printing Works, Vienna)

1970 (2 Mar). *Gandhi Centenary Year* (1969). *T* **129** *and similar multicoloured design. P* 12.
376 10 c. Type **129** 25 10
377 30 c. Head of Gandhi and Indian flag (*horiz*) .. 50 30

131 Symbols of Culture, Science, Arts and Technology

132 New U.P.U. H.Q. Building

(Des G. Lee. Photo State Printing Works, Vienna)

1970 (26 June). *25th Anniv of United Nations. T* **131/2** *and similar designs. Multicoloured. P* 12 (30 c.), 13½ × 14 (10 c.) *or* 13½ (*others*).
378 5 c. Type **131** 5 5
379 10 c. Children of different races, map and flag (34 × 25 *mm*) 10 5
380 20 c. Noah's Ark, rainbow and dove (35 × 24 *mm*) 15 10
381 30 c. Type **132** 25 20

NATIONAL
COMMERCIAL
BANK
ESTABLISHED
1.7.70

(**133**)

134 "East Indian Immigrants" (J. Cazabon)

1970 (1 July). *Inauguration of National Commercial Bank. No.* 341A *optd with T* **133**.
382 5 c. multicoloured 5 5

(Des from paintings by Cazabon. Litho Questa)

1970 (Oct). *125th Anniv of San Fernando. T* **134** *and similar designs. W w* **12** *(sideways on 5 c. and 40 c.). P* 13½.
383 3 c. multicoloured 5 5
384 5 c. black, blue and yellow-ochre 10 5
385 40 c. black, blue and yellow-ochre 60 30
Designs: *Horiz*—5 c. "San Fernando Town Hall"; 40 c. "San Fernando Harbour, 1860".

135 "The Adoration of the Shepherds" (detail, School of Seville)

(Des G. Drummond. Litho Format)

1970 (8 Dec). *Christmas. Paintings. T* **135** *and similar ve designs. Multicoloured. P* 13½.
386 3 c. Type **135** 8
387 5 c. "Madonna and Child with Saints" (detail, Titian) 10
388 30 c. "The Adoration of the Shepherds" (detail, Le Nain) 20 1
389 40 c. "The Virgin and Child, St. John and an Angel" (Morando) 30 2
390 $1 "The Adoration of the Kings" (detail, Veronese) .. .. 95 1·2
MS391 114 × 153 mm. Nos. 386/9 .. .. 2·00 2·2

136 Brocket Deer

(Des State Printing Works, Vienna. Litho Questa)

1971 (9 Aug). *Trinidad Wildlife. T* **136** *and similar horiz designs. Multicoloured. W w* **12** *(sideways). P* 13½.
392 3 c. Type **136** 25 12
393 5 c. Quenk (pig) 35 12
394 6 c. Lappe (rodent) 40 15
395 30 c. Agouti (rodent) .. .. 1·75 2·00
396 40 c. Ocelot .. .. 2·00 2·25

137 A. A. Cipriani

138 "Virgin and Child with St. John" (detail, Bartolommeo)

(Litho D.L.R.)

1971 (30 Aug*). *Ninth Anniv of Independence. T* **137** *and similar vert design. Multicoloured. W w* **12**. *P* 14.
397 5 c. Type **137** 5 5
398 30 c. Chaconia medal 20 15
*This was the local release date, but the New York agency issued the stamps on 25 August.

(Litho Harrison)

1971 (25 Oct). *Christmas. T* **138** *and similar vert designs. Multicoloured. W w* **12** *(sideways on 10 and 15 c.). P* 14 × 14½.
399 3 c. Type **138** 5 5
400 5 c. Local crèche 5 5
401 10 c. "Virgin and Child with Saints Jerome and Dominic" (detail, Lippi) 15 10
402 15 c. "Virgin and Child with St. Anne" (detail, Gerolamo dai Libri) 30 30

139 Satellite Earth Station, Matura

(Litho Harrison)

1971 (18 Nov). *Satellite Earth Station. T* **139** *and similar vert designs. Multicoloured. W w* **12** *(sideways on 10 c.). P* 14 (10 c.) *or* 14 × 13½ (*others*).
403 10 c. Type **139** 12 10
404 30 c. Dish antennae 30 30
405 40 c. Satellite and the earth 40 40
MS406 140 × 76 mm. Nos. 403/5 (wmk sideways). Imperf .. .. 1·50 1·75
a. Yellow and pale blue omitted .. ..

140 Morpho Hybrid

(Des G. Drummond. Photo Harrison)

1972 (18 Feb). *Butterflies. T* **140** *and similar horiz designs. Multicoloured. W w* **12** *(sideways on 5 c.). P* 14.
407 3 c. Type **140** 20 5
408 5 c. Purple Mort Bleu 25 5
409 6 c. Jaune d'Abricot 30 10

410 10 c. Purple King Shoemaker 45 15
411 20 c. Southern White Page .. .. .. 1·00 1·25
412 30 c. Little Jaune .. .. .. 1·50 2·00
407/12 .. .. Set of 6 3·25 3·25

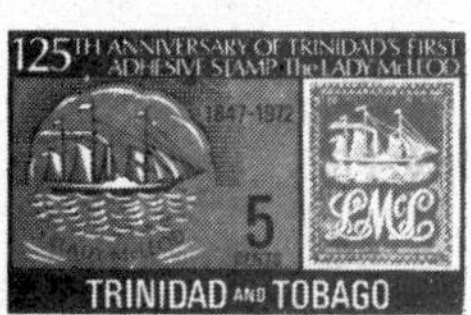

141 S.S. *Lady McLeod* and McLeod Stamp

142 Trinity Cross

(Des J. Cooter. Litho Harrison)

1972 (24 Apr*). *125th Anniv. of First Trinidad Postage Stamp. T* **141** *and similar horiz designs. W w* **12**. *P* 14.
413 5 c. multicoloured 10 5
414 10 c. multicoloured 20 10
415 30 c. greenish blue, reddish chestnut and black 50 45
MS416 83 × 140 mm. Nos. 413/15 .. .. 1·25 1·25
a. Wmk sideways .. .. 20·00 22·00

Designs:—10 c. Map and Lady McLeod stamp; 30 c. Lady McLeod stamp and inscription.

*This was the local release date, but the New York Agency issued the stamps on 12 April.

(Des G. Drummond. Photo Enschedé)

1972 (28 Aug). *Tenth Anniv of Independence. T* **142** *and similar vert designs. Multicoloured. W w* **12**. *P* 13½ × 13.
417 5 c. Type **142** 5 5
418 10 c. Chaconia Medal 10 5
419 20 c. Hummingbird Medal 20 15
420 30 c. Medal of Merit 30 25
MS421 93 × 121 mm. Nos. 417/20 .. .. 1·10 1·25

One example of MS421 has been seen with the blue (background and frame) omitted from the 10 c. Another example has been seen with carmine (background and frame) omitted from the 30 c.

See also Nos. 440/4.

143 Bronze Medal, 1964 Relay

144 "Adoration of the Kings" (detail, Dosso)

145 E.C.L.A. Building, Chile

(Des G. Drummond. Litho Questa)

1972 (7 Sept). *Olympic Games, Munich. T* **143** *and similar horiz designs. Multicoloured. W w* **12**. *P* 14.
422 10 c. Type **143** 15 5
423 20 c. Bronze, 1964 200 metres 25 15
424 30 c. Silver, 1952 weightlifting 35 25
425 40 c. Silver, 1964 400 metres 40 40
426 50 c. Silver, 1948 weightlifting 50 50
MS427 153 × 82 mm. Nos. 422/6 .. .. .. 1·75 2·00

(Des G. Drummond. Photo J.W.)

1972 (9 Nov). *Christmas. T* **144** *and similar horiz design. Multicoloured. W w* **12**. *P* 14.
428 3 c. Type **144** 10 5
429 5 c. "The Holy Family and a Shepherd" (Titian) 12 5
430 30 c. As 5 c. 60 65
MS431 73 × 99 mm. Nos. 428/30 .. .. .. 1·25 1·50

1973–74. *Nos. 340/2, but W w* **12** *(upright). Glazed, ordinary paper.*
432 3 c. multicoloured (9.74?) 50 45
433 5 c. multicolourex (1973) .. .. .. 4·75 1·50
a. Yellow (background) omitted £125
434 6 c. multicoloured (1974) 45 45

(Des G. Drummond. Litho Questa)

1973 (15 Aug). *Anniversaries. Events described on stamps. T* **145** *and similar horiz designs. Multicoloured. W w* **12**. *P* 14.
435 10 c. Type **145** 5 5
436 20 c. Interpol emblem 30 10
437 30 c. W.M.O. emblem 30 20
438 40 c. University of the West Indies 35 30
MS439 155 × 92 mm. Nos. 435/8 .. .. .. 1·40 1·50

(Des J. Cooter. Litho Harrison)

1973 (30 Aug). *Eleventh Anniv of Independence. Vert designs as T* **142**. *Multicoloured. W w* **12**. *P* 14½ × 14.
440 10 c. Trinity Cross 5 5
441 20 c. Medal of Merit 15 10
442 30 c. Chaconia Medal 20 20
443 40 c. Hummingbird Medal 30 30
MS444 75 × 122 mm. Nos. 440/3. P 14 .. .. 1·25 1·40

146 G.P.O., Port-of-Spain

147 "Madonna with Child" (Murillo)

(Des J. Cooter. Photo J.W.)

1973 (8 Oct). *Second Commonwealth Conference of Postal Administrations, Trinidad. T* **146** *and similar horiz design. Multicoloured. W w* **12** *(sideways). P* 14.
445 30 c. Type **146** 20 20
446 40 c. Conference Hall, Chaguaramas* 30 30
MS447 115 × 115 mm. Nos. 445/6 .. .. 70 90

*Wrongly inscr "CHAGARAMAS" on stamp.

(Des PAD Studio. Photo Harrison)

1973 (22 Oct). *Christmas. W w* **12** *(sideways on* **MS**450). *P* 14½ × 14.
448 **147** 5 c. multicoloured 5 5
449 $1 multicoloured .. .. .. 85 1·00
MS450 94 × 88 mm. Nos. 448/9. P 14 .. .. 1·25 1·40

148 Berne H.Q. within U.P.U. Emblem

(Des PAD Studio. Photo Harrison)

1974 (18 Nov). *Centenary of Universal Postal Union. T* **148** *and similar horiz design. Multicoloured. W w* **12** *(sideways). P* 13 × 14.
451 40 c. Type **148** 35 45
452 50 c. Map within emblem 40 55
MS453 117 × 104 mm. Nos. 451/2. P 13 × 14½ 18·00 20·00

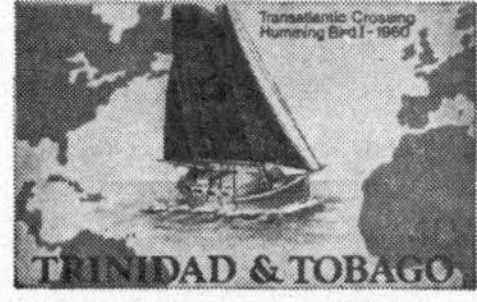

149 *Humming Bird I* crossing Atlantic Ocean (1960)

(Des and photo Harrison)

1974 (2 Dec). *First Anniv of World Voyage by H. and K. La Borde. T* **149** *and similar horiz design. Multicoloured. W w* **12** *(sideways). P* 14.
454 40 c. Type **149** 35 35
455 50 c. *Humming Bird II* crossing globe 40 40
MS456 109 × 84 mm. Nos. 454/5 (wmk upright) .. 3·25 4·00

150 "Sex Equality"

(Des Hetty J. Mejias de Grannes; adapted V. Whiteley. Litho Harrison)

1975 (23 June). *International Women's Year. W w* **14** *(sideways). P* 14.
457 **150** 15 c. multicoloured 10 10
458 30 c. multicoloured 25 25

151 Vampire Bat, Microscope and Syringe

(Des PAD Studio. Photo Harrison)

1975 (23 Sept). *Isolation of Rabies Virus. T* **151** *and similar horiz design. Multicoloured. W w* **14**. *P* 14 × 14½.
459 25 c. Type **151** 25 20
460 30 c. Dr. Pawan, instruments and book .. 30 25

152 Route-map and Tail of Boeing "707"

(Des C. Abbott. Litho Walsall)

1975 (27 Nov). *35th Anniv of British West Indian Airways. T* **152** *and similar horiz designs. W w* **14** *(sideways). P* 14.
461 20 c. Type **152** 25 15
462 30 c. "707" on ground 35 25
463 40 c. "707" in flight 45 45
MS464 119 × 110 mm. Nos. 461/3 .. .. 1·00 1·00

153 "From the Land of the Humming Bird"

(Des and photo Harrison)

1976 (12 Jan). *Carnival. 1974 Prizewinning Costumes. T* **153** *and similar horiz design. Multicoloured. W w* **14** *(sideways). P* 14.
465 30 c. Type **153** 15 10
466 $1 "The Little Carib" 60 70
MS467 83 × 108 mm. Nos. 465/6 .. .. .. 90 90

154 Angostura Building, Port-of-Spain

(Des Jennifer Toombs. Litho J.W.)

1976 (14 July). *150th Anniv. of Angostura Bitters. T* **154** *and similar horiz designs. Multicoloured. W w* **14** *(sideways). P* 13.
468 5 c. Type **154** 5 5
469 35 c. Medal, New Orleans 1885/6 .. .. 25 25
470 45 c. Medal, Sydney 1879 .. .. .. 40 40
471 50 c. Medal, Brussels 1897 .. .. .. 40 40
MS472 119 × 112 mm. Nos. 468/71. P 14 .. .. 1·25 1·40

REPUBLIC

1976 (2 Aug). *As No.* 344B *but W w* **14**.
473 10 c. multicoloured 40 20

1976 (4 Oct). *West Indian Victory in World Cricket Cup. As Nos. 559/60 of Barbados.*
474 35 c. Caribbean map 60 60
475 45 c. Prudential Cup 65 65
MS476 80 × 80 mm. Nos. 474/5 .. .. .. 1·75 1·75

155 "Columbus sailing through the Bocas" (Campins)

(Des J.W. Litho Questa)

1976 (1 Nov)–**78**. *Paintings, Hotels and Orchids. Horiz designs as T* **155**. *Multicoloured. W w* **14**. *P* 14.
479 5 c. Type **155** 5 5
480 6 c. Robinson Crusoe Hotel, Tobago (17.1.78) 5 5
482 10 c. "San Fernando Hill" (J. Cazabon) .. 5 5
483 12 c. *Paphinia cristata* (7.6.78) 20 5
484 15 c. Turtle Beach Hotel (17.1.78) 10 5
485 20 c. "East Indians in a Landscape" (J. Cazabon) 15 5
485 25 c. Mt Irvine Hotel (17.1.78) 15 5
487 30 c. *Caularthon bicornutum* (7.6.78) .. 30 10
488 35 c. "Los Gallos Point" (J. Cazabon) .. 25 25
489 40 c. *Miltassia* (7.6.78) 35 25
490 45 c. "Corbeaux Town" (J. Cazabon) .. 30 30
491 50 c. *Oncidium ampliatum* (7.6.78) 45 30
492 70 c. Beach facilities, Mt Irvine Hotel (17.1.78) 40 50
494 $2.50, *Oncidium papilio* (7.6.78) .. .. 1·50 1·50
495 $5 Trinidad Holiday Inn (17.1.78) .. .. 2·00 2·25
479/95 .. .. Set of 15 5·75 5·00
MS497 171 × 100 mm. Nos. 479, 482, 485, 488 and 490. Wmk sideways 55 65
MS498 171 × 88 mm. Nos. 480, 484, 486, 492 and 495. Wmk sideways (17.1.78) .. .. 2·75 3·25
MS499 170 × 90 mm. Nos. 483, 487, 489, 491 and 494. Wmk sideways (7.6.78) .. .. 2·50 2·75

156 Hasely Crawford and Olympic Gold Medal

(Des J.W. Litho D. L. R.)

1977 (4 Jan). *Hasely Crawford Commemoration. W w* **14** (*sideways*). *P* 12 × 12½.
501 **156** 25 c. multicoloured 25 20
MS502 93 × 70 mm. No. 501 .. .. .. 40 40

157 Lindbergh's Sikorsky "S-38", 1929

158 National Flag

(Des and litho J.W.)

1977 (4 Apr). *50th Anniv of Airmail Service. T* **157** *and similar horiz designs. Multicoloured. W w* **14** (*sideways*). *P* 13.
503 20 c. Type **157** 25 15
504 35 c. Arrival of Charles and Anne Lindbergh 35 20
505 45 c. Boeing "707", *c.* 1960 .. .. .. 45 30
506 50 c. Boeing "747", 1969 .. .. .. 1·10 1·40
MS507 130 × 100 mm. Nos. 503/6. P 14 .. .. 3·50 3·50

(Des and litho J.W.)

1977 (26 July). *Inauguration of the Republic. T* **158** *and similar vert designs. Multicoloured. W w* **14**. *P* 13.
508 20 c. Type **158** 10 10
509 35 c. Coat of Arms 20 20
510 45 c. Government House 30 30
MS511 125 × 84 mm. Nos. 508/10. P 14 .. .. 65 80

159 White Poinsettia

160 Miss Janelle (Penny) Commissiong with Trophy

(Des J.W. Litho Walsall)

1977 (11 Oct). *Christmas. T* **159** *and similar vert design. Multicoloured. W w* **14**. *P* 14 × 14½.
512 10 c. Type **159** 5 5
513 35 c. Type **159** 30 20
514 45 c. Red Poinsettia 40 35
515 50 c. As 45 c. 50 40
MS516 112 × 142 mm. Nos. 512/15 .. .. 1·00 1·10

(Des BG Studio. Litho Questa)

1978 (2 Aug). *Miss Janelle (Penny) Commissiong ("Miss Universe 1977") Commemoration. T* **160** *and similar vert designs showing Miss Commissiong. Multicoloured. W w* **14**. *P* 14½.
517 10 c. Type **160** 10 5
518 35 c. Portrait 20 20
519 45 c. In evening dress 25 30
MS520 186 × 120 mm. Nos. 517/19 .. .. 70 75
a. 45c. value imperf on three sides .. ..

161 Tayra

162 "Burst of Beauty"

(Des G. Drummond. Litho Walsall)

1978 (7 Nov). *Wildlife. T* **161** *and similar horiz designs. Multicoloured. W w* **14** (*sideways*). *P* 13½.
521 15 c. Type **161** 20 10
522 25 c. Ocelot 30 20
523 40 c. Porcupine 50 30
524 70 c. Yellow Tamandua 65 80
MS525 128 × 101 mm. Nos. 521/4 .. .. 1·50 1·60

(Des C. Abbott. Litho Format)

1979 (1 Feb). *Carnival* 1978. *T* **162** *and similar vert designs. P* 13½.
526 5 c. multicoloured 5 5
527 10 c. multicoloured 5 5
528 35 c. multicoloured 20 20
529 45 c. multicoloured 25 25
530 50 c. yellow-brown, rosine and deep lilac .. 25 25
531 $1 multicoloured 45 45
526/31 .. .. *Set of* 6 1·10 1·10
Designs:—10 c. Rain worshipper; 35 c. "Zodiac"; 45 c. Praying mantis; 50 c. "Eye of the Hurricane"; $1 Steel orchestra.

163 Day Care

164 Geothermal Exploration

(Des BG Studio. Litho J.W.)

1979 (5 June). *International Year of the Child. T* **163** *and similar vert designs. Multicoloured. P* 13.
532 5 c. Type **163** 5 5
533 10 c. School feeding programme 5 5
534 35 c. Dental care 20 20
535 45 c. Nursery school 25 25
536 50 c. Free bus transport 25 25
537 $1 Medical care 55 55
532/7 .. .. *Set of* 6 1·25 1·25
MS538 114 × 132 mm. Nos. 532/7. P 14 × 13½ .. 1·50 1·60

(Des local artist; adapted L. Curtis. Litho Format)

1979 (3 July). *4th Latin American Geological Congress. T* **164** *and similar horiz designs. Multicoloured. W w* **14** (*sideways*). *P* 13½.
539 10 c. Type **164** 10 5
540 35 c. Hydrogeology 35 20
541 45 c. Petroleum exploration 45 25
542 70 c. Environmental preservation 65 50
MS543 185 × 89 mm. Nos. 539/42 .. .. 1·50 1·60

165 1879 1d. rose and Map of Tobago

(Des J. Cooter. Litho Format)

1979 (1 Aug). *Tobago Stamp Centenary. T* **165** *and similar horiz designs in black, rose-lilac and dull orange* ($1) *or multicoloured* (*others*). *W w* **14** (*sideways*). *P* 13½ × 14.
544 10 c. Type **165** 5 5
545 15 c. 1879 3d. and 1880 ½d. surcharged on half of 6d. 10 5
546 35 c. 1879 6d. and 1886 ½d. surcharged on 6d. 25 25
547 45 c. 1879 1s. and 1886 ½d. surcharged on 2½d. 30 30
548 70 c. 1879 5s. and Great Britain 1856 1s. with "A14" (Scarborough, Tobago) postmark 45 45
549 $1 1879 £1 and General Post Office, Scarborough, Tobago 60 60
544/9 .. .. *Set of* 6 1·60 1·50
MS550 165 × 155 mm. Nos. 544/9 .. .. 1·60 1·60

166 1962 60 c. Independence Commemorative and Sir Rowland Hill

(Des and litho J.W.)

1979 (4 Oct). *Death Centenary of Sir Rowland Hill. T* **166** *and similar horiz designs showing stamps and Sir Rowland Hill. Multicoloured. W w* **14** (*sideways*). *P* 13.
551 25 c. Type **166** 15 12
552 45 c. 1977 35 c. Inauguration of Republic commemorative 25 25
553 $1 1879 Trinidad ½d. surcharge and Tobago 1880 4d. 50 50
MS554 115 × 125 mm. No. 551/3. P 13½ × 14 .. 1·00 1·00

167 Poui Tree in Churchyard

1844–
1980
POPULATION
CENSUS
12th MAY 1980

(**168**)

(Des G. Hutchins. Litho Format)

1980 (21 Jan). *Centenary of Princes Town. T* **167** *and similar horiz designs. Multicoloured. W w* **14** (*sideways*). *P* 14½ × 14.
555 5 c. Type **167** 5 5
556 10 c. Princes Town Court House 5 5
557 50 c. Locomotive of the Royal Train 45 45
558 $1.50, H.M.S. *Bacchante* .. .. .. 1·10 1·10
MS559 177 × 102 mm. Nos. 555/8 .. .. 1·60 1·75

1980 (8 Apr). *Population Census. Nos.* 479/80 *and* 482 *optd with T* **168**.
560 5 c. Type **155** 5 5
561 6 c. Robinson Crusoe Hotel, Tobago 5 5
562 10 c. "Old View" (Cazabon) 8 8

169 Scarlet Ibis (male)

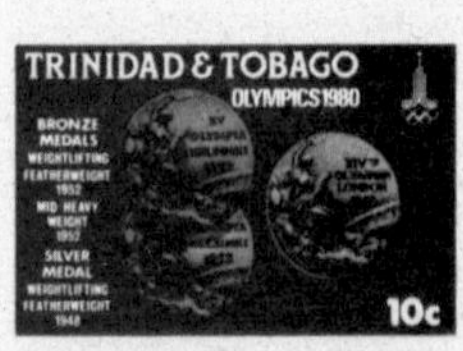

170 Silver and Bronze Medals for Weightlifting, 1948 and 1952

(Des G. Drummond. Litho Questa)

1980 (6 May). *Scarlet Ibis. T* **169** *and similar vert designs. Multicoloured. W w* **14**. *P* 14.
563 50 c. Type **169** 40 40
a. Strip of 5. Nos. 563/7 .. .. .. 1·75
564 50 c. Male and female 40 40
565 50 c. Hen and nest 40 40
566 50 c. Nest and eggs 40 40
567 50 c. Chick in nest 40 40
Nos. 563/7 were printed together, *se-tenant*, in horizontal and vertical strips of 5 throughout.

(Des G. Hutchins. Litho Walsall)

1980 (22 July). *Olympic Games, Moscow. T* **170** *and similar designs. W w* **14** (*sideways*). *P* 14.
568 10 c. multicoloured 5 5
569 15 c. multicoloured 10 5
570 70 c. multicoloured 45 50
MS571 110 × 149 mm. $2.50, black, silver and orange-vermilion (wmk upright) .. .. .. 1·00 1·10
Designs: *Horiz*—15 c. Hasely Crawford (100 metres sprint winner, 1976) and gold medal; 70 c. Silver medal for 400 metres and bronze medals for 4 × 400 metres relay, 1964. *Vert*—$2.50, Olympic Games emblems for Moscow, 1980, Olympia, 776 B.C. and Athens, 1896.

171 Charcoal Production

(Des J. Cooter. Litho Walsall)

1980 (8 Sept). *11th Commonwealth Forestry Conference. T* **171** *and similar horiz designs. Multicoloured. W w* **14** (*sideways*). *P* 14.
572 10 c. Type **171** 5 5
573 55 c. Logging 35 35
574 70 c. Teak plantation 40 45
575 $2.50, Watershed management .. .. 1·50 1·50
MS576 135 × 87 mm. Nos. 572/5 .. .. 2·50 2·75

172 Beryl McBurnie (dance and culture) and Audrey Jeffers (social worker)

(Des BG Studio. Litho Questa)

1980 (29 Sept). *Decade for Women. T* **172** *and similar horiz designs. Multicoloured. W w* **14** (*sideways*). *P* 14.
577 $1 Type **172** 55 65
578 $1 Elizabeth Bourne (judiciary) and Isabella Teshier (government) 55 65
579 $1 Dr. Stella Abidh (public health) and Louise Horne (nutrition) 55 65

173 Netball Stadium

(Des BG Studio. Litho Format)

1980 (21 Oct). *World Netball Tournament. W w* **14** (*sideways*). *P* 13½ × 14.
580 **173** 70 c. multicoloured 40 45

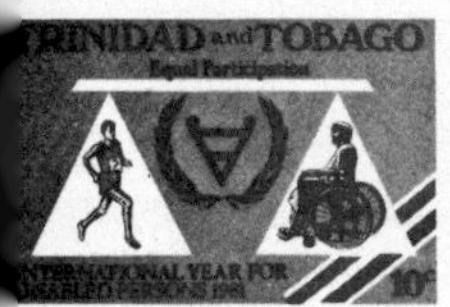

174 I.Y.D.P. Emblem, Athlete and Disabled Person
175 "Our Land Must Live"

(Des BG Studio. Litho Format)

1981 (23 Mar). *International Year for Disabled Persons. T* **174** *and similar horiz designs. W* w **14**. *P* 14½.
581 10 c. black, vermilion and dull yellowish green .. 12 15
582 70 c. black, vermilion and buff 85 90
583 $1.50, black, vermilion and cobalt .. .. 1·90 2·00
584 $2 black, vermilion and flesh .. .. 2·40 2·50

Designs:—70 c. I.Y.D.P. emblem and doctor with disabled person; $1.50, Emblem, and blind man and woman; $2 Emblem and inscription.

(Des Debbie Galt; adapted G. Vasarhelyi. Litho J.W.)

1981 (7 July). *Environmental Preservation. T* **175** *and similar horiz designs. Multicoloured. W* w **14** (*sideways*). *P* 13 × 13½.
585 10 c. Type **175** 10 5
586 55 c. "Our seas must live" 35 35
587 $3 "Our skies must live" .. .. .. 1·75 1·90
MS588 142 × 89 mm. Nos. 585/7 .. .. .. 2·10 2·25

176 "Food or Famine"
177 "First Aid Skills"

(Des and litho Harrison)

1981 (16 Oct). *World Food Day. T* **176** *and similar horiz designs. Multicoloured. W* w **14** (*sideways*). *P* 14½ × 14.
589 10 c. Type **176** 5 5
590 15 c. "Produce more" (threshing and milling rice) 5 5
591 45 c. "Fish for food" (Bigeye) 30 30
592 55 c. "Prevent hunger" 35 35
593 $1.50, "Fight malnutrition" 85 90
594 $2 "Fish for food" (Smallmouth Grunt) .. 1·10 1·25
589/94 .. .. *Set of* 6 2·40 2·50
MS595 164 × 98 mm. Nos. 589/94 .. .. 2·40 2·50

(Des L. Curtis. Litho Format)

1981 (17 Nov). *President's Award Scheme. T* **177** *and similar vert designs. Multicoloured. W* w **14**. *P* 14.
596 10 c. Type **177** 5 5
597 70 c. "Motor mechanics" 40 45
598 $1 "Expedition" 55 55
599 $2 Presenting an award .. .. 1·10 1·25

178 Pharmacist at Work
179 "Production"

(Des C. Abbott. Litho Questa)

1982 (12 Feb). *Commonwealth Pharmaceutical Conference. T* **178** *and similar vert designs. W* w **14**. *P* 14½ × 14.
600 10 c. Type **178** 5 5
601 $1 Gerritoute (plant) 55 55
602 $2 Rachette (plant) .. .. 1·10 1·10

(Des Debbie Galt; adapted G. Vasarhelyi. Litho Questa)

1982 (28 June). *75th Anniv of Boy Scout Movement. T* **179** *and similar vert designs. Multicoloured. W* w **14**. *P* 14.
603 15 c. Type **179** 10 5
604 55 c. "Tolerance" 35 35
605 $5 "Discipline" .. .. 2·75 2·75

180 Charlotteville
181 "Pa Pa Bois"

(Des Harrison. Litho Format)

1982 (18 Oct). *25th Anniv of Tourist Board. T* **180** *and similar vert designs. Multicoloured. W* w **14**. *P* 13½ × 14.
606 55 c. Type **180** 35 35
607 $1 Boating 55 55
608 $3 Fort George .. .. 1·75 1·90

(Des D. Louison. Litho Harrison)

1982 (8 Nov). *Folklore. Local Spirits and Demons. T* **181** *and similar horiz designs. Multicoloured. W* w **14** (*sideways*). *P* 14.
609 10 c. Type **181** 5 8
610 15 c. "La Diablesse" 8 10
611 65 c. "Lugarhoo", "Phantom" and "Soucouyant" 35 40
612 $5 "Bois de Soleil", "Davens" and "Mamma de l'Eau" .. .. 2·75 2·90
MS613 133 × 100 mm. Nos. 609/12 .. .. 3·25 3·50

182 Cane Harvesting

((Des W. Fenton. Litho Harrison)

1982 (13 Dec). *Canefarmers' Association Centenary. T* **182** *and similar horiz designs. Multicoloured. W* w **14** (*sideways*). *P* 14.
614 30 c. Type **182** 15 20
615 70 c. Farmers loading bullock cart 40 45
616 $1.50, Cane field in bloom 85 90
MS617 72 × 117 mm. Nos. 614/16. P 14½. .. 1·40 1·50

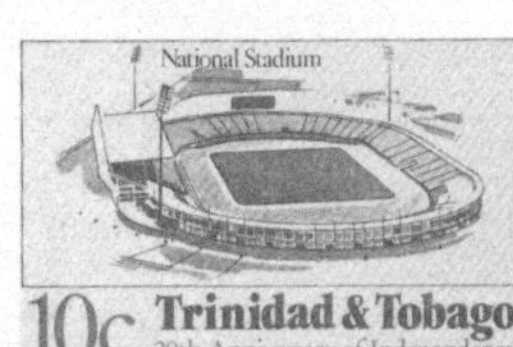

183 National Stadium

(Des McCombie Skinner. Litho Harrison)

1982 (28 Dec). *20th Anniv of Independence. T* **183** *and similar horiz designs. Multicoloured. W* w **14** (*sideways*). *P* 13 × 14.
618 10 c. Type **183** 5 8
619 35 c. Caroni water treatment plant 20 25
620 50 c. Mount Hope Maternity Hospital 30 35
621 $2 National Insurance Board Mall, Tobago 1·10 1·25

184 Commonwealth Flags

(Des C. Abbott. Litho Harrison)

1983 (14 Mar). *Commonwealth Day. T* **184** *and similar multicoloured designs. W* w **14** (*sideways on* 10, 55 *c*.). *P* 14.
622 10 c. Type **184** 5 8
623 55 c. Satellite view of Trinidad and Tobago .. 30 35
624 $1 "Nodding donkey" oil pump (*vert*) .. 55 60
625 $2 Map of Trinidad and Tobago (*vert*) .. 1·10 1·25

185 BW1A "Tristar"

(Des D. Miller. Litho Format)

1983 (11 July). *10th Anniv of CARICOM. W* w **14** (*sideways*). *P* 14.
626 **185** 35 c. multicoloured 20 25

186 V.D.U. Operator

(Des G. Vasarhelyi. Litho Harrison)

1983 (5 Aug). *World Communications Year. T* **186** *and similar horiz designs. Multicoloured. W* w **14** (*sideways*). *P* 14.
627 15 c. Type **186** 8 10
628 55 c. Scarborough Post Office, Tobago 30 35
629 $1 Textel building 55 60
630 $3 Morne Blue E.C.M.S. station .. .. 1·75 1·90

187 Financial Complex

(Des D. Miller. Litho Format)

1983 (19 Sept). *Conference of Commonwealth Finance Ministers. W* w **14** (*sideways*). *P* 14.
631 **187** $2 multicoloured .. .. .. 1·10 1·25

188 Kingfish
189 Bois Pois

(Des N. Weaver. Litho Format)

1983 (17 Oct). *World Food Day. T* **188** *and similar horiz designs. Multicoloured. W* w **14** (*sideways*). *P* 14 × 13½ (10 *c*., 55 *c* .) *or* 13½ (*others*).
632 10 c. Type **188** 5 8
633 55 c. Flying Fish 30 35
634 70 c. Queen Conch 40 45
635 $4 Red Shrimp .. .. 2·25 2·40

(Des I. Loe. Litho Questa)

1983 (14 Dec)–**84**. *Flowers. T* **189** *and similar multicoloured designs. W* w **14** (*sideways on* 5 *c. to* $1.50). *P* 14. A. *Without imprint date*. B. *With imprint date* ("1984") (10.84).

		A		B	
636	5 c. Type **189**	5	5	5	5
637	10 c. Maraval Lily	5	8	5	8
638	15 c. Star Grass	10	12	10	12
639	20 c. Bois Caco	12	15	†	
640	25 c. Strangling Fig	15	20	15	20
641	30 c. *Cassia moschata*	20	25	†	
642	50 c. Chalice Flower	30	35	†	
643	65 c. Black Stick	40	45	†	
644	80 c. *Columnea scandens* ..	50	55	†	
645	95 c. Cat's Claw	65	70	†	
646	$1 Bois L'agli	65	70	†	
647	$1.50, *Eustoma exaltatum* ..	95	1·00		
648	$2 Chaconia	1·25	1·40	†	
649	$2.50, *Chrysothemis pulchella*	1·50	1·60	†	
650	$5 *Centratherum punctatum* ..	3·25	3·50	†	
651	$10 Savanna Flower	6·50	7·00	†	
636/51	.. .. *Set of* 16	15·50	16·00	†	

Nos. 648/51 are horizontal, 39 × 29 mm.

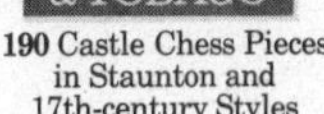

190 Castle Chess Pieces in Staunton and 17th-century Styles
191 Swimming

(Des L. Curtis. Litho Questa)

1984 (14 Sept). *60th Anniv of World Chess Federation. T* **190** *and similar vert designs. Multicoloured. W* w **14**. *P* 14.
652 50 c. Type **190** 30 35
653 70 c. Staunton and 12th-century Bishops .. 45 50
654 $1.50, Staunton and 13th-century Queens .. 95 1·00
655 $2 Staunton and 19th-century Kings .. 1·25 1·40

(Des Garden Studio. Litho Harrison)

1984 (21 Sept). *Olympic Games, Los Angeles. T* **191** *and similar vert designs. Multicoloured. W* w **14**. *P* 14 × 14½.
656 15 c. Type **191** 10 12
657 55 c. Track and field events 40 45
658 $1.50, Sailing .. .. 1·10 1·25
659 $4 Cycling .. .. 3·00 3·25
MS660 132 × 85 mm. Nos. 656/9 .. .. .. 5·00 5·50

192 Slave Ship and Shackles
193 Children's Band

(Des O. Bell. Litho Walsall)

1984 (22 Oct). *150th Anniv of Abolition of Slavery. T* **192** *and similar vert designs. Multicoloured. W w* **14**. *P* 13½ × 13.

No.	Description	Unused	Used
661	35 c. Type **192**	25	30
662	55 c. Slave and "Slave Triangle" map	40	45
663	$1 *Capitalism and Slavery* (book by Dr. Eric Williams)	70	75
664	$2 Toussaint l'Ouverture (Haitian revolutionary)	1·75	1·90
MS665	95 × 100 mm. Nos. 661/4	3·00	3·25

(Des G. Vasarhelyi. Litho J.W.)

1984 (13 Nov). *125th Anniv of St. Mary's Children's Home. T* **193** *and similar horiz designs. Multicoloured. W w* **14** *(sideways). P* 13½.

No.	Description	Unused	Used
666	10 c. Type **193**	8	10
667	70 c. St. Mary's Children's Home	50	55
668	$3 Group of children	2·25	2·40

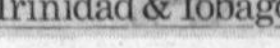

194 Parang Band

(Des D. Miller. Litho Questa)

1984 (26 Nov). *Parang Festival. T* **194** *and similar horiz designs. Multicoloured. W w* **14** *(sideways). P* 14 × 14½.

No.	Description	Unused	Used
669	10 c. Type **194**	8	10
670	30 c. Music and poinsettia	20	25
671	$1 Bandola, bandolin and cuatro (musical instruments)	70	75
672	$3 Double bass, fiddle and guitar (musical instruments)	2·25	2·40

POSTAGE DUE STAMPS

D 1

D 2

(Typo D.L.R.)

1885 (1 Jan). *Wmk Crown CA. P* 14.

No.	Type	Description	Unused	Used
D1	D 1	½d. slate-black	20·00	14·00
D2		1d. slate-black	90	30
D3		2d. slate-black	6·00	35
D4		3d. slate-black	11·00	85
D5		4d. slate-black	11·00	5·00
D6		5d. slate-black	11·00	1·50
D7		6d. slate-black	17·00	7·00
D8		8d. slate-black	18·00	7·00
D9		1s. slate-black	21·00	16·00
D1/9		*Set of* 9	£100	48·00

1905–6. *Wmk Mult Crown CA. P* 14.

No.	Type	Description	Unused	Used
D10	D 1	1d. slate-black	45	25
D11		2d. slate-black	1·25	30
D12		3d. slate-black	1·50	75
D13		4d. slate-black	3·50	4·00
D14		5d. slate-black	4·00	4·75
D15		6d. slate-black	7·50	8·00
D16		8d. slate-black	9·00	13·00
D17		1s. slate-black	14·00	18·00
D10/17		*Set of* 8	38·00	45·00

1923–45. *Wmk Mult Script CA. P* 14.

No.	Type	Description	Unused	Used
D18	D 1	1d. black (1923)	35	70
D19		2d. black (1923)	35	60
D20		3d. black (1925)	40	75
D21		4d. black (1929)	1·75	3·50
D22		5d. black (1944)	10·00	8·00
D23		6d. black (1945)	13·00	8·50
D24		8d. black (1945)	17·00	17·00
D25		1s. black (1945)	32·00	32·00
D18/25		*Set of* 8	65·00	65·00
D18/25 Optd/Perf "Specimen"		*Set of* 8	£140	

1947 (1 Sept)–**61.** *Value in cents. Wmk Mult Script CA. P* 14.

No.	Type	Description	Unused	Used
D26	D 1	2 c. black, O	90	2·50
		aa. Chalky paper (20.1.53)	20	85
		a. Error. Crown missing. W **9***a*, C	35·00	
		b. Error. St. Edward's Crown. W **9***b*, C	18·00	
D27		4 c. black, O	1·25	3·50
		a. Chalky paper (10.8.55)	45	1·00
D28		6 c. black, O	1·25	3·75
		aa. Chalky paper (20.1.53)	45	1·50
		a. Error. Crown missing. W **9***a*, C	45·00	
		b. Error. St. Edward's Crown. W **9***b*, C	26·00	
D29		8 c. black, O	1·25	5·00
		a. Chalky paper (10.9.58)	45	1·50
D30		10 c. black, O	1·25	3·50
		a. Chalky paper (10.8.55)	75	1·00
D31		12 c. black, O	1·25	5·00
		aa. Chalky paper (20.1.53)	75	2·25
		a. Error. Crown missing. W **9***a*, C	55·00	
		b. Error. St. Edward's Crown, W **9***b*, C	35·00	
D32		16 c. black, O	2·75	8·00
		a. Chalky paper (22.8.61)	1·25	3·00
D33		24 c. black, O	4·50	8·00
		a. Chalky paper (10.8.55)	2·00	4·50
D26/33a		*Set of* 8	5·75	14·00
D26/33 Perf "Specimen"		*Set of* 8	£140	

(Litho B.W.)

1969 (25 Nov)–**70.** *Size* 19 × 24 *mm. P* 14 × 13½.

No.	Type	Description	Unused	Used
D34	D 2	2 c. pale blue-green	10	35
D35		4 c. magenta (1970)	25	60
D36		6 c. brown (1970)	45	95
D37		8 c. slate-lilac (1970)	50	1·25
D38		10 c. dull red (1970)	50	1·25
D39		12 c. pale orange (1970)	70	1·40
D40		16 c. bright apple-green (1970)	8	10
D41		24 c. grey (1970)	12	15
D42		50 c. grey-blue (1970)	25	30
D43		60 c. sage-green (1970)	30	35
D34/43		*Set of* 10	3·00	6·00

(Litho Questa)

1976 (3 May)*–**77.** *Redrawn in smaller size* (17 × 21 *mm*). *P* 13½ × 14.

No.	Type	Description	Unused	Used
D44	D 2	2 c. pale blue-green (31.3.77)	5	5
D45		4 c. light claret	5	5
D46		6 c. brown (31.3.77)	5	5
D47		8 c. bright lilac (31.3.77)	5	5
D48		10 c. dull red (31.3.77)	5	5
D49		12 c. pale orange	5	5
D44/9		*Set of* 6	12	15

*The date for the 4 and 12 c. is the local date; the Crown Agents released the stamps on 19 March.

"TOO LATE" STAMPS

A handstamp with the words "TOO LATE" was used upon letters on which a too-late fee had been paid, and was sometimes used for cancelling the stamps on such letters.

OFFICIAL STAMPS

O S (O 1) OFFICIAL (O 2) OFFICIAL (O 3)

1894. *Optd with Type* O **1** (*a*) *Wmk Crown CA. P* 14.

No.	Type	Description	Unused	Used
O1	**10**	½d. dull green	24·00	24·00
O2		1d. carmine	30·00	30·00
O3		2½d. ultramarine	30·00	30·00
O4		4d. grey	32·00	32·00
O5		6d. olive-black	32·00	32·00
O6		1s. orange-brown	45·00	45·00
		(*b*) *Wmk Crown CC. P* 12½.		
O7	**5**	5s. rose-lake	80·00	£100

1909. *Optd with Type* O **2**. *Wmk Mult Crown CA. P* 14.

No.	Type	Description	Unused	Used
O8	**11**	½d. green, O	25	35
O9		1d. rose-red, O	20	30
		a. Opt double	—	£200
		b. Opt vertical	27·00	
		c. Opt inverted	—	£150

1910. *Optd with Type* O **2**. *Wmk Crown CA. P* 14.

No.	Type	Description	Unused	Used
O10	**14**	½d. green, O	15	20

1913. *Optd with Type* O **3**.

No.	Type	Description	Unused	Used
O11	**17**	½d. green, O	15	15
		a. Overprint vertical		

OFFICIAL (O 4) OFFICIAL (O 5) **OFFICIAL** (O 6)

1914. *Optd with Type* O **4**.

No.	Type	Description	Unused	Used
O12	**17**	½d. green, O	70	90

1914–17. *Optd with Type* O **5** (*without stop*).

No.	Type	Description	Unused	Used
O13	**17**	½d. green	35	45
		a. Blue-green (*thick paper*) (1917)	35	45

1916. *Optd with Type* O **5** (*with stop*).

No.	Type	Description	Unused	Used
O14	**17**	½d. yellow-green, O	25	25
		a. Overprint double	12·00	

1917 (22 Aug). *Optd with Type* O **6**.

No.	Type	Description	Unused	Used
O15	**17**	½d. green, O	25	35
		a. Yellow-green	35	65
		b. Blue-green (*thick paper*)	20	35

Tristan Da Cunha

Although first settled in 1817 no surviving mail is known from Tristan da Cunha until two whaler's letters written in 1836 and 1843, these being carried home in other whaling ships. Then there is a long gap until the late 1800's when other letters are known—surprisingly only some seven in number, up to 1908 when the first of the island cachet handstamps came into use.

The collecting of postal history material from 1908 to 1952, when Tristan's first stamps were issued, revolves around the numerous cachets of origin which were struck on mail from the island during these 44 years. The handstamps producing these cachets were supplied over the years by various people particularly interested in the island and the islanders, and were mostly used by the clergymen who volunteered to go and serve as the community's ministers.

The postal cachets are illustrated below. The use of the different cachets on mail frequently overlapped, at one period in 1930 there were five different types of handstamp in use. As there was no official source for providing them they appeared on the island from various donors; then disappeared without trace once they became worn out. Only one of these early rubber handstamps has apparently survived, Cachet Va.

Covers bearing the cachets are recognised collector's items, but are difficult to value in general terms. As elsewhere the value is discounted by poor condition of the cover, and may be increased by use on a scarce date or with additional postal markings.

Cachet Types V and VII on cover are the commonest, Type Va, used only for three months, and Type IVa are the scarcest, equalling the scarcest use of Type I examples. All cacheted covers, particularly if non-philatelic, are desirable forerunner items. Even a philatelic cover of Type V is, at present, worth in the region of £35.

Dates given are of the first recorded use.

Cachet I

Cachet II

Cat. No.	Date	Cachet	*Value on cover*
C1	**1908** (19 Dec).	Cachet I	*from* £1800
C2	**1919** (31 July).	Cachet II	*from* £350

Cachet III

C3	**1921** (8 Feb).	Cachet III	*from* £100

Cachet IVa

C4	**1928** (25 Feb).	Cachet IV (*as* IVa, *but without centre label*)	*from* £800
C5	**1928** (28 Oct).	Cachet IVa	*from* £5500

Cachet V

Cachet VI

C6	**1929** (24 Feb).	Cachet V	*from* 35·00
C7	**1929** (15 May).	Cachet Va (*as* V, *but without break in inner ring. Shows* "T" "C" *and* "N" *damaged*)	*from* £6500
C8	**1936** (Aug).	Cachet VI	*from* 50·00

Cachet VII

C9 **1936** (1 Feb). Cachet VII . . . . . . *from* 20·00

During World War II there was little mail from the island as its function as a meteorological station was cloaked by security. Such covers as are known are generally struck with the "tombstone" naval censor mark and postmarked "maritime mail" or have South African postal markings. A few philatelic items from early in the war bearing cachets exist, but this usage was soon stopped by the military commander and the handstamps were put away until peace returned. Covers from the period would be worth from £50 to, at least, £170.

Cachet VIII

C10 **1946** (8 May). Cachet VIII . . . . . . *from* 45·00

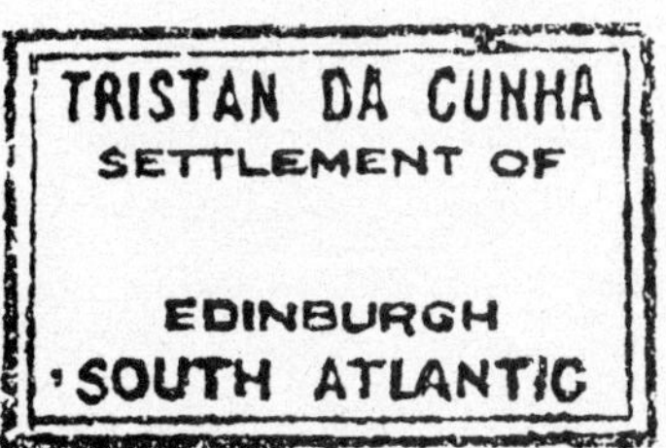

Cachet IX

C11 **1948** (29 Feb). Cachet IX . . . . . . *from* 40·00

Cachet X

C12 **1950** (Mar). Cachet X . . . . . . *from* 30·00

Cachet XI

Cachet XII

RESETTLEMENT
SURVEY - 1962

Cachet XIII

Cachets XI to XIII from the 1961/63 "volcano eruption" and "return to the island" period vary in value from £30 to £120, due to philatelic usage on the one hand and scarce mailings from the small survey parties on shore during this period on the other.

The large format 350 page handbook—*The History and Postal History of Tristan da Cunha* by George Crabb, who provided the brief notes above, can be obtained from Stanley Gibbons Ltd, 399 Strand, London, price £16, plus £1 postage.

TRISTAN
DA CUNHA
(1)

1952 (1 Jan). *Stamps of St. Helena, optd with T* 1.

No.	Type	Description	Unused	Used
1	33	½d. violet	50	75
2		1d. black and green	50	1·00
3		1½d. black and carmine	50	1·50
4		2d. black and scarlet	50	1·75
5		3d. grey	80	2·00
6		4d. ultramarine	1·25	2·50
7		6d. light blue	2·50	3·00
8		8d. sage-green	3·00	5·50
9		1s. sepia	3·00	7·50
10		2s. 6d. maroon	22·00	25·00
11		5s. chocolate	30·00	48·00
12		10s. purple	75·00	90·00
1/12		*Set of* 12	£120	£170

1953 (2 June). *Coronation. As No. 47 of Aden.*

No.	Description	Unused	Used
13	3d. black and grey-green	2·00	3·50

2 Tristan Crawfish   3 Carting Flax for Thatching

(Recess D.L.R.)

1954 (2 Jan). *T 2/3 and similar designs. Wmk Mult Script CA. P* 12½ × 13 (*horiz*) *or* 13 × 12½ (*vert*).

No.	Description	Unused	Used
14	½d. red and deep brown	20	20
15	1d. sepia and bluish green	20	15
16	1½d. black and reddish purple	75	40
17	2d. grey-violet and brown-orange	60	40
18	2½d. black and carmine-red	1·50	60
19	3d. ultramarine and olive-green	1·00	45
20	4d. turquoise-blue and deep blue	1·25	50
21	5d. emerald and black	1·25	50
22	6d. deep green and violet	1·25	55
23	9d. reddish violet and Venetian red	1·25	75
24	1s. deep yellow-green and sepia	1·40	80
25	2s. 6d. deep brown and light blue	22·00	14·00
26	5s. black and red-orange	42·00	35·00
27	10s. brown-orange and purple	48·00	45·00
14/27	*Set of* 14	£110	90·00

Designs: *Vert*—1½d. Rockhopper Penguin; 3d. Island boat. *Horiz*—2d. Big Beach factory; 2½d. Yellow-nosed Albatross; 4d. Tristan from the south-west; 5d. Girls on donkeys; 6d. Inaccessible Island from Tristan; 9d. Nightingale Island; 1s. St. Mary's Church; 2s. 6d. Elephant Seal at Gough Island; 5s. Inaccessible Island Rail; 10s. Island spinning wheel.

16 Starfish

17 Concha Fish

(Des Mr. and Mrs. G. F. Harris. Recess Waterlow)

1960 (1 Feb). *Marine Life. Vert designs as T* **16/17**. *W w* **12**. *P* 13.

No.	Description	Unused	Used
28	½d. black and orange	25	30
29	1d. black and bright purple	30	20
30	1½d. black and light turquoise-blue	40	20
31	2d. black and bluish green	50	20
32	2½d. black and sepia	60	20
33	3d. black and brown-red	60	20
34	4d. black and yellow-olive	75	25
35	5d. black and orange-yellow	85	30
36	6d. black and blue	1·00	40
37	9d. black and rose-carmine	1·50	65
38	1s. black and light brown	1·75	70
39	2s. 6d. black and ultramarine	15·00	16·00
40	5s. black and light emerald	32·00	32·00
41	10s. black and violet	48·00	50·00
28/41	*Set of* 14	95·00	95·00

Designs:—1½d. Klip Fish; 2d. Heron Fish; 2½d. Swordfish; 3d. Tristan Crawfish; 4d. Soldier Fish; 5d. "Five Finger" Fish; 6d. Mackerel; 9d. Stumpnose Fish; 1s. Blue Fish; 2s. 6d. Snoek; 5s. Shark; 10s. Atlantic Right Whale.

1961 (15 Apr). *As Nos. 28/30 and 32/41 but values in South African decimal currency.*

No.	Description	Unused	Used
42	½ c. black and orange (as ½d.)	10	12
43	1 c. black and bright purple (as 1d.)	15	15
44	1½ c. black and light turquoise-blue (as 1½d.)	35	25
45	2 c. black and sepia (as 2½d.)	40	30
46	2½ c. black and brown-red (as 3d.)	50	30
47	3 c. black and yellow-olive (as 4d.)	65	30
48	4 c. black and orange-yellow (as 5d.)	80	40
49	5 c. black and blue (as 6d)	85	45
50	7½ c. black and rose-carmine (as 9d.)	1·25	75
51	10 c. black and light brown (as 1s.)	1·50	80
52	25 c. black and ultramarine (as 2s. 6d.)	12·00	15·00
53	50 c. black and light emerald (as 5s.)	32·00	35·00
54	1 r. black and violet (as 10s.)	48·00	60·00
42/54	*Set of* 13	90·00	£100

Following a volcanic eruption the island was evacuated on 10 October 1961, but resettled in 1963.

TRISTAN DA CUNHA
RESETTLEMENT
1963
(30)

1963 (12 Apr). *Tristan Resettlement. As Nos. 176/88 of St. Helena, but Wmk Mult Script CA (sideways on 1d., 2d., 7d., 10d., 2s. 6d., 10s), optd with T* **30**.

No.	Description	Unused	Used
55	1d. bright blue, dull violet, yellow & carmine	12	8
56	1½d. yellow, green, black and light drab	20	12
57	2d. scarlet and grey	25	12
58	3d. light blue, black, pink and deep blue	30	15
59	4½d. yellow-green, green, brown and grey	50	25
60	6d. red, sepia and light yellow-olive	55	20
61	7d. red-brown, black and violet	60	20
62	10d. brown-purple and light blue	70	25
63	1s. greenish yellow, bluish green & brown	75	20
64	1s. 6d. grey, black and slate-blue	1·50	70
65	2s. 6d. red, pale yellow and turquoise	2·75	1·25
66	5s. yellow, brown and green	7·00	3·25
67	10s. orange-red, black and blue	16·00	8·00
55/67	*Set of* 13	28·00	14·00

1963 (1 Oct). *Freedom from Hunger. As No. 76 of Aden.*

No.	Description	Unused	Used
68	1s. 6d. carmine	3·50	1·25

1964 (1 Feb). *Red Cross Centenary. As Nos. 147/8 of Antigua.*

No.	Description	Unused	Used
69	3d. red and black	1·25	50
70	1s. 6d. red and blue	2·75	1·50

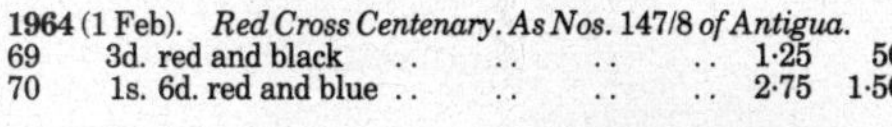

31 South Atlantic Map

32 Queen Elizabeth II

(Queen's portrait by Anthony Buckley. Des, eng and recess B.W.)

1963 (17 Feb)–**67**. *Designs as T* **31/2**. *W w* **12** (*sideways on* £1). *P* 11½ × 11 (*vert*) *or* 11 × 11½ (*horiz*).

No.	Description	Unused	Used
71	½d. black and ultramarine	20	20
72	1d. black and emerald-green	25	15
73	1½d. black and blue	25	15
74	2d. black and purple	25	20
75	3d. black and turquoise-blue	35	25
75*a*	4d. black and orange (1.9.67)	2·50	2·25
76	4½d. black and brown	70	50
77	6d. black and green	70	40
78	7d. black and rose-red	60	45
79	10d. black and chocolate	65	50
80	1s. black and carmine	65	45
81	1s. 6d. black and yellow-olive	2·75	1·25
82	2s. 6d. black and orange-brown	4·00	1·75
83	5s. black and violet	9·50	4·50
84	10s. deep blue and carmine	9·00	6·50
84*a*	10s. black and deep turquoise-blue (1.9.67)	32·00	18·00
84*b*	£1 deep blue and orange-brown (1.9.67)	32·00	16·00
71/84*b*	*Set of* 17	85·00	48·00

Designs: *Horiz as T* **31**—1d. Flagship of Tristão da Cunha; 1½d. *Heemstede*; 2d. New England whaler; 3d. *Shenandoah*; 4d. H.M.S. *Challenger*; 4½d. H.M.S. *Galatea*; 6d. H.M.S. *Cilicia*; 7d. H.M. Yacht *Britannia*; 10d. H.M.S. *Leopard*; 1s. M.V. *Tjisadane*; 1s. 6d. M.V. *Tristania*; 2s. 6d. M.V. *Boissevain*; 5s. M.S. *Bornholm*; 10s. (No. 84*a*), Research Vessel *R.S.A*. *Vert*—10s. (No. 84), £1, Type **32**.

1965 (11 May*). *I.T.U. Centenary. As Nos. 166/7 of Antigua.*

No.	Description	Unused	Used
85	3d. orange-red and grey	1·75	75
86	6d. reddish violet and yellow-orange	2·00	1·00

*This is the local date of issue; the stamps were not released in London until 17 May.

1965 (25 Oct). *International Co-operation Year. As Nos. 168/9 of Antigua.*

No.	Description	Unused	Used
87	1d. reddish purple and turquoise-green	80	35
88	6d. deep bluish green and lavender	3·50	1·50

1966 (24 Jan). *Churchill Commemoration. As Nos. 170/3 of Antigua.*

No.	Description	Unused	Used
89	1d. new blue	90	30
90	3d. deep green	3·50	1·25
91	6d. brown	5·00	2·25
92	1s. 6d. bluish violet	6·00	3·75

NEW INFORMATION

The editor is always interested to correspond with people who have new information that will improve or correct the Catalogue.

45 Ship at Tristan and Soldier of 1816

(Des V. Whiteley. Litho Harrison)

1966 (15 Aug). *150th Anniv of Tristan Garrison. W* w **12** *(sideways). P* 14½.
93 **45** 3d. multicoloured 45 15
94 6d. multicoloured 65 25
95 1s. 6d. multicoloured .. .. 1·00 50
96 2s. 6d. multicoloured .. .. 1·10 65

1966 (1 Oct*). *World Cup Football Championships. As Nos.* 176/7 *of Antigua.*
97 3d. violet, yellow-grn, lake & yell-brn .. 75 30
98 2s. 6d. chocolate, blue-grn, lake & yellow-brn 3·00 1·25
*Released in St. Helena on 1 July in error.

1966 (1 Oct). *Inauguration of W.H.O. Headquarters, Geneva. As Nos.* 178/9 *of Antigua.*
99 6d. black, yellow-green and light blue .. 3·25 1·50
100 5s. black, light purple and yellow-brown .. 3·75 1·75

1966 (1 Dec). *20th Anniv of U.N.E.S.C.O. As Nos.* 196/8 *of Antigua.*
101 10d. slate-violet, red, yellow and orange .. 1·75 45
102 1s. 6d. orange-yellow, violet and deep olive 2·00 60
103 2s. 6d. black, bright purple and orange .. 2·75 1·50

46 Calshot Harbour

(Des V. Whiteley. Litho D.L.R.)

1967 (2 Jan). *Opening of Calshot Harbour. P* 14 × 14½.
104 **46** 6d. multicoloured 20 15
105 10d. multicoloured 20 15
106 1s. 6d. multicoloured 25 15
107 2s. 6d. multicoloured 30 20

(47)

48 Prince Alfred, First Duke of Edinburgh

1967 (10 May). *No.* 76 *surch with T* **47**.
108 4d. on 4½d. black and brown 10 15

(Des M. Goaman. Litho Harrison)

1967 (10 July). *Centenary of First Duke of Edinburgh's Visit to Tristan. W* w **12**. *P* 14½.
109 **48** 3d. multicoloured 20 10
110 6d. multicoloured 20 10
111 1s. 6d. multicoloured 25 15
112 2s. 6d. multicoloured 30 20

49 Wandering Albatross

(Des V. Whiteley. Photo Harrison)

1968 (15 May). *Birds. T* **49** *and similar horiz designs. Multicoloured. W* w **12**. *P* 14 × 14½.
113 4d. Type **49** 80 30
114 1s. Wilkin's Finch 85 35
115 1s. 6d. Tristan Thrush 90 40
116 2s. 6d. Greater Shearwater .. .. 1·90 75

53 Union Jack and Dependency Flag

(Des Jennifer Toombs. Litho D.L.R.)

1968 (1 Nov). *30th Anniv of Tristan da Cunha as a Dependency of St. Helena. T* **53** *and similar horiz design. W* w **12** *(sideways). P* 14.
117 **53** 6d. multicoloured 45 40
118 – 9d. sepia, blue and turquoise-blue .. 45 40
119 **53** 1s. 6d. multicoloured 50 45
120 – 2s. 6d. carmine, blue and turquoise-blue 55 50
Design:—9d., 2s. 6d. St. Helena and Tristan on chart.

55 Frigate

(Des and recess B.W.)

1969 (1 June). *Clipper Ships. T* **55** *and similar horiz designs. W* w **12**. *P* 11 × 11½.
121 4d. new blue .. .. 1·00 45
122 1s. carmine (Cape Horner) .. .. .. 1·00 70
123 1s. 6d. blue-green (Barque) .. .. .. 1·25 90
124 2s. 6d. chocolate (Tea Clipper) .. .. 1·25 1·00

59 Sailing Ship off Tristan da Cunha

(Des Jennifer Toombs. Litho Format)

1969 (1 Nov). *United Society for the Propagation of the Gospel. T* **59** *and similar horiz designs. Multicoloured. W* w **12** *(sideways). P* 14½ × 14.
125 4d. Type **59** 60 50
126 9d. Islanders going to first Gospel service .. 60 55
127 1s. 6d. Landing of the first minister .. 65 60
128 2s. 6d. Procession outside St. Mary's Church 70 65

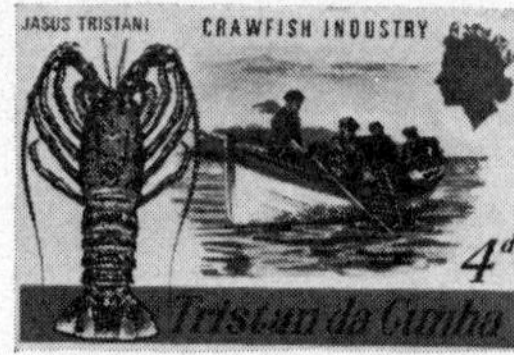

63 Globe and Red Cross Emblem

(Des and litho B.W.)

1970 (1 June). *Centenary of British Red Cross. T* **63** *and similar designs. W* w **12** *(sideways on vert designs). P* 13.
129 **63** 4d. lt emerald, scarlet & dp bluish green 55 45
130 9d. bistre, scarlet and deep bluish green 80 65
131 – 1s. 9d. light drab, scarlet & ultramarine 1·00 80
132 – 2s. 6d. reddish purple, scarlet & ultram 1·10 1·10
Design: *Vert*—1s. 9d., 2s. 6d., Union Jack and Red Cross Flag.

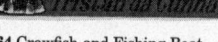

64 Crawfish and Fishing Boat

(65)

(Des Harrison. Litho Enschedé)

1970 (1 Nov). *Crawfish Industry. T* **64** *and similar horiz design. Multicoloured. W* w **12**. *P* 12½ × 13.
133 4d. Type **64** .. .. 1·00 70
134 10d. Packing and storing Crawfish .. .. 1·25 80
135 1s. 6d. Type **64** .. .. 1·50 1·00
136 2s. 6d. As 10d. .. .. 1·75 1·50

1971 (14 Feb).* *Decimal Currency. As Nos.* 71/84*a surch as T* **65**, *by B. W. in typo. Glazed paper.*
137 ½p. on 1d. black and emerald-green .. 20 20
138 1p. on 2d. black and purple 20 20
139 1½p. on 4d. black and orange 30 30
140 2½p. on 6d. black and green 45 45
141 3p. on 7d. black and rose-red 45 45
142 4p. on 10d. black and chocolate 60 60
143 5p. on 1s. black and carmine 65 65
144 7½p. on 1s. 6d. black and yellow-olive .. 95 95
145 12½p. on 2s. 6d. black and orange-brown .. 2·50 2·75
146 15p. on 1½d. black and blue .. .. 3·50 3·50
147 25p. on 5s. black and violet .. .. 6·00 8·00
148 50p. on 10s. black and deep turquoise-blue 17·00 20·00
137/48 .. .. *Set of* 12 28·00 35·00
*This was the local release date, but the Crown Agents issued the stamps one day later.

66 *Quest*

(Des V. Whiteley. Litho J.W.)

1971 (1 June). *50th Anniv of Shackleton–Rowett Expedition. T* **66** *and similar horiz designs. W* w **12** *(sideways). P* 13½ × 14.
149 1½p. multicoloured .. .. .. 2·25 1·75
150 4p. sepia, pale green and apple-green .. 2·50 2·00
151 7½p. black, bright purple and pale green .. 2·50 2·00
152 12½p. multicoloured .. .. .. 2·75 2·75
Designs:—4p. Presentation of Scout Troop flag; 7½p. Cachet on pair of 6d. G.B. stamps; 12½p. Shackleton, postmarks and boat taking mail to the *Quest*.

67 H.M.S. *Victory* at Trafalgar and Thomas Swain catching Nelson

68 Cow Pudding

(Des R. Granger Barrett. Litho Questa)

1971 (1 Nov). *Island Families. T* **67** *and similar horiz designs showing ships and the names of families associated with them. Multicoloured. W* w **12** *(sideways). P* 13½.
153 1½p. Type **67** 65 65
154 2½p. *Emily of Stonington* (P. W. Green) .. 75 75
155 4p. *Italia* (Lavarello and Repetto) .. 1·00 1·25
156 7½p. H.M.S. *Falmouth* (William Glass) .. 1·75 2·50
157 12½p. American whaler (Rogers and Hagan) 2·25 3·75

(Des M. and Sylvia Goaman. Recess and litho B.W. (50p., £1); Litho A. & M. (others))

1972 (29 Feb). *T* **68** *and similar multicoloured designs showing flowering plants. W* w **12** *(sideways on horiz designs). P* 13.
158 ½p. Type **68** 15 12
159 1p. Peak Berry 25 15
160 1½p. Sand Flower (*horiz*) 25 20
161 2½p. N.Z. Flax (*horiz*) 40 30
162 3p. Island Tree 40 30
163 4p. Bog Fern 45 35
164 5p. Dog Catcher 45 35
165 7½p. Celery 75 50
166 12½p. Pepper Tree .. .. 1·25 90
167 25p. Foul Berry (*horiz*) .. .. .. 2·50 2·75
168 50p. Tussock .. .. 4·50 4·75
169 £1 Tussac (*horiz*) .. .. .. 8·50 10·00
158/69 .. .. *Set of* 12 18·00 19·00

69 Launching

(Des R. Svensson. Litho Walsall)

1972 (1 June). *Tristan Longboats. T* **69** *and similar multicoloured designs. W* w **12** *(sideways on* 2½*p. and* 4*p.). P* 14.
170 2½p. Type **69** 70 50
171 4p. Under oars 70 60
172 7½p. Coxswain Arthur Repetto (*vert*) .. 80 70
173 12½p. Under sail for Nightingale Island (*vert*) 85 75

70 Tristan Thrushes and Wandering Albatrosses

(Des (from photographs by D. Groves) and photo Harrison)

1972 (20 Nov). *Royal Silver Wedding. Multicoloured; background colours given. W* w **12**. *P* 14 × 14½.
174 **70** 2½p. red-brown 75 75
175 7½p. dull ultramarine 50 75

71 Church Altar

(Des J. Cooter. Litho Questa)

1973 (8 July). *Golden Jubilee of St. Mary's Church.* W w **12**. *P* 13½.
176 **71** 25p. multicoloured .. .. .. 2·50 2·00

72 H.M.S. *Challenger's* Laboratory

(Des V. Whiteley Studio. Litho Questa)

1973 (15 Oct). *Centenary of H.M.S. Challenger's Visit. T* **72** *and similar horiz designs. Multicoloured.* W w **12**. *P* 13½.
177 4p. Type **72** 80 80
178 5p. H.M.S. *Challenger* off Tristan .. 85 85
179 7½p. *Challenger's* pinnace off Nightingale Is 95 1·00
180 12½p. Survey route .. .. 1·40 1·60
MS181 145 × 96 mm. Nos. 177/80 .. .. .. 3·50 5·00

73 Approaching English Port

(Des Jennifer Toombs. Litho Questa)

1973 (10 Nov). *Tenth Anniv of Return to Tristan da Cunha. T* **73** *and similar horiz designs. Multicoloured (except 4p.).* W w **12**. *P* 14.
182 4p. Type **73** (reddish brn, lemon & gold) 1·00 1·00
183 5p. Survey party .. .. 1·00 1·00
184 7½p. Embarking on *Bornholm* .. .. 1·25 1·40
185 12½p. Approaching Tristan .. .. .. 1·60 1·75

1973 (14 Nov). *Royal Wedding. As Nos.* 165/6 *of Anguilla.*
186 7½p. bright blue 25 25
187 12½p. light turquoise-green 30 30

74 Rockhopper Penguin and Egg

(Des R. Granger Barrett. Litho Questa)

1974 (1 May). *Rockhopper Penguins. T* **74** *and similar horiz designs.* W w **12**. *P* 14.
188 2½p. Type **74** .. .. 3·50 1·75
189 5p. Rockhopper Colony, Inaccessible Island 4·00 2·50
190 7½p. Penguin fishing .. .. .. 4·50 2·75
191 25p. Adult and fledgling .. .. .. 5·00 5·00

75 Map with Rockhopper Penguin and Wandering Albatross

(Des J.W. Litho Questa)

1974 (1 Oct). *"The Lonely Island". Sheet* 154 × 104 *mm.* W w **12** *(sideways). P* 13½.
MS192 **75** 35p. multicoloured .. .. .. 3·75 4·50

76 Blenheim Palace

(Des Sylvia Goaman. Litho Questa)

1974 (30 Nov). *Birth Centenary of Sir Winston Churchill. T* **76** *and similar horiz design.* W w **14** *(sideways). P* 14.
193 7½p. pale yellow and black 60 60
194 25p. black, sepia and grey .. .. .. 1·00 1·00
MS195 93 × 93 mm. Nos. 193/4. W w **12** (sideways) 1·75 2·25
Design:—25p. Churchill with Queen Elizabeth II.

77 *Plocamium fuscorubrum*

(Des Sylvia Goaman. Litho Harrison)

1975 (16 Apr). *Sea Plants. T* **77** *and similar horiz designs.* W w **12** *(sideways). P* 13 × 13½.
196 4p. rose-carmine, light lilac and black .. 50 50
197 5p. apple-green, light violet-blue and deep bluish green 55 55
198 10p. red-orange, stone and brown-purple .. 60 65
199 20p. multicoloured .. .. 90 1·25
Designs:—5p. *Ulva lactua;* 10p. *Epymenia flabellata;* 20p. *Macrocystis pyrifera.*

78 Killer Whale

(Des G. Drummond. Litho Walsall)

1975 (1 Nov). *Whales. T* **78** *and similar horiz designs. Multicoloured.* W w **12** *(sideways). P* 13½.
200 2p. Type **78** 70 70
201 3p. Rough-toothed Dolphin 70 70
202 5p. Atlantic Right Whale 80 80
203 20p. Finback Whale .. .. 2·00 2·00

79 ½d. Stamp of 1952 **80** Island Cottage

(Des C. Abbott. Litho J.W.)

1976 (27* May). *Festival of Stamps, London. T* **79** *and similar designs.* W w **14** *(sideways on 5 and 25p). P* 13½.
204 5p. black, violet and light lilac 50 55
205 9p. black, deep green and turquoise 60 70
206 25p. multicoloured .. .. 80 1·00
Designs: *Vert*—9p. 1953 Coronation stamp. *Horiz*—25p. Mail carrier *Tristania II.*
*This is the local date of issue. The stamps were released by the Crown Agents on 4 May.
For miniature sheet containing No. 206 see No. **MS**218 of Ascension.

(Des C. Abbott. Litho Questa)

1976 (4 Oct). *Paintings by Roland Svensson (1st series). T* **80** *and similar multicoloured designs.* W w **14** *(sideways on 5p., 10p. and* **MS**211). *P* 14.
207 3p. Type **80** 30 30
208 5p. The potato patches (*horiz*) 45 50
209 10p. Edinburgh from the sea (*horiz*) .. 60 75
210 20p. Huts, Nightingale Island .. .. 85 1·00
MS211 125 × 112 mm. Nos. 207/10 .. .. 2·50 3·00
See also Nos. 234/8 and 272/6.

81 The Royal Standard

(Des and litho J.W.)

1977 (7 Feb). *Silver Jubilee. T* **81** *and similar horiz designs. Multicoloured.* W w **14** *(sideways). P* 13.
212 10p. Royal Yacht *Britannia* 70 80
213 15p. Type **81** 40 50
214 25p. Royal family 50 70
For Nos. 213/14 surcharged, see Nos. 232/3.

82 H.M.S. *Eskimo*

(Des L. Curtis. Litho Walsall)

1977 (1 Oct). *Ships' Crests. T* **82** *and similar horiz designs. Multicoloured.* W w **14** *(sideways). P* 14.
215 5p. Type **82** 50 30
216 10p. H.M.S. *Naiad* 60 45
217 15p. H.M.S. *Jaguar* 70 55
218 20p. H.M.S. *London* 85 65
MS219 142 × 140 mm. Nos. 215/18 .. .. 2·75 3·25

83 Great-winged Petrel **(84)**

(Des BG Studio. Litho Walsall)

1977 (1 Dec). *Multicoloured designs as T* **83** *showing birds.* W w **14** *(sideways on 1 and 2p.). P* 13½.
220 1p. Type **83** 10 10
221 2p. White-faced Storm Petrel 15 15
222 3p. Hall's Giant Petrel 15 15
223 4p. Soft-plumaged Petrel 20 20
224 5p. Wandering Albatross 20 20
225 10p. Kerguelen Petrel 30 30
226 15p. Swallow-tailed Tern 50 50
227 20p. Greater Shearwater 55 55
228 25p. Broad-billed Prion 65 65
229 50p. Great Skua .. .. 1·25 1·25
230 £1 Common Diving Petrel .. .. .. 2·00 2·00
231 £2 Yellow-nosed Albatross .. .. .. 3·75 3·75
220/31 .. .. *Set of* 12 9·00 9·00
The 3p. to £2 are vertical designs.

1978 (19 Jan*). *Provisional definitives. Nos.* 213/14 *surch as T* **84**.
232 4p. on 15p. Type **81** .. .. 10·00 15·00
233 7½p. on 25p. Royal family .. .. .. 10·00 15·00
*This is the local date of issue. Covers dated 26 November 1977 are philatelic mail forwarded to the island for cancellation, the stamps having been released in London on 31 October 1977. Supplies for the island population did not arrive until 19 January.

(Des C. Abbott. Litho Questa)

1978 (1 Mar). *Paintings by Roland Svensson (2nd series). Horiz designs as T* **80**. *Multicoloured.* W w **14** *(sideways). P* 14.
234 5p. St. Mary's Church 30 30
235 10p. Longboats 45 45
236 15p. A Tristan home 60 60
237 20p. The harbour, 1970 .. .. .. 75 75
MS238 115 × 128 mm. Nos. 234/7 .. .. 2·50 2·75

85 King's Bull **86** Sodalite

(Des Jennifer Toombs. Litho Questa)

1978 (21 Apr). *25th Anniv of Coronation. T* **85** *and similar vert designs.* W w **14**. *P* 15.
239 25p. bistre, bright violet and silver 65 65
a. Sheetlet Nos. 239/41 × 2 .. .. 4·00
240 25p. multicoloured 65 65
241 25p. bistre, bright violet and silver 65 65
Designs:—No. 239, Type **85**; No. 240, Queen Elizabeth II; No. 241, Tristan crawfish.
Nos. 239/41 were printed together in small sheets of 6, containing two *se-tenant* strips of 3, with horizontal gutter margin between.

(Des J.W. Litho Questa)

1978 (9 June). *Local Minerals. T* **86** *and similar horiz designs. Multicoloured.* W w **14** *(sideways). P* 13½.
242 3p. Type **86** 30 25
243 5p. Aragonite 40 25
244 10p. Sulphur 60 50
245 20p. Lava containing pyroxene crystal .. 90 85

87 Klipfish

(Des R. Granger Barrett. Litho Harrison)

1978 (29 Sept). *Fish. T* **87** *and similar horiz designs.* W w **14** *(sideways). P* 14.
246 5p. black, yellow-brown and yellow-green .. 30 25
247 10p. black, yellow-brown and emerald .. 40 35
248 15p. multicoloured 60 55
249 20p. multicoloured 90 75
Designs:—10p. Fivefinger; 15p. Concha; 20p. Soldier.

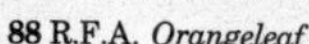

88 R.F.A. *Orangeleaf* **89** Elephant Seal

(Des R. Granger Barrett. Litho Cartor S.A., France)

1978 (24 Nov). *Royal Fleet Auxiliary Vessels. T* **88** *and similar horiz designs. Multicoloured.* W w **14** *(sideways). P* 12½ × 12.

250 5p. Type **88** 25 20
251 10p. R.F.A. *Tarbatness* 50 30
252 20p. R.F.A. *Tidereach* 90 60
253 25p. R.F.A. *Reliant* .. .. 1·25 90
MS254 136 × 140 mm. Nos. 250/3 (Wmk inverted) 3·00 3·50

(Des J.W. Litho Questa)

1979 (3 Jan). *Wildlife Conservation. T* **89** *and similar vert designs. Multicoloured.* W w **14**. *P* 14.

255 5p. Type **89** 30 30
256 10p. Fur Seal 40 40
257 15p. Tristan Thrush 60 60
258 20p. Nightingale Finch 80 70

90 Tristan Longboat

(Des R. Granger Barrett. Litho Questa)

1979 (8 Feb). *Visit of R.M.S. "Queen Elizabeth 2". T* **90** *and similar horiz designs. Multicoloured.* W w **14** *(sideways). P* 14½.

259 5p. Type **90** 35 45
260 10p. R.M.S. *Queen Mary* 45 55
261 15p. R.M.S. *Queen Elizabeth* 50 65
282 20p. R.M.S. *Q.E.2* 60 80
MS263 148 × 96 mm. 25p. R.M.S. *Q.E.2* (131 × 27 mm) .. .. 4·00 6·00

91 1952 "TRISTAN DA CUNHA" overprinted St. Helena 10s. Definitive

(Des J.W. Litho Questa)

1979 (27 Aug). *Death Centenary of Sir Rowland Hill. T* **91** *and similar designs showing stamps.* W w **14** *(sideways on 5 and 10p.). P* 14.

264 5p. black, lilac and bistre-yellow 25 25
265 10p. black, red and apple-green 35 35
266 25p. multicoloured 50 65
MS267 83 × 103 mm. 50p. black and vermilion .. 1·10 1·40

Designs: *Horiz*—10p. 1954 5s. definitive. *Vert*—25p. 1963 3d. Tristan da Cunha Resettlement commemorative; 50p. 1946 1d. 4 Potatoes local label.

92 "The Padre's House" **93** Mail Ship

(Des G. Hutchins. Litho Questa)

1979 (26 Nov). *International Year of the Child. Children's Drawings. T* **92** *and similar horiz designs. Multicoloured.* W w **14** *(sideways). P* 14.

268 5p. Type **92** 20 15
269 10p. "Houses in the Village" 30 25
270 15p. "St. Mary's Church" 45 35
271 20p. "Rockhopper Penguins" 45 45

(Des C. Abbott. Litho Questa)

1980 (29 Feb). *Paintings by Roland Svensson (3rd series). Landscapes. Multicoloured designs as T* **80**. W w **14** *(sideways on 5 and 10p.). P* 14.

272 5p. "Stoltenhoff Island" [*horiz*] 20 15
273 10p. "Nightingale from the East" (*horiz*) .. 30 25
274 15p. "The Administrator's Abode" 35 35
275 20p. "Ridge where the Goat jump off" .. 45 45
MS276 126 × 109 mm. Nos. 272/5 (wmk sideways) 1·50 1·60

1980 (6 May). *"London 1980" International Stamp Exhibition. T* **93** *and similar vert designs. Multicoloured.* W w **14**. *P* 14.

277 5p. Type **93** 25 25
278 10p. Unloading mail at Calshot Harbour .. 30 30
279 15p. Tractor transporting mail to Post Office 35 35
280 20p. Ringing the "dong" to summons people to Post Office 45 45
281 25p. Distributing mail 50 50

94 Queen Elizabeth the Queen Mother **95** *Golden Hinde*

1980 (11 Aug*). *80th Birthday of Queen Elizabeth the Queen Mother.* W w **14** *(sideways). P* 14.

282 **94** 14p. multicoloured 60 70

*This is the local date of issue. The Crown Agents released this stamp in London on 4 August.

(Des G. Vasarhelyi. Litho Walsall)

1980 (6 Sept). *400th Anniv of Sir Francis Drake's Circumnavigation of the World. T* **95** *and similar vert designs. Multicoloured.* W w **14**. *P* 14½ × 14.

283 5p. Type **95** 35 20
284 10p. Drake's route 40 30
285 20p. Sir Francis Drake 45 45
286 25p. Queen Elizabeth I 55 45

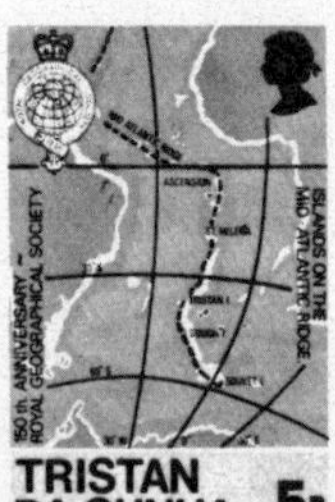

96 "Humpty Dumpty" **97** South Atlantic Ocean showing Islands on Mid-Atlantic Ridge

(Des G. Vasarhelyi. Litho J.W.)

1980 (31 Oct). *Christmas. Scenes from Nursery Rhymes. T* **96** *and similar horiz designs. Multicoloured.* W w **14** *(sideways). P* 13.

287 15p. Type **96** 35 35
a. Sheetlet Nos. 287/95 .. .. 2·75
288 15p. "Mary had a little Lamb" 35 35
289 15p. "Little Jack Horner" 35 35
290 15p. "Hey Diddle Diddle" 35 35
291 15p. "London Bridge" 35 35
292 15p. "Old King Cole" 35 35
293 15p. "Sing a Song of Sixpence" 35 35
294 15p. "Tom, Tom the Piper's Son" 35 35
295 15p. "The Owl and the Pussy Cat" 35 35
287/95 .. .. *Set of* 9 2·75 2·75

Nos. 287/95 were printed together, *se-tenant*, within a small sheet of 9 stamps.

(Des A. Crawford, adapted BG Studio. Litho Rosenbaum Bros, Vienna)

1980 (15 Dec). *150th Anniv of Royal Geographical Society. Maps. T* **97** *and similar vert designs. Multicoloured.* W w **14**. *P* 13½.

296 5p. Type **97** 20 15
297 10p. Tristan da Cunha group (Beauforts Survey, 1806) 30 25
298 15p. Tristan Island (Crawford, 1937–38) .. 40 35
299 20p. Gough Island (1955–56) 45 45

98 Revd. Edwin Dodgson as Young Man **99** Detail from Captain Denham's Plan, 1853

(Des Jennifer Toombs. Litho Questa)

1981 (23 Mar). *Centenary of Revd. Edwin Dodgson's Arrival on Tristan da Cunha. T* **98** *and similar multicoloured designs.* W w **14** *(sideways on 20p.). P* 14.

300 10p. Type **98** 30 30
301 20p. Dodgson and view of Tristan da Cunha (*horiz*) 50 50
302 30p. Dodgson with people of Tristan da Cunha 65 70
MS303 140 × 134 mm. Nos. 300/2 (wmk sideways) 1·40 1·75

(Des L. McCombie. Litho Questa)

1981 (22 May). *Early Maps. T* **99** *and similar horiz designs Multicoloured.* W w **14** *(sideways). P* 13½ × 14.

304 5p. Type **99** 20 2
305 14p. Detail from map by A. Dalrymple, 17 March 1781 .. .. 35 3
306 21p. Detail from Captain Denham's plan, 1853 (*different*) 45 4
MS307 110 × 70 mm. 35p. Detail from map by J. van Keulen, *circa* 1700 .. .. 80 95

100 Wedding Bouquet from Tristan da Cunha **101** Explorer with Rucksack

(Des J.W. Litho Walsall)

1981 (22 July). *Royal Wedding. T* **100** *and similar vert designs Multicoloured.* W w **14**. *P* 14.

308 5p. Type **100** 30 3
309 20p. Prince of Wales at Investiture 55 55
310 50p. Prince Charles and Lady Diana Spencer 1·10 1·10

(Des BG Studio. Litho Questa)

1981 (14 Sept). *25th Anniv of Duke of Edinburgh Award Scheme. T* **101** *and similar vert designs. Multicoloured.* W w **14**. *P* 14.

311 5p. Type **101** 30 20
312 10p. Explorer at campsite 45 30
313 20p. Explorer map reading 65 50
314 25p. Duke of Edinburgh 80 65

102 Inaccessible Island Rail on Nest

(Des R. Granger Barrett. Litho Walsall)

1981 (1 Nov). *Inaccessible Island Rail. T* **102** *and similar horiz designs. Multicoloured.* W w **14** *(sideways). P* 13½ × 14.

315 10p. Type **102** 30 30
a. Strip of 4. Nos. 315/18 .. .. .. 1·10
316 10p. Inaccessible Island Rail eggs 30 30
317 10p. Rail chicks 30 30
318 10p. Adult Rail 30 30

Nos. 315/18 were printed together, *se-tenant*, in horizontal and vertical strips of 4 throughout the sheet.

103 Six-gilled Shark

(Des I. Loe. Litho Enschedé)

1982 (8 Feb). *Sharks. T* **103** *and similar horiz designs. Multicoloured.* W w **14** *(sideways). P* 13½.

319 5p. Type **103** 25 20
320 14p. Porbeagle Shark 45 30
321 21p. Blue Shark 60 60
322 35p. Hammerhead Shark 70 70

104 *Marcella* **105** Lady Diana Spencer at Windsor, July 1981

(Des J. Cooter. Litho Questa)

1982 (5 Apr). *Sailing Ships (1st series). T* **104** *and similar horiz designs. Multicoloured.* W w **14** *(sideways). P* 13½.

323 5p. Type **104** 25 25
324 15p. *Eliza Adams* 45 45
325 30p. *Corinthian* 70 70
326 50p. *Samuel and Thomas* .. .. 1·00 1·00

See also Nos. 341/4.

(Des Jennifer Toombs. Litho Walsall)

1982 (1 July). *21st Birthday of Princess of Wales. T* **105** *and similar vert designs. Multicoloured. W* w **14**. *P* 14½ × 14.

327	5p. Tristan da Cunha coat of arms	15	15
328	15p. Type **105**	40	40
329	30p. Prince and Princess of Wales in wedding portrait	60	60
330	50p. Formal portrait	1·00	1·00

106 Lord Baden-Powell

1ST PARTICIPATION
COMMONWEALTH
GAMES 1982

(**107**)

(Des C. Abbott. Litho J.W.)

1982 (20 Sept). *75th Anniv of Boy Scout Movement. T* **106** *and similar multicoloured designs. W* w **14** (*sideways on No.* 333). *P* 13 × 13½ (50*p.*) *or* 13½ × 13 (*others*).

331	5p. Type **106**	25	20
332	20p. First Scout camp, Brownsea, 1907	50	50
333	50p. Local Scouts on parade (*horiz*)	1·00	1·00
MS334	88 × 104 mm. 50p. Moral of the Acorn and the Oak. P 14	1·00	1·10

1982 (28 Sept). *Commonwealth Games, Brisbane. Nos.* 224 *and* 228 *optd with T* **107**.

335	5p. Wandering Albatross	10	12
336	25p. Broad-billed Prion	50	55

108 Formation of Island

109 Tractor pulling Trailer

(Des J.W. Litho Questa)

1982 (1 Nov). *Volcanoes. T* **108** *and similar horiz designs. Multicoloured. W* w **14** (*sideways*). *P* 14 × 14½.

337	5p. Type **108**	10	12
338	15p. Plan of surface cinder cones and cross-section of volcano showing feeders	30	35
339	25p. Eruption	50	55
340	35p. 1961 Tristan eruption	70	75

(Des J. Cooter. Litho Questa)

1983 (1 Feb). *Sailing Ships* (2*nd series*). *Multicoloured designs as T* **104**. *W* w **14** (*sideways on* 20*p.*, 35*p.*). *P* 13½.

341	5p. *Islander* (*vert*)	10	12
342	20p. *Roscoe*	40	45
343	35p. *Columbia*	70	75
344	50p. *Emeline* (*vert*)	1·00	1·10

(Des C. Abbott. Litho Format)

1983 (2 May). *Land Transport. T* **109** *and similar horiz designs. Multicoloured. W* w **14** (*sideways*). *P* 14.

345	5p. Type **109**	10	12
346	15p. Pack donkeys	30	35
347	30p. Bullock cart	60	65
348	50p. Landrover	1·00	1·10

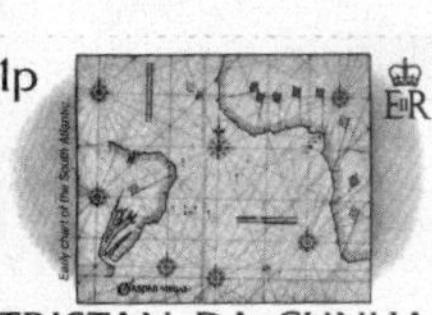

110 Early Chart of South Atlantic

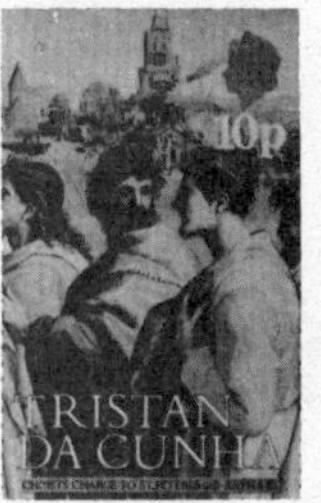

111 "Christ's Charge to St. Peter" (detail) (Raphael)

(Des L. Curtis. Litho Questa)

1983 (1 Aug). *Island History. T* **110** *and similar horiz designs. Multicoloured* (*except* 50*p. black, bright scarlet and buff*). *W* w **14** (*sideways*). *P* 14.

349	1p. Type **110**	5	5
350	3p. Tristao d'Acunha's flagship	5	8
351	4p. Notice left by Dutch on first landing, 1643	8	10
352	5p. 17th-century views of the island	8	10
353	10p. British army landing party, 1815	20	25
354	15p. 19th-century view of the settlement	25	30
355	18p. Governor Glass's house	30	35
356	20p. The Revd. W. F. Taylor and Peter Green	35	40
357	25p. *John and Elizabeth* (American whaler)	45	50
358	50p. Letters Patent declaring Tristan da Cunha a dependency of St. Helena	90	95
359	£1 Commissioning H.M.S. *Atlantic Isle*, 1944	1·75	2·00
360	£2 Evacuation, 1961	3·50	3·75
349/60	*Set of* 12	7·00	8·00

(Des and litho Walsall)

1983 (27 Oct). *500th Birth Anniv of Raphael. T* **111** *and similar designs, showing different details of "Christ's Charge to St. Peter". W* w **14**. *P* 14.

361	10p. multicoloured	25	30
362	25p. multicoloured	55	60
363	40p. multicoloured	85	85
MS364	115 × 90 mm. 50p. multicoloured (*horiz*). Wmk sideways	1·00	1·10

On No. **MS**364 the Queen's head has been replaced by the Royal Cypher.

112 1952 6d. Stamp

113 *Agrocybe praecox var. cutefracta*

(Des C. Abbott. Litho Questa)

1984 (3 Jan). *150th Anniv of St. Helena as a British Colony. T* **112** *and similar horiz designs showing 1952 overprints on St. Helena stamps. Multicoloured. W* w **14** (*sideways*). *P* 14.

365	10p. Type **112**	20	25
366	15p. 1952 1s. stamp	30	35
367	25p. 1952 2s. stamp	50	55
368	60p. 1952 10s. stamp	1·25	1·40

(Des McCombie Skinner Studio. Litho Questa)

1984 (25 Mar). *Fungi. T* **113** *and similar multicoloured designs. W* w **14** (*sideways on* 30 *p.*, 50 *p.*). *P* 14.

369	10p. Type **113**	20	25
370	20p. *Laccaria tetraspora*	40	45
371	30p. *Agrocybe cylindracea* (*horiz*)	60	65
372	50p. *Sacoscypha coccinea* (*horiz*)	1·00	1·10

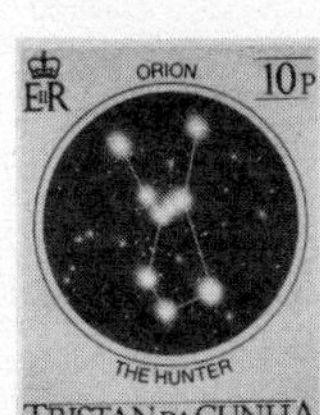

114 Constellation of "Orion"

115 Sheep-shearing

(Des Harrison. Litho Questa)

1984 (30 July). *The Night Sky. T* **114** *and similar vert designs. Multicoloured. W* w **14**. *P* 14½ × 14.

373	10p. Type **114**	20	25
374	20p. "Scorpius"	40	45
375	25p. "Canis Major"	50	55
376	50p. "Crux"	1·00	1·10

(Des G. Wilby. Litho Walsall)

1984 (1 Oct). *Tristan Woollens Industry. T* **115** *and similar vert designs. Multicoloured. W* w **14**. *P* 14½.

377	9p. Type **115**	20	25
378	17p. Carding wool	35	40
379	29p. Spinning	60	65
380	45p. Knitting	90	95
MS381	120 × 85 mm. As Nos. 377/80, but without white borders around the designs	2·00	2·10

116 "Christmas Dinner-table"

117 "H.M.S. *Julia* Ashore, 1817" (Midshipman C. W. Browne

(Des G. Vasarhelyi. Litho Questa)

1984 (3 Dec). *Christmas. Children's Drawings. T* **116** *and similar horiz designs. Multicoloured. W* w **14** (*sideways*). *P* 14.

382	10p. Type **116**	20	25
383	20p. "Santa Claus in ox cart"	40	45
384	30p. "Santa Claus in longboat"	60	65
385	50p. "The Nativity"	1·00	1·10

(Des A. Crawford, adapted G. Vasarhelyi. Litho Questa)

1985 (4 Feb). *Shipwrecks* (1*st series*). *T* **117** *and similar designs. W* w **14** (*sideways on* 35*p.*). *P* 14 × 13½ (10, 25*p.*) *or* 13½ × 14 (35, 60*p.*).

386	10p. royal blue and light grey-blue	20	25
387	25p. red-brown and emerald	50	55
388	35p. yellow-brown and orange-yellow	70	75
MS389	142 × 101 mm. 60p. multicoloured. Wmk sideways	1·25	1·40

Designs: *Vert*—25p. *Mabel Clark's* Bell, St. Mary's Church. *Horiz*—35p. "Barque *Glenhuntley* foundering, 1898" (John Hagan); 60p. Map of Tristan da Cunha showing sites of shipwrecks.

POSTAGE DUE STAMPS

D 1

D 2

(Typo D.L.R.)

1957 (1 Feb). *Chalk-surfaced paper. Wmk Mult Script CA*. *P* **14**.

D1	D 1	1d. scarlet	3·50	3·75
D2		2d. orange-yellow	4·50	6·00
D3		3d. green	5·50	7·00
D4		4d. ultramarine	6·00	9·50
D5		5d. lake	8·50	15·00

(Des J.W. Litho Questa)

1976 (27 May*). *W* w **12** (*sideways*). *P* 13½ × 14.

D 6	D 2	1p. magenta	70	85
D 7		2p. dull emerald	80	1·00
D 8		4p. bluish violet	90	1·25
D 9		5p. new blue	1·25	1·50
D10		10p. chestnut	2·50	4·25

*This is the local date of issue; the Crown Agents released the stamps four days later.

1976 (3 Sept). *W* w **14** (*sideways*). *P* 13½ × 14.

D11	D 2	1p. magenta	5	5
D12		2p. dull emerald	5	5
D13		4p. bluish violet	8	8
D14		5p. new blue	10	10
D15		10p. chestnut	20	25

POSTAL FISCAL STAMPS

NATIONAL
SAVINGS

(**F 1**)

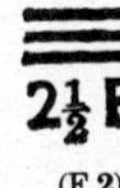

(**F 2**)

1970 (15 May). *No.* 77 *optd with Type* **F 1** *in red.*

F1	6d. black and green	20	30

No. F1 was originally intended as a National Savings Stamp, but also retained postal validity.

(Handstamped locally by rubber handstamp)

1971 (Feb). *Decimal currency. No.* F 1 *handstamped with Type* **F 2**, *in violet.*

F2	2½p. on 6d. black and green	16·00	20·00
	a. Pair, one without handstamp	£350	£350

Beware of forgeries of this handstamp.

Trucial States

The Trucial States consisted of Abu Dhabi, Ajman (with Manama), Dubai, Fujeira, Ras al Khaima, Sharjah and Umm al Qiwain. However the following issue of stamps was only put into use in Dubai, despite the inscription "TRUCIAL STATES".

The first organised postal service in Dubai commenced on 19 August 1909 when an Indian Branch Office, administered from Karachi, was opened, using the unoverprinted stamps of India, principally the ½ a. and 1 a. values.

The initial cancellation was a single-ring type inscribed "DUBAI B.O. PERSIAN GULF", which remained in use until 1933.

1909 Cancellation

Its replacement was of the Indian double-circle type showing a similar inscription.

Dubai was upgraded to Sub-Post Office status on 1 April 1942 and this change was reflected in a new double-ring mark inscribed "DUBAI" only. At the same time the office was provided with a single-ring handstamp which also incorporated a cancelling device of seven wavy lines.

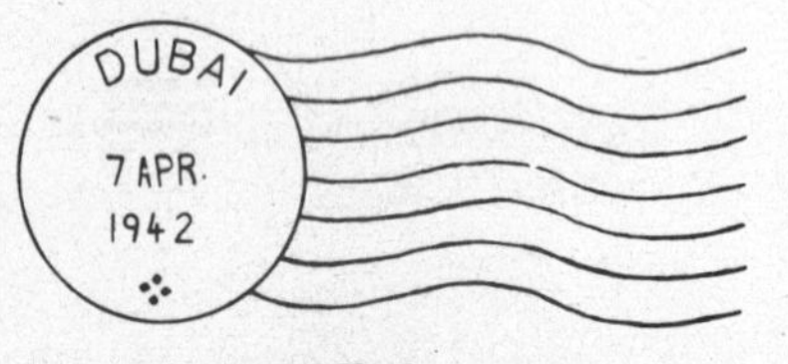

1942 Handstamp

(*illustration reduced: actual size 65 × 27 mm*)

A further version of the double-ring type appeared in 1946, showing the "PERSIAN GULF" inscription restored to the lower segment of the postmark.

In October 1947 control of the Dubai Post Office passed to Pakistan whose stamps were used there until the end of March 1948.

On 1 April 1948 the post office was transferred, yet again, to British control and Great Britain stamps surcharged for use in the British Postal Agencies in Eastern Arabia were then sold in Dubai until 6 January 1961, being cancelled with British style single and double-ring postmarks.

1 Palms

2 Dhow

(Des M. Goaman. Photo Harrison (T 1). Des M. Farrar-Bell. Recess D.L.R. (T 2))

1961 (7 Jan). *P* 15 × 14 (*T* 1) *or* 13 × 12½ (*T* 2).

No.	Type	Description	Unused	Used
1	1	5 n.p. green	8	5
2		15 n.p. red-brown	12	8
3		20 n.p. bright blue	15	12
4		30 n.p. orange-red	20	20
5		40 n.p. reddish violet	20	10
6		50 n.p. bistre	25	25
7		75 n.p. grey	40	30
8	2	1 r. green	1·75	35
9		2 r. black	2·50	3·00
10		5 r. carmine-red	3·50	8·00
11		10 r. deep ultramarine	11·00	20·00
1/11		*Set of* 11	18·00	29·00

The Dubai Post Department took over the postal services on 14 June 1963. Later issues for Dubai will be found in Part 19 (*Middle East*) of this catalogue.

Turks and Caicos Islands

TURKS ISLANDS

DEPENDENCY OF JAMAICA

Local postal markings are known from the islands during the early 1840's and the provision of No. CC1 in 1853 suggests that a branch of the British G.P.O. was operating on Grand Turk sometime before the establishment of the Turks and Caicos Islands Post Office on 11 December 1854.

For illustrations of the handstamp types see BRITISH POST OFFICES ABROAD notes, following GREAT BRITAIN.

GRAND TURK

CROWNED-CIRCLE HANDSTAMPS

CC1 CC 4 TURKS-ISLANDS (*circa*. 1853)

PRICES FOR STAMPS ON COVER TO 1945	
Nos. 1/5	*from* × 10
No. 6	—
Nos. 7/20	*from* × 10
Nos. 20*a*/48	—
Nos. 49/52	*from* × 3
Nos. 53/7	*from* × 4
Nos. 58/65	*from* × 10
Nos. 66/9	*from* × 4
Nos. 70/2	*from* × 8
Nos. 101/9	*from* × 5
Nos. 110/26	*from* × 4
Nos. 129/39	*from* × 3
Nos. 140/53	*from* × 10
Nos. 154/90	*from* × 3
Nos. 191/3	*from* × 10
Nos. 194/205	*from* × 2

1

(Recess P.B.)

1867 (4 April). *No wmk. P* 11–12.

No.	Type	Description	Unused	Used
1	1	1d. dull rose	23·00	32·00
2		6d. black	45·00	45·00
3		1s. dull blue	42·00	42·00

1873–79. *Wmk Small Star. W* w **2** (*sideways on Nos.* 5 *and* 6). *P* 11–12 × 14½–15½.

No.	Type	Description	Unused	Used
4	1	1d. dull rose-lake (7.73)	30·00	30·00
		a. Wmk sideways		
5		1d. dull red (1.79)	40·00	40·00
		a. Imperf between (pair)	£8000	
		c. Wmk upright		
6		1s. lilac (1.79)	£5500	£2000

1881 (1 Jan). *Stamps of the preceding issues surcharged locally, in black.*

There are twelve different settings of the ½d., nine settings of the 2½d., and six settings of the 4d.

(2) (3)

Setting 1. *T* **2**. *Long fraction bar. Two varieties repeated fifteen times in the sheet.*

No.	Description	Unused	Used
7	½ on 6d. black	40·00	45·00

Setting 2. *T* **3**. *Short fraction bar. Three varieties in a vertical strip repeated ten times in sheet.*

Setting 3. *Similar to setting* 2, *but the middle stamp of the three varieties has a longer bar.*

No.	Description	Unused	Used
8	½ on 6d. black (*setting* 2 *only*)	32·00	
9	½ on 1s. dull blue	38·00	50·00
	a. Surch double	£3500	

(4) (5) (6)

Three varieties in a vertical strip repeated ten times in sheet.

Section 4. *Types* **4, 5, 6.**

Setting 5. *Types* **4** (*without bar*), **5, 6.**

Setting 6. *Types* **4, 5, 6** (*without bar*).

Setting 7. *Types* **4** (*shorter thick bar*), **6, 6.**

No.	Description	Unused	Used
10	½ on 1d. dull red (*setting* 7 *only*) (T **6**)	£1000	
	a. Type **4** (shorter thick bar)	£1700	
11	½ on 1s. dull blue (*setting* 6 *and* 7) (T **4**)	£450	
	a. Type **4** (shorter thick bar)	£450	
	b. Type **5**	£450	
	c. Type **6**	£275	
	d. Type **6** (without bar)	£450	
	e. Surch double (T **6** without bar)		
12	½ on 1s. lilac (T **4**)	£275	£275
	a. Without bar	£450	
	b. With short thick bar	£450	
	c. Surch double		
13	½ on 1s. lilac (T **5**)	£110	£110
	a. Surch double	£1200	
14	½ on 1s. lilac (T **6**)	90·00	
	a. Without bar	£450	

(7) (8) (9) (10)

Setting 8. *T* **7**. *Three varieties in a vertical strip. All have a very short bar.*

No.	Description	Unused	Used
15	½ on 1d. dull red	25·00	

Setting 9. *T* **8**. *Three varieties in a vertical strip. Bars long and thick and* "1" *leaning a little to left.*

No.	Description	Unused	Used
16	½ on 1d. dull red	£100	
	a. Surch double		

Setting 10. *T* **9** *and* **10**. *Fifteen varieties repeated twice on a sheet. Ten are of T* **9**, *five of T* **10**.

No.	Description	Unused	Used
17	½ on 1d. dull red (T **9**)	20·00	20·00
	a. Surch double		
18	½ on 1d. dull red (T **10**)	26·00	35·00
19	½ on 1s. lilac (T **9**)	45·00	45·00
20	½ on 1s. lilac (T **10**)	£120	£150
20*a*	½ on 1s. dull blue (T **9**)		

Types **9** *and* **11**. The difference is in the position of the "2" in relation to the "1". In setting 10 the "2" is to the left of the "1" except on No. 10 and in setting 11 it is to the right except on No. 2

(11) (12) (13) (14)

Setting 11. *T* **11** *to* **14**. *Fifteen varieties repeated twice in a sheet. Ten of T* **11**, *three of T* **12**, *and one each of T* **13** *and* **14**.

Setting 12. *Similar to last, but T* **13** *replaced by another T* **12**.

No.	Description	Unused	Used
21	½ on 1d. dull red (T **11**)	35·00	
22	½ on 1d. dull red (T **12**)	65·00	
23	½ on 1d. dull red (T **13**)	£1000	
24	½ on 1d. dull red (T **14**)	£275	
24*a*	½ on 1s. dull blue (T **11**)	£8000	

(15) (16)

Setting 1. *T* **15**. *Fraction in very small type.*

No.	Description	Unused	Used
25	2½ on 6d. black	£6500	

Setting 2. *T* **16**. *Two varieties repeated fifteen times in a sheet. Large* "2" *on level with top of the* "1", *long thin bar.*

No.	Description	Unused	Used
26	2½ on 6d. black	£225	
	a. Imperf between (pair)		
	b. Surch double	£4000	

(17) (18) (19)

Setting 3. *T* **17**. *As T* **16**, *but large* "2" *not so high up.*

No.	Description	Unused	Used
27	2½ on 1s. lilac	£1300	

Setting 4. *T* **18**. *Three varieties in a vertical strip repeated ten times in sheet. Large* "2" *placed lower and small bar.*

No.	Description	Unused	Used
28	2½ on 6d. black	£110	£110
	a. Surch double		

Setting 5. *T* **19**. *Three varieties in a vertical strip repeated ten times in sheet* "2" *further from* "½", *small fraction bar.*

No.	Description	Unused	Used
29	2½ on 1s. lilac	£600	£500

(20) (21)

Setting 6. *T* **20** *and* **21**. *Fifteen varieties. Ten of T* **20** *and five of T* **21**, *repeated twice in a sheet.*

No.	Description	Unused	Used
30	2½ on 1s. lilac (T **20**)	£5500	
31	2½ on 1s. lilac (T **21**)		

(22) (23) (24)

Setting 7. *T* **22**. *Three varieties in a vertical strip, repeated ten times in a sheet.*

No.	Description	Unused	Used
32	2½ on 6d. black	£7000	
33	2½ on 1s. dull blue	£7000	

Setting 8. *T* **23** *and* **24**. *Fifteen varieties. Ten of T* **23** *and five of T* **24**, *repeated twice in a sheet.*

No.	Description	Unused	Used
34	2½ on 1d. dull red (T **23**)	£225	
35	2½ on 1d. dull red (T **24**	£350	
36	2½ on 1s. lilac (T **23**)	£450	
	a. Surch "½" double	£2000	
37	2½ on 1s. lilac (T **24**)	£1200	

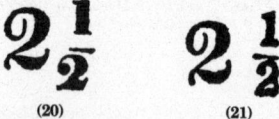

(25) (26) (27)

Setting 9. T 25, 26, and 27. Fifteen varieties. Ten of T 25, three of T 26, one of T 26 without bar, and one of T 27, repeated twice in a sheet.

38 2½ on 1s. dull blue (T 25) .. £375
39 2½ on 1s. dull blue (T 26) .. £1200
40 2½ on 1s. dull blue (T 26) (without bar) .. £6000
41 2½ on 1s. dull blue (T 27) .. £6000

4 (28) **4** (29) **4** (30)

Setting 1. T 28. "4" 8 mm high, pointed top.
42 4 on 6d. black .. £150 £150

Settings 2–6. T 29 and 30.
43 4 on 6d. black (T 29) .. 23·00
44 4 on 6d. black (T 30) .. £325 £325
45 4 on 1s. lilac (T 29) .. £325
a. Surch double ..
46 4 on 1s. lilac (T 30) .. £2000
a. Surch double ..
47 4 on 1d. dull red (T 29) .. £400 £325
48 4 on 1d. dull red (T 28) .. £400 £350

The components of these settings can only be distinguished when in blocks. Details are given in the handbook by John J. Challis.

TURKS ISLANDS HALF PENNY
31

One Penny
(32)

(Typo D.L.R.)

1881. *Wmk Crown CC (sideways; upright on 4d.). P 14.*
49 1 1d. brown-red (Oct) .. 24·00 24·00
50 31 4d. ultramarine (Die I) (Aug) .. 45·00 45·00
51 1 6d. olive-black (Oct) .. 65·00 65·00
52 1s. slate-green (Oct) .. 90·00 95·00

1882–85. *Wmk Crown CA. P 14.*
53 31 ½d. blue-green (Die I) (2.82) .. 6·50 17·00
a. Pale green (12.85) .. 1·10 3·00
55 1 1d. orange-brown (10.83) .. 24·00 32·00
a. Bisected (½d.) (on cover) .. † £1100
56 31 2½d. red-brown (Die I) (2.82) .. 11·00 16·00
57 4d. grey (Die I) (10.84) .. 4·50 5·50
a. Bisected (2d.) (on cover) .. † £900

1887 (July)–**89.** *Wmk Crown CA. (a) P 12.*
58 1 1d. crimson-lake .. 5·00 5·50
a. Imperf between (pair) ..
(b) P 14
59 1 6d. yellow-brown (2.89) (Optd S. £30) 5·00 6·50
60 1s. sepia .. 5·00 6·50

1889 (May). *Surch at Grand Turk with T 32.*
61 31 1d. on 2½d. red-brown .. 7·50 9·00

1889–93. *Wmk Crown CA. P 14.*
62 1 1d. crimson-lake (7.89) .. 1·75 4·50
63 1d. lake .. 1·40 4·00
64 1d. pale rosy lake .. 1·25 5·00
65 31 2½d. ultram (Die II) (4.93) (Optd S. £55) .. 2·00 1·90

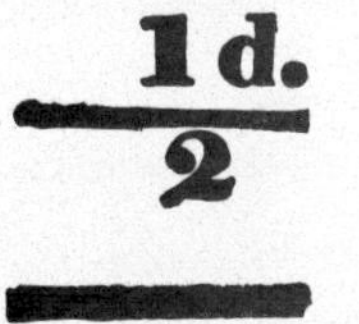
(33)

34

1893 (July). *No. 57 surch at Grand Turk with T 33.*

Setting 1. Bars between "1d." and "2" separate, instead of continuous across the rows of stamps.
66 ½d. on 4d. grey .. £180 £120

Setting 2. Continuous bars. Thin and thick bar 10¾ mm apart. "2" under the "1".
67 ½d. on 4d. grey .. 90·00 90·00

Setting 3. As last, but bars 11¾ mm apart.
68 ½d. on 4d. grey .. 90·00 90·00

Setting 4. Bars 11 mm apart. Five out of the six varieties in the strip have the "2" below the space between the "1" and "d".
69 ½d. on 4d. grey .. 90·00

There is a fifth setting, but the variation is slight.

(Typo D.L.R.)

1894–95. *Wmk Crown CA. P 14.*
70 31 ½d. dull green (Die II) (1894) .. 40 75
71 4d. dull purple & ultram (Die II) (5.95) 4·50 10·00
72 34 5d. olive-green and carmine (6.94) .. 2·50 9·00
a. Bisected (2½d.) (on cover) .. † £1600
71/2 Optd "Specimen" .. *Set of 2* £110

ALTERED CATALOGUE NUMBERS

Any Catalogue numbers altered from the last edition are shown as a list in the introductory pages.

TURKS AND CAICOS ISLANDS

35

36

Salt raking

The dates on the stamps have reference to the political separation from Bahamas.

(Recess D.L.R.)

1900 (10 Nov)–**04.** *Wmk Crown CA* (½d. to 1s.) *or Wmk Crown CC* (2s., 3s.). *P 14.*
101 35 ½d. green .. 2·25 3·75
102 1d. red .. 2·25 1·90
103 2d. sepia .. 2·40 2·40
104 2½d. blue .. 4·25 8·50
a. Greyish blue (1904) .. 2·25 3·00
105 4d. orange .. 4·25 7·00
106 6d. dull mauve .. 3·00 6·50
107 1s. purple-brown .. 2·75 7·00
108 36 2s. purple .. 45·00 65·00
109 3s. lake .. 45·00 65·00
101/9 .. *Set of 9* £100 £140
101/9 Optd "Specimen" .. *Set of 9* £300

1905–08. *Wmk Mult Crown CA. P 14.*
110 35 ½d. green .. 75 50
111 1d. red .. 6·50 2·00
112 3d. purple/*yellow* (1908) (Optd S. £60) .. 3·00 6·50

37 Turk's-head Cactus

38

(Recess D.L.R.)

1909 (2 Sept)–**11.** *Wmk Mult Crown CA. P 14.*
115 37 ¼d. rosy mauve (1910) .. 50 1·00
116 ¼d. red (1911) .. 25 30
117 38 ½d. yellow-green .. 30 30
118 1d. red .. 30 35
119 2d. greyish slate .. 3·00 4·25
120 2½d. blue .. 2·00 4·50
121 3d. purple/*yellow* .. 2·75 4·50
122 4d. red/*yellow* .. 5·00 7·50
123 6d. purple .. 8·00 10·00
124 1s. black/*green* .. 5·00 9·00
125 2s. red/*green* .. 19·00 32·00
126 3s. black/*red* .. 24·00 38·00
115/26 .. *Set of 12* 65·00 £100
115/26 Optd "Specimen" .. *Set of 12* £300

See also Nos. 154 and 162.

39

WAR TAX
(40)

1913 (1 Apr)–**21.** *Wmk Mult Crown CA. P 14.*
129 39 ½d. green .. 30 1·00
130 1d. red .. 1·40 1·10
a. Bright scarlet .. 1·40 1·40
b. Rose-carmine (1918) .. 1·40 1·40
131 2d. greyish slate .. 95 1·50
132 2½d. ultramarine .. 3·25 4·50
a. Bright blue (1918) .. 3·25 4·50
133 3d. purple/*yellow* .. 2·50 5·00
a. On lemon .. 12·00
b. On yellow-buff .. 3·00 4·50
c. On orange-buff .. 2·00
d. On pale yellow .. 3·00 4·25
134 4d. red/*yellow* .. 2·75 6·00
a. On orange-buff (Optd S. £48) .. 2·00 6·50
b. Carmine on pale yellow .. 3·00 7·00
135 5d. pale olive-green (18.5.16) .. 4·25 8·00
136 6d. dull purple .. 4·50 8·00
137 1s. brown-orange .. 2·50 5·50
138 2s. red/*blue-green* .. 9·00 14·00
a. On greenish white (1919) .. 16·00 30·00
b. On emerald (3.21) (Optd S. £48) .. 13·00 22·00
139 3s. black/*red* .. 17·00 25·00
129/39 .. *Set of 11* 42·00 70·00
129/39 Optd "Specimen" .. *Set of 11* £225

1917 (3 Jan). *Optd with T 40 at bottom of stamp.*
140 39 1d. red .. 20 65
a. Overprint double .. £150
b. "TAX" omitted ..
c. "WAR TAX" omitted in vert pair with normal ..
d. Opt inverted at top .. £100
e. Opt double, one inverted* ..
f. Opt inverted only, in pair with No. 140e* ..
141 3d. purple/*yellow-buff* .. 45 1·25
a. Opt double .. 38·00
142 3d. purple/*lemon* .. 70 1·60
a. Opt double .. 35·00
b. Opt double, one inverted ..

*In Nos. 140e/f the inverted overprint is at foot and reads "TAX WAR" owing to displacement. No. 140e also exists with "WAR" omitted from the inverted overprint.

In both values of the first printings the stamp in the bottom left-hand corner of the sheet has a long "T" in "TAX", and on the first stamp of the sixth row the "X" is damaged and looks like a reversed "K".

1917 (Oct). *Second printing with overprint at top or in middle of stamp.*
143 39 1d. red .. 20 50
a. Inverted opt at bottom or centre .. 23·00
c. Overprint omitted, in pair with normal .. £140
d. Double overprint, one at top, one at bottom .. 35·00
e. As d., but additional overprint in top margin .. 90·00
f. Vertical pair, one as d., the other normal .. £180
g. Pair, one overprint inverted, one normal .. £225
h. Double overprint at top (in pair with normal .. £180
i. Overprint double .. 35·00 35·00
144 3d. purple/*yellow* .. 40 1·00
a. Opt double .. 19·00
b. Opt double, one inverted ..
144*c* 3d. purple/*lemon* ..

1918. *Overprinted with T 40.*
145 39 3d. purple/*yellow* (R.) .. 2·50 4·00
a. Opt double ..

WAR TAX
(41)

WAR TAX
(42)

WAR TAX
(43)

1918. *Optd with T 41 in London by D.L.R.*
146 39 1d. rose-carmine .. 40 1·25
a. Bright rose-scarlet .. 25 65
147 3d. purple/*yellow* .. 30 75
146/7 Optd. "Specimen" .. *Set of 2* £110

1919. *Optd with T 41 in London by D.L.R.*
148 39 3d. purple/*orange-buff* (R.) .. 35 1·00
148 Optd "Specimen" .. 65·00

1919. *Local overprint. T 40, in violet.*
149 39 1d. bright rose-scarlet .. 35 75
a. "WAR" omitted .. 95·00
b. Opt double .. 16·00
c. Opt double in pair with normal .. 95·00
d. Rose-carmine .. 3·25 4·75
da. Opt double ..

1919. *Optd with T 42.*
150 39 1d. scarlet .. 20 60
a. Opt double .. 95·00 95·00
151 3d. purple/*orange-buff* .. 75 1·60

1919 (17 Dec). *Optd with T 43 in London by D.L.R.*
152 39 1d. scarlet .. 20 60
a. Opt inverted ..
153 3d. purple/*orange-buff* .. 20 75

The two bottom rows of this setting have the words "WAR" and "TAX" about 1 mm further apart.

1921 (23 April). *Wmk Mult Script CA. P 14.*
154 37 ¼d. rose-red .. 25 1·40
155 39 ½d. green .. 60 2·50
156 1d. carmine-red .. 60 1·75
157 2d. slate-grey .. 1·25 4·00
158 2½d. bright blue .. 2·00 5·50
159 5d. sage-green .. 4·25 8·50
160 6d. purple .. 6·00 14·00
161 1s. brown-orange .. 12·00 23·00
154/161 .. *Set of 8* 24·00 55·00
154/61 Optd "Specimen" .. *Set of 8* £225

44

45

(Recess D.L.R.)

1922 (20 Nov)–**26.** *P 14. (a) Wmk Mult Script CA.*
162 37 ¼d. black (11.10.26) .. 20 50
163 44 ½d. yellow-green .. 30 70
a. Bright green .. 50 85
b. Apple-green .. 1·50 2·25
164 1d. brown .. 65 1·75
165 1½d. scarlet (24.11.25) .. 1·50 2·00
166 2d. slate .. 1·00 2·00
167 2½d. purple/*pale yellow* .. 30 70
168 3d. bright blue .. 1·25 2·00
169 4d. red/*pale yellow* .. 1·50 2·75
a. Carmine/pale yellow .. 3·00 5·50
170 5d. sage-green .. 1·50 4·75
171 6d. purple .. 1·60 3·50
172 1s. brown-orange .. 1·90 4·75
173 2s. red/*emerald* .. 5·50 10·00
(b) Wmk Mult Crown CA
174 44 2s. red/*emerald* (24.11.25) .. 17·00 26·00
175 3s. black/*red* (24.11.25) .. 9·00 15·00
162/75 .. *Set of 14* 38·00 70·00
162/75 Optd "Specimen" .. *Set of 14* £300

1928 (1 Mar). *Inscr "POSTAGE & REVENUE". Wmk Mult Script CA. P 14.*
176 45 ½d. green .. 35 40
177 1d. brown .. 35 60
178 1½d. scarlet .. 35 90

179 **45** 2d. grey 45 40
180 2½d. purple/*yellow* . . . . 70 1·00
181 3d. bright blue . . . . 70 1·40
182 6d. purple . . . . 1·10 2·00
183 1s. brown-orange . . . . 2·00 3·50
184 2s. red/*emerald* . . . . 7·00 15·00
185 5s. green/*yellow* . . . . 24·00 40·00
186 10s. purple/*blue* . . . . 45·00 70·00
176/86 . . . . *Set of* 11 75·00 £120
176/86 Optd "Specimen" . . . . *Set of* 11 £250

1935 (6 May). *Silver Jubilee. As Nos.* 91/4 *of Antigua, but ptd by Waterlow. P* 11 × 12.
187 ½d. black and green 20 50
188 3d. brown and deep blue . . . . . . 1·25 1·75
189 6d. light blue and olive-green . . . . 1·60 2·25
190 1s. slate and purple . . . . 4·00 7·50
187/90 Perf "Specimen" . . . . *Set of* 4 60·00

1937 (12 May). *Coronation. As Nos.* 13/15 *of Aden.*
191 ½d. myrtle-green 15 15
a. Deep green . . . .
192 2d. grey-black 30 30
193 3d. bright blue 40 40
191/3 Perf "Specimen" . . . . *Set of* 3 35·00

46 Raking Salt

47 Salt Industry

(Recess Waterlow)

1938 (18 June)–**45**. *Wmk Mult Script CA. P* 12½.
194 **46** ¼d. black 10 10
195 ½d. yellowish green 45 35
a. Deep green (6.11.44) 15 20
196 1d. red-brown 15 10
197 1½d. scarlet 15 20
198 2d. grey 15 15
199 2½d. yellow-orange 35 30
a. Orange (6.11.44) 35 30
200 3d. bright blue 15 15
201 6d. mauve . . . . 4·50 3·50
201*a* 6d. sepia (9.2.45) 35 40
202 1s. yellow-bistre . . . . . . 2·50 6·00
202*a* 1s. grey-olive (9.2.45) 55 55
203 **47** 2s. deep rose-carmine . . . . 5·50 4·50
a. Bright rose-carmine (6.11.44) 5·00 4·00
204 5s. yellowish green . . . . 12·00 11·00
a. Deep green (6.11.44) . . . . 11·00 11·00
205 10s. bright violet . . . . . . 8·50 10·00
194/205 . . . . . . *Set of* 14 30·00 32·00
194/205 Perf "Specimen" . . . . *Set of* 14 £200

1946 (4 Nov). *Victory. As Nos.* 28/9 *of Aden.*
206 2d. black 15 30
207 3d. blue 20 30
206/7 Perf "Specimen" . . . . *Set of* 2 50·00

1948 (13 Sept). *Royal Silver Wedding. As Nos.* 30/1 *of Aden.*
208 1d. red-brown 15 15
209 10s. mauve . . . . 6·50 13·00

50 Badge of the Islands

53 Queen Victoria and King George VI

(Recess Waterlow)

1948 (14 Dec). *Centenary of Separation from Bahamas. T* **50**, **53** *and similar designs. Wmk Mult Script CA. P* 12½.
210 **50** ½d. blue-green 20 20
211 2d. carmine 40 30
212 – 3d. blue 50 45
213 – 6d. violet 50 60
214 **53** 2s. black and bright blue . . . . 80 1·10
215 5s. black and green . . . . . . 1·25 4·00
216 10s. black and brown . . . . . . 1·50 6·50
210/16 . . . . . . *Set of* 7 4·50 12·00
Designs: *Horiz*—3d. Flag of Turks and Caicos Islands; 6d. Map of islands.

1949 (10 Oct). 75*th Anniv of Universal Postal Union. As Nos.* 114/17 *of Antigua.*
217 2½d. red-orange 15 30
218 3d. deep blue 45 55
219 6d. brown 60 70
220 1s. olive 70 90

65 Bulk Salt Loading

66 Dependency's Badge

(Recess Waterlow)

1950 (1 Aug). *T* **65** *and similar horiz designs, and T* **66**. *Wmk Mult Script CA. P* 12½.
221 ½d. green 15 40
222 1d. red-brown 15 50
223 1½d. deep carmine 20 50
224 2d. red-orange 15 40
225 2½d. grey-olive 20 50
226 3d. bright blue 20 50
227 4d. black and rose . . . . 80 1·25
228 6d. black and blue . . . . 80 1·25
229 1s. black and blue-green . . . . . . 70 1·25
230 1s. 6d. black and scarlet . . . . . . 1·40 3·00
231 2s. emerald and ultramarine . . . . 1·75 3·50
232 5s. blue and black . . . . 8·50 11·00
233 10s. black and violet . . . . . . 20·00 27·00
221/33 . . . . . . *Set of* 13 32·00 45·00
Designs:—1d. Salt Cay; 1½d. Caicos mail; 2d. Grand Turk; 2½d. Sponge diving; 3d. South Creek; 4d. Map; 6d. Grand Turk Light; 1s. Government House; 1s. 6d. Cockburn Harbour; 2s. Government Offices; 5s. Loading salt.

1953 (2 June). *Coronation. As No.* 47 *of Aden, but ptd by B.W. & Co.*
234 2d. black and orange-red 15 80

67 M.V. *Kirksons*

(Recess Waterlow)

1955 (1 Feb). *T* **67** *and similar horiz design. Wmk Mult Script CA. P* 12½.
235 5d. black and bright green 50 40
236 8d. black and brown 50 25
Design:—8d. Greater Flamingoes in flight.

69 Queen Elizabeth II (after Annigoni)

70 Bonefish

82 Dependency's Badge

(Recess B.W.)

1957 (25 Nov). *T* **69/70**, **82** *and similar horiz design as T* **70**. *W* w **12**. *P* 13½ × 14 (1*d.*), 14 (10*s.*) *or* 13½ (*others*).
237 1d. deep blue and carmine 12 20
238 1½d. grey-green and orange 20 35
239 2d. red-brown and olive 20 25
240 2½d. carmine and green 20 25
241 3d. turquoise-blue and purple 20 15
242 4d. lake and black 20 15
243 5d. slate-green and brown 25 50
244 6d. carmine-rose and blue 30 12
245 8d. vermilion and black 50 10
246 1s. deep blue and black 30 10
247 1s. 6d. sepia and deep ultramarine 80 80
248 2s. deep ultramarine and brown . . . . 2·00 2·50
249 5s. black and carmine . . . . . . 1·75 3·00
250 10s. black and purple . . . . . . 9·00 12·00
237/250 *and* 253 . . . . *Set of* 15 35·00 42·00
Designs:—2d. Red Grouper; 2½d. Spiny Lobster; 3d. Albacore; 4d. Muttonfish Snapper; 5d. Permit; 6d. Conch; 8d. Greater Flamingoes; 1s. Spanish Mackerel; 1s. 6d. Salt Cay; 2s. Caicos sloop; 5s. Cable Office.

83 Map of the Turks and Caicos Islands

(Photo D.L.R.)

1959 (4 July). *New Constitution. Wmk Mult Script CA P* 13½ × 14.
251 **83** 6d. deep olive and light orange 25 30
252 8d. violet and light orange 25 20

84 Brown Pelican

(Des Mrs. S. Hurd. Photo Harrison)

1960 (1 Nov). *W* w 12. *P* 14 × 14½.
253 **84** £1 sepia and deep red . . . . . . 24·00 26·00

CROWN COLONY

1963 (4 June). *Freedom from Hunger. As No.* 76 *of Aden.*
254 8d. carmine 30 20

1963 (2 Sept). *Red Cross Centenary. As Nos.* 147/8 *of Antigua.*
255 2d. red and black 20 10
256 8d. red and blue 45 30

1964 (23 April). 400*th Birth Anniv of William Shakespeare. As No.* 164 *of Antigua.*
257 8d. green 12 10

1965 (17 May). *I.T.U. Centenary. As Nos.* 166/7 *of Antigua.*
258 1d. vermilion and brown 10 5
259 2s. light emerald and turquoise-blue . . 40 25

1965 (25 Oct). *International Co-operation Year. As Nos.* 168/9 *of Antigua.*
260 1d. reddish purple and turquoise-green . . 5 5
261 8d. deep bluish green and lavender 25 15

1966 (24 Jan). *Churchill Commemoration. As Nos.* 170/3 *of Antigua.*
262 1d. new blue 5 5
263 2d. deep green 15 8
264 8d. brown 30 20
265 1s. 6d. bluish violet 40 40

1966 (4 Feb). *Royal Visit. As Nos.* 174/5 *of Antigua.*
266 8d. black and ultramarine 25 10
267 1s. 6d. black and magenta 45 25

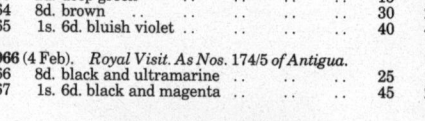

85 Andrew Symmer going ashore

(Des V. Whiteley. Photo D.L.R.)

1966 (1 Oct). *Bicentenary of "Ties with Britain" T* **85** *and similar horiz designs. P* 13½.
268 1d. deep blue and orange 5 5
269 8d. red, blue and orange-yellow 15 10
270 1s. 6d. multicoloured 20 20
Designs:—8d. Andrew Symmer and Royal Warrant; 1s. 6d. Arms and Royal Cypher.

1966 (1 Dec). 20*th Anniv of U.N.E.S.C.O. As Nos.* 196/8 *of Antigua.*
271 1d. slate-violet, red, yellow and orange . . 10 5
272 8d. orange-yellow, violet and deep olive . . 30 10
273 1s. 6d. black, bright purple and orange . . 40 40

88 Turk's-head Cactus

89 Boat-building

90 Arms of Turks and Caicos Islands

91 Queen Elizabeth II

(Des V. Whiteley. Photo Harrison)

1967 (1 Feb). *Designs as T* **88/91**. W w **12**. *P* 14½ × 14 (*vert*) *or* 14 × 14½ (*horiz*).

274 1d. olive-yellow, vermilion & brt bluish vio .. 5 5
275 1½d. brown and orange-yellow 5 5
276 2d. deep slate and deep orange-yellow .. 8 5
277 3d. agate and dull green 8 5
278 4d. bright mauve, black and turquoise .. 10 5
279 6d. sepia and new blue 12 5
280 8d. yellow, turquoise-blue and deep blue .. 15 5
281 1s. maroon and turquoise 25 5
282 1s. 6d. orange-yellow, lake-brn & dp turq-bl 80 40
283 2s. multicoloured 85 60
284 3s. maroon and turquoise-blue 85 40
285 5s. ochre, blue and new blue .. .. 1·75 1·75
286 10s. multicoloured .. .. 2·50 3·25
287 £1 Prussian blue, silver and crimson .. 5·00 8·00
274/287 .. .. *Set of* 14 11·00 13·00

Designs: *Vert as T* **88**—2d. Donkey; 3d. Sisal industry; 6d. Salt industry; 8d. Skin-diving; 1s. 6d. Water-skiing. *Horiz as T* **89**—4d. Conch industry; 1s. Fishing; 2s. Crawfish industry; 3s. Maps of Turks and Caicos Islands and West Indies; 5s. Fishing industry.

102 Turks Islands 1d. Stamp of 1867

(Des R. Granger Barrett. Photo Harrison)

1967 (1 May). *Stamp Centenary. T* **102** *and similar horiz designs.* W w **12**. *P* 14½.

288 1d. black and light magenta.. .. .. 5 5
289 6d. black and bluish grey 10 10
290 1s. black and turquoise-blue 15 15

Designs:—6d. Queen Elizabeth "stamp" and Turks Islands 6d. stamp of 1867; 1s. Turks Islands 1s. stamp of 1867.

104 Human Rights Emblem and Charter

(Des R. Granger Barrett. Photo Harrison)

1968 (1 Apr). *Human Rights Year.* W w **12**. *P* 14 × 14½.

291 **104** 1d. multicoloured 5 5
292 8d. multicoloured 8 8
293 1s. 6d. multicoloured 12 12

105 Dr Martin Luther King and "Freedom March"

(Des V. Whiteley. Photo Harrison)

1968 (1 Oct). *Martin Luther King Commemoration.* W w **12**. *P* 14 × 14½.

294 **105** 2d. yellow-brown, blackish brn & dp bl 5 5
295 8d. yellow-brown, blackish brn & lake 8 8
296 1s. 6d. yellow-brn, blackish brn & vio .. 12 12

(New Currency. 100 cents=1 dollar)

1c

(106)

107 "The Nativity with John the Baptist"

1969 (8 Sept). *Decimal currency. Nos.* 274/87 *surch as T* **106** *by Harrison & Sons, and new value* (¼ c.) *as T* **90**.

297 ¼ c. multicoloured (*shades*) 5 5
298 1 c. on 1d. olive-yell, verm & brt bluish vio .. 5 5
a. Wmk sideways 5 5
299 2 c. on 2d. deep slate and deep orange-yellow 5 5
a. Wmk sideways 5 5
300 3 c. on 3d. agate and dull green 5 5
a. Wmk sideways 5 5
301 4 c. on 4d. bright mauve, black and turquoise 8 5
302 5 c. on 6d. sepia and new blue 10 5
a. Wmk sideways 10 5
303 7 c. on 8d. yellow, turquoise-blue & dp blue .. 12 5
a. Wmk sideways 12 5
304 8 c. on 1½d. brown and orange-yellow .. 12 5
305 10 c. on 1s. maroon and turquoise 20 5
306 15 c. on 1s. 6d. orange-yellow, lake-brown and deep turquoise-blue 35 10
a. Wmk sideways 30 30
307 20 c. on 2s. multicoloured 40 35
308 30 c. on 3s. maroon and turquoise-blue .. 70 50
309 50 c. on 5s. ochre, blue and new blue .. 1·25 80
310 $1 on 10s. multicoloured .. .. .. 2·00 2·00
311 $2 on £1 Prussian blue, silver and crimson 9·50 16·00
a. Wmk sideways .. .. 3·00 4·75
297/311a .. .. *Set of* 15 7·50 8·00

The 4, 8, 10, 20, 30, 50 c., and $1 exist with PVA gum as well as gum arabic.

No. 311 was only on sale through the Crown Agents.

(Des adapted by V. Whiteley. Litho D.L.R.)

1969 (20 Oct). *Christmas. Scenes from 16th-cent Book of Hours. T* **107** *and similar vert design. Multicoloured.* W w **12**. *P* 13 × 12½.

312 1 c. Type **107** 5 5
313 3 c. "The Flight into Egypt" 10 10
314 15 c. Type **107** 15 15
315 30 c. As 3 c. 20 20

109 Coat of Arms

110 "Christ bearing the Cross"

(Des L. Curtis. Litho B.W.)

1970 (2 Feb). *New Constitution. Multicoloured; background colours given.* W w **12** (*sideways*). *P* 13 × 12½.

316 **109** 7 c. brown 10 10
317 35 c. deep violet-blue 40 30

(Des, recess and litho Enschedé)

1970 (17 Mar). *Easter. Details from the "Small Engraved Passion" by Dürer. T* **110** *and similar vert designs.* W w **12** (*sideways*). *P* 13 × 13½.

318 5 c. olive-grey and blue 10 5
319 7 c. olive-grey and vermilion.. .. .. 10 10
320 50 c. olive-grey and red-brown 50 70

Designs:—7 c. "Christ on the Cross"; 50 c. "The Lamentation of Christ".

113 Dickens and Scene from *Oliver Twist*

(Des Sylvia Goaman. Recess and litho D.L.R.)

1970 (17 June). *Death Centenary of Charles Dickens. T* **113** *and similar horiz designs.* W w **12** (*sideways*). *P* 13.

321 1 c. black and yellow-brown/*yellow* 5 5
322 3 c. black and Prussian blue/*flesh* 5 5
323 15 c. black and grey-blue/*flesh* 25 15
324 30 c. black and drab/*blue* 40 35

Designs (each incorporating portrait of Dickens as in T **113**, and a scene from one of his novels):—3 c. *A Christmas Carol*; 15 c. *Pickwick Papers*; 30 c. *The Old Curiosity Shop*.

114 Ambulance—1870

(Des Harrison. Litho B.W.)

1970 (4 Aug). *Centenary of British Red Cross. T* **114** *and similar horiz design. Multicoloured.* W w **12**. *P* 13½ × 14.

325 1 c. Type **114** 5 5
326 5 c. Ambulance—1970 .. .. .. 10 10
a. Wmk sideways 10 10
327 15 c. Type **114** 20 15
a. Wmk sideways 20 15
328 30 c. As 5 c. 30 30
a. Wmk sideways 30 30

No. 326a is known with grey omitted.

OMNIBUS ISSUES

Details, together with prices for complete sets, of the various Omnibus issues from the 1935 Silver Jubilee series to date are included in a special section following Zululand at the end of the catalogue.

115 Duke of Albermarle and Coat of Arms

(Des V. Whiteley. Litho Enschedé)

1970 (1 Dec). *Tercentenary of Issue of Letters Patent. T* **115** *and similar horiz design. Multicoloured.* W w **12**. *P* 12½ × 13½.

329 1 c. Type **115** 5 5
330 8 c. Arms of Charles II and Elizabeth II .. 40 40
331 10 c. Type **115** 40 30
332 35 c. As 8 c. .. .. 75 1·00

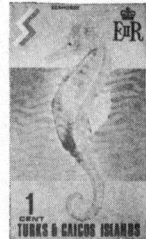

116 Boat-building 117 Seahorse

1971 (2 Feb). *Designs as T* **88/91** *etc., but inscr in decimal currency as in T* **116**. W w **12** (*sideways on* 1 c., 2 c., 3 c., 5 c., 7 c., 15 c. *and* $2).

333 1 c. olive-yell, verm & brt bluish vio (as 1d.) 10 5
334 2 c. deep slate & deep orange-yell (as 2d.) .. 12 5
335 3 c. agate and dull green (as 3d.) 15 5
336 4 c. bright mauve, black & turquoise (as 4d.) 20 5
337 5 c. sepia and new blue (as 6d.) 20 5
338 7 c. yellow, turquoise-blue & dp blue (as 8d.) 25 5
339 8 c. brown and orange-yellow 30 5
340 10 c. maroon and turquoise (as 1s.) 30 5
341 15 c. orange-yellow, lake-brown and deep turquoise-blue (as 1s. 6d.) 60 40
342 20 c. multicoloured (as 2s.) 75 75
343 30 c. maroon and turquoise-blue (as 3s.) .. 1·25 1·00
344 50 c. ochre, blue and new blue (as 5s.) .. 2·25 2·25
345 $1 multicoloured (as 10s.) .. .. .. 3·50 4·50
346 $2 Prussian blue, silver and crimson (as £1) 6·50 9·00
333/46 .. .. *Set of* 14 15·00 16·00

The ¼ c. value was also re-issued, but it can only be distinguished from No. 297 by its revised sheet format of 25 instead of 60.

(Des G. Vasarhelyi. Litho J.W.)

1971 (4 May). *Tourist Development. T* **117** *and similar multicoloured designs.* W w **12** (*sideways on Nos.* 348/50). *P* 14 × 14½ (1 c.) *or* 14½ × 14 (*others*).

347 1 c. Type **117** 5 5
348 3 c. Queen Conch Shell (*horiz*) 5 5
349 15 c. Oystercatcher (*horiz*) 40 20
350 30 c. Blue Marlin (*horiz*) 55 30

118 Pirate Sloop 119 The Wilton Diptych (Left Wing)

(Des and litho J.W.)

1971 (27 July). *Pirates. T* **118** *and similar horiz designs. Multicoloured.* W w **12** (*sideways*). *P* 14.

351 2 c. Type **118** 10 10
352 3 c. Pirate treasure 12 10
353 15 c. Marooned sailor 70 45
354 30 c. Buccaneers .. .. 1·00 75

(Des J.W. Litho Questa)

1971 (12 Oct). *Christmas. T* **119** *and similar vert design. Multicoloured.* W w **12**. *P* 13½.

355 2 c. Type **119** 5 5
a. Horiz pair. Nos. 355/6 .. .. .. 10 10
356 2 c. The Wilton Diptych (Right Wing) .. 5 5
357 8 c. Type **119** 15 20
a. Horiz pair. Nos. 357/8 .. .. .. 30 40
358 8 c. As No. 356 .. .. 15 20
359 15 c. Type **119** 20 20
a. Horiz pair. Nos. 359/60 .. .. .. 40 40
360 15 c. As No. 356 .. .. 20 20
355/60 .. .. *Set of* 6 70 80

The two stamps of each denomination were printed in horizontal *se-tenant* pairs throughout the sheet.

120 Cape Kennedy Launching Area   121 "Christ before Pilate" (Rembrandt)

(Des V. Whiteley. Litho A. & M.)

1972 (21 Feb). *Tenth Anniv of Colonel Glenn's Splashdown. T* **120** *and similar multicoloured designs.* W w **12** (*sideways on* 5, 10 *and* 15 *c.*). *P* 13½.

361 5 c. Type **120** .. 10 5
362 10 c. "Friendship 7" space capsule .. 20 15
363 15 c. Map of Islands and splashdown .. 25 25
364 20 c. N.A.S.A. Space Medal (*vert*) .. 30 30

(Des and litho J.W.)

1972 (21 Mar). *Easter. T* **121** *and similar designs.* W w **12** (*sideways on* 15 *c.*). *P* 13½.

365 2 c. black and lilac .. 5 5
366 15 c. black and rose-pink .. 20 15
367 30 c. black and greenish yellow .. 35 25

Designs: *Horiz*—15 c. "The Three Crosses" (Rembrandt). *Vert*—30 c. "The Descent from the Cross" (Rembrandt).

122 Christopher Columbus   123 Turk's-head Cactus and Spiny Lobster

(Des P. Powell. Litho J.W.)

1972 (28 July*). *Discoverers and Explorers. T* **122** *and similar multicoloured designs.* W w **12** (*sideways on* 8 *and* 30 *c.*). *P* 13½.

368 ¼ c. Type **122** .. 5 5
369 8 c. Sir Richard Grenville (*horiz*) .. 35 25
370 10 c. Capt. John Smith .. 40 30
371 30 c. Juan Ponce de Leon (*horiz*) .. 1·40 1·25

*This was the local date of issue; the Crown Agents released the stamps on 4 July.

(Des (from photograph by D. Groves) and photo Harrison)

1972 (20 Nov). *Royal Silver Wedding. Multicoloured; background colour given.* W w **12**. *P* 14 × 14½.

372 **123** 10 c. dull ultramarine .. 15 20
373 20 c. myrtle-green .. 25 25

124 Treasure Hunting, *circa* 1700   125 Arms of Jamaica and Turks & Caicos Islands

(Des C. Abbott. Litho Questa)

1973 (18 Jan). *Treasure. T* **124** *and similar vert designs.* W w **12** (*sideways*). *P* 14 × 14½.

374 3 c. multicoloured .. 10 5
375 5 c. reddish purple, silver and black .. 10 5
376 10 c. magenta, silver and black .. 40 25
377 30 c. multicoloured .. 1·10 85
MS378 127 × 108 mm. Nos. 374/7 .. 2·25 2·25

Designs:—5 c. Silver Bank medallion (obverse); 10 c. Silver Bank medallion (reverse); 30 c. Treasure hunting, 1973.

(Des PAD Studio. Litho Walsall)

1973 (16 Apr). *Centenary of Annexation to Jamaica.* W w **12** (*sideways*). *P* 13½ × 14.

379 **125** 15 c. multicoloured .. 30 20
380 35 c. multicoloured .. 60 50

126 Sooty Tern   **127** Bermuda Sloop

(Des R. Granger Barrett. Litho Questa)

1973 (1 Aug). *T* **126** *and similar vert designs.* W w **12** (*sideways*). *P* 14.

381 ¼ c. Type **126** .. 5 10
382 1 c. Magnificent Frigate Bird .. 20 20
383 2 c. Common Noddy .. 30 30
384 3 c. Blue-grey Gnatcatcher .. 50 40
385 4 c. Little Blue Heron .. 30 25
386 5 c. Catbird .. 30 25
387 7 c. Black Whiskered Vireo .. 35 30
388 8 c. Osprey .. 50 40
389 10 c. Greater Flamingo .. 50 30
390 15 c. Brown Pelican .. 70 60
391 20 c. Parula Warbler .. 2·00 1·50
392 30 c. Northern Mockingbird .. 1·25 1·25
393 50 c. Ruby-throated Hummingbird .. 2·00 2·00
394 $1 Bananaquit .. 3·75 3·75
395 $2 Cedar Waxwing .. 6·00 6·00
381/95 .. *Set of* 15 17·00 16·00

See also Nos. 411/14 and 451/64.

(Des R. Granger Barrett. Litho Questa)

1973 (14 Aug). *Vessels. T* **127** *and similar horiz designs. Multicoloured.* W w **12**. *P* 13½.

396 2 c. Type **127** .. 5 5
397 5 c. H.M.S. *Blanche* .. 15 15
398 8 c. U.S. privateer *Grand Turk* and P.O. packet *Hinchinbrooke* .. 25 25
399 10 c. H.M.S. *Endymion* .. 30 30
400 15 c. R.M.S. *Medina* .. 60 80
401 20 c. H.M.S. *Daring* .. 70 90
396/401 .. *Set of* 6 1·90 2·25
MS402 198 × 101 mm. Nos. 396/401 .. 2·25 3·00

1973 (14 Nov). *Royal Wedding. As Nos.* 165/6 *of Anguilla.*

403 12 c. light turquoise-blue .. 12 12
404 18 c. dull indigo .. 15 15

128 Duho (stool)

(Des Jennifer Toombs. Litho Questa)

1974 (17 July). *Lucayan Remains. T* **128** *and similar horiz designs. Multicoloured.* W w **12** (*sideways*). *P* 14½ × 14.

405 6 c. Type **128** .. 10 10
406 10 c. Broken wood bowl .. 15 15
407 12 c. Greenstone axe .. 20 20
408 18 c. Wood bowl .. 30 30
409 35 c. Fragment of duho .. 60 60
MS410 240 × 90 mm. Nos. 405/9 .. 1·75 1·90

1974–75. *As Nos.* 381 *etc, but* W w **12** (*upright*).

411 1 c. Magnificent Frigate Bird (11.6.75) .. 45 55
412 2 c. Common Noddy (27.9.74) .. 55 55
413 3 c. Blue-grey Gnatcatcher (19.3.75) .. 1·00 1·00
414 20 c. Parula Warbler (11.6.75) .. 2·75 2·50

Nos. 415/25 vacant.

129 G.P.O., Grand Turk

(Des G. Drummond. Litho Questa)

1974 (9 Oct). *Centenary of Universal Postal Union. T* **129** *and similar horiz designs. Multicoloured.* W w **12**. *P* 14.

426 4 c. Type **129** .. 12 5
427 12 c. Sloop and island map .. 30 20
428 18 c. "U.P.U." and globe .. 40 30
429 55 c. Posthorn and emblem .. 95 80

130 Churchill and Roosevelt   131 Spanish Captain, *circa* 1492

(Des V. Whiteley. Litho Questa)

1974 (30 Nov). *Birth Centenary of Sir Winston Churchill. T* **130** *and similar horiz design. Multicoloured.* W w **14** (*sideways*). *P* 14.

430 12 c. Type **130** .. 25 20
431 18 c. Churchill and vapour-trails .. 30 25
MS432 85 × 85 mm. Nos. 430/1 .. 70 80

(Des J.W. Litho Questa)

1975 (26 Mar). *Military Uniforms. T* **131** *and similar vert designs. Multicoloured.* W w **14**. *P* 14.

433 5 c. Type **131** .. 10 10
434 20 c. Officer, Royal Artillery, 1783 .. 50 30
435 25 c. Officer, 67th Foot, 1798 .. 65 50
436 35 c. Private, 1st West India Regt, 1833 .. 95 85
MS437 145 × 88 mm. Nos. 433/6 .. 2·50 2·50

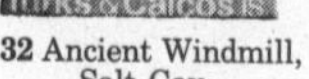

132 Ancient Windmill, Salt Cay   133 Star Coral

(Des P. Powell. Litho Questa)

1975 (16 Oct). *Salt-raking Industry. T* **132** *and similar multicoloured designs.* W w **12** (*sideways on* 10 *and* 20 *c.*). *P* 14.

438 6 c. Type **132** .. 20 15
439 10 c. Salt pans drying in sun (*horiz*) .. 30 20
440 20 c. Salt-raking (*horiz*) .. 60 40
441 25 c. Unprocessed salt heaps .. 65 50

(Des C. Abbott. Litho Questa)

1975 (4 Dec). *Island Coral. T* **133** *and similar horiz designs. Multicoloured.* W w **14** (*sideways*). *P* 14.

442 6 c. Type **133** .. 20 15
443 10 c. Elkhorn Coral .. 30 20
444 20 c. Brain Coral .. 60 40
445 25 c. Staghorn Coral .. 65 50

134 American Schooner   135 1s. 6d. Royal Visit Stamp of 1966

(Des J.W. Litho Questa)

1976 (28 May). *Bicentenary of American Revolution. T* **134** *and similar vert designs. Multicoloured.* W w **14**. *P* 13½.

446 6 c. Type **134** .. 40 20
447 20 c. British ship of the line .. 1·25 60
448 25 c. American frigate *Grand Turk* .. 1·25 65
449 55 c. British ketch .. 2·25 1·50
MS450 95 × 151 mm. Nos. 446/9 .. 5·50 5·50

Each value depicts, at the top, the engagement between the *Grand Turk* and the P.O. Packet *Hinchinbrooke*, as in T **134**.

1976–77. *As Nos.* 381/95, *and new value* ($5), *but* W w **14** (*upright*).

451 ¼ c. Type **126** (12.77) .. 5 10
452 1 c. Magnificent Frigate Bird (12.77) .. 20 15
453 2 c. Common Noddy (12.77) .. 25 20
454 3 c. Blue-grey Gnatcatcher (14.6.76) .. 60 20
455 4 c. Little Blue Heron (12.77) .. 30 20
456 5 c. Catbird (12.77) .. 30 20
457 10 c. Greater Flamingo (12.77) .. 40 25
458 15 c. Brown Pelican (12.77) .. 70 45
459 20 c. Parula Warbler (30.11.76) .. 2·00 75
460 30 c. Northern Mockingbird (12.77) .. 1·25 75
461 50 c. Ruby-throated Hummingbird (12.77) .. 1·50 1·25
462 $1 Bananaquit (12.77) .. 2·25 2·00
463 $2 Cedar Waxwing (12.77) .. 3·75 3·75
464 $5 Painted Bunting (24.11.76) .. 5·50 6·00
451/64 .. *Set of* 14 17·00 14·50

No. 465 vacant.

(Des V. Whiteley Studio. Litho Walsall)

1976 (14 July). *Tenth Anniv of Royal Visit. T* **135** *and similar horiz design. Multicoloured.* W w **14** (*sideways*). *P* 14½ × 14.

466 20 c. Type **135** .. 80 50
467 25 c. 8d. Royal Visit stamp .. 80 50

136 "The Virgin and Child with Flowers" (C. Dolci)

137 Balcony Scene, Buckingham Palace

(Des G. Drummond. Litho Questa)

1976 (10 Nov). *Christmas. T* **136** *and similar vert designs. Multicoloured. W w* **14**. *P* 13½.

468	6 c. Type **136**	10	10
469	10 c. "Virgin and Child with St. John and an Angel" (Studio of Botticelli)	15	15
470	20 c. "Adoration of the Magi" (Master of Paraiso)	40	40
471	25 c. "Adoration of the Magi" (French miniature)	45	45

(Des J.W. (**MS**475), C. Abbott (others) Litho Questa)

1977 (7 Feb–6 Dec). *Silver Jubilee. T* **137** *and similar vert designs. Multicoloured. W w* **14**. *P* 14 × 13½ (**MS**475) *or* 13½ (*others*).

472	6 c. Queen presenting O.B.E. to E. T. Wood	10	10
473	25 c. The Queen with regalia	35	40
474	55 c. Type **137**	65	75
MS475	120 × 97 mm. $5 Queen Elizabeth II (6.12.77)	3·25	4·25

138 Col. Glenn's "Mercury" Capsule

139 "Flight of the Holy Family" (Rubens)

(Des and litho J.W.)

1977 (20 June). *25th Anniv of U.S. Tracking Station. T* **138** *and similar multicoloured designs. W w* **14** (*sideways on horiz designs*). *P* 13½.

476	1 c. Type **138**	5	5
477	3 c. Moon buggy "Rover" (*vert*)	8	8
478	6 c. Tracking Station, Grand Turk	10	12
479	20 c. Moon landing craft (*vert*)	35	35
480	25 c. Col. Glenn's rocket launch (*vert*)	45	45
481	50 c. "Telstar 1" satellite	85	1·00
476/81	*Set of* 6	1·75	1·75

(Des J.W. Litho Questa)

1977 (23 Dec). *Christmas and 400th Birth Anniv of Rubens. T* **139** *and similar vert designs. Multicoloured. P* 14.

482	¼ c. Type **139**	5	5
483	½ c. "Adoration of the Magi" (1634)	5	5
484	1 c. "Adoration of the Magi" (1624)	5	5
485	6 c. "Virgin within Garland"	10	10
486	20 c. "Madonna and Child Adored by Angels"	35	25
487	$2 "Adoration of the Magi" (1618)	2·50	2·75
482/7	*Set of* 6	2·75	3·00
MS488	100 × 81 mm. $1 detail of 20 c.	1·75	1·90

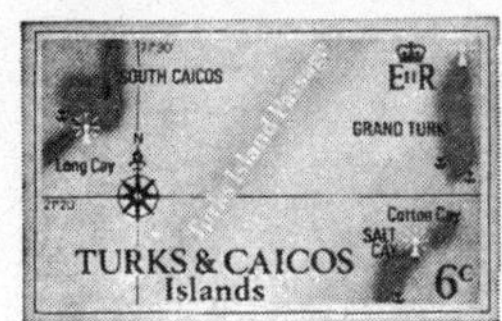

140 Map of Passage

(Des R. Granger Barrett. Litho J.W.)

1978 (2 Feb). *Turks Islands Passage. T* **140** *and similar horiz designs. Multicoloured. P* 13½. *A. No wmk. B. W w* **14** (*sideways*).

		A		B	
489	6 c. Type **140**	10	10	10	10
490	20 c. Sailing boat, passing Grand Turk Lighthouse	35	40	35	40
491	25 c. Motor launch	40	45	40	45
492	55 c. S.S. *Jamaica Planter*	85	1·00	85	1·00
MS493	136 × 88 mm. Nos. 489/92. P 14½	2·25	2·25	55·00	—

MINIMUM PRICE

The minimum price quoted is 5p which represents a handling charge rather than a basis for valuing common stamps. For further notes about prices see introductory pages.

141 "Queen Victoria" (Sir George Hayter)

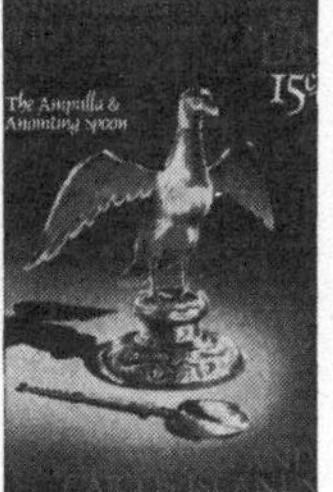

142 Ampulla and Anointing Spoon

(Manufactured by Walsall (Nos. 499/501). Des PAD Studio. Litho Questa (others))

1978 (2 June–July). *25th Anniv of Coronation. Multicoloured.*

(*a*) *Sheet stamps. Vert designs as T* **141** *showing British monarchs in coronation robes. P* 14

494	6 c. Type **141**	15	15
495	10 c. "King Edward VII" (Sir Samuel Fildes)	20	20
496	25 c. King George V	40	40
497	$2 King George VI	2·00	2·00
MS498	161 × 113 mm. $2.50, Queen Elizabeth II	2·75	2·75

(*b*) *Booklet stamps. Vert designs as T* **142**. *Imperf × roul 5*. Self-adhesive* (July)

499	15 c. Type **142**	15	25
	a. Booklet pane. Nos. 499/501	2·50	
	b. Booklet pane. Nos. 499/500, each × 3	1·25	
500	25 c. St. Edward's Crown	15	20
501	$2 Queen Elizabeth II in coronation robes	2·25	2·75

Nos. 494/7 also exist perf 12 (*Price for set of* 4 £2.50 *mint or used*) from additional sheetlets of 3 stamps and 1 label. Stamps perforated 14 are from normal sheets of 50.

*Nos. 499/501 are separated by various combinations of rotary-knife (giving a straight edge) and roulette.

143 Wilbur Wright and *Flyer III*

(Des Curtis Design. Litho Format)

1978 (July). *75th Anniv of Powered Flight. T* **143** *and similar horiz designs. Multicoloured. P* 14½.

502	1 c. Type **143**	5	5
503	6 c. Wright brothers and Cessna "337"	12	12
504	10 c. Orville Wright and "Electra"	15	15
505	15 c. Wilbur Wright and "C-47"	20	20
506	35 c. Wilbur Wright and "Islander"	50	55
507	$2 Wilbur Wright and Wright biplane	2·25	2·50
502/7	*Set of* 6	3·00	3·25
MS508	111 × 84 mm. $1 Orville Wright and Wright glider	1·50	1·60

144 Hurdling

(Des J.W. Litho Format)

1978 (3 Aug). *Commonwealth Games, Edmonton. T* **144** *and similar horiz designs. Multicoloured. P* 14½.

509	6 c. Type **144**	5	5
510	20 c. Weightlifting	20	20
511	55 c. Boxing	60	60
512	$2 Cycling	1·90	1·90
MS513	105 × 79 mm. $1 Sprinting	1·25	1·40

145 Indigo Hamlet

146 "Madonna of the Siskin"

(Des G. Drummond. Litho Questa)

1978 (17 Nov)–**83**. *Fishes. Horiz designs as T* **145**. *Multicoloured.*

A. *P* 14. *No imprint date*
B. *P* 12. *Printed with imprint date at the foot of design*

		A		B	
514	1 c. Type **145**	5	5	5	5
515	2 c. Tobacco fish	5	5	†	
516	3 c. Passing Jack	5	5	†	
517	4 c. Porkfish	5	5	†	
518	5 c. Spanish Grunt	5	5	5	5
519	7 c. Yellowtail Snapper	5	5	†	
520	8 c. Foureye Butterflyfish	12	10	†	
521	10 c. Yellowfin Grouper	15	15	15	15
522	15 c. Beau Gregory	20	25	20	25
523	20 c. Queen Angelfish	30	30	30	30
524	30 c. Hogfish	40	40	†	
525	50 c. Fairy Basslet	70	65	70	60
526	$1 Clown Wrasse	1·40	1·60	1·40	1·50
527	$2 Stoplight Parrotfish	2·75	2·50	2·75	2·50
528	$5 Queen Triggerfish	7·00	6·50	7·00	6·50
514/28	*Set of* 15	12·00	11·00		
514/28	*Set of* 9			11·00	11·00

Dates of issue:—Nos. 514A, 516A, 518A and 521/3A 17.11.78; Nos. 515A, 517A, 519/20A and 524/8A 19.1.79; Nos. 514B, 518B, 521B, 523B and 525B/8B 15.12.81; No. 522B 25.1.83.

(Des BG Studio. Litho Questa)

1978 (11 Dec). *Christmas. Paintings by Dürer. T* **146** *and similar multicoloured designs. P* 14.

529	6 c. Type **146**	10	10
530	20 c. "The Virgin and Child with St. Anne"	25	25
531	35 c. "Paumgärtner Nativity" (*horiz*)	40	40
532	$2 "Praying Hands"	1·75	2·00
MS533	137 × 124 mm. $1 "Adoration of the Magi" (*horiz*)	1·10	1·25

147 Osprey

(Des G. Drummond. Litho Questa)

1979 (29 May). *Endangered Wildlife. T* **147** *and similar horiz designs. Multicoloured. P* 14.

534	6 c. Type **147**	25	10
535	20 c. Green Turtle	35	25
536	25 c. Queen Conch	45	30
537	55 c. Rough Toothed Dolphin	85	60
538	$1 Humpback Whale	1·50	1·50
MS539	117 × 85 mm. $2 Iguana	2·75	2·75

148 "The Beloved" (painting by D. G. Rossetti)

(Des G. Vasarhelyi. Litho Questa)

1979 (2 July). *International Year of the Child. T* **148** *and similar horiz designs showing paintings and I.Y.C. emblem. Multicoloured. P* 14.

540	6 c. Type **148**	5	5
541	25 c. "Tahitian Girl" (P. Gauguin)	30	30
542	55 c. "Calmady Children" (Sir Thomas Lawrence)	60	60
543	$1 "Mother and Daughter" (detail, P. Gauguin)	1·00	1·00
MS544	112 × 85 mm. $2 "Marchesa Elena Grimaldi" (A. van Dyck)	2·00	2·50

149 R.M.S.P. *Medina* and Handstamped Cover

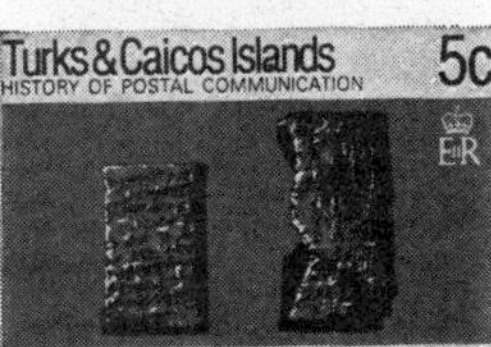

150 Cuneiform Script

(Des J.W. Litho Questa (Nos. 545/51). Des and litho Walsall (Nos. 552/64))

1979 (27 Aug)–**80**. *Death Centenary of Sir Rowland Hill.*

(*a*) *Sheet stamps. Horiz designs as T* **149**. *Multicoloured. P* 12 ($2) *or* 14 (*others*)

545	6 c. Type **149**	5	5
546	20 c. Sir Rowland Hill and map of Caribbean	25	25
547	45 c. R.M.S. *Orinoco* and cover bearing Penny Black stamp	50	50
548	75 c. R.M.S. *Shannon* and letter to Grand Turk	80	80
549	$1 R.M.S.P. *Trent* and map of Caribbean	1·10	1·10
550	$2 Turks Islands 1867 and Turks and Caicos Islands 1900 1d. stamps (6.5.80)	1·90	1·90
545/50	*Set of* 6	4·25	4·25
MS551	170 × 113 mm. As No. 550	2·25	2·25

Nos. 545/9 also exist perf 12 (*Price for set of* 5 £2.75 *mint or used*) from additional sheetlets of 5 stamps and 1 label. No. 550 only exists in this format. Stamps perforated 14 are from normal sheets of 40.

No. 550 has the inscription "International Stamp Exhibition Earls Court—London 6–14 May 1980. LONDON 1980" overprinted on the sheet margin. The individual stamps are not overprinted.

(b) *Booklet stamps. Designs as T* **150**. *Imperf × roul 5*. Self-adhesive* (27.9.79)

552 5 c. black and bright emerald 5 5
a. Booklet pane. Nos. 552/7 80
553 5 c. black and bright emerald 5 5
554 5 c. black and bright emerald 5 5
555 15 c. black and light blue 20 20
556 15 c. black and light blue 20 20
557 15 c. black and light blue 20 20
558 25 c. black and light blue 30 30
a. Booklet pane. Nos. 558/63 2·25
559 25 c. black and light blue 30 30
560 25 c. black and light blue 30 30
561 40 c. black and bright rosine 45 45
562 40 c. black and bright rosine 45 45
563 40 c. black and bright rosine 45 45
564 $1 black and lemon 1·10 1·25
a. Booklet pane of 1 1·10

Designs: *Horiz*—No. 552. Type **150**; No. 553, Egyptian papyrus; No. 554, Chinese paper; No. 555, Greek runner; No. 556, Roman post horse; No. 557, Roman post ship; No. 558, Pigeon post; No. 559, Railway post; No. 560, Steamship postal packet; No. 561, Balloon post; No. 562, First airmail; No. 563, Supersonic airmail. *Vert*—No. 564, Original stamp press.

*Nos. 552/63 are separated by various combinations of rotary knife (giving a straight edge) and roulette. No. 564 exists only with straight edges.

BRASILIANA 79

(151)

152 "St. Nicholas", Prikra, Ukraine

1979 (10 Sept). *"Brasiliana 79" International Stamp Exhibition, Rio de Janeiro. No.* **MS**551 *optd with T* **151**.
MS565 170 × 113 mm. $2 Turks Islands 1867 and Turks and Caicos Islands 1900 1d. stamps 2·00 2·25

Stamps from Nos. **MS**551 and **MS**565 are identical as the overprint on **MS**565 appears on the background of the sheet.

(Des M. Diamond. Litho Questa)

1979 (19 Oct). *Christmas. Art. T* **152** *and similar vert designs. Multicoloured. P* 13½ × 14.
566 1 c. Type **152** 5 5
567 3 c. "Emperor Otto II with Symbols of Empire" (Master of the Registrum Gregorii) 8 8
568 6 c. "Portrait of St. John" (Book of Lindisfarne) 10 10
569 15 c. "Adoration of the Majestas Domini" (Prayer Book of Otto II) 25 25
570 20 c. "Christ attended by Angels" (Book of Kells) 30 30
571 25 c. "St. John the Evangelist" (Gospels of St. Medard of Soissons), Charlemagne 35 35
572 65 c. "Christ Pantocrator", Trocany, Ukraine 75 75
573 $1 "Portrait of St. John" (Canterbury Codex Aureus) 1·00 1·00
566/73 *Set of* 8 2·50 2·50
MS574 106 × 133 mm. $2 "Portrait of St. Matthew" (Book of Lindisfarne) 2·00 2·25

153 Pluto and Starfish

(Litho Format)

1979 (2 Nov). *International Year of the Child. Walt Disney Cartoon Characters. T* **153** *and similar vert designs showing characters at the seaside. Multicoloured. P* 11.
575 ¼ c. Type **153** 5 5
576 ½ c. Minnie Mouse in summer outfit 5 5
577 1 c. Mickey Mouse underwater 5 5
578 2 c. Goofy and turtle 5 5
579 3 c. Donald Duck and dolphin 5 5
580 4 c. Mickey Mouse fishing 5 5
581 5 c. Goofy surfing 5 5
582 25 c. Pluto and crab 45 45
583 $1 Daisy water-skiing 2·00 2·00
575/83 *Set of* 9 2·50 2·50
MS584 126 × 96 mm. $1.50, Goofy after water-skiing accident. P 13½ 2·10 2·25
a. Error. Imperf £180

154 "Christina's World" (painting by Andrew Wyeth)

(Des J.W. Litho Format)

1979 (19 Dec). *Works of Art. T* **154** *and similar multicoloured designs. P* 13½.
585 6 c. Type **154** 5 5
586 10 c. Ivory Leopards, Benin (19th-cent) 12 12
587 20 c. "The Kiss" (painting by Gustav Klimt) (*vert*) 25 25
588 25 c. "Portrait of a Lady" (painting by R. van der Weyden) (*vert*) 35 35
589 80 c. Bull's head harp, Sumer, *c.* 2600 B.C. (*vert*) 85 85
590 $1 "The Wave" (painting by Hokusai) 1·10 1·10
585/90 *Set of* 6 2·50 2·50
MS591 110 × 140 mm. $2 "Holy Family" (painting by Rembrandt) (*vert*) 2·00 2·25

155 Pied-billed Grebe

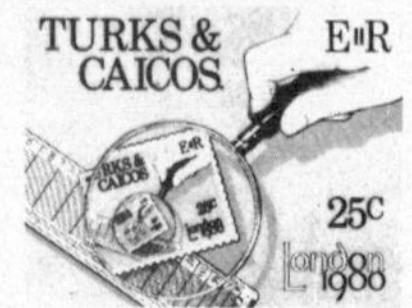

156 Stamp, Magnifying Glass and Perforation Gauge

(Des G. Drummond. Litho Questa)

1980 (20 Feb). *Birds. T* **155** *and similar horiz designs. Multicoloured. P* 14.
592 20 c. Type **155** 35 30
593 25 c. Ovenbirds at nest 40 35
594 35 c. Hen Harrier 60 55
595 55 c. Yellow-bellied Sapsucker 75 70
596 $1 Blue-winged Teal 1·40 1·25
MS597 107 × 81 mm. $2 Glossy Ibis 2·25 2·50

(Des BG Studio. Litho Questa)

1980 (6 May). *"London 1980" International Stamp Exhibition. T* **156** *and similar horiz designs. P* 14.
598 25 c. black and chrome-yellow 25 30
599 40 c. black and bright green 45 45
MS600 76 × 97 mm. $2 vermilion, black and blue 2·00 2·00

Designs:—40 c. Stamp, tweezers and perforation gauge; $2, Earls Court Exhibition Centre.

157 Trumpet Triton

158 Queen Elizabeth the Queen Mother

(Des G. Drummond. Litho Questa)

1980 (26 June). *Shells. T* **157** *and similar horiz designs. Multicoloured. P* 14.
601 15 c. Type **157** 25 25
602 20 c. Measled Cowry 30 30
603 30 c. True Tulip 40 40
604 45 c. Lion's Paw 55 55
605 55 c. Sunrise Tellin 65 65
606 70 c. Crown Cone 85 85
601/6 *Set of* 6 2·75 2·75

(Des G. Vasarhelyi. Litho Questa)

1980 (4 Aug). *80th Birthday of Queen Elizabeth the Queen Mother. P* 14.
607 **158** 80 c. multicoloured 1·25 1·00
MS608 57 × 80 mm. **158** $1.50, multicoloured. P 12. 1·90 1·90

159 Doctor examining Child and Lions International Emblem

(Des Design Images. Litho Questa)

1980 (29 Aug). *"Serving the Community". T* **159** *and similar horiz designs. Multicoloured. P* 14.
609 10 c. Type **159** 12 12
610 15 c. Students receiving scholarships and Kiwanis International emblem 20 20
611 45 c. Teacher with students and Soroptimist emblem 50 50
612 $1 Lobster boat and Rotary International emblem 1·10 1·10
MS613 101 × 74 mm. $2 School receiving funds and Rotary International emblem 2·00 2·25

No. **MS**613 also commemorates the 75th anniversary of Rotary International.

(Litho Walsall)

1980 (30 Sept). *Christmas. Scenes from Walt Disney's Cartoon Film "Pinocchio". Horiz designs as T* **153**. *Multicoloured. P* 11.
614 ¼ c. Scene from *Pinocchio* 5 5
615 ½ c. As puppet 5 5
616 1 c. Pinocchio changed into a boy 5 5
617 2 c. Captured by fox 5 5
618 3 c. Pinocchio and puppeteer 5 5
619 4 c. Pinocchio and bird's nest nose 5 5
620 5 c. Pinocchio eating 5 5
621 75 c. Pinocchio with ass ears 1·00 1·00
622 $1 Pinocchio underwater 1·25 1·25
614/22 *Set of* 9 2·40 2·40
MS623 127 × 102 mm. $2 Pinocchio dancing (*vert*) 2·10 2·25

160 Martin Luther King Jr

(Des Design Images Studio. Litho Questa)

1980 (22 Dec). *Human Rights. Personalities. T* **160** *and similar horiz designs. Multicoloured. P* 14 × 13½.
624 20 c. Type **160** 20 12
625 30 c. John F. Kennedy 45 35
626 45 c. Roberto Clemente (baseball player) 60 45
627 70 c. Sir Frank Worrel (cricketer) 1·10 75
628 $1 Harriet Tubman 1·40 95
MS629 103 × 80 mm. $2 Marcus Garvey 1·90 2·00

161 Yachts

162 Night Queen Cactus

(Litho Questa)

1981 (29 Jan). *South Caicos Regatta. T* **161** *and similar horiz designs. Multicoloured. P* 14.
630 6 c. Type **161** 10 5
631 15 c. Trophy and yachts 20 20
632 35 c. Spectators watching speedboat race 45 40
633 $1 Yachts (*different*) 1·25 1·10
MS634 113 × 85 mm. $2 Queen Elizabeth II and map of South Caicos (*vert*) 2·25 2·50

(Des J. Cooter. Litho Questa)

1981 (10 Feb). *Flowering Cacti. T* **162** *and similar vert designs. Multicoloured. P* 13½ × 14.
635 25 c. Type **162** 35 40
636 35 c. Ripsaw Cactus 45 50
637 55 c. Royal Strawberry Cactus 65 70
638 80 c. Caicos Cactus 1·00 1·10
MS639 72 × 86 mm. $2 Turks Head Cactus. P 14½ 2·40 2·75

(Litho Format)

1981 (16 Feb). *50th Anniv of Walt Disney's Cartoon Character, Pluto. Vert designs as T* **153**. *Multicoloured. P* 13½.
640 10 c. Pluto playing on beach with shell 10 10
641 75 c. Pluto on raft, and porpoise 1·10 1·10
MS642 127 × 101 mm. $1.50 Pluto in scene from film *Simple Things* 1·60 1·75

(Litho Format)

1981 (20 Mar). *Easter. Walt Disney Cartoon Characters. Vert designs as T* **153**. *Multicoloured. P* 11.
643 10 c. Donald Duck and Louie 20 20
644 25 c. Goofy and Donald Duck 40 40
645 60 c. Chip and Dale 85 85
646 80 c. Scrooge McDuck and Huey 1·25 1·25
MS647 126 × 101 mm. $4 Chip (or Dale). P 13½ 4·00 4·00

163 "Woman with Fan"

164 Kensington Palace

(Des J.W. Litho Questa)

981 (28 May). *Birth Centenary of Picasso. T* **163** *and similar vert designs. Multicoloured. P* 13½ × 14.

48 20 c. Type **163** 30 30
49 45 c. "Woman with Pears" 55 55
50 80 c. "The Accordionist" . . . . 1·00 1·00
51 $1 "The Aficionado" . . . . . . 1·25 1·25
MS652 102 × 127 mm. $2 "Girl with a Mandolin" 2·10 2·25

(Des J.W. Litho Questa)

981 (23 June). *Royal Wedding. T* **164** *and similar vert designs. Multicoloured. P* 14.

53 35 c. Prince Charles and Lady Diana Spencer 40 40
54 65 c. Type **164** 75 75
55 90 c. Prince Charles as Colonel of the Welsh Guards 95 95
MS656 96 × 82 mm. $2 Glass Coach . . . . 2·00 2·00

Nos. 653/5 also exist perforated 12 (*price for set of* 3 £2 *mint or used*) from additional sheetlets of five stamps and one label. These stamps have changed background colours.

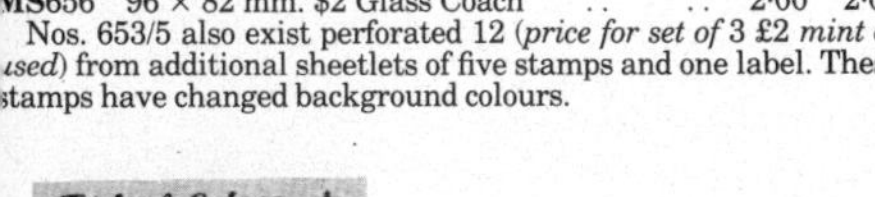

165 Lady Diana Spencer **166** Marine Biology Observation

(Manufactured by Walsall)

1981 (7 July). *Royal Wedding. Booklet stamps. T* **165** *and similar vert designs. Multicoloured. Roul* 5 × *imperf*. Self-adhesive.*

657 20 c. Type **165** 25 25
a. Booklet pane. Nos. 657/8, each × 3 . . 3·75
658 $1 Prince Charles . . . . . . 1·00 1·00
659 $2 Prince Charles and Lady Diana Spencer 2·75 2·75
a. Booklet pane of 1 . . . . . . 2·75

*The 20 c. and $1 values were each separated by various combinations of rotary knife (giving a straight edge) and roulette. The $2 value exists only with straight edges.

(Des G. Drummond. Litho Questa)

1981 (21 Aug). *Diving. T* **166** *and similar horiz designs. Multicoloured. P* 14.

660 15 c. Type **166** 20 20
661 40 c. Underwater photography 50 50
662 75 c. Wreck diving 90 90
663 $1 Diving with dolphins . . . . 1·25 1·25
MS664 91 × 75 mm. $2 Diving flag . . . . 2·25 2·50

(Litho Questa)

1981 (2 Nov). *Christmas. Horiz designs as T* **153** *showing scenes from Walt Disney's cartoon film "Uncle Remus". P* 13½.

665 ¼ c. multicoloured 5 5
666 ½ c. multicoloured 5 5
667 1 c. multicoloured 5 5
668 2 c. multicoloured 5 5
669 3 c. multicoloured 5 5
670 4 c. multicoloured 5 5
671 5 c. multicoloured 5 5
672 75 c. multicoloured 90 90
673 $1 multicoloured . . . . . . 1·25 1·25
665/73 . . . . . . *Set of* 9 2·25 2·25
MS674 128 × 103 mm. $2 multicoloured . . . . 2·25 2·50

167 Map of Grand Turk, and Lighthouse **168** Caribbean Buckeye

(Des J.W. Litho Questa)

1981 (1 Dec). *Tourism. T* **167** *and similar horiz designs. Multicoloured. P* 14.

675 20 c. Type **167** 25 30
a. Vert strip of 10. Nos. 675/84 . . 2·25
676 20 c. Map of Salt Cay, and "industrial archaeology" 25 30
677 20 c. Map of South Caicos, and "island flying" 25 30
678 20 c. Map of East Caicos, and "beach combing" 25 30
679 20 c. Map of Grand Caicos (middle), and cave exploring 25 30
680 20 c. Map of North Caicos, and camping and hiking 25 30
681 20 c. Map of North Caicos, Parrot Cay, Dellis Cay, Fort George Cay, Pine Cay and Water Cay, and "environmental studies" 25 30
682 20 c. Map of Providenciales, and scuba diving 25 30
683 20 c. Map of West Caicos, and "cruising and bird sanctuary" 25 30
684 20 c. Turks and Caicos Islands flag . . 25 30
675/84 . . . . . . *Set of* 10 2·25 2·75

Nos. 675/84 were printed together, *se-tenant*, in vertical strips of 10 throughout the sheet of 40, the two panes (2 × 10), separated by a gutter margin, being *tête-bêche*.

(Des J. Cooter. Litho Questa)

1982 (21 Jan). *Butterflies. T* **168** *and similar vert designs. Multicoloured. P* 14.

685 20 c. Type **168** 30 30
686 35 c. Clench's Hairstreak 50 50
687 65 c. Gulf Fritillary 90 90
688 $1 Bush Sulphur . . . . . . 1·40 1·40
MS689 72 × 56 mm. $2 Turk Island Leaf Butterfly 2·50 2·75

169 Flag Salute on Queen's Birthday **170** Footballer

(Litho Questa)

1982 (17 Feb). *75th Anniv of Boy Scout Movement. T* **169** *and similar vert designs. Multicoloured. P* 14.

690 40 c. Type **169** 50 50
691 50 c. Raft building 60 60
692 75 c. Sea scout cricket match . . . . 1·10 1·10
693 $1 Nature study . . . . . . 1·50 1·50
MS694 100 × 70 mm. $2 Lord Baden-Powell and scout salute . . . . . . 2·25 2·50

(Des G. Vasarhelyi. Litho Questa)

1982 (30 Apr). *World Cup Football Championship, Spain. T* **170** *and similar designs showing footballers. P* 14.

695 10 c. multicoloured 12 12
696 25 c. multicoloured 35 35
697 45 c. multicoloured 50 50
698 $1 multicoloured . . . . . . 1·25 1·25
MS699 117 × 83 mm. $2 multicoloured (*horiz*) . . 2·25 2·50

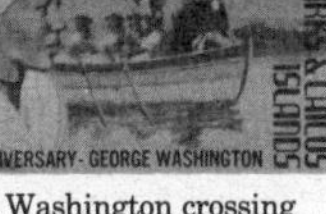

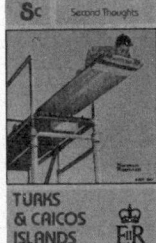

171 Washington crossing the Delaware and Phillis Wheatley (poetess) **172** "Second Thoughts"

(Des Design Images Studio. Litho Questa)

1982 (3 May). *250th Birth Anniv of George Washington* (20, 35 c.) *and Birth Centenary of Franklin D. Roosevelt* (65, 80 c.). *T* **171** *and similar horiz designs. Multicoloured. P* 14.

700 20 c. Type **171** 30 30
701 35 c. George Washington and Benjamin Banneker (surveyor) 45 45
702 65 c. Franklin D. Roosevelt meeting George Washington Carver (agricultural researcher) 80 80
703 80 c. Roosevelt as stamp collector . . 1·00 1·00
MS704 100 × 70 mm. $2 Roosevelt with stamp showing profile of Washington . . . . 2·25 2·50

(Litho Questa)

1982 (23 June). *Norman Rockwell (painter) Commemoration. T* **172** *and similar vert designs. Multicoloured. P* 14 × 13½.

705 8 c. Type **172** 12 12
706 15 c. "The Proper Gratuity" 25 25
707 20 c. "Before the Shot" 30 30
708 25 c. "The Three Umpires" 35 35

173 Princess of Wales **174** "Skymaster" over Caicos Cays

(Des PAD Studio. Litho Questa)

1982 (1 July–18 Nov). *21st Birthday of Princess of Wales. T* **173** *and similar vert designs. Multicoloured. P* 14½ × 14.

(*a*) *Sheet stamps. Pale green frames*

709 55 c. Sandringham 80 65
710 70 c. Prince and Princess of Wales . . 95 80
711 $1 Type **173** . . . . . . 1·60 1·40
MS712 102 × 76 mm. $2 Princess Diana (*different*) 3·00 2·50

(*b*) *Booklet stamps. As Nos.* 709/11 *but printed with new values and blue frame* (18.11.82)

713 8 c. Sandringham 25 12
714 35 c. Prince and Princess of Wales . . 60 50
715 $1.10, Type **173** . . . . . . 1·60 1·60

Nos. 713/15 also exist from sheets printed in horizontal *tête-bêche* pairs throughout.

(Des MBI Studios. Litho Questa)

1982 (23 Aug). *Aircraft. T* **174** *and similar horiz designs. Multicoloured. P* 14.

716 8 c. Type **174** 12 12
717 15 c. "Jetstar" over Grand Turk 25 25
718 65 c. Helicopter over South Caicos . . 80 80
719 $1.10, Seaplane over Providenciales . . 1·40 1·40
MS720 99 × 69 mm. $2 Boeing "727" over Turks and Caicos Islands . . . . . . 2·25 2·50

(Litho Questa)

1982 (1 Dec). *Christmas. Scenes from Walt Disney's Cartoon Film "Mickey's Christmas Carol". Horiz designs as T* **153**. *Multicoloured. P* 13½.

721 1 c. Donald Duck, Mickey Mouse and Scrooge 5 5
722 1 c. Goofy (Marley's ghost) and Scrooge . . 5 5
723 2 c. Jiminy Cricket and Scrooge 5 5
724 2 c. Huey, Dewey and Louie 5 5
725 3 c. Daisy Duck and youthful Scrooge . . 5 5
726 3 c. Giant and Scrooge 5 5
727 4 c. Two bad wolves, a wise pig and a reformed Scrooge 5 5
728 65 c. Donald Duck and Scrooge 85 90
729 $1.10, Mortie and Scrooge . . . . 1·40 1·45
721/9 . . . . . . *Set of* 9 2·25 2·50
MS730 126 × 101 mm. $2 Mickey and Minnie Mouse with Mortie . . . . . . 2·75 3·00

175 West Caicos Trolley Tram

(Des N. Waldman. Litho Questa)

1983 (18 Jan). *Trams and Locomotives. T* **175** *and similar horiz designs. Multicoloured. P* 14

731 15 c. Type **175** 20 25
732 55 c. West Caicos steam locomotive . . 75 80
733 90 c. East Caicos sisal locomotive . . 1·10 1·25
734 $1.60, East Caicos steam locomotive . . 2·10 2·25
MS735 99 × 69 mm. $2.50, Steam engine pulling cars of sisal . . . . . . 2·75 2·75

176 Policewoman on Traffic Duty **177** "St. John and the Virgin Mary" (detail)

(Des N. Waldman. Litho Questa)

1983 (14 Mar). *Commonwealth Day. T* **176** *and similar horiz designs. Multicoloured. P* 14

736 1 c. Type **176** 5 5
a. Vert strip of 4. Nos. 736/9 . . 2·25
737 8 c. Stylised sun and weather vane . . 10 12
738 65 c. Yacht 85 90
739 $1 Cricket . . . . . . 1·50 1·60

Nos. 736/9 were printed together, *se-tenant*, in vertical strips of four throughout the sheet.

(Des Design Images. Litho Questa)

1983 (7 Apr). *Easter. T* **177** *and similar vert designs showing details from the "Mond Crucifixion" by Raphael. Multicoloured. P* 13½ × 14.

740 35 c. Type **177** 45 50
741 50 c. "Two Women" 65 70
742 95 c. "Angel with two jars" . . . . 1·10 1·25
743 $1.10, "Angel with one jar" . . . . 1·40 1·50
MS744 100 × 130 mm. $2.50, "Christ on the Cross" 2·75 2·75

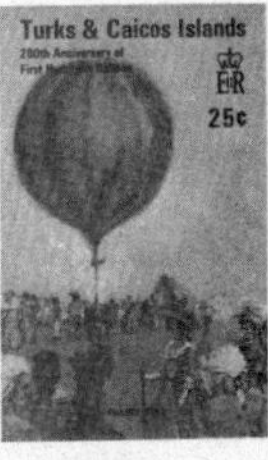

178 Piked Whale **179** First Hydrogen Balloon, 1783

(Des D. Hamilton. Litho Questa)

1983 (16 May–13 June). *Whales. T* **178** *and similar horiz designs. Multicoloured. P* 13½.

745 50 c. Type **178** 65 70
746 65 c. Right Whale (11.7.83) 85 90

747	70 c. Killer Whale (13.6.83)	90	95
748	95 c. Sperm Whale (13.6.83)	1·10	1·25
749	$1.10, Goosebeak Whale (11.7.83)	1·40	1·50
750	$2 Blue Whale (13.6.83)	2·75	3·00
751	$2.20, Humpback Whale	3·00	3·25
752	$3 Longfin Pilot Whale	4·00	4·25
745/52	*Set of* 8	13·00	14·00
MS753	112 × 82 mm. $3 Fin Whale (11.7.83)	4·00	4·50

Nos. 745/52 were each issued in sheetlets of four.

(Des BG Studio. Litho Questa)

1983 (30 Aug). *Bicentenary of Manned Flight. T* **179** *and similar vert designs. Multicoloured. P* 14.

754	25 c. Type **179**	35	40
755	35 c. *Friendship 7*	45	50
756	70 c. First hot air balloon, 1783	90	95
757	95 c. Space shuttle *Columbia*	1·10	1·25
MS758	112 × 76 mm. $2 Montgolfier balloon and Space shuttle	2·75	3·00

180 Fiddler Pig

181 Bermuda Sloop

(Litho Format)

1983 (4 Oct). *Christmas. Walt Disney Cartoon Characters. T* **180** *and similar vert designs. Multicoloured. P* 11.

759	1 c. Type **180**	5	5
760	1 c. Fifer Pig	5	5
761	2 c. Practical Pig	5	5
762	2 c. Pluto	5	5
763	3 c. Goofy	5	5
764	3 c. Mickey Mouse	5	5
765	35 c. Gyro Gearloose	45	50
766	50 c. Ludwig von Drake	65	70
767	$1.10, Huey, Dewey and Louie	1·40	1·50
759/67	*Set of* 9	2·50	2·50
MS768	127 × 102 mm. $2.50, Mickey and Minnie Mouse with Huey, Dewey and Louie. P 13½	3·25	3·50

(Des G. Drummond. Litho Questa)

1983 (5 Oct)–**84**. *Ships. T* **181** *and similar horiz designs. Multicoloured. P* 14.

769	4 c. Arawak dug-out canoe (9.1.84)	5	5
770	5 c. *Santa Maria* (9.1.84)	8	10
771	8 c. British and Spanish ships in battle (16.12.83)	12	15
772	10 c. Type **181**	15	20
773	20 c. U.S. privateer, *Grand Turk* (9.1.84)	30	35
774	25 c. H.M.S. *Boreas* (16.12.83)	35	40
775	30 c. H.M.S. *Endymion* attacking French ship, 1790s	45	50
776	35 c. Bark *Caesar* (9.1.84)	50	55
777	50 c. *Grapeshot*, three-masted schooner (16.12.83)	70	75
778	65 c. Battlecruiser H.M.S. *Invincible*	95	1·00
779	95 c. H.M.S. *Magicienne* (16.12.83)	1·40	1·50
780	$1.10, H.M.S. *Durban*	1·60	1·75
781	$2 C.S. *Sentinel*	3·00	3·25
782	$3 H.M.S. *Minerva*	4·50	4·75
783	$5 Caicos sloop (9.1.84)	7·25	7·50
769/83	*Set of* 15	19·00	20·00

182 President Kennedy and Signing of Civil Rights Legislation

(Des Design Images. Litho Questa)

1983 (22 Dec). *20th Death Anniv of President J. F. Kennedy. P* 14.

784	**182**	20 c. multicoloured	30	35
785		$1 multicoloured	1·60	1·75

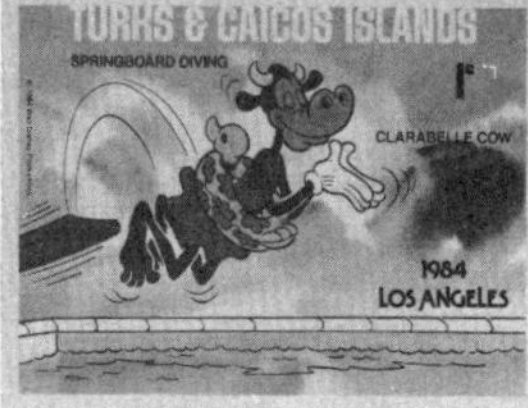
183 Clarabelle Cow Diving

(Litho Questa)

1984 (21 Feb–Apr). *Olympic Games, Los Angeles. T* **183** *and similar horiz designs showing Disney cartoon characters in Olympic events. Multicoloured.* A. *Inscr* "1984 LOS ANGELES". *P* 14 × 13½. B. *Inscr* "1984 OLYMPICS LOS ANGELES" *and Olympic emblem. P* 14 × 13½ (**MS** 795B) *or* 12 (*others*) (4.84).

		A		B	
786	1 c. Type **183**	5	5	5	5
787	1 c. Donald Duck in 500m kayak race	5	5	5	5
788	2 c. Huey, Dewey and Louie in 1000m kayak race	5	5	5	5
789	2 c. Mickey Mouse in single kayak	5	5	5	5
790	3 c. Donald Duck highboard diving	5	5	5	5
791	3 c. Minnie Mouse in kayak slalom	5	5	5	5
792	25 c. Mickey Mouse freestyle swimming	40	45	40	45
793	75 c. Donald Duck playing water-polo	1·25	1·40	1·25	1·40
794	$1 Uncle Scrooge and Donald Duck yachting	1·60	1·75	1·60	1·75
786/94	*Set of* 9	3·25	3·50	3·25	3·50
MS795	117 × 90 mm. $2 Pluto platform diving	3·25	3·50	3·25	3·50

184 "Cadillac V–16", 1933

185 "Rest during the Flight to Egypt, with St. Francis"

(Des N. Waldman. Litho Questa)

1984 (15 Mar). *Classic Cars and 125th Anniv of first Commercial Oil Well. T* **184** *and similar horiz designs. Multicoloured. P* 14.

796	4 c. Type **184**	5	5
797	8 c. Rolls-Royce "Phantom III", 1937	12	15
798	10 c. Saab "99", 1969	15	20
799	25 c. Maserati "Bora", 1973	40	45
800	40 c. Datsun "260Z", 1970	65	70
801	55 c. Porsche "917", 1971	90	95
802	80 c. Lincoln "Continental", 1939	1·25	1·40
803	$1 Triumph "TR3A", 1957	1·60	1·75
796/803	*Set of* 8	4·50	5·00
MS804	70 × 100 mm. $2 Daimler, 1886	3·25	3·50

(Des S. Karp. Litho Walsall)

1984 (9 Apr). *Easter. 450th Death Anniv of Correggio (painter). T* **185** *and similar vert designs. Multicoloured. P* 14.

805	15 c. Type **185**	25	30
806	40 c. "St. Luke and St. Ambrose"	65	70
807	60 c. "Diana and her Chariot"	1·00	1·10
808	95 c. "The Deposition of Christ"	1·50	1·60
MS809	100 × 79 mm. $2 "The Nativity with Saints Elizabeth and John the younger" (*horiz*)	3·25	3·50

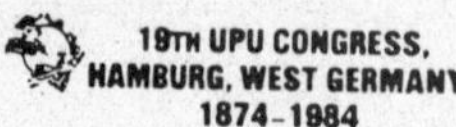

(186)

1984 (19 June). *Universal Postal Union Congress, Hamburg. Nos.* 748/9 *and* **MS**753 *optd with T* **186**.

810	95 c. Sperm Whale	1·60	1·75
811	$1.10, Goosebeak Whale	1·75	1·90
MS812	112 × 82 mm. $3 Fin Whale	4·50	4·75

187 "The Adventure of the Second Stain"

188 Clown-Fish

(Des S. Karp. Litho Walsall)

1984 (16 July). *125th Birth Anniv of Sir Arthur Conan Doyle (author). T* **187** *and similar horiz designs showing scenes from Sherlock Holmes stores. Multicoloured. P* 14.

813	25 c. Type **187**	40	45
814	45 c. "The Adventure of the Final Problem"	75	80
815	70 c. "The Adventure of the Empty House"	1·10	1·25
816	85 c. "The Adventure of the Greek Interpreter"	1·40	1·50
MS817	100 × 70 mm. $2 Sir Arthur Conan Doyle	3·25	3·50

(Des S. Karp. Litho Walsall)

1984 (16 July). *125th Birth Anniv of Sir Arthur Conan Doyl (author). T* **187** *and similar horiz designs showing scenes fron Sherlock Holmes stories. Multicoloured. P* 14.

813 25 c. Type **187** 40 45
814 45 c. "The Adventure of the Final Problem" 75 80
815 70 c. "The Adventure of the Empty House" 1·10 1·25
816 85 c. "The Adventure of the Greek Interpreter" 1·40 1·50
MS817 100 × 70 mm. $2 Sir Arthur Conan Doyle 3·25 3·50

CAICOS ISLANDS

CAICOS ISLANDS

(1)

1981 (24 July). *Nos.* 514A, 518A, 520A, 523A *and* 525A/7A *of Turks and Caicos Islands optd with T* 1.

No.	Description	Unused	Used
1	1 c. Indigo Hamlet	5	8
2	5 c. Spanish Grunt	8	10
3	8 c. Foureye Butterflyfish	10	12
4	20 c. Queen Angelfish	25	30
5	50 c. Fairy Basslet	65	70
6	$1 Clown Wrasse	1·25	1·40
7	$2 Stoplight Parrotfish	2·75	3·00
1/7	.. .. *Set of* 7	4·75	5·25

(2) (3)

1981 (24 July). *Royal Wedding. Nos.* 653/6 *of Turks and Caicos Islands optd. A. With T* 2 *in London. B. With T* 3 *in New York.*

No.	Description	A		B	
8	35 c. Prince Charles and Lady Diana Spencer	50	50	2·75	2·75
	a. Opt inverted		†	£130	—
9	65 c. Kensington Palace ..	85	85	4·75	4·75
	a. Opt inverted		†	95·00	—
10	90 c. Prince Charles as Colonel of the Welsh Guards	1·00	1·00	6·00	6·00
	a. Opt inverted		†	£110	—
	b. Opt double		†	£110	—
MS11	96 × 82 mm. $2 Glass Coach	10·00	10·00	12·00	12·00

Nos. 8B/10 come either in sheets of 40 (2 panes 4 × 5) or in sheetlets of 5 stamps and one label. Examples of Nos. 8Ba, 9Ba and 10Ba are known from both formats, but No. 10Bb only exists from sheetlets.

Nos. 8/10 also exist perforated 12 (*Price for set of* 3 *with London opt £7 or with New York opt £20, mint or used*) from additional sheetlets of five stamps and one label. These stamps have changed background colours.

1981 (29 Oct). *Royal Wedding. Booklet stamps. As Nos.* 657/9 *of Turks and Caicos Islands, but each inscr* "Caicos Islands". *Multicoloured. Roul* 5 × *imperf*. Self-adhesive.*

No.	Description	Unused	Used
12	20 c. Lady Diana Spencer	80	60
	a. Booklet pane. Nos. 12/13, each × 3 ..	4·00	
13	$1 Prince Charles	3·75	2·75
14	$2 Prince Charles and Lady Diana Spencer	10·00	6·00
	a. Booklet pane of 1	10·00	

*The 20 c. and $1 values were each separated by various combinations of rotary knife (giving a straight edge) and roulette. The $2 value exists only with straight edges.

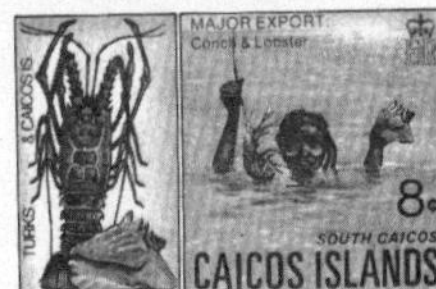

4 Conch and Lobster Fishing, South Caicos

1983 (6 June)–**84**. *T* 4 *and similar horiz designs. Multicoloured. Litho. P* 14.

No.	Description	Unused	Used
15	8 c. Type 4	12	15
16	10 c. Hawksbill Turtle, East Caicos ..	15	20
17	20 c. Arawak Indians and idol, Middle Caicos	30	35
18	35 c. Boat-building, North Caicos	50	55
19	50 c. Marine biologist at work, Pine Cay ..	70	75
20	95 c. Boeing "707" airliner at new airport, Providenciales	1·40	1·50
21	$1.10, Columbus' *Pinta*, West Caicos ..	1·60	1·75
22	$2 Fort George Cay (18.5.84)	3·00	3·25
23	$3 Pirates Anne Bonny and Calico Jack at Parrot Cay (18.5.84)	4·50	4·75
15/23	.. .. *Set of* 9	11·00	11·50

5 Goofy and Patch

6 "Leda and the Swan"

(Litho Walsall)

1983 (7 Nov). *Christmas. T* 5 *and similar vert designs showing Disney cartoon characters. Multicoloured. P* 11.

No.	Description	Unused	Used
30	1 c. Type 5	5	5
31	1 c. Chip and Dale	5	5
32	2 c. Morty	5	5
33	2 c. Morty and Ferdie	5	5
34	3 c. Goofy and Louie	5	5
35	3 c. Donald Duck, Huey, Dewey and Louie ..	5	5
36	50 c. Uncle Scrooge	85	90
37	70 c. Mickey Mouse and Ferdie	1·10	1·25
38	$1.10, Pinocchio, Jiminy Cricket and Figaro	1·75	1·90
30/8	.. .. *Set of* 9	3·50	3·75
MS39	126 × 101 mm. $2 Morty and Ferdie. P 13½ × 14	3·25	3·50

(Des and litho Questa)

1983 (15 Dec). *500th Birth Anniv of Raphael. T* 6 *and similar vert designs. Multicoloured. P* 14.

No.	Description	Unused	Used
40	35 c. Type 6	60	65
41	50 c. "Study of Apollo for Parnassus"	85	90
42	95 c. "Study of two figures for the battle of Ostia"	1·50	1·60
43	$1.10, "Study for the Madonna of the Goldfinch"	1·75	1·90
MS44	71 × 100 mm. $2.50, "The Garvagh Madonna"	4·00	4·25

7 High Jumping

8 Horace Horsecollar and Clarabelle Cow

(Litho Questa)

1984 (1 Mar). *Olympic Games, Los Angeles. T* 7 *and similar designs. P* 14.

No.	Description	Unused	Used
45	4 c. multicoloured	8	10
46	25 c. multicoloured	40	45
47	65 c. black, deep grey-blue and new blue ..	1·10	1·25
48	$1.10, multicoloured	1·75	1·90
MS49	105 × 75 mm. $2 multicoloured	3·25	3·50

Designs: *Vert*—25 c. Archery; 65 c. Cycling; $1.10, Football. *Horiz*—$2 Show jumping.

(Des Walt Disney Productions. Litho Questa)

1984 (23 Apr). *Easter. Walt Disney Cartoon Characters. T* 8 *and similar horiz designs. Multicoloured. P* 14 × 13½.

No.	Description	Unused	Used
50	35 c. Type 8	60	65
51	45 c. Mickey and Minnie Mouse, and Chip ..	75	80
52	75 c. Gyro Gearloose, Chip 'n Dale	1·25	1·40
53	85 c. Mickey Mouse, Chip 'n Dale	1·40	1·50
MS54	127 × 101 mm. $2.20, Donald Duck ..	3·50	3·75

UNIVERSAL POSTAL UNION 1874-1984

AUSIPEX 1984

(9) (10)

1984 (19 June). *Universal Postal Union Congress, Hamburg. Nos.* 20/1 *optd with T* 9.

No.	Description	Unused	Used
55	95 c. Boeing "707" airliner at new airport, Providenciales	1·50	1·60
56	$1.10, Columbus' *Pinta*, West Caicos ..	1·75	1·90

1984 (22 Aug). *"Ausipex" International Stamp Exhibition, Melbourne. No.* 22 *optd with T* 10.

No.	Description	Unused	Used
57	$2 Fort George Cay	3·25	3·50

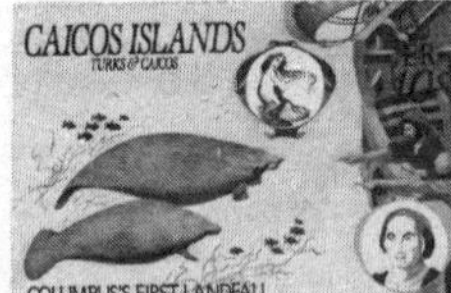

11 Seamen sighting Manatees

(Des L. Lightbourne. Litho Walsall)

1984 (12 Sept). *492nd Anniv of Columbus' First Landfall. T* 11 *and similar horiz designs. Multicoloured. P* 14.

No.	Description	Unused	Used
58	10 c. Type 11	15	20
59	70 c. Columbus' fleet of ships	1·10	1·25
60	$1 First landing in West Indies	1·60	1·75
MS61	99 × 69 mm. $2 Columbus' fleet of ships (*different*)	3·25	3·50

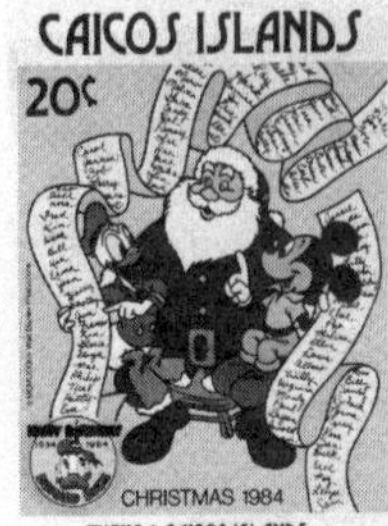

12 Donald Duck and Mickey Mouse with Father Christmas

(Litho Questa)

1984 (26 Nov). *Christmas. Walt Disney Cartoon Characters. T* 12 *and similar vert designs. Multicoloured. P* 12 ($2) *or* 13½ × 14 (*others*).

No.	Description	Unused	Used
62	20 c. Type 12	35	40
63	35 c. Donald Duck opening refrigerator ..	60	65
64	50 c. Mickey Mouse, Donald Duck and toy train	85	90
65	75 c. Donald Duck and parcels	1·25	1·40
66	$1.10, Donald Duck and carol singers ..	1·75	1·90
MS67	127 × 102 mm. $2 Donald Duck as Christmas tree	3·25	3·50

No. 65 was printed in sheetlets of 8 stamps.

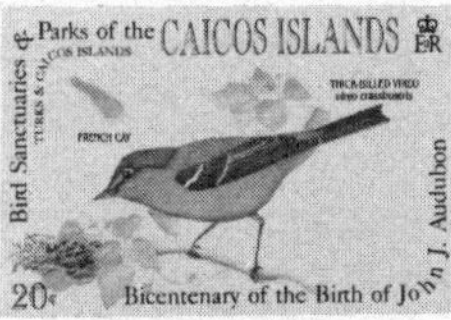

13 Thick-billed Vireo

(Des Susan David. Litho Walsall)

1985 (12 Feb). *Birth Bicentenary of John J. Audubon (ornithologist). T* 13 *and similar horiz designs. Multicoloured. P* 14.

No.	Description	Unused	Used
68	20 c. Type 13	35	40
69	35 c. Black-faced Grassquit	60	65
70	50 c. Pearly-eyed Thrasher	85	90
71	$1 Greater Antillean Bullfinch	1·60	1·75
MS72	100 × 70 mm. $2 Stripe-headed Tanager ..	3·25	3·50

Tuvalu

Formerly known as the Ellice Islands when they shared a joint administration with the Gilbert group. On 1 January 1976 the two island-groups separated and the Ellice Islands were renamed Tuvalu.

CROWN COLONY

1 Gilbertese and Tuvaluan

(Des Iakopo Nivatui; adapted J. Cooter. Litho Questa)

1976 (1 Jan). *Separation of the Islands. T* **1** *and similar multi-coloured designs.* W w **14** *(sideways on* 4 *and* 35 c.). *P* 13½.
1 4 c. Type **1** .. .. 1·50 2·00
2 10 c. Map of the islands (*vert*) .. .. .. 2·00 2·00
3 35 c. Canoes .. .. 3·00 2·50

TUVALU

(2)

3 50 c. Coin and Octopus

1976 (1 Jan). *Nos.* 173 *etc. of Gilbert & Ellice Is optd as T* **2** *in silver* (35 c.) *or blue (others). (a)* W w **12** (upright).
4 2 c. Lagoon fishing £600 £120
5 5 c. Gilbertese canoe .. .. .. 1·00 60
6 8 c. Weaving pandanus fronds 95 60
7 10 c. Weaving a basket .. .. .. 1·50 70
8 50 c. Local handicrafts .. .. .. 32·00 18·00
9 $1 Weaving coconut screen .. .. 85·00 70·00

(b) W w **12** *(sideways)*
10 2 c. Lagoon fishing .. .. £130 45·00
11 3 c. Cleaning pandanus leaves 70 60
12 5 c. Gilbertese canoe .. .. .. 1·90 1·50
13 25 c. Loading copra .. .. .. 4·00 3·50

(c) W w **14** *(inverted)*
14 1 c. Cutting toddy 25 20
15 6 c. De-husking coconuts 75 40
16 15 c. Tiger shark .. .. 1·50 90
17 50 c. Local handicrafts .. .. .. 7·00 4·50
18 $1 Weaving coconut screen .. .. 11·00 10·00
19 $2 Coat of arms .. .. 12·00 10·00

(d) W w **14** *(sideways)*
20 2 c. Lagoon fishing 65 30
21 3 c. Cleaning pandanus leaves 65 30
22 4 c. Casting nets 80 35
23 20 c. Beating a rolled pandanus leaf .. .. 1·75 1·00
24 25 c. Loading copra .. .. 2·25 1·50
25 35 c. Fishing at night .. .. 3·50 2·25
5/7 *and* 14/25 .. .. .. *Set of* 15 40·00 30·00

(Des G. Drummond. Litho Walsall)

1976 (21 Apr). *New Coinage. Vert designs, each showing coin as in T* **3**. *Multicoloured.* W w **14** *(inverted). P* 13½.
26 5 c. Type **3** .. .. 1·00 1·00
27 10 c. Red-eyed Crab .. .. 1·75 1·25
28 15 c. Flying Fish .. .. 2·25 1·75
29 35 c. Green Turtle .. .. 2·75 2·00

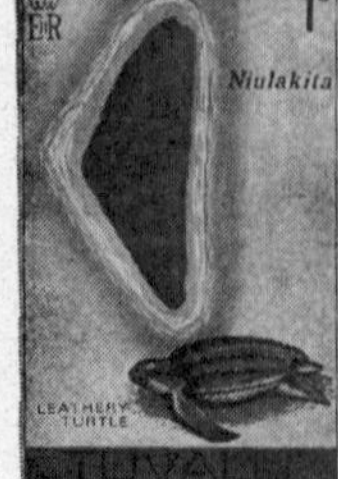

4 Niulakita and Leathery Turtle

5 Title page of New Testament

(Des J. Cooter. Litho Questa)

1976 (1 July–1 Sept). *Vert designs showing maps* (1 *to* 25 c.) *or horiz designs showing scenes (others). Multicoloured.* W w **14** *(sideways on* 35 c. *to* $5). *P* 13½.
30 1 c. Type **4** 70 45
31 2 c. Nukulaelae and sleeping mat 40 30
32 4 c. Nui and talo (vegetable) 40 30
33 5 c. Nanumanga and grass skirt .. .. 1·25 40
34 6 c. Nukufetau and Coconut Crab 70 40
35 8 c. Funafuti and Banana tree 75 50
36 10 c. Map of Tuvalu .. .. 1·25 45
37 15 c. Niutao and Flying fish .. .. .. 1·00 50
38 20 c. Vaitupu and Maneapa (house) .. .. 1·00 40
39 25 c. Nanumea and fish-hook .. .. 9·00 3·75
40 35 c. Te Ano (game) .. .. 1·50 55
41 50 c. Canoe pole fishing .. .. .. 2·00 1·25
42 $1 Reef fishing by flare .. .. .. 2·50 2·50
43 $2 Living house .. .. 6·50 5·00
44 $5 M.V. *Nivanga* (1.9.76) .. .. .. 90·00 30·00
30/44 .. .. *Set of* 15 £110 42·00
See also Nos. 58/72.

(Des G. Drummond. Litho Harrison)

1976 (6 Oct). *Christmas. T* **5** *and similar horiz designs. Multi-coloured.* W w **14**. *P* 14 × 14½.
45 5 c. Type **5** .. .. 2·75 1·50
46 20 c. Lotolelei Church .. .. 3·50 1·50
47 25 c. Kelupi Church .. .. 3·50 1·50
48 30 c. Mataloa o Tuvalu Church .. .. 3·50 1·50
49 35 c. Palatasio o Keliso Church .. .. 3·50 1·75

6 Queen Elizabeth and Prince Philip

(Des G. Vasarhelyi. Litho Format)

1977 (9 Feb). *Silver Jubilee. T* **6** *and similar horiz designs. Multi-coloured. P* 13½.
50 15 c. Type **6** .. .. 3·00 2·50
51 35 c. Prince Philip carried ashore at Vaitupu 4·00 3·25
52 50 c. Queen and attendants .. .. .. 4·00 3·75
MS53 98 × 144 mm. Nos. 50/2. P 15 .. .. 13·00 13·00

7 "Health"

(Des I. Oliver. Litho Format)

1977 (4 May). *30th Anniv of South Pacific Commission. T* **7** *and similar horiz designs. Multicoloured. P* 13½.
54 5 c. Type **7** .. .. 1·25 90
55 20 c. "Education" .. .. 1·50 1·10
56 30 c. "Fruit-growing" .. .. 1·50 1·10
57 35 c. Map of S.P.C. area .. .. .. 1·75 1·10

1977 (13 June)–**78**. *As Nos.* 30/6, 38/9 *and* 44, *but no wmk, or new values and designs.* (30, 40 c.).
58 1 c. Type **4** (9.77) 25 25
59 2 c. Nukulaelae and sleeping mat (3.78) .. 60 60
60 4 c. Nui and talo (vegetable) (3.78) 70 60
61 5 c. Nanumanga and grass skirt (9.77) .. 70 60
62 6 c. Nukufetau and Coconut Crab (3.78) .. 70 70
63 8 c. Funafuti and Banana tree (9.77) .. 70 75
64 10 c. Map of Tuvalu (9.77) .. .. .. 1·00 90
65 20 c. Vaitupu and Maneapa (house) (10.78) .. 4·00 5·00
66 25 c. Nanumea and fish-hook (9.77) .. .. 1·00 65
67 30 c. Fatele (local dancing) (19.4.78) .. .. 1·00 35
68 40 c. Screw Pine (19.4.78) .. .. .. 1·10 35
69 $5 M.V. *Nivanga* .. .. 22·00 12·00
58/69 .. .. *Set of* 12 30·00 21·00
No. 70/2 vacant.

8 Scout Promise

(Des I. Oliver. Litho Format)

1977 (10 Aug). *50th Anniv of Scouting in the Central Pacific. T* **8** *and similar horiz designs. Multicoloured. P* 13½.
73 5 c. Type **8** .. .. 1·50 1·00
74 20 c. Canoeing .. .. 1·50 1·00
75 30 c. Scout shelter .. .. 1·75 1·00
76 35 c. Lord Baden-Powell .. .. .. 1·75 1·00

9 Hurricane Beach (Expedition photo)

(Des I. Oliver. Litho Format)

1977 (2 Nov). *Royal Society Expeditions, 1896/7. T* **9** *and similar designs. P* 13½ × 14 (5 *and* 35 c.) *or* 14 × 13½ *(others).*
77 5 c. multicoloured .. .. 1·00 75
78 20 c. black and light blue .. .. .. 1·50 1·10
79 30 c. black and light blue .. .. .. 1·50 1·10
80 35 c. multicoloured .. .. 1·50 1·10
Designs: *Vert*—20 c. Boring apparatus on H.M.S. *Porpoise*; 30 c. Dredging chart. *Horiz*—35 c. Charles Darwin and H.M.S. *Beagle*.

10 Pacific Pigeon

11 S.M.V. *Lawedua*

(Des G. Drummond. Litho Format)

1978 (25 Jan). *Wild Birds. T* **10** *and similar vert designs. Multi-coloured. P* 14 × 13½.
81 8 c. Type **10** .. .. 2·50 1·60
82 20 c. Eastern Reef Heron .. .. .. 3·00 2·00
83 30 c. White Tern .. .. 3·25 2·25
84 40 c. Lesser Frigate Bird .. .. .. 3·50 2·50

(Des I. Oliver. Litho Format)

1978 (5 Apr). *Ships. T* **11** *and similar horiz designs. Multi-coloured. P* 13½ × 14.
85 8 c. Type **11** 60 50
86 10 c. Tug *Wallacia* 75 55
87 30 c. M.V. *Cenpac Rounder* 85 70
88 40 c. M.V. *Pacific Explorer* 90 70

(Des G. Drummond. Litho Format)

1978 (2 June). *25th Anniv of Coronation. Horiz designs as Nos.* 422/5 *of Montserrat. Multicoloured. P* 13½ × 14.
89 8 c. Canterbury Cathedral 25 20
90 30 c. Salisbury Cathedral 35 35
91 40 c. Wells Cathedral 45 40
92 $1 Hereford Cathedral .. .. .. 1·00 85
MS93 137 × 108 mm. Nos. 89/92. P 15 .. .. 1·90 1·60
Nos. 89/92 were each printed in sheets containing 2 *se-tenant* stamp-size labels.

INDEPENDENT

INDEPENDENCE
1ST OCTOBER
1978

(12)

13 White Frangipani

1978 (1 Oct). *Independence. Nos.* 63/4, 65, 67/8 *and as Nos.* 37 *and* 40, *but without wmk, optd as T* **12** *by Format.*
94 8 c. Funafuti and Banana tree 20 20
95 10 c. Map of Tuvalu 25 25
96 15 c. Niutao and Flying fish 30 25
97 20 c. Vaitupu and Maneapa (house) 30 30
98 30 c. Fatele (local dancing) 40 45
99 35 c. Te Ano (game) 45 25
100 40 c. Screw Pine 45 45
94/100 .. .. *Set of* 7 2·10 1·90

(Des J. Cooter. Litho Format)

1978 (4 Oct). *Wild Flowers. T* **13** *and similar vert designs. Multi-coloured. P* 14.
101 8 c. Type **13** 35 30
102 20 c. Susana 35 30
103 30 c. Tiale 45 40
104 40 c. Inato 60 50

14 Squirrelfish

(Des G. Drummond. Litho Format)

1979 (24 Jan)–**81**. *Fishes. Multicoloured designs as T* **14**. *P* 14.
105 1 c. Type **14** 5 5
106 2 c. Yellow-banded Goatfish 5 5
107 4 c. Imperial Angelfish 10 5
108 5 c. Rainbow Butterfly 12 8
109 6 c. Blue Angelfish 12 8

110 8 c. Blue Striped Snapper 15 10
111 10 c. Orange Clownfish 25 12
112 15 c. Chevroned Coralfish 25 15
113 20 c. Fairy Cod 35 25
114 25 c. Clown Triggerfish 35 30
115 30 c. Long-nosed Butterfly 40 35
116 35 c. Yellowfin Tuna 50 40
117 40 c. Spotted Eagle Ray 60 50
117*b* 45 c. Black-tipped Rock Cod (16.6.81) .. 70 55
118 50 c. Hammerhead Shark 65 65
119 70 c. Lionfish (*vert*) 80 80
120 $1 White-barred Triggerfish (*vert*).. .. 1·10 1·10
121 $2 Beaked Coralfish (*vert*) .. .. .. 2·25 2·25
122 $5 Tiger Shark (*vert*) .. .. .. 5·50 5·50
105/22 .. .. *Set of* 19 13·00 12·00

Nos. 105/22 were each printed in sheets containing 2 *se-tenant* stamp-size printed labels.

15 "Explorer of the Pacific"

(Des J. Cooter. Litho Format)

1979 (14 Feb). *Death Bicentenary of Captain Cook. T* **15** *and similar horiz designs. Multicoloured. P* 14 × 14½.

123 8 c. Type **15** 65 65
a. Horiz strip of 4. Nos. 123/6 .. .. 3·00
124 30 c. "A new island is discovered" 80 80
125 40 c. "Transit of Venus, Tahiti, 3 June, 1769" 80 80
126 $1 Death of Captain Cook, Hawaii, 14 February, 1779 .. .. 1·10 1·10

Nos. 123/6 were printed together, *se-tenant*, in horizontal strips of 4 throughout the sheet.

16 Grumman "Goose G21A" and Nukulaelae Island

(Des J. Cooter. Litho Format)

1979 (16 May). *Internal Air Service. T* **16** *and similar horiz designs. Multicoloured. P* 13½.

127 8 c. Type **16** 30 30
128 20 c. "Goose" and Vaitupu 40 40
129 30 c. "Goose" and Nui 50 50
130 40 c. "Goose" and Funafuti 60 50

17 Sir Rowland Hill, 1976 4 c. Separation Commemorative and London's First Pillar Box, 1855

18 Child's Face

(Des J. Cooter. Litho Format)

1979 (27 Aug). *Death Centenary of Sir Rowland Hill. T* **17** *and similar horiz designs. Multicoloured. P* 13½ × 14.

131 30 c. Type **17** 55 55
132 40 c. Sir Rowland Hill, 1976 10 c. Separation commemorative and Penny Black .. 55 55
133 $1 Sir Rowland Hill, 1976 35 c. Separation commemorative and mail coach.. .. 75 85
MS134 148 × 140 mm. Nos. 131/3. P 15 .. .. 2·25 2·25

(Des G. Vasarhelyi. Litho Format)

1979 (20 Oct). *International Year of the Child. T* **18** *and similar vert designs showing children's faces. P* 14 × 13½.

135 8 c. multicoloured 20 25
136 20 c. multicoloured 25 25
137 30 c. multicoloured 30 30
138 40 c. multicoloured 35 40

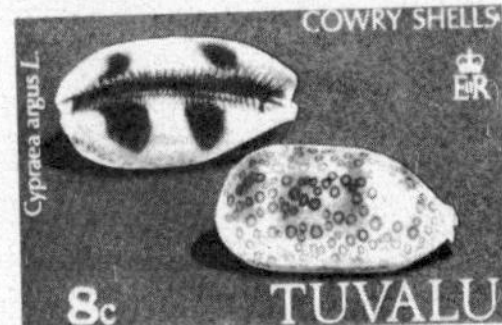

19 *Cypraea argus*

(Des J. Cooter. Litho Format)

1980 (20 Feb). *Cowrie Shells. T* **19** *and similar horiz designs. Multicoloured. P* 13½ × 14.

139 8 c. Type **19** 25 25
140 20 c. *Cypraea scurra* 25 25
141 30 c. *Cypraea carneola* 35 35
142 40 c. *Cypraea aurantium* 50 50

20 Philatelic Bureau, Funafuti, and 1976 8 c. Definitive

21 Queen Elizabeth the Queen Mother

(Des J. Cooter. Litho Questa)

1980 (30 Apr). *"London 1980" International Stamp Exhibition. T* **20** *and similar horiz designs. Multicoloured. P* 13½ × 14.

143 10 c. Type **20** 25 25
144 20 c. Gilbert and Ellice Islands stamp with Nukulaelae postmark of 1946 and 1976 2 c. definitive 30 30
145 30 c. Fleet Post Office, U.S. Navy, airmail letter of 1943 .. .. 45 45
146 $1 Tuvalu coat of arms and map 80 80
MS147 160 × 136 mm. Nos. 143/6 .. .. 1·90 2·25

(Des G. Drummond. Litho Format)

1980 (14 Aug). *80th Birthday of Queen Elizabeth the Queen Mother. P* 13½.

148 **21** 50 c. multicoloured 75 65

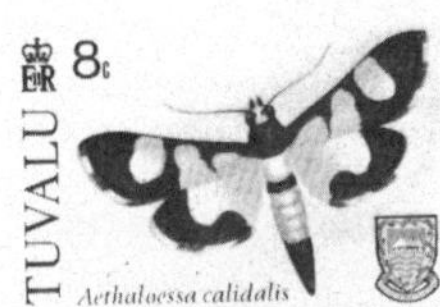

22 *Aethaloessa calidalis*

(Des J. Cooter. Litho Format)

1980 (20 Aug). *Moths. T* **22** *and similar horiz designs. Multicoloured. P* 14.

149 8 c. Type **22** 25 25
150 20 c. *Parotis suralis* 30 30
151 30 c. *Dudua aprobola* 40 40
152 40 c. *Decadarchis simulans* 45 45

23 Air Pacific "Heron"

45
CENTS

(**24**)

(Des G. Drummond. Litho Format)

1980 (5 Nov). *Aviation Commemorations. T* **23** *and similar horiz designs. Multicoloured. P* 13½ × 14.

153 8 c. Type **23** 20 20
154 20 c. Hawker Siddeley "748" 30 30
155 30 c. "Sunderland" flying boat 40 40
156 40 c. Orville Wright and *Flyer* 50 50

Commemorations:—8 c. 1st regular air service to Tuvalu, 1964; 20 c. Air service to Tuvalu; 30 c. War time R.N.Z.A.F. flying boat service to Funafuti, 1945; 40 c. Wright Brothers' 1st flight, 17 December 1903.

TWO TYPES OF SURCHARGE FOR NO. 157

Type I

Type II

Type I. Applied by lithography. Clean lines with an even distribution of the ink.

Type II. Applied by typography. Ragged lines with an uneven distribution of the ink, especially at the edges of the figures and bars. On some stamps the impression of the surcharge is visible on the back.

1981 (19 Jan). *No.* 118 *surch with T* **24**.

157 45 c. on 50 c. Hammerhead Shark (I).. .. 70 70
a. Type II (typo) surch .. .. .. 2·75 1·75

25 *Hypolimnas bolina elliciana* (male)

26 Brig *Elizabeth*, 1809

(Des J. Cooter. Litho Questa)

1981 (3 Feb). *Butterflies. T* **25** *and similar horiz designs. Multicoloured. P* 14 × 14½.

158 8 c. Type **25** 25 25
159 20 c. *Hypolimnas bolina elliciana* (female) .. 35 35
160 30 c. *Hypolimnas bolina elliciana* (female) (*different*).. .. .. .. 45 45
161 40 c. *Junonia vallida* 55 55

(Des R. Granger Barrett. Litho Format)

1981 (13 May). *Ships* (1*st series*). *T* **26** *and similar horiz designs. Multicoloured. W w* **15** (*sideways*). *P* 14.

162 10 c. Type **26** 40 25
163 25 c. Brigantine *Rebecca*, 1819 .. .. 45 40
164 35 c. Whaler *Independence II*, 1821 .. .. 50 50
165 40 c. H.M.S. *Basilisk*, 1872 .. .. .. 55 55
166 45 c. H.M.S. *Royalist*, 1890 .. .. .. 65 65
167 50 c. *Olivebank*, 1920 .. .. 70 70
162/7 .. .. *Set of* 6 3·00 3·00

Nos. 162/7 were each produced in sheets of six stamps and two labels, these occurring in the second horizontal row.

See also Nos. 235/40.

(Des D. Shults. Litho Questa)

1981 (10 July–26 Nov). *Royal Wedding. Horiz designs as T* **26/27** *of Kiribati. Multicoloured.* (*a*) *W w* **15**. *P* 14.

168 10 c. *Carolina* 10 12
a. Sheetlet. No. 168 × 6 and No. 169 .. 1·00
169 10 c. Prince Charles and Lady Diana Spencer 40 40
170 45 c. *Victoria and Albert III* 40 45
a. Sheetlet. No. 170 × 6 and No. 171 .. 3·00
171 45 c. As No. 169 .. .. 60 60
172 $2 *Britannia* .. .. 1·90 2·00
a. Sheetlet No. 172 × 6 and No. 173 .. 16·00
173 $2 As No. 169 .. .. 5·00 5·00
MS174 120 × 109 mm. $1.50, As No. 169. Wmk sideways. P 12 (26 Nov) .. .. .. 2·25 2·00

(*b*) *Booklet stamps. No wmk. P* 12 (26 Nov)

175 10 c. As No. 168 .. .. 12 15
a. Booklet pane. No. 175 × 4 50
176 45 c. As No. 171 .. .. 75 80
a. Booklet pane. No. 176 × 2 .. .. 1·50

Nos. 168/73 were printed in sheetlets of seven stamps of the same face value, each containing six of the "Royal Yacht" design and one of the larger design showing Prince Charles and Lady Diana.

Nos. 175/6 come from $1.70 stamp booklets.

27 U.P.U. Emblem

28 Map of Funafuti and Anchor

(Des, eng and recess Harrison)

1981 (19 Nov). *U.P.U. Membership. W* 4 *of Maldive Islands. P* 14½ × 14.

177 **27** 70 c. deep ultramarine 70 70
178 $1 red-brown .. .. 1·00 1·00
MS179 86 × 71 mm. Nos. 177/8. No wmk .. 2·25 2·25

(Des J. Cooter. Litho Questa)

1982 (17 Feb). *Amatuku Maritime School. T* **28** *and similar horiz designs. Multicoloured. W w* **15** (*sideways*). *P* 13½ × 14.

180 10 c. Type **28** 15 15
181 25 c. Motor launch 30 30

182 35 c. School buildings and jetty 40 40
183 45 c. School flag and freighters 50 50

TONGA CYCLONE
RELIEF
1982 +20c
(30)

29 Caroline of Brandenburg–Ansbach, Princess of Wales, 1714

(Des D. Shults and J. Cooter. Litho Format)

1982 (19 May). *21st Birthday of Princess of Wales. T* **29** *and similar vert designs. Multicoloured. W* w **15**. *P* 13½ × 14.
184 10 c. Type **29** 20 15
185 45 c. Coat of arms of Caroline of Brandenburg-Ansbach 60 55
186 $1.50, Diana, Princess of Wales .. .. .. 2·25 1·75

1982 (20 May). *Tonga Cyclone Relief. Nos.* 170/1 *surch as T* **30** (*words in one line on No.* 188).
187 45 c. + 20 c. *Victoria and Albert III* 75 75
a. Sheetlet. No. 187 × 6 and No. 188 .. 5·50
b. Surch inverted .. .. 32·00
c. Surch inverted (horiz pair) .. .. 55·00
d. Surch double .. .. 32·00
188 45 c. + 20 c. Prince Charles and Lady Diana Spencer .. .. 1·00 1·00
a. Surch inverted .. .. 60·00
b. Surch double .. .. 55·00

No. 187c shows the long surcharge, intended for No. 188, inverted and struck across a horizontal pair of No. 187. No. 188a shows two examples of Type **30** inverted on the same stamp.

1982 (14 July). *Birth of Prince William of Wales. Nos.* 184/6 *optd with T* 19 *of St. Kitts*.
189 10 c. Type 29 .. .. 20 15
190 45 c. Coat of Arms of Caroline of Brandenburg-Ansbach 60 55
a. Opt inverted .. .. 50·00
191 $1.50, Diana, Princess of Wales .. .. 1·60 1·75

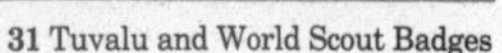

31 Tuvalu and World Scout Badges

32 Tuvalu Crest and Duke of Edinburgh's Standard

(Des J. Cooter. Litho Walsall)

1982 (18 Aug). *75th Anniv of Boy Scout Movement. T* **31** *and similar horiz designs. Multicoloured. W* w **15** (*sideways*). *P* 13½ × 14.
192 10 c. Type **31** 15 15
193 25 c. Camp-fire 40 40
194 35 c. Parade 45 45
195 45 c. Boy Scout 55 55

(Des J. Cooter. Litho Format)

1982 (26 Oct). *Royal Visit. T* **32** *and similar vert designs. Multicoloured. W* w **15**. *P* 14.
196 25 c. Type **32** 35 35
197 45 c. Tuvalu flag and Royal Standard 55 55
198 50 c. Portrait of Queen Elizabeth II 55 55
MS199 104 × 85 mm. Nos. 196/8 .. .. .. 1·40 1·50

33 Fisherman's Hat and Equipment

(Des G. Drummond. Litho Walsall)

1983 (14 Mar)–**84**. *Handicrafts. T* **33** *and similar multicoloured designs. W* w **15** (*sideways on* 1 c. *to* 45 c.). *P* 14.
200 1 c. Type **33** 5 5
201 2 c. Cowrie shell handbags 5 5
202 5 c. Wedding and babyfood baskets 5 8
203 10 c. Model canoe 10 12
203*a* 15 c. Ladies' sun hats (30.4.84) 15 20
204 20 c. Palm climbing rope and platform with toddy pot 20 25
205 25 c. Pandanus baskets 25 30
205*a* 30 c. Basket tray and coconut stands (18.4.84) 30 35
206 35 c. Pandanus pillows and shell necklaces .. 35 40
207 40 c. Round baskets and fans 40 45
208 45 c. Reef sandals and fish trap 45 50
209 50 c. Rat trap (*vert*) 50 55
209*a* 60 c. Fisherman's waterproof boxes (*vert*) (18.4.84) 60 65
210 $1 Pump drill and adze (*vert*) .. .. 1·00 1·10
211 $2 Fisherman's hat and canoe bailers (*vert*) 2·00 2·10
212 $5 Fishing rod, lures and scoop nets (*vert*) .. 5·00 5·50
200/12 .. .. *Set of* 16 10·50 11·00

34 *Te Tautai* (fishing vessel)

(Des G. Drummond. Litho Format)

1983 (14 Mar). *Commonwealth Day. T* **34** *and similar horiz designs. Multicoloured. W* w **15** (*sideways*). *P* 14.
213 20 c. Type **34** 20 25
214 35 c. Traditional dancing, Motufoua School .. 40 45
215 45 c. Satellite view of Pacific 50 55
216 50 c. *Morning Star* (container ship) 60 65

No. 214 is incorrectly inscribed "MOTOFOUA SCHOOL".

35 *Pantala flavescens*

(Des J. Cooter. Litho Format)

1983 (25 May). *Dragonflies. T* **35** *and similar horiz designs. Multicoloured. W* w **15** (*sideways*). *P* 14.
217 10 c. Type **35** 12 15
218 35 c. *Anax guttatus* 40 45
219 40 c. *Tholymis tillarga* 45 50
220 50 c. *Diplacodes bipunctata* 60 65

36 Brigade Members Racing

(37)

(Des J. Cooter. Litho Format)

1983 (10 Aug). *Centenary of Boys' Brigade. T* **36** *and similar multicoloured designs. W* w **15** (*sideways on* 10 c., 35 c.). *P* 13½.
221 10 c. Type **36** 12 15
222 35 c. B. B. members in outrigger 40 45
223 $1 On parade (*vert*) .. .. 1·25 1·40

1983 (26 Aug). *No.* 210 *surch with T* **37**.
224 60 c. on $1 Pump drill and adze 65 70

38 Montgolfier Balloon, 1783

39 Early Communications

(Des A. Theobald. Litho Format)

1983 (21 Sept). *Bicentenary of Manned Flight. T* **38** *and similar multicoloured designs. W* w **15** (*sideways on* 35 c., 45 c.). *P* 14.
225 25 c. Type **38** 30 35
226 35 c. McKinnon (Grumman) "Turbo-goose" (*horiz*) 40 45
227 45 c. Beechcraft "Super King Air 200" (*horiz*) 50 55
228 50 c. *Double Eagle II* balloon 60 65
MS229 114 × 145 mm. Nos. 225/8. Wmk sideways 1·75 1·90

(Des J.W. Litho Questa)

1983 (18 Nov). *World Communications Year. T* **39** *and similar horiz designs. Multicoloured. W* w **15**. *P* 14.
230 25 c. Type **39** 30 35
231 35 c. Radio operator 40 45
232 45 c. Modern telephone 50 55
233 50 c. Funafuti transmitting station 60 65

30c

(40)

1984 (1 Feb). *No.* 208 *surch with T* **40**.
234 30 c. on 45 c. Reef sandals and fish trap .. 35 40

(Des R. Granger Barrett. Litho Format)

1984 (16 Feb). *Ships* (*2nd series*). *Horiz designs as T* **26.** *Multicoloured. W* w **15** (*sideways*). *P* 14.
235 10 c. S.S. *Titus*, 1897 .. .. 12 15
236 20 c. S.S. *Malaita*, 1905 .. .. 20 25
237 25 c. S.S. *Aymeric*, 1906 .. .. 30 35
238 35 c. S.S. *Anshun*, 1965 .. .. 40 45
239 45 c. M.V. *Beaverbank*, 1970 .. .. .. 55 60
240 50 c. M.V. *Benjamin Bowring*, 1981 .. .. 60 65
235/40 .. .. *Set of* 6 2·00 2·25

Nos. 235/40 were each produced in sheets of six stamps and two labels, these occurring in the second horizontal row.

41 Class "GS-4"

(Des J.W. Litho Format)

1984 (29 Feb). *Leaders of the World. Railway Locomotives* (*1st series*). *T* **41** *and similar horiz designs, the first in each pair showing technical drawings and the second the locomotive at work. P* 12½.
241 1 c. multicoloured 5 5
a. Vert pair. Nos. 241/2 .. .. .. 10 10
242 1 c. multicoloured 5 5
243 15 c. multicoloured 20 25
a. Vert pair. Nos. 243/4 .. .. .. 40 50
244 15 c. multicoloured 20 25
245 40 c. multicoloured 55 60
a. Vert pair. Nos. 245/6 .. .. .. 1·10 1·10
246 40 c. multicoloured 55 60
247 60 c. multicoloured 75 80
a. Vert pair. Nos. 247/8 .. .. .. 1·50 1·60
248 60 c. multicoloured 75 80
241/8 .. .. *Set of* 8 2·75 3·25

Designs:—Nos. 241/2, Class "GS-4" (1941); 243/4, Class "AD 60" (1952); 245/6, Class "C 38" (1943); 247/8, *Lord of the Isles* (1892).

See also Nos. 253/68 and 273/80.

42 *Ipomoea pes-caprae*

(Des Michael and Sylvia Goaman. Litho Questa)

1984 (30 May). *Beach Flowers. T* **42** *and similar horiz designs. Multicoloured. W* w **15**. *P* 14.
249 25 c. Type **42** 30 35
250 45 c. *Ipomoea macrantha* 50 55
251 50 c. *Triumfetta procumbens* 55 60
252 60 c. *Portulaca quadrifida* 65 70

(Des J.W. Litho Format)

1984 (27 June). *Leaders of the World, Railway Locomotives* (*2nd series*). *Designs as T* **41**, *the first in each pair showing technical drawings and the second the locomotive at work. P* 12½.
253 10 c. multicoloured 12 15
a. Vert pair. Nos. 253/4 .. .. .. 25 30
254 10 c. multicoloured 12 15
255 15 c. multicoloured 15 20
a. Vert pair. Nos. 255/6 .. .. .. 30 40
256 15 c. multicoloured 15 20
257 20 c. multicoloured 25 30
a. Vert pair. Nos. 257/8 .. .. .. 50 60
258 20 c. multicoloured 25 30
259 25 c. multicoloured 30 35
a. Vert pair. Nos. 259/60 .. .. .. 60 70
260 25 c. multicoloured 30 35
261 40 c. multicoloured 45 50
a. Vert pair. Nos. 261/2 .. .. .. 90 1·00
262 40 c. multicoloured 45 50
263 50 c. multicoloured 55 60
a. Vert pair. Nos. 263/4 .. .. .. 1·10 1·25
264 50 c. multicoloured 55 60
265 60 c. multicoloured 65 70
a. Vert pair. Nos. 265/6 .. .. .. 1·25 1·40
266 60 c. multicoloured 65 70
267 $1 multicoloured .. .. 1·10 1·25
a. Vert pair. Nos. 267/8 .. .. .. 2·25 2·50
268 $1 multicoloured .. .. 1·10 1·25
253/68 .. .. *Set of* 16 6·50 7·25

Designs:—Nos. 253/4, "Casey Jones" engine (1896); 255/6, Triplex type (1914); 257/8, A.P.T. Class "370" (1981); 259/60, Class "F4" (1924); 261/2, Tornado Rover Class (1888); 263/4, "Broadlands" Class (1967); 265/6, *Locomotion No.* 1 (1825); 267/8, "C57" Class (1937).

Nos. 253/68 were issued in a similar sheet format to Nos. 241/8.

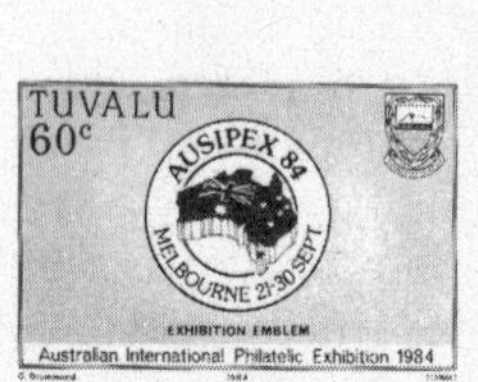

43 Exhibition Emblem

44 A. Shrewsbury

(Des G. Drummond. Litho Format)

1984 (21 Aug). *"Ausipex" International Stamp Exhibition, Melbourne (Nos. 269/70) and 15th South Pacific Forum (others). T* **43** *and similar horiz designs. Multicoloured. W w* **15** *(sideways). P* 14.

269 60 c. Type **43** 65 70
270 60 c. Royal Exhibition Building, Melbourne .. 65 70
271 60 c. Arms of Tuvalu 65 70
272 60 c. Tuvalu flag 65 70

(Des J.W. Litho Format)

1984 (4 Oct). *Leaders of the World. Railway Locomotives (3rd series). Horiz designs as T* **41**, *the first in each pair showing technical drawings and the second the locomotive at work. P* 12½.

273 1 c. multicoloured 5 5
a. Vert pair. Nos. 273/4 .. .. .. 5 5
274 1 c. multicoloured 5 5
275 15 c. multicoloured 15 20
a. Vert pair. Nos. 275/6 .. .. .. 30 40
276 15 c. multicoloured 15 20
277 30 c. multicoloured 35 40
a. Vert pair. Nos. 277/8 .. .. .. 70 80
278 30 c. multicoloured 35 40
279 $1 multicoloured .. .. 1·10 1·25
a. Vert pair. Nos. 279/80 .. .. .. 2·25 2·50
b. Error. Wmk W **15** .. .. .. 17·50
ba. Vert pair. Nos. 279b/80b.. .. .. 35·00
280 $1 multicoloured .. .. 1·10 1·25
b. Error. Wmk W **15** .. .. .. 17·50
273/80 .. .. *Set of* 8 3·00 3·50

Designs:—Nos. 273/4, Class "9700" (1897); 275/6, P.L.M. Class "231C/K"; 277/8, Class "640" (1907); 279/80, P.O. Class "4500" (1906).

Nos. 273/80 were issued in a similar sheet format to Nos. 241/8.

(Des Court House Studio. Litho Format)

1984 (5 Nov). *Leaders of the World. Cricketers. T* **44** *and similar vert designs, the first listed in each pair showing the cricketer in action and the second a head portrait. P* 12½.

281 5 c. multicoloured 8 10
a. Horiz pair. Nos. 281/2 .. .. .. 15 20
282 5 c. multicoloured 8 10
283 30 c. multicoloured 35 40
a. Horiz pair. Nos. 283/4 .. .. .. 70 80
284 30 c. multicoloured 35 40
285 50 c. multicoloured 55 60
a. Horiz pair. Nos. 285/6 .. .. .. 1·10 1·25
286 50 c. multicoloured 55 60
287 60 c. multicoloured 65 70
a. Horiz pair. Nos. 287/8 .. .. .. 1·25 1·40
288 60 c. multicoloured 65 70
281/8 .. .. *Set of* 8 3·00 3·25

Designs:—Nos. 281/2, A. Shrewsbury; 283/4, H. Verity; 285/6, E. H. Hendren; 287/8, J. Briggs.

Nos. 281/2, 283/4, 285/6 and 287/8 were printed together, *se-tenant*, in horizontal pairs throughout the sheets.

45 Trees and Stars

(Des Jennifer Toombs. Litho Format)

1984 (14 Nov). *Christmas. Children's Drawings. T* **45** *and similar horiz designs. Multicoloured. W w* **15** *(sideways). P* 14½ × 14.

289 15 c. Type **45** 15 20
290 40 c. Fishing from outrigger canoes 45 50
291 50 c. Three Wise Men bearing gifts 55 60
292 60 c. The Holy Family.. .. .. .. 65 70

46 Morris Minor

47 Common Flicker

(Des J.W. ($1), Artists International (others). Litho Format)

1984 (7 Dec). *Leaders of the World. Automobiles. T* **46** *and similar horiz designs, the first in each pair showing technical drawings and the second paintings. P* 12½.

293 1 c. black, pale cinnamon and yellow-ochre .. 5 5
a. Vert pair. Nos. 293/4 .. .. .. 5 5
294 1 c. multicoloured 5 5
295 15 c. black, pale flesh and brown-lilac .. 15 20
a. Vert pair. Nos. 295/6 .. .. .. 30 40
296 15 c. multicoloured 15 20
297 50 c. black, pale cinnamon and dull mauve .. 55 60
a. Vert pair. Nos. 297/8 .. .. .. 1·10 1·25
298 50 c. multicoloured 55 60
299 $1 black, pale green and cobalt .. .. 1·10 1·25
a. Vert pair. Nos. 299/300 .. .. .. 2·25 2·50
300 $1 multicoloured .. .. 1·10 1·25
293/300 .. .. *Set of* 8 3·25 3·75

Designs:—Nos. 293/4, Morris "Minor"; 295/6, Studebaker "Avanti"; 297/8, Chevrolet "International Six"; 299/300, Allard "J2".

Nos. 293/4, 295/6, 297/8 and 299/300 were printed together, *se-tenant*, in vertical pairs throughout the sheets.

(Des R. Vigurs. Litho Format)

1985 (12 Feb). *Leaders of the World. Birth Bicentenary of John J. Audubon (ornithologist). T* **47** *and similar vert designs. Multicoloured. P* 12½.

301 1 c. Type **47** 5 5
a. Horiz pair. Nos. 301/2 .. .. .. 5 5
302 1 c. Say's Phoebe 5 5
303 25 c. Townsend's Warbler 30 35
a. Horiz pair. Nos. 303/4 .. .. .. 60 70
304 25 c. Bohemian Waxwing 30 35
305 50 c. Prothonotary Warbler 55 60
a. Horiz pair. Nos. 305/6 .. .. .. 1·10 1·25
306 50 c. Worm-eating Warbler 55 60
307 70 c. Broad-winged Hawk 80 85
a. Horiz pair. Nos. 307/8 .. .. .. 1·60 1·75
308 70 c. Northern Harrier 80 85
301/8 .. .. *Set of* 8 3·00 3·25

Nos. 301/2, 303/4, 305/6 and 307/8 were printed together, *se-tenant*, in horizontal pairs throughout the sheets.

48 Black-naped Tern

(Des G. Drummond. Litho Format)

1985 (27 Feb). *Birds and their Eggs. T* **48** *and similar horiz designs. Multicoloured. W w* **15** *(sideways). P* 14.

309 15 c. Type **48** 15 20
310 40 c. Black Noddy 45 50
311 50 c. White-tailed Tropicbird 55 60
312 60 c. Sooty Tern 65 70

POSTAGE DUE STAMPS

D 1 Tuvalu Crest

(Des G. Drummond. Litho Questa)

1981 (3 May). *P* 13½ × 14.

D1 D 1 1 c. black and bright purple 5 5
D2 2 c. black and greenish blue 5 5
D3 5 c. black and ochre 5 5
D4 10 c. black and blue-green 20 20
D5 20 c. black and purple-brown 35 35
D6 30 c. black and bright orange 35 40
D7 40 c. black and blue 45 50
D8 50 c. black and yellow-green 55 60
D9 $1 black and deep mauve .. .. 1·00 1·10
D1/9 .. .. *Set of* 9 2·75 3·00

1982 (25 Nov)–**83**. *As Nos.* D1/9 *but P* 14½ × 15 *and with imprint date at foot.*

D10 D 1 1 c. black and bright purple 5 5
D11 2 c. black and greenish blue 5 5
D12 5 c. black and ochre 5 8
D13 10 c. black and blue-green 10 12
D14 20 c. black and purple-brown 20 25
D15 30 c. black and bright orange (25.5.83) .. 30 35
D16 40 c. black and blue (25.5.83) 40 45
D17 50 c. black and yellow-green (25.5.83) .. 50 55
D18 $1 black and deep mauve (25.5.83) .. 1·00 1·10
D10/18 .. .. *Set of* 9 2·40 2·75

The imprint date on Nos. D10/14 is "1982" and on Nos. D15/18 "1983".

OFFICIAL STAMPS

For the use of the Philatelic Bureau.

OFFICIAL (O 1) OFFICIAL (O 2)

TWO TYPES OF OVERPRINT FOR NOS. O1/19

This issue was overprinted using two different processes.

All values, except for the 35, 45 and 50 c., come with the overprint applied by typography. This process results in ragged lines, uneven distribution of the ink, especially at the edges of the letters, and often has the impression of the letters visible from the reverse.

In addition nine of these values have been found with overprints applied by lithography. These show clean lines and an even distribution of the ink.

The 35, 45 and 50 c. values have only been seen with overprints applied by lithography.

1981 (2 July). *Nos.* 105/22 *optd with Type* O 1.

O 1 1 c. Type **14** .. .. 2·50 1·50
O 2 2 c. Yellow-banded Goatfish 5 5
O 3 4 c. Imperial Angelfish 5 5
O 4 5 c. Rainbow Butterfly 5 5
O 5 6 c. Blue Angelfish 8 8
a. Litho opt 30 30
O 6 8 c. Blue Striped Snapper 25 25
O 7 10 c. Orange Clownfish 15 15
a. Litho opt 30 25
O 8 15 c. Chevroned Coralfish 20 20
O 9 20 c. Fairy Cod 25 25
O10 25 c. Clown Triggerfish .. .. .. 20·00
a. Litho opt 30 30
O11 30 c. Long-nosed Butterfly 30 30
a. Litho opt
O12 35 c. Yellowfin Tuna (*litho opt*) 35 35
O13 40 c. Spotted Eagle Ray 40 40
O14 45 c. Black-tipped Rock Cod (*litho opt*) .. 45 45
O15 50 c. Hammerhead Shark (*litho opt*) .. 50 50
O16 70 c. Lionfish 75 75
a. Litho opt .. .. 4·00 3·00
O17 $1 White-barred Triggerfish .. .. 1·10 1·10
a. Litho opt .. .. 2·50 2·50
O18 $2 Beaked Coralfish .. .. .. 3·25 3·00
a. Litho opt .. .. 2·25 2·25
O19 $5 Tiger Shark .. .. 5·50 6·00
a. Litho opt .. .. 15·00 12·00
O1/19 .. .. *Set of* 19 11·00 11·00

1983 (26 Aug)–**84**. *Nos.* 202/3a, 205/12, 224 *and* 234 *optd as Type* O 1, *but* 20½ × 4 *mm.* (5 c.), *or as Type* O 2 *(others).*

O20 5 c. Wedding and baby food baskets (1.2.84) 5 8
O21 10 c. Hand-carved model of canoe (1.2.84) .. 10 12
O22 15 c. Ladies' sun hats (30.4.84) 15 20
O23 25 c. Pandanus baskets (1.2.84) 25 30
O24 30 c. on 45 c. Reef sandals and fish trap (1.2.84) 30 35
O25 30 c. Basket tray and coconut stand (30.4.84) 30 35
O26 35 c. Pandanus pillows and shell necklaces (1.2.84) 35 40
O27 40 c. Round baskets and fans (1.2.84) .. 40 45
O28 45 c. Reef sandals and fish trap (1.2.84) .. 45 50
O29 50 c. Rat trap (1.2.84) 50 55
O30 60 c. on $1 Pump drill and adze 60 65
O31 60 c. Fisherman's waterproof boxes (30.4.84) 70 75
O32 $1 Pump drill and adze (1.2.84) .. .. 1·00 1·10
O33 $2 Fisherman's hat and canoe bailers (1.2.84) .. .. 2·00 2·25
O34 $5 Fishing rod, lures and scoop nets (1.2.84) 5·00 5·50
O20/34 .. .. *Set of* 15 11·00 12·00

Appendix

The following issues for individual islands of Tuvalu fall outside the criteria for full listing as detailed on page viii of this edition.

FUNAFUTI

1984

Leaders of the World. Railway Locomotives (1st series). Two designs for each value, the first showing technical drawings and the second the locomotive at work. 15, 20, 30, 40, 50, 60 c., *each* × 2

Leaders of the World. Automobiles (1st series). Two designs for each value, the first showing technical drawings and the second the car in action. 1, 10, 40 c., $1, *each* × 2

Leaders of the World. Railway Locomotives (2nd series). Two designs for each value, the first showing technical drawings and the second the locomotive at work. 5, 15, 25, 35, 40, 55, 60 c., $1, *each* × 2

1985

Leaders of the World. Automobiles (2nd series). Two designs for each value, the first showing technical drawings and the second the car in action. 1, 30, 55, 60 c., *each* × 2

NANUMAGA

1984

Leaders of the World. Automobiles (1st series). Two designs for each value, the first showing technical drawings and the second the car in action. 5, 10, 25, 30, 40 c., $1, *each* × 2

Leaders of the World. British Monarchs. Two designs for each value, forming a composite picture. 10, 20, 30, 40, 50 c., $1, *each* × 2

Leaders of the World. Automobiles (2nd series). Two designs for each value, the first showing technical drawings and the second the car in action. 5, 10, 50 c., $1, *each* × 2

1985

Leaders of the World. Railway Locomotives. Two designs for each value, the first showing technical drawings and the second the locomotive at work. 10, 25, 50, 60 c., *each* × 2.

NANUMEA

1984

Leaders of the World. Railway Locomotives (1st series). Two designs for each value, the first showing technical drawings and the second the locomotive at work. 15, 20, 30, 40, 50, 60 c., *each* × 2

Leaders of the World. Famous Cricketers. Two designs for each value, the first showing a portrait and the second the cricketer in action. 1, 10, 40 c., $1, *each* × 2

1985

Leaders of the World. Automobiles (1st series). Two designs for each value, the first showing technical drawings and the second the car in action. 5, 40, 50, 60 c., *each* × 2

Leaders of the World. Railway Locomotives (2nd series). Two designs for each value, the first showing technical drawings and the second the locomotive at work. 1, 35, 50, 60 c., *each* × 2

Leaders of the World. Automobiles (2nd series). Two designs for each value, the first showing technical drawings and the second the car in action. 15, 20, 50, 60 c., *each* ×2.

NIUTAO

1984

Leaders of the World. Automobiles. Two designs for each value, the first showing technical drawings and the second the car in action. 15, 30, 40, 50 c., *each* × 2

Leaders of the World. Railway Locomotives. Two designs for each value, the first showing technical drawings and the second the locomotive at work. 5, 10, 20, 40, 50 c., $1, *each* × 2

1985

Leaders of the World. Famous Cricketers. Two designs for each value, the first showing a portrait and the second the cricketer in action. 1, 15, 50 c., $1, *each* × 2

Leaders of the World. Birth Bicent of John J. Audubon (ornithologist). Birds. 5, 15, 25 c., $1, *each* × 2.

NUI

1984

Leaders of the World. Railway Locomotives (1st series). Two designs for each value, the first showing technical drawings and the second the locomotive at work. 15, 25, 30, 50 c., *each* × 2

Leaders of the World. British Monarchs. Two designs for each value, forming a composite picture. 1, 5, 15, 40, 50 c., $1, *each* × 2

Leaders of the World. Railway Locomotives (2nd series). Two designs for each value, the first showing technical drawings and the second the locomotive at work. 5, 15, 25 c., $1, *each* × 2.

Leaders of the World. Automobiles. Two designs for each value, the first showing technical drawings and the second the car in action. 25, 30, 40, 50 c., *each* × 2.

NUKUFETAU

1984

Leaders of the World. Automobiles. Two designs for each value, the first showing technical drawings and the second the car in action. 10, 25, 30, 50, 60 c., *each* × 2

Leaders of the World. British Monarchs. Two designs for each value, forming a composite picture. 1, 10, 30, 50, 60 c., $1, *each* × 2

1985

Leaders of the World. Famous Cricketers. Two designs for each value, the first showing a portrait and the second the cricketer in action. 1, 10, 55 c., $1, *each* × 2

Leaders of the World. Railway Locomotives. Two designs for each value, the first showing technical drawings and the second the locomotive at work. 1, 10, 60, 70 c., *each* × 2

NUKULAELAE

1984

Leaders of the World. Railway Locomotives (1st series). Two designs for each value, the first showing technical drawings and the second the locomotive at work. 5, 15, 40 c., $1, *each* × 2

Leaders of the World. Famous Cricketers. Two designs for each value, the first showing a portrait and the second the cricketer in action. 5, 15, 30 c., $1, *each* × 2

Leaders of the World. Railway Locomotives (2nd series). Two designs for each value, the first showing technical drawings and the second the locomotive at work. 5, 20, 40 c., $1, *each* × 2

1985

Leaders of the World. Automobiles. Two designs for each value, the first showing technical drawings and the second the car in action. 5, 35, 50, 70 c., *each* × 2

VAITUPU

1984

Leaders of the World. Automobiles (1st series). Two designs for each value, the first showing technical drawings and the second the car in action. 15, 25, 30, 50 c., *each* × 2

Leaders of the World. British Monarchs. Two designs for each value, forming a composite picture. 1, 5, 15, 40, 50 c., $1, *each* × 2

Leaders of the World. Automobiles (2nd series). Two designs for each value, the first showing technical drawings and the second the car in action. 5, 15, 25, 30, 40, 50, 60 c., $1, *each* × 2

1985

Leaders of the World. Railway Locomotives. Two designs for each value, the first showing technical drawings and the second the locomotive at work. 10, 25, 50, 60 c., *each* × 2.

Leaders of the World. Butterflies. 5, 15, 50, 75 c., *each* × 2.

Leaders of the World. Automobiles (3rd series). Two designs for each value, the first showing technical drawings and the second the car in action. 15, 30, 40, 60 c., *each* × 2.

Uganda

PRICES FOR STAMPS ON COVER TO 1945

The type-written stamps of Uganda, Nos. 1/53, are very rare used on cover.

Nos. 54/60	*from* × 8
No. 61	—
Nos. 70/5	*from* × 8
No. 76	—
Nos. 84/90	*from* × 12
No. 91	—
Nos. 92/3	*from* × 20

PROTECTORATE

1

2

TYPE-WRITTEN STAMPS. Nos. 1/53 were type-written by the Revd. E. Millar at Mengo. For all "printings" a thin laid paper was used, and all issues were imperforate.

The original typewriter used had wide letters, but in late April, 1895 Millar obtained a new machine on which the type face was in a narrower fount.

Each sheet was made up of whatever values were required at the time, so that different values can be found *se-tenant* or *tête-bêche*. These last were caused by the paper being inverted in the machine so that space at the foot could be utilised.

For the first issue the sheets were of 117 (9 × 13), but with the introduction of the narrower width (Nos. 17 onwards) a larger number of stamps per sheet, 143 (11 × 13), was adopted.

The manuscript provisionals, Nos. 9*a*/16, come from the Mission at Ngogwe, most of the manuscript surcharges including the initials of the Revd. G. R. Blackledge stationed there.

1895 (20 Mar). *Wide letters. Wide stamps, 20 to 26 mm wide.*

1	1	5 (cowries), black	£2000	
2		10 (cowries), black	£1200	
3		15 (cowries), black		
4		20 (cowries), black	—	£1000
5		25 (cowries), black		
6		30 (cowries), black	£1100	£1000
7		40 (cowries), black	£1200	
8		50 (cowries), black	£1000	£950
9		60 (cowries), black	£1200	

A strip of three of No. 2 is known on cover of which one copy has the value "10" altered to "5" in manuscript and initialled.

1895 (May). *Wide stamps with pen-written surcharges, in black.*

9*a*	1	10 on 30 (c.) black		
10		10 on 50 (c.) black	—	£2250
11		15 on 10 (c.) black	—	£2250
12		15 on 20 (c.) black	—	£3500
13		15 on 40 (c.) black	—	£2250
14		15 on 50 (c.) black	—	£3750
15		25 on 50 (c.) black	—	£3500
16		50 on 60 (c.) black	—	£3500

1895 (April). *Wide letters. Narrow stamps, 16 to 18 mm wide.*

17	1	5 (c.) black	—	£850
18		10 (c.) black	£950	£950
19		15 (c.) black	£750	£700
20		20 (c.) black	£650	£600
21		25 (c.) black	£750	£700
22		30 (c.) black	£950	£950
23		40 (c.) black	£950	
24		50 (c.) black	£1000	
25		60 (c.) black	£1100	

1895 (May). *Narrow letters. Narrow stamps 16 to 18 mm wide.*

26	2	5 (c.) black	£325
27		10 (c.) black	£325
28		15 (c.) black	£400
29		20 (c.) black	£200
30		25 (c.) black	£325
31		30 (c.) black	£375
32		40 (c.) black	£325
33		50 (c.) black	£325
34		60 (c.) black	£325

1895 (Nov). *Narrow letters. Narrow stamps, 16–18 mm wide. Change of colour.*

35	2	5 (c.) violet	£275	£300
36		10 (c.) violet	£275	£275
37		15 (c.) violet	£275	£275
38		20 (c.) violet	£300	£275
		a. "G U" for "U G"		
39		25 (c.) violet	£300	
40		30 (c.) violet	£300	
41		40 (c.) violet	£300	
42		50 (c.) violet	£300	
43		100 (c.) violet	£2750	

Stamps of 35 (c.) and 45 (c.) have been chronicled in both colours. They were never prepared for postal use, and did not represent a postal rate, but were type-written to oblige a local official.

3

1896 (June).

44	3	5 (c.) violet	£150	£125
45		10 (c.) violet	£150	£125
46		15 (c.) violet	£150	£125
47		20 (c.) violet	£150	£125
48		25 (c.) violet	£200	
49		30 (c.) violet	£200	
50		40 (c.) violet	£200	
51		50 (c.) violet	£200	
52		60 (c.) violet	£550	
53		100 (c.) violet	£600	£550

4 (Thin "1")

5 (Thick "1")

6

7

In the 2 a. and 3 a. the dagger points upwards; the stars in the 2 a. are level with the top of "VR". The 8 a. is as **T 6** but with left star at top and right star at foot. The 1 r. has three stars at foot. The 5 r. has central star raised and the others at foot.

(Printed by the Revd. F. Rowling at Lubwa's, in Usoga)

1896 (7 Nov). (*a*) *Types* **4/6**.

A. *Normal.* B. *Small* "o" *in* "POSTAGE"

			A		B	
54	4	1 a. black	15·00	20·00	60·00	60·00
55	5	1 a. black	5·00	5·50	15·00	15·00
56	6	2 a. black	5·50	6·00	12·00	12·00
57		3 a. black	5·50	6·00	16·00	16·00
58		4 a. black	5·50	6·50	16·00	16·00
59		8 a. black	6·50	9·00	30·00	30·00
60		1 r. black	20·00	25·00	£130	£130
61		5 r. black	90·00	£130	£180	£180

(*b*) *Optd* "L", *in black as in T* **7** *for local use, by a postal official, R. R. Racey, at Kampala*

			A		B	
70	4	1 a. black	16·00	30·00	£275	—
71	6	2 a. black	16·00	30·00	40·00	50·00
72		3 a. black	25·00	42·00	£350	—
73		4 a. black	25·00	42·00	50·00	—
74		8 a. black	50·00	55·00	£120	—
75		1 r. black	£100	£120	£275	—
76		5 r. black	—	£1600	—	—

Tête-bêche pairs of all values may be found owing to the settings being printed side by side or above one another. They are worth a premium.

8

9

UGANDA

(10)

(Recess D.L.R.)

1898–1902. *P* 14. (*a*) *Wmk Crown CA.*

84	8	1 a. scarlet	30	25
		a. Carmine-rose (1902)	30	35
86		2 a. red-brown	40	85
87		3 a. pale grey	1·75	2·00
		a. Bluish grey	1·25	1·50
88		4 a. deep green	1·25	2·00
89		8 a. pale olive	2·00	5·00
		a. Grey-green	2·00	5·00
		(*b*) *Wmk Crown CC*		
90	9	1 r. dull blue	8·50	8·50
		a. Bright blue	12·00	13·00
91		5 r. brown	35·00	42·00
84/91		*Set of* 7	45·00	55·00
84/91 Optd "Specimen"		*Set of* 7	£180	

1902. *T* **11** *of British East Africa optd with T* **10**.

92	½ a. yellow-green	35	40
	a. Opt omitted (in pair with normal)	£850	
	b. Opt inverted (at foot)	£450	
	c. Opt double	£650	
93	2½ a. deep blue (R.)	50	85
	a. Opt double	£600	

For issues between 1903 and 1976 see KENYA, UGANDA AND TANGANYIKA.

OMNIBUS ISSUES

Details, together with prices for complete sets, of the various Omnibus issues from the 1935 Silver Jubilee series to date are included in a special section following Zululand at the end of the catalogue.

SELF-GOVERNMENT

11 Ripon Falls and Speke Memorial

(Des S. Scott. Recess B.W.)

1962 (28 July). *Centenary of Speke's Discovery of Source of the Nile. W w* **12**. *P* 14.
95 **11** 30 c. black and red 10 5
96 50 c. black and slate-violet 10 5
97 1s. 30, black and green 15 10
98 2s. 50, black and blue 30 75

INDEPENDENT

12 Murchison Falls

13 Tobacco-growing

14 Mulago Hospital

(Des V. Whiteley. Photo Harrison)

1962 (9 Oct). *Independence. Various designs as T* **12/14**. *P* 15 × 14 (5 *c. to* 50 *c.*) *or* 14½ (*others*).
99 5 c. deep bluish green 10 5
100 10 c. reddish brown (*shades*) 5 5
101 15 c. black, red and green 8 5
102 20 c. plum and buff 10 5
103 30 c. blue 10 5
104 50 c. black and turquoise-green 12 5
105 1s. sepia, red and turquoise-green 15 5
106 1s. 30, yellow-orange and violet 20 5
107 2s. black, carmine and light blue 40 15
108 5s. vermilion and deep green . . . . 2·75 90
109 10s. slate and chestnut . . . . 3·50 2·00
110 20s. brown and blue . . . . 12·00 16·00
99/110 . . . . *Set of* 12 18·00 18·00

Designs: *As T* **12/13**—10 c. Tobacco growing; 15 c. Coffee growing; 20 c. Ankole cattle; 30 c. Cotton; 50 c. Mountains of the Moon. *As T* **14**—1s. 30, Cathedrals and Mosque; 2s. Makerere College; 5s. Copper mining; 10s. Cement industry; 20s. Parliament Buildings.

15 Crowned Crane

(Photo Harrison)

1965 (20 Feb). *International Trade Fair, Kampala. P* 14½ × 14.
111 **15** 30 c. multicoloured 20 10
112 1s. 30, multicoloured 40 20

16 Black Bee Eater

17 African Jacana

18 Ruwenzori Turaco

(Des Mrs. R. Fennessy. Photo Harrison)

1965 (9 Oct). *Birds. Various designs as T* **16/18**. *P* 15 × 14 (5 *c.,* 15 *c.,* 20 *c.,* 40 *c.,* 50 *c.*), 14 × 15 (10 *c.,* 30 *c.,* 65 *c.*) *or* 14½ (*others*).
113 5 c. multicoloured 10 10
114 10 c. chestnut, black and light blue 10 5
115 15 c. yellow and sepia 12 5
116 20 c. multicoloured 15 10
117 30 c. black and brown-red 20 5
118 40 c. multicoloured 25 20
119 50 c. grey-blue and reddish violet 25 5
a. White bird (grey-blue omitted) . . . . 75·00
120 65 c. orange-red, black and light grey 70 75
121 1s. multicoloured 45 5
122 1s. 30, chestnut, black and yellow . . . . 1·50 15
123 2s. 50, multicoloured . . . . . . 3·00 65
124 5s. multicoloured . . . . . . 4·75 2·00
125 10s. multicoloured . . . . . . 8·00 7·00
126 20s. multicoloured . . . . . . 17·00 20·00
113/26 . . . . *Set of* 14 32·00 28·00

Designs: *Vert as T* **16**—15 c. Orange Weaver; 20 c. Narina Trogon; 40 c. Blue-breasted Kingfisher; 50 c. Whale-headed Stork. *Horiz as T* **17**—30 c. Sacred Ibis; 65 c. Red-crowned Bishop. *As T* **18**. *Vert*—1s. 30, African Fish Eagle; 5s. Lilac-breasted Roller. *Horiz*—2s. 50, Great Blue Turaco; 10s. Black-collared Lovebird; 20s. Crowned Crane.

The 15 c., 40 c., 65 c., and 1s. exist with PVA gum as well as gum arabic.

19 Carved Screen

(Des Mrs. R. Fennessy. Photo Harrison)

1967 (26 Oct). *13th Commonwealth Parliamentary Association Conference. T* **19** *and similar horiz designs. Multicoloured. P* 14.
127 30 c. Type **19** 5 5
128 50 c. Arms of Uganda 8 5
129 1s. 30, Parliamentary Building 20 5
130 2s. 50, Conference Chamber . . . . 40 1·00

20 *Cordia abyssinica*

21 *Acacia drepanolobium*

(Des Mrs. R. Fennessy. Photo Harrison)

1969 (9 Oct)–**73**. *Flowers. Various designs as T* **20/1**. *Chalk-surfaced paper. P* 14½ × 14 (5 *c. to* 70 *c.*) *or* 14 (*others*).
131 5 c. brown, green and light olive-yellow . . 5 5
a. Glazed, ordinary paper (11.4.73) . . 15 5
132 10 c. multicoloured 5 5
a. Glazed, ordinary paper (27.9.72) . . 15 5
133 15 c. multicoloured 10 5
134 20 c. bluish violet, yellow-ol & pale sage-grn . . 10 5
a. Glazed, ordinary paper (27.9.72) . . 20 5
135 30 c. multicoloured 12 5
136 40 c. reddish violet, yellow-green and pale olive-grey 15 5
137 50 c. multicoloured 15 5
138 60 c. multicoloured 35 30
a. Glazed, ordinary paper (9.5.73) . . 50 50
139 70 c. multicoloured 35 25
a. Glazed, ordinary paper (27.9.72) . . 50 60
140 1s. multicoloured 25 5
a. Glazed, ordinary paper (22.1.71) . . 30 5
141 1s. 50, multicoloured (*shades*) 35 10
a. Glazed, ordinary paper (3.2.71) . . 50 10
142 2s. 50, multicoloured 90 25
a. Glazed, ordinary paper (3.2.71) . . 1·25 10
143 5s. multicoloured . . . . . . 2·00 60
a. Glazed, ordinary paper (3.2.71) . . 1·75 25
144 10s. multicoloured . . . . . . 4·00 1·50
a. Glazed, ordinary paper (3.2.71) . . 3·75 30
145 20s. multicoloured . . . . . . 9·00 2·75
a. Glazed, ordinary paper (22.1.71) . . 9·50 40
131/45 . . . . *Set of* 15 16·00 5·50
131a/45a . . . . *Set of* 11 17·00 2·25

Designs: *As T* **20**—10 c. *Grewia similis*; 15 c. *Cassia didymobotrya*; 20 c. *Coleus barbatus*; 30 c. *Ockna ovata*; 40 c. *Ipomoea spathulata*; 50 c. *Spathodea nilotica*; 60 c. *Oncoba spinosa*; 70 c. *Carissa edulis*. *As T* **21**—1s. 50, *Clerodendrum myricoides*; 2s. 50, *Acanthus arboreus*; 5s. *Kigelia aethiopium*; 10s. *Erythrina abyssinica*; 20s. *Monodora myristica*.

2/-

(22)

1975 (29 Sept). *Nos.* 141/2 *and* 145a *surch as T* **22**.
146 2s. on 1s. 50, multicoloured . . . . 1·50 1·25
147 3s. on 2s. 50, multicoloured . . . . 20·00 17·00
148 40s. on 20s. multicoloured . . . . 7·00 6·00
a. Surch on No. 145 . . . . — 7·00

23 Millet

24 Maize

(Des Mrs. R. Fennessy. Photo Harrison)

1975 (9 Oct). *Ugandan Crops. T* **23/4** *and similar horiz designs. P* 14 × 14½ (10 *to* 80 *c.*) *or* 14 (*others*).
149 10 c. black, apple-green and yellow-brown . . 5 5
150 20 c. multicoloured 5 5
151 30 c. multicoloured 8 5
152 40 c. multicoloured 10 5
153 50 c. multicoloured 10 5
154 70 c. black, apple-green and light blue-green 12 5
155 80 c. multicoloured 12 5
156 1s. multicoloured 15 5
157 2s. multicoloured 30 25
158 3s. multicoloured 50 35
159 5s. multicoloured 90 60
160 10s. multicoloured . . . . . . 1·50 1·25
161 20s. apple-green, black and bright purple . . 3·25 2·40
162 40s. apple-green, black and yellow-orange . . 6·50 4·75
149/62 . . . . *Set of* 14 12·00 9·00

Designs: *As T* **23**—20 c. Sugar; 30 c. Tobacco; 40 c. Onions; 50 c. Tomatoes; 70 c. Tea; 80 c. Bananas. *As T* **24**—2s. Pineapples; 3s. Coffee; 5s. Oranges; 10s. Groundnuts; 20s. Cotton; 40s. Runner Beans.

Face value colours: 5s. green; 10s. brown; 20s. bright purple; 40s. yellow-orange. For 5s. to 40s. with colours changed see Nos. 220/3.

Nos. 149 and 153 exist in coils constructed from normal sheets.

1976 (15 Apr). *Telecommunications Development. As Nos.* 56/60 *of Kenya, but inscr* "UGANDA".
163 50 c. Microwave tower 12 5
164 1s. Cordless switchboard 25 5
165 2s. Telephone 35 40
166 3s. Message Switching Centre 50 60
MS167 120 × 120 mm. Nos. 163/6 . . . . 1·40 1·40

1976 (5 July). *Olympic Games, Montreal. As Nos.* 61/5 *of Kenya, but inscr* "UGANDA".
168 50 c. Akii Bua, hurdler 15 5
169 1s. Filbert Bayi, runner 30 5
170 2s. Steve Muchoki, boxer 55 50
171 3s. East African flags 70 60
MS172 129 × 154 mm. Nos. 168/71 . . . . 6·00 4·50

1976 (4 Oct). *Railway Transport. As Nos.* 66/70 *of Kenya, but inscr* "UGANDA".
173 50 c. Tanzania–Zambia railway 20 5
174 1s. Nile Bridge, Uganda 35 5
175 2s. Nakuru Station, Kenya 75 55
176 3s. Class A loco, 1896 . . . . . . 95 70
MS177 154 × 103 mm. Nos. 173/6 . . . . 3·25 2·25

1977 (10 Jan). *Game Fish of East Africa. As Nos.* 71/5 *of Kenya, but inscr* "UGANDA".
178 50 c. Nile Perch 15 5
179 1s. Tilapia 30 5
180 3s. Sailfish 90 45
181 5s. Black Marlin . . . . . . 1·25 85
MS182 153 × 129 mm. Nos. 178/81 . . . . 3·25 1·75

1977 (15 Jan). *Second World Black and African Festival of Arts and Culture, Nigeria. As Nos.* 76/80 *of Kenya, but inscr* "UGANDA".
183 50 c. Maasai Manyatta (village) 15 5
184 1s. "Heartbeat of Africa" (Ugandan dancers) 30 5
185 2s. Makonde sculpture 65 55
186 3s. "Early Man and Technology" (skinning animal) 80 90
MS187 132 × 109 mm. Nos. 183/6 . . . . 2·25 2·25

1977 (5 Apr). *25th Anniv of Safari Rally. As Nos.* 81/5 *of Kenya, but inscr* "UGANDA".
188 50 c. Rally-car and villagers 15 5
189 1s. Starting-line 30 10
190 2s. Car fording river 80 80
191 5s. Car and elephants . . . . . . 1·60 1·90
MS192 126 × 93 mm. Nos. 188/91 . . . . 2·75 3·00

1977 (30 June). *Centenary of Ugandan Church. As Nos.* 86/90 *of Kenya, but inscr* "UGANDA".
193 50 c. Canon Kivebulaya 12 5
194 1s. Modern Namirembe Cathedral 25 5
195 2s. Old Namirembe Cathedral 70 55
196 5s. Early congregation, Kigezi . . . . 1·25 1·25
MS197 126 × 89 mm. Nos. 193/6 . . . . 2·25 2·25

80c ═

(25)

26 Shot Putting

1977 (22 Aug). *Design as No.* 155 *surch with T* **25** *in mauve by Harrison*.
198 80 c. on 60 c. multicoloured 25 20
a. Surch omitted £175

A 60 c. stamp was to have been added to Nos. 149/62 using the design of the 80 c. (bananas), but it was cancelled and those already printed were surcharged to make No. 198.

1977 (26 Sept). *Endangered Species. As Nos.* 96/101 *of Kenya, but inscr* "UGANDA".
199 50 c. Pancake Tortoise 20 5
200 1s. Nile Crocodile 35 5
201 2s. Hunter's Hartebeest . . . . . . 1·25 55

202 3s. Red Colobus monkey .. .. .. 1·50 1·10
203 5s. Dugong .. .. 2·25 1·75
MS204 127 × 101 mm. Nos. 200/3 .. .. 5·00 3·50

1978 (10 Apr). *World Cup Football Championship, Argentina* (1st *issue*). *As Nos.* 122/6 *of Kenya but inscr* "UGANDA".
205 50 c. Joe Kadenge and forwards 15 5
206 1s. Mohamed Chuma and cup presentation 30 5
207 2s. Omari Kidevu and goalmouth scene .. 80 60
208 5s. Polly Ouma and forwards .. .. 1·50 1·60
MS209 136 × 81 mm. Nos. 205/8 .. .. .. 2·50 2·50

(Litho Questa)

1978 (28 Aug). *Commonwealth Games, Edmonton. T* **26** *and similar horiz designs. Multicoloured. P* 14.
210 50 c. Type **26** 15 5
211 1s. Long jumping 30 5
212 2s. Running 80 60
213 5s. Boxing .. .. 1·60 1·60
MS214 114 × 85 mm. Nos. 210/13. P 12 × 12½ .. 3·25 3·25

1978 (11 Sept). *World Cup Football Championship, Argentina* (2*nd issue*). *Designs as Nos.* 205/8 *but additionally inscr* "WORLD CUP 1978".
215 50 c. Polly Ouma and forwards 15 5
216 2s. Omari Kidevu and goalmouth scene .. 60 55
217 5s. Joe Kadenge and forwards .. .. 1·50 1·10
218 10s. Mohamed Chuma and cup presentation 2·25 1·90
MS219 140 × 87 mm. Nos. 215/18 .. .. 4·00 3·50

(Litho Questa)

1978. *As Nos.* 159/62 *but printing process and colours changed.*
220 5s. multicoloured (face value in blue) .. 70 70
221 10s. multicoloured (face value in magenta) .. 1·50 1·50
222 20s. multicoloured (face value in brown) .. 2·50 3·00
223 40s. multicoloured (face value in red) .. 4·50 6·00

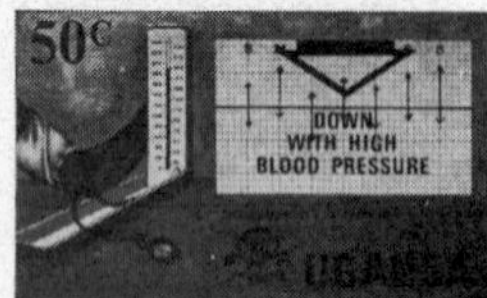

27 Measurements of High Blood Pressure

(Litho Questa)

1978 (25 Sept). *"Down with High Blood Pressure". T* **27** *and similar horiz designs. Multicoloured. P* 14 × 13½.
224 50 c. Type **27** 15 5
225 1s. Hypertension and the heart 25 5
226 2s. Fundus of the eye in hypertension .. 55 45
227 5s. Kidney and high blood pressure .. .. 1·25 1·10
MS228 180 × 115 mm. Nos. 224/7 .. .. 2·00 1·90

28 Off Loading Cattle

(Litho Questa)

1978 (16 Dec). *75th Anniv of Powered Flight. T* **28** *and similar horiz designs. Multicoloured. P* 14.
229 1s. Type **28** 20 5
230 1s. 50, "Domestic services" (passengers boarding "Islander" light aircraft) .. 30 25
231 2s. 70, Export of Uganda coffee 60 50
232 10s. "Time machines in the air" (Wright *Flyer* and "Concorde") .. .. 1·75 1·40
MS233 166 × 110 mm. Nos. 229/32 .. .. 2·50 2·25

29 Queen Elizabeth II leaving Owen Falls Dam

(Des BG Studio. Litho Ashton-Potter)

1979 (15 Feb). *25th Anniv of Coronation* (1978). *T* **29** *and similar horiz designs. Multicoloured. P* 12½ × 12.
234 1s. Type **29** 20 5
235 1s. 50, Regalia 30 10
236 2s. 70, Coronation ceremony 60 40
237 10s. Royal family on balcony of Buckingham Palace .. .. 1·40 1·10
MS238 150 × 102 mm. Nos. 234/7 .. .. 2·25 2·25

30 Dr. Joseph Kiwanuka (first Ugandan bishop)

(Des G. Vasarhelyi. Litho Questa)

1979 (15 Feb). *Centenary of Catholic Church in Uganda. T* **30** *and similar horiz designs. Multicoloured. P* 14.
239 1s. Type **30** 15 5
240 1s. 50, Lubaga Cathedral 25 25
241 2s. 70, Ugandan pilgrimage to Rome, Holy Year, 1975 .. .. 50 50
242 10s. Friar Lourdel-Mapeera (early missionary) .. .. 1·40 1·40
MS243 128 × 91 mm. Nos. 239/42 .. .. 2·00 2·25

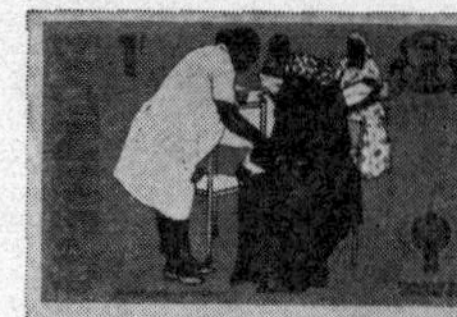

31 Immunisation of Children

(Des J.W. Litho Questa)

1979 (28 June). *International Year of the Child. T* **31** *and similar horiz designs. Multicoloured. P* 14.
244 1s. Type **31** 15 5
245 1s. 50, Handicapped children at play .. 20 20
246 2s. 70, Ugandan I.Y.C. emblem 50 50
247 10s. Children in class .. .. 1·10 1·25
MS248 136 × 113 mm. Nos. 244/7 .. .. 1·75 2·00

UGANDA LIBERATED 1979 (32)
UGANDA LIBERATED 1979 (33)
UGANDA LIBERATED 1979 (34)

1979 (12 July–16 Aug?). *Liberation.*

(*a*) *Nos.* 149/55 *optd with T* **32** *and* 156/62 *with T* **33** (12 July)
249 10 c. black, apple-green and yellow-brown .. 5 5
250 20 c. multicoloured 5 5
251 30 c. multicoloured 5 5
252 40 c. multicoloured 5 5
253 50 c. multicoloured 5 5
254 70 c. black, apple-green and light blue-green 8 10
255 80 c. multicoloured 10 12
a. Opt double £110
256 1s. multicoloured 12 15
257 2s. multicoloured 20 25
258 3s. multicoloured 35 40
259 5s. multicoloured 55 60
260 10s. multicoloured .. .. 1·10 1·25
261 20s. apple-green, black and bright purple .. 2·25 2·40
262 40s. apple-green, black and yellow-orange .. 4·50 4·75
a. Opt double £130

(*b*) *Nos.* 210/13 (*Commonwealth Games*) *optd with T* **34** (1 Aug)
263 50 c. Type **26** 8 10
264 1s. Long jumping 15 20
265 2s. Running 25 30
266 5s. Boxing 60 65

(*c*) *Nos.* 207, 215 *and* 217/18 (*World Cup Football Championships*) *optd with T* **34** (1 Aug)
267 50 c. Polly Ouma and forwards 8 10
268 2s. Omari Kidevu and goal-mouth scene .. 25 30
a. Optd on No. 216 .. .. .. 26·00 30·00
269 5s. Joe Kadenge and forwards 60 65
270 10s. Mohamed Chuma and cup presentation 1·25 1·40

(*d*) *Nos.* 220/3 *optd with T* **33** (1979)
271 5s. multicoloured 55 60
272 10s. multicoloured .. .. 1·10 1·25
273 20s. multicoloured .. .. 2·25 2·40
274 40s. multicoloured .. .. 4·50 4·75

(*e*) *Nos.* 229/32 (*75th Anniv of Powered Flight*) *optd with T* **34** (1 Aug)
275 1s. Type **28** 15 20
276 1s. 50, "Domestic services" (passengers boarding "Islander" light aircraft) .. 20 25
277 2s. 70, Export of Uganda coffee 40 45
278 10s. "Time machines in the air" (Wright *Flyer* and "Concorde") .. .. 1·25 1·40

(*f*) *Nos.* 234/7 (*25th Anniv of Coronation*) *optd as T* **33** *or surch also and No.* **MS**238 *additionally inscr* "Diplomatic Relations Normalised" *with Ugandan and British flags replacing portrait of Amin* (12 July)
279 1s. Type **29** 15 20
280 1s. 50, Regalia 20 25
281 2s. 70, Coronation ceremony 40 45
282 15s. on 10s. Royal family on balcony of Buckingham Palace .. .. 1·75 1·90
MS283 150 × 102 mm. Nos. 234/7* .. .. 2·25 2·50
* The sheet contains the original unoverprinted stamps; the additional inscriptions and changes in design appear only on the sheet margin.

(*g*) *Nos.* 239/42 (*Centenary of Catholic Church in Uganda*) *optd with T* **34** *and No.* **MS**243 *with additional inscr* "FREEDOM OF WORSHIP DECLARED" *replacing part of the margin decoration* (1 Aug)
284 1s. Type **30** 15 20
285 1s. 50, Lubaga Cathedral 20 25
286 2s. 70, Ugandan pilgrimage to Rome, Holy Year, 1975 .. .. 40 45
287 10s. Friar Lourdel-Mapeera (early missionary) .. .. 1·25 1·40
MS288 128 × 91 mm. Nos. 239/42* (1979) .. 2·25 2·50
* The sheet contains the original unoverprinted stamps; the additional inscription appears on the sheet margin.

(*h*) *Nos.* 244/8 (*International Year of the Child*) *optd with T* **34** (16 Aug)
289 1s. Type **31** 15 20
290 1s. 50, Handicapped children at play .. 20 25
291 2s. 70, Ugandan I.Y.C. emblem 40 45
292 10s. Children in class .. .. 1·25 1·40
MS293 136 × 113 mm. Nos. 289/92 .. .. 2·25 2·50
249/82, 284/7 and 289/92 .. .. *Set of* 42 26·00 29·00

35 Radio Wave Symbol

(Des G. Vasarhelyi. Litho Questa)

1979 (11 Sept). *50th Anniv of International Consultative Radio Committee and International Telecommunications Union. P* 14.
294 **35** 1s. multicoloured 15 5
295 1s. 50, multicoloured 20 10
296 2s. 70, multicoloured 50 50
297 10s. multicoloured .. .. .. 1·10 1·25

36 20s. Definitive Stamp of 1965 and Sir Rowland Hill

(Des BG Studio. Litho Questa)

1979 (Oct). *Death Centenary of Sir Rowland Hill. T* **36** *and similar horiz designs showing stamps and Sir Rowland Hill. Multicoloured. P* 14.
298 1s. Type **36** 15 5
299 1s. 50, 1967 13th Commonwealth Parliamentary Association Conference 50 c. commemorative 20 10
300 2s. 70, 1962 Independence 20s. commemorative 50 50
301 10s. Uganda Protectorate 1898 1 a. .. .. 1·10 1·25
MS302 154 × 98 mm. Nos. 298/301 .. .. 1·75 2·00

37 Impala 38 Lions with Cub

(Des G. Drummond. Litho Questa)

1979 (3 Dec)–**82.** *Wildlife. Horiz designs as T* **37** (10 *to* 80 *c.*) *or T* **38** (1 *to* 40*s.*). *Multicoloured. P* 14 × 13½ (10 *to* 80 *c.*) *or* 14 (1 *to* 40*s.*). *A. No imprint date. B. With imprint date* ("1982") *at foot of design* (1982).

		A		B	
303	10 c. Type **37**	5	5	†	
304	20 c. Large Spotted Genet ..	5	5	†	
305	30 c. Thomson's Gazelle ..	10	5	†	
306	50 c. Bush Baby	10	5	†	
307	80 c. Hunting Dog ..	15	5	†	
308	1s. Type **38**	15	5	10	5
309	1s. 50, Mountain Gorilla ..	25	5	†	
310	2s. Common Zebra ..	25	10	25	8
311	2s. 70, Leopard with cub ..	30	10	†	
312	3s. 50, Black Rhinoceros ..	35	15	†	
313	5s. Defassa Waterbuck ..	35	25	40	25
314	10s. African Black Buffalo ..	40	35	†	
315	20s. Hippopotamus ..	70	70	†	
316	40s. African Elephant ..	1·25	1·25	†	
303/16	.. .. *Set of* 14	4·00	2·75		

For designs as Nos. 308/12 and 315/16, but with face values in revalued currency, see Nos. 433/9.

LONDON 1980
(39)

40 Rotary Emblem

1980 (6 May). *"London 1980" International Stamp Exhibition. Nos.* 298/302 *optd with T* **39**.
317 1s. Type **36** 15 5
318 1s. 50, 1967 13th Commonwealth Parliamentary Association Conference 50 c. commemorative 20 20
319 2s. 70, 1962 Independence 20s. commemorative 50 50
320 10s. Uganda Protectorate 1898 1a. .. .. 1·10 1·40
MS321 154 × 99 mm. Nos. 317/20 .. .. 1·75 2·00

(Des BG Studio. Litho Questa)

1980 (25 Aug). *75th Anniv of Rotary International. T* **40** *and similar multicoloured design. P* 14.
322 1s. Type **40** 10 5
323 20s. Paul Harris (founder) with wheel-barrow containing "Rotary projects" (*horiz*) .. 2·10 2·25
MS324 100 × 76 mm. Nos. 322/3. Imperf. .. .. 2·40 2·50

FOOTBALL
GOLD MEDALISTS, C.S.S.R.

41 Football (42)

(Des G. Vasarhelyi. Litho Questa)

1980 (29 Dec). *Olympic Games, Moscow. T* **41** *and similar horiz designs. Multicoloured. P* 14.

325 1s. Type **41** 10 5
326 2s. Relay 20 25
327 10s. Hurdles .. .. 1·10 1·25
328 20s. Boxing .. .. 2·25 2·25
MS329 118 × 90 mm. 2s. 70, 3s., 5s., 25s. As Nos. 325/8 .. .. 3·50 3·50

1980 (29 Dec). *Olympic Games, Moscow. Medal Winners. Nos.* 325/9 *optd as T* **42**.

330 1s. Type **41** 10 12
331 2s. Relay 20 25
332 10s. Hurdles .. .. 1·10 1·25
333 20s. Boxing .. .. 2·25 2·25
MS334 118 × 90 mm. 2s. 70, 3s., 5s., 25s. As Nos. 330/3 .. .. 3·50 3·50

Overprints:—2s. "RELAY GOLD MEDALIST U.S.S.R."; 10s. "HURDLES 110 m. GOLD MEDALIST THOMAS MUNKLET, D.D.R."; 20s. "BOXING WELTERWEIGHT SILVER MEDALIST JOHN MUGABI, UGANDA".

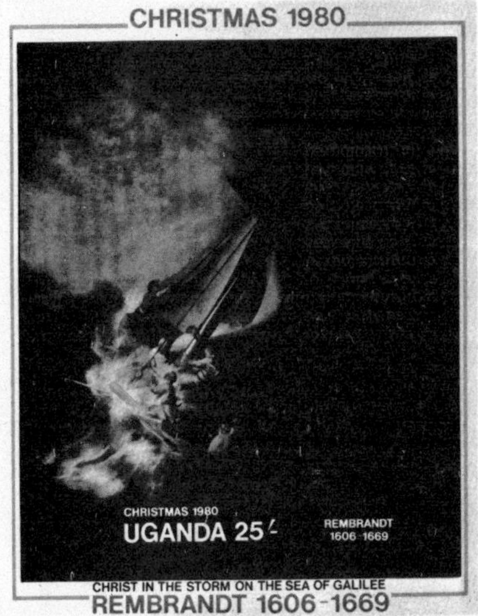

43 "Christ in the Storm on the Sea of Galilee" (painting, Rembrandt)

1980 (31 Dec). *Christmas. Sheet* 79 × 101 *mm. Litho. Imperf.*

MS335 **43** 25s. multicoloured .. .. 2·75 3·00

44 Heinrich von Stephan and U.P.U. Emblem

45 Tower of London

(Des BG Studio. Litho Questa)

1981 (2 June). *150th Birth Anniv of Heinrich von Stephan (founder of U.P.U.). T* **44** *and similar horiz designs. Multicoloured. P* 14.

336 1s. Type **44** 15 12
337 2s. U.P.U. Headquarters 25 25
338 2s. 70, Air mail, 1935 .. .. .. 30 30
339 10s. Mail transport by train, 1927 .. .. 1·40 1·40
MS340 112 × 95 mm. Nos. 336/9 .. .. .. 1·90 1·90

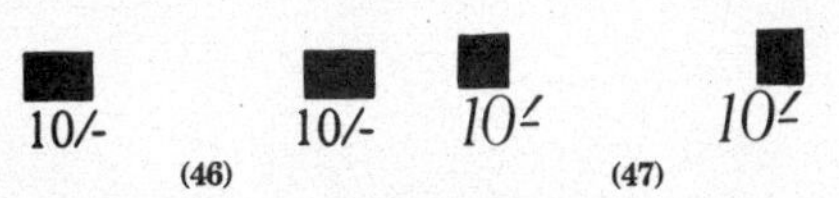

(46) (47)

(Des J.W. Litho Questa)

1981 (July). *Royal Wedding. T* **45** *and similar vert designs. Multicoloured. P* 14. *(a) Unissued stamps surcharged* (13 July).

A. *As T* **46**. B. *As T* **47**.

		A		B	
341	10s. on 1s. Prince Charles and Lady Diana Spencer ..	75	75	35	35
	a. Surch on 5s. value ..	£125	—	†	
	b. Surch on 20s. value ..	£110	—	†	
	c. Surch omitted	£140	—	†	
342	50s. on 5s. Type **45**	1·75	1·75	55	55
	a. Surch omitted	£125	—	†	
343	200s. on 20s. Prince Charles at Balmoral	5·50	5·50	3·25	3·25
	a. Surch omitted	£200	—	†	
	b. Surch inverted	£125	—	†	
	c. Surch inverted on 1s. value	£125	—	†	
	d. Surch inverted on 5s. value	£125	—	†	
MS344	95 × 80 mm. 250s. on 25s. Royal Mews	15·00	15·00	5·00	5·00
	a. Surch omitted	—	—	†	

(b) Redrawn with new face values. Background colours changed (29 July)

345 10s. As No. 341 .. .. 25 25
346 50s. Type **45** 80 80
347 200s. As No. 343 .. .. 2·75 2·75
MS348 95 × 80 mm. 250s. As No. **MS**344 .. 3·50 3·50

Nos. 345/7 also exist perforated 12 (*price for set of* 3 £3·75 *mint or used*) from additional sheetlets of 5 stamps and one label. These stamps have changed background colours.

The issue was originally printed with face values of 1, 5 and 20s. and 25s. for the miniature sheet. Before it could be placed on sale the Uganda currency was devalued and the stamps were surcharged, and later reprinted with corrected face values.

48 "Sleeping Woman before Green Shutters"

(Des J.W. Litho Questa)

1981 (21 Sept). *Birth Centenary of Picasso. T* **48** *and similar multicoloured designs. P* 14 × 13½.

349 10s. Type **48** 15 15
350 20s. "Bullfight" 30 30
351 30s. "Detail of a Nude asleep in a Landscape" 45 45
352 200s. "Interior with a Girl Drawing" .. .. 2·75 3·00
MS353 120 × 146 mm. 250s. "Minotaure" (112 × 139 *mm*). Imperf .. .. 3·25 3·50

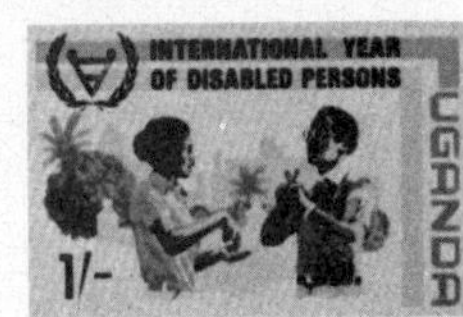

49 Deaf People using Sign Language

(Des Design Images Studio. Litho Format)

1981 (28 Dec). *International Year for Disabled Persons. T* **49** *and similar horiz designs. Multicoloured. P* 14½.

354 1s. Type **49** 5 5
355 10s. Disabled teacher in classroom 15 15
356 50s. Teacher and disabled children 70 70
357 200s. Blind person with guide dog .. .. 3·00 3·00
MS358 122 × 93 mm. Nos. 354/7 .. .. .. 3·50 3·75

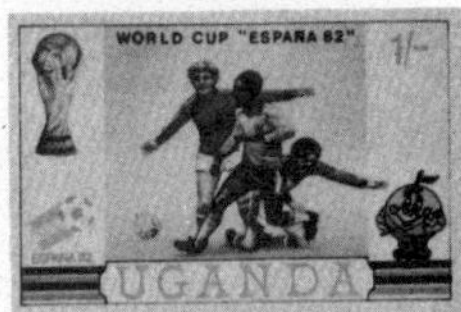

50 Footballers

(Des G. Vasarhelyi. Litho Questa)

1982 (11 Jan). *World Cup Football Championship, Spain. T* **50** *and similar horiz designs showing World Cup* (250s.) *or footballers (others). P* 14.

359 1s. multicoloured 5 5
360 10s. multicoloured 15 15
361 50s. multicoloured 70 70
362 200s. multicoloured .. .. 3·00 3·00
MS363 116 × 77 mm. 250s. multicoloured .. .. 3·25 3·50

51 Mpoma Satellite Earth Station

(Des Artists International. Litho Format)

1982 (10 May). *"Peaceful Use of Outer Space". T* **51** *and similar horiz designs. Multicoloured. P* 15.

364 5s. Type **51** 10 10
365 10s. *Pioneer II* (satellite) 15 15
366 50s. Space Shuttle 80 80
367 100s. *Voyager 2* (satellite) .. .. .. 1·60 1·60
MS368 118 × 89 mm. 150s. Space Shuttle (*different*) .. .. 2·00 2·00

21st BIRTHDAY
HRH Princess of Wales
JULY 1 1982

52 Dr. Robert Koch (53)

(Des R. Vigurs. Litho Questa)

1982 (14 June). *Centenary of Robert Koch's Discovery of Tubercle Bacillus. T* **52** *and similar multicoloured designs. P* 14.

369 1s. Type **52** 10 8
370 10s. Microscope 20 15
371 50s. Ugandans receiving vaccinations .. 80 80
372 100s. Tubercle virus .. .. 1·60 1·75
MS373 85 × 64 mm. 150s. Medical College classroom scene (*horiz*) .. .. 2·00 2·10

1982 (7 July). *21st Birthday of Princess of Wales. Nos.* 345/8 *optd with T* **53**. *P* 14.

374 10s. Prince Charles and Lady Diana Spencer 20 20
375 50s. Type **45** 75 75
376 200s. Prince Charles at Balmoral .. .. 2·75 3·00
MS377 95 × 82 mm. 250s. Royal Mews .. .. 3·25 3·50

Nos. 374/6 also exist perforated 12 (*price for set of* 3 £3·25 *mint or used*) from additional sheetlets of 5 stamps and one label. These stamps have changed background colours.

These sheetlets and miniature sheet No. **MS**377 also exist with the top line of the overprint shown as "21st Birthday". (*Price for set of* 3 *and miniature sheet* £15 *mint*).

54 Yellow-billed Hornbill

55 Scout Band

(Des Artists International. Litho Questa)

1982 (12 July). *Birds. T* **54** *and similar vert designs. Multicoloured. P* 14.

378 1s. Type **54** 5 5
379 20s. Superb Starling 35 35
380 50s. Bateleur 80 80
381 100s. Saddle-bill Stork .. .. 1·75 1·75
MS382 115 × 85 mm. 200s. Laughing Dove .. 3·25 3·25

(Des G. Vasarhelyi. Litho Questa)

1982 (23 Aug). *75th Anniv of Boy Scout Movement. T* **55** *and similar horiz designs. Multicoloured. P* 14.

383 5s. Type **55** 12 10
384 20s. Scout receiving Bata Shoe trophy .. 35 35
385 50s. Scouts with wheelchair patient 80 80
386 100s. First aid instruction .. .. 1·75 1·75
MS387 112 × 85 mm. 150s. Lord Baden-Powell .. 2·50 2·50

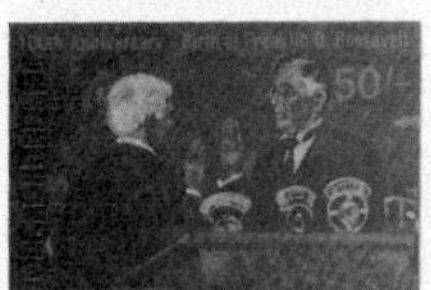

56 Swearing-in of Roosevelt

(Des Design Images. Litho Format)

1982 (8 Nov). *250th Birth Anniv of George Washington (Nos.* 389/90) *and Birth Centenary of Franklin D. Roosevelt (others). T* **56** *and similar horiz designs. Multicoloured. P* 14½.

388 50s. Type **56** 35 40
389 200s. Swearing-in of Washington .. .. .. 1·40 1·50
MS390 100 × 69 mm. 150s. Washington at Mt Vernon .. .. 1·10 1·25
MS391 100 × 70 mm. 150s. Roosevelt at Hyde Park Mansion .. .. 1·10 1·25

57 Italy v West Germany

(Des D. Miller. Litho)

1982 (30 Dec). *World Cup Football Championship Winners. T* **57** *and similar horiz designs. Multicoloured. P* 14½.

392 10s. Type **57** 8 8
393 200s. Victorious Italian team .. .. .. 1·40 1·50
MS394 97 × 117 mm. 250s. Espana '82 emblem with Spanish and Italian flags .. .. .. 1·75 1·90

58 Dancers

59 "St. George and the Dragon" (Raphael)

(Des and litho J.W.)

1983 (14 Mar). *Commonwealth Day. Cultural Art. T* **58** *and similar horiz designs. Multicoloured. P* 14.

395 5s. Type **58** 5 5
396 20s. Traditional currency 15 20
397 50s. Homestead 40 45
398 100s. Drums 80 85

(Des Design Images. Litho Questa)

1983 (16 Apr). *500th Birth Anniv of Raphael (painter). T* **59** *and similar vert designs. Multicoloured. P* 13½.

399 5s. Type **59** 5 5
400 20s. "St. George and the Dragon" (*different*) 15 20
401 50s. "Crossing the Red Sea" (*detail*) 40 45
402 200s. "The Expulsion of Heliodorus" (*detail*) .. 1·50 1·60
MS403 126 × 101 mm. 250s. "The Meeting of Pope Leo the Great and Attila the Hun" (*detail*) .. 1·50 1·60

60 Map showing Namibia and U.N. Flag

(Des R. Vigurs. Litho Format)

1983 (15 Aug). *Commemorations. T* **60** *and similar horiz design. Multicoloured. P* 14½.

404 5s. Type **60** 5 5
405 200s. 7th Non-aligned Summit Conference logo 1·25 1·40

61 Elephants in "Elephants' Graveyard"

BOYS BRIGADE CENTENARY 1883-1983

(62)

(Des J. Iskowitz. Litho Format)

1983 (22 Aug). *Wildlife. T* **61** *and similar multicoloured designs. P* 14½.

406 5s. Type **61** 5 5
407 10s. Elephants moving through grassland .. 10 10
408 30s. Elephants at waterhole 25 25
409 70s. Elephants having dust bath 50 55
MS410 87 × 64 mm. 300s. Zebra drinking (*vert*) .. 1·75 1·90

1983 (19 Sept). *Centenary of Boys' Brigade. Nos. 383/7 optd with T* **62** *or surch also.*

411 5s. Type **55** 5 5
412 20s. Scout receiving Bata Shoe trophy .. 12 15
413 50s. Scouts with wheelchair patient.. .. 25 30
414 400s. on 100s. First aid instruction .. .. 2·40 2·50
MS415 112 × 85 mm. 150s. Lord Baden-Powell .. 90 1·00

63 Mpoma Satellite Earth Station

100/-

(64)

(Des D. Dorfman. Litho Format)

1983 (3 Oct). *World Communications Year. T* **63** *and similar horiz designs. Multicoloured. P* 14½.

416 20s. Type **63** 10 12
417 50s. Railroad computer and operator .. 25 30
418 70s. Cameraman filming lions 35 40
419 100s. Aircraft cockpit 45 50
MS420 128 × 103 mm. 300s. Communications satellite .. .. 1·40 1·50

No. 416 has the "o" omitted from "Station".

1983 (7 Nov). *Nos.* 303, 305/7, 308A, 309 *and* 313A *surch as T* **64**.

421 100s. on 10 c. Type **37** 40 45
422 135s. on 1s. Type **38** 55 60
423 175s. on 30 c. Thomson's Gazelle 70 75
424 200s. on 50 c. Bush Baby 80 85
425 400s. on 80 c. Hunting Dog .. .. .. 1·60 1·75
426 700s. on 5s. Defassa Waterbuck .. .. 2·75 3·00
427 1000s. on 1s. 50, Mountain Gorilla .. .. 4·00 4·25
421/7 .. .. *Set of* 7 9·75 10·50

65 The Nativity

(Des PAD Studio. Litho Questa)

1983 (12 Dec). *Christmas. T* **65** *and similar horiz designs. Multicoloured. P* 14.

428 10s. Type **65** 5 8
429 50s. Shepherds and Angels 25 30
430 175s. Flight into Egypt 80 85
431 400s. Angels blowing trumpets .. .. 1·90 2·00
MS432 85 × 57 mm. 300s. The Three Kings .. 1·40 1·50

1983 (19 Dec). *Designs as Nos.* 308/12 *and* 315/16 *but with face values in revalued currency.*

433 100s. Type **38** 30 35
434 135s. Mountain Gorilla 40 45
435 175s. Common Zebra 50 55
436 200s. Leopard with cub 55 60
437 400s. Black Rhinoceros .. .. .. 1·10 1·25
438 700s. African Elephant .. .. .. 1·90 2·00
439 1000s. Hippopotamus .. .. 2·75 3·00
433/9 .. .. *Set of* 7 6·75 7·25

66 Ploughing with Oxen

(Des J.W. Litho Questa)

1984 (16 Jan). *World Food Day. T* **66** *and similar horiz design. Multicoloured. P* 14.

440 10s. Type **66** 5 8
441 300s. Harvesting bananas .. .. .. 1·40 1·50

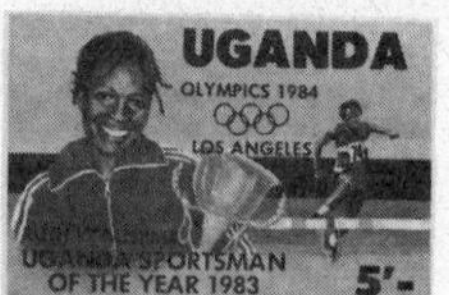

67 Ruth Kyalisiima, Sportsman of the Year 1983

(Des J. Iskowitz. Litho Format)

1984 (1 Oct). *Olympic Games, Los Angeles. T* **67** *and similar multicoloured designs. P* 15.

442 5s. Type **67** 5 5
443 115s. Javelin-throwing 40 45
444 155s. Wrestling 50 55
445 175s. Rowing 60 65
MS446 108 × 79 mm. 500s. Fund-raising walk (*vert*) .. .. 1·50 1·60

68 Entebbe Airport

(Des BG Studio. Litho Format)

1984 (29 Oct). *40th Anniv of International Civil Aviation Organization. T* **68** *and similar horiz designs. Multicoloured. P* 15.

447 5s. Type **68** 5 5
448 115s. Loading cargo plane 40 45
449 155s. Uganda police helicopter 50 55
450 175s. East African Civil Flying School, Soroti 60 65
MS451 100 × 70 mm. 250s. Balloon race 75 80

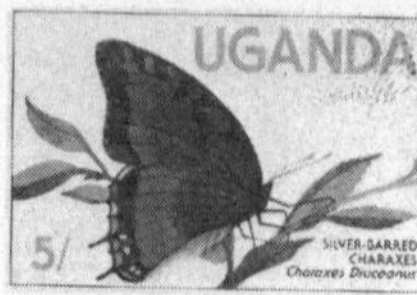

69 Silver-barred Charaxes

(Des J. Johnson. Litho Questa)

1984 (19 Nov). *Butterflies. T* **69** *and similar horiz designs. Multicoloured. P* 14.

452 5s. Type **69** 5 5
453 115s. Western Emperor Swallowtail 40 45
454 155s. African Giant Swallowtail 50 55
455 175s. Blue Salamis 60 65
MS456 127 × 90 mm. 250 s. Veined Yellow .. 75 80

POSTAGE DUE STAMPS

The Postage Due stamps of Kenya, Uganda and Tanganyika were used in Uganda until 2 January 1967.

D 1

LIBERATED 1979

(D 2)

UGANDA 5/ Postage Due

D 3 Lion

(Litho D.L.R.)

1967 (3 Jan). *Chalk-surfaced paper. P* 14 × 13½.

D1 D 1 5 c. scarlet 20 50
D2 10 c. green 20 50
D3 20 c. deep blue 35 90
D4 30 c. red-brown .. .. 40 1·00
D5 40 c. bright purple .. .. 60 1·60
D6 1s. orange .. .. 1·50 4·25
D1/6 .. .. *Set of* 6 3·00 8·00

1970 (31 Mar). *As Nos.* D1/6, *but on glazed ordinary paper. P* 14 × 15.

D 7 D 1 5 c. scarlet 15 40
D 8 10 c. green (*shades*) 15 40
D 9 20 c. deep blue 25 65
D10 30 c. red-brown (*shades*) 35 90
D11 40 c. bright purple .. .. 55 1·25

1973 (12 Dec). *Glazed, ordinary paper. P* 15.

D12 D 1 5 c. scarlet 15 40
D13 10 c. emerald 15 40
D14 20 c. deep blue 25 50
D15 30 c. red-brown 35 60
D16 40 c. bright mauve 45 80
D17 1s. bright orange .. .. 85 1·10
D12/17 .. .. *Set of* 6 2·00 3·50

"UGANDA LIBERATED" OVERPRINTS. Nos. D1/12 and D14/17 were overprinted "UGANDA LIBERATED 1979", in very limited quantities, using a style of overprint similar to Type **32** (*Prices: Nos.* D1/6 *set of* 6 £275; D7/11 *set of* 5 £125; D12, 14/17 *set of* 5 £100, *all mint*).

(Litho Questa)

1979 (Dec). *Liberation. As Nos.* D1/6 *optd with Type* D **2**. *Chalk-surfaced paper. P* 13½ × 14.

D18 D 1 5 c. scarlet 5 5
D19 10 c. green 5 5
D20 20 c. dull ultramarine 5 5
D21 30 c. red-brown 5 5
D22 40 c. bright purple 5 5
D23 1s. orange 8 10
D18/23 .. .. *Set of* 6 30 30

(Litho Questa)

1985 (11 Mar). *Animals. Type* D 3 *and similar vert designs. P* 14½ × 14.

D24 5s. black and bright turquoise-green .. 5 5
D25 10s. black and dull rose-lilac 5 5
D26 20s. black and dull orange 5 5
D27 40s. black and bright lilac 10 12
D28 50s. black and pale greenish blue .. 12 15
D29 100s. black and mauve 25 30
D24/9 .. .. *Set of* 6 55 65

Designs:—10s. African Buffalo; 20s. Uganda Kob; 40s. Elephant; 50s. Zebra; 100s. Rhinoceros.

Vanuatu

(*formerly* New Hebrides

The former Condominium of the New Hebrides became the Republic of Vanuatu on 30 July 1980 and was admitted as a member of the Commonwealth.

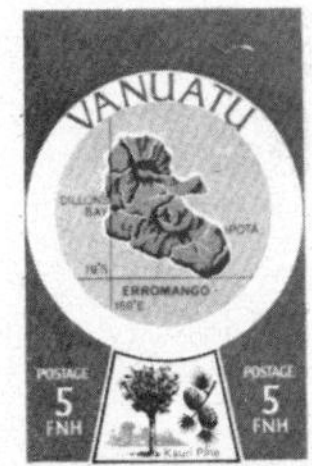

99 Island of Erromango and Kauri Pine

100 Rotary International

(Des L. Curtis. Litho J.W. (15, 30, 40 f.), Walsall (10, 35, 70, 500 f.), Questa (others))

1980 (30 July). *As Nos. 242/54 of New Hebrides but inscr "VANUATU" and without cyphers as in T* **99.** *P* 13 (15, 30, 40 *f.*) *or* 14 (*others*).
E. *Inscr in English. W* w **14.** F. *Inscr in French. No wmk.*

		E		F	
287	5 f. Type **99**	15	15	15	15
288	10 f. Territory map and man splitting coconuts ..	15	15	15	15
289	15 f. Espiritu Santo and cattle	25	25	25	25
290	20 f. Efate and Vila P.O. ..	30	30	30	30
291	25 f. Malakula and head-dresses	35	35	35	35
292	30 f. Aoba, Maewo and pigs' tusks	45	45	45	45
293	35 f. Pentecost and land diver	50	50	50	50
294	40 f. Tanna and volcano ..	70	60	70	60
295	50 f. Shepherd Island and canoe	75	70	75	70
296	70 f. Banks Island and custom dancers	1·25	1·00	1·25	1·00
297	100 f. Ambrym and idols ..	1·75	1·40	1·75	1·40
298	200 f. Aneityum and baskets ..	2·50	2·50	2·50	2·50
299	500 f. Torres Island and archer	6·50	6·50	6·50	6·50
287/99	.. .. .. *Set of* 13	14·00	13·00	14·00	13·00

(Des L. Curtis. Litho Walsall)

1980 (16 Sept). *75th Anniv of Rotary International. T* **100** *and similar vert design. P* 14. E. *Inscr in English. W* w **14** (*sideways on* 10 *f.*). F. *Inscr in French. No wmk.*

		E		F	
300	10 f. Type **100**	20	20	20	20
301	40 f. Rotary emblem (*vert*) ..	60	60	60	60

101 Kiwanis Emblem and Globe

102 "The Virgin and Child enthroned with Saints and Angels" (Umkreis Michael Pacher)

(Des L. Curtis. Litho Walsall)

1980 (16 Sept). *Kiwanis International (service club), New Zealand District Convention, Port Vila. T* **101** *and similar design. P* 14. E. *Inscr in English. W* w **14** (*sideways on* 40 *f.*). F. *Inscr in French. No wmk.*

		E		F	
302	10 f. gold, ultram & chestnut ..	20	20	20	20
303	40 f. gold, blue-grn & brt bl ..	60	60	60	60

Design: *Horiz*—40 f. Kiwanis and Convention emblems.

(Des BG Studio. Litho Questa)

1980 (12 Nov). *Christmas. Details from Paintings. T* **102** *and similar vert designs. Multicoloured. W* w **14.** *P* 14 × 13½.

304	10 f. Type **102**	20	20
305	15 f. "The Virgin and Child with Saints, Angels and Donors" (Hans Memling) ..	25	25
306	30 f. "The Rest on the Flight to Egypt" (Adriaen van der Werff)	40	40

103 Blue-faced Parrot Finch

104 Tribesman with Portrait of Prince Philip

(Des G. Drummond. Litho Questa)

1981 (18 Feb). *Birds (1st series). T* **103** *and similar vert designs. Multicoloured. W* w **14.** *P* 14.

307	10 f. Type **103**	30	20
308	20 f. Emerald Dove	50	40
309	30 f. Golden Whistler	70	55
310	40 f. Silver-shouldered Fruit Dove	75	65

See also Nos. 327/30.

(New Currency. Vatus)

(Des A. Theobald. Litho Format)

1981 (10 June). *60th Birthday of Prince Philip, Duke of Edinburgh. T* **104** *and similar vert designs. Multicoloured. W* w **14.** *P* 14 × 14½.

311	15 v. Type **104**	30	30
312	25 v. Prince Philip in casual dress	45	45
313	35 v. Queen and Prince Philip with Princess Anne and Master Peter Phillips ..	60	60
314	45 v. Prince Philip in ceremonial dress ..	75	75

105 Prince Charles with his Dog, Harvey

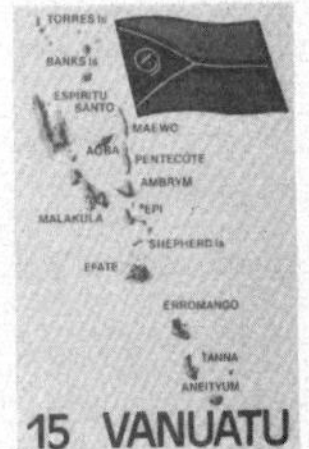

106 National Flag and Map of Vanuatu

(Des J.W. Litho Walsall)

1981 (22 July). *Royal Wedding. T* **105** *and similar vert designs. Multicoloured. W* w **14.** *P* 14.

315	15 v. Wedding bouquet from Vanuatu ..	30	30
316	45 v. Type **105**	80	80
317	75 v. Prince Charles and Lady Diana Spencer	1·10	1·25

(Des C. Abbott. Litho Format)

1981 (30 July). *First Anniv of Independence. T* **106** *and similar designs. W* w **14** (*sideways on* 25 *and* 45 *v.*). *P* 14.

318	15 v. multicoloured	20	25
319	25 v. multicoloured	35	40
320	45 v. greenish yellow and brown-lake ..	65	70
321	75 v. multicoloured	1·10	1·25

Designs: *Horiz*—25 v. Vanuatu emblem; 45 v. Vanuatu national anthem. *Vert*—75 v. Vanuatu coat of arms.

107 Three Wise Men

108 New Caledonian Myiagra Flycatcher

(Adapted G. Vasarhelyi. Litho Questa)

1981 (11 Nov). *Christmas. Children's Paintings. T* **107** *and similar multicoloured designs. W* w **14** (*sideways on* 25 *and* 45 *v.*). *P* 14.

322	15 v. Type **107**	20	25
323	25 v. Shepherd with lamb (*vert*)	35	40
324	35 v. Angel as butterfly	50	55
325	45 v. Boy carrying torch and gifts (*vert*) ..	65	70
MS326	133 × 94 mm. Nos. 322/5 (wmk sideways)	1·60	1·75

(Des G. Drummond. Litho Questa)

1982 (8 Feb). *Birds (2nd series). T* **108** *and similar vert designs. Multicoloured. W* w **14.** *P* 14½ × 14.

327	15 v. Type **108**	30	25
328	20 v. Rainbow Lorys	40	35
329	25 v. Buff-bellied Flycatchers	45	40
330	45 v. Collared Grey Fantails	70	75

109 *Flickingeria comata*

110 Scouts round Camp-fire

(Des Jennifer Toombs. Litho Enschedé)

1982 (15 June). *Orchids. Multicoloured designs as T* **109.** *W* w **14** (*sideways on* 35, 45, 50 *and* 75 *v.*). *P* 13½.

331	1 v. Type **109**	5	5
332	2 v. *Calanthe triplicata*	5	5
333	10 v. *Dendrobium sladei*	12	15
334	15 v. *Dendrobium mohlianum*	20	25
335	20 v. *Dendrobium macrophyllum*	25	30
336	25 v. *Dendrobium purpureum*	30	35
337	30 v. *Robiquetia mimus*	40	45
338	35 v. *Dendrobium mooreanum* (*horiz*) ..	45	50
339	45 v. *Spathoglottis plicata* (*horiz*) ..	60	65
340	50 v. *Dendrobium seemannii* (*horiz*) ..	65	70
341	75 v. *Dendrobium conanthum* (*horiz*) ..	95	1·00
342	100 v. *Phaius tankervilliae*	1·25	1·40
343	200 v. *Coelogyne lamellata*	2·50	2·75
344	500 v. *Bulbophyllum longioscapum*	6·25	6·50
331/44	.. .. *Set of* 14	12·50	13·50

(Des L. Curtis. Litho Questa)

1982 (1 Sept). *75th Anniv of Boy Scout Movement. T* **110** *and similar horiz designs. Multicoloured. W* w **14** (*sideways*). *P* 14.

345	15 v. Type **110**	25	25
346	20 v. First aid	30	30
347	25 v. Constructing tower	35	40
348	45 v. Constructing raft	65	70
349	75 v. Scout saluting	1·10	1·25

111 Baby Jesus

112 *Euploea sylvester*

(Des G. Vasarhelyi. Litho Questa)

1982 (1 Nov). *Christmas. Nativity Scenes. T* **111** *and similar multicoloured designs. W* w **14** (*sideways on* 15, 25 *v.*). *P* **14.**

350	15 v. Type **111**	20	25
351	25 v. Mary and Joseph	35	40
352	35 v. Shepherds (*vert*)	50	55
353	45 v. Kings bearing gifts (*vert*)	65	70
MS354	132 × 92 mm. As Nos. 350/3 but without yellow borders	1·60	1·75

(Des J. Cooter. Litho Questa)

1983 (17 Jan). *Butterflies. T* **112** *and similar horiz designs. Multicoloured. W* w **14** (*sideways*). *P* 14 × 14½.

355	15 v. Type **112**	20	25
	a. Pair. Nos. 355/6	40	50
356	15 v. *Hypolimnas octocula*	20	25
357	20 v. *Papilio canopus hypsicles*	30	35
	a. Pair. Nos. 357/8	60	70
358	20 v. *Polyura sacco*	30	35
359	25 v. *Luthrodes cleotas*	35	40
	a. Pair. Nos. 359/60	70	80
360	25 v. *Parantica pumila*	35	40

Nos. 355/6, 357/8 and 359/60 were each printed in *se-tenant* pairs, horizontally and vertically throughout the sheets.

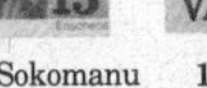

113 President Afi George Sokomanu

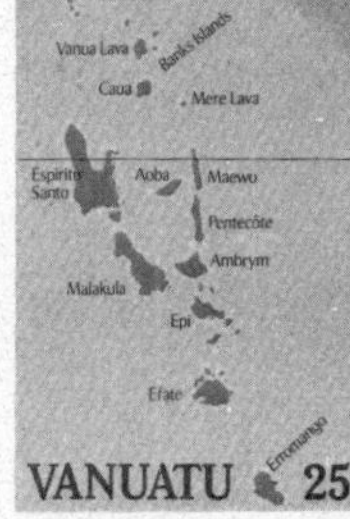

114 Map of Northern Vanuatu

(Des L. Curtis. Litho Enschedé)

1983 (14 Mar). *Commonwealth Day. T* **113** *and similar horiz designs. Multicoloured. W* w **14** (*sideways*). *P* 13½ × 14.

361	15 v. Type **113**	20	25
362	20 v. Fishing	30	35
363	25 v. Herdsman and cattle	35	40
364	75 v. World map showing position of Vanuatu with Commonwealth and Vanuatu flags	1·10	1·25

(Des A. Theobald. Litho Harrison)

1983 (23 May). *Economic Zone. Sheet* 120 × 120 *mm containing T* **114** *and similar vert designs. Multicoloured.* W w **14**. *P* 13½ × 13.
MS365 25 c. × 6 *Thunnus albacares* (fish); Type **114**; Map of Umaenupne; Map of Umaeneag; *Epinephelus morrhua* and *Etelis carbunculus* (fish); *Katsuwonus pelamis* (fish) .. .. .. 1·75 1·90

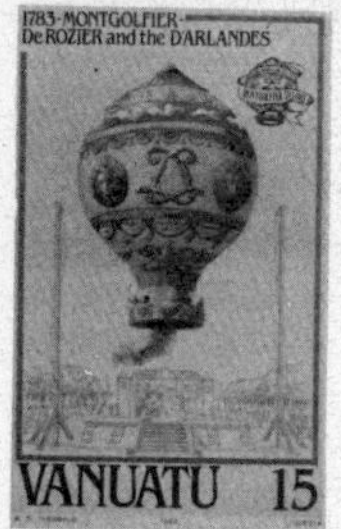

115 Montgolfier Balloon of De Rozier and D'Arlandes, 1783

116 Mail at Bauerfield Airport

(Des A. Theobald. Litho Questa)

1983 (4 Aug). *Bicentenary of Manned Flight. T* **115** *and similar multicoloured designs, each with manned flight logo.* W w **14** (*sideways on* 35, 40 *and* 45 *v.*). *P* 13½.

366	15 v. Type **115** ..	20	25
367	20 v. J. A. C. Charles balloon (first use of hydrogen), 1783 ..	30	35
368	25 v. Blanchard and Jeffries crossing English Channel, 1785 ..	35	40
369	35 v. Giffard's airship, 1852 (*horiz*) ..	50	55
370	40 v. *La France* (airship of Renard and Krebs), 1884 (*horiz*) ..	55	60
371	45 v. *Graf Zeppelin* (first aerial circumnavigation), 1929 (*horiz*) ..	65	70
366/71	.. *Set of* 6	2·25	2·50

(Des L. McCombie. Litho Questa)

1983 (10 Sept). *World Communications Year. T* **116** *and similar horiz designs. Multicoloured.* W w **14** (*sideways*). *P* 14.

372	15 v. Type **116** ..	20	25
373	20 v. Switchboard operator ..	30	35
374	25 v. Telex operator ..	35	40
375	45 v. Satellite Earth station ..	65	70
MS376	138 × 95 mm. Nos. 372/5 ..	1·50	1·60

117 *Cymatoderma elegans var. lamellatum*

118 Port Vila

(Des P. Cox. Litho Questa)

1984 (9 Jan). *Fungi. T* **117** *and similar multicoloured designs.* W w **14** (*sideways on* 35 *v., inverted on* 45 *v.*). *P* 14.

377	15 v. Type **117** ..	25	30
378	25 v. *Lignosus rhinoceros* ..	40	45
379	35 v. *Stereum ostreu* (*horiz*) ..	55	60
380	45 v. *Ganoderma boninense* ..	85	90

(Des D. Miller. Litho Questa)

1984 (30 Apr). *250th Anniv of "Lloyd's List" (newspaper). T* **118** *and similar vert designs. Multicoloured.* W w **14**. *P* 14½ × 14.

381	15 v. Type **118** ..	20	25
382	20 v. Cargo ship *Induna* ..	30	35
383	25 v. Air Vanuatu aircraft ..	35	40
384	45 v. Cargo ship *Brahman Express* ..	65	70

(Des A. Theobald. Litho Questa)

1984 (11 June). *Universal Postal Union Congress, Hamburg. As No.* 371 *but inscribed* "UPU CONGRESS HAMBURG" *and with U.P.U. logo.* W w **14** (*sideways*). *P* 13½ × 14.
385 45 v. multicoloured 65 70

119 Charolais

(Des Doreen McGuinness. Litho J.W.)

1984 (24 July). *Cattle. T* **119** *and similar horiz designs. Multicoloured.* W w **14** (*sideways*). *P* 14.

386	15 v. Type **119** ..	20	25
387	25 v. Charolais-afrikander ..	35	40
388	45 v. Friesian ..	65	70
389	75 v. Charolais-brahman ..	1·10	1·25

120 *Makambo*

(Des L. Dunn. Litho Walsall)

1984 (7 Sept). *"Ausipex" International Stamp Exhibition, Melbourne. T* **120** *and similar horiz designs showing ships. Multicoloured.* W w **14** (*sideways*). *P* 14.

390	25 v. Type **120** ..	35	40
391	45 v. *Rockton* ..	65	70
392	100 v. *Waroonga* ..	1·40	1·50
MS393	140 × 70 mm. Nos. 390/2 ..	2·40	2·50

121 Father Christmas in Children's Ward

122 Ambrym Island Ceremonial Dance

(Des D. Slater. Litho Questa)

1984 (19 Nov). *Christmas. T* **121** *and similar horiz designs. Multicoloured.* W w **14** (*sideways*). *P* 14.

394	25 v. Type **121** ..	35	40
395	45 v. Nativity play ..	65	70
396	75 v. Father Christmas distributing presents	1·10	1·25

(Des D. Slater. Litho Questa)

1985 (22 Jan). *Traditional Costumes. T* **122** *and similar vert designs. Multicoloured.* W w **14**. *P* 14.

397	20 v. Type **122** ..	30	35
398	25 v. Pentecost Island Marriage Ceremony ..	35	40
399	45 v. Women's Grade Ceremony, South West Malakula ..	65	70
400	75 v. Ceremonial Dance, South West Malakula	1·10	1·25

(123)

1985 (22 Jan). *No.* 331 *surch with T* **123**.
401 5 v. on 1 v. Type **109** 8 10

Victoria

PRICES FOR STAMPS ON COVER

Nos. 1/29	*from* × 2
Nos. 30/8	*from* × 4
Nos. 39/43	*from* × 3
Nos. 44/8	*from* × 2
Nos. 49/51	*from* × 4
No. 52	*from* × 8
No. 53	—
No. 54	*from* × 6
Nos. 55/90	*from* × 2
No. 91	—
Nos. 92/186	*from* × 3
Nos. 187/220	*from* × 4
Nos. 221/2	*from* × 10
Nos. 223/38	*from* × 5
Nos. 239/67	*from* × 10
Nos. 268/82	—
Nos. 283/91	*from* × 10
Nos. 292/6	—
Nos. 297/303	*from* × 12
Nos. 304/22	*from* × 8
Nos. 323/4	—
Nos. 325/6	*from* × 4
Nos. 327/9	*from* × 10
Nos. 330/45	*from* × 15
Nos. 346/7	*from* × 2
Nos. 348/75	*from* × 10
Nos. 376/7	—
Nos. 378/87	*from* × 10
Nos. 388/98	—
Nos. 399/409	*from* × 10
Nos. 410/12	—
Nos. 413/23	*from* × 4
Nos. 424/33	—
Nos. 434/43	*from* × 10
No. 444	—
No. 445	*from* × 10
Nos. 446/52	*from* × 6
No. 453	—
No. 454	*from* × 6
Nos. F1/6	—
Nos. F7/15	*from* × 20
Nos. F16/22	—
Nos. F23/5	*from* × 20
Nos. F26/40	—
Nos. F41/5	*from* × 20
Nos. F46/50	—
Nos. F51/2	*from* × 20
Nos. F53/9	—
Nos. D1/8	*from* × 30
Nos. D9/10	—
Nos. D11/67	*from* × 30

Unlike many British colonies, Victoria, with three exceptions only, produced her own dies, plates and stamps. The exceptions were the 1d. and 6d. "Queen-on-Throne" (the dies and plates for which were produced and the stamps printed by Perkins, Bacon) and the 2d. of 1870 for which though it was printed throughout in Victoria, the die and plates were produced by De La Rue. Being the products of local endeavour in a remote country, the stamps of Victoria possess great technical interest for students although its issues are too complicated for many collectors. The present list is an attempt alike to demonstrate their interest and to clarify their complications, particularly by the inclusion of carefully written notes on various aspects of their production.

A. THE PRIVATE CONTRACT PERIOD, 1850–59 (Ham, Campbell & Co, Campbell and Fergusson, Calvert, Robinson)

1 Queen Victoria ("Half Length")

(Des engraved on a single piece of steel by Thomas Ham, Melbourne)

I. Lithographed by Thomas Ham, Melbourne

1850 (3 Jan). *T* **1**. *Imperf except groups* (9) *and* (10).

1d. Thin line at top

2d. Fine border and background

3d. White area to left of orb

(1) Original state of dies: 1d. *(tops of letters of "VICTORIA" reach to top of stamp)*; 2d. *(fine border and background)*; 3d. *(thicker white outline around left of orb, central band of orb does not protrude at left). No frame-lines on dies.*

No.	Description	Unused	Used
1	1d. orange-vermilion	—	£950
	a. Orange-brown	—	£500
	b. Dull chocolate-brown (shades)	—	£450
2	2d. lilac-mauve *(shades)*	—	£275
3	2d. brown-lilac *(shades)*	£2250	£250
	a. Grey-lilac	—	£250
4	3d. bright blue *(shades)*	—	£275
	a. Blue (shades)	—	£170
	ab. Retouched (Nos. 10 and 11 in transfer-group only)	—	£275

Periods of use: 1d., 2d. and 3d. No. 4 (January 1850); 3d. No. 4*a* March 1850 to October 1851).

Note on Group (1). With the exception of No. 4*a* all the above were printed from a small stone of 30 (5 × 6), laid down without the use of an Intermediate stone. The 3d. No. 4*a* was the first "Half Length" to appear in sheets of 120, which was the case for all subsequent Ham printings. It was produced from an Intermediate stone of 15 (5 × 3). The 2d. No. 2 was the first printing (from Stone "A") and Nos. 3 and 3*a* the second (from Stone "B"). Impressions clear and fine.

Note on margins found in the Ham printings: These stamps divide into two groups—Nos. 1 to 7—which were from 5-wide groups (or sheets) and Nos. 8 to 17—which were from 6-wide groups. The spacing between stamps horizontally is greater for Nos. 1 to 7 than Nos. 8 to 17 (and see later notes).

1d. Thick line at top

2d. Coarse background

3d. White area small and band protruding to left of orb

(2) Second state of dies: 1d. *(more colour over top of letters of "VICTORIA")*; 2d. *(fine border as (1) but with coarse background)*; 3d. *(thinner white outline around left of orb, central band of orb protrudes at left).*

No.	Description	Unused	Used
5	1d. red-brown *(shades)*	£2750	£275
	a. Pale dull red-brown	—	£275
6	2d. grey-lilac *(shades)*	£1000	80·00
	a. Dull grey	—	80·00
7	3d. blue *(shades)*	—	£110
	a. Retouched (22 varieties) .. *from*	—	£225

Periods of use: 1d. (Feb–Sept 1850); 2d. (Jan–April 1850); 3d. (Oct 1851 to Dec 1852).

Note on Group (2). These were all printed in sheets of 120 (10 × 12), the Printing stones for the 1d. and 2d. being produced from an Intermediate stone of 30 (5 × 6), and that for the 3d. from one of 10 (5 × 2). Impressions are clear and fine.

Frame-lines added

(3) Third state of dies: *As in* (2) *but with frame-lines added, very close up, on all four sides.*

No.	Description	Unused	Used
8	1d. dull orange-vermilion	—	£120
	a. Dull red (shades)	—	£120
9	1d. deep red-brown	—	£600
	a. Brownish red (shades)	—	£110
	b. Dull rose (shades)	—	£110
10	2d. grey *(shades)*	—	£120
	a. Olive-grey (shades)	—	£120
11	3d. blue *(shades)*	—	50·00
	a. Deep blue (shades)	—	50·00
	b. Pale greenish blue (shades)	—	95·00

Periods of use: 1d. No. 8 (Oct 1850 to April 1851); 1d. No. 9 (April 1851 to March 1854): 2d. (Aug–Oct 1850); 3d. (Dec 1852 to April 1854).

Note on Group (3). Although the above were all printed in sheets of 120 the format was 12 × 10—and continued so—and not 10 × 12 as in Group (2). For No. 8 (i.e. third 1d. printing) an Intermediate stone of 30 (6 × 5) was used, but for all the others (i.e. fourth printings) one of 12 (6 × 2) was employed. These stamps (and those under Group (4) following) are very closely spaced as compared with the (1) and (2) groups. Group (3) represented the last state of the 1d. and 3d. dies but not of the 2d. Impressions vary from medium to fine.

White veil

(4) *As* (3) *but altered to give, for the* 1d. *and* 3d., *the so-called "white veils", and for the* 2d., *the effect of vertical drapes to the veil.*

No.	Description	Unused	Used
12	1d. reddish brown	—	£100
	a. Bright pinky red (shades)	£450	£100
13	2d. drab	—	£110
	a. Grey-drab	—	£110
	b. Lilac-drab	—	£110
	c. Red-lilac	—	£650
	d. Void S.W. corner	—	£1200
14	3d. blue *(shades)*	—	45·00
	a. Deep blue (shades)	—	45·00
	b. Greenish blue (shades)	—	45·00
	c. Retouched (9 varieties)	—	£120

Periods of use: 1d. (April 1851–March 1854); 2d. (Aug–Oct 1850); 3d. (April–June 1854).

Note on Group (4): The alterations to the veils were made to each of the 12 impressions on the Intermediate Stones used for Group (3), and there are therefore 12 varieties of the veil in each value. Impressions are relatively coarse, particularly of the 2d. (save for No. 13c). Spacing of stamps is very close as in (3). In the 1d. and 2d. the shades found in Group (4) differ considerably from those met in (3).

2d. Coarse border and background

(5) Fourth state of die. 2d. value only: *Coarse border and background. Veil details as in original die.*

No.	Description	Unused	Used
15	2d. red-lilac *(shades)*	—	£180
	a. Lilac	—	£180
	b. Grey	—	£275
	c. Dull brownish lilac	—	£100
	d. Retouched lower label—value omitted. (Nos. 15 to 15c)	—	£1800
	e. Other retouches (Nos. 15 to 15c) (17 varieties) .. *from*	—	£225

Period of use: May–August 1850.

Note on Group (5): This comprised the sixth printing of this value and was printed from Stone "A". For it (and also for Groups (6) and (7) below) Ham utilized an Intermediate Stone of 30 (6 × 5). This was the only printing of the 2d. value in which retouches were made to the printing stone. Impressions (save for No. 15*a*) are generally good, sometimes fine.

No. 15*b* can generally, and No. 15*c* can always be readily distinguished as they are on *thin* wove paper of good quality, not found elsewhere.

(6) 2d. only: *As* (5) *but with veils altered to give effect of vertical drapes.*

No.	Description	Unused	Used
16	2d. lilac-grey	—	£110
	a. Deep grey	—	£110
	b. Brown-lilac (shades)	—	60·00
17	2d. cinnamon *(shades)*	£425	95·00
	a. Drab (shades)	—	45·00
	b. Pale dull brown (shades)	—	60·00
	c. Greenish grey	—	60·00
	d. Olive-drab (shades)	—	£110
	e. Buff	—	£120

Periods of use: No. 16 etc. (Nov 1850–March 1851), No. 17 etc. (March 1851–Dec 1852).

Note on Group (6): The 2d. Stone "B" (No. 16, etc.) and Stone "C" (No. 17, etc.) constituted Ham's seventh and eighth printings respectively. Two shades in the Stone "B" printings do not differ greatly from shades in the Stone "A" printings, but all those listed under No. 17 are entirely and peculiarly distinctive. The veil alterations were again made to each of the impressions on the Intermediate Stones so that there are 30 varieties of these.

General note on Ham printings. Ham's contract was completed in May 1850 but his 1d. and 3d. stamps remained in use up till March and June 1854 respectively. The 2d. "Half Length" design was, however, as the result of an injury to the die, superseded by Ham's "Queen-on-Throne" design in December 1852. In all Ham made five printings of each of the 1d. and 3d. and eight of the 2d. The paper employed by the three contractors was distinctive. For instance, for the whole of the Campbell and Fergusson printings (1d. and 3d. only) a coarse wove paper of poor quality, easily thinned and with a marked "mesh" (horizontal or vertical) was used. This paper is nothing like any paper used for the Ham or Campbell printings, and affords the best preliminary test for all 1d. and 3d. "Half Lengths".

II. Lithographed by J. S. Campbell & Co, Melbourne

(7) *Wide settings. Stamps* 2½–3 *mm apart* (1d.) *or* 1½–2 *mm apart* (3d.).

No.	Description	Unused	Used
18	1d. orange-red *(shades)*	£400	£120
	a. Rose	—	£350
19	3d. blue *(shades)*	£425	32·00
	a. Retouched (No. 17 in group)	—	£120

Periods of use: 1d. (Mar 1854–Jan 1855); 3d. (June 1854–April 1855, also 1858/9).

Note on Group (7): The Campbell 1d. was printed from a stone of 192 impressions (96 × 2), and the 3d. from a stone of 320 (160 × 2). For each value an intermediate stone of 24 (6 × 4) was used. Impressions are generally good.

III. Lithographed by Campbell and Fergusson, Melbourne

(8) *Wide settings as* (7). *Impressions medium to poor, depending on state of printing stones. Paper used is distinctive (see final note after Ham printings).*

(*a*) *Same intermediate stones as had been employed for Group* (7)

No.	Description	Unused	Used
20	1d. brown *(shades)*	£325	95·00
	a. Brick-red (shades)	—	75·00
	b. Dull red (shades)	—	75·00
21	1d. orange-brown *(shades)*	—	£100
	a. Dull rose-red (shades)	—	60·00
	b. Bright rose-pink	—	£100
	c. Retouched (4 varieties)	—	£400
22	1d. pink *(shades)*	£300	32·00
	a. Rose (shades)	£300	32·00
	b. Lilac-rose (shades)	—	32·00
	c. Dull brown-red (shades)	—	£100
	d. Retouched (9 varieties)	—	£325
23	3d. bright blue *(shades)*	£400	48·00
	a. Greenish blue (shades)	£350	40·00
	b. Retouched (No. 17 in group)	—	95·00
24	3d. Prussian blue *(shades)*	—	70·00
	a. Milky blue	—	£110
	b. Retouched (No. 17 in group)	—	£225

Periods of use: 1d. No. 20, etc. (Stone 2, July 1854 and December 1855–May 1856): 1d. No. 21, etc. (Stone 3, Aug–Nov 1855); 1d. No. 22, etc. (Stones 4, 5, Feb–Aug 1855 and May–Oct 1856); 3d. No. 23, etc. (Stone "B", July 1857–Dec 1858); 3d. No. 24 etc. (Stone "C", Nov 1856–June 1857).

(*b*) *New intermediate stone of similar size* (6 × 4) *and spacing* 2½–3 *mm apart horizontally. (Stone "D")*

No.	Description	Unused	Used
25	3d. steel-blue *(shades)*	—	42·00
	a. Greenish blue (shades)	£325	30·00
	b. Blue (shades)	£325	30·00
	c. Deep blue (shades)	£325	30·00
	d. Indigo (shades)	—	38·00

Period of use: May 1855 to November 1856. Impressions generally heavier than previous 3d.

Note on Group (8): All printing stones were of 400 impressions, consisting of an upper and lower pane of 200 (20 × 10) save in two cases, viz.: the 3d. No. 23 which was of 320 (160 × 2) and No. 24 which was probably of 200 (20 × 10) impressions. The 3d. No. 24, etc., presents a considerably worn appearance. No. 25 (steel-blue) comprised the earlier part of the printing and is, comparatively, of good appearance and impression.

No. 21*b* is only found with barred oval cancellations as these were not used after the end of 1855 they are of assistance in identification.

IV. 3d. stamps rouletted and perforated in 1857 and 1859 respectively

(9) *Rouletted* 7 *to* 8½ *at G.P.O., Melbourne (see later notes).*

(*a*) *Campbell printing* (No. 19)

No.	Description	Unused	Used
26	3d. blue (shades)	—	£150
	a. Retouched (No. 17 in group)		

(*b*) *Campbell & Fergusson printing* (No. 23)

No.	Description	Unused	Used
27	3d. bright blue *(shades)*	—	£160
	a. Greenish blue (shades)	—	£140
	b. Retouched (No. 17 in group)		

Period of use: Sept–Dec 1858.

(10) *Perforated* 12 *by Robinson*. (*a*) *Campbell printing* (No. 19).

No.	Description	Unused	Used
28	3d. blue *(shades)*	—	£110
	a. Retouched (No. 17 in group)	—	£250

(*b*) *Campbell & Fergusson printing* (No. 23)

No.	Description	Unused	Used
29	3d. greenish blue *(shades)*	—	£350
	a. Retouched (No. 17 in group)		

Period of use: Jan 1859 to Jan 1860.

Note on Groups (9) *and* (10): The roulettes are seldom found on all four sides. The great majority of the perforated stamps are badly off-centre.

Lithographic Reprints of the three values (the 2d. die then being in a defaced condition) were made in 1891, on paper wmk V over Crown (Type V2) *W* **23**, perf 12½. The 1891 Reprints of all issues were the direct result of Victoria, in that year, joining the Universal Postal Union. As a member she was expected to supply specimens of her old issues to other members. None of these being available and most of the old plates having been destroyed she was, in the majority of cases, compelled to make new plates for which, fortunately, all the original dies (save the "Emblems" (3) and the "Woodblocks" (4) were available.

FURTHER INFORMATION on these interesting issues, including the details of the numbers printed, the plating of the Transfer Groups, the papers used, the retouches, creased transfers, "abnormal" combinations, "stitch" watermarks, etc., etc., will be found in "The Half-Lengths of Victoria", the work by J. R. W. Purves, F.R.P.S.L., on which the above list is based.

2 Queen on Throne

1852–54. *T* **2**. *Imperf.*

Corner letters: Each of the fifty subjects of the original plate show different letter combinations of A to Z, except J.

I. Dec 1852. *Recess-printed by Thomas Ham from a steel plate of* 50 (10 × 5) *impressions, engraved by him by hand.*

No.	Description	Unused	Used
30	2d. reddish brown	£110	24·00
	a. Chestnut	—	£110
	b. Purple-brown	£110	24·00

Reprints were made in 1891 (and later) using the original plate, on paper wmk V over Crown Type V2, both imperf and perf 12½.

II. Dec 1853–May 1854. *Lithographed by Campbell & Co, transfers for the stones being taken from Ham's steel plate. Period of issue: Dec 1853–April 1855 and May 1856–May 1857. On various types of good quality paper, hand-made and machine-wove.*

(i) *Early printings: full impression, detail around back of throne generally complete. Impressions fine and clear; colours rich*

No.	Description	Unused	Used
31	2d. brownish purple	£150	22·00
	a. Grey-brown	—	22·00
	b. Purple-black	—	22·00
	c. Dull lilac-brown (spotty print on toned)	—	25·00

Papers: The papers used for (i) and (ii) were, save in the two cases indicated, distinguished by their *whiteness*, as compared with the toned (yellowish) character of all that follow. This toning is due in part to the type of gum used but also to the larger proportion of wood pulp used in manufacture. The *hand-made* paper, which is always *white*, is found in (i) and (ii) only.

(ii) *Intermediate printings. Impressions not so full or sharp, background round top of throne not so fully defined*

No.	Description	Unused	Used
32	2d. violet-black	—	22·00
	a. Grey-black	—	24·00
	b. Grey-lilac	—	24·00
	c. Dull brown (on toned)	—	24·00
	d. Substituted transfer (in pair)	—	£2750

(iii) *Later printings, on toned paper only. Background round top of throne generally whiter. Stamps lack the detail of* (i) *and* (ii) *although impression is reasonably good*

33 2d. grey-black .. .. £110 19·00
 a. Purple-black .. .. £110 19·00

(iv) *Last printing; on toned paper only. Background generally full as* (i) *but impression is singularly flat, and lacking in fineness and sharpness. Normal colour is distinctive*

34 2d. grey-drab (*shades*) .. .. .. — 19·00
 a. Black .. .. — 60·00

Notes on the Campbell & Co Printings

(*a*) *Stones*: In all, 2,000,000 stamps were printed (and issued) under this contract. They were not printed on the one occasion but on several. A total of 22 transfers were taken from the steel plate, *nine* printing stones being used. Of these the first eight were of 100 impressions (one "fifty" over another "fifty") and the ninth was of 300 impressions (three "fifties" over three "fifties"). Only three of these stones were used to a point where they showed wear and in those cases the wear was nothing like that found in the Campbell & Fergusson printings. Whiteness in the background around the throne, where it occurs, is more often the result of weak pressure in the taking of the transfers.

(*b*) *Shades*: These should be readily distinguishable from the C. & F. printings, with the possible exception of No. 32*b* which has a pinkish element.

(*c*) *Papers*: At least *six* varieties, all of good quality (comprising both hand and machine made papers) were used but they were all so different (and of so much better quality) to that employed for the C. & F. contract that, once a C. & F. stamp is acquired, no difficulty should be encountered in identifying a Campbell.

(*d*) *Vertical pairs* (they are rare) have been met from four of the Campbell stones, with *wide* distances (up to 19 mm) between the stamps. In such cases the top stamp is from the lower row of a top transfer of fifty and the bottom stamp from the top row of a similar lower transfer.

(*e*) *"Substituted Transfers"*. These (a block of four in the S.W. corner of a sheet) occurred on one out of the 22 transfers on printing stone 5. The horizontal pairs read WA–HN and GM–SX respectively and the vertical pairs VZ over VZ and WA over WA respectively. They are all of the greatest rarity.

(*f*) No *"Creased Transfer"* varieties are to be met in the Campbell printings where the method followed for laying down the printing stones differed from that employed for the Campbell & Fergussons. The same is true of the "Half-Lengths" printed by these two contractors.

Some instances of *retouching* (they are rare) may be met. One stone only was affected.

III. June 1854. *Lithographed by Campbell & Fergusson; transfers for the stones again being taken from Ham's steel plate. Period of issue: March 1855–May 1856. Printed, like the Campbell & Fergusson Half-Lengths, on a machine-wove paper of poor quality (easily thinned and torn). This factor alone provides an unfailing guide for distinguishing the products of the two contractors.*

(i) *Printings from stones which were not over-used; background around top of throne generally full and detail good*

35 2d. lilac (*shades*) .. .. £130 19·00
 a. Purple (*shades*) .. .. — 19·00
 b. Variety "TVO" .. .. — £550

(ii) *Early printings from stones which were over-used. Similar characteristics to* (i) *above, though detail is not quite so full. Distinctive shades*

36 2d. brown .. .. — 70·00
 a. Brown-purple .. .. £160 22·00
 b. Warm purple .. .. — 22·00
 c. Rose-lilac .. .. — 22·00
 d. Substituted transfer (pair) .. .. — £800

(iii) *Later printings from the same stones used for* (ii) *when in a worn condition. Impressions heavy, coarse and overcoloured; details blurred; generally white background around top of throne*

37 2d. dull lilac-mauve .. .. £110 22·00
 a. Dull mauve .. .. £110 22·00
 b. Grey-violet .. .. — 22·00
 c. Red-lilac .. .. — 24·00
 d. Substituted transfer (pair) .. .. — £800

(iv) *Printings from a stone giving* (*from the start*) *blotchy and unpleasing results, with poor definition. Mainly shows in extra colour patches found on most stamps*

38 2d. dull purple .. .. — 22·00
 a. Dull grey-lilac .. .. £160 22·00
 b. On thick card paper .. .. .. — £500

Notes on the Campbell & Fergusson Printings

(*a*) *Stones*: 3,000,000 stamps in all were printed under this contract, of which, however, 1,500,000 (deemed to be in excess of requirements) were destroyed. A total of four printing stones (comprising 16 transfers from the steel plate) were used. The greater size of the printing and the smaller number taken of transfers of fifty (and hence of printing impressions) explains the *over-use* of certain stones, and the badly-worn prints (with filled-in colour, finer details missing, etc.) that are often met.

(*b*) *Shades*: At least 95 per cent of these printings, whatever their actual shade names, have—by comparison with the Campbell stamps—a *pink* quality. Only about 2 per cent of the Campbells, a proportion of the stamps printed from one stone only, have such a quality, but in that case the paper used was wholly different.

(*c*) *Paper* is invariably of vertical mesh. *Both* horizontal and vertical meshes are found in the Campbells.

(*d*) *Vertical pairs* with *wide* spacing have been found. They are rare: See note above on similar Campbell pairs.

(*e*) *"Substituted Transfers"*: Here the entire *five* impressions comprising the left vertical row of a sheet were affected. The *horizontal* pairs (starting at the top and going down) are as follows: UY-BF, TX-MQ, DI-WA, SW-GM and CH-RW. The *vertical* pairs are UY over TX and DI over SW. They occur in various shades and stages of wear.

(*f*) *"Creased Transfer"* varieties. As in the C. & F. "Half-Length" printings, various major instances are met, including the "TVO" variety. At least two transfer groups of 50 were affected.

No retouching has been met in any printing.

3

4 Queen on Throne

(Die engraved and stamps lithographed by Campbell & Fergusson)

1854–65. *T* 3. (*a*) *Imperf.*

39 1s. blue (*shades*) (6.7.54) .. .. .. £600 22·00
 a. Greenish blue .. .. £700 22·00
 b. Indigo-blue .. .. — £110

(*b*) *Rouletted 7–7½ at G.P.O., Melbourne* (*see later notes*)

40 1s. greenish blue (27.8.57) .. .. .. — 80·00
 a. Blue .. .. — 80·00

(*c*) *Perf 12 by Robinson, early in* 1859

41 1s. blue (*shades*)(13.4.59) .. .. .. £120 15·00
 a. Greenish blue .. .. £110 11·00
 b. Indigo-blue .. .. — 22·00

For this stamp four printing stones, each of 400 impressions (in four panes of 100), were used. These were built up from an "intermediate" stone of 40 (8 × 5) impressions. Retouches and "creased transfer" varieties also exist. At least two classes of paper were used.

This stamp was reprinted (by lithography) in 1891, wmk V over Crown, Type V2, perf 12½. The transfers were taken from the original die.

(Recess P.B.)

1856–58. *T* 4. *Wmk Large Star, W w* 1. (*a*) *Imperf.*

42 1d. yellow-green (23.10.56) .. .. .. 95·00 19·00

(*b*) *Rouletted 5½–6½ by F. W. Robinson, in Melbourne*

43 6d. bright blue (1.11.58) .. .. .. 85·00 12·00
 a. Light blue .. .. £150 24·00

The gumming for the 6d. was deemed unsatisfactory and it was not used until the exhaustion of Nos. 44–48. The stock was imperf and was rouletted by Robinson before issue. It only exists imperf, obliterated "CANCELLED" in London, in 1861.

Re-entries and re-cuts occur in both values.

These two stamps were reprinted in 1891, Wmk V over Crown, Type V2, imperf, using the original steel plates. The 1d. is found in two colours—a dull yellow-green and a bright blue-green. The 6d. has an indigo quality and can be found in two shades.

5 6 7

1854–59. *T* 5 *to* 7 (*the "Woodblocks"*). *Typo.*

I. *T* **5.** *6d.: Printed in sheets of 100 stamps, representing two impressions from a plate of 50 woodblocks* (*in two panes of 25—5 × 5*), *engraved individually by S. Calvert. These all differ but are of two main types:—*

A. *Small white mark after* "VICTORIA" *like an apostrophe.*
B. *No white mark after* "VICTORIA".

(*a*) *Imperf*

44 6d. reddish brown (13.9.54) .. .. .. 75·00 22·00
 a. Dull orange .. .. 65·00 18·00
 b. Orange-yellow .. .. 65·00 19·00

(*b*) *Rouletted 7–9*

45 6d. reddish brown (12.8.57) .. .. .. — 42·00
 a. Dull orange (3.12.57) .. .. .. — 30·00
 b. Orange-yellow .. .. — 42·00

These stamps may be met rouletted on two sides only, and also (with finer points) on all four sides. The first class emanates from some "rouletters" used by the window-clerks at the G.P.O., Melbourne (see note after No. 62). The latter class were "perforated" by Calvert, and this gauge was also used for the Rouletted "Emblems" of early 1858.

(*c*) *Serpentine Roulette* 10½

46 6d. orange-yellow (5.12.57) .. .. .. — 55·00

(*d*) *Serrated 18–19 × serpentine 10½; also serrated compound on one side with serpentine*

47 6d. orange-yellow (19.10.57) .. .. .. — 55·00

(*e*) *Serrated 18–19*

48 6d. orange-yellow .. .. — 55·00

Part of (*b*) and all of (*c*), (*d*) and (*e*) were "perforated" by Calvert under his contract of 14.10.57, a total of 163,000 stamps being so treated. The "pin-perf about 10" variety previously listed belongs to 1856 and is clearly not of official origin.

II. *T* **5.** *2s.: For this value Calvert employed a plate of 25* (*5 × 5*) *separately engraved wood-blocks, two impressions of which made up the sheet of* 50. (*a*) *Imperf.*

49 2s. dull bluish green (1.9.54) £900 £110

(*b*) *Rouletted 7–7½*

50 2s. dull bluish green .. .. — £350

(*c*) *Perf 12* (*by Robinson*), 1859

51 2s. dull bluish green .. .. £200 30·00
 a. Pale bluish green .. .. £200 25·00

Nos. 49–51 were printed on a printed *yellow* background which is usually faint. For the blue-on-green printings of 1864–81 see Nos. 127, 130, 140 and 147. These latter were printed in sheets of 30, in two panes of 15 (3 × 5). The plate comprised 18 of the original woodblocks and 12 electros.

III. *T* 6. REGISTRATION *stamp.* (*a*) *Imperf.*

52 1s. rose-pink and blue (1.12.54) .. .. £600 60·00

(*b*) *Rouletted 7–7½*

53 1s. rose-pink and blue £3000 £180

IV. *T* 7. "TOO LATE" *stamp. Imperf.*

54 6d. lilac and green (1.1.55) £450 £120

The *same* main plate of 25 woodblock impressions (5 × 5 printed four times make up a sheet of 100) was originally used for both the "Registered" and "Too Late" stamps. For the portions printed in blue and green respectively separate stereotype plates were used of each stamp.

A second woodblock plate of 25 (5 × 5) impressions from a different model was used (with the first plate) for later printings of the "Registered" only. Die 2 is distinguished by the longer head "R" of "VICTORIA" and the absence of the small white letters "V" and "R" etc. The "Registered" stamp ceased to be so used from 5.1.58 although Postmasters were then instructed to use up remainin stocks for normal postal purposes. The "Too Late" stamp was wit drawn from issue as from 1.7.57. A very few used multiples of bot these stamps are known. They all represent abnormal usage.

8

1857–60. *T* 8 (*"Emblems"*). *Typo.*

For these stamps the dies were "wood-blocks" engraved by Calvert, and the "plates" consisted of 120 individual electrotypes clamped together. In all, six settings were employed for the 4d value and three each for the 1d. and 2d. values.

I. 1857: Printed by Calvert

(i) *Wmk Large Star, W w* 1. (*a*) *Imperf*

55 1d. yellow-green (18.2.57) .. .. .. 95·00 13·0(
 a. Deep green .. .. £110 26·0(
 b. Printed on both sides .. .. .. — £70(
56 4d. vermilion (26.1.57) .. .. .. £200 7·5(
 a. Brown-vermilion .. .. £190 7·5(
 b. Printed on both sides .. .. .. — £55(
57 4d. dull red (20.7.57) .. .. .. £160 7·5(
58 4d. dull rose (6.9.57) .. .. .. £180 7·5(

(*b*) *Rouletted 7–9* (*often on two sides only*)

59 1d. yellow-green .. .. £275 65·00
60 4d. vermilion .. .. — 85·00
61 4d. dull red (1.8.57) .. .. .. — 38·00
62 4d. dull rose .. .. — 26·00

Nos. 59–62 were not rouletted by Calvert, but by one or other of three "rouletters" used by the clerks at the selling windows of the G.P.O., Melbourne. One of these "rouletters" gauged 6½–7½ and another 7¾–9. The most effective of them was purchased from one Raymond early in August 1857.

(*c*) *P* 12

63 1d. yellow-green .. .. — £275

This stamp and Nos. 66, 66*a*, 72 and 77 were the result of the perforating (by Robinson), probably in 1860, of a few sheets of old stock.

(ii) *No wmk. On good quality medium-wove paper.* (*a*) *Imperf*

64 2d. pale lilac (25.5.57) .. .. .. £160 10·00
 a. Grey-lilac .. .. £160 10·00

(*b*) *Rouletted 7–9* (*often on two sides only*)

65 2d. pale lilac .. .. — 23·00
 a. Grey-lilac .. .. — 23·00

See note following No. 62.

(*c*) *P* 12

66 2d. pale lilac .. .. — £225
 a. Grey-lilac .. .. — £225

See note following No. 63.

(*d*) *Serrated 18–19*

67 2d. grey-lilac £400 £250

This variety is probably the result of an experiment by Calvert. Most of the copies seen are unused.

II. 1858: Printed by Calvert on white wove paper of good quality

(*a*) *Rouletted all round 8–9* (*usually fine points*)

68 1d. pale emerald (19.1.58) .. .. .. £160 14·00
 a. Emerald-green .. .. £160 14·00
 b. Roulette horiz only .. .. .. — £325
69 4d. rose-pink (10.1.58) .. .. .. £200 5·50
 a. Bright rose .. .. £200 5·50
 b. Reddish pink .. .. — 11·00
 c. Roulette horiz only .. .. .. — £250
 d. Roulette vert only .. .. .. — £250

(*b*) *Imperf* (April 1858)

70 1d. pale emerald .. .. £190 10·00
 a. Emerald-green .. .. — 13·00
71 4d. rose-pink .. .. £250 23·00
 a. Bright rose .. .. — 23·00
 b. Reddish pink .. .. — 30·00

The imperf varieties above were stamps which *should* have been rouletted by Calvert. On the cancellation of his contract they were taken over from him but since supplies were urgently required (and Robinson not having then commenced his contract) the stamps were put into use as they were. They *follow* and do not precede the roulettes.

(*c*) *P* 12

72 1d. emerald-green .. .. — £275
 a. Imperf between (horiz pair) .. ..

III. 1858–9: Printed under contract by F. W. Robinson, first outside and later (1859) inside the Post Office Establishment

(i) *On wove paper of a somewhat poorer quality than Calvert's. Imperf*

73 4d. dull rose (5.58) .. .. — 60·00

(ii) *On smooth vertically laid paper of good quality.* (*a*) *Imperf*

74 4d. dull rose (8.5.58) .. .. .. — 23·00
 a. Dull rose-red .. .. — 23·00
 b. Dull rose-red (*normal ink*) .. .. £375 15·00

The imperforate stamps Nos. 73, 74 and 74*a* can be easily distinguished by their distinctive *heavy, coarse* impression and the *oily* nature of the ink employed. They were the *first* stamps printed by Robinson and because of the demand were rushed into circulation without being rouletted, as also was No. 74*b* which was the first stamp printed by him using a more satisfactory quality of ink.

(*b*) *Rouletted 5½–6½*

75 2d. brown-lilac (*shades*) (9.58) .. .. £200 9·50
76 4d. pale dull rose (5.58) .. .. .. — 3·50
 a. Dull rose-red .. .. £120 3·50
 b. Rose-red .. .. £120 3·25

(*c*) *P* 12

77 4d. dull rose .. .. — £300

See note following No. 63.

(*d*) *Serrated* 19

78 4d. rose-red .. .. — £300

(iii) *On smooth horizontally laid paper of same quality as* (ii) *above*

(*a*) *Rouletted* 5½–6½

79 2d. brown-lilac (*shades*) (7.58) .. .. £120 5·50
a. Violet (*shades*) (27.11.58) .. .. £150 5·50
b. Dull violet .. .. .. — 18·00
80 4d. pale dull rose .. .. .. — £600

(iv) *On good quality wove paper.* (*a*) *Rouletted* 5½–6½

81 1d. yellow-green (25.12.58) .. .. .. £275 23·00
82 4d. dull rose .. .. — £325

(*b*) *Perf* 12 (*the first perforated stamps to be issued in Victoria*)

83 1d. yellow-green (*shades*) (11.1.59) .. .. £160 11·00
a. Imperf × perf (vert pair) .. .. — £225
84 4d. dull rose (16.2.59) .. .. .. £150 2·75

Note: No. 83 is found on two classes of paper.

(v) *P* 12. *On poorer quality wove paper of coarser mesh*

85 1d. dull green (7.59) .. .. .. £120 7·50
a. Green (11.59) .. .. .. £120 7·50
86 4d. dull rose (19.4.59) .. .. .. — 5·00
a. Rose-carmine (6.59) .. .. £150 5·00
b. Rose-pink (12.59) .. .. .. — 9·00

Save in the rouletted 1d. (where a second paper of *vertical* mesh was also employed) all the paper used for (iv) above was of *horizontal* mesh, whereas under (v) except for No. 86*b* (which was printed on a tough, thick, handmade paper) it is always of *vertical* mesh. In two printings of the 1d. *both* wove and laid papers were included.

(vi) *P* 12. *On horizontally laid papers, of coarser quality and not so smooth as those previously employed by Robinson*

(*a*) *Laid lines closer together*

87 1d. dull green (July 1859) .. .. .. — 15·00
88 4d. rose-pink (23.12.59) .. .. .. — 7·00

(*b*) *Laid lines farther apart*

89 1d. green (*shades*) (October 1859) .. .. £130 9·50
90 4d. rose-pink (*shades*) (January 1860) .. £120 7·50

(vii) *P* 12. *On thin glazed paper, emanating from Bordeaux*

91 1d. deep yellow-green (July 1859) .. .. — £150

This stamp must have been printed *before* the "dull greens" of July 1859.

PLATES: 1857–68

The plates prepared for use between January 1857 and December 1867 (with one exception, see note after No. 51 on 2s. value) consisted of a number of individual electros (usually 120) clamped together in a "forme" and spaced and arranged to fit the pattern of the watermarked paper. Five such schemes are to be found, viz.: (*a*) from 1857 to Sept 1863 when (save for the 2d. of May 1857) the forme comprised 4 blocks of 30 (6 × 5) electros; (*b*) for the 2d. of May 1857 only, the sheet consisted of 20 blocks of 6 (2 × 3); (*c*) from Sept 1863 to Feb 1866 when *three* separate arrangements, constant for any one value, are found. These were based on the face value of the stamps in the unit group and were as follows:—(i) For the 1d., 2d. and 4d. values the forme was composed of 8 blocks of 15 (3 × 5) separated by "gutters"; (ii) for the 3d., 6d. and 1s. values of 6 blocks (or 3, in the case of the 1s.) of 20 (4 × 5) separated by "gutters" and (iii) in the case of the 10d. of 20 blocks of 6 (3 × 2) separated by "gutters"; (*d*) over and following the period Jan–July 1866, in anticipation of the introduction of the V over Crown watermarked paper, the old formes (with the exception of the 10d.) were reset and the new formes (e.g. 3d. and 6d.) arranged to give one block of 120 (12 × 10) evenly spaced units without "gutters". For various values, therefore, two "settings" were employed of the same electrotypes. Those interested in this subject should consult an article in *Philately from Australia* for March 1954. From 1869 to 1874 new printing plates consisted of 4 electrotypes each of 30 impressions (6 × 5) clamped together. These were produced via one (or two) "master" electrotypes of the same size. From 1875 (with four exceptions in the 1885 issues) all new printing plates consisted of a continuous surface electrotype of 120 (12 × 10) impressions. The foregoing remarks apply to normal size stamps only and require modification for other sizes.

B. GOVERNMENT STAMP PRINTING.
THE FIRST PERIOD, 1860–1884

Robinson was employed, in April 1858, to finish Calvert's uncompleted Contracts of 1857. Subsequently, under further Contracts, he printed more stamps. The work being satisfactory the Government (on 12.4.59) undertook to continue his employment and at the same time purchased the whole of his equipment, paper stocks, etc. As from 1.1.60 a Government Stamp Printing Branch was set up, Robinson was appointed its Chief Officer and there was no more Stamp Printing in terms of Private Contract. He was succeeded in 1867 by James Atkinson, and from 1883 to 1906 the same work was performed by William Bond. In December 1885 printing operations were transferred from the Post Office to the Government Printing Office and the Stamp Printer then joined the staff of the Government Printer. The Stamp Printers after Bond were J. Kemp and J. B. Cooke (1909–12), the latter being also appointed the first Commonwealth Stamp Printer.

Note: All issues of this period, 1860–84, were printed by typography from electrotypes.

9

10

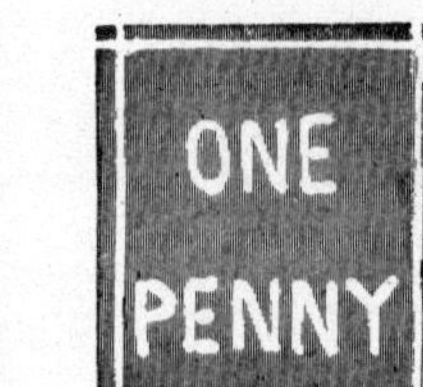

11 12

(Dies for 3d., 4d. and 6d. (T **9**) designed and engraved by Frederick Grosse. The die for the 6d. T **11** consisted of a frame die engraved by Grosse into which was plugged a head portion, cut out of his die for the 6d. T **9**. The design, die and plate for the 1d. T **10** were all supplied by Messrs. De Gruchy and Leigh of Melbourne)

1860–66. *T* **5, 8, 9, 10** *and* **11.** *P* 12.

(i) *No wmk. On horizontally laid paper* (*lines further apart, as* (vi) (*b*) *above*)

92 **9** 3d. deep blue (31.1.60) .. .. £300 23·00
a. Light blue £1000 £110

(ii) *No wmk. On thin glazed paper emanating from Bordeaux* (*see also under* (vii) *above*)

93 **8** 1d. bright green (25.5.60) .. .. — 22·00
94 **9** 4d. rose (21.4.60) .. .. .. £275 12·00
a. Rose-pink .. .. — 7·50

(iii) *No wmk. On a thicker coarser paper*

95 **9** 4d. rose-pink (7.60) .. .. .. £275 7·50

(iv) 1860–66: *Watermarked with the appropriate words of value as W* **12**. *The paper, which was hand-made, was supplied by T. H. Saunders of London*

96 **8** 1d. pale yellowish green (8.7.60) .. 65·00 4·50
a. Yellow-green .. .. .. 75·00 4·75
b. Wmk "FOUR PENCE" .. .. — £1200
97 **10** 1d. pale green (1.10.61) .. .. 75·00 5·50
a. Olive-green .. .. .. — 6·00
b. Pale green (deep brown gum) (2.63) 75·00 6·00
98 **8** 2d. brown-lilac (7.7.61) .. .. — 15·00
99 2d. bluish slate (8.61, 6.62) .. £100 4·75
a. Greyish lilac (9.61) .. .. £110 4·75
b. Slate-grey (1.62) .. .. .. — 4·75
100 **9** 3d. pale blue (1.61) .. .. .. £120 7·00
a. Bright blue (8.61) .. .. .. £120 8·00
b. Blue (deep brown gum) (2.63) .. £130 6·00
ba. "TRREE" for "THREE" in wmk ..
c. Deep blue (1864) .. .. .. £130 6·00
101 3d. maroon (13.2.66) .. .. .. 95·00 22·00
a. Perf 13 .. .. £110 25·00
102 4d. rose-pink (1.8.60) .. .. .. — 4·75
a. Rose-red (shades) (9.60) .. .. 80·00 3·00
b. Rose-carmine (12.60) .. .. — 7·50
c. Dull rose (shades) (1861) .. .. 80·00 3·00
103 6d. orange (18.10.60) £1600 £200
104 **5** 6d. black (22.6.61) .. .. .. £150 26·00
105 **9** 6d. black (20.8.61) .. .. .. 95·00 5·50
a. Grey-black .. .. 95·00 5·50
106 **11** 6d. grey (26.4.62) .. .. .. 80·00 5·00
a. Grey-black .. .. 80·00 6·50
b. Jet black (deep brown gum) (3.63) 85·00 7·50

Reprints on paper wmkd V over Crown (*W* **23**), perf 12½, were made in 1891 of the 1d. Type **10**, 3d. and 4d. Type **9** and 6d. Type **11**. In all cases new plates were used, and certain "die flaws" are found on the "Reprints" which are not met on the originals.

13

14

1862–63. *Emergency printings owing to supplies of the appropriate paper not being available.*

(*a*) *On paper wmkd* "FIVE SHILLINGS", *W* **13**

107 **9** 4d. dull rose-pink (11.9.62) .. .. £1500 20·00
a. Dull rose .. .. — 20·00

(*b*) *On paper wmkd* "THREE PENCE", *W* **12**

108 **8** 2d. pale slate (27.12.62) .. .. £110 10·00
a. Bluish grey (deep brown gum) (2.63) .. .. .. £120 12·00

Note: Certain stamps are to be met on the "words of value" papers with wmk *reversed* under Nos. 99, 100, 102, also 173 and 176. *Inverted* wmks may also be found in several cases. All these wmk varieties are scarce to rare.

(v) 1862–64: *Same types as before but wmkd with the appropriate single-lined numeral of value, as W* **14**, *the paper being supplied by De La Rue. P* 12 *unless otherwise described*

109 **10** 1d. olive-green (1.2.63) .. .. .. 55·00 4·50
a. Pale green (9.63) .. .. .. 55·00 4·50
b. Apple-green (4.64) .. .. .. — 4·50
110 **8** 2d. dull reddish lilac (21.4.63) .. £160 5·50
111 2d. grey-lilac (10.63) .. .. .. £150 12·00
a. Wmk "6" (10.63) .. .. .. — £4000
b. Grey-violet (shades) (11.63) .. — 9·00
c. Slate (12.63) .. .. £150 18·00
112 **9** 4d. dull rose-pink (9.10.62) .. .. 90·00 4·50
a. Dull rose (deep brown gum) (2.63) .. 95·00 4·75
b. Rose-red .. .. — 4·50
113 **11** 6d. grey (18.6.63) .. .. .. 70·00 4·50
a. Grey-black (2.64) .. .. .. 70·00 4·75
b. Intense black .. .. .. — 5·50
114 6d. jet-black (*p* 13) (12.64) .. .. 80·00 5·00
a. Grey-black .. .. 80·00 5·50

July–Aug 1863: *Varieties due to a temporary break-down of the perforating machine.*

115 **9** 4d. dull rose-pink (*imperf*) .. .. — 48·00
116 4d. dull rose-pink (*roul*) .. .. — £250

Notes on plate varieties found on stamps printed from plates made by Robinson.

The electros prepared by Robinson over the period 1860–66 (many, e.g. the 4d., which lasted until 1881, remaining in use for a long time after) furnish perhaps the most interesting varieties found in typographed stamps. Since the lead moulds for these were struck by hand, on semifused metal, and without the aid of a "collar", the stamps present us with certain constant abnormalities, viz *partial strikes, double strikes* and *internal distortion* varieties of a nature and extent not found in any other issues, as well as also providing all the more usual types of flaw found in typographed stamps. The whole of the Robinson "Beaded Ovals" and "Laureates" are plateable since the process used made it *impossible* for any stamp to be a perfect reproduction of the die. The 6d. black (Type **11**) is the most interesting of all since the die here was in two parts. This meant the adherence of lead along the line of junction, etc, and gave rise to yet further classes of plate variety. For information on this stamp see various articles in the *London Philatelist*.

Notes on the two single-line numeral watermark papers.

Two different English firms supplied the single-line numeral wmk papers used from October 1862 onwards. The two classes of paper supplied are so distinct that they have now been given separate listing. Their characteristics are as follows:—

1. *De La Rue papers* (several consignments). Comprised *white* paper wmkd "1", "2", "4", "6" and "8" respectively, *blue* paper wmkd "1" and *green* paper wmkd "2". In certain printings particularly in the 1d., 2d. and 4d. Laureates and the 6d. black (1863–65) on this paper, a *pelure* type—thin, hard and semi-transparent—may be found. This variety has not been separately listed but is worthy of the specialist's attention. Generally the quality of these De La Rue papers varied considerably among the different consignments.

2. *T. H. Saunders papers* (one consignment only). Comprised *white* paper wmkd "1", "4" and "6" respectively, *blue* paper wmkd "1", *green* paper wmkd "2", and *pink* paper wmkd "10". It was first used in December 1865 and the white papers were exhausted by August 1867. The paper was (apart from the *blue* variety, which was rather thinner than the rest) of even quality throughout and was smoother, thicker, more brittle and (in the white variety) not so white as the De La Rue product. It will be noted that the "2" and "8" papers were supplied by De La Rue only, whereas the "10" paper (pink) was supplied by Saunders only. Comparison of these should assist collectors in accurate classification. The *coloured* papers lasted much longer than the white, as will be seen from the listings. The *blue* lasted until 1875, and the *green* and *pink* until 1879.

In both papers, in practically all cases, *reversed* and/or *inverted* wmks may be met. *Sideways* wmks have been found under Nos. 113, 124 and 200. Stamps showing little or no wmk are from the left or right sides of badly cut sheets.

15

16

17

18 19

(The *"Laureated"* series: Dies engraved by Frederick Grosse. Printing plates (see previous note) made by F. W. Robinson until late in 1867.)

Note. Since various printings of the 2s. Calvert (Type **5**) were also made between 1864 and 1881 these have been included where appropriate.

1863–80.

(i) 1863–64. *Early printings. Wmkd with appropriate single-lined numeral as W* **14**, *on paper supplied by De La Rue. P* 12

117 **15** 1d. pale green (8.9.64) .. .. .. 75·00 7·00
118 2d. violet (4.64) .. .. 65·00 4·75
a. Dull violet (10.64) .. .. .. 70·00 5·00
119 4d. deep rose (4.9.63) .. .. .. — 3·50
a. Doubly printed .. .. .. — £500
b. Rose-pink (9.63) .. .. .. 85·00 2·50
c. Pink (4.64) .. .. 85·00 2·50

Emergency printings on Perkins, Bacon paper wmkd double-lined numerals "1" *and* "4" *respectively, supplied by Tasmania. P* 12.

120 **10** 1d. yellow-green (10.12.63) .. .. £110 7·00
a. Dull green (4.64) .. .. .. — 7·00
b. Imperf between (pair) .. ..
121 **15** 4d. deep rose (7.1.64) .. .. .. £110 3·75
a. Pale rose .. .. — 3·75

Like the 1d. and 4d. Perkins, Bacon types of Van Diemen's Land most of the Victorian stamps printed on the above two papers may occasionally be found with wmk *inverted*. This applies both to the 1d. and 4d. above and also the various "Laureates" of the 1867–68 printings. Instances are also known where the wmk is *reversed* and one (in No. 132) where it is *sideways*. Most of these varieties are rare.

(ii) *Printings of* October 1864 *onwards. As* (i) *but P* 13

122 **15** 1d. pale green (10.10.64) .. .. 70·00 3·50
a. Bluish green (12.64) .. .. .. 65·00 2·75
aa. Doubly printed .. .. .. — £550
b. Green (shades) (8.65) .. .. 65·00 3·50
c. Deep green (12.65) .. .. .. — 3·00
123 2d. dull violet (10.64) .. .. .. 55·00 3·75
a. Dull lilac (shades) (4.65) .. .. 55·00 3·50
b. Reddish mauve (11.65) .. .. 60·00 3·50
124 4d. dull rose (10.64) .. .. .. 75·00 2·50
a. Dull rose-red (2.65) .. .. .. 75·00 2·50
125 8d. orange (22.2.65) .. .. .. £300 40·00
126 **18** 1s. blue/*blue* (10.4.65) .. .. 85·00 3·50
127 **5** 2s. light blue/*green* (22.11.64) .. £150 5·00
a. Deep blue/green (1865) .. .. £150 5·00

The above 1s. stamp can be immediately identified by the white patches (comprising an *albino* impression) due to the lack of a *make-ready* which are found on all stamps. The 8d. was withdrawn from issue on 11.6.69.

(iii) July–August 1865. *As before but P* 12 *or* 12 × 13 *from repaired state of* 12 *machine, with larger holes and sharper teeth than previously.* (*a*) *Perf* 12

128 **15** 1d. green (*shades*) .. .. .. 70·00 3·00
a. Deep green .. .. 70·00 3·00
129 4d. dull rose-red (8.65) .. .. £120 7·50
130 **5** 2s. dark blue/*green* .. .. .. £170 8·50

(*b*) *Perf* 12 × 13

131 **15** 1d. deep green .. .. — 6·00

August and December 1865. *Emergency printings (2) on Perkins, Bacon paper wmkd double-lined "4" supplied by Tasmania.*

132 15 4d. dull reddish rose (p 13) (11.8.65) .. £110 3·50
 a. Perf 12 .. — 3·75
 b. Perf 12 × 13 .. — 11·00
133 4d. red (p 13) (16.12.65) .. £120 3·50

October 1865. *Emergency printing on De La Rue paper wmkd single-lined "8", no "10" paper having arrived. P 13.*

134 17 10d. grey (21.10.65) .. £450 £130
 a. Grey-black .. £450 £130

(iv) December 1865–66 *printings. These, in general, were of finer impression than the previous 1865 printings*

A. *On Saunders paper, wmkd with the appropriate single-line numerals as W* **14.**

135 15 1d. deep yellow-green (p 13) (1.66) .. 65·00 2·75
 a. Perf 12 .. — 6·50
 b. Perf 12 × 13 .. — 5·50
136 4d. rose-red (p 13) (12.12.65) .. 75·00 3·00
 a. Perf 12 .. — 4·75
 b. Perf 12 × 13 .. — 5·50
137 17 6d. blue (p 13) (13.2.66) .. 21·00 1·50
 a. Perf 12 .. 23·00 3·00
 b. Perf 12 × 13 .. 21·00 1·75
 c. Imperf between (pair) .. — £550
138 10d. dull purple/*pink* (p 13) (22.3.66) .. 65·00 3·00
 a. Perf 12 × 13 .. 70·00 4·00
 b. Blackish brown/pink (p 13) (1869) .. 75·00 4·00
139 18 1s. indigo-blue/*blue* (p 13) (1870) .. 55·00 3·25
 a. Perf 12 (1873) .. — 5·00
 b. Bright blue/blue (p 13) (1.71) .. 55·00 2·50
 ba. Perf 12 .. — 3·25
 c. Pale dull blue/blue (p 13) (1.75) .. — 7·00
 ca. Perf 12 .. — 3·25
140 5 2s. dark blue/*green* (12.67) .. £160 5·50
 a. Perf 12 (1875) .. £180 5·50
 b. Blue/green (1872, 1878) .. £160 3·75
 c. Greenish blue/green (p 12) (1875) .. £180 5·50
 d. Deep greenish blue/green (p 12½) (1880) .. £160 7·50

The 1s. on Saunders paper was issued later than 1866 but it and the 2s. printing are included here for the sake of convenience. The Saunders green paper is distinctly *deeper* in shade and more apparently *green* than the De La Rue variety.

B. *On De La Rue paper wmkd with the appropriate single-line numerals as W* **14.** *P* 13.

141 15 1d. bright yellow-green (1.67) .. — 15·00
142 2d. rosy lilac (1.66) .. 55·00 4·75
 a. Perf 12 × 13 .. 55·00 4·75
143 2d. dull lilac (6.66) .. — 4·75
 a. Perf 12 .. — 6·00
 b. Perf 12 × 13 .. — 7·50
144 2d. grey (25.7.66) .. 55·00 3·00
 a. Perf 12 .. 85·00 6·00
145 17 6d. blue (13.2.66) .. 23·00 2·50
 a. Perf 12 .. 23·00 4·00
 b. Perf 12 × 13 .. 21·00 1·75
146 18 1s. blue/*blue* (1866, 1869) .. 55·00 3·00
 a. Perf 12 × 13 (1866) .. 55·00 3·50
 b. Bright blue/blue (p 13) (1867, 1871) .. — 3·00
 ba. Perf 12 (1871) .. — 3·50
 c. Indigo/blue (p 13) .. — 2·75
 d. Dull blue/blue (p 12) (1874) .. — 3·50
 e. Imperf between (vert pair) (12 × 13) .. — £550
147 5 2s. blue/*green* (1868) .. £140 3·75
 a. Greenish blue/green (1873) .. £140 3·75
 aa. Perf 12 .. £160 4·75
 b. Dark blue/green (p 12½) (1880) .. £140 3·75

The 1d. of 1867 on De La Rue, distinguishable only by its shade, was presumably the result of the discovery of a small quantity of old stock. The 2d. and 4d. of 1866 may also be found 13 × 12 but are rare in *this* condition. The 10d. was withdrawn from issue on 21.6.71. There were, between 1864 and 1881, no less than 21 different printings of the 2s. blue on green. Only the main schools of colour have been listed.

1866 (Sept)–**67.** *Various Emergency printings, all the results of the non-arrival of the first shipment of "V over Crown" paper.*

1. *Printings on De La Rue paper wmkd single-lined "8". P* 13.

148 15 1d. bright yellow-green (27.12.66) .. £120 9·50
149 2d. grey (18.1.67) .. £110 4·50
150 16 3d. lilac (29.9.66) .. £160 15·00
151 15 4d. rose-red (?date) ..

Only one copy of the 4d. has been recorded and that is understood to have been lost, although its authenticity seems to have been established.

2. *Printings on Saunders paper wmkd single-lined "4". P* 13.

152 15 1d. bright yellow-green (6.3.67) .. 85·00 6·50
153 2d. grey (21.2.67) .. 75·00 4·75

3. *Printings on paper wmkd single-lined "6". P* 13.

(*a*) *On De La Rue paper*

154 15 1d. bright yellow-green (6.67) .. — 14·00

(*b*) *On Saunders paper*

155 15 1d. bright yellow-green (6.67) .. £120 11·00
156 2d. grey (13.5.67) .. £130 6·00

9 9
NINEPENCE

20 (V1) (21)

WATERMARKS. Many stamps watermarked V and Crown may be found with watermark inverted or sideways.

1867–68. *Printings on first consignment of paper wmkd "V over Crown", W* **20**, *received in July* 1867. *P* 13.

157 15 1d. bright yellow-green (10.8.67) .. 85·00 3·50
158 2d. slate-grey (*shades*) (26.8.67) .. 70·00 3·50
 a. Grey-lilac (1.68) .. — 4·75
159 16 3d. lilac (8.67) .. £200 19·00
 a. Grey-lilac (8.68) .. £225 21·00
160 15 4d. dull rose (11.67) .. 75·00 5·00
161 17 6d. dark blue (12.67) .. — 3·00
162 19 5s. blue/*yellow* (26.12.67) .. £1600 £300
 a. Wmk reversed .. — £500

The above shades (there are also paper differences) are sufficiently distinctive to enable separation of the five lower values from *later* "V over Crown" printings. The 5s. was printed from the first electros prepared by Atkinson. There were two printings, both in sheets of 25 (5 × 5). The first (1200) was from a single vertical column of 5 electros clamped together. The second (2000) was from a plate of 25 impressions, comprising a different "5 vertical", repeated 5 times (i.e. giving 5 types). The reversed wmk variety belongs to the first printing and was created *deliberately* to avoid the appearance of the "page number" on the front of one stamp in every four sheets of 25.

1867 (Sept)–**68 and 1870.** *Various Emergency printings due first to the 1867 shipment of white "V over Crown" paper being so small, later to its exhaustion and the non-arrival of the second shipment ordered, later still* (1870) *to a further shortage of this paper.*

1. *Printings on the Perkins, Bacon paper wmkd double-lined "1" received from Tasmania in* 1863. *P* 13.

163 15 1d. pale yellowish green (24.9.67) .. 65·00 3·50
 a. Deep yellow-green (6.68) .. — 3·50
164 2d. slate (5.68) .. £110 5·50
 a. Mauve (30.6.68) .. £110 6·50
165 16 3d. grey-lilac (8.68) .. £150 32·00
166 17 6d. blue (28.7.68) .. 55·00 4·25

2. *Printings on the Perkins, Bacon paper wmkd double-lined "4" received from Tasmania in* 1863. *P* 13.

167 15 1d. pale yellow-green (27.5.68) .. £750 80·00
168 2d. grey-lilac (3.2.68) .. £110 4·25
 a. Slate (28.3.68) .. £110 3·50
 b. Mauve (3.7.68) .. — 4·50
169 4d. dull rose-red (5.68) .. £110 5·00
170 17 6d. blue (20.6.68) .. £150 13·00
 a. Indigo-blue .. — 15·00

3. *Printing on Saunders paper wmkd* "SIX PENCE" *as W* **12.** *P* 13.

171 15 1d. pale yellow-green (5.6.68) .. £325 15·00
172 2d. slate-grey .. — £1100
173 17 6d. blue (23.5.68) .. £150 11·00
 a. Indigo-blue .. — 15·00

Only one copy is apparently known of No. 172. From its shade it would appear to belong to an 1867–68 printing. No 171 is known with the wmk *sideways.*

4. *Printings on lilac paper wmkd V over Crown from* 1867 *consignment. P* 13.

174 15 2d. mauve/*lilac* (12.8.68) .. 55·00 6·50
 a. Lilac/lilac .. 55·00 6·00

5. 1870: 6d. *value only. Printings on various wmkd papers as indicated. P* 13.

175 17 6d. dull blue (THREE PENCE) (23.4.70) £130 6·00
 a. Deep blue .. — 7·00
176 6d. dull blue (FOUR PENCE) (18.6.70) £250 22·00
 a. Deep blue .. — 23·00
177 6d. dull blue ("4") (21.5.70) .. — £1100
178 6d. dull blue ("2") (1870) .. — £1100

Of the six or seven copies known of No. 177 all but one have the watermark reversed.

1868 (Aug)–**71.** *Printings on second and later consignments of V over Crown paper. W* **20.** *P* 13 *only.* (i) *Printed from Robinson plates.*

179 15 2d. lilac (26.8.68) .. 50·00 3·25
 a. Dull mauve (*shades*) (10.68) .. 50·00 3·25
 b. Lilac-grey (1.69) .. — 3·50
 c. Lilac-rose (2.69) .. — 3·00
180 16 3d. yellow-orange (12.6.69) .. 15·00 3·00
181 15 4d. pale red (*aniline*) (21.4.69) .. — 6·50
 a. Deep red (*aniline*) (16.7.69) .. — 6·50
 b. Rose-pink (2.70) .. — 5·00
182 17 6d. blue (*shades*) .. 14·00 1·10
 a. Indigo-blue (1869) .. 14·00 1·10
183 19 5s. indigo-blue and carmine (I) (8.10.68) £200 15·00
 a. Blue and carmine (1869) .. £170 11·00

Nos. 179*b/c* were printed from badly worn plates.

For the frame-plate of the 5s. (I) the electros of the 1867 plate, with the Crown, "VICTORIA" and "FIVE SHILLINGS" cut out, were employed. A new plate, also produced via cut-out portions of the 1867 plate, was brought into use for the red portion.

(ii) *Printed from new plates made by Atkinson*

184 15 1d. bright yellow-green (10.68) .. 65·00 2·50
 a. Bright olive-green (1.69) .. — 14·00
 b. Dull yellow-green (4.69) .. — 2·10
 c. Dull green (3.70) .. 65·00 2·10
 d. Very pale green (10.70) .. — 2·10
185 2d. lilac-grey (15.1.69) .. — 3·75
 a. Lilac-rose (*shades*) (24.2.69) .. 55·00 3·75
 b. Mauve (20.4.69) .. — 3·25
 c. Red-lilac (*shades*) (5.69) .. 55·00 3·00
 d. Dull lilac (*shades*) (6.69) .. 55·00 2·50
 e. Silver-grey (2.9.69) .. £110 7·00

The Atkinson plates, produced by an improved technique; do not show the *double* and *partial strikes* and *internal distortion* varieties met on a large proportion of the stamps from the Robinson plates. Further, the later printings from the 2d. and 6d. Robinson plates show obvious signs of wear. These factors and the differing shades should make classification relatively easy. For the first two printings of the 2d. in 1869 the first of the new Atkinson plates was used in conjunction with the old Robinson plate, following which the latter was replaced by a second Atkinson plate. The dates of introduction of the Atkinson plates were 1d., October 1868; 2d., January 1869 and 6d., December 1875.

1871. *Provisional. Surch with T* **21**, *in blue. On Saunders paper wmkd single-lined "10". P* 13.

186 17 9d. on 10d. purple-brown/*pink* (22.4.71) £180 8·00
 a. Blackish brown/pink .. — 9·50
 b. Surch double .. — £700

PERFORATIONS (TO 1883)

The perforations of Victoria, particularly those of the period October 1864–80, form a complex study for specialists. We have adopted in this listing a simplified classification based on *three* descriptions—Perf 12, Perf 13 and Perf 12½ respectively, the latter being substituted for Perf 13 for the period 1881 on. The position can be concisely put as follows:—

A. *"Perf 12"*: Here the gauge is *never* quite 12 and nearer 11½. It is not found after 1883. There were two machines (both single-line), the first introduced by Robinson in January 1859 and the second purchased in 1871. No "perf 12" are found in the period mid 1866–mid 1871. At various periods, more particularly in 1865 and 1880, one or both of the machines was repaired, to give larger holes and sharper teeth over a succeeding period.

B. *"Perf 13"*: Here the gauge is invariably *over* 12 and with a sole exception (covering a section of the pins on one machine over the period 1876–80) invariably *under* 13. Generally speaking up to the end of 1880, these machines gauged 12½ to 12¾. Two classes of machine are found:

(i) *Single-line* machines. These were three in number—purchased on October 1864, 1866 and 1873 respectively. Two of them were converted into combs in 1873. The other was repaired on several occasions, particularly in 1879–80, to give larger holes and sharper teeth.

(ii) *Comb* machines. First introduced in 1873 (see above). Over the period of use they gave various gauges, depending on the machine and its state of repair. They were all *vertical* combs adapted only for normal size stamps of either dimension as likewise (until 1913) were all other comb-machines used in Victoria for perforating stamps.

C. *"Perf 12½"*: Found from late 1876 onwards, in both single-line (used mainly for the larger-size stamps) and vertical comb machines. Gradually superseded the A and B gauges. Certain stamps of the 1879–80 period are found in both B and C gauges but these are no longer differentiated as separate varieties, being only listed under the one or the other gauge. This applies also to the Postal Fiscal section.

"Compound" perforations: In previous editions certain 12 × 13 perforations were listed which were not true compounds of A and B but simply the product of one or other of the *comb* machines. Such varieties have now been eliminated. The "Compounds" now listed are all true compounds (or "mixeds") of A and B. They generally fall into two categories: (i) those of the 1865–66 period where the two machines were both used for the original perforating, one in the one direction (top to bottom) and the other in the other (sides); (ii) isolated examples, better termed "mixed" perfs, from 1873 on, where one gauge machine was used to correct off-centre perforating done by the other gauge machine. Such cases are almost invariably associated with "mends", viz the pasting of gummed strips down the back of the faulty line of perforations.

1871–84 PRINTINGS

These are listed separately from the 1868–71 printings because of the perforation changes made in the period, viz the reintroduction of the 12 gauge (1871), the introduction of comb machines (1873), the repairs of various 12 and 13 machines (1879), and the introduction of the 12½ gauge (1879–80). Many stamps issued in the latter period are found both perf 13 and 12½ but no distinction is made. The 13 gauge disappears in 1880–81.

Papers: All printings on white paper made after April 1878 and also the last 8d. printing were on the *"glazed"* variety of paper and this furnishes another means of identification. Some shades, e.g. 6d. blue of 1878–79 are found on *both* papers.

Shades are different from those found in the 1868–71 printings.

1871–84.

(i) *Printed from Robinson plates; W* **20**; *P* 13, 12½ *unless otherwise described*

187 16 3d. dull orange (1871) .. 14·00 1·90
 a. Perf 12 (1872) .. 14·00 20·00
 b. Orange (1874) .. — 2·25
 ba. Perf 12 .. — 2·10
 c. Bright orange .. — 2·50
 ca. Perf 12 .. — 2·50
188 3d. orange-brown (1878) .. 20·00 5·50
189 3d. dull orange-yellow (1881) .. 22·00 2·50
 a. Perf 12 ..
190 15 4d. rose (*shades*) (1871–78) .. 70·00 3·00
 a. Perf 12 .. 70·00 3·00
 b. Dull rose (5.3.79) .. — 3·00
 ba. Perf 12 .. — 3·00
 c. Dull rose-red (23.12.79) .. — 3·00
 ca. Perf 12 .. — 3·00
 d. Bright lilac-rose (*aniline*) (3.3.80) .. 75·00 3·75
 da. Perf 12 .. — 6·50
191 4d. rosine (*aniline*) (22.9.80) .. £200 5·00
 a. Perf 12 .. 80·00 4·75
 b. Compound perf 12 with 12½ .. — £325
192 17 6d. Prussian blue (1872, 1874) .. 12·00 90
 a. Perf 12 .. 14·00 1·10
 b. Indigo (1873) .. 14·00 1·40
 ba. Perf 12 .. 18·00 1·75
 c. Dull blue (worn plate) .. — 90
193 15 8d. lilac-brown/*pink* (24.1.77) .. 75·00 5·00
 a. Purple-brown/pink (21.3.78) .. 75·00 5·00
 b. Chocolate/pink (6.8.78) .. 80·00 4·00
 bb. Compound perf 13 × 12 .. — £325
194 8d. red-brown/*pink* (20.5.78) .. 75·00 4·00
195 8d. dark red-brown/*pink* (p 12) (*glazed*) (30.11.80) .. 75·00 5·00
 a. Perf 12½ ..
196 18 1s. light blue/*blue* (5.75) .. 75·00 6·50
 a. Perf 12 .. — 6·50
197 19 5s. pale bright blue and carmine (I) (7.77) — 15·00
 a. Grey-blue and carmine (8.78) .. £160 13·00
 b. Deep lavender-blue and carmine (5.80) .. £160 13·00
198 5s. bright blue and red (II) (12.5.81) .. £140 11·00
 a. Perf 12 .. £130 12·00
 b. Indigo-blue and red .. — 15·00
 ba. Perf 12 .. — 16·00
 c. Second "I" in "SHILLINGS" short at foot .. — 90·00

The 4d. "pink" previously listed is a *faded* rosine. For the 5s. (Type II) new dies were made for *each* portion of the design. All Type I stamps have a blue line under the Crown, which is missing in Type II. The latter were printed in sheets of 100 (10 × 10), as compared with 25 (5 × 5) for Type I.

No. 197*b* has the watermark sideways.

1877–79. *Printings of the 8d. value on Saunders paper wmkd single-lined "10". P* 13, 12½ *unless otherwise stated.*

199 15 8d. lilac-brown/*pink* (12.77) .. — £550
 a. Purple-brown/pink (20.2.78) .. £100 5·50
200 8d. red-brown/*pink* (8.8.79) .. 85·00 4·50
 a. Perf 12 .. — 7·00

The 8d. printings (save that of 1880) were *mixed* and comprised stamps on *both* V over Crown and "10" papers.

½ ½

HALF

(22)

(ii) *Printed from plates made by Atkinson. The ½d. made by surch with T* **22**, *in red*

201 **15** ½d. on 1d. green (25.6.73) . . . . 36·00 4·50
a. Perf 12 . . . . 45·00 6·00
b. *Grass-green* . . . . 40·00 4·50
ba. Perf 12 . . . . 45·00 6·00
c. Short "1" at right . . — 60·00
202 1d. pale green (1871) . . . . 60·00 2·25
a. Perf 12 (10.71) . . . . 70·00 2·40
b. *Green (shades)* . . . . 60·00 2·25
ba. Perf 12 . . . . 60·00 2·25
c. *Grass-green* . . . . — 2·40
ca. Perf 12 . . . . — 2·40
d. *Bluish green (shades)* . . . . 60·00 2·40
da. Perf 12 . . . . — 2·40
203 **17** 6d. dull ultramarine (2.12.75) . . . . 19·00 1·25
a. *Light Prussian-blue* (29.12.75) . . — 1·25
b. *Dull violet-blue* (4.78) . . — 5·50
c. Blue (13.5.78) . . . . 20·00 90
ca. Perf 12 . . — 90
d. *Dull milky blue* (7.3.79) . . . . 19·00 1·10
da. Perf 12 . . — 1·10
e. *Blue (light ink)* (8.80) . . — 90
f. *Light blue* (10.5.81) . . . . 20·00 1·10
fa. Perf 12 . . — 2·40
g. *Deep blue* (15.1.82) . . . . 19·00 90

23 (V2)

24

The types of V over Crown watermark (1867–1912)

In all, *five* types were employed.

The first two types (*V1* and *V2*) belong to the contracts made with De La Rue to supply postage stamp paper. That firm lost the contract in 1895 to Waterlow and Sons, who held it until 1912. The third and fourth types are therefore products of the Waterlow contracts. The fifth type (found only in 1912) was supplied by James Spicer & Sons. The change in the pattern from *V1* to *V2* is explained by the dandyroll (which was the property of De La Rue) requiring replacement. Since *all* the changes in pattern are also associated with changes in the nature and texture of the paper supplied, little difficulty should be encountered, with the new descriptions, in identifying the various types. Each pattern (save in a few cases of "left over" stock) succeeded the previous pattern.

Types *V1* and *V2* are mainly to be distinguished from one another by the four "points" around the top of the Crown which are found in *V1* but not in *V2*. Also, as compared with *V2*, the shapes of the top ornaments in *V1* resemble diamonds, and not ovals. It must be remembered that *V1 coloured* papers continued in use long after the exhaustion of the *V1* white paper, the earliest date met for the *V2* white paper being 15.8.82. The first *V2* coloured papers (blue and green) were not used until February 1890. In general the papers supplied by De La Rue were whiter than their successors. The quality found with the *V1* wmk varied greatly both with and without a pronounced mesh. The quality of the *V2* papers on the other hand varied little. It is generally more "loaded" and opaque than any of the *V1* papers and the wmk clearer when held to the light.

(iii) 1882–4. *As* (ii) *above but on paper wmkd V over Crown* (*V2*), *W* **23.** *P* 12½

204 **16** 3d. yellow-orange (13.4.83) . . . . 18·00 4·50
a. *Dull brownish orange* . . . . 22·00 6·50
205 **17** 6d. dull violet-blue (10.11.82) . . . . 11·00 1·00
a. *Indigo-blue* (11.83) . . . . 11·00 1·10
b. *Light ultramarine* (9.84) . . . . 11·00 1·25

The above 3d. was printed from two new plates made by Atkinson. For the 6d. the same Atkinson plates introduced in December 1875 were employed.

Reprints were made, in 1891, on V over Crown paper, Type **23**, perf 12½, of the 1d., 2d., 3d., 4d., 6d., 8d., 10d., 1s. and 5s. "Laureates". The shades are distinctive and a number of values show "die flaws" not found in the originals. The 3d. was printed in yellow, the 8d. in orange-yellow, the 10d. in greenish slate and the 5s. in blue and red.

(Printed in Melbourne from a double electrotyped plate of 240 subjects supplied by D.L.R.)

1870 (28 Jan). *Wmk V over Crown* (*V1*), *W* **20.** *P* 13.
206 **24** 2d. brown-lilac . . . . 48·00 1·10
a. *Dull lilac-mauve* (9.70) . . . . 36·00 70
aa. Perf 12 (1871) . . . . 48·00 1·10
b. *Mauve* (worn plate, 3.73) . . . . 36·00 1·00
ba. Perf 12 . . . . 48·00 75

PRICES OF SETS

Set prices are given for many issues, generally those containing five stamps or more. Definitive sets include one of each value or major colour change, but do not cover different perforations, die types or minor shades. Where a choice is possible the set prices are based on the cheapest versions of the stamps included in the listings.

25

26

27

8d 8d

EIGHTPENCE

(28)

29

30

31 (Die I)

32 (Die II)

(Des and dies eng by William Bell and stamps printed from electrotyped plates)

1873–84. *Two dies of 2d.: I, single-lined outer oval; II, double-lined outer oval. The 8d. is made by surch with T* **28** *in blue. P* 13 *unless otherwise described.*

(*a*) *On Saunders paper, wmkd single-lined* "10"

207 **29** 9d. pale brown/*pink* (25.3.73) . . . . 50·00 5·00
a. Perf 12 . . . . 55·00 8·00
b. *Red-brown/pink* (8.74) . . . . 45·00 5·50

(*b*) *Wmk V over Crown* (*V1*), *W* **20**

208 **25** ½d. rose-red (10.2.74) . . . . 4·50 50
a. Perf 12 . . . . 5·00 70
b. *Lilac-rose* (1874) . . . . 5·00 70
ba. Perf 12 . . . . 4·50 70
c. *Rosine (shades)* (12.80) . . . . 3·75 50
ca. Perf 12 . . . . 4·50 35
d. *Pale red* (1882) . . . . 4·50 35
da. Perf 12 . . . . 4·50 40
e. Mixed perf 13 and 12 . . — £110
209 **26** 1d. dull bluish green (14.12.75) . . 13·00 75
a. Perf 12 . . . . 15·00 75
b. *Green (shades)* (1877) . . . . 13·00 70
ba. Perf 12 . . . . 14·00 4·50
c. *Yellow-green* (1878 and 1880) . . 13·00 55
ca. Perf 12 . . — 1·75
210 **27** 2d. deep lilac-mauve, Die I (1.10.73) . . 13·00 35
a. Perf 12 . . — 1·50
b. *Dull violet-mauve* . . . . 13·00 35
ba. Perf 12 . . — 1·40
c. *Dull mauve* . . . . 13·00 35
ca. Perf 12 . . . . 15·00 50
d. *Pale mauve (worn plate)* (1.79) . . 14·00 50
da. Perf 12 . . — 65
e. Mixed perf 13 and 12 . . £130 £100
211 2d. lilac-mauve, Die II (17.12.78) . . 10·00 35
a. Perf 12 . . . . 14·00 35
b. *Grey-mauve* (1.80) . . — 40
ba. Perf 12 . . — 80
c. *Pale mauve* (6.80) . . — 40
ca. Perf 12 . . — 1·25
d. Imperf (pair) . . — £450
e. Imperf between (pair) . . — £450
212 **29** 8d. on 9d. lilac-brn/*pink* (*p* 12) (1.7.76) . . 90·00 9·50
a. "F.IGHT" (broken "E") . . — £120
213 9d. lilac-brown/*pink* (*p* 12) (1.12.75) . . 60·00 8·00
214 **30** 1s. indigo-blue/*blue* (16.8.76) . . 25·00 3·75
a. *Deep blue/blue* (1877) . . 25·00 3·75
aa. Perf 12 (10.80) . . — 7·00
b. *Blue/blue* (1878) . . 25·00 3·75
ba. Perf 12 . . — 7·00
c. *Ultramarine/blue* (1879) . . 38·00 7·00
d. *Bright blue/blue* (11.83) . . 35·00 4·50

(*c*) 18 February–April 1878. *Emergency printings on various coloured papers, due to the exhaustion of white V1 paper. W* **20** (*V1*), *P* 13 *only*

215 **25** ½d. rose-red/*pink* (1.3.78) . . 15·00 5·00
216 **26** 1d. yellow-green/*yellow* (25.2.78) . . 38·00 5·50
217 1d. yellow-green/*drab* (4.78) . . 75·00 32·00
218 **27** 2d. violet-mauve/*green* (18.2.78) . . £110 3·00
219 2d. violet-mauve/*lilac* (21.2.78) . . £850 £250
220 2d. violet-mauve/*brown* (21.3.78) . . £110 3·75

Two shades of yellow paper, termed *pale canary* and *deep canary* respectively, are found.

All supplies of *V1* paper received in Victoria after 15.3.78 were, as compared with previous supplies, highly surfaced on the printing side. An experimental printing was made on the new paper in July 1877 (1d., 2d., 6d. and 5s.) and all printings on white *V1* paper from April 1878 on were made on this glazed paper. The glazed *V1* coloured papers, with few exceptions, made their appearance later.

(*d*) 1882–83. *On white paper wmkd V over Crown* (*V2*). *W* **23.** *P* 13
221 **25** ½d. rosine (4.83) . . . . 5·00 65
a. Perf 12 . . — 15·00
222 **26** 1d. yellow-green (9.82) . . . . 14·00 1·00
a. Perf 12

Reprints: The ½d., 1d., 2d. (Die II), 9d. and 1s. values were reprinted in 1891, perf 12½. The first four from new plates, made from Dies containing *die flaws* not found in the originals. The 9d. was on *V1* and the others on *V2* paper.

33

34

35

(Des and eng by Charles Naish (T **33** & **34**) and William Bell (T **35**). Typo from electrotyped plates)

1880–84. *P* 12½ *unless otherwise described, this description including the P* 13 *varieties found in* 1880. (*a*) *W* **20** (*V1*).

223 **33** 2d. sepia (3.11.80) . . . . 14·00 30
a. Perf 12 . . — 38·00
b. *Sepia-brown* (2.81) . . . . 11·00 30
ba. Perf 12 . . . . £130 38·00
c. *Brown (aniline)* (5.81) . . . . 14·00 30
ca. Perf 12 . . — 38·00
d. *Dull black-brown* (10.81) . . — 30
e. *Dull grey-brown* (3.82) . . . . 10·00 30
f. Mixed perf 13 and 12 . . — £190
224 2d. mauve (*worn plate*) (2.84) . . — 4·50
225 **34** 4d. rose-carmine (10.81) . . . . 12·00 3·00
a. *Rosine* (8.82) . . . . 12·00 2·75
226 **35** 2s. dark blue (*shades*)/*green* (8.7.81) . . 60·00 17·00
a. *Light blue/green* (wmk sideways) (8.83) . . . . 65·00 21·00
b. *Ultramarine/green* (7.84) . . — 27·00
ba. Wmk sideways . . — 48·00

(*b*) *W* **23** (*V2*)

227 **33** 2d. dull grey-brown (15.8.82) . . . . 10·00 30
228 2d. chocolate (3.83) . . . . 10·00 30
a. Perf 12 . . — 19·00
229 2d. mauve (20.12.83) . . . . 7·00 20
a. Worn plate . . . . 7·50 20
b. Perf 12 . . — £180
c. Mixed perfs 12½ and 12 . . — £180
230 **34** 4d. rose-red (3.83) . . . . 13·00 3·50

For the scarce perf 12 stamps listed above the holes are large and the teeth sharp. See also the note about perf 12 stamps after No. 186b.

The first printings of the 2d. in mauve were from the two plates used for the browns. Later printings were from two new plates. Reprints were made in 1891 of the 2d. (brown), 4d. (in pale red) and 2s., all on *V2* paper.

36

(Des and die eng Charles Naish. Typo)

1883 (29 Oct)–**84.** *P* 12½. (*a*) *W* **20** (*V1*).
231 **36** 1d. green (2.84) . . . . 90·00 6·00

(*b*) *W* **23** (*V2*)

232 **36** 1d. yellow-green (29.10.83) . . . . 11·00 90
a. *Green* . . . . 11·00 90
b. *Pale green* (5.84) . . . . 11·00 90

Nos. 224 and 231 represent a printing on old stocks of paper.

C. THE "POSTAGE AND REVENUE" PERIOD, 1884–1901

Under the provisions of the Postage Act 1883 the stamps of the three series then in use (Postage, Duty, Fee) became, as from 1.1.84, mutually interchangeable. It was, at the same time, decided to issue (as soon as possible) the *one* stamp only, for any value, to serve *all* purposes. Since there were available many more dies (and plates) inscribed "Stamp Duty" than there were of either the "Postage" or "Fee" (Stamp Statute) series it was agreed that all values should be inscribed "Stamp Duty" by the beginning of 1885. All stamps *printed* after 1.1.84 are therefore true "Postage and Revenue" stamps whereas all Stamp Duty and Fee stamps printed before that date are Postal Fiscals, since they were originally printed solely for fiscal purposes. These principles have been strictly adhered to in our listing. Little difficulty should however be met in distinguishing between the printings of the one stamp found respectively in the main list and in the "Postal Fiscal" section since there are many major differences of printing, watermark, perforation and shade. On 1.1.84 there were no "Stamp Duty" designs for the ½d., 2d., 4d., 8d. and 2s. 6d. values. Also the existing "Stamp Duty" designs for the 1d., 6d., 1s. and 2s. were deemed to be too large to be convenient for general and extensive use. For all these values it was therefore necessary to produce new and smaller designs inscribed "Stamp Duty". Pending the preparation of new dies and plates, printings were made in 1884 (for the ½d., 1d., 2d., 4d., 6d., 1s. and 2s. values) from the existing "Postage" plates. These printings are also "Postage and Revenue" stamps but have naturally been included, for the sake of convenience, in the previous period. By the beginning of 1885 printings were available, in the new designs, of all values save the 1s. and 2s., and these latter appeared later.

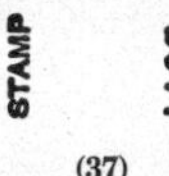

(37)

I. **1885.** *Postage Stamps optd with T* **37.** *The* 1s. *and* 2s. *appeared in February* 1885, 3d. *and* 4d. *in November* 1885. *P* 12½.

(*a*) *W* **20** (*V1*)

233 **16** 3d. dull orange-yellow (Pl 1) (B.) . . — £130
234 **30** 1s. ultramarine/*blue* . . . . 95·00 19·00
a. *Dull blue/blue* . . — 22·00
235 1s. deep ultramarine/*blue* (B.) (F.C. £14) . . — £400
236 **35** 2s. ultramarine/*blue* . . . . 75·00 12·00
a. Wmk sideways . . . . 90·00 17·00

(*b*) *W* **23** (*V2*)

237	**16**	3d. yellow-orange (Pl 2) (B.)	60·00	21·00
		a. Dull brownish orange (B.)	65·00	23·00
238	**34**	4d. rose-carmine (B.)	48·00	19·00

The overprinted 1s. was replaced by the 1s. Type **44** on lemon. Collectors should beware of faded black overprints purporting to be the "blue". In genuine examples the blue of the overprint is difficult to distinguish in the blue of the stamp.

Reprints of the 4d. and 1s. (with and without overprint) were made in 1895–6. The 1s. is wmkd *V2* and the 4d. (from a new plate) is a pale red. Examples of the latter genuinely postally used are sometimes met.

38 39 40

41 42 43

(Typo. Dies for ½d., 2d., 3d., 4d., 8d. and 2s. 6d. eng by Charles Naish, the other values being derived from these)

II. 1884–95. *New designs inscr* "STAMP DUTY". *P* 12½.

(*a*) *W* **20** (*V1*)

239	**42**	8d. rose/*pink* (*shades*) (1.1.85)	19·00	4·00
		a. Rose-red/pink	20·00	4·00
240	**40**	1s. deep dull blue/*lemon* (11.85)	32·00	3·00
		a. Dull blue/yellow (6.86)	32·00	3·50
241	**42**	2s. olive/*bluish green* (*shades*) (6.86)	25·00	3·00

(*b*) *W* **23** (*V2*)

243	**38**	½d. pale rosine (1.1.85)	4·50	55
		a. Deep rosine (7.85)	5·00	1·00
		b. Salmon (9.85)	5·50	1·25
244	**39**	1d. yellowish green (*shades*) (1.1.85)	5·25	30
		a. Dull pea-green (2.85)	8·00	1·75
245	**40**	2d. lilac (*shades*) (1.1.85)	3·75	20
		a. Mauve (1.86)	4·00	20
		b. Rosy-mauve (6.86)	5·50	50
246	**39**	3d. yellowish brown (1.1.85)	7·00	60
		a. Pale ochre (11.86)	6·50	60
		b. Bistre-yellow (12.92)	7·00	60
247	**41**	4d. magenta (1.1.85)	21·00	3·00
		a. Bright mauve-rose (1.87)	23·00	3·50
248		4d. dull lilac (*error*) (12.86)	£2250	£400
249	**39**	6d. chalky blue (1.1.85)	27·00	2·50
		a. Bright blue (2.85)	21·00	2·10
		b. Cobalt (9.85)	21·00	2·10
250	**42**	8d. bright scarlet/*pink* (1892)	21·00	7·50
251		2s. olive-green/*pale green* (*shades*) (3.90)	25·00	3·00
252		2s. apple-green (12.8.95)	19·00	5·25
253		2s. blue-green (29.10.95)	18·00	4·75
254	**43**	2s. 6d. brown-orange (23.4.84)	80·00	11·00
		a. Yellow (1885)	75·00	10·00
		b. Lemon-yellow (1.93)	75·00	9·50

In each of the 1d., 6d., 1s. and 2s. values six types are to be found differing, *inter alia*, in the engraving of the words of value.

In the 2d. two die states are found: the *original* (1) which occurs on all but seven stamps in the Plate 1 sheet and the *damaged* (1a) which occurs on seven stamps in the Plate 1 sheet and on all 120 stamps in the Plate 2 sheet. The damage consists of a clear break in the top frame just in from the top right corner.

4d. "error": This comprised a printing of 6000 stamps, 1886, in a *dull lilac* shade. It is true that only some seven unused specimens are known but it is not true (as previously stated) that it is unknown used, since a leading authority has himself seen upwards of 30 undoubted used copies, all of which have certain characteristics which distinguish them from certain colour changelings, accidental or deliberate. The records show that the whole printing of 6000 was issued which confirms the findings of so many used copies.

The 8d. value was withdrawn from sale on 24.8.95.

Reprints were made in 1891, using one of the original plates in each case, of the ½d., 1d., 2d., 4d., 6d. and 1s. values. In the three lower values the shades are fairly distinctive. The 1s. was wmkd *V1*. In all cases the wmk is equally common normal and inverted and this applies to *all* the Reprints made in 1891 or later.

44 45 46 47

48 49 50 51

52 53 54 55

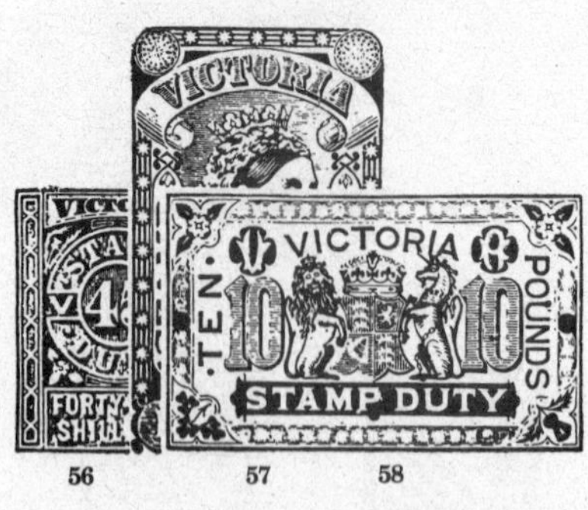

56 57 58

III. 1884–96. *New printings, all typographed from electrotypes, of* "STAMP DUTY" *designs first issued in* 1879. (*Des Charles Jackson and Ludwig Lang. Dies eng by Charles Jackson, Arthur Williams, Charles Evans and possibly others, supplied* (1879) *by Messrs Sands and McDougall of Melbourne*). *P* 12½. *Wmk sideways save where shown as upright* (U). (*a*) *W* **20** (*V1*).

255	**44**	1s. ultramarine/*blue* (11.84)	13·00	4·00
256		1s. chalky blue/*lemon* (3.3.85)	£100	25·00
257	**46**	3s. maroon/*blue* (8.84)	10·00	3·00
258	**48**	5s. reddish purple/*lemon* (6.87)	7·50	2·75
		a. Brown-red/yellow (1.94)	50·00	10·00
259	**52**	£1 orange/*yellow* (9.84)	—	48·00
		a. Reddish orange/yellow (12.90)	32·00	48·00

(*b*) *W* **23** (*V2*)

260	**45**	1s. 6d. pink (2.85)	£140	19·00
		a. Bright rose-carmine (5.86)	£120	15·00
261	**46**	3s. drab (11.85)	70·00	15·00
		a. Olive-drab (10.93)	65·00	15·00
262	**47**	4s. red-orange (27.5.86)	75·00	12·00
		a. Yellow-orange (S, U)	£100	8·50
263	**48**	5s. rosine (8.5.96)	65·00	19·00
264	**49**	6s. pea-green (12.11.91)	£110	32·00
		a. Apple-green (U) (4.96)	£100	32·00
265	**50**	10s. dull bluish green (10.85)	75·00	35·00
		a. Grey-green (9.87)	65·00	32·00
266	**51**	15s. purple-brown (12.85)	38·00	25·00
267		15s. brown (U) (5.95)	75·00	45·00
268	**53**	£1 5s. pink† (U) (6.8.90)	75·00	15·00
269	**54**	£1 10s. pale olive† (10.88)	£100	25·00
270	**55**	£2 blue† (8.88)	£100	32·00
271	**56**	45s. lilac† (15.8.90)	—	32·00
272	**57**	£5 pink (10.85)	—	50·00
273	**58**	£10 lilac (7.85)	—	50·00
		a. Mauve† (7.93)	—	38·00

Stamps of the above designs printed by lithography or line-engraving, or similar designs not found in the above list should be looked for among the Postal Fiscals.

†Both here and later indicates that prices quoted are for stamps postmarked to order by the Victorian postal authorities for sale in sets.

59

IV. 1896–1900. *T* **59** *and similar types. W* **23** (*V2*) *sideways* (S) *or upright* (U). *The line-engraved stamps were all printed singly direct from the dies and both the lithographed and typographed stamps were in sheets of* 10 (2 × 5). (i) *Lithographed. Printings of* 1886 *to* 1889.

274	£25 dull yellowish green (S, U) (1.86)	F.C.	45·00
	a. Dull blue-green (U) (10.88)	F.C.	45·00
275	£50 bright violet (U) (2.86)	F.C.	55·00
	a. Dull purple (U) (10.87)	F.C.	55·00
276	£100 rosine (S, U) (1.86)	F.C.	65·00

(ii) *Recess-printed. Printings of November* 1890 *to April* 1897

277	£25 bright blue-green (S, U) (11.90)	F.C.	45·00
278	£50 black-violet (S) (11.90)	F.C.	55·00
279	£100 crimson (aniline) (S, U) (11.90)	F.C.	55·00
	a. Scarlet-red† (1897)	—	75·00

For earlier recess-printed printings, see under "POSTAL FISCALS".

(iii) *Typographed from electrotyped plates. Printings of November* 1897 *on*

280	£25 dull blue-green† (U)	—	40·00
281	£50 bright mauve† (U)	—	55·00
282	£100 pink-red† (U) (10.00)	—	55·00

Collectors should beware of stamps with cleaned fiscal markings particularly in the higher values. Some of these bear forged cancellations but others, in fraud of the revenue, did genuine postal service.

60 61 62

63 64 65

66 67

(Typo. Previous 2d. and 4d. dies "lined" by Charles Naish; 1s. 6d. des and eng Charles Naish; rest des Philip Astley, probably eng Samuel Reading and supplied by Fergusson and Mitchell)

1886–96. *W* **23** (*V2*) *upright save in ½d.,* 1s. *and high values* (*excepting the* £6) *where it is sideways. P* 12½.

283	**60**	½d. lilac-grey (20.8.86)	15·00	3·00
		a. Grey-black	—	35·00
284		½d. pink (15.2.87)	5·00	25
		a. Rosine (*aniline*) (12.89)	4·75	25
		b. Rose-red (5.91)	4·50	20
		c. Vermilion (3.96)	4·75	35
285	**61**	1d. green (26.7.86)	5·25	20
		a. Yellow-green (7.87)	5·25	20
286	**62**	2d. pale lilac (17.12.86)	2·75	20
		a. Pale mauve (1887)	2·50	20
		b. Deep lilac (1888, 1892)	2·50	20
		c. Purple (5.94)	2·75	25
		d. Violet (5.95)	2·50	20
		e. Imperforate (1890)	—	£700
287	**63**	4d. rose-red (1.4.87)	6·50	1·00
		a. Red (1893)	5·75	90
288	**64**	6d. bright ultramarine (27.8.86)	7·50	65
		a. Pale ultramarine (10.87)	7·00	50
		b. Dull blue (2.91)	6·50	50
289	**65**	1s. dull purple-brown (14.3.87)	15·00	1·25
		a. Lake (2.90)	15·00	1·50
		b. Carmine-lake (5.92)	14·00	90
		c. Brownish red (1.96)	15·00	1·00
290	**66**	1s. 6d. pale blue (6.88)	£100	65·00
291		1s. 6d. orange (18.9.89)	15·00	4·50
		a. Red-orange	15·00	5·00
292	**67**	£5 pale blue and maroon† (7.2.88)	£850	50·00
293		£6 yellow and pale blue† (1.10.87)	£1000	60·00
294		£7 rosine and black† (17.10.89)	£1200	85·00
295		£8 mauve and brown-orange† (U) (2.8.90)	£1300	£120
296		£9 apple-green and rosine† (21.8.88)	£1600	£130

Reprints of the ½d. grey and 1s. 6d. blue were made in 1894–5. They differ from the originals in shade. A £10 (T **67**) was prepared for use, but not issued.

An imperforate sheet of the 2d. was on sale at the Mortlake Post Office in 1890 and a pair was noted in 1902.

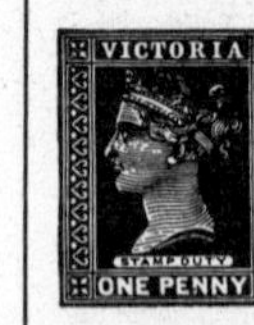

68

69

70

(1d. die supplied, des and eng by Samuel Reading; 2½d. and 5d. des by M. Tannenberg; 9d. first printed from the new Reprint plate of 1891. Typo)

1890–96. *New designs and values. P* 12½. (*a*) *W* **20** (*V1*).

297	**68**	1d. orange-brown/*pink* (16.6.91)	2·50	75

This was an emergency printing, caused by a temporary shortage of white *V2* paper.

(*b*) *W* **23** (*V2*)

298	**68**	1d. dull chestnut (1.1.90)	2·10	15
		a. Deep red-brown (1.90)	2·10	30
		b. Orange-brown (4.90)	2·10	15
		c. Yellow-brown (1891)	1·90	15
		d. Brown-red (1890, 1892)	1·90	15
		e. Bright yellow-orange (1.94)	9·50	30
		f. Brownish orange (8.94)	1·75	15
299	**69**	2½d. red-brown/*lemon* (18.12.90)	4·75	90
300		2½d. brown-red/*yellow* (1892)	4·50	90
		a. Red/yellow (1893)	4·50	90
301	**70**	5d. purple-brown	6·00	1·10
		a. Pale reddish brown (1892)	5·50	1·00
302	**29**	9d. apple-green (18.10.92)	15·00	4·00
303		9d. carmine-rose (18.10.95)	11·00	2·40
		a. Rosine (*aniline*) (1896)	12·00	2·50

The yellow papers used for the 2½d. value differed considerably in tint.

71

72 (V3)

(Eng A. Williams (1½d.))

1896 (June)–**1899** (Aug). *W* **72** (V3). *Paper supplied by Waterlow and Sons. This paper differs noticeably from the previous De La Rue products. It is less white, softer and generally thicker, and has a coarser grain or mesh than any previous V over Crown paper. It will be noted that some coloured V2 papers of earlier manufacture were utilised during this period. T* **60, 65, 71** *and the larger size stamps have the wmk sideways unless marked* U (*upright*). *P* 12½.

No.	Type	Description	Unused	Used
304	**60**	½d. light scarlet (1.7.96)	3·50	15
		a. Carmine-rose (11.97)	3·75	15
		b. Deep carmine-red (coarse impression) (1899)	—	75
305	**68**	1d. brown-red (13.6.96)	2·00	15
		a. Brownish orange (1899)	1·90	15
306	**71**	1½d. apple-green (8.10.97)	3·75	1·50
307	**62**	2d. violet (*shades*) (12.6.96)	2·10	15
308	**39**	3d. ochre (11.96)	7·00	55
		a. Buff (2.98)	6·50	50
309	**63**	4d. red (6.97)	5·00	90
310	**70**	5d. red-brown (7.97)	7·00	95
311	**64**	6d. dull blue (9.96)	6·50	55
312	**29**	9d. rosine (10.96)	14·00	1·90
		a. Rose-carmine (4.98)	—	1·90
		b. Dull rose (6.98)	11·00	1·90
313	**65**	1s. brownish red (3.97)	11·00	1·10
314	**66**	1s. 6d. brown-orange (8.98)	23·00	7·50
315	**42**	2s. blue-green (4.97)	21·00	5·00
316	**43**	2s. 6d. yellow (9.96)	90·00	11·00
		a. Yellow (U) (9.98)	£100	11·00
317	**46**	3s. olive-drab (12.96)	15·00	11·00
		a. Olive-drab (U) (10.98)	16·00	10·00
318	**47**	4s. orange (9.97)	15·00	4·50
319	**48**	5s. rosine (2.97)	15·00	5·00
		a. Rose-carmine (11.97)	12·00	5·00
		b. Rosine (U) (3.99)	19·00	5·50
320	**49**	6s. pale yellow-green† (4.99)	15·00	5·00
321	**50**	10s. grey-green (4.97)	23·00	11·00
		a. Blue-green (7.98)	23·00	11·00
322	**51**	15s. brown† (4.97)	25·00	10·00
323	**59**	£25 dull bluish green† (U) (1899)	—	80·00
324		£50 dull purple† (U) (11.97)	—	65·00

73

74

(Des M. Tannenberg. Eng R. R. Mitchelhill)

1897 (7 Oct). *Charity. W* **72** (V3) *sideways. P* 12½.

No.	Type	Description	Unused	Used
325	**73**	1d. (1s.) blue	18·00	18·00
326	**74**	2½d. (2s. 6d.) red-brown	70·00	60·00
325/6		Optd "Specimen" *Set of* 2	£140	

These stamps, sold at 1s. and 2s. 6d. respectively, paid postage of 1d. and 2½d. only, the difference being given to a Hospital Fund.

1899 (1 Aug)–**1900.** *Colours changed for ½d., 1d., 1½d. and 2½d. P* 12½.

(*a*) *W* **23** (V2)

No.	Type	Description	Unused	Used
327	**71**	1½d. brown-red/*yellow* (1.8.99)	2·50	1·50

(*b*) *W* **72** (V3)

No.	Type	Description	Unused	Used
328	**60**	½d. emerald (8.99)	5·00	50
329	**69**	2½d. blue (1.8.99)	5·00	1·75

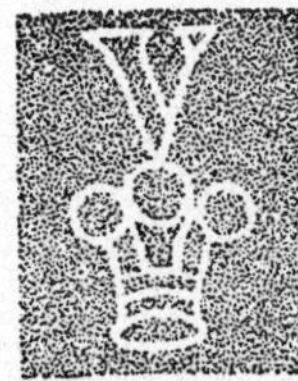

75 (V4)

(*c*) *W* **75** (V4)

This wmk and paper, like V3, was supplied by Waterlow and Sons and it continued in use until 1905. It was the result of an amended specification. Like the V3 paper it has a marked mesh but is whiter, smoother and harder. The 1s. and the four higher values have the wmk sideways, the ½d. being found with both positions.

No.	Type	Description	Unused	Used
330	**60**	½d. emerald (1.8.99)	4·75	50
		a. Deep blue-green	5·00	50
331	**68**	1d. rosine (1.8.99)	3·75	15
		a. Rose-red (1900)	3·75	15
332	**62**	2d. violet (*shades*)(1.8.99)	2·50	15
333	**69**	2½d. blue (2.00)	3·00	1·75
334	**39**	3d. bistre-yellow (9.99)	5·25	55
335	**63**	4d. rose-red (12.99)	4·75	95
336	**70**	5d. red-brown (10.99)	4·75	95
337	**64**	6d. dull ultramarine (2.00)	7·00	55
338	**29**	9d. rose-red (8.99)	8·00	1·50
339	**65**	1s. brown-red (5.00)	10·00	1·40
340	**66**	1s. 6d. orange (12.99)	14·00	4·75
341	**42**	2s. blue-green (6.00)	15·00	4·25
342	**43**	2s. 6d. yellow (1.00)	90·00	8·00
343	**46**	3s. pale olive† (5.00)	£130	10·00
344	**48**	5s. rose-red (4.00)	£130	12·00
345	**50**	10s. green† (3.00)	£130	11·00

76

77

(Eng S. Reading)

1900 (May). *Charity. W* **75** (V4) *sideways. P* 12½.

No.	Type	Description	Unused	Used
346	**76**	1d. (1s.) olive-brown	35·00	25·00
347	**77**	2d. (2s.) emerald-green	£100	80·00

These stamps were sold for a Boer War Patriotic Fund, on a similar basis to the issue of 1897.

V over Crown Wmks: A Note on "Abnormal" Watermark Positions

It should always be remembered that the block of 120 wmks (12 × 10) in the sheet was designed to fit the normal size stamp in an upright position. *Other* sizes, larger and smaller, were printed, at various times, with the wmk *both* upright and sideways. The following note concerns only varieties as they are found on stamps of normal size.

Inverted Wmks: This description also embraces cases of wmks lying sideways with V at right found on stamps of Type **60** etc. which are of the same dimensions (but reversed) as the usual size stamps. In printings before 1882 all inverted wmks may be regarded as "abnormals". In this period all sheets of 240 wmks were, where necessary, cut into two before printing. From 1882 to mid-1896 the *only* inverted "abnormals" are found in certain of the common values where the area of the printing surface (i.e. 2 plates of 120) more or less equalled the area of the complete sheet of watermarked paper as it was supplied by De La Rue's. This was of 240 wmks, consisting of one pane of 120 wmks over another pane of 120. In this period the sheet of 240 wmks was not cut up before printing from single plates as had been done previously. Where only one plate was employed the sheet was fed in in one direction, removed, dried, and fed in the other direction, giving in the result of 120 normal and 120 inverted wmks. (This fact is of assistance when distinguishing certain Reprints.) From 1896 the same principle applied save that the complete sheets supplied were of 480 wmks so that the only "abnormal" inverteds found are in those cases, e.g. 1d. and 2d. where the stamps were printed from a block of similar size viz. of 4 plates of 120 impressions clamped together.

However, in 1901 to 1912, following a change in postal rates, resulting in a smaller demand for the 2d. value, this was again printed from two plates so that inverted watermarks in this period are always normal.

Sideways Wmks: This description includes upright wmks on stamps of the dimensions of Type **60** etc. They usually arose through the suppliers placing the paper in the wrong direction in the bound books (and later unbound reams) of paper supplied. *Three* periods concern us in this regard.

(i) 1867–1882: Before 1867 paper was supplied in single sheets of 120 wmks and from 1867 in double sheets of 240 wmks. From 1867 to 1882 wherever it was necessary (i.e. where only one plate was used) the double sheets were cut into half before printing. The variety may be found under the following numbers. All are extremely rare—viz. 174, 180, 190, 192, 193, 202, 214, 225.

(ii) 1882–1896. In this period no "abnormal" sideways wmks are met since the paper supplied was not cut up before printing and since the complete sheet supplied was rectangular and *not square* in shape.

(iii) 1896–1912: Here the wmkd paper supplied was of 480 (120 × 4) wmks and such sheets were practically square. One meets "abnormals" under the following numbers, many of these being extremely rare—viz. 304, 305, 307, 308, 312, 313, 328, 330, 331, 332, 334, 338, 356, 357, 359, 366, 367, 368, 371, 373, 386, 400, 405, 407, 414, 417, 445, 447, 451.

Reversed Wmks: These involved a printing on the wrong side of the paper. Since the side which should have been printed was usually "surfaced" to some degree these varieties almost invariably show the impression of the stamp coarser than normally and the back of the stamp smoother and glossier. From 1878 to 1896 the back of the paper supplied by De La Rue was treated with a special preparation to prevent the gum soaking through to the front. This preparation was susceptible to moisture and when printed upon and subsequently exposed to moisture occasionally shed portions of the design, so that in this period such varieties often bear the superficial appearance of having been printed on the gum, whereas in fact, up to July 1912, all gumming was done after printing. Reversed wmks, many of them very rare, have been found under the following Nos.—158, 162, 179, 181, 183, 184, 185, 187, 190, 192, 193, 197, 198, 206, 210, 211, 214, 228, 243, 244, 245, 263, 283, 284, 285, 286, 287, 288, 289, 298, 305, 307, 310, 331, 332, 356, 357, 366, 373, 400, 401, 403, 406, 407, 408, 447, 448—also in certain of the £25, £50 and £100 stamps (in both sections) and in various items in the Postal Fiscal list. In the reversed V over Crown cases—looking through the front of the stamp in a normal upright position—the double side of the "V" will appear on the *right* and not on the left as it should do.

D. THE COMMONWEALTH PERIOD, 1901–12

All postage stamps issued by the States in this period were in reality COMMONWEALTH stamps. This viewpoint has now received official endorsement ("Commonwealth of Australia Philatelic Bulletin" No. 2, October 1953). Prior to the actual coming into being of the Commonwealth it had been agreed between the States that the Postal Services were to be the concern of the Commonwealth and that the postal revenue was to go to it. This decision meant, for Victoria, the separation of the Postal and the Fiscal systems. So long, however, as the Commonwealth lacked printing facilities and a Postal administration of its own the work had to be done by each State on its behalf. Separate series of Postage stamps (for which the State was obliged to account to the Commonwealth) and of Duty stamps (which were to continue as a State concern) therefore became necessary. The first Kangaroo stamps were not issued by the Commonwealth until January 1913, but in the intervening period a long chain of philatelic events had contributed to make this issue possible. From the beginning of 1902 all the stamps of Tasmania and Western Australia were printed in Melbourne, on Victorian paper. Later Papua (1907) and later again South Australia (1909) were added to these. In the same year (1902) the first Commonwealth Postage Dues, printed in Sydney on New South Wales paper, appeared. In 1903 a 9d. stamp of the same "Commonwealth" design was issued in New South Wales and Queensland. In 1905 all States commenced using one or other of four types of Crown over A paper, marginally wmkd "COMMONWEALTH OF AUSTRALIA". In 1909, printed in Melbourne, appeared new bi-coloured Postage Dues, the first stamps to be inscribed "AUSTRALIA". This followed the appointment of J. B. Cooke, the South Australian stamp printer, as Commonwealth Stamp Printer. As from 13.10.10 the stamps of any State could legally be used in any other State, and in April 1911 the first Commonwealth Postal Stationery was issued. In short, in the period 1901 to 1912, although certain States printed and issued postage stamps, this was a privilege, subject at all times to Commonwealth control and direction and conducted, in respect of the nett revenue received, solely for the Commonwealth's benefit.

The Commonwealth was proclaimed as from 1 January 1901. In only three cases in the first issue, viz. the 1d., 2½d. and 5d. values was there sufficient time to alter the dies and produce new plates. In all the other cases the same plates were used as had been employed to produce the 1891 Reprints.

1901 (29 Jan)–**1905.** *P* 12½ *or* 12 × 12½.

(*a*) *Without the word* "POSTAGE" *in the design.* (i) *W* **72** (V3)

No.	Type	Description	Unused	Used
348	**35**	2s. blue/*pink*	30·00	9·50

(ii) *W* **75** (V4)

No.	Type	Description	Unused	Used
349	**25**	½d. bluish green	1·50	70
		a. "VICTCRIA"	23·00	19·00
350	**33**	2d. reddish violet	3·75	15
351	**16**	3d. dull orange	8·00	1·00
352	**34**	4d. bistre-yellow	25·00	6·50
353	**17**	6d. emerald	7·00	3·00
354	**30**	1s. yellow	15·00	4·75
355	**19**	5s. pale red and deep blue	45·00	15·00

78

79

80

(*b*) *With the word "POSTAGE" in the design. W* **75** (V4)

No.	Type	Description	Unused	Used
356	**78**	1d. rose (Die I)	1·25	15
		a. Dull red (12.01)	1·25	15
357		1d. rose (Die II) (2.4.01)	1·25	15
		a. Dull red (12.01)	1·25	15
358		1d. pale rose-red (Die III) (3.5.05)	2·00	15
359	**79**	2½d. dull blue (1901)	2·75	35
		a. Deep blue (1902)	2·75	35
360	**80**	5d. reddish brown	4·75	55
		a. Purple-brown (1903)	4·00	55

I

II

III

I and II

III

Three dies of the 1d.: Principal differences are:

I. Horizontal lines over Queen's head fill oval surround under "VICTORIA". Found in two plates employed January 1901–February 1903.

II. Practically all the lines of shading to the left of and on top of the head have been "thinned", giving a lighter appearance. Some lines at the top have been cut away, leaving small white patches, particularly under the "OR". Found in ten plates in use between April 1901 and April 1905.

III. As II but with stop at lower left clearly separated from circle line at its right; spot of colour in shading between "O" and "R"; two lines of shading meet in lower left portion of "P" of "PENNY". Found in twelve plates in use between May 1905 and the end of 1912.

1901 (June). *W* **75** (*V4*). *P* 12 × 12½.

No.	Type	Description	Unused	Used
361	**68**	1d. olive (6.6.01)	5·25	4·75
362	**39**	3d. slate-green (20.6.01)	21·00	4·75

These stamps were available for postal purposes to 30 June 1901, afterwards for fiscal purposes only.

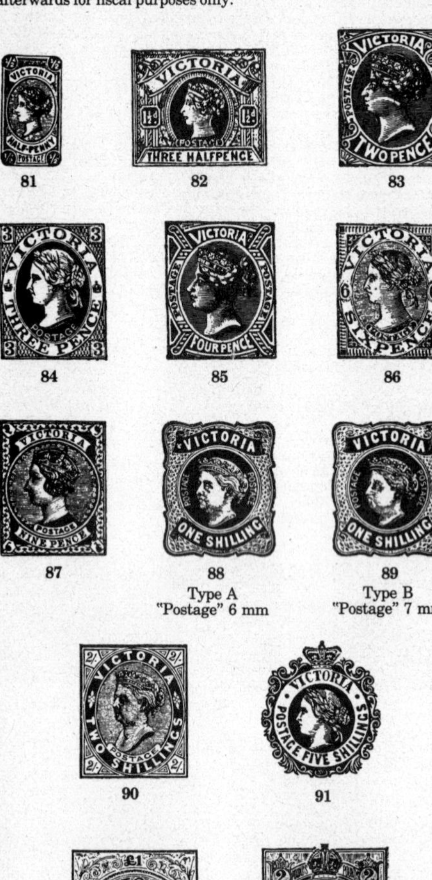

81 82 83

84 85 86

87 88 Type A "Postage" 6 mm 89 Type B "Postage" 7 mm

90 91

92 93

1901 (June)–**10**. *Similar to former types but "POSTAGE" inserted in design. W* **75** (V4). (*a*) *P* 12½ *or* 12 × 12½.

No.	Type	Description	Unused	Used
363	**81**	½d. blue-green (*shades*) (Die I) (26.6.01)	1·90	15
		a. Blue-green (U)	1·90	15
364		½d. pale blue-green (Die II) (6.04)	2·10	15
365		½d. pale bluish green (Die III) (6.05)	3·50	50
366	**82**	1½d. maroon/*yellow* (9.7.01)	3·00	60
		a. Brown-red/yellow (1901)	2·10	55
		b. Dull red/yellow (1906)	2·10	55
367	**83**	2d. lilac (16.7.01)	1·90	35
		a. Reddish violet (1902)	1·90	35
		b. Violet (1904)	3·00	35
		c. Bright purple (1905)	3·00	50
368	**84**	3d. dull orange-brown (2.7.01)	4·75	55
		a. Chestnut (1901)	4·75	55
		b. Yellowish brown (1903)	4·75	55
369	**85**	4d. bistre-yellow (26.6.01)	4·75	55
		a. Brownish bistre (1905)	5·25	70
370	**86**	6d. emerald (5.7.01)	7·50	1·00
		a. Dull green (1904)	9·00	1·25
371	**87**	9d. dull rose-red (5.7.01)	9·50	1·40
		a. Pale red (1901)	10·00	1·25
		b. Dull brownish red (1905)	10·00	1·75
372	**88**	1s. yellow-orange (Type A) (5.7.01)	9·50	2·50
		a. Yellow (1902)	10·00	2·40
373	**89**	1s. yellow (Type B) (4.03)	10·00	3·00
		a. Yellow-orange (1903)	10·00	2·50
374	**90**	2s. blue/*rose* (5.7.01)	22·00	2·75
375	**91**	5s. rose-red and pale blue (5.7.01)	70·00	11·00
		a. Scarlet and deep blue (1902)	65·00	9·00
		b. Rosine and blue (1905)	65·00	9·00
376	**92**	£1 carmine-rose (18.11.01)	£350	£100
377	**93**	£2 deep blue (2.6.02)	£700	£250

(*b*) *P* 11

No.	Type	Description	Unused	Used
378	**81**	½d. blue-green (Die I) (9.02)	3·50	75
		a. Blue-green (U)	2·75	20
379		½d. blue-green (Die II)	2·50	25
380		½d. bluish green (Die III)	3·00	50
381	**78**	1d. dull red (Die I)	—	22·00
382		1d. dull red (Die II)	—	18·00
		a. Pale red (*aniline*) (3.03)	2·50	75
		b. Pale rose (*aniline*)(1904)	—	3·00
383		1d. pale rose-red (Die III)	38·00	23·00
384	**82**	1½d. dull red/*yellow* (1910)	28·00	28·00
385	**83**	2d. violet (1904)	—	£140
		a. Bright purple (1905)	—	£140
386	**84**	3d. orange-brown (1903)	5·25	3·00
387	**86**	6d. emerald (1903)	9·50	3·75
		a. Dull green (1905)	£250	£160
388	**92**	£1 carmine-red (1905)	£400	£130
389	**93**	£2 deep blue (1905)	£900	£650

(*c*) *Compound or mixed perf* 12½ *and* 11

No.	Type	Description	Unused	Used
390	**81**	½d. blue-green (Die I)	—	3·00
		a. Blue-green (U) (1903)	—	3·00
391		½d. blue-green (Die II) (1904)	14·00	10·00
392	**78**	1d. dull red (Die I)	—	£150
393		1d. dull red (Die II)	—	£110
394	**82**	1½d. dull red/*yellow*	—	£200
395	**83**	2d. reddish violet	—	£250
396	**84**	3d. orange-brown	—	£200
397	**86**	6d. emerald	—	£200
398	**91**	5s. rose and blue	£800	

I II III

Three dies of the ½d.; Principal differences are:

I. Outer of two vertical lines of colour to left of "V" is continuous save for a marked break opposite top of "V". Found in two plates in use 1901–May 1904.

II. Outer vertical line to left of "V" is broken in three places; the triangular space S.W. of "V", has also been "opened up" and shows more white lines than in I. Found in two plates in use June 1904–June 1905.

III. As II but the vertical coloured line to right of the "A" of "VICTORIA" (previously broken in the middle) is now broken in four or five places. The triangular ornament to S.E. of the same "A" has also been "opened up", the white cross-hatching now being stronger than in I and II. Found in two plates introduced in June 1905 and in two subsequent plates introduced late in 1909.

The paper used for the 1½d. value for two printings in 1908–9 was yellow-buff in colour but in used copies the difference is not so marked as to warrant separate description.

There were two main states of the 2d. Die, the original showing the S.E. corner correctly squared and the later showing it damaged and blunter. There are other differences. The original state is found in all printings before April 1904 but not after, and the later state to a small extent (5 per cent) in the printings before April 1904 and *solely* in the printings from that date.

For the 1s. Type A the same plate was used as for the 1s. "No Postage" of 1901, the words "POSTAGE" being separately punched on. For Type B two new plates, prepared via an etched line-block, were introduced.

Certain *unlisted shades* (due to their being unsatisfactory) are found *only* punctured O.S. Marked instances of this are found in the 2d., 3d. and 4d. values.

1905–13. *Wmk Crown over A, W w* **11**. I. *Medium paper, supplied, like the V4 paper, by Waterlow & Sons.*

(*a*) *P* 12½ *or* 12 × 12½

No.	Type	Description	Unused	Used
399	**81**	½d. blue-green (21.10.05)	1·60	15
		a. Light bluish green	1·60	15
400	**78**	1d. rose-red (*shades*)(16.7.05)	1·25	15
		a. Pale rose (1907)	1·25	15
		b. Rose-carmine (9.11)	2·10	15
401	**83**	2d. dull mauve (13.9.05)	2·50	40
		a. Bright mauve (1906)	2·50	40
		b. Reddish violet (1907)	2·50	40
		c. Lilac (1910)	2·10	40
402	**79**	2½d. blue (*shades*)(4.08)	3·00	50
		a. Indigo (1909)	3·00	50
403	**84**	3d. orange-brown (11.11.05)	4·00	55
		a. Yellow-orange (1908)	5·00	30
		b. Dull orange-buff (1909)	4·75	30
		c. Ochre (1912)	4·75	30
404	**85**	4d. yellow-bistre (15.1.06)	6·00	65
		a. Bistre (1908)	6·00	65
		b. Yellow-olive (1912)	6·00	70
405	**80**	5d. chocolate (14.8.06)	5·00	90
		a. Dull reddish brown (1908)	5·00	65
406	**86**	6d. dull green (25.10.05)	8·00	1·10
		a. Dull yellow-green (1907)	7·50	1·00
		b. Emerald (1909)	7·50	1·10
		c. Yellowish green (1911)	7·50	1·00
407	**87**	9d. rose-red (11.12.05)	9·50	1·25
		a. Pale salmon-red (1906)	9·50	1·25
		b. Brown-red (1908)	10·00	1·25
		c. Pale dull rose (worn plate)	11·00	2·40
		d. Rose-carmine (new plate) (12.09)	9·50	1·25
408	**89**	1s. yellow-orange (13.2.06)	8·00	2·25
		a. Yellow (1906)	8·00	2·25
		b. Lemon (1908)	9·50	2·25
409	**91**	5s. rose-red and ultramarine (U) (11.07)	70·00	13·00
		a. Rose-red and blue (U) (1912)	80·00	13·00
		b. Rose-red and blue (S)	80·00	16·00
410	**92**	£1 salmon (2.07)	£350	£100
411		£1 dull rose (1910)	£350	£120
		a. Deep dull rose (U) (1912)	£350	£120
412	**93**	£2 dull blue (1906)	£750	£250

Perforations of period 1901–12

In general, up to 1910, five machines were available at any one time—three single-line (two "11" and one "12½") and two vertical combs (12 × 12½). Only single-line machines were used for the 5s., £1 and £2 values. The "12½" single line was used on many occasions for the ½d. and occasionally for other values. The "11" machines were primarily employed for larger size stamps, e.g. Victorian Duty Stamps, Tasmanian Pictorials and Papua, and their use for the normal size Victorian postage stamps was in the main restricted to emergencies. At certain periods, e.g. 1909–10 one encounters the true "compounds" i.e. the products of two single-line machines, 12½ and 11 respectively. For the ½d. the vertical comb 12 × 12½ was also used, particularly in the earlier period, on the sheet turned sideways. In the result the alternate vertical margins between stamps were left imperforate and a single-line machine (either 12½ or 11) was often used to complete the perforating, in the latter case (11) giving us a variety for separate listing. "Mixed" perforations in this period are, like their predecessors of the 70s, the result of the correction—with another machine—of faultily centred lines of perforation (either single-line or comb), the back of these faulty lines being usually pasted over with gummed strips to assist in tearing down the corrected lines.

The rotary-comb machines gauging 11½ × 12¼ were brought over from South Australia by J. B. Cooke when he moved to Melbourne in 1909.

The ½d. perf 11 and the 2½d. and 5s. first printings (all perforated with single line machines) may be met with *full imperforate base margins*. Likewise in the Crown over A issues the ½d. perf 12½ and the 5s. perf 12½ (1912) have been similarly found. Such varieties are, of course, rare.

(*b*) *P* 11

No.	Type	Description	Unused	Used
413	**81**	½d. light bluish green	1·60	15
		a. Blue-green	1·60	15
414	**78**	1d. rose-red (1905)	1·40	75
		a. Pale rose (1907)	1·75	75
		b. Rose-carmine (1911)	3·00	2·75
415	**83**	2d. mauve (1906)	—	£150
		a. Reddish violet (1908)	65·00	15·00
		b. Lilac (1910)	19·00	7·50
416	**79**	2½d. blue (1909)	15·00	7·50
		a. Indigo (1909)	5·50	3·25
417	**84**	3d. brown (1908)	7·00	5·00
		a. Orange-buff (1909)	14·00	9·50
		b. Dull orange-yellow (1911)	—	£125
		c. Ochre (1912)	6·50	1·50
418	**85**	4d. yellow-bistre (1908)	7·00	
		a. Yellow-olive (1912)	6·50	3·00
419	**80**	5d. reddish brown	—	£300
420	**86**	6d. emerald (1910)	8·50	2·40
		a. Yellowish green (1911)	11·00	2·40
421	**87**	9d. rose-carmine	—	£325
422	**89**	1s. yellow-orange	£275	
		a. Yellow	—	£225
423	**91**	5s. rose-red and ultramarine	70·00	9·50
424	**92**	£1 salmon (1907)	£400	£100
425	**93**	£2 dull blue (1906)	£700	£250

(*c*) *Compound or mixed perfs* 12½ *and* 11

No.	Type	Description	Unused	Used
426	**81**	½d. light bluish green (6.09)	15·00	14·00
427	**78**	1d. rose-red	32·00	32·00
428	**83**	2d. mauve	—	£200
429	**84**	3d. brown (1908)	£190	£225
		a. Ochre (1912)	—	£190
430	**85**	4d. bistre	—	£275
431	**86**	6d. yellowish green	—	£300
432	**87**	9d. dull rose-red	—	£375
433	**89**	1s. yellow-orange	—	£400

(*d*) *Rotary comb perf* 11½ × 12¼

No.	Type	Description	Unused	Used
434	**78**	1d. pale scarlet-red (2.10)	3·00	20
		a. Rose-red (3.10)	2·25	60
435	**83**	2d. lilac (*shades*)	3·50	75

II. *On thinner paper, ready gummed with white gum.* (July–Nov 1912).

(*a*) *P* 12½ *or* 12 × 12½

No.	Type	Description	Unused	Used
436	**81**	½d. blue-green	3·00	25
437	**78**	1d. rose-red	4·50	25
438	**83**	2d. lilac	7·00	2·25
439	**80**	5d. brown	6·50	1·75
440	**86**	6d. emerald	9·50	2·25
441	**89**	1s. dull yellow (11.12)	15·00	6·00
		a. Pale orange (1.13)	15·00	6·00

(*b*) *P* 11

No.	Type	Description	Unused	Used
442	**81**	½d. blue-green	12·00	7·50
443	**78**	1d. rose-red	5·00	2·25

(*c*) *P* 11 × 12½

No.	Type	Description	Unused	Used
444	**81**	½d. blue-green	£100	80·00

(*d*) *Rotary comb perf* 11½ × 12¼

No.	Type	Description	Unused	Used
445	**78**	1d. rose-carmine (2.7.12)	2·25	15
		a. Rose-red (10.12)	2·40	15

Two qualities of the "thin" paper were supplied, the first supply (earliest date 2.7.12) being thicker and with a less obvious mesh than the second (earliest date 2.10.12). The ½d. and 1d. are found on both classes of paper, the 2d. on the first only, and the 5d., 6d. and 1s. on the second only. There was a shortage pending the arrival of the second supply, and this gap was filled by the use of the "Stamp Duty" paper next described and the ONE PENNY overprint of 1.7.12. The 5d. perforated O.S. on the thin paper may be met in *dull red-brown*.

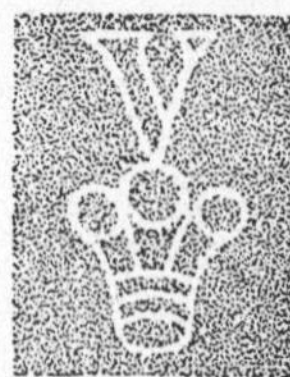

94 (V5)

ONE PENNY

(95)

III. *Printed on "Stamp Duty" paper, W* **94** (V5). *This paper is rather softer and of a more pronounced mesh than the V4 paper.* (Aug–Oct 1912). (*a*) *P* 12½ *or* 12 × 12½.

No.	Type	Description	Unused	Used
446	**81**	½d. bluish green	2·50	25
447	**78**	1d. rose-carmine (7.8.12)	2·25	20
448	**83**	2d. reddish violet	2·50	50
		a. Lilac	3·75	1·40
449	**87**	9d. carmine-red	9·50	2·10

(*b*) *P* 11

No.	Type	Description	Unused	Used
450	**81**	½d. bluish green	12·00	9·00
451	**78**	1d. rose-carmine (8.12)	20·00	6·50
452	**87**	9d. carmine-red	13·00	3·50

(*c*) *Compound perf* 11 *with* 12½

No.	Type	Description	Unused	Used
453	**87**	9d. carmine-red	—	£350

This paper was supplied by Spicer Bros at the beginning of 1911 and continued to be used for many years in the production of Duty Stamps for this State.

1912 (1 July). *Surch with T* **95** *in red. Wmk Crown over A. P* 11½ × 12¼.

No.	Type	Description	Unused	Used
454	**83**	1d. on 2d. lilac	90	55

Late in June 1912 the first consignment of "thin" paper was xhausted and the second had not arrived. A further supply of the d. value was urgently required, and the expedient of overprinting urrent 2d. stock was employed to fill the gap. The same reason also roduced the 1d. and 2d. overprints of Tasmania and Western ustralia, respectively.

POSTAL FISCALS

This section embraces those printings of Duty and Fee stamps nade before 1.1.84. These were made available for postal purposes s from 1.1.84. The two series were in concurrent use between)ecember 1879 and 1884.

A. The "STAMP STATUTE" series

This series was first issued on 26 April 1871 and it was in the nain used to record the payment of various Court fees. The issue of he series ceased in April 1884.

F 1 F 2 F 3

F 4

1870–83. *Large rectangular stamps of various designs as Types* **F 1** *to* **F 4.** *All save the 3d. and 2s. 6d. (eng by James Turner) have the Queen's head included in the design (eng by William Bell). Typo at the Stamp Printing Office, Melbourne.*

(a) *Wmk single-lined numerals (1, 2, and 10) as used for Postage Stamps (1863–67). On Saunders paper unless otherwise noted. Both sideways and upright wmks are found in certain cases*

F 1 1s. blue/*blue* (*p* 13) .. 5·50 6·00
a. Perf 12 .. 9·50
F 2 2s. blue/*green* (D.L.R.) (*p* 13) .. 9·50 11·00
a. Perf 12 .. 9·50 11·00
F 3 2s. deep blue/*green* (S), (*p* 13) .. 12·00
a. Perf 12 .. — 12·00
F 4 10s. brown-olive/*pink* (*p* 13) (6.71) ..
F 5 10s. red-brown/*pink* (*p* 13) (1879) .. 55·00 16·00
a. Perf 12 ..

(b) *Wmk V over Crown,* **W 20** (V1)

The wmk is usually *sideways* but in certain cases the whole of a printing was *upright.* One also meets "abnormal" upright wmks.

F 7 ½d. on 1d. pale green (R.) (*p* 13) .. 4·00 4·00
F 8 1d. pale green (*p* 13) .. 3·75 2·25
a. Green (*p* 12½) (U) (1880) .. 4·50 5·50
F 9 3d. mauve (*p* 13) (9.79) .. 20·00 14·00
F10 4d. rose (*p* 13) .. 6·50 6·50
F11 6d. blue (*p* 13) (1871) .. 8·00 6·50
a. Dull ultramarine (*p* 13) (1876) .. 3·75 1·90
aa. Perf 12 .. — 3·75
F12 1s. blue/*blue* (*p* 13) (6.76) .. 7·25
a. Perf 12 .. — 6·00
b. Ultramarine/blue (*p* 12½) (1882) .. — 6·00
ba. Perf 12 .. — 6·00
c. Deep blue/blue (*p* 12½) (1883) .. 8·00 6·00
ca. Perf 12 .. — 6·00
F13 2s. blue/*green* (*p* 13) (7.76) .. 20·00 14·00
a. Perf 12 ..
b. Deep blue/blue-green (*p* 13) (1883) .. 20·00 9·50
ba. Perf 12 .. 20·00 11·00
F15 2s. 6d. orange (*p* 13) (7.76) .. — 15·00
a. Perf 12 ..
b. Yellow (*p* 13) (11.78) .. 22·00
ba. Perf 12 .. 22·00 20·00
c. Orange-yellow (*p* 12½) (1882) ..
ca. Perf 12 ..
F16 5s. blue/*yellow* (*p* 13) .. 27·00 14·00
a. Perf 12 ..
b. Ultramarine/lemon (*p* 12½) (1881) .. 27·00 14·00
F17 10s. brown/*pink* (*p* 13) (8.76) .. 55·00
a. Purple-brown/pink (*p* 12½) (1882) .. 55·00
aa. Perf 12 ..
F18 £1 slate-violet/*yellow* (S, U) (*p* 13) (1871) .. 55·00
a. Perf 12 (1880) .. 55·00
b. Mauve/yellow (*p* 13) (1873)
ba. Perf 12 (1881) .. 55·00
bb. Perf 12½ (1882) ..
F19 £5 black and yellow-green (*p* 12) (11.71) ..
a. Perf 13 ..
b. Perf 12½ (U) ..

(c) 1882–3: *Wmk V over Crown,* **W 23** (V2)

F20 1d. yellowish green (*p* 12½) .. 6·00 6·00
F21 2s. 6d. pale orange-yellow (*p* 12½) .. 20·00
F22 £5 black and yellow-green (*p* 12) ..

Reversed watermarks, all rare, have been found under Nos. F12, F15, F18 and F19.

All the values of the "Stamp Statute" series were reprinted in 1891 on paper wmkd V1 (5s., 10s. and £1) and V2 (the rest). The colours used, in all cases, differed radically from the originals. Except for the £5, for which the old electrotypes were used, new plates were made for the Reprints, from dies which showed "die flaws" not to be found on the originals. In 1877 a 12s. 6d. value was prepared for use but although it was placed on sale at the Law Courts and was available there for some months not a single copy was sold, and it was withdrawn. Proofs are known.

B. The "STAMP DUTY" series

This series was used mainly to record the payment of duties on the sale of land, receipts and numerous other documents.

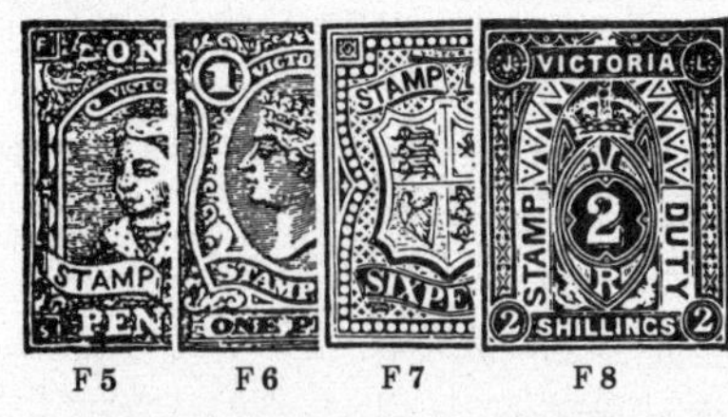

F 5 F 6 F 7 F 8

F 9 F 10 F 11

(Dies for these issues (except 1d. of 1880) supplied by Messrs. Sands and McDougall. Des Charles Jackson and Ludwig Lang. Eng Charles Jackson, Arthur Williams and others (See previously). The 1d. of 1880 was eng by Charles Naish)

1879 (Dec)–**1883** (Dec). I. *December 1879. Litho Stamp Printing Office, Melbourne. Wmk V over Crown,* **W 20** (V1). *Sideways unless otherwise indicated* (U). *P* 13.

F23 F 5 1d. blue-green .. 2·40 2·40
a. Perf 12 .. 4·25 2·40
F24 45 1s. 6d. rosine .. 4·25 4·25
a. Perf 12 ..
F25 46 3s. purple/*blue* .. 6·50 6·00
a. Perf 12 .. — 9·50
F26 47 4s. orange-red .. 6·50 4·00
a. Perf 12 .. 6·50 4·00
F27 40 6s. apple-green (U) .. 6·50 4·00
a. Perf 12 (U)
F28 50 10s. brown/*rose* (S, U) .. 29·00 13·00
a. Perf 12 (S, U)
F29 51 15s. mauve .. — 20·00
F30 52 £1 red-orange .. — 20·00
F31 53 £1 5s. dull rose (U) .. — 26·00
F32 54 £1 10s. deep grey-olive (S, U) .. — 16·00
F33 35s. grey-violet (U) .. F.C. £35
F34 55 £2 blue .. — 32·00
F35 56 45s. dull brown-lilac (U) .. — 32·00
F36 57 £5 rose-red (U) .. — 48·00
F37 F 9 £6 blue/*pink* (U) .. — £140
F38 F 10 £7 violet/*blue* (U) .. — £140
F39 F 11 £8 brownish red/*yellow* (U) .. — £140
F40 — £9 yellow-green/*green* (U) F.C. £25

Apart from the "Half-Lengths", the 2d. Queen-on-Throne, the first 1s. Octagonal and the £25, £50 and £100 of 1886–89 these were the only stamps of Victoria to be printed by lithography and its adoption on this occasion was dictated by the necessity for speed of production. *All* the Lithographed stamps can be distinguished from the typographed stamps of the same design by their colours which are highly distinctive. Other differences, of wmk and perf, will be found. Some values, e.g. the 6s., 25s. and 30s. (1884–91) were available for postage over a considerable period.

No. F32 occurs with *reversed* watermark (rare).

II. Dec 1879–1882: *Typographed from electrotypes at Stamp Printing Office, Melbourne*

(i) *Wmk V over Crown,* **W 20** (V1)

F41 F 5 1d. yellowish green (*p* 13) (12.79) .. 2·50 1·25
a. Perf 12 .. 2·40 2·25
F42 F 6 1d. pale bistre (*p* 12½) (6.80) .. 90 30
a. Perf 12 .. 1·60 50
F43 F 7 6d. dull blue (*p* 13) (12.79) .. 2·50 1·25
a. Perf 12 ..
F44 44 1s. deep blue/*blue* (*p* 13) (12.79) .. 2·40 40
a. Perf 12 .. 2·50 1·25
b. Bright blue/blue (*p* 12½) (1882) .. 2·50 90
ba. Perf 12 .. — 1·25
F45 F 8 2s. deep blue/*green* (*p* 13) (12.79) .. 3·75 1·90
a. Perf 12 .. — 2·25
b. Indigo/green .. 17·00 9·00
ba. Perf 12 .. 17·00 9·00
F46 48 5s. claret/*yellow* (*p* 13) (12.79) .. 6·50 1·90
a. Perf 12 .. — 3·75
b. Pale claret/yellow (*p* 12½) (1880) .. 7·50 1·90
ba. Perf 12 .. 9·00 3·75
F47 50 10s. chocolate/*rose* (*p* 13) (S, U) (12.79) — 17·00
a. Perf 12 (S, U) ..
F48 52 £1 yellow-orange/*yellow* (*p* 12) (1882)
F49 55 £2 deep blue (*p* 12½) (1881) .. — 17·00
F50 58 £10 dull mauve (*p* 12) (1879) ..
a. Deep red-lilac (1882) .. — 45·00

(ii) 1882–3: *Wmk V over Crown,* **W 23** (V2)

F51 F 6 1d. ochre (*shades*) (*p* 12½) .. 75 30
a. Perf 12 .. 1·25 35
F52 F 7 6d. ultramarine (*p* 12½) .. 2·25 1·25
a. Perf 12 .. 2·25 1·25
F53 55 £2 blue (*p* 12) .. — 26·00
F54 57 £5 rose-pink (*p* 12) .. — 50·00

III. 1879–80: *Recess-printed direct from the die*

(i) *Wmk V over Crown,* **W 20** (V1). *P* 13

F55 59 £25 yellow-green (1879) .. F.C. 40·00
a. Deep green (1880) .. F.C. 40·00
F56 £50 bright mauve (1879) .. F.C. 65·00
F57 £100 crimson-lake (1879) .. F.C. 65·00

(ii) 1882–3: *Wmk V over Crown,* **W 23** (V2). *P* 12½

F58 59 £50 dull lilac-mauve .. F.C. 80·00
F59 £100 crimson .. F.C. 95·00
a. Perf 12 .. F.C. 95·00

Nos. F44 and F45 occur with *reversed* watermark (both rare).

Reprints of Stamp Duty Series: The only stamps in this series to be reprinted in 1891 (on wmk V2) were the two types of 1d. which by then had become obsolete. Again the colours are distinctive from the originals.

In 1879 certain other values inscribed "STAMP DUTY" (of varying heraldic designs) viz; 7s., 8s., 9s., 11s., 12s., 13s., 14s., 16s., 17s., 18s. and 19s. were prepared for use but were not issued. Proofs are known.

POSTAGE DUE STAMPS

D 1

(Dies eng Arthur Williams (values) and John McWilliams (frame). Typo)

1890–1908. *Type* **D 1.** A. *Wmk V over Crown,* **W 23** (V2). *P* 12 × 12½. (i) 1 Nov 1890 (½d., 24.12.90).

D 1 ½d. dull blue and brown-lake .. 2·25 1·60
D 2 1d. dull blue and brown-lake .. 3·50 1·40
D 3 2d. dull blue and brown-lake .. 3·00 1·10
D 4 4d. dull blue and brown-lake .. 6·00 1·50
D 5 5d. dull blue and brown-lake .. 5·00 1·75
D 6 6d. dull blue and brown-lake .. 6·50 1·75
D 7 10d. dull blue and brown-lake .. 60·00 35·00
D 8 1s. dull blue and brown-lake .. 28·00 6·50
D 9 2s. dull blue and brown-lake .. £100 42·00
D10 5s. dull blue and brown-lake .. £140 85·00

The blue shades vary considerably.

(ii) 1890–94

D11 ½d. dull blue and deep claret (1890) .. 1·90 1·40
D12 1d. dull blue and brownish red (20.1.93) .. 3·00 1·10
D13 2d. dull blue and brownish red (28.3.93) .. 3·75 90
D14 4d. dull blue and pale claret (28.5.94) .. 6·00 1·75

Nos. D1 and D11 were separate printings, both made in December 1890.

(iii) 17 Jan 1895. *Colours changed*

D15 ½d. rosine and bluish green .. 2·10 1·60
D16 1d. rosine and bluish green .. 1·60 40
D17 2d. rosine and bluish green .. 2·25 30
D18 4d. rosine and bluish green .. 4·50 1·50
D19 5d. rosine and bluish green .. 4·75 2·50
D20 6d. rosine and bluish green .. 4·50 2·75
D21 10d. rosine and bluish green .. 12·00 9·00
D22 1s. rosine and bluish green .. 6·50 3·25

(iv) 28 March 1895

D23 2s. pale red and yellowish green .. 40·00 20·00
D24 5s. pale red and yellowish green .. 80·00 40·00

(v) March 1896 onwards

D25 ½d. pale scarlet and yellow-green .. 2·25 1·10
D26 1d. pale scarlet and yellow-green .. 1·75 35
D27 2d. pale scarlet and yellow-green .. 2·50 30
D28 4d. pale scarlet and yellow-green .. 5·50 1·00
D29 5d. pale scarlet and yellow-green .. 5·00 2·25

B. **W 72** (V3). *P* 12½ *or* 12 × 12½. (i) July 1897 onwards

D30 1d. pale scarlet and yellow-green .. 2·00 30
D31 2d. pale scarlet and yellow-green .. 3·00 30
D32 4d. pale scarlet and yellow-green .. 4·50 1·25
D33 5d. pale scarlet and yellow-green .. 5·00 1·90
D34 6d. pale scarlet and yellow-green .. 5·00 2·75

(ii) July–Sept 1899

D35 1d. dull red and bluish green .. 2·50 30
D36 2d. dull red and bluish green .. 3·00 35
D37 4d. dull red and bluish green .. 5·50 1·10

C. **W 75** (V4). *P* 12½ *or* 12 × 12½. (i) 1900–1

D38 ½d. rose-red and pale green .. 2·50 1·00
D39 1d. rose-red and pale green .. 2·00 35
D40 2d. rose-red and pale green .. 2·50 30
D41 4d. rose-red and pale green .. 6·00 1·75

(ii) 1901–2

D42 ½d. pale red and deep green .. 1·50 1·00
D43 1d. pale red and deep green .. 1·50 35
D44 2d. pale red and deep green .. 2·75 35
D45 4d. pale red and deep green .. 5·00 1·40

(iii) 1902–3

D45*a* ½d. scarlet and deep green ..
D46 1d. scarlet and deep green .. 2·50 30
D47 2d. scarlet and deep green .. 2·75 30
D48 4d. scarlet and deep green .. 5·50 1·00
D49 5d. scarlet and deep green .. 4·00 2·25
D50 1s. scarlet and deep green .. 8·00 2·75
D51 2s. scarlet and deep green .. £100 60·00
D52 5s. scarlet and deep green .. £120 60·00

The deep green of Nos. D45*a*–52 has more "yellow" than that of D42–45.

(iv) 1904

D53 ½d. rosine (*aniline*) and green .. 2·75 1·50
D54 1d. rosine (*aniline*) and green .. 2·00 40
D55 2d. rosine (*aniline*) and green .. 2·50 45
D56 4d. rosine (*aniline*) and green .. 6·00 1·50

D. *Wmk Crown over A* (W w 11). *P* 12½ *or* 12 × 12½. (i) Jan 1906

D57 ½d. rosine (*aniline*) and pale green .. 3·25 2·40
D58 1d. rosine (*aniline*) and green .. 22·00 2·75

(ii) March 1906

D59 ½d. scarlet and pale yellow-green .. 2·00 1·10
D60 1d. scarlet and pale yellow-green .. 2·00 30

(iii) Dec 1906

D61	1d. scarlet (*aniline*) and deep yellow-green	2·25	30
D62	2d. scarlet (*aniline*) and deep yellow-green	3·00	45

(iv) 1907–8

D63	½d. dull scarlet and pea-green	1·75	1·10
D64	1d. dull scarlet and pea-green	2·00	35
D65	2d. dull scarlet and pea-green	3·25	35
D66	4d. dull scarlet and pea-green	7·00	3·75

Perf compound 12 × 12½ *with* 11

D67	½d. dull scarlet and pea-green	50·00	40·00

In D59 and D60 the centre is more clearly printed than in the later printings. A 5d. value was prepared and printed on Crown over A paper but was not issued. A few copies are known postmarked to order from presentation sets.

Victoria now uses the stamps of Australia.

Virgin Islands *see* British Virgin Islands

Western Australia

PRICES FOR STAMPS ON COVER

Nos. 1/14	*from* × 3
Nos. 15/32	*from* × 2
Nos. 33/46	*from* × 3
Nos. 49/51	*from* × 4
Nos. 52/62	*from* × 6
Nos. 63/*a*	*from* × 5
No. 67	*from* × 4
Nos. 68/93*a*	*from* × 5
Nos. 98/102	*from* × 30
Nos. 103/5	*from* × 4
Nos. 107/10*a*	*from* × 8
Nos. 111*a*/*b*	—
Nos. 112/16	*from* × 15
Nos. 117/25	*from* × 10
Nos. 126/8	—
Nos. 129/34	*from* × 8
Nos. 135/6	—
Nos. 138/48	*from* × 10
Nos. 151/63	*from* × 3
Nos. 168/9	*from* × 15
Nos. 170/1	*from* × 2
Nos. 172/3	*from* × 40
Nos. F1/5	*from* × 3
Nos. F6/8	—
Nos. F9/22	*from* × 3
Nos. T1/2	—

1

2

3

4

GUM. The 1854 issues are hardly ever seen with gum and so the unused prices quoted are for examples without gum.

(Eng W. Humphrys. Recess P.B.)

1854 (1 Aug). *W* 4 (*sideways*). (*a*) *Imperf.*

1	1	1d. black	£1200	£325

(*b*) *Rouletted* 7½ *to* 14 *and compound*

2	1	1d. black	£1500	£450

In addition to the supplies received from London a further printing, using the original plate and watermarked paper from Perkins, Bacon, was made in the colony before the date of issue.

The 1d. is also known pin-perforated.

(Litho H. Samson (later A. Hillman), Government Lithographer)

1854 (1 Aug)–**55**. *W* 4 (*sideways*). (*a*) *Imperf.*

3	2	4d. pale blue	£325	£225
		a. Blue	£325	£225
		b. Deep dull blue	£1500	£750
		c. Slate-blue (1855)	£1400	£850
4	3	1s. salmon	—	£1800
		a. Deep red-brown	£800	£500
		b. Grey-brown (1.55)	£600	£400
		c. Pale brown (10.55)	£450	£350

(*b*) *Rouletted* 7½ *to* 14 *and compound*

5	2	4d. pale blue	£1500	£550
		a. Blue	—	£550
		b. Slate-blue (1855)	—	£1600
6	3	1s. grey-brown (1.55)	£1800	£850
		a. Pale brown (10.55)	£1800	£850

The 1s. is also known pin-perforated.

The 4d. value was prepared from the Perkins, Bacon 1d. plate. A block of 60 (5 × 12) was taken as a transfer from this plate, the frames painted out and then individually replaced by transfers taken from a single impression master plate of the frame. Four transfers were then taken from this completed intermediate stone to construct the printing stone of 240 impressions. This first printing stone was used by H. Samson to print the initial supplies in July 1854.

The intermediate stone had carried several transfer errors, the most prominent of which was the "T" of "POSTAGE" sliced at foot, which appeared on four positions of the printing stone.

3d. "T" of "POSTAGE" shaved off to a point at foot (R.7/5, 7/10, 7/15, 7/20)	£750	£700

The original printing stone also contained three scarce creased transfers, whose exact positions in the sheet have yet to be established.

3e. Top of letters of "AUSTRALIA" cut off so that they are barely 1 mm high	—	£6500
f. "PEICE" instead of "PENCE"	—	£6000
g. "CE" of "Pence" close together	—	£7500

Further supplies were required in January 1855 and Samson's successor, A. Hillman, used the original printing stone to produce three further sheets, after which this first stone was discarded. He then returned to the intermediate stone to produce a second printing stone. On inspection it was found that two of the impressions on the intermediate stone were defective so two new transfers of the frame, for use in these positions, were prepared. Unfortunately when these frames were replaced one was inverted and the other tilted. Each error occurs in four positions on the second printing stone, as do the transfer errors shown on the intermediate stone.

3h. Frame inverted (R.8/1, 8/6, 8/11, 8/16)	—	£50000
i. Tilted border (R.7/4, 7/9, 7/14, 7/19)	£800	£750

None of the creased transfers from the first printing stone appear on the second, which exhibits its own range of similar varieties.

3j. "WEST" in squeezed-down letters and "F" of "FOUR" with pointed foot (R.2/17)	£900	£850
k. "ESTERN" in squeezed-down letters and "U" of "FOUR" squeezed-up (R.3/17)	£1600	£1500
l. Small "S" in "POSTAGE" (R.4/17)	£900	£850
m. "EN" of "PENCE" shorter (R.6/4)	£800	£750
n. "N" of "PENCE" tilted to right with thin first downstroke (R.6/16)	£750	£700
o. Swan and water above "ENCE" damaged (R.6/20)	£800	£750
p. "F" of "FOUR" slanting to left (R.7/17)	£800	£750
q. "WESTERN" in squeezed-down letters only 1½ mm high (R.8/17)	£950	£900
r. "P" of "PENCE" with small head (R.9/15)	£800	£750
s. "RALIA" in squeezed-down letters only 1½ mm high (R.9/16)	£900	£850
t. "PE" of "PENCE" close together (R.10/15)	£800	£750
u. "N" of "PENCE" narrow (R.10/16)	£800	£750
v. Part of right cross-stroke and down-stroke of "T" of "POSTAGE" cut off (R.11/15)	£800	£750
w. "A" in "POSTAGE" with thin right limb (R.11/16)	£750	£700

For the third printing in October 1855 the impressions showing the inverted frame were replaced on the printing stone with fresh individual transfers of the frame. On two of the positions traces of the original frame transfer remained visible.

3x. Coloured line above "AGE" of "POSTAGE" (R.8/6)	£750	£700
y. No outer line above "GE" of "POSTAGE" and coloured line under "FOU" of "FOUR" (R.8/11)	£800	£750

The same stone was used for a further printing in December 1855 and it is believed that the slate-blue shade occurred from one of the 1855 printings.

The above varieties, with the exception of Nos. 3e/g, also occur on the rouletted stamps.

The 1s. value was produced in much the same way, based on a transfer from the Perkins, Bacon 1d. plate.

5

(Litho A. Hillman, Government Lithographer)

1857 (7 Aug)–**59**. *W* 4 (*sideways*). (*a*) *Imperf.*

15	5	2d. brown-black/*red* (26.2.58)	£2500	£800
		a. Printed both sides	£2750	£1200
16		2d. brown-black/*Indian red* (26.2.58)	—	£1200
		a. Printed both sides	£2500	£1300
17		6d. golden bronze	£3750	£2000
18		6d. black-bronze	£2250	£900
19		6d. grey-black (1859)	£2500	£800

(*b*) *Rouletted* 7½ *to* 14 *and compound*

20	5	2d. brown-black/*red*	£3500	£1500
		a. Printed both sides		
21		2d. brown-black/*Indian red*	—	£1800
22		6d. black-bronze	£3000	£950
23		6d. grey-black	—	£1100

The 2d. and 6d. are known pin-perforated.

Prices quoted for Nos. 15/23 are for "cut-square" examples. Collectors are warned against "cut-round" copies with corners added.

(Recess in the colony from P.B. plates)

1860 (11 Aug)–**64**. *W* 4 (*sideways*). (*a*) *Imperf.*

24	1	2d. pale orange	90·00	70·00
25		2d. orange-vermilion	80·00	60·00
25*a*	1	2d. deep vermilion	£300	£400
26		4d. blue (21.6.64)	£250	£500
27		4d. deep blue	£250	£600
28		6d. sage-green (27.7.61)	£1300	£600
28*a*		6d. deep sage-green	—	£700

(*b*) *Rouletted* 7½ *to* 14

29	1	2d. pale orange	£450	£175
30		2d. orange-vermilion	£550	£175
31		4d. deep blue	£2250	
32		6d. sage-green	—	£550

(Recess P.B.)

1861. *W* 4 (*sideways*). (*a*) *Intermediate perf* 14–16.

33	1	1d. rose	£250	80·00
34		2d. blue	£120	45·00
35		4d. vermilion	£300	£180
36		6d. purple-brown	£300	60·00
37		1s. yellow-green	£375	90·00

(*b*) *P* 14 *at Somerset House*

38	1	1d. rose	£120	40·00
39		2d. blue	50·00	29·00
40		4d. vermilion	£140	90·00

(*c*) *Perf clean-cut* 14–16

41	1	2d. blue	65·00	30·00
		a. Imperf between (pair)		
42		6d. purple-brown	£150	35·00
43		1s. yellow-green	£325	45·00

(*d*) *P* 14–16 *very rough* (July)

44	1	1d. rose-carmine	£180	25·00
45		6d. purple/*blue*	£550	£100
46		1s. deep green	£800	£180

Perkins, Bacon experienced considerable problems with their perforating machine during the production of these stamps.

The initial printing showed intermediate perforation 14–16. Further supplies were then sent, in late December 1860, to Somerset House to be perforated on their comb 14 machine. The Inland Revenue Board were only able to process the three lower values, although the 6d. purple-brown and 1s. yellow-green are known from this perforation overprinted "SPECIMEN".

The Perkins, Bacon machine was repaired the following month and the 6d., 1s. and a further supply of the 2d. were perforated on it to give a clean-cut 14–16 gauge.

A final printing was produced in July 1861, but by this time the machine had deteriorated so that it produced a very rough 14–16.

(Recess D.L.R. from P.B. plates)

1863 (16 Dec)–**64**. *No wmk. P* 13.

49	1	1d. carmine-rose	38·00	9·00
50		1d. lake	38·00	8·00
51		6d. deep lilac (15.4.64)	75·00	28·00
51*a*		6d. dull violet (15.4.64)	90·00	32·00

Both values exist on thin and on thick papers, the former being the scarcer.

Both grades of paper show a marginal sheet watermark, "T H SAUNDERS 1860" in double-lined large and small capitals, but parts of this watermark rarely occur on the stamps.

(Recess D.L.R. from P.B. plates)

1864 (27 Dec)–**79**. *Wmk Crown CC* (*sideways on* 1*d.*). *P* 12½.

52	1	1d. bistre	35·00	1·75
53		1d. yellow-ochre (16.10.74)	42·00	5·00
54		2d. chrome-yellow (18.1.65)	38·00	1·25
55		2d. yellow	35·00	1·25
		a. Wmk sideways (5.79)		
		b. Error. Mauve (1879)	£7500	£3500
56		4d. carmine (18.1.65)	38·00	5·00
		a. Doubly printed	£6000	
57		6d. violet (18.1.65)	60·00	9·00
		a. Doubly printed	†	—
		b. Wmk sideways		
58		6d. indigo-violet	£225	28·00
59		6d. lilac (1872)	£120	9·00
60		6d. mauve (12.5.75)	£110	9·00
61		1s. bright green (18.1.65) (H/S S. £85)	70·00	10·00
62		1s. sage-green (10.68)	£200	16·00

Beware of fakes of No. 55b made by altering the value tablet of No. 60.

7

ONE PENNY

(8)

(Typo D.L.R.)

1871 (29 Oct)–**73**. *Wmk Crown CC* (*sideways*). *P* 14.

63	7	3d. pale brown (H/S S. £75)	18·00	4·00
		a. Cinnamon (1873)	17·00	3·50

1874 (10 Dec). *No.* 55 *surch with T* 8 *by Govt Printer.*

67	1	1d. on 2d. yellow (G.)	95·00	28·00
		a. Pair, one without surch		
		b. Surch triple	—	£900
		c. "O" of "ONE" omitted		

Forged surcharges of T 8 are known on stamps wmk Crown CC perf 14, and on Crown CA, perf 12 and 14.

(Recess D.L.R. from P.B. plates)

1876–81. *Wmk Crown CC* (*sideways*). *P* 14.

68	1	1d. ochre	28·00	70
69		1d. bistre (1878)	30·00	2·75
70		1d. yellow-ochre (1879)	27·00	70
71		2d. chrome-yellow	29·00	60
		a. Wmk upright (1877)	29·00	60
74		4d. carmine (1881)	£200	75·00
75		6d. lilac (1877)	75·00	4·50
		a. Wmk upright (1879)		
75*b*		6d. reddish lilac (1879)	75·00	5·50

(Recess D.L.R. from P.B. plates)

1882 (Mar)–**85**. *Wmk Crown CA* (*sideways*). (*a*) *P* 14.

76	1	1d. yellow-ochre	10·00	65
77		2d. chrome-yellow	12·00	65
		a. Wmk upright	†	—

78 1 4d. carmine (8.82) .. .. .. 60·00 8·00
a. Wmk upright (1885) .. ..
79 6d. reddish lilac (1882) .. .. 70·00 3·25
80 6d. lilac (1884) (H/S S. £75) .. .. 70·00 4·00

(b) P 12 × 14

81 1 1d. yellow-ochre (2.83).. .. .. £1000 £140

(c) P 12

82 1 1d. yellow-ochre (2.83).. .. .. 42·00 1·25
83 2d. chrome-yellow (6.83) .. .. 55·00 1·25
a. Imperf between (pair) .. ..
84 4d. carmine (5.83) .. .. .. 95·00 25·00
85 6d. lilac (6.83) .. .. £160 19·00

(Typo D.L.R.)

1882 (July)–95. *Wmk Crown CA (sideways). P 14.*

86 **7** 3d. pale brown .. .. 8·00 70
87 3d. red-brown (12.95) .. .. .. 8·50 70

The 3d. stamps in other colours, watermark Crown CA and perforated 12, are colour trials dating from 1883.

½ 1d. 1d.

(9) (10) (11)

1884 (19 Feb). *Surch with T* **9**, *in red, by Govt Printer.*

89 **1** ½ on 1d. yellow-ochre (No. 76). .. 13·00 7·00
a. Thin bar .. .. .. 70·00 40·00
90 ½ on 1d. yellow-ochre (No. 82). .. 9·00 2·75

Inverted or double surcharges are forgeries made in London about 1886.

The "Thin bar" varieties occur on R12/3, R12/8, R12/13 and R12/18, and show the bar only 0.2 mm thick.

1885 (May). *Nos. 63/a surch, in green, by Govt Printer.*

(a) Thick "1" with slanting top, T **10** (Horizontal Rows 1/5)

91 1d. on 3d. pale brown .. .. .. 24·00 6·00
a. Cinnamon .. .. .. 14·00 4·75
b. Vert pair. Nos. 91/2 ..

(b) Thin "1" with straight top, T **11** (Horizontal Row 6)

92 1d. on 3d. pale brown .. .. .. 38·00 6·00
a. Cinnamon .. .. .. 22·00 7·00

12 13

14 15

(Typo D.L.R.)

1885 (May)–93. *Wmk Crown CA (sideways). P 14.*

94 **12** ½d. yellow-green 95 12
94*a* ½d. green 95 12
95 **13** 1d. carmine (2.90) .. .. .. 1·60 12
96 **14** 2d. bluish grey (6.90) .. .. .. 3·00 25
96*a* 2d. grey .. .. .. 2·00 25
97 **15** 2½d. deep blue (1.5.92) .. .. .. 5·50 50
97*a* 2½d. blue .. .. .. 6·00 50
98 4d. chestnut (7.90) .. .. .. 5·00 45
99 5d. bistre (1.5.92) .. .. .. 10·00 1·25
100 6d. bright violet (1.93).. .. .. 13·00 90
101 1s. pale olive-green (4.90) .. .. 19·00 1·25
102 1s. olive-green.. .. .. .. 18·00 90
94, 96*a*, 97*a*/99, 101 Optd/H/S "Specimen" *Set of* 6 £150

(Recess D.L.R. from P.B. plates)

1888 (Mar–Apr). *Wmk Crown CA (sideways). P 14.*

103 **1** 1d. carmine-pink .. .. .. 11·00 60
104 2d. grey .. .. 19·00 1·60
105 4d. red-brown (April) .. .. 90·00 18·00
103/5 H/S "Specimen" .. .. *Set of* 3 90·00

ONE PENNY Half-penny

(16) (17)

1893 (Feb). *Surch with T* **16**, *in green, by Govt Printer.*

107 **7** 1d. on 3d. pale brown (No. 63) .. .. 8·00 4·00
108 1d. on 3d. cinnamon (No. 63*a*) .. .. 8·00 4·50
a. Double surcharge £450
109 1d. on 3d. pale brown (No. 86) .. .. 24·00 6·00

1895 (21 Nov). *Surch with T* **17** *by Govt Printer. (a) In green.*

110 **7** ½d. on 3d. pale brown (No. 63).. .. 11·00 11·00
110*a* ½d. on 3d. cinnamon (No. 63*a*).. .. 5·50 5·50
b. Surcharge double £450

(b) In red and in green

111*a* **7** ½d. on 3d. cinnamon (No. 63*a*).. .. 90·00
111*b* ½d. on 3d. red-brown (No. 87) .. .. 50·00

Green was the adopted surcharge colour but a trial had earlier been made in red on stamps watermarked Crown CC. As they proved unsatisfactory they were given another surcharge in green. The trial stamps were inadvertently issued and, to prevent speculation, a further printing of the duplicated surcharge was made, but on both papers, Crown CC (No. 111*a*) and Crown CA (No. 111*b*).

18 19

20 21

(Typo D.L.R.)

1898 (Dec)–1907. *Wmk W Crown A, W* **18**. *P* 14.

112 **13** 1d. carmine .. .. .. 2·50 12
113 **14** 2d. bright yellow (1.99) .. .. 3·00 25
114 **19** 2½d. blue (1.01) .. .. .. 4·00 40
115 **20** 6d. bright violet (10.06) .. .. 11·00 65
116 **21** 1s. olive-green (4.07) .. .. 18·00 4·50

22 23 24

25 26 27

28 29 30

31 32 33

(Typo Victorian Govt Printer, Melbourne)

1902 (Oct)–12. *Wmk V and Crown, W* **33** *(sideways on horiz designs).*

(a) P 12½ or 12½ × 12 (horiz), 12 × 12½ (vert)

117 **22** 1d. carmine-rose (1.03) .. .. .. 1·60 12
a. Wmk upright (10.02) .. ..
118 **23** 2d. yellow (4.1.03) .. .. 2·75 12
a. Wmk upright (12.7.04) .. ..
119 **24** 4d. chestnut (4.03) .. .. 4·50 50
a. Wmk upright .. ..
120 **15** 5d. bistre (4.9.05) .. .. 55·00 35·00
121 **25** 8d. apple-green (3.03) .. .. 20·00 2·75
122 **26** 9d. yellow-orange (5.03).. .. 26·00 4·25
a. Wmk upright (11.03) .. ..
123 **27** 10d. red (3.03) .. .. .. 30·00 4·25
124 **28** 2s. bright red/*yellow* .. .. 65·00 14·00
a. Wmk sideways .. ..
b. Orange/yellow (7.06) .. .. 48·00 8·50
c. Brown-red/yellow (5.11) .. .. 48·00 8·50
125 **29** 2s. 6d. deep blue/*rose* .. .. 40·00 9·00
126 **30** 5s. emerald-green .. .. £120 17·00
127 **31** 10s. deep mauve .. .. £250 45·00
a. Bright purple (1910).. .. £275 70·00
128 **32** £1 orange-brown (4.11.02) £500 £200
a. Orange (10.7.09) £950 £350

(b) P 11

129 **22** 1d. carmine-rose .. .. .. 80·00 4·00
a. Wmk upright .. ..
130 **23** 2d. yellow .. .. .. £100 4·50
a. Wmk upright .. ..
131 **24** 4d. chestnut £300 £100
132 **15** 5d. bistre .. .. .. 38·00 16·00
133 **26** 9d. yellow-orange .. .. 55·00 30·00
134 **28** 2s. bright red/*yellow* .. .. £100 50·00
a. Orange/yellow £200 £100

(c) Perf compound of 12½ or 12 and 11

135 **22** 1d. carmine-rose .. .. .. — £160
136 **23** 2d. yellow .. .. .. — £200
137 **24** 4d. chestnut .. ..

Type **22** is similar to Type **13** but larger.

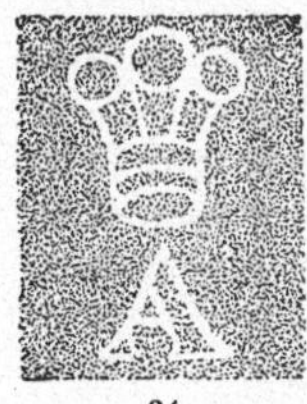

34 35

1905–12. *Wmk Crown and A, W* **34** *(sideways).*

(a) P 12½ or 12½ × 12 (horiz), 12 × 12½ (vert)

138 **12** ½d. green (6.10) 90 15
139 **22** 1d. rose-pink (10.05).. .. .. 1·75 15
a. Wmk upright (1.06) .. .. 1·50 15
b. Carmine (1909) .. .. 1·75 15
c. Carmine-red (1912) .. .. 1·50 15
140 **23** 2d. yellow (15.11.05) .. .. .. 1·40 15
a. Wmk upright (4.10) .. ..
141 **7** 3d. brown (2.06) .. .. .. 3·25 50
142 **24** 4d. bistre-brown (12.06) .. .. 5·00 60
a. Pale chestnut (1908) .. .. 8·00 30
b. Bright brown-red (14.10.10) .. 7·00 30
143 **15** 5d. pale olive-bistre (8.05) .. .. 10·00 75
a. Olive-green (1.09) .. .. 10·00 90
b. Pale greenish yellow (5.12) .. 42·00 27·00
144 **25** 8d. apple-green (22.4.12) .. .. 17·00 3·50
145 **26** 9d. orange (11.5.06) .. .. 17·00 2·40
a. Red-orange (6.10) .. .. 24·00 2·50
b. Wmk upright (7.12) .. .. 21·00 2·50
146 **27** 10d. rose-orange (16.2.10) .. .. 17·00 7·00
148 **30** 5s. emerald-green (9.07) .. .. 70·00 35·00

(b) P 11

150 **12** ½d. green .. .. ..
151 **22** 1d. rose-pink .. .. .. 4·00 75
a. Carmine-red .. .. 4·00 70
b. Wmk upright .. .. 4·00 70
152 **23** 2d. yellow .. .. .. 7·00 1·50
153 **7** 3d. brown .. .. .. 7·00 1·50
154 **24** 4d. yellow-brown .. .. .. £350 85·00
a. Pale chestnut .. ..
155 **15** 5d. pale olive-bistre .. .. 28·00 9·50
a. Olive-green .. .. 15·00 2·50
157 **27** 9d. orange .. .. .. 70·00 75·00
a. Red-orange .. .. — 65·00

(c) Perf compound of 12½ or 12 and 11

161 **22** 1d. rose-pink .. .. .. £150 75·00
162 **23** 2d. yellow .. .. .. £170 80·00
163 **7** 3d. brown .. .. .. £190 85·00
164 **27** 9d. red-orange .. ..

1912 (Mar). *Wmk Crown and A (sideways).* **W 35.** *P* 11½ × 12.

168 **20** 6d. bright violet .. .. .. 12·00 1·25
169 **21** 1s. sage-green .. .. .. 19·00 3·25
a. Perf 12½ (single line) .. ..

1912 (7 Aug). **W 34** *(sideways). Thin paper and white gum (as Victoria).*

170 **7** 3d. brown (*p* 12½) .. .. .. 19·00 17·00
a. Wmk upright .. .. .. 19·00 17·00
171 3d. brown (*p* 11) .. ..
a. Wmk upright .. ..

ONE PENNY

(36)

1912 (6 Nov). *Nos. 140 and 162 surch with T* **36** *in Melbourne.*

(a) P 12½ or 12 × 12½

172 **23** 1d. on 2d. yellow 70 30
a. Wmk upright 70 30

(b) Perf compound of 12½ and 11

173 **23** 1d. on 2d. yellow £275

POSTAL FISCAL STAMPS

I. R.

TWO PENCE I R

(F 1) (F 2)

The Post & Telegraph Act of 5 September 1893 authorised the use of fiscal stamps with values up to and including 1s. for postal purposes and initially stamps Nos. F1/15, issued earlier than 1893, were available.

1893 (5 Sept). *De La Rue provisional issue of Nov 1881 with surch as Type* **F 1**. *Wmk Crown CC. P* 14.

F1 **7** 1d. on 3d. lilac .. .. .. £200 60·00
F2 2d. on 3d. lilac .. .. .. 13·00 5·50
F3 3d. on 3d. lilac .. .. .. 18·00 6·50
F4 6d. on 3d. lilac .. .. .. £110 80·00
F5 1s. on 3d. lilac £300 £190

1893 (5 Sept). *Local provisional issue of* 1881 *with opt Type* **F 2**, *in green. (a) Wmk Crown CC. P* 12½.

F 6 **1** 1d. bistre (52) .. .. .. 90·00 45·00

(b) Wmk Crown CC. P 14

F 7 **1** 1d. ochre (68) .. .. .. 70·00 32·00
F 8 1d. bistre (69) .. .. .. 70·00 32·00
F 9 1d. yellow-ochre (70) .. .. 65·00 30·00

(c) Wmk Crown CA. P 14

F10 **1** 1d. yellow-ochre (76) .. .. 32·00 16·00

Postally used copies of some of the above basic stamps, together with some other issues and values, have been fraudulently overprinted in green, red or black.

F 3

(Typo D.L.R.)

1893 (5 Sept). *Definitive fiscal stamps of Feb* 1882. *Wmk CA over Crown. P* 14.

F11	F 3	1d. dull purple	3·50	75
F12		2d. dull purple	48·00	27·00
F13		3d. dull purple	12·00	1·75
F14		6d. dull purple	16·00	2·75
F15	–	1s. dull purple	20·00	3·00

The 1s. value is as Type F 3 but with rectangular outer frame and circular frame surrounding swan.

Higher values in this series were not validated by the Act for postal use.

The letters CA of the watermark are narrow. A second printing about 1896 had the letters wider.

1897. *Wmk W Crown A, W* **18.** *P* 14.

F19	F 3	1d. dull purple	3·00	65
F20		3d. dull purple	6·00	85
F21		6d. dull purple	8·00	1·25
F22	–	1s. dull purple	13·00	2·00

TELEGRAPH STAMPS USED FOR POSTAGE

The 1d. Telegraph stamps were authorised for postal purposes from 25 October 1886.

T 1

1886 (25 Oct). *Wmk Crown CC.*

T1	T 1	1d. bistre (*p* 12½)	11·00	2·50
T2		1d. bistre (*p* 14)	13·00	4·00

Copies of a similar 6d. value are known postally used, but such use was unauthorised.

OFFICIAL STAMPS

Stamps of the various issues from 1854–85 are found with a circular hole punched out, the earlier size being about 3 mm. in diameter and the later 4 mm. These were used on official correspondence by the Commissariat and Convict Department, branches of the Imperial administration separate from the colonial government. This system of punching ceased by 1886. Subsequently many stamps between Nos. 94 and 148 may be found punctured, "PWD", "WA" or "OS".

Western Australia now uses the stamps of AUSTRALIA.

Western Samoa *see* Samoa

Zambia
(*formerly* Northern Rhodesia)

INDEPENDENT

11 Pres. Kaunda and Victoria Falls

12 College of Further Education, Lusaka

(Des M. Goaman (3d., 6d.), Mrs. G. Ellison (1s. 3d.). Photo Harrison)

1964 (24 Oct). *Independence. T* **11/12** *and similar vert design. P* 13½ × 14½ (6*d.*) *or* 14½ × 13½ (*others*).

91	3d. sepia, yellow-green and blue	8	5
92	6d. deep violet and yellow	10	5
93	1s. 3d. red, black, sepia and orange ..	15	20

Design:—1s. 3d. Barotse dancer.

14 Maize-Farmer and Silo

15 Health—Radiographer

21 Fishing at Mpulungu

22 Tobacco Worker

(Des Mrs. G. Ellison. Photo Harrison)

1964 (24 Oct). *T* **14/15, 21/2** *and similar designs. P* 14½ (½*d. to* 4*d.*), 14½ × 13½ (1*s.* 3*d.*, 2*s. and* £1) *or* 13½ × 14½ (*others*).

94	½d. red, black and yellow-green	5	5
95	1d. brown, black and bright blue	5	5
96	2d. red, deep brown and orange	5	5
97	3d. black and red	5	5
98	4d. black, brown and orange	8	5
99	6d. orange, deep brown & deep bluish green	10	5
100	9d. carmine, black and bright blue.. ..	15	5
101	1s. black, yellow-bistre and blue	25	5
102	1s. 3d. light red, yellow, black and blue ..	25	5
103	2s. bright blue, black, deep brown & orange	35	5
104	2s. 6d. black and orange-yellow	50	35
105	5s. black, yellow and green..	95	65
106	10s. black and orange	2·50	1·25
107	£1 black, brown, yellow and red	3·75	3·75
94/107	.. .. *Set of* 14	8·00	6·00

Designs: *Vert* (*as T* **15**)—2d. Chinyau dancer; 3d. Cotton-picking. (*As T* **22**)—2s. Tonga basket-making; £1 Makishi dancer. *Horiz* (*as T* 14)—4d. Angoni bull. (*As T* **21**)—6d. Communications, old and new; 9d. Zambezi sawmills and Redwood flower; 2s. 6d. Luangwa Game Reserve; 5s. Education—student; 10s. Copper mining.

28 I.T.U. Emblem and Symbols

29 I.C.Y. Emblem

(Photo Harrison)

1965 (26 July). *I.T.U. Centenary. P* 14 × 14½.

108	28	6d. light reddish violet and gold	20	10
109		2s. 6d. brownish grey and gold	60	60

(Photo Harrison)

1965 (26 July). *International Co-operation Year. P* 14½.

110	29	3d. turquoise and gold	15	5
111		1s. 3d. ultramarine and gold	45	45

30 State House, Lusaka

34 W.H.O. Building and U.N. Flag

(Des Mrs. G. Ellison. Photo Harrison)

1965 (18 Oct). *First Anniv of Independence. T* **30** *and similar multicoloured designs. No wmk. P* 13½ × 14½ (3*d.*), 14 × 13½ (6*d.*) *or* 13½ × 14 (*others*).

112	3d. Type **30**	5	5
113	6d. Fireworks, Independence Stadium ..	5	5
114	1s. 3d. Clematopsis (*vert*)	25	25
115	2s. 6d. *Tithonia diversifolia* (*vert*)	50	70

(Des M. Goaman. Photo Harrison)

1966 (18 May). *Inauguration of W.H.O. Headquarters, Geneva. P* 14½.

116	34	3d. lake-brown, gold and new blue ..	12	5
		a. Gold omitted..	40·00	
117		1s. 3d. gold, new blue & deep bluish vio	30	30

ALTERED CATALOGUE NUMBERS

Any Catalogue numbers altered from the last edition are shown as a list in the introductory pages.

35 University Building

36 National Assembly Building

(Des Mrs. G. Ellison. Photo Harrison)

1966 (12 July). *Opening of Zambia University. P* 14½.

118	35	3d. blue-green and copper-bronze ..	5	5
119		1s. 3d. reddish violet and copper-bronze	20	10

(Des Mrs. G. Ellison. Photo Harrison)

1967 (2 May). *Inauguration of National Assembly Building. P* 14½.

120	36	3d. black and gold	5	5
121		6d. olive-green and gold	10	5

37 Airport Scene

(Des Mrs. G. Ellison. Photo Harrison)

1967 (2 Oct). *Opening of Lusaka International Airport. P* 13½ × 14½.

122	37	6d. violet-blue and copper-bronze ..	12	8
123		2s. 6d. brown and copper-bronze ..	40	50

38 Youth Service Badge

39 "Co-operative Farming"

(Des Mrs. G. Ellison. Photo Harrison)

1967 (23 Oct). *National Development. T* **38/9** *and similar designs. P* 13½ × 14½ (6*d.*, 1*s.* 6*d.*) *or* 14½ × 13½ (*others*).

124	4d. black, red and gold	8	5
125	6d. black, gold and violet-blue	12	5
126	9d. black, grey-blue and silver	20	15
127	1s. multicoloured	25	15
128	1s. 6d. multicoloured	40	75

Designs: *Vert*—9d "Communications"; 1s. Coalfields. *Horiz*—1s. 6d. Road link with Tanzania.

(New Currency. 100 ngwee=1 kwacha)

43 Lusaka Cathedral

44 Baobab Tree

52 Chokwe Dancer

53 Kafue Railway Bridge

(Des Mrs. G. Ellison. Photo Harrison)

1968 (16 Jan). *Decimal Currency. T* **43/4, 52/3** *and similar designs. P* 13½ × 14½ (1, 3, 15, 50 *n.*) *or* 14½ × 13½ (*others*).

129	1 n. multicoloured	5	5
	a. Copper-bronze (including value) omitted	35·00	
130	2 n. multicoloured	5	5
131	3 n. multicoloured	8	5
132	5 n. bistre-brown and copper-bronze ..	20	5
133	8 n. multicoloured	20	5
	a. Copper-bronze (background) omitted ..		
134	10 n. multicoloured	25	5
135	15 n. multicoloured	1·75	5
136	20 n. multicoloured	50	5
137	25 n. multicoloured	50	5
138	50 n. chocolate, red-orange & copper-bronze ..	70	25
139	1 k. royal blue and copper-bronze	3·00	90
140	2 k. black and copper-bronze	4·00	3·00
129/40	.. .. *Set of* 12	10·00	4·00

Designs: *Horiz* (*as T* **43**)—3 n. Zambia Airways jetliner. (*As T* **53**)—15 n. *Nudaurelia zambesina*; 2 k. Eland. *Vert* (*as T* **44**) —5 n National Museum, Livingstone; 8 n. Vimbuza dancer; 10 n. Tobacco picking. (*As T* **52**)–20 n. South African Crowned Cranes; 25 n. Angoni warrior.
All values exist with PVA gum as well as gum arabic.

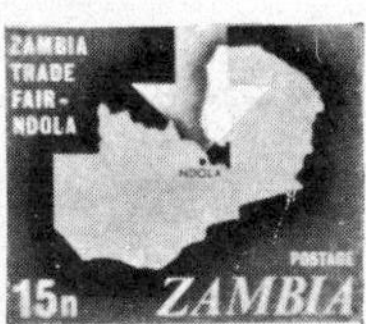

55 Ndola on Outline of Zambia

56 Human Rights Emblem and Heads

(Des Mrs G. Ellison. Photo Harrison)

1968 (29 June). *Trade Fair, Ndola. P* 14.
141 **55** 15 n. green and gold 30 10

(Des Mrs. G. Ellison. Photo and die-stamped (gold emblem) Harrison)

1968 (23 Oct). *Human Rights Year. P* 14.
142 **56** 3 n. deep blue, pale violet and gold . . 10 5

57 W.H.O. Emblem

58 Group of Children

(Des Mrs. G. Ellison. Photo and die-stamped (gold staff and "20") Harrison)

1968 (23 Oct). *20th Anniv of World Health Organization. P* 14.
143 **57** 10 n. gold and bluish violet 20 5

(Des Mrs. G. Ellison. Photo and die-stamped (gold children) Harrison)

1968 (23 Oct). *22nd Anniv. of U.N.I.C.E.F. P* 14.
144 **58** 25 n. black, gold and ultramarine . . 45 70

59 Copper Miner

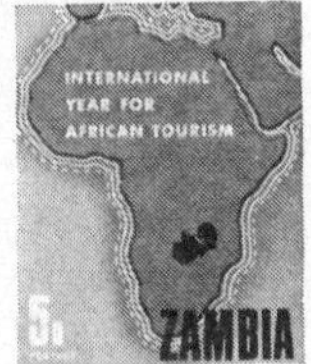

61 Zambia outlined on Map of Africa

(Des Mrs. G. Ellison. Photo Harrison)

1969 (18 June). *50th Anniv of International Labour Organization. T* **59** *and similar design. P* 14½ × 13½ (3 *n.*) *or* 13½ × 14½ (25 *n.*).
145 3 n. copper-bronze and deep violet 15 5
146 25 n. pale yell, copper-bronze & blackish brn 55 70
Design: *Horiz*—25 n. Poling a furnace.
A used example of No. 145 exists with the copper-bronze omitted.

(Des Mrs. G. Ellison. Photo Harrison)

1969 (23 Oct). *International African Tourist Year. T* **61** *and similar multicoloured designs. P* 14 × 14½ (5 *n.*, 25 *n.*) *or* 14½ × 14 (*others*).
147 5 n. Type **61** 15 5
148 10 n. Defassa Waterbuck (*horiz*) 30 5
149 15 n. Golden Perch (*horiz*) 45 35
150 25 n. Carmine Bee Eater . . . . . . 1·25 80

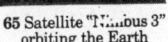

65 Satellite "Nimbus 3" orbiting the Earth

66 Woman collecting Water from Well

(Des Mrs. G. Ellison. Litho Enschedé)

1970 (23 Mar). *World Meteorological Day. P* 13 × 10½.
151 **65** 15 n. multicoloured 40 60

(Des V. Whiteley (from local designs). Litho B.W.)

1970 (4 July). *Preventive Medicine. T* **66** *and similar vert designs. P* 13½ × 12.
152 3 n. multicoloured 12 5
153 15 n. multicoloured 30 40
154 25 n. greenish blue, rosine and sepia 50 65
Designs:—15 n. Child on scales; 25 n. Child being immunized.

67 "Masks" (mural by Gabriel Ellison

68 Ceremonial Axe

(Des Mrs. G. Ellison. Litho Harrison)

1970 (8 Sept). *Conference of Non-Aligned Nations. P* 14 × 14½.
155 **67** 15 n. multicoloured 40 50

(Des Mrs. G. Ellison. Litho D.L.R.)

1970 (30 Nov). *Traditional Crafts. T* **68** *and similar multicoloured designs. P* 13½ (15 *n.*), 12½ (25 *n.*) *or* 14 (*others*).
156 3 n. Type **68** 12 5
157 5 n. Clay Smoking-Pipe Bowl 15 5
158 15 n. Makishi Mask (30 × 47 *mm*) 50 50
159 25 n. Kuomboka Ceremony (72 × 19 *mm*) . . 90 1·25
MS160 133 × 83 mm. Nos. 156/9. Imperf. . . 5·50 7·00

69 Dag Hammarskjöld and U.N. General Assembly

(Des J.W. Litho Questa)

1971 (18 Sept). *Tenth Death Anniv of Dag Hammarskjöld. T* **69** *and similar horiz designs, each with portrait of Hammarskjöld. Multicoloured. P* 13½.
161 4 n. Type **69** 5 5
162 10 n. Tail of aircraft 10 5
163 15 n. Dove of Peace 25 20
164 25 n. Memorial tablet . . . . 50 1·10

70 Red-breasted Bream

71 Porcupine

(Des G. Drummond. Litho J.W.)

1971 (10 Dec). *Fish. T* **70** *and similar horiz designs. Multicoloured. P* 13½.
165 4 n. Type **70** 12 10
166 10 n. Green-headed Bream 35 20
167 15 n. Tiger fish . . . . 75 1·25

(Des and litho J.W.)

1972 (15 Mar). *Conservation Year* (1st issue). *T* **71** *and similar multicoloured designs. P* 13½.
168 4 n. Cheetah (58 × 21 *mm*) 25 25
169 10 n. Lechwe (58 × 21 *mm*) 60 60
170 15 n. Type **71** . . . . 1·00 1·00
171 25 n. Elephant . . . . 2·25 2·25

(Des and litho J.W.)

1972 (30 June). *Conservation Year* (2nd issue). *Designs similar to T* **71**. *Multicoloured. P* 13½.
172 4 n. Soil conservation 25 25
173 10 n. Forestry 60 60
174 15 n. Water (58 × 21 *mm*) 85 85
175 25 n. Maize (58 × 21 *mm*) . . . . . . 1·60 1·60

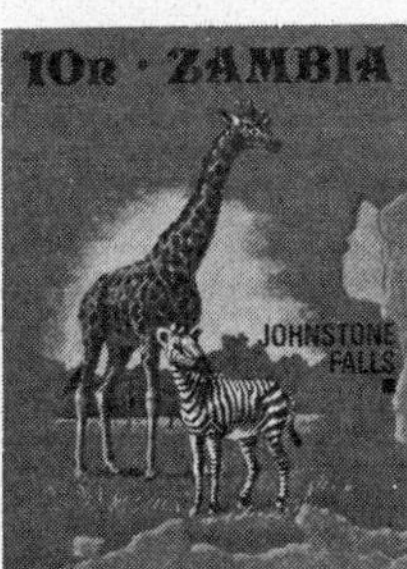

72 Giraffe and Zebra

(Des and litho J.W.)

1972 (30 June). *National Parks. Sheet* 114 × 140 *mm containing T* **72** *and similar vert designs. Multicoloured. P* 13½.
MS176 10 n. (× 4) giraffe and zebra; rhino; hippo and deer; lion . . . . 7·00 9·00
Each design includes part of a map showing Zambian National Parks, the four forming a composite design.

73 Zambian Flowers

(Des and litho J.W.)

1972 (22 Sept). *Conservation Year* (3rd issue). *T* **73** *and similar horiz designs. Multicoloured. P* 13½.
177 4 n. Type **73** 40 40
178 10 n. Citrus Swallowtail Butterfly 90 90
179 15 n. Bees . . . . 1·50 1·50
180 25 n. Red Locusts . . . . 2·25 2·25

74 Mary and Joseph

75 *Oudenodon* and *Rubidgea*

(Des V. Whiteley. Litho Questa)

1972 (1 Dec). *Christmas. T* **74** *and similar horiz designs. Multicoloured. P* 14.
181 4 n. Type **74** 5 5
182 9 n. Mary, Joseph and Jesus 10 5
183 15 n. Mary, Jesus and the shepherds 30 20
184 25 n. The Three Wise Men 45 80

(Des Mrs. G. Ellison; adapted J.W. Litho Questa)

1973 (1 Feb). *Zambian Prehistoric Animals. T* **75** *and similar horiz designs. Multicoloured. P* 14 × 13½ (4 *n.*) *or* 13½ × 14 (*others*).
185 4 n. Type **75** . . . . 1·00 90
186 9 n. Broken Hill Man . . . . 1·10 1·00
187 10 n. *Zambiasaurus* . . . . 1·40 1·25
188 15 n. *Luangwa drysdalli* . . . . . . 1·75 1·90
189 25 n. *Glossopteris* . . . . 2·50 2·75
Nos. 186/9 are smaller (38 × 21 mm) and show fossils.

76 "Dr. Livingstone, I Presume"

(Des J.W. Litho Format)

1973 (1 May). *Death Centenary of Dr. Livingstone. T* **76** *and similar horiz designs. Multicoloured. P* 13½.
190 3 n. Type **76** 20 15
191 4 n. Scripture Lesson 20 15
192 9 n. Victoria Falls 45 40
193 10 n. Scattering slavers 45 45
194 15 n. Healing the sick 85 90
195 25 n. Burial place of Livingstone's heart . . 1·25 1·50
190/5 . . . . *Set of* 6 3·00 3·25

77 Parliamentary Mace

(Des Mrs. G. Ellison. Litho Questa)

1973 (24 Sept). *Third Commonwealth Conference of Speakers and Presiding Officers, Lusaka. P* 13½.
196 **77** 9 n. multicoloured . . . . . . 1·25 80
197 15 n. multicoloured . . . . . . 1·50 1·50
198 25 n. multicoloured . . . . . . 2·25 2·25

78 Inoculation

79 U.N.I.P. Flag

(Des Mrs. G. Ellison. Litho Questa)

1973 (16 Oct). *25th Anniv of W.H.O. T* **78** *and similar multi-coloured designs. P* 14.

199	4 n. Mother washing baby (*vert*)	48·00	20·00
200	9 n. Nurse weighing baby (*vert*)	45	55
201	10 n. Type **78**	50	65
202	15 n. Child eating meal	90	1·50

Only a small quantity of No. 199 was produced, and most examples were issued to post offices for local use.

(Des Mrs. G. Ellison. Litho Questa)

1973 (13 Dec). *1st Anniv of Second Republic. T* **79** *and similar vert designs. Multicoloured. P* 14 × 13½.

203	4 n. Type **79**	14·00	6·50
204	9 n. Freedom House	50	50
205	10 n. Army band	50	55
206	15 n. "Celebrations" (dancers)	90	1·25
207	25 n. Presidential chair	1·75	2·25

80 President Kaunda at Mulungushi

81 Nakambala Sugar Estate

(Des Mrs. G. Ellison. Litho Harrison)

1974 (28 Apr). *President Kaunda's 50th Birthday. T* **80** *and similar horiz designs. Multicoloured. P* 14½ × 14 (4 *n.*) *or* 14 × 14½ (*others*).

208	4 n. Type **80**	1·40	1·25
209	9 n. President's former residence	80	90
210	15 n. President holding Independence flame	1·60	2·25

(Des G. Vasarhelyi. Litho Questa)

1974 (23 Oct). *Tenth Anniv of Independence. T* **81** *and similar horiz designs. Multicoloured. P* 13½.

211	3 n. Type **81**	20	15
212	4 n. Local market	20	15
213	9 n. Kapiri glass factory	45	45
214	10 n. Kafue hydro-electric scheme	50	50
215	15 n. Kafue hook bridge	90	1·00
216	25 n. Non-aligned Conference, Lusaka, 1970	1·40	1·50
211/16	*Set of* 6	3·25	3·25
MS217	141 × 105 mm. 15 n. (× 4) Academic Education; Teacher Training College; Technical Education; Zambia University	6·00	6·50

82 Mobile Post-van

(Des Mrs. G. Ellison. Litho Format)

1974 (15 Nov). *Centenary of Universal Postal Union. T* **82** *and similar horiz designs. Multicoloured. P* 13½.

218	4 n. Type **82**	25	20
219	9 n. Aeroplane on tarmac	60	50
220	10 n. Chipata Post Office	60	55
221	15 n. Modern training centre	1·10	1·75

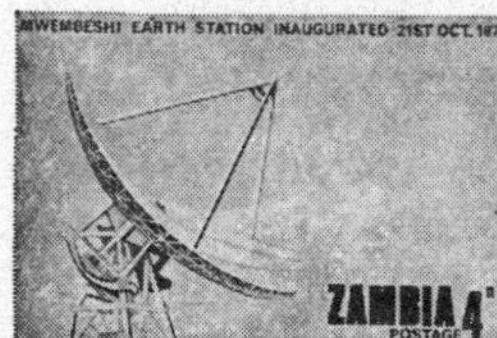

83 Dish Aerial

(Des Mrs. G. Ellison. Litho Questa)

1974 (15 Dec). *Opening of Mwembeshi Earth Station* (21 *October*). *T* **83** *and similar horiz designs. Multicoloured. P* 13½.

222	4 n. Type **83**	30	30
223	9 n. View at dawn	65	65
224	15 n. View at dusk	1·00	1·00
225	25 n. Aerial view	1·75	2·25

84 Rhinoceros and Calf

85 Independence Monument

(Des Mrs. G. Ellison. Litho J.W.)

1975 (2 Jan). *T* **84/5** *and similar horiz designs. Multicoloured.*

(*a*) *Size as T* **84**. *P* 13½ × 14

226	1 n. Type **84**	5	5
227	2 n. Helmet Guineafowl	10	5
228	3 n. National Dancing Troupe	10	5
229	4 n. African Fish Eagle	15	5
230	5 n. Knife-edge Bridge	15	5
231	8 n. Sitatunga (antelope)	15	5
232	9 n. Elephant, Kasaba Bay	20	5
233	10 n. Giant Pangolin	20	5

(*b*) *Size as T* **85**. *P* 13

234	15 n. Type **85**	25	5
	a. Magenta omitted		
235	20 n. Harvesting groundnuts	25	15
236	25 n. Tobacco-growing	30	10
237	50 n. Flying-Doctor service	65	60
238	1 k. Lady Ross's Turaco	1·75	1·50
239	2 k. Village scene	2·25	2·75
226/39	*Set of* 14	6·00	5·00

No. 234a shows much of the design in yellow-green due to the omission of the magenta which was used as an overlay on other colours.

86 Map of Namibia

87 Erection of Sprinkler Irrigation

(Des PAD Studio. Litho Questa)

1975 (26 Aug). *Namibia Day. P* 13½.

240	**86**	4 n. green and light yellow-green	35	20
241		9 n. steel-blue and light turquoise-green	40	30
242		15 n. orange-yellow and greenish yellow	75	65
243		25 n. orange and light orange	1·00	1·10

(Des and litho J.W.)

1975 (16 Dec). *Silver Jubilee of the International Commission on Irrigation and Drainage. T* **87** *and similar horiz designs. Multi-coloured. P* 13.

244	4 n. Type **87**	25	25
245	9 n. Sprinkler irrigation (*different*)	55	55
246	15 n. Furrow irrigation	1·00	1·50

88 Mutondo

(Des A. Chimfwembe. Litho J.W.)

1976 (22 Mar). *World Forestry Day. T* **88** *and similar horiz designs showing trees. Multicoloured. P* 13.

247	3 n. Type **88**	10	5
248	4 n. Mukunyu	10	5
249	9 n. Mukusi	25	25
250	10 n. Mopane	25	25
251	15 n. Musuku	45	70
252	25 n. Mukwa	55	85
247/52	*Set of* 6	1·50	1·90

89 Passenger Train

(Des A. Chimfwembe. Litho J.W.)

1976 (10 Dec). *Opening of Tanzania-Zambia Railway. T* **89** *and similar horiz designs. Multicoloured. P* 13½ (**MS**257) *or* 13 (*others*).

253	4 n. Type **89**	30	30
254	9 n. Copper exports	55	55
255	15 n. Machinery imports	90	95
256	25 n. Goods train	1·40	1·75
MS257	140 × 106 mm. 10 n. Clearing bush; 15 n. Laying track; 20 n. Railway workers; 25 n. Completed track	3·50	4·00

90 Kayowe Dance

91 Grimwood's Longclaw

(Des BG Studio. Litho Questa)

1977 (18 Jan). *Second World Black and African Festival of Arts and Culture, Nigeria. T* **90** *and similar horiz designs. Multi-coloured. P* 13½.

258	4 n. Type **90**	15	10
259	9 n. Lilombola dance	35	35
260	15 n. Initiation ceremony	60	60
261	25 n. Munkhwele dance	95	1·40

(Des Mrs. G. Ellison. Litho Questa)

1977 (1 July). *Birds of Zambia. T* **91** *and similar vert designs. Multicoloured. P* 14½.

262	4 n. Type **91**	40	10
263	9 n. Shelley's Sunbird	70	60
264	10 n. Black-cheeked Sunbird	70	60
265	15 n. Locust Finch	1·40	1·40
266	20 n. Black-chinned Tinkerbird	1·60	1·75
267	25 n. Chaplin's Barbet	2·00	2·10
262/7	*Set of* 6	6·00	6·00

92 Girls with Building Blocks

(Des Mrs. G. Ellison. Litho Questa)

1977 (20 Oct). *Decade for Action to Combat Racism and Racial Discrimination. T* **92** *and similar horiz designs. Multicoloured. P* 14 × 14½.

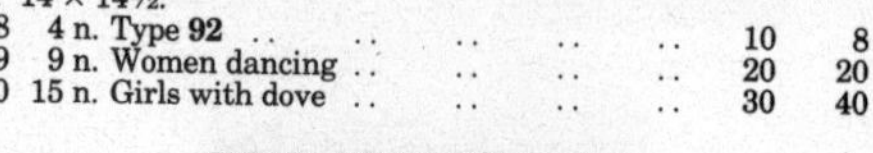

268	4 n. Type **92**	10	8
269	9 n. Women dancing	20	20
270	15 n. Girls with dove	30	40

93 Angels and Shepherds

(Des Mrs. G. Ellison. Litho J.W.)

1977 (20 Dec). *Christmas. T* **93** *and similar horiz designs. Multi-coloured. P* 14.

271	4 n. Type **93**	8	8
272	9 n. The Holy Family	15	20
273	10 n. The Magi	20	20
274	15 n. Jesus presented to Simeon	30	35

94 Elephant and Road Check

=8n

(95)

(Des Mrs. G. Ellison. Litho Questa)

1978 (1 Aug). *Anti-Poaching Campaign. T* **94** *and similar horiz designs. Multicoloured. P* 14 × 14½.

275	8 n. Type **94**	12	12
276	18 n. Kafue Lechwe and river-boat patrol	30	35
277	28 n. Warthog and helicopter	45	55
278	32 n. Cheetah and game guard patrol	50	65

1979 (15 Mar). *Nos.* 228, 232, 234 *and* 236 *surch as T* **95**.

279	8 n. on 9 n. Elephant, Kasaba Bay	8	8
	a. Surch inverted		
280	10 n. on 3 n. National Dancing Troupe	8	8
	a. Surch inverted		

281 18 n. on 25 n. Tobacco-growing 12 15
a. Surch inverted .. ..
282 28 n. on 15 n. Type **85** 20 25
a. Surch inverted .. .. 7·00
b. Albino surch .. ..

96 Kayowe Dance

97 "Kalulu and the Tug of War"

(Des Mrs. G. Ellison. Litho Questa)

1979 (1 Aug). *Commonwealth Summit Conference, Lusaka. T* **96** *and similar horiz designs. Multicoloured. P* 14.
283 18 n. Type **96** 25 30
284 32 n. Kutambala dance 35 50
285 42 n. Chitwansombo drummers 50 75
286 58 n. Lilombola dance 70 95

(Des Mrs. G. Ellison. Litho Questa)

1979 (21 Sept). *International Year of the Child. Illustrations from Children's Books. T* **97** *and similar vert designs. Multicoloured. P* 14.
287 18 n. Type **97** 30 30
288 32 n. "Why the Zebra has no Horns" 45 50
289 42 n. "How the Tortoise got his Shell" 50 75
290 58 n. "Kalulu and the Lion" 70 95
MS291 90 × 120 mm. Nos. 287/90 .. .. 2·25 2·50

98 Children of Different Races holding Anti-Apartheid Emblem

(Des Mrs. G. Ellison. Litho Questa)

1979 (13 Nov). *International Anti-Apartheid Year. T* **98** *and similar horiz designs showing children of different races together. Multicoloured. P* 14½.
292 18 n. Type **98** 25 30
293 32 n. Children with toy car 35 50
294 42 n. Young children with butterfly 50 75
295 58 n. Children with microscope 70 95

99 Sir Rowland Hill and 2s. Definitive Stamp of 1964

LONDON 1980

(**100**)

(Des Mrs. G. Ellison. Litho Format)

1979 (20 Dec). *Death Centenary of Sir Rowland Hill. T* **99** *and similar horiz designs. Multicoloured. P* 14½.
296 18 n. Type **99** 20 25
297 32 n. Sir Rowland Hill and mailman 40 45
298 42 n. Sir Rowland Hill and Northern Rhodesia 1963 ½d. definitive stamp 50 55
299 58 n. Sir Rowland Hill and mail-carrying oxwaggon 65 85
MS300 112 × 89 mm. Nos. 296/9 .. .. .. 2·00 2·25

1980 (6 May). *"London 1980" International Stamp Exhibition. Nos. 296/300 optd with T* **100**.
301 18 n. Type **99** 35 25
302 32 n. Sir Rowland Hill and mailman 55 45
303 42 n. Sir Rowland Hill and Northern Rhodesia 1963 ½d. definitive stamp 70 65
304 58 n. Sir Rowland Hill and mail-carrying oxwaggon 90 85
MS305 112 × 89 mm. Nos. 301/4 .. .. .. 2·25 2·50

101 Rotary Anniversary Emblem

(Des J.W. Litho Questa)

1980 (18 June). *75th Anniv of Rotary International. P* 14.
306 **101** 8 n. multicoloured 10 12
307 32 n. multicoloured 50 50
308 42 n. multicoloured 55 60
309 58 n. multicoloured 80 90
MS310 115 × 89 mm. Nos. 306/9 .. .. .. 1·90 2·10

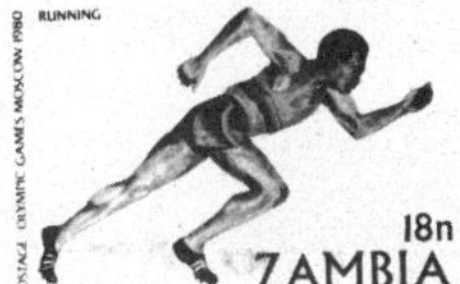

102 Running

(Des Mrs. G. Ellison. Litho J.W.)

1980 (19 July). *Olympic Games, Moscow. T* **102** *and similar horiz designs. Multicoloured. P* 13.
311 18 n. Type **102** 25 30
312 32 n. Boxing 40 45
313 42 n. Football 45 55
314 58 n. Swimming .. .. 80 1·00
MS315 142 × 144 mm. Nos. 311/14. P 14 .. .. 1·90 2·10

103 Zaddach's Forester

104 Zambia Coat of Arms

(Des Mrs. G. Ellison. Litho Questa)

1980 (27 Aug). *Butterflies. T* **103** *and similar horiz designs. Multicoloured. P* 14.
316 18 n. Type **103** 25 30
317 32 n. Northern Highflier 45 50
318 42 n. Zambezi Skipper 55 65
319 58 n. Modest Blue 70 90
MS320 114 × 86 mm. Nos. 316/19 .. .. 1·90 2·40

(Des Mrs. G. Ellison. Litho Format)

1980 (22 Sept). *26th Commonwealth Parliamentary Association Conference, Lusaka. P* 14.
321 **104** 18 n. multicoloured 25 30
322 32 n. multicoloured 40 50
323 42 n. multicoloured 45 70
324 58 n. multicoloured 65 95

105 Nativity and St. Francis of Assisi (stained glass window, Ndola Church)

106 Musikili

(Des Mrs. G. Ellison. Litho Questa)

1980 (3 Nov). *50th Anniv of Catholic Church on the Copperbelt. P* 13½.
325 **105** 8 n. multicoloured 10 12
326 28 n. multicoloured 35 50
327 32 n. multicoloured 35 50
328 42 n. multicoloured 40 65

(Des Mrs. G. Ellison. Litho Questa)

1981 (21 Mar). *World Forestry Day. Seedpods. T* **106** *and similar horiz designs. Multicoloured. P* 14.
329 8 n. Type **106** 10 10
330 18 n. Mupapa 30 40
331 28 n. Mulunguti 40 50
332 32 n. Mulama 45 65

107 I.T.U. Emblem

108 Mask Maker

(Des J.W. Litho Format)

1981 (15 May). *World Telecommunications and Health Day. T* **107** *and similar vert design. Multicoloured. P* 14½.
333 8 n. Type **107** 10 10
334 18 n. W.H.O. emblems 35 35
335 28 n. Type **107** 60 60
336 32 n. As 18 n. 75 75

(Des Mrs. G. Ellison. Litho Harrison)

1981 (2 June)–**83**. *Multicoloured designs as T* **108**. *P* 14 × 13½ *(50 n., 75 n., 1 k., 2 k.) or* 14½ *(others).*
337 1 n. Type **108** 5 5
338 2 n. Blacksmith 5 5
339 5 n. Pottery making 5 5
340 8 n. Straw-basket fishing 5 8
341 10 n. Thatching 8 10
342 12 n. Mushroom picking (17.2.83) 10 12
343 18 n. Millet grinding on stone 12 15
344 28 n. Royal Barge paddler (11.11.81) 20 25
345 30 n. Makishi tightrope dancer (11.11.81) .. 20 25
346 35 n. Tonga Ila granary and house (11.11.81) 25 30
347 42 n. Cattle herding (11.11.81) 30 35
348 50 n. Traditional healer (38 × 26 *mm*) (11.11.81) 35 40
349 75 n. Women carrying water (38 × 26 *mm*) (17.2.83) 50 55
350 1 k. Pounding maize (38 × 26 *mm*) (17.2.83) 70 75
351 2 k. Pipe-smoking, Gwembe Valley Belle (38 × 26 *mm*) .. .. 1·40 1·50
337/48 .. .. *Set of* 15 4·00 5·50

109 Kankobele

110 Banded Ironstone

(Des Mrs. G. Ellison. Litho Format)

1981 (30 Sept*). *Traditional Musical Instruments. T* **109** *and similar vert designs. Multicoloured. P* 15.
356 8 n. Type **109** 10 10
357 18 n. Inshingili 25 25
358 28 n. Ilimba 35 35
359 32 n. Bango 40 40

*It has been reported that the Ndola Philatelic Bureau inadvertently sold some of these stamps some days earlier, and that cancelled-to-order examples exist postmarked 14 or 15 September.

(Des Mrs. G. Ellison. Litho Questa)

1982 (5 Jan). *Minerals (1st series). T* **110** *and similar vert designs. Multicoloured. P* 14.
360 8 n. Type **110** 10 10
361 18 n. Cobaltocalcite 40 30
362 28 n. Amazonite 45 35
363 32 n. Tourmaline 45 35
364 42 n. Uranium ore 70 50

See also Nos. 370/4.

111 Zambian Scouts

(Des Mrs. G. Ellison. Litho Questa)

1982 (30 Mar). *75th Anniv of Boy Scout Movement. T* **111** *and similar horiz designs. Multicoloured. P* 14.
365 8 n. Type **111** 15 10
366 18 n. Lord Baden-Powell and Victoria Falls .. 40 35
367 28 n. Buffalo and Zambian Scout patrol pennant 40 40
368 1 k. African Fish Eagle and Zambian Conservation badge .. .. 1·50 1·50
MS369 105 × 78 mm. Nos. 365/8 .. .. .. 2·25 2·50

(Des Mrs. G. Ellison. Litho Questa)

1982 (1 July). *Minerals (2nd series). Vert designs as T* **110**. *Multicoloured. P* 14.
370 8 n. Bornite 10 10
371 18 n. Chalcopyrite 40 30
372 28 n. Malachite 45 40
373 32 n. Azurite 45 40
374 42 n. Vanadinite 70 60

112 Drilling Rig, 1926

(Des Mrs G. Ellison. Litho Harrison)

1983 (26 Jan). *Early Steam Engines. T* **112** *and similar horiz designs. Multicoloured. P* 14 × 14½.
375 8 n. Type **112** 10 8
376 18 n. Fowler road locomotive, 1900 .. .. 20 20
377 28 n. Borsig ploughing engine, 1925 .. .. 35 40
378 32 n. 7th Class locomotive, 1900 .. .. .. 35 40

113 Cotton Picking

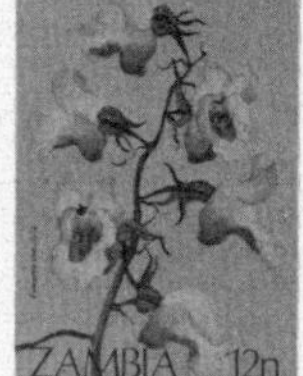

114 *Eulophia cucullata*

(Des Mrs G. Ellison. Litho Harrison)

1983 (10 Mar). *Commonwealth Day. T* **113** *and similar horiz designs. Multicoloured. P* 14 × 13½.

379	12 n. Type **113**	15	12
380	18 n. Mining	20	20
381	28 n. Ritual pot and traditional dances	30	35
382	1 k. Violet-crested Turaco and Victoria Falls	1·00	1·10

(Des Mrs G. Ellison. Litho Questa)

1983 (26 May). *Wild Flowers. T* **114** *and similar vert designs. Multicoloured. P* 14.

383	12 n. Type **114**	15	12
384	28 n. *Kigelia africana*	30	30
385	35 n. *Protea gaguedi*	35	40
386	50 n. *Leonotis nepetifolia*	55	70
MS387	141 × 71 mm. Nos. 383/6. P 12	1·25	1·50

115 Thornicroft's Giraffe

(Des Mrs. G. Ellison. Litho Harrison)

1983 (21 July). *Zambia Wildlife. T* **115** *and similar horiz designs. Multicoloured. P* 14 × 13½.

388	12 n. Type **115**	15	12
	a. Orange-brown and brown (inscr and face value) omitted		
389	28 n. Cookson's Wildebeest	30	30
390	35 n. Black Lechew	35	45
391	1 k. Yellow-backed Duiker	1·00	1·40

116 Tiger Fish

117 The Annunciation

(Des Mrs. G. Ellison. Litho J.W.)

1983 (29 Sept). *Zambia Fishes. T* **116** *and similar horiz designs. Multicoloured. P* 14.

392	12 n. Type **116**	15	12
393	28 n. Silver Barbel	30	35
394	35 n. Spotted Squeaker	35	45
395	38 n. Red-breasted Bream	35	45

(Des Mrs. G. Ellison. Litho J.W.)

1983 (12 Dec). *Christmas. T* **117** *and similar vert designs. Multicoloured. P* 14.

396	12 n. Type **117**	10	12
397	28 n. The Shepherds	25	30
398	35 n. Three Kings	30	35
399	38 n. Flight into Egypt	35	40

118 Boeing "737"

(Des Mrs. G. Ellison. Litho Harrison)

1984 (26 Jan). *Air Transport. T* **118** *and similar horiz designs. Multicoloured. P* 14 × 13½.

400	12 n. Type **118**	10	12
401	28 n. "Beaver"	25	30
402	35 n. Short "Solent" flying boat	30	35
403	1 k. "D.H.66 Hercules"	80	85

119 Receiving Flowers

120 Football

(Des and litho J.W.)

1984 (28 Apr). *60th Birthday of President Kaunda. T* **119** *and similar multicoloured designs. P* 14½ × 14 (12 *n*., 60 *n*.) *or* 14 × 14½ (*others*).

404	12 n. Type **119**	10	12
405	28 n. Swearing-in ceremony (*vert*)	20	25
406	60 n. Planting cherry tree	50	55
407	1 k. Opening of 5th National Assembly (*vert*)	80	85

(Des Mrs. G. Ellison. Litho Format)

1984 (18 July). *Olympic Games, Los Angeles. T* **120** *and similar vert designs. Multicoloured. P* 14½ × 14.

408	12 n. Type **120**	10	12
409	28 n. Running	20	25
410	35 n. Hurdling	25	30
411	50 n. Boxing	40	45

121 Gaboon Viper

(Des Mrs. G. Ellison. Litho Harrison)

1984 (5 Sept). *Reptiles. T* **121** *and similar horiz designs. Multicoloured. P* 14.

412	12 n. Type **121**	10	12
413	28 n. Chameleon	20	25
414	35 n. Nile Crocodile	25	30
415	1 k. Blue-headed Agama	80	85
MS416	120 × 101 mm. Nos. 412/15	1·40	1·50

122 Pres. Kaunda and Mulungushi Rock

123 *Amanita flammeola*

(Des Mrs. G. Ellison. Litho Harrison)

1984 (22 Oct). *26th Anniv of United National Independence Party* (12 *n*.) *and 20th Anniv of Independence* (*others*). *T* **122** *and similar horiz designs. Multicoloured. P* 14.

417	12 n. Type **122**	10	12
418	28 n. Freedom Statue	20	25
419	1 k. Pres. Kaunda and agricultural produce ("Lima Programme")	80	85

(Des Mrs. G. Ellison. Litho J.W.)

1984 (12 Dec). *Fungi. T* **123** *and similar vert designs. Multicoloured. P* 14 × 14½.

420	12 n. Type **123**	10	12
421	28 n. *Amanita zambiana*	20	25
422	32 n. *Termitomyces letestui*	25	30
423	75 n. *Cantharellus miniatescens*	55	60

POSTAGE DUE STAMPS

D 3

(Des D. Smith. Litho Govt Printer, Lusaka)

1964 (24 Oct). *P* 12½.

D11	D 3	1d. orange	30	65
D12		2d. deep blue	45	80
D13		3d. lake	55	1·10
D14		4d. ultramarine	60	1·60
D15		6d. purple	75	1·75
D16		1s. light emerald	1·50	3·75
D11/16		*Set of* 6	3·75	8·75

In all values the left-hand vertical row of the sheet is imperf at left and the bottom horizontal row is imperf at bottom. The above were crudely perforated, resulting in variations in the sizes of the stamps.

The above were withdrawn on 15 January 1968 and thereafter decimal currency postage stamps were used for postage due purposes with appropriate cancellations.

Appendix

The following stamps have either been issued in excess of postal needs, or have not been made available to the public in reasonable quantities at face value. Miniature sheets, imperforate stamps etc., are excluded from this section.

1984

Olympic Games, Los Angeles. 90 *n*. × 5, *each embossed on gold foil*.

Zanzibar

Stamps of INDIA were used in Zanzibar from 1 October 1875 until 10 November 1895, when the administration of the postal service was transferred from India to British East Africa.

A French post office was opened on the island in January 1889 and this service used the stamps of FRANCE until 1894 when specific stamps for this office were provided. The French postal service on the island closed on 31 July 1904 and it is known that French stamps were again utilised during the final month.

A German postal agency operated in Zanzibar between 27 August 1890 and 31 July 1891, using the stamps of GERMANY.

PRICES FOR STAMPS ON COVER TO 1945

Nos. 1/2	—
Nos. 3/18	*from* × 12
Nos. 19/21	—
Nos. 22/40	*from* × 4
Nos. 41/6	*from* × 5
Nos. 156/74	*from* × 3
Nos. 175/7	—
Nos. 178/87	*from* × 10
Nos. 188/204	*from* × 3
Nos. 205/9	*from* × 5
Nos. 210/38	*from* × 3
Nos. 239/45	—
Nos. 246/59	*from* × 3
Nos. 260/*f*	—
Nos. 261/330	*from* × 2
Nos. D1/17	*from* × 10
Nos. D18/24	*from* × 12
Nos. D25/30	*from* × 10

PROTECTORATE

Zanzibar
(1)

1895 (10 Nov). *Contemporary stamps of India optd with T* **1**.

(a) In blue

1	**23**	½ a. blue-green	£2250	£700
2	**25**	1 a. plum	£700	£250
		j. "Zanzidar"	—	£3250

(b) In black

3	**23**	½ a. blue-green	2·25	2·50
		j. "Zanzidar"	£225	£160
		k. "Zanibar"	£250	£180
		l. Diaeresis over last "a"	£110	
4	**25**	1 a. plum	2·50	2·25
		j. "Zanzidar"	£275	£200
		k. "Zanibar"	£250	£200
5	**26**	1 a. 6 p. sepia	2·75	2·75
		j. "Zanzidar"	£325	£250
		k. "Zanibar"	£250	£200
		l. "Zanizbar"	£500	
		m. Diaeresis over last "a"	£110	
6	**27**	2 a. pale blue	2·50	2·75
7		2 a. blue	3·00	3·25
		j. "Zanzidar"	£500	£425
		k. "Zanibar"	£350	£275
		l. Diaeresis over last "a"	£120	
		m. Opt double	£130	
8	**36**	2½ a. yellow-green	3·25	3·00
		j. "Zanzidar"	£350	£250
		k. "Zanibar"	£120	£150
		l. "Zapzibar"		
		m. "Zanzipar"	£350	
		n. Diaeresis over last "a"	£130	
		o. Second "z" italic	30·00	
9	**28**	3 a. orange	5·50	6·50
10		3 a. brown-orange	4·50	6·50
		j. Zanzidar"	£160	£190
		k. "Zanizbar"	£800	£800
11	**29**	4 a. olive-green	8·50	8·50
12		4 a. slate-green	7·50	8·50
		j. "Zanzidar"	£600	£425
13	**21**	6 a. pale brown	8·00	9·00
		j. "Zanzidar"	£450	£450
		k. "Zanibar"	£275	£275
		l. "Zanzibarr"	£600	£600
		m. Opt double		
14	**31**	8 a. dull mauve	12·00	12·00
		j. "Zanzidar"	£700	£700
15		8 a. magenta	8·00	9·00
16	**32**	12 a. purple/*red*	8·00	10·00
		j. "Zanzidar"	£700	£700
17	**33**	1 r. slate	50·00	55·00
		j. "Zanzidar"	£1100	£1100
18	**37**	1 r. green and carmine	9·00	11·00
		j. Opt vert downwards	£160	
19	**38**	2 r. carmine and yellow-brown	23·00	26·00
		j. "r" omitted	£1100	
		k. "r" inverted	£400	£400
20		3 r. brown and green	20·00	23·00
		j. "r" omitted	£1100	
		k. "r" inverted	£375	£425
21		5 r. ultramarine and violet	20·00	23·00
		j. "r" omitted	£1100	
		k. "r" inverted	£375	£425
		l. Opt double, one inverted	£225	
3/21		*Set of* 15	£150	£170

Many forgeries of this overprint exist and also bogus errors.

MINOR VARIETIES. The following minor varieties of type exist on Nos. 1/21:

A. First "Z" antique (all values)
B. Broken "p" for "n" (all values to 1 r.)
C. Tall second "z" (all values)
D. Small second "z" (all values)
E. Small second "z" and inverted "q" for "b" (all values)
F. Second "z" Gothic (½ a. to 12 a. and 1 r.) (No. 18) (black opts only)
G. No dot over "i" (all values to 1 r.)
H. Inverted "q" for "b" (all values to 1 r.)
I. Arabic "2" for "r" (all values to 1 r.) (black opts only)

The scarcity of these varieties varies from normal catalogue value (D. and E.) to 4 times catalogue value (B.).

1895–98. *Provisionals.* I *Stamps used for postal purposes.*

2½ (2) 2½ (3) 2½ (4) 2½ (5)

1895 (Dec.) *No.* 5 *surch with T* **2** *in red.*

22		2½ on 1½ a. sepia	14·00	16·00
		j. "Zanzidar"	£425	£425
		k. "Zanizbar"	£500	£500
		l. Inverted "1" in "½"	£275	£275

1896 (11 May). *No.* 4 *surch in black.*

23	**3**	2½ on 1 a. plum	55·00	40·00
24	**4**	2½ on 1 a. plum	£100	70·00
		j. Inverted "1" in "½"	£650	
25	**5**	2½ on 1 a. plum	55·00	40·00

2½ (6) 2½ (7) 2½ (8)

1896 (15 Aug). *No.* 6 *surch in red.*

26	**6**	2½ on 2 a. pale blue	17·00	15·00
		j. Inverted "1" in "½"	£110	£100
		k. Roman "I" in "½"	£150	£130
27	**7**	2½ on 2 a. pale blue	55·00	40·00
		j. "2" of "½" omitted	£700	
		k. "22" for "2½"	£700	
		l. "1" of "½" omitted	£700	£650
28	**8**	2½ on 2 a. pale blue	£500	£400

No. 28 only exists with small "z".

1896 (15 Nov). *No* 5 *surch in red.*

29	**6**	2½ on 1½ a. sepia	60·00	45·00
		j. Inverted "1" in "½"	£250	£250
		k. Roman "I" in "½"	£250	£250
30	**7**	2½ on 1½ a. sepia	£140	
31	**8**	2½ on 1½ a. sepia	£900	

No. 31 only exists with small "z".

II. *Stamps prepared for official purposes*

1898 (Jan). *Nos.* 4, 5 *and* 7 *surch as before in red.*

32	**3**	2½ on 1 a. plum	£110	£125
33	**4**	2½ on 1 a. plum	£160	£175
34	**5**	2½ on 1a. plum	£110	£125
35	**3**	2½ on 1½ a. sepia	50·00	60·00
		j. Diaeresis over last "a"	£300	£300
36	**4**	2½ on 1½ a. sepia	75·00	85·00
37	**5**	2½ on 1½ a. sepia	50·00	60·00
38	**3**	2½ on 2 a. dull blue	45·00	55·00
39	**4**	2½ on 2 a. dull blue	70·00	80·00
40	**5**	2½ on 2 a. dull blue	45·00	55·00

It is doubtful whether Nos. 32/40 were issued to the public.

1896. *Stamps of British East Africa, T* **11**, *optd with T* **1**.

41	½ a. yellow-green (1 June)	16·00	15·00
42	1 a. carmine-rose (1 June)	16·00	15·00
	j. Opt double	£225	£225
43	2½ a. deep blue (R.) (1 June)	45·00	35·00
44	4½ a. orange-yellow (12 Aug)	16·00	18·00
45	5 a. olive-bistre (12 Aug)	18·00	20·00
	j. "r" omitted	—	£500
46	7½ a. mauve (12 Aug)	22·00	23·00
41/6	*Set of* 6	£120	£110

MINOR VARIETIES. The various minor varieties of type detailed in the note below No. 21 also occur on Nos. 22 to 46 as indicated below:

A. Nos. 23, 27, 30, 35, 38, 41/6
B. Nos. 22, 26, 29/30, 32/3, 36, 39, 44/6
C. Nos. 22, 25/6, 36, 40/6
D. Nos. 22/46
E. Nos. 22/46
F. Nos. 22, 25/6, 29, 41/6
G. Nos. 25/6, 29, 35, 37/8, 40/6
H. Nos. 22, 41/6 (on the British East Africa stamps this variety occurs in the same position as variety C.)
I. Nos. 26, 35, 38, 41/6

The scarcity of these varieties on the surcharges (Nos. 22/40) is similar to those on the basic stamps, but examples on the British East Africa values (Nos. 41/6) are more common.

PRINTERS. All Zanzibar stamps up to Type **37** were printed by De La Rue & Co.

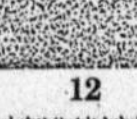
12

13

14 Sultan Seyyid Hamed-bin-Thwain

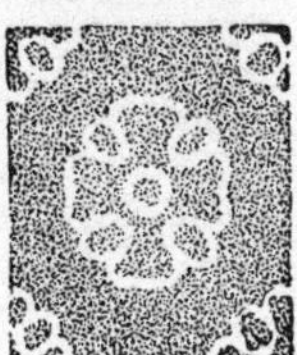
18

1896 (20 Sept). *Recess. Flags in red on all values. W* **12**. *P* 14.

156	**13**	½ a. yellow-green	45	40
157		1 a. indigo	85	70
158		1 a. violet-blue	1·40	70
159		2 a. red-brown	70	65
160		2½ a. bright blue	95	50
161		2½ a. pale blue	1·00	60
162		3 a. grey	1·50	1·90
163		3 a. bluish grey	2·25	2·25
164		4 a. myrtle-green	1·50	1·75
165		4½ a. orange	1·60	2·25
166		5 a. bistre	1·75	1·75
		a. Bisected (2½ a.) (on cover)	†	£400
167		7½ a. mauve	1·90	2·00
168		8 a. grey-olive	1·75	1·90
169	**14**	1 r. blue	8·00	9·00
170		1 r. deep blue	8·50	9·00
171		2 r. green	8·50	9·50
172		3 r. dull purple	18·00	13·00
173		4 r. lake	18·00	13·00
174		5 r. sepia	25·00	18·00
156/74		*Set of* 15	80·00	70·00
156/74 Optd "Specimen"		*Set of* 15	£170	

The ½, 1, 2, 2½, 3 and 8 a. are known without wmk, these being from edges of the sheets.

1897 (5 Jan). *No.* 164 *surch as before, in red.*

175	**3**	2½ on 4 a. myrtle-green	25·00	25·00
176	**4**	2½ on 4 a. myrtle-green	50·00	50·00
177	**5**	2½ on 4 a. myrtle-green	25·00	25·00

1898 (May). *Recess. W* **18**. *P* 14.

178	**13**	½ a. yellow-green	40	35
179		1 a. indigo	55	45
		a. Greenish black	1·25	70
180		2 a. red-brown	60	70
		a. Deep brown	1·00	1·00
181		2½ a. bright blue	80	35
182		3 a. grey	1·00	60
183		4 a. myrtle-green	1·25	1·00
184		4½ a. orange	1·50	75
185		5 a. bistre	1·75	1·50
		a. Pale bistre	2·50	2·00
186		7½ a. mauve	1·90	2·25
187		8 a. grey-olive	2·75	2·00
178/87		*Set of* 10	11·00	9·00

19

20 Sultan Seyyid Hamoud-bin-Mohammed bin Said

1899 (Sept)–**1901**. *Recess. Flags in red. W* **18** *(Nos.* 188/99*) or W* **12** *(others). P* 14.

188	**19**	½ a. yellow-green	40	25
189		1 a. indigo	70	25
190		1 a. carmine (1901)	55	20
191		2 a. red-brown	65	30
192		2½ a. bright blue	75	35
193		3 a. grey	90	90
194		4 a. myrtle-green	90	1·00
195		4½ a. orange	2·00	2·50
196		4½ a. blue-black (1901)	2·50	3·00
197		5 a. bistre	1·50	1·25
198		7½ a. mauve	2·50	3·00
199		8 a. grey-olive	2·25	3·00
200	**20**	1 r. blue	15·00	13·00
201		2 r. green	15·00	15·00
202		3 r. dull purple	15·00	15·00
203		4 r. lake	22·00	24·00
204		5 r. sepia	26·00	38·00
188/204		*Set of* 17	95·00	£110
188/204 Optd "Specimen"		*Set of* 17	£170	

One (21) — Two & Half (22) — Two & Half (22*a*) Thin open "w" — Two & Half (22*b*) Serif to foot of "f"

1904. *Stamps of* 1899/1901 *surch as T* **21** *and* **22**, *in black or lake* (L.).

205	**19**	1 on 4½ a. orange	1·40	2·50
206		1 on 4½ a. blue-black (L.)	4·25	5·00
207		2 on 4 a. myrtle-green (L.)	11·00	11·00
208		2½ on 7½ a. mauve	11·00	11·00
		a. Opt Type **22*a***	45·00	45·00
		b. Opt Type **22*b***	50·00	50·00
		c. "Hlaf" for "Half"		
209		2½ on 8 a. grey-olive	12·00	14·00
		a. Opt Type **22*a***	60·00	60·00
		b. Opt Type **22*b***	70·00	70·00
		c. "Hlaf" for "Half"	—	£500

23

24

Monogram of Sultan Seyyid Ali bin Hamoud bin Naherud

1904 (8 June). *Typo. Background of centre in second colour. W* **18**. *P* 14.
210 **23** ½ a. green 45 15
211 1 a. rose-red 45 12
212 2 a. brown 1·00 45
213 2½ a. blue 1·00 35
214 3 a. grey 1·25 1·00
215 4 a. deep green 1·60 1·00
216 4½ a. black 2·75 2·75
217 5 a. yellow-brown 3·00 1·75
218 7½ a. purple 3·25 3·25
219 8 a. olive-green 3·25 2·50
220 **24** 1 r. blue and red 8·00 7·00
221 2 r. green and red 12·00 14·00
222 3 r. violet and red 30·00 32·00
223 4 r. claret and red 35·00 40·00
224 5 r. olive-brown and red 38·00 42·00
210/24 *Set of* 15 £130 £130
210/24 Optd "Specimen" *Set of* 15 £100

25

26

27 Sultan Ali bin Hamoud

28 View of Port

1908 (May)–**09**. *Recess. W* **18**. *P* 14.
225 **25** 1 c. pearl-grey (10.09) 20 30
226 3 c. yellow-green 40 12
227 6 c. rose-carmine 60 12
228 10 c. brown (10.09) 1·25 1·50
229 12 c. violet 1·00 35
230 **26** 15 c. ultramarine 1·50 75
231 25 c. sepia 1·90 80
232 50 c. blue-green 2·75 2·75
233 75 c. grey-black (10.09) 4·75 6·00
234 **27** 1 r. yellow-green 5·50 4·00
235 2 r. violet 10·00 11·00
236 3 r. orange-bistre 16·00 24·00
237 4 r. vermilion 27·00 35·00
238 5 r. steel-blue 30·00 35·00
239 **28** 10 r. blue-green and brown (S. £22) 65·00 70·00
240 20 r. black and yellow-green (S. £30) £100 £100
241 30 r. black and sepia (S. £40) £170 £180
242 40 r. black and orange-brown (S. £50) £400
243 50 r. black and mauve (S. £60) £350
244 100 r. black and steel-blue (S. £100) £450
245 200 r. brown and greenish black (S. £150) £750
225/38 *Set of* 14 90·00 £110
225/38 Optd "Specimen" *Set of* 14 £140
Specimen copies of Nos. 239/45 are all overprinted.

29 Sultan Kalif bin Harub

30 Native Craft

31

1913. *Recess. W* **18** (*sideways on* 75 c. *and T* **31**). *P* 14.
246 **29** 1 c. grey 10 20
247 3 c. yellow-green 15 25
248 6 c. rose-carmine 25 10
249 10 c. brown 60 60
250 12 c. violet 50 15
251 15 c. blue 60 40
252 25 c. sepia 70 45
253 50 c. blue-green 1·50 1·25
254 75 c. grey-black 1·00 1·00
255 **30** 1 r. yellow-green 2·50 1·75
256 2 r. violet 7·50 9·00
257 3 r. orange-bistre 9·00 13·00
258 4 r. scarlet 14·00 18·00
259 5 r. steel-blue 17·00 17·00
260 **31** 10 r. green and brown 40·00 40·00
260*a* 20 r. black and green (S. £20) 55·00 48·00
260*b* 30 r. black and brown (S. £30) 85·00 75·00
260*c* 40 r. black and vermilion (S. £50) £170 £170
260*d* 50 r. black and purple (S. £55) £180 £170
260*e* 100 r. black and blue (S. £80) £250 £190
260*f* 200 r. brown and black (S. £110) £500 £425
246/60 *Set of* 15 85·00 95·00
246/60 Optd "Specimen" *Set of* 15 £100
Specimen copies of Nos. 260*a*/*f* are all overprinted.

1914–22. *Wmk Mult Crown CA. P* 14.
261 **29** 1 c. grey 12 25
262 3 c. yellow-green 30 12
a. Dull green 40 20
263 6 c. deep carmine 45 12
a. Bright rose-carmine 45 12
264 8 c. purple/*pale yellow* (1922) 50 85
265 10 c. myrtle/*pale yellow* (1922) 50 45
266 15 c. deep ultramarine 50 75
268 50 c. blue-green 3·00 3·00
269 75 c. grey-black 2·25 3·50
270 **30** 1 r. yellow-green 3·25 1·60
271 2 r. violet 3·50 3·75
272 3 r. orange-bistre 7·00 11·00
273 4 r. scarlet 12·00 16·00
274 5 r. steel-blue 15·00 18·00
275 **31** 10 r. green and brown 38·00 42·00
261/75 *Set of* 14 80·00 95·00
261/75 Optd "Specimen" *Set of* 14 £120

1921–29. *Wmk Mult Script CA. P* 14.
276 **29** 1 c. slate-grey 12 40
277 3 c. yellow-green 15 80
278 3 c. yellow (1922) 12 12
279 4 c. green (1922) 35 70
280 6 c. carmine-red 25 90
281 6 c. purple/*blue* (1922) 25 15
282 10 c. brown 70 1·25
283 12 c. violet 30 95
284 12 c. carmine-red (1922) 40 50
285 15 c. blue 45 85
286 20 c. indigo (1922) 90 50
287 25 c. sepia 60 1·00
288 50 c. myrtle-green 90 1·00
289 75 c. slate 1·75 3·00
290 **30** 1 r. yellow-green 1·25 1·60
291 2 r. deep violet 1·75 3·00
292 3 r. orange-bistre 3·25 4·25
293 4 r. scarlet 7·50 11·00
294 5 r. Prussian blue 9·00 13·00
295 **31** 10 r. green and brown 19·00 19·00
296 20 r. black and green (Optd S. £32) 60·00 60·00
297 30 r. black and brown (1929) (Perf S. £38) £150 £150
276/95 *Set of* 20 45·00 60·00
276/95 Optd "Specimen" *Set of* 20 £130

32 Sultan Kalif bin Harub 33

1926–27. *T* **32** ("CENTS" *in serifed capitals*). *Recess. Wmk Mult Script CA. P* 14.
299 **32** 1 c. brown 15 15
300 3 c. yellow-orange 15 15
301 4 c. deep dull green 20 40
302 6 c. violet 15 15
303 8 c. slate 75 1·25
304 10 c. olive-green 65 50
305 12 c. carmine-red 75 20
306 20 c. bright blue 40 40
307 25 c. purple/*yellow* (1927) 1·75 1·25
308 50 c. claret 80 65
309 75 c. sepia (1927) 90 3·00
299/309 *Set of* 11 6·00 7·25
299/309 Optd "Specimen" *Set of* 11 80·00

(New Currency. 100 cents = 1 shilling)

1936 (1 Jan). *T* **33** "CENTS" *in sans-serif capitals*), *and T* **30/1**, *but values in shillings. Recess. Wmk Mult Script CA. P* 14 × 13½–14.
310 **33** 5 c. green 5 5
311 10 c. black 5 5
312 15 c. carmine-red 5 20
313 20 c. orange 5 5
314 25 c. purple/*yellow* 5 10
315 30 c. ultramarine 5 8
316 40 c. sepia 12 20
317 50 c. claret 12 5
318 **30** 1s. yellow-green 35 12
319 2s. slate-violet 55 35
320 5s. scarlet 2·25 2·75
321 7s. 50, light blue 5·50 7·00
322 **31** 10s. green and brown 4·50 4·00
310/22 *Set of* 13 12·00 13·50
310/22 Perf "Specimen" *Set of* 13 38·00

36 Sultan Kalif bin Harub

1936 (9 Dec). *Silver Jubilee of Sultan. Recess. Wmk Mult Script CA. P* 14.
323 **36** 10 c. black and olive-green 70 75
324 20 c. black and bright purple 70 75
325 30 c. black and deep ultramarine 70 80
326 50 c. black and orange-vermilion 70 90
323/6 Perf "Specimen" *Set of* 4 45·00

ALTERED CATALOGUE NUMBERS

Any Catalogue numbers altered from the last edition are shown as a list in the introductory pages.

37 Dhow

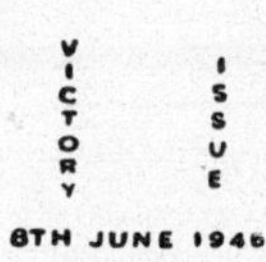

(38)

1944 (20 Nov). *Bicentenary of Al Busaid Dynasty. Recess. Wmk Mult Script CA. P* 14.
327 **37** 10 c. ultramarine 10 40
328 20 c. red 10 40
329 50 c. blue-green 10 30
330 1s. dull purple 10 45
327/30 Perf "Specimen" *Set of* 4 65·00

1946 (11 Nov). *Victory. Optd with T* **38**.
331 **33** 10 c. black (R.) 20 30
332 30 c. ultramarine (R.) 20 55
331/2 Perf "Specimen" *Set of* 2 45·00

1949 (10 Jan). *Royal Silver Wedding. As Nos.* 30/1 *of Aden.*
333 20 c. orange 25 25
334 10s. brown 10·00 15·00

1949 (10 Oct). *75th Anniv of U.P.U. As Nos.* 114/17 *of Antigua.*
335 20 c. red-orange 25 20
336 30 c. deep blue 80 60
337 50 c. magenta 90 75
338 1s. blue-green 1·25 1·25

39 Sultan Kalif bin Harub

40 Seyyid Khalifa Schools, Beit-el-Ras

(Recess D.L.R.)

1952 (26 Aug). *Wmk Mult Script CA. P* 12½ (*cent values*) *or* 13 (*shilling values*).
339 **39** 5 c. black 5 5
340 10 c. red-orange 5 5
341 15 c. green (*shades*) 12 5
342 20 c. carmine-red 20 5
343 25 c. reddish purple 25 5
344 30 c. deep bluish green (*shades*) 15 5
345 35 c. bright blue 20 45
346 40 c. deep brown (*shades*) 20 20
347 50 c. violet (*shades*) 20 5
348 **40** 1s. deep green and deep brown 25 5
349 2s. bright blue and deep purple 65 30
350 5s. black and carmine-red 1·50 1·25
351 7s. 50, grey-black and emerald 6·00 15·00
352 10s. carmine-red and black 4·50 2·75
339/352 *Set of* 14 13·00 18·00

41 Sultan Kalif bin Harub

(Photo Harrison)

1954 (26 Aug). *Sultan's 75th Birthday. Wmk Mult Script CA. Chalk-surfaced paper. P* 13 × 12.
353 **41** 15 c. deep green 10 10
354 20 c. rose-red 10 10
355 30 c. bright blue 15 10
356 50 c. purple 15 10
357 1s. 25, orange-red 30 40

42 Cloves

43 Dhows

44 Sultan's Barge

45 Map of East African Coast

46 Minaret Mosque 47 Dimbani Mosque 48 Kibweni Palace

(Des W. J. Jennings (T **42**), A. Farhan (T **43**), Mrs. M. Broadbent (T **44**, **46**), R. A. Sweet (T **45**), A. S. B. New (T **47**), B. J. Woolley (T **48**). Recess B.W.)

1957 (26 Aug). W w **12**. *P* 11½ (5 *c*., 10 *c*.), 11 × 11½ (15 *c*., 30 *c*., 1*s*. 25), 14 × 13½ (20 *c*., 25 *c*., 35 *c*., 50 *c*.), 13½ × 14 (40 *c*., 1*s*., 2*s*.) *or* 13 × 13½ (5*s*., 7*s*. 50, 10*s*.).

358	**42**	5 c. orange and deep green	5	5
359		10 c. emerald and carmine-red	5	5
360	**43**	15 c. green and sepia	10	5
361	**44**	20 c. ultramarine	10	5
362	**45**	25 c. orange-brown and black	10	5
363	**43**	30 c. carmine-red and black	15	5
364	**45**	35 c. slate and emerald	15	20
365	**46**	40 c. brown and black	15	5
366	**45**	50 c. blue and grey-green	15	5
367	**47**	1s. carmine and black	25	5
368	**43**	1s. 25, slate and carmine	45	5
369	**47**	2s. orange and deep green	50	20
370	**48**	5s. deep bright blue	2·50	1·75
371		7s. 50, green	2·50	4·00
372		10s. carmine	2·75	2·00
358/72		*Set of* 15	9·00	7·50

49 Sultan Seyyid Sir Abdulla bin Khalifa 50 "Protein Foods"

(Recess B.W.)

1961 (17 Oct). *As T* **42/8**, *but with portrait of Sultan Sir Abdulla as in T* **49**. W w **12**. *P* 13 × 13½ (20*s*.), *others as before*.

373	**49**	5 c. orange and deep green	5	5
374		10 c. emerald and carmine-red	8	5
375	**43**	15 c. green and sepia	12	5
376	**44**	20 c. ultramarine	12	5
377	**45**	25 c. orange-brown and black	12	5
378	**43**	30 c. carmine-red and black	15	5
379	**45**	35 c. slate and emerald	15	15
380	**46**	40 c. brown and black	15	5
381	**45**	50 c. blue and grey-green	15	5
382	**47**	1s. carmine and black	25	5
383	**43**	1s. 25, slate and carmine	45	35
384	**47**	2s. orange and deep green	40	40
385	**48**	5s. deep bright blue	90	90
386		7s. 50, green	2·25	4·75
387		10s. carmine	2·25	3·00
388		20s. sepia	8·50	13·00
373/88		*Set of* 16	14·00	20·00

(Des M. Goaman. Photo Harrison)

1963 (4 June). *Freedom from Hunger*. W w **12**. *P* 14 × 14½.

389	**50**	1s. 30, sepia	40	35

INDEPENDENT

51 Zanzibar Clove 53 "Religious Tolerance" (mosques and churches)

(Photo Harrison)

1963 (10 Dec). *Independence. Portrait of Sultan Seyyid Jamshid bin Abdulla. T* **51, 53** *and similar vert designs. P* 12½.

390	30 c. multicoloured	8	20
391	50 c. multicoloured	10	25
392	1s. 30, multicoloured	15	75
393	2s. 50, multicoloured	25	1·75

Designs: 50 c. "To Prosperity" (Zanzibar doorway); 2s. 50, "Towards the Light" (Mangapwani Cave).

REPUBLIC

When the Post Office opened on 14 January 1964, after the revolution deposing the Sultan, the stamps on sale had the portrait cancelled by a manuscript cross. Stamps thus cancelled on cover or piece used between January 14 and 17 are therefore of interest.

JAMHURI 1964

(55= "Republic")

1964 (17 Jan). *Locally handstamped as T* **55** *in black*.

(i) *Nos*. 373/88.

394	**49**	5 c. orange and deep green	5	5
395		10 c. emerald and carmine-red	5	5
396	**43**	15 c. green and sepia	5	5
397	**44**	20 c. ultramarine	8	5
398	**45**	25 c. orange-brown and black	8	5
399	**43**	30 c. carmine-red and black	10	5
400	**45**	35 c. slate and emerald	12	5
401	**46**	40 c. brown and black	12	5
402	**45**	50 c. blue and grey-green	12	5
403	**47**	1s. carmine and black	15	5
404	**43**	1s. 25, slate and carmine	20	10
405	**47**	2s. orange and deep green	60	20
406	**48**	5s. deep bright blue	1·25	55
407		7s. 50, green	1·75	1·00
408		10s. carmine	1·75	90
409		20s. sepia	2·50	2·25

(ii) *Nos*. 390/3 (*Independence*)

410	30 c. multicoloured	10	5
411	50 c. multicoloured	15	5
412	1s. 30, multicoloured	25	10
413	2s. 50, multicoloured	40	25
394/413	*Set of* 20	9·00	5·50

T **55** occurs in various positions—diagonally, horizontally or vertically.

NOTE. Nos. 394 to 413 are the only stamps officially authorised to receive the handstamp but it has also been seen on Nos. 353/7, 389 and the Postage Dues. There are numerous errors but it is impossible to distinguish between cases of genuine oversight and those made deliberately at the request of purchasers.

JAMHURI 1964 (56)

JAMHURI 1964 (57)

1964 (28 Feb). *Optd by Bradbury, Wilkinson*.

(i) *As T* **56** *on Nos*. 373/88

414	**49**	5 c. orange and deep green	5	5
415		10 c. emerald and carmine-red	5	5
416	**43**	15 c. green and sepia	5	5
417	**44**	20 c. ultramarine	5	5
418	**45**	25 c. orange-brown and black	5	5
419	**43**	30 c. carmine-red and black	5	5
420	**45**	35 c. slate and emerald	5	5
421	**46**	40 c. brown and black	10	5
422	**45**	50 c. blue and grey-green	10	5
423	**47**	1s. carmine and black	12	5
424	**43**	1s. 25, slate and carmine	15	10
425	**47**	2s. orange and deep green	25	15
426	**48**	5s. deep bright blue	60	45
427		7s. 50, green	75	1·00
428		10s. carmine	85	1·00
429		20s. sepia	1·50	1·75

The opt T **56** is set in two lines on Types **46/8**.

(*ii*) *As T* **57** *on Nos*. 390/3 (*Independence*)

430	30 c. multicoloured	5	5
431	50 c. multicoloured	5	5
432	1s. 30, multicoloured	10	5
433	2s. 50, multicoloured	20	15
414/33	*Set of* 20	4·75	4·75

The opt T **57** is set in one line on No. 432.

For the set inscribed "UNITED REPUBLIC OF TANGANYIKA AND ZANZIBAR" see Nos. 124/7 of Tanzania.

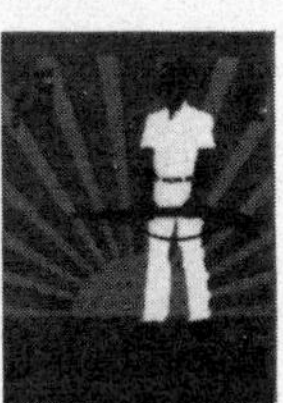

58 Axe, Spear and Dagger 59 Zanzibari with Rifle

(Litho German Bank Note Ptg Co, Leipzig)

1964 (21 June). *T* **58/9** *and similar designs inscr*. "JAMHURI ZANZIBAR 1964". *Multicoloured. P* 13 × 13½ (*vert*) *or* 13½ × 13 (*horiz*).

434	5 c. Type **58**	5	5
435	10 c. Bow and arrow breaking chains	5	5
436	15 c. Type **58**	5	5
437	20 c. As 10 c.	5	5
438	25 c. Type **59**	8	5
439	30 c. Zanzibari breaking manacles	8	5
440	40 c. Type **59**	10	5
441	50 c. As 30 c.	12	5
442	1s. Zanzibari, flag and Sun	15	5
443	1s. 30, Hands breaking chains (*horiz*)	20	5
444	2s. Hand waving flag (*horiz*)	25	10
445	5s. Map of Zanzibar and Pemba on flag (*horiz*)	65	30
446	10s. Flag on Map	1·75	1·25
447	20s. National flag (*horiz*)	2·75	4·50
434/47	*Set of* 14	5·50	6·50

68 Soldier and Maps 69 Building Construction

(Litho German Bank Note Ptg Co, Leipzig)

1965 (12 Jan). *First Anniv of Revolution. P* 13 × 13½ (*vert*) *or* 13½ × 13 (*horiz*).

448	**68**	20 c. apple-green and deep green	5	5
449	**69**	30 c. chocolate and yellow-orange	8	5
450	**68**	1s. 30, light blue and ultramarine	15	15
451	**69**	2s. 50, reddish violet and rose	30	40

70 Planting Rice

(Litho German Bank Note Ptg Co, Leipzig)

1965 (17 Oct). *Agricultural Development. T* **70** *and similar horiz design. P* 13 × 12½.

452	**70**	20 c. sepia and blue	5	5
453	–	30 c. sepia and magenta	8	5
454	–	1s. 30, sepia and yellow-orange	20	25
455	**70**	2s. 50, sepia and emerald	40	85

Design:—30 c., 1s. 30, Hands holding rice.

72 Ship, Tractor, Factory, and Open Book and Torch 73 Soldier

(Litho German Bank Note Ptg Co, Leipzig)

1966 (12 Jan). *2nd Anniv of Revolution. P* 12½ × 13.

456	**72**	20 c. multicoloured	10	5
457	**73**	50 c. multicoloured	12	5
458	**72**	1s. 30, multicoloured	30	20
459	**73**	2s. 50, multicoloured	45	65

For stamps with similar inscription or inscribed "TANZANIA" only, and with commemorative date 26th April 1966, see Nos. Z142/5 of TANZANIA.

74 Tree-felling 75 Zanzibar Street

(Litho German Bank Note Ptg Co, Leipzig)

1966 (5 June). *Horiz designs as T* **74**, *and T* **75**. *P* 12½ × 13 (50 *c*., 10*s*.) *or* 13 × 12½ (*others*).

460	5 c. maroon and yellow-olive	5	5
461	10 c. brown-purple and bright emerald	5	5
462	15 c. brown-purple and light blue	5	5
463	20 c. ultramarine and light orange	5	5
464	25 c. maroon and orange-yellow	5	5
465	30 c. maroon and ochre-yellow	5	5
466	40 c. purple-brown and rose-pink	5	5
467	50 c. green and pale greenish yellow	8	5
468	1s. maroon and bright blue	15	5
469	1s. 30, maroon and turquoise	20	5
470	2s. brown-purple and light blue-green	30	20
471	5s. rose-red and pale blue	80	2·50
472	10s. crimson and pale yellow	2·50	6·00
473	20s. deep purple-brown and magenta	5·50	11·00
460/473	*Set of* 14	9·00	18·00

Designs:—5 c., 20s. Type **74**; 10 c., 1s. Clove cultivation; **15, 40 c.** Chair-making; 20 c., 5s. Lumumba College; 25 c., 1s. 30, Agriculture; 30 c., 2s. Agricultural workers; 50 c., 10s. Type **75**.

81 "Education"

(Litho D.L.R.)

1966 (25 Sept). *Introduction of Free Education. P* 13½ × 13.

474	**81**	50 c. black, light blue and orange	10	5
475		1s. 30, black, lt blue and yellow-green	20	30
476		2s. 50, black, light blue and pink	50	1·60

82 A.S.P. Flag

(Litho D.L.R.)

1967 (5 Feb). *Tenth Anniv of Afro-Shirazi Party (A.S.P.). T* **82** *and similar multicoloured design. P* 14.

477 30 c. Type **82** .. 5 5
478 50 c. Vice-President M. A. Karume of Tanzania, flag and crowd (*vert*) .. 8 5
479 1s. 30, As 50 c. .. 20 35
480 2s. 50, Type **82** .. 30 90

84 Voluntary Workers

(Photo Delrieu)

1967 (20 Aug). *Voluntary Workers Brigade. P* 12½ × 12.

481 **84** 1s. 30, multicoloured .. 25 30
482 2s. 50, multicoloured .. 45 1·25

POSTAGE DUE STAMPS

D 1

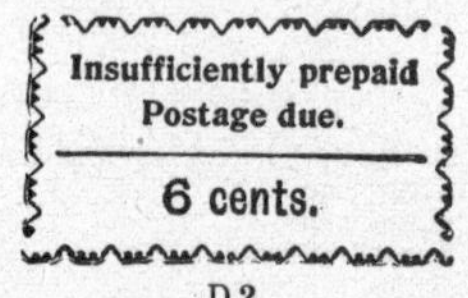

D 2

(Types D 1 and D 2 typo by the Government Printer)

1929–30. *Rouletted* 10, *with imperf sheet edges. No gum.*

D 1 **D 1** 1 c. black/*orange* .. 1·10 2·50
D 2 2 c. black/*orange* .. 1·10 2·50
D 3 3 c. black/*orange* .. 1·10 2·50
a. "cent.s" for "cents." .. 6·00
D 4 6 c. black/*orange* ..
a. "cent.s" for "cents." ..
D 5 9 c. black/*orange* .. 1·25 2·75
a. "cent.s" for "cents." .. 6·50 10·00
D 6 12 c. black/*orange* ..
a. "cent.s" for "cents." ..
D 7 12 c. black/*green* .. £150 £100
a. "cent.s" for "cents." .. £750 £500
D 8 15 c. black/*orange* .. 1·10 1·60
a. "cent.s" for "cents." .. 6·00 7·50
D 9 18 c. black/*salmon* .. 4·00 5·00
a. "cent.s" for "cents." .. 20·00 28·00
D10 18 c. black/*orange* .. 2·25 3·00
a. "cent.s" for "cents." .. 10·00 12·00
D11 20 c. black/*orange* .. 2·25 3·00
a. "cent.s" for "cents." .. 10·00 14·00
D12 21 c. black/*orange* .. 2·00 3·00
a. "cent.s" for "cents." .. 10·00 14·00
D13 25 c. black/*magenta* .. £800 £450
a. "cent.s" for "cents." ..
D14 25 c. black/*orange* ..
D15 31 c. black/*orange* .. 5·00 9·00
a. "cent.s" for "cents." .. 25·00
D16 50 c. black/*orange* .. 13·00 22·00
a. "cent.s" for "cents." .. 50·00
D17 75 c. black/*orange* .. 30·00 45·00
a. "cent.s" for "cents." .. 90·00

Sheets of the first printings of all values except the 1 c. and 2 c. contained one stamp showing the error "cent.s" for "cents."

1930–33. *Rouletted* 5. *No gum.*

D18 **D 2** 2 c. black/*salmon* .. 1·40 3·25
D19 3 c. black/*rose* .. 1·50 3·50
D21 6 c. black/*yellow* .. 1·75 4·25
D22 12 c. black/*blue* .. 2·50 4·00
D23 25 c. black/*rose* .. 7·00 9·50
D24 25 c. black/*lilac* .. 3·25 9·50
D18/24 .. *Set of* 6 16·00 30·00

D 3

(Typo D.L.R.)

1936 (1 Jan)–**62**. *Wmk Mult Script CA. P* 14.

D25 **D 3** 5 c. violet, **O** .. 25 75
a. Chalky paper (18.7.56) .. 20 75
D26 10 c. scarlet, **O** .. 25 60
a. Chalky paper (6.3.62) .. 20 60
D27 **D 3** 20 c. green, **O** .. 60 1·75
a. Chalky paper (6.3.62) .. 20 75
D28 30 c. brown, **O** .. 1·25 2·50
a. Chalky paper (18.7.56) .. 30 85
D29 40 c. ultramarine, **O** .. 1·25 3·25
a. Chalky paper (18.7.56) .. 40 95
D30 1s. grey, **O** .. 2·75 5·00
a. Chalky paper (18.7.56) .. 1·00 1·75
D25a/30a .. *Set of* 6 2·10 5·00
D25/30 Perf "Specimen" .. *Set of* 6 50·00

See footnote after No. 413.

All Zanzibar issues were withdrawn on 1 January 1968 and replaced by Tanzania issues. Zanzibar stamps remained valid for postage in Zanzibar for a limited period.

Zimbabwe

(formerly Rhodesia)

Rhodesia became independent under majority rule on 18 April 1980 and was renamed Zimbabwe.

PRINTERS. All stamps of Zimbabwe were printed in lithography by Mardon Printers (Pvt) Ltd, Harare, *unless otherwise stated.*

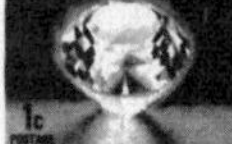

113 Morganite

114 Rotary Anniversary Emblem

1980 (18 Apr)–**83**. *As Nos.* 555/69 *of Rhodesia but inscr* "ZIMBABWE" *as in T* **113**.

576 1 c. Type **113** .. 5 5
577 3 c. Amethyst .. 5 5
578 4 c. Garnet .. 5 5
579 5 c. Citrine .. 5 5
580 7 c. Blue Topaz .. 5 5
581 9 c. Rhinoceros .. 8 10
582 11 c. Lion .. 10 12
583 13 c. Warthog .. 12 15
584 15 c. Giraffe .. 15 20
585 17 c. Zebra .. 15 20
586 21 c. Odzani Falls .. 20 25
587 25 c. Goba Falls .. 25 30
588 30 c. Inyangombi Falls .. 30 35
588*a* 40 c. Bundi Falls (14.3.83) .. 40 45
589 $1 Bridal Veil Falls .. 90 1·00
590 $2 Victoria Falls .. 1·75 1·90
576/90 .. *Set of* 16 4·50 5·00

1980 (18 June). *75th Anniv of Rotary International. P* 14½.

591 **114** 4 c. multicoloured .. 10 5
592 13 c. multicoloured .. 25 25
593 21 c. multicoloured .. 45 40
594 25 c. multicoloured .. 60 50
MS595 140 × 84 mm. Nos. 591/4. .. 1·25 1·40

115 Olympic Rings

(Des Nancy Abrey)

1980 (19 July). *Olympic Games, Moscow. P* 14½.

596 **115** 17 c. multicoloured .. 30 30

116 Gatooma Post Office, 1912 **117** Stylised Blind Person

(Des Mortimer Tiley and Partners Ltd)

1980 (17 Oct). *75th Anniv of Post Office Savings Bank. T* **116** *and similar horiz designs. P* 14.

597 5 c. black and yellow-brown .. 10 10
598 7 c. black and red-orange .. 12 12
599 9 c. black and olive-yellow .. 20 20
600 17 c. black and light blue .. 45 45
MS601 125 × 84 mm. Nos. 597/600 .. 1·25 1·25

Designs:—7 c. Salisbury Post Office, 1912; 9 c. Umtali Post Office, 1901; 17 c. Bulawayo Post Office, 1895.

(Des Rose Martin)

1981 (23 Sept). *International Year for Disabled Persons. T* **11**[7] *and similar vert designs showing stylised figures. Multicoloure*[d]*. P* 14.

602 5 c. Type **117** .. 10
603 7 c. Deaf person .. 15 1
604 11 c. Person with one leg .. 25 1
605 17 c. Person with one arm .. 35 3

118 Msasa **119** Painting from Gwamgwadza Cave, Mtoko Area

(Des Nancy Abrey)

1981 (4 Dec). *National Tree Day. T* **118** *and similar vert designs. Multicoloured. P* 14½.

606 5 c. Type **118** .. 10 5
607 7 c. Mopane .. 15 12
608 21 c. Flat-crowned Acacia .. 40 35
609 30 c. Pod Mahogany .. 45 45

1982 (17 Mar). *Rock Paintings. T* **119** *and similar horiz designs showing paintings from various locations. Multicoloured. P* 14½.

610 9 c. Type **119** .. 15 15
611 11 c. Epworth Mission, near Harare .. 15 15
612 17 c. Diana's Vow, near Harare .. 30 30
613 21 c. Gwamgwadza Cave, Mtoko Area (*different*) .. 30 30
614 25 c. Mucheka Cave, Msana Communal Land 40 45
615 30 c. Chinzwini Shelter, Chiredzi Area .. 45 55
610/15 .. *Set of* 6 1·60 1·75

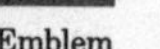

120 Scout Emblem **121** Dr. Robert Koch

(Des Rose Martin)

1982 (21 July). *75th Anniv of Boy Scout Movement. T* **120** *and similar vert designs. Multicoloured. P* 14½ × 14.

616 9 c. Type **120** .. 15 12
617 11 c. Scouts around campfire .. 15 12
618 21 c. Scouts map-reading .. 30 30
619 30 c. Lord Baden-Powell .. 45 50

(Des Rose Martin)

1982 (17 Nov). *Centenary of Dr. Robert Koch's Discovery of Tubercle Bacillus. T* **121** *and similar horiz design. P* 14.

620 11 c. salmon, black and greenish grey .. 15 20
621 30 c. multicoloured .. 45 45

Design:—30 c. Man looking through microscope.

122 "Wing Woman" (Henry Mudzengerere) **123** Traditional Ploughing Team (moving right)

1983 (14 Mar). *Commonwealth Day. Sculptures. T* **122** *and similar multicoloured designs. P* 14.

622 9 c. Type **122** .. 10 12
623 11 c. "Telling Secrets" (Joseph Ndandarika) (*horiz*) .. 15 20
624 30 c. "Hornbill Man" (John Takawira) (*horiz*) 40 45
625 $1 "The Chief" (Nicholas Mukomberanwa) 1·40 1·50

(Des Rose Martin)

1983 (13 May). *30th World Ploughing Contest, Zimbabwe. T* **123** *and similar horiz designs. Multicoloured. P* 14.

626 21 c. Type **123** .. 25 30
a. Horiz pair. Nos. 626/7 .. 50 60
627 21 c. Traditional ploughing team (moving left) 25 30
628 30 c. Tractor ploughing .. 40 45
a. Horiz pair. Nos. 628/9 .. 80 90
629 30 c. Modern plough .. 40 45

The two designs of each value were issued in horizontal *se-tenant* pairs, forming composite designs, throughout the sheets.

124 Postman on Cycle

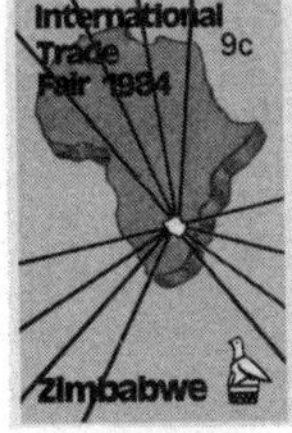

125 Map of Africa showing Zimbabwe

(Des R. Phillips)

1983 (12 Oct). *World Communications Year. T* **124** *and similar multicoloured designs. P* 14.

630	9 c. Type **124** . .	10	12
631	11 c. Aircraft controller directing aircraft . .	15	20
632	15 c. Switchboard operator . .	20	25
633	17 c. Printing works . .	20	25
634	21 c. Road transport (*horiz*) . .	25	30
635	30 c. Rail transport (*horiz*) . .	40	45
630/5	. . *Set of* 6	1·10	1·40

(Des Bunty Woods and Nancy Abrey)

1984 (11 Apr). *Zimbabwe International Trade Fair. T* **125** *and similar vert designs. Multicoloured. P* 14½.

636	9 c. Type **125** . .	10	12
637	11 c. Globe . .	10	12
638	30 c. Zimbabwe flag and Trade Fair logo . .	30	35

126 Cycling

(Des Vivienne Fick (11 c.), Joanna Hogg (21 c.), Blessing Chikoore (30 c.), Wayne Gubb (40 c.))

1984 (18 July). *Olympic Games, Los Angeles. Children's Pictures. T* **126** *and similar horiz designs. Multicoloured. P* 14½.

639	11 c. Type **126** . .	10	12
640	21 c. Swimming . .	20	25
641	30 c. Running . .	30	35
642	40 c. Hurdling . .	40	45

127 Liberation Heroes

128 Fish Eagle

(Des N. Pearce (11 c.), J. Akester (others))

1984 (8 Aug). *Heroes' Days. T* **127** *and similar multicoloured designs showing various aspects of Heroes' Acre. P* 14½.

643	9 c. Type **127** . .	10	12
644	11 c. Symbolic tower and flame (*vert*) . .	10	12
645	17 c. Bronze sculpture (*vert*) . .	15	20
646	30 c. Section of bronze mural . .	30	35

(Des B. Finch)

1984 (10 Oct). *Birds of Prey. T* **128** *and similar vert designs. Multicoloured. P* 14½.

647	9 c. Type **128** . .	10	12
648	11 c. Long Crested Eagle . .	10	12
649	13 c. Bateleur . .	15	20
650	17 c. Black Eagle . .	15	20
651	21 c. Martial Eagle . .	20	25
652	30 c. African Hawk Eagle . .	30	35
647/52	. . *Set of* 6	90	1·10

POSTAGE DUE STAMPS

D 4 Zimbabwe Bird (soapstone sculpture)

1980. *As Nos.* D11/15 *of Rhodesia but inscr* "ZIMBABWE" *as in Type* D **4**.

D16	D 4	1 c. bright green . .	5	5
D17		2 c. ultramarine . .	5	5
D18		5 c. bright reddish violet . .	5	5
		a. Imperf (pair) . .	85·00	
D19		6 c. pale lemon . .	5	8
D20		10 c. cerise . .	10	12

Zululand

PRICES FOR STAMPS ON COVER

Nos. 1/10	*from* × 5
No. 11	—
Nos. 12/16	*from* × 3
Nos. 20/6	*from* × 4
Nos. 27/9	—
No. F1	—

ZULULAND (1) ZULULAND. (2)

1888 (1 May)–**93**. (*a*) *Stamps of Great Britain optd with T* **1**.

1	**71**	½d. vermilion (11.88) . .	4·00	4·50
2	**57**	1d. deep purple . .	9·00	7·00
3	**73**	2d. green and carmine . .	11·00	15·00
4	**74**	2½d. purple/*blue* (9.91) . .	14·00	17·00
5	**75**	3d. purple/*yellow* . .	18·00	20·00
6	**76**	4d. green and brown . .	22·00	27·00
7	**78**	5d. dull purple and blue (3.93) . .	42·00	48·00
8	**79**	6d. purple/*rose-red* . .	20·00	20·00
9	**80**	9d. dull purple and blue (4.92) . .	65·00	65·00
10	**82**	1s. green (4.92) . .	85·00	95·00
11	**59**	5s. rose (4.92) . .	£950	£1000
1/11		. . *Set of* 11	£1100	£1200
1 and 3/11 H/S "Specimen"		. . *Set of* 10	£1200	

(*b*) *No. 97a of Natal optd with T* **2**.

12	**23**	½d. green (7.88) . .	16·00	27·00
		a. Opt double . .	£1200	
		b. Opt inverted . .	£1300	
		c. Without stop . .	40·00	45·00
		d. Opt omitted (pair with normal) . .	£3000	£3000

1894 (Jan). *No. 103 of Natal optd with T* **1**.

16	**15**	6d. mauve . .	45·00	45·00

3

4

(Typo D.L.R.)

1894 (18 Apr)–**96**. *Wmk Crown CA. P* 14.

20	3	½d. dull mauve and green . .	1·75	3·00
21		1d. dull mauve and carmine . .	5·50	1·50
22		2½d. dull mauve and ultramarine . .	13·00	10·00
23		3d. dull mauve and olive-brown . .	13·00	6·00
24	4	6d. dull mauve and black . .	16·00	16·00
25		1s. green . .	25·00	27·00
26		2s. 6d. green and black (2.96) . .	55·00	55·00
27		4s. green and carmine . .	80·00	£100
28		£1 purple/*red* . .	£400	£450
29		£5 purple and black/*red* (Optd S. £500)	£3000	£1100
20/8		. . *Set of* 9	£550	£600
20/8 Optd "Specimen"		. . *Set of* 9	£450	

Dangerous forgeries exist of the £1 and £5.

FISCAL STAMP USED FOR POSTAGE

1891 (June). *Fiscal stamp of Natal* (*Wmk Crown, CA, P* 14) *optd with T* 1.

F1	1d. dull mauve (Optd S. £80) . .	3·50	5·50

Other values, 1s. to £20 as No. F1 exist apparently with postmarks, but, as these were never authorised for postal use, they are no longer listed.

The issue of Zululand stamps ceased on 30 June 1898, the territory having been annexed to Natal on 31 December, 1897.

Set Prices for British Commonwealth Omnibus Issues

The composition of these sets is in accordance with the tables on the following pages. Up to 1973 only such items considered basic stamps are included; varieties such as shades, perforation changes and watermark changes are excluded. Great Britain issues which come on both ordinary paper and on paper with phosphor bands are however covered.

Stamps issued in connection with any of the events by countries which are no longer in the British Commonwealth and which are not listed in the Part 1 Catalogue are omitted.

		Price Un	Used
1935. Silver Jubilee.	*Complete set of* 250 *stamps*	£1000	£1200

The concept initiated by the 1935 Silver Jubilee omnibus issue has provided a pattern for a series of Royal commemoratives over the past 50 years which have introduced countless collectors to the hobby.

The Crown Colony Windsor Castle design by Harold Fleury is, surely, one of the most impressive produced in the 20th-century and its reproduction in the recess process by three of the leading stamp-printing firms of the era has provided a subject for philatelic research which has yet to be exhausted.

Each of the three, Bradbury, Wilkinson & Co. and Waterlow and Sons, who both produced fifteen issues, together with De La Rue & Co. who printed fourteen, used a series of vignette (centre) plates coupled with individual frame plates for each value. All were taken from dies made by Waterlow. Several worthwhile varieties exist on the frame plates, but most interest has been concentrated on the centre plates, each of which was used to print a considerable number of different stamps.

Sheets printed by Bradbury, Wilkinson were without printed plate numbers, but careful study since the initial work by Douglas Armstrong in 1936 has produced two further centre plates to add to the six originally identified. Stamps from some of these eight plates have revealed a number of prominent plate flaws, the most famous of which, the extra flagstaff, has been eagerly sought by collectors for many years. Research has subsequently confirmed three comparable varieties and these are now included in the catalogue listings.

Extra flagstaff (Plate "1" R.9/1)

Short extra flagstaff (Plate "2" R.2/1)

Lightning conductor (Plate "3" R.2/5)

Double flagstaff (Plate "6" R.5/2)

De La Rue sheets were initially printed with plate numbers, but in many instances these were subsequently trimmed off. Surviving examples do, however, enable a positive identification of four centre plates, 2A, 2B, 4 and 4/ to be made. The number of major plate flaws is not so great as on the Bradbury, Wilkinson sheets, but two examples are now included in the catalogue.

Horizontal line from turret (Plate 2A R.10/2)

Dash by turret (Plate 4/ R.3/6)

Much less is known concerning the Waterlow centre plate system. Two plates have been identified and it has been suggested that there may be two more.

All of the Silver Jubilee plate varieties listed have been confirmed by actual examples. It is recorded that the centre plates involved were used for other stamps, so it is quite possible that other instances do exist.

1937. Coronation. *Complete set of* 202 *stamps* £130 £120

1945–46. Victory. *Complete set of* 164 *stamps* 27·00 32·00

1948–49. Royal Silver Wedding. *Complete set of* 138 *stamps* £1600 £2000

1949. U.P.U. 75th Anniversary *Complete set of* 310 *stamps* £300 £375

1951. B.W.I. University College *Complete set of* 28 *stamps* 10·00 11·00

1953. Coronation. *Complete set of* 106 *stamps* £100 £100

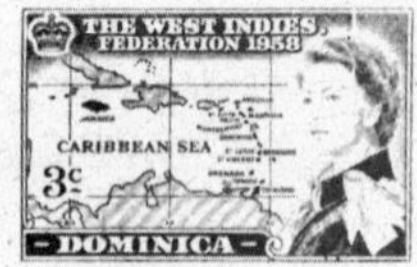

1953–54. Royal Visit. *Complete set of* 13 *stamps* 6·00 4·75

1958. Caribbean Federation. *Complete set of* 30 *stamps* 7·00 6·50

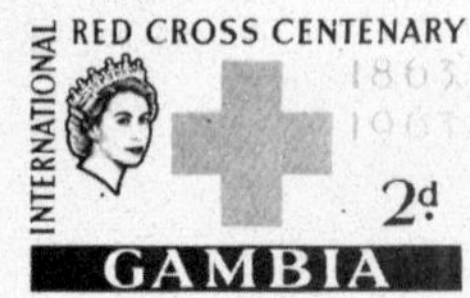

1963. Freedom from Hunger. *Complete set of* 77 *stamps* £200 £100

1963. Red Cross Centenary. *Complete set of* 108 *stamps and* 2 *miniature sheets* £250 £160

1964. Shakespeare. 400th Birth Anniversary. *Complete set of* 25 *stamps* 30·00 22·00

1965. I.T.U. Centenary. *Complete set of* 112 *stamps and* 1 *miniature sheet* £190 £100

1965. I.C.Y. *Complete set of* 108 *stamps and* 2 *miniature sheets* £120 70·00

965–67. Churchill. *Complete set of* 182 *stamps* £275 £140

966. Royal Visit to the Caribbean.
Complete set of 34 *stamps* 28·00 14·00

1966. World Cup Football Championship.
Complete set of 76 *stamps and* 2 *miniature sheets* 65·00 40·00

1966. W.H.O. New Headquarters.
Complete set of 62 *stamps and* 1 *miniature sheet* 70·00 35·00

1966–67. U.N.E.S.C.O. 20th Anniversary.
Complete set of 110 *stamps and* 1 *miniature sheet* £160 90·00

1972. Royal Silver Wedding.
Complete set of 78 *stamps* 40·00 38·00

1973. Royal Wedding.
Complete set of 72 *stamps and* 6 *miniature sheets* 38·00 35·00

1977. Silver Jubilee. *Set of* 220 *basic stamps* £200 £160
Set of 24 *miniature sheets* £100 £100

1977. Royal Visit. *Set of* 46 *basic stamps* 26·00 23·00
Set of 8 *miniature sheets* 21·00 22·00

1978. Coronation. 25th Anniversary.
Set of 195 *basic stamps* £100 £100
Set of 21 *sheetlets* 70·00
Set of 27 *miniature sheets* 70·00 70·00

1980. Queen Mother's Birthday.
Set of 41 *stamps* 32·00 32·00
Set of 12 *miniature sheets* 27·00 27·00

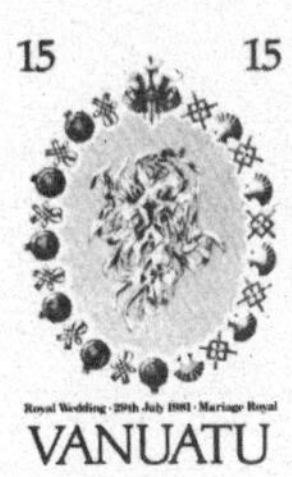

1981. Royal Wedding. *Set of* 247 *basic stamps* £225 £225
Set of 36 *miniature sheets* £100 £100

1982. Princess Diana's 21st Birthday.
Set of 164 *basic stamps* £100 £100
Set of 19 *miniature sheets* 48·00 50·00

1982. Birth of Prince William.
Set of 125 *basic stamps* £150 £120
Set of 22 *miniature sheets* 80·00 80·00

1935 SILVER JUBILEE TO 1973 ROYAL WEDDING

Issuing Countries	1935 *Silver Jubilee*	1937 *Coronation*	1945–46 *Victory*	1948 *Silver Wedding*	1949 *U.P.U.*	1951 *B.W.I. Univ*	1953 *Coronation*	1953–54 *Royal Visit*	1958 *Caribbean Fed.*	1963 *F.F.H.*	1963 *Red Cross*	1964 *Shakespeare*	1965 *I.T.U.*	1965 *I.C.Y.*	1965–66 *Churchill*	1966 *Royal Visit*	1966 *Football Cup*	1966 *W.H.O.*	1966–67 *UNESCO*	1972 *Silver Wedding*	1973 *Royal Wedding*
Great Britain	4	1	2	2	4	—	4	—	—	2+2	3+3	5+4	2+2	2+2	2+2	—	3+3	—	—	2	2
Guernsey	—	—	—	—	—	—	—	—	—	—	—	—	—	—	—	—	—	—	—	4	1
Isle of Man	—	—	—	—	—	—	—	—	—	—	—	—	—	—	—	—	—	—	—	—	1
Jersey	—	—	—	—	—	—	—	—	—	—	—	—	—	—	—	—	—	—	—	4	2
Aden/South Arabian Fed.	—	3	2	2	4	—	1	1	—	1	2	—	—	2	4	—	2	2	3	—	—
Seiyun	—	—	2	2	4	—	1	—	—	—	—	—	7	—	1	—	7	—	—	—	—
Shihr and Mukalla	—	—	2	2	4	—	1	—	—	—	—	—	—	8	3	—	8	—	—	—	—
Anguilla	—	—	—	—	—	—	—	—	—	—	—	—	—	—	—	—	—	—	—	2	2
Antigua	4	3	2	2	4	2	1	—	3	1	2	1	2	2	4	2	2	2	3	2	2+M
Barbuda	—	—	—	—	—	—	—	—	—	—	—	—	—	—	—	—	—	—	—	—	2
Ascension	4	3	2	2	4	—	1	—	—	1	2	—	2	2	4	—	2	2	3	2	2
Australia	3	—	3	—	1	—	3	3	—	—	1	—	1	1	1	—	—	—	—	—	—
Bahamas	4	3	2	2	4	—	1	—	—	1	2	1	2	2	4	2	2	2	3	2	—
Bahrain	—	—	—	2	4	—	4	—	—	—	—	—	—	—	—	—	—	—	—	—	—
Barbados	4	3	2	2	4	2	1	—	3	—	—	—	2	—	4	2	—	—	3	—	—
Basutoland/Lesotho	4	3	3×2	2	4	—	1	—	—	1	2	—	2	2	4	—	—	—	4	—	—
Bechuanaland	4	3	3×2	2	4	—	1	—	—	1	2	1	2	2	4	—	—	—	—	—	—
Bermuda	4	3	2	2	4	—	1	1	—	1	2	—	2	2	4	—	2	—	3	2	2
British Antarctic Territory	—	—	—	—	—	—	—	—	—	—	—	—	—	—	4	—	—	—	—	2	2
British Forces in Egypt	1	—	—	—	—	—	—	—	—	—	—	—	—	—	—	—	—	—	—	—	—
British Guiana	4	3	2	2	4	2	1	—	—	1	2	—	2	2	2	2	—	—	—	—	—
British Honduras/Belize	4	3	2	2	4	2	1	—	—	1	2	—	2	2	4	—	—	—	—	2	2
British Indian Ocean Terr.	—	—	—	—	—	—	—	—	—	—	—	—	—	—	—	—	—	—	—	2	—
British P.A's in Eastern Arabia	—	—	—	2	4	—	4	—	—	—	—	—	—	—	—	—	—	—	—	—	—
British Virgin Islands	4	3	2	2	4	2	1	—	—	1	2	1	2	2	4	2	—	—	3	2	2
Brunei	—	—	—	—	4	—	—	—	—	1	—	—	2	2	4	—	2	2	3	2	2
Burma	—	—	4	—	—	—	—	—	—	—	—	—	—	—	—	—	—	—	—	—	—
Canada	6	1	—	—	—	—	1	—	—	—	—	—	—	1	1	—	—	—	—	—	—
Cayman Islands	4	3	2	2	4	—	1	—	—	1	2	1	2	2	4	2	2	2	3	2	2
Ceylon/Sri Lanka	4	3	2	—	3	—	1	1	—	2	—	—	2	2	—	—	—	2	2	—	—
Cook Islands	3	3	4	—	—	—	2	—	—	—	—	—	—	—	6	—	—	—	—	4	3+M
Aitutaki	—	—	—	—	—	—	—	—	—	—	—	—	—	—	—	—	—	—	—	2	2+M
Penrhyn	—	—	—	—	—	—	—	—	—	—	—	—	—	—	—	—	—	—	—	—	3
Cyprus	4	3	2	2	4	—	1	—	—	2	2	4	3	2	—	—	—	—	1	—	—
Dominica	4	3	2	2	4	2	1	—	3	1	2	1	2	2	4	2	2	2	3	2	2+M
Falkland Islands	4	3	2	2	4	—	1	—	—	1	2	1	2	2	4	—	—	—	—	2	2
Falkland Islands Dependencies	—	—	2	2	4	—	1	—	—	—	—	—	—	—	—	—	—	—	—	—	—
South Georgia	—	—	—	—	—	—	—	—	—	—	—	—	—	—	—	—	—	—	—	2	2
Fiji	4	3	2	2	4	—	1	1	—	1	2	—	2	2	4	—	2	2	—	2	—
Gambia	4	3	2	2	4	—	1	—	—	1	2	1	2	—	3	—	—	—	—	—	—
Gibraltar	4	3	2	2	4	—	1	1	—	1	2	1	2	2	4	—	2	2	3	2	2
Gilbert and Ellice Islands	4	3	2	2	4	—	1	—	—	1	2	—	2	2	4	—	2	2	3	2	2
Gold Coast/Ghana	4	3	2	2	4	—	1	—	—	3	4+MS	—	4+MS	4+MS	—	—	5+MS	4+MS	5+MS	—	—
Grenada	4	3	2	2	4	2	1	—	3	1	2	—	2	2	4	2	2	2	3	2	2+M
Grenadines	—	—	—	—	—	—	—	—	—	—	—	—	—	—	—	—	—	—	—	—	2+M
Hong Kong	4	3	2	2	4	—	1	—	—	1	2	—	2	2	4	—	—	2	3	2	2
India	7	—	4	—	4	—	—	—	—	1	1	—	1	1	—	—	—	—	—	—	—
Hyderabad	—	—	1	—	—	—	—	—	—	—	—	—	—	—	—	—	—	—	—	—	—
Ireland	—	—	—	—	—	—	—	—	—	2	2	—	2	2	—	—	—	—	—	—	—
Jamaica	4	3	2	2	4	2	1	1	3	2	2	—	1	—	2	4	—	—	—	—	—
K.U.T./East Africa	4	3	2	2	4	—	1	1	—	4	2	—	4	4	—	—	—	—	4	—	—
Kuwait	—	—	—	2	4	—	4	—	—	—	—	—	—	—	—	—	—	—	—	—	—
Leeward Islands	4	3	2	2	4	2	1	—	—	—	—	—	—	—	—	—	—	—	—	—	—
Malayan States, etc.	4	3	—	22	44	—	11	—	—	3	—	—	3	—	—	—	—	—	—	—	—
Maldive Islands	—	—	—	—	—	—	—	—	—	7	5	—	—	6+MS	6	—	8+MS	4	6	—	—
Malta	4	3	2	2	4	—	1	1	—	1	2	—	—	—	4	—	—	—	—	—	—
Mauritius	4	3	2	2	4	—	1	—	—	1	2	—	2	2	4	—	—	—	3	—	—
Montserrat	4	3	2	2	4	2	1	—	3	1	2	1	2	2	4	2	—	2	3	2	2
Morocco Agencies/Tangier	15	3	2	4	4	—	4	—	—	—	—	—	—	—	—	—	—	—	—	—	—
Nauru	4	4	—	—	—	—	—	—	—	—	—	—	—	—	—	—	—	—	—	—	—
Newfoundland	4	14	—	—	—	—	—	—	—	—	—	—	—	—	—	—	—	—	—	—	—
New Guinea	2	4	—	—	—	—	—	—	—	—	—	—	—	—	—	—	—	—	—	—	—
New Hebrides (English & French inscr)	—	—	—	—	4+4	—	1	—	—	1+1	2+2	—	2+2	2+2	4+4	—	2+2	2+2	3+3	2+2	—
New Zealand	3	3	11	—	—	—	5	2	—	—	—	—	1	1	1	—	—	—	—	—	—
Tokelau Islands	—	—	—	—	—	—	1	—	—	—	—	—	—	—	—	—	—	—	—	—	—
Nigeria	4	3	2	2	4	—	1	—	—	2	3+MS	—	3	3	—	—	—	—	3	—	—
Niue	3	3	4	—	—	—	2	—	—	—	—	—	—	—	—	—	—	—	—	—	—
North Borneo	—	—	—	2	4	—	1	—	—	1	—	—	—	—	—	—	—	—	—	—	—
Northern Rhodesia/Zambia	4	3	2	2	4	—	1	—	—	—	—	—	2	2	—	—	—	2	—	—	—
Nyasaland	4	3	2	2	4	—	1	—	—	—	—	—	—	—	—	—	—	—	—	—	—
Pakistan	—	—	—	—	—	—	—	—	—	2	1	—	1	2	—	—	—	—	1	—	—
Bahawalpur Postage and Officials	—	—	1	—	4+4	—	—	—	—	—	—	—	—	—	—	—	—	—	—	—	—
Papua/P.N.G.	4	4	—	—	—	—	—	—	—	—	1	—	—	—	—	—	—	—	—	—	—
Pitcairn Islands	—	—	2	2	4	—	1	—	—	1	2	—	2	2	4	—	2	2	3	2	2
Rhodesia and Nyasaland	—	—	—	—	—	—	—	—	—	—	1	—	—	—	—	—	—	—	—	—	—
St. Helena	4	3	2	2	4	—	1	—	—	1	2	—	2	2	4	—	2	2	3	2	2
St. Kitts-Nevis	4	3	2	2	4	2	1	—	3	—	2	—	2	2	4	2	2	2	3	2	2
St. Lucia	4	3	2	2	4	2	1	—	3	1	2	1	2	2	4	2	2	2	3	2	2
St. Vincent	4	3	2	2	4	2	1	—	3	1	2	—	2	—	4	2	—	2	3	2	2
Grenadines	—	—	—	—	—	—	—	—	—	—	—	—	—	—	—	—	—	—	—	—	2
Samoa	3	—	4	—	—	—	2	—	—	—	—	—	—	—	—	—	—	4	—	—	—
Sarawak	—	—	—	2	4	—	1	—	—	1	—	—	—	—	—	—	—	—	—	—	—
Seychelles	4	3	2	2	4	—	1	—	—	1	2	—	2	2	4	—	2	2	3	2	2
Sierra Leone	4	3	2	2	4	—	1	—	—	2	3	—	—	—	11	—	—	—	—	—	—
Singapore	—	—	—	2	4	—	1	—	—	—	—	—	—	—	—	—	—	—	—	—	—
Solomon Islands	4	3	2	2	4	—	1	—	—	1	2	—	2	2	4	—	2	2	3	2	2
Somaliland Protectorate	4	3	2	2	4	—	1	—	—	—	—	—	—	—	—	—	—	—	—	—	—
South Africa	4×2	5×2	3×2	1×2	3×2	—	1	—	—	—	2	—	2	—	—	—	—	—	—	—	—
South West Africa	4	8×2	3×2	1×2	3×2	—	5	—	—	—	2	—	—	—	—	—	—	—	—	—	—
Southern Rhodesia/Rhodesia	4	4	4	—	2	—	1	—	—	—	—	—	3	—	1	—	—	—	—	—	—
Swaziland	4	3	3×2	2	4	—	1	—	—	1	2	—	2	2	4	—	—	—	3	—	—
Tonga	—	—	—	—	4	—	—	—	—	1	2	—	—	—	—	—	—	—	—	—	—
Trinidad and Tobago	4	3	2	2	4	2	1	—	3	3	—	—	—	1	—	4	—	—	—	—	—
Tristan da Cunha	—	—	—	—	—	—	1	—	—	1	2	—	2	2	4	—	2	2	3	2	2
Turks and Caicos Islands	4	3	2	2	4	—	1	—	—	1	2	1	2	2	4	2	—	—	3	2	2
Zanzibar	—	—	2	2	4	—	—	—	—	1	—	—	—	—	—	—	—	—	—	—	—
Total number of stamps	250	202	164	138	310	28	106	13	30	77	108 +2 MS	25	112 +MS	108 +2 MS	182	34	76 +2 MS	62 + MS	110 + MS	78	72 +6 MS

NOTE Countries marked with an asterisk are those which comprise the Crown Agents Omnibus issue.

1977 SILVER JUBILEE

Country	Catalogue Nos.	Stamps	MS
Great Britain	1033/7	5	—
Guernsey	149/50	2	—
Isle of Man	94/6	3	—
Jersey	168/70	3	—
Anguilla	269/73	4	1
Antigua	526/33a	5	1
Barbuda	298/304, 323/28	11	2
Ascension*	222/4	3	—
Australia	645/6	2	—
Bahamas	488/92	4	1
Bangladesh	93/6	3	1
Barbados*	574/6	3	—
Belize*	449/51	3	—
Bermuda*	371/3	3	—
Botswana*	391/3	3	—
British Antarctic Territory*	83/5	3	—
British Virgin Islands*	364/6	3	—
Brunei	264/6	3	—
Canada	855	1	—
Cayman Islands*	427/9	3	—
Christmas Island	83	1	—
Cook Islands	564/70	6	1
Aitutaki	225/9	4	1
Penrhyn	100/3	3	1
Cyprus	485	1	—
Dominica	562/7	5	1
Falkland Islands*	325/7ba	3	—
South Georgia*	50/2	3	—
Fiji*	536/8	3	—
Gambia*	365/7	3	—
Gibraltar	371/3	2	1
Gilbert Islands*	48/50	3	—
Grenada	857/66	5	1
Grenadines of Grenada	215/22	3	1
Hong Kong*	361/3	3	—
Kenya	295/9	4	2
Maldive Islands	673/9	6	1
Mauritius*	516/18	3	—
Montserrat	396/8	3	—
New Hebrides* (English & French inscr)	217/19, F231/3	3+3	—
New Zealand	**MS**1137	—	1
Niue	213/15	2	1
Norfolk Island	196	1	—
Papua New Guinea	330/2	3	—
Pitcairn Islands*	171/3	3	—
St. Helena*	332/4	3	—
St. Kitts-Nevis*	367/9	3	—
St. Lucia	443/7	4	1
St. Vincent	502/26	12	1
Grenadines of St. Vincent	93/5	3	—
Samoa	479/82	4	—
Seychelles	393/401	8	1
Sierra Leone	597/8	2	—
Solomon Islands*	334/6	3	—
Swaziland*	268/70	3	—
Tanzania	218/22	4	1
Tonga	598/607, O151/3	13	—
Tristan da Cunha*	212/14	3	—
Turks and Caicos Islands*	472/5	3	1
Tuvalu	50/3	3	1
Total number of items		220	24

The Turks and Caicos Islands miniature sheet, **MS**475, did not form part of the Crown Agents Omnibus issue.

1977 ROYAL VISIT

Country	Catalogue Nos.	Stamps	MS
Anguilla	298/302	4	1
Antigua	548/53	5	1
Barbuda	345/54	8	2
Bahamas	500/4	4	1
Barbados	590/2	3	—
British Virgin Islands	371/3	3	—
Dominica	591/6	5	1
Grenada	894/9	5	1
Grenadines of Grenada	239/42	3	1
Monserrat	409/11	3	—
St. Vincent	540	1	—
Grenadines of St. Vincent	104/5	2	—
Total number of items		46	8

1978 CORONATION ANNIVERSARY

Country	Catalogue Nos.	Stamps	Sheetlets	MS
Great Britain	1059/62	4	—	—
Guernsey	167	1	—	—
Isle of Man	132	1	—	—
Jersey	195/6	2	—	—
Anguilla	320/4	4	—	1
Antigua	581/9	5	—	1
Barbuda	408/23, 445/6	12	—	3
Ascension*	233/5	3	1	—
Bahamas	515/17	2	—	1
Bangladesh	116/20	4	—	1
Barbados*	597/9	3	1	—
Belize*	464/6, 495/503	11	1	2
Bermuda	384/6	3	—	—
British Antarctic Territory*	86/8	3	1	—
British Virgin Islands*	384/6	3	1	—
Brunei	/9	3	—	—
Cayman Islands*	468/70	3	1	—
Christmas Island*	96/8	3	1	—
Cook Islands	593/601	8	—	1
Aitutaki	257/60	3	—	1
Penrhyn	121/4	3	—	1
Dominica	612/15	3	—	1
Falkland Islands*	348/50	3	1	—
South Georgia*	67/9	3	1	—
Fiji*	549/51	3	1	—
Gambia*	397/9	3	1	—
Gibraltar	400/6	4	—	—
Gilbert Islands*	68/70	3	1	—
Grenada	946/52	3	—	1
Grenadines of Grenada	272/8	3	—	1
Hong Kong	373/4	2	—	—
Maldive Islands	755/61	6	—	1
Mauritius*	549/51	3	1	—
Montserrat	422/6	4	—	1
New Hebrides* (English & French inscr)	262/4, F276/8	3+3	1+1	—
New Zealand Dependency of Tokelau	61/4	4	—	—
Niue	245/8	3	—	1
Norfolk Island	207/8	2	—	—
Pitcairn Islands	**MS**189	—	—	1
St. Helena*	338/40	3	1	—
St. Kitts-Nevis*	389/91	3	1	—
St. Lucia	468/72	4	—	1
St. Vincent	556/60	4	—	1
Grenadines of St. Vincent	130/4	4	—	1
Samoa*	508/10	3	1	—
Seychelles	428/32	4	—	1
Sierra Leone	601/3	3	—	—
Solomon Islands*	357/9	3	1	—
Swaziland	293/5	3	1	—
Tanzania	233/7	4	—	1
Tristan da Cunha*	239/41	3	1	—
Turks and Caicos Islands	494/501	4	—	1
Tuvalu	89/93	4	—	1
Uganda	234/38	4	—	1
Total number of items		195	27	25

The Crown Agents Omnibus issue was printed in matching sheetlets, each containing two *se-tenant* strips of the three designs.

Barbuda Nos. 445/6 form part of a general anniversaries issue.

Belize Nos. 495/503 were not part of the Crown Agents Omnibus issue.

1980 QUEEN MOTHER's 80th BIRTHDAY

Country	Catalogue Nos.	Stamps	MS
Great Britain	1129	1	—
Anguilla	411/15	4	1
Antigua	663/5	2	1
Barbuda	533/5	2	1
Ascension*	269	1	—
Bangladesh	172/4	2	1
Belize	586/7	1	1
Bermuda*	425	1	—
Cayman Islands*	506	1	—
Cook Islands	701/2	1	1
Penrhyn	150/1	1	1
Dominica	732/4	2	1
Falkland Islands*	383	1	—
Gambia*	440	1	—
Gibraltar*	436	1	—
Hong Kong*	390	1	—
Lesotho	423/5	3	—
Maldive Islands	886/7	1	1
Niue	364/5	1	1
Norfolk Island	252/3	2	—
Pitcairn Islands*	206	1	—
St. Helena*	366	1	—
St. Kitts-Nevis			
St. Kitts	48	1	—
Nevis	50	1	—
St. Lucia	534/6	2	1
Samoa*	572	1	—
Solomon Islands*	421	1	—
Tristan da Cunha*	282	1	—
Turks and Caicos Islands	607/8	1	1
Tuvalu	148	1	—
Total number of items		41	12

1981 ROYAL WEDDING

Country	Catalogue Nos.	Stamps	MS
Great Britain	1160/1	2	—
Guernsey	232/9	7	1
Isle of Man	202/4	2	1
Jersey	284/5	2	—
Anguilla	464/9†	3	1
Antigua	702/12a	3	1
Barbuda	565/75†, 580/6	9	2
Ascension*	302/4	3	—
Australia	801/2	2	—
Bahamas	586/8	2	1
Barbados*	674/6	3	—
Belize	608/14	6	1
Bermuda*	436/8	3	—
British Virgin Islands*	463/5	3	—
Brunei*	304/6	3	—
Cayman Islands*	534/6	3	—
Cocos (Keeling) Islands	70/1	2	—
Cook Islands	812/14	2	1
Aitutaki	391/3†	3	—
Penrhyn	223/8†	5	1
Cyprus	580	1	—
Turkish Cypriot Posts	121	1	—
Dominica	747/53†	3	1
Falkland Islands*	402/4	3	—
Dependencies*	95/7	3	—
Fiji*	612/14	3	—
Gambia*	454/6	3	—
Ghana	948/56†	6	1
Gibraltar	450	1	—
Grenada	1130/8†	5	1
Grenadines of Grenada	444/52†	5	1
Guyana	769/70, 841/3, 930/6	12	—
Hong Kong*	399/401	3	—
Jamaica	516/20†	4	1
Kenya	411/15†	4	1
Kiribati	149/57†	6	1
Lesotho*	451/4	3	1
Maldive Islands	918/21	3	1
Mauritius*	615/17	3	—
Montserrat	510/18†	6	1
New Zealand	1247/8	2	—
Niue	430/3†	3	1
Norfolk Island*	262/4	3	—
Pitcairn Islands*	219/21	3	—
St. Helena*	378/80	3	—
St. Kitts-Nevis			
St. Kitts	75/83†	6	1
Nevis	72/80†	6	1
St. Lucia	576/82†	3	1
St. Vincent	668/76†	6	1
Grenadines of St. Vincent	195/203†	6	1
Samoa*	599/601	3	—
Seychelles	505/13†	6	1
Zil Elwagne Sesel	23/31†	6	1
Sierra Leone*	668/74†	6	1
Solomon Islands*	445/7	3	—
Swaziland*	376/8	3	—
Tanzania	325/7	2	1
Tonga	785/8	4	—
Tristan da Cunha*	308/10	3	—
Turks and Caicos Islands	653/9†	3	1
Caicos Islands	8/11	3	—
Tuvalu	168/76†	6	1
Uganda	341/8†	6	2
Vanuatu*	315/17	3	—
Total number of items		247	36

The Lesotho miniature sheet, No. **MS**454, and Sierra Leone Nos. 671/3 do not form part of the Crown Agents Omnibus issue.

Issues available in sheetlet form are indicated by a †. Some of these sets were also available from normal sized sheets, others were not.

1982 PRINCESS DIANA'S 21st BIRTHDAY

Country	Catalogue Nos.	Stamps	MS
Anguilla	507/14	6	2
Antigua	748/51	3	1
Barbuda	624/30	6	2
Ascension*	322/5	4	—
Bahamas*	622/5	4	—
Barbados*	705/8	4	—
Belize	674/80	6	1
British Antarctic Territory*	109/12	4	—
British Virgin Islands*	488/91	4	—
Cayman Islands*	549/52	4	—
Cook Islands	833/7	4	1
Aitutaki	411/14	3	1
Penrhyn	250/5	5	1
Dominica	821/4	3	1
Falkland Islands*	426/9	4	—
Dependencies*	108/11	4	—
Fiji*	640/3	4	—
Gambia*	476/9	4	—
Grenada	1188/94	6	1
Grenadines of Grenada	493/9	6	1
Guyana	979/81	3	—
Jamaica	551/7	6	1
Kiribati	183/5	3	—
Lesotho*	514/17	4	—
Maldive Islands	964/7	3	1
Mauritius*	643/6	4	—
Montserrat	542/4	3	—
Niue	454/7	3	1
Pitcairn Islands*	226/9	4	—
St. Helena*	397/400	4	—
St. Kitts-Nevis			
St. Kitts	95/7	3	—
Nevis	85/7	3	—
St. Lucia	625/8	3	1
St. Vincent	694/6	3	—
Grenadines of St. Vincent	229/31	3	—
Sierra Leone	707/9	3	1
Solomon Islands*	467/70	4	—
Swaziland*	404/7	4	—
Tristan da Cunha*	327/30	4	—
Turks and Caicos Islands	709/12	3	1
Tuvalu	184/6	3	—
Uganda	374/7	1	1
Total number of items		164	19

1982 BIRTH OF PRINCE WILLIAM

Country	Catalogue Nos.	Stamps	MS
Great Britain			
Isle of Man	**MS**227	—	1
Antigua	757/60	3	1
Barbuda	613/16, 632/85	6	2
Belize	701/14	12	2
Cook Islands	838/47, 856/61	13	3
Aitutaki	415/24	9	1
Penrhyn	256/72	15	2
Dominica	830/3	3	1
Grenada	1200/6	6	1
Grenadines of Grenada	505/11	6	1
Guyana	982/7	6	—
Jamaica	558/64	6	1
Kiribati	186/8	3	—
Lesotho	521/2	2	—
Maldive Islands	968/71	3	1
Mauritius	647	1	—
Niue	458/74	13	4
St. Kitts-Nevis			
St. Kitts	98/100	3	—
Nevis	88/90	3	—
St. Vincent	699/701	3	—
Grenadines of St. Vincent	234/6	3	—
Sierra Leone	711/14	3	1
Tuvalu	189/91	3	—
Total number of items		125	22

Addenda and Corrigenda

ANGUILLA

112 Christmas in Sweden

(Litho Questa)

1984 (12 Nov). *Christmas. Walt Disney Cartoon Characters. T* **112** *and similar horiz designs showing national scenes. Multicoloured. P* 12 ($2) *or* 14 × 13½ (*others*).

636 1 c. Type **112** 5 5
637 2 c. Italy 5 5
638 3 c. Holland 5 5
639 4 c. Mexico 5 5
640 5 c. Spain 5 5
641 10 c. Disneyland, U.S.A. 5 8
642 $1 Japan 60 65
643 $2 Anguilla . . . . 1·25 1·40
644 $4 Germany . . . . 2·40 2·50
636/44 . . . . *Set of* 9 4·00 4·50
MS645 126 × 102 mm. $5 England . . . . 3·00 3·25

No. 643 was printed in sheetlets of 8 stamps.

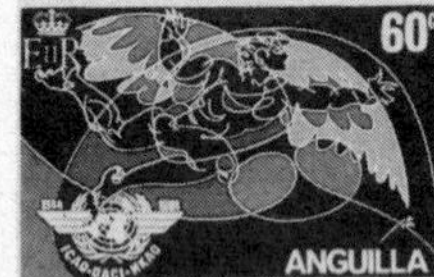

113 Icarus in Flight

(Des H. Herni (60 c.), S. Diouf (75 c.), adapted R. Granger Barrett. Litho Ueberreuter)

1984 (3 Dec). *40th Anniv of International Civil Aviation Authority. T* **113** *and similar multicoloured designs. P* 14.

646 60 c. Type **113** 35 40
647 75 c. "Solar Princess" (abstract) 45 50
648 $2.50, I.C.A.O. emblem (*vert*) . . . . 1·50 1·60
MS649 65 × 49 mm. $5 Map of air routes serving Anguilla . . . . 3·00 3·25

ANTIGUA

BARBUDA

1984 (30 Nov). *150th Birth Anniv of Edgar Degas (painter). Nos.* 883/7 *of Antigua optd with T* **95** (*No.* 762/5) *or T* **99** (*No.* **MS**766), *all in silver.*

762 15 c. "The Blue Dancers" 8 10
763 50 c. "The Pink Dancers" 30 35
764 70 c. "Two Dancers" 45 50
765 $4 "Dancers at the Bar" . . . . . . 2·40 2·50
MS766 90 × 60 mm. $5 "The Folk Dancers" (40 × 27 *mm*) . . . . 3·00 3·25

AUSTRALIA

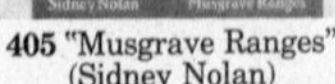

405 "Musgrave Ranges" (Sidney Nolan)

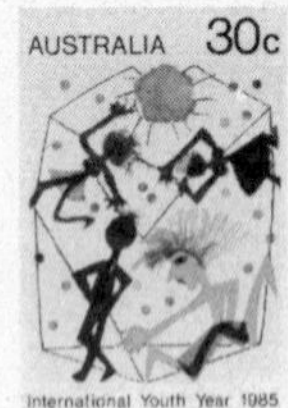

406 Young People of Different Races, and Sun

(Des Sue Titcher. Litho Leigh-Mardon Ltd, Melbourne)

1985 (25 Jan). *Australia Day. Birth Centenary of Dorothea Mackellar (author of poem "My Country"). T* **405** *and similar horiz design. Multicoloured. P* 14½.

961 30 c. Type **405** 35 40
a. *Tête-bêche* (vert pair) 70 80
b. Vert pair. Nos. 961/2 . . . . . . 70 80
962 30 c. "The Walls of China" (Russell Drysdale) . 35 40
a. *Tête-bêche* (vert pair) 70 80

Nos. 961/2 were issued together, *se-tenant*, within the same sheet. In each pane of 25 No. 961 occurs in horizontal rows 1, 4, 5, 8 and 9, and No. 962 in rows 2, 3, 6, 7 and 10. Horizontal rows 3/4 and 7/8 are inverted forming *tête-bêche* pairs of the same design in addition to the vertical *se-tenant* pairs containing both designs.

(Des Derryn Vogelnest. Litho Cambec Press, Melbourne)

1985 (13 Feb). *International Youth Year. P* 14 × 13½.

963 **406** 30 c. multicoloured 35 40

407 Royal Victorian Volunteer Artillery

408 District Nurse of early 1900's

(Des Pam Andrews. Litho Leigh-Mardon Ltd, Melbourne)

1985 (25 Feb). *19th-Century Australian Military Uniforms. T* **407** *and similar vert designs. Multicoloured. P* 14½.

964 33 c. Type **407** 40 45
a. Horiz strip of 5. Nos. 964/8 . . . . 1·90
965 33 c. Western Australian Pinjarrah Cavalry . . 40 45
966 33 c. New South Wales Lancers 40 45
967 33 c. New South Wales Contingent to the Sudan 40 45
968 33 c. Victorian Mounted Rifles 40 45

Nos. 964/8 were issued in horizontal strips of 5, *se-tenant*, throughout the sheet.

(Des Wendy Tamlyn. Litho Leigh-Mardon Ltd, Melbourne)

1985 (13 Mar). *Centenary of District Nursing Services. P* 14½.

969 **408** 33 c. multicoloured 40 45

BAHAMAS

1985 (2 Jan). *Air. As Nos.* 663/6, *but without Manned Flight logo. W* w **14** (*sideways*). *P* 14.

699 10 c. Type **150** 15 20
700 25 c. Avro "Tudor IV" 35 40
701 31 c. Avro "Lancastrian" 45 50
702 35 c. Consolidated "Commodore" 50 55

158 Brownie Emblem and Conch

(Des Berta Dallen Sands. Litho Walsall)

1985 (22 Feb). *International Youth Year. 75th Anniv of Girl Guide Movement. T* **158** *and similar horiz designs. Multicoloured. W* w **14** (*sideways*). *P* 14.

703 5 c. Type **158** 8 10
704 25 c. Tents and coconut palm 40 45
705 31 c. Guide salute and flamingos 50 55
706 35 c. Ranger emblem and marlin 55 60
MS707 95 × 74 mm. Nos. 703/6 . . . . 1·50 1·60

BANGLADESH

72 Eagle attacking Hen with Chicks

73 Abbasuddin Ahmad

(Des K. Mostafa. Litho Harrison)

1984 (3 Dec). *Centenary of Postal Life Insurance. T* **72** *and similar vert design. Multicoloured. P* 14.

235 1 t. Type **72** 5 8
236 5 t. Bangladesh family and postman's hand with insurance cheque 30 35

(Des K. Mostafa. Litho Harrison)

1984 (24 Dec). *Abbasuddin Ahmad (singer) Commemmoration. P* 14.

237 **73** 3 t. multicoloured 20 25

BARBADOS

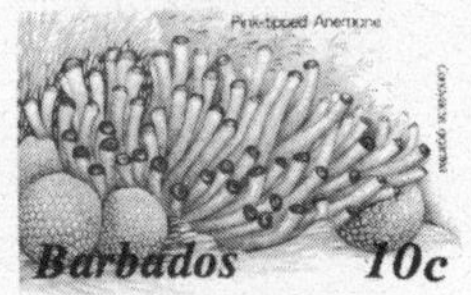

173 Pink-tipped Anemone

(Des I. Loe. Litho Questa)

1985 (26 Feb). *Marine Life. T* **173** *and similar horiz designs Multicoloured. W* w **14** (*sideways*). *P* 14.

766 10 c. Type **173** 5 8
767 20 c. Christmas Tree Worm 15 20
768 25 c. Hermit Crab 15 20
772 50 c. Ghost Crab 35 40
776 $2.50, Green Turtle . . . . 1·75 1·90
777 $5 Rock Beauty (fish) . . . . . . 3·50 3·75
766/77 . . . . *Set of* 6 5·25 5·75

Two further instalments of this set are expected.

BECHUANALAND

CORRECTION: Replace Nos. 194/7 on page 78 as follows.

1965 (25 Oct). *International Co-operation Year. As Nos.* 168/9 *of Antigua.*

192 1 c. reddish purple and turquoise-green . . 10 10
193 12½ c. deep bluish green and lavender . . 1·00 55

1966 (24 Jan). *Churchill Commemoration. As Nos.* 170/3 *of Antigua.*

194 1 c. new blue 15 12
195 2½ c. deep green 40 10
196 12½ c. brown 85 50
197 20 c. bluish violet 95 50

BERMUDA

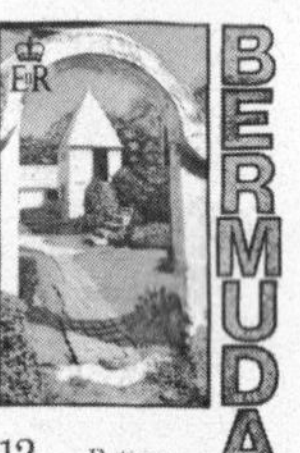

125 Buttery

(Des D. Miller. Litho Walsall)

1985 (24 Jan). *Bermuda Architecture. T* **125** *and similar multicoloured designs. W* w **14** (*inverted on* 12 *c.*, $1.50, *sideways on* 30 *c.*, 40 *c.*). *P* 13½ × 13 (12 *c.*, $1.50) *or* 13 × 13½ (30 *c.*, 40 *c.*).

486 12 c. Type **125** 20 25
487 30 c. Limestone rooftops (*horiz*) 45 50
488 40 c. Chimneys (*horiz*) 65 70
489 $1.50, Entrance archway . . . . . . 2·25 2·40

BRITISH ANTARCTIC TERRITORY

34 M.Y. *Penola* in Stella Creek

(Des A. Theobald. Litho Questa)

1985 (23 Mar). *50th Anniv of British Graham Land Expedition. T* **34** *and similar horiz designs. Multicoloured. W* w **14** (*sideways*). *P* 14½.

139 7p. Type **34** 15 20
140 22p. Northern Base, Winter Island 45 50
141 27p. D. H. Fox "Moth" at Southern Base, Barry Island 55 60
142 54p. Dog Team near Ablation Point, George VI Sound . . . . 1·10 1·25

CANADA

507 Heart and Arrow

508 Astronaut in Space, and Planet Earth

(Des F. Dallaire. Litho Ashton-Potter)

985 (8 Feb). *International Youth Year. P* 12½.
142 **507** 32 c. multicoloured 40 45

(Des L. Holloway. Litho Ashton-Potter)

985 (15 Mar). *Canadian Space Programme. P* 13½.
143 **508** 32 c. multicoloured 40 45

CHRISTMAS ISLAND

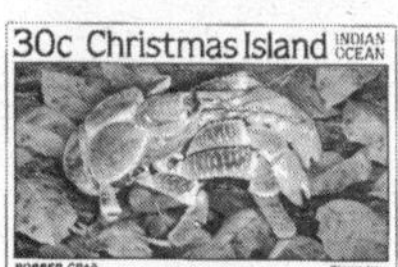

44 Robber Crab

(Des L. Curtis. Litho Walsall)

985 (30 Jan). *Crabs* (1*st series*). *T* **44** *and similar horiz designs. Multicoloured. P* 13 × 13½.
95 30 c. Type **44** 35 40
196 40 c. Horn-eyed Ghost Crab 45 50
197 55 c. Purple Hermit Crab 60 65
198 85 c. Little Nipper .. .. 95 1·00

COOK ISLANDS

Commemorating-
15 Sept. 1984

(**212**)

213 "Virgin on Throne with Child" (Giovanni Bellini)

1984 (15 Oct). *Birth of Prince Henry. Nos.* 812 *and* 833/6 *optd or surch* (*No.* 1007) *as T* **212**.
1003 $1.25, Type **191** (optd with T **212**) (Gold) .. 1·75 1·10
a. Pair. Nos. 1003/4.. .. .. 3·00 2·25
1004 $1.25, As Type **191**, but inscr "1 July 1982" (optd "Birth H.R.H. Prince Henry") (Gold) 1·75 1·10
1005 $2.50, Princess Diana (inscr "21st Birthday") (optd with T **212**) (Gold) .. .. 3·00 2·00
a. Pair. Nos. 1005/6.. .. .. 6·00 4·00
1006 $2.50, As No. 835, but inscr "1 July 1982" (optd "Birth H.R.H. Prince Henry") (Gold) 3·00 2·00
1007 $3 on $1 Type **187** (surch "Royal Birth Prince Henry 15 Sept. 1984") (Sil.) .. .. 6·00 4·00

1984 (21 Nov). *Christmas. T* **213** *and similar vert designs. Multicoloured. P* 14.
1008 36 c. Type **213** 30 35
1009 48 c. "Virgin and Child" (anonymous, 15th century) 40 45
1010 60 c. "Virgin and Child with Saints" (Alvise Vivarini) 45 50
1011 96 c. "Virgin and Child with Angels" (H. Memling) 75 80
1012 $1.20, "Adoration of Magi" (G. Tiepolo) .. 90 95
MS1013 120 × 113 mm. As Nos. 1008/12, but each with a premium of 5 c. P 13½. .. .. .. 2·10 2·25

1984 (10 Dec). *Christmas. Designs as Nos.* 1008/12 *in separate miniature sheets,* 62 × 76 *mm, each with a face value of* 95 c. + 5 c. *P* 13½.
MS1014 As Nos. 1008/12 .. .. *Set of 5 sheets* 3·75 4·00

AITUTAKI

70 Princess Diana with Prince Henry

1984 (10 Dec). *Birth of Prince Henry* (2*nd issue*). *T* **70** *and similar vert designs. Multicoloured. P* 14.
514 48 c. Type **70** 40 45
515 60 c. Prince William with Prince Henry 45 50
516 $2.10, Prince and Princess of Wales with children .. .. 1·50 1·60
MS517 113 × 65 mm. As Nos. 514/16, but each with a face value of 96 c. + 7 c. P13½.. .. .. 2·25 2·40

CYPRUS

TURKISH CYPRIOT POSTS

55 Kemal Ataturk, Flag and Crown

56 Taekwondo Bout

(Des H. Ulucam (20 l.), F. Isiman (70 l.). Litho Tezel Ofset, Lefkosa)

1984 (15 Nov). 1*st Anniv of Turkish Republic of Northern Cyprus. T* **55** *and similar multicoloured design. W* **51** (*sideways on* 20 *l., inverted on* 70 *l.*). *P* 12½.
159 20 l. Type **55** 8 10
160 70 l. Legislative Assembly voting for Republic (*horiz*) 25 30

(Des H. Ulucam. Litho Tezel Ofset, Lefkosa)

1984 (10 Dec). *International Taekwondo Championship, Girne. T* **56** *and similar horiz design. W* **51** (*sideways on* 10 *l.*). *P* 12½.
161 10 l. black, pale cinnamon and grey-black .. 5 8
162 70 l. multicoloured 25 30
Design:—70 l. Emblem and flags of competing nations.

57 "Le Regard" (Saulo Mercader)

58 Musical Instruments and Music

(Litho Tezel Ofset, Lefkosa)

1984 (10 Dec). *Exhibition by Saulo Mercader (artist). T* **57** *and similar multicoloured design. W* **51** (*sideways on* 20 *l.*). *P* 12½ × 13 (20 *l.*) *or* 13 × 12½ (70 *l.*).
163 20 l. Type **57** 8 10
164 70 l. "L'equilibre De L'esprit (*horiz*) 25 30

(Des H. Ulucam. Litho Tezel Ofset, Lefkosa)

1984 (10 Dec). *Visit of Nurnberg Chamber Orchestra. W* **51** (*sideways*). *P* 12½.
165 **58** 70 l. multicoloured 25 30

59 Dr. Fazil Kucuk (politician)

(Des Y. Calli (20 l.), E. Cizenel (70 l.). Litho Tezel Ofset, Lefkosa)

1985 (15 Jan). 1*st Death Anniv of Dr. Fazil Kucuk (politician). T* **59** *and similar vert design. Multicoloured. W* **51** (*inverted on* 70 *l.*).*P* 12½ × 12.
166 20 l. Type **59** 8 10
167 70 l. Dr. Fazil Kucuk reading newspaper .. 25 30

DOMINICA

203 Tabby

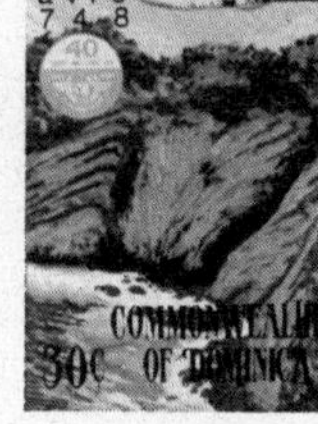

204 Avro "748"

(Des I. MacLaury. Litho Format)

1984 (12 Nov). *Cats. T* **203** *and similar horiz designs. Multicoloured. P* 15.
912 10 c. Type **203** 5 8
913 15 c. Calico Shorthair 8 10
914 20 c. Siamese 12 15
915 25 c. Manx 15 20
916 45 c. Abyssinian 25 30
917 60 c. Tortoise-shell Longhair 35 40
918 $1 Rex 60 65
919 $2 Persian .. .. 1·25 1·40
920 $3 Himalayan .. .. 1·75 1·90
921 $5 Burmese .. .. 3·00 3·25
912/21 .. .. *Set of* 10 7·00 7·50
MS922 105 × 75 mm. $5 Grey Burmese, Persian and American Shorthair .. .. 3·00 3·25

(Des Bonny Redecker. Litho Questa)

1984 (26 Nov). 40*th Anniv of International Civil Aviation Organisation. T* **204** *and similar vert designs. Multicoloured. P* 14.
923 30 c. Type **204** 15 20
924 60 c. Twin "Otter" 35 40
925 $1 "Islander" 60 65
926 $3 "Casa" .. .. 1·75 1·90
MS927 102 × 75 mm. $5 Boeing "747" .. .. 3·00 3·25

205 Donald Duck, Mickey Mouse and Goofy with Father Christmas

(Litho Questa)

1984 (30 Nov). *Christmas. Walt Disney Cartoon Characters. T* **205** *and similar vert designs. Multicoloured. P* 12 ($2) *or* 13½ × 14 (*others*).
928 45 c. Type **205** 25 30
929 60 c. Donald Duck as Father Christmas with toy train 35 40
930 90 c. Donald Duck as Father Christmas in sleigh 55 60
931 $2 Donald Duck and nephews in sledge .. 1·25 1·40
932 $4 Donald Duck in snow with Christmas tree 2·40 2·50
MS933 127 × 102 mm. $5 Donald Duck and nephews opening present .. .. 3·00 3·25
No. 931 was printed in sheetlets of 8 stamps.

206 Mrs. M. Bascom presenting Trefoil to Chief Guide Lady Baden-Powell

(Des Marlise Najaka. Litho Questa)

1985 (28 Feb). 75*th Anniv of Girl Guide Movement. T* **206** *and similar multicoloured designs. P* 14.
934 35 c. Type **206** 20 25
935 45 c. Lady Baden-Powell inspecting Dominican Brownies 25 30
936 60 c. Lady Baden-Powell with Mrs. M. Bascom and Mrs. A. Robinson (Guide leaders) .. 35 40
937 $3 Lord and Lady Baden-Powell (*vert*) .. 1·75 1·90
MS938 77 × 105 mm. $5 Flags of Dominica and Girl Guide Movement .. .. 3·00 3·25

FALKLAND ISLANDS

146 Technical Drawing of "Wren" Class Locomotive

(Des C. Abbott. Litho Questa)

1985 (18 Feb). 70*th Anniv of Camber Railway. T* **146** *and similar horiz designs, each black, deep brown and pale cinnamon. W w* **14** (*sideways*). *P* 14.
497 7p. Type **146** 15 20
498 22p. Sail-propelled trolley 45 50
499 27p. Locomotive at work 55 60
500 54p. "Falkland Islands Express" passenger train (75 × 25 *mm*). .. .. .. 1·10 1·25

FALKLAND ISLANDS DEPENDENCIES

23 Zavodovski Island

(Des. J.W. Litho Questa)

1984 (8 Nov). *Volcanoes of South Sandwich Islands. T* **23** *and similar horiz designs. Multicoloured.* W w **14** *(sideways). P* 14 × 14½.

121	6p. Type **23**	12	15
122	17p. Mt Michael, Saunders Island	35	40
123	22p. Bellingshausen Island	45	50
124	52p. Bristol Island	1·00	1·10

GHANA

VALERIE
BRISCO-HOOKS
U.S.A.
(413)

1984 (3 Dec). *Olympic Medal Winners, Los Angeles. Nos.* 1102/7 *optd as T* **413** *in gold.*

1132	1 c. Type **408** (optd with T **413**)	5	5
1133	1 c. 40, Boxing (optd "U.S. WINNERS")	5	8
1134	2 c. 30, Field hockey (optd "PAKISTAN (FIELD HOCKEY)")	8	10
1135	3 c. Men's 400 metre hurdle race (optd "EDWIN MOSES U.S.A.")	10	12
1136	50 c. Rhythmic gymnastics (optd "LAURI FUNG CANADA")	1·50	1·60
MS1137	103 × 78 mm. 70 c. Football (optd "FRANCE")	2·10	2·25

Nos. 1133 and **MS**1137 have the overprint in one line and Nos. 1134/6 in two.

GIBRALTAR

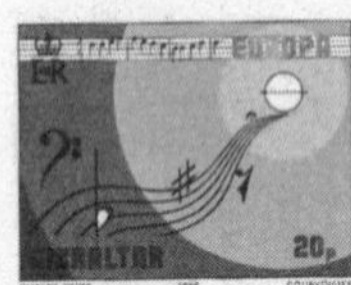

146 Musical Symbols, and Score from Beethoven's 9th (Choral) Symphony

(Des Olympia Reyes. Photo Courvoisier)

1985 (26 Feb). *Europa. Music. T* **146** *and similar horiz design. Multicoloured. Granite paper. P* 12½.

516	**146**	20p. multicoloured	40	45
517	–	29p. multicoloured	60	65

The 29p. is as T **146** but shows different symbols.

GRENADA

303 Honda "XL500R"

(Des R. Sentnor. Litho Questa)

1985 (11 Mar). *Centenary of the Motor Cycle. T* **303** *and similar horiz designs. Multicoloured. P* 14.

1383	25 c. Type **303**	15	20
1384	50 c. Suzuki "GS1100ES"	30	35
1385	90 c. Kawasaki "KZ700"	55	60
1386	$4 BMW "K100"	2·40	2·50
MS1387	109 × 81 mm. $5 Yamaha "500CC V Four"	3·00	3·25

GUYANA

——— (305)

25  130 (306)

1984 (307)

1984 (308)

1984 (309)

1984 (Sept–Nov). *Various stamps surch or optd.*

(a) As T **294** *or as T* **298** (60 c.)

1328	20 c. on 15 c. on 2 c. Type **132** (No. 1030)	8	10
1329	20 c. on 15 c. on 2 c. Type **132** (No. 1034)	8	10
1330	20 c. on 15 c. on 2 c. Type **132** (No. 1063)	8	10
1331	60 c. on 110 c. on 8 c. on 3 c. Hanging Heliconia (as No. 868, but without T **219**) (two vert obliterating panels)		
	a. One vert obliterating panel*		
1332	120 c. on 125 c. on 8 c. on 6 c. Cannon-ball tree (No. 893)		
1333	120 c. on 125 c. on $2 *Norantea guianensis* (No. 834)	45	50
1334	120 c. on 125 c. on $2 *Norantea guianensis* (No. O8)	45	50
1335	120 c. on 140 c. on $1 *Chelonanthus uliginoides* (No. 796)	45	50
1336	200 c. on 220 c. on 1 c. Pitcher Plant of Mt Roraima (No. 922) (B.)	80	85
1337	320 c. on 110 c. on $2 *Norantea guianensis* (No. 804) (B.)		
1338	350 c. on 375 c. on $5 *Odontadenia grandiflora* (No. 803) (B.)	1·25	1·40
1339	390 c. on 400 c. on $5 *Odontadenia grandiflora* (No. 1091) (B.)	1·50	1·60
1340	450 c. on $5 *Odontadenia grandiflora* (No. O4) (B.)	1·75	1·90

*The small original printing of the 60 c. surcharge has the "8 c" and "110" values obliterated by a single vertical block of six lines. On the vast majority of the supply these features were covered by two vertical blocks of six lines each.

(b) As T **305** *(figures handstamped, bar in ballpoint pen)*

1341	25 c. on 10 c. Cattleya (No. 547)	10	12
	a. Surch on No. 547a	40	50
1342	25 c. on 15 c. Christmas Orchid (No. 864a)	10	12

(c) As T **306**

1343	25 c. on 15 c. Christmas Orchid (No. 548)		
1344	25 c. on 15 c. Christmas Orchid (No. 809)	10	12
1345	25 c. on 15 c. Christmas Orchid (No. 864)	10	12
1346	25 c. on 15 c. Christmas Orchid (No. 977)	10	12
	a. Surch on No. 977a		
1347	25 c. on 15 c. Christmas Orchid (No. 1009)	10	12
1348	25 c. on 15 c. Christmas Orchid (No. O11)	10	12
1349	130 c. on 110 c. on $2 *Norantea guianensis* (No. 804)	75	80
1350	130 c. on 110 c. on $2 *Norantea guianensis* (No. O10)	16·00	16·00
1351	600 c. on $7.20 on $1 *Chelonanthus uliginoides* (No. 770A)	2·25	2·50
	a. Surch on No. 770B	2·25	2·50

(d) With T **307** (Nov)

1352	20 c. *Paphinia cristata* (No. 549)	8	10
	a. Optd on No. 549a		
1353	$3.60 on $5 *Odontadenia grandiflora* (No. 769A)	18·00	2·00
	a. Optd on No. 769B	20·00	2·00

(e) With T **308** *vertically in blue* (Nov)

1354	50 c. on 8 c. Type **136** (No. 1062)	20	25
1355	60 c. on 1 c. Pitcher Plant of Mt Roraima (No. 1000)	20	25
1356	$2 *Norantea guianensis* (No. O22)	80	85

(f) With T **309**

1357	20 c. *Paphinia cristata* (No. 549)	10	12
	a. Optd on No. 549a	10	12
1358	25 c. Marabunta (No. 550)		
1359	25 c. Marabunta (No. F4)	10	12
	a. Optd on No. F4a	40	50
1360	$3.60 on $5 *Odontadenia grandiflora* (No. 769A)		

HONG KONG

115 Hung Sing Temple

(Des M. Harris. Litho J.W.)

1985 (14 Mar). *Historic Buildings. T* **115** *and similar horiz designs. Multicoloured. P* 13½.

467	40 c. Type **115**	8	10
468	$1 St. John's Cathedral	20	25
469	$1.30, The Old Supreme Court Building	25	30
470	$5 Wan Chai Post Office	1·00	1·10

INDIA

940 "Herdsman and Cattle in Forest" (H. Kassam)

1984 (14 Nov). *Children's Day. P* 13 × 13½.

1137	**940**	50 p. multicoloured	8	10

941 Indira Gandhi

(Des C. Lal)

1984 (19 Nov). *Prime Minister Indira Gandhi Commemoration (1st issue). P* 15 × 14.

1138	**941**	50 p. black, lavender and bright orange	8	10

See also No. 1147.

942 Congress Emblem

943 Swami Haridas

1984 (20 Nov). *12th World Mining Congress, New Delhi. P* 13 × 13½.

1139	**942**	1 r. black and orange-yellow	12	15

1984 (27 Nov). *Swami Haridas (philosopher) Commemoration. P* 13.

1140	**943**	1 r. multicoloured	12	15

944 Dr. Rajendra Prasad at Desk

945 Mrinalini (rose)

1984 (3 Dec). *Birth Centenary of Dr. Rajendra Prasad (former President). P* 13.

1141	**944**	50 p. multicoloured	8	10

1984 (23 Dec). *Roses. T* **945** *and similar vert design. Multicoloured. P* 13.

1142	1 r. 50, Type **945**	20	25
1143	2 r. Sugandha	25	30

946 "Fergusson College" (Gopal Deuskar)

947 Narhar Vishnu Gadgil

1985 (2 Jan). *Centenary of Fergusson College, Pune. P* 13.

1144	**946**	1 r. multicoloured	12	15

1985 (10 Jan). *Narhar Vishnu Gadgil (politician) Commemoration. P* 13.

1145	**947**	50 p. chestnut, bright orange & dp grn	8	10

948 Gunner and Howitzer from Mountain Battery

985 (15 Jan). *50th Anniv of Regiment of Artillery*. *P* 13½ × 13.
146 **948** 1 r. multicoloured 12 15

949 Indira Gandhi making Speech

(Des R. Chopra)

985 (31 Jan). *Indira Gandhi Commemoration* (*2nd issue*). *P* 14.
147 **949** 2 r. multicoloured 25 30

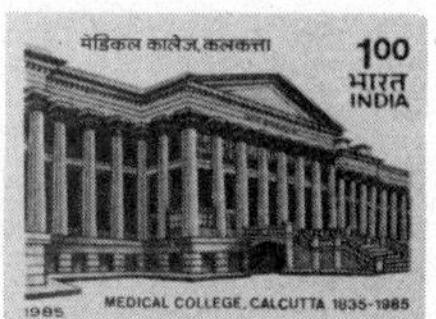

950 Minicoy Lighthouse **951** Medical College Hospital

985 (2 Feb). *Centenary of Minicoy Lighthouse*. *P* 13.
148 **950** 1 r. multicoloured 12 15

985 (20 Feb). *150th Anniv of Medical College, Calcutta*. *P* 13½ × 13.
149 **951** 1 r. yellow, reddish brown and deep reddish purple 12 15

952 Medical College, Madras

1985 (6 Mar). *150th Anniv of Medical College, Madras*. *P* 13½ × 13.
1150 **952** 1 r. yellow-brown and reddish brown .. 12 15

IRELAND

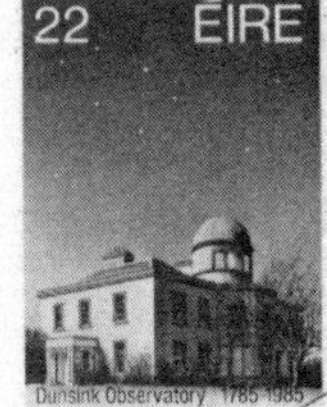

214 "Love" and Heart-shaped Balloon **215** Dunsink Observatory (Bicentenary)

(Des Susan Dubsky (22p.), Patricia Jorgensen (26p.). Litho Irish Security Stamp Ptg Ltd)

1985 (31 Jan). *Greetings Stamps. T* **214** *and similar multicoloured design. P* 15 × 14 (22*p*.) *or* 14 × 15 (26*p*.).
603 22p. Type **214** 35 40
604 26p. Bouquet of hearts and flowers (*vert*) .. 40 45

(Des R. Ballagh (22, 44p.), K. Thomson (26p.), M. Lunt (37p.). Litho Irish Security Stamp Ptg Ltd)

1985 (14 Mar). *Anniversaries. T* **215** *and similar designs. Multicoloured. P* 15 × 14 (26*p*.) *or* 14 × 15 (*others*).
605 22p. Type **215** 35 40
606 26p. "A Landscape at Tivoli, Cork, with Boats" (Nathanial Grogan) (800th anniv of city of Cork) (*horiz*) 40 45
607 37p. Royal Irish Academy (Bicentenary) .. 65 70
608 44p. Richard Crosbie's balloon flight (Bicentenary of first aeronautic flight by an Irishman) 70 75

MINIMUM PRICE

The minimum price quoted is 5p which represents a handling charge rather than a basis for valuing common stamps. For further notes about prices see introductory pages.

JAMAICA

226 "Accompong Madonna" (Namba Roy)

(Des G. Vasarhelyi. Litho Harrison)

1984 (6 Dec). *Christmas. Sculptures. T* **226** *and similar vert designs. Multicoloured. W* **111**. *P* 14.
616 20 c. Type **226** 8 10
617 25 c. "Head" (Alvin Marriott) 10 12
618 55 c. "Moon" (Edna Manley) 15 20
619 $1.50, "All Women are Five Women" (Mallica Reynolds (Kapo)) 45 50

KIRIBATI

40 Tang

(Des G. Drummond. Litho Questa)

1985 (19 Feb). *Reef Fishes. T* **40** *and similar horiz designs. Multicoloured. W* w **15**. *P* 14.
232 12 c. Type **40** 15 20
233 25 c. White-barred Triggerfish 30 35
234 35 c. Surgeon Fish 40 45
235 80 c. Squirrel Fish 90 95
MS236 140 × 107 mm. Nos. 232/5. Wmk sideways 1·60 1·75

MALDIVE ISLANDS

196 Facade of the Malé Mosque

(Litho Format)

1984 (11 Nov). *Opening of Islamic Centre. T* **196** *and similar multicoloured design. P* 15.
1057 2 r. Type **196** 45 50
1058 5 r. Malé Mosque and minaret (*vert*) .. .. 1·10 1·25

197 Air Maldives Boeing "737" **198** "Edmond Iduranty" (Degas)

(Des G. Drummond. Litho Questa)

1984 (19 Nov). *40th Anniv of International Civil Aviation Authority. T* **197** *and similar horiz designs. Multicoloured. P* **14**.
1059 7 l. Type **197** 5 8
1060 4 r. Airlanka Lockheed "L–1011 TriStar" .. 90 95
1061 6 r. Air Alitalia McDonnell Douglas "DC10–30" .. .. 1·25 1·40
1062 8 r. L.T.U. Lockheed "L–1011 TriStar" .. 1·75 1·90
MS1063 110 × 92 mm. 15 r. Air Maldives Shorts "SC7 Skyvan" .. .. 3·25 3·50

(Litho Questa)

1984 (10 Dec). *150th Birth Anniv of Edgar Degas* (*artist*). *T* **198** *and similar vert designs. P* 14.
1064 75 l. Type **198** 15 20
1065 2 r. "James Tissot" 45 50
1066 5 r. "Achille de Gas in Uniform" .. .. 1·10 1·25
1067 10 r. "Lady with Chrysanthemums" .. 2·25 2·40
MS1068 100 × 70 mm. 15 r. "Self-portrait" .. 3·25 3·50

PAKISTAN

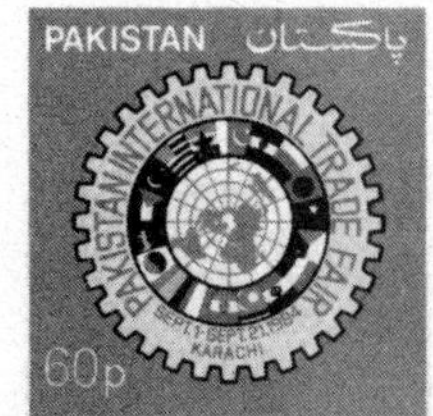

348 Gearwheel Emblem and Flags of Participating Nations

(Des A. Zafar)

1984 (1 Sept). *Pakistan International Trade Fair*. *P* 13.
656 **348** 60 p. multicoloured 5 8

349 Interior of Main Dome

1984 (5 Nov). *Tourism Convention. Shahjahan Mosque, Thatta. T* **349** *and similar horiz designs. Multicoloured. P* 13½.
657 1 r. Type **349** 10 12
658 1 r. Brick and glazed tile work 10 12
659 1 r. Gateway 10 12
660 1 r. Symmetrical archways 10 12
661 1 r. Interior of a dome 10 12
Nos. 657/61 were printed together, *se-tenant*, in horizontal strips of 5 throughout the sheet

350 Bank Emblem in Floral Pattern

(Des A. Zafar)

1984 (7 Nov). *25th Anniv of United Bank Ltd*. *P* 13½.
662 **350** 60 p. multicoloured 5 8

351 Conference Emblem **352** Postal Life Insurance Emblem within Hands

(Des A. Salahuddin)

1984 (24 Dec). *20th United Nations Conference on Trade and Development*. *P* 14.
663 **351** 60 p. multicoloured 5 8

(Des A. Zafar and J. Sultana)

1984 (29 Dec). *Centenary of Postal Life Insurance. T* **352** *and similar vert design. Multicoloured. P* 13½.
664 60 p. Type **352** 5 8
665 1 r. "100" and Postal Life Insurance emblem 10 12

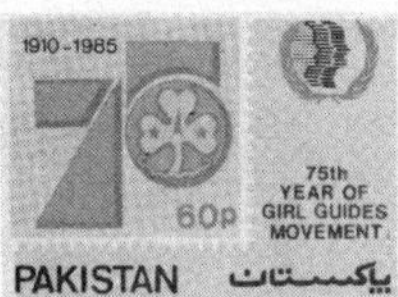

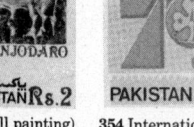

353 Bull (Wall painting) **354** International Youth Year Emblem and "75"

(Des A. Salahuddin and M. Munawar)

1984 (31 Dec). *U.N.E.S.C.O. Save Moenjadoro Campaign. T* **353** *and similar vert design. Multicoloured. P* 13½.
666 2 r. Type **353** 20 25
667 2 r. Bull (seal) 20 25
Nos. 666/7 were printed together, *se-tenant*, in horizontal pairs throughout the sheet.

(Des A. Salahuddin)

1985 (6 Jan). *75th Anniv of Girl Guide Movement. P* 13½.
668 **354** 60 p. multicoloured 5 8

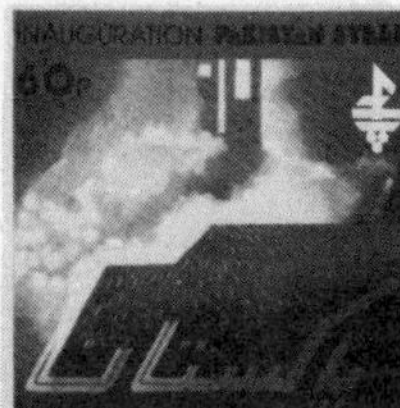

355 Smelting Ore

1985 (15 Jan). *Inauguration of Pakistan Steel Corporation. T* **355** *and similar multicoloured design. P* 13.
669 60 p. Type **355** 5 8
670 1 r. Pouring molten steel from ladle (28 × 46 mm) 10 12

ST. KITTS–NEVIS

NEVIS

(Des G. Turner (10 c.), J.W. (others). Litho Format)

1985 (20 Feb). *Leaders of the World. Automobiles (3rd series). Horiz designs as T* **25**, *the first in each pair showing technical drawings and the second paintings. P* 12½.
249 1 c. black, light green and pale green .. 5 5
a. Vert pair. Nos. 249/50 10
250 1 c. multicoloured 5 5
251 5 c. black, cobalt and pale violet-blue .. 5 5
a. Vert pair. Nos. 251/2 10
252 5 c. multicoloured 5 5
253 10 c. black, grey-olive and pale green.. .. 5 8
a. Vert pair. Nos. 253/4 10
254 10 c. multicoloured 5 8
255 50 c. black, sage-green and pale cinnamon .. 30 35
a. Vert pair. Nos. 255/6 60
256 50 c. multicoloured 30 35
257 60 c. black, dull yellowish green and pale blue 35 40
a. Vert pair. Nos. 257/8 70
258 60 c. multicoloured 35 40
259 75 c. black, dull vermilion and pale orange .. 45 50
a. Vert pair. Nos. 259/60 90
260 75 c. multicoloured 45 50
261 $2.50, black, light green and azure.. .. 1·50 1·60
a. Vert pair. Nos. 261/2 .. .. .. 3·00
262 $2.50, multicoloured .. .. .. 1·50 1·60
263 $3 black, bright yellow-green and pale green 1·75 1·90
a. Vert pair. Nos. 263/4 .. .. .. 3·50
264 $3 multicoloured .. .. 1·75 1·90
249/64 .. .. *Set of* 16 8·00 9·00
Designs:—Nos. 249/50, Delahaye "Type 35 Cabriolet" (1935); 251/2, Ferrari "Testa Rossa" (1958); 253/4, Voisin "Aerodyne" (1934); 255/6, Buick "Riviera" (1963); 257/8, Cooper "Climax" (1960); 259/60, Ford "999" (1904); 261/2, MG "M-Type Midget" (1930); 263/4, Rolls-Royce "Corniche" (1971).
Nos. 249/64 are in a similar sheet format to Nos. 165/80

ST. LUCIA

155 *Clossiana selene*

(Des Jennifer Toombs. Litho Format)

1985 (28 Feb). *Leaders of the World. Butterflies. T* **155** *and similar vert designs. Multicoloured. P* 12½.
781 15 c. Type **155** 8 10
a. Horiz pair. Nos. 781/2 15
782 15 c. *Inachis io*.. .. .. 8 10
783 40 c. *Philaethria werneckei* 25 30
a. Horiz pair. Nos. 783/4 50
784 40 c. *Catagramma sorana* 25 30
785 60 c. *Kallima inachus* 35 40
a. Horiz pair. Nos. 785/6 70
786 60 c. *Hypanartia paullus* 35 40
787 $2.25, *Morpho rhetenor helena* .. .. 1·40 1·50
a. Horiz pair. Nos. 787/8 .. .. .. 2·75
788 $2.25, *Ornithoptera meridionalis* .. .. 1·40 1·50
781/8 .. .. *Set of* 8 3·75 4·00
Nos. 781/2, 783/4, 785/6 and 787/8 were printed together, *se-tenant*, in horizontal pairs throughout the sheets.

ST. VINCENT

145 Brown Pelican

(Des R. Vigurs. Litho Format)

1985 (7 Feb). *Leaders of the World. Birth Bicentenary of John J. Audubon (ornithologist). T* **145** *and similar vert designs. Multicoloured. P* 12½.
854 15 c. Type **145** 8 10
a. Horiz pair. Nos. 854/5 15
855 15 c. Green Heron 8 10
856 40 c. Pileated Woodpecker 25 30
a. Horiz pair. Nos. 856/7 50
857 40 c. Common Flicker.. .. .. .. 25 30
858 60 c. Painted Bunting.. .. .. .. 35 40
a. Horiz pair. Nos. 858/9 70
859 60 c. White-winged Crossbill 35 40
860 $2.25, Red-shouldered Hawk .. .. 1·40 1·50
a. Horiz pair. Nos. 860/1 .. .. .. 2·75
861 $2.25, Crested Caracara .. .. .. 1·40 1·50
854/61 .. .. *Set of* 8 3·75 4·00
Nos. 854/5, 856/7, 858/9 and 860/1 were printed together, *se-tenant*, in horizontal pairs throughout the sheets.

SIERRA LEONE

AUSIPEX 84
(176)

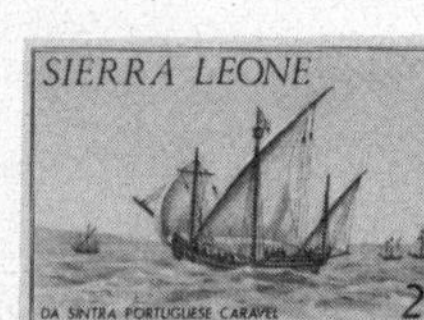

177 *Da Sintra*

1984 (22 Aug). *"Ausipex" International Stamp Exhibition, Melbourne. Optd with T* **176**. *(a) On Nos.* 632 *and* 635. *A. No imprint. B. Imprint date at foot.*

			A		B	
816	50 c. Black Crake (*vert*)	..	5·00	5·00	5·00	5·00
817	5 l. Barrow's Bustard	..	15·00	15·00	15·00	15·00

(b) On Nos. 770 *and* 773
818 50 c. Black Crake .. .. 1·00 1·00
819 5 l. Barrow's Bustard .. .. 3·00 3·00
Nos. 816B/17B exist with either "1981" or "1982" imprint dates (*same price for either issue*).

(Des G. Drummond. Litho Questa)

1984 (5 Sept–7 Nov). *History of Shipping. T* **177** *and similar horiz designs. Multicoloured. P* 14.
820 2 c. Type **177** 5 5
821 5 c. *Merlin* of Bristol 5 5
822 10 c. *Golden Hind* 5 5
823 15 c. *Mordaunt* 5 5
824 20 c. R. N. transport *Atlantic* 5 5
825 25 c. H.M.S. *Lapwing* 5 8
826 30 c. Brig *Traveller* 8 10
827 40 c. Schooner *Amistad* 10 12
828 50 c. H.M.S. *Teazer* 12 15
829 70 c. Cable ship *Scotia*.. .. .. .. 15 20
830 1 l. H.M.S. *Alecto* 25 30
831 2 l. H.M.S. *Blonde* (9.10) 45 50
832 5 l. H.M.S. *Fox* (9.10) .. .. .. 1·25 1·40
833 10 l. R.M.S. *Accra* (7.11) .. .. .. 2·50 2·75
820/33 .. .. *Set of* 14 4·25 5·25

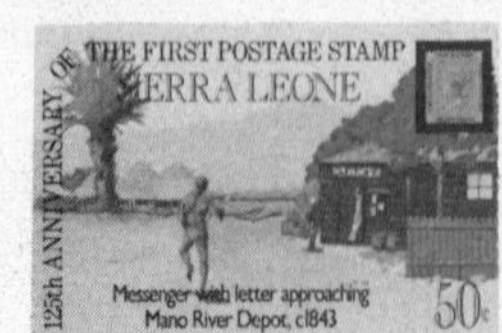

178 Mail Runner approaching Mano River Depot, *c* 1843

(Des Susan David. Litho Walsall)

1984 (9 Oct). *125th Anniv of First Postage Stamps. T* **178** *and similar horiz designs. Multicoloured. P* 14.
834 50 c. Type **178** 12 15
835 2 l. Isaac Fitzjohn, First Postmaster, receiving letters, 1855 .. .. 50 55
836 3 l. 1859 packet franked with four 6d. stamps 75 80
MS837 100 × 70 mm. 5 l. Sierra Leone 1859 6d. purple and Great Britain 1840 Penny Black stamps .. .. 1·25 1·40

179 "Madonna and Child" (Pisanello)

(Litho Walsall)

1984 (15 Nov). *Christmas. Madonna and Child paintings b artists named. T* **179** *and similar vert designs. Multicoloured P* 14.
838 20 c. Type **179** 5
839 1 l. Memling 25 3
840 2 l. Raphael 50 5
841 3 l. Van der Werff 75 8
MS842 100 × 69 mm. 6 l. Picasso.. .. .. 1·50 1·6

SINGAPORE

149 Coleman Bridge

(Des Eng Siak Loy. Recess Harrison)

1985 (15 Mar). *Bridges of Singapore. T* **149** *and similar hori designs. One phosphor band* (10 c.) *or phosphorised pape (others). P* 14½ × 14.
487 10 c. black (Type **149**) 8 1
488 35 c. black (Cavenagh Bridge) 25 3
489 75 c. black (Elgin Bridge) 55 6
490 $1 black (Benjamin Sheares Bridge) .. 70 7

SOUTH AFRICA

268 "Reflections" (Frans Oerder)

1985 (22 Feb). *Paintings by Frans Oerder. T* **268** *and similar horiz designs. Multicoloured. Litho. P* 14.
577 11 c. Type **268** 12 15
578 25 c. "Ladies in a Garden" 20 25
579 30 c. "Still-life with Lobster" 25 30
580 50 c. "Still-life with Marigolds" 45 50
MS581 129 × 74 mm. Nos. 577/80 .. .. 1·00 1·25

SWAZILAND

10c
(111)

112 Rotary International Logo and Map of World

1984 (15 Dec). *Nos.* 340B, 342A, 343A, 345B *and* 346A *surch as T* **111**.
471 10 c. on 4 c. *Aloe marlothii* 8 10
472 15 c. on 7 c. *Cyrtanthus bicolor* 12 15
473 20 c. on 3 c. *Haemanthus magnificus*.. .. 15 20
474 25 c. on 6 c. *Aloe kniphofioides* 20 25
475 30 c. on 1 c. Type **83** 20 25

(Des G. Vasarhelyi. Litho Questa)

1985 (23 Feb). *80th Anniv of Rotary International. T* **112** *and similar horiz designs. Multicoloured.* W w **14** *(sideways). P* 14.
476 10 c. Type **112** 10 12
477 15 c. Teacher and handicapped children .. 15 20
478 50 c. Youth exchange 45 50
479 1 e. Nurse and children 85 90

NOTE. The first Supplement recording new stamps not in this Catalogue or the Addenda appeared in the August 1985 number of *Stamp Monthly*.

ALBUMS

THE UNIVERSAL SYSTEM

The 'Universal' Multi-Ring system offers today's collector everything he needs – flexibility combined with quality. Stamps, covers and stamp booklets can be mounted with a selection of leaves – twelve different formats – giving your collection a united attractive presentation, either in the same 22-ring binder or series of binders. **Universal Binders (3860)** are available in red, blue or brown grained PVC, gold-blocked on the spine and presented in a smart slip box.

TRADITIONAL STAMP PAGES

There are three types of traditional album page, in a new larger size – 11 x 9½in.; white leaves faced with transparent glassine interleaving, white leaves unfaced, and black leaves faced.

3861 Universal Album with 50 white unfaced leaves
3862 Extra white unfaced leaves
3863 Universal Album with 40 white faced leaves
3864 Extra white faced leaves
3365 Universal Album with 40 black faced leaves
3866 Extra black faced leaves

BOOKLET PAGES

Both current British Post Office folding booklets and the older-style stitched booklets can be displayed. Folded booklets can be seen on both sides, without handling, and booklets from many other countries can be taken too. Leaves, size 11 x 8¾in., are available in packs of three as follows:

3563 Universal Booklet Album
3571 3 extra 15 pocket leaves
3572 3 extra 8 pocket leaves
3573 3 extra 8 strip leaves
3574 3 extra 5 strip leaves
3587 3 extra 2 strip leaves

PRESENTATION PACK PAGES

Every British Post Office Presentation Pack, Year Pack and Souvenir Book can be safely housed and securely mounted and protected in these pages – even the larger size packs issued since February 1982.

3595 Universal Presentation Pack Album
3596 5 extra double pocket leaves
3597 5 extra single pocket leaves

CO OCKETS

No ne oto-corners or separate albums anym t day and other covers can be mounted with t issue! There are two Universal cover pocke single and double crystal clear pockets 11 x 9 th open at the top, ensuring that covers do not against the album ring; both take the Post Office Cover size – single pockets take covers up to 8½in.

3560 U Cover Album
3562 gle pockets
3561 ble pockets

Now y e display medium you need – but can spend your money on stamps!!

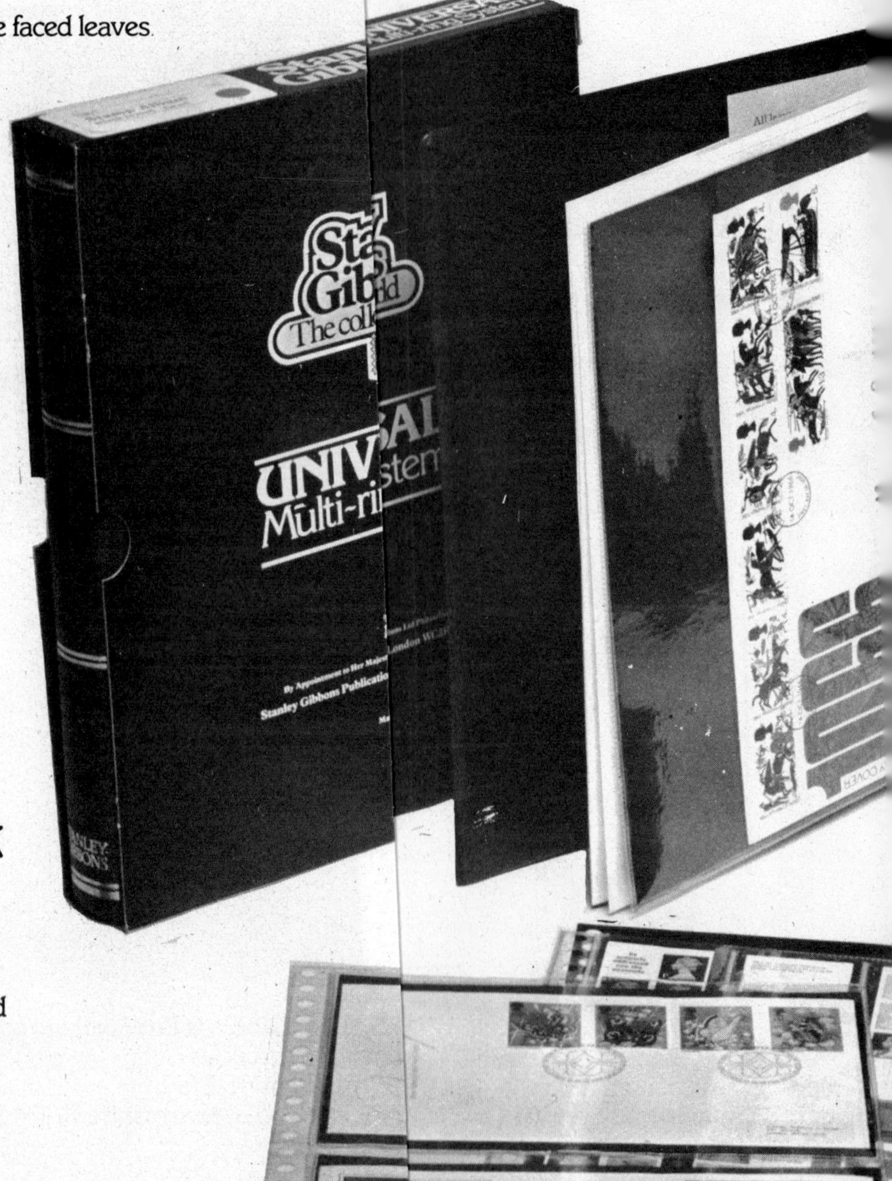

ALBUMS

PEG-FITTING ALBUMS

Superb binders with peg-fitting release action are a feature of the five albums in this quality range; four have double linen-hinged cartridge leaves with transparent facing. The advantage of this leaf is that it lies flat when the album is opened, enhancing the appearance of the collection and, by minimising friction, aiding stamp preservation.

3834 Devon
The large capacity binder is available in maroon, green, black or blue and contains 200 fine quality white cartridge feint quadrille-ruled leaves, size 10¾ x 9¾in. Boxed.

3832 Exeter
A quality binder in a choice of red, blue or green, containing 40 double linen-hinged transparent faced leaves, 10³/8 x 9³/4in., of special matt white cartridge; feint grey quadrille rules.

0392 Plymouth
A connoisseur's album, with a binder choice of maroon, green, black or blue, and protective slip case. The binder contains forty double linen-hinged transparent faced leaves, 10³/8 x 9³/4in., of special matt white cartridge, feint grey quadrille rules.

The Philatelic
The largest album in the whole of the Stanley Gibbons range. It not only accommodates more stamps per page than other albums, but also allows sheets and blocks, etc., to be mounted and arranged on its 12⅞ x 10¾in. leaves. It is bound in handsome deep green cloth with leather corners and spine. Supplied with 80 double linen-hinged leaves of matt white cartridge, feint quadrille-ruled, with transparent interleaving, it is presented complete in a sturdy slip case.

3921 Philatelic
With transparent interleaving.

0395 Oriel
Supreme among luxury blank albums, this will enhance the finest collection, specially designed to provide the most prestigious home for your stamps. With a telescopic peg-fitting action, the 'Oriel' is half-bound in rich red leather, finished with gold tooling. Each album contains 50 superior quality feint quadrille-ruled transparent faced, double linen-hinged, gilt-edged leaves of matt-white cartridge, size 10⅜ x 9¾in. It is supplied in a luxury matching slip case.

SAFE 'N' CLEAR

Stanley Gibbons Safe 'n' Clear leaves combine the versatility of blank leaves with the ease of use of a hingeless album — just slip the stamps into the strips and build a permanent collection or rearrange them instantly as required. Nine different leaf formats for singles, pairs, strips, blocks, gutter pairs or cylinder blocks and even early postal history and presentation packs — in fact a Safe 'n' Clear leaf for every need! There is also one to house stamps and covers of the same set on the same leaf.

Stanley Gibbons Safe 'n' Clear is safe because the entire system is manufactured only from highest quality materials guaranteed to give maximum protection to stamps, covers and postal history. The leaves are of tough, matt board, colour fast and completely free of harmfull chemicals. The crystal clear polyester strips contain no softeners, acids, solvents or plasticisers and offer substantial protection against ultra-violet light, humidity and friction. The bonding between strips and leaf is likewise chemically inert, ensuring the leaves will not warp or buckle under adverse conditions, whilst holding stamps and covers firmly in place.

Stanley Gibbons Safe 'n' Clear leaves are 280 × 215mm. The multi-punched holes are designed to fit a vast range of ring binders from 2 to 22 ring: Whatever the ring system Safe 'n' Clear is likely to fit it. Alternatively use the special Stanley Gibbons Safe 'n' Clear Album.

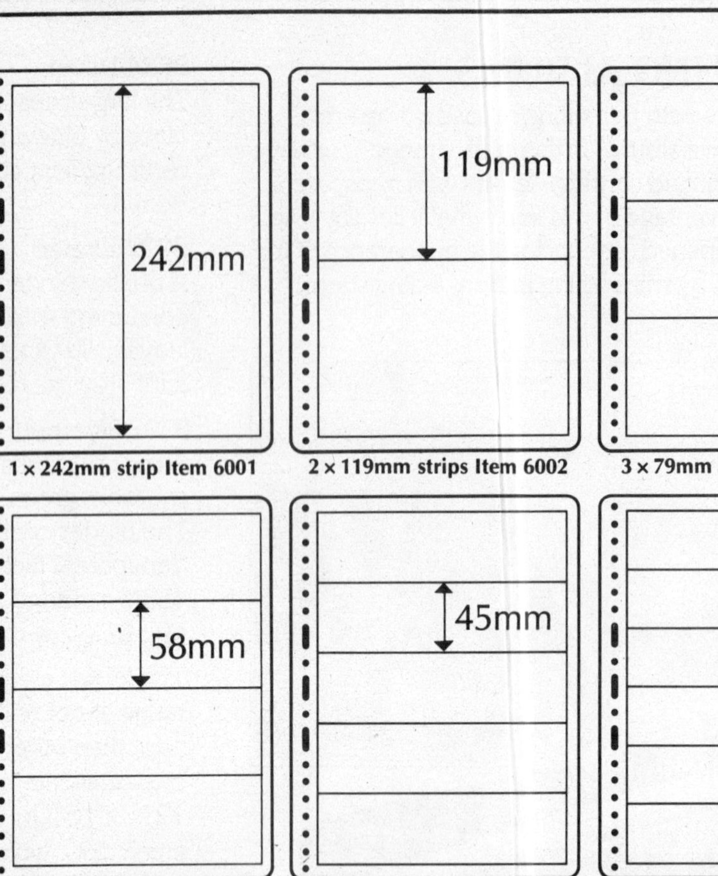

1 × 242mm strip Item 6001

2 × 119mm strips Item 6002

3 × 79mm strips Item 6003

4 × 58mm strips Item 6004

5 × 45mm strips Item 6005

6 × 37mm strips Item 6006

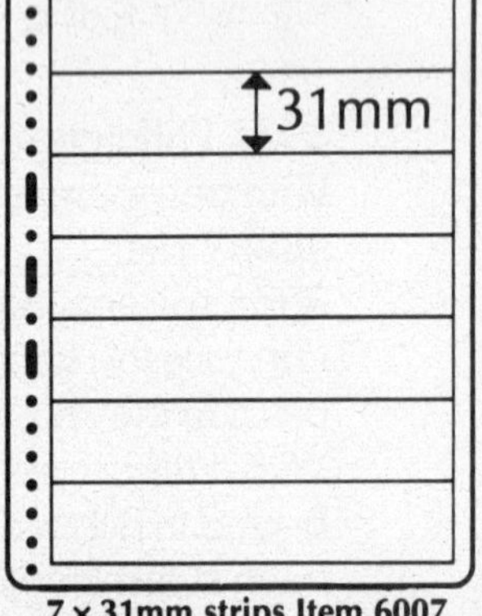

7 × 31mm strips Item 6007

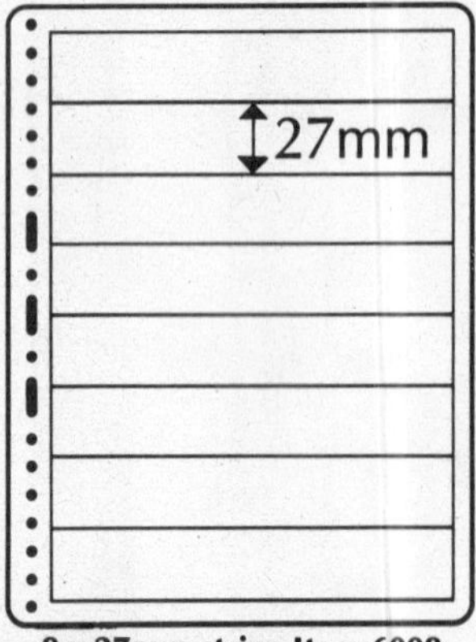

8 × 27mm strips Item 6008

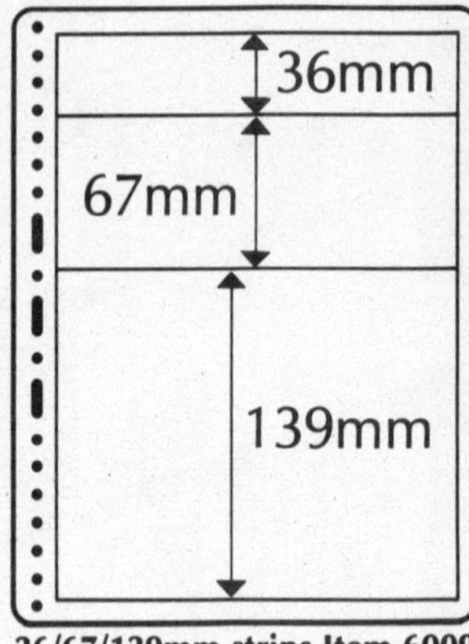

36/67/139mm strips Item 6009